D1292006

Organic Chemistry

Principles and Mechanisms

Organic Chemistry
Principles and Mechanisms

THIRD EDITION

Joel M. Karty
Elon University

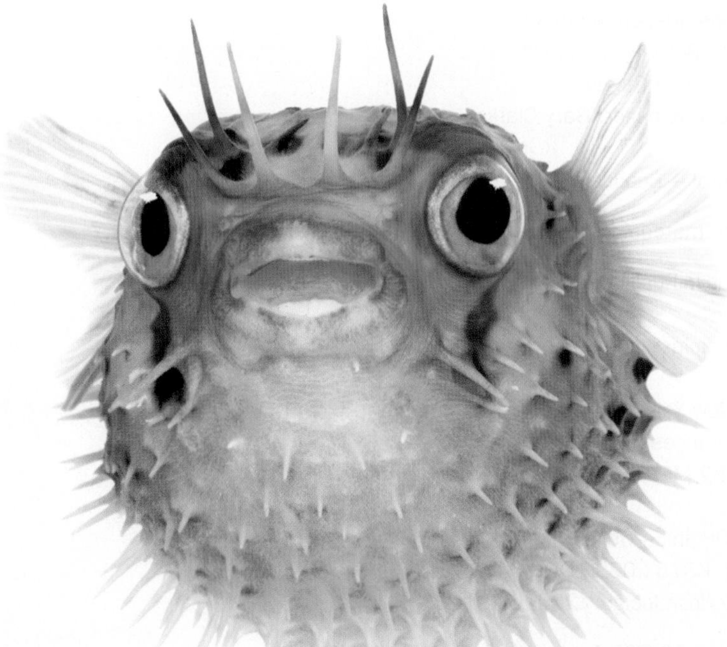

W. W. NORTON & COMPANY
Independent Publishers Since 1923

W. W. Norton & Company has been independent since its founding in 1923, when William Warder Norton and Mary D. Herter Norton first published lectures delivered at the People's Institute, the adult education division of New York City's Cooper Union. The firm soon expanded its program beyond the Institute, publishing books by celebrated academics from America and abroad. By midcentury, the two major pillars of Norton's publishing program—trade books and college texts—were firmly established. In the 1950s, the Norton family transferred control of the company to its employees, and today—with a staff of five hundred and hundreds of trade, college, and professional titles published each year—W. W. Norton & Company stands as the largest and oldest publishing house owned wholly by its employees.

Copyright © 2022, 2018, 2014 by W. W. Norton & Company, Inc.

All rights reserved
Printed in Canada

Editors: Erik Fahlgren and Rob Bellinger
Project Editor: Taylere Peterson
Assistant Editor: Selin Tekgurler
Developmental Editor: Carol Pritchard-Martinez
Copyeditors: Heather Whirlow Cammarn and Christopher Curioli
Managing Editor, College: Marian Johnson
Managing Editor, College Digital Media: Kim Yi
Associate Director of Production, College: Benjamin Reynolds
Media Editors: Cailin Barrett-Bressack and Marilyn Rayner
Chemistry Content Development Specialist: Dr. Richard L. Jew
Associate Media Editor: Liz Vogt
Associate Digital Media Project Editor: Sarah McGinnis
Media Editorial Assistant: Manny Ruiz
Ebook Production Manager and Coordinator: Megan Crayne
Marketing Research and Strategy Director: Stacy Loyal
Design Directors: Lissi Sigillo and Marisa Nakasone
Photo Editor: Mike Cullen
Director of College Permissions: Megan Schindel
College Permissions Manager: Bethany Salminen
Text Permissions Specialist: Joshua Garvin
Composition: GW, Inc. / Project Manager: Gary Clark
Illustrations: GW, Inc.
Manufacturing: Transcontinental—Beauceville QC

Permission to use copyrighted material is included at the back of the book.

Library of Congress Cataloging-in-Publication Data
Names: Karty, Joel M., author.
Title: Organic chemistry : principles and mechanisms / Joel M. Karty, Elon University.
Description: Third edition. | New York : W.W. Norton & Company, [2022] | Includes bibliographical references and index.
Identifiers: LCCN 2021033782 | **ISBN 9780393544015 (hardcover)** | ISBN 9780393877465 (epub)
Subjects: LCSH: Chemistry, Organic—Textbooks.
Classification: LCC QD253.2 .K375 2022 | DDC 547—dc23
LC record available at https://lccn.loc.gov/2021033782

W. W. Norton & Company, Inc., 500 Fifth Avenue, New York, NY 10110
wwnorton.com
W. W. Norton & Company Ltd., 15 Carlisle Street, London W1D 3BS
2 3 4 5 6 7 8 9 0

To Pnut, Fafa, and Jakers

About the Author

JOEL KARTY earned his B.S. in chemistry at the University of Puget Sound and his Ph.D. at Stanford University. He joined the faculty of Elon University in 2001, where he currently holds the rank of full professor. He teaches primarily the organic chemistry sequence and also teaches general chemistry. In the summer, Joel teaches at the Summer Biomedical Sciences Institute through the Duke University Medical Center. His research interests include investigating the roles of resonance and inductive effects in fundamental chemical systems and studying the mechanism of pattern formation in Liesegang reactions.

Brief Contents

The [E] icon refers to content in online chapters.

Contents

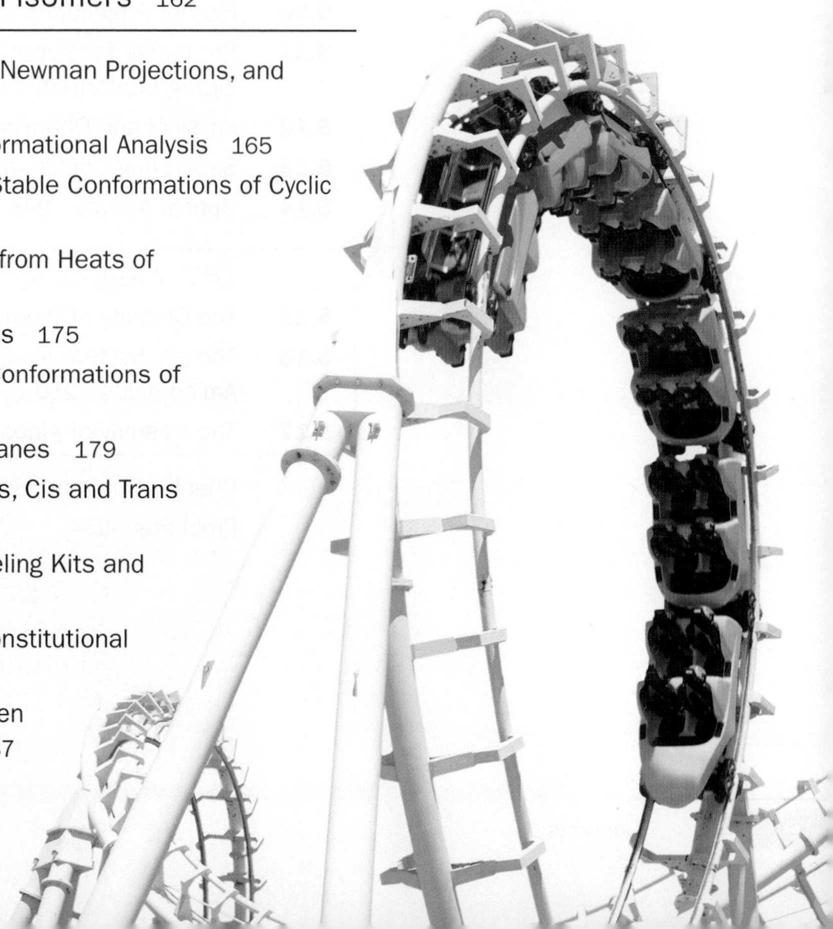

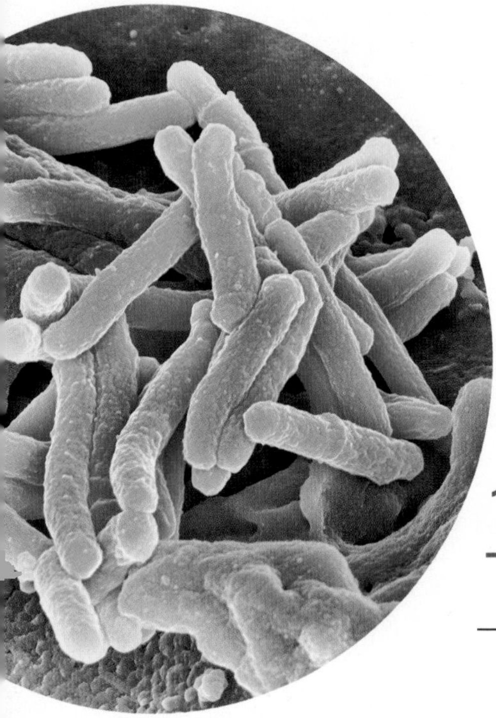

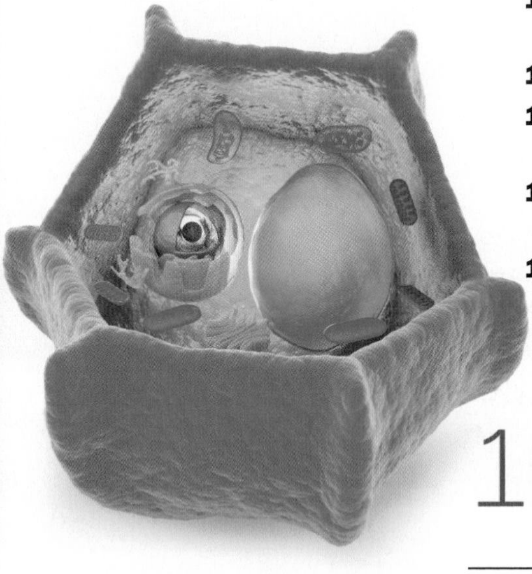

17 Structure Determination 3

Nuclear Magnetic Resonance Spectroscopy 819

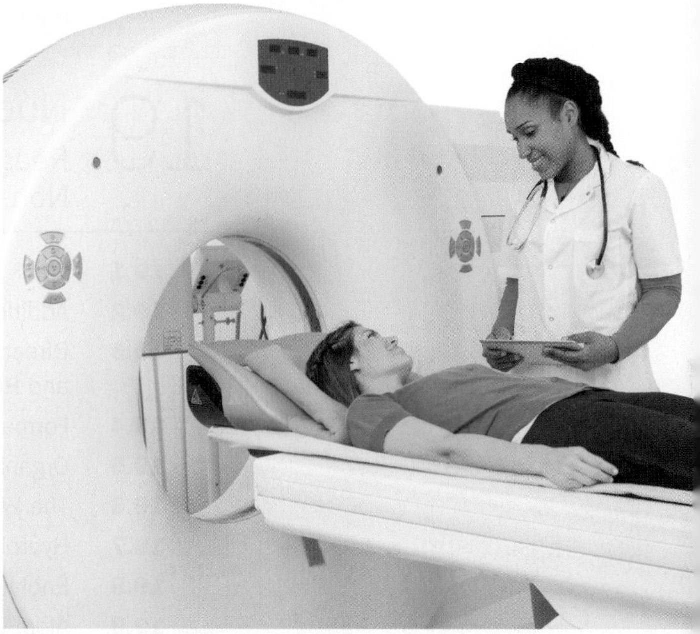

18 Nucleophilic Addition to Polar π Bonds 1

Reagents That Are Strongly Nucleophilic 878

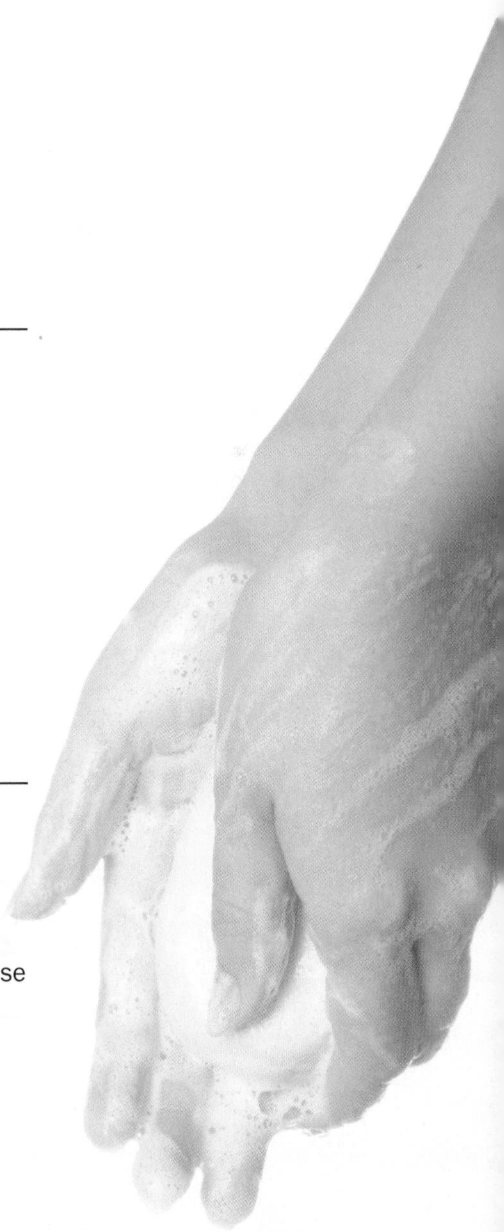

23 Nucleophilic Addition–Elimination Reactions 2

Reagents That Are Weakly Nucleophilic or Non-nucleophilic 1099

24 Aromatic Substitution 1

Electrophilic Aromatic Substitution on Benzene, and Useful Accompanying Reactions 1156

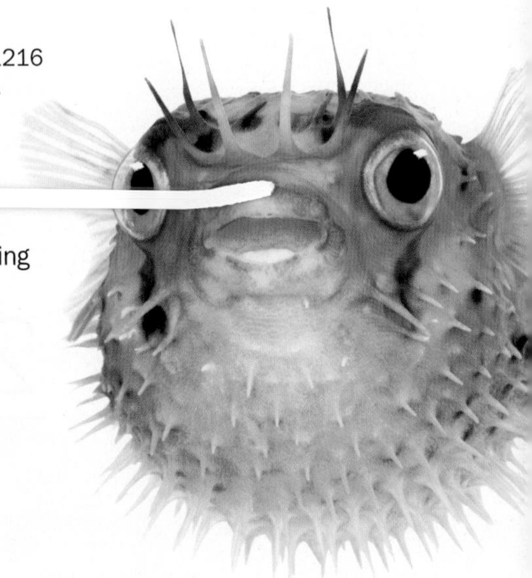

Biochemistry Topics

For a more in-depth coverage of biomolecules, see the Table of Contents for Chapters 29 and 30.

Proteins and Amino Acids

Organic Chemistry of Biomolecules

Interest Boxes

Nucleic Acids

Organic Chemistry of Biomolecules

Interest Boxes

Carbohydrates

Organic Chemistry of Biomolecules

Interest Boxes

Lipids

Organic Chemistry of Biomolecules

Interest Boxes

Interest Boxes

Connections Boxes

Green Chemistry Boxes

Mechanisms

Preface

Focused on the Student, Organized by Mechanism

When an organic reaction is presented to a novice, only the structural differences between the reactants and products are immediately apparent. Students tend to see only *what* happens, such as the transformation of one functional group into another, changes in connectivity, and aspects of stereochemistry. It should therefore not be surprising that students, when presented with reactions, are tempted to commit the reactions to memory. But there are far too many reactions and accompanying details for memorization to work in organic chemistry.

This is where mechanisms come into play. Mechanisms allow us to understand the sequences of elementary steps—the step-by-step pathways—that convert the reactants to products, so we can see *how* and *why* reactions take place as they do. Moreover, the mechanisms that describe the large number of reactions in the course are constructed from just a handful of elementary steps, so mechanisms allow us to see *similarities* among reactions that are not otherwise apparent. In other words, mechanisms actually *simplify* organic chemistry. Thus, teaching mechanisms—enabling students to understand and simplify organic chemistry—is an enormous key to success in the course.

At the outset of my teaching career, I fully appreciated the importance of mechanisms, so during my first couple years of teaching, I emphasized mechanisms *very* heavily. I did so under a functional group organization where reactions are pulled together according to the functional groups that react. That is the organization under which I learned organic chemistry, and it is also the way that most organic chemistry textbooks are organized. Despite my best efforts, the majority of my students struggled with even the basics of mechanisms and, consequently, turned to flash cards as their primary study tool. They tried to memorize their way through the course, which made matters worse.

I began to wonder what impact the *organization*—an organization according to functional group—had on deterring my students from mechanisms. I had good reason to be concerned, because as I alluded to earlier, functional groups tend to convey the *what* of chemical reactions, whereas mechanisms convey the *how* and *why*. What kinds of mixed messages were my students receiving when I was heavily emphasizing mechanisms, while the organization of the material was giving priority to functional groups? To probe that question, I made a big change to my teaching.

The third year I taught organic chemistry, I rearranged the material to pull together reactions that had the same or similar mechanisms; that is, I taught under a *mechanistic organization*. I made no other changes that year; the course content, course structure, and my teaching style all remained the same. I even taught out of the same textbook organized according to functional group. But that year I saw dramatic improvements in my students' mastery of mechanisms.[1] Students had *command* over the material, which

[1]Bowman, B. G.; Karty, J. M.; Gooch, G. Teaching a Modified Hendrickson, Cram, and Hammond Curriculum in Organic Chemistry. *J. Chem. Educ.* **2007**, *84*, 1209.

proved to be a tremendous motivator. They were better able to solve different kinds of problems with confidence. Ultimately, I saw significant improvements in student performance, morale, and retention. I became convinced that students benefit remarkably from learning under a mechanistic organization.

My goal in writing this book is to support instructors who are seeking what I was seeking: getting students to use mechanisms to learn organic chemistry in order to achieve better performances and to have better experiences in their organic courses. Using a functional group organization to achieve these outcomes can be an uphill battle because of the high priority that it inherently places on functional groups, which ultimately promotes memorization. This textbook, on the other hand, allows students to receive the same message from both their instructor and their textbook: a clear and consistent message that mechanisms simplify learning organic chemistry and are vital to success in the course.

A Closer Look: Why Is a Mechanistic Organization Better?

Consider what the novice sees when they begin a new *functional group chapter* in a traditionally organized textbook. In an alcohols chapter, for example, students first learn how to recognize and name alcohols, then they study the physical properties of alcohols. Next, students might spend time on special spectroscopic characteristics of alcohols, after which they learn various routes that can be used to synthesize alcohols from other species. Eventually, students move into the heart of the chapter: new reactions that alcohols undergo and the mechanisms that describe them. Finally, students deal with how those reactions are incorporated into synthesis. Within a particular functional group chapter, students find themselves bouncing among *several different themes.*

Even within the discussion of new reactions and mechanisms that a particular functional group can undergo, students are typically faced with widely varying reaction types and mechanisms. Take again the example of an alcohols chapter in a book organized according to functional group. Students learn that alcohols can act as an acid or as a base; alcohols can act as nucleophiles to attack a saturated carbon, in a substitution reaction, or to attack the carbon atom of a polar π bond, in a nucleophilic addition reaction; protonated alcohols can act as electrophiles in a substitution or an elimination reaction; and alcohols can undergo oxidation, too.

With the substantial jumping around that takes place within a particular functional group chapter, it is easy to see how students can become overwhelmed. Under a functional group organization, students don't receive intrinsic and clear guidance as to what they should focus on, not only within a particular functional group chapter but also from one chapter to the next. Without clear guidance, and without substantial time for focus, students often see no choice but to memorize. And they will memorize what they perceive to be most important: predicting products of reactions, typically ignoring (or giving short shrift to) fundamental concepts and mechanisms.

Under the mechanistic organization in this book, students experience a *coherent story* of chemical reactivity. The story begins with molecular structure and energetics and then guides students into reaction mechanisms through a few transitional chapters. Thereafter, students study how and why reactions take place as they do, focusing on one type of mechanism at a time. Ultimately, students learn how to intuitively use reactions in synthesis. In this manner, students have clear and consistent guidance as to what their focus should be on, both within a single chapter and throughout the entire book.

The *patterns* we, as experts, see become clear to students when they learn under this mechanistic organization. Consider the following four mechanisms:

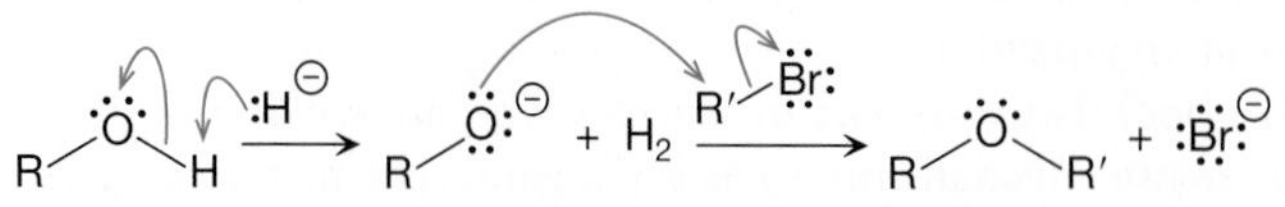
(P-1)

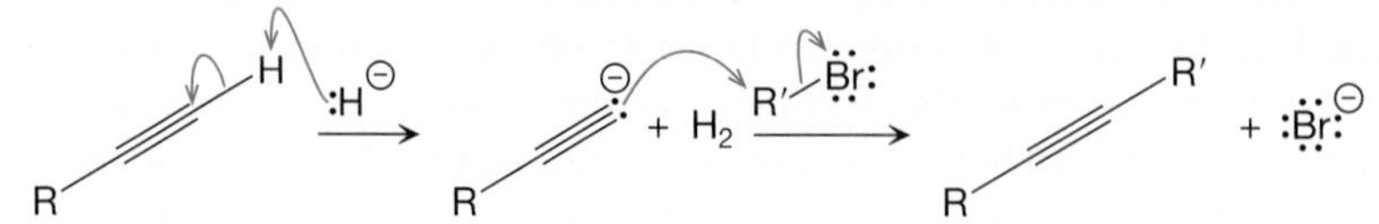
(P-2)

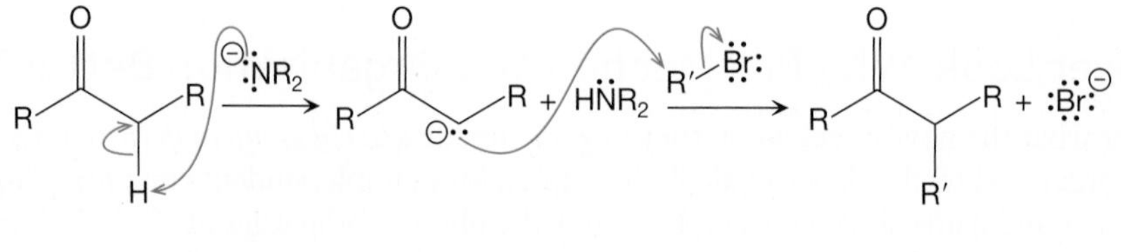
(P-3)

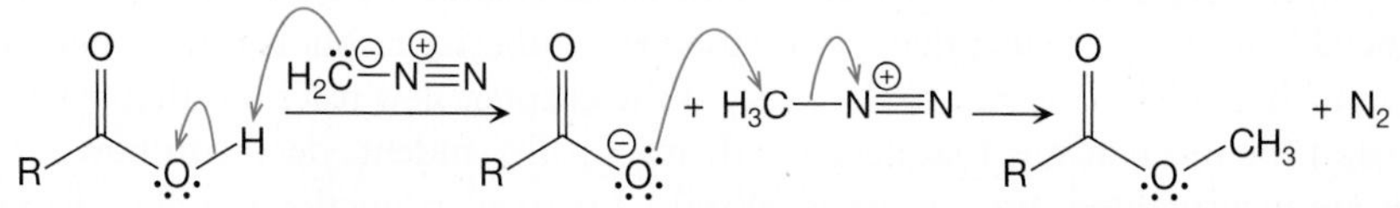
(P-4)

The mechanism in Equation P-1 is for the Williamson synthesis of an ether; the one in Equation P-2 is for alkylation of a terminal alkyne; the one in Equation P-3 is for alkylation of a ketone; and the one in Equation P-4 is for conversion of a carboxylic acid to a methyl ester. In these four reactions, the reactants are an alcohol, an alkyne, a ketone, and a carboxylic acid. In a functional group organization, these reactions will be taught in *four separate chapters* that can be located in distinctly different parts of the book. Because all four reaction mechanisms are identical, consisting of a deprotonation followed by an S_N2 step, all four reactions are taught *together* in this book, in the pair of connected chapters dealing with substitution reactions in synthesis: Chapters 10 and 11.

Seeing these patterns early, students more naturally embrace mechanisms and use them when solving problems. Moreover, as students begin to see such patterns unfold in one chapter, they develop a better toolbox of mechanisms to draw on in subsequent chapters. Ultimately, students gain *confidence* in using mechanisms to predict what will happen and why. I believe this is vital to their success throughout the course, in later biochemistry courses where organic chemistry is routinely applied, and on admission exams such as the MCAT.

Details about the Organization

Continuing with the success of the second edition, the book remains divided into three major parts:

Part I: Atomic and Molecular Structure

- Chapter 1: Atomic structure, Lewis structures and the covalent bond, and resonance theory, culminating in an introduction to functional groups
- Chapter 2: Aspects of three-dimensional geometry and its impacts on intermolecular forces
- Chapter 3: Structure in terms of hybridization, valence bond (VB) theory, and molecular orbital (MO) theory
- Chapters 4 and 5: Isomerism in its entirety, including constitutional isomerism, conformational isomerism, and stereoisomerism

Much of the material in Chapters 1–5 will be new to students, such as organic functional groups, protic and aprotic solvents, effective electronegativity, conformers and cyclohexane chair structures, and stereoisomers. Chapters 1–5 also contain a significant amount of material that students will recognize from general chemistry, such as electronic configurations, Lewis structures and resonance, intermolecular forces, valence shell electron pair repulsion (VSEPR) theory and hybridization, and constitutional isomers. Because most students do not retain everything they should from general chemistry, I have made the general chemistry topics in this textbook more extensive than in other textbooks. Knowing that this extended coverage is in the book, instructors should feel comfortable covering as much or as little of it as they see fit for their students.

Part II: Developing a Toolbox for Working with Mechanisms

- Chapters 6 and 7: Ten common elementary steps of mechanisms
- Chapter 8: Beginnings of multistep mechanisms, with S_N1 and E1 reactions as examples

Mechanisms are vital to succeeding in organic chemistry, but before tackling mechanisms, students must have the proper tools. Chapters 6–8 give students those tools, dealing with aspects of elementary steps in Chapters 6 and 7 before dealing with aspects of multistep mechanisms in Chapter 8. Therefore, the chapters in Part II act a transition from Part I to Part III, which deals more intently with reactions.

Chapter 7 is a particularly important part of this transition. Students learn how to work with elementary steps in Chapter 7 in a low-risk environment, where there are no demands to predict products from mixing reactants and reagents. Thus, there is no pressure to memorize overall reactions. Furthermore, the fact that Chapter 7 brings together the 10 most common elementary steps, which make up the mechanisms of the many hundreds of reactions students will encounter through Chapter 25, sends a strong message to students that *mechanisms simplify organic chemistry*. As such, students take to heart from the outset that mechanisms are worthwhile to learn.

Part III: Major Reaction Types

- Chapters 9–11: Nucleophilic substitution and elimination
- Chapters 12 and 13: Electrophilic addition
- Chapters 18 and 19: Nucleophilic addition
- Chapter 20: Redox reactions
- Chapters 22 and 23: Nucleophilic addition–elimination
- Chapters 24 and 25: Aromatic substitution
- Chapter 26: Diels–Alder reactions and other pericyclic reactions
- Chapter 27: Radical reactions
- Chapter 28: Polymerization

Several of these chapters come in pairs, where the first chapter is used to introduce key ideas about the reaction or mechanism and the second chapter explores the reaction or mechanism to greater depth and breadth. Pairing the chapters this way provides flexibility. An instructor could teach all the chapters in order. Alternatively, following the guidelines set by the American Chemical Society, an instructor could teach the first in each set of paired chapters in the first term as part of "foundational" coursework. Then the remaining chapters would represent "in-depth" coursework for the second term. Teaching the chapters in this order would also allow an instructor to teach carbonyl chemistry in the first term.

Interspersed in Part III are chapters dealing with multistep synthesis (Chapters 10, 11, and 21), conjugation and aromaticity (Chapter 14), and structure determination by mass spectrometry and spectroscopy (Chapters 15–17). The structure determination chapters are self-contained and can be taught earlier, at the instructor's discretion. They can even be taught separately in the laboratory. The spectroscopy chapters are movable like this because, with the mechanistic organization of the book, important aspects of spectroscopy are not integrated in reaction chapters like they typically are in a functional group text.

The three chapters devoted to multistep synthesis (Chapters 10, 11, and 21), on the other hand, are strategically located. Chapters 10 and 11 appear after students have spent a few chapters working with reactions. Having a decent number of reactions under their belts, students can appreciate cataloging reactions as either functional group transformations or reactions that alter the carbon skeleton. Students can also appreciate retrosynthetic analysis after having learned some reactions that form carbon–carbon bonds. Moreover, Chapters 10 and 11 appear early enough so students can practice their skills devising multistep syntheses throughout the entire second half of the book; each subsequent chapter has multiple synthesis problems.

Chapter 21 (the third chapter devoted to synthesis) is delayed a few more chapters because it deals with content related to reactions from Chapters 18–20, including protecting groups and choosing carbon–carbon bond-forming reactions that result in the desired relative positioning of heteroatoms. The multistep synthesis topics in Chapter 21 are somewhat more challenging than the ones in Chapters 10 and 11, so whereas Chapters 10 and 11 might be covered in most mainstream courses, instructors can choose to cover only certain sections of Chapter 21.

I have found that treating multistep synthesis in dedicated chapters makes it more meaningful to students. When I taught synthesis under a functional group organization, I saw synthesis become a distraction to the reactions that students were simultaneously learning. I also found that students often associated a synthetic strategy only with the functional group for which it was introduced. For example, when the idea of protecting groups is introduced in the ketones/aldehydes chapter of a textbook organized by functional group, students tended to associate protecting groups with ketones and aldehydes *only*. My dedicated synthesis chapters help students focus on synthesis without compromising their focus on reactions. Furthermore, synthesis strategies are discussed more holistically, so students can appreciate them in a much broader context rather than being applicable to just a single functional group.

Another major organizational feature of the book pertains to nomenclature. Nomenclature is separated out from the main chapters, in three relatively short interchapters: Interchapters A, B, and D. Separating nomenclature from the main chapters in this way removes distractions. It also allows students to focus on specific rules of nomenclature instead of specific compound classes. With each new nomenclature interchapter, the complexity of the material increases as new rules are applied to the ones introduced earlier.

The instructor has flexibility as to how to work with these nomenclature interchapters. They can be covered in lecture or easily assigned for self-study. They can be split over two terms or could all be covered in the first. The locations of the interchapters in the book (i.e., immediately after Chapters 1, 3, and 7), however, should be taken as indicators as to the earliest that each interchapter should be assigned or taught. Covering a nomenclature interchapter substantially earlier than it appears in the book would expose students to compound classes well before those types of compounds are dealt with in the main chapters.

Finally, the application of molecular orbitals (MOs) toward chemical reactions is separated from the main reaction chapters and is presented, instead, as an optional, self-contained unit in Interchapter C. This interchapter appears just after Chapter 7, the overview of the 10 most common elementary steps. Each elementary step from Chapter 7 is revisited from the perspective of frontier MO theory. Because this interchapter is optional, chapters later in the book do not rely on coverage of this material.

Presenting this frontier MO theory material together in an optional unit, as I have done in Interchapter C in this book, offers two main advantages to students. First, it removes a potential distraction from the main reaction chapters, and instructors have the choice of not covering it at all. Another advantage comes from the fact that the MO pictures of all 10 common elementary steps appear together in the interchapter. Therefore, instructors who wish to cover this interchapter can expect their students to come away with a better understanding of the bigger picture of MO theory as it pertains to chemical reactions.

In addition to Chapters 1–28 (Parts I–III) in the main part of the textbook, Chapters 29 and 30, which are devoted to bioorganic chemistry, have been added as online-only chapters. Chapter 29 compiles material from The Organic Chemistry of Biomolecules sections found at the ends of several chapters in the main part of the textbook, focusing on structure, properties, and laboratory characterization of biomolecules. Chapter 30 discusses the organic chemistry principles behind some biochemical pathways. The aim of Chapter 30 is to showcase how organic chemistry applies to complex processes in the body and to provide students a glimpse of the kinds of things they will see in a biochemistry course.

Helping Every Student Think about, Practice, and Apply Organic Chemistry

While the organization provides a coherent story, I've included pedagogy that promotes active learning and makes this book a more valuable tool for students and instructors.

New section-level learning objectives. I provide learning objectives at the beginning of each section, making transparent for students the competencies expected of them. Instructors can then tie assessments to each learning objective, since Smartwork and the Test Bank use objectives closely aligned with those in the text.

Building problem-solving skills through the consistent Think-Solve approach. Helping students become expert problem solvers, in this course and beyond, is one of my major goals. To that end, I have developed a consistent Think-Solve approach for Solved Problems, and I have written special Strategies for Success sections.

SECTION 7.1 OBJECTIVES

You will be able to:

1. Identify electron-rich and electron-poor sites within a species.
2. Articulate how the curved arrow notation for a proton transfer step represents the flow of electrons from an electron-rich site to an electron-poor site.
3. Identify organometallic reagents and hydride reagents as sources of carbanions and hydride, respectively.

SOLVED PROBLEM **7.1**

How to determine the proper electron flow and outcome for a proton transfer

Break It Down **Identify the electron-poor H atom in methanol. Draw the mechanism by which methanol acts as an acid in a proton transfer reaction with H_2N^-.**

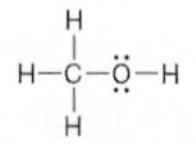

Methanol

Every Solved Problem in this book uses a Think/Solve strategy to guide you through the solution. After you consider a question posed on the Think side of the table, read the answer on the Solve side.

Think	Solve
What kinds of charges characterize electron-poor atoms? Which H in methanol bears that kind of charge?	An electron-poor atom tends to have a partial or full positive charge. Because the O atom in methanol is highly electronegative, the attached H bears a substantial partial positive charge and is therefore electron-poor.
Should H_2N^- be considered electron-rich or electron-poor?	The negative charge on H_2N^- indicates it is electron-rich.
When H_2N^- and CH_3OH are combined, how do we draw a curved arrow to depict the flow of electrons from an electron-rich site to an electron-poor site?	A curved arrow is drawn from the electrons on N to H, indicating the flow of electrons from an electron-rich site (denoted by the red screen) to an electron-poor site (blue screen). That arrow also indicates the formation of a new N—H bond. 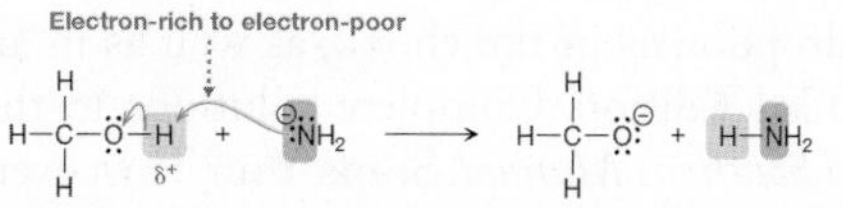 Electron-rich to electron-poor
When that curved arrow is drawn to depict bond formation, do any other bonds have to break?	The H in methanol gains a new bond, but there cannot be two bonds to H, so the initial O—H bond must break. A curved arrow from the O—H bond to the O represents the breaking of that bond. The O on the product side picks up that pair of electrons and ends up with a −1 formal charge.

Try It Identify the electron-rich and electron-poor sites in the reactant molecules shown here. Draw the curved arrows and the products for the proton transfer between these two molecules, and label the curved arrow that represents the flow of electrons from an electron-rich site to an electron-poor site. *Hint*: Are all the relevant electron pairs shown?

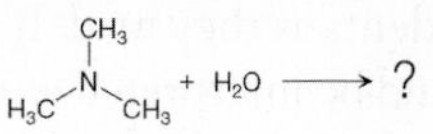

Answers to all Try It exercises can be found in the Solutions Manual.

I designed each Solved Problem to help build a focused set of skills for a specific type of problem; in fact, the skills for a given Solved Problem can be identified by the "How to ..." statement in the problem's title. Step-by-step solutions to Solved Problems are presented in tables made up of two columns: ***Think*** and ***Solve***. In each row of the table, I present a guided *question* in the Think column, and that question is answered in the Solve column. The scaffolded, two-column format of the Solved Problems helps students understand how to approach problems and motivates them to proceed through the table methodically, considering the Think and Solve columns for one set of questions before facing the next set of questions. This helps students learn how to approach problems by asking the right questions, and it mirrors the strategy I use to help students during office hours.

Importantly, students can self-assess their proficiency with Solved Problems because each one has a follow-up Try It exercise that can be tackled by using the same Think-Solve approach, and the solutions for all Try It exercises are provided in the *Study Guide and Solutions Manual.*

Over 230 Solved Problems are in the Third Edition, giving students numerous opportunities to receive guidance on the strategies they should use when solving a problem. Each chapter averages eight Solved Problems, and all of them follow the consistent Think-Solve format.

Strategies for Success sections coach students through solving broader types of problems, and thus each one helps develop a more extensive set of skills. There are 20 of these sections throughout the book. For example, a Strategies for Success section in Chapter 1 shows students how to draw all resonance structures of a given species. As another example, a Strategies for Success section in Chapter 4 shows students how to use molecular modeling kits to help derive and draw the more stable chair conformation of a substituted cyclohexane. Almost every Strategy for Success section now has an accompanying video embedded in the ebook.

▶ LOOKING AHEAD

The simplifications that allow us to treat organometallic compounds as R^- (Fig. 7-2) are convenient, and so are the simplifications that allow us to treat hydride reagents as H^- (Fig. 7-3). However, the nature of the covalent bond that we simplify can be important. As you will learn in Chapter 18, for example, RLi, RMgBr, and R_2CuLi behave substantially differently, as do $LiAlH_4$ and $NaBH_4$.

◀ RECALL

A charged species is stabilized when the formal charge appears on different atoms of the resonance structures (Section 6.8d). Moreover, inductive effects stabilize an anion when electron-withdrawing groups appear near the atom bearing the negative charge (Section 6.8e). In both cases, the outcome is a decrease in the concentration of charge within the species.

New cross-references to help students make connections across chapters. The most effective learning in organic chemistry comes when students can use a small number of concepts or ideas to arrive at a large number of outcomes. We instructors, as experts, fully appreciate how those relatively few concepts act as threads to connect material throughout an entire year of organic chemistry. In the Third Edition, **Looking Ahead** and **Recall** boxes, located in the margins, give students regular reminders of such threads. Looking Ahead boxes call out specific topics where newly introduced ideas will be applied later in the book, emphasizing the importance of mastering the topic at hand. Recall boxes jog students' memories, giving a short recap of the topic and indicating where it was introduced or applied earlier in the book. For many students, the information in a Recall box is all that is needed to gain confidence to press on; other students who need more in-depth review will find the section number references in the Recall boxes helpful. In the ebook, each box provides a direct link to the relevant section.

Your Turn exercises. Getting students to read *actively* can be challenging, so I wrote the Your Turns in each chapter to motivate this type of behavior. Your Turns are exercises that students tackle as they read the chapter. Short answers to all Your Turns are provided via interactive dropdowns in the ebook, as well as in an appendix in all printed student copies of the Third Edition. Complete solutions to these exercises are provided in the *Study Guide and Solutions Manual.* Some Your Turn exercises are basic, asking students to answer a relatively straightforward question, look something up in a table, construct a molecule using a model kit, or interact with art in a figure or data in a plot. Other Your Turn exercises are a bit more challenging, asking students to apply what they just read toward solving a problem. These exercises serve two purposes. One is to provide "reality checks" for students as they read. If a student cannot solve or answer a Your Turn exercise easily, this should be interpreted as a signal to either reread the previous section(s) or seek help. The other purpose is to build students' confidence as they read: each time a student successfully answers a Your Turn exercise, their confidence grows.

YOUR TURN 7.1

Consider the proton transfer step shown here. **(a)** Identify the electron-rich and electron-poor sites, and label the curved arrow that connects the two as "electron-rich to electron-poor." **(b)** Explain why the curved arrow notation would be faulty if the curved arrow on the right were not drawn.

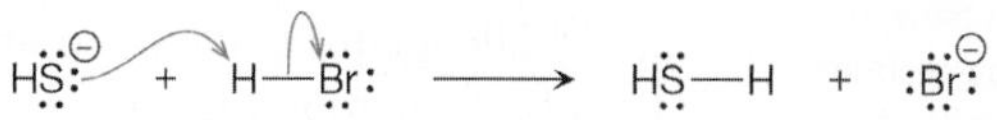

HS:
+
H—Br:
HS—H
+
:Br:

Answers to Your Turns are in the back of the book.

A flexible approach to biochemistry. Many students taking organic chemistry are biology majors or are seeking a career in a health profession. They appreciate seeing how organic chemistry relates to their interests and look for ways in which this course will prepare them for the admissions exams (such as the MCAT) that may have a large impact on their future.

Rather than relegating biochemistry solely to the end of the book, I have placed self-contained sections on The Organic Chemistry of Biomolecules at the ends of several chapters, beginning with Chapter 1. These sections can be taught at the instructor's discretion; they are optional and flexible. The topics chosen for these sections cover many of the topics dealt with on the MCAT, which means that The Organic Chemistry of Biomolecules sections are not *in addition to* what students are expected to know for the MCAT; they are topics that students *should know* for the test. In even the earliest of chapters, students have the tools to start learning aspects of this traditional biochemistry coverage. More importantly, these sections provide reinforcement of topics. In each of these sections, the material is linked directly back to concepts encountered earlier in the chapter.

For instructors who prefer to teach biochemical topics together near the end of the course, I have written two new online chapters dealing with the organic chemistry of biomolecules (see digital.wwnorton.com/karty3).

A range of interesting applications. Students often ask, "How does organic chemistry apply to me?" For the chemistry major or the student going on to medical school , the long-term answer might be apparent. Connections boxes and Interest boxes are designed to help answer that question as it relates to the immediate.

Several Connections boxes are located in the margins of each chapter, which highlight the importance or application of a recently introduced molecule. Students might see that the molecule is integral in the synthesis of a pharmaceutical drug, or that the molecule is important in the manufacture of a material that students use daily in consumer products. Connections boxes are short and are deliberately kept light, so students can quickly learn something interesting about the molecule with little investment.

In addition to Connections boxes, every chapter has one or two Interest boxes. These are much more in-depth, applying a concept in the chapter toward a discovery or process that can have significant appeal to students, perhaps delving into a biochemical process or examining novel materials. In addition to reinforcing concepts from the chapter, these Interest boxes are intended to provide *meaning* to what students are learning and to motivate students to dig deeper.

Green chemistry. Section 11.6 provides an overview of green chemistry and its importance, and then its subsections delve into three of the 12 main principles of green chemistry outlined by the American Chemical Society: fewer toxic reagents and solvents, safer synthesis routes, and minimal by-products and other waste. In subsequent reaction

CONNECTIONS 7.1

Your nose knows trimethylamine Trimethylamine [$(CH_3)_3N$, Solved Problem 7.1, Try It] is a gas that is often associated with the odor of rotting fish. Sensors have been developed to test for trimethylamine to assess the freshness of fish.

GREEN CHEMISTRY
Peroxy acids such as MCBPA are convenient reagents to produce an epoxide from an alkene. One problem, however, is that these reactions suffer from a low percent atom economy. As we can see in Equations 13-6 and 13-7, a fairly massive carboxylic acid by-product tends to go to waste. A variety of much more efficient epoxidation reactions that use catalysts have been developed. One such reaction uses polyoxometalate-supported gold nanoparticles (Au/BaPOM) as catalysts and uses molecular oxygen as the reactant.

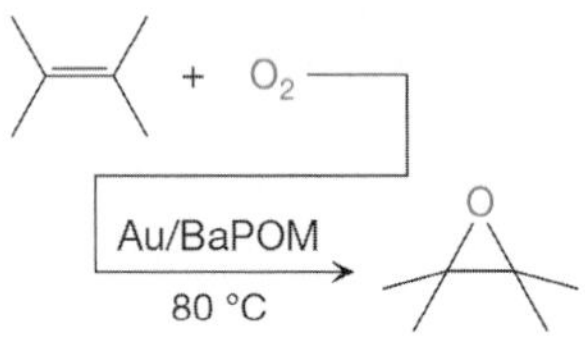

+ O2
Au/BaPOM
80 °C
O

chapters, students will find Green Chemistry boxes in the margins, which highlight green aspects of some reactions and provide green alternatives to others. For students planning on a career in chemistry, the goal is to instill in them the importance of considering green chemistry when designing and carrying out a synthesis. All students should be familiar with green chemistry and should come to appreciate the fact that chemists in the 21st century are increasingly prioritizing the well-being of our planet.

Strategies for spectral analysis. Even with a strong foundation in the principles that underlie IR and NMR spectroscopy and mass spectrometry, it can still be quite a challenge for students to analyze a spectrum in a way that brings the individual pieces of information together. Therefore, I present separate strategies up front to analyze mass, IR, and NMR spectra, with sequential steps that students can follow. Then I show students how to apply these strategies to analyze the spectra of unknown compounds. Students are encouraged to develop other strategies that might work better for them, but until then, students have an effective strategy that they can use and rely on.

End-of-chapter problems. At the end of each chapter, problems are grouped by concept or section so students can easily identify the types of problems they need to work on. A set of Integrated Problems follows those sets of focused problems. These Integrated Problems require students to bring together major concepts from multiple sections within the chapter, or from multiple chapters, as they would on an exam. These problems also help students stay familiar with material from earlier in the book, thus reducing the time that students would need to spend separately for review. In addition to organizing problems this way, problems that relate to aspects of synthesis are labeled (SYN), so students and instructors can find those types of problems quickly.

Updates and Changes to Content Based on User and Reviewer Feedback

The following changes, all of which are the direct result of instructor feedback, are designed to make the Third Edition more flexible:

Streamlined nomenclature presentation. Nomenclature is now presented in three interchapters rather than five. Stereochemical designations are now covered in a Chapter 5 section on stereoisomers. I've combined two nomenclature interchapters on functional groups that call for suffixes into Interchapter D, in order to streamline presentation. Finally, to keep the focus of the nomenclature interchapters on IUPAC rules, I moved most trivial nomenclature to the new Appendix E.

Consistent orbital treatment. In the Third Edition, valence bond (VB) theory is cleanly separated from molecular orbital (MO) theory. Orbital explanations are consistently introduced with VB theory, and they are followed up with MO theory explanations in separate sections. This allows you, as an instructor, to tailor MO theory coverage to what is best for your students.

A Deeper Look sections. For optional-coverage topics that are a bit more quantitative, take discussions to a greater depth, or are more specialized, A Deeper Look sections allow you to tailor your coverage. Examples include using molecular orbital theory to extend explanations by valence bond theory, calculating relative stabilities from heats of combustion and heats of hydrogenation, and transition state theory. The main text does not rely on A Deeper Look sections, so you can cover as much or as little material in these sections as you like.

Updated presentation of carbocation and alkene stability. In the second edition, alkene stability was covered in the context of stereoisomer properties, and carbocation stability was covered in the context of charge stability. In the Third Edition, these concepts are introduced when students learn to apply them. Carbocation stability is now introduced in Chapter 7 as students are learning about factors that contribute to the driving force for chemical reactions. Alkene stability is now introduced in Chapter 9 in the context of Zaitsev's rule, as students are learning how to predict the outcome of $S_N2/S_N1/E2/E1$ competitions.

New strategy to predict the outcome of $S_N2/S_N1/E2/E1$ competitions. A four-step procedure replaces the table-constructing exercise used in the first two editions. Students are now asked to:

(1) Determine whether an $S_N2/S_N1/E2/E1$ competition is feasible.
(2) Rule out reactions that are unfeasible.
(3) Determine which of the remaining reactions are favored by the attacking species.
(4) Apply the appropriate tiebreaker to the remaining reactions.

Students are explicitly shown how to carry out each step by applying their understanding of concepts from earlier in the chapter.

Earlier introduction of synthesis. Instructors asked for a way to introduce multistep synthesis earlier, and they also asked if the reactions in Chapter 10 could be introduced in a more methodical way. To address both requests, I combined and reorganized chapters from the previous edition. Chapters 10 and 11 now introduce aspects of multistep synthesis in the context of substitution and elimination reactions that are useful for synthesis. All the reactions in Chapter 10 are functional group transformations, and all the reactions in Chapter 11 are reactions that alter the carbon skeleton.

Structure determination in three chapters rather than two. The Third Edition now presents mass spectrometry (MS) in Chapter 15, infrared spectroscopy and ultraviolet–visible (UV–vis) spectroscopy in Chapter 16, and nuclear magnetic resonance (NMR) spectroscopy in Chapter 17. MS is presented first and in its own chapter for two reasons: (1) MS is fundamentally different from spectroscopy, as it does not involve transitions that result from photon absorption, and (2) structure determination from various forms of spectroscopy often rely on knowing the molecular formula of a compound, which is a result that is obtained from MS.

New section on two-dimensional NMR spectra. I added a short A Deeper Look section that introduces students to 2-D NMR spectra. The new section shows students how to use off-diagonal peaks in COSY and HETCOR 2-D spectra to determine which nuclei are coupled.

New chapter on redox reactions. Rather than discussing redox reactions separately throughout the book, I have written a dedicated chapter (Chapter 20) on them. This chapter reexamines redox reaction from previous chapters in the context of a carbon's bonds to hydrogen versus electronegative atoms, as well as in the context of oxidation states. The chapter also introduces other reactions that are redox reactions or involve redox steps in their mechanisms, including coupling and alkene metathesis reactions.

New online chapters for biomolecules. In the first two editions, I presented aspects of organic chemistry involving biomolecules in special sections at the ends of most chapters. Because of the success of this approach, I am continuing with this practice for the Third Edition. However, some instructors prefer to teach topics involving biomolecules together at the end of the course. Therefore, I have written two new online-only chapters dealing with the organic chemistry of biomolecules.

The material found in The Organic Chemistry of Biomolecules sections throughout the book is presented again in Chapter 29, now organized into four parts according to biomolecule class: proteins and amino acids, carbohydrates and monosaccharides, nucleic acids and nucleotides, and lipids. Whereas Chapter 29 deals with aspects of structure and properties of biomolecules, as well as some of their laboratory reactions, Chapter 30 deals with some key biochemical processes involving biomolecules in the body. This chapter examines how enzymes function, discusses key metabolic pathways, shows how genetic information is stored and accessed, and explores the fundamentals of cell signaling. Chapter 30 is a special topics chapter designed to give students an appreciation for how organic chemistry and organic reaction mechanisms apply to complex biochemical processes, and it also provides a foundation for students who plan to take a course in biochemistry.

Streamlined organization and numbering of problems. Every chapter contains Your Turn exercises (an average of 25 per chapter), as well as a Try It exercise at the end of each Solved Problem. All numbered problems are now gathered at the end of each chapter, rather than being scattered through the text.

Nearly 200 new end-of-chapter problems. Based on user and reviewer feedback, several new problems have been added to each chapter to provide students even more opportunities to hone their problem-solving skills and to assess their mastery of the material. Some of these new problems are specifically geared toward material from The Organic Chemistry of Biomolecules sections from within the chapter; these are grouped together to make them easily identifiable.

More Solved Problems. Almost 30 additional Solved Problems have been added to the third edition. All of them follow the Think-Solve format.

Acknowledgments

As always, my biggest thanks and appreciation go to my wife Valerie and my boys Joshua and Jacob, as they continue to be my biggest fans. They always motivate me to be better, and their love and immense support continue to make my achievements worthwhile.

Many thanks to my colleagues in the chemistry department at Elon for your understanding, especially Karl Sienerth and Kathy Matera, who served as my department chairs during this endeavor. Kathy, thank you especially for the real-time feedback you continue to give me and for your remarkable patience every time I barge into your office to pick your brain about a quandary with the book.

I remain indebted to my students. Thank you for bringing such great energy to learning organic chemistry year in and year out, and thank you for allowing me to learn from you. You are the reason I wrote this book in the first place, and you motivate me to make each new edition better than the last.

I am blown away by the talent on the Norton team. Erik Fahlgren and Rob Bellinger, thank you for your leadership on this project. And thank you for your continued belief in me and in the potential this book has to help teachers teach and to help students learn. Carol Pritchard-Martinez, you are an amazing developmental editor. You helped me think creatively to come up with a bold vision for the Third Edition, and you were instrumental at every step of the way to turn that vision into a reality. Taylere Peterson and Selin Tekgurler, I'm in disbelief as to how you have been able to manage so many intricate moving parts so masterfully. Wow! To Heather Cammarn and Chris Curioli, many thanks for holding me to a high standard in the copyediting stages. Heather, I can't imagine anyone else on the planet with your talent and skills, and nobody takes more pride in their work than you do! Mike Cullen and Josh Garvin, thank you for your patience and persistence searching for photos and spectra. Thanks to Cailin Barrett-Bressack and Marilyn Rayner for your leadership of the digital resources team, and thanks to Richard Jew, Liz Vogt, and Manny Ruiz for the work you did to develop the online resources for the book. I am especially grateful for your work to bring our new groundbreaking videos to life. Lissi Sigillo and Marisa Nakasone, what a fantastic job on the interior (and ebook!) design, maintaining a warm and inviting feel. And Stacy Loyal, thank you for your continued tireless work in marketing the book, and especially for everything you do to build and maintain strong relationships with instructors. A special thanks to Taylor Mach, who has had two major roles: coauthor on the *Study Guide and Solutions Manual*, and accuracy reviewer. I'm tremendously impressed by your work on the *Study Guide and Solutions Manual*, not only with the quality but also with your depth of thought. Your passion for teaching organic chemistry really comes through. And your work as an accuracy reviewer is no less impressive.

Steve Pruett, I again thank you for your work on the polymers chapter in the first edition and for your continued feedback throughout the entire life of the book.

Kristen Barrett, thank you for your excellent work on our new video series.

Roger Miesfeld, I can't thank you enough for all the figures that went into the new bioorganic chemistry chapters.

Finally, I am indebted to the many reviewers, whose feedback has been instrumental in making several significant improvements throughout the Third Edition. A special thanks to

Sachin Nedungadi, who stepped in to accuracy-check the last few chapters of the book. I am especially grateful to Jeffrey Pruet, Jonathan Mills, and Nicholas Leadbeater, who have accuracy-checked nearly the entire book along with Taylor.

Reviewers of the Third Edition

Ruquia Ahmed-Schofield, Goucher College
John Antos, Western Washington University
Kristen Barrett, Rowan University
Josh Beaver, University of North Carolina at Chapel Hill
Jesse Bergkamp, California State University, Bakersfield
Thomas Bertolini, University of Southern California
Ngong Kodiah Beyeh, Oakland University
Krishna Bhat, Widener University
Shannon Biros, Grand Valley State University
Jeffrey Bjorklund, North Central College
Tim Brunker, Towson University
Brock Casselman, The University of Alabama at Birmingham
Manashi Chatterjee, Hunter College
Joe Chihade, Carleton College
Daniel Christen, The University of North Carolina at Greensboro
Sean Curtis, Des Moines Area Community College
Debra Dillner, United States Naval Academy
Ken Doxsee, University of Oregon
Alexandre Drouin, Bishop's University
Doug Duquette, Occidental College
Lisa Eytel, Boise State University
Kevin Francis, Texas A&M University—Kingsville
Brian Fulton, Northeastern University
Stephen Gabriel, Pitt Community College
Elijah St. Germain, Florida Atlantic University
Cynthia Gilley, San Diego Miramar College
Christopher Gorman, North Carolina State University
Jeff Grell, North Central Missouri College
Jennifer Griffith, Western Washington University
Jan Gryko, Jacksonville State University
Jennifer Guerard, University of Alaska Fairbanks
Jeff Gustafson, San Diego State University
Melissa Harman, Riverside City College
Carrie Hayes, Otterbein University
Chris Hobbs, Sam Houston State University
Jacob Horger, University of North Carolina at Charlotte
Syed Hussaini, The University of Tulsa
Subash Jonnalagadda, Rowan University
Adam Kiefer, Mercer University
Brett Kite, Shenandoah University
Monique Koppel, University of Maryland
Rebecca Laird, The University of Iowa
Angus Lamar, The University of Tulsa
Erik Larsen, Bloomsburg University
Nicholas Leadbeater, University of Connecticut
Douglas Linebarrier, Salem College
Pamela Lundin, High Point University
Taylor Mach, Concordia University, St. Paul
Daniel Marous, Wittenberg University
Ronald Marks, North Greenville University
Christopher Markworth, Western Washington University
Justin Massing, University of Michigan—Flint
Dominic McGrath, The University of Arizona
LuAnne McNulty, Butler University
Galina Melman, Clarkson University
Christine Miller, Lee College
Jonathan Mills, Illinois State University
Suazette Mooring, Georgia State University
Andrew Morehead, East Carolina University
Therese Myers, Northern Arizona University
Sri Kamesh Narasimhan, Corning Community College
Sachin Nedungadi, University of Nebraska Omaha
Bryan Nell, University of Minnesota, Morris
Jackie Nikles, The University of Alabama at Birmingham
Emily Pelton, University of Minnesota
Angela Perkins, University of Minnesota
Matt Peterson, Brigham Young University
Josh Pierce, North Carolina State University
Sarah Pierce, Cumberland University
Pamela Pollet, Georgia Institute of Technology

Jeffrey Pruet, Valparaiso University
Kenneth Raymond, Eastern Washington University
Jacquie Richardson, University of Colorado Boulder
Amber Schaefer, Texas A&M University
Michael Schulz, Virginia Tech
Rico Del Sesto, Dixie State University
Matthew Siebert, Missouri State University—Springfield
Chester Simocko, San Jose State University
Chatu Sirimanne, California State University Los Angeles
Mike Slade, University of Evansville
Kevin Smith, Southern Illinois University
Roxanne Smith, Skagit Valley College
Corey Stilts, Elmira College
Nicole Snyder, Davidson College
Anne Szklarski, King's College
Ming Lee Tang, University of Utah
James Tanko, Virginia Tech
Kerri Taylor, Columbus State University
Jessica Tischler, University of Michigan—Flint
Rob Tobolowsky, Los Angeles Pierce College
Nancy Totah, Syracuse University
James Wollack, St. Catherine University
Brian Woods, Saint Louis University
Michael Wentzel, Augsburg University
Laura Wysocki, Wabash College
Danielle Zurcher, University of North Carolina at Chapel Hill

Reviewers of Previous Editions

Robert Allen, Arkansas Tech University
Niels Andersen, University of Washington
Aron Anderson, Gustavus Adolphus College
Amelia Anderson-Wile, Ohio Northern University
Herman Ammon, University of Maryland
Carolyn Anderson, Calvin University
Aaron Aponick, University of Florida
Phyllis Arthasery, Ohio University
Jared Ashcroft, Pasadena City College
Athar Ata, The University of Winnipeg
Jovica Badjic, The Ohio State University
Christina Bagwill, Saint Louis University
Joshua Beaver, University of North Carolina at Chapel Hill
John Bellizzi, The University of Toledo
David Bergbreiter, Texas A&M University
Daniel Berger, Bluffton University
Shannon Biros, Grand Valley State University
Anthony Bishop, Amherst College
Dan Blanchard, Kutztown University
Elizabeth Blue, Campbell University
Luc Boisvert, University of Puget Sound
Michelle Boucher, Utica College
Rebecca Broyer, University of Southern California
Rick Bunt, Middlebury College
Larry Calhoun, University of New Brunswick
Shawn Campagna, The University of Tennessee, Knoxville
Nancy Carpenter, University of Minnesota, Morris
Brad Chamberlain, Luther College
Timothy Clark, University of San Diego
Robert Coleman, The Ohio State University
Kimberly Cousins, California State University, San Bernardino
Ashton Cropp, Virginia Commonwealth University
Tammy Davidson, University of Florida
Lorraine Deck, The University of New Mexico
Anna Drotor, Metropolitan State University of Denver
Nathan Duncan, Maryville College
Brendan Dutmer, Highland Community College
Sergei Dzyuba, Texas Christian University
Todd Eckroat, Penn State Behrend
Jeff Elbert, University of Northern Iowa
Seth Elsheimer, University of Central Florida
Daniel Esterline, Thomas More University
Amanda Evans, California State University, Fullerton
Christoph Fahrni, Georgia Institute of Technology
Suzanne Fernandez, Lehigh University
Michael Findlater, Texas Tech University

Eric Finney, University of Washington
Abbey Fischer, University of Wisconsin Eau Claire—Barron County
Stephen Foley, University of Saskatchewan
Malcolm Forbes, Bowling Green State University
Denis Fourches, North Carolina State University
Andrew Frazer, University of Central Florida
Larry French, St. Lawrence University
Gregory Friestad, The University of Iowa
Brian Frink, Lakeland University
Brian Ganley, University of Missouri
Kevin Glaeske, Wisconsin Lutheran College
Sarah Goforth, Campbell University
Harold Goldston Jr., Des Moines Area Community College
Anne Gorden, Auburn University
Christopher Gorman, North Carolina State University
Oliver Graudejus, Arizona State University
Dustin Gross, Sam Houston State University
Robert Grossman, University of Kentucky
Daniel Gurnon, DePauw University
Jeffrey Hansen, DePauw University
Bryan Hanson, DePauw University
Andrew Harned, University of Minnesota
Matthew Hart, Grand Valley State University
Stewart Hart, Arkansas Tech University
Allan Headley, Texas A&M University
John Hershberger, Arkansas State University
Ian Hill, Gustavus Adolphus College
Daniel Holley, Columbus State University
Gail Horowitz, Brooklyn College
Roger House, Auburn University
Robert Hughes, East Carolina University
Philip Hultin, University of Manitoba
Kevin Jantzi, Valparaiso University
William Jenks, Iowa State University
Amanda Jones, Wake Forest University
Jeff Jones, Washington State University
Paul Jones, Wake Forest University
Robert Kane, Baylor University
Arif Karim, Austin Community College
Steven Kass, University of Minnesota
Stephen Kawai, Concordia University Montreal
Valerie Keller, University of Chicago
Mark Keranen, University of Tennessee at Martin
Kristopher Keuseman, Mount Mercy College
Angela King, Wake Forest University
Jesudoss Kingston, Iowa State University
Brett Kite, Shenandoah University
Francis Klein, Creighton University
Jeremy Klosterman, University of California, San Diego
Kazunori Koide, University of Pittsburgh
Dalila Kovacs, Grand Valley State University
Shane Lamos, Saint Michael's College
Nicholas Leadbeater, University of Connecticut
Carl Lecher, Marian University
Larry Lee, Camosun College
Diana Leung, The University of Alabama
Nicholas Llewellyn, Emory University
Jason Locklin, University of Georgia
Brian Long, The University of Tennessee, Knoxville
Carl Lovely, The University of Texas at Arlington
Claudia Lucero, California State University, Sacramento
Breeyawn Lybbert, University of Wisconsin—Green Bay
David Madar, Arizona State University Polytechnic
Helena Malinakova, The University of Kansas
Richard Manderville, University of Guelph
Kirk Manfredi, University of Northern Iowa
Kristen Mascall, Brandeis University
Eugene Mash, The University of Arizona
Eric Masson, Ohio University
Daniell Mattern, The University of Mississippi
Anita Mattson, The Ohio State University
Gerald Mattson, University of Central Florida
Jimmy Mays, The University of Tennessee, Knoxville
Vanessa McCaffrey, Albion College
Alison McCurdy, California State University, Los Angeles
Dominic McGrath, The University of Arizona
Mark McMills, Ohio University

Marie Melzer, Old Dominion University
Ognjen Miljanic, University of Houston
Justin Miller, Hobart and William Smith Colleges
Stephen Miller, University of Florida
Justin Mohr, University of Illinois, Chicago
Suazette Mooring, Georgia State University
Jesse More, Loyola University Maryland
Andrew Morehead, East Carolina University
Barbora Morra, University of Toronto
Cheryl Moy, University of North Carolina at Chapel Hill
R. Scott Murphy, Regina University
Joan Mutanyatta-Comar, Georgia State University
David Nagib, The Ohio State University
Felix Ngassa, Grand Valley State University
Joseph O'Connor, University of California, San Diego
Taeboem Oh, California State University, Northridge
Joshua Osbourn, West Virginia University
James Parise, University of Notre Dame
Keith Pascoe, Georgia State University
Gitendra Paul, Malcolm X College
Noel Paul, The Ohio State University
Michael Pelter, Purdue University Northwest
Angela Perkins, University of Minnesota
Joanna Petridou-Fischer, Spokane Falls Community College
Tarakeshwar Pilarsetty, Arizona State University
Smitha Pillai, Arizona State University
Kyle Plunkett, Southern Illinois University
Pamela Pollet, Georgia Institute of Technology
James Poole, Ball State University
Brian Popp, West Virginia University
Walda Powell, Meredith College
Stephen Pruett, Jefferson Community and Technical College
Christine Pruis, Arizona State University
Harold Rogers, California State University, Fullerton
Frank Rossi, State University of New York, Cortland
Sheryl Rummel, Pennsylvania State University
Nicholas Salzameda, California State University, Fullerton
Robert Sammelson, Ball State University
Joachim Schantl, University of Florida
Jacob Schroeder, Clemson University
Adrian Schwan, University of Guelph
Colleen Scott, Southern Illinois University, Carbondale
Reza Sedaghat-Herati, Missouri State University
Jia Sheng, University of Albany
Abbas Shilabin, East Tennessee State University
Alan Shusterman, Reed College
Matthew Siebert, Missouri State University
Joseph Simard, University of New England
Chatu Sirimanne, California State University, Los Angeles
Heather Sklenicka, Rochester Community and Technical College
Chad Snyder, Western Kentucky University
Mike Slade, University of Evansville
Greg Slough, Kalamazoo College
John Sorensen, University of Manitoba
Gary Spessard, The University of Arizona
Levi Stanley, Iowa State University
Laurie Starkey, California State Polytechnic University, Pomona
Nicholas Stephanopoulos, Arizona State University
Robert Ternansky, University of California, San Diego
Tracy Thompson, Alverno College
Nathan Tice, Butler University
John Tomlinson, Wake Forest University
Melissa VanAlstine-Parris, Adelphi University
Nanine Van Draanen, California Polytechnic State University
Sadanandan Velu, The University of Alabama at Birmingham
Martin Walker, The State University of New York at Potsdam
Qian Wang, University of South Carolina
Don Warner, Boise State University
Michael Weaver, University of Florida
Haim Weizman, University of California, San Diego
Lyndon West, Florida Atlantic University
Lisa Whalen, The University of New Mexico
Anne Wilson, Butler University
James Wilson, University of Miami

Laurie Witucki, Grand Valley State University
James Wollack, St. Catherine University
Kai Ylijoki, Saint Mary's University
Andrei Yudin, University of Toronto
Michael Zagorski, Case Western Reserve University
Rui Zhang, Western Kentucky University
Yimin Zhu, Pennsylvania State University, Altoona
Regina Zibuck, Wayne State University
Eugene Zubarev, Rice University
James Zubricky, The University of Toledo

Resources for Students

Study Guide and Solutions Manual

by Taylor Mach, Concordia University, St. Paul; Joel Karty, Elon University; and Marie Melzer

Written by dedicated organic chemistry instructors, this guide provides students with fully worked solutions to all unworked problems in the text, including all Try It, Your Turn, and end-of-chapter problems. Every solution follows a Think-Solve format similar to the one used in the textbook, so the approach to problem solving is modeled consistently. To ensure clarity and accuracy, every solution is reviewed by undergraduate students in addition to organic chemistry professors.

The *Study Guide and Solutions Manual* is an ebook that is available for purchase at digital.wwnorton.com/karty3ssm.

NEW Animations and Videos

by Joel Karty, Elon University, and Kristen Barrett, Rowan University

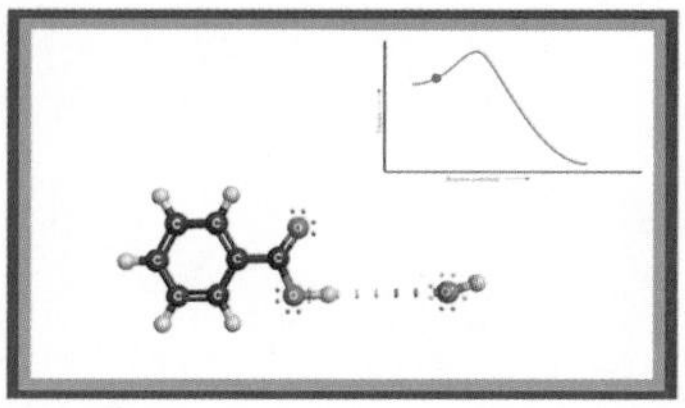

The Third Edition offers over 80 videos and narrated animations on elementary steps, mechanisms, and important organic chemistry problem-solving skills. Like the book itself, the videos help students to develop and apply critical thinking skills, and they are specifically designed to counter common student misconceptions. The three video types are as follows:

- **15 Elementary Step animations** help students to visualize what is happening on a molecular level during the elementary steps, and to understand the concomitant changes in energy. Each animation begins after the curved arrow notation has been presented, so students can see that all changes represented by the curved arrows occur simultaneously rather than as separate events.
- **20 Strategies for Success videos** guide students through solving challenging types of problems, and they help students gain command over difficult topics. They feature Joel Karty on camera, often narrating a combination of whiteboard drawings and model kit manipulations.
- **50 Mechanism Drawing videos** help students gain the skills to draw mechanisms on their own. Whereas the textbook provides mechanisms that are already complete, each mechanism is drawn from scratch in these videos, which brings the process to life. Moreover, the starting materials for these mechanism videos are different from the those used for the mechanisms in the textbook, which gives students more variety. Twenty-five mechanism videos have been recorded by Joel Karty, and the remaining 25 have been recorded by Kristen Barrett, Rowan University, to provide an additional instructor's perspective.

Students can watch the videos in the ebook, or you can assign them in Smartwork online homework questions. The videos are also available with pedagogical notes and discussion questions on our Norton Teaching Tools site. Ten additional mechanism-drawing videos will be released each year for the life of the edition.

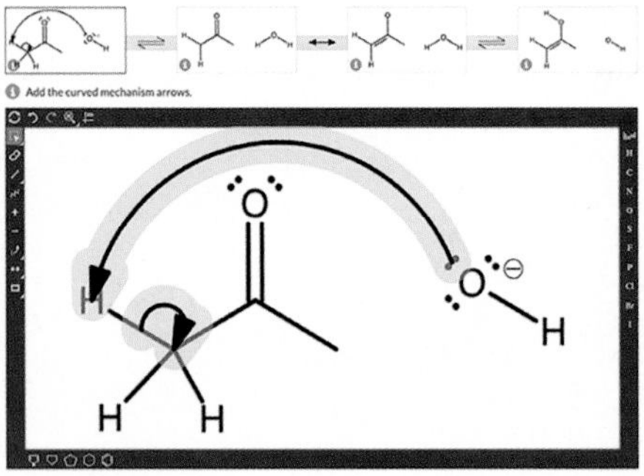

Smartwork Online Homework (digital.wwnorton.com/karty3)

Smartwork is an easy-to-use online homework system that helps students become better problem solvers through a variety of interactive question types, book-specific hints, and extensive answer-specific feedback. Over 4000 problems, including over 1100 graded mechanism problems, support the text's organization and pedagogy. The intuitive 2-D molecular drawing and multistep tools allow students to practice drawing mechanisms while receiving coaching in real time; every problem in Smartwork has hints and answer-specific feedback to guide students and provide the help they need, when they need it. Each problem in Smartwork links directly to the appropriate page in the ebook, so students have an instant reference and are prompted to read.

Get started quickly with our premade assignments for each chapter, plus new MCAT skill-building assignments, or take advantage of Smartwork's flexibility by customizing questions and adding your own content. Integration with your campus learning management system (LMS) saves you time by allowing Smartwork grades to report directly to your LMS gradebook, while individual and classwide performance reports help you see students' progress, identify challenging concepts, and intervene to help students who struggled with those concepts.

New Smartwork questions will be released each year throughout the life of the edition, allowing instructors to refresh their assignments.

The Smartwork course for the Third Edition features the following:

- **An expert author team.** The Smartwork course was authored by instructors who teach at a diverse group of schools: Arizona State University, Brigham Young University, Butler University, Craven Community College, Florida State University, Kent State University, Mesa Community College, and Rochester Community and Technical College. The authors' experience in teaching diverse student populations has resulted in a question library that will appeal to instructors at all schools.
- **An unparalleled drawing tool.** Smartwork contains an upgraded 2-D drawing tool that mimics drawing on paper, reduces frustration, and helps students focus on the problem at hand. This intuitive tool supports both multistep mechanism and multistep synthesis problems and provides students with answer-specific feedback for every problem. The 2-D drawing tool has a variety of features that make drawing easy and efficient. Students are provided with templates including a variety of common rings and a carbon chain drawing tool. In addition, Smartwork presents students with a toolbar of commonly used elements, the ability to add lone pairs with a single click, and easy-to-use features such as undo, redo, single-click erase, and zoom-in/zoom-out.
- **100+ Video- and animation-based problems.** These questions make the new suite of videos assignable and assessable.
- **Pooled problem sets.** Smartwork features sets of pooled problems to promote independent work. Groups of similar problems are "pooled" into one problem so different students receive different problems from the pool. Instructors can choose our preset pools or create their own.
- **NEW MCAT skill-building assignments.** These assignments designed to help premed students practice applying the skills the exam will assess.
- **Question variety.** The Smartwork course offers a diverse set of problems including nomenclature, multistep mechanism, multistep synthesis, reaction, and spectroscopy problems. Conceptual question types include ranking, sorting, labeling, numeric entry, multiple-choice/multiple-select, and short answer.

Ebook (digital.wwnorton.com/karty3)

Norton Ebooks offer an enhanced reading experience at a fraction of the cost of a print textbook. New videos are embedded directly inline with text, helping students visualize mechanisms and elementary steps as they are introduced. The ebook provides an active reading experience, featuring click-to-reveal answers for Your Turn exercises, as well as enabling students to take notes, bookmark, search, highlight, and read offline. Instructors can even embed their own videos or notes that students can see as they are reading the text. Norton Ebooks can be viewed on all computers and mobile devices.

The online ebook is available at no extra cost with the purchase of a new print text, or it may be purchased as a stand-alone with Smartwork.

Resources for Instructors

Norton Teaching Tools (https://iig.wwnorton.com/karty3/full)

by Michelle Boucher, Utica College, and Andrew Robak, Keuka College

Written by users of the text, our new Norton Teaching Tools provide all the support resources that instructors need to make the switch to organization by mechanism and to continually refresh their syllabus with creative, diverse resources.

Based on their experiences teaching with the second edition, Michelle and Andrew have compiled a wealth of resources in this searchable, sortable online repository. Sample content includes:

- lecture PowerPoint slides with integrated figures from the book
- classroom response system (or "clicker") questions
- an explanation of the differences between Joel Karty's organizational approach and what a professor may be familiar with in other textbooks
- outlines of each chapter with presentation suggestions
- commentary on common student misunderstandings
- descriptions of each video and animation, including a summary, discussion questions, specific usage suggestions, and Smartwork questions that use that video
- activities, classroom demonstrations, and lab experiment suggestions
- select photographs and every piece of line art in both JPEG and PowerPoint formats

Lecture PowerPoint Slides and Clicker Questions

by Sarah Pierce, Cumberland University

Our PowerPoint slides reflect the dynamic and diverse ways instructors lecture. These slides have been revised and streamlined to highlight larger color figures from the text, and new problem slides encourage in-class problem solving.

Around 400 clicker questions allow instructors to immediately assess student understanding and advance their problem-solving skills. All clicker questions are available in PowerPoint format or can be delivered via Squarecap classroom response system.

All lecture PowerPoint slides and clicker questions have been optimized to be fully accessible for visually impaired students.

Clickers in Action: Active Learning in Organic Chemistry

by Suzanne M. Ruder, Virginia Commonwealth University

This instructor-oriented resource provides information on implementing clickers in organic chemistry courses. Part I gives instructors information on how to choose and manage a classroom response system, develop effective questions, and integrate the questions into their courses. Part II contains 140 class-tested, lecture-ready questions. Most questions include histograms that show actual student response, generated in large classes with 200–300 students over multiple terms. Each question also includes insights and suggestions for implementation. The 140 questions in *Clickers in Action* are sorted to correspond to the chapters in the textbook.

Norton Testmaker

by Jennifer Griffith, Western Washington University, and James Wollack, St. Catherine University

Norton uses evidence-based models to deliver high-quality and pedagogically effective testing materials. Over 1600 questions, at least 20% new or revised for this edition, are organized by a new set of learning objectives that align with new section objectives in the text as well as organizing objectives in Smartwork and the Norton Teaching Tools site.

The test bank is available for the first time in Norton Testmaker, which brings Norton's high-quality testing materials online. Create assessments for your course from anywhere with an Internet connection, without downloading files or installing specialized software. Search and filter test bank questions by chapter, type, difficulty, learning objectives, Bloom's taxonomy, or keyword. You can also customize test bank questions to fit your course.

Easily export your tests or Norton's ready-to-use quizzes to Microsoft Word or Common Cartridge files for your LMS.

Author Blog: www.teachthemechanism.com

In July 2012, Joel Karty started a blog about his organizational approach and his experience teaching from the text. Now there are more than 218 guest blog posts written by professors who use Joel's book, which have garnered nearly 115,000 views. What once was an informational blog has now grown into a platform for a community of instructors to share their experiences and insights, have open-forum discussions, view sample materials, and watch videos of Joel as he discusses a number of topics, including how he believes a mechanistic organization allows users of his book to have increased expectations about student understanding. Visit the blog and join the community!

Molecular Model Kits

Norton partners with two model kit providers and can package either kit with the textbook for an additional cost.

Darling Molecular Model Kit. Tetrahedral atoms are constructed by snapping together two V-shaped pieces in a jigsaw style, emphasizing bond angles and symmetry elements of the atoms. Double bonds are independent, rectangular units to emphasize the planarity of sp^2-hybridized atoms. Large substituents can be represented by various colored marker balls.

This kit includes 120 pieces:

- 57 sp^3 V-shaped pieces (black, red, blue, silver)
- 16 sp^2 V-shaped pieces (gray)
- 18 marker balls (white, red, green, blue)
- 7 double bonds (gray)
- 6 half double bonds (gray)
- 2 trigonal atoms (gray)
- 2 linear bonds (gray)
- 4 bond extenders (hot pink)
- 4 octahedral pieces (hot pink)
- 2 Atom Visions™ balls (hot pink, black)

HGS Molecular Structure Model Kit. The HGS kit reflects the traditional ball-and-stick model for constructing molecules. Conjugation can be illustrated by using trigonal planar atoms that have five holes to accommodate three bonds and the two lobes of a *p* orbital. Double bonds can be constructed by using curved sticks to occupy two valences of a tetrahedral atom.

This kit includes 130 pieces:

- 30 hydrogen atoms, white
- 6 carbon atoms (sp^2, dsp^3), black
- 9 carbon atoms (sp^3), black
- 1 nitrogen atom (sp^3), blue
- 1 nitrogen atom (sp^2, dsp^3), blue
- 4 oxygen atoms (sp^3), red
- 1 sulfur atom (sp^3), yellow
- 1 chlorine atom (sp^3), green
- 2 miscellaneous atoms (sp, d^2sp^3), gray
- 70 bonds (pink, green, white, yellow, bent blue)
- 4 orbital plates (green, blue)
- 1 bond puller (black)

Please contact your Norton representative about ordering and pricing options for packaging model kits.

Preface for the Student

Some Suggestions for How to Use This Book

Perhaps you have heard that organic chemistry is difficult. Perhaps you have heard that it requires an enormous amount of memorization. Are these statements true? It depends on how you approach the course. It is true that this book contains a lot of information: much more than you can memorize. There is a better way.

You can understand organic chemistry through models and theories that are built on fundamental concepts. Consider, for example, that when two compounds react under a given set of conditions, the outcome of that reaction is precisely the same, each and every time. Is this because the reactant molecules have memorized what products they are supposed to make? No—they are obeying certain chemical laws, and you can learn those laws.

You will spend considerable effort throughout this course developing those models and theories. *Reaction mechanisms*—detailed steps that show how reactions take place—are among the most important ideas to develop. If you devote your time and energy to understanding mechanisms and learning how they are applied toward solving problems, you will find that much of organic chemistry can be conquered without rote memorization, and you will find the course to be quite rewarding and enjoyable. Moreover, the skills you develop in organic chemistry will apply to complex situations you will face beyond this course.

If you are planning on a career in a health profession, it is particularly important for you to focus on understanding and applying concepts as opposed to memorizing. On standardized exams like the MCAT, you will often need to choose between answers that look equally good to students who have memorized the material. To a student who is well-versed in applying concepts and mechanisms toward solving problems, on the other hand, those choices are more easily discernible.

In light of how important it is to understand concepts and mechanisms, your success in this course will demand a lot of time and devotion. Therefore, you should consider the following suggestions for using that time, and this book, most efficiently:

- **Read actively and diligently.** You should try to read the assigned sections before class if possible. Reading prior to class means that you will see the material for the second time in class. This will allow you to better process information and give you ample opportunity to ask pertinent questions. When you read, you should have a pen or pencil in hand so you can underline or highlight what you feel is important, and take notes about what you find enlightening or confusing. Note that you can also highlight and take notes in the ebook. *Pay attention to the objectives listed at the beginning*

SECTION 7.1 OBJECTIVES

You will be able to:

1. Identify electron-rich and electron-poor sites within a species.
2. Articulate how the curved arrow notation for a proton transfer step represents the flow of electrons from an electron-rich site to an electron-poor site.
3. Identify organometallic reagents and hydride reagents as sources of carbanions and hydride, respectively.

Elementary Step for Equation 7-1

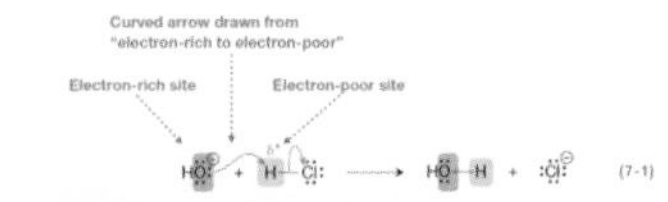

Curved arrow drawn from "electron-rich to electron-poor"

Electron-rich site   Electron-poor site

$H\overset{..}{\underset{..}{S}}^{\ominus} + H-\overset{..}{\underset{..}{Br}}: \longrightarrow H\overset{..}{\underset{..}{S}}-H + :\overset{..}{\underset{..}{Br}}:^{\ominus}$ (7-1)

▶️ Video: Proton Transfer

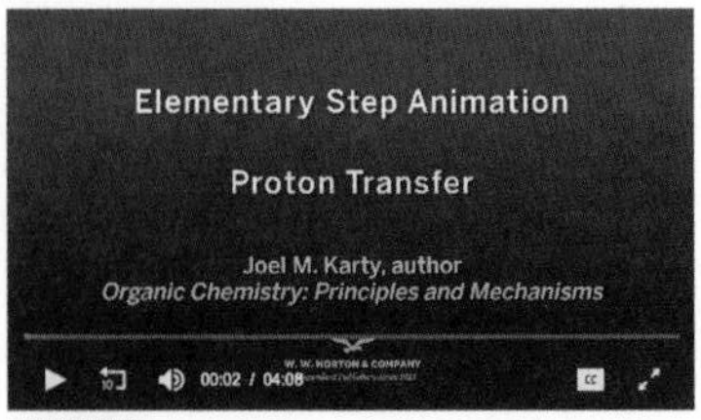

Elementary Step Animation

Proton Transfer

Joel M. Karty, author
Organic Chemistry: Principles and Mechanisms

W. W. NORTON & COMPANY
▶ ⟲ 🔊 00:02 / 04:08   CC ⛶

▶ Transcript

YOUR TURN 7.1

Consider the proton transfer step shown here. **(a)** Identify the electron-rich and electron-poor sites, and label the curved arrow that connects the two as "electron-rich to electron-poor." **(b)** Explain why the curved arrow notation would be faulty if the curved arrow on the right were not drawn.

$H\overset{..}{\underset{..}{S}}:^{\ominus} + H-\overset{..}{\underset{..}{Br}}: \longrightarrow H\overset{..}{\underset{..}{S}}-H + :\overset{..}{\underset{..}{Br}}:^{\ominus}$

▶ SHOW ANSWER

▼ HIDE ANSWER

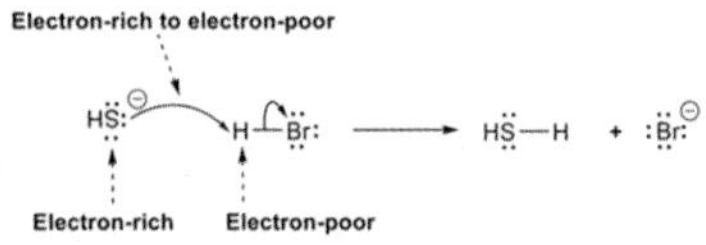

Electron-rich to electron-poor

$H\overset{..}{\underset{..}{S}}:^{\ominus} \quad H-\overset{..}{\underset{..}{Br}}: \longrightarrow H\overset{..}{\underset{..}{S}}-H + :\overset{..}{\underset{..}{Br}}:^{\ominus}$

Electron-rich   Electron-poor

Without the curved arrow on the right, the H—Br bond would remain unbroken and H would have two bonds, exceeding its duet.

SOLVED PROBLEM 7.1

How to determine the proper electron flow and outcome for a proton transfer

Break It Down Identify the electron-poor H atom in methanol. Draw the mechanism by which methanol acts as an acid in a proton transfer reaction with H_2N^-.

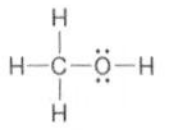

$$H-\overset{\overset{\displaystyle H}{|}}{\underset{\underset{\displaystyle H}{|}}{C}}-\overset{..}{\underset{..}{O}}-H$$
Methanol

Every Solved Problem in this book uses a Think/Solve strategy to guide you through the solution. After you consider a question posed on the Think side of the table, read the answer on the Solve side.

Think	Solve
What kinds of charges characterize electron-poor atoms? Which H in methanol bears that kind of charge?	An electron-poor atom tends to have a partial or full positive charge. Because the O atom in methanol is highly electronegative, the attached H bears a substantial partial positive charge and is therefore electron-poor.
Should H_2N^- be considered electron-rich or electron-poor?	The negative charge on H_2N^- indicates it is electron-rich.
When H_2N^- and CH_3OH are combined, how do we draw a curved arrow to depict the flow of electrons from an electron-rich site to an electron-poor site?	A curved arrow is drawn from the electrons on N to H, indicating the flow of electrons from an electron-rich site (denoted by the red screen) to an electron-poor site (blue screen). That arrow also indicates the formation of a new N—H bond. 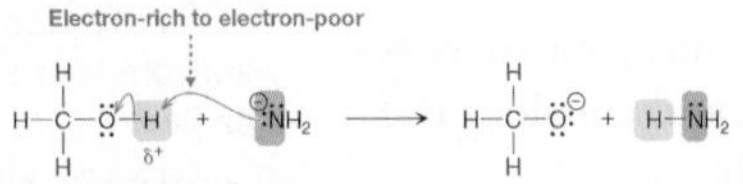 **Electron-rich to electron-poor** $H-\overset{\overset{\displaystyle H}{|}}{\underset{\underset{\displaystyle H}{|}}{C}}-\overset{..}{\underset{\delta+}{O}}-H + {}^{\ominus}:NH_2 \longrightarrow H-\overset{\overset{\displaystyle H}{|}}{\underset{\underset{\displaystyle H}{|}}{C}}-\overset{..}{\underset{..}{O}}:^{\ominus} + H-NH_2$
When that curved arrow is drawn to depict bond formation, do any other bonds have to break?	The H in methanol gains a new bond, but there cannot be two bonds to H, so the initial O—H bond must break. A curved arrow from the O—H bond to the O represents the breaking of that bond. The O on the product side picks up that pair of electrons and ends up with a −1 formal charge.

Try It Identify the electron-rich and electron-poor sites in the reactant molecules shown here. Draw the curved arrows and the products for the proton transfer between these two molecules, and label the curved arrow that represents the flow of electrons from an electron-rich site to an electron-poor site. *Hint:* Are all the relevant electron pairs shown?

$$H_3C-\overset{\overset{\displaystyle CH_3}{|}}{N}-CH_3 + H_2O \longrightarrow ?$$

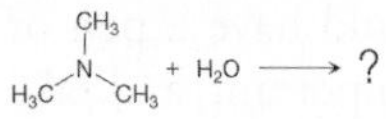

Answers to all Try It exercises can be found in the Solutions Manual.

---

of each section, as those are the things you will be expected to do on completion of the section. When the text refers to a figure or reaction mechanism, take that as a cue to study that figure now. Be sure that what the text is describing makes sense to you before you move on. If you are referred to a previous chapter, flip to the appropriate page to refresh your memory.

- **Visualize and understand with videos.** We've created over 80 videos to help you visualize mechanisms and develop problem-solving skills. Watch them when they appear in the ebook. When you see the video icon in your print book, head to digital.wwnorton.com/karty3 to watch them. Pay particular attention to the videos that accompany the Strategies for Success sections, as these illustrate skills and techniques that you will need to master and apply throughout the course.

- **Engage with Your Turns.** These relatively short activities ask you to complete a task or solve a problem based on what you have just read. I developed them to help you remain actively engaged while you read. They will also help you quickly evaluate whether you understand the topic at hand, ultimately giving you confidence to press on each time you successfully complete one. I encourage you to work through all Your Turn exercises in each chapter and quickly check the answers by clicking to reveal them in the ebook or referring to page ANS-1 in the print book.

- **Use the Think-Solve approach to work through Solved Problems.** Multiple Solved Problems appear in each chapter, designed to help you build critical skills to solve problems on your own. The skills you will gain from each Solved Problem can be identified by its title, which begins with "How to ..." You will notice that every Solved Problem has a Think-Solve table immediately after the problem statement, which will help guide you through the solution to the problem. In each row, questions are given in the Think column on the left side of the table, which point you toward the kinds of things you should consider as you approach solving the problem. Those questions are answered in the Solve column on the right side of the table. As you work your way through the Solved Problem, make sure to read each Think question, followed by its corresponding Solve answer. At the end of every Solved Problem, you will find a Try It exercise that is similar to the problem that was just solved. Give every Try It exercise your best attempt, using the corresponding Solved Problem as a guide, and check the solution in the *Study Guide and Solutions Manual* Ebook. Doing so will give you valuable feedback.

- **Practice solving end-of-chapter problems.** As with anything new you attempt, mastery requires practice. Most of your practice should come from solving problems. I have included more than 2000 problems throughout this book, located at the end of each chapter. Take the time to work through as many problems as possible, and use them to assess areas of strength and weakness.

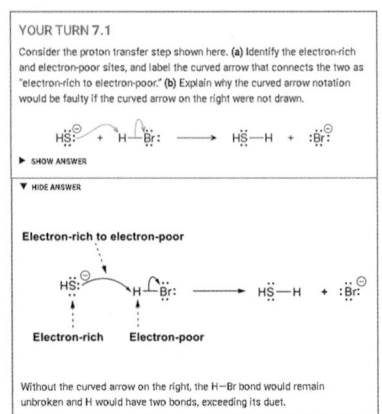

Organic Chemistry and You

You are taking organic chemistry for a reason: you might be pursuing a career in which an understanding of organic chemistry is crucial, or the course might be required for your particular field of study, or both. You might even be taking the course simply out of interest. Regardless of the reason, organic chemistry impacts your life in significant ways.

Consider, for example, the growing concern about the increasing resistance of bacteria to antibiotics over the past several decades. Perhaps no pathogen has caused more alarm than methicillin-resistant *Staphylococcus aureus* (MRSA), a type of bacteria responsible for staph infections. Methicillin is a member of the penicillin family of antibiotics, and resistance to methicillin in these bacteria was first observed in 1961. Today MRSA, which has been called a superbug, is resistant to most antibiotics, including all penicillin-derived antibiotics.

A breakthrough in the fight against MRSA occurred in 2006 with the discovery of a compound called platensimycin, isolated from *Streptomyces* spores. The way that platensimycin targets bacteria is different from that of any other antibiotic in use and, therefore, it is not currently susceptible to bacterial resistance.

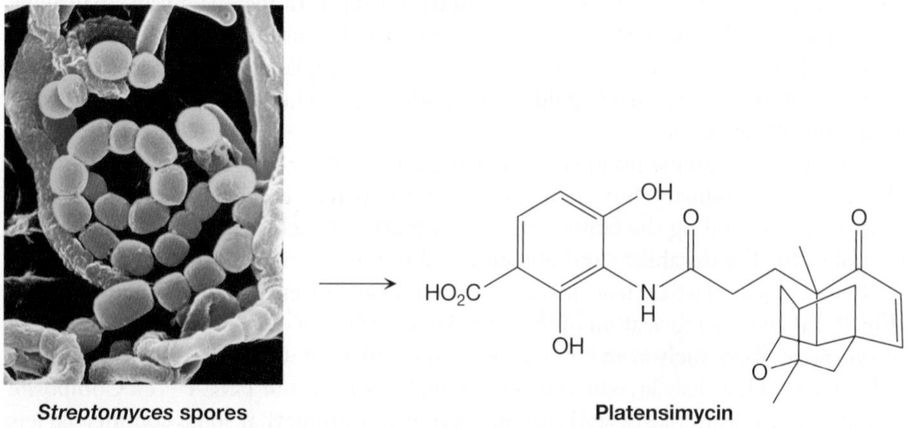
OH
O
O
HO_2C
N
H
OH
O

***Streptomyces* spores** **Platensimycin**

Platensimycin is isolated from a South African soil bacterium, *Streptomyces platensis*, and was discovered by screening 250,000 natural product extracts for antibacterial activity. Sheo B. Singh (Merck Research Laboratories) and coworkers determined the structure of platensimycin using a technique called nuclear magnetic resonance (NMR) spectroscopy, which we discuss in Chapter 17. Not long after, K. C. Nicolaou and co-workers from the Scripps Research Institute (La Jolla, California) and the University of California, San Diego, were the first to devise a synthesis of platensimycin from other readily available chemicals.

The story of platensimycin, from discovery to synthesis, involves several of the subdisciplines that make up the field of organic chemistry.

- **Biological chemistry (biochemistry):** the study of the behavior of biomolecules and the nature of chemical reactions that occur in living systems.
- **Structure determination:** the use of established experimental techniques to determine the structure of newly discovered compounds.
- **Organic synthesis:** the design of pathways for making new compounds from existing, readily available compounds by means of known organic reactions.

Because each of these areas typically focuses on solving existing and practical problems, they are considered to be applied areas of organic chemistry. However, other areas of organic chemistry, considered to be theoretical in nature, provide the foundations on which such applications rest. They focus on answering questions about the how and why of chemical processes. For example, an understanding of the basic principles of NMR spectroscopy (an analytical technique discussed in Chapter 17) underlies our

(a) (b) (c) (d)

POLICE
787

FIGURE P-1 Some uses of plastics Plastics, which are designed and created in the laboratories of organic chemists, are found in a wide range of products, such as (a) food packaging, (b) an artificial heart, (c) body armor made from Kevlar, and (d) a Boeing 787, a commercial jet whose body consists largely of composite materials made from plastics and carbon fibers.

(a)

(b)

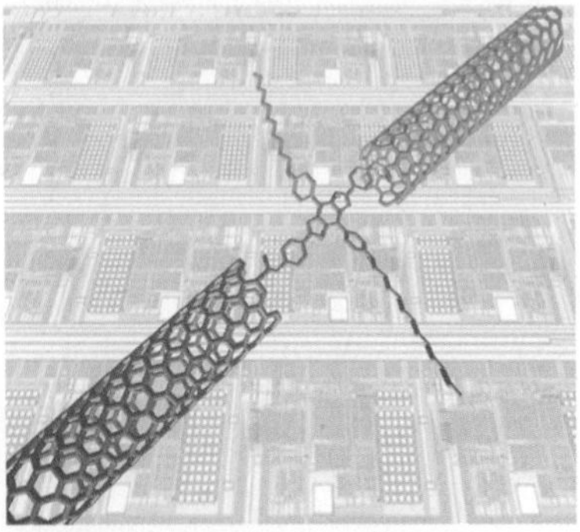

FIGURE P-2 Organic chemistry in the electronics industry (a) A smartphone whose display is made from organic light-emitting diodes (OLEDs). (b) A molecular switch in which an organic molecule joins together two carbon nanotubes, which are sheets of carbon in the form of cylinders with a diameter on the order of 10^{-9} meter.

ability to determine molecular structure. Understanding the principles that govern organic reactions (such as those involved in the synthesis of platensimycin) may allow us to enhance yields, not only by altering reaction conditions but also perhaps by devising entirely new synthesis schemes. And understanding platensimycin's specific mode of attack on bacteria will likely guide us in modifying its chemical structure to make it even more effective.

The story of platensimycin showcases the importance of organic chemistry in the pharmaceutical industry, but organic chemistry is at the center of other high-profile areas as well, including the fabrication of new materials such as polymers (the topic of Chapter 28). The durability and chemical stability of thermoplastic polymers (often shortened to just plastics) have made them excellent choices for use in food packaging (Fig. P-1a) and the fabrication of the artificial heart (Fig. P-1b). Plastics are the source of synthetic fibers such as nylon and polyester, which are often used in the clothing industry, as well as Kevlar, which is used to make body armor (Fig. P-1c). Composite materials made from plastic and carbon fibers are so strong that some commercial jets are now constructed with a body made largely from plastics (Fig. P-1d).

Organic chemistry has also been at the forefront of generating new materials for electronic devices. Organic light-emitting diodes (OLEDs) are the main components of electronic displays for many high-end smartphones (Fig. P-2a), and single organic molecules can be used to make electronic switches tens of thousands of times smaller than those used in today's integrated circuits (Fig. P-2b).

Perhaps even more important to our lives is the impact that organic chemistry can have on our ability to understand, and solve, environmental problems, such as overflowing landfills (Fig. P-3a), the destruction of the stratospheric ozone layer (Fig. P-3b), and global warming (Fig. P-3c). Organic chemistry, for example, is helping provide new ways to recycle waste materials. Additionally, organic chemistry has been used to engineer new coolants that are safer for the environment than the chlorofluorocarbons (CFCs) used in the late 20th century in refrigerators and air conditioners. Finally, organic chemistry may lead us to economically feasible processes by which we can synthesize hydrogen gas, a fuel whose combustion product is only water. This could be a welcome alternative to coal and oil, whose combustion products not only cause air and water pollution but also generate carbon dioxide, one of several greenhouse gases responsible for global warming.

(a)

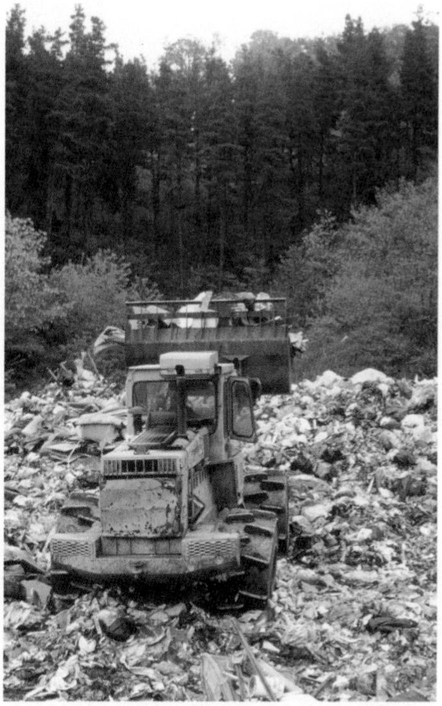

(b) September 2020

(c)

FIGURE P-3 Organic chemistry and the environment Organic chemistry continues to play a significant role in solving environmental problems, such as (a) overflowing landfills, (b) ozone depletion (the area in red represents the ozone hole over Antarctica), and (c) global warming (the ice sheets in Montana's Glacier National Park have been melting at a dramatically accelerating rate over the past 90 years).

Because organic chemistry is important in so many ways, you will find one or two Interest boxes in the main part of each chapter, which show how the material in the chapter directly connects to issues that you might find more relevant or more interesting. Take the time to read those boxes, and consider researching them even further. In addition to those Interest boxes, you will find several Connections boxes in the margins of each chapter, each of which provides a glimpse into how a molecule you just encountered relates to an aspect of everyday life.

All this being said, it's time to get started. Keep your focus on concepts and mechanisms, work hard, and ask questions!

Organic chemistry is often referred to as the chemistry of life because biological compounds such as DNA, proteins, and carbohydrates are themselves organic molecules. In this chapter, we examine some of the bonding characteristics of these and other organic molecules, which are constructed primarily from carbon, hydrogen, nitrogen, and oxygen.

1

Atomic and Molecular Structure

Organic chemistry is often called "the chemistry of life" because organic compounds, and the reactions they undergo, are responsible for sustaining life. What are the characteristics of such compounds and what advantages do those compounds offer living organisms? Here in Chapter 1 we begin to answer these questions.

We review several aspects of atomic and molecular structure typically covered in a general chemistry course, including ionic and covalent bonding, the basics of Lewis dot structures, and resonance theory. We then tighten our focus on organic molecules, presenting various types of shorthand notation that organic chemists often use, and we introduce common bonding arrangements, called functional groups, encountered in organic chemistry.

Toward the end of this chapter, we will apply some of the ideas discussed in this chapter, especially functional groups, to certain classes of biomolecules: specifically, amino acids, monosaccharides, and nucleotides. With this early introduction to some basic aspects of biochemistry, you will begin to appreciate the relevance of organic chemistry to biological systems.

1.1 What Is Organic Chemistry?

SECTION 1.1 OBJECTIVES

You will be able to:

1. Distinguish organic compounds from inorganic ones.
2. Explain why organic compounds are not limited to those synthesized by living things.

Organic chemistry is the branch of chemistry involving *organic compounds*. What, then, is an organic compound?

In the late 1700s, scientists defined organic compounds as ones that could be obtained from a *living* organism: compounds such as glucose (a sugar), testosterone (a hormone), and deoxyribonucleic acid (DNA; genetic material) (**Figure 1-1**). According to a theory called **vitalism**, only living systems could summon up a mysterious "vital force" needed to synthesize organic compounds. All other compounds, including ones synthesized in the lab, were defined as inorganic.

The vitalist definition of organic compounds became obsolete in 1828, when Friedrich Wöhler (1800–1882), a German physician and chemist, synthesized urea by heating a solution of ammonium cyanate (Eq. 1-1); urea is a major component of mammalian urine and is organic, but ammonium cyanate is inorganic.

An inorganic compound | An organic compound

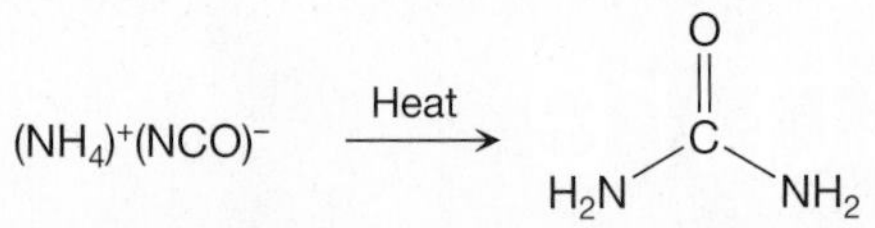
$(NH_4)^+(NCO)^-$
Heat
O
C
H_2N
NH_2

Ammonium cyanate | **Urea** (1-1)

If vitalism couldn't account for the distinction between organic and inorganic compounds, what could? Gradually, chemists arrived at our modern definition:

An **organic compound** contains a substantial amount of carbon and hydrogen, whereas an **inorganic compound** does not.

This definition is still imperfect because it leaves some room for interpretation, but it does allow chemists to classify most molecules.

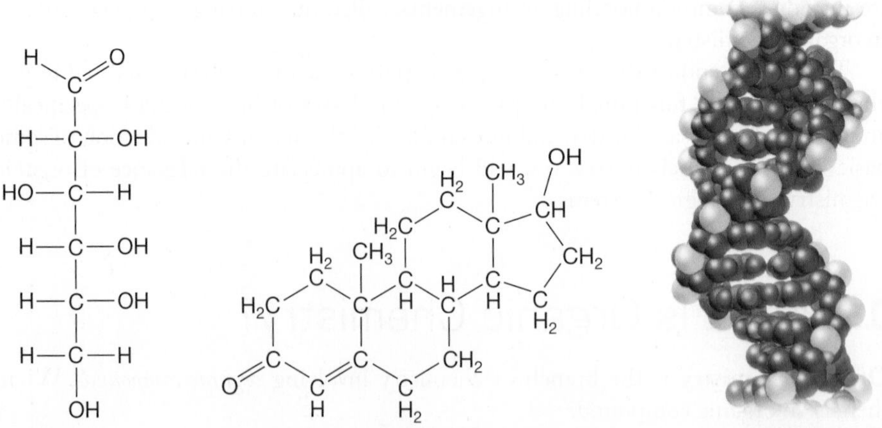

Glucose | **Testosterone** | **DNA**

FIGURE 1-1 Some familiar organic compounds Glucose, testosterone, and DNA are organic compounds produced by living organisms.

The birth of organic chemistry as a distinct field occurred around the time that vitalism was dismissed, making the discipline less than 200 years old. However, humans have taken advantage of organic reactions and the properties of organic compounds for thousands of years! Since about 6000 BCE, for example, civilizations have fermented grapes to make wine. Some evidence suggests that Babylonians, as early as 2800 BCE, could convert oils into soaps.

Organic chemistry has matured tremendously since its inception. Today, we can not only use organic reactions to reproduce complex molecules found in nature but also engineer new molecules never before seen.

CONNECTIONS 1.1

Organic compounds in ancient civilizations Royal purple, also called Tyrian purple, is a natural dye that was obtained by ancient Phoenicians from the aquatic snail *Bolinus brandaris*, shown here. About 10,000 of these snails had to be processed to obtain a single gram of dye.

1.2 Why Carbon?

Why does the carbon atom play such a central role in the chemistry of life? First of all, carbon is capable of forming incredibly *diverse* compounds. As will be explained in Section 1.6, the carbon atom can form four covalent bonds to other atoms, especially other carbon atoms.

Consequently, carbon atoms can link together in chains of almost any length (**Figure 1-2a**) as well as in rings of various sizes. Moreover, each carbon atom is capable of forming not only single bonds but also double and triple bonds (Fig. 1-2b). Finally, the ability to form four bonds means that *branching* can occur at each carbon (Fig. 1-2c). These characteristics make possible a tremendous number of compounds, even with a relatively small number of carbon atoms. Indeed, to date, tens of millions of organic compounds are known, and the list is growing rapidly as we continue to discover or synthesize new compounds.

SECTION 1.2 OBJECTIVES

You will be able to:

1. Describe how the diversity in the structure of organic molecules is an outcome of carbon's ability to form four bonds.
2. Explain the role of bond strength in the stability of organic molecules.

If carbon works so well, then why *not* silicon, which appears just below carbon in the periodic table? Elements in the same group (column) of the periodic table tend to have similar chemical properties, so silicon, too, can form four covalent bonds, giving it the same potential for diversity as carbon. The answer is *stability*. As we will see in Section 1.4, a bond formed between silicon atoms has about half the strength of a bond formed between carbon atoms, making it much easier to break a bond between silicon atoms. Thus, compounds based on silicon would be much less stable.

Let's entertain the idea of silicon atoms replacing carbon atoms in biomolecules such as glucose ($C_6H_{12}O_6$). Glucose is broken down by our bodies through cellular respiration to extract energy, according to the overall reaction in Equation 1-2. One of the by-products is carbon dioxide, a gas, which is exhaled from the lungs. If the molecules of life were based on silicon, the glucose analog would be $Si_6H_{12}O_6$, and its by-product would be silicon dioxide (SiO_2), as shown in Equation 1-3. Silicon

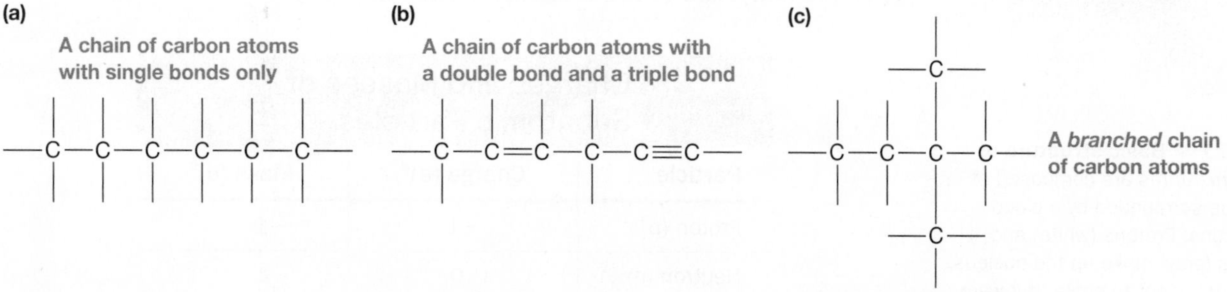
(a)
A chain of carbon atoms with single bonds only
(b)
A chain of carbon atoms with a double bond and a triple bond
(c)
A *branched* chain of carbon atoms

FIGURE 1-2 Carbon's ability to generate structurally diverse compounds Organic molecules can have such diverse structures because carbon atoms can (a) link together to form chains, (b) participate in double and triple bonds, and (c) participate in branching.

FIGURE 1-3 Quartz crystal Quartz (silicon dioxide) is the silicon analog of carbon dioxide. Whereas carbon dioxide is gaseous, silicon dioxide is solid.

dioxide, a solid, is the main component of sand; in its crystalline form, it is known as quartz (**Figure 1-3**).

$$C_6H_{12}O_6(s) + 6\ O_2(g) \rightarrow 6\ CO_2(g) + 6\ H_2O(l) \quad (1\text{-}2)$$

$$Si_6H_{12}O_6(s) + 6\ O_2(g) \rightarrow 6\ SiO_2(s) + 6\ H_2O(l) \quad (1\text{-}3)$$

1.3 Atomic Structure and Ground State Electron Configurations

In Section 1.2, we saw that carbon's bonding characteristics give rise to the large variety of organic molecules. Those bonding characteristics, and the bonding characteristics of all atoms, are governed by the atom's electrons.

In this section, we consider the nature of electrons in atoms. We'll first review the basic structure of an atom, including the role of orbitals and shells. Then we'll review some rules governing electron configurations, distinguishing between *valence electrons*, which can be used for bonding, and *core electrons*.

SECTION 1.3 OBJECTIVES

You will be able to:

1. Specify the number of protons and electrons in an atom or atomic ion.
2. Write the ground state electron configuration of an atom or atomic ion.
3. Distinguish valence electrons from core electrons.

1.3a The Structure of the Atom

At the center of an atom (**Figure 1-4**) is a positively charged nucleus, composed of *protons* and *neutrons*. Surrounding the nucleus is a cloud of negatively charged *electrons*, attracted to the nucleus by simple **electrostatic forces** (the interactions by which opposite charges attract one another and like charges repel one another). Individual electrons are incredibly small, much smaller than the nucleus, but the space that electrons occupy (i.e., the *electron cloud*) is much larger than the nucleus. In other words:

- The size of an atom is essentially defined by the size of its electron cloud.
- The vast majority of an electron cloud (and thus the vast majority of an atom) is empty space.

Table 1-1 lists the mass and charge of each elementary particle. Notice that the masses of the proton and neutron are significantly greater than that of the electron, so the mass of an atom is essentially the mass of just the nucleus.

An atom, by definition, has no net charge, so *the number of electrons in an atom must equal the number of protons*. The number of protons in the nucleus, called the **atomic number (*Z*)**, defines the element. For example, a nucleus that has six protons has an atomic number of 6 and can only be a carbon nucleus.

If the number of protons and the number of electrons are *unequal*, then the entire **species** (that particular combination of protons, neutrons, and electrons) bears a net charge and is called an **ion**. A negatively charged ion, an **anion** (pronounced AN-eye-on), results from an excess of electrons. A positively charged ion, a **cation** (pronounced CAT-eye-on), results from a deficiency of electrons.

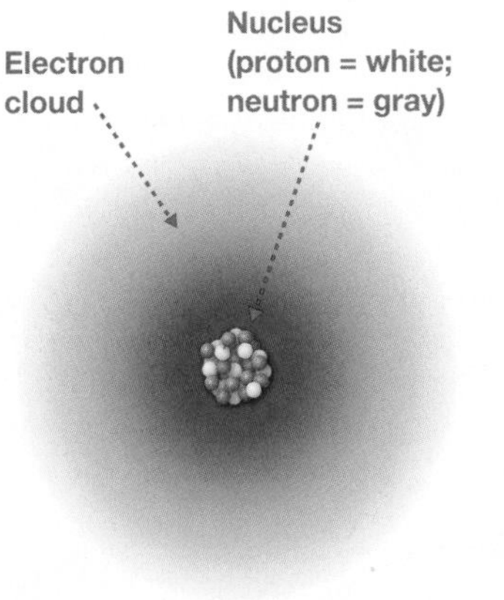
Electron cloud
Nucleus (proton = white; neutron = gray)

FIGURE 1-4 Basic structure of the atom Atoms are composed of a nucleus surrounded by a cloud of electrons. Protons (white) and neutrons (gray) make up the nucleus. (This figure is not to scale. If it were, the size of the electron cloud, which is much larger in size than the nucleus, would have a radius on the order of 500 meters!)

TABLE 1-1 Charges and Masses of Subatomic Particles

Particle	Charge (e)[a]	Mass (u)[b]
Proton (p^+)	+1	~1
Neutron (n)	0	~1
Electron (e^-)	−1	~0.0005

[a] e = Elementary charge.
[b] u = Unified atomic mass unit.

Chemistry with Chicken Wire

Some of the most exciting chemistry today involves extended frameworks of *only* carbon, as shown in **Figure 1-5**. *Graphene*, for example, is a framework of carbon atoms arranged in a single flat layer resembling molecular chicken wire. Wrapped around to form a cylinder, a graphene sheet forms what is called a *carbon nanotube*. Pure carbon can even take the form of a soccer ball: the so-called *buckminsterfullerene*.

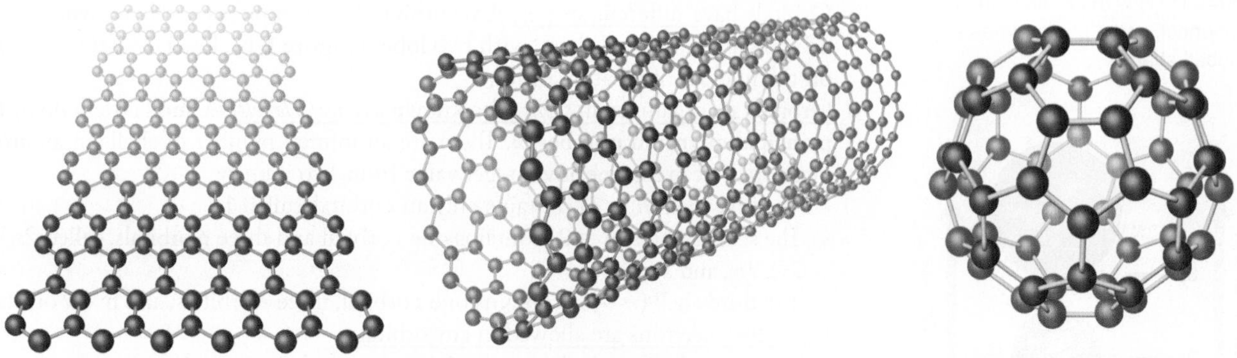

A sheet of graphene
A carbon nanotube
Buckminsterfullerene

FIGURE 1-5

These structures have quite interesting electronic properties, giving them a bright future in nanoelectronics. Moreover, carbon nanotubes and buckminsterfullerenes have high tensile strength, making them useful for structural reinforcement in concrete, sports equipment, and body armor. Chemical modification gives these structures an even wider variety of potential uses. Graphene oxide, for example, has promising antimicrobial activity, and attaching certain molecular groups to the surface of a carbon nanotube or buckminsterfullerene has potential for use as drug carriers for cancer therapeutics.

SOLVED PROBLEM **1.1**

How to determine the number of protons and electrons in an atomic ion

Break It Down How many protons and electrons does a cation of the carbon atom have if its net charge is +1?

Every Solved Problem in this book uses a Think/Solve strategy to guide you through the solution. After you consider a question posed on the Think side of the table, read the answer on the Solve side.

Think	Solve
How many protons are there in the nucleus of a carbon atom?	A carbon atom's nucleus has six protons.
Does a cation have more protons than electrons, or vice versa?	A cation must have more protons (positive charges) than electrons (negative charges).
What does the net charge tell you about the relative numbers of protons and electrons?	The +1 charge indicates that there is one more proton than there are electrons, so the ion must have five electrons.

Try It **(a)** How many protons and electrons does an anion of the carbon atom have if its net charge is −1? **(b)** How many protons and electrons does a cation of the oxygen atom have if its net charge is +1? **(c)** How many protons and electrons does an anion of the oxygen atom have if its net charge is −1?

Answers to all Try It exercises can be found in the Solutions Manual.

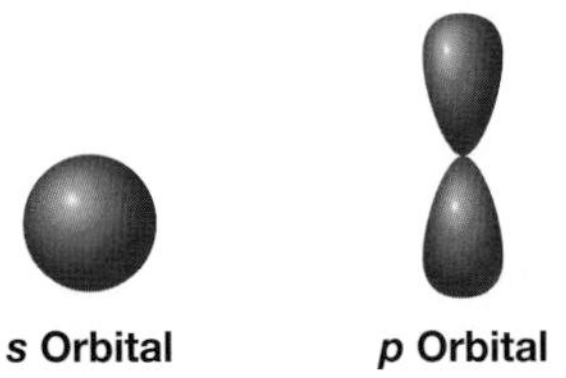

s Orbital
p Orbital

FIGURE 1-6 Orbitals Orbitals represent regions in space where an electron is likely to be. An s orbital is spherical, and a *p* orbital has a dumbbell shape.

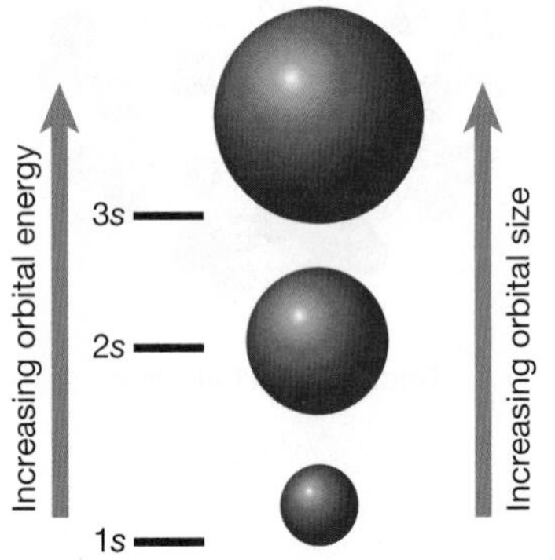

Increasing orbital energy
3s
2s
1s
Increasing orbital size

FIGURE 1-7 Relationship between principal quantum number, orbital size, and orbital energy As the shell number of an orbital increases, its size and energy increase, too. The horizontal black lines indicate each orbital's energy.

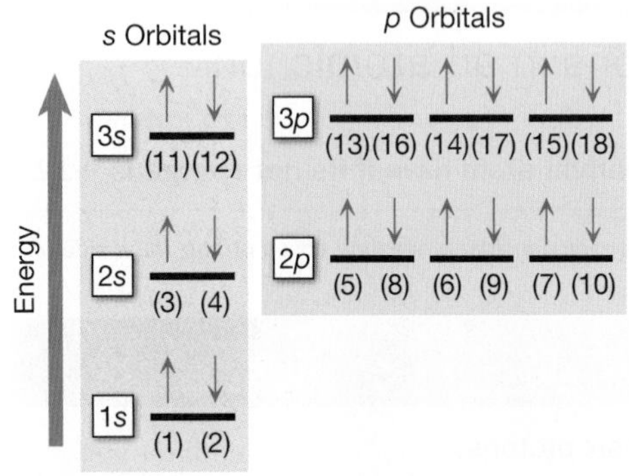

s Orbitals
p Orbitals
Energy
3s
(11)(12)
3p
(13)(16) (14)(17) (15)(18)
2s
(3) (4)
2p
(5) (8) (6) (9) (7) (10)
1s
(1) (2)

FIGURE 1-8 Energy diagram of orbitals for the first 18 electrons Each horizontal black line represents a single orbital. The order of electron filling is indicated in parentheses. Each successive electron (red arrow) fills the lowest energy orbital available. Notice that when the 2*p* set of orbitals begins to fill, the first three electrons (electrons 5, 6, and 7) go into different *p* orbitals, and each of the next three electrons (electrons 8, 9, and 10) results in a completely filled orbital. The 3*p* orbitals fill in a similar fashion.

1.3b Orbitals and Shells

Electrons in an isolated atom reside in **orbitals**. As we will see, the exact location of an electron can never be pinpointed. An orbital, however, describes the region of space where the *probability* of finding a given electron is high. More simplistically, we can view orbitals as "rooms" that house electrons. Orbitals are examined in greater detail in Chapter 3; for now, it will suffice to review some of their more basic properties.

- Orbitals have different shapes. An *s* orbital, for example, is a sphere, whereas a *p* orbital has a dumbbell shape with two lobes (**Figure 1-6**). Each orbital is centered on the nucleus of its atom or ion.
- Orbitals are organized in *shells* (also known as *energy levels*). A **shell** is defined by the **principal quantum number, *n***. There are an infinite number of shells in an atom, given that *n* can assume any integer value from 1 to infinity.
  - The first shell ($n = 1$) contains only an *s* orbital, called 1*s*.
  - The second shell ($n = 2$) contains one *s* orbital and three *p* orbitals, called 2*s*, $2p_x$, $2p_y$, and $2p_z$.
  - The third shell ($n = 3$) contains one *s* orbital, three *p* orbitals, and five *d* orbitals.
- Up to two electrons are allowed in any orbital.
  - Therefore, the first shell can contain up to two electrons: a **duet**.
  - The second shell can contain up to eight electrons: an **octet**.
  - The third shell can contain up to 18 electrons.
- With increasing shell number, the *size* and *energy* of the orbital increase. For example, comparing *s* orbitals in the first three shells, the size and energy increase in the order $1s < 2s < 3s$, as shown in **Figure 1-7**. Similarly, a 2*p* orbital is smaller in size and lower in energy than a 3*p* orbital.
- Within a given shell, an orbital's energy increases in the following order: $s < p < d$, etc. In the second shell, for example, the 2*s* orbital is lower in energy than the 2*p* orbital.

1.3c Ground State Electron Configurations: Valence Electrons and Core Electrons

The way in which electrons are arranged in orbitals is called the atom's **electron configuration**. The *most stable* (i.e., the lowest energy) electron configuration is called the **ground state** configuration. Knowing an atom's ground state configuration provides insight into the atom's chemical behavior, as we will see.

With the relative energies of orbitals established, an atom's ground state electron configuration can be obtained by applying the following three rules:

1. **Pauli exclusion principle:** No more than two electrons (i.e., zero, one, or two electrons) can occupy a single orbital; two electrons in the same orbital must have opposite spins.
2. **Aufbau principle:** Each successive electron must fill the lowest energy orbital available.
3. **Hund's rule:** Before a second electron can be paired in the same orbital, all other orbitals *at the same energy* must contain a single electron.

According to these three rules, the first 18 electrons fill orbitals as indicated in **Figure 1-8**. Each arrow represents an electron, and the direction of the arrow (up or down) represents the electron's spin.

YOUR TURN 1.1

In Figure 1-8, draw a box around all of the electrons that occupy orbitals in the second shell and draw a circle around the electrons that occupy orbitals in the third shell.

Answers to Your Turns are in the back of the book.

In the ground state, the six electrons found in a carbon atom would fill the orbitals as shown in **Figure 1-9**, with two electrons in the 1*s* orbital, two electrons in the 2*s* orbital, and one electron in each of two different 2*p* orbitals (it doesn't matter which two). The shorthand notation for this electron configuration is $1s^22s^22p^2$.

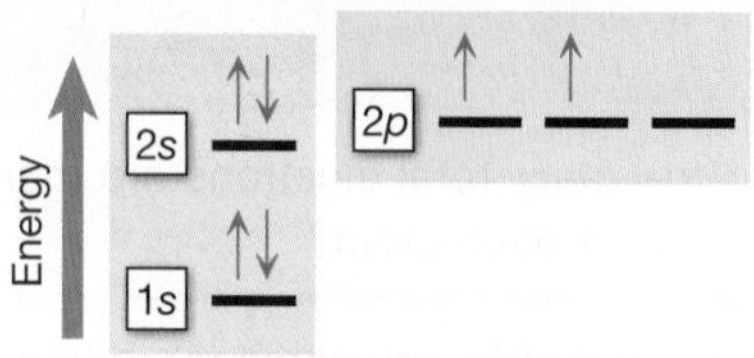

Energy
1s
2s
2p

FIGURE 1-9 Energy diagram for the ground state electron configuration of the carbon atom This configuration is abbreviated $1s^22s^22p^2$.

Knowing the ground state electron configuration of an atom, we can distinguish *valence* electrons from *core* electrons:

- **Valence electrons** are those occupying the highest energy (i.e., valence) shell. For the carbon atom, the valence shell is the $n = 2$ shell.
- **Core electrons** occupy the remaining lower energy shells of the atom. For the carbon atom, the core electrons occupy the $n = 1$ shell.

Valence electrons are important because, as we will discuss in Section 1.5, they participate in covalent bonds. As we can see in Figure 1-9, for example, carbon has four valence electrons and two core electrons, so bonding involving carbon is governed by those four valence electrons.

YOUR TURN 1.2

In Figure 1-9, draw a circle around the valence electrons and label them. Draw a box around all of the core electrons and label them.

We can use the periodic table (a copy of which appears inside the book's front cover) to quickly determine how many valence electrons an atom has:

The number of valence electrons in an atom is the same as the atom's *group number*.

Carbon is located in group 4A, consistent with its four valence electrons, whereas chlorine (group 7A) has seven. According to its ground state electron configuration ($1s^22s^22p^63s^23p^5$), chlorine's valence electrons occupy the third shell.

Elements in group 8A have a special property:

Atoms that have a completely filled valence shell, such as helium and neon, are particularly stable and are called the **noble gases** (group 8A).

Noble gases are so stable that they rarely form bonds to make molecules. Although the specific origin of this "extra" stability is beyond the scope of this book, the consequences are the basis for the octet and duet rules we routinely use when drawing Lewis structures (Section 1.5).

SOLVED PROBLEM **1.2**

How to determine the ground state electron configuration of an atom

Break It Down **Write the ground state electron configuration of the nitrogen atom. How many valence electrons does it have? How many core electrons does it have?**

Think	Solve
How many total electrons are there in a nitrogen atom?	Nitrogen has seven total electrons ($Z = 7$ for N).
In what order are nitrogen's orbitals filled (see Fig. 1-8)?	The first two electrons are placed in the 1s orbital and the next two in the 2s orbital, leaving one electron for each of the three 2*p* orbitals. The electron configuration is $1s^22s^22p^3$.
What is nitrogen's valence shell and where do its core electrons reside?	Nitrogen's valence shell is the second shell, so there are five valence electrons. The remaining two electrons occupying the first shell are core electrons.

Try It Write the ground state electron configuration of the oxygen atom. How many valence electrons and how many core electrons are there?

SECTION 1.4 OBJECTIVES

You will be able to:

1. Describe the makeup of a covalent bond.
2. Explain how bond strength and bond length relate to the lowest energy separation between atoms involved in the bond.
3. Describe the relationship between the strength and length of a covalent bond when the bond holding the atoms together goes from single to double to triple.

1.4 The Covalent Bond: Bond Energy and Bond Length

In a compound, nuclei are held together by chemical bonds. Two types of fundamental bonds in chemistry are the *covalent bond* and the *ionic bond* (see Section 1.8). A **covalent bond** is characterized by the *sharing of valence electrons* between two or more atoms, as shown for two H atoms in a molecule of H_2 (hydrogen gas) in **Figure 1-10**.

In Section 1.5, we will explore how various molecules can be constructed from atoms through the formation of covalent bonds, but first let's examine the nature of covalent bonds more closely. Why do they form at all?

We can begin to answer this question by examining **Figure 1-11a**, which illustrates how the energy of two H atoms changes as a function of the distance between their nuclei. In particular, when two H atoms separated by a large distance are brought together, their total energy begins to decrease:

Lower energy corresponds to greater stability.

At one particular internuclear distance, the energy of the molecule is at a minimum, while at shorter distances the energy rises dramatically.

The internuclear distance at which energy is the lowest is called the **bond length** of the H—H bond. The energy that is required to remove the H atoms from that internuclear distance to infinity (toward the right in the figure) is the **bond strength**, or **bond energy**, of the H—H bond.

The idea of a lowest energy distance between two H atoms is analogous to a ball on a hill (Fig. 1-11b). A ball at the top of a hill has more potential energy than a ball at the bottom, so the ball at the top tends to roll downhill, coming to rest at the bottom. By the same token, it takes energy to roll the ball from the bottom of the hill back to the top.

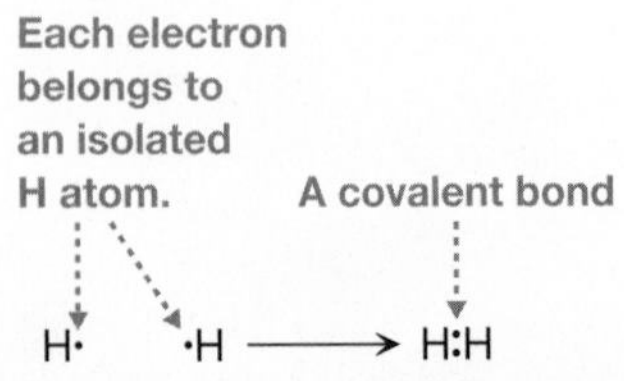
Each electron belongs to an isolated H atom.
A covalent bond
H·
·H
H:H

FIGURE 1-10 **A covalent bond** A covalent bond is the sharing of two electrons between nuclei.

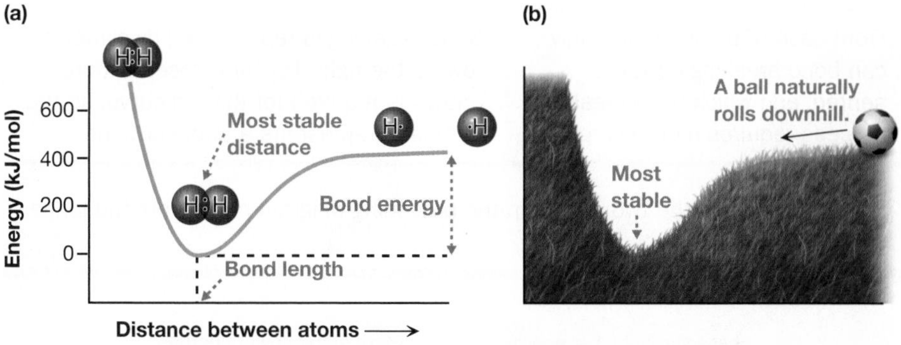
(a)
(b)
H:H
600
400
200
0
Energy (kJ/mol)
Most stable distance
H·
·H
H:H
Bond energy
Bond length
Distance between atoms
A ball naturally rolls downhill.
Most stable

FIGURE 1-11 Formation of a chemical bond (a) Plot of energy as a function of the internuclear distance for two H atoms. The H atoms are most stable at the distance at which energy is a minimum. (b) A ball at the top of a hill becomes more stable at the bottom of the hill, and therefore it tends to roll downhill.

YOUR TURN **1.3**

Estimate the bond energy of the bond represented by Figure 1-11a.

It is often convenient to *think of a covalent bond as a spring that connects two atoms.* Just as it takes energy to lengthen or shorten a covalent bond from its bond length, it takes energy to stretch or compress a spring from its rest position, as shown in **Figure 1-12.**

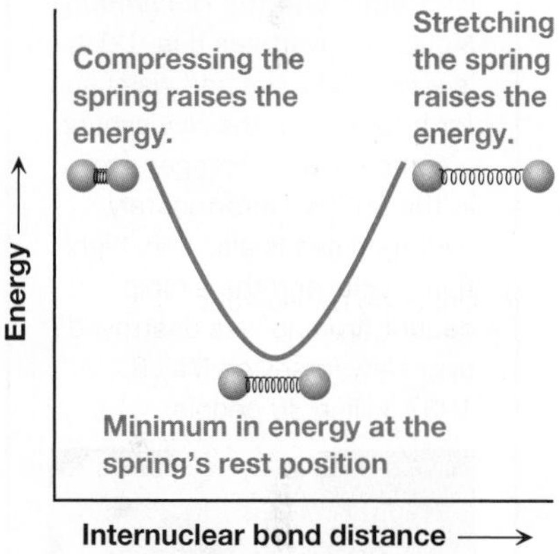
Compressing the spring raises the energy.
Stretching the spring raises the energy.
Energy
Minimum in energy at the spring's rest position
Internuclear bond distance

FIGURE 1-12 The spring model of a covalent bond The energy curve of a spring connecting two masses resembles that of the covalent bond shown in Figure 1-11a. Both stretching and compressing the spring from its rest position increase energy.

CONNECTIONS 1.2

Oscillating bonds and the greenhouse effect The warming of the atmosphere by greenhouse gases such as carbon dioxide (CO_2) and methane (CH_4) is a consequence of the springlike behavior of covalent bonds (Fig. 1-12), whereby the bonds vibrate at frequencies corresponding to infrared radiation

SOLVED PROBLEM **1.3**

How to identify bond strength and bond length from an energy diagram

Break It Down In the diagram shown here, which curve represents the stronger covalent bond?

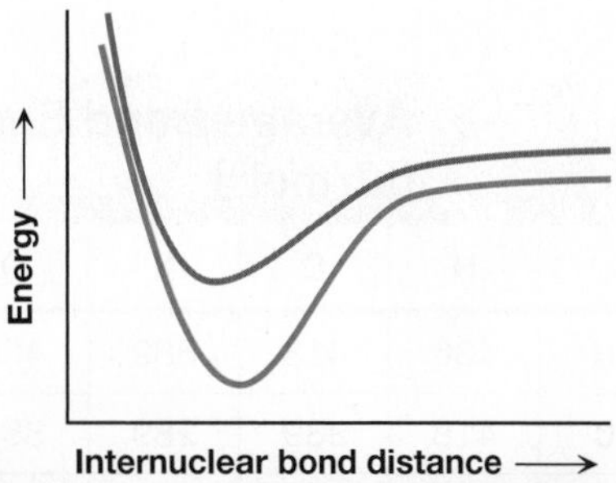
Energy
Internuclear bond distance

Think	Solve
At which point on each curve are the atoms in the bond the most stable?	The atoms in each bond are most stable at the bottom of the curve.
Does bond energy depend on the horizontal or vertical location of those points?	Bond energy depends on the vertical location of those points.

(continued)

From each of those points, how can bond breaking be represented, and which bond-breaking process requires more energy?	Bond breaking is represented by climbing toward the right. For this process, more energy is required for the red curve, so the red curve represents a stronger bond.

Try It Which of the two curves in the preceding diagram represents the longer bond?

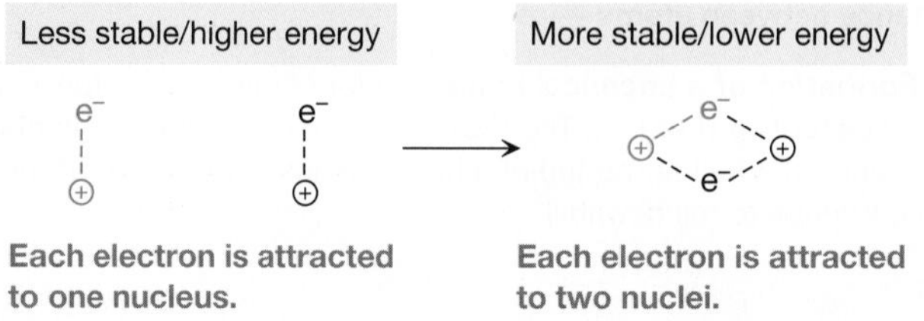

Less stable/higher energy
More stable/lower energy
e⁻
e⁻
e⁻
e⁻
Each electron is attracted to one nucleus.
Each electron is attracted to two nuclei.

FIGURE 1-13 Stabilization of electrons in a covalent bond In an isolated H atom (*left*), each electron is attracted to a single nucleus (represented by the circled + charges). In a covalent bond (*right*), each electron is attracted simultaneously to two H nuclei, thus lowering the energy of each electron.

Why is a H_2 molecule more stable than two isolated H atoms? As shown in **Figure 1-13**, when the nuclei are a bond length apart, the sharing of the electrons allows each electron to be simultaneously attracted to two nuclei rather than one. This simultaneous attraction causes the electrons to slow down, thus lowering their energy.

Single bonds are the most common type of bond found in organic molecules, but we frequently encounter double bonds and triple bonds, too. Whereas two electrons are shared between two nuclei involved in a single bond, four electrons are shared in a double bond, and six electrons are shared in a triple bond.

Tables 1-2 and 1-3 list average bond energies for a variety of common bonding partners found in organic molecules. Table 1-2 describes only single bonds, whereas Table 1-3 compares bond energies and lengths for some common single, double, and triple bonds.

Notice the trend in Table 1-3:

As the number of bonds between a pair of atoms increases, the bond energy increases and the bond length decreases (**Figure 1-14**).

CONNECTIONS 1.3

Hydrogen and the *Hindenburg* Molecular hydrogen (Fig. 1-10) is a very light gas and was used for buoyancy in the *Hindenburg*, a commercial passenger airship in the 1930s. Unfortunately, hydrogen gas is also very highly flammable, and the airship caught fire and was destroyed over New Jersey on May 6, 1937, killing 36 people.

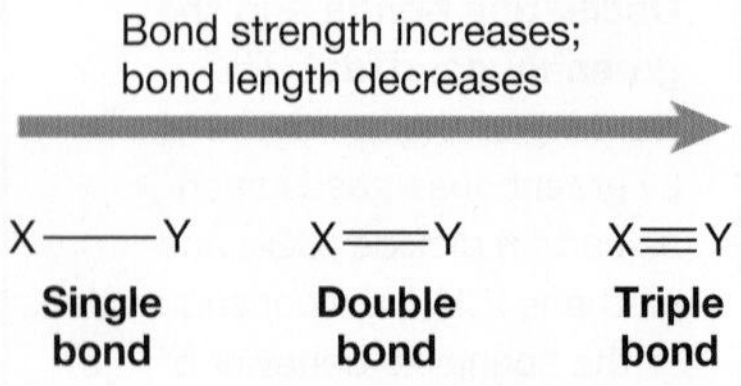

Bond strength increases; bond length decreases
X—Y
X=Y
X≡Y
Single bond
Double bond
Triple bond

FIGURE 1-14 Bond strength and bond length For a particular pair of atoms that are covalently bonded (X and Y), a triple bond is shorter and stronger than a double bond, which is shorter and stronger than a single bond.

TABLE 1-2 Average Bond Energies of Common Single Bonds (kJ/mol[a])

	H	C	N	O	F	Cl	Br	I	Si
H	436	418	389	460	569	431	368	297	301
C	418	339	289	351	439	331	280	238	289
N	389	289	159	180	272	201	243	169	355
O	460	351	180	138	209	209	222	238	430
F	569	439	272	209	159	251	251	280	586
Cl	431	331	201	209	251	243	222	209	402
Br	368	280	243	222	251	222	192	180	289
I	297	238	169	238	280	209	180	151	209
Si	301	289	355	430	586	402	289	209	223

[a]Values are given in kilojoules per mole. To convert to kilocalories per mole, use the conversion 1 kcal/mol = 4.18 kJ/mol.

TABLE 1-3 Average Bond Energies and Bond Lengths of Single, Double, and Triple Bonds

Atoms Bonded Together	SINGLE BOND		DOUBLE BOND		TRIPLE BOND	
	Energy (kJ/mol)[a]	Length (pm)[b]	Energy (kJ/mol)	Length (pm)	Energy (kJ/mol)	Length (pm)
C—C	339	154	619	134	812	120
C—N	289	147	619	129	891	116
C—O	351	143	720	120	1072	113
N—N	159	145	418	125	946	110
O—O	138	148	498	121		

[a]Values are given in kilojoules per mole. To convert to kilocalories per mole, use the conversion 1 kcal/mol = 4.18 kJ/mol.
[b]Lengths are given in picometers (pm).

Thus, double and triple bonds can be viewed as shorter, stronger springs than single bonds.

YOUR TURN 1.4

Refer to Tables 1-2 and 1-3 to answer the following questions, which are designed to acquaint you with the range of strengths of common bonds.

(a) What is the value of the strongest *single* bond listed? ______________
(b) What atoms does that bond involve? ______________
(c) What is the value of the weakest *single* bond listed? ______________
(d) What atoms does that bond involve? ______________
(e) What is the value of the strongest bond of any type listed? ______________
(f) What atoms does that bond involve, and what type of bond is it? ______

▸ LOOKING AHEAD

Radicals are discussed in greater detail in Chapter 27. Reactions that involve radicals are important in synthesizing organic molecules, including a variety of polymers. Radicals are also involved in some key biochemical processes.

1.5 Lewis Dot Structures and the Octet Rule

SECTION 1.5 OBJECTIVES

You will be able to:

1. Evaluate whether a given structure is a valid Lewis structure.
2. Draw the Lewis structure for a small molecule or molecular ion, given its molecular formula.

To understand a molecule's chemical behavior, it is necessary to know its **connectivity**: that is, which atoms are bonded together and by what types of bonds (single, double, or triple). It is also useful to know which valence electrons participate in bonding and which do not. **Lewis dot structures** (or **Lewis structures**) are a convenient way to convey this information. Let's review some basic conventions of Lewis structures.

- Lewis structures take into account only valence electrons. In a complete Lewis structure, such as those in **Figure 1-15** for isolated C and Cl atoms, *all* valence electrons are shown.
- Bonding and nonbonding electrons are clearly shown.
  - Single bonds (—) represent the sharing of two electrons, double bonds (═) represent the sharing of four electrons, and triple bonds (≡) represent the sharing of six electrons. Thus, each line represents a shared pair, or **bonding pair**, of electrons.
  - Nonbonding electrons are indicated by dots and are usually paired (:). Nonbonding electrons that occur in pairs are called **lone pairs** of electrons. Nonbonding electrons that are unpaired are represented by single dots, and the species in which they appear are called **radicals** (see Looking Ahead box).

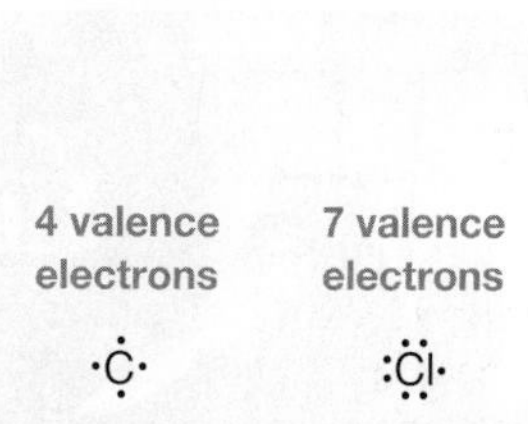
4 valence electrons
7 valence electrons

FIGURE 1-15 Lewis dot representations of isolated atoms

CONNECTIONS 1.4

Chlorine radicals and the ozone hole Chlorine radicals (Fig. 1-15) in the stratosphere catalyze the breakdown of stratospheric ozone. Unnaturally high concentrations of chlorine radicals in the stratosphere, produced from synthetic coolants called chlorofluorocarbons (CFCs), have, since the middle of the 20th century, led to the development of the ozone hole over Antarctica (shown in blue).

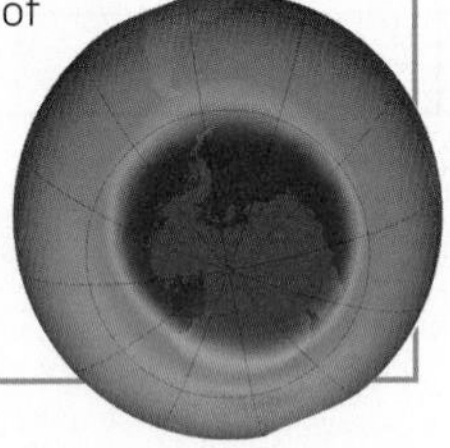

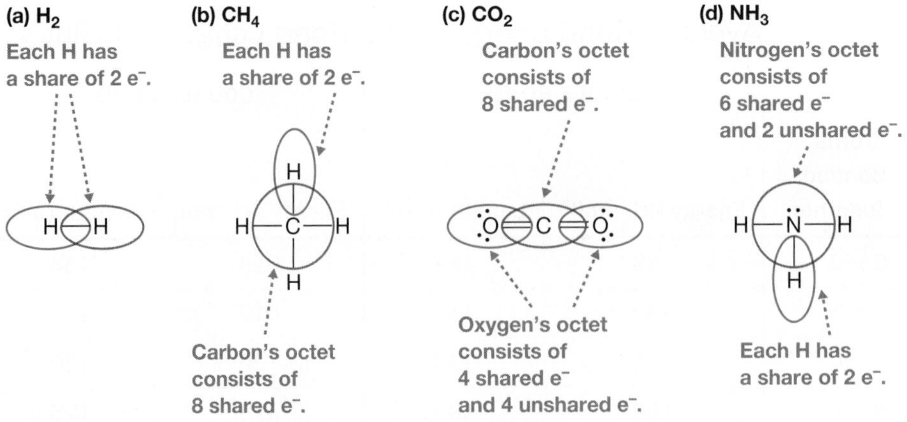

(a) H_2
Each H has a share of 2 e⁻.
(b) CH_4
Each H has a share of 2 e⁻.
Carbon's octet consists of 8 shared e⁻.
(c) CO_2
Carbon's octet consists of 8 shared e⁻.
Oxygen's octet consists of 4 shared e⁻ and 4 unshared e⁻.
(d) NH_3
Nitrogen's octet consists of 6 shared e⁻ and 2 unshared e⁻.
Each H has a share of 2 e⁻.

FIGURE 1-16 Covalent bonding: Sharing electrons to produce full valence shells In each of these molecules, all atoms have completely filled valence shells: H has a share of two electrons (a, b, and d), whereas C (b and c), O (c), and N (d) each have an octet of electrons made up of a total of 8 shared and unshared valence electrons.

- Atoms in Lewis structures obey the duet rule and the octet rule. The shared electrons of a covalent bond count as the valence electrons of each atom involved in the bond. Thus, atoms tend to form covalent bonds to achieve a full valence shell (two electrons for hydrogen; eight electrons for atoms in the second row of the periodic table). Examples are shown in **Figure 1-16**.

YOUR TURN **1.5**

Using Figure 1-16 as your guide, circle the electrons in the Lewis structure of CH_3OH that represent carbon's octet, oxygen's octet, and each hydrogen's duet.

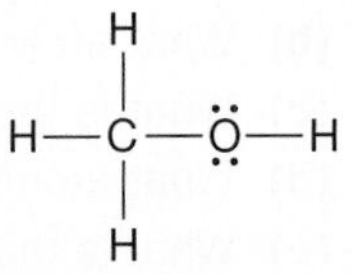

Because of their widespread use in organic chemistry, you must be able to draw Lewis structures quickly and accurately. The following steps allow you to do so in a systematic way:

CONNECTIONS 1.5

Methanol and its uses Methanol (CH_3OH, Your Turn 1.5), also called methyl alcohol or wood alcohol, is used industrially as a feedstock to produce formaldehyde, which is integral in the production of some plastics, paints, and explosives. Methanol is also the primary fuel used in many types of racing vehicles.

TO

Steps for Drawing Lewis Structures

1. Count the total number of *valence* electrons in the molecule.
   a. The number of valence electrons contributed by each atom is the same as its group number (H = 1, C = 4, N = 5, O = 6, F = 7).
   b. Each negative charge increases the number of valence electrons by one; each positive charge decreases the number of electrons by one.
2. Write the skeleton of the molecule.
   a. Show only the atoms and the single bonds required to hold them together.
   b. If molecular connectivity is not given to you, the central atom (the one with the greatest number of bonds) is usually the nonhydrogen atom with the lowest electronegativity. (Electronegativity is reviewed in Section 1.7.)
3. Subtract two electrons from the total in Step 1 for each single covalent bond drawn in Step 2.
4. Distribute the remaining electrons as lone pairs.
   a. Start with the outer atoms and work inward.
   b. Try to achieve an octet on each atom other than hydrogen.
5. If there is an atom with less than an octet, increase the atom's share of electrons by converting lone pairs from *neighboring* atoms into bonding pairs, thereby creating double or triple bonds.

SOLVED PROBLEM **1.4**

How to draw the Lewis structure of a small molecule or molecular ion

Break It Down **Draw a Lewis structure of HCO_2^-, where carbon is the central atom.**

Think	Solve
How many total valence electrons are there?	The number of valence electrons each atom contributes is the atom's group number. The −1 charge represents one additional electron. 1 H atom: 1 × 1 valence electron = 1 valence electron 1 C atom: 1 × 4 valence electrons = 4 valence electrons 2 O atoms: 2 × 6 valence electrons = 12 valence electrons −1 charge: 1 × 1 valence electron = 1 valence electron Total: = 18 valence electrons
How should you draw the skeleton? How many electrons must still be accounted for after drawing the skeleton?	The carbon is given as the central atom. Therefore, the central carbon is connected by a single bond to hydrogen and to each oxygen, which accounts for six valence electrons. That leaves 12 valence electrons still to account for. 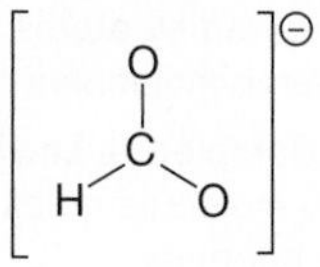
How should the remaining electrons be added? Can each nonhydrogen atom achieve an octet?	The 12 remaining electrons are added as lone pairs to the oxygen atoms, as shown in the first structure, which gives each oxygen atom an octet. To give carbon an octet, convert a lone pair from one oxygen into a bonding pair to create a double bond, as shown in the second structure. 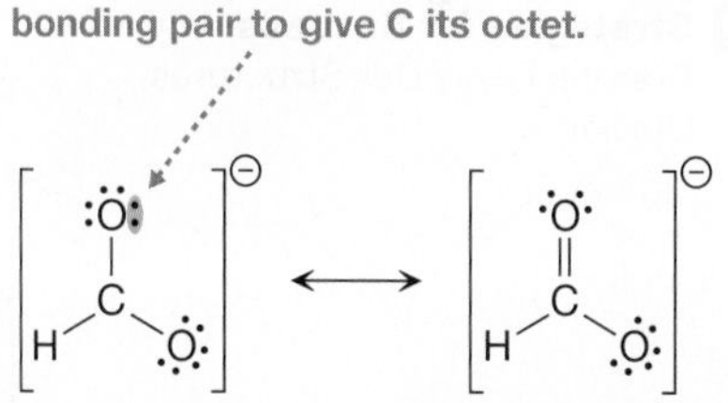 Convert a lone pair into a bonding pair to give C its octet.

Try It Draw a Lewis structure for C_2H_3N. One carbon is bonded to three hydrogen atoms and to the second carbon. The nitrogen atom is bonded only to a carbon atom.

Some molecular species do not have enough electrons to allow all atoms to have a complete valence shell. In borane (BH_3, **Figure 1-17a**), for example, the B atom has a share of only six valence electrons. The same is true of C^+ in the methyl cation (H_3C^+, Fig. 1-17b), a species characterized as a **carbocation** due to its positively charged carbon. Similarly, in thionyl chloride ($SOCl_2$, Fig. 1-17c), the S atom has a share of 10 electrons but, being in the third row of the periodic table, its valence shell can contain up to 18 electrons.

CONNECTIONS 1.6

You'll get a charge out of thionyl chloride

Thionyl chloride ($SOCl_2$, Fig. 1-17c) is used in lithium–thionyl chloride batteries, where it acts as the positive electrode.

SAFT
LS
14250
3.6V

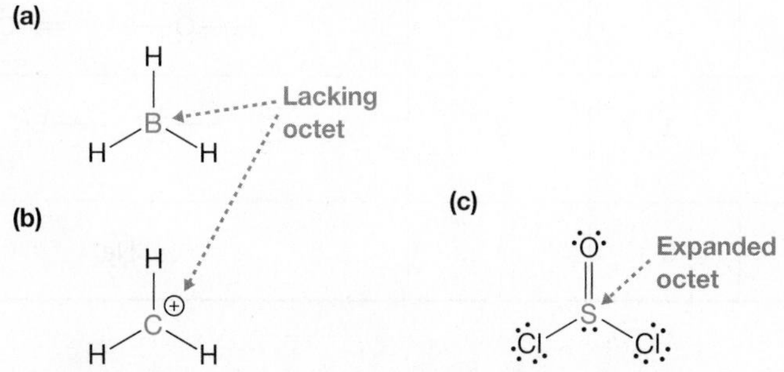
(a)
Lacking octet
(b)
(c)
Expanded octet

FIGURE 1-17 **Exceptions to the octet rule** (a) Boron and (b) carbon are in the second row and have less than an octet. (c) Sulfur is in the third row and has an expanded octet.

Even though atoms in the third row and below can have more than eight electrons in their valence shell, we often apply the idea of an octet to those atoms, too. In $SOCl_2$, for example, both Cl atoms have a share of eight valence electrons, so we say that each Cl atom has an octet. The S atom, on the other hand, has a share of 10 electrons, so we say that S has an **expanded octet**. Be careful, however, when using this terminology, because only atoms in the third row and below can have an expanded octet:

Atoms in the second row cannot exceed the octet!

SECTION 1.6 OBJECTIVES

You will be able to:

1. Specify the most common number of bonds and lone pairs exhibited by atoms that form organic molecules.
2. Complete a Lewis structure of a molecule quickly, given its connectivity.

Strategies for Success
Drawing Lewis Dot Structures Quickly

1.6 Strategies for Success: Drawing Lewis Dot Structures Quickly

After you've used the systematic steps (p. 12) to construct Lewis structures of several species, you may begin to notice that each type of atom tends to form a specific number of bonds and to have a specific number of lone pairs of electrons. Table 1-4 summarizes these patterns. What you will learn later is that *those are the number of bonds and lone pairs for atoms that bear no formal charge*. Atoms that are charged have combinations of bonds and lone pairs that are different from those in Table 1-4.

The patterns shown in Table 1-4 are really helpful when drawing Lewis structures of relatively large molecules, as shown in Solved Problem 1.5.

TABLE 1-4 Common Numbers of Covalent Bonds and Lone Pairs for Selected Uncharged Atoms

Atom	Number of Bonds	Number of Lone Pairs	Examples
H	1	0	—H
C	4	0	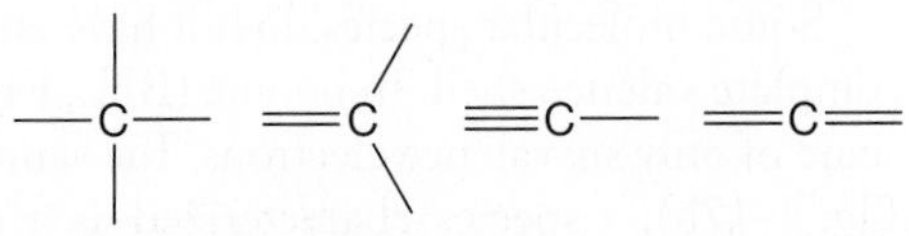
N	3	1	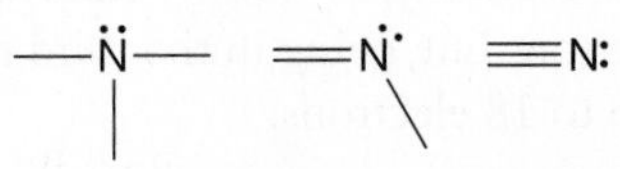
O	2	2	
X (X = F, Cl, Br, I)	1	3	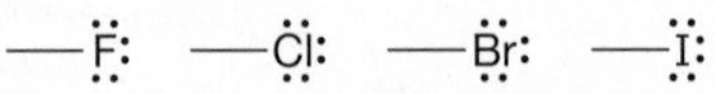
Ne	0	4	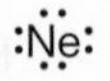

SOLVED PROBLEM **1.5**

How to complete a Lewis structure quickly

Break It Down **Complete the Lewis structure for the compound whose skeleton is shown here. Assume that all atoms are uncharged.**

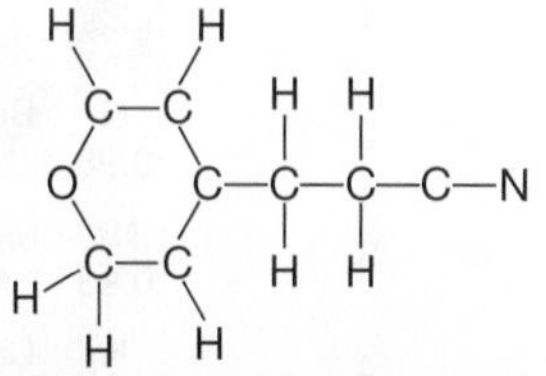

H H
C C H H
O C C C C N
H C C H H
H H

Think	Solve
Which atoms (other than hydrogen) have an octet and which atoms don't?	The atoms not shown with an octet are highlighted in red below on the left.
How many bonds and lone pairs are typical for each element?	According to Table 1-4, we need to add two lone pairs to O, convert two C—C single bonds of the ring into double bonds, convert the C—N single bond into a triple bond, and add a lone pair to N. The completed Lewis structure is shown below on the right.

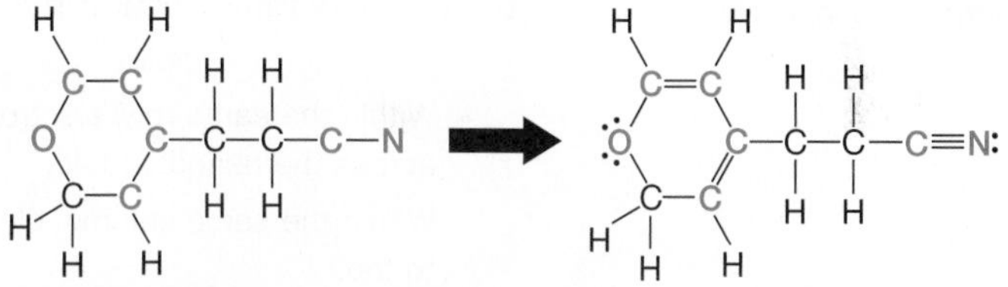

Atoms shown in red lack an octet. All atoms now have an octet.

Try It Complete the Lewis structure for the molecule with the connectivity shown here. Assume that all atoms have the number of bonds and lone pairs listed in Table 1-4.

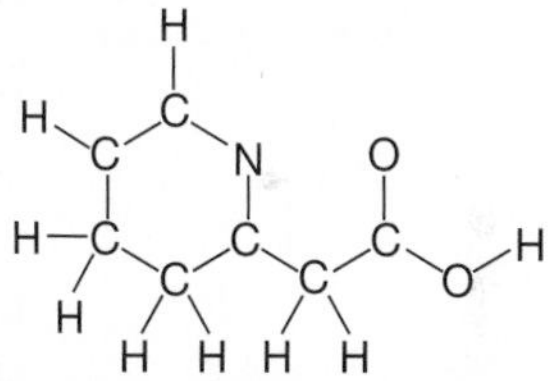

1.7 Electronegativity, Polar Covalent Bonds, and Bond Dipoles

SECTION 1.7 OBJECTIVES

You will be able to:

1. Use electronegativities to determine the direction and relative magnitude of a bond dipole.
2. Determine the relative electronegativities of atoms from their locations in the periodic table.

We've seen that covalent bonds are characterized by the sharing of electrons between two atomic nuclei. If the atoms are identical, the electrons are shared equally and the bond is called a **nonpolar covalent bond**. Otherwise, one nucleus will attract electrons more strongly than the other. The ability to attract electrons in a covalent bond is defined as the element's **electronegativity (EN)**.

There are a variety of different electronegativity scales that assign values to each element, but the one developed by Linus Pauling, which ranges from 0 to about 4

Electronegativity (EN) using the Pauling scale

Group (vertical)	1	2	3	4	5	6	7	8	9	10	11	12	13	14	15	16	17	18
Period (horizontal)	1A																	8A
1	H 2.20	2A											3A	4A	5A	6A	7A	He
2	Li 0.98	Be 1.57											B 2.04	C 2.55	N 3.04	O 3.44	F 3.98	Ne
3	Na 0.93	Mg 1.31											Al 1.61	Si 1.90	P 2.19	S 2.58	Cl 3.16	Ar
4	K 0.82	Ca 1.00	Sc 1.36	Ti 1.54	V 1.63	Cr 1.66	Mn 1.55	Fe 1.83	Co 1.88	Ni 1.91	Cu 1.90	Zn 1.65	Ga 1.81	Ge 2.01	As 2.18	Se 2.55	Br 2.96	Kr 3.00
5	Rb 0.82	Sr 0.95	Y 1.22	Zr 1.33	Nb 1.6	Mo 2.16	Tc 1.9	Ru 2.2	Rh 2.28	Pd 2.20	Ag 1.93	Cd 1.69	In 1.78	Sn 1.96	Sb 2.05	Te 2.1	I 2.66	Xe 2.60
6	Cs 0.79	Ba 0.89	La 1.1	Hf 1.3	Ta 1.5	W 2.36	Re 1.9	Os 2.2	Ir 2.20	Pt 2.28	Au 2.54	Hg 2.00	Tl 1.62	Pb 2.33	Bi 2.02	Po 2.0	At 2.2	Rn 2.2

EN = 1.0 — EN = 4.0

FIGURE 1-18 Pauling's electronegativity scale for the elements In the periodic table, electronegativity generally increases from left to right across a row and from bottom to top in a column.

(see **Figure 1-18**), is perhaps the most well known. For main group elements, electronegativity values exhibit the following periodic trends:

- Within the same row, electronegativity values tend to increase from left to right across the periodic table.
- Within the same column, electronegativity values tend to increase from bottom to top.

As a result, the elements with the highest electronegativities (not counting the noble gases) tend to be in the upper right corner of the periodic table (e.g., N, O, F, Cl, and Br), whereas the elements with the lowest electronegativities tend to be in the lower left corner (e.g., K, Rb, Cs, Sr, and Ba).

In a covalent bond, electrons are more likely to be found near the nucleus of the more electronegative atom and less likely near the nucleus of the less electronegative atom. This creates a separation of partial positive and partial negative charges along the bond, called a **bond dipole**, and the bond is referred to as a **polar covalent bond**. More specifically:

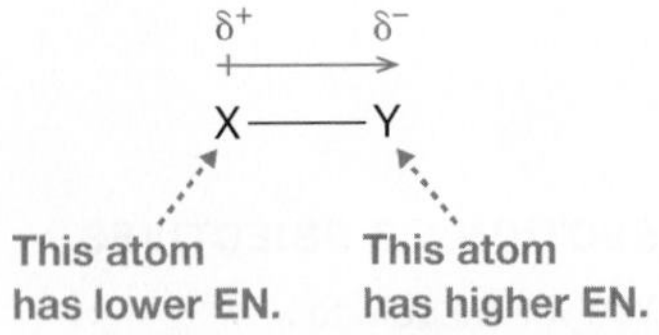

δ+
δ−
X—Y
This atom has lower EN.
This atom has higher EN.

FIGURE 1-19 Bond dipole arrow

- The more electronegative atom of a covalent bond bears a partial negative charge (δ^-, "delta minus").
- The less electronegative atom bears a partial positive charge (δ^+, "delta plus").
- A **dipole arrow** (**Figure 1-19**) can be drawn from the less electronegative atom (δ^+) toward the more electronegative atom (δ^-).

These ideas are shown for HF, CH_4, and CO_2 in **Figure 1-20**.

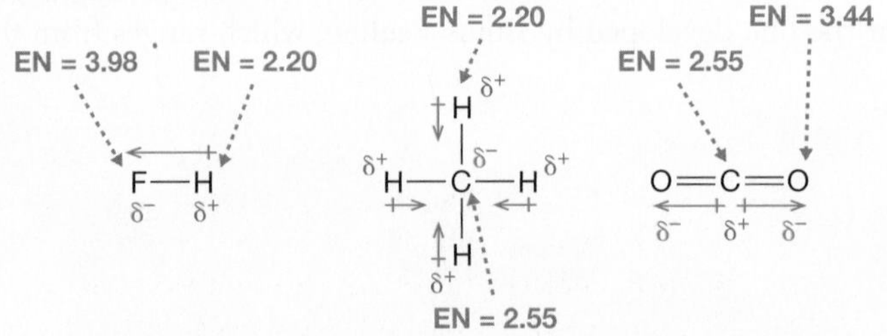

EN = 3.98
EN = 2.20
F—H
EN = 2.20
EN = 2.55
EN = 3.44
EN = 2.55
O=C=O

FIGURE 1-20 Bond dipoles in various molecules The dipoles are represented by the red arrows. Each arrow points from the less electronegative atom (δ^+) to the more electronegative atom (δ^-). The length of the arrow indicates the relative magnitude of the bond dipole. EN = electronegativity.

The magnitude of a bond dipole depends on the *difference* in electronegativity between the atoms involved in the bond. A larger difference in electronegativity results in a larger bond dipole. Relative magnitudes of a bond dipole are often depicted by the *lengths* of dipole arrows. For example, the difference in electronegativity between hydrogen and fluorine is larger than that between carbon and hydrogen. In Figure 1-20, therefore, the dipole arrow along the H—F bond is longer than the dipole arrows along the H—C bonds.

YOUR TURN 1.6

Draw a dipole arrow along the C≡N bond in H—C≡N, and add the δ^+ and δ^- symbols.

SOLVED PROBLEM **1.6**

How to identify the most polar covalent bond in a molecule

Break It Down Identify the most polar bond(s) in the molecule shown here. Draw a dipole arrow along that bond to indicate the direction in which the bond dipole points.

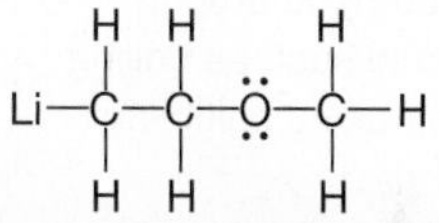

Think	Solve
What property of atoms should we consider to evaluate bond polarity?	In a covalent bond, we should consider the electronegativity of each atom bonded together. The relevant electronegativity (EN) values are shown here.
How should we use that property to determine the relative magnitude of a bond dipole?	We determine the relative magnitude of a bond dipole from the *difference* in electronegativity (ΔEN) between two atoms bonded. The ΔEN values for the four distinct bonds are shown here. The Li—C bond has the largest difference, making it the most polar bond in the molecule. We draw the bond dipole from the less electronegative Li toward the more electronegative C.

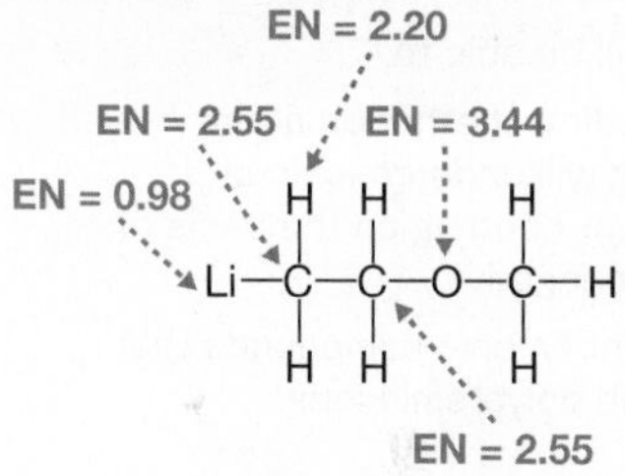

EN = 2.20
EN = 2.55
EN = 3.44
EN = 0.98
EN = 2.55

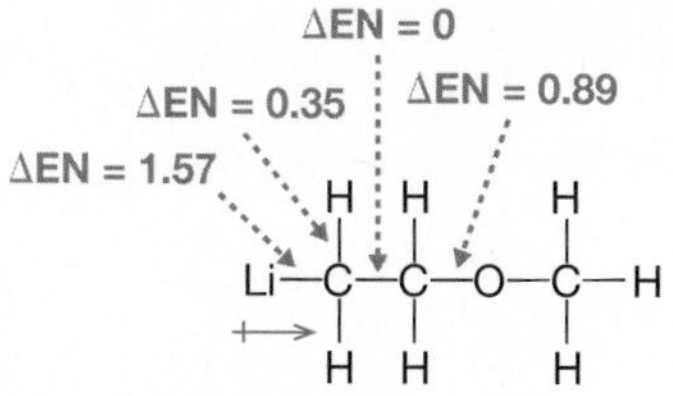

ΔEN = 0
ΔEN = 0.35
ΔEN = 0.89
ΔEN = 1.57

Try It Identify the most polar bond in each of the following molecules.

(a)

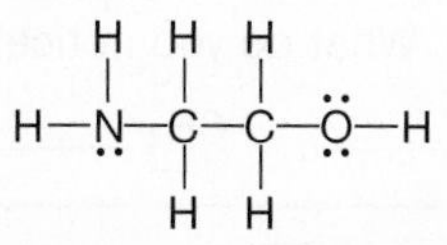

(b)

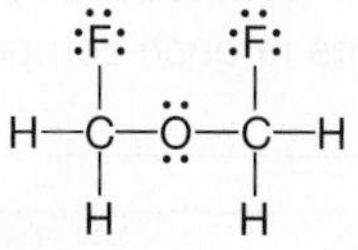

(c)

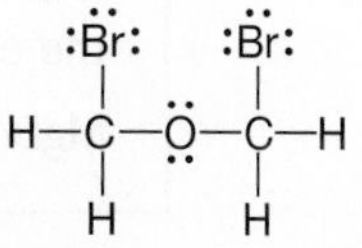

An **electrostatic potential map** offers another useful way to illustrate the distribution of charge along a covalent bond. Examples are shown in **Figure 1-21** (next page). An electrostatic potential map depicts a molecule's electron cloud in colors that indicate its *relative* charge. Red corresponds to a buildup of negative charge, whereas blue

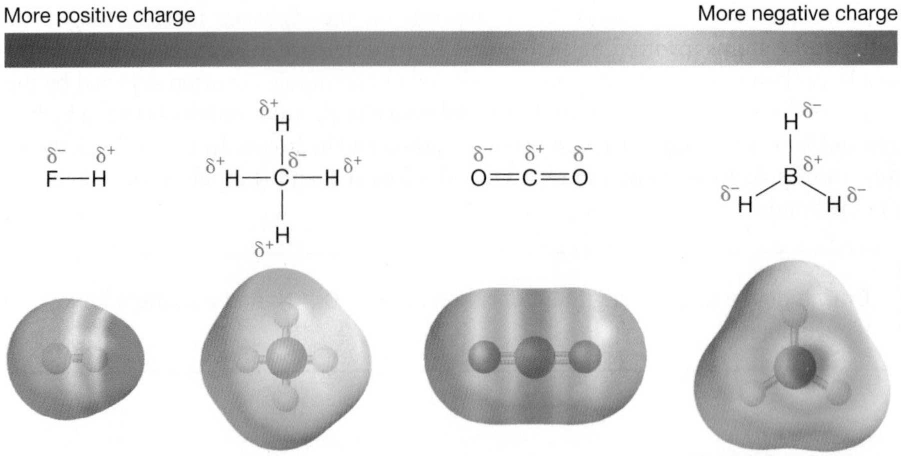
More positive charge
More negative charge
δ⁻ δ⁺
F—H
H—C—H
O=C=O
B
H

FIGURE 1-21 Electrostatic potential maps of four molecules Red indicates a buildup of negative charge; blue indicates a buildup of positive charge.

▸ **LOOKING AHEAD**

In Chapter 2, we will learn how the overall distribution of charge within a molecule dictates the way that molecules interact with one another, impacting characteristic properties of the molecule such as boiling point, melting point, and solubility.

represents a buildup of positive charge. Colors between red and blue in the spectrum, such as green, represent a more neutral charge.

Some of the structures in Figures 1-20 and 1-21 demonstrate that a single molecule can have more than one bond dipole. When this occurs, the bond dipoles' orientations and relative magnitudes dictate the overall distribution of charge within the molecule. We will explore this concept further in Chapter 2 (see Looking Ahead box).

SECTION 1.8 OBJECTIVES

You will be able to:

1. Predict whether an atom pairing will undergo ionic or covalent bonding on the basis of electronegativity.
2. Identify ionic compounds that contain polyatomic ions.

1.8 Ionic Bonds

When elements in a compound have large enough differences in electronegativity, the more electronegative atom can acquire electrons given up by the less electronegative atom, forming oppositely charged ions. The electrostatic attraction between the positively charged cation and the negatively charged anion describes ionic bonding.

An **ionic bond** typically occurs when the electronegativity *difference* between two atoms is greater than about 1.7. Sodium chloride (NaCl), for example, consists of sodium cations (Na^+) and chloride anions (Cl^-), and the electronegativity difference between Na (0.93) and Cl (3.16) is 2.23. Large electronegativity differences like this tend to occur when one atom is a metal from the left side of the periodic table and the other is a nonmetal from the right side of the periodic table. Consequently:

Most ionic compounds (e.g., NaCl and $MgBr_2$) consist of a metal and a nonmetal, whereas most covalent compounds (e.g., CH_4) consist of nonmetals only.

While covalent compounds are generally found as discrete uncharged molecules, the ions in an ionic solid are arranged in a regular pattern, called a **crystal lattice**, as shown for NaCl in **Figure 1-22**.

YOUR TURN 1.7

It was previously mentioned that $MgBr_2$ is an ionic compound, whereas CH_4 is a covalent compound. Calculate the difference in electronegativity between the elements in each compound. What do you notice?

$MgBr_2$ ____________________ CH_4 ____________________

Polyatomic ions, such as the hydroxide (HO^-), methoxide (CH_3O^-), and methylammonium ($CH_3NH_3^+$) ions shown in **Figure 1-23**, contain more than one atom. Polyatomic ions usually consist only of nonmetals, and their atoms are held together by covalent bonds.

Figure 1-23 also shows that polyatomic ions can be either *anions* (HO^- and CH_3O^-) or *cations* ($CH_3NH_3^+$). As will be explained in Section 1.9, most polyatomic

FIGURE 1-22 Representation of the solid crystal structure of NaCl(s) The Na^+ and Cl^- ions are held together by electrostatic forces, called ionic bonds, whereby opposite charges attract. As a solid, the ions form a regular array called a crystal lattice.

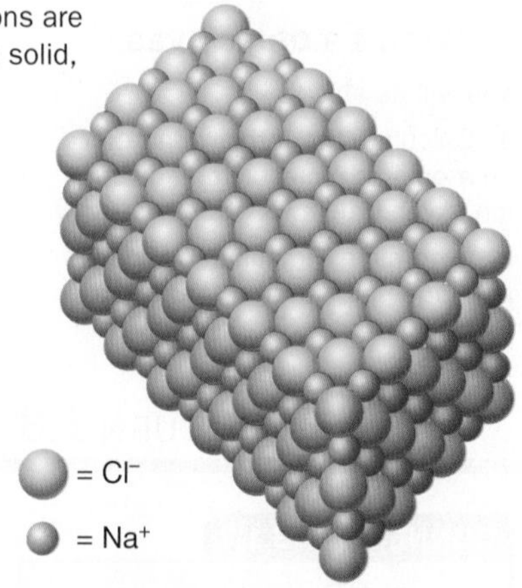

= Cl⁻
= Na⁺

cations possess a nitrogen atom participating in four covalent bonds (another common example is ammonium ion, NH_4^+). Interestingly, the existence of these kinds of polyatomic cations makes possible the formation of ionic compounds composed entirely of nonmetals (e.g., CH_3NH_3Cl and NH_4Br).

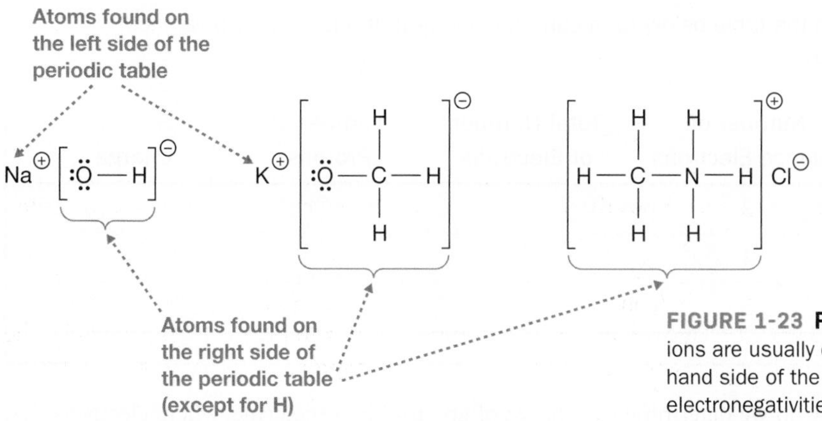

Atoms found on the left side of the periodic table
Atoms found on the right side of the periodic table (except for H)

FIGURE 1-23 Polyatomic ions in ionic compounds Polyatomic ions are usually composed of nonmetal elements from the right-hand side of the periodic table. Those elements have similar electronegativities, allowing covalent bonds to form between them.

SOLVED PROBLEM **1.7**

How to identify ionic versus covalent compounds

Break It Down Identify each of the following as either an ionic compound (i.e., one containing ionic bonds) or a covalent compound (i.e., one containing only covalent bonds): (a) NH_4CHO_2; (b) $LiOCH_2CH_3$; (c) $CH_3CH_2CH_2OH$. (In these *condensed formulas*, which are discussed in Section 1.12, you may assume that each hydrogen appearing immediately to the right of a non-hydrogen atom forms a covalent bond to that non-hydrogen atom.)

Think	Solve
Which compounds contain elements from both the left and right sides of the periodic table?	In $LiOCH_2CH_3$, Li is a metal and the remaining elements are nonmetals. Therefore, $LiOCH_2CH_3$ is an ionic compound in which Li exists as Li^+, and the remaining nonmetals make up the negatively charged ion $(OCH_2CH_3)^-$.
Which compounds contain recognizable polyatomic ions?	In NH_4CHO_2, the four H atoms appearing immediately to the right of N are all bonded to N, which makes up the polyatomic ion NH_4^+. The remaining nonmetals must therefore make up a negatively charged ion, $(CHO_2)^-$, so NH_4CHO_2 is an ionic compound.
Which compounds have neither of these features?	$CH_3CH_2CH_2OH$ consists of only nonmetals and has no recognizable polyatomic ions, so it is a covalent compound.

Try It Which of the following are ionic compounds (i.e., ones containing ionic bonds) and which are covalent compounds (i.e., ones containing only covalent bonds)?

(a)

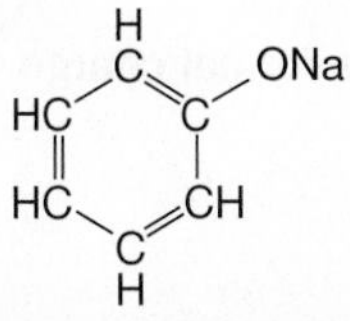

(b)

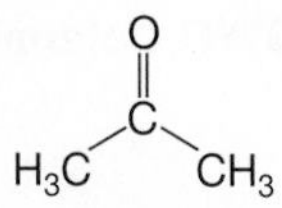

(c) NH_4CN

SECTION 1.9 OBJECTIVES

You will be able to:

1. Calculate the formal charge of an atom in a molecule or molecular ion, given the Lewis structure.
2. Determine the number of bonds and lone pairs an atom has from its formal charge.

1.9 Assigning Electrons to Atoms in Molecules: Formal Charge

In an *isolated* atom or atomic ion, charge is determined by the difference between the atom's group number and the actual number of valence electrons it possesses. A carbon atom, for example, has zero charge if it possesses four valence electrons, because its group number is 4. It carries a charge of −1 if it has five valence electrons, and it carries a charge of +1 if it has only three valence electrons.

YOUR TURN **1.8**

Fill in the table below for a carbon nucleus that has 3, 4, or 5 valence electrons.

Number of Valence Electrons	Total Number of Electrons	Number of Protons	Charge
3			
4			
5			

CONNECTIONS 1.7

The formate anion in the body The formate anion, HCO_2^- (Solved Problem 1.8), is produced in significant amounts in the mitochondria of embryonic liver cells and also in cancer cells. Mitochondrial formate contributes the majority of the one-carbon units that are used for an important biochemical process called methylation.

CONNECTIONS 1.8

Oximes and their uses Oximes (Solved Problem 1.8, Try It) are important intermediates in organic synthesis, including the industrial production of nylon-6. Some oximes are used as nerve-agent antidotes, and one (perillartine) is an artificial sweetener that is 2000 times sweeter than sucrose.

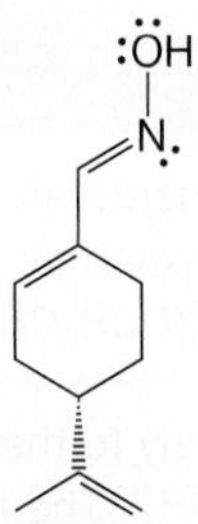

:ÖH
N

Perillartine

How do we determine the charge of an atom in a molecule, where electrons that make up covalent bonds are being *shared* between atoms? One way is to use the rules for **formal charge** to assign electrons:

Formal Charge

1. Assign electrons to atoms with the assumption that each covalent bond is perfectly covalent (i.e., shared equally).
   - In a given covalent bond, assign half the electrons to each atom involved in the bond.
   - Assign both electrons of a lone pair to the atom on which they appear.
2. Compute the formal charge of an atom by comparing the number of electrons assigned to the atom with the atom's group number.
   - Formal charge is 0 if the number of assigned electrons is the same as the atom's group number.
   - Each excess electron contributes −1 to the formal charge.
   - Each electron that is lacking contributes +1 to the formal charge.

Solved Problem 1.8 shows how to apply these rules to a Lewis structure of HCO_2^-.

SOLVED PROBLEM **1.8**

How to calculate the formal charge of an atom in a molecular species

Break It Down Determine the formal charge on every atom in the formate anion, HCO_2^-, shown here.

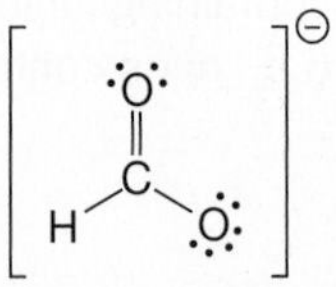

O
C
H
O

(continued)

Think	Solve
How are lone pairs and bonding pairs assigned to atoms?	Lone pair electrons are assigned to the atom on which they appear. Electrons that make up a covalent bond are equally divided between the two atoms in the bond. So, in the H—C bond, one of the two electrons is assigned to H and the other to C; similarly, we assign one of the two electrons from the C—O bond to C and the other to O. We assign two of the four electrons from the C═O bond to C and the remaining two to O.
How is an atom's formal charge computed from the number of electrons it is assigned?	We compare each atom's group number with the number of electrons it is assigned. As seen in the diagram, the H atom, the C atom, and the double-bonded O atom are assigned formal charges of 0 because they have the same number of valence electrons as their corresponding group numbers. The single-bonded O is assigned seven valence electrons, which is one more than its group number of 6. It is therefore assigned a formal charge of −1. 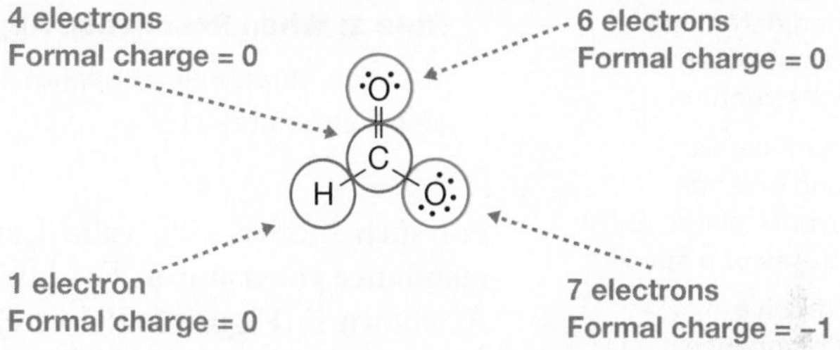 4 electrons Formal charge = 0 6 electrons Formal charge = 0 1 electron Formal charge = 0 7 electrons Formal charge = −1

Try It Determine the formal charge of each atom in the molecule shown here, which belongs to a class of compounds called *oximes*.

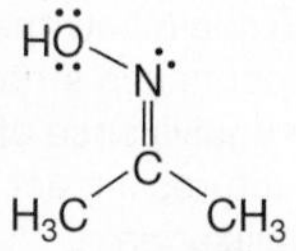

Assigning formal charges to atoms is simply a way of distributing the electrons that are already present within a particular species. Therefore:

> The formal charges of all atoms must sum to the total charge of the species.

YOUR TURN 1.9

Sum the formal charges assigned in Solved Problem 1.8. What do you notice?

1.10 Resonance Theory

Some species are not described well by Lewis structures. In HCO_2^-, for example (refer to Solved Problems 1.4 and 1.8), both of the C—O bonds are identical experimentally; they have the same bond length and bond strength, intermediate between those of a single and a double bond (**Figure 1-24a**, next page). However, the Lewis structure of HCO_2^- (Fig. 1-24b) shows one C—O single bond and one C═O double bond, suggesting that the two bonds are different. Furthermore, experiments show that both oxygen atoms carry an identical partial negative charge (δ^-), whereas the Lewis structure suggests that one oxygen atom bears a full negative charge and the other is uncharged. In other words, the Lewis structure suggests that the C═O double bond and the −1 charge are both confined to a specific region in space, or **localized**, whereas in the real species, they are spread out, or **delocalized**.

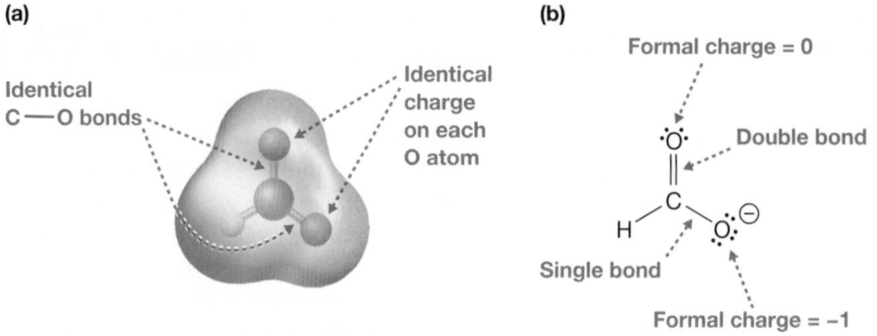
(a)
Identical C—O bonds
Identical charge on each O atom
(b)
Formal charge = 0
Double bond
Single bond
Formal charge = −1

FIGURE 1-24 Limitations of Lewis structures The actual structure of HCO_2^- differs from that suggested by the Lewis structure. (a) In the actual structure, both carbon–oxygen bonds are identical and the charge on each O atom is the same. (b) The Lewis structure, on the other hand, suggests the species has a C—O single bond and a C═O double bond, as well as different charges on each O atom.

SECTION 1.10 OBJECTIVES

You will be able to:

1. Describe what resonance structures are, and determine whether two given structures are indeed resonance structures.
2. Explain the significance of a resonance hybrid and how the resonance hybrid relates to the resonance structures of a species.
3. Evaluate the relative contributions of resonance structures to the resonance hybrid.
4. Explain how the number of resonance structures and the equivalence of resonance structures impact resonance stabilization.

How, then, do we reconcile the differences between the Lewis structures of species like HCO_2^- and their observed characteristics? The answer is through **resonance theory**, the key points of which can be summarized by the following four rules:

Rule 1: When Resonance Applies

The idea of resonance applies to species for which there are two or more valid Lewis structures.

For such species, each valid Lewis structure is called a **resonance structure** or a **resonance contributor**. For HCO_2^-, there are two possible resonance contributors. As shown in **Figure 1-25**, we can think of the two resonance structures resulting from two different ways to complete Step 5 (the final step) of drawing Lewis structures (p. 12)—that is, using lone pairs from two different neighboring atoms to construct the C═O double bond and complete carbon's octet. As a result:

Resonance structures differ only in the placement of their valence electrons, not their atoms.

Rule 2: Significance of the Resonance Hybrid

An individual resonance structure does not accurately describe the structure of the species; the one, true species is better characterized by the **resonance hybrid**, which is a *weighted average of all resonance structures*.

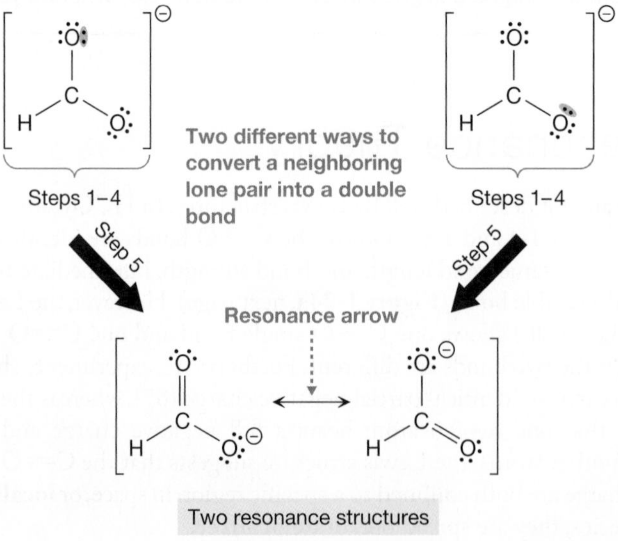
Steps 1–4
Two different ways to convert a neighboring lone pair into a double bond
Steps 1–4
Step 5
Step 5
Resonance arrow
Two resonance structures

FIGURE 1-25 Resonance structures of HCO_2^- Each of the identical structures at the top is the outcome of carrying out Steps 1–4 of drawing Lewis structures (p. 12). To complete the octet on carbon, Step 5 of drawing Lewis structures can be applied in two ways. A lone pair from the oxygen on top can be converted into a C═O double bond, resulting in the first resonance structure. Alternatively, a lone pair from the oxygen on the right can be converted into a C═O double bond, resulting in the second resonance structure.

In the case of HCO_2^-, the hybrid is an average of two resonance structures, as shown in **Figure 1-26**. Averaging the two C—O bonds (a single and a double bond) makes each one an identical 1.5 bond, which is more than a single bond but less than a double bond. (A partial bond is represented in a resonance hybrid by a dashed line connecting the two atoms, -----.) Averaging the charge on each oxygen atom gives each an identical −0.5 charge. This resonance hybrid is now consistent with experimental results.

To help us remember that resonance structures are hypothetical and contribute to the same hybrid, we draw square brackets, [ ], around the group of resonance structures and we place double-headed **resonance arrows** (⟷) between them, as shown previously in both Figures 1-25 and 1-26. These are *not* equilibrium arrows (⇌), which indicate a chemical reaction, because a compound does not rapidly interconvert between its resonance structures. Rather, think of a resonance hybrid in the same way as you might think of a duck-billed platypus (**Figure 1-27**). That is, a platypus has characteristics of both a duck and an otter, but it is a unique species that does *not* rapidly interconvert between those two animals!

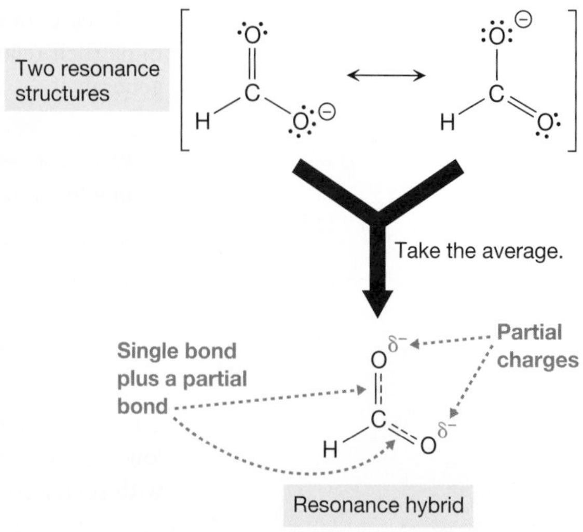

Two resonance structures
Take the average.
Single bond plus a partial bond
Partial charges
Resonance hybrid

FIGURE 1-26 The resonance hybrid of HCO_2^- Each resonance structure of HCO_2^- (top) is averaged to arrive at the resonance hybrid (bottom).

Rule 3: Relative Contribution to the Resonance Hybrid

The resonance hybrid resembles the lowest energy (most stable) resonance structure the most.

The two resonance contributors of HCO_2^- are *equivalent*. Each is composed of one H—C bond, one C═O double bond, and one C—O single bond, and each has a −1 formal charge on the singly bonded O. As a result, the resonance structures have identical energies and they contribute equally to the resonance hybrid.

Duck
Otter
Duck-billed platypus

FIGURE 1-27 An analogy of resonance A duck-billed platypus has characteristics of a duck and an otter, just as a resonance hybrid has characteristics from its resonance contributors.

In cases in which resonance structures are *not* equivalent, we must be able to determine their relative energies to determine their relative contributions to the hybrid. In general:

When two resonance structures are compared, the more stable structure (i.e., the one lower in energy) is the one that has:

1. More atoms with a completed octet.
2. Fewer atoms with a nonzero formal charge.
3. A −1 formal charge appearing on the more electronegative atom and/or a +1 formal charge appearing on the less electronegative atom.

These factors are presented in order of importance, which will help you predict the lower energy resonance structure when two factors contradict each other. We deal with such a contradiction in Solved Problem 1.9.

SOLVED PROBLEM **1.9**

How to determine the more important resonance contributor

Break It Down Which of these resonance structures makes a greater contribution to the resonance hybrid?

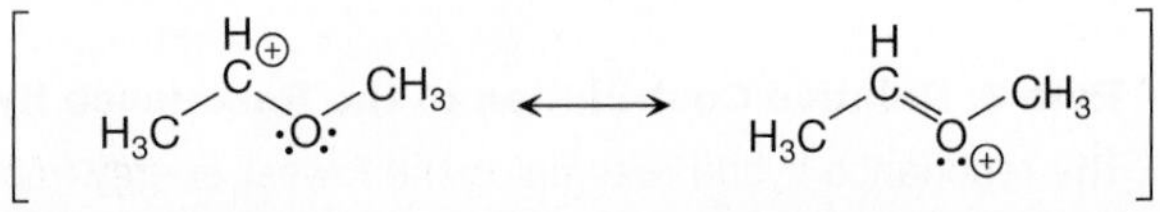

H⊕
C
CH3
H3C
O
H
C
CH3
H3C
O⊕

Think	Solve
Which resonance structure has more atoms with an octet?	The resonance structure on the right has more atoms with octets, because the positively charged carbon in the resonance structure on the left lacks an octet.
Which resonance structure has fewer atoms with a nonzero formal charge?	Neither does, because each resonance structure has one atom with a +1 formal charge.
Which resonance structure has the +1 formal charge on the less electronegative atom?	The resonance structure on the left does, given that carbon is less electronegative than oxygen.
Is there a contradiction among these factors? If so, which factor is more important?	We see a contradiction between the first factor (octets) and the third factor (electronegativity). The first factor is more important, so the resonance structure on the right is lower in energy and makes a greater contribution to the hybrid.

Try It Which of these resonance structures makes a greater contribution to the resonance hybrid? *Note*: Formal charges are not shown.

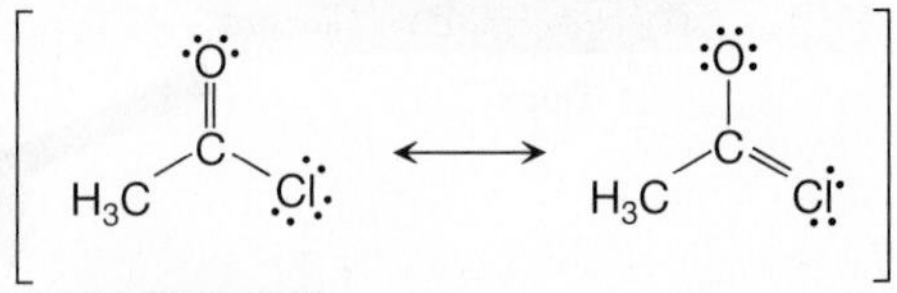

O
C
H3C
Cl
O
C
H3C
Cl

Rule 4: Resonance and Stabilization

A species that exhibits resonance tends to be more stable than a similar species that does not.

- As the number of resonance structures increases, the species tends to be more stable.
- A species that has equivalent resonance structures tends to be highly stabilized.

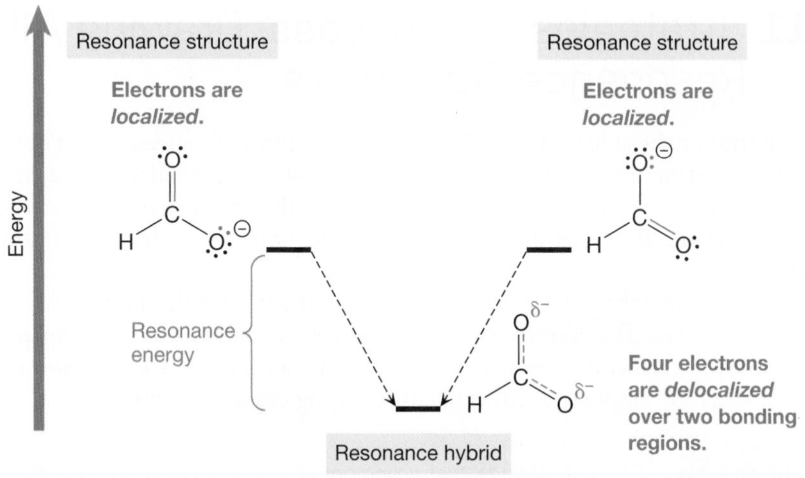
Resonance structure
Electrons are localized.
Resonance structure
Electrons are localized.
Energy
Resonance energy
Four electrons are delocalized over two bonding regions.
Resonance hybrid

FIGURE 1-28 Resonance stabilization In each resonance structure of HCO_2^-, the four electrons in red are localized. In the resonance hybrid, those four electrons are delocalized over three atoms. Delocalization results in lower energy and greater stability.

The stabilization due to resonance is an outcome of the **delocalization** of electrons; that is, electrons have lower energy when they are less confined. In the resonance hybrid of HCO_2^-, we can see that four electrons are delocalized over two bonding regions (**Figure 1-28**). In one of the hypothetical resonance structures, on the other hand, those electrons would be *localized.* The extent by which a species is stabilized in this fashion is called its **resonance energy** or its **delocalization energy**.

Resonance stabilization increases with additional resonance structures because each additional resonance structure allows electrons to be delocalized over a greater amount of space. Similarly, resonance stabilization tends to be large when a species has equivalent resonance structures because equivalent resonance structures contribute equally to the hybrid, which maximizes electron delocalization.

We saw previously that the two resonance structures of HCO_2^- are equivalent, so its resonance energy is quite substantial. Another example is benzene, whose resonance structures and hybrid are shown in **Figure 1-29** (see Looking Ahead box).

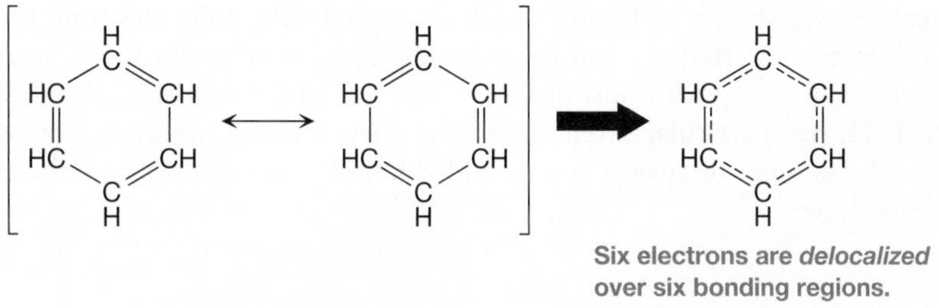
Six electrons are delocalized over six bonding regions.

FIGURE 1-29 Equivalent resonance structures The two resonance structures of benzene (*left*) are equivalent, so they contribute equally to the resonance hybrid (*right*).

▸ LOOKING AHEAD

We will discuss benzene in greater detail in Chapter 14, where we explain that much of benzene's resonance energy is due to a phenomenon called *aromaticity*.

CONNECTIONS 1.9

Benzene and gasoline

Benzene (Fig. 1-29) is an aromatic hydrocarbon that is naturally found in crude oil and, because of its high octane number, is an important component of gasoline.

CONNECTIONS 1.10

Acetic acid and its uses

Acetic acid (Fig. 1-30), when it is diluted to about 5% by volume, is familiar to us as vinegar. In organic chemistry, acetic acid is used as a reagent in a wide variety of organic reactions. It can also be used as a solvent.

SUPREME STAR
White Distilled
Vinegar

Acetic acid (CH_3CO_2H) is *not* stabilized greatly by resonance. Although it has two resonance structures, only the one on the left in **Figure 1-30** contributes significantly. The one on the right is much higher in energy because two charges are present. Therefore, the electrons involved in resonance in this compound are not very highly delocalized.

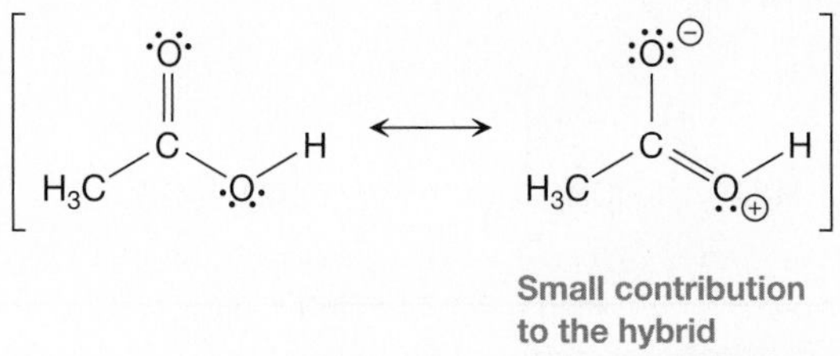
Small contribution to the hybrid

FIGURE 1-30 Nonequivalent resonance structures The two resonance structures of acetic acid are nonequivalent, so they contribute unequally to the resonance hybrid. The one on the left is lower in energy, so it has the greater contribution.

SECTION 1.11 OBJECTIVES

You will be able to:

1. Use curved arrow notation to indicate the electron movement necessary to convert one resonance structure into another.
2. Identify features in a given Lewis structure that indicate the structure will have another resonance structure.
3. Draw all resonance structures of a species when you are given an initial Lewis structure.

1.11 Strategies for Success: Drawing All Resonance Structures

It is important to be able to draw *all* resonance structures of a species. That's because all resonance structures contribute to the features of the resonance hybrid, and the total number of resonance structures is related to the stability of the species. We therefore devote this section to giving you insights into drawing resonance structures.

To begin, remember that any two resonance structures differ only in where the *electrons* are located. Therefore, one resonance structure can be obtained from another just by moving valence electrons (see Looking Ahead box), but *atoms must remain frozen in place!* We emphasize this explicitly by using **curved arrows**:

A curved arrow  illustrates the movement of a pair of valence electrons.

- A curved arrow can originate from a lone pair of electrons or from the center of a double or triple bond to indicate the specific pair of electrons that is being moved.
- The arrow points to an atom if the electrons being moved become a lone pair. Otherwise, the arrow points to the center of an existing single or double bond to represent the formation of a new double or triple bond there.

▸ LOOKING AHEAD

The electrons that can be moved to convert one resonance structure into another must be π (pi) electrons. As we will learn in Sections 3.4 and 3.5, double and triple bonds contain π electrons. In Section 14.4, we will learn that π electrons can also take the form of lone pairs in Lewis structures.

Each curved arrow illustrates the movement of an electron pair.

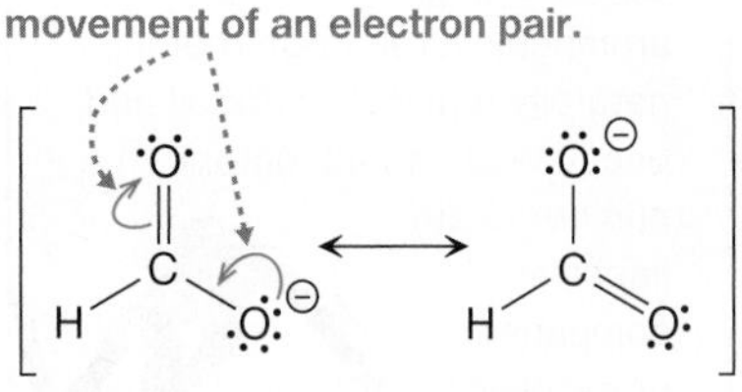

FIGURE 1-31 Curved arrow notation in resonance Shifting the four electrons indicated by the two curved arrows converts the resonance structure on the left into the one on the right.

Curved arrow notation is shown for HCO_2^- in **Figure 1-31**. The curved arrow on the right represents the conversion of a lone pair into a new bond between C and O. The other curved arrow represents a bond from the C═O double bond being converted into a lone pair on the O atom.

The curved arrow notation drawn in Figure 1-31 is feasible because the species contains a particular feature: a lone pair of electrons on an atom (the single-bonded O) adjacent to a multiple bond (the C═O bond). This feature, shown again as Feature 1 in **Figure 1-32a**, is one of five features a species can have that would allow electrons to be moved to arrive at another resonance structure. The other four features are shown in Figure 1-32b through 1-32e. Take the time to study these five features so that you can immediately recognize them in Lewis structures and so that you can quickly add the curved arrows with confidence. As you study Figure 1-32, pay particular attention to the curved arrow notation, not only in terms of the number of curved arrows added but also in terms of how the curved arrows are drawn.

YOUR TURN 1.10

Examine the first resonance structure in each pair, and determine which feature from Figure 1-32 it possesses. Then supply the necessary curved arrow(s) to convert the first structure into the second structure.

(a)

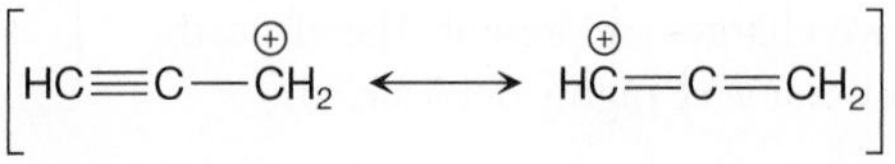

(b)

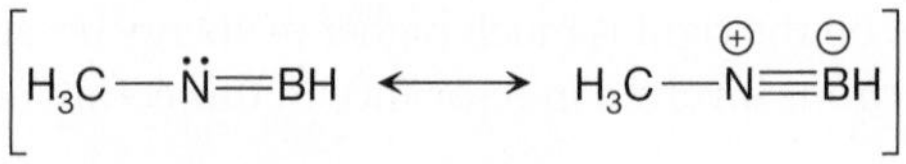

(c)

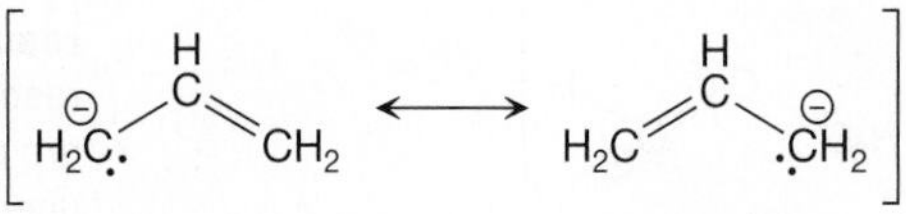

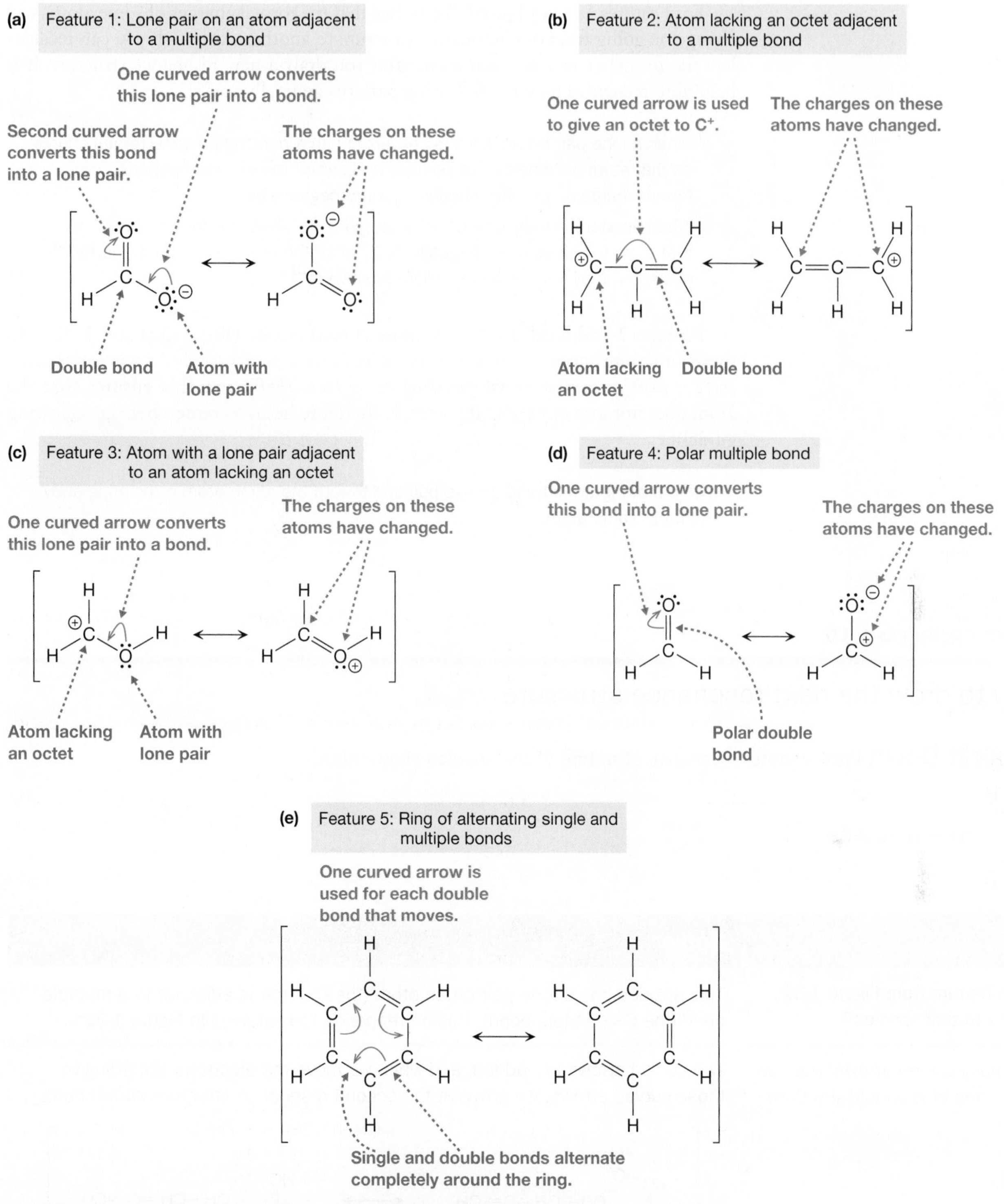
(a) Feature 1: Lone pair on an atom adjacent to a multiple bond
One curved arrow converts this lone pair into a bond.
Second curved arrow converts this bond into a lone pair.
The charges on these atoms have changed.
Double bond
Atom with lone pair
(b) Feature 2: Atom lacking an octet adjacent to a multiple bond
One curved arrow is used to give an octet to C⁺.
The charges on these atoms have changed.
Atom lacking an octet
Double bond
(c) Feature 3: Atom with a lone pair adjacent to an atom lacking an octet
One curved arrow converts this lone pair into a bond.
The charges on these atoms have changed.
Atom lacking an octet
Atom with lone pair
(d) Feature 4: Polar multiple bond
One curved arrow converts this bond into a lone pair.
The charges on these atoms have changed.
Polar double bond
(e) Feature 5: Ring of alternating single and multiple bonds
One curved arrow is used for each double bond that moves.
Single and double bonds alternate completely around the ring.

FIGURE 1-32 Features that indicate the existence of another resonance structure
When a Lewis structure has one of these features, a new resonance structure can be drawn by adding the corresponding curved arrows and moving the electrons accordingly.

For Features 1–4 in Figure 1-32, notice that the formal charges of some atoms will change on going from one resonance structure to another. Although you can recalculate the formal charge on each atom after you draw a new resonance structure, it is helpful to recognize how the following patterns generally apply:

- When a lone pair on an atom is converted into a bonding pair, the formal charge on that atom becomes more positive by 1; when the reverse happens, the formal charge on the atom becomes more negative by 1.
- When an atom initially lacking an octet gains its octet, the formal charge on that atom becomes more negative by 1; when the reverse happens, the formal charge on that atom becomes more positive by 1.

Features 1 and 5 call for two or more curved arrows (Fig. 1-32a and 1-32e). In these situations, notice that *when one curved arrow points toward a particular atom, there is another curved arrow pointing away from that atom.* This ensures that the atom does not lose or exceed its octet. It therefore helps to remember the following guideline:

Avoid drawing two curved arrows pointing toward the same atom or pointing away from the same atom.

SOLVED PROBLEM **1.10**

How to draw the next resonance structure

Break It Down **Draw another resonance structure of the species shown here.**

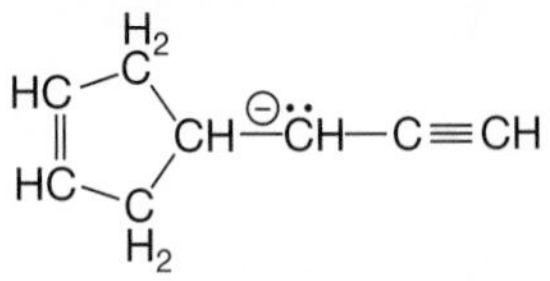

Think	Solve
Which feature from Figure 1-32 applies to this species?	This species has a lone pair on an atom (the C^-) that is adjacent to a multiple bond (the $C{\equiv}C$ triple bond); this corresponds to Feature 1 in Figure 1-32a.
How many curved arrows must be added, and how should you draw them?	Two curved arrows are added, and when we move the electrons according to those curved arrows, we arrive at the second resonance structure shown here. 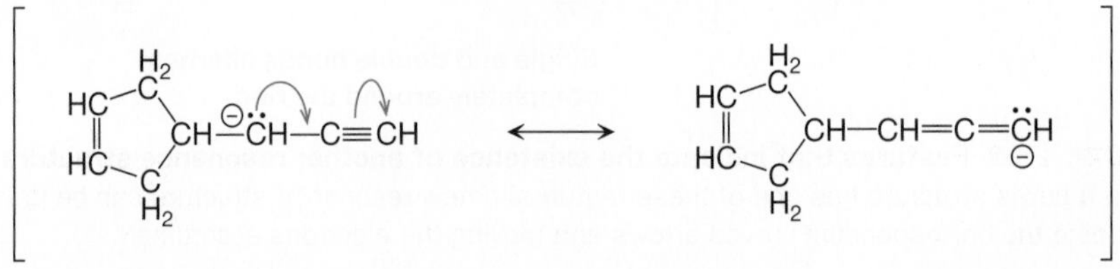
What happens to the respective formal charges?	The charge on C^- becomes more positive by 1 because a lone pair is turned into a bond. The opposite is true for the triply bonded C that gains a lone pair.

(continued)

Try It Draw a resonance structure for each of the following species.

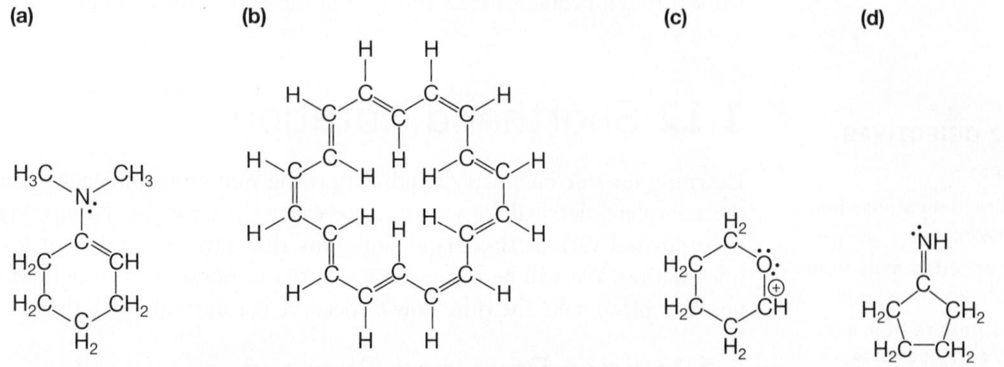

(a)
(b)
(c)
(d)

Frequently, a species will have more than two resonance structures. To draw all resonance structures of these species, it helps to approach the problem systematically.

Strategies for Success
Drawing All Resonance Structures

Drawing All Resonance Structures

1. Identify the feature. Which feature in Figure 1-32 does the species have?
2. Add the curved arrow(s). Each feature calls for a certain number of curved arrows to be added in a particular way.
3. Move the electrons. Draw the new resonance structure by moving only the electrons indicated by the curved arrow(s).
4. Examine the new resonance structure. Does the new resonance structure have a feature from Figure 1-32? If so, repeat Steps 2–4.
5. Continue this process until you have exhausted all your options for moving electrons.

Figure 1-33 gives an example of how to apply this strategy. The first structure exhibits Feature 1 from Figure 1-32a: a lone pair on an atom (C^-) that is adjacent to a multiple bond (the leftmost C=C bond). To arrive at the second structure, we add the two curved arrows and move the valence electrons accordingly to arrive at the second resonance structure. Examining the second resonance structure, we see that it, too, exhibits Feature 1, so we add two curved arrows again to arrive at the third resonance structure. The process is repeated one more time to arrive at the final structure.

YOUR TURN **1.11**

Draw in the curved arrows needed to convert the third resonance structure in Figure 1-33 to the fourth.

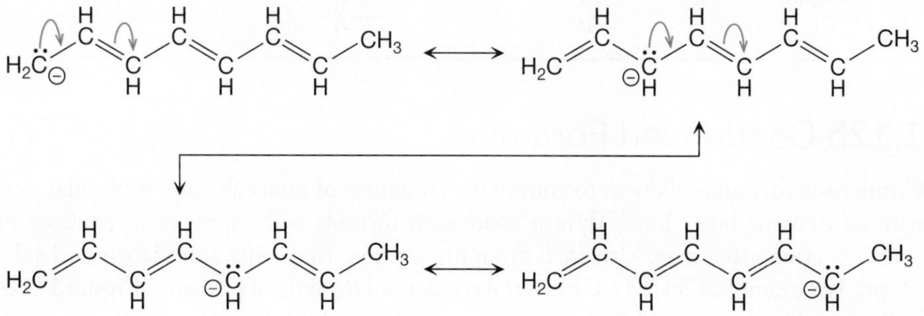

FIGURE 1-33 Multiple resonance structures involving an atom with a lone pair adjacent to a multiple bond Each structure exhibits Feature 1 from Figure 1-32, so two curved arrows are drawn each time to convert one resonance structure into the next.

Species that have multiple resonance structures can contain any of the five features in Figure 1-32. To gain practice drawing all resonance structures of a given species, work through Problems 1.22 and 1.23 at the end of the chapter.

SECTION 1.12 OBJECTIVES

You will be able to:

1. Add lone pairs to an atom when they are not shown.
2. Draw a condensed formula from a Lewis structure and vice versa.
3. Draw a line structure from a Lewis structure and vice versa.

1.12 Shorthand Notations

Learning organic chemistry requires drawing numerous molecules. Because drawing the complete, detailed Lewis structure every time can be tedious, organic chemists have devised various shorthand notations that save time without loss of structural information. We will be using these shorthand notations throughout the rest of the book, so please take the time now to become comfortable with them.

1.12a Lone Pairs and Charges

Lone pairs of electrons are frequently omitted from Lewis structures. Because lone pairs have vital roles in many organic reactions, you need to be able to put them back in as necessary. Knowing where lone pairs belong requires an understanding of how formal charge relates to the numbers of bonds and lone pairs on various atoms. Table 1-5 illustrates formal charges in various bonding arrangements. Note that the atoms have octets in all of the scenarios shown, except in the case of a positively charged carbon, C^+.

TABLE 1-5 Formal Charges on Atoms with Various Bonding Scenarios

	FORMAL CHARGE		
Atom	**-1**	**0**	**+1**
Carbon	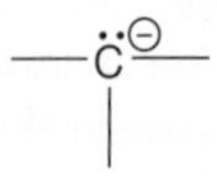	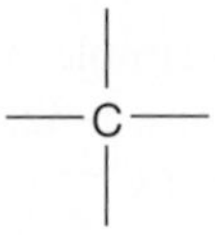	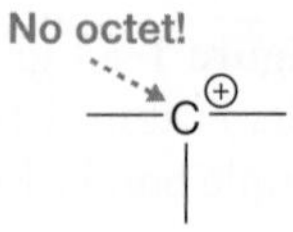No octet!
Nitrogen	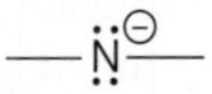	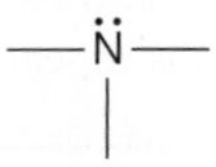	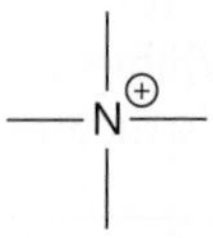
Oxygen	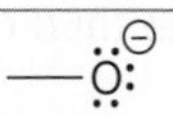	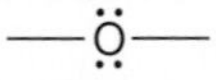	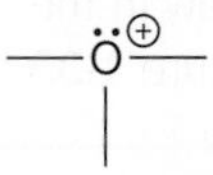
Halogen (X = F, Cl, Br, I)		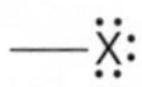	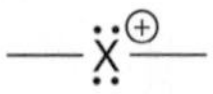

1.12b Condensed Formulas

Condensed formulas allow us to convey the structures of molecules and molecular ions without drawing bond lines. Thus, a condensed formula will appear as a sequence of common atom groupings, with each grouping written using only atom labels and subscripts. For example, $CH_3CH_2CH_3$ is the condensed formula of propane (**Figure 1-34**), indicating that the central CH_2 group is bonded to two CH_3 groups.

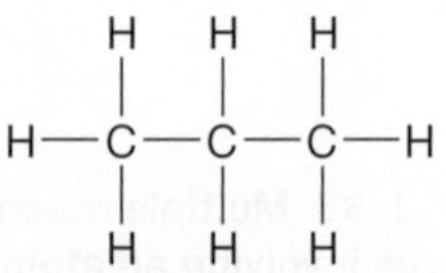

$CH_3CH_2CH_3$

Propane

FIGURE 1-34 Condensed formula of propane

In general, condensed formulas are written according to the following rules:

Rules for Drawing Condensed Formulas

- Each non-hydrogen atom is identified, followed immediately by the number of hydrogen atoms that are bonded to it.
- Adjacent non-hydrogen atoms are interpreted as being covalently bonded to each other.

To see how we can draw a Lewis structure from a condensed formula, consider CH_3CHN^-. Three hydrogens are bonded to the first carbon, and one hydrogen is bonded to the second carbon. Furthermore, the central C atom is bonded to another C atom and to a N atom, giving rise to the skeleton that appears on the left in **Figure 1-35**. The structure is completed by adding the electrons shown in red: a double bond between C and N and two lone pairs on N.

FIGURE 1-35 Lewis structure of CH_3CHN^- To convert from the skeleton on the left to the Lewis structure on the right, an extra C—N bond and two lone pairs (in red) must be added.

SOLVED PROBLEM **1.11**

How to draw a Lewis structure from a condensed formula

Break It Down **Draw the Lewis structure for crotonaldehyde, $CH_3CHCHCHO$.**

Think	Solve
Which non-hydrogen atoms are bonded together?	The four C atoms and the O atom are connected to make a chain: C—C—C—C—O.
How many H atoms are bonded to each non-hydrogen atom?	Each non-hydrogen atom is bonded to the hydrogen atoms that immediately follow it in the condensed formula: three hydrogens on the first carbon, and one hydrogen on each of the other carbons. 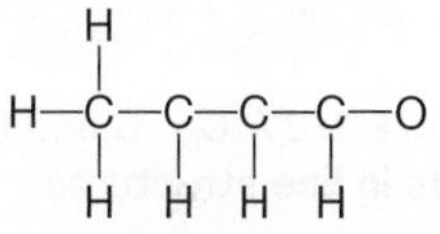
How can we add bonds and lone pairs to maximize the number of octets and also make sure that the total charge is zero?	None of the atoms bears a formal charge. Therefore, according to Table 1-5 (p. 30), each C atom should have four bonds, and the O atom should have two bonds and two lone pairs. The electrons that must be added to complete the Lewis structure are shown in red. 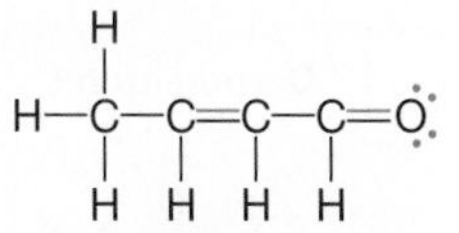 **Crotonaldehyde**

Try It Draw the Lewis structure for **(a)** $CHCCH_2CHCHCH_3$, **(b)** $CH_3OCH_2CHCH_2$, and **(c)** $NH_2CH_2CHNCH_2CHCF_2$.

Many organic molecules have multiple CH_2 groups bonded together. In these cases, we can simplify a condensed formula by using the notation $(CH_2)_n$. Thus, $CH_3CH_2CH_2CH_2CH_3$ simplifies to $CH_3(CH_2)_3CH_3$.

Parentheses are also used to clarify situations in which three or four groups are attached to the same atom. In 2-methylbutane (**Figure 1-36a**, next page), for example, the second C atom from the left is bonded to two CH_3 groups and one CH_2CH_3 group. Its condensed formula is written as $CH_3CH(CH_3)CH_2CH_3$, indicating that the CH_3 group in parentheses and the CH_2 group are both bonded to the preceding CH carbon.

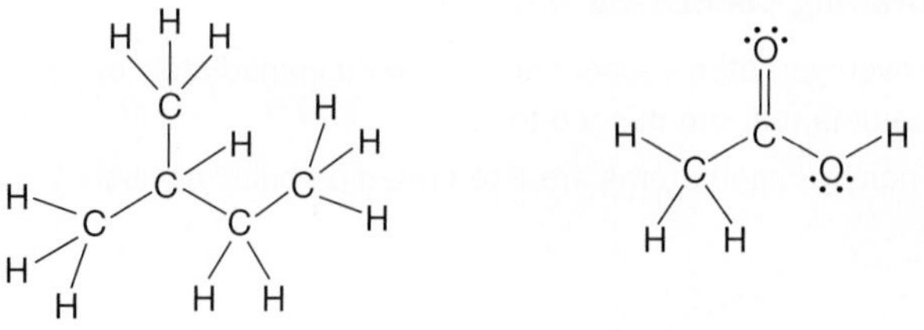

FIGURE 1-36 **Condensed formulas and branching** Condensed formulas are shown on the top and Lewis structures are shown on the bottom. (a) Parentheses in a condensed formula denote that the group is attached to the previous C. (b) The CO_2 notation represents a C atom that is doubly bonded to one O atom and singly bonded to another.

(a) $CH_3CH(CH_3)CH_2CH_3$
Same as

2-Methylbutane

(b) CH_3CO_2H
Same as

Ethanoic acid (Acetic acid)

CONNECTIONS 1.11

Crotonaldehyde and its uses

Crotonaldehyde (Solved Problem 1.11) is found in some foodstuffs, such as soybean oil. It is also used as a precursor in the industrial synthesis of vitamin E and sorbic acid, a food preservative.

Life
E
1000 IU
50

Many common organic compounds contain a bonding arrangement in which a carbon atom is bonded to one oxygen atom by a double bond and to a second oxygen atom by a single bond. We can write this arrangement in the form CO_2, as shown in Figure 1-36b for acetic acid (CH_3CO_2H). Another common bonding arrangement is CH═O, which is often abbreviated as CHO, as shown previously in Solved Problem 1.11.

1.12c Line Structures

Line structures, like condensed formulas, are compact and can be drawn quickly and easily. Unlike condensed formulas, however, they are not intended to be written as part of text. The rules for drawing line structures are as follows:

Rules for Drawing Line Structures

- Carbon atoms are not drawn explicitly. Carbon atoms are implied at the intersection of every two or more lines and at the end of every bond that is drawn, unless another atom is written there already. This includes carbon atoms that are parts of double bonds and triple bonds (**Figure 1.37**).
- All non-carbon and non-hydrogen atoms, called **heteroatoms**, are drawn.
- Hydrogen atoms bonded to carbon are not drawn. Hydrogen atoms bonded to all other atoms are drawn.
- Bonds to hydrogen are not drawn. All other bonds are drawn explicitly.
- Several carbon atoms bonded in a single chain are represented by a zigzag structure (**Figure 1.38**).
- Lone pairs of electrons are generally not shown. Lone pairs can be drawn explicitly to emphasize an important aspect of an atom.

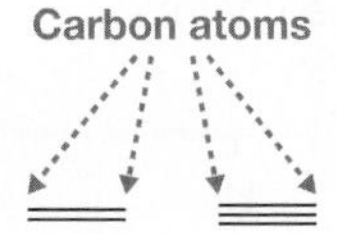

Carbon atoms

FIGURE 1-37 **C═C and C≡C bonds in line structures**

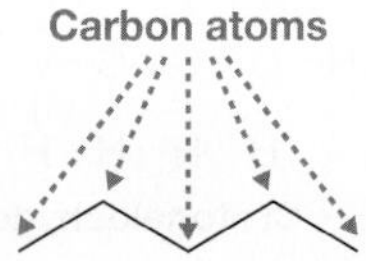

Carbon atoms

FIGURE 1-38 **Zigzags in line structure**

The line structure of $CH_3CH_2CH_2CH_2CH_2CH_2CH_2NH_2$ is shown in **Figure 1-39**. Notice that the intersection of each bond line represents a C atom, as does the end of the bond on the left side of the molecule. The NH_2 group is written in explicitly.

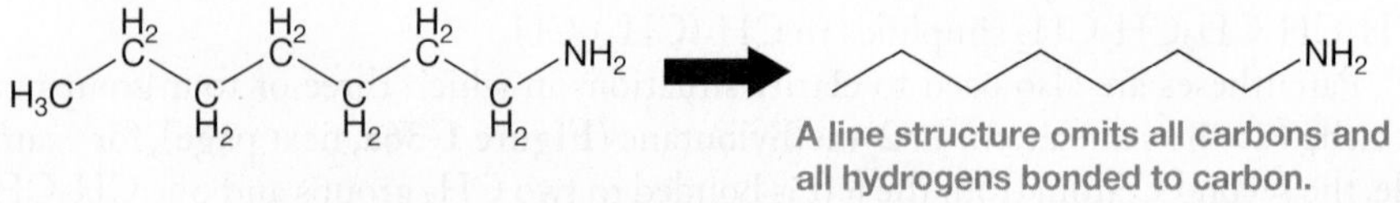

A line structure omits all carbons and all hydrogens bonded to carbon.

FIGURE 1-39 **Line structure of $CH_3(CH_2)_6NH_2$** In the line structure on the right, neither the C atoms nor the H atoms attached to C are shown. However, the N atom is shown, and so are the H atoms attached to N.

YOUR TURN 1.12

A student mistakenly interprets the line structure shown here as but-2-yne ($CH_3C{\equiv}CCH_3$). What mistake did the student make?

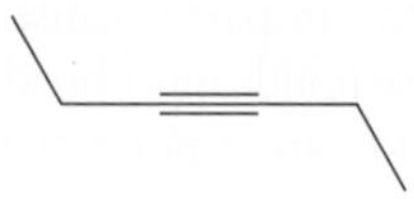

SOLVED PROBLEM 1.12

How to use line structures when drawing resonance structures

Break It Down **Why is it incorrect to draw resonance structures for propene as shown here?**

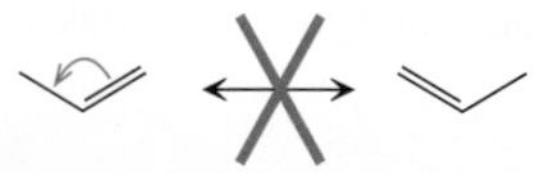

Think	Solve
Does the first structure have any of the five features illustrated Figure 1-32?	None of the features from Figure 1-32 is present. There are no atoms with a lone pair and no atoms lacking an octet, which eliminates Features 1 through 3. There is no polar multiple bond (Feature 4), and neither is there a ring of alternating single and multiple bonds (Feature 5).
What would the initial structure look like as a complete Lewis structure (i.e., with all hydrogen atoms drawn in)? How would that structure change after the electrons are moved?	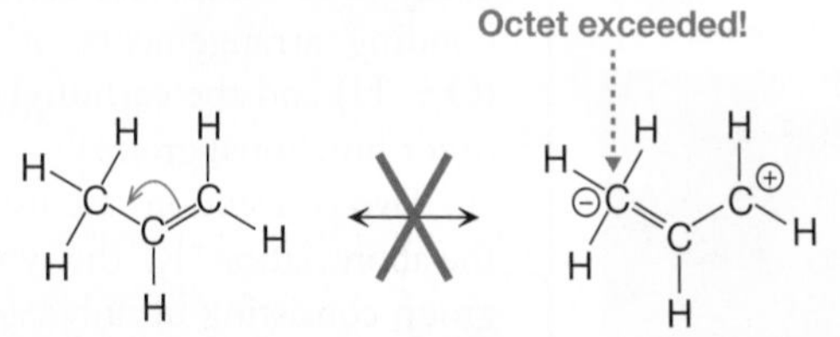Octet exceeded!
What rule is broken in the transformation from the first structure to the second?	As shown above, the CH_3 carbon would exceed its octet after gaining the bond indicated by the curved arrow. Atoms in the second row of the periodic table must not exceed their octet.

Try It Draw all resonance structures for each of the ions represented here as line structures. If no additional resonance structures exist, explain why.

(a)

(b)

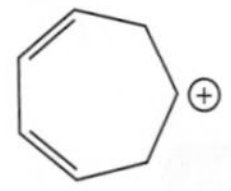

(c)

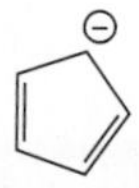

1.13 An Overview of Organic Compounds: Functional Groups

SECTION 1.13 OBJECTIVES

You will be able to:

1. Explain why functional groups are important.
2. Identify functional groups within a molecular species and name the compound classes they characterize.

Certain types of bonds and arrangements of atoms appear especially frequently in organic chemistry. The most common types of bonds we encounter are C—C and C—H single bonds. Compounds consisting of only C—C and C—H single bonds are called **alkanes**. Examples include methane, 2-methyloctane, and ethylcyclohexane (**Figure 1-40**, next page).

CH_4

Methane

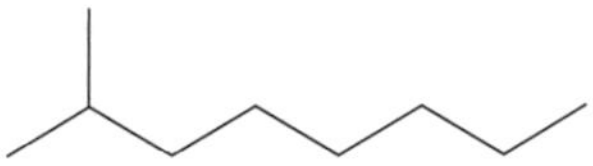

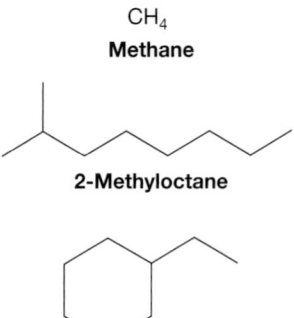

2-Methyloctane

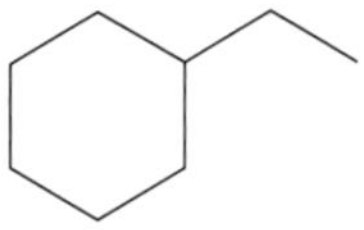

Ethylcyclohexane

FIGURE 1-40 Examples of alkanes Alkanes consist entirely of carbon and hydrogen and have only single bonds.

Alkanes tend to be among the most *unreactive* organic compounds. For this reason, liquid alkanes (e.g., pentane and hexane) are often used as solvents in which to carry out organic reactions.

Alkanes are relatively unreactive in part because C—C and C—H bonds are so strong; for a reaction to occur, these bonds must break. In fact, as indicated in Table 1-2 (p. 10), C—C and C—H bonds are among the strongest single bonds we will encounter.

Alkanes also tend to be unreactive because C—C and C—H bonds are either nonpolar or are only very slightly polar. In Chapter 7, we explain that a large driving force behind many chemical reactions depends on the existence of substantial bond dipoles.

Organic molecules having atoms other than C and H, or bonds other than single bonds, tend to be more reactive than alkanes. In some cases, this may be due to the introduction of weaker bonds, and in other cases, to the presence of large bond dipoles.

As you will learn throughout this book, specific arrangements of atoms connected by specific types of bonds tend to react in characteristic ways. Even though such arrangements may consist of only two or three atoms, they dictate the *function* (i.e., the chemical behavior) of the entire molecule; thus these structural components are called **functional groups**. Consequently:

An organic molecule's reactivity is governed by its functional groups.

The most common functional groups are listed in Table 1-6, along with the compound classes in which they are found. Take the time to commit these functional groups and compound classes to memory and review them frequently. Note that the bonding arrangements of some functional groups, such as the **hydroxyl group** (O—H) and the **carbonyl group** (C═O), appear in the bonding arrangements for other functional groups.

Two conventions are used in Table 1-6 to represent generalized structures. One is the abbreviation "R," the symbol used to represent an **alkyl group**, which is an attached group consisting of only carbon and hydrogen. Like alkanes, alkyl groups tend to be unreactive. The benefit of replacing large, unreactive alkyl groups with R is that it allows us to focus on just the reactive portion of the molecule (i.e., the functional group).

We will learn more about alkyl groups in the first *nomenclature* unit (Interchapter A), following this chapter, which pertains to the naming of molecules. For now, you just need to know that *a bond to R specifically indicates a bond to a carbon atom.*

The second convention used in Table 1-6 pertains to the absence of atoms at the ends of specific bonds. These bonds indicate that *either* an alkyl group (R) or a hydrogen atom can be attached.

With these conventions understood, the following conclusions can be drawn from Table 1-6:

General Conclusions about Functional Groups

1. Functional groups can be distinguished by the type of atoms they contain. R—S—H and R—O—H, for example, are different functional groups.
2. Functional groups can differ in type of bond. C═C and C≡C are different functional groups.
3. Some functional groups contain the bonding arrangements of smaller functional groups. A carboxyl group (CO_2H), for example, contains both C—O—H and C═O bonding arrangements.
4. Alkanes are considered to have no functional groups. They are relatively unreactive, and when they do react, the reaction tends to be very unselective (see Chapter 27).

CONNECTIONS 1.12

Cyclohexanone and nylon
Cyclohexanone (Solved Problem 1.13, p. 36) is an important industrial compound because it is a precursor in the synthesis of nylon, the material used to make this parachute.

CONNECTIONS 1.13

δ-Valerolactone, pentanoic acid, and their uses
δ-Valerolactone (Solved Problem 1.13, Try It, p. 36) is used as a precursor in the industrial synthesis of polyesters, whereas pentanoic acid is used to produce esters that have pleasant odors or pleasant flavors. These esters are used in perfumes and cosmetics or as food additives.

5. Rings generally do not constitute new functional groups. In most cases, the reactivity of a functional group that is part of a ring is very similar to its reactivity in an open chain.
   a. *Arenes* are exceptions, which are discussed in depth in Chapter 14.
   b. Another exception is an *epoxide*, which is a three-membered-ring ether. As we discuss in Chapter 4, this is because small rings are highly strained, which tends to make them more reactive than an analogous open-chain ether group.

TABLE 1-6 Common Functional Groups[a]

Functional Group (Red)	Compound Class	Functional Group (Red)	Compound Class	Functional Group (Red)	Compound Class
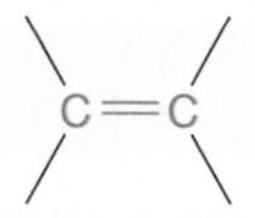	Alkene	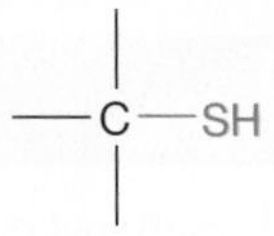	Thiol	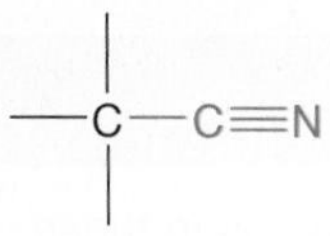	Nitrile
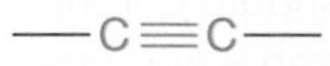	Alkyne	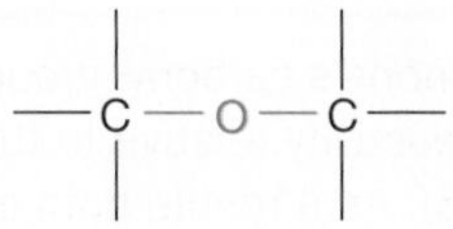	Ether	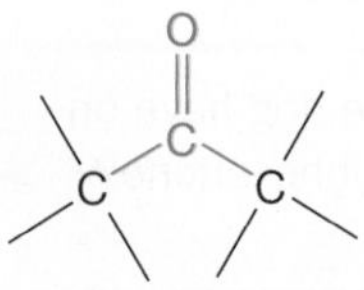	Ketone
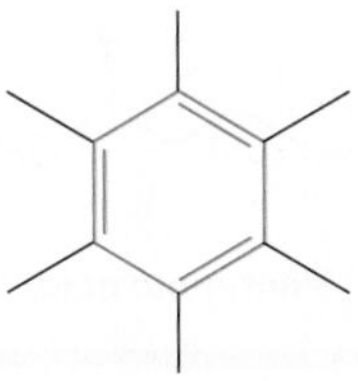	Arene or Aromatic compound	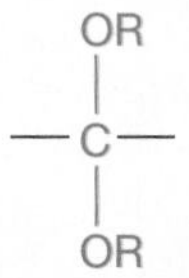	Acetal	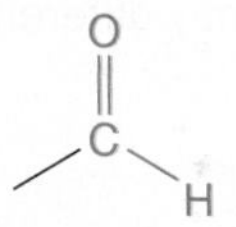	Aldehyde
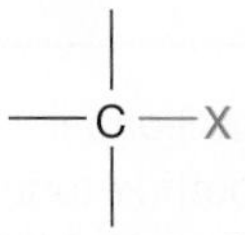 (X = F, Cl, Br, I)	Alkyl halide	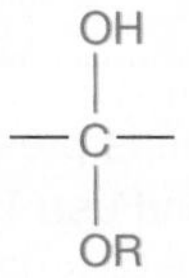	Hemiacetal	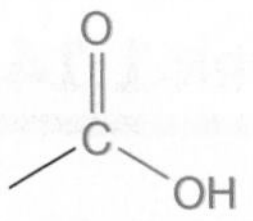	Carboxylic acid
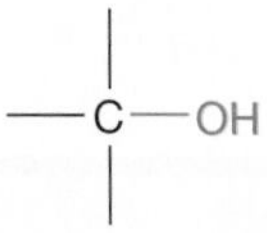	Alcohol	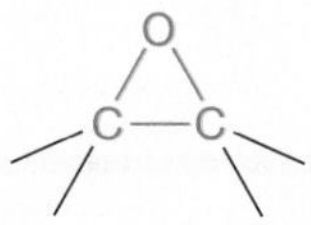	Epoxide	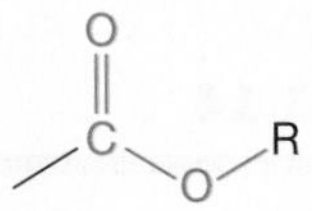	Ester
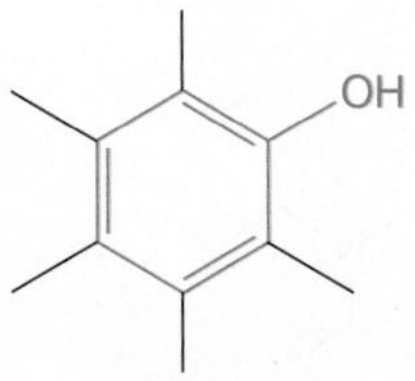	Phenol	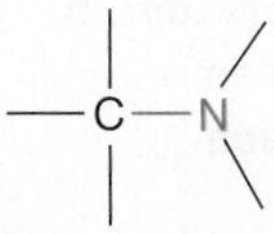	Amine	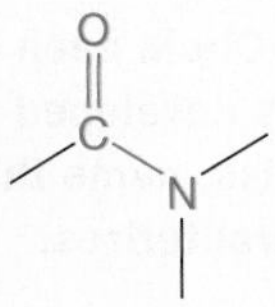	Amide

[a]R indicates an alkyl group, and the absence of an atom at the end of a bond indicates that either R or H may be attached.

YOUR TURN **1.13**

Table 1-6 illustrates eight functional groups that contain the bonding arrangements of functional groups with fewer atoms. One of these is the carboxyl group (CO_2H), as noted previously. What are the other seven functional groups, and what are the smaller functional groups that they appear to contain?

SOLVED PROBLEM **1.13**

How to use functional groups to evaluate similarities in reactivity of molecules

Break It Down **Will the chemical reactivities of these compounds be similar or significantly different? Explain.**

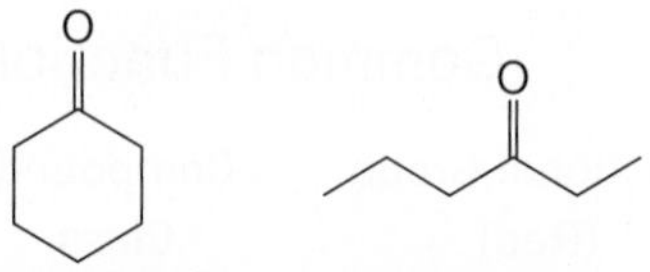

Cyclohexanone **Hexan-3-one**

Think	Solve
Are the functional groups in these molecules the same or different?	Both compounds have a carbonyl group of the form $C_2C{=}O$, characteristic of ketones.
What impact will the ring have on the reactivity of cyclohexanone?	Although cyclohexanone's carbonyl group is part of a ring, this should not significantly alter its reactivity relative to that of the open-chain hexan-3-one (see Conclusion 5, p. 35). As a result, both compounds should behave similarly.

Try It Will the chemical reactivity of δ-valerolactone and pentanoic acid be similar or significantly different? Explain.

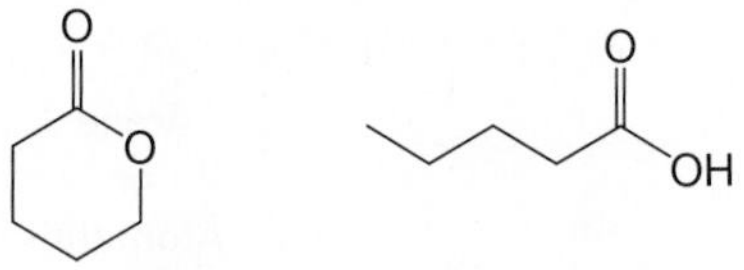

δ-Valerolactone **Pentanoic acid**

YOUR TURN **1.14**

Circle the functional groups present in cyclohexanone and hexan-3-one in Solved Problem 1.13, and use Table 1-6 to verify that they are both ketones.

SOLVED PROBLEM **1.14**

How to identify functional groups in a large molecule

Break It Down **Circle each of the functional groups present in ebalzotan, which was developed as an antidepressant and an antianxiety agent. Also, name the compound class that each functional group characterizes.**

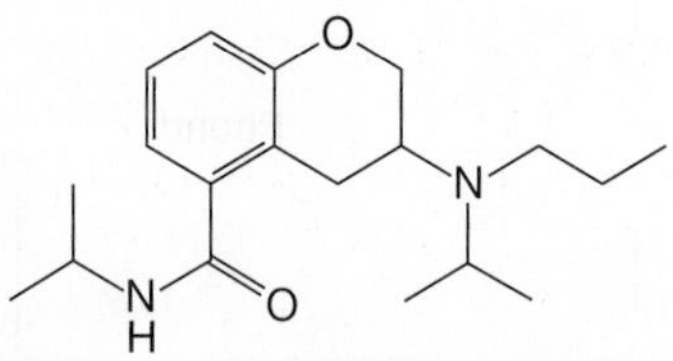

Ebalzotan

(continued)

Think	Solve
Are there any multiple bonds between carbon atoms? Are there any special rings present?	There are three C=C double bonds. These are *not* separate C=C groups that characterize alkenes, because they alternate with single bonds completely around the six-membered ring. The functional group is characteristic of an arene.
Are any heteroatoms present? If so, in what kinds of bonds are they involved? Are there cases in which two heteroatoms belong to the same functional group?	Recall that heteroatoms are atoms other than carbon or hydrogen. There are two O atoms and two N atoms present, each providing the potential for another functional group. The N atom at the right of the molecule is part of a N—C bond, characteristic of an amine. The O atom at the top of the molecule is part of a C—O—C functional group, characteristic of an ether. The O atom and the N atom at the bottom left of the molecule are part of the O=C—N functional group, characteristic of an amide.

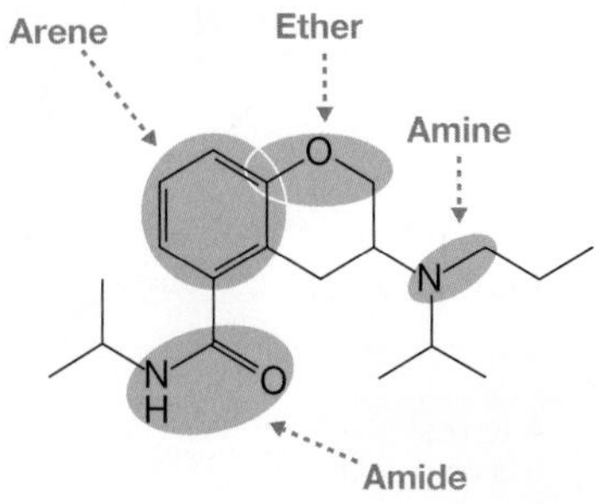

Arene
Ether
Amine
Amide

Try It Circle each functional group present in this structure of ciprofloxacin, a powerful antibiotic commonly sold under the brand name Cipro. Also, name the compound class that each functional group characterizes.

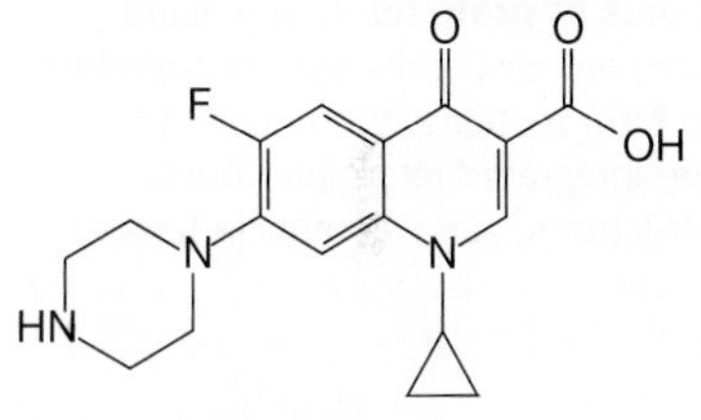

Ciprofloxacin (Cipro)

THE ORGANIC CHEMISTRY OF BIOMOLECULES

1.14 An Introduction to Proteins, Carbohydrates, and Nucleic Acids: Fundamental Building Blocks and Functional Groups

SECTION 1.14 OBJECTIVES

You will be able to:

1. Draw the general structure of an amino acid and distinguish one amino acid from another on the basis of their side chains.
2. Identify carbohydrates and monosaccharides on the basis of their molecular formulas.
3. Characterize the three components of a nucleotide, and distinguish one nucleotide from another on the basis of their nitrogenous bases.
4. Explain how amino acids relate to proteins, how monosaccharides relate to polysaccharides, and how nucleotides relate to nucleic acids.

Organic chemistry plays a pivotal role in biology at the molecular level. As we saw in Section 1.1, the original definition of an organic compound was a substance of plant or animal origin, and even today many people still think of "organic" as synonymous with "natural" and distinct from a "synthetic" substance made in a laboratory or an industrial plant. To the chemist, however, organic molecules are those composed chiefly of carbon and hydrogen and usually of other nonmetals such as oxygen, nitrogen, phosphorus, sulfur, and the halogens (fluorine, chlorine, bromine, and iodine). The particular organic molecules found almost exclusively in living organisms are more properly called **biomolecules**.

Because they are generally the products of millions of years of evolution, the structures of biomolecules are highly adapted to serve specific biological functions and are often large and complex. Despite their size and complexity, however, biomolecules behave basically the same way in living cells as they do in a flask. In other words:

> The chemistry of living cells is ultimately the chemistry of organic compounds.

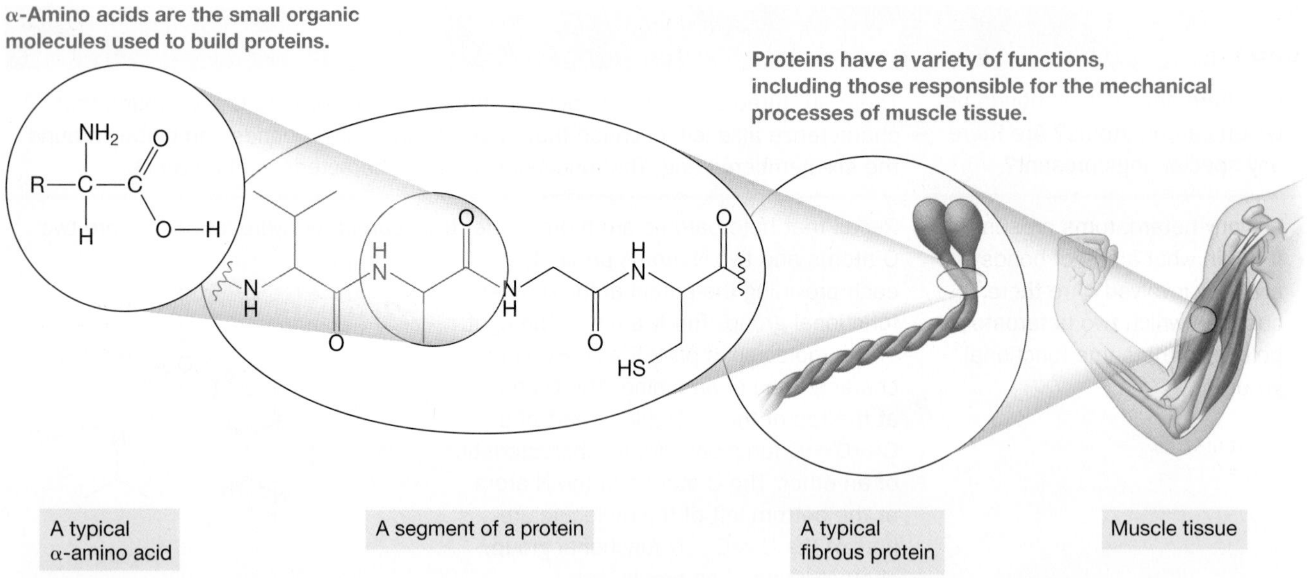

α-Amino acids are the small organic molecules used to build proteins.
Proteins have a variety of functions, including those responsible for the mechanical processes of muscle tissue.
A typical α-amino acid
A segment of a protein
A typical fibrous protein
Muscle tissue

FIGURE 1-41 Organizational levels of proteins Amino acids (*left*) are covalently bonded together to form proteins. Proteins, in turn, are integrated into more familiar structures, such as muscle tissue.

Four major classes of biomolecules are discussed throughout this book: *proteins*, *carbohydrates*, *nucleic acids*, and *lipids*. In this section, we introduce proteins, carbohydrates, and nucleic acids, leaving the introduction of lipids to Section 2.10. We choose this organization because *proteins, carbohydrates, and nucleic acids have a common attribute: they are typically very large structures that are constructed from relatively few types of small organic molecules*. By contrast, lipids are relatively small- to medium-sized molecules, characterized by their insolubility in water; water solubility is covered in Chapter 2.

The small organic molecules that compose large proteins, carbohydrates, and nucleic acids are recognizable; they are building blocks that have distinct structural features and characteristic functional groups from Table 1-6 (p. 35). We review some of those characteristics in the remainder of this chapter.

1.14a Proteins and Amino Acids

Proteins are versatile biomolecules. Some are responsible for mechanical processes; for example, the proteins actin and myosin cause the contraction of muscle tissue. Others, such as cortactin, are responsible for regulating cell shape. Many different proteins are classified as **enzymes**, which act as catalysts for biological reactions; they facilitate biological reactions but are not consumed while doing so. Acetylcholinesterase, for example, catalyzes the breakdown of acetylcholine, a neurotransmitter.

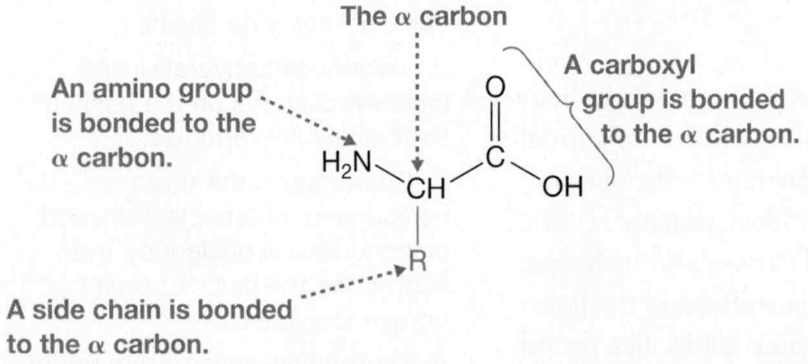

The α carbon
An amino group is bonded to the α carbon.
A carboxyl group is bonded to the α carbon.
A side chain is bonded to the α carbon.

FIGURE 1-42 An α-amino acid All α-amino acids have the same basic structure, shown in black; they differ by the identity of the side chain (R) highlighted in red.

Proteins have different organizational levels, as depicted in **Figure 1-41**. At the left of the figure, we can see that proteins are constructed from relatively few types of small organic molecules called α-amino acids. The general structure of an amino acid is shown in **Figure 1-42**.

All α-amino acids have the following features:

- An **α-amino acid** contains both an NH_2 and a CO_2H group, which are characteristic of amines and carboxylic acids, respectively.
- Both the NH_2 and CO_2H groups are attached to the same carbon atom, called the **α (alpha) carbon**.
- The α carbon is also covalently bonded to a **side chain**, which is sometimes called an **R group**.

The side chain of an amino acid is what distinguishes one amino acid from another. In particular, there are 20 naturally occurring side chains, so there are 20 different naturally occurring amino acids. Their structures are shown in Table 1-7.

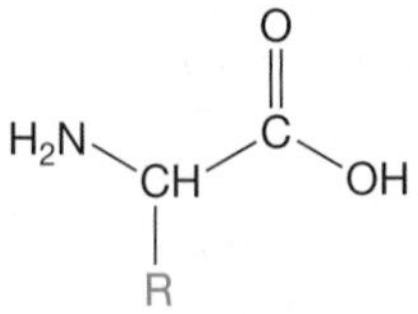

O
H2N
CH
C
OH
R

TABLE 1-7 The 20 Naturally Occurring Amino Acids

Name (abbreviation)[a]	Side Chain (R)	Name (abbreviation)[a]	Side Chain (R)	Name (abbreviation)[a]	Side Chain (R)
NONPOLAR AMINO ACIDS					
Alanine (Ala or A)	$-CH_3$	**Glycine** (Gly or G)	—H	**Isoleucine** (Ile or I)	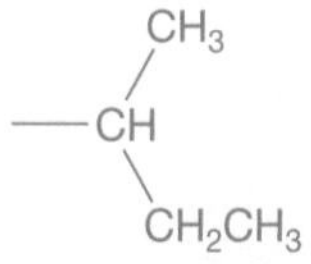
Leucine (Leu or L)	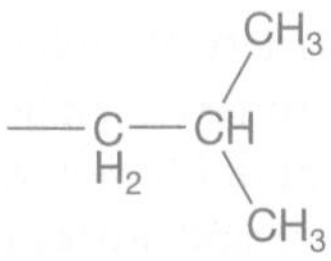	**Methionine** (Met or M)	$-(CH_2)_2SCH_3$	**Phenylalanine** (Phe or F)	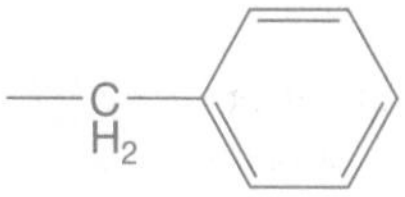
Proline (Pro or P)	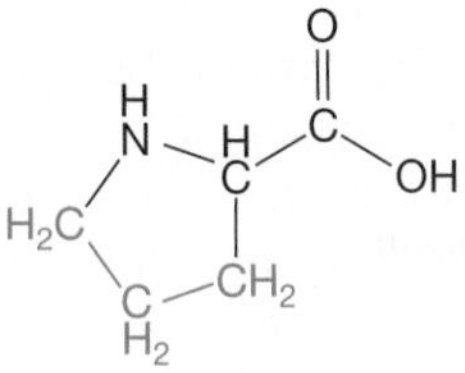	**Tryptophan** (Trp or W)	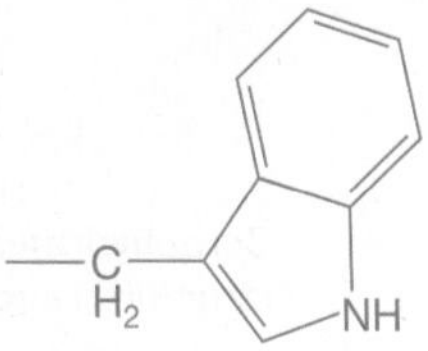	**Valine** (Val or V)	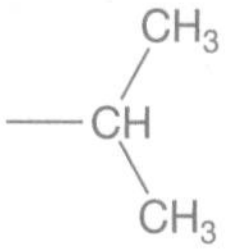
POLAR AMINO ACIDS					
Asparagine (Asn or N)	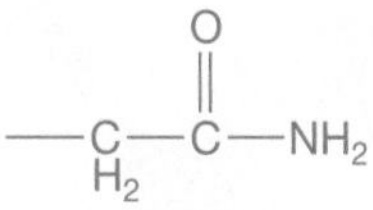	**Cysteine** (Cys or C)	$-CH_2SH$	**Glutamine** (Gln or Q)	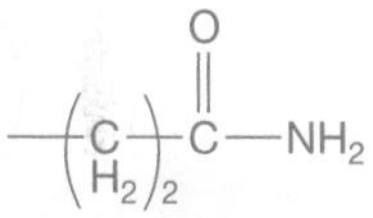
Serine (Ser or S)	$-CH_2OH$	**Threonine** (Thr or T)	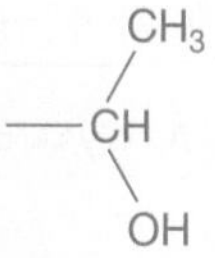	**Tyrosine** (Tyr or Y)	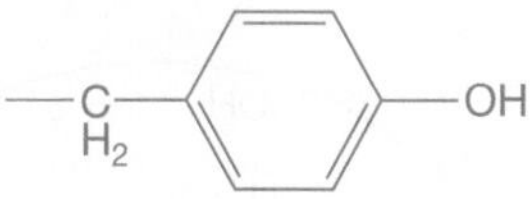
ACIDIC AMINO ACIDS					
Aspartic acid (Asp or D)	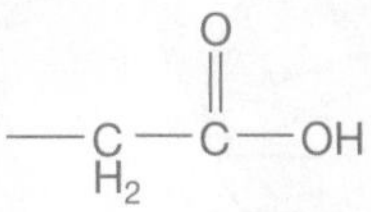	**Glutamic acid** (Glu or E)	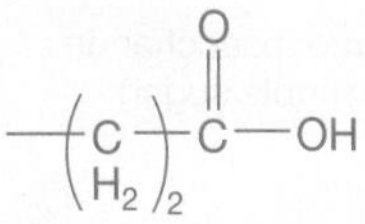		
BASIC AMINO ACIDS					
Arginine (Arg or R)	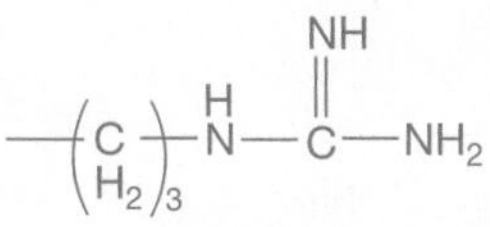	**Lysine** (Lys or K)	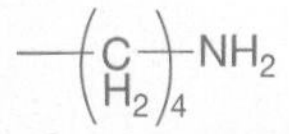	**Histidine** (His or H)	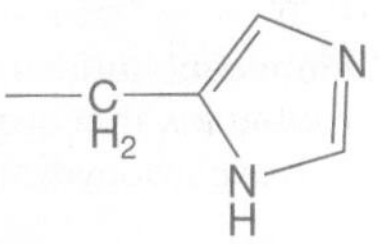

[a]Each amino acid has a one- and three-letter abbreviation.

Notice in Table 1-7 that amino acid side chains contain a variety of functional groups. The side chain of serine, for example, contains an OH group, characteristic of alcohols, whereas aspartic acid has a CO_2H group, characteristic of carboxylic acids, and lysine has an NH_2 group, characteristic of amines. Some amino acids, such as phenylalanine, contain an aromatic ring.

YOUR TURN 1.15

Use Table 1-7 to help you circle the functional groups just mentioned for serine, aspartic acid, lysine, and phenylalanine.

Note in Table 1-7 that the side chains of amino acids can be polar or nonpolar, and they can be acidic or basic. These properties are largely what govern an amino acid's function when it forms part of a protein. We will revisit these properties in greater depth as we continue our discussion of biomolecules throughout this book.

1.14b Carbohydrates and Monosaccharides

Carbohydrates, also called **saccharides**, serve a variety of biological functions. Sugar, starch, and glycogen, for example, are fuels for primary metabolic pathways such as glycolysis, and cellulose is the structural component of the cell walls in plants. Derivatives of carbohydrates are involved in many important processes, too, such as those related to blood clotting and the immune system.

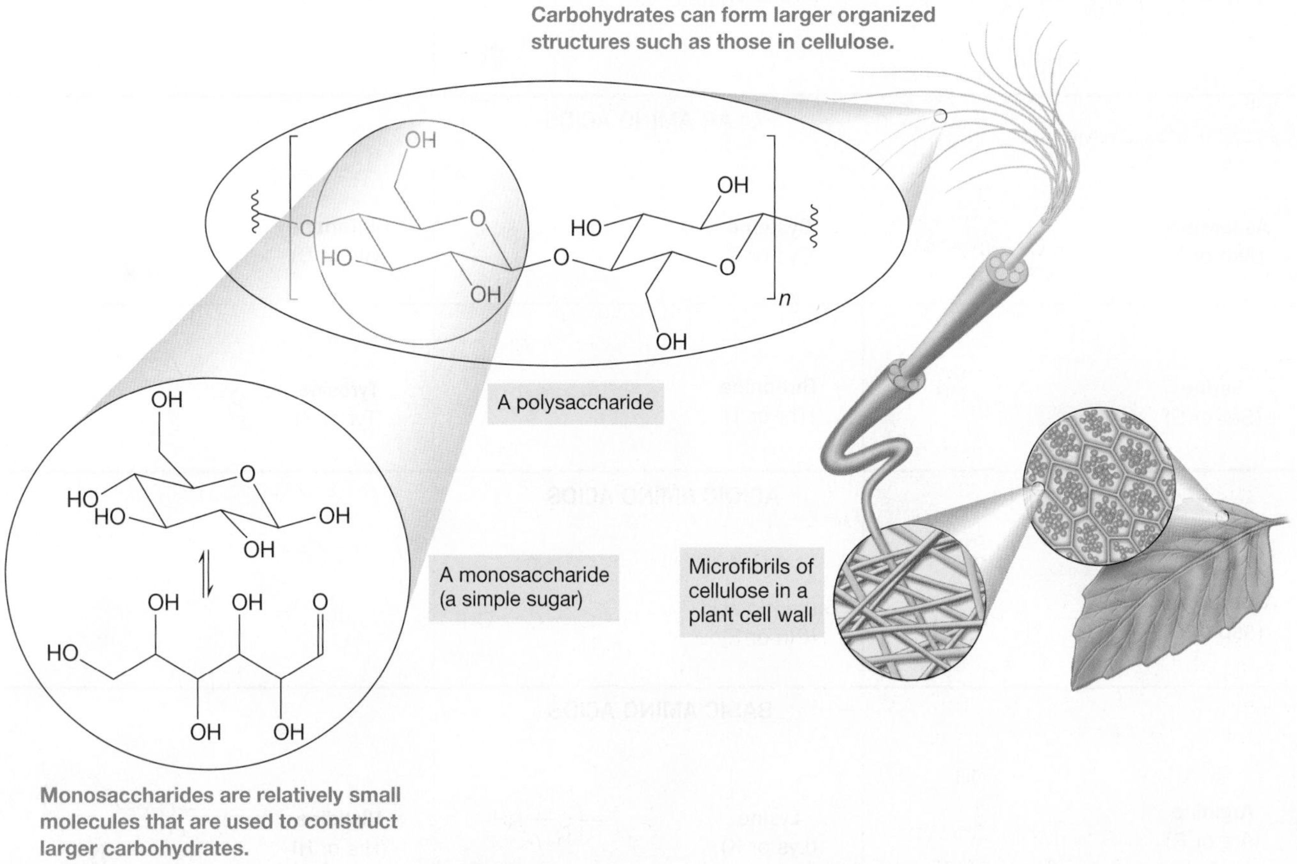

Carbohydrates can form larger organized structures such as those in cellulose.
A polysaccharide
A monosaccharide (a simple sugar)
Microfibrils of cellulose in a plant cell wall
Monosaccharides are relatively small molecules that are used to construct larger carbohydrates.

FIGURE 1-43 Organizational levels of carbohydrates Monosaccharides (*left*) can exist in acyclic and cyclic forms. The cyclic forms are used to construct polysaccharides (*middle*). Cellulose (*right*) is a polysaccharide that makes up the cell walls in plants.

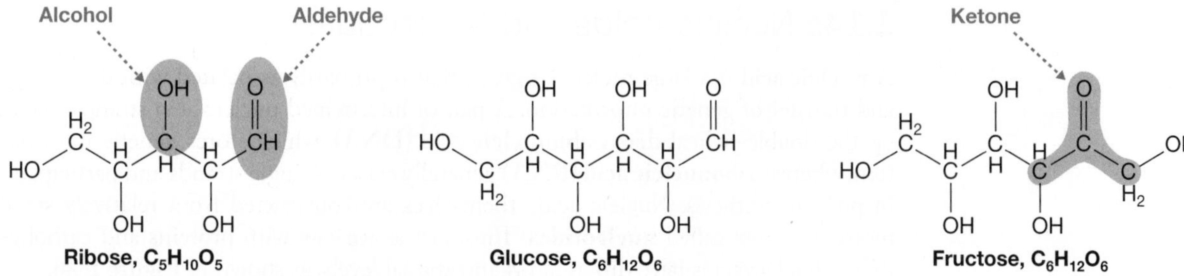
Alcohol
Aldehyde
Ketone
Ribose, $C_5H_{10}O_5$
Glucose, $C_6H_{12}O_6$
Fructose, $C_6H_{12}O_6$

FIGURE 1-44 Examples of monosaccharides The C—OH group (found in alcohols) and the C═O group (found in aldehydes and ketones) appear in these monosaccharides.

Carbohydrates are characterized by their chemical composition:

- Carbohydrates are composed of only carbon, oxygen, and hydrogen.
- There are two hydrogen atoms for every oxygen atom, regardless of how many carbon atoms are present, giving each carbohydrate the general molecular formula $C_xH_{2y}O_y$.

Thus, in carbohydrates, hydrogen and oxygen are present in the same ratio as in water, which is why "hydrate" appears in the name.

Similar to proteins, carbohydrates have different organizational levels, as shown in **Figure 1-43**. Shown at the left of the figure are **monosaccharides** or **simple sugars**, which link together to form large carbohydrates called **polysaccharides**. Monosaccharides are themselves carbohydrates, with one additional restriction to their chemical composition:

In a monosaccharide, the number of oxygen atoms is the same as the number of carbon atoms, giving it the general formula $C_xH_{2x}O_x$.

As shown in **Figure 1-44**, for example, ribose (a sugar found in the backbone of DNA) has the molecular formula $C_5H_{10}O_5$, whereas glucose and fructose have the formula $C_6H_{12}O_6$.

Notice in these structures that each C atom is bonded to a single O atom. One O atom in each monosaccharide is part of a C═O group that is characteristic of an aldehyde or ketone. The remaining O atoms are part of C—OH groups, characteristic of alcohols.

YOUR TURN **1.16**

Circle and label all of the functional groups in the structure of glucose in Figure 1-44. In which compound class is each functional group typically found?

As individual molecules, monosaccharides continually interconvert between their acyclic and cyclic forms, as shown for ribose in **Figure 1-45**. This process is discussed in greater detail in Section 19.14. Only the cyclic forms of monosaccharides, however, are linked together in polysaccharides.

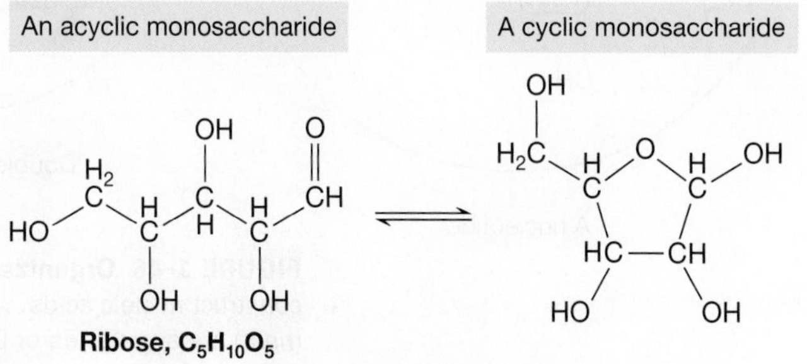
An acyclic monosaccharide
A cyclic monosaccharide
Ribose, $C_5H_{10}O_5$

FIGURE 1-45 Cyclization of a monosaccharide A monosaccharide such as ribose can equilibrate between its cyclic and acyclic forms.

1.14c Nucleic Acids and Nucleotides

A **nucleic acid** is a large molecular chain that is primarily associated with the storage and transfer of genetic information. A pair of intertwined nucleic acid strands makes up the double-helical **deoxyribonucleic acid (DNA)**, which stores genetic information, whereas **ribonucleic acid (RNA)** generally exists as single strands and participates in protein synthesis. Nucleic acids themselves are constructed from relatively small molecular units called **nucleotides**. Thus, just as we saw with proteins and carbohydrates, nucleic acids have different organizational levels, as shown in **Figure 1-46**.

All nucleotides have three distinct components (**Figure 1-47a**):

- an inorganic phosphate ($-OPO_3$) group,
- a cyclic monosaccharide (or sugar), and
- a nitrogenous base.

In both RNA (Fig. 1-47b) and DNA (Fig. 1-47c), the backbone of a single strand consists of alternating sugar and phosphate groups. Thus, adjacent nucleotides are connected by a bond between the sugar group of one nucleotide and the phosphate group of another.

In RNA, the sugar group is ribose, whereas in DNA, it is deoxyribose. As the name suggests, deoxyribose has one fewer oxygen atom than ribose; specifically, it lacks the oxygen attached to the 2′ carbon (compare Fig. 1-47b and Fig. 1-47c).

Nucleotides are distinguished from one another by the identity of the nitrogenous base. In both RNA and DNA, the specific sequence of the nitrogenous bases determines the genetic information that is stored or carried. Four types of nitrogenous bases appear in RNA: uracil, guanine, adenine, and cytosine (abbreviated U, G, A, and C, respectively; **Figure 1-48**). Four types of nitrogenous bases appear in DNA, too: G, A, C, and thymine (T). Thus, three of the bases appearing in DNA are the same as the bases appearing in RNA. Thymine appears only in DNA, whereas uracil appears only in RNA.

Notice the functional groups in these nitrogenous bases. An O═C—N group, for example, which is characteristic of an amide, appears in guanine, and a C═C bond, which characterizes an alkene, appears in uracil and thymine. (In Chapter 14, we will learn that this C═C bond is better classified as being part of an aromatic ring rather than an alkene.)

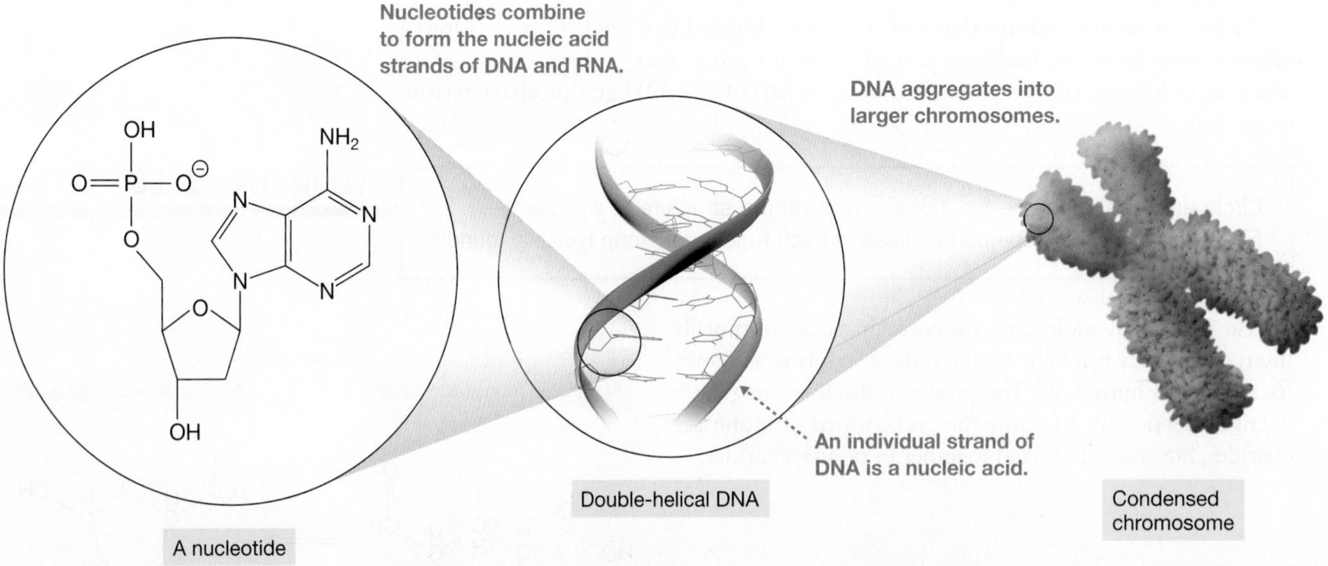

Nucleotides combine to form the nucleic acid strands of DNA and RNA.
DNA aggregates into larger chromosomes.
OH
NH2
O═P—O⊖
O
N
N
N
N
O
OH
An individual strand of DNA is a nucleic acid.
Double-helical DNA
Condensed chromosome
A nucleotide

FIGURE 1-46 Organizational levels of nucleic acids Nucleotides (*left*) are used to construct nucleic acids, which form the strands of RNA and DNA (*middle*). Chromosomes (*right*) are aggregates of DNA.

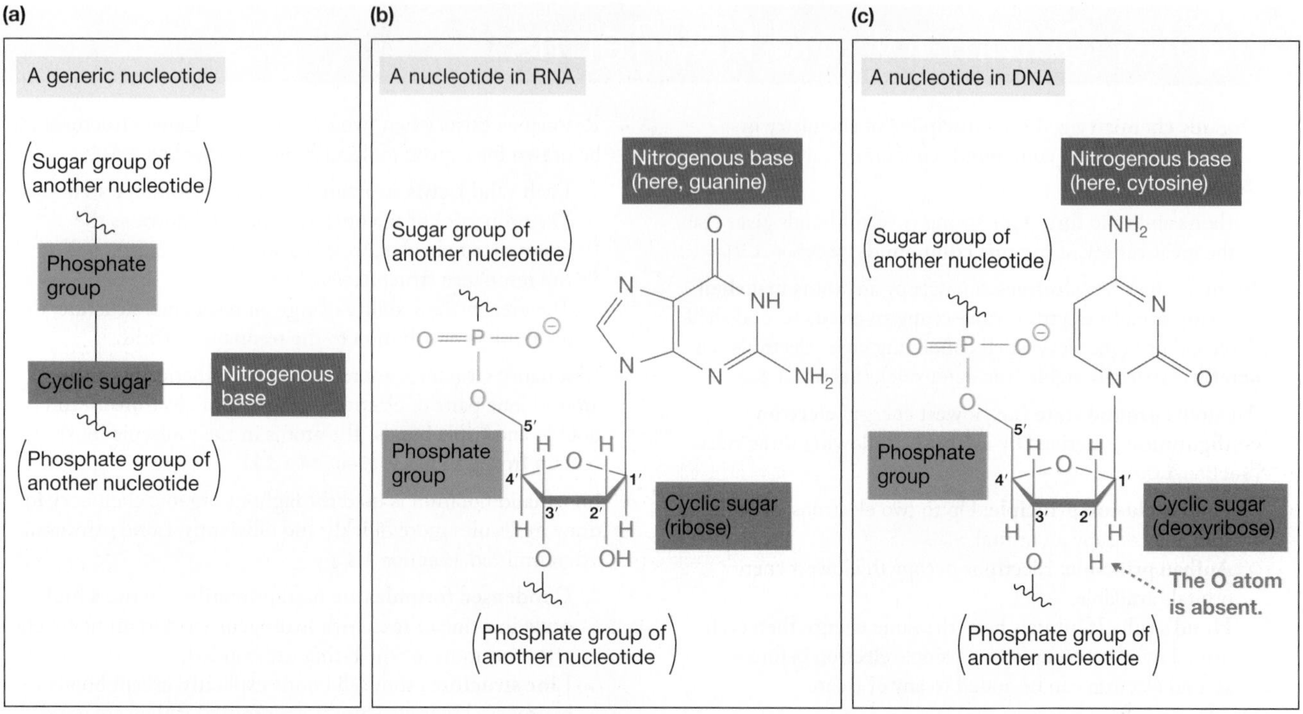
(a)
A generic nucleotide
Sugar group of another nucleotide
Phosphate group
Cyclic sugar
Nitrogenous base
Phosphate group of another nucleotide
(b)
A nucleotide in RNA
Nitrogenous base (here, guanine)
Sugar group of another nucleotide
Phosphate group
Cyclic sugar (ribose)
Phosphate group of another nucleotide
(c)
A nucleotide in DNA
Nitrogenous base (here, cytosine)
Sugar group of another nucleotide
Phosphate group
Cyclic sugar (deoxyribose)
The O atom is absent.
Phosphate group of another nucleotide

FIGURE 1-47 Composition of a nucleotide (a) Every nucleotide has three components: a phosphate group (green), a cyclic sugar (red), and a nitrogenous base (blue). The backbone of a nucleic acid consists of alternating sugar and phosphate groups. (b) A nucleotide in a ribonucleic acid. In RNA, the cyclic sugar component must be ribose. The nitrogenous base shown is guanine, but it could also be adenine, cytosine, or uracil. (c) A nucleotide in a deoxyribonucleic acid. In DNA, the cyclic sugar must be deoxyribose, in which the ribose oxygen indicated is not present. The nitrogenous base shown is cytosine, but it could also be adenine, guanine, or thymine.

YOUR TURN 1.17

Circle and label the functional groups that appear in U, G, A, C, and T in Figure 1-48.

In subsequent units on biomolecules, we will examine some of the chemical processes by which information is encoded in DNA and RNA. In Section 14.9, for example, we will examine the complementarity among the nitrogenous bases.

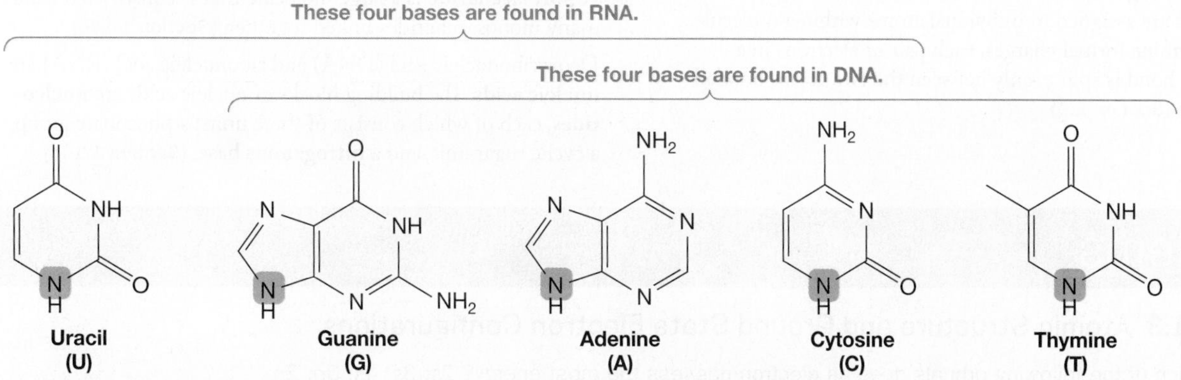
These four bases are found in RNA.
These four bases are found in DNA.
Uracil (U)
Guanine (G)
Adenine (A)
Cytosine (C)
Thymine (T)

FIGURE 1-48 Nitrogenous bases The identity of a nucleotide is specified by the nitrogenous base bonded to the sugar ring. U, G, A, and C are found in RNA, whereas G, A, C, and T are found in DNA. In a nucleotide, the 1′ carbon of the ribose sugar unit connects to the highlighted nitrogen atom.

Chapter Summary and Key Terms

- **Organic chemistry** is the subdiscipline of chemistry in which the focus is on compounds containing carbon atoms. **(Section 1.1)**
- Carbon's ability to form four strong covalent bonds gives rise to the great variety of **organic compounds**. **(Section 1.2)**
- No more than two electrons can occupy an atom's first **shell**. As many as eight electrons can occupy an atom's second shell. A second or higher level shell containing eight electrons (an **octet**) is especially stable (the octet rule). **(Section 1.3b)**
- An atom's **ground state** (i.e., lowest energy) **electron configuration** is derived by use of the following three rules. **(Section 1.3c)**
    - **Pauli exclusion principle**: Up to two electrons, opposite in spin, may occupy an orbital.
    - **Aufbau principle**: Electrons occupy the lowest energy orbitals available.
    - **Hund's rule**: If orbitals have the same energy, then each orbital must be occupied by a single electron before a second electron can be added to any of them.
- Sharing of a pair of electrons by two atoms lowers the energy of the system, creating a **covalent bond**. Some atoms can share two or three pairs of electrons, creating double or triple bonds, respectively. Double bonds are shorter and stronger than single bonds, and triple bonds are shorter and stronger than double bonds. **(Section 1.4)**
- **Lewis structures** illustrate a molecule's **connectivity**. Lewis structures account for *all* **valence electrons**, differentiating between **bonding pairs** and **lone pairs** of electrons. They indicate, moreover, which atoms are bonded together and by what types of bonds. Lewis structures are constructed so that the maximum number of atoms have filled valence shells (i.e., duets or octets). **(Section 1.5)**
- The electrons in a **nonpolar covalent bond** are shared equally. **Polar covalent bonds** arise when atoms with moderate differences in **electronegativity** are bonded together. **Ionic bonds** arise when there are large differences in electronegativity. **(Sections 1.7 and 1.8)**
- **Formal charge** represents a particular way in which valence electrons are assigned to individual atoms within a molecule. To determine formal charges, each pair of electrons in a covalent bond is split evenly between the two atoms bonded together. **(Section 1.9)**
- Resonance exists when two or more valid Lewis structures can be drawn for a given molecular species. **(Section 1.10)**
    - Each valid Lewis structure is called a **resonance structure**.
    - The properties of the one, true species, known as the **resonance hybrid**, represent a weighted average of all the resonance structures.
    - The greater the stability of a given resonance structure, the greater its contribution to the resonance hybrid.
- Resonance structures are related by hypothetically shifting around lone pairs of electrons and pairs of electrons from double and triple bonds. The atoms in the molecule must remain frozen in place. **(Section 1.11)**
- Shorthand notation is used throughout organic chemistry to draw molecules more quickly and efficiently. Lone pairs are often omitted. **(Section 1.12)**
    - **Condensed formulas** are used primarily to write a molecule in a line of text, with hydrogens written immediately after the atom to which they are bonded.
    - **Line structures** show all bonds explicitly, except bonds to hydrogen. Hydrogen atoms are omitted if they are bonded to carbon. Carbon atoms are not drawn explicitly but are assumed to reside at the intersection of two lines and at the end of a line (unless otherwise indicated).
- **Functional groups** are common bonding arrangements of relatively few atoms. Functional groups dictate the behavior of entire molecules; that is, molecules with the same functional groups tend to behave similarly. **(Section 1.13)**
- A **protein** is a large molecule composed of *α-amino acids*; α-amino acids can be viewed as building blocks of proteins. **(Section 1.14a)**
- There are 20 naturally occurring *α-amino acids*. In every **α-amino acid**, an **α carbon** is attached to an amino group, a carboxyl group, a hydrogen, and a **side chain** (or **R group**). **(Section 1.14a)**
- A **carbohydrate** has the general molecular formula $C_xH_{2y}O_y$, and a **monosaccharide** has the general molecular formula $C_xH_{2x}O_x$. **(Section 1.14b)**
- A **polysaccharide** is a large molecule that is constructed from many monosaccharides linked together. **(Section 1.14b)**
- Deoxyribonucleic acid (DNA) and ribonucleic acid (RNA) are **nucleic acids**. The building blocks of nucleic acids are **nucleotides**, each of which consists of three units: a phosphate group, a cyclic sugar unit, and a **nitrogenous base**. **(Section 1.14c)**

Problems

Section 1.3 Atomic Structure and Ground State Electron Configurations

1.1 In which of the following orbitals does an electron possess the most energy? 2s; 3s; 4s; 3*p*; 2*p*

1.2 For each pair, identify the orbital in which an electron possesses more energy. **(a)** 4s or 5s; **(b)** 5*p* or 5*d*

1.3 Write the ground state electron configuration of each of the following atoms. For each atom, identify the valence electrons and the core electrons. **(a)** Al; **(b)** S; **(c)** O; **(d)** N; **(e)** F

Section 1.4 The Covalent Bond: Bond Energy and Bond Length

1.4 Consider a molecule of N_2. For each pair of distances between the two N atoms, determine which distance represents a higher energy. Explain. *Hint*: Consult Table 1-3. **(a)** 50 or 75 pm; **(b)** 75 or 110 pm; **(c)** 110 or 150 pm; **(d)** 150 or 160 pm

1.5 In which of the following molecules is the bond between carbon and nitrogen the shortest, and in which molecule is it the strongest? $H{-}C{\equiv}N$; $H_2C{=}NH$; $H_3C{-}NH_2$

1.6 According to Table 1-2, which of the following compounds has the strongest single bond, and which has the weakest? HCl; CH_4; H_2O; HF; Cl_2

Sections 1.5–1.8 Lewis Dot Structures, Polarity, and Ionic Bonds

1.7 Determine whether each structure shown here is a legitimate Lewis structure. If not, explain why not.

(a)
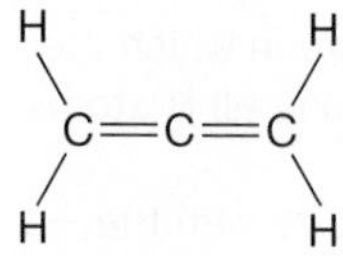
(b)
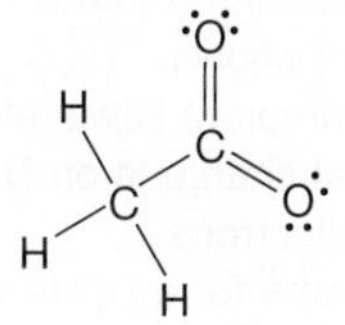
(c)
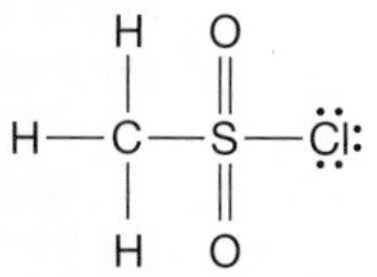
(d)
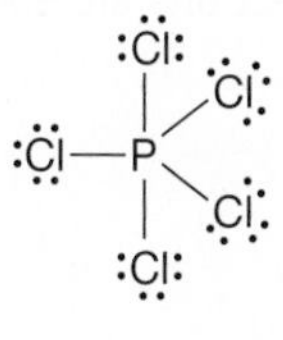
(e)
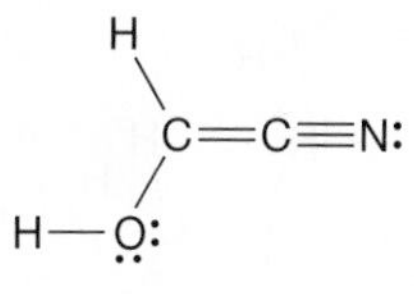

1.8 Determine whether each structure shown here is a legitimate Lewis structure. If not, explain why not.

(a)
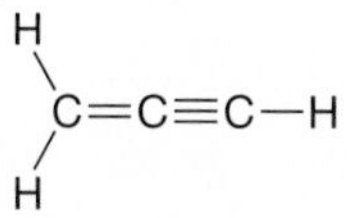
(b)
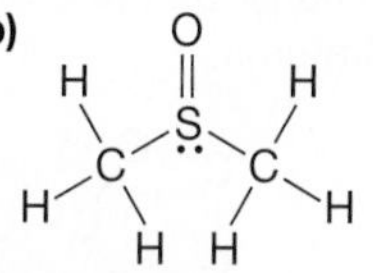
(c)
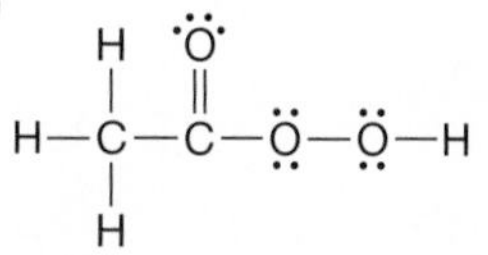
(d)
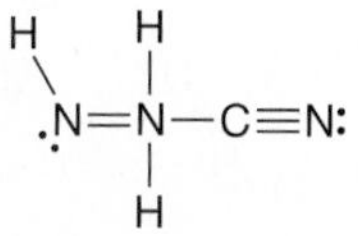
(e)
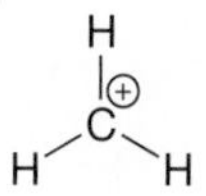

1.9 Draw Lewis structures for each of these molecules: **(a)** CH_5N (contains a bond between C and N); **(b)** CH_3NO_2 (contains a bond between C and N but no bonds between C and O); **(c)** CH_2O; **(d)** CH_2Cl_2; **(e)** BrCN

1.10 Complete the Lewis structure for each of the following molecules, using the information provided in Table 1-4. You may assume that all formal charges are zero. All H atoms are shown; add only bonding pairs and lone pairs of electrons.

(a)
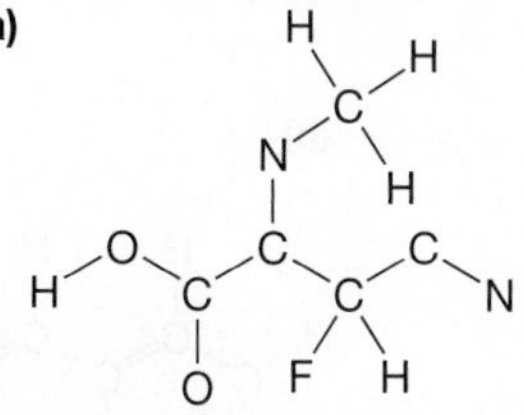
(b)
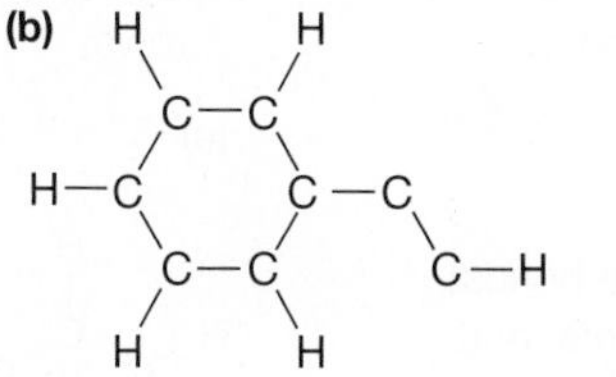
(c)
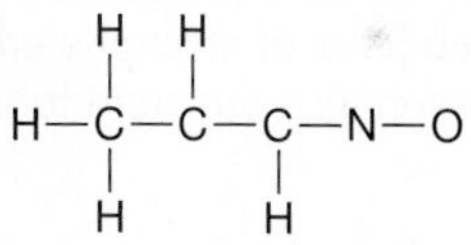

1.11 Rank the molecules in order of increasing negative charge on carbon: $CH_3{-}CH_3$; $CH_3{-}MgBr$; $CH_3{-}Li$; $CH_3{-}F$; $CH_3{-}OH$; $CH_3{-}NH_2$

1.12 Which of the compounds below is consistent with the electrostatic potential map shown? Explain.

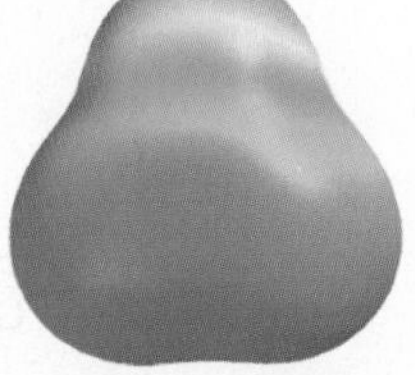
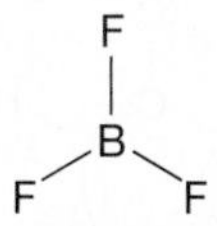
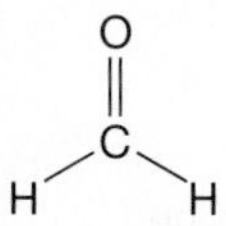
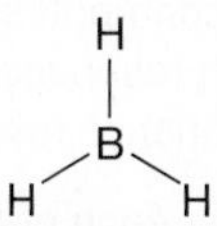
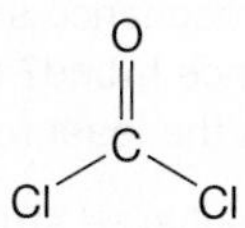

1.13 Which of the following compounds contains an ionic bond? **(a)** H_2; **(b)** NaCl; **(c)** NaOH; **(d)** CH_3ONa; **(e)** CH_4; **(f)** $HOCH_2CH_3$; **(g)** $LiNHCH_3$; **(h)** $CH_3CH_2CO_2K$; **(i)** $C_6H_5NH_3Cl$

Section 1.9 Assigning Electrons to Atoms in Molecules: Formal Charge

1.14 Determine the formal charge of each atom in the species shown here, which is an intermediate in a reaction called the Wolff-Kishner reduction (Chapter 19). Assume that each atom has a filled valence shell.

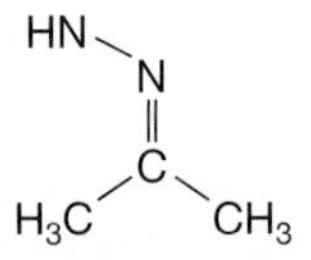

1.15 In the methoxide anion (CH_3O^-), is it possible for a double bond to exist between C and O, given that the negative charge resides on O? Explain why or why not.

1.16 Draw Lewis structures for each of the following ions. One atom in each ion has a formal charge that is not zero. Determine which atom it is and what its formal charge is. **(a)** C_2H_5 anion; **(b)** CH_3O cation; **(c)** CH_6N cation; **(d)** CH_5O cation; **(e)** C_3H_3 anion (with all three H atoms on the same carbon)

1.17 Identify the formal charge on each atom in the following species. Assume that all valence electrons are shown.

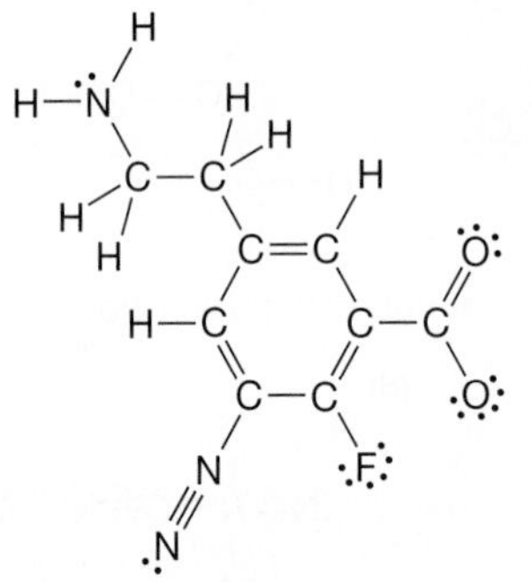

1.18 The structure shown here is a skeleton of an anion having the overall formula $C_6H_6NO^-$. The hydrogen atoms are not shown.

(a) Draw a complete Lewis structure in which the −1 formal charge is on N. Include all H atoms and valence electrons.

(b) Do the same for a Lewis structure with the −1 formal charge on O.

(c) Do the same for a Lewis structure with the −1 formal charge on the C atom that is bonded to three other C atoms.

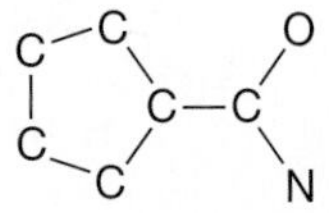

Sections 1.10 and 1.11 Resonance Theory and Drawing All Resonance Structures

1.19 Draw all resonance contributors for each of the following molecules or ions. Be sure to include the curved arrows that indicate which pairs of electrons are shifted in going from one resonance structure to the next.

(a) CH_3NO_2

(b) $CH_3CO_2^-$

(c) $CH_3CHCHCH_2^-$ (the ion has two C—C single bonds)

(d) C_5H_5N (a ring is formed by the C and N atoms, and each H is bonded to C)

(e) C_4H_5N (a ring is formed by the C and N atoms, the N is bonded to one H, and each C is bonded to one H)

1.20 Draw the resonance hybrid of CH_3NO_2 in Problem 1.19(a).

1.21 **(a)** Draw all resonance contributors for sulfuric acid, H_2SO_4 (the S atom is bonded to four O atoms). **(b)** Which resonance structure contributes the most to the resonance hybrid? **(c)** Which resonance structure contributes the least to the resonance hybrid?

1.22 Draw all resonance structures for each of the following species. Make sure to include all appropriate curved arrows.

(a)

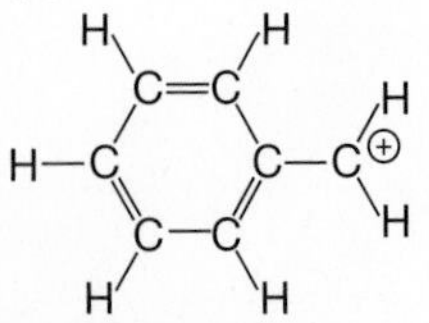

(b)

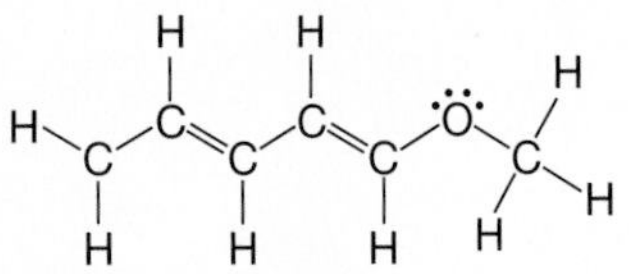

1.23 Draw all resonance structures for each of the following species. Make sure to include all appropriate curved arrows.

(a)

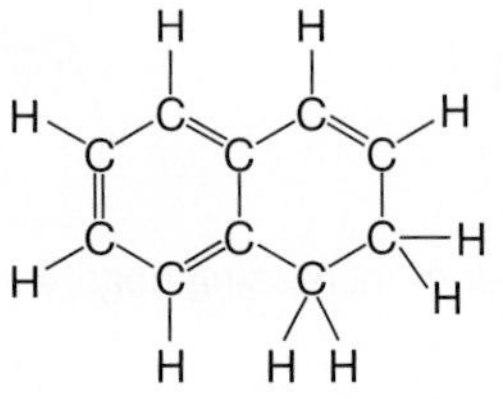

(b)

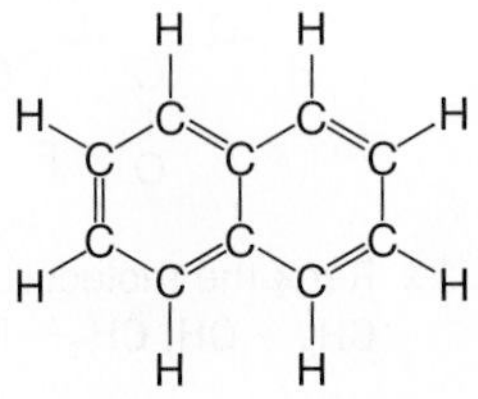

(c)

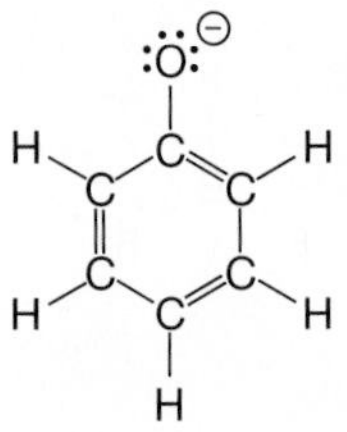

(d)

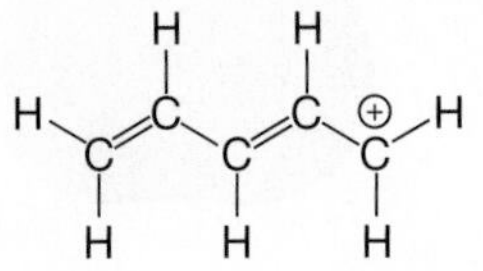

1.24 Experiments indicate that the carbon–carbon bonds in cyclobutadiene are of two different lengths. Discuss whether cyclobutadiene has a resonance structure.

Cyclobutadiene

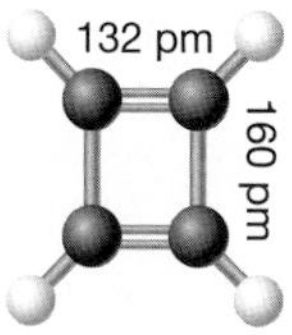
132 pm
160 pm

1.25 The two species shown are structurally very similar. Draw all resonance structures for each species. Determine which species is more stable and explain why.

(a)
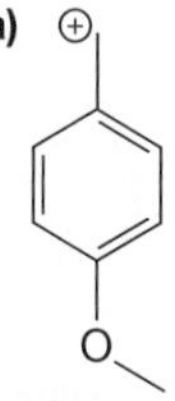

(b)
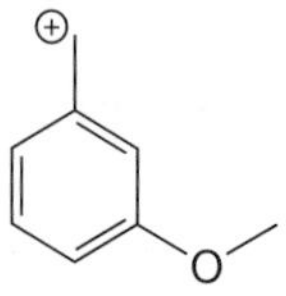

1.26 The two species shown are structurally very similar. Draw all resonance structures for each species. Determine which species is more stable and explain why.

(a)
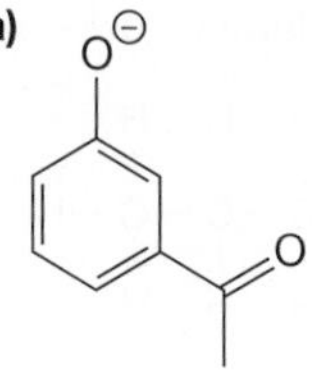

(b)
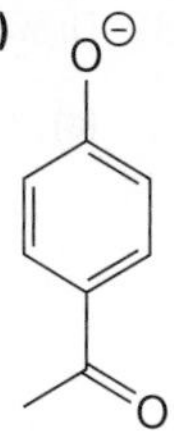

Section 1.12 Shorthand Notations

1.27 Draw the complete Lewis structure of each of the following species, including lone pairs. Indicate whether the Lewis structure is already complete.

(a)
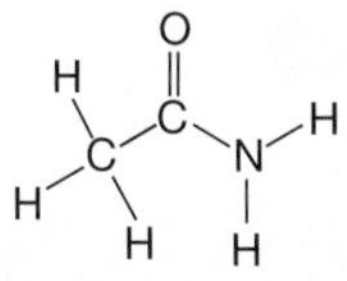

(b)
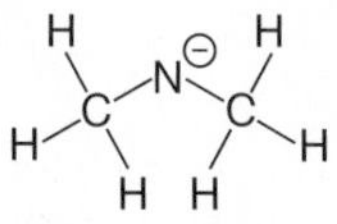

(c)
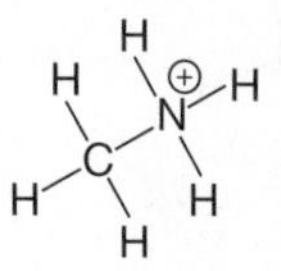

(d)
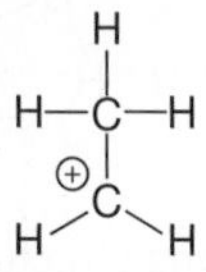

(e)
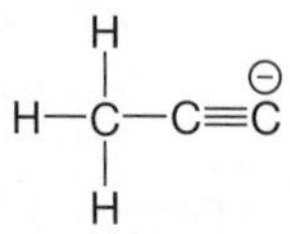

1.28 Redraw each of the following Lewis structures as the corresponding line structure.

(a)
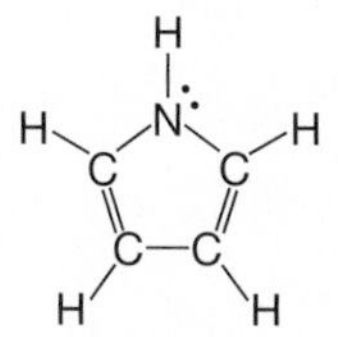

(b)
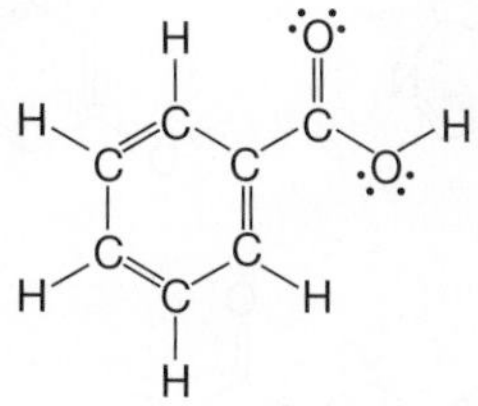

(c)
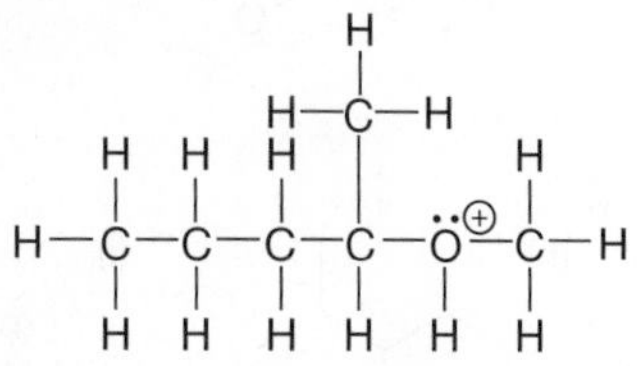

1.29 For each of the following line structures, draw in all carbon atoms, hydrogen atoms, and lone pairs.

(a)
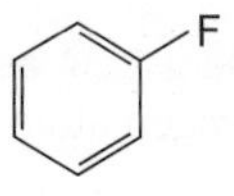

(b)
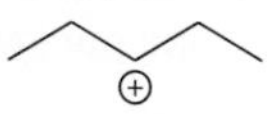

(c)

1.30 Redraw the following structure of glucose as a line structure.

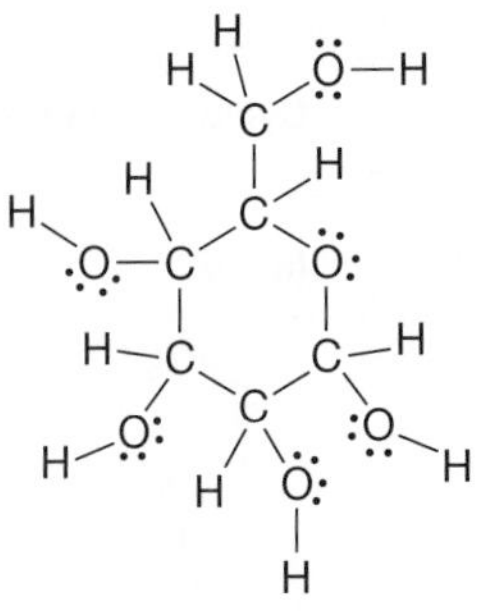

Glucose

1.31 Redraw the following line structure of sucrose as a complete Lewis structure. Include all hydrogen atoms and lone pairs.

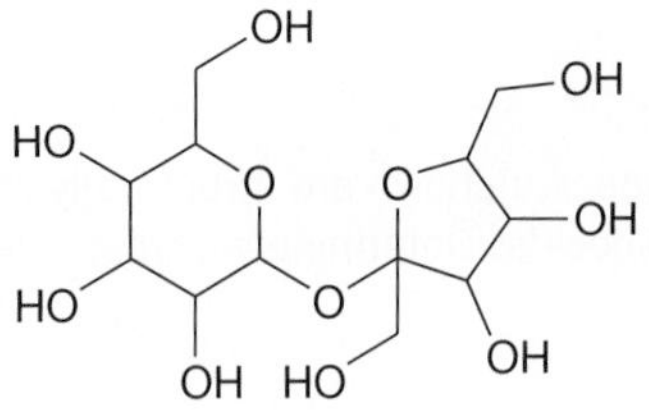

Sucrose

1.32 Draw the following Lewis structures as condensed formulas.

(a)

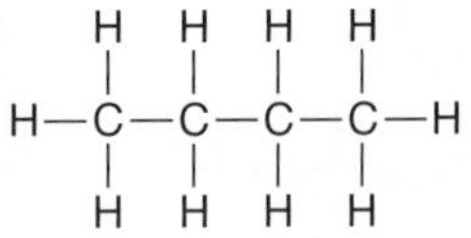

(b)

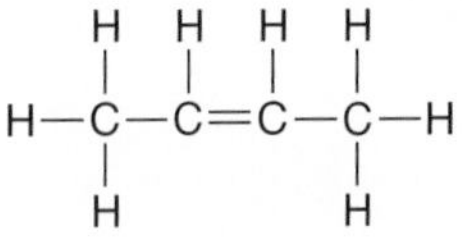

(c)

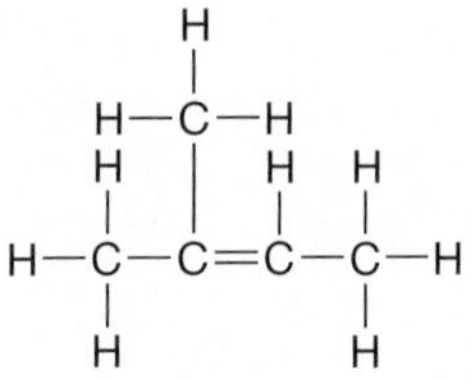

(d)

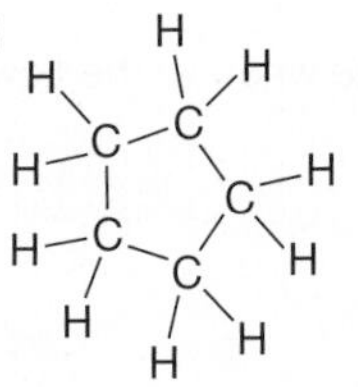

(e)

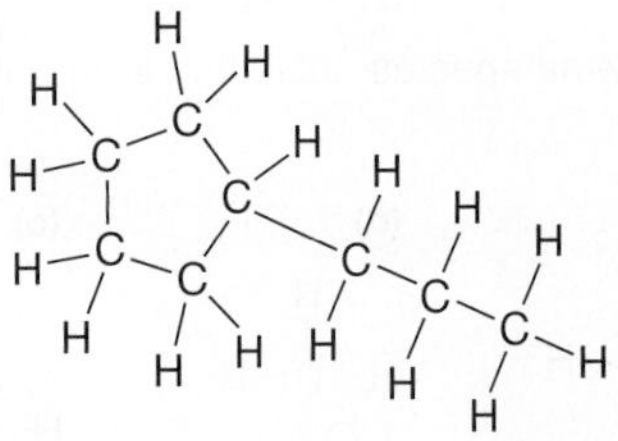

(f)

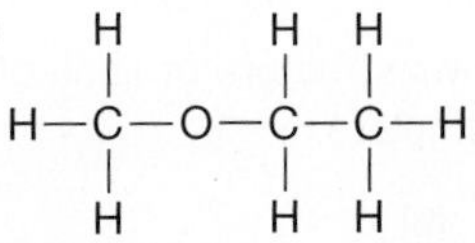

1.33 Draw the molecules in Problem 1.32 as line structures.

1.34 Draw Lewis structures for the following molecules. Include all lone pairs and H atoms.

(a)

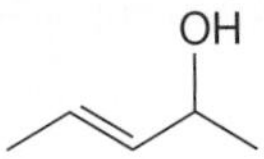

(b)

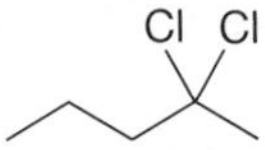

(c)

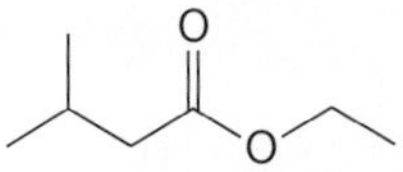

(d)

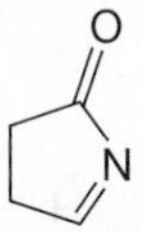

(e)

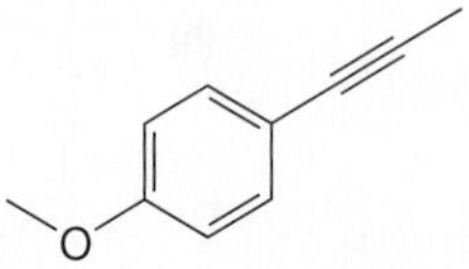

(f)

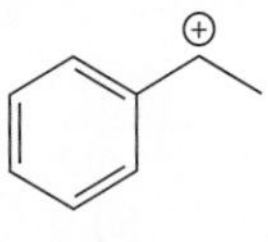

(g)

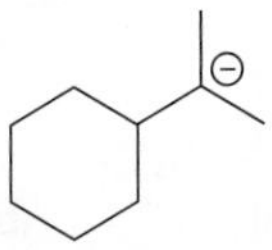

(h)

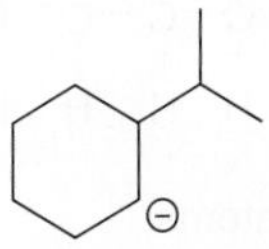

(i)

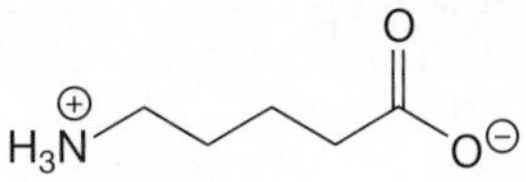

1.35 Draw each species in Problem 1.34 as a condensed formula. Explicitly draw all bonds between non-hydrogen atoms in which at least one non-hydrogen atom belongs to a ring.

1.36 Redraw the line structure of cholesterol (shown here) as a condensed formula. Explicitly draw all bonds between non-hydrogen atoms in which at least one non-hydrogen atom belongs to a ring. What advantages do line structures have?

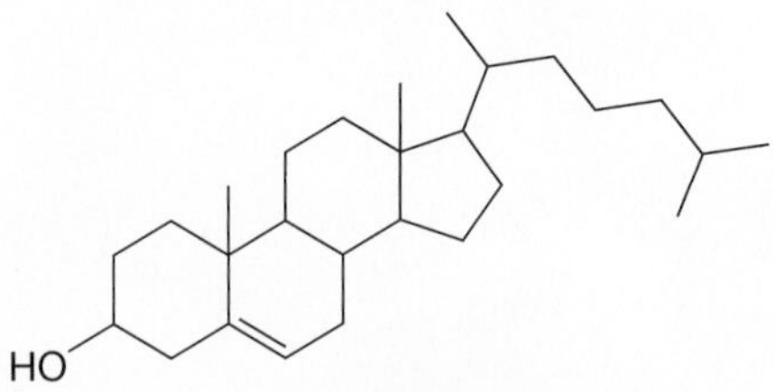

Cholesterol

Section 1.13 An Overview of Organic Compounds: Functional Groups

1.37 Circle each functional group in glucose (Problem 1.30) and sucrose (Problem 1.31). What compound class is characteristic of each functional group?

1.38 Dimethyl sulfide ($H_3C—S—CH_3$) contains a functional group that is not listed in Table 1-6. Which functional group in Table 1-6 do you think its reactivity might resemble?

1.39 Which one of the following compounds do you think will behave most similarly to ethanol (CH_3CH_2OH)? Explain.

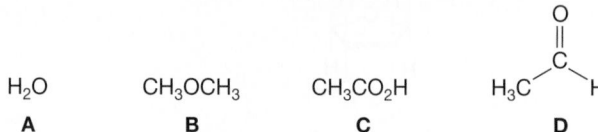

H_2O **A** CH_3OCH_3 **B** CH_3CO_2H **C**

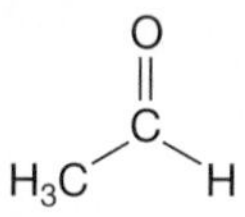

O
C
H3C
H

D

1.40 Identify all functional groups that are present in strychnine, a highly toxic alkaloid used as a pesticide to kill rodents, whose line structure is shown here. What compound class is characteristic of each of those functional groups?

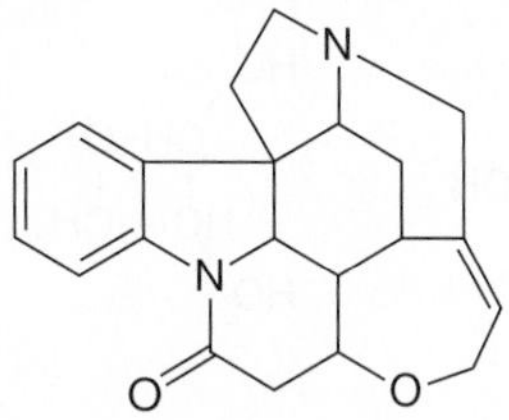

N
N
O
O

Strychnine

1.41 Identify all functional groups that are present in doxorubicin, a drug used as an antibiotic and cancer therapeutic, whose line structure is shown here. What compound class is characteristic of each of those functional groups?

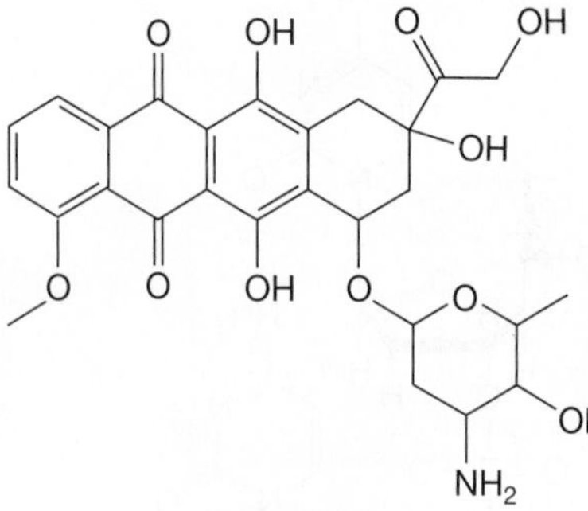

O
OH
O
OH
OH
O
O
OH
O
O
OH
NH2

Doxorubicin

Section 1.14 The Organic Chemistry of Biomolecules

1.42 Identify all of the amino acids whose side chains contain functional groups found in these compound classes: **(a)** alcohol; **(b)** amide; **(c)** carboxylic acid; **(d)** amine; **(e)** arene

1.43 The R group in alanine is CH_3, whereas the R group in aspartic acid is CH_2CO_2H. After consulting Figure 1-42 (p. 38), draw the complete Lewis structure for each of these amino acids.

1.44 Shown here is a tripeptide, which consists of three amino acids linked together in a chain. Circle and name each amino acid. *Hint*: After consulting Figure 1-42 (p. 38), can you identify each of the three α-carbons in this tripeptide?

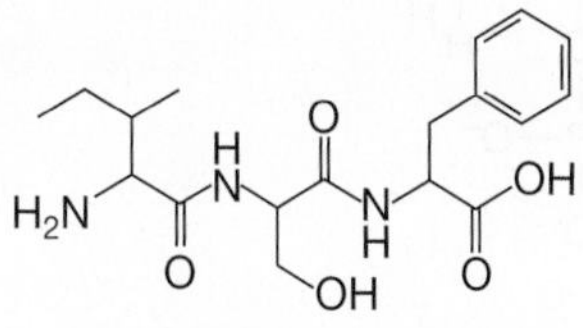

H2N
O
H
N
O
N
H
OH
OH
O

1.45 Which of the following molecules are carbohydrates? Which are monosaccharides?

(a)

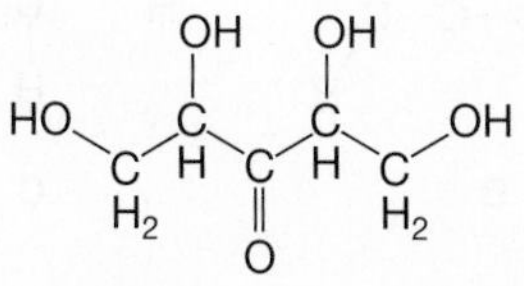

OH
OH
HO
C
C
OH
C
H
C
H
C
H2
O
H2

(b)

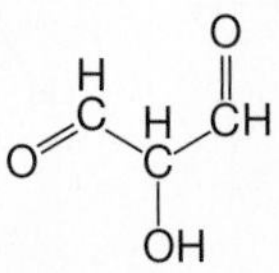

O
H
C
H
CH
O
C
OH

(c)

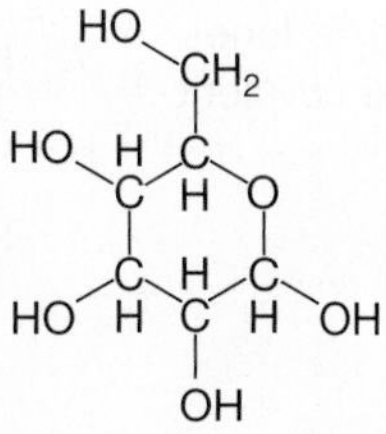

HO
CH2
HO
H
C
C
H
O
C
H
C
HO
H
C
H
OH
OH

(d)

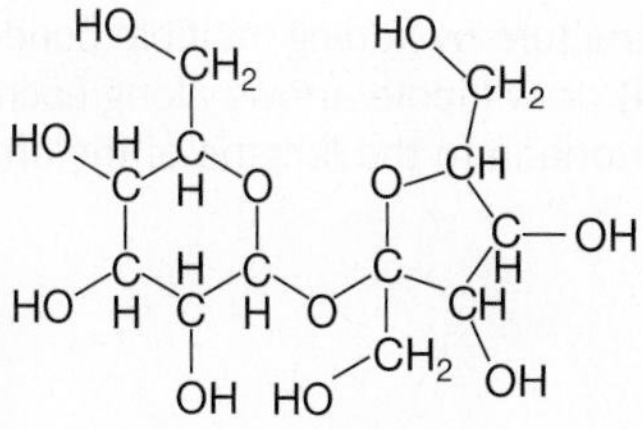

HO
CH2
HO
CH2
HO
H
C
CH
C
H
O
O
C
OH
C
H
C
H
HO
H
C
H
O
CH
CH2
OH
HO
OH

1.46 For each of the following nucleotides, **(a)** circle and label the phosphate group, the sugar group, and the nitrogenous base; **(b)** determine whether it can be part of RNA or DNA; and **(c)** identify the nitrogenous base that it contains

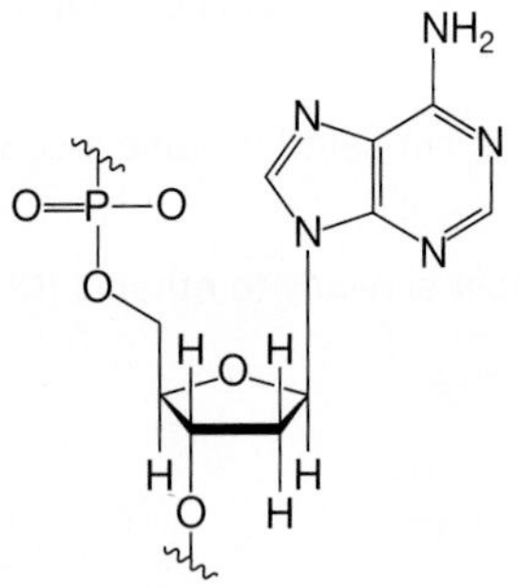

1

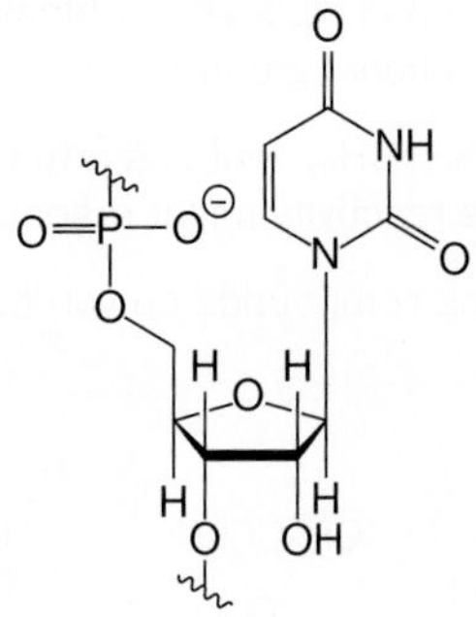

2

1.47 This is a segment of a nucleic acid. **(a)** Is this a segment of RNA or DNA? **(b)** Circle and name each nucleotide.

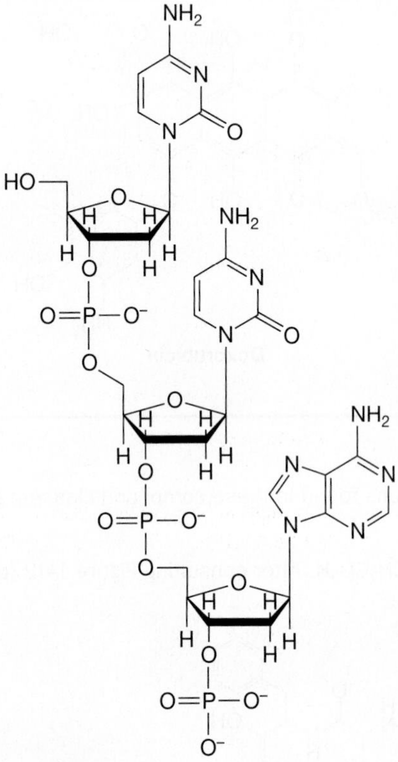

1.48 Determine whether each of the following structures is a carbohydrate. If so, is it also a monosaccharide?

(a)

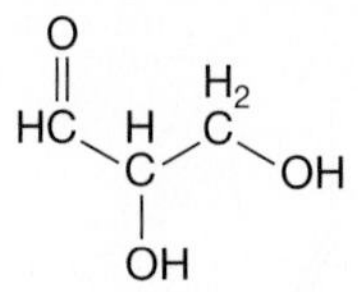

(b)

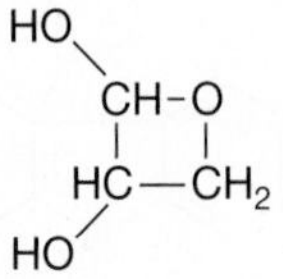

(c)

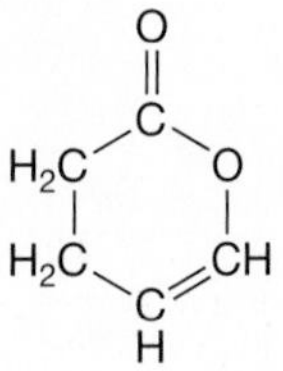

Integrated Problems

1.49 For each *uncharged* molecule shown here, **(a)** complete the Lewis structure by adding multiple bonds and/or lone pairs and **(b)** draw dipole arrows along each polar covalent bond. Pay attention to the lengths of the arrows.

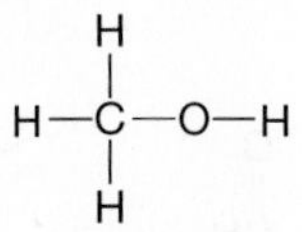

A

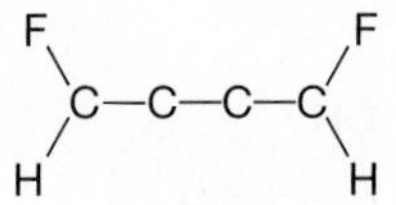

B

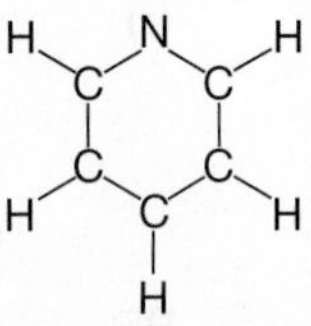

C

1.50 Which of the following pairs are *not* resonance structures of one another? Lone pairs of electrons are not shown. Identify where each lone pair that is not shown belongs.

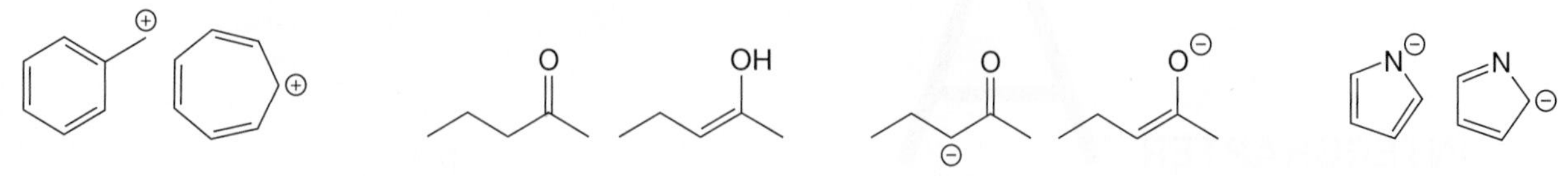

A B C D

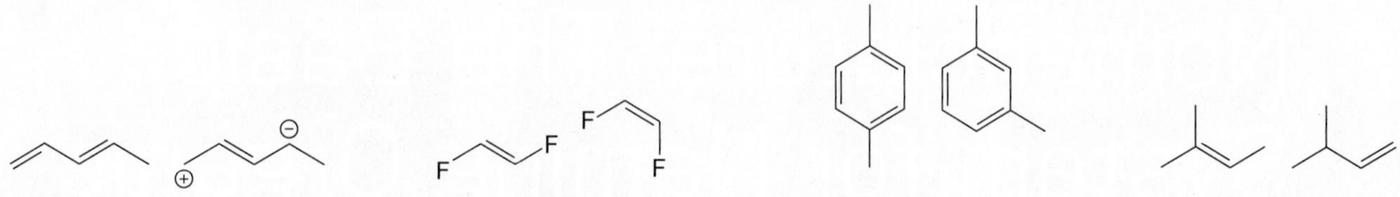

E F G H

1.51 Which of the following electrostatic potential maps best represents nitromethane (CH_3NO_2)? Explain.

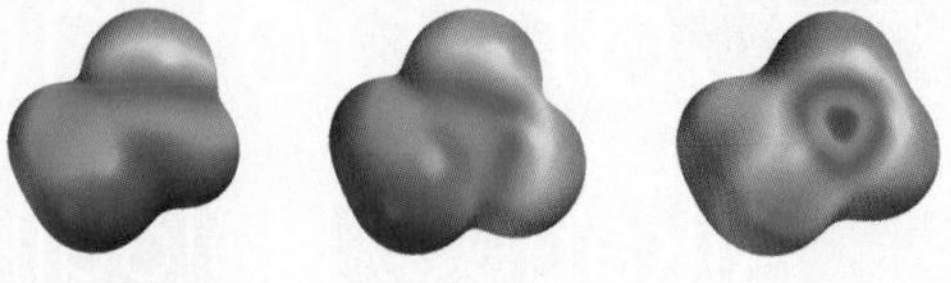

A B C

1.52 Which of the following species is responsible for the electrostatic potential map provided? Explain.

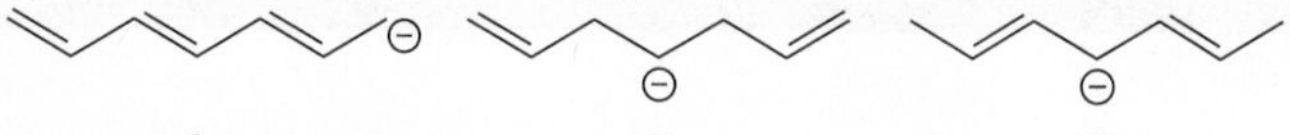

A B C

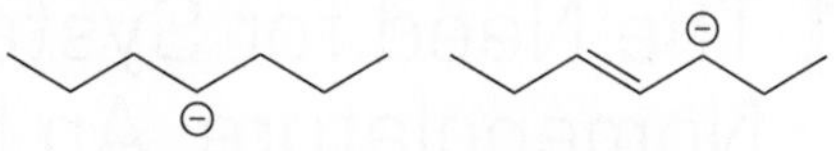

D E

1.53 Draw the structure of a molecule with formula C_5H_9N that contains functional groups characteristic of **(a)** an alkyne and an amine; **(b)** two alkenes and an amine; **(c)** a nitrile

1.54 Draw all of the resonance structures for each of the following species. Be sure to include the curved arrows that indicate which pairs of electrons are shifted in going from one resonance structure to the next. Draw the resonance hybrid of each species.

(a) 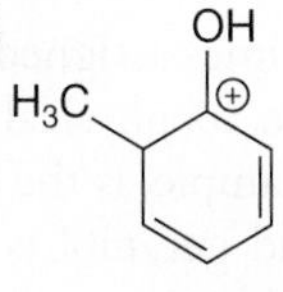 **(b)** 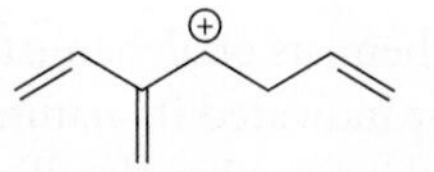 **(c)** 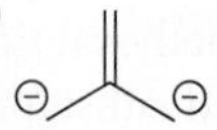 **(d)** 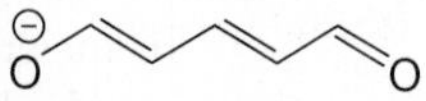

1.55 **(a)** Draw all valid resonance contributors for this ion. Show how the electrons can be moved by using curved arrows. **(b)** Draw the resonance hybrid.

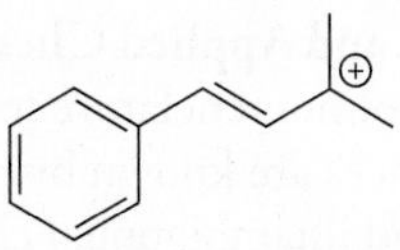

1.56 Diazomethane has the formula H_2CN_2. Draw all valid resonance contributors for diazomethane and, using Table 1-3, propose which one contributes more to the resonance hybrid. *Hint*: There are no structures that avoid charged atoms.

1.57 **(a)** Draw all resonance contributors for the following ion. In drawing each additional resonance structure, use curved arrows to indicate which pairs of electrons are being shifted. **(b)** Draw the resonance hybrid. **(c)** Which C—C bond is the longest?

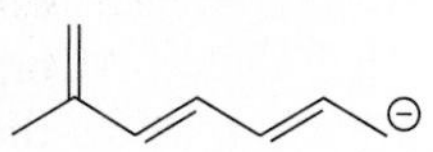

INTERCHAPTER A

Nomenclature: The Basic System for Naming Organic Compounds

Alkanes, Haloalkanes, Nitroalkanes, Cycloalkanes, and Ethers

SECTION A.1 OBJECTIVES

You will be able to:

1. Explain why the IUPAC system of nomenclature is beneficial.

A.1 The Need for Systematic Nomenclature: An Introduction to the IUPAC System

Learning how to name specific substances—that is, learning **nomenclature**—is an essential task. Nomenclature is not unique to chemistry; every discipline of study, from accounting and art history to zoology, has its specialized vocabulary. Organic nomenclature, in particular, is designed so that each unique molecule is assigned a unique name.

In ancient and medieval times, chemists or alchemists sometimes assigned a name to a newly discovered substance that indicated its natural source, its physical characteristics, or its chemical or medicinal properties. Vanillin, for example, is the primary component extracted from the vanilla bean (**Figure A-1a**), and geraniol is derived from the geranium plant (Fig. A-1b). Azulene, which is a dark blue crystalline solid, derives its name from *azul*, the Spanish word for "blue" (Fig. A-1c), and morphine, a powerful sedative isolated from opium, was named for Morpheus, the Greek god of dreams (Fig. A-1d).

In 1919, the **International Union of Pure and Applied Chemistry (IUPAC)** was established, which began developing a system of nomenclature for both inorganic and organic substances. Today, while many substances are known by more than one name, thanks to the IUPAC one *standard* (unique and unambiguous) chemical name can be assigned for every chemical structure.

Rules for deriving IUPAC names are based on the molecule's structure:

- Given a molecular structure, you can derive its IUPAC name, piece by piece.
- Given the IUPAC name, you can draw its structure, piece by piece.

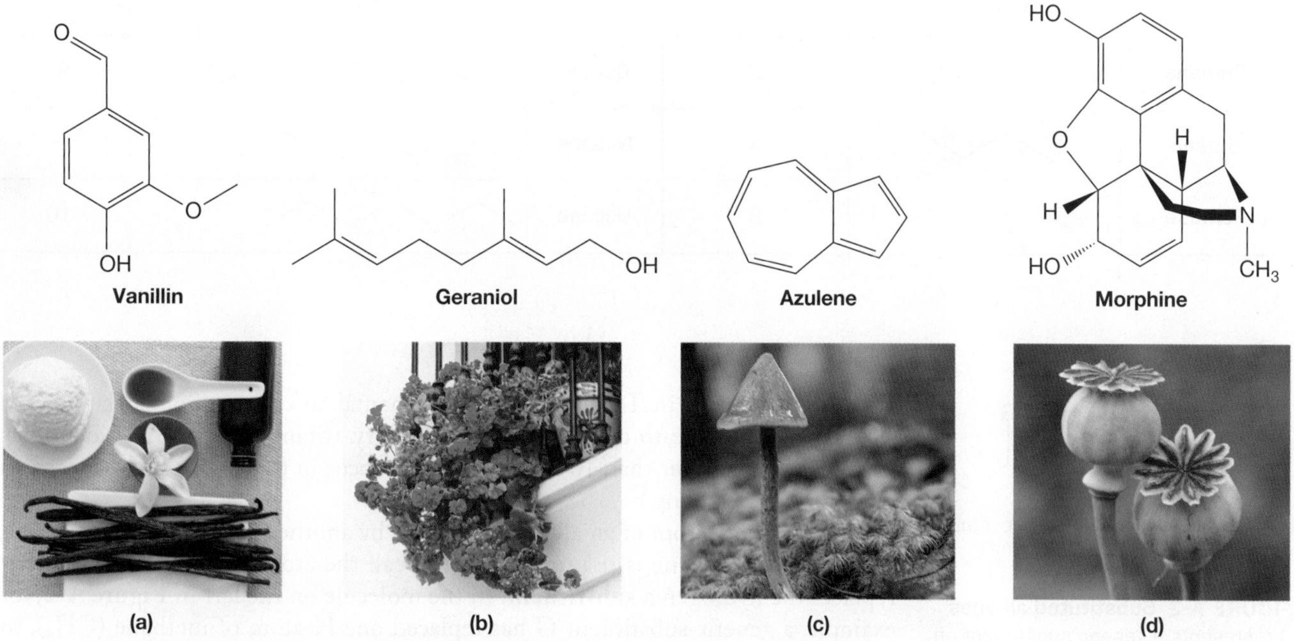

Vanillin
Geraniol
Azulene
Morphine
(a)
(b)
(c)
(d)

FIGURE A-1 Naturally occurring organic compounds (a) Vanillin can be isolated from vanilla beans. (b) Geraniol occurs in geranium oil. (c) Azulene gives this mushroom its blue color. (d) Morphine is derived from opium poppy.

In the sections that follow, we step through the various nomenclature rules and provide several examples, and you will have many opportunities to practice those rules.

A.2 Alkanes and Substituted Alkanes

SECTION A.2 OBJECTIVES

You will be able to:

1. Draw and name the straight-chain alkanes up to 10 carbons.
2. Distinguish a substituted alkane from an alkane with no substituents.

We begin by learning the names of the **straight-chain alkanes**, or **linear alkanes**, shown in Table A-1, because they form the basis for the entire system of organic nomenclature. Recall from Section 1.13 that *alkanes* make up the simplest class of organic compounds, because they contain only C—C and C—H single bonds; that is, they contain *no functional groups*. Straight-chain alkanes, furthermore, form *one continuous chain* from one end of the molecule to the other: No carbon atom is bonded to more than two others. The following rules govern the naming of such compounds:

Naming Straight-Chain Alkanes

- All straight-chain alkanes have the suffix *ane*.
- A numerical identifier (e.g., *meth*, *eth*, *prop*, *but*) is used to specify the number of carbon atoms in the chain.

TABLE A-1 Straight-Chain Alkanes

Name	Molecule	Number of Carbon Atoms	Name	Molecule	Number of Carbon Atoms
Methane	CH_4	1	**Hexane**		6
Ethane	H_3C-CH_3	2	**Heptane**		7
Propane		3	**Octane**		8
Butane		4	**Nonane**		9
Pentane		5	**Decane**		10

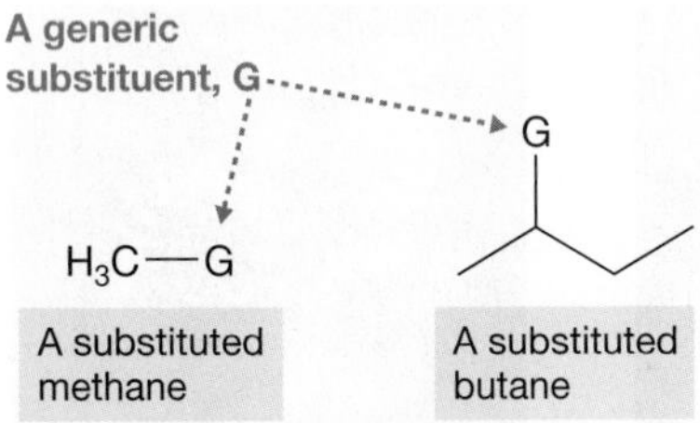
A generic substituent, G
G
H3C—G
A substituted methane
A substituted butane

FIGURE A-2 Substituted alkanes G represents a generic substituent on methane (*left*) and butane (*right*).

Because the names in Table A-1 are fundamental to organic nomenclature, you should take the time to commit them to memory. (Standard numerical identifiers exist for chains longer than 10 carbons, but our focus in this book will be on chains of 10 or fewer carbons.)

If a hydrogen atom of an alkane is replaced by another atom or group of atoms, we say that the alkane is *substituted*, and we call the atom or group of atoms that replaces the hydrogen a **substituent**. In the molecule on the left in **Figure A-2**, for example, a generic substituent G has replaced one H atom of methane (CH_4), so the molecule is a substituted methane. The molecule on the right is a substituted butane.

YOUR TURN A.1

How would you describe each of the molecules shown here, where G is a generic substituent?

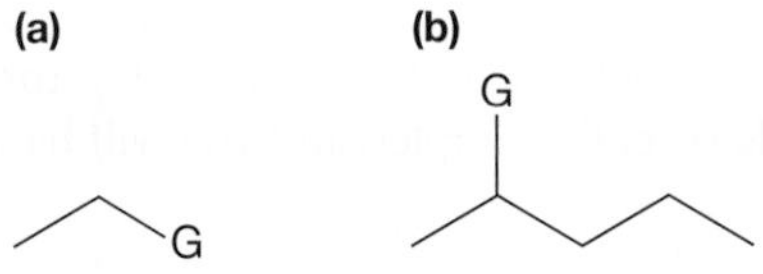
(a)
(b)
G
G

Answers to Your Turns are in the back of the book.

YOUR TURN A.2

Using G as a generic substituent, draw **(a)** a substituted propane and **(b)** a substituted hexane.

The IUPAC name must account for multiple substituents in a molecule. The rules for doing so depend on which of two types of substituents the molecule has. Here in Interchapter A we consider the easier case involving *halo*, *nitro*, *alkyl*, and *alkoxy* substituents, all of which require only prefixes to be added to the IUPAC name. Naming the other type of substituents involves consideration of both prefixes and suffixes and is dealt with in Interchapter D.

A.3 Haloalkanes and Nitroalkanes: Roots, Prefixes, and Locator Numbers

SECTION A.3 OBJECTIVES

You will be able to:

1. Determine the longest carbon chain and establish the numbering system for a halo- or nitro-substituted alkane.
2. Write the complete IUPAC name for an alkane having one or more halo or nitro substituents.

To specify a particular substituent in an IUPAC name, you must be able to recognize the substituent in the molecule's structure and you must know the corresponding name for the substituent. We begin with *halo* and *nitro* substituents:

- The *halo* substituents –F, –Cl, –Br, and –I are called *fluoro*, *chloro*, *bromo*, and *iodo*, respectively.
- The *nitro* substituent is $–NO_2$.

With this information, we can name a substituted straight-chain alkane that has a single halo or nitro substituent, so-called **haloalkanes** and **nitroalkanes**, according to the following rules:

Naming a Straight-Chain Alkane with One Substituent

1. Identify the main chain. The **main chain** or **parent chain** is the *longest continuous chain of carbon atoms*. The name of the corresponding alkane from Table A-1 will be the **root** of the molecule's name.
2. Add the name of the substituent. The substituent's name should be written as a *prefix*, to the left of the root.
3. Number the carbon atoms of the chain. Begin with C-1 (pronounced *see one*) at one end of the chain, so that the carbon atom to which the substituent is bonded receives the *lowest possible number*, called the **locator number** or **locant.**
4. Add the locator number. Write the locator number to the left of the substituent name. Use a hyphen to separate the locator number from the first letter of the substituent's name. *No spaces should appear in these IUPAC names.*

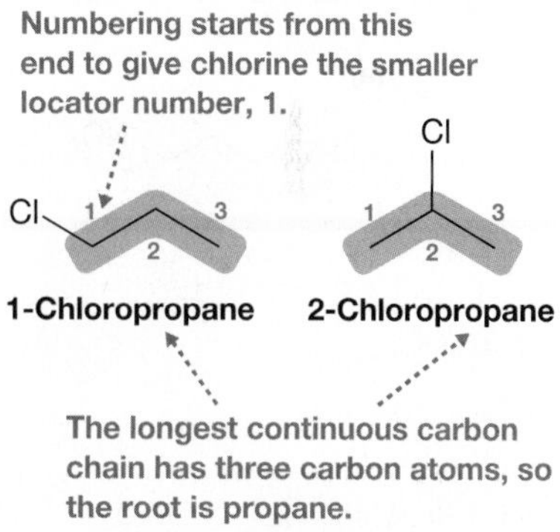

Numbering starts from this end to give chlorine the smaller locator number, 1.
Cl
1
2
3
Cl
1
2
3
1-Chloropropane
2-Chloropropane
The longest continuous carbon chain has three carbon atoms, so the root is propane.

FIGURE A-3 Naming a straight-chain alkane with a single substituent Highlighting indicates the longest continuous carbon chain. Locator numbers are shown in blue.

Examples of how to apply these rules are shown in **Figure A-3** for 1-chloropropane and 2-chloropropane.

SOLVED PROBLEM **A.1**

How to name a straight-chain alkane that has one substituent

Break It Down What is the IUPAC name of this molecule?

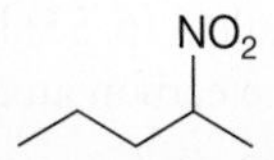

NO_2

Think	Solve
How many carbon atoms does the longest continuous carbon chain have? What is the corresponding root?	The longest continuous carbon chain has five carbon atoms, as highlighted here, so the root is *pentane*. 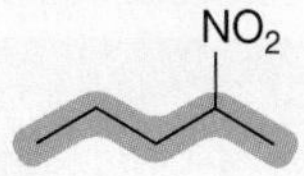

(continued)

What are the two choices for assigning C-1? Which of those choices gives the NO_2 group the lower locator number?	C-1 must be at the end of the chain, so there are two possibilities: (1) If carbons are numbered from left to right, the locator number for the NO_2 group is 4, whereas (2) if the carbons are numbered from right to left, the locator number is 2. Since the substituent must be assigned the lowest possible number, the second choice is correct.

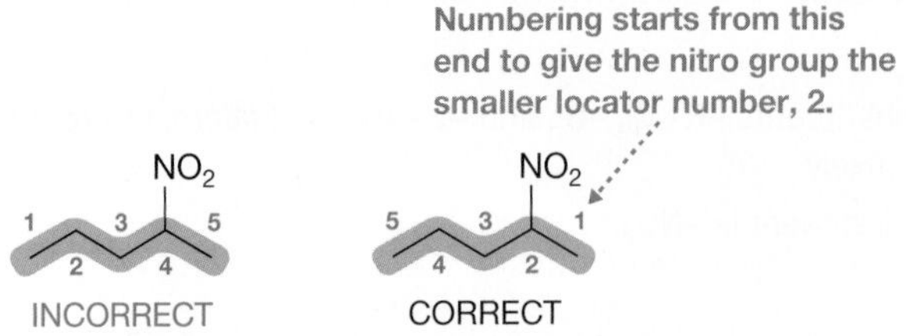

Numbering starts from this end to give the nitro group the smaller locator number, 2.
NO2
1 3 5
2 4
INCORRECT
NO2
5 3 1
4 2
CORRECT

How should the locator number and substituent be indicated in the IUPAC name of this molecule?	The substituent name, *nitro*, is added as a prefix to the root (which is *pentane*). The locator number 2 precedes the substituent name and is separated by a hyphen. The complete IUPAC name is 2-nitropentane.

Try It Write the IUPAC name for each of the following molecules.

(a)

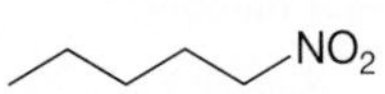

NO2

(b)

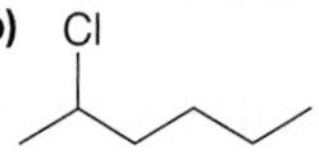

Cl

(c)

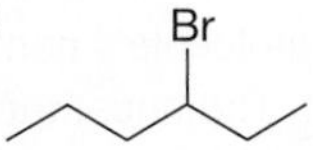

Br

(d)

F

Answers to all Try It exercises can be found in the Solutions Manual.

Sometimes there is only one possible locator number for a particular substituent, regardless of the end of the chain to which C-1 is assigned:

> When there is only one possible locator number for a substituent, the locator number is not added to the IUPAC name.

Bromomethane and iodoethane, for example, do not require a locator number, as shown in **Figure A-4.** Bromomethane has just a single carbon, so the Br substituent must be attached to C-1. Iodoethane, on the other hand, has two carbon atoms, so you might think that the I substituent could be bonded to C-1 or C-2, yielding 1-iodoethane and 2-iodoethane as possible IUPAC names. But the name 2-iodoethane would violate Rule 3 (p. 55) because its C-1 assignment does *not* give the lowest possible number to the carbon atom that is attached to the substituent.

CONNECTIONS A.1

The good and bad side of a pesticide Bromomethane is (Fig. A-4) a fumigant pesticide, which helped revolutionize the strawberry industry. Phasing out of this pesticide began in the early 2000s, however, because it is believed to deplete Earth's ozone layer.

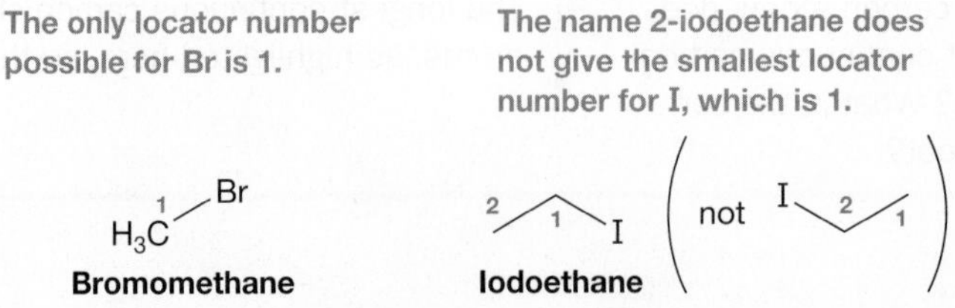

The only locator number possible for Br is 1.
The name 2-iodoethane does not give the smallest locator number for I, which is 1.
1
Br
H3C
Bromomethane
2
1
I
Iodoethane
not
I
2
1

FIGURE A-4 Molecules that do not require a locator number

If the molecule has two or more substituents, then additional considerations are necessary to establish the numbering system:

Establishing the Numbering System for a Main Chain Having Two or More Substituents

1. Minimize the first locator number. Choose C-1 so that the substituent that is encountered first has the lowest locator number.
2. Use the next locator number to break a tie. If each choice for C-1 results in a tie for the locator number of the first substituent, then C-1 is chosen so that the second substituent encountered has the lowest locator number. If there is still a tie, keep looking to break the tie by giving the lowest possible locator number to the next substituent encountered.
3. Use substituent names to break persisting ties. If a tie cannot be broken by minimizing locator numbers in Step 2, repeat these steps so that the lowest locator number is assigned to the substituent whose name is alphabetically first.

The examples in **Figure A-5** show the proper numbering system for molecules containing multiple generic substituents, G.

Additional considerations for prefixes apply when a molecule has two or more substituents:

Adding Prefixes When the Main Chain Has Two or More Substituents

1. Write the name of each substituent as a prefix. Order the substituent names alphabetically.
2. Add multiplying prefixes if necessary. When there are two or more of the *same* substituent, write the appropriate multiplying prefix just before the name of the substituent:

Number of Substituents	2	3	4	5	6	7	8	9	10
Multiplying Prefix	di	tri	tetra	penta	hexa	hepta	octa	nona	deca

Note: These multiplying prefixes are not part of the substituent name, so do not consider them when arranging substituent names alphabetically.

3. Add one locator number for *each* substituent. Remember to use a hyphen to separate any number from a letter.
   - If there is just one of a particular substituent, the locator number appears immediately to the left of the substituent it describes.
   - If there are two or more of the same substituent, the locator numbers appear immediately to the left of the multiplying prefix *di*, *tri*, etc. Furthermore, the locator numbers for a particular type of substituent are written in increasing numerical order, separated from each other by commas.

CONNECTIONS A.2

A cool molecule Freon 142b (Solved Problem A.2, Try It, p. 58) is a refrigerant, but it is being phased out for this use because it contributes to the depletion of stratospheric ozone. Freon 142b is also used as feedstock in the production of poly(vinylidene fluoride), a plastic used to make this modular conveyor belt.

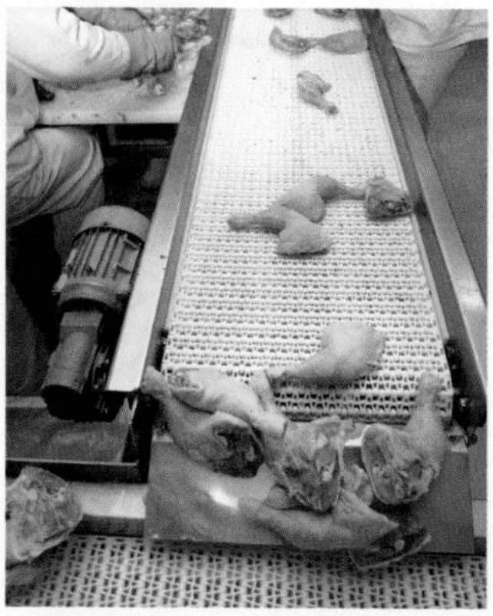

FIGURE A-5 Establishing the numbering system in a chain

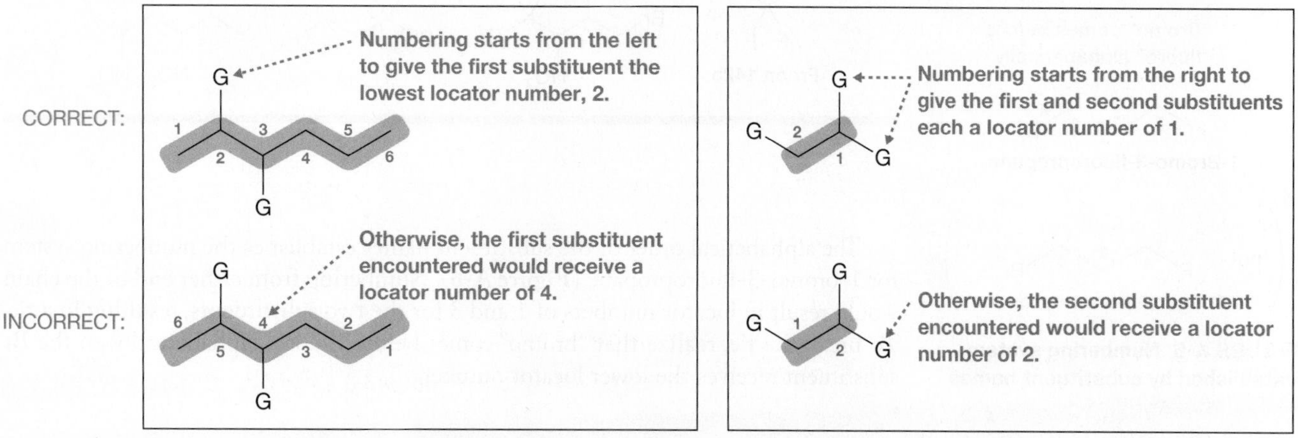
CORRECT:
Numbering starts from the left to give the first substituent the lowest locator number, 2.
INCORRECT:
Otherwise, the first substituent encountered would receive a locator number of 4.
Numbering starts from the right to give the first and second substituents each a locator number of 1.
Otherwise, the second substituent encountered would receive a locator number of 2.

SOLVED PROBLEM **A.2**

How to name a straight-chain alkane having multiple substituents

Break It Down What is the IUPAC name of this molecule?

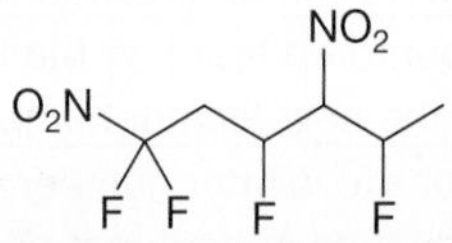

NO_2
O_2N
F F F F

Think	Solve
How many carbon atoms does the longest continuous carbon chain have, and what is the corresponding root name?	The longest continuous carbon chain has six carbon atoms, so the root is *hexane*.
On which end of the chain should numbering begin?	Numbering must begin on the left to give the first substituent encountered the smallest locator number, 1, as shown here. 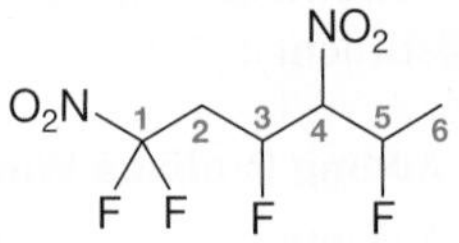
What are the names of the substituents, and which comes first alphabetically?	This molecule has two types of substituents: *nitro* and *fluoro*. "Fluoro" comes first alphabetically, so it appears first in the IUPAC name.
How do you indicate the number of each kind of substituent, and what locator number is assigned to each substituent?	The prefix tetra is added to indicate that there are four fluoro substituents, and the locator numbers 1,1,3,5 are added to indicate their positions along the chain. The prefix *di* is added to indicate two nitro substituents, and the corresponding locator numbers are 1,4. The IUPAC name, therefore, is 1,1,3,5-tetrafluoro-1,4-dinitrohexane.

Try It Write the IUPAC name for each of the following molecules.

(a)

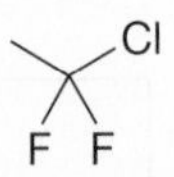

Cl
F F

Freon 142b

(b)

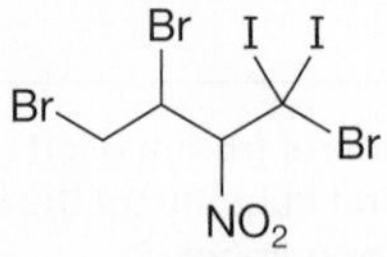

Br I I
Br
Br
NO_2

(c)

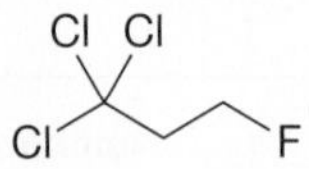

Cl Cl
Cl
F

(d)

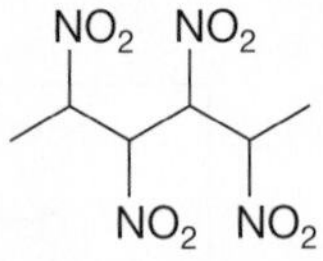

NO_2 NO_2
NO_2 NO_2

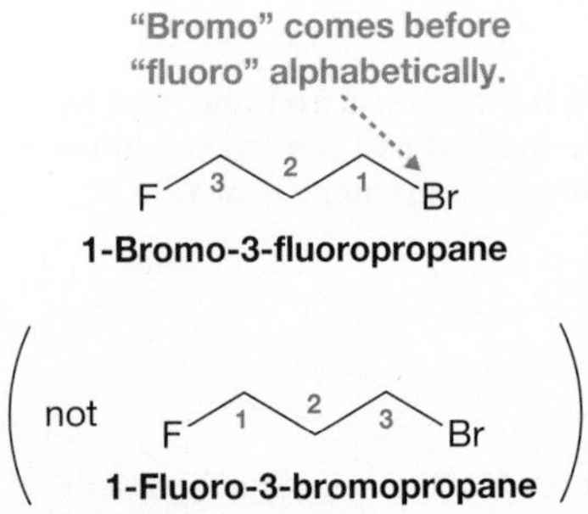

"Bromo" comes before "fluoro" alphabetically.
F 3 2 1 Br
1-Bromo-3-fluoropropane
not
F 1 2 3 Br
1-Fluoro-3-bromopropane

FIGURE A-6 Numbering system established by substituent names

The alphabetical order of the substituent names establishes the numbering system for 1-bromo-3-fluoropropane (**Figure A-6**). Numbering from either end of the chain would result in locator numbers of 1 and 3 for the two substituents, resulting in a tie. To break the tie, realize that "bromo" comes before "fluoro" alphabetically, so the Br substituent receives the lower locator number.

A.4 Alkyl Substituents: Branched Alkanes and Substituted Branched Alkanes

SECTION A.4 OBJECTIVES

You will be able to:

1. Identify the longest continuous chain of carbons in a branched alkane.
2. Identify and name alkyl groups and branched alkyl groups.
3. Write the IUPAC name for a branched alkane, including those that have branched alkyl groups.

Alkyl groups are substituents that contain only carbon and hydrogen atoms that are all connected by single bonds. You can envision an alkyl group constructed by removing a hydrogen atom from an alkane, leaving one of the carbon atoms available for bonding. The most straightforward alkyl groups to name are *straight-chain alkyl groups*, which are derived by removing a hydrogen atom from the terminal carbon of a straight-chain alkane. Some examples are shown in **Figure A-7**.

Naming these alkyl substituents is relatively straightforward:

Naming Straight-Chain Alkyl Groups

1. Identify the corresponding alkane (Table A-1, p. 54). The corresponding alkane is the straight-chain alkane that has the same number of carbon atoms as the alkyl substituent.
2. Replace the *ane* suffix with the suffix *yl*.

The $-CH_3$ substituent, for instance, is called the **methyl group** because it has a single carbon atom, the same as methane (CH_4). Similarly, the $-CH_2CH_3$ substituent is called the **ethyl group** because it is derived from ethane, CH_3CH_3.

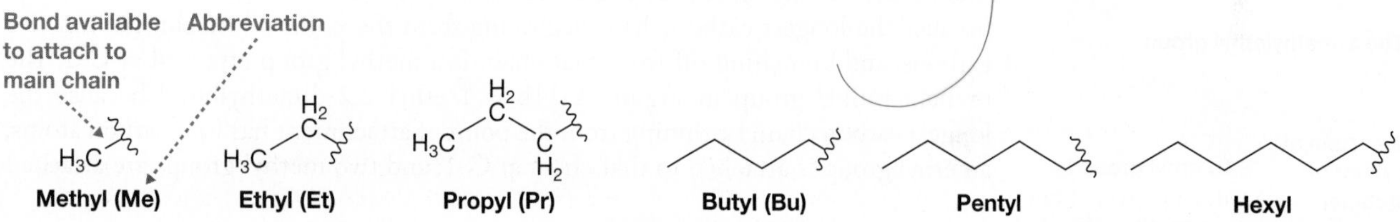

Bond available to attach to main chain
Abbreviation
H_3C
Methyl (Me)
H_3C H_2 C
Ethyl (Et)
H_3C H_2 C C H_2
Propyl (Pr)
Butyl (Bu)
Pentyl
Hexyl

FIGURE A-7 Straight-chain alkyl groups and their abbreviations

When the main chain of a molecule has attached alkyl groups, the molecule is said to be **branched** because not all of the carbon atoms connected together form a single straight chain. The rules for naming branched alkanes are no different from those used to name halo- and nitro-substituted alkanes. Examples are shown for 3-methylhexane and 4,4-dichloro-5-propyloctane in **Figure A-8**.

Be careful when dealing with alkyl substituents; it will not always be immediately obvious which is the longest continuous chain of carbons. The molecule in **Figure A-9a**,

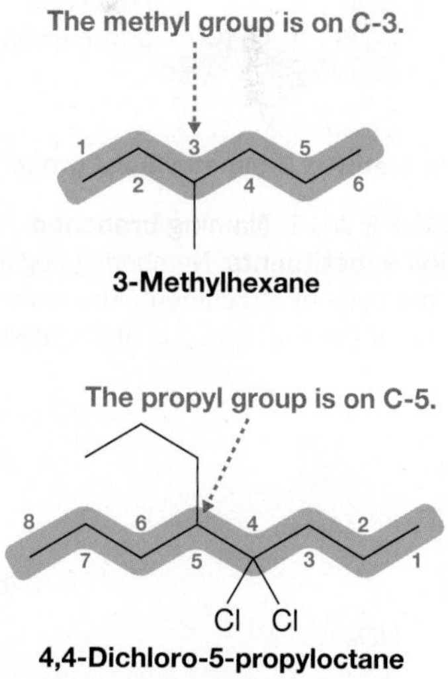

The methyl group is on C-3.
1 2 3 4 5 6
3-Methylhexane
The propyl group is on C-5.
8 7 6 5 4 3 2 1
Cl Cl
4,4-Dichloro-5-propyloctane

FIGURE A-8 Naming alkanes with alkyl substituents

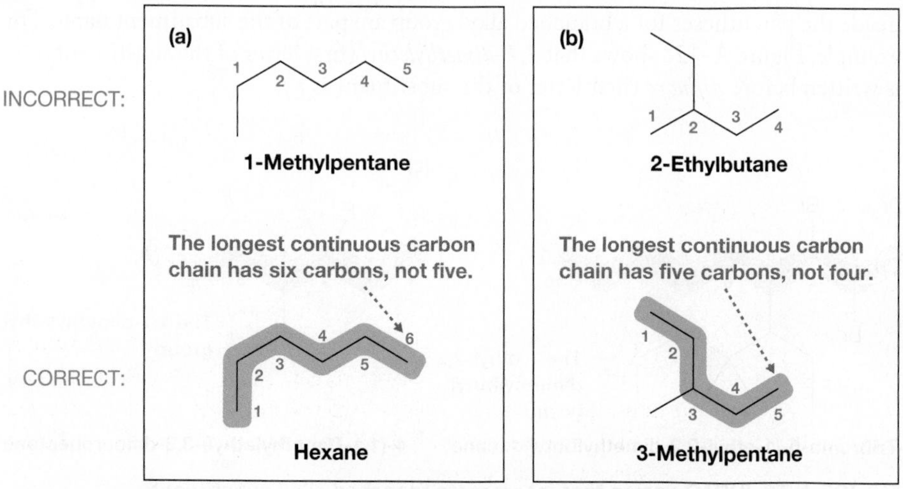

INCORRECT:
CORRECT:
(a)
1 2 3 4 5
1-Methylpentane
The longest continuous carbon chain has six carbons, not five.
1 2 3 4 5 6
Hexane
(b)
1 2 3 4
2-Ethylbutane
The longest continuous carbon chain has five carbons, not four.
1 2 3 4 5
3-Methylpentane

FIGURE A-9 Distinguishing alkyl substituents from the main chain

This branched alkyl group has two terminal carbons.

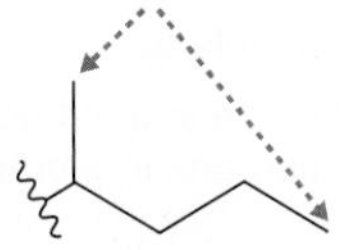

FIGURE A-10 A branched alkyl substituent Notice that, beginning from the point of attachment, there is more than one path to arrive at a terminal carbon.

(a)

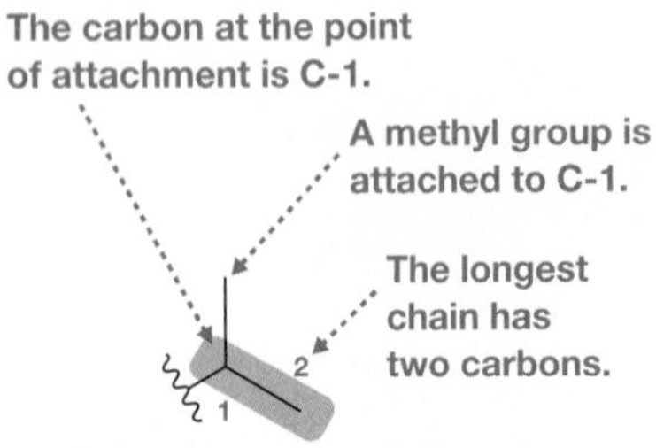

The carbon at the point of attachment is C-1.
A methyl group is attached to C-1.
The longest chain has two carbons.
1
2

The 1-methylethyl group

(b)

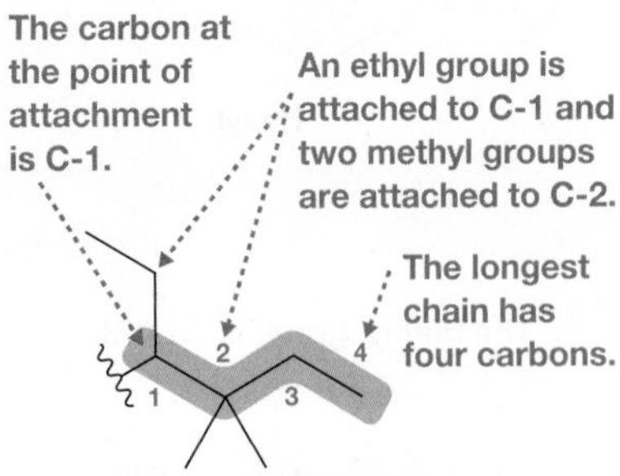

The carbon at the point of attachment is C-1.
An ethyl group is attached to C-1 and two methyl groups are attached to C-2.
The longest chain has four carbons.
1
2
3
4

The 1-ethyl-2,2-dimethylbutyl group

FIGURE A-11 Naming branched alkyl substituents Numbering begins at the point of attachment. The main chain of the alkyl group is highlighted.

for example, might appear to have five carbons in its longest carbon chain, making it 1-methylpentane, but the methyl group is part of the longest continuous chain of six carbons, so the molecule is simply hexane. Likewise, in Figure A-9b, what might appear to be 2-ethylbutane is in fact 3-methylpentane instead.

Alkyl groups that have more than one terminal carbon atom are said to be branched. An example is shown in **Figure A-10**. The IUPAC rules for naming these branched alkyl groups apply the same logic as some of the rules we have already encountered:

Naming Branched Alkyl Groups

1. Identify the main chain of the branched alkyl group. The main chain of an alkyl group is the longest continuous chain of carbons in the alkyl group, beginning at the substituent's point of attachment.
2. Assign the alkyl group's *root name*. The root name of the branched alkyl group is the name of the straight-chain alkyl group (i.e., *ethyl*, *propyl*, etc.) that has the same number of carbons.
3. Number the carbon atoms of the branched alkyl group's main chain. The atom at the alkyl group's point of attachment is C-1.
4. Add prefixes and locator numbers. These additions account for smaller alkyl groups attached along the substituent's main chain.

The branched alkyl group in **Figure A-11a**, for example, is named 1-methylethyl because the longest carbon chain beginning from the point of attachment has two carbons, and branching off from that chain is a methyl group attached at C-1. The branched alkyl group in Figure A-11b is 1-ethyl-2,2-dimethylbutyl because the longest carbon chain beginning from the point of attachment has four carbon atoms, an ethyl group is attached to that chain at C-1, and two methyl groups are attached at C-2.

Incorporating branched alkyl groups into an IUPAC name follows the same rules as straight-chain alkanes, with one additional rule:

Incorporating Branched Alkyl Groups into an IUPAC Name

Enclose the entire name of a branched alkyl group in parentheses.

Parentheses help to avoid confusion between the numbering system for the substituent's main chain and that for the main chain of the entire molecule. Examples are shown in **Figure A-12**.

When determining the alphabetical order in which substituents should be written in a complete IUPAC name, realize that the multiplier prefixes (*di*, *tri*, etc.) appearing inside the parentheses for a branched alkyl group are part of the substituent name. For example, Figure A-12c shows that *1,1-dimethylethyl* (first letter of the substituent is *d*) is written before *difluoro* (first letter of the substituent is *f*).

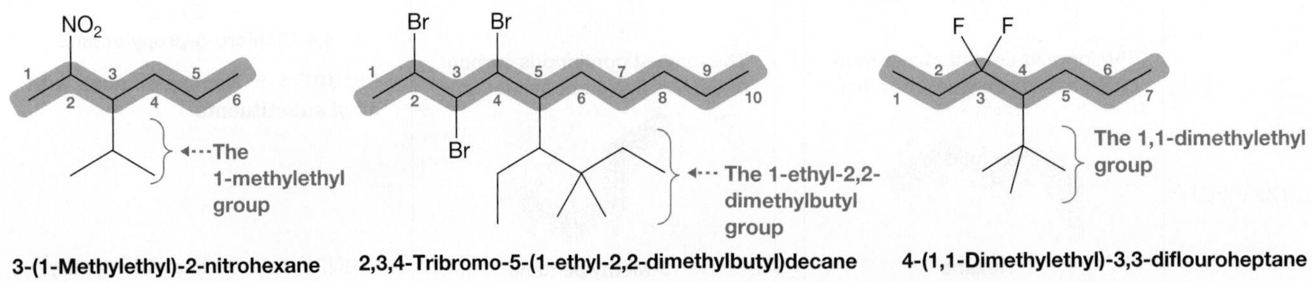

(a)
NO_2
1
2
3
4
5
6
The 1-methylethyl group
3-(1-Methylethyl)-2-nitrohexane
(b)
Br
Br
Br
1
2
3
4
5
6
7
8
9
10
The 1-ethyl-2,2-dimethylbutyl group
2,3,4-Tribromo-5-(1-ethyl-2,2-dimethylbutyl)decane
(c)
F
F
1
2
3
4
5
6
7
The 1,1-dimethylethyl group
4-(1,1-Dimethylethyl)-3,3-diflouroheptane

FIGURE A-12 IUPAC names that incorporate branched alkyl substituents

Draw the structure that corresponds to each IUPAC name.
(a) 3,3-dibromo-5-(2-methylpropyl)nonane; **(b)** 4,5-di(1,1-dimethylethyl)octane

YOUR TURN **A.3**

A.5 Cyclic Alkanes and Cyclic Alkyl Groups

SECTION A.5 OBJECTIVES

You will be able to:

1. Determine whether a ring of carbons in a molecule should establish the root of the IUPAC name or should be treated as a substituent.
2. Write the complete IUPAC name of a molecule containing a ring of carbons.

If a molecule contains at least one ring made entirely of carbon atoms, then a ring could establish the root as a **cycloalkane**, such as the ones in **Figure A-13**.

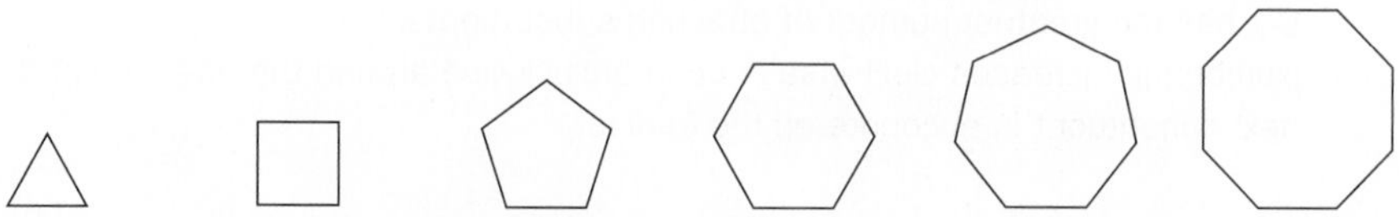

Cyclopropane **Cyclobutane** **Cyclopentane** **Cyclohexane** **Cycloheptane** **Cyclooctane**

FIGURE A-13 **Cycloalkanes**

Alternatively, the rings could be treated as substituents, called **cycloalkyl groups**, examples of which are shown in **Figure A-14**.

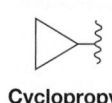

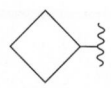

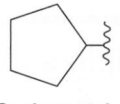

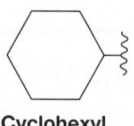

Cyclopropyl **Cyclobutyl** **Cyclopentyl** **Cyclohexyl**

FIGURE A-14 **Cycloalkyl substituents**

Whether a ring is treated as a root or a substituent depends on its relative number of carbon atoms:

Establishing the Root of a Molecule Containing a Carbon Ring

1. Distinguish ring carbons from chain carbons. A carbon that is part of a ring is *not* counted as part of a chain.
2. Compare the number of carbon atoms in the carbon ring to the number in the longest continuous carbon chain.
   - If the ring has as many or more carbons than the longest continuous carbon chain, then the ring establishes the root as a cycloalkane.
   - Otherwise, the longest continuous carbon chain establishes the root and the ring is treated as a cycloalkyl substituent.

For example, in **Figure A-15a**, the root is *octane* because the straight-chain alkane has eight carbons, whereas the ring has only five carbons. In Figure A-15b, the *cyclooctane*

(a)

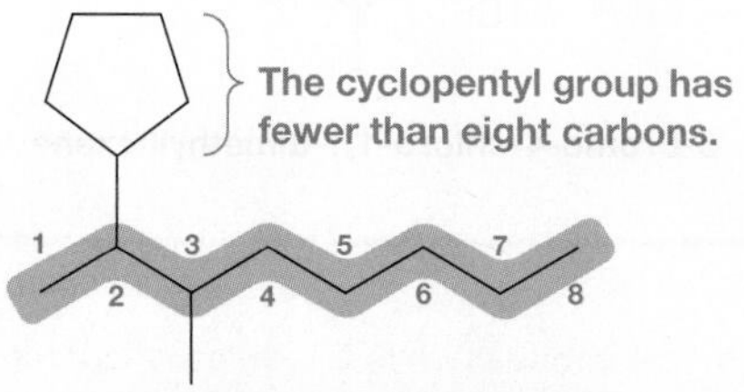
The cyclopentyl group has fewer than eight carbons.
1
2
3
4
5
6
7
8

2-Cyclopentyl-3-methyloctane

(b)

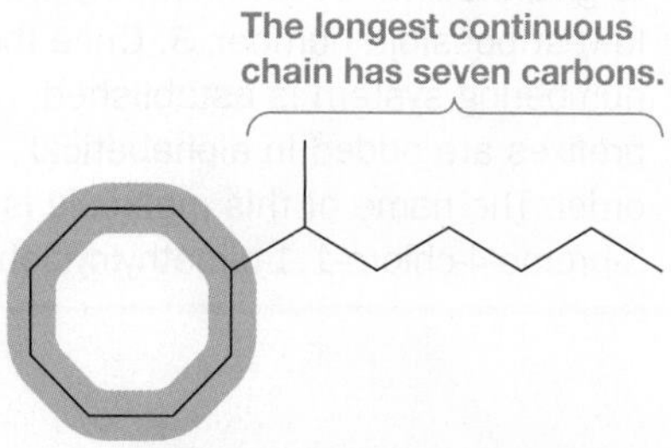
The longest continuous chain has seven carbons.

(1-Methylhexyl)cyclooctane

FIGURE A-15 **Naming molecules that contain a carbon ring**

ring establishes the root because the longest continuous chain has only seven carbons, whereas the ring has eight.

If a molecule's root is a cycloalkane, we establish the numbering system just as we did with alkanes. Namely, C-1 is chosen so that the first substituent encountered receives the lowest possible locator number. If two or more choices of C-1 result in a tie for the locator number of the first substituent, then we break the tie by choosing C-1 to give the next substituent encountered the lowest possible locator number, and so on.

Because of the cyclic nature of the ring, you should be aware of the following consequences of the rule for establishing numbering systems:

Establishing the Numbering System of a Cycloalkane

1. C-1 has the greatest number of attached substituents.
2. Numbering increases clockwise or counterclockwise around the ring so that the next substituent is encountered the earliest.

Moreover, because all carbons of a cycloalkane are indistinguishable, locator numbers are unnecessary for monosubstituted cycloalkanes. For example, (1-methylhexyl) cyclooctane (Fig. A-15b) does not include a locator number.

SOLVED PROBLEM **A.3**

How to name a cycloalkane that has multiple substituents

Break It Down

Write the IUPAC name for this molecule.

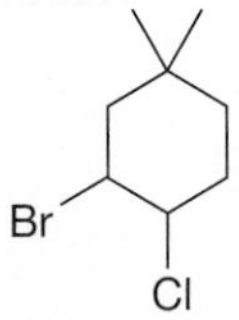

Br
Cl

Think	Solve
How many carbon atoms are in the longest carbon chain and the largest carbon ring? Which one establishes the root?	The longest carbon chain has one carbon and the largest carbon ring has six, so the root is *cyclohexane*.
Which carbon atom gives the lowest locator number to the first substituent? To the second substituent?	The top carbon of the ring is chosen to be C-1 because the locator number is 1 for both the first and second substituents (both CH_3 groups in this case). If, on the other hand, C-1 were chosen to be the carbon attached to either Br or Cl, then the locator number of the next substituent would be 2.
Should numbering increase clockwise or counterclockwise?	We increase the numbers counterclockwise to give the next substituent, Br, the lowest possible number, 3. Once the numbering system is established, prefixes are added in alphabetical order. The name of this molecule is 3-bromo-4-chloro-1,1-dimethylcyclohexane. 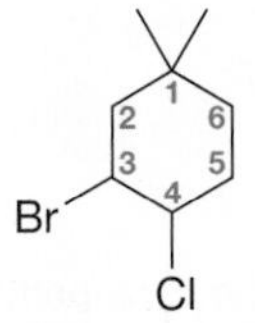 1 2 3 4 5 6 Br Cl **3-Bromo-4-chloro-1,1-dimethylhexane**

(continued)

Try It Write the IUPAC name for each of the following molecules.

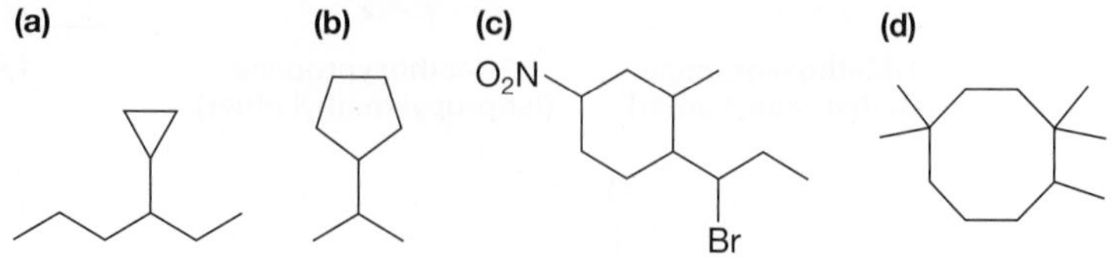
(a)
(b)
(c)
(d)
O_2N
Br

A.6 Ethers and Alkoxy Groups

An ether can be represented as R—O—R′, in which an oxygen atom joins two alkyl groups, R and R′ (review Section 1.13). The alkyl groups can be the same or they can be different. To name an ether, we mentally divide the molecule into two portions. One portion, R, contains the main chain. The remaining portion, –OR′, is treated as a substituent called an **alkoxy group** (alkyl group + oxygen), as shown in **Figure A-16**.

Naming an Ether

1. Establish the root. The alkane or cycloalkane that has the same number of carbons as the main chain or ring in R (Fig. A-16) is assigned as the root.
2. Name the alkoxy group. Remove the suffix *yl* from the name of the corresponding alkyl or cycloalkyl group (R′) and add the suffix *oxy*. For example, $-OCH_3$ is the **methoxy group**, and $-OCH_2CH_3$ is the **ethoxy group**.
3. Assemble the IUPAC name by using previous rules. Establish the numbering system of the main chain or ring. Then add prefixes and locator numbers (if necessary), treating an alkoxy group as a substituent.

The examples in **Figure A-17** demonstrate how ethers are named.

In methoxymethane, the longest carbon chain has one carbon, so the root is *methane*. The remaining alkoxy substituent is $-OCH_3$, the *methoxy* group. In ethoxyethane, the longest carbon chain has two carbons, so the root is *ethane*, and the remaining $-OCH_2CH_3$ group is the *ethoxy* substituent. In propoxycyclohexane, *cyclohexane* is the root because it has more C atoms (six) than the propyl group (three), and the remaining $-OCH_2CH_2CH_3$ group is the *propoxy* substituent. (The names in parentheses under the molecules are common names, as we will discuss in Section A.7.)

SECTION A.6 OBJECTIVES

You will be able to:

1. Distinguish the main chain or ring of an ether from the alkoxy substituent.
2. Write the complete IUPAC name of an ether when given the structure.
3. Draw the structure of an ether when given the IUPAC name.

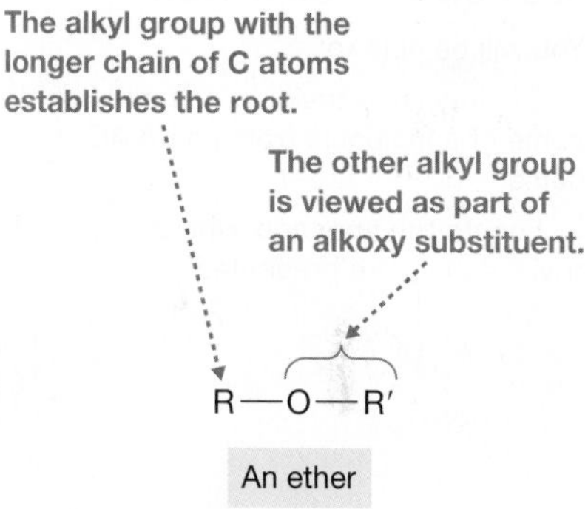
The alkyl group with the longer chain of C atoms establishes the root.
The other alkyl group is viewed as part of an alkoxy substituent.
R—O—R′
An ether

FIGURE A-16 Composition of an ether An ether is composed of an alkyl group (R) and an alkoxy group (–OR′).

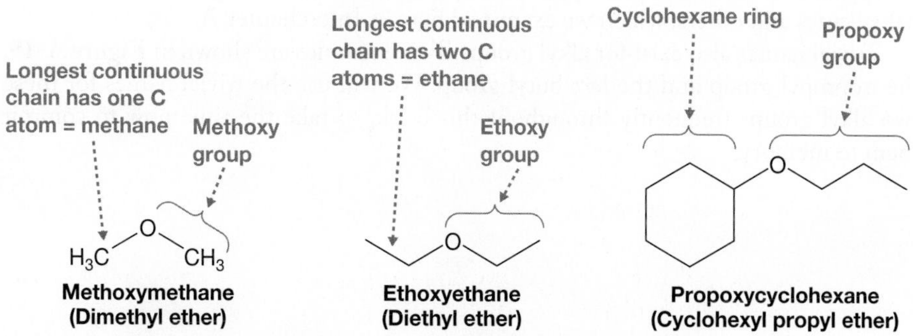
Longest continuous chain has one C atom = methane
Methoxy group
H_3C
O
CH_3
Methoxymethane (Dimethyl ether)
Longest continuous chain has two C atoms = ethane
Ethoxy group
O
Ethoxyethane (Diethyl ether)
Cyclohexane ring
Propoxy group
O
Propoxycyclohexane (Cyclohexyl propyl ether)

FIGURE A-17 Naming ethers that do not require locator numbers

FIGURE A-18 Naming ethers that require locator numbers

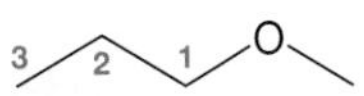
3
2
1
O

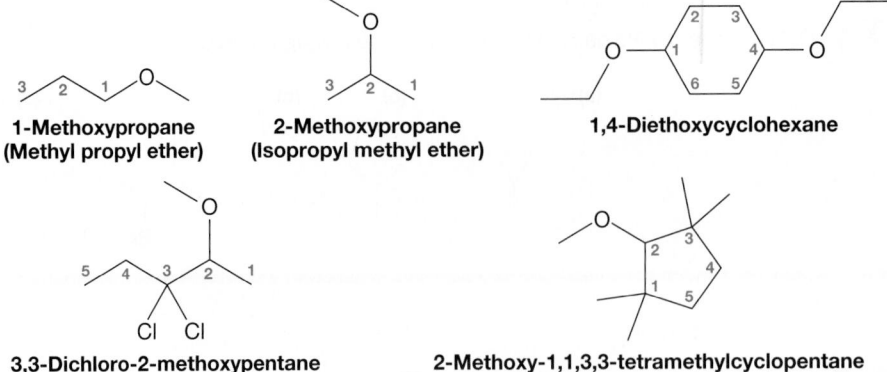

1-Methoxypropane (Methyl propyl ether)

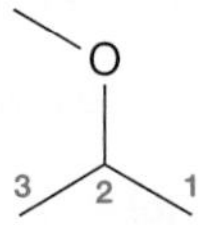
O
3
2
1

2-Methoxypropane (Isopropyl methyl ether)

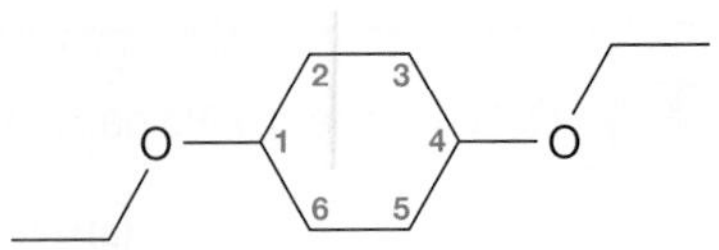
O
2
3
1
4
6
5
O

1,4-Diethoxycyclohexane

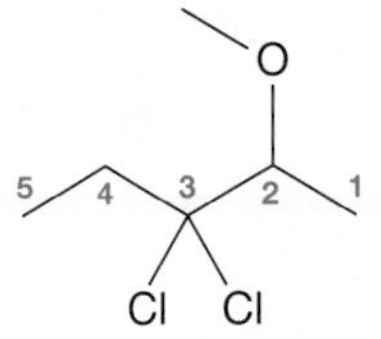
O
5
4
3
2
1
Cl
Cl

3,3-Dichloro-2-methoxypentane

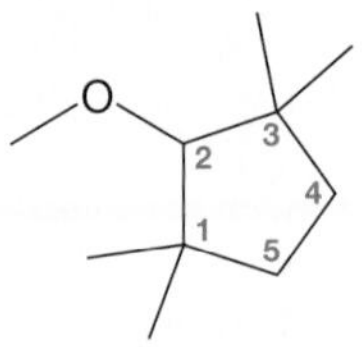
O
2
3
4
1
5

2-Methoxy-1,1,3,3-tetramethylcyclopentane

For the compounds in Figure A-17, numbers are unnecessary to locate the alkoxy substituents because only one locator number is possible. In the examples in **Figure A-18**, however, substituent locators are necessary.

YOUR TURN **A.4**

Draw the structure for each of the following compounds. **(a)** 3,3-diethoxypentane; **(b)** 1-chloro-5-methoxyhexane; **(c)** 1,2-diethoxy-1-methylcyclopentane

SECTION A.7 OBJECTIVES

You will be able to:

1. Distinguish a trivial or common name of a molecule from an IUPAC name.
2. Locate the appendix where trivial names are presented.

A.7 Trivial Names or Common Names

Many organic compounds were assigned names before the IUPAC system of nomenclature was established. Such names that do not follow the IUPAC rules are referred to as **trivial names** or **common names**.

Although we will minimize the use of trivial names in this book, they are so frequently employed by professionals in the chemical field that you will need to know them to communicate effectively. Therefore, where appropriate, we will provide both the IUPAC name and the trivial name together:

In this book, trivial or common names will generally appear in parentheses, whereas IUPAC names will not.

As we mentioned in Section A.1, trivial names were frequently assigned on the basis of the compound's properties or its natural source. Trivial names also come from naming systems that predate the IUPAC system, and those systems are covered in Appendix E. For example, Appendix E presents trivial naming systems of alkanes, haloalkanes and ethers, which we examined here in Interchapter A.

Trivial names also exist for alkyl groups. Two examples are shown in **Figure A-19**: the isopropyl group and the *tert*-butyl group. We will use the trivial names for these two alkyl groups frequently throughout this book, so take the time now to commit them to memory.

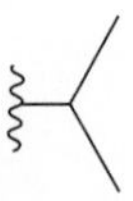

Isopropyl

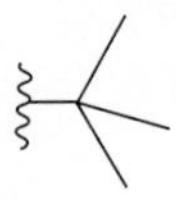

***tert*-Butyl**

FIGURE A-19 Trivial names of alkyl groups

Problems

Sections A.2 and A.3 Alkanes, Substituted Alkanes, Haloalkanes, and Nitroalkanes

A.1 Using G as a generic substituent, draw three different molecules that would be described as substituted heptanes.

A.2 Assuming G is a generic substituent, describe each of these molecules as a substituted alkane.

(a)
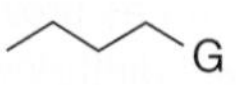
G

(b)
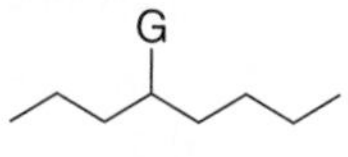
G

A.3 Draw structures for the following haloalkanes. **(a)** 1,2,3-tribromohexane; **(b)** 2,2,3,3,4-pentachlorohexane; **(c)** 1,2-dichloro-4-nitrohexane; **(d)** 1,2-dichloro-3-methoxycyclopentane

A.4 Draw structures for the following haloalkanes. **(a)** 2,2-dichloro-3-cyclopropylbutane; **(b)** 1-bromo-1-chloro-1-iodobutane; **(c)** 2-bromo-1,1-diiodohexane; **(d)** 3-chloro-1,1,2,2-tetrafluoropentane

A.5 Draw structures for the following molecules. **(a)** 3-bromo-2-nitropentane; **(b)** 2,2-dichloro-4,4,5-trinitroheptane; **(c)** 1,2,3,4-tetranitrobutane; **(d)** 6-iodo-1,2-difluorohexane

A.6 Write the IUPAC name for each of the following molecules:

(a)
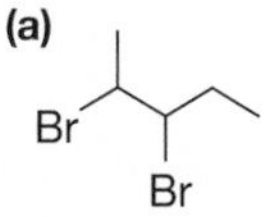
Br
Br

(b)
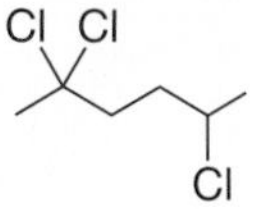
Cl Cl
Cl

(c)
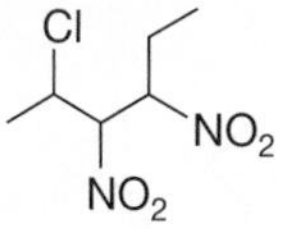
Cl
NO2
NO2

Section A.4 Branched Alkanes and Substituted Branched Alkanes

A.7 Write the IUPAC name for each of these molecules:

(a)
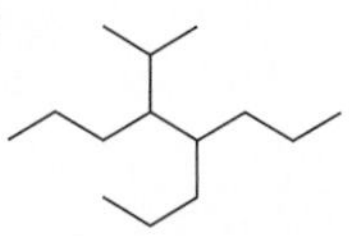

(b)
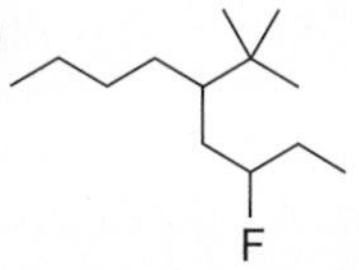
F

A.8 Given each of the IUPAC names provided, draw the corresponding structure. **(a)** 2-methylhexane; **(b)** 3-methylhexane; **(c)** 2,3-dimethylbutane; **(d)** 2,2,3-trimethylbutane

A.9 Given each of the IUPAC names provided, draw the corresponding structure. **(a)** 2,2,4-trimethylpentane; **(b)** 3-ethyl-2,3-dimethylpentane; **(c)** 2,2,3,3-tetramethylhexane

A.10 Given each of the IUPAC names provided, draw the corresponding structure. **(a)** 4-(1-methylethyl)heptane; **(b)** 3-(1,1-dimethylethyl)-4-(1,2-dimethylpropyl)decane

A.11 Given each of the structures provided, write the corresponding IUPAC name.

(a)
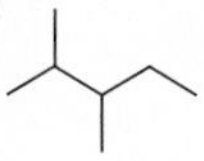

(b)
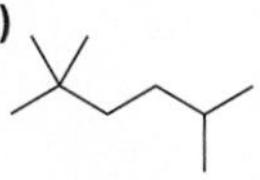

(c)
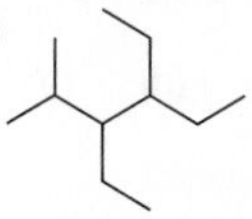

A.12 Write the IUPAC name for each of the following molecules.

(a)
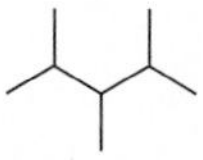

(b)
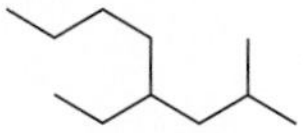

(c)
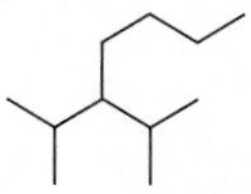

(d)
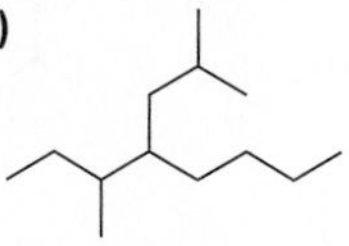

Section A.5 Cyclic Alkanes and Cyclic Alkyl Groups

A.13 Given each of the IUPAC names provided, draw the corresponding structure. **(a)** 1,1-dimethylcyclohexane; **(b)** 1,2-dimethylcyclohexane; **(c)** 1,2,3-trimethylcyclobutane

A.14 Given each of the IUPAC names provided, draw the corresponding structure. **(a)** 1-cyclopentylhexane; **(b)** cyclohexylcyclohexane; **(c)** 1,2-dicyclopropylnonane

A.15 Given each of the IUPAC names provided, draw the corresponding structure.
(a) 1-(1,1-dimethylethyl)-2,4-diethylcyclohexane; **(b)** 1,4-dibutyl-2-(1-methylpropyl)cyclooctane;
(c) 1,1-dicyclopropyl-3-(1,1-dimethylethyl)cycloheptane

A.16 Given each of the structures provided, write the corresponding IUPAC name.

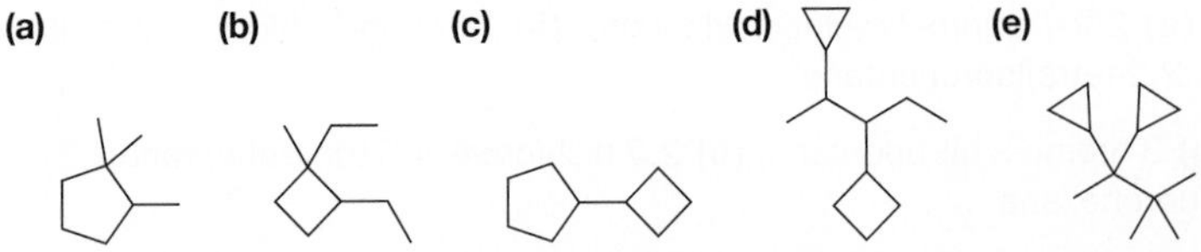

(a)
(b)
(c)
(d)
(e)

A.17 Given each of the structures provided, write the corresponding IUPAC name.

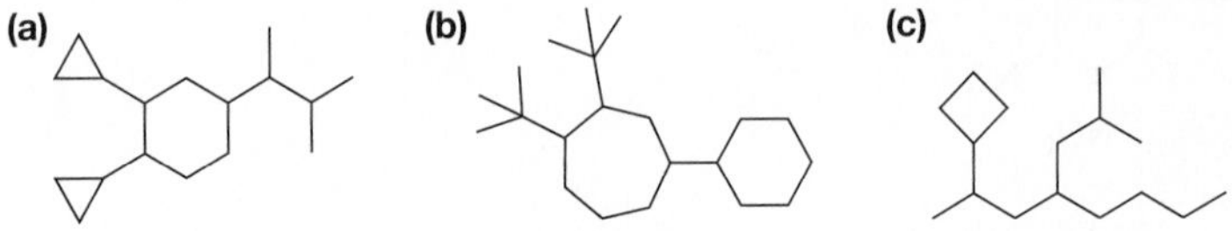

(a)
(b)
(c)

Section A.6 Ethers and Alkoxy Groups

A.18 What is the IUPAC name for each of the following ethers?

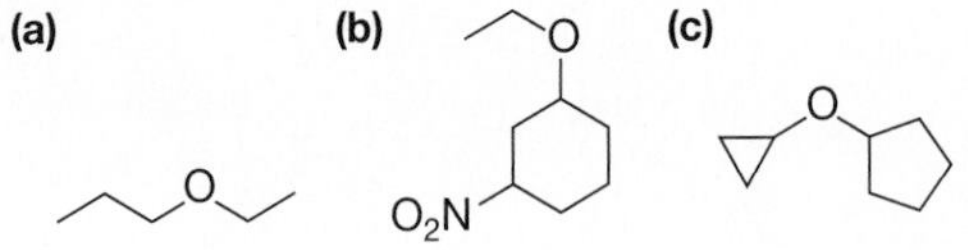

(a)
O
(b)
O
O2N
(c)
O

A.19 Given each of the IUPAC names provided, draw the corresponding structure. **(a)** 1-ethoxypropane; **(b)** 2-ethoxypropane; **(c)** 1,2,3-trimethoxybutane

A.20 Given each of the IUPAC names provided, draw the corresponding structure. **(a)** 1-ethoxy-3-methoxyhexane; **(b)** 1,5-dipropoxypentane; **(c)** 4-butoxy-1,2-dimethoxyheptane

A.21 Given each of the IUPAC names provided, draw the corresponding structure. **(a)** 2-cyclopropoxypentane; **(b)** 1,2-dimethoxy-4-propylcyclohexane; **(c)** 4-(1,1-dimethylethyl)-1,2-dipropoxycyclooctane

A.22 Given each of the structures provided, write the corresponding IUPAC name.

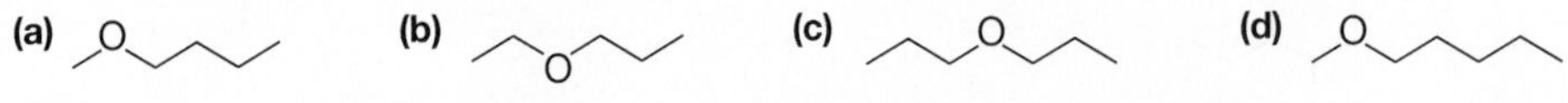

(a)
O
(b)
O
(c)
O
(d)
O

A.23 Given each of the structures provided, write the corresponding IUPAC name.

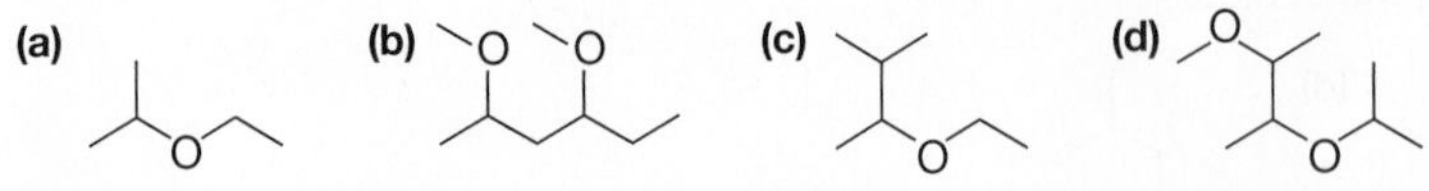

(a)
O
(b)
O
O
(c)
O
(d)
O
O

Integrated Problems

A.24 Given each of the IUPAC names provided, draw the corresponding structure.

(a) 2,4-dicyclopropyl-2-ethoxyhexane
(b) 1,2-dichloro-1-(2-methylpropyl)-4-nitrocyclohexane
(c) 1,3-dicyclopentyl-1,2,3,4-tetramethoxycyclooctane
(d) 1-cyclobutyl-4-(1,1-dimethylethyl)-2,4-dinitrononane
(e) 1-(1,1-dimethylbutyl)-2-ethoxy-1,2,3-trinitrocyclobutane
(f) 1,2,4-tricyclopropyl-1-(2,2-dichloropentyl)cyclohexane
(g) 4-(2-chloro-1-methoxyethyl)-1,1-dinitroheptane
(h) 3,3,4-trichloro-1-cyclohexoxy-4-(1,1-dichloroethyl)decane

A.25 Given each of the structures provided, write the corresponding IUPAC name.

(a)
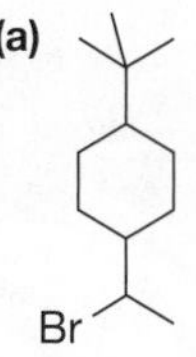
Br

(b)
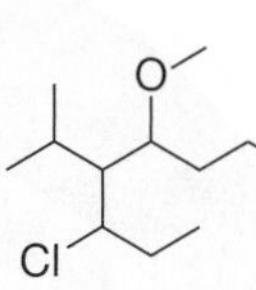
O
Cl

(c)
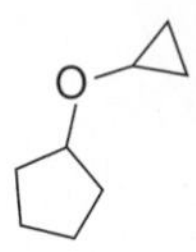
O

(d)
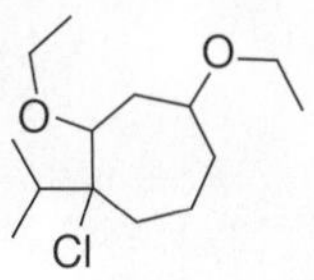
O
O
Cl

(e)
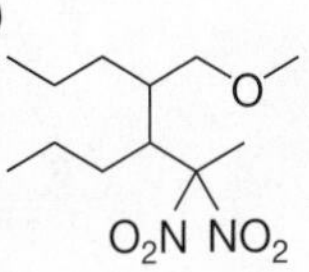
O
O2N NO2

(f)
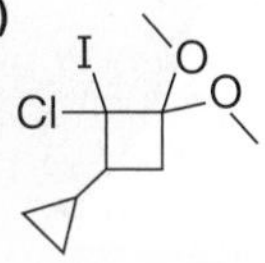
I
O
O
Cl

(g)
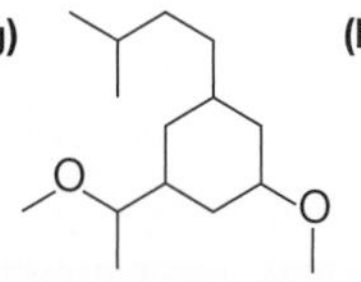
O
O

(h)
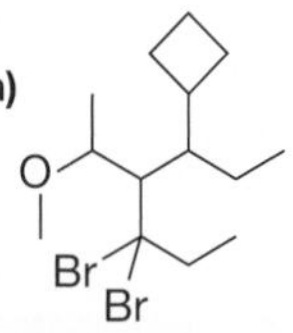
O
Br
Br

A.26 What is the IUPAC name for each of the following compounds?

(a)
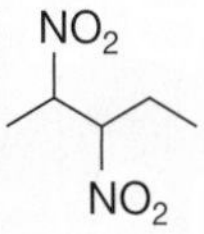
NO2
NO2

(b)
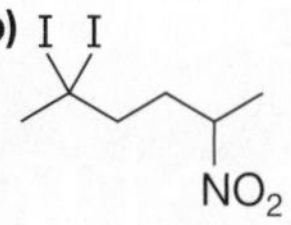
I I
NO2

(c)
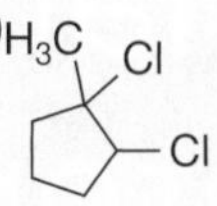
H3C
Cl
Cl

(d)
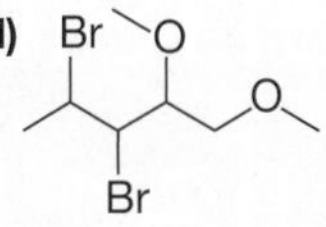
Br
O
O
Br

(e)
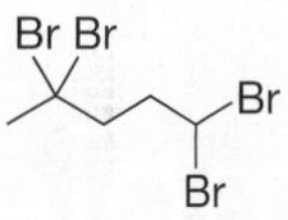
Br Br
Br
Br

(f)
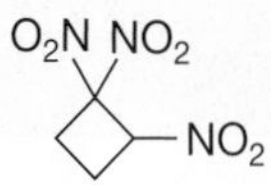
O2N NO2
NO2

(g)
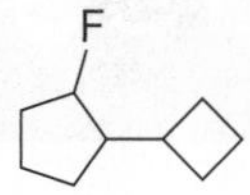
F

(h)
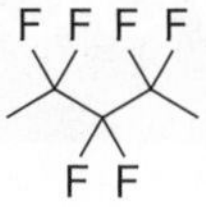
F F F F
F F

(i)
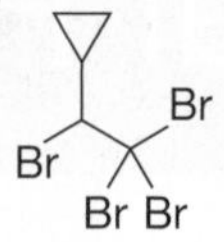
Br
Br
Br Br

(j)
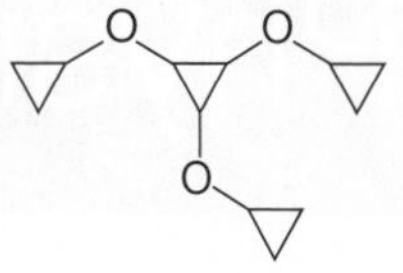
O
O
O

2

Geckos can climb effortlessly on almost every surface. Their ability to do so is attributed to ultrafine hairs on their feet, which give rise to a very large contact surface area. This allows for rather strong dispersion forces—an attraction that results from the interaction between the electron clouds surrounding the molecules on the gecko's feet and the molecules that make up the surface. Dispersion forces are one of the intermolecular interactions we examine in this chapter.

Three-Dimensional Geometry, Intermolecular Interactions, and Physical Properties

Carbon dioxide (CO_2) and methanoic acid (HCO_2H), also called formic acid, are similar in their chemical makeup, but as shown in **Figure 2-1**, the boiling point of CO_2 is −78 °C, whereas that of HCO_2H is 101 °C. Moreover, CO_2 is only slightly soluble in water, whereas HCO_2H is soluble in any proportion (infinitely soluble) in water. Why are their physical properties so vastly different?

As we discuss here in Chapter 2, compounds such as CO_2 and HCO_2H behave differently because they undergo different *intermolecular interactions*. Those

O═C═O
O
C
H
OH

Carbon dioxide	Methanoic acid (Formic acid)
Molar mass = 44 g/mol	Molar mass = 46 g/mol
Boiling point = –78 °C	Boiling point = 101 °C
Water solubility = slight	Water solubility = infinite

FIGURE 2-1 **Widely different physical properties of compounds with similar chemical makeup**

Chapter Outline

intermolecular interactions are governed, in turn, by a variety of factors, including the three-dimensional shapes of the molecules and the functional groups they contain. We begin, therefore, with a review of the factors that determine molecular geometry, and then we discuss the different types of intermolecular interactions that are important in organic chemistry.

Molecular geometry and intermolecular interactions explain many phenomena of organic chemistry. Toward the end of this chapter, for example, you will learn that intermolecular interactions determine how soaps function. You will also learn how the properties of cell membranes are governed by intermolecular interactions. In Chapter 5, we will explain how molecular geometry is central to the important concept of *chirality*—that is, whether a molecule is different from its mirror image. And, in Chapter 9, we will explain how intermolecular interactions can have a dramatic effect on the outcome of chemical reactions.

2.1 Valence Shell Electron Pair Repulsion (VSEPR) Theory: Three-Dimensional Geometry

SECTION 2.1 OBJECTIVES

You will be able to:

1. Outline the basic principles of VSEPR theory.
2. Predict the electron and molecular geometries of an atom within a given Lewis structure.

Chemists routinely use two different theories to explain molecular geometry: *valence shell electron pair repulsion (VSEPR) theory*, which we examine in this chapter, and *molecular orbital (MO) theory*, which we will deal with in Chapter 3. Although MO theory constitutes a more powerful model than VSEPR theory, VSEPR theory remains extremely useful because of its simplicity: Its concepts are easier to grasp, and it allows us to arrive at answers much more quickly.

Valence shell electron pair repulsion (VSEPR) theory is based on the following ideas:

1. Electrons in a Lewis structure are viewed as groups.
   - A lone pair of electrons, a single bond, a double bond, and a triple bond each constitute one *group* of electrons (Table 2-1).
2. The negatively charged electron groups strongly repel one another. Thus, they tend to arrange themselves as far away from each other as possible.
   - Two electron groups tend to be 180° apart (a linear configuration).
   - Three groups tend to be 120° apart (a trigonal planar configuration).
   - Four groups tend to be 109.5° apart (a tetrahedral configuration).

TABLE 2-1 Various Types of Electron Groups in VSEPR Theory

Type of Group	Total Number of e^-	Number of Groups
Lone pair	2	1
Single bond	2	1
Double bond	4	1
Triple bond	6	1

TABLE 2-2 Correlations between Electron Geometry and Bond Angle in VSEPR Theory

Number of Electron Groups	Electron Geometry	Approximate Bond Angle
2	 Linear	180°
3	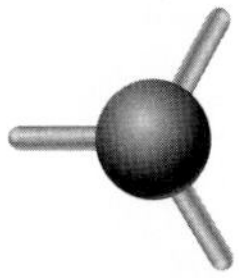 Trigonal planar	120°
4	 Tetrahedral	109.5°

3. **Electron geometry** describes the orientation of the *electron groups* about a particular atom. These configurations are summarized in Table 2-2.
4. **Molecular geometry** describes the arrangement of *atoms* about a particular atom. Because atoms must be attached by bonding pairs of electrons, an atom's molecular geometry is governed by its electron geometry.

Common molecular geometries are summarized in Table 2-3. Notice the following relationships between a molecule's electron geometry and its molecular geometry:

- If all the electron groups are bonds (depicted in gray), then the molecular geometry is the *same* as the electron geometry. This is because each bond has an attached atom, so a central atom's arrangements of its electron groups and its attached atoms are the same.
- If one or more of the electron groups is a lone pair (depicted in yellow, with red dots), then the molecular geometry is *different* than the electron geometry. This is because lone pairs do *not* have an attached atom.

TABLE 2-3 Molecular Geometries in VSEPR Theory[a]

	ELECTRON GEOMETRY		
Number of Bonded Atoms/Groups	Linear (180°)	Trigonal Planar (120°)	Tetrahedral (109.5°)
2	 Linear	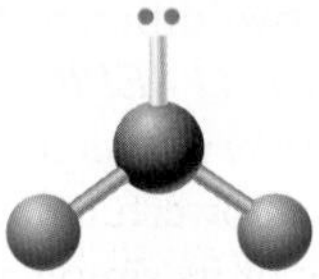 Bent	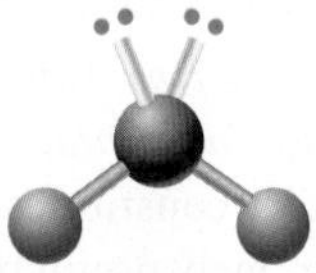 Bent
3		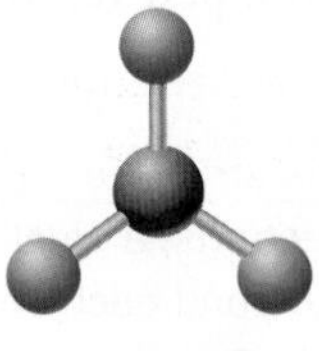 Trigonal planar	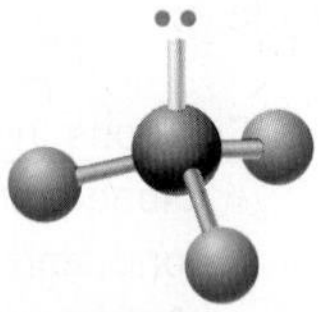 Trigonal pyramidal
4			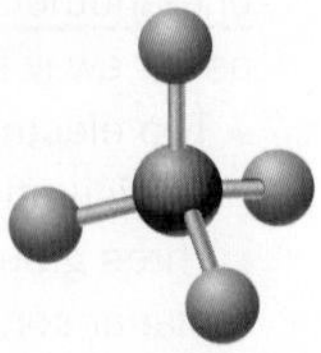 Tetrahedral

[a]Bonding electron groups are depicted with gray sticks; nonbonding electron groups are depicted as yellow sticks terminating in a red lone pair.

CONNECTIONS 2.1

Acetonitrile, acetone, and their uses Acetonitrile (Fig. 2-2a) is a polar organic solvent used in the manufacture of DNA oligonucleotides and numerous pharmaceuticals. Acetone (Fig. 2-2b) is another organic solvent. Acetone can dissolve hardened nail polish, which is why it is the active ingredient in nail polish remover. Ethane (Fig. 2-2c) is a gas that is important in the petrochemical industry.

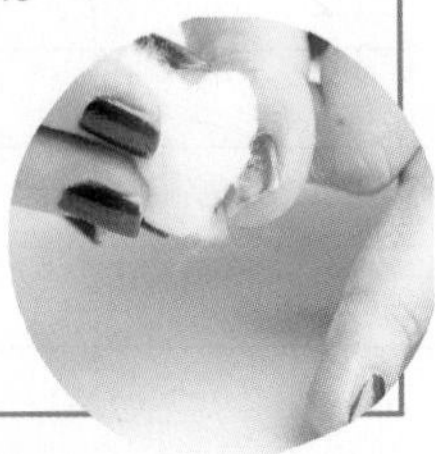

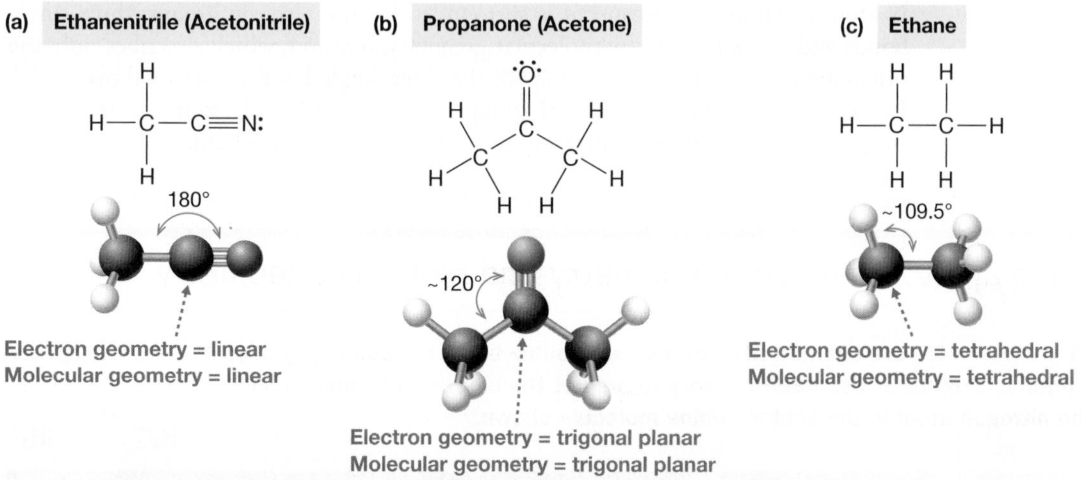
(a) Ethanenitrile (Acetonitrile)
180°
Electron geometry = linear
Molecular geometry = linear
(b) Propanone (Acetone)
~120°
Electron geometry = trigonal planar
Molecular geometry = trigonal planar
(c) Ethane
~109.5°
Electron geometry = tetrahedral
Molecular geometry = tetrahedral

FIGURE 2-2 Compounds in which the central atom lacks lone pairs Because there are no lone pairs about the central atom, the molecular geometries of (a) ethanenitrile (acetonitrile), (b) propanone (acetone), and (c) ethane are identical to their electron geometries.

Some examples of molecules containing central atoms without lone pairs are shown in **Figure 2-2**. The electron and molecular geometries of these central atoms are the same.

YOUR TURN 2.1

How many electron groups surround **(a)** the triply bonded C in Figure 2-2a, **(b)** the central C in Figure 2-2b, and **(c)** each C atom in Figure 2-2c?

Answers to Your Turns are in the back of the book.

Notice that each molecule in Figure 2-2 has more than one atom that can be described by an electron geometry and a molecular geometry. This is explored in Your Turn 2.2.

YOUR TURN 2.2

What is the electron geometry that describes the CH_3 carbon in ethanenitrile (Fig. 2-2a)? What is that atom's molecular geometry? What is the approximate H—C—C bond angle?

In 2-aminoethanol (ethanolamine, **Figure 2-3**), the molecular geometries of the N and O atoms are different than their electron geometries. The electron geometry of the

CONNECTIONS 2.2

2-Aminoethanol and its uses
2-Aminoethanol (Fig. 2-3) is commonly used in the production of a variety of industrial compounds, including shampoos and detergents. It is also used as an injectable treatment for hemorrhoids.

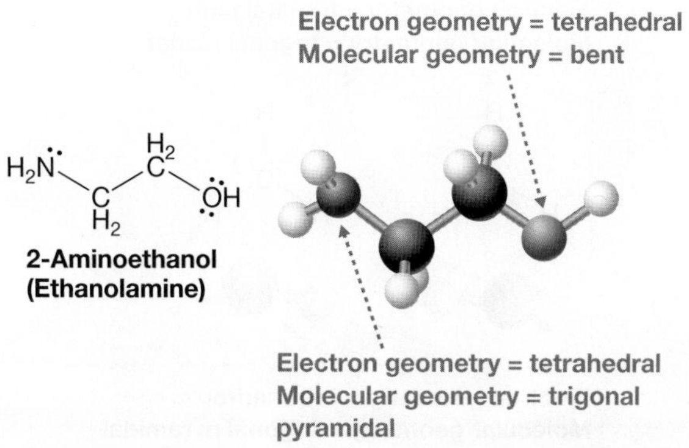
2-Aminoethanol
(Ethanolamine)
Electron geometry = tetrahedral
Molecular geometry = bent
Electron geometry = tetrahedral
Molecular geometry = trigonal pyramidal

FIGURE 2-3 Lewis structure and VSEPR geometries about the atoms in 2-aminoethanol The electron geometries about the NH_2 nitrogen and the OH oxygen atoms are both tetrahedral, but they have different molecular geometries because N has one lone pair and O has two.

N atom is tetrahedral because it is surrounded by four electron groups: three single bonds and one lone pair. Its molecular geometry, however, which describes only the orientation of the atoms at the ends of the three single bonds, is trigonal pyramidal. Likewise, the O atom of the OH group has a tetrahedral electron geometry (two single bonds and two lone pairs), but its molecular geometry is bent.

SOLVED PROBLEM **2.1**

How to determine an atom's electron geometry and molecular geometry

Break It Down Imines, which are characterized by a C=N double bond, are commonly used as intermediates in organic synthesis. Use VSEPR theory to predict the electron and molecular geometries about the nitrogen atom in the acetone imine molecule shown.

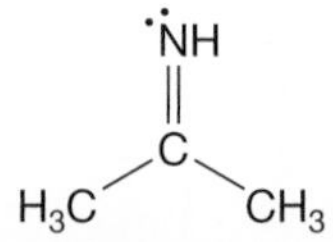
NH
C
H3C
CH3

Think	Solve
How many electron groups surround the N atom? What does that suggest about the electron geometry?	Three electron groups surround the nitrogen atom: one double bond, one single bond, and one lone pair. From Table 2-2, we therefore predict a trigonal planar electron geometry.
Are any electron groups lone pairs? How does that impact the molecular geometry of N?	One of the electron groups on N is a lone pair, so the molecular and electronic geometries will not be the same. According to Table 2-3, the N atom's molecular geometry is bent.

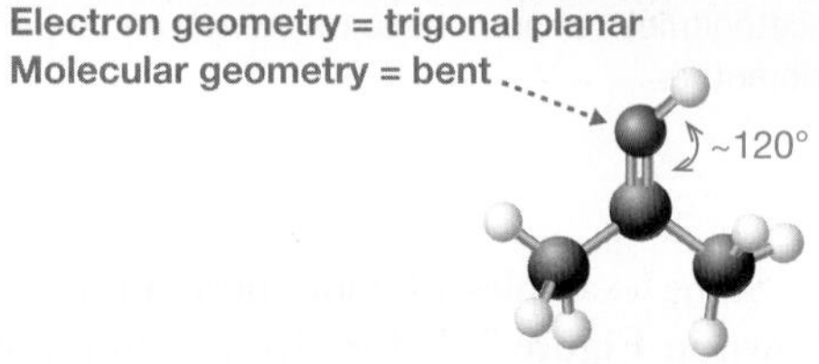
Electron geometry = trigonal planar
Molecular geometry = bent
~120°

Try It Prop-2-yn-1-ol (propargyl alcohol) is used as an intermediate in organic synthesis and can be polymerized to make poly(propargyl alcohol), a polymer that has been studied for use in humidity detectors. Use VSEPR theory to predict the electron and molecular geometries about each nonhydrogen atom in the molecule.

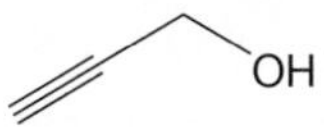
OH

Prop-2-yn-1-ol (Propargyl alcohol)

Answers to all Try It exercises can be found in the Solutions Manual.

The rules of VSEPR theory apply equally well to ions. **Figure 2-4a** shows, for example, that the methyl cation, CH_3^+, has a trigonal planar electron geometry, consistent with a carbon atom that is surrounded by three groups of electrons (i.e., three single bonds). The methyl anion (Fig. 2-4b), on the other hand, is surrounded by four groups of electrons (i.e., three single bonds and a lone pair). Its electron geometry, therefore, is tetrahedral, and its molecular geometry is trigonal pyramidal.

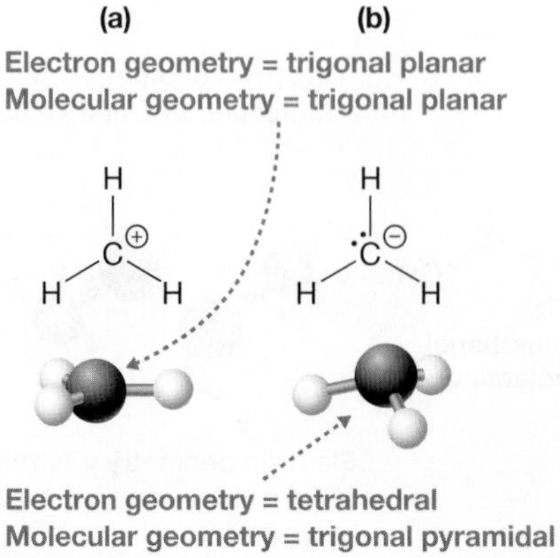
(a)
(b)
Electron geometry = trigonal planar
Molecular geometry = trigonal planar
H
C
H
H
H
C
H
H
Electron geometry = tetrahedral
Molecular geometry = trigonal pyramidal

FIGURE 2-4 **Lewis structures and three-dimensional geometries of the methyl cation and methyl anion** (a) The central C atom in CH_3^+ is surrounded by three single bonds only (i.e., no lone pairs), so its electron and molecular geometries are the same. (b) The central C atom in CH_3^-, on the other hand, is surrounded by three single bonds and one lone pair, so its electron and molecular geometries are different.

YOUR TURN **2.3**

Circle each electron group in the Lewis structures of CH_3^+ and CH_3^- in Figure 2-4.

2.2 Dash–Wedge Notation

SECTION 2.2 OBJECTIVES

You will be able to:

1. Outline the basic rules of dash–wedge notation.
2. Use dash–wedge notation to accurately depict the three-dimensional nature of tetrahedral atoms.

Molecules are three-dimensional, but the page on which we draw them is two-dimensional. To work around this problem, chemists use **dash–wedge notation** (see Looking Ahead box), which allows us to represent atoms both in front of and behind the plane of the paper. Dash–wedge notation has three basic rules:

Rules for Dash–Wedge Notation

1. A straight line (——) represents a bond that lies in the plane of the page.
   - Atoms at either end of the bond are also in the plane of the page.
2. A wedge (◀) represents a bond that points toward you.
   - In general, the atom at the thinner end of the wedge is in the plane of the page, whereas the atom bonded at the thicker end is in front of the page.
3. A dash (┈┈) represents a bond that points away from you.
   - In general, you may assume in this book that the atom bonded at the thicker end of the dash is behind the plane of the page. (You may see different conventions in other books.)

▸ LOOKING AHEAD

In Chapter 5, we will see how dash–wedge notation is used to distinguish *stereoisomers*, which are types of isomers that differ by the spatial arrangements of their atoms. Distinguishing stereoisomers is important, especially because they can have vastly different properties in the body.

Using dash–wedge notation, **Figure 2-5** shows two ways to represent the tetrahedral atom in CH_4. Both illustrations represent the same molecule with the same 109.5° bond angles. The only difference is the vantage point from which you view the molecule. Figure 2-5a is the most common representation, whereas Figure 2-5b is the basis for a shorthand notation of tetrahedral carbon atoms, called the *Fischer projection*, which we will introduce in Chapter 5.

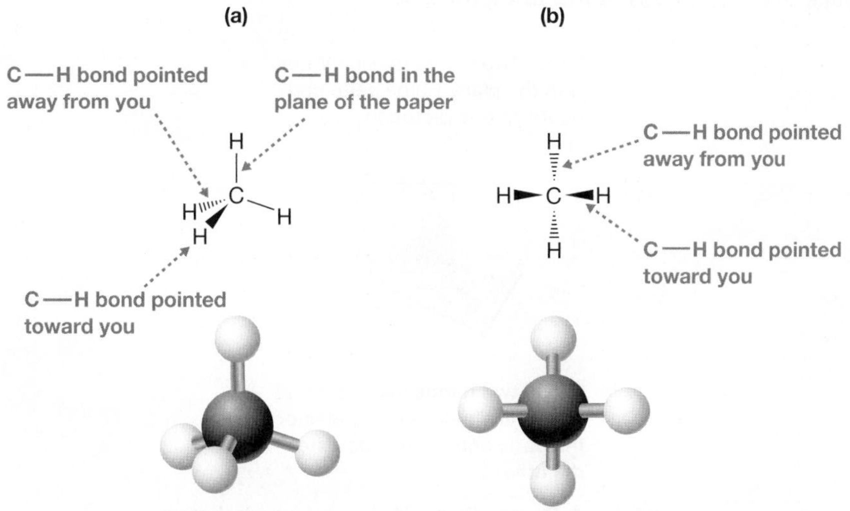
(a)
(b)
C—H bond pointed away from you
C—H bond in the plane of the paper
C—H bond pointed toward you
C—H bond pointed away from you
C—H bond pointed toward you

FIGURE 2-5 Representations of CH_4 using dash–wedge notation The two different depictions in parts (a) and (b) imply views of the same molecule from different vantage points.

YOUR TURN **2.4**

Ball-and-stick representations of NH_4^+ from two different vantage points are provided. Next to each one, draw the corresponding cation using dash–wedge notation.

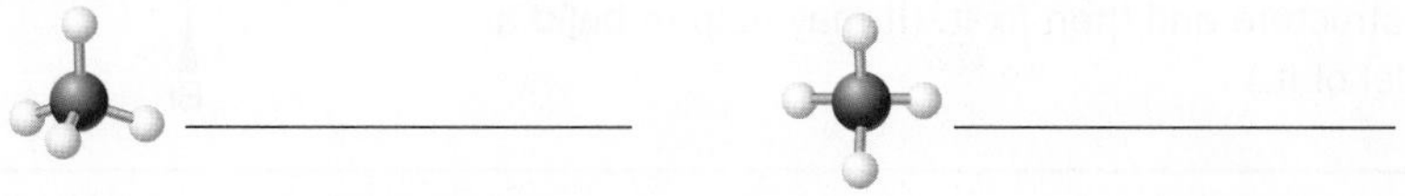

CONNECTIONS 2.3

Butan-2-ol and its use in industry Butan-2-ol (Fig. 2-6) is used industrially as a precursor to butan-2-one, which has applications as an industrial solvent and as a welding agent for connecting polystyrene parts of scale models.

Dash–wedge notation can be combined with line structures to illustrate the three-dimensional geometry of more complex molecules such as butan-2-ol, shown in **Figure 2-6**.

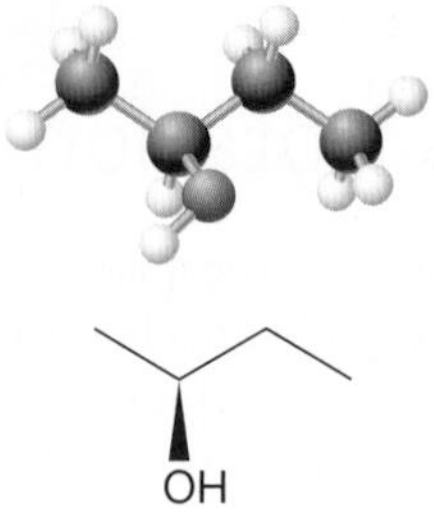
OH
Butan-2-ol

FIGURE 2-6 Line structures combined with dash–wedge notation The line structure indicates a chain of four tetrahedral carbon atoms. The wedge indicates that the bond to OH points toward you.

YOUR TURN 2.5

In the box provided, draw the line structure of butan-2-ol using dash–wedge notation. Note that the C—O bond points away from you.

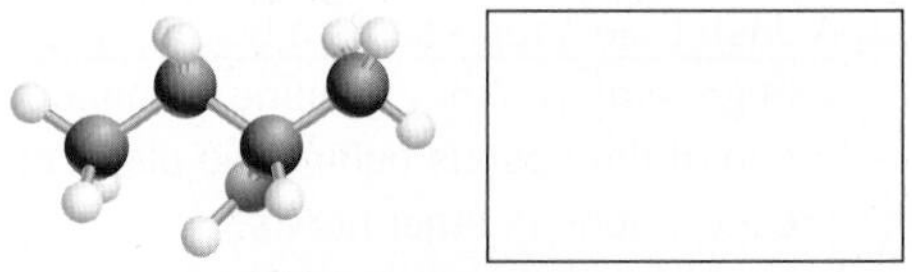

When drawing the dash–wedge notation for a tetrahedral atom, it is important to add the dash and wedge bonds accurately. Looking back at Figure 2-5a, notice that only two of the four bonds can be in the plane of the page. One of the remaining two bonds points toward you, and it is in front of the final bond that points away. To remember this, it helps to see that the four bonds make up two Vs that are perpendicular to each other, as shown in **Figure 2-7**.

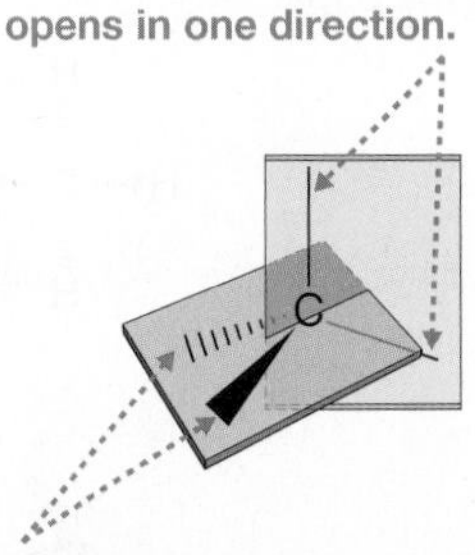
These two bonds make a V that is in the plane of the page and opens in one direction.
C
These two bonds make a V that is perpendicular to the plane of the page and opens opposite the other V.

FIGURE 2-7 Perpendicular Vs in a tetrahedral atom

YOUR TURN 2.6

A common mistake is made in the dash–wedge notation at the right. Explain what is incorrect about the structure and then fix it. (It may help to build a model of it.)

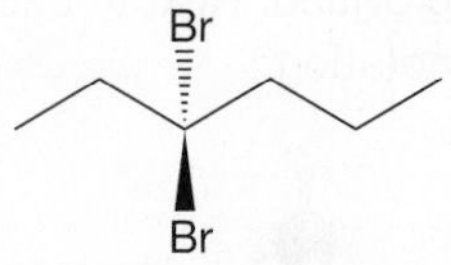
Br
Br

2.3 Strategies for Success: The Molecular Modeling Kit

SECTION 2.3 OBJECTIVES

You will be able to:

1. Construct a molecular model accurately, given the dash–wedge notation of a molecule.
2. Use a molecular model to help draw the dash–wedge notation of a molecule accurately.

Strategies for Success
The Molecular Modeling Kit

Much of organic chemistry requires us to manipulate molecules in three dimensions. Unfortunately, we are limited to two dimensions when we represent a molecule on paper, even when we use dash–wedge notation. **Molecular modeling kits** can help. Instead of having to rotate a three-dimensional image mentally, you can construct real models and rotate them in your hands. For example, let's use a modeling kit to determine what the following cyclopentane derivative looks like after it has been flipped over vertically.

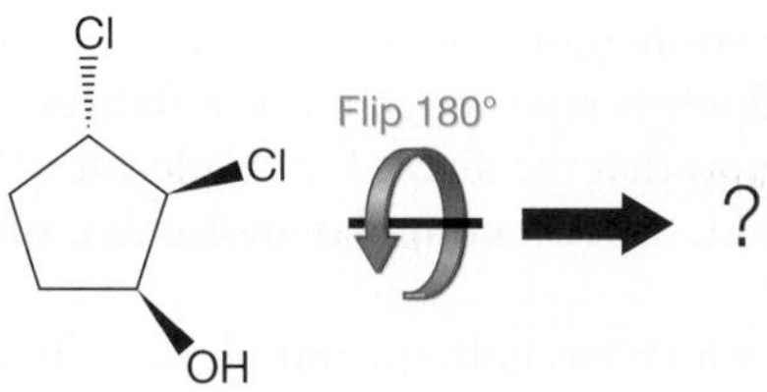

Cl
Cl
OH
Flip 180°
?

(2-1)

You may develop your own process for these kinds of manipulations, but for now carry out the following steps, which are depicted in **Figure 2-8**:

1. Construct the molecular model exactly as indicated in the accurate dash–wedge notation.
2. Change the orientation of the molecule as indicated.
3. Redraw the molecule in its dash–wedge notation, using the reoriented model as a guide.

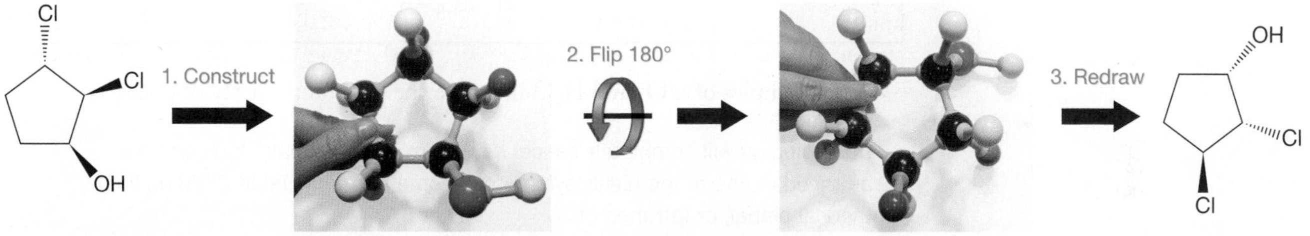

Cl
Cl
OH
1. Construct
2. Flip 180°
3. Redraw
OH
Cl
Cl

FIGURE 2-8 Modeling kits and 3-D manipulations To draw the molecule in Equation 2-1 after it is flipped 180°, follow these steps: (1) Construct the molecule with a modeling kit, (2) flip the molecule over 180°, and (3) use the model as a guide to redraw the molecule in dash–wedge notation.

YOUR TURN **2.7**

Construct the molecule shown here, using a molecular modeling kit, and then draw its structure using dash–wedge notation after each successive 180° flip.

Cl
Cl
OH
180°
180°

SECTION 2.4 OBJECTIVES

You will be able to:

1. Explain how molecules with polar covalent bonds can be nonpolar overall.
2. Determine whether a molecule with polar covalent bonds will be polar or nonpolar.

2.4 Net Molecular Dipoles

Recall from Section 1.7 that a *polar covalent bond* arises when atoms having different electronegativities are bonded together, and the resulting bond dipole points toward the more electronegative atom. If there is only one polar covalent bond in the entire molecule, as in HF (**Figure 2-9a**), then the molecule will have a **net molecular dipole**, or **permanent dipole**. That is, one end of the molecule bears a partial positive charge and the other end bears a partial negative charge of equal magnitude. In HF, the partial negative charge builds up on the side with the fluorine atom (electronegativity = 3.98; see Fig. 1-18, p. 16), while the partial positive charge is left in the vicinity of the hydrogen atom (electronegativity = 2.20), so the net molecular dipole points toward F and the entire molecule is **polar** (see Looking Ahead box).

The *magnitude* of a dipole is reported in units of **debyes** (D). To get a feel for this type of unit, it helps to know that the dipole for a molecule of HF, which is quite polar, has a magnitude of 1.8 D. Strictly **nonpolar** molecules, such as H_2, have a dipole magnitude of 0 D.

A dipole is a **vector**, which has both magnitude and direction, so we arrive at the net dipole of a molecule by adding the vectors of the bond dipoles together. CO_2 (Fig. 2-9b), for example, is nonpolar, despite having two polar covalent bonds. CO_2 is linear and symmetrical, so the two C═O bond dipoles point in exactly opposite directions, resulting in complete cancellation. Water (Fig. 2-9c), on the other hand, is polar because its two bond dipoles do not point in exactly opposite directions.

▸ LOOKING AHEAD

As we will learn in Chapter 7, the distribution of charge within a molecule, which describes polarity, is a major factor that controls how molecules participate in chemical reactions. Specifically, we will see that many reactions are driven by the attractive force between sites that have opposite charges.

YOUR TURN 2.8

Like CO_2, BeH_2 is a linear nonpolar molecule. Using the structure shown, draw dipole arrows above each Be—H bond. (For the necessary electronegativity values, see Fig. 1-18, p. 16.)

H—Be—H

The examples of CO_2 and H_2O illustrate the general property of polarity:

Bond dipoles will completely cancel if they are of equal magnitude and are arranged in one of the highly symmetric geometries from Table 2-2 (i.e., linear, trigonal planar, or tetrahedral).

CONNECTIONS 2.4

Tetrachloromethane and its uses in the past Historically, CCl_4 (Fig. 2-10a) was a common organic solvent and was also used widely as a pesticide and in fire extinguishers like this one. We now know, however, that substantial exposure to CCl_4 causes acute liver failure and other severe health problems, including cancer, so these uses have largely been phased out.

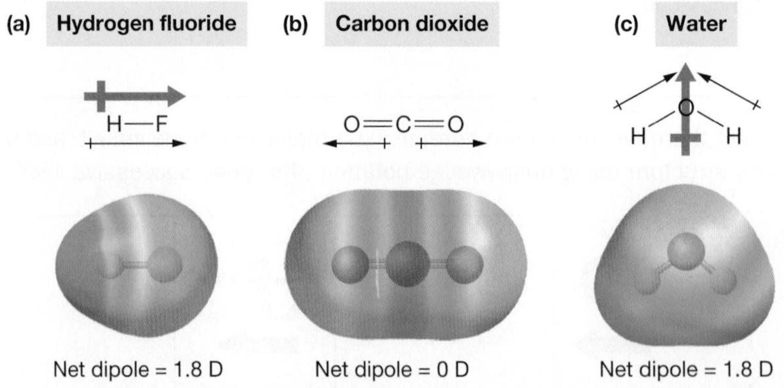

(a) Hydrogen fluoride
(b) Carbon dioxide
(c) Water
H—F
O═C═O
O
H
H
Net dipole = 1.8 D
Net dipole = 0 D
Net dipole = 1.8 D

FIGURE 2-9 Bond dipoles and net molecular dipoles Bond dipoles are shown as thin black arrows, and net molecular dipoles are shown as thick red arrows. (a) HF is a polar molecule. The net dipole points toward the F atom and has a magnitude of 1.8 D. (b) CO_2 is nonpolar, because the two C═O bond dipoles point in exactly opposite directions and completely cancel by vector addition. (c) Water is a polar molecule. The net dipole points from midway between the H atoms toward the O atom and has a magnitude of 1.8 D.

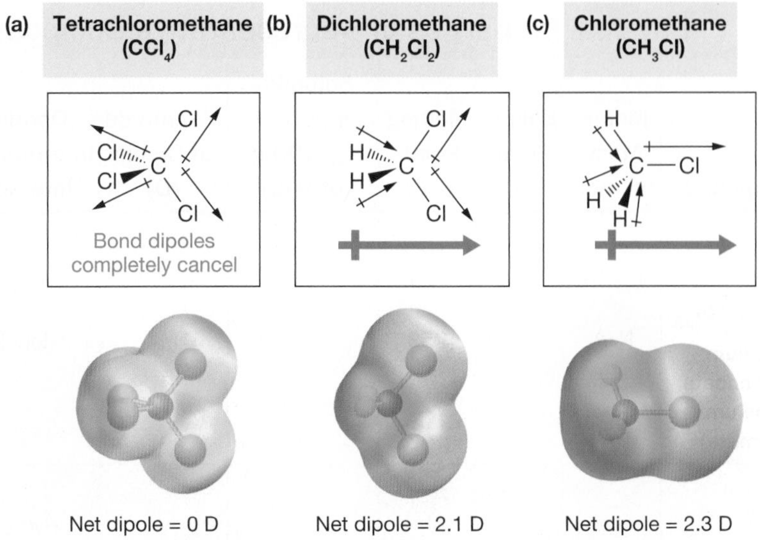
(a) Tetrachloromethane (CCl_4)
(b) Dichloromethane (CH_2Cl_2)
(c) Chloromethane (CH_3Cl)
Bond dipoles completely cancel
Net dipole = 0 D
Net dipole = 2.1 D
Net dipole = 2.3 D

FIGURE 2-10 Vector addition of bond dipoles in tetrahedral molecules (a) Tetrachloromethane, (b) dichloromethane, and (c) chloromethane all have a tetrahedral molecular geometry. Individual bond dipoles are shown as thin black arrows in the top row, and the net molecular dipole is indicated by the thick red arrow. The bottom row shows the electrostatic potential map of each species.

CONNECTIONS 2.5

Dichloromethane and its uses
CH_2Cl_2 (Fig. 2-10b), commonly called methylene chloride, has uses as a paint stripper and degreaser and has been used in the food industry to decaffeinate coffee. Because of its low boiling point, it is used as the liquid inside the "drinking bird" toy.

CONNECTIONS 2.6

Chloromethane and its uses
CH_3Cl (Fig. 2-10c) was once used as a refrigerant, but this is no longer the case due to its toxicity and flammability. Nowadays, it finds use as a local anesthetic and as an herbicide.

We can see how this idea applies to CCl_4, CH_2Cl_2, and CH_3Cl (all of which are tetrahedral molecules) as shown in **Figure 2-10**. Only CCl_4 (Fig. 2-10a) is nonpolar because the four C—Cl bond dipoles are equal in magnitude and are arranged in a tetrahedron. By contrast, the bond dipoles of the polar C—Cl bonds in CH_2Cl_2 (Fig. 2-10b) and CH_3Cl (Fig. 2-10c) do not completely cancel. In CH_2Cl_2, the two C—Cl bonds are arranged in a bent geometry, and CH_3Cl has just one bond with significant polarity, the C—Cl bond.

YOUR TURN **2.9**

A molecule of CF_4 is shown with dash–wedge notation. Draw the bond dipoles along each of the C—F bonds and determine whether the molecule is polar.

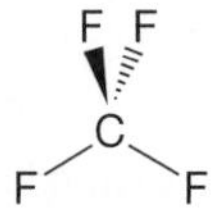

2.5 Physical Properties, Functional Groups, and Intermolecular Interactions

SECTION 2.5 OBJECTIVES

You will be able to:

1. Determine whether compounds of similar size have similar physical properties on the basis of the functional groups they possess.
2. Explain how charge concentration within a species impacts the strength of the intermolecular interactions in which it can participate.

Now that we have reviewed some of the basic concepts of molecular geometry and polarity, it's time to explore how these factors affect the physical properties of compounds. We can begin to understand these influences by examining the boiling points, melting points, and water solubilities of some representative compounds, as shown in Table 2-4.

All of the compounds in Table 2-4 are covalent except sodium methanoate (sodium formate, $Na^+ \; ^-OCH{=}O$), which is ionic. The covalent compounds are all similar in size, shape, and molar mass, with the exception of ethane, which is roughly 30% lighter. Differences in their physical properties must therefore be due mainly to differences in the *functional groups* present:

The functional groups in a compound can significantly influence its physical properties.

CONNECTIONS 2.7

Sodium methanoate and its uses Sodium methanoate (sodium formate, Table 2-4) is used as a dye activator in fabric and leather dyeing processes because it helps promote the fixation of a dye to the material. It has also been used in the food industry as a preservative and flavor enhancer.

CONNECTIONS 2.8

Methanoic acid in nature and its industrial uses Methanoic acid (formic acid, Table 2-4) is found in the venom of ants, and it also has several uses in industry and agriculture. It is used in the production of leather and in dyeing textiles, and it is also used to treat animal feed because of its properties as a preservative and an antibacterial agent.

TABLE 2-4 Physical Properties of Representative Compounds

Compound	Molar Mass (g/mol)	Boiling Point (°C)	Melting Point (°C)	Solubility in Water (g/100 g of H_2O)	Magnitude of Dipole (D)	Dominant Intermolecular Interaction
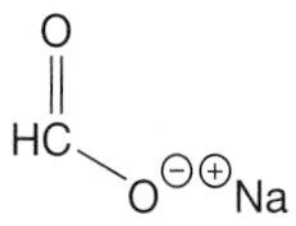 **Sodium methanoate (Sodium formate)**	N/A	>253	253	77	N/A	Ion–ion
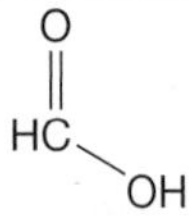 Methanoic acid (Formic acid)	46	101	8	Infinite	1.4	Hydrogen bonding
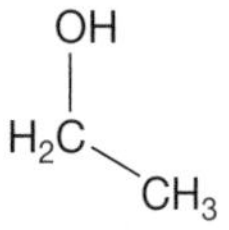 Ethanol	46	78	−114	Infinite	1.7	Hydrogen bonding
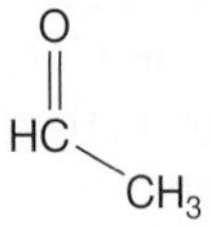 Ethanal (Acetaldehyde)	44	20	−117	>100	3.0	Dipole–dipole
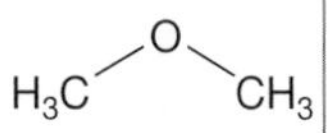 Methoxymethane (Dimethyl ether)	46	−25	−139	6.9	1.3	Dipole–dipole
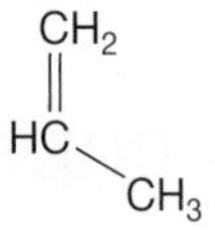 Propene	42	−48	−185	0.00061	0.3	Induced dipole–induced dipole
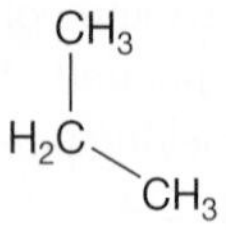 Propane	44	−45	−188	0.00039	0	Induced dipole–induced dipole
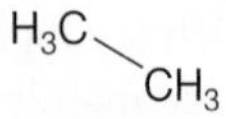 Ethane	30	−89	−183	0.006	0	Induced dipole–induced dipole

YOUR TURN **2.10**

Circle the functional group that is present in each covalent compound in Table 2-4 and identify the compound class to which each molecule belongs.

Why do functional groups have such a profound effect on the physical properties of organic compounds? Functional groups can differ in the atoms they possess or in the arrangement of those atoms in space, both of which will impact how charge is distributed within a molecule. Charge distribution will in turn affect **intermolecular interactions** (also called **intermolecular forces**), which are the ways in which various species attract (or repel) each other. We will examine the following types of intermolecular interactions:

- ion–ion interactions
- dipole–dipole interactions
- hydrogen bonding
- induced dipole–induced dipole interactions (or London dispersion forces)
- ion–dipole interactions

The first four of these intermolecular interactions are discussed in Sections 2.6a–d in the context of boiling points and melting points. We will examine the fifth and final intermolecular interaction in Section 2.7a in the context of a compound's solubility in a given solvent.

Although they have different names, intermolecular interactions all originate from the same fundamental law: *opposite charges attract*. As a result, the strength of each intermolecular interaction depends on the concentrations of charge involved:

All else being equal, the greater the concentrations of charge that are involved in an intermolecular interaction, the stronger is the resulting attraction.

2.6 Melting Points, Boiling Points, and Intermolecular Interactions

SECTION 2.6 OBJECTIVES

You will be able to:

1. Identify the following types of intermolecular interactions in a pair of interacting species: ion–ion, dipole–dipole, hydrogen bonding, or London dispersion.
2. Determine the dominant type of intermolecular interaction between a pair of interacting species.
3. Evaluate the relative strengths of intermolecular interactions in different pairs of interacting species when each pair has the same dominant type of interaction.

Melting points and boiling points can provide a wealth of information about intermolecular interactions. To help you see why, review the molecular-level representations of solid, liquid, and gas in **Figure 2-11** (next page).

- Solid. The atoms, ions, or molecules that make up the compound are in contact with one another and are essentially immobile. This allows intermolecular interactions to be maximized.
- Liquid. The species that make up the compound are in close contact, but they can rotate and slide past one another, so intermolecular interactions are less substantial than in a solid.
- Gas. The species that make up the compound are far apart and are effectively isolated from one another, so they can move freely. Intermolecular interactions are essentially nonexistent.

Melting, therefore, decreases the intermolecular interactions that exist in the solid phase, and boiling disrupts the remaining intermolecular interactions that exist in the liquid phase. Consequently, as the strength of the intermolecular interactions that exist in a particular substance increases, more energy (in the form of heat) is required for the substance to melt or boil:

- Melting points increase as the intermolecular interactions in a solid increase.
- Boiling points increase as the intermolecular interactions in a liquid increase.

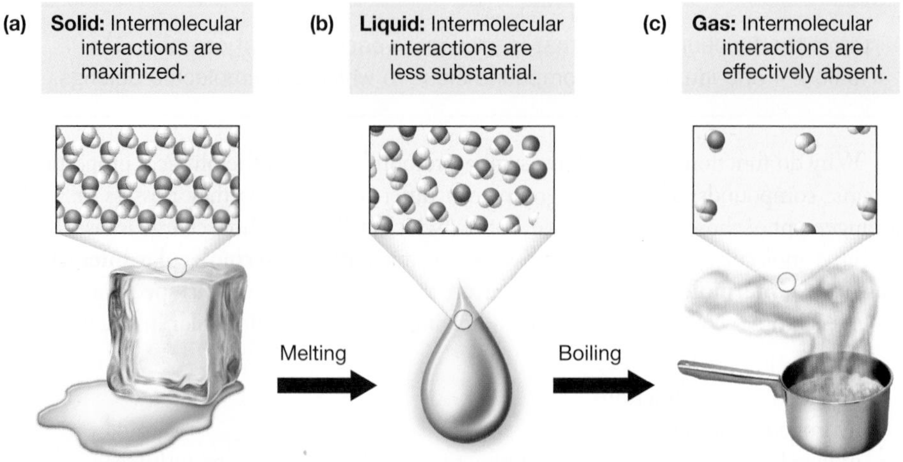
(a) Solid: Intermolecular interactions are maximized.
(b) Liquid: Intermolecular interactions are less substantial.
(c) Gas: Intermolecular interactions are effectively absent.
Melting
Boiling

FIGURE 2-11 Molecular-level representations of the three phases of matter (a) In a crystalline solid, molecules or ions form a well-ordered structure called a crystal lattice, in which movement is limited to vibration and intermolecular forces are maximized. (b) In a liquid, molecules are free to move around, because intermolecular forces are somewhat less substantial. (c) In the gas phase, molecules are so far apart that intermolecular forces are effectively absent.

Let's now apply these ideas to interpret the relative strengths of various types of intermolecular interactions.

2.6a Ion–Ion Interactions

Of all the compounds in Table 2-4 on page 78, sodium methanoate (sodium formate, $Na^+ \ ^-OCH{=}O$) has the highest melting point and boiling point, suggesting that it has particularly strong intermolecular attractions in both its solid and liquid phases. Sodium methanoate is an ionic compound, composed of Na^+ and HCO_2^- ions, held together (as we saw in Section 1.8) by the electrostatic attraction of oppositely charged ions (that is, by ionic bonds) or, more generally, by **ion–ion interactions**:

Ion–ion interactions are the strongest type of intermolecular interaction because ions have very high concentrations of positive and negative charge.

2.6b Dipole–Dipole Interactions

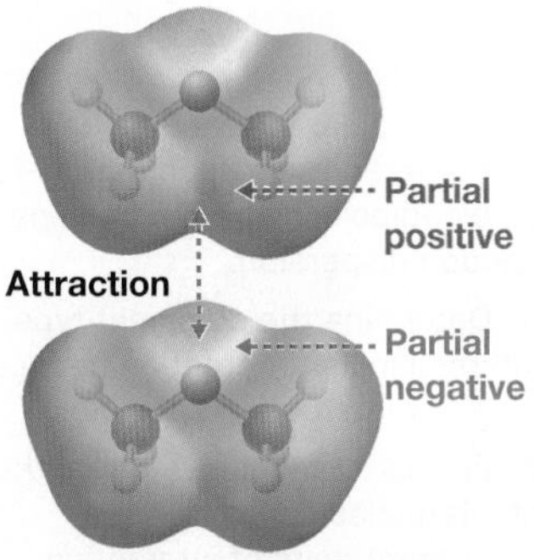
Partial positive
Attraction
Partial negative

FIGURE 2-12 Dipole–dipole interaction The dominant intermolecular force between two molecules of dimethyl ether is a dipole–dipole interaction. The positive end of one ether molecule attracts the negative end of the other.

Referring again to Table 2-4, notice that the compounds with significant dipoles—methanoic acid (formic acid), ethanol, ethanal (acetaldehyde), and methoxymethane (dimethyl ether)—have boiling points and melting points that are significantly higher than those of the remaining compounds, which are essentially nonpolar:

Polar molecules are attracted to each other more strongly than similar nonpolar molecules.

The stronger attractions among polar molecules are due to dipole–dipole interactions. **Dipole–dipole interactions** arise because the positive end of one molecule's *net dipole* is attracted to the negative end of another molecule's net dipole, as shown in **Figure 2-12**. Therefore:

All other factors being equal, the strength of dipole–dipole interactions increases as the magnitude of the dipole increases.

Notice in Table 2-4, for example, that the highly polar ethanal ($CH_3CH{=}O$) has a higher melting point and a higher boiling point than the less polar dimethyl ether (CH_3OCH_3).

YOUR TURN **2.11**

The boiling point of CH_3CH_2F is -37.1 °C. How does this compare to the boiling point of $CH_3CH{=}O$? Which compound, therefore, is more polar?

Although dipole–dipole interactions can be quite strong, they involve the attraction of *partial* charges, which are smaller in magnitude than the *full* charges in ion–ion interactions. Therefore:

Dipole–dipole interactions are generally much weaker than ion–ion interactions.

As a result, compounds such as ethanal (acetaldehyde) melt and boil at lower temperatures than ionic compounds.

SOLVED PROBLEM **2.2**

How to determine relative melting points of an ionic versus a covalent compound

Break It Down **Which compound has the higher melting point, $NaOCH_2CH_3$ or $CH_3CH{=}O$?**

Think	Solve
What is the strongest intermolecular interaction in $NaOCH_2CH_3$?	$NaOCH_2CH_3$ is an ionic compound. It consists of Na^+ and $CH_3CH_2O^-$, which are held together by ion–ion interactions.
What is the strongest intermolecular interaction in $CH_3CH{=}O$?	$CH_3CH{=}O$ is a polar covalent compound, so it experiences dipole–dipole interactions.
Which type of interaction is stronger? How does that affect the melting point?	Ion–ion interactions are stronger than dipole–dipole interactions, so the melting point of $NaOCH_2CH_3$ is higher than the melting point of $CH_3CH{=}O$.

Try It Which compound in each pair has the higher melting point? **(a)** $NaSCH_3$ or CH_3CH_2OH; **(b)** $(CH_3)_2C{=}NCH_3$ or $(CH_3)_2C{=}NK$

2.6c Hydrogen Bonding

Dipole–dipole interactions alone cannot account for some of the data for polar compounds in Table 2-4. Methanoic acid (formic acid, HCO_2H) and ethanol (CH_3CH_2OH), for example, have substantially higher melting points and boiling points than ethanal (acetaldehyde, $CH_3CH{=}O$), even though ethanal's net dipole is the largest of the three. These apparent anomalies arise because methanoic acid and ethanol can form *hydrogen bonds*, whereas acetaldehyde cannot.

Each **hydrogen bond** (H-bond) requires a *hydrogen-bond donor* and a *hydrogen-bond acceptor*, as shown in **Figure 2-13**.

- A **hydrogen-bond donor** is a covalent bond, Do—H, where Do (donor) is a highly electronegative atom, such as N, O, or F.
- A **hydrogen-bond acceptor**, A, can be any atom with a large concentration of negative charge and a lone pair of electrons. For the hydrogen bond to be substantial, an uncharged H-bond acceptor must be F, O, or N.

The high electronegativity of the F, O, or N atom ensures that the Do—H covalent bond is highly polar, giving the H atom a large partial positive charge. This sets up a strong attraction between the H atom and the oppositely charged acceptor.

The actual H-bond is created when a lone pair of electrons on the H-bond acceptor is shared with the hydrogen atom of the H-bond donor. In this book, the H-bond is depicted by a red hashed line. **Figure 2-14** (next page) shows how hydrogen bonding might be depicted between two molecules of ethanol (Fig. 2-14a) and

CONNECTIONS 2.9

Ethanol and its uses Ethanol (Table 2-4) is probably most commonly known as the alcohol found in alcoholic beverages, but it is also an important organic solvent, fuel, and antiseptic.

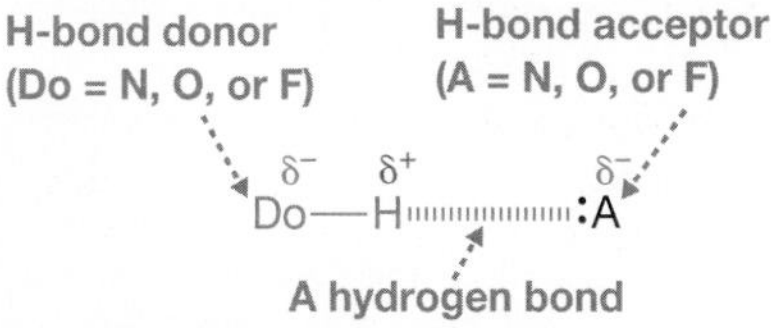

H-bond donor
(Do = N, O, or F)
H-bond acceptor
(A = N, O, or F)
δ− δ+ δ−
Do—H:A
A hydrogen bond

FIGURE 2-13 **Hydrogen bonds** A hydrogen bond consists of a hydrogen-bond donor (Do—H) and a hydrogen-bond acceptor (A). If the Do and A atoms are uncharged, they must be nitrogen, oxygen, or fluorine for the hydrogen bond to be substantial.

FIGURE 2-14 **Hydrogen bonding between ethanol molecules and between methanoic acid molecules** (a) A hydrogen bond can form between two molecules of ethanol because the H atom is covalently bonded to an O atom in one molecule and is attracted to the second molecule's O atom, which has a lone pair of electrons and a significant partial negative charge. The H-bond is indicated by a red hashed line. (b) Two different H-bonds are shown between two molecules of methanoic acid (formic acid).

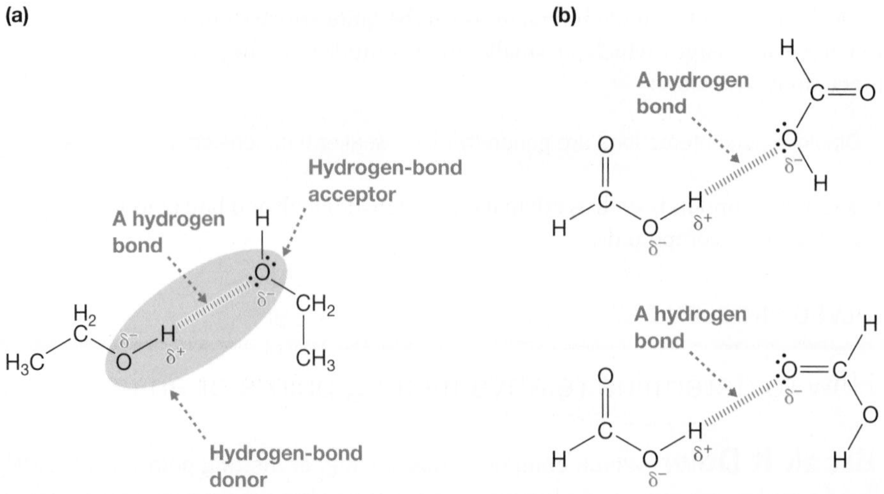

(a)
A hydrogen bond
Hydrogen-bond acceptor
Hydrogen-bond donor
(b)
A hydrogen bond
A hydrogen bond

between two molecules of methanoic acid (Fig. 2-14b). Notice that either O atom in methanoic acid can serve as a H-bond acceptor.

YOUR TURN **2.12**

Circle and label the H-bond donor and H-bond acceptor in *each* H-bond shown in Figure 2-14b.

Hydrogen bonding in uncharged species involves only *partial* charges, so like dipole–dipole interactions:

Hydrogen bonding is weaker than ion–ion interactions.

Hydrogen bonds, however, are distinct from dipole–dipole interactions for two main reasons: (1) fluorine, oxygen, and nitrogen are highly electronegative, so the partial charges involved are large; and (2) the hydrogen atom is very small, which allows the partial positive charge on hydrogen to be very close to the partial negative charge on the H-bond acceptor. For these reasons:

Hydrogen bonding is often (but not always) stronger than dipole–dipole interactions.

It is important to be able to gauge the *extent* of hydrogen bonding among molecules of a particular compound—that is, the collective strength of all the hydrogen bonds present. As a general rule:

The extent of hydrogen bonding increases as the total number of *potential* H-bond donors and acceptors increases between the species involved.

With more potential donor–acceptor pairs involving two molecules, there are more ways in which hydrogen bonding can take place.

The extent of hydrogen bonding explains why methanoic acid (formic acid) has a higher boiling point and melting point than ethanol. As shown in **Figure 2-15a**, a single molecule of ethanol has one potential H-bond donor and one potential H-bond acceptor. In an intermolecular interaction between a pair of ethanol molecules, there are therefore two potential donors and two potential acceptors. In a single molecule of methanoic acid (formic acid, Fig. 2-15b), on the other hand, there is one potential donor and there are *two* potential acceptors. Thus, in a pair of methanoic acid molecules there are two potential donors and *four* potential acceptors. As a result, there are more ways in which hydrogen bonding can take place in methanoic acid than in ethanol.

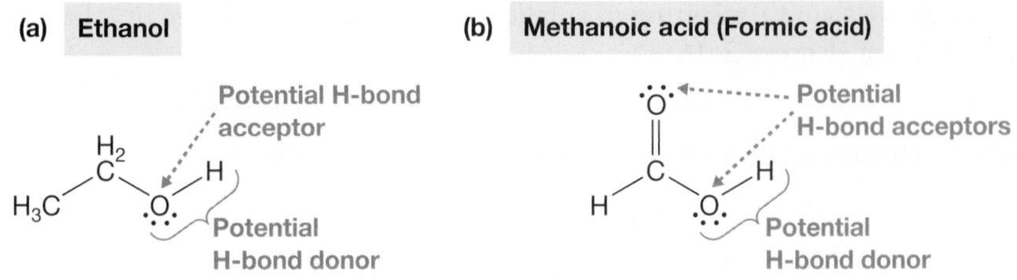
(a) Ethanol
Potential H-bond acceptor
Potential H-bond donor
(b) Methanoic acid (Formic acid)
Potential H-bond acceptors
Potential H-bond donor

FIGURE 2-15 Potential hydrogen-bond donors and acceptors (a) In a molecule of ethanol, the OH bond is a potential H-bond donor and the O atom is a potential H-bond acceptor. (b) In a molecule of methanoic acid (formic acid), the OH bond is a potential H-bond donor and each O atom is a potential H-bond acceptor.

YOUR TURN **2.13**

Which functional groups in Table 1-6 (p. 35) possess at least one H-bond acceptor but no H-bond donors? Which functional groups possess at least one H-bond donor and one H-bond acceptor? Which functional groups possess no H-bond donors and no H-bond acceptors?

SOLVED PROBLEM **2.3**

How to evaluate hydrogen bonding to determine the higher boiling compound

Break It Down 1,2-Ethanediol (ethylene glycol, A) is used as an automotive antifreeze. Hydroxyacetaldehyde (B) is believed to be an intermediate in the metabolism of proteins and carbohydrates. Which of these compounds would you expect to have a higher boiling point? Why?

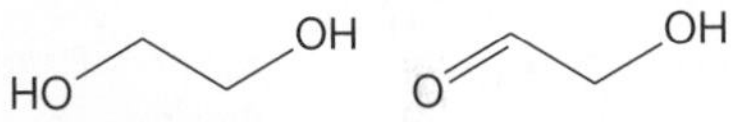

A **B**

Think	Solve
What is the most important intermolecular interaction that will occur between two molecules of **A**? Between two molecules of **B**?	Both **A** and **B** are polar molecules, so each should experience dipole–dipole interactions. Both are also subject to hydrogen bonding, because each molecule contains at least one potential H-bond donor (an OH bond) and at least one potential H-bond acceptor (an O atom). Hydrogen bonding is often stronger than dipole–dipole interactions, so hydrogen bonding is the most important intermolecular interaction for both molecules.
How many *potential* H-bond donors and H-bond acceptors are there for each pair of molecules?	In a molecule of **A**, there are two potential donors (each OH bond) and two potential acceptors (each O atom), so there are four of each in a pair of **A** molecules. In a molecule of **B**, there is one potential donor (the OH bond) and there are two potential acceptors (each O atom), so there are two potential donors and four potential acceptors in a pair of **B** molecules.
Which compound will undergo more extensive hydrogen-bonding interactions, and how would it affect the boiling points of **A** and **B**?	We would expect compound **A** to have more extensive hydrogen bonding because there are more potential donor–acceptor interactions. Thus, we expect **A** to have the higher boiling point.

Try It Which compound, **C** or **D**, would you expect to have a higher boiling point? Why?

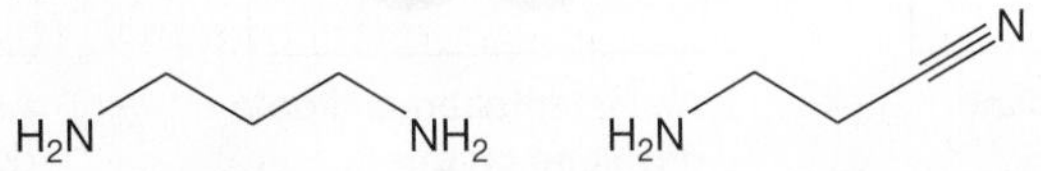

C **D**

The strength of hydrogen bonding also depends on the concentrations of charge in the H-bond donors and H-bond acceptors. Ethanamine ($CH_3CH_2NH_2$), for example, has a lower boiling point than ethanol (CH_3CH_2OH) because N is less electronegative than O, resulting in smaller concentrations of charge in ethanamine than in ethanol (**Figure 2-16**).

YOUR TURN 2.14

Which H-bond would you expect to be stronger, **E** or **F**? Why?

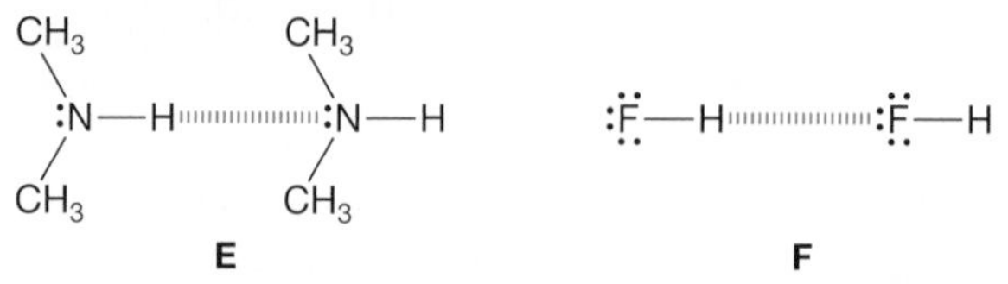

E
F

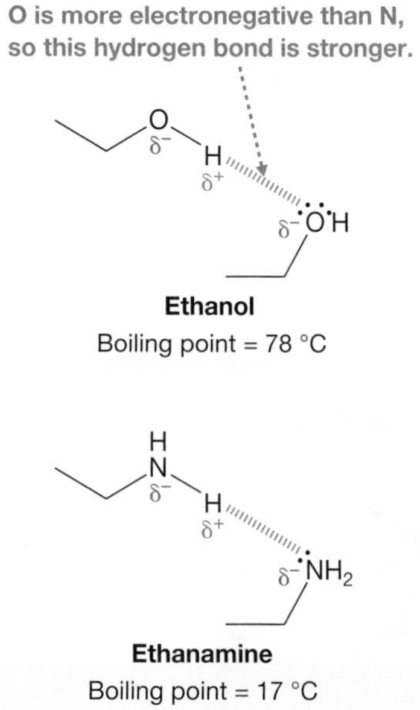

O is more electronegative than N, so this hydrogen bond is stronger.
Ethanol
Boiling point = 78 °C
Ethanamine
Boiling point = 17 °C

FIGURE 2-16 Hydrogen bonding and electronegativity Hydrogen bonding is stronger in ethanol than in ethanamine because O is more electronegative than N, thus giving rise to larger concentrations of positive and negative charges. As a result, the boiling point of ethanol is higher than the boiling point of ethanamine.

2.6d Induced Dipole–Induced Dipole Interactions (London Dispersion Forces)

Nonpolar molecules must attract each other through intermolecular interactions; otherwise, nonpolar compounds could never condense from gas to liquid. **Induced dipole–induced dipole interactions**, or **London dispersion forces**, are responsible for the attractions among nonpolar molecules.

How do induced dipole–induced dipole interactions arise? Although the *average* electron distribution in a molecule such as propane ($CH_3CH_2CH_3$) does not give rise to a significant permanent dipole (**Figure 2-17a**), any electron cloud can be distorted; that is, any electron cloud is **polarizable**. Electrons are constantly moving around, and at some instant in time, there may be more electrons on one side of the molecule than there are on the other side. The extra electrons on that one side give rise to an **instantaneous dipole** (Fig. 2-17b), which can alter the electron distribution on a second molecule by repelling or attracting nearby electrons. The second molecule then develops an **induced dipole** that is attracted to the first molecule (Fig. 2-17c).

Although they are most important in nonpolar molecules, induced dipole–induced dipole interactions are present when any two species interact.

To gain a sense of the relative strength of induced dipole–induced dipole interactions, notice in Table 2-4 (p. 78) that the nonpolar compounds tend to have the lowest boiling points and melting points. The low boiling points and melting points suggest that:

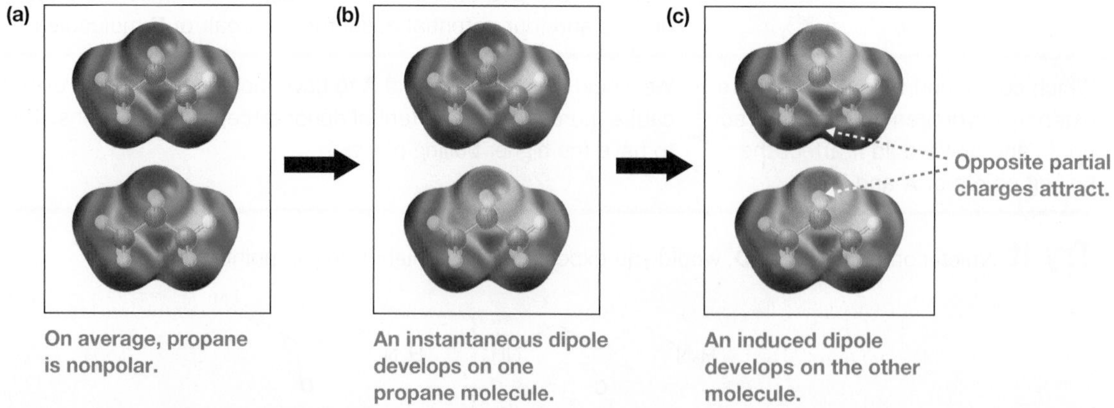

(a)
(b)
(c)
Opposite partial charges attract.
On average, propane is nonpolar.
An instantaneous dipole develops on one propane molecule.
An induced dipole develops on the other molecule.

FIGURE 2-17 Induced dipole–induced dipole interaction (a) On average, two isolated molecules of propane are nonpolar. (b) Because electrons are not static, electron density can build up on one side of a molecule at some instant in time, resulting in a temporary dipole. (c) That temporary dipole, in turn, can alter the electron distribution of a second, adjacent molecule, giving the second molecule an induced dipole. The oppositely charged ends of these induced dipoles attract one another.

Induced dipole–induced dipole interactions are generally the weakest of all intermolecular forces.

However, the strength of induced dipole–induced dipole interactions is highly variable and can even be stronger than other intermolecular interactions, depending on the *polarizability* of the species involved:

Polarizability, which can be thought of as the ease with which the electron cloud of a species can be distorted, tends to increase as the number of total electrons increases.

A small species like CH_4 has just 10 total electrons, so it is not very polarizable. Therefore, the induced dipole–induced dipole interactions in a sample of CH_4 are rather weak, giving rise to a low melting point (−182 °C) and a low boiling point (−161 °C), as shown in Table 2-5. On the other hand, pentane ($CH_3CH_2CH_2CH_2CH_3$), with 42 electrons, is significantly more polarizable, giving it a higher melting point (−130 °C) and boiling point (36 °C). Iodine (I_2) has 106 electrons, so its melting point (114 °C) and boiling point (184 °C) are higher still. Notice that I_2 melts above 0 °C, which is the melting point of water, indicating that the induced dipole–induced dipole interactions in I_2 are even stronger than the hydrogen bonding in water!

CONNECTIONS 2.10

Iodine and its uses Elemental iodine (Table 2-5) dissolved in water, which is yellow-brown, is commonly used as a disinfectant. In nonpolar solvents, I_2 has a deep violet color, and its reactivity with compounds such as alkenes makes it useful in analytical chemistry to determine end points of titrations.

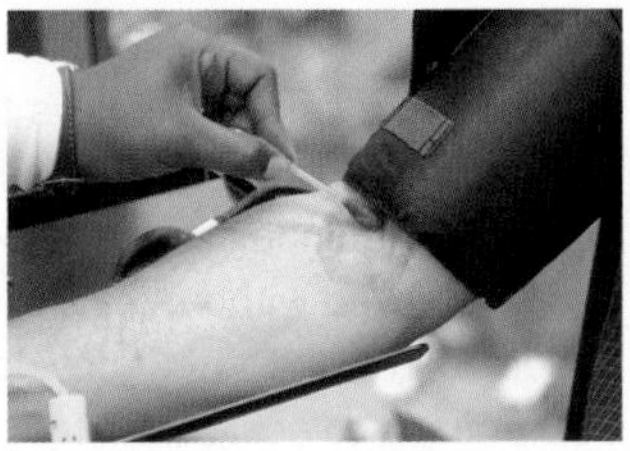

YOUR TURN 2.15

On the graph provided, plot boiling point as a function of total number of electrons for the straight-chain alkanes in Table 2-5 (i.e., methane, ethane, propane, butane, and pentane). What do you notice?

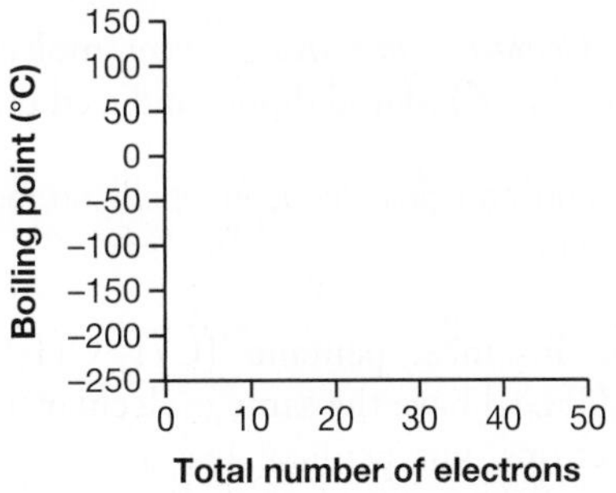
Boiling point (°C)
150
100
50
0
−50
−100
−150
−200
−250
0 10 20 30 40 50
Total number of electrons

TABLE 2-5 Melting Points and Boiling Points of Nonpolar Compounds

Molecule	Total Number of Electrons	Melting Point (°C)	Boiling Point (°C)	Molecule	Total Number of Electrons	Melting Point (°C)	Boiling Point (°C)
CH_4 Methane	10	−182	−161	 Dimethylpropane	42	−17	10
CH_3CH_3 Ethane	18	−183	−89	 Pentane	42	−130	36
 Propane	26	−188	−42	Br_2 Bromine	70	−7	59
Cl_2 Chlorine	34	−101	−34	I_2 Iodine	106	114	184
 Butane	34	−138	−1				

Climbing Like Geckos

We noted in opening this chapter that dispersion forces are responsible for the astonishing ability of geckos to effortlessly climb up just about any surface. Geckos have a specialized hierarchical structure in their toes, culminating in large numbers of very small hairs less than 200 nm in diameter, called setae (see again the image on p. 68). Setae extensively increase the contact surface area of each toe, giving a gecko's foot an adhesive pressure of up to 30 pounds per square inch on glass. This means that the gecko can, in principle, cling to glass by just one toe.

Scientists have known the gecko's secret for many years but were unable to harness it until recently, when Professors Duncan Irschick and Alfred Crosby of the University of Massachusetts Amherst unveiled Geckskin in 2014. Geckskin is made from polydimethylsiloxane, a common polymer, and the adhesive pad mimics the structure of the gecko's toe to maximize its contact surface area. One of the keys to the success of Geckskin is that it is woven into a synthetic tendon to maintain both stiffness and rotational freedom. And successful it is. A piece about the size of an index card has been shown to hold 700 pounds on a smooth wall and is easily removed without leaving any residue. Inspired by this, the Defense Advanced Research Projects Agency (DARPA) developed a system that enables an adult human weighing more than 200 pounds to scale a 25-foot vertical glass wall (**Figure 2-18**).

FIGURE 2-18

Contact surface area between molecules is another important factor governing the strength of induced dipole–induced dipole interactions:

> Induced dipole–induced dipole interactions tend to increase in strength as the contact surface area increases.

For instance, pentane [$CH_3(CH_2)_3CH_3$] and dimethylpropane [neopentane, $C(CH_3)_4$] have the same molecular formula (C_5H_{12}), and thus the same number of electrons, but pentane has a more extended shape than the relatively compact dimethylpropane. As a result, two molecules of pentane have a greater surface area available for interaction than two molecules of dimethylpropane do, as shown in **Figure 2-19**. Greater contact surface area means that pentane has more effective induced dipole–induced dipole interactions and a higher boiling point than dimethylpropane.

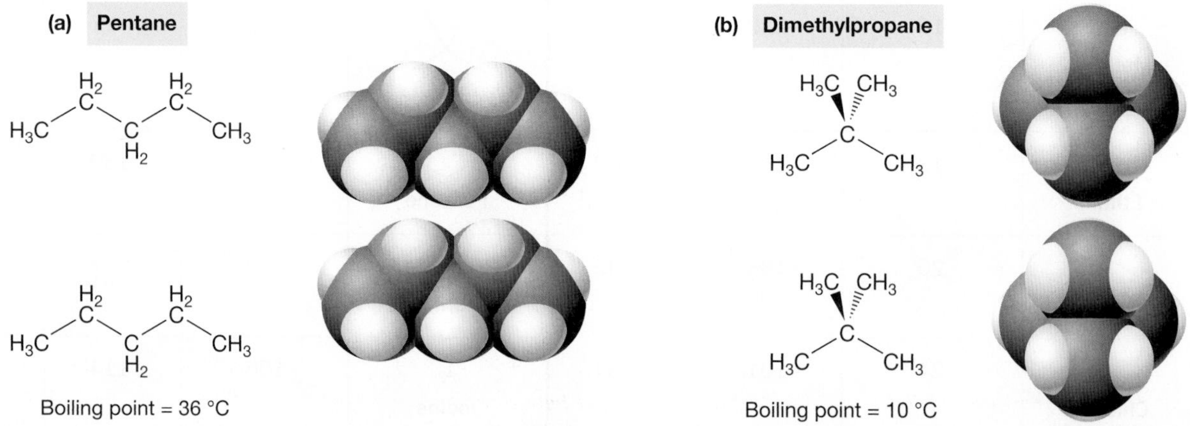
(a) Pentane
Boiling point = 36 °C
(b) Dimethylpropane
Boiling point = 10 °C

FIGURE 2-19 Contact surface area and induced dipole–induced dipole interactions The contact surface area between (a) two molecules of pentane is greater than that between (b) two molecules of dimethylpropane. The result is stronger induced dipole–induced dipole interactions in pentane and a correspondingly higher boiling point.

In Figure 2-19, shade in the contact surface area for each pair of molecules. What do you notice?

YOUR TURN **2.16**

2.7 Solubility

SECTION 2.7 OBJECTIVES

You will be able to:

1. Explain the roles that entropy and intermolecular forces play in the solubility of a compound.
2. Describe what solvation is, and explain the importance of solvation in the solubility of an ionic compound.
3. Predict the more soluble of two compounds in a particular solvent, given only their structures.

The general rule of solubility is that "like dissolves like." This means that polar compounds tend to be soluble in polar solvents but insoluble in nonpolar solvents, whereas nonpolar compounds tend to be soluble in nonpolar solvents but insoluble in polar solvents. These tendencies are outcomes of two major factors: (1) entropy and (2) intermolecular interactions at play in the pure solute, the pure solvent, and the mixture of the two (the solution).

Let's first discuss how entropy impacts solubility. As you may recall from general chemistry, **entropy** is a thermodynamic quantity that increases with the number of equivalent ways the energy in a system can be arranged. Many people think of entropy as a *measure of disorder*. A system with greater entropy (i.e., one that is more disordered) tends to be more favored than a system with less entropy. Importantly, two substances have greater entropy when they are mixed. Therefore:

An increase in entropy provides the driving force for two substances to mix.

If entropy were the only factor, then a given solute would be soluble in any solvent. How do we account for situations in which a solute remains insoluble in a solvent? To answer this question, we need to consider the intermolecular interactions present in both the mixed and unmixed states:

Substances tend *not* to mix if the intermolecular interactions in the pure solute and pure solvent are sufficiently stronger than those in the hypothetical solution.

Consider, for example, that hexane ($CH_3CH_2CH_2CH_2CH_2CH_3$), a nonpolar compound, is essentially insoluble in water. As shown in **Figure 2-20**, induced dipole–induced dipole interactions dominate in pure hexane, whereas hydrogen bonding dominates in pure water. In the *hypothetical* solution that would result if hexane were to dissolve in water, induced dipole–induced dipole interactions would dominate. The

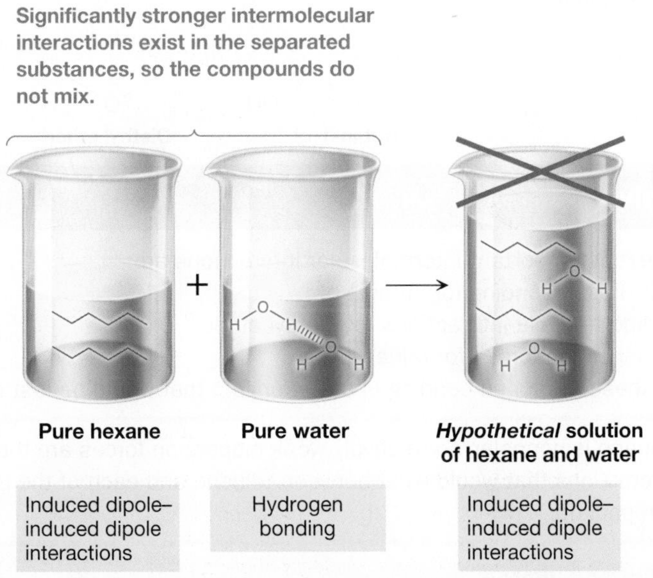

Significantly stronger intermolecular interactions exist in the separated substances, so the compounds do not mix.
Pure hexane
Pure water
Hypothetical solution of hexane and water
Induced dipole–induced dipole interactions
Hydrogen bonding
Induced dipole–induced dipole interactions

FIGURE 2-20 Intermolecular interactions and the insolubility of hexane in water The dominant intermolecular interactions present in pure hexane are induced dipole–induced dipole interactions. The dominant intermolecular interaction in pure water is hydrogen bonding. When we consider the *hypothetical* solution that would result if hexane were to dissolve in water, induced dipole–induced dipole interactions would remain but hydrogen bonding would be diminished. Because the stronger hydrogen bonding in pure water is preferred, mixing does not occur.

FIGURE 2-21 Intermolecular interactions and the solubility of ethanol in water Hydrogen bonding exists in pure ethanol (blue) and in pure water (red). Substantial hydrogen bonding occurs between molecules of water and ethanol in a solution, allowing the two substances to dissolve readily and in any proportion.

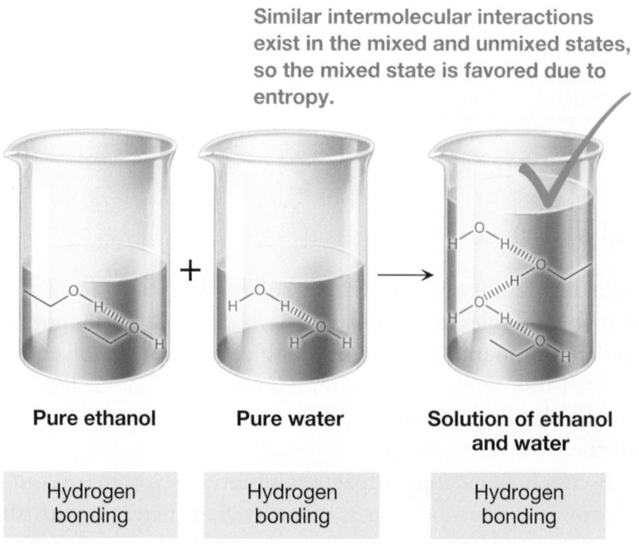

Similar intermolecular interactions exist in the mixed and unmixed states, so the mixed state is favored due to entropy.
Pure ethanol
Pure water
Solution of ethanol and water
Hydrogen bonding
Hydrogen bonding
Hydrogen bonding

CONNECTIONS 2.11

Toluene and its uses Toluene (Solved Problem 2.4) is an important organic solvent, but it is also a precursor in the production of 2,4,6-trinitrotoluene (TNT) and other industrial compounds. In biochemistry, red blood cells can be lysed by toluene to extract hemoglobin.

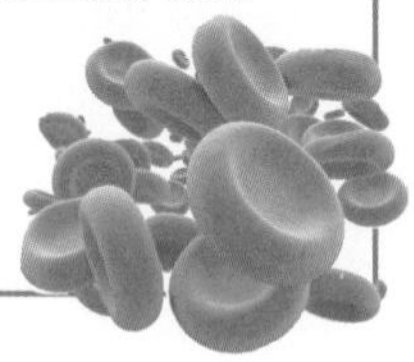

much stronger hydrogen bonding that exists in the unmixed state prevents the solute and solvent from mixing.

The story changes when the solute and solvent are both polar or both nonpolar. Ethanol (CH_3CH_2OH), for example, is infinitely soluble in water. As shown in **Figure 2-21**, the strongest intermolecular interaction that exists in the pure separated substances is hydrogen bonding (both in water and in ethanol). Substantial hydrogen bonding also occurs between the solute and solvent molecules in the ethanol–water solution, so the intermolecular interactions are similar in strength in the mixed and unmixed states. In this case, the intermolecular interactions in the unmixed state do not overcome the driving force for the substances to mix due to entropy, so the substances mix and form the solution.

SOLVED PROBLEM **2.4**

How to predict the more soluble compound

Break It Down **Would you expect butan-1-ol or diethyl ether to be more soluble in toluene ($C_6H_5CH_3$)? Explain.**

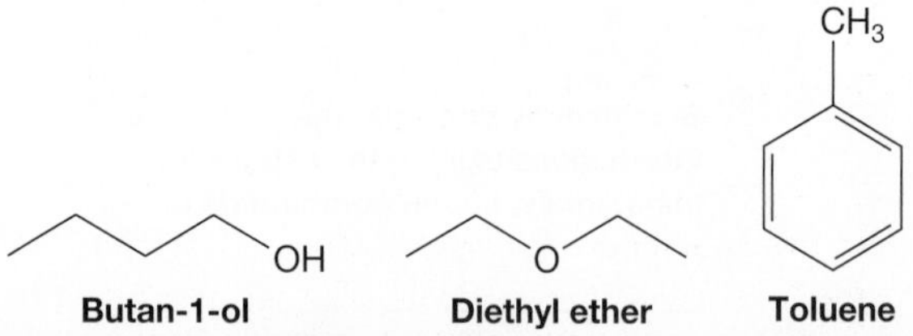

OH
O
CH3
Butan-1-ol
Diethyl ether
Toluene

Think	Solve
What are the most important intermolecular interactions in the pure solutes? In the pure solvent? What is the strongest intermolecular interaction that would be lost on mixing?	The most important intermolecular interactions are: • hydrogen bonding for butan-1-ol • dipole–dipole interactions for diethyl ether • dispersion forces for toluene Of these, hydrogen bonding is the strongest that would be lost on mixing.
What is the most important intermolecular interaction that would be present in each mixed state?	Toluene is nonpolar, so relatively weak dispersion forces are the only interactions that would exist between toluene and each of the given compounds.

(continued)

For which solute is there a more favorable trade-off of intermolecular interactions on mixing with the solvent?	Because each mixed state would have only weak dispersion forces, the most favorable trade-off would occur with the solute that loses the weakest intermolecular interactions: diethyl ether. Diethyl ether is therefore more soluble in toluene.

Try It Which compound, **A** or **B**, do you expect to be more soluble in H_2O? Which compound, **C** or **D**, would you expect to be more soluble in toluene ($C_6H_5CH_3$)? Explain.

A

NH2

B

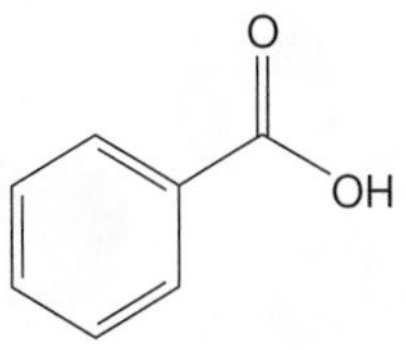
O
OH

C

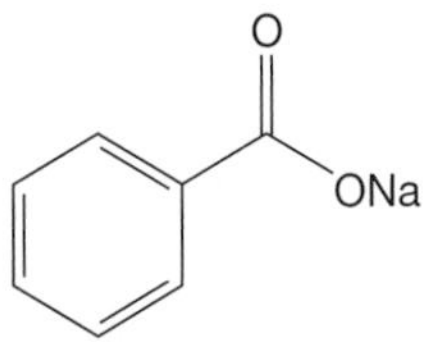
O
ONa

D

2.7a The Solubility of Ionic Compounds: Ion–Dipole Interactions and Solvation

Based on what we've discussed so far, it might seem peculiar that an ionic compound such as sodium methanoate (sodium formate, $Na^+HCO_2^-$) dissolves in a polar solvent like water, because it would require the loss of ion–ion interactions, the strongest of the intermolecular forces. Yet sodium methanoate *does* dissolve in water, and its water solubility (like that of most ionic compounds) is quite high (Table 2-4, p. 78). Why?

When an ionic compound like sodium methanoate dissolves in water, it does so as its individual ions, Na^+ and HCO_2^-, not as uncharged formula units. These free ions can interact with water molecules through **ion–dipole interactions**, a different kind of intermolecular interaction from the ones we have examined thus far. In this example, the positive end of water's dipole attracts a HCO_2^- anion and the negative end attracts a Na^+ cation (**Figure 2-22**).

Notice that an ion–dipole interaction involves a full charge and a partial charge. The concentration of charge involved in an ion–dipole interaction is generally less than in an ion–ion interaction but more than in a dipole–dipole interaction. Consequently:

> The strength of an ion–dipole interaction is intermediate between that of an ion–ion interaction and that of a dipole–dipole interaction.

How, then, are ion–dipole interactions capable of overcoming the stronger ion–ion interactions to dissolve an ionic compound? A major factor is **solvation**, depicted in

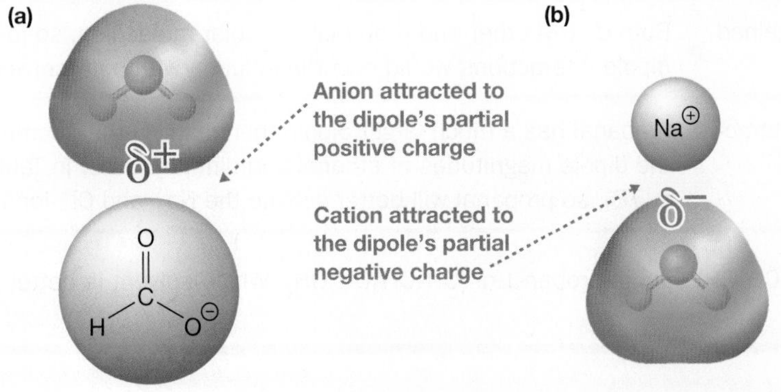
(a)
(b)
δ+
Anion attracted to the dipole's partial positive charge
Cation attracted to the dipole's partial negative charge
Na⊕
δ−
O
C
H
O⊖

FIGURE 2-22 Ion–dipole interactions (a) An ion–dipole interaction between the methanoate anion, HCO_2^-, and H_2O. The anion interacts with the positive end of water's dipole. (b) An ion–dipole interaction between the sodium cation, Na^+, and H_2O. The cation interacts with the negative end of water's dipole.

FIGURE 2-23 Solvation Ionic compounds can dissolve in water as a result of solvation of the respective ions. (a) The positive end of water's dipole solvates the anion, HCO_2^-. (b) The negative end of water's dipole solvates the cation, Na^+.

(a) The positive end of water's dipole solvates the methanoate anion through multiple ion–dipole interactions.

(b) The negative end of water's dipole solvates the sodium cation through multiple ion–dipole interactions.

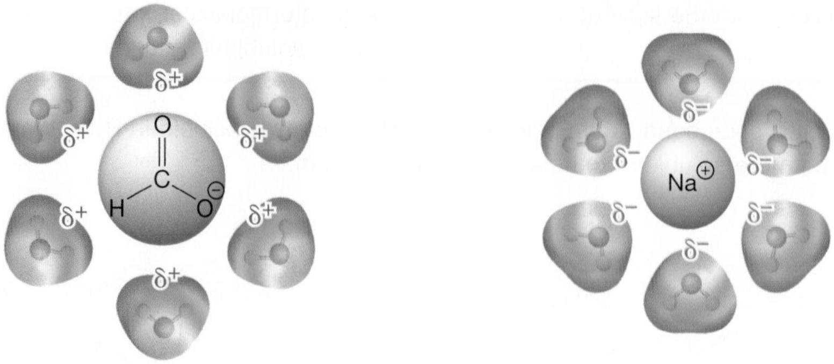

δ+
O
C
H
O⊖
Na⊕
δ−

Figure 2-23, in which an individual ion participates in *multiple* ion–dipole interactions with the solvent. When this occurs, the ions are said to be *solvated*. The collective stability from all of these ion–dipole interactions can be substantially greater than that of the ion–ion interactions in an ionic compound, thus favoring the mixture (that is, the mixture is more stable).

YOUR TURN **2.17**

Redraw Figure 2-23, using methanol (CH_3OH) as the solvent instead of water. Draw just the Lewis structures, not the space-filling models, but do include the symbols for the relevant partial charges.

The strength of an individual ion–dipole interaction depends on the polarity of the solvent molecule, so the collective stability provided by solvation does, too (see Solved Problem 2.5). This is important because, as we will discuss in Chapter 9, a solvent's ability to solvate ions can have a dramatic effect on the outcome of reactions.

SOLVED PROBLEM **2.5**

How to predict the relative solubility of an ionic compound in different solvents

Break It Down In which solvent would you expect NaCl to be more soluble: diethyl ether ($CH_3CH_2OCH_2CH_3$) or propanal ($CH_3CH_2CH{=}O$)?

Think	Solve
What are the most important intermolecular interactions that would be disrupted on dissolving?	Very strong ion–ion interactions are disrupted when NaCl dissolves.
What intermolecular interactions would be gained in the solution?	Both diethyl ether and propanal are polar molecules, so ion–dipole interactions would occur in solution with both solvents.
In which solvent are those intermolecular interactions stronger?	Propanal has a much larger dipole than diethyl ether (compare the dipole magnitudes of ethanal and dimethyl ether in Table 2-4, p. 78), so propanal will better solvate the Na^+ and Cl^- ions.

Try It NaCl is more soluble in methanol (CH_3OH) than in propan-1-ol ($CH_3CH_2CH_2OH$). Which solvent is better at solvating ions?

2.7b The Effect of Hydrocarbon Groups on Solubility

The types of functional groups present in a molecule have a direct effect on its solubility in various solvents, because the functional groups determine the kinds of intermolecular interactions that are available to the molecule. Alcohols, for example, can always form hydrogen bonds with water due to the presence of the **hydrophilic** ("water-loving") OH group. Thus, small alcohols like methanol (CH_3OH), ethanol (CH_3CH_2OH), and propan-1-ol ($CH_3CH_2CH_2OH$) are infinitely soluble in water, as shown in Table 2-6.

Table 2-6 shows that the water solubility of an alcohol *decreases* as the size of the R group (the hydrocarbon portion of the molecule) *increases*. This is because R groups are highly nonpolar; they are **hydrophobic** ("water-fearing"). We can generalize this trend as follows:

> A species behaves more like a nonpolar alkane as the size of its alkyl group increases.

YOUR TURN 2.18

Which functional groups in Table 1-6 (p. 35) would be considered hydrophilic? Which would be considered hydrophobic?

Monoalcohols (i.e., alcohols with one OH group) are generally considered insoluble in water if they contain six or more carbons. The effect of the alkyl group, however, can be overcome by increasing the number of hydrophilic functional groups:

> Molecules are generally very water-soluble if the ratio of their total number of carbon atoms to the number of hydrophilic functional groups is less than about 3:1.

Sucrose (table sugar), for example, is highly soluble in water even though it has 12 carbon atoms (**Figure 2-24**). Sucrose is soluble because it contains

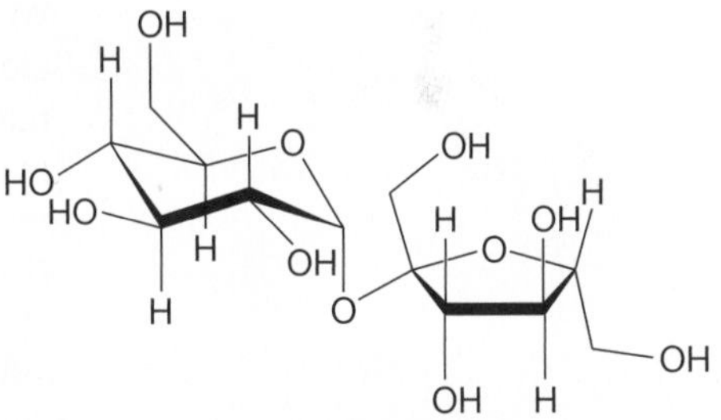
OH
H
HO
HO
H
O
H
OH
H
OH
H
OH
O
O
H
OH
OH
H

Sucrose, $C_{12}H_{22}O_{11}$

FIGURE 2-24 The water solubility of sucrose The large number of OH groups compared to C atoms makes sucrose soluble in water.

TABLE 2-6 Water Solubility of Some Simple Alcohols (R—OH)

Alcohol	Water Solubility (g/100 g of H_2O)	Alcohol	Water Solubility (g/100 g of H_2O)
CH_3OH **Methanol**	Infinitely soluble	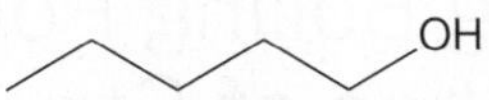 **Pentan-1-ol**	2.7
CH_3CH_2OH **Ethanol**	Infinitely soluble	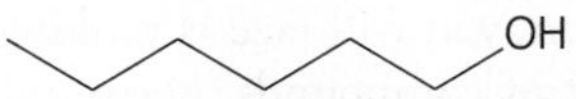 **Hexan-1-ol**	0.6
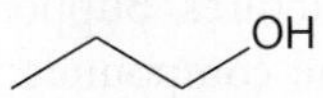 **Propan-1-ol**	Infinitely soluble		
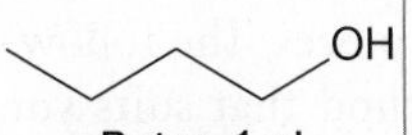 **Butan-1-ol**	7.7	 **Heptan-1-ol**	0.1

CONNECTIONS 2.12

2-Naphthol and dyes
2-Naphthol (molecule **C** in Solved Problem 2.6) is widely used as a precursor in the production of dyes, such as Sudan I.

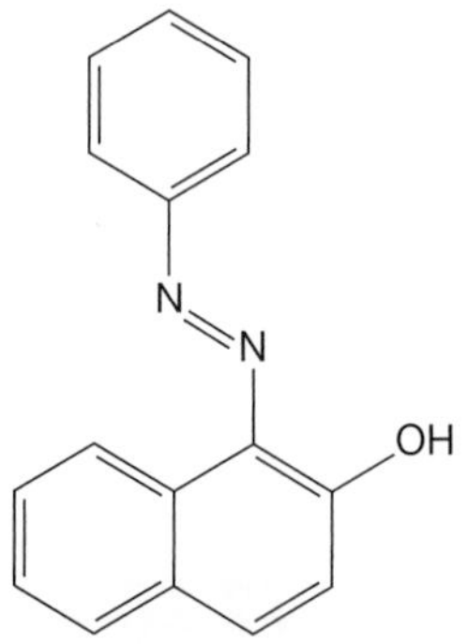

Sudan I

eight hydrophilic OH groups, so its ratio of carbon atoms to hydrophilic groups is 12:8 = 1.5:1, which is less than 3:1.

SOLVED PROBLEM **2.6**

How to predict a compound's water solubility

Break It Down Would you expect each of the following compounds to be soluble in water? Why or why not?

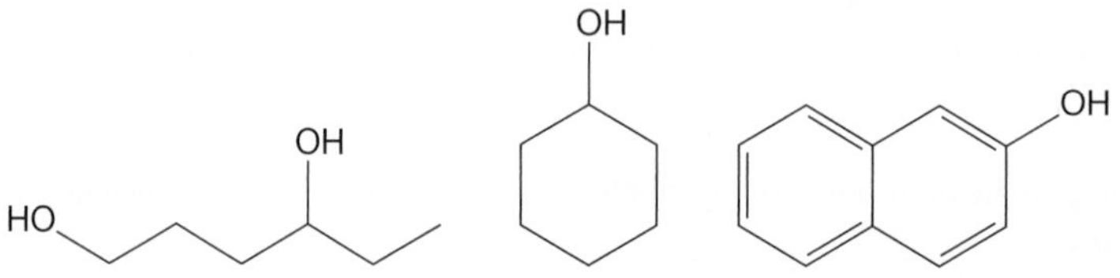

A **B** **C**
2-Naphthol

Think	Solve
What is the ratio of alcohol groups to the number of carbon atoms in each molecule?	Molecule **A** contains six carbons and two hydrophilic OH groups, giving it a ratio of 3:1. For molecules **B** and **C**, the ratios are 6:1 and 10:1, respectively.
How does each ratio compare to the 3:1 cutoff?	Molecule **A** matches the 3:1 cutoff, so we expect **A** to be highly water-soluble. Molecules **B** and **C** exceed the cutoff, so we expect the nonpolar groups in **B** and **C** to dominate the intermolecular interactions, causing the molecules to be *insoluble* in water.

Try It Like alcohols, aldehydes (R—CH═O) become less soluble in water as the number of carbon atoms in the alkyl group R increases. Do you think the maximum number of carbon atoms for water-soluble aldehydes will be greater than or less than that for water-soluble alcohols? Explain.

SECTION 2.8 OBJECTIVES

You will be able to:

1. Rank the boiling points of several structurally similar compounds, on the basis of intermolecular forces.
2. Predict the order of solubility of several structurally similar solutes in a given solvent, on the basis of intermolecular forces.

Strategies for Success
Ranking Boiling Points and Solubilities of Structurally Similar Compounds

2.8 Strategies for Success: Ranking Boiling Points and Solubilities of Structurally Similar Compounds

One type of problem you will face is ranking the boiling points, melting points, or solubilities of a set of compounds, given only their molecular structures. Suppose, for example, that you were asked to rank the boiling points of the compounds in **Figure 2-25**, from lowest to highest.

Because there are a number of factors at play simultaneously, you should find ways to break this large problem into smaller, more manageable pieces. The following method can help, but you might also discover another method that suits you better:

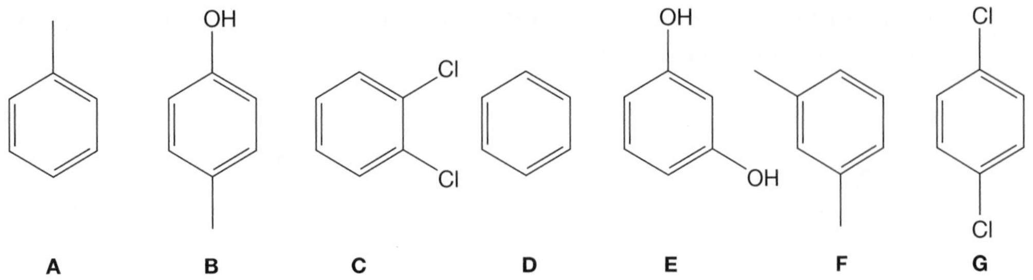
OH
Cl
Cl
OH
OH
Cl
Cl
A
B
C
D
E
F
G

FIGURE 2-25 Compounds A–G to rank in order of boiling point

Ranking Boiling Points

1. Identify the most important intermolecular interactions in each pure compound and group the compounds accordingly.
2. Arrange those groups of compounds according to the typically observed strength of the intermolecular interactions, which increase from low to high as follows:

induced dipole–induced dipole < dipole–dipole < hydrogen bonding < ion–dipole < ion–ion

3. Within each group, arrange the compounds according to the major factor that dictates the strength of the interaction. For example,
   - Induced dipole–induced dipole interactions become stronger with greater polarizability.
   - Dipole–dipole interactions become stronger with larger dipoles.
   - Hydrogen bonding becomes more extensive with greater numbers of potential H-bond donors and H-bond acceptors.
4. Assign the relative boiling points the same overall order because, to overcome stronger intermolecular interactions, more heat energy is required.

Applying Steps 1 and 2 to compounds **A–G**, we arrive at the groupings in **Figure 2-26**:

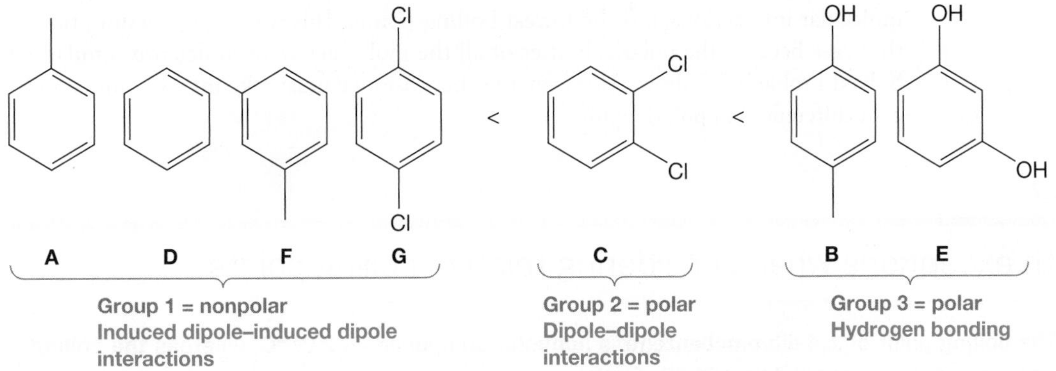
Cl
Cl
Cl
Cl
OH
OH
OH
<
<
A
D
F
G
C
B
E
Group 1 = nonpolar
Induced dipole–induced dipole interactions
Group 2 = polar
Dipole–dipole interactions
Group 3 = polar
Hydrogen bonding

FIGURE 2-26 Compounds A–G grouped by dominant intermolecular interactions

Next we apply Step 3 to each group of molecules. For the nonpolar molecules in group 1, polarizability dictates the strength of the induced dipole–induced dipole interactions, and polarizability tends to increase with the number of total electrons. Therefore, the strength of the intermolecular interactions increases in the order **D** < **A** < **F** < **G**.

For the group 3 molecules, which undergo hydrogen bonding, we examine the number of potential donors and acceptors in a pair of each. In a pair of molecules **B**, there are two donors and two acceptors, whereas in a pair of molecules **E**, there are four of each. Therefore, H-bonding is more extensive in **E** than in **B**.

Putting it all together, we predict that the strength of intermolecular interactions increases as shown in **Figure 2-27**:

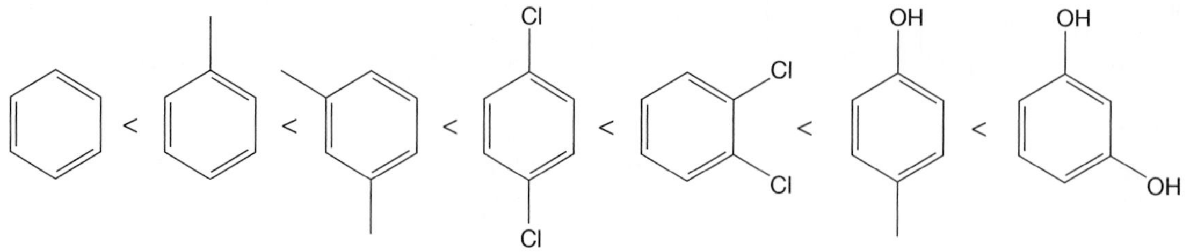

Boiling point:	D	A	F	G	C	B	E
	80 °C	111 °C	139 °C	173 °C	181 °C	202 °C	281 °C

FIGURE 2-27 Compounds A–G in order of increasing boiling point

We therefore predict that the boiling points of these compounds increase in the same order (actual boiling points are included for comparison).

YOUR TURN **2.19**

Rank compounds **H–L** in order of increasing boiling point.

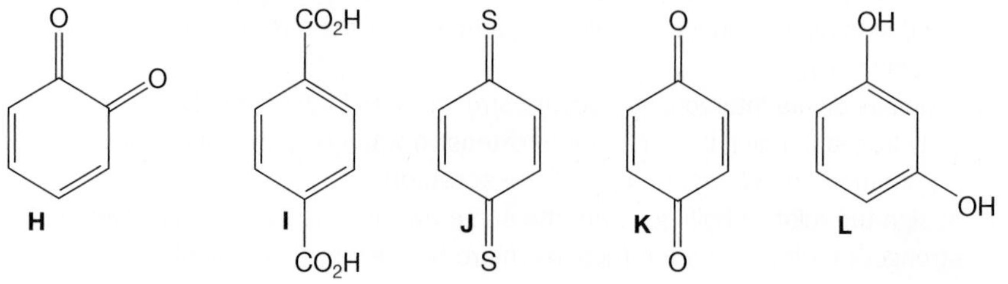
H
I
J
K
L

In solving the previous ranking problem, we assumed that the molecules possessing only induced dipole–induced dipole interactions (group 1) had the weakest intermolecular interactions and the lowest boiling points. This was a good assumption in that case because the polarizabilities of all the molecules were sufficiently similar. As Solved Problem 2.7 shows, however, in other cases we must take into account significant differences in polarizability.

SOLVED PROBLEM **2.7**

How to deal with exceptions when considering relative boiling points

Break It Down The boiling point of 1,4-dibromobenzene, a nonpolar compound, is 219 °C, whereas the boiling point of 1,2-dichlorobenzene, a polar compound, is 181 °C. Explain.

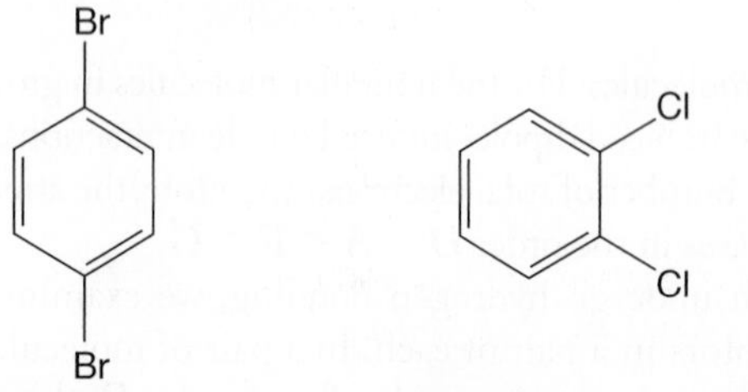

1,4-Dibromobenzene
Boiling point = 219 °C

1,2-Dichlorobenzene
Boiling point = 181 °C

(continued)

Think	Solve
What intermolecular interactions are present in each compound?	1,4-Dibromobenzene is nonpolar, so it has only induced dipole–induced dipole interactions. 1,2-Dichlorobenzene, on the other hand, is polar, so it has both dipole–dipole interactions and induced dipole–induced dipole interactions.
Are the intermolecular interactions of similar strength in each compound?	Dipole–dipole interactions are generally assumed to be the more important interaction when comparing compounds with similar polarizabilities. In this case, however, the two molecules should have different polarizabilities. More specifically, 1,4-dibromobenzene should be significantly more polarizable than 1,2-dichlorobenzene because it has 36 more electrons (146 vs. 110), the difference between two Br atoms and two Cl atoms. As a result, induced dipole–induced dipole interactions are stronger in 1,4-dibromobenzene: enough to give 1,4-dibromobenzene the higher boiling point.

Try It Which of the compounds shown here do you think has the higher boiling point? Explain.

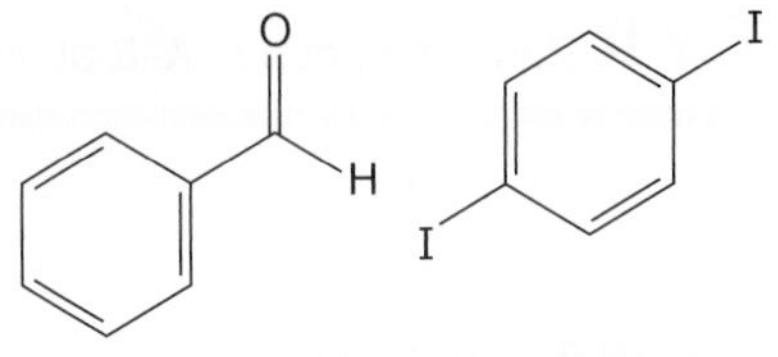

O
H
I
I

A B

We can apply a similar strategy to predict relative solubilities in a given solvent. In doing so, however, we must consider the disruption of intermolecular interactions in the pure separated substances as well as the formation of intermolecular interactions in the mixture. This is illustrated in Solved Problem 2.8.

SOLVED PROBLEM **2.8**

How to predict relative solubilities of several compounds in a given solvent

Break It Down Rank compounds A–E from lowest solubility in hexane, $CH_3(CH_2)_4CH_3$, to highest solubility in hexane.

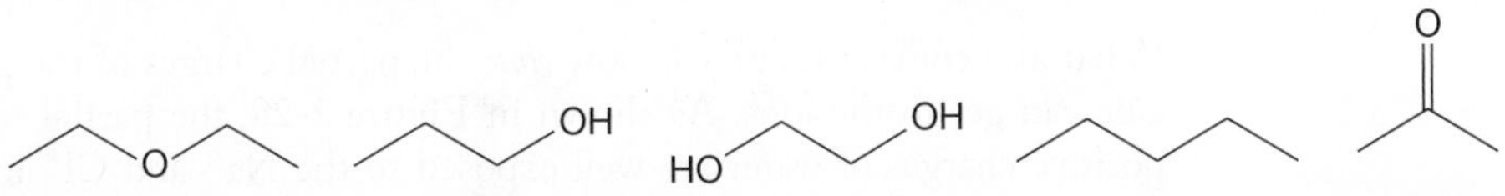

O
OH
OH
HO
O

A B C D E

Think	Solve
What are the most important intermolecular interactions that would be lost from the pure solutes? From the pure solvent? What are their relative strengths?	For pure solutes: • Compound **D** (nonpolar) would lose London dispersion forces. • Compounds **A** and **E** (polar) would lose dipole–dipole interactions; these would be stronger in **E** because it has a larger dipole. • Compounds **B** and **C** would lose hydrogen bonding, this would be more extensive in **C** because **C** has more H-bond donors and acceptors. The hexane solvent (nonpolar) would lose only London dispersion forces.
What are the most important intermolecular interactions that would be gained in each solution?	Hexane is nonpolar, so London dispersion forces will be the only intermolecular interactions gained in each solution.

(continued)

Which intermolecular interactions have the greatest impact on solubility: the ones lost from the pure solutes, lost from the pure solvent, or gained in the solutions?	Only London dispersion forces (the weakest of the intermolecular interactions) would be lost from the pure solvent or gained in the solutions, so the intermolecular interactions lost from the pure solutes (compounds **A–E**) will dictate the relative solubilities. The solutes with weaker interactions will be more soluble, so solubility will increase in the following order:

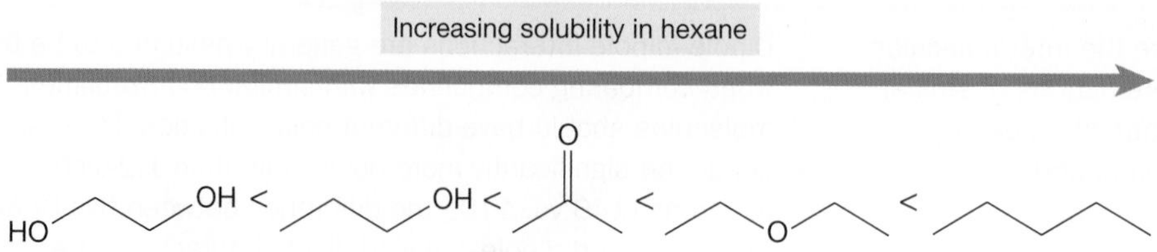

Increasing solubility in hexane
HO
OH <
OH <
O
<
O
<

C **B** **E** **A** **D**

Try It Rank compounds **A–E** above in order from least to most soluble in water.

SECTION 2.9 OBJECTIVES

You will be able to:

1. Identify a solvent as either protic or aprotic.
2. Explain why ionic compounds tend to be more soluble in protic solvents than in aprotic solvents.

2.9 Protic and Aprotic Solvents

As we learned in Section 2.7, ionic compounds can have very high solubility in a polar solvent such as water, due to the strong solvation set up by ion–dipole interactions in the resulting solution. For example, about 35 g of sodium chloride (NaCl) dissolves in 100 mL of water. The magnitude of the water's dipole (1.9 D), however, is not the only factor influencing solubility. For instance, dimethyl sulfoxide [DMSO, $(CH_3)_2S{=}O$] is even more polar (magnitude = 4.0 D) than water, but it dissolves only about 0.4 g of NaCl.

$$\text{35 g of NaCl(s)} \xrightarrow[H_2O]{} Na^{\oplus} + Cl^{\ominus} \qquad \text{(2-2a)}$$

NaCl is highly soluble in water but not in DMSO.

$$\text{0.4 g of NaCl(s)} \xrightarrow[\text{DMSO}]{} Na^{\oplus} + Cl^{\ominus} \qquad \text{(2-2b)}$$

What also comes into play is how *close* the partial charges of the polar solvent molecule can get to the ions. As shown in **Figure 2-28**, the partial negative and partial positive charges of water are well exposed to the Na^+ and Cl^- ions, respectively, so these partial charges and the ions can get rather close to each other. Thus, the solvation of each ion is relatively strong.

(a) The negative end of water's dipole solvates the sodium cation strongly. **(b) The positive end of water's dipole solvates the chloride anion strongly.**

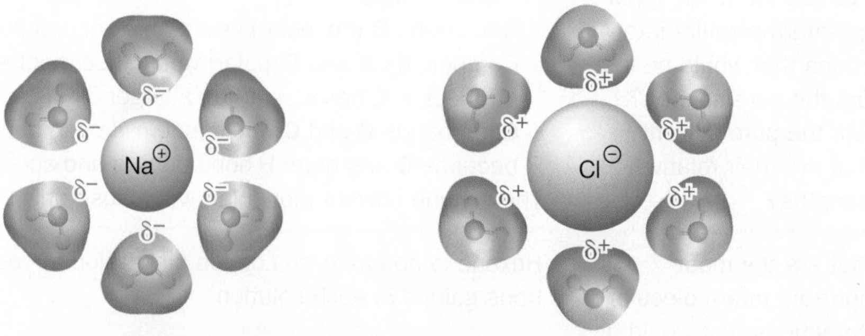

δ−
Na⊕
δ+
Cl⊖

FIGURE 2-28 **Solvation of NaCl in water** (a) The Na^+ ion is strongly solvated because the partial negative charge of water is well exposed. (b) The Cl^- ion is strongly solvated because the partial positive charge of water is well exposed.

Now let's examine the solvation of NaCl in DMSO. As we can see in **Figure 2-29a**, the partial negative charge of DMSO is well exposed, so Na^+ is strongly solvated by DMSO, just as it is strongly solvated by water. The partial positive charge of DMSO, however, is flanked by two bulky CH_3 groups, which makes it difficult for the partial positive charge to approach the Cl^- ion (Fig. 2-29b). The obstruction due to the bulkiness of the methyl groups in this instance is an example of **steric hindrance**. Thus, Cl^- is not solvated very strongly and NaCl is less soluble.

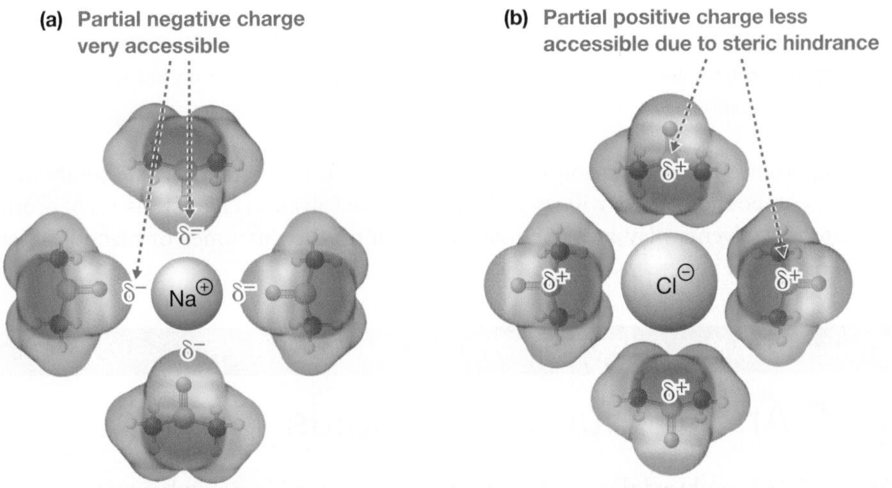
(a) Partial negative charge very accessible
δ−
δ−
Na⊕
δ−
δ−
(b) Partial positive charge less accessible due to steric hindrance
δ+
δ+
Cl⊖
δ+
δ+

FIGURE 2-29 Solvation in DMSO (a) Na^+ is solvated strongly in DMSO because the partial negative charge of DMSO is well exposed. (b) Cl^- is not solvated very strongly by DMSO because the partial positive charge of DMSO is buried inside the molecule. This is an example of steric hindrance.

CONNECTIONS 2.13

DMSO in chemistry and medicine In addition to being an important solvent in chemistry, DMSO (Fig. 2-29) has a variety of medicinal uses. It is used topically to treat some chronic inflammatory conditions and, because it was discovered to penetrate organs without damaging them, it can be used to deliver some drugs into biological systems. Interestingly, when DMSO contacts the skin, some people taste garlic in the mouth.

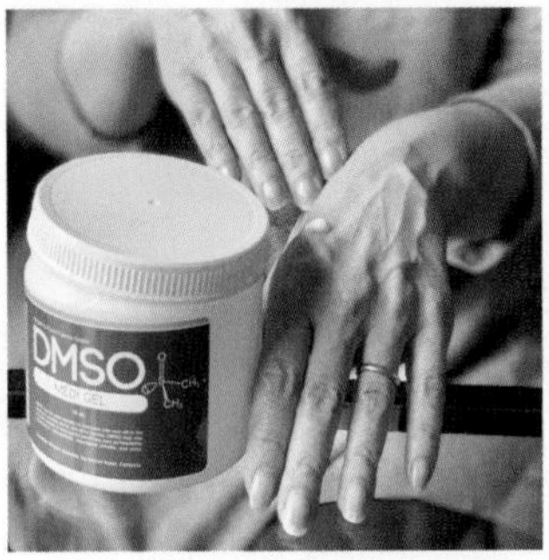
DMSO

Water is a particularly good solvent for ionic compounds because it has a H-bond donor (in this case, an O—H covalent bond), which classifies water as a **protic solvent**. DMSO has no H-bond donors, so it is an **aprotic solvent**. Other examples of polar protic solvents and polar aprotic solvents are shown in Table 2-7.

TABLE 2-7 Common Polar Protic Solvents and Polar Aprotic Solvents

POLAR PROTIC SOLVENTS		POLAR APROTIC SOLVENTS	
Structure	**Name**	**Structure**	**Name**
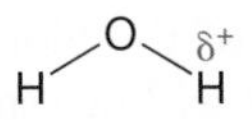	**Water**	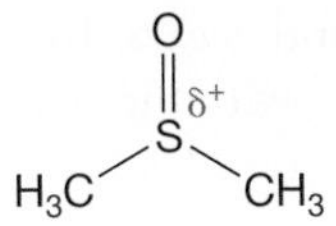	**Dimethyl sulfoxide (DMSO)**
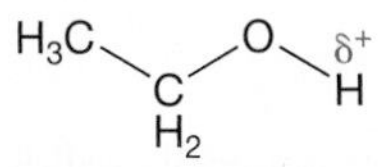	**Ethanol**	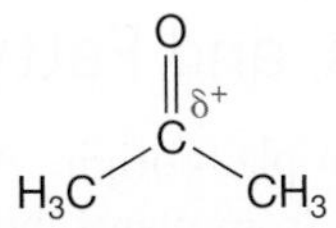	**Propanone (Acetone)**
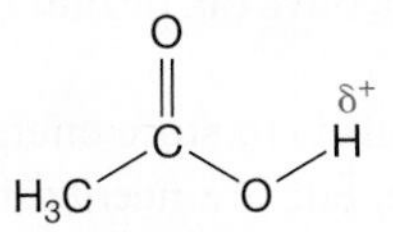	**Ethanoic acid (Acetic acid)**	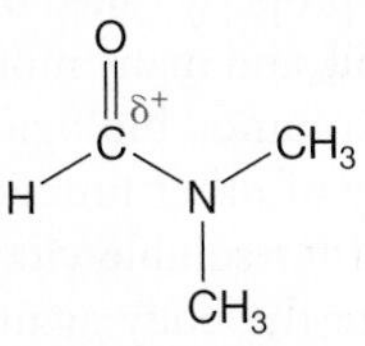	***N,N*-Dimethylformamide (DMF)**

YOUR TURN **2.20**

In Table 2-7, circle and label each potential hydrogen-bond donor.

▶ LOOKING AHEAD

In Chapter 9, we will study the competition between four reactions, called S_N1, S_N2, E1, and E2. One factor that impacts which reaction dominates is how strongly solvated the reactant and product ions are. The strength of solvation depends not only on the nature of the ions but also on whether the solvent is protic or aprotic.

Like water, all polar protic solvents have easily accessible partial negative and positive charges. Polar aprotic solvents, on the other hand, have well-exposed partial negative charges, but their partial positive charges tend not to be very accessible. Therefore:

- Polar protic solvents tend to solvate both cations and anions very strongly.
- Polar aprotic solvents tend to solvate cations very strongly but do not strongly solvate anions.

The importance of these attributes extends far beyond understanding the solubilities of ionic compounds. As we will see in Chapter 9, the solvation characteristics of protic and aprotic solvents play a major role in governing the outcomes of reactions (see Looking Ahead box).

THE ORGANIC CHEMISTRY OF BIOMOLECULES

2.10 An Introduction to Lipids

SECTION 2.10 OBJECTIVES

You will be able to:

1. Distinguish lipids from other biomolecules on the basis of their solubility characteristics.
2. Identify fatty acids and fats/oils, phospholipids, steroids, and waxes from their structures.
3. Describe the chemical makeup of a lipid bilayer for a cell membrane.

Section 1.14 introduced three of the four major classes of biomolecules: proteins, carbohydrates, and nucleic acids. Here in Section 2.10, we introduce the fourth: *lipids*.

Recall that proteins, carbohydrates, and nucleic acids can be very large molecules, but they are constructed from just a few types of small organic molecules. Proteins, for instance, are constructed from α-amino acids, polysaccharides are constructed from monosaccharides (simple sugars), and nucleic acids are constructed from nucleotides. Moreover, these smaller molecules can be unambiguously identified by the specific functional groups they possess.

Lipids, on the other hand, are characterized by their solubility:

Lipids are biomolecules that are relatively *insoluble* in water.

Thus, most lipids are highly nonpolar, consisting primarily of carbon and hydrogen, with very little oxygen or nitrogen content. Consequently, they tend to be soluble in nonpolar or weakly polar organic solvents, such as diethyl ether.

Because lipids are characterized in such a broad way, they can have a variety of structures. Nevertheless, lipids can be divided into subclasses based on the structural features they have in common. We examine four of these subclasses in this unit: *fats*, *phospholipids*, *steroids*, and *waxes*. In particular, we describe some of the biological functions of lipids, along with the structural features shared by lipids within a specific subclass.

2.10a Fats, Oils, and Fatty Acids

Fats can be of animal or plant origin. Animal fats, such as lard, are generally solids at room temperature. Fats from plants, however, are generally liquids at room temperature and are thus more properly called **oils**. These include corn oil, olive oil, peanut oil, safflower oil, coconut oil, and many more.

Perhaps the most common biological function of fats and oils is to store energy, but they have a variety of other functions as well. For example, fats are needed for the intake of so-called fat-soluble vitamins, such as vitamins A, D, E, and K. Fats can be used to insulate the body against heat loss and to insulate internal organs

How Do Soaps Work?

Washing your hands with water alone is ineffective at removing dirt or oil because dirt and oil are nonpolar and hydrophobic. But using soap along with water is quite effective. Why?

The structure of soap is key to its cleansing ability. Soaps are typically *salts of fatty acids*, which are ionic compounds of the form RCO_2^- Na^+ or RCO_2^- K^+. In these compounds, R is a long hydrocarbon chain, and the fatty acid salts generally contain from 12 to 18 carbons. Examples include potassium oleate and sodium palmitate, shown in **Figure 2-30**.

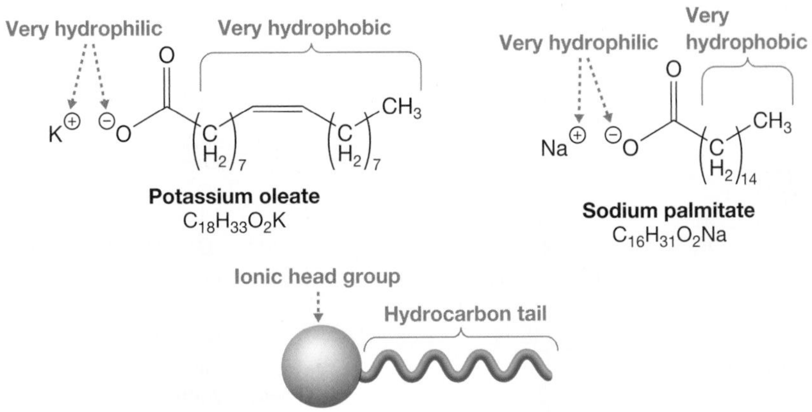
Very hydrophilic
Very hydrophobic
Potassium oleate
C18H33O2K
Very hydrophilic
Very hydrophobic
Sodium palmitate
C16H31O2Na
Ionic head group
Hydrocarbon tail

FIGURE 2-30

When a soap dissolves in water, it does so as its individual ions: the metal cation (Na^+ or K^+) and the carboxylate anion (RCO_2^-). Of these two species, the carboxylate anion is the one that is directly responsible for the soap's cleansing properties, because it has vastly different characteristics at its two ends. As the structures show, the CO_2^- portion (the ionic head group) is very hydrophilic, whereas the large nonpolar R group (the hydrocarbon tail) is very hydrophobic.

When dissolved in water, the soap's RCO_2^- ions form spherical aggregates, called *micelles*, as shown in **Figure 2-31**. In a micelle, the nonpolar tails are on the inside, where they can interact with one another via extensive induced dipole–induced dipole interactions, whereas the charged head groups are on the outside, where they can interact favorably with the surrounding water molecules. As a result, micelles are highly solvated (review Section 2.7a).

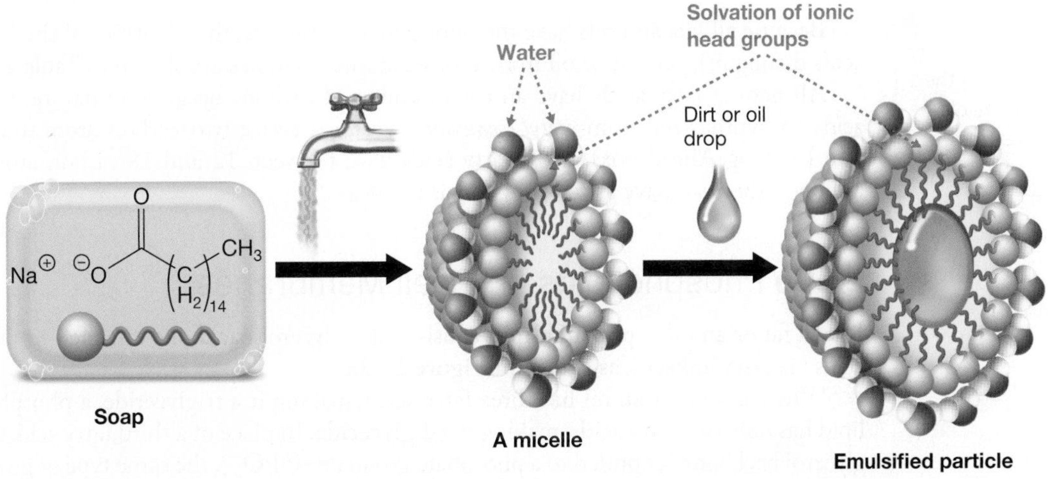
Solvation of ionic head groups
Water
Dirt or oil drop
Soap
A micelle
Emulsified particle

FIGURE 2-31

When dirt or oil encounters the water–soap solution, the dirt or oil effectively becomes dissolved by the nonpolar tails of the soap, as indicated in Figure 2-31. Soap is said to *emulsify* such substances; that is, it disperses them in a solvent (water) in which they are normally insoluble. Such emulsified particles can then be washed away by water.

against physical impact. Fats can help protect organisms from foreign substances, either chemical or biological, by temporarily locking them away in new fat tissue. And fats contain **fatty acids**, which are long-chain carboxylic acids that help regulate blood pressure and blood lipid levels and play major roles in the inflammatory response to injury.

Although there are several different kinds of fats and oils (having different plant or animal sources), they all share the same general structure:

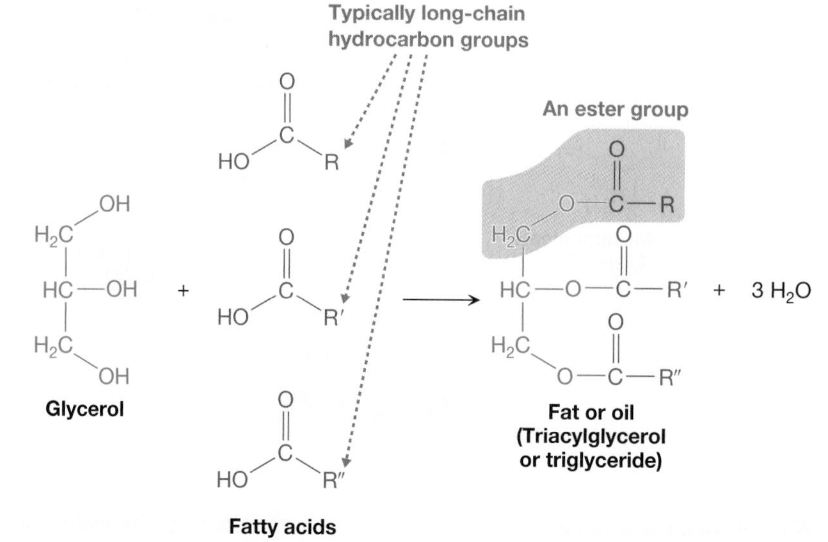

Typically long-chain hydrocarbon groups
An ester group
Glycerol
Fatty acids
Fat or oil (Triacylglycerol or triglyceride)
+ 3 H2O

(2-3)

Notice that a fat or oil contains three adjacent ester groups, each of which can be produced from a *fatty acid* and one of the OH groups from *glycerol*. (The chemical reactions involved are discussed in Chapter 23.) Thus, a fat or oil is often described as a **triacylglycerol** or a **triglyceride**.

YOUR TURN **2.21**

Circle and label the two unlabeled ester groups in the fat molecule in Equation 2-3.

▶ LOOKING AHEAD

In Section 30.3 we will examine the biosynthetic pathway responsible for synthesizing fatty acids from acetyl coenzyme A.

Because all fats and oils have the same general structure, the identities of the fatty acids distinguish one fat or oil from another. Some examples are shown in Table 2-8.

All natural fatty acids have an even number of carbons because, in nature, fatty acids are synthesized from *acetyl coenzyme A* (*acetyl-CoA*), a two-carbon-atom source (see Looking Ahead box). Most fatty acids have between 12 and 18 carbon atoms, although they can have as few as 4 and as many as 22.

2.10b Phospholipids and Cell Membranes

Like a fat or an oil, a **phospholipid** consists of a glycerol backbone attached to fatty acids via ester linkages, as shown in **Figure 2-32a**.

Whereas a fat or an oil has three fatty acids, making it a triglyceride, a phospholipid has only two fatty acids, making it a **diglyceride**. In place of a third fatty acid, the glycerol backbone is bonded to a phosphate group ($—OPO_3^-$), the same type of group that appears in nucleotides in DNA and RNA (Section 1.14). Typically, the phosphate group is bonded to a second molecular fragment, such as choline (Fig. 2-32b).

Because of their structural similarities to fats and oils, phospholipids can efficiently store energy, too. More importantly, however, phospholipids are integral in the formation of *cell membranes*. Such a role is possible because the two ends of a phospholipid have vastly different properties: the phosphate portion is ionic (hydrophilic),

TABLE 2-8 Some Common Fatty Acids

Fatty Acid	Structure	Sources
Lauric acid $C_{12}H_{24}O_2$	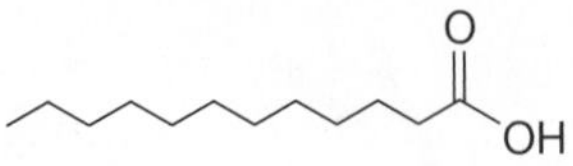	Coconut oil, palm kernel oil
Palmitic acid $C_{16}H_{32}O_2$	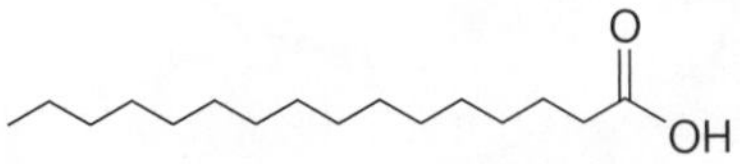	Coconut oil, palm oil, palm kernel oil, meats, cheeses
Stearic acid $C_{18}H_{36}O_2$	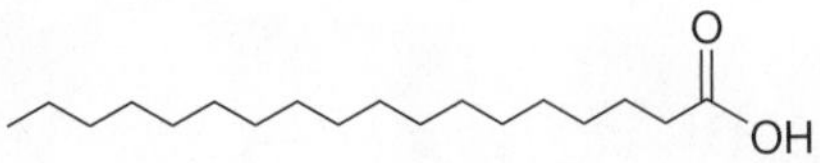	Animal fats, cocoa butter
Oleic acid $C_{18}H_{34}O_2$	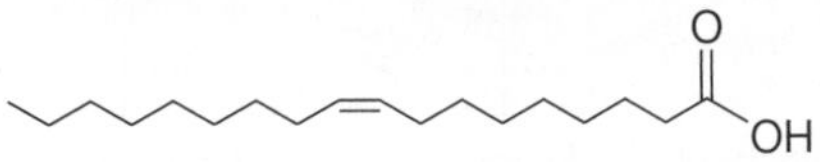	Olive oil, pecan oil, peanut oil
Linoleic acid $C_{18}H_{32}O_2$	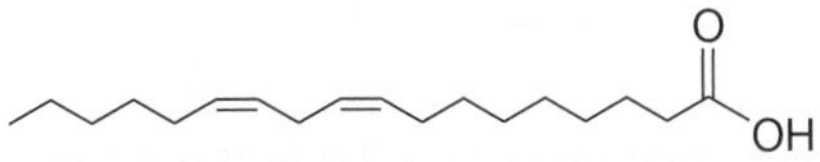	Safflower oil, grape–seed oil
Linolenic acid $C_{18}H_{30}O_2$	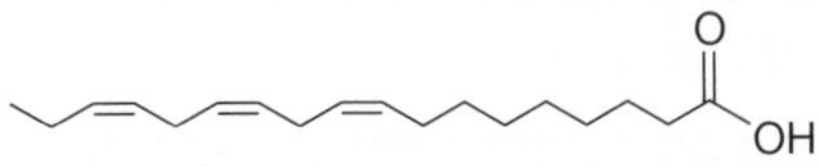	Kiwifruit seeds, flax

whereas the alkyl chains of the fatty acids are nonpolar (hydrophobic). These characteristics, which are also observed in soaps (see Fig. 2-30, p. 99), can be seen in the simplified representation of a phospholipid on the right in Figure 2-32b, in which the red sphere represents the ionic head group and the two blue wavy lines represent the two nonpolar alkyl chains.

Under physiological conditions, the hydrophobic tails from multiple phospholipids associate into a **lipid bilayer** to escape the aqueous environment, as illustrated in

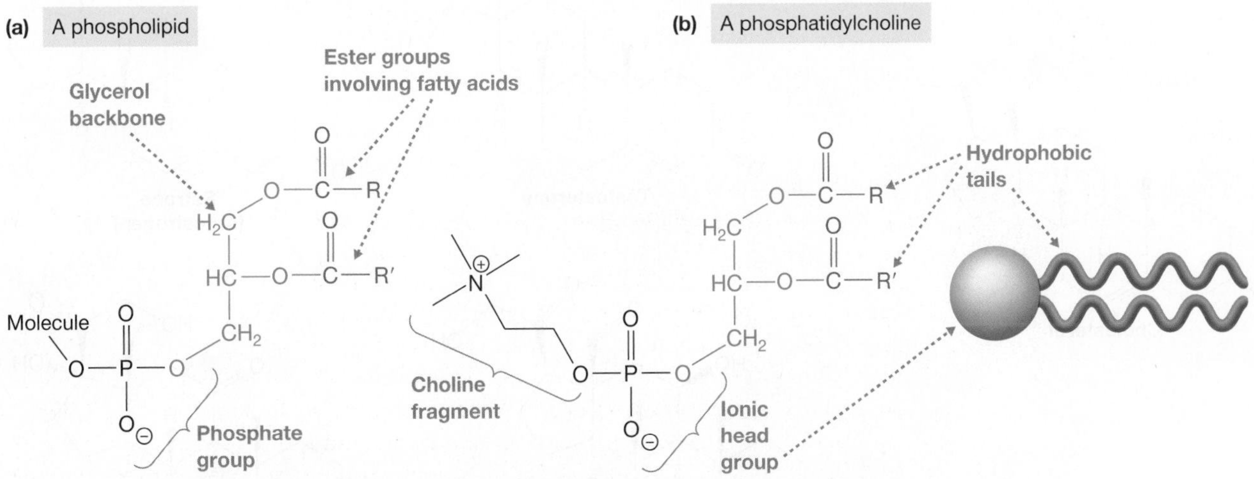
(a) A phospholipid
(b) A phosphatidylcholine
Glycerol backbone
Ester groups involving fatty acids
Molecule
Phosphate group
Choline fragment
Ionic head group
Hydrophobic tails

FIGURE 2-32 Diglycerides in nature (a) A phospholipid and (b) a phosphatidylcholine are both diglycerides because two fatty acids (blue) are linked to the glycerol backbone (red).

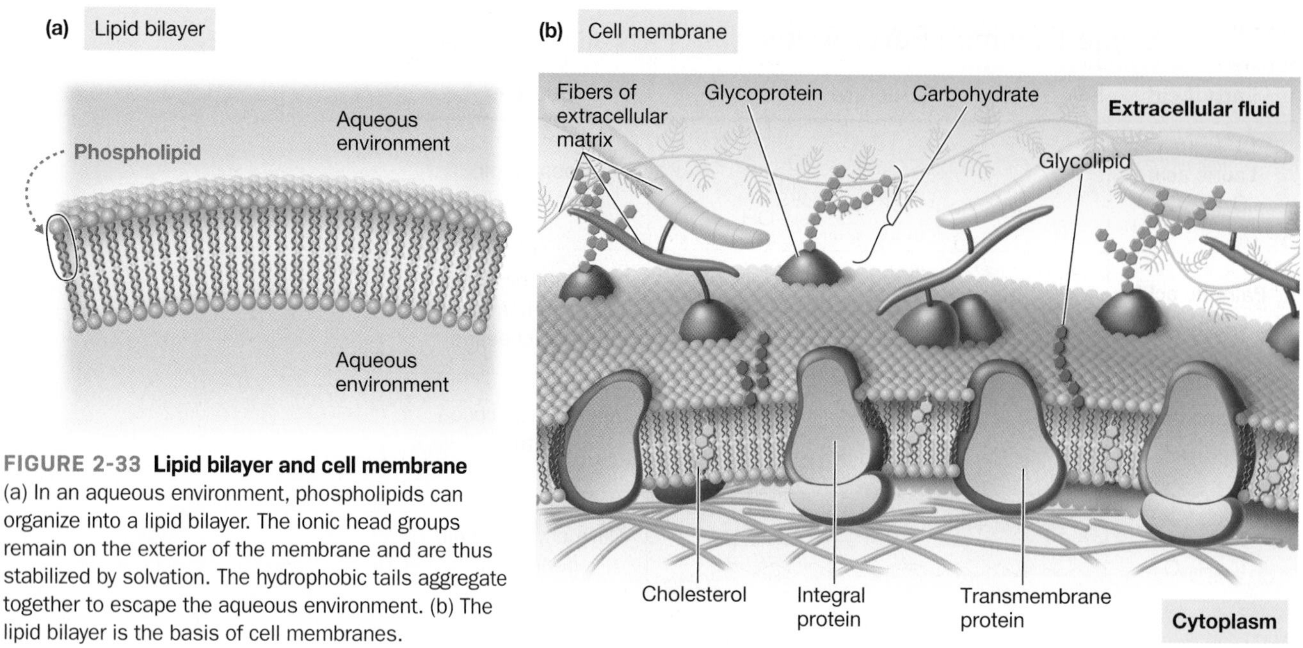
(a) Lipid bilayer
Phospholipid
Aqueous environment
Aqueous environment
(b) Cell membrane
Fibers of extracellular matrix
Glycoprotein
Carbohydrate
Extracellular fluid
Glycolipid
Cholesterol
Integral protein
Transmembrane protein
Cytoplasm

FIGURE 2-33 Lipid bilayer and cell membrane (a) In an aqueous environment, phospholipids can organize into a lipid bilayer. The ionic head groups remain on the exterior of the membrane and are thus stabilized by solvation. The hydrophobic tails aggregate together to escape the aqueous environment. (b) The lipid bilayer is the basis of cell membranes.

Figure 2-33a (similar to the formation of micelles by soaps; see Fig. 2-31, p. 99). This lipid bilayer is the basis of a cell membrane, the basic features of which are shown in Figure 2-33b.

YOUR TURN **2.22**

Identify and label the hydrophobic regions in Figure 2-33a and 2-33b.

The cell membrane's hydrophobic interior and hydrophilic exterior are critical, because they restrict the free passage of most molecules from one side of the membrane to the other. Hydrophobic molecules, such as cholesterol, reside in the membrane's interior. Hydrophilic molecules, such as carbohydrates, are located on the outside. As we can see, however, some specialized proteins can exist in both regions

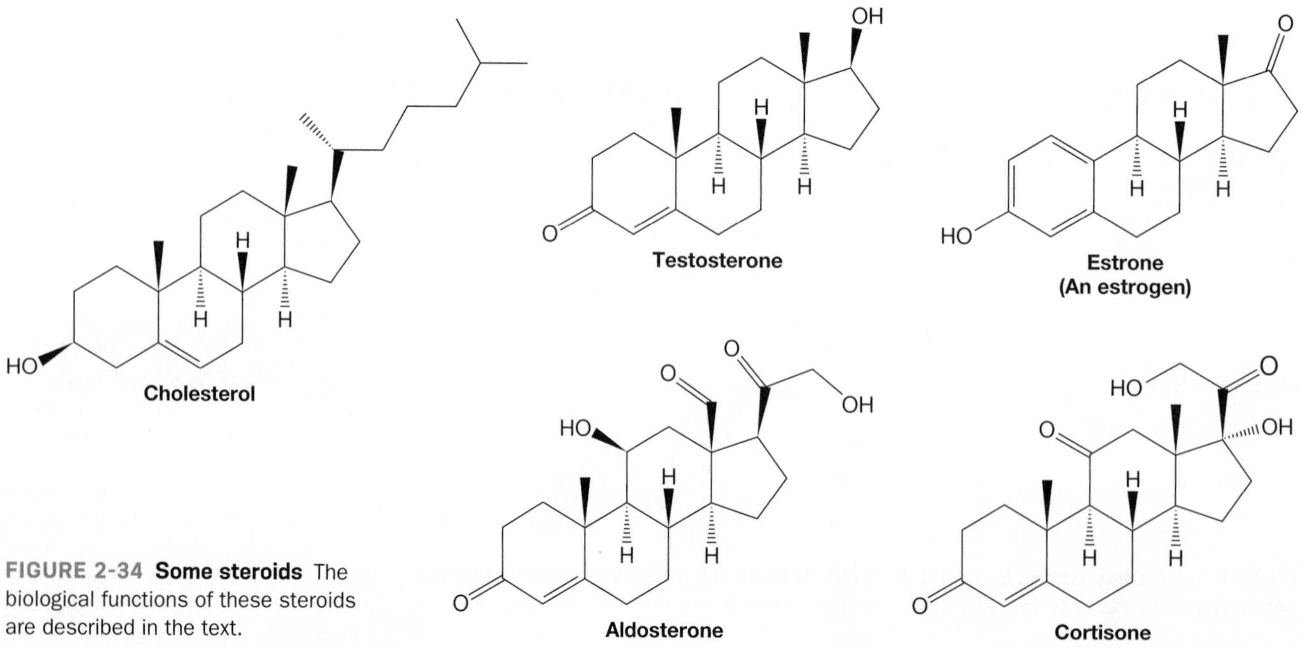
HO
H
H
H
Cholesterol
OH
O
Testosterone
HO
Estrone
(An estrogen)
O
OH
Aldosterone
HO
Cortisone

FIGURE 2-34 Some steroids The biological functions of these steroids are described in the text.

simultaneously. Although we will not examine the details, these proteins tend to have separate hydrophilic and hydrophobic regions, and some are capable of shuttling molecules across the membrane.

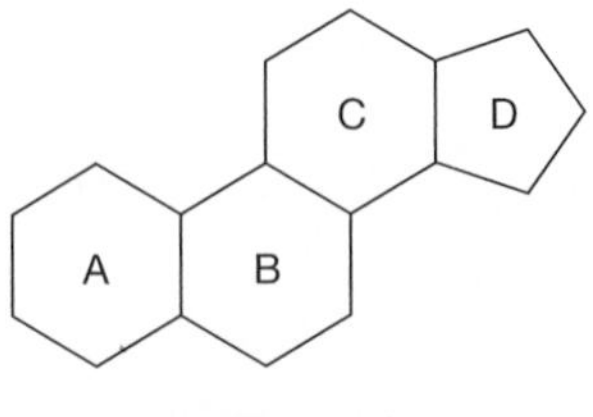
A
B
C
D

FIGURE 2-35 The steroid ring system All steroids are made of three six-membered rings and one five-membered ring, designated as the A, B, C, and D rings, fused in the arrangement shown.

2.10c Steroids

Steroids (**Figure 2-34**) have a wide variety of biological functions. *Cholesterol*, one of the most well-known steroids, is responsible for maintaining the permeability of cell membranes in mammals. *Testosterone* and *estrone* (an estrogen), on the other hand, are male and female sex hormones, respectively. *Aldosterone* helps regulate blood pressure, and *cortisone* suppresses the immune system and is used to treat inflammatory conditions.

All steroids have the same basic ring structure (**Figure 2-35**), in which three six-membered rings and one five-membered ring (designated as the A, B, C, and D rings) are fused together; that is, they have a bond in common. This ring structure is a common feature among steroids because every steroid is produced by chemical modification of *lanosterol*, as shown in Equation 2-4. Lanosterol, in turn, is produced from *squalene*.

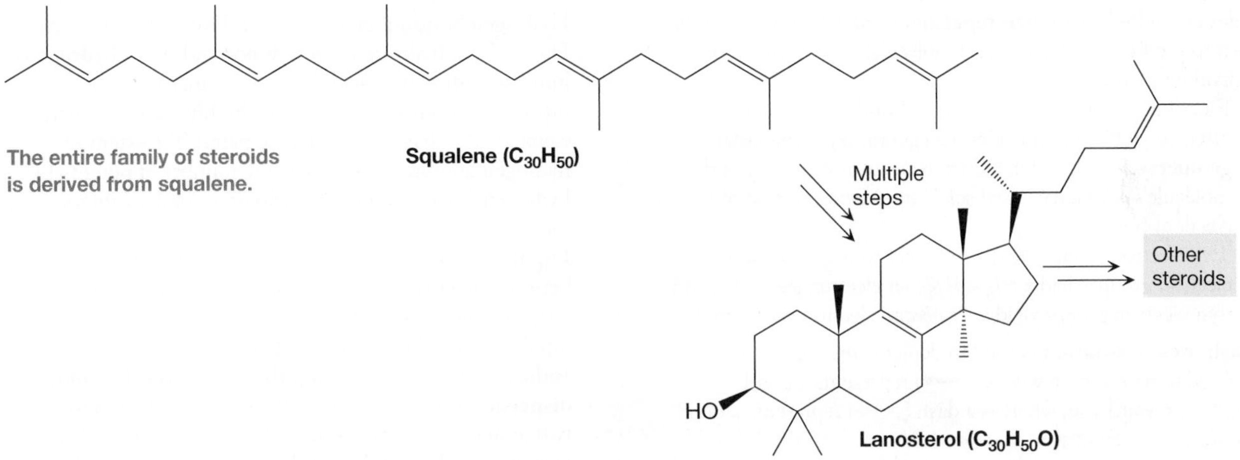
The entire family of steroids is derived from squalene.
Squalene ($C_{30}H_{50}$)
Multiple steps
HO
Lanosterol ($C_{30}H_{50}O$)
Other steroids

(2-4)

Squalene belongs to a family of naturally occurring compounds called *terpenes*, which consist of multiple five-carbon units called *isoprene units*. We will discuss terpenes and their biosynthesis in Section 12.12.

2.10d Waxes

Waxes are secretions from plants and animals that are solid at room temperature but melt at relatively low temperatures. Waxes are typically soft and malleable and are very hydrophobic. Bees use beeswax (**Figure 2-36a**) to store honey and protect their eggs. More commonly in nature, however, wax is used as a protective coating; examples include carnauba wax (Fig. 2-36b), lanolin (Fig. 2-36c), and human earwax (Fig. 2-36d).

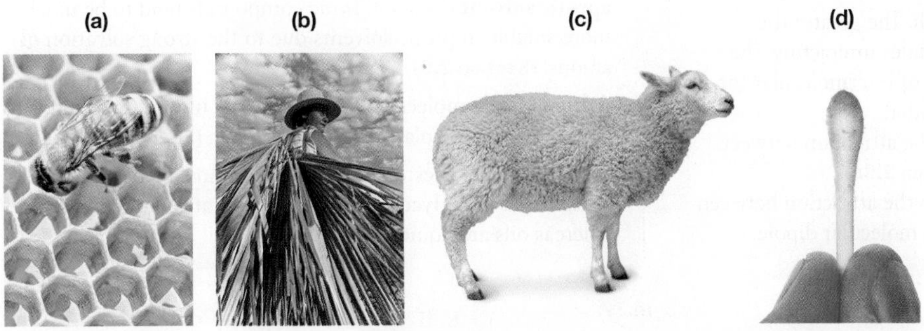
(a)
(b)
(c)
(d)

FIGURE 2-36 Sources of various kinds of natural wax (a) Beeswax is used to make compartments for storing honey and protecting eggs. (b) The carnauba palm, native to Brazil, has wax deposits on its leaves to protect from excessive water loss. (c) Wool has a coating of lanolin, which helps shed water. (d) Human earwax protects the ear canal from bacteria and other foreign substances.

Waxes are generally mixtures of compounds, consisting principally of long-chain esters and alkanes. Tetracosyl hexadecanoate (**Figure 2-37**), for example, is a main constituent of beeswax. Any polarity that might originate from the ester functional group is overwhelmed by the large, highly nonpolar alkyl groups, making the molecule hydrophobic overall.

FIGURE 2-37 Structure of tetracosyl hexadecanoate

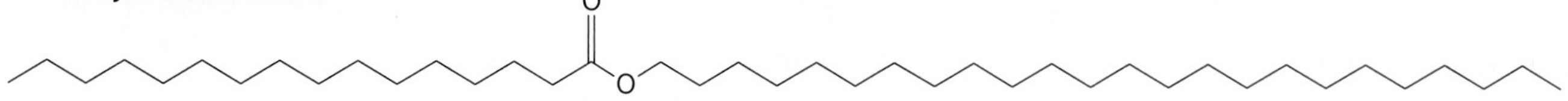
Principal component of beeswax
O
O

Chapter Summary and Key Terms

- **Valence shell electron pair repulsion (VSEPR)** theory can be used to predict the electron and molecular geometries about individual atoms. (Section 2.1a)
  - Electron groups (i.e., lone pairs or bonds) repel each other to yield an atom's **electron geometry**. **Molecular geometry**, which is derived from electron geometry, is the molecule's geometry based solely on the orientation of its covalent bonds.
  - Two electron groups yield a *linear* electron geometry, three electron groups yield a *trigonal planar* electron geometry, and four electron groups yield a *tetrahedral* electron geometry.
- **Dash–wedge notation** is used to depict three-dimensional molecular geometry; a wedge (▬) represents a bond pointing toward you, whereas a dash (⋯) represents a bond pointing away from you. (Section 2.2)
- Bond dipoles are treated as vectors and are added together to yield a molecule's **net molecular dipole** or **permanent dipole**. If bond dipoles do not perfectly cancel, then the molecule is **polar**. If the bond dipoles perfectly cancel, then the molecule is **nonpolar**. (Section 2.4)
- Differences in the physical properties of compounds similar in their makeup and mass are due to the presence of different functional groups. (Section 2.5)
- Boiling points and melting points increase as the strength of **intermolecular interactions** increases in the liquid and solid phases, respectively. (Section 2.6)
- Two compounds will generally mix if the intermolecular forces in the solution are roughly the same strength as or stronger than those that exist in the pure separated compounds. (Section 2.7)
- Intermolecular forces differ in strength. The greater the concentration of charges on the molecules interacting, the stronger their attraction. The strength of intermolecular forces generally decreases in the following order:
  - **Ion–ion interactions** result from the attraction between two oppositely charged ions. (Section 2.6a)
  - **Ion–dipole interactions** are due to the attraction between a positive or negative ion and a net molecular dipole. (Section 2.7a)
  - **Hydrogen bonding** takes the form Do—H⋯A, where Do—H is a **hydrogen-bond donor** and A is a **hydrogen-bond acceptor**. The Do and A atoms are each either nitrogen, oxygen, or fluorine (i.e., highly electronegative elements that have available lone pairs). The extent of hydrogen bonding increases as the number of potential hydrogen-bond donors and hydrogen-bond acceptors increases. (Section 2.6c)
  - **Dipole–dipole interactions** result from the attraction between two net molecular dipoles. The strength of the attraction increases as the magnitudes of the molecular dipoles involved increase. (Section 2.6b)
  - **Induced dipole–induced dipole interactions (London dispersion forces)** are due to the attraction between two temporary dipoles. These interactions increase with increasing **polarizability** of the species involved and with increasing contact surface area. Polarizability generally increases as the number of total electrons increases. (Section 2.6d)
- With enough electrons, induced dipole–induced dipole interactions can become the dominant intermolecular force. (Section 2.6d)
- Even though ion–dipole interactions are weaker than ion–ion interactions, ionic compounds may dissolve in polar solvents as a result of **solvation** of the ions. (Section 2.7a)
- As the size of hydrocarbon groups increases, compounds become less polar and less soluble in polar solvents. A compound tends to be insoluble in water if the ratio of carbons to hydrophilic functional groups exceeds 3 : 1. (Section 2.7b)
- A **protic solvent** contains a H-bond donor, whereas an **aprotic solvent** does not. Ionic compounds tend to be much more soluble in protic solvents due to the strong solvation of anions. (Section 2.9)
- A **lipid** is a biomolecule that is insoluble in water and tends to be soluble in nonpolar solvents like ether. (Section 2.10)
- A **fat** or **oil** is a triester of glycerol and three **fatty acids** and is classified as a **triglyceride**. Fats are solid at room temperature, whereas oils are liquids. (Section 2.10a)

- A **phospholipid** is a **diglyceride** of glycerol, in which two ester groups join fatty acids and a phosphate group joins another molecular fragment. Phospholipids make up the **lipid bilayer** of cell membranes. (Section 2.10b)
- All **steroids** have a system of four fused rings (three six-membered rings and one five-membered ring) called the A, B, C, and D rings. (Section 2.10c)
- **Waxes** generally consist of long-chain esters and alkanes and are secreted by plants and animals for protective coatings. (Section 2.10d)

Problems

Sections 2.1–2.3 Valence Shell Electron Pair Repulsion (VSEPR) Theory, Dash–Wedge Notation, and the Molecular Modeling Kit

2.1 Brassinolide, a naturally occurring steroid derivative found in a wide variety of plants, is thought to promote plant growth. Identify the electron geometry for each atom indicated by an arrow. Where applicable, describe the atom's molecular geometry and estimate the bond angle.

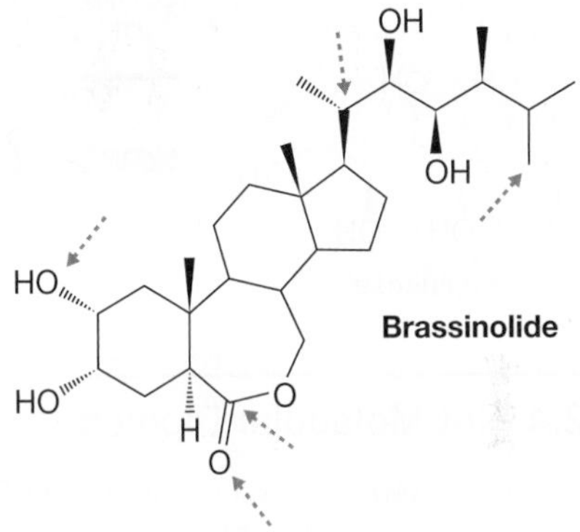
OH
OH
HO
HO
H
O
O

Brassinolide

2.2 Falcarinol, a naturally occurring pesticide found in carrots, is being studied as an anticancer agent. Identify the electron geometry for each atom indicated by an arrow. Where applicable, describe the atom's molecular geometry and estimate the bond angle.

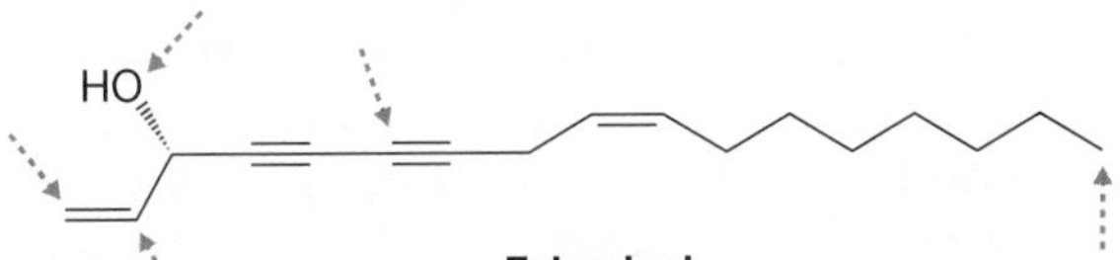
HO

Falcarinol

2.3 Identify the electron geometry about each charged atom. Where appropriate, indicate the molecular geometry and approximate bond angle as well.

(a)
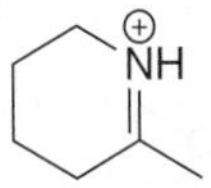
NH

(b)
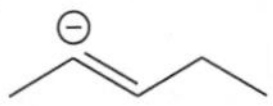

(c)
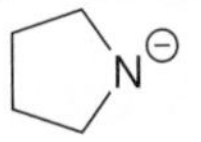
N

(d)
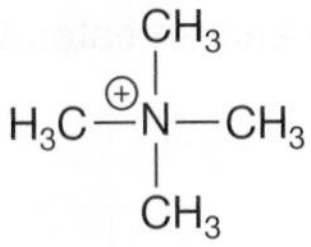
CH3
H3C—N—CH3
CH3

(e)
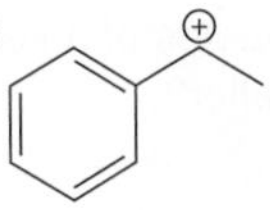

(f)
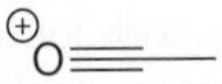
O

2.4 What would VSEPR theory predict as the value for each C—C—C bond angle in cyclopropene? What are the actual bond angles?

Cyclopropene

2.5 Add dash–wedge notation to each line structure provided to accurately depict the ball-and-stick model appearing above it.

(a)
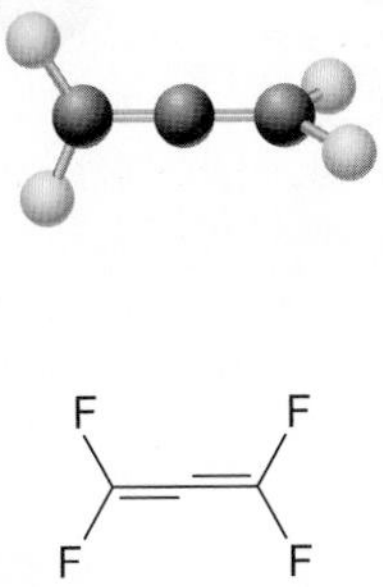
F
F
F
F

(b)
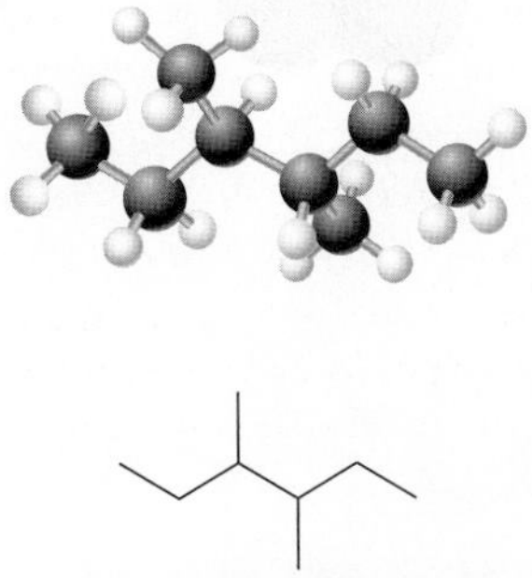

(c)
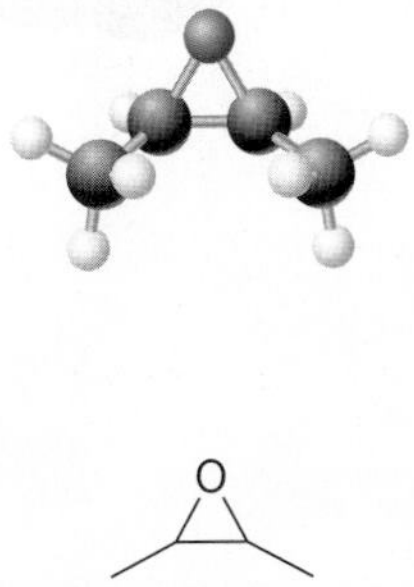
O

(d)
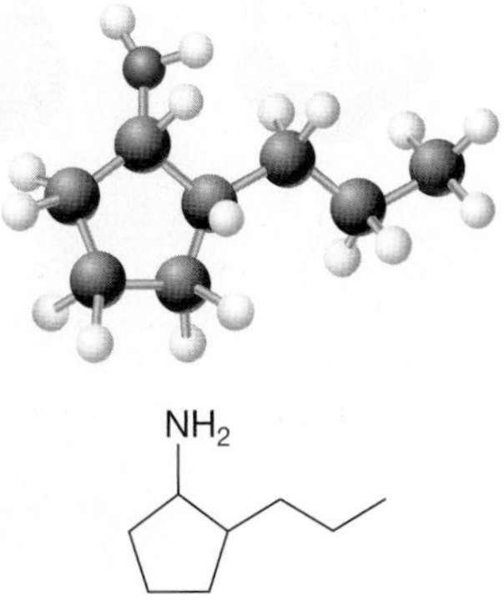
NH2

2.6 Draw line structures of each of these molecules using dash–wedge notation. Assume that no atoms have formal charges. *Note*: Black = carbon, white = hydrogen, green-yellow = chlorine, and blue = nitrogen.

(a)

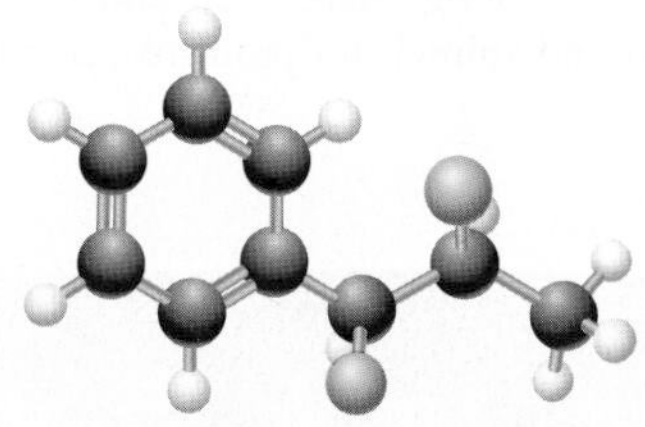

(b)

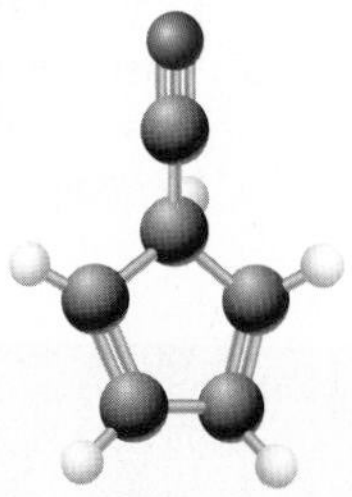

(c)

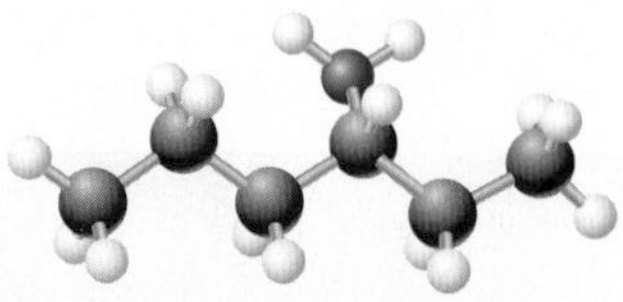

2.7 The structure of D-glucose using dash–wedge notation is shown in parts (a) and (b) here. Draw its structure using dash–wedge notation after each reorientation indicated.

(a)

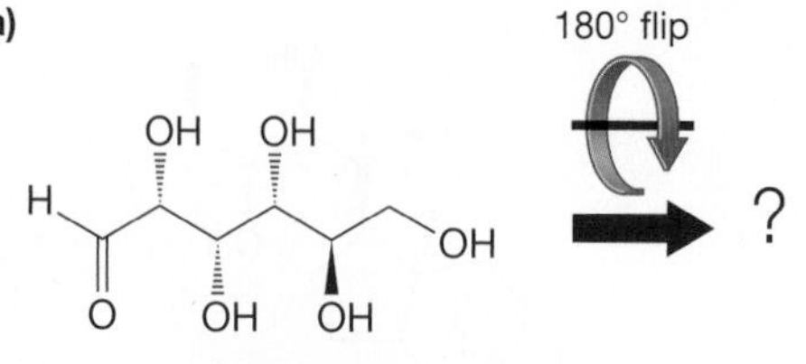

180° flip
OH OH
H
OH
O OH OH
?

D-Glucose

(b)

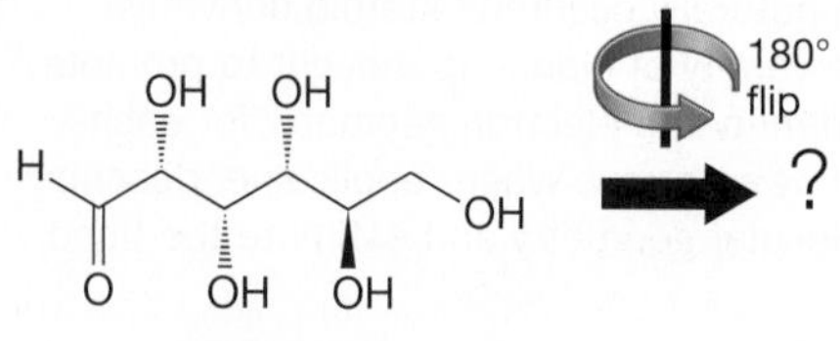

180° flip
OH OH
H
OH
O OH OH
?

D-Glucose

Section 2.4 Net Molecular Dipoles

2.8 Which of the following molecules are polar? For those that are, draw a dipole arrow indicating the direction of the net molecular dipole. *Hint*: Are the molecular geometries depicted accurately?

(a)

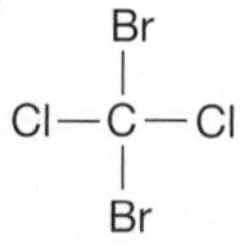

Br
Cl—C—Cl
Br

(b)

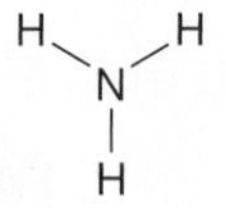

H H
N
H

(c)

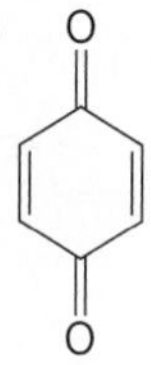

O
O

(d)

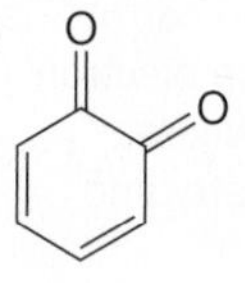

O
O

(e)

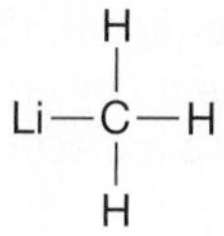

H
Li—C—H
H

2.9 Rank BF_3, BF_2H, and BFH_2 from least polar to most polar.

2.10 The magnitudes are given for the dipoles of a ketone and an ester. Why is the magnitude of the ester's dipole smaller?

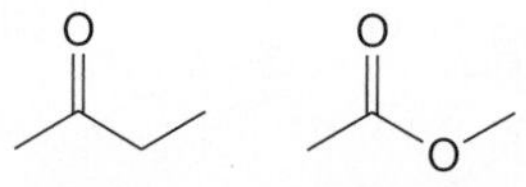

O
O
O

3.0 D 1.8 D

2.11 Use the following electrostatic potential maps of a variety of uncharged molecules to determine which ones are polar (i.e., have nonzero molecular dipoles) and which ones are nonpolar. For each one that is polar, indicate the direction of the net molecular dipole. (You may want to review the color scheme in Figure 1-21 on p. 18.)

(a)

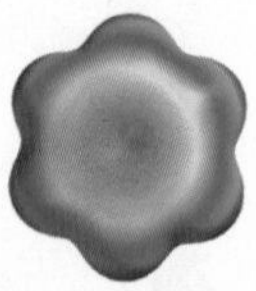

(b)

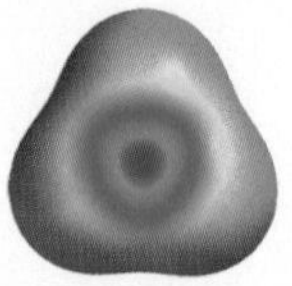

(c)

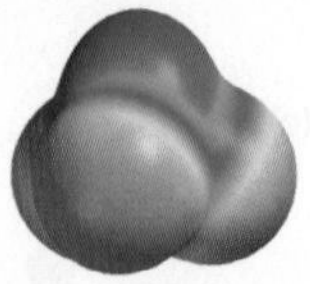

(d)

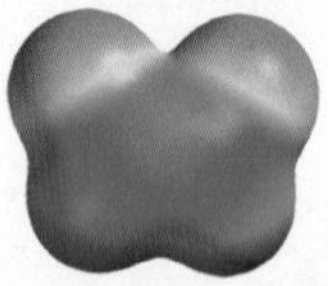

(e)

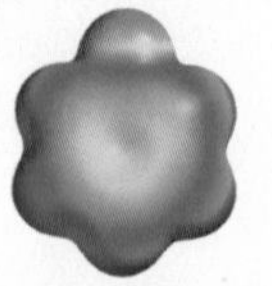

(f)

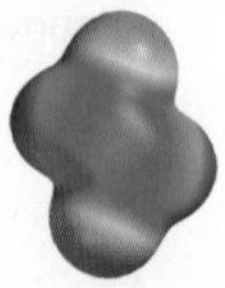

2.12 Determine whether each of the following molecules is polar. For those that are polar, indicate the direction of the net dipole.

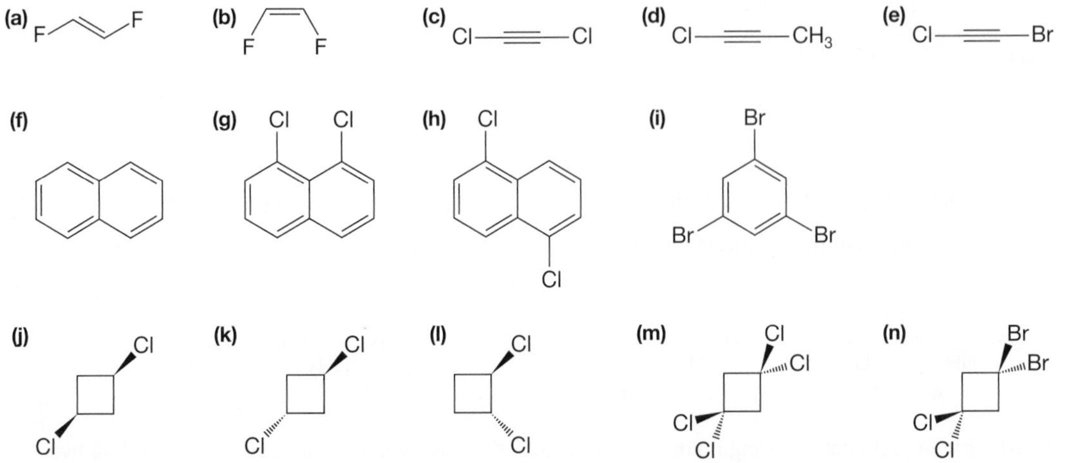

(a)
F
F
(b)
F
F
(c)
Cl
Cl
(d)
Cl
CH3
(e)
Cl
Br
(f)
(g)
Cl
Cl
(h)
Cl
Cl
(i)
Br
Br
Br
(j)
Cl
Cl
(k)
Cl
Cl
(l)
Cl
Cl
(m)
Cl
Cl
Cl
Cl
(n)
Br
Br
Cl
Cl

2.13 In 1874, Dutch chemist Jacobus van't Hoff (1852–1911) and French chemist Joseph Le Bel (1847–1930) independently deduced that a carbon atom bonded to four atoms assumes a tetrahedral geometry. Prior to that time, it was believed that tetravalent carbons assumed a square planar geometry. One piece of evidence that can be used to support a tetrahedral geometry is the fact that molecules with the general formula CX_2Y_2 (where X and Y are either hydrogen or halogen atoms) are always polar. Explain how this supports a tetrahedral geometry and rules out a square planar geometry.

Tetrahedral geometry **Square planar geometry**

Sections 2.6 and 2.7 Melting Points, Boiling Points, Solubility, and Intermolecular Interactions

2.14 Which ions or molecules would be attracted to CH_3^+? Indicate the type of intermolecular forces involved in the attraction. **(a)** H_2O; **(b)** Na^+; **(c)** Cl^-; **(d)** F^-; **(e)** $H_2C{=}O$

2.15 Which pair of ions will attract each other most strongly? Explain.

$Mg^{2+}O^{2-}$	$Al^{3+}O^{2-}$	Na^+O^{2-}
A	**B**	**C**

2.16 Which compound has the higher boiling point, CH_4 or CH_3F?

2.17 Would you expect 1,2-difluorobenzene or 1,3-difluorobenzene to have a higher boiling point? Explain.

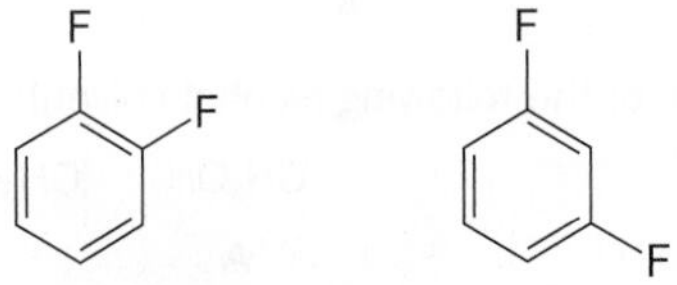

F
F
F
F

1,2-Difluorobenzene **1,3-Difluorobenzene**

2.18 High levels of cholesterol, a naturally occurring steroid, have been linked to cardiovascular disease. Octanoic acid (caprylic acid) is a fatty acid found in milk and is used commercially to manufacture perfumes and dyes. Identify the number of *potential* H-bond donors and H-bond acceptors in cholesterol and in octanoic acid.

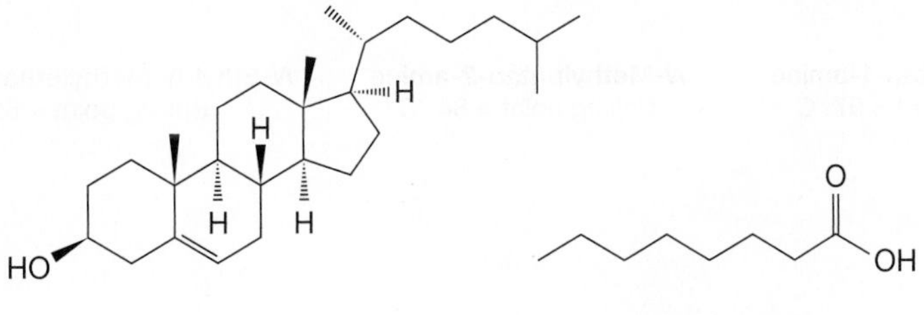

H
H
H
H
HO
O
OH

Cholesterol **Octanoic acid (Caprylic acid)**

2.19 How many potential H-bond donors and H-bond acceptors are there in each of the following molecules?

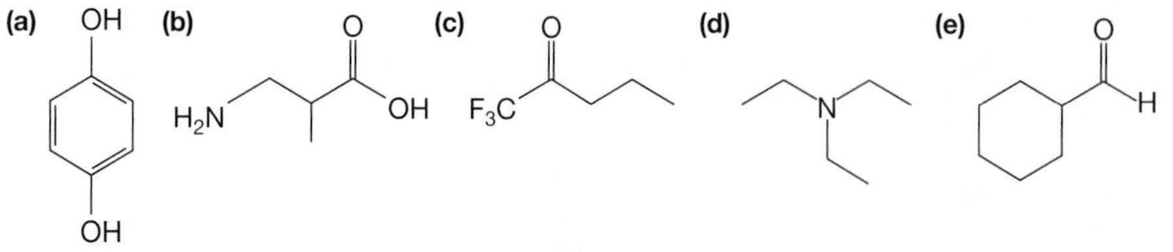
(a)
OH
OH
(b)
O
H_2N
OH
(c)
O
F_3C
(d)
N
(e)
O
H

2.20 Draw the complete Lewis structure of $(CH_3)_2CHCH(NH_2)CO_2H$ and identify all H-bond donors and all H-bond acceptors.

2.21 Which pair of species will give rise to the strongest intermolecular interactions? Which will give rise to the weakest interactions?

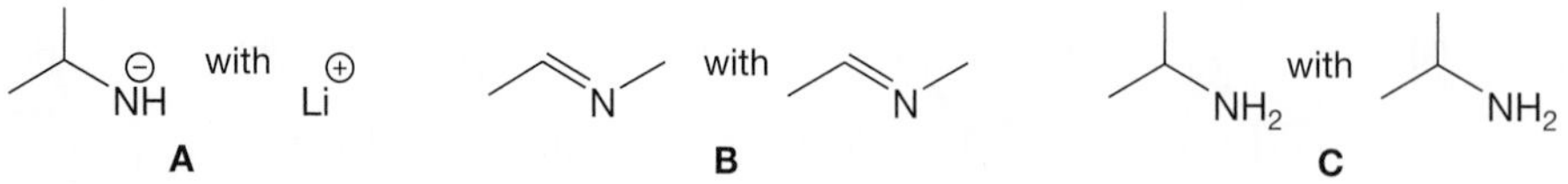
NH
with
Li
A
N
with
N
B
NH_2
with
NH_2
C

2.22 The substance with the lowest known boiling point (−269 °C, or 4 K) is helium, an atomic element that has two electrons. Hydrogen is a diatomic molecule and also has two electrons, but its boiling point is significantly higher, at −253 °C, or 20 K.

(a) What is the dominant intermolecular force between a pair of helium atoms and a pair of H_2 molecules?

(b) Why do you think H_2 has a higher boiling point?

2.23 Which molecule, in each pair, would you expect to have a higher boiling point? Why?

(a)

2,2-Dimethylbutane **2-Methylpentane**

(b)

1,1-Dimethylcyclopropane **1,2-Dimethylcyclopropane**

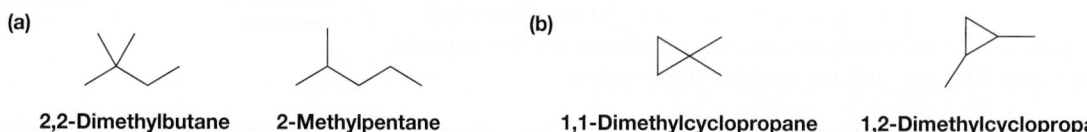

2.24 In this chapter, we did not discuss the interaction that is primarily responsible for the attraction that exists between an anion like CH_3O^- and a nonpolar molecule like Br_2.

(a) What name would be used to describe the strongest interaction that exists between those two species?

(b) For which pair of species would you expect that type of attractive interaction to be stronger: between CH_3O^- and Br_2 or between CH_3O^- and I_2? Why?

2.25 Which of these organic solvents would be most soluble in water? Explain your choice.

A	B	C	D
$CH_3CH_2CH_2CH_2CH_2CH_3$	$CH_3OCH_2CH_2CH_2CH_3$	$CH_3OCH_2CH_2OCH_3$	$CH_3CH_2CH_2CH_3$

2.26 In which of the following alcohol solvents do you think NaCl would be the most soluble?

A	B	C	D
CH_3OH	CH_3CH_2OH	$CH_3CH_2CH_2OH$	$CH_3CH_2CH_2CH_2OH$

2.27 The following amines have the same molecular formula ($C_5H_{13}N$), but their boiling points are significantly different. Explain why.

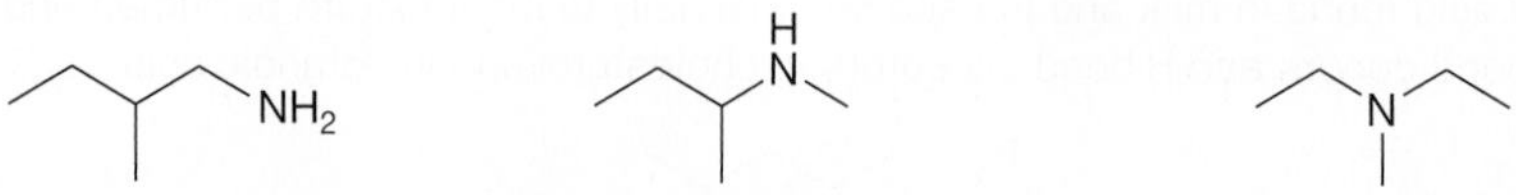
NH_2
H
N
N

2-Methylbutan-1-amine
Boiling point = 97 °C

***N*-Methylbutan-2-amine**
Boiling point = 84 °C

***N*-Ethyl-*N*-methylethan-1-amine**
Boiling point = 65 °C

Section 2.8 Ranking Boiling Points and Solubilities of Structurally Similar Compounds

2.28 Rank molecules **A–H** in order from lowest to highest boiling point.

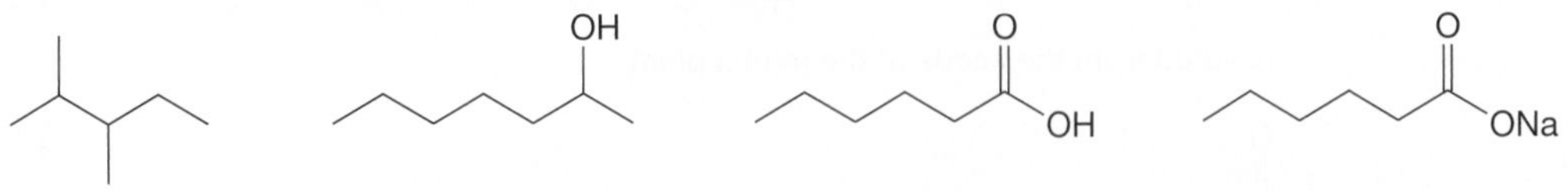

A **B** **C** **D**

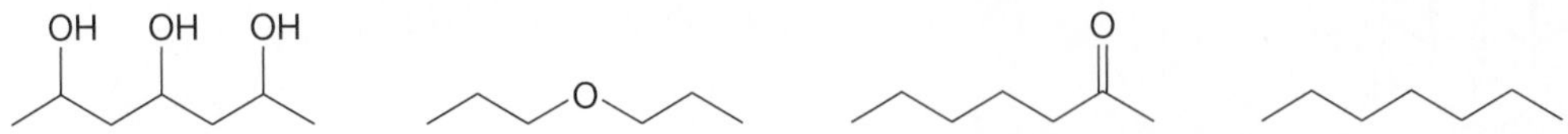

E **F** **G** **H**

2.29 Rank molecules **A–D** in order from lowest to highest boiling point. Briefly rationalize your choice.

$CH_3CH_2OCH_2CH_3$	$CH_3CH_2CH_2CH_2CH_3$	$CH_3CH(OH)CH_2CH_3$	$FCH_2CH_2OCH_2CH_3$
A	**B**	**C**	**D**

2.30 Rank molecules **A–D** in order from lowest to highest boiling point. Briefly rationalize your choice.

$CH_3CH_2CH(OH)CH_2OH$	$CH_3CH_2CH_2CH_2OH$	$CH_3CH(OH)CH(OH)CH_2OH$	$FCH_2CH_2CH_2CH_3$
A	**B**	**C**	**D**

Section 2.9 Protic and Aprotic Solvents

2.31 Identify each of the following compounds as either a *protic* solvent or an *aprotic* solvent.

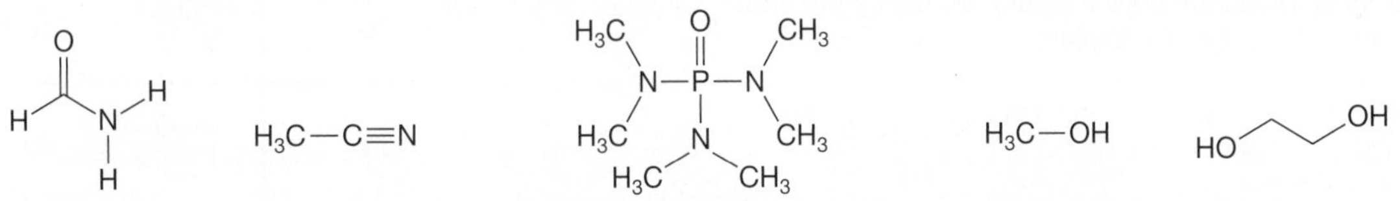

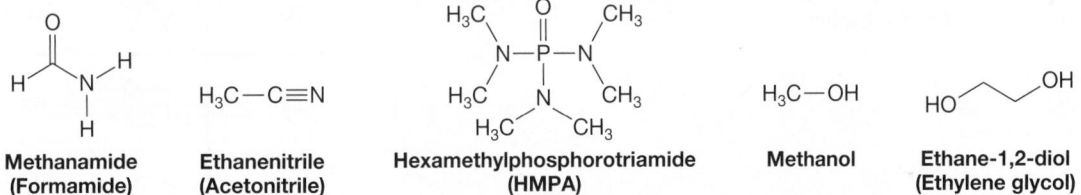

Methanamide (Formamide) **Ethanenitrile (Acetonitrile)** **Hexamethylphosphorotriamide (HMPA)** **Methanol** **Ethane-1,2-diol (Ethylene glycol)**

2.32 In which solvents in Problem 2.31 do you think NaCl will have a substantially greater solubility than in dimethyl sulfoxide (DMSO)? Explain.

2.33 Do you think NaCl is more soluble in acetone, $(CH_3)_2C{=}O$, or di-*tert*-butyl ketone, $[(CH_3)_3C]_2C{=}O$? Explain.

2.34 Will $KSCH_3$ be more soluble in ethanol or acetone? Explain.

Section 2.10 The Organic Chemistry of Biomolecules

2.35 Draw a triacylglycerol in which **(a)** all three fatty acids are lauric acid and **(b)** one fatty acid is linoleic acid and two are oleic acid.

2.36 Draw a fat or oil molecule that is constructed from **(a)** three molecules of stearic acid and **(b)** two molecules of oleic acid and one molecule of linolenic acid.

2.37 Identify each of the following molecules as a steroid, a fatty acid, or a wax.

(a)

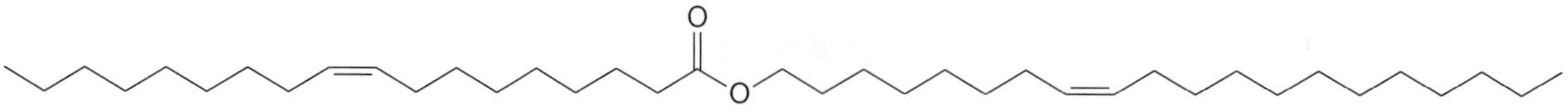

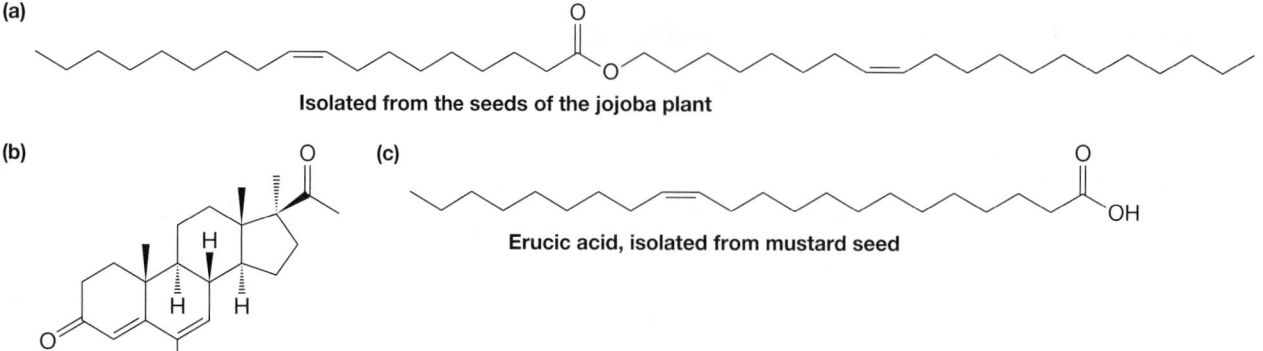

Isolated from the seeds of the jojoba plant

(b)

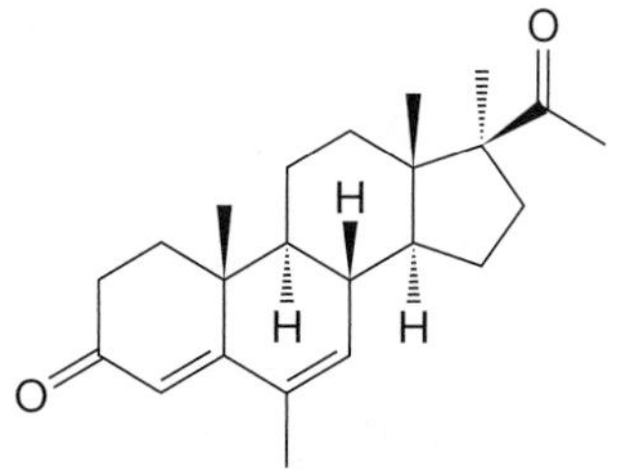

Medrogestone, a synthetic drug

(c)

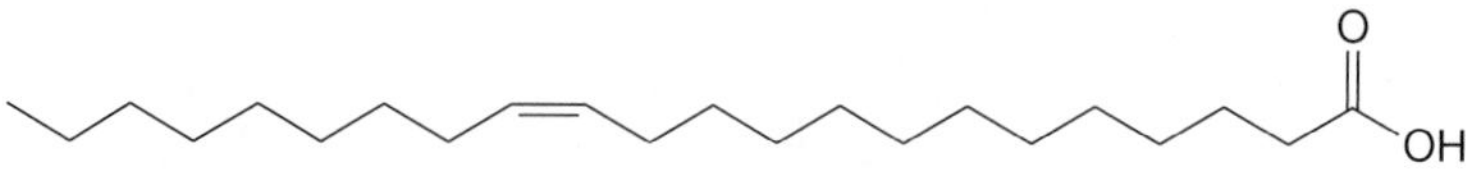

Erucic acid, isolated from mustard seed

2.38 Circle and label all functional groups in the molecules in Problem 2.37.

Integrated Problems

2.39 Propan-1-ol ($CH_3CH_2CH_2OH$) and propan-2-ol [$(CH_3)_2CHOH$] are both alcohols that have the same formula (C_3H_8O) but significantly different boiling points: 97.5 °C for propan-1-ol and 82 °C for propan-2-ol. Explain.

2.40 The boiling points of several cyclic alkanes and ethers are listed in the table shown here. For small rings, there is a significant difference in boiling points between the cyclic alkane and the cyclic ether (e.g., −76 °C vs. 10.7 °C), but for large rings, the boiling points are nearly the same (e.g., 80.7 °C vs. 88 °C). Explain.

Cyclic Alkane	Boiling Point (°C)	Cyclic Ether	Boiling Point (°C)
	–76		10.7
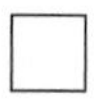	–13	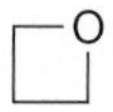	50
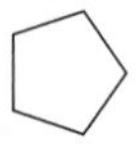	49		66
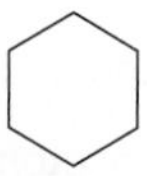	80.7	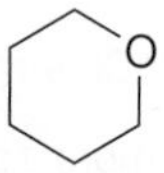	88

2.41 Naturally occurring unsaturated fatty acids, such as **A**, contain only cis double bonds, in which the two non-hydrogen substituents appear on the same side of the double bond. A corresponding saturated fatty acid (**B**) is also shown. **A** is a liquid at room temperature, whereas **B** is a solid. What does this suggest about the strength of the intermolecular forces in each substance? Can you explain? *Hint*: Build a model and compare the surface area of contact for a pair of each molecule.

Liquid

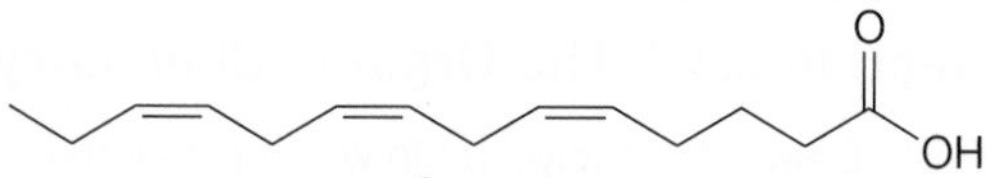

A

Solid

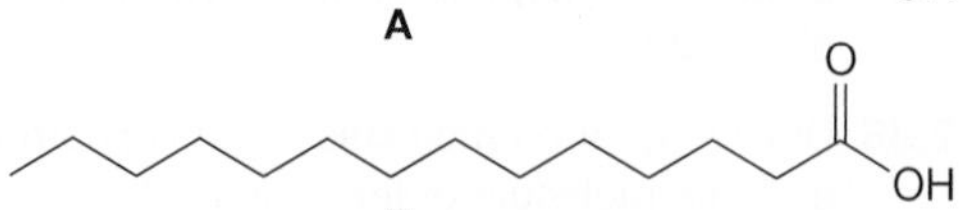

B

2.42 Benzene and hexafluorobenzene have nearly identical boiling points, even though hexafluorobenzene has significantly more total electrons than benzene. Why do you think this is so?

Benzene
Boiling point = 80 °C

Hexafluorobenzene
Boiling point = 81 °C

2.43 An uncharged oxygen atom has two lone pairs of electrons, so it can participate in two different hydrogen bonds (i.e., with two separate H-bond donors), as shown here. Estimate the angle between the two hydrogen bonds.

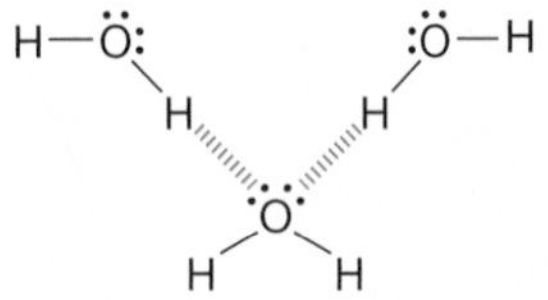

2.44 All of the following alcohols have the same molecular formula ($C_5H_{12}O$), but they have significantly different boiling points. Explain why.

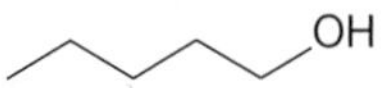
OH

Pentan-1-ol
Boiling point = 136–138 °C

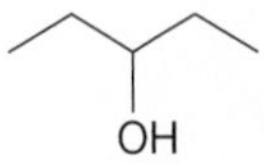
OH

Pentan-3-ol
Boiling point = 114–115 °C

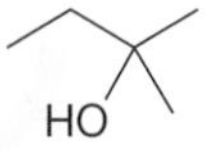
HO

2-Methylbutan-2-ol
Boiling point = 102 °C

2.45 Explain why 1,2-dihydroxybenzene and 1,3-dihydroxybenzene have such different boiling points.

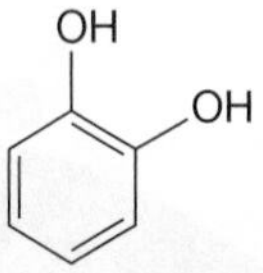
OH
OH

1,2-Dihydroxybenzene
Boiling point = 245 °C

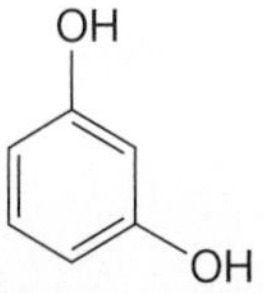
OH
OH

1,3-Dihydroxybenzene
Boiling point = 281 °C

3

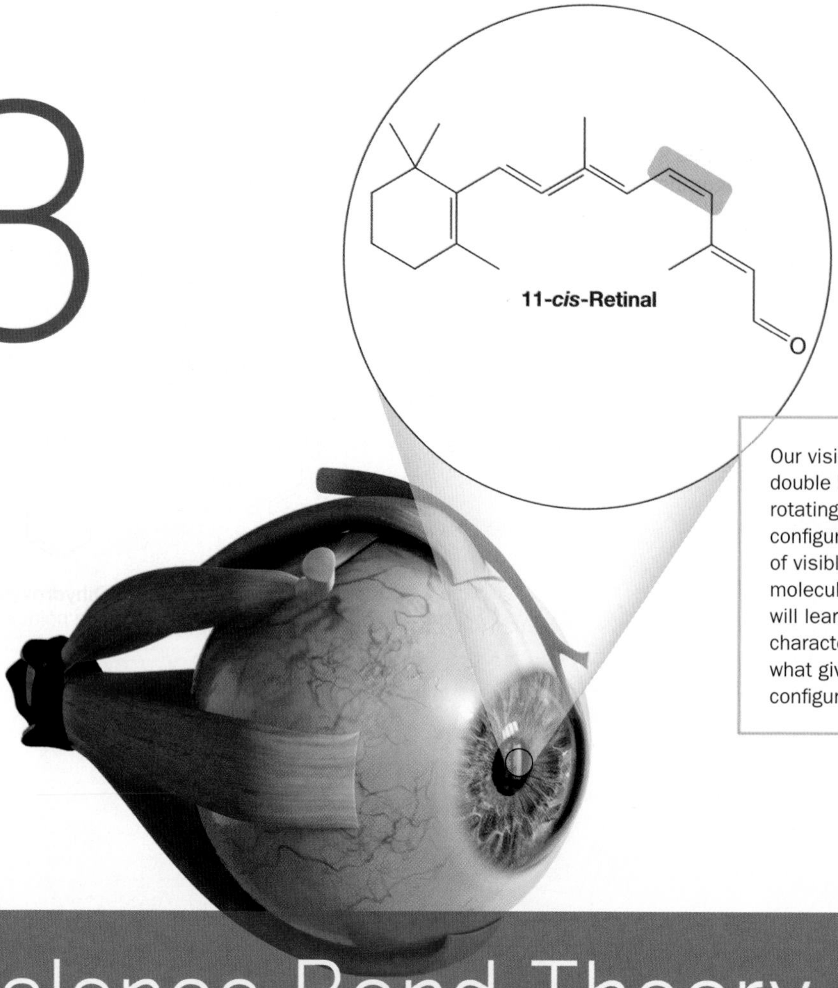
11-*cis*-Retinal
O

Our vision relies on the highlighted double bond in 11-*cis*-retinal rotating from the cis to the trans configuration when a photon of visible light collides with the molecule. Here in Chapter 3, we will learn about the rotational characteristics of bonds and what gives rise to cis and trans configurations for double bonds.

Valence Bond Theory and Molecular Orbital Theory

In Chapters 1 and 2, we reviewed Lewis structures and valence shell electron pair repulsion (VSEPR) theory: two very useful models that help us describe molecular structure. Lewis structures describe the connectivity of the atoms (i.e., which atoms are bonded together and whether they are connected by single, double, or triple bonds), whereas VSEPR theory allows us to make reliable predictions of the geometries about the atoms.

Despite their usefulness, Lewis structures and VSEPR theory have significant limitations. Neither model explains certain important experimental findings, such as why a molecule of ethene ($H_2C{=}CH_2$, **Figure 3-1**), is entirely planar (that is, why all six of its atoms lie in the same plane) without the CH_2 groups rotating relative to each other.

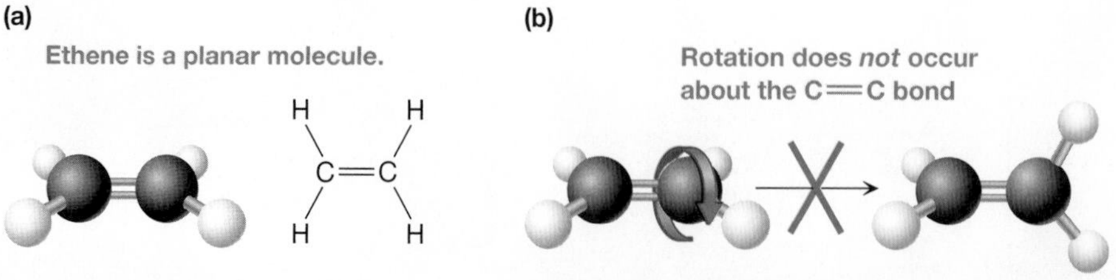
(a)
Ethene is a planar molecule.
H
H
C=C
H
H
(b)
Rotation does *not* occur about the C=C bond

FIGURE 3-1 Ethene (a) All six atoms of ethene lie in the same plane. (b) Rotation does not occur about the C=C double bond. These characteristics of ethene cannot be explained by Lewis structures or VSEPR theory.

Chapter Outline

This chapter presents models of bonding that go beyond the limitations of Lewis structures and VSEPR theory. To better explain molecular geometry and bond rotations, we introduce the concepts of *hybridization* and *valence bond theory*. Then, toward the end of this chapter, we delve into the model of *molecular orbital theory*, which, as will be seen in later chapters, provides insights into the dynamics of chemical reactions (Chapter 7), resonance stabilization (Chapter 14), and spectroscopy (which deals with how molecules interact with light; Chapters 16 and 17).

3.1 An Introduction to Valence Bond Theory and σ Bonds: An Example with H_2

SECTION 3.1 OBJECTIVES

You will be able to:

1. Use valence bond theory to describe the origin of a bond.
2. Characterize a σ bond according to the type of overlap from contributing orbitals.
3. Draw the valence bond picture of a single bond in a diatomic molecule.

Recall that Lewis structures describe a covalent bond as the sharing of valence electrons between two atoms. *Valence bond (VB) theory* takes this idea further, focusing on the orbitals in which those electrons reside, both before and after bond formation:

Valence Bond (VB) Theory

- A covalent bond forms when two half-filled valence orbitals, from two separate atoms, overlap in space.
- The overlapping orbitals mix to create a new orbital that is built up in the region between the two atoms.
- The new orbital accommodates bonding electrons, allowing them to be shared between the two atoms.

(You may recall from general chemistry that the buildup of the orbitals in an internuclear region is an outcome of electrons behaving as waves, a topic we will discuss in greater detail in Section 3.10.)

To begin to apply VB theory, we must be familiar with *s* and *p* orbitals (**Figure 3-2**), which make up the valence shells of the atoms that are most common to organic

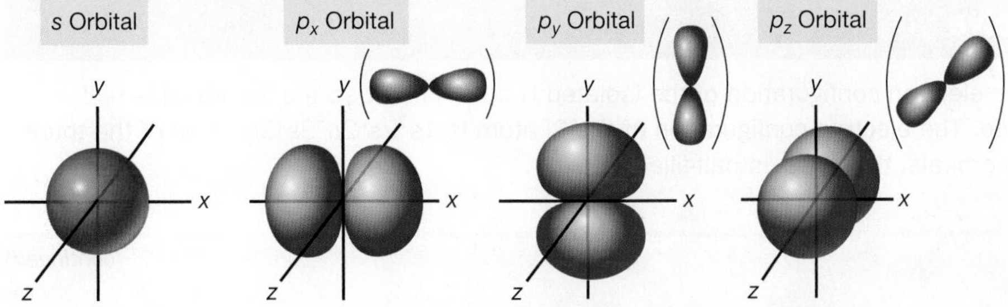

s Orbital
p_x Orbital
p_y Orbital
p_z Orbital
y
x
z

FIGURE 3-2 ***s* and *p* Orbitals** An *s* orbital is spherical, whereas a *p* orbital consists of two lobes and is dumbbell-shaped. A *p* orbital can be aligned along the *x*, *y*, or *z* axis, characterizing it as a p_x, p_y, or p_z orbital, respectively. The depictions in parentheses are streamlined representations of *p* orbitals.

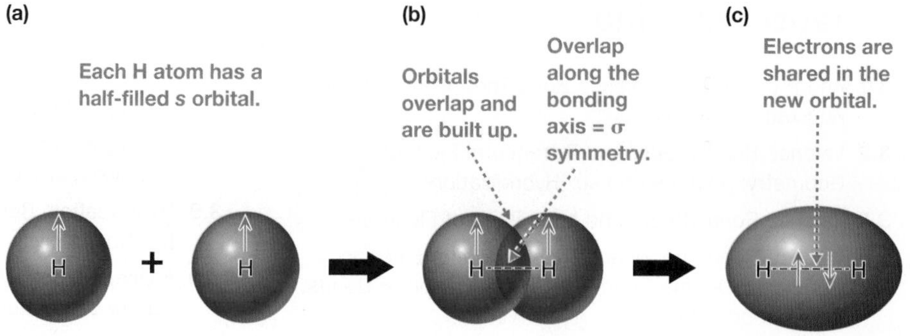
(a)
Each H atom has a half-filled s orbital.
H
+
H
(b)
Orbitals overlap and are built up.
Overlap along the bonding axis = σ symmetry.
H
H
(c)
Electrons are shared in the new orbital.
H
H

FIGURE 3-3 Valence bond theory applied to H_2 (a) Each separate H atom has a half-filled valence s orbital. (b) When the two H atoms come together in space, the orbitals overlap. (c) This overlap produces a new orbital that belongs to both nuclei simultaneously. The overlap of the orbitals along the bonding axis (black dashed line) gives the new orbital σ symmetry, and the bond is a σ bond.

CONNECTIONS 3.1

Molecular hydrogen and its uses H_2 (Fig. 3-3) has a wide variety of uses industrially, including the processing of fossil fuels and the production of ammonia, NH_3. It is also used as a reducing agent in the synthesis of chemicals and as a fuel source in the hydrogen fuel cells that power electric cars.

FuelCell
GF 41 863

chemistry. Recall from Section 1.3 that the first shell consists of only an *s* orbital, whereas the second and higher shells have one *s* and three *p* orbitals. An *s* orbital is spherical, whereas the three *p* orbitals (called p_x, p_y, and p_z) are dumbbell-shaped and align along the *x*, *y*, and *z* axes, respectively. Often *p* orbitals are depicted with the streamlined representations shown in parentheses in Figure 3-2.

Let's now apply VB theory to the simplest molecule, H_2. The two hydrogen atoms are held together by a single covalent bond, so the Lewis structure is simply H—H, and we can envision the molecule being constructed from two isolated H atoms. The electron configuration of an isolated H atom is $1s^1$, so the 1*s* orbital of each atom is a half-filled valence orbital (**Figure 3-3a**). When the H atoms come together, the two 1*s* orbitals overlap (Fig. 3-3b), and the new orbital that is produced (Fig. 3-3c) ends up with both electrons.

Symmetry is an important property of new orbitals that are produced by overlapping orbitals from different atoms. The most common type is *σ (sigma) symmetry*:

- An orbital having **σ symmetry** will be produced when orbitals from different atoms overlap *along* the bonding axis, which is the line connecting the two nuclei.
- A pair of electrons occupying an orbital with σ symmetry is called a **σ bond**.

The H—H single bond in H_2 is an example of a σ bond. This simple example reflects a general outcome:

All single bonds are σ bonds, regardless of the molecule in which they are found.

Solved Problem 3.1 takes us through another example.

SOLVED PROBLEM **3.1**

How to use valence bond theory to describe a single bond

Break It Down **The H and Cl atoms in HCl are held together by a single covalent bond. Apply VB theory to describe that bond. What type of symmetry does that bond have?**

Think	Solve
What is the electron configuration of each isolated atom? What valence orbitals are half-filled?	The electron configuration of the isolated H atom is $1s^1$, so the 1s orbital is half-filled. The electron configuration of the Cl atom is $1s^2 2s^2 2p^6 3s^2 3p^5$. One of the three 3*p* orbitals, therefore, is half-filled.

(continued)

How do those orbitals overlap to form a new orbital that would allow the electrons of the bond to be shared?	When the orbitals overlap as shown here, a new orbital results, which has been built up in the overlap region. 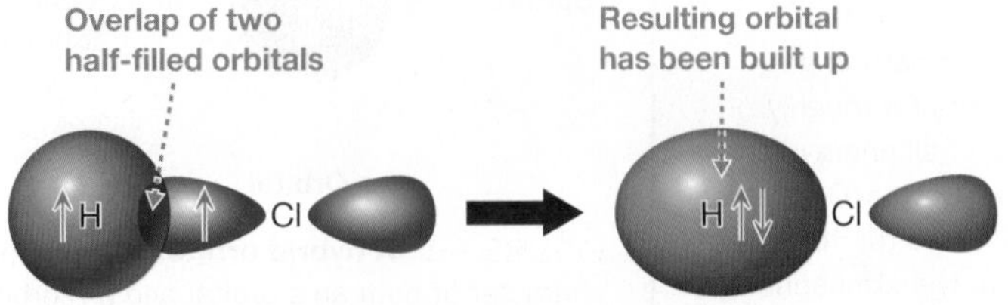 Overlap of two half-filled orbitals Resulting orbital has been built up H Cl H Cl
Do the orbitals overlap along the bonding axis? What type of symmetry, therefore, is the resulting bond?	The 1*s* orbital of hydrogen overlaps the 3*p* orbital from Cl along the bonding axis, so the resulting orbital has σ symmetry and the resulting bond is a σ bond. 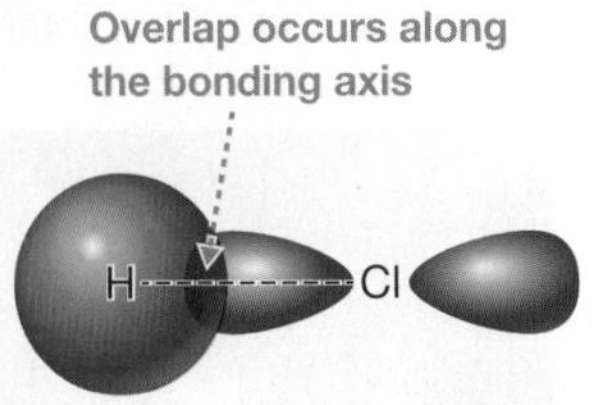 Overlap occurs along the bonding axis H Cl

Try It The two Cl atoms in Cl_2 are held together by a covalent single bond. Apply VB theory to describe that bond. What type of symmetry does that bond have?

Answers to all Try It exercises can be found in the Solutions Manual.

The examples in this section deal only with σ symmetry. Another common type of symmetry is π (pi) symmetry, which we will discuss in Section 3.4.

3.2 Valence Bond Theory and Tetrahedral Electron Geometry: Alkanes and *sp*^{3} Hybridization

SECTION 3.2 OBJECTIVES

You will be able to:

1. Identify the hybridization of an atom that has a tetrahedral electron geometry.
2. Describe the orbitals that such an atom contributes to the VB picture of a molecule.
3. Draw the VB picture of an alkane.

When we apply VB theory to methane (CH_4), we immediately run into an issue concerning the number of bonds possible and the geometry. In an isolated C atom, the ground state electron configuration is $1s^22s^22p^2$. Therefore, the *s* orbital in the valence shell is filled and two of the valence *p* orbitals are half-filled. If only those half-filled *p* orbitals are used to form C—H bonds, then carbon would be able to form only two bonds. Moreover, as shown in **Figure 3-4**, those C—H bonds would be 90° apart because the *p* orbitals are perpendicular. However, the carbon in CH_4 forms four bonds and the actual H—C—H bond angle is 109.5°. How, then, does VB theory account for the tetrahedral geometry of CH_4?

We begin by invoking the concept of *hybridization*, where we consider pure (unhybridized) *s* and *p* orbitals from the valence shell mixing together to form new orbitals, called **hybrid orbitals.** We will discuss hybridization and orbital mixing in greater detail in Section 3.10. For now, it will suffice to know that each hybrid orbital that results from mixing *s* and *p* orbitals has character of both an *s* and a *p* orbital, so its shape is somewhat different from either. Specifically, as shown in **Figure 3-5** (next page), each hybrid orbital consists of one large lobe and one small lobe.

In the case of CH_4, we consider all four of carbon's valence orbitals (the 2*s* orbital and all three 2*p* orbitals) mixing together in what is called ***sp*^{3} hybridization** (viewed

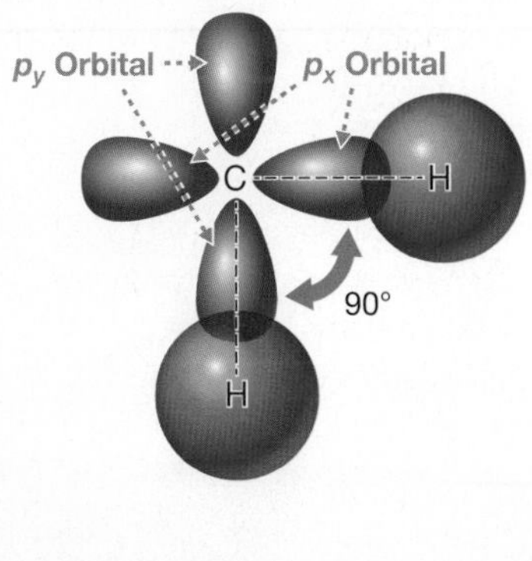
p_y Orbital
p_x Orbital
C
H
H
90°

FIGURE 3-4 Hypothetical H—C—H angle in CH_4 If only carbon's two half-filled 2*p* orbitals were used for the C—H bonds in methane, the bond angle would be 90°, which disagrees with the actual bond angle of 109.5°.

CONNECTIONS 3.2

The good and bad of methane
Methane (Fig. 3-4) is the principal fuel in natural gas, which accounts for roughly one-quarter of all energy usage in the United States. Care must be taken to avoid the release of methane into the atmosphere, because it is a greenhouse gas at least 30 times more potent than carbon dioxide.

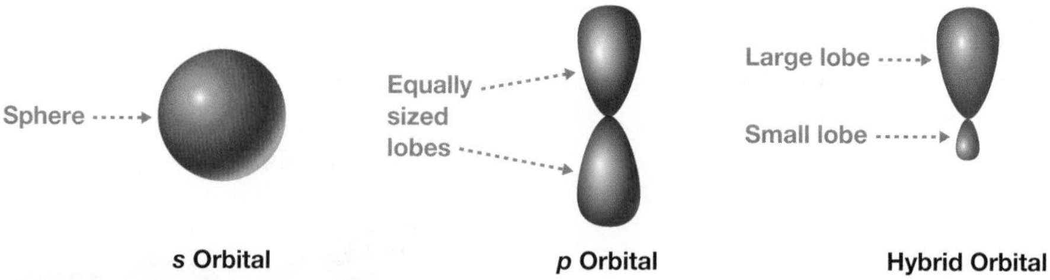

Sphere
Equally sized lobes
Large lobe
Small lobe
s Orbital
p Orbital
Hybrid Orbital

FIGURE 3-5 A hybrid orbital A hybrid orbital that results from mixing s and p orbitals has character of both an s orbital and a p orbital. Whereas an s orbital is a sphere and a p orbital has two lobes of equal size, the resulting hybrid orbital has one large lobe and one small lobe.

as s^1p^3, the superscripts indicate that one *s* orbital and all three *p* orbitals are used). Four new orbitals are produced, called ***sp*³ hybrid orbitals**, as shown in the energy diagrams in **Figure 3-6**, and the carbon atom is said to be sp^3-hybridized:

> Any atom that has a tetrahedral electron geometry is **sp^3-hybridized.**
>
> - Four sp^3 hybrid orbitals are contributed from the atom's valence shell.
> - Those sp^3 hybrid orbitals point to the corners of a tetrahedron.
> - Because sp^3 hybrid orbitals are generated by mixing one s orbital and three p orbitals, each sp^3 hybrid orbital has 25% **s-character** (one part out of four) and 75% ***p*-character** (three parts out of four).

With the four sp^3 hybrid orbitals accounting for carbon's tetrahedral geometry, we can construct the VB picture of CH_4 shown in **Figure 3-7**. We begin by adding the atoms in the proper locations along with the valence orbitals that they contribute. Figure 3-7a shows the four sp^3 hybrid orbitals (purple) from the carbon atom arranged in a tetrahedron. (Notice that the small lobe from each hybrid orbital is omitted to avoid cluttering the picture.) The four half-filled 1*s* orbitals (red) are also included: one from each of the four hydrogen atoms. Figure 3-7b shows the resulting orbitals (green) in the CH_4 molecule, all of which result from the buildup along the bonding axes identified in Figure 3-7a. Therefore, each pair of bonding electrons makes up a σ bond, in agreement with the observation made earlier that all single bonds are σ bonds.

CONNECTIONS 3.3

Uses of ethane and propane
Ethane and propane (Solved Problem 3.2) are two common alkanes. The principal use of ethane is in the industrial production of ethene, $H_2C{=}CH_2$, which has a wide variety of uses. Propane is commonly used as a fuel for barbecues and to heat homes where natural gas pipelines are unavailable.

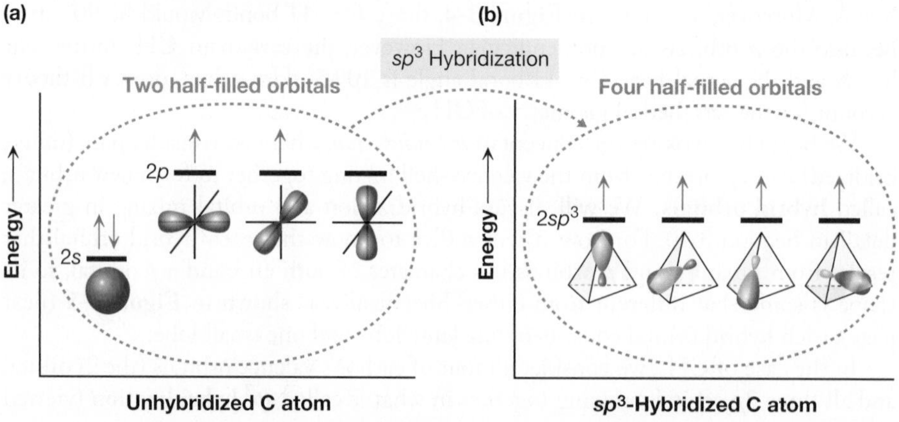

(a)
(b)
sp3 Hybridization
Two half-filled orbitals
Four half-filled orbitals
Energy
2p
2s
2sp3
Unhybridized C atom
sp3-Hybridized C atom

FIGURE 3-6 *sp*³ Hybridization in CH₄ (a) In an unhybridized carbon atom, the four valence electrons occupy the pure (unhybridized) 2s and 2p orbitals. (b) In an sp^3-hybridized carbon atom, one electron occupies each of four sp^3 hybrid orbitals, which point to the corners of a tetrahedron. According to VB theory, all four sp^3 orbitals are available for forming bonds, and the bond angle will be 109.5°.

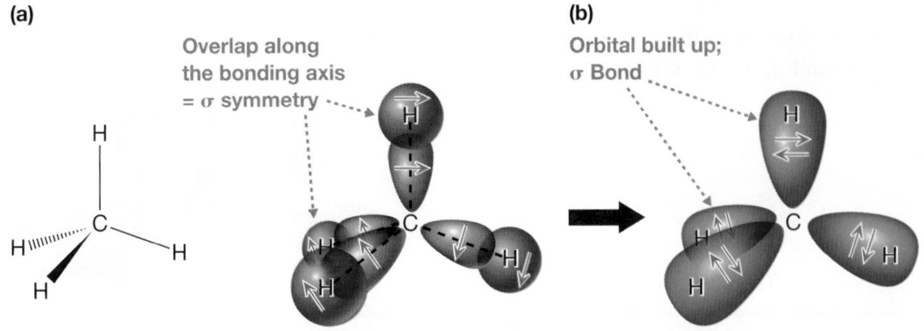

(a)
Overlap along
the bonding axis
= σ symmetry
H
C
H
H
H
(b)
Orbital built up;
σ Bond
H
C
H
H
H

FIGURE 3-7 The valence bond picture of methane (a) Valence orbitals and electrons contributed by each atom. Each H atom contributes a half-filled 1*s* orbital (red). The sp^3-hybridized C atom contributes four sp^3 hybrid orbitals (purple), all of which are half-filled. Each region of overlap between a 1*s* orbital and a hybrid orbital occurs along the bonding axis, which characterizes σ symmetry. (b) Resulting orbitals (green) containing the bonding electrons. The four regions of orbital overlap along bonding axes lead to four σ bonds.

YOUR TURN **3.1**

Draw the valence bond picture that describes the ammonium ion, NH_4^+, using the valence bond picture of CH_4 (Fig. 3-7) as a guide.

Answers to Your Turns are in the back of the book.

VB theory can be used to describe larger alkanes, too. Solved Problem 3.2, for example, shows you how to draw the VB picture of ethane (CH_3CH_3) and then challenges you to do the same for propane ($CH_3CH_2CH_3$).

SOLVED PROBLEM **3.2**

How to draw the valence bond picture of an alkane

Break It Down Draw the VB picture of ethane, CH_3CH_3. How many σ bonds does the molecule have?

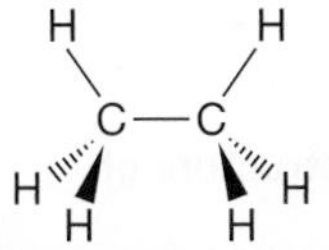

Think	Solve
What is the hybridization of each C atom, and what valence orbitals does it contribute? What orbital does each H atom contribute?	Each C atom has a tetrahedral electron geometry, so each is sp^3-hybridized and contributes four half-filled sp^3 hybrid orbitals that point to the corners of a tetrahedron. Each H atom contributes a half-filled 1*s* orbital.
How many regions of orbital overlap are there along bonding axes? What type of bond does that kind of overlap characterize?	To help draw the locations of the atoms and the orientations of the orbitals, use the dash–wedge notation above as a guide. To better visualize the dash–wedge notation, you should use a modeling kit to build a model of the molecule. There are seven regions of orbital overlap along the bonding axes: six along the H—C bonding axes and one along the C—C bonding axis. Each of those will produce a σ bond. 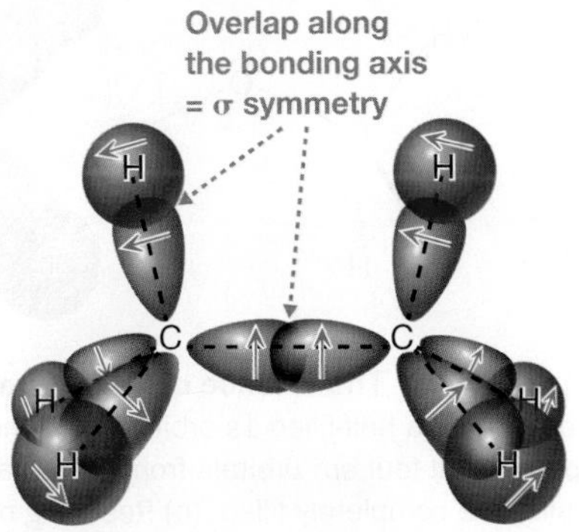

Overlap along
the bonding axis
= σ symmetry

(continued)

How is each resulting orbital derived from that overlap?	Each overlap results in an orbital that has been built up in the region of overlap. 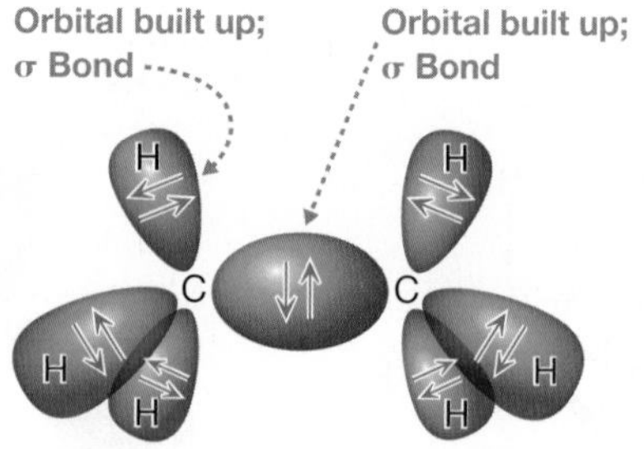

Orbital built up; σ Bond
Orbital built up; σ Bond
H
C
C
H
H
H
H
H

Try It Draw the VB picture of propane, $CH_3CH_2CH_3$. How many σ bonds does the molecule have?

YOUR TURN **3.2**

In Solved Problem 3.2, the graphic that shows the contributing orbitals has two regions of overlap labeled as characterizing σ symmetry. Identify and label the remaining regions of overlap that characterize σ symmetry.

SECTION 3.3 OBJECTIVES

You will be able to:

1. Draw the VB picture of a molecular species containing an atom that has a tetrahedral electron geometry and a lone pair of electrons.
2. Identify the type of orbital that holds such a lone pair of electrons.

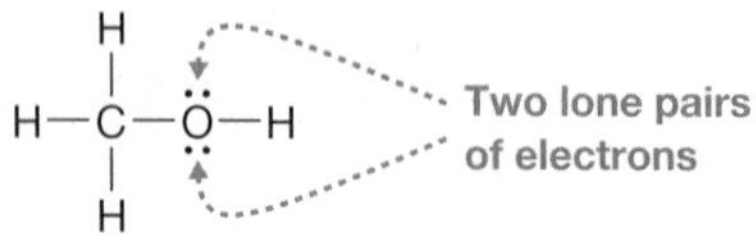

Two lone pairs of electrons

FIGURE 3-8 **Lewis structure of methanol**

3.3 Valence Bond Theory and Lone Pairs of Electrons

In Section 3.2, we used VB theory to describe alkanes, which have no lone pairs of electrons. Let's see how to apply VB theory to methanol, CH_3OH, in which the O atom has two lone pairs of electrons (**Figure 3-8**).

As in applying VB theory to alkanes, we first determine the valence orbitals contributed by each atom in CH_3OH and identify the valence electrons occupying those orbitals (**Figure 3-9a**). The C atom has a tetrahedral electron geometry, so as we learned in Section 3.2, it is sp^3-hybridized and contributes four half-filled sp^3 hybrid orbitals. The O atom, with its four electron groups (two single bonds and two lone pairs), also has a tetrahedral electron geometry: it, too, is sp^3-hybridized and contributes four sp^3 hybrid orbitals. Unlike C, the O atom contributes six valence electrons,

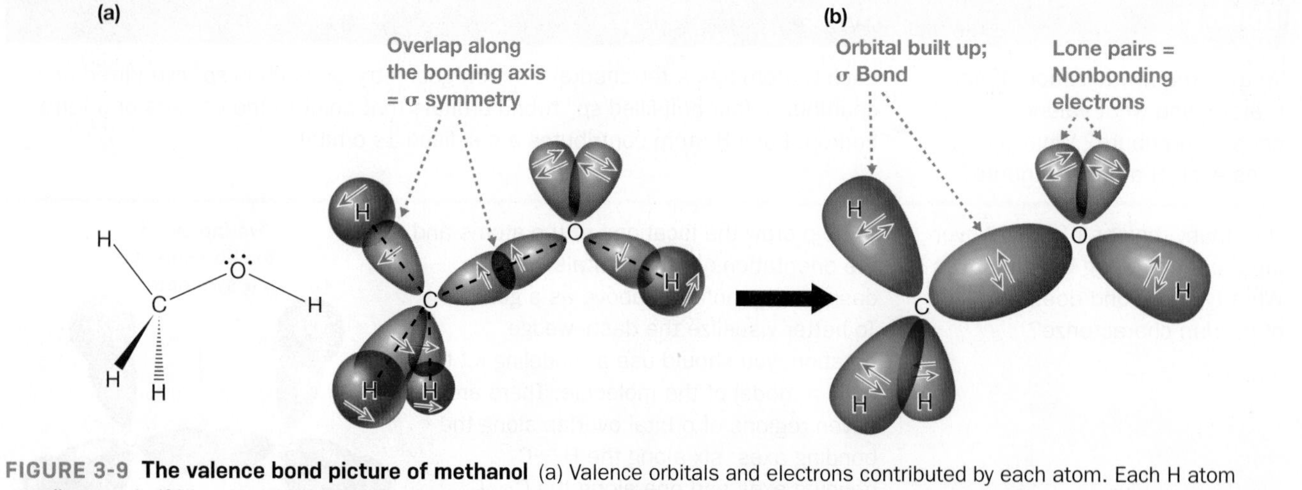

(a)
Overlap along the bonding axis = σ symmetry
(b)
Orbital built up; σ Bond
Lone pairs = Nonbonding electrons

FIGURE 3-9 **The valence bond picture of methanol** (a) Valence orbitals and electrons contributed by each atom. Each H atom contributes a half-filled 1s orbital (red). The C and O atoms have a tetrahedral electron geometry, so they each contribute four sp^3 orbitals (purple). All four sp^3 orbitals from C are half-filled. Two sp^3 orbitals from O are half-filled, and the other two, representing the two lone pairs, are completely filled. (b) Resulting orbitals containing the bonding electrons and lone pairs. The five regions of orbital overlap along bonding axes lead to σ bonds (green), whereas the orbitals containing the lone pairs (purple) remain unaffected.

so two of the four hybrid orbitals are completely filled and the other two remain half-filled (see Your Turn 3.3). Finally, each of the four H atoms contributes a half-filled 1*s* orbital.

YOUR TURN 3.3

Redraw the energy diagram from Figure 3-6b (p. 116) so that it describes an oxygen atom that has tetrahedral electron geometry. How many hybrid orbitals are completely filled? How many are half-filled? How many are empty? Do your answers agree with Figure 3-9a?

Figure 3-9b shows the orbitals after taking into account the buildup in each region where half-filled orbitals overlap is considered. The five regions of overlap along the bonding axes result in five σ bonds (green). The two remaining orbitals (purple) represent the hybrid orbitals from O that were shown to be completely filled in Figure 3-9a. Those hybrid orbitals do not overlap with orbitals from another atom, so no buildup occurs. Those hybrid orbitals therefore end up holding the two lone pairs of electrons on O.

SOLVED PROBLEM **3.3**

How to draw a valence bond picture when a tetrahedral atom has a lone pair

Break It Down As we learned in Section 1.12, a carbon atom has a formal charge of −1 if it has three bonds and a lone pair of electrons. With that in mind, draw the VB picture of $CH_3CH^-CH_3$. How many σ bonds does the ion have?

Think	Solve
What is the complete Lewis structure of the species? How do you include dash–wedge notation? (You might construct a model to better visualize it.)	In the Lewis structure, the two terminal carbons have formal charge of 0, so they each have four bonds and no lone pairs. The central carbon has a −1 formal charge, giving it three bonds and one lone pair. Each of the three carbons has a tetrahedral electron geometry, which is shown in the dash–wedge notation. 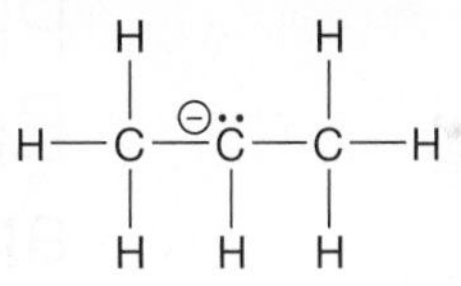 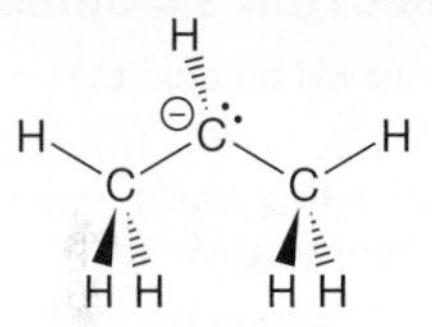
What valence orbitals does each atom contribute? How many valence electrons does each atom contribute?	Each H atom contributes a half-filled 1s orbital. Because each of the three C atoms has a tetrahedral electron geometry, each is sp^3-hybridized and contributes four hybrid orbitals. Each uncharged C contributes four valence electrons, making each hybrid orbital half-filled. The negatively charged C contributes one additional valence electron, for a total of five. These occupy the four hybrid orbitals to give three half-filled hybrid orbitals and one that is completely filled (see Your Turn 3.4).
How many regions of orbital overlap are there along bonding axes? What type of symmetry does that kind of overlap characterize?	There are nine regions of orbital overlap along the bonding axes: seven along the H—C bonding axes and two along the C—C bonding axes. Each overlap along a bonding axis characterizes σ symmetry. 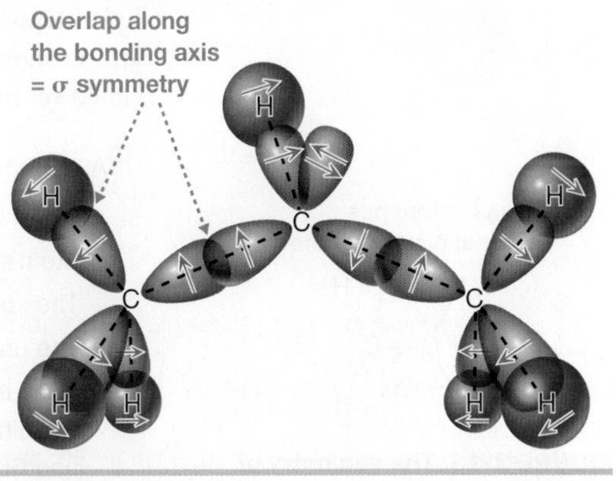 Overlap along the bonding axis = σ symmetry H C

(continued)

How is each resulting orbital derived from the overlapping orbitals?	Each pair of overlapping orbitals results in a new orbital (green) that has been built up where the overlap occurs. A pair of electrons filling such an orbital characterizes a σ bond, and there are nine such σ bonds. The remaining orbital, shaded purple, does not overlap with another orbital; it contains the lone pair of electrons.	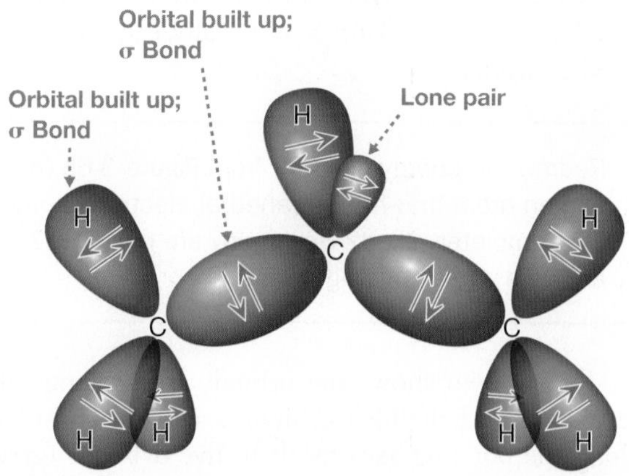 Orbital built up; σ Bond Orbital built up; σ Bond Lone pair H C H

Try It Draw the VB picture of CH_3NH^-. How many σ bonds does the molecule have?

YOUR TURN **3.4**

Redraw the energy diagram from Figure 3-6b (p. 116) so that it describes a carbon atom having a −1 charge. How many hybrid orbitals are completely filled? How many are half-filled? How many are empty? How do your answers compare with the numbers given in Solved Problem 3.3?

SECTION 3.4 OBJECTIVES

You will be able to:

1. Identify the hybridization of an atom that has a trigonal planar electron geometry.
2. Describe the orbitals that such an atom contributes to the VB picture of a molecule.
3. Draw the VB picture of a molecular species that contains atoms with trigonal planar electron geometry.
4. Characterize a π bond according to the type of overlap from contributing orbitals.

3.4 Valence Bond Theory and Trigonal Planar Electron Geometry: Double Bonds, sp^2 Hybridization, π Bonds, and Carbocations

So far we have applied VB theory to species that contain single bonds only, in which each non-hydrogen atom has a tetrahedral electron geometry. In this section, we extend VB theory to describe species containing atoms with trigonal planar geometry. For example, each of the two C atoms in ethene (**Figure 3-10**) has a trigonal planar geometry.

What types of valence orbitals do the C atoms in ethene contribute to the VB picture? To answer this question, we turn again to hybridization. In this case, each C atom needs three hybrid orbitals to accommodate three electron groups. To arrive at those three hybrid orbitals, we consider mixing three pure orbitals from the valence shell: the *s* orbital and two of the three valence *p* orbitals. This concept is called ***sp*² hybridization** (the superscript 2 indicates that two of the three *p* orbitals are used) and is shown schematically in **Figure 3-11**. The new orbitals that are produced are called ***sp*² hybrid orbitals**, and the atom is said to be sp^2-hybridized:

Any atom that has a trigonal planar electron geometry is **sp^2-hybridized**.

- Three sp^2 hybrid orbitals and one unhybridized *p* orbital are contributed from the atom's valence shell.
- The sp^2 hybrid orbitals point to the corners of a triangle.
- The unhybridized *p* orbital is perpendicular to that triangle.
- Because sp^2 hybrid orbitals are generated by mixing one s orbital and two *p* orbitals, each sp^2 hybrid orbital has 33.33% *s*-character (one part out of three) and 66.67% *p*-character (two parts out of three).

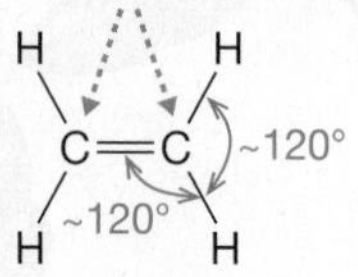
Each C atom has trigonal planar geometry.
H
H
C
C
~120°
~120°
H
H

FIGURE 3-10 The geometry of ethene

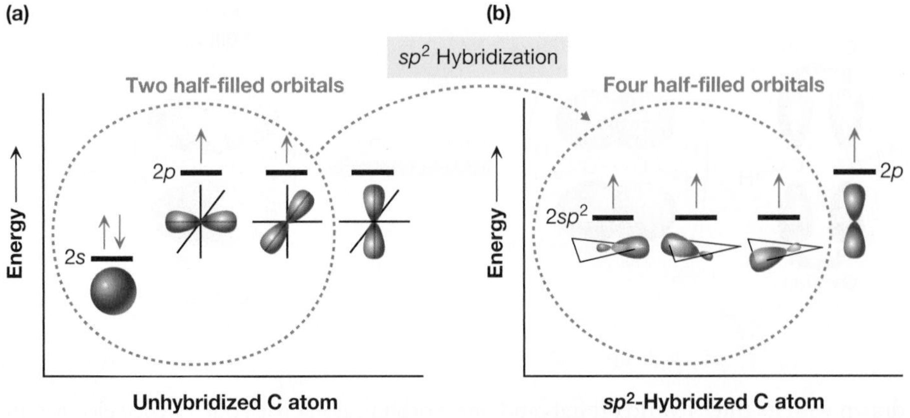
(a)
(b)
sp^2 Hybridization
Two half-filled orbitals
Four half-filled orbitals
Energy
2p
2s
Energy
$2sp^2$
2p
Unhybridized C atom
sp^2-Hybridized C atom

FIGURE 3-11 ***sp*^{2} Hybridization in $H_2C{=}CH_2$** (a) The s orbital and two of the *p* orbitals from the valence shell of the unhybridized atom mix in sp^2 hybridization. (b) Those three orbitals become sp^2 hybrid orbitals in an sp^2-hybridized carbon atom, and they point to the corners of a triangle. The remaining *p* orbital is perpendicular to the triangle that contains the hybrid orbitals.

Carbon, moreover, contributes four valence electrons, so the three sp^2 orbitals and the *p* orbital in Figure 3-11 are each half-filled.

In Figure 3-11, the plane of the triangle containing the hybrid orbitals is perpendicular to the page. The unhybridized *p* orbital, which lies vertically in the page (i.e., along the *y*-axis), is the p_y orbital. **Figure 3-12a** shows how the sp^2-hybridized atom would appear with all four of these orbitals drawn together, but an sp^2-hybridized atom can have other orientations, too, as shown in Figure 3-12b and 3-12c.

CONNECTIONS 3.4

Ethene and its uses Ethene (Fig. 3-10), also called ethylene, is the starting material used to produce polyethylene, a widely used plastic. Ethene is also very useful in the chemical laboratory because the C=C double bond can undergo highly selective reactions, including ones we will encounter in Chapter 12.

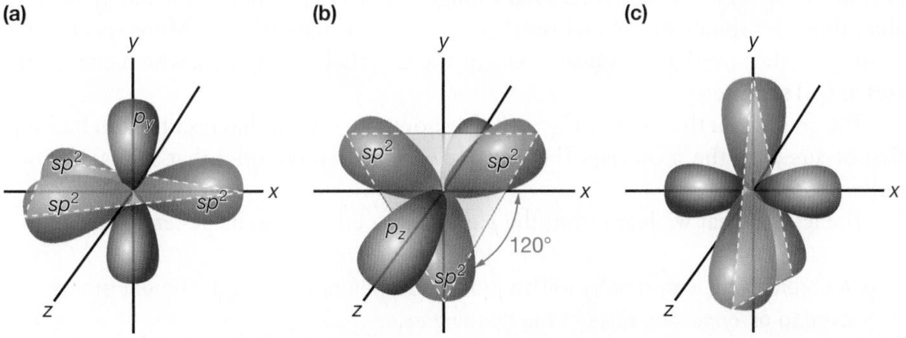
(a)
(b)
(c)
y
p_y
sp^2
sp^2
sp^2
x
z
y
sp^2
sp^2
p_z
sp^2
120°
x
z
y
x
z

FIGURE 3-12 Different orientations of an *sp*^{2}-hybridized atom In all three orientations, the sp^2 hybrid orbitals (purple) lie in a plane and point to the corners of a triangle (small lobes are omitted), and an unhybridized *p* orbital is perpendicular to that triangle. (a) The triangle is perpendicular to the page, and the unhybridized *p* orbital is the p_y. (b) The triangle lies in the plane of the page, and the unhybridized *p* orbital is the p_z. (c) The triangle is perpendicular to the page, and the unhybridized *p* orbital is the p_x.

YOUR TURN 3.5

In Figure 3-12c, label each orbital as either sp^2, p_x, p_y, or p_z.

Now that we know the valence orbitals contributed by each C atom in ethene, let's construct the molecule's VB picture. We begin by drawing all of the contributing valence orbitals and valence electrons, as shown in **Figure 3-13**. Each sp^2-hybridized C atom is

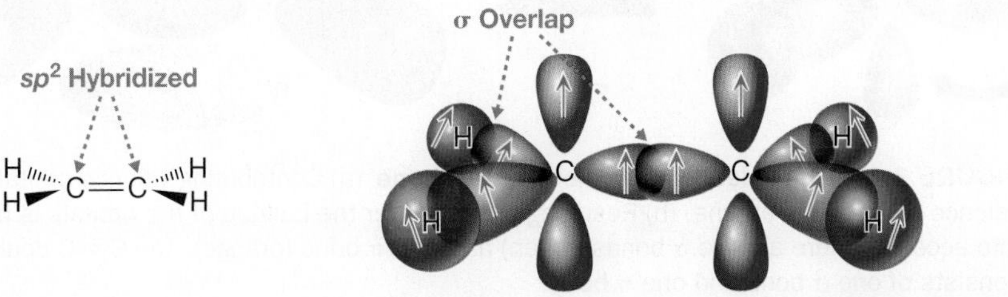
sp^2 Hybridized
σ Overlap
H
C
H

FIGURE 3-13 Valence orbitals and electrons in ethene The dash–wedge notation of ethene is shown on the left, and the contributing orbitals are shown on the right. The H atoms each contribute a half-filled 1s orbital (red). The sp^2-hybridized C atoms each contribute three sp^2 hybrid orbitals (purple) and one unhybridized *p* orbital (blue), all of which are half-filled. Overlaps of orbitals, along the four H—C bonding axes and the one C—C bonding axis, all characterize σ symmetry.

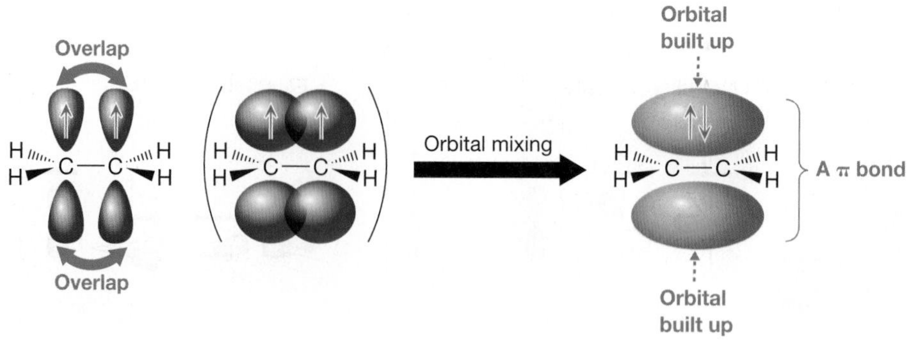
Overlap
Overlap
Orbital mixing
Orbital built up
Orbital built up
A π bond

FIGURE 3-14 **π Overlap and π bonds** (*Left*) Adjacent half-filled *p* orbitals overlap in a side-by-side fashion. Such overlap on opposite sides of the C—C bonding axis characterizes π overlap. (*Right*) In the resulting orbital that has been built up, the pair of electrons characterizes a π bond.

drawn with its three hybrid orbitals and one *p* orbital, along with one valence electron in each orbital. Each H atom contributes an *s* orbital and one valence electron.

Overlap of orbitals occurs with σ symmetry along each of the four H—C bonding axes and along the C—C bonding axis, resulting in five σ bonds. With that in mind, let's temporarily ignore the orbitals undergoing σ overlap so we can focus on just the *p* orbitals, as we have done in **Figure 3-14**.

The *p* orbitals shown on the left in Figure 3-14, which are aligned side by side, do not overlap along a bonding axis. In fact, the *p* orbitals do not appear to overlap at all. Remember, however, that our depictions of orbitals represent regions of high probability of finding electrons, and there is significant probability of electrons existing beyond those regions. Therefore, even though the overlap is not immediately noticeable, those *p* orbitals do indeed overlap as shown in parentheses. More specifically, those *p* orbitals overlap on *opposite sides* of the C—C bonding axis, which characterizes **π (pi) symmetry**.

The graphic on the right in Figure 3-14 shows the orbital that results from buildup that occurs from the π overlap. The pair of electrons that occupies that orbital characterizes a π *bond.*

The lessons that we learn from the *p* orbitals in ethene can be generalized:

- An orbital with π symmetry will be produced when orbitals from different atoms overlap on *opposites sides* of the bonding axis.
- A pair of electrons occupying an orbital with π symmetry is called a **π bond**.

To complete the VB picture of ethene, we show in **Figure 3-15** the σ and π bonds together. Notice that the C=C double bond is made up of two bond types: one σ bond and one π bond. In fact, it is always true that:

Any double bond consists of one σ bond and one π bond.

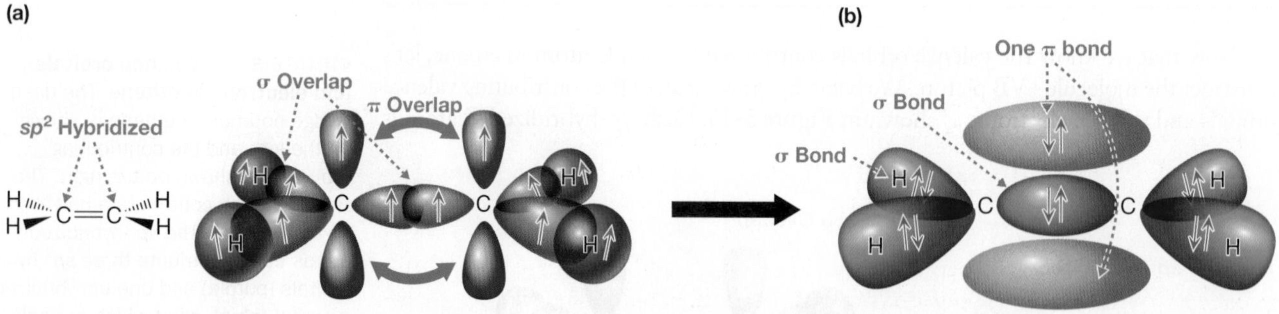
(a)
σ Overlap
π Overlap
sp^2 Hybridized
(b)
One π bond
σ Bond
σ Bond

FIGURE 3-15 **The valence bond picture of ethene** (a) Contributing valence orbitals and valence electrons in ethene. (b) Resulting orbitals after the buildup of the orbitals is taken into account. There are five σ bonds (green) and one π bond (orange). The C=C double bond consists of one σ bond and one π bond.

SOLVED PROBLEM **3.4**

How to draw the valence bond picture of a molecule that has a double bond

Break It Down **Draw the valence bond picture of methanal (formaldehyde, $H_2C{=}O$). How many σ bonds does the molecule have? How many π bonds?**

Think	Solve
What electronic geometry do the C and O atoms have? What is each atom's hybridization?	Both the C and O atoms have trigonal planar electron geometry and are sp^2-hybridized. The molecule is entirely planar, as shown in the dash–wedge notation. (You might build a molecular model to better visualize the molecule.) 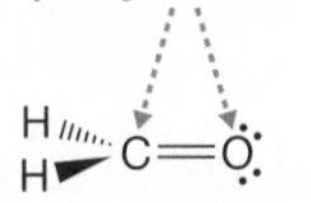 sp^2 Hybridized
What valence orbitals does each atom contribute? How many valence electrons does each orbital contain?	Each H atom contributes a 1*s* orbital containing one valence electron. The C and O atoms, which are sp^2-hybridized, each contribute three hybrid orbitals and one *p* orbital (review Fig. 3-11). The C atom contributes four valence electrons: one valence electron in each orbital. The O atom contributes six valence electrons: Two of oxygen's hybrid orbitals contain two electrons, whereas the third hybrid orbital and the *p* orbital each contain one electron.
How many regions of orbital overlap are there along bonding axes? How many are there on opposite sides of a bonding axis?	Orbitals overlap along three bonding axes: the two H—C bonding axes and the C—O bonding axis. The two *p* orbitals are adjacent and they overlap on opposite sides of the C—O bonding axis. 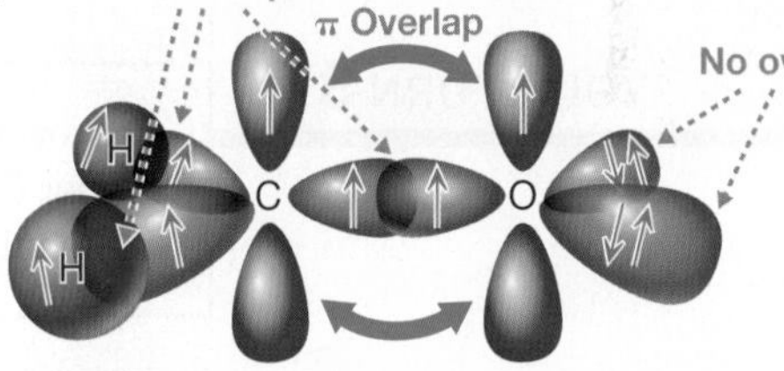 σ Overlap π Overlap No overlap
What type of bond does each kind of overlap lead to?	The orbitals overlapping along the bonding axes are half-filled, and each pair of those overlapping orbitals forms a σ bond (green). The overlapping *p* orbitals are each half-filled and form a π bond (orange). The final two hybrid orbitals on oxygen do not overlap with other orbitals and remain unchanged. The molecule has a total of three σ bonds and one π bond. 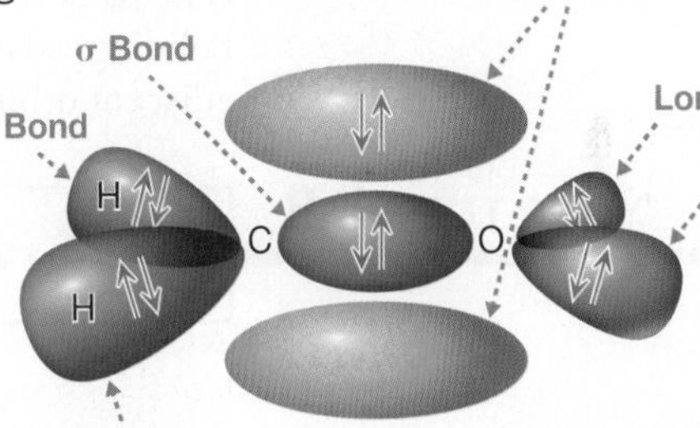 π Bond σ Bond σ Bond Lone pair Lone pair σ Bond

Try It Draw the valence bond picture of $CH_3CH{=}NH$. How many σ bonds does the molecule have? How many π bonds?

YOUR TURN **3.6**

Draw an energy diagram, similar to that in Figure 3-11b (p. 121), to describe an sp^2-hybridized oxygen atom. Which orbitals are half-filled? Completely filled? Empty? Do your answers agree with the statement in Solved Problem 3.4?

To this point in Section 3.4, we have considered atoms with trigonal planar electron geometry involved in double bonds, but an atom involved in only single bonds can have a trigonal planar geometry, too. For example, a carbon atom that has three single bonds and no lone pairs (and thus bears a +1 formal charge) has a trigonal planar geometry and, like other atoms with this geometry, is sp^2-hybridized. With this in mind, we can draw the VB picture of a carbocation like $CH_3CH_2^+$, as shown in **Figure 3-16** (next page).

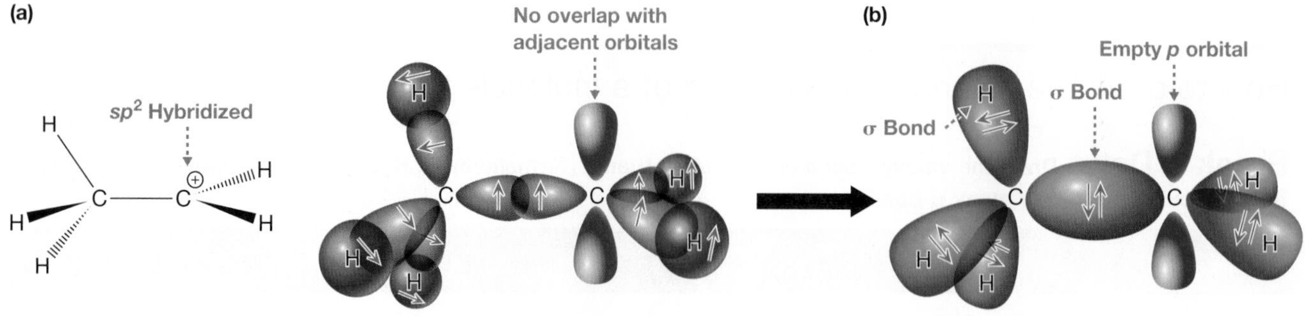
(a)
sp² Hybridized
No overlap with adjacent orbitals
(b)
Empty p orbital
σ Bond
σ Bond

FIGURE 3-16 The valence bond picture of $CH_3CH_2^+$ (a) Contributing valence orbitals and valence electrons in $CH_3CH_2^+$. (b) Resulting bonds after the buildup of the orbitals is taken into account. There are six σ bonds (green) and one empty, unhybridized *p* orbital (blue).

▸ LOOKING AHEAD

Although the *p* orbital in Figure 3-16 does not overlap with an adjacent orbital, a significant interaction called *hyperconjugation* does occur. Hyperconjugation can have a substantial impact on stability, a topic we will discuss in Section 7.9a.

The uncharged C atom, which is sp^3-hybridized, contributes four half-filled sp^3 hybrid orbitals, and each H atom contributes a half-filled 1*s* orbital (Fig. 3-16a). The C^+ atom, being sp^2-hybridized, contributes three sp^2 hybrid orbitals lying in a plane and an unhybridized *p* orbital perpendicular to that plane. Unlike what we saw with ethene (Fig. 3-13), C^+ contributes only three valence electrons, so the three hybrid orbitals are half-filled but the *p* orbital is empty.

YOUR TURN 3.7

Redraw the energy diagram from Figure 3-11b, this time assuming a trigonal planar C^+. How many electrons occupy each hybrid orbital? How many occupy the *p* orbital? Do your answers agree with the above statements?

Figure 3-16b shows the resulting orbitals, taking into account the overlap of adjacent pairs of orbitals. Overlap along the five H—C bonding axes and the C—C bonding axis leads to six σ bonds. The *p* orbital, however, does not overlap with an adjacent orbital, so it remains unchanged and empty (see Looking Ahead box).

YOUR TURN 3.8

Draw the VB picture of CH_3BH_2, which is analogous to that of $CH_3CH_2^+$.

SECTION 3.5 OBJECTIVES

You will be able to:

1. Determine the hybridization of an atom that has a linear electron geometry.
2. Identify the orbitals that an atom with linear electron geometry contributes to the VB picture of a molecule.
3. Draw the VB picture of a molecular species that contains atoms with linear electron geometry.

3.5 Valence Bond Theory and Linear Electron Geometry: Triple Bonds and *sp* Hybridization

We have invoked sp^3 hybridization to describe atoms with tetrahedral electron geometry (Sections 3.2 and 3.3) and sp^2 hybridization to describe atoms with trigonal planar electron geometry (Section 3.4). We now turn to atoms with linear electron geometry, such as the two C atoms in ethyne (acetylene, **Figure 3-17**).

An atom with a linear geometry needs two hybrid orbitals to accommodate its two electron groups; to arrive at those hybrid orbitals, we consider *sp* hybridization. In ***sp* hybridization**, the valence *s* orbital mixes with just one of the three valence *p* orbitals, producing two new orbitals called ***sp* hybrid orbitals** (**Figure 3-18**).

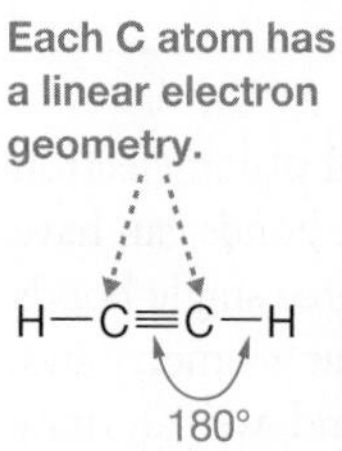
Each C atom has a linear electron geometry.
H—C≡C—H
180°

FIGURE 3-17 Lewis structure of ethyne (acetylene)

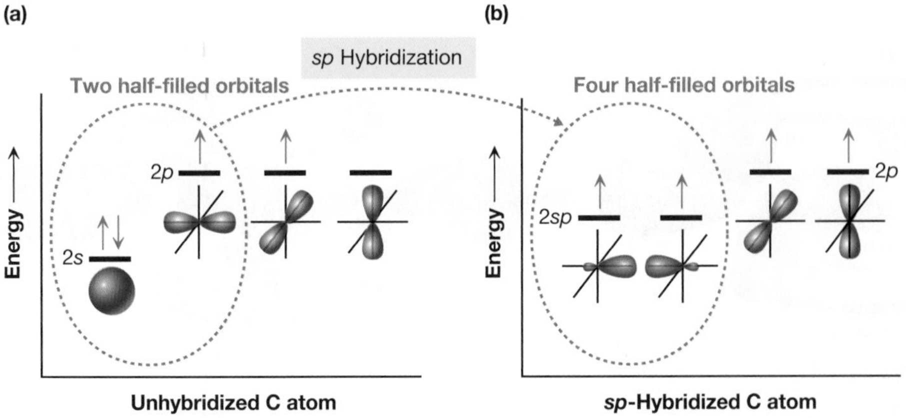
(a)
(b)
sp Hybridization
Two half-filled orbitals
Four half-filled orbitals
Energy
2p
2s
2sp
2p
Energy
Unhybridized C atom
sp-Hybridized C atom

FIGURE 3-18 ***sp* Hybridization in HC≡CH** (a) The s orbital and one of the *p* orbitals from the valence shell of the unhybridized atom mix in *sp* hybridization. (b) Those two orbitals become *sp* hybrid orbitals in an *sp*-hybridized carbon atom, and they point 180° apart. The two remaining *p* orbitals are perpendicular to the line containing the hybrid orbitals and are perpendicular to each other.

Any atom that has a linear electron geometry is ***sp*-hybridized.**

- An *sp*-hybridized atom contributes two *sp* hybrid orbitals and two unhybridized *p* orbitals from the valence shell.
- The *sp* hybrid orbitals point 180° apart along the same line.
- The two unhybridized *p* orbitals are perpendicular to the *sp* hybrid orbitals and are perpendicular to each other.
- Because *sp* hybrid orbitals are generated by mixing one s orbital and one *p* orbital, each *sp* hybrid orbital has 50% s-character (one part out of two) and 50% *p*-character (one part out of two).

Because an uncharged C atom contributes four valence electrons, the two *sp* orbitals and the two *p* orbitals in Figure 3-18 are each half-filled.

In Figure 3-18, the line containing the hybrid orbitals is the *x*-axis, and the unhybridized *p* orbitals are the p_y and p_z. All four of these orbitals are shown together on the same *sp*-hybridized atom in **Figure 3-19a**. Two other orientations of an *sp*-hybridized atom are shown in Figure 3-19b and 3-19c. Notice in the three orientations that the unhybridized *p* orbitals are aligned along different axes, so they receive different labels.

The VB picture of HC≡CH is presented in **Figure 3-20** (next page). Figure 3-20a shows the contributed valence orbitals and valence electrons. Each H atom (red) contributes a half-filled 1*s* orbital. Each *sp*-hybridized C atom contributes two *sp* hybrid orbitals and two unhybridized *p* orbitals. σ Overlap occurs along each of the two H—C bonding axes and along the C—C bonding axis. π Overlap involving the two p_y orbitals (blue) occurs above and below the C—C bonding axis. In addition, π overlap occurs with the

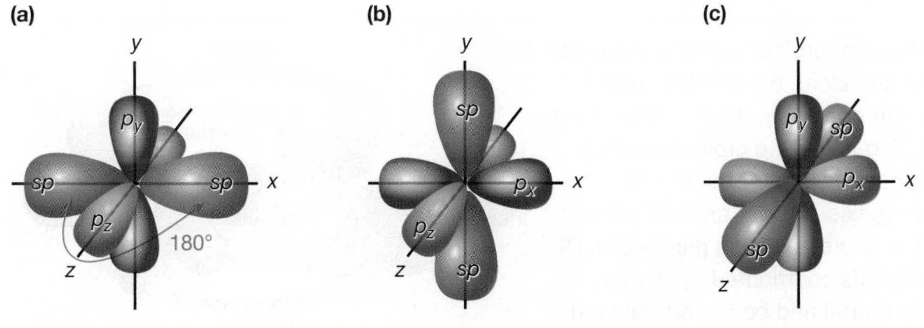
(a)
(b)
(c)
y
p_y
sp
sp
x
p_z
180°
z
y
sp
p_x
x
p_z
z
sp
y
p_y
sp
p_x
x
sp
z

FIGURE 3-19 **Different orientations of an *sp*-hybridized atom** In all three orientations, the *sp* hybrid orbitals (shown in purple; small lobes are omitted) lie along the same line and point 180° apart, and the two unhybridized *p* orbitals are perpendicular to that line. The *sp* hybrid orbitals lie along (a) the *x*-axis, (b) the *y*-axis, and (c) the *z*-axis.

CONNECTIONS 3.5

Acetylene and its uses
Acetylene (Fig. 3-17) is one of the hottest burning fuels, reaching temperatures over 3300 °C (6000 °F), which made it popular in the welding industry until a few decades ago. Arc welding, which uses electrical arcs, is now the technique of choice in most applications.

CONNECTIONS 3.6

A useful poison HCN (Solved Problem 3.5, p. 126) is hydrogen cyanide, also called hydrocyanic acid. It is used industrially to make precursors of some polymers such as poly(methyl methacrylate) and nylon-6,6. HCN is poisonous, and the larvae of the eucalyptus leaf beetle release the compound as a defense mechanism.

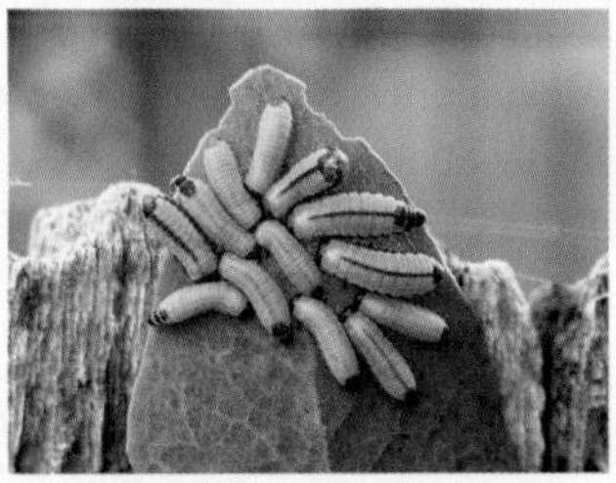

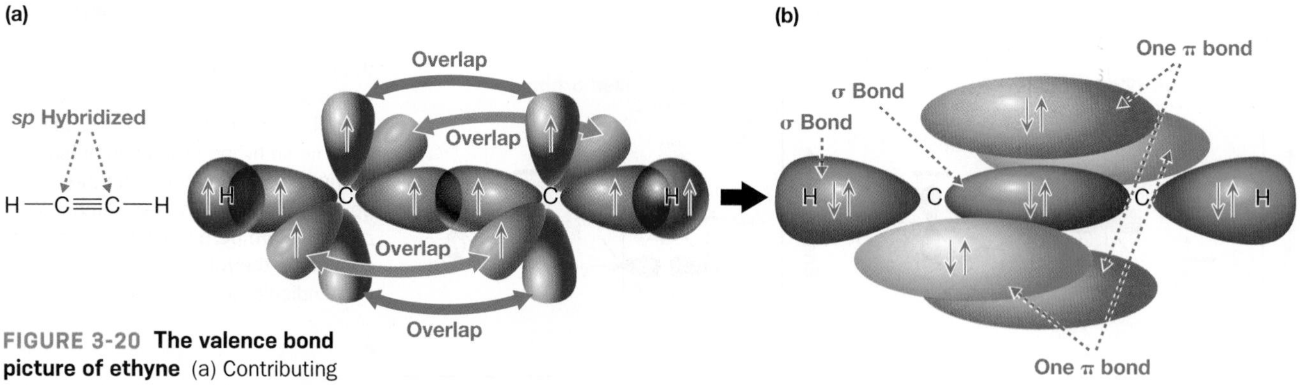
(a)
sp Hybridized
H—C≡C—H
Overlap
Overlap
Overlap
Overlap
H
C
C
H
(b)
σ Bond
σ Bond
One π bond
One π bond
H
C
C
H

FIGURE 3-20 The valence bond picture of ethyne (a) Contributing valence orbitals and valence electrons in HC≡CH. σ Overlap takes place along each of the two H—C bonding axes and along the C—C bonding axis. The adjacent p_y orbitals (blue) undergo π overlap, as do the adjacent p_z orbitals (teal). (b) Bonds formed by the build-up of the orbitals: Three σ bonds (green) and two π bonds (orange and yellow). The C≡C triple bond consists of one σ bond and two π bonds.

two p_z orbitals (teal) in front of and behind the bonding axis. Figure 3-20b shows the resulting bonds. Three σ bonds (green) appear in the molecule: two H—C σ bonds and one C—C σ bond. There are also two C—C π bonds (one orange and one yellow).

The VB picture of ethyne in Figure 3-20b illustrates that the triple bond consists of one σ bond and two π bonds, an outcome that is true for other triple bonds, too:

> Any triple bond consists of one σ bond and two π bonds.

Another example of a triple bond is illustrated in Solved Problem 3.5.

SOLVED PROBLEM **3.5**

How to draw the valence bond picture of a molecule that has a triple bond

Break It Down **Draw the VB picture of HCN. How many σ bonds does the molecule have? How many π bonds?**

Think	Solve
What electron geometry and hybridization do the C and N atoms have?	Both C and N atoms have linear electron geometry and are *sp*-hybridized. 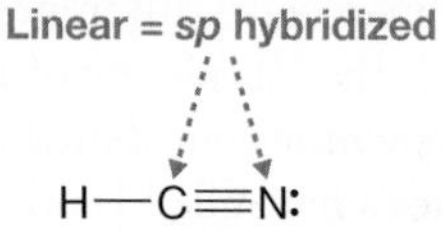 Linear = *sp* hybridized H—C≡N:
What valence orbitals does each atom contribute? How many valence electrons does each atom contribute?	The H atom contributes a 1*s* orbital and one valence electron. Both the C and N atoms contribute two hybrid orbitals, 180° apart, as well as two *p* orbitals perpendicular to the hybrid orbitals. The C atom contributes four valence electrons, whereas the N atom contributes five.
How many regions of orbital overlap occur along the bonding axes? How many occur on opposite sides of the bonding axis? How many valence electrons occupy each orbital?	Two pairs of orbitals overlap along bonding axes: one along the H—C bonding axis and one along the C—N bonding axis. Two pairs of *p* orbitals overlap on opposite sides of the C—N bonding axis. All four orbitals contributed by C are half-filled (Fig. 3-18). Of the orbitals contributed by N, one hybrid orbital and both *p* orbitals are half-filled; the other hybrid orbital is completely filled. 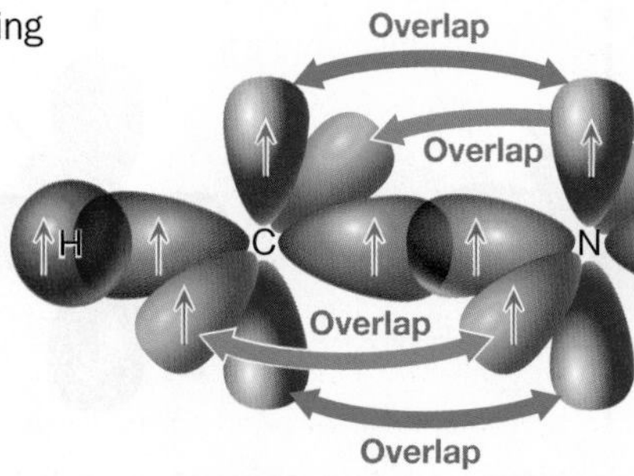 Overlap Overlap Overlap Overlap H C N

(continued)

What type of bond does each pair of overlapping half-filled orbitals produce?	Each pair of half-filled orbitals overlapping along a bonding axis produces a σ bond (green). Each pair of half-filled orbitals overlapping on opposite sides of a bonding axis produces a π bond (orange and yellow). There is one nonoverlapping orbital that contains a lone pair of electrons (purple). Thus, there are two σ bonds and two π bonds in the molecule.

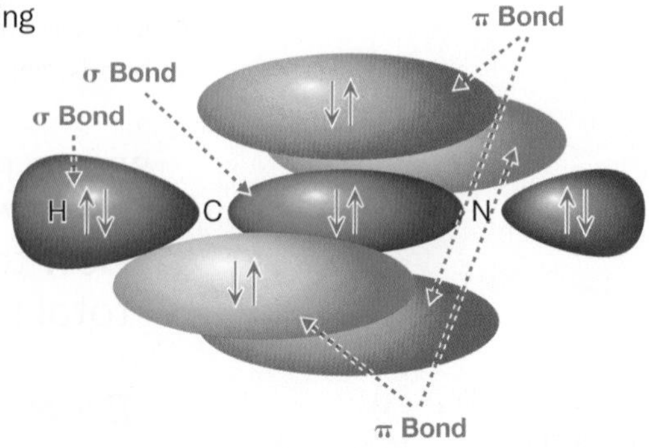
π Bond
σ Bond
σ Bond
H
C
N
π Bond

Try It Draw the valence bond picture of HC≡C—CH_2—C≡N. How many σ bonds does the molecule have? How many π bonds?

YOUR TURN **3.9**

Redraw the energy diagram from Figure 3-18b, assuming an uncharged N atom. Which orbitals are half-filled? Completely filled? Empty? Do your answers agree with the statement in Solved Problem 3.5?

SECTION 3.6 OBJECTIVES

You will be able to:

1. Quickly derive the hybridization of an atom from a Lewis structure.
2. Quickly determine the number of σ and π bonds from a Lewis structure.

3.6 Strategies for Success: Quickly Identifying Hybridization and the Number of σ and π Bonds from a Lewis Structure

Strategies for Success
Quickly Identifying Hybridization and the Number of σ and π Bonds from a Lewis Structure

We developed the basic ideas of VB theory in Section 3.1. Then, in Sections 3.2–3.5, we applied those ideas toward drawing the VB pictures of molecules containing atoms with various geometries and in which the valence electrons belong to single bonds, double bonds, triple bonds, or lone pairs. Along the way, we arrived at some generalizations that we will find very useful throughout the rest of this book. We devote this section to reviewing those generalizations and applying them to molecular species without completely drawing the VB picture.

One important lesson we learned from previous sections of this chapter, summarized in Table 3-1, relates an atom's electron geometry to its hybridization.

Another important lesson comes from the types of bonds that make up single, double, and triple bonds:

- All single bonds are σ bonds.
- All double bonds consist of one σ bond and one π bond.
- All triple bonds consist of one σ bond and two π bonds.

TABLE 3-1 The Relationship between Hybridization and VSEPR Theory

Number of e^- groups	Electron Geometry in VSEPR Theory	Atom's Hybridization	Orientation of Hybrid Orbitals	Bond Angles
2	Linear	*sp*		180°
3	Trigonal planar	sp^2		120°
4	Tetrahedral	sp^3		109.5°

With these lessons in mind, we can quickly determine the hybridization of an atom in a Lewis structure, and we can also quickly determine the total number of σ and π bonds. Solved Problem 3.6 takes you through an example.

SOLVED PROBLEM **3.6**

How to quickly determine atom hybridization and the total number of σ and π bonds from a Lewis structure

Break It Down **What is the hybridization of each non-hydrogen atom in this molecule? How many total σ and π bonds are there?**

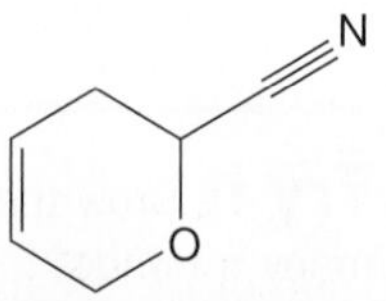
N
O

Think	**Solve**
What is the electron geometry of each non-hydrogen atom? What hybridization is associated with that geometry?	To answer questions about electron geometry, it helps to draw all the C—H bonds and all lone pairs, as shown here. Knowing the number of electron groups surrounding each atom, we can then determine the electron geometry and hybridization. 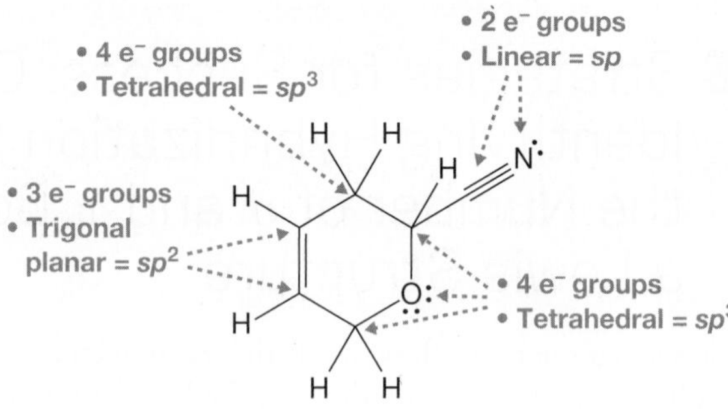
What types of bonds make up single, double, and triple bonds? How many single, double, and triple bonds are there in the molecule?	There are 13 single bonds (σ bonds). As shown here, there is one double bond (consisting of one σ and one π bond) and one triple bond (consisting of one σ bond and two π bonds). In total, there are 15 σ bonds and three π bonds. 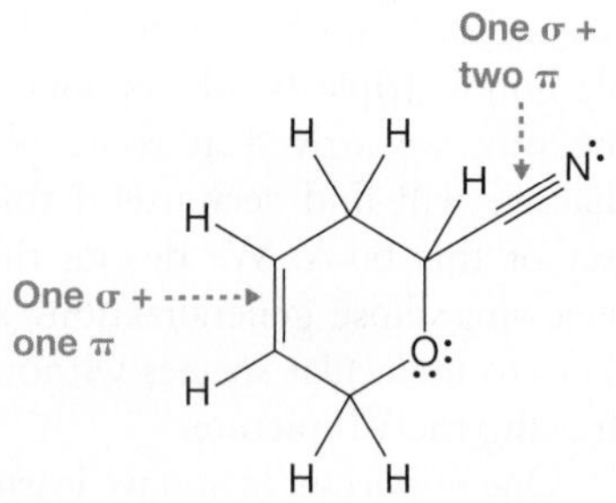

• 4 e⁻ groups
• Tetrahedral = sp3
• 2 e⁻ groups
• Linear = sp
• 3 e⁻ groups
• Trigonal planar = sp2
• 4 e⁻ groups
• Tetrahedral = sp3
H
N
O

One σ + two π
One σ + one π
H
N
O

Try It In each of the following molecular species, determine the hybridization of each non-hydrogen atom and the total number of σ and π bonds.

(a)

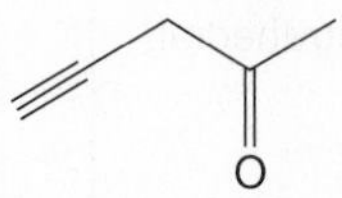
O

(b)

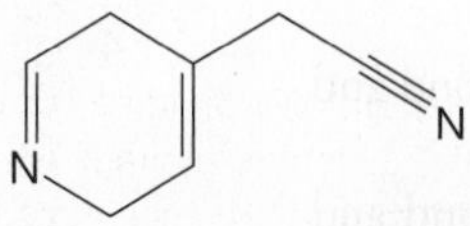
N
N

(c)

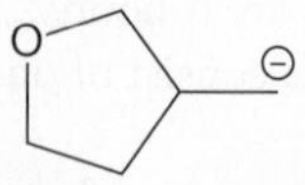
O

(d)

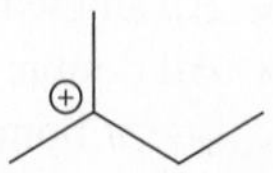

3.7 Bond Rotations about Single and Double Bonds: Cis and Trans Configurations

SECTION 3.7 OBJECTIVES

You will be able to:

1. Explain the different rotational characteristics of single and double bonds.
2. Determine whether a double bond in a molecule could exist as one of two possible configurations.

There is a significant difference between single and double bonds that goes well beyond the differences in bond strength and bond length that we reviewed in Chapter 1:

> *Free rotation* can occur about single bonds but not about double bonds.

In a molecule of ethane ($H_3C{-}CH_3$), for example, the two CH_3 groups freely rotate relative to one another about the single bond that connects them (**Figure 3-21a**). In a molecule of ethene ($H_2C{=}CH_2$, Fig. 3-21b), on the other hand, no rotation occurs. Instead, the entire molecule is planar, with the two CH_2 groups locked in place.

The CH_3 groups in ethane can rotate freely because, *during rotation, the σ bond that connects the two groups is unaffected* (**Figure 3-22a**). The picture is somewhat different with a molecule containing a double bond, which consists of one σ bond and one π bond. Imagine trying to rotate the CH_2 groups in $H_2C{=}CH_2$ relative to each other. The σ bond of the double bond would be unaffected, but the π bond would be broken because rotation would destroy the overlap between the *p* orbitals (Fig. 3-22b). The substantial energy cost associated with breaking the π bond is what locks the CH_2 groups of ethene in place.

For the π bond in $H_2C{=}CH_2$ to remain intact, all six atoms must be in the same plane. In general:

> When two atoms are connected by a double bond, those atoms and any atoms to which they are directly bonded prefer to lie in the same plane.

This principle is illustrated in **Figure 3-23**.

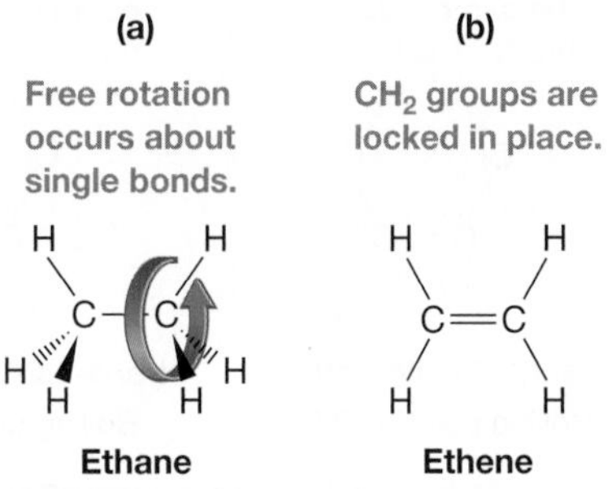

(a)
(b)
Free rotation occurs about single bonds.
CH₂ groups are locked in place.
Ethane
Ethene

FIGURE 3-21 Bond rotation Groups connected by a single bond rotate freely relative to each other, but groups connected by a double bond do not.

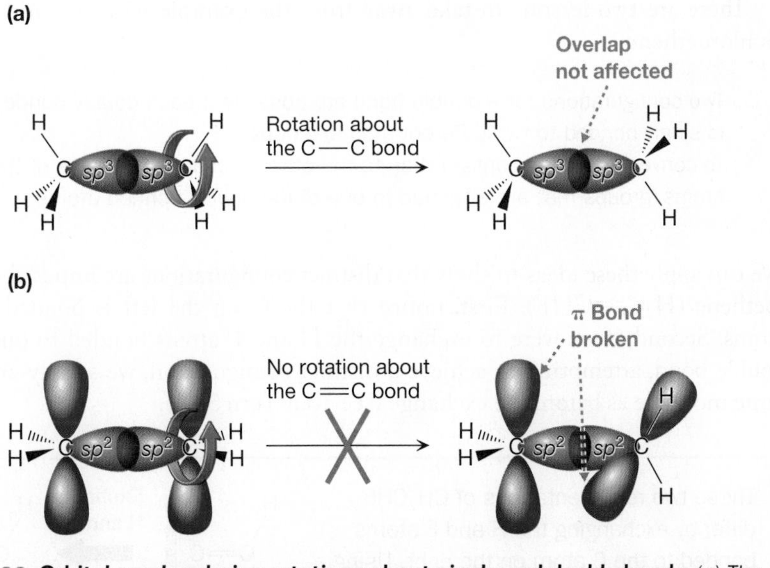

(a)
Overlap not affected
Rotation about the C—C bond
(b)
π Bond broken
No rotation about the C═C bond

FIGURE 3-22 Orbital overlap during rotations about single and double bonds (a) The overlap of the hybrid orbitals forming the σ bond remains intact when the CH_3 groups rotate about the C—C bond in $H_3C{-}CH_3$. (b) Rotation of the CH_2 groups about the C═C bond in $H_2C{=}CH_2$ does not affect the σ bond but would break the π bond.

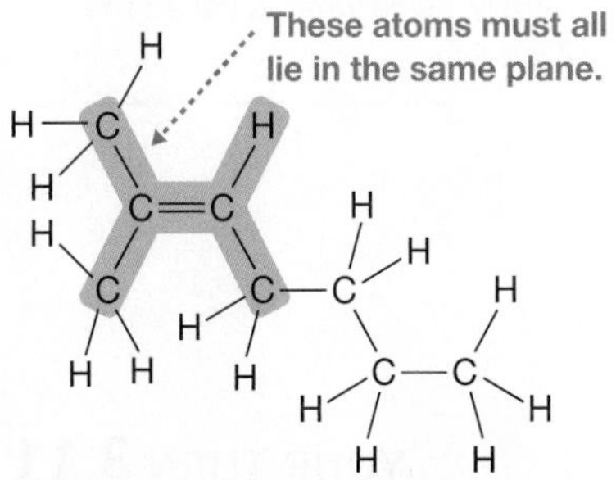

These atoms must all lie in the same plane.

FIGURE 3-23 Planar geometry imposed by a double bond In a molecule of 2-methylhept-2-ene, the five C atoms and the H atom indicated must all lie in the same plane for the π bond to remain intact.

YOUR TURN 3.10

In each of the molecules shown here, circle the atoms that must be in the same plane with the atoms connected by the double bond. (Because these are line structures, some H atoms may need to be added back in.)

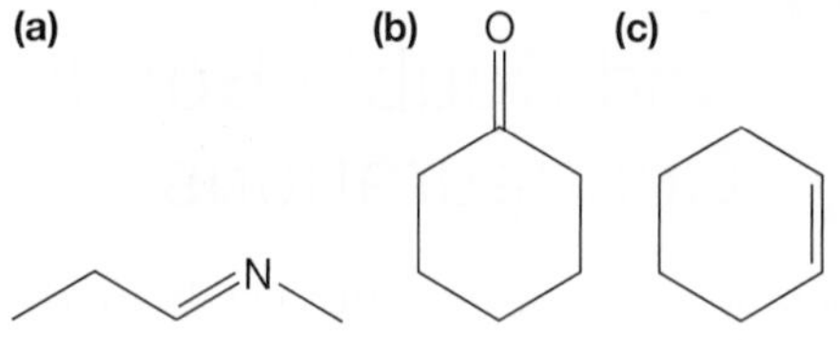
(a)
(b)
(c)
N
O

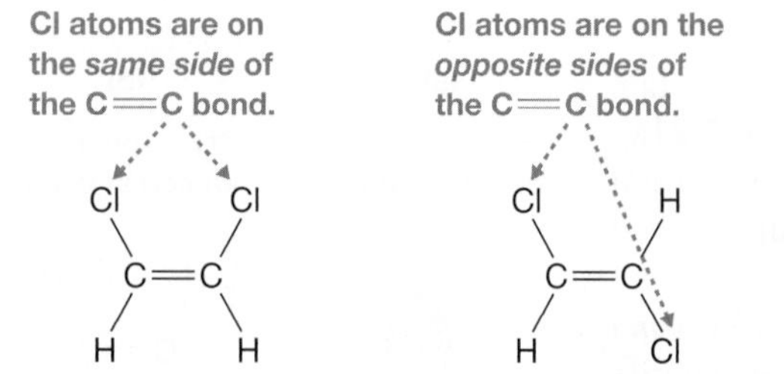
Cl atoms are on the *same side* of the C═C bond.
Cl atoms are on the *opposite sides* of the C═C bond.
Cl
Cl
C═C
H
H
Cl
H
C═C
H
Cl

***cis*-1,2-Dichloroethene**
Boiling point = 60.3 °C

***trans*-1,2-Dichloroethene**
Boiling point = 47.5 °C

FIGURE 3-24 Cis and trans configurations These two molecules differ by the relative positions of H and Cl on one of the doubly bonded C atoms. The two configurations do not interconvert. The H atoms are on the same side of the double bond in the cis configuration; they are on opposite sides in the trans configuration.

Because no rotation takes place about double bonds, some double bonds can exist in one of two distinct *configurations*. Each configuration has the same connectivity (i.e., which atoms are connected together and by what types of bonds), but they have different arrangements of atoms in space. Molecules like this typically do not interconvert, so they can be isolated from each other and studied separately. This is the case with the two molecules of 1,2-dichloroethene shown in **Figure 3-24**. In both molecules, notice that each doubly bonded C is singly bonded to one H and one Cl. In the first molecule, both Cl atoms are on the *same side* of the doubly bonded carbons, whereas in the second molecule, the Cl atoms are on *opposite sides*. Notice that the two forms of 1,2-dichloroethene have significantly different boiling points.

The configurations about a C═C double bond can be named either cis or trans if each carbon has an attached H (see Looking Ahead box):

The configuration about a C═C double bond is:

- **cis** if the two non-hydrogen substituents are on the *same side* of the two carbons in the double bond.
- **trans** if two non-hydrogen substituents are on *opposite sides* of the two carbons in the double bond.

▸ LOOKING AHEAD

To describe the configuration of a C═C double bond as either cis or trans, each C atom must be bonded to one H. In Section 5.8, we will learn how to distinguish the configurations of double bonds more generally, using what is called the *E*/*Z* system.

There are two lessons to take away from the example with *cis*- and *trans*-1,2-dichloroethene:

1. Two configurations for a double bond are possible if each doubly bonded atom is singly bonded to two different atoms/groups.
2. To convert from one configuration to the other, exchange locations of the atoms/groups that are attached to one of the doubly bonded atoms.

We can apply these ideas to show that distinct configurations are impossible for fluoroethene ($H_2C{=}CHF$). First, notice that the C on the left is bonded to two H atoms. Second, if we were to exchange the H and F atoms bonded to one C of the double bond, attempting to achieve a distinct configuration, we simply arrive at the same molecule as before the exchange (see Your Turn 3.11).

YOUR TURN 3.11

These two representations of CH_2CHF differ by exchanging the H and F atoms bonded to the C atom on the right. Using a molecular modeling kit, construct the two molecules and try to line one up with the other. Are they the same or different? (Try all orientations of the two molecules.)

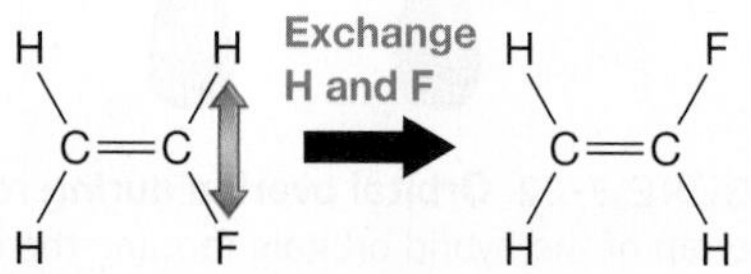
H
H
C═C
H
F
Exchange H and F
H
F
C═C
H
H

SOLVED PROBLEM **3.7**

How to determine whether two configurations exist about a double bond

Break It Down **Does this molecule have two distinct configurations about the double bond?**

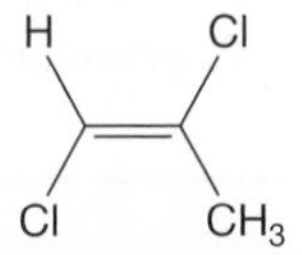

H
Cl
Cl
CH3

Think	Solve
Are two different atoms/groups attached to each doubly bonded C?	On both ends of the C═C bond, the two substituents are different (H and Cl on one end, and Cl and CH_3 on the other end). Therefore, two unique configurations about the double bond must exist. 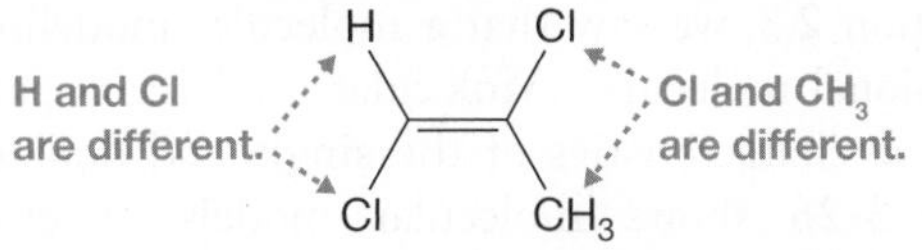
Alternatively, will exchanging the two groups attached to a doubly bonded C give rise to a different molecule? How can you tell?	The graphic illustrates the exchange of the Cl and CH_3 groups attached to one of the doubly bonded C atoms. The molecules before and after are different: they have different configurations about the C═C bond. Before the exchange, the Cl atoms are on opposite sides of the double bond, whereas after the exchange, the Cl atoms are on the same side. 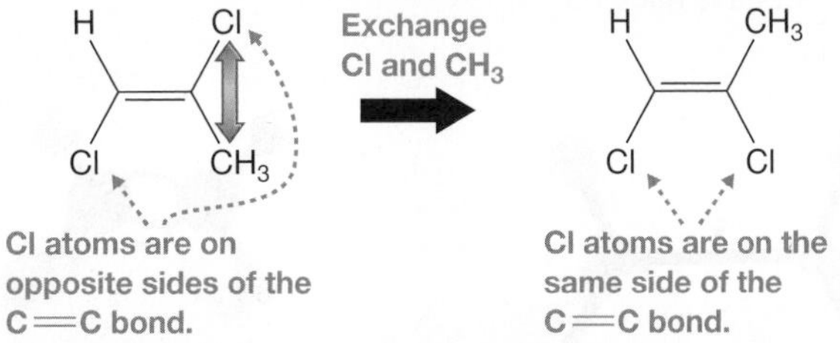

H and Cl are different.
Cl and CH3 are different.

Exchange Cl and CH3
Cl atoms are on opposite sides of the C═C bond.
Cl atoms are on the same side of the C═C bond.

Try It Determine which of the following molecules **A–D** have a double bond for which two distinct configurations are possible.

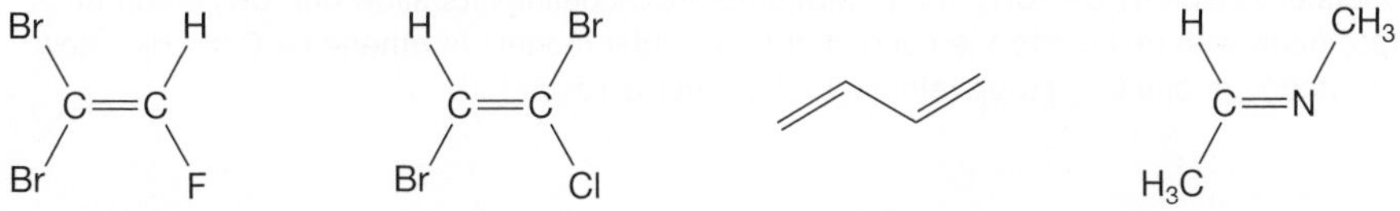

A B C D

Some molecules have more than one C═C double bond, and each double bond can potentially have different configurations. There are three double bonds, for example, in a molecule of α-linolenic acid (**Figure 3-25**), a natural fatty acid. Notice that

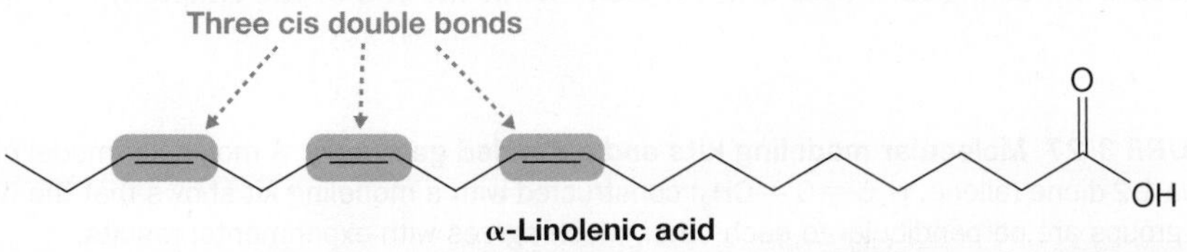

Three cis double bonds
α-Linolenic acid

FIGURE 3-25 α-Linolenic acid and its three cis double bonds

CONNECTIONS 3.7

Protecting the Goodyear blimp Fluoroethene (Your Turn 3.11), also called vinyl fluoride, is used to make poly(vinyl fluoride), a polymer developed by DuPont. Poly(vinyl fluoride) was given the brand name Tedlar, and it is typically produced in thin films and used as protective coatings. This Goodyear blimp, for example, is protected by Tedlar.

GOODYEAR

CONNECTIONS 3.8

Important dietary oils α-Linolenic acid (Fig. 3-25), a type of omega-3 fatty acid, is classified as an essential fatty acid for humans because it has vital roles but is not produced by the body. Rather, it must be consumed as part of the diet, from sources such as walnuts and vegetable oils.

each double bond in α-linolenic acid is in the cis configuration: in each case, the two hydrogen atoms (not shown) are bonded to one side of the C═C double bond, and the two carbons are bonded to the C═C on the other side.

YOUR TURN 3.12

Label each of these double bonds as either cis or trans.

(a)

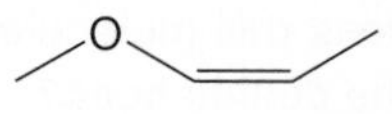

(b)

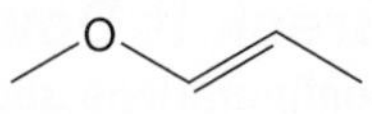

3.8 Strategies for Success: Molecular Modeling Kits, Bond Rotations, and Extended Geometries

SECTION 3.8 OBJECTIVES

You will be able to:

1. Use a molecular modeling kit to demonstrate rotational characteristics about single and double bonds.
2. Obtain the extended three-dimensional geometry of a molecule with double bonds by using a molecular modeling kit.

Strategies for Success
Molecular Modeling Kits and Single versus Double Bonds: Bond Rotations and Extended Geometry

In Section 2.3, we saw that a molecular modeling kit can help us visualize three-dimensional molecules. Molecular models are particularly helpful for studying the *rotational* characteristics of the single and double bonds discussed in Section 3.7. **Figure 3-26** shows molecular models of ethane ($H_3C—CH_3$) and ethene ($H_2C═CH_2$), constructed using different modeling kits. Take the time to build these two molecules with your own kit and try to rotate one group relative to the other. You will find that your model allows groups to rotate about single bonds but not double bonds, mimicking what takes place in real molecules.

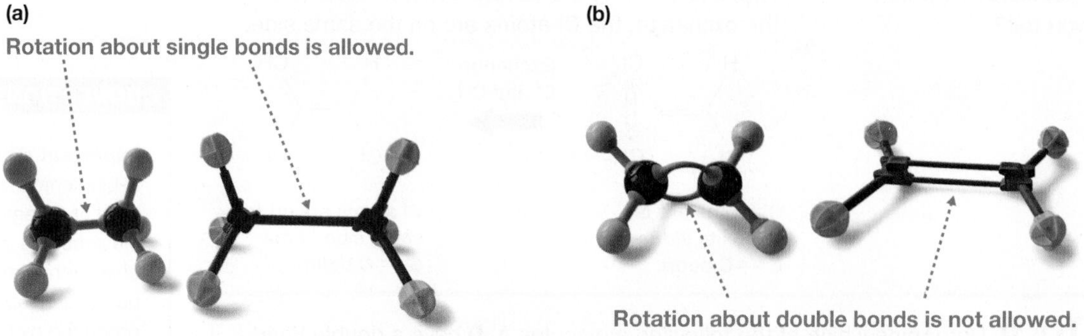

(a)
Rotation about single bonds is allowed.
(b)
Rotation about double bonds is not allowed.

FIGURE 3-26 Modeling kits and rotational characteristics of molecules (a) Molecular models of ethane ($H_3C—CH_3$) made with different modeling kits allow one CH_3 group to rotate freely with respect to the second. (b) Molecular models of ethene ($H_2C═CH_2$) show that rotation of one CH_2 group relative to the other is restricted.

Modeling kits also do a good job of showing accurate *extended* geometries about double bonds—that is, the three-dimensional location of the atoms directly attached to each double bond. Because of the planar nature of double bonds, for example, it might be tempting to think that the entire propa-1,2-diene (allene, $H_2C═C═CH_2$) molecule is planar. Experiments show, however, that one CH_2 group is perpendicular to the other. As we can see in **Figure 3-27**, these are the same results we obtain from molecular modeling kits! (See also Problem 3.5 at the end of the chapter.)

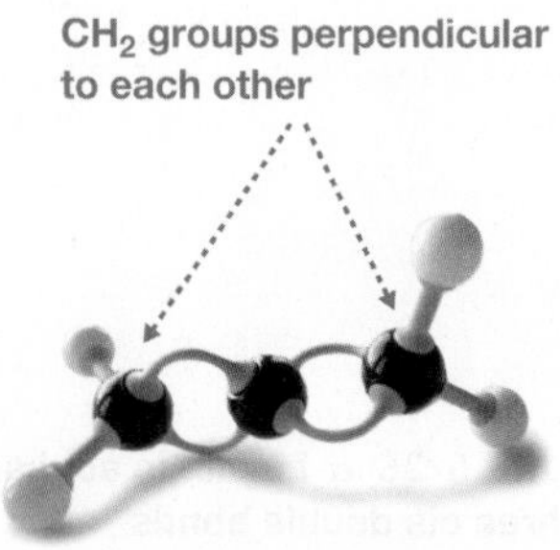

CH2 groups perpendicular to each other

FIGURE 3-27 Molecular modeling kits and extended geometry A molecular model of propa-1,2-diene (allene, $H_2C═C═CH_2$) constructed with a modeling kit shows that the two CH_2 groups are perpendicular to each other, which agrees with experimental results.

YOUR TURN **3.13**

(a) Using a molecular modeling kit, construct a molecule of $H_2C{=}C{=}C{=}CH_2$. Is the entire molecule planar? **(b)** Next, construct a molecule of $H_2C{=}C{=}C{=}C{=}CH_2$. Is that molecule entirely planar?

3.9 Hybridization, Bond Characteristics, and Effective Electronegativity

SECTION 3.9 OBJECTIVES

You will be able to:

1. Determine which of two atoms, differing only in their hybridization, has the greater effective electronegativity.
2. Identify the relative lengths and strengths of bonds that differ by the hybridization of the atoms involved in the bond.

Thus far, we have not treated the various types of hybrid orbitals as being significantly different, but their differences do have some important consequences in chemistry. One is the effect on bond length and bond strength:

As the hybridization of an atom goes from sp^3 to sp^2 to sp, its bonds become shorter and stronger.

This can be seen in **Figure 3-28** (top) with the C—H single bonds in ethane ($H_3C{-}CH_3$), ethene ($H_2C{=}CH_2$), and ethyne ($HC{\equiv}CH$).

The main difference in these molecules is the hybridization of the orbital from C (Fig. 3-28, bottom). More specifically, the *s*-character of that orbital increases going from sp^3 to sp^2 to sp. A 2*s* orbital is more compact than a 2*p* orbital, so the hybrid orbital becomes more compact as the *s*-character increases, as illustrated in **Figure 3-29** (next page). With a shorter hybrid orbital, bonds made from it must also be shorter in order to maintain sufficient orbital overlap. And, as we learned in Section 1.4, shorter bonds connecting the same atoms are typically stronger.

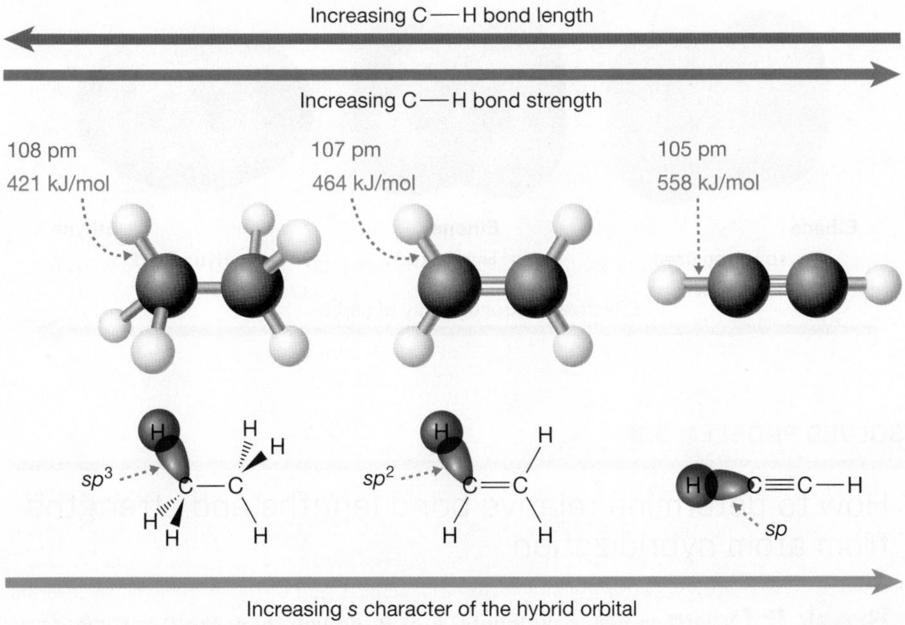

Increasing C—H bond length
Increasing C—H bond strength
108 pm
421 kJ/mol
107 pm
464 kJ/mol
105 pm
558 kJ/mol
sp3
sp2
sp
Increasing s character of the hybrid orbital

FIGURE 3-28 Relationship between hybridization, bond length, and bond strength (*Top*) The C—H bonds become shorter and stronger on going from ethane to ethene to ethyne. (*Bottom*) In all cases, the C—H bond involves the overlap of the 1*s* orbital of a H atom with a hybrid orbital from C. The *s*-character of the C atom's hybrid orbital increases in the order $sp^3 < sp^2 < sp$.

YOUR TURN **3.14**

Review the percent *s*-character in each of the hybrid orbitals in Figure 3-29, and write that percentage above the appropriate orbital.

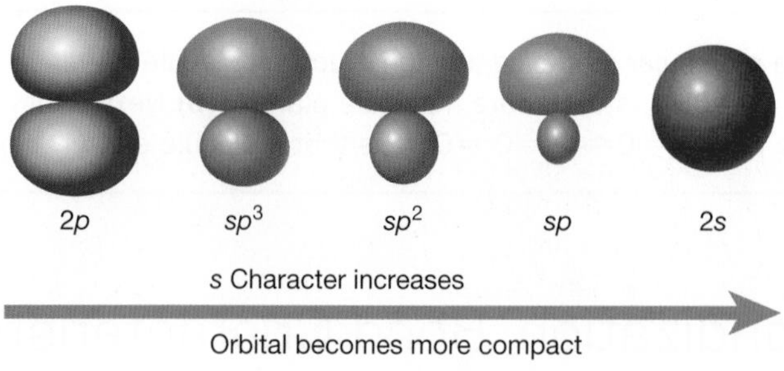
2p
sp3
sp2
sp
2s
s Character increases
Orbital becomes more compact

FIGURE 3-29 Comparison of pure and hybrid orbitals As s-character increases, an orbital becomes more compact and therefore holds electrons closer to the nucleus, on average.

In addition to bond lengths and bond strengths, hybridization can also affect bond polarity. This can be seen in the electrostatic potential maps in **Figure 3-30**, where the concentration of positive charge (blue) on H increases on going from ethane (sp^3) to ethene (sp^2) to ethyne (sp).

As the hybrid orbital on carbon becomes more compact from increased *s*-character, electrons occupying that orbital are held closer to the nucleus. The C atom therefore *behaves* as if its electronegativity is increasing. However, because the nucleus is not changing (it is carbon in all cases), the actual electronegativity is not changing either. Instead, we say that the carbon atom's **effective electronegativity** increases. In general:

> As the hybridization of an atom goes from sp^3 to sp^2 to sp (i.e., as the s-character increases), its effective electronegativity increases.

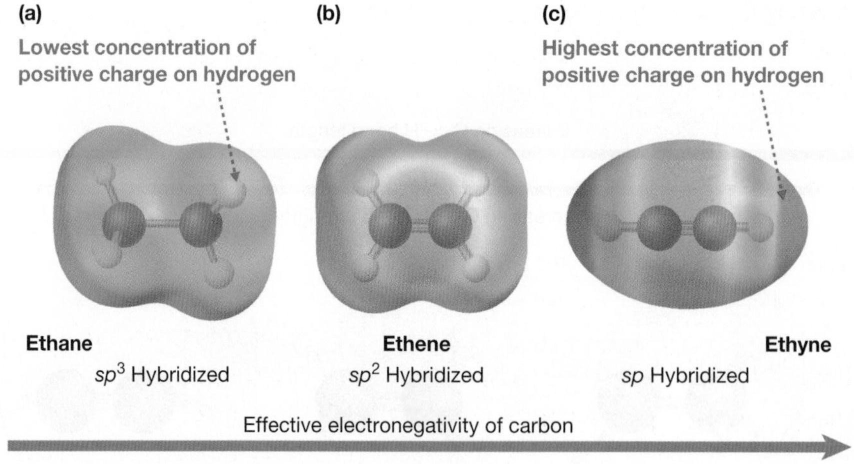
(a)
Lowest concentration of positive charge on hydrogen
(b)
(c)
Highest concentration of positive charge on hydrogen
Ethane
sp3 Hybridized
Ethene
sp2 Hybridized
Ethyne
sp Hybridized
Effective electronegativity of carbon

FIGURE 3-30 Hybridization and effective electronegativity Electrostatic potential maps of (a) ethane, $H_3C{-}CH_3$, (b) ethene, $H_2C{=}CH_2$, and (c) ethyne, $HC{\equiv}CH$. Ethyne has the highest concentration of positive charge on hydrogen. Therefore, as the hybridization of carbon goes from sp^3 to sp^2 to sp, the effective electronegativity of carbon increases.

SOLVED PROBLEM **3.8**

How to determine relative bond lengths and strengths from atom hybridization

Break It Down In which molecule, A or B, do you think the C═C distances are longer? In which molecule are the C═C bonds stronger?

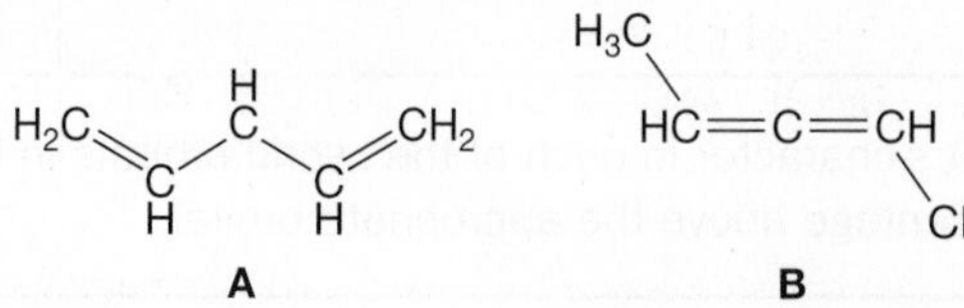
A
B

(continued)

Carbyne: The World's Strongest Material

In Section 3.9, we saw that an atom's bonds tend to get stronger as the atom's hybridization goes from sp^3 to sp^2 to sp. Scientists are looking to take advantage of this property by developing materials composed entirely of *sp*-hybridized carbon atoms. Because each carbon atom would have a linear geometry, the material, called carbyne, would necessarily consist of one-dimensional chains, a portion of whose structure might be represented as in **Figure 3-31**.

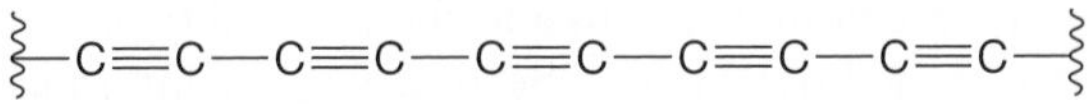

FIGURE 3-31

In 2013, Professor Boris Yakobson at Rice University carried out a theoretical study on carbyne. He concluded that carbyne is 3 times stiffer than diamond and its tensile strength (i.e., its ability to withstand stretching) is twice that of graphene, the two-dimensional sheet of carbon atoms that wraps into cylinders to form carbon nanotubes (see Chemistry with Chicken Wire in Section 1.3). And that's saying something, because carbon nanotubes have found applications in toughening materials in everyday use, including those used in tennis racquets and bicycle frames.

In addition to its mechanical properties, carbyne is theorized to have other properties that are potentially very useful. For example, it has a band gap (a property that determines its electrical conductivity) that varies from 3.2 to 4.4 eV simply by stretching the chain 10%. And molecules can be attached to the ends of the chain that, when twisted 90°, give the chain the helical *highest occupied molecular orbital* (see Section 3.11) shown in **Figure 3-32** and turn carbyne into a magnetic semiconductor.

Unfortunately, the potential for carbyne is far from being fully realized, in large part because it is difficult to synthesize. To date, researchers have been able to synthesize only very small chains, up to 44 carbon atoms long. If this hurdle can be overcome, however, carbyne has a bright future.

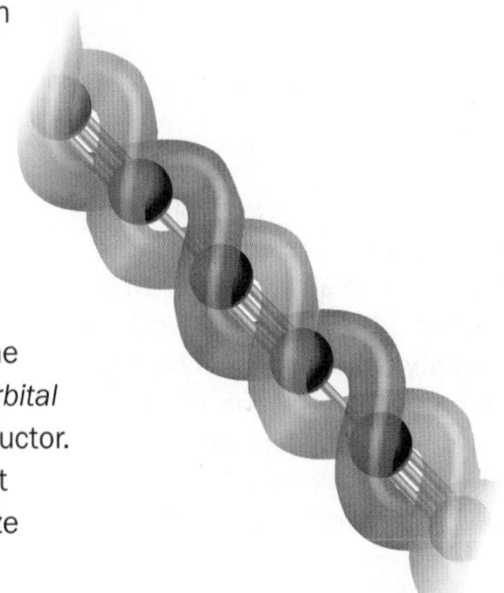

FIGURE 3-32

Think	Solve
What is the hybridization of each atom involved in the C=C bonds?	In **A**, each C=C bond involves two sp^2-hybridized C atoms. In **B**, each C=C bond involves one sp^2-hybridized C atom and one *sp*-hybridized C atom.
What is the *s*-character in each of those C atoms? How does the *s*-character of an atom affect bond length and bond strength?	An *sp* hybrid orbital has greater *s*-character (50%) than an sp^2 hybrid orbital (33.33%). With greater *s*-character, hybrid orbitals are more compact, so the C=C bonds in **B** are shorter and stronger than the ones in **A**.

Try It **(a)** In which molecule, **C** or **D**, is the C—C bond shorter? In which molecule is it stronger? Explain. **(b)** Answer the same questions about the carbon–nitrogen bonds.

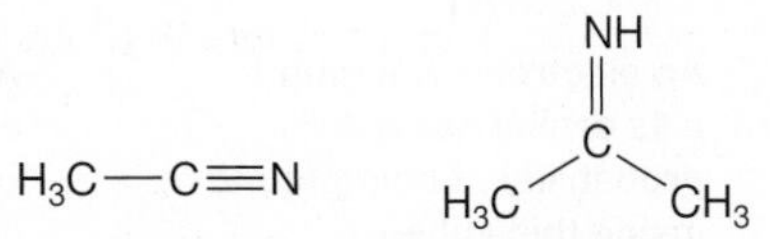

C **D**

3.10 A Deeper Look: Molecular Orbital Theory and the Wave Nature of Electrons

SECTION 3.10 OBJECTIVES

You will be able to:

1. Identify regions of constructive and destructive interference when orbitals with particular phases mix.
2. Explain how molecular orbitals are derived from atomic orbitals and distinguish between bonding, nonbonding, and antibonding molecular orbitals.
3. Draw the molecular orbital energy diagram of H_2 and identify the highest occupied and lowest unoccupied molecular orbitals.

Valence bond (VB) theory, which we developed in Sections 3.1–3.5, gives us insight into bond formation and accounts for important characteristics of a molecule, such as why single bonds rotate but double bonds do not. But VB theory has significant limitations, failing to account for other important outcomes such as the delocalization of electrons over three or more atoms and the availability of empty orbitals in a molecule (see Looking Ahead box). Here in Section 3.10, we introduce a more powerful model called *molecular orbital (MO) theory* that explains aspects of bonding that cannot be explained by VB theory.

▸ LOOKING AHEAD

We will further discuss how MO theory explains electron delocalization via resonance in Section 14.8. In Section 7.9a, we will examine the role empty orbitals play in chemical reactions, and in Section 16.11, we discuss how empty orbitals are involved in ultraviolet–visible (UV–vis) spectroscopy.

Very small particles, such as electrons, have characteristics of both particles and waves; this concept is known as *wave–particle duality*. The branch of chemistry and physics that deals with wave–particle duality is called **quantum mechanics**. As with any wave:

> An electron can be described by a *wave function* (Ψ) that has a numerical value, called the *amplitude*, at each point in space.

The amplitude of an electron's wave function is analogous to the displacement of a rope when a wave is generated along the rope. Just as a rope can be displaced in either direction from rest (**Figure 3-33**), an electron's amplitude can be positive or negative, characterizing the electron's **phase** as positive or negative.

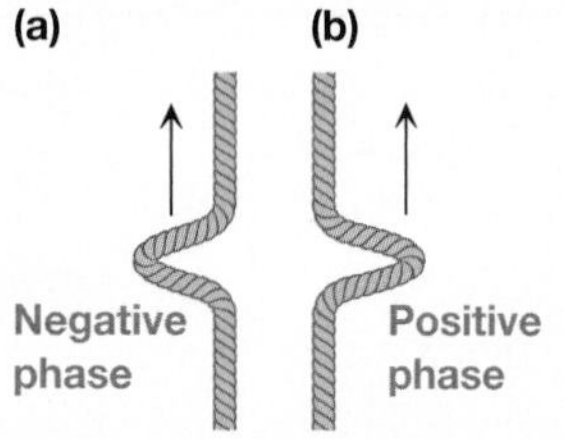
(a)
(b)
Negative phase
Positive phase

FIGURE 3-33 Waves generated on a rope

Electrons in different orbitals are characterized by different wave functions. An electron in a 1*s* orbital, for example, would be described by the Ψ_{1s} wave function, whereas an electron in a 2*p* orbital would be described by Ψ_{2p}.

The amplitude of an electron's wave function at a particular point in space has no physical meaning. The square of that value, however, gives the relative probability of finding the electron there. Mapping those probability values throughout space is what gives us the shape of an orbital. As shown in **Figure 3-34a**, for example, an electron described by Ψ_{1s} has a 90% probability of being found inside a sphere. For an electron described by Ψ_{2p} (Fig. 3-34b) a dumbbell shape encompasses 90% of the probability. The dumbbell consists of two lobes on opposite sides of the nucleus, and at the nucleus there is a **node**: a region where there is zero probability of finding an electron in the orbital.

Notice in Figure 3-34 that relative phase is depicted using dark and light shading of the orbital surfaces. An *s* orbital (Fig. 3-34a) is represented entirely in one shade, indicating that it has the same phase everywhere. The two lobes of a *p* orbital

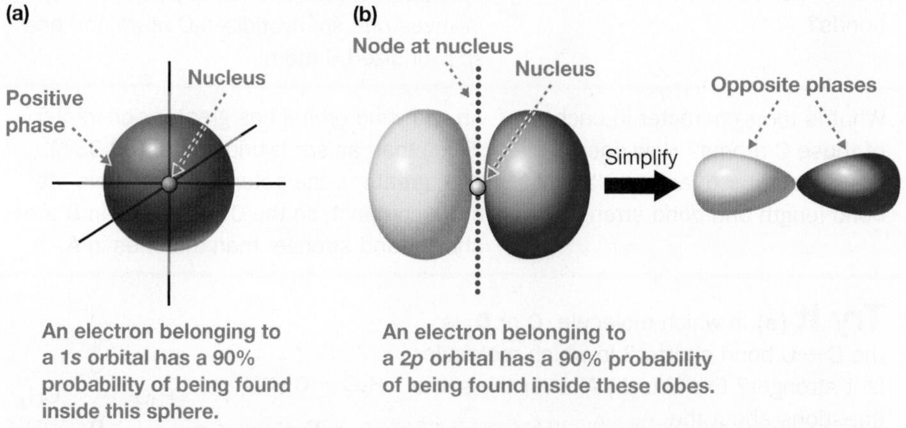
(a)
(b)
Node at nucleus
Nucleus
Nucleus
Opposite phases
Positive phase
Simplify
An electron belonging to a 1s orbital has a 90% probability of being found inside this sphere.
An electron belonging to a 2p orbital has a 90% probability of being found inside these lobes.

FIGURE 3-34 Representations of the 1*s* and 2*p* orbitals (a) The 1*s* orbital is spherical and has the same phase everywhere. (b) The 2*p* orbital consists of two spherical lobes of opposite phase (dark and light shading), located on opposite sides of the nucleus.

(Fig. 3-34b) are represented in two different shades, indicating that the lobes have opposite phases.

Even though an electron's phase has no physical meaning, phase does play an important role when orbitals overlap in space and mix. To get a better feel for the role that phase plays, consider two waves generated on opposite ends of a rope: one case in which the two waves have the same phase (**Figure 3-35a**) and another case in which the two waves have opposite phases (Fig. 3-35b).

In both cases, the waves on the rope propagate toward each other, and when the waves overlap, their amplitudes add together to produce a new wave. If the original waves had the same phase (Fig. 3-35a), then the amplitude of the new wave is larger than either of the original amplitudes, and the original waves are said to have undergone **constructive interference**. Conversely, if the original waves had opposite phases (Fig. 3-35b), then the amplitude of the new wave is diminished or cancelled entirely, and the original waves are said to have undergone **destructive interference**.

YOUR TURN **3.15**

(a) Redraw Figure 3-35a with both initial waves generated on the left side of the rope to represent negative phases. **(b)** Redraw Figure 3-35b, but this time generate the top wave on the left side of the rope (negative phase) and generate the bottom wave on the right side of the rope (positive phase).

Similar to waves on a rope, orbitals mix together to produce new orbitals, dictated by the relative phases of the orbitals where overlap takes place:

- *Constructive interference* occurs in regions of space where overlapping orbitals have the same phase.
- *Destructive interference* occurs where the respective overlapping orbitals have opposite phases.

When orbitals mix to produce new orbitals, it helps to know ahead of time that the number of orbitals cannot change by mixing; that is, the number of orbitals must be conserved:

Conservation of Number of Orbitals

If the number of orbitals that mix is *n*, then the number of new orbitals produced from mixing must also be *n*.

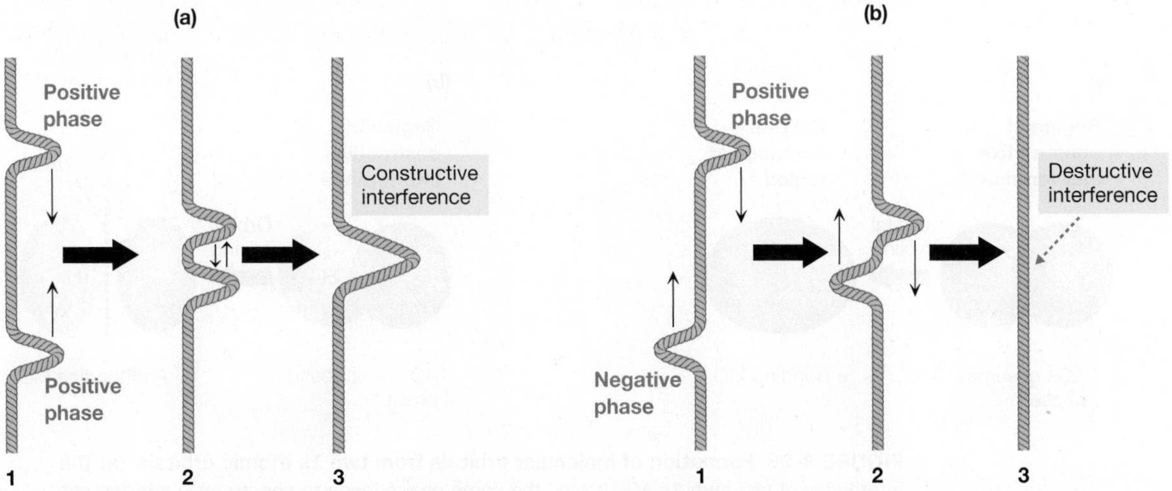

(a)
(b)
Positive
phase
Positive
phase
Constructive
interference
Positive
phase
Negative
phase
Destructive
interference
1
2
3
1
2
3

FIGURE 3-35 Constructive and destructive interference (a) Waves with the same phase (**1** and **2**) propagate toward each other. When the waves meet (**3**), they undergo *constructive interference*, creating a new wave with twice the amplitude of the original ones. (b) Waves with opposite phases (**1** and **2**) propagate toward each other. When the waves meet (**3**), they undergo *destructive interference* and completely cancel.

With these ideas in mind, let's look at some basic principles of molecular orbital (MO) theory:

Molecular Orbital Theory

- Electrons occupy **molecular orbitals (MOs)**, each of which is generated by mixing **atomic orbitals (AOs)** contributed by individual atoms. *All* AOs from all atoms in the molecule mix simultaneously. (For the sake of simplicity, we will consider only valence and core AOs in this book.)
- Only pure AOs (*s*, *p*, etc.) contribute to MOs; hybrid AOs are not considered at all.
- Each MO is produced by a different **linear combination of atomic orbitals (LCAO)**, whereby the AOs have different phase combinations or are weighted differently.
- The number of MOs produced must be the same as the number of AOs contributed (conservation of number of orbitals).

Let's apply these ideas to a molecule of H_2. Each H atom contributes a 1*s* AO, in a manner similar to that described by valence bond theory (Fig. 3-3, p. 114). Two AOs mix, so two MOs must be produced. One MO is produced from mixing the 1*s* AOs having the same phase (in-phase overlap), as shown in **Figure 3-36a**. The in-phase overlap results in constructive interference in the internuclear region, so the resulting MO is built up there. The second MO is produced from mixing 1*s* AOs having opposite phases (out-of-phase overlap), as shown in Figure 3-36b. In this case, destructive interference takes place in the internuclear region, so the resulting MO is reduced in size there. In fact, midway between the two nuclei, the out-of-phase AOs completely cancel one another to produce a *node*.

The MOs in Figure 3-36 have different energies. The buildup of the MO in Figure 3-36a represents a greater probability of finding an electron in the internuclear region, where the simultaneous attraction to both nuclei lowers the electron's energy. The opposite takes place in Figure 3-36b, where orbital cancellation would exclude an electron in the internuclear region and raise the electron's energy. These energy differences characterize MOs as being *bonding*, *antibonding*, or *nonbonding*:

- A **bonding MO** is significantly lower in energy than its contributing AOs.
- An **antibonding MO** (often denoted by *) is significantly higher in energy than its contributing AOs.
- A **nonbonding MO** has about the same energy as its contributing AOs.

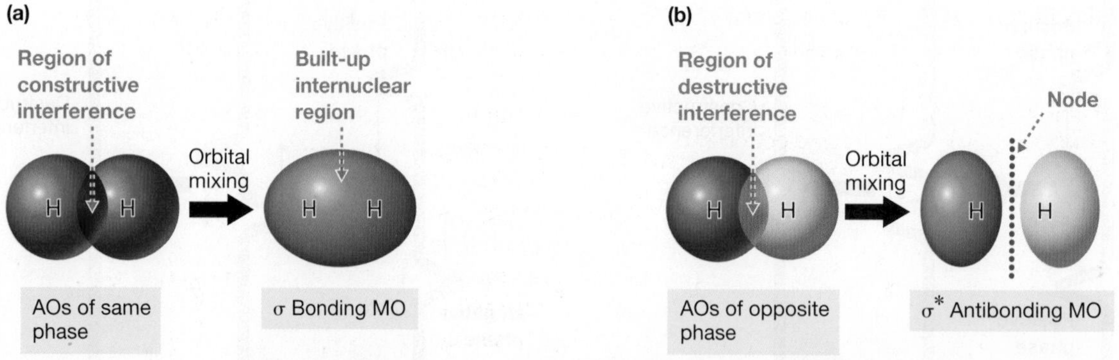
(a)
Region of constructive interference
Built-up internuclear region
Orbital mixing
H
H
H
H
AOs of same phase
σ Bonding MO
(b)
Region of destructive interference
Node
Orbital mixing
H
H
H
H
AOs of opposite phase
σ* Antibonding MO

FIGURE 3-36 Formation of molecular orbitals from two 1s atomic orbitals (a) The interaction of two pure 1s AOs having the same phase leads to constructive interference between the two nuclei. (b) The interacting 1s AOs have opposite phases, which leads to destructive interference. The resulting MO undergoes cancellation in the internuclear region, resulting in a node.

Notice that both of the MOs in Figure 3-36 have σ symmetry because they both result from the overlap of AOs along the bonding axis (Section 3.1). Thus, the MO in Figure 3-36a is a **σ bonding MO**, and the one in Figure 3-36b is a **σ* antibonding MO**. H_2 has no nonbonding MOs.

Figure 3-37 shows the MO energy diagram for H_2. On the left are the two 1*s* AOs, prior to undergoing mixing. On the right are the σ and σ* MOs: you can see that the σ MO is lower in energy than the contributing 1*s* AOs, and the opposite is true for the σ* MO.

With the two MOs in place in Figure 3-37, we can finally add the two electrons of H_2. As usual, the electrons add to the lowest energy orbitals first, which results in two electrons occupying the σ MO and no electrons in the σ* MO.

From any completed MO energy diagram, we can identify two MOs that have special significance:

- The **highest occupied molecular orbital (HOMO)** is the highest-energy MO that contains an electron.
- The **lowest unoccupied molecular orbital (LUMO)** is the lowest-energy MO that is empty.

The HOMO and LUMO play a significant role in dictating whether a particular chemical reaction can take place, as we will see in Interchapter C. Chapter 16 shows how the HOMO and LUMO of a species relate to the features of an ultraviolet–visible spectrum.

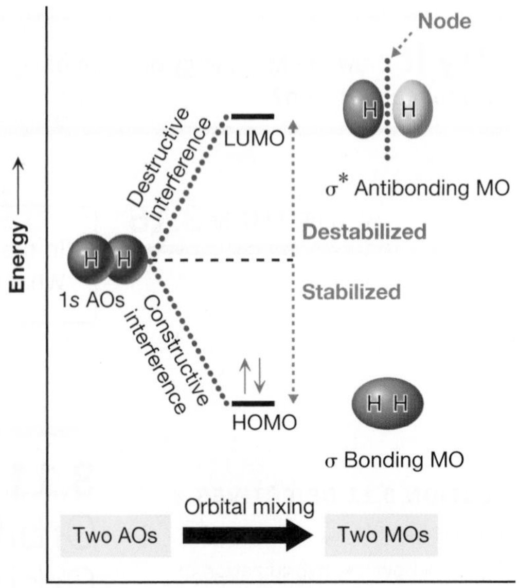

Node
H H
LUMO
σ* Antibonding MO
Destructive interference
Destabilized
Energy
H H
1s AOs
Stabilized
Constructive interference
HOMO
H H
σ Bonding MO
Orbital mixing
Two AOs
Two MOs

FIGURE 3-37 Molecular orbital energy diagram of H_2 The overlap of two 1s AOs from separate H atoms results in the formation of one σ MO and one σ* MO. The individual AOs are on the left, and the resulting MOs are on the right. The σ MO is the highest occupied molecular orbital (HOMO), and the σ* MO is the lowest unoccupied molecular orbital (LUMO).

SOLVED PROBLEM **3.9**

How to draw the MO energy diagram of an H_2 ion

Break It Down Draw the MO energy diagram of H_2^+. Is H_2^+ more stable, less stable, or about the same as the isolated H atom and H^+ ion?

Think	Solve
What AOs do H and H^+ contribute? How many MOs will be produced from mixing those AOs?	H and H^+ each contribute a 1s AO. Two MOs will result from mixing two AOs (conservation of number of orbitals).
What MO will be produced from mixing the 1s AOs having the same phase? What about opposite phases?	As in Figure 3-36a, a σ bonding MO will be produced when two 1s AOs having the same phase mix. And as in Figure 3-36b, a σ* antibonding MO will be produced when the 1s AOs having opposite phases mix.
What are the relative energies of the σ and σ* MOs? How many electrons does H_2^+ have, and how do you fill the MOs with those electrons?	As we saw with H_2 (Fig. 3-37), the σ MO is lowered in energy relative to the isolated 1s AOs, and the σ* MO is raised in energy, as shown in the MO energy diagram here. The H_2^+ ion has one electron total, and it goes in the lowest energy MO available, which is the σ MO. Because the energy of the electron is lower in H_2^+ than it is in the isolated H and H^+, H_2^+ is more stable than if H and H^+ were separated.

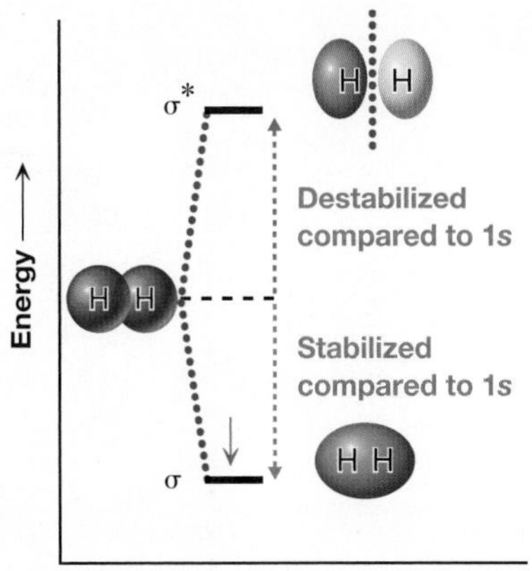

σ*
H H
Destabilized compared to 1s
Energy
H H
Stabilized compared to 1s
σ
H H

(continued)

Try It Draw the MO energy diagram of H_2^-. Is H_2^- more stable, less stable, or about the same as the isolated H atom and H^- ion?

YOUR TURN **3.16**

In the H_2^+ molecule described in Solved Problem 3.9, what is the HOMO? What is the LUMO?

SECTION 3.11 OBJECTIVES

You will be able to:

1. Show how the hybridization of pure *s* and *p* AOs leads to hybrid AOs that consist of one large lobe and one small lobe having opposite phases.
2. Derive a molecular orbital–valence bond picture for a molecular species, and the corresponding energy diagram, when given the Lewis structure.

3.11 A Deeper Look: Hybrid Atomic Orbitals and a Combined Molecular Orbital–Valence Bond Model

As we learned in Section 3.10, each MO in a molecule is the product of mixing all pure AOs (*s*, *p*, etc.) from every atom. For a molecule of H_2, we saw that two MOs (one σ and one σ*) are produced when the 1*s* AOs from each isolated H atom are mixed (review Fig. 3-37). The problem becomes somewhat complex for organic molecules, however, even when they are relatively small. For ethane (CH_3CH_3), for example, there are 16 MOs produced from 16 contributing AOs—one AO from each H atom (1*s*) and five AOs from each C atom (1*s*, 2*s*, $2p_x$, $2p_y$, and $2p_z$)—and each MO is produced by mixing all 16 contributing AOs. Indeed, sophisticated computer programs have been written to deal with these kinds of situations.

Here we apply some simplifications to make MO theory more manageable. First, we consider AOs contributed only from the valence shell of the atoms, since it is the valence electrons that are involved in bonding. Moreover, valence AOs from different atoms tend to have similar energies, so they will have the greatest interactions when mixing. Second, we will incorporate two ideas from VB theory: (1) the key orbital interactions are from overlapping AOs on adjacent atoms, and (2) atoms having a particular electron geometry are hybridized and contribute hybrid AOs from their valence shell. Thus, our blended treatment of bonding in this section is more properly characterized as a *molecular orbital–valence bond (MO–VB) model.*

To incorporate hybrid AOs into the MO–VB model, we need to know their shapes and phases. Section 3.2 showed the general shape of a hybrid AO; it consists of one large lobe and one small lobe on opposite sides of the nucleus. But what are the relative phases of those lobes?

To answer this question, let's consider how *sp* hybrid AOs are produced by mixing one *s* AO and one *p* AO (a p_x in this case) with different phase combinations (**Figure 3-38**). In Figure 3-38a, the *s* and *p* AOs overlap with the same phase (constructive interference) to the right of the nucleus, and they overlap with opposite phases (destructive interference) to the left. This produces an *sp* hybrid AO that has a large lobe of a single phase on the right and a small lobe of the opposite phase on the left. In the other phase combination of the contributing *s* and *p* AOs, shown in Figure 3-38b, constructive interference takes place to the left of the nucleus and destructive interference takes place on the right. Thus, the large lobe of the resulting *sp* AO appears on the left and has one phase, and the small lobe with the opposite phase appears on the right.

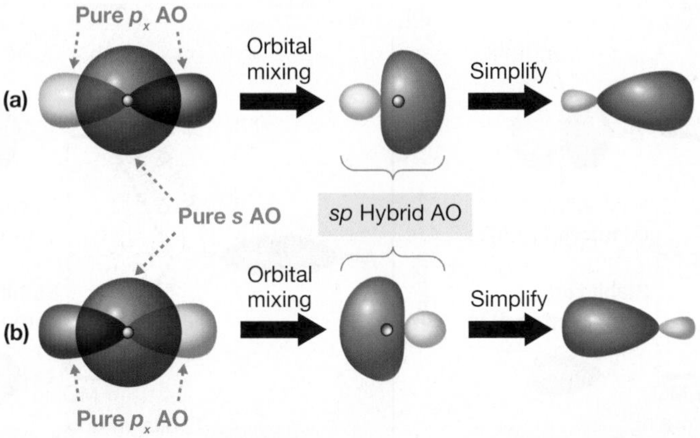
Pure p_x AO
(a)
Orbital mixing
Simplify
Pure s AO
sp Hybrid AO
Orbital mixing
Simplify
(b)
Pure p_x AO

FIGURE 3-38 Generation of two *sp* hybrid orbitals from pure atomic orbitals
(a) Constructive interference (same phase of the orbitals) occurs to the right of the nucleus and destructive interference (opposite phases) occurs to the left, so the resulting *sp* hybrid orbital (middle) becomes larger on the right and smaller on the left. (b) Constructive interference occurs to the left and destructive interference occurs to the right, so the resulting *sp* hybrid orbital (middle) becomes larger on the left and smaller on the right. Simplified versions of the hybrid orbitals are shown on the right.

YOUR TURN **3.17**

Figure 3-38 shows how two *sp* AOs are produced from an s AO and a p_x AO, but the contributing *p* AO could instead be a p_y or a p_z. Show how two *sp* AOs would be produced by mixing an s AO with **(a)** a p_y AO and **(b)** a p_z AO.

The concepts we used to derive *sp* hybrid AOs can also be used to derive sp^2 and sp^3 hybrid AOs. The exercises to derive those other hybrid AOs, however, are more involved and beyond the scope of this book. Suffice it to say, however, that sp^2 and sp^3 AOs are qualitatively similar in shape and phase to *sp* hybrid AOs:

Any *sp*, sp^2, or sp^3 hybrid AO consists of one large lobe of a single phase and one small lobe of the opposite phase.

There are just three key orbital interactions that arise when the MO–VB model is applied to organic molecules: the interactions between (1) one hybrid AO and one *s* AO (**Figure 3-39a**, next page) (2) two hybrid AOs (Fig. 3-39b), and (3) two *p* AOs (Fig. 3-39c). Just as we saw for the interaction of two 1*s* AOs in a molecule of H_2 (review Fig. 3-37, p. 139), each pair of AOs in Figure 3-39 will mix to produce two new MOs: one *bonding* MO, which is lower in energy than the contributing AOs, and one *antibonding* MO, which is higher in energy than the AOs.

Notice that the symmetry of the MOs in Figure 3-39a and 3-39b differs from the symmetry of the MOs in Figure 3-39c. In Figure 3-39a, overlap occurs along the bonding axis (σ symmetry), so each interaction produces one σ bonding MO and one σ^* antibonding MO. In Figure 3-39c, on the other hand, overlap occurs on opposite sides of the bonding axis (π symmetry) to produce one **π bonding MO** and one **π^* antibonding MO**.

In an organic molecule, there can be multiple orbital interactions of the types shown in Figure 3-39. In general:

- Each pair of AOs undergoing σ overlap will produce one σ MO and one σ^* MO.
- Each pair of AOs undergoing π overlap will produce one π MO and one π^* MO.

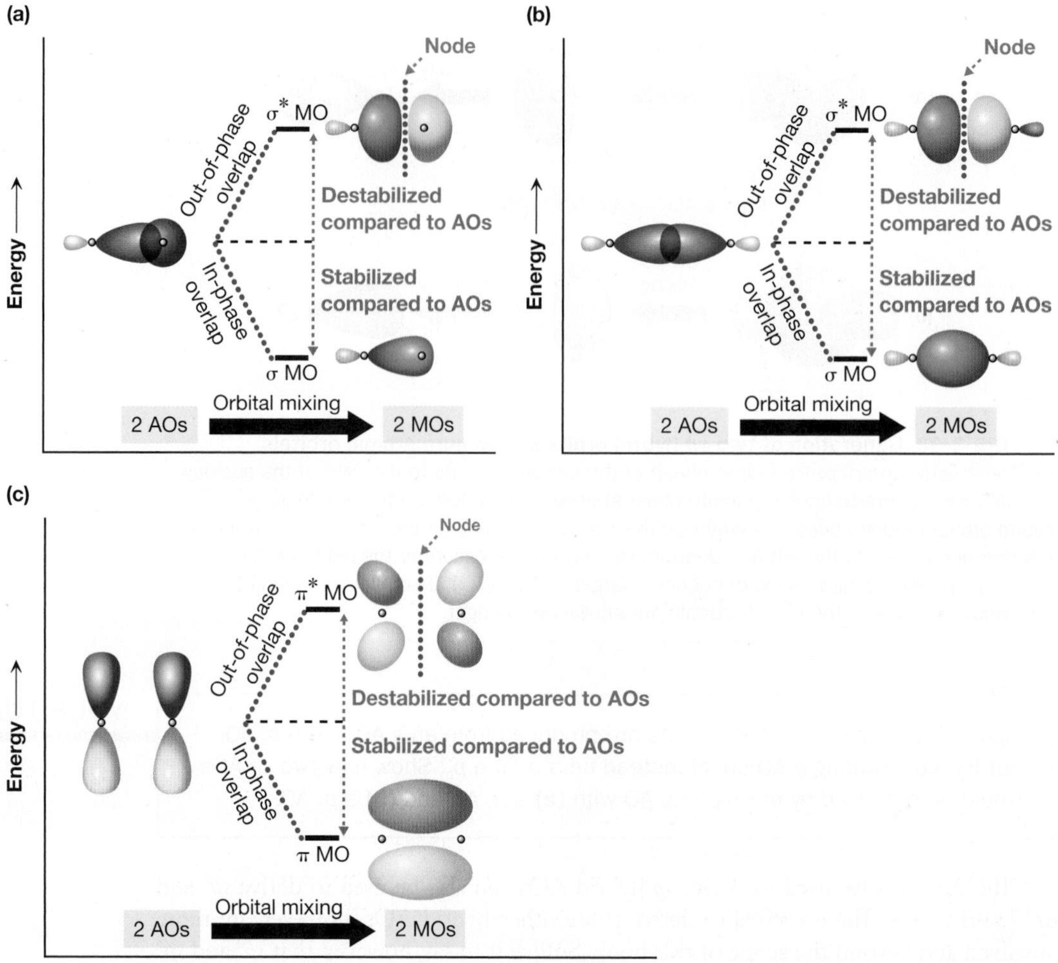
(a)
Node
σ* MO
Out-of-phase overlap
Destabilized compared to AOs
Stabilized compared to AOs
In-phase overlap
σ MO
Energy
Orbital mixing
2 AOs
2 MOs
(b)
Node
σ* MO
Out-of-phase overlap
Destabilized compared to AOs
Stabilized compared to AOs
In-phase overlap
σ MO
Energy
Orbital mixing
2 AOs
2 MOs
(c)
Node
π* MO
Out-of-phase overlap
Destabilized compared to AOs
Stabilized compared to AOs
In-phase overlap
π MO
Energy
Orbital mixing
2 AOs
2 MOs

FIGURE 3-39 Key atomic orbital interactions in the qualitative molecular orbital–valence bond model (a) A hybrid AO mixes with a 1*s* AO. (b) Two hybrid AOs mix. (c) Two *p* AOs mix. The AOs in (a) and (b) undergo σ overlap, so they mix to produce a σ bonding MO and a σ* antibonding MO. The AOs in (c) undergo π overlap, so they mix to produce a π bonding MO and a π* antibonding MO. In all three cases, the bonding MO is lowered in energy due to constructive interference in the internuclear region, and the antibonding MO is raised in energy due to destructive interference in the internuclear region and the appearance of a node there.

YOUR TURN **3.18**

Consider the AO interaction in Figure 3-39a. Draw the AOs with the particular phases that, on mixing, would produce the antibonding MO shown. Do the same for the AO interactions in Figure 3-39b and 3-39c.

Having laid the foundation for the MO–VB model, let's now apply the model to some of the molecules we examined using the VB model earlier in this chapter.

3.11a Applying the MO–VB Model to Ethane

As illustrated in the energy diagram for ethane ($H_3C—CH_3$), shown in **Figure 3-40**, 14 contributing valence AOs (previously shown in Solved Problem 3.2, p. 117) generate 14 MOs. More specifically, each of the seven σ interactions generates one σ MO and one σ * MO, totaling seven σ MOs and seven σ* MOs. The 14 valence electrons of ethane fill the seven σ MOs, leaving seven σ* MOs empty. Thus, one of the σ MOs would be the HOMO, and one of the σ* MOs would be the LUMO.

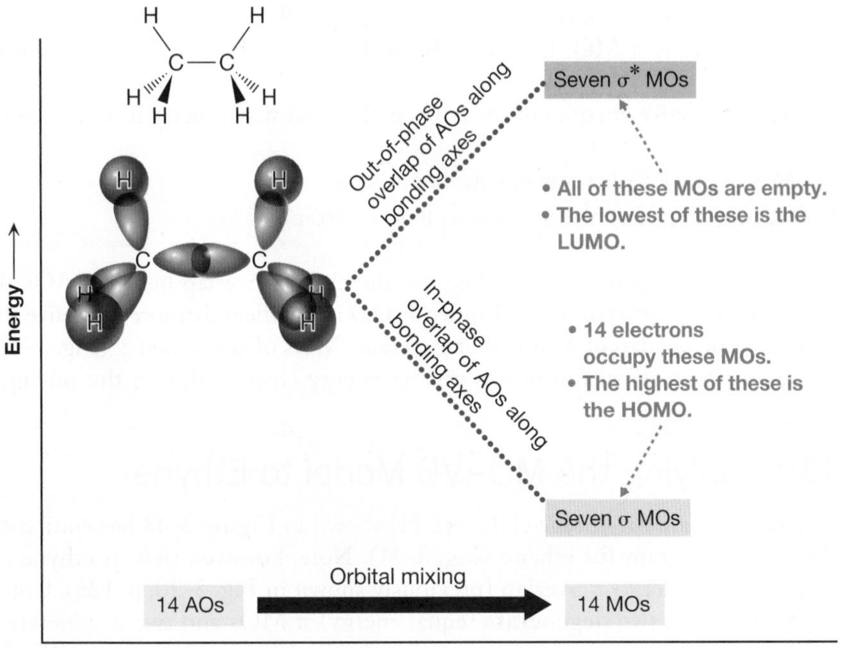
Seven σ* MOs
Out-of-phase overlap of AOs along bonding axes
• All of these MOs are empty.
• The lowest of these is the LUMO.
Energy
In-phase overlap of AOs along bonding axes
• 14 electrons occupy these MOs.
• The highest of these is the HOMO.
Seven σ MOs
Orbital mixing
14 AOs
14 MOs

FIGURE 3-40 Energy diagram for the formation of ethane from its constituent atoms The individual AOs are shown on the left. Interaction among those orbitals generates 14 MOs of σ symmetry, seven bonding (σ) MOs and seven antibonding (σ*) MOs, shown on the right.

3.11b Applying the MO–VB Model to Ethene

The energy diagram for ethene ($H_2C{=}CH_2$) is derived in **Figure 3-41**. The contributing 12 valence AOs (previously shown in Fig. 3-13, p. 121) mix to produce 12 MOs. Five pairs of AOs undergo σ overlap, resulting in five σ MOs and five σ* MOs. The two *p* AOs undergo π overlap to produce one π MO and one π* MO. Finally, the

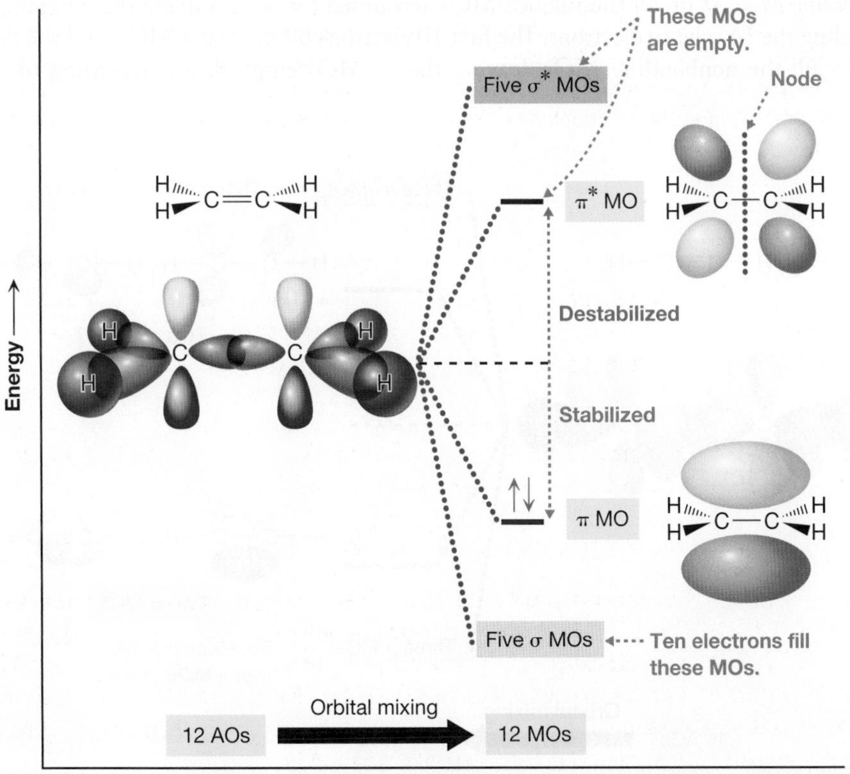
These MOs are empty.
Five σ* MOs
Node
π* MO
Energy
Destabilized
Stabilized
π MO
Five σ MOs
Ten electrons fill these MOs.
Orbital mixing
12 AOs
12 MOs

FIGURE 3-41 Energy diagram for the formation of ethene from its constituent atoms The AOs are shown on the left, and the resulting MOs are shown on the right. The energies of the five σ MOs are lower than that of the π MO, whereas the energies of the five σ* MOs are higher than that of the π* MO.

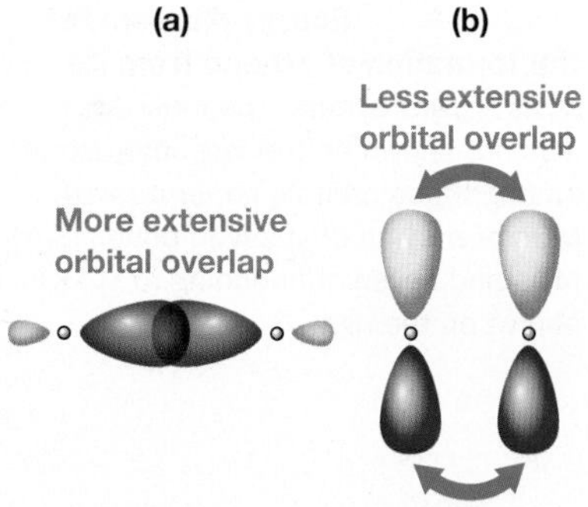

(a)
(b)
Less extensive orbital overlap
More extensive orbital overlap

FIGURE 3-42 Comparison of orbital overlap for orbitals of σ and π symmetry (a) Overlap of two hybrid AOs in the formation of a MO with σ symmetry. (b) Overlap of two *p* AOs in the formation of a MO with π symmetry. There is significantly more extensive orbital overlap in (a) than in (b).

12 valence electrons are added. The first 10 electrons fill the five σ MOs, and the last two electrons fill the π MO. Thus, the HOMO is the π MO and the LUMO is the π* MO.

Notice the relative energies of the MOs with σ and π symmetry in Figure 3-41:

- σ MOs are typically lower in energy than π MOs.
- σ* MOs are typically higher in energy than π* MOs.

We observe these relative energies because the end-on overlap between AOs that generates MOs with σ symmetry (**Figure 3-42a**) is significantly more extensive than the side-by-side overlap of *p* AOs that generates MOs of π symmetry (Fig. 3-42b). The greater extent of overlap means greater energy changes during the mixing of the AOs.

3.11c Applying the MO–VB Model to Ethyne

The energy diagram for ethyne (HC≡CH) shown in **Figure 3-43** has similarities to the energy diagram for ethene (Fig. 3-41). Note, however, that in ethyne *two* pairs of *p* AOs undergo π overlap (previously shown in Fig. 3-20, p. 126). Consequently, ethyne has two **degenerate** (equal energy) π MOs and two degenerate π* MOs. To complete the energy diagram, we add the 10 valence electrons. The first six fill the three σ MOs, and the final four fill the two π MOs. Thus, the π MOs form equivalent HOMOs and the π* MOs form equivalent LUMOs.

3.11d Applying the MO–VB Model to Methanol

Figure 3-44 shows the energy diagram for methanol (CH_3OH), whose Lewis structure exhibits lone pairs. The 12 AOs (previously shown in Fig. 3-9, p. 118) mix to produce 12 MOs. The five pairs of AOs undergoing σ overlap produce five σ MOs and five σ* MOs. The remaining two AOs, which are sp^3 hybrid AOs contributed from the O atom, do not overlap with any AOs from other atoms. These sp^3 hybrid AOs therefore produce MOs that are similar in energy to the AOs; that is, they are *nonbonding MOs*. With all the valence MOs accounted for, we complete the diagram by adding the 14 valence electrons. The first 10 electrons fill the five σ MOs, and the final four fill the nonbonding MOs, leaving the σ* MOs empty. Thus, according to the

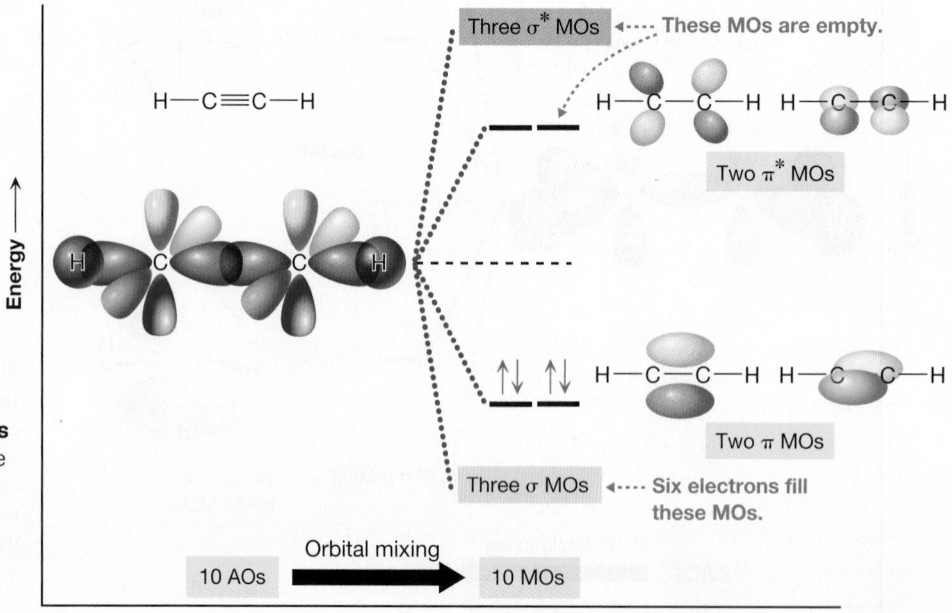

Three σ* MOs
These MOs are empty.
H—C≡C—H
Two π* MOs
Energy
Two π MOs
Three σ MOs
Six electrons fill these MOs.
Orbital mixing
10 AOs
10 MOs

FIGURE 3-43 Energy diagram for the formation of molecular orbitals in ethyne The AOs are shown on the left, and the MOs are shown on the right. Six electrons occupy three σ MOs and four electrons occupy two π MOs, thus accounting for all 10 valence electrons in ethyne.

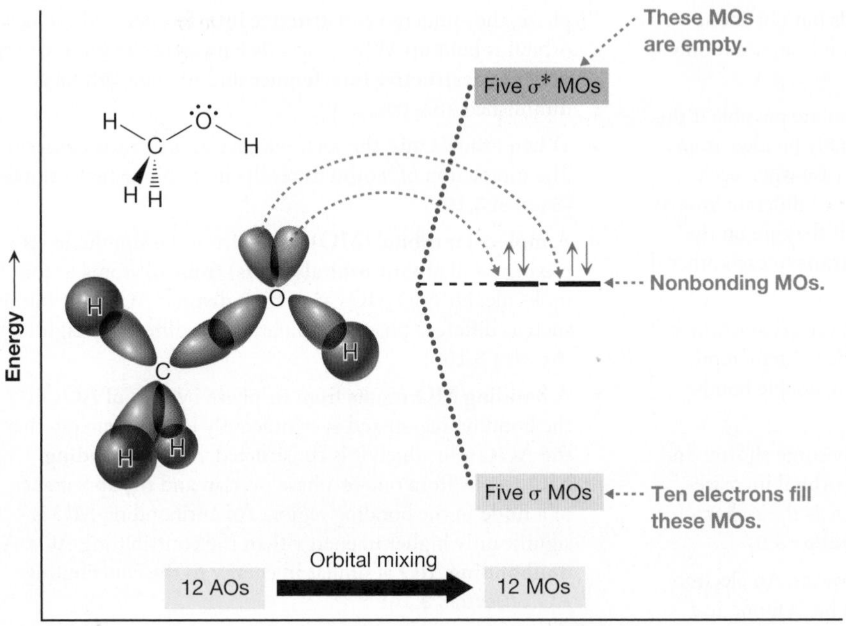

These MOs are empty.
Five σ* MOs
Nonbonding MOs.
Energy
Five σ MOs
Ten electrons fill these MOs.
Orbital mixing
12 AOs
12 MOs

FIGURE 3-44 Energy diagram for the formation of molecular orbitals in methanol The AOs are shown on the left, and the MOs are shown on the right. Ten electrons occupy five σ MOs and four electrons occupy two nonbonding MOs, thus accounting for all 14 valence electrons in methanol.

MO-VB model, the nonbonding MOs form a degenerate pair of HOMOs, and the LUMO is one of the σ* MOs.

Notice in Figure 3-44 that there are two filled nonbonding MOs and there are two lone pairs of electrons in the Lewis structure. In general:

> A lone pair of electrons in a Lewis structure is associated with a filled nonbonding MO.

Chapter Summary and Key Terms

- **Valence bond (VB) theory** treats a covalent bond as the outcome of mixing two half-filled orbitals, one from each of two adjacent atoms. The resulting orbital that holds the pair of electrons in the bond has been built up in the region where the orbitals overlap. **(Section 3.1)**
- Orbitals that overlap along a bonding axis result in a new orbital that has **σ symmetry**; a pair of electrons occupying an orbital that has σ symmetry constitutes a **σ bond**. Orbitals that overlap on opposite sides of a bonding axis result in a new orbital that has **π symmetry**; a pair of electrons occupying an orbital that has π symmetry constitutes a **π bond**. **(Sections 3.1 and 3.4)**
- A single bond is a σ bond. A double bond consists of one σ bond and one π bond. A triple bond consists of one σ bond and two π bonds. **(Sections 3.1, 3.4, and 3.5)**
- According to VB theory, a lone pair occupies an orbital that does not overlap with orbitals from other atoms. **(Section 3.3)**
- To account for various electron geometries, VB theory invokes hybridization, in which valence *s* and *p* orbitals mix to produce **hybrid orbitals**. A hybrid orbital consists of one large lobe and one small lobe. **(Section 3.2)**
- An atom that has a tetrahedral electron geometry is sp^3-hybridized. Four sp^3 **hybrid orbitals** result from the mixing of one *s* and three *p* orbitals from the valence shell. The four hybrid orbitals point to the corners of a tetrahedron. An sp^3 hybrid orbital has 25% *s*-character and 75% *p*-character. **(Sections 3.2 and 3.6)**
- An atom that has a trigonal planar electron geometry is sp^2-hybridized. Three sp^2 **hybrid orbitals** result from the mixing of one *s* and two *p* orbitals from the valence shell. The three hybrid orbitals point to the corners of a triangle, and one *p* orbital perpendicular to that triangle remains unhybridized. Each sp^2 hybrid orbital has 33.33% *s*-character and 66.67% *p*-character. **(Sections 3.4 and 3.6)**
- An atom that has a linear electron geometry is *sp*-hybridized. Two ***sp* hybrid orbitals** result from the mixing of one *s* and one *p* orbital from the valence shell. The two hybrid orbitals point in opposite directions along the same line, and two *p* orbitals perpendicular to that line remain unhybridized. Each *sp* hybrid orbital has 50% *s*-character and 50% *p*-character. **(Sections 3.5 and 3.6)**

- Free rotation can occur about single bonds but not about double bonds. Rotation about a double bond can occur only by breaking the π bond. **(Section 3.7)**
- For a given double bond, two *configurations* are possible if the exchange of two groups on one of the doubly bonded atoms results in a different molecule. This is the case when each doubly bonded atom is singly bonded to two different atoms/groups. Two groups are **cis** to each other if they are on the *same* side of a double bond, and they are **trans** to each other if they are on *opposite* sides. **(Section 3.7)**
- Molecular modeling kits display the rotational characteristics about single and double bonds and provide accurate representations of *extended* geometries involving double bonds. **(Section 3.8)**
- Single bonds involving a hybrid orbital become shorter and stronger as the *s*-character of the hybrid orbital increases. **Effective electronegativity** also increases as the *s*-character of the atom's hybridization increases. **(Section 3.9)**
- **Quantum mechanics** treats electrons as waves. An electron is described by a wave function, Ψ, which has a numerical value called the amplitude at each point in space. Electrons in different orbitals are described by different wave functions. **(Section 3.10)**
- At a particular location in space, the square of the wave function's amplitude, Ψ^2, is the relative probability of finding the electron there. A map of those probabilities in space gives the shape of an orbital: an *s* orbital is a sphere, whereas a *p* orbital is dumbbell-shaped. **(Section 3.10)**
- **Phase** describes whether a wave function's amplitude is positive or negative. Positive phase for an orbital is indicated in this book by dark shading of the orbital's surface, whereas negative phase is indicated by light shading. **(Section 3.10)**
- The phase of an orbital in a region of space is important to consider when orbitals mix. Where orbitals have the same phase, they undergo **constructive interference** and the new orbital is built up. Where orbitals have opposite phases, they undergo **destructive interference** and the new orbital is diminished. **(Section 3.10)**
- When orbitals mix, the total number of orbitals is conserved: The interaction of *n* orbitals results in *n* unique new orbitals. **(Section 3.10)**
- A **molecular orbital (MO)** results from the simultaneous mixing of all **atomic orbitals (AOs)** from all atoms in the molecule. Distinct MOs arise from distinct AO contributions, such as different phase combinations or different weightings. **(Section 3.10)**
- A **bonding MO** results from in-phase overlap of AOs in the bonding region and is significantly lower in energy than the AOs from which it is constructed. An **antibonding MO** results from out-of-phase overlap and the appearance of a **node** in the bonding region. An antibonding MO is significantly higher in energy than the contributing AOs. A **nonbonding MO** is similar in energy to the contributing AOs. **(Section 3.10)**
- The highest-energy MO containing an electron is called the **highest occupied molecular orbital (HOMO)**, and the lowest-energy empty MO is called the **lowest unoccupied molecular orbital (LUMO)**. **(Section 3.10)**
- A qualitative molecular orbital–valence bond (MO–VB) model considers simplifications to MO theory. **(Section 3.11)**
  - Interactions are considered only between pairs of valence AOs contributed from adjacent atoms.
  - Atoms with characteristic molecular geometries are considered to be hybridized.
- The shape and phase of a hybrid AO is derived from mixing valence *s* and *p* AOs with different phase combinations. Every hybrid AO consists of a large lobe having one phase and a small lobe having the opposite phase. **(Section 3.11)**

Problems

Sections 3.1–3.5 Valence Bond Theory

3.1 Draw the VB picture for butane, $CH_3CH_2CH_2CH_3$, similar to Figures 3-7, 3-9, 3-15, 3-16, and 3-20. Identify all regions of σ overlap and π overlap.

3.2 Draw the VB picture for diethyl ether, $CH_3CH_2OCH_2CH_3$, similar to Figures 3-7, 3-9, 3-15, 3-16, and 3-20. Identify all regions of σ overlap and π overlap.

3.3 Draw the VB picture for acetone, $(CH_3)_2C{=}O$, similar to Figures 3-7, 3-9, 3-15, 3-16, and 3-20. Identify all regions of σ overlap and π overlap.

3.4 Draw the VB picture for :C≡O:, similar to Figures 3-7, 3-9, 3-15, 3-16, and 3-20. Identify all regions of σ overlap and π overlap.

3.5 Draw the VB picture for propa-1,2-diene, $H_2C{=}C{=}CH_2$, similar to Figures 3-7, 3-9, 3-15, 3-16, and 3-20. Identify all regions of σ overlap and π overlap. *Hint*: The three-dimensional geometry of propa-1,2-diene is shown in the chapter.

3.6 Draw the VB picture for buta-1,2,3-triene, $H_2C{=}C{=}C{=}CH_2$, similar to Figures 3-7, 3-9, 3-15, 3-16, and 3-20. Identify all regions of σ overlap and π overlap. *Hint*: See Your Turn 3.13.

3.7 Draw the VB picture for CH_3^+, similar to Figures 3-7, 3-9, 3-15, 3-16, and 3-20. Identify all regions of σ overlap and π overlap.

Section 3.6 Quickly Identifying Hybridization and the Number of σ and π Bonds From a Lewis Structure

3.8 For each of the following species, determine both the electron geometry and the hybridization for all non-hydrogen atoms.
(a) CH_3NH_2 **(b)** $CH_3N{=}O$ **(c)** CH_2Cl_2 **(d)** BrCN

3.9 For each of the following species, determine both the electron geometry and the hybridization for all non-hydrogen atoms.
(a) $C_2H_5^+$ **(b)** $C_2H_5^-$ **(c)** $H_2C{=}OH^+$ **(d)** $CH_3NH_3^+$
(e) $CH_3OH_2^+$ **(f)** $C_3H_3^-$ (all hydrogens are on the same carbon)

3.10 Levomenol, a naturally occurring sesquiterpene alcohol, has a sweet-smelling aroma and has been used as a component in fragrances. It also is known to have antimicrobial and anti-inflammatory properties. Determine the electron geometry, hybridization, and molecular geometry for each non-hydrogen atom in levomenol.

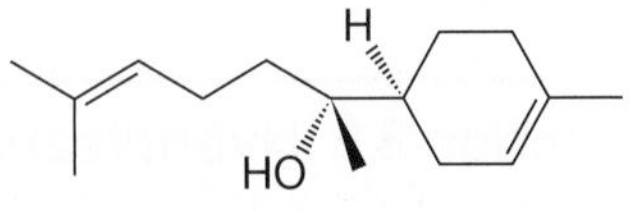
H
HO

Levomenol

3.11 Which of the following molecules has a single bond connecting an *sp*-hybridized atom to an *sp*²-hybridized atom?

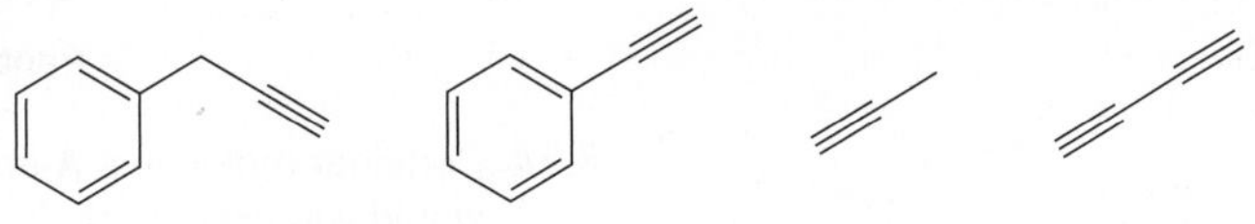

A **B** **C** **D**

3.12 Determine the total number of σ bonds and the total number of π bonds in levomenol (Problem 3.10).

3.13 According to VB theory, how many total electrons reside in MOs of π symmetry in this cation?

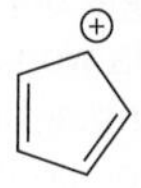

3.14 Norethynodrel is a synthetic hormone used in Enovid, the first oral contraceptive. **(a)** Determine the hybridization of each non-hydrogen atom. **(b)** How many total σ bonds and π bonds does norethynodrel have?

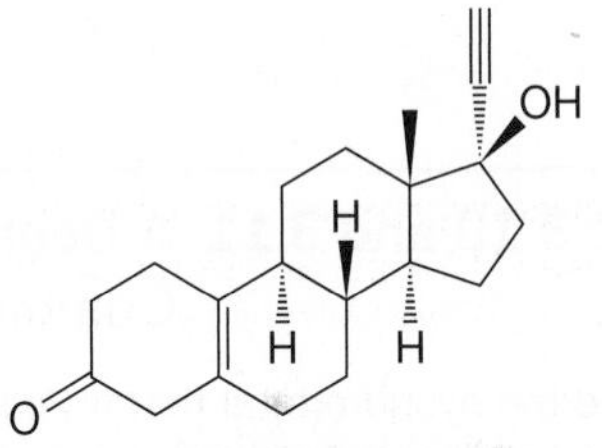
OH
H
H
H
O

Norethynodrel

3.15 β-Carotene is the compound responsible for the orange color of carrots and is the precursor to vitamin A. Judging from the Lewis structure shown here, how many π bonds does β-carotene have?

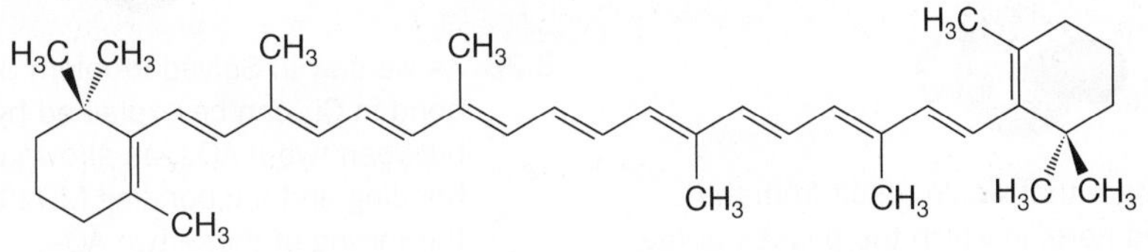
H3C CH3
CH3
CH3
CH3
H3C
CH3
CH3
H3C CH3

β-Carotene

Section 3.7 Bond Rotations about Single and Double Bonds: Cis and Trans Configurations

3.16 Bombykol is a pheromone produced by silkworm moths. Label each C=C double bond's configuration as cis or trans.

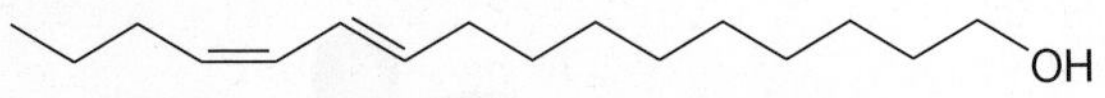
OH

Bombykol

3.17 For which of the following molecules are two configurations about the double bond possible? Explain. **(a)** $(CH_3)_2C{=}CHCl$; **(b)** $H_2C{=}CHCH_2CH_3$; **(c)** $ClHC{=}CHBr$; **(d)** $HC{\equiv}CCH{=}CHCl$

3.18 Does cyclooctene have two possible configurations about its C=C bond? *Hint*: Consider using a model kit.

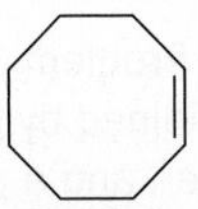

Cyclooctene

3.19 Draw the form of α-linolenic acid (Fig. 3-25, p. 131) in which all three double bonds are trans. How many unique structures can be made by changing the cis/trans configurations about the double bonds in α-linolenic acid?

3.20 Adenine, cytosine, guanine, and thymine are the four nitrogenous bases found in DNA. For each molecule, identify all of the non-hydrogen atoms that are required to be in the same plane.

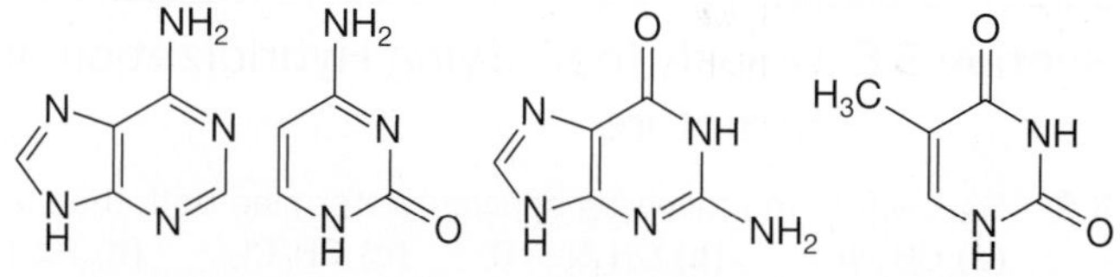

NH₂
N
N
N
H
N
NH₂
N
N
H
O
O
N
NH
N
H
N
NH₂
O
H₃C
NH
N
H
O

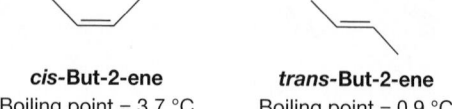

Adenine **Cytosine** **Guanine** **Thymine**

3.21 Do all of the atoms in buta-1,3-diene have to reside in the same plane? Why or why not?

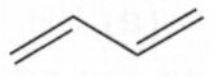

Buta-1,3-diene

Section 3.9 Hybridization, Bond Characteristics, and Effective Electronegativity

3.22 The boiling point of *cis*-but-2-ene is 3.7 °C, whereas that of *trans*-but-2-ene is 0.9 °C. Explain. *Hint*: Identify which intermolecular interaction is responsible for the difference in boiling points.

***cis*-But-2-ene**
Boiling point = 3.7 °C

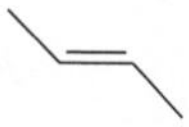

***trans*-But-2-ene**
Boiling point = 0.9 °C

3.23 There are two C—C single bonds in penta-1,3-diyne. **(a)** Which of those bonds would you expect to be stronger? **(b)** Which of those bonds would you expect to be shorter? **(c)** The molecule is moderately polar, with a dipole moment of 1.37 D. In which direction would you expect the dipole moment to point? Explain.

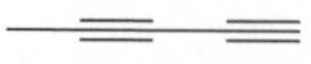

Penta-1,3-diyne

3.24 Consider molecules **A** and **B**. **(a)** In which molecule would you expect the C—Cl bond to be stronger? **(b)** In which molecule would you expect the C—Cl bond to be shorter? **(c)** In which molecule would you expect there to be a greater concentration of negative charge on the Cl atom? Explain.

Cl

A

Cl

B

Sections 3.10 and 3.11 A Deeper Look: Molecular Orbital Theory, Hybrid Atomic Orbitals, and a Combined Molecular Orbital–Valence Bond Model

3.25 Derive the hybrid orbital that would result from the interaction illustrated here, in which the phases of the s and p_x orbitals are opposite those in Figure 3-38a (p. 141). Is the resulting orbital different from the ones in Figure 3-38a and 3-38b? Explain.

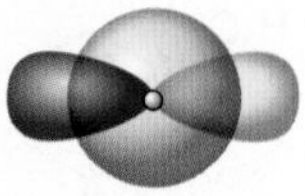

3.26 Derive the hybrid orbital that would result from the interaction illustrated here, in which the phases of the s and p_x orbitals are opposite those in Figure 3-38b (p. 141). Is the resulting orbital different from the ones in Figure 3-38a and 3-38b? Explain.

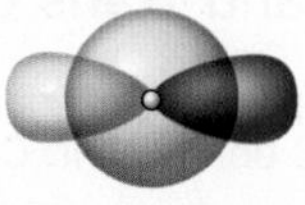

3.27 As we saw in Solved Problem 3.1 (p. 115), the bond in H—Cl can be explained by the overlap between an s orbital from hydrogen and a *p* orbital from chlorine, as shown in this diagram. Draw the bonding and antibonding MOs that would result from the mixing of these two AOs.

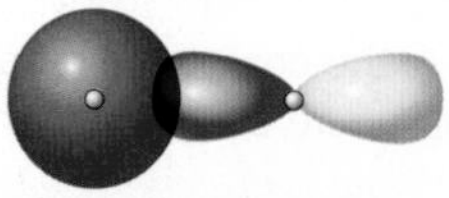

3.28 As we saw in Solved Problem 3.1, Try It (p. 115), the bond in Cl_2 can be explained by the end-on overlap between two *p* AOs, as shown in this diagram. Draw the bonding and antibonding MOs that would result from the mixing of these two AOs.

3.29 One of the orbital interactions we did not consider in this chapter is that between an s AO from one atom and a *p* AO from another atom in the fashion shown here. These orbitals will not interact while in this orientation. Explain why.

3.30 In Chapter 16, we will learn that light can promote an electron to a higher-energy MO. Suppose that light is used to promote one of the two electrons in the H_2 molecule from the σ MO to the σ^* MO, as illustrated here. What is the HOMO? Is this state more stable, less stable, or about the same stability as the two separated hydrogen atoms?

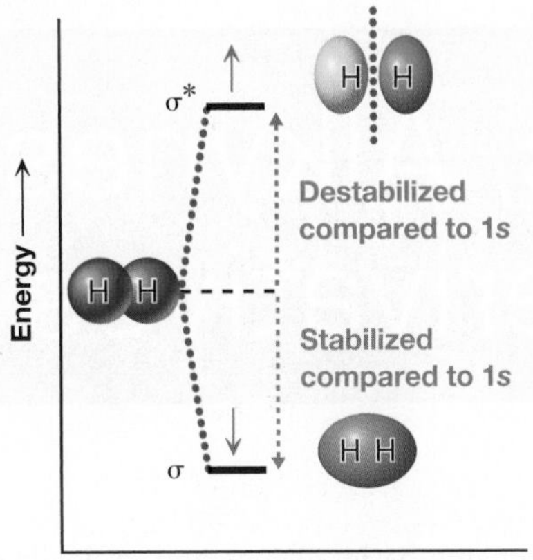
Energy
σ*
σ
H H
Destabilized compared to 1s
Stabilized compared to 1s

3.31 Suppose a linear molecule were constructed from three atoms, all of which are found in the second row of the periodic table. How many valence shell AOs would these three atoms contribute toward the production of MOs? How many MOs would be produced by the mixing of these valence shell AOs? *Hint*: The answer is independent of which orbitals overlap.

3.32 **(a)** Draw the MO–VB energy diagram for butane, $CH_3CH_2CH_2CH_3$, similar to Figures 3-40, 3-41, 3-43, and 3-44. **(b)** Identify the HOMO and LUMO.

3.33 **(a)** Draw the MO–VB energy diagram for diethyl ether, $CH_3CH_2OCH_2CH_3$, similar to Figures 3-40, 3-41, 3-43, and 3-44. **(b)** Identify the HOMO and LUMO.

3.34 **(a)** Draw the MO–VB energy diagram for acetone, $(CH_3)_2C{=}O$, similar to Figures 3-40, 3-41 3-43, and 3-44. **(b)** Identify the HOMO and LUMO.

3.35 **(a)** Draw the MO–VB energy diagram for :C≡O:, similar to Figures 3-40, 3-41, 3-43, and 3-44. **(b)** Identify the HOMO and LUMO.

3.36 **(a)** Draw the MO–VB energy diagram for propa-1,2-diene, $H_2C{=}C{=}CH_2$. *Hint*: The three-dimensional geometry is shown in the chapter. **(b)** What is the HOMO? What is the LUMO?

3.37 **(a)** Draw the MO-VB energy diagram for buta-1,2,3-triene, $H_2C{=}C{=}C{=}CH_2$. **(b)** What is the HOMO? What is the LUMO? *Hint*: See Your Turn 3.13.

3.38 **(a)** Draw the MO-VB energy diagram for CH_3^+. **(b)** What is the HOMO? What is the LUMO?

3.39 Suppose that an electron were added to CH_3^+, the species in Problem 3.38, yielding uncharged CH_3. What is the HOMO? What is the LUMO?

Integrated Problems

3.40 Suppose a linear molecule were constructed from three atoms, all of which are found in the second row of the periodic table. Suppose that two orbitals from the first atom were to mix with two orbitals from the second atom and that two other orbitals from the second atom were to mix with two orbitals from the third atom. In the resulting molecule, how many bonding MOs would there be in total? How many antibonding MOs? How many nonbonding MOs?

3.41 Octocrylene is an ingredient found in topical sunscreens. It is a water-resistant molecule that helps protect skin against harmful UVA and UVB radiation. **(a)** What is the hybridization of each non-hydrogen atom? **(b)** Circle all atoms bonded to the acyclic C═C double bond that are required to be in the same plane. **(c)** Are there two unique configurations possible about the acyclic C═C double bond? Explain. **(d)** Which of the two C—C single bonds indicated by arrows would you expect to be shorter? Explain.

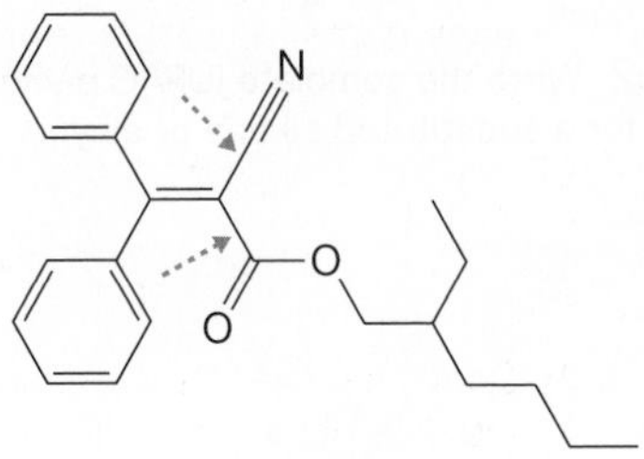
N
O
O

Octocrylene

3.42 In the chapter, we mentioned that ethene ($H_2C{=}CH_2$) does not undergo free rotation about the C═C double bond because the π bond must be broken to achieve the twisted ethene configuration in which the two CH_2 groups are perpendicular to each other (Fig. 3-22b, p. 129). **(a)** Draw the MO–VB energy diagram for the twisted ethene and identify the HOMO and LUMO. **(b)** By comparing the diagram for this molecule to that in Figure 3-41 (p. 143), explain why the molecule is more stable when it is all planar.

3.43 An amide is typically drawn with a single bond connecting the carbonyl C atom to the N atom. If this representation were accurate, we would expect the N atom to be pyramidal, and we would also expect C—N to undergo free rotation. In actuality, however, the N atom is rather planar, and the rotation is quite hindered: properties that give rise to important secondary structures of proteins, such as α-helices and β-sheets (Chapter 28). Explain these properties of the amide.

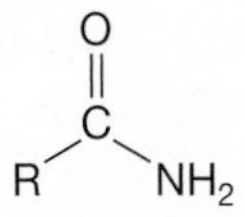
O
C
R
NH2

An amide

INTERCHAPTER B

Naming Alkenes, Alkynes, and Benzene Derivatives

Interchapter A discussed how to name basic alkanes and cycloalkanes (hydrocarbons with only single bonds) as well as haloalkanes, nitroalkanes, and ethers. This interchapter on nomenclature extends what we have already learned, enabling us to name *alkenes* (molecules that contain the C=C group) and *alkynes* (molecules that contain the C≡C group). We also discuss how to name simple *benzene derivatives* (compounds that contain a benzene ring), which are related to alkenes because the Lewis structure for benzene (C_6H_6) contains three alternating C=C bonds.

SECTION B.1 OBJECTIVES

You will be able to:

1. Determine the root name and numbering system for a molecule containing one C=C or C≡C bond.
2. Write the complete IUPAC name for a substituted alkene or alkyne.

B.1 Alkenes, Alkynes, Cycloalkenes, and Cycloalkynes: Molecules with One C=C or C≡C Bond

In Interchapter A, we learned that our first task in determining an IUPAC name is to establish the root (also called the parent compound) by identifying the longest continuous carbon chain or largest carbon ring: that is, the main chain or ring. The naming of an alkene, alkyne, cycloalkene, or cycloalkyne similarly requires determining the root, but the rules for doing so are modified for the following reason:

The C=C and C≡C functional groups have higher priorities than any of the substituents encountered in Interchapter A.

Having these priorities for the C=C and C≡C groups, we establish the root as follows:

Determining the Root of a Compound Containing One C=C or C≡C Bond

1. Identify the analogous alkane or cycloalkane. Count the number of carbons in the longest continuous carbon chain or largest carbon ring that contains the *entire* C=C or C≡C bond. Use Table A-1 (p. 54) to identify the alkane or cycloalkane that has the same number of carbons.
2. Replace the alkane suffix. Remove the *ane* suffix of the alkane or cycloalkane and add either:
   - *ene* if the molecule contains a C=C functional group.
   - *yne* if the molecule contains a C≡C functional group.

Chapter Outline

Figure B-1 shows a few examples of how these rules are applied. Notice in each of the first two molecules in Figure B-1 that the longest carbon chain has more carbon atoms than specified by the root. In the first molecule, the longest carbon chain has six carbon atoms, and in the second molecule, it has five carbons. But neither of those chains contains the *complete* C═C group.

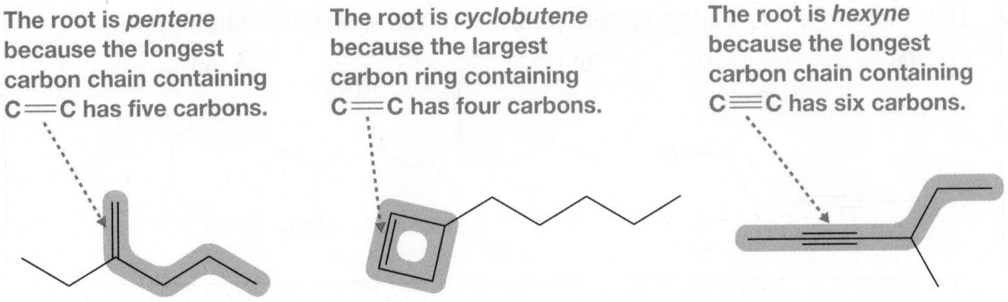
The root is *pentene* because the longest carbon chain containing C═C has five carbons.
The root is *cyclobutene* because the largest carbon ring containing C═C has four carbons.
The root is *hexyne* because the longest carbon chain containing C≡C has six carbons.

FIGURE B-1 Establishing the root for molecules with one C═C or C≡C bond

YOUR TURN B.1

Determine the root for each of the following molecules.

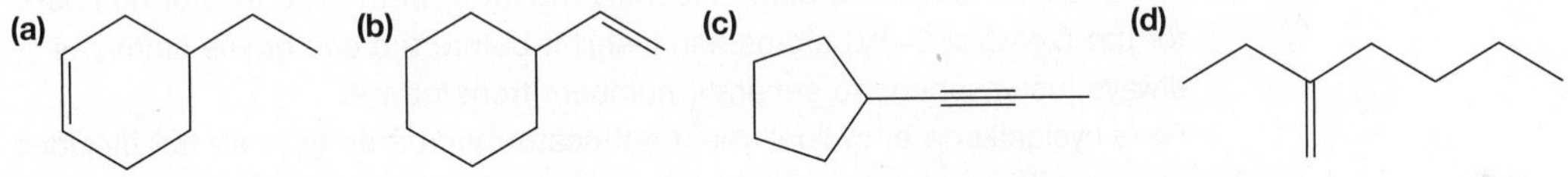
(a)
(b)
(c)
(d)

Answers to Your Turns are in the back of the book.

Once the root is determined, the next step is to establish the numbering system for that main chain or ring. In Interchapter A, which dealt with roots containing only C—C single bonds, the numbering system was dictated only by the locations of the substituents. For an alkene or alkyne, the location of the C═C or C≡C establishes the numbering system:

The Numbering System for a Main Chain or Ring Containing One C═C or C≡C Bond

- For a chain, assign C-1 to the end from which the C═C or C≡C is encountered the earliest. If the C═C or C≡C bond is same distance from each end, break the tie using the rules from Interchapter A (p. 57) to minimize the locator numbers (or locants) for the substituents.
- For a ring, assign the two carbon atoms of the C═C or C≡C bond as C-1 and C-2. Which of those carbon atoms is C-1 is determined by the rules described in Interchapter A to minimize the locator numbers for the substituents.

The molecules in **Figure B-2** (next page) demonstrate how these rules are applied.

FIGURE B-2 The numbering system for molecules with one C═C or C≡C bond

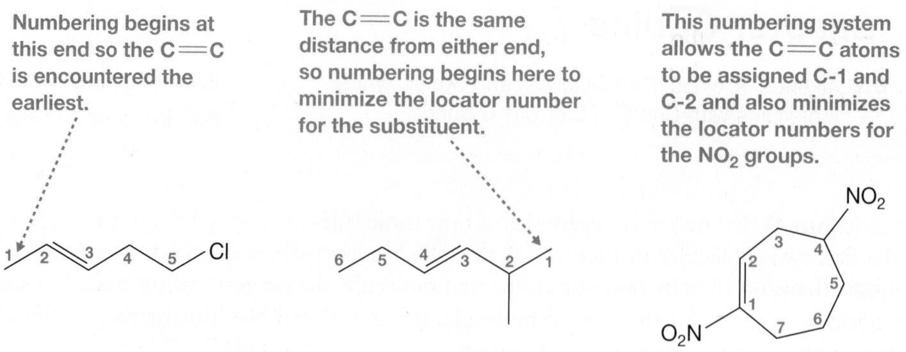
Numbering begins at this end so the C═C is encountered the earliest.
The C═C is the same distance from either end, so numbering begins here to minimize the locator number for the substituent.
This numbering system allows the C═C atoms to be assigned C-1 and C-2 and also minimizes the locator numbers for the NO_2 groups.
1 2 3 4 5 Cl
6 5 4 3 2 1
NO_2
O_2N
1 2 3 4 5 6 7

YOUR TURN **B.2**

Determine the numbering system for each of the molecules shown here.

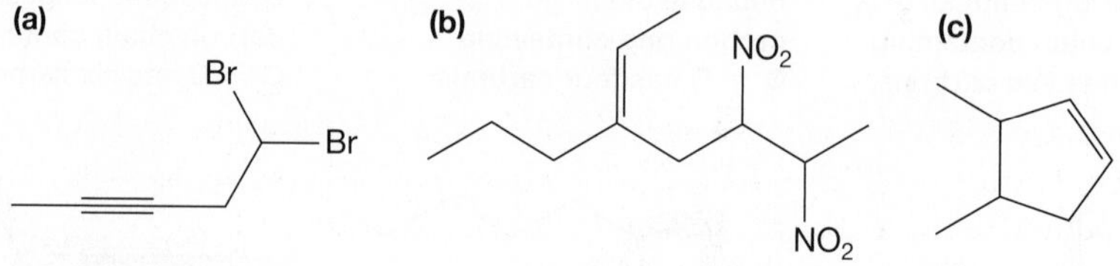
(a)
Br
Br
(b)
NO_2
NO_2
(c)

Finally, the IUPAC name for an alkene or an alkyne can be constructed according to the following rules:

Writing the IUPAC Name of a Molecule Containing One C═C or C≡C Bond

1. Write the root name:
   - For an acyclic alkene or alkyne, identify the lower of the two locator numbers for the C═C or C≡C atoms and insert it before the *ene* or *yne* suffix. As always, use hyphens to separate numbers from letters.
   - For a cycloalkene or cycloalkyne, that locator number is typically not included because it is understood to be 1.
2. Add prefixes. Use the rules from Interchapter A (p. 57) to account for various substituents and their locations.

Solved Problem B.1 shows how these rules are applied. Make sure you understand that example, and then work through the Try It exercise that follows it.

SOLVED PROBLEM **B.1**

How to name an alkene that has one C═C bond

Break It Down **Write the IUPAC name for the molecule shown here.**

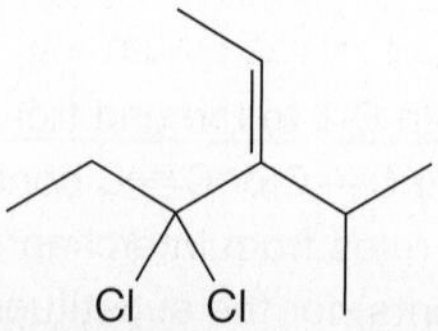
Cl
Cl

Think	Solve
What is the longest carbon chain that entirely contains the C═C bond? What is the corresponding root name? ➤	The longest carbon chain that entirely contains the C═C (highlighted below) has six carbon atoms, so the root is *hexene*.

(continued)

On which end of the chain should numbering begin to allow the C=C group to be encountered the earliest?	Numbering begins at the terminal carbon at the top to encounter the C=C group the earliest, so the locator numbers for those two carbon atoms are C-2 and C-3. 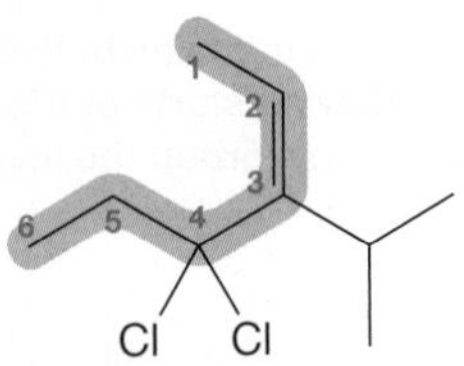 1 2 3 4 5 6 Cl Cl
Which locator number of the C=C atoms should be included in the IUPAC name?	The lower of those two numbers, 2, is added to the root immediately before the *ene* suffix, and prefixes are added to account for the chloro and the 1-methylethyl substituents. The IUPAC name is 4,4-dichloro-3-(1-methylethyl)hex-2-ene.

Try It What is the IUPAC name of each of the compounds in Your Turn B.2 (p. 152)?

Answers to all Try It exercises can be found in the Solutions Manual.

For alkene and alkyne roots containing two or three carbon atoms (namely ethene, ethyne, propene, and propyne), it is not necessary to add a locator number for the alkene or alkyne group. For these cases, the lower of the two locator numbers must be 1, so adding the locator number would be redundant.

Also, placing the locator number immediately before the *ene* or *yne* suffix reflects a relatively recent change to the IUPAC rules. Historically, the locator number was placed immediately before the root, so you will commonly encounter names such as 2-methyl-1-pentene, but the current IUPAC rules call for 2-methylpent-1-ene.

B.2 Molecules with Multiple C=C or C≡C Bonds

SECTION B.2 OBJECTIVES

You will be able to:

1. Derive the root name and numbering system for a molecule containing more than one C=C or C≡C bond.
2. Write the complete IUPAC name for such a molecule having various substituents.

For a molecule that has more than one double bond or triple bond, the IUPAC name must indicate the number of double bonds or triple bonds present as well as their locations:

Naming a Molecule with More Than One C=C or C≡C Bond

1. Establish the root. This is derived from the longest carbon chain or largest carbon ring that contains the greatest number of entire C=C or C≡C groups.
2. Establish the numbering system for the chain or ring.
   a. The first C=C or C≡C group should be encountered the earliest.
   b. If there is a tie, then the next C=C or C≡C group should be encountered the earliest.
3. Locate each C=C or C≡C bond. For *each* pair of C=C or C≡C atoms, write the lower of the two locator numbers.
4. Modify the suffix. Immediately before the *ene* or *yne* suffix, add the letter "a" followed by the above set of locator numbers, and then add a multiplier prefix (*di*, *tri*, etc.) to specify how many double or triple bonds are present.

The examples in **Figure B-3** (next page) demonstrate how these rules are applied.

The root contains both C=C bonds. Numbering starts at the top C to give the propyl group the lowest locator number.

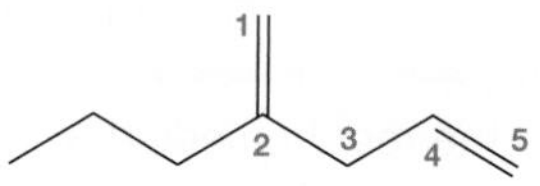

1
2
3
4
5

2-Propylpenta-1,4-diene

The root contains both C=C bonds. Numbering starts at the bottom-right C so both C=C groups are encountered the earliest and the locator number of the methoxy group is minimized.

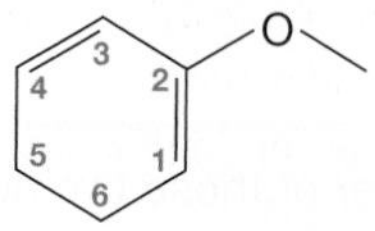

O
1
2
3
4
5
6

2-Methoxycyclohexa-1,3-diene

The root contains all three C≡C groups. Numbering starts from the right so the C≡C groups are encountered the earliest.

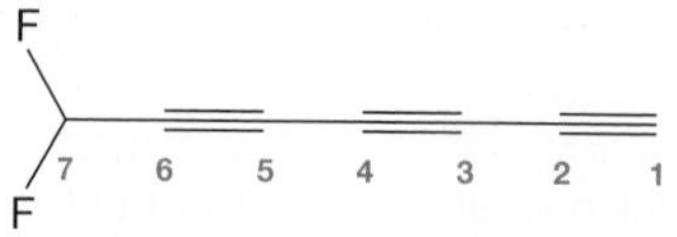

F
F
7
6
5
4
3
2
1

7,7-Difluorohepta-1,3,5-triyne

FIGURE B-3 **Naming molecules containing more than one C=C or C≡C bond**

SOLVED PROBLEM **B.2**

How to name a molecule that has two or more C=C bonds

Break It Down **Write the IUPAC name for the molecule shown here.**

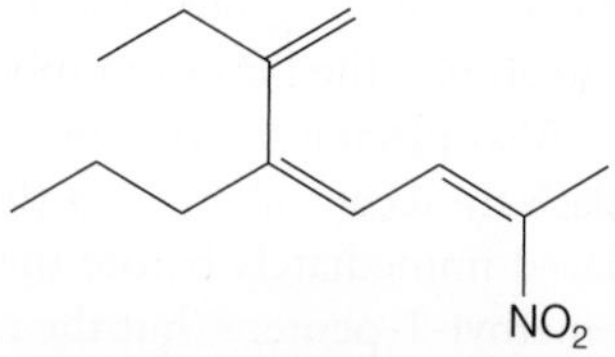

NO_2

Think	Solve
What is the longest carbon chain that entirely contains all of the C=C groups?	There are three C=C groups and the longest carbon chain that contains all of them has seven C atoms.
On which end of the chain should numbering begin so that the first C=C group is encountered the earliest? How do you determine the set of locator numbers for the C=C groups?	Numbering begins at the top-right terminal carbon because that gives the first C=C group the lowest locator number (in this case, 1), so the set of locator numbers assigned to the C=C groups is 1,3,5. 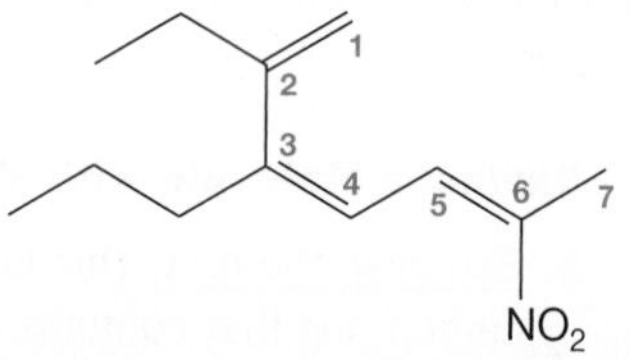 1 2 3 4 5 6 7 NO_2
When do you add the letter "a" before the suffix?	Because of the multiple C=C groups, the letter "a" is added before the suffix, so this is a *heptatriene*. The complete IUPAC name is 2-ethyl-6-nitro-3-propylhepta-1,3,5-triene.

Try It Write the IUPAC name for each of the compounds shown here.

(a)

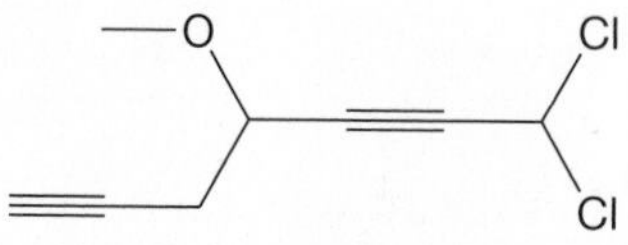

O
Cl
Cl

(b)

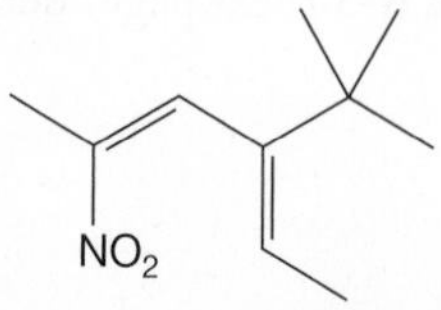

NO_2

(c)

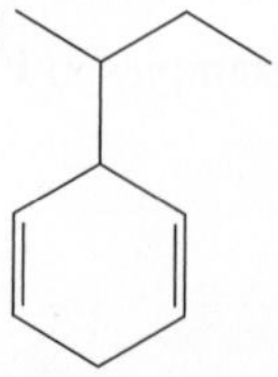

If a molecule contains both C=C and C≡C functional groups, it is called an *enyne*. The following modified rules are used for naming enynes:

Naming Enynes: Molecules Having both C=C and C≡C Groups

1. Establish the root. Identify the longest carbon chain or largest carbon ring that contains all C=C and C≡C groups and use the suffix *enyne*.
2. Establish the numbering system. To do so, minimize the locator number for each successive C=C or C≡C group.
   - The C=C and C≡C groups are given equal priority unless there is a tie between two numbering systems.
   - If there is a tie, the tie is broken by giving priority to the C=C group.
3. Add the locator numbers. Add the locator numbers for the C=C groups immediately before *en* and add those for the C≡C groups immediately before *yne*.
4. Account for multiple C=C and C≡C groups. Add the letter "a" immediately before the corresponding locator numbers, and add the proper multiplier prefix (*di*, *tri*, etc.) immediately after.

Examples of how to apply these rules are shown in **Figure B-4**. Numbering starts from the left in the first molecule to give the C=C group the lowest locator number, whereas numbering starts from the right in the second molecule to give the C≡C the lowest number. The third example shows how to account for two C=C groups.

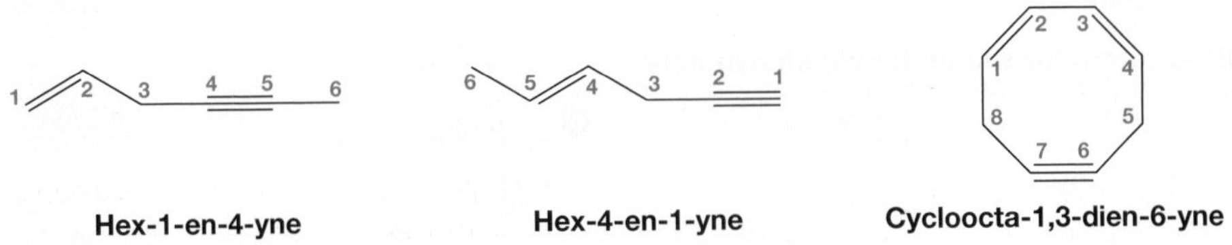

1
2
3
4
5
6
Hex-1-en-4-yne
6
5
4
3
2
1
Hex-4-en-1-yne
2
3
1
4
8
5
7
6
Cycloocta-1,3-dien-6-yne

FIGURE B-4 Naming enynes

YOUR TURN B.3

Draw the structures for pent-3-en-1-yne and 1,2-dimethylcycloocta-1,3-dien-6-yne.

B.3 Benzene and Benzene Derivatives

SECTION B.3 OBJECTIVES

You will be able to:

1. Name compounds for which benzene is the root or parent name.
2. Incorporate the ortho/meta/para system for naming disubstituted benzenes.
3. Identify phenyl and benzyl substituents.

The Lewis structure of **benzene** (C_6H_6), shown in **Figure B-5**, consists of three C=C double bonds that alternate with three C—C single bonds in a six-membered ring. On the basis of the rules presented so far for naming alkenes, it might be tempting to rename benzene as "cyclohexa-1,3,5-triene." This name is unacceptable, however, because the behavior of benzene is significantly different than that of a typical alkene. Benzene is an *aromatic* compound (see Chapter 14 for an in-depth discussion),

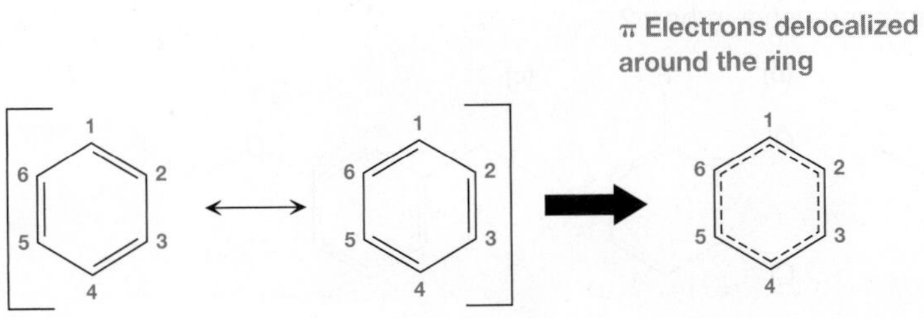

π Electrons delocalized around the ring
1
2
3
4
5
6

FIGURE B-5 Benzene The Lewis structures of benzene are shown inside the brackets, and the resonance hybrid is shown on the right.

◀ RECALL

The alternating single and double bonds that make up the benzene ring characterize a feature for resonance, which we first encountered in Section 1.10. Both resonance structures contribute to the resonance hybrid, which accurately represents the one, true molecule.

and as its resonance hybrid indicates, its π electrons are fully delocalized around the ring (see Recall box). Thus, all six carbon atoms of benzene are identical, and we cannot formally assign any of the double bonds to a single pair of carbon atoms.

Because of the unique behavior of the benzene ring, the following rules are applied to naming relatively simple molecules in which benzene has attached substituents, so-called **benzene derivatives**:

Naming Benzene Derivatives

1. Establish the root as *benzene*. The groups attached to the benzene ring are treated as substituents.
2. Establish the numbering system of the ring. Give the lowest locator number to each successive substituent.
3. Add prefixes and locator numbers. As usual, account for the number, type, and location of each substituent.

These ideas are applied in Solved Problem B.3. Make sure you understand that example and then work through the Try It exercise that follows it.

SOLVED PROBLEM **B.3**

How to name a benzene derivative

Break It Down **Provide the IUPAC name for the molecule shown here.**

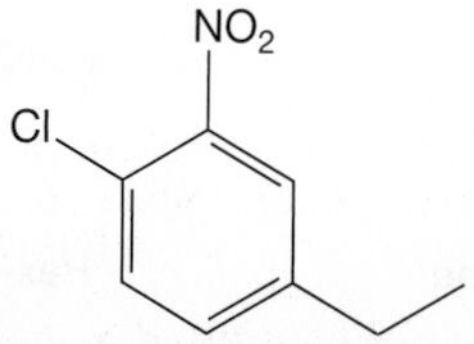

NO_2
Cl

Think	Solve
Is there a six-membered ring of alternating C—C and C=C bonds? What root is assigned in such cases? ➤	The six-membered ring of alternating C—C and C=C bonds requires the root *benzene*.
Where should C-1 be assigned to allow each successive substituent to be encountered the earliest? Should numbering proceed clockwise or counterclockwise? ➤	To encounter each successive substituent the earliest, numbering begins at the C atom attached to Cl and proceeds clockwise. 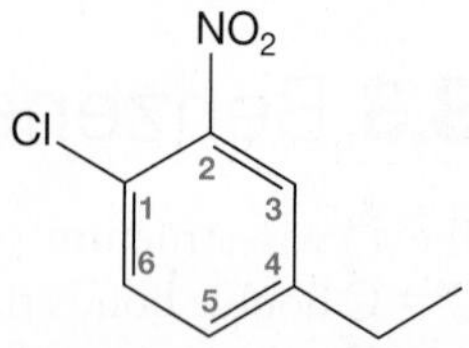NO_2 Cl 1 2 3 4 5 6
How should you add prefixes to complete the name? ➤	The substituent names are arranged alphabetically, and they appear along with their locator numbers before the root. The complete IUPAC name is 1-chloro-4-ethyl-2-nitrobenzene.

Try It What is the name of each of the compounds shown here?

(a)

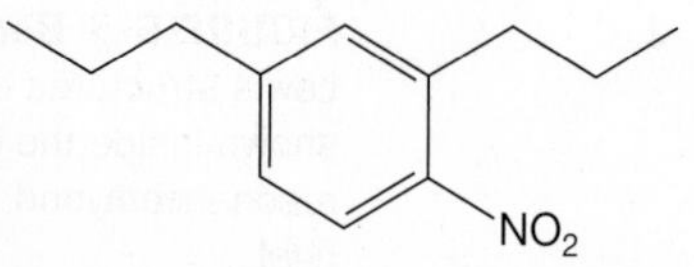

NO_2

(b)

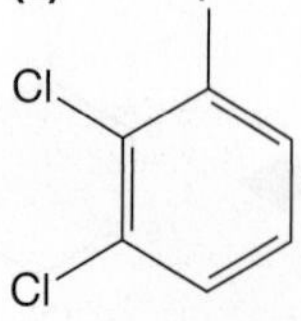

F
Cl
Cl

(c)

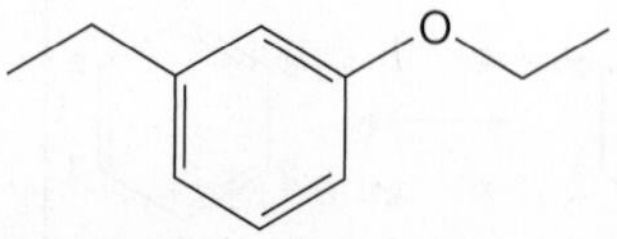

O

B.3a Disubstituted Benzenes: Ortho, Meta, and Para Designations

Although the numbering system outlined in the previous section is always valid, the following nonnumerical system can be used in the special case of **disubstituted benzenes**, in which two substituents are attached to the benzene ring.

Relative Positioning of Substituents in Disubstituted Benzenes

- *ortho* = *o* = 1,2-positioning
- *meta* = *m* = 1,3-positioning
- *para* = *p* = 1,4-positioning

Note: When more than two substituents are attached to the ring, the ortho, meta, and para prefix system is never used.

The examples of disubstituted benzenes in **Figure B-6** show how to use the ortho, meta, and para notation. Make sure that the ortho/meta/para designation is applied only when benzene is the root. It would be a mistake, for example, to name 1,2-dibromocyclohexane as *ortho*-dibromocyclohexane.

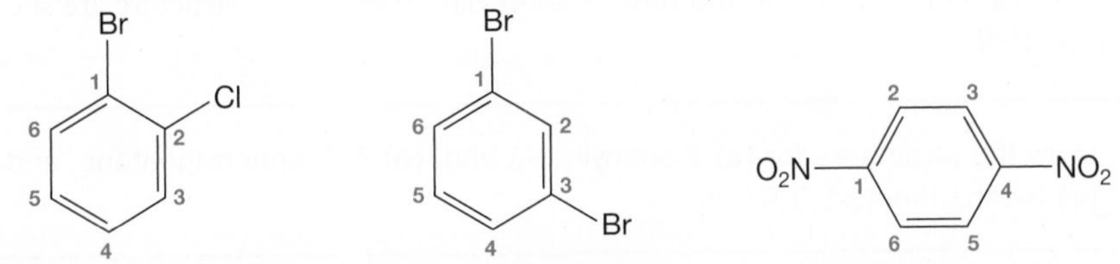

Br
Cl
1
2
3
4
5
6
Br
Br
1
2
3
4
5
6
O_2N
NO_2
1
2
3
4
5
6

1-Bromo-2-chlorobenzene
***ortho*-Bromochlorobenzene**
***o*-Bromochlorobenzene**

1,3-Dibromobenzene
***meta*-Dibromobenzene**
***m*-Dibromobenzene**

1,4-Dinitrobenzene
***para*-Dinitrobenzene**
***p*-Dinitrobenzene**

FIGURE B-6 **Naming disubstituted benzenes**

YOUR TURN **B.4**

Draw the structures for *p*-dichlorobenzene and *m*-bromoethoxybenzene. What are the corresponding IUPAC names using locator numbers instead?

B.3b Phenyl and Benzyl Substituents

If a substituent attached to a benzene ring is sufficiently complicated, it could be more straightforward to name the molecule if we treat the benzene ring as a substituent or part of a substituent instead. One example is C_6H_5, the **phenyl (Ph)** substituent (pronounced FEN-uhl, the same as the spice fennel), as shown in **Figure B-7a**. Another example is $C_6H_5CH_2$, the **phenylmethyl** substituent, also called the **benzyl (Bn)**

(a)

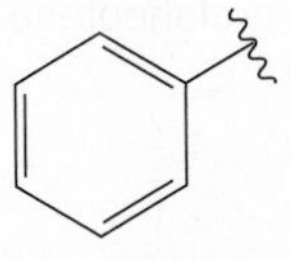

The phenyl (Ph) substituent

(b)

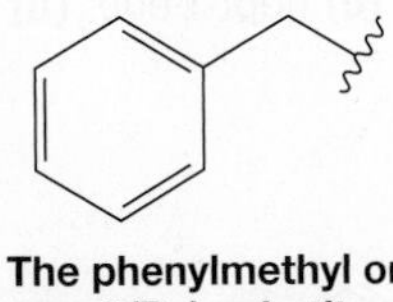

The phenylmethyl or benzyl (Bn) substituent

FIGURE B-7 **Substituents containing a benzene ring** (a) The phenyl substituent. (b) The phenylmethyl or benzyl substituent. Incorporating these substituents into the IUPAC name can often lead to a simpler name than if benzene were treated as the root.

▸ LOOKING AHEAD

As with any class of organic compounds, alkenes, alkynes, and benzene derivatives have trivial names that are firmly entrenched in nomenclature. Appendix E presents some of the ways in which trivial names apply to these types of compounds.

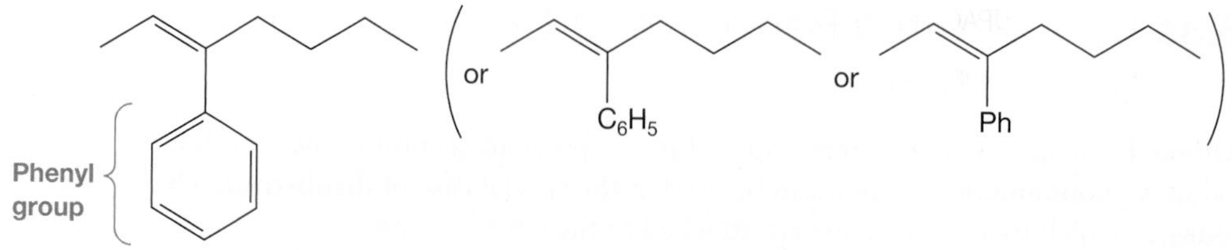
or
or
C6H5
Ph
Phenyl group

3-Phenylhept-2-ene

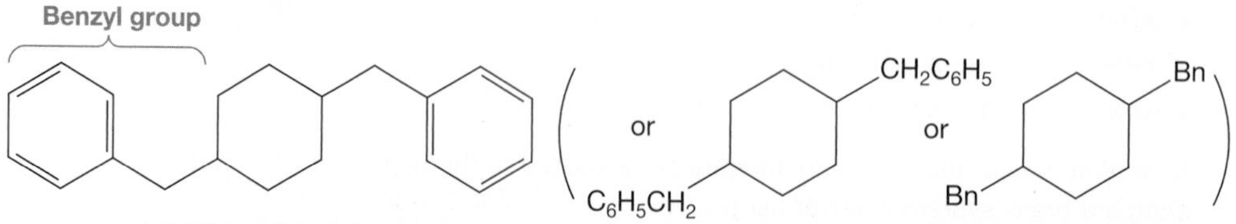
Benzyl group
or
or
CH2C6H5
Bn
C6H5CH2
Bn

1,4-Dibenzylcyclohexane

FIGURE B-8 **Naming molecules with benzene-containing substituents**

substituent, as shown in Figure B-7b. Examples of how to incorporate these substituents into a molecule's name and how to abbreviate them in the structure are shown in **Figure B-8**.

YOUR TURN **B.5**

Draw the structures for **(a)** 2-phenylhex-1-ene, **(b)** 1,5-diphenylpentane, and **(c)** 3-benzylhepta-1,3,5-triene.

Problems

Section B.1 Alkenes, Alkynes, Cycloalkenes, and Cycloalkynes: Molecules with One C=C or C≡C Bond

B.1 Write the IUPAC name for each of the following compounds.

(a) 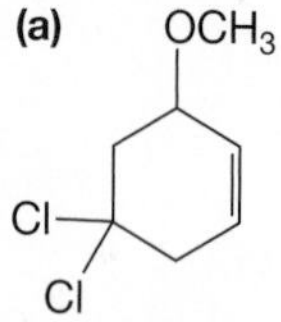
OCH3
Cl
Cl

(b) 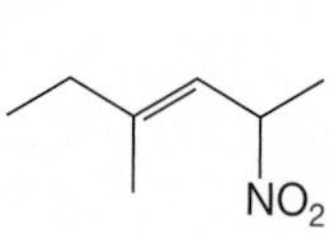
NO2

(c) 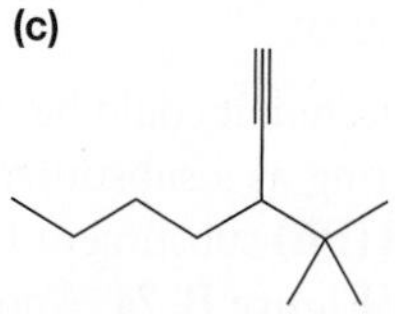

B.2 Write the IUPAC name for each of the following molecules.

(a) $H_2C{=}CH_2$ **(b)** 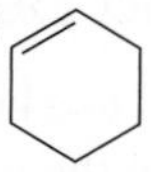 **(c)** 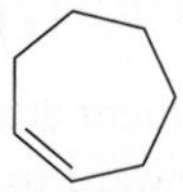

B.3 Write the IUPAC name for each of the following compounds.

(a) 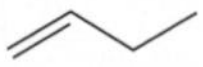 **(b)** 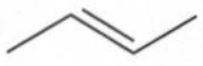 **(c)** 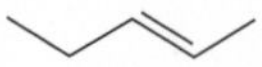 **(d)** 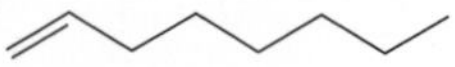 **(e)** 

B.4 Draw the structures for **(a)** hex-2-ene; **(b)** hex-3-ene; **(c)** hept-1-ene; **(d)** oct-2-yne; **(e)** cycloheptene.

B.5 Name the following structures.

(a) 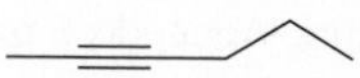 **(b)** 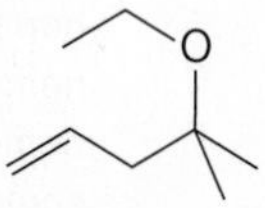
O

(c) 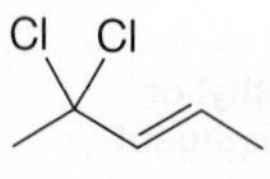
Cl Cl

B.6 Provide the IUPAC names for the following compounds.

(a) 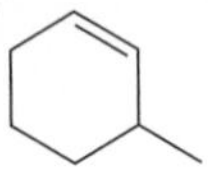
(b) 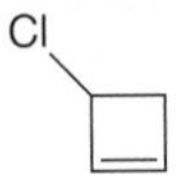
Cl
(c) 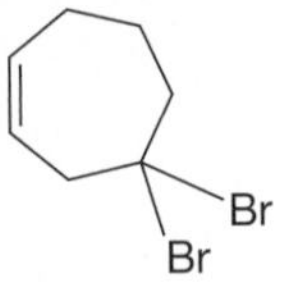
Br
Br
(d) 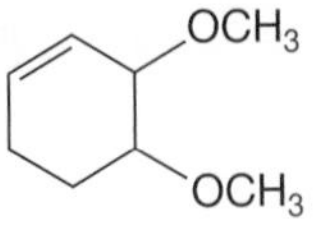
OCH3
OCH3
(e) 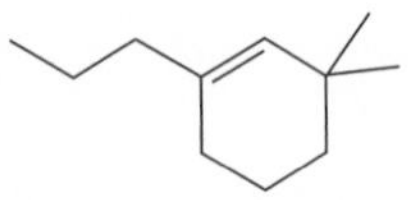
(f) 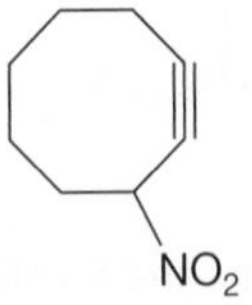
NO2

B.7 Provide the IUPAC names for the following compounds.

(a) 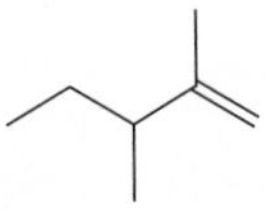
(b) 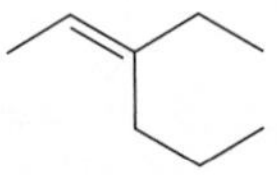
(c) 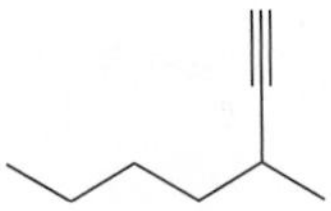

B.8 2-Propylbut-1-ene is an incorrect name under the IUPAC system. What is the correct name for this compound? *Hint*: Draw the structure based on the incorrect name and rename it.

B.9 Draw the structures for these molecules. **(a)** 2-chloropropene; **(b)** 3-methylbut-1-ene; **(c)** 2,3-dimethyl-2-butene; **(d)** 2-ethoxy-3,3-dimethylcyclohexene; **(e)** 3,4,5-trimethoxycycloheptene; **(f)** 3-bromo-2-methyl-4-nitrocyclopentene; **(g)** 3,3-dibromo-4-methylcyclopentene; **(h)** 4-methylpent-2-yne

B.10 Write the IUPAC name for each of the following molecules.

(a) 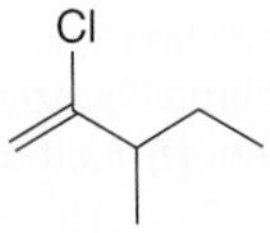
Cl
(b) 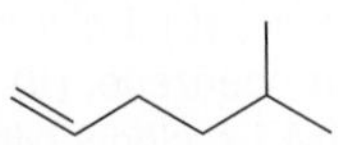
(c) 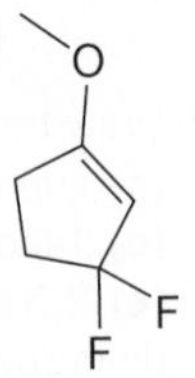
O
F
F
(d) 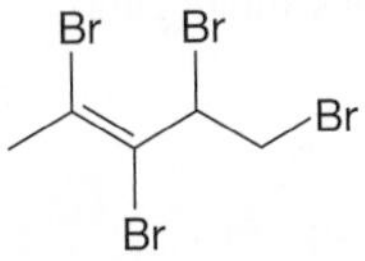
Br
Br
Br
Br

(e) 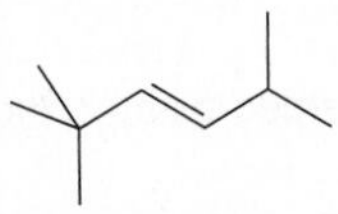
(f) 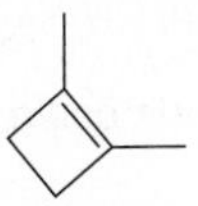
(g) 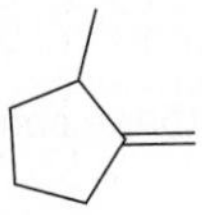
(h) 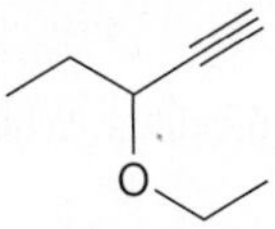
O
(i) 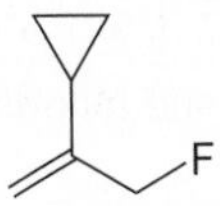
F

Section B.2 Molecules with Multiple C═C or C≡C Bonds

B.11 The name 1,4-cyclohexadiene is derived by applying an IUPAC rule that has since been revised. Draw the structure of 1,4-cyclohexadiene. Then write the IUPAC name according to the new rule.

B.12 Draw the structures for penta-1,4-diene and cyclopenta-1,3-diene.

B.13 What is the name for the following structure?

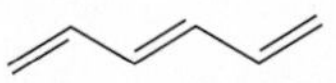

B.14 Draw the structures for **(a)** 2-methylhexa-1,3,5-triene and **(b)** 1,6-dimethoxyhexa-1,5-diene.

B.15 Determine the IUPAC name for each of the following molecules.

(a) 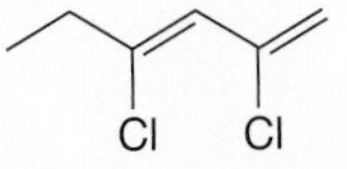
Cl
Cl
(b) 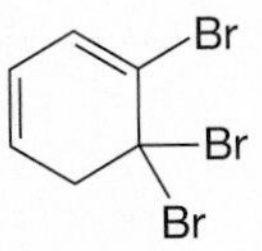
Br
Br
Br
(c) 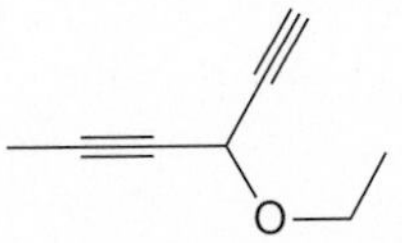
O
(d) 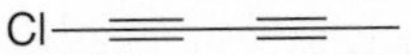
Cl

(e) 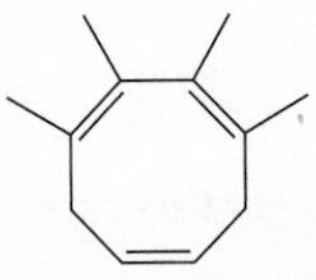
(f) 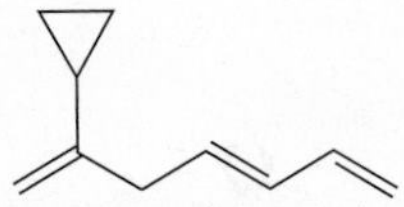
(g) 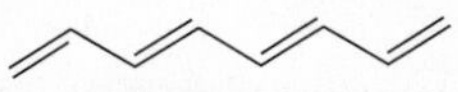

B.16 What is the name of this compound?

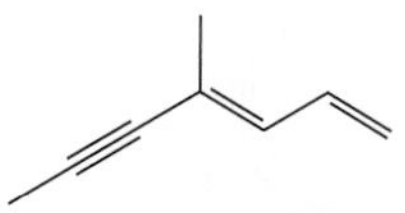

B.17 Determine the IUPAC name for each of the following molecules.

(a)

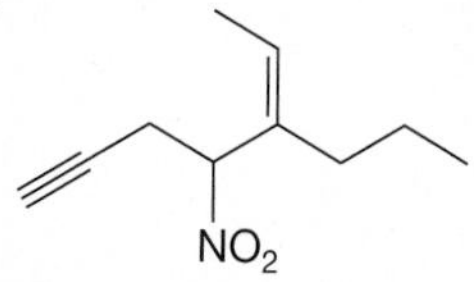

NO2

(b)

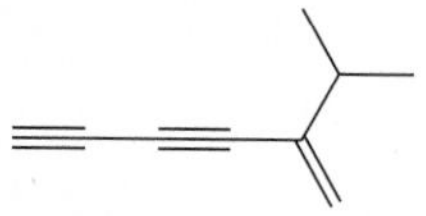

(c)

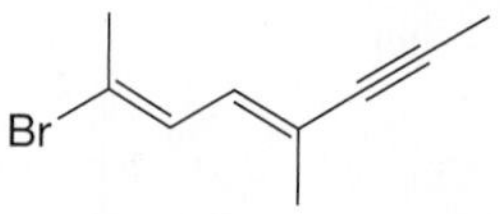

Br

(d)

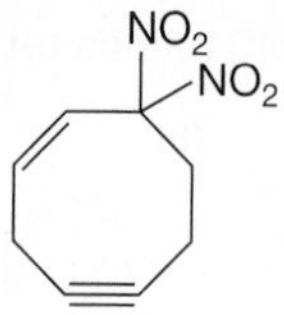

NO2
NO2

Section B.3 Benzene and Benzene Derivatives

B.18 Draw the structures of **(a)** hexylbenzene and **(b)** bromobenzene.

B.19 Draw the structures of **(a)** 1,2,3-trimethylbenzene and **(b)** 4-bromo-2-chloro-1-nitrobenzene.

B.20 What is the name of this compound?

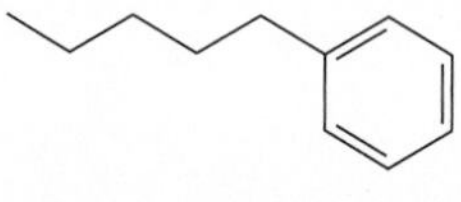

B.21 What are the IUPAC names for the following molecules?

(a)

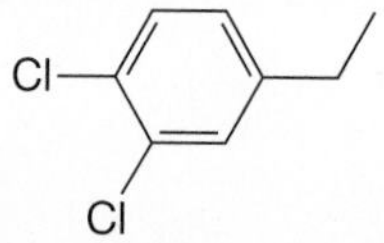

Cl
Cl

(b)

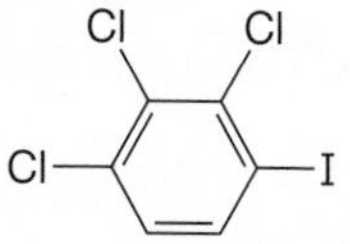

Cl
Cl
Cl
I

B.22 Draw the structures for each of the following molecules. **(a)** fluorobenzene; **(b)** 1-chloro-2-fluorobenzene; **(c)** 1-iodo-4-nitrobenzene; **(d)** 1,3-dibromobenzene; **(e)** 2,3-dimethyl-1-cyclopentylbenzene; **(f)** 4-ethoxy-1,2-dinitrobenzene

B.23 Give the IUPAC name for each of the following molecules. Which of these compounds could be named using *ortho*, *meta*, or *para* as a prefix?

(a)

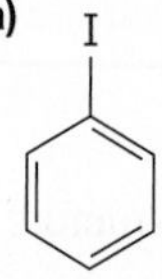

I

(b)

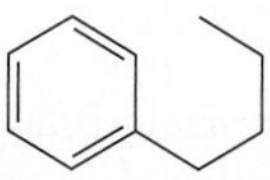

(c)

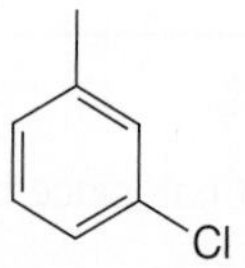

Cl

(d)

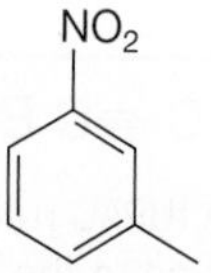

NO2

(e)

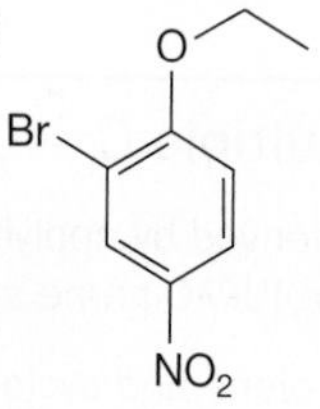

O
Br
NO2

(f)

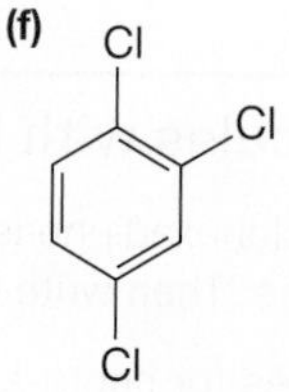

Cl
Cl
Cl

(g)

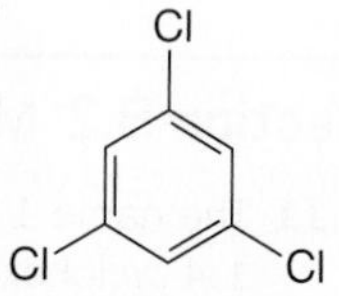

Cl
Cl
Cl

B.24 What is the name of this compound?

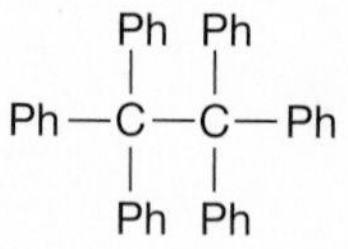

Ph Ph
Ph—C—C—Ph
Ph Ph

Integrated Problems

B.25 Provide the IUPAC name for each of the following molecules.

(a)

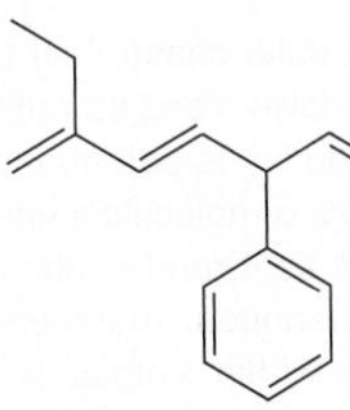

(b)

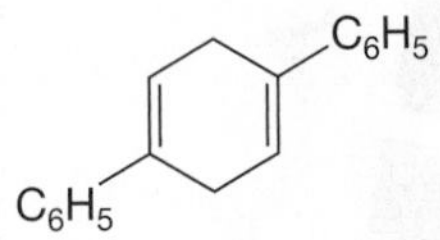
C6H5
C6H5

(c)

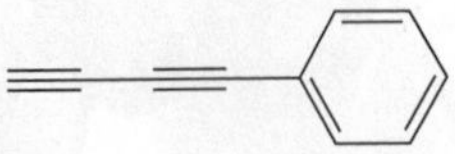

(d)

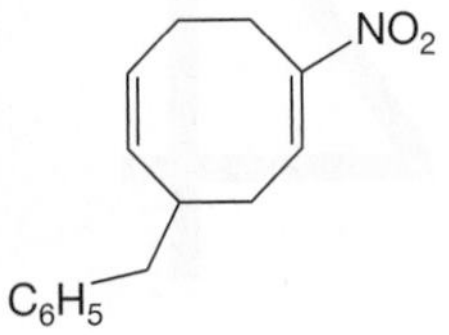
NO2
C6H5

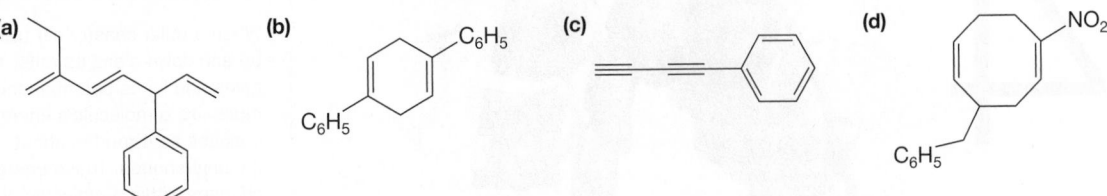

B.26 Provide the IUPAC name for each of the following molecules.

(a)

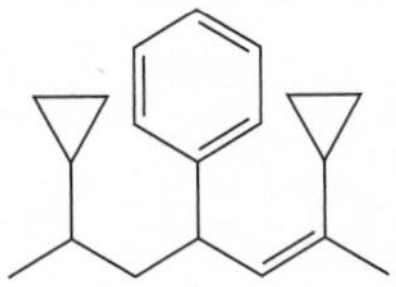

(b)

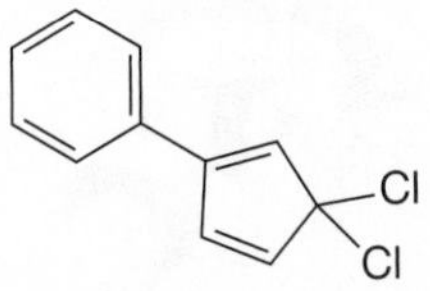
Cl
Cl

(c)

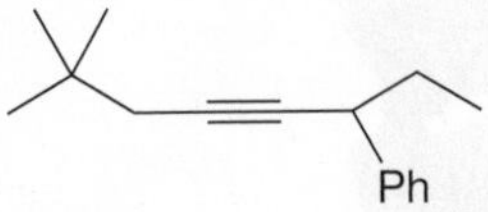
Ph

B.27 Draw the structure for each of these molecules. **(a)** 3-phenylmethylhex-4-en-1-yne; **(b)** 7-phenylcyclohepta-1,3,5-triene; **(c)** 3,5,6-trinitro-4-phenylmethylhepta-1,3,5-triene; **(d)** 5,5-dichloro-6-ethenyl-7-phenylcyclooct-3-en-1-yne

4

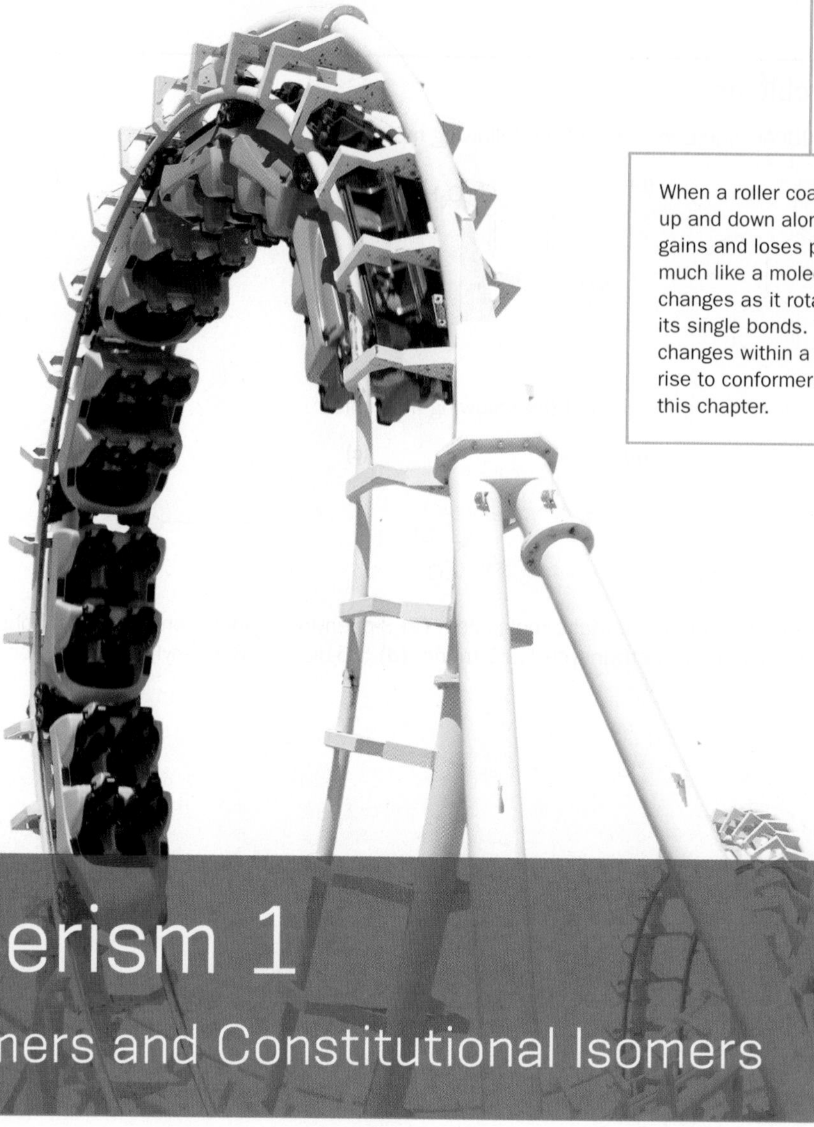

When a roller coaster car travels up and down along its rails, it gains and loses potential energy, much like a molecule's energy changes as it rotates about its single bonds. These energy changes within a molecule give rise to conformers, a topic of this chapter.

Isomerism 1

Conformers and Constitutional Isomers

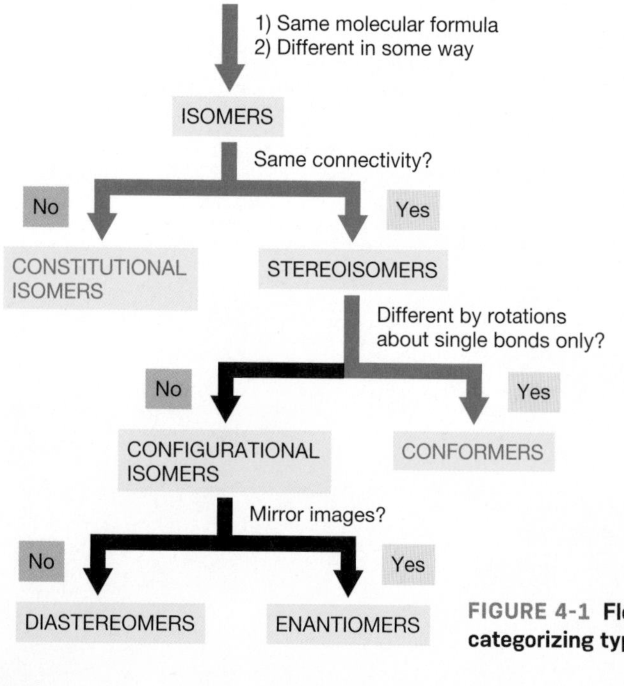

1) Same molecular formula
2) Different in some way
ISOMERS
Same connectivity?
No
Yes
CONSTITUTIONAL ISOMERS
STEREOISOMERS
Different by rotations about single bonds only?
No
Yes
CONFIGURATIONAL ISOMERS
CONFORMERS
Mirror images?
No
Yes
DIASTEREOMERS
ENANTIOMERS

FIGURE 4-1 Flowchart for categorizing types of isomers

There are tens of millions of known organic compounds, and more are being isolated, synthesized, and identified every year! Fortunately, the chemical behavior of every compound is *not* entirely unique. Instead, certain relationships among molecules' structures give us an idea about how similarly or differently the molecules behave. For example, as we learned in Chapter 1, molecules having the same functional group tend to react similarly.

Here in Chapter 4 and later in Chapter 5, we develop a broader understanding of how molecules are related, and we delve into the consequences of those relationships. Specifically, we will examine relationships among **isomers**, which are distinct molecules that have the same molecular formulas. As it turns out, isomers can differ from each other in a variety of ways, as shown in **Figure 4-1**. *Constitutional isomers* and *conformers* (the categories shown in red lettering in Fig. 4-1) are examined in depth here in Chapter 4; *configurational isomers*, which include *diastereomers* and *enantiomers*, will be discussed in Chapter 5.

Chapter Outline

4.1 Conformers: Rotational Conformations, Newman Projections, and Dihedral Angles

SECTION 4.1 OBJECTIVES

You will be able to:

1. Draw a Newman projection to depict a molecule in a specific conformation about a particular bond.
2. Draw a Lewis structure from a given Newman projection.

As indicated in Figure 4-1, **conformers** differ only by rotations about single bonds. (Conformers are sometimes referred to as conformational isomers, but we will avoid that term in this book because conformers generally cannot be isolated from each other.) To more easily study conformers, it is helpful to have a systematic way of depicting molecules having different angles of rotation about single bonds—that is, different **rotational conformations**. One convenient way to illustrate rotational conformations is with a **Newman projection** (**Figure 4-2**), a two-dimensional representation of a molecule *viewed down the bond of interest*. The following conventions apply to Newman projections:

Newman Projections

- The two atoms directly connected by the bond of interest are shown explicitly.
  - The nearer atom is depicted as a point.
  - The more distant atom is depicted as a circle.
- Bonds to the front atom converge at the point, whereas bonds to the back atom connect to the circle.

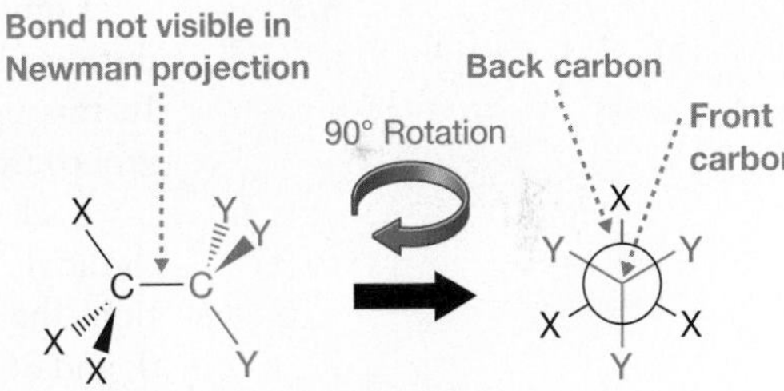

Bond not visible in Newman projection
Back carbon
Front carbon
90° Rotation

FIGURE 4-2 Interpretation of a Newman projection The generic molecule on the left is depicted by a Newman projection on the right. Each carbon in the Newman projection has three substituents pointing outward.

YOUR TURN **4.1**

From the Newman projection given, label the front carbon and the back carbon in the structure on the left.

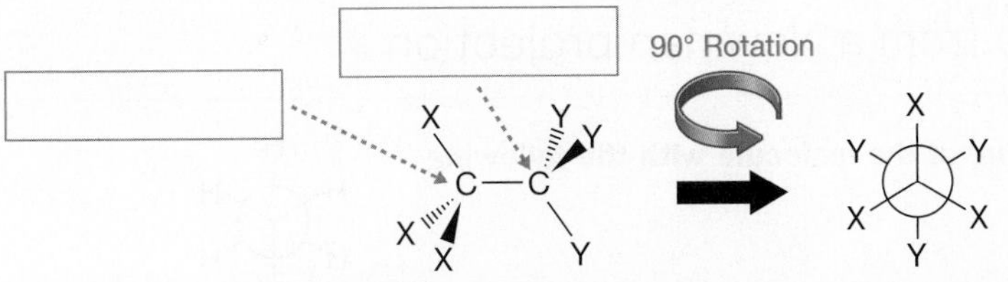

90° Rotation

Answers to Your Turns are in the back of the book.

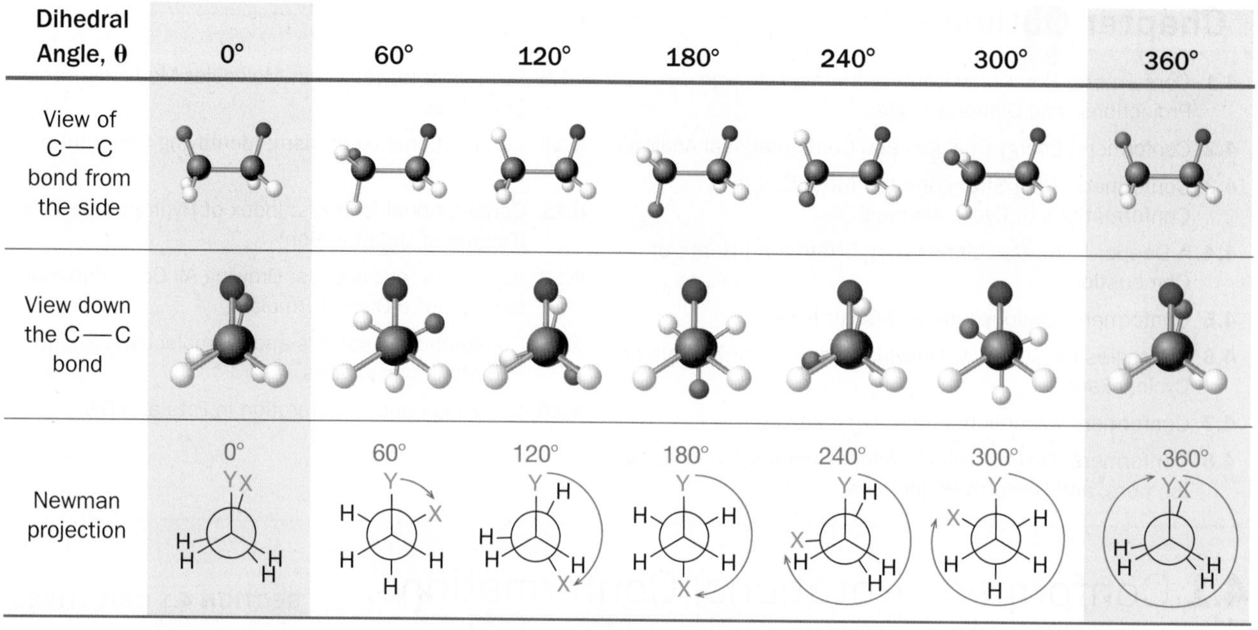

Dihedral Angle, θ
0°
60°
120°
180°
240°
300°
360°
View of C—C bond from the side
View down the C—C bond
Newman projection

FIGURE 4-3 **Newman projections and bond rotations** A generic molecule of XCH_2—CH_2Y is shown at various angles of rotation (dihedral angles, θ) about the C—C bond. (*Top row*) Views of the molecule from the side. (*Middle row*) Views of the molecule down the C—C bonding axis (from the right end). (*Bottom row*) Newman projections of the molecule that correspond to the view down the C—C bond.

As illustrated in Figure 4-2, *in a Newman projection the bond of interest is not visible; instead, it must be imagined as connecting the front and back carbons.* A Newman projection does, however, explicitly show the other bonds to the front and back atoms.

Figure 4-3 shows the Newman projections for several conformations that arise during a 360° rotation about the C—C bond of a generic molecule, XCH_2—CH_2Y. In this figure, we have arbitrarily chosen to leave the C atom in front (the CH_2Y group) frozen in place and to rotate the C atom in back (the CH_2X group).

Each angle of rotation defines a particular **dihedral angle (θ)**, corresponding to the angle between the C—X and C—Y bonds as they appear in the Newman projection. The angle θ can assume values between 0° and 360°, where the conformations at 0° and 360° are exactly the same.

YOUR TURN **4.2**

Add the substituents to the incomplete Newman projections to represent the first molecule after 60° and 120° rotations of the back carbon.

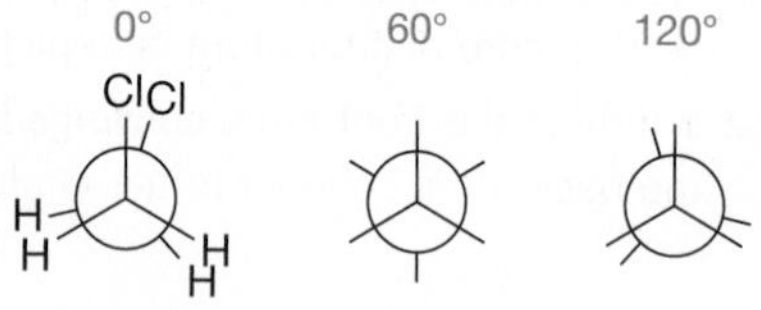

0°
60°
120°
ClCl
H
H
H
H

SOLVED PROBLEM **4.1**

How to draw a Lewis structure from a Newman projection

Break It Down **Draw the Lewis structure of the molecule with the following Newman projection.**

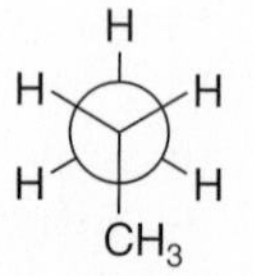

H
H
H
H
H
CH3

(continued)

Think	Solve
Which atoms are connected by the bond not observable in the Newman projection?	The bond not shown is a C—C single bond. The front C atom is represented by a point, and the back C atom is represented by a circle.
What atoms or groups are attached to each of those atoms?	The front C atom is bonded to two H atoms and a CH_3 group, whereas the back C atom is bonded to three H atoms. Thus, the structure consists of three C atoms bonded together. The compound is propane. 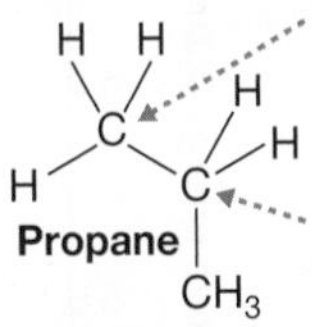 Back carbon of Newman projection (circle) Front carbon of Newman projection (point) Propane

Try It Draw the Lewis structure that corresponds to each of the following Newman projections.

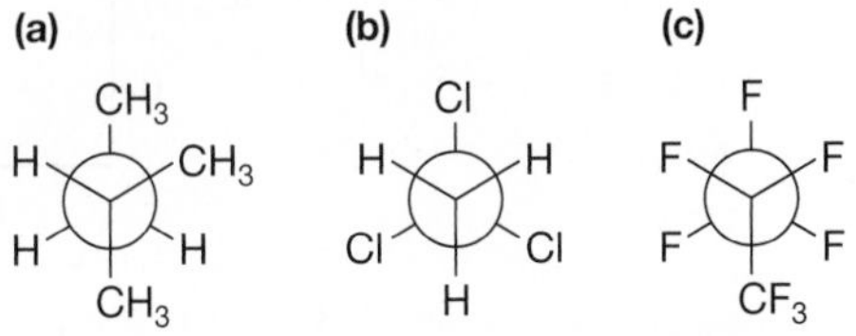

Answers to all Try It exercises can be found in the Solutions Manual.

YOUR TURN **4.3**

The Newman projection shown here is of the same generic molecule used in Figure 4-3. Taking this dihedral angle to be 0°, draw Newman projections for each 60° rotation about the C—C single bond, from 0° to 360°, in which *the front carbon remains frozen in place.*

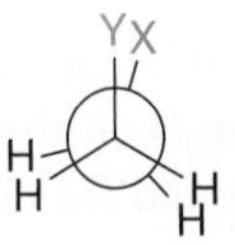

4.2 Conformers: Energy Changes and Conformational Analysis

SECTION 4.2 OBJECTIVES

You will be able to:

1. Characterize eclipsed and staggered conformations about a particular single bond and explain their energy difference.
2. Characterize gauche and anti conformations about a particular single bond and explain their energy difference.
3. Carry out a conformational analysis about a particular single bond in a given molecule.

To better understand the nature of a rotation about a given bond, we can perform a **conformational analysis**, which is a plot of a molecule's relative energy as a function of that bond's dihedral angle. Here, we will examine the conformational analyses of ethane (Section 4.2a) and 1,2-dibromoethane (Section 4.2b), which exemplify key types of strain.

4.2a Conformational Analysis of Ethane: Torsional Strain and Eclipsed and Staggered Conformations

Figure 4-4 depicts the conformational analysis of ethane ($H_3C—CH_3$) about the C—C bond. The rear CH_3 group is rotated 360° while the front CH_3 group remains frozen in place. There are three rotational conformations in Figure 4-4 in which ethane's energy is at a *maximum* (i.e., $\theta = 0°, 120°$, and 240°). These are called **eclipsed conformations** because the C—H bonds on the front carbon atom cover, or *eclipse*, those on the rear carbon atom in the Newman projections. Because the hydrogen substituents are all identical, these three conformations are indistinguishable.

There are also three rotational conformations of $H_3C—CH_3$ in which the energy is at a minimum (i.e., $\theta = 60°, 180°$, and 300°). In the Newman projections of these

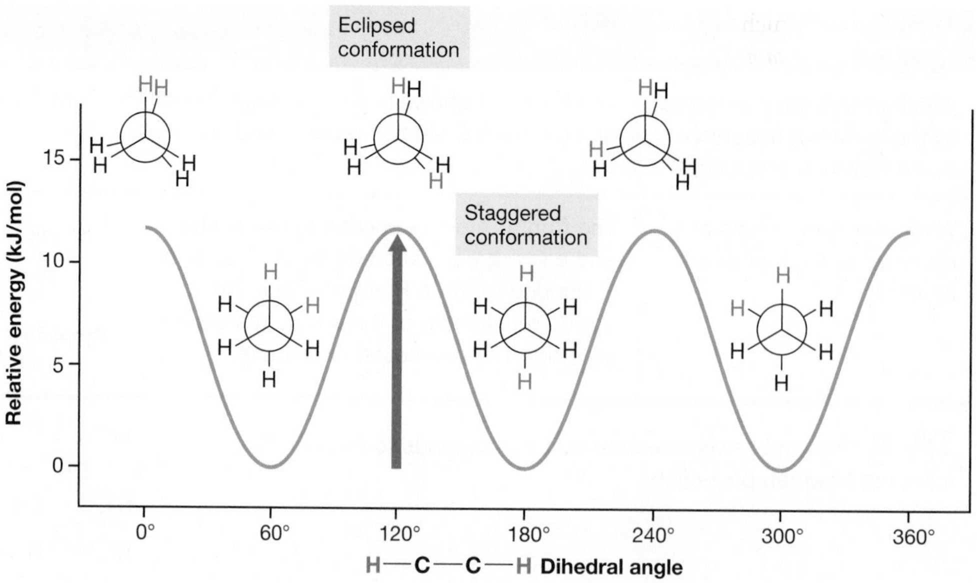
Eclipsed conformation
Staggered conformation
Relative energy (kJ/mol)
15
10
5
0
0°
60°
120°
180°
240°
300°
360°
H—C—C—H Dihedral angle

FIGURE 4-4 Conformational analysis of ethane, $H_3C—CH_3$ The plot shows the relative energy of ethane as a function of the H—C—C—H dihedral angle. Energies are relative to the lowest-energy conformation. The thick red arrow represents the energy barrier for rotation about that bond.

conformations, each C—H bond on the front carbon atom bisects a pair of C—H bonds on the rear carbon, so the bonds to the front and rear carbon atoms alternate around the circle in what are called **staggered conformations**.

YOUR TURN **4.4**

In Figure 4-4, label each of the unlabeled conformations as either eclipsed or staggered.

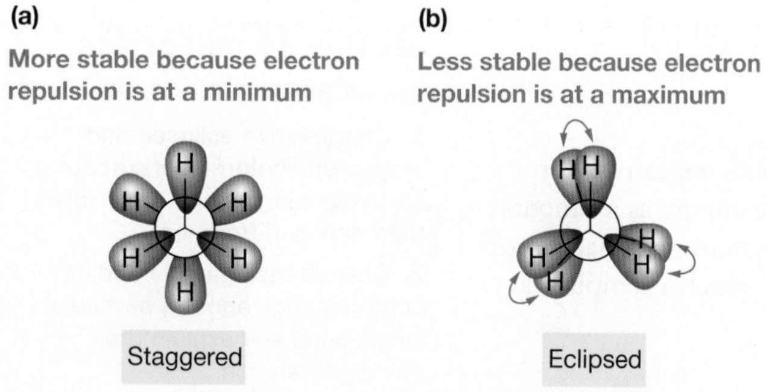
(a)
More stable because electron repulsion is at a minimum
Staggered
(b)
Less stable because electron repulsion is at a maximum
Eclipsed

FIGURE 4-5 Origin of torsional strain (a) In the staggered conformation, repulsion among the electrons in the C—H bonds is at a minimum, making it the more stable conformation. (b) In the eclipsed conformation, repulsion is at a maximum, making it the less stable conformation.

Why are eclipsed conformations higher in energy than staggered conformations? As we can see in **Figure 4-5**, the electrons making up the C—H bonds on the adjacent C atoms are closer in an eclipsed conformation (build a molecular model to see this for yourself!), and the resulting electron repulsion causes energy to rise. Because this rise in energy, or *strain*, occurs on rotation of the single bond connecting the C atoms, we call it **torsional strain**. Also, because the C—H electron groups are closest when the conformation is eclipsed and are the farthest apart when it is staggered, we can say the following:

Eclipsed conformations possess torsional strain, and staggered conformations do not.

YOUR TURN **4.5**

Use Figure 4-4 to estimate the torsional strain in a molecule of ethane in an eclipsed conformation. ____________ kJ/mol

Although they appear in the conformational analysis of ethane, eclipsed conformations do not exist for significant amounts of time because they represent energy maxima (see Fig. 4-4). Instead, essentially all molecules of ethane exist in staggered conformations, which appear at energy minima. Nevertheless, ethane molecules are not locked in the *same* staggered conformation indefinitely:

At room temperature, staggered conformations of ethane constantly interconvert through rotation about the C—C single bond.

To get from one staggered conformation to another requires the molecule to have enough energy to surmount the *rotational energy barrier*. A **rotational energy barrier** between two conformations, in general, is the difference in energy between the beginning conformation and the highest-energy conformation through which the molecule must pass to arrive at the ending conformation. In the case of ethane, this is simply the difference in energy between the staggered and eclipsed conformations (Fig. 4-4), which is 12 kJ/mol.

From where does ethane acquire enough energy to surmount the rotational energy barrier? The answer is **thermal energy**, which is the average energy available through molecular collisions, and it increases as temperature increases. The average thermal energy is calculated as the product *RT*, where *R* is the universal gas constant (8.314 J/mol·K) and *T* is the temperature in kelvins. If *T* is 298 K, then the average thermal energy is ~2.5 kJ/mol. This is less than the 12 kJ/mol rotational energy barrier in ethane, but a fast interconversion from one staggered conformation to another does not require every molecule's energy to exceed the energy barrier simultaneously. Rather, all that is required is for a significant percentage of molecules to exceed that energy at any given time. As we can see from **Figure 4-6**, about 2% of the molecules at any given time have sufficient energy.

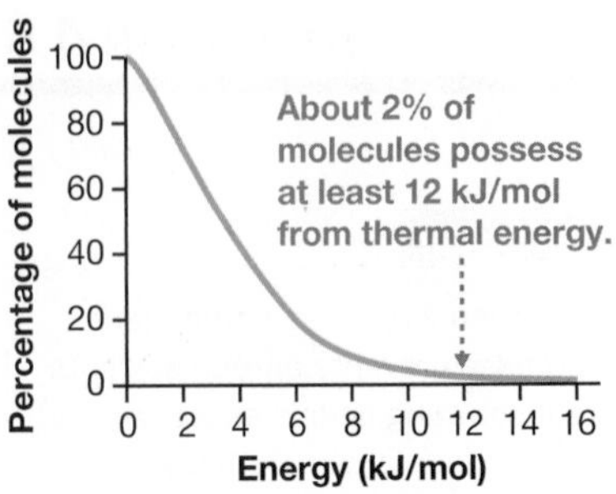

Percentage of molecules
100
80
60
40
20
0
0 2 4 6 8 10 12 14 16
Energy (kJ/mol)
About 2% of molecules possess at least 12 kJ/mol from thermal energy.

FIGURE 4-6 Distribution of thermal energy in molecules at 298 K For each energy level plotted on the *x* axis, the percentage of molecules possessing at least that much energy at 298 K is plotted on the *y* axis. At any given time, about 2% of molecules possess enough energy to surmount an energy barrier of 12 kJ/mol, the rotational energy barrier for ethane.

4.2b Conformational Analysis of 1,2-Dibromoethane: Steric Strain and Gauche and Anti Conformations

If one H atom of each CH_3 group in ethane ($H_3C—CH_3$) is replaced by another substituent, the energies of the three staggered conformations will no longer be the same. Neither are the energies of the three eclipsed conformations. This can be seen in the conformational analysis of 1,2-dibromoethane ($Br—CH_2—CH_2—Br$) shown in **Figure 4-7**.

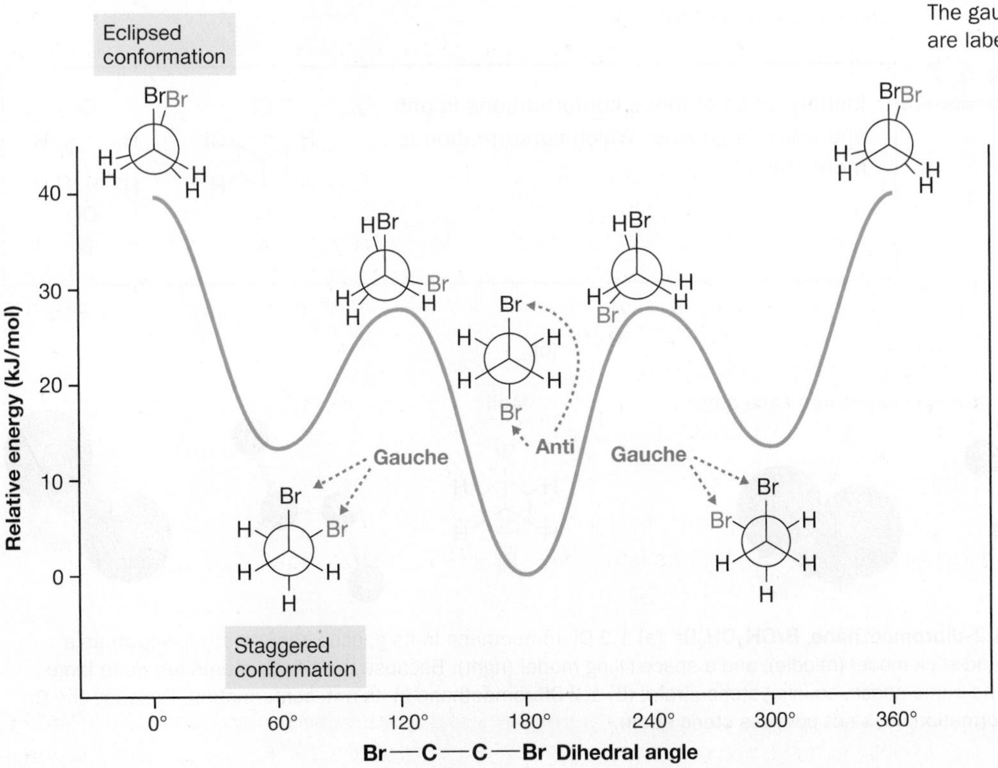

Eclipsed conformation
Staggered conformation
Gauche
Anti
Gauche
Relative energy (kJ/mol)
40
30
20
10
0
0° 60° 120° 180° 240° 300° 360°
Br—C—C—Br Dihedral angle

FIGURE 4-7 Conformational analysis of 1,2-dibromoethane, $Br—CH_2—CH_2—Br$ The energy of 1,2-dibromoethane is plotted as a function of the Br—C—C—Br dihedral angle. Energies are relative to that of the most stable conformation. The gauche and anti conformations are labeled.

YOUR TURN 4.6

Label each unlabeled structure in Figure 4-7 as either eclipsed or staggered.

◂ RECALL

In Section 2.9, we saw that *steric hindrance* prevents aprotic solvents from solvating anions as well as protic solvents can. Both steric hindrance and steric strain are outcomes of repulsion between bulky groups not directly bonded together.

The differences in energy among the staggered conformations and among the eclipsed conformations are mainly due to the much larger size of a bromine atom relative to a hydrogen atom. As the Br atoms are brought closer together through rotation about the C—C bond, their electrons, forced to occupy the same space, repel one another. This is a form of strain called *steric strain* (see Recall box), depicted in **Figure 4-8**. More generally:

Steric strain is an increase in energy that results from electron repulsion between atoms or groups of atoms that are not directly bonded together but occupy the same space.

CONNECTIONS 4.1

Controlling destructive pests
1,2-Dibromoethane (Figs. 4-7 and 4-8) is used for the control of bark beetles and termites in trees that have fallen, and for the control of wax moths in beehives.

Because of the energy changes caused by bulky groups like bromine atoms, the staggered conformations are further distinguished as anti and gauche:

- **Anti conformation:** Bulky groups are 180° apart in a Newman projection.
- **Gauche conformation:** Bulky groups are 60° apart in a Newman projection.

Notice in Figure 4-7 that 1,2-dibromoethane has two gauche conformations and one anti conformation. The anti conformation, moreover, has the lowest energy of all the conformations. This is to say:

- Substituents that are gauche to each other contribute steric strain to the molecule.
- Substituents that are anti to each other do not.

In the case of 1,2-dibromoethane, the two gauche conformations have the same amount of steric strain (about 12 kJ/mol).

Similar arguments explain why the eclipsed conformations have different energies. There is greater steric strain when the Br—C—C—Br dihedral angle is 0° than when it is 120° or 240°.

YOUR TURN 4.7

Identify which of these conformations is anti and which is gauche. Which conformation is more stable?

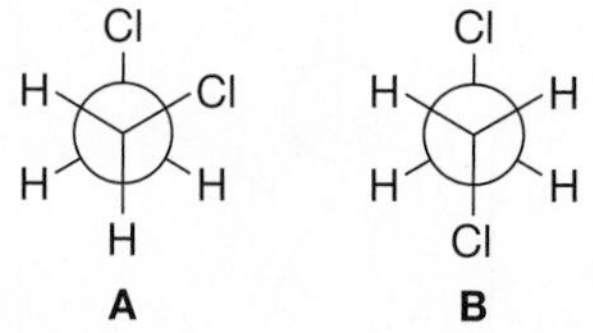

Cl
H
Cl
H
H
H
A
Cl
H
H
H
H
Cl
B

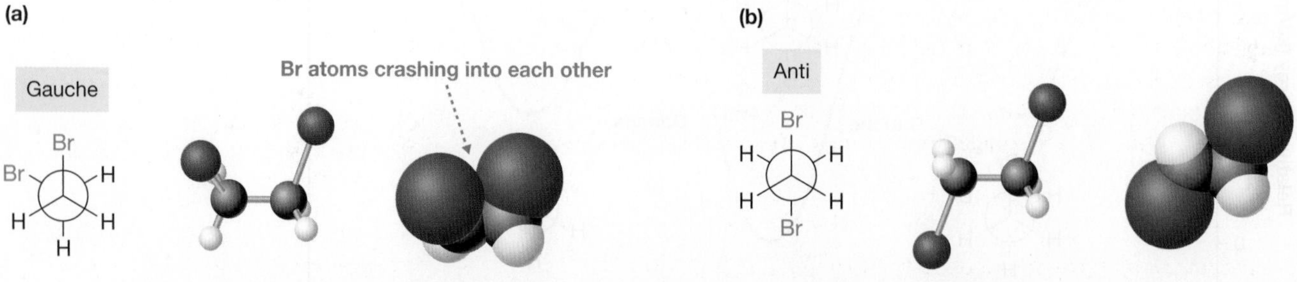

(a)
Gauche
Br atoms crashing into each other
Br
Br
H
H
H
H
(b)
Anti
Br
H
H
H
H
Br

FIGURE 4-8 Steric strain in 1,2-dibromoethane, $BrCH_2CH_2Br$ (a) 1,2-Dibromoethane in its gauche conformation, shown as a Newman projection (left), a ball-and-stick model (middle), and a space-filling model (right). Because the two Br atoms are quite large, their electrons begin to occupy the same space, causing steric strain. (b) 1,2-Dibromoethane in its anti conformation. Because the Br atoms are 180° apart, this conformation does not possess steric strain.

The three staggered (i.e., the two gauche and one anti) conformations of Br—CH_2—CH_2—Br occur at energy minima, so they are stable relative to the eclipsed conformations. Furthermore, these three conformations have the same molecular formula yet are not exactly the same. Therefore, according to Figure 4-1 (p. 162):

Gauche and anti conformations are *conformers* of each other.

> **▸ LOOKING AHEAD**
>
> As we will learn in Chapter 8, the ability of a compound to achieve the anti conformation about a single bond can dramatically impact the outcome of *bimolecular elimination (E2)* reactions.

Like those in ethane, all three staggered conformations of 1,2-dibromoethane interconvert rapidly at room temperature (see top Looking Ahead box). That is because, similar to ethane, the thermal energy available at room temperature gives a significant percentage of 1,2-dibromoethane molecules sufficient energy to surmount the rotational energy barrier.

YOUR TURN 4.8

Estimate the rotational energy barrier on going from the anti conformation of 1,2-dibromoethane (Fig. 4-7) to one of its gauche conformations. How does that value compare to the energy barrier on going from one staggered conformation of ethane to another (Fig. 4-4)? What accounts for the difference?

Even though the gauche and anti conformations of 1,2-dibromoethane rapidly interconvert, they do not exist in equal abundance:

An anti conformation is lower in energy (more stable) than the corresponding gauche conformation, so an anti conformation is preferred.

In fact, Br—CH_2—CH_2—Br molecules at room temperature are 99% anti and 1% gauche (see bottom Looking Ahead box).

> **▸ LOOKING AHEAD**
>
> The relative amounts of anti and gauche conformers at room temperature are an outcome of an equilibrium that is established, a topic we will discuss in greater detail in Chapter 6. The discussion of equilibrium in Chapter 6 will shed light on how relative amounts of such conformers can be calculated.

YOUR TURN 4.9

Which molecule do you think has a larger rotational energy barrier about the C—C bond: 1,2-dibromoethane or 1,2-difluoroethane? Why?

4.2c Longer Molecules and the Zigzag Conformation

Longer molecules, such as hexane ($CH_3CH_2CH_2CH_2CH_2CH_3$), have several single bonds about which rotation can occur, giving rise to many possible conformations. Each of the three interior C—C bonds in hexane has the form R—CH_2—CH_2—R, in which R is an alkyl group. As a result, each of these bonds can exist in either a gauche or an anti conformation. Just as we saw with 1,2-dibromoethane, anti conformations are favored over gauche, so the most stable conformation of hexane is the **all-anti conformation**, often called the **zigzag conformation** (**Figure 4-9a**). This is the basis for the zigzag convention we use to depict alkyl chains in line structures (Fig. 4-9b).

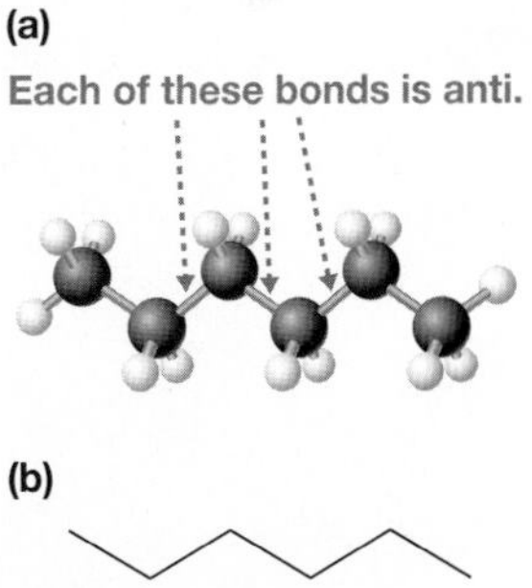

(a)
Each of these bonds is anti.
(b)

FIGURE 4-9 The all-anti conformation of hexane (a) Ball-and-stick model of hexane. The all-anti conformation is most stable, giving rise to a zigzag structure. (b) Line structure of hexane.

YOUR TURN 4.10

The following line structure of octane is not in a zigzag conformation. **(a)** Redraw the molecule in its zigzag conformation. **(b)** Explain why the zigzag conformation is more stable.

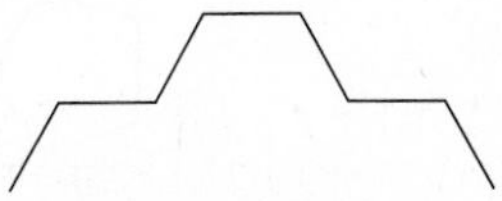

SECTION 4.3 OBJECTIVES

You will be able to:

1. Explain what ring strain is, and account for contributions to ring strain in rings of various sizes.
2. Predict relative amounts of ring strain in cyclic molecules from the size of the ring.
3. Describe the most stable conformations of cyclohexane, cyclopentane, cyclobutane, and cyclopropane.

4.3 Conformers: Ring Strain and the Most Stable Conformations of Cyclic Alkanes

Ring structures consisting only of single bonds are abundant in nature (**Figure 4-10**). Menthol, for example, is a natural oil that contains a six-membered ring. Androsterone, a steroid, consists of three six-membered rings and one five-membered ring. Diamond, one of the hardest substances known, is an extended network of six-membered rings. And five-membered rings called ribose and deoxyribose are principal components of RNA and DNA, respectively.

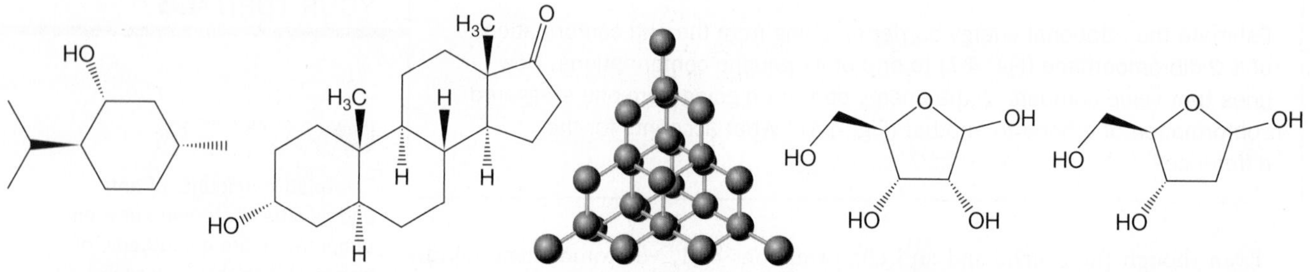

Menthol
Androsterone
Diamond
Ribose
Deoxyribose

FIGURE 4-10 Rings in nature Menthol, androsterone, and diamond have rings made of only carbon. Ribose and deoxyribose have rings that consist of carbon and oxygen.

Although compounds can exist with rings of any size, five- and six-membered rings are most abundant in nature, suggesting that rings of these sizes are particularly stable. This idea is supported by the values of *ring strain* for various cycloalkanes; **ring strain** is the increase in energy (decrease in stability) due to geometric constraints of the ring. As shown in Table 4-1, cyclohexane (six-membered ring) has no ring strain. Cyclopentane (five-membered ring) and cycloheptane (seven-membered ring) have a small amount of ring strain, and cyclobutane (four-membered ring) and cyclopropane (three-membered ring) have substantial ring strain.

The ring strain values in Table 4-1 are for cycloalkanes, but the trend that we observe for how ring strain varies with ring size can be applied to other compounds that are not simply cycloalkanes. An example is shown in Solved Problem 4.2.

SOLVED PROBLEM **4.2**

How to determine relative ring strain in cyclic molecules

Break It Down **Rank the following compounds in order from least ring strain to greatest ring strain.**

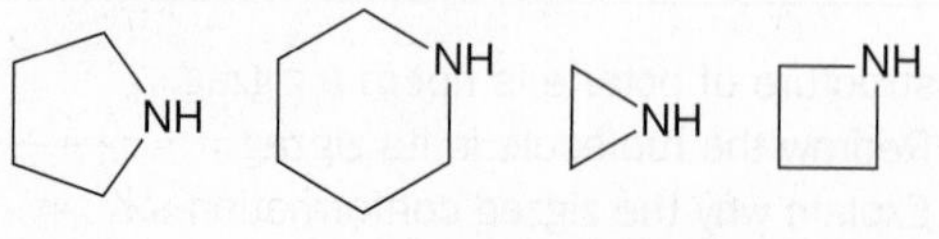

A B C D

(continued)

Think	Solve
What is the hybridization of the atoms that make up the ring? How does this compare to the atoms that make up a cycloalkane ring?	All the atoms that make up the ring, including N, are sp^3-hybridized, the same as for the cycloalkanes in Table 4-1. Therefore, we expect ring strain for molecules **A–D** to depend on ring size, similar to how cycloalkanes depend on ring size.
How does ring strain depend on ring size for cycloalkanes?	For the cycloalkanes having ring sizes of three through six, the six-membered ring has the least ring strain. Presuming the same is true for the above molecules, **B** would have the least ring strain, followed by the five-membered ring **A**, the four-membered ring **D**, and finally the three-membered ring **C**. From least to greatest ring strain, the order is **B** < **A** < **D** < **C**.

Try It Rank the following compounds in order from least to greatest ring strain.

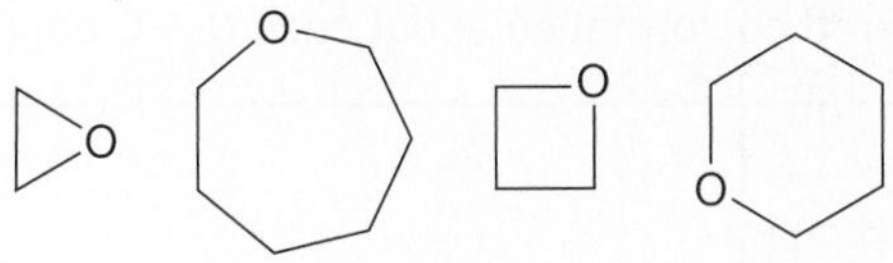

O
O
O
O

E F G H

Because cycloalkanes consist of C—C single bonds, it should not be surprising to know that *torsional strain* and *steric strain* are two major contributions to the ring strain values in Table 4-1. A third major contribution to ring strain is **angle strain**, which arises when the actual bond angles differ significantly from the ideal bond angles.

We devote the rest of Section 4.3 to understanding how torsional strain, steric strain, and angle strain contribute to ring strain in rings of various sizes. In Section 4.4, we will examine how ring strain values are determined experimentally.

TABLE 4-1 Ring Strain in Cycloalkanes

Cycloalkane	Ring Strain (kJ/mol)
 Cyclopropane	115.8
 Cyclobutane	110.0
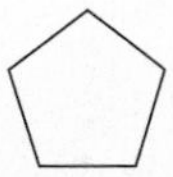 Cyclopentane	27.0
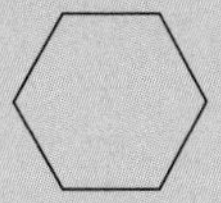 Cyclohexane	0
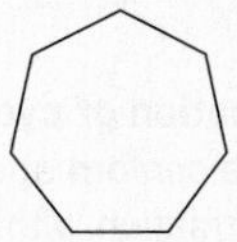 Cycloheptane	26.6

4.3a Cyclohexane

Table 4-1 indicates that cyclohexane has virtually no ring strain. Why is this? Cyclohexane experiences very little ring strain because its atoms are not confined to the same plane. When it is lowest in energy, cyclohexane exists in a **chair conformation**, in which the bonds connecting the carbon atoms trace out a shape resembling a chair (**Figure 4-11a**, next page). In a chair conformation, one C atom is designated the "head" of the chair and the opposite C atom is designated the "foot." Because all bond angles of the ring are about 111° (Fig. 4-11b), which is very close to the ideal tetrahedral angle of 109.5° (Section 2.1), the six-membered ring of cyclohexane has essentially no angle strain. It also has little to no torsional strain (Section 4.2a), because all of the rotational conformations about the C—C bonds are staggered, which can be seen in both the ball-and-stick model in Figure 4-11c and the Newman projection in Figure 4-11d.

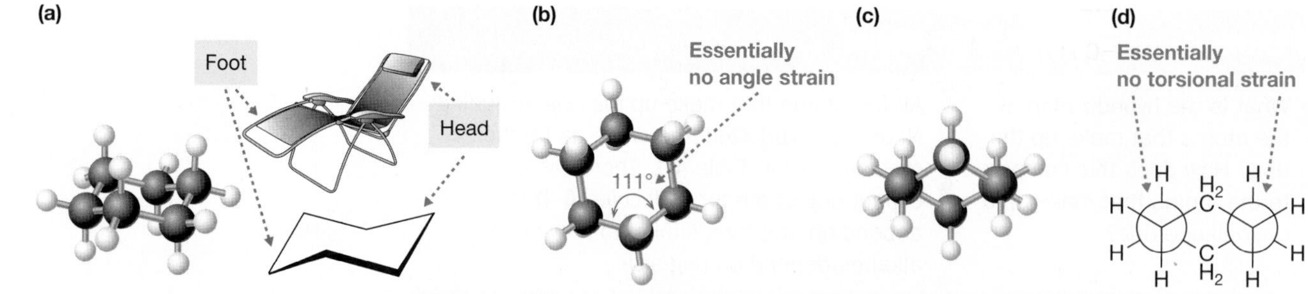
(a)
Foot
Head
(b)
Essentially
no angle strain
111°
(c)
(d)
Essentially
no torsional strain

FIGURE 4-11 Various representations of cyclohexane (a) Ball-and-stick model and line structure of cyclohexane viewed from the side, illustrating its chair conformation. (b) Ball-and-stick model of cyclohexane viewed from the top. All C—C—C bond angles are about 111°. (c) Ball-and-stick model of cyclohexane viewed down two parallel C—C bonds, illustrating that those bonds are in staggered conformations. (d) Newman projection of cyclohexane.

YOUR TURN **4.11**

Using a molecular modeling kit, build a molecule of cyclohexane in its chair conformation, then rotate it in space until it appears as in Figure 4-11c. Observe the staggered conformation about each C—C bond.

4.3b Cyclopentane

Like cyclohexane, the lowest-energy conformation of cyclopentane is not entirely planar, as shown in **Figure 4-12**. Four of its five carbon atoms lie essentially in one plane, but the fifth carbon is outside that plane. If you imagine cyclopentane's carbon atoms located at the five corners of the envelope in Figure 4.12a, you can see why this geometry is referred to as an **envelope conformation.**

Unlike cyclohexane, cyclopentane has a small amount of ring strain (see Table 4-1). It possesses some angle strain, because its bond angles range from 102° to 106°, which are somewhat farther from the ideal tetrahedral bond angle of 109.5° than are the 111° angles of cyclohexane. Furthermore, as shown in **Figure 4-13**, cyclopentane's C—C bonds have slightly eclipsed conformations.

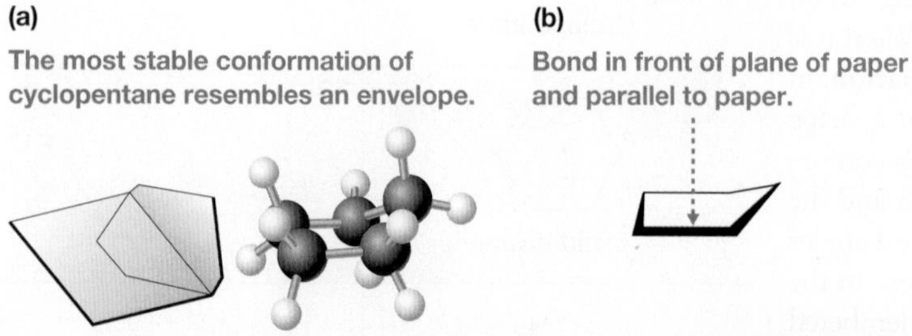
(a)
The most stable conformation of cyclopentane resembles an envelope.
(b)
Bond in front of plane of paper and parallel to paper.

FIGURE 4-12 The envelope conformation of cyclopentane (a) Ball-and-stick representation of the envelope conformation of cyclopentane. (b) Line structure of the envelope conformation with dash–wedge notation. The thicker bond on the bottom indicates that it is in front of, and parallel to, the plane of the paper.

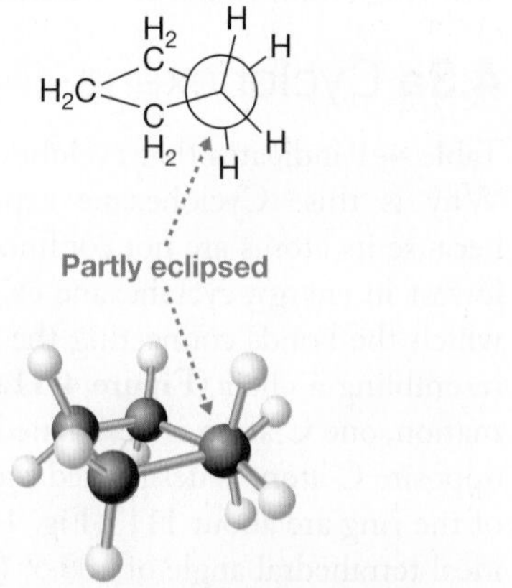
Partly eclipsed

FIGURE 4-13 Torsional strain in cyclopentane (*Top*) Newman projection of cyclopentane. The dihedral angle shown is partly eclipsed, giving rise to a small amount of torsional strain. (*Bottom*) Ball-and-stick model of cyclopentane.

YOUR TURN **4.12**

Identify the C—C bond in Figure 4-12 that has the most torsional strain. It may help if you use a modeling kit to build a model of cyclopentane in its envelope conformation.

4.3c Cyclobutane and Cyclopropane

The most stable conformation for cyclobutane is close to square, but not exactly; instead, the ring is slightly puckered, with interior angles of about 88° (**Figure 4-14**). This large deviation from the ideal bond angle of 109.5° leaves cyclobutane with a substantial amount of angle strain. Furthermore, as we can see in **Figure 4-15**, the conformation of each C—C bond remains mostly eclipsed, giving cyclobutane a substantial amount of torsional strain, too.

For cyclopropane, there is no alternative to having all three carbon atoms in the same plane, because three points define a plane. All three angles of the ring are exactly 60° and all three C—C bonds are the same length, so the ring forms an equilateral triangle. As a result, cyclopropane has more angle strain than the other cyclic molecules we have examined. Furthermore, the conformation at all of the C—C bonds is fully eclipsed, as shown in **Figure 4-16**, resulting in a large amount of torsional strain.

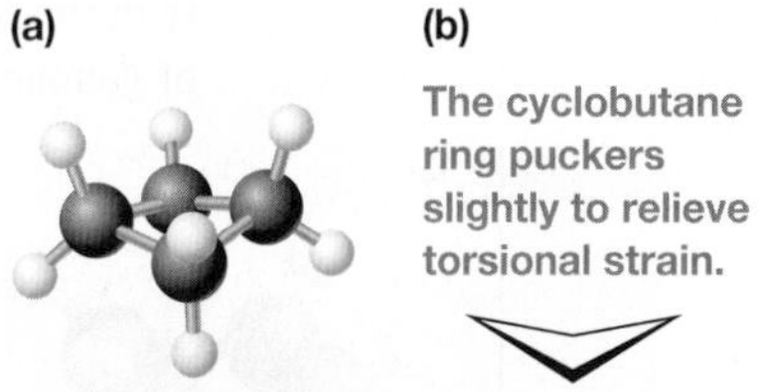
(a)
(b)
The cyclobutane ring puckers slightly to relieve torsional strain.

FIGURE 4-14 Puckered conformation of cyclobutane (a) Ball-and-stick representation of cyclobutane. (b) Line structure. The most stable conformation of cyclobutane has a slightly puckered ring.

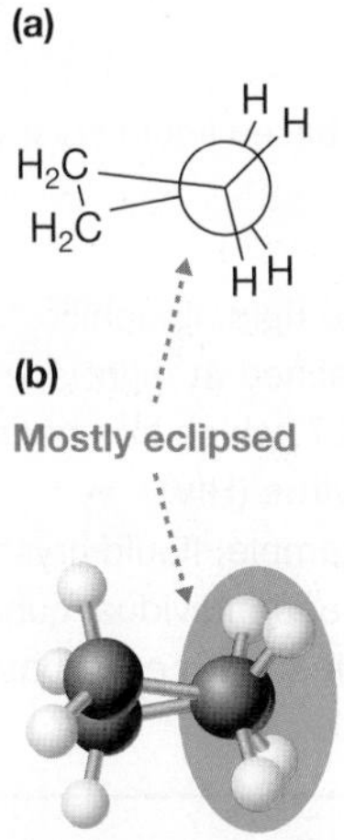
(a)
H
H
H_2C
H_2C
H
H
(b)
Mostly eclipsed

FIGURE 4-15 Torsional strain in cyclobutane (a) Newman projection of puckered cyclobutane, illustrating that the C—C bond is mostly eclipsed. (b) Ball-and-stick model of cyclobutane.

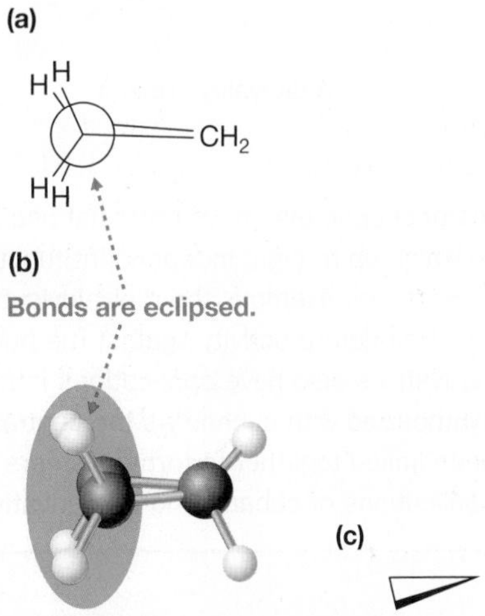
(a)
H
H
CH_2
H
H
(b)
Bonds are eclipsed.
(c)

FIGURE 4-16 Cyclopropane (a) Newman projection and (b) ball-and-stick model of cyclopropane, showing that the C—C bonds are eclipsed. (c) Line structure of cyclopropane.

4.4 A Deeper Look: Calculating Ring Strain from Heats of Combustion

SECTION 4.4 OBJECTIVES

You will be able to:

1. Explain how ring strain is calculated from a cyclohexane's heat of combustion.
2. Calculate the ring strain for a cycloalkane, given its heat of combustion.

In Table 4-1 (p. 171), we saw values of ring strain listed for cycloalkanes of various ring sizes. Here in Section 4.4, we learn how ring strain can be calculated from the **heat of combustion**, the energy given off in the form of heat ($\Delta H°$) during a combustion reaction.

Like any hydrocarbon, when a cycloalkane undergoes combustion, it reacts with O_2 to produce CO_2 and H_2O, along with heat. The balanced chemical equation for

Cubane: A Useful "Impossible" Compound?

Cubane (C_8H_8, **Figure 4-17**) is an exotic molecule in which the eight carbon atoms are located at the corners of a cube. It was once thought to be an impossible compound, unable to exist due to excessive strain. In 1964, however, Philip Eaton and Thomas W. Cole, Jr., at the University of Chicago, successfully carried out its synthesis. At the time, such a synthesis was more a novelty than anything else. But since then, cubane and its derivatives have found widespread potential applications. One of the longest-studied applications is its potential use as a high-energy fuel. With the large amount of strain it has, combined with its relatively high density (nearly twice that of gasoline), cubane can store energy more efficiently than conventional fuels.

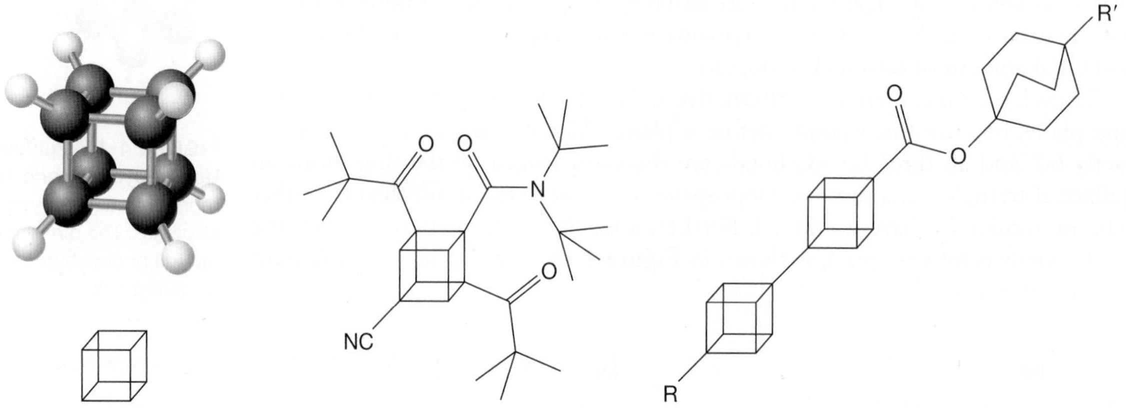
O
O
N
O
NC
O
O
R′
R

Cubane **A dipivaloylcubane** **A cubane-based liquid crystal**

FIGURE 4-17

Derivatives of cubane also have potential use in medicine, owing to the rigid, lipophilic framework to which up to eight independent functional groups can be attached at eight specific locations. Consider, for example, the dipivaloylcubane shown in Figure 4-17, which has been shown to exhibit moderate activity against the human immunodeficiency virus (HIV).

Cubane derivatives also have applications in materials science. For example, liquid crystals have been synthesized with cubane as the central structural component, and individual cubane units have been linked together to form polymers with interesting properties. With each passing year, more applications of cubane and its derivatives are sure to be found.

this process is shown in Equation 4-1, where $(CH_2)_n$ is the general formula for a cycloalkane and n is the number of carbons in the ring; for example, $(CH_2)_6$ would represent C_6H_{12} for cyclohexane:

$$(CH_2)_n + \frac{3n}{2} O_2 \rightarrow n\,CO_2 + n\,H_2O + \text{heat} \quad (4\text{-}1)$$

The numbers of moles of O_2, CO_2, and H_2O in the balanced equation are proportional to the size of the ring, n. To adjust for this, we can think of dividing all of the above terms by n to yield the balanced chemical equation in Equation 4-2 that is independent of ring size, which contains each ring's heat of combustion *per CH_2* group, $\frac{\text{heat}}{n}$:

$$\text{"}(CH_2)\text{"} + \frac{3}{2} O_2 \rightarrow CO_2 + H_2O + \frac{\text{heat}}{n} \quad (4\text{-}2)$$

Because cyclohexane has no ring strain, cyclohexane's value of $\frac{\text{heat}}{n}$ is considered a strain-free reference. Therefore, we can obtain the ring strain per CH_2 group of a particular cycloalkane by comparing that cycloalkane's value of $\frac{\text{heat}}{n}$ against cyclohexane's value of $\frac{\text{heat}}{n}$. We then obtain the total ring strain by multiplying the ring strain per

	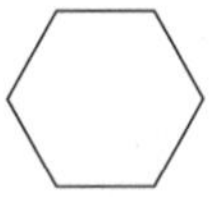	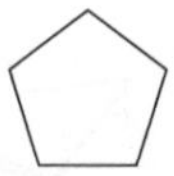
Heat of combustion	3690.7 kJ/mol	3102.5 kJ/mol
Heat of combustion per CH_2 group $\left(\frac{\text{heat}}{n}\right)$	(3690.7 kJ/mol) ÷ 6 = 615.1 kJ/mol	(3102.5 kJ/mol) ÷ 5 = 620.5 kJ/mol
Strain per CH_2 group	0 (reference)	620.5 kJ/mol − 615.1 kJ/mol = 5.4 kJ/mol
Total ring strain	0 (reference)	5(5.4 kJ/mol) = 27.0 kJ/mol

FIGURE 4-18 Ring strain derived from heat of combustion

CH_2 group by the cycloalkane's number of CH_2 groups. We can see how this is done in **Figure 4-18**, where we calculate the ring strain of cyclopentane.

YOUR TURN **4.13**

The heat of combustion of cyclopropane is 1961.0 kJ/mol. Calculate the ring strain in cyclopropane.

4.5 Conformers: Cyclohexane and Chair Flips

SECTION 4.5 OBJECTIVES

You will be able to:

1. Identify cyclohexane's C—H bonds as axial or equatorial.
2. Describe how a cyclohexane chair flip takes place through partial single-bond rotations.
3. Carry out a chair flip on a molecular model of cyclohexane.

In cyclohexane, all six carbon atoms are completely indistinguishable, but the hydrogen atoms occupy two distinct types of position, as shown in **Figure 4-19**. Six hydrogen atoms occupy *equatorial* positions and six occupy *axial* positions. Each carbon atom in cyclohexane is bonded to one equatorial hydrogen and one axial hydrogen:

- **Equatorial** bonds lie almost in the plane that is roughly defined by the ring (i.e., the *equator* of the molecule; see Fig. 4-19) and point outward from the center of the ring.
- **Axial** bonds are perpendicular to the plane.

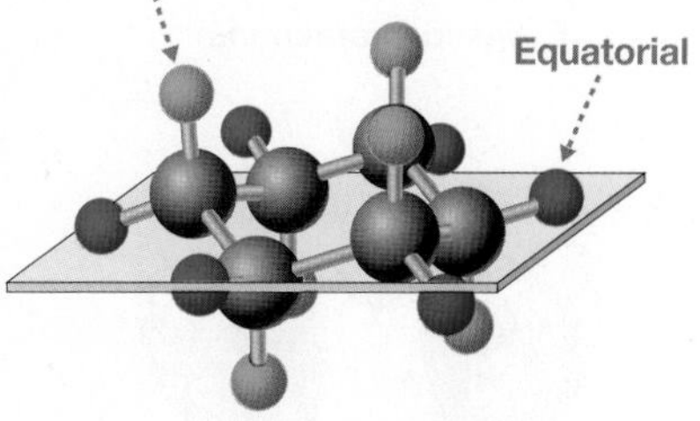

Axial
Equatorial

FIGURE 4-19 Axial and equatorial hydrogens in cyclohexane This chair conformation of cyclohexane shows that there are six axial H atoms (orange) and six equatorial H atoms (green). Bonds to axial H atoms are perpendicular to the plane indicated, whereas bonds to equatorial H atoms are nearly in the plane.

Even though they occupy different positions, the axial and equatorial hydrogens in cyclohexane are indistinguishable in most experiments. That is because cyclohexane undergoes a process called a **chair flip** or **ring flip**, in which two chair conformations interconvert very rapidly, on the order of millions of times per second at room temperature. As shown in **Figure 4-20** (next page), the head of the chair becomes the foot after a chair flip, and vice versa. Moreover:

A chair flip converts axial hydrogens into equatorial hydrogens, and vice versa.

Converting from one chair conformation to the other requires only partial rotations about the C—C bonds of the ring (see Your Turn 4.14). A cyclohexane chair flip does not occur in a single step but rather in multiple independent steps, as illustrated in **Figure 4-21** (next page). In the process of a chair flip, cyclohexane assumes key conformations known as the *half-chair*, the *twist-boat*, and the *boat*.

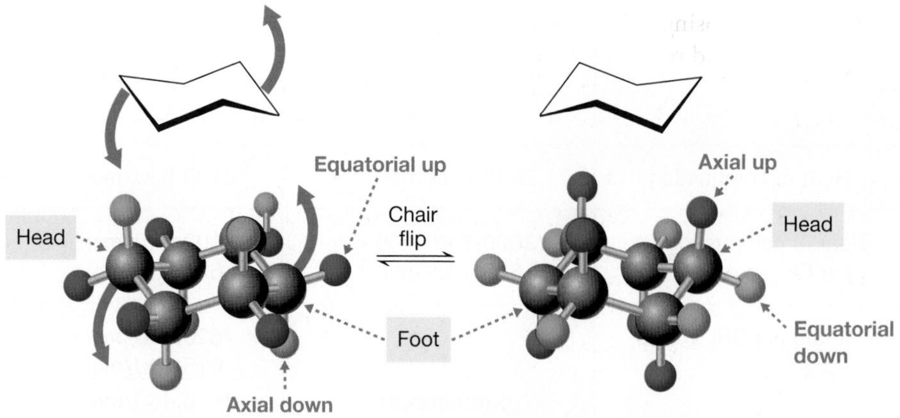
Equatorial up
Axial up
Head
Chair
flip
Head
Foot
Equatorial
down
Axial down

FIGURE 4-20 Chair flip of a cyclohexane ring The chair conformation on the left can be converted into the chair conformation on the right when the two specified C atoms move in the directions indicated by the red arrows. Notice that all the equatorial positions in the structure on the left (green) become axial after the chair flip, and all the axial positions (orange) become equatorial.

YOUR TURN **4.14**

Use a molecular modeling kit to construct a model of cyclohexane and position it to resemble the view of the left-hand structure in Figure 4-20. Perform a chair flip by moving the two carbon atoms indicated by the red arrows to obtain the conformation seen on the right in the figure. Reverse and repeat this procedure several more times. As you flip the chair back and forth, identify the bonds of the ring that rotate and the directions in which they rotate. Circle and label those bonds in the drawing on the left in Figure 4-20.

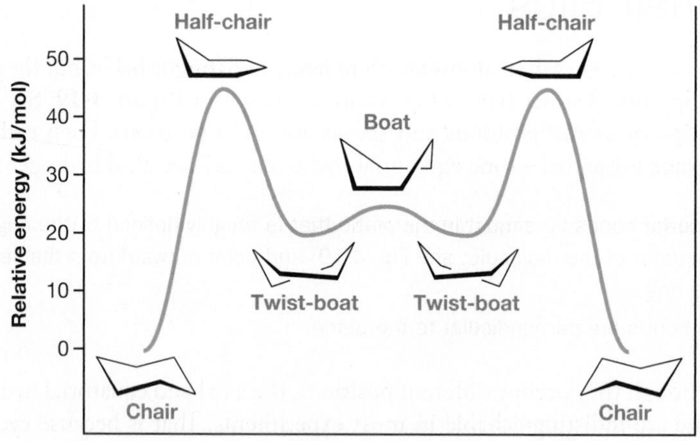
Half-chair
Half-chair
Boat
Relative energy (kJ/mol)
50
40
30
20
10
0
Twist-boat
Twist-boat
Chair
Chair

FIGURE 4-21 Energy diagram of a chair flip A chair flip that converts the conformation on the left into the one on the right goes through several key conformations, including the half-chair, twist-boat, and boat. Energies are relative to the chair conformation.

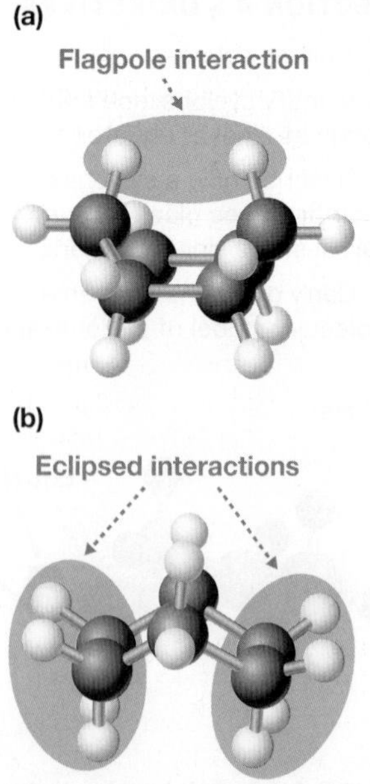
(a)
Flagpole interaction
(b)
Eclipsed interactions

FIGURE 4-22 Strain in the boat conformation of cyclohexane
(a) The boat conformation, viewed from the side, shows the flagpole interaction, a form of steric strain.
(b) The boat conformation, viewed from one end, shows the two eclipsed interactions.

As can be seen from Figure 4-21:

The half-chair, twist-boat, and boat conformations in a chair flip are higher in energy than the chair conformation itself, due to added ring strain.

Let's take a closer look at the contributions to strain in the boat conformation (**Figure 4-22**). In Figure 4-22a, note the **flagpole interaction** between hydrogen atoms on an opposing pair of carbon atoms, which represents substantial *steric strain* (each C—H bond resembles a boat's mast that might be used to fly a flag). In Figure 4-22b, note that two of the C—C bonds are in an eclipsed conformation and contribute substantial *torsional strain*. Despite the strain that develops during a chair flip, however, the energy barrier is still small enough to allow the chair conformations to interconvert rapidly.

Even though a chair flip interconverts axial and equatorial positions on a cyclohexane ring, it does *not* allow substituents to switch sides of the ring's plane. During a chair flip, a hydrogen atom in an axial position on one side of the ring's plane becomes an equatorial hydrogen on the same side. Likewise, an equatorial hydrogen on one side of the plane becomes an axial hydrogen on that same side. Viewing the cyclohexane ring from the side, as in Figure 4-20:

- A chair flip converts axial-up positions to equatorial-up (and vice versa).
- A chair flip converts axial-down positions to equatorial-down (and vice versa).

CONNECTIONS 4.2

Don't let it rain on your parade Most cyclohexane (Figs. 4-19–4-22) is oxidized to produce adipic acid, a precursor to nylon, which is used to make the fabric for this umbrella.

YOUR TURN **4.15**

Use a molecular modeling kit to build the half-chair conformation shown. Examine the model from different points of view, and note the different types of strain. In the figure provided here, indicate where the strain exists, as well as the type of strain (i.e., angle, steric, or torsional). With these observations, can you justify why the half-chair conformation is so high in energy?

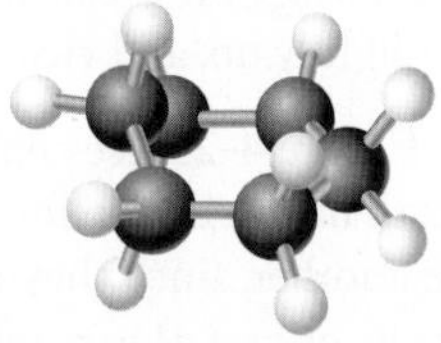

4.6 Strategies for Success: Drawing Chair Conformations of Cyclohexane

SECTION 4.6 OBJECTIVES

You will be able to:

1. Interpret a shorthand drawing of a chair conformation of cyclohexane accurately.
2. Draw a chair conformation of cyclohexane quickly and accurately.

Given the abundance of cyclohexane rings, it would soon become cumbersome if we always had to represent chair conformations three-dimensionally as ball-and-stick models (**Figure 4-23a**) or in dash–wedge notation (Fig. 4-23b). Chemists, therefore, have devised the shorthand notation for drawing chair conformations shown in Figure 4-23c. Working with these structures is not trivial, so we devote this section to both drawing and interpreting chair structures using this shorthand method.

Strategies for Success Drawing Chair Conformations of Cyclohexane Using a Modeling Kit

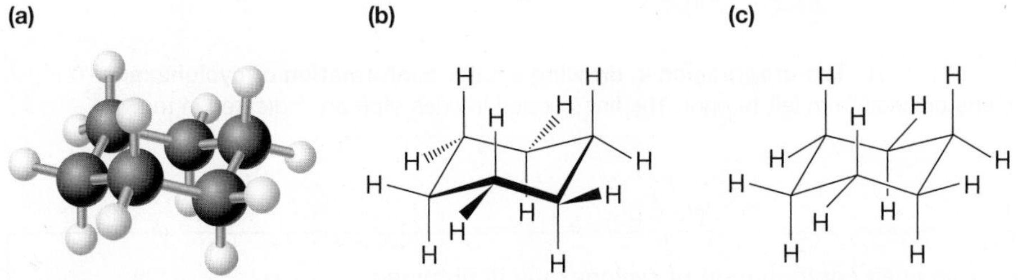

(a)
(b)
(c)
H

FIGURE 4-23 Various representations of the chair conformation of cyclohexane (a) Ball-and-stick model. (b) Dash–wedge notation. (c) Shorthand notation.

Before we begin, note the following features of the shorthand notation:

- By convention, the C—C bonds toward the bottom of the ring are interpreted as being in front of the plane of the paper (**Figure 4-24a**, next page).
- When the ring is oriented as it is in Figure 4-23, all of the axial bonds (red) are perfectly vertical, *alternating up and down* around the ring (Fig. 4-24b).

Strategies for Success Drawing Chair Conformations of Cyclohexane without a Modeling Kit

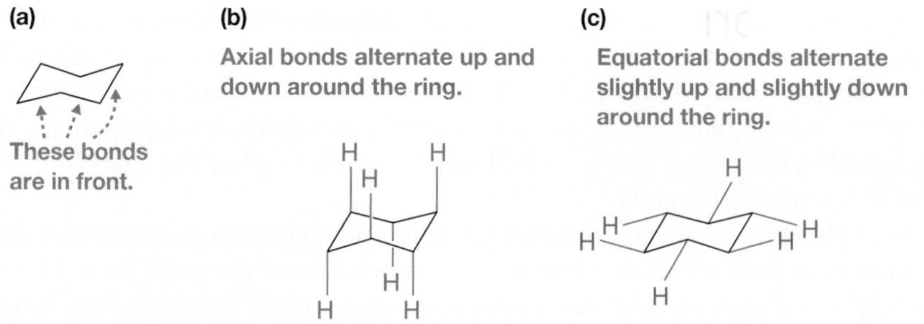
(a)
These bonds are in front.
(b)
Axial bonds alternate up and down around the ring.
(c)
Equatorial bonds alternate slightly up and slightly down around the ring.

FIGURE 4-24 Interpreting the shorthand notation for the chair conformation of cyclohexane (a) By convention, the bonds on the bottom are in front of the plane of the paper. (b) Axial bonds (red) are vertical and alternate up and down around the ring. (c) Equatorial bonds (blue) alternate slightly up and slightly down around the ring.

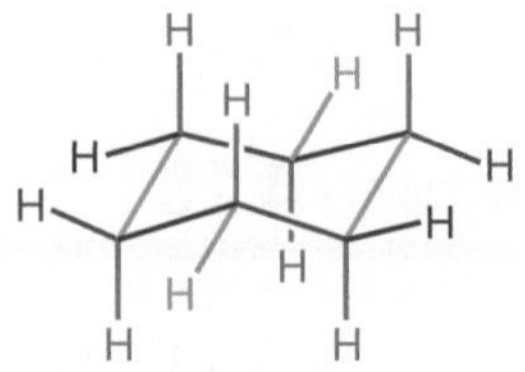

FIGURE 4-25 Parallel bonds in the shorthand notation for cyclohexane The chair conformation of cyclohexane is color-coded to show its four sets of parallel bonds. Each C—C bond is parallel to the one opposite it in the ring and to a pair of equatorial C—H bonds. The six axial C—H bonds are also parallel to one another.

- All equatorial bonds (blue) are either slightly up or slightly down, *alternating around the ring*; on a carbon where the axial bond is down, there is an equatorial bond slightly up, and vice versa (Fig. 4-24c).

Figure 4-25 uses color coding to illustrate which sets of bonds are parallel in the shorthand notation for cyclohexane. All six axial C—H bonds (red) are parallel to one another, since they are all drawn vertically. Each equatorial C—H bond (brown, purple, or green) is parallel to one equatorial C—H bond on the opposite side of the ring and to two C—C bonds that are part of the ring. With these sets of parallel lines in mind, examine **Figure 4-26** to learn one way to draw a complete chair structure from scratch. (If you learn another way that suits you better, then use that.) You should practice these steps until you can draw the complete chair structure without having to refer to the figure.

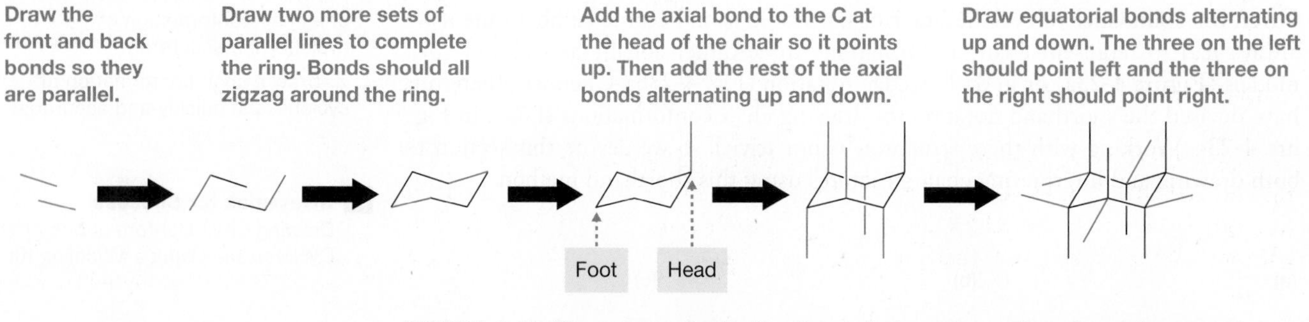
Draw the front and back bonds so they are parallel.
Draw two more sets of parallel lines to complete the ring. Bonds should all zigzag around the ring.
Add the axial bond to the C at the head of the chair so it points up. Then add the rest of the axial bonds alternating up and down.
Draw equatorial bonds alternating up and down. The three on the left should point left and the three on the right should point right.
Foot
Head

FIGURE 4-26 The progression in drawing a chair conformation of cyclohexane The steps proceed from left to right. The lines added in each step are indicated in red.

YOUR TURN **4.16**

This chair conformation of cyclohexane is obtained after the one in Figure 4-25 has undergone a chair flip. Use the steps in Figure 4-26 to practice drawing this chair conformation until you can draw it without having to refer to the figure.

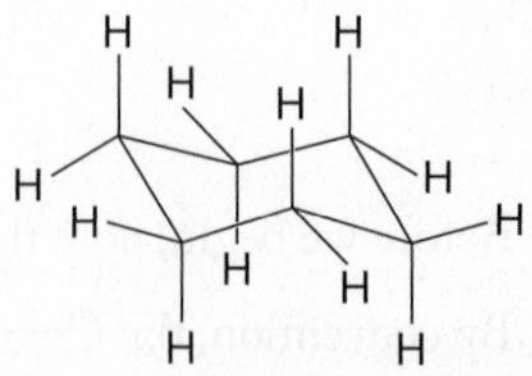

4.7 Conformers: Monosubstituted Cyclohexanes

SECTION 4.7 OBJECTIVES

You will be able to:

1. Draw a monosubstituted cyclohexane in both of its chair conformations.
2. Evaluate which of the two chair conformations is more stable.

If one of the hydrogen atoms in cyclohexane is replaced by a substituent such as CH_3, the result is a **monosubstituted cyclohexane**:

The two chair conformations of a monosubstituted cyclohexane are *not* equivalent.

For example, the CH_3 group of methylcyclohexane is axial in one chair form (**Figure 4-27**, left), whereas it is equatorial in the other (Fig. 4-27, right).

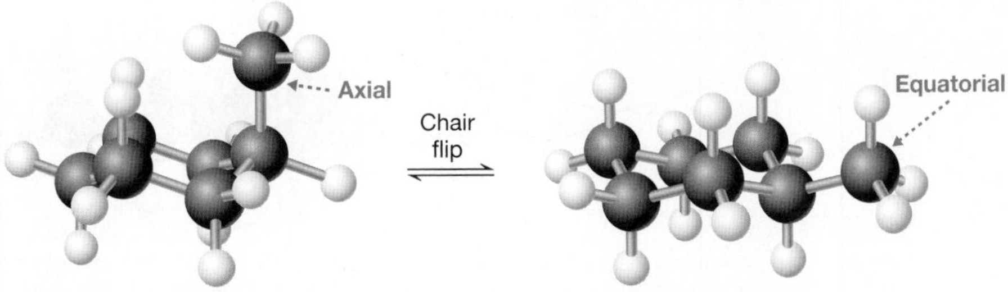

Axial
Chair flip
Equatorial

FIGURE 4-27 The two chair conformations of methylcyclohexane (*Left*) The methyl group occupies an axial position. (*Right*) The methyl group occupies an equatorial position. The two chair conformations of monosubstituted cyclohexanes are not equivalent.

YOUR TURN 4.17

In both chair conformations in Figure 4-27, label each of the 11 hydrogen atoms bonded to the ring as either axial or equatorial.

Because they have the same molecular formula but differ due to rotations about single bonds:

Two nonequivalent chair forms are *conformers* of each other.

The two chair conformations of methylcyclohexane rapidly interconvert, but they are not equally favored. At any given time, about 95% of the molecules exist in the form with an equatorial CH_3 group, and the remaining 5% exist in the form with an axial CH_3 group. Other monosubstituted cyclohexanes exhibit the same trend:

A monosubstituted cyclohexane is lower in energy (more stable) when the substituent occupies an equatorial position.

The equatorial conformer is more stable than the axial conformer because *there is more room for the substituent in the equatorial position*. To see why, compare methylcyclohexane with an axial CH_3 group (**Figure 4-28a**, next page) to methylcyclohexane with an equatorial CH_3 group (Fig. 4-28b).

In the axial position, the CH_3 group experiences significant steric strain from gauche interactions, one of which is illustrated in the Newman projection in Figure 4-28a. Notice that the CH_2 group containing C-3 of the ring is gauche to the CH_3 substituent (red) bonded to C-1. Repulsion between the electrons from the respective CH_3 and CH_2 groups gives rise to the strain.

CONNECTIONS 4.3

Methylcyclohexane in industry One of the principal uses of methylcyclohexane (Fig. 4-27) is as a solvent for cellulose ethers. Cellulose ethers have a wide variety of applications, including construction products, foods, cosmetics, pharmaceuticals, and paints.

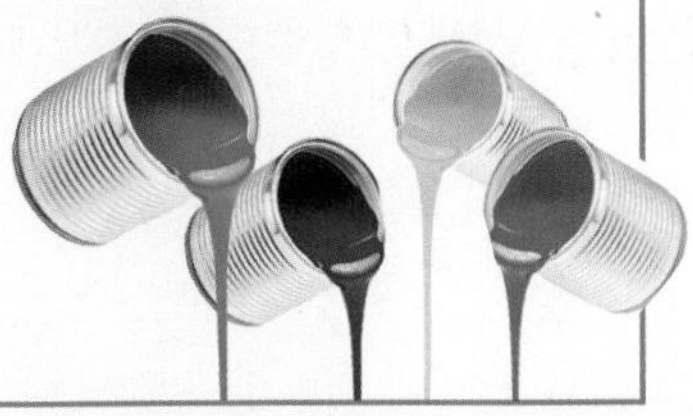

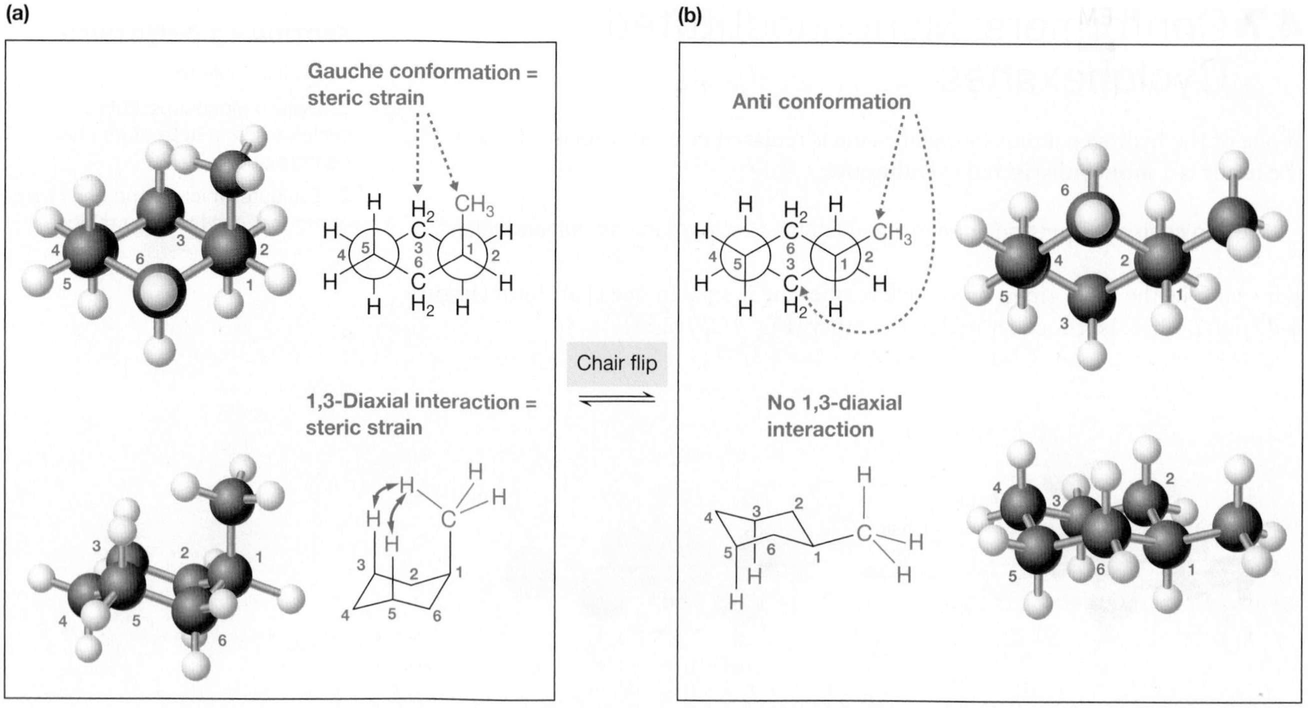

(a)
(b)
Gauche conformation = steric strain
Anti conformation
Chair flip
1,3-Diaxial interaction = steric strain
No 1,3-diaxial interaction

FIGURE 4-28 Strain from axial versus equatorial substituents on cyclohexane (a) The methyl group is in an axial position. A Newman projection looking down the C1—C2 and C5—C4 bonds (top) shows strain from a gauche interaction between the CH_3 substituent on the ring and a CH_2 group of the ring. A chair representation (bottom) shows strain from 1,3-diaxial interactions. (b) The methyl group is in an equatorial position. A Newman projection (top) shows that the CH_3 substituent on the ring is anti to the CH_2 group of the ring. A chair representation (bottom) shows that no 1,3-diaxial interactions are present.

A major contribution to the strain in these gauche interactions comes specifically from repulsion between the electrons on the axial CH_3 group bonded to C-1 and those on the axial H atoms two positions away on the ring (i.e., at positions 3 and 5). There are two of these **1,3-diaxial interactions** (the "1,3" identifies the *relative* positions on the ring for the interacting substituents), as indicated in Figure 4-28a.

No such steric strain exists when the CH_3 group is in the equatorial position (Fig. 4-28b). In the equatorial position, the CH_2 group at position 3 on the ring is anti to the CH_3 group, so no steric strain arises from their interaction. More specifically, the 1,3-diaxial interactions are eliminated because the CH_3 group is relatively far away from the axial H atoms at positions 3 and 5.

YOUR TURN 4.18

This model of methylcyclohexane corresponds to the top structure in Figure 4-28a. It shows two hydrogen atoms on the ring involved in 1,3-diaxial interactions with the CH_3 group. Identify these two hydrogens. Also, *two* different CH_2 groups are gauche to the CH_3 group. One is indicated in Figure 4-28a. Identify the second one in the structure shown. *Hint*: Build a molecular model of methylcyclohexane.

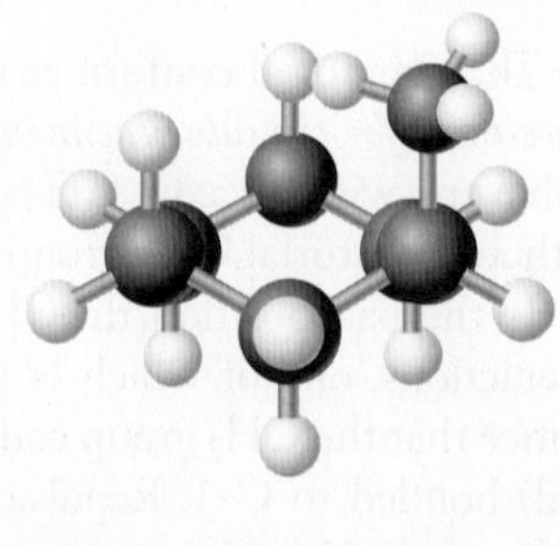

SOLVED PROBLEM **4.3**

How to identify the more stable monosubstituted cyclohexane

Break It Down **Which species, A or B, is more stable?**

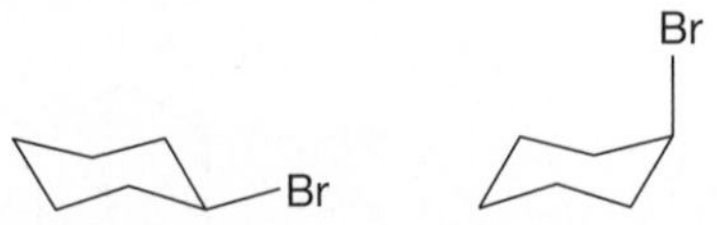
Br
Br

A **B**

Think	Solve
How are the two molecules related? What is different between the two molecules?	The C—Br bond is equatorial in **A** and is axial in **B**, so the two structures are related by a chair flip. 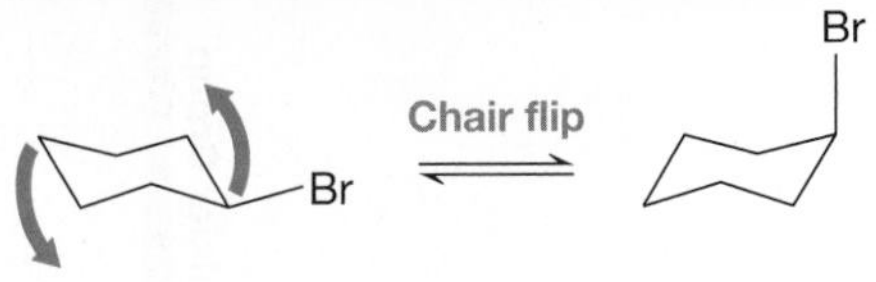 Br Chair flip Br **A** **B**
How does that difference translate into relative stabilities?	Bromine is much bulkier than any of the 11 H atoms also bonded to the cyclohexane ring, so it requires more room. Because the equatorial position provides more room than the axial position, conformation **A** is more stable.

Try It Draw both chair conformations of cyclohexane-d_1, in which a hydrogen atom on cyclohexane has been replaced by a deuterium atom. Which conformation would you expect to be in greater abundance, if any? Explain. *Hint*: Deuterium is an isotope of hydrogen, possessing one more neutron than hydrogen. Recall from Chapter 1 that the size of an atom is dictated by the size of its electron cloud.

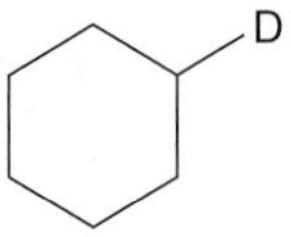
D

Cyclohexane-d_1

Even though all non-hydrogen groups prefer the equatorial position over the axial position, some groups have a stronger preference than others. This can be seen in Table 4-2 (next page), which shows the relative percentages of the two chair conformations of various monosubstituted cyclohexanes.

The preference a substituent has for equatorial versus axial reflects how bulky the substituent is:

> The bulkier the substituent on a cyclohexane ring, the more favored is the chair conformation with the substituent in the equatorial position.

With the above idea in mind, we can identify two key trends in Table 4-2. The first trend is captured by the fact that bulkiness increases in the order OH < NH_2 < CH_3:

> The bulkiness of a substituent increases as the atom at the point of attachment has more σ bonding pairs of electrons and fewer lone pairs.

The reason is that a pair of electrons involved in a σ bond extends farther away from the atom at the point of attachment than does a lone pair.

The second trend from Table 4-2 is captured by the fact that bulkiness increases in the order CH_3 < CH_2CH_3 < $CH(CH_3)_2$ < $C(CH_3)_3$:

> The bulkiness of a substituent increases as the atom at the point of attachment is bonded to more alkyl groups.

In fact, the *tert*-butyl group [$C(CH_3)_3$] is so bulky that only a very small percentage of molecules exist with the group in the axial position; the *tert*-butyl group is effectively locked in the equatorial position.

TABLE 4-2 **Relative Percentages of Chair Conformations of Monosubstituted Cyclohexanes**

Substituted Cyclohexane	Percent Axial	Percent Equatorial
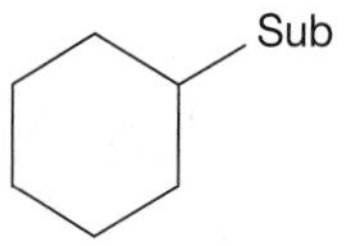	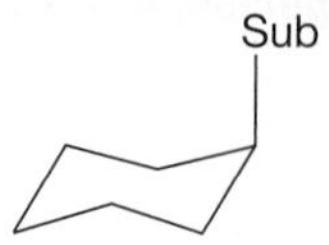	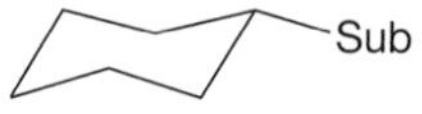
Sub = H	50.0	50.0
OH	18.7	81.3
NH_2	6.3	93.7
CH_3	5.3	94.7
CH_2CH_3	4.5	95.5
$CH(CH_3)_2$	2.8	97.2
$C(CH_3)_3$	0.02	99.98

Bulkier Group ↓

YOUR TURN **4.19**

For which compound, triiodomethylcyclohexane or trifluoromethylcyclohexane, would you expect to find a greater percentage of molecules that have the substituent in the axial position? Explain.

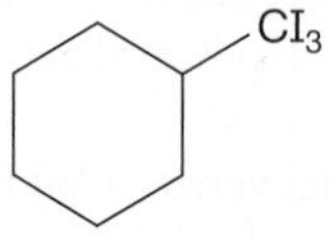

CI_3

Triiodomethylcyclohexane

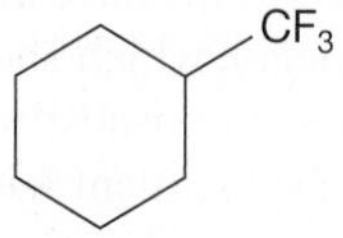

CF_3

Trifluoromethylcyclohexane

SECTION 4.8 OBJECTIVES

You will be able to:

1. Draw a Haworth projection, given the top view of a cyclic molecule, and vice versa.
2. Convert a Haworth projection of a substituted cyclohexane to a chair structure and vice versa.
3. Draw the more stable chair conformation of a disubstituted cyclohexane.

4.8 Conformers: Disubstituted Cyclohexanes, Cis and Trans Isomers, and Haworth Projections

With **disubstituted** cyclohexanes (i.e., those with two substituents), we have to take into account the relationship of each substituent to the plane of the ring. Are they on the same side of the ring (i.e., cis to each other), or are they on opposite sides (i.e., trans)? A chair flip does *not* switch a substituent from one side of the plane to the other, so *the cis–trans relationship between any pair of substituents on a cyclohexane ring is independent of the particular chair conformation the species is in*:

Substituents that are cis to each other on a cyclohexane ring remain cis after a chair flip; substituents that are trans to each other remain trans.

FIGURE 4-29 **Top views and Haworth projections of disubstituted cyclohexanes** (a) A cis isomer of a generic 1,2-disubstituted cyclohexane is shown in its top view using dash–wedge notation (top) and as a Haworth projection (bottom). (b) A trans isomer of a generic 1,2-disubstituted cyclohexane is similarly depicted.

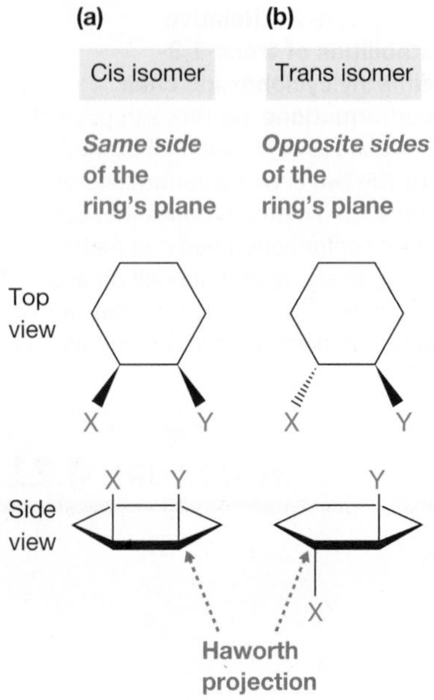

(a)
(b)
Cis isomer
Trans isomer
Same side of the ring's plane
Opposite sides of the ring's plane
Top view
Side view
X
Y
Haworth projection

Because the cis–trans relationship of any pair of substituents is unaffected by a chair flip, chemists often find it more convenient to represent substituted cyclohexanes (and rings of other size, for that matter) using a top view of the ring (top structures in **Figure 4-29**). Sometimes it is convenient to depict these structures from the side, using *Haworth projections* (bottom structures in Fig. 4-29). In a **Haworth projection**, the ring is depicted as being planar, and bonds to substituents are drawn perpendicular to that plane. Despite their convenience, both top views and Haworth projections are inaccurate representations of the true structure and should be used with caution. In particular, they are incapable of portraying axial versus equatorial positions, so they do not accurately represent steric interactions.

YOUR TURN 4.20

Draw each top view as a Haworth projection, and draw each Haworth projection as a top view including dash–wedge notation.

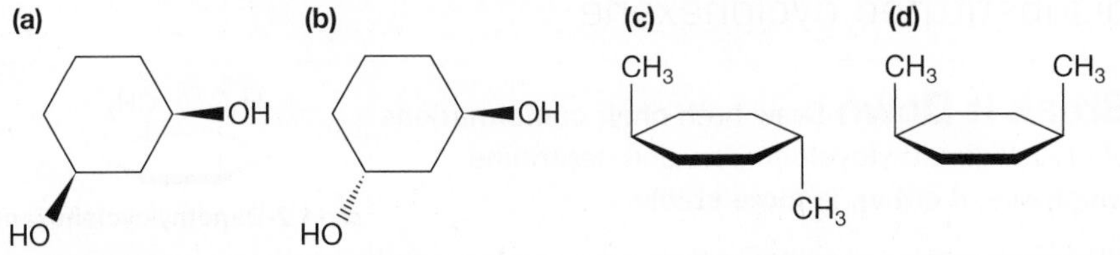

(a)
(b)
(c)
(d)
OH
HO
CH_3

Because each substituent on a cyclohexane ring is more stable in an equatorial position than in an axial position, we can reasonably predict the more stable chair conformation of a number of disubstituted cyclohexanes. In *cis*-1,3-dimethylcyclohexane (**Figure 4-30**), for example, one chair conformation has two equatorial CH_3 groups, whereas the other has both groups axial. The diequatorial conformer is favored over the diaxial conformer.

In *trans*-1,3-dimethylcyclohexane (**Figure 4-31**, next page), both chair conformations are equally favored because each conformation has one axial and one equatorial CH_3 group. With a chair flip, the axial CH_3 group becomes equatorial and the equatorial group becomes axial, which results in a conformation that is identical to the first.

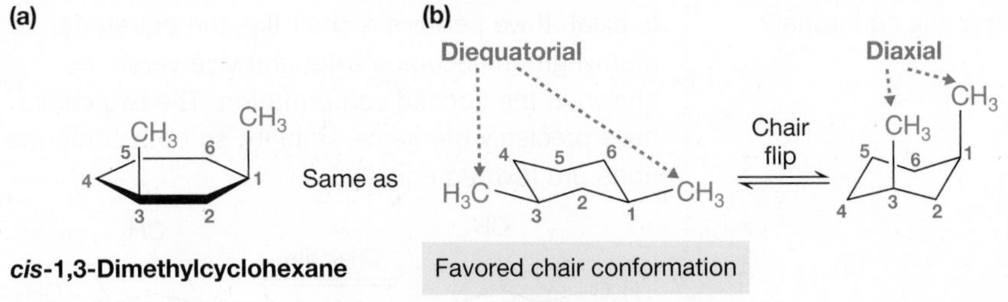

(a)
(b)
Diequatorial
Diaxial
CH_3
H_3C
Same as
Chair flip
cis-1,3-Dimethylcyclohexane
Favored chair conformation

FIGURE 4-30 **Relative stabilities of *cis*-1,3-dimethylcyclohexane chair conformations** (a) Haworth projection of *cis*-1,3-dimethylcyclohexane. (b) The two chair conformations of *cis*-1,3-dimethylcyclohexane. The diequatorial conformation is favored over the diaxial.

FIGURE 4-31 Relative stabilities of *trans*-1,3-dimethylcyclohexane chair conformations (a) Haworth projection of *trans*-1,3-dimethylcyclohexane. (b) The two chair conformations of *trans*-1,3-dimethylcyclohexane. Each chair conformation has one methyl group in an equatorial position and one in an axial position, so the two conformations are favored equally.

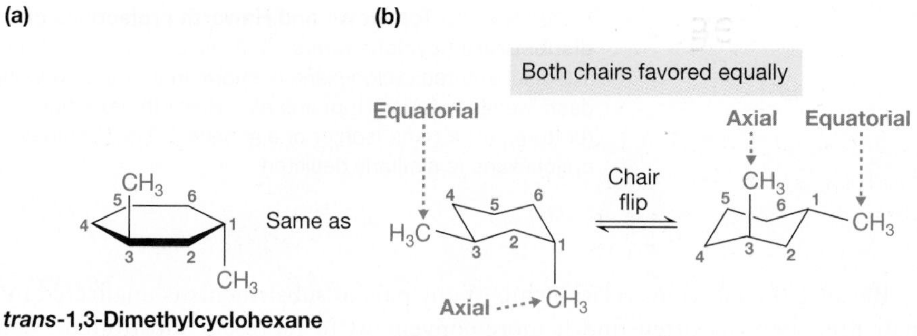

(a)
(b)
Both chairs favored equally
Equatorial
Axial
Equatorial
Chair flip
Same as
CH_3
H_3C
Axial
trans-1,3-Dimethylcyclohexane

YOUR TURN **4.21**

Use a molecular modeling kit to build a model of *trans*-1,3-dimethylcyclohexane so that it looks exactly like the chair conformation shown on the left in Figure 4-31b. Without carrying out a chair flip of the molecule, simply reorient the molecule so it looks like the chair conformation on the right.

SOLVED PROBLEM **4.4**

How to draw the more stable chair conformation of a disubstituted cyclohexane

Break It Down **Draw both chair conformations of *cis*-1,2-dimethylcyclohexane and determine which one, if either, is more stable.**

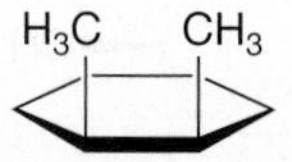

H_3C
CH_3

***cis*-1,2-Dimethylcyclohexane**

Think	Solve
Which substituents require the most room?	The two methyl groups are the largest substituents on the ring and therefore require the most room.
Which position, axial or equatorial, offers more room?	The equatorial position offers more room than axial, so each methyl group has preference for equatorial. The first methyl group can be drawn equatorial, as shown here. 
Can both substituents achieve that position? If not, which substituent has a greater preference for being equatorial?	The first methyl group added points up (slightly), and for the two methyl groups to be cis, the methyl group on the adjacent carbon must also point up. As shown here in the first conformation, that bond is axial. If we perform a chair flip, the equatorial methyl group becomes axial and vice versa, as shown in the second conformation. The two chairs have precisely the same stability, so both conformations are favored equally. 

Try It Draw the most stable chair conformation of *trans*-1,2-dimethylcyclohexane.

4.9 Strategies for Success: Molecular Modeling Kits and Chair Flips

As we have seen, molecular modeling kits can be really useful because they help us "see" molecules in three dimensions from different vantage points and they accurately portray the rotational characteristics of single bonds. This makes molecular modeling kits *especially* helpful in problems that ask you to compare chair conformations.

For example, instead of working Solved Problem 4.4 entirely on paper, you can simplify the problem by making the modeling kit do much of the work for you. First, build a cyclohexane ring in its chair conformation, temporarily leaving off all the hydrogen atoms, as shown in **Figure 4-32a**. Being able to see all of the bonding positions on the ring that are available, you can then attach two CH_3 groups on adjacent carbon atoms, on the same side of the plane of the ring. As shown in Figure 4-32b, one position is axial, pointing straight up, and the other is equatorial, pointing slightly up. After you add the remaining hydrogen atoms, one of the two chair conformations of *cis*-1,2-dimethylcyclohexane is complete. Flipping the chair as indicated in Figure 4-32b, you arrive at the second chair conformation in Figure 4-32c, which also has one axial and one equatorial CH_3 group. Hence, the two conformations are equivalent.

SECTION 4.9 OBJECTIVES

You will be able to:

1. Use a modeling kit to construct a molecular model of a substituted cyclohexane.
2. Carry out a chair flip on the molecular model to evaluate the more stable conformation.

Strategies for Success
Molecular Modeling Kits and Chair Flips

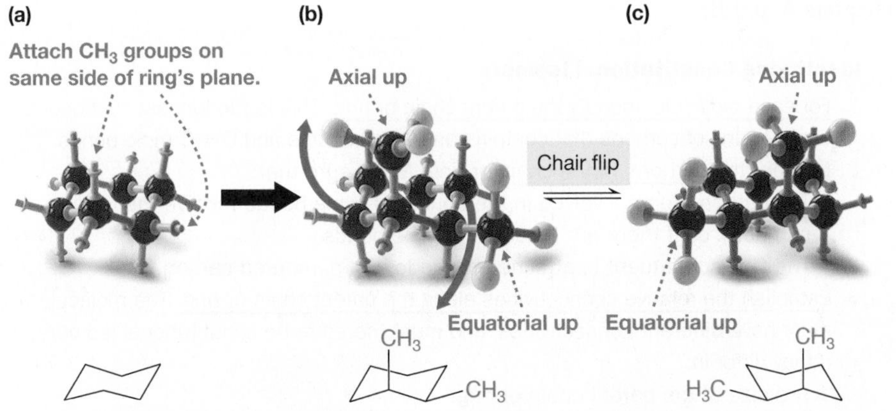

(a)
(b)
(c)
Attach CH3 groups on same side of ring's plane.
Axial up
Chair flip
Axial up
Equatorial up
Equatorial up
CH3
CH3
CH3
H3C

FIGURE 4-32 Model kits and chair flips (a) A cyclohexane ring without hydrogen atoms. Bonds on the same side of the ring's plane and on adjacent C atoms are identified. (b) CH_3 groups have been added. One is axial and the other is equatorial. Twisting the C atoms on the left and right sides, according to the red arrows, flips the chair. (c) The model after the chair flip. Both CH_3 groups remain up, with one axial and the other equatorial.

CONNECTIONS 4.4

Keeping the water flowing
But-1-ene (Fig. 4-34) is used to produce polybutylene, a polymer that was heavily used in the late twentieth century for manufacturing plastic pipes used for plumbing.

4.10 Constitutional Isomerism: Identifying Constitutional Isomers

Constitutional isomers are the second type of isomers we discuss in this chapter. As you can see from the portion of the Figure 4-1 flowchart reproduced in **Figure 4-33** (next page):

> **Constitutional isomers**, also called **structural isomers**, have the same molecular formula but *differ in their connectivity*.

Unlike conformers, constitutional isomers generally do not interconvert and can be separated from each other. Recall from Chapter 1 that the *connectivity* of a molecule describes its *bonding scheme*, including which atoms are bonded together and by what

SECTION 4.10 OBJECTIVES

You will be able to:

1. Describe the relationship between constitutional isomers.
2. Use a systematic method to determine whether a pair of molecules are constitutional isomers.

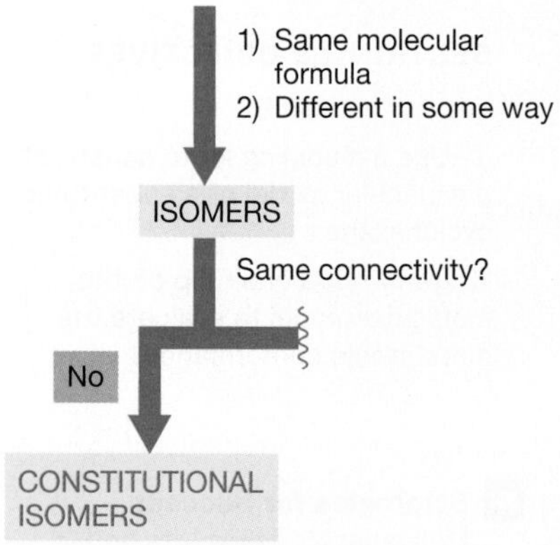
1) Same molecular formula
2) Different in some way
ISOMERS
Same connectivity?
No
CONSTITUTIONAL ISOMERS

FIGURE 4-33 Constitutional isomers Constitutional isomers have the same formula but different connectivities.

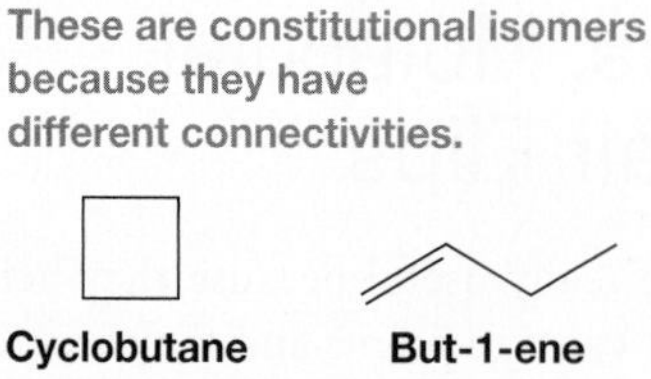
These are constitutional isomers because they have different connectivities.
Cyclobutane
But-1-ene

FIGURE 4-34 Different connectivities

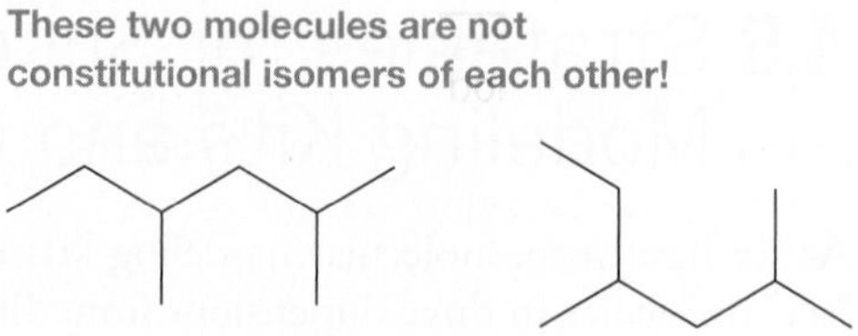
These two molecules are not constitutional isomers of each other!

FIGURE 4-35 Identical connectivities

type of bond (e.g., single, double, or triple). Cyclobutane and but-1-ene (**Figure 4-34**) are constitutional isomers, for example, because both have the molecular formula C_4H_8 but their connectivities are different. Cyclobutane has only single bonds, whereas but-1-ene contains a C=C double bond. Furthermore, the C—C single bonds in cyclobutane form a ring, whereas but-1-ene is acyclic.

Both of the structures in **Figure 4-35** have the molecular formula C_8H_{18}, but are they constitutional isomers? Although they are drawn differently, they actually have the same connectivity, so they are *not* constitutional isomers of each other. How can we tell?

A straightforward method for determining whether two molecules with the same formula are constitutional isomers builds on nomenclature rules introduced in Interchapters A and B:

Identifying Constitutional Isomers

1. For each molecule, identify the parent chain or ring. This is the longest continuous chain or ring of carbons that contains any C=C double and C≡C triple bonds.
2. Number the carbons in the chain or ring. Make sure that:
   - The carbon atoms involved in the double or triple bonds receive the lowest numbers, or, if there are no such multiple bonds,
   - The first substituent is attached to the lowest-numbered carbon.
3. Establish the relative connectivities along the parent chain or ring. The molecules must have different connectivities, and must therefore be constitutional isomers, if they differ in:
   - The size of the parent chain or ring.
   - The numbers assigned to the carbons involved in the multiple bonds.
   - The numbers assigned to the carbons to which any substituent is attached.
   - The identities of the substituents attached to the same-numbered carbon.

Otherwise, the molecules have the same connectivity and are not constitutional isomers.

CONNECTIONS 4.5

Cyclobutane and DNA
Cyclobutane (Fig. 4-34) is not very useful itself, but the strained four-membered carbon ring does have significance in biochemistry and medicine. The motif is found in the thymine dimer, for example, which is produced in DNA on exposure to ultraviolet light and is repaired enzymatically.

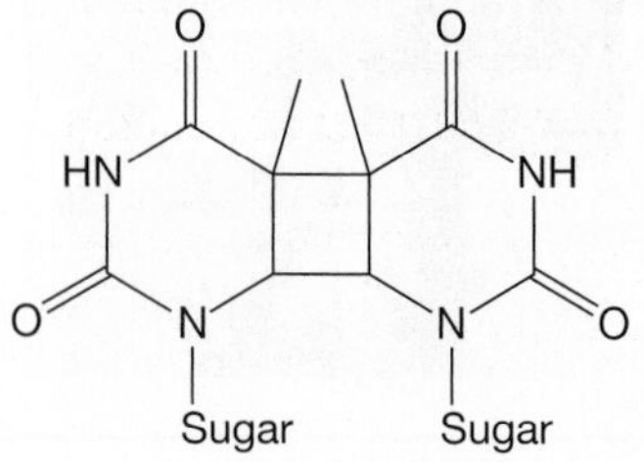
O
O
HN
NH
O
N
N
O
Sugar
Sugar

Thymine dimer

Figure 4-36 shows how to apply this method to the two molecules shown in Figure 4-35. For Step 1, the longest continuous chain of carbon atoms in each molecule has six carbons. For Step 2, the carbons are numbered 1 through 6 so that the first methyl group is encountered on C-2. Because the methyl groups are attached to C-2 and C-4 in both cases, the molecules have the same connectivity and therefore are not constitutional isomers.

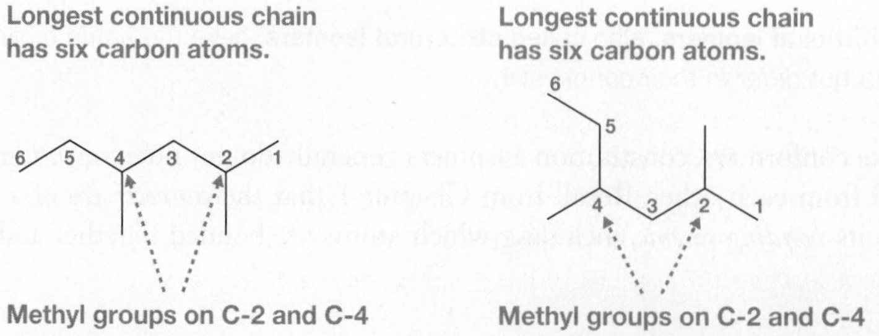
Longest continuous chain has six carbon atoms.
6 5 4 3 2 1
Methyl groups on C-2 and C-4
Longest continuous chain has six carbon atoms.
6
5
4 3 2 1
Methyl groups on C-2 and C-4

FIGURE 4-36 Comparing connectivities

Using the method just described, show that the molecule depicted here is *not* a constitutional isomer of the two molecules depicted in Figure 4-35.

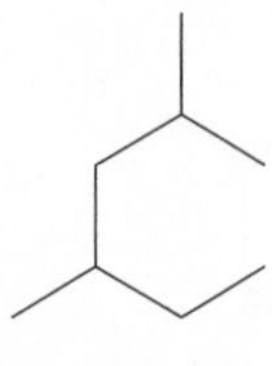

YOUR TURN **4.22**

SOLVED PROBLEM **4.5**

How to determine whether two structures are constitutional isomers

Break It Down **Are these two molecules constitutional isomers of each other?**

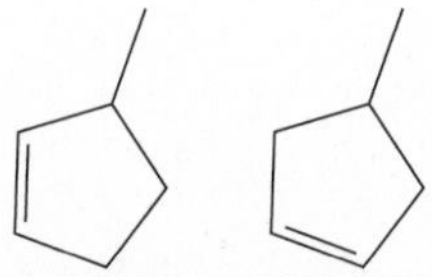

Think	Solve
Do both compounds have the same molecular formula?	Both compounds have a molecular formula of C_6H_{10}. Therefore, if the connectivities are different, they must be constitutional isomers.
Is the largest continuous chain or ring in each molecule the same? Are the C atoms that are involved in the double bonds assigned the same numbers in each molecule?	In each molecule, the largest continuous ring has five C atoms. As shown at the right, the numbers assigned to the doubly bonded C atoms are the same in each molecule. 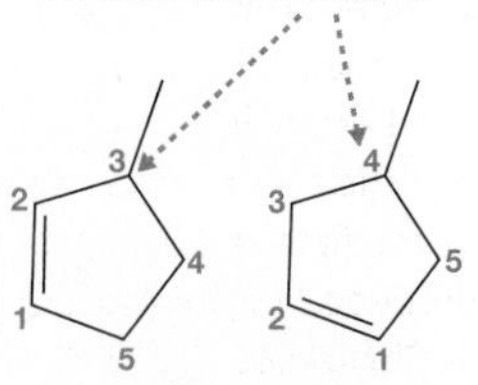 Methyl groups attached to different carbons 1 2 3 4 5 1 2 3 4 5
In each molecule, is the C atom to which the methyl group is attached assigned the same number?	The molecules differ in the number assigned to the C atom to which the methyl group is attached. In the first molecule, the methyl group is attached to C-3, whereas it is attached to C-4 in the second. Thus, the molecules have different connectivities, making them constitutional isomers.

Try It For each pair of molecules shown here, determine whether they are constitutional isomers.

(a)

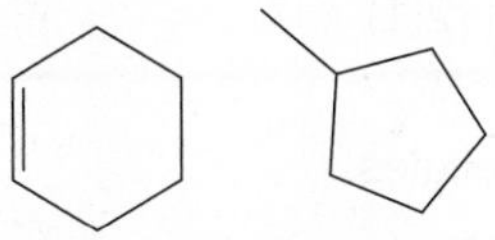

(b)

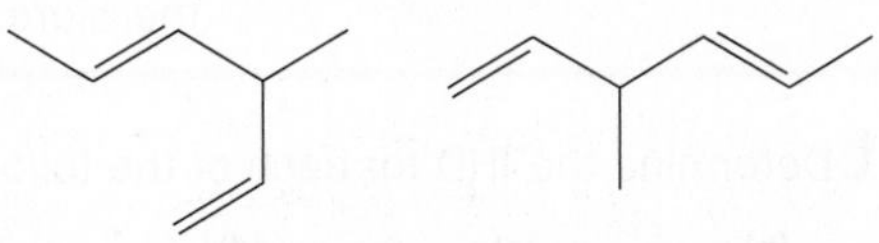

(c)

4.11 Constitutional Isomers: Index of Hydrogen Deficiency (Degree of Unsaturation)

SECTION 4.11 OBJECTIVES

You will be able to:

1. Determine the IHD of a molecule when given either the structure or a molecular formula.
2. Characterize a molecule as being saturated or unsaturated.

As we have seen, constitutional isomers have the same molecular formula. An important consequence of this requirement is that *constitutional isomers must have the same total number of π bonds and rings*, a number that is called the **index of hydrogen deficiency (IHD)** or the **degree of unsaturation**. For example, each of the three constitutional isomers in **Figure 4-37** (next page) has an IHD of 5, although they have very different connectivities.

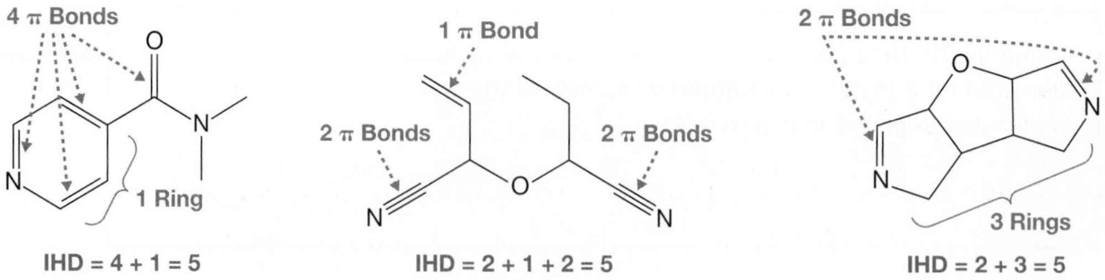
4 π Bonds
O
N
N
1 Ring
IHD = 4 + 1 = 5
1 π Bond
2 π Bonds
2 π Bonds
N
O
N
IHD = 2 + 1 + 2 = 5
2 π Bonds
O
N
N
3 Rings
IHD = 2 + 3 = 5

FIGURE 4-37 Constitutional isomers of $C_8H_{10}N_2O$ For each of the three molecules, the IHD is 5.

As we will see in Section 4.12, knowing that constitutional isomers must have the same IHD is quite useful when it comes to drawing constitutional isomers. You should therefore take the time to work through Solved Problem 4.6 and the corresponding Try It exercise.

SOLVED PROBLEM **4.6**

How to determine the IHD of a molecule from its structure

Break It Down What is the IHD of naphthalene?

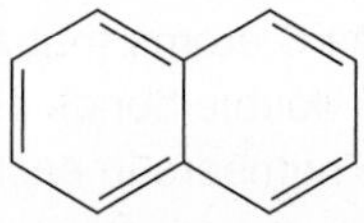

Naphthalene

Think	Solve
How many π bonds are there? How many rings are there?	There are five π bonds, one in each of the five C═C double bonds. There are two rings.
How much does each π bond and ring contribute to the overall IHD?	Each π bond contributes 1 to the IHD, and each ring contributes 1. The total IHD, therefore, is 5(1) + 2(1) = 7.

Try It Determine the IHD for each of the following molecules.

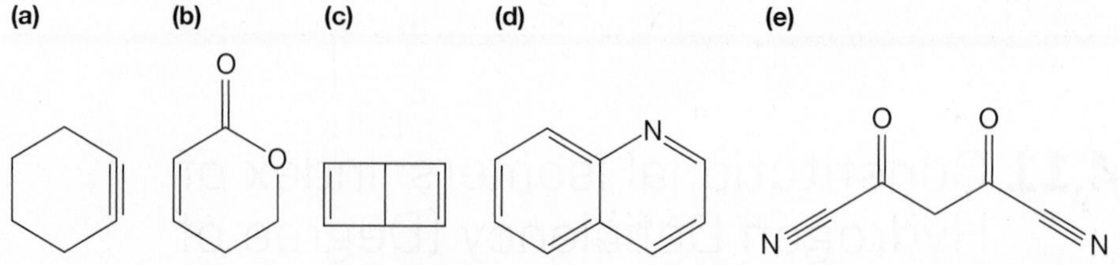
(a)
(b)
(c)
(d)
(e)
O
O
N
O
O
N
N

Why should constitutional isomers have the same IHD? Fundamentally, it is because the presence of each π bond or ring requires an additional bond between two non-hydrogen atoms, which uses up two bonds (one from each non-hydrogen atom) that could otherwise be used to attach hydrogens. This means that *each unit of IHD in a molecule reduces the number of hydrogen atoms by two*, as shown in **Figure 4-38**.

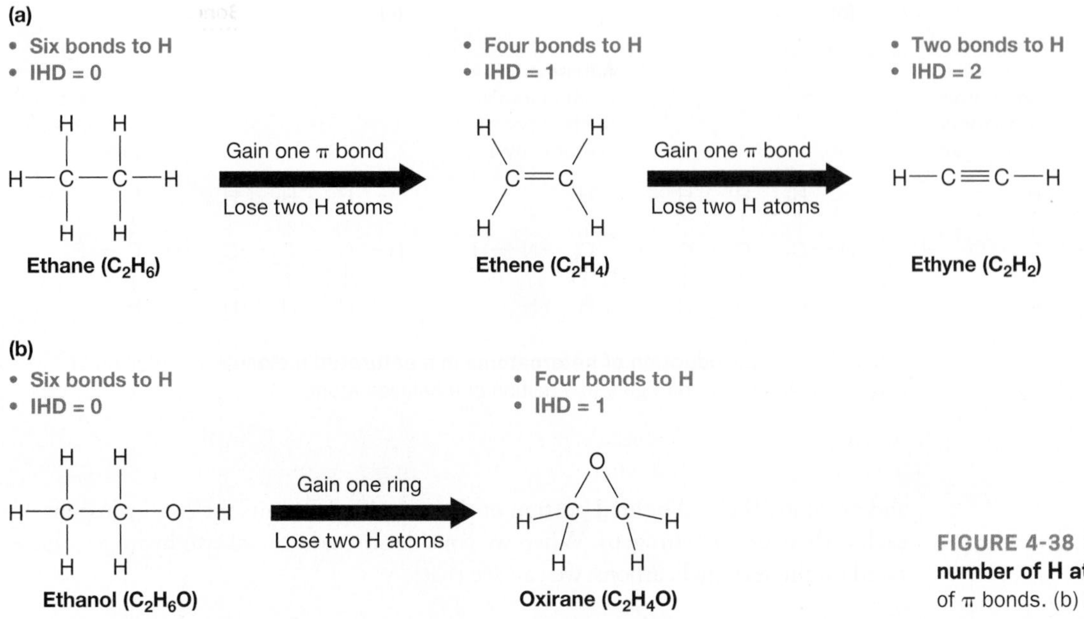
(a)
• Six bonds to H
• IHD = 0
Gain one π bond
Lose two H atoms
• Four bonds to H
• IHD = 1
Gain one π bond
Lose two H atoms
• Two bonds to H
• IHD = 2
Ethane (C_2H_6)
Ethene (C_2H_4)
Ethyne (C_2H_2)
(b)
• Six bonds to H
• IHD = 0
Gain one ring
Lose two H atoms
• Four bonds to H
• IHD = 1
Ethanol (C_2H_6O)
Oxirane (C_2H_4O)

FIGURE 4-38 Impact of IHD on the number of H atoms (a) Introduction of π bonds. (b) Introduction of a ring.

With this in mind, suppose we begin with a molecule for which IHD = 0; it would have the maximum number of H atoms possible, making it **saturated**. If π bonds or rings are introduced in various ways, the resulting molecules will be **unsaturated** because they have fewer than the maximum possible number of H atoms. As long as the unsaturated molecules have the same IHD, the same number of H atoms would have to be removed from the saturated molecule (two H atoms for each unit of IHD). After removal of those hydrogens, the unsaturated molecules would be left with the same number of hydrogens and would therefore have the same molecular formula.

Knowing that each unit of IHD corresponds to the removal of two H atoms from a saturated molecule, we can determine IHD from a molecular formula rather than from a completed molecular structure:

> The IHD of a given molecular formula is half the number of H atoms missing from the molecular formula of an analogous (same number and type of each non-hydrogen atom) saturated molecule.

How, then, do we determine the number of hydrogens in an analogous saturated molecule? One method has us focus on patterns that relate the number of hydrogens in a saturated molecule to the number of carbons, nitrogens, oxygens, and halogens appearing in the formula. Consider, for example, the Lewis structure of an alkane with n carbons, shown in **Figure 4-39**. The molecule is saturated because it has no π bonds

CONNECTIONS 4.6

Oxirane and its uses Oxirane (Fig. 4-38b) is used as a reactant in a wide variety of organic reactions, including the production of ethylene glycol (a component of some brands of antifreeze for your car) and acrylonitrile (used to make the plastic polyacrylonitrile). Oxirane is also used in the health-care industry to sterilize medical devices.

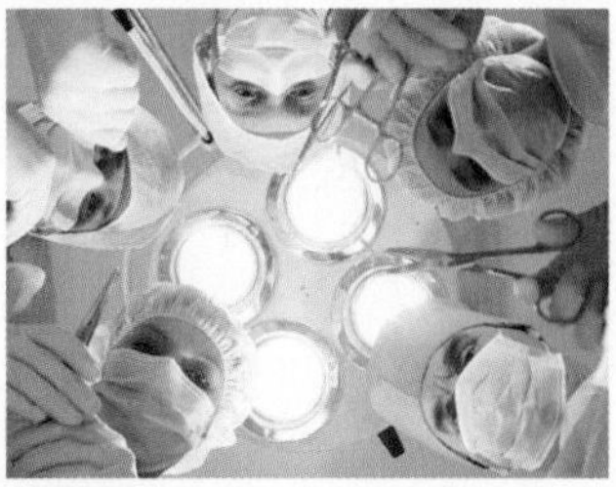

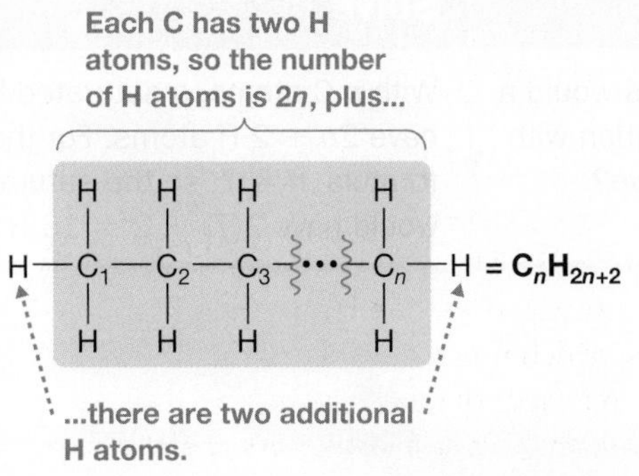
Each C has two H atoms, so the number of H atoms is 2n, plus...
= C_nH_{2n+2}
...there are two additional H atoms.

FIGURE 4-39 Molecular formula of a saturated hydrocarbon

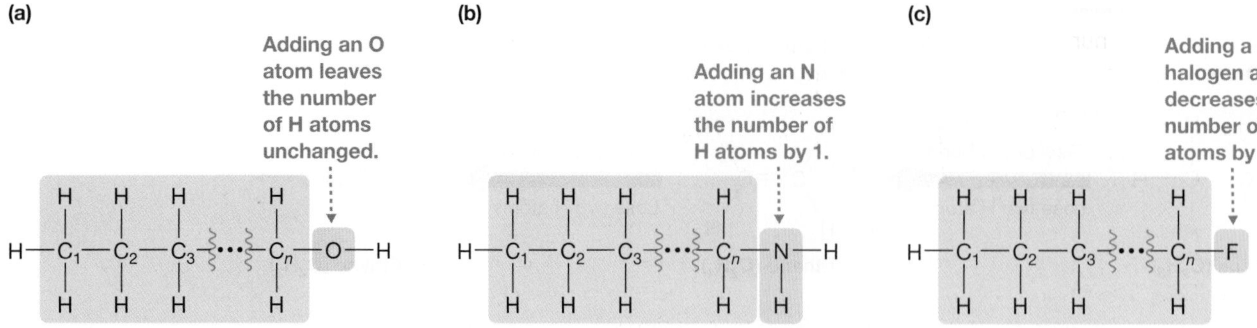
(a)
Adding an O atom leaves the number of H atoms unchanged.
(b)
Adding an N atom increases the number of H atoms by 1.
(c)
Adding a halogen atom decreases the number of H atoms by 1.

FIGURE 4-40 Introduction of heteroatoms in a saturated molecule (a) Addition of oxygen. (b) Addition of nitrogen. (c) Addition of a halogen atom.

and no rings. The highlighted portion of the structure accounts for two hydrogens on each carbon, or $2n$ hydrogens. When we consider the additional two hydrogens indicated on the terminal carbons, we can see that:

A saturated hydrocarbon with n carbons has $2n + 2$ hydrogens, giving it the formula C_nH_{2n+2}.

Now consider how the value of $2n + 2$ changes when oxygen, nitrogen, or halogen atoms are inserted into the Lewis structure of a saturated hydrocarbon. **Figure 4-40a** shows that when an oxygen is added, the number of hydrogen atoms does not change; Figure 4-40b shows that the addition of a nitrogen atom increases the number of hydrogens by 1; and Figure 4-40c shows that the addition of a halogen atom reduces the number by 1.

The lessons from Figures 4-39 and 4-40 can be summarized as follows:

The number of hydrogen atoms in a saturated molecule with n carbons is:

$$\text{\# of H atoms} = 2n + 2 + (\text{\# of N atoms}) - (\text{\# of halogen atoms}) \quad (4\text{-}3)$$

To see how Equation 4-3 is applied toward determining the IHD of a molecular formula, study Solved Problem 4.7 and then work through the Try It exercise.

SOLVED PROBLEM **4.7**

How to determine the IHD of a given molecular formula

Break It Down **Determine the IHD for a compound whose molecular formula is $C_7H_8NO_2Cl_3$.**

Think	Solve
How many H atoms would a saturated hydrocarbon with seven C atoms have?	With n C atoms, a saturated hydrocarbon would have $2n + 2$ H atoms. For the given molecular formula, $n = 7$, so the saturated hydrocarbon would have $2(7) + 2 = 16$ H atoms.

(continued)

How should that number of H atoms be adjusted for each O, N or halogen atom?	Adding O atoms does not change the number of H atoms. Each N atom increases the number by 1 and each halogen decreases the number by 1. Therefore, the number of H atoms in the saturated molecule is $16 + 1 - 3 = 14$ H atoms.
How many H atoms in the given molecular formula are missing from an analogous saturated molecule? How does that number correspond to the IHD?	The given molecular formula has eight H atoms, which is six fewer than in the 14 H atoms in the analogous saturated molecule. The IHD is half the number of missing H atoms, so IHD $= \frac{6}{2} = 3$.

Try It Compute the IHD for a compound whose molecular formula is $C_4N_2OH_7F$.

4.12 Strategies for Success: Drawing All Constitutional Isomers of a Given Formula

SECTION 4.12 OBJECTIVES

You will be able to:

1. Use a systematic method to draw various constitutional isomers of a given molecular formula.
2. Avoid redundancies when drawing constitutional isomers.

Strategies for Success Drawing All Constitutional Isomers of a Given Formula

Being able to draw all constitutional isomers of a given molecular formula can be useful, especially when you are trying to determine a compound's structure using results from spectroscopy (Chapters 16 and 17). More immediately, however, the exercise of drawing constitutional isomers will deepen your understanding of connectivity; it is particularly important to be able to work comfortably with the idea of connectivity before we delve into the isomers in Chapter 5 that involve other types of relationships.

It helps to have a systematic method to tackle these kinds of problems. Here we present one method, and you may even develop your own:

Drawing Constitutional Isomers of a Given Formula

1. Determine the formula's IHD. This will tell you the possible combinations of double bonds, triple bonds, and rings required in each isomer you draw.
2. Draw all possible backbones. Omit double bonds, triple bonds, and halogen atoms. (It is most convenient to work with line structures so that the H atoms are accounted for appropriately when features are added in Steps 3 and 4.)
   - Double bonds, triple bonds, and halogen atoms will be added later.
   - Include rings. The number of rings must not exceed the IHD calculated in Step 1.
3. Add double or triple bonds. For each structure generated in Step 2, add double or triple bonds to satisfy the total IHD calculated in Step 1. Try to add the multiple bonds at various locations to generate as many unique connectivities as possible.
4. Add halogens. For each structure generated in Step 3, add halogen atoms at various locations to generate as many unique connectivities as possible.

How we apply these steps depends specifically on the nature of the formula we are given. We present two examples in Sections 4.12a and 4.12b.

4.12a Drawing All Constitutional Isomers of $C_4H_8F_2$

Let's draw all possible constitutional isomers having the formula $C_4H_8F_2$. For Step 1, we determine the IHD of the formula to be 0. That means that every constitutional isomer we draw must have *no double bonds*, *no triple bonds*, and *no rings*.

YOUR TURN **4.23**

Verify that the IHD is 0 for the formula $C_4H_8F_2$.

Steps 2 through 4 are shown in **Figure 4-41**. Make sure to work your way through those steps, progressing left to right. As you do, notice the following aspects:

- We skip Step 3 because the IHD is 0, so no double or triple bonds can be added.
- We split Step 4 into two stages, adding one F atom (red) in the first stage and the other F atom (blue) in the second stage.
- When the first F atom is added in Step 4, we add it only to C-1 or C-2 because adding the F atom to the other C atoms would result in redundant structures.
- When we add the second F atom to the various C atoms in structures **C** through **F**, four unique connectivities (and thus four constitutional isomers) result from structure **C**, two from **D**, three from **E**, and none from **F**. Thus, there are nine constitutional isomers: **G, H, I, J, L, M, O, P,** and **Q**.

4.12b Drawing All Constitutional Isomers of C_3H_6O

Let's now consider the formula C_3H_6O. For Step 1, we determine the IHD to be 1, so every isomer must have one double bond or one ring.

YOUR TURN **4.24**

Verify that the IHD is 1 for the formula C_3H_6O.

Similar to the previous example, Steps 2 through 4 are carried out in **Figure 4-42** (p. 194). Again, make sure to work your way through the figure, progressing left to right, and pay attention to the following aspects as you do:

- For Step 2, six backbones can have up to one ring to avoid exceeding an IHD of 1. Three of those backbones contain one ring: structures **A, B,** and **C**. Three backbones contain no rings: **D, E,** and **F**.
- For Step 3, we add a double bond in various locations to achieve the IHD of 1. We can add a double bond to structure **D** to produce structures **G, H,** and **I**, all of which have an IHD of 1. There is only one location to add a double bond in structure **E**, because a double bond involving the O atom would give three bonds to O, requiring a +1 formal charge. For structure **F**, we add the double bond to three locations to yield structures **K, L,** and **M**, but **L** is redundant with **K**.
- We skip Step 4 because there are no halogens. Therefore, there are nine constitutional isomers of C_3H_6O: **A, B, C, G, H, I, J, K,** and **M** (see Looking Ahead box).

▸ LOOKING AHEAD

Isomers **H** and **K** in Figure 4-42 fall into a class of compounds called *enols*. We explain in Section 7.10 that such molecules tend to be unstable and will undergo a rearrangement reaction in solution to form isomers that are more stable. In this case, **H** and **K** rearrange to **I** and **M**, respectively.

YOUR TURN **4.25**

Identify the functional groups present in *each* constitutional isomer of C_3H_6O in Figure 4-42.

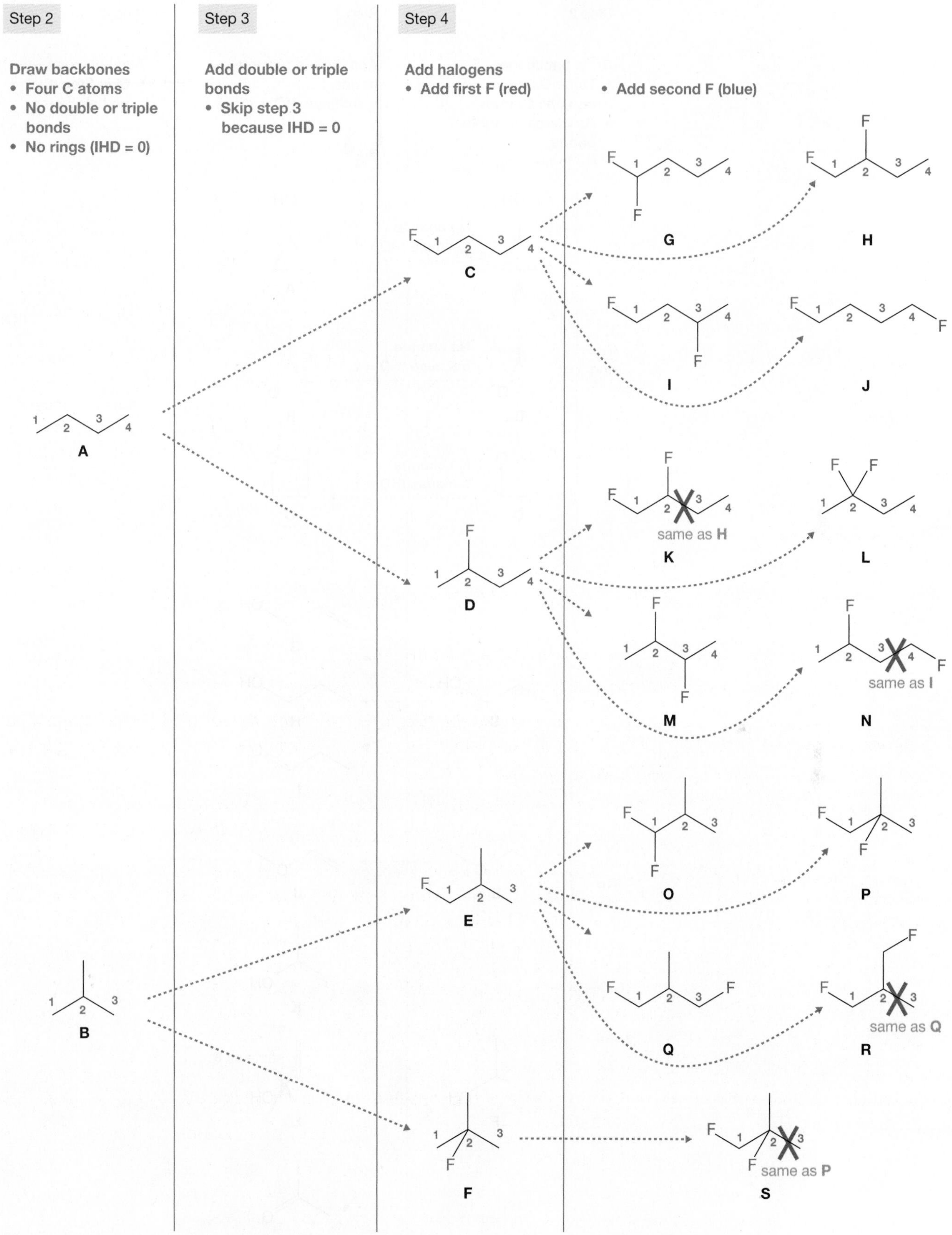

Step 2
Draw backbones
• Four C atoms
• No double or triple bonds
• No rings (IHD = 0)
Step 3
Add double or triple bonds
• Skip step 3 because IHD = 0
Step 4
Add halogens
• Add first F (red)
• Add second F (blue)
A
B
C
D
E
F
G
H
I
J
same as H
K
L
M
same as I
N
O
P
Q
same as Q
R
same as P
S

FIGURE 4-41 Drawing constitutional isomers of $C_4H_8F_2$

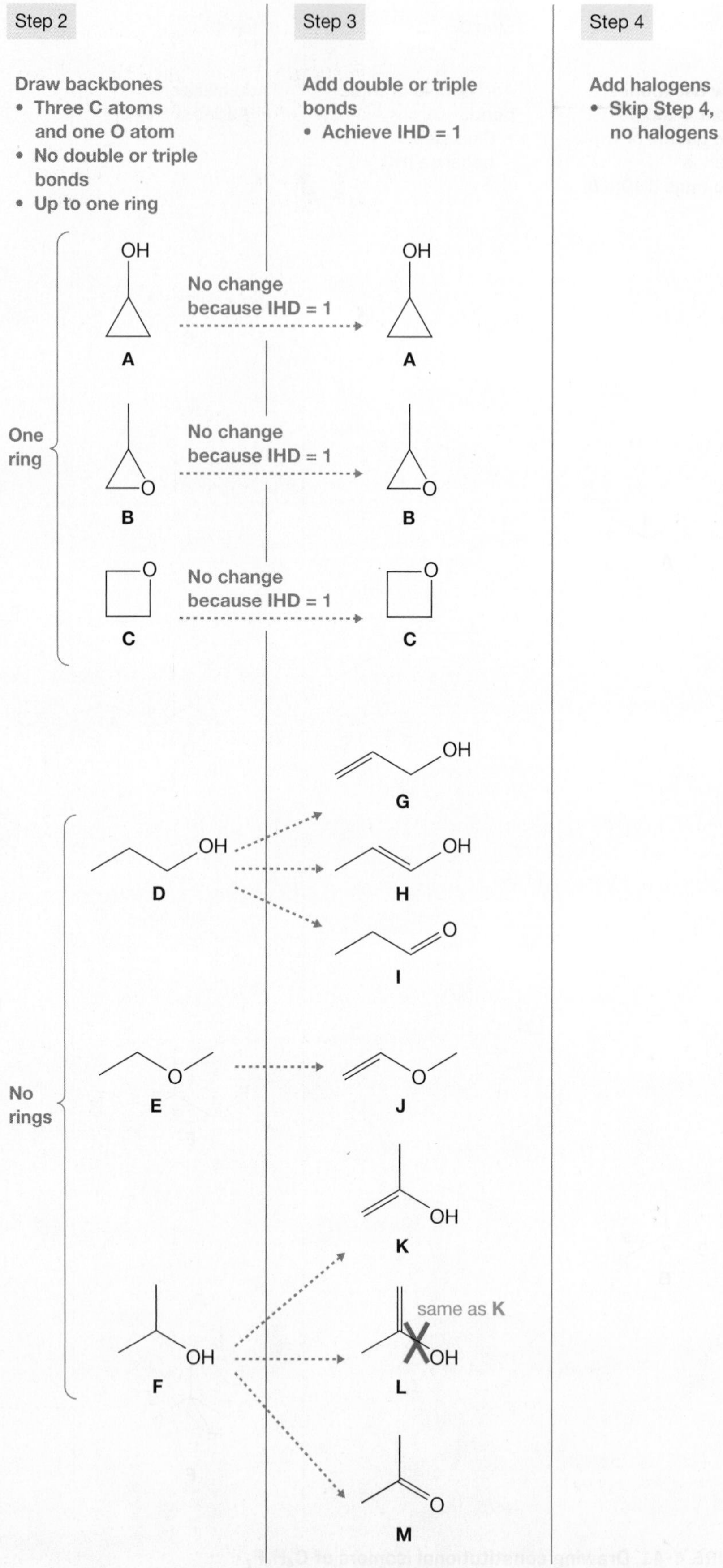
Step 2
Draw backbones
• Three C atoms and one O atom
• No double or triple bonds
• Up to one ring
Step 3
Add double or triple bonds
• Achieve IHD = 1
Step 4
Add halogens
• Skip Step 4, no halogens
One ring
OH
A
No change because IHD = 1
B
O
C
No rings
D
E
F
G
H
I
J
K
L
M
same as K

FIGURE 4-42 **Drawing constitutional isomers of C_3H_6O**

4.13 Constitutional Isomers and Biomolecules: Amino Acids and Monosaccharides

SECTION 4.13 OBJECTIVES

You will be able to:

1. Identify constitutional isomers of some amino acids and monosaccharides.
2. Characterize a monosaccharide as an aldose or pentose, and further distinguish it by the number of carbons it has.

A variety of biomolecules can exist as constitutional isomers. Leucine and isoleucine (**Figure 4-43**), for example, which are two naturally occurring amino acids, are constitutional isomers because they have the same molecular formula but differ in their connectivities. (The prefix *iso*, in fact, stands for "isomer.") Notice, in particular, that the only difference between the two molecules is in the location of a methyl group.

Monosaccharides provide many more examples of constitutional isomers. The cyclic and acyclic forms of ribose are constitutional isomers, for instance, as are the cyclic and acyclic forms of glucose (**Figure 4-44**).

Among the acyclic forms of monosaccharides, ribose and ribulose are constitutional isomers, as are glucose and fructose (**Figure 4-45**, next page). These isomers differ by the location of the carbonyl group (C═O). In ribose, for example, the carbonyl group involves a terminal carbon, characteristic of an aldehyde, whereas in ribulose, it involves an internal carbon, characteristic of a ketone. Thus, ribose is classified as an **aldose**, whereas ribulose is a **ketose**. Glucose is similarly classified as an aldose, whereas fructose is a ketose.

To further distinguish sugars on the basis of their carbon atoms, ribose and ribulose are **pentoses**, because they both contain five carbons, whereas glucose and fructose are **hexoses**, containing six carbons. Combining these terminologies, we say that ribose is an **aldopentose**, ribulose is a **ketopentose**, glucose is an **aldohexose**, and fructose is a **ketohexose**.

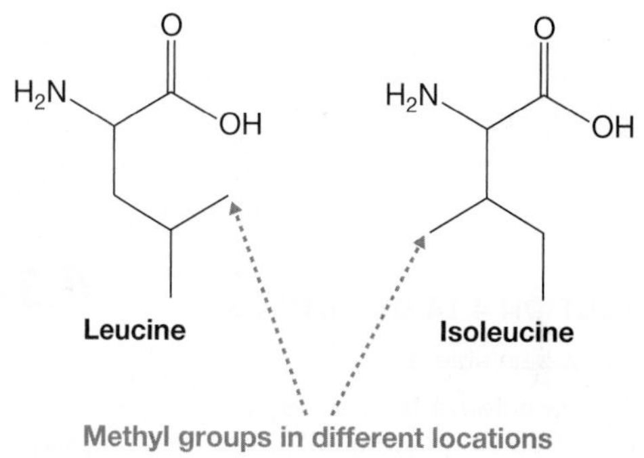

H2N
O
OH
Leucine
Isoleucine
Methyl groups in different locations

FIGURE 4-43 Isomeric amino acids Leucine and isoleucine are naturally occurring amino acids that have the same formula but different connectivities, so they are constitutional isomers.

YOUR TURN 4.26

Draw the Lewis structure of each of the following: **(a)** an aldotetrose; **(b)** a ketotetrose; **(c)** an aldotriose; **(d)** a ketotriose; **(e)** a ketohexose different from fructose. (*Hint*: You may wish to review the characteristics of monosaccharides in Section 1.14b.)

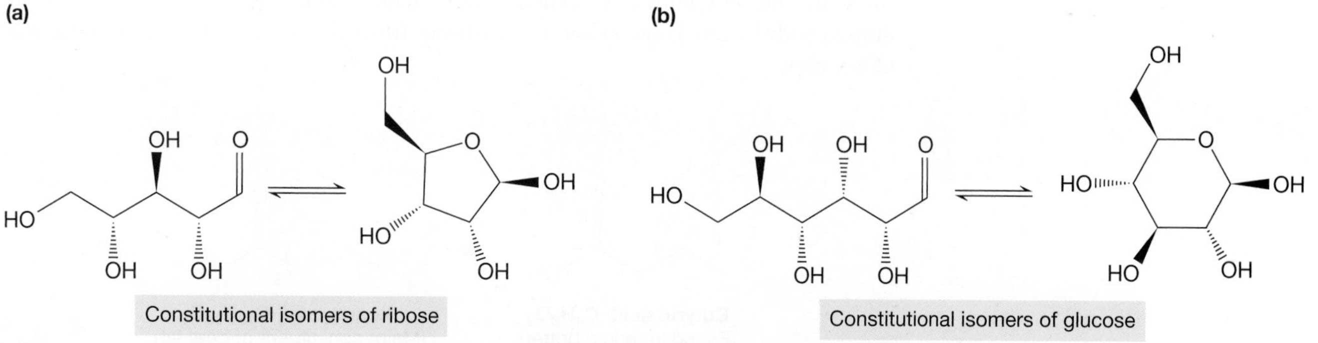

(a)
(b)
OH
O
HO
Constitutional isomers of ribose
Constitutional isomers of glucose

FIGURE 4-44 Acyclic and cyclic forms of sugars as constitutional isomers (a) Acyclic and cyclic ribose have the same formula ($C_5H_{10}O_5$) but different connectivities. (b) Acyclic and cyclic glucose have the same formula ($C_6H_{12}O_6$) but different connectivities.

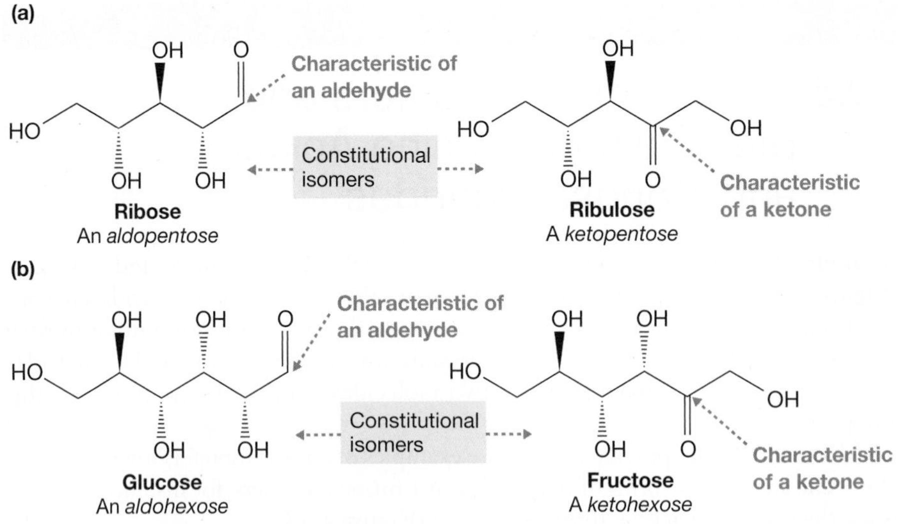
(a)
OH
O
Characteristic of an aldehyde
HO
OH
OH
Ribose
An aldopentose
Constitutional isomers
OH
HO
OH
OH
O
Ribulose
A ketopentose
Characteristic of a ketone
(b)
OH
OH
O
Characteristic of an aldehyde
HO
OH
OH
Glucose
An aldohexose
Constitutional isomers
OH
OH
HO
OH
OH
O
Fructose
A ketohexose
Characteristic of a ketone

FIGURE 4-45 Acyclic sugars as constitutional isomers (a) Ribose and ribulose have the same formula ($C_5H_{10}O_5$) but different connectivities. (b) Glucose and fructose have the same formula ($C_6H_{12}O_6$) but different connectivities.

SECTION 4.14 OBJECTIVES

You will be able to:

1. Characterize fatty acids as saturated or unsaturated.
2. Predict the relative melting points of fatty acids from the number of cis double bonds they possess.

4.14 Saturation and Unsaturation in Fats and Oils

Diets high in saturated fats, typically of animal origin, are generally regarded as unhealthy because they increase the risk of coronary heart disease. Conversely, unsaturated fats, typically derived from plants, are a healthy part of our diets.

The concepts of saturation and unsaturation apply to the hydrocarbon chains of fats and oils in the same way they do to other organic compounds (see Section 4.11). That is, each C=C double bond that is present adds 1 unit of unsaturation (or IHD) to the molecule. Thus, fats that contain fatty acids such as butyric acid or stearic acid (**Figure 4-46**) are *saturated*, because they contain no C=C double bonds, whereas fats that contain oleic, linoleic, or linolenic acids (**Figure 4-47**) are *unsaturated*, because these fatty acids have one or more C=C double bonds.

We can distinguish the extent of unsaturation from the number of C=C double bonds present. For example, oleic acid is a **monounsaturated** fatty acid, because it has just one C=C double bond, whereas linolenic acid is a **polyunsaturated** fatty acid, because it has three.

Linoleic and linolenic acids are further classified as **essential fatty acids** because these are the only naturally occurring fatty acids that cannot be synthesized in the human body by any known chemical pathway. Instead, they must be consumed as part of our diet.

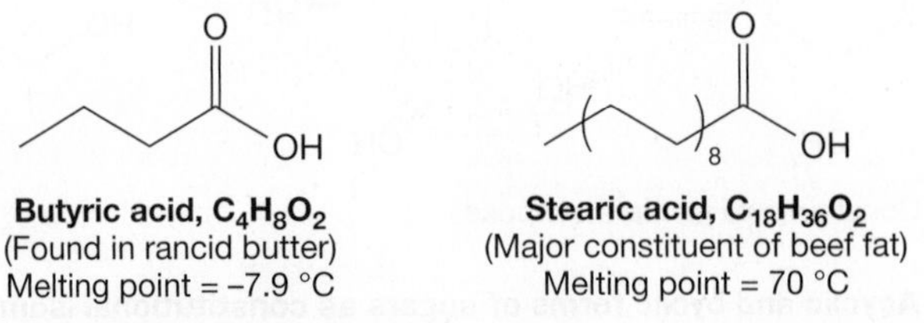
O
OH
Butyric acid, $C_4H_8O_2$
(Found in rancid butter)
Melting point = −7.9 °C
O
8
OH
Stearic acid, $C_{18}H_{36}O_2$
(Major constituent of beef fat)
Melting point = 70 °C

FIGURE 4-46 Saturated fatty acids Butyric acid and stearic acid are saturated fatty acids because they contain the maximum possible number of hydrogen atoms in their hydrocarbon chains. In stearic acid, the two-carbon component appearing in parentheses is repeated eight times.

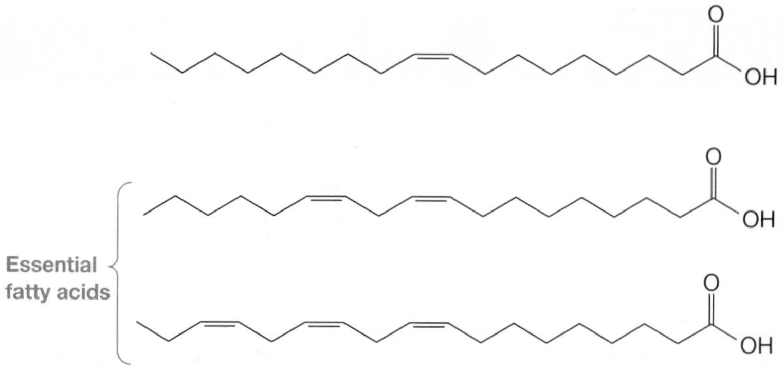

O
OH
Essential
fatty acids

Oleic acid, $C_{18}H_{34}O_2$
(Major constituent of olive oil)
Melting point = 16 °C

Linoleic acid, $C_{18}H_{32}O_2$
(Major constituent of safflower oil)
Melting point = −7 °C

Linolenic acid, $C_{18}H_{30}O_2$
(Major constituent of flaxseed oil)
Melting point = −11 °C

FIGURE 4-47 Unsaturated fatty acids Oleic acid, linoleic acid, and linolenic acid are unsaturated fatty acids because they contain units of unsaturation (i.e., C═C bonds) in their carbon chains.

The different health effects of saturated and unsaturated fats seem to correlate with their different physical properties. Namely:

> Each cis C═C double bond (**Figure 4-48**) that is present in a fatty acid lowers the melting point.

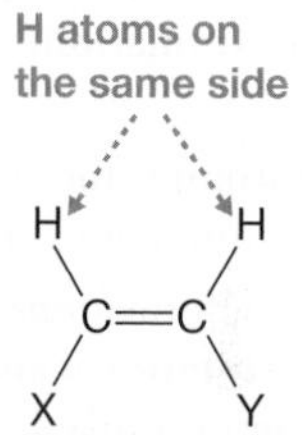

H atoms on
the same side
H
H
C═C
X
Y

FIGURE 4-48 A cis double bond

Notice, in particular, that stearic acid, a saturated fatty acid, melts at 70 °C, well *above* room temperature (~25 °C), and is therefore a solid under normal conditions. By contrast, oleic (16 °C), linoleic (−7 °C), and linolenic acids (−11 °C) melt well *below* room temperature and are therefore liquids, despite having the same number of carbon atoms as stearic acid.

The number of double bonds affects the melting points of these compounds because all C═C double bonds found in naturally occurring fatty acids are cis. Thus, each double bond introduces a kink in the carbon chain, as shown for oleic acid in **Figure 4-49**. Such a kink makes it more difficult for separate fatty acid molecules to align, so the contact surface area among the molecules is decreased. In turn, this weakens the induced dipole–induced dipole interactions (Section 2.6d), resulting in a lower melting point.

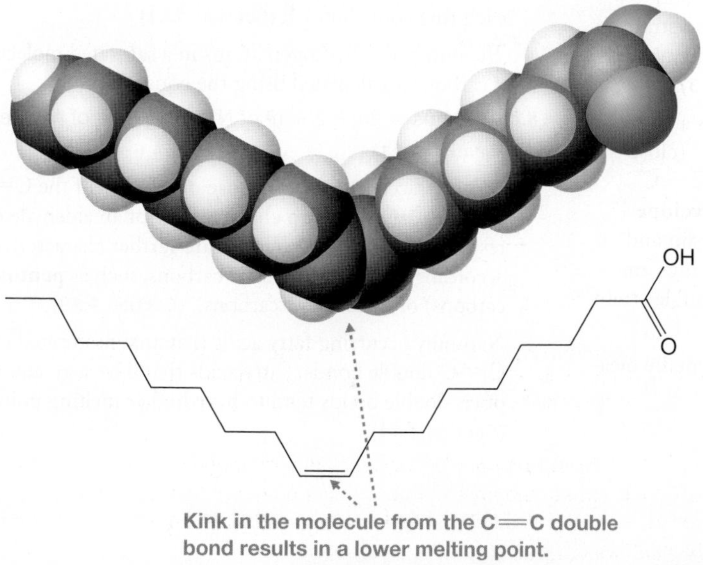

OH
O
Kink in the molecule from the C═C double
bond results in a lower melting point.

FIGURE 4-49 Space-filling model of oleic acid A cis double bond introduces a kink in the carbon chain of a naturally occurring fatty acid such as oleic acid. Kinks decrease the contact surface area among separate fatty acid molecules, which reduces the strength of their intermolecular interactions and thus decreases the melting point.

Chapter Summary and Key Terms

- Isomerism is a relationship between two or more molecular species. Molecules are **isomers** of each other if they have the same molecular formula but are different in some way.
- **Conformers** differ by rotations about single bonds, whereas **constitutional isomers** have different connectivities. (Sections 4.1 and 4.10)
- **Newman projections** are used to show conformations about bonds. They depict the view down a bonding axis. The atom in front is represented as a point and the atom in back is represented as a circle. (Section 4.1)
- In a **conformational analysis** of ethane, energy is plotted as a function of the H—C—C—H **dihedral angle (θ)**. In a 360° rotation, we observe three equivalent **staggered conformations**, each at an energy minimum, and three equivalent **eclipsed conformations**, each at an energy maximum. (Section 4.2a)
- **Torsional strain** is the energy increase that appears in an eclipsed conformation. (Section 4.2a)
- Staggered conformations in ethane rapidly interconvert because the **rotational energy barrier** is comparable to the **thermal energy** available. (Section 4.2a)
- Based on conformational analysis of $BrCH_2—CH_2Br$, one staggered conformation, called the **anti conformation**, is lower in energy than the other two, called **gauche conformations**. Energy differences arise due to differences in **steric strain**. Similarly, one eclipsed conformation is higher in energy than the other two. (Section 4.2b)
- Although the anti conformation is more stable than the gauche, the two conformers rapidly interconvert because the energy barrier between them is comparable to the available thermal energy. (Section 4.2b)
- The lowest-energy conformation of an alkyl chain is the **zigzag** or **all-anti conformation**, which has the anti conformation at each C—C bond. (Section 4.2c)
- Cyclohexane (a six-membered ring) has essentially no **ring strain**. Cyclopentane and cycloheptane (five- and seven-membered rings, respectively) have mild ring strain. Cyclopropane and cyclobutane (three- and four-membered rings, respectively) are highly strained. (Section 4.3)
- Cyclohexane has no ring strain because it adopts a **chair conformation**, in which all angles are about 111° (close to the ideal tetrahedral angle of 109.5°) and all C—C bonds are staggered. Cyclopentane adopts an **envelope conformation**, which has slightly more angle strain and torsional strain. Cyclobutane and cyclopropane rings are highly strained due to substantial torsional and angle strain. (Section 4.3)
- Ring strain values can be obtained from experimentally measured **heats of combustion**. (Section 4.4)
- Chair conformations of cyclohexane interconvert via **chair flips**, which involve partial single-bond rotations about the C—C bonds of the ring. (Section 4.5)
- In each chair conformation of cyclohexane, one hydrogen atom on each carbon is in an **axial** position and one is in an **equatorial** position. The two positions interconvert during a chair flip. (Section 4.5)
- The two chair conformations of a **monosubstituted cyclohexane** are no longer equivalent. Because the substituent is larger than the hydrogen atoms, the cyclohexane ring is more stable with the substituent in an equatorial position, where there is more room. (Section 4.7)
- The bulkier a substituent is, the greater its tendency to occupy an equatorial position. A *tert*-butyl group, $C(CH_3)_3$, is so bulky that it is almost exclusively found in an equatorial position. (Section 4.7)
- **Disubstituted** cyclohexanes introduce cis and trans relationships relative to the plane of the ring. **Haworth projections** illustrate cis and trans relationships well, but they do not accurately convey three-dimensional relationships or steric strain because they portray the cyclohexane ring as planar. (Section 4.8)
- The more stable chair conformation of a disubstituted cyclohexane is the one in which the substituents experience the least amount of strain. This usually calls for the larger substituent to occupy an equatorial position. (Section 4.8)
- Molecular modeling kits effectively demonstrate the changes that occur during a chair flip. (Section 4.9)
- A molecule's **index of hydrogen deficiency (IHD)**, also called its **degree of unsaturation**, is half the number of hydrogen atoms missing from that molecule compared to an analogous completely *saturated* molecule. A **saturated** molecule has an IHD of 0 and therefore has the most possible hydrogen atoms given the non-hydrogen atoms it contains. (Section 4.11)
- A molecule with π bonds or rings is **unsaturated**. Each π bond a molecule possesses contributes 1 to its IHD, and each ring contributes 1. (Section 4.11)
- The number of hydrogen atoms in a saturated molecule with n carbons is calculated using the equation:

$$\text{\# of H atoms} = 2n + 2 + (\text{\# of N atoms}) - (\text{\# of halogen atoms})$$

(Section 4.11)

- A monosaccharide is an **aldose** or a **ketose** if the C=O bond is part of a group characteristic of an aldehyde or ketone, respectively. Monosaccharides are further characterized according to their number of carbons, such as **pentose** (five carbons) or **hexose** (six carbons). (Section 4.13)
- Naturally occurring fatty acids that are unsaturated contain cis C=C double bonds. Fatty acids that have a greater number of cis double bonds tend to have higher melting points. (Section 4.14)

Problems

Section 4.1 Rotational Conformations, Newman Projections, and Dihedral Angles

4.1 Draw the Newman projection for each of the following species, looking down the bond that is indicated in red.

(a)

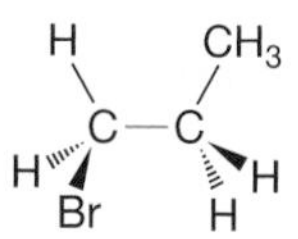

(b)

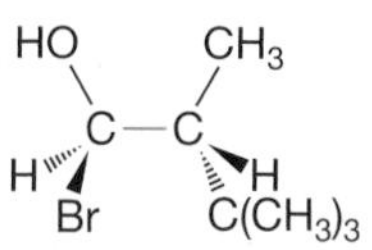

(c)

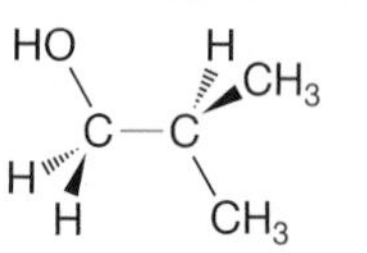

(d)

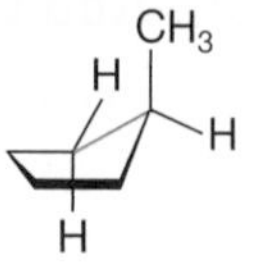

(e)

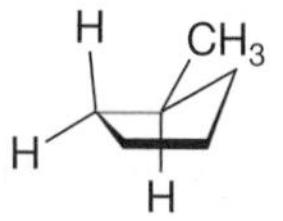

(f)

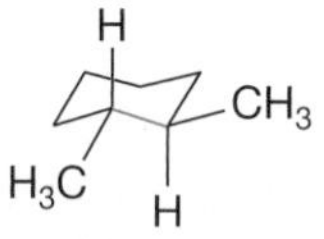

(g)

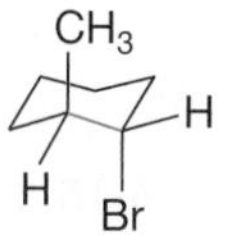

(h)

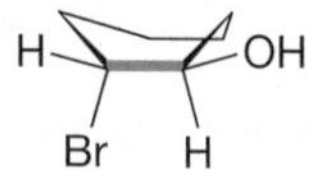

4.2 Draw the corresponding dash–wedge structure for each of the following Newman projections.

(a)

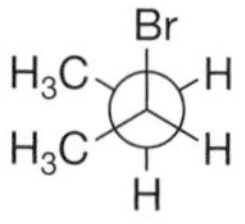

(b)

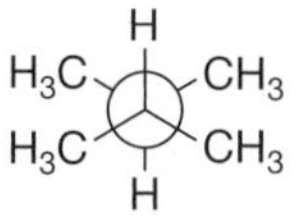

(c)

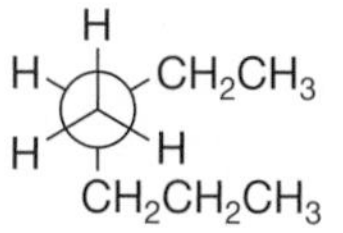

(d)

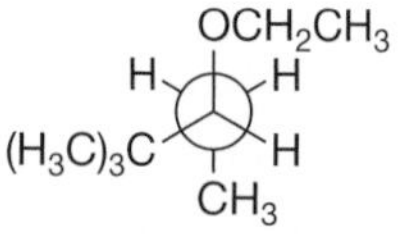

4.3 Identify which C—H bonds are axial and which are equatorial in the following Newman projection for cyclohexane.

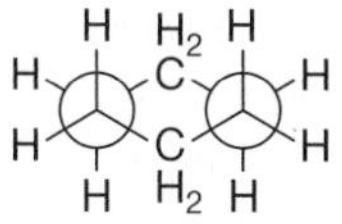

4.4 **(a)** Draw the Newman projection for each molecule shown here, looking down the C—C bond indicated by the arrow. **(b)** Which configuration do you think is more stable? Explain.

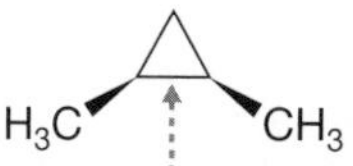

***cis*-1,2-Dimethylcyclopropane**

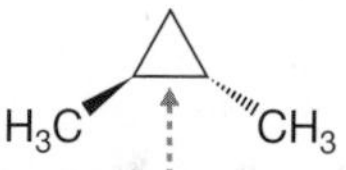

***trans*-1,2-Dimethylcyclopropane**

Section 4.2 Energy Changes and Conformational Analysis

4.5 Rank conformations **A–F** in order from least stable to most stable.

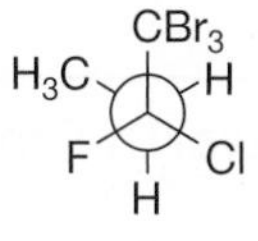

A

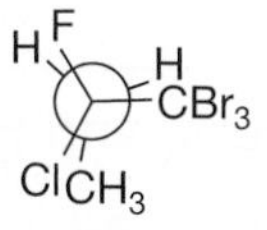

B

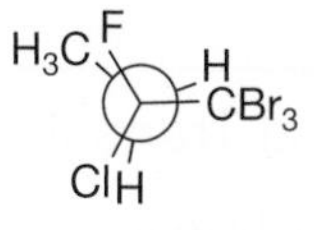

C

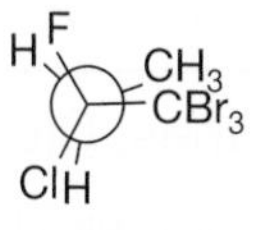

D

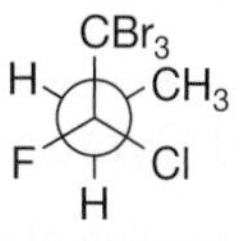

E

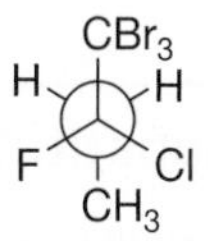

F

4.6 Perform a conformational analysis of 1,2-dichloroethane ($ClCH_2—CH_2Cl$) by sketching its energy as a function of the dihedral angle about the C—C bond. Make sure the *relative* energies are correct, but do not concern yourself with the exact values. *Hint*: First draw Newman projections for each staggered and eclipsed conformation encountered during the 360° rotation, and identify the anti and gauche conformations.

4.7 Perform a conformational analysis of propane, $CH_3CH_2CH_3$. Pay attention to the relative energies of the various conformations, but do not concern yourself with the actual energy values.

4.8 Perform a conformational analysis of butane, $CH_3CH_2CH_2CH_3$, looking down the C-2—C-3 bond. Pay attention to the relative energies of the various conformations, but do not concern yourself with the actual energy values.

4.9 Perform a conformational analysis of 1-bromo-2-chloroethane, $BrCH_2CH_2Cl$. Pay attention to the relative energies of the various conformations, but do not concern yourself with the actual energy values.

4.10 Perform a conformational analysis of 2-methylbutane, $(CH_3)_2CHCH_2CH_3$, looking down the C-2—C-3 bond. Pay attention to the relative energies of the various conformations, but do not concern yourself with the actual energy values.

4.11 Perform a conformational analysis of 1,2-dibromo-1-fluoroethane, BrFCH—CH_2Br. Pay attention to the relative energies of the various conformations, but do not concern yourself with the actual energy values.

Sections 4.3–4.7 Ring Strain, Stable Conformations of Rings, and Chair Conformations of Monosubstituted Cyclohexanes

4.12 Rank compounds **A–E** in order from the least amount of ring strain to the greatest amount. You may assume that the strain for each ring is additive.

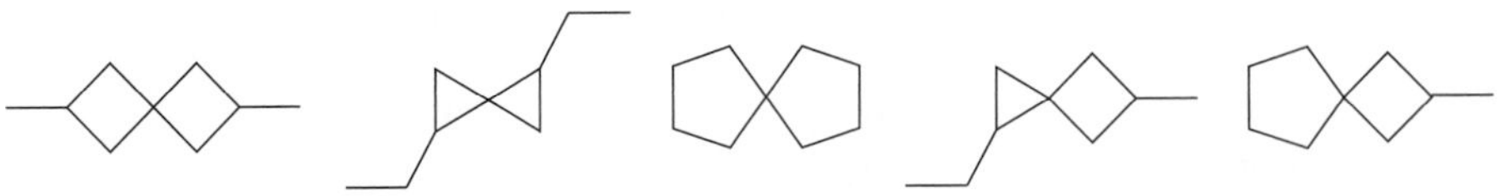

A B C D E

4.13 Rank compounds **F–I** in order from the least amount of ring strain to the greatest amount. You may assume that the strain for each ring is additive.

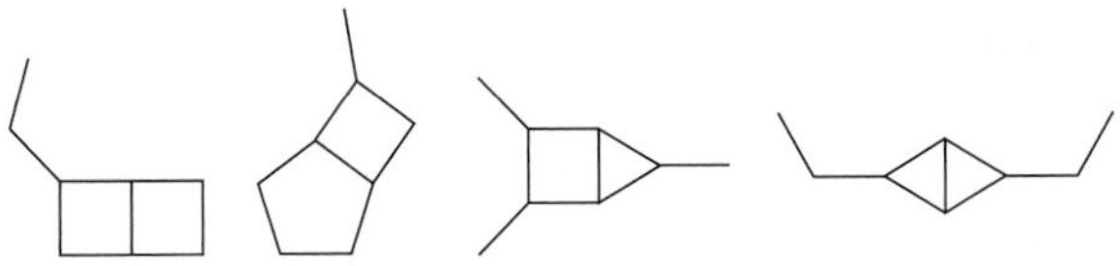

F G H I

4.14 There are three distinct chair conformations for cyclohexylcyclohexane. **(a)** Draw all three conformations and **(b)** determine which one is the most stable.

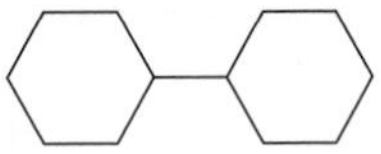

Cyclohexylcyclohexane

4.15 These two compounds are each in their more stable chair conformation. **(a)** Which occupies more space, a lone pair of electrons or a N—H bond? **(b)** Which occupies more space, a lone pair of electrons or a CH_3 group?

H
N
N
CH3

4.16 For which isomer would you expect a greater equilibrium percentage of molecules with the alkyl group in the axial position, isopropylcyclohexane or propylcyclohexane? Explain.

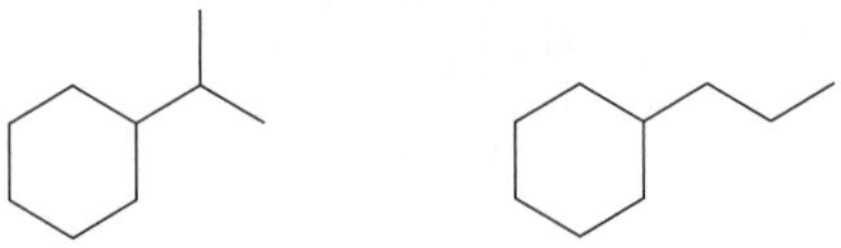

Isopropylcyclohexane **Propylcyclohexane**

4.17 Rank compounds **A–E** in Problem 4.12 in order from smallest heat of combustion to largest.

4.18 The heat of combustion of cyclononane is 5586 kJ/mol (1335 kcal/mol). Calculate the ring strain per CH_2 group and the total ring strain of cyclononane. Which compound has more ring strain, cyclononane or cycloheptane?

Section 4.8 Disubstituted Cyclohexanes, Cis and Trans Isomers, and Haworth Projections

4.19 Draw the most stable conformation of the molecule shown here.

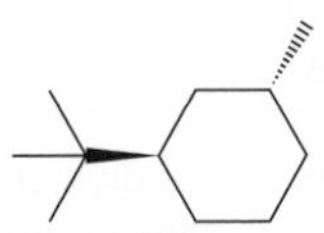

4.20 Draw the most stable conformation of *cis*-1-methyl-4-trichloromethylcyclohexane.

4.21 Draw the more stable chair conformation of each of the following molecules.

(a) (b) (c) (d) (e) (f) (g)

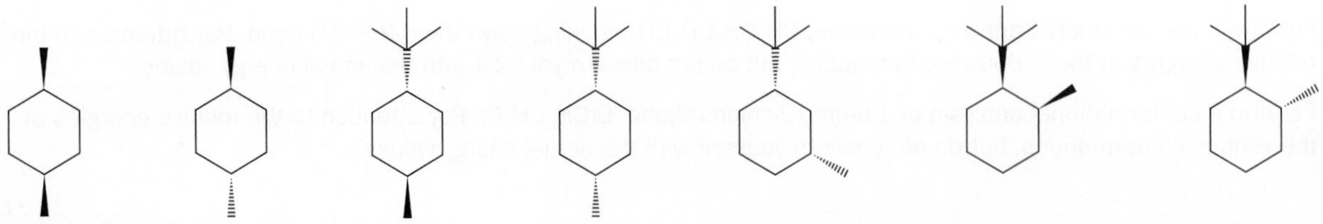

4.22 Draw a chair conformation of this molecule with **(a)** all CH_3 groups in axial positions and **(b)** all CH_3 groups in equatorial positions.

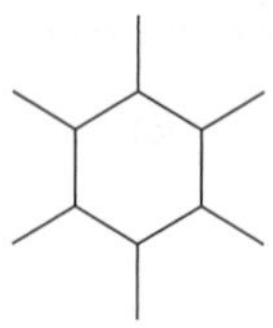

4.23 Identify each of the following disubstituted cyclohexanes as either a cis or a trans isomer.

(a)

Br
Cl

(b)

Br
CH3

(c)

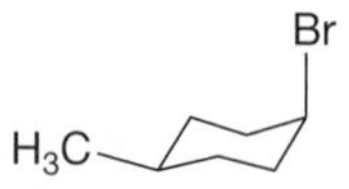
Br
H3C

(d)

Cl
CH3

(e)

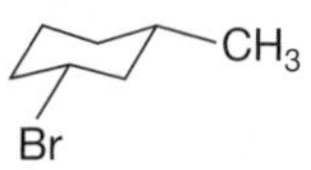
CH3
Br

(f)

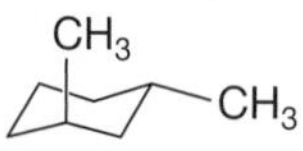
CH3
CH3

4.24 For each of the following disubstituted cyclohexanes, determine whether the cis or trans isomer is more stable.

(a)

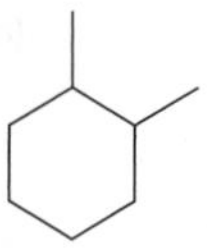

(b)

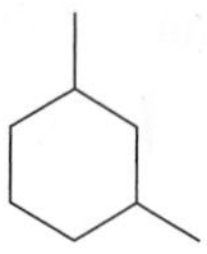

(c)

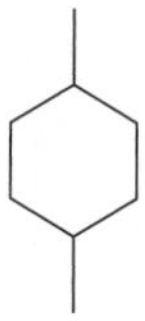

4.25 Both cis and trans isomers exist for this molecule. Which one is more stable?

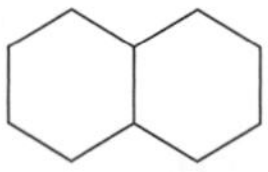

4.26 Draw the more stable chair conformation for each of the following disubstituted cyclohexanes.

(a)

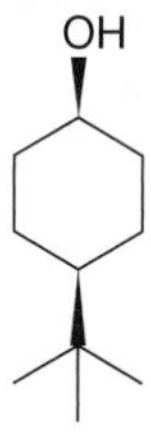
OH

(b)

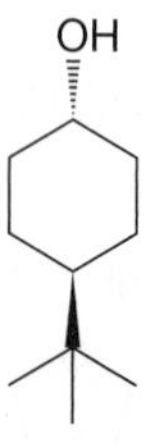
OH

(c)

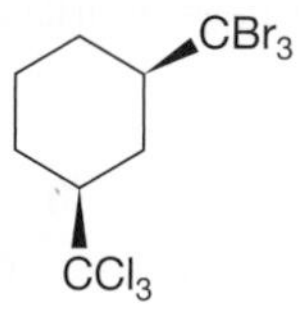
CBr3
CCl3

(d)

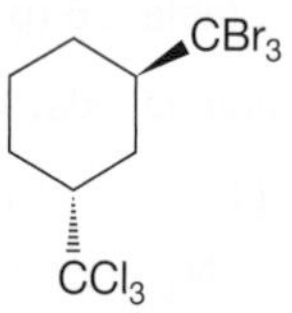
CBr3
CCl3

(e)

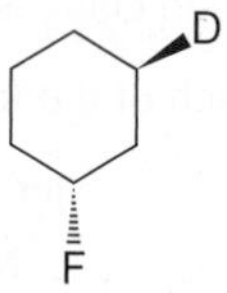
D
F

(f)

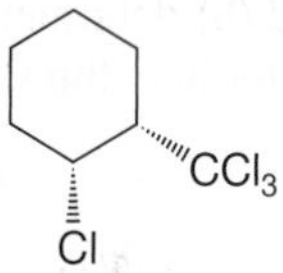
CCl3
Cl

Sections 4.10 and 4.11 Constitutional Isomers and Index of Hydrogen Deficiency

4.27 For each pair of molecules, determine whether they are constitutional isomers.

(a)

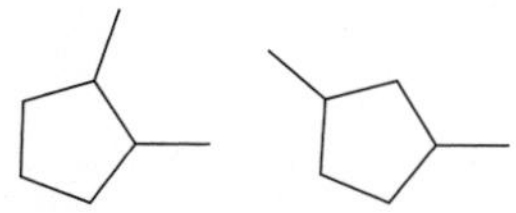

(b)

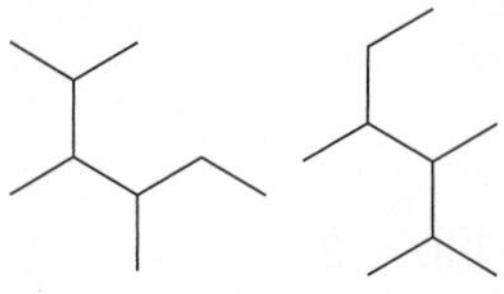

(c)

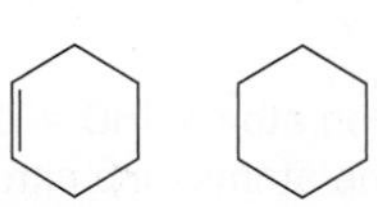

(d)

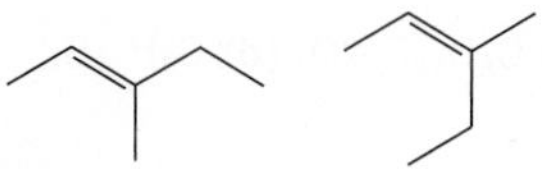

(e)

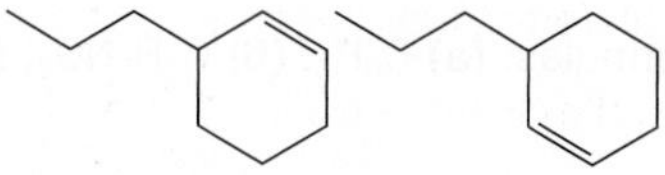

(f)

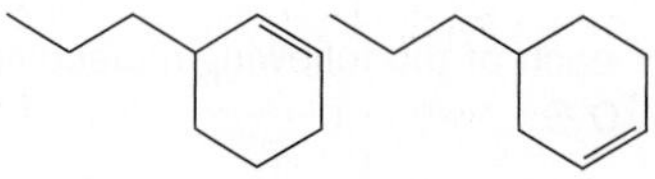

4.28 For each pair of molecules, determine whether they are constitutional isomers.

(a) (b) (c) (d)

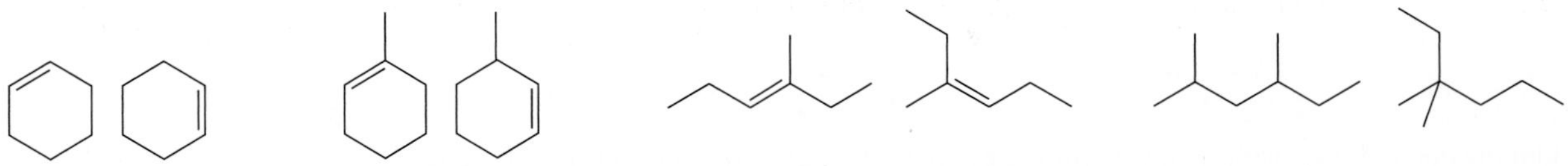

(e) (f) (g) (h)

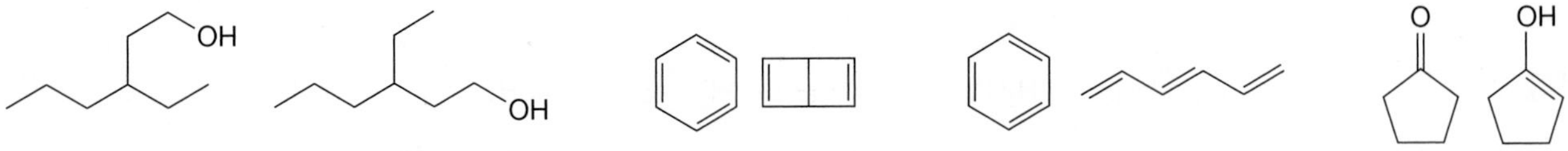

OH
OH
O
OH

4.29 For each pair of molecules, determine whether they are constitutional isomers.

(a) (b) (c) (d)

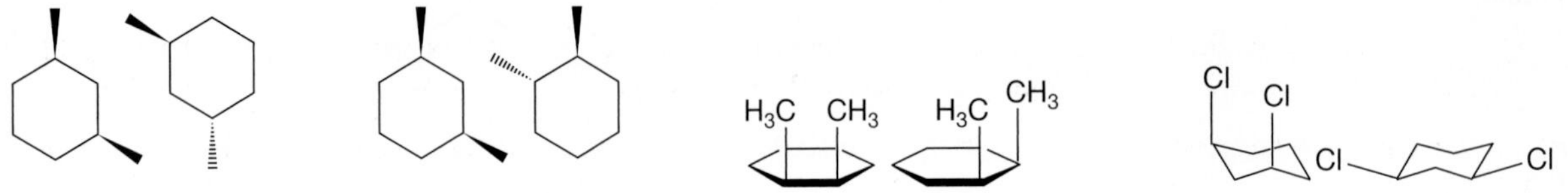

H_3C CH_3
H_3C CH_3
Cl
Cl
Cl
Cl

(e) (f) (g)

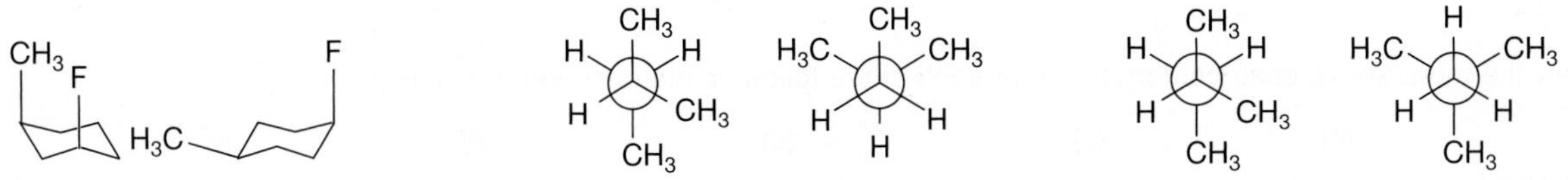

CH_3
F
H_3C
F
CH_3
H
H
H
CH_3
CH_3
CH_3
H_3C
CH_3
H
H
H
CH_3
H
H
H
CH_3
CH_3
H
H_3C
CH_3
H
H
CH_3

4.30 Identify all of the compound classes listed in Table 1-6 (p. 35) that have an IHD of **(a)** 1, **(b)** 2, **(c)** 3, and **(d)** 4.

4.31 Determine the IHD for each of the following compounds.

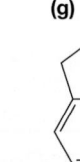

(a) (b) (c) (d) (e) (f) (g) (h)

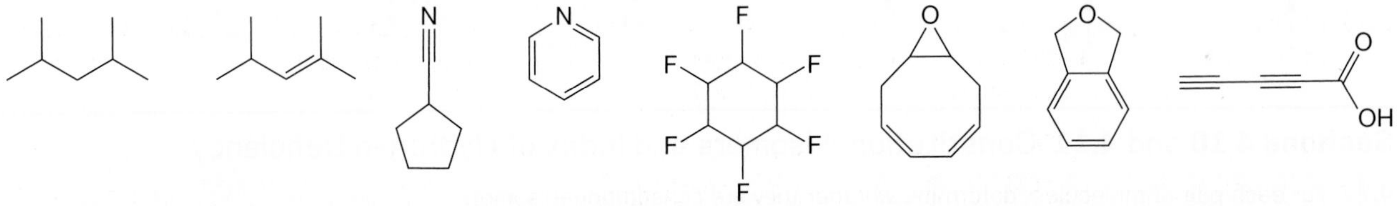

N
N
F
F
F
F
F
F
O
O
O
OH

4.32 Determine the number of hydrogen atoms in each compound, given the number and type of non-hydrogen atoms it contains and its IHD.

(a) Four carbon atoms; IHD = 0
(b) Four carbon atoms; IHD = 2
(c) Three carbon atoms, two oxygen atoms; IHD = 1
(d) Five carbon atoms, two chlorine atoms, one nitrogen atom; IHD = 3
(e) One carbon atom, one nitrogen atom; IHD = 2
(f) Six carbon atoms, two nitrogen atoms, one oxygen atom, three fluorine atoms; IHD = 4

4.33 Calculate the IHD for each of the following molecular formulas: **(a)** C_6H_6; **(b)** $C_6H_5NO_2$; **(c)** $C_8H_{13}F_2NO$; **(d)** $C_4H_{12}Si$; **(e)** C_6H_5BrO; **(f)** $C_4H_6O_3S$

Section 4.12 Drawing All Constitutional Isomers of a Given Formula

4.34 Draw all constitutional isomers that have the formula $C_5H_{11}Br$.

4.35 Draw all constitutional isomers that have the molecular formula $C_3H_6F_2O$, in which the oxygen is bonded to only one carbon atom. (There are 14 isomers.)

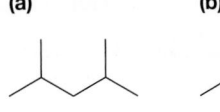

4.36 Draw all constitutional isomers that have the molecular formula $C_3H_6F_2O$, in which the oxygen is bonded to two carbon atoms.

4.37 Draw all constitutional isomers that have the molecular formula C_4H_6. (There are nine isomers.)

Sections 4.13 and 4.14 The Organic Chemistry of Biomolecules

4.38 Behenic acid and erucic acid are two fatty acids isolated from rapeseed oil. Which fatty acid has a higher melting point?

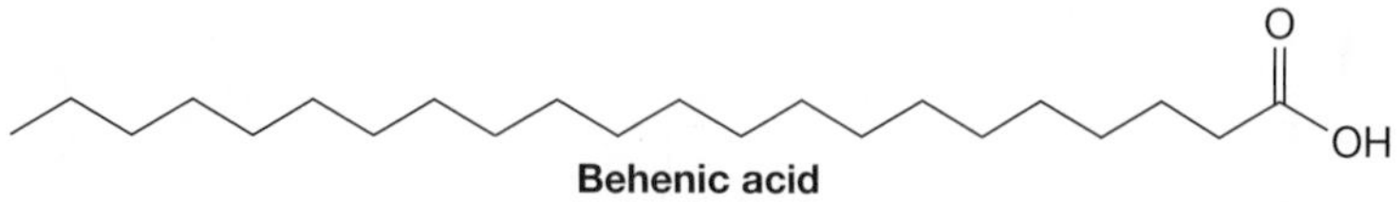
O
OH
Behenic acid

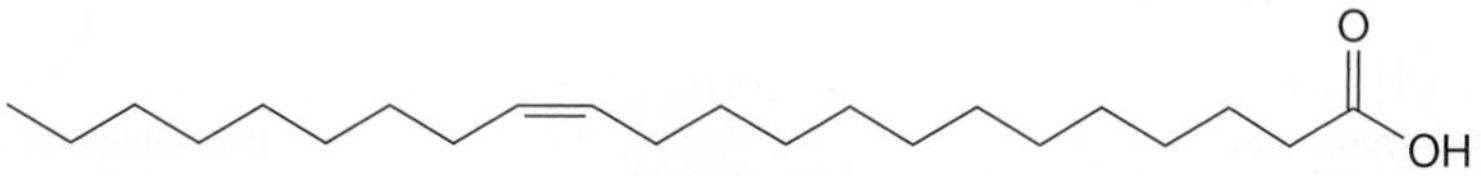
O
OH
Erucic acid

4.39 As we saw in Section 4.14, oleic acid has one C═C double bond that is in the cis configuration. Elaidic acid is identical to oleic acid, but the C═C is in the trans configuration. Which fatty acid has the higher melting point? Explain.

4.40 How many constitutional isomers of acyclic monosaccharides are there that can be classified as aldohexoses? As ketohexoses?

4.41 Mannoheptulose is a monosaccharide found in avocados and, by blocking the enzyme hexokinase, it inhibits glucose phosphorylation. Classify mannoheptulose according to the distinctions made in Section 4.13 (e.g., aldohexose).

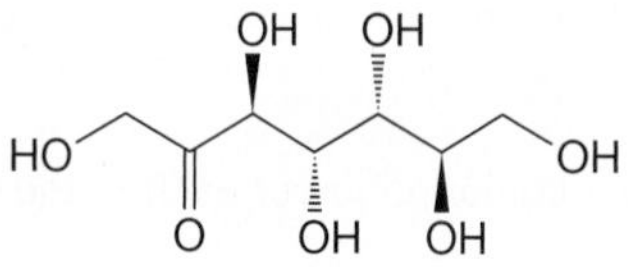
OH
OH
HO
OH
O
OH
OH
Mannoheptulose

4.42 Olive oil melts around −6 °C and palm oil melts around +35 °C. What does this say about the relative amount of unsaturation in the fatty acids that make up these oils?

Integrated Problems

4.43 For each of the following substituted cyclohexane rings, **(a)** draw the corresponding dash–wedge structure, **(b)** draw the corresponding Haworth projection, **(c)** determine whether the given conformation is the most stable one, and **(d)** if it is *not* the most stable conformation, draw the Newman projection of the most stable conformation.

(1)

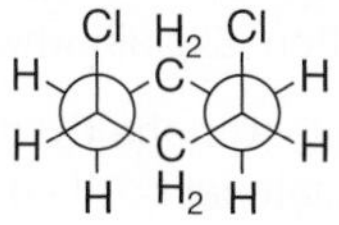
Cl
H2
Cl
H
C
H
H
C
H
H
H2
H

(2)

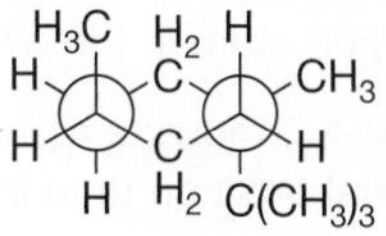
H3C
H2
H
H
C
CH3
H
C
H
H
H2
C(CH3)3

(3)

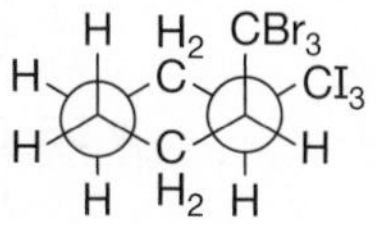
H
H2
CBr3
H
C
CI3
H
C
H
H
H2
H

4.44 Rank compounds **A–D** in order from smallest heat of combustion to largest heat of combustion.

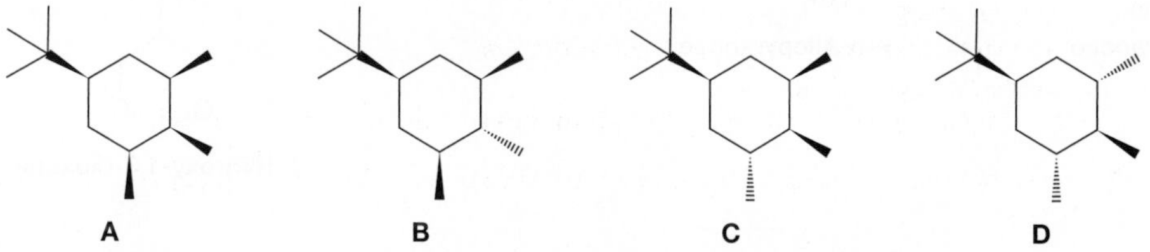
A
B
C
D

4.45 Draw all constitutional isomers that have the formula C_3H_5N. In each isomer, identify any functional groups that are listed in Table 1-6 (p. 35).

4.46 Draw all constitutional isomers of C_9H_{12} that contain a benzene ring.

4.47 Draw all constitutional isomers of $C_5H_8O_2$ that are carboxylic acids.

4.48 Draw all constitutional isomers of C_5H_8O that are ketones that do *not* contain a C═C group.

4.49 Draw all constitutional isomers of all-*cis*-ethylmethylisopropylcyclohexane: that is, in which a methyl group (CH_3), an ethyl group (CH_2CH_3), and an isopropyl group [$CH(CH_3)_2$] are all bonded to a cyclohexane ring on the same side of the ring's plane. Which of those isomers do you think is the most stable? Explain.

4.50 Glucose, a monosaccharide, has both acyclic and cyclic forms. One of the cyclic forms is called β-D-glucopyranose. Draw the more stable chair conformation of β-D-glucopyranose.

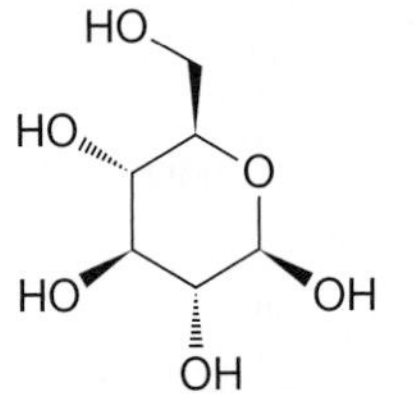
HO
HO
O
HO
OH
OH

β-D-Glucopyranose

4.51 In addition to β-D-glucopyranose (see Problem 4.50), glucose can exist in another cyclic form, called β-D-glucofuranose. Which form is more stable, β-D-glucopyranose or β-D-glucofuranose? Explain.

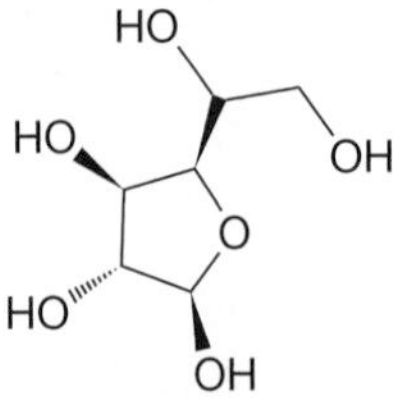
HO
HO
OH
O
HO
OH

β-D-Glucofuranose

4.52 Draw the more stable chair conformation of each of the following compounds in which an sp^3-hybridized heteroatom is part of the ring.

(a)

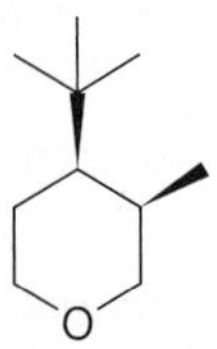
O

(b)

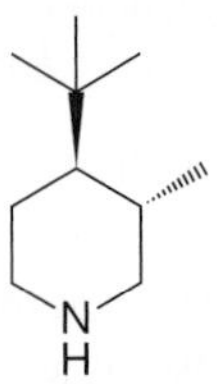
N
H

(c)

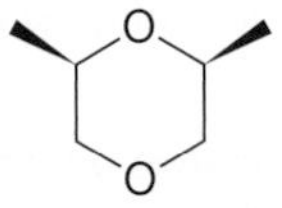
O
O

4.53 Draw the more stable chair conformation of each of the following compounds in which an sp^2-hybridized carbon atom is part of the ring.

(a)

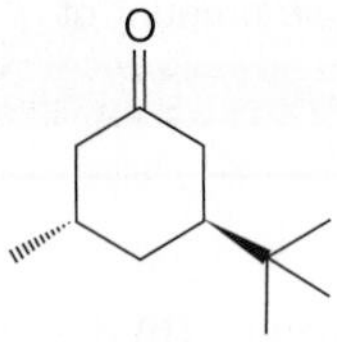
O

(b)

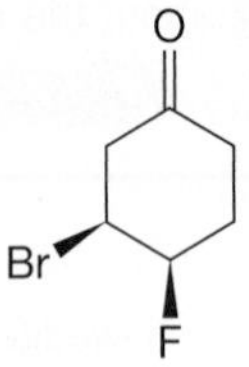
O
Br
F

(c)

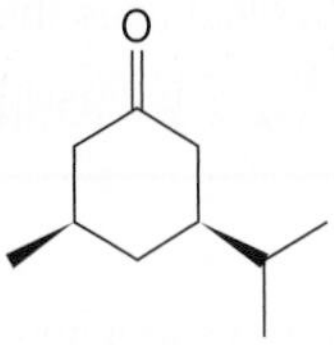
O

(d)

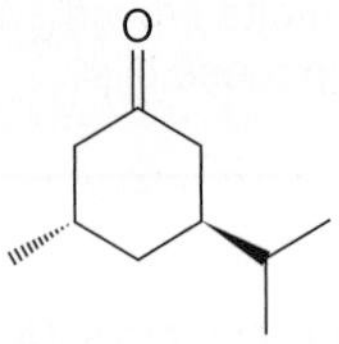
O

(e)

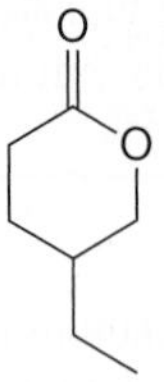
O
O

4.54 Which monosaccharide has a greater heat of combustion, β-D-glucopyranose or β-D-allopyranose? Explain.

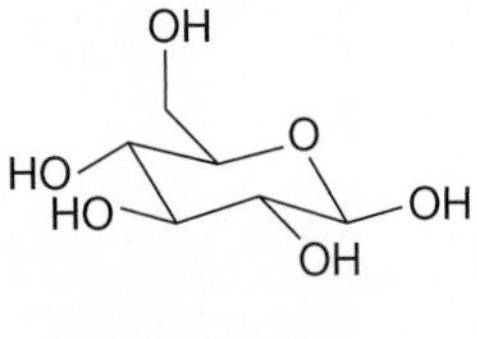
OH
O
HO
HO
OH
OH

β-D-Glucopyranose

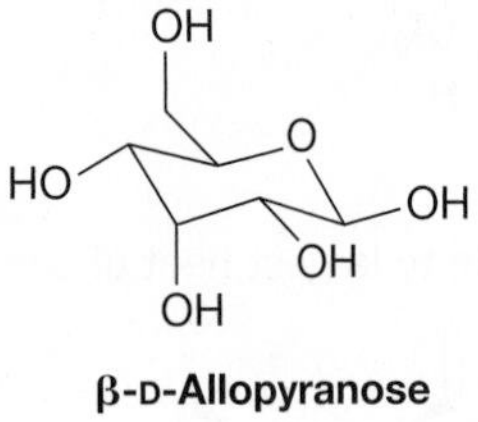
OH
O
HO
OH
OH
OH

β-D-Allopyranose

4.55 Even though an iodine atom is larger in size than a bromine atom, both bromocyclohexane and iodocyclohexane exist with 31% of molecules having the halogen atom in the axial position. Explain why.

4.56 5-Hydroxy-1,3-dioxane is more stable with the OH group in the axial position than in the equatorial position. Explain why.

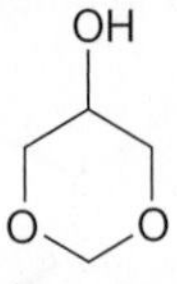
OH
O
O

5-Hydroxy-1,3-dioxane

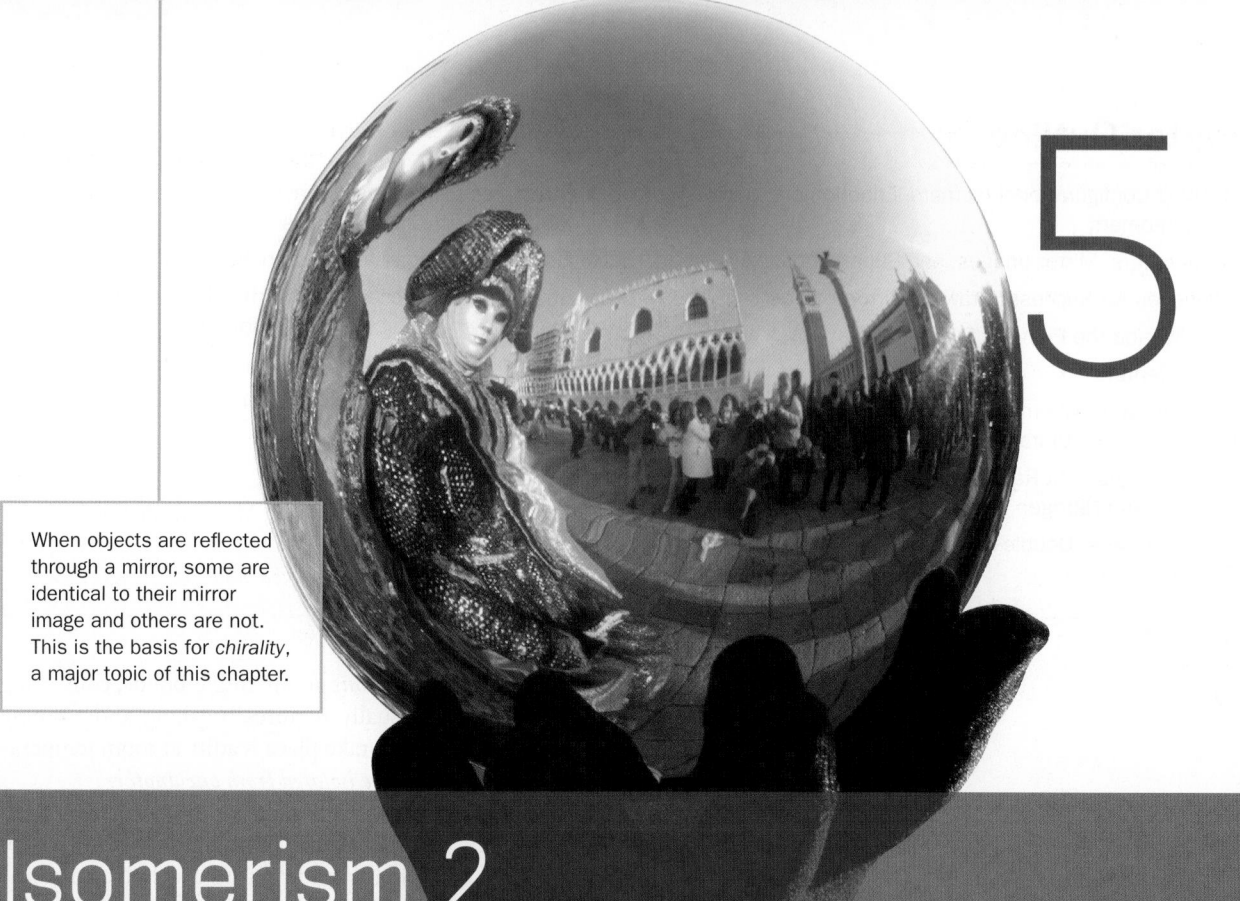

When objects are reflected through a mirror, some are identical to their mirror image and others are not. This is the basis for *chirality*, a major topic of this chapter.

5

Isomerism 2

Chirality, Enantiomers, and Diastereomers

In Chapter 4, we examined *conformers* and *constitutional isomers* in detail. Here in Chapter 5, we examine *configurational isomers*, of which there are two types: *enantiomers* and *diastereomers*. We will study the structural relationships among these types of isomers, and we will learn how those relationships affect their respective physical and chemical behaviors. Whether molecules are enantiomers or diastereomers can have dramatic consequences in chemical reactions, as we will study in greater depth in Chapter 8 and beyond.

5.1 Defining Configurational Isomers, Enantiomers, and Diastereomers

SECTION 5.1 OBJECTIVES

You will be able to:

1. Define configurational isomers, enantiomers, and diastereomers.
2. Distinguish configurational isomers from conformers and constitutional isomers.

To formally define *configurational isomers*, *enantiomers*, and *diastereomers*, review the flowchart shown in **Figure 5-1** (next page; the same flowchart we saw in Chapter 4). The types of isomers we are interested in here are shown in red lettering in Figure 5-1. According to the flowchart:

Configurational isomers have the same connectivity, making them a type of **stereoisomers**, but they differ in a way *other* than by rotations about single bonds. They include two types:

- **Enantiomers:** Configurational isomers that are mirror images of each other.
- **Diastereomers:** Configurational isomers that are *not* mirror images of each other.

Chapter Outline

Whereas conformers are related only by *rotations* about single bonds, converting from one configurational isomer to another usually requires breaking and forming covalent bonds: something that generally does not take place readily at room temperature. Therefore, *configurational isomers can usually be isolated from one another*.

Even though the structural differences between a pair of configurational isomers may seem subtle, the differences in their behavior may not be. For example, one of two enantiomers (mirror images) of the drug thalidomide acts as a sedative and anti-nausea medication for pregnant people suffering from morning sickness, whereas the other enantiomer causes terrible birth defects in newborns. Widely marketed in Europe during the late 1950s and early 1960s, thalidomide is now used to treat multiple myeloma (a kind of cancer) and erythema nodosum leprosum (an inflammation of fat cells under the skin). We will have more to say about this phenomenon later in the chapter.

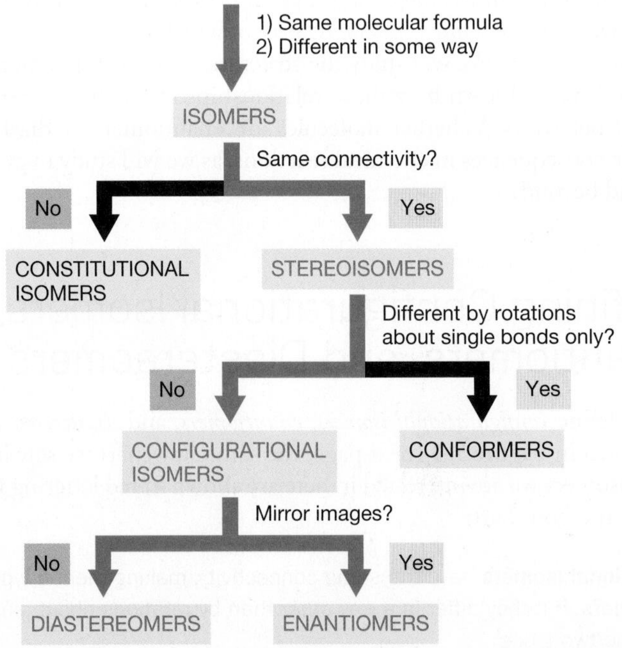

1) Same molecular formula
2) Different in some way
ISOMERS
Same connectivity?
No
Yes
CONSTITUTIONAL ISOMERS
STEREOISOMERS
Different by rotations about single bonds only?
No
Yes
CONFIGURATIONAL ISOMERS
CONFORMERS
Mirror images?
No
Yes
DIASTEREOMERS
ENANTIOMERS

FIGURE 5-1 Flowchart illustrating the subcategories of isomers Categories shown in red are examined in detail in this chapter, whereas categories shown in black were discussed in Chapter 4.

5.2 Enantiomers, Mirror Images, and Superimposability

Enantiomers are mirror images of each other. To be *isomers* of each other, however, they must be *different* in some way. Enantiomers, therefore, are *nonsuperimposable mirror images*:

Molecules are **nonsuperimposable** if there is no orientation in which *all* atoms of both molecules can be lined up perfectly (i.e., superimposed).

The two molecules of CHBrClF in **Figure 5-2a** are enantiomers. They are mirror images of each other; that is, if we were to hold a mirror between the two molecules, as shown in Figure 5-2b, then one molecule would appear as the mirror reflection of the other. There is no orientation of the two molecules, however, that allows *all* of the atoms to be superimposed (see Your Turn 5.1).

SECTION 5.2 OBJECTIVES

You will be able to:

1. Identify a pair of molecules as superimposable or nonsuperimposable.
2. Determine whether molecules that are mirror images are also enantiomers.

YOUR TURN 5.1

The molecule on the left and part of the molecule on the right in Figure 5-2a are redrawn here. Using a molecular modeling kit, construct the molecule on the right in Figure 5-2a and orient it so that the C, Br, and F atoms occupy the positions shown in the second structure here. Complete the drawing of the molecule by adding the H and Cl atoms in the positions where they appear in your model. When you compare these two structures, are the molecules superimposable?

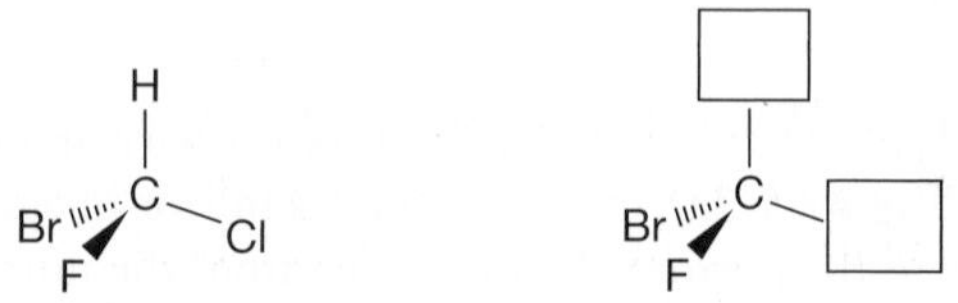

H
C
Br
Cl
F
C
Br
F

Molecule on the left in Figure 5-2a **Molecule on the right in Figure 5-2a**

Answers to Your Turns are in the back of the book.

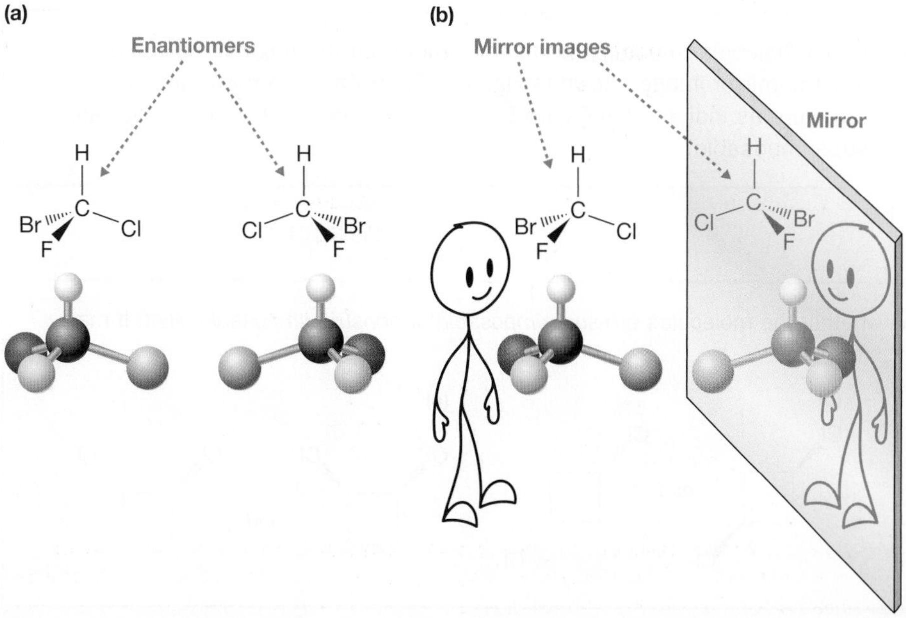

(a)
Enantiomers
H
C
Br
Cl
F
(b)
Mirror images
Mirror

FIGURE 5-2 Enantiomers
(a) The two molecules of CHBrClF are enantiomers because (b) they are nonsuperimposable mirror images of each other. A ball-and-stick model is shown below each dash–wedge structure.

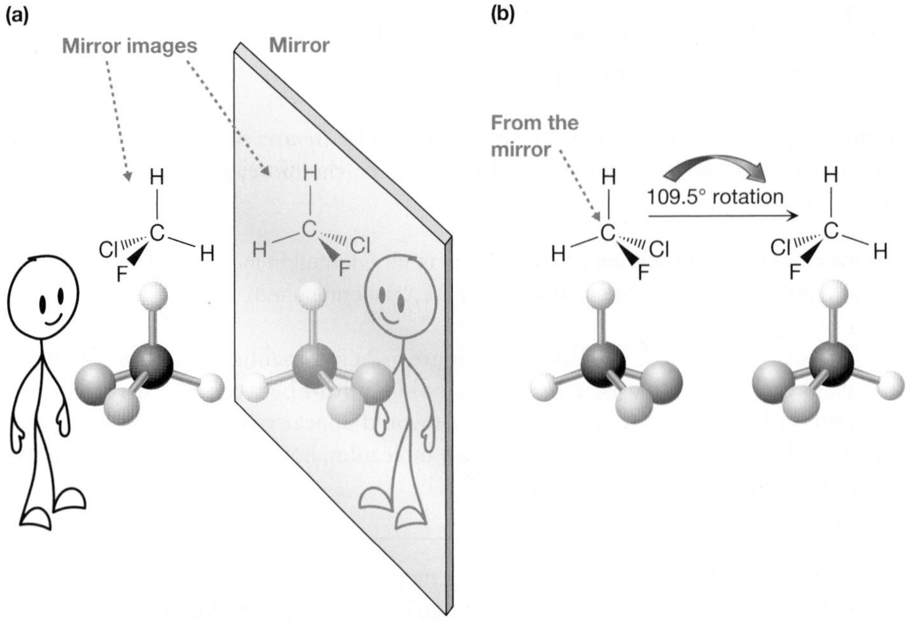
(a)
Mirror images
Mirror
(b)
From the mirror
109.5° rotation

FIGURE 5-3 Superimposable mirror images (a) CH_2ClF does not have an enantiomer because the molecule and its mirror image are superimposable. (b) If the image from the mirror is rotated by 109.5°, then it is exactly the same as the original molecule. A ball-and-stick model is shown below each dash–wedge structure.

Unlike CHBrClF, a molecule of CH_2ClF does *not* have an enantiomer. CH_2ClF has a mirror image (**Figure 5-3a**), of course, but its mirror image is exactly the same as itself. If the image in the mirror is first removed from the mirror and then rotated, as shown in Figure 5-3b, we find that it can be superimposed on the original molecule (see Your Turn 5.2). Remember:

Every molecule has a mirror image, but not every molecule has a *nonsuperimposable* mirror image.

YOUR TURN 5.2

Use a molecular modeling kit to construct both the original molecule and the mirror image shown in Figure 5-3a. Rotate the mirror image structure as indicated in Figure 5-3b to verify that the two molecules are superimposable.

YOUR TURN 5.3

For each pair shown here, determine whether the molecules are *superimposable* or *nonsuperimposable*. *Hint*: It may help to build models.

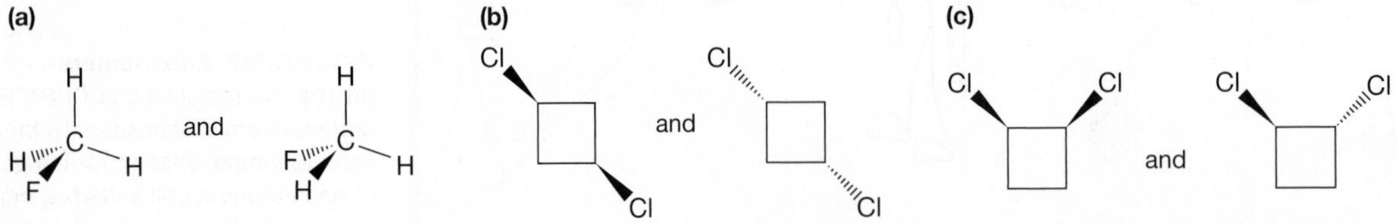
(a)
and
(b)
and
(c)
and

5.3 Strategies for Success: Drawing Mirror Images

Learning to draw a molecule's mirror image quickly and correctly is an essential skill in this chapter. One method involves drawing the mirror image of each atom one at a time, following these three guiding principles:

SECTION 5.3 OBJECTIVES

You will be able to:

1. Use a systematic method to draw the mirror image of a given molecule.
2. Recognize when molecules are mirror images on the basis of the relative positions of their atoms.

Characteristics of Mirror Image Molecules

- An atom and its mirror image are directly opposite each other on opposite sides of the mirror.
- An atom and its mirror image are identical distances *away from* the mirror.
- When the mirror is placed next to a molecule, as in Figures 5-2 and 5-3, dash–wedge notation in the mirror image is identical to that in the original molecule.

Let's practice this step-by-step process in **Figure 5-4** by drawing the mirror image of the molecule shown on the left in Figure 5-2. (The blue dotted line represents a mirror perpendicular to the page.)

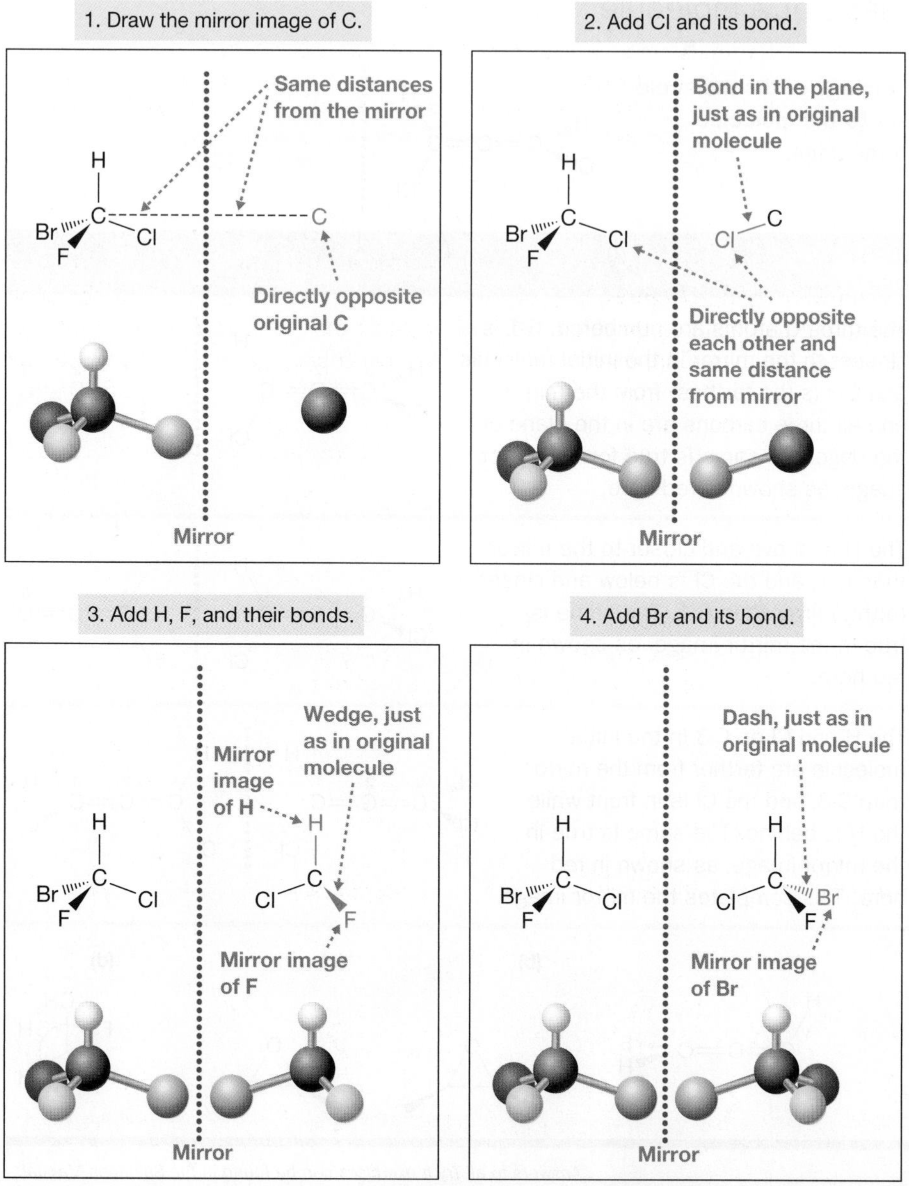

1. Draw the mirror image of C.
Same distances from the mirror
Directly opposite original C
Mirror
2. Add Cl and its bond.
Bond in the plane, just as in original molecule
Directly opposite each other and same distance from mirror
Mirror
3. Add H, F, and their bonds.
Mirror image of H
Wedge, just as in original molecule
Mirror image of F
Mirror
4. Add Br and its bond.
Dash, just as in original molecule
Mirror image of Br
Mirror

FIGURE 5-4 Progression of drawing the mirror image of CHFClBr In each frame, the mirror is represented by the blue dotted line, the original molecule is on the left, and the mirror image is on the right. The atoms and bonds added to the mirror image of the dash–wedge structure in each step are highlighted in red. A ball-and-stick model is shown below each dash–wedge structure.

YOUR TURN 5.4

Carry out the steps in Figure 5-4 again, but this time place the perpendicular mirror on the left of the initial molecule. How does the resulting mirror image compare to the one shown in Figure 5-4?

YOUR TURN 5.5

If the mirror in Figure 5-4 were instead oriented parallel to the plane of the page, the mirror image would appear as shown here. In this case, the mirror image is drawn only by reversing the dash–wedge notation of the initial molecule. Is the molecule shown here superimposable on the mirror image shown in frame 4 of Figure 5-4? (It would help to build models of the two molecules.)

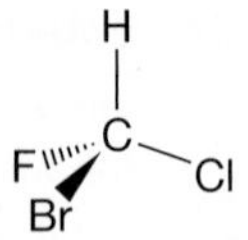

SOLVED PROBLEM **5.1**

How to draw the mirror image of a molecule

Break It Down **Draw the mirror image of the molecule shown here. The blue dotted line next to the molecule represents a mirror perpendicular to the page.**

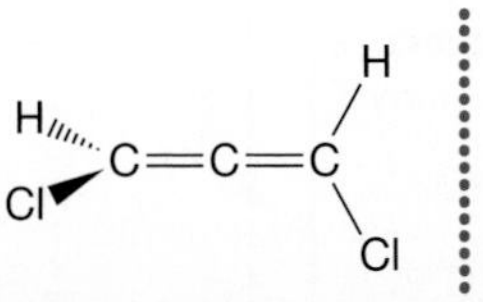

Think	Solve
How do you apply the three characteristics of mirror images just presented to draw the mirror image of the three C atoms?	The three C atoms are numbered. C-1 is closest to the mirror in the initial molecule and C-3 is the farthest from the mirror, and all three carbons are in the plane of the page; the same is true for the mirror image, as shown in red here. 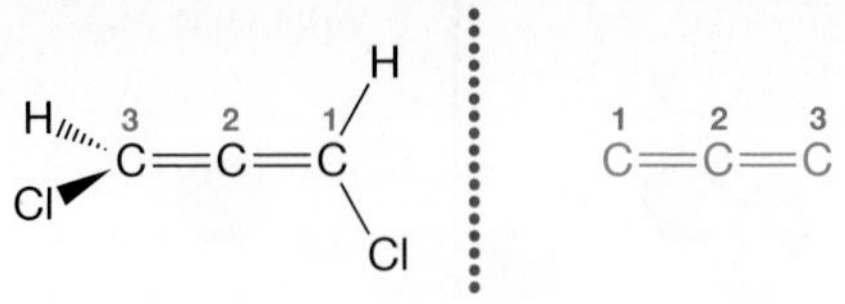
How do you apply the characteristics of mirror images to draw the H and Cl atoms attached to C-1?	The H is above and closer to the mirror than C-1, and the Cl is below and closer to the mirror than C-1. The same is true in the mirror image, as shown in red here. 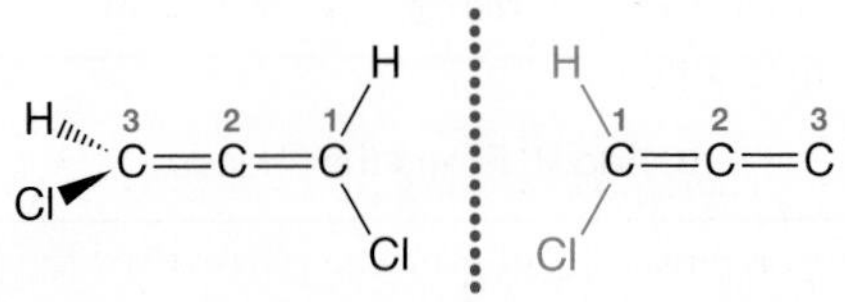
How do you apply the characteristics of mirror images to draw the H and Cl atoms attached to C-3?	The H and Cl on C-3 in the initial molecule are farther from the mirror than C-3, and the Cl is in front while the H is behind. The same is true in the mirror image, as shown in red here. This completes the mirror image. 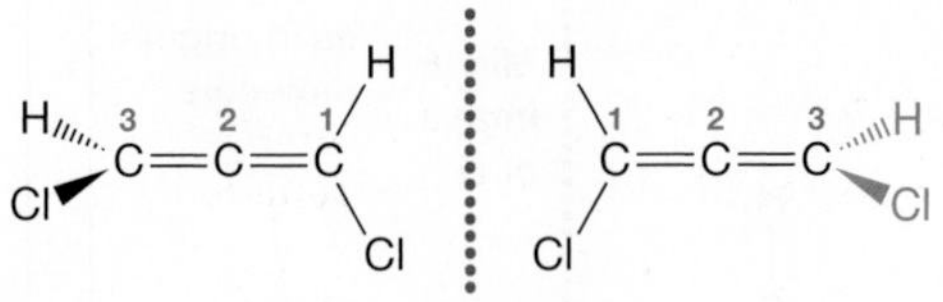

Try It Draw the mirror image of each of the following molecules.

(a)

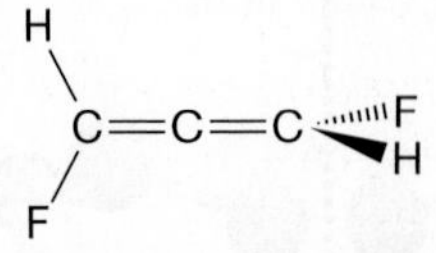

(b)

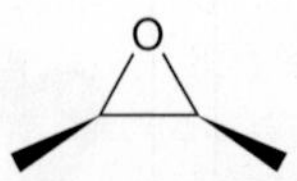

(c)

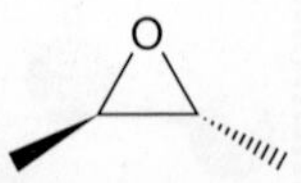

(d)

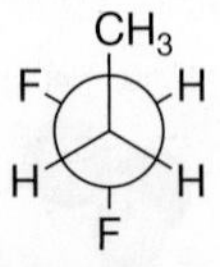

Answers to all Try It exercises can be found in the Solutions Manual.

YOUR TURN **5.6**

For each molecule in Solved Problem 5.1, Try It, determine whether the mirror image you drew is superimposable on the original molecule.

5.4 Chirality and the Plane of Symmetry Test

SECTION 5.4 OBJECTIVES

You will be able to:

1. Identify a molecule as chiral or achiral.
2. Determine whether a molecule has a plane of symmetry and therefore must be achiral.

Whether a molecule has an enantiomer can have important implications for the molecule's physical and chemical properties:

- A molecule is **chiral** (KAI-ruhl) if it *has* an enantiomer.
- A molecule is **achiral** if it *does not* have an enantiomer.

The word *chiral* is derived from Greek for "hand," given that your hands are chiral. In fact, the enantiomer of your left hand is your right hand, and vice versa, because your left and right hands are mirror images of each other but they are not superimposable (**Figure 5-5a**). Other objects with handedness, or chirality, include corkscrews (Fig. 5-5b) and certain seashells (Fig. 5-5c). Certain biomolecules such as amino acids and sugars are chiral, too (see Section 5.15).

(a)

(b)

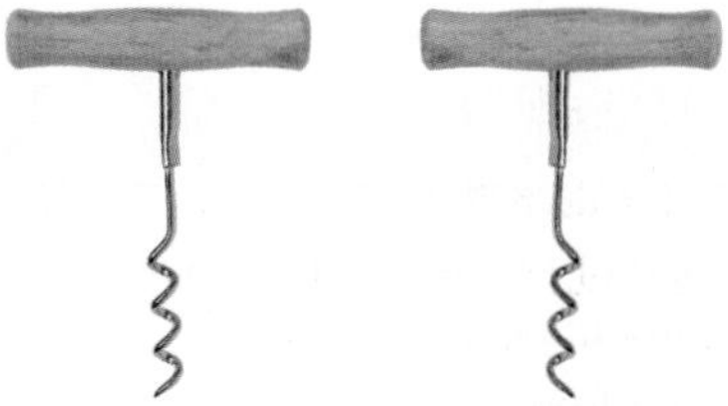

(c)

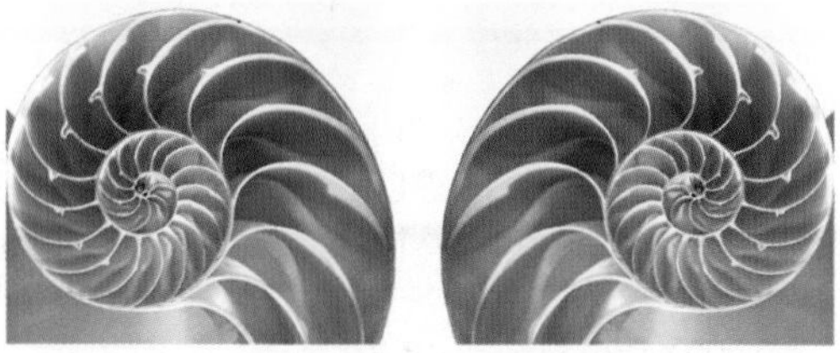

FIGURE 5-5 Familiar objects that are chiral (a) Hands. (b) A corkscrew. (c) A seashell.

Of the molecules we have examined so far, CHBrClF (Fig. 5-2) is chiral, whereas CH_2ClF (Fig. 5-3) is achiral. Both molecules have mirror images (as all molecules do), but only for CHBrClF do we find that the molecule and its mirror image are not superimposable.

SOLVED PROBLEM **5.2**

How to determine whether a molecule is chiral

Break It Down Determine whether *trans*-1,2-dichlorocyclopropane is chiral or achiral.

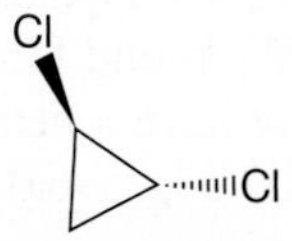
Cl
Cl

***trans*-1,2-Dichlorocyclopropane**

Think	Solve
How do you draw the mirror image of the given molecule?	If we place the mirror next to the molecule and perpendicular to the page, we arrive at the mirror image shown here in red. 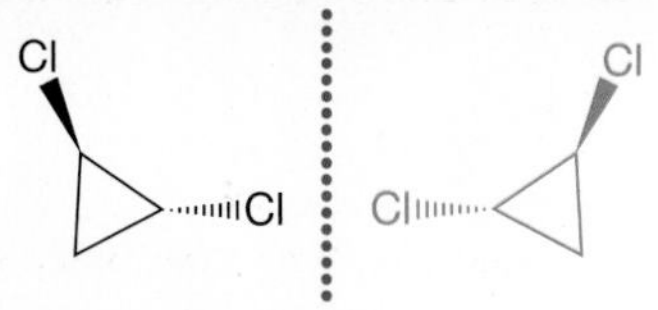

Cl
Cl
Cl
Cl

(continued)

How do you determine whether the two molecules are superimposable?	For the two molecules to be superimposable, every atom in one molecule must line up perfectly with every atom in the second molecule. We must try every possible orientation of the two molecules, two of which are shown here. 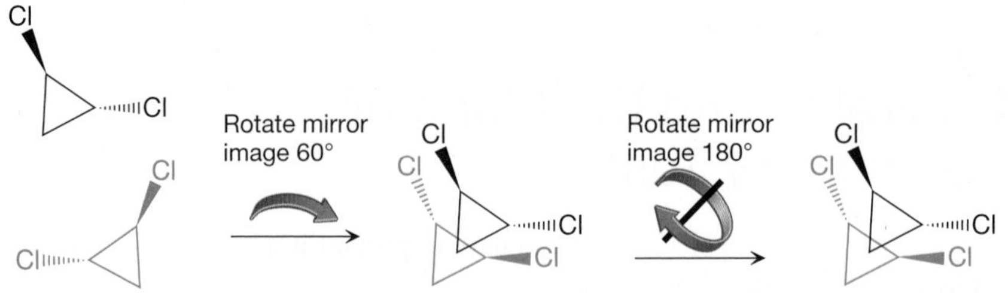 Cl Cl Cl Cl Rotate mirror image 60° Cl Cl Cl Cl Rotate mirror image 180° Cl Cl Cl Cl
For the molecule to be chiral, does it need to be superimposable or nonsuperimposable on its mirror image?	There are no orientations of the two molecules in which all atoms line up perfectly (*if you are unconvinced, then you must use your model kit to build both molecules and try various orientations yourself*). Consequently, the molecule and its mirror image are nonsuperimposable, so the given molecule must be chiral.

Try It Determine whether each of the following molecules is chiral or achiral.

(a)

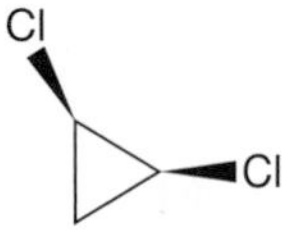

Cl
Cl

(b)

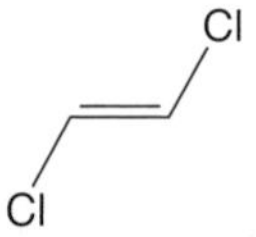

Cl
Cl

(c)

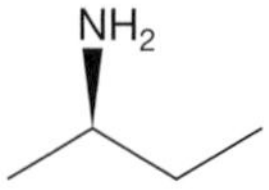

NH2

YOUR TURN **5.7**

Is the mirror image of the molecule in Solved Problem 5.2 (i.e., the molecule shown in red) chiral or achiral?

A convenient way to determine whether a molecule is achiral is to search for a *plane of symmetry*. A molecule has a **plane of symmetry** if it can be bisected in such a way that *one half of the molecule is the mirror image of the other half*. If a molecule has at least one plane of symmetry, then its mirror image is the same as itself. Thus:

A molecule that possesses a plane of symmetry must be achiral.

Most molecules that do not possess a plane of symmetry are chiral, though there are some exceptions. (See Problem 5.54 at the end of the chapter.)

Previously we found that CH_2ClF is achiral (Fig. 5-3, p. 208). **Figure 5-6a** shows that CH_2ClF has a plane of symmetry that bisects the H—C—H bond angle. We found CHBrClF to be chiral (Fig. 5-2, p. 207), on the other hand, so it must *not* have a plane of symmetry. Notice that what was a plane of symmetry in CH_2ClF (Fig. 5-6a) is no longer one in CHBrClF (Fig. 5-6b).

YOUR TURN **5.8**

Use a model kit to construct the four molecules in Solved Problem 5.2 and the corresponding Try It exercise, and view the models from various angles. **(a)** Locate a plane of symmetry in the model of each achiral molecule, and indicate those planes of symmetry in the structures in Solved Problem 5.2. **(b)** Verify that each chiral molecule does *not* have a plane of symmetry.

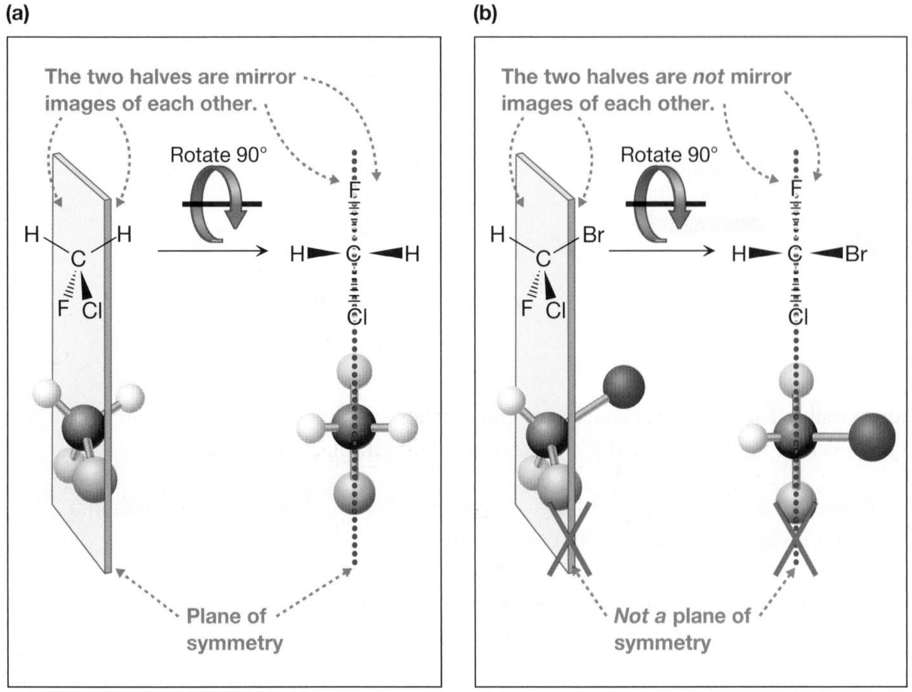
(a)
The two halves are mirror images of each other.
Rotate 90°
H
H
C
F
Cl
H
C
H
F
Cl
Plane of symmetry
(b)
The two halves are *not* mirror images of each other.
Rotate 90°
H
Br
C
F
Cl
H
C
Br
F
Cl
Not a plane of symmetry

FIGURE 5-6 Plane of symmetry test for chirality (a) Two orientations of CH_2ClF. To obtain the orientation on the right, the molecule on the left is rotated 90° about the axis indicated. In both orientations, the molecule possesses a plane of symmetry (indicated in blue) that bisects the H—C—H angle. As a result, CH_2ClF is achiral. (b) Two orientations of CHBrClF that differ by a rotation of 90° about the axis. Replacing one of the H atoms from CH_2ClF with a Br atom destroys the plane of symmetry that exists in CH_2ClF. This is consistent with CHBrClF being chiral.

5.5 Chiral Centers

SECTION 5.5 OBJECTIVES

You will be able to:

1. Locate all chiral centers in a given molecule and determine whether a molecule is meso.
2. Describe the two ways to convert a chiral center having a particular configuration into its opposite configuration.
3. Identify stereoisomers as enantiomers from the relative configurations of their chiral centers.

In Section 5.4, we learned that a molecule is chiral if it is not superimposable on its mirror image. We can apply this idea of chirality to an *atom* within a molecule, too: An atom is a **chiral center**, also called a **stereocenter** or an **asymmetric atom**, if it (along with its attached substituents having a particular arrangement in space) and its mirror image are nonsuperimposable. The specific arrangement of a chiral atom's substituents is called the **stereochemical configuration** (or simply **configuration**) of the chiral center.

In this book, the only chiral centers we will encounter are ones that are tetrahedral, which can be quickly identified:

A tetrahedral atom is a *chiral center* if it is bonded to *four different substituents*.

A generic chiral center of this type is represented by the structure shown in black in **Figure 5-7**, where W, X, Y and Z can be any four distinct substituents. Reflecting that chiral center through a mirror results in the structure shown in red, and as we can see, the black and red mirror images are not superimposable.

Even without knowing how to precisely characterize the configuration of a chiral center (the topic of Section 5.6), we can say that the black and red chiral centers in Figure 5-7 have different *relative configurations*. And because only two configurations

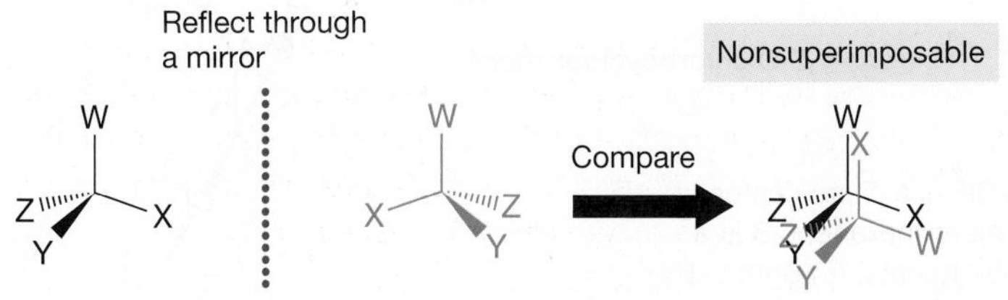
Reflect through a mirror
Nonsuperimposable
Compare
W
Z
X
Y
W
X
Z
Y

FIGURE 5-7 Nonsuperimposability of a chiral center and its mirror image The structure in black represents a generic chiral center with substituents W, X, Y and Z. The structure in red is the result of reflecting through the mirror. In an attempt to line up the mirror image with the original structure, as shown at the right, we can see that the two structures are not superimposable.

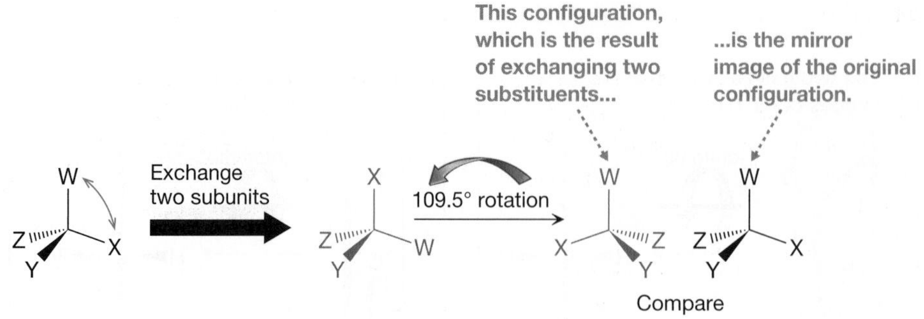
This configuration, which is the result of exchanging two substituents...
...is the mirror image of the original configuration.
Exchange two subunits
109.5° rotation
Compare
W
X
Y
Z

FIGURE 5-8 Relationships between stereochemical configurations The structure in black (left) represents a generic chiral center with a particular configuration. Exchanging substituents W and X results in the structure in blue. After rotating the structure in blue, we can compare it to the structure in black (right) to see that the two are mirror images of each other. Thus, exchanging two substituents on a chiral center is equivalent to taking the chiral center's mirror image.

are possible for any chiral center, we can further say that the configuration of the red chiral center is *opposite* (or the *reverse* of) the one in black. In general:

> Reflecting a chiral center with a given configuration through a mirror results in a mirror image with the opposite configuration.

In addition to being mirror images of each other, the two configurations of a chiral center have another very important relationship:

> Exchanging any two substituents attached to a chiral center with a given configuration results in the opposite configuration.

This second relationship between the two stereochemical configurations can be seen by carrying out the exercise shown in **Figure 5-8** for a generic chiral center.

Figure 5-9 gives some specific examples of chiral centers, which are represented by asterisks (*). The C atom in CHBrClF (Fig. 5-9a) is a chiral center because the four atoms to which it is bonded are all different. Figure 5-9b shows that 3-methylhexane has one chiral center, too, which is C-3. That carbon atom is bonded to H, CH_3, CH_2CH_3, and $CH_2CH_2CH_3$, which are all different substituents. Notice that the last

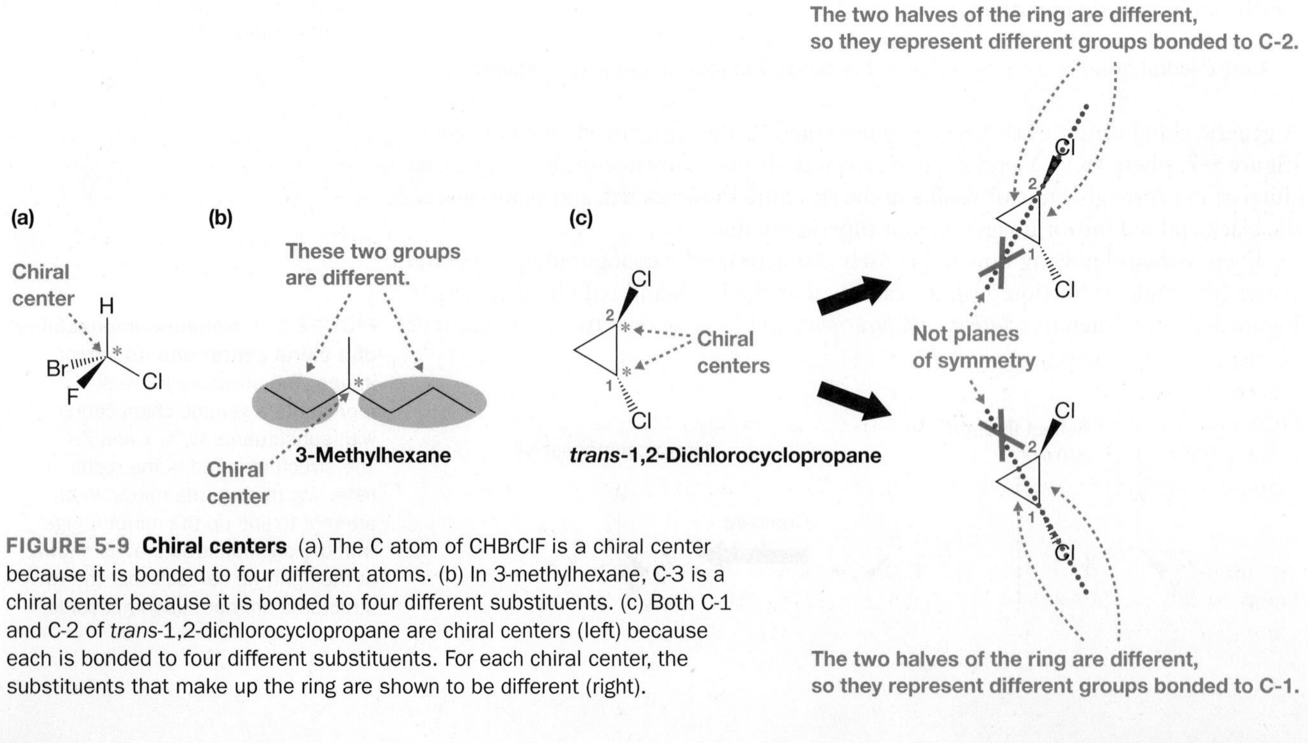
The two halves of the ring are different, so they represent different groups bonded to C-2.
(a)
Chiral center
H
Br
Cl
F
(b)
These two groups are different.
Chiral center
3-Methylhexane
(c)
Cl
Chiral centers
trans-1,2-Dichlorocyclopropane
Not planes of symmetry
The two halves of the ring are different, so they represent different groups bonded to C-1.

FIGURE 5-9 Chiral centers (a) The C atom of CHBrClF is a chiral center because it is bonded to four different atoms. (b) In 3-methylhexane, C-3 is a chiral center because it is bonded to four different substituents. (c) Both C-1 and C-2 of *trans*-1,2-dichlorocyclopropane are chiral centers (left) because each is bonded to four different substituents. For each chiral center, the substituents that make up the ring are shown to be different (right).

two substituents are distinct, even though they both have CH_2 groups at their points of attachment.

Figure 5-9c shows that *trans*-1,2-dichlorocyclopropane contains two chiral centers: namely, C-1 and C-2. Each of those C atoms has bonds to H and Cl, and the remaining two bonds are part of the ring. How can we tell that the two bonds to the ring have attached substituents that should be treated as different? Here is one way to tell:

Identifying a Chiral Center That Is Part of a Ring

1. Divide the ring in half. Bisect the angle made by the two bonds of the ring in which the atom in question is involved (shown on the right in Fig. 5-9c).
2. Evaluate the two halves of the ring.
   - If the two halves of the ring are different, treat the two substituents as different.
   - If the two halves of the ring are the same, treat the two substituents as the same.

When we apply this strategy to either C-1 or C-2 in Figure 5-9c, one half of the ring contains a C—Cl bond and the other half of the ring does not. Thus, C-1 and C-2 are each attached to four different substituents.

Chiral centers are not limited to just carbon atoms. Nitrogen atoms can also be tetrahedral and form four bonds. Therefore:

A nitrogen atom that is bonded to four different substituents is a chiral center.

An example is shown in **Figure 5-10**. Notice that, to be a chiral center, a nitrogen atom, unlike carbon, must have a +1 formal charge.

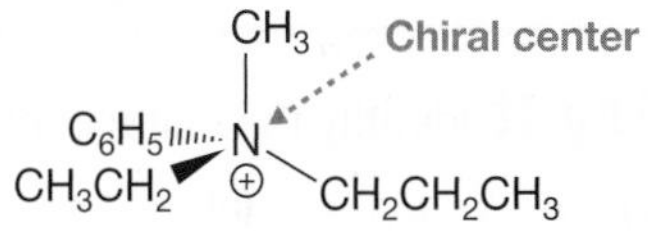
CH3
Chiral center
C6H5
N
CH3CH2
CH2CH2CH3

A quaternary ammonium ion

FIGURE 5-10 A nitrogen chiral center The nitrogen atom is tetrahedral and is bonded to four different substituents, so it is a chiral center.

SOLVED PROBLEM **5.3**

How to identify chiral centers in a molecule

Break It Down Identify the chiral centers in this molecule.

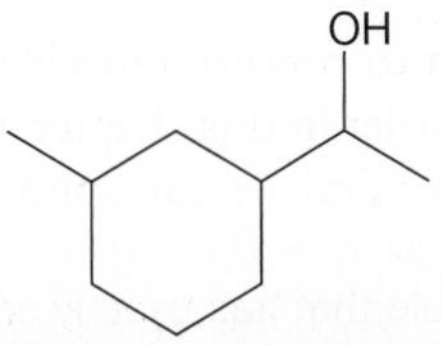
OH

Think	Solve
Which atoms are bonded to four substituents?	Every C atom is bonded to four substituents. If the C atom is bonded to four *different* substituents, then it is a chiral center. The O atom is bonded to only two substituents, so it cannot be a chiral center.
Which C atoms have two or more identical substituents (which would rule them out as chiral centers)? Which C atoms remain as candidates?	For each of the two CH_3 groups, the C atom is bonded to three identical H atoms. For the four CH_2 groups, the C atoms are bonded to two identical H atoms. Those six C atoms, therefore, cannot be chiral centers. The three other C atoms indicated by a ? remain as candidates for chiral centers. 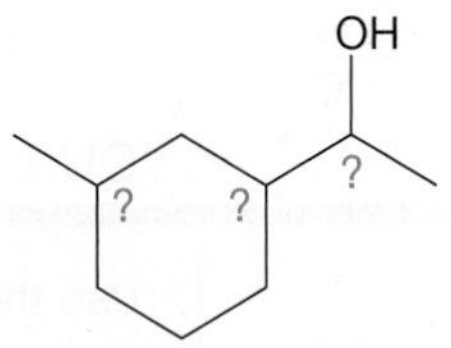 OH ? ? ?
Is the rightmost C atom marked with a ? bonded to four *different* substituents?	The rightmost C atom with a ? is bonded to OH, CH_3, H, and the ring. All of those substituents are different, so this C atom is a chiral center.

(continued)

How do we tell if the atoms that are part of the ring are chiral centers?

The C with a ? on the left side of the ring has a bond to H, a bond to CH_3, and two bonds that are part of the ring. The C with a ? on the right side of the ring has a bond to H, $CH(OH)CH_3$, and two bonds that are part of the ring. As shown here, when we split the ring in half through each of those carbons, the two halves of the ring are different, so we treat the two substituents making up the ring as being different. Thus, both C atoms in the ring marked ? have four different substituents and are chiral centers.

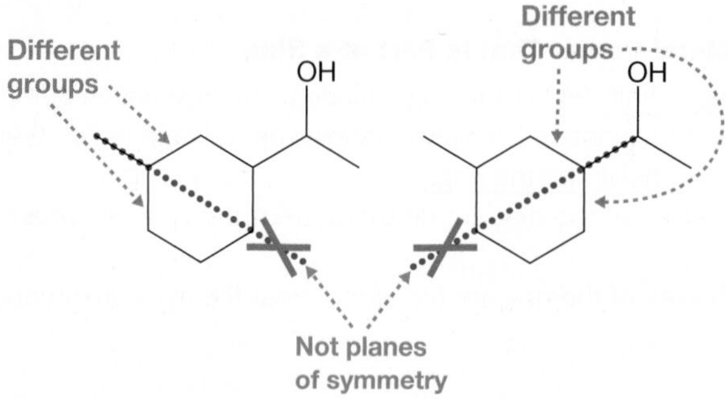

Different groups
OH
Different groups
OH
Not planes of symmetry

Try It Identify the chiral centers in each of the following molecules.

(a)
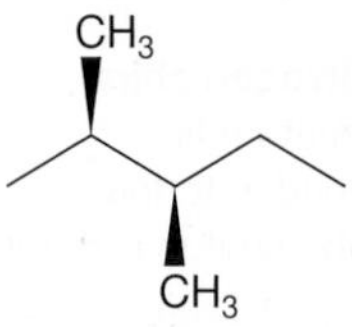

CH3
CH3

(b)
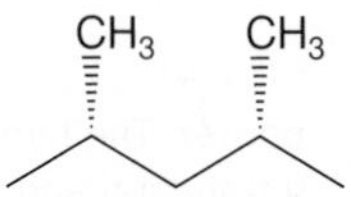

CH3
CH3

(c)
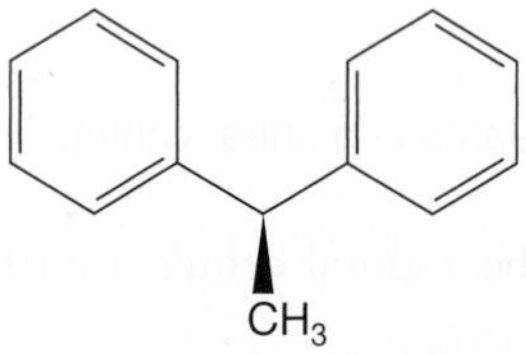

CH3

(d)
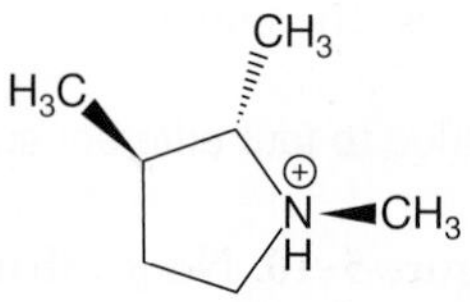

CH3
H3C
N
CH3
H

(e)
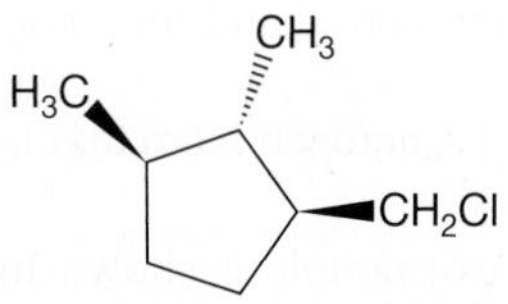

CH3
H3C
CH2Cl

5.5a Chiral Molecules, Meso Compounds, and Enantiomers

One reason to concern ourselves with chiral centers is to help streamline some tasks we faced earlier in this chapter. For example, when it comes to determining whether a molecule is chiral, we can apply the following generalization:

A molecule that has exactly one chiral center must be chiral.

We can see why this generalization is true by revisiting Figure 5-7 (p. 213), which shows that one configuration of a generic chiral center (drawn in black) is not superimposable on its mirror image (drawn in red). Notice that the substituents W, X, Y, and Z in that figure are unspecified, so we can take them to represent *any* substituent, big or small, that does not contain another chiral center. Thus, the black structure can represent *any* molecule that contains a single chiral center, and because it is not superimposable on its mirror image (the red structure), it must be chiral.

YOUR TURN 5.9

Use the generalization just described to determine which of these molecules must be chiral.

(a)
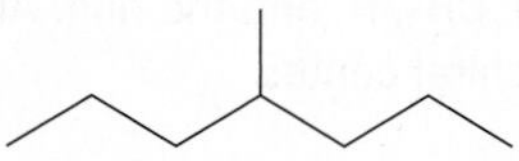

(b)

(c)

(d)
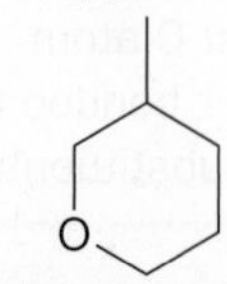

O

(e)
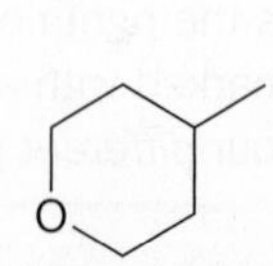

O

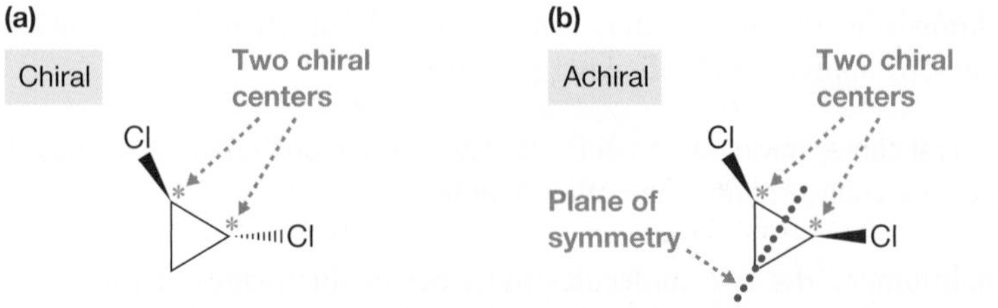
(a)
Chiral
Two chiral centers
Cl
Cl
(b)
Achiral
Two chiral centers
Cl
Plane of symmetry
Cl

trans-1,2-Dichlorocyclopropane

cis-1,2-Dichlorocyclopropane (*meso*-1,2-Dichlorocyclopropane)

FIGURE 5-11 Chiral and achiral molecules containing two chiral centers (a) *trans*-1,2-Dichlorocyclopropane is chiral. (b) *cis*-1,2-Dichlorocyclopropane is achiral because one chiral center is the mirror image of the other.

A molecule that has two chiral centers could be chiral or achiral. For example, both the trans and cis forms of 1,2-dichlorocyclopropane, shown in **Figure 5-11**, have two chiral centers. As we saw previously in Solved Problem 5.2 (p. 211), *trans*-1,2-dichlorocyclopropane is chiral (Fig. 5-11a). However, *cis*-1,2-dichlorocyclopropane, which was presented in Solved Problem 5.2, Try It (p. 212), is achiral (Fig. 5-11b).

As we can see in Figure 5-11b, a plane of symmetry is the feature that makes *cis*-1,2-dichlorocyclopropane achiral even though it contains chiral centers. Such molecules are called *meso*:

> A molecule is **meso** if it contains at least two chiral centers but has a plane of symmetry that makes it achiral *overall*.

The term *meso* comes from the Greek word for "middle" and refers to the fact that the molecule reflects about its middle: its plane of symmetry.

SOLVED PROBLEM **5.4**

How to determine if a molecule is meso

Break It Down Determine whether molecules A and B are meso.

A B

Think	Solve
Which of the molecules has two or more chiral centers?	Both molecules have two chiral centers, which are the carbons marked by an * here. Each of those carbons is bonded to four different groups: H, CH_3, and two halves of the ring that are different.  A B
Which of the molecules possesses a plane of symmetry?	As shown here, **A** has a plane of symmetry, and because it also has two chiral centers, it is meso. The plane of symmetry in **A** is not a plane of symmetry in **B** because, for the CH_3 groups to be reflections of each other, both must be on the same side of the plane of the ring. In fact, **B** is chiral, so it has no plane of symmetry anywhere in the molecule. Therefore, **B** must not be meso. 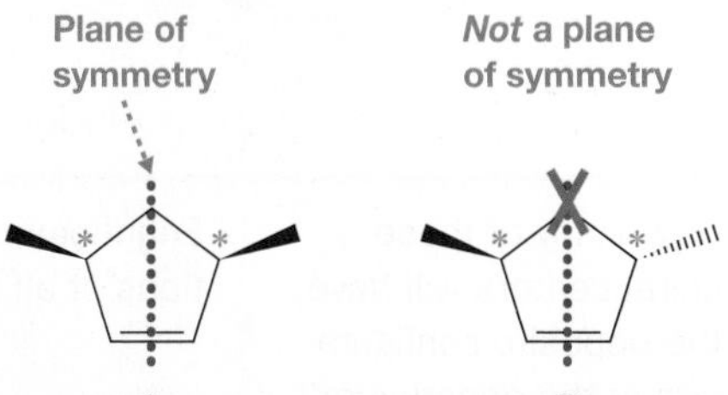 Plane of symmetry *Not* a plane of symmetry A B

Try It Determine whether molecules **C**–**E** are meso.

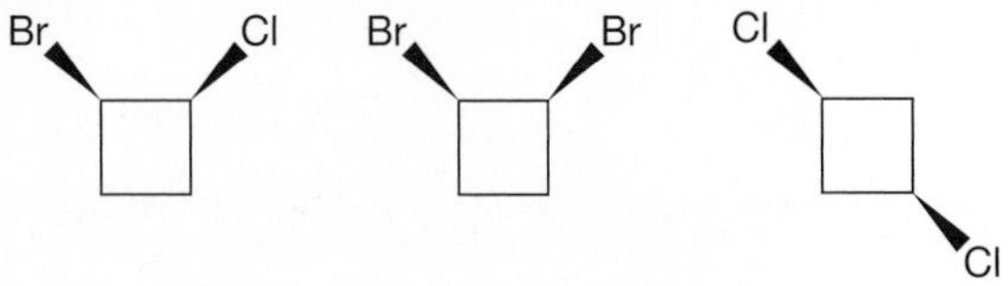
Br
Cl
Br
Br
Cl
Cl

C D E

Our knowledge of chiral centers can also be helpful when drawing or identifying enantiomers, by applying the following principle:

> Every chiral center having a particular configuration in one enantiomer must have the opposite configuration in the other enantiomer.

To be enantiomers, the two molecules must be mirror images of each other, so on going from one enantiomer to the other, *all* chiral centers are reflected through a mirror. As we learned earlier in Section 5.5, each such reflection ends up reversing the chiral center's configuration.

If you also recall that exchanging any two substituents on a chiral center has the effect of reversing the configuration, then identifying enantiomers is often quite straightforward, as shown in Solved Problem 5.5.

SOLVED PROBLEM **5.5**

How to use relative stereochemical configurations to identify enantiomers

Break It Down The molecule shown in the box is chiral. Which of the molecules A–E is its enantiomer?

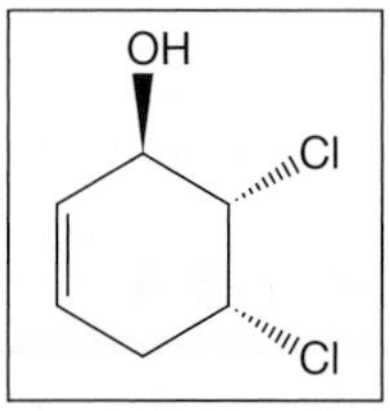
OH
Cl
Cl

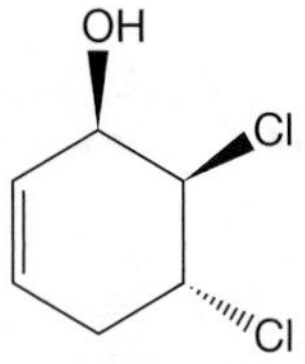
OH
Cl
Cl

A

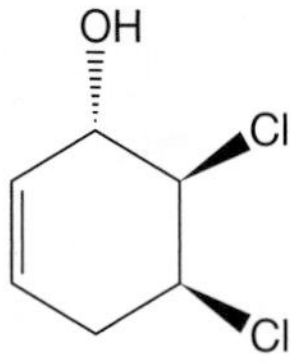
OH
Cl
Cl

B

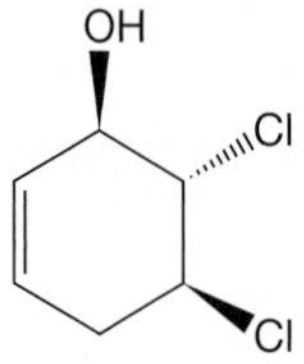
OH
Cl
Cl

C

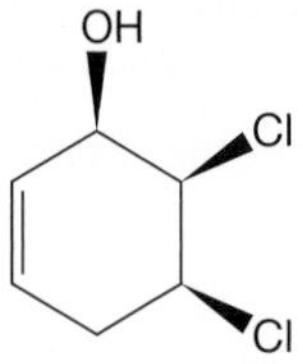
OH
Cl
Cl

D

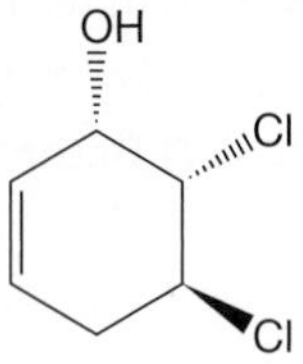
OH
Cl
Cl

E

Think	Solve
How many chiral centers does the molecule shown in the box have?	The molecule has three chiral centers, each of which is marked by an * in the structure shown here. 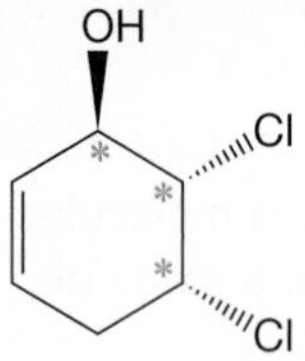
How many of those chiral centers will have the opposite configuration in the enantiomer?	Enantiomers are mirror images, so in the enantiomer of the given molecule the configurations of all three chiral centers must be reversed.

(continued)

How can you convert each chiral center from the given configuration to its opposite configuration?

To arrive at the opposite configuration for all chiral centers, we can exchange two substituents attached to each chiral center. On each chiral center, the most convenient substituents to exchange are the ones that are not part of the ring: the H and OH substituents on the chiral center at the top, and the H and Cl substituents on each of the other two chiral centers. The result, as shown here, is molecule **B**.

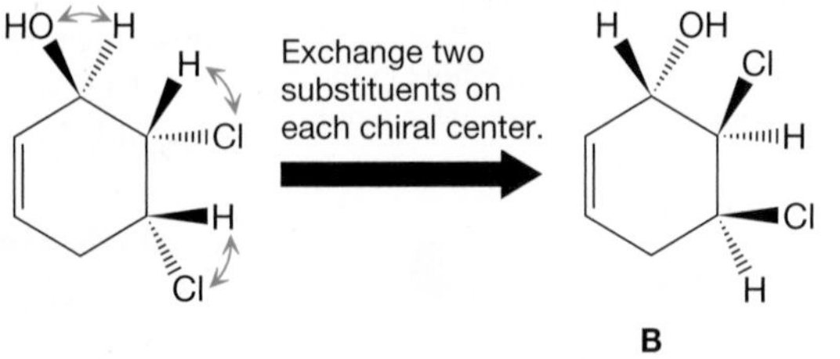
HO
H
H
Cl
H
Cl
Exchange two substituents on each chiral center.
H
OH
Cl
H
Cl
H
B

Try It The molecule shown in the box is chiral. Which of the molecules **F–I** is its enantiomer?

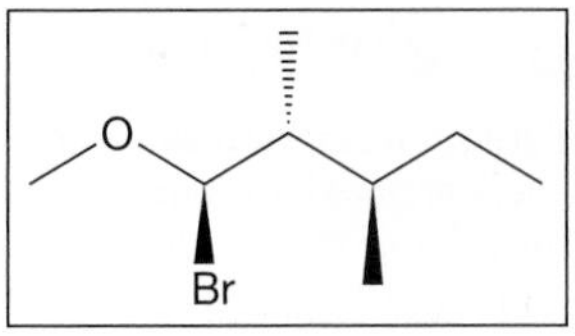
O
Br

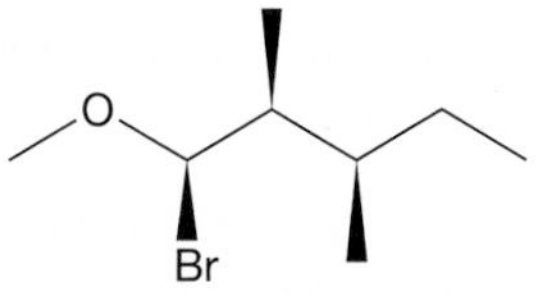
O
Br

F

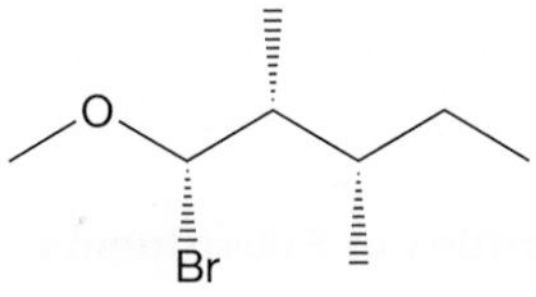
O
Br

G

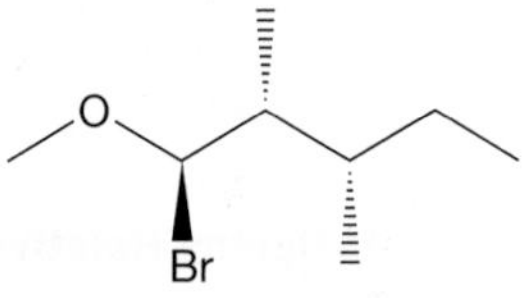
O
Br

H

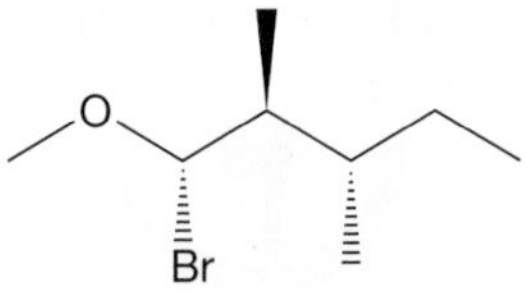
O
Br

I

5.6 Absolute Stereochemical Configurations: *R/S* Designations of Chiral Centers

SECTION 5.6 OBJECTIVES

You will be able to:

1. Determine the absolute configuration of a given chiral center as either *R* or *S*.
2. Incorporate the absolute configurations of chiral centers into a molecule's name.

In Section 5.5, we learned how to judge the *relative* configurations of a chiral center: Opposite configurations of a chiral center are related by either reflecting through a mirror or exchanging two of its substituents. Here in Section 5.6, we learn how to establish a chiral center's *absolute configuration*, which identifies the specific arrangement of the substituents in space. We will see, in particular, how to assign each configuration as either *R* or *S*.

One of the main reasons for establishing absolute configurations is to incorporate them into a molecule's name to distinguish one stereoisomer from others. For example, the name (2*S*,3*R*)-6-bromo-1,2,3-trichlorohexane, whose structure is shown in **Figure 5-12a**, indicates that there are two chiral centers in the molecule; the one at C-2 has the *S* configuration and the one at C-3 has the *R* configuration. The

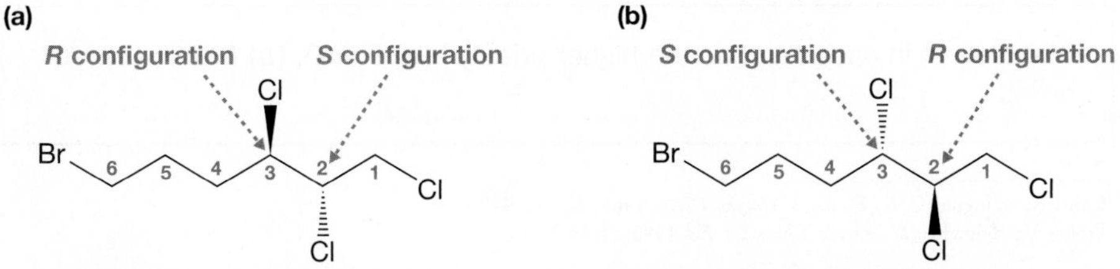
(a)
R configuration
S configuration
Cl
Br
6
5
4
3
2
1
Cl
Cl
(b)
S configuration
R configuration
Cl
Br
6
5
4
3
2
1
Cl
Cl

(2*S*,3*R*)-6-Bromo-1,2,3-trichlorohexane **(2*R*,3*S*)-6-Bromo-1,2,3-trichlorohexane**

FIGURE 5-12 Enantiomers and absolute configurations (a) (2*S*,3*R*)-6-Bromo-1,2,3-trichlorohexane and (b) (2*R*,3*S*)-6-bromo-1,2,3-trichlorohexane have opposite configurations at chiral centers 2 and 3.

(a) R configuration

Turning a steering wheel in the *clockwise* direction turns a car to the *right*.

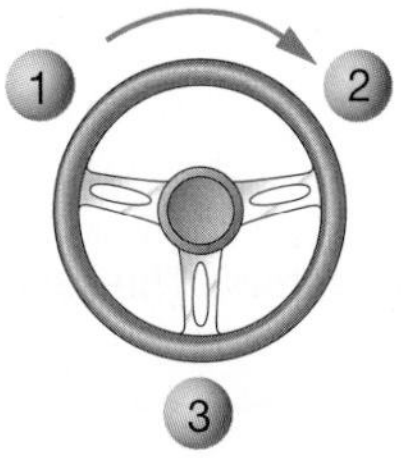
1
2
3

(b) S configuration

Turning a steering wheel in the *counterclockwise* direction turns a car to the *left*.

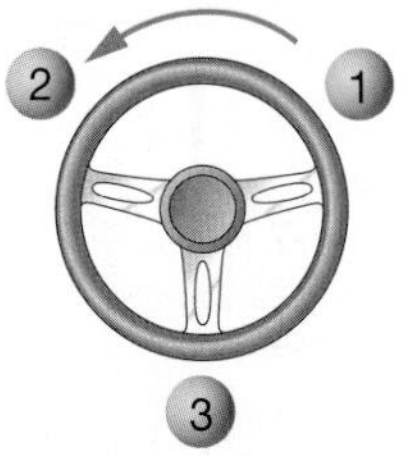
2
1
3

FIGURE 5-13 *R* and *S* configurations (a) With the lowest-priority substituent pointed away (as if down the column of a steering wheel), a clockwise arrangement of the top-three-priority substituents defines an *R* configuration. (b) A counterclockwise arrangement of these substituents defines an *S* configuration.

enantiomer shown in Figure 5-12b, in which the configurations of both chiral centers have been reversed, is named (2*R*,3*S*)-6-bromo-1,2,3-trichlorohexane.

To assign an absolute configuration, we use a collection of rules called the **Cahn–Ingold–Prelog system**,[1,2] which involves three basic steps:

Basic Steps for Assigning an *R* or *S* Configuration to a Chiral Center

1. Assign priorities, 1 through 4, to the substituents. The highest priority is 1 and the lowest priority is 4.
2. Orient the molecule properly so the lowest-priority substituent points away.
3. Observe the arrangement of substituents 1 through 3 and assign the configuration as *R* or *S*.
   a. If the substituents having priorities 1 through 3 are arranged *clockwise*, then the chiral center is assigned the ***R* configuration** (**Figure 5-13a**). (*R* derives from Latin, in which *rectus* means right.)
   b. If the substituents are arranged *counterclockwise*, then the chiral center is assigned the ***S* configuration** (Fig. 5-13b). (*S* derives from Latin, in which *sinistra* means left.)

As you can see, determining the relative priorities of substituents is a key part of assigning an *R* or *S* configuration to a chiral center. Establishing the substituent priorities involves applying the following rules that involve tiebreakers:

Assigning Relative Priorities of Substituents

1. Assign the substituent priorities on the basis of the atoms at the points of attachment. The atoms at the points of attachment are the ones responsible for attaching the substituents to the chiral center.
   a. Atoms that have higher atomic number receive higher priority.
   b. If two atoms are isotopes of the same element, the atom with the higher atomic mass receives the higher priority.
   c. For any ties, continue to Step 2.
2. Assign the substituent priorities on the basis of the sets of three atoms located one bond away from the points of attachment.
   a. Arrange the three atoms in each set in order from highest priority to lowest priority.
   b. Compare the first atom in each set and assign the higher priority to the substituent with the higher priority atom. If there is a tie, then:
   c. Compare the second atom in each set and assign the higher priority to the substituent with the higher priority atom. If there is a tie, then:
   d. Compare the third atom in each set and assign the higher priority to the substituent with the higher priority atom. If there is a tie, then continue to Step 3.
3. Repeat Steps 2a–2d using the sets of three atoms located one additional bond away from the points of attachment. If ties persist, continue repeating Steps 2a–2d, moving one more bond away from the points of attachment each time.

YOUR TURN **5.10**

Which atom in each pair has the higher priority? **(a)** F or O; **(b)** P or F; **(c)** ^{13}C or ^{12}C

[1]Cahn, R. S.; Ingold, C. K.; Prelog, V. *Angew. Chem.* **1966**, *78*, 413–447.
[2]Prelog, V.; Helmchen, G. *Angew. Chem. Int. Ed.* **1982**, *21*, 567–583.

YOUR TURN **5.11**

The atoms in each of the following sets are arranged alphabetically. Reorder the substituents in each set from *highest* to *lowest* priority. **(a)** Br, CH_3, Cl, F; **(b)** Br, CH_3, H, I; **(c)** CH_3, F, O, NH_2

Let's apply this system to determine the absolute configuration of the chiral center (which is at C-3) in the stereoisomer of 6-bromo-1,3-dichlorohexane shown in **Figure 5-14**. The substituents attached to the chiral center are Cl, H, $CH_2CH_2CH_2Br$, and CH_2CH_2Cl. According to Step 1 of **Assigning Relative Priorities of Substituents** (p. 220), we begin by examining just the atoms at the points of attachment, which are Cl, H, C, and C. According to Step 1a (illustrated in **Figure 5-15**), we assign Cl as the first priority because it has the highest atomic number, whereas we assign H as the fourth priority because it has the lowest atomic number. The other two substituents remain tied.

To break the tie between the two substituents attached by C, we proceed to Step 2 (illustrated on the left in **Figure 5-16**). For each substituent, we identify the set of three atoms that are one bond away from the point of attachment, and we arrange the three atoms in order of decreasing priority. The set of atoms is {C,H,H} for both substituents, so the tie remains.

Proceeding to Step 3 (illustrated on the right in Fig. 5-16), we examine the set of three atoms that are two bonds away from the point of attachment. The set of atoms is {C,H,H} for the Br-containing substituent and {Cl,H,H} for the Cl-containing substituent. Because Cl has a higher atomic number than C, the Cl-containing substituent has the higher priority. Therefore, of the four substituents attached to the chiral center, the Cl-containing substituent has the second priority and the Br-containing substituent has the third priority.

Having established the relative priorities of the four substituents, we note that the fourth-priority substituent is pointing away and that the first-, second-, and third-priority substituents are arranged clockwise, as indicated by the red arrow in **Figure 5-17**. Thus, the chiral center's configuration is *R*. In the IUPAC name, the stereochemical designation appears in parentheses and is typically written in front of the substituents: (*R*)-6-Bromo-1,3-dichlorohexane.

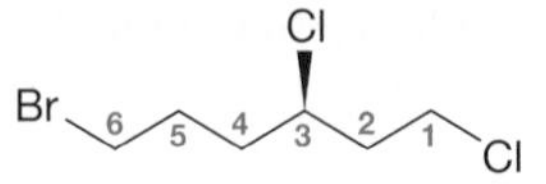

Cl
Br
6 5 4 3 2 1
Cl

6-Bromo-1,3-dichlorohexane

FIGURE 5-14 **One stereoisomer of 6-bromo-1,3-dichlorohexane**

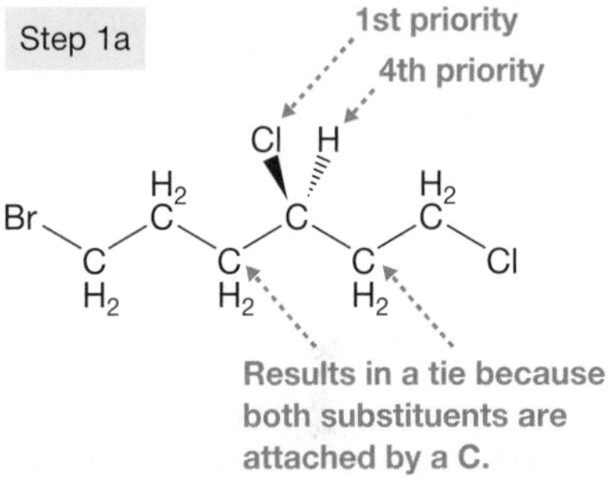

Step 1a
1st priority
4th priority
Results in a tie because both substituents are attached by a C.

FIGURE 5-15 **Step 1a in assigning substituent priorities to a chiral center**

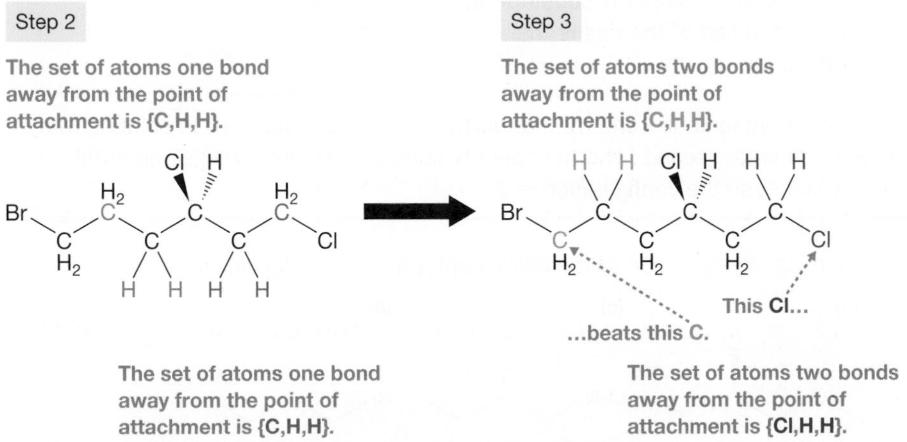

Step 2
The set of atoms one bond away from the point of attachment is {C,H,H}.
The set of atoms one bond away from the point of attachment is {C,H,H}.
Step 3
The set of atoms two bonds away from the point of attachment is {C,H,H}.
This Cl...
...beats this C.
The set of atoms two bonds away from the point of attachment is {Cl,H,H}.

FIGURE 5-16 **Steps 2 and 3 in assigning substituent priorities to a chiral center**

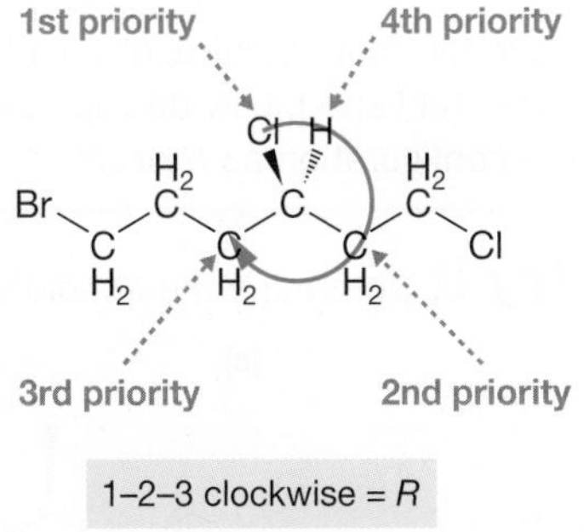

1st priority
4th priority
3rd priority
2nd priority
1–2–3 clockwise = R

FIGURE 5-17 **Absolute configuration of a chiral center**

SOLVED PROBLEM **5.6**

How to determine the absolute configuration of a chiral center

Break It Down **Determine the absolute stereochemical configuration of the chiral center in the molecule shown here.**

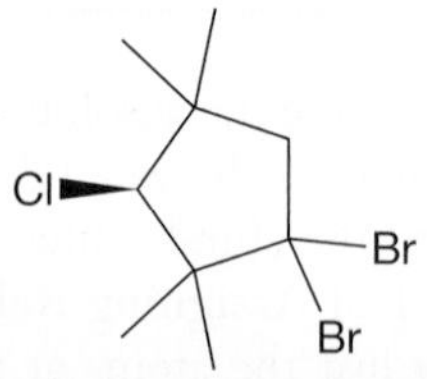

Cl
Br
Br

Think	Solve
What four substituents are attached to the chiral center?	Two of the substituents are Cl and H. The other two substituents make up the two halves of the ring, where one half of the ring contains the two Br atoms and the other does not.
Does Step 1 establish any group priorities unambiguously?	According to Step 1 in assigning relative priorities, we examine the atoms by which the four substituents are attached: Cl, H, C and C. The first-priority substituent is Cl because it has the highest atomic number. The fourth-priority is H because it has the lowest atomic number. The two substituents that are part of the ring are both attached by C, leaving a tie.
Does Step 2 establish the relative priorities of the two substituents that make up the ring?	The set of three atoms that are *one* bond away from the point of attachment is {C,C,C} for *both* the top and bottom halves of the ring. So the tie remains. 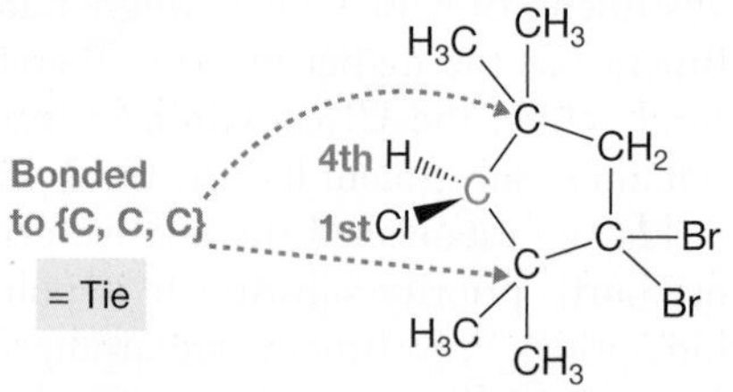 Bonded to {C, C, C} = Tie 4th H 1st Cl H_3C CH_3 CH_2 Br Br
Does Step 3 break the tie?	As illustrated, the set of atoms *two* bonds away from the point of attachment is {C,H,H} for the top half of the ring and is {Br,Br,C} for the bottom half. Because Br has a higher atomic number than C, the bottom half of the ring is the second-priority substituent, and the top half of the ring is the third-priority substituent. 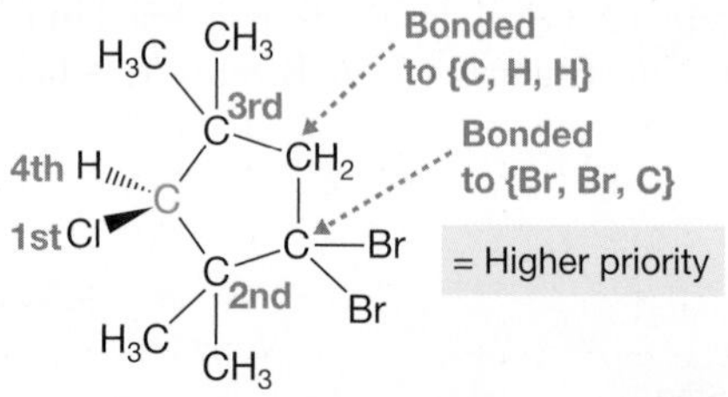 Bonded to {C, H, H} Bonded to {Br, Br, C} = Higher priority 3rd 2nd 4th H 1st Cl H_3C CH_3 CH_2 Br Br
Once the four substituent priorities are established, how do you assign the configuration as *R* or *S*?	In the representation shown, the fourth-priority substituent (H) is pointing away, and the first-, second-, and third-priority substituents are arranged counterclockwise, so the configuration is *S*.

Try It Determine the absolute stereochemical configuration of the chiral center in each molecule.

(a)

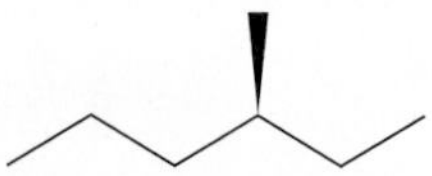

(b)

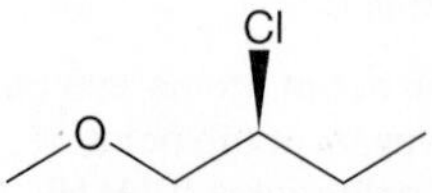

Cl
O

(c)

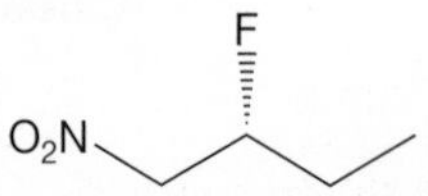

F
O_2N

(d)

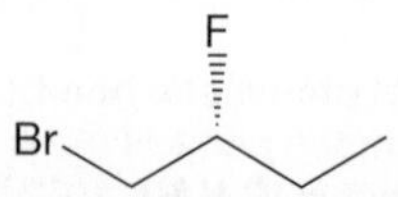

F
Br

Occasionally you will encounter substituents that contain double or triple bonds. To ensure that we can write a set of three atoms any number of bonds away from the point of attachment (and therefore apply Steps 2 and 3 of assigning substituent priorities), we replace the double and triple bonds as illustrated in **Figure 5-18**.

(a)

HC=CH2 is treated as HC—CH2
HC=NH is treated as HC—NH
HC=O is treated as HC—O

(b)

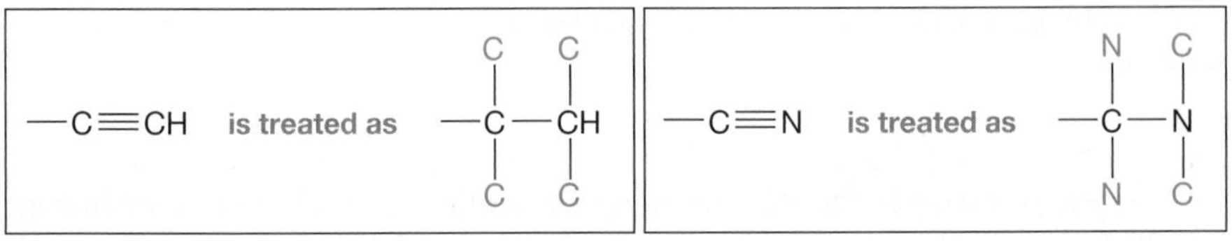
—C≡CH is treated as —C—CH
—C≡N is treated as —C—N

FIGURE 5-18 Priorities of substituents with double and triple bonds (a) An atom that is doubly bonded to another atom is treated as having two single bonds to the atom: one real atom (black) and one imaginary (red). (b) An atom that is triply bonded to another atom is treated as having three single bonds to the atom: one real atom (black) and two imaginary (red).

We apply this type of replacement to the stereoisomer of 3-methylhex-1-ene in **Figure 5-19**. Applying Step 1 of assigning substituent priorities, we identify H as the fourth-priority substituent. The other three substituents ($CH_2CH_2CH_3$, CH_3, and $CH{=}CH_2$) are all attached by C, resulting in a tie. Before applying Step 2, we replace the C=C double bond (Fig. 5-19a) with two C—C single bonds (Fig. 5-19b). According to Step 2, we then establish that the $C{=}CH_2$ substituent has first priority, $CH_2CH_2CH_3$ has second priority, and CH_3 has third priority. Because the top three priority substituents are arranged counterclockwise with the fourth-priority substituent pointing away, the configuration is *S*.

In all of the examples so far, the fourth-priority substituent on each chiral center has been pointed away. When the fourth-priority substituent is *not* pointed away, you can always reorient the molecule so the substituent does point away (a model kit is very helpful when reorienting molecules!) and proceed with the steps as outlined previously. Alternatively, you could apply one of the following methods:

Assigning *R* and *S* Configurations When the Fourth-Priority Substituent Does Not Point Away

- If the fourth-priority substituent points toward you, determine whether the first-, second-, and third-priority substituents are arranged clockwise or counterclockwise and reverse that arrangement before assigning *R* or *S*.
- If the fourth-priority substituent is in the plane of the page, exchange the fourth-priority substituent with the substituent that points away, then determine whether the first-, second-, and third-priority substituents are arranged clockwise or counterclockwise, and reverse that arrangement before assigning *R* or *S*.

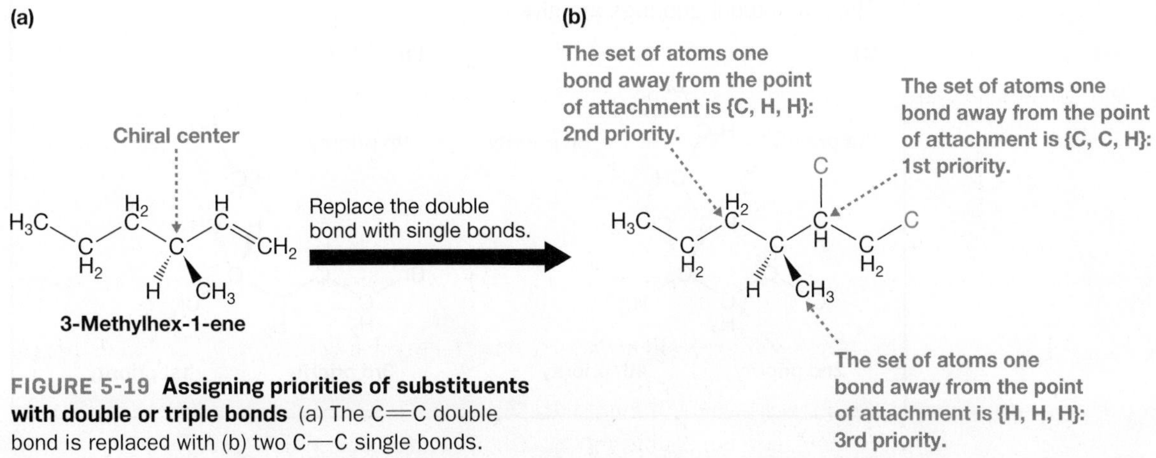
(a)
Chiral center
3-Methylhex-1-ene
Replace the double bond with single bonds.
(b)
The set of atoms one bond away from the point of attachment is {C, H, H}: 2nd priority.
The set of atoms one bond away from the point of attachment is {C, C, H}: 1st priority.
The set of atoms one bond away from the point of attachment is {H, H, H}: 3rd priority.

FIGURE 5-19 Assigning priorities of substituents with double or triple bonds (a) The C=C double bond is replaced with (b) two C—C single bonds.

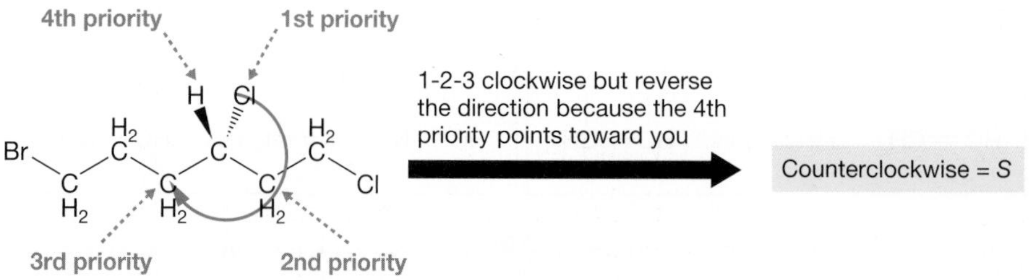
4th priority
1st priority
1-2-3 clockwise but reverse the direction because the 4th priority points toward you
Counterclockwise = *S*
3rd priority
2nd priority

FIGURE 5-20 Assigning a configuration when the 4th-priority substituent points toward you

Consider, for example, the stereoisomer of 6-bromo-1,3-dichlorohexane in **Figure 5-20**, for which the relative substituent priorities are labeled (these are the same substituents we examined in Figs. 5-14–5-17). The first-, second-, and third-priority substituents are arranged clockwise (red arrow), but the fourth-priority substituent (H) points toward you. If we reverse the arrangement to counterclockwise, the *S* configuration can be assigned.

In the example in **Figure 5-21** (with the same four substituents on the chiral center once again), the fourth-priority substituent is in the plane of the page. We first swap the H and Cl substituents so that H (the fourth-priority substituent) points away. Then we establish the configuration in the resulting structure, which is *S*. Finally, we assign the opposite configuration, *R*, to the chiral center in the original structure, because swapping the H and Cl substituents reversed the configuration.

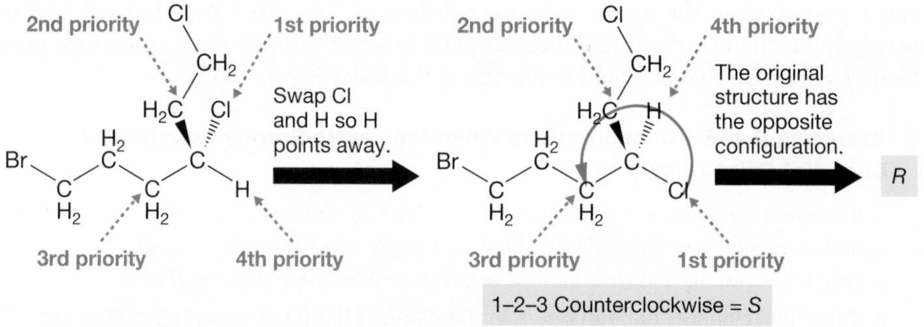
2nd priority
1st priority
Swap Cl and H so H points away.
3rd priority
4th priority
2nd priority
4th priority
The original structure has the opposite configuration.
R
3rd priority
1st priority
1–2–3 Counterclockwise = *S*

FIGURE 5-21 Assigning a configuration when the 4th-priority substituent is in the plane of the page

YOUR TURN **5.12**

Determine the absolute configuration of the chiral center in each structure. The substituent priorities are given.

(a) **(b)**

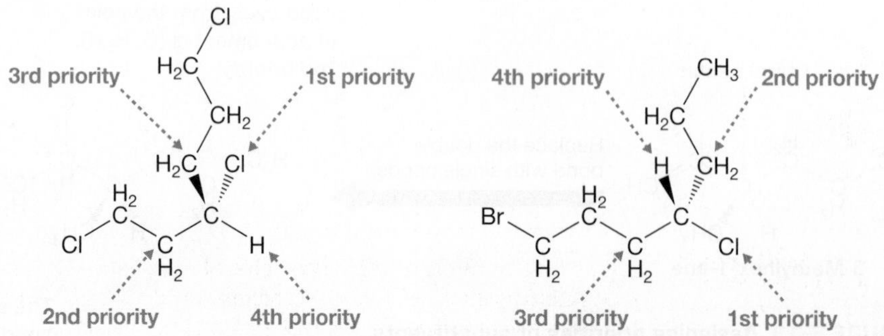
3rd priority
1st priority
2nd priority
4th priority
4th priority
2nd priority
3rd priority
1st priority

5.7 Mirror Images That Rapidly Interconvert: Single-Bond Rotation and Nitrogen Inversion

In our discussion about chirality so far, the nonsuperimposable mirror images we have examined do not interconvert; doing so would require breaking covalent bonds. However, in some cases, nonsuperimposable mirror images do rapidly interconvert, making it impossible to separate the mirror images:

> If a molecule and its mirror image rapidly interconvert, then the molecule is effectively *achiral*.

Conformers, for example, can often interconvert rapidly. Consider the gauche conformation of 1,2-dibromoethane shown in black in **Figure 5-22a** (see Recall box). Its mirror image is the gauche conformation shown in red. The two gauche conformations are nonsuperimposable (build models to convince yourself!), but they rapidly interconvert through rotation about the C—C bond (Fig. 5-22b), which indicates that 1,2-dibromoethane is achiral (Fig. 5-22c).

SECTION 5.7 OBJECTIVES

You will be able to:

1. Identify whether a molecule and its nonsuperimposable mirror image rapidly interconvert, and on that basis, determine whether the molecule is chiral.
2. Use Haworth projections to evaluate the chirality of substituted cyclohexanes.

◂ RECALL

In Section 4.1, we learned that the Newman projections in Figure 5-22 represent looking down the bond joining the front carbon (shown as a point) to the rear carbon (shown as a circle). In Section 4.2b, we distinguished gauche conformations of 1,2-dibromoethane as conformers that rapidly interconvert.

YOUR TURN 5.13

Determine whether each of these molecules is chiral or achiral.

(a) (b) (c)

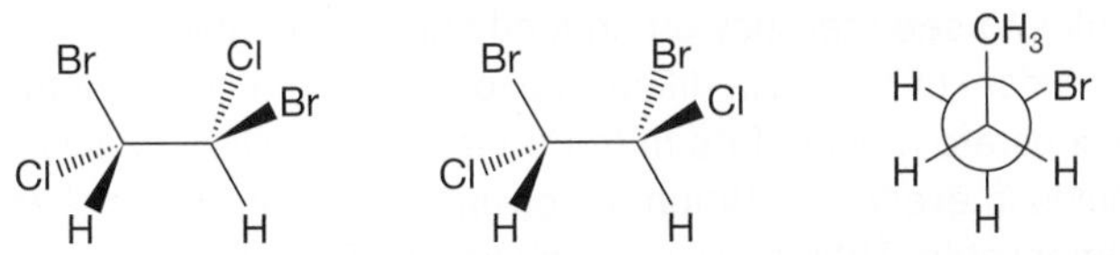

Br
Cl
Br
H
H
Cl
Br
Cl
H
H
CH3
Br
H
H
H
H

YOUR TURN 5.14

Determine whether each of these molecules is meso.

(a) (b)

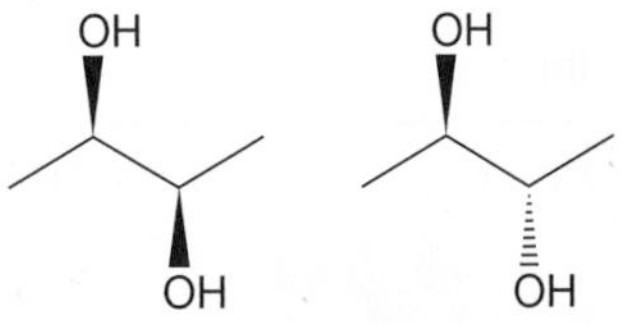

OH
OH
OH
OH

(a) (b) (c)

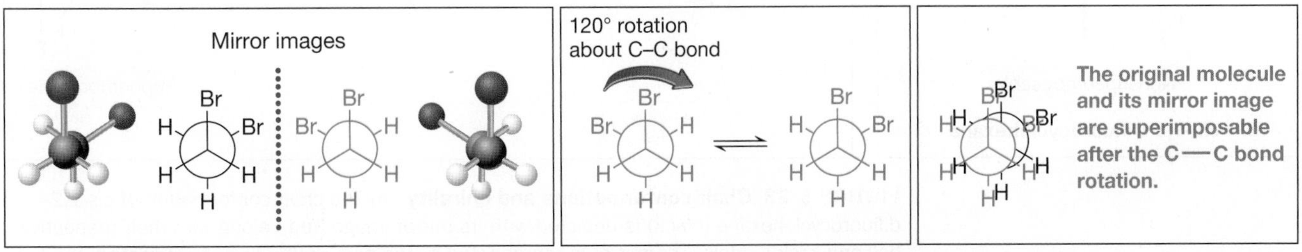

Mirror images
120° rotation
about C–C bond
The original molecule and its mirror image are superimposable after the C—C bond rotation.

Gauche 1,2-dibromoethane

FIGURE 5-22 Bond rotations and chirality (a) Newman projections and corresponding ball-and-stick models of 1,2-dibromoethane in a gauche conformation (black) and its mirror image (red). The mirror is indicated by the blue dotted line. (b) The mirror image after a 120° rotation of the rear CH_2Br group about the C—C single bond. (c) Overlaying the rotated conformer with the original molecule shows that the two are superimposable.

CONNECTIONS 5.1

Butane-2,3-diol in nature The compound in Your Turn 5.14a, a stereoisomer of butane-2,3-diol, is produced naturally by certain organisms via a process called butanediol fermentation. It is found in sweet corn, rotten mussels, and cocoa butter.

PALMER'S
COCOA BUTTER FORMULA
with Vitamin E
HEALS
NET WT. 100g/3.5 oz

The same principle applies to conformers of cyclohexane chairs. **Figure 5-23a**, for example, shows that one chair conformation of *cis*-1,2-difluorocyclohexane is nonsuperimposable on its mirror image. Figure 5-23b shows, however, that the mirror image is simply the *other* chair conformation (see Recall box). And, because the two chair conformations rapidly interconvert, *cis*-1,2-difluorocyclohexane is *achiral*.

The preceding example suggests that, when determining the chirality of substituted cyclohexanes, we do not need to consider the details surrounding the conformation of the chair. Rather, what matters is the *relative* positioning of the substituents with respect to the plane of the ring (i.e., cis or trans). Therefore, we can simplify the problem by working with structures that assume a flat ring, such as Haworth projections or regular line structures that are viewed from the top and incorporate dash–wedge notation. For example, the Haworth projection of *cis*-1,2-difluorocyclohexane (**Figure 5-24a**) has a plane of symmetry, so it is achiral. *trans*-1,2-Difluorocyclohexane, on the other hand, is chiral; note that its Haworth projection (Fig. 5-24b) has no plane of symmetry.

YOUR TURN 5.15

Carry out the following steps using molecular models to prove to yourself that *cis*-1,2-difluorocyclohexane is achiral and *trans*-1,2-difluorocyclohexane is chiral, as predicted using Haworth projections.

(a) Build a model of *cis*-1,2-difluorocyclohexane in a chair conformation and a separate model of its mirror image. Try to align the two molecules in every orientation to convince yourself that they are not superimposable. Then carry out a chair flip of just the mirror image and align the two molecules to see that they are indeed superimposable.

(b) Build a model of *trans*-1,2-difluorocyclohexane in a chair conformation and a separate model of its mirror image. Try to align the two molecules in every orientation to convince yourself that they are not superimposable. Then carry out a chair flip of just the mirror image and try to align the two molecules again in every orientation to see that they are still *not* superimposable.

◀ RECALL

In Section 4.5, we learned that the two chair conformations of cyclohexane rapidly interconvert via a chair flip. When a chair flip occurs, substituents that are axial become equatorial and vice versa, but the substituents remain on the same side of the ring's plane in both chair conformations.

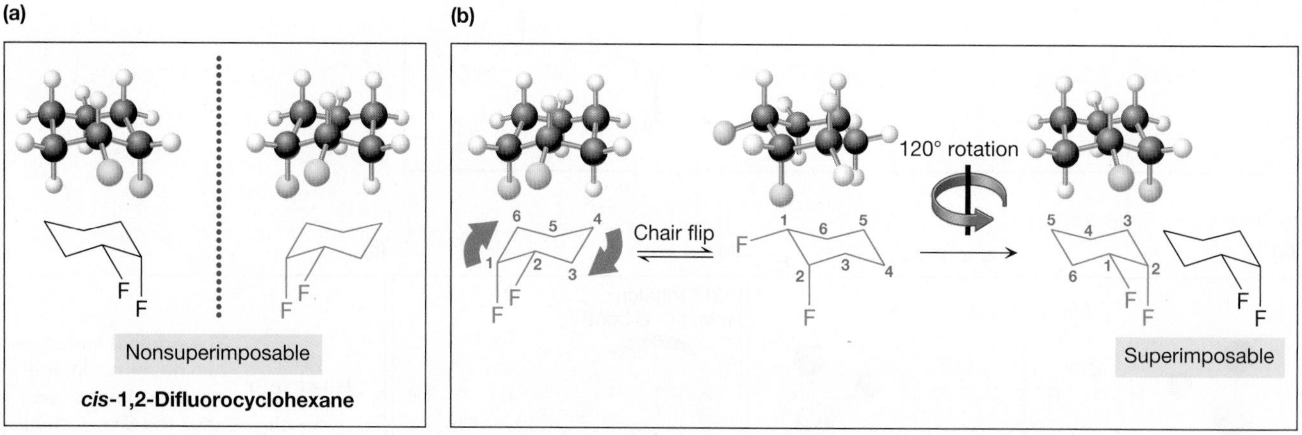

(a)
(b)
Nonsuperimposable
cis-1,2-Difluorocyclohexane
Chair flip
120° rotation
Superimposable

FIGURE 5-23 Chair conformations and chirality (a) The chair conformation of *cis*-1,2-difluorocyclohexane (black) is depicted with its mirror image (red), along with their respective ball-and-stick models. The mirror is represented by the blue dotted line. As indicated, the two structures are nonsuperimposable. (b) The mirror image (red) undergoes a chair flip, followed by a rotation of 120°. The resulting orientation is superimposable on the original molecule (black). Therefore, *cis*-1,2-difluorocyclohexane is achiral.

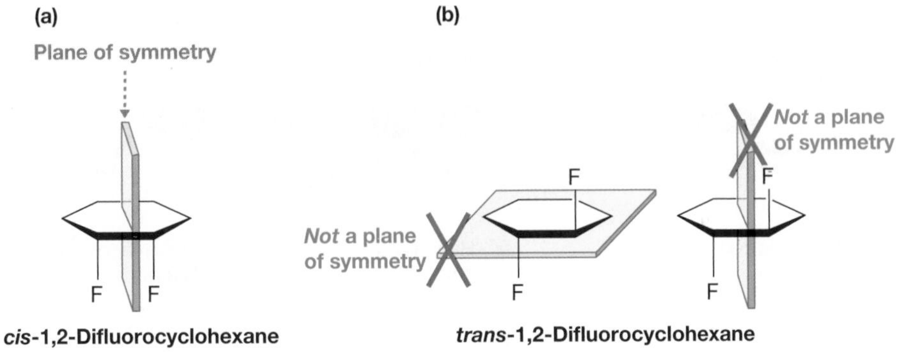
(a)
Plane of symmetry
F
F
cis-1,2-Difluorocyclohexane
(b)
Not a plane of symmetry
F
F
Not a plane of symmetry
F
F
trans-1,2-Difluorocyclohexane

FIGURE 5-24 Haworth projections and chirality Haworth projections accurately depict the chirality of a substituted cyclohexane ring. (a) The Haworth projection of *cis*-1,2-difluorocyclohexane has a plane of symmetry, so it is achiral. (b) *trans*-1,2-Difluorocyclohexane is chiral, so the Haworth projection does not have a plane of symmetry.

YOUR TURN 5.16

Determine whether each of the following molecules is chiral or achiral.

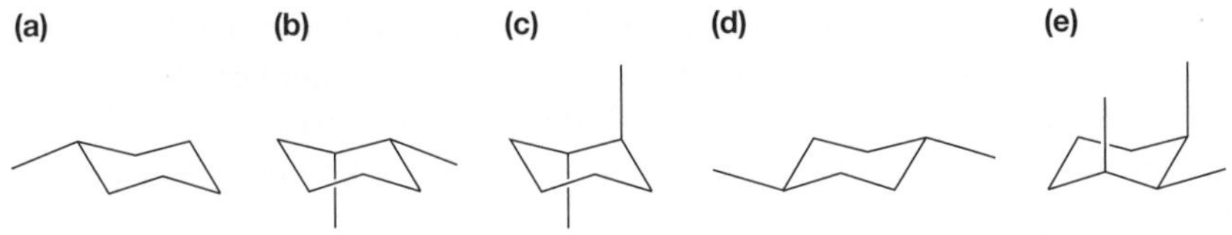
(a)
(b)
(c)
(d)
(e)

Nonsuperimposable mirror images that rapidly interconvert are not limited to conformers. Consider, for example, uncharged nitrogen atoms in molecules such as *N*-methylethanamine (ethylmethylamine), shown in **Figure 5-25**. Notice that the molecule and its mirror image are nonsuperimposable and therefore appear to be enantiomers. The N atom, furthermore, *appears* to be a chiral center because it is tetrahedral and has four different groups: H, CH_3, CH_2CH_3, and a lone pair of electrons. However, the mirror images rapidly interconvert through a process called **nitrogen inversion**, the dynamics of which are depicted in **Figure 5-26** (next page). Because of this rapid interconversion, the mirror images cannot be separated and *N*-methylethanamine is achiral. Thus, the N atom cannot be counted as a chiral center. In general:

Uncharged nitrogen atoms that undergo *nitrogen inversion* are not chiral centers.

Nitrogen inversion is analogous to an umbrella that turns inside out in a gust of wind. As shown on the left in Figure 5-26, the N atom is initially pyramidal and sp^3-hybridized, with its three bonds pointing toward the left. Those bonds and the attached

CONNECTIONS 5.2

Paving roads and cleaning your clothes 1-Bromopropane (Your Turn 5.13c) has been used as a solvent, finding applications in asphalt production, aerosol glues, and synthetic fiber production. In the 21st century, with the phasing out of tetrachloroethylene, 1-bromopropane has found increasing use as a dry-cleaning solvent.

DRY
CLEANING
LAUNDRY

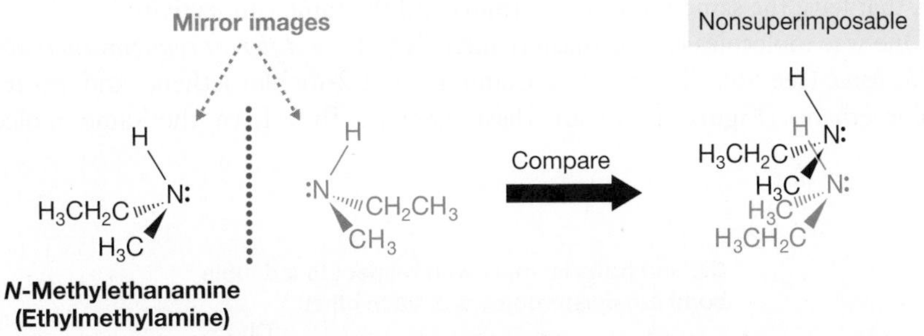
Mirror images
Nonsuperimposable
H
N:
H3CH2C
H3C
H
:N
CH2CH3
CH3
Compare
N-Methylethanamine
(Ethylmethylamine)

FIGURE 5-25 Uncharged nitrogen atoms that might appear as chiral centers When the lone pair of electrons is counted as a group, *N*-methylethanamine has a tetrahedral nitrogen atom with four different groups, suggesting that *N* should be a chiral center. Additionally, the mirror image is nonsuperimposable on the original molecule, suggesting that ethylmethylamine should be chiral.

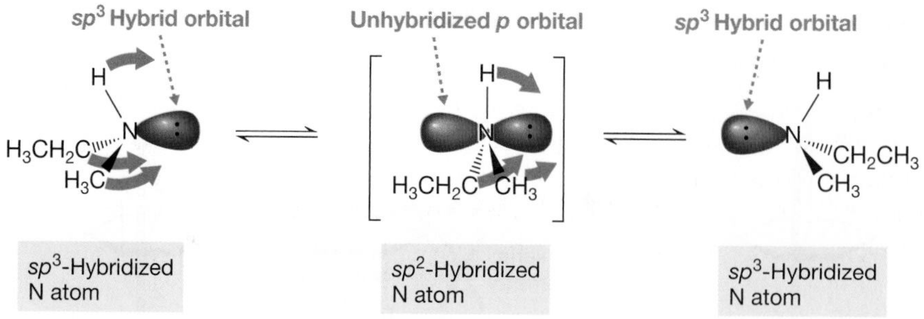

sp3 Hybrid orbital
Unhybridized p orbital
sp3 Hybrid orbital
H
H
H
N
N
N
H3CH2C
H3C
H3CH2C
CH3
CH2CH3
CH3
sp3-Hybridized N atom
sp2-Hybridized N atom
sp3-Hybridized N atom

FIGURE 5-26 Nitrogen inversion *N*-Methylethanamine is achiral because the two pyramidal mirror images rapidly interconvert via a planar intermediate with an sp^2-hybridized N atom. Consequently, the uncharged nitrogen atom is not a chiral center.

groups swing to the right to proceed through a planar species that is sp^2-hybridized, which continues on to ultimately produce the structure shown at the right of the figure, in which N is again pyramidal and sp^3-hybridized.

This process occurs with relative ease, in large part because the lone pair of electrons can freely move from one side of the N atom to the other. If that lone pair were instead tied up in a covalent bond, as is the case with the quaternary ammonium ion we saw previously in Figure 5-10 (p. 215), then nitrogen inversion would not take place, and the N atom, if it were bonded to four *different* groups, would be a chiral center.

YOUR TURN **5.17**

How many chiral centers are present in each of the following species?

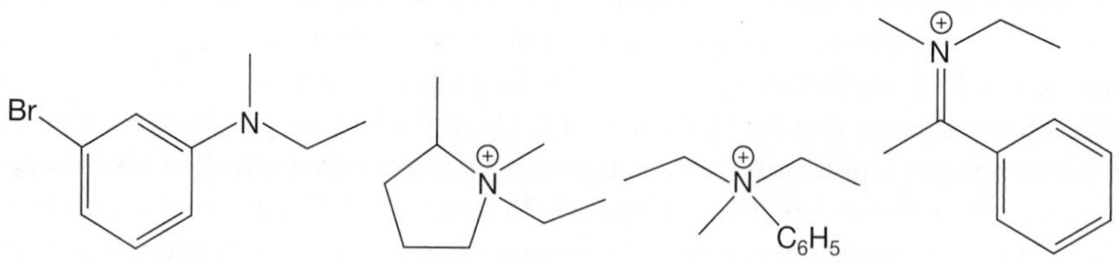

(a)
(b)
(c)
(d)
Br
N
N
N
C6H5
N

5.8 Diastereomers: Double-Bond Configurations and Chiral Centers

SECTION 5.8 OBJECTIVES

You will be able to:

1. Identify diastereomers from the configurations of the double bonds or chiral centers they possess.
2. Establish the absolute configuration of a double bond as either *Z* or *E*.

Recall that *diastereomers* are *stereoisomers that are not mirror images of each other* (review the flowchart in Fig. 5-1, p. 206). To be stereoisomers, they must be different molecules that have the same molecular formula and the same connectivity.

One way molecules can be diastereomers is to have *different configurations about a double bond* (see Recall box). For example, *cis*-1,2-dichloroethene and *trans*-1,2-dichloroethene (**Figure 5-27**) are diastereomers. They have the same molecular

◂ RECALL

In Section 3.7 we learned a C═C double bond has two possible configurations if neither of the carbon atoms is bonded to two identical substituents. The two configurations of the double bond are related by the exchange of the two substituents attached to one of the carbons.

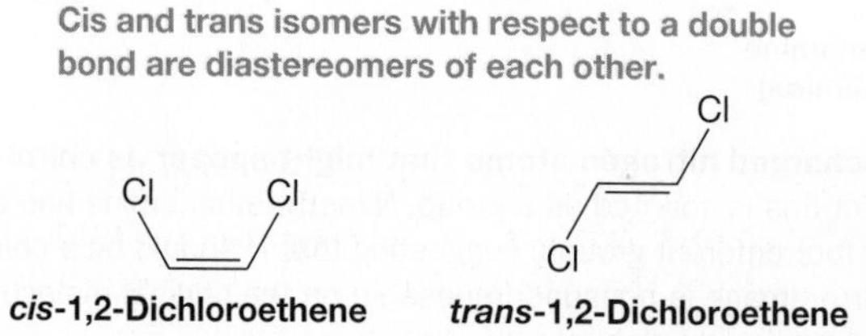

Cis and trans isomers with respect to a double bond are diastereomers of each other.
Cl
Cl
Cl
Cl
cis-1,2-Dichloroethene
trans-1,2-Dichloroethene

FIGURE 5-27 Diastereomers of an alkene

Nanocars

Can you imagine an electric car about 10,000 times smaller than the thickness of a human hair? Dr. Ben Feringa, who shared the Nobel Prize in Chemistry for the design and synthesis of molecular machines, could imagine such a car, and in 2011, he and his research team at the University of Groningen (The Netherlands) constructed one! It is a single molecule, roughly 1 nm long, as shown in **Figure 5-28a**. Each of the four "wheels" comprises a planar three-ring system.

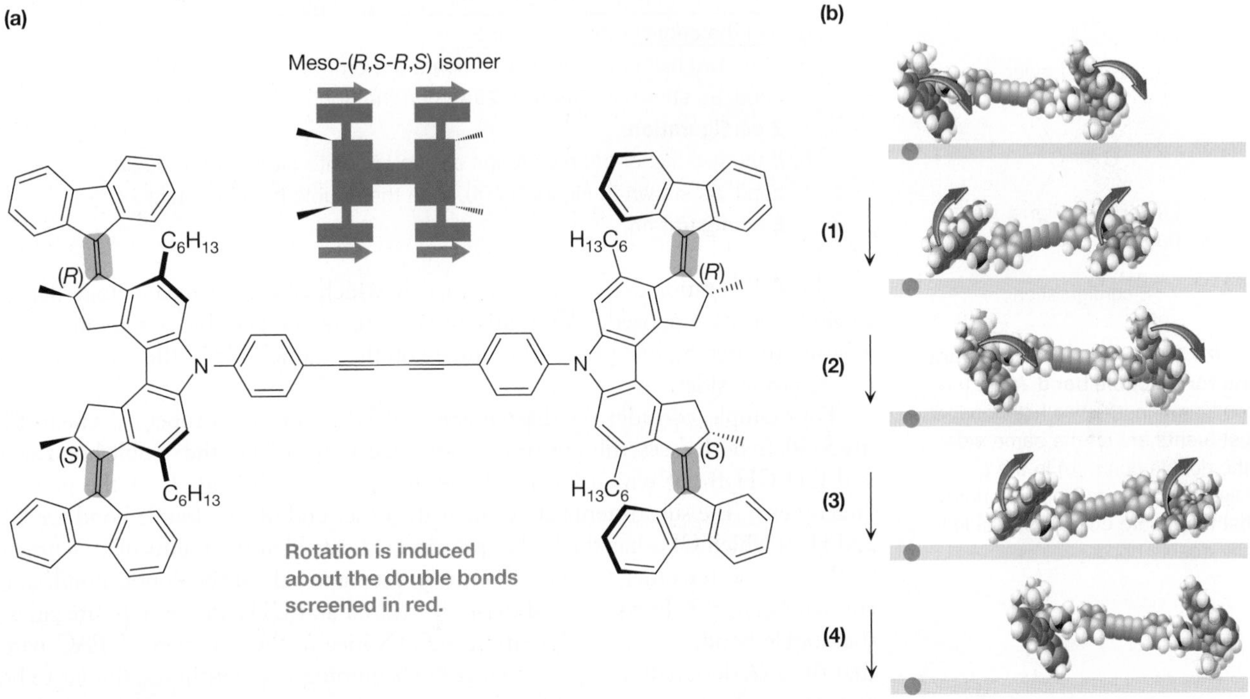

(a)
Meso-(R,S-R,S) isomer
C_6H_{13}
(R)
(S)
N
$H_{13}C_6$
Rotation is induced about the double bonds screened in red.
(b)
(1)
(2)
(3)
(4)

FIGURE 5-28

After the car is deposited via vapor onto a copper surface, it is powered by electrons from a scanning tunneling microscope (STM). Each wheel functions independently of the others, making the nanocar analogous to a four-wheel-drive vehicle. As shown in Figure 5-28b, a full rotation of each wheel takes place in four separate steps. First, excitation by a pulse from the STM provides energy to temporarily break the π bond of the double bond that connects the wheel. Each such STM pulse isomerizes the double bond, resulting in a partial turn. The wheel is left in a sterically strained conformation as a result, and in Step 2 that strain is relieved by relaxing into a more stable conformation. Steps 3 and 4 are the same as Steps 1 and 2.

The direction in which each wheel rotates is governed by the specific configuration of its four chiral centers. With the configurations shown, the four wheels work in concert to propel the nanocar forward. Other configurations can lead to the wheels working against each other, resulting either in no net motion or in the car turning.

Powering a nanocar in a single direction like this provides a proof of concept for more advanced nanomachines that could carry out specific tasks within our bodies. One task that scientists envision is targeting and killing cancer cells.

formula and the same connectivity, but they are different molecules, given that one has chlorine atoms on the same side of the double bond and the other has chlorine atoms on opposite sides. Moreover, they are *not* mirror images of each other.

Because double-bond configurations can distinguish diastereomers, it is helpful to characterize the absolute configuration of double bonds in a way similar to how we use

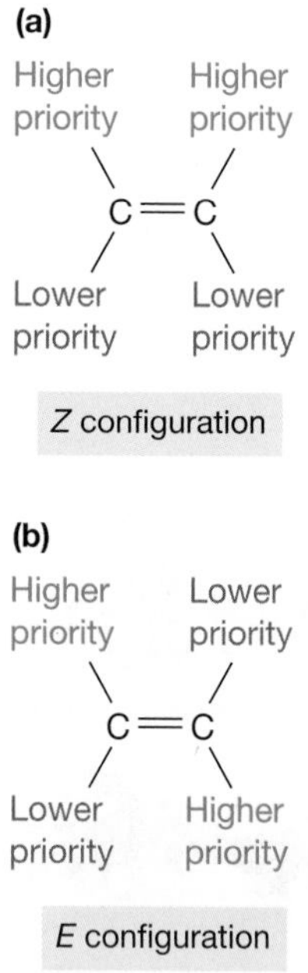
(a)
Higher priority
Higher priority
C=C
Lower priority
Lower priority
Z configuration
(b)
Higher priority
Lower priority
C=C
Lower priority
Higher priority
E configuration

FIGURE 5-29 Absolute configurations for a double bond (a) In the *Z* configuration, the two higher-priority substituents are on the same side of the double bond. (b) In the *E* configuration, the two higher-priority substituents are on opposite sides of the double bond.

R or *S* to characterize the absolute configurations of a chiral center (Section 5.6). For double bonds, however, we use *Z* or *E* to designate the configuration:

Rules for Determining a *Z* or *E* Configuration of a Double Bond

1. Determine the higher priority substituent attached to one atom of the double bond. Use the rules involving tiebreakers from Section 5.6 (p. 220) to establish the relative priorities.
2. Determine the higher priority substituent attached to the other atom of the double bond. Again use the rules involving tiebreakers from Section 5.6.
3. Observe the relative positions of the two higher-priority substituents and assign the configuration as *Z* or *E*.
   a. If the two higher-priority substituents are on the same side of the double bond, as shown in **Figure 5-29a**, then the double bond is assigned the ***Z* configuration**.
   b. If the two higher-priority groups are on opposite sides of the double bond, as shown in Figure 5-29b, then the double bond is assigned the ***E* configuration**.

The *Z*/*E* notation derives from German, in which *zusammen* means "together" and *entgegen* means "opposed." Alternatively, you can remember this mnemonic, noting whether the two higher-priority groups are on the "Zame" side of the double bond or on "Epposite" sides.

For example, consider the diastereomers of 5-bromo-3-chloropent-2-ene in **Figure 5-30**. In both cases, the substituents attached at one end of the double bond are Cl and CH_2CH_2Br, of which Cl has the higher priority (Cl beats C at the points of attachment). The substituents attached at the other end of the double bond are CH_3 and H, of which CH_3 has the higher priority (C beats H at the points of attachment). In the first diastereomer, Cl and CH_3 are on the same side of the double bond, so the configuration is *Z*. In the second diastereomer, Cl and CH_3 are on opposite sides of the double bond, so the configuration is *E*. (Notice in the complete IUPAC names that the *Z*/*E* designations are written at the beginning in parentheses, similar to how *R*/*S* designations are indicated for chiral centers.)

YOUR TURN 5.18

What is the configuration, *Z* or *E*, for each of the following double bonds?

(a) *cis*-1,2-Dichloroethene

(b) *trans*-1,2-Dichloroethene

(c)

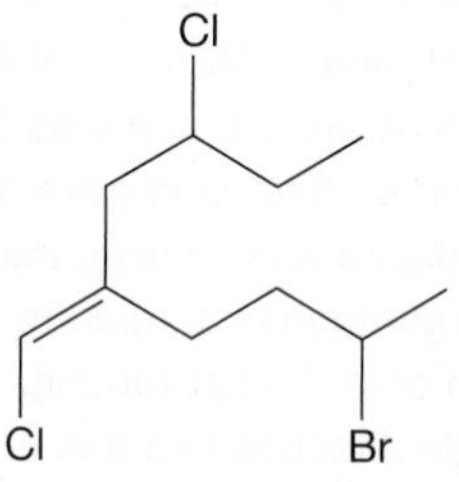
Cl
Cl
Br

(d)

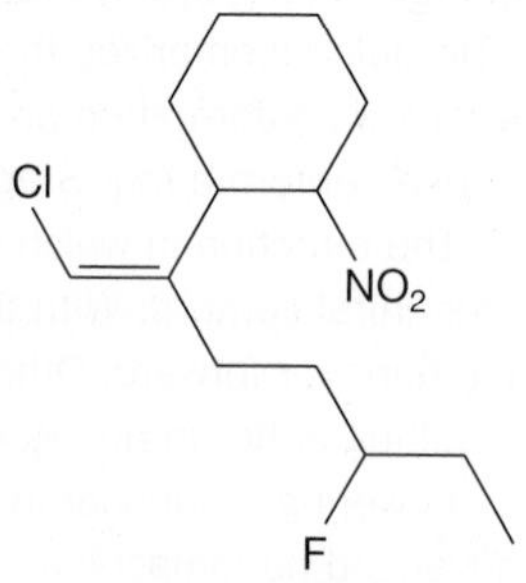
Cl
NO2
F

Diastereomers don't necessarily have a double bond. For example, the stereoisomers of 1-bromo-3-chlorocyclopentane in **Figure 5-31** are diastereomers. The two structures have the same molecular formula and the same connectivity, but they are different molecules and are not mirror images of each other.

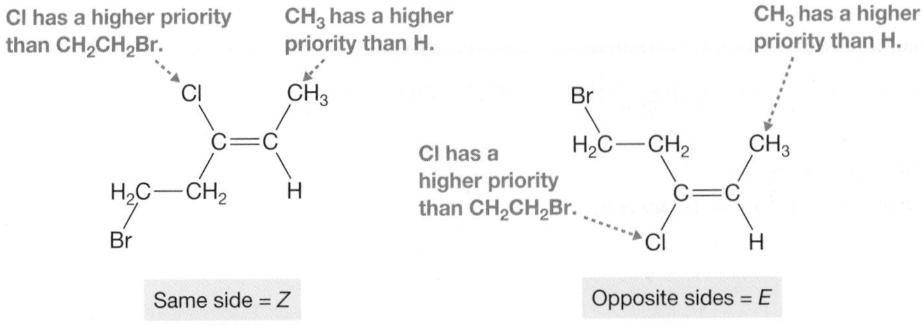
Cl has a higher priority than CH_2CH_2Br.
CH_3 has a higher priority than H.
Cl
CH_3
C=C
H_2C—CH_2
H
Br
Same side = *Z*
CH_3 has a higher priority than H.
Br
H_2C—CH_2
CH_3
Cl has a higher priority than CH_2CH_2Br.
C=C
Cl
H
Opposite sides = *E*

(*Z*)-5-Bromo-3-chloropent-2-ene (*E*)-5-Bromo-3-chloropent-2-ene

FIGURE 5-30 Assigning *Z* and *E* configurations

The stereoisomers in Figure 5-31 are different molecules because the configurations of the chiral centers at C-1 and C-3 in the first molecule are not the same as in the second molecule. Specifically, the molecules have opposite configurations at C-3 but the same configuration at C-1, indicated by the (1*S*,3*R*) and (1*S*,3*S*) designations in the names of the two molecules.

Furthermore, we know that the stereoisomers in Figure 5-31 are not mirror images because, as we learned in Section 5.5a, enantiomers have opposite configurations at *all* chiral centers. In this case, the molecules have different configurations at only one of the two chiral centers.

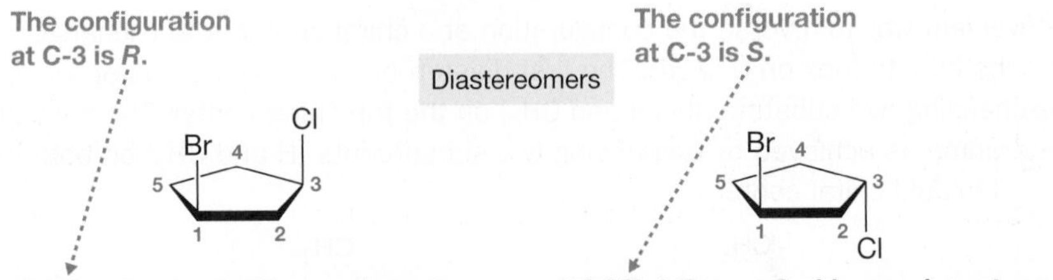
The configuration at C-3 is *R*.
Diastereomers
The configuration at C-3 is *S*.
Br
Cl
4
5
3
1
2
Br
4
5
3
1
2
Cl

(1*S*,3*R*)-1-Bromo-3-chlorocyclopentane (1*S*,3*S*)-1-Bromo-3-chlorocyclopentane

FIGURE 5-31 Diastereomers with no double bonds

The ideas we just used can be generalized to help us distinguish diastereomers from enantiomers:

- If two isomers are related by reversing the configurations of some, but not all, chiral centers, then the two molecules are *diastereomers* of each other.
- Recall from Section 5.5a that if two isomers are related by reversing the configurations of *all* chiral centers, then the two molecules are *enantiomers*.

YOUR TURN **5.19**

Determine whether the molecules shown here are diastereomers.

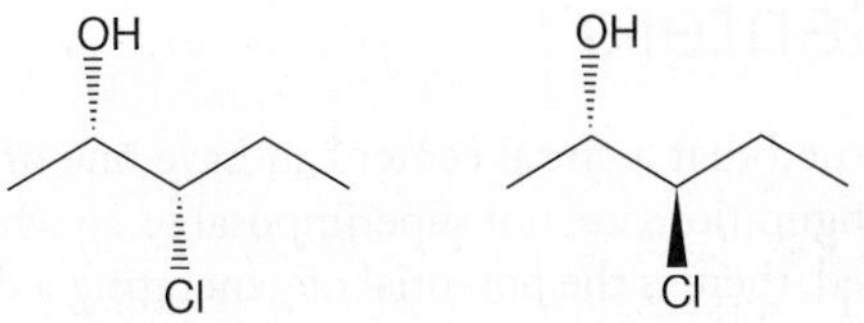
OH
Cl
OH
Cl

SOLVED PROBLEM **5.7**

How to draw diastereomers of a molecule with chiral centers

Break It Down **Given this configurational isomer of 1-chloro-2,3-dimethylcyclopentane, draw one of its diastereomers.**

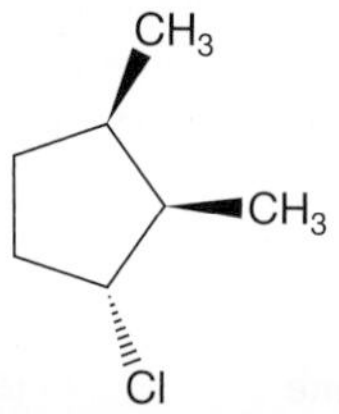

CH3
CH3
Cl

Think	Solve
How many chiral centers are there?	The three chiral centers in the molecule are indicated by * in the structure shown here. 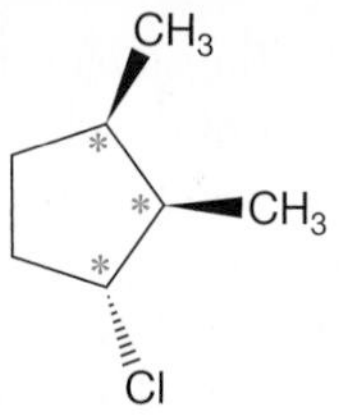 CH3 CH3 Cl
To draw a diastereomer, how many chiral centers should have their configurations reversed?	To draw a diastereomer, we must reverse the configurations at some, but not all, of the chiral centers. In this case, we could reverse the configuration at one chiral center, or at two of the chiral centers, but not at all three.
How can you accomplish the reversal of a configuration at a chiral center?	A convenient way to reverse the configuration at a chiral center is to exchange two substituents (box on p. 214). The first diastereomer shown here is achieved by exchanging two substituents (H and CH_3) on the top chiral center. The second diastereomer is achieved by exchanging two substituents (H and CH_3) on both the top and middle chiral centers. 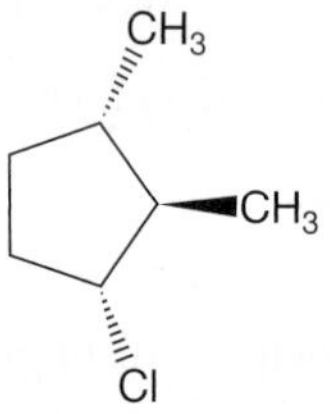 CH3 CH3 Cl 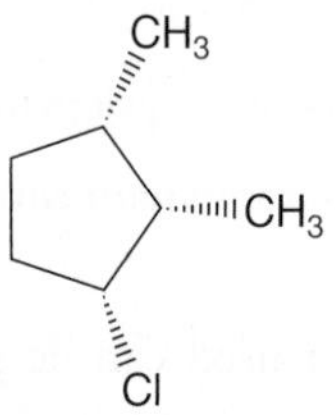 CH3 CH3 Cl

Try It Draw two more diastereomers of the molecule given in Solved Problem 5.7.

SECTION 5.9 OBJECTIVES

You will be able to:

1. Determine the maximum number of stereoisomers that can exist for a structure, on the basis of the number of chiral centers present.
2. Draw all stereoisomers of a given structure that possesses chiral centers.

Strategies for Success
Drawing All Stereoisomers of a Molecule with Chiral Centers

5.9 Strategies for Success: Drawing All Stereoisomers of a Molecule with Chiral Centers

In Section 5.5, we learned that a chiral center can have one of two configurations: *R* or *S*. The opposite configurations are not superimposable, so whenever a chiral center's configuration is reversed, there is the potential of generating a distinct stereoisomer. If there is just one chiral center, two stereoisomers exist: (*R*) and (*S*). If there are two chiral centers, there are four combinations, (*R*,*R*), (*R*,*S*), (*S*,*R*), and (*S*,*S*), giving rise to four potential stereoisomers. Notice that on going from one chiral center to two chiral centers, the number of *R*/*S* combinations doubles from two to four. In fact, the number of *R*/*S* combinations doubles with the addition of *each* chiral center. Therefore:

> The maximum number of configurational isomers that can exist for a molecule with *n* chiral centers is 2^n.

This number represents the *maximum* because, depending on the symmetry of the molecule, some of those *R*/*S* combinations could end up being the same stereoisomer.

How can we draw all stereoisomers of a given structure? One way is to use the following systematic method:

Drawing All Stereoisomers of a Given Structure

1. Identify all chiral centers. To keep track of them, it helps to label the chiral centers 1, 2, etc.
2. Draw the first structure by specifying the configuration at every chiral center. Use dash–wedge notation to specify each configuration; for the first structure, the choice of configurations does not matter.
3. Draw the second structure by reversing the configuration only at chiral center 1.
4. Draw the next two structures by reversing the configuration at chiral center 2. Repeat the configurations you drew for all other chiral centers in Steps 2 and 3.
5. Draw the next four structures by reversing the configuration at chiral center 3. Repeat the configurations you drew for all other chiral centers in Steps 2–4.
6. Continue this pattern for each remaining chiral center. The number of structures will double each time.

Finally: Look for any redundant structures and omit them.

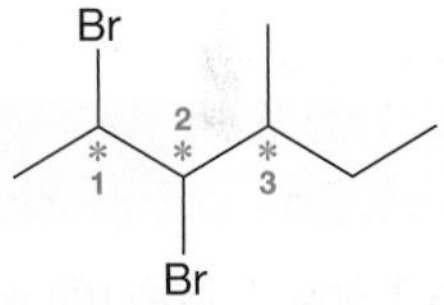

Br
Br
1
2
3

2,3-Dibromo-4-methylhexane

FIGURE 5-32 Step 1 in drawing all stereoisomers

Let's apply this method to 2,3-dibromo-4-methylhexane, whose connectivity is shown in **Figure 5-32**. For Step 1, we note that there are three chiral centers, numbered 1–3. Steps 2–5 are shown in **Figure 5-33**. For Step 2, we draw structure **A**, arbitrarily choosing to have all H atoms (not shown) on the chiral centers point away. For Step 3, we draw structure **B** by reversing the configuration only at chiral center 1, leaving alone the configurations at the other two chiral centers. For Step 4, we draw structures **C** and **D** by reversing the configuration at chiral center 2, repeating the configurations at chiral center 1 from Steps 2 and 3. For Step 5, we draw structures **E**, **F**, **G**, and **H** by reversing the configuration at chiral center 3, repeating the configurations at chiral centers 1 and 2 from Steps 2–4. Finally, we note that there are no

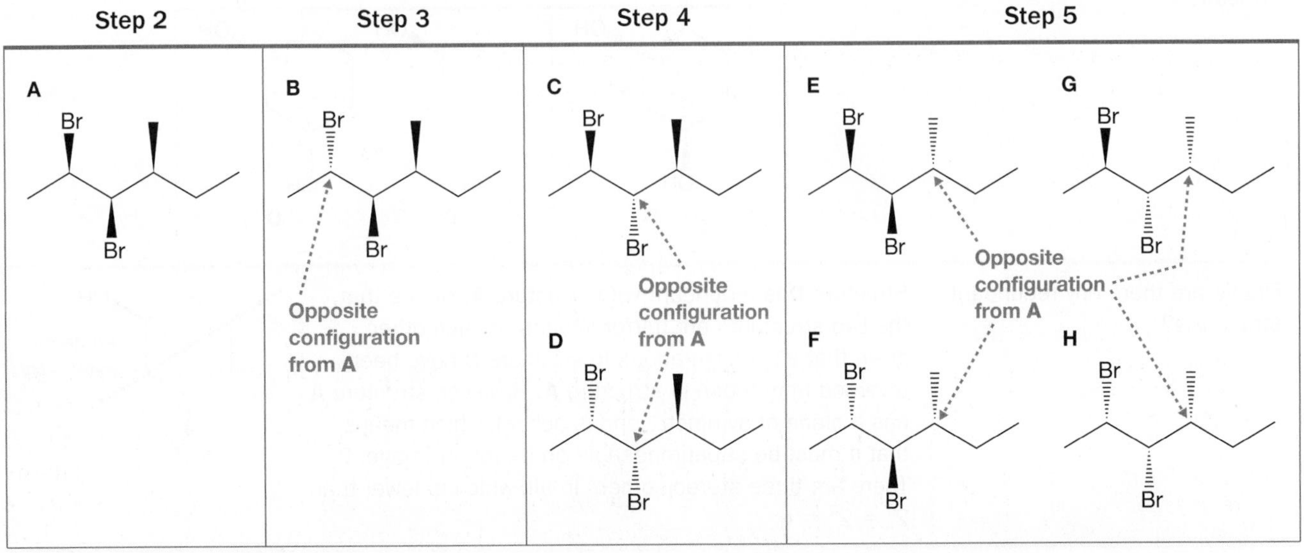

Step 2
Step 3
Step 4
Step 5
A
B
C
D
E
F
G
H
Br
Opposite configuration from A

FIGURE 5-33 Steps 2–5 in drawing all stereoisomers 2,3-Dibromo-4-methylhexane has three chiral centers, giving rise to a total of $2^3 = 8$ configurational isomers.

redundancies in any of the structures (convince yourself of this!), so there are eight unique stereoisomers.

YOUR TURN 5.20

> Which molecules in Figure 5-33 are enantiomers of molecule **A**? Which molecules are diastereomers of molecule **A**? *Hint*: How many chiral centers are there? In each structure, how many chiral centers are reversed relative to those in molecule **A**?

SOLVED PROBLEM **5.8**

How to draw all stereoisomers of a given structure

Break It Down Draw all stereoisomers of cyclohexane-1,3-diol. Does the total number of configurational isomers equal 2^n? Explain.

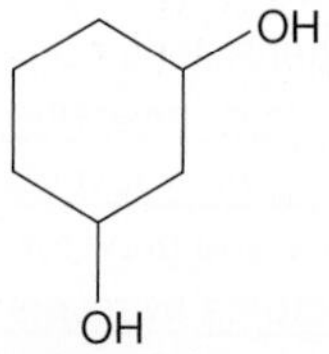
OH
OH

Cyclohexane-1,3-diol

Think	Solve
Steps 1 and 2: How many chiral centers are there? How can you draw the first stereo-isomer using dash–wedge notation?	There are two chiral centers, denoted by * and numbered 1 and 2. We draw the first stereoisomer, structure **A**, by using wedge bonds to each OH group to specify the configuration at each of those chiral centers. 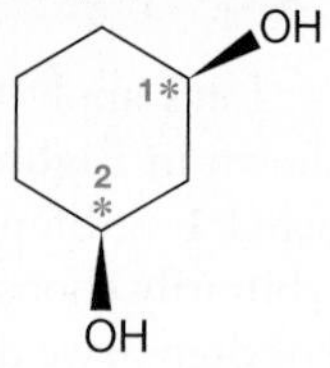 OH 1* 2* OH **A**
Steps 3 and 4: How can you adjust the dash–wedge notation to arrive at the second structure? The third and fourth structures?	For Step 3, we reverse the configuration only at chiral center 1 to yield structure **B**. For Step 4, we reverse the configuration at chiral center 2, repeating the previous two configurations at chiral center 1, yielding structures **C** and **D**. **Step 3** **Step 4** 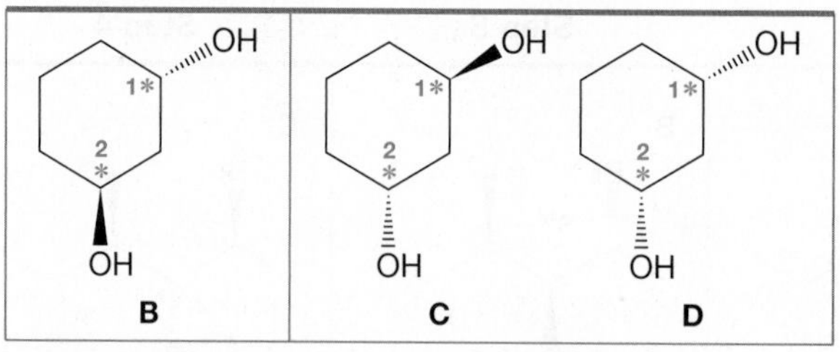 OH 1* 2* OH B; OH 1* 2* OH C; OH 1* 2* OH D
Finally, are there any redundant structures?	Structure **D** is redundant with structure **A**. Notice that the two structures are mirror images of each other, given that all configurations in structure **D** have been reversed from those in structure **A**. However, structure **A** has a plane of symmetry and is achiral, which means that it must be superimposable on its mirror image, **D**. There are three stereoisomers in all, which is fewer than $2^n = 2^2 = 4$. 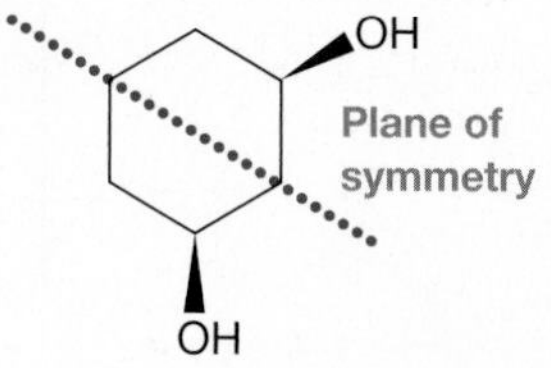 OH Plane of symmetry OH

(continued)

Try It Draw all possible configurational isomers of each molecule. How many chiral centers are there? Does the number of configurational isomers equal 2^n? Explain.

(a)

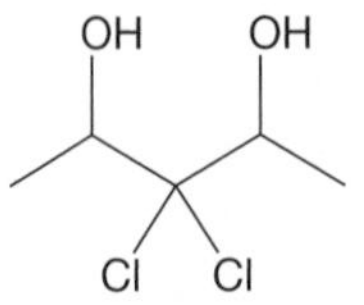

OH
OH
Cl
Cl

(b)

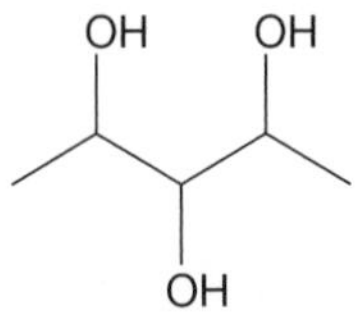

OH
OH
OH

5.10 Fischer Projections and Stereochemistry

SECTION 5.10 OBJECTIVES

You will be able to:

1. Interpret a Fischer projection by adding dash and wedge bonds.
2. Describe how two molecules are related when their Fischer projections differ by a 90° rotation.

In his study of simple sugars (saccharides) in the late 19th century, Emil Fischer found himself working with several asymmetric carbons (chiral centers) in a given molecule and several molecules at a time. This led Fischer to develop a quicker and more convenient way to depict configurations about these chiral centers, now known as **Fischer projections**. There are two conventions for drawing Fischer projections, which are captured in **Figure 5-34**:

Fischer Projection Conventions

- The intersection of a horizontal line and a vertical line indicates a carbon atom, typically an asymmetric carbon.
- The substituents on the horizontal bonds are understood to point toward you, reminiscent of a bow tie, whereas the substituents on the vertical bonds are understood to point away from you.

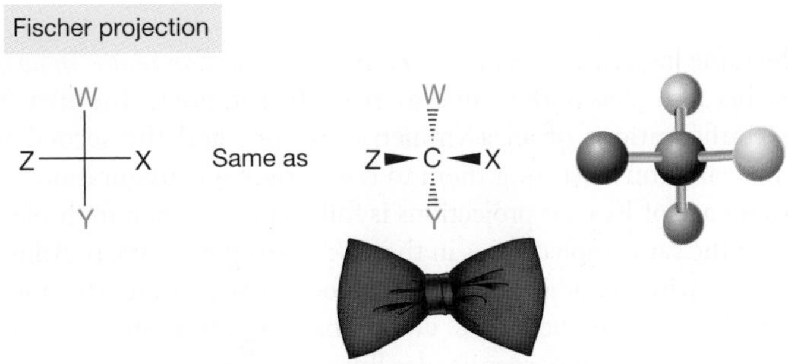

Fischer projection
W
Z
X
Y
Same as
W
Z
C
X
Y

FIGURE 5-34 Fischer projection (*Left*) A generic Fischer projection of an asymmetric carbon, where W, X, Y, and Z are different substituents. (*Middle*) The dash–wedge structure that corresponds to the Fischer projection. The horizontal substituents point toward you, reminiscent of a bow tie, whereas the vertical substituents point away from you. (*Right*) A ball-and-stick model of the molecule.

YOUR TURN 5.21

Build a model of the molecule represented by the Fischer projection in Figure 5-34 (shown again on the left here). Use different colored balls to represent the four different substituents. View the molecule from the vantage point indicated on the right and fill in the atoms in the boxes provided.

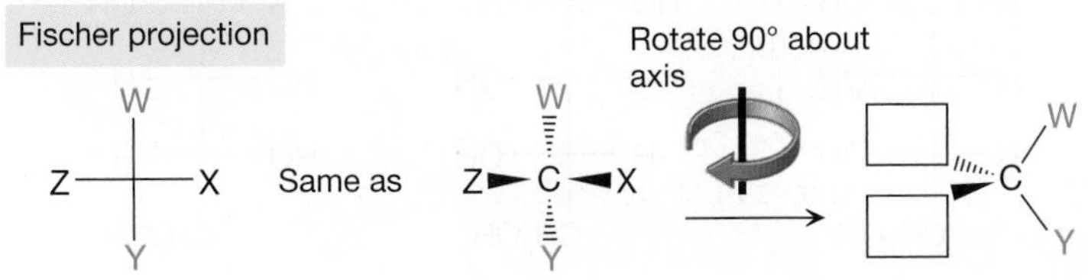

Fischer projection
W
Z
X
Y
Same as
W
Z
C
X
Y
Rotate 90° about axis
C
W
Y

To work comfortably with Fischer projections, we must know how certain manipulations affect the configurations about their chiral centers:

Properties of Fischer Projections

- Exchanging any two substituents on an asymmetric carbon in a Fischer projection gives the opposite stereochemical configuration.
- Taking the mirror image of a Fischer projection gives the opposite stereochemical configuration.
- Rotating a Fischer projection 90° in the plane of the page gives the opposite stereochemical configuration.

The first two properties apply to dash–wedge representations, too, whereas the third property is peculiar to Fischer projections. When a Fischer projection is rotated 90°, the bonds that were pointing toward us instead point away from us, and vice versa. As illustrated in **Figure 5-35**, this results in a configuration that is nonsuperimposable on the original molecule.

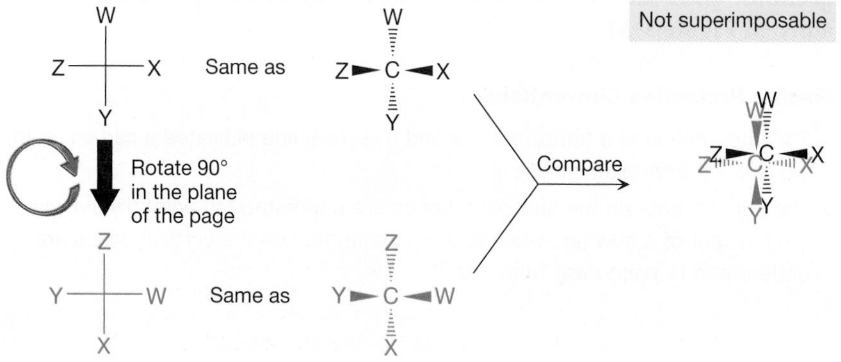

Not superimposable
Same as
Rotate 90° in the plane of the page
Compare
Same as

FIGURE 5-35 Rotation of a Fischer projection by 90° (*Top left*) A generic Fischer projection and its dash–wedge representation. (*Bottom left*) Rotation of the Fischer projection by 90° and the resulting dash–wedge structure. (*Right*) The two structures are nonsuperimposable, demonstrating that rotation of a Fischer projection by 90° gives the opposite configuration at an asymmetric carbon.

Using the same logic, *a 180° rotation of a Fischer projection results in no change in the configuration*, because this is the same as two 90° rotations. The first 90° rotation reverses the configurations of all asymmetric carbons and the second 90° rotation reverses them again, thus restoring them to their original configurations.

The convenience of Fischer projections is fully realized when multiple asymmetric carbons exist in the same molecule, as in the case of simple sugars. D-Allose, for example, is a molecule with six adjacent C atoms, four of which are asymmetric carbons (**Figure 5-36**). Notice that the two C atoms that are not asymmetric are *not* represented by the intersection of perpendicular lines.

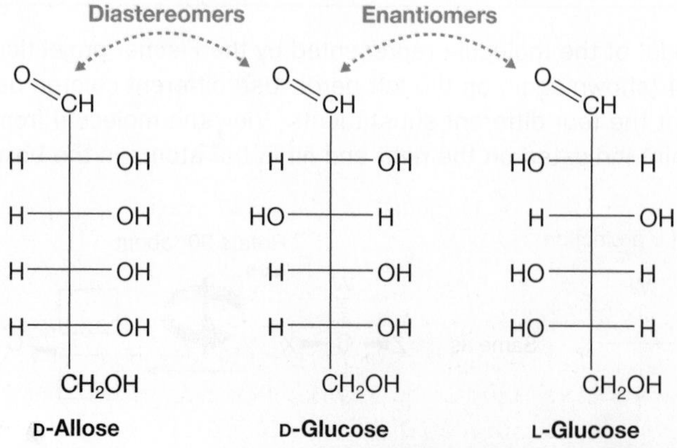

Diastereomers
Enantiomers
D-Allose
D-Glucose
L-Glucose

FIGURE 5-36 Fischer projections with multiple stereocenters Each Fischer projection represents four asymmetric carbons. D-Allose and D-glucose differ in the configuration at one of these carbons, so they are diastereomers. D-Glucose and L-glucose are nonsuperimposable mirror images, so they are enantiomers.

D-Glucose has the same molecular formula and the same connectivity as D-allose. Based on their Fischer projections, however, they are diastereomers of each other (not enantiomers), because their stereochemical configurations are opposite at only one of the four asymmetric carbons. Similarly, we can see from their Fischer projections that L-glucose and D-glucose are enantiomers of each other: They are mirror images that are nonsuperimposable.

YOUR TURN 5.22

Identify the C atoms at which the stereochemical configurations are different in D-allose and D-glucose.

YOUR TURN 5.23

(a) What is the stereochemical relationship between D-allose and L-glucose? Explain. **(b)** Draw the enantiomer of D-allose as a Fischer projection.

R and *S* configurations can be assigned straightforwardly using Fischer projections. For example, consider the Fischer projection in **Figure 5-37**. The substituents attached to the chiral center, in order from highest to lowest priority, are OH, CH=O, CH_2OH, and H. As we can see, the top three priority groups are arranged counterclockwise, but notice that H, the 4th priority group, appears on a horizontal bond. Because horizontal bonds in a Fischer projection point toward you, the arrangement of the top three priority groups must be reversed to clockwise before assigning the configuration, which is *R*.

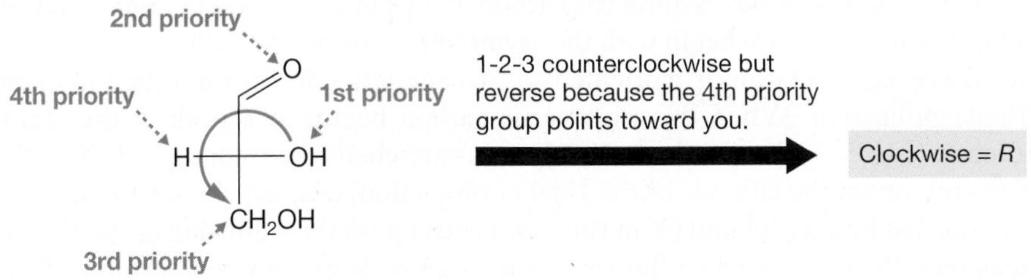
2nd priority
O
4th priority
1st priority
H
OH
CH2OH
3rd priority
1-2-3 counterclockwise but reverse because the 4th priority group points toward you.
Clockwise = R

FIGURE 5-37 Absolute configurations and Fischer projections

YOUR TURN 5.24

Determine the absolute configurations of the chiral centers in each Fischer projection.

(a)

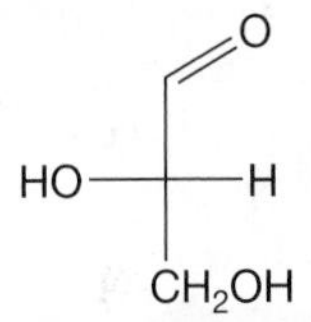
O
HO
H
CH2OH

(b)

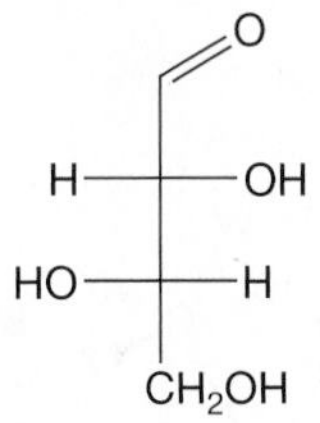
O
H
OH
HO
H
CH2OH

5.11 Strategies for Success: Converting between Fischer Projections and Zigzag Conformations

SECTION 5.11 OBJECTIVES

You will be able to:

1. Draw a Fischer projection of a molecule from its zigzag structure.
2. Draw a zigzag structure of a molecule from its Fischer projection.

A molecule containing a chain of carbon atoms is frequently represented in its zigzag conformation. If it contains multiple asymmetric carbons, however, it may be more convenient to work with its Fischer projection. How does one convert from a zigzag conformation to a Fischer projection?

Strategies for Success
Converting between Fischer Projections and Zigzag Conformations

FIGURE 5-38 **Beginning the conversion of a zigzag structure to a Fischer projection** The horizontal substituents must be added to establish the configurations of the chiral centers.

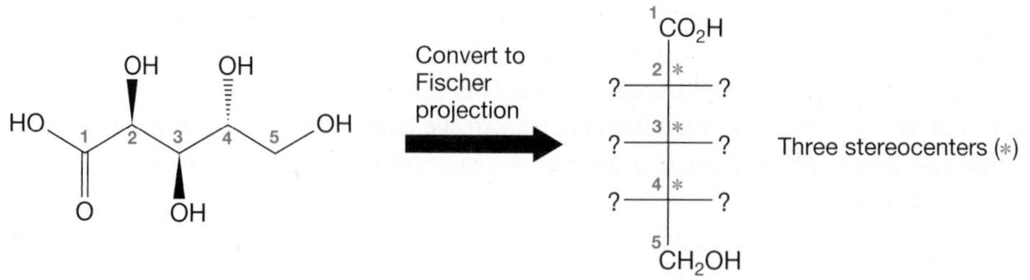

HO
OH
OH
OH
O
OH
Convert to Fischer projection
CO_2H
?
CH_2OH
Three stereocenters (*)

Consider, for example, the molecule shown in its zigzag conformation on the left in **Figure 5-38**. The zigzag conformation consists of a chain of five C atoms, each of which is numbered; C-2, C-3, and C-4 are asymmetric carbons. With this information, we can partially draw the Fischer projection, as shown on the right in Figure 5-38, where the three adjacent asymmetric carbons are denoted by *. Two of the bonds on each asymmetric carbon are designated with a question mark because two substituents must still be added to each (in this case, the substituents to be added are H and OH), and we must add them so that the stereochemical configuration at each of those carbons in the Fischer projection matches the dash–wedge notation.

To tackle a problem like this, look for patterns when an individual chiral center is turned in space from its zigzag representation (with two bonds in the plane of the page) to the orientation that is required for a Fischer projection (with the horizontal bonds pointing toward you and the vertical bonds pointing away). **Figure 5-39** shows two ways in which these kinds of reorientations can occur with a generic asymmetric carbon, in which W, X, Y, and Z represent any substituents. In Figure 5-39a, we begin with the asymmetric carbon at a peak in the zigzag representation, and in Figure 5-39b, we begin with the asymmetric carbon at a valley. In both cases, the zigzag representation is reoriented so that the left side becomes the top of the Fischer projection. When the asymmetric carbon begins at a peak in the zigzag structure (Fig. 5-39a), the substituent that was attached by a wedge bond (X in this case) ends up on the left side of the Fischer projection, whereas the substituent that was attached by a dash bond (Y in this case) ends up on the right side of the Fischer projection. By contrast, when the asymmetric carbon begins at a valley in the zigzag structure (Fig. 5-39b), the opposite is true.

FIGURE 5-39 **Reorienting an asymmetric carbon from a zigzag to a Fischer representation** The asymmetric carbon may begin at (a) a peak or (b) a valley in the zigzag representation (left). In both cases, the left end of the molecule becomes the top of the Fischer projection (right). The substituents attached by wedge and dash bonds in the zigzag representation (X and Y) end up attached by horizontal bonds in the Fischer projection. Whether X and Y appear on the left or right side of the Fischer projection depends on whether the asymmetric carbon was at a peak or valley in the zigzag structure.

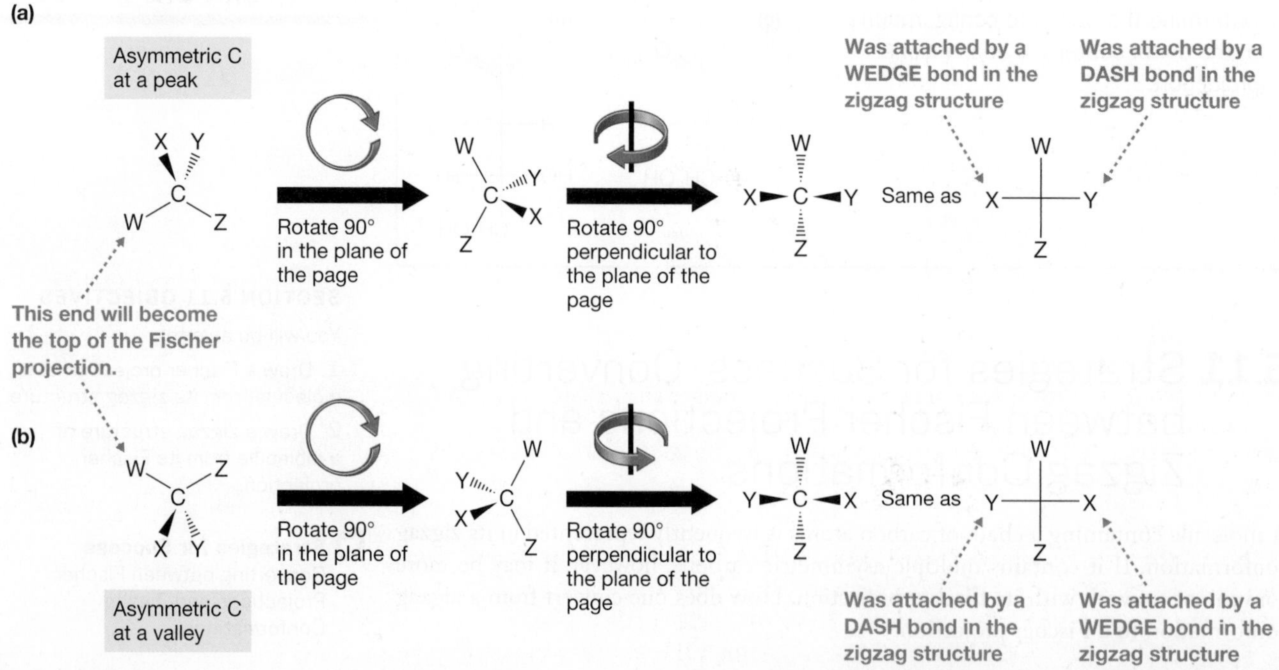

(a)
Asymmetric C at a peak
Rotate 90° in the plane of the page
Rotate 90° perpendicular to the plane of the page
Same as
Was attached by a WEDGE bond in the zigzag structure
Was attached by a DASH bond in the zigzag structure
This end will become the top of the Fischer projection.
(b)
Rotate 90° in the plane of the page
Rotate 90° perpendicular to the plane of the page
Same as
Asymmetric C at a valley
Was attached by a DASH bond in the zigzag structure
Was attached by a WEDGE bond in the zigzag structure

YOUR TURN 5.25

(a) Use a model kit to construct the molecule shown on the left in Figure 5-39a (you can use four different colored balls to represent the four substituents W, X, Y, and Z). Then reorient the molecule so it appears as shown on the right in Figure 5-39a. **(b)** Repeat this exercise for the molecule shown in Figure 5-39b.

Figure 5-40 shows how to apply the insights from Figure 5-39 to convert the zigzag structure shown previously in Figure 5-38 into a Fischer projection. Take the time to work through Figure 5-40.

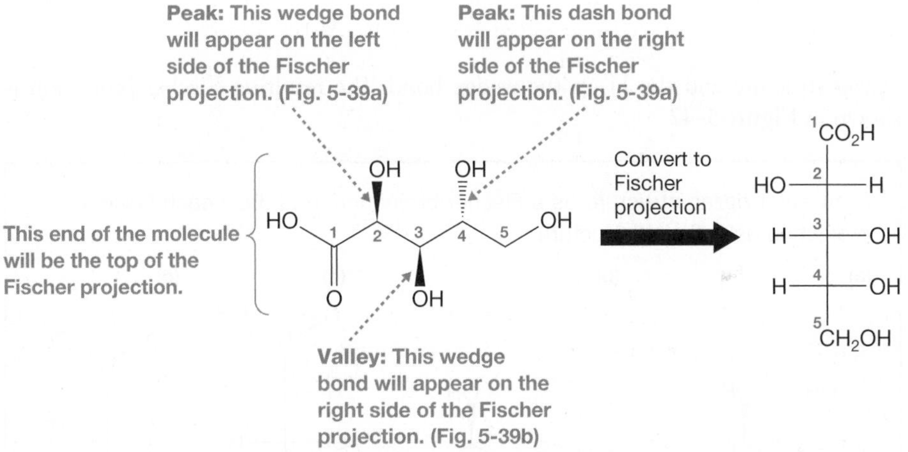

Peak: This wedge bond will appear on the left side of the Fischer projection. (Fig. 5-39a)
Peak: This dash bond will appear on the right side of the Fischer projection. (Fig. 5-39a)
This end of the molecule will be the top of the Fischer projection.
Valley: This wedge bond will appear on the right side of the Fischer projection. (Fig. 5-39b)
Convert to Fischer projection

FIGURE 5-40 Completing the conversion of a zigzag structure to a Fischer projection The horizontal substituents are added to the Fischer projection in Figure 5-38 on the basis of whether they appear at a peak or valley in the zigzag structure.

To convert from a Fischer projection to a zigzag conformation, we can apply a similar strategy, just in reverse. Suppose, for example, that we want to convert the Fischer projection shown on the left in **Figure 5-41** into the zigzag conformation shown on the right, where the top of the Fischer projection becomes the left end of the zigzag structure. There are four carbon atoms in the chain, two of which are asymmetric: C-2 and C-3. To complete the zigzag structure, we must add the remaining H and OH substituents so that the configurations agree with those given in the Fischer projection.

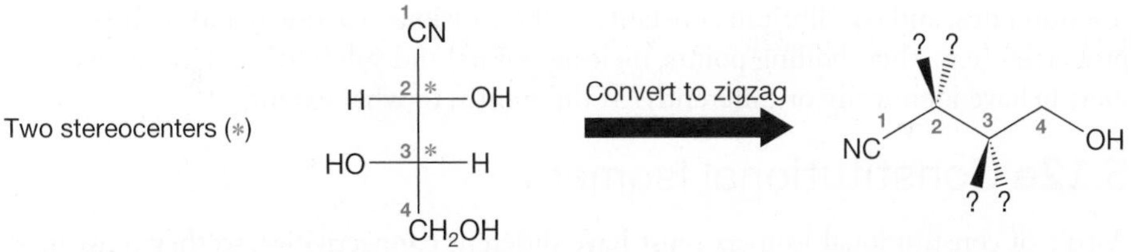

Two stereocenters (*)
Convert to zigzag

FIGURE 5-41 Beginning the conversion of a Fischer projection to a zigzag structure The top of the Fischer projection becomes the left end of the zigzag structure. The substituents attached by horizontal bonds in the Fischer projection are to be added as wedge and dash bonds in the zigzag representation.

Notice that C-2 is at a peak in the zigzag structure. Therefore, we follow the guidelines in Figure 5-39a to draw the H on the wedge bond in the zigzag structure and the OH on the dash bond. On the other hand, C-3 is at a valley in the zigzag structure, so we follow the guidelines in Figure 5-39b to draw the OH on the dash bond in the

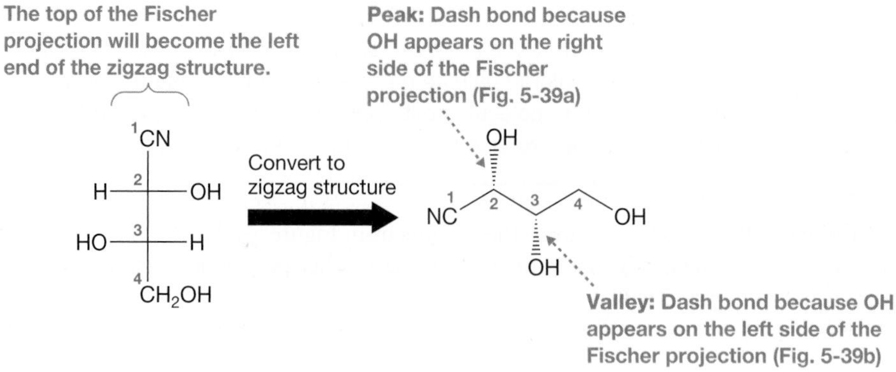
The top of the Fischer projection will become the left end of the zigzag structure.
Peak: Dash bond because OH appears on the right side of the Fischer projection (Fig. 5-39a)
Convert to zigzag structure
Valley: Dash bond because OH appears on the left side of the Fischer projection (Fig. 5-39b)

FIGURE 5-42 Completing the conversion of a Fischer projection to a zigzag structure The substituents attached by wedge or dash bonds are added to the zigzag structure in Figure 5-41 on the basis of whether they appear at a peak or valley in the zigzag structure.

zigzag structure and the H on the wedge bond. The resulting Fischer projection is shown in **Figure 5-42**.

YOUR TURN **5.26**

Draw each zigzag structure as a Fischer projection, and draw each Fischer projection as a zigzag structure.

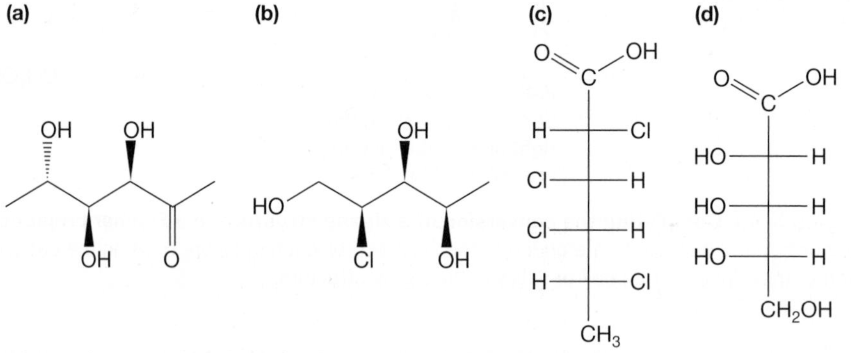

5.12 Physical and Chemical Properties of Isomers

SECTION 5.12 OBJECTIVES

You will be able to:

1. Use the relationship between two molecules to determine whether they must have identical or different properties in an achiral environment.
2. Explain the impact of a chiral environment on whether enantiomers have identical properties.

One benefit of knowing the specific relationship between two isomers is the insight it provides into their relative behavior: both their chemical behavior (e.g., the products, reaction rates, and equilibrium constants of their various reactions) and their physical properties (e.g., their boiling points, melting points, and solubilities). Do the two isomers behave identically or differently? If differently, to what extent?

5.12a Constitutional Isomers

A pair of constitutional isomers must have different connectivities, so they must have some difference in bonding, too. For example, one of two constitutional isomers may have a C=O double bond, whereas the second molecule may have a C=C double bond. Or one constitutional isomer may contain a ring and the other may not. These differences in connectivity lead to differences in polarities and bond energies. As a result:

Constitutional isomers must have different physical and chemical properties.

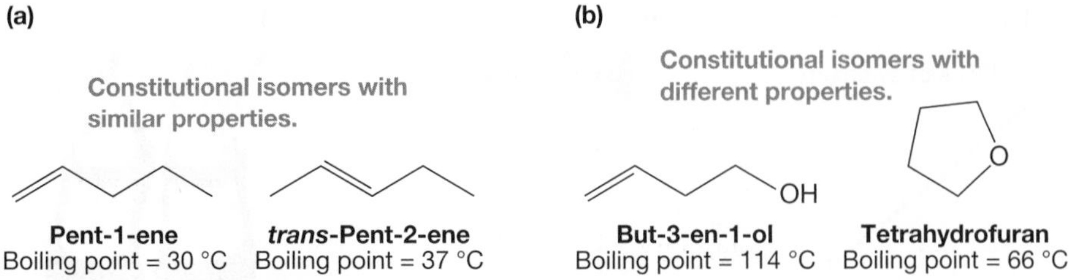

(a)
Constitutional isomers with similar properties.
Pent-1-ene
Boiling point = 30 °C
trans-Pent-2-ene
Boiling point = 37 °C
(b)
Constitutional isomers with different properties.
OH
O
But-3-en-1-ol
Boiling point = 114 °C
Tetrahydrofuran
Boiling point = 66 °C

FIGURE 5-43 Different properties of constitutional isomers (a) The connectivities of pent-1-ene and *trans*-pent-2-ene are similar, and so are their boiling points. (b) The connectivities of but-3-en-1-ol and tetrahydrofuran are substantially different, and so are their boiling points.

CONNECTIONS 5.3

Tetrahydrofuran and its uses
Tetrahydrofuran (Fig. 5-43b) is principally used as a solvent, both industrially and in the organic chemistry laboratory. When it is treated with a strong acid, it forms the polymer poly(tetramethylene ether) glycol, which is used to make elastic fibers such as Spandex.

How differently constitutional isomers behave depends largely on the degree to which their connectivities differ. For example, pent-1-ene and *trans*-pent-2-ene, shown in **Figure 5-43a**, are two constitutional isomers of C_5H_{10}. They both contain one C=C double bond in addition to C—C and C—H single bonds. Although they have different connectivities, the differences are not great; the double bonds are simply found at different locations within the molecules. As a result, these two molecules behave similarly, both physically and chemically. On the other hand, but-3-en-1-ol and tetrahydrofuran, shown in Figure 5-43b, are two constitutional isomers of C_4H_8O that have quite different physical and chemical behavior because of their different functional groups.

5.12b Enantiomers

Enantiomers are mirror images of each other, so they have exactly the same connectivity and precisely the same polarity. For these reasons, it might seem that enantiomers should behave identically. Indeed, as shown in **Figure 5-44**, both enantiomers of butan-2-ol boil at 99 °C.

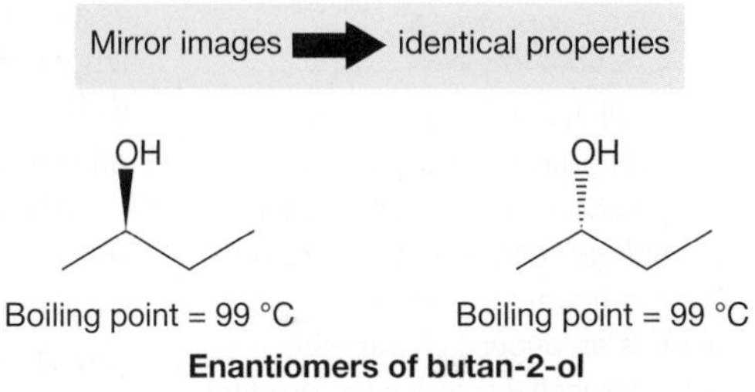

Mirror images → identical properties
OH
OH
Boiling point = 99 °C
Boiling point = 99 °C
Enantiomers of butan-2-ol

FIGURE 5-44 Identical properties of enantiomers

In general, however, whether enantiomers have identical properties depends on whether they are in a *chiral environment* or an *achiral environment*:

- A **chiral environment** is one that is nonsuperimposable on its mirror image.
  - Chiral species must be present, other than the enantiomers of interest.
  - At least one of those chiral species must be present in an amount that is different from its enantiomer.
- An **achiral environment** is one that is superimposable on its mirror image.
  - This can occur if no chiral species are present other than the enantiomers of interest.
  - This can also occur if chiral species (other than the enantiomers of interest) have equal proportions of their enantiomers.

Most environments we encounter in the laboratory are *achiral*. This is the case, for example, when a pure enantiomer boils. Furthermore, most solvents, solutes, and reactants an enantiomer might encounter are achiral.

Chiral environments can occur in a variety of ways. For example, in chromatography (a lab separation method where a sample travels through a stationary phase), a chiral stationary phase can be used. In chemical reactions, we can use chiral catalysts. Perhaps more importantly, biological systems are chiral environments because biomolecules such as proteins, sugars, and DNA are chiral and, in the body, are each present as exclusively one of their enantiomers (see Section 5.15).

FIGURE 5-45 **Chiral and achiral environments** (a) A sock has a plane of symmetry and is therefore achiral. (b) Because a sock is an achiral environment for feet, socks fit both the left and right feet equally well. (c) A shoe is chiral and is therefore a chiral environment for feet. This is why a left shoe fits a left foot far better than a right shoe and why a right shoe fits a right foot far better than a left shoe.

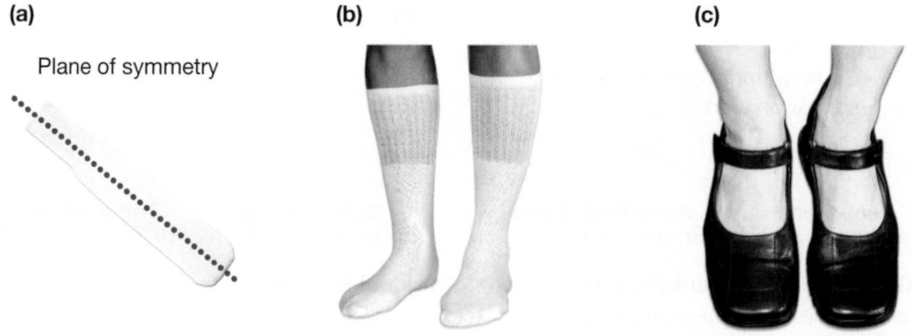

(a)
Plane of symmetry
(b)
(c)

With an understanding of chiral and achiral environments, we can now be more precise in our statement regarding the relative behavior of enantiomers:

- In an *achiral environment*, enantiomers have exactly the same physical and chemical properties.
- In a *chiral environment*, enantiomers must have different physical and chemical properties.

Depending on the specific situation, the behavior of the enantiomers can be slightly different or dramatically different.

To better understand the behavior of enantiomers in chiral versus achiral environments, let's consider an analogy using feet, socks, and shoes. Your left and right feet are chiral; they are enantiomers of each other. A sock, however, which can be thought of as an environment for your feet, is achiral because it has a plane of symmetry along its length (**Figure 5-45a**). From experience we know that a sock will fit either foot equally well (Fig. 5-45b). Thus, both a left foot and right foot "behave" identically in the achiral environment of a sock.

Shoes, however, are chiral objects (left and right shoes are enantiomers), so we can think of a shoe as a chiral environment for your feet. From experience, we know that a right shoe fits the right foot better than the left (Fig. 5-45c) and vice versa. Thus, we can say that left and right feet "behave" differently in the presence of the chiral environment of a given shoe.

▸ LOOKING AHEAD

As we will see in Chapter 8, reactions can produce mixtures of configurational isomers. Whether the configurational isomers are produced in equal or unequal amounts (which is an aspect of the reaction's *stereochemistry*) is dictated by whether the configurational isomers are enantiomers or diastereomers.

5.12c Diastereomers

Like enantiomers, diastereomers have the same connectivity. They are *not* mirror images of each other, however, so they must behave differently:

> Diastereomers must have different physical and chemical properties (see Looking Ahead box).

The properties of diastereomers can be quite different, as we can see for the boiling points of the 1,2-dichloroethene diastereomers shown in **Figure 5-46a**. The trans

FIGURE 5-46 **Different properties of diastereomers** (a) One diastereomer of 1,2-dichloroethene is nonpolar while the other is polar, so they have quite different boiling points. (b) The diastereomers of butane-2,3-diol have similar boiling points.

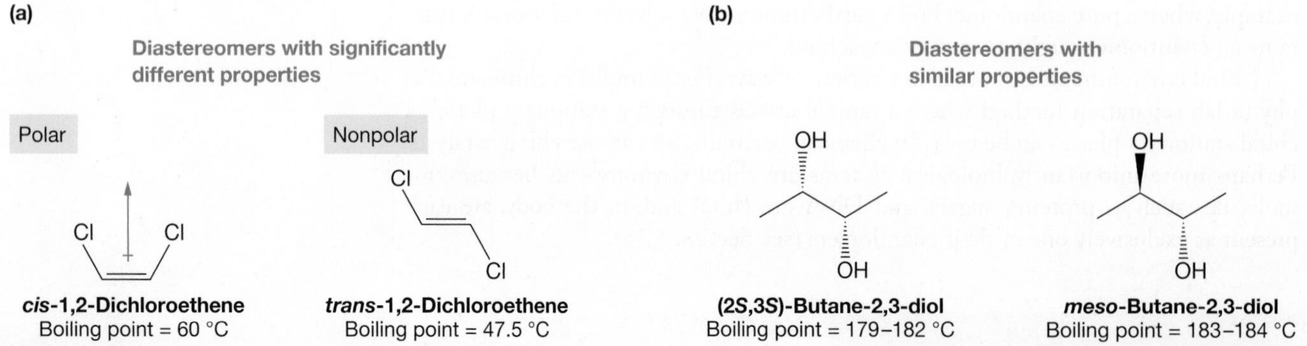

(a)
Diastereomers with significantly different properties
Polar
Nonpolar
Cl
Cl
Cl
Cl
cis-1,2-Dichloroethene
Boiling point = 60 °C
trans-1,2-Dichloroethene
Boiling point = 47.5 °C
(b)
Diastereomers with similar properties
OH
OH
OH
OH
(2S,3S)-Butane-2,3-diol
Boiling point = 179–182 °C
meso-Butane-2,3-diol
Boiling point = 183–184 °C

isomer is nonpolar whereas the cis isomer is polar, so the cis isomer undergoes significantly stronger intermolecular forces. Often, however, diastereomers have very similar properties because they have subtle differences in their structures, as in the case of the butane-2,3-diol diastereomers shown in Figure 5-46b. Notice how similar their boiling points are.

SOLVED PROBLEM **5.9**

How to determine relative properties of molecules from isomeric relationships

Break It Down In Chapter 8, you will learn that 2-bromo-4-methylhexane (molecule Z) can undergo the substitution reaction shown here when treated with NaCl.

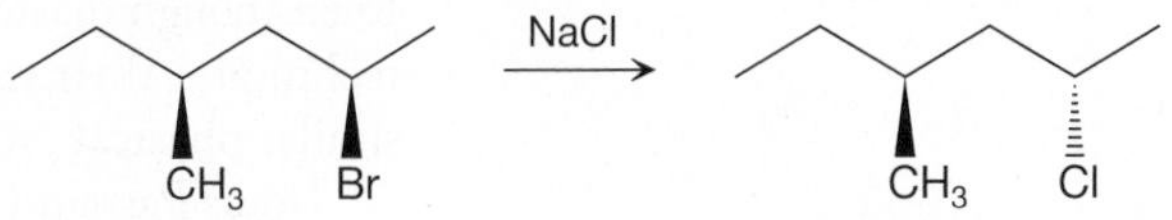
NaCl
CH3
Br
CH3
Cl

Z

Molecules A–E undergo a similar substitution reaction with NaCl. For which of these molecules will the *rate* of the reaction be precisely the same as that of the reaction involving Z? Explain.

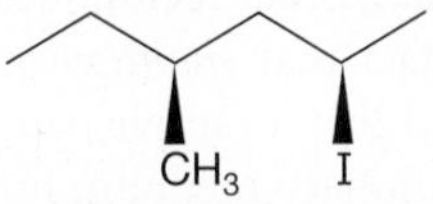
CH3
I
A

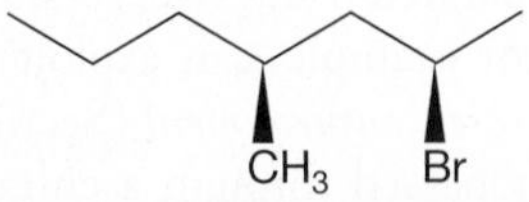
CH3
Br
B

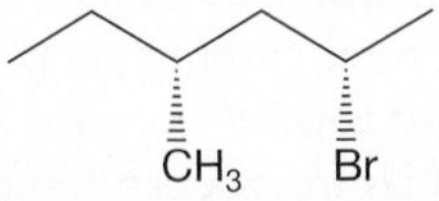
CH3
Br
C

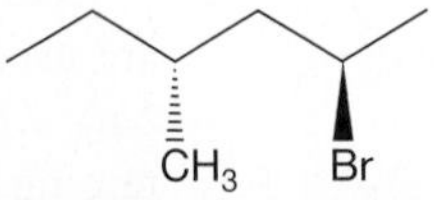
CH3
Br
D

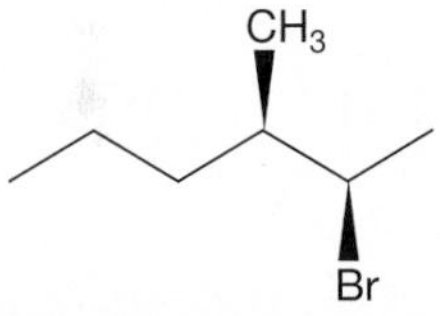
CH3
Br
E

Think	Solve
How is each molecule **A–E** related to **Z**?	**A** and **B** are unrelated to **Z** because they have different molecular formulas. **C**, **D**, and **E** are all isomers of **Z**. **C** is its enantiomer, **D** is a diastereomer of it, and **E** is one of its constitutional isomers.
How do those relationships translate into relative behavior?	Only enantiomers have precisely the same behavior, so the correct answer is **C**.

Try It Molecule **Y** is a carboxylic acid (RCO_2H), so it is moderately acidic (see Chapter 6 for details). Which of the molecules **A–E** have an acidity that is *different* from that of **Y**? Explain.

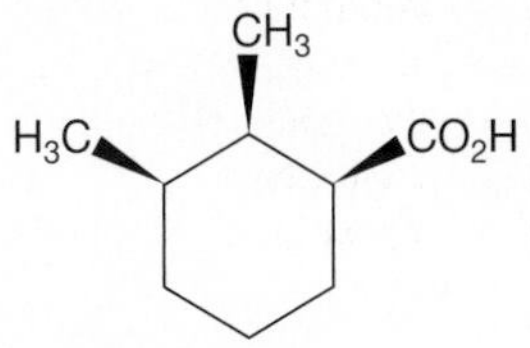
CH3
H3C
CO2H
Y

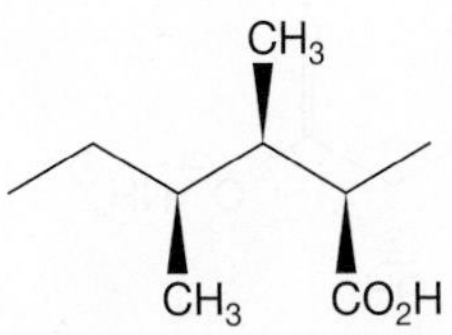
CH3
CH3
CO2H
A

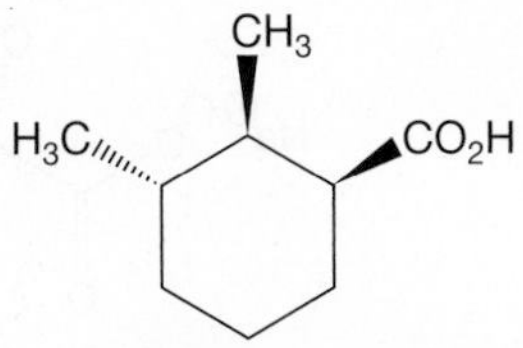
CH3
H3C
CO2H
B

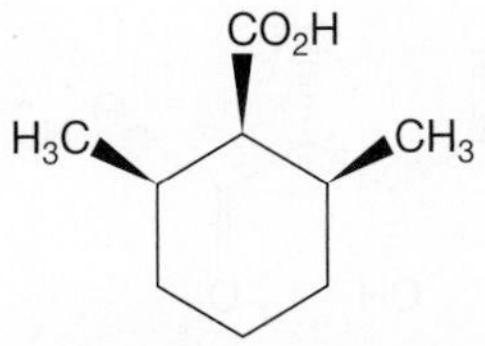
CO2H
H3C
CH3
C

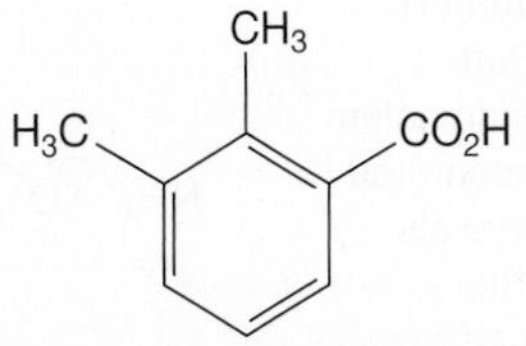
CH3
H3C
CO2H
D

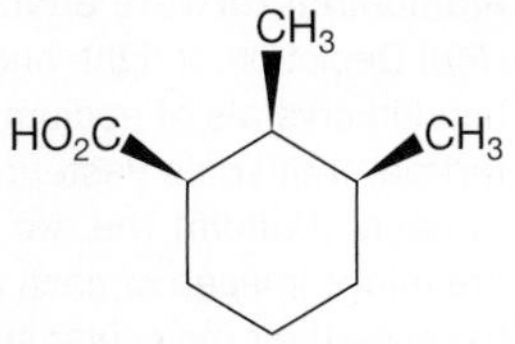
CH3
HO2C
CH3
E

SECTION 5.13 OBJECTIVES

You will be able to:

1. Explain why it is often difficult to separate configurational isomers, especially enantiomers.
2. Describe two general strategies that can be used to separate enantiomers.

5.13 Separating Configurational Isomers

As we discuss in Chapter 8, if a chemical reaction forms a chiral product, it usually forms a mixture of stereoisomers. How, then, do we separate stereoisomers from one another to isolate just the desired stereoisomer?

Recall that diastereomers have different physical properties, whereas enantiomers have identical properties in achiral environments. Consequently:

- Diastereomers often can be separated by common laboratory techniques that rely on different physical properties, such as fractional distillation, crystallization, and simple chromatography.
- Enantiomers generally cannot be separated by these methods

Even though diastereomers can be separated using these kinds of common laboratory techniques, their separation can still be quite difficult, particularly when they have very similar physical properties (see Fig. 5-46b).

Louis Pasteur (1822–1895) was the first to isolate a pair of enantiomers from each other. The enantiomers he separated were those of sodium ammonium tartrate, an ionic compound that forms crystals (**Figure 5-47**). As Pasteur noted, the crystals appeared to grow in one of two varieties, left-handed crystals and right-handed crystals, that are mirror images of each other. Using nothing more than a microscope and a pair of tweezers, he physically separated the two types of crystals.

Most enantiomers cannot be separated using tweezers, so today, other techniques are used. Chiral chromatography, for example, can exploit the fact that *enantiomers have different physical properties in a chiral environment* (Section 5.12b). A sample containing a mixture of enantiomers is passed through a chiral stationary medium, for which the enantiomers have different affinities. Traveling through the chiral medium at different rates allows the two enantiomers to be collected separately.

A second method of separating enantiomers takes advantage of diastereomers being separable due to their different physical properties (Section 5.12c). This method involves three steps:

1. Temporarily converting the enantiomers into a pair of diastereomers.
2. Separating those diastereomers from each other.
3. Regenerating the enantiomers from the separated diastereomers.

See Problem 5.31 at the end of the chapter for a specific example of how this method is applied.

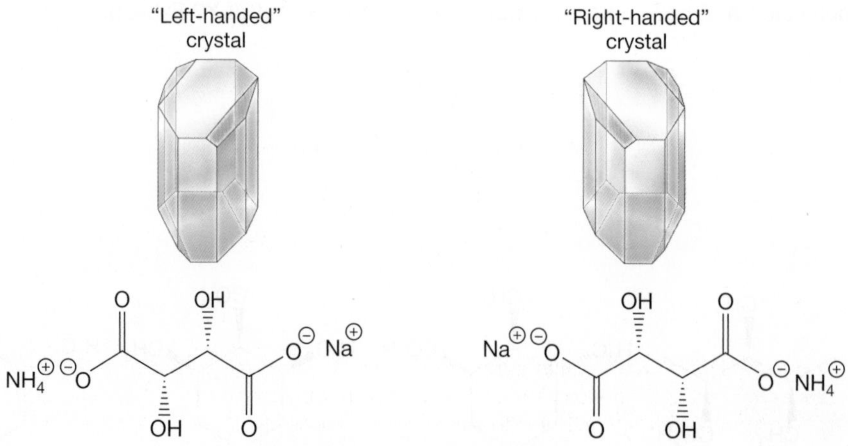

"Left-handed" crystal
"Right-handed" crystal

Sodium ammonium tartrate

FIGURE 5-47 Separation of sodium ammonium tartrate enantiomers (*Top*) Depiction of right- and left-handed crystals of sodium ammonium tartrate that Louis Pasteur separated by hand. (*Bottom*) The two crystals are mirror images of each other because their molecular structures are enantiomers.

5.14 Optical Activity

Although enantiomers have identical physical and chemical properties in an achiral environment, they behave differently in a chiral environment (Section 5.12b). They also interact differently with *plane-polarized* light, as we will discuss.

Light can be regarded as both a particle and a wave. When it is treated as a particle, we think of light as consisting of **photons**, each of which carries a specific quantity of energy that can be associated with its frequency and wavelength (see Looking Ahead box). When it is treated as a wave, we think of light as consisting of oscillating electric and magnetic fields. The frequency of oscillation of those fields defines the frequency of light.

As a ray of light travels through space, its electric and magnetic fields oscillate in planes perpendicular to each other and also perpendicular to the direction it travels (**Figure 5-48**). If all photons from a light source have their electric fields oscillating in the same plane, then the light is **plane-polarized.** A red double-headed arrow is used to represent that plane of polarization in Figure 5-48. The plane in which the magnetic field oscillates is perpendicular to the electric field's plane of oscillation.

SECTION 5.14 OBJECTIVES

You will be able to:

1. Describe how a polarimetry experiment works.
2. Use polarimetry data to calculate the value for a measured angle of rotation, specific rotation, sample concentration, or sample length, given any three of these values.
3. Work with polarimetry data for a mixture of enantiomers to interconvert the mixture's specific rotation and its composition.

▸ LOOKING AHEAD

The existence of light as photons is the basis of *spectroscopy*, the study of light (more generally, electromagnetic radiation) interacting with matter. We will discuss three types of spectroscopy in Chapters 16 and 17).

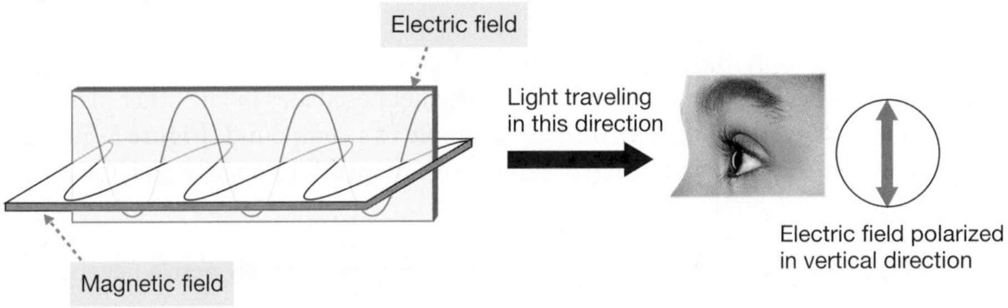
Electric field
Light traveling in this direction
Electric field polarized in vertical direction
Magnetic field

FIGURE 5-48 Plane-polarized light (*Left*) The electric field (shown in red) oscillates in a vertical direction and the magnetic field (shown in black) oscillates in the plane perpendicular to the page as the light wave travels to the right. (*Right*) A red, double-headed arrow represents the electric field's plane of oscillation.

Most light sources emit light that is **unpolarized.** That is, if we could view all of the photons traveling in the same direction, we would see each one's electric field oscillating in a different plane. A **polarizer** (**Figure 5-49**) generates plane-polarized light by

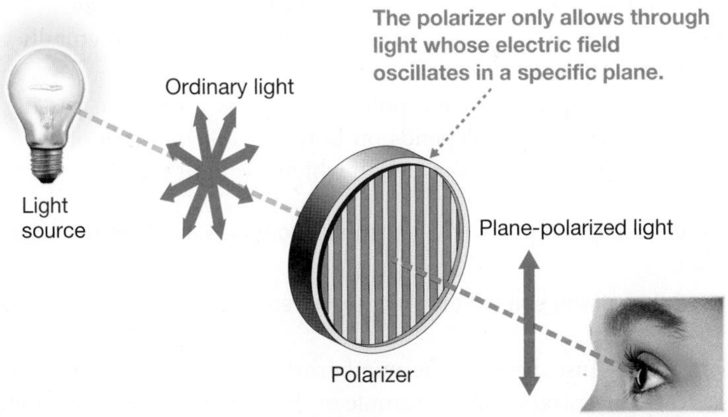
The polarizer only allows through light whose electric field oscillates in a specific plane.
Ordinary light
Light source
Plane-polarized light
Polarizer

FIGURE 5-49 Function of a polarizer (*Left*) Light emitted from most sources is unpolarized. The electric-field vectors of its photons oscillate in all planes perpendicular to the direction of travel. (*Middle*) A polarizer effectively filters out photons whose electric-field vector does not oscillate in the specified plane (in this case, the vertical direction). (*Right*) The light that passes through the polarizer is plane-polarized.

CONNECTIONS 5.4

Polarized sunglasses The lenses of polarized sunglasses effectively act as polarizers (Fig. 5-49), allowing through only plane-polarized light. If two such lenses are stacked and the polarization planes of the lenses are perpendicular, then any light that passes through the first lens is filtered out by the second lens.

FIGURE 5-50 **Polarimetry** (*Left*) Plane-polarized light enters a tube containing a solution of a compound being studied. (*Middle*) If the compound is optically active, the plane of polarization is rotated as the light passes through the tube. (*Right*) The angle of rotation, α, is measured using an analyzer.

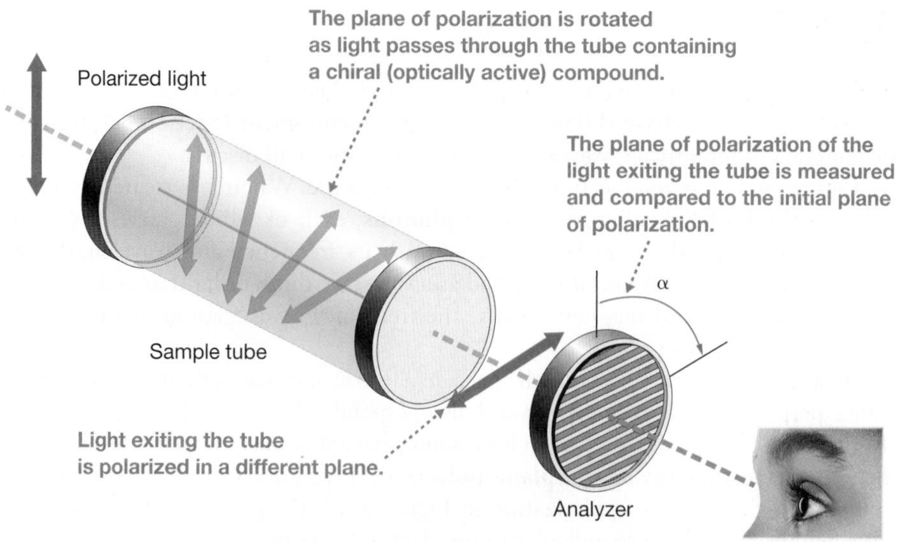

Polarized light
The plane of polarization is rotated as light passes through the tube containing a chiral (optically active) compound.
The plane of polarization of the light exiting the tube is measured and compared to the initial plane of polarization.
α
Sample tube
Light exiting the tube is polarized in a different plane.
Analyzer

allowing through only those photons whose electric field is oscillating in a specified plane, effectively filtering out light whose electric field oscillates in any other plane.

If plane-polarized light passes through a sample of a compound (**Figure 5-50**), the plane in which the light is polarized can change, depending on whether the compound is chiral or achiral:

- Enantiomerically pure chiral compounds are said to be **optically active** because they rotate the plane of polarization.
- Achiral compounds are said to be **optically inactive** because they leave the plane of polarization unchanged.

Polarimetry is an experimental technique that measures the optical activity of a sample. After the plane-polarized light exits the sample, the light enters an analyzer, which is used to determine the angle by which the plane of polarization has been rotated. Some chiral compounds rotate light clockwise, in the (+) direction, and are called **dextrorotatory** (from Latin, meaning "rotating to the right"). Others rotate light counterclockwise, in the (−) direction, and are called **levorotatory** (meaning "rotating to the left"). *The direction of rotation generally cannot be known without performing the experiment.* In fact, two chiral compounds that are structurally very similar may rotate light in opposite directions!

The amount by which the plane-polarized light is rotated on passing through a sample of a chiral compound depends on both the *concentration* of the chiral compound and the *length of the sample* through which the light travels:

- As the concentration of a chiral compound increases, so does the angle of rotation.
- As the length of the sample tube increases, so does the angle of rotation.

This should make sense, because the number of molecules encountered by the light increases as the concentration of the sample or the length of the sample tube increases.

The **measured angle of rotation (α)** can thus be expressed by Equation 5-1, where *c* is the concentration of the sample in units of grams per milliliter (g/mL) and *l* is the length of the sample tube in units of decimeters (dm; 1 dm = 0.1 meter):

$$\alpha = [\alpha]_{\lambda}^{T}(l)(c) \quad \textbf{(5-1)}$$

The **specific rotation**, $[\alpha]_\lambda^T$, is a constant that is *unique for a given chiral compound.* The specific rotation is the angle of rotation of light of a given wavelength (λ, in nanometers) that passes through a sample whose concentration is 1 g/mL, whose length is 1 dm, and whose temperature is T °C. Most often, the light used for measurement is the sodium D line (589.6 nm), abbreviated simply D, and the temperature is 20 °C. Therefore, the specific rotation is usually reported as $[\alpha]_D^{20}$.

CONNECTIONS 5.5

Sodium street lights The sodium D line used for polarimetry experiments is produced when electrons in excited sodium atoms relax to a lower energy state. A similar process is responsible for generating light in some types of street lamps.

SOLVED PROBLEM **5.10**

How to work with polarimetry data for a single enantiomer

Break It Down **Suppose that 20.00 g of a chiral compound is dissolved in 0.1000 L of solution and is placed in a tube that is 20.00 cm long. What is its specific rotation of light if the observed rotation is determined experimentally to be +45.00°?**

Think	Solve
Which variable in Equation 5-1 are we solving for?	We are asked for $[\alpha]_\lambda^T$ and are given the value for α, which is +45.00°. Equation 5-1 must therefore be rearranged as follows: $[\alpha]_\lambda^T = \frac{\alpha}{(l)(c)}$
The equation calls for concentration; how do we calculate it?	We can calculate concentration in units of grams per milliliter by dividing 20.00 g of sample by 100.0 mL of solution, to yield 0.2000 g/mL.
Are the units correct for the length of the tube, *l*?	The length of the tube, *l*, is given to us as 20.00 cm but must be converted to decimeters. Because 1 dm = 0.1 m = 10 cm, the length of our tube is 2.000 dm. Therefore, the specific rotation is $[\alpha]_\lambda^T = \frac{(+45.00°)}{(2.000\ \text{dm})(0.2000\ \text{g/mL})} = 112.5°\ \text{mL dm}^{-1}\ \text{g}^{-1}$

Try It Penicillin V has a specific rotation of +223° mL dm^{-1} g^{-1}. What would the measured angle of rotation of a 0.00300 g/mL solution be, if it were measured in a tube 10.0 cm long?

Recall that enantiomers interact differently with plane-polarized light. In fact:

Enantiomers have equal but opposite specific rotations.

Just as enantiomers are mirror images of each other, the mirror image of a rotation in the clockwise direction is an identical rotation in the counterclockwise direction. For this reason, one enantiomer can always be designated as the (+) enantiomer and the other as the (−) enantiomer.

A **racemic mixture** (pronounced ruh-SEE-mik) contains equal amounts of the (+) and (−) enantiomers of a chiral molecule. That is, light traveling through a racemic mixture encounters an equal number of molecules of each enantiomer. Therefore, the tendency of one enantiomer to rotate the light in one direction is exactly balanced by the tendency of the other enantiomer to rotate the light in the opposite direction. The net result is zero rotation of the light. Consequently:

A racemic mixture of enantiomers is optically inactive, despite being made up of chiral molecules.

If a mixture of enantiomers is not racemic, then it will be optically active, but it will not rotate light as much as one of the pure enantiomers. Such a mixture can be viewed as being a certain percentage racemic, with the remaining percentage, called the **enantiomeric excess (ee)**, viewed as being composed of one of the pure enantiomers. The percentage that is racemic will not contribute toward the rotation of plane-polarized light, but the enantiomeric excess will. This idea is summarized in Equation 5-2:

(specific rotation of mixture) = (% ee)(specific rotation of pure enantiomer)/100 (5-2)

Because (% ee)/100 must be a fraction between 0 and 1, *the specific rotation of a mixture of enantiomers must be smaller in magnitude than the specific rotation of the pure enantiomers.*

If you know the relative amounts of two enantiomers in solution, you can solve for the enantiomeric excess by first determining the percentage of the solution that is racemic. Suppose, for example, that a solution consists of 70% enantiomer A and 30% enantiomer B. The percent of the solution that is racemic is determined by combining all of the enantiomer in the smaller amount (B) with an equal amount of the other enantiomer (A). In this case, that would be 30% B + 30% A = 60% racemic. The remaining 40% of the solution is entirely A, and therefore, the enantiomeric excess of A is 40%.

YOUR TURN **5.27**

Determine the enantiomeric excess of a solution that consists of 95% A and 5% B.

SOLVED PROBLEM **5.11**

How to work with polarimetry data for a mixture of enantiomers

Break It Down Suppose a solution of a pure chiral molecule has a specific rotation of −32°. What is the specific rotation of a solution that is 90% (+) enantiomer and 10% (−) enantiomer?

Think	Solve
Which enantiomer is in excess and what is its ee?	There is more (+) enantiomer than (−), so the (+) enantiomer is in excess. The 10% that is the (−) enantiomer can be combined with 10% of the solution that is the (+) enantiomer, such that 20% of the solution is effectively racemic, leaving 80% ee of the (+) enantiomer.
In Equation 5-2, what value should you use for the pure compound's specific rotation?	Our choices are +32° for the pure (+) enantiomer or −32° for the pure (−) enantiomer. We choose +32° because it agrees with the enantiomer that is in excess, which is the (+) enantiomer. Substituting the values into Equation 5-2: (specific rotation of mixture) = (% ee)(specific rotation of pure enantiomer)/100 = (80)(+32°)/100 = 26°

Try It Suppose that a pure compound has a specific rotation of +49°. In the laboratory, a solution in which the compound is mixed with its enantiomer is found to have a specific rotation of +12°. What is the ee of the mixture? What percentage of the mixture is the (+) enantiomer and what percentage is the (−) enantiomer?

5.15 The Chirality of Biomolecules

SECTION 5.15 OBJECTIVES

You will be able to:

1. Give examples of biomolecules that contribute to making the body a chiral environment.
2. Explain the implications that the body, as a chiral environment, can have on chiral drugs.

The tragedy of thalidomide was mentioned briefly in Section 5.1. In the 1950s and 1960s, thalidomide was prescribed as an anti-nausea medication for pregnant people with morning sickness. Unfortunately, thalidomide is teratogenic: It causes birth defects. As a direct result of taking the drug, it is estimated that more than 10,000 children worldwide were born with deformed or missing limbs.

Like many drugs, thalidomide is chiral and was sold as a *racemic mixture* of its two enantiomers (**Figure 5-51**). Later testing on mice showed that the enantiomer on the left is primarily responsible for suppressing nausea, whereas the one on the right is primarily responsible for the teratogenic properties. (It turns out, however, that administering only the enantiomer on the left would not have solved the problem because the two enantiomers interconvert in the body.)

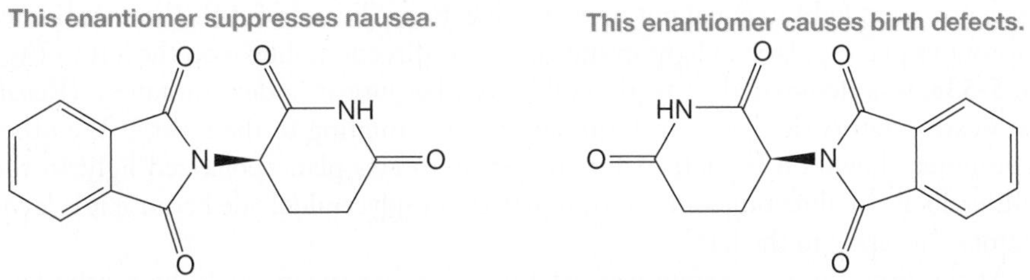
This enantiomer suppresses nausea.
This enantiomer causes birth defects.

FIGURE 5-51 Enantiomers of thalidomide

How can enantiomers, molecules that are mirror images of each other, behave so differently? It is possible because:

The body acts as a chiral environment.

Recall from Section 5.12b that *enantiomers have different physical and chemical properties in a chiral environment.*

Most biomolecules, including those encountered in previous chapters, are chiral. For example, as shown in **Figure 5-52**, a typical amino acid has a single chiral center (marked by *) and is thus chiral. (There is one exception: see Problem 5.37). Glucose, in its acyclic form, has four chiral centers: each C atom that is bonded to an H and an OH group. A nucleotide in DNA has three chiral centers, and the steroid testosterone has six chiral centers.

Despite the presence of these chiral compounds, the body would remain an achiral environment if each pair of enantiomers were present in equal amounts. (This is analogous to a racemic mixture being optically inactive, as discussed in Section 5.14.) Instead:

Natural amino acids and monosaccharides appear in the body exclusively in one enantiomeric form.

FIGURE 5-52 Chiral centers in biomolecules In each of these biomolecules, chiral centers are marked by asterisks.

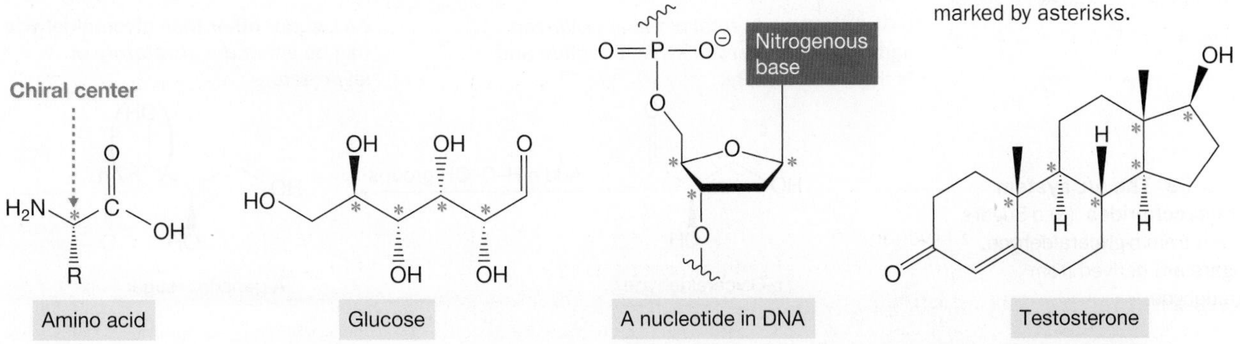
Chiral center
Nitrogenous base
Amino acid
Glucose
A nucleotide in DNA
Testosterone

For amino acids, that form is the L enantiomer, and for monosaccharides, it is the D enantiomer. (These designations are discussed in greater detail in Section 5.16.) Reasons why these compounds appear exclusively in these forms are not known and are the subject of debate.

5.16 The D/L System for Classifying Monosaccharides and Amino Acids

SECTION 5.16 OBJECTIVES

You will be able to:

1. Describe the origin of the D/L system for naming sugars.
2. Assign a D or L designation to a monosaccharide from its structure, and do the same for an α-amino acid.

Each chiral amino acid and monosaccharide has two enantiomers, specified using the D/L system. The system was established around 1910, before the advent of the IUPAC system of nomenclature and before the technology existed to determine the specific location of atoms in three-dimensional space.

The basis of the D/L system is the optical rotation of glyceraldehyde, $HOCH_2CH(OH)CH{=}O$. Glyceraldehyde is an *aldotriose*, a three-carbon monosaccharide possessing a $CH{=}O$ group characteristic of an aldehyde (see Section 4.13). It has a single asymmetric carbon, which is C-2, and thus has enantiomers that rotate plane-polarized light in equal but opposite directions (Section 5.14). The enantiomer that rotates plane-polarized light in the clockwise direction, shown on the left in **Figure 5-53a**, was designated as D-glyceraldehyde because it is dextrorotatory. (Recall that dextrorotatory derives from Latin and means "rotating to the right.") The other enantiomer, shown on the left in Figure 5-53b, rotates plane-polarized light in the counterclockwise direction and was designated as L-glyceraldehyde because it is levorotatory ("rotating to the left").

At the time the D/L system was established, other sugars could be synthesized from glyceraldehyde by lengthening the molecule at the $CH{=}O$ end of the molecule, while leaving unchanged the configuration of glyceraldehyde's chiral center. Sugars synthesized in this way from D-glyceraldehyde (Fig. 5-53a) were designated as D-sugars, and sugars synthesized from L-glyceraldehyde (Fig. 5-53b) were designated as L-sugars.

On the basis of its origin from either D- or L-glyceraldehyde, a sugar *other* than glyceraldehyde is assigned a D/L designation only as part of the *name*. In those cases,

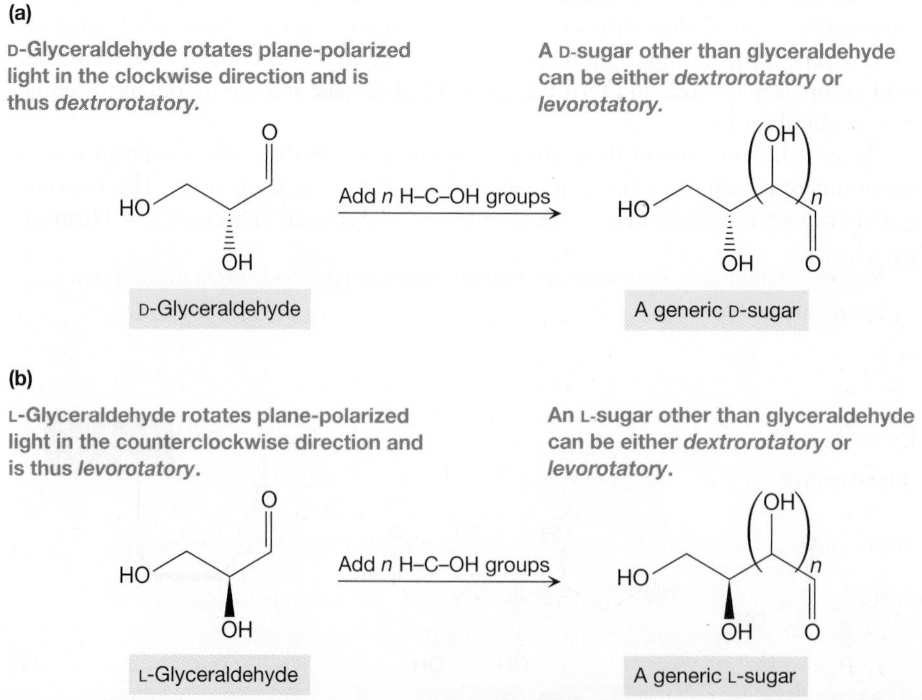
(a)
D-Glyceraldehyde rotates plane-polarized light in the clockwise direction and is thus *dextrorotatory.*
A D-sugar other than glyceraldehyde can be either *dextrorotatory* or *levorotatory.*
O
HO
OH
Add *n* H–C–OH groups
OH
n
HO
OH
O
D-Glyceraldehyde
A generic D-sugar
(b)
L-Glyceraldehyde rotates plane-polarized light in the counterclockwise direction and is thus *levorotatory*.
An L-sugar other than glyceraldehyde can be either *dextrorotatory* or *levorotatory*.
O
HO
OH
Add *n* H–C–OH groups
OH
n
HO
OH
O
L-Glyceraldehyde
A generic L-sugar

FIGURE 5-53 The D/L system for monosaccharides (a) D-Sugars are derived from D-glyceraldehyde. (b) L-Sugars are derived from L-glyceraldehyde.

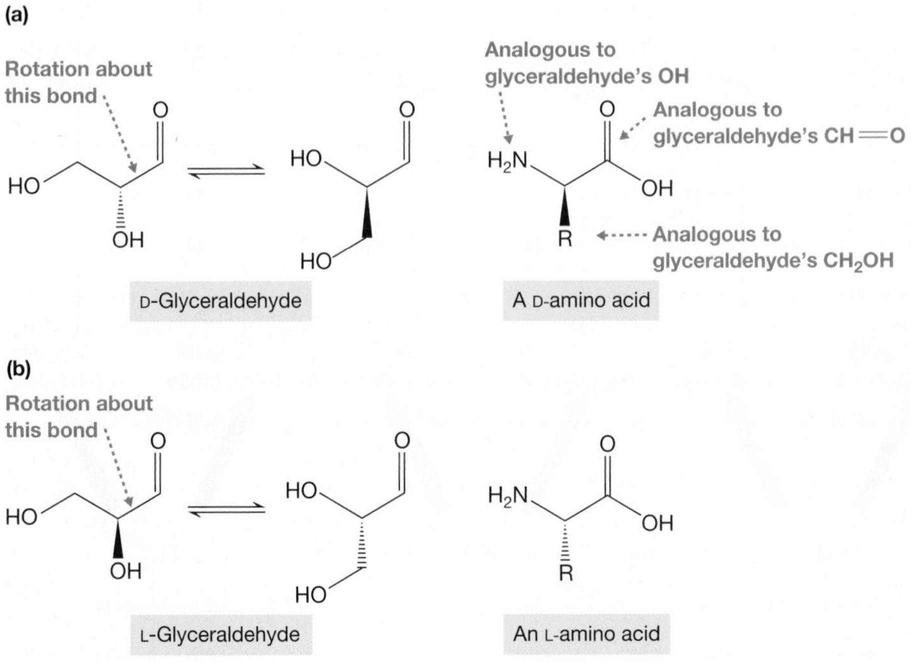
(a)
Rotation about this bond
HO
OH
O
HO
HO
O
D-Glyceraldehyde
Analogous to glyceraldehyde's OH
Analogous to glyceraldehyde's CH=O
Analogous to glyceraldehyde's CH₂OH
H₂N
O
OH
R
A D-amino acid
(b)
Rotation about this bond
HO
OH
O
HO
HO
O
L-Glyceraldehyde
H₂N
O
OH
R
An L-amino acid

FIGURE 5-54 The D/L system for amino acids (a) The structure of a D-amino acid is analogous to that of D-glyceraldehyde. (b) The structure of an L-amino acid is analogous to that of L-glyceraldehyde.

the D/L designation has no connection to the direction in which the sugar rotates plane-polarized light:

- Some D-sugars rotate plane-polarized light in the clockwise direction, and others rotate it in the counterclockwise direction.
- Some L-sugars rotate plane-polarized light in the clockwise direction, and others rotate it in the counterclockwise direction.

The D and L designations for amino acids are assigned by analogy. The second conformation of each glyceraldehyde enantiomer in **Figure 5-54** resembles the configuration of the amino acid next to it: specifically, the HC=O, OH, and CH_2OH groups of glyceraldehyde are analogous to the CO_2H, NH_2, and R groups of the amino acid. Thus, the amino acid in Figure 5-54a is the D enantiomer, because its R group points toward you, just as the CH_2OH group of D-glyceraldehyde does. For similar reasons, the amino acid in Figure 5-54b is the L enantiomer.

5.17 The D Family of Aldoses

SECTION 5.17 OBJECTIVES

You will be able to:

1. Determine whether two monosaccharides are epimers.
2. Draw a D-monosaccharide when given the structure of its L form, and vice versa.

D-Glyceraldehyde is the only possible D-aldotriose, which is shown at the bottom of **Figure 5-55** (next page) in its Fischer projection. Each H—C—OH group added to glyceraldehyde introduces a new chiral center, which can have either of two stereochemical configurations. Thus, two D-aldotetroses are possible: namely, D-erythrose and D-threose. Two more D-aldoses can be produced from each of those sugars on the addition of another H—C—OH group, giving rise to four possible D-aldopentoses: namely, D-ribose, D-arabinose, D-xylose, and D-lyxose. And, with yet another H—C—OH group, there are eight possible D-aldohexoses: namely, D-allose, D-altrose, D-glucose, D-mannose, D-gulose, D-idose, D-galactose, and D-talose.

Notice in the Fischer projection of D-glyceraldehyde that the OH group attached to the chiral center (shown in purple) appears on the right. Similarly:

Any D-sugar is distinguished by having the OH group of the highest-numbered asymmetric carbon (i.e., farthest away from the C=O carbon) appear on the right in its Fischer projection.

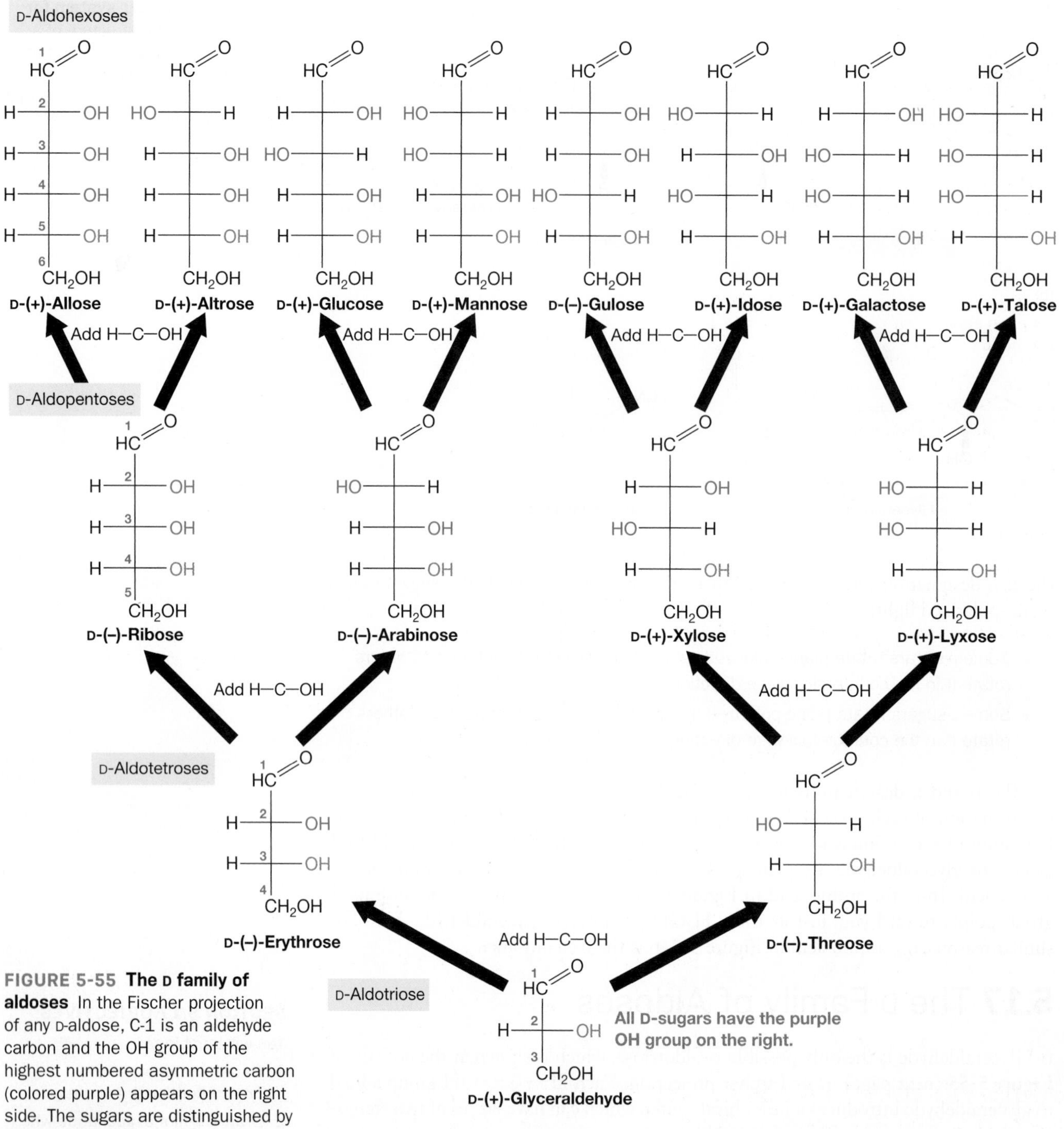

D-Aldohexoses
D-(+)-Allose
D-(+)-Altrose
D-(+)-Glucose
D-(+)-Mannose
D-(–)-Gulose
D-(+)-Idose
D-(+)-Galactose
D-(+)-Talose
Add H—C—OH
D-Aldopentoses
D-(–)-Ribose
D-(–)-Arabinose
D-(+)-Xylose
D-(+)-Lyxose
D-Aldotetroses
D-(–)-Erythrose
D-(–)-Threose
D-Aldotriose
D-(+)-Glyceraldehyde
All D-sugars have the purple OH group on the right.

FIGURE 5-55 The D family of aldoses In the Fischer projection of any D-aldose, C-1 is an aldehyde carbon and the OH group of the highest numbered asymmetric carbon (colored purple) appears on the right side. The sugars are distinguished by the number of carbon atoms (bottom to top) and the stereochemical configuration at each asymmetric carbon (left to right).

Notice, too, that D-glyceraldehyde rotates plane-polarized light in the clockwise direction, denoted by (+), but this is not true of all D-sugars. For example, D-erythrose rotates plane-polarized light in the counterclockwise direction, denoted by (−). Finally, sugars in the same row all have the same connectivity but are not mirror images. Thus:

> Any two sugars in the same row of Figure 5-55 are diastereomers.

Recall from Section 5.12c that diastereomers have different physical and chemical properties, which is why no two sugars in the same row have the same name.

Among the various diastereomers in a particular row in Figure 5-55, some differ only by the stereochemical configuration at one carbon atom. Compounds with this specific relationship are called **epimers**. For example, D-allose and D-altrose are epimers, differing only in the configuration at C-2; they are called C-2 epimers. D-Allose and D-glucose are C-3 epimers.

YOUR TURN **5.28**

Name the sugar that fits each of the following descriptions: **(a)** The C-2 epimer of D-glucose; **(b)** the C-3 epimer of D-talose; **(c)** the C-4 epimer of D-talose; **(d)** the C-3 epimer of D-xylose.

The mirror image of any D-sugar would result in a Fischer projection in which the OH group of the highest-numbered asymmetric carbon appears on the left. This is shown for D-glucose in **Figure 5-56**. As a result, the enantiomer of any D-sugar must not be a D-sugar. Instead:

The enantiomer of a D-sugar is designated as an L-sugar of the same name, and in its Fischer projection, the OH group of the highest-numbered asymmetric carbon appears on the left.

Thus, the enantiomer of D-glucose is L-glucose.

YOUR TURN **5.29**

Draw the Fischer projection of each of the following sugars: **(a)** L-mannose; **(b)** L-arabinose; **(c)** L-threose; **(d)** the C-2 epimer of L-arabinose.

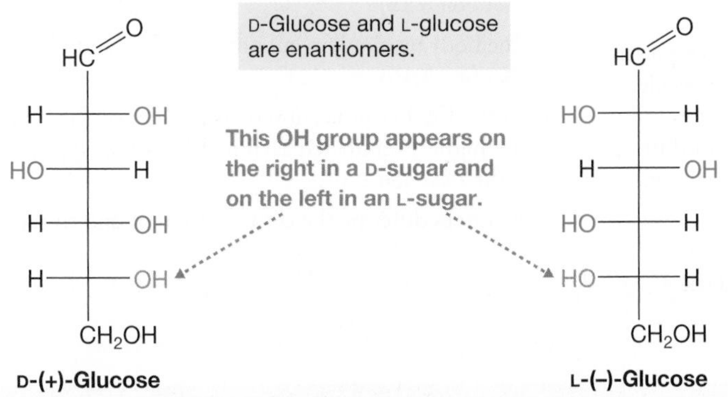

HC
O
H
OH
HO
H
H
OH
H
OH
CH_2OH
D-(+)-Glucose
D-Glucose and L-glucose are enantiomers.
This OH group appears on the right in a D-sugar and on the left in an L-sugar.
HC
O
HO
H
H
OH
HO
H
HO
H
CH_2OH
L-(–)-Glucose

FIGURE 5-56 Enantiomers of glucose

Chapter Summary and Key Terms

- **Configurational isomers** are isomers that have the same connectivity but are **nonsuperimposable. Enantiomers** and **diastereomers** are types of configurational isomers; enantiomers are mirror images of each other, whereas diastereomers are not. **(Sections 5.1 and 5.2)**
- A molecule is **chiral** if it has an enantiomer. Otherwise it is **achiral**. **(Section 5.4)**
- A molecule that has at least one **plane of symmetry** must be achiral. A molecule that is chiral must have no plane of symmetry. **(Section 5.4)**
- A tetrahedral **chiral center**, also called a **stereocenter** or an **asymmetric atom**, is an atom bonded to four *different* substituents. **(Section 5.5)**
- Every chiral center has two different configurations possible, related to each other by either (1) reflection through a mirror or (2) the interchange of any two groups. **(Section 5.5)**
- A molecule that contains exactly one chiral center must be chiral. **(Section 5.5a)**
- A molecule with at least two chiral centers is **meso** if it contains a plane of symmetry. **(Section 5.5a)**

- All chiral centers in one enantiomer have configurations that are opposite their corresponding chiral centers in the second enantiomer. **(Section 5.5a)**
- A chiral center's absolute configuration can be assigned as *R* or *S* on the basis of how the top three priority substituents are arranged when the fourth-priority substituent points away. **(Section 5.6)**
- If a molecule and its mirror image rapidly interconvert, the molecule is achiral. Interconversions can occur through single-bond rotations or **nitrogen inversion**. **(Section 5.7)**
- Because chair conformations rapidly interconvert, the chirality of a substituted cyclohexane can be evaluated by using representations that treat the cyclohexane ring as flat, such as Haworth projections. **(Section 5.7)**
- A nitrogen atom may be a chiral center if it is bonded to four different groups (and thus bears a +1 formal charge). An uncharged nitrogen atom that undergoes nitrogen inversion is not a chiral center. **(Sections 5.5 and 5.7)**
- A double bond that has two possible configurations can be assigned as *Z* or *E* on the basis of whether the higher priority substituents attached to each end of the double bond appear on the same side of the double bond or opposite sides. **(Section 5.8)**
- Molecules that differ by the configuration of a double bond are diastereomers. **(Section 5.8)**
- If a molecule contains two or more chiral centers, then the reversal of some, but not all, of their configurations gives a different diastereomer. **(Section 5.8)**
- For a molecule that contains *n* chiral centers, there are, at most, 2^n configurational isomers. **(Section 5.9)**
- **Fischer projections** are shorthand notations used to represent the configurations about asymmetric carbons in a molecule. Perpendicular intersecting lines represent a carbon atom, typically a chiral center. Horizontal bonds point toward the viewer, whereas vertical bonds point away from the viewer. **(Section 5.10)**
- Rotation of a Fischer projection by 90° in the plane of the page gives the opposite configuration at all asymmetric carbons. Rotation by 180° leaves all stereochemical configurations unchanged. Taking a mirror image of a chiral Fischer projection gives the molecule's enantiomer. **(Section 5.10)**
- Constitutional isomers have different chemical and physical properties. Similarly, diastereomers have different chemical and physical properties. In an **achiral environment**, enantiomers have *identical* physical and chemical properties. In a **chiral environment**, enantiomers have *different* properties. **(Section 5.12)**
- Diastereomers can be separated on the basis of their physical properties. Enantiomers can be separated in a chiral environment, such as a chromatography column containing a chiral stationary phase. **(Section 5.13)**
- Chiral compounds rotate **plane-polarized** light and are therefore **optically active**. Achiral compounds are **optically inactive**. **(Section 5.14)**
- A compound's **specific rotation**, $[\alpha]_\lambda^T$, characterizes its ability to rotate plane-polarized light and is a constant that is unique to every chiral compound. **(Section 5.14)**
- Enantiomers have equal but opposite specific rotations. A **racemic mixture** of enantiomers is optically inactive. **(Section 5.14)**
- The **enantiomeric excess (ee)** is the fraction of a mixture that is not racemic. It is the fraction of a mixture that contributes to the rotation of plane-polarized light. **(Section 5.14)**
- The body acts as a chiral environment because biomolecules such as amino acids and monosaccharides are chiral and exist in only one of their enantiomeric forms in the body. **(Section 5.15)**
- The body uses only D-monosaccharides and L-amino acids. **(Section 5.16)**
- In the Fischer projection of any D-aldose, the OH group on the highest numbered asymmetric carbon appears on the right. **(Section 5.17)**
- **Epimers** differ by the configuration of one chiral center. **(Section 5.17)**

Problems

Sections 5.2–5.5 Enantiomers, Chirality, and Chiral Centers

5.1 For each pair, determine whether the molecules are superimposable.

(a)

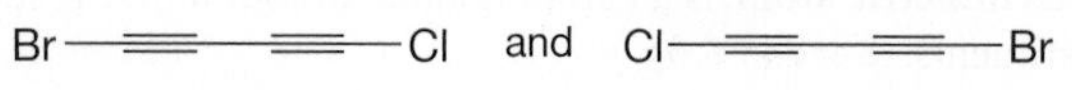
Br
Cl
and
Cl
Br

(b)

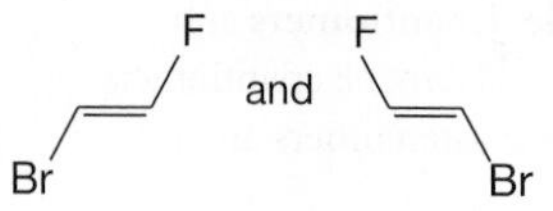
F
Br
and
F
Br

(c)

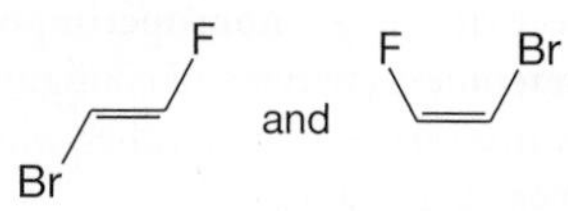
F
Br
and
F
Br

(d)

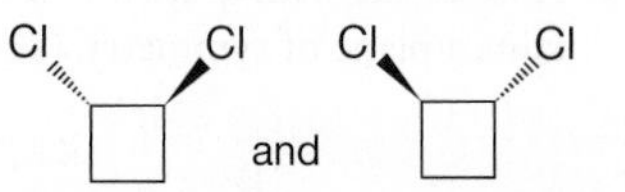
Cl
Cl
and
Cl
Cl

(e)

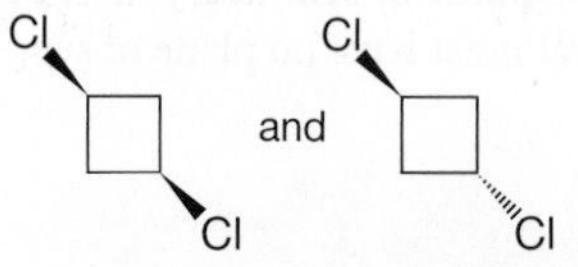
Cl
Cl
and
Cl
Cl

5.2 Determine which pairs of molecules are mirror images.

(a)

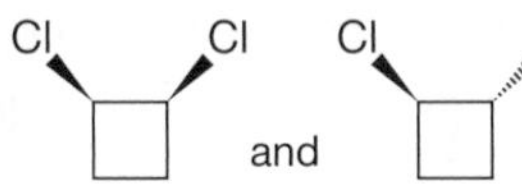

(b)

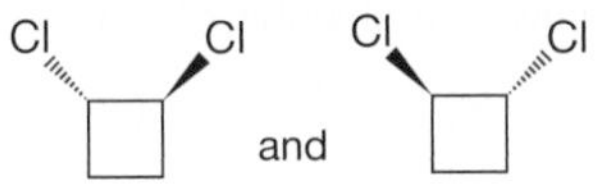

(c)

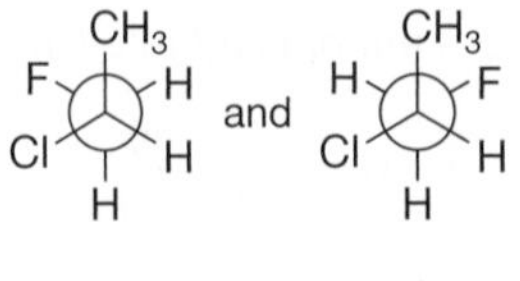

5.3 Determine whether each of the following objects is chiral or achiral. (Assume that there are no graphics on any of these objects.)

(a) A coffee mug **(b)** Your ears **(c)** A bowling ball **(d)** An automobile **(e)** A pair of scissors
(f) A t-shirt **(g)** Eyeglasses **(h)** A piano **(i)** Golf clubs **(j)** A tennis racquet

5.4 Determine whether each of the following molecules possesses a plane of symmetry. If it does, indicate the plane of symmetry using a dashed line.

(a)

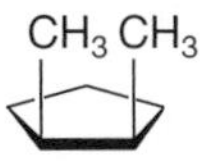

(b)

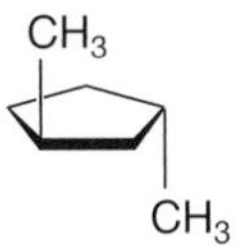

(c)

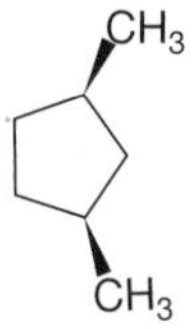

(d)

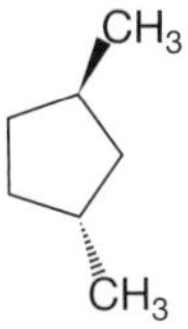

(e)

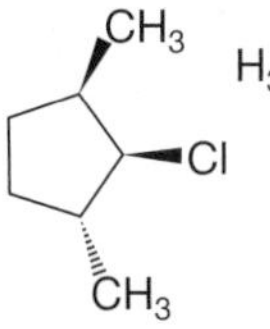

(f)

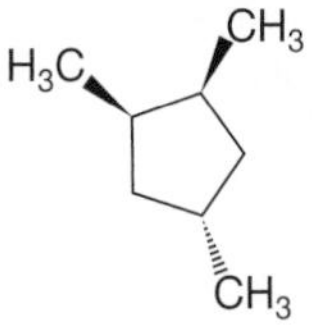

5.5 Draw the Newman projection of 1,2-dichloroethane in its anti conformation and in each of its gauche conformations. Determine which of these conformers possess a plane of symmetry. For those that do, indicate the plane of symmetry using a dashed line.

5.6 For each molecule shown below, determine whether it is the same enantiomer as the one shown in the box.

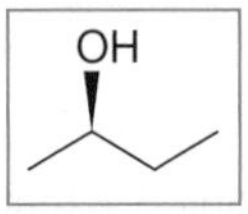

(a)

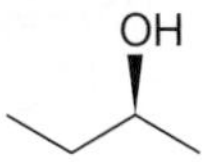

(b)

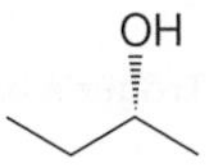

(c)

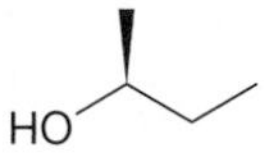

(d)

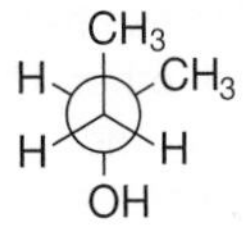

(e)

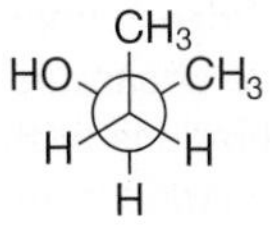

(f)

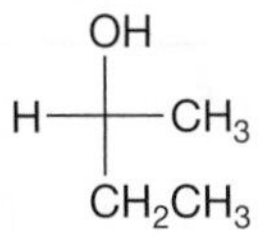

(g)

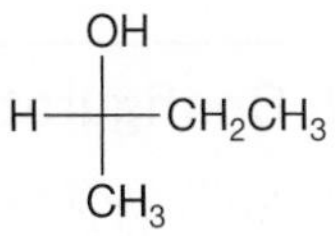

(h)

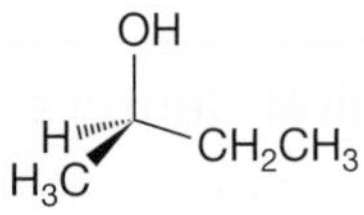

5.7 Which of the following species are chiral?

(a)

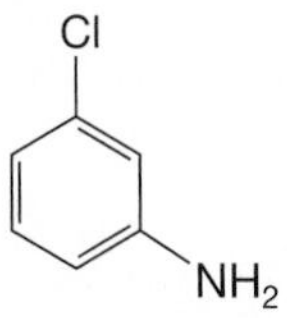

(b)

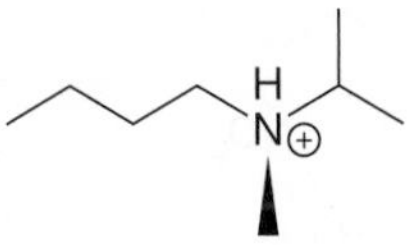

(c)

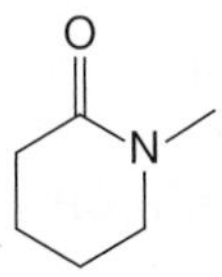

(d)

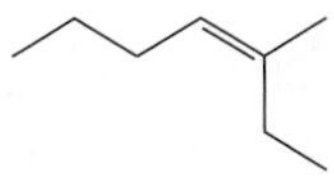

(e)

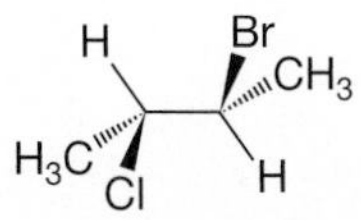

(f)

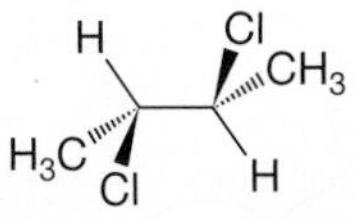

(g)

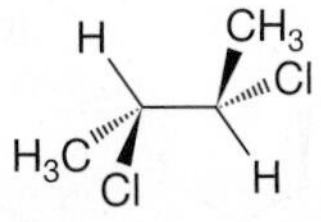

(h)

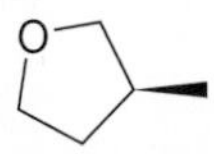

5.8 For each molecule in Problem 5.7, identify all of the chiral centers. Which of those molecules, if any, are meso?

5.9 Is it possible for a meso compound to contain three chiral centers? Why or why not?

5.10 How many chiral centers are present in each of the following molecules? Mark each one with an asterisk.

(a)

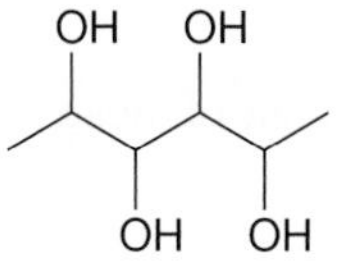
OH OH
OH OH

(b)

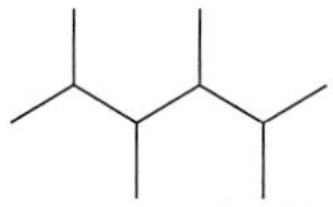

(c)

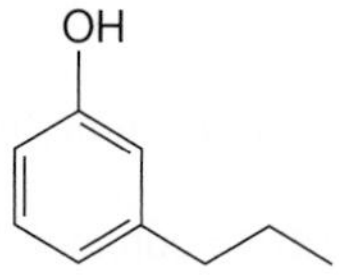
OH

(d)

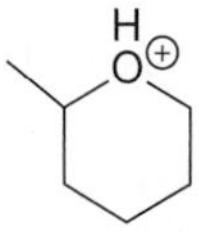
H
O⊕

(e)

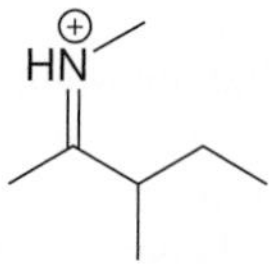
⊕
HN

(f)

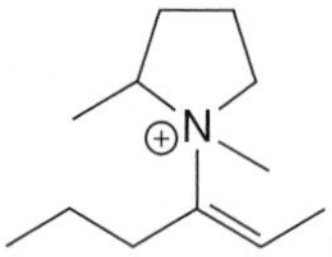
⊕N

(g)

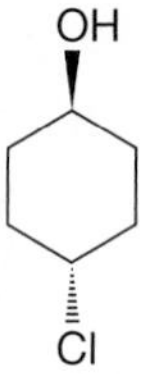
OH
Cl

5.11 Aldosterone, a steroid involved in regulating blood pressure, is shown here without dash–wedge notation. How many chiral centers does aldosterone have?

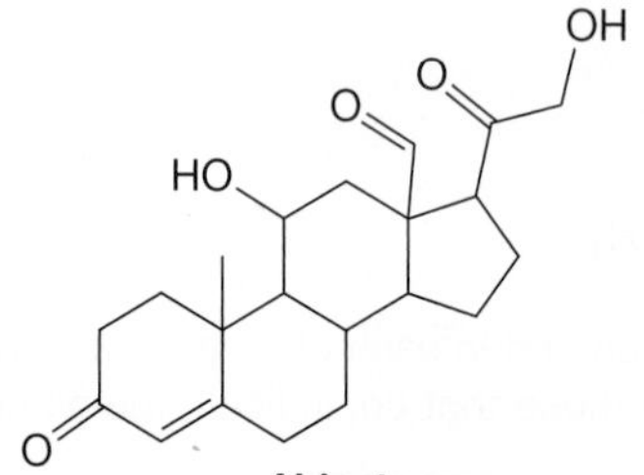
OH
O
O
HO
O

Aldosterone

5.12 Taxol, an anticancer drug, is shown here without dash–wedge notation. How many chiral centers does Taxol have?

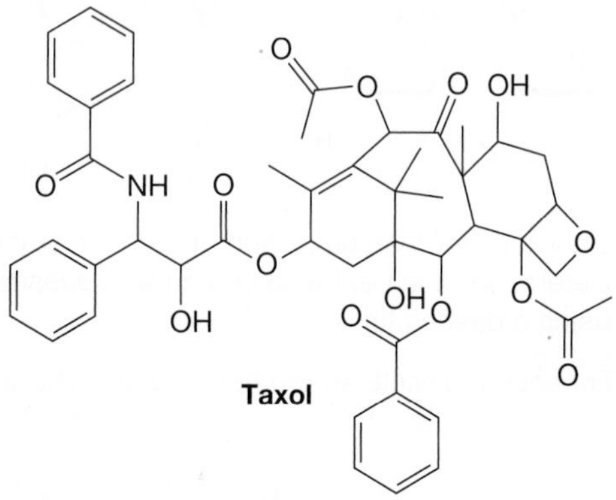
O
O
O OH
O
NH
O
O
O
OH
OH
O
O
O
O
O

Taxol

5.13 Although we learned in Section 5.7 that uncharged nitrogen atoms generally cannot be chiral centers (due to nitrogen inversion), an exception is Tröger's base. Tröger's base has two enantiomers that can be separated from each other. They are different in their configurations at the N atoms. One enantiomer is shown here, viewed from two different perspectives. **(a)** Draw the second enantiomer of Tröger's base. **(b)** Explain why the two enantiomers do not interconvert.

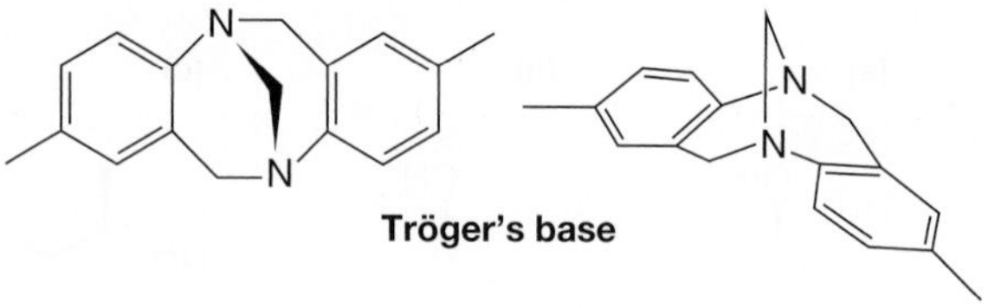
N
N
N
N

Tröger's base

Sections 5.6 and 5.8 *R/S* Configurations of Chiral Centers and *Z/E* Configurations of Double Bonds

5.14 Designate the configuration of each chiral center in the following molecules as *R* or *S*.

(a)

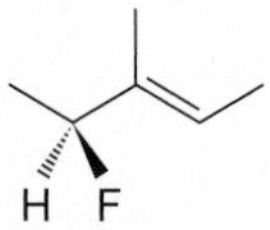
H F

(b)

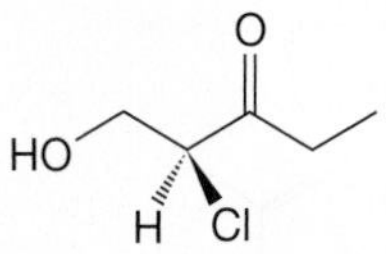
O
HO
H Cl

(c)

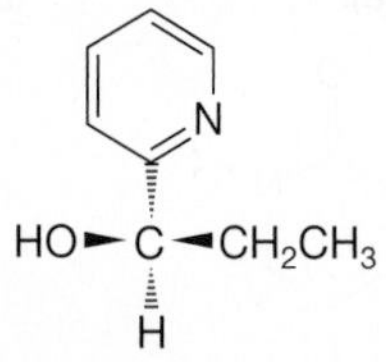
N
HO C CH2CH3
H

(d)

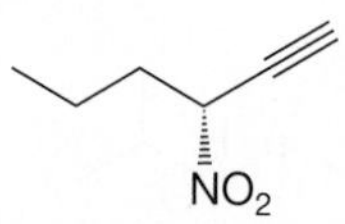
NO2

5.15 Assign the configuration of each asymmetric carbon as *R* or *S*.

(a)

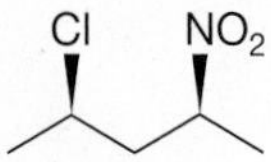
Cl NO2

(b)

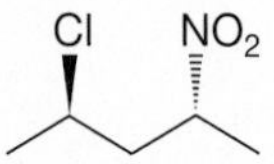
Cl NO2

(c)

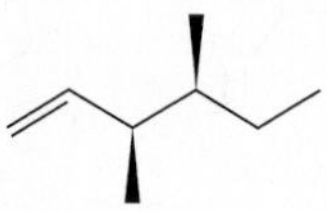

(d)

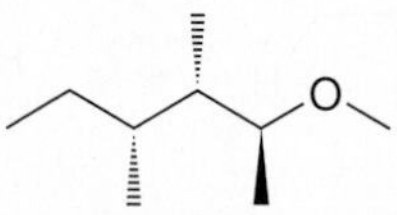
O

5.16 Assign the configuration of each asymmetric carbon as *R* or *S*.

(a)

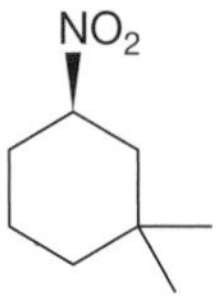
NO_2

(b)

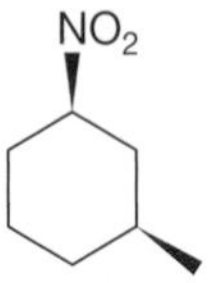
NO_2

(c)

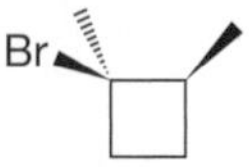
Br

(d)

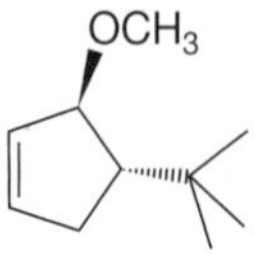
OCH_3

5.17 What is the configuration, *Z* or *E*, of each of the following double bonds?

(a)

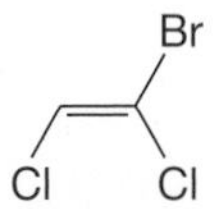
Br
Cl
Cl

(b)

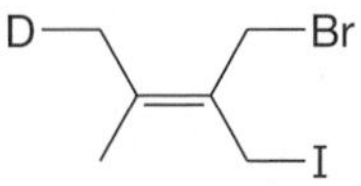
D
Br
I

(c)

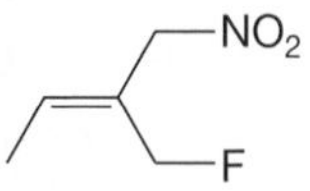
NO_2
F

(d)

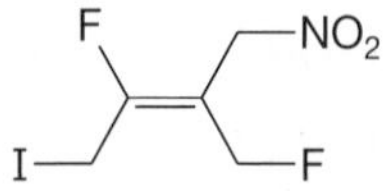
F
NO_2
I
F

5.18 What is the configuration, *Z* or *E*, of each of the following double bonds?

(a)

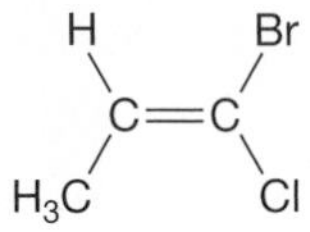
H
Br
C=C
H_3C
Cl

(b)

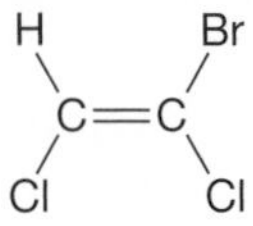
H
Br
C=C
Cl
Cl

(c)

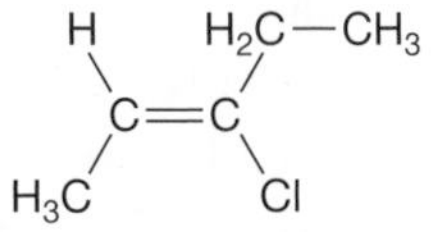
H
H_2C-CH_3
C=C
H_3C
Cl

(d)

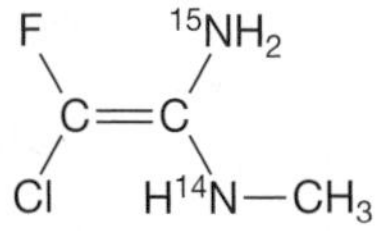
F
$^{15}NH_2$
C=C
Cl
$H^{14}N-CH_3$

5.19 What is the configuration, *Z* or *E*, of each of the following double bonds?

(a)

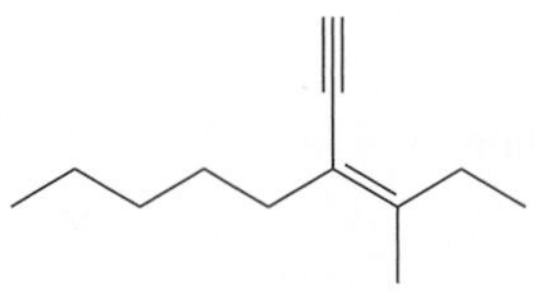

(b)

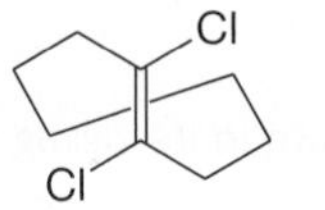
Cl
Cl

Note: **Make a model; the diagonal bond is *behind* the double bond.**

5.20 Assign the configuration *Z* or *E* to each double bond, where appropriate, in the following molecules.

(a)

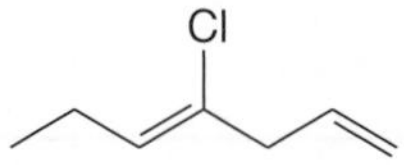
Cl

(b)

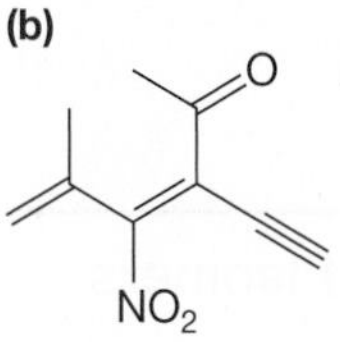
O
NO_2

(c)

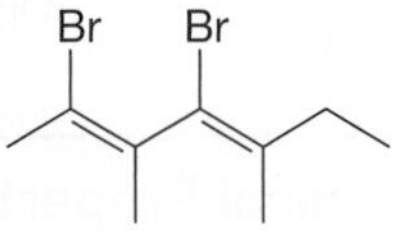
Br
Br

Sections 5.8–5.11 Diastereomers, Drawing Stereoisomers, and Fischer Projections

5.21 Consider the molecule shown here. **(a)** How many chiral centers does it have? **(b)** How many total stereoisomers are possible? *Hint*: Determine whether it is possible for any of the stereoisomers to be meso.

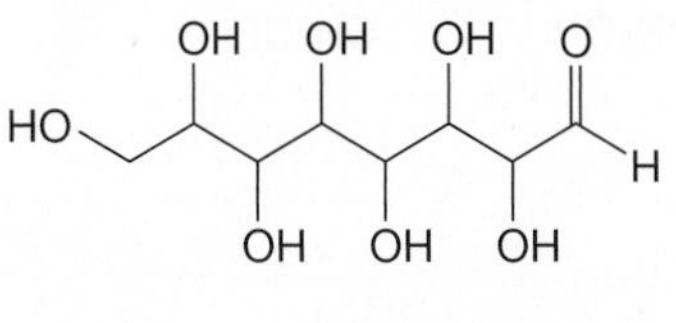
OH OH OH O
HO
H
OH OH OH

5.22 Draw all possible stereoisomers of the molecule shown here. Which ones are meso?

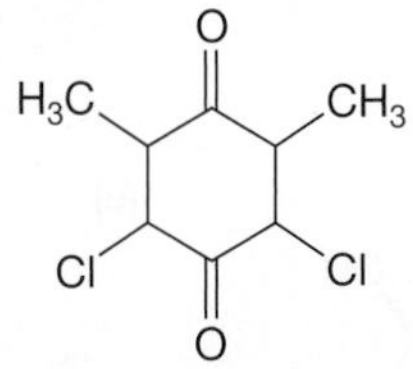
O
H_3C
CH_3
Cl
Cl
O

5.23 Draw all possible stereoisomers of the molecule shown here.

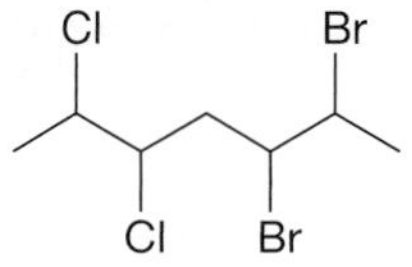
Cl
Br
Cl
Br

5.24 Which of the following species are chiral?

(a)

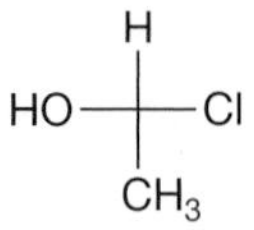
H
HO
Cl
CH$_3$

(b)

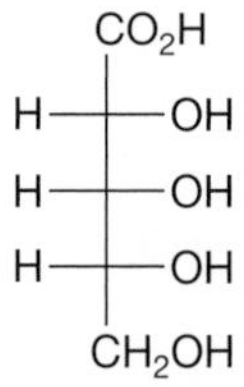
CO$_2$H
H
OH
H
OH
H
OH
CH$_2$OH

(c)

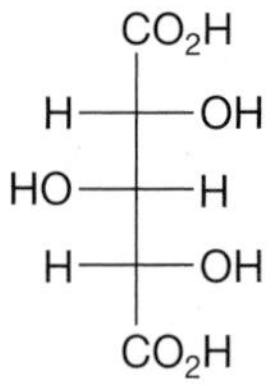
CO$_2$H
H
OH
HO
H
H
OH
CO$_2$H

(d)

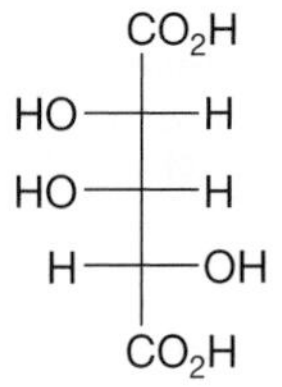
CO$_2$H
HO
H
HO
H
H
OH
CO$_2$H

5.25 For each molecule in Problem 5.24, identify all chiral centers that exist. Which of those molecules, if any, are meso?

5.26 Draw each of the following molecules in a zigzag conformation.

(a)

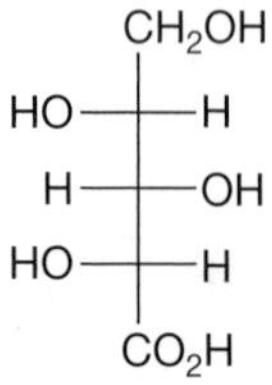
CH$_2$OH
HO
H
H
OH
HO
H
CO$_2$H

(b)

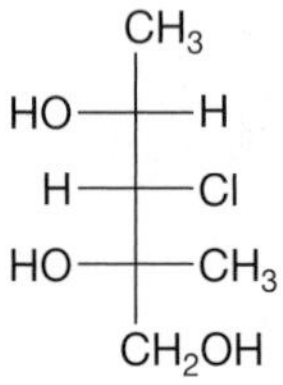
CH$_3$
HO
H
H
Cl
HO
CH$_3$
CH$_2$OH

(c)

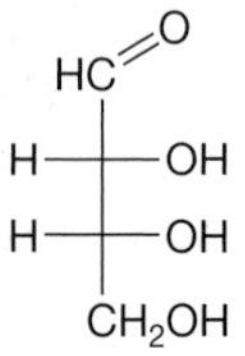
HC
O
H
OH
H
OH
CH$_2$OH

(d)

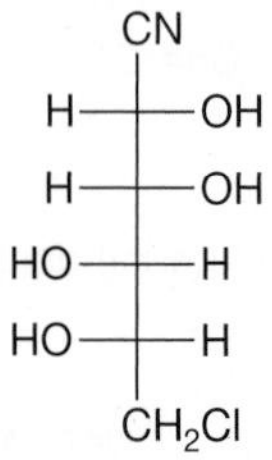
CN
H
OH
H
OH
HO
H
HO
H
CH$_2$Cl

5.27 Draw a Fischer projection for each of the following molecules shown in its zigzag conformation.

(a)

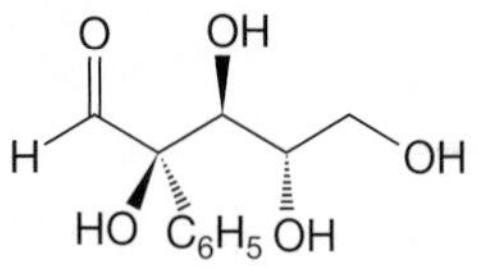
O
OH
H
OH
HO
C$_6$H$_5$
OH

(b)

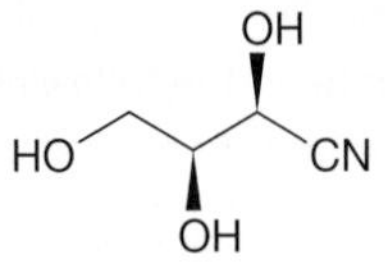
OH
HO
CN
OH

(c)

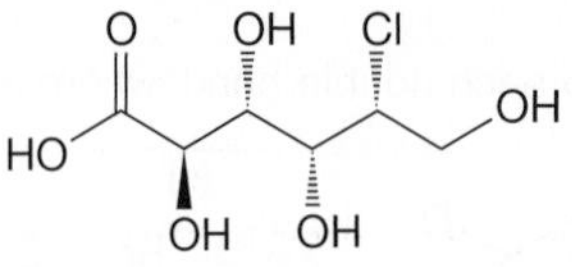
O
OH
Cl
OH
HO
OH
OH

Sections 5.12 and 5.13 Physical and Chemical Properties of Isomers

5.28 For each of the following pairs, determine if the compounds have the same boiling point or different boiling points.

(a)

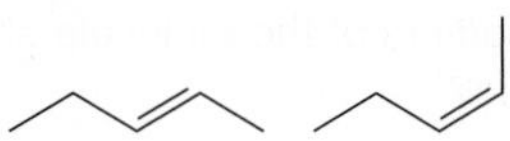

(b)

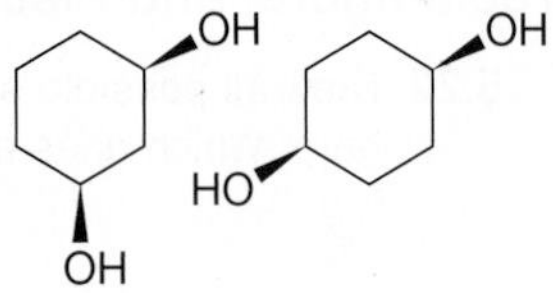
OH
OH
OH
HO

(c)

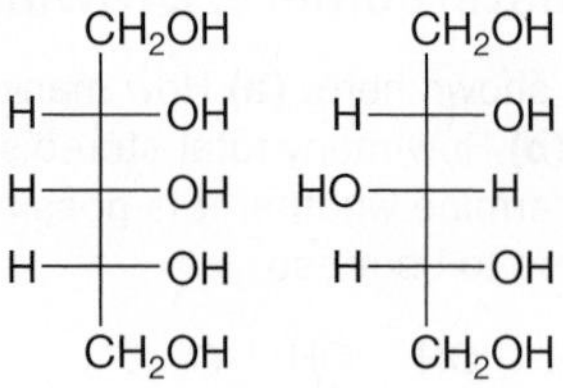
CH$_2$OH
H
OH
H
OH
H
OH
CH$_2$OH
CH$_2$OH
H
OH
HO
H
H
OH
CH$_2$OH

(d)

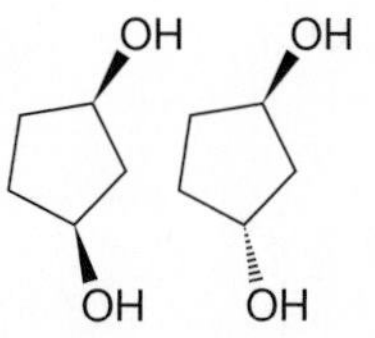
OH
OH
OH
OH

(e)

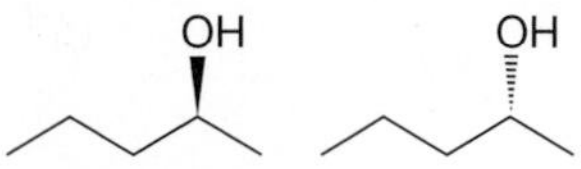
OH
OH

5.29 Would you expect any of the isomers **A–C** to have the same heat of combustion? Explain.

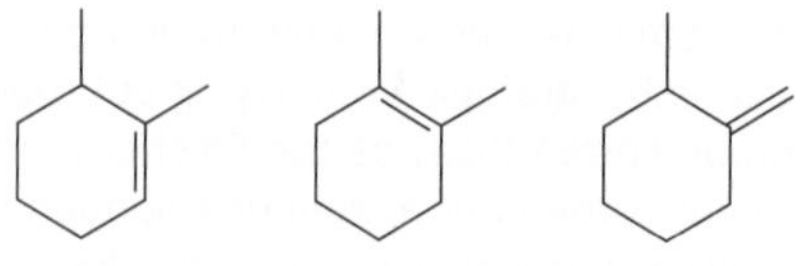

A
B
C

5.30 Would you expect any of the isomers **A–C** to have the same heat of combustion? Explain.

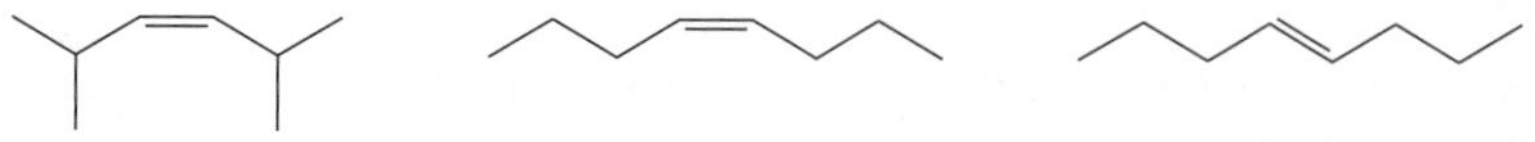

A
B
C

5.31 Molecule **A** is an acid that has a single chiral center and is therefore chiral. As with any chiral compound, the enantiomers of **A** have identical physical and chemical properties and therefore cannot be separated in an achiral environment. However, when a racemic mixture of **A** is reacted with an enantiomerically pure chiral base such as **B**, then two salts of the form **C** are produced.

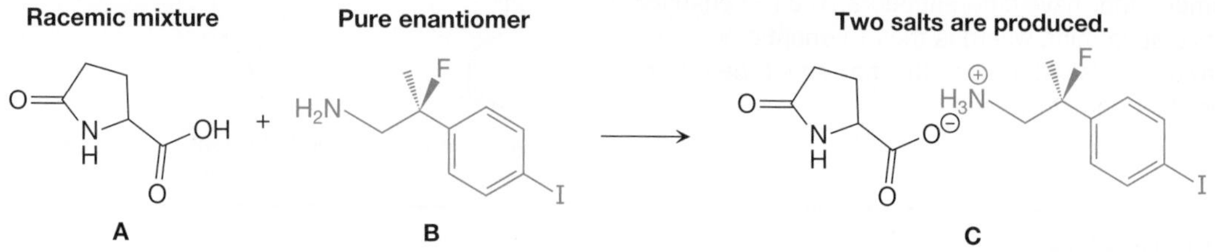

Racemic mixture
Pure enantiomer
Two salts are produced.
A
B
C

The two product salts have *different* physical and chemical properties, which allow them to be separated in an achiral environment.

(a) Draw the two salts that are produced, including their complete dash–wedge notations.

(b) Explain why the two salts have different physical and chemical properties.

Section 5.14 Optical Activity

5.32 Which of the molecules you drew in Problem 5.23 are optically active?

5.33 If Taxol (see Problem 5.12) has a specific rotation of −49°, then what is the specific rotation of its enantiomer?

5.34 Consider a mixture that is 60% (+) enantiomer and 40% (−) enantiomer. In which direction will the mixture rotate plane-polarized light? What is the enantiomeric excess of the mixture?

5.35 (S)-2-Bromobutane has a specific rotation of +23.1°. Suppose that a solution is made by dissolving 20.00 g of (S)-2-bromobutane in 1.00 L of total solution. What would be the measured rotation of plane-polarized light sent through a 10.00-cm tube containing that solution?

5.36 Ibuprofen is a drug used to manage mild pain, fever, and inflammation. It is a chiral drug, and only the *S* enantiomer, whose specific rotation is +25.0°, is effective. The *R* enantiomer exhibits no biological activity. If a particular process is capable of producing ibuprofen with 84% enantiomeric excess of the *S* enantiomer, then what is the specific rotation of that mixture? What is the percentage of *S* enantiomer in that mixture?

Sections 5.15–5.17 Organic Chemistry of Biomolecules

5.37 In this chapter, we saw that amino acids typically have a single chiral center and are therefore chiral. One amino acid, however, is achiral. Which one? Explain. *Hint*: Review Table 1-7, page 39.

5.38 How many D-aldoheptoses are possible? Draw the Fischer projection of one of them and its enantiomer.

5.39 Identify which D-aldopentoses are C-2 epimers. Identify which ones are C-3 epimers.

5.40 Draw the Fischer projection of **(a)** L-lyxose and **(b)** L-talose.

5.41 In the late 1800s, Emil Fischer was able to determine the stereochemical relationships among the four asymmetric carbons in D-glucose by strategically carrying out reactions on various known sugars and studying their optical activities. His proof, known today as the Fischer proof, is a very elegant application of logic in chemistry. As one piece of the proof, Fischer carried out a Wohl degradation reaction on D-glucose to produce D-arabinose. He then oxidized D-arabinose with warm nitric acid, which converted both the CH=O group at C-1 and the C—OH group at C-5 to CO_2H functional groups. He found that the resulting compound, a type of *aldaric acid*, was optically active. On the basis of this result, which aldopentose structures could be ruled out for D-arabinose? Which aldohexose structures could be ruled out for D-glucose?

5.42 As another piece of the Fischer proof (see Problem 5.41), D-glucose was reacted in such a way as to convert the CH=O group at C-1 to a CH_2OH group and to convert the CH_2OH group at C-6 to a CH=O group. The same was done to D-mannose. When this transformation was carried out on D-glucose, a sugar other than D-glucose was produced, but when it was carried out on D-mannose, D-mannose was returned as the product. How do these results agree with the currently known structures of the two sugars? What sugar was produced when D-glucose was reacted?

5.43 Carvone is present in many essential oils. It is chiral, and its two enantiomers are shown here. Even though they are enantiomers, they have different odors. The (−) enantiomer smells like spearmint, whereas the (+) enantiomer smells like caraway seeds. What does this say about the olfactory receptors that detect carvone?

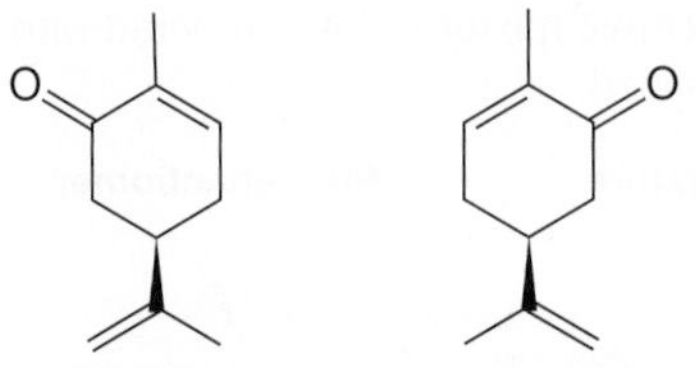

(−)-Carvone **(+)-Carvone**

Integrated Problems

5.44 If molecules **A** and **B** are isomers of each other, then what kinds of isomers could they be (i.e., *enantiomers*, *diastereomers*, or *constitutional isomers*) under each of the following conditions?

(a) Both molecules have the same index of hydrogen deficiency (IHD).
(b) Molecule **A** has a ring but molecule **B** does not.
(c) Molecules **A** and **B** contain different functional groups.
(d) Molecules **A** and **B** share exactly the same functional groups.
(e) Molecule **A** has a plane of symmetry but molecule **B** does not.

5.45 Identify the specific relationship between each of the following pairs of molecules (*same*, *constitutional isomers*, *enantiomers*, *diastereomers*, *conformers*, or *unrelated*).

(a)

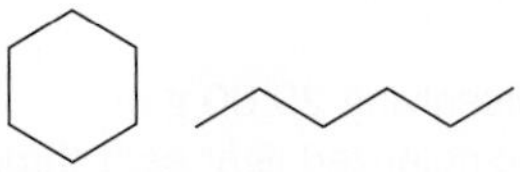

(b)

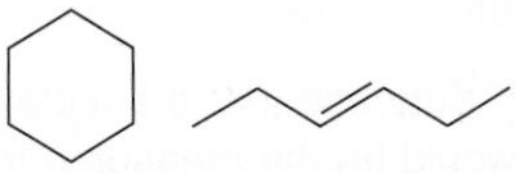

(c)

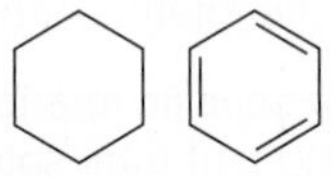

(d)

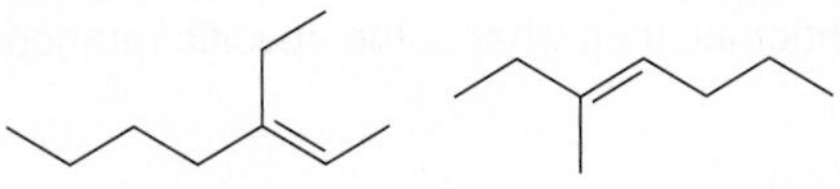

(e)

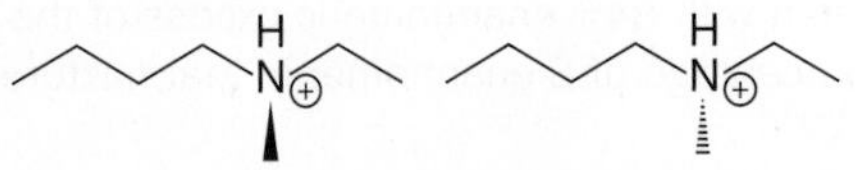

(f)

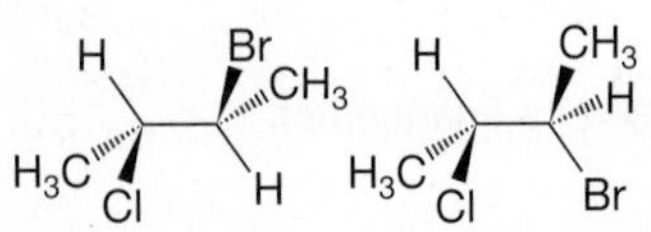

(g)

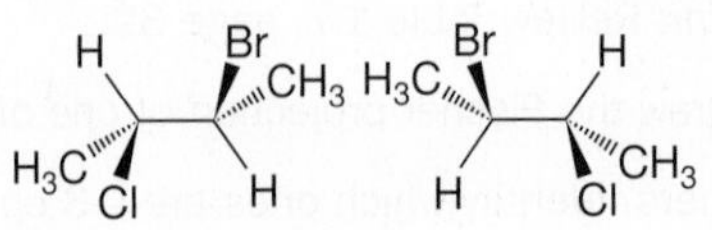

(h)

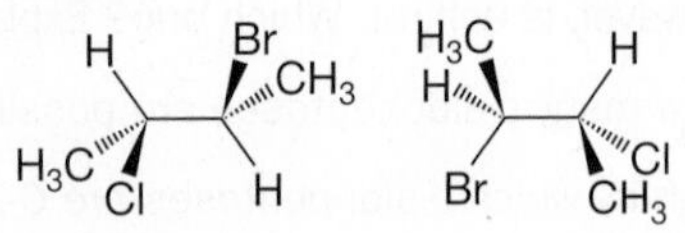

5.46 Identify the specific relationship between each of the following pairs of molecules (*same*, *constitutional isomers*, *enantiomers*, *diastereomers*, *conformers*, or *unrelated*).

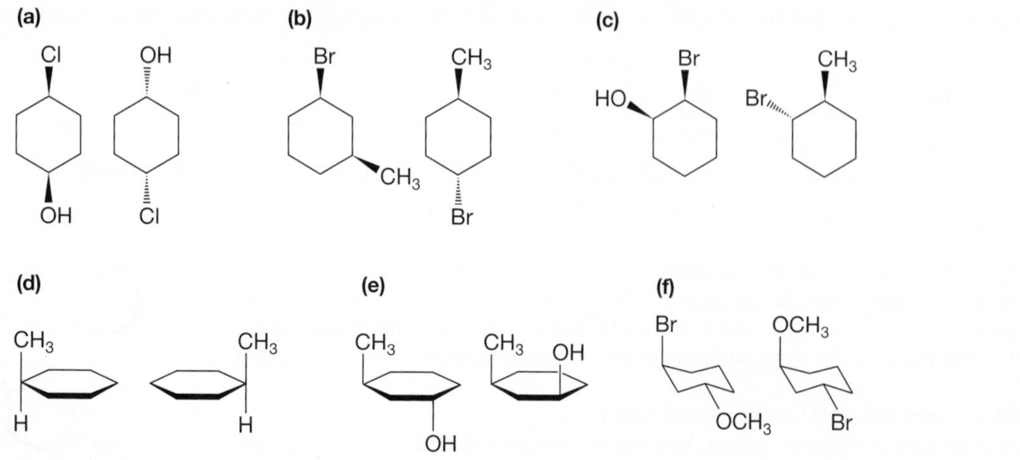
(a)
(b)
(c)
(d)
(e)
(f)

5.47 Identify the specific relationship between each of the following pairs of molecules (*same*, *constitutional isomers*, *enantiomers*, *diastereomers*, *conformers*, or *unrelated*).

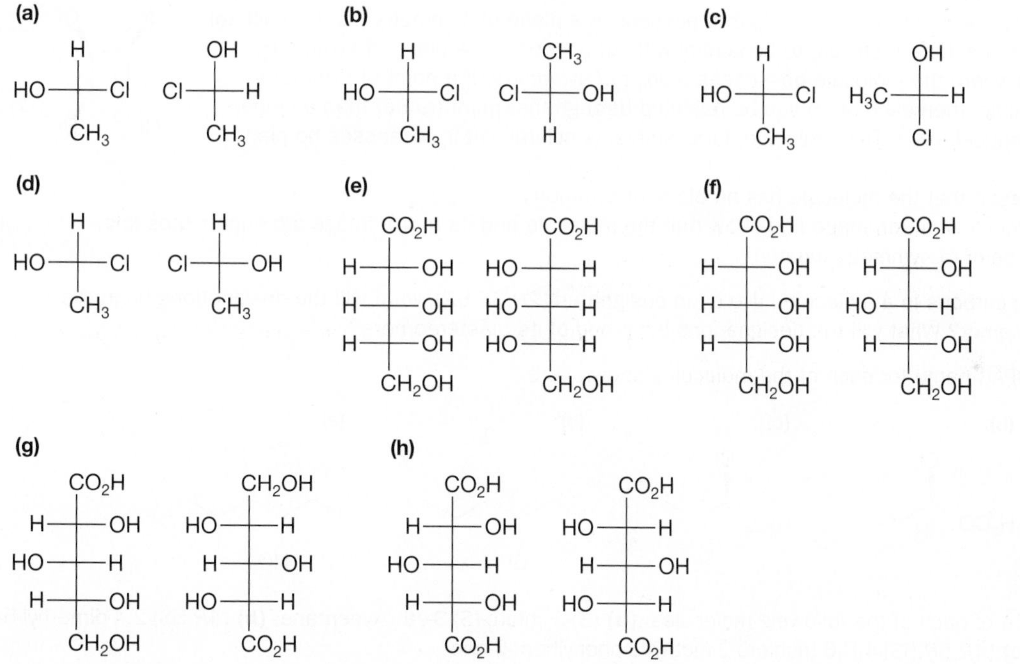
(a)
(b)
(c)
(d)
(e)
(f)
(g)
(h)

5.48 Draw all configurational isomers of $C_4H_{11}N$ that are optically active.

5.49 Butanal (C_4H_8O) has eight H atoms. Suppose that any of these H atoms can be replaced by a Cl atom to yield a molecule with the formula C_4H_7ClO. Identify two H atoms where this substitution would yield **(a)** *constitutional isomers* of C_4H_7ClO, **(b)** *enantiomers* of C_4H_7ClO, and **(c)** *conformers* of C_4H_7ClO.

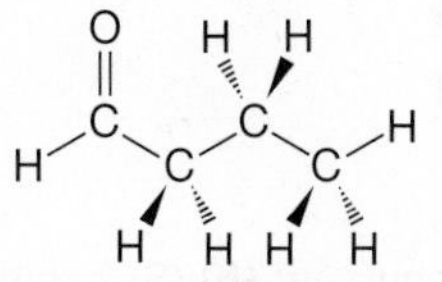

Butanal

5.50 2,3-Dibromoprop-1-ene ($C_3H_4Br_2$) has four H atoms. Suppose that any of these H atoms can be replaced by a Cl atom to yield a molecule with the formula $C_3H_3Br_2Cl$. Identify two H atoms where this substitution would yield **(a)** *constitutional isomers* of $C_3H_3Br_2Cl$; **(b)** *enantiomers* of $C_3H_3Br_2Cl$; **(c)** *diastereomers* of $C_3H_3Br_2Cl$.

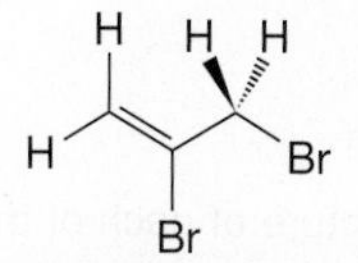

2,3-Dibromoprop-1-ene

5.51 An unknown compound is optically active and has the molecular formula C_6H_{12}. Draw all possible isomers of the compound.

5.52 Which of the molecules shown here are chiral? *Hint*: Do these Lewis structures accurately depict the three-dimensional geometry?

(a)

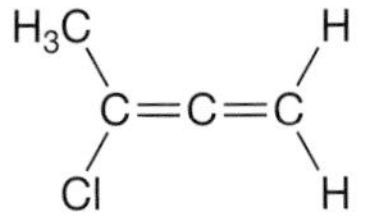
H3C
H
C=C=C
Cl
H

(b)

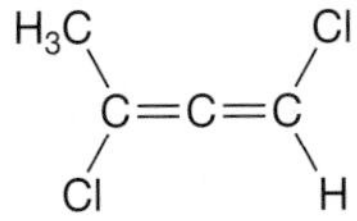
H3C
Cl
C=C=C
Cl
H

(c)

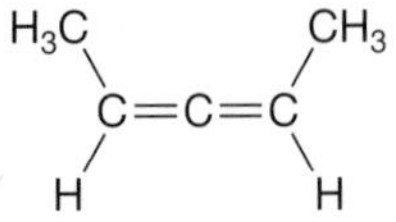
H3C
CH3
C=C=C
H
H

(d)

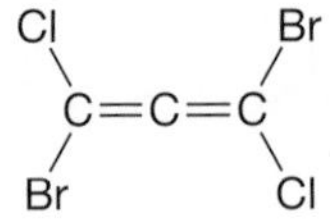
Cl
Br
C=C=C
Br
Cl

(e)

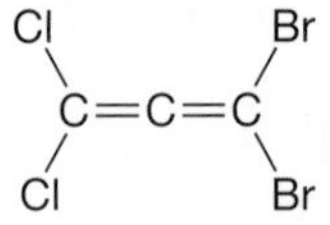
Cl
Br
C=C=C
Cl
Br

5.53 1,1′-Bi-2-naphthol is a chiral compound, and its enantiomers can be separated from each other. The enantiomer shown here has a specific rotation of −32.70° when dissolved in tetrahydrofuran. (Notice that the two fused-ring systems are not in the same plane. In the top ring system, the left side is in front of the plane of the page, whereas in the bottom ring system, the right side is in front.)

(a) How many chiral centers does 1,1′-bi-2-naphthol have?

(b) Draw the enantiomer of the molecule shown. What is its specific rotation?

(c) Aside from being mirror images of each other, how else are the two enantiomers related? Why do you think they do not readily interconvert? *Hint*: It may help to construct a molecular model.

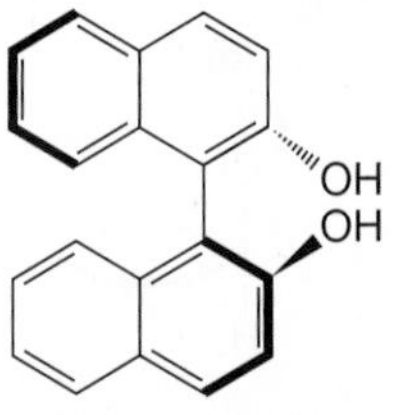
OH
OH

1,1′-Bi-2-naphthol

5.54 In this chapter, you learned that a molecule that possesses a plane of symmetry must be achiral. It is possible, however, for a molecule to be achiral without possessing a plane of symmetry, such as in cases where the molecule possesses a *point of symmetry*. If a point of symmetry exists for a molecule, then each atom can be reflected through that point (rather than a plane) to arrive at an identical atom. This molecule, for example, is achiral, yet it possesses no plane of symmetry.

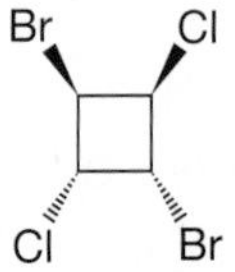
Br
Cl
Cl
Br

(a) Convince yourself that the molecule has no plane of symmetry.

(b) Draw the molecule's mirror image and show that the molecule and its mirror image are superimposable.

(c) Where is the point of symmetry located?

5.55 If the asymmetric carbons in a molecule have been designated (2*R*,3*S*,5*R*), what will the designations be in the molecule's enantiomer? What will the designations be in *one* of its diastereomers?

5.56 Determine the IUPAC name for each of the molecules shown here.

(a)

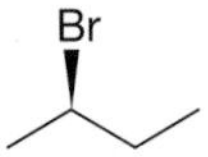
Br

(b)

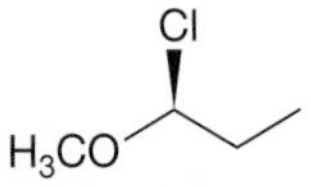
Cl
H3CO

(c)

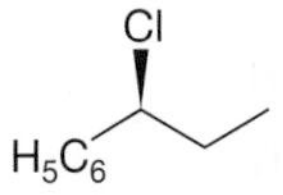
Cl
H5C6

(d)

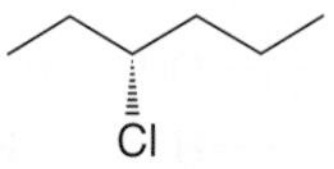
Cl

(e)

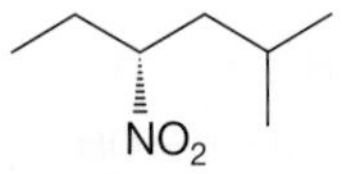
NO2

5.57 Draw the structure of each of the following molecules. **(a)** (*S*)-2-chloro-(*S*)-3-ethoxypentane; **(b)** (4*R*,5*S*)-2,4-dimethyl-5-nitrohex-2-ene; **(c)** (4*R*,5*R*,6*S*)-4,5,6-trichloro-2-methyl-3-phenylhept-2-ene

5.58 Draw the structure of each of the following molecules. **(a)** (*S*)-1-chloro-2,2-dimethyl-1-phenylcyclopentane; **(b)** (1*R*,2*S*)-1-methyl-1,2-dinitrocyclopropane; **(c)** (*R*)-4-ethoxycyclohexene; **(d)** (3*S*,4*S*)-3-chloro-4-fluoro-2-methylhepta-1,6-diene

5.59 Determine the IUPAC name for each of the molecules shown here.

(a)

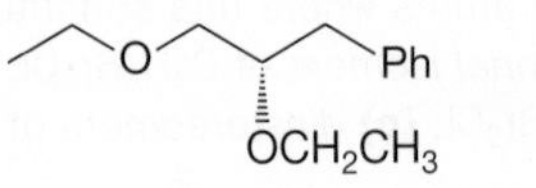
O
Ph
OCH2CH3

(b)

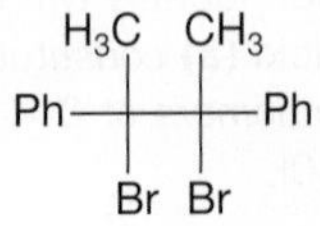
H3C CH3
Ph
Ph
Br Br

(c)

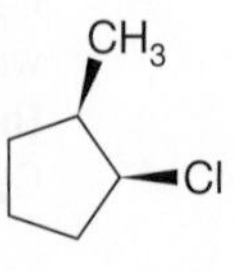
CH3
Cl

(d)

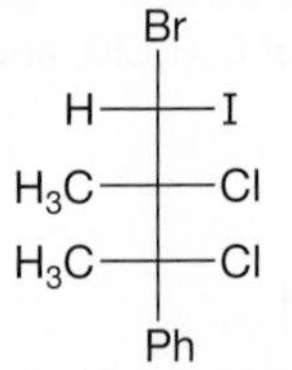
Br
H
I
H3C
Cl
H3C
Cl
Ph

5.60 Draw the structure of each of the following molecules. **(a)** (*R*)-1-chloro-1-fluorobutane; **(b)** (*S*)-2-chloropentane; **(c)** (*R*)-2-chloro-2-methoxypentane; **(d)** (*R*)-2,2,3-trichlorobutane; **(e)** (*S*)-3-methylhexane; **(f)** (*S*)-2-bromo-1-nitropentane

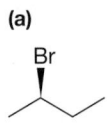

5.61 Draw the structure of each of the following molecules. **(a)** (*R*)-3-chloropent-1-ene; **(b)** (2*S*,3*S*)-2-bromo-3-chloropentane; **(c)** (*R*)-1-bromo-(*R*)-2-iodocyclopentane; **(d)** (*S*)-3-chlorocyclohexene; **(e)** (1*R*,2*S*)-1,2-dibromocyclopentane

5.62 What is the complete IUPAC name for each of the molecules shown here?

(a)

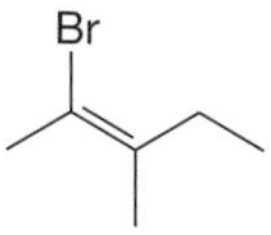

(b)

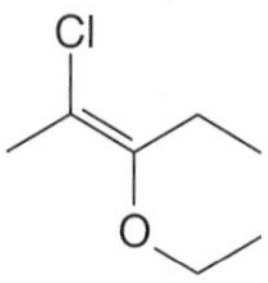

(c)

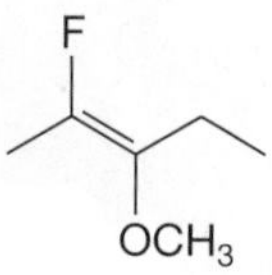

(d)

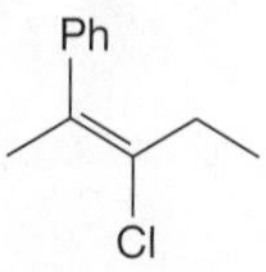

5.63 What is the complete IUPAC name for each of the molecules shown here?

(a)

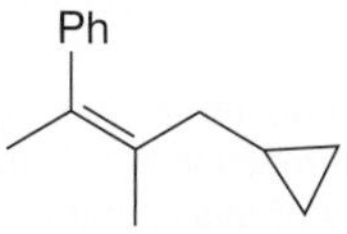

(b)

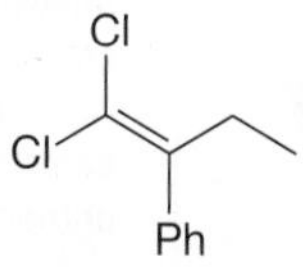

(c)

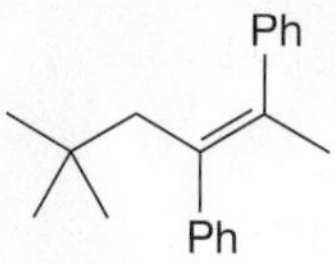

5.64 For each of the following names, draw the corresponding structure. **(a)** (*Z*)-2-methoxypent-2-ene; **(b)** (*E*)-3-methylpent-2-ene; **(c)** (*Z*)-1-chloro-2-methylpent-1-ene; **(d)** (*E*)-2-chloro-3-methoxybut-2-ene; **(e)** (*Z*)-1-bromo-1-chloropent-1-ene; **(f)** (*Z*)-3-methylpent-2-ene

5.65 For each of the following names, draw the corresponding structure. **(a)** (*Z*)-3-phenylhex-2-ene; **(b)** 1,2-dichlorocyclopentene; **(c)** (2*E*,4*E*)-2-ethoxyhexa-2,4-diene; **(d)** (1*E*,3*E*,5*E*)-1,3,4,6-tetrachlorohexa-1,3,5-triene

5.66 Determine whether each of the following names describes a single stereoisomer unambiguously. For each one that does, rewrite the name using the *R* and *S* designations for the chiral centers if appropriate. **(a)** *cis*-1,2-difluorocyclohexane; **(b)** *trans*-1,2-difluorocyclohexane; **(c)** *trans*-1,4-difluorocyclohexane; **(d)** *cis*-1-chloro-2-fluorocyclohexane; **(e)** *trans*-1,4-dimethylcycloheptane

6

This statue of George Washington (Washington Square Park, New York City) exhibits damage from acid rain. Sulfuric acid in rainwater (acid rain) reacts with calcium carbonate in the stone via a proton transfer reaction, the same type of reaction that is the primary focus of this chapter.

The Proton Transfer Reaction

An Introduction to Mechanisms, Equilibria, Free Energy Diagrams, and Charge Stability

In Chapters 1 through 5, we focused primarily on structural aspects of atoms, molecules, and ions. We asked questions about the nature of the chemical bond, about how electrons are distributed in a given molecule or ion, and about the similarities and differences among the various types of isomers. Here in Chapter 6, we shift our focus to *chemical reactions*. A **chemical reaction** is the transformation of one substance (a reactant) into another substance (a product), typically through changes in chemical bonds.

When we watch a chemical reaction take place in the laboratory, it may seem to proceed smoothly, with the reactants disappearing and the products appearing in one continuous process. If we could observe the reaction on the molecular level, however, we would see that it actually takes place in distinct events called **elementary steps**, each of which is a near-instantaneous change in geometry that involves the breaking and/or formation of specific bonds. The precise sequence of elementary steps that accounts for the conversion of the original reactants to the final products is called the **mechanism** of the reaction. Depending on the nature of the particular reaction, the mechanism may consist of a single elementary step (i.e., Reactants $\rightarrow$ Products) or multiple elementary steps (e.g., Reactants $\rightarrow$ A $\rightarrow$ B $\rightarrow$ C $\rightarrow$ Products).

Chapter Outline

Reaction mechanisms help us understand *how* and *why* reactions take place as they do, which allows us to predict the outcomes of reactions without having to memorize. Moreover, as we will see throughout the rest of the book, there are many seemingly different reactions whose mechanisms are constructed from just a handful of different elementary steps, so *mechanisms simplify organic chemistry*. We will therefore spend a great deal of focus on mechanisms throughout this book. But first we must work on gaining insight into key aspects of elementary steps.

We begin with the *proton transfer reaction*, the topic of this entire chapter, because it is one of the simplest reactions that you will encounter in organic chemistry and it is also the most common elementary step found in organic reaction mechanisms. Then, in Chapter 7, we will examine a handful of other elementary steps, to which the concepts we learn here about proton transfers can be applied.

6.1 An Introduction to Reaction Mechanisms: The Proton Transfer Reaction and Curved Arrow Notation

SECTION 6.1 OBJECTIVES

You will be able to:

1. Identify the acid and the base of a proton transfer reaction when given the reactants and products.
2. Draw the curved arrow notation and products of a proton transfer reaction when the acid and base have been identified.

A **proton transfer reaction** (or a **Brønsted–Lowry acid–base reaction**) is one in which a *Brønsted–Lowry base* reacts with a *Brønsted–Lowry acid*:

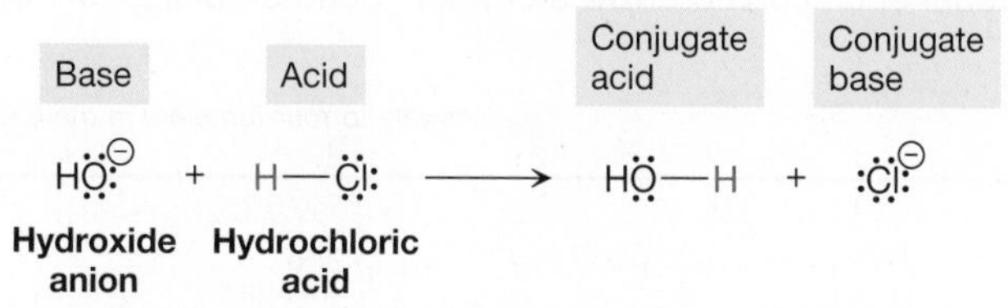

Base
Acid
Conjugate acid
Conjugate base
HO:⁻ + H—Cl: → HO—H + :Cl:⁻
Hydroxide anion
Hydrochloric acid

(6-1)

In Equation 6-1, HO^- is the **Brønsted–Lowry base** because it *accepts a proton* (H^+), and HCl is the **Brønsted–Lowry acid** because it *donates a proton*. Overall, a proton (shown in blue) is transferred from the acid to the base; the formal charge of the base, therefore, increases by 1, whereas the formal charge of the acid decreases by 1. The **conjugate acid** is the species that results after the base picks up a proton, and the **conjugate base** is the species that results after the acid loses a proton.

Proton transfer reactions take place as a single event, which is to say:

> A proton transfer reaction consists of a single *elementary step*.

As a result, all of the changes that occur in the reaction at the molecular level do so simultaneously; they are said to be **concerted**.

▸ LOOKING AHEAD

In Chapter 7, we will see how the curved arrow notation rules for proton transfers apply to other elementary steps, including steps that involve the making or breaking of π bonds.

Organic chemists follow these changes by keeping track of the arrangement of the valence electrons. As shown in Equation 6-2, a single bond between H and Cl in the reactants is broken, while a single bond between H and O in the products is formed:

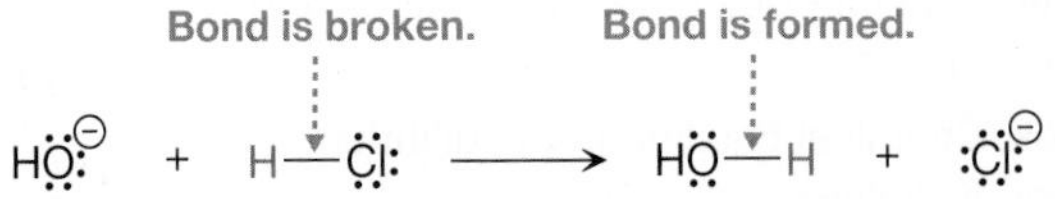
Bond is broken.
Bond is formed.

(6-2)

Curved arrow notation (also called **arrow pushing**) allows us to keep track of the valence electrons as they move throughout a mechanism. There are essentially four rules to using curved arrow notation for a proton transfer (see Looking Ahead box):

Rules for Curved Arrow Notation for a Proton Transfer

1. A curved arrow represents the movement of *valence electrons*, not *atoms*.
2. Each *double-barbed curved arrow* (⟶) represents the movement of two valence electrons.
3. A curved arrow that originates from the center of a bond represents the breaking of that bond.
4. A curved arrow that points to an atom represents:
   (a) the formation of a new σ bond if the electrons were originally on another atom.
   (b) the formation of a new lone pair if the electrons were originally from a bond involving that atom.

The curved arrow notation for the reaction in Equation 6-1 is illustrated in Equation 6-3:

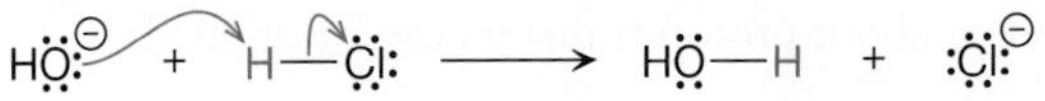

(6-3)

Two curved arrows are required because the reaction involves a total of four electrons (Rule 2). The curved arrow on the left shows that a lone pair on O becomes an O—H bond (Rule 4a). The curved arrow on the right shows that the H—Cl bond breaks (Rule 3) and those electrons become an additional lone pair on Cl (Rule 4b). You will learn in Solved Problem 6.1 that this set of curved arrows can be used to describe other proton transfer reactions as well.

CONNECTIONS 6.1

Ammonia: More than a window cleaner Ammonia (Solved Problem 6.1) is commonly used as an active ingredient in window cleaners, but most of the ammonia produced worldwide is used for fertilizers that feed nearly half the world's population. Industrially, ammonia is produced via the Haber–Bosch process, in which nitrogen gas, the principal component of the atmosphere, reacts with gaseous hydrogen.

Windex
ORIGINAL

YOUR TURN **6.1**

In Equation 6-3, circle all of the electrons that are involved in the chemical reaction. Label each curved arrow as either "bond breaking" or "bond formation."

Answers to Your Turns are in the back of the book.

SOLVED PROBLEM **6.1**

How to draw the curved arrow notation for a proton transfer reaction

Break It Down **Draw the curved arrow notation for the proton transfer between ammonia (NH_3) and water, where water acts as the acid and ammonia acts as the base.**

Think	Solve
What does it mean to be an acid? A base?	Because water acts as an acid (H^+ donor) and ammonia acts as a base (H^+ acceptor), write the reaction as follows: 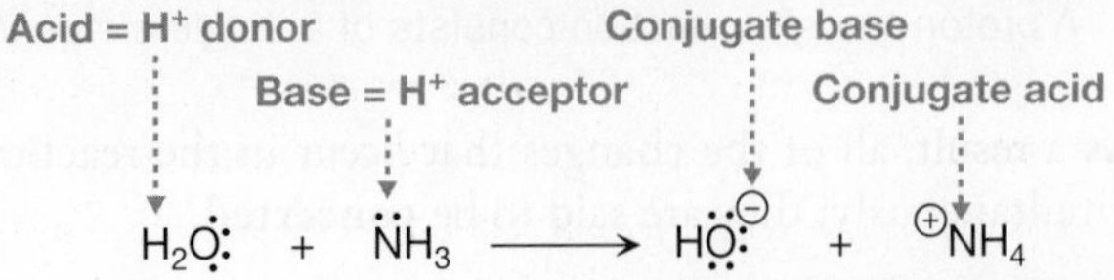

Acid = H⁺ donor
Base = H⁺ acceptor
Conjugate base
Conjugate acid

(continued)

What bonds are broken? What bonds are formed?	An O—H bond in water breaks and the electrons become a new lone pair on O. The lone pair on N in ammonia becomes a new N—H bond. 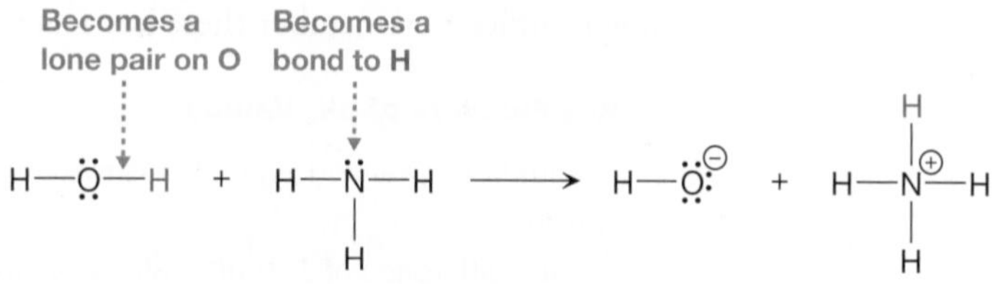 Becomes a lone pair on O Becomes a bond to H
How do you show those changes using curved arrows?	One curved arrow is drawn from the lone pair on N to the H on water (Rule 4a). A second curved arrow originates from the center of the O—H bond (Rule 3) and points to O (Rule 4b). 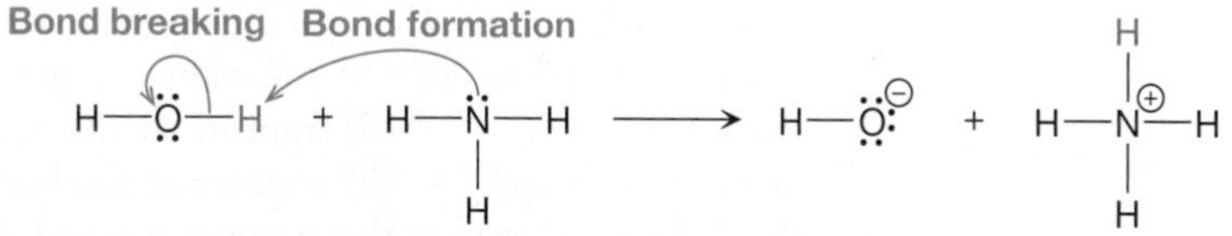 Bond breaking Bond formation

Try It Draw the curved arrow notation for the reverse of the reaction in the above exercise.

Answers to all Try It exercises can be found in the Solutions Manual.

6.2 Proton Transfer Reaction Outcomes: pK_a Values and Acid and Base Strengths

SECTION 6.2 OBJECTIVES

You will be able to:

1. Identify the stronger of two acids or two bases from the relevant pK_a values.
2. Use pK_a values to determine whether a proton transfer reaction is reactant-favored or product-favored and to what extent.
3. Determine whether the leveling effect will allow a species to exist in a given solvent.
4. Determine the ionization state of an acid when given the pH of the solution.

Even though a proton transfer reaction can be *written* for any combination of acid and base, not every reaction will actually *occur*; that is, not every proton transfer reaction will favor products. A proton transfer reaction between HCl and HO^- does favor products, for example, producing Cl^- and H_2O, but the proton transfer between NH_3 and HO^- to produce NH_2^- and H_2O does not.

Knowing how to predict the outcome of a proton transfer reaction is an essential skill in organic chemistry. As we mentioned earlier, proton transfers are the most common elementary steps found in reaction mechanisms, so predicting the outcome of a proton transfer will give you insight into whether a specific proton transfer that might be proposed for a mechanism is actually feasible.

To better understand why some proton transfer reactions favor products and others do not, examine the generic proton transfer reaction in Equation 6-4:

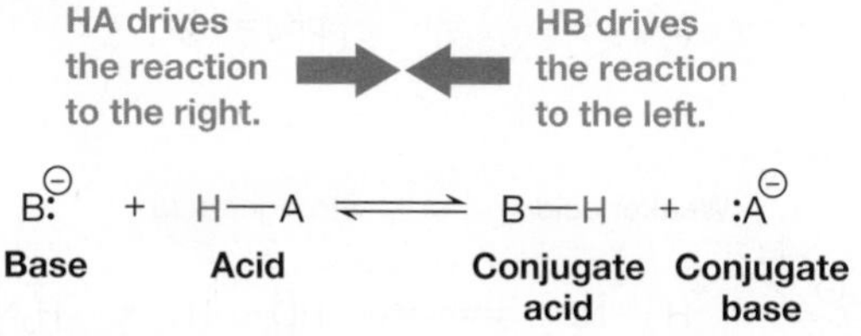
HA drives the reaction to the right.
HB drives the reaction to the left.
Base
Acid
Conjugate acid
Conjugate base

(6-4)

The reactant acid, HA, can donate its proton to B^- to form the products. But the reverse reaction is also possible (indicated by the bidirectional arrow, $\rightleftharpoons$), where the product acid, HB, can donate its proton to A^- to form the reactants. Thus, we can view the two acids as being in competition with each other, and the stronger acid will win, succeeding in donating its proton:

- If the reactant acid is stronger, then the reaction will tend to result in more products than reactants; the product side will be favored.
- If the product acid is stronger, then the reaction will tend to result in more reactants than products; the reactant side will be favored.

To know which of two acids is stronger, we can turn to the **pK_a** values of the acids, which are experimentally determined values of acid strengths. In Section 6.3, we will discuss pK_a values in greater depth, including how they are derived. For now, it will suffice to remember these key features:

Key Features of pK_a Values

- A lower pK_a value (i.e., less positive or more negative) represents a stronger acid.
- Each difference of 1 in pK_a values represents a factor of 10 difference in acid strength.

With these features in mind, you should familiarize yourself with Table 6-1, which contains pK_a values of several representative acids in order of decreasing acid strength (a more complete table of pK_a values is provided in Appendix A). The strongest of these acids (pK_a = −13) appears at the top of the first column, and the weakest of these acids (pK_a = 50) appears at the bottom of the second column. Notice that the difference between those values is 63 pK_a units, which corresponds to a difference in acid strength of 10^{63}!

YOUR TURN **6.2**

Rank these acids from weakest to strongest. (Consult Table 6-1 for the pK_a value of phenol.)

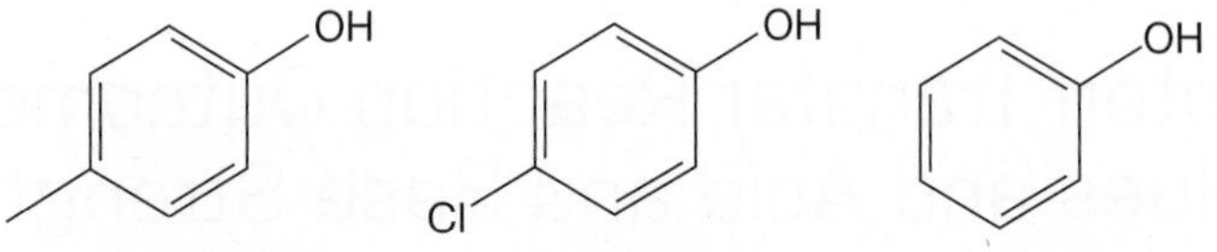

OH
OH
Cl
OH

4-Methylphenol pK_a = 10.26 | **4-Chlorophenol** pK_a = 9.43 | **Phenol**

CONNECTIONS 6.2

4-Methylphenol in nature and in industry 4-Methylphenol (Your Turn 6.2), also called *para*-cresol, is one of the compounds responsible for the odor of pigs. The compound is also found in human sweat and attracts female mosquitoes. One of the main industrial uses of 4-methylphenol is in the production of antioxidants.

Having pK_a values at our disposal, let's now revisit the two proton transfer reactions mentioned at the beginning of this section, shown in Equations 6-5 and 6-6:

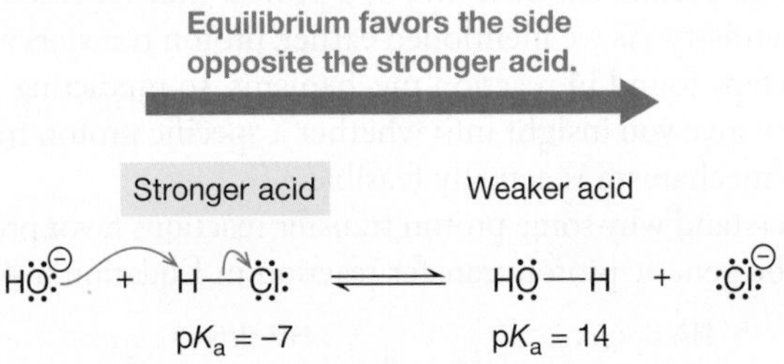

Equilibrium favors the side opposite the stronger acid.
Stronger acid
Weaker acid
HO:⊖ + H—Cl: ⇌ HO—H + :Cl:⊖
pKa = −7
pKa = 14

(6-5)

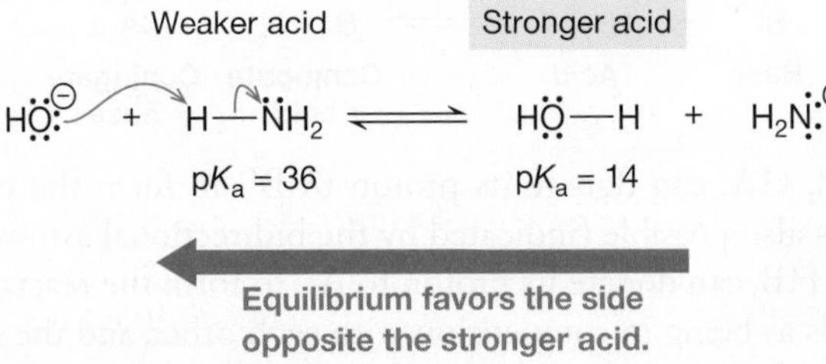

Weaker acid
Stronger acid
HO:⊖ + H—NH2 ⇌ HO—H + H2N:⊖
pKa = 36
pKa = 14
Equilibrium favors the side opposite the stronger acid.

(6-6)

In Equation 6-5, the stronger acid is on the reactant side, so the product side of the reaction is favored. Moreover, because the difference in pK_a values between −7 and 14 is 21 units, the reactant acid is 10^{21} times stronger (one power of 10 for each unit of pK_a difference), so the *extent* to which the product side is favored is 10^{21}. In Equation 6-6, the stronger acid is on the product side, so the reactant side of the reaction

TABLE 6-1 Values of pK_a for Various Acids[a]

Acid	Conjugate Base	pK_a
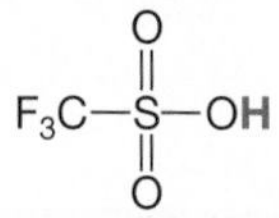 Trifluoromethanesulfonic acid	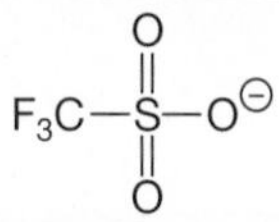	−13
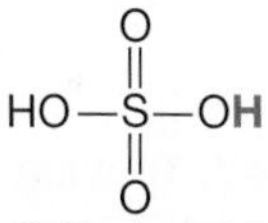 Sulfuric acid	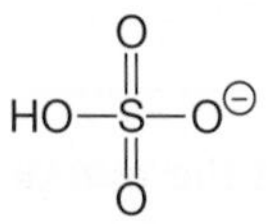	−9
HCl Hydrochloric acid	$Cl^{\ominus}$	−7
$H_3O^{\oplus}$ Hydronium ion	H_2O	0[b]
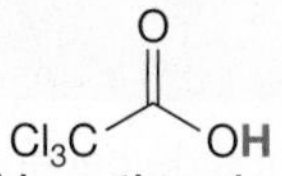 Trichloroethanoic acid (Trichloroacetic acid)	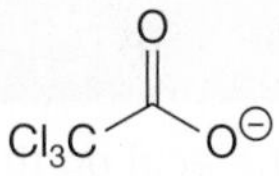	0.77
HF Hydrofluoric acid	$F^{\ominus}$	3.2
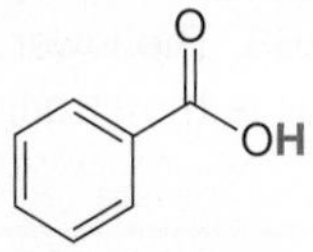 Benzoic acid	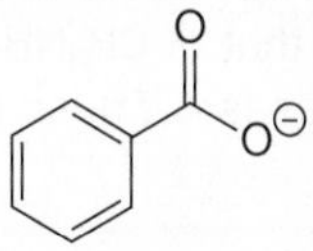	4.2
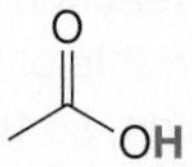 Ethanoic acid (Acetic acid)	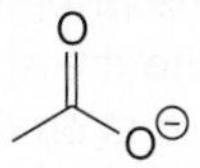	4.75
H_2S Hydrogen sulfide	$HS^{\ominus}$	7.2
$H_4N^{\oplus}$ Ammonium ion	NH_3	9.4
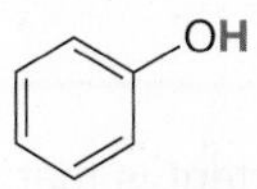 Phenol	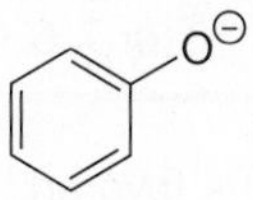	10.0
$H_3C-\overset{\oplus}{N}H_3$ Methylammonium ion	H_3C-NH_2	10.63
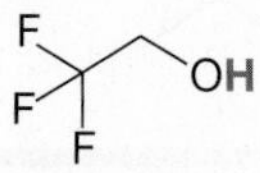 2,2,2-Trifluoroethanol	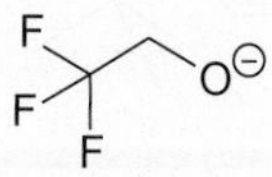	12.4
H_2O Water	$HO^{\ominus}$	14[b]
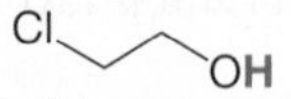 2-Chloroethanol	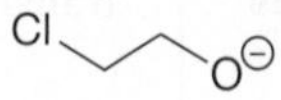	14.3
CH_3OH Methanol	$CH_3O^{\ominus}$	15.5
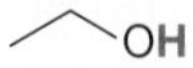 Ethanol	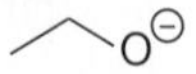	16
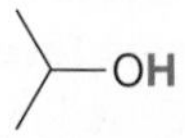 Propan-2-ol (Isopropyl alcohol)	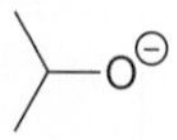	16.5
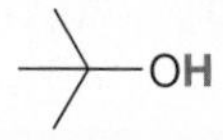 Methylpropan-2-ol (*tert*-Butyl alcohol)	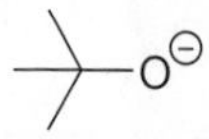	19
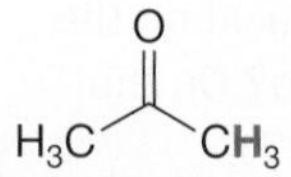 Propanone (Acetone)	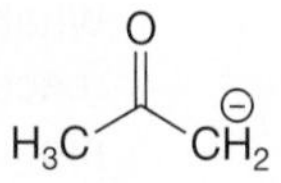	20
$HC\equiv CH$ Ethyne (Acetylene)	$HC\equiv C^{\ominus}$	25
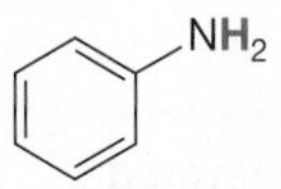 Aniline (Phenylamine)	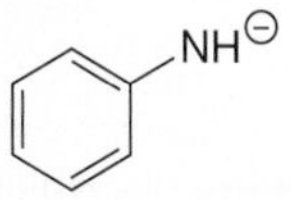	27
H_2 Hydrogen gas	$H^{\ominus}$	35
NH_3 Ammonia	$H_2N^{\ominus}$	36
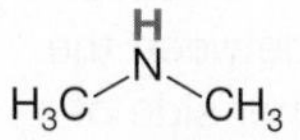 *N*-Methylmethanamine (Dimethylamine)	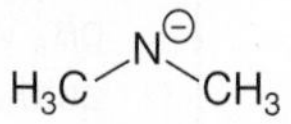	38
$H_2C=CH_2$ Ethene (Ethylene)	$H_2C=\overset{\ominus}{C}H$	44
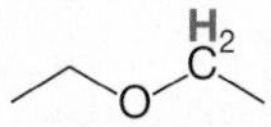 Ethoxyethane (Diethyl ether)	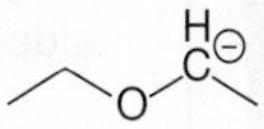	45
CH_4 Methane	$H_3C^{\ominus}$	48
CH_3CH_3 Ethane	$CH_3\overset{\ominus}{C}H_2$	50

[a]pK_a = −log K_a. The less positive (or more negative) the pK_a value, the stronger the acid relative to another acid.
[b]In older textbooks, the pK_a values of H_3O^+ and H_2O are reported to be −1.7 and 15.7, respectively, but by definition they are 0 and 14.

CONNECTIONS 6.3

Phenol: The first plastics and the first successful surgeries Phenol (Your Turn 6.2) is primarily used to make precursors to plastics, including nylon, resins, and Bakelite. In the 1920s, billiard balls were made out of Bakelite as a substitute for ivory. Phenol was the first antiseptic to be used successfully in surgery, a technique pioneered by Joseph Lister, 1st Baron Lister (1827–1912). It is still used as an active ingredient in oral analgesics.

is favored. And, because the difference in pK_a values between 36 and 14 is 22, the extent to which the reactant side is favored is 10^{22}. (In Section 6.3, we will show more explicitly how pK_a values relate to the extent to which a particular side of a proton transfer equilibrium is favored.)

SOLVED PROBLEM **6.2**

How to use pK_a values to predict the outcome of a proton transfer reaction

Break It Down **Predict which side of the reaction is favored. To what extent is that side favored?**

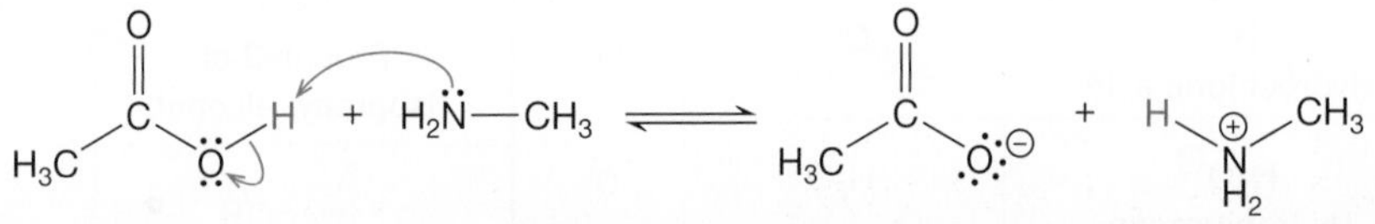

Think	Solve
What is the acid on the reactant side? On the product side?	CH_3CO_2H is the acid on the reactant side because it is donating a proton. The conjugate acid on the product side is $CH_3NH_3^+$.
Which of those two acids is stronger? How can you tell?	We can use pK_a values found in Table 6-1 to determine the stronger acid. The pK_a value of CH_3CO_2H is 4.75, and that of $CH_3NH_3^+$ is 10.63. The lower of the two values is 4.75, so CH_3CO_2H is the stronger acid.
Which is the favored side of a proton transfer reaction: the side that has the stronger acid or the side opposite the stronger acid?	The stronger acid has a greater tendency to donate its proton, so the favored side of the reaction is the side opposite the stronger acid. In this case, the stronger acid is on the reactant side, so the product side of the reaction is favored.
What is the difference in pK_a values between the acids on either side of the reaction? How much stronger does that make one acid than the other?	The difference between the pK_a values 4.75 and 10.63 is 5.88. Each difference of 1 in pK_a values corresponds to a factor of 10 difference in acid strength. Therefore, the acid on the reactant side is $10^{5.88}$ times stronger, so the product side is favored by $10^{5.88}$ (or 7.6×10^5).

Try It Predict which side of this reaction is favored. To what extent is that side favored?

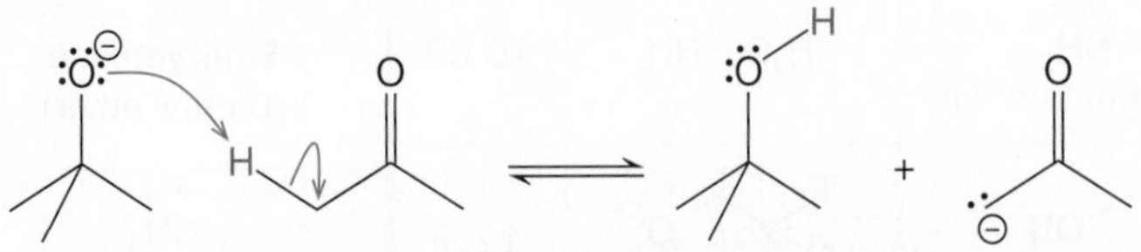

CONNECTIONS 6.4

Methanamine: What's that putrid smell? Methanamine (CH_3NH_2, Solved Problem 6.2) is a common reagent used in the production of a wide variety of compounds, including some pesticides, pharmaceuticals, and surfactants. Biologically, methanamine is produced in putrefaction, one of the stages in the decomposition of dead animals.

Although pK_a values represent acid strengths, they can also be used to determine the stronger of two bases:

- The stronger base is the one that has the weaker conjugate acid.
- The weaker base is the one that has the stronger conjugate acid.

This inverse relationship between the strength of an acid and the strength of its conjugate base arises because an acid and its conjugate base are found on opposite sides of a proton transfer reaction.

Suppose we want to know which base is stronger, H^- or $HC{\equiv}C^-$. We first write each conjugate acid by adding H^+ to the bases: The conjugate acid of H^- is H_2 (pK_a = 35), and the conjugate base of $HC{\equiv}C^-$ is $HC{\equiv}CH$ (pK_a = 25). The weaker of the two conjugate acids is H_2 (higher pK_a), so the stronger of the two bases is H^-.

YOUR TURN 6.3

For each pair of species given, use Table 6-1 (p. 269) to determine the stronger base. **(a)** H_2O or CH_3NH_2; **(b)** $CH_3CO_2^-$ or NH_3; **(c)** $CH_3CH_2O^-$ or $C_6H_5O^-$

6.2a The Leveling Effect

Knowing which side of a proton transfer reaction is favored helps us understand an important phenomenon called the **leveling effect**, which tells us the kinds of acids that can exist in a particular solvent. The leveling effect can be summarized as follows:

The Leveling Effect

- The strongest acid that can exist in solution to any appreciable concentration is the *protonated solvent*.
- The strongest base that can exist in solution is the *deprotonated solvent*.

In water, for example, H_3O^+ (protonated water) is the strongest acid that can exist and HO^- (deprotonated water) is the strongest base that can exist.

To see why this is so, let's examine what would happen if an acid stronger than H_3O^+ or a base stronger than HO^- were placed in water. For example, HCl is a stronger acid than H_3O^+, and being an acid, HCl could donate its proton to water according to the proton transfer reaction in Equation 6-7:

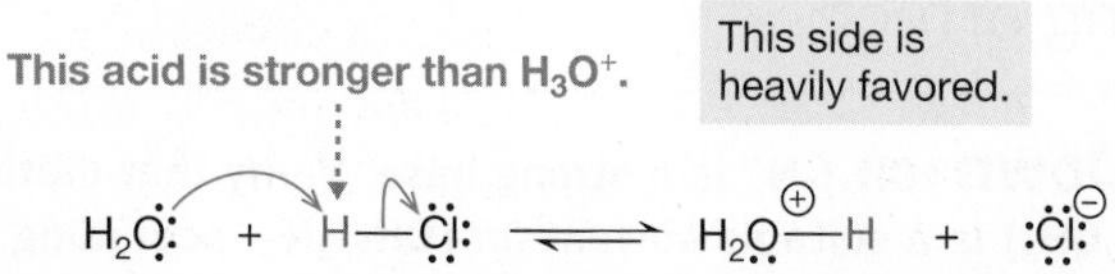
This acid is stronger than H3O+.
This side is heavily favored.

(6-7)

Because HCl is a significantly stronger acid than H_3O^+, HCl wins the competition and the product side is heavily favored. This means that when HCl is added to water, the above reaction will take place until HCl is essentially depleted, producing H_3O^+ instead.

YOUR TURN 6.4

What are the pK_a values of HCl and H_3O^+ in Equation 6-7, and do they verify that HCl is a stronger acid than H_3O^+?

A similar story happens when a base stronger than HO^-, such as $(CH_3)_2N^-$, is added to water. Being a base, $(CH_3)_2N^-$ could remove a proton from water, according to the proton transfer reaction in Equation 6-8:

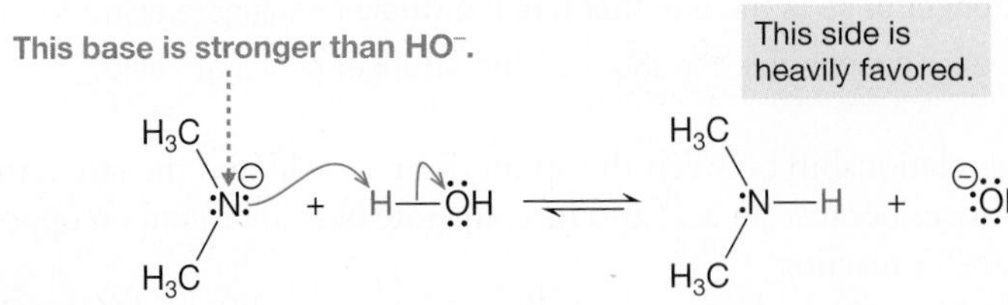
This base is stronger than HO⁻.
This side is heavily favored.

(6-8)

The product side of Equation 6-8 is heavily favored because the acid on the reactant side (H_2O) is much stronger than the acid on the product side [$(CH_3)_2NH$]. Therefore, when $(CH_3)_2N^-$ is added to water, it is consumed by the above reaction, leaving HO^- as the base instead of $(CH_3)_2N^-$.

YOUR TURN **6.5**

What are the pK_a values of H_2O and $(CH_3)_2NH$ in Equation 6-8, and do they verify that H_2O is a much stronger acid than $(CH_3)_2NH$?

The important lesson to take away from these examples is that if we want to carry out a particular reaction involving either HCl or $(CH_3)_2N^-$ as a reactant, then water is a poor choice of solvent because each of these species will be consumed by an *undesired proton transfer* with water (either Eq. 6-7 or Eq. 6-8). We would say that, with respect to the leveling effect, water is an *unsuitable* solvent for either HCl or $(CH_3)_2N^-$. In general:

With respect to the leveling effect, a solvent is unsuitable for a particular reactant R if:

- R is a stronger acid than the solvent's conjugate acid (i.e., R has the lower pK_a).
- R is a stronger base than the solvent's conjugate base (i.e., the conjugate acid of R has a higher pK_a than the solvent).

If one solvent is unsuitable with respect to the leveling effect, we would need to choose another solvent. For example, diethyl ether ($CH_3CH_2OCH_2CH_3$) would be a suitable solvent for $(CH_3)_2N^-$. (See Solved Problem 6.3.)

SOLVED PROBLEM **6.3**

How to determine if a solvent is suitable according to the leveling effect

Break It Down **$(CH_3)_2N^-$ is a strong base. Verify that diethyl ether ($CH_3CH_2OCH_2CH_3$) is a suitable solvent for $(CH_3)_2N^-$, according to the leveling effect.**

Think	Solve
Is $(CH_3)_2N^-$ a stronger base than the conjugate base of $CH_3CH_2OCH_2CH_3$?	For $(CH_3)_2N^-$ to be a stronger base than $CH_3CH_2OCH^-CH_3$, $(CH_3)_2NH$ must be a weaker acid (higher pK_a) than $CH_3CH_2OCH_2CH_3$. Note instead that the opposite is true: the pK_a of $(CH_3)_2NH$ (which is 38) is lower than the pK_a of $CH_3CH_2OCH_2CH_3$ (which is 45).

(continued)

Will an undesired proton transfer reaction between $(CH_3)_2N^-$ and diethyl ether be favored?	The potential undesired proton transfer reaction would be: $(CH_3)_2N^- + CH_3CH_2OCH_2CH_3 \rightarrow (CH_3)_2NH + CH_3CH_2OCH^-CH_3$ The stronger acid is on the product side, so this reaction will *not* be favored. Therefore, $(CH_3)_2N^-$ will *not* be consumed by a reaction with the solvent. When $(CH_3)_2N^-$ is dissolved, it will remain predominantly as $(CH_3)_2N^-$, meaning that the solvent would be suitable.

Try It The acetylide anion ($HC{\equiv}C{:}^-$) is a strong base. With respect to the leveling effect, determine whether each of the following solvents would be suitable for a reaction involving $HC{\equiv}C{:}^-$ as a reactant. *Hint*: You might need pK_a values from Table 6-1 (p. 269) or Appendix A.

(a) **(b)** **(c)** **(d)** **(e)**

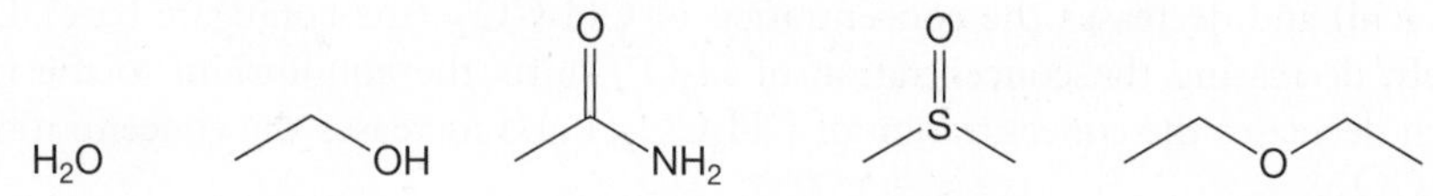
H2O
OH
O
NH2
O
S
O

Water | **Ethanol (EtOH)** | **Acetamide** | **Dimethyl Sulfoxide (DMSO)** | **Diethyl ether (Et_2O)**

6.2b Le Châtelier's Principle, pH, and Ionization States

In Section 6.2a, we saw that if an acid or base is too strong (relative to the solvent's conjugate acid or conjugate base), then it cannot exist in solution at any substantial concentration. In many cases, however, both an acid and its conjugate base *can* exist in solution in substantial concentrations, when neither the acid nor the conjugate base is excessively strong. That is, an acid and its conjugate base can exist in solution together when they are in *equilibrium* with each other. You might recall from general chemistry that a reaction is at **equilibrium** when the rate of the reaction in the forward direction (reactants forming products) equals the rate of the reaction in the reverse direction (products forming reactants), in which case the concentrations of reactants and products do not change. (We will discuss equilibria in greater detail in Section 6.3.) For example, as shown in Equation 6-9, ethanoic acid (acetic acid, CH_3CO_2H) can exist in equilibrium with its conjugate base, the ethanoate anion (acetate anion, $CH_3CO_2^-$), in water:

Can exist in water because it is a weaker acid than H_3O^+

Can exist in water because it is a weaker base than HO^-

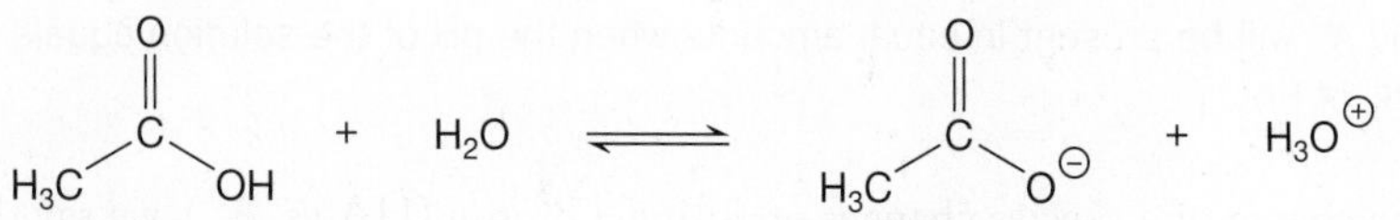
O
C
H3C
OH
+
H2O
O
C
H3C
O
+
H3O

(6-9)

Ethanoic acid (Acetic acid)

Ethanoate anion (Acetate anion)

When an acid and its conjugate base are in equilibrium with each other in water, their relative concentrations can be controlled by the concentration of H_3O^+ because of *Le Châtelier's principle*:

Le Châtelier's Principle

If a reaction at equilibrium experiences a change in reaction conditions (e.g., concentrations, temperature, pressure, or volume), then the equilibrium will shift to counteract that change. Specifically:

- A reaction at equilibrium can be shifted in the forward direction (i.e., to form more products) by the addition of reactants or the removal of products.
- A reaction at equilibrium can be shifted in the reverse direction (i.e., to form more reactants) by the addition of products or the removal of reactants.

In the case of Equation 6-9, increasing the concentration of H_3O^+ (a product) shifts the equilibrium to the left, which increases the concentration of CH_3CO_2H (the acid) and decreases the concentration of $CH_3CO_2^-$ (the conjugate base). Conversely, decreasing the concentration of H_3O^+ shifts the equilibrium to the right, which decreases the concentration of CH_3CO_2H and increases the concentration of $CH_3CO_2^-$.

The standard unit of concentration is moles per liter, but when considering H_3O^+, it is often more convenient to work with units of pH:

$$pH = -\log [H_3O^+] \qquad (6\text{-}10)$$

where $[H_3O^+]$ is the concentration of H_3O^+ in units of moles per liter. The pH of a solution is a measure of the solution's *acidity*: A lower pH corresponds to a higher concentration of H_3O^+ and a more acidic solution, and vice versa. With this in mind, we can apply Le Châtelier's principle toward a proton transfer reaction involving water more generally:

For the acid–base equilibrium in water, $HA + H_2O \rightleftharpoons A^- + H_3O^+$:

- Lowering the pH of the solution (increasing the concentration of H_3O^+) shifts the equilibrium toward HA.
- Raising the pH of the solution (decreasing the concentration of H_3O^+) shifts the equilibrium toward A^-.

For a particular acid (HA), it turns out that the pK_a value is also the threshold value of pH that dictates whether HA or A^- is in higher concentration at equilibrium:

- HA will be the dominant form when the pH of the solution is lower than the pK_a of HA.
- A^- will be the dominant form when the pH of the solution is higher than the pK_a of HA.
- HA and A^- will be present in equal amounts when the pH of the solution equals the pK_a of HA.

▸ LOOKING AHEAD

The dependence of a species' ionization state on solution pH has wide application in organic chemistry. In Section 6.10, for example, we will learn how pH dictates the structure of an amino acid. And in Section 10.7, we will see how this idea applies to a laboratory technique called *acid workup*.

Because the charge of a species changes on losing a proton (HA vs. A^-), we say that the acid has different *ionization states*, and the dominant ionization state depends on the solution's pH (see Looking Ahead box). (In Section 6.3, we will see why the threshold pH value for changing ionization states is the acid's pK_a value.)

pK_a and the Absorption and Secretion of Drugs

Ibuprofen (**Figure 6-1a**) and morphine (Fig. 6-1b) are both drugs that are taken to relieve pain, but when they are taken orally, they have different routes for absorption into the blood. Ibuprofen is absorbed when it is in the stomach, whereas morphine is absorbed when it is in the upper bowel. Their excretion routes are different, too. Whereas ibuprofen is excreted in the urine, morphine is excreted via the stomach. What gives rise to these different absorption and excretion routes?

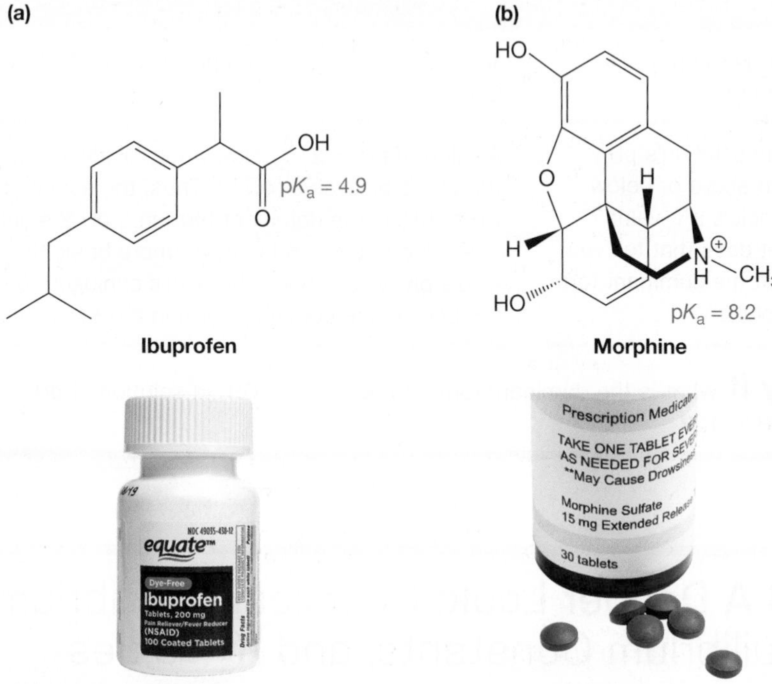

(a)
OH
O
pK_a = 4.9
Ibuprofen
(b)
HO
O
H
H
N
H
CH_3
HO
pK_a = 8.2
Morphine
equate
Dye-Free
Ibuprofen
Tablets, 200 mg
(NSAID)
100 Coated Tablets
Prescription Medication
Morphine Sulfate
15 mg Extended Release
30 tablets

FIGURE 6-1

The answer has to do with the different pK_a values of the two drugs. Ibuprofen has a CO_2H group and its pK_a is 4.9. Morphine, on the other hand, has an R_3NH^+ group, whose pK_a is 8.2. In the stomach, where the pH of gastric juice is roughly 2, both drugs retain their protons because their respective pK_a values are above the pH. Ibuprofen, therefore, is uncharged in the stomach, which allows it to diffuse across a cell's lipophilic membrane. Morphine, on the other hand, is positively charged in the stomach, which makes it hydrophilic. Morphine therefore remains soluble in the aqueous environment of the stomach until it reaches the large intestine, where the pH can be as high as about 7. With the higher pH, a greater percentage of morphine exists in the deprotonated, uncharged state, in which case it can diffuse across the cell membrane.

The same ideas account for the different excretion routes of these drugs. Morphine is water-soluble in the stomach due to the low pH, whereas ibuprofen is water-soluble in urine, which has a pH of 6.5–8.

SOLVED PROBLEM **6.4**

How to determine the dominant ionization state of an acid in solution

Break It Down **What is the dominant form of CH_3CO_2H in solution at pH = 2? At pH = 6?**

Think	Solve
What is the pK_a of CH_3CO_2H?	Table 6-1 (p. 269) gives a pK_a value of 4.75 for CH_3CO_2H.
Is the solution's pH value above or below the acid's pK_a value? What does that tell you about the dominant form in solution?	A value of pH = 2 is below (more acidic than) the acid's pK_a value (4.75). Thus, the acid itself, CH_3CO_2H, is the dominant form in a pH 2 solution. A value of pH = 6 is above (more basic than) the acid's pK_a value. Thus, the acid's conjugate base, $CH_3CO_2^-$, is the dominant form in a pH 6 solution.

Try It What is the dominant form of phenol (C_6H_5OH) in solution at pH = 7? At pH = 12?

SECTION 6.3 OBJECTIVES

You will be able to:

1. Write the K_a expression for any acid.
2. Use the Henderson–Hasselbalch equation to relate the pH of a solution to the relative concentrations of an acid and its conjugate base.
3. Calculate the K_{eq} of a proton transfer reaction when given the pK_a values of the acids on the reactant and product sides.

6.3 A Deeper Look: Chemical Equilibrium, Equilibrium Constants, and K_a Values

In Section 6.2, we saw how pK_a values are used to indicate relative strengths of an acid, and we learned how to use pK_a values to predict the outcome of a proton transfer reaction: that is, whether the reaction would favor the reactant or product side, and to what extent. We also saw how the ionization state of an acid depends on the solution's pH. Here in Section 6.3, we revisit these ideas in a more quantitative way.

We begin by reviewing a reaction's **equilibrium constant (K_{eq})**, which describes the reaction's tendency to form products. An equilibrium constant for a given reaction can be obtained experimentally by allowing that reaction to come to equilibrium (the point at which the net concentrations of reactants and products no longer change) and then measuring the concentrations of all products and all reactants. Those equilibrium concentrations are then substituted into the equilibrium constant expression (pure solids and pure liquids are omitted); for the generic reaction in Equation 6-11a, the equilibrium constant expression takes the form of Equation 6-11b:

$$a\,\mathrm{A} + b\,\mathrm{B} + c\,\mathrm{C} + \cdots \rightleftharpoons w\,\mathrm{W} + x\,\mathrm{X} + y\,\mathrm{Y} + \cdots \quad \textbf{(6-11a)}$$

$$K_{eq} = \frac{[\mathrm{W}]_{eq}^{w}[\mathrm{X}]_{eq}^{x}[\mathrm{Y}]_{eq}^{y}\cdots}{[\mathrm{A}]_{eq}^{a}[\mathrm{B}]_{eq}^{b}[\mathrm{C}]_{eq}^{c}\cdots} \quad \textbf{(6-11b)}$$

In this reaction, the uppercase letters are the reactants (A, B, C, . . .) and products (W, X, Y, . . .), and the corresponding lowercase letters (*a*, *b*, *c*, . . . and *w*, *x*, *y*, . . .) are the stoichiometric coefficients used to balance the equation. The numerator of the K_{eq} expression contains the equilibrium concentrations of the products, whereas the denominator contains the equilibrium concentrations of the reactants. Each concentration is raised to a power specified by the exponent corresponding to its stoichiometric coefficient.

For a proton transfer reaction between HA (a generic acid) and B^- (a generic base) shown in Equation 6-12a, the equilibrium constant expression is written as in Equation 6-12b:

$$HA + B^- \rightleftharpoons A^- + HB \tag{6-12a}$$

$$K_{eq} = \frac{[A^-]_{eq}[HB]_{eq}}{[HA]_{eq}[B^-]_{eq}} \tag{6-12b}$$

If the equilibrium concentrations of the products are high (and hence the equilibrium concentrations of the reactants are low), then the value of the numerator will be large and the value of the denominator will be small. The converse is true, as well. Thus:

- A very large K_{eq} value (e.g., 10^{10}) heavily favors products.
- A very small K_{eq} value (e.g., 10^{-10}) heavily favors reactants.
- A K_{eq} value close to 1 favors significant concentrations of both reactants and products.

YOUR TURN 6.6

From the K_{eq} values, which reaction tends to form more products at equilibrium?

$CH_3CO_2H + CH_3CH_2OH \rightleftharpoons CH_3CO_2^- + CH_3CH_2OH_2^+$ $\quad K_{eq} = 7.1 \times 10^{-8}$

$CF_3CO_2H + CH_3CH_2OH \rightleftharpoons CF_3CO_2^- + CH_3CH_2OH_2^+$ $\quad K_{eq} = 4.0 \times 10^{-3}$

Acid strengths can be obtained experimentally from the equilibrium that is established between a particular acid (HA) and water, producing the acid's conjugate base (A^-) and the *hydronium ion* (H_3O^+), as shown in Equation 6-13a. In this case, water is both the base, denoted by $H_2O(\ell)$, and the solvent, denoted by (*aq*) to indicate that the other species are dissolved in aqueous solution:

$$HA(aq) + H_2O(\ell) \rightleftharpoons A^-(aq) + H{-}OH_2^+(aq) \tag{6-13a}$$

$$K_{eq} = \frac{[A^-]_{eq}[H_3O^+]_{eq}}{[HA]_{eq}} = K_a \tag{6-13b}$$

The expression for the equilibrium constant is shown in Equation 6-13b. (Notice that water is omitted from the expression because it is a pure liquid.) Because this particular equilibrium constant expression characterizes an acid's strength, it is more specifically referred to as an **acidity constant (K_a)**.

All K_a values are obtained with the same base (water), so any difference in K_a for two compounds reflects a difference in the strength of the acid:

When two acids are compared, the one with the larger K_a value is the stronger acid.

For example, the K_a of ethanol (CH_3CH_2OH) is 1×10^{-16}, whereas the K_a for ammonia (NH_3) is 1×10^{-36}. Because 10^{-16} is larger than 10^{-36} by a factor of 10^{20}, ethanol is a stronger acid than ammonia by a factor of 10^{20}.

Chemists frequently work with values of pK_a, which is related to K_a through Equation 6-14:

$$pK_a = -\log K_a \tag{6-14}$$

The negative sign in front of the log function in Equation 6-14 has the effect of reversing the relative values of K_a. That is, a larger value of K_a corresponds to a lower (i.e., more negative or less positive) value of pK_a. Moreover, the log function has the following property: $\log 10^x = x$. Thus, Equation 6-14 is what leads to the key features of pK_a values we saw previously in Section 6.2: namely, that a lower pK_a value represents a stronger acid, and each unit of difference in pK_a values represents a factor of 10 difference in acid strength.

We are now ready to see why the relative values of pH and pK_a dictate whether an acid or its conjugate base is in higher concentration, as we learned in Section 6.2. Let's take the −log of both sides of the K_a expression in Equation 6-13b, apply the property of logarithms: $\log(xy) = \log(x)\log(y)$, and then rearrange:

$$-\log(K_a) = -\log\left(\frac{[A^-]_{eq}[H_3O^+]_{eq}}{[HA]_{eq}}\right)$$

$$-\log(K_a) = -\log[H_3O^+]_{eq} - \log\left(\frac{[A^-]_{eq}}{[HA]_{eq}}\right)$$

$$pK_a = pH - \log\left(\frac{[A^-]_{eq}}{[HA]_{eq}}\right)$$

$$pK_a + \log\left(\frac{[A^-]_{eq}}{[HA]_{eq}}\right) = pH \qquad (6\text{-}15)$$

The expression in Equation 6-15 is called the **Henderson–Hasselbalch equation.** If $pH > pK_a$, then $\log([A^-]_{eq}/[HA]_{eq})$ must be a positive number, which means $([A^-]_{eq}/[HA]_{eq}) > 1$, and $[A^-]_{eq} > [HA]_{eq}$. The opposite is true when $pH < pK_a$. And, if $pH = pK_a$, then $\log([A^-]_{eq}/[HA]_{eq})$ must be 0, which means $([A^-]_{eq}/[HA]_{eq}) = 1$, and $[A^-]_{eq} = [HA]_{eq}$.

We are also poised to see how the outcome of a proton transfer equilibrium is dictated by the pK_a values of the acids on the reactant and product sides. The K_{eq} expression for a proton transfer reaction between an acid HA and a base B^- (Eq. 6-12b) can be written in terms of the K_a values of HA and HB:

For the proton transfer equilibrium $HA + B^- \rightleftharpoons A^- + HB$, $K_{eq} = K_a(HA)/K_a(HB)$.

YOUR TURN **6.7**

Verify that $K_{eq} = K_a(HA)/K_a(HB)$ by plugging in the expressions for $K_a(HA)$ and $K_a(HB)$, described in Equation 6-13b, and comparing the result to Equation 6-12b.

Next we rearrange the definition $pK_a = -\log K_a$ to solve $K_a = 10^{-pK_a}$ and replace the two instances of K_a in the above expression. Finally, we apply the property of exponents, $10^x/10^y = 10^{(x-y)}$, to arrive at the expression on the right:

$$K_{eq} = \frac{K_a(HA)}{K_a(HB)} = \frac{10^{[-pK_a(HA)]}}{10^{[-pK_a(HB)]}} = 10^{[-pK_a(HA)]-[-pK_a(HB)]} = 10^{[pK_a(HB)-pK_a(HA)]}$$

Therefore, we can say:

For the proton transfer equilibrium $HA + B^- \rightleftharpoons A^- + HB$:

$$K_{eq} = 10^{\Delta pK_a}, \text{ where } \Delta pK_a = pK_a(HB) - pK_a(HA) \qquad (6\text{-}16)$$

If HA is the stronger acid, then $pK_a(HA)$ is lower than $pK_a(HB)$ and ΔpK_a is a positive value. Thus, $K_{eq} = 10^{\Delta pK_a}$ is greater than 1 and, as we saw in Section 6.2, the product side of the reaction is favored. If HB is the stronger acid, the reverse is true.

YOUR TURN **6.8**

Using the appropriate pK_a values, compute K_{eq} for the proton transfer reaction in **(a)** Solved Problem 6.2 (p. 270) and **(b)** the corresponding Try It exercise. How do these K_{eq} values compare to the answers obtained for those exercises?

6.4 Gibbs Free Energy and the Reaction Free Energy Diagram

SECTION 6.4 OBJECTIVES

You will be able to:

1. Determine the more stable of two species on the basis of their relative Gibbs free energies.
2. Specify whether a reaction is product-favored or reactant-favored on the basis of ΔG°_{rxn}.
3. Describe the changes in geometry that occur for a given reaction when the reaction coordinate increases.
4. Identify the features of a reaction free energy diagram that correspond to reactants, products, the transition state, ΔG°_{rxn}, and $\Delta G^{\circ\ddagger}$ for a proton transfer reaction.

In Section 6.2, we learned how to determine the favored side of a proton transfer reaction (i.e., reactants or products) by comparing the strength of the acid on the reactant side to the strength of the acid on the product side. We can also identify the favored side of a reaction by considering *standard Gibbs free energy*:

The side of a reaction that is favored is the one that has the lower **standard Gibbs free energy (G°)**.[1]

We will discuss standard Gibbs free energy in greater detail in Section 6.5, but for now we can think of it as a measure of stability:

A lower standard Gibbs free energy corresponds to greater stability.

For example, recall from Equation 6-5 (p. 268) that the product side is favored for the reaction $HO^- + HCl \rightarrow H_2O + Cl^-$. Therefore, G° for the products ($G^\circ_{products}$) is lower than G° for the reactants ($G^\circ_{reactants}$), which allows us to say that the products H_2O and Cl^- are more stable than the reactants $HO^- + HCl$.

When discussing free energies, it is often more convenient to consider the **standard Gibbs free energy difference** for the reaction, $\Delta G^\circ_{rxn} = G^\circ_{products} - G^\circ_{reactants}$:

- A reaction is product-favored if $\Delta G^\circ_{rxn} < 0$. Such a reaction is said to be **exergonic** (energy out), because it releases free energy.
- A reaction is reactant-favored if $\Delta G^\circ_{rxn} > 0$. Such a reaction is said to be **endergonic** (energy in), because it absorbs free energy.

YOUR TURN 6.9

Review the proton transfer reaction in Equation 6-6 (p. 268): $HO^- + NH_3 \rightarrow H_2O + H_2N^-$. Which side of the reaction has the lower standard Gibbs free energy? Which side is more stable? Is $\Delta G^\circ_{rxn} > 0$ or < 0?

The quantity ΔG°_{rxn} corresponds only to the end points of the reaction: namely, the reactants and the products. However, the changes that the reactants undergo to become products are continuous, not instantaneous. To help discuss these changes, chemists often use free energy diagrams.

In a **reaction free energy diagram**, Gibbs free energy is plotted as a function of the *reaction coordinate*. A **reaction coordinate** is a variable that corresponds to the changes in geometry, on a molecular level, as reactants are converted into products. In essence:

As the reaction coordinate increases, the geometries of the species involved in the reaction increasingly resemble the geometries of the products.

This becomes clearer if we examine the specific examples in **Figure 6-2** (next page). Figure 6-2a is the free energy diagram for the proton transfer between HCl and HO^-, whereas Figure 6-2b is the diagram for the reverse reaction, between Cl^- and H_2O.

For the reaction in Figure 6-2a, a H—Cl bond is broken during the course of the reaction and an O—H bond is formed; the proton in HCl departs from Cl and

[1] The naught (°) signifies *standard conditions*, in which all pure substances are in their most stable states at 298 K, the partial pressures of all gases are 1 atm, and the concentrations of all solutions are 1 mol/L.

FIGURE 6-2 Free energy diagrams (a) Free energy diagram for the proton transfer between HCl and HO^-. The reaction is exergonic ($\Delta G^\circ_{rxn} < 0$), but it still has an energy barrier. (b) Free energy diagram for the proton transfer between Cl^- and H_2O, an endergonic reaction ($\Delta G^\circ_{rxn} > 0$).

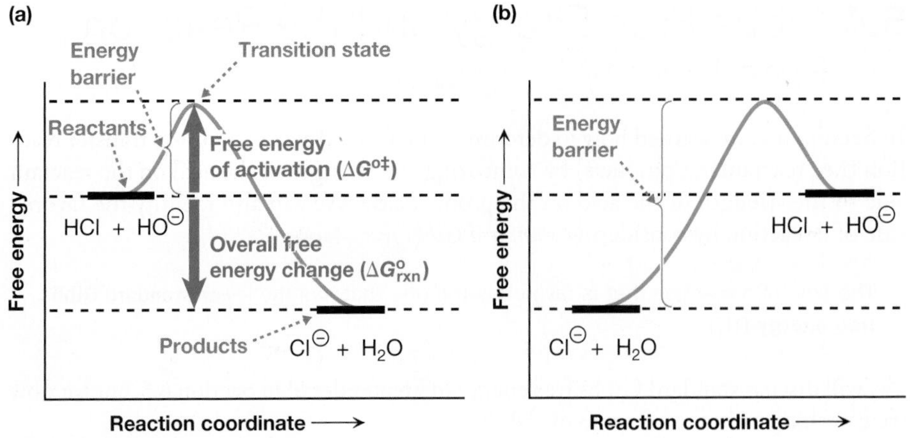

(a)
Energy barrier
Transition state
Reactants
Free energy of activation (ΔG°‡)
HCl + HO⊖
Overall free energy change (ΔG°rxn)
Products
Cl⊖ + H2O
Free energy
Reaction coordinate
(b)
Energy barrier
HCl + HO⊖
Cl⊖ + H2O
Free energy
Reaction coordinate

joins O. Therefore, as the reaction coordinate increases, the distance between the H and Cl atoms increases and the distance between H and O decreases.

YOUR TURN 6.10

In Figure 6-2b, as the reaction coordinate increases, does the distance between Cl and H increase or does it decrease? Does the distance between the HO and H increase or decrease?

One of the main benefits of free energy diagrams is that they allow us to see quickly whether $\Delta G^\circ_{rxn} < 0$ or $\Delta G^\circ_{rxn} > 0$. In Figure 6-2a, for example, the products are lower in energy than the reactants, so $\Delta G^\circ_{rxn} < 0$, indicated by the thick blue arrow pointing downward. For the reverse reaction (Fig. 6-2b), $\Delta G^\circ_{rxn} > 0$.

Notice in Figure 6-2a and 6-2b that there is an *energy maximum* along the reaction coordinate. The structure that corresponds to this energy maximum is the elementary step's **transition state**. Because there is a maximum in energy between the reactants and products, an *energy barrier* must be surmounted to form products. This energy barrier, called the **free energy of activation ($\Delta G^{\circ\ddagger}$)** and pronounced "delta-*G*-naught-double-dagger," is the difference in standard free energy between the reactants and the transition state (see Looking Ahead box). $\Delta G^{\circ\ddagger}$ is an important factor that governs reaction rates:

> As the free energy of activation decreases (i.e., as the energy barrier becomes smaller), the rate of the reaction increases and the reactants are said to be more *reactive*.

▸ LOOKING AHEAD

In Chapter 9, we will learn how to use free energy diagrams to predict relative sizes of $\Delta G^{\circ\ddagger}$, which will help us predict the outcome when certain types of reactions compete.

YOUR TURN 6.11

Indicate ΔG°_{rxn} and $\Delta G^{\circ\ddagger}$ in Figure 6-2b the way it is done in Figure 6-2a. Which reaction has a greater $\Delta G^{\circ\ddagger}$, the one in Figure 6-2a or the one in Figure 6-2b?

6.5 A Deeper Look: Gibbs Free Energy, Equilibrium Constants, Enthalpy, and Entropy

SECTION 6.5 OBJECTIVES

You will be able to:

1. Relate a reaction's ΔH°_{rxn} and its ΔS°_{rxn} to the types of structural changes that occur in the reaction.
2. Calculate the value of ΔG°_{rxn} when given ΔH°_{rxn} and ΔS°_{rxn}.

In Section 6.3, we saw that the equilibrium constant (K_{eq}) for a reaction tells us whether the reaction favors products ($K_{eq} > 1$) or reactants ($K_{eq} < 1$). In Section 6.4, we saw that $\Delta G^\circ_{rxn} < 0$ for a reaction that favors products and $\Delta G^\circ_{rxn} > 0$ for a reaction that favors reactants. Both of these quantities, K_{eq} and ΔG°_{rxn}, are associated with the favored side of a reaction because they are mathematically related according to Equation 6-17:

$$\Delta G^\circ_{rxn} = -RT \ln K_{eq} \qquad (6\text{-}17)$$

where R is the universal gas constant (8.314 J/mol·K) and T is the temperature in kelvins.

The quantity ΔG°_{rxn} can be expressed in terms of the reaction's *enthalpy change* and *entropy change*, as follows:

$$\Delta G^\circ_{rxn} = \Delta H^\circ_{rxn} - T\Delta S^\circ_{rxn} \qquad (6\text{-}18)$$

The ΔH°_{rxn} term in Equation 6-18 is the **standard enthalpy difference** between the reactants and products. At constant pressure, ΔH°_{rxn} equals the heat absorbed or released by the reaction. If ΔH°_{rxn} is positive, then the reaction absorbs heat and is said to be **endothermic**; if ΔH°_{rxn} is negative, then the reaction releases heat and is **exothermic**.

YOUR TURN **6.12**

For each set of values for ΔH°_{rxn} and ΔS°_{rxn}, determine whether the reaction would be reactant-favored or product-favored at 298 K. **(a)** $\Delta H^\circ_{rxn} = +200$ kJ/mol, $\Delta S^\circ_{rxn} = +0.100$ kJ/mol·K; **(b)** $\Delta H^\circ_{rxn} = +10$ kJ/mol, $\Delta S^\circ_{rxn} = +0.100$ kJ/mol·K

ΔH°_{rxn} is governed by the bonds that are formed or broken during the course of a reaction:

- Breaking a bond requires heat and is endothermic.
- Forming a bond releases heat and is exothermic.

As described in Section 1.4, typical bond energies are on the order of 300–400 kJ/mol. The magnitude of ΔH°_{rxn}, therefore, can often exceed 100 kJ/mol or even 1,000 kJ/mol.

In Equation 6-18, T is the temperature in kelvins and ΔS°_{rxn} is the **standard entropy difference** between the reactants and products. As mentioned in Section 2.7, entropy is related to the number of different states available to a system and is often thought of as a "measure of disorder."

The largest magnitudes for ΔS°_{rxn} are associated with reactions that substantially change the freedom of movement available to the species involved in the reaction:

- A reaction in which the number of separate species increases (e.g., A—B → A + B) has $\Delta S^\circ_{rxn} > 0$, and vice versa.
- A reaction in which a ring breaks open has $\Delta S^\circ_{rxn} > 0$, and vice versa.

YOUR TURN **6.13**

Consider the structural changes in each reaction given to determine whether ΔS°_{rxn} is substantially >0, substantially <0, or ≈0.

(a)

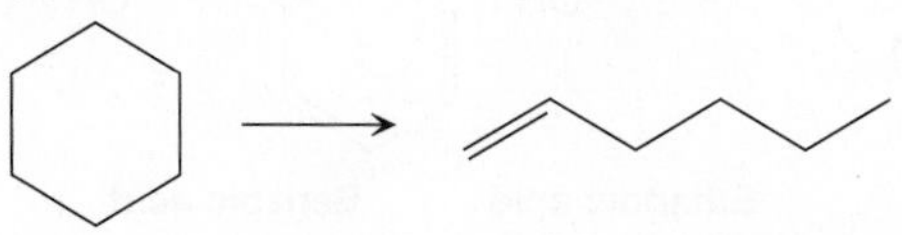

(b)

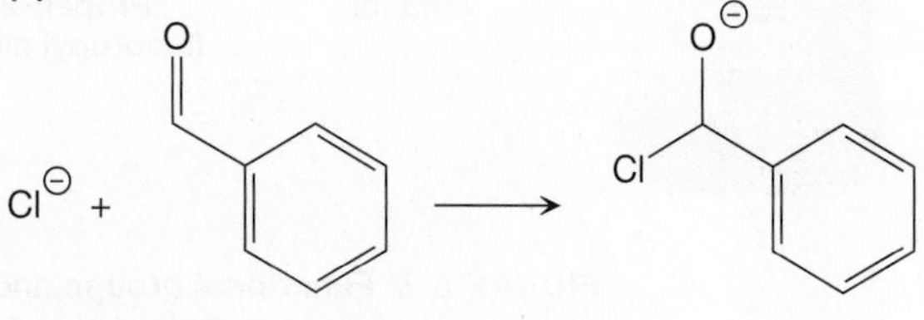
O
Cl⁻ +
O⁻
Cl

(c)

$CH_3CH_2O^- + H_2O \longrightarrow CH_3CH_2OH + HO^-$

Even for reactions that have substantial entropy changes, the magnitude of $T\Delta S^\circ_{rxn}$ at room temperature tends to be on the order of 50 kJ/mol or less. Therefore, for most organic reactions at room temperature, the magnitude of $T\Delta S^\circ_{rxn}$ is substantially smaller than the magnitude of ΔH°_{rxn}. In such cases, ΔH°_{rxn} dominates and $\Delta G^\circ_{rxn} \approx \Delta H^\circ_{rxn}$. In other words:

For most organic reactions, ΔH°_{rxn} governs whether ΔG°_{rxn} is positive or negative.

In situations where $T\Delta S^\circ_{rxn}$ and ΔH°_{rxn} are similar in magnitude, the sign of ΔG°_{rxn} depends on the signs of both ΔH°_{rxn} and ΔS°_{rxn}, as well as the temperature. We will discuss this idea further in situations where it becomes relevant.

SECTION 6.6 OBJECTIVES

You will be able to:

1. Determine whether the strengths of two acids should be similar or substantially different on the basis of their functional groups.
2. Estimate the pK_a value of an acid on the basis of the functional group that contains the acidic proton.

6.6 Functional Groups and Acidity

Table 6-1 (p. 269) lists the pK_a values for only a small fraction of the millions of compounds known. There is a good chance, then, that the exact compound for which you need to know the pK_a value is not included in the table. How can you obtain the pK_a values for those other compounds?

One way is to *estimate* the value on the basis of structural similarities to a compound that is listed in the table. Recall from Section 1.13 that the chemical behavior of a compound is governed largely by the *functional groups* it possesses. Therefore:

For two acids in which the acidic proton is part of the same functional group, the pK_a values tend to be similar.

For example, consider ethanol (CH_3CH_2OH) and propan-2-ol [isopropyl alcohol, $(CH_3)_2CHOH$], shown in **Figure 6-3a**. Both compounds are alcohols (R—OH), so we should expect their pK_a values to be similar. Indeed, Table 6-1 indicates the pK_a of ethanol is 16 and the pK_a of propan-2-ol is 16.5. Likewise, ethanoic acid (acetic acid, CH_3CO_2H) and benzoic acid ($C_6H_5CO_2H$), shown in Figure 6-3b, are both carboxylic acids (R—CO_2H), so we should expect their pK_a values to be similar, too. Indeed, we see from Table 6-1 that the pK_a of ethanoic acid is 4.75 and that of benzoic acid is 4.2.

Notice that carboxylic acids are substantially more acidic than alcohols. Ethanoic acid (acetic acid, CH_3CO_2H) has a pK_a of 4.75, whereas ethanol (CH_3CH_2OH) has

CONNECTIONS 6.5

Isopropyl alcohol as an antiseptic and a solvent
Isopropyl alcohol (Fig. 6-3a), as a concentrated aqueous solution, is sold commercially as rubbing alcohol, a topical antiseptic. The alcohol kills germs by effectively disrupting the fat membrane that encases the bacteria or virus cell. It is also useful as a solvent in the laboratory because it can dissolve a variety of nonpolar compounds.

70%
Isopropyl
RUBBING ALCOHOL
16 FL OZ (473 mL)

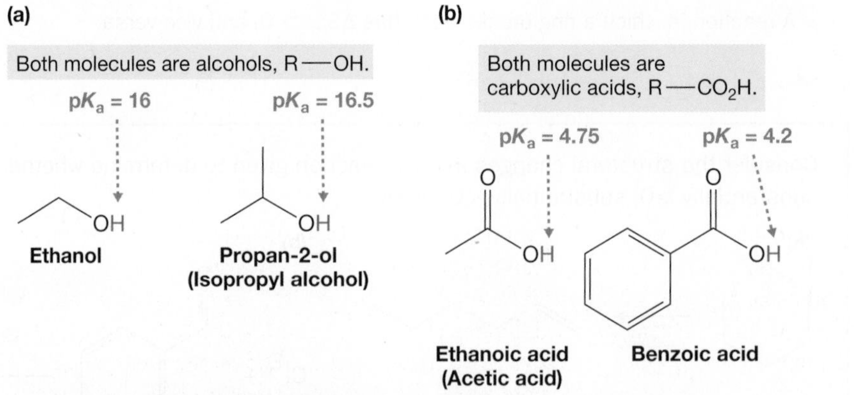

(a)
Both molecules are alcohols, R—OH.
pKa = 16
pKa = 16.5
OH
OH
Ethanol
Propan-2-ol
(Isopropyl alcohol)
(b)
Both molecules are carboxylic acids, R—CO2H.
pKa = 4.75
pKa = 4.2
O
OH
O
OH
Ethanoic acid
(Acetic acid)
Benzoic acid

FIGURE 6-3 Functional groups and pK_a (a) The acidic proton (shown in blue) in both molecules is part of an OH functional group, characteristic of alcohols, and the pK_a values are similar. (b) The acidic proton (shown in blue) in both molecules is part of a CO_2H functional group, characteristic of carboxylic acids, and the pK_a values are similar. The pK_a value of a carboxylic acid, however, is significantly different from that of an alcohol.

a pK_a of 16: a difference in acid strength of $>10^{11}$. We do not expect these acids to have similar pK_a values because the acidic protons in the two compounds are part of different functional groups.

SOLVED PROBLEM **6.5**

How to estimate a pK_a value on the basis of functional groups

Break It Down Using Table 6-1 (p. 269), estimate the pK_a values for the indicated CH_2 protons in cyclohexanone.

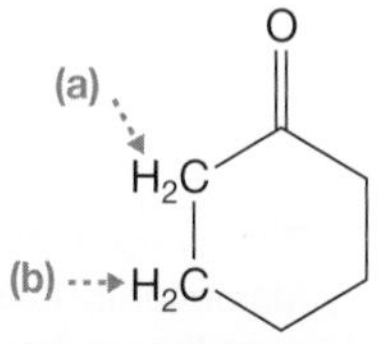

O
(a)
H_2C
(b)
H_2C

Cyclohexanone

Think	Solve
On what functional group do the acidic protons appear?	Protons (a) are attached to a carbon that is part of an $R_2C{=}O$ functional group, characteristic of ketones. Protons (b) are attached to a carbon that is not part of any functional group.
For what molecule(s) in Table 6-1 is the acidic proton part of the same functional group?	According to Table 6-1, the pK_a of acetone [$(CH_3)_2C{=}O$], another ketone, is 20. Therefore, we should expect the pK_a of protons (a) to be about 20, too. For protons (b), the pK_a should be similar to that of an alkane, because alkanes have no functional groups. Two examples in Table 6-1 are methane (CH_4, pK_a = 48) and ethane (CH_3CH_3, pK_a = 50), so the pK_a of protons (b) should be about 48–50, too.

Try It Using Table 6-1 and/or Appendix A, estimate the pK_a for the proton(s) explicitly shown on each of the following compounds.

(a)

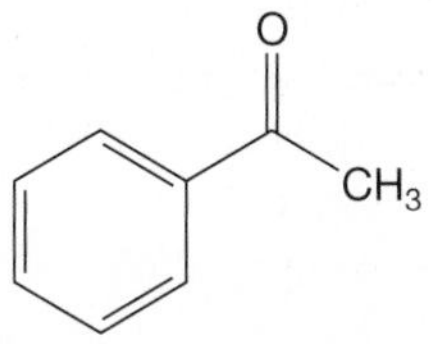

O
CH_3

(b)

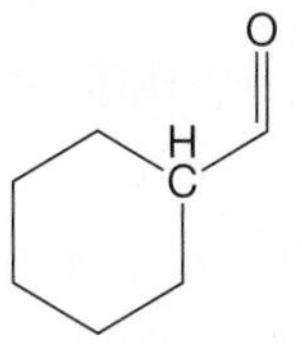

O
H
C

(c)

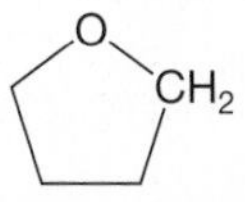

O
CH_2

(d)

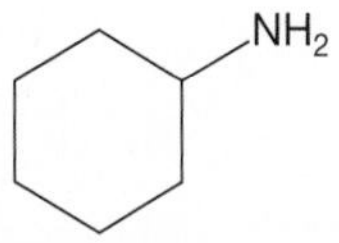

NH_2

(e)

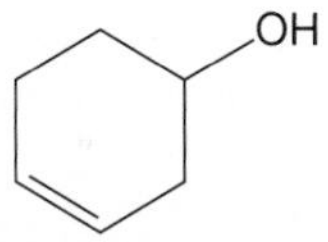

OH

6.7 Relative Strengths of Charged and Uncharged Acids: The Reactivity of Charged Species

SECTION 6.7 OBJECTIVES

You will be able to:

1. Determine the stronger of two acids that have similar structure but different charges.
2. Construct a free energy diagram that illustrates the deprotonations of two distinct acids that are similar in structure but have different charges.

Section 6.6 described how compounds tend to have similar acid strengths when the acidic protons are part of the same functional group in the two compounds. When the acidic protons are part of different functional groups, on the other hand, the acid strengths can be remarkably different. Here in Section 6.7 and later in Section 6.8, we explore how and why the relative strengths of acids depend on the *structures* of the acids.

Perhaps the most noticeable trend for the pK_a values in Table 6-1 involves the charge on the atom to which a proton is attached:

A proton is dramatically more acidic when it is attached to a positively charged atom than when that atom is uncharged.

For example, the pK_a of H_2O is 14, whereas that of H_3O^+ is 0. Additionally, the pK_a of H_3N is 36, whereas that of H_4N^+ is 9.4. Why should the presence of a charge have this effect?

To answer this question, first consider Equation 6-19, the *autoionization* equilibrium for water:

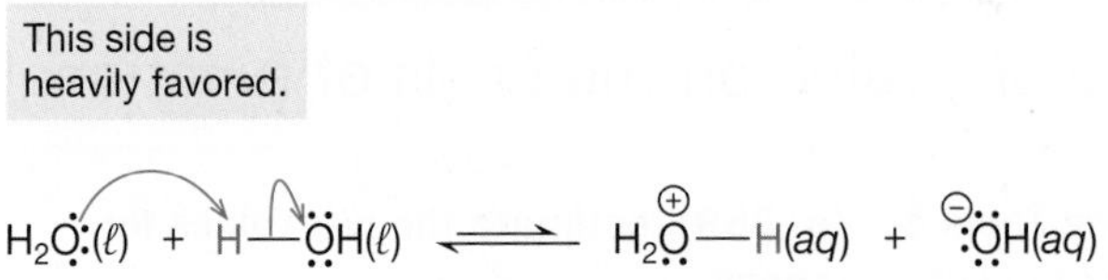

This side is heavily favored.
H₂Ö:(ℓ) + H—ÖH(ℓ) ⇌ H₂O⊕—H(aq) + ⊖:ÖH(aq)

(6-19)

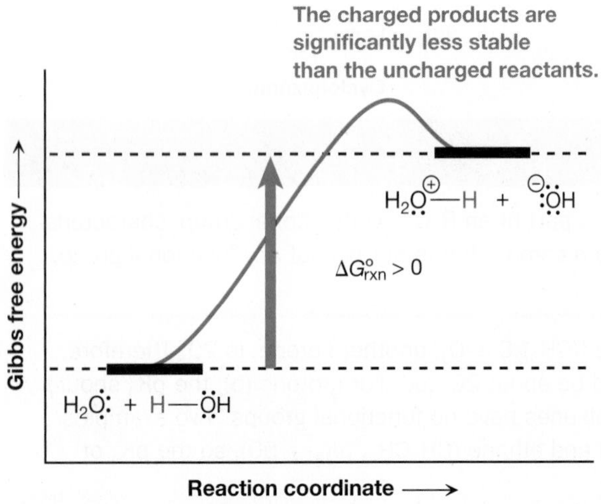

The charged products are significantly less stable than the uncharged reactants.
Gibbs free energy
ΔG°rxn > 0
H₂O⊕—H + ⊖:ÖH
H₂Ö: + H—ÖH
Reaction coordinate

FIGURE 6-4 Free energy diagram for autoionization of H_2O (Eq. 6-19) The charged products are much higher in energy and less stable than the uncharged reactants.

As indicated, the reactant side of the reaction is heavily favored (you might recall from general chemistry that the equilibrium constant for this reaction, called K_w, is very small: 1.0×10^{-14}). Therefore, as we learned in Section 6.4, the standard Gibbs free energy is much lower for the reactants than for the products ($\Delta G^\circ_{rxn} > 0$); this outcome is captured in the free energy diagram in **Figure 6-4**. The H_3O^+ and HO^- products, which are charged, are much less stable than the uncharged reactants. Generally speaking:

A charged species is significantly higher in energy (and thus less stable) than its uncharged counterpart.

The tendency of charged species to be less stable than similar uncharged species helps us understand the relative strengths of a variety of charged versus uncharged acids. Consider the reactions shown in Equation 6-20a and 6-20b, in which water deprotonates NH_3 and H_4N^+, respectively:

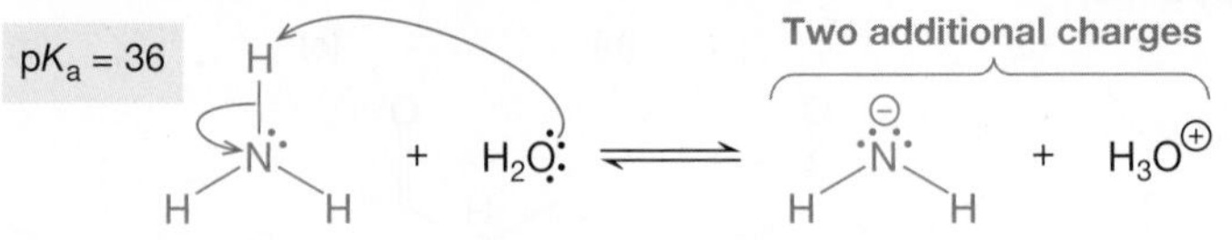

pKa = 36
Two additional charges
+ H₂Ö:
+ H₃O⊕

(6-20a)

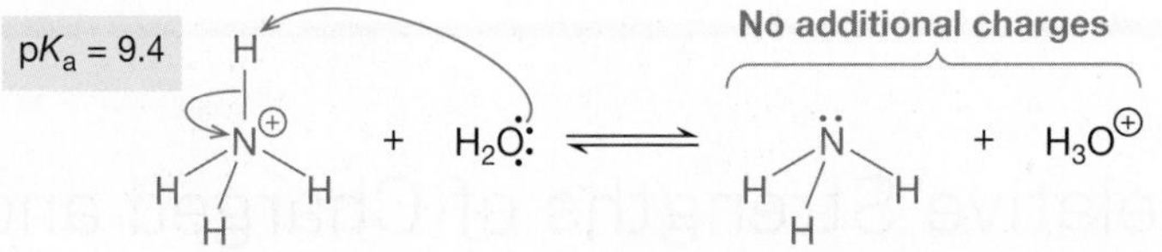

pKa = 9.4
No additional charges
+ H₂Ö:
+ H₃O⊕

(6-20b)

Notice in Equation 6-20a that the deprotonation of NH_3 results in two new charges. The red curve in the corresponding free energy diagram in **Figure 6-5** shows that the products are considerably higher in energy than the reactants. On the other hand, when H_4N^+ is deprotonated (Eq. 6-20b), no new charges appear; the corresponding free energy diagram (blue curve in Fig. 6-5) shows that the reactants and products are closer in energy. In short, H_4N^+ is the stronger acid because it is energetically easier for H_4N^+ to lose a proton.

YOUR TURN **6.14**

In Figure 6-5, why are the reactants for the blue curve shown at a higher energy than the reactants for the red curve? Why are the products for the blue curve shown at a lower energy than the products for the red curve?

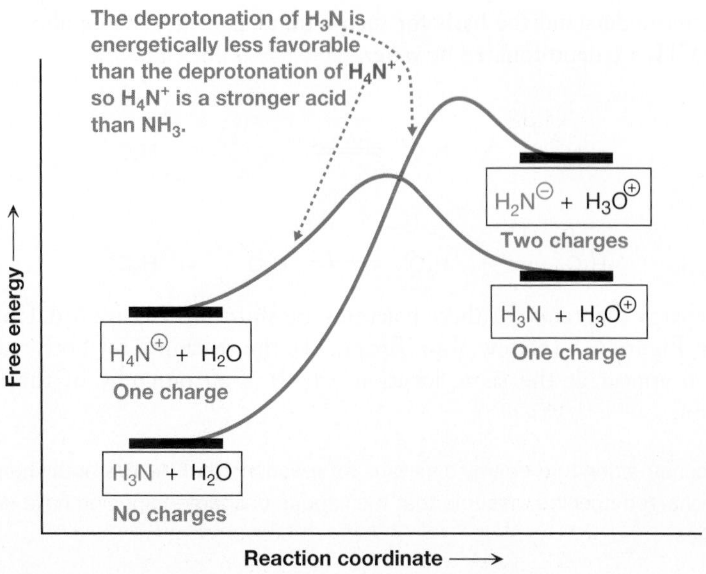
The deprotonation of H3N is energetically less favorable than the deprotonation of H4N+, so H4N+ is a stronger acid than NH3.
Free energy
H2N⊖ + H3O⊕
Two charges
H3N + H3O⊕
One charge
H4N⊕ + H2O
One charge
H3N + H2O
No charges
Reaction coordinate

FIGURE 6-5 Energy diagram for deprotonation of H_3N and H_4N^+ by water In the deprotonation of H_3N by water (red curve), two additional charges appear in the products, which makes the products much less stable (higher energy) than the reactants. In the deprotonation of H_4N^+ by water (blue curve), no new charges appear, so the reactants and products are closer together in energy. The deprotonation of H_4N^+ is more energetically favorable than the deprotonation of H_3N, so H_4N^+ is a stronger acid than H_3N.

YOUR TURN **6.15**

Draw an energy diagram similar to the one in Figure 6-5, with H_3O^+ and H_2O as the acids instead of H_4N^+ and H_3N. From your energy diagram, which acid is predicted to be stronger, H_3O^+ or H_2O? Is this consistent with their relative pK_a values?

6.8 Relative Acidities of Protons on Atoms with Like Charges

SECTION 6.8 OBJECTIVES

You will be able to:

1. Predict the stronger of two acids when the acidic protons are attached to atoms that are different or have different hybridization.
2. Use resonance delocalization to predict the stronger of two acids.
3. Determine the stronger of two acids on the basis of inductive effects.
4. Construct free energy diagrams to use as tools when predicting the stronger of two acids.

Section 6.7 explained the greater acidity of a positively charged species relative to a comparable uncharged molecule. Here in Section 6.8, we will examine trends involving acids that have the *same* charge. In Sections 6.8a and 6.8b, for example, we discuss how the identity of an atom affects the acidity of protons attached to it; in Section 6.8c, we describe how hybridization affects acidity; and in Sections 6.8d and 6.8e, we explain how acid strength is affected by π bonds and certain atoms or groups that are nearby.

6.8a Protons on Different Atoms in the Same Row of the Periodic Table

The acidic protons in CH_4, H_3N, H_2O, and HF are bonded to different atoms in the second row of the periodic table: namely, C, N, O, and F. The pK_a values of these acids are 48, 36, 14, and 3.2, respectively. Notice that:

The farther to the right an atom appears in the periodic table, the more acidic the protons that are attached to it.

To better understand the basis for such a trend, consider the equilibria in which H_3N and CH_4 are deprotonated by water:

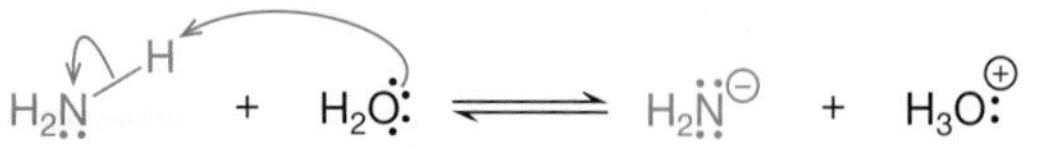

(6-21a)

(6-21b)

The free energy diagrams for these reactions are shown in **Figure 6-6**. Unlike what we saw in Figure 6-5 (review Your Turn 6.14), the reactants for both reactions in Figure 6-6 appear at the same location, which is an outcome of the following assumption:

> When constructing free energy diagrams for reactions that involve both charged and uncharged species, assume that the various uncharged species have similar stabilities.

In reality, NH_3 and CH_4 have different free energies, but the above assumption works because the free energy difference between uncharged species is typically much smaller than the free energy difference between their charged counterparts.

Next, notice that, for both reactions represented in Figure 6-6, the products have two more charges than the reactants. Therefore, as the free energy diagrams for these reactions show, the products are significantly higher in energy than the reactants. Because NH_3 is a stronger acid than CH_4, the deprotonation of NH_3 (red curve) is more energetically favorable than the deprotonation of CH_4 (blue curve). The products of NH_3 deprotonation are thus lower in energy than the products of CH_4 deprotonation, which means that H_2N^- is more stable than H_3C^-.

The example of the relative stabilities of H_2N^- and H_3C^- leads to the following general rule:

> When two uncharged acids are compared, the stronger acid is the one whose negatively charged conjugate base (a product) is more stable.

Why should H_2N^- be more stable than H_3C^-? The answer lies in the difference between the atoms on which the charge resides. As described in Section 1.7, N is more electronegative than C, meaning that N has a stronger attraction for electrons (i.e., for

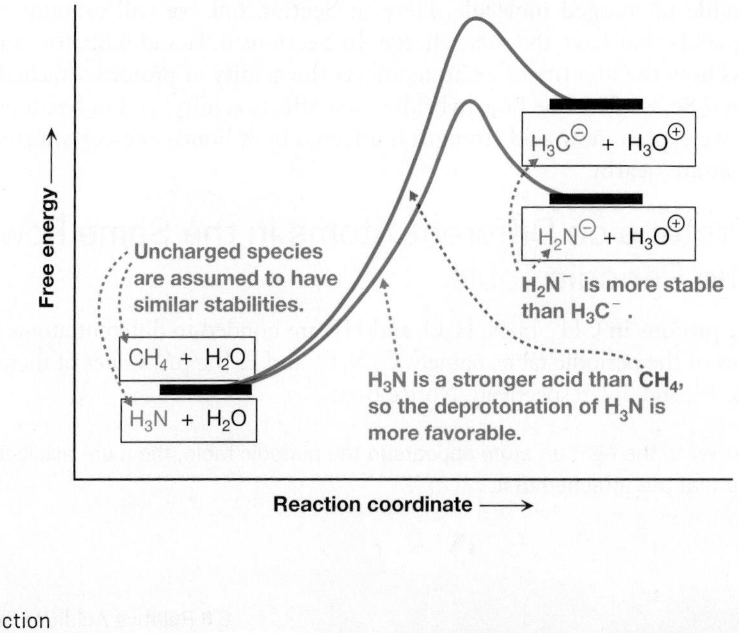

Free energy
Reaction coordinate
Uncharged species are assumed to have similar stabilities.
CH4 + H2O
H3N + H2O
H3C⊖ + H3O⊕
H2N⊖ + H3O⊕
H2N⁻ is more stable than H3C⁻.
H3N is a stronger acid than CH4, so the deprotonation of H3N is more favorable.

FIGURE 6-6 Relative stabilities of H_3C^- and H_2N^- Because H_3N is a stronger acid than CH_4, the reaction in Equation 6-21a (red curve) is more favorable than the reaction in Equation 6-21b (blue curve). Thus, H_2N^- is more stable than H_3C^-.

negative charge). Thus, although both species are destabilized by the presence of a negative charge, the negative charge is better accommodated by N; in other words, N is less destabilized by the negative charge than is C.

A similar analysis shows that H_2N^- is less stable than HO^-, which, in turn, is less stable than F^-. In general:

> An anion becomes more stable as the electronegativity of the atom bearing the negative charge increases (**Figure 6-7**).

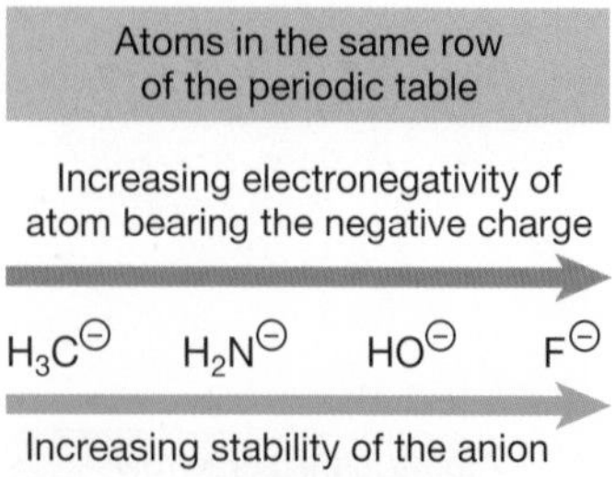

Atoms in the same row of the periodic table
Increasing electronegativity of atom bearing the negative charge
$H_3C^{\ominus}$ $H_2N^{\ominus}$ $HO^{\ominus}$ $F^{\ominus}$
Increasing stability of the anion

FIGURE 6-7 Periodic table trend for negative charge stability

The same trend is observed among acids with acidic protons bonded to atoms in other rows of the periodic table. For example, HCl ($pK_a = -7$) is a stronger acid than H_2S ($pK_a = 7.2$) because Cl is more electronegative than S, allowing Cl to better accommodate the negative charge that appears when the proton is lost.

YOUR TURN 6.16

Use the location of S and P in the periodic table to determine whether H_2S or H_3P is the stronger acid. What does that suggest about the relative stabilities of HS^- and H_2P^-?

The preceding analysis involving uncharged acids applies equally well to positively charged acids. H_3O^+ ($pK_a = 0$), for example, is a stronger acid than H_4N^+ ($pK_a = 9.4$). The proton transfer equilibria for H_3O^+ and H_4N^+ with water are shown in Equation 6-22a and 6-22b:

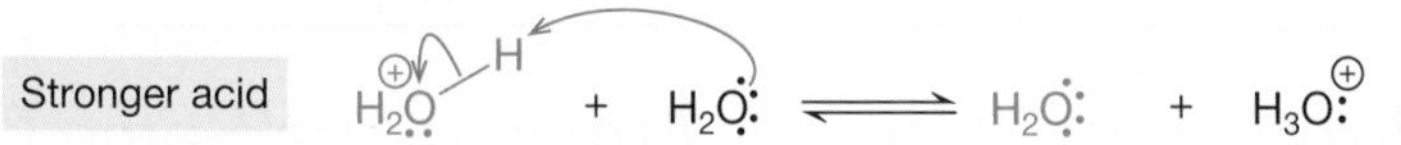

Stronger acid

(6-22a)

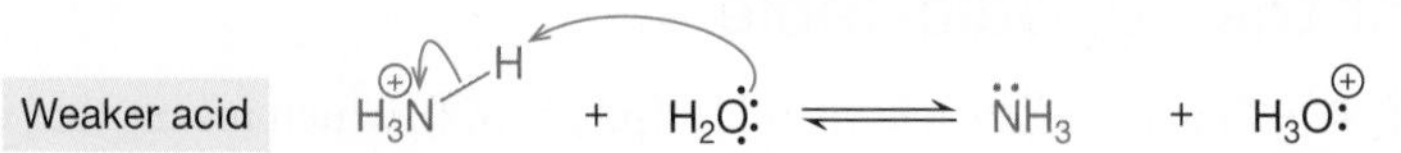

Weaker acid

(6-22b)

On the product side, the difference in these reactions is H_2O versus NH_3. Relative to the charged species on the reactant sides, we assume that these uncharged molecules have similar stabilities. Therefore, in the free energy diagrams for these reactions shown in **Figure 6-8**, the products are placed at the same height.

Next, because H_3O^+ is more acidic than H_4N^+, we know that the reaction in Equation 6-22a (red curve in Fig. 6-8) is more energetically favorable than the reaction in

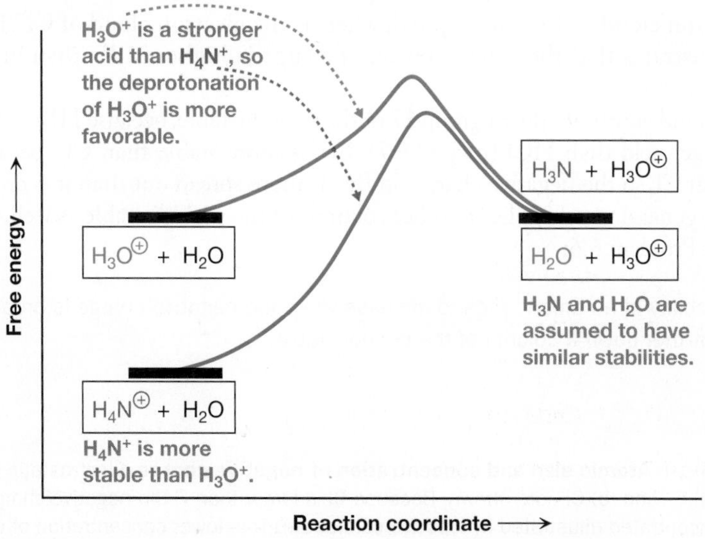

H_3O^+ is a stronger acid than H_4N^+, so the deprotonation of H_3O^+ is more favorable.
$H_3N + H_3O^{\oplus}$
$H_3O^{\oplus} + H_2O$
$H_2O + H_3O^{\oplus}$
H_3N and H_2O are assumed to have similar stabilities.
$H_4N^{\oplus} + H_2O$
H_4N^+ is more stable than H_3O^+.
Free energy
Reaction coordinate

FIGURE 6-8 Relative stabilities of H_3O^+ and H_4N^+ H_3O^+ is a stronger acid than H_4N^+, so the reaction in Equation 6-22a (red curve) is more favorable than the reaction in Equation 6-22b (blue curve). Thus, H_4N^+ is more stable than H_3O^+.

Equation 6-22b (blue curve in Fig. 6-8). Therefore, in the free energy diagrams, the reactants for Equation 6-22a appear above the reactants for Equation 6-22b. This allows us to conclude that H_3O^+ is less stable than H_4N^+. In general:

When two positively charged acids are compared, the stronger acid (a reactant) is less stable.

Why is H_3O^+ less stable than H_4N^+? Once again, it can be attributed to a difference in electronegativity. The O atom bearing the positive charge in H_3O^+ is more electronegative than the N atom bearing the positive charge in H_4N^+. Whereas an atom with higher electronegativity can accommodate a *negative* charge better, it does the opposite for a *positive* charge. Thus, N accommodates a *positive* charge better than O.

The relative stabilities of H_3O^+ and H_4N^+ are consistent with the following periodic table trend for the stabilities of positively charged ions:

The stability of a cation decreases as the electronegativity of the atom bearing the positive charge increases (**Figure 6-9**).

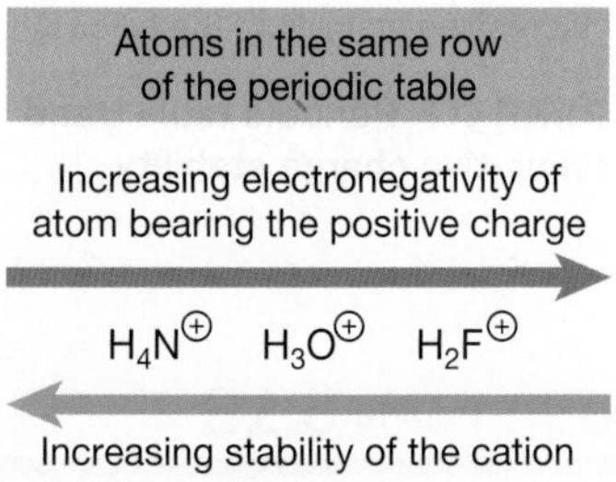
Atoms in the same row of the periodic table
Increasing electronegativity of atom bearing the positive charge
$H_4N^{\oplus}$ $H_3O^{\oplus}$ $H_2F^{\oplus}$
Increasing stability of the cation

FIGURE 6-9 Periodic table trend for positive charge stability

YOUR TURN **6.17**

Use the location of S and P in the periodic table to determine whether H_3S^+ or H_4P^+ is the stronger acid. What does that suggest about the relative stabilities of the two cations?

6.8b Protons on Different Atoms in the Same Column of the Periodic Table

HCl (pK_a = −7) is a *stronger* acid than HF (pK_a = 3.2), which means that Cl^- is *more* stable than F^-. F is *more* electronegative than Cl, however, so you might expect that F could accommodate a negative charge better than Cl.

To untangle this apparent discrepancy, recall that *Cl is a substantially larger atom than F*, because Cl is one row below F in the periodic table; going down one row of the periodic table represents adding a new (larger) valence shell. A negative charge on Cl is therefore less concentrated than a negative charge on F because the same −1 charge is spread out over a larger volume in Cl. This lower concentration of charge contributes to the greater stability of Cl^- than F^-. The electrostatic potential maps of F^- and Cl^-, shown in **Figure 6-10**, are consistent with this analysis. The electron cloud of F^- is a deep red, whereas the electron cloud of Cl^- is orange, which illustrates that the concentration of charge is higher in F^- than in Cl^- (see Recall box).

This trend continues down group 17 of the periodic table, because HBr (pK_a = −9) is a stronger acid than HCl (pK_a = −7). Br^- is more stable than Cl^- because Br is larger than Cl, so the negative charge on Br^- is more spread out than it is on Cl^-. The following general trend applies to other columns of the periodic table as well, as shown in Solved Problem 6.6:

The stability of an anion tends to increase when the negative charge is on an atom farther down a column of the periodic table.

◀ RECALL

As discussed in Section 1.7, an electrostatic potential map depicts a molecule's electron cloud in colors that indicate relative charge. Red corresponds to a buildup of negative charge, whereas blue represents a buildup of positive charge.

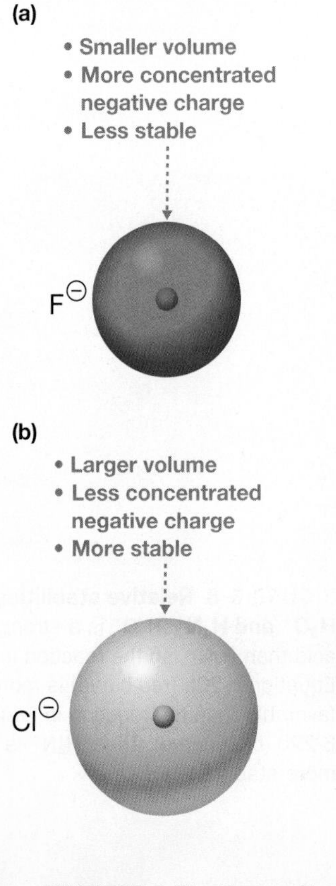
(a)
• Smaller volume
• More concentrated negative charge
• Less stable
$F^{\ominus}$
(b)
• Larger volume
• Less concentrated negative charge
• More stable
$Cl^{\ominus}$

FIGURE 6-10 Atomic size and concentration of negative charge Electrostatic potential maps of (a) F^- and (b) Cl^- are shown. Because Cl is larger than F, the negative charge on Cl^- is less concentrated (illustrated by less red coloration). This lower concentration of charge helps make Cl^- more stable than F^-.

SOLVED PROBLEM **6.6**

How to predict relative acid strength for protons on different atoms in the same column of the periodic table

Break It Down **Predict which has a lower pK_a: CH_4 or SiH_4.**

Think	Solve
In the deprotonation of these acids, do the acids or the conjugate bases bear the charge?	The deprotonation reactions are shown below. Each acid is uncharged, whereas the conjugate bases are negatively charged. 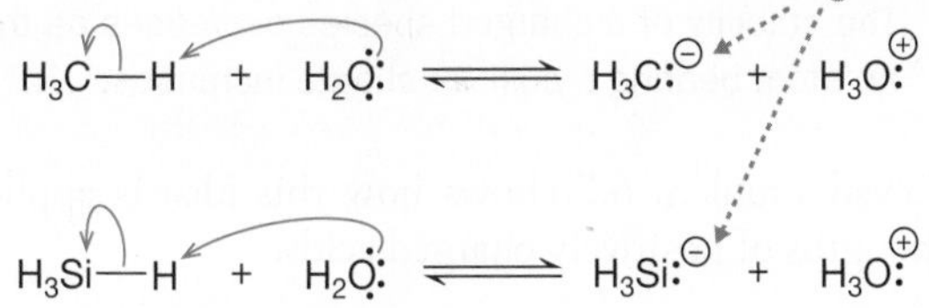 The conjugate bases are negatively charged.
Which ion is more stable, H_3C^- or H_3Si^-?	The negative charges in H_3C^- and H_3Si^- appear on C and Si, respectively, which are different atoms in the same column of the periodic table. Because Si is significantly larger than C (Si is below C in the periodic table), H_3Si^- is more stable than H_3C^-.
Which ion's formation is more favorable in the deprotonation reactions shown? How does that correspond to the relative acid strengths?	Because H_3Si^- is more stable, its formation is more favorable than H_3C^-. Therefore, SiH_4 loses a proton more easily than CH_4, meaning that SiH_4 is the stronger acid and has the lower pK_a (34 vs. 48).

Try It Which is the stronger acid in each pair? Explain. **(a)** HBr or HI; **(b)** CH_4 or PH_3

6.8c Hybridization of the Atom to Which the Proton Is Attached

According to Table 6-1, $H_3C{-}CH_3$ is an extremely weak acid (among the weakest known), $H_2C{=}CH_2$ is somewhat stronger, and $HC{\equiv}CH$ is much stronger; in fact, the acid strength of $HC{\equiv}CH$ is within about 5–10 pK_a units of alcohols (R—OH).

YOUR TURN **6.18**

Verify the relative acidities of ethane, ethene, and ethyne by looking up their pK_a values in Table 6-1 (p. 269). Which one has the lowest pK_a value? The highest?

pK_a: $H_3C{-}CH_3$ __________ $H_2C{=}CH_2$ __________ $HC{\equiv}CH$ __________

Because ethane, ethene, and ethyne are uncharged acids, their differences in acidity must be caused by differences in the stability of their negatively charged conjugate bases. In other words, $HC{\equiv}C^-$ must be more stable than $H_2C{=}CH^-$, which, in turn, must be more stable than $H_3C{-}CH_2^-$. These differences in stability cannot

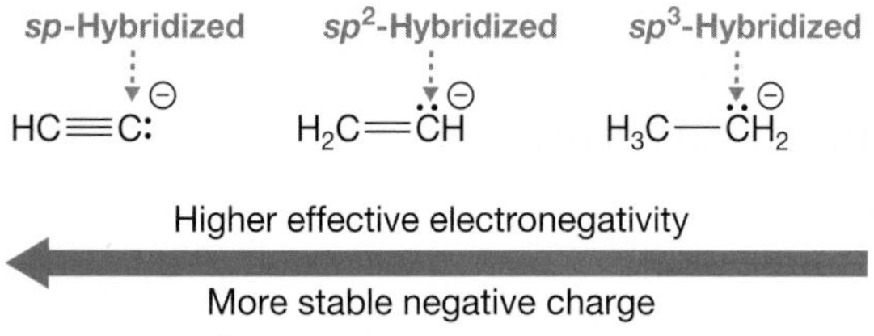
sp-Hybridized
sp²-Hybridized
sp³-Hybridized
HC≡C:
H₂C=CH
H₃C—CH₂
Higher effective electronegativity
More stable negative charge

FIGURE 6-11 Charge stability and effective electronegativity

come from differences in the size of the charged atom, because the negative charge is on carbon in each conjugate base. Instead, they arise from differences in the carbon atom's *effective electronegativity* in each of these species. As explained in Section 3.9, the effective electronegativity of an atom depends on its hybridization, increasing in the order $sp^3 < sp^2 < sp$ (see Recall box). The effective electronegativity has the same effect on charge stability that true electronegativity does:

The stability of a charged species increases as the *effective electronegativity* of an atom bearing a *negative* charge increases (**Figure 6-11**).

As you might expect, effective electronegativity has the opposite effect on the stability of positively charged species:

The stability of a charged species decreases as the *effective electronegativity* of an atom bearing a *positive* charge increases.

Solved Problem 6.7 shows how this idea is applied toward predicting the relative strengths of positively charged acids.

◂ RECALL

Recall from Section 3.9 that effective electronegativity derives from the *s*-character the atom has in its hybrid orbitals. An *s* orbital is more compact than a *p* orbital, so with greater *s*-character, the atom's electrons are held closer to the nucleus. This property of holding electrons close to the nucleus is reminiscent of the atom's actual electronegativity.

SOLVED PROBLEM **6.7**

How to predict the stronger acid when the atoms with acidic protons have different hybridizations

Break It Down Predict which acid is stronger.

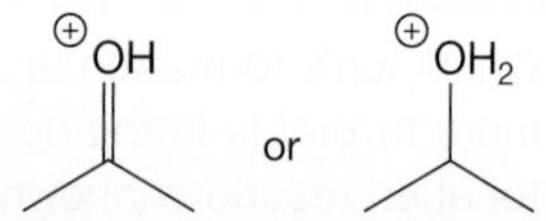
OH
or
OH₂

Think	Solve
Which species are charged: the acids or the conjugate bases? Are the acidic protons on the same atom or different atoms?	The acids are both positively charged, so those are the species we should compare. In both cases, the acidic proton is bonded to a positively charged O. Those atoms, therefore, have the same size and electronegativity, so we can't use these factors to predict the stronger acid.
Do the positively charged O atoms have the same hybridization? If not, which one has the higher effective electronegativity?	The O atom in $(CH_3)_2C{=}OH^+$ is sp^2-hybridized, whereas the O atom in $(CH_3)_2CH{-}OH_2^+$ is sp^3-hybridized, giving the O atom in $(CH_3)_2C{=}OH^+$ a higher effective electronegativity.
Which acid exhibits the greater charge stability? How does that impact the relative acid strengths?	With a greater effective electronegativity, the O atom in $(CH_3)_2C{=}OH^+$ does not accommodate the positive charge as well as the O atom in $(CH_3)_2CH{-}OH_2^+$. Therefore, $(CH_3)_2C{=}OH^+$ is less stable and its donation of a proton is more energetically favorable. Consequently, $(CH_3)_2C{=}OH^+$ is the stronger acid.

Try It Which is the stronger acid: $CH_3{-}NH_3^+$ or $HC{\equiv}NH^+$?

6.8d Effects from Adjacent Double and Triple Bonds: Resonance Effects

In both ethanoic acid (acetic acid, CH_3CO_2H) and ethanol (CH_3CH_2OH), the acidic proton is part of an OH group, but as **Figure 6-12** indicates, ethanoic acid is a much stronger acid. The presence of the adjacent C=O double bond makes the acid stronger.

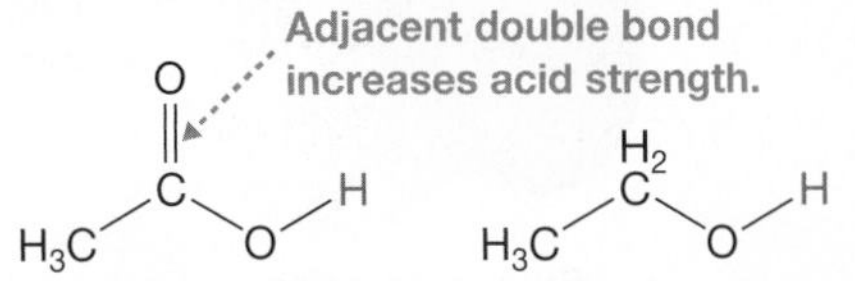
Adjacent double bond
increases acid strength.

Ethanoic acid (Acetic acid) **Ethanol**

FIGURE 6-12 Impact of an adjacent C=O bond on acidity

YOUR TURN **6.19**

Use Table 6-1 (p. 269) to look up the pK_a values of ethanoic acid and ethanol. Identify which acid has the lower pK_a.

pK_a: Ethanoic acid ____________ Ethanol ____________

Both ethanoic acid and ethanol are uncharged acids (of the type shown in Eq. 6-21, p. 286), so the difference in their acidities is largely due to differences in the stability of their negatively charged conjugate bases, $CH_3CO_2^-$ and $CH_3CH_2O^-$ (Eq. 6-23a and 6-23b). Because ethanoic acid is more acidic, we can say that $CH_3CO_2^-$ is more stable than $CH_3CH_2O^-$ (review Fig. 6-6, p. 286):

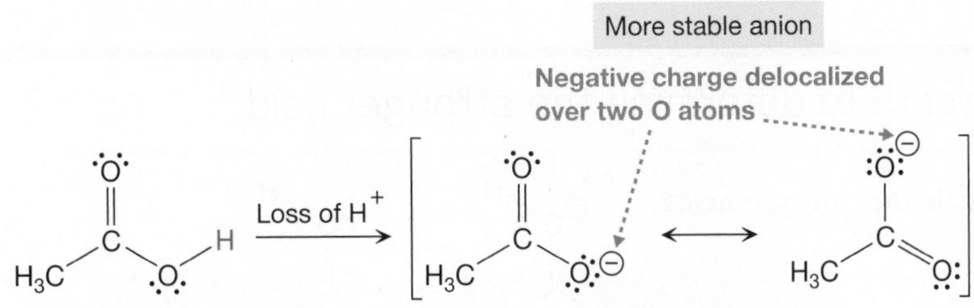
More stable anion
Negative charge delocalized
over two O atoms
Loss of H+

Ethanoic acid (Acetic acid) **Ethanoate anion (Acetate anion)** (6-23a)

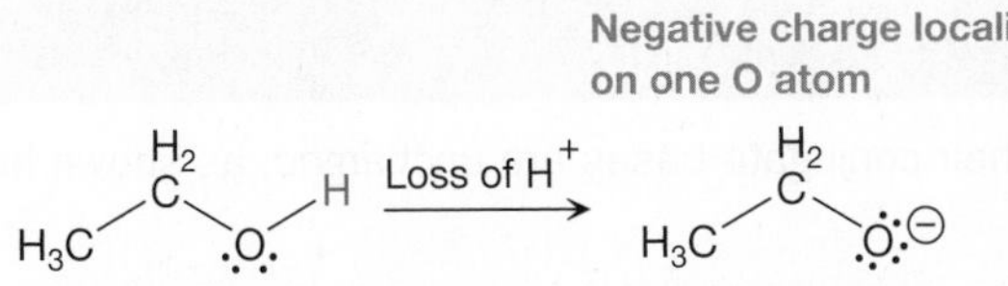
Negative charge localized
on one O atom
Loss of H+

Ethanol **Ethoxide anion** (6-23b)

As we can see in Equation 6-23a, $CH_3CO_2^-$ has two resonance structures, each of which has the negative charge on a different O atom; that is, the negative charge is *delocalized* over the two O atoms. On the other hand, the negative charge in $CH_3CH_2O^-$ is *localized* on a single O atom, shown in Equation 6-23b. In other words, the negative charge is *less concentrated* in the $CH_3CO_2^-$ anion than it is in the $CH_3CH_2O^-$ anion, as confirmed by the electrostatic potential maps of the two anions in **Figure 6-13** (next page). With lower concentration of charge comes greater charge stability. In general:

Delocalization of a charge via resonance lowers the *concentration* of the charge and increases the stability of the charged species.

The impact that this charge delocalization has on acid strength is called a **resonance effect**.

FIGURE 6-13 Resonance delocalization of a negative charge (a) An electrostatic potential map of the ethoxide anion ($CH_3CH_2O^-$) shows that the negative charge is localized on just the one O atom. (b) An electrostatic potential map of the ethanoate anion ($CH_3CO_2^-$) shows that the negative charge is delocalized onto both O atoms, consistent with its resonance hybrid. The concentration of negative charge is lower (illustrated by less red coloration) in the ethanoate anion, so the ethanoate anion is more stable than the ethoxide anion.

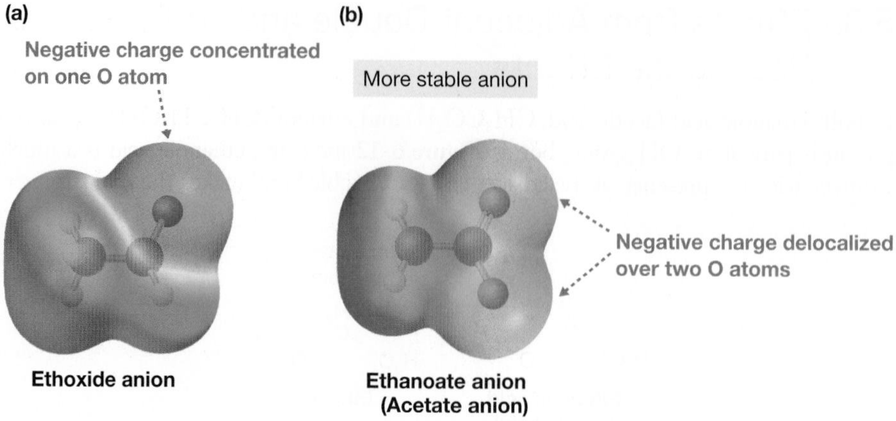
(a)
Negative charge concentrated on one O atom
Ethoxide anion
(b)
More stable anion
Negative charge delocalized over two O atoms
Ethanoate anion (Acetate anion)

YOUR TURN **6.20**

Draw the curved arrow notation for the conversion of one of the ethanoate anion's resonance structures into the other, and draw the resonance hybrid. (You may want to review Section 1.10.)

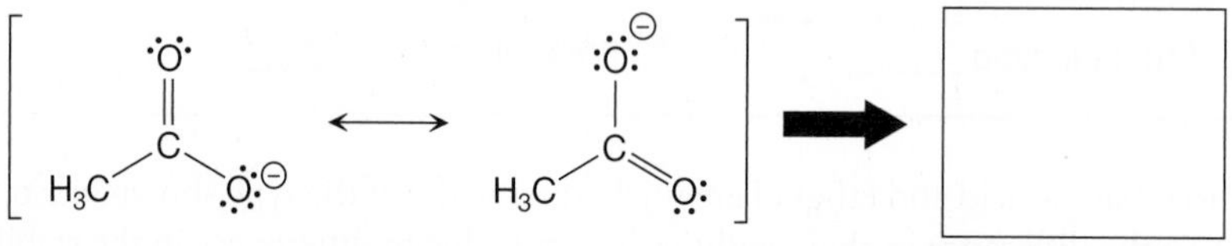
Resonance hybrid

SOLVED PROBLEM **6.8**

How to identify resonance effects to determine the stronger acid

Break It Down Which species, A or B, is the stronger acid?

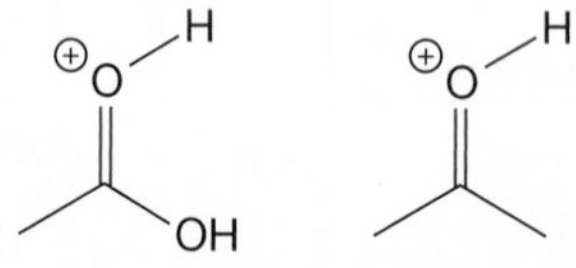

A B

Think	Solve
Which species are charged: the acids or the conjugate bases?	The two acids are charged and their conjugate bases are uncharged, as shown here.

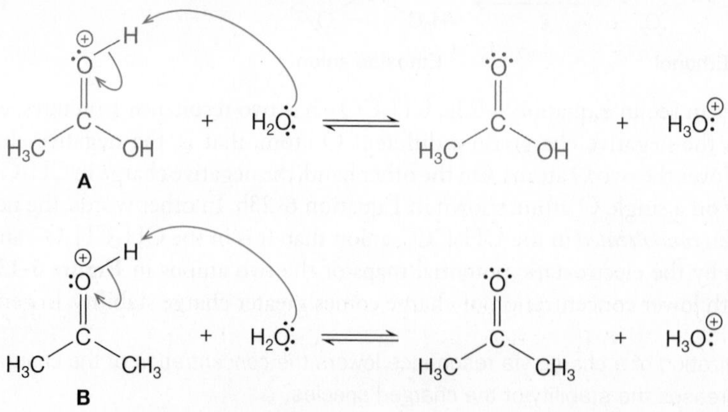

(continued)

To predict relative acid strengths, should we consider the stabilities of the acids or their conjugate bases?	Because both acids are positively charged, the acid that is less stable should be stronger. We must therefore determine the relative stabilities of the two acids.
Are the charge-bearing atoms different in the two acids? Do the atoms have different effective electronegativities?	In both acids, the acidic proton is attached to a positively charged O atom, so there is no significant difference in atom size or electronegativity. Both of those O atoms are sp^2-hybridized, so effective electronegativity does not play a role.
Are there differences in charge delocalization via resonance?	Acid **A** has two major resonance structures, which results in the positive charge being shared over two O atoms, as shown here. 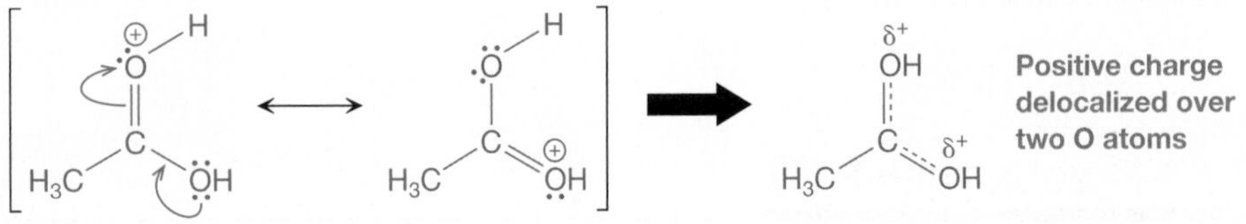 Positive charge delocalized over two O atoms **A** Acid **B**, by contrast, has only a weaker resonance contributor that lacks an octet, so the positive charge is more *localized* on one oxygen atom. As a result, acid **B** is less stable and is therefore the stronger acid. 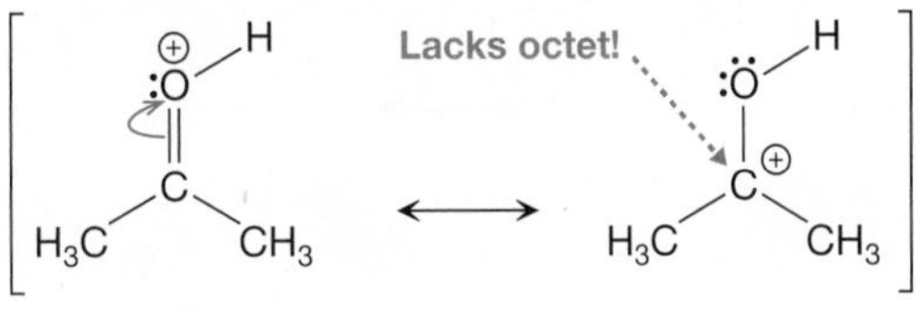 Lacks octet! **B**

Try It Which compound, **C** or **D**, is the stronger acid? Explain.

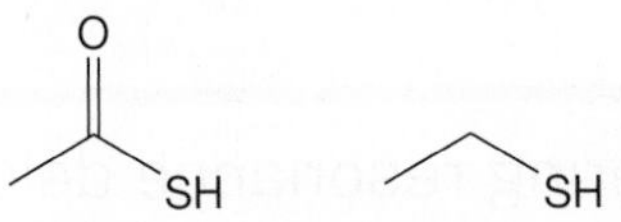

C **D**

The number of atoms over which a charge is delocalized by resonance affects charge stability:

> Stabilization via resonance generally increases as the number of atoms over which a charge is delocalized increases.

For example, sulfuric acid (H_2SO_4; $pK_a = -9$) is a stronger acid than ethanoic acid (CH_3CO_2H; $pK_a = 4.75$). Both acids are uncharged, so the conjugate base of the stronger acid must be more stable than that of the weaker acid (recall Eq. 6-21 and Fig. 6-6, p. 286); HSO_4^- is more stable than $CH_3CO_2^-$. In HSO_4^-, the negative charge is delocalized over three O atoms, whereas in $CH_3CO_2^-$, the negative charge is delocalized over only two O atoms. Delocalizing over more atoms in HSO_4^- means the negative charge is less concentrated, leading to greater stability. The electrostatic potential maps in **Figure 6-14** confirm that the negative charge is more delocalized in HSO_4^- than in $CH_3CO_2^-$.

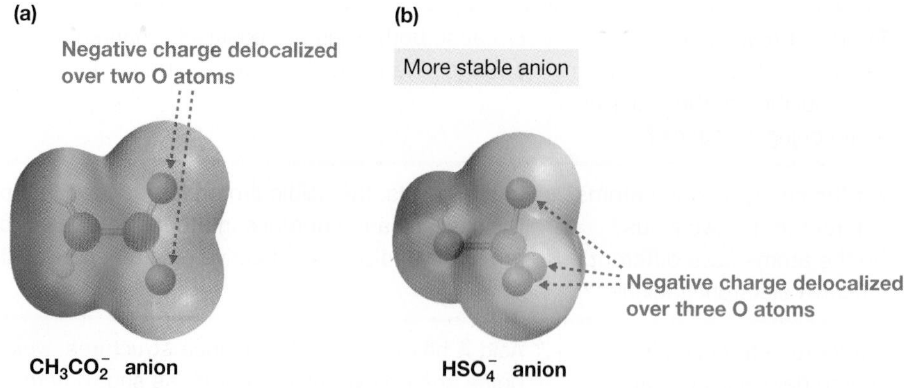
(a)
Negative charge delocalized over two O atoms
$CH_3CO_2^-$ anion
(b)
More stable anion
Negative charge delocalized over three O atoms
HSO_4^- anion

FIGURE 6-14 Resonance delocalization of a negative charge onto different numbers of atoms (a) An electrostatic potential map of the ethanoate anion ($CH_3CO_2^-$) shows that the negative charge is delocalized by resonance over two O atoms. (b) An electrostatic potential map of the hydrogen sulfate anion (HSO_4^-) shows that the negative charge is delocalized over three O atoms. The concentration of negative charge is lower in HSO_4^- (illustrated by less red around the O atoms), so HSO_4^- is more stable than $CH_3CO_2^-$.

YOUR TURN 6.21

Draw the two remaining resonance structures of HSO_4^- that illustrate the sharing of its negative charge. Be sure to include the appropriate curved arrows. Then draw the corresponding resonance hybrid.

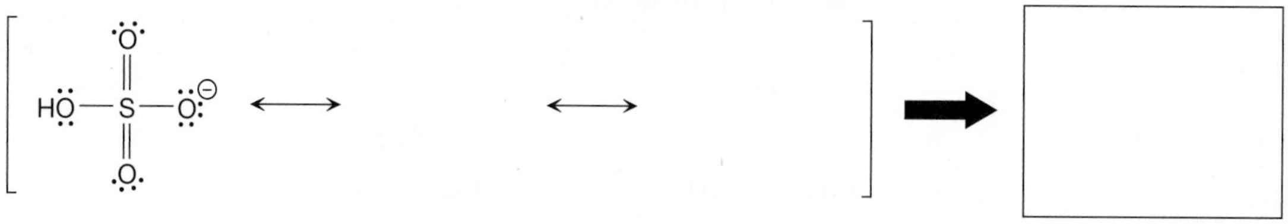
Resonance hybrid

SOLVED PROBLEM 6.9

How to determine the most acidic site by considering resonance delocalization

Break It Down Deprotonation in pentane-2,4-dione may occur at a terminal C atom or at the central C atom. Which site is more acidic? Explain.

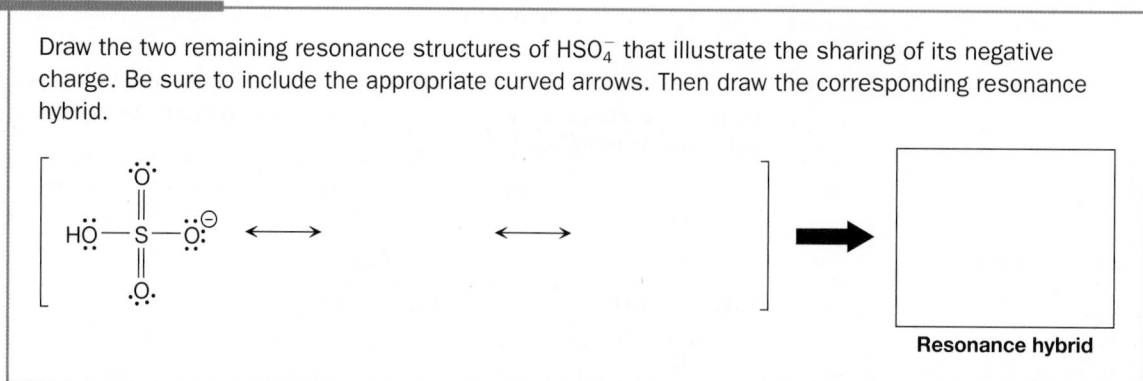

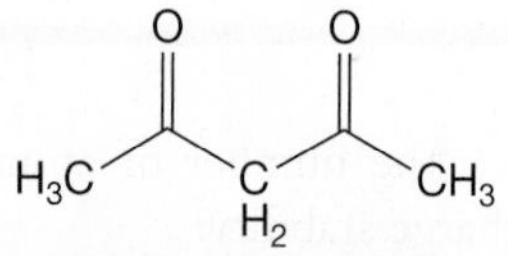

Pentane-2,4-dione

Think	Solve
Does charge stability play a role in the acid or in the conjugate bases?	The acid is uncharged, so we must look for differences in charge stability in the possible conjugate bases, which will be negatively charged.
In the possible charged conjugate bases, are the charge-bearing atoms different?	Since both the CH_2 and CH_3 protons are attached to sp^3-hybridized C atoms, neither the type of atom nor effective electronegativity should play a role. In both cases, the negative charge appears on C in the conjugate base.

(continued)

Is there a difference in charge delocalization in the conjugate bases?	There is a difference in resonance stabilization of the resulting charge, as shown here. 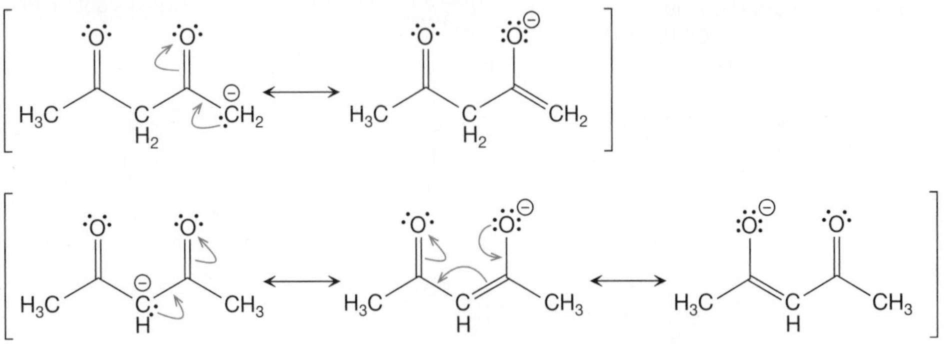 If deprotonation occurs at a terminal C, then the resulting negative charge in the conjugate base (top row) is delocalized over the C atom and one O atom by resonance. If deprotonation occurs at the central C, however, then the negative charge is delocalized over the C atom and *two* O atoms (bottom row). As a result, the negative charge that develops is less concentrated, so the conjugate base is more stable. This makes the central C atom more acidic than a terminal C atom.

Try It On the basis of differences in resonance delocalization, predict whether HNO_3 or CH_3CO_2H is the stronger acid. Explain. *Hint*: In this case, you can ignore the fact that the O atoms are bonded to different atoms (i.e., N vs. C).

6.8e Effects from Nearby Atoms: Inductive Effects

2-Chloroethanol ($ClCH_2CH_2OH$; $pK_a = 14.3$) is more acidic than ethanol (CH_3CH_2OH; $pK_a = 16$) by almost two pK_a units, even though they are very similar in structure: the only difference is a Cl atom in place of H on the leftmost carbon. Both acids are uncharged, so the conjugate base of 2-chloroethanol ($ClCH_2CH_2O^-$) must be more stable than that of ethanol ($CH_3CH_2O^-$).

In both conjugate bases, the negative charge is on the same type of atom (oxygen) with the same hybridization (sp^3). Furthermore, neither conjugate base has any resonance structures that place the negative charge on other atoms. Therefore, the difference in charge stability must come from another factor.

The electrostatic potential maps of the two anions are shown in **Figure 6-15**. Notice that the negative charge (illustrated by red) surrounding the O atom is diminished

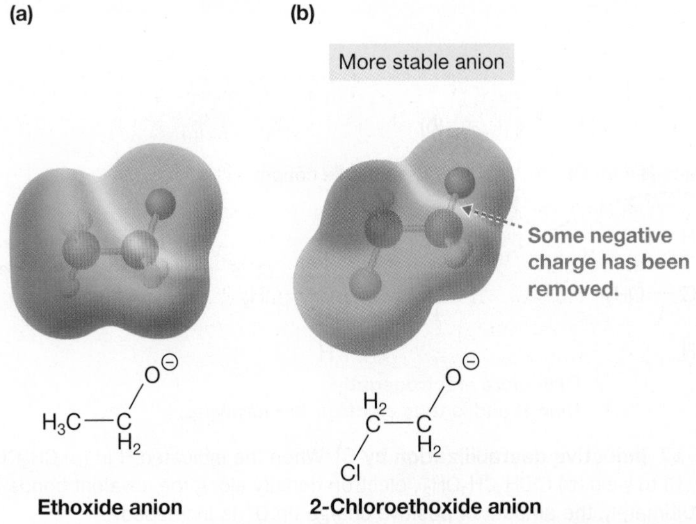
(a)
(b)
More stable anion
Some negative charge has been removed.
Ethoxide anion
2-Chloroethoxide anion

FIGURE 6-15 Delocalization of a negative charge via induction Electrostatic potential maps of (a) the ethoxide anion ($CH_3CH_2O^-$) and (b) the 2-chloroethoxide anion ($ClCH_2CH_2O^-$) are shown. The presence of the Cl atom in place of a H atom removes some electron density (illustrated by a smaller red area) from the negatively charged O atom. This decrease in charge concentration stabilizes the anion.

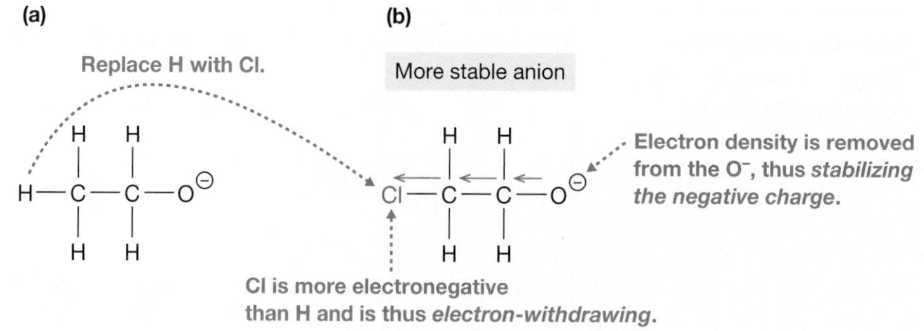
(a)
(b)
Replace H with Cl.
More stable anion
Electron density is removed from the O⁻, thus *stabilizing the negative charge.*
Cl is more electronegative than H and is thus *electron-withdrawing.*

FIGURE 6-16 Inductive stabilization by Cl When the indicated H in (a) $CH_3CH_2O^-$ is replaced by Cl to yield (b) $ClCH_2CH_2O^-$, electron density along the covalent bonds is shifted toward Cl. Ultimately, the amount of negative charge on O^- is diminished.

when the Cl atom is present. In other words, the O atom bears less of a negative charge in $ClCH_2CH_2O^-$ (Fig. 6-15b) than it does in $CH_3CH_2O^-$ (Fig. 6-15a). Just as with charge delocalization via resonance, this decrease in the concentration of charge makes the anion more stable.

Why does the Cl atom reduce electron density from the nearby O atom? Consider what would happen if Cl replaced a H atom on CH_3 in $CH_3CH_2O^-$, as shown in **Figure 6-16**. Because Cl is more electronegative than H, Cl is **electron-withdrawing** relative to H. Therefore, Cl causes electron density in $ClCH_2CH_2O^-$ (Fig. 6-16b) to be shifted toward itself along its covalent bonds. As indicated by the red arrows, this shift of electron density continues down the chain and ultimately draws electron density (negative charge) away from the O atom bearing the negative charge. In general:

Anions are *stabilized* by electron-withdrawing groups near the negative charge.

The electron-withdrawing phenomenon just discussed is an example of **induction**: the distortion of electron density along covalent bonds, brought about by the replacement of a H atom with another substituent. The effect that induction has on stability is called an **inductive effect**. In $ClCH_2CH_2O^-$, for example, the Cl atom is *inductively stabilizing*.

The presence of a nearby electron-withdrawing substituent does not always lead to stabilization. If electron density (i.e., negative charge) is drawn away from an atom that already has a *positive* charge, then that will leave behind *more* positive charge, which is destabilizing. This is what we observe in $ClCH_2CH_2OH_2^+$, the conjugate acid of 2-chloroethanol (**Figure 6-17**). In this case, the Cl atom is *inductively destabilizing*. In general:

Cations are *destabilized* by electron-withdrawing groups near the positive charge.

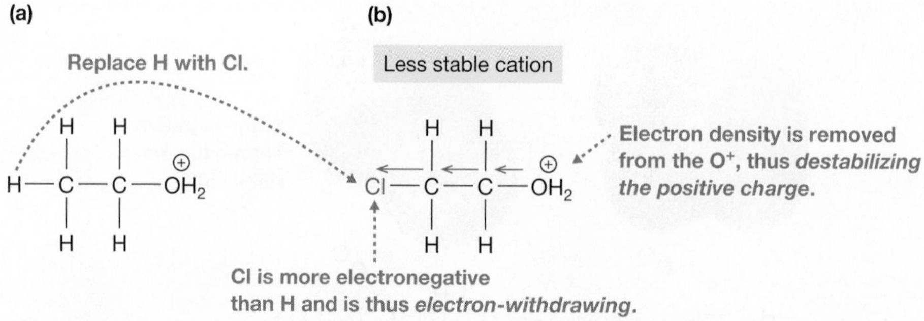
(a)
(b)
Replace H with Cl.
Less stable cation
Electron density is removed from the O⁺, thus *destabilizing the positive charge.*
Cl is more electronegative than H and is thus *electron-withdrawing.*

FIGURE 6-17 Inductive destabilization by Cl When the indicated H in (a) $CH_3CH_2OH_2^+$ is replaced by Cl to yield (b) $ClCH_2CH_2OH_2^+$, electron density along the covalent bonds is shifted toward Cl. Ultimately, the amount of positive charge on O^+ is increased.

YOUR TURN 6.22

Predict which of the following protonated alcohols is the stronger acid.

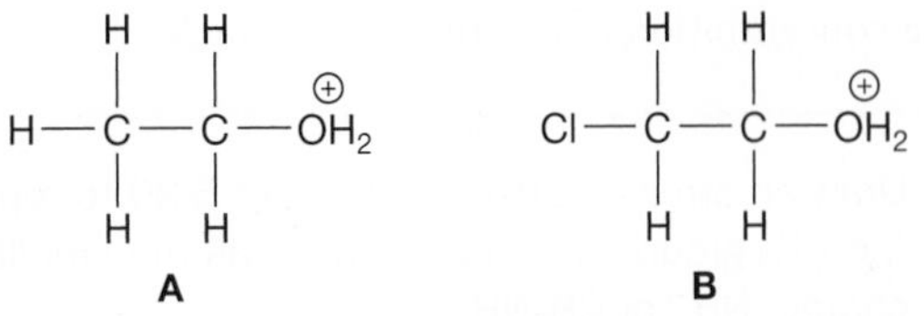
A
B

Most substituents, like chlorine, are inductively electron-withdrawing groups because most atoms common in organic compounds are more electronegative than hydrogen. However, a handful of substituents are inductively **electron-donating** and distort electron density away from themselves along covalent bonds. A silicon atom, for example, is electron-donating relative to hydrogen because silicon is less electronegative than hydrogen (1.90 vs. 2.20). Moreover:

The most common electron-donating groups in organic chemistry are *alkyl groups*.

The inductive electron-donating ability of alkyl groups can be explained by the small difference in electronegativity between carbon and hydrogen (EN = 2.55 for carbon; EN = 2.20 for hydrogen). Each C—H bond therefore results in a small bond dipole that points toward the C atom, as we can see in **Figure 6-18** for CH_3, the simplest alkyl group. As a consequence of these bond dipoles, the carbon atom takes on a partial negative charge (δ^-); the buildup of negative charge enables that carbon atom to donate some electron density to a group to which it is bonded (see Looking Ahead box).

Because electron-donating groups distort electron density away from themselves, which is opposite to what electron-withdrawing groups do, the impact that electron-donating groups have on ion stability is opposite that of electron-withdrawing groups:

- Anions are generally *destabilized* by electron-donating groups near the negative charge.
- Cations are generally *stabilized* by electron-donating groups near the positive charge.

The impact of electron-donating groups on *anion* stability can be seen from the fact that $(CH_3)_2NH$ ($pK_a = 38$) is a weaker acid than NH_3 ($pK_a = 36$), which indicates that $(CH_3)_2N^-$ is less stable than H_2N^-. As shown in **Figure 6-19**, electron donation from the methyl groups causes a buildup of negative charge on N^-; the greater concentration of charge results in decreased stability.

The impact of electron-donating groups on *cation* stability can be seen from the fact that $CH_3NH_3^+$ ($pK_a = 10.63$) is a weaker acid than NH_4^+ ($pK_a = 9.4$), indicating that $CH_3NH_3^+$ is the more stable cation. As shown in **Figure 6-20**, $CH_3NH_3^+$ is more

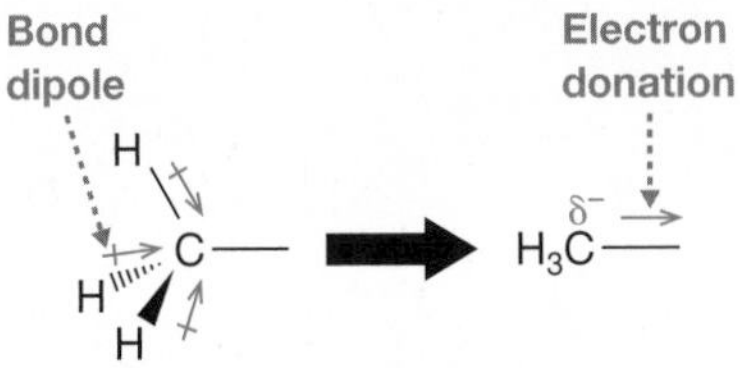
Bond dipole
Electron donation

FIGURE 6-18 Electron-donating ability of an alkyl group (*Left*) C is slightly more electronegative than H, so each C—H bond dipole points toward C. (*Right*) The electron density (δ^-) built up on C can be donated to adjacent atoms.

▸ LOOKING AHEAD

In Section 7.9a, we will see that alkyl groups can also be electron-donating via *hyperconjugation*, which requires the alkyl group to be attached to an atom that has a low-energy unoccupied orbital.

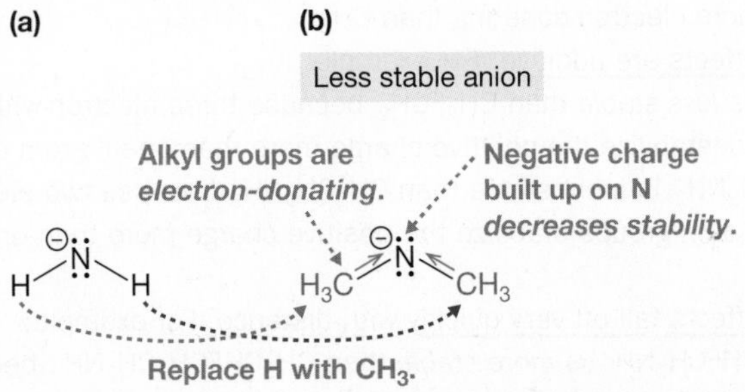
(a)
(b)
Less stable anion
Alkyl groups are electron-donating.
Negative charge built up on N decreases stability.
Replace H with CH3.

FIGURE 6-19 Inductive destabilization by an alkyl group When the indicated H atoms in (a) H_2N^- are replaced by CH_3 groups to yield (b) $(CH_3)_2N^-$, electron density along the covalent bonds is shifted away from the alkyl groups. Ultimately, the amount of negative charge on N^- is increased.

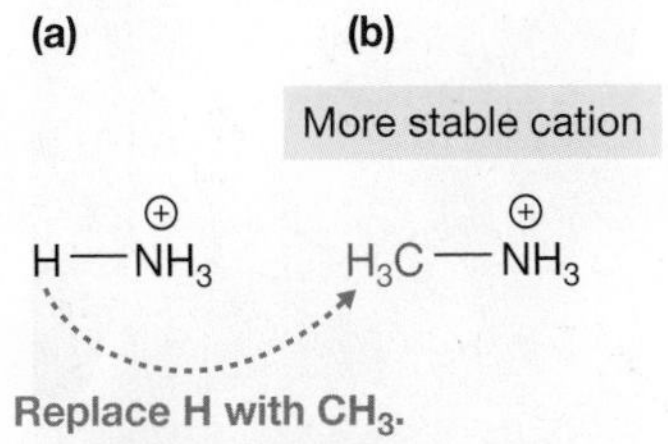
(a)
(b)
More stable cation
Replace H with CH3.

FIGURE 6-20 Inductive stabilization by an alkyl group When the indicated H atom in (a) NH_4^+ is replaced by CH_3, the resulting cation (b) $CH_3NH_3^+$ is stabilized.

stable because the electron-donating ability of the CH_3 group compared to H reduces the concentration of positive charge on N.

YOUR TURN 6.23

Draw an arrow in $CH_3NH_3^+$ in Figure 6-20 to represent the inductive effect of the CH_3 group. Indicate which N has the smaller concentration of positive charge: NH_4^+ or $CH_3NH_3^+$.

YOUR TURN 6.24

Predict which compound, **A** or **B**, is the stronger acid. Explain.

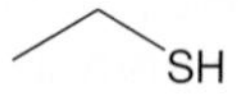

A

H_2S

B

Alkyl groups of different sizes have different electron-donating capabilities, but the difference is typically very small:

Alkyl groups that differ in chain length typically have very similar electron-donating capabilities.

For example, the alkyl group attached to the acidic OH in ethanol (CH_3CH_2OH) is twice the size of that in methanol (CH_3OH), but both have pK_a values of about 16.

Thus far, we have discussed inductive effects on ion stability in a qualitative way: electron-withdrawing groups stabilize nearby negative charges and destabilize nearby positive charges, whereas electron-donating groups destabilize nearby negative charges and stabilize nearby positive charges. These trends can be described quantitatively as well:

Trends Involving Inductive Effects

1. The magnitude of an inductive effect caused by an uncharged atom depends on the atom's electronegativity. The inductive effect becomes more pronounced when there is a bigger difference in electronegativity between the atom and hydrogen. For example:
   - F and Cl are both electron-withdrawing, but F is more electron-withdrawing because it is more electronegative than Cl.
   - The H_3Si and H_3C groups are both electron-donating, but the H_3Si group is more electron-donating because Si is less electronegative than C.
2. Charged substituents have more pronounced inductive effects than uncharged substituents. A full positive charge signifies a substituent that is very highly electron-deficient. A full negative charge, on the other hand, signifies a large excess of electron density. For example:
   - $(CH_3)_3N^+$ is more electron-withdrawing than F.
   - CO_2^- is more electron-donating than CH_3.
3. Inductive effects are additive. For example:
   - $CF_3CH_2^+$ is *less stable* than $CH_2FCH_2^+$ because three electron-withdrawing F atoms destabilize the positive charge more than one F atom does.
   - $(CH_3CH_2)_2NH_2^+$ is *more stable* than $CH_3CH_2NH_3^+$ because two electron-donating alkyl groups stabilize the positive charge more than one alkyl group does.
4. Inductive effects fall off very quickly with distance. For example:
   - $CH_3CH_2CHFCH_2NH^-$ is *more stable* than $CH_3CHFCH_2CH_2NH^-$ because the electron-withdrawing F atom better stabilizes the negative charge on N when it is closer.

CONNECTIONS 6.6

Got acne? Trichloroacetic acid (Cl_3CCO_2H, the first molecule listed in Solved Problem 6.10, Try It) is used in cosmetic treatments, such as wart removal and chemical peels that treat acne, sunspots, and wrinkles.

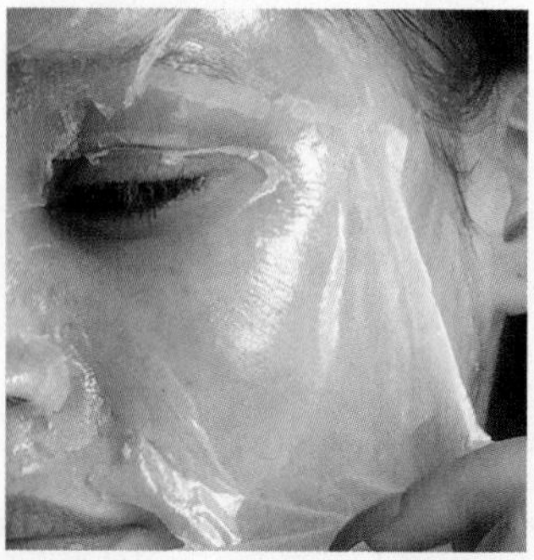

SOLVED PROBLEM **6.10**

How to evaluate inductive effects to determine the stronger acid

Break It Down **Predict which carboxylic acid, A or B, is more acidic.**

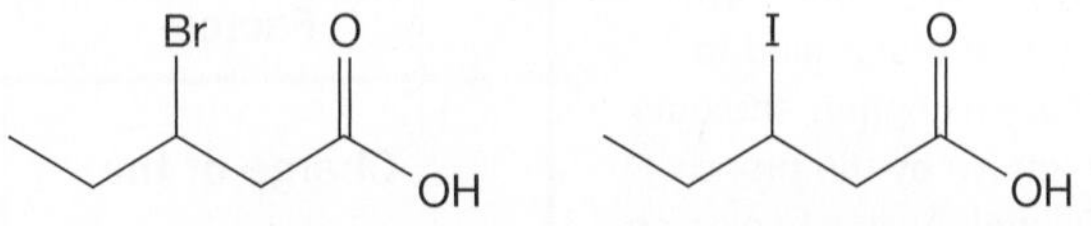

Br
O
OH
A
I
O
OH
B

Think	Solve
For each acid, does the stability of the acid or the stability of the conjugate base dictate pK_a?	**A** and **B** are uncharged acids, so their pK_a values are dictated by the stability of their negatively charged conjugate bases, in which the OH group has become O^-.
Do electron-donating or electron-withdrawing effects stabilize those species? Are the Br and I substituents electron-donating or electron-withdrawing?	Each negatively charged O^- would be stabilized by a nearby electron-withdrawing group, which would decrease the concentration of charge. Both Br and I are electron-withdrawing substituents (they are more electronegative than H), so they both stabilize the O^-.
Which substituent invokes stronger inductive effects?	Br is more electronegative than I (Rule 1), so Br better stabilizes the conjugate base, in which case **A** is a stronger acid than **B**. (Notice that the larger size of I compared to Br does *not* come into play because in neither case does the negative charge appear on those atoms.)

Try It For each pair of compounds, determine the stronger acid and explain your reasoning. *Hint*: Draw out the complete Lewis structure for each. **(a)** Cl_3CCO_2H or $Cl_3CCH_2CO_2H$; **(b)** $O_2NCH_2CH_2OH$ or $H_2NCH_2CH_2OH$

6.9 Strategies for Success: Ranking Acid and Base Strengths by Using the CARDIN-al Rule

SECTION 6.9 OBJECTIVES

You will be able to:

1. Determine the relative stabilities of species when multiple charge-stability factors are at play.
2. Predict the order of acid strengths or base strengths when multiple charge-stability factors are at play.

Strategies for Success
Ranking Acid and Base Strengths by Using the CARDIN-al Rule

So far in this chapter, we have analyzed relative acid strengths by considering only one charge-stability factor at a time. Often in organic chemistry, however, we must consider multiple factors simultaneously. To do so, we need to understand the relative importance of each factor in evaluating the stability of a particular species.

With relatively few exceptions, the order of priority for these factors follows the "CARDIN"-al rule:

> Charge > Atom > Resonance Delocalization > Inductive effects

That is to say: Whether a species is *charged or uncharged* is typically the most important factor; the next-most-important factor is the type of *atom* on which the charge appears, which includes the hybridization of the atom; this is followed by the extent of charge delocalization via *resonance*; and *inductive effects* are usually the least important factor.

The relative importance of these factors is reflected in the magnitude of their effect on pK_a, as shown in Table 6-2. Notice that an acid's pK_a can differ by over 20 units depending on the charge or the type of atom to which the acidic proton is attached.

CONNECTIONS 6.7

What do blue jeans and Tylenol have in common? Aniline ($C_6H_5NH_2$, Your Turn 6.25) is a precursor used to make acetaminophen, the pain reliever known by the brand name Tylenol. Aniline is also an important compound in the dye industry, where it is a precursor to indigo, the dye commonly associated with blue jeans.

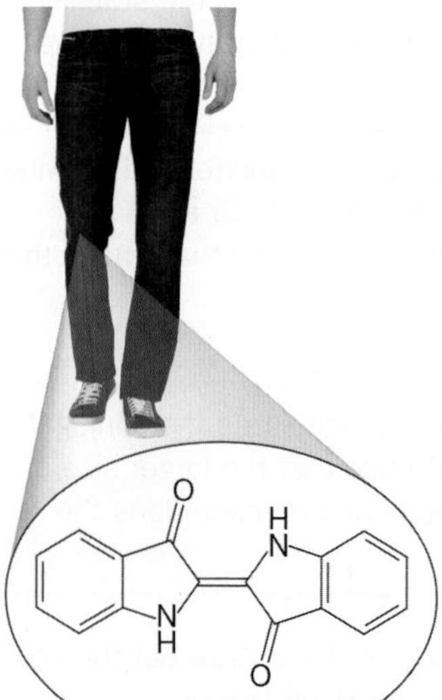

Indigo

TABLE 6-2 Relative Importance of Charge-Stability Factors: The "CARDIN"-al Rule

Charge-Stability Factor	Examples	pK_a Difference
Charge of the atom	H_4N^+ vs. NH_3 pK_a 9.4 36	36 − 9.4 = 26.6
Atom type	H_2O vs. NH_3 pK_a 14 36	36 − 14 = 22
	HC≡CH vs. H_3C—CH_3 pK_a 25 48	48 − 25 = 23
Resonance delocalization	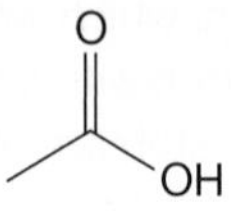 vs.  pK_a 4.75 16	16 − 4.75 = 11.25
Inductive effects	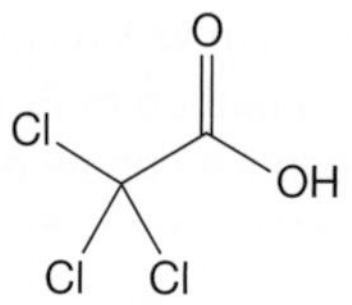 vs. 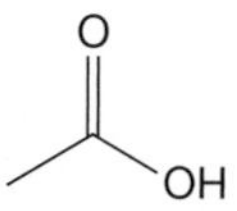 pK_a 0.17 4.75	4.75 − 0.17 = 4.58

The impact of resonance delocalization tends to be somewhat smaller, and the impact from inductive effects tends to be smaller still.

YOUR TURN 6.25

(a) Use Table 6-1 (p. 269) to determine the pK_a difference between the two acids in each of the four given pairs **A–D**. **(b)** Identify the CARDIN-al rule factor that is primarily responsible for the pK_a difference between the two acids in each pair **A–D**. **(c)** Do your findings generally agree with the CARDIN-al rule order of priorities?

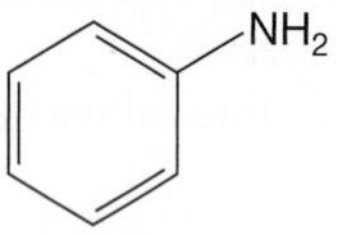 vs. 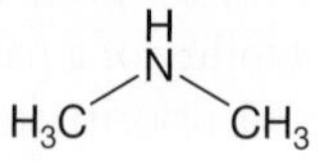

A

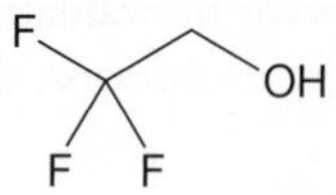 vs. 

B

HCl vs. H_2S

C

H_2O vs. $H_3O^{\oplus}$

D

With the CARDIN-al rule priorities in mind, you should ask the following questions, in order, when evaluating the relative stabilities of two species. The first question to which the answer is "yes" will likely correspond to the factor that most influences the relative stabilities:

Applying the CARDIN-al Rule to Determine Relative Charge Stability

1. Do the species have different charges? A charged species is generally more reactive than a species that bears no formal charge.
2. Do the charges appear on different atoms? If the charges appear on the same atoms, do the atoms have different hybridization?
   - A charge, positive or negative, is better accommodated on a larger atom (i.e., one farther down the periodic table).
   - A *negative* charge is better accommodated on an atom with greater electronegativity or effective electronegativity; a *positive* charge is better accommodated on an atom with less electronegativity or effective electronegativity.
3. Are the charges delocalized differently via resonance? All else being equal, stability increases as a charge is shared over a greater number of atoms.
4. Are there differences in inductive effects?
   - Electron-withdrawing groups stabilize nearby negative charges but destabilize nearby positive charges.
   - Electron-donating groups stabilize nearby positive charges but destabilize nearby negative charges.

Let's now apply this knowledge toward ranking the strengths of the four acids, **A–D**, shown in **Figure 6-21**.

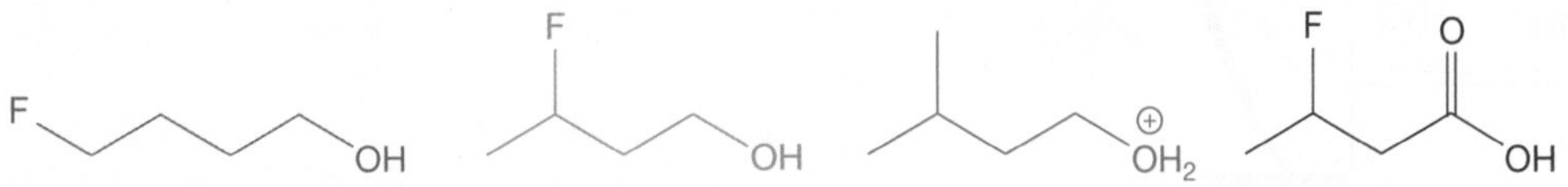

F
OH
F
OH
OH2
F
O
OH

A **B** **C** **D**

FIGURE 6-21 Acids to be ranked according to strength

Because pK_a is defined in terms of each acid's reaction with water, we begin by writing out these reactions, as shown in Equation 6-24:

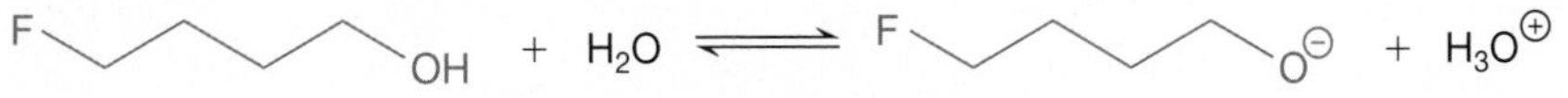

(6-24a)

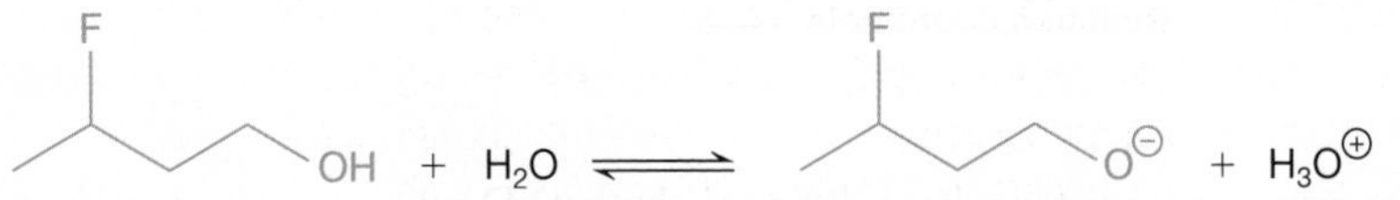

(6-24b)

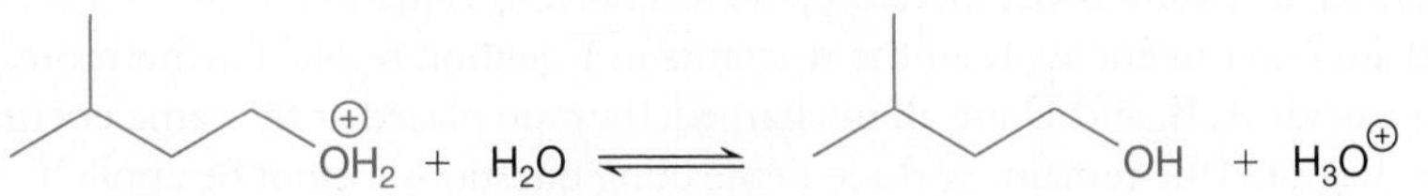

(6-24c)

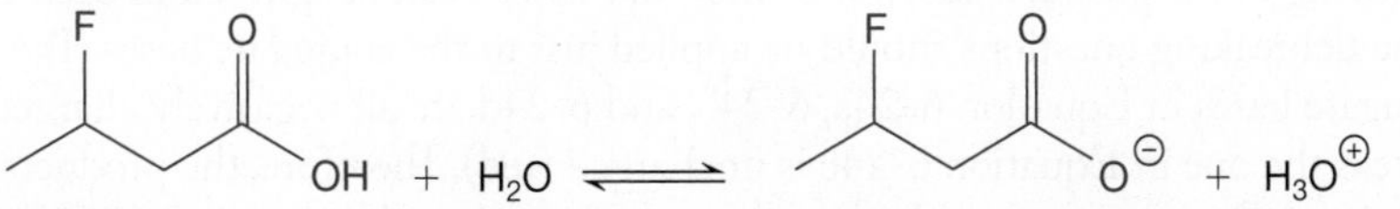

(6-24d)

To help determine how favorable each reaction is (the more favorable the reaction, the stronger the acid), construct a free energy diagram of all four reactions on a single plot (see **Figure 6-22**, see next page). We do so by determining the relative stabilities of the various reactant and product species. H_2O (a reactant) can be ignored because it appears in all cases. The remaining reactants can be evaluated by use of these tiebreaking questions.

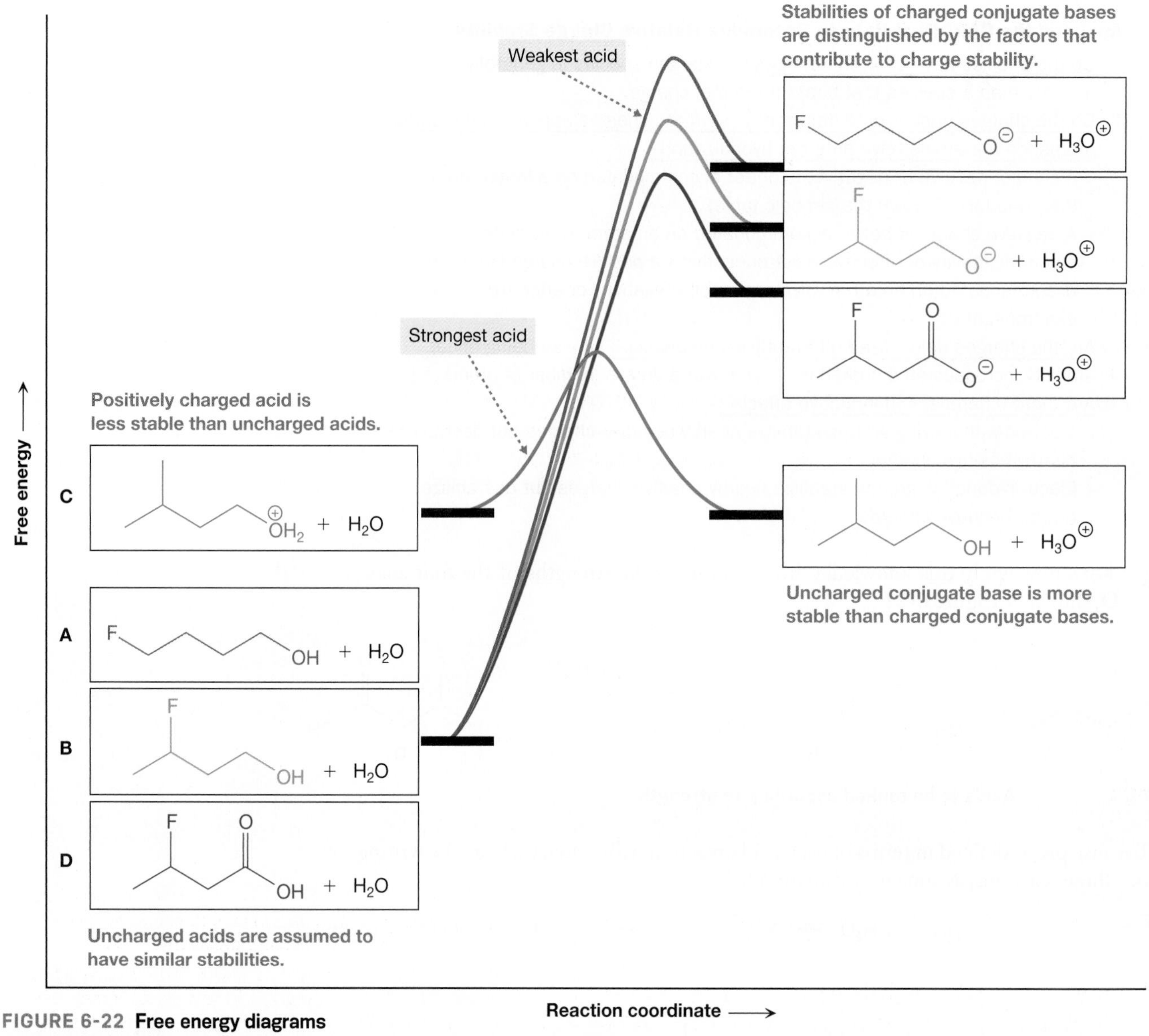

Weakest acid
Stabilities of charged conjugate bases are distinguished by the factors that contribute to charge stability.
Strongest acid
Positively charged acid is less stable than uncharged acids.
Free energy
C
A
B
D
+ H2O
Uncharged acids are assumed to have similar stabilities.
+ H3O
Uncharged conjugate base is more stable than charged conjugate bases.
Reaction coordinate

FIGURE 6-22 Free energy diagrams for proton transfer reactions shown in Equation 6-24 The reactants for the red curve are highest in energy because the acid in that reaction is charged, whereas the reactants for the other reactions are uncharged. The products for the red curve are lowest in energy because the conjugate base in that reaction is uncharged; the conjugate bases for the other reactions are charged. The products of the purple curve are next lowest in energy because the negative charge on the conjugate base is resonance-delocalized. The products for the green curve are lower in energy than the products for the blue curve due to inductive effects. In the conjugate base shown in green, F is closer to the negative charge, which more substantially decreases the concentration of negative charge on O^-.

1. Do the remaining reactants have different charges? Do the remaining products have different charges? Acid **C** is charged, whereas acids **A**, **B**, and **D** are uncharged. In Figure 6-22, therefore, the reactants in Equation 6-24a, 6-24b, and 6-24d are lower in energy than the reactants in Equation 6-24c. Furthermore, because acids **A**, **B**, and **D** are all uncharged, they are placed at the same energy in the diagram (the remaining three tiebreaking questions cannot be applied to them).

   Moving to the product side, notice first that H_3O^+ can be ignored in each case, so the tiebreaking questions should be applied just to the conjugate bases. The conjugate bases in Equation 6-24a, 6-24b, and 6-24d are all negatively charged, whereas the one in Equation 6-24c is uncharged (red). Therefore, the products of Equation 6-24c are more stable than the ones from the other reactions.
2. Do the charges appear on different atoms? This question applies only to the charged conjugate bases in Equation 6-24a, 6-24b, and 6-24d. In those species, the −1 charge appears on O in all three cases, so the answer is no.
3. Are the charges delocalized differently via resonance? Again, this question applies only to the conjugate bases in Equation 6-24a, 6-24b, and 6-24d. The conjugate

base in Equation 6-24d (purple) has two resonance structures that delocalize the negative charge over the two O atoms, making it more stable than the negatively charged conjugate bases in Equation 6-24a (blue) and 6-24b (green).

4. Are there differences in inductive effects? The only remaining species to consider are the conjugate bases in Equation 6-24a and 6-24b. Each has a highly electron-withdrawing F atom that inductively stabilizes the negative charge, but the one in Equation 6-24b (green) is closer to the negative charge, so the conjugate base in Equation 6-24b is more stable than the one in Equation 6-24a.

By establishing the relative stabilities of all four sets of reactants and products, we can see in Figure 6-22 that deprotonation of the acids becomes more favorable (less positive ΔG°_{rxn}) in the order **A** < **B** < **D** < **C**. This, then, is the order of increasing acid strength.

If you know how to rank species according to acid strength, then you can rank species according to base strength by applying the concept from Section 6.2: *The stronger base is the one that has the weaker conjugate acid.* Thus, the conjugate bases in Equation 6-24 increase in base strength in the order shown in **Figure 6-23**.

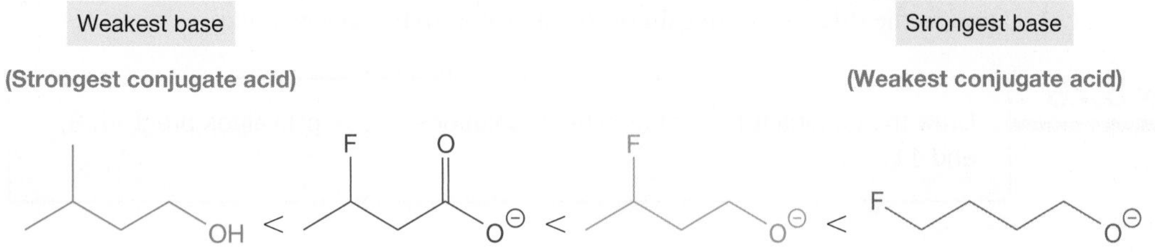

Weakest base
Strongest base
(Strongest conjugate acid)
(Weakest conjugate acid)

FIGURE 6-23 Conjugate bases of acids from Figure 6-21

THE ORGANIC CHEMISTRY OF BIOMOLECULES

6.10 The Structure of Amino Acids in Solution as a Function of pH

SECTION 6.10 OBJECTIVES

You will be able to:

1. Determine the ionization state for any amino acid when the pH of the solution is specified.
2. Draw an amino acid's zwitterion and determine the pH range for which the zwitterion is dominant.

Recall from Section 1.14a that the general form of an α-amino acid contains both an amino group (NH_2) and a carboxyl group (CO_2H) bonded to the same C atom, as shown in **Figure 6-24**. It turns out, however, that this is never the dominant form of an α-amino acid in aqueous solution because the carboxyl group is weakly acidic and the amino group is weakly basic.

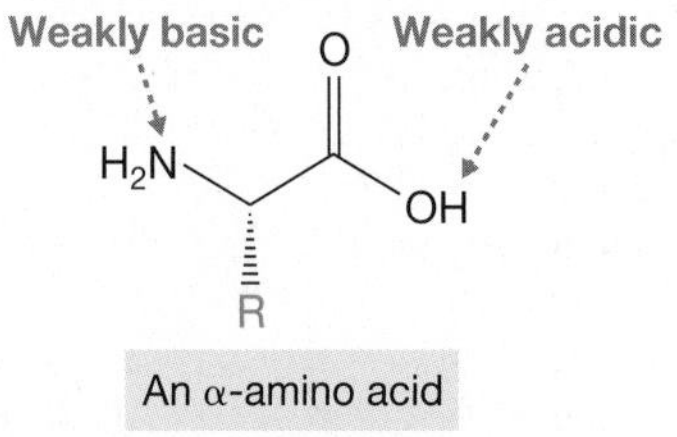

Weakly basic
Weakly acidic
An α-amino acid

FIGURE 6-24 General structure of an α-amino acid

What form, then, does an α-amino acid take in aqueous solution? The answer depends on the pH of the solution. Under very acidic conditions (pH < 2), the weakly basic N atom is protonated. The resulting species, which bears an overall charge of +1, is shown on the left in Equation 6-25:

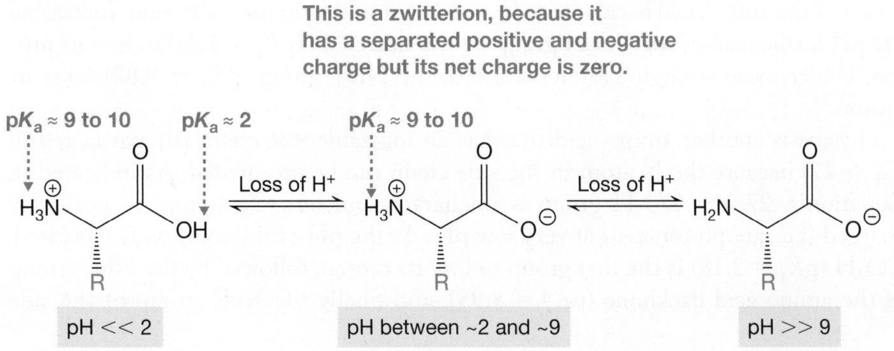

This is a zwitterion, because it has a separated positive and negative charge but its net charge is zero.
pKa ≈ 9 to 10
pKa ≈ 2
pKa ≈ 9 to 10
Loss of H+
Loss of H+
pH << 2
pH between ~2 and ~9
pH >> 9

(6-25)

As the solution becomes more basic (i.e., as the pH of the solution increases), a proton can be removed. It does *not* come from the NH_3^+ group, however, because the most acidic proton in the cationic species is the one that belongs to the CO_2H group: its pK_a is around 2, whereas that of the NH_3^+ group is around 9 to 10. (The exact pK_a values depend on the specific amino acid, characterized by the side-chain R.) Therefore, as we learned in Section 6.2b, the CO_2H proton is lost when the pH of the solution has risen significantly above 2 (the pK_a of the acidic proton), at which point the dominant form is the middle species in Equation 6-25. This species, called a **zwitterion** (pronounced ZVITTER-eye-on), has both a positive and a negative formal charge but a net charge of zero.

As the solution becomes more basic still, the proton of the NH_3^+ group is lost, yielding the species on the right in Equation 6-25. This second deprotonation takes place when the pH of the solution is significantly above 9 or 10, the pK_a of the NH_3^+ proton.

Table 6-3 lists the pK_a values associated with the 20 naturally occurring amino acids. For the majority of these amino acids, only two pK_a values are listed: one for the CO_2H group and one for the NH_3^+ group. For seven of them, however, a third pK_a value is given. Those amino acids have side chains that are **ionizable**, meaning that an atom in the side chain can gain or lose a proton to become charged.

YOUR TURN 6.26

Draw the dominant form of alanine in solutions whose pH values are 1, 4, 8, and 11.

Aspartic acid is one of the seven amino acids with an ionizable side chain. Its side chain (shown in red in Eq. 6-26) contains a second CO_2H group:

Aspartic acid

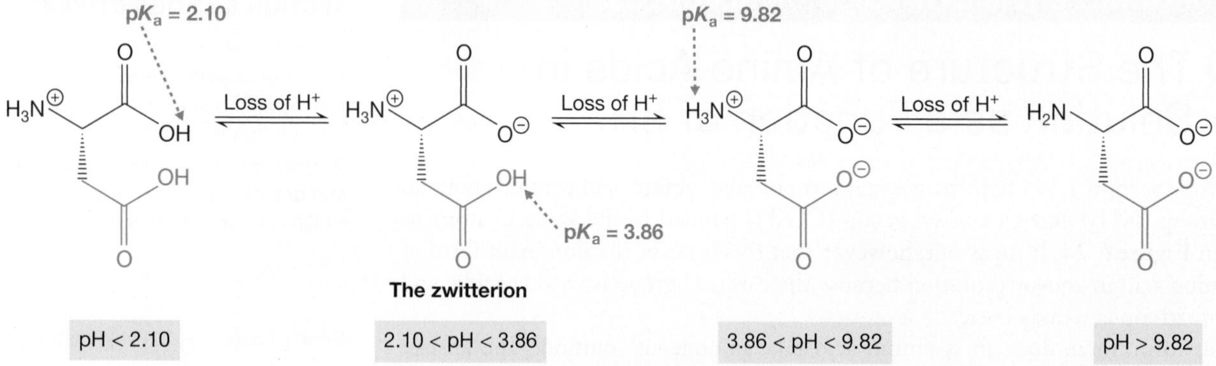

pKa = 2.10
H3N
OH
OH
O
Loss of H+
pKa = 9.82
pKa = 3.86
H2N
The zwitterion
pH < 2.10
2.10 < pH < 3.86
3.86 < pH < 9.82
pH > 9.82

(6-26)

At low pH (i.e., strongly acidic conditions), aspartic acid is in its fully protonated form, in which both CO_2H groups are uncharged and the NH_3^+ group is positively charged. As the pH is increased, the first proton that is lost comes from the CO_2H group that is part of the amino acid backbone ($pK_a = 2.10$), resulting in the zwitterion. Increasing the pH further causes the CO_2H group on the side chain ($pK_a = 3.86$) to lose its proton. Under more strongly basic conditions, the NH_3^+ group ($pK_a = 9.82$) loses its proton.

Lysine is another amino acid that has an ionizable side chain (shown in red in Eq. 6-27) because the N atom in the side chain can be protonated. As indicated in Equation 6-27, the CO_2H group is uncharged and both N atoms are positively charged (i.e., are protonated) at very low pH. As the pH of the solution is increased, CO_2H ($pK_a = 2.18$) is the first group to lose its proton, followed by the NH_3^+ group of the amino acid backbone ($pK_a = 8.95$), and finally the NH_3^+ group of the side

TABLE 6-3 pK_a Values of the 20 Naturally Occurring Amino Acids

Amino Acid	Side Chain	pK_a of CO_2H	pK_a of NH_3^+	pK_a of Side Chain
Alanine	$-CH_3$	2.35	9.87	-
Arginine	$-CH_2-(CH_2)_2-NH-C(=\overset{\oplus}{N}H_2)-NH_2$	2.01	9.04	12.48
Asparagine	$-CH_2-C(=O)-NH_2$	2.02	8.80	-
Aspartic acid	$-CH_2-C(=O)-OH$	2.10	9.82	3.86
Cysteine	$-CH_2-SH$	2.05	10.25	8.00
Glutamic acid	$-CH_2-CH_2-C(=O)-OH$	2.10	9.47	4.07
Glutamine	$-CH_2-CH_2-C(=O)-NH_2$	2.17	9.13	-
Glycine	$-H$	2.35	9.78	-
Histidine	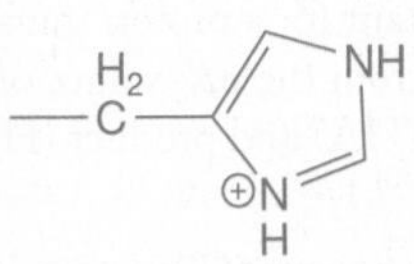	1.77	9.18	6.10
Isoleucine	$-CH(CH_3)-CH_2CH_3$	2.32	9.76	-
Leucine	$-CH_2-CH(CH_3)_2$	2.33	9.74	-
Lysine	$-CH_2-(CH_2)_3-\overset{\oplus}{N}H_3$	2.18	8.95	10.53
Methionine	$-CH_2-CH_2-S-CH_3$	2.28	9.21	-
Phenylalanine	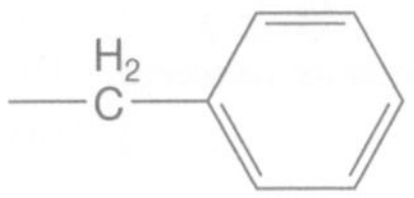	2.58	9.24	-
Proline[a]	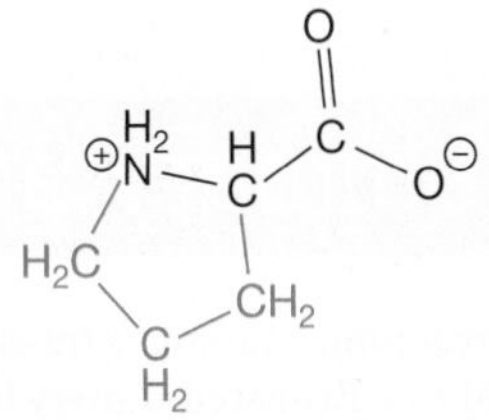	2.00	10.60	-
Serine	$-CH_2-OH$	2.21	9.15	-
Threonine	$-CH(CH_3)-OH$	2.09	9.10	-
Tryptophan	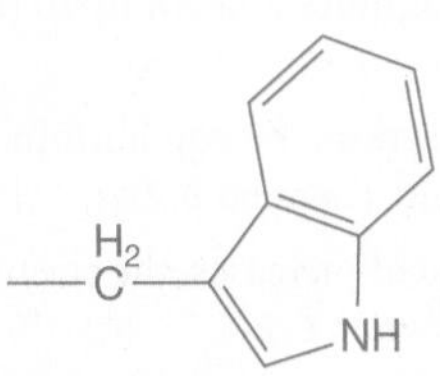	2.38	9.39	-
Tyrosine		2.20	9.11	10.07
Valine	$-CH(CH_3)_2$	2.29	9.72	-

[a]For proline, the side chain is shown in red and the amino acid backbone is shown in black.

chain (pK_a = 10.53). With lysine, the zwitterion is the product of the second deprotonation, not the first:

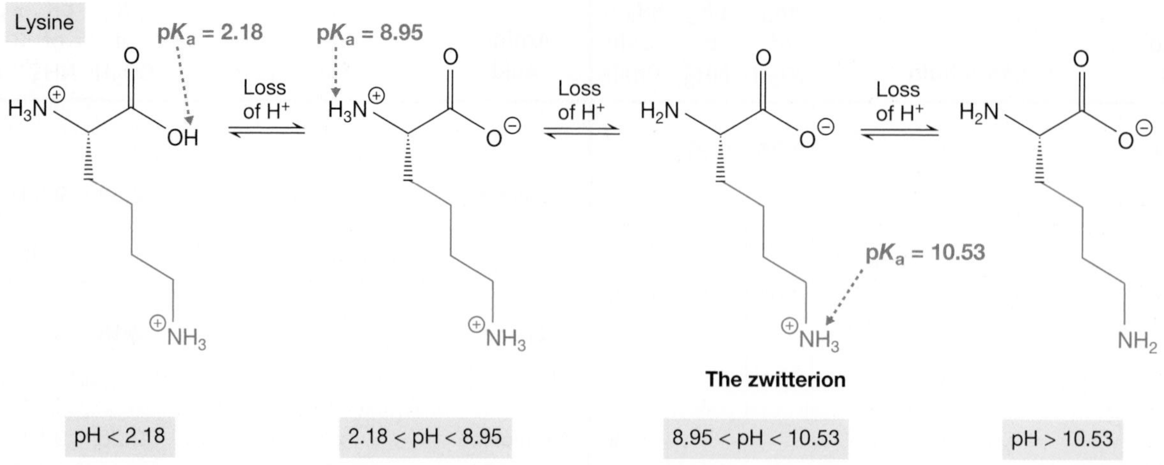

Lysine
pK_a = 2.18
pK_a = 8.95
Loss of H^+
Loss of H^+
Loss of H^+
pK_a = 10.53
The zwitterion
pH < 2.18
2.18 < pH < 8.95
8.95 < pH < 10.53
pH > 10.53

(6-27)

YOUR TURN **6.27**

Draw the structure of the most abundant form of arginine in solutions whose pH values are 1, 4, 8, 10, and 14.

Chapter Summary and Key Terms

- In a **proton transfer reaction**, a proton is transferred from a **Brønsted–Lowry acid** to a **Brønsted–Lowry base** in a single **elementary step**; that is, one bond is broken and another is formed simultaneously. **(Section 6.1)**
- **Curved arrow notation** describes the movement of electrons in an elementary step of a mechanism, showing explicitly the breaking and/or forming of bonds. A *double-barbed* curved arrow (⟶) represents the movement of a pair of valence electrons. **(Section 6.1)**
- An acid's **pK_a** value depicts the acid's strength. A lower pK_a value represents a stronger acid, and each difference of 1 unit in an acid's pK_a value signifies a factor of 10 difference in acid strength. **(Section 6.2)**
- In a proton transfer reaction, the equilibrium favors the side *opposite* the stronger acid. **(Section 6.2)**
- As the strength of an acid increases, the strength of its conjugate base decreases. **(Section 6.2)**
- A solvent's **leveling effect** dictates the maximum strength of an acid or a base that can exist in solution. The strongest acid that can exist is the protonated solvent; the strongest base that can exist is the deprotonated solvent. **(Section 6.2a)**
- According to **Le Châtelier's principle**, a reaction at equilibrium shifts toward products when the concentration of a reactant is increased or the concentration of a product is decreased. Conversely, a reaction at equilibrium shifts toward reactants when the concentration of a reactant is decreased or the concentration of a product is increased. **(Section 6.2b)**
- The ionization state of an acid depends on the pH of the solution. The acid is the dominant form when the pH is lower than the acid's pK_a, whereas the conjugate base is the dominant form when the pH is higher than the acid's pK_a. **(Section 6.2b)**
- A reaction's **equilibrium constant (K_{eq})** reflects the tendency of that reaction to form products. A reaction with K_{eq} >1 favors products, and one with K_{eq} <1 favors reactants. **(Section 6.3)**
- The equilibrium between an acid (HA) and water is described by the **acidity constant (K_a)** where: $K_a = [A^-]_{eq}[H_3O^+]_{eq}/[HA]_{eq}$. **(Section 6.3)**
  - Rearranging this expression gives the **Henderson–Hasselbalch equation,** which relates the pH of the solution to the relative amounts of an acid and its conjugate base: pH = pK_a + log ([A$^-$]/[HA]).
  - The equilibrium constant for a proton transfer reaction can be obtained from the pK_a values of the acids on the reactant (HA) and product (HB) sides: $K_{eq} = 10^{[pK_a(HB) - pK_a(HA)]}$.
- The **standard Gibbs free energy ($G°$)** is associated with relative stability: A species with a lower $G°$ is more stable. A reaction is product favored if $\Delta G°_{rxn} < 0$ and is reactant favored if $\Delta G°_{rxn} > 0$. **(Section 6.4)**
- A **reaction free energy diagram** plots free energy as a function of the **reaction coordinate**: a measure of geometric changes of the species involved in a reaction as reactants are transformed into products. **(Section 6.4)**

- The **transition state** for an elementary step is the geometry that corresponds to the highest free energy (least stability) in the conversion of reactants into products. The **free energy of activation ($\Delta G^{\circ\ddagger}$)** is the difference in Gibbs free energy between the reactants and the transition state in an elementary step. **(Section 6.4)**
- A reaction's **standard Gibbs free energy difference, ΔG°_{rxn}**, is related to the reaction's equilibrium constant: $\Delta G^{\circ}_{rxn} = -RT \ln K_{eq}$. **(Section 6.5)**
- ΔG°_{rxn} consists of a **standard enthalpy difference** term and a **standard entropy difference** term: $\Delta G^{\circ}_{rxn} = \Delta H^{\circ}_{rxn} - T\Delta S^{\circ}_{rxn}$. **(Section 6.5)**
    - A reaction's ΔH°_{rxn} depends primarily on the bonds that are broken and formed.
    - Typically, $\Delta S^{\circ}_{rxn} > 0$ for a reaction in which the species involved gain freedom of movement, such as when a ring opens or when the number of independent species increases.
    - For most reactions, the magnitude of $T\Delta S^{\circ}_{rxn}$ is substantially smaller than the magnitude of ΔH°_{rxn}, so $\Delta G^{\circ}_{rxn} \approx \Delta H^{\circ}_{rxn}$.
- A compound's pK_a is governed primarily by the functional group on which the acidic proton resides. **(Section 6.6)**
- Positively charged acids are stronger acids than their uncharged counterparts, indicating that charged species are generally high in energy and tend to be unstable and reactive. **(Section 6.7)**
- Relative pK_a values for acids reflect the relative *charge stability* of the reactants and products. For an uncharged acid (HA), the stability of the conjugate base (A^-) increases as the pK_a decreases. For a positively charged acid (HA^+), the stability of the acid decreases as the pK_a decreases. **(Section 6.8)**
- For two ions in which the formal charge is on a different atom in the same row of the periodic table, the electronegativity of the atom governs the stability of the species. A negative charge is energetically favored on the more electronegative atom, whereas a positive charge is energetically favored on the less electronegative atom. **(Section 6.8a)**
- For two ions in which the formal charge is on a different atom in the same column of the periodic table, the size of the atom governs stability. The charge is favored on the atom that is larger, which is in a lower row of the periodic table. **(Section 6.8b)**
- For two ions in which the formal charge is on an atom of the same element, hybridization governs stability. A negative charge is energetically favored on the atom with the higher effective electronegativity (i.e., $sp^3 < sp^2 < sp$). A positive charge is energetically favored on the atom with the lower effective electronegativity. **(Section 6.8c)**
- **Resonance effects** can stabilize a charged species. A species in which a charge is *delocalized* by resonance is more stable than one in which the charge is *localized*. All else being equal, the stability of the charged species increases as the number of atoms over which the charge is delocalized increases. **(Section 6.8d)**
- **Inductive effects** can affect the stability of a charged species by shifting electron density through covalent bonds. An atom that is more electronegative than hydrogen is considered to be **electron-withdrawing**, so it stabilizes a nearby negative charge but destabilizes a nearby positive charge. An **electron-donating** group, such as an alkyl group or an atom that is less electronegative than hydrogen, stabilizes a nearby positive charge but destabilizes a nearby negative charge. **(Section 6.8e)**
- Inductive effects are additive. The greater the number of groups that contribute to an inductive effect, the greater the effect. **(Section 6.8e)**
- Inductive effects fall off quickly with distance. **(Section 6.8e)**
- In general, the order of importance for factors affecting charge stability follows the "CARDIN-al" rule. From most important to least important, the general order is (1) the presence of formal charges, (2) the type of atom on which the charge resides, (3) resonance effects, and (4) inductive effects. **(Section 6.9)**
- An amino acid's NH_2 and CO_2H groups are **ionizable**. At low pH, the NH_2 group is protonated to become NH_3^+ and the CO_2H group retains its proton. At higher pH, the uncharged form of an amino acid is a **zwitterion**, which has both a positive and a negative charge. **(Section 6.10)**
- Some amino acid side chains are ionizable, establishing the amino acid as acidic or basic. **(Section 6.10)**

Problems

Sections 6.1 and 6.2 The Proton Transfer Reaction and pK_a Values

6.1 Given the curved arrow notation for each of the following proton transfer reactions, draw the appropriate products.

(a)

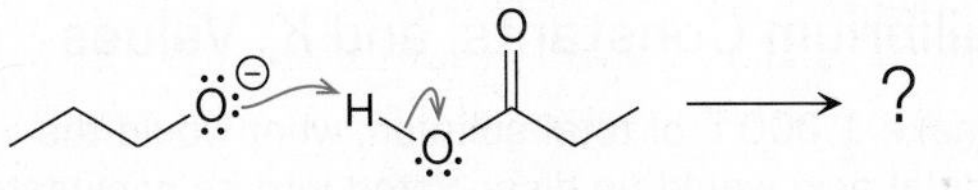

(b)

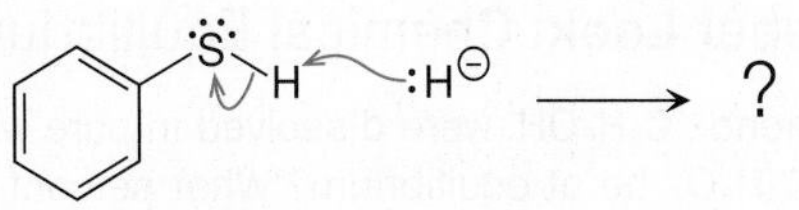

(c)

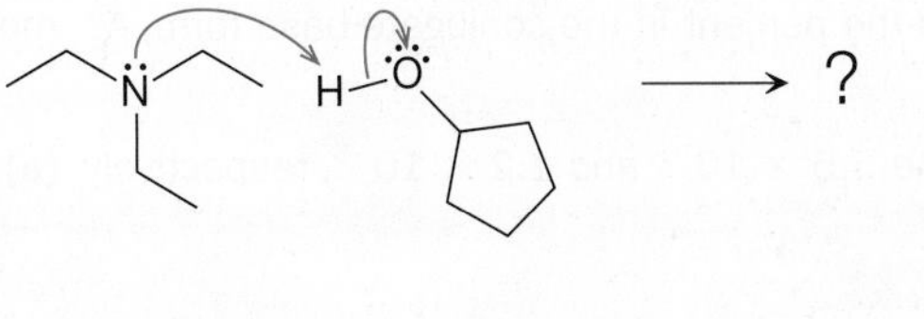

(d)

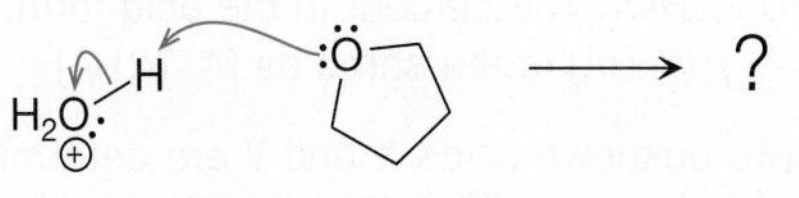

6.2 Given the reactants and products in each of the following proton transfer reactions, supply the missing curved arrows. Add relevant electrons if they are not shown.

(a)

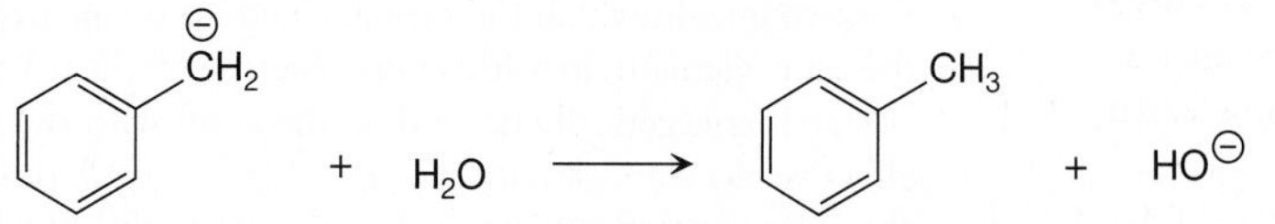

(b)

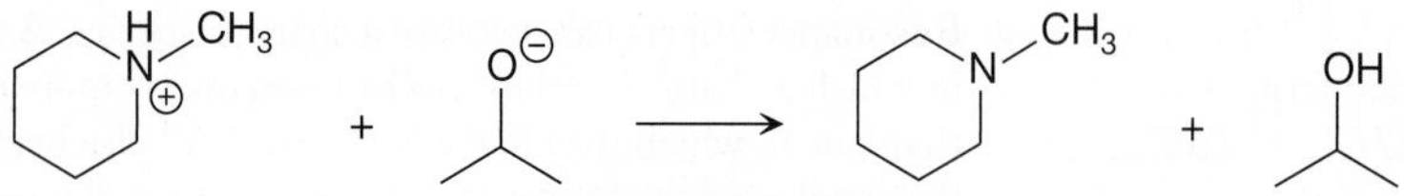

(c)

(d)

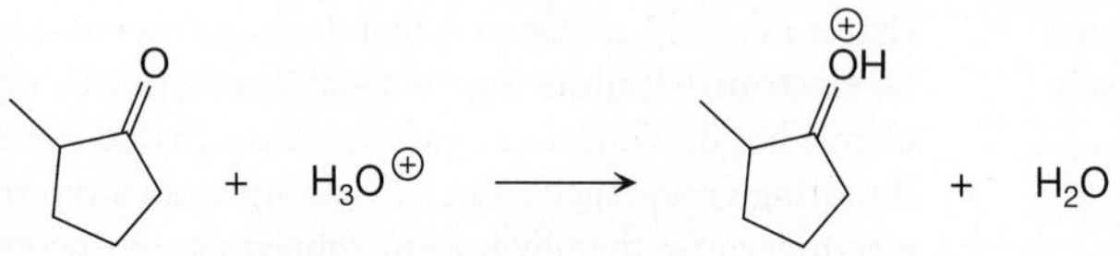

6.3 Draw the curved arrow notation for the proton transfer reaction between NH_3 and H_2O, in which NH_3 acts as the acid and H_2O acts as the base.

6.4 Draw the curved arrow notation for the proton transfer reaction between the hydride anion (H^-) and ethanol (CH_3CH_2OH). Using the pK_a values listed in Table 6-1 (p. 269), predict which side of this reaction is favored. By what numerical factor is that side favored?

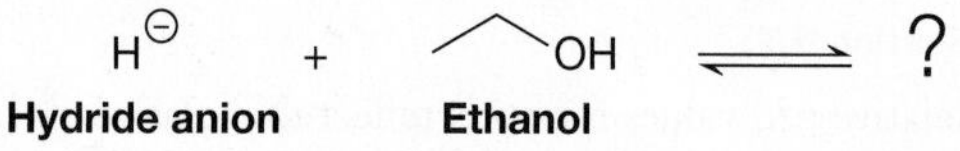

Hydride anion
Ethanol

6.5 The protonated form of aniline has a pK_a of about 4.6. At what pH would you expect the protonated (cationic) form to have a greater concentration than the uncharged form? At what pH would you expect an equal mixture of the two forms?

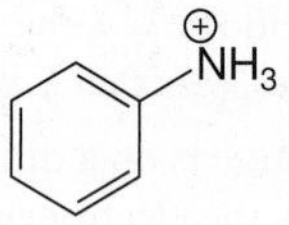

pK_a = 4.6

6.6 Keeping in mind the leveling effect, determine if each of the following bases can exist at a substantial concentration in ethanol.

(a) $^-NH_2$ **(b)** 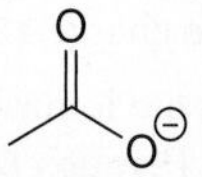 **(c)** Cl^- **(d)** 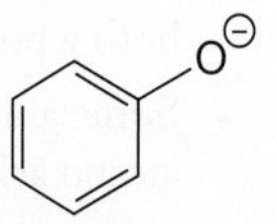 **(e)** ^-CN **(f)** 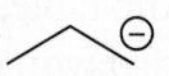

6.7 Keeping in mind the leveling effect, determine if each of the following bases can exist at a substantial concentration in ethanamine ($CH_3CH_2NH_2$).

(a) Cl^- **(b)** $CH_3CO_2^-$ **(c)** $^-CH_3$ **(d)** $^-NH_2$ **(e)** ^-SH **(f)** ^-OH

6.8 What is the strongest acid that can exist in significant amounts in each of the following solvents? **(a)** CH_3OH; **(b)** CH_3CO_2H; **(c)** $C_6H_5NH_2$; **(d)** CH_3SCH_3

Section 6.3 A Deeper Look: Chemical Equilibrium, Equilibrium Constants, and K_a Values

6.9 If 0.100 mol of phenol, C_6H_5OH, were dissolved in pure water to make 1.000 L of total solution, what would the concentration of $C_6H_5O^-$ be at equilibrium? What percent of the initial acid would be dissociated into its conjugate base?

6.10 At what pH will Cl_3CCO_2H dissociate 50% into its conjugate base in water? At what pH will it dissociate 90%? At what pH will it dissociate 10%? *Hint*: The percent in the acid form, HA, and the percent in the conjugate base form, A^-, must sum to 100%. Also, (% A^-)/(% HA) is the same as [A^-]/[HA].

6.11 The K_a values for two unknown acids **X** and **Y** are determined to be 5.5×10^{-8} and 1.2×10^{-5}, respectively. **(a)** What are the pK_a values for the two acids? **(b)** Which acid is stronger?

6.12 Calculate K_{eq} for the following proton transfer reaction.

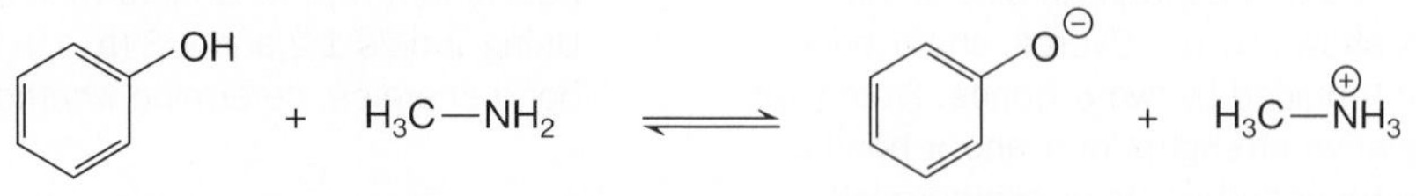

6.13 An unknown acid **Z** is determined to exist in equal amounts of its acid and conjugate base forms at pH = 4.2. What acid(s) in Table 6-1 (p. 269) could **Z** be?

6.14 A student dissolved 0.500 mol of an acid HA in water to make 1.000 L of solution and measured the pH to be 3.5. Calculate the K_a of the acid.

Section 6.4 Gibbs Free Energy and the Reaction Free Energy Diagram

6.15 Consider the proton transfer reaction shown here. As the reaction coordinate increases: **(a)** Does the distance between N and the indicated H increase or decrease? **(b)** Does the distance between S and the indicated H increase or decrease? **(c)** Does the C—N bond length increase or decrease? *Hint*: Consider resonance structures of the conjugate base.

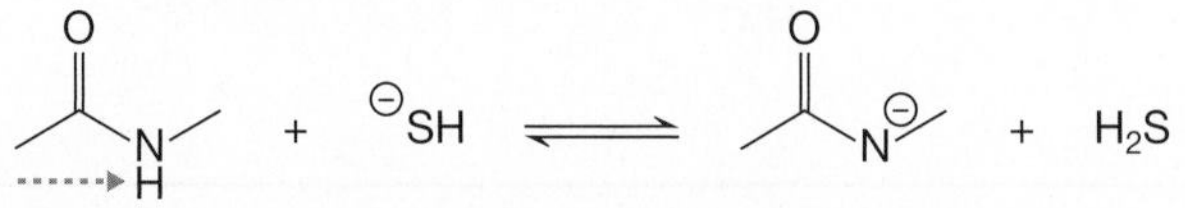

6.16 **(a)** Draw the products of the proton transfer reaction shown here. **(b)** Draw a free energy diagram for this reaction, indicating whether it is endergonic or exergonic.

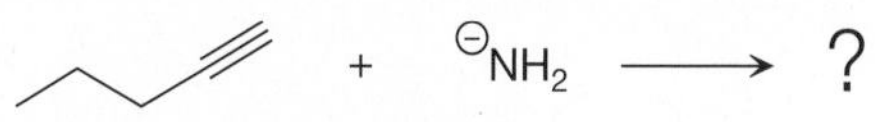

6.17 **(a)** Draw the products of the proton transfer reaction shown here. **(b)** Draw a free energy diagram for this reaction, indicating whether it is endergonic or exergonic.

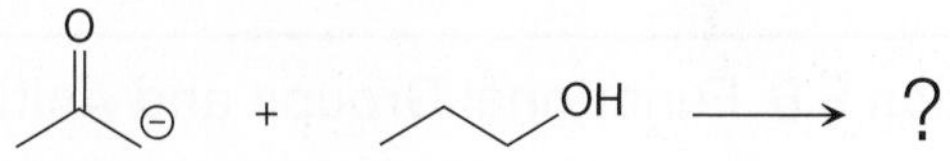

6.18 A reactant **W** can undergo two separate reactions to yield either **X** or **Y**. **(a)** If the free energy diagram on the left were to describe these competing reactions, which product would be more stable? Which product would be formed faster? **(b)** If the free energy diagram on the right were to describe these competing reactions, which product would be more stable? Which product would be formed faster?

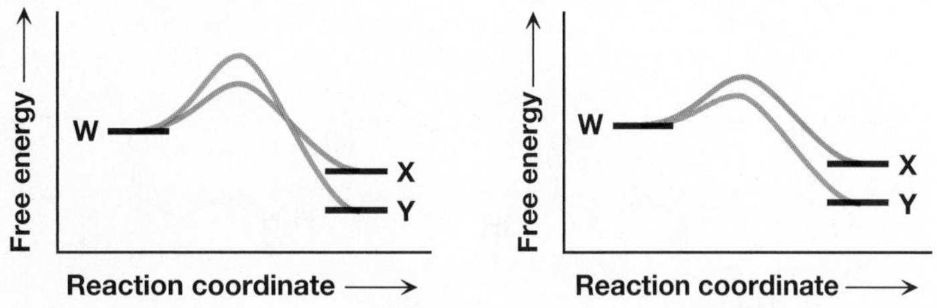
Free energy
W
X
Y
Reaction coordinate
Free energy
W
X
Y
Reaction coordinate

Section 6.5 A Deeper Look: Gibbs Free Energy, Equilibrium Constants, Enthalpy, and Entropy

6.19 In Chapter 9 you will learn that the following reactants can undergo competing reactions to make different products. Relevant to this competition, which reaction, **A** or **B**, has the more positive ΔS°_{rxn}? Explain.

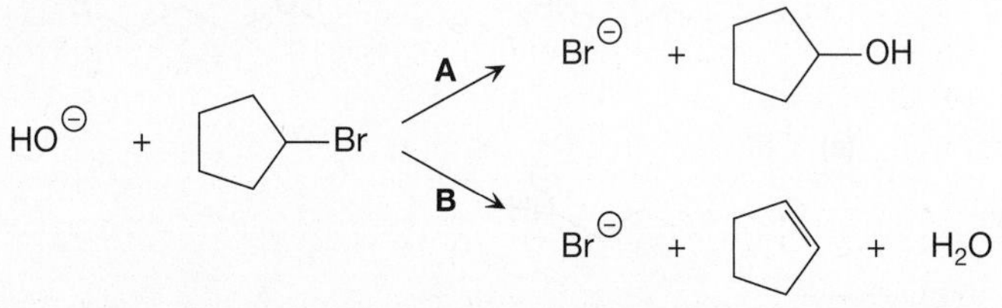

6.20 For a given reaction at 298 K, ΔH°_{rxn} is −25 kJ/mol and ΔS°_{rxn} is −0.15 kJ/mol·K. At 298 K, does this reaction favor the reactant side or the product side? At what temperature will the opposite side of the reaction be favored?

6.21 In Chapter 12 you will learn that a strong acid like HCl can add to the C=C double bond of an alkene, an example of which is shown below. Overall, one σ bond and one π bond are replaced by two σ bonds. From your knowledge of the relative strengths of σ and π bonds, should this reaction be endothermic or exothermic? Explain.

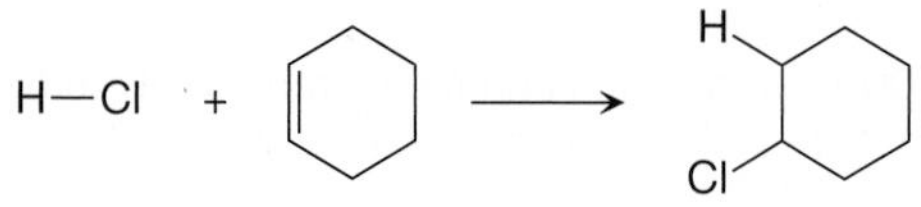

H—Cl
+
H
Cl

6.22 Which transformation, **A** or **B**, has the more positive value for ΔS°_{rxn}? Explain.

A
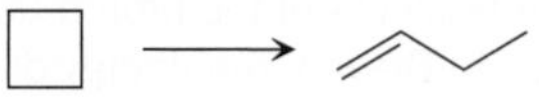

B
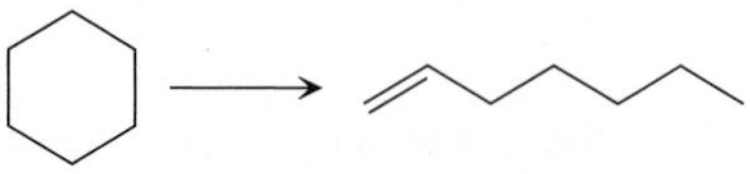

6.23 In Chapter 7 you will learn that a ketone exists in equilibrium with its enol form, as shown here for acetone. Using Tables 1-2 and 1-3 (p. 10–11) to find the relevant bond energies, determine whether ΔH°_{rxn} is >0 or <0.

O
C
H3C
CH3
OH
C
H3C
CH2

Keto form **Enol form**

6.24 In Chapter 26 you will learn that ethene and buta-1,3-diene can undergo a Diels–Alder reaction to produce cyclohexene, as shown here. **(a)** From what you know about the relative strengths of σ and π bonds, determine whether ΔH°_{rxn} is >0 or <0. **(b)** Determine whether ΔS°_{rxn} is >0 or <0. **(c)** For a Diels–Alder reaction, is it possible to change the sign of ΔG°_{rxn} just by changing temperature?

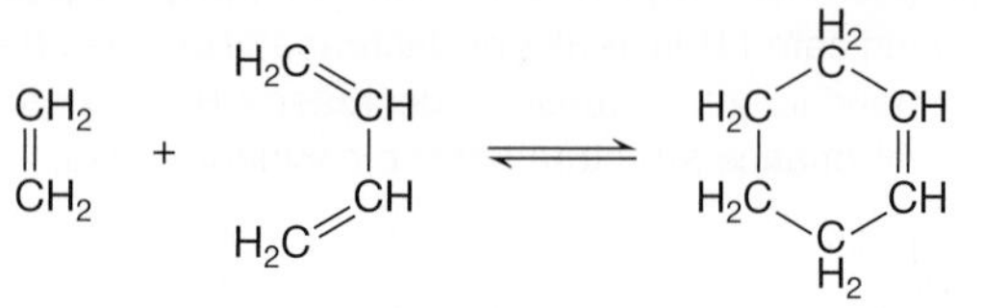

CH2
CH2
+
H2C
CH
CH
H2C
H2
C
H2C
CH
H2C
CH
C
H2

Section 6.6 Functional Groups and Acidity

6.25 For each of the following species, identify the most acidic proton and estimate its pK_a.

(a)
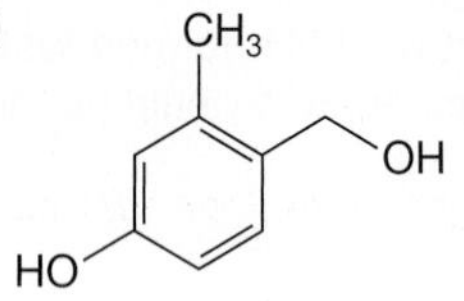

CH3
OH
HO

(b)
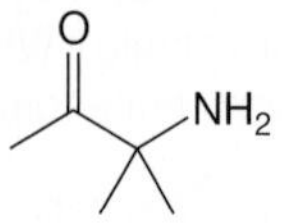

O
NH2

(c)
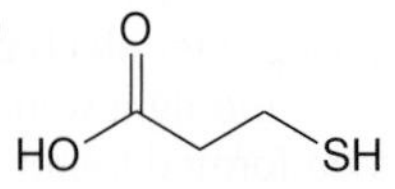

O
HO
SH

(d)

N
H
N

(e)
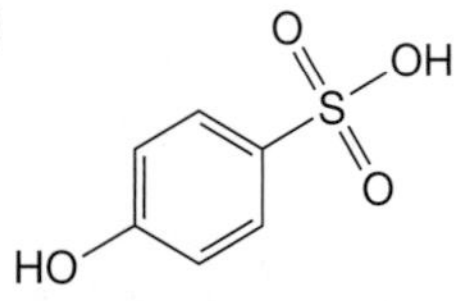

O
OH
S
O
HO

(f)
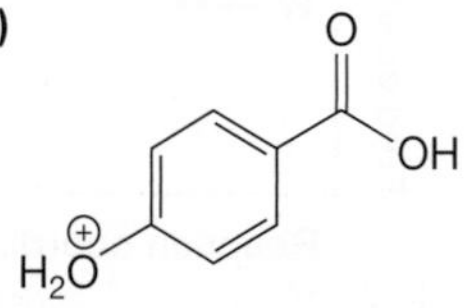

O
OH
H2O

(g)
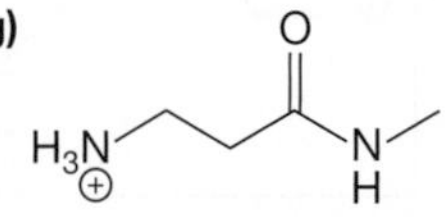

O
H3N
N
H

(h)
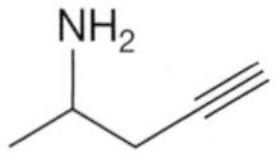

NH2

6.26 For each of the following species, identify the most basic site. *Hint*: Estimate the pK_a values of the corresponding conjugate acids.

(a)
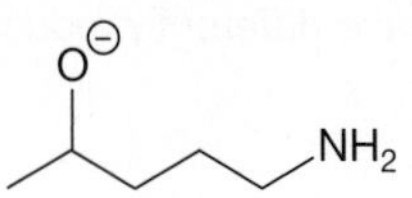

O
NH2

(b)
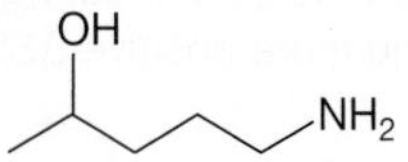

OH
NH2

(c)

O
S

(d)
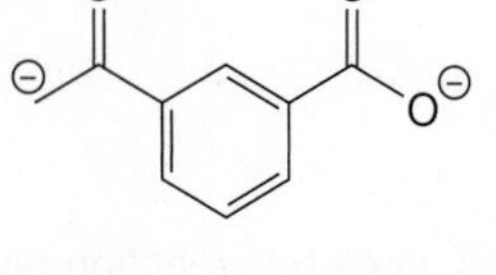

O
O
O

(e)
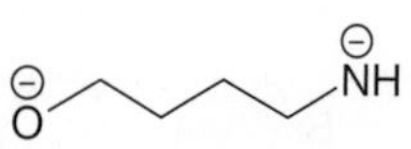

NH
O

6.27 For which of the following molecules, **A–D**, do you expect the pK_a value of the OH proton to be the most similar to that of cyclohexanol? Which do you expect to be the most different? Explain.

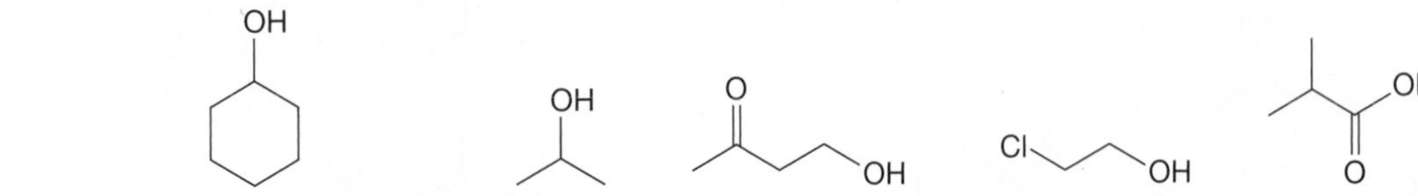

OH
OH
O
OH
Cl
OH
OH
O

Cyclohexanol **A** **B** **C** **D**

6.28 For which of the following molecules, **A–D**, do you expect the pK_a value of the indicated proton(s) to be most similar to the indicated protons in 2-amino-2-methyl-1-phenylpropanone? Explain.

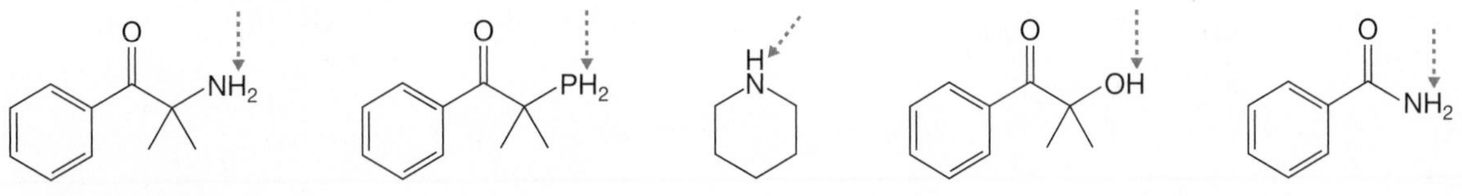

O
NH2
O
PH2
H
N
O
OH
O
NH2

2-Amino-2-methyl-1-phenylpropanone **A** **B** **C** **D**

Sections 6.7 and 6.8 Relative Acidities and Charge-Stability Factors

6.29 Students are often taught in general chemistry that HCl, HBr, and HI are all "strong acids" and no distinction is made among them. On the basis of charge stability, rank these acids from least acidic to most acidic.

6.30 For each pair of molecules, predict which is the stronger acid and explain your reasoning.

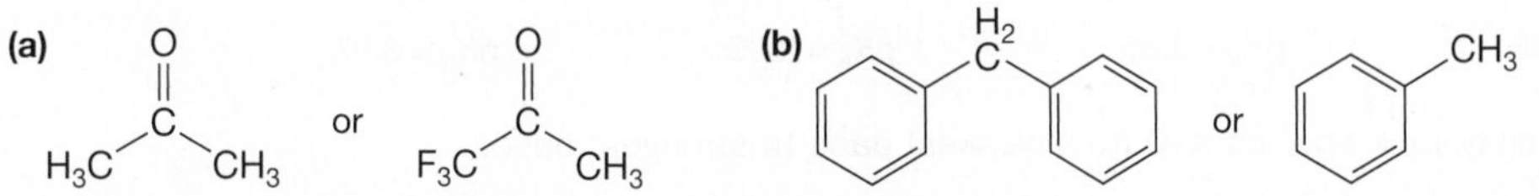

(a)
O
C
H3C
CH3
or
O
C
F3C
CH3
(b)
H2
C
or
CH3

6.31 Sulfuric acid (H_2SO_4) is called a *diprotic acid* because it has two acidic protons. The pK_a for the first deprotonation is −9, whereas the pK_a for the second deprotonation is 2. Explain these relative acid strengths.

6.32 From the pK_a values of the following substituted acetic acids, which is a stronger electron-withdrawing group, CO_2H or NO_2? Can you explain why? *Hint*: Write out the complete Lewis structures.

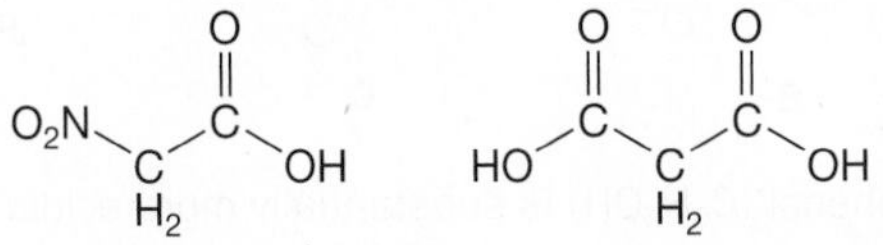

O
O2N
C
C
OH
H2
O
O
HO
C
C
C
OH
H2

pK_a = 1.68 pK_a = 2.83

6.33 Use the electrostatic potential maps provided to predict whether C≡N or CF_3 is a stronger electron-withdrawing substituent. Explain.

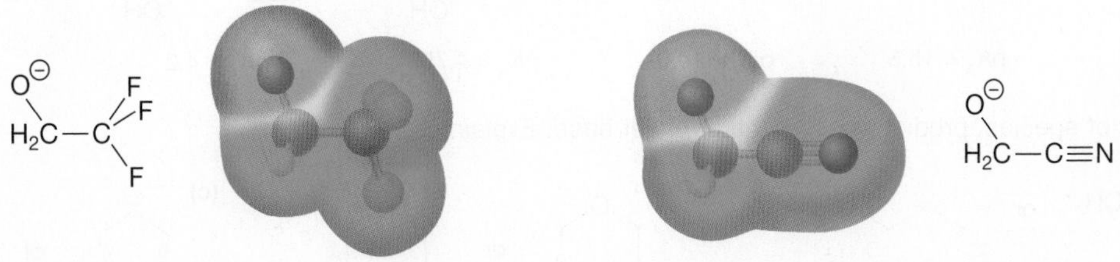

O
F
F
H2C—C
F
O
H2C—C≡N

6.34 Which do you expect to be the stronger base: HCN or HNC? Explain. *Hint*: Draw out the complete Lewis structure for each molecule.

6.35 The pK_a values of acids **A–C** are 9.0, 9.1, and 9.2. Match each of these values with its structure.

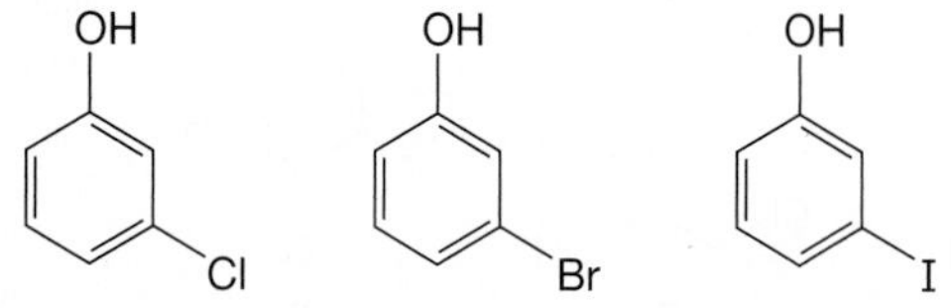

A **B** **C**

6.36 Which of the compounds shown here do you expect to be the stronger base? Explain.

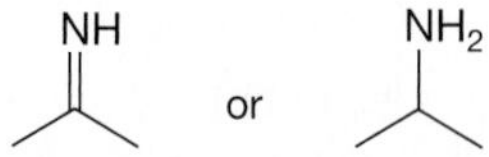

6.37 Which carboxylic acid is more acidic? Explain.

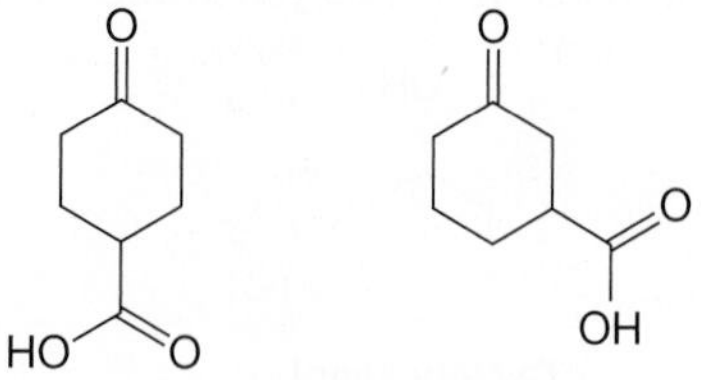

A **B**

Section 6.9 Strategies for Success: Ranking Acid and Base Strengths by Using the CARDIN-al Rule

6.38 From the following pK_a values, which do you think is more important in determining inductive effects: electronegativity or distance from the reaction center? Explain.

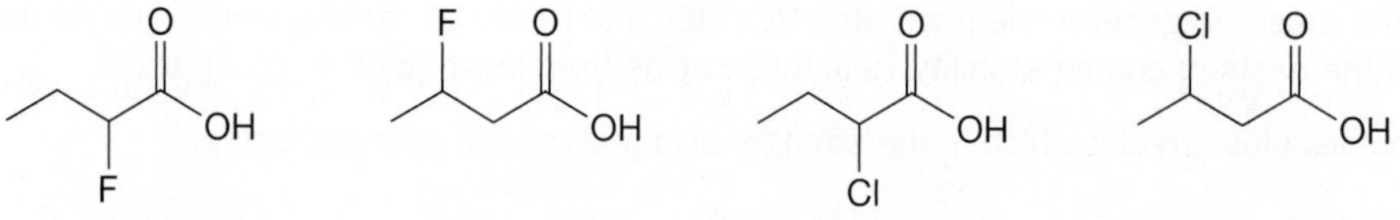

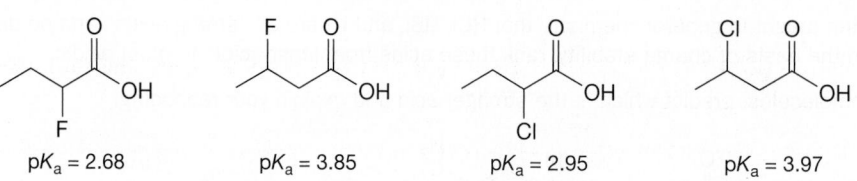

$pK_a = 2.68$ $pK_a = 3.85$ $pK_a = 2.95$ $pK_a = 3.97$

6.39 On the basis of charge stability, rank species **A–G** from weakest base to strongest base.

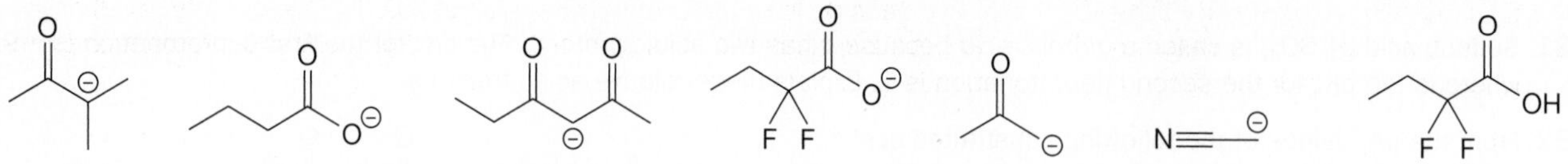

A **B** **C** **D** **E** **F** **G**

6.40 Explain why phenol (C_6H_5OH) is substantially more acidic than methanol (CH_3OH) but benzoic acid ($C_6H_5CO_2H$) is not much more acidic than acetic acid (CH_3CO_2H).

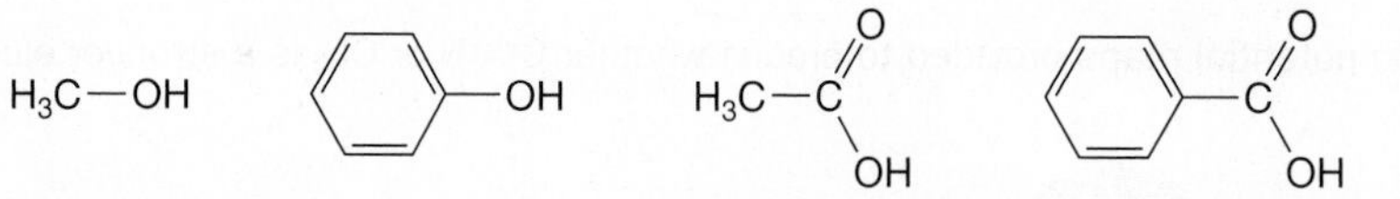

$pK_a = 15.5$ $pK_a = 10.0$ $pK_a = 4.75$ $pK_a = 4.2$

6.41 For each pair of species, predict which is the stronger base. Explain.

(a) 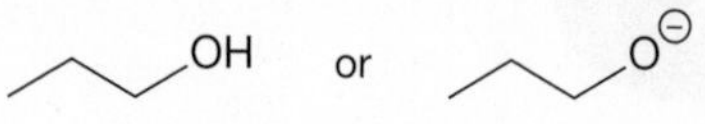

(b) 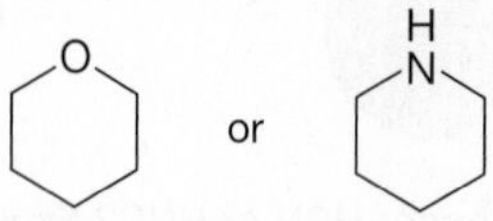

(c) 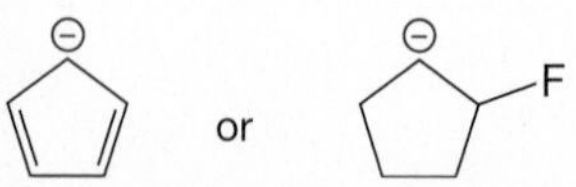

(d) 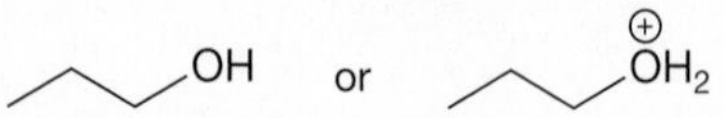

(e) 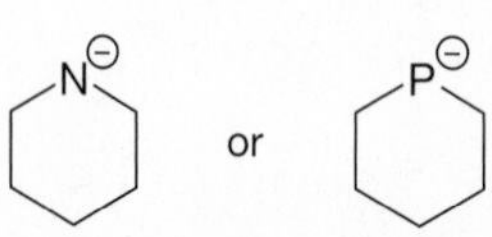

(f) 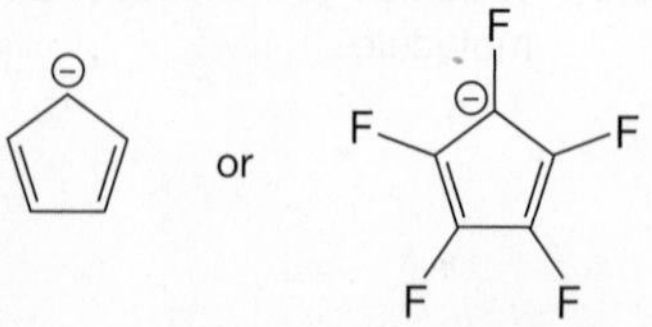

(g) 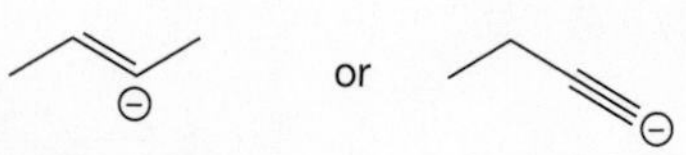

(h) 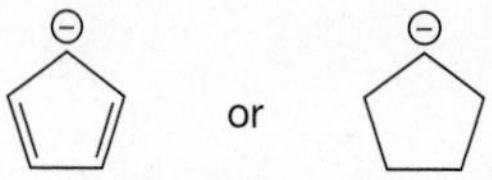

(i) 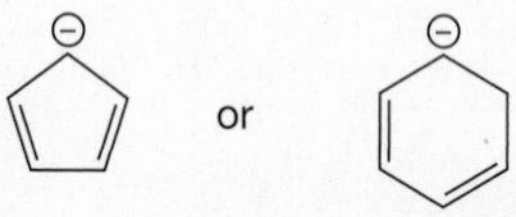

6.42 Acid-catalyzed hydrolysis converts an ester into a carboxylic acid and an alcohol. Although there are two O atoms that can be protonated, the first step in the mechanism is believed to be protonation of the oxygen in the C═O group. Based on charge stability, why is it favorable to protonate that oxygen? *Hint*: Draw out the products of each protonation.

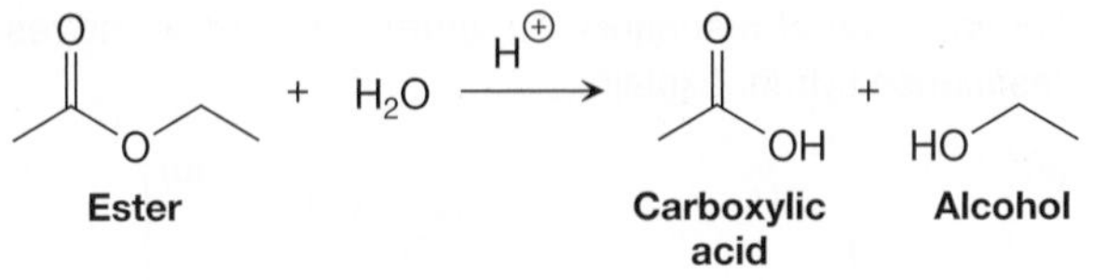

Ester
Carboxylic acid
Alcohol

Section 6.10 The Organic Chemistry of Biomolecules

6.43 Draw the structure of the most abundant form of cysteine in solutions whose pH values are 1, 4, 6, 9, and 11.

6.44 Draw the structure of the most abundant form of histidine in solutions whose pH values are 1, 3, 5, 7, and 11.

6.45 Gel electrophoresis is a laboratory technique that can be used to separate species on the basis of their charge. A sample is spotted onto the surface of a gel, and a high voltage is applied by a positively charged terminal (the anode) at one end of the gel and a negatively charged terminal (the cathode) at the other end. Therefore, negatively charged species will migrate toward the anode and positively charged species will migrate toward the cathode. Toward which terminal will glutamic acid migrate at each of these gel pH values: 1, 5, 7, and 11?

6.46 In a gel electrophoresis experiment (see Problem 6.45) where the pH of the gel is 9, will cysteine migrate toward the anode or the cathode? Explain.

6.47 In a gel electrophoresis experiment (see Problem 6.45) where the pH of the gel is 5, will histidine migrate toward the anode or the cathode? Explain.

6.48 In a gel electrophoresis experiment (see Problem 6.45) where the pH of the gel is 11, will tyrosine migrate toward the anode or the cathode? Explain.

Integrated Problems

6.49 For each of the following proton transfer reactions, **(a)** draw the products, **(b)** determine which side of the equilibrium is favored, and **(c)** determine the extent to which that side is favored. *Hint*: For acids not listed in Table 6-1 (p. 269) or in Appendix A, you will need to estimate pK_a values from charge stability and the functional group in which the acidic proton appears.

(1)

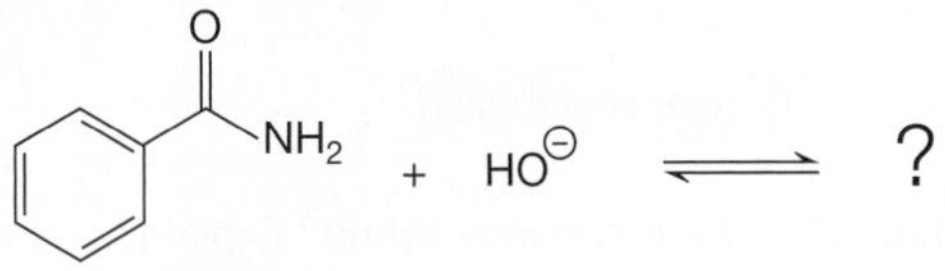

(2)

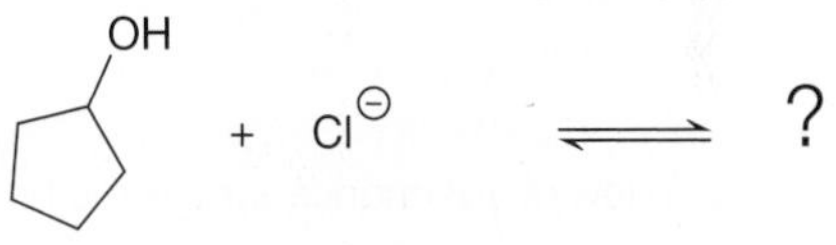

(3)

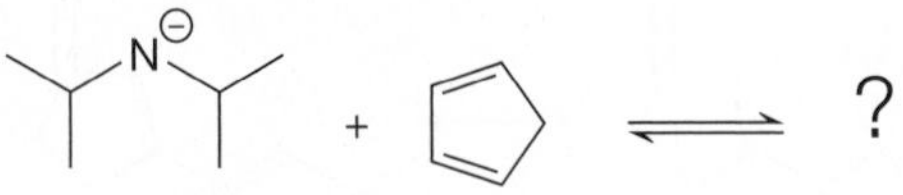

(4)

(5)

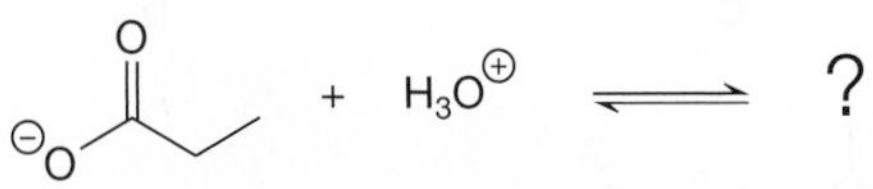

(6)

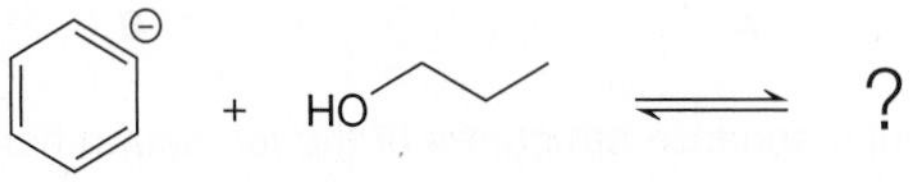

(7)

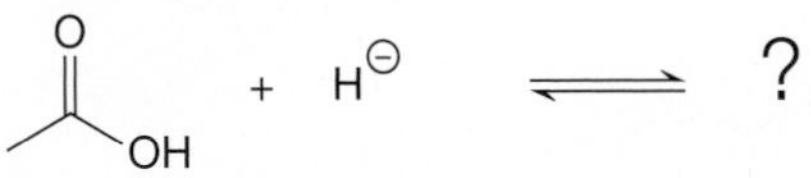

6.50 For each pair of resonance structures, determine the resonance structure that has a greater contribution to the resonance hybrid. Explain.

(a) 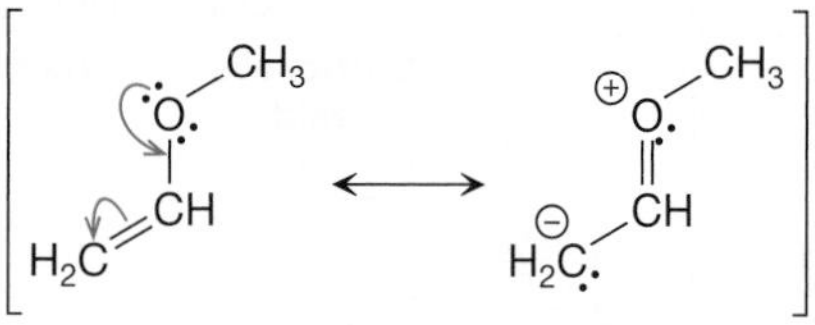

(b) 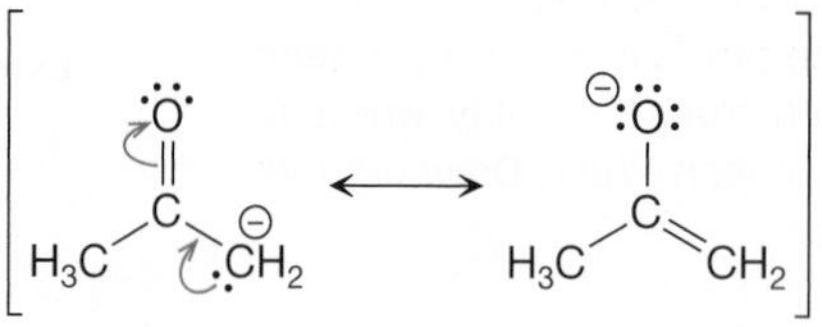

(c) 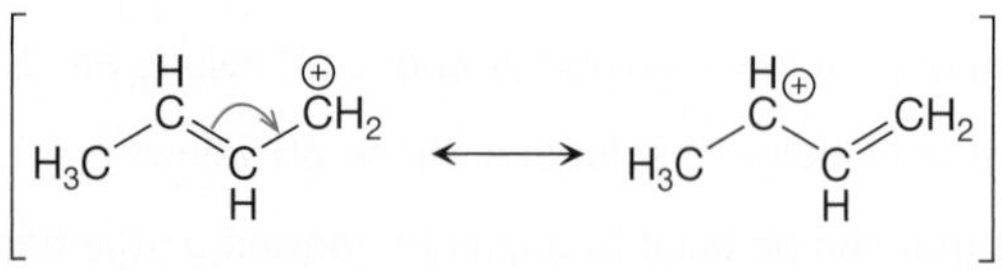

6.51 For each pair of resonance structures, determine which one has a greater contribution to the resonance hybrid. Explain.

(a) 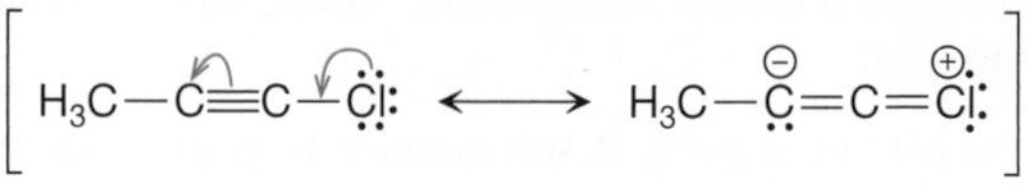

(b) 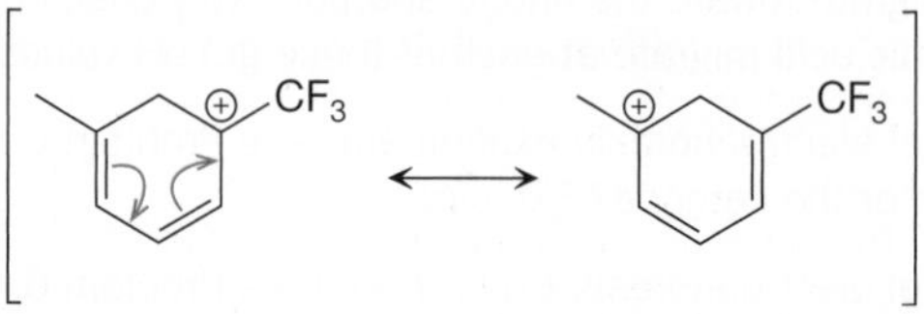

(c) 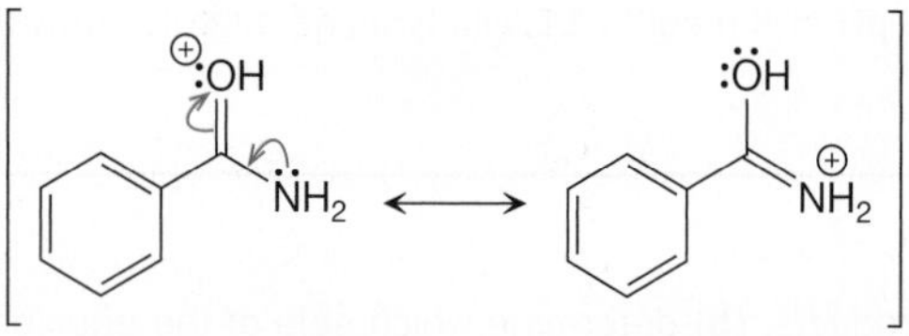

6.52 Of these two resonance structures, the greater contribution is from the second one. **(a)** Explain why this is counterintuitive based on charge stability. **(b)** Why does the structure on the right contribute more?

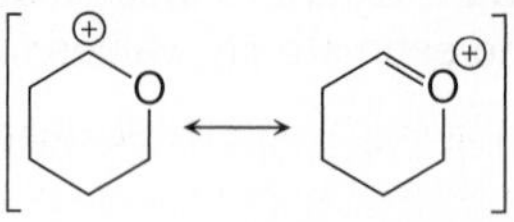

Greater contribution

6.53 Which of the following resonance structures has the greatest contribution to the resonance hybrid? Explain.

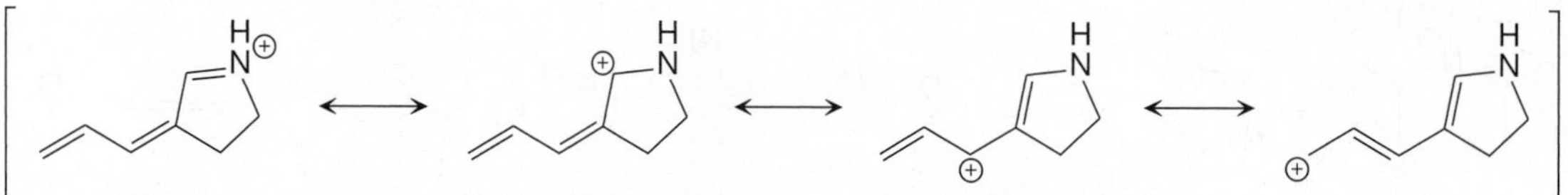

A B C D

6.54 Draw all resonance structures of the ion shown here and determine which is the strongest contributor to its resonance hybrid.

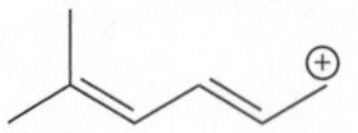

6.55 Draw all resonance structures of the ion shown here and rank them in order from strongest to weakest contributor.

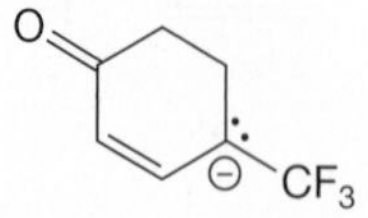

6.56 Each molecule **A–C** has a resonance structure that exhibits separated positive and negative charges. Which molecule will resemble that resonance structure the most? Which will resemble it the least? Explain.

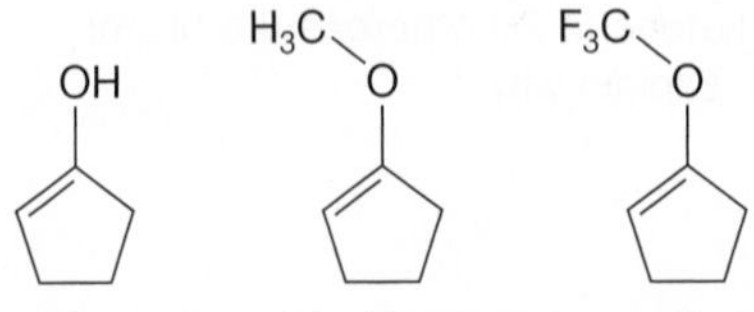

OH
H_3C
O
F_3C
O

A **B** **C**

6.57 The pK_a of acetone is substantially lower than that of toluene. **(a)** Explain why this result might be counterintuitive. **(b)** Why is acetone the stronger acid?

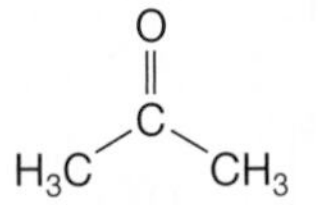

O
C
H_3C
CH_3

Acetone

pK_a = 20

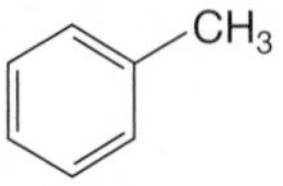

CH_3

Toluene

pK_a = 40

6.58 An important step in one synthesis of carboxylic acids is the deprotonation of diethyl malonate and its alkyl-substituted derivative:

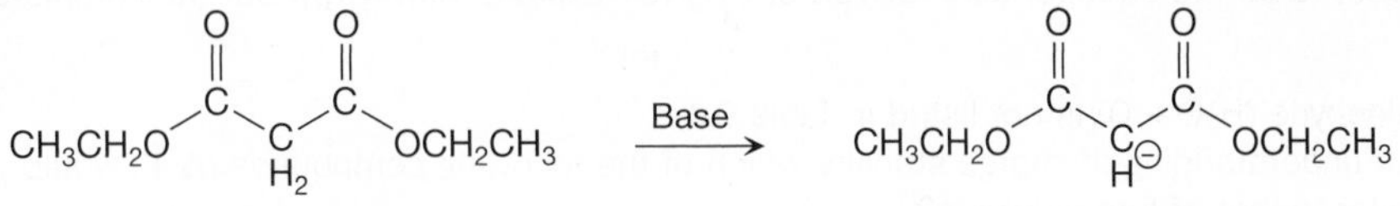

CH_3CH_2O
H_2
OCH_2CH_3
Base
CH_3CH_2O
H
OCH_2CH_3

Diethyl malonate

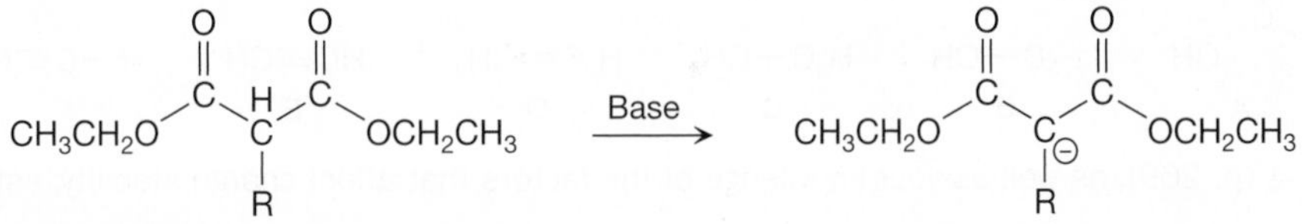

CH_3CH_2O
H
R
OCH_2CH_3
Base
CH_3CH_2O
R
OCH_2CH_3

Alkyl-substituted diethyl malonate

NaOH can deprotonate diethyl malonate effectively, but $NaOC(CH_3)_3$ is typically used to deprotonate the alkyl-substituted derivative. Explain why.

6.59 The pK_a of phenol (C_6H_5OH) is 10.0. When a nitro group (NO_2) is attached to the ring, the pK_a decreases, as shown here for the ortho, meta, and para isomers.
(a) Explain why the pK_a values of all three isomers are lower than the pK_a of phenol itself.
(b) Explain why the meta isomer has the highest pK_a of the three isomers.

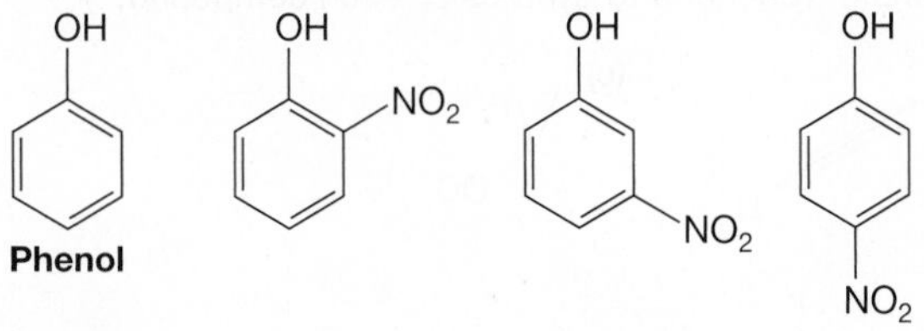

OH
OH
NO_2
OH
NO_2
OH
NO_2

Phenol

pK_a = 10.0   7.23   8.35   7.14

6.60 The pK_a of phenol (C_6H_5OH) is 10.0. When a methyl group (CH_3) is attached to the ring, the pK_a increases, as shown here for the ortho, meta, and para isomers.
(a) Explain why the pK_a values of all three isomers are higher than the pK_a of phenol itself.
(b) Explain why the meta isomer has the lowest pK_a of the three isomers.

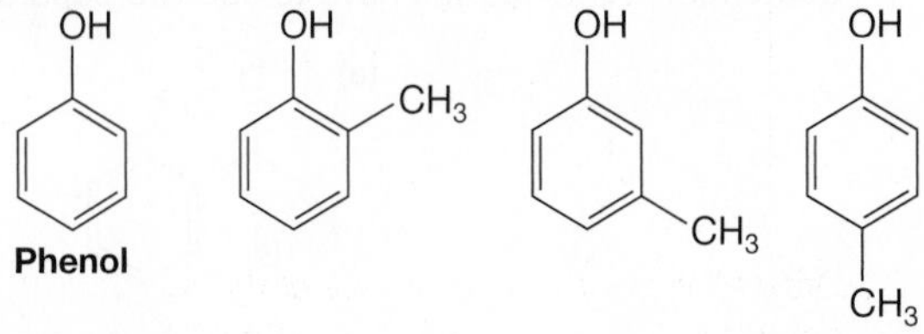

OH
OH
CH_3
OH
CH_3
OH
CH_3

Phenol

pK_a = 10.0   10.3   10.1   10.2

6.61 *cis*-Cyclohexane-1,2-diol is more acidic than *trans*-cyclohexane-1,2-diol. On the basis of charge stability, explain why this is the case.

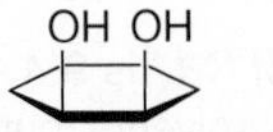

OH OH

***cis*-Cyclohexane-1,2-diol**

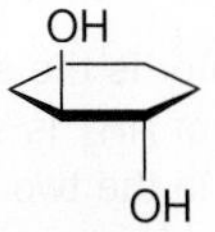

OH
OH

***trans*-Cyclohexane-1,2-diol**

6.62 The pK_a of a typical ketone is 20, whereas the pK_a of a typical ester is 25. Explain why.

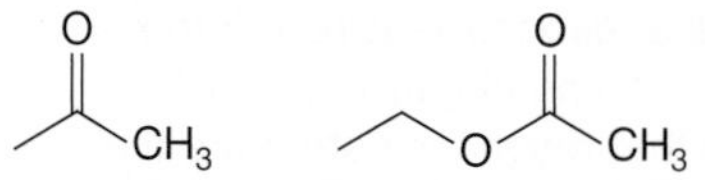

$pK_a = 20$ $pK_a = 25$

6.63 Which do you predict will be a stronger acid: *m*-hydroxybenzaldehyde or *p*-hydroxybenzaldehyde? Explain.

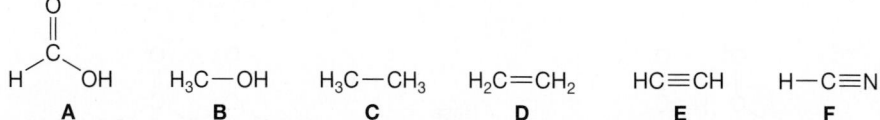

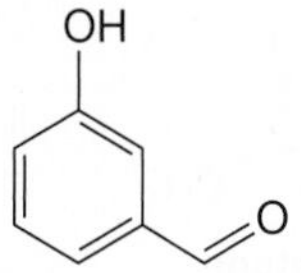

***m*-Hydroxybenzaldehyde**

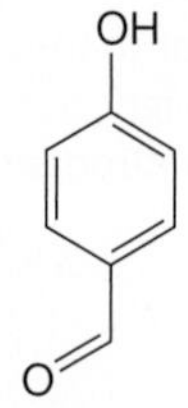

***p*-Hydroxybenzaldehyde**

6.64 Which do you expect to be the stronger acid: CH_3CN or CH_3NC? Explain. *Hint*: Draw out the complete Lewis structure for each molecule.

6.65 The pK_a of formaldehyde ($H_2C{=}O$) is not listed in Table 6-1.

(a) Based on your understanding of charge stability, which of the following compounds (**A–F**) would you expect to have a pK_a most similar to that of formaldehyde?

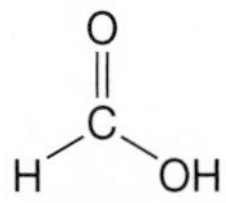	$H_3C{-}OH$	$H_3C{-}CH_3$	$H_2C{=}CH_2$	$HC{\equiv}CH$	$H{-}C{\equiv}N$
A	**B**	**C**	**D**	**E**	**F**

(b) Using Table 6-1 (p. 269), as well as your knowledge of the factors that affect charge stability, estimate the pK_a of formaldehyde.

6.66 Two possible proton transfer reactions can take place between the reactants shown here.

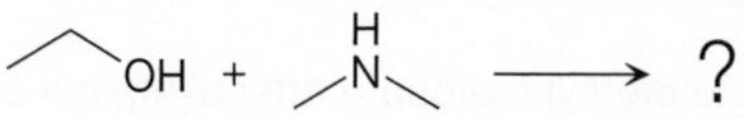

(a) Write the products of each possible proton transfer reaction.

(b) Determine which reaction is more energetically favorable.

6.67 Deuterium (D) is an isotope of H. Both D and H have one proton and one electron; H has no neutrons and D has one neutron. Consequently, D and H have nearly identical behavior, but they can be distinguished from each other experimentally due to their different masses. Therefore, replacing a H with a D in a molecule, known as *deuterium isotope labeling*, can provide valuable information about a mechanism. With this in mind, how would you synthesize each of the following deuterium-labeled compounds from the analogous unlabeled compound, using D_2O as your only source of deuterium? *Hint*: You will have to use two separate proton transfer reactions to synthesize each compound.

(a)

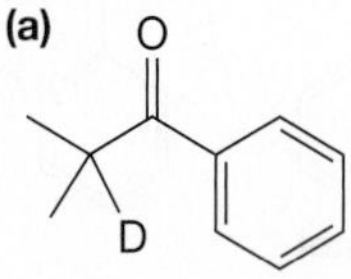

(b)

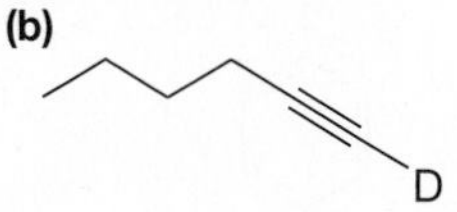

(c)

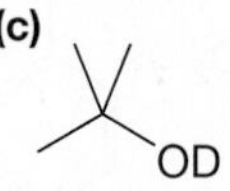

6.68 When water is the solvent, the pK_a of acetic acid (CH_3CO_2H) is 4.75, but when dimethyl sulfoxide (DMSO) is the solvent, the pK_a is 12.6. Explain why. *Hint*: Review Section 2.9 and consider the ability of each solvent to solvate cations and anions.

6.69 When water is the solvent, the pK_a of NH_4^+ is 9.4, but when DMSO is the solvent, the pK_a is 10.5. Explain why the acid strength of NH_4^+ is similar in the two solvents, but, as shown in Problem 6.68, the acid strength of acetic acid is very different in the two solvents. *Hint*: Review Section 2.9 and consider the ability of each solvent to solvate cations and anions.

6.70 In which solvent **A–E** will CH_3NH_2 be the *weakest* base? Explain.

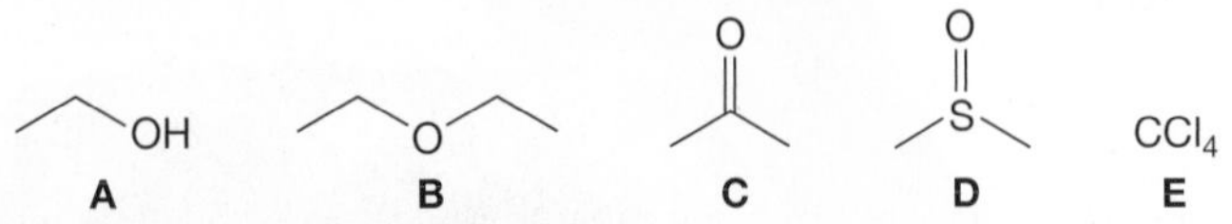
OH
A
O
B
O
C
O
S
D
CCl4
E

6.71 The pK_a value for a protonated amine (R_3NH^+) depends on the number of alkyl groups attached to N, as shown here. This order disagrees with what we would predict by using charge stability.

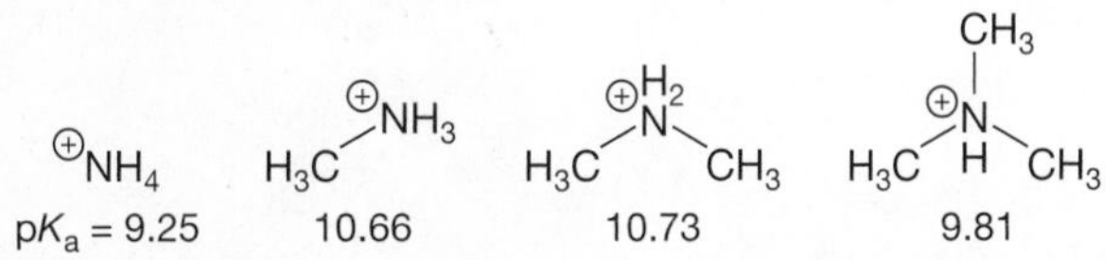
⊕NH4
pKa = 9.25
⊕NH3
H3C
10.66
⊕H2
N
H3C
CH3
10.73
CH3
⊕N
H3C
H
CH3
9.81

(a) From least acidic to most acidic, what is the order that would be predicted by using charge stability?
(b) Can you explain the reason for the discrepancy? *Hint*: These pK_a values are all measured in water.

7

Pollen sticks to this bee due to electrostatic attraction. When it flies, a bee loses electrons and builds up a positive electrical charge. The flower's pollen, on the other hand, is negatively charged, so when the bee lands, the pollen experiences a driving force from the flower to the bee. Similarly, the elementary steps we examine here in Chapter 7 are driven by the flow of electrons from a site with excess negative charge toward a site with excess positive charge.

An Overview of the Most Common Elementary Steps

In Chapter 6, we learned that a proton transfer is an *elementary step*: it occurs as a single event. The proton transfer steps we saw throughout Chapter 6 were considered in isolation from other steps. Frequently, however, a proton transfer makes up one step of a *multistep mechanism*, something we will discuss more extensively in Chapter 8.

There are a handful of other quite common elementary steps, too, which can be combined in various ways to produce mechanisms for numerous reactions. Chapter 7 provides an overview of nine of these elementary steps:

> The nine new elementary steps we learn here in Chapter 7, along with the proton transfer step (10 in all), make up nearly all of the reaction mechanisms you will encounter through Chapter 25.

Knowing that the same 10 elementary steps make up the mechanisms for a large number of reactions, you can be confident that *mechanisms simplify organic chemistry*. Therefore, the time and effort you spend mastering these elementary steps will be very worthwhile as you continue to learn reactions throughout the rest of this book.

Each of the nine elementary steps introduced here in Chapter 7 (in Sections 7.2–7.7) can be depicted using curved arrow notation, much as proton transfer steps were

Chapter Outline

depicted in Chapter 6. However, it is not enough to merely describe how each step takes place; it is important to know *why* the step would (or would not) take place. Therefore, two sections of this chapter are devoted to developing this understanding: Section 7.1 shows how the curved arrow notation for each step represents a natural direction of electron flow, and Section 7.8 deals with the *driving force* for elementary steps.

Keep in mind that this chapter serves to provide an *overview* of the common elementary steps; later chapters describe in more detail the central roles these elementary steps play in more complex mechanisms. For now, your goal is to learn just three aspects of each elementary step: (1) the types of species that are required as reactants and products, (2) the curved arrows that describe the electron movement (bonds forming and breaking), and (3) the driving force.

To help you see the similarities and differences among the various elementary steps:

> General forms of all 10 elementary steps are described in the chapter summary on pages 350–351.

Think of the Chapter 7 summary as a reference to be revisited frequently, not only as you first make your way through this chapter but also when you encounter these elementary steps in reaction mechanisms in later chapters.

7.1 Mechanisms as Predictive Tools: The Proton Transfer Step Revisited

SECTION 7.1 OBJECTIVES

You will be able to:

1. Identify electron-rich and electron-poor sites within a species.
2. Articulate how the curved arrow notation for a proton transfer step represents the flow of electrons from an electron-rich site to an electron-poor site.
3. Identify organometallic reagents and hydride reagents as sources of carbanions and hydride, respectively.

A reaction mechanism can be very helpful as a *predictive* tool. In this section, we revisit curved arrow notation for a proton transfer step to see how it can be used to make predictions about bond formation and bond breaking. Pay close attention to the main lessons in this section because we will be applying them to other elementary steps described in later sections of this chapter.

7.1a Curved Arrow Notation: Electron-Rich to Electron-Poor

Curved arrow notation was introduced in Section 6.1 as a means for keeping track of valence electrons in an elementary step. It can be far more powerful than that, though, if we recall two concepts:

- Opposite charges attract; like charges repel.
- Atoms in the first and second rows of the periodic table must obey the duet and octet rules, respectively.

With these ideas in mind, examine Equation 7-1, which shows the curved arrows for the proton transfer between HCl and HO^-:

Elementary Step
Proton Transfer

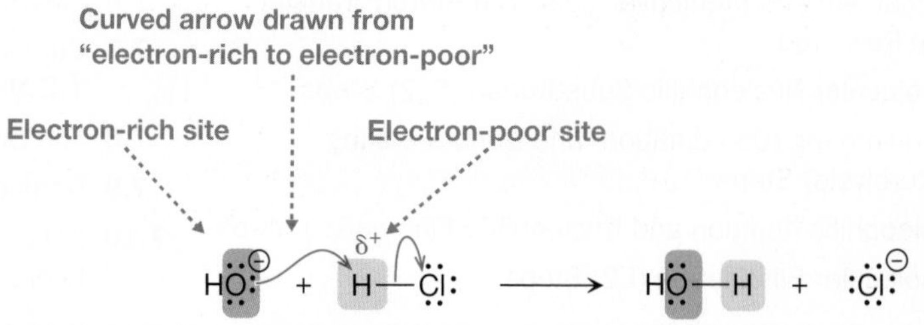

Curved arrow drawn from "electron-rich to electron-poor"
Electron-rich site
Electron-poor site

(7-1)

Notice that HO^- bears a full negative charge. This excess electron density on O means the electrons on O are somewhat destabilized due to their mutual repulsion. The proton on HCl bears a partial positive charge, δ^+, because Cl is more electronegative than H. As a result, the electrons on O are attracted to the proton on HCl. This simultaneous charge repulsion among the electrons on O and their attraction to H facilitates the flow of electrons from O to H and results in the formation of the new O—H bond.

Equation 7-1 illustrates one of the most important guidelines for drawing curved arrows:

> In an elementary step, electrons tend to flow from an *electron-rich* site to an *electron-poor* site.
>
> - An electron-rich atom typically has a full or partial *negative* charge.
> - An electron-poor atom typically has a full or partial *positive* charge or lacks an octet.

In Equation 7-1, the HO^- anion is relatively electron-rich, denoted by the light red screen, and the H atom on HCl is relatively electron-poor, denoted by the light blue screen. (This is the same color scheme used in electrostatic potential maps to represent areas of more and less electron density, respectively.) To help you keep track of those atoms, we have kept the red and blue screens the same in the products.

Having identified the key electron-rich and electron-poor sites in HO^- and HCl, we can now see that the curved arrow on the left in Equation 7-1 represents the flow of electrons from an electron-rich site to an electron-poor site, as well as the formation of a new bond to H. The curved arrow on the right represents the breaking of the initial H—Cl bond, which is necessary to avoid having two bonds to H.

YOUR TURN 7.1

Consider the proton transfer step shown here. **(a)** Identify the electron-rich and electron-poor sites, and label the curved arrow that connects the two as "electron-rich to electron-poor." **(b)** Explain why the curved arrow notation would be faulty if the curved arrow on the right were not drawn.

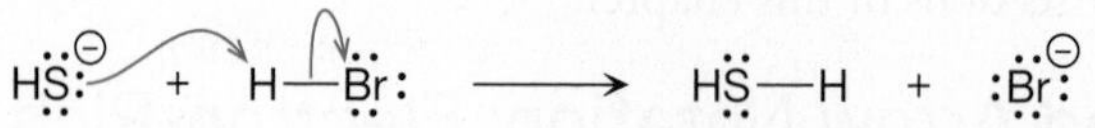

Answers to Your Turns are in the back of the book.

SOLVED PROBLEM **7.1**

How to determine the proper electron flow and outcome for a proton transfer

Break It Down **Identify the electron-poor H atom in methanol. Draw the mechanism by which methanol acts as an acid in a proton transfer reaction with H_2N^-.**

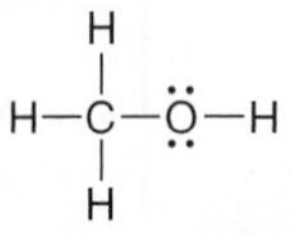

Methanol

Every Solved Problem in this book uses a Think/Solve strategy to guide you through the solution. After you consider a question posed on the Think side of the table, read the answer on the Solve side.

Think	Solve
What kinds of charges characterize electron-poor atoms? Which H in methanol bears that kind of charge?	An electron-poor atom tends to have a partial or full positive charge. Because the O atom in methanol is highly electronegative, the attached H bears a substantial partial positive charge and is therefore electron-poor.
Should H_2N^- be considered electron-rich or electron-poor?	The negative charge on H_2N^- indicates it is electron-rich.
When H_2N^- and CH_3OH are combined, how do we draw a curved arrow to depict the flow of electrons from an electron-rich site to an electron-poor site?	A curved arrow is drawn from the electrons on N to H, indicating the flow of electrons from an electron-rich site (denoted by the red screen) to an electron-poor site (blue screen). That arrow also indicates the formation of a new N—H bond. 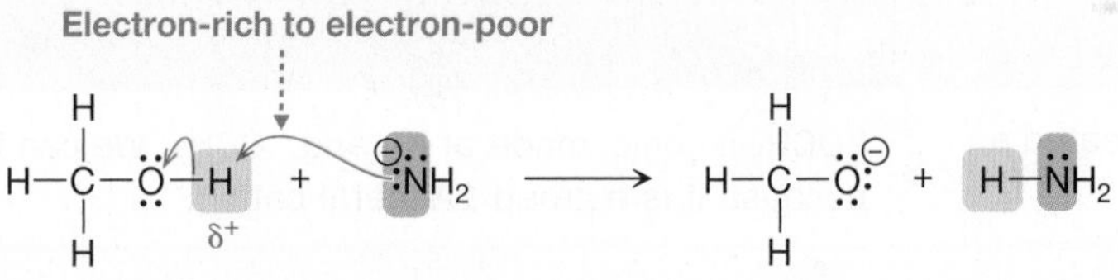 Electron-rich to electron-poor
When that curved arrow is drawn to depict bond formation, do any other bonds have to break?	The H in methanol gains a new bond, but there cannot be two bonds to H, so the initial O—H bond must break. A curved arrow from the O—H bond to the O represents the breaking of that bond. The O on the product side picks up that pair of electrons and ends up with a −1 formal charge.

Try It Identify the electron-rich and electron-poor sites in the reactant molecules shown here. Draw the curved arrows and the products for the proton transfer between these two molecules, and label the curved arrow that represents the flow of electrons from an electron-rich site to an electron-poor site. *Hint*: Are all the relevant electron pairs shown?

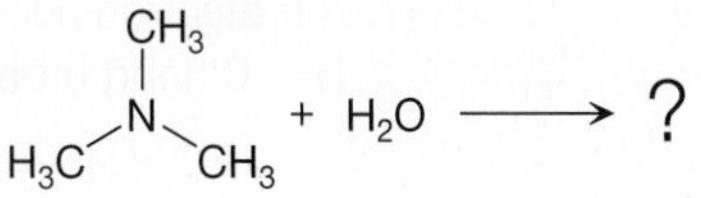

Answers to all Try It exercises can be found in the Solutions Manual.

CONNECTIONS 7.1

Your nose knows trimethylamine Trimethylamine [$(CH_3)_3N$, Solved Problem 7.1, Try It] is a gas that is often associated with the odor of rotting fish. Sensors have been developed to test for trimethylamine to assess the freshness of fish.

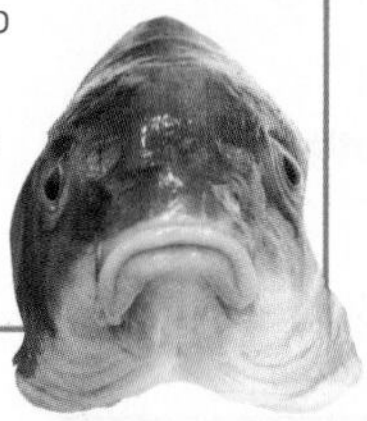

7.1b Simplifying Assumptions Regarding Electron-Rich and Electron-Poor Species

Contrary to what is suggested in Equation 7-1, we cannot simply add hydroxide anion (HO^-) to HCl to carry out a proton transfer reaction, because of the following restriction:

> Anions do not exist in the solid or liquid phase without the presence of cations, and vice versa, because the charges must balance.

We can, however, add a *source* of HO^-, such as NaOH; NaOH is an ionic compound, so in solution it dissolves as Na^+ and HO^-.

Dealing with NaOH rather than just HO^- may at first seem to complicate the picture, because Na^+ is electron-poor. Wouldn't Na^+ react with an electron-rich site of another species? As it turns out, Na^+ behaves as a **spectator ion**, meaning that it does not take part in a chemical reaction in solution:

> In general, group 1A metal cations (i.e., Li^+, Na^+, and K^+) tend to behave as spectator ions in solution, due to their stable noble gas electron configurations.

Consequently, we can disregard these metal cations when we envision the flow of electrons from an electron-rich site to an electron-poor site.

SOLVED PROBLEM **7.2**

How to simplify an ionic compound with a group 1A metal in a proton transfer

Break It Down **Draw the necessary curved arrows for the proton transfer between $KOCH_3$ and HCN in solution.**

Think	Solve
In $KOCH_3$, what can be treated as a spectator ion?	$KOCH_3$ is ionic, made of K^+ and $^-OCH_3$. We can treat K^+ as a spectator ion because it is a group 1A metal cation.
What reactive species remains in solution? Should it be considered electron-rich or electron-poor?	By disregarding K^+, we consider just $^-OCH_3$ as the reactive species that remains in solution. It bears a full negative charge, so we should consider it as an electron-rich species.
Which H should be considered electron-poor? How should the curved arrows be added?	HCN has an electron-poor H atom due to the high effective electronegativity of the *sp*-hybridized C atom and due to the high electronegativity of N. Therefore, we draw a curved arrow from the electrons of the electron-rich O of $^-OCH_3$ to the electron-poor H of HCN. We draw a second curved arrow to show that the H—C bond breaks because there cannot be two bonds to H. 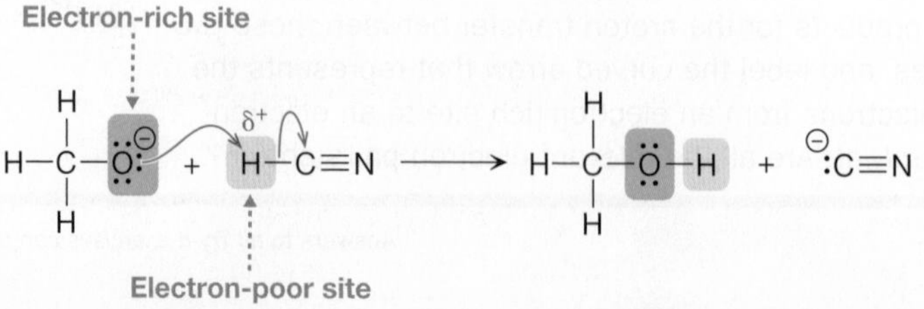 Electron-rich site Electron-poor site

Try It Draw the necessary curved arrows for the proton transfer between NaSH and CH_3CO_2H.

Analogously, we can make simplifying assumptions for reactions involving **organometallic** compounds, which contain a metal atom bonded directly to a carbon atom. Examples of organometallic compounds include alkyllithium (R—Li); alkylmagnesium halide (R—MgX, where X = Cl, Br, or I), also called a **Grignard reagent**; and lithium dialkyl cuprate $[Li^+(R—Cu—R)^-]$. These kinds of organometallic compounds are useful reagents for forming new carbon–carbon bonds (discussed in Chapter 11).

Consider that the C—Metal bond in an organometallic compound is a *polar* covalent bond. The carbon atom's electronegativity (2.55) is significantly greater than that of the metal (Li = 0.98, Mg = 1.31, and Cu = 1.90), so there is a large partial negative charge on carbon (making it electron-rich) and a large partial positive charge on the metal atom (making it electron-poor), as shown in **Figure 7-1**.

In most reactions involving organometallic compounds, the product that we are interested in isolating contains the organic portion of the organometallic compound and not the metal-containing portion. Therefore, even though the C—Metal bond of an organometallic compound is covalent, we can *think of* the bond as ionic [that is, as $C:^-$ and $^+$(Metal)] and in effect ignore the metal-containing portion. So, in much the same way as we did with the group 1A metal cations:

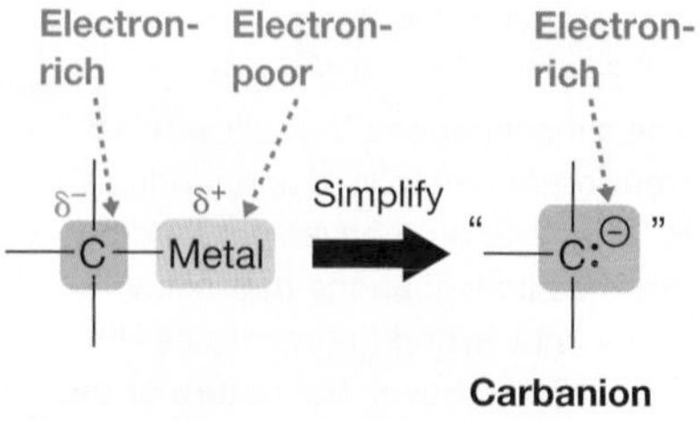

Electron-rich
Electron-poor
Electron-rich
δ−
δ+
C
Metal
Simplify
"C:⊖"
Carbanion

FIGURE 7-1 Simplifying assumptions in organometallic compounds (*Left*) Because of the high polarity in a C—Metal bond, organometallic compounds contain an electron-rich site on C and an electron-poor site on the metal. (*Right*) We can usually ignore the reactivity of the metal-containing portion and treat the organometallic compound simply as a carbanion, which is electron-rich. The quotation marks remind us that the carbanion does not actually exist in solution.

When we consider organometallic compounds in the flow of electrons from an electron-rich site to an electron-poor site, we can often treat the metal-containing portion as a spectator.

This simplifying assumption allows us to treat organometallic compounds as electron-rich **carbanions**, compounds in which a negative formal charge and a lone pair of electrons appear on C (Fig. 7-1). Thus, as shown in **Figure 7-2**, we can treat CH_3CH_2Li as a source of $CH_3CH_2^-$, C_6H_5MgBr as a source of $C_6H_5^-$, and $(CH_3)_2CuLi$ as a source of CH_3^- (see Looking Ahead box, p. 324).

The strategy for simplifying organometallic compounds also works for simplifying **hydride reagents**, such as lithium aluminum hydride ($LiAlH_4$) and sodium borohydride ($NaBH_4$), which are commonly used as *reducing agents* (discussed in Chapter 18). $LiAlH_4$ consists of Li^+ ions and AlH_4^- ions, as shown on the left in **Figure 7-3a**. We can treat Li^+ as a spectator ion because it is a group 1A metal cation, which leaves AlH_4^- as the reactive species (Fig. 7-3a, middle). The Lewis structure of AlH_4^- shows the H atoms bonded to an Al metal atom. Those Al—H bonds are covalent, but because the electronegativity of H (2.20) is higher than that of Al (1.61), each

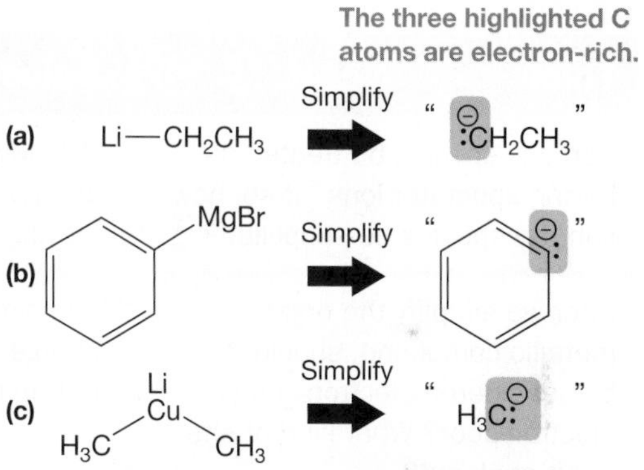

The three highlighted C atoms are electron-rich.
(a)
Li—CH2CH3
Simplify
"⊖:CH2CH3"
(b)
MgBr
Simplify
(c)
Li
Cu
H3C
CH3
Simplify
"H3C:⊖"

FIGURE 7-2 Simplifying some specific organometallic compounds (a) $LiCH_2CH_3$ is simplified to $^-CH_2CH_3$. (b) C_6H_5MgBr is simplified to $C_6H_5^-$. (c) $(CH_3)_2CuLi$ is simplified to H_3C^-.

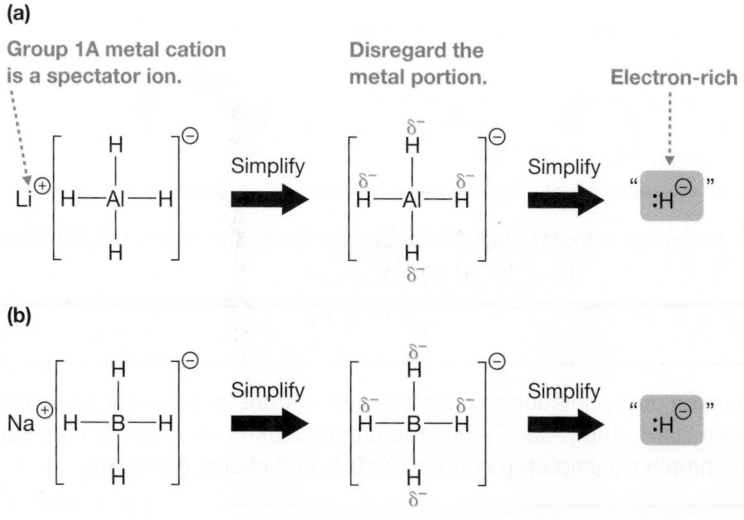

(a)
Group 1A metal cation is a spectator ion.
Disregard the metal portion.
Electron-rich
Li⊕
H—Al—H
Simplify
δ−
Simplify
":H⊖"
(b)
Na⊕
H—B—H
Simplify
Simplify
":H⊖"

FIGURE 7-3 Simplifying assumptions in hydride reagents (a) Lithium aluminum hydride, $LiAlH_4$, consists of Li^+ and AlH_4^- ions. The reactive species is AlH_4^- (middle), which can be treated simply as $H:^-$. The quotation marks indicate that $H:^-$ does not actually exist in solution. (b) Sodium borohydride, $NaBH_4$, consists of Na^+ and BH_4^- ions. The reactive species is BH_4^- (middle), which can be treated as $H:^-$, too.

▸ LOOKING AHEAD

The simplifications that allow us to treat organometallic compounds as R⁻ (Fig. 7-2) are convenient, and so are the simplifications that allow us to treat hydride reagents as H⁻ (Fig. 7-3). However, the nature of the covalent bond that we simplify can be important. As you will learn in Chapter 18, for example, RLi, RMgBr, and R_2CuLi behave substantially differently, as do $LiAlH_4$ and $NaBH_4$.

Al—H bond is polar and each H bears a δ^- charge. As we did for organometallic compounds, if we *think of* these Metal—H bonds as ionic [that is, as H:⁻ and ⁺(Metal)] then we can disregard the metal portion as indicated on the right of Figure 7-3a. In other words:

We can *treat* $LiAlH_4$ simply as a source of **hydride anion (H:⁻)**.

Figure 7-3b shows how to apply similar arguments to $NaBH_4$. Therefore:

We can also *treat* $NaBH_4$ simply as a source of hydride anion (H:⁻).

SOLVED PROBLEM **7.3**

How to simplify an organometallic compound when drawing curved arrows

Break It Down **What are the products of the proton transfer step between C_6H_5MgBr and H_2O?**

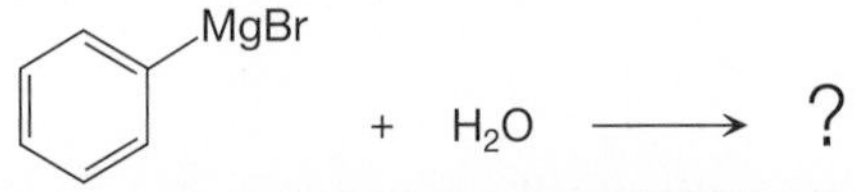

MgBr
+ H₂O
?

Think	Solve
Can any species be treated as having spectator ions? If so, how can the species be simplified? ➤	C_6H_5MgBr is organometallic because it has a C—Mg bond. We simplify the compound by treating the metal-containing portion $(MgBr)^+$ as a spectator ion, leaving just $C_6H_5^-$ to consider as the reactive species.
After we simplify the organometallic compound, should it be considered electron-rich or electron-poor? What kind of site will it seek out? ➤	The simplified version of the organometallic compound, $C_6H_5^-$, has a negative charge and a lone pair on a C atom, so we treat it as electron-rich. It will seek out an electron-poor site, such as the partially positive H atom on H_2O.
What curved arrow can be drawn to signify electron flow from electron-rich to electron-poor? What curved arrow is necessary to avoid having too many bonds to any one atom? ➤	A curved arrow drawn from the electrons on C:⁻ to the H of water represents the flow of electrons from electron-rich (red screen) to electron-poor (blue screen). It also signifies the formation of a new bond to H, so a second curved arrow is needed to indicate the breaking of the initial H—O bond. 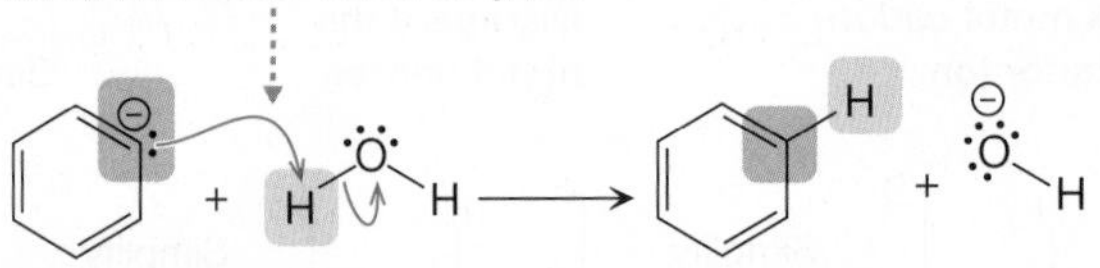 Electron-rich to electron-poor + H O H H + O H

Try It Use curved arrow notation to show the proton transfer step that occurs between CH_3Li and CH_3OH. Predict the products of this reaction.

YOUR TURN **7.2**

Use curved arrow notation to show the proton transfer step that takes place between $LiAlH_4$ and water. Predict the products of the reaction. Do the same for the proton transfer step between $NaBH_4$ and phenol (C_6H_5OH).

7.2 Bimolecular Nucleophilic Substitution (S_N2) Steps

In a **bimolecular nucleophilic substitution (S_N2)** step, a molecular species, called a **substrate**, undergoes *substitution* in which one atom or group of atoms is replaced by another. Examples are shown in Equation 7-2, where HO^- substitutes for Cl^-, and in Equation 7-3, where H_3N substitutes for $CH_3SO_3^-$ (see Looking Ahead box).

S_N2 step

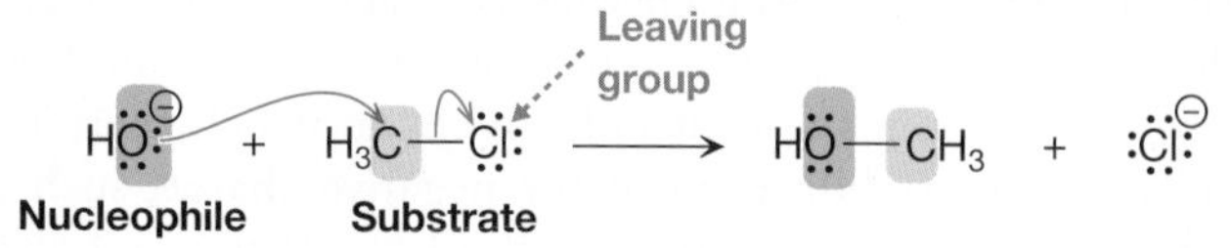

Leaving group
Nucleophile
Substrate

(7-2)

S_N2 step

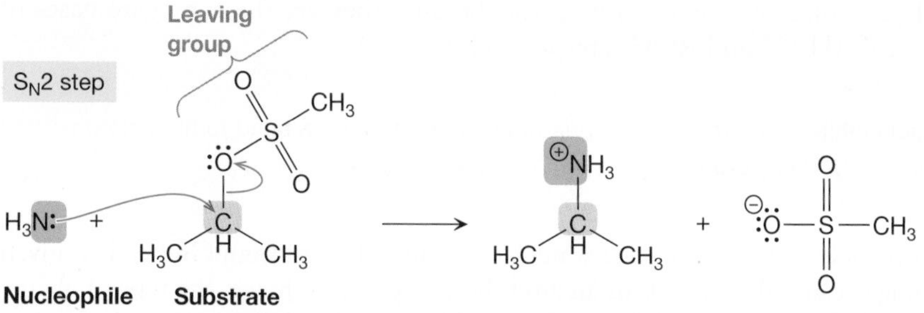

Leaving group
Nucleophile
Substrate

(7-3)

During the course of the S_N2 steps in Equations 7-2 and 7-3, a *nucleophile* (which we will define shortly) forms a bond to the substrate at the same time a bond to the **leaving group** (the group that is displaced) is broken. The step is said to be *bimolecular* because it contains two separate reacting species in an elementary step. In other words, the step's **molecularity** is 2. It is called *nucleophilic* simply because the reaction involves a nucleophile as a reactant.

Just as we saw with proton transfer steps, an S_N2 step is an *elementary step*, meaning that the reactants are converted into products in a *single event*. In other words, the reaction proceeds through a single transition state, as shown in the energy diagram in **Figure 7-4** for a generic nucleophile Nu^- and a generic substrate R—L. Notice, in particular, that both the Nu—R and R—L bonds are partial bonds in the transition state, as those are the bonds that undergo forming or breaking in the reaction. Also notice that the −1 charge disappears from Nu and appears on L as the reaction proceeds, so a partial negative charge appears on both Nu and L in the transition state (see top Looking Ahead box, p. 326).

SECTION 7.2 OBJECTIVES

You will be able to:

1. Identify an S_N2 step when given the reactants and products.
2. Draw the curved arrow notation, transition state, and products for an S_N2 step when given the reactants.
3. Identify nucleophiles and substrates (electrophiles) that can participate in S_N2 steps.

Elementary Step
Bimolecular Nucleophilic Substitution (S_N2)

LOOKING AHEAD

Reactions involving S_N2 steps are really important in organic chemistry, especially in *organic synthesis* (Chapter 10). The product of an S_N2 reaction might be the compound you want to synthesize. Alternatively, an S_N2 reaction might be used to alter the reactivity of a molecule in ways that make further reactions possible. Because of this central role in synthesis, we revisit S_N2 reactions in Chapters 8–11.

YOUR TURN **7.3**

For each of the S_N2 steps in Equations 7-2 and 7-3, draw the transition state by replacing Nu, R, and L in Figure 7-4 with the actual molecular fragments appearing in the reaction.

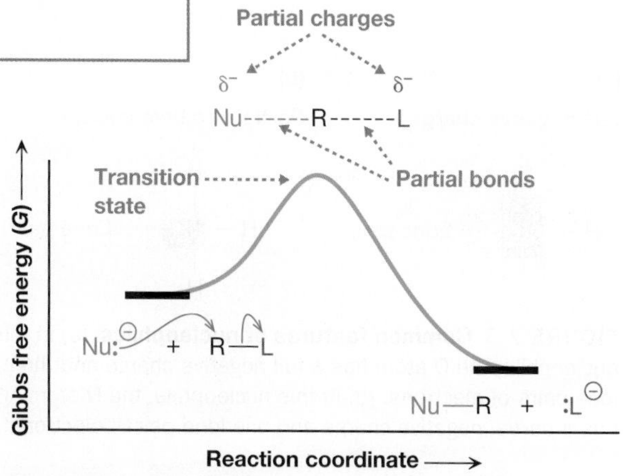

Partial charges
δ−
δ−
Nu------R------L
Partial bonds
Transition state
Gibbs free energy (G)
Nu:
+
R—L
Nu—R + :L
Reaction coordinate

FIGURE 7-4 Free energy diagram for an S_N2 step An S_N2 step proceeds through a single transition state because the process is an elementary step. The Nu—R bond forms at the same time the R—L bond breaks, so both bonds are partially formed in the transition state. During the course of the reaction, the −1 charge disappears from Nu and appears on L, so a partial negative charge appears on both Nu and L in the transition state.

▸ LOOKING AHEAD

We can use the strategy presented here to depict the general structure of a transition state, but the exact geometry will depend on how the reactants approach each other (*stereochemistry*) and whether ΔG for the reaction is positive or negative. We will cover these topics in Chapter 9.

Equations 7-2 and 7-3 show the leaving group coming off in the form of a negatively charged species. *Common leaving groups are able to accommodate that negative charge well* (see Recall box). Applying what we learned in Sections 6.8 and 6.9, we can say that:

> Leaving groups are typically *conjugate bases of strong acids.*

Common leaving groups therefore include Cl^-, Br^-, and I^- (conjugate bases of the strong acids HCl, HBr, and HI, respectively) because, in each case, the negatively charged atom is either relatively large or electronegative (see bottom Looking Ahead box). Common leaving groups also include anions in which there is substantial resonance and inductive stabilization of the negative charge, such as an alkylsulfonate anion, RSO_3^- (the conjugate base of RSO_3H). Water and alcohols (ROH) are common leaving groups, too, because they are the conjugate bases of strong acids (H_3O^+ and ROH_2^+, respectively).

◂ RECALL

A charged species is stabilized when the formal charge appears on different atoms of the resonance structures (Section 6.8d). Moreover, inductive effects stabilize an anion when electron-withdrawing groups appear near the atom bearing the negative charge (Section 6.8e). In both cases, the outcome is a decrease in the concentration of charge within the species.

> A **nucleophile** tends to donate a pair of electrons to form a bond to an electron-poor non-hydrogen atom.

The term *nucleophile* literally means "nucleus loving" (derived from Greek). It is given this name because the nucleus of an atom bears a positive charge, the type of charge we might find on an electron-poor atom to which a nucleophile is attracted.

How can we recognize common nucleophiles?

> Species that act as nucleophiles in S_N2 steps generally have an atom with the following two features:
>
> - A full negative charge or a partial negative charge.
> - A lone pair of electrons.

▸ LOOKING AHEAD

Chapter 9 will examine a broader range of leaving groups and deal with the idea of *leaving group ability*, which is the tendency of a leaving group to depart from a substrate.

The full or partial negative charge makes the nucleophile electron-rich, and the lone pair of electrons is used to form a new bond to an atom in the substrate, as shown in **Figure 7-5**. In the HO^- nucleophile in Equation 7-2, for example, the O atom has a full negative charge and three lone pairs of electrons (Fig. 7-5a). The H_3N nucleophile in Equation 7-3 has a N atom bearing a *partial* negative charge and one lone pair of electrons (Fig. 7-5b). These and other common nucleophiles, both negatively charged and uncharged, are shown in **Figure 7-6**.

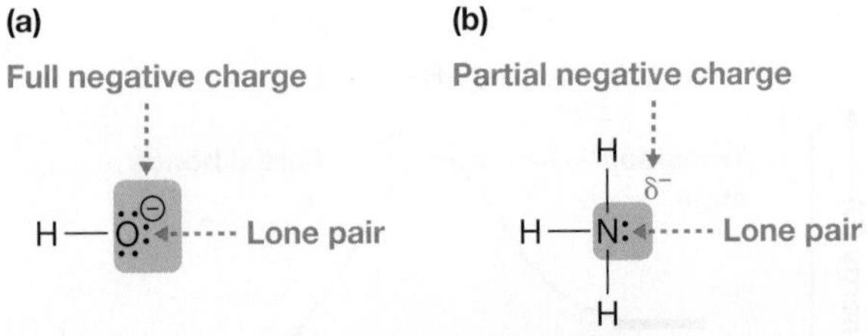
(a)
Full negative charge
Lone pair
(b)
Partial negative charge
Lone pair

FIGURE 7-5 Common features of nucleophiles (a) In this nucleophile, the O atom has a full negative charge and three lone pairs of electrons. (b) In this nucleophile, the N atom has a *partial* negative charge and one lone pair of electrons.

Common negatively charged nucleophiles			Common uncharged nucleophiles		
HO^-	CH_3O^-	HS^-	H_3N	CH_3NH_2	H_2O
CH_3S^-	H_2N^-	CH_3NH^-	CH_3OH	H_2S	CH_3SH
Cl^-	Br^-	I^-			
NC^-	HCC^-	N_3^-			

FIGURE 7-6 Common negatively charged and uncharged nucleophiles

SOLVED PROBLEM **7.4**

How to identify a species that can act as a nucleophile in an S_N2 step

Break It Down **Can CH_4 act as a nucleophile in an S_N2 step? Why or why not?**

Think	Solve
Does CH_4 have an atom that carries a partial or full negative charge?	Draw the Lewis structure for CH_4. We see that the C atom has a formal charge of 0 but has a small partial negative charge because C is slightly more electronegative than H. 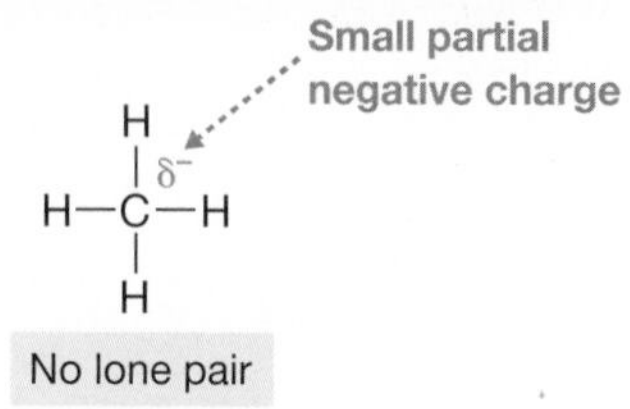 Small partial negative charge No lone pair
Does that atom have a lone pair of electrons that can be used to form a bond to another atom?	The C atom does *not* possess a lone pair of electrons that can be used to form a bond with another atom. Therefore, CH_4 would *not* act as a nucleophile in an S_N2 step.

Try It Which of the following species can behave as a nucleophile in an S_N2 step? Explain. **(a)** SiH_4; **(b)** NaSCN; **(c)** NH_4^+; **(d)** CH_3Li

YOUR TURN **7.4**

Draw the complete Lewis structures for three of the *negatively charged* nucleophiles (other than HO^-) and for three of the uncharged nucleophiles (other than H_3N) listed in Figure 7-6. Include all lone pairs. For each of the uncharged nucleophiles, write "δ^-" next to the atom bearing a partial negative charge.

Recall from Section 7.1a that the electrons in an elementary step tend to flow from an *electron-rich* site to an *electron-poor* site. In the proton transfer in Equation 7-1 (shown again in Eq. 7-4a), for example, where HO^- acts as a base, a curved arrow is drawn from a lone pair on the O in HO^- to the H in HCl. A second curved arrow is drawn to show the initial bond to H being broken, with its electrons becoming a lone pair on Cl^-.

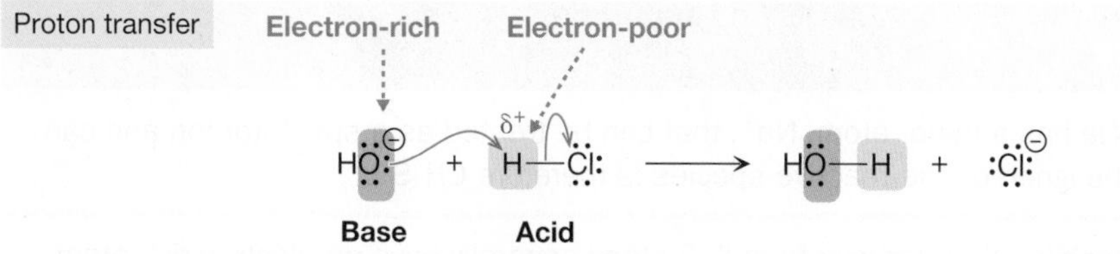
Proton transfer
Electron-rich
Electron-poor
Base
Acid

(7-4a)

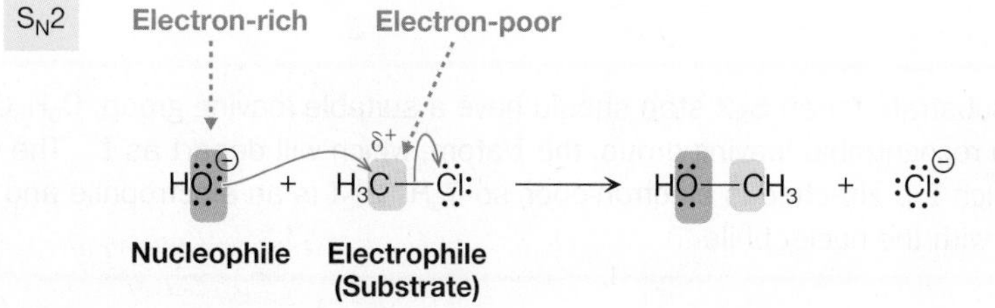
S_N2
Electron-rich
Electron-poor
Nucleophile
Electrophile (Substrate)

(7-4b)

Similarly, in the S_N2 step in Equation 7-4b, HO^- is still relatively electron-rich, but the C atom of CH_3Cl is relatively electron-poor because it carries a partial positive charge. Therefore, HO^- acts as a nucleophile, and a curved arrow is drawn from a pair of electrons on O to the C atom to signify bond formation. Because five bonds would exceed the C atom's octet, a second curved arrow shows that the pair of electrons initially making up the C—Cl bond becomes a lone pair on Cl.

In a proton transfer step (Eq. 7-4a), the electron-poor species acts as an acid because it is donating a proton. In an S_N2 step (Eq. 7-4b), on the other hand, the electron-poor substrate is not behaving as an acid (it is not donating a proton) but rather is behaving as an *electrophile*:

An **electrophile** is an electron-poor species to which a nucleophile forms a bond.

The term means "electron-loving," because an electron bears a negative charge, the kind of charge to which an electrophile tends to be attracted.

Now that we have defined *nucleophile* and *electrophile*, we can restate a general lesson from Section 7.1a regarding the flow of electrons from an electron-rich species to an electron-poor species:

A nucleophile (electron-rich) will tend to form a bond to an electrophile (electron-poor).

So far, we have seen how this applies to an S_N2 step. Throughout the rest of this chapter, we will see how it applies to other elementary steps, too.

YOUR TURN **7.5**

The following S_N2 step is similar to the one in Equation 7-4b:

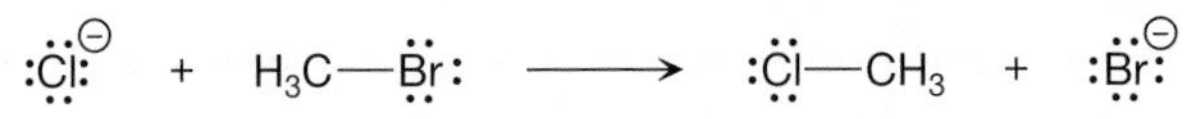

Cl
H3C—Br
Cl—CH3
Br

Draw in the curved arrows and label the appropriate reacting species as "electron-rich" or "electron-poor." Also label each reacting species as "nucleophile" or "electrophile."

SOLVED PROBLEM **7.5**

How to draw a reasonable S_N2 step when the reactants are given

Break It Down **Draw the S_N2 step that would occur between $C_6H_5CH_2I$ and CH_3SNa.**

Think	Solve
Can any portions of the reactants be treated as spectator ions?	CH_3SNa has a metal atom, Na^+, that can be treated as a spectator ion and can thus be ignored. The reactive species is therefore CH_3S^-.
What are the general characteristics of a nucleophile for an S_N2 step? Which reactant species has those characteristics?	Nucleophiles that participate in S_N2 steps generally have an electron-rich atom with a lone pair of electrons. The negatively charged S atom has those characteristics, so CH_3S^- will behave as the nucleophile.
What are the general characteristics of a substrate for an S_N2 step? Which species has those characteristics?	The substrate for an S_N2 step should have a suitable leaving group. $C_6H_5CH_2I$ has a recognizable leaving group, the I atom, which will depart as I^-. The C atom to which I is attached is electron-poor, so $C_6H_5CH_2I$ is an electrophile and can bond with the nucleophile.

(continued)

With the nucleophile and substrate (electrophile) identified, how should the curved arrows be drawn for the S_N2 step?	An S_N2 step requires two curved arrows. The first curved arrow begins from the lone pair of the electron-rich species (the nucleophile) and points to the electron-poor C atom of the substrate (the electrophile). To avoid five bonds to C, the initial bond to the leaving group must break, which is indicated by the curved arrow drawn from the center of the bond that attaches the leaving group and points toward the leaving group.

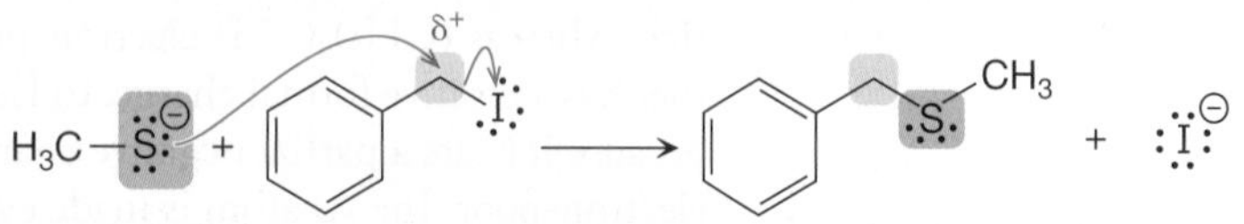

Try It Draw the S_N2 step that would occur between these two compounds.

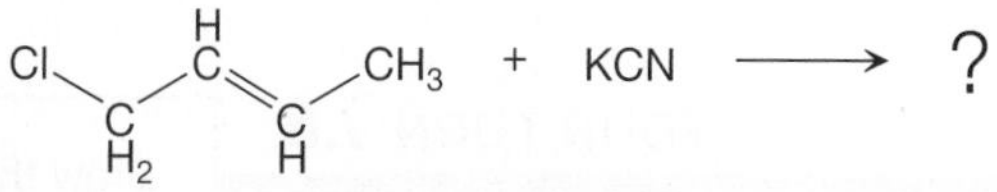

7.3 Bond-Forming (Coordination) and Bond-Breaking (Heterolysis) Steps

SECTION 7.3 OBJECTIVES

You will be able to:

1. Identify a coordination or heterolysis step when given the reactants and products.
2. Draw the curved arrow notation, transition state, and products for a coordination or heterolysis step when given the reactants.
3. Describe how the reactants of a coordination step behave as a nucleophile and an electrophile.

In the proton transfer and S_N2 steps we have examined so far, a bond is formed and a separate bond is broken simultaneously. It is possible, however, for bond formation and bond breaking to occur as independent steps. Equations 7-5 and 7-6 are examples of **coordination steps**, in which a single covalent bond is formed and no bonds are broken.

Elementary Step Coordination

Coordination step

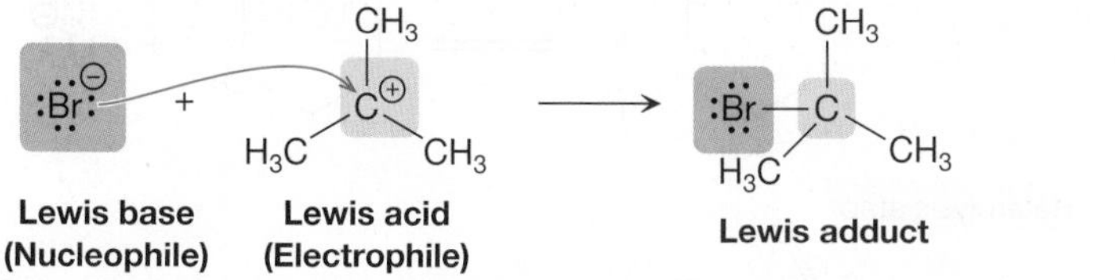
Lewis base
(Nucleophile)
Lewis acid
(Electrophile)
Lewis adduct

(7-5)

Coordination step

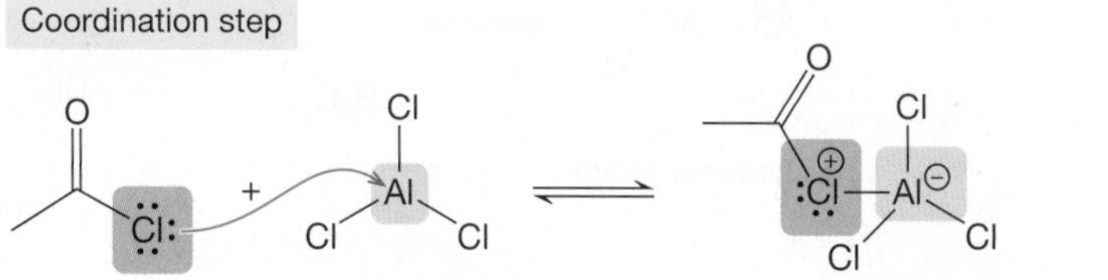

(7-6)

You may have learned in general chemistry that coordination steps are also called *Lewis acid–base reactions*. A **Lewis acid** is an electron-pair acceptor, having an atom that lacks an octet. A **Lewis base**, on the other hand, is an electron-pair donor. In Equation 7-5, $(CH_3)_3C^+$ is the Lewis acid and Br^- is the Lewis base. The product, $Br—C(CH_3)_3$, is called the **Lewis adduct**.

Notice in Equation 7-5 that the Lewis base is labeled as a nucleophile and the Lewis acid is labeled as an electrophile. That is because the Lewis base is electron-rich and forms a bond to the Lewis acid, which is electron-poor.

YOUR TURN 7.6

Label each species in Equation 7-6 as a Lewis acid, Lewis base, or Lewis adduct. Also label the nucleophile and the electrophile.

YOUR TURN 7.7

Draw the transition states for the reactions in Equations 7-5 and 7-6, taking into account just the partial bonds and partial charges.

Notice how the single curved arrow in each coordination step in Equations 7-5 and 7-6 depicts the flow of electrons from an electron-rich site to an electron-poor site (Section 7.1a). In Equation 7-5, Br^- is negatively charged and is therefore electron-rich, whereas $(CH_3)_3C^+$ is electron-poor; it has a C atom that lacks an octet and further has a positive formal charge. In Equation 7-6, the Cl of CH_3COCl is electron-rich because it bears a partial negative charge, whereas the Al of $AlCl_3$ lacks an octet and is electron-poor. The Al atom is made even more electron-poor by the attached electron-withdrawing Cl atoms on $AlCl_3$ (Section 6.6e).

YOUR TURN 7.8

Draw the appropriate curved arrows for the coordination step between $FeCl_3$ and Cl^-. Draw the reaction products. Identify which reactant species is electron-rich and which is electron-poor. Identify which reactant is the nucleophile and which is the electrophile.

An elementary step can also occur in which only a single bond is broken, which releases a leaving group, as shown in Equations 7-7 and 7-8. In such a **heterolytic bond dissociation** step, or **heterolysis** step (*hetero* = different; *lysis* = break), both electrons from the broken bond end up on the atom in the leaving group that was initially involved in the bond. The other atom of the original bond is left without an octet. You can think of *heterolysis steps as the reverse of coordination steps* (see Looking Ahead box).

▸ LOOKING AHEAD

Coordination and heterolysis steps usually comprise one step of a mechanism involving two or more elementary steps (a so-called *multistep mechanism*) because the reactant or product lacking an octet can be highly unstable. We will see, for example, coordination and heterolysis steps as parts of multistep mechanisms in the reactions we learn in Chapters 8, 12, and 24.

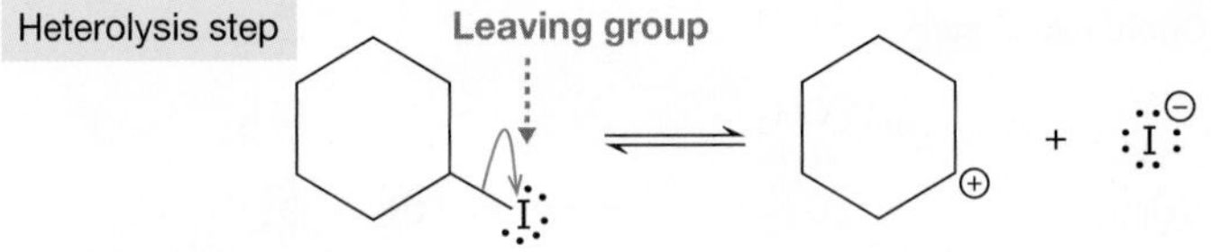

Heterolysis step
Leaving group

(7-7)

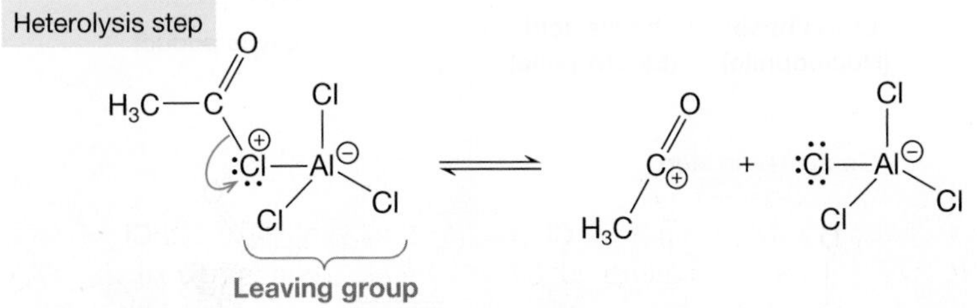

Heterolysis step
Leaving group

(7-8)

Elementary Step
Heterolysis

YOUR TURN 7.9

In Equations 7-7 and 7-8, identify all atoms lacking an octet. Also, draw the transition state for each reaction, taking into account the partial bonds and partial charges.

YOUR TURN 7.10

Use curved arrow notation to show the product from Your Turn 7.8 undergoing heterolysis to regenerate $FeCl_3$ and Cl^-.

7.4 Nucleophilic Addition and Nucleophile Elimination Steps

SECTION 7.4 OBJECTIVES

You will be able to:

1. Identify a nucleophilic addition or nucleophile elimination step when given the reactants and products.
2. Draw the curved arrow notation, transition state, and products for a nucleophilic addition or nucleophile elimination step when given the reactants.
3. Describe how the reactants of a nucleophilic addition step behave as a nucleophile and an electrophile.

Section 7.2 introduced the S_N2 step, in which a nucleophile forms a bond to an atom containing a suitable leaving group. A nucleophile can also form a bond to an atom that is initially involved in a *polar π bond*; that is, a π bond that is part of a double or triple bond connecting atoms with significantly different electronegativities, such as those in carbonyl groups (C═O), imine groups (C═N), and cyano groups (C≡N). Specifically, as shown in Equations 7-9 through 7-11, the nucleophile forms a bond to the less electronegative atom and the π bond breaks, becoming a lone pair on the more electronegative atom. A nucleophile adds to the polar π bond in these steps, so they are called **nucleophilic addition steps**.

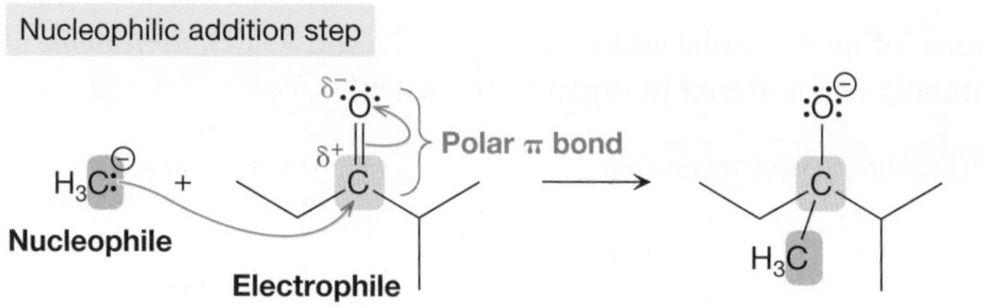

Nucleophilic addition step
Polar π bond
Nucleophile
Electrophile

(7-9)

Elementary Step Nucleophilic Addition

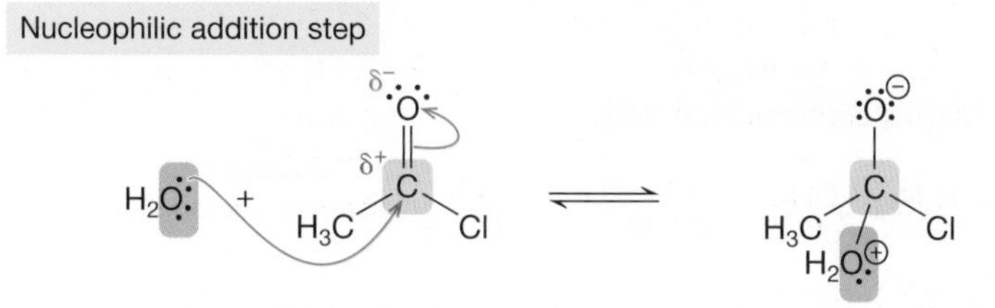

Nucleophilic addition step

(7-10)

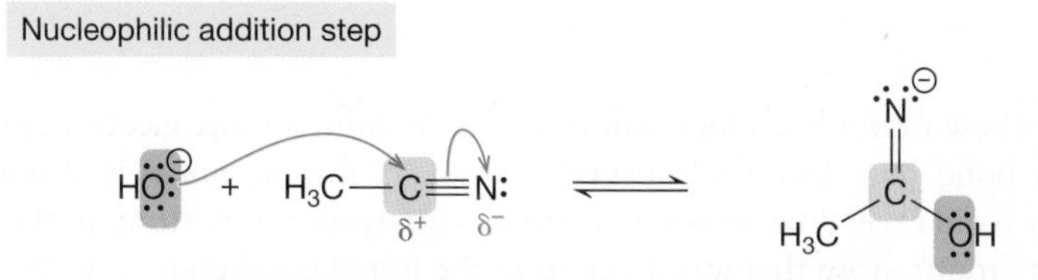

Nucleophilic addition step

(7-11)

YOUR TURN 7.11

For each of the nucleophilic addition steps in Equations 7-9 through 7-11, draw the transition state, taking into account the partial bonds and partial charges.

The *electron-rich to electron-poor* nature of a nucleophilic addition step is fairly straightforward. As shown in **Figure 7-7**, the nucleophile in a nucleophilic addition step, which has an excess of negative charge, is relatively electron-rich. The electrophile is the less electronegative atom of the polar π bond because it is relatively electron-poor. Thus, the curved arrow drawn from the electrons on the nucleophile to the polar π bond represents the flow of electrons from an electron-rich site to an electron-poor site. The second curved arrow, drawn from the center of the double (or triple) bond to the electronegative atom (Z), is necessary to avoid exceeding an octet on the less electronegative atom (C).

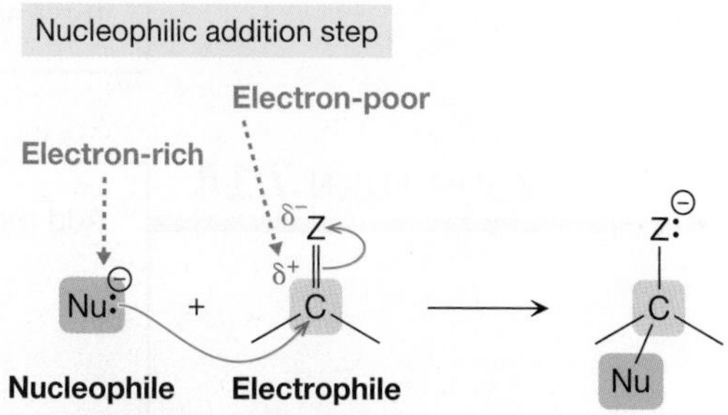

Nucleophilic addition step
Electron-poor
Electron-rich
Nucleophile
Electrophile

FIGURE 7-7 Electron-rich and electron-poor sites in nucleophilic addition

YOUR TURN 7.12

For the following nucleophilic addition step, label the pertinent electron-rich and electron-poor sites and label each reactant as either the nucleophile or the electrophile. Add the appropriate curved arrows and draw the product. Identify the curved arrow that is drawn from the electron-rich site to the electron-poor site.

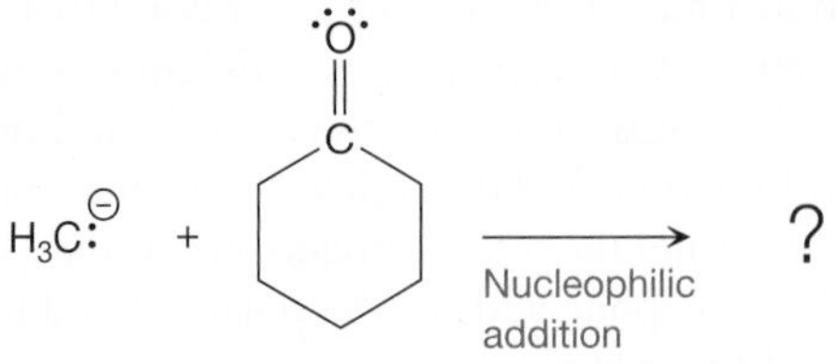

H₃C:⊖
+
Nucleophilic addition
?

The reverse of nucleophilic addition (Eqs. 7-12 and 7-13), *nucleophile elimination*, is also commonly encountered in organic chemistry.

Elementary Step
Nucleophilie Elimination

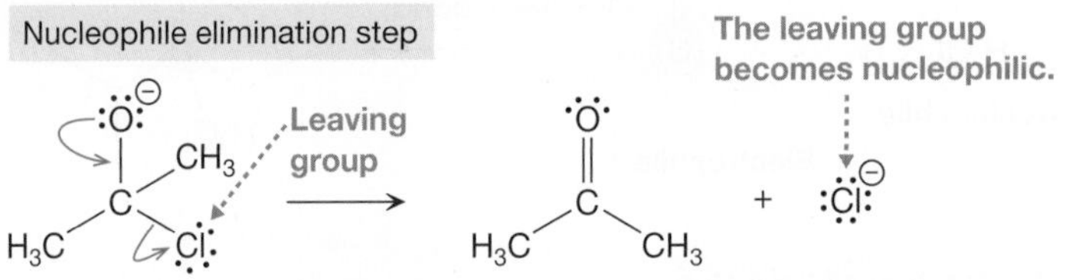

Nucleophile elimination step
Leaving group
The leaving group becomes nucleophilic.
H₃C
CH₃

(7-12)

> **▸ LOOKING AHEAD**
>
> Nucleophilic addition steps are often part of multistep mechanisms that also contain proton transfer steps (Chapters 18 and 19). Substitution can take place when nucleophilic addition and nucleophile elimination steps occur back-to-back (Chapters 22 and 23). Many biochemical reactions involve nucleophilic addition and nucleophile elimination steps, too (Chapters 19 and 23).

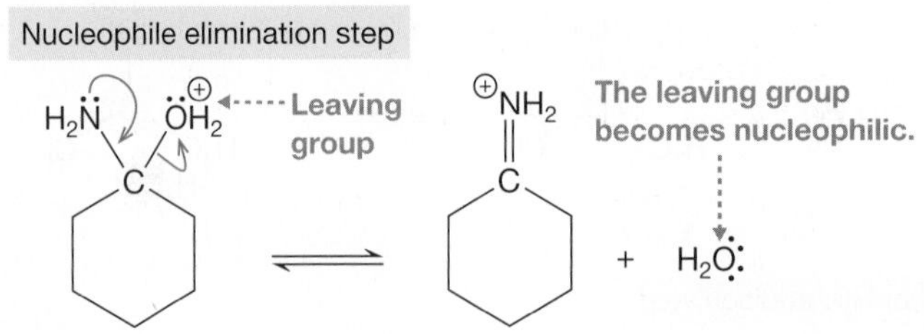

Nucleophile elimination step
Leaving group
The leaving group becomes nucleophilic.
H₂N
OH₂
NH₂
H₂O:

(7-13)

In both of these examples, a lone pair of electrons from a more electronegative atom forms a π bond to a less electronegative atom. A *leaving group* is simultaneously expelled to avoid exceeding an octet on the less electronegative atom. In the products, the leaving group's atom that was involved in the initial bond ends up with a lone pair of electrons and an excess of negative charge, both of which are characteristics of a nucleophile. As a result, we call these **nucleophile elimination steps** (see Looking Ahead box).

YOUR TURN 7.13

For each of the nucleophile elimination steps in Equations 7-12 and 7-13, draw the transition state, taking into account the partial bonds and partial charges.

YOUR TURN 7.14

Add the appropriate curved arrows to the following nucleophile elimination step.

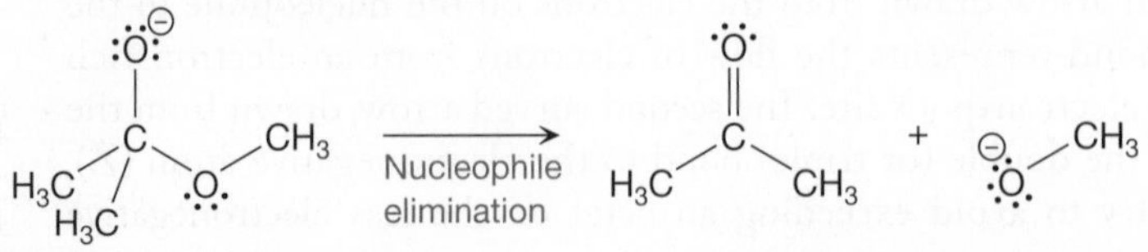

Nucleophile elimination
H₃C
CH₃

Draw the appropriate curved arrows and the products for each of the following elementary steps, as indicated below the reaction arrows. If electron pairs involved in the reaction are not shown, you must draw them in. *Hint*: Consider simplifying the electron-rich species.

(a)

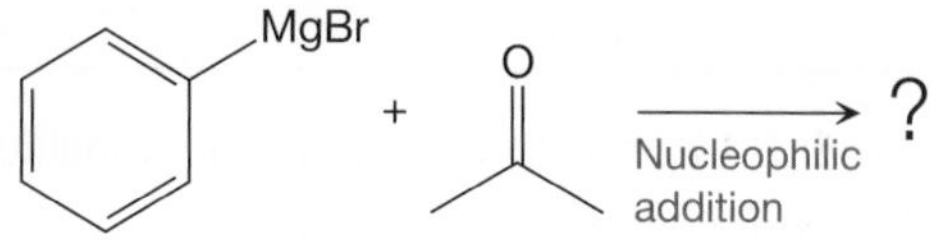
MgBr
O
?
Nucleophilic
addition

(b)

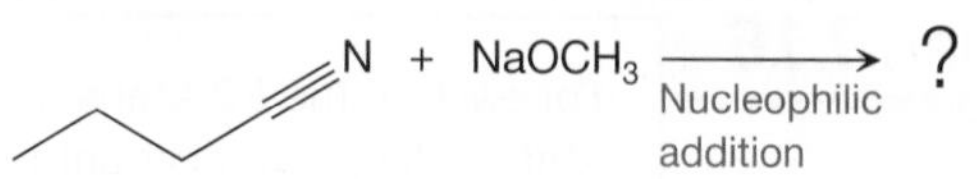
N + NaOCH3
?
Nucleophilic
addition

(c)

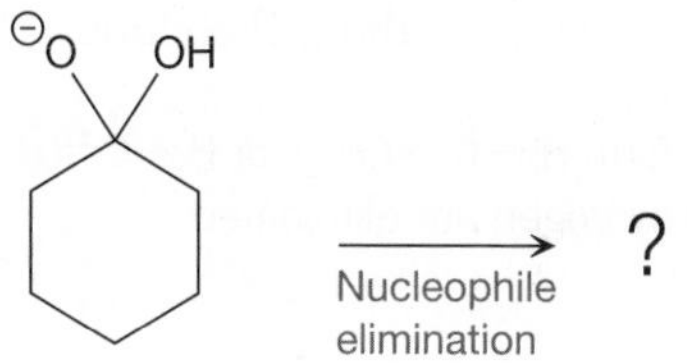
O
OH
?
Nucleophile
elimination

(d)

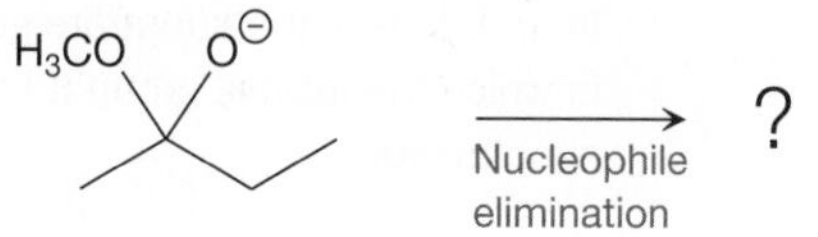
H3CO
O
?
Nucleophile
elimination

7.5 Bimolecular Elimination (E2) Steps

SECTION 7.5 OBJECTIVES

You will be able to:

1. Identify an E2 step when given the reactants and products.
2. Draw the curved arrow notation, transition state, and products for an E2 step when given the reactants.
3. Describe the role of the base in an E2 step.

Each of the elementary steps we have examined so far involves only one or two curved arrows. A *bimolecular elimination (E2) step*, however, is an example of an elementary step that requires three curved arrows, as shown in Equations 7-14 through 7-16.

E2 step

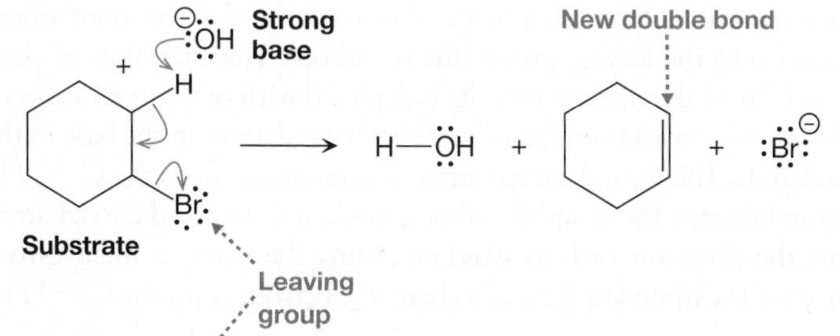
OH
Strong
base
H
Br
Substrate
H—OH
New double bond
Br
Leaving
group

(7-14)

E2 step

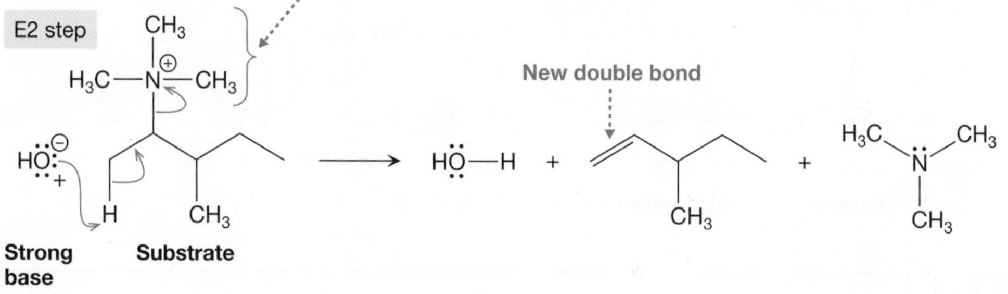
CH3
H3C—N—CH3
HO
H
CH3
Strong
base
Substrate
HO—H
New double bond
CH3
H3C
CH3
N
CH3

(7-15)

E2 step

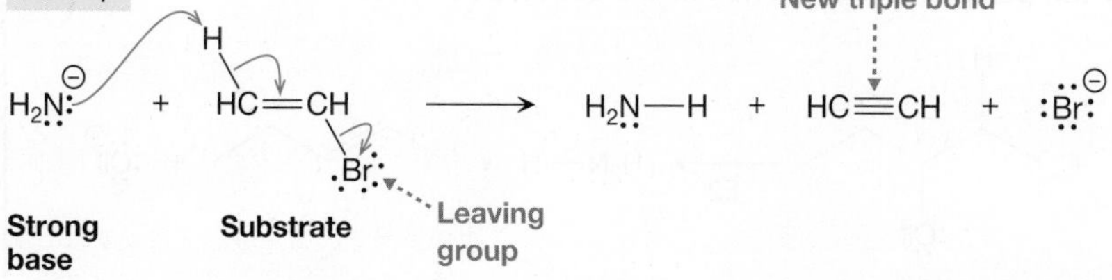
H2N
H
HC═CH
Br
Strong
base
Substrate
Leaving
group
H2N—H
HC≡CH
New triple bond
Br

(7-16)

Elementary Step
Bimolecular Elimination (E2)

A **bimolecular elimination (E2) step** is one in which a proton and a leaving group (L) are eliminated from a substrate, resulting in the formation of a new double or triple bond. Like S_N2 steps, E2 steps are called *bimolecular* because they have two reactant species. As the examples above illustrate, an *E2 step typically takes place when a strong base reacts with a substrate in which a leaving group (L) and a hydrogen atom are on adjacent carbon atoms.*

YOUR TURN 7.16

For each of the E2 steps in Equations 7-14 through 7-16, draw the transition state, taking into account the partial bonds and partial charges.

In elimination reactions, the carbon attached to the L is known as the alpha (α) carbon and the adjacent carbon is known as the beta (β) carbon. Therefore:

In an E2 step, the substrate generally has the form H—$\overset{\beta}{C}$—$\overset{\alpha}{C}$—L or H—$\overset{\beta}{C}$=$\overset{\alpha}{C}$—L, in which the leaving group (L) and the beta (β) hydrogen are eliminated simultaneously.

▸ LOOKING AHEAD

The C=C double bond or C≡C triple bond formed in an E2 reaction can itself undergo reaction, as we discuss later in this chapter, as well as in Chapters 12 and 13. We therefore revisit E2 steps in greater detail in Chapters 8 and 9.

For this reason, an E2 reaction is a type of **β elimination.**

Equations 7-14, 7-15, and 7-16 illustrate the diversity of reactants and products that can be involved in E2 steps. The base is HO^- in Equations 7-14 and 7-15, whereas it is H_2N^- in Equation 7-16. The leaving group can come off as a negatively charged species, as in Equations 7-14 and 7-16, or it can be uncharged, as in Equation 7-15. And the α and β carbon atoms in the substrate may be joined by either a single bond (Eqs. 7-14 and 7-15) or a double bond (Eq. 7-16), resulting in the formation of a new C=C double bond or C≡C triple bond, respectively (see Looking Ahead box).

The base in an E2 step is the electron-rich species, but the β hydrogen atom that the base attacks is not particularly electron-poor; instead, the electron-poor atom is the carbon atom bonded to the leaving group (the α carbon). Thus, the flow of electrons from the *electron-rich* site to the *electron-poor* site is depicted with two curved arrows (Eq. 7-17). One curved arrow is drawn from the negatively charged atom in the base to the β hydrogen in the substrate. The second curved arrow is then drawn from the C—H bond to the bonding region between the α and β carbon atoms, and the third curved arrow is necessary to depict the departure of L to avoid exceeding the octet on the α carbon. Overall, the electron-poor α carbon atom gains a share of electrons from the C—H bond.

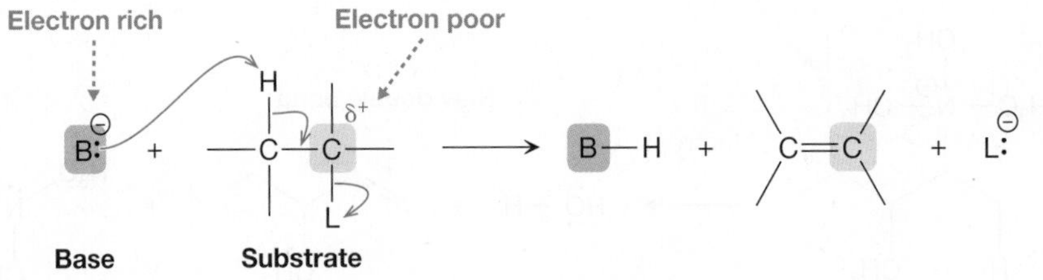

Electron rich
Electron poor
B:
H
δ+
C
C
L
B—H
C=C
L:
Base
Substrate

(7-17)

YOUR TURN 7.17

The reactants and products for this E2 step are shown, but the curved arrow notation has been omitted. Supply the missing curved arrow notation and identify the pertinent electron-rich and electron-poor sites.

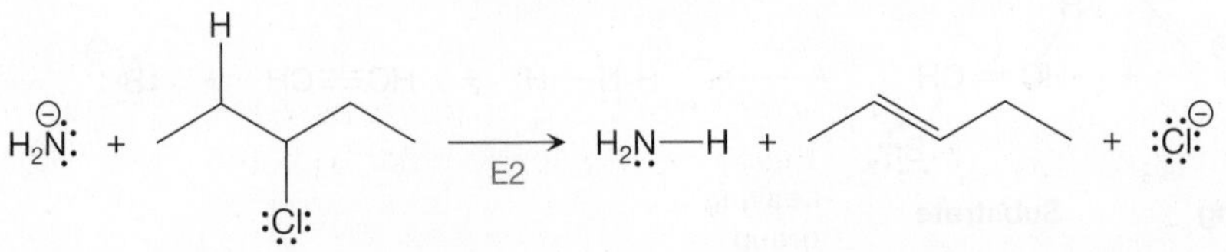

H
H_2N:
:Cl:
E2
H_2N—H
:Cl:

YOUR TURN **7.18**

Supply the appropriate curved arrows and the products for each of the following E2 steps. If atoms or electron pairs involved in the reaction are not shown, you must draw them in. *Hint*: Consider simplifying the electron-rich species.

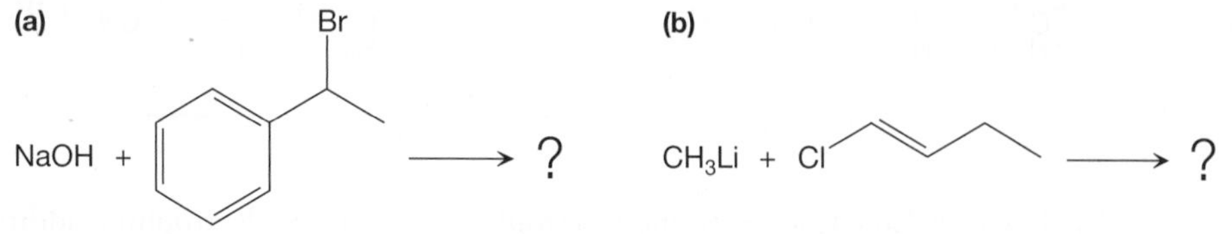

(a)
Br
NaOH +
?
(b)
CH3Li + Cl
?

7.6 Electrophilic Addition and Electrophile Elimination Steps

SECTION 7.6 OBJECTIVES

You will be able to:

1. Identify an electrophilic addition or electrophile elimination step when given the reactants and products.
2. Draw the curved arrow notation, transition state, and products for an electrophilic addition or electrophile elimination step when given the reactants.
3. Describe how the reactants of an electrophilic addition step behave as a nucleophile and an electrophile.

Elementary Step
Electrophilic Addition

An **electrophilic addition step** occurs when a species containing a nonpolar π bond (as part of a double or triple bond) approaches a strongly electron-deficient species (an *electrophile*), and a bond forms between an atom of the π bond and the electrophile (Eqs. 7-18 and 7-19).

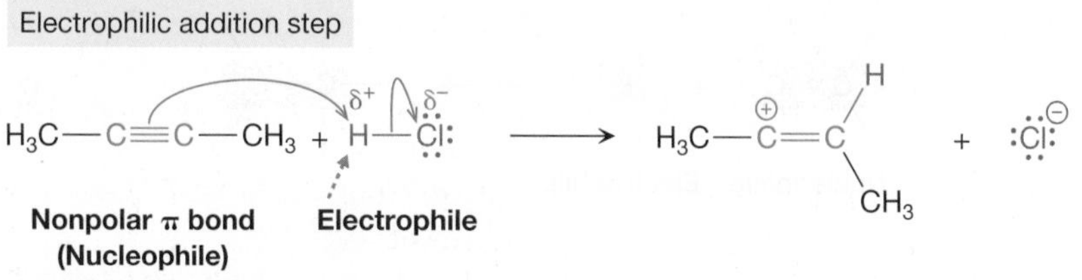

Electrophilic addition step
H3C—C≡C—CH3 + H—Cl:
δ+ δ−
H3C—C=C
H
CH3
+ :Cl:
Nonpolar π bond (Nucleophile)
Electrophile

(7-18)

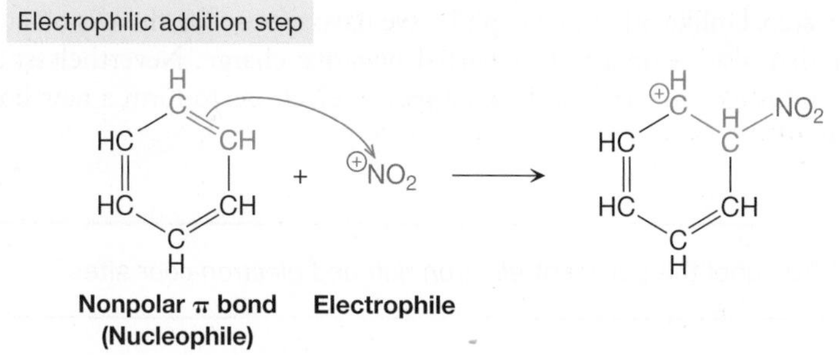

Electrophilic addition step
HC
CH
HC
CH
C
H
+ NO2
HC
HC
CH
H
NO2
Nonpolar π bond (Nucleophile)
Electrophile

(7-19)

The nonpolar π bonds involved in electrophilic addition steps are typically ones that join a pair of carbon atoms. The electrophile, on the other hand, can have a variety of different forms. For example, the electrophile can be $H^{\delta+}$ from a Brønsted acid, such as HCl in Equation 7-18. Alternatively, the electrophile can exist on its own, as shown for the NO_2^+ species in Equation 7-19. In both electrophilic addition steps, however, notice that a carbocation is produced.

YOUR TURN **7.19**

For each of the electrophilic addition steps in Equations 7-18 and 7-19, draw the transition state, taking into account the partial bonds and partial charges.

YOUR TURN 7.20

Add the appropriate curved arrows for the electrophilic addition step shown here.

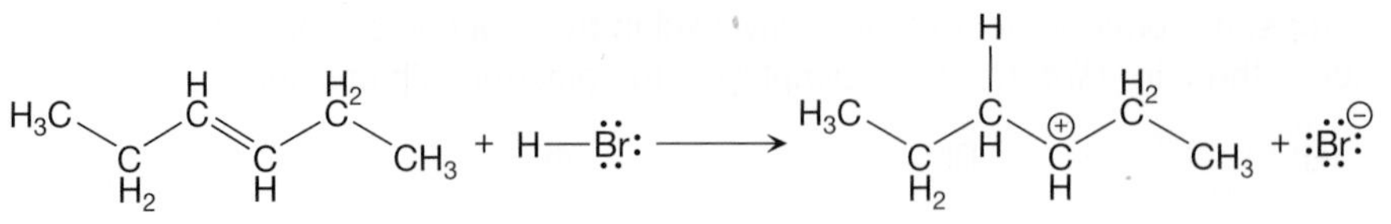

As shown in Equation 7-20, the electrophile (E^+) in an electrophilic addition step is relatively electron-poor because it either carries a full positive charge (Eq. 7-19) or has an atom with a significant partial positive charge (Eq. 7-18). The double or triple bond, on the other hand, is relatively electron-rich. In a C=C double bond, for example, four electrons are localized in the region between the two atoms, and in a C≡C triple bond, six electrons are localized between the two atoms. Therefore, the movement of electrons from *electron-rich* to *electron-poor* is indicated by a curved arrow that begins at the center of the multiple bond and points to the electrophile.

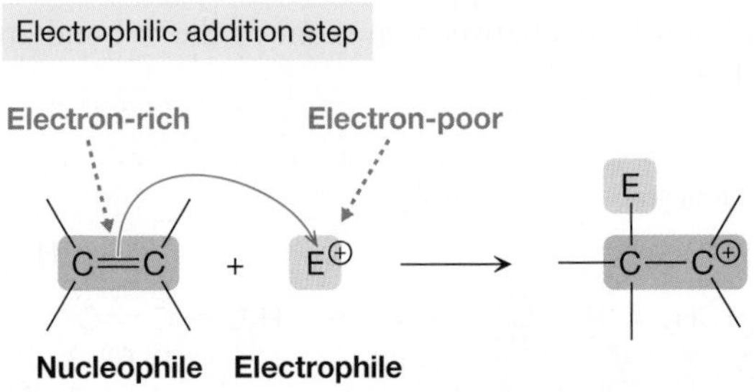
Electrophilic addition step
Electron-rich
Electron-poor
Nucleophile
Electrophile

(7-20)

Notice in Equation 7-20 that the nonpolar π bond acts as a *nucleophile* in an electrophilic addition step. Unlike other nucleophiles we have seen so far, there is no atom with a lone pair that also bears a full or partial negative charge. Nevertheless, the C=C double bond is electron-rich and uses a pair of electrons to form a new bond to an electrophile.

YOUR TURN 7.21

In Your Turn 7.20, label the pertinent *electron-rich* and *electron-poor* sites.

Elementary Step
Electrophile Elimination

▸ LOOKING AHEAD

Electrophilic addition and electrophile elimination steps generally involve carbocations, which tend to be highly reactive because they lack an octet and are positively charged. Therefore, electrophilic addition and electrophile elimination steps are usually part of a multistep mechanism, such as the ones we will explore in greater detail in Chapters 8, 12, 13, 24, and 25.

Carbocations are typically quite unstable, so the reverse of electrophilic addition is also a common elementary step in organic reactions. In the reverse step, called **electrophile elimination** (Eq. 17-21), an electrophile is *eliminated* from the carbocation, generating a stable, uncharged organic species (see Looking Ahead box).

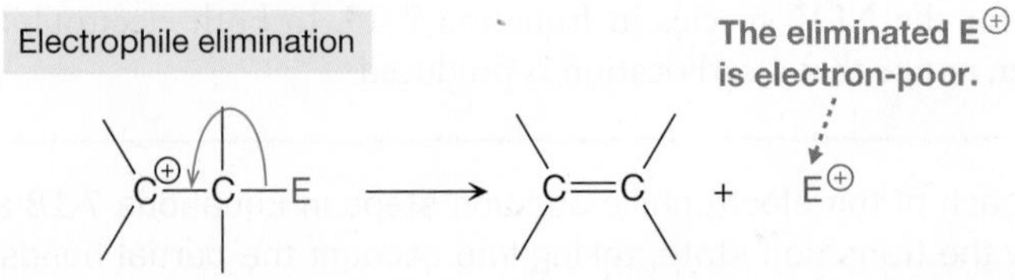
Electrophile elimination
The eliminated E⊕ is electron-poor.

(7-21)

Equations 7-22 and 7-23 show examples in which the eliminated electrophile is SO_3H^+ or H^+, respectively.

Electrophile elimination

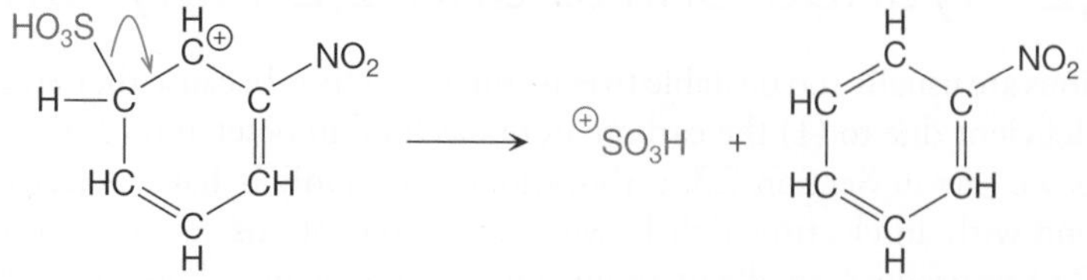

Nitrobenzene

(7-22)

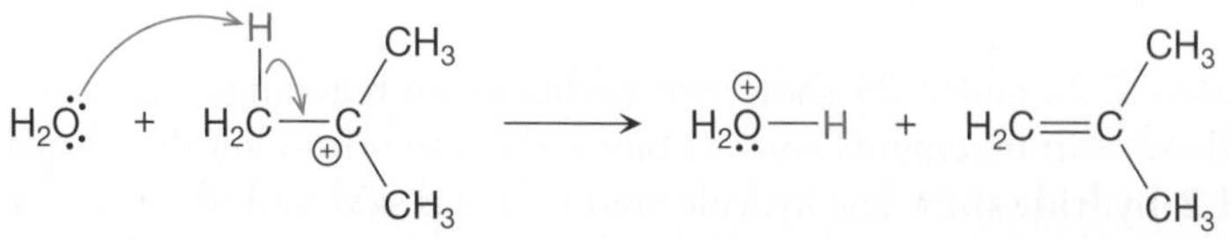

Methylpropene

(7-23)

In Equation 7-22, the SO_3H^+ electrophile is eliminated on its own. In Equation 7-23, however, the H^+ that is eliminated is simultaneously picked up by water, which acts as a Brønsted base. Such participation of a base is necessary because H^+ does not exist on its own in solution.

CONNECTIONS 7.2

Nitrobenzene: Explosives, perfumes, and blue jeans

Nitrobenzene ($C_6H_5NO_2$, Eq. 7-22) has an odor that resembles almonds, which once made it useful in the fragrance industry. Now, nitrobenzene is used primarily in the production of aniline, which is a precursor to a variety of compounds, including explosives, pharmaceutical drugs, and dyes such as indigo, the dye associated with blue jeans.

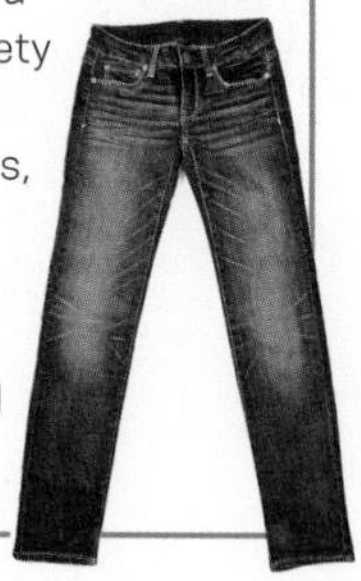

YOUR TURN 7.22

For each of the electrophile elimination steps in Equations 7-22 and 7-23, draw the transition state, taking into account the partial bonds and partial charges.

YOUR TURN 7.23

Add the appropriate curved arrow(s) to the electrophile elimination step shown here, which is essentially the reverse of the addition step in Your Turn 7.20.

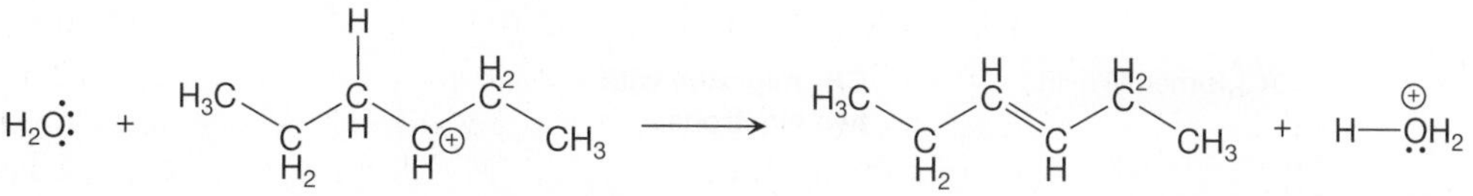

YOUR TURN 7.24

Supply the appropriate curved arrows and draw the product of each of the elementary steps shown here, indicated underneath the reaction arrows. If atoms or electron pairs involved in the reaction are not shown, you must draw them in.

(a)

Electrophilic addition

(b)

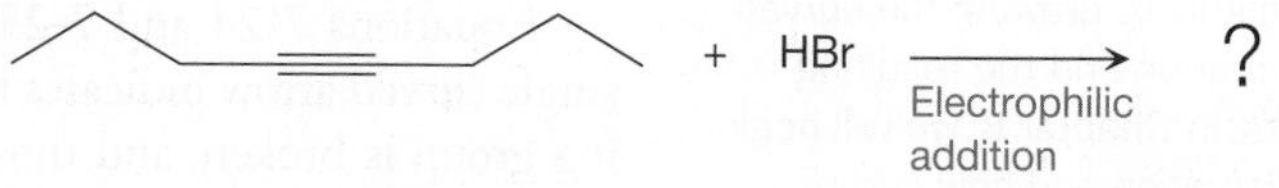
Electrophilic addition

(c)

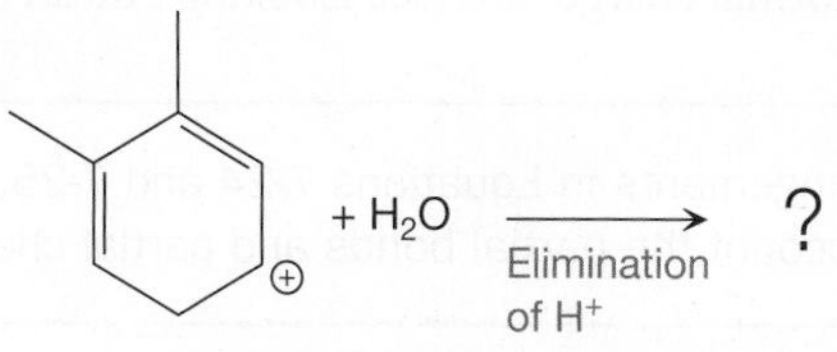
Elimination of H+

(d)

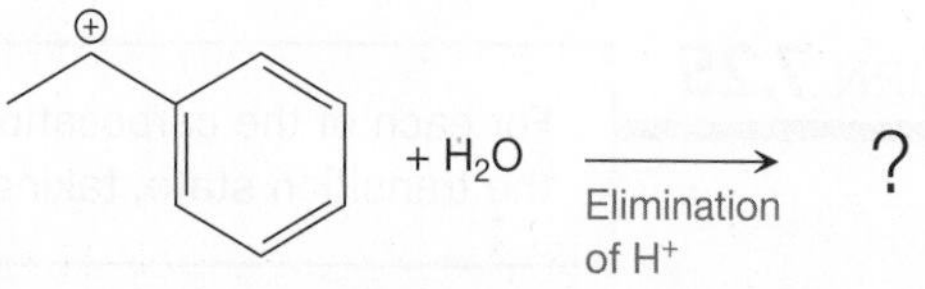
Elimination of H+

SECTION 7.7 OBJECTIVES

You will be able to:

1. Identify a 1,2-hydride shift or 1,2-methyl shift when given the reactants and products.
2. Draw the curved arrow notation, transition state, and product for a 1,2-hydride shift or 1,2-methyl shift when given the reactant.

7.7 Carbocation Rearrangements: 1,2-Hydride Shifts and 1,2-Alkyl Shifts

Carbocations are usually too unstable to exist for a long time because they are extremely electron-deficient due to (1) the carbon atom's lack of an octet and (2) its +1 formal charge. As we saw in Section 7.3, carbocations commonly behave as Lewis acids to form a bond with an electron-rich Lewis base. Carbocations can also eliminate H^+ (Section 7.6) to produce an alkene or alkyne. Given a chance, however, carbocations can also undergo a *rearrangement* before taking part in one of these steps with another species.

Equations 7-24 and 7-25 show two **carbocation rearrangements**; as the name suggests, these rearrangements convert one carbocation into another. Equation 7-24 depicts a **1,2-hydride shift**. The hydride anion (H^-) is said to shift because a hydrogen atom migrates along with the pair of electrons initially making up the C—H bond. The numbering system denotes the number of atoms over which the hydride anion migrates; the atom to which the hydrogen is initially bonded is designated as the number 1 atom, and any adjacent atom can be designated as a number 2 atom. Thus, a "1,2" shift refers to the hydrogen migrating to an adjacent atom.

Elementary Step
Carbocation Rearrangement

A 1,2-hydride shift

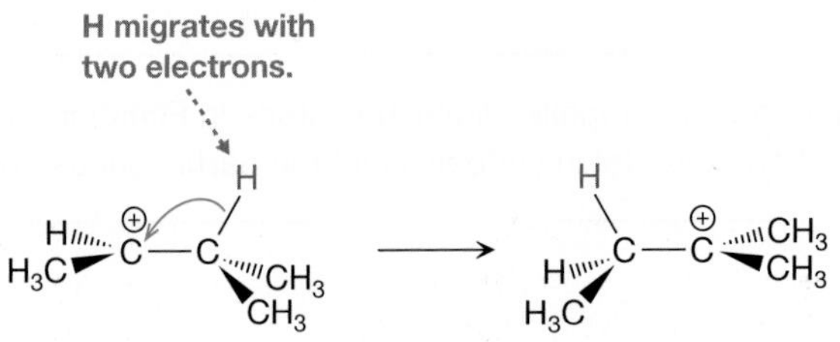
H migrates with
two electrons.
H
H
H₃C
C
C
CH₃
CH₃
H
C
C
CH₃
CH₃
H
H₃C

(7-24)

A 1,2-methyl shift

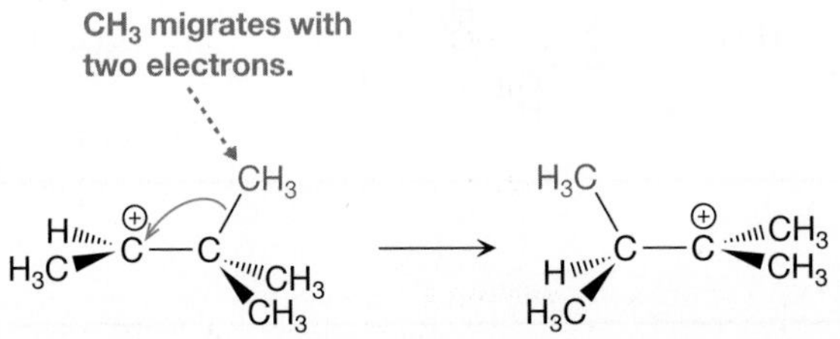
CH₃ migrates with
two electrons.
CH₃
H
H₃C
C
C
CH₃
CH₃
H₃C
C
C
CH₃
CH₃
H
H₃C

(7-25)

Equation 7-25 shows a **1,2-alkyl shift**; more specifically, a methyl group is transferred, so this rearrangement is called a **1,2-methyl shift**. Again the numbering system indicates that the migrating group (the methyl group) is transferred to an adjacent atom.

Equations 7-24 and 7-25 have identical curved arrow notation. In both cases, a single curved arrow indicates that the initial bond between the C atom and the migrating group is broken, and those electrons are used to form a bond to the adjacent C. Meanwhile, the C that is left behind by the migrating group loses an octet and ends up with a formal charge of +1, whereas the C that is joined by the migrating group gains a complete octet and ends up with a formal charge of 0 (see Looking Ahead box).

▸ LOOKING AHEAD

Here in Chapter 7, our focus on carbocation rearrangements is limited primarily to drawing the curved arrow notation and the resulting products. In Chapter 8, we will begin to predict when and how carbocation rearrangements participate in multistep mechanisms.

YOUR TURN 7.25

For each of the carbocation rearrangements in Equations 7-24 and 7-25, draw the transition state, taking into account the partial bonds and partial charges.

YOUR TURN **7.26**

Supply the curved arrow notation for the carbocation rearrangement shown here.

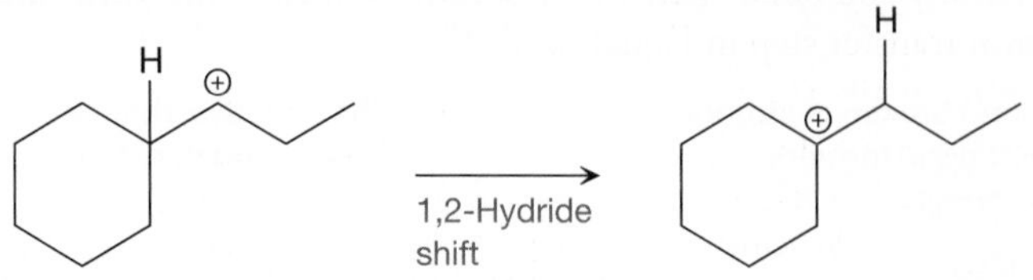
H
H
1,2-Hydride
shift

YOUR TURN **7.27**

Supply the appropriate curved arrows and draw the product for this carbocation undergoing **(a)** a 1,2-hydride shift and **(b)** a 1,2-methyl shift. If atoms or electron pairs involved in the reaction are not shown, you must draw them in.

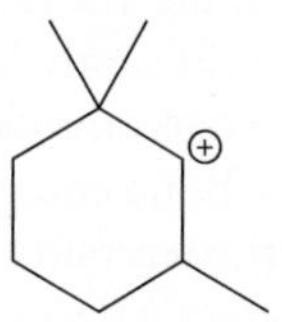

7.8 The Driving Force for Chemical Reactions

SECTION 7.8 OBJECTIVES

You will be able to:

1. Determine the side of an elementary step that is favored by charge stability and by total bond strength.
2. Predict the side of an elementary step that is favored when the factors of charge stability and bond strength disagree.

So far, our focus on elementary steps has been on *how* they occur, using curved arrows to account for bonds breaking and bonds forming. But why should these elementary steps occur in the first place? That is, what is their *driving force*?

The **driving force** for a reaction reflects the extent to which the reaction favors products over reactants, which, as we learned in Section 6.4, is associated with the reaction's Gibbs free energy change (see Recall box). That tendency to favor products increases with increasing stability of the products relative to the reactants. Thus, understanding a reaction's driving force is a matter of identifying and evaluating the factors that help stabilize the products, destabilize the reactants, or both.

Although various factors dictate the stability of a species, we can often make reasonable predictions about a reaction's driving force by examining just two factors. One is *charge stability* (see Recall box, p. 340), and the other is *total bond energy*:

◀ RECALL

In Section 6.4, we saw that the Gibbs free energy (G) of a species corresponds to its stability: A lower G indicates greater stability, and a higher G indicates less stability. Therefore, as the Gibbs free energy change (ΔG) for a reaction becomes more negative (less positive), the reaction is more product favored. As ΔG becomes less negative (more positive), the reaction is more reactant favored.

Major Contributions to Driving Force

A reaction's driving force generally increases with:

- Greater charge stabilization in the products relative to the reactants.
- Greater total bond energy in the products relative to the reactants.

With this in mind, we can see that a coordination step like that in Equation 7-26 is unambiguously driven toward products.

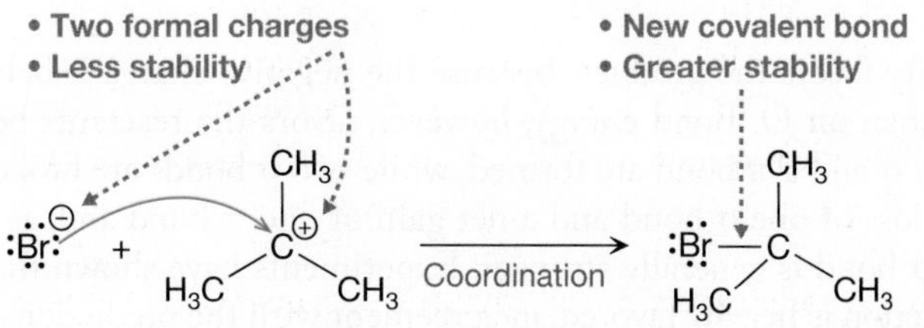
• Two formal charges
• Less stability
• New covalent bond
• Greater stability
CH3
:Br:
+
C
H3C
CH3
Coordination
CH3
:Br—C
H3C
CH3

(7-26)

Charge stability heavily favors the products in this reaction because there are two formal charges in the reactants but no formal charges in the products. Furthermore, total bond energy favors the products because, during the course of the reaction, a covalent bond is formed, giving carbon an octet, and no bonds are broken.

Charge stability and bond energy do not always work in the same direction. Consider the proton transfer step in Equation 7-27.

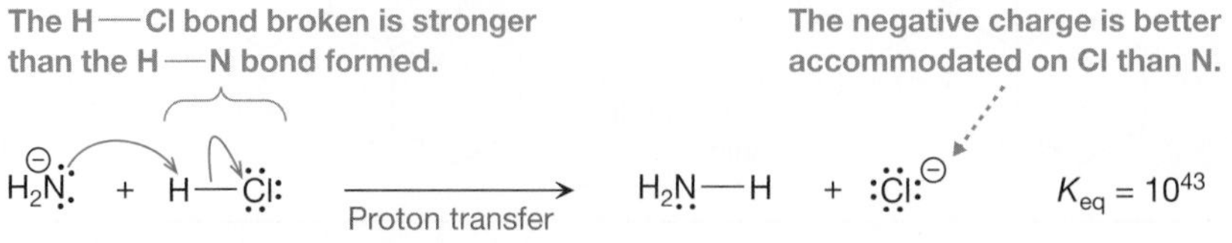
The H—Cl bond broken is stronger than the H—N bond formed.
The negative charge is better accommodated on Cl than N.
Proton transfer
$K_{eq} = 10^{43}$
(7-27)

In this case, a negative charge appears in both the reactants and the products. In the reactants, the negative charge is on N, whereas in the products, it is on Cl. Because Cl is significantly larger (i.e., lower in the periodic table) than N, the negative charge is better accommodated on Cl than on N, so we say that charge stability favors the products. Bond energy, however, favors the reactants because the H—Cl bond that appears on the reactant side (431 kJ/mol) is stronger than the H—N bond that appears on the product side (389 kJ/mol). Despite the disagreement, notice that the products are heavily favored ($K_{eq} = 10^{43}$), because HCl (pK_a = −7) is a much stronger acid than NH_3 (pK_a = 36).

The previous example leads to the following general rule:

> When charge stability and bond energy favor opposite sides of a chemical reaction, charge stability usually wins.

◄ RECALL

Chapter 6 discussed how to assess charge stability according to the CARDIN-al rule: The *charge* of the species; the type of *atom* holding the charge; *resonance delocalization* of the charge; and *inductive effects* from substituents attached to the charged atom. Recall also that each covalent bond in a species contributes to the species' stability. (Review bond energies in Tables 1-2 and 1-3 on pp. 10–11.)

YOUR TURN 7.28

Consider the proton transfer reaction shown here. The product side is heavily favored because H_2O (pK_a = 14) is a much stronger acid than NH_3 (pK_a = 36). **(a)** Which side of the reaction exhibits greater charge stability? **(b)** Which side of the reaction exhibits greater total bond energy? *Hint*: Use Table 1-2 on p. 10 to find the H—O and H—N bond energies. **(c)** Do your answers to parts (a) and (b) agree? If not, which factor appears to be more important?

$$H_2N^{\ominus} + H{-}OH \longrightarrow H_2N{-}H + {}^{\ominus}OH$$

The greater importance of charge stability compared to bond energy is evident in the E2 step in Equation 7-28:

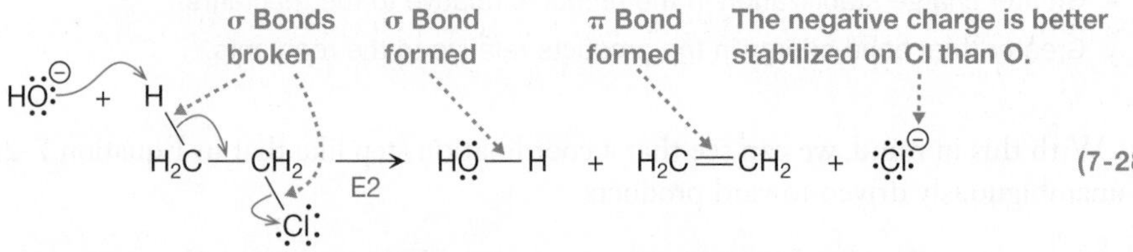
σ Bonds broken
σ Bond formed
π Bond formed
The negative charge is better stabilized on Cl than O.
E2
(7-28)

Charge stability favors the products because the negative charge is better accommodated on Cl than on O. Bond energy, however, favors the reactants because, on the product side, a σ and a π bond are formed, while two σ bonds are broken. Effectively, there is a net loss of one σ bond and a net gain of one π bond and, as we learned in Chapter 3, a σ bond is generally stronger. Experiments have shown that the product side of the reaction is heavily favored, in agreement with the prediction obtained from charge stability.

SOLVED PROBLEM **7.6**

How to determine the favored side of an elementary step

Break It Down

Which side of this nucleophilic addition step is favored?

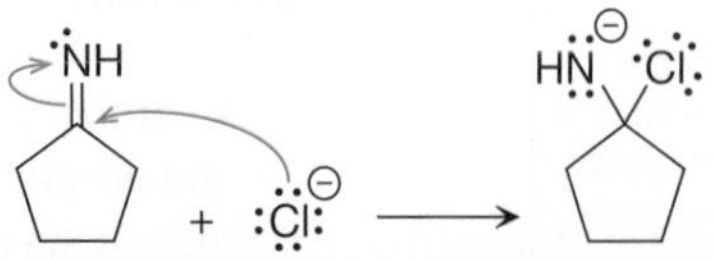

Think	Solve
On the two sides of the reaction, is there a difference in charge stability?	The negative charge is on Cl in the reactants and on N in the product. Because Cl is the larger atom, the charge is better accommodated on Cl, so charge stability favors the reactant side.
Is there a substantial difference in total bond energy on the two sides of the reaction?	During the course of the reaction, the π bond from C=N breaks and a C—Cl σ bond forms. A σ bond tends to be stronger than a π bond, in which case bond energy would favor the product side.
Do the answers to the above two questions agree? If not, which factor wins?	Charge stability favors the reactant side, but bond energy favors the product side. When the two factors disagree like this, charge stability usually wins, in which case we would predict that the reaction favors the reactant side.

Try It Determine which side of each elementary step is favored.

(a)

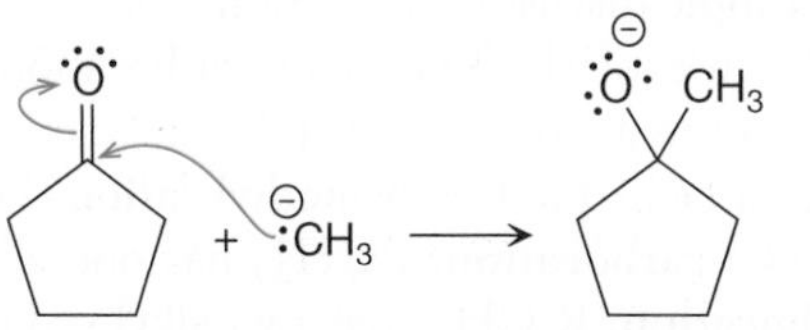

(b)

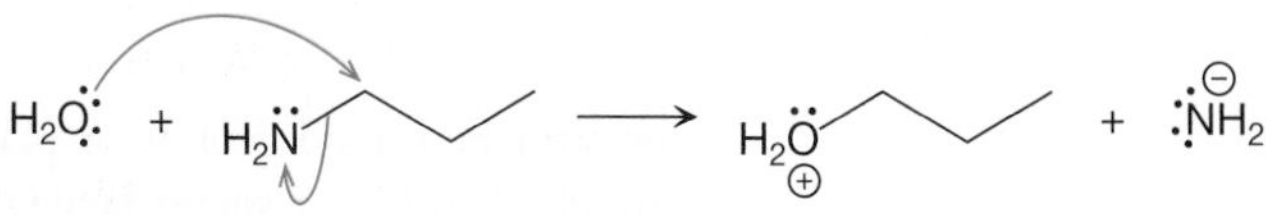

Using charge stability and total bond energy to predict the outcome of a reaction is generally quite reliable, but some exceptions exist. For example, the product side of a reaction might be favored, but an excessively large energy barrier can prevent the reaction from forming products; the rate would be too small. Alternatively, charge stability and bond energy can heavily favor the reactant side, but the reaction might still proceed if other factors, such as entropy or stabilization from the solvent, favor products. We will discuss cases like these in later chapters when they become relevant.

7.9 Carbocations and Charge Stability

Carbocations, which carry a +1 charge, are involved in several of the elementary steps presented earlier in this chapter, as a reactant, a product, or both. Those elementary steps include heterolysis, coordination, electrophilic addition, electrophile elimination, and carbocation rearrangements. We just saw in Section 7.8 how important charge stability is to the driving force for chemical reactions. This section, therefore, takes a closer look at factors that control the relative stabilities of carbocations.

SECTION 7.9 OBJECTIVES

You will be able to:

1. Determine the relative stabilities of carbocations on the basis of resonance delocalization and the number of alkyl groups attached to C^+.
2. Determine the relative driving force for elementary steps involving carbocations.

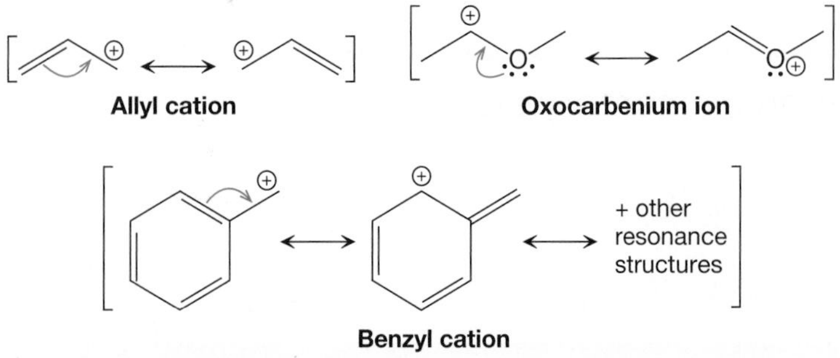
Allyl cation
Oxocarbenium ion
+ other resonance structures
Benzyl cation

FIGURE 7-8 Stabilization of carbocations via resonance

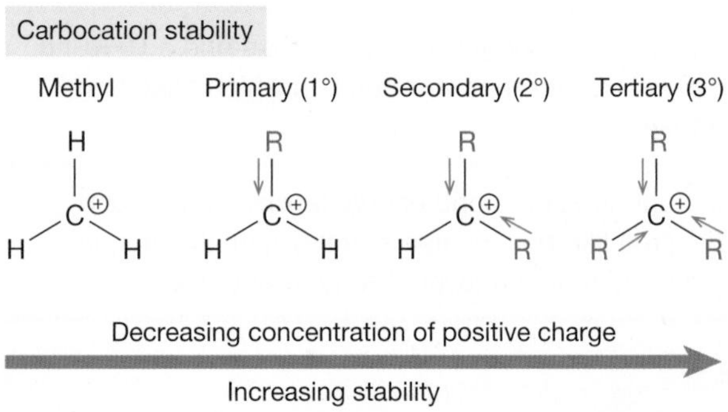
Carbocation stability
Methyl
Primary (1°)
Secondary (2°)
Tertiary (3°)
Decreasing concentration of positive charge
Increasing stability

FIGURE 7-9 Stabilization of carbocations via attached alkyl groups

Carbocations in general are quite unstable, due to the lack of an octet on carbon and the appearance of a positive charge, but as we have seen for other charged species, *resonance* (Section 6.8d) can play a major role:

> A carbocation undergoes substantial stabilization if its charge is delocalized via resonance.

Some common examples are shown in **Figure 7-8**. In the allyl cation and the benzyl cation, resonance involves a pair of electrons from the double bond attached to C^+. In the oxocarbenium ion, resonance involves a lone pair of electrons from O.

Additionally, as shown in **Figure 7-9**:

> Carbocation stability generally increases with each additional alkyl group attached to the positively charged carbon atom.

Alkyl groups stabilize the carbocation in part because they are inductively electron-donating (Section 6.8e), which helps to reduce the concentration of positive charge on C^+. Alkyl groups attached to C^+ also stabilize carbocations through *hyperconjugation*, a topic discussed in Section 7.9a.

Because of the impact on carbocation stability, carbocations are distinguished by the number of alkyl groups attached to C^+. A **methyl cation** (H_3C^+) has no attached alkyl groups; a **primary (1°) carbocation**, RCH_2^+, has one alkyl group attached to C^+; a **secondary (2°) carbocation**, R_2CH^+, has two alkyl groups; and a **tertiary (3°) carbocation**, R_3C^+, has three alkyl groups. Thus, carbocation stability increases in the following order: methyl < 1° < 2° < 3°.

Taking into account both resonance delocalization and the electron-donating effects from alkyl groups, the general order for carbocation stability is shown in **Figure 7-10**. Notice that resonance delocalization has a greater stabilizing effect than does a single alkyl group (allyl vs. 1°), similar to what we saw with other ions we examined in Section 6.9. As it turns out, however, multiple alkyl groups attached to the same C^+ can provide more stabilization than resonance delocalization.

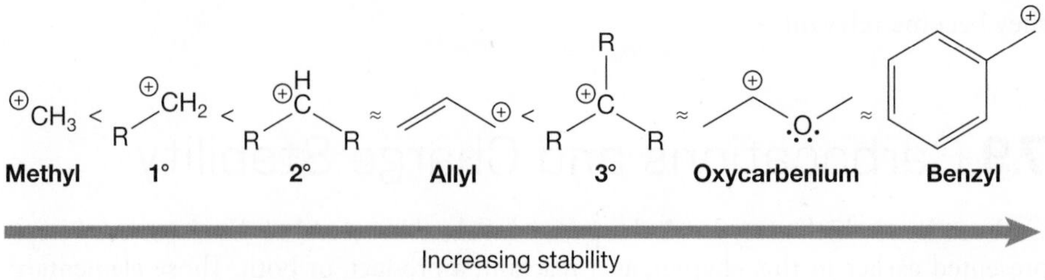
Methyl
1°
2°
Allyl
3°
Oxycarbenium
Benzyl
Increasing stability

FIGURE 7-10 Relative stabilities of carbocations

SOLVED PROBLEM **7.7**

How to determine the favored side of carbocation rearrangement

Break It Down **Which side of this carbocation rearrangement is favored?**

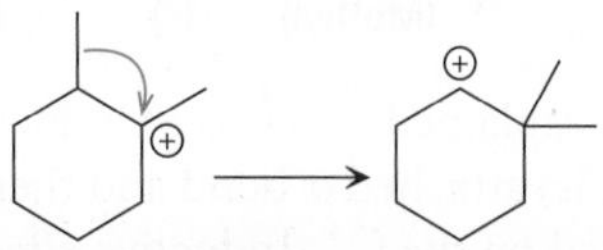

Think	Solve
On the two sides of the reaction, is there a difference in charge stability?	The positive charge is on a tertiary carbon in the reactant and on a secondary carbon in the product. Because a tertiary carbocation is more stable, charge stability favors the reactant side.
Is there a substantial difference in total bond energy on the two sides of the reaction?	Total bond energy is not a significant factor in this reaction because a C—C σ bond is broken in the reactant and another one is formed in the product.
Do the answers to the above two questions conflict?	Charge stability is substantially different on either side of the reaction, but total bond energy is not. Charge stability favors the reactant side, so overall this carbocation rearrangement will favor the reactant side.

Try It Determine which side of each of the carbocation rearrangements shown here is favored.

(a)

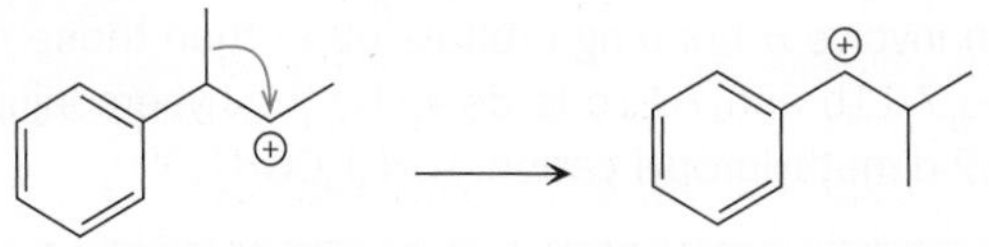

(b)

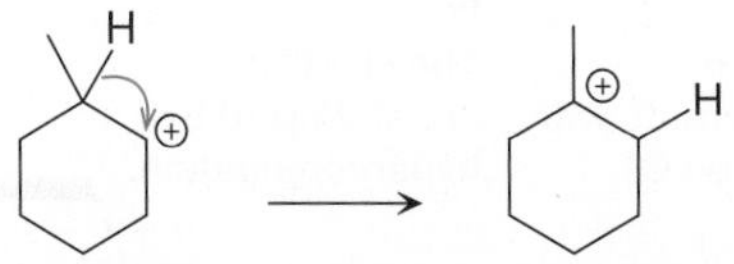

H
H

7.9a A Deeper Look: Carbocation Stability and Hyperconjugation

We just learned that the stability of a carbocation increases as the number of alkyl groups bonded to the positively charged carbon increases:

Carbocation stability: $CH_3^+ < RCH_2^+ < R_2CH^+ < R_3C^+$
(Methyl) (1°) (2°) (3°)

These relative stabilities were explained in terms of inductive effects: Each alkyl group is electron-donating through its attached σ bond and therefore reduces the amount of positive charge that is localized on the C^+. Inductive effects, however, are only part of the story. The other major contribution comes from **hyperconjugation**, which is an outcome of orbital interactions, illustrated in **Figure 7-11**.

Figure 7-11a highlights a key feature of CH_3^+, which is an outcome of molecular orbital (MO) theory discussed in Section 3.11. Namely, the C—H bonds, each of which represents two electrons occupying a σ bonding MO, are perpendicular to the empty *p* atomic orbital (AO) on carbon. Therefore, the empty *p* AO does not interact with any of the C—H σ bonds; the *p* AO is effectively isolated. By contrast, the *p* AO in $CH_3CH_2^+$ (Fig. 7-11b) is aligned with one of the C—H bonds in the adjacent CH_3 group. The empty *p* AO and that σ bonding MO therefore interact. As with any pair of interacting orbitals, two new orbitals are produced: In this case, constructive interference results in a new orbital that is more stable than the σ bonding MO, and destructive interference results in a new orbital that is less stable than the *p* AO. The two electrons from the σ bonding MO end up in the lower energy of the two new orbitals and are thus stabilized, as shown in Figure 7-11c. Such a stabilizing effect would occur for each additional alkyl group attached to C^+.

The constructive interference that leads to the stabilization we see in Figure 7-11c also results in delocalization of the resulting orbital and the electrons that occupy it. In this case, the electrons from the C—H bond are delocalized into the empty *p* AO on C^+. Hyperconjugation therefore effectively transfers some electron density from the alkyl group into the empty *p* AO. In this way, the alkyl group is electron-donating, in agreement with how we view alkyl groups from the perspective of inductive effects.

YOUR TURN **7.29**

Hyperconjugation can involve σ bonding orbitals other than those from C—H bonds. Redraw Figure 7-11b and 7-11c to describe the hyperconjugation that takes place in the 2,2-dimethylpropyl cation, $(CH_3)_3CCH_2^+$.

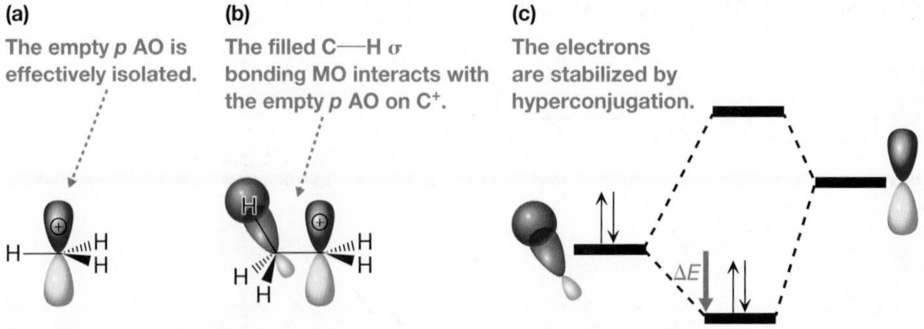
(a)
The empty p AO is effectively isolated.
H
H
H
(b)
The filled C—H σ bonding MO interacts with the empty p AO on C⁺.
H
H
H
H
H
(c)
The electrons are stabilized by hyperconjugation.
ΔE

FIGURE 7-11 Hyperconjugation in carbocations (a) In CH_3^+, the *p* atomic orbital (AO) on carbon is empty and does not interact with any adjacent orbitals. (b) In $CH_3CH_2^+$, the empty *p* AO overlaps with the σ bonding molecular orbital (MO) of the adjacent C—H bond, so the two orbitals can interact. (c) The orbital interaction in $CH_3CH_2^+$ (shown in part b), called hyperconjugation, stabilizes the electrons from the σ bonding orbital.

7.10 Keto–Enol Tautomerization: An Example of Bond Energies as the Major Driving Force

SECTION 7.10 OBJECTIVES

You will be able to:

1. Draw the keto form of a tautomerization when given the enol form, and vice versa, and explain why the keto form is usually more stable.
2. Draw the mechanism for a tautomerization under acidic or basic conditions.

In aqueous basic or acidic conditions, ketones and aldehydes exist in rapid equilibrium with a rearranged form, called an *enol*:

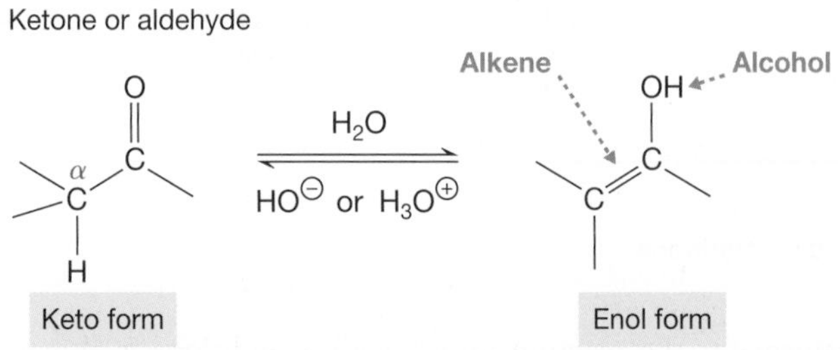

Ketone or aldehyde
Alkene
Alcohol
H2O
HO⊖ or H3O⊕
Keto form
Enol form

(7-29)

As a ketone or aldehyde, the species is called the **keto form**. In the **enol form**, the species has a carbon atom that is simultaneously part of a C=C bond characteristic of an alkene and is bonded to OH, characteristic of an alcohol. Because the keto and enol forms are constitutional isomers in equilibrium, they are called **tautomers** (Greek: *tauto* = same; *mer* = part), and the equilibrium is called **keto–enol tautomerization**. In later chapters, we will see that this equilibrium has important consequences in a variety of chemical reactions.

In the equilibrium shown in Equation 7-29, notice that the keto form has one additional hydrogen atom on the **α (alpha) carbon** (the carbon atom that is adjacent to the C=O group), whereas the enol form has one additional hydrogen appearing on oxygen. We can therefore account for this transformation with a mechanism consisting of two steps, where a proton is removed from the α carbon in one step, and a proton is added to oxygen in the other step. Which step occurs first, however, depends on the presence of a strong base or strong acid. Because a base is a proton acceptor and an acid is a proton donor:

- Under basic conditions, a proton tends to be removed before one is added.
- Under acidic conditions, a proton tends to be added before one is removed.

The mechanism for the tautomerization reaction (Eq. 7-29) under basic conditions is shown in Equation 7-30, and it consists of back-to-back proton transfer steps. The strong base (HO^-) removes a proton from the α carbon in Step 1, producing an **enolate anion**, which has a resonance-delocalized negative charge. In the resonance structure on the right, the O atom is electron-rich, and in Step 2 of the mechanism, it picks up a proton from water, which acts as the acid.

Mechanism Drawing
Keto-to-Enol/Enol-to-Keto Tautomerization under Basic Conditions

Mechanism for keto-to-enol tautomerization (Eq. 7-29) under basic conditions

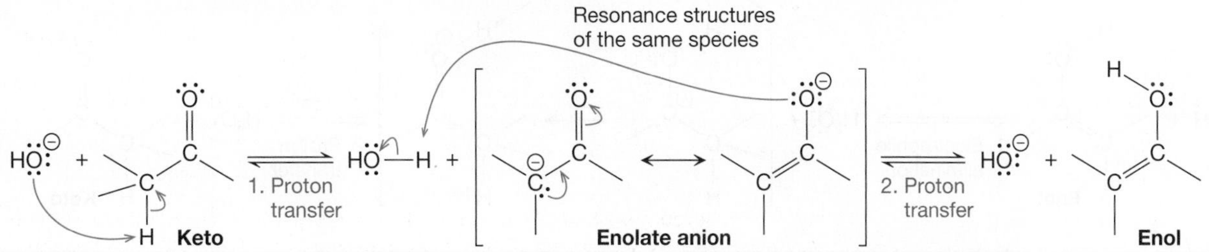

Resonance structures
of the same species
1. Proton transfer
2. Proton transfer
Keto
Enolate anion
Enol

(7-30)

Mechanism for keto-to-enol tautomerization (Eq. 7-29) under acidic conditions

(7-31)

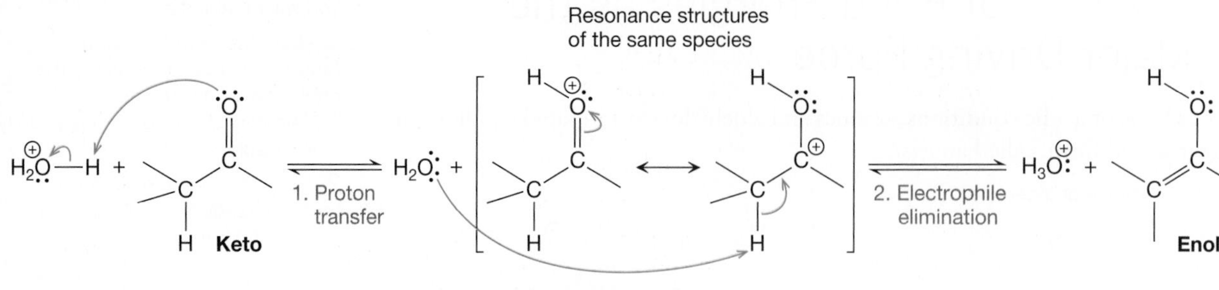
Resonance structures
of the same species
Keto
1. Proton
transfer
2. Electrophile
elimination
Enol

Mechanism Drawing
Keto-to-Enol/Enol-to-Keto Tautomerization under Acidic Conditions

▸ LOOKING AHEAD

The tautomerization mechanisms presented here incorporate two ideas we will revisit in Chapter 8:

1. A mechanism can differ under acidic versus basic conditions, an idea we will revisit in Section 8.6a.
2. Species with multiple resonance structures can appear in a mechanism, an idea we will revisit in Section 8.7.

The mechanism for the reaction under acidic conditions is shown in Equation 7-31. The strong acid (H_3O^+) donates a proton to the O atom of the C═O group in Step 1, a proton transfer step. In Step 2, which is an electrophile elimination step, the proton is eliminated from the α carbon and is picked up by water (a weak base), resulting in a C═C double bond.

Because it is an equilibrium, the tautomerization reaction in Equation 7-29 takes place in the reverse direction, too. Equations 7-32 and 7-33 are the mechanisms showing how the enol form produces the keto form under basic and acidic conditions, respectively. Notice how the steps in Equations 7-32 and 7-33 are the same as in Equations 7-30 and 7-31, respectively, but in reverse order.

Mechanism for enol-to-keto tautomerization (reverse of Eq. 7-29) under basic conditions

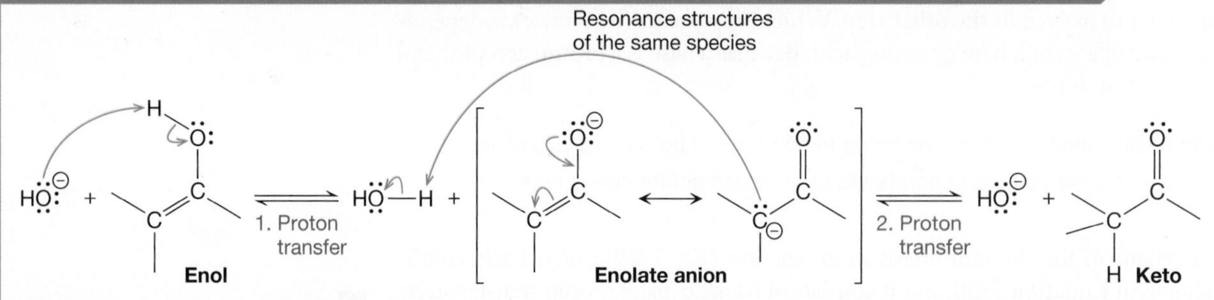
Resonance structures
of the same species
Enol
1. Proton
transfer
Enolate anion
2. Proton
transfer
Keto

(7-32)

Mechanism Drawing
Keto-to-Enol/Enol-to-Keto Tautomerization under Basic Conditions

Mechanism for enol-to-keto tautomerization (reverse of Eq. 7-29) under acidic conditions

(7-33)

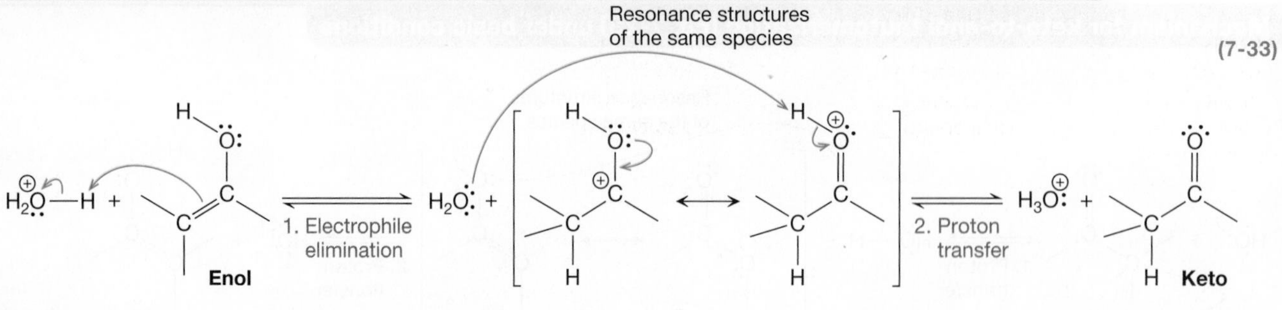
Resonance structures
of the same species
Enol
1. Electrophile
elimination
2. Proton
transfer
Keto

Mechanism Drawing
Keto-to-Enol/Enol-to-Keto Tautomerization under Acidic Conditions

Even though tautomerization takes place readily in both the forward and reverse directions:

> For most aldehydes and ketones, the tautomerization equilibrium (Eq. 7-29, p. 345) heavily favors the keto form over the enol form.

Table 7-1 illustrates this point, showing the relative abundance of keto and enol forms for a variety of tautomers. The enol form is present only in trace amounts, suggesting that the keto form is significantly more stable. In other words, the driving force for these reactions favors the keto form.

Unlike the reactions we saw in Section 7.9, the reactant and product of the tautomerization equilibrium are both uncharged. Therefore, charge stability cannot contribute to the driving force. Instead, the keto form is favored because it has a greater total bond energy than the enol form. To show that the keto form has a greater total bond energy, **Figure 7-12** compares and tallies the energies of the bonds (see Tables 1-2 and 1-3, pp. 10-11) that appear in one form but not the other.

Although three bonds in the keto form differ from the enol form, the greater stability of the keto form comes primarily from the strength of the C=O bond. Consider Table 7-2, which compares similar bonds in the two forms. Notice that the average C=O bond is 101 kJ/mol stronger than the average C=C bond. The differences are substantially smaller when we compare the strengths of the other bonds.

TABLE 7-1 Relative Percentages of Keto and Enol Forms

Tautomerization Reaction Keto ⇌ Enol	Keto	Enol
	99.99994%	0.00006%
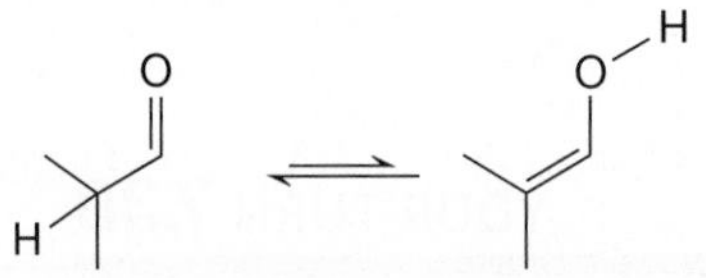	99.986%	0.014%
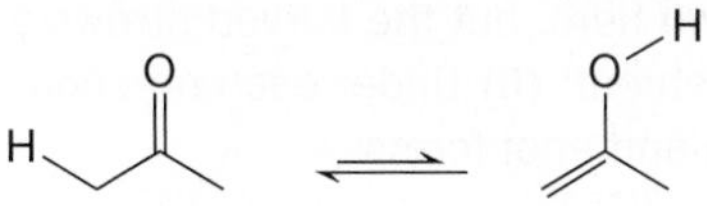	99.9999995%	0.0000005%
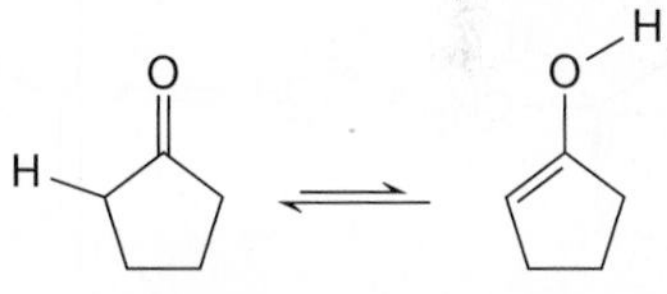	99.9999988%	0.0000012%
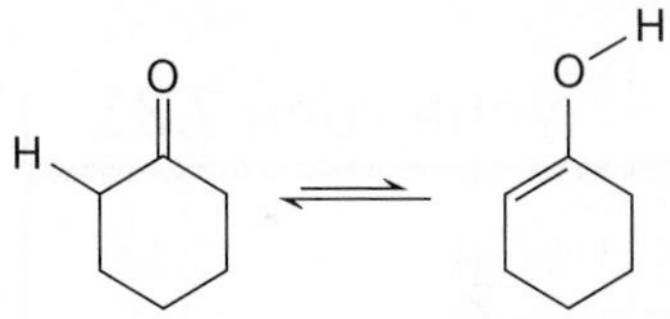	99.99996%	0.00004%

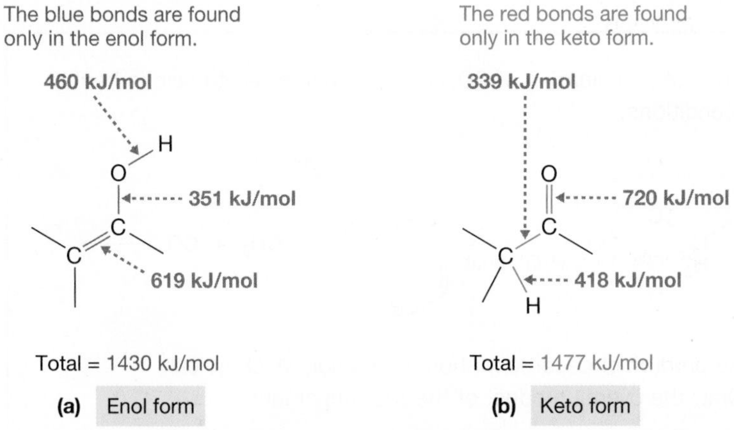

The blue bonds are found only in the enol form.
460 kJ/mol
351 kJ/mol
619 kJ/mol
Total = 1430 kJ/mol
(a) Enol form
The red bonds are found only in the keto form.
339 kJ/mol
720 kJ/mol
418 kJ/mol
Total = 1477 kJ/mol
(b) Keto form

FIGURE 7-12 Relative stabilities of enol and keto forms (a) Energies of bonds that appear in the enol form but not in the keto form. The sum of these energies is 1430 kJ/mol. (b) Energies of bonds that appear in the keto form but not in the enol form. The sum of these energies is 1477 kJ/mol. Because of its greater total bond energy, the keto form is more stable than the enol form.

TABLE 7-2 The Driving Force in Tautomerization

KETO FORM		ENOL FORM		
Bond	Bond Energy (kJ/mol)	Bond	Bond Energy (kJ/mol)	Difference in Bond Energy (kJ/mol)
C=O	720	C=C	619	101
C—C	339	C—O	351	−12
C—H	418	O—H	460	−42

YOUR TURN 7.30

The mechanism for the tautomerization of 2-methylcyclohexanone to its enol form under basic conditions is shown here, but the curved arrows are not shown. **(a)** Draw the curved arrows that account for all electron movement. **(b)** Under each reaction arrow, write the name of the elementary step taking place. **(c)** Label the keto and enol forms.

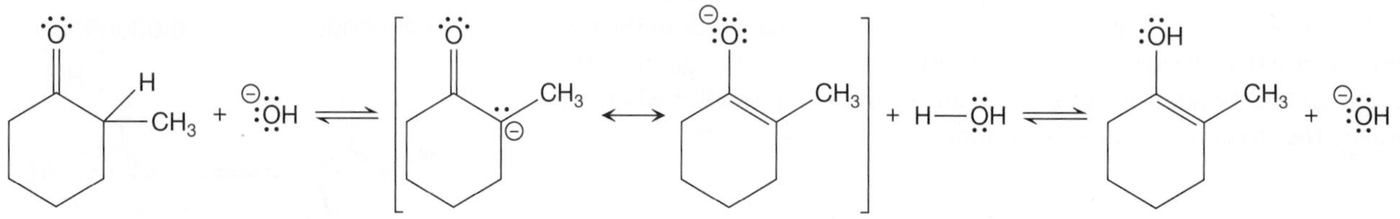

O
H
CH3
+
OH
O
CH3
O
CH3
+ H—OH
OH
CH3
+
OH

YOUR TURN 7.31

Decarboxylation (i.e., elimination of CO_2) occurs when a β-keto acid is heated under acidic conditions.

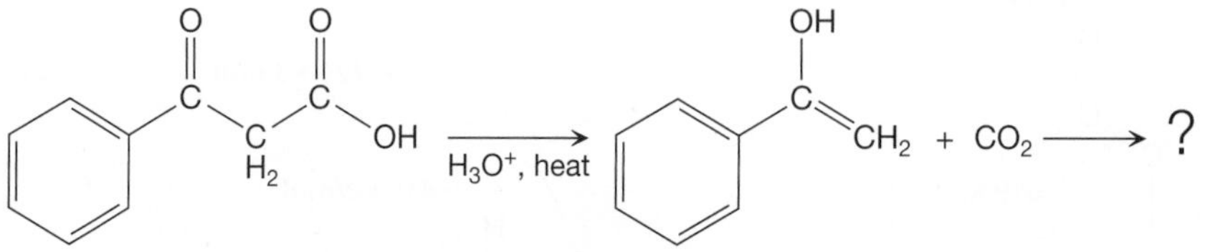

O
O
C
C
C
H2
OH
H3O+, heat
OH
C
CH2
+ CO2
?

The immediate product of decarboxylation is an enol, which quickly rearranges. Draw the overall product of the rearrangement.

Sugar Transformers: Tautomerization in the Body

A sugar inside a cell can be different from the one that might be needed for a particular purpose, but the body has developed an elegant way to deal with this: It can transform one sugar into another using keto–enol tautomerization reactions (Section 7.10). This is exemplified in **Figure 7-13**, which shows a key part of *glycolysis*, a metabolic pathway that breaks down simple carbohydrates for energy.

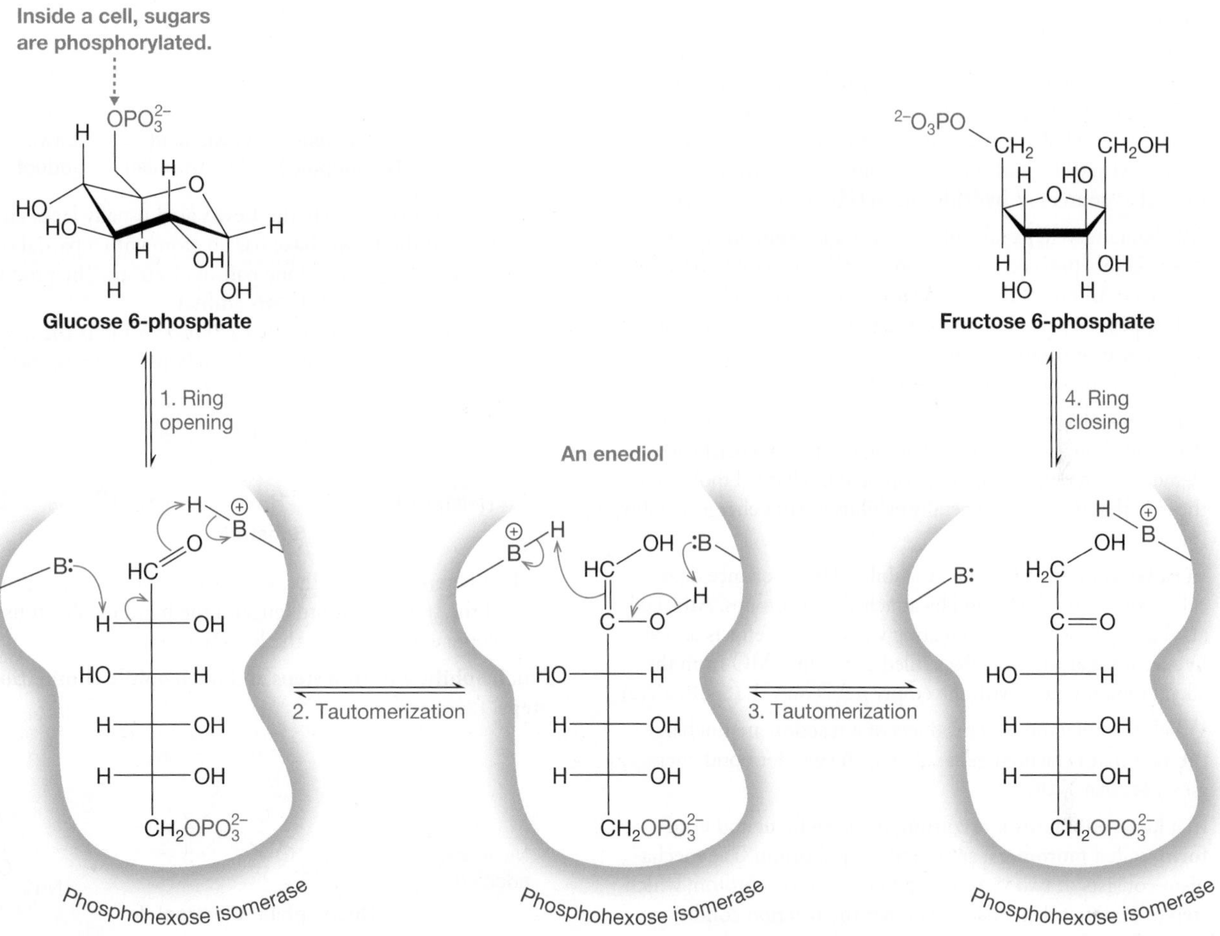

Inside a cell, sugars are phosphorylated.
Glucose 6-phosphate
Fructose 6-phosphate
1. Ring opening
4. Ring closing
An enediol
2. Tautomerization
3. Tautomerization
Phosphohexose isomerase
Phosphohexose isomerase
Phosphohexose isomerase

FIGURE 7-13

When D-glucose enters a cell, it is *phosphorylated* to become glucose 6-phosphate (shown on the left), in which the hydroxyl group on C-6 (the bottommost carbon in the Fischer projection) has been replaced by a phosphate group ($-OPO_3^{2-}$). Before it can be broken down, however, glucose 6-phosphate must be converted into fructose 6-phosphate (shown on the right). This conversion involves back-to-back tautomerization reactions catalyzed by the enzyme phosphohexose isomerase (the active site is shown in purple). The enzyme supplies the basic site (B:) and acidic site (B^+—H) necessary for the proton transfer steps. The first tautomerization produces an enol that contains two different OH groups, so it is more precisely called an *enediol*. The second tautomerization converts the enediol back into a keto form, but on doing so, the C═O bond is part of a different carbon atom than in the initial sugar. The result is a different phosphorylated sugar, known as fructose 6-phosphate.

This process of transforming one sugar into another is not limited to just six-carbon sugars. At a later stage in glycolysis, an enzyme called *phosphotriose isomerase* converts one three-carbon sugar into another. These kinds of processes truly are a testament to the efficiency of biological organisms.

Chapter Summary and Key Terms

- The curved arrow notation for an elementary step reflects the flow of electrons from an *electron-rich* site to an *electron-poor* site. **(Section 7.1a)**
- Metal cations from group 1A of the periodic table behave as **spectator ions**, so they can be disregarded when identifying electron-rich sites in an elementary step. **(Section 7.1b)**
- **Organometallic** reagents, such as alkyllithium reagents (RLi), **Grignard reagents** (RMgX), and lithium dialkylcuprates (R_2CuLi), can be treated as sources of R^-, called **carbanions**. **Hydride reagents**, such as lithium aluminum hydride ($LiAlH_4$) and sodium borohydride ($NaBH_4$), can be treated as sources of **hydride anion ($H\!:^-$)**. **(Section 7.1b)**
- All elementary steps take place in a single event, in which the reactants proceed through one transition state to become products. All bonds that break or form during an elementary step appear as partial bonds in the transition state. All charges that appear or disappear during the step appear as partial charges in the transition state. **(Section 7.2)**
- Charge stability and total bond energy are two major factors that contribute to a reaction's **driving force**. For a reaction or elementary step involving both ions and uncharged molecules, the side that is favored generally exhibits greater charge stability. **(Section 7.8)**
- In carbocations, the C^+ can be stabilized by resonance delocalization of the charge and by attached alkyl groups. Attached alkyl groups are electron-donating via inductive effects and via **hyperconjugation**, whereby a filled σ bonding MO from the alkyl group interacts with the empty *p* AO on C^+. **(Section 7.9)**
- When the reactants and products of a reaction are uncharged, the side that is favored generally has the greater bond energies. **(Section 7.10)**
- In a **keto–enol tautomerization**, the **keto form** and **enol form**, called **tautomers**, are in rapid equilibrium. The mechanism consists of two steps that add or remove a proton; which step occurs first depends on whether the reaction conditions are acidic or basic. In general, the keto form is much more stable than, and therefore favored over, the enol form because it has a greater total bond energy. **(Section 7.10)**
- **Bimolecular nucleophilic substitution (S_N2) steps.** **(Section 7.2)**

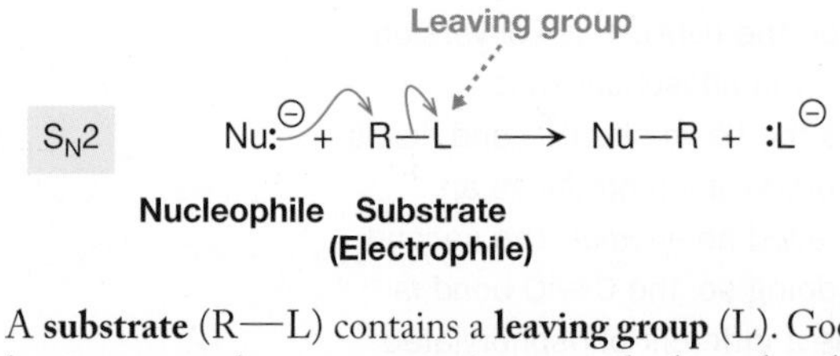

Leaving group
SN2
Nu: + R—L ⟶ Nu—R + :L
Nucleophile
Substrate (Electrophile)

  - A **substrate** (R—L) contains a **leaving group** (L). Good leaving groups have strong conjugate acids. A **nucleophile** that participates in an S_N2 step contains an atom that has a full or partial negative charge and possesses a lone pair of electrons.
  - The nucleophile is relatively *electron-rich*. The atom attached to the leaving group is relatively *electron-poor* and is characterized as an **electrophile**.
- **Coordination steps** and **heterolytic bond dissociation (heterolysis) steps.** **(Section 7.3)**

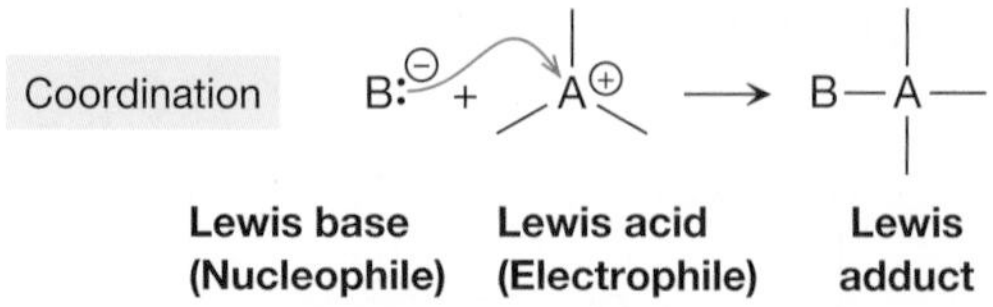

Coordination
B: + A ⟶ B—A—
Lewis base (Nucleophile)
Lewis acid (Electrophile)
Lewis adduct

  - In a coordination step, the **Lewis acid** usually lacks an octet, and the **Lewis base** has an atom with a partial or full negative charge and a lone pair of electrons. The product of such a step is called a **Lewis adduct**.
  - The Lewis base is relatively *electron-rich* and is the nucleophile, whereas the Lewis acid is relatively *electron-poor* and is the electrophile.

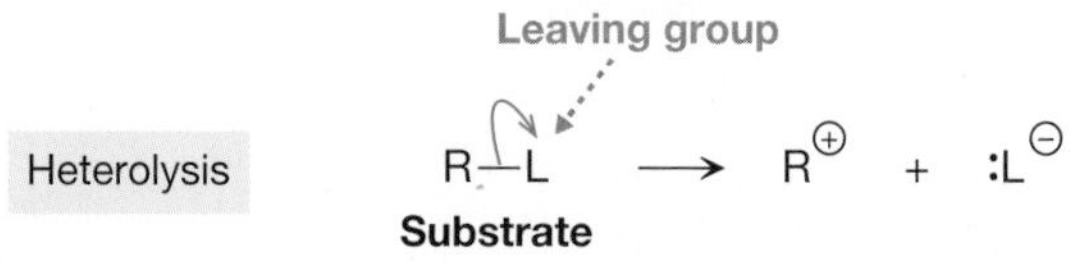

Leaving group
Heterolysis
R—L ⟶ R + :L
Substrate

  - In a heterolysis step, the bond between the leaving group and the substrate is broken, and the bonding electrons become a lone pair on the leaving group.
- **Nucleophilic addition steps** and **nucleophile elimination steps.** **(Section 7.4)**

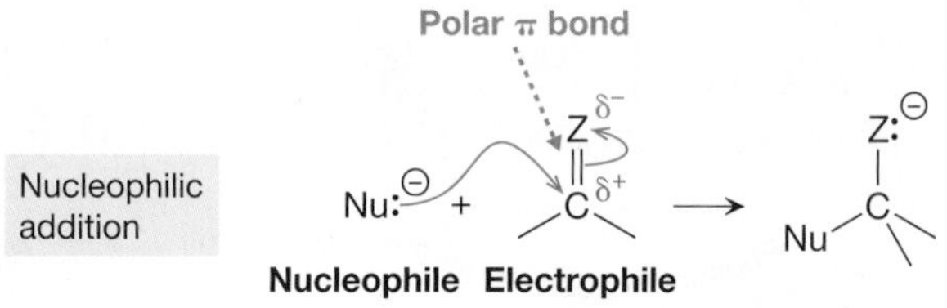

Polar π bond
Nucleophilic addition
Nu: + Z=C ⟶ Nu—C—Z:
Nucleophile
Electrophile

  - In a nucleophilic addition step, a nucleophile forms a bond to the positive end of a polar C—Z π bond, forcing a pair of electrons from the π bond onto Z.
  - The nucleophile is relatively *electron-rich*. The atom at the positive end of the polar C—Z π bond is relatively *electron-poor* and acts as the electrophile.

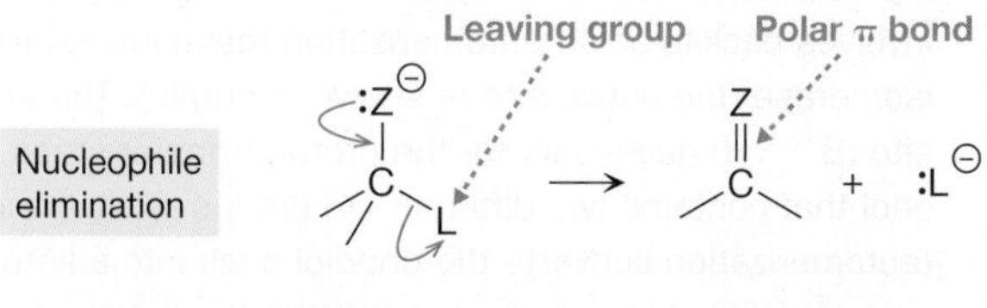

Leaving group
Polar π bond
Nucleophile elimination
:Z—C—L ⟶ Z=C + :L

  - In a nucleophile elimination step, a new C—Z π bond is formed at the same time that a leaving group is expelled.

- **Bimolecular elimination (E2) steps.** (Section 7.5)

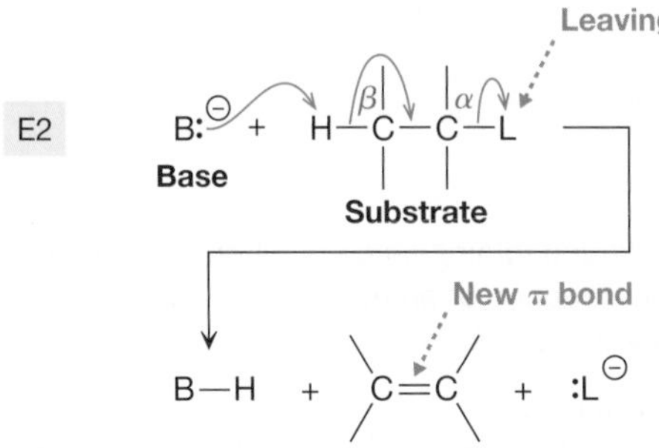
Leaving group
E2
B:
Base
H—C—C—L
β
α
Substrate
New π bond
B—H + C=C + :L

  - An E2 step is a type of **β-elimination**. A base deprotonates an atom designated β on the substrate at the same time that a leaving group is expelled from the atom designated α, forming an additional π bond between the α and β atoms.
  - The base is relatively *electron-rich*. The α carbon atom, which is bonded to the leaving group, is relatively *electron-poor*.

- **Electrophilic addition steps** and **electrophile elimination steps.** (Section 7.6)

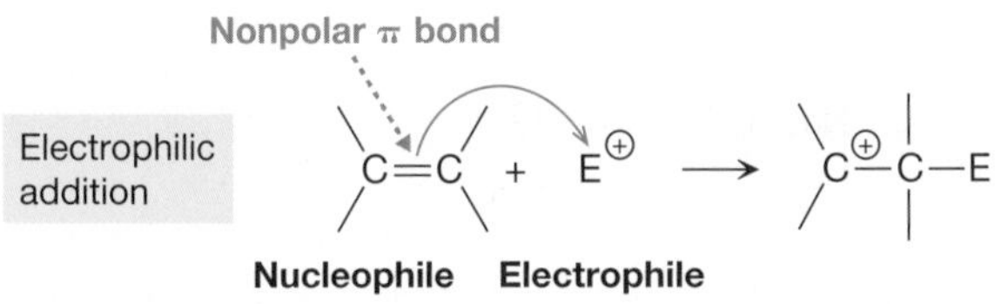
Nonpolar π bond
Electrophilic addition
C=C + E
C—C—E
Nucleophile
Electrophile

  - In an electrophilic addition step, a pair of electrons from a nonpolar π bond forms a bond to an *electrophile*.
  - The nonpolar π bond is relatively *electron-rich*, so it acts as the nucleophile. The electrophile is relatively *electron-poor*.

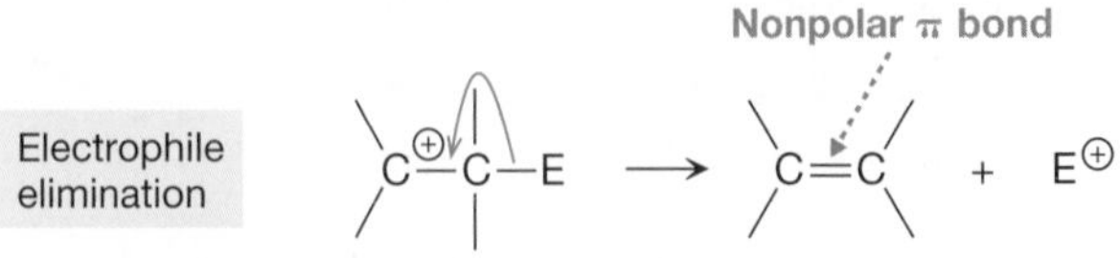
Nonpolar π bond
Electrophile elimination
C—C—E
C=C + E

  - In an electrophile elimination step, an electrophile is eliminated from a carbocation species and a nonpolar π bond is formed simultaneously.

- **Carbocation rearrangements.** (Section 7.7)

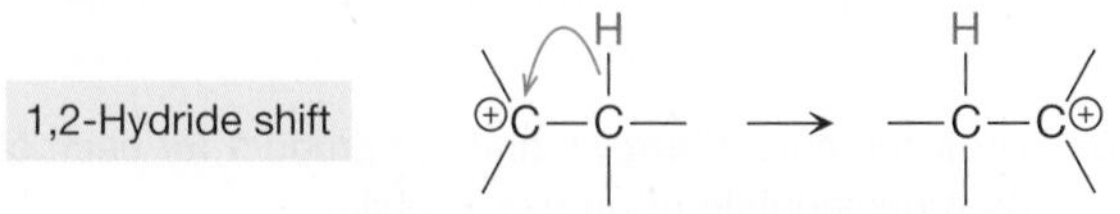
1,2-Hydride shift
H

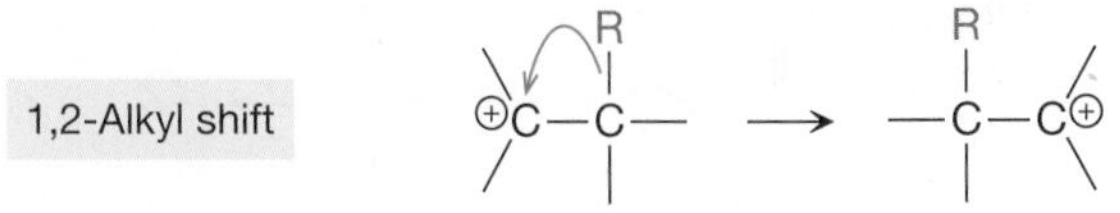
1,2-Alkyl shift
R

  - In a **1,2-hydride shift** or **1,2-alkyl shift**, a C—H or C—C bond adjacent to a C^+ is broken, and the bond is re-formed to the C atom that initially carried the positive charge. The positive charge moves to the C atom whose bond was broken.
  - A **1,2-methyl shift** is a 1,2-alkyl shift in which a methyl group (CH_3) migrates.

Problems

Sections 7.1–7.7 Curved Arrow Notation and Elementary Steps

7.1 Predict the product of the reaction between phenol (C_6H_5OH) and each of the compounds shown here. *Hint*: First determine which elementary step is likely to occur.

(a) CH_3OK (b) CH_3Li (c) 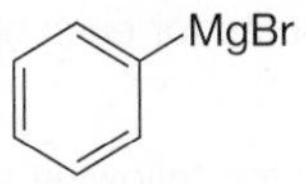 (d) $LiAlH_4$

MgBr

7.2 Determine whether each of the following elementary steps is acceptable. For those that are, draw the products. For those that are not, explain why. *Hint*: Explaining why may involve drawing the products.

(a)
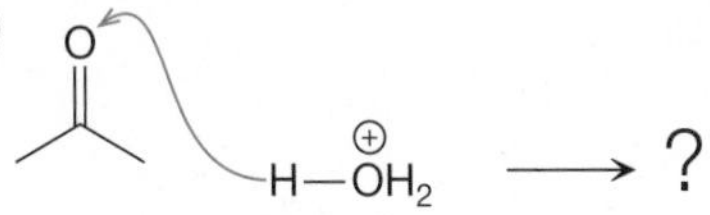
O
H—OH2
?

(b)
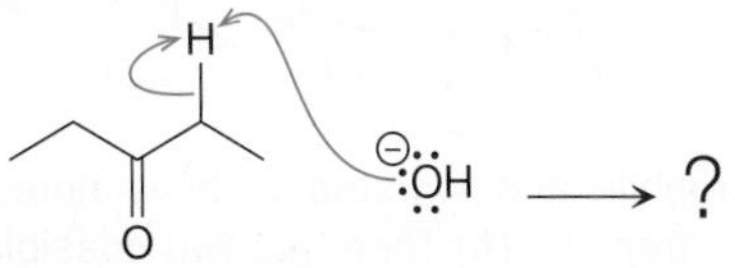
H
O
:OH
?

(c)
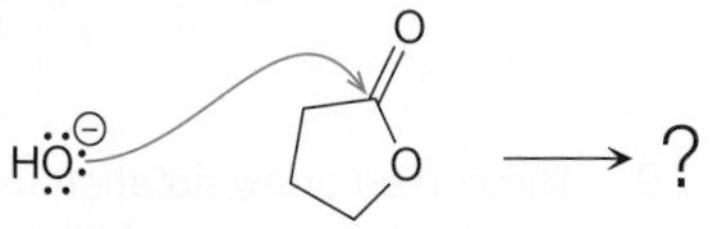
HO:
O
O
?

(d)
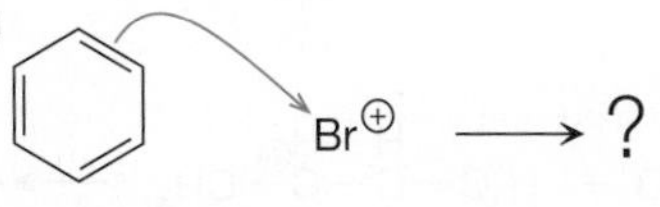
Br
?

(e)
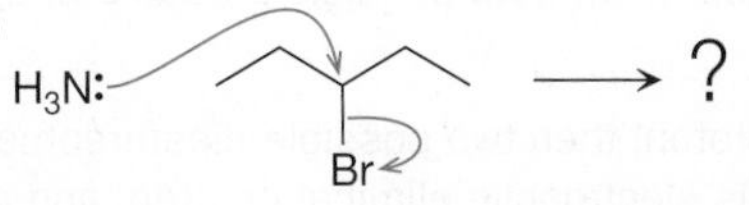
H3N:
Br
?

7.3 Draw the curved arrows and the product for each of the following S_N2 steps.

(a) 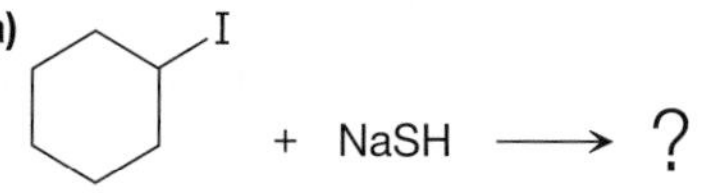

(b) 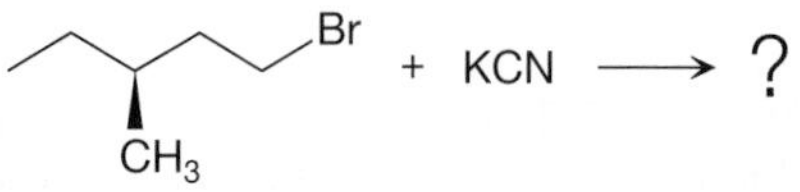

7.4 Draw the appropriate curved arrows and products for each set of reactants undergoing a coordination step. Then, identify each reactant species as either a Lewis acid or a Lewis base and as a nucleophile or an electrophile. Finally, use curved arrow notation to show each product undergoing heterolysis to regenerate reactants.

(a) 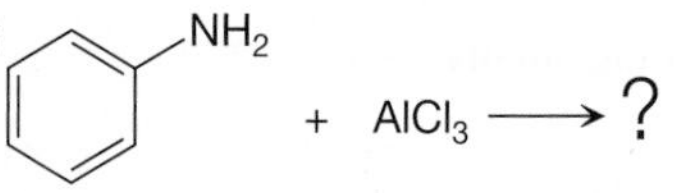

(b) 

(c) 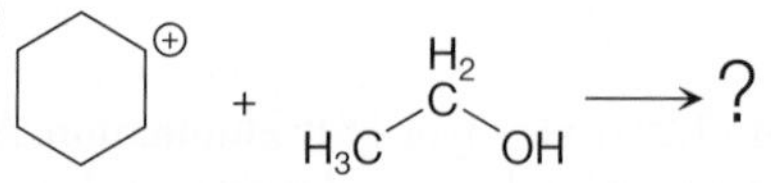

7.5 Draw the curved arrows and the product for each of the following nucleophilic addition steps, and identify each reactant as a nucleophile or an electrophile.

(a) 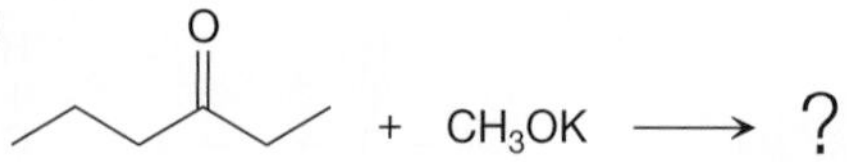

(b) 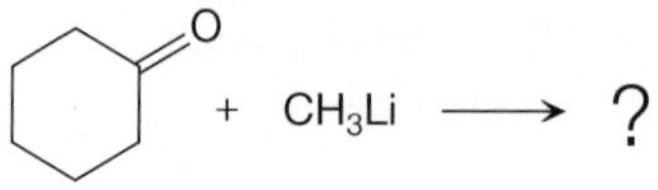

(c) 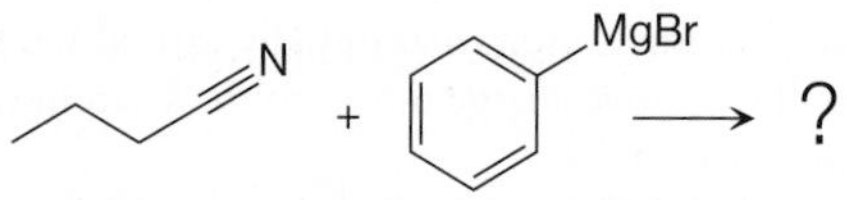

(d) 

(e) 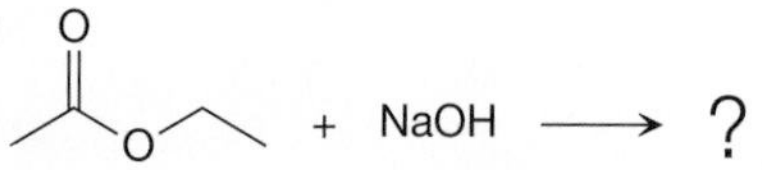

(f) 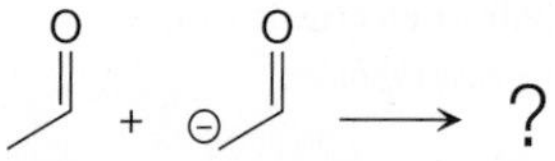

7.6 For each of the steps in Problem 7.5, determine whether the product can eliminate a leaving group to produce a compound that is different from the reactants. For those that can, draw the appropriate curved arrows and the new product that forms.

7.7 If the anionic species shown here were to eliminate a leaving group, the three possibilities would be H_3C^-, Cl^-, or CH_3O^-. Draw the curved arrow notation and the products for each of these elimination steps. Which is the major product? Why?

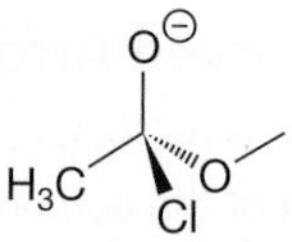

7.8 Which of the following substrates can undergo an E2 step with H_2N^- as the base? For those that can, draw the curved arrow notation and the products.

(a) 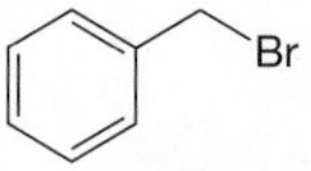

(b) 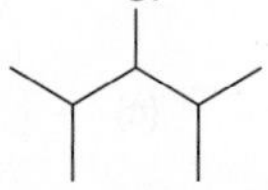

(c) 

(d) 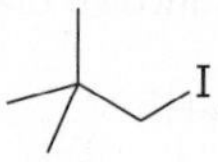

(e) 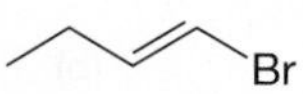

7.9 The curved arrow notation for an electrophilic addition step is shown here. **(a)** Identify the nucleophile and the electrophile. **(b)** There are two possible products of this electrophilic addition step. Draw both possible products and predict which one is more stable.

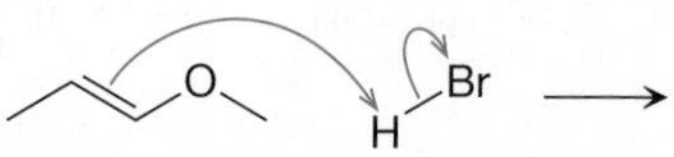

7.10 If the H colored red is eliminated as a proton, then two possible diastereomers can form. Draw the curved arrows for this electrophile elimination step, and draw each of the diastereomeric products.

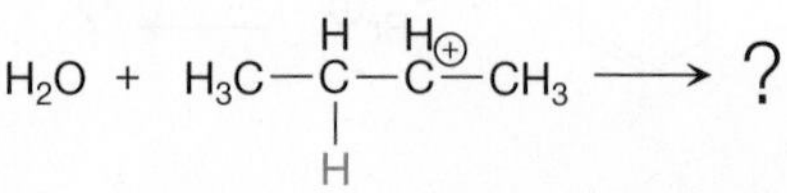

7.11 If H^+ is eliminated from the carbocation shown here in an electrophile elimination step, then three possible constitutional isomers can form. Draw the mechanism for the formation of each of the three products.

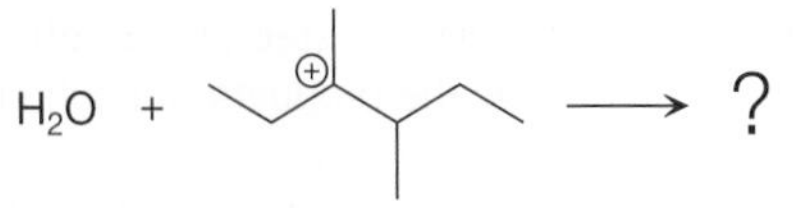

H2O +
?

7.12 In the electrophilic addition step shown here, NO_2^+ can add to phenol either ortho, meta, or para to the OH substituent on the ring. **(a)** Draw the curved arrows and products of each electrophilic addition step. **(b)** Identify each reactant as either the nucleophile or the electrophile.

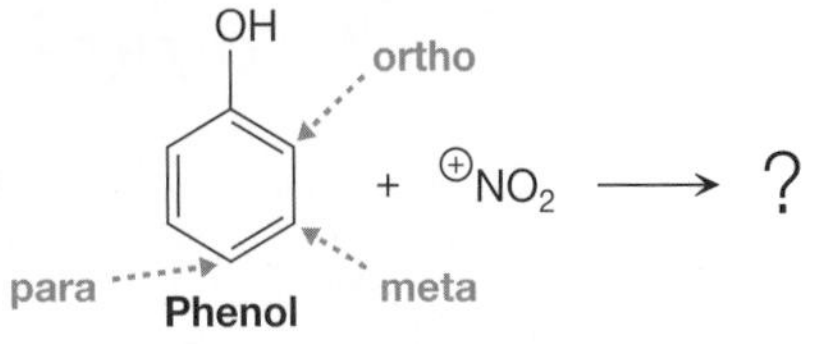

OH
ortho
+ NO2
?
para
meta
Phenol

7.13 A proton (H^+) from trifluoromethanesulfonic acid, CF_3SO_2OH, can add to the alkyne shown here to yield two different carbocation products. **(a)** Draw the mechanism for each of these steps, along with the corresponding products. **(b)** Which carbocation is more stable?

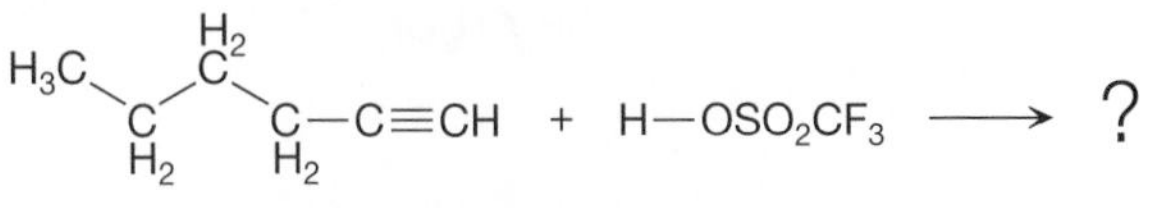

H3C
H2
C≡CH
+ H—OSO2CF3
?

7.14 The carbocation shown here is formed in one step of an electrophilic aromatic substitution reaction (discussed in Chapter 24). **(a)** Draw the curved arrow notation and the product for the elimination of H^+. **(b)** Do the same for the elimination of SO_3H^+.

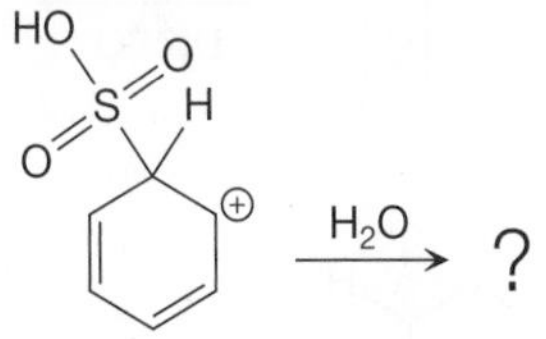

HO
O
S
H
O
H2O
?

7.15 For each of these carbocations, draw the curved arrow notation and product for all possible 1,2-hydride shifts and all possible 1,2-methyl shifts.

(a)
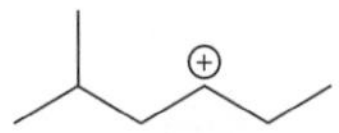

(b)
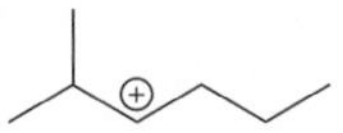

(c)
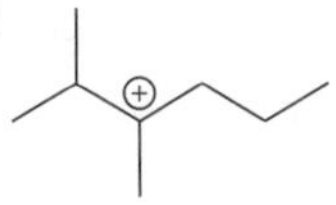

(d)
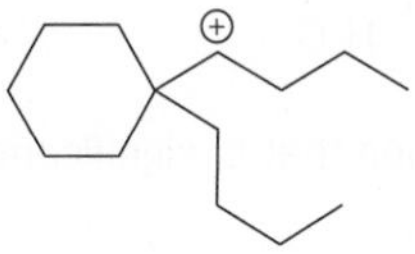

(e)
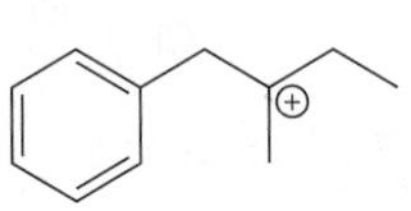

(f)
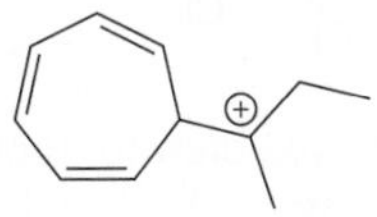

Sections 7.8–7.10 The Driving Force for Chemical Reactions and Keto–Enol Tautomerization

7.16 For each elementary step given, determine whether the reactant or product side is favored.

(a)

:Cl:
OH
?

(b)
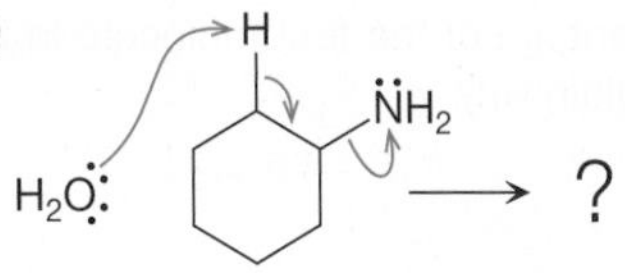

H
NH2
H2O:
?

(c)
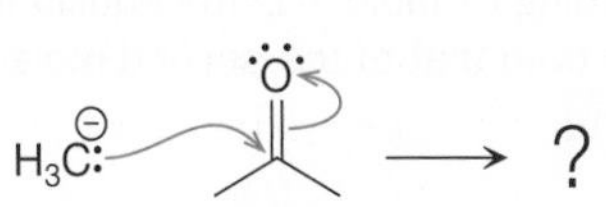

O
H3C:
?

(d)
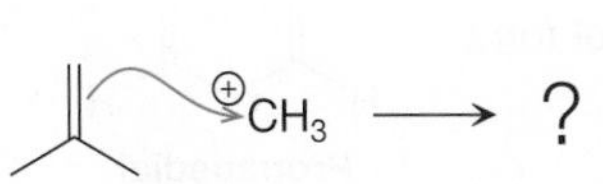

CH3
?

(e)
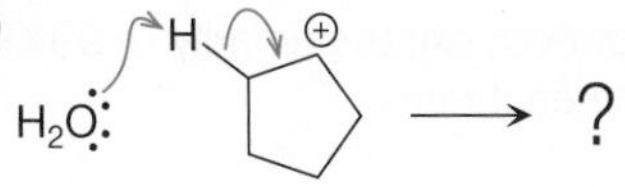

H
H2O:
?

(f)
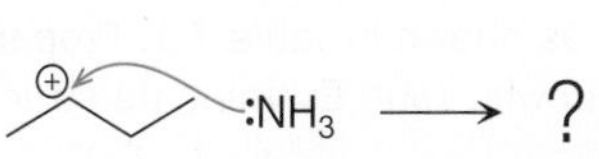

:NH3
?

7.17 Each heterolysis step on the left does not readily occur, but the corresponding one on the right does. Explain why. *Hint*: Draw the products of each heterolysis and determine the contributions to their driving force.

(a)

Br
CH3CH2OH
?
Br
CH3CH2OH
?

(b)

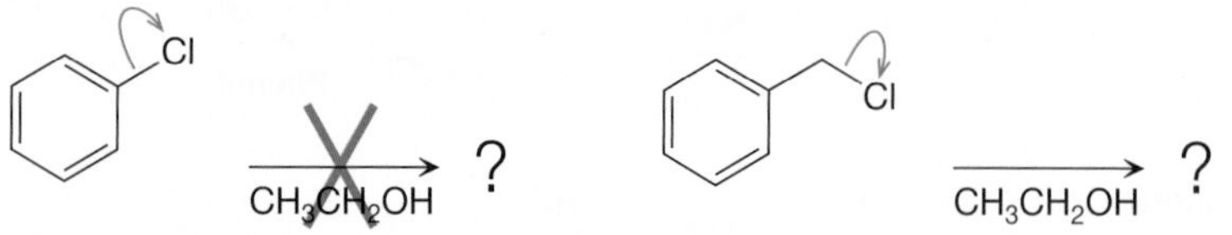
Cl
CH3CH2OH
?
Cl
CH3CH2OH
?

(c)

Br
DMSO
?
Br
CH3CH2OH
?

(d)

H
CH3CH2OH
?
I
CH3CH2OH
?

7.18 The first of the two heterolysis reactions shown here takes place readily, but the second one does not. Explain why.

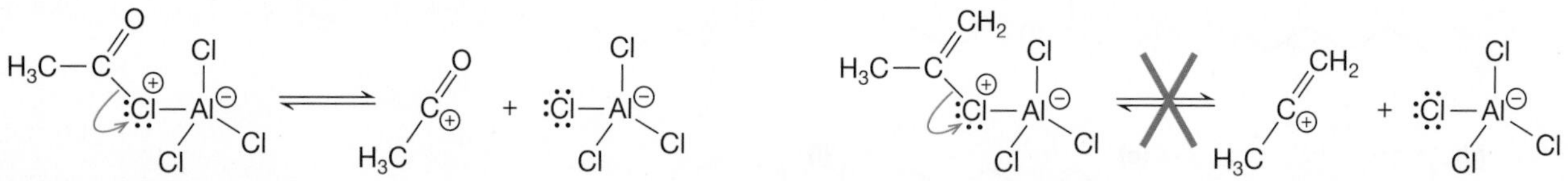

7.19 Determine which carbocation rearrangements you drew for Problem 7.15 produce a carbocation that is significantly more stable than the reactant.

7.20 According to Table 7-1, the equilibrium percentage of the first molecule in its keto form is lower than that of the second molecule. Explain why. *Hint:* What do you know about the stability of C=C double bonds?

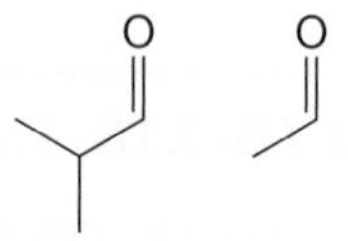

7.21 According to Table 7-1, the equilibrium percentage of the first molecule in its keto form is lower than that of the second molecule. Explain why.

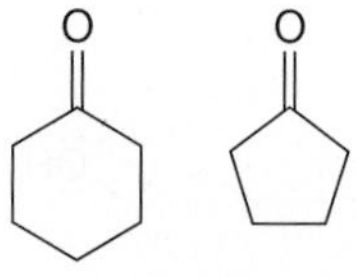

7.22 Recall from Section 7.10 that most ketones and aldehydes exist primarily in their keto form, as shown in Table 7-1. Propanedial, however, exists primarily (>99%) in its enol form. Explain why. *Hint:* Examine its structure in the enol form.

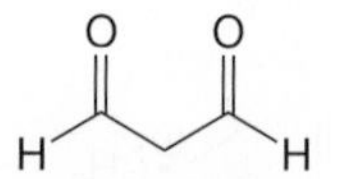

Propanedial

7.23 Draw the mechanisms for the conversion of propanedial (see Problem 7.22) in its keto form to its enol form under basic and acidic conditions. Do the same for the conversion from the enol form to the keto form.

7.24 A tautomerization reaction can occur with an imine in a way analogous to that of a ketone or aldehyde. Using the appropriate bond energies from Section 1.4, determine which form is more stable, the imine or enamine.

NH
NH2

Imine **Enamine**

Integrated Problems

7.25 The following reaction, which is discussed in Chapter 8, is an example of a unimolecular nucleophilic substitution (S_N1) reaction. It consists of the four elementary steps shown here. For each step (1–4), **(a)** identify all nucleophiles, electrophiles, Brønsted acids, and Brønsted bases on the reactant side of each elementary step; **(b)** draw in the appropriate curved arrows to show the bond formation and bond breaking that occur; and **(c)** name the elementary step.

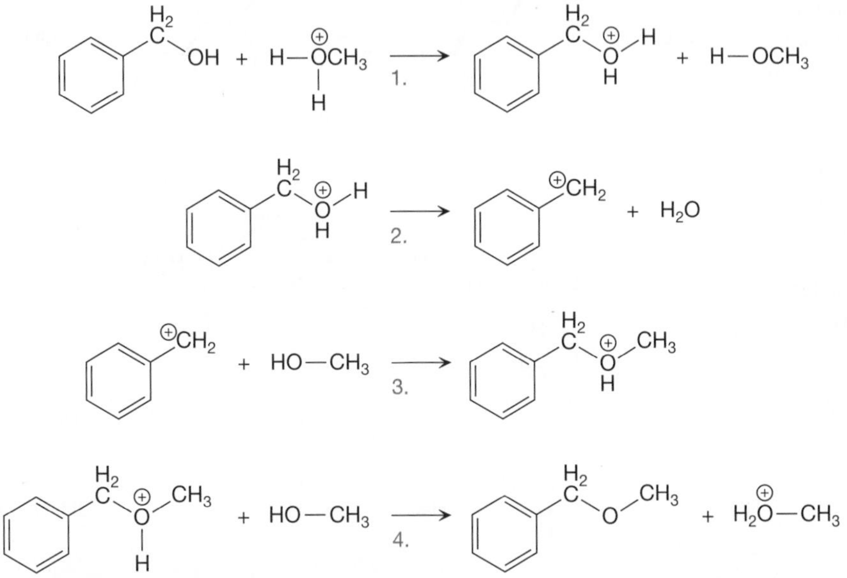

7.26 The reaction shown here, which is discussed in Chapter 8, is an example of a unimolecular elimination (E1) reaction and consists of the three elementary steps shown. For each step (1–3), **(a)** identify all nucleophiles, electrophiles, Brønsted acids, and Brønsted bases on the reactant side of each elementary step; **(b)** draw in the appropriate curved arrows to show the bond formation and bond breaking that occur; and **(c)** name the elementary step.

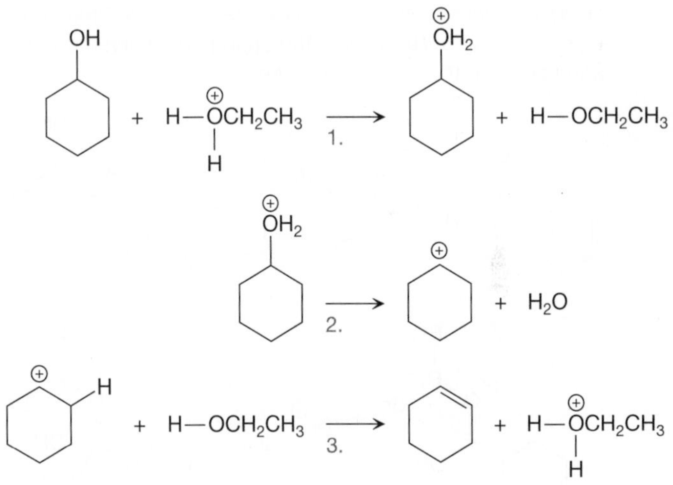

7.27 The reaction shown here, which converts an epoxide into a bromohydrin, is discussed in Chapter 10. It consists of the two elementary steps shown. For each step (1 and 2), **(a)** identify all nucleophiles, electrophiles, Brønsted acids, and Brønsted bases on the reactant side of each elementary step; **(b)** draw in the appropriate curved arrows to show the bond formation and bond breaking that occur; and **(c)** name the elementary step.

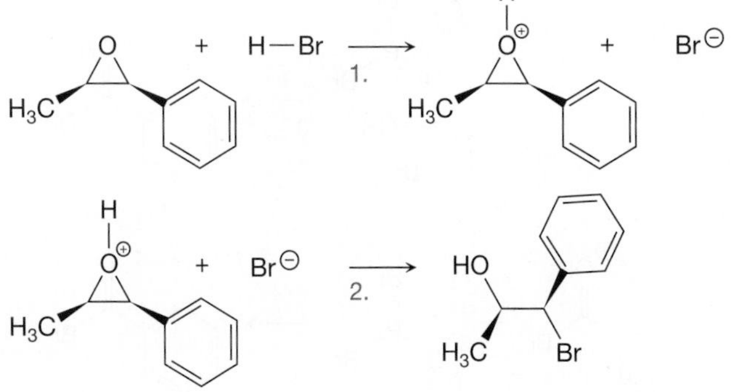

7.28 The reaction shown here, which is discussed in Chapter 10, consists of the two elementary steps shown. For each step (1 and 2), **(a)** identify all nucleophiles, electrophiles, Brønsted acids, and Brønsted bases on the reactant side of each elementary step; **(b)** draw in the appropriate curved arrows to show the bond formation and bond breaking that occur; and **(c)** name the elementary step.

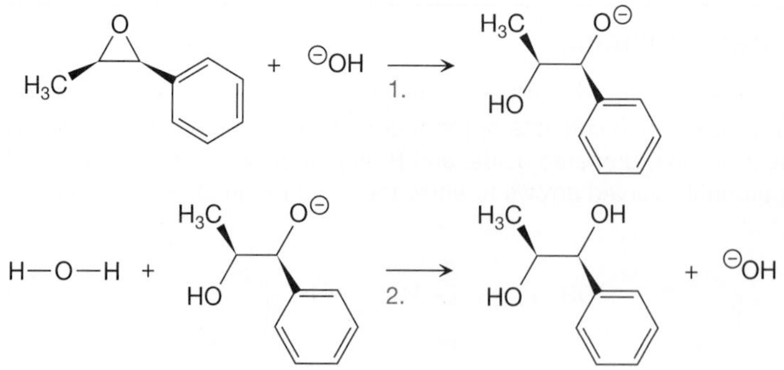

7.29 The following reaction, which converts a cyclic ether into a diol, is discussed in Chapter 8. It consists of the three elementary steps shown. For each step (1–3), **(a)** identify all nucleophiles, electrophiles, Brønsted acids, and Brønsted bases on the reactant side of each elementary step; **(b)** draw in the appropriate curved arrows to show the bond formation and bond breaking that occur; and **(c)** name the elementary step.

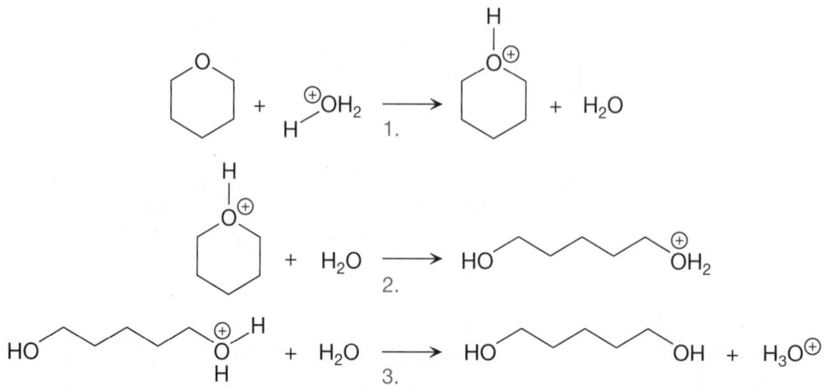

7.30 The following reaction, which is discussed in Chapter 23, consists of the four elementary steps shown. For each step (1–4), **(a)** identify all nucleophiles, electrophiles, Brønsted acids, and Brønsted bases on the reactant side of each elementary step; **(b)** draw in the appropriate curved arrows to show the bond formation and bond breaking that occur; and **(c)** name the elementary step.

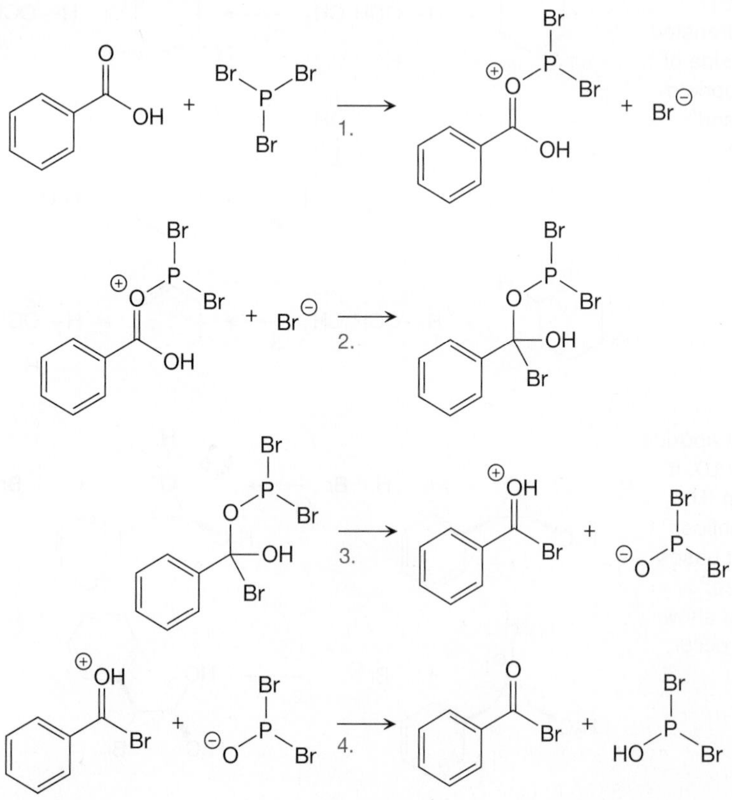

7.31 The following reaction, which is discussed in Chapter 18, consists of the two elementary steps shown. For each step (1 and 2), **(a)** identify all nucleophiles, electrophiles, Brønsted acids, and Brønsted bases on the reactant side of each elementary step; **(b)** draw in the appropriate curved arrows to show the bond formation and bond breaking that occur; and **(c)** name the elementary step.

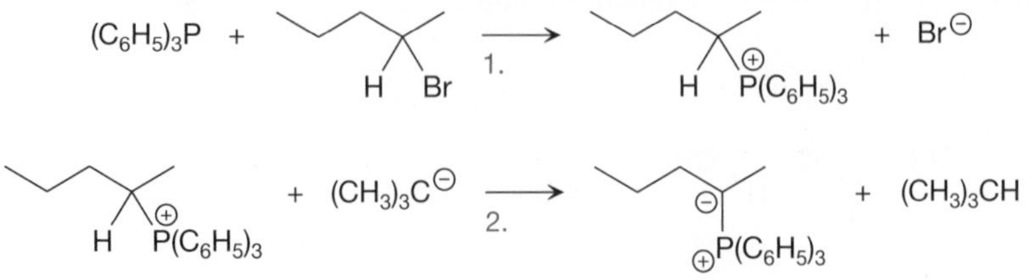

(C6H5)3P
H
Br
1.
H
P(C6H5)3
Br
H
P(C6H5)3
(CH3)3C
2.
P(C6H5)3
(CH3)3CH

7.32 The following is an example of a Fischer esterification reaction, which is discussed in Chapter 23. The mechanism consists of the six elementary steps shown. For each step (1–6), **(a)** identify all nucleophiles, electrophiles, Brønsted acids, and Brønsted bases on the reactant side of each elementary step; **(b)** draw in the appropriate curved arrows to show the bond formation and bond breaking that occur; and **(c)** name the elementary step.

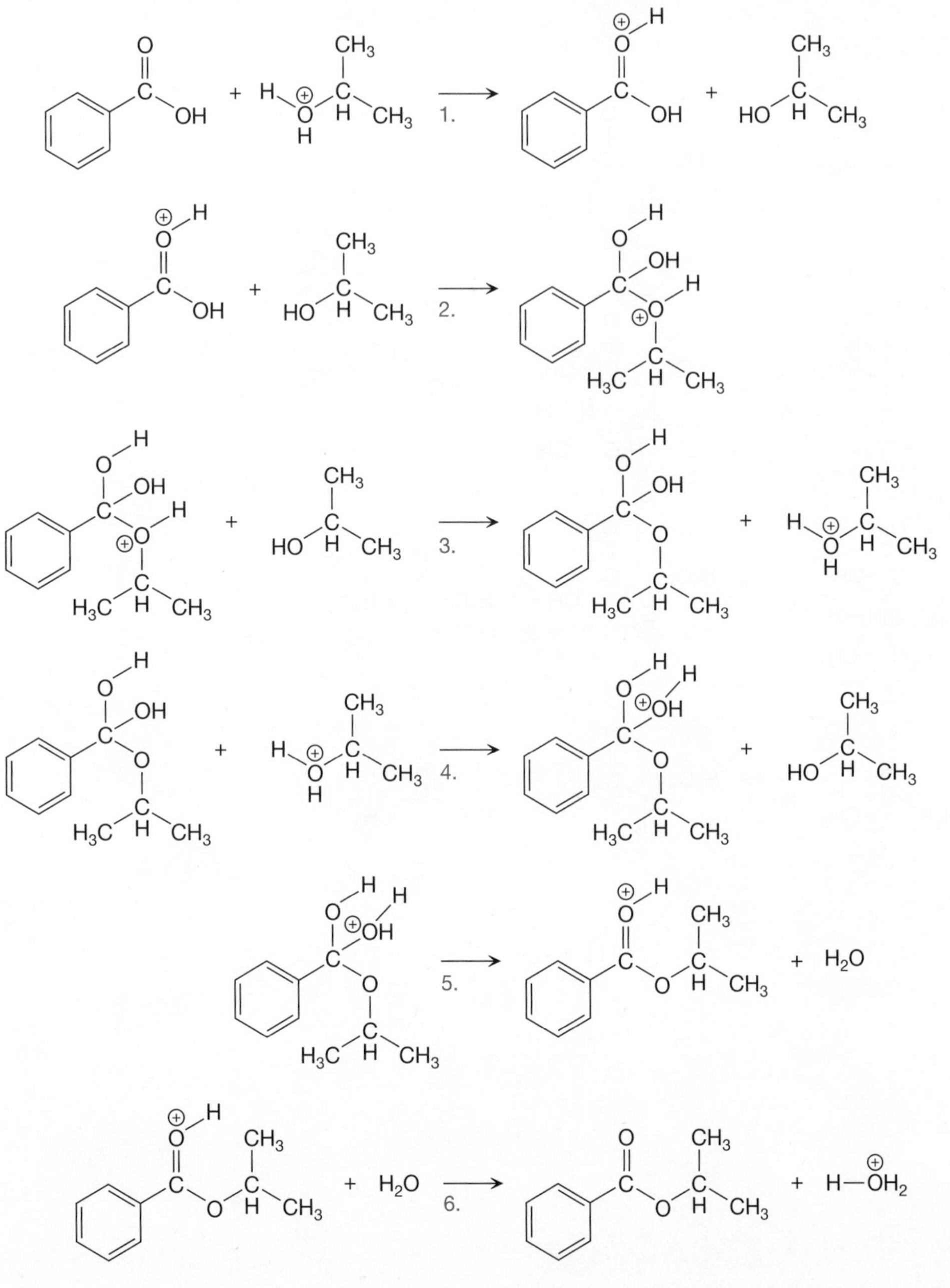

1.
2.
3.
4.
5.
6.
H2O
H—OH2

7.33 The following reaction is an example of an acid-catalyzed hydrolysis of an amide. This reaction, which is the same one that breaks down proteins into amino acids in your stomach, is discussed in Chapter 23. The mechanism consists of the six elementary steps shown. For each step (1–6), **(a)** identify all nucleophiles, electrophiles, Brønsted acids, and Brønsted bases on the reactant side of each elementary step; **(b)** draw in the appropriate curved arrows to show the bond formation and bond breaking that occur; and **(c)** name the elementary step.

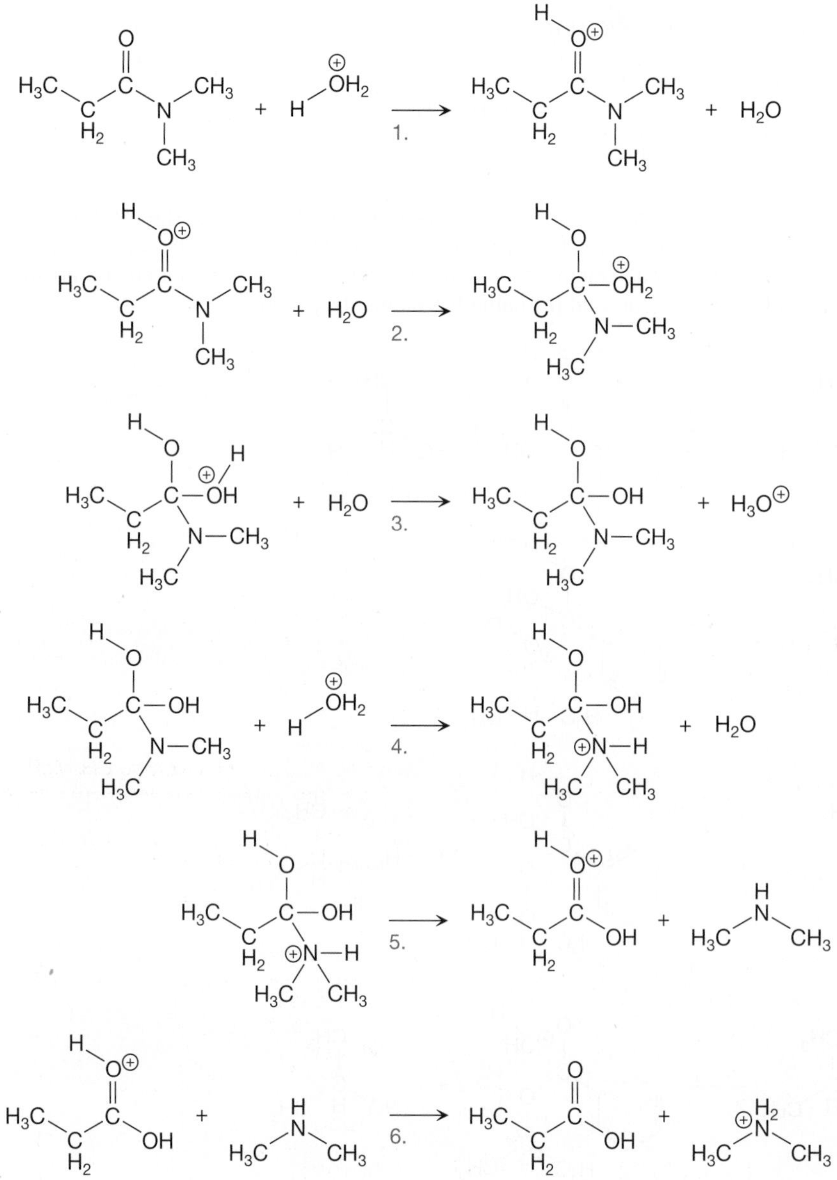

7.34 Shown here is an example of an electrophilic aromatic substitution reaction, which we examine in Chapter 24. The mechanism consists of the four elementary steps shown. For each step (1–4), **(a)** identify all nucleophiles, electrophiles, Brønsted acids, and Brønsted bases on the reactant side of each elementary step; **(b)** draw in the appropriate curved arrows to show the bond formation and bond breaking that occur; and **(c)** name the elementary step.

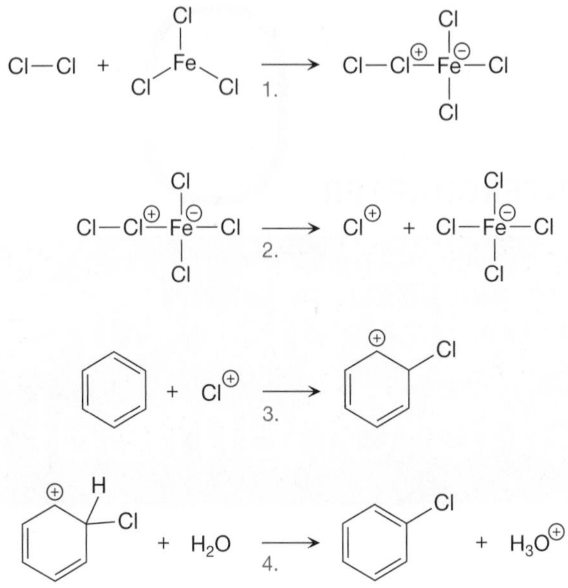

Cl—Cl
Cl
Fe
Cl
Cl
1.
Cl—Cl—Fe—Cl
2.
Cl
3.
H
Cl
H2O
4.
H3O

7.35 Draw the curved arrow notation and products for each elementary step described by the sequence shown here. *Note:* The products of the first step should be used as reactants in the second step.

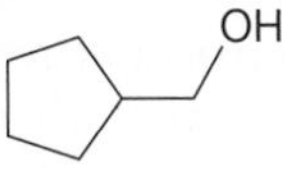

OH

1. Proton transfer involving HCl
2. S_N2 involving $Cl^{\ominus}$

?

7.36 Draw the curved arrow notation and products for each elementary step described by the sequence shown here. *Note:* The products of each step should be used as reactants in the subsequent step.

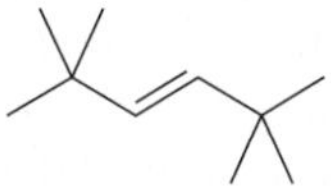

1. Electrophilic addition of $H^{\oplus}$ from HCl
2. 1,2-Methyl shift
3. Electrophile elimination of $H^{\oplus}$ involving H_2O

?

7.37 Draw the curved arrow notation and products for each elementary step described by the sequence shown here. *Note:* The products of each step should be used as reactants in the subsequent step.

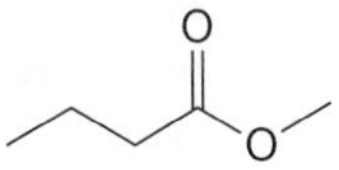

O
O

1. Nucleophilic addition involving CH_3MgBr
2. Nucleophile elimination
3. Nucleophilic addition involving CH_3MgBr
4. Proton transfer involving $H_3O^{\oplus}$

?

7.38 Draw the curved arrow notation and products for each elementary step described by the sequence shown here. *Note:* The products of each step should be used as reactants in the subsequent step.

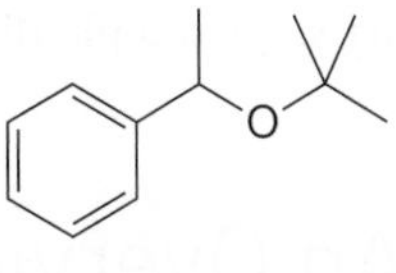

O

1. Proton transfer involving $H_3O^{\oplus}$
2. Heterolysis
3. Coordination involving H_2O
4. Proton transfer involving H_2O

?

7.39 Draw the curved arrow notation and products for each elementary step described by the sequence shown here. *Note:* The products of each step should be used as reactants in the subsequent step.

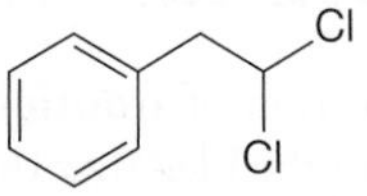

Cl
Cl

1. E2 involving $NaNH_2$
2. E2 involving $NaNH_2$
3. Proton transfer involving $NaNH_2$
4. Proton transfer involving $H_3O^{\oplus}$

?

INTERCHAPTER C

Molecular Orbital Theory and Chemical Reactions

Chapters 6 and 7 introduced 10 of the most common elementary steps that make up organic reaction mechanisms. For each step, we examined the curved arrow notation that enables us to depict the changes that take place among valence electrons throughout the course of the reaction. Furthermore, we discussed how such changes in valence electrons tend to represent a flow of electrons from an electron-rich site to an electron-poor site. Thus far, however, these aspects have been discussed only in terms of the Lewis structure model; there has been no mention of orbitals, which, as we learned in Chapter 3, help govern the structure and stability of a species. Here in Interchapter C, we explore the important roles of orbitals in chemical reactions.

We begin by giving an overview of what is called *frontier molecular orbital (FMO) theory*. Then we apply FMO theory to each of the elementary steps presented in Chapters 6 and 7. We will see how FMO theory explains why each step occurs and how it accounts for the flow of electrons from an electron-rich site to an electron-poor one. Additionally, we will see how FMO theory justifies the *stereochemistry* of certain elementary steps, a topic that will be discussed more fully in Chapter 8.

C.1 An Overview of Frontier Molecular Orbital Theory

SECTION C.1 OBJECTIVES

You will be able to:

1. Describe the role of frontier molecular orbitals in stabilizing the transition state for an elementary step.
2. Distinguish an allowed elementary step from an elementary step that is forbidden on the basis of frontier molecular orbital overlap.

◂ RECALL

Section 3.10 explained that the HOMO is the highest-energy molecular orbital that contains electrons. The LUMO is the lowest-energy molecular orbital that is empty.

The application of **frontier molecular orbital (FMO) theory** to chemical reactions begins with the idea that the reactants in an elementary step must typically surmount a significant energy barrier, the free energy of activation ($\Delta G^{\circ\ddagger}$, Section 6.4), to get to products. The energy barrier arises because the transition state is less stable than the reactants. If the transition state does not have a source of significant stabilization, the energy barrier could be very large (red curve, **Figure C-1**), making the elementary step's rate excessively slow; there would effectively be no reaction. Conversely, stabilization of the transition state can lower the energy barrier to allow the elementary step to take place at a reasonable rate (blue curve, Fig. C-1).

How might the transition state be stabilized to lower the energy barrier and increase the reaction rate? One of the main contributions comes from the **frontier molecular orbitals** of the reacting species, which are defined as its *highest occupied* and *lowest unoccupied* molecular orbitals (i.e., the HOMO and LUMO, respectively; see Recall box):

Chapter Outline

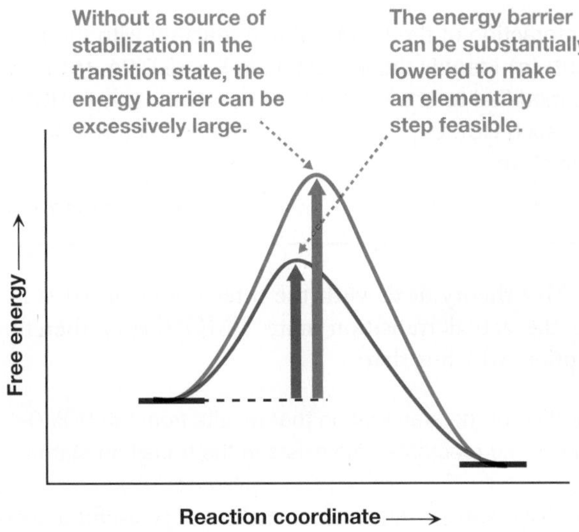
Without a source of stabilization in the transition state, the energy barrier can be excessively large.
The energy barrier can be substantially lowered to make an elementary step feasible.
Free energy
Reaction coordinate

FIGURE C-1 Energy barriers and transition-state stabilization The red curve represents an elementary step in which the transition state is not significantly stabilized (large energy barrier), making the reaction excessively slow. When the transition state is significantly stabilized (smaller energy barrier), as indicated by the blue curve, the reaction rate is substantially increased.

- If the HOMO of one reactant and the LUMO of another have substantial net overlap in the transition state, then the transition state tends to be significantly stabilized, and the reaction of interest is said to be *allowed*.
- If there is little or no net overlap between the above HOMO and LUMO orbitals, then the transition state tends *not* to be sufficiently stabilized, and the reaction of interest is said to be *forbidden*.

The frontier orbitals of the reactants are the focus for two reasons:

1. Of all imaginable interactions of a filled orbital with an empty orbital, the HOMO–LUMO interaction is generally the one that involves orbitals that are closest in energy (**Figure C-2a**). The similar energies of the HOMO and LUMO maximize any interaction that takes place when the orbitals mix.

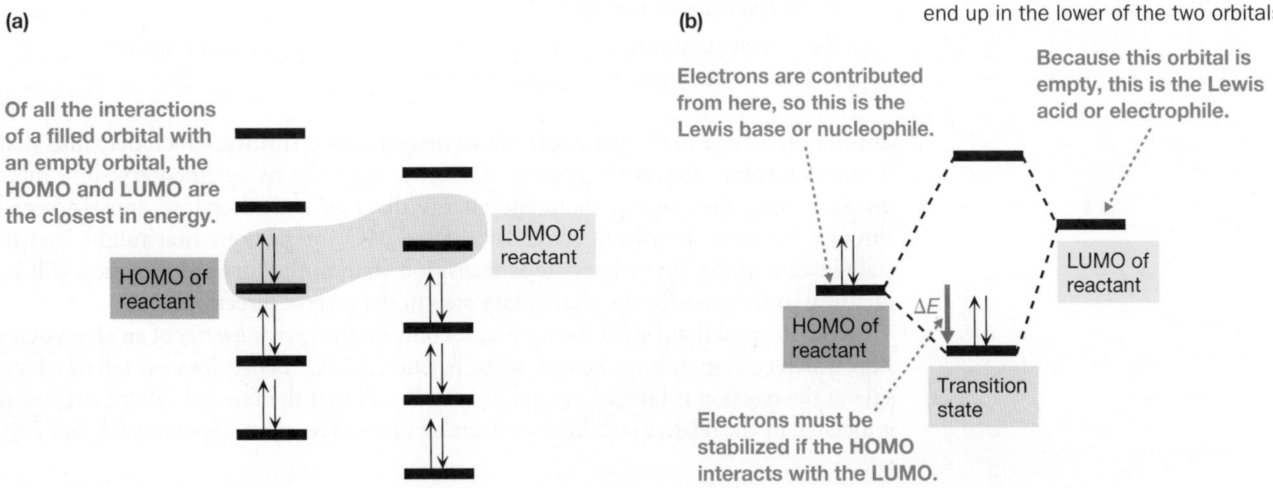
(a)
Of all the interactions of a filled orbital with an empty orbital, the HOMO and LUMO are the closest in energy.
HOMO of reactant
LUMO of reactant
(b)
Electrons are contributed from here, so this is the Lewis base or nucleophile.
Because this orbital is empty, this is the Lewis acid or electrophile.
HOMO of reactant
LUMO of reactant
ΔE
Transition state
Electrons must be stabilized if the HOMO interacts with the LUMO.

FIGURE C-2 HOMO–LUMO interactions (a) The similar energies of the HOMO and LUMO maximize any interaction between the two orbitals. (b) If an interaction takes place between the HOMO of one reactant and the LUMO of another, then stabilization is guaranteed. When the two orbitals interact, two new orbitals in the transition state (center) are produced: one that is lower in energy than either the HOMO or LUMO and one that is higher in energy. The electrons contributed by the HOMO end up in the lower of the two orbitals.

2. If the HOMO and LUMO orbitals can interact, then the interaction will stabilize the entire species (Fig. C-2b). The interaction between the HOMO and LUMO must be stabilizing because, by definition, the HOMO contains electrons and the LUMO is empty (see Recall box).

YOUR TURN C.1

Consider the interaction of the HOMO of one reactant with the HOMO of a second reactant. **(a)** Identify those orbitals in Figure C-2a. **(b)** How would Figure C-2b be modified to show the interaction of those two HOMOs? **(c)** Explain why such HOMO–HOMO interaction does not lead to stabilization in the transition state.

Answers to Your Turns are in the back of the book.

◀ RECALL

Section 3.10 showed that when orbitals from different atoms mix (via constructive and destructive interference), two new orbitals are produced: one that has been lowered in energy and one that has been raised in energy. Furthermore, the new orbital that is lower in energy will be filled before the higher-energy orbital becomes occupied.

Notice that FMO theory deals with the interactions of MOs in the reactants, not the MOs in the actual transition state. FMO theory therefore requires an important assumption, which is that:

A substantial portion of the stabilization that results from the HOMO–LUMO interaction between the reactants also exists in the transition state.

With what we have seen so far, we can make a very useful association between FMO interactions and the tendency of electrons to flow from an electron-rich site to an electron-poor one. Notice in Figure C-2b that the pertinent electrons originate from the HOMO of one species and interact with the empty LUMO of the other. Thus, there is an effective flow of electrons from the HOMO to the LUMO:

- The species that contributes the pertinent HOMO in the FMO interaction is relatively electron-rich; it is the Lewis base or the nucleophile.
- The species that contributes the pertinent LUMO is relatively electron-poor; it is the Lewis acid or the electrophile.

One of the important messages from Chapter 7 is that some elementary steps might simply be the reverse of each other but receive different names. Examples include coordination and heterolysis (Section 7.3), nucleophilic addition and nucleophile elimination (Section 7.4), and electrophilic addition and electrophile elimination (Section 7.6). We could apply FMO theory separately to the elementary steps in each reversible pair, but it is much more convenient to take advantage of the following idea:

- If an elementary step is allowed in the forward direction, then it will be allowed in the reverse direction as well.
- If an elementary step is forbidden in the forward direction, then it will be forbidden in the reverse direction as well.

This idea is related to the **principle of microscopic reversibility**, which demands that if one elementary step is the reverse of another, then the two elementary steps must proceed along the same path in the energy diagram and, therefore, must proceed through the same transition state. Thus, the FMO interactions that might lead to stabilization of the elementary step's transition state in the forward direction will be identical to the ones for the elementary step in the reverse direction.

Keep in mind that FMO theory focuses only on the *energy barrier* of an elementary step, which corresponds to the *rate* of the reaction. FMO theory does *not* tell us which side of the reaction is favored at equilibrium. Recall that the favored side of a reaction is dictated by the relative stabilities of the reactants and products (Sections 6.5 and 7.8).

C.2 Frontier Molecular Orbital Theory and Elementary Steps

SECTION C.2 OBJECTIVES

You will be able to:

1. Use frontier molecular orbital theory to illustrate whether the following elementary steps are allowed: proton transfer; S_N2; coordination; heterolysis; nucleophilic addition; nucleophile elimination; E2; electrophilic addition; electrophile elimination; carbocation rearrangement.
2. Explain how the spatial arrangement of the reactants in S_N2 and E2 steps can dictate whether the elementary step is allowed.

Now let's see how FMO theory applies to the various elementary steps introduced in Chapters 6 and 7. In each case, we must first determine the relevant FMOs in the reacting species and then determine whether they have substantial net overlap to stabilize the transition state.

C.2a Proton Transfer Steps

A typical proton transfer step, including curved arrow notation, is shown in Equation C-1. In this case, HO^- is electron-rich and the H atom of HCl is relatively electron-poor. Thus, the flow of electrons from an electron-rich site to an electron-poor site is represented by the curved arrow drawn from a pair of electrons on O to the H atom of HCl. This means that HO^- is the species that contributes the pertinent HOMO to the FMO interaction, whereas HCl is the species that contributes the pertinent LUMO:

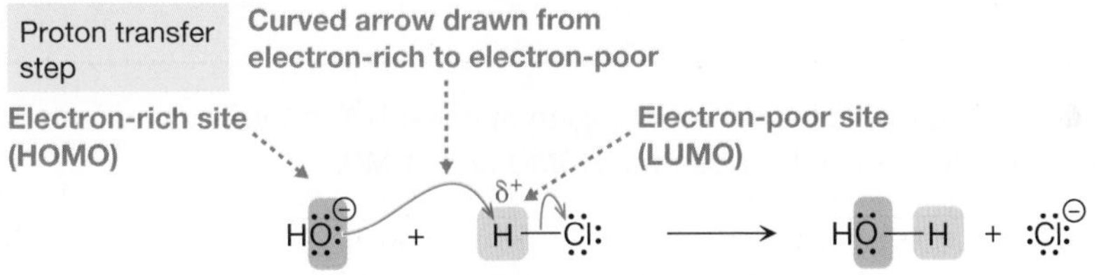
Proton transfer step
Curved arrow drawn from electron-rich to electron-poor
Electron-rich site (HOMO)
Electron-poor site (LUMO)
(C-1)

It is now a matter of identifying the HOMO of HO^- and the LUMO of HCl and determining whether they have substantial net overlap. In the qualitative molecular orbital–valence bond (MO–VB) approach introduced in Section 3.11, the HOMO of HO^- is a nonbonding orbital containing a pair of electrons, as shown in **Figure C-3**, and the LUMO of HCl is a σ^* antibonding MO. When HO^- approaches HCl from the end opposite the Cl atom (Fig. C-3a), the HOMO and LUMO will undergo substantial interaction. The specific phases shown in the figure will lead to a net constructive interference, whereas destructive interference would result from

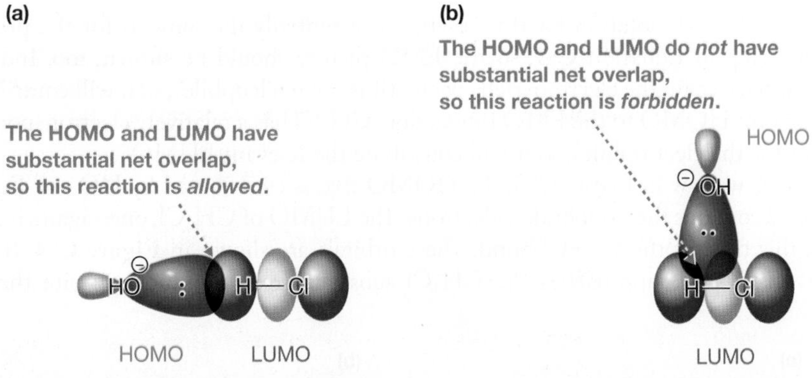
(a)
The HOMO and LUMO have substantial net overlap, so this reaction is *allowed*.
HOMO
LUMO
(b)
The HOMO and LUMO do *not* have substantial net overlap, so this reaction is *forbidden*.
HOMO
LUMO

FIGURE C-3 Frontier orbital interactions for the proton transfer involving HO^- and HCl (a) The approach of HO^- from the end opposite the Cl atom is shown. As indicated, the HOMO and LUMO have substantial net overlap. The specific phases shown would lead primarily to constructive interference, whereas reversing the phase of one of the orbitals would lead primarily to destructive interference. (b) The approach of HO^- from the side of the H—Cl bond is shown. The HOMO and LUMO do not have a significant net interaction. Whereas the left side in this depiction (shaded dark red and dark blue) indicates constructive interference, the right side (shaded dark red and light blue) contributes to destructive interference.

reversing the phase of one of the orbitals. As we learned in the previous section (Fig. C-2b), this kind of HOMO–LUMO interaction will lead to stabilization in the transition state and the reaction is *allowed.*

YOUR TURN **C.2**

Construct the atomic orbital overlap and MO energy diagrams separately for HO^- and HCl (review Figs. 3-39 through 3-44). From these diagrams, determine the HOMO of HO^- and the LUMO of HCl. Do they agree with the ones shown in Figure C-3?

Is there a transition state for which these frontier orbitals do *not* undergo significant interaction? One example is shown in Figure C-3b, in which HO^- approaches HCl from the side of the H—Cl bond. In that transition state, one portion of the orbital overlap leads to constructive interference (in this case, the left side), whereas the other portion (the right side) leads to destructive interference. Thus, there is very little net interaction, so the transition state remains unstabilized and the reaction is *forbidden.*

YOUR TURN **C.3**

In Figure C-3a and C-3b, label every region of constructive interference and destructive interference between the HOMO and LUMO.

C.2b Bimolecular Nucleophilic Substitution (S_N2) Steps

The S_N2 step we first encountered in Chapter 7 is shown once again in Equation C-2:

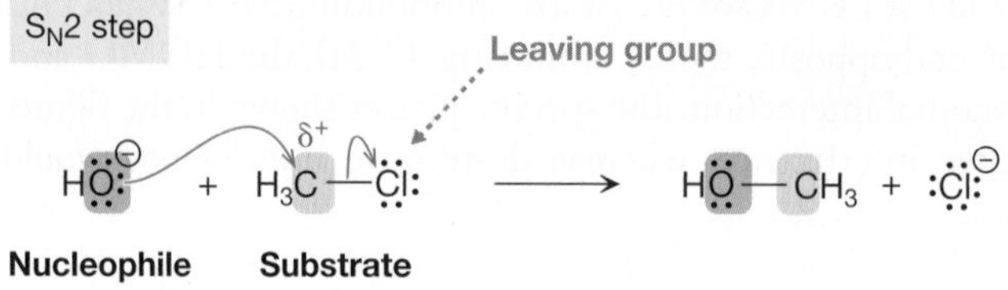

S_N2 step
Leaving group
δ+
HO: + H₃C—Cl: → HO—CH₃ + :Cl:
Nucleophile
Substrate

(C-2)

The curved arrow notation for this reaction is essentially the same as for the proton transfer step in Equation C-1, so the FMO picture should be similar, too. Indeed, HO^- is once again the electron-rich species (it is the nucleophile), so it will contribute the relevant HOMO to the FMO interaction. CH_3Cl has a relatively electron-poor C atom (it is the electrophile), so it will contribute the relevant LUMO.

Just as we saw in Figure C-3, the HOMO that is contributed by HO^- in Equation C-2 contains the nonbonded electrons. The LUMO of CH_3Cl, once again, is a σ^* MO, this time of the C—Cl bond. These orbitals are shown in **Figure C-4**. If the HO^- nucleophile approaches the CH_3Cl substrate from the end opposite the Cl

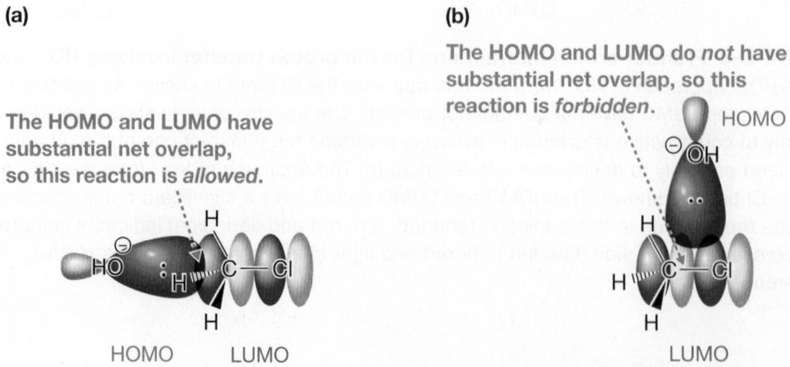

(a)
The HOMO and LUMO have substantial net overlap, so this reaction is *allowed.*
H
HO
H
C
Cl
H
HOMO
LUMO
(b)
The HOMO and LUMO do *not* have substantial net overlap, so this reaction is *forbidden.*
HOMO
OH
H
H
C
Cl
H
LUMO

FIGURE C-4 Frontier orbital interactions for the S_N2 step involving HO^- and CH_3Cl (a) The approach of HO^- from the end opposite the Cl leaving group is shown. As indicated, the HOMO and LUMO have substantial net overlap. (b) The approach of HO^- from the side of the C—Cl bond is shown. The HOMO and LUMO do not have a significant net interaction. Whereas the right side in this depiction (shaded dark red and dark blue) indicates constructive interference, the left side (shaded dark red and light blue) contributes to destructive interference.

leaving group (Fig. C-4a), then the resulting overlap of the HOMO and LUMO orbitals will lead to significant interaction, the transition state will be stabilized, and the reaction will be allowed. Also, similar to what we saw in Figure C-3b, if the approach of the HO^- nucleophile is from the side of the C—Cl bond (Fig. C-4b), then there will be no significant interaction between the FMOs, making the reaction forbidden.

YOUR TURN C.4

Construct the atomic orbital overlap and MO energy diagrams for CH_3Cl (review Figs. 3-39 through 3-44) and use these diagrams to determine its LUMO. Does your answer agree with the one shown in Figure C-4? *Hint*: A C—Cl single bond is weaker than a C—H single bond.

YOUR TURN C.5

In Figure C-4a and C-4b, label every region of constructive interference and destructive interference between the HOMO and LUMO.

We just saw that an S_N2 reaction may be allowed or forbidden, depending on the way the nucleophile approaches the substrate:

For an S_N2 reaction to occur, the nucleophile must approach and form a bond to the substrate on the side opposite the leaving group (see Looking Ahead box).

▸ LOOKING AHEAD

The requirement that the nucleophile in an S_N2 reaction must attack from the side opposite the leaving group dictates the *stereochemistry* of the reaction, as we will discuss in Chapter 8. In short, if the carbon atom bonded to the leaving group is a chiral center, then its stereochemical configuration in the product will be the reverse of what it was in the reactant.

C.2c Bond-Forming (Coordination) and Bond-Breaking (Heterolysis) Steps

The coordination step depicted in Equation C-3 was shown previously in Section 7.3:

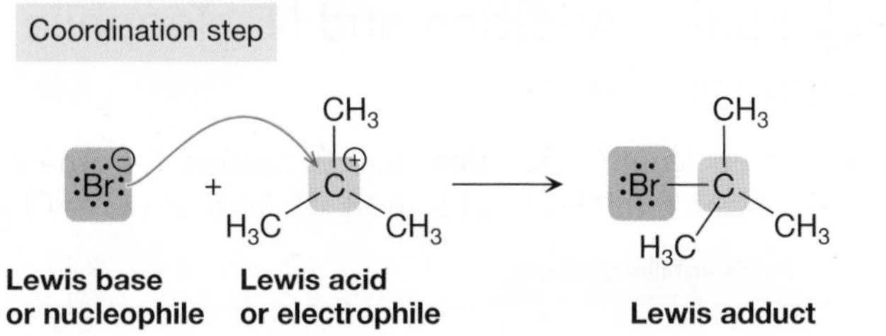
Coordination step
:Br:
+
CH3
C
H3C
CH3
CH3
:Br—C
H3C
CH3
Lewis base
or nucleophile
Lewis acid
or electrophile
Lewis adduct

(C-3)

Br^- is relatively electron-rich and is the Lewis base or nucleophile, so it will contribute a nonbonding orbital as the relevant HOMO to the FMO interaction. By contrast, the $(CH_3)_3C^+$ carbocation is electron-poor, so it serves as the Lewis acid or electrophile, and it will contribute the relevant LUMO (the empty *p* orbital in **Figure C-5**) to the FMO interaction.

Figure C-5a shows that the HOMO and LUMO have substantial net overlap when the Br^- nucleophile approaches from the left face of the plane established by

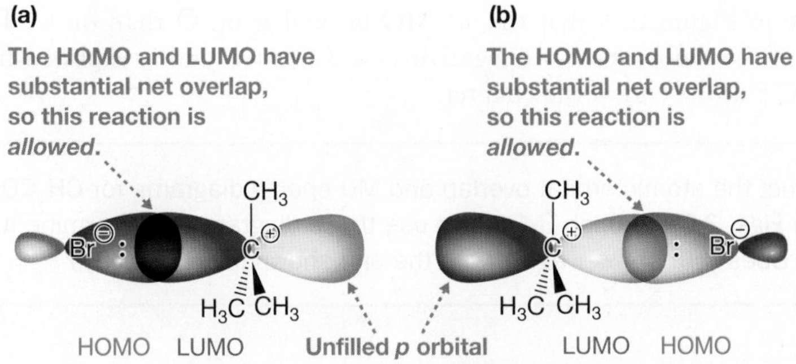
(a)
The HOMO and LUMO have substantial net overlap, so this reaction is *allowed*.
(b)
The HOMO and LUMO have substantial net overlap, so this reaction is *allowed*.
Br
CH3
C
H3C CH3
HOMO LUMO
Unfilled *p* orbital
LUMO HOMO

FIGURE C-5 Frontier orbital interactions for the coordination of Br^- and $(CH_3)_3C^+$ The approach of Br^- is shown from (a) the left face and (b) the right face of the plane established by the electron groups of C^+. As indicated, the HOMO and LUMO have substantial net overlap for both approaches, so the elementary step is allowed for either approach.

the electron groups of C^+. Figure C-5b shows that the same is true for the approach of the nucleophile from the right face of the plane, too. (Notice that we reversed the phases of the orbitals to illustrate this.) Thus, coordination is allowed from either face (see Looking Ahead box).

YOUR TURN **C.6**

Construct the atomic orbital overlap and MO energy diagrams for $(CH_3)_3C^+$ (review Figs. 3-39 through 3-44) and use these diagrams to determine its LUMO. Does your answer agree with the one shown in Figure C-5?

YOUR TURN **C.7**

In Figure C-5a and C-5b, label every region of constructive interference and destructive interference between the HOMO and LUMO.

▸ **LOOKING AHEAD**

The ability of a nucleophile to approach and form a bond to either face of the electrophile in a coordination step has important implications in the *stereochemistry* of some reactions, which we will explore further in Chapter 8. In short, if the atom that gains the bond becomes a chiral center, then both the *R* and *S* configurations of the chiral center will be produced.

Let's now consider heterolysis, the reverse of coordination. An example that we previously encountered in Chapter 7 is shown again in Equation C-4:

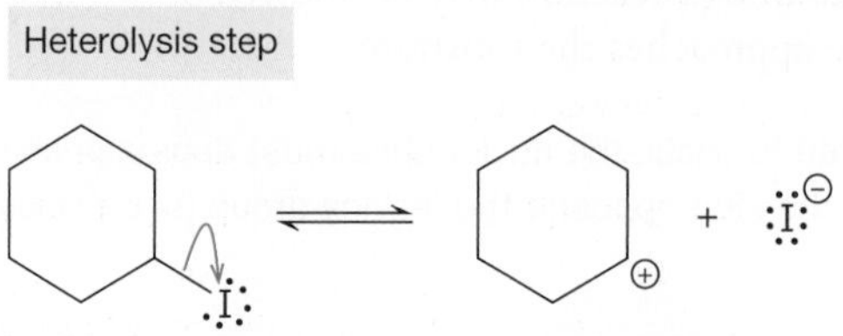
Heterolysis step
I
+
I

(C-4)

We don't need a new FMO analysis to determine whether this reaction is allowed or forbidden. The principle of microscopic reversibility (Section C.1) tells us that because coordination steps are allowed, heterolysis steps must be allowed too.

C.2d Nucleophilic Addition and Nucleophile Elimination Steps

We first introduced nucleophilic addition steps in Section 7.4. An example is shown in Equation C-5, in which the HO^- adds to the C atom of a C═O group:

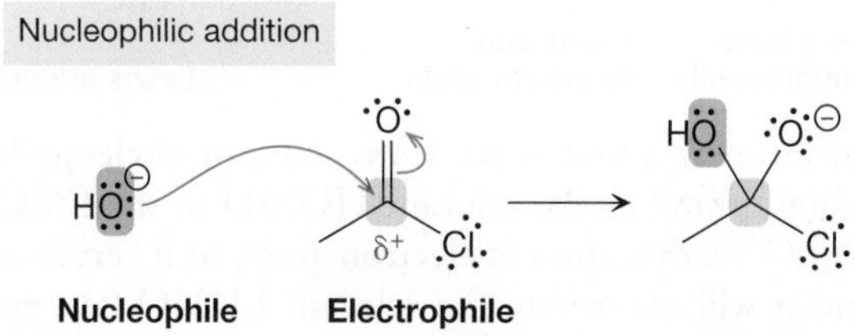
Nucleophilic addition
HO
O
δ+
Cl
HO
O
Cl
Nucleophile
Electrophile

(C-5)

Once again, the HO^- is the nucleophile and contributes the relevant HOMO. The C atom of the C═O group is relatively electron-poor (it has a partial positive charge). As a result, the C═O group acts as the electrophile and contributes the relevant LUMO. As shown in **Figure C-6**, the HOMO of HO^- is a nonbonding orbital, and the LUMO of the C═O group is a π* MO.

Notice in Figure C-6 that the π* MO is smaller on O than on C. This is an outcome of the different electronegativities of O and C and is explored further in Problem C.8 at the end of the chapter.

YOUR TURN **C.8**

Construct the atomic orbital overlap and MO energy diagrams for CH_3COCl (review Figs. 3-39 through 3-44) and use these diagrams to determine its LUMO. Does your answer agree with the one shown in Figure C-6a?

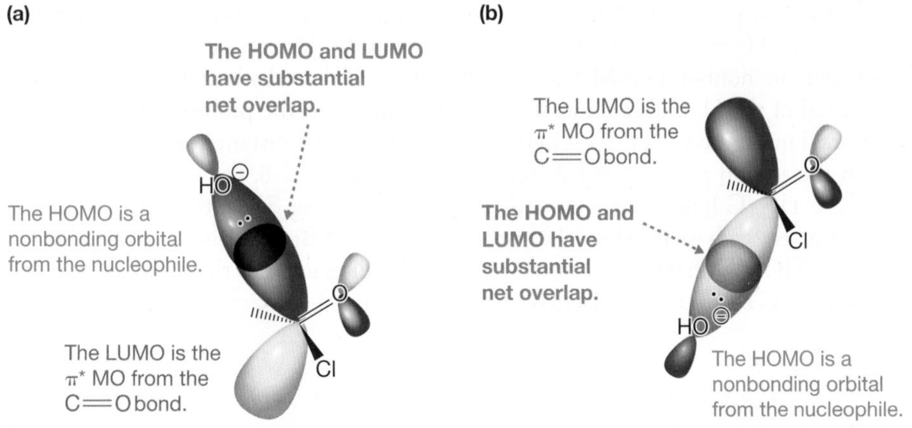
(a)
The HOMO and LUMO have substantial net overlap.
HO
The HOMO is a nonbonding orbital from the nucleophile.
O
The LUMO is the π* MO from the C═O bond.
Cl
(b)
The LUMO is the π* MO from the C═O bond.
O
The HOMO and LUMO have substantial net overlap.
Cl
HO
The HOMO is a nonbonding orbital from the nucleophile.

FIGURE C-6 Frontier orbital interaction for the nucleophilic addition of HO^- to CH_3COCl The approach of HO^- is shown from (a) the left face or (b) the right face of the plane established by the electron groups of the carbonyl carbon. The nonbonding orbital of the HO^- nucleophile (red; HOMO) has substantial net overlap with the π* orbital of the C═O bond (blue; LUMO) for both approaches, so this nucleophilic addition is allowed.

YOUR TURN C.9

In Figure C-6a and C-6b, label every region of constructive interference and destructive interference between the HOMO and LUMO.

Figure C-6 shows the approach of the nucleophile from either of the two faces of the plane containing the electron groups of the carbonyl carbon. Regardless of the nucleophile's approach, the HOMO and LUMO have substantial net overlap, so either approach leads to an allowed nucleophilic addition.

The reverse of nucleophilic addition is nucleophile elimination. An example is shown in Equation C-6, in which Cl^- is eliminated from a reactant species:

Nucleophile elimination

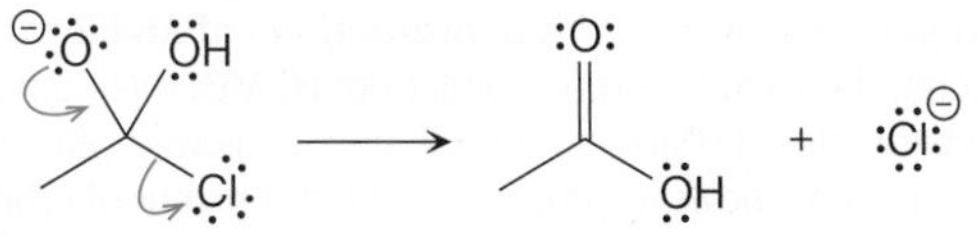
O
OH
Cl
O
OH
+
Cl

(C-6)

According to the principle of microscopic reversibility, nucleophile elimination steps are allowed because nucleophilic addition steps are allowed.

C.2e Bimolecular Elimination (E2) Steps

Section 7.5 introduced the bimolecular elimination (E2) step, in which a base reacts with a substrate. An example is shown in Equation C-7:

E2 step

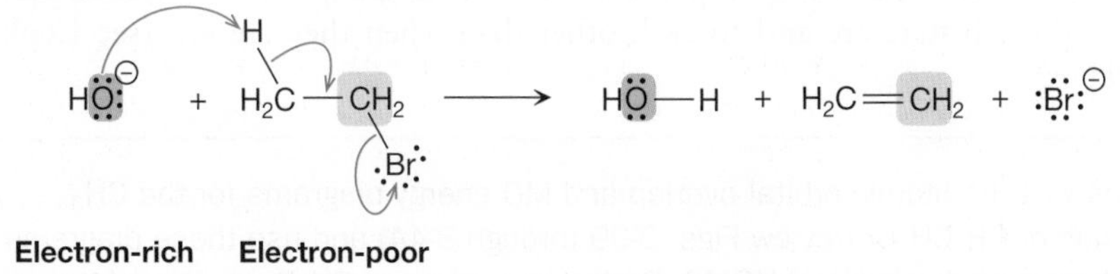
H
HO
+ H2C—CH2
Br
HO—H + H2C═CH2 + Br
Electron-rich
Electron-poor

(C-7)

Unlike the previous elementary steps we have analyzed using FMO theory, an E2 step involves the formation of two separate bonds (in this case, the HO—H bond and the π bond) and the breaking of another two bonds (in this case, the H—C and C—Br bonds). To simplify the picture using FMO theory, we can treat the entire process as two separate parts that take place at essentially the same time: one part that forms the HO—H bond and breaks the H—C bond (ignoring the presence of Br), and the second part that forms the π bond and breaks the C—Br bond (ignoring the presence of HO^-).

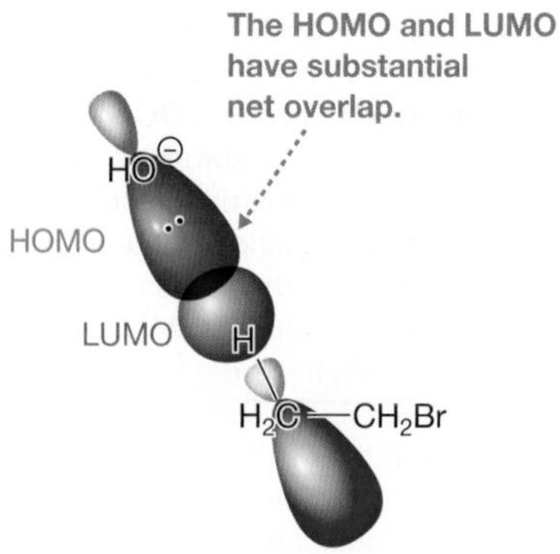
The HOMO and LUMO
have substantial
net overlap.
HO
HOMO
LUMO
H
H_2C
CH_2Br

FIGURE C-7 First part of frontier orbital interactions of an E2 step The nonbonding orbital of the HO^- base (red; HOMO) has substantial net overlap with the σ^* orbital of the H—C bond (blue; LUMO), so this part of the E2 step is allowed.

In the first part of the E2 step, shown in **Figure C-7**, the HO^- base is electron-rich and the H—C bond of the substrate is relatively electron-poor. Thus, HO^- will contribute its nonbonding MO as the HOMO, and the substrate will contribute its σ^* orbital of the H—C bond as the LUMO. Similar to the proton transfer step we examined in Figure C-3, the HOMO and LUMO have substantial net overlap.

In the second part of the E2 step, shown in **Figure C-8**, the electrons originate from the H—C bond that is undergoing bond-breaking. Thus, the H—C bond is treated as electron-rich, while the carbon of the C—Br bond is electron-poor. As such, the HOMO that is contributed to the FMO interaction is the σ bonding orbital of the H—C bond, and the LUMO is the σ^* orbital of the C—Br bond.

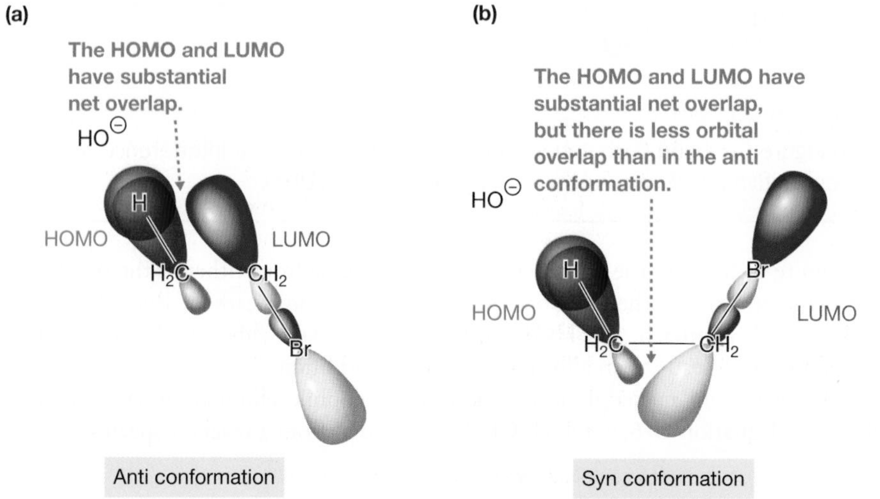
(a)
The HOMO and LUMO
have substantial
net overlap.
HO
H
HOMO
LUMO
H_2C
CH_2
Br
Anti conformation
(b)
The HOMO and LUMO have
substantial net overlap,
but there is less orbital
overlap than in the anti
conformation.
HO
H
Br
HOMO
LUMO
H_2C
CH_2
Syn conformation

FIGURE C-8 Second part of frontier orbital interactions of an E2 step In both the (a) anti and (b) syn conformations, the filled C—H σ orbital (red; HOMO) has substantial net overlap with the empty C—Br σ^* orbital (blue; LUMO), so the E2 step is allowed with either conformation. The anti conformation is favored, however, due to the greater extent of orbital overlap.

▸ LOOKING AHEAD

The preference of an E2 reaction for a substrate in the anti conformation has important implications for the *stereochemistry* of the reaction, which we will explore further in Chapter 8. In short, the favored C=C configuration in the product is the one that resembles the substrate in its anti conformation.

Notice that there are two orientations in Figure C-8 in which the HOMO and LUMO have substantial net overlap. In the *anti conformation* (Fig. C-8a), the H—C and C—Br bonds are on opposite sides of the C—C bond and are said to be anti to each other. In the **syn conformation** (Fig. C-8b), the H—C and C—Br bonds are on the same side of the C—C bond and are said to be syn to each other. Thus, an E2 step is allowed in either of these conformations. The HOMO and LUMO overlap to a greater extent, however, when the two bonds are anti. As a result, an E2 step tends to proceed faster when the hydrogen and the leaving group on the adjacent carbon atom in the substrate are anti to each other than when they are syn (see Looking Ahead box).

YOUR TURN **C.10**

Construct the atomic orbital overlap and MO energy diagrams for the CH_3 portion of CH_3CH_2Br (review Figs. 3-39 through 3-44) and use these diagrams to determine that group's HOMO. Do the same for the CH_2Br portion of the molecule to determine that group's LUMO. Do your answers agree with the ones shown in Figure C-8a?

YOUR TURN **C.11**

In Figure C-8a and C-8b, label every region of constructive interference and destructive interference between the HOMO and LUMO.

C.2f Electrophilic Addition and Electrophile Elimination Steps

Electrophilic addition was first discussed in Section 7.6. An example is shown in Equation C-8, in which a C atom of a C═C bond forms a new bond to the proton of H—Cl:

Electrophilic addition

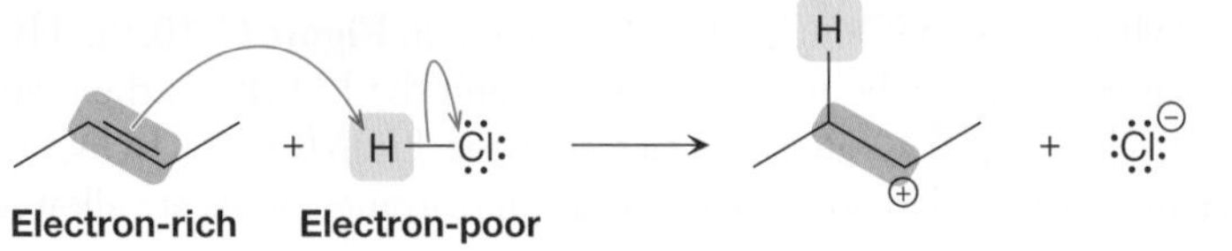
H
H
Cl
Cl

(C-8)

Electron-rich   Electron-poor

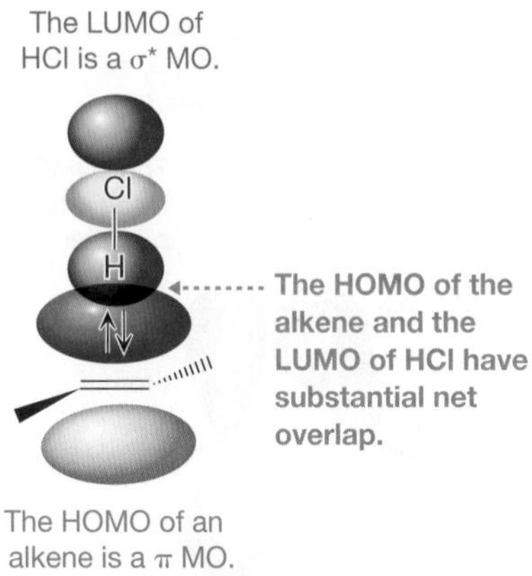
The LUMO of HCl is a σ* MO.
Cl
H
The HOMO of the alkene and the LUMO of HCl have substantial net overlap.
The HOMO of an alkene is a π MO.

FIGURE C-9 Frontier orbital interaction for electrophilic addition involving an alkene and HCl The π MO of the alkene (red; HOMO) has substantial net overlap with the σ* orbital of the H—Cl bond (blue; LUMO), so this electrophilic addition step is allowed.

Recall that the C═C double bond of an alkene is relatively electron-rich and acts as the nucleophile, whereas the proton of HCl is electron-poor and acts as the electrophile. Therefore, the alkene donates the relevant HOMO to the FMO interaction, and HCl donates the relevant LUMO. As shown in **Figure C-9**, the HOMO of the alkene is a π MO, and the LUMO of H—Cl is a σ* orbital. Notice that those two MOs have substantial overlap, so the elementary step is allowed.

YOUR TURN **C.12**

Construct the atomic orbital overlap and MO energy diagrams for $CH_3CH{=}CHCH_3$ (review Figs. 3-39 through 3-44) and use these diagrams to determine its HOMO. Does your answer agree with the one shown in Figure C-9?

YOUR TURN **C.13**

In Figure C-9, label every region of constructive interference and destructive interference between the HOMO and LUMO.

Electrophile elimination is the reverse of electrophilic addition, so electrophile elimination is allowed, too, according to the principle of microscopic reversibility. A typical electrophile elimination step is shown in Equation C-9, in which water, an electron-rich base, abstracts a H^+ from the carbocation species. Thus, the H^+ electrophile is eliminated from a carbocation species, producing a new π bond:

Electrophile elimination

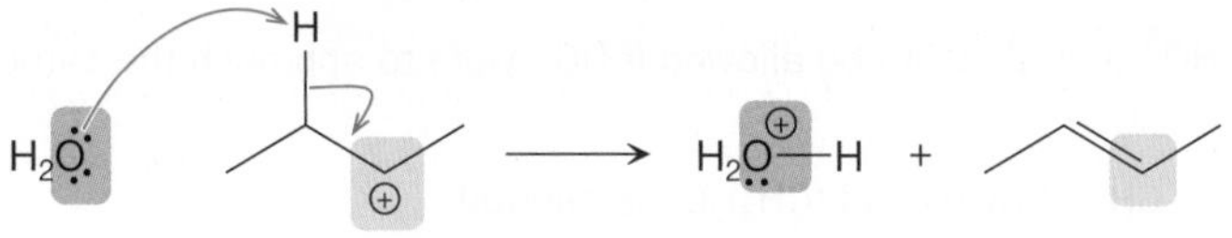
H
H2O
H2O
H

(C-9)

C.2g Carbocation Rearrangements

Carbocation rearrangements, specifically 1,2-hydride shifts and 1,2-methyl shifts, were discussed in Section 7.7. An example of a 1,2-hydride shift is shown in Equation C-10:

1,2-Hydride shift

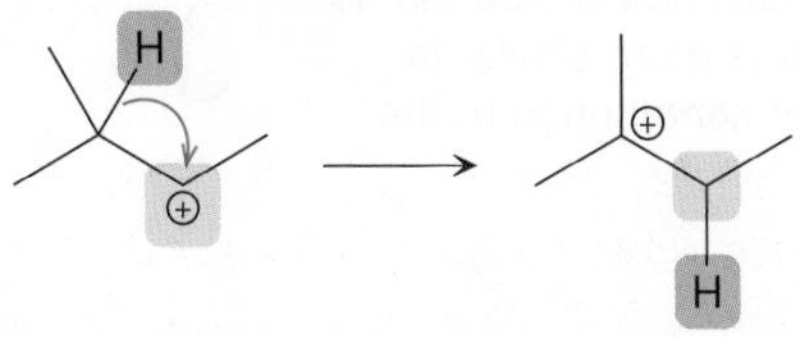
H
H

(C-10)

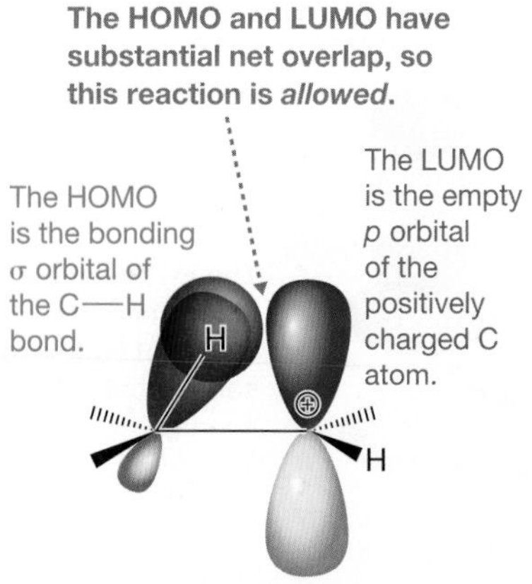
The HOMO and LUMO have substantial net overlap, so this reaction is *allowed*.
The HOMO is the bonding σ orbital of the C—H bond.
The LUMO is the empty *p* orbital of the positively charged C atom.
H
H

FIGURE C-10 Frontier orbital interaction for a 1,2-hydride shift The geometry of the carbocation shows the H partially transferred from the C—H bond to the C^+ atom. The σ orbital of the C—H bond (red; HOMO) has substantial net overlap with the empty *p* orbital of the positively charged carbon atom (blue; LUMO), so this carbocation rearrangement step is allowed.

This reaction involves just one species, so the carbocation must provide both the HOMO and the LUMO to the FMO interaction. As shown in **Figure C-10**, the HOMO is the σ orbital that connects to the migrating group, and the LUMO is the empty *p* orbital of the positively charged C atom. Notice that the HOMO and LUMO do, indeed, have substantial net overlap, so these carbocation rearrangements are allowed.

YOUR TURN C.14

Construct the atomic orbital overlap and MO energy diagrams for the $(CH_3)_2CH$ portion of $(CH_3)_2CHC^+HCH_3$ (review Figs. 3-39 through 3-44) and use these diagrams to determine that group's HOMO. Do the same for the $^+CHCH_3$ portion to determine that group's LUMO. Do your answers agree with the ones shown in Figure C-10?

YOUR TURN C.15

In Figure C-10, label every region of constructive interference and destructive interference between the HOMO and LUMO.

Problems

Section C.2 Frontier Molecular Orbital Theory and Elementary Steps

C.1 Would the proton transfer between HO^- and HCl be allowed if HO^- were to approach HCl from the same end as Cl (i.e., directly opposite the H)? If your answer is yes, would you expect that elementary step to take place? Why or why not?

C.2 Would the S_N2 step between HO^- and CH_3Cl be allowed if HO^- were to approach CH_3Cl from the same end as Cl (i.e., directly opposite the CH_3)? If your answer is yes, would you expect that elementary step to take place? Why or why not?

C.3 Would the coordination step between Br^- and $(CH_3)_3C^+$ be allowed if Br^- were to approach from within the plane that contains the electron groups of the C^+? Explain.

C.4 Would the nucleophilic addition step between HO^- and CH_3COCl be allowed if HO^- were to approach the carbonyl C atom directly along the C═O bond? Explain.

C.5 Show that the electrophilic addition involving $CH_3CH{=}CHCH_3$ and $(CH_3)_3C^+$ is allowed.

C.6 Show that a 1,2-methyl shift involving $(CH_3)_3CC^+HCH_3$ is allowed.

C.7 Determine whether the addition of a nucleophile to the O atom of a C═O group is allowed or forbidden. If you determine that it is allowed, would you expect that elementary step to take place? Why or why not?

C.8 In Figure C-6 (p. 367), the π* MO is shown to be larger on the C atom than on the O atom. This is an outcome of oxygen being more electronegative than carbon, which causes oxygen's 2*p* AOs to be lower in energy than carbon's 2*p* AOs, as shown here. When two AOs of unequal energy are mixed, each new orbital that is produced has a greater contribution from the AO to which it is more similar in energy. With this in mind, which atom's 2*p* AO has a greater contribution to the π MO? To the π* MO? Does this agree with Figure C-6?

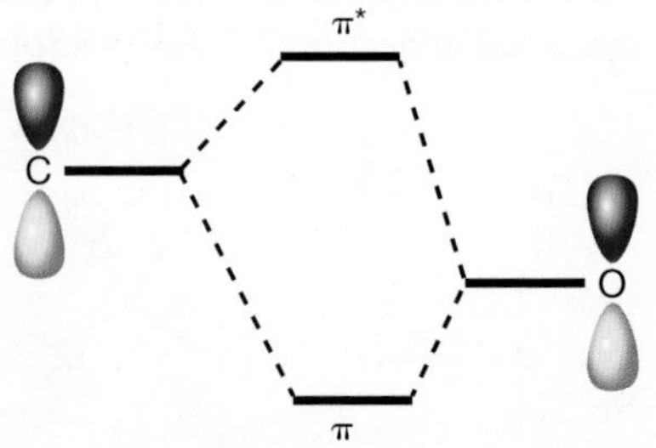
π*
C
O
π

C.9 Using FMO theory, determine whether a carbanion rearrangement, analogous to the 1,2-hydride shift in Equation C-10, is allowed or forbidden.

INTERCHAPTER D

Naming Compounds with a Functional Group That Calls for a Suffix

Alcohols, Amines, Ketones, Aldehydes, Carboxylic Acids, and Carboxylic Acid Derivatives

In previous nomenclature interchapters (A and B), we saw that the presence of a functional group requires a very specific modification to a compound name. When the compound is an alkene or alkyne, for example, the corresponding alkane's root (parent compound) is identified by *ene* or *yne*, respectively. Groups such as halogen atoms, nitro groups, and ethers, on the other hand, are indicated by appropriate prefixes. Here in Interchapter D, you will learn that a *suffix* must be added to the appropriate root if functional groups other than the ones just mentioned are present in a molecule. These ideas are captured in **Figure D-1**.

The root (parent compound) indicates the longest chain or ring of carbons and the presence of C═C and C≡C bonds.

Prefixes indicate the presence and locations of substituents.

The suffix indicates the presence of a functional group other than halo, nitro, ether, C═C, or C≡C.

prefixesrootsuffix

FIGURE D-1 General structure of an IUPAC name that requires adding a suffix

Section D.1 provides the basic rules for naming compounds that require adding a suffix, and in Section D.2, we begin applying them to alcohols and amines. In Section D.3, we extend these rules to aldehydes and ketones. Then, in Section D.4, we deal with naming carboxylic acids, acid chlorides, amides, and nitriles. Finally, in Section D.5, we learn how to name esters and acid anhydrides.

Chapter Outline

SECTION D.1 OBJECTIVES

You will be able to:

1. Determine whether the IUPAC name for a particular compound class requires adding a suffix.
2. Describe the basic structure of an IUPAC name for a compound requiring a suffix.
3. Outline the rules for naming compounds that require a suffix.

◀ RECALL

In Interchapter A, we learned that the root of a molecule is identified as the longest continuous carbon chain (Section A.3) or the largest carbon ring (Section A.5).

◀ RECALL

As discussed in Interchapter A, a chain is numbered so that C-1 is the end closest to the first substituent. For a ring, C-1 has the maximum number of attached substituents, and numbering continues clockwise or counterclockwise to encounter the next substituent the earliest.

D.1 The Basic System for Naming Compounds with a Functional Group That Calls for a Suffix

To name a compound with a functional group that requires a suffix, all of the rules we learned in Interchapters A and B remain in effect, and the following additional rules are applied:

Basic Rules for Naming Compounds with a Functional Group That Requires a Suffix

1. Use Table D-1 to determine the highest-priority functional group present.
2. Establish the main chain or ring. The main chain or ring (see top Recall box) must contain the highest-priority functional group.
3. Use Table D-1 to add the appropriate suffix.
   a. Choose the suffix that corresponds to the highest-priority functional group.
   b. Remove the "e" from the normal *ane*, *ene*, or *yne* ending before adding the suffix. (Nitriles are an exception to this rule.)
4. Number the main chain or ring. The carbon atom involving the highest-priority functional group should receive the lowest number possible (see bottom Recall box).
5. Add the locator number (locant) for the highest-priority functional group. It should appear immediately before the suffix, unless it is redundant.
6. Add prefixes and the remaining locator numbers (locants). All functional groups in the molecule, other than the one corresponding to the suffix, are treated as substituents. They and their locator numbers (locants) appear in the name as prefixes.

SECTION D.2 OBJECTIVES

You will be able to:

1. Write the IUPAC name of an alcohol or amine when given its structure.
2. Draw the structure of an alcohol or amine when given its IUPAC name.

D.2 Naming Alcohols and Amines

Let's apply the rules set out in Section D.1 to name the alcohols shown in **Figure D-2**, each of which has just one OH functional group. Those four compounds would be alkanes if the OH groups were absent. More specifically, the molecules in Figure D-2a and D-2b would be *propane*, the one in Figure D-2c would be *ethane*, and the one in Figure D-2d would be *cyclohexane*. Following the basic rules listed earlier (and as noted in Table D-1), to name an alcohol, we drop the final "e" from the alkane name and add the *ol* suffix; thus the molecules in Figure D-2a and D-2b become *propanol*, the one in Figure D-2c becomes *ethanol*, and the one in Figure D-2d becomes *cyclohexanol*. Locator numbers are added to the names of molecules in Figure D-2a and D-2b, immediately before the *ol* suffix, to indicate where the OH group is located in the molecule. For the molecules in Figure D-2c and D-2d, locator numbers are not added to the name because the carbon atoms are equivalent without the OH group; a locator number would be redundant.

TABLE D-1 Common Functional Groups, Their Relative Priorities, and Corresponding Suffixes and Prefixes

		SUFFIX					SUFFIX		
Functional Group Priority[a]	Compound Class	Drop "e" from Root?	Add	Prefix	Functional Group Priority[a]	Compound Class	Drop "e" from Root?	Add	Prefix
1 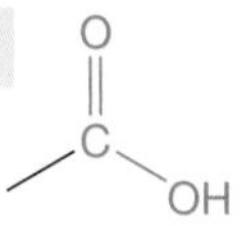	Carboxylic acid	Yes	oic acid	carboxy	6 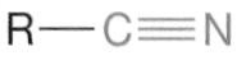	Nitrile	No	nitrile	cyano
2 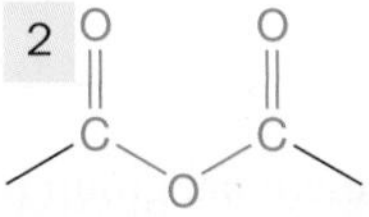	Acid anhydride	Yes	oic anhydride	—	7 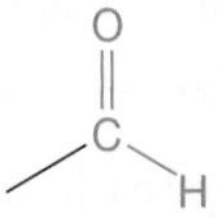	Aldehyde	Yes	al	oxo
3 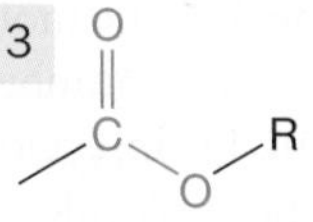	Ester	See Section D.4a		—	8 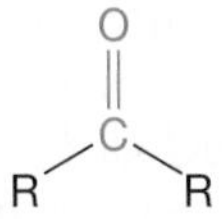	Ketone	Yes	one	oxo
4 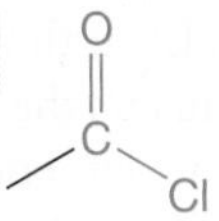	Acid chloride	Yes	oyl chloride	chloro-carbonyl	9 	Alcohol	Yes	ol	hydroxy
5 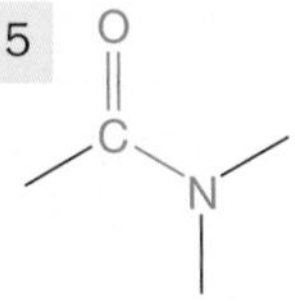	Amide	Yes	amide	carbamoyl	10 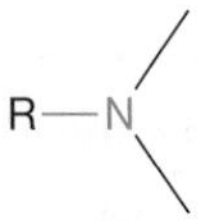	Amine	Yes	amine	amino

Note: R indicates an alkyl group, and the absence of an atom at the end of a bond indicates that either R or H may be attached.
[a]A functional group that appears earlier in the table has the higher priority.

(a) OH group located on C-1 (b) OH group located on C-2 (c) No locator number added (d) No locator number added

Propan-1-ol Propan-2-ol Ethanol Cyclohexanol

FIGURE D-2 Alcohols containing a single OH group

YOUR TURN D.1

Write the IUPAC name for each of the following compounds.

(a) (b) (c)

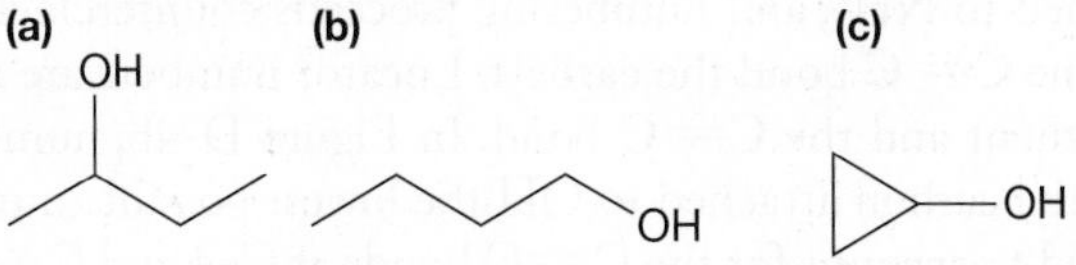

Answers to Your Turns are in the back of the book.

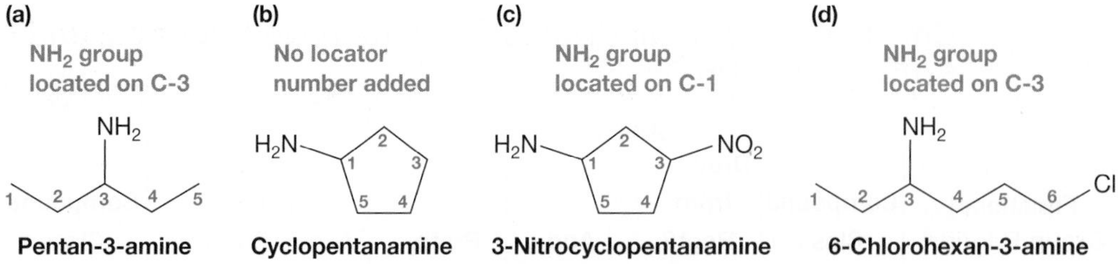
(a)
NH2 group located on C-3
NH2
1 2 3 4 5
Pentan-3-amine
(b)
No locator number added
H2N
1 2 3 4 5
Cyclopentanamine
(c)
NH2 group located on C-1
H2N
NO2
1 2 3 4 5
3-Nitrocyclopentanamine
(d)
NH2 group located on C-3
NH2
Cl
1 2 3 4 5 6
6-Chlorohexan-3-amine

FIGURE D-3 Amines containing a single NH_2 group

YOUR TURN D.2

Draw the structure for each of the following molecules. **(a)** pentan-3-ol; **(b)** cyclobutanol; **(c)** hexan-1-ol

For each molecule shown in **Figure D-3**, the highest-priority functional group is NH_2, characteristic of amines. According to Table D-1, they each receive the suffix *amine* after the final "e" is removed from the corresponding alkane name. For the molecule in Figure D-3a, the *pentane* root becomes *pentanamine* and the locator number 3 is included immediately before the *amine* suffix. The molecule in Figure D-3b, cyclopentanamine, does not require a locator number in the name. For the molecule in Figure D-3c, C-1 is assigned to the carbon attached to NH_2 and numbering increases clockwise around the ring so the nitro group is encountered the earliest. Even though the locator number for the NH_2 group is not included in this molecule's name, the one for the nitro group is necessary. In Figure D-3d, numbering starts from the left end of the chain to give the lowest locator number to the carbon attached to NH_2, which is the highest-priority group in the molecule.

YOUR TURN D.3

Write the IUPAC name for each of the following compounds.

(a) (b) (c)

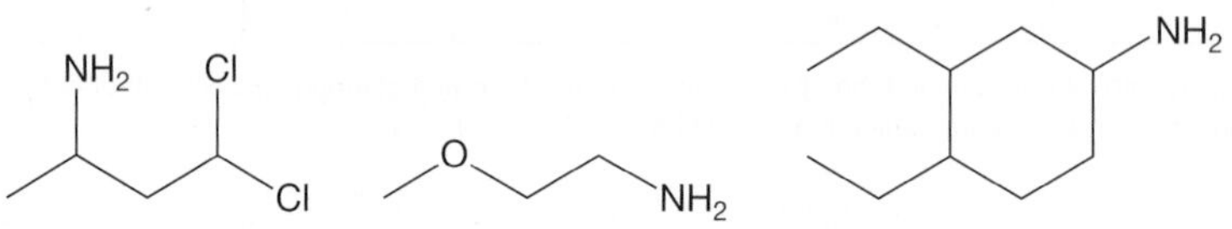
NH2
Cl
Cl
O
NH2
NH2

YOUR TURN D.4

Draw the structure for each of the following molecules.
(a) 4,4-dibromocyclohexanamine; **(b)** 2-nitroethan-1-amine; **(c)** 2-methylpropan-1-amine; **(d)** 5-cyclopropylheptan-2-amine

CONNECTIONS D.1

What does camping gear have to do with cyclohexanol? Millions of tons of cyclohexanol (Fig. D-2d) are produced annually, primarily as a precursor in the production of nylon. Nylon is an important synthetic fiber used in a variety of consumer products, such as this tent.

Figure D-4 shows three molecules that contain one or more C═C or C≡C bonds in addition to an OH or NH_2 group. To name these molecules, we must add the appropriate *ol* or *amine* suffix after first dropping the final "e" from the normal *ene* or *yne* ending. We must also apply the rules we learned in Interchapter B to establish the presence and location of the C═C and C≡C bonds. In Figure D-4a, C-1 is the carbon attached to NH_2, and numbering proceeds counterclockwise around the ring to arrive at the C═C bond the earliest. Locator numbers are required for both the chloro substituent and the C═C bond. In Figure D-4b, numbering begins on the right to give the carbon attached to OH the lowest possible number, and locator numbers are added to account for the C═C bonds at C-4 and C-6. Remember that *di* is added to specify that there are two C═C bonds. In Figure D-4c, the carbon

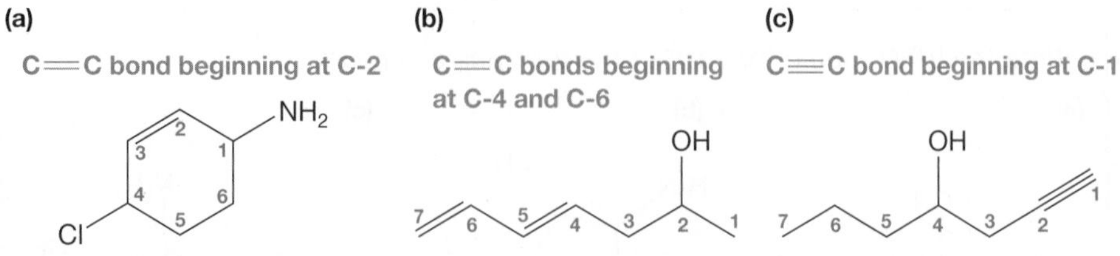

(a)
C=C bond beginning at C-2
NH_2
Cl
(b)
C=C bonds beginning at C-4 and C-6
OH
(c)
C≡C bond beginning at C-1
OH

4-Chlorocyclohex-2-en-1-amine   Hepta-4,6-dien-2-ol   Hept-1-yn-4-ol

FIGURE D-4 Molecules that require a suffix and also have C=C or C≡C bonds

attached to OH would receive the same locator number regardless of the end at which numbering begins, so we begin at the right to encounter the C≡C bond the earliest.

YOUR TURN D.5

Write the IUPAC name for each of the following compounds. You may disregard stereochemistry in this case.

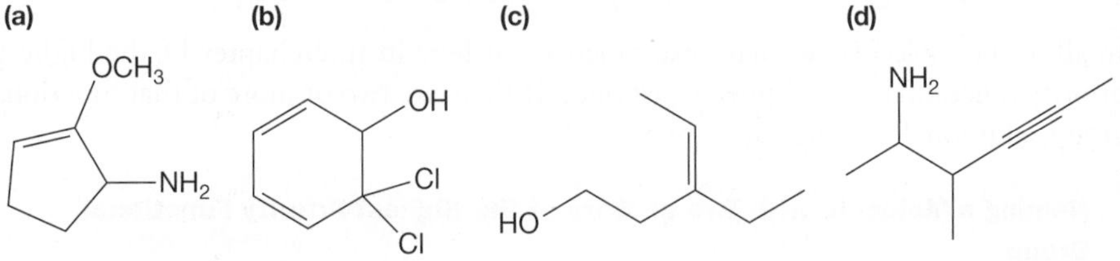

(a)
(b)
(c)
(d)
OCH_3
NH_2
OH
Cl
Cl
HO
NH_2

YOUR TURN D.6

Draw the structure for each of the following molecules. **(a)** pent-4-en-1-amine; **(b)** 3-cyclopropylcyclopent-3-en-1-amine; **(c)** 6-chlorohexa-1,4-diyn-3-amine; **(d)** 2-methylcycloocta-3,6-dien-1-ol

Each molecule shown in **Figure D-5** contains both OH and NH_2 groups. Both the NH_2 and OH functional groups require adding a suffix to the IUPAC name, but only one suffix can be added. According to Table D-1 (p. 373), the higher priority goes to OH, so each molecule receives the suffix *ol* and numbering is established to give the carbon attached to OH the lowest possible number. In Figure D-5a, then, the numbering must begin at the right, and in Figure D-5b, the carbon attached to OH is C-1 and numbering increases clockwise around the ring. The NH_2 groups are then treated as substituents and, according to Table D-1, are named with *amino* prefixes.

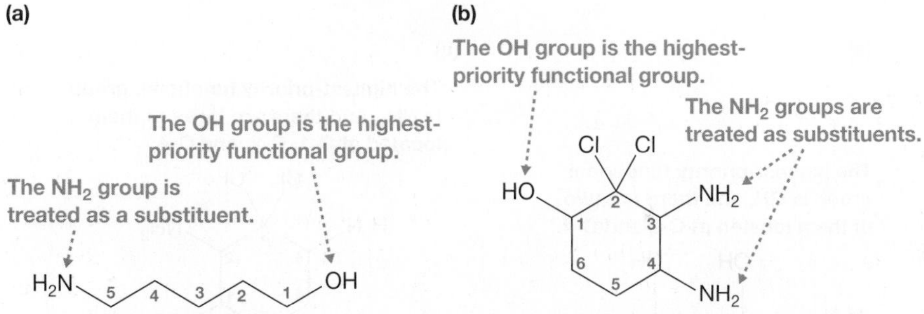

(a)
The OH group is the highest-priority functional group.
The NH_2 group is treated as a substituent.
H_2N
OH
(b)
The OH group is the highest-priority functional group.
The NH_2 groups are treated as substituents.
Cl
Cl
HO
NH_2
NH_2

5-Aminopentan-1-ol   3,4-Diamino-2,2-dichlorocyclohexanol

FIGURE D-5 Molecules containing both OH and NH_2 groups

CONNECTIONS D.2

Sponges that fight tumors

5-Aminopentan-1-ol (Fig. D-5a) is used in the synthesis of manzamines, a class of compounds that exhibit antitumor activity. Manzamines were originally isolated from marine sponges like the one shown here.

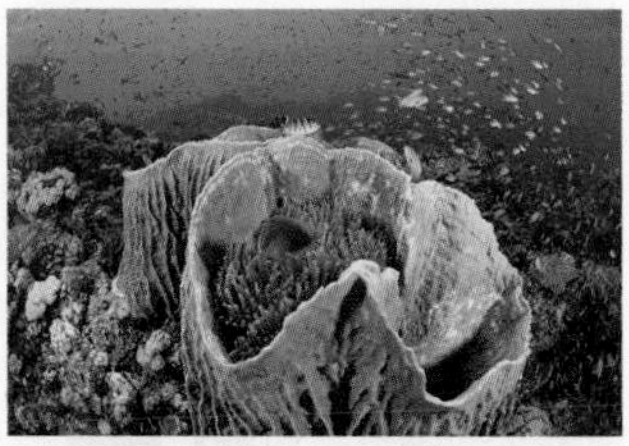

YOUR TURN D.7

Write the IUPAC name for each of the following compounds.

(a)

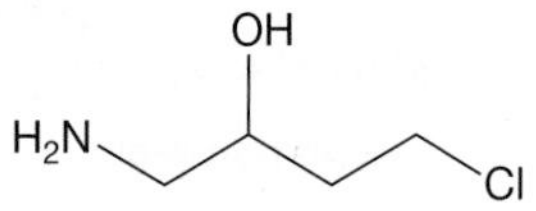
OH
H2N
Cl

(b)

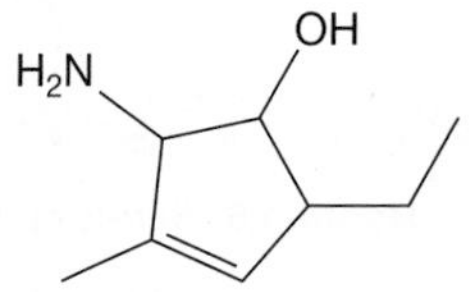
OH
H2N

(c)

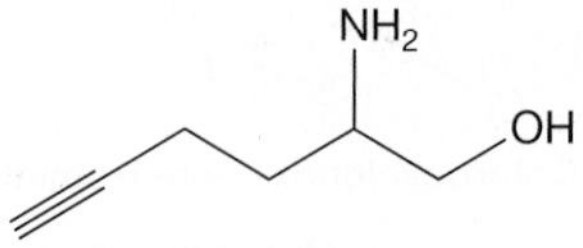
NH2
OH

YOUR TURN D.8

Draw the structure for each of the following molecules. **(a)** 4,5-diaminoheptan-2-ol; **(b)** 2,3,4-triaminocycloheptanol

D.2a Naming Molecules with Two or More of the Highest-Priority Functional Group

In all of the molecules we have examined so far here in Interchapter D, the highest-priority functional group appears just once. If there are two or more of that functional group, additional naming rules are needed:

Naming a Molecule with Two or More of the Highest-Priority Functional Group

1. Keep the final "e." Normally we remove the final "e" of *ane*, *ene*, or *yne* prior to adding the suffix, but this is not the case when there are two or more of the highest-priority functional groups.
2. Add the multiplying prefix for the highest-priority functional group. Add *di*, *tri*, etc. (p. 57) immediately before the suffix to specify how many of the highest-priority functional groups appear.
3. Add locator numbers. Add one locator number for *each* of the highest-priority functional groups immediately before the multiplying prefix.

Let's apply these rules to the examples in **Figure D-6**. In Figure D-6a, the OH groups establish the suffix because they are the highest-priority functional group in the molecule. There are two of them, so we keep the "e" at the end of *pentane*, add *di* immediately before the *ol* suffix, and add locator numbers 2 and 4 to specify where they are attached. In Figure D-6b, the highest-priority functional group is NH_2 and there are three of them. Because the molecule is cyclic, one of the carbons attached to NH_2 must be assigned C-1. The carbon at the bottom right is correct, because assigning it as C-1 allows the next two NH_2 groups to be encountered the earliest.

CONNECTIONS D.3

Keep your car running with propane-1,2-diol Propane-1,2-diol (Your Turn D.9a), more commonly known as propylene glycol, is the principal ingredient used in antifreeze for automobiles. The role of antifreeze is to prevent engines from seizing up in very cold weather.

(a)

The highest-priority functional group is OH, and there are two of them located at C-2 and C-4.

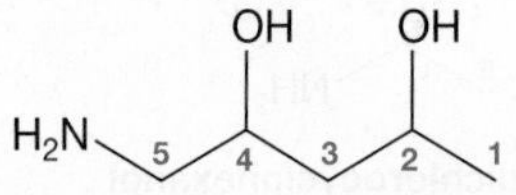
OH
OH
H2N
5
4
3
2
1

5-Aminopentane-2,4-diol

(b)

The highest-priority functional group is NH_2, and there are three of them located at C-1, C-2, and C-4.

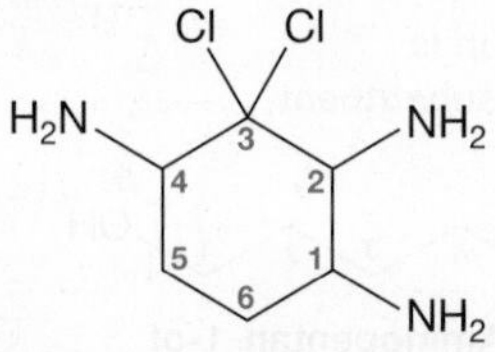
Cl
Cl
H2N
NH2
NH2
3
4
2
5
1
6

3,3-Dichlorocyclohexane-1,2,4-triamine

FIGURE D-6 **Molecules containing multiple highest-priority functional groups**

SOLVED PROBLEM **D.1**

How to name an amino alcohol

Break It Down Write the IUPAC name for the compound shown here.

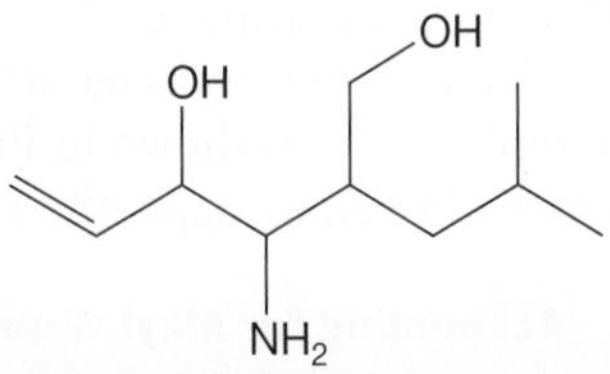
OH
OH
NH2

Think	Solve
Are there any functional groups that require adding a suffix to the name? If there are two or more different ones, which one has priority?	The molecule contains OH and NH_2 groups, both of which call for a suffix to be added. According to Table D-1 (p. 373), an OH group has a higher priority than NH_2, so the suffix is *ol*.
What is the longest carbon chain that contains the highest-priority functional groups? How should you number the main chain so those groups are encountered the earliest?	There are two OH groups, and the longest carbon chain that contains both of them has six carbons, as shown with the numbering system here. The chain is numbered so the first OH encountered receives the lowest possible number: in this case, C-1. 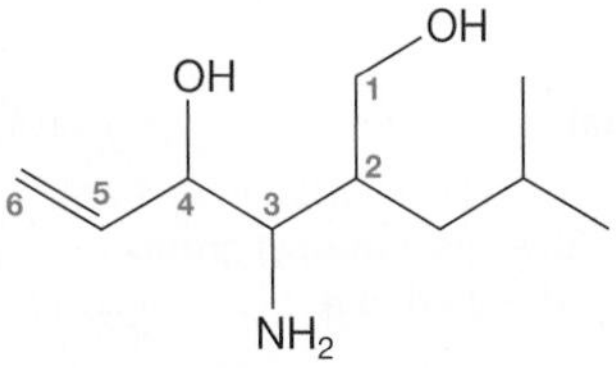
Are there any C=C or C≡C bonds within that main chain? Should you drop the final "e" before adding the suffix? How should you account for the names, numbers, and locations of all functional groups?	There is one C=C bond that is part of that chain, located at C-5. Because there are two OH groups, we keep the final "e" in *ene* before adding the suffix, we add *di* before *ol* to indicate how many OH groups there are, and we specify the location of the OH groups using the locator numbers 1 and 4. Finally, we use prefixes to account for the amino substituent at C-3 and the (2-methylpropyl) substituent at C-2. The name thus is 3-amino-2-(2-methylpropyl)-hex-5-ene-1,4-diol.

OH
OH
1
2
3
4
5
6
NH2

Try It Write the IUPAC name for each of the following compounds.

(a)

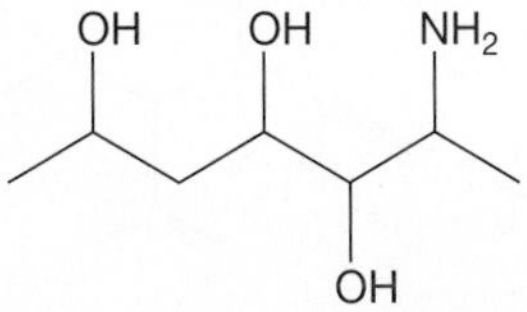
OH
OH
NH2
OH

(b)

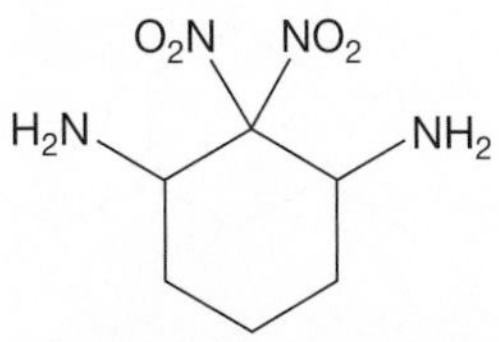
O2N
NO2
H2N
NH2

(c)

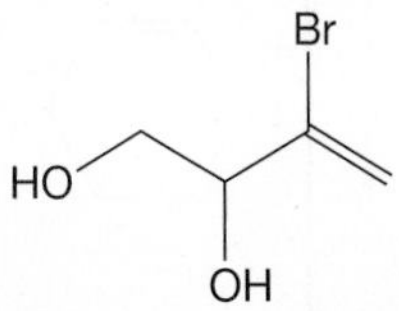
Br
HO
OH

Answers to all Try It exercises can be found in the Solutions Manual.

YOUR TURN **D.9**

Draw the structure for each of the following molecules. **(a)** propane-1,2-diol; **(b)** 1-methoxypentane-2,3-diamine; **(c)** but-2-ene-1,4-diol

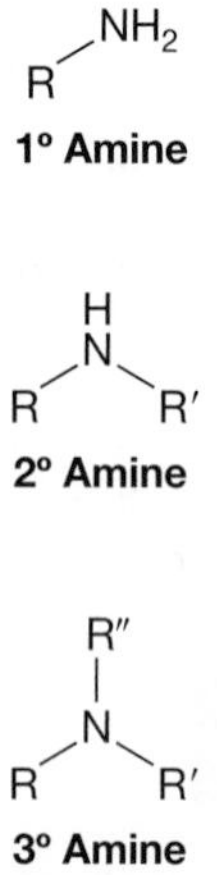

NH_2
R
1° Amine
H
N
R
R′
2° Amine
R″
N
R
R′
3° Amine

FIGURE D-7 Amine classifications Amines are classified as primary (1°), secondary (2°), or tertiary (3°) according to the number of bonds the amine N has to carbon.

D.2b Naming Amines in Which More Than One Alkyl Group Is Bonded to Nitrogen

In the amines we have examined so far, the amine nitrogen has been bonded to two H atoms, appearing as R—NH_2. An amine N can have up to three alkyl groups bonded to it, however, characterizing the amine as either primary (1°), secondary (2°), or tertiary (3°), as shown in **Figure D-7**. To account for these additional alkyl groups attached to N, we apply the following rules:

Accounting for Alkyl Groups Bonded to an Amine Nitrogen

1. Determine which alkyl group attached to N establishes the root. The root for an amine is established by the longest carbon chain or largest carbon ring attached to N.
2. Treat the other alkyl groups attached to N as prefixes. Each of these alkyl groups is given an italic *N* as a locator instead of a number.

Consider the amines shown in **Figure D-8** as examples. The molecule in Figure D-8a has two alkyl groups attached to N, and the six-carbon ring establishes the root: It is a *cyclohexenamine*. The methyl group that is attached to N is treated as a substituent and is given *N* as its locator. In Figure D-8b, the longest carbon chain that is attached to N has five carbons, so it is a *pentanamine*. There is one ethyl substituent that is attached to N, so it appears as a prefix and is given the locator *N*. There are two methyl substituents in the molecule, one attached to N and one attached to C-3, so *dimethyl* appears as a prefix along with the locators "*N*,3."

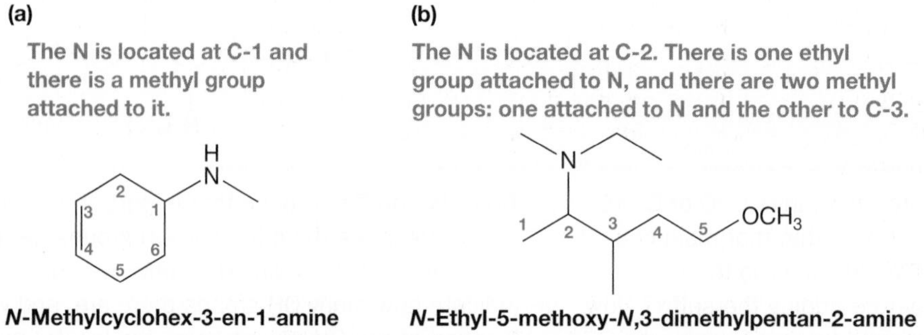

(a)
The N is located at C-1 and there is a methyl group attached to it.
H
N
1
2
3
4
5
6
N-Methylcyclohex-3-en-1-amine
(b)
The N is located at C-2. There is one ethyl group attached to N, and there are two methyl groups: one attached to N and the other to C-3.
N
1
2
3
4
5
OCH_3
N-Ethyl-5-methoxy-*N*,3-dimethylpentan-2-amine

FIGURE D-8 Alkyl groups attached to the amine nitrogen

YOUR TURN **D.10**

Write the IUPAC name for each of the following compounds.

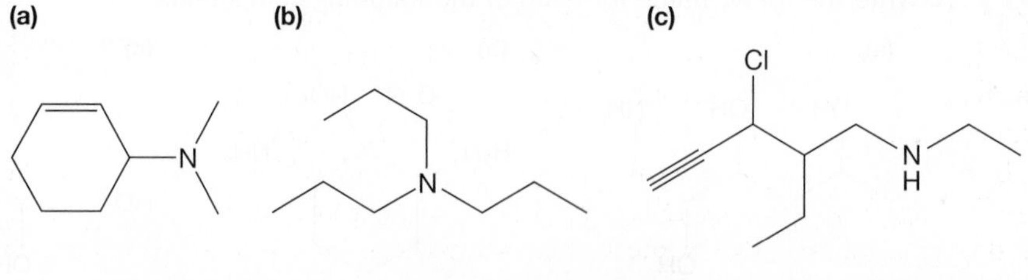

(a)
N
(b)
N
(c)
Cl
N
H

YOUR TURN **D.11**

Draw the structure for each of the following molecules. **(a)** *N*-methylhepta-1,6-dien-4-amine; **(b)** *N*,*N*,3-tricyclopropylcyclobutanamine

D.3 Naming Ketones and Aldehydes

SECTION D.3 OBJECTIVES

You will be able to:

1. Write the IUPAC name of a ketone or aldehyde when given its structure.
2. Draw the structure of ketone or aldehyde when given its IUPAC name.

Both ketones and aldehydes (**Figure D-9**) contain a C═O bond, the *carbonyl group*. In a ketone, the carbonyl carbon is bonded to two alkyl and/or aryl groups, whereas in an aldehyde, the carbonyl carbon is bonded on one side to a H atom and on the other side to an alkyl group, an aryl group, or a second H.

Ketones and aldehydes require adding a suffix to the IUPAC name and therefore follow the rules we learned in Section D.1. Let's first see how those rules are applied to the ketones shown in **Figure D-10**.

The longest carbon chain in the molecule in Figure D-10a has three carbons and no C═C or C≡C bonds, so we begin with *propane*. According to Table D-1 (p. 373), we drop the "e" at the end and add the suffix *one* because the C═O group is part of a ketone. We do not add a locator number because the carbonyl carbon must be at C-2 for the compound to be a ketone rather than an aldehyde. The name, therefore, is just propanone.

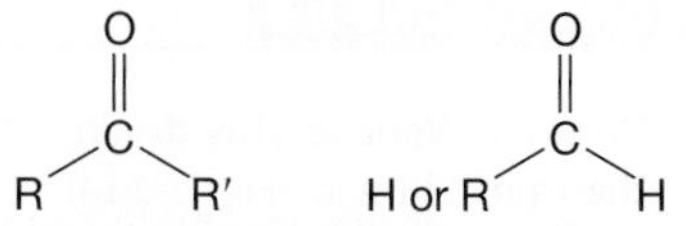

O
R
C
R′
O
H or R
C
H

Ketone **Aldehyde**

FIGURE D-9 **General structures of a ketone and an aldehyde**

The molecule in Figure D-10b has two functional groups that require a suffix: a C═O group that establishes a ketone and an OH group that characterizes an alcohol. According to Table D-1, priority goes to the C═O group, so we name the compound as a ketone and treat the OH group as a substituent, adding the prefix *hydroxy*. The ketone has five carbons in its longest carbon chain, making it a *pentanone*. Unlike propanone, a locator number is necessary for this molecule because a pentanone can have the C═O group at more than one location. In this case, we begin numbering from the right to give the C═O the lowest number, C-2 instead of C-4. The name, therefore, is 4-hydroxypentan-2-one.

For the molecule in Figure D-10c, the longest carbon chain has six carbon atoms, but the longest carbon chain that contains *both* C═O functional groups has just five carbon atoms. Therefore, it is a pentanedione. Because there is more than one C═O, we keep the "e" at the end of *pentane*. Furthermore, locator numbers are required for each C═O. Finally, the propyl group at C-3 is treated as a substituent.

The molecule in Figure D-10d is a cyclic ketone. To give the lowest locator number to the first C═O group, we begin numbering at one of the C═O carbons. To encounter the next two C═O groups the earliest, we must begin with the C═O on the right and number the carbons counterclockwise. Again, we keep the "e" at the end of *ane*, add a multiplying prefix, and include a locator number for each C═O.

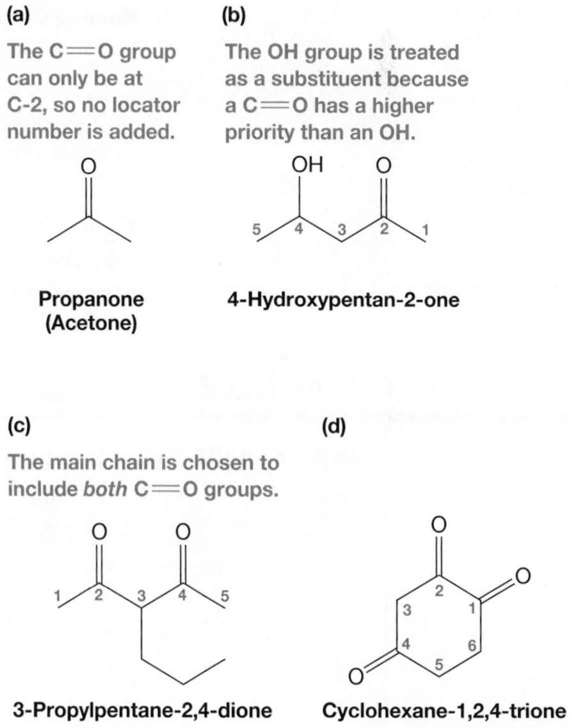

(a)
The C═O group can only be at C-2, so no locator number is added.
O
Propanone
(Acetone)
(b)
The OH group is treated as a substituent because a C═O has a higher priority than an OH.
OH
O
5
4
3
2
1
4-Hydroxypentan-2-one
(c)
The main chain is chosen to include *both* C═O groups.
O
O
1
2
3
4
5
3-Propylpentane-2,4-dione
(d)
O
O
O
2
1
3
4
5
6
Cyclohexane-1,2,4-trione

FIGURE D-10 **Examples of ketones**

To see how the rules are applied for aldehydes, let's name the molecules shown in **Figure D-11** (next page). The molecule shown in Figure D-11a has four carbons in the main chain and, according to Table D-1, an aldehyde requires dropping the final "e" and adding the *al* suffix. Therefore, *butane* becomes *butanal*. Notice that no locator number is needed because an aldehyde C═O must be at a terminal carbon.

In Figure D-11b, the molecule has both a ketone C═O group and an aldehyde C═O group, both of which call for a suffix. According to Table D-1, priority goes to the aldehyde, so the ═O of the ketone is treated as an *oxo* substituent. A locator number is required for the ketone C═O but not for the aldehyde C═O group.

The molecule shown in Figure D-11c has five carbons in the longest carbon chain, but the main chain is assigned as the four-carbon chain that contains both aldehyde C═O groups. A locator number is required for the ethyl substituent but not for the aldehyde C═O groups, so the name is 2-ethylbutanedial. Notice that *di* is added to account for the two aldehyde C═O groups, and the "e" in *ane* is kept.

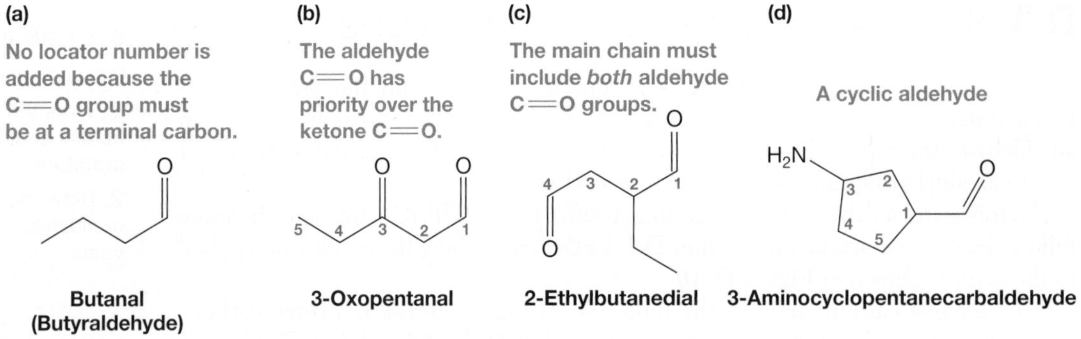
(a)
No locator number is added because the C=O group must be at a terminal carbon.
O
Butanal
(Butyraldehyde)
(b)
The aldehyde C=O has priority over the ketone C=O.
O
O
5
4
3
2
1
3-Oxopentanal
(c)
The main chain must include *both* aldehyde C=O groups.
O
O
4
3
2
1
2-Ethylbutanedial
(d)
A cyclic aldehyde
H_2N
O
3
2
1
4
5
3-Aminocyclopentanecarbaldehyde

FIGURE D-11 **Examples of aldehydes**

CONNECTIONS D.4

Butanal: Want to stay dry in the rain? Butanal (Fig. D-11a) occurs naturally in lavender and eucalyptus oil. It is an industrial precursor for di-(2-ethylhexyl) phthalate (DEHP), a plasticizer used in the production of a variety of consumer products made from poly(vinyl chloride) or PVC, such as this raincoat.

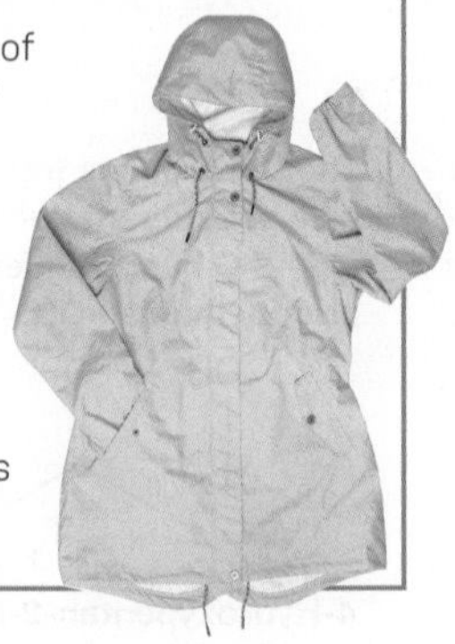

The molecule in Figure D-11d is a cyclic aldehyde. Unlike the functional groups we have dealt with previously, the carbon of an aldehyde C=O cannot be part of the carbon ring. Rather, it is external to the ring but is attached directly to it. In situations like this, we apply the following rule:

Naming Cyclic Aldehydes

1. Establish the root as *cycloalkanecarbaldehyde*. The *cycloalkane* portion is dictated by the size of the ring attached to the HC=O group.
2. Number the carbons of the ring. C-1 is the ring carbon attached to the HC=O group, and numbering increases around the ring.

In Figure D-11d, the ring is a cyclopentane, so the molecule is a *cyclopentanecarbaldehyde*. The ring carbon attached to HC=O is assigned C-1, and numbering increases counterclockwise around the ring to encounter the NH_2 group the earliest. The molecule is 3-aminocyclopentanecarbaldehyde.

YOUR TURN D.12

Write the IUPAC name for each of the following compounds.

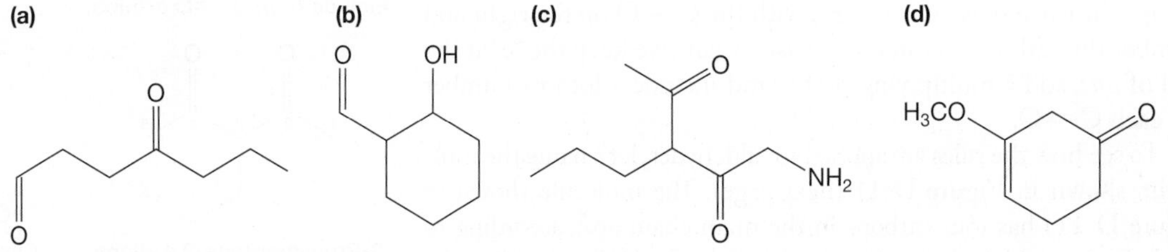
(a)
O
O
(b)
O
OH
(c)
O
NH_2
O
(d)
H_3CO
O

YOUR TURN D.13

Draw the structure for each of the following molecules.
(a) cyclopentane-1,2,3-trione; **(b)** 3,3,3-trichloro-2-oxopropanal;
(c) 2,4,4-trinitrocycloheptanecarbaldehyde; **(d)** 4-hydroxyhept-2-ynedial

D.4 Naming Carboxylic Acids, Acid Chlorides, Amides, and Nitriles

SECTION D.4 OBJECTIVES

You will be able to:

1. Write the IUPAC name of a carboxylic acid, acid chloride, amide, or nitrile when given its structure.
2. Draw the structure of a carboxylic acid, acid chloride, amide, or nitrile when given its IUPAC name.

The nomenclature rules for carboxylic acids, acid chlorides, amides, and nitriles are presented together in this section for two reasons: (1) they are named according to the same basic rules that were presented in Section D.1, and (2) they are related chemically, as water can react with acid chlorides, amides, and nitriles to produce carboxylic acids (reactions that we will study in Chapters 22 and 23). Thus, acid chlorides, amides, and nitriles are types of **carboxylic acid derivatives**.

Let's begin by naming the molecules in **Figure D-12**. The molecule shown in Figure D-12a has two functional groups found in Table D-1 (p. 373): a carbonyl group, characteristic of a ketone, and a carboxyl group, characteristic of a carboxylic acid. The carboxyl group has the higher priority, so numbering begins at the right to give its carbon the lowest number. The longest carbon chain containing the carboxyl group has 10 carbons and a C=C bond, making the root *decene*. After we remove the final "e" and add the suffix *oic acid*, the root becomes *decenoic acid*. The location of the carboxyl group is not included in the name because it must be at C-1, but the locator numbers for the C=C bond at C-2 and the carbonyl group of the ketone at C-9 are included. Those groups are named according to the rules we have encountered previously. Notice, specifically, that the ketone's C=O group is given the prefix *oxo*. Finally, as discussed in Section 5.8, the configuration about the double bond (*E* in this case) is indicated in parentheses at the beginning of the name (see top Recall box).

◂ RECALL

In Section 5.8, we learned how to assign *E* and *Z* configurations to double bonds. The two substituents attached to each end of the double bond are assigned higher or lower priority. The double bond is *E* if the two higher-priority substituents appear on the same side of the double bond and is *Z* if they are on opposite sides.

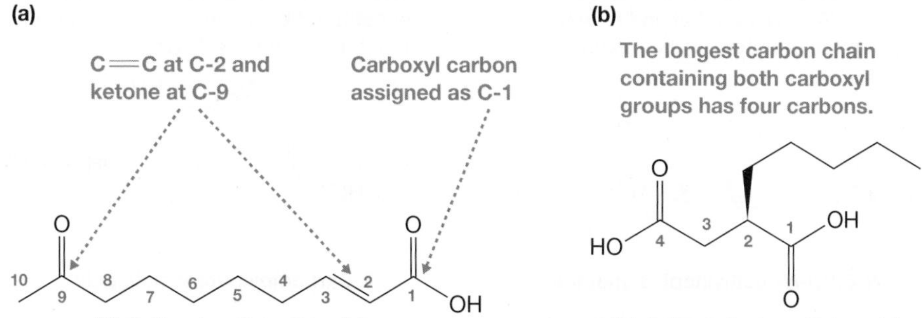

(a)
C=C at C-2 and ketone at C-9
Carboxyl carbon assigned as C-1
O
O
OH
10 9 8 7 6 5 4 3 2 1
(b)
The longest carbon chain containing both carboxyl groups has four carbons.
O
HO
4 3 2 1
OH
O

(*E*)-9-Oxodec-2-enoic acid

(*R*)-2-Pentylbutanedioic acid

FIGURE D-12 Examples of carboxylic acids

The molecule in Figure D-12b has two carboxyl groups, and the longest carbon chain that contains both of them has four carbons. In this case, the final "e" is kept, so the molecule is a *butanedioic acid*. The pentyl group is indicated at C-2, and according to the rules from Section 5.6, the *R* configuration of the asymmetric carbon appears at the beginning of the name (see bottom Recall box). Notice that no numbers are used to locate the two carboxyl groups because they must be at the ends of the chain.

Let's now look at two molecules containing a CN group (see **Figure D-13**, next page). In Figure D-13a, the CN group is the highest-priority functional group present, so according to Table D-1, the molecule is given the suffix *nitrile* and the carbon that is part of the CN group is designated C-1. In Figure D-13b, the CN group is treated as the substituent *cyano* because the highest-priority functional group present is O=C—Cl, characteristic of an acid chloride. Notice, in this case, that the carbon belonging to the CN group is not counted as part of the longest carbon chain that establishes the root because, when treated as a substituent, the cyano group already accounts for that carbon.

CONNECTIONS D.5

A royal carboxylic acid

(*E*)-9-Oxodec-2-enoic acid (Fig. D-12a) is a pheromone that attracts drones to queen bees over long distances.

◂ RECALL

In Section 5.6, we learned how to assign *R* and *S* configurations to chiral centers. The four substituents attached to the chiral center are assigned priorities 1 through 4. With the lowest priority substituent pointing away, the configuration is *R* if substituents 1–3 are arranged clockwise, and it is *S* if they are arranged counterclockwise.

FIGURE D-13 Compounds containing C≡N groups

(a)

CN is the highest-priority functional group, so the suffix is *nitrile* and its carbon is assigned C-1.

(b)

O═C—Cl is the highest-priority functional group, so the suffix is *oyl chloride*. The CN group is a substituent, so its C atom is not numbered.

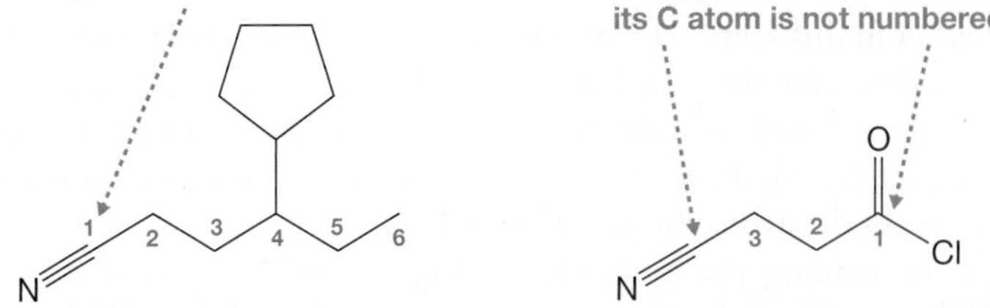

1
2
3
4
5
6
N
O
3
2
1
Cl
N

4-Cyclopentylhexanenitrile

3-Cyanopropanoyl chloride

We next examine the two amides (containing the characteristic O═C—N group) in **Figure D-14**. In Figure D-14a, O═C—N is the highest-priority functional group (see Table D-1), so we add the suffix *amide*. Notice that the ethyl and methyl groups attached to the amide N are indicated using the same rules we learned in Section D.2b to specify alkyl groups attached to an amine N. Furthermore, there are three alkyl groups attached to the amide N, characterizing it as a tertiary amide according to **Figure D-15**.

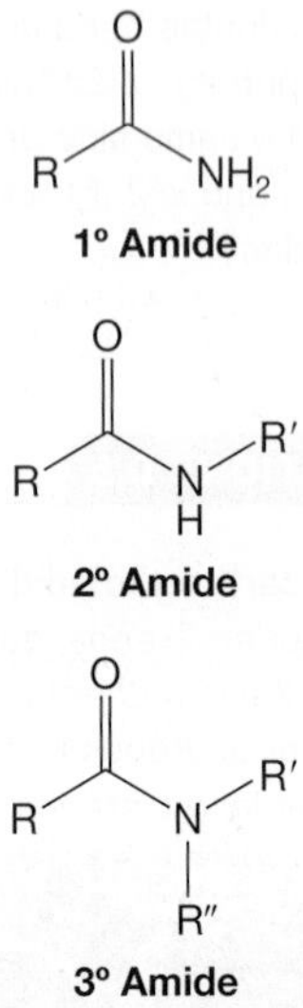

O
R
NH₂
1° Amide
O
R
N
R′
H
2° Amide
O
R
N
R′
R″
3° Amide

FIGURE D-15 Amide classifications As for amines in Figure D-7, amides are classified as primary (1°), secondary (2°), or tertiary (3°) according to the number of bonds the amide N has to carbon.

(a)

The highest-priority functional group is O═C—N. An ethyl and a methyl group are attached to the amide N.

(b)

The O═C—N group is treated as a substituent because the highest-priority functional group is CO_2H.

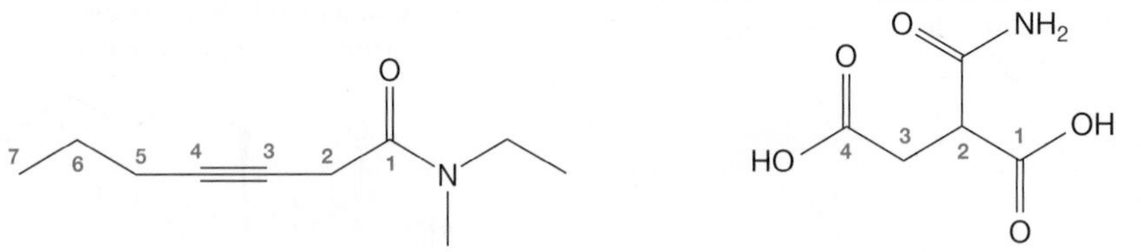

O
7
6
5
4
3
2
1
N
O
NH₂
O
3
1
OH
HO
4
2
O

***N*-Ethyl-*N*-methylhept-3-ynamide**

2-Carbamoylbutanedioic acid

FIGURE D-14 Compounds containing O═C—N groups

For the molecule in Figure D-14b, the highest-priority functional group is CO_2H, so the O═C—N group is treated as a substituent, indicated by the prefix *carbamoyl* (Table D-1). Just as we saw with CN groups, *the carbon atom of an O═C—N group is not numbered when the O═C—N group is treated as a substituent* (see also Solved Problem D.2).

SOLVED PROBLEM **D.2**

How to name a carboxylic acid derivative

Break It Down **Write the IUPAC name for L-asparagine, one of the naturally occurring amino acids, which is shown here in its un-ionized form. (Do not be concerned with stereochemical designations in this case.)**

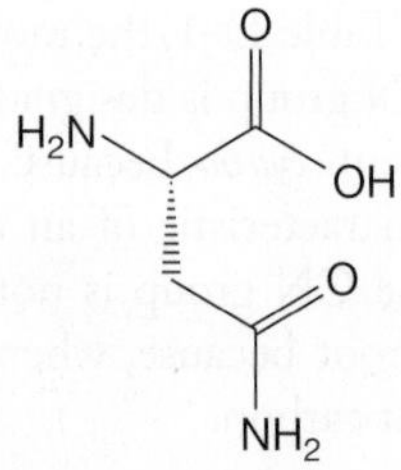

O
H₂N
OH
O
NH₂

(continued)

Think	Solve
What is the highest-priority functional group present, and what corresponding suffix must be added?	The highest-priority functional group in the molecule is CO_2H (Table D-1, p. 373), so the suffix is *oic acid* and numbering begins at the CO_2H carbon. 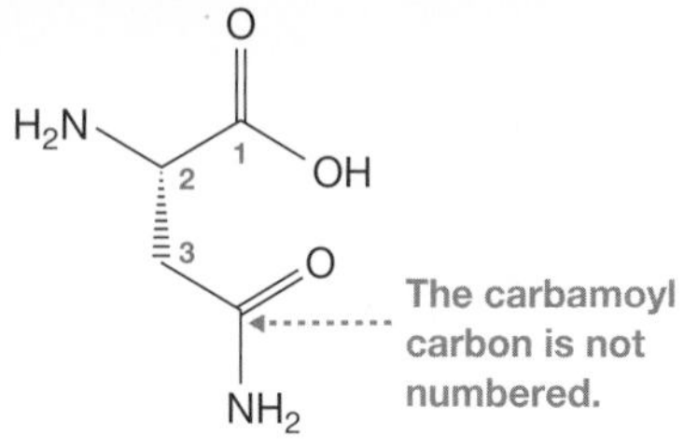 O H_2N 1 2 OH 3 O NH_2 The carbamoyl carbon is not numbered.
What other functional groups are present, and how are those named as substituents?	The other functional groups present are NH_2 and O=C—N, which must be treated as substituents and receive the prefixes *amino* and *carbamoyl*, respectively.
How many carbon atoms are in the longest carbon chain? Where along the chain are the substituents located?	The prefix *carbamoyl* accounts for the O=C—N carbon, so there are three carbon atoms in the longest carbon chain containing the CO_2H group, making the molecule a *propanoic acid*. The amino group is attached to C-2 and the carbamoyl group is attached to C-3. The IUPAC name for this amino acid is thus 2-amino-3-carbamoylpropanoic acid.

Try It Write the IUPAC name for each of the following compounds.

(a)

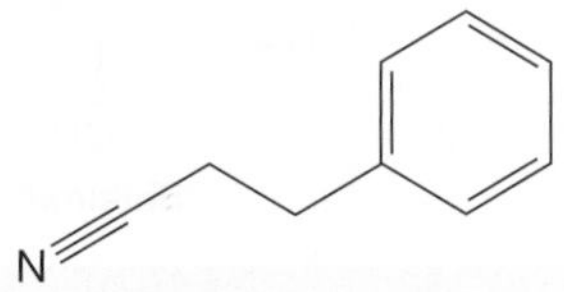
N

(b)

O
HO
N

(c)

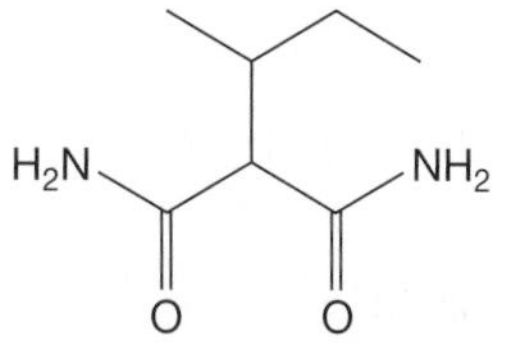
H_2N
NH_2
O
O

YOUR TURN **D.14**

Draw the structure for each of the following molecules.
(a) 4-chlorocarbonylbutanoic acid; **(b)** 4-hydroxy-*N*-methyl-5-phenylpentanamide; **(c)** 2,3-dimethylhex-2-enedinitrile; **(d)** 2-carboxy-1,4-butanedioic acid

The functional groups characterizing carboxylic acids, primary amides, and nitriles cannot be incorporated into a ring structure, but they can be *attached* directly to a ring. In such cases, we apply the following rules, which are similar to the ones we used to name cyclic aldehydes (Section D.3):

Naming Cyclic Carboxylic Acids, Primary Amides, and Nitriles

1. Include both the ring and the functional group in the root name.
   - A cyclic carboxylic acid takes the form *cycloalkanecarboxylic acid*.
   - A cyclic amide takes the form *cycloalkanecarboxamide*.
   - A cyclic nitrile takes the form *cycloalkanecarbonitrile*.
2. Number the carbons of the ring. C-1 is the ring carbon attached to the carbonyl-containing group, and numbering increases around the ring.

Let's apply these rules to the molecules in **Figure D-16** (next page). The molecule shown in Figure D-16a is a *cyclohexanecarboxylic acid* and the C=O that characterizes a ketone is located at C-3. In Figure D-16b, the five-membered ring attached to

CONNECTIONS D.6

Naturally occurring carboxylic acids and carboxylic acid derivatives In Solved Problem D.2, Try It, compound (a) is isolated from watercress. Compound (b) is a fungal metabolite isolated from *Lepista diemii*, shown here.

FIGURE D-16 Cyclic carboxylic acids and carboxylic acid derivatives

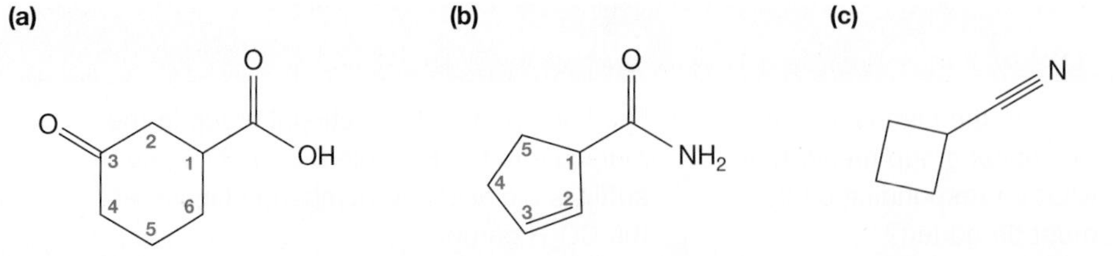
(a)
(b)
(c)

3-Oxocyclohexanecarboxylic acid **Cyclopent-2-enecarboxamide** **Cyclobutanecarbonitrile**

the O═C—N carbon would establish the root as *cyclopentanecarboxamide*. The C═C bond requires *ane* to become *ene*, and it is located at C-2. The molecule in Figure D-16c has no substituents on the ring and is named cyclobutanecarbonitrile, which accounts for the attached four-membered ring.

SOLVED PROBLEM **D.3**

How to name a cyclic acid derivative

Break It Down Write the IUPAC name for shikimic acid. (Do not be concerned with stereochemical designations in this case.)

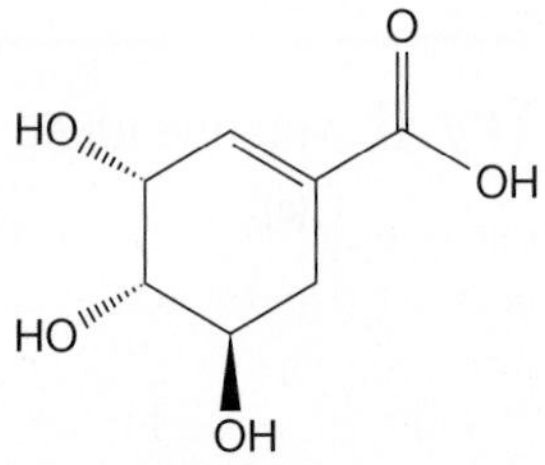

Shikimic acid

Think	Solve
What is the highest-priority functional group present? Given the ring structure and the functional group, what general form does this cyclic acid take?	The highest-priority functional group present is CO_2H, and because it is directly attached to a cyclohexene ring, the molecule is a *cyclohexenecarboxylic acid*.
Should the highest-priority functional group be numbered as part of the root? What other functional groups are present? How many of them are there, and where are they located on the ring?	The carbon atoms of the ring are numbered, with C-1 being the carbon that is attached to the carboxyl group. The C═C bond begins at C-1, and three hydroxy substituents are attached at C-3, C-4, and C-5. 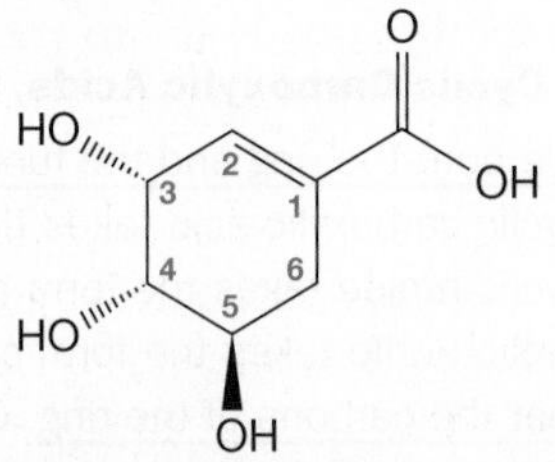
How do you construct the IUPAC name from this information?	The IUPAC name for shikimic acid is 3,4,5-trihydroxycyclohex-1-enecarboxylic acid.

(continued)

CONNECTIONS D.7

The use of shikimic acid toward flu medication
Shikimic acid (Solved Problem D.3) can be isolated from the Japanese star anise flower and is used as a starting material in the production of oseltamivir, an antiviral medication marketed under the trade name Tamiflu.

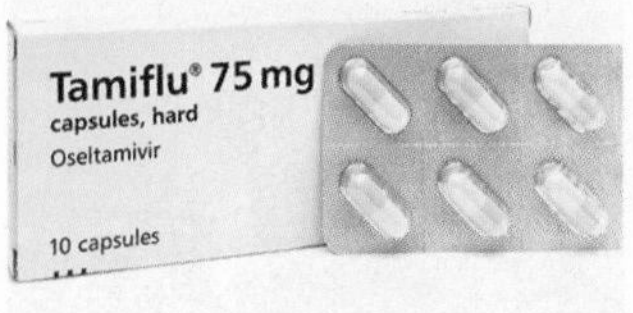
Tamiflu® 75 mg
capsules, hard
Oseltamivir
10 capsules

Try It Write the IUPAC name for each of the following compounds.

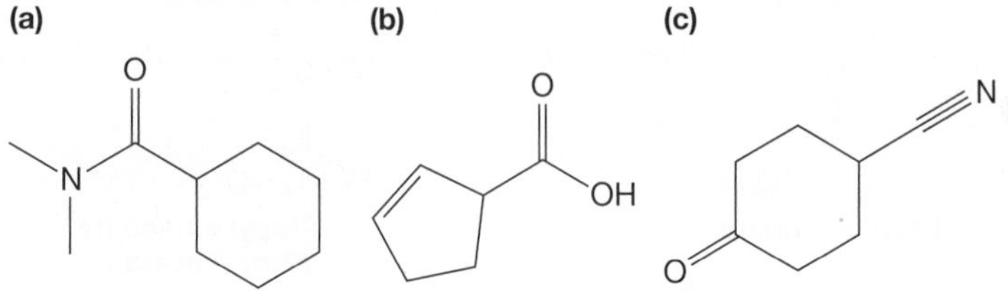

(a)
(b)
(c)
O
N
O
OH
N
O

YOUR TURN **D.15**

Draw the structure for each of the following molecules.
(a) 2,2-dimethylcyclopentanecarboxylic acid; **(b)** cyclohepta-3,5-diene-1-carboxamide; **(c)** 4-cyanocyclooctane-1-carboxylic acid; **(d)** 2-hydroxy-*N*-(1-methylethyl)cyclobutane-1-carboxamide; **(e)** cyclohexa-2,4-diene-1-carbonitrile

D.5 Naming Esters and Acid Anhydrides

SECTION D.5 OBJECTIVES

You will be able to:

1. Write the IUPAC name of an ester or acid anhydride when given its structure.
2. Draw the structure of an ester or acid anhydride when given its IUPAC name.

Like acid chlorides, amides, and nitriles, it turns out that esters and acid anhydrides can react with water to produce carboxylic acids; thus, esters and acid anhydrides are also types of *carboxylic acid derivatives*. The rules for naming esters and acid anhydrides differ from the rules for other compound classes described in Sections D.1–D.4. Section D.5a presents the nomenclature rules for esters, and Section D.5b deals with acid anhydrides.

D.5a Naming Esters

As shown in **Figure D-17a**, an ester consists of an O═C—O group with H or an alkyl group (R) attached to the carbonyl carbon and another alkyl group (R′) attached to the singly bonded O. Because the two groups attached to O═C—O can consist of any number of carbon atoms, the name of the ester must accurately account for both groups. We begin by dividing the molecule into two parts, as shown in Figure D-17b. One part is simply the R′ alkyl group bonded to the O atom, highlighted in blue. The other is the RCO_2 group, called the **alkanoate group**, which is highlighted in red and contains the carbonyl (C═O) group and the singly bonded O atom.

With the ideas from Figure D-17 in mind, we name esters as follows:

Rules for Naming Esters

1. Establish the alkanoate portion as the root for the ester. The name of the alkanoate is determined by the number of carbons in the chain. For example, HCO_2 is named *methanoate*; CH_3CO_2 is named *ethanoate*; and $CH_3CH_2CO_2$ is named *propanoate*.
2. Number the alkyl and alkanoate chains. C-1 of the alkanoate chain is assigned to the CO_2 carbon, and C-1 of the alkyl group is assigned to the carbon that is attached to the ester oxygen.
3. Establish the alkyl portion of the ester. The alkyl group is named precisely as described in Section A.4 (i.e., *methyl*, *ethyl*, *propyl*, etc.)
4. Write the parent name of the ester in the format *alkyl alkanoate.* Notice that there is a space between the two portions of the name.
5. Add the names and locator numbers (locants) of the substituents. Substituents can appear on both the alkyl and the alkanoate portions of the ester.

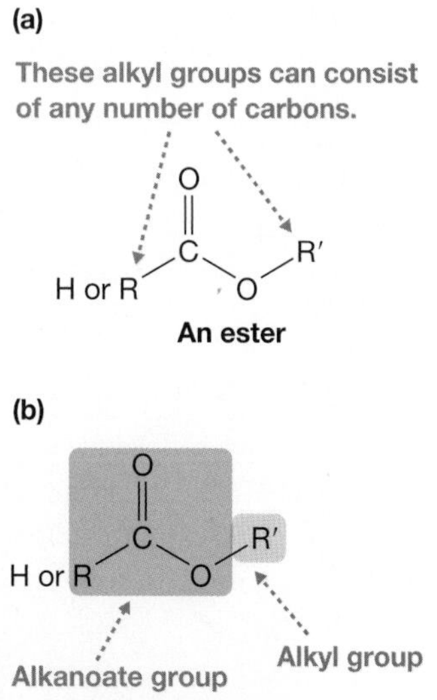

(a)
These alkyl groups can consist of any number of carbons.
O
C
R′
H or R
O
An ester
(b)
O
C
R′
H or R
O
Alkanoate group
Alkyl group

FIGURE D-17 The two parts that make up an ester

(a)

(b)

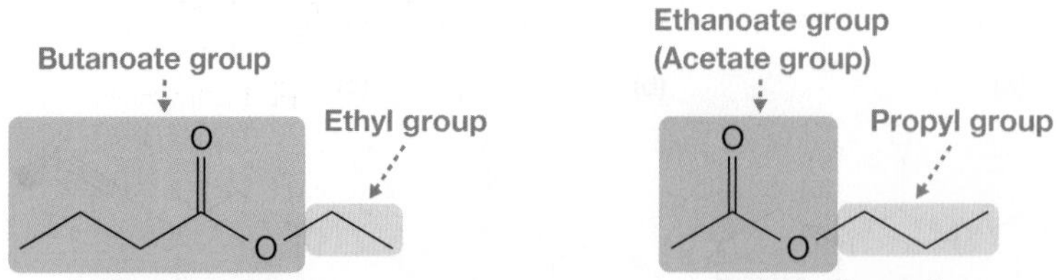
Butanoate group
Ethyl group
Ethanoate group
(Acetate group)
Propyl group

Ethyl butanoate

Propyl ethanoate
(Propyl acetate)

FIGURE D-18 **Naming esters**

CONNECTIONS D.8

Esters in your orange juice
Ethyl butanoate (Fig. D-18a) tastes like oranges and is commonly used as a flavoring agent, including in many brands of orange juice.

Let's see how these rules apply to the esters shown in **Figure D-18**. In ethyl butanoate (Figure D-18a), an ethyl group is attached to the singly bonded O atom. The alkanoate group is named *butanoate* because it is made up of a four-carbon chain. In propyl ethanoate (propyl acetate, Figure D-18b), the alkyl group is a propyl group and the alkanoate group has two C atoms, so it is the ethanoate group (acetate group). (The name acetate derives from the trivial name for the analogous carboxylic acid, acetic acid; see Appendix E.)

The examples in **Figure D-19** show how to deal with substituents attached to the alkyl and alkanoate groups. In Figure D-19a, a methyl group is attached to C-1 of the propyl group, and C-3 of the butanoate portion is part of a carbonyl group. In Figure D-19b, hydroxy substituents are attached to C-3 and C-4 of the pentanoate portion. The *S* configurations (Section 5.6) at those two carbons are indicated at the beginning of the alkanoate portion of the name.

(a)

(b)

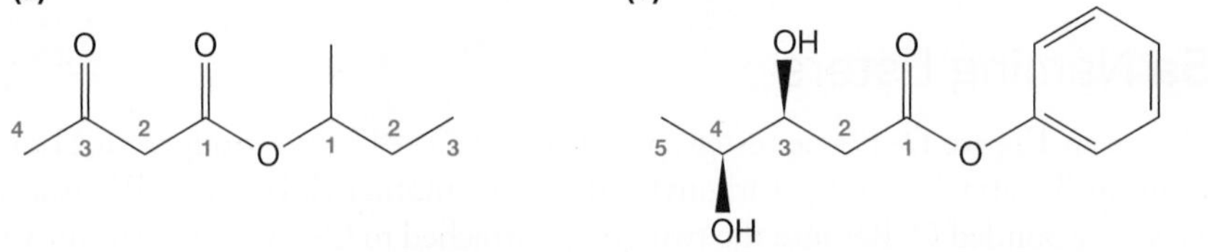

1-Methylpropyl 3-oxobutanoate

Phenyl (3*S*,4*S*)-3,4-dihydroxypentanoate

FIGURE D-19 **Esters with substituents attached**

SOLVED PROBLEM **D.4**

How to name an ester

Break It Down Write the IUPAC name for the molecule shown here. (The configuration of the asymmetric carbon is S.)

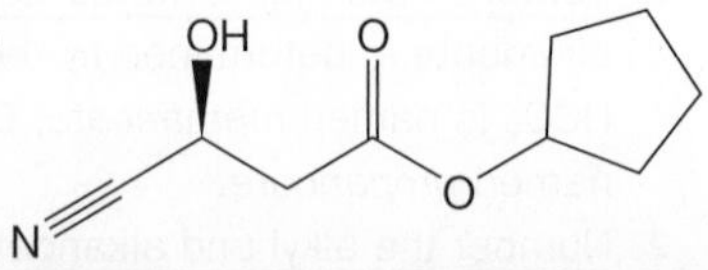

Think	Solve
What functional groups are present? Which one has the highest priority?	Three functional groups are present: C≡N (nitrile), OH (alcohol), and CO_2R (ester). According to Table D-1 (p. 373), the ester group has the highest priority.

(continued)

What are the names of the alkyl and alkanoate portions of the ester?	The alkyl group is *cyclopentyl*. The alkanoate chain has three carbons, as shown with the numbering system here (the C of CN is not included because it is already accounted for as a substituent). It is therefore a *propanoate*. 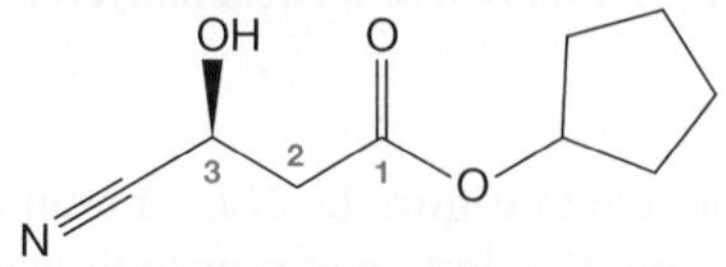
How do you account for the names and locations of the substituents, as well as the configuration of the asymmetric carbon?	The OH and CN groups at C-3 belong to the alkanoate group, so their names and locator numbers are written at the front of the alkanoate portion of the name. Similarly, the asymmetric carbon belongs to the alkanoate, so the *S* configuration is written at the front of the alkanoate's name, too. The IUPAC name is thus cyclopentyl (*S*)-3-cyano-3-hydroxypropanoate.

Try It What is the IUPAC name for each of the following molecules?

(a)

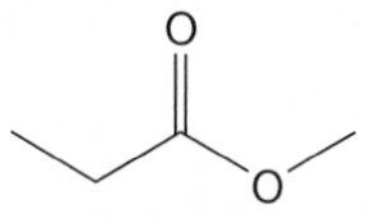

(b)

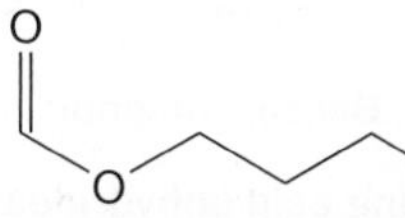

(c)

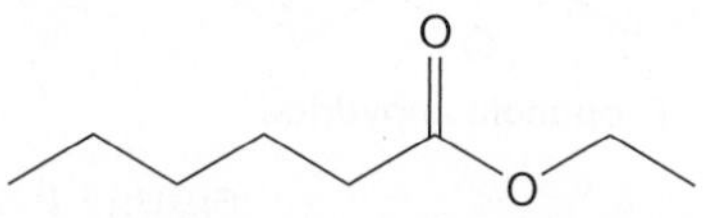

YOUR TURN **D.16**

Draw the molecules that correspond to the following IUPAC names. **(a)** pentyl pentanoate; **(b)** propyl butanoate; **(c)** ethyl methanoate; **(d)** ethyl 3-methylpent-2-enoate; **(e)** 3-chlorobutyl 2-hydroxypropanoate

D.5b Naming Acid Anhydrides

The rules for naming acid anhydrides are derived from the fact that an acid anhydride can be produced from two carboxylic acids in what is called a dehydration reaction, as shown in **Figure D-20** (next page). (A dehydration reaction involves removal of water; these reactions are described in detail in Chapter 23.) The R and R′ groups can be the same, in which case the acid anhydride would be *symmetric*, or they can be different, in which case the acid anhydride would be *unsymmetric*:

Rules for Naming Acid Anhydrides

- For a symmetric acid anhydride, name the molecule according to the general form *alkanoic anhydride*. Here, *alkanoic* corresponds to the specific carboxylic acid that could undergo dehydration to produce the anhydride.
- If the acid anhydride is unsymmetric, then name the molecule according to the general form *alkanoic alkanoic anhydride*.
  - The two instances of *alkanoic* will be different, each corresponding to one of the two different carboxylic acids that would be required to form the anhydride via dehydration.
  - The two instances of *alkanoic* should appear in alphabetical order.

CONNECTIONS D.9

Acetic anhydride and aspirin The molecule in Your Turn D.17a, whose trivial name is acetic anhydride, is commonly used to acetylate certain functional groups, including alcohols, phenols, and amines. It is used, for instance, to acetylate salicylic acid in the production of acetylsalicylic acid, more commonly known as aspirin.

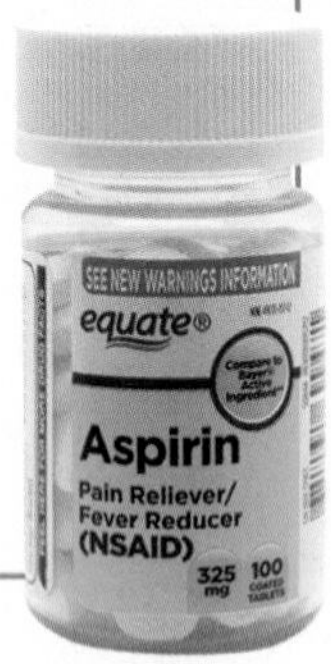

SEE NEW WARNINGS INFORMATION
equate
Aspirin
Pain Reliever/
Fever Reducer
(NSAID)
325 mg
100

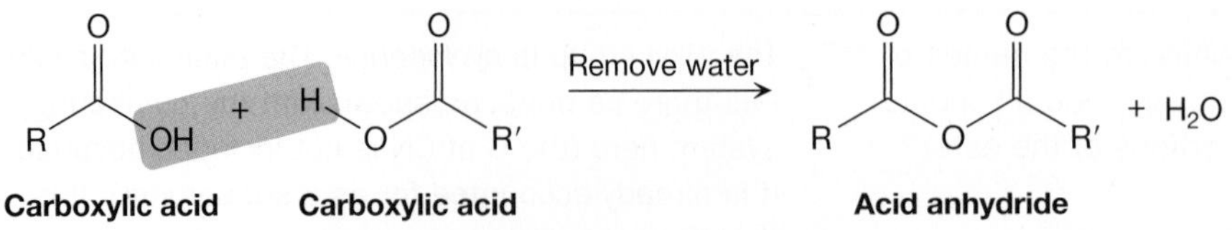

R
OH
+
H
O
R′
Remove water
R
O
R′
+ H_2O
Carboxylic acid
Carboxylic acid
Acid anhydride

FIGURE D-20 Formation of an acid anhydride via dehydration

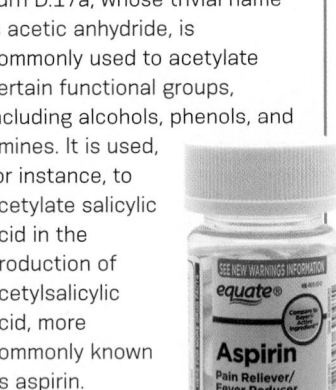

The molecule in **Figure D-21a**, for example, is a symmetric anhydride that would be produced on dehydration of propanoic acid. Therefore, its name is propanoic anhydride. The molecule in Figure D-21b is an unsymmetric anhydride, which would be produced on the dehydration of ethanoic acid (acetic acid) and benzoic acid. It is named benzoic ethanoic anhydride.

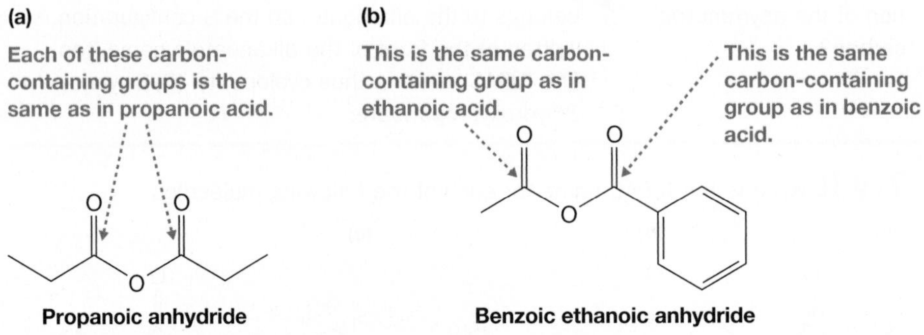

(a)
Each of these carbon-containing groups is the same as in propanoic acid.
Propanoic anhydride
(b)
This is the same carbon-containing group as in ethanoic acid.
This is the same carbon-containing group as in benzoic acid.
Benzoic ethanoic anhydride

FIGURE D-21 Naming acid anhydrides

YOUR TURN D.17

What is the IUPAC name for each of the following molecules?

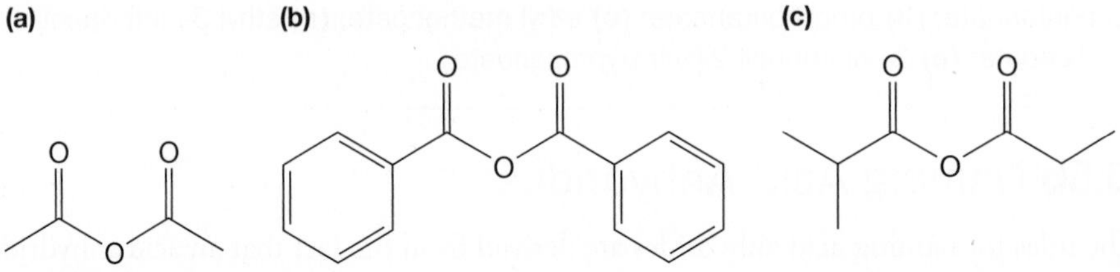

(a)
(b)
(c)

YOUR TURN D.18

Draw the molecules that correspond to the following IUPAC names. **(a)** butanoic anhydride; **(b)** butanoic propanoic anhydride; **(c)** 2-methylbutanoic anhydride; **(d)** benzoic 2-methylbutanoic anhydride

▸ LOOKING AHEAD

As with any class of organic compounds, the compound classes we examined here in Interchapter D (alcohols, amines, ketones, aldehydes, carboxylic acids, and carboxylic acid derivatives) have trivial names that are firmly entrenched in nomenclature. Appendix E presents some of the ways in which trivial names apply to these types of compounds.

Problems

Section D.2 Naming Alcohols and Amines

D.1 Provide the IUPAC name for each of the following alcohols.

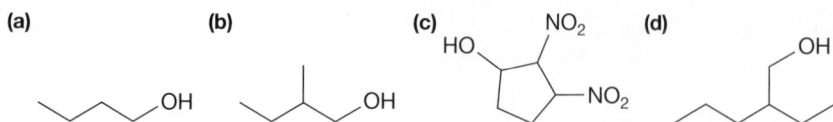

(a) 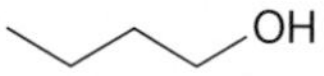
OH

(b) 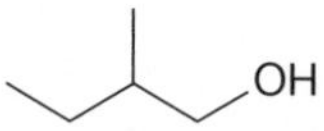
OH

(c) 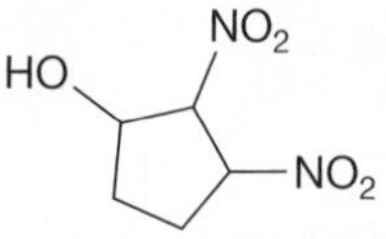
HO
NO2
NO2

(d) 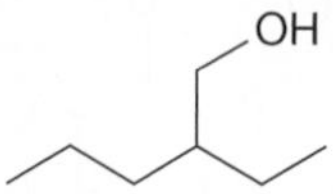
OH

D.2 Provide the IUPAC name for each of the following amines.

(a) 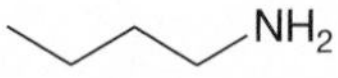
NH2

(b) 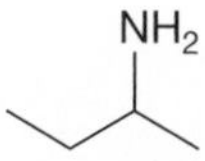
NH2

(c) 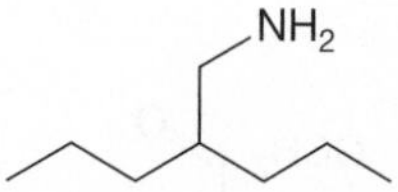
NH2

(d) 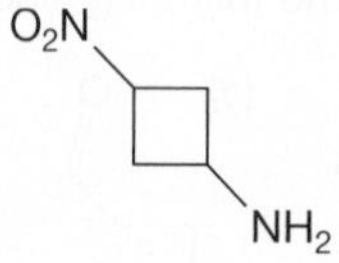
O2N
NH2

D.3 Draw the molecule that corresponds to each IUPAC name. **(a)** 3,3-dipropoxypentan-1-amine; **(b)** 2,3,4-trichlorocyclohexanol; **(c)** 3-cyclopropylpentan-1-ol; **(d)** 3-(1-methylethyl)cycloheptanamine

D.4 Provide the IUPAC name for each of the following compounds.

(a) 
H2N
Cl

(b) 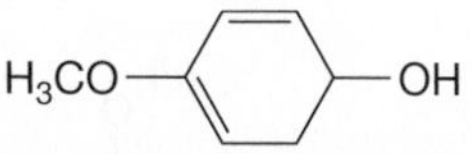
H3CO
OH

(c) 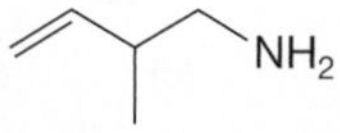
NH2

D.5 Provide the IUPAC name for each of the following compounds.

(a) 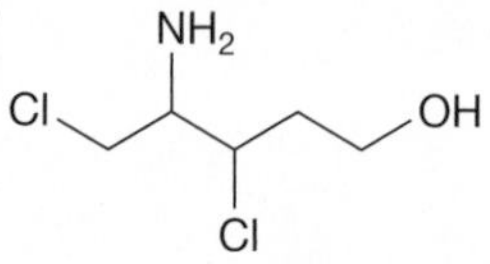
NH2
Cl
OH
Cl

(b) 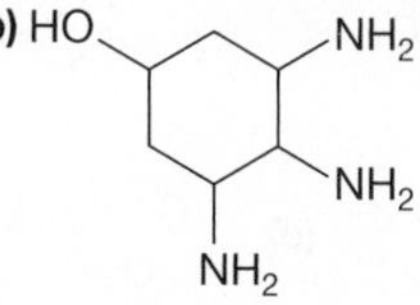
HO
NH2
NH2
NH2

(c) 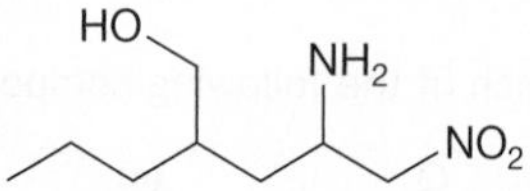
HO
NH2
NO2

D.6 Draw the molecule that corresponds to each IUPAC name. **(a)** 5-amino-2,3,4-trimethylpentan-1-ol; **(b)** 3-amino-4,5-diethoxyoctan-1-ol; **(c)** 3,4-diamino-5-bromocyclohexanol; **(d)** 4-amino-3,3-diethylhexan-1-ol

D.7 Provide the IUPAC name for each of the following compounds.

(a) 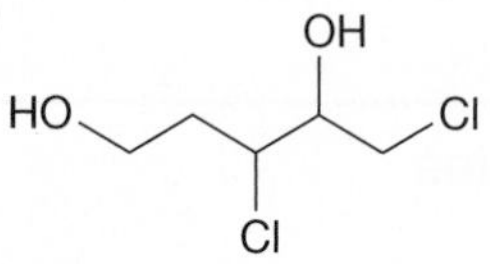
OH
HO
Cl
Cl

(b) 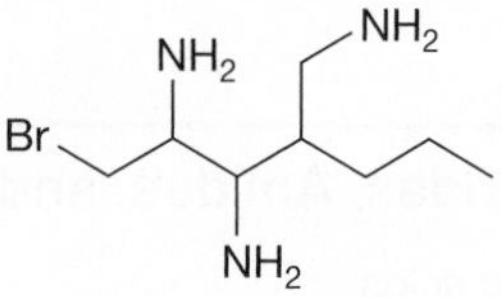
NH2
NH2
Br
NH2

(c) 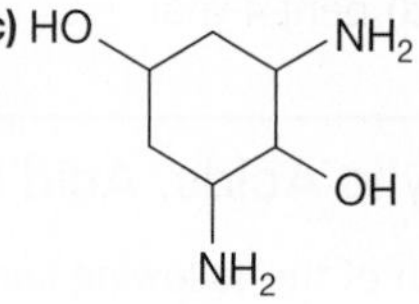
HO
NH2
OH
NH2

D.8 Provide the IUPAC name for each of the following compounds.

(a) 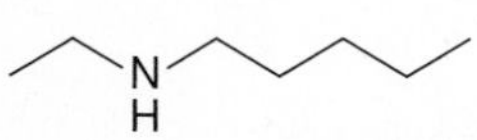
N
H

(b) 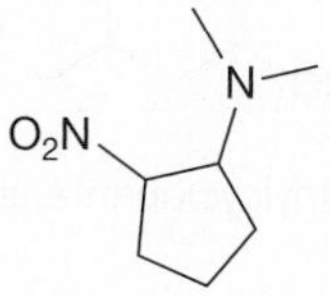
N
O2N

(c) 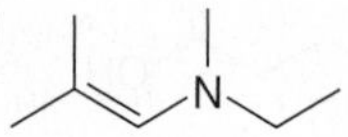
N

D.9 Provide the IUPAC name for each of the following compounds.

(a) 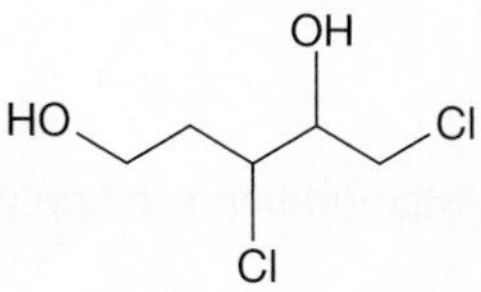
OH
HO
Cl
Cl

(b) 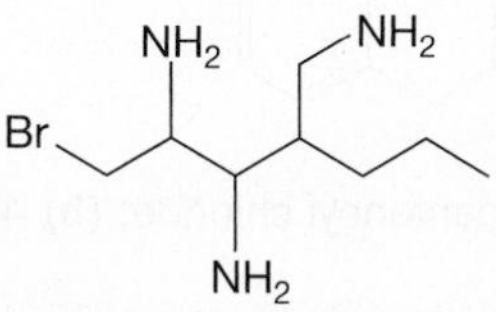
NH2
NH2
Br
NH2

(c) 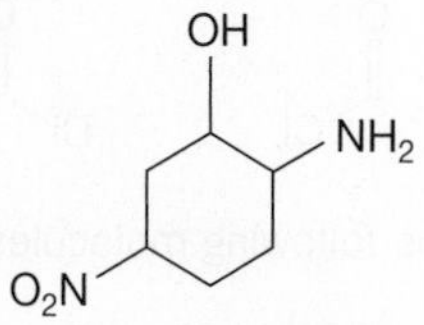
OH
NH2
O2N

D.10 Draw the molecule that corresponds to each IUPAC name. **(a)** hexan-3-amine; **(b)** 4-aminopentan-2-ol; **(c)** 4-nitrocycloheptane-1,3-diamine

Section D.3 Naming Ketones and Aldehydes

D.11 Provide the IUPAC name for each of the following ketones.

(a)
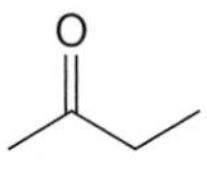

(b)
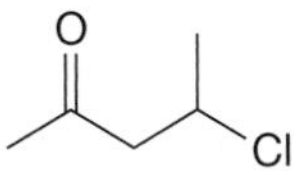
O
Cl

(c)
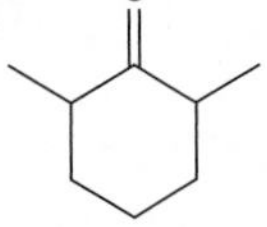

(d)
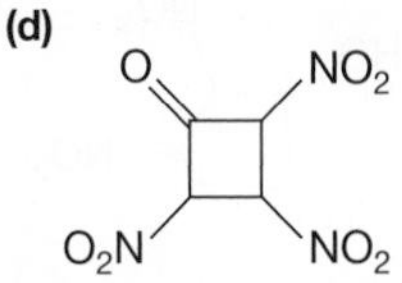
O
NO_2
O_2N
NO_2

D.12 Provide the IUPAC name for each of the following aldehydes.

(a)
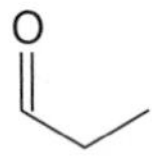

(b)

(c)
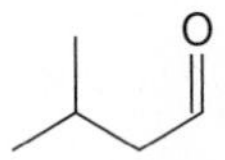

(d)
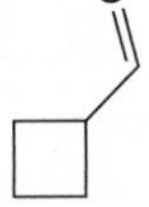

(e)
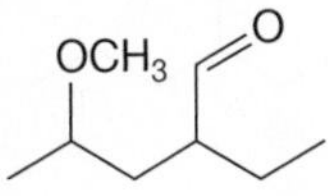
OCH_3
O

D.13 Draw the molecule that corresponds to each IUPAC name. **(a)** 2,3-dimethylcyclopentanone; **(b)** 4,4-difluoroheptanal; **(c)** 1,1,1-trichloropentan-3-one; **(d)** 3-ethoxycyclohexanecarbaldehyde

D.14 Provide the IUPAC name for each of the following compounds.

(a)
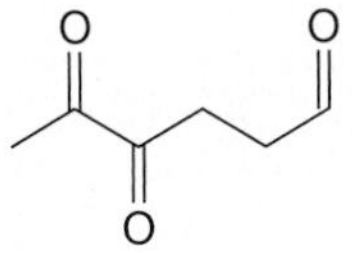

(b)
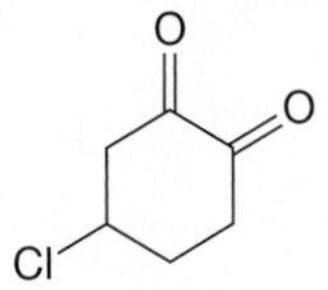
O
O
Cl

(c)
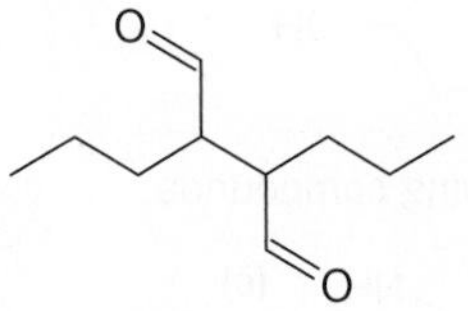

(d)
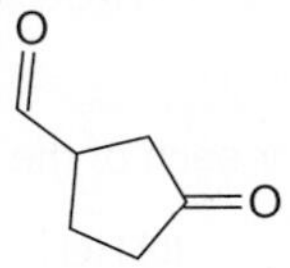

D.15 Provide the IUPAC name for each of the following compounds.

(a)
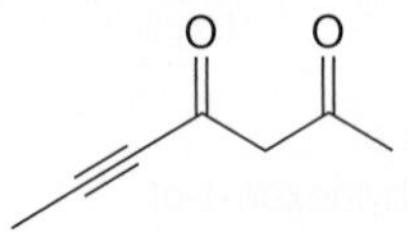

(b)
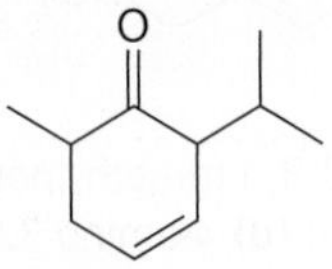

(c)
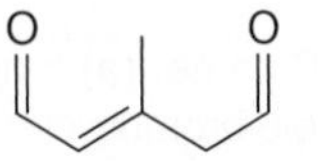

(d)
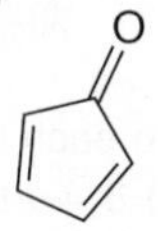

D.16 Draw the molecule that corresponds to each IUPAC name. **(a)** hept-3-enedial; **(b)** 2,2-diethoxy-4-oxopentanal; **(c)** cyclohept-4-ene-1,3-dione; **(d)** pent-4-ynal

Section D.4 Naming Carboxylic Acids, Acid Chlorides, Amides, and Nitriles

D.17 Provide the IUPAC name for each of the following carboxylic acids.

(a)
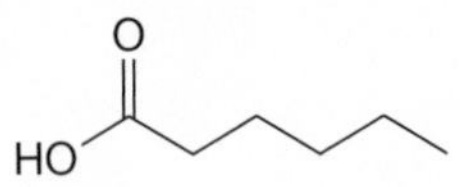
O
HO

(b)
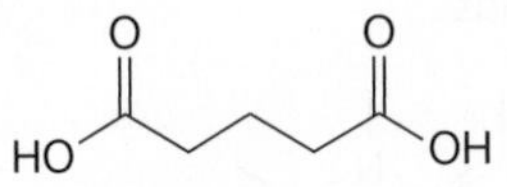
O
O
HO
OH

(c)
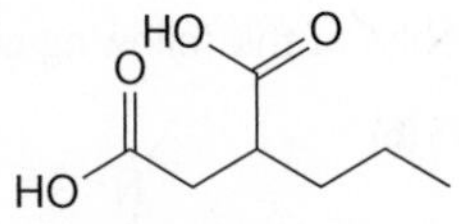
HO
O
O
HO

D.18 Draw the structure of each of the following molecules. **(a)** 2,2-dimethylcyclopentane-1-carboxylic acid; **(b)** 3-chloropentanoic acid; **(c)** 2,3-dinitrobutanedioic acid

D.19 Provide the IUPAC name for each of the following acid chlorides.

(a)
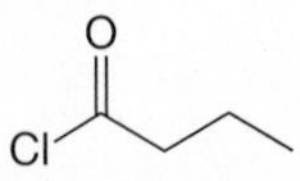
O
Cl

(b)
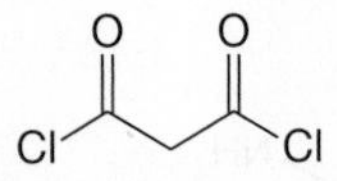
O
O
Cl
Cl

(c)
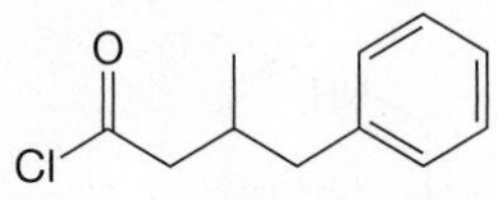
O
Cl

D.20 Draw the structure of each of the following molecules. **(a)** pentanoyl chloride; **(b)** 4-(2-methylpropyl)heptanedioyl chloride; **(c)** 5-phenyloctanoyl chloride

D.21 Provide the IUPAC name for each of the following amides.

(a) 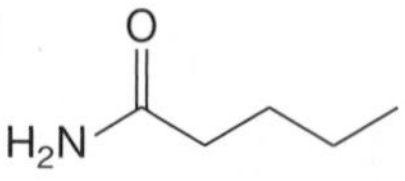 (b) 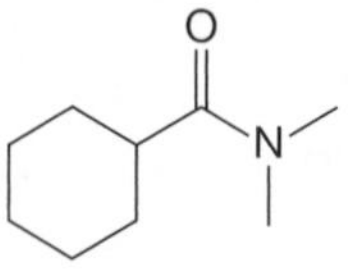 (c) 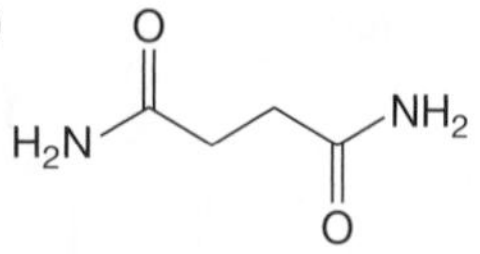

D.22 Draw the structure of each of the following molecules. **(a)** 5-phenylpentanamide; **(b)** 2,3-dimethoxyhexanediamide; **(c)** *N*-phenylcyclobutanecarboxamide

D.23 Provide the IUPAC name for each of the following nitriles.

(a) 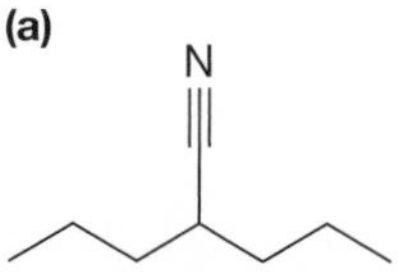 (b) 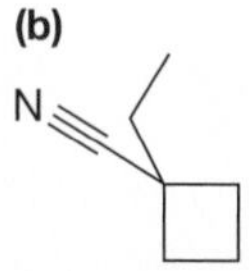 (c) 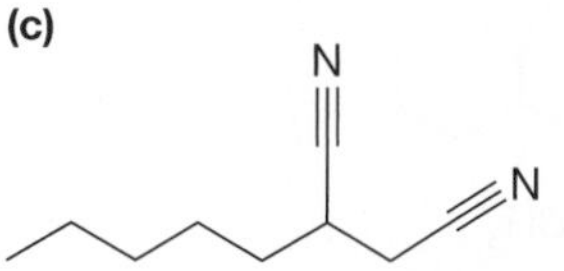

D.24 Draw the structure of each of the following molecules. **(a)** hexanedinitrile; **(b)** 4-nitroheptanenitrile; **(c)** 4,4-diethylcyclohexanecarbonitrile

Section D.5 Naming Esters and Acid Anhydrides

D.25 Provide the IUPAC name for each of the following esters.

(a) 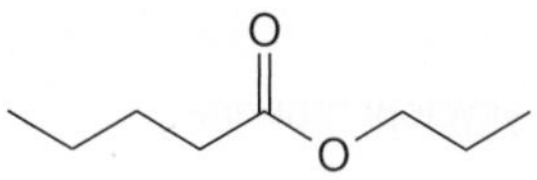 (b) 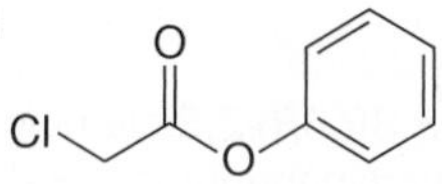 (c) 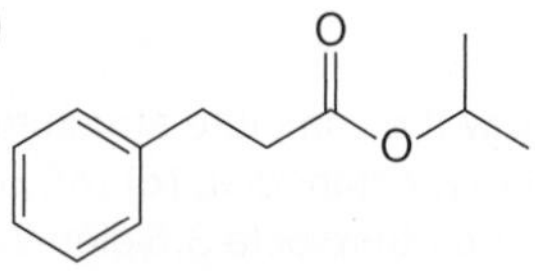

D.26 Draw the structure of each of the following molecules. **(a)** cyclohexyl butanoate; **(b)** 1,1-dimethylethyl hexanoate; **(c)** phenyl 4,4-dinitroheptanoate

D.27 Provide the IUPAC name for each of the following acid anhydrides.

(a) 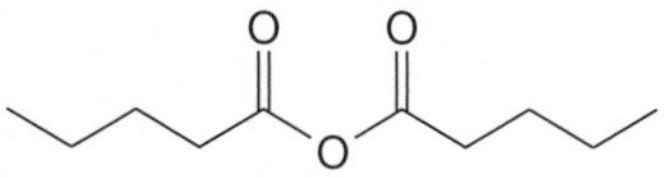 (b) 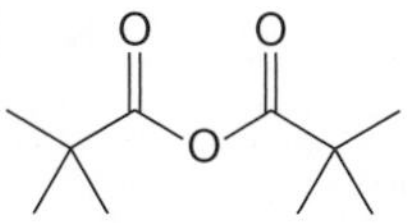 (c) 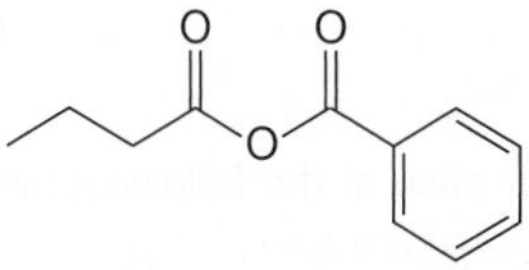

D.28 Draw the structure of each of the following molecules. **(a)** pentanoic anhydride; **(b)** hexanoic propanoic anhydride; **(c)** ethanoic 3-methylpentanoic anhydride

Integrated Problems

D.29 Provide the IUPAC name for each of the following compounds.

(a) 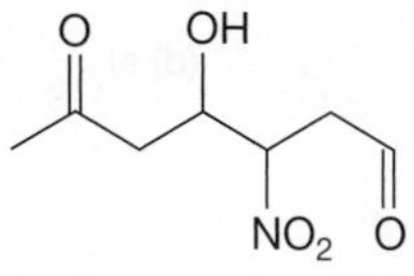 (b) 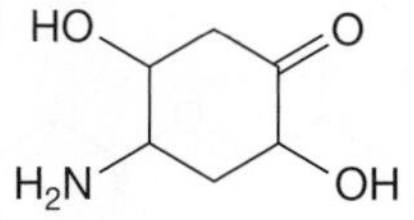 (c) 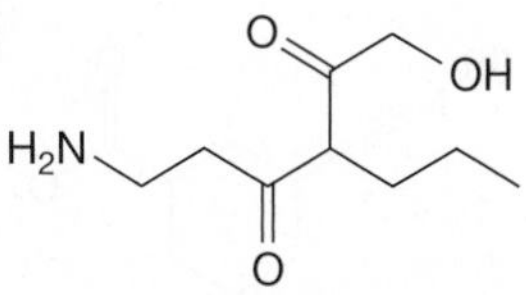

D.30 Provide the IUPAC name for each of the following compounds.

(a) 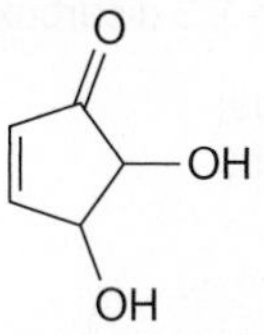 (b) 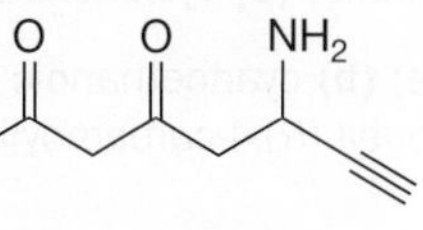 (c) 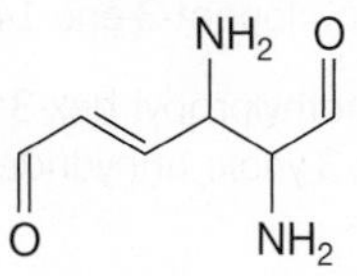

D.31 Provide the IUPAC name for each of the following compounds. Pay attention to stereochemistry.

(a)

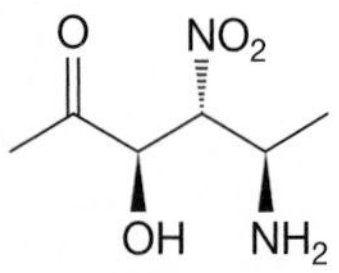

(b)

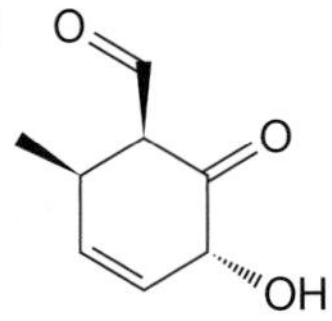

(c)

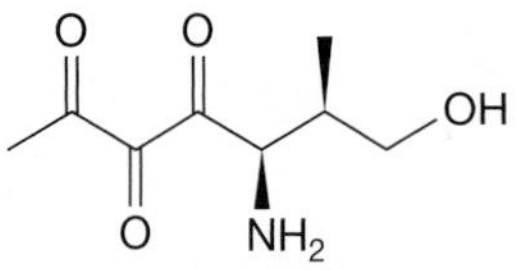

D.32 Write the IUPAC name for each of the following compounds, including stereochemical designations.

(a)

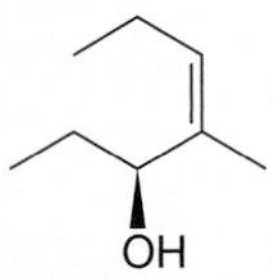

(b)

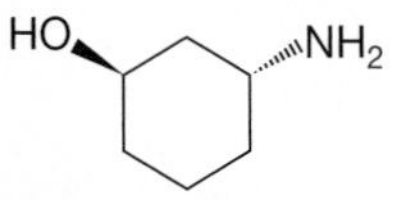

(c)

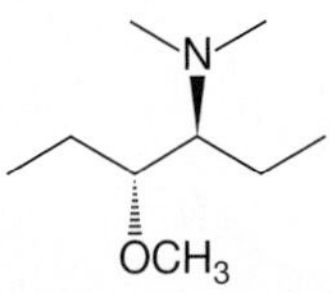

D.33 Draw the structure for each of the following molecules. **(a)** (1*R*,3*S*)-cyclooct-6-ene-1,3-diol; **(b)** (3*S*,4*Z*)-6-amino-5-chlorohex-4-en-3-ol

D.34 Provide the IUPAC name for each of the following compounds.

(a)

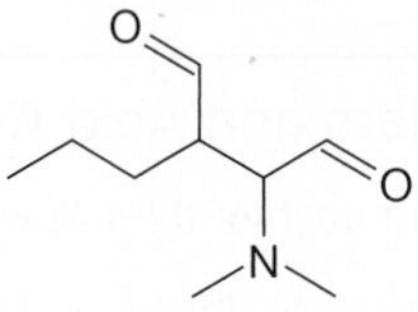

(b)

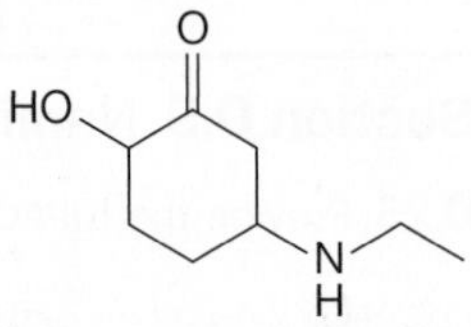

D.35 For each IUPAC name, draw the complete structure. **(a)** (2*S*,3*R*,4*R*)-2,3-diamino-4-hydroxycyclopentanone; **(b)** (2*R*,3*R*)-2-butyl-3-hydroxypentanedial; **(c)** (4*S*,5*R*)-4,5-diaminoheptane-2,3,6-trione; **(d)** (3*E*,5*R*,6*Z*)-5-hydroxy-7-methoxyocta-3,6-dien-2-one

D.36 Provide the IUPAC name for each of the following molecules.

(a)

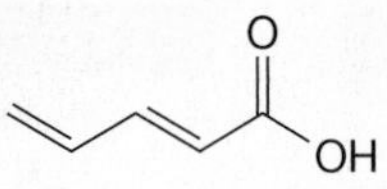

(b)

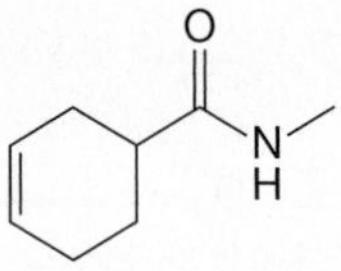

(c)

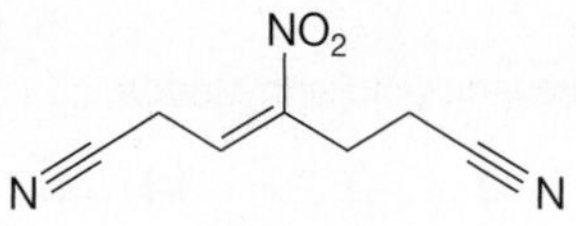

(d)

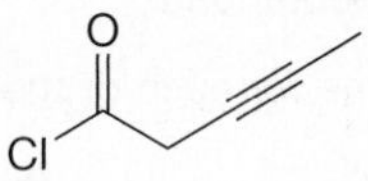

D.37 Provide the IUPAC name for each of the following molecules.

(a)

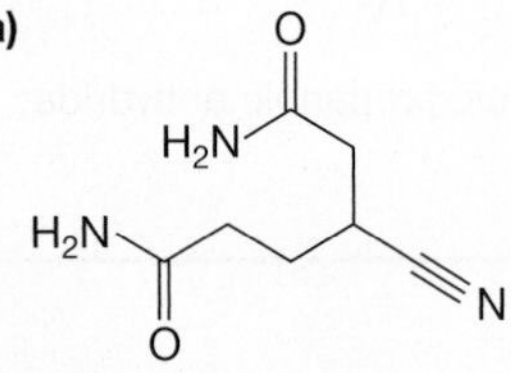

(b)

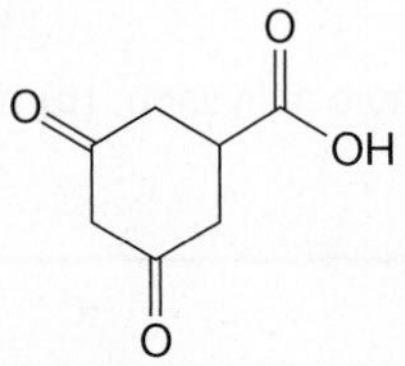

(c)

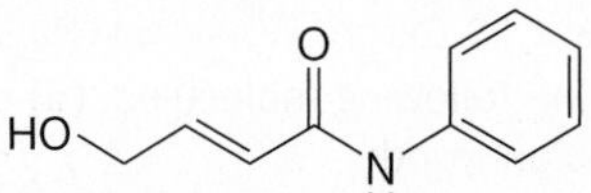

(d)

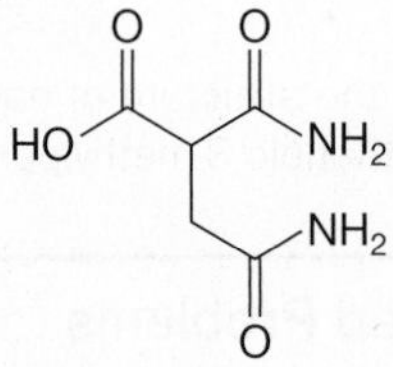

D.38 Provide the IUPAC name for each of the following molecules.

(a)

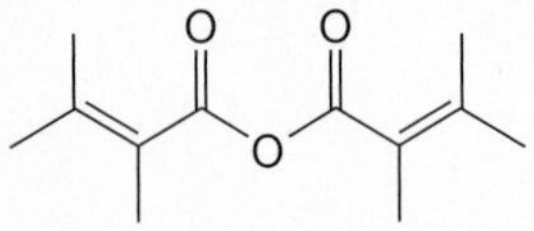

(b)

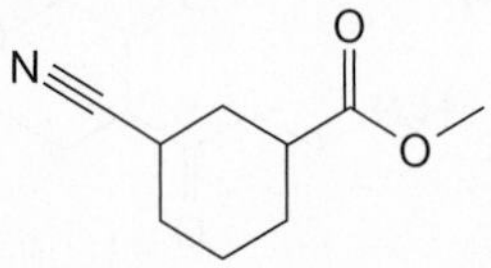

(c)

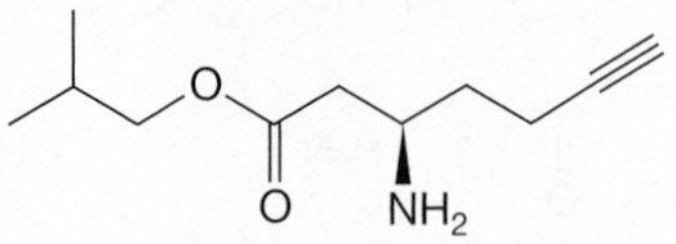

(d)

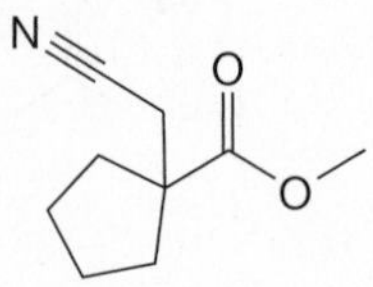

D.39 Draw the structure of each molecule. **(a)** (*E*)-4-carbamoylbut-3-enoic acid; **(b)** 3-carbamoylpentanediamide; **(c)** 4,6-dioxohexanenitrile; **(d)** (1*S*,2*S*)-2-methoxycyclopent-3-ene-1-carbonitrile; **(e)** cyclohexa-3,6-diene-1,3-dicarboxylic acid

D.40 Draw the structure of each molecule. **(a)** 2,2-dimethylpropyl hex-3-ynoate; **(b)** cyanoethanoic anhydride; **(c)** cyanomethyl 5,5-dibromopentanoate; **(d)** hex-3-ynoic anhydride; **(e)** butyl (*R*)-4-carbamoylhexanoate

Eventually, all of these dominoes will fall, but they must do so in a particular order. Analogously, the overall reactions we will learn in this chapter (S_N1 and E1 reactions) take place via multistep mechanisms constructed from precise sequences of elementary steps.

8

An Introduction to Multistep Mechanisms

S_N1 and E1 Reactions and Their Comparisons to S_N2 and E2 Reactions

In Chapters 6 and 7, we examined 10 common elementary steps. Many organic reactions take place by mechanisms that consist of two or more elementary steps, called **multistep mechanisms**. Just as letters of the alphabet can be combined in various ways to create a large number of different words, the elementary steps we have already learned can be combined in various ways to create a large number of different reaction mechanisms.

Here in Chapter 8, we introduce two of the simplest multistep mechanisms: the unimolecular nucleophilic substitution (S_N1) reaction and the unimolecular elimination (E1) reaction. In doing so, we will also revisit the single-step S_N2 and E2 reactions to see the similarities and differences. Even though S_N1 and E1 reactions consist of just two steps each, by studying them we can learn much about multistep mechanisms in general, including those with three, four, five, or more steps.

We begin Chapter 8 by examining key aspects of S_N1 and E1 reactions; namely, we will examine their curved arrow notation, reaction energy diagrams, chemical kinetics (reaction rates), and stereoselectivity (the tendency to form one stereoisomer over another). We then present general guidelines for reasonable multistep mechanisms, which are intended to help you develop a certain level of "chemical intuition" that can be applied to other reaction mechanisms in subsequent chapters.

Chapter Outline

SECTION 8.1 OBJECTIVES

You will be able to:

1. Draw the mechanism for an S_N1 reaction and distinguish it from an S_N2 reaction.
2. Distinguish a mechanism from its overall reaction.
3. Identify the overall reactants, overall products, and intermediates in a multistep mechanism.
4. Draw and interpret the free energy diagram for an S_N1 reaction.

8.1 The Unimolecular Nucleophilic Substitution (S_N1) Reaction: Intermediates, Overall Reactants, and Overall Products

In Section 7.2, we saw that a nucleophile (Nu^-) can replace a leaving group (L) on a substrate (R—L) in a single step via a bimolecular nucleophilic substitution (S_N2) reaction (Eq. 8-1):

Mechanism for the general S_N2 reaction

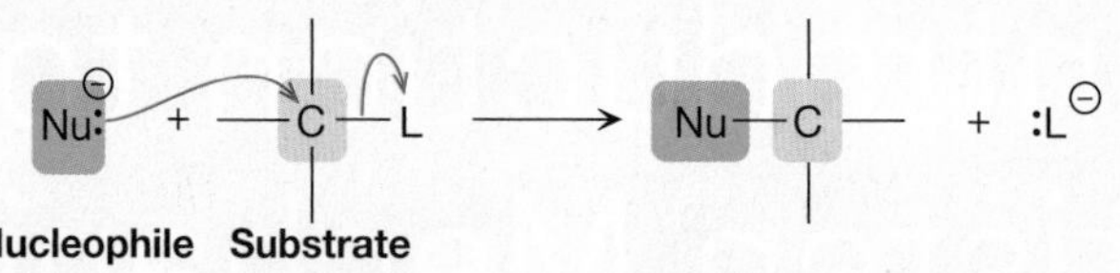

Nu:
C
L
Nu
C
:L
Nucleophile
Substrate

(8-1)

However, we can also envision a nucleophilic substitution reaction taking place in two steps, as shown in Equation 8-2. Equation 8-2 presents the general mechanism of a **unimolecular nucleophilic substitution (S_N1) reaction**. (Why the reaction is characterized as unimolecular will become clearer in Section 8.3.)

Mechanism for the general S_N1 reaction

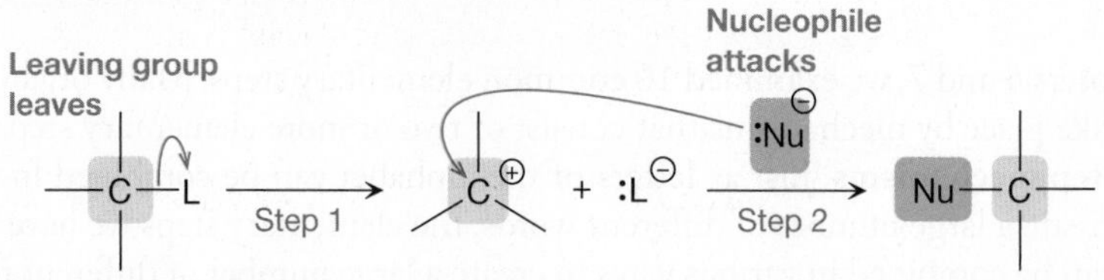

Leaving group leaves
Nucleophile attacks
:Nu
C
L
Step 1
C
:L
Step 2
Nu
C

(8-2)

▸ LOOKING AHEAD

Although S_N1 and S_N2 mechanisms both describe substitutions, the reactions tend to produce different distributions of stereoisomers (Section 8.5). We will also see that the carbon backbone can rearrange in an S_N1 mechanism, but it cannot in an S_N2 mechanism (Section 8.6d).

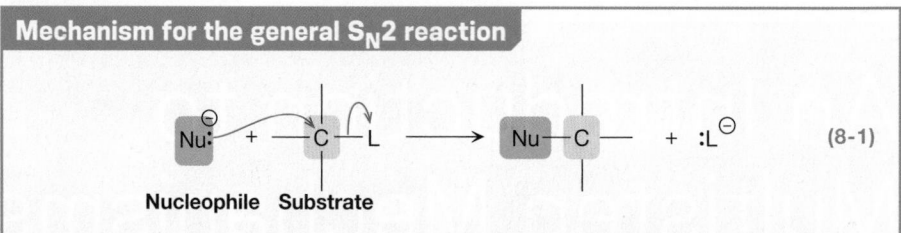

Equation 8-2 shows that the leaving group (L) simply leaves in the first step of an S_N1 mechanism, producing L^- and a carbocation. In the second step, the nucleophile (Nu^-) forms a bond to the carbocation (which is a very reactive electrophile) to complete the reaction (see Looking Ahead box). Even though this mechanism is different from what we have seen before, it is composed of elementary steps with which we are familiar (see Your Turn 8.1).

YOUR TURN **8.1**

Under each arrow in Equation 8-2, write the name of the elementary step that is occurring. *Hint*: See the Chapter 7 summary beginning on page 350.

Answers to Your Turns are in the back of the book.

Using curved arrow notation, draw **(a)** an S_N2 mechanism and **(b)** an S_N1 mechanism for the substitution reaction shown here.

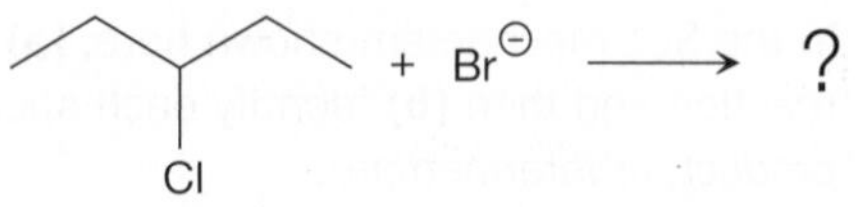
+ Br
?
Cl

In any reaction that takes place in multiple steps, we must be able to distinguish the *overall reaction* from the elementary steps of its mechanism:

The **overall reaction** (or **net reaction**) describes the changes that occur throughout the course of a complete mechanism and can be obtained by simply adding together all of the elementary steps.

To add elementary steps together, write each step on a separate line and then cancel a species if it appears as a product in one step and a reactant in another. **Figure 8-1**, for example, shows how to add the steps for the S_N1 mechanism from Equation 8-2. Notice that the carbocation is cancelled and the net reaction is $Nu^- + R\text{—}L \rightarrow Nu\text{—}R + L^-$.

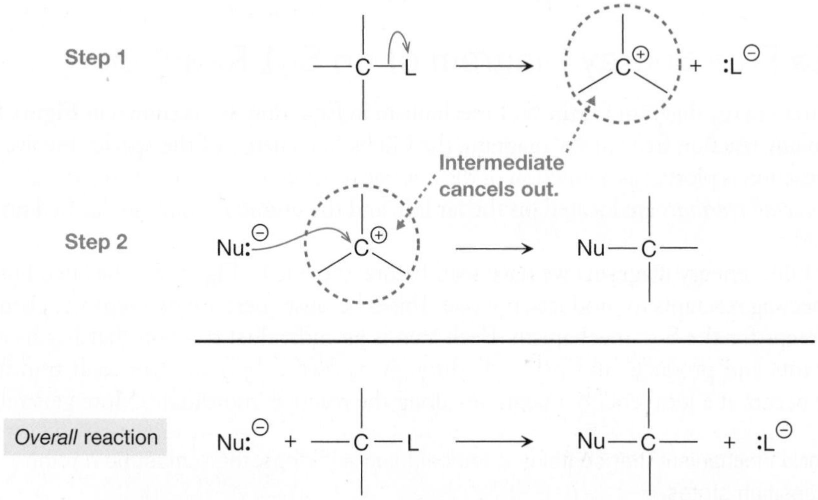
Step 1
C
L
C
+ :L
Intermediate
cancels out.
Step 2
Nu:
C
Nu—C—
Overall reaction
Nu:
+ —C—L
Nu—C—
+ :L

FIGURE 8-1 Adding the steps of an S_N1 mechanism Steps 1 and 2 make up the general S_N1 mechanism in Equation 8-2. When the steps are added, the carbocation intermediate (circled) cancels because it is produced in Step 1 and is consumed in Step 2. The other species appear in the overall reaction.

By comparing the mechanism to the overall reaction, we can distinguish between *overall reactants*, *overall products*, and *intermediates*:

- A species is an **overall reactant** or an **overall product** if it appears in the overall (i.e., net) reaction.
  - Overall reactants are physically added together to initiate a reaction.
  - Overall products are the newly formed compounds found in the reaction mixture after the reaction has come to completion. Overall products can often be isolated.
- A species is an **intermediate** if it is *produced* in a mechanism but does *not* appear in the overall reaction.
  - Intermediates tend to be unstable and highly reactive.
  - Usually, intermediates cannot be isolated.

The overall reactants in Figure 8-1 (and Eq. 8-2) are R—L and Nu^-, whereas the overall products are Nu—R and L^-. The carbocation (R^+) is the only intermediate.

YOUR TURN **8.3**

In the S_N1 mechanism shown here, **(a)** sum the steps to yield the overall reaction and then **(b)** identify each species as an *overall reactant*, *overall product*, or *intermediate*.

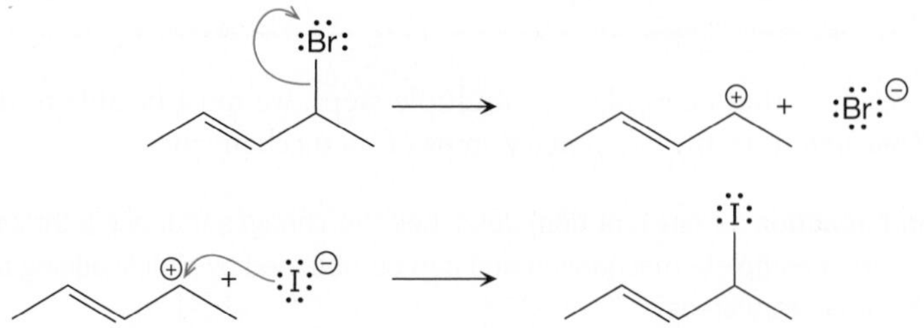

:Br:
+
:Br:
:I:
+
:I:

YOUR TURN **8.4**

For the S_N1 reaction in Your Turn 8.2, identify the overall reactants, overall products, and any intermediates.

8.1a Free Energy Diagram of an S_N1 Reaction

◂ RECALL

Section 6.4 showed that a reaction coordinate describes the geometry changes that occur for a molecule as reactants are converted to products. As the reaction coordinate increases from left to right, the geometries less closely resemble the reactants and more closely resemble the products.

The free energy diagram for the S_N1 mechanism in Equation 8-2 is shown in **Figure 8-2**. As in any reaction free energy diagram, the Gibbs free energy of the species involved in the reaction is plotted as a function of the *reaction coordinate* (Section 6.4; see Recall box). The *overall reactants* are located on the far left, and the *overall products* are located on the far right.

Unlike energy diagrams we have seen before, the one in Figure 8-2 has two humps connecting reactants to products, not one. This is because there are two separate elementary steps for the S_N1 mechanism. Each step is an individual reaction that has its own reactants and products and proceeds through its own *transition state*; each transition state occurs at a local energy maximum along the reaction coordinate. More generally:

For a mechanism that contains *n* total elementary steps, there must be *n* total transition states.

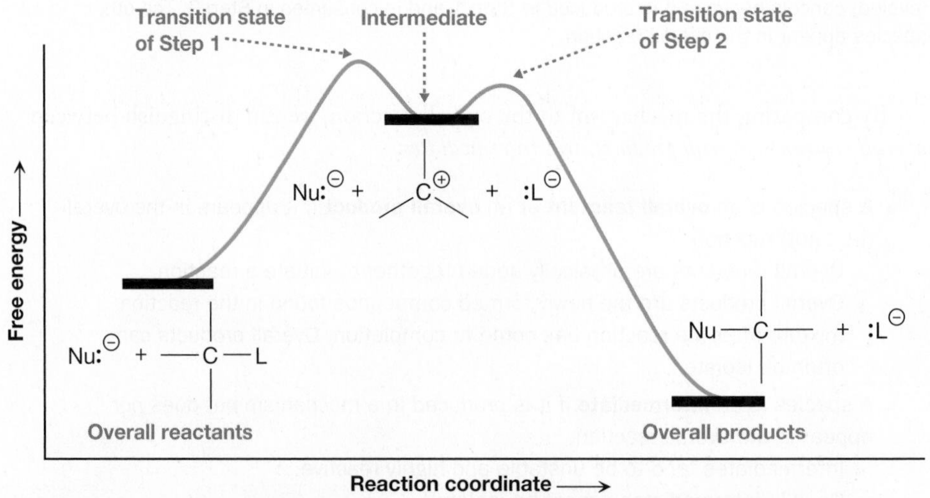

Transition state of Step 1
Intermediate
Transition state of Step 2
Nu: + C + :L
Free energy
Nu: + —C—L
Overall reactants
Nu—C— + :L
Overall products
Reaction coordinate

FIGURE 8-2 Free energy diagram for an S_N1 reaction The overall reactants are on the far left, the overall products are on the far right, and the intermediate appears at the local minimum in energy between them.

Because an intermediate is located in between two transition states, there must be $n - 1$ locations in the energy diagram that represent intermediates.

The free energy diagram for an S_N1 reaction shows two noteworthy characteristics of the intermediate:

- The intermediate is higher in energy (less stable) than the overall reactants and the overall products.
- The intermediate occurs at a **local minimum** in energy along the reaction coordinate, so energy increases when going either forward or backward from the intermediate along the reaction coordinate.

The energy of the reaction intermediate in Figure 8-2 is high because the C atom has lost its octet and also because two additional charges have been created in the process. Although the intermediate is itself highly unstable, even more destabilization is created when *partial bonds* are introduced as the reaction proceeds either forward or backward from the intermediate along the reaction coordinate.

YOUR TURN **8.5**

How many elementary steps are there in the mechanism represented by this free energy diagram? How many locations in the energy diagram represent intermediates? Mark the locations of the overall reactants (R), intermediates (I), transition states (TS), and overall products (P) on the diagram.

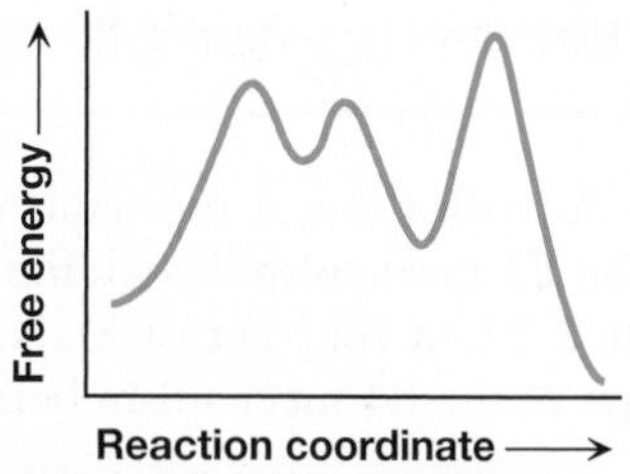
Free energy
Reaction coordinate

YOUR TURN **8.6**

Draw a detailed free energy diagram for the S_N1 reaction in Your Turn 8.2. Include and label the overall reactants, the overall products, the intermediate(s), and the transition state(s).

8.2 The Unimolecular Elimination (E1) Reaction

SECTION 8.2 OBJECTIVES

You will be able to:

1. Draw the mechanism for an E1 reaction and distinguish it from an E2 reaction.
2. Draw and interpret the free energy diagram for an E1 reaction.

In Section 7.5, we saw that a leaving group and a proton (H^+) are eliminated from adjacent carbon atoms in a *bimolecular elimination (E2) reaction*, resulting in an additional π bond between those two carbon atoms. Equation 8-3 shows an E2 reaction between a generic base (B^-) and a generic substrate (R—L):

Mechanism for the general E2 reaction

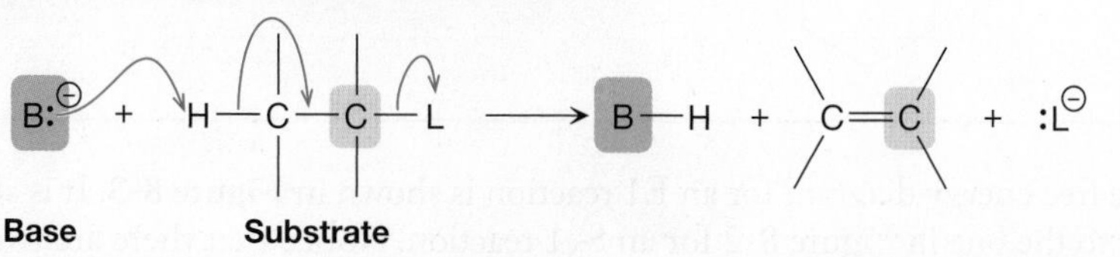
B:
H
C
C
L
B
H
C
C
:L
Base
Substrate

(8-3)

Elimination reactions can also take place in two steps, via a **unimolecular elimination (E1) reaction**, as shown in Equation 8-4. As with S_N1 and S_N2 reactions, the numbers in the names of the elimination reactions do *not* refer to the number of steps in each mechanism:

Mechanism for the general E1 reaction

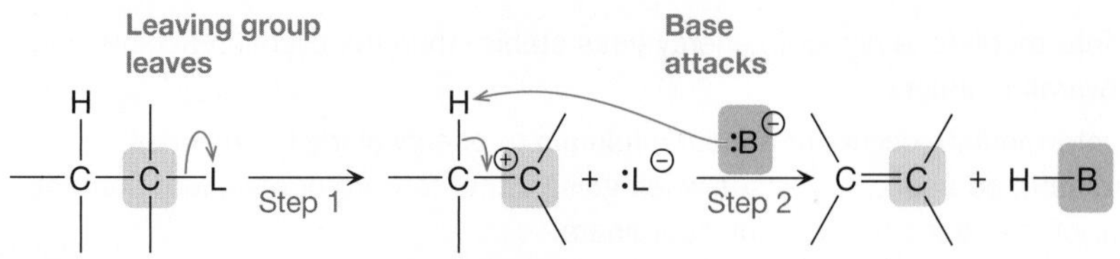

Leaving group leaves
Base attacks
Step 1
Step 2

(8-4)

Notice that the first step in an E1 reaction (Eq. 8-4) is precisely the same as the first step in an S_N1 reaction (Eq. 8-2); namely, the leaving group leaves. The difference between the S_N1 and E1 mechanisms is in the second step: coordination in the S_N1 mechanism versus elimination of H^+ in the E1 mechanism.

YOUR TURN **8.7**

Under each arrow in Equation 8-4, name the elementary step that is occurring. *Hint*: Start by reviewing the Chapter 7 summary that begins on page 350.

As with the S_N1 mechanism, we can obtain the overall reactants and products of an E1 mechanism by adding together the steps in Equation 8-4, yielding Equation 8-5 (see Your Turn 8.8). Notice once again that the carbocation is an intermediate in the E1 mechanism because it does not appear in the overall reaction.

Overall reaction for the E1 mechanism in Equation 8-4

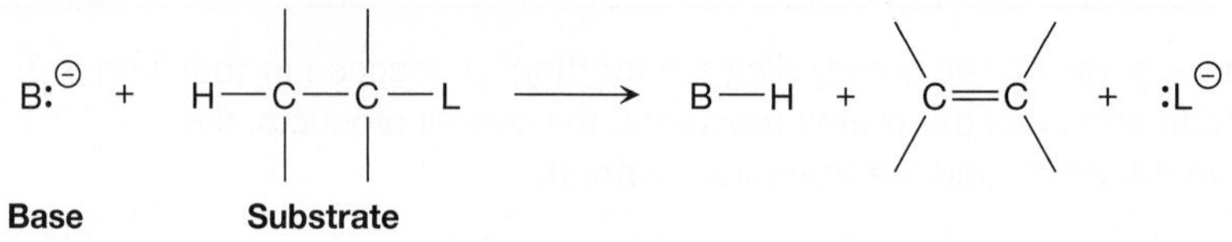

Base
Substrate

(8-5)

YOUR TURN **8.8**

Add together the steps of the E1 mechanism in Equation 8-4, as was done in Figure 8-1. Does the result agree with Equation 8-5?

YOUR TURN **8.9**

Draw the mechanism for the E1 reaction that would take place between the two species shown here, with $HOCH_3$ as the base. Label each species in the mechanism as an overall reactant, an overall product, or an intermediate.

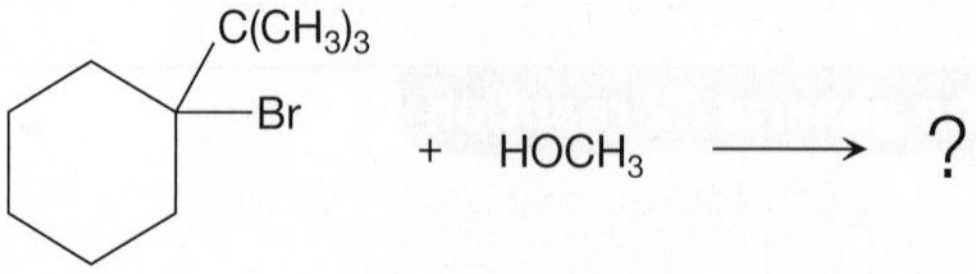

C(CH3)3
Br
+ HOCH3
?

The free energy diagram for an E1 reaction is shown in **Figure 8-3**. It is strikingly similar to the one in Figure 8-2 for an S_N1 reaction. Notice that there are two transition states (energy maxima), because the E1 mechanism consists of two separate steps. Also note the single intermediate that appears at a *local minimum* in energy between

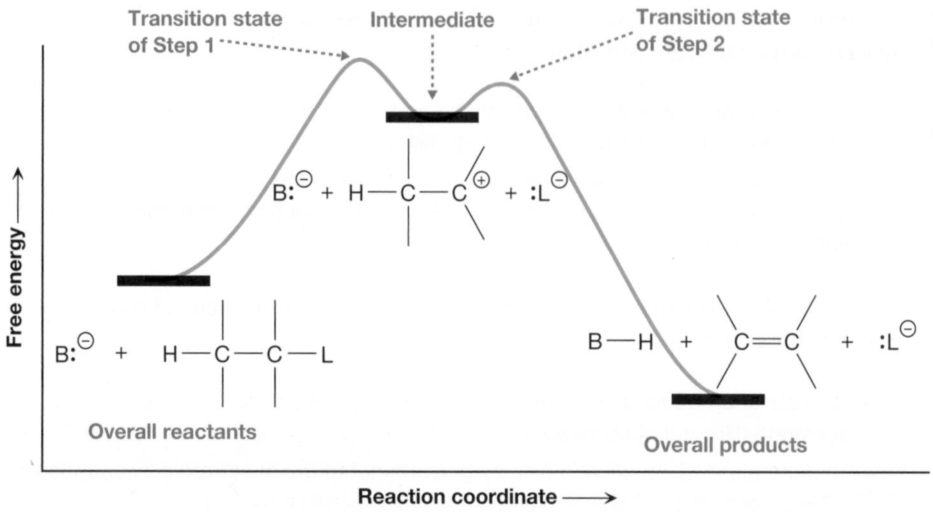
Transition state
of Step 1
Intermediate
Transition state
of Step 2
Free energy
Overall reactants
Overall products
Reaction coordinate

FIGURE 8-3 Free energy diagram for an E1 reaction The overall reactants are on the far left, the overall products are on the far right, and the intermediate appears at the local minimum in energy between them.

the two transition states. Finally, as in the S_N1 reaction, the energy of the intermediate is substantially higher than the energy of either the reactants or the products, due to the loss of an octet on carbon and the appearance of charges.

YOUR TURN **8.10**

Draw the energy diagram for the E1 reaction in Your Turn 8.9. Include and label the overall reactants, the overall products, the transition state(s), and the intermediate(s).

8.3 The Kinetics of S_N2, S_N1, E2, and E1 Reactions: Evidence for Reaction Mechanisms

SECTION 8.3 OBJECTIVES

You will be able to:

1. Use kinetic data to determine whether a reaction has taken place by the S_N2, S_N1, E2, or E1 mechanism.
2. Identify the rate-determining step of an S_N2, S_N1, E2, or E1 reaction and justify why that step is the rate-determining step.
3. Explain why the rate of an S_N2 or E2 reaction depends on the nucleophile or base concentration but those concentrations do not impact the rate of an S_N1 or E1 reaction.

So far in this chapter, we have seen that S_N1 products are similar to S_N2 products and that E1 products are similar to E2 products. How can we tell when a nucleophilic substitution reaction has taken place by the S_N1 or S_N2 mechanism? How can we tell when an elimination reaction has taken place by the E1 or E2 mechanism?

One way to tell which mechanism has taken place is from the reaction's **empirical rate law**: an equation derived from experiments that explicitly shows how the rate of the reaction depends on initial reactant concentrations. The empirical rate laws for the S_N2, S_N1, E2, and E1 reactions are shown in Equations 8-6 through 8-9:

$$S_N2 \text{ Rate} = k_{S_N2}[Nu^-][R{-}L] \tag{8-6}$$

$$S_N1 \text{ Rate} = k_{S_N1}[R{-}L] \tag{8-7}$$

$$E2 \text{ Rate} = k_{E2}[B^-][R{-}L] \tag{8-8}$$

$$E1 \text{ Rate} = k_{E1}[R{-}L] \tag{8-9}$$

In these equations, recall that brackets indicate concentrations: $[Nu^-]$ is the concentration of the nucleophile, $[B^-]$ is the concentration of the base, and $[R{-}L]$ is the concentration of the substrate. The proportionality constant in each equation (k_{S_N2}, k_{S_N1}, k_{E2}, or k_{E1}) is the reaction's **rate constant**.

Notice how the rate laws for the S_N2 and S_N1 reactions exhibit different dependencies on reactant concentrations:

- The rate of an S_N2 reaction is directly proportional to both the nucleophile ($[Nu^-]$) and substrate ([R—L]) concentrations.
- The rate of an S_N1 reaction is directly proportional to the substrate concentration ([R—L]) only; that is, the S_N1 rate is *independent* of the nucleophile concentration.

Similarly, notice how the rate laws for the E1 and E2 reactions depend differently on reactant concentrations:

- The rate of an E2 reaction is directly proportional to both the base ($[B^-]$) and substrate ([R—L]) concentrations.
- The rate of an E1 reaction is directly proportional to the substrate concentration ([R—L]) only; the E1 rate is *independent* of the base concentration.

Knowing these concentration dependencies, we can determine which mechanism has taken place if we are given data from kinetics experiments involving different initial reactant concentrations. An example is shown in Solved Problem 8.1.

SOLVED PROBLEM **8.1**

How to use kinetic data to determine whether a reaction is S_N1 or S_N2

Break It Down To determine whether the reaction shown here proceeds via an S_N1 or S_N2 reaction, you carry out kinetics experiments, measuring the dependence of the reaction rate on the initial concentrations of each reactant. Your results are tallied in the accompanying table.

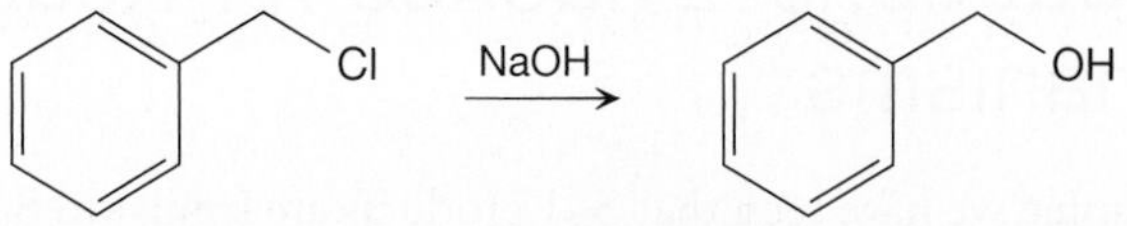

Cl
NaOH
OH

Trial Number	$[C_6H_5CH_2Cl]$	$[HO^-]$	Rate (M/s)
1	0.10 M	0.10 M	2.6×10^{-6}
2	0.10 M	0.20 M	5.1×10^{-6}
3	0.20 M	0.20 M	1.0×10^{-5}

On the basis of these results, does the reaction proceed by the S_N1 or S_N2 mechanism?

Think	Solve
Which trials should you compare to determine the dependence of the reaction rate on the nucleophile concentration? What is that dependence?	On going from Trial 1 to Trial 2, the concentration of HO^- (the nucleophile) doubles, but the concentration of $C_6H_5CH_2Cl$ remains the same. This causes the reaction rate to double, from 2.6×10^{-6} M/s to 5.1×10^{-6} M/s, suggesting that the rate is directly proportional to the concentration of the nucleophile.

(continued)

Which trials should you compare to determine the dependence of the reaction rate on the substrate concentration? What is that dependence?	On going from Trial 2 to Trial 3, the concentration of $C_6H_5CH_2Cl$ (the substrate) doubles, but the concentration of HO^- remains the same, and the rate also doubles. Thus, the rate is directly proportional to the concentration of the substrate as well.
Does the concentration dependence agree with the rate law for an S_N1 or an S_N2 reaction?	With the rate directly proportional to *both* the substrate and nucleophile concentrations, these results indicate an empirical rate law of the form: Rate = $k[C_6H_5CH_2Cl][HO^-]$, which is consistent with an S_N2 reaction.

Try It Rate data for the substitution reaction shown here are presented in the accompanying table. Are these data consistent with an S_N1 reaction or an S_N2 reaction?

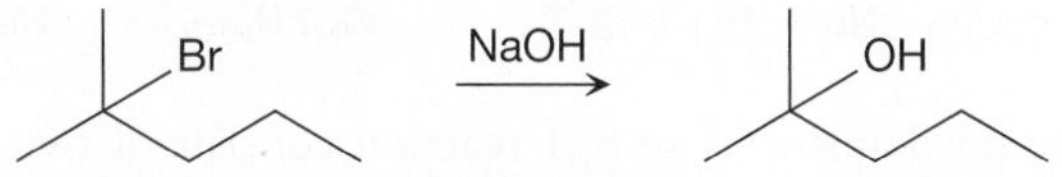
Br
NaOH
OH

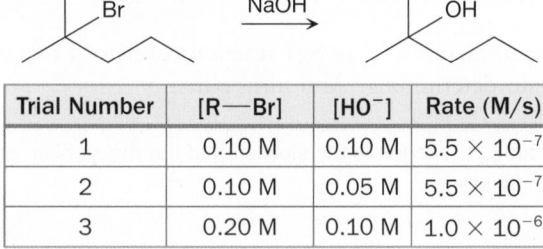

Trial Number	[R—Br]	$[HO^-]$	Rate (M/s)
1	0.10 M	0.10 M	5.5×10^{-7}
2	0.10 M	0.05 M	5.5×10^{-7}
3	0.20 M	0.10 M	1.0×10^{-6}

Answers to all Try It exercises can be found in the Solutions Manual.

CONNECTIONS 8.1

Benzyl chloride in the fight against COVID-19 Benzyl chloride ($C_6H_5CH_2Cl$, Solved Problem 8.1) is used as a reagent with tertiary amines to produce quaternary ammonium ions that can serve as active ingredients in cleaning products, such as the ones shown here. Quaternary ammonium ions are effective at killing viruses on surfaces, including COVID-19, though they are less potent than alcohol disinfectants. Unlike alcohol sanitizers, however, quaternary ammonium ions do not evaporate quickly, so they remain effective longer.

CLOROX
DISINFECTING WIPES
Scrubbing Bubbles
BATHROOM CLEANER
PENETRATING FOAM

YOUR TURN **8.11**

In the S_N2 reaction of $BrCH_2CH_2CH_2CH_3$ with $NaSCH_3$, how would the reaction rate be affected if the concentration of $NaSCH_3$ were doubled?

Why do the S_N2 and S_N1 reactions have different rate laws? Why do the E2 and E1 reactions have different rate laws? To answer these questions, we need to understand the concept of a *rate-determining step* in a mechanism:

The **rate-determining step** of a mechanism (also called the *slow step*) is the elementary step that dictates the rate of the overall reaction.

To understand how the slow step of a multistep mechanism can control the rate of an overall reaction, consider the situation involving traffic shown in **Figure 8-4**, often referred to as a "bottleneck." When fewer lanes on a road are open (analogous to the slow step of a mechanism), traffic flow (the number of cars in a given time) is reduced. On the other side of the bottleneck, when the lanes are open again, the traffic flow is the same as the flow of traffic through the bottleneck. In the same sense, the rate of the slow step of a mechanism is essentially the same as the overall reaction rate.

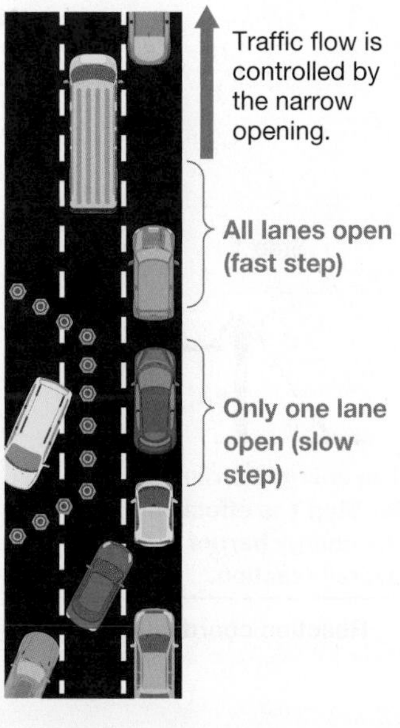
Traffic flow is controlled by the narrow opening.
All lanes open (fast step)
Only one lane open (slow step)

FIGURE 8-4 Rate-determining steps The narrower and wider openings in the road represent slower and faster elementary steps, respectively. Just as the rate that traffic can flow is governed by the narrow opening in the road, the rate of an overall reaction is governed by its slow step: that is, the rate-determining step.

By examining the rate-determining step of a mechanism, we can determine which reactant concentrations should impact the overall reaction rate, according to the following idea:

> If a species appears as a reactant in the rate-determining step of a mechanism, then the overall reaction rate will depend on the concentration of that species.

For an S_N2 reaction, the mechanism consists of just one elementary step. Therefore, that S_N2 step must be the rate-determining step of the reaction. As we can see in Equation 8-10, both the nucleophile and the substrate are reactants in that step, so the overall reaction rate depends on the concentrations of both species; this is the same dependence we saw previously in the empirical rate law for an S_N2 reaction (Eq. 8-6):

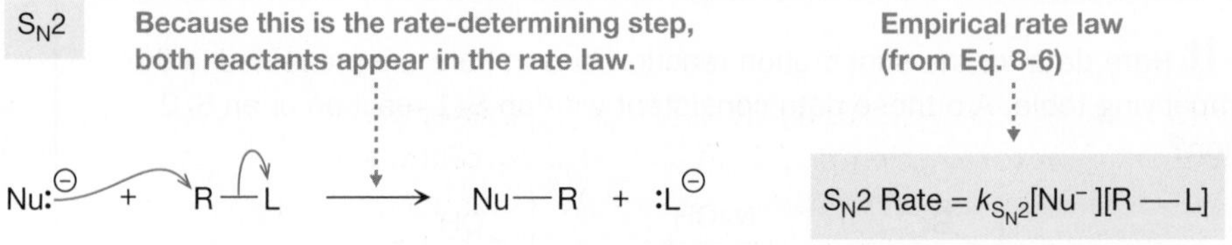

SN2
Because this is the rate-determining step, both reactants appear in the rate law.
Empirical rate law (from Eq. 8-6)
Nu: + R—L → Nu—R + :L
SN2 Rate = kSN2[Nu⁻][R—L]

$$S_N2 \text{ Rate} = k_{S_N2}[\text{Nu}^-][\text{R—L}] \quad (8\text{-}10)$$

In contrast, the mechanism of an S_N1 reaction consists of two elementary steps, but which one is rate-determining? As it turns out:

> The first step of an S_N1 reaction is the slow step of the mechanism and is therefore the rate-determining step.

The first step of an S_N1 reaction is slow because, as shown in Equation 8-11, the products are much less stable than the reactants; a carbon atom loses its octet and two new formal charges appear. Thus, the products of the first step are difficult to form:

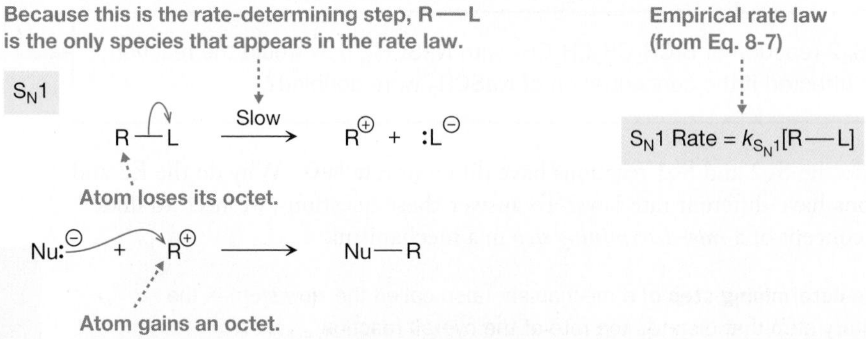

Because this is the rate-determining step, R—L is the only species that appears in the rate law.
Empirical rate law (from Eq. 8-7)
SN1
R—L
Slow
R + :L
SN1 Rate = kSN1[R—L]
Atom loses its octet.
Nu: + R → Nu—R
Atom gains an octet.

$$S_N1 \text{ Rate} = k_{S_N1}[\text{R—L}] \quad (8\text{-}11)$$

For a better understanding of why the first step of an S_N1 mechanism is the rate-determining step, examine **Figure 8-5**, the free-energy diagram for an S_N1 reaction. The intermediate is much higher in energy than the overall reactants or overall products, and the transition state for the first step is higher energy still, making the transition state of the first step the highest energy point along the entire path. Therefore, the energy barrier for the overall reaction, which establishes the overall reaction rate, is essentially the same as the energy barrier for the first step.

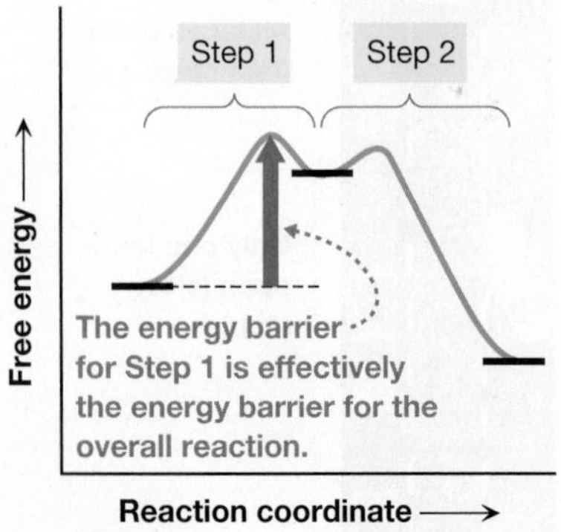

Step 1
Step 2
Free energy
The energy barrier for Step 1 is effectively the energy barrier for the overall reaction.
Reaction coordinate

FIGURE 8-5 Rate-determining step of an S_N1 reaction The transition state for Step 1 has the highest energy along the reaction coordinate. Effectively, the energy barrier for Step 1 establishes the energy barrier of the overall reaction, consistent with Step 1 being the rate-determining step.

Now that we know how to identify the rate-determining step of the S_N1 reaction, take a closer look at that rate-determining step in Equation 8-11. Notice that the substrate (R—L) is the only reactant species in that step. Therefore, the overall reaction rate depends only on the concentration of R—L, the same dependence we saw previously in the empirical rate law for the S_N1 reaction (Eq. 8-7).

The different rate laws for E2 and E1 reactions are explained in much the same way. The rate-determining step of an E2 reaction is the only elementary step in the mechanism, as shown in Equation 8-12:

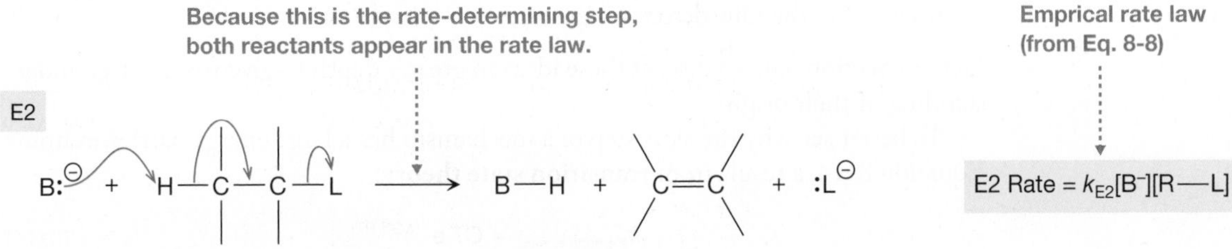

Because this is the rate-determining step,
both reactants appear in the rate law.
Emprical rate law
(from Eq. 8-8)
E2

$$\text{E2 Rate} = k_{E2}[B^-][R\text{—}L] \qquad (8\text{-}12)$$

In the rate-determining step, both the base (B^-) and the substrate (R—L) appear as reactants, so the overall reaction rate depends on the concentration of both species. This is in agreement with the empirical rate law we previously saw in Equation 8-8.

By contrast, the two-step E1 reaction presents a different situation:

> The first step of an E1 reaction is the slow step of the mechanism and is therefore the rate-determining step.

Like the S_N1 mechanism, the first step of an E1 mechanism is slow because the products of that step are much less stable than the reactant, as shown in Equation 8-13:

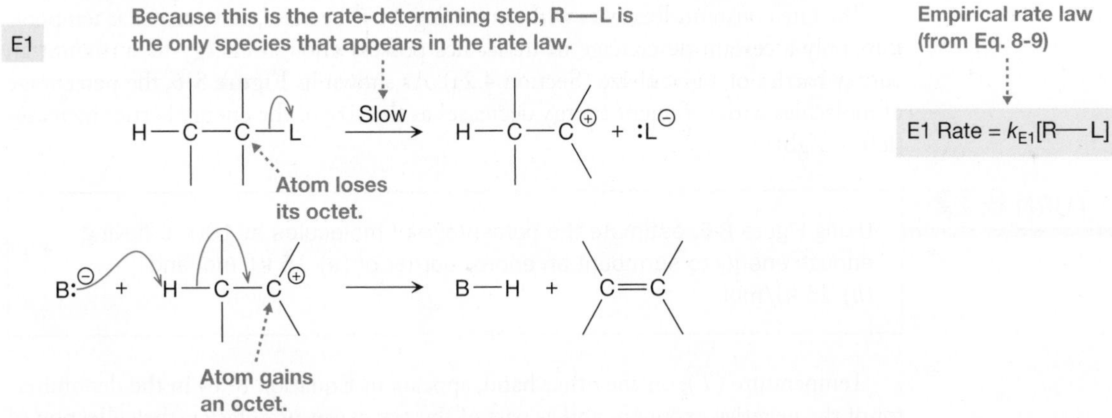

E1
Because this is the rate-determining step, R—L is
the only species that appears in the rate law.
Empirical rate law
(from Eq. 8-9)
Slow
Atom loses
its octet.
Atom gains
an octet.

$$\text{E1 Rate} = k_{E1}[R\text{—}L] \qquad (8\text{-}13)$$

Now that we have identified the rate-determining steps for the S_N2, S_N1, E2, and E1 reactions, the significance of the terms *unimolecular* and *bimolecular* in the names of the reactions becomes apparent. These terms refer to the *molecularity* of each reaction's rate-determining step:

> The **molecularity** of a multistep mechanism is the number of reactant species in the rate-determining step:
>
> - S_N2 and E2 reactions are **bimolecular** because there are two reactant species in each reaction's rate-determining step: the substrate and either the nucleophile or the base.
> - S_N1 and E1 reactions, on the other hand, are **unimolecular** because there is just one reacting species in each reaction's rate-determining step: only the substrate.

SECTION 8.4 OBJECTIVES

You will be able to:

1. Explain how the rate constant of an elementary step relates to $\Delta G^{\circ\ddagger}$ for that step, and how it relates to temperature.
2. Derive the theoretical rate law of an elementary step.

8.4 A Deeper Look: Theoretical Rate Laws and Transition State Theory

In Section 8.3, we took advantage of two important ideas:

- The slow step of a mechanism has a large energy barrier.
- The overall reaction rate depends on the concentrations of the species that appear as reactants in the rate-determining step.

Here in Section 8.4, we discuss these ideas in greater depth to give you a better understanding of their origin.

To better see why the slow step of a mechanism has a large energy barrier, examine Equation 8-14, a result from **transition state theory**:

$$k_{\text{elementary step}} = CT\,e^{-(\Delta G^{\circ\ddagger}/RT)} \quad (8\text{-}14)$$

◀ RECALL

In Section 6.4, we learned that $\Delta G^{\circ\ddagger}$ is the difference in standard free energy between the reactants and the transition state of an elementary step, and it represents an energy barrier that must be surmounted for reactants to become products.

Here, $k_{\text{elementary step}}$ is the rate constant for an elementary step, C is a constant, T is the absolute temperature (in kelvins), $\Delta G^{\circ\ddagger}$ is the standard Gibbs free energy of activation (see Recall box), and R is the universal gas constant.

Because $\Delta G^{\circ\ddagger}$ appears in the numerator of a negative exponent in Equation 8-14:

> The rate constant ($k_{\text{elementary step}}$) decreases as $\Delta G^{\circ\ddagger}$ increases, so the corresponding reaction rate decreases, too.

Thus, when $\Delta G^{\circ\ddagger}$ is sufficiently large, the rate for the corresponding elementary step is slow enough to make it the rate-determining step.

The rate constant decreases with increasing $\Delta G^{\circ\ddagger}$ because, at a particular temperature, only a certain percentage of molecules possess enough energy to surmount an energy barrier of a given size (Section 4.2a). As shown in **Figure 8-6**, the percentage of molecules with sufficient energy decreases as the size of the energy barrier increases (left to right).

YOUR TURN 8.12

Using Figure 8-6, estimate the percentage of molecules at 100 °C having enough energy to surmount an energy barrier of **(a)** 15 kJ/mol and **(b)** 25 kJ/mol.

Temperature (T), on the other hand, appears in Equation 8-14 in the denominator of the negative exponent and as part of the *pre-exponential factor* (the collection of terms, CT, that multiply the exponential factor). Consequently:

> The rate constant ($k_{\text{elementary step}}$) increases as T increases, so the reaction rate increases.

A higher temperature provides the reactants with more kinetic energy, so a greater percentage of molecules have enough energy to surmount the energy barrier. Figure 8-6 supports this idea: At each value of $\Delta G^{\circ\ddagger}$, the red curve (100 °C) corresponds to a greater percentage of molecules than the blue curve (0 °C).

YOUR TURN 8.13

Using Figure 8-6, estimate the percentage of molecules having enough energy to surmount an energy barrier of 20 kJ/mol at **(a)** 0 °C and **(b)** 100 °C.

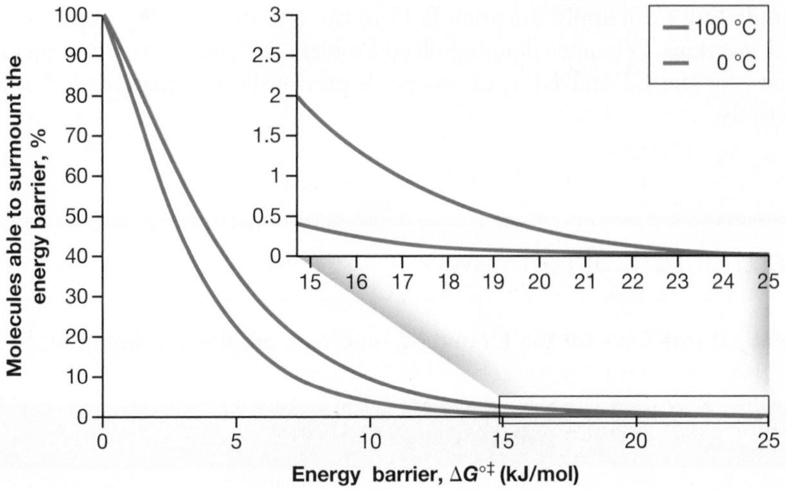

Molecules able to surmount the energy barrier, %
100
90
80
70
60
50
40
30
20
10
0
0
5
10
15
20
25
Energy barrier, ΔG°‡ (kJ/mol)
3
2.5
2
1.5
1
0.5
0
15
16
17
18
19
20
21
22
23
24
25
100 °C
0 °C

FIGURE 8-6 Percentage of molecules able to surmount an energy barrier ($\Delta G^{\circ\ddagger}$) The percentage of molecules able to surmount an energy barrier is plotted against the size of the energy barrier for two different temperatures: 0 °C (blue curve) and 100 °C (red curve). The region inside the box is expanded in the inset. Notice that as the size of the energy barrier increases, the percentage of molecules having enough energy to react decreases dramatically. Notice also that, for a given energy barrier, increasing the temperature significantly increases the percentage of molecules able to react.

Now let's consider why the S_N2, S_N1, E2, and E1 reactions have the specific concentration dependencies that they do. We begin by introducing one of the foundational principles of chemical kinetics:

> For an *elementary step*, $a\,A + b\,B \rightarrow$ products, where A and B are reactants and *a* and *b* are the coefficients required to balance the chemical equation, the **theoretical rate law** is:
>
> $$\text{Rate (theoretical)} = k[A]^a[B]^b \qquad (8\text{-}15)$$

The quantities [A] and [B] are the concentrations of the reactants. The exponents *a* and *b* represent the **order** of the reaction with respect to the reactants A and B, respectively; *a* is the order of the reaction with respect to A, and *b* is the order of the reaction with respect to B. Importantly, *a* and *b* are the same as the coefficients used to balance the elementary step. This is because the reactants must collide at effectively the same time for an elementary step to take place, and the frequency of these collisions is proportional to $[A]^a[B]^b$. Note that Equation 8-15 is referred to as a *theoretical* rate law (not an *empirical* rate law) because it is derived from a proposed elementary step, not from an experiment.

When we apply Equation 8-15 to the S_N2 and S_N1 rate-determining steps, we derive a different theoretical rate law for each mechanism. The rate-determining step for an S_N2 reaction is $Nu^- + R{-}L \rightarrow Nu{-}R + L^-$. The coefficient in front of Nu^- is 1, and so is the coefficient in front of R—L. Therefore, according to Equation 8-15:

$$S_N2 \text{ Rate (theoretical)} = k[Nu^-]^1[R{-}L]^1 = k[Nu^-][R{-}L] \qquad (8\text{-}16)$$

This has precisely the same form as the empirical rate law we previously saw in Equation 8-6.

By contrast, the rate-determining step for an S_N1 reaction is $R{-}L \rightarrow R^+ + L^-$. The coefficient in front of R—L is 1, giving the theoretical rate law for that step, according to Equation 8-15:

$$S_N1 \text{ Rate (theoretical)} = k[R{-}L]^1 = k[R{-}L] \qquad (8\text{-}17)$$

Again, this theoretical rate law has the same form as the empirical rate law we saw previously in Equation 8-7.

Similarly, we can apply Equation 8-15 to the rate-determining steps for the E2 and E1 reactions. When we do (see Solved Problem 8.2), we arrive at the theoretical rate laws for the E2 and E1 reactions given previously in Equations 8-8 and 8-9, respectively.

SOLVED PROBLEM **8.2**

How to derive and evaluate a theoretical rate law

Break It Down **Show how the theoretical rate laws for the E2 and E1 reactions are derived from their respective mechanisms.**

Think	Solve
What are the rate-determining steps for the E2 and E1 reactions?	For an E2 reaction (Eq. 8-12), the rate-determining step is the only step of the mechanism: $B^- + R{-}L \rightarrow$ products. For an E1 reaction (Eq. 8-13), the rate-determining (slow) step is the leaving of the leaving group: $R{-}L \rightarrow R^+ + L^-$.
What is the theoretical rate law for each of those rate-determining steps?	For the rate-determining step of an E2 reaction, the coefficients in front of B^- and R—L are each 1, so the theoretical rate law would be: E2 Rate (theoretical) $= k[B^-]^1[R{-}L]^1 = k[B^-][R{-}L]$. For the rate-determining step of an E1 reaction, the coefficient in front of R—L is 1, so the theoretical rate law would be: E1 Rate (theoretical) $= k[R{-}L]^1 = k[R{-}L]$.
How do these theoretical rate laws compare to the empirical rate laws in Equations 8-8 and 8-9?	The empirical rate law for an E2 reaction (Eq. 8-8) is: E2 Rate $= k_{E2}[B^-][R{-}L]$. The empirical rate law for an E1 reaction (Eq. 8-9) is: E1 Rate $= k_{E1}[R{-}L]$. Thus, the theoretical rate laws we derived for E2 and E1 reactions have the same concentration dependencies as their respective empirical rate laws.

Try It Derive the theoretical rate law for an E1 reaction, assuming (falsely) that the first step of the mechanism is much faster than the second step. Does the resulting theoretical rate law show that the E1 reaction rate is independent of the base concentration, in agreement with Equation 8-9?

SECTION 8.5 OBJECTIVES

You will be able to:

1. Take stereochemistry into account when drawing the product of an S_N2, S_N1, E2, or E1 reaction.
2. Explain why S_N2, S_N1, E2, and E1 reactions exhibit the particular stereochemistries they do.

8.5 Stereochemistry of Nucleophilic Substitution and Elimination Reactions

From the general S_N2 and S_N1 mechanisms shown previously in Equations 8-1 and 8-2 (p. 394), it may appear that both the S_N2 and S_N1 reactions yield the same products. Likewise, from Equations 8-3 and 8-4, it may appear that E2 and E1 reactions yield the same products. However, differences in the *stereochemistry* of these reactions can result in subtle but important differences in the products that are formed:

The **stereochemistry** of a reaction describes:

- Which stereoisomers are produced (see Recall box).
- The relative proportions of the stereoisomers that are produced.

◀ RECALL

Recall from Section 5.1 that stereoisomers have the same connectivity but differ in the arrangement of their atoms in space. Enantiomers are mirror images, whereas diastereomers are not.

Here in Section 8.5, we will examine the stereochemistry of each of these reactions to understand how they differ.

8.5a Stereochemistry of an S_N2 Reaction

Equation 8-18, which shows the outcome of an S_N2 reaction between I^- and (*S*)-1-chloro-1-phenylethane, illustrates the stereochemistry of S_N2 reactions:

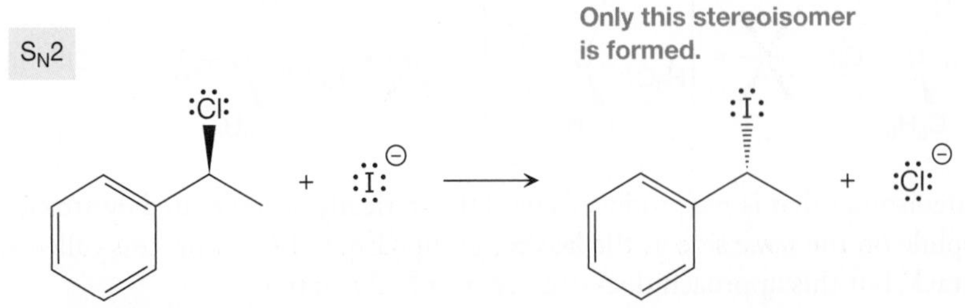

SN2
Only this stereoisomer is formed.

(8-18)

(*S*)-1-Chloro-1-phenylethane **(*R*)-1-Iodo-1-phenylethane**

There are two possible enantiomers of the initial substrate, 1-chloro-1-phenylethane, but the reaction in Equation 8-18 begins only with the *S* isomer; that is, the initial substrate is *enantiomerically pure* (see Recall box). Similarly, there are two possible enantiomers of the product, whose configurations differ by the arrangement of the new C—I bond, but only the *R* enantiomer is produced from this reaction. This observation can be generalized to describe the stereochemistry of the S_N2 reaction:

◀ RECALL

In Sections 5.5 and 5.6, we learned that a chiral center is a tetrahedral atom bonded to four different substituents, and it can exist in one of two configurations: *R* or *S*. The inversion of a chiral center with one stereochemical configuration results in the opposite configuration.

Stereochemistry of the S_N2 Reaction

An S_N2 reaction results in the inversion of the stereochemical configuration at the carbon initially attached to the leaving group.

Moreover, because the precise stereoisomer that is produced depends on the exact stereoisomer that reacts, we say that the S_N2 reaction is **stereospecific**.

Why should S_N2 reactions be stereospecific in this way? To begin to understand, notice in Equation 8-18 that the initial C—Cl bond points toward you, whereas the new C—I bond points away. For this to occur in a single elementary step, the I^- nucleophile must approach the substrate from the side of the molecule opposite the initial C—Cl bond. In general:

In an S_N2 reaction, the nucleophile attacks the substrate exclusively from the side opposite the leaving group, in a **backside attack**.

Such a backside attack is illustrated in Equation 8-19a:

Backside attack (does occur)

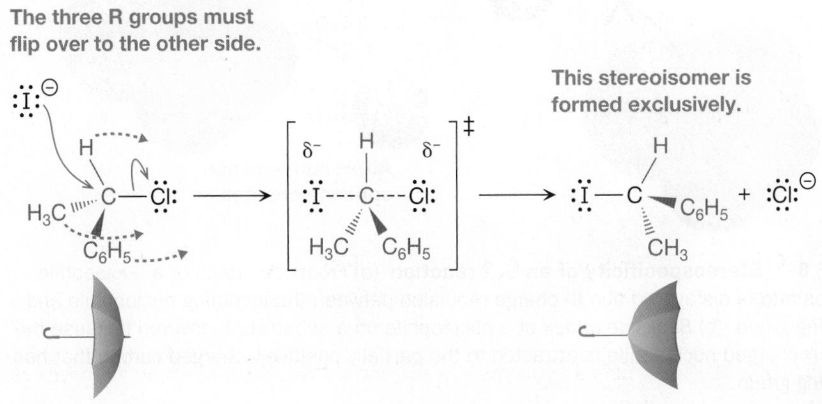

The three R groups must flip over to the other side.
This stereoisomer is formed exclusively.

(8-19a)

Mechanism Drawing
S_N2 Mechanism and Stereochemistry

Frontside attack (does NOT occur)

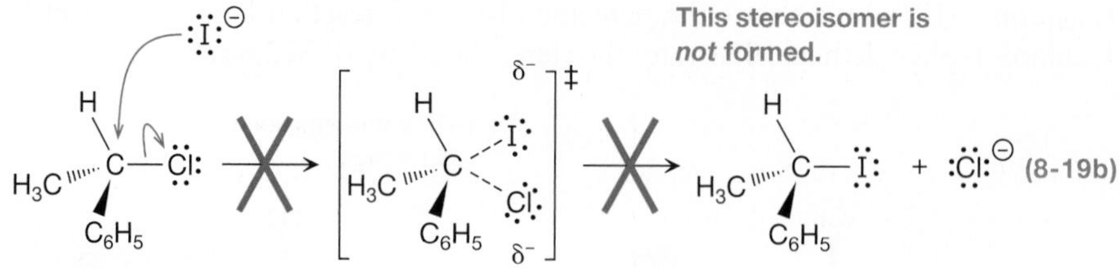

This stereoisomer is *not* formed.
(8-19b)

The stereoisomer that is *not* produced could theoretically be generated by attack of the nucleophile on the *same* side as the leaving group (Eq. 8-19b), a process called **frontside attack**, but this approach does not occur in S_N2 reactions.

YOUR TURN **8.14**

Which is the correct product of an S_N2 reaction, **A** or **B**?

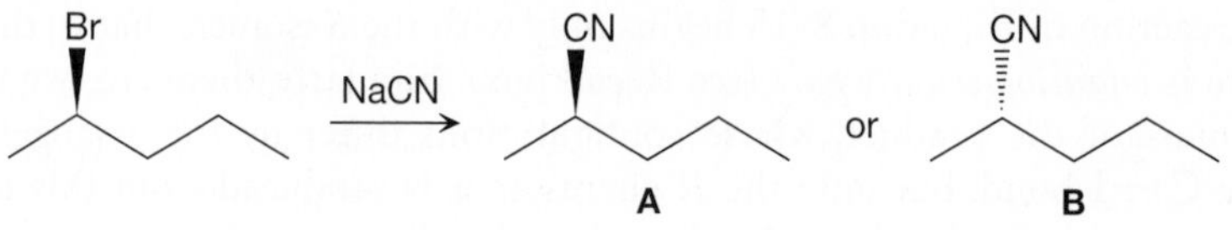

Br
NaCN
CN
A
or
CN
B

◂ RECALL

Steric hindrance was introduced in Section 2.9 to explain why polar aprotic solvents do not solvate anions as strongly as protic solvents do. Recall that in a polar aprotic solvent, the partial positive charge is buried inside bulky groups. Thus, an anion cannot get very close to the partial positive charge.

◂ RECALL

The requirement for backside attack in an S_N2 reaction was explained from a molecular orbital point of view in Interchapter C (Section C.2b). Backside attack allows the frontier MOs to undergo substantial interaction, which lowers the free energy of activation and enables reactants to form products.

As shown in Equation 8-19a, the backside attack requires the remaining three groups of the substrate to flip over to the side that was occupied by the leaving group, a process known as a **Walden inversion**. A Walden inversion is analogous to an umbrella inverting in a windstorm. In a frontside attack, the three groups would remain on the same side throughout the course of the reaction.

What causes the S_N2 reaction to be stereospecific? *Steric hindrance* (bulkiness) is one factor (see top Recall box); the leaving group is often large (otherwise it could not accommodate the negative charge with which it leaves), so it would crash into any nucleophile approaching in a frontside attack. Thus, frontside attack would be disfavored.

In addition, frontside attack is disfavored due to charge repulsion, as shown in **Figure 8-7**. The atom of the leaving group bonded to the substrate is typically highly electronegative, so it usually bears a significant partial negative charge. The nucleophile, which itself bears either a partial or a full negative charge, is thus repelled from that side of the substrate (Fig. 8-7a). In a backside attack (Fig. 8-7b), on the other hand, the nucleophile is instead attracted to the partial positive charge on carbon (see bottom Recall box).

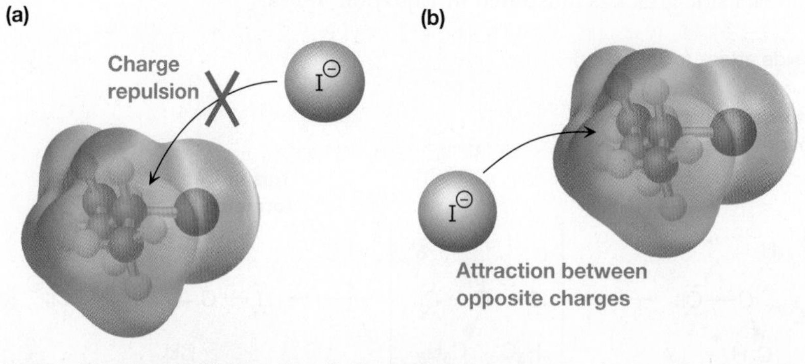

(a)
Charge repulsion
(b)
Attraction between opposite charges

FIGURE 8-7 Stereospecificity of an S_N2 reaction (a) *Frontside attack* of a nucleophile on a substrate is disfavored due to charge repulsion between the incoming nucleophile and the leaving group. (b) *Backside attack* of a nucleophile on a substrate is favored because the negatively charged nucleophile is attracted to the partially positively charged carbon that has the leaving group.

SOLVED PROBLEM **8.3**

How to predict the stereochemical outcome of an S_N2 reaction

Break It Down **Draw the complete, detailed mechanism for the following reaction, assuming that it takes place by an S_N2 mechanism. Pay attention to stereochemistry.**

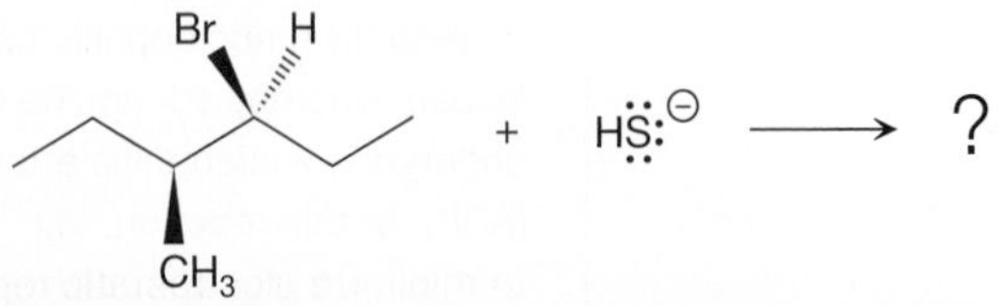
Br
H
CH3
+
HS:
?

Think	Solve
What acts as the nucleophile? What best serves as the leaving group?	HS^- is highly electron-rich and is the nucleophile. The leaving group is Br^- because the large atom can best accommodate the negative charge it acquires when it departs from the substrate.
How many steps make up an S_N2 mechanism? How do curved arrows show this?	An S_N2 reaction must take place in a single elementary step, so the curved arrow notation must show the new S—C bond forming at the same time the C—Br bond breaks. Two curved arrows are required for the S_N2 reaction, as shown below.
How must the nucleophile approach the substrate? What does this require of the new bond that is formed?	The HS^- nucleophile must attack from the side opposite the initial bond to the Br^- leaving group. Because the initial C—Br bond points toward you, HS^- must attack from behind the substrate, and the new S—C bond points away, as shown on the right.

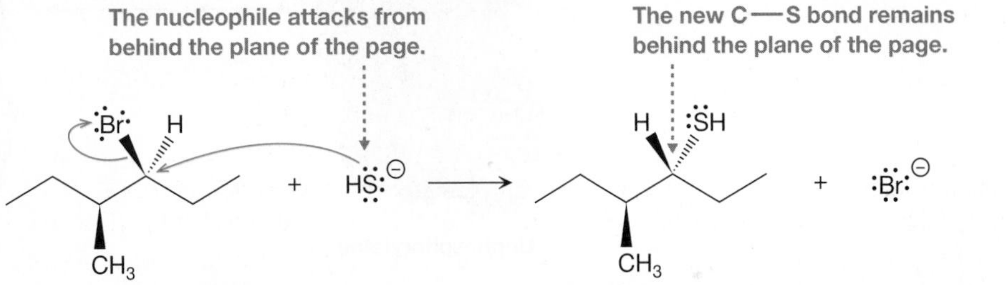
The nucleophile attacks from behind the plane of the page.
The new C—S bond remains behind the plane of the page.
Br
H
CH3
+
HS:
H
SH
CH3
+
Br:

Try It Draw the complete mechanism and the products for each of the following S_N2 reactions, paying close attention to stereochemistry.

(a)

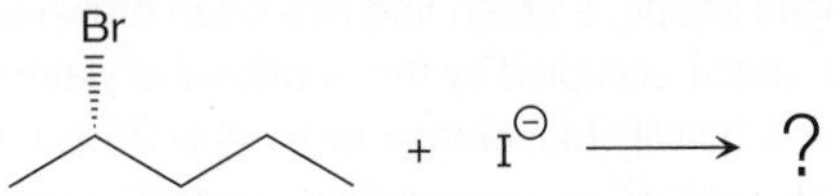
Br
+ I
?

(b)

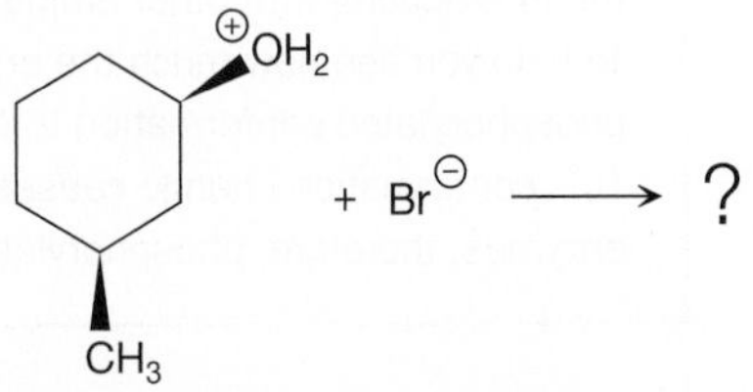
OH2
CH3
+ Br
?

Phosphorylation: An Enzyme's On/Off Switch

Phosphorylation is a process that regulates the function of certain enzymes, such as glycogen phosphorylase (**Figure 8-8**), which catalyzes the breaking down of glycogen. The process is essentially a nucleophilic substitution reaction and is facilitated by another enzyme called a *kinase*, whereby adenosine triphosphate (ATP, abbreviated $^{2-}O_3P$—ADP), acting as the substrate, undergoes nucleophilic attack to produce the phosphorylated product and adenosine diphosphate (ADP). In this reaction, Mg^{2+} (not shown) coordinates with the negatively charged O atoms of ATP to minimize electrostatic repulsion with the incoming nucleophile.

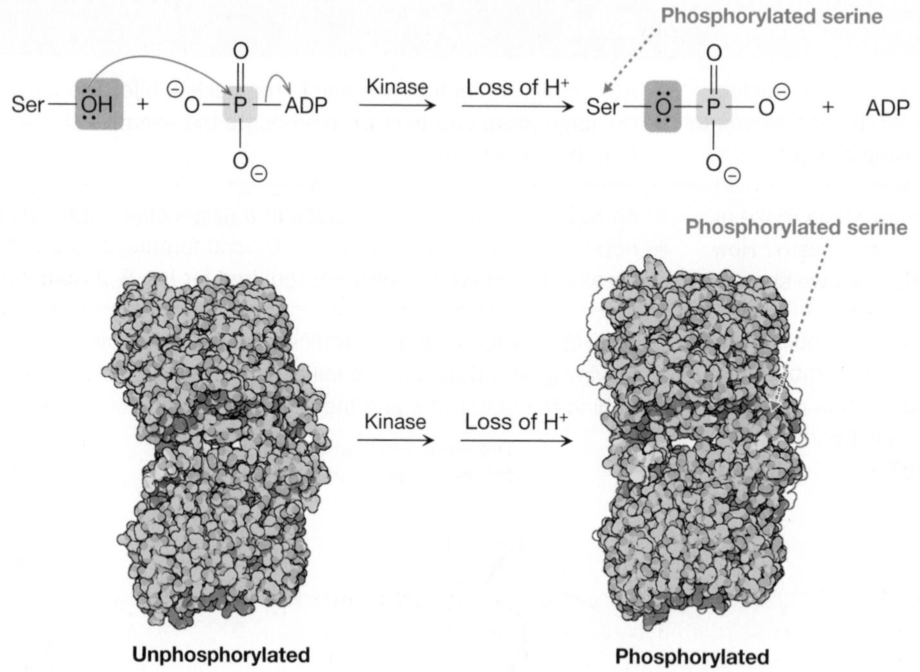

Phosphorylated serine
Ser
OH
O
P
ADP
Kinase
Loss of H+
Phosphorylated serine
Unphosphorylated
Phosphorylated

FIGURE 8-8

In glycogen phosphorylase, in particular, a serine amino acid in the enzyme's active site is subject to phosphorylation, owing to the nucleophilic character of the OH group in serine's side group. The introduction of the negatively charged phosphate group onto that residue (pink) significantly changes the interactions with other amino acid residues, causing a change in the conformation of the enzyme. To help you see how much the enzyme changes shape, a green line has been drawn around the phosphorylated conformation to indicate the space occupied by the unphosphorylated conformation. This conformation change causes the enzyme's activity to increase by roughly 25%. For this and other enzymes, therefore, phosphorylation can be thought of as a convenient "on/off" switch.

8.5b Stereochemistry of an S_N1 Reaction

If an S_N1 reaction is carried out on a stereochemically pure substrate, such as the one shown in Equation 8-20, then a *mixture* of both the *R* and *S* enantiomers is produced:

S_N1

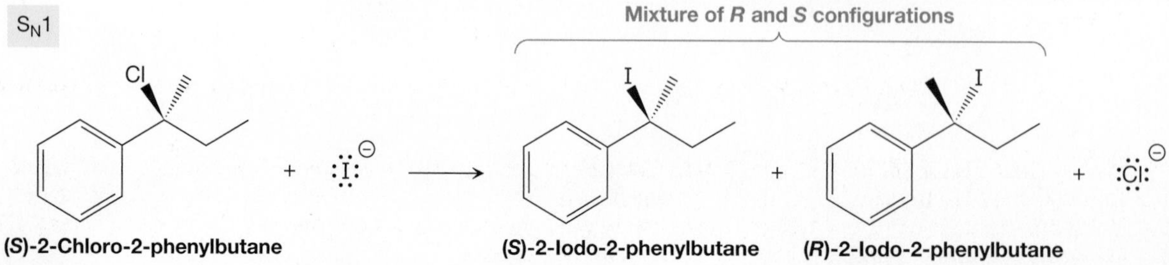

Mixture of R and S configurations
Cl
I
I
I
Cl
(S)-2-Chloro-2-phenylbutane
(S)-2-Iodo-2-phenylbutane
(R)-2-Iodo-2-phenylbutane

(8-20)

Unlike S_N2 reactions, *S_N1 reactions are not stereospecific.* Rather, we can describe the stereochemistry of the S_N1 reaction as follows:

Stereochemistry of the S_N1 Reaction

If the atom that gains the nucleophile is a chiral center in the product, then a mixture of two stereoisomers will be produced: one with an *R* configuration at the chiral center and the other with the *S* configuration.

Why does the reaction produce both configurations of the chiral center?

To answer this question, let's look at the mechanism, shown in Equation 8-21:

Mechanism for S_N1 reaction (Eq. 8-20), including stereochemistry

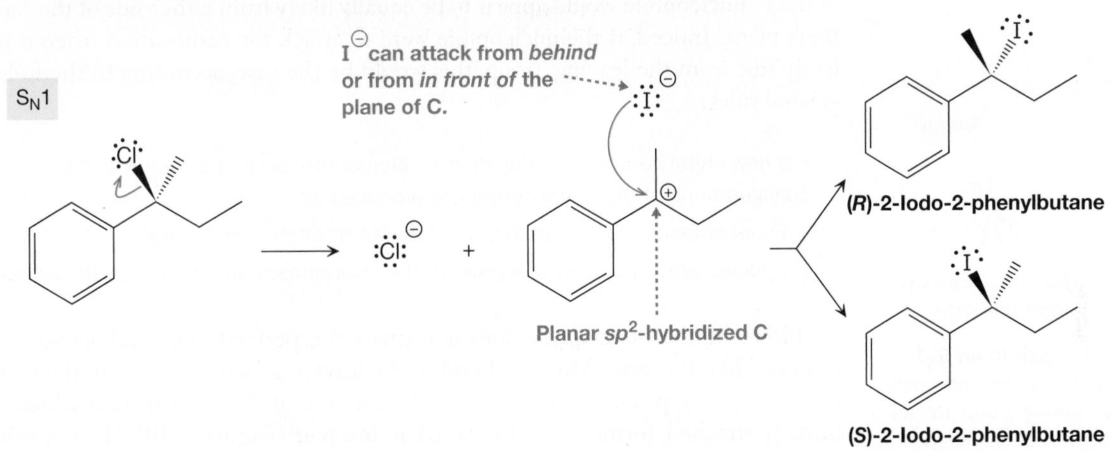

S_N1
I^- can attack from *behind* or from *in front of* the plane of C.
Planar sp^2-hybridized C
(*R*)-2-Iodo-2-phenylbutane
(*S*)-2-Iodo-2-phenylbutane

(8-21a)

(8-21b)

In the first step, Cl^- simply departs, leaving behind a planar carbocation. The C atom that was initially bonded to Cl becomes sp^2-hybridized in the carbocation and is no longer a chiral center (i.e., the stereochemistry of that C atom has been lost). In the second step, in which I^- forms a bond to the carbocation, that same C atom becomes a chiral center once again.

Mechanism Drawing
S_N1 Mechanism and Stereochemistry

YOUR TURN **8.15**

Label all organic species in Equation 8-21a and 8-21b as either *chiral* or *achiral*.

In **Figure 8-9**, we focus on the second step of the mechanism. The carbocation intermediate is shown at the left in Figure 8-9a and 8-9b, and the plane indicated is

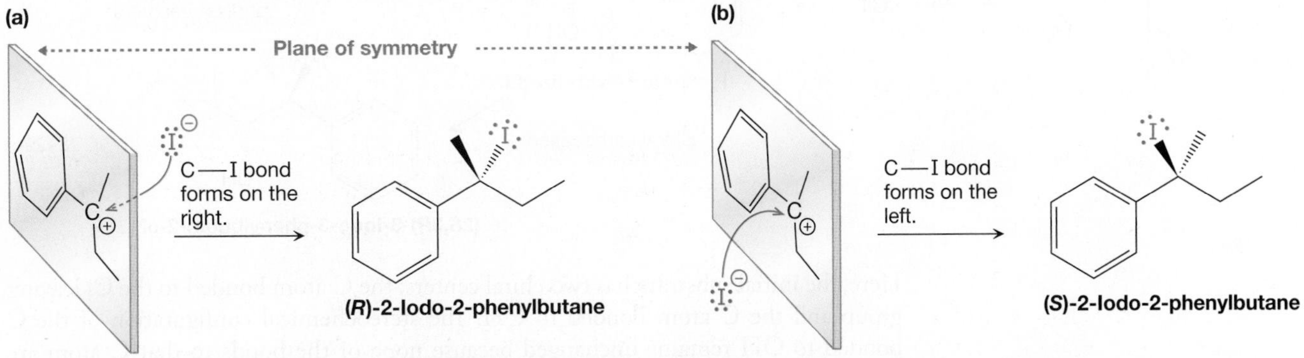

(a)
(b)
Plane of symmetry
C—I bond forms on the right.
(*R*)-2-Iodo-2-phenylbutane
C—I bond forms on the left.
(*S*)-2-Iodo-2-phenylbutane

FIGURE 8-9 Generating a mixture of stereoisomers in an S_N1 reaction The specific stereoisomer that is formed in the reaction in Equation 8-20 is determined by the approach of the I^- nucleophile. The planes shown are defined by the bonds to the positively charged C. (a) I^- approaches from the right, generating the new C—I bond shown, thus producing the *R* enantiomer. (b) I^- approaches from the left, generating the new C—I bond shown, thus producing the *S* enantiomer.

◂ RECALL

Section 5.12b defined a chiral environment as a set of surroundings that is not superimposable on its mirror image. By analogy, a left shoe would represent a chiral environment for your left and right feet, whereas a sock would represent an achiral environment.

defined by the bonds to the positively charged C. When I^- attacks, it can do so from either side of that plane. The approach of I^- from one side of the plane leads to formation of the *R* enantiomer (Fig. 8-9a), whereas the approach of I^- from the other side of the plane leads to formation of the *S* enantiomer (Fig. 8-9b). This idea can be generalized as follows:

> If a chiral center is generated in an elementary step from an atom that is not a chiral center initially, then both *R* and *S* configurations will usually be produced.

You might expect the enantiomeric products of the reaction in Equation 8-20 to be produced in equal amounts: that is, as a *racemic mixture*. The carbocation shown in Figure 8-9 has a plane of symmetry and is therefore achiral, in which case the attack of the I^- nucleophile would appear to be equally likely from either side of the carbocation's plane. Indeed, if the nucleophile were to attack the carbocation when it is perfectly free from the leaving group, this would be the case, according to the following general rules:

> If a new chiral center is produced in an elementary step, then the *R* and *S* configurations of the chiral center are produced in:
> - *Equal* amounts if the reactants and the environment are *achiral*.
> - *Unequal* amounts if the reactants or the environment are *chiral* (see Recall box).

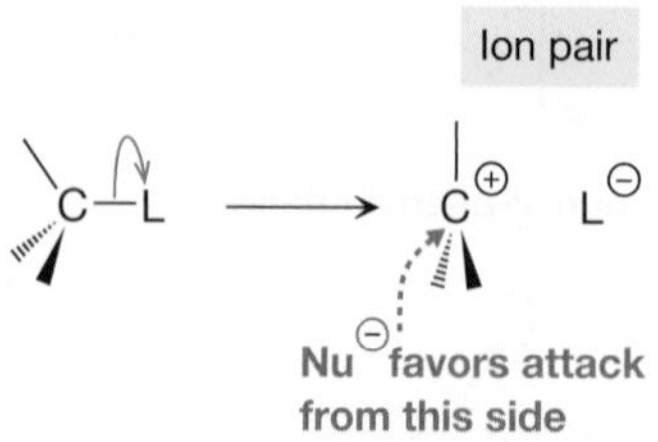

Ion pair
C
L
Nu favors attack from this side

FIGURE 8-10 Ion pair in an S_N1 reaction An ion pair is formed when the bond to the leaving group breaks but electrostatic attractions keeps the leaving group associated with the carbocation. A nucleophile can attack from either side of the carbocation's plane, but a backside attack is favored.

However, the nucleophile does not attack the perfectly free carbocation in S_N1 reactions like this one. After the bond to the leaving group is broken in the first step, the leaving group remains associated with the side of the carbon from which it was initially attached, forming what is called an **ion pair** (**Figure 8-10**). The ion pair produced in the reaction in Equation 8-20 retains some of the chiral character from the original substrate when the nucleophile attacks. Effectively, then, this type of S_N1 reaction behaves somewhat like an S_N2 reaction, favoring backside attack of the nucleophile over frontside attack. The result is a mixture that is close to racemic but slightly favors inversion of configuration.

The stereochemistry of the S_N1 reaction in Equation 8-22 is more clear-cut:

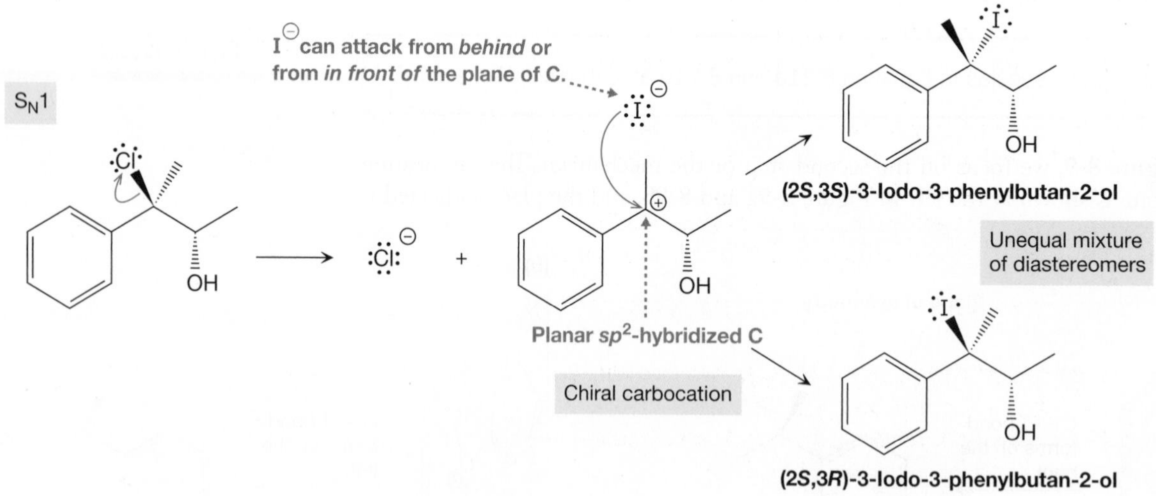

S_N1
I⁻ can attack from *behind* or from *in front of* the plane of C.
Cl
OH
Cl
I
Planar *sp*²-hybridized C
Chiral carbocation
(2*S*,3*S*)-3-Iodo-3-phenylbutan-2-ol
Unequal mixture of diastereomers
(2*S*,3*R*)-3-Iodo-3-phenylbutan-2-ol

(8-22a)

(8-22b)

Here, the initial substrate has two chiral centers: the C atom bonded to the Cl leaving group and the C atom bonded to OH. The stereochemical configuration of the C bonded to OH remains unchanged because none of the bonds to that C atom are involved in the reaction. Just as in Equation 8-21, though, the C atom bonded to Cl reacts to form both the *R* and *S* configurations in the product. As indicated in Equation 8-22, the result is a mixture of two *diastereomers*.

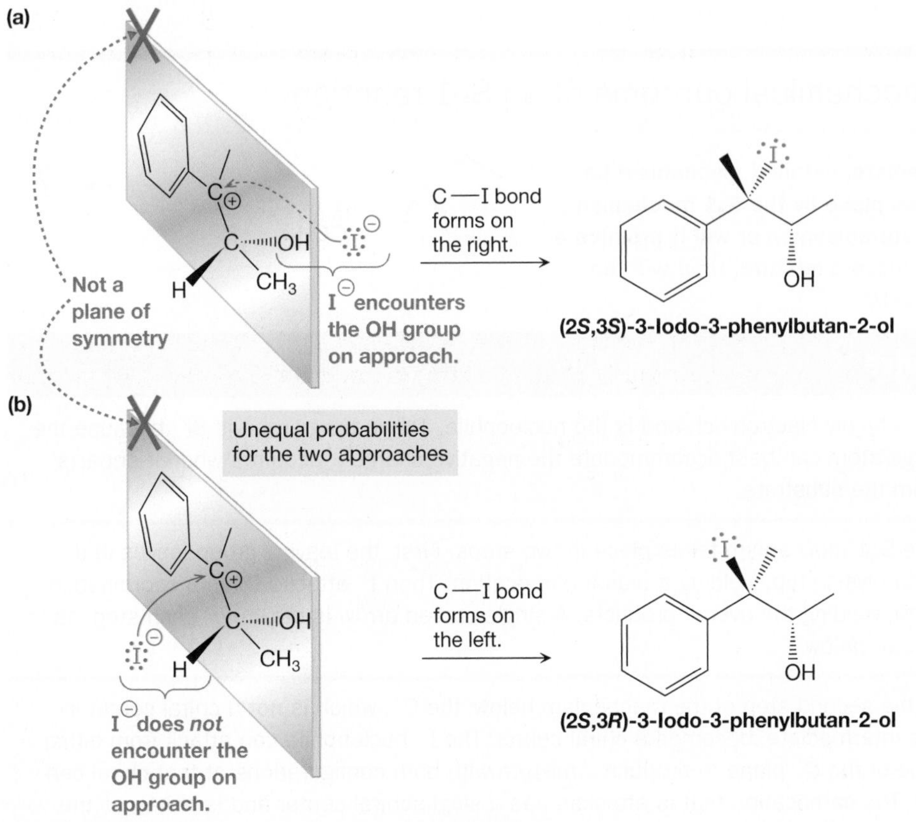
(a)
C—I bond
forms on
the right.
Not a
plane of
symmetry
I⁻ encounters
the OH group
on approach.
(2S,3S)-3-Iodo-3-phenylbutan-2-ol
(b)
Unequal probabilities
for the two approaches
C—I bond
forms on
the left.
I⁻ does not
encounter the
OH group on
approach.
(2S,3R)-3-Iodo-3-phenylbutan-2-ol

FIGURE 8-11 Formation of an unequal mixture of diastereomers in an S_N1 reaction The planes indicated are defined by the bonds to the positively charged C, but they are not planes of symmetry because the molecule is chiral. The OH group is present only on one side of the plane, so whether it interacts with an approaching I^- depends on the direction from which the ion arrives. (a) If the I^- nucleophile comes from the right, it encounters the OH group. (b) If the I^- nucleophile comes from the left, it avoids the OH group. The two possible resulting reactions thus occur with different probabilities, producing an unequal mixture of diastereomers.

Unlike the previous situation shown in Equation 8-21, the carbocation intermediate shown in Equation 8-22 has a single chiral center, so it is unambiguously chiral and has no plane of symmetry. Without a plane of symmetry in the carbocation, the nucleophile will be influenced differently depending on which side of the carbocation it approaches. In **Figure 8-11**, the nucleophile would encounter the OH group on the right side (Fig. 8-11a) but not on the left side (Fig. 8-11b). Thus the likelihood of each approach would be unequal, and the diastereomeric products would be produced in *unequal* amounts.

You may be tempted to try to predict which diastereomer is produced in greater abundance. We caution against it, however, because the factors that favor the production of one configuration over another can be subtle, involving the interplay between steric effects and electronic effects (such as hydrogen bonding, inductive effects, and polarizability). As a result, we limit such discussions to reactions in which these factors are straightforward.

YOUR TURN **8.16**

Determine whether each carbocation will undergo coordination with I^- to produce a single product, an equal mixture of stereoisomers, or an unequal mixture of stereoisomers. (Assume each carbocation is free from any leaving group.)

(a)

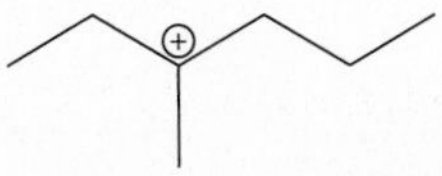

(b)

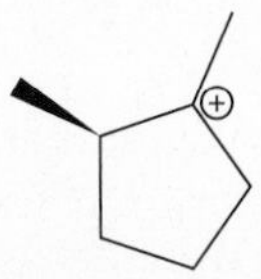

(c)

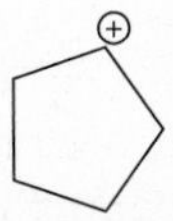

SOLVED PROBLEM **8.4**

How to predict the stereochemical outcome of an S_N1 reaction

Break It Down **Draw the complete, detailed mechanism for this reaction, assuming that it takes place by the S_N1 mechanism. Will the reaction produce a single stereoisomer, or will it produce a mixture of stereoisomers? If it produces a mixture, then will the isomers be produced in equal amounts?**

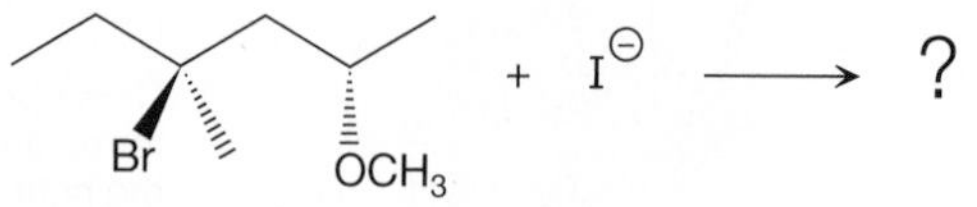

Br
OCH₃
+ I⊖
?

Think	Solve
What acts as the nucleophile? What best serves as the leaving group?	I^- is highly electron-rich and is the nucleophile. The leaving group is Br^- because the large atom can best accommodate the negative charge it acquires when it departs from the substrate.
What are the steps of the S_N1 mechanism? How are the curved arrows drawn for each step?	The S_N1 mechanism takes place in two steps. First, the leaving group leaves in a heterolysis step, yielding a planar carbocation. Then I^- attacks C^+ in a coordination step, yielding the overall products. A single curved arrow is drawn for each step, as shown below.
Is there an elementary step where an atom that is not a chiral center becomes a chiral center? In that step, is the reactant chiral or achiral?	In the second step of the mechanism below, the C^+, which is not a chiral center in the intermediate, becomes a chiral center. The I^- nucleophile can attack from either side of the C^+ plane to produce a mixture with both configurations at that chiral center. The carbocation that is attacked has a single chiral center and is chiral, so the resulting diastereomers must be produced in unequal amounts.

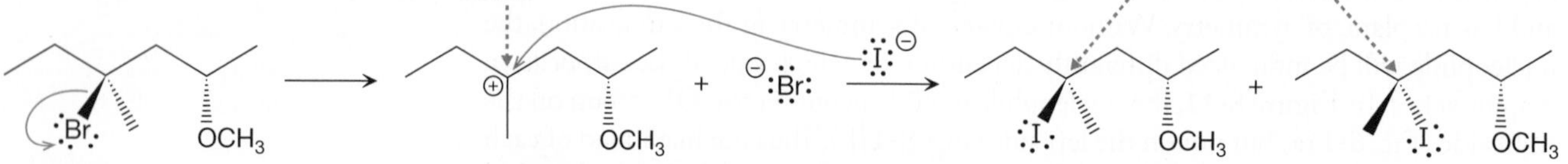

Not a chiral center
Chiral center
Br
OCH₃
+
I

Try It Draw the complete mechanism and products for an S_N1 reaction between the following reactants. Will the reaction produce a single stereoisomer, or will it produce a mixture of stereoisomers? If it produces a mixture, will those isomers be produced in equal amounts?

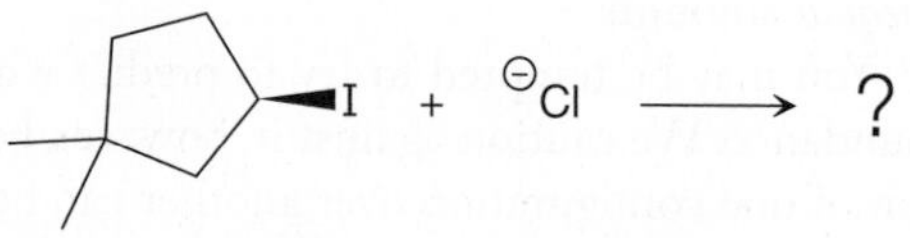

I
+ ⊖Cl
?

8.5c Stereochemistry of an E2 Reaction

In the E2 reaction shown in Equation 8-23, the new C=C double bond that is formed has *E* and *Z* configurations possible, but only the *E* isomer is produced. Therefore, like the S_N2 reaction, *the E2 reaction is stereospecific.*

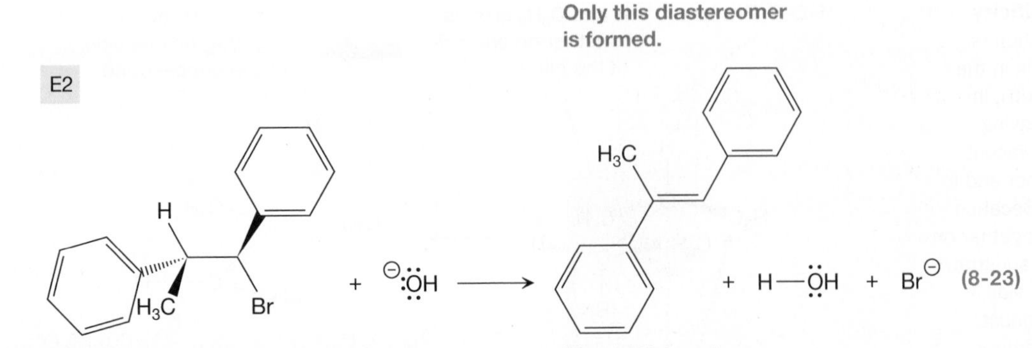
Only this diastereomer
is formed.
E2
H
H₃C
Br
+
:ÖH
H₃C
+ H—ÖH + Br
(8-23)
(1S,2R)-1-Bromo-1,2-diphenylpropane
(E)-1,2-Diphenylpropene

We account for this stereospecificity with the following general rule:

Stereochemistry of the E2 Reaction

E2 reactions are favored by the substrate conformation in which the leaving group and the hydrogen atom that are eliminated are anti to each other.

This rule becomes important for the reaction in Equation 8-23 because, as shown in **Figure 8-12**, the C atoms to which the H and Br are attached are themselves connected by a C—C single bond that rotates rapidly. As we learned in Section 4.2, the three stable conformations of that C—C bond are staggered. One of those conformations has the H and Br anti to each other; more specifically, because the H, Br, and the two C atoms to which they are attached all lie in the same plane, that conformation is called **anticoplanar** or **antiperiplanar**. In the other two conformations, the H and Br are gauche to each other.

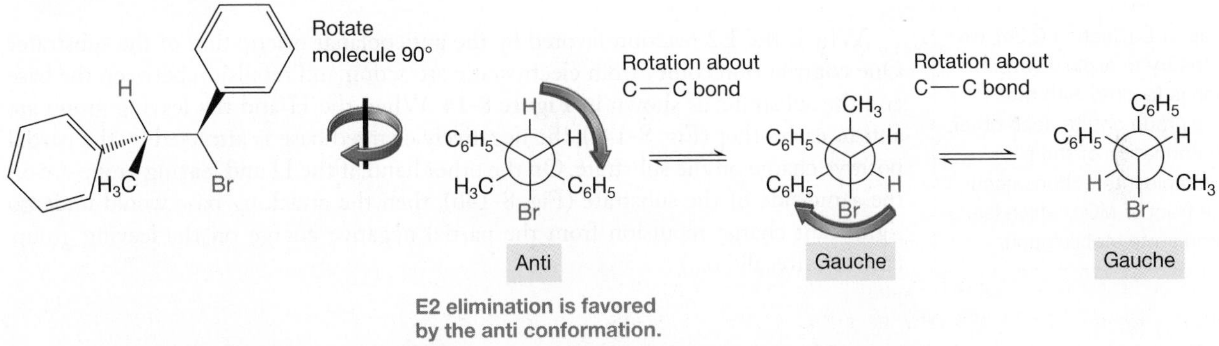
Rotate
molecule 90°
Rotation about
C—C bond
Rotation about
C—C bond
Anti
Gauche
Gauche
E2 elimination is favored
by the anti conformation.

FIGURE 8-12 Favored substrate conformation for an E2 reaction The C atoms attached to the H and Br that can be eliminated in an E2 reaction are connected by a single bond. In the stable conformations for that C—C bond (shown as Newman projections), the H and Br are either anti or gauche, but E2 reactions are favored only when they are anti to each other.

Figure 8-13 shows that, with the substrate in the anticoplanar conformation, the stereoisomer formed is determined by the location of the other substituents on the carbon atoms of the substrate. Notice in particular that H and one C_6H_5 group are together on one side of the plane in the substrate, so they are together on one side of the double bond in the product, too. Similarly, CH_3 and the second C_6H_5 group are together on the other side of the double bond in the product because they both began

FIGURE 8-13 Stereospecificity in E2 reactions An E2 reaction is favored when the substrate is in the *anticoplanar* conformation (left), in which the H atom and the leaving group (in this case, Br) on adjacent C atoms are anti to each other and in the same plane (coplanar). Because the H and C_6H_5 groups are together on one side of the plane in the substrate, they end up together on one side of the double bond in the product. Similarly, the CH_3 and C_6H_5 groups are together on the other side of the plane in the substrate, so they end up together on the other side of the double bond in the product.

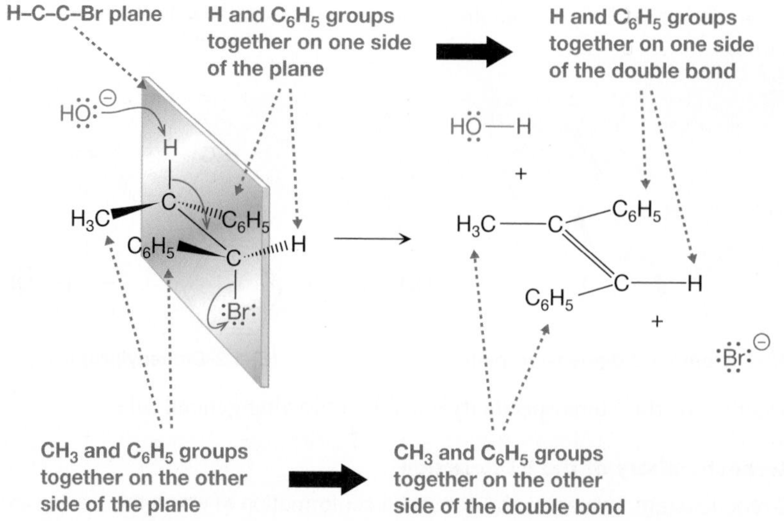

H–C–C–Br plane
H and C6H5 groups together on one side of the plane
H and C6H5 groups together on one side of the double bond
HO:
H
H3C
C
C6H5
C6H5
C
H
:Br:
HO—H
+
H3C—C
C6H5
C6H5
C—H
+
:Br:
CH3 and C6H5 groups together on the other side of the plane
CH3 and C6H5 groups together on the other side of the double bond

Mechanism Drawing E2 Mechanism and Stereochemistry

on the other side of the plane in the substrate. (To better see these relationships, construct a model of the substrate from Eq. 8-23, paying attention to the dash–wedge notation; rotate about the single bond so H and Br are anti to each other; and examine which substituents are on each side of the H—C—C—Br plane.)

YOUR TURN **8.17**

Draw a substrate that would undergo an E2 reaction to yield the diastereomer of the product alkene shown in Equation 8-23. Be sure to include accurate dash–wedge notation.

◀ RECALL

In Interchapter C (Section C.2e), we used MO theory to explain why an E2 reaction is favored with the H and leaving group anti to each other. In that conformation of the substrate, favorable interactions occur among the frontier MOs, which leads to transition state stabilization.

Why is the E2 reaction favored by the anticoplanar orientation of the substrate? One contribution comes from electrostatic attraction and repulsion between the base and the substrate, as shown in **Figure 8-14**. When the H and the leaving group are anti to each other (Fig. 8-14a), the negatively charged base is attracted by the partial positive charge on the substrate. On the other hand, if the H and leaving group are on the same side of the substrate (Fig. 8-14b), then the attacking base would undergo significant charge repulsion from the partial negative charge on the leaving group. (See also Recall box.)

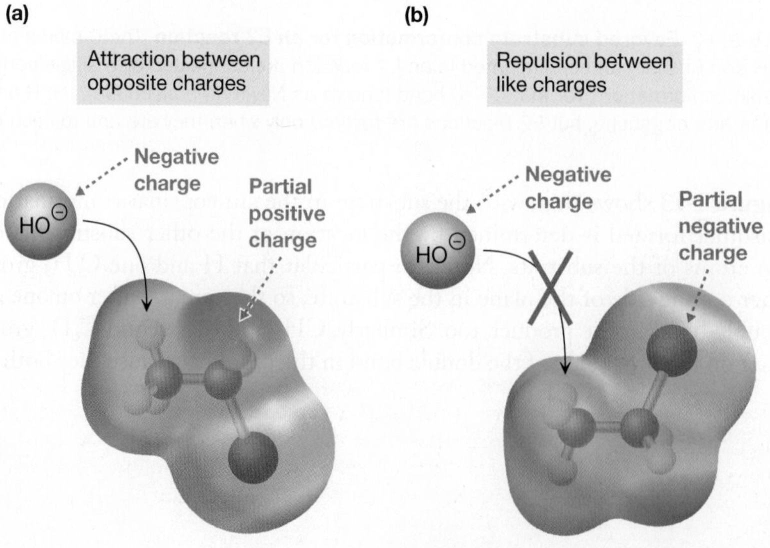

(a)
Attraction between opposite charges
Negative charge
Partial positive charge
HO
(b)
Repulsion between like charges
Negative charge
Partial negative charge
HO

FIGURE 8-14 Stereospecificity in E2 reactions E2 reactions with the substrate in different conformations. (a) With the H and leaving group oriented anti to each other, the incoming base is attracted by the positively charged end of the substrate. (b) With the H and leaving group oriented on the same side of the substrate, the base is repelled by the partial negative charge on the leaving group.

If two different H atoms could be eliminated from the same C atom, as shown in Equation 8-24, then a *mixture* of diastereomers can form in an E2 reaction:

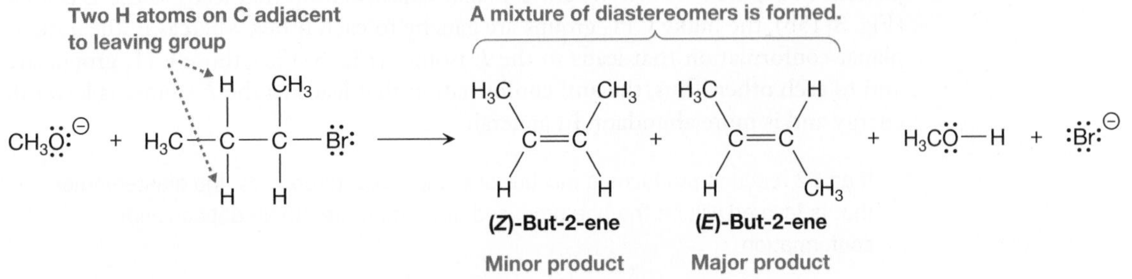

Two H atoms on C adjacent to leaving group
A mixture of diastereomers is formed.
(Z)-But-2-ene
Minor product
(E)-But-2-ene
Major product

(8-24)

Each product in Equation 8-24 is the result of an E2 elimination from the substrate. **Figure 8-15** shows that there are two different anticoplanar conformers, in which different H atoms are anti to the Br atom; these conformers are related by rotation about the C—C single bond. One of them leads to the *E* configuration about the C=C double bond (Fig. 8-15a), whereas the other leads to the *Z* configuration (Fig. 8-15b; see bottom Recall box).

◀ RECALL

Section 5.8 showed how to distinguish *Z* and *E* configurations for a C=C double bond by identifying the higher-priority substituent attached to each doubly bonded C. Those substituents are on the same side of the double bond in a *Z* configuration and are on opposite sides in an *E* configuration.

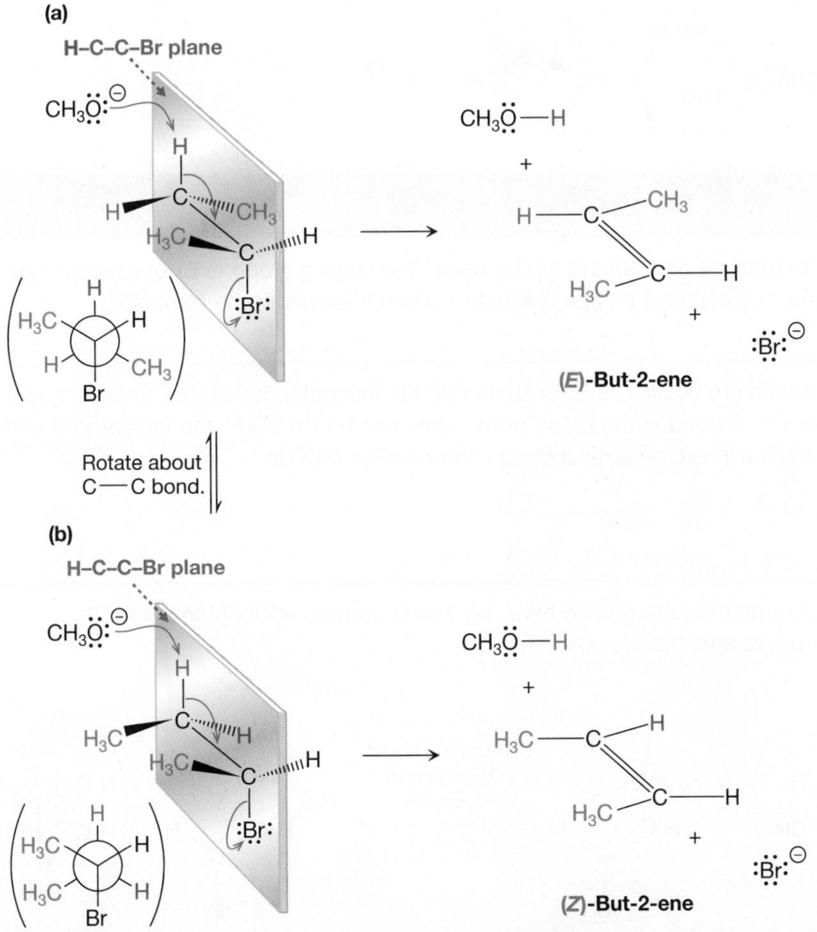

(a)
H–C–C–Br plane
Rotate about C—C bond.
(b)
H–C–C–Br plane
(E)-But-2-ene
(Z)-But-2-ene

FIGURE 8-15 Formation of diastereomers in an E2 reaction The substrate in Equation 8-24 (left) has two different conformers in which an H atom and the Br atom are anti, favoring an E2 reaction. (a) In this conformer, the methyl groups are on opposite sides of the H—C—C—Br plane, so the *E* diastereomer is formed. (b) In this conformer, the methyl groups are on the same side of the H—C—C—Br plane, so the *Z* diastereomer is formed.

Notice in Equation 8-24 that the *E* isomer is favored over the *Z* isomer. Steric strain in the substrate accounts for this selectivity, as we can see in the Newman projections in Figure 8-15. In the anticoplanar conformation that leads to the *Z* isomer (Fig. 8-15b), the bulky CH_3 groups are gauche to each other, whereas in the anticoplanar conformation that leads to the *E* isomer (Fig. 8-15a), those CH_3 groups are anti to each other. Thus, the anti conformation that leads to the *E* isomer is lower in energy and is more abundant. In general:

> If an E2 reaction produces a mixture of *E* and *Z* diastereomers, the diastereomer that is favored will be the one produced from the more stable anticoplanar conformation.

SOLVED PROBLEM **8.5**

How to predict the stereochemical outcome of an E2 reaction

Break It Down **Draw the products of E2 elimination involving (a) the D atom and (b) the H atom indicated. Pay attention to stereochemistry, and note that D is an isotope of H, so the two atoms exhibit nearly identical chemical behavior.**

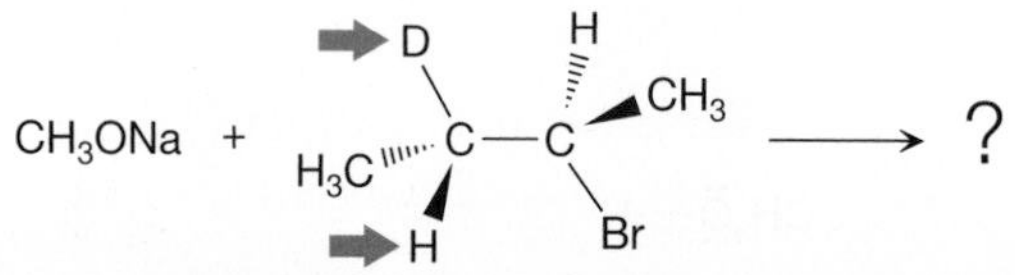

CH₃ONa +
D
H
CH₃
H₃C
C—C
H
Br
?

Think	Solve
What acts as the base? What best serves as the leaving group?	CH_3O^- is electron-rich and will act as the base. The leaving group is Br because it can accommodate the negative charge it acquires when it leaves in the form of Br^-.
What conformations of the substrate facilitate an E2 reaction? Can the H and D indicated above both achieve that conformation?	For an E2 reaction to occur, the H (or D) should be anticoplanar with the Br leaving group. Because the C—C bond in the plane of the page can rotate 360°, the indicated H and D atoms can each achieve an anticoplanar conformation with Br.
How should you draw each conformation, taking into account the particular configuration at each chiral center?	The two conformations are shown here. (a) The D atom is anticoplanar with Br. (b) The H atom is anticoplanar with Br. 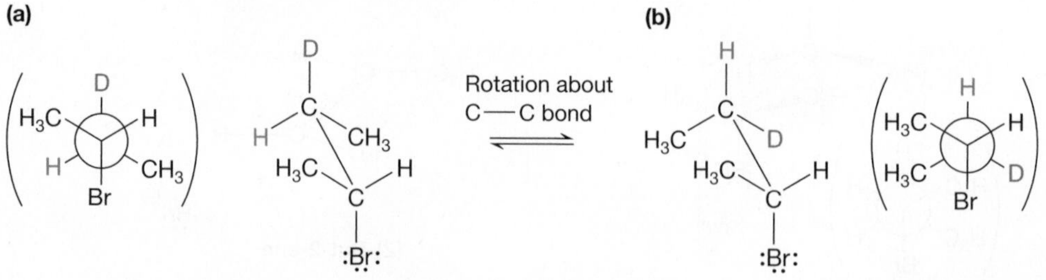 (a) (b) Rotation about C—C bond D H H₃C CH₃ Br :Br: D

(continued)

In each anticoplanar conformation, what substituents appear on either side of the H/D—C—C—Br plane? How do those relationships in the substrate dictate the arrangement of the substituents attached to the new C═C bond in the product?

The relationships of the substituents relative to the H/D—C—C—Br plane are shown on the left. As indicated, those relationships are conserved relative to the new C═C bond produced.

(a)

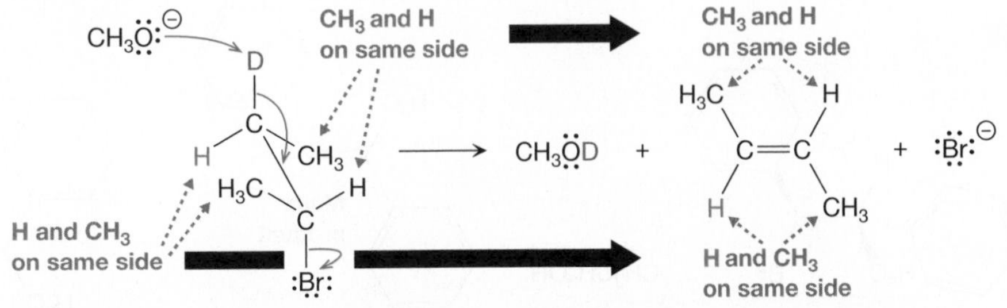
CH₃ and H on same side
H and CH₃ on same side
CH₃ and H on same side
H and CH₃ on same side

(b)

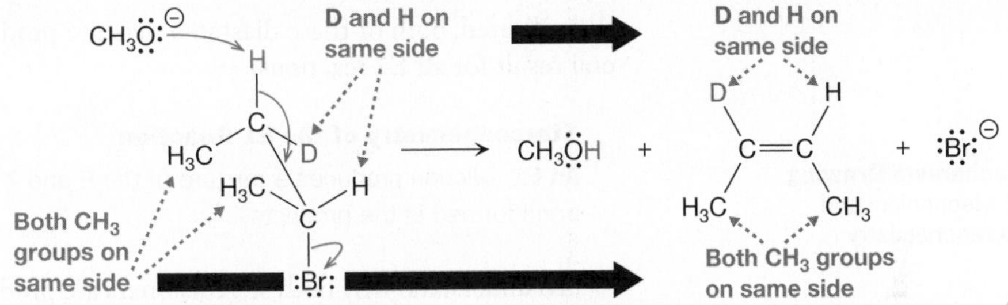
D and H on same side
Both CH₃ groups on same side
D and H on same side
Both CH₃ groups on same side

Try It Draw the products of E2 elimination involving **(a)** the H atom and **(b)** the D atom indicated, and compare these products to the ones in Solved Problem 8.5. Pay attention to stereochemistry.

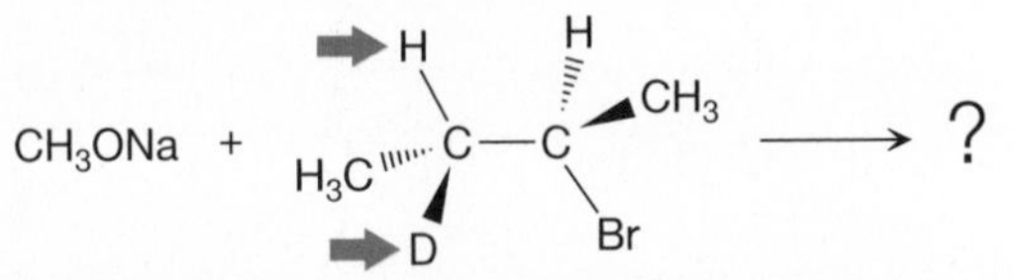

The anticoplanar requirement for the eliminated H and leaving group can impact more than the stereochemistry of an E2 reaction: it can also impact *which* H is eliminated. This is of particular concern in cyclic substrates, because the bonds of the ring cannot undergo complete rotations, sometimes making it impossible for the H—C—C—L to be anticoplanar. For an example, see Your Turn 8.18.

YOUR TURN **8.18**

Explain why the double bond appears in different locations in the products of these two E2 reactions.

A

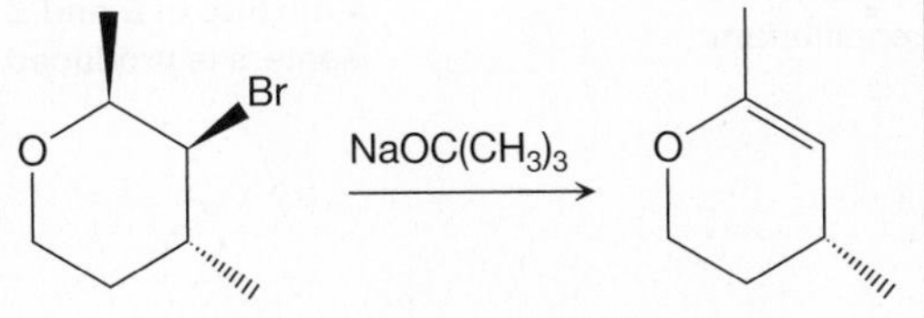

B

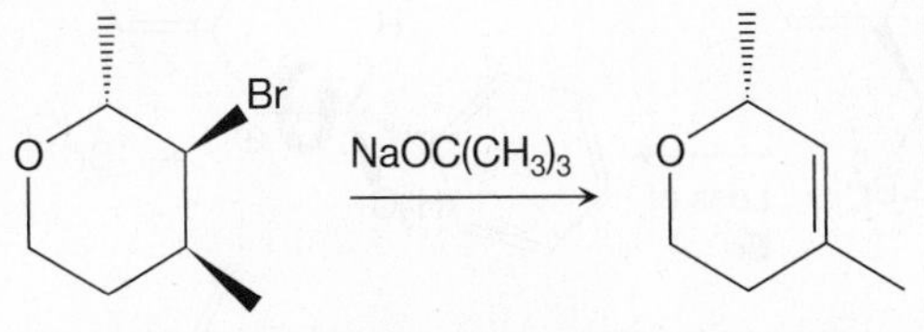

8.5d Stereochemistry of an E1 Reaction

When an E1 reaction produces a new double bond, stereochemistry is an issue if both *E* and *Z* configurations about the double bond exist. An example is shown in Equation 8-25:

Both *E* and *Z* isomers are produced in an E1 mechanism.

E1

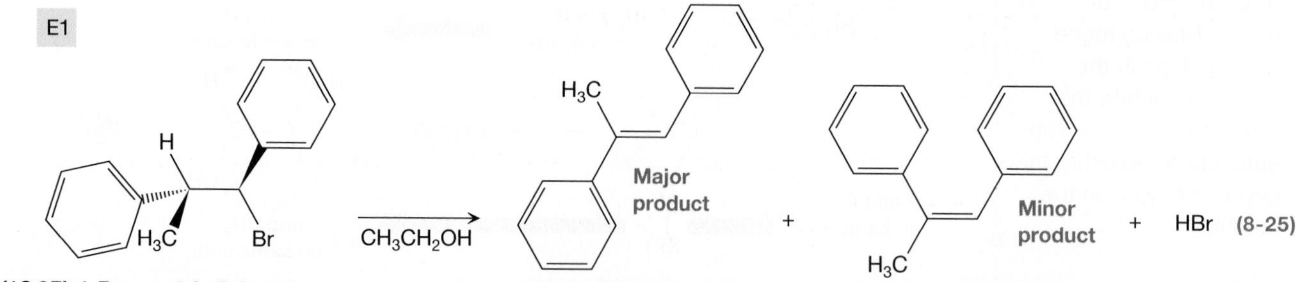

H
H_3C
Br
CH_3CH_2OH
H_3C
Major product
+
Minor product
H_3C
+ HBr
(8-25)

(1*S*,2*R*)-1-Bromo-1,2-diphenylpropane **(*E*)-1,2-Diphenylpropene** **(*Z*)-1,2-Diphenylpropene**

As indicated, both of these diastereomers are produced in the reaction. This is a general result for all E1 reactions:

Stereochemistry of the E1 Reaction

An E1 reaction produces a mixture of the *E* and *Z* configurations about a double bond formed in the products.

Mechanism Drawing
E1 Mechanism and Stereochemistry

To understand why both stereoisomers are produced, we turn to the mechanism of the E1 reaction, shown in Equation 8-26:

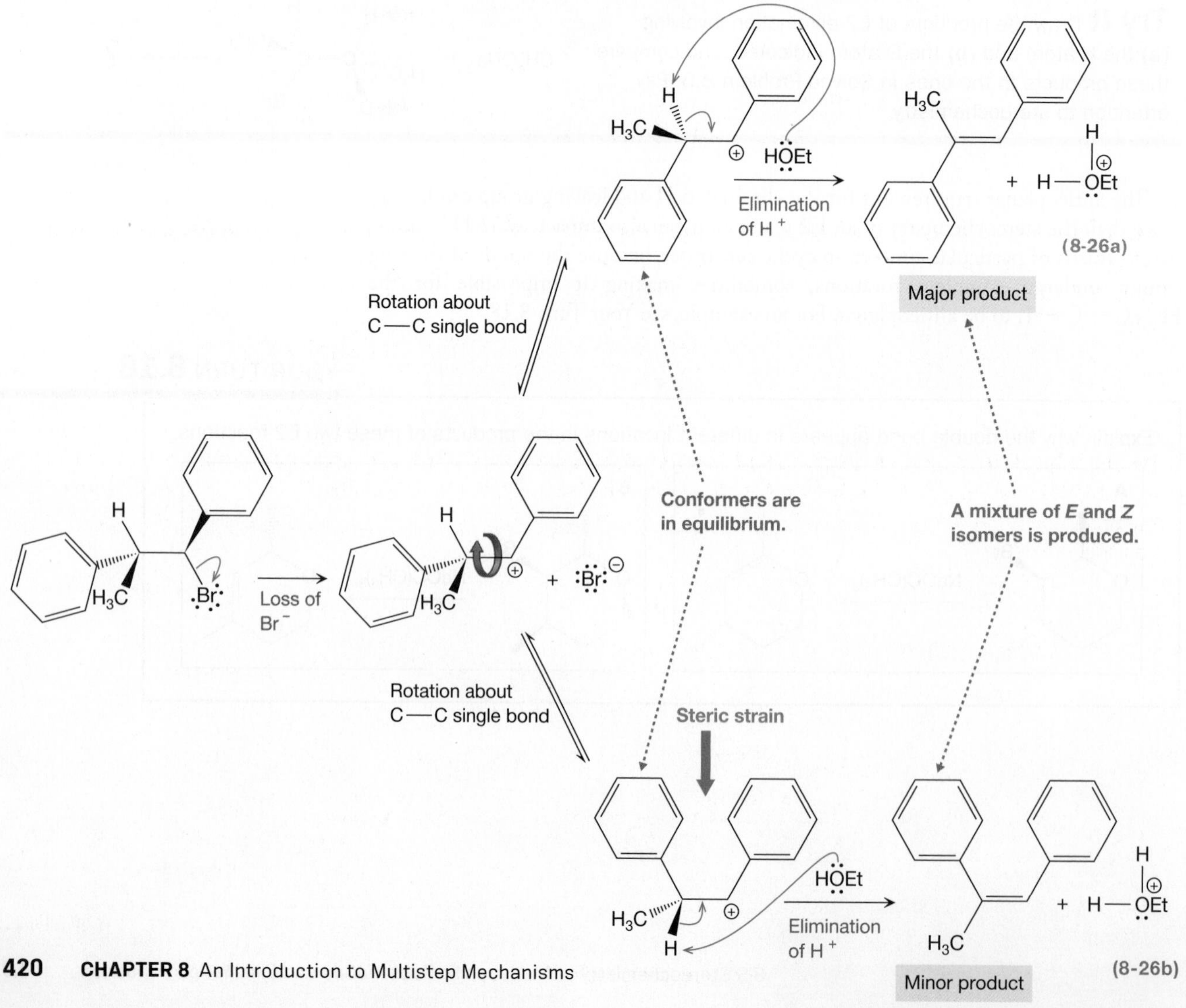

H
H_3C
HÖEt
Elimination of H^+
H_3C
H
+ H—OEt
(8-26a)
Major product
Rotation about C—C single bond
H
H_3C
:Br:
Loss of Br^-
H
H_3C
+ :Br:
Conformers are in equilibrium.
A mixture of *E* and *Z* isomers is produced.
Rotation about C—C single bond
Steric strain
HÖEt
H_3C
H
Elimination of H^+
H_3C
H
+ H—OEt
Minor product
(8-26b)

The C=C bond in the product forms when a base pulls off H^+ from the $H—C—C^+$ group in the carbocation intermediate. Prior to the base attacking, that $C—C^+$ single bond rotates rapidly to establish an equilibrium among the various conformers. Unlike what we saw for E2 reactions, there is no attached leaving group to dictate when the base can attack. Therefore, each time the base attacks, either the *E* isomer (Eq. 8-26a) or the *Z* isomer (Eq. 8-26b) can be produced, depending on the particular conformation about the $C—C^+$ bond of the carbocation.

SOLVED PROBLEM **8.6**

How to predict the stereochemical outcome of an E1 reaction

Break It Down Draw the complete, detailed mechanism for this reaction, assuming it proceeds via an E1 mechanism. Pay attention to stereochemistry.

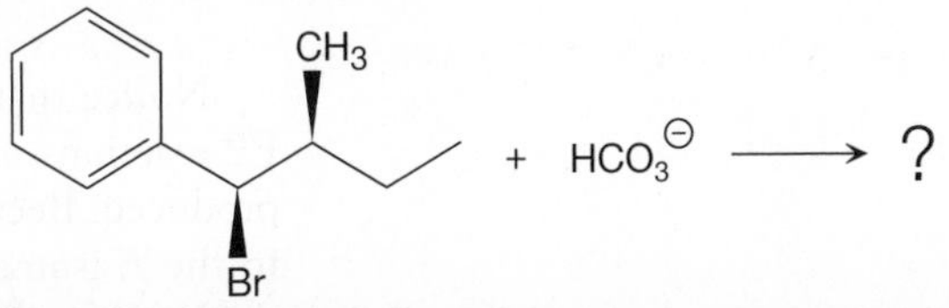
CH3
Br
+ HCO3⁻
?

Think	Solve
What can act as the leaving group? What is the product of the first step of an E1 mechanism?	Br can act as the leaving group because it can accommodate the negative charge it acquires when it departs as Br^-. In the first step of an E1 mechanism, the carbocation intermediate shown here is produced when the leaving group departs. 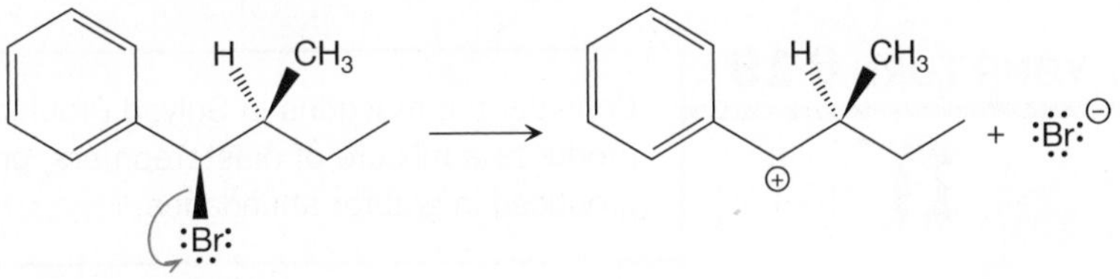 H CH3 :Br: H CH3 + :Br:⁻
Which proton can be removed in the second step of an E1 mechanism? What can act as the base?	In the second step, HCO_3^- can act as a base to remove a proton from the C atom that is adjacent to C^+, as shown here, which will produce an alkene. 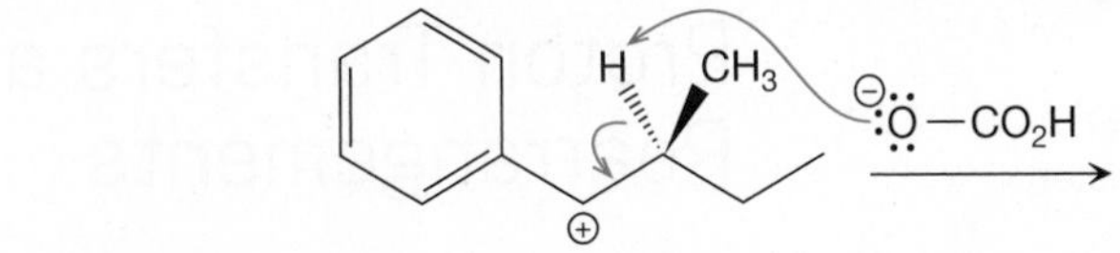 H CH3 :Ö—CO2H
Do *E* and *Z* configurations exist for the new double bond in the product? If so, can both be formed?	Both *E* and *Z* configurations exist about that double bond, and because the bond indicated in the carbocation can undergo rotation, both the *E* and *Z* isomers are formed. 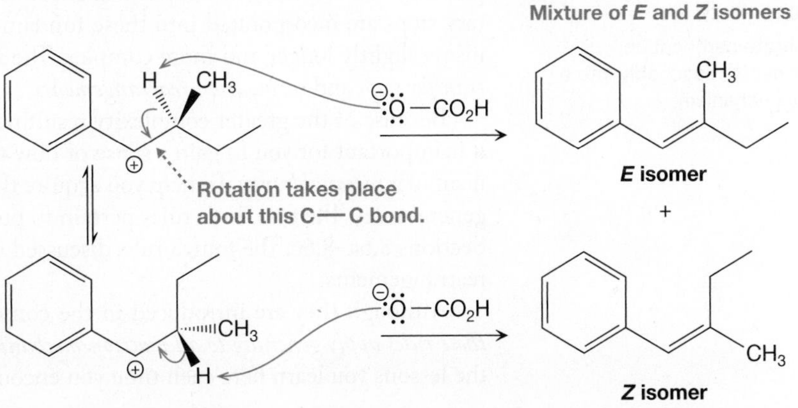 Mixture of E and Z isomers H CH3 :Ö—CO2H CH3 Rotation takes place about this C—C bond. E isomer + CH3 H :Ö—CO2H CH3 Z isomer

(continued)

Try It Draw the complete, detailed mechanism for each of the following reactions, assuming they proceed via E1 mechanisms. Pay attention to stereochemistry.

(a)

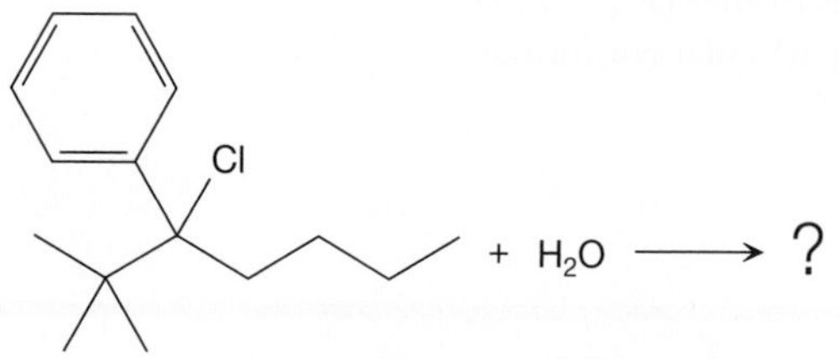

Cl
+ H₂O
?

(b)

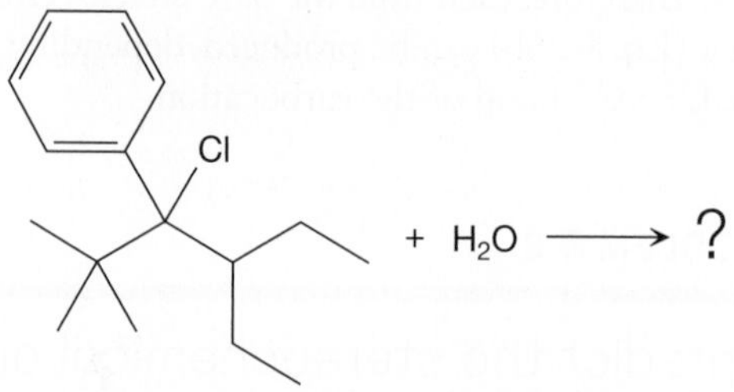

Cl
+ H₂O
?

Notice that the *E* isomer in Equation 8-25 is favored over the *Z* isomer. As in E2 reactions, steric strain accounts for the relative amounts of the *E* and *Z* isomers produced. Because the phenyl rings are somewhat bulky, the conformer that leads to the *E* isomer (Eq. 8-26a) will be in greater abundance than the one that leads to the *Z* isomer (Eq. 8-26b). This idea can be generalized for other E1 reactions as well:

If an E1 reaction produces both *E* and *Z* isomers, the isomer with less steric strain will generally be favored.

YOUR TURN **8.19**

Consider the reactions in Solved Problem 8.6, Try It. For each reaction that produces a mixture of diastereomers, predict which diastereomer will be produced in greater abundance.

SECTION 8.6 OBJECTIVES

You will be able to:

1. Incorporate proton transfer steps reasonably into a multistep mechanism.
2. Construct a multistep mechanism using unimolecular and bimolecular steps, avoiding termolecular steps and steps of higher molecularity.
3. Incorporate carbocation rearrangements reasonably into a multistep mechanism.

8.6 The Reasonableness of a Mechanism: Proton Transfers and Carbocation Rearrangements

So far, we have considered just the simplest of nucleophilic substitution and elimination reactions. Each S_N2 and E2 mechanism that has been presented consists of precisely one step, and each S_N1 and E1 reaction that has been presented consists of precisely two steps. However, you will encounter many instances where other elementary steps are incorporated into these fundamental mechanisms, making the mechanisms slightly longer and more complex. The most common of these steps are *proton transfer steps* and *carbocation rearrangements*.

Because of the greater complexity resulting from including these additional steps, it is important for you to gain a sense of how they can be incorporated into a mechanism in a *reasonable* way. To help you acquire this "chemical intuition," we present four general rules. The first three rules pertain to proton transfer steps and are discussed in Sections 8.6a–8.6c. The fourth rule, discussed in Section 8.6d, pertains to carbocation rearrangements.

Although they are introduced in the context of S_N2, S_N1, E2, and E1 reactions, *these rules apply generally to all reaction mechanisms*. Therefore, you should try to apply the lessons you learn here each time you encounter a new reaction mechanism.

8.6a Acidic and Basic Conditions: Proton Transfer Steps Are Fast

The first general rule addresses the conditions under which a reaction takes place:

Rule 1: Avoid the Appearance of Incompatible Acids and Bases

- Strong acids generally should not appear in mechanisms under basic conditions.
- Strong bases generally should not appear in mechanisms under acidic conditions.

Under basic conditions, the equilibrium concentration of a strongly acidic species is extremely small, and under acidic conditions, the equilibrium concentration of a strongly basic species is extremely small.

Proton transfer steps are fast, so they can be incorporated before or after another elementary step, as necessary, to avoid incompatible species. You can gain a sense of how fast proton transfers are by recalling the acid–base titrations you have carried out in lab. Changes in the pH of a solution occur almost instantaneously on the addition of acid or base. On the other hand, many organic reactions require hours to reach completion, even at an elevated temperature.

To apply this rule correctly, we must be able to recognize strong acids and strong bases. You may recall from general chemistry that H_3O^+ is a strong acid and HO^- is a strong base. Those species are also convenient cutoffs for defining other strong acids and bases:

- Strong acids are roughly as strong or stronger than H_3O^+, whereas weak acids are significantly weaker than H_3O^+.
- Strong bases are roughly as strong or stronger than HO^-, whereas weak bases are significantly weaker than HO^-.

◀ RECALL

As we saw in Section 6.2, the stronger of two acids is the one that has the lower pK_a value. The stronger of two bases is the one that has the weaker conjugate acid, which is the conjugate acid with the higher pK_a value.

Knowing these cutoffs, we can use pK_a values to characterize acids and bases (see Recall box). The pK_a of H_3O^+ is 0, so any acid whose pK_a is <0 will be a strong acid, too. The conjugate acid of HO^- is H_2O, which has a pK_a of 14. Therefore, any base whose conjugate acid has a pK_a that is >14 will also be a strong base.

With these pK_a comparisons in mind, we can classify some common acids and bases:

- Examples of strong acids: H_3O^+, $CH_3OH_2^+$, $H_3CCH_2^+$
- Examples of weak acids: H_2O, NH_3, H_4N^+, $CH_3NH_3^+$
- Examples of strong bases: HO^-, H_2N^-, H_3C^-, H^-
- Examples of weak bases: H_2O, NH_3, Cl^-, Br^-, I^-, HSO_4^-, HCO_2^-

YOUR TURN 8.20

Use Table 6-1 (p. 269) to look up or estimate the pK_a values of $CH_3OH_2^+$, $CH_3NH_3^+$, H_2, and HCl. Do those values indicate that $CH_3OH_2^+$ is a strong acid, whereas $CH_3NH_3^+$ is a weak acid? Do those values indicate that H^- is a strong base, whereas Cl^- is a weak base?

Notice that some patterns emerge in these classifications. For example, strong bases generally have a negative charge localized on an atom from the first or second row of the periodic table. As we learned in Chapter 6, these relatively small atoms do not accommodate the negative charge very well. Weak bases are generally uncharged but can be negatively charged if the charge is heavily stabilized. In the halides listed (Cl^-, Br^- and I^-), for example, the negative charge appears on a large atom, and in HSO_4^- and HCO_2^-, the negative charge is stabilized by resonance and inductive effects.

Strong acids generally have a positive charge, but some positively charged acids, such as H_4N^+, are weak. A nitrogen atom can handle the positive charge fairly well because it is not very highly electronegative. You might think that a carbocation should be a weak acid, too, because carbon is even less electronegative than nitrogen, but remember that a carbon atom in a carbocation lacks an octet. Therefore, a proton on an atom *adjacent* to C^+ is easily removed.

Let's now apply these ideas toward the substitution reaction shown in Equation 8-27, in which phenylmethanol is converted to 1-benzyloxyprop-2-yne under *basic* conditions (indicated by the presence of KOH):

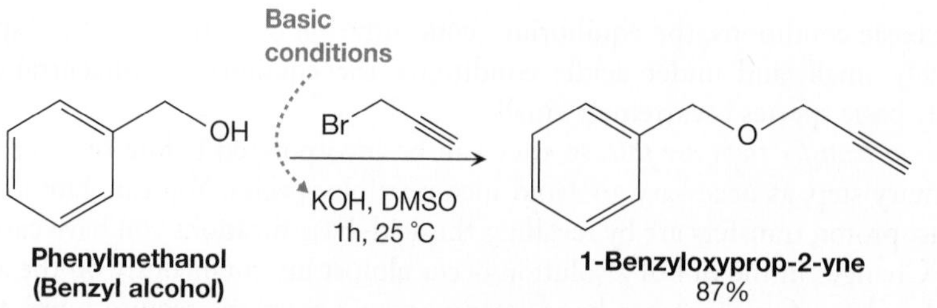

Basic conditions
OH
Br
KOH, DMSO
1h, 25 °C
O
Phenylmethanol
(Benzyl alcohol)
1-Benzyloxyprop-2-yne
87%

(8-27)

In one proposed mechanism, shown in Equation 8-28, the alcohol acts as a nucleophile in an S_N2 reaction, followed by a proton transfer step:

Unreasonable S_N2 mechanism involving an alcohol under basic conditions (Eq. 8-27)

Unreasonable

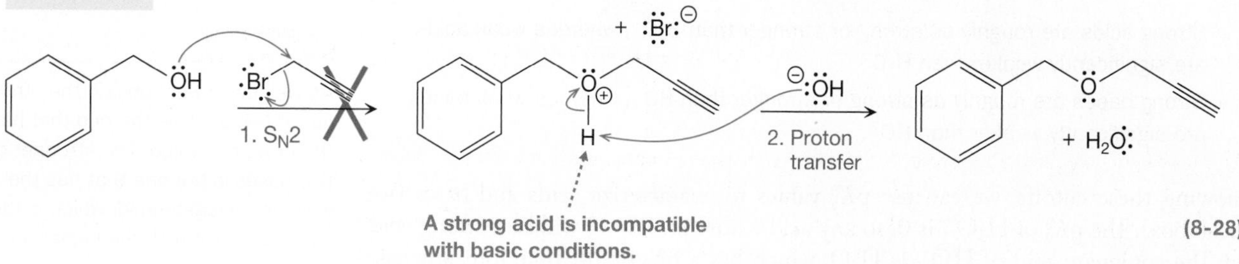

ÖH
Br
1. S$_N$2
+ :Br:⊖
O⊕
H
⊖:ÖH
2. Proton transfer
O
+ H$_2$Ö:
A strong acid is incompatible with basic conditions.

(8-28)

The mechanism proposed in Equation 8-28, however, is unreasonable because the product of the first step has a strongly acidic proton, which is incompatible with the basic conditions of the reaction.

Mechanism Drawing
S_N2 Mechanism under Basic Conditions

A more reasonable mechanism is shown in Equation 8-29, in which HO^- first deprotonates phenylmethanol to produce an alkoxide anion, RO^-. The alkoxide anion then acts as the nucleophile to displace Br^-. In contrast to Equation 8-28, no strongly acidic species appear in this mechanism:

Reasonable S_N2 mechanism involving an alcohol under basic conditions (Eq. 8-27)

Reasonable

No strong acids appear.

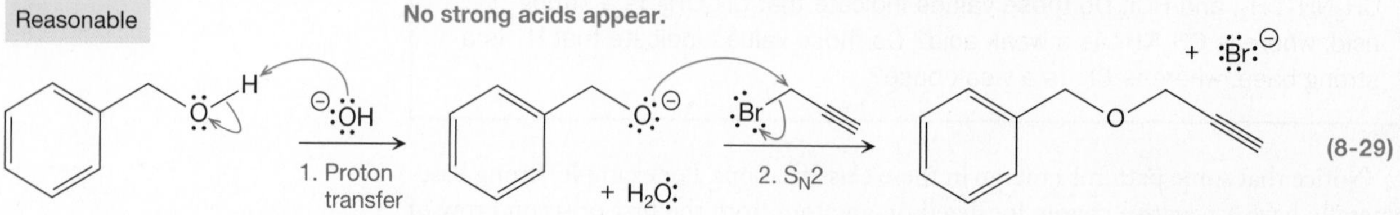

O
H
⊖:ÖH
1. Proton transfer
O:⊖
+ H$_2$Ö:
Br
2. S$_N$2
+ :Br:⊖
O

(8-29)

YOUR TURN 8.21

The reaction shown in the box takes place under *basic* conditions. The following proposed mechanism is unreasonable. **(a)** Label the incompatible species that makes the mechanism unreasonable. **(b)** Draw a reasonable mechanism for this reaction.

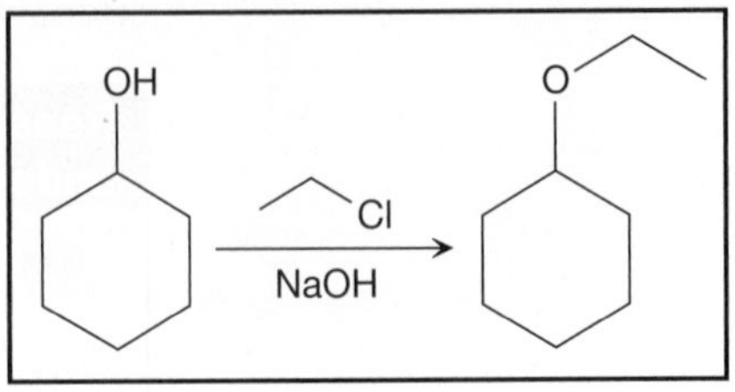

OH
Cl
NaOH
O

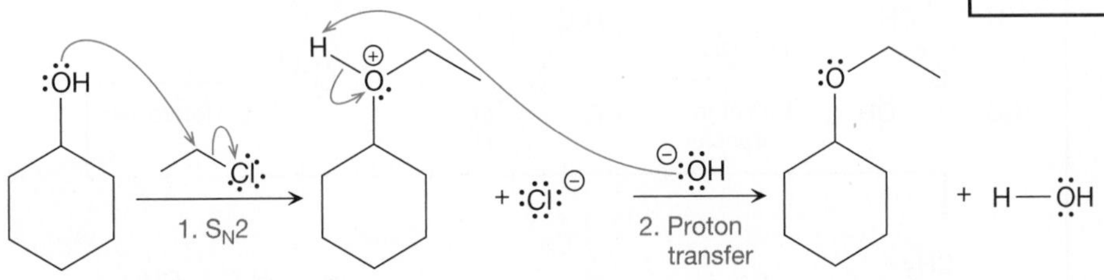

:ÖH
Cl
1. S_N2
H
O
+ :Cl:
:ÖH
2. Proton transfer
:O
+ H—ÖH

The substitution reaction shown in Equation 8-30 takes place under *acidic* conditions:

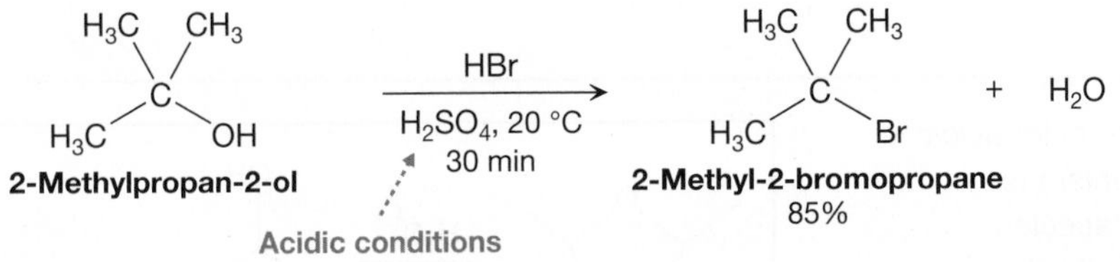

H3C CH3
C
H3C OH
2-Methylpropan-2-ol
HBr
H2SO4, 20 °C
30 min
Acidic conditions
H3C CH3
C
H3C Br
2-Methyl-2-bromopropane
85%
+ H2O

(8-30)

The proposed S_N1 mechanism shown in Equation 8-31 accounts for the formation of the product, but it is *unreasonable*. Notice that the product of the first step is HO^-, which is a strong base and is thus incompatible with the acidic conditions of the reaction. (In Chapter 9, we will also learn that this mechanism is unreasonable because *strong bases are poor leaving groups*.)

Unreasonable S_N1 mechanism involving an alcohol under acidic conditions (Eq. 8-30)

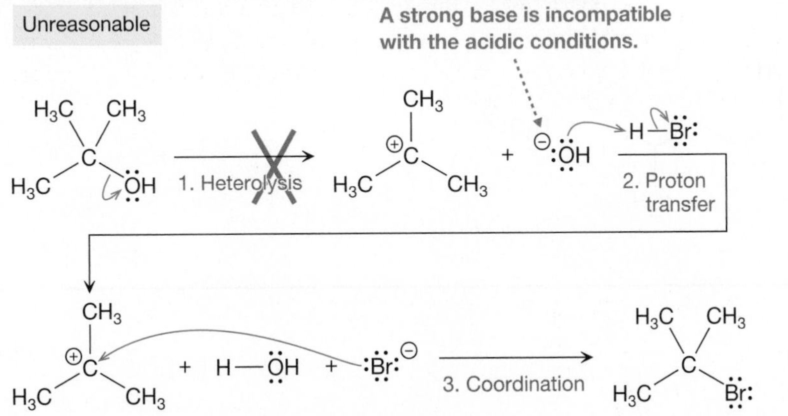

Unreasonable
A strong base is incompatible with the acidic conditions.
H3C CH3
C
H3C ÖH
1. Heterolysis
CH3
C
H3C CH3
+ :ÖH
H—Br:
2. Proton transfer
CH3
C
H3C CH3
+ H—ÖH + :Br:
3. Coordination
H3C CH3
C
H3C Br:

(8-31)

A more reasonable mechanism is shown in Equation 8-32, in which the OH group is protonated first. Then the leaving group departs as H_2O instead of HO^-, and no strongly basic species appear at any stage of the mechanism:

Reasonable S_N1 mechanism involving an alcohol under acidic conditions (Eq. 8-30)

Reasonable

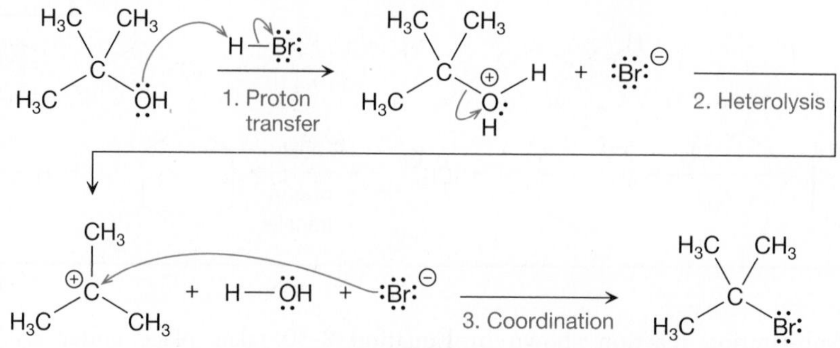

H₃C CH₃
H—Br:
1. Proton transfer
H₃C CH₃
+ :Br:
2. Heterolysis
CH₃
+ H—OH +
3. Coordination
H₃C CH₃
H₃C Br:

(8-32)

Mechanism Drawing
S_N1 Mechanism under Acidic Conditions

YOUR TURN 8.22

The reaction shown in the box takes place under *acidic* conditions. The following proposed mechanism is unreasonable. **(a)** Label the incompatible species that makes the mechanism unreasonable. **(b)** Draw a reasonable mechanism for this reaction.

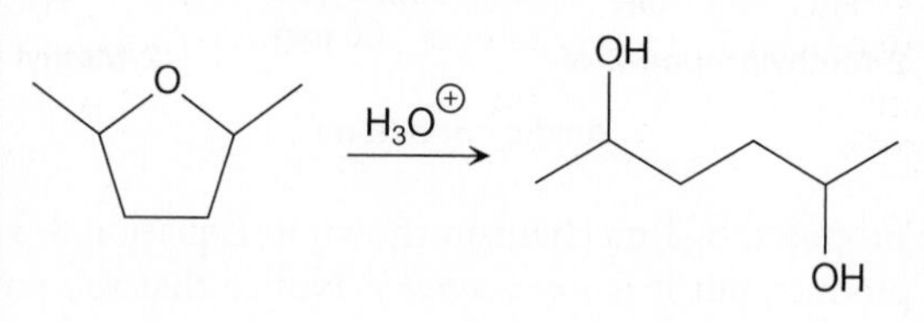

O
H₃O⊕
OH
OH

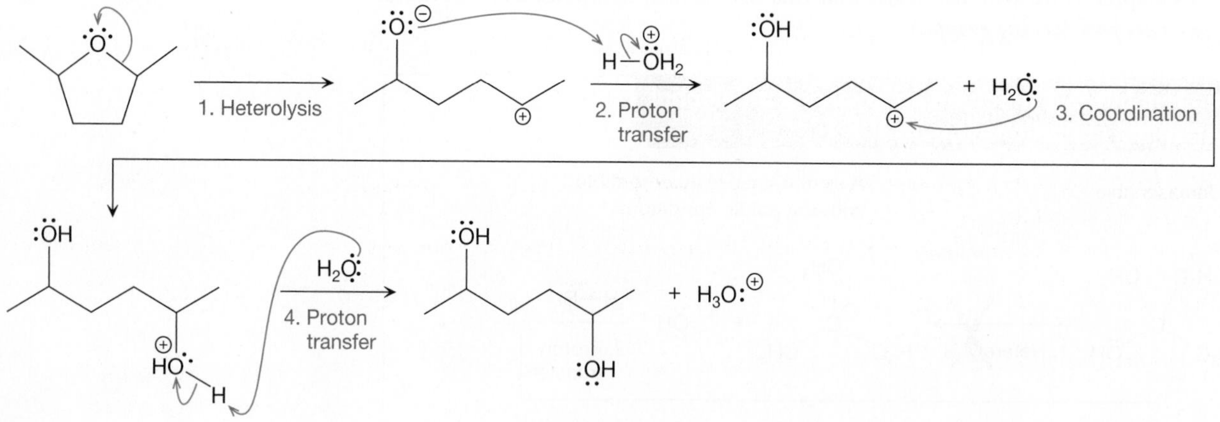

1. Heterolysis
H—OH₂
2. Proton transfer
:OH
+ H₂O:
3. Coordination
:OH
H₂O:
4. Proton transfer
:OH
+ H₃O:
:OH

SOLVED PROBLEM **8.7**

How to include a proton transfer in an elimination mechanism under acidic conditions

Break It Down **Draw a reasonable mechanism for the elimination reaction shown here, assuming it takes place by an E1 mechanism.**

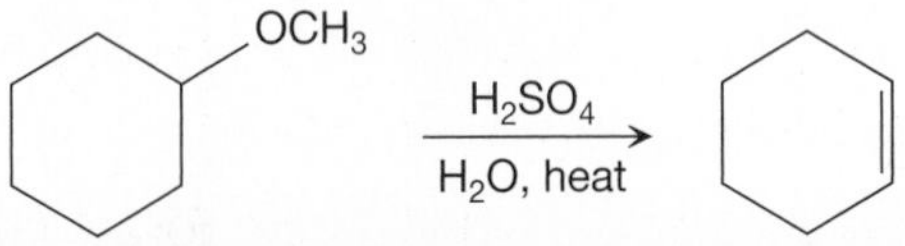

OCH3
H2SO4
H2O, heat

Think	Solve
What are the first and second steps of the regular two-step E1 mechanism?	The regular two-step E1 mechanism includes a heterolysis step, followed by elimination of H^+ to form the double bond.

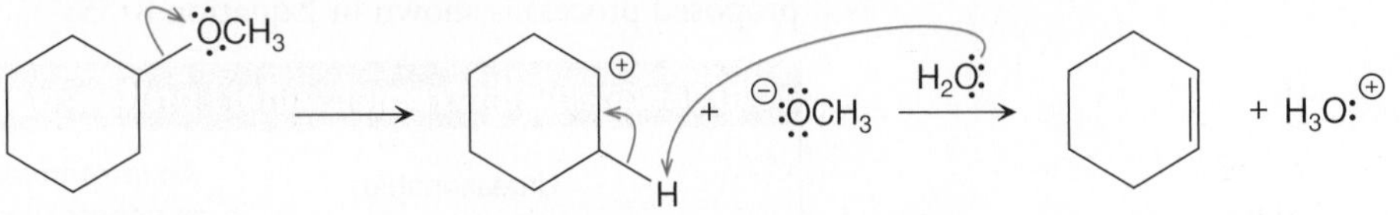

OCH3
H
H2O:
+ H3O:

Think	Solve
Do any incompatible species appear in the two-step E1 mechanism for this reaction?	The regular two-step E1 mechanism above shows the formation of CH_3O^-, which is a strong base. Since the reaction takes place under acidic conditions, CH_3O^- is incompatible and this proposed mechanism is *unreasonable*.
Is it possible to incorporate a proton transfer step in a reasonable way to avoid the formation of incompatible species?	To avoid the formation of CH_3O^-, the strong acid can protonate oxygen prior to the heterolysis step (remember, proton transfer steps are *fast*). Therefore, in the step where the C—O bond is broken, a weakly basic CH_3OH molecule is formed instead:

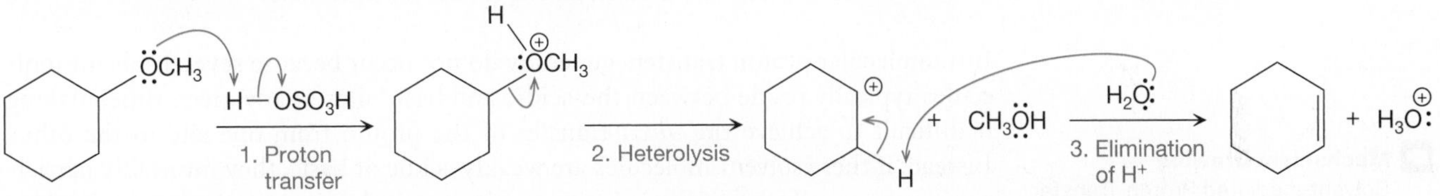

OCH3
H—OSO3H
1. Proton transfer
H
OCH3
2. Heterolysis
H
+ CH3OH
H2O:
3. Elimination of H+
+ H3O:

Try It Draw a reasonable mechanism for the reaction in Solved Problem 8.7, assuming that it proceeds by an E2 rather than an E1 mechanism.

8.6b Intramolecular versus Solvent-Mediated Proton Transfer Reactions

Some mechanisms must account for the removal of a proton at one site within a molecular species and the addition of a proton at another site within the *same* species. Consider, for example, the reaction shown in Equation 8-33, in which ammonia attacks oxirane to produce 2-aminoethanol. (We will discuss this type of ring-opening reaction in greater detail in Chapter 10.)

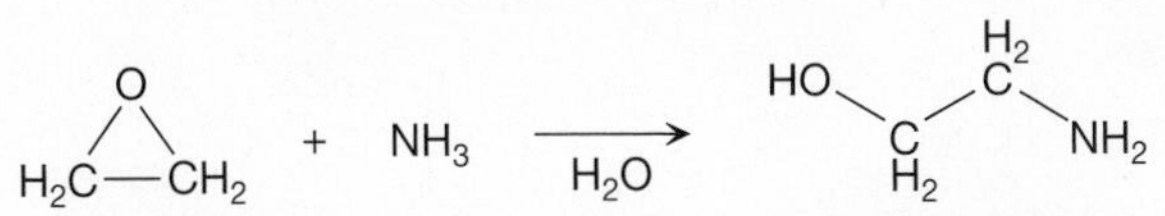

O
H2C—CH2
+ NH3
H2O
HO
H2
C
C
H2
NH2

Oxirane (Ethylene oxide) **2-Aminoethanol** 70% (8-33)

CONNECTIONS 8.2

Cyclohexene: Hang tight! One of the main uses of cyclohexene (the product in Solved Problem 8.7) is as a precursor of adipic acid, a monomer of the polymer nylon-6,6. Nylon-6,6 can be used to make synthetic fibers, such as the ones in this rope.

A reasonable first step is shown in Equation 8-34, in which an S_N2 reaction opens the ring to produce a species with a positively charged ammonium ion ($R—NH_3^+$) and a negatively charged alkoxide anion (RO^-). From there, the N atom must be deprotonated and the negatively charged O atom must be protonated to arrive at the final, uncharged product. But how does this happen?

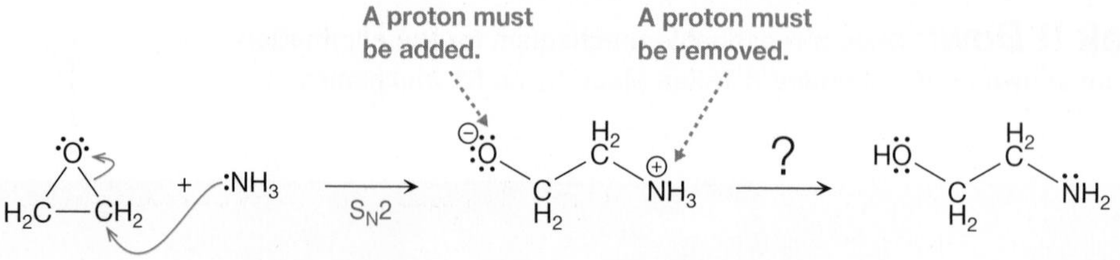

A proton must be added.
A proton must be removed.
S_N2
?

(8-34)

We could imagine that the proton is transferred directly from the N to the O, through an ***intra*molecular proton transfer** step. The curved arrow notation for that proposed process is shown in Equation 8-35:

Unreasonable (intramolecular) proton transfer mechanism (Eq. 8-34)

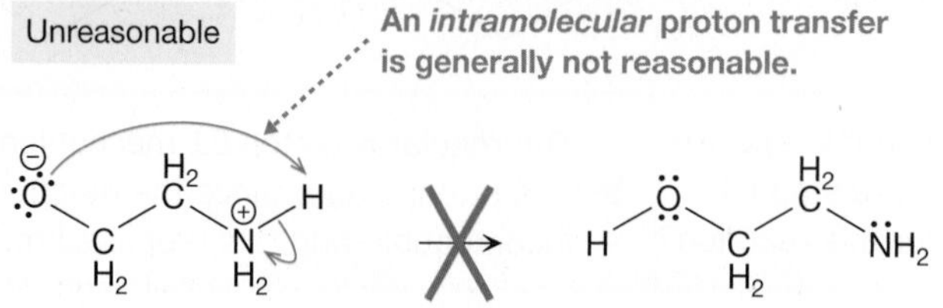

Unreasonable
An *intramolecular* proton transfer is generally not reasonable.

(8-35)

However:

Rule 2: Avoid Intramolecular Proton Transfer Steps

Intramolecular proton transfer steps are usually unreasonable.

Mechanism Drawing
Solvent-mediated Proton Transfer in S_N2

Intramolecular proton transfers generally do not occur because several solvent molecules typically reside between the acidic and basic sites at any given time, making it difficult to achieve the *direct* transfer of the proton from one site to the other. Instead, if these solvent molecules are weakly acidic or basic, they invariably participate in the transfer of a proton from one site to another in a particular species, by a **solvent-mediated proton transfer.** In Equation 8-33, the solvent (water) is both weakly acidic and weakly basic. Therefore, the solvent-mediated proton transfer shown in Equation 8-36 is reasonable:

Reasonable (solvent-mediated) proton transfer mechanism (Eq. 8-34)

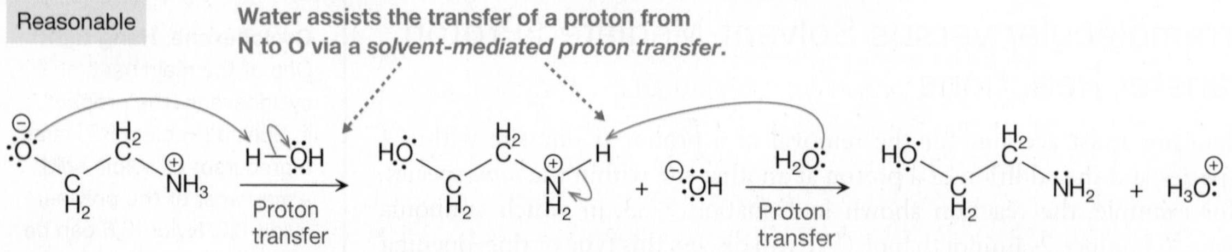

Reasonable
Water assists the transfer of a proton from N to O via a *solvent-mediated proton transfer.*
Proton transfer
Proton transfer

(8-36)

Methanethiol ($HSCH_3$) attacks β-propiolactone to open the ring, as shown in the overall reaction in the box. The following proposed mechanism for this reaction is *unreasonable*. **(a)** Label the step that is unreasonable and explain why. **(b)** Draw a reasonable mechanism for this reaction.

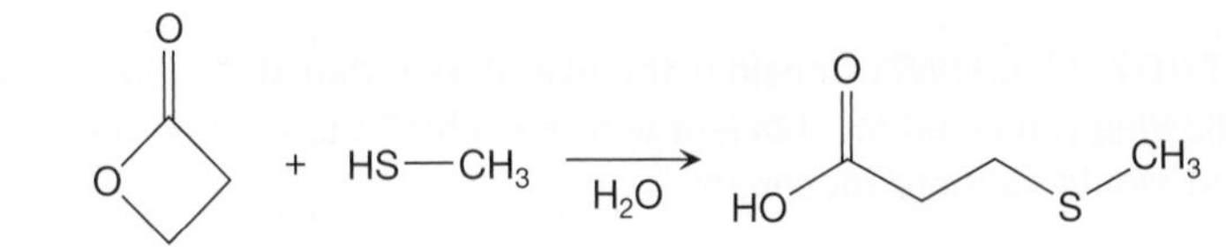
H2O

β-Propiolactone **3-Methylthiopropanoic acid**

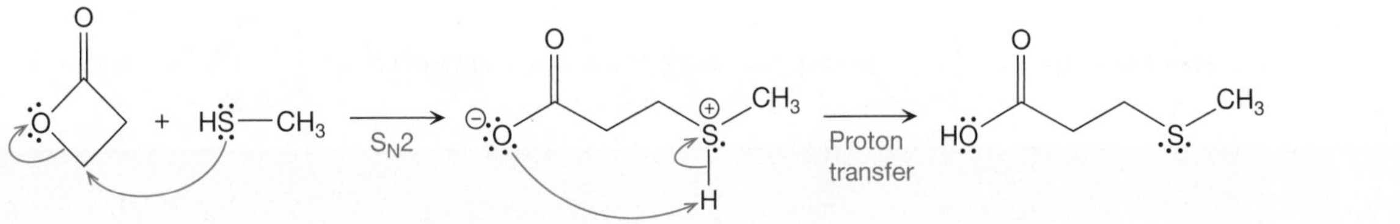
SN2
Proton transfer

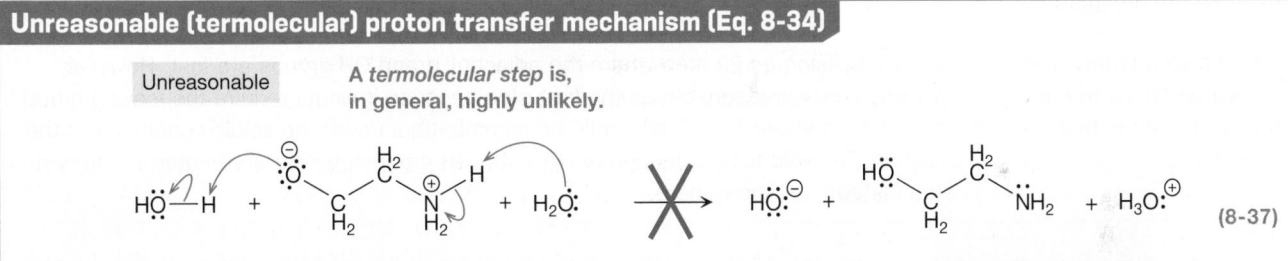

8.6c Molecularity

A third general rule addresses the number of reactant species in a particular elementary step. The proposed mechanism in Equation 8-37, for example, accomplishes the same proton transfers we saw previously in Equation 8-36 but is unreasonable:

Unreasonable (termolecular) proton transfer mechanism (Eq. 8-34)

Unreasonable

A *termolecular step* is, in general, highly unlikely.

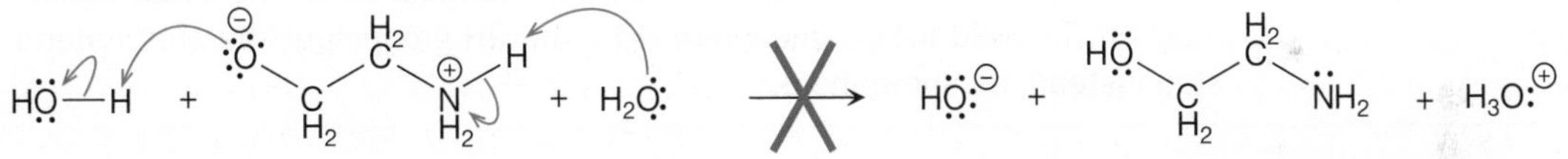 (8-37)

Equation 8-37 is unreasonable because it is a **termolecular** elementary step, which involves three reactant species simultaneously:

Rule 3: Avoid Termolecular Steps

Termolecular steps (and steps of higher molecularity) are generally unreasonable.

Why are termolecular steps generally unreasonable? By definition, an elementary step takes place in a *single event*: that is, the breaking and/or forming of bonds occur simultaneously. Therefore, a termolecular step would require the collision of all three reactant species at precisely the same moment, the probability of which is vanishingly small. By contrast, bimolecular and unimolecular steps are reasonable because a bimolecular step requires the collision of just two species, and a unimolecular step is a spontaneous transformation that does not require a collision with another reactant species at all.

CONNECTIONS 8.3

β-Propiolactone (BPL) and the fight against viruses

β-Propiolactone (Your Turn 8.23) has been used as a sterilizing agent for blood plasma, tissue grafts, and antiviral vaccines. BPL has been found to inactivate viruses by inhibiting membrane fusion, a key process in viral attachment to animal cells.

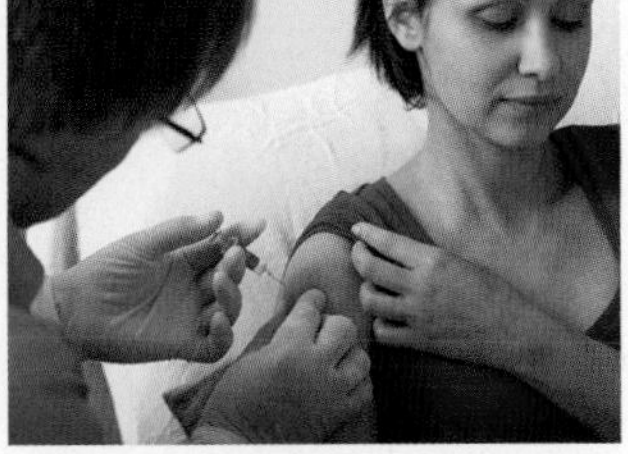

SOLVED PROBLEM **8.8**

How to draw a reasonable mechanism by avoiding termolecular steps

Break It Down **Consider the overall reaction shown in the box. Why is the following proposed mechanism unreasonable? Suggest an alternate mechanism that would be more reasonable.**

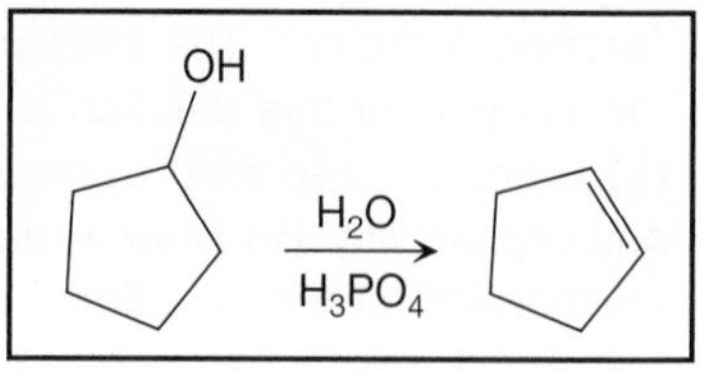

OH
H2O
H3PO4

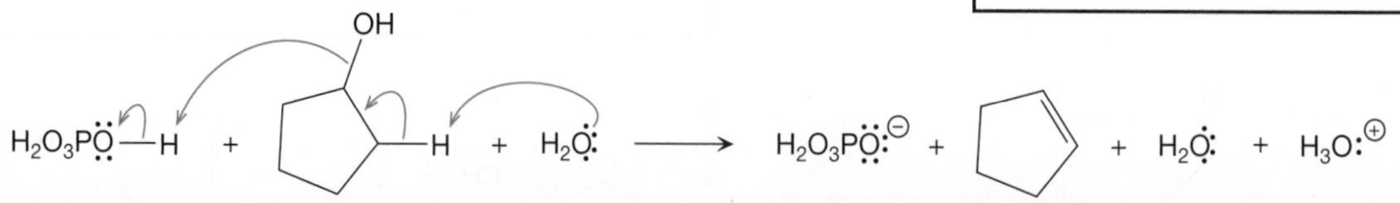

Think	Solve
Are there any incompatible acids or bases? Is there an intramolecular proton transfer? Is there a termolecular step?	The reaction takes place under acidic conditions. All the species that appear are either strongly acidic or neutral, so they are compatible with the reaction conditions. The elementary step shown is not a proton transfer, so we are not concerned about it being an intramolecular proton transfer. The step shown is termolecular, however, because it involves the alcohol, H_2O, and H_3PO_4, which makes the step unreasonable.
What major changes does the reactant undergo to become the product?	An H and an OH are lost from adjacent C atoms in the alcohol reactant, and a new π bond joins those two C atoms. The alcohol therefore undergoes an elimination reaction.
Can the elementary step shown be split into multiple other steps that are reasonable?	We can envision an E2 step where the adjacent H and OH groups are lost. However, this would be unreasonable as the first step because it would require the leaving group to be HO^-, a strong base that would be incompatible under the acidic conditions of the reaction. To avoid the production of HO^-, the OH group could be protonated in the first step instead, as shown here.

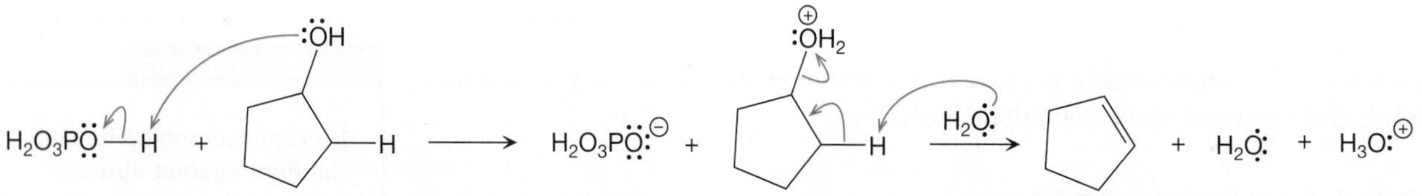

Try It Suggest why the following S_N2 step is unreasonable and provide an alternate mechanism that is reasonable.

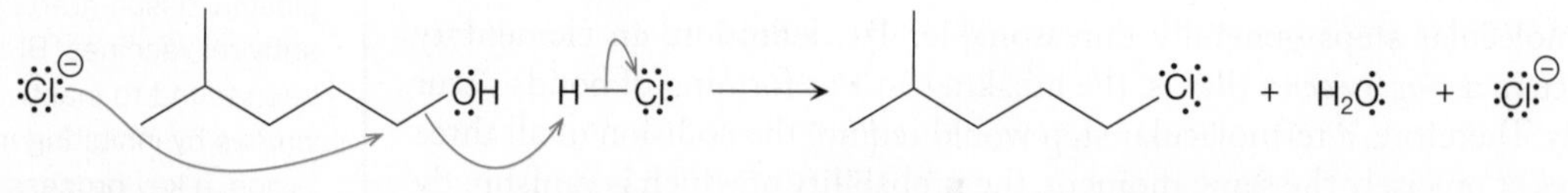

8.6d Carbocation Rearrangements

Carbocations, because of their net positive charge and lack of an octet, are inherently quite unstable. Once formed, they tend to react quickly to become more stable. As we have seen, they can undergo coordination with a nucleophile to form S_N1 products (Section 8.1), and they can lose H^+ to form E1 products (Section 8.2).

Furthermore, as we learned in Section 7.7, they can undergo *carbocation rearrangements*, in which both the reactant and the product carbocations are isomers of each other.

S_N1 reactions provide clear evidence of these carbocation rearrangements. Consider the S_N1 reaction shown in Equation 8-38, between 2-iodo-3-methylbutane and water. It *appears* that substitution occurs at a C atom that is not initially attached to the leaving group!

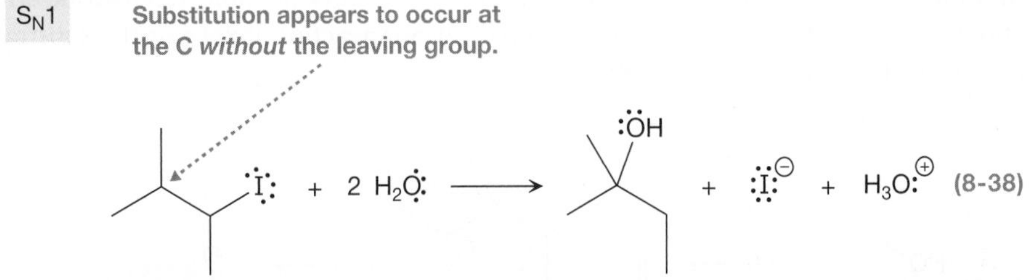

SN1
Substitution appears to occur at the C *without* the leaving group.
+ 2 H2O:
+ :I:⊖
+ H3O:⊕
:OH
(8-38)

2-Iodo-3-methylbutane **2-Methylbutan-2-ol**

The mechanism in Equation 8-39 shows that a carbocation rearrangement takes place. In Step 1, the leaving group leaves as in the usual S_N1 reaction, yielding I^- and a secondary carbocation intermediate. In Step 2, a 1,2-hydride shift converts the secondary carbocation into the tertiary carbocation. In Step 3, the normal second step of an S_N1 reaction (coordination) takes place between H_2O and the carbocation. A final proton transfer in Step 4 yields the uncharged alcohol product:

CONNECTIONS 8.4

2-Methyl-2-butanol: Sweet dreams! 2-Methylbutan-2-ol (also called *tert*-amyl alcohol; Eq. 8-38) is a by-product of grain fermentation and has physiological effects similar to ethanol. It was once used as an anesthetic under the name amylene hydrate but has been replaced by safer drugs.

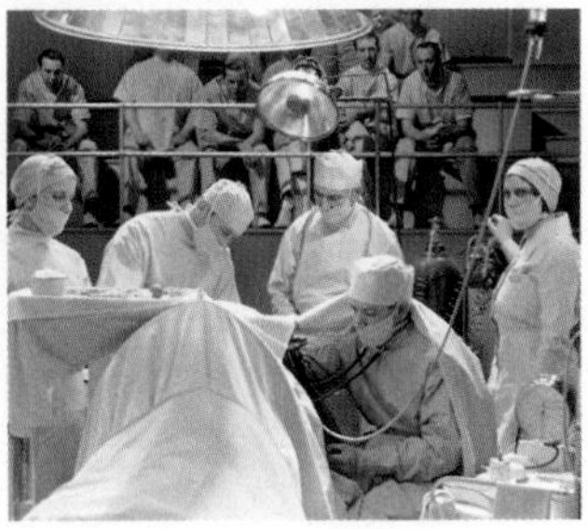

Mechanism for an S_N1 reaction with a carbocation rearrangement (Eq. 8-38)

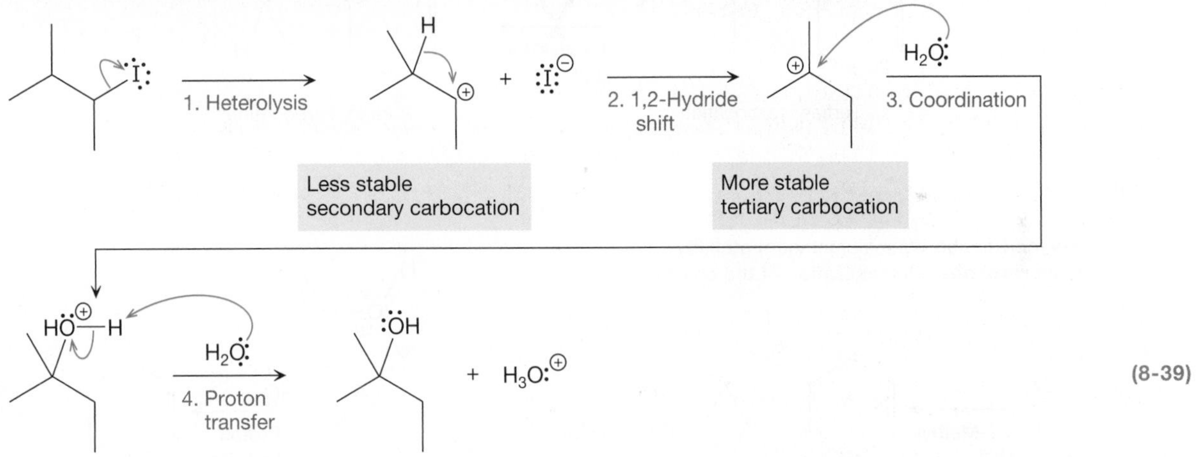

1. Heterolysis
2. 1,2-Hydride shift
3. Coordination
Less stable secondary carbocation
More stable tertiary carbocation
H2O:
4. Proton transfer
+ H3O:⊕
(8-39)

Why should this carbocation rearrangement take place? As we learned in Section 7.9, a tertiary carbocation is more stable than a secondary carbocation because the additional alkyl group stabilizes the positive charge (see Recall box). Moreover, H is very light and moves easily. Therefore, the 1,2-hydride shift in Equation 8-39 is very fast and beats out the coordination step that would otherwise take place.

Methyl (CH_3) groups, although heavier than H, are still rather light and can move easily. Consequently, 1,2-methyl shifts that are energetically favorable also tend to be very fast and typically beat out other elementary steps. This brings us to a very useful rule for reasonable mechanisms:

Rule 4: Favorable 1,2-Hydride and 1,2-Methyl Shifts Will Usually Win

If an energetically favorable 1,2-hydride shift or 1,2-methyl shift competes with another possible elementary step, the carbocation rearrangement is usually faster.

Mechanism Drawing
S_N1 Mechanism with a Carbocation Rearrangement

◂ RECALL

Section 7.9 showed that a carbocation becomes more stable with an increasing number of alkyl groups attached directly to C^+. Alkyl groups are electron-donating due to inductive effects (Section 6.8e) and hyperconjugation (Section 7.9a), so each attached alkyl group reduces the concentration of charge on C^+.

Other alkyl groups, such as ethyl and propyl groups, tend not to shift in carbocation rearrangements because the alkyl groups are too massive. Therefore, alkyl shifts other than 1,2-methyl shifts are usually too slow to beat out other competing elementary steps. (One exception involves the relief of ring strain; see Problems 8.46 and 8.47 at the end of the chapter.)

Because energetically favorable 1,2-hydride and 1,2-methyl shifts tend to be so fast, it is important that you pay attention whenever you see a carbocation produced in a mechanism. In such cases, you should consider every possible 1,2-hydride shift and 1,2-methyl shift. Consider, for example, an S_N1 reaction involving the substrate and nucleophile in Equation 8-40:

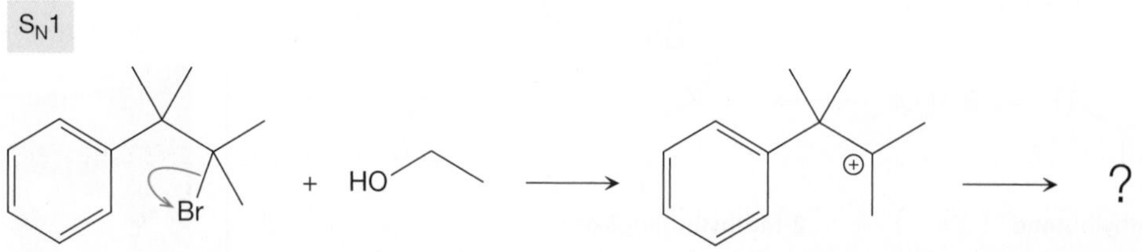

S_N1
Br
+ HO
?

(8-40)

Once the carbocation is produced, there are two possible carbocation rearrangements to consider. Equation 8-41 shows a 1,2-hydride shift, and Equation 8-42 shows a 1,2-methyl shift:

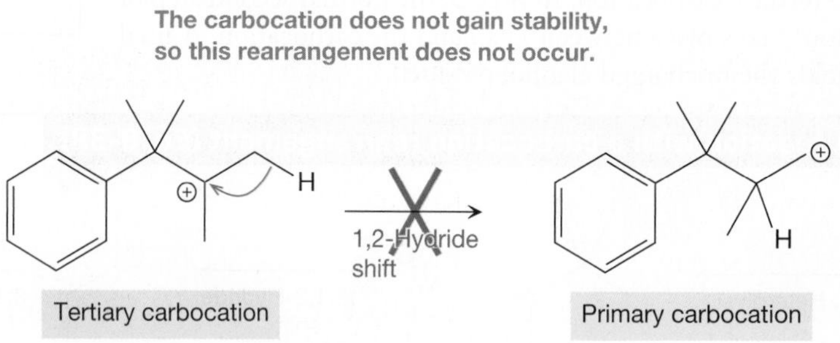

The carbocation does not gain stability, so this rearrangement does not occur.
H
1,2-Hydride shift
H
Tertiary carbocation
Primary carbocation

(8-41)

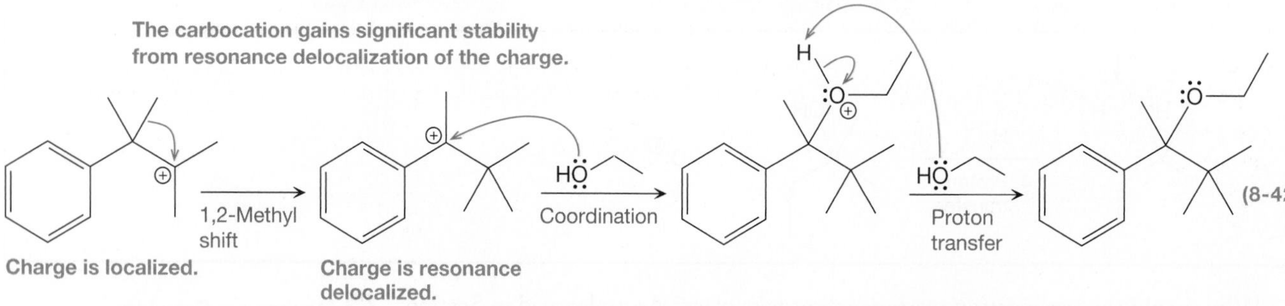

The carbocation gains significant stability from resonance delocalization of the charge.
1,2-Methyl shift
Charge is localized.
Charge is resonance delocalized.
HO
Coordination
H
HO
Proton transfer

(8-42)

As indicated, the 1,2-hydride shift does not take place because a more stable tertiary carbocation would be converted to a less stable primary one. On the other hand, the 1,2-methyl shift is expected to take place rapidly because it produces a carbocation that has gained significant stability from resonance delocalization of the charge. From there, a coordination step and a proton transfer step complete the S_N1 mechanism.

Three different carbocations are shown in Equations 8-41 and 8-42 (the initial carbocation is the same in both equations). **(a)** Draw all resonance structures of each carbocation. **(b)** Rank the three carbocations from most stable to least stable.

YOUR TURN **8.24**

E1 reactions are also susceptible to carbocation rearrangements, as illustrated in Solved Problem 8.9. Later in this book, we will discuss other reactions in which carbocation intermediates appear in the mechanism. Keep in mind the possibility of carbocation rearrangements in those reactions as well.

SOLVED PROBLEM **8.9**

How to predict carbocation rearrangements in E1 reactions

Break It Down Predict the products of the reaction shown here, which takes place via an E1 mechanism.

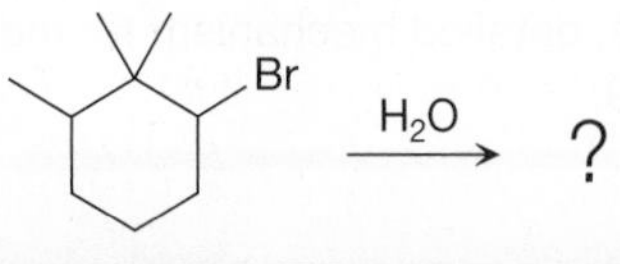

Br
H_2O
?

Think

What is the first step of an E1 mechanism?

Solve

In the first step of an E1 mechanism, the leaving group departs to produce a carbocation intermediate, as shown here.

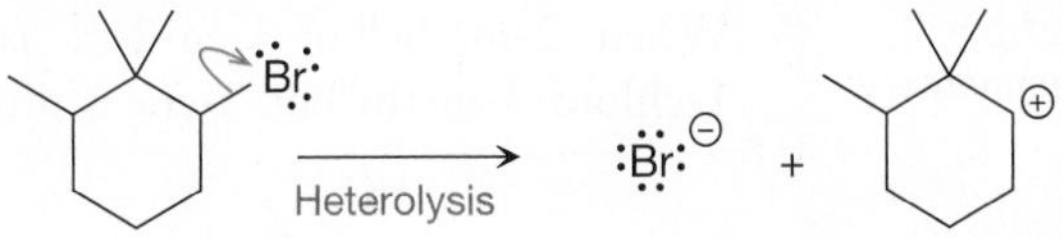

Br
Heterolysis
Br
+

Think

If a carbocation is produced, what are the possible 1,2-hydride and 1,2-methyl shifts? Does one of these allow the carbocation to become significantly more stable?

Solve

A secondary carbocation intermediate is generated in the first step. As shown here, a 1,2-hydride shift and a 1,2-methyl shift are both available. The hydride shift produces a secondary carbocation, which is similar in stability to the initial carbocation. The methyl shift, on the other hand, produces a tertiary carbocation that is significantly more stable.

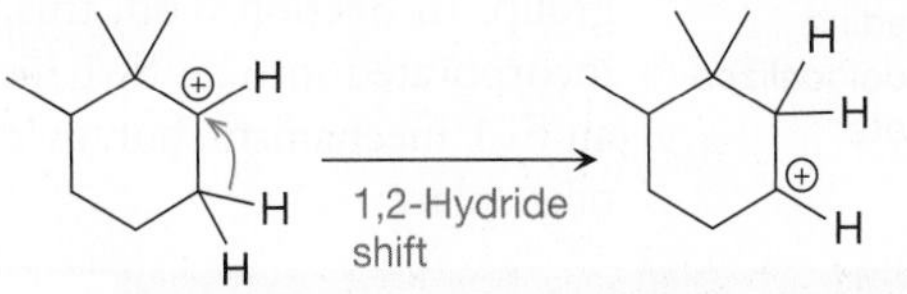

H
H
H
1,2-Hydride
shift
H
H
H

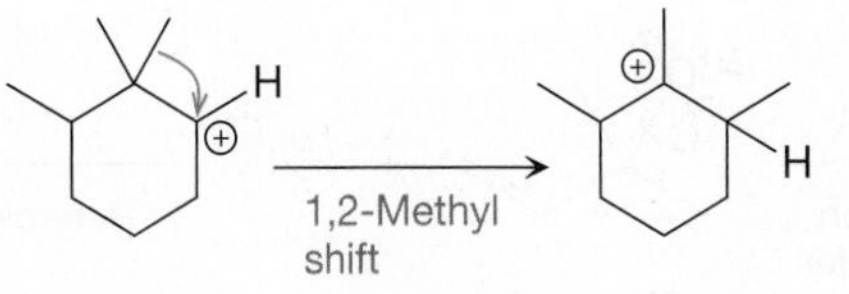

H
1,2-Methyl
shift
H

(continued)

Should the E1 mechanism include a carbocation rearrangement? If so, how should it be incorporated?	The 1,2-methyl shift produces a more stable carbocation, so it should be incorporated into the E1 mechanism before the normal next step, which is elimination of H^+ to produce the alkene. The complete mechanism is shown here.

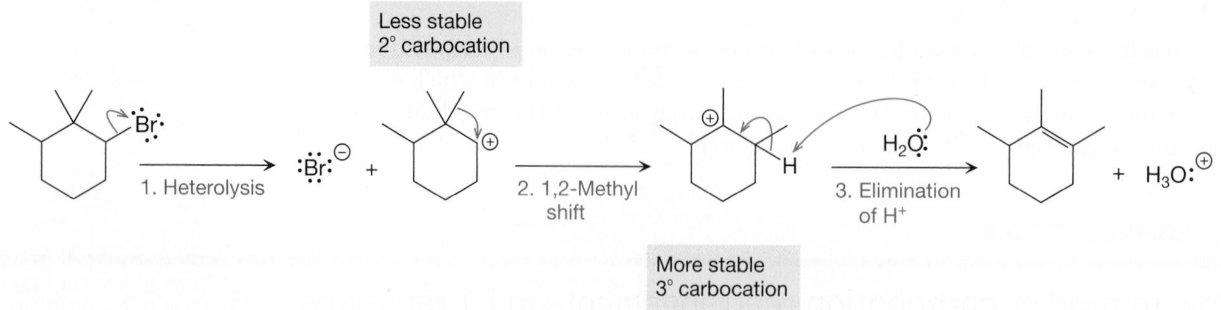

Less stable
2° carbocation
Br
1. Heterolysis
Br
2. 1,2-Methyl
shift
H
H_2O
3. Elimination
of H^+
+ H_3O
More stable
3° carbocation

Try It Draw the complete, detailed mechanism for the S_N1 reaction (rather than the E1 reaction) between the reactants in Solved Problem 8.9.

SECTION 8.7 OBJECTIVES

You will be able to:

1. Distinguish curved arrows used for resonance structures from curved arrows used for elementary steps.
2. Use curved arrows to incorporate resonance structures into mechanisms.

Mechanism Drawing
S_N1 Mechanism Proceeding through a Resonance-delocalized Carbocation Intermediate

8.7 Resonance-Delocalized Intermediates in Mechanisms

When 2-methylbut-3-en-2-ol is treated with concentrated hydrochloric acid, 1-chloro-3-methylbut-2-ene is produced, as shown in Equation 8-43:

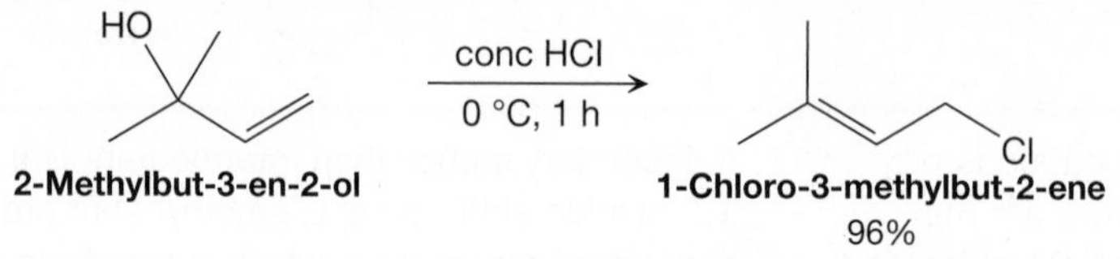

HO
conc HCl
0 °C, 1 h
Cl
2-Methylbut-3-en-2-ol
1-Chloro-3-methylbut-2-ene
96%

(8-43)

This is a substitution reaction, and as we saw with the examples in Section 8.6d, substitution appears to take place at a carbon atom that initially does *not* have the leaving group. In Section 8.6d, this puzzle was explained by a carbocation rearrangement incorporated into an S_N1 mechanism. The reaction in Equation 8-43 does undergo an S_N1 mechanism, but, as shown in Equation 8-44, no carbocation rearrangement takes place:

Mechanism for an S_N1 reaction whose carbocation intermediate has resonance structures (Eq. 8-43)

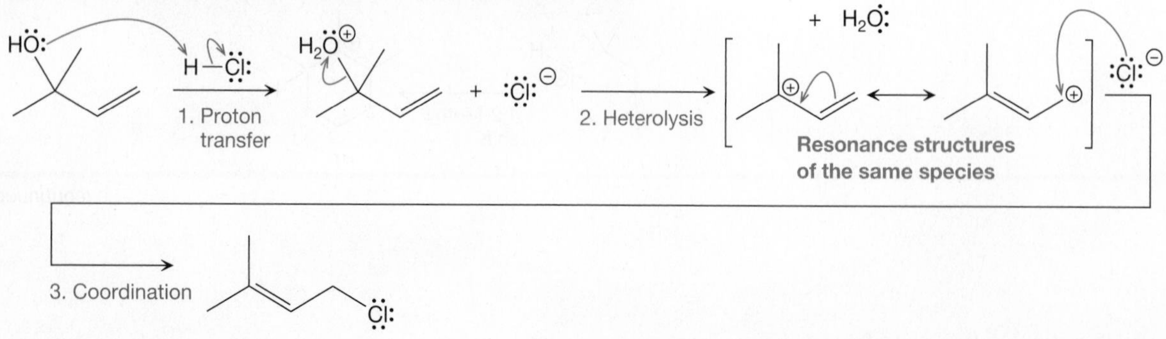

HO
H—Cl
1. Proton
transfer
H_2O
+ Cl
2. Heterolysis
+ H_2O
Cl
Resonance structures
of the same species
3. Coordination
Cl

(8-44)

Instead, the carbocation produced in Step 2 has two resonance structures, showing that the positive charge is shared over two carbon atoms: the carbon to which the leaving group was attached and the terminal carbon. To produce the particular alkyl chloride shown in Equation 8-43, Cl^- must attack the terminal carbon, as indicated by the curved arrow notation in Step 3.

When resonance structures are incorporated into a mechanism like this, keep in mind two important points. First:

The conversion of one resonance structure to another is *NOT* an elementary step.

An individual resonance structure is hypothetical and the one, true species is most accurately represented by the resonance hybrid. Therefore, resonance structures are just different depictions of the *same* species. This leads to the second point:

When an intermediate has two or more resonance structures, *any* resonance structure can be shown to participate as a reactant in the next step of the mechanism.

In Equation 8-44, the second resonance structure was used, but the first resonance structure could have been used instead, as shown in Equation 8-45:

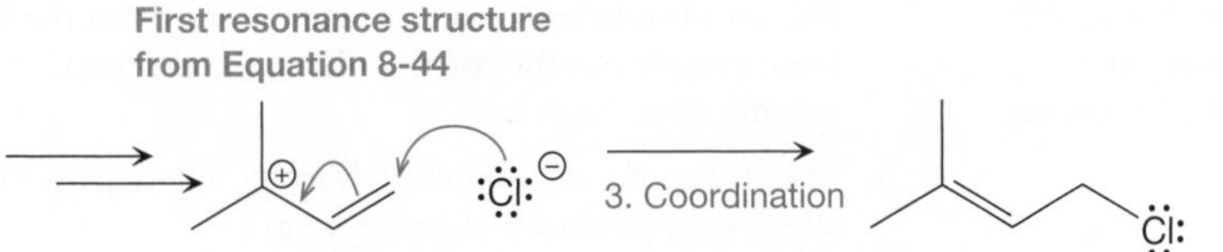

First resonance structure
from Equation 8-44
3. Coordination

(8-45)

Notice, however, that the choice of resonance structure will impact the curved arrow notation for the subsequent elementary step. In Equation 8-44, a single curved arrow was used to depict the final coordination step. In Equation 8-45, two curved arrows must be used.

CONNECTIONS 8.5

2-Methylbut-3-en-2-ol: A problem and solution for deforestation 2-Methylbut-3-en-2-ol (Eq. 8-43) is a pheromone for the bark beetle, a species that has been responsible for destroying millions of acres of forest in the western United States since 2005. One method to manage bark beetle outbreaks is to use traps containing this pheromone.

YOUR TURN 8.25

Draw the complete, detailed mechanism for the following E1 reaction.

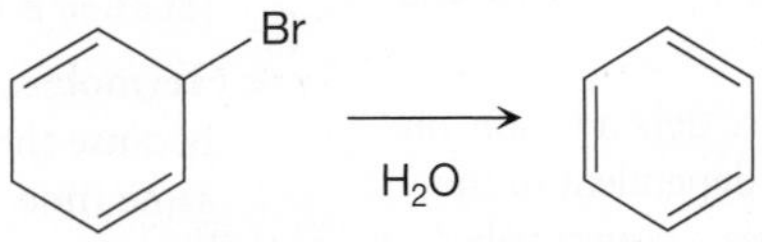

Chapter Summary and Key Terms

- A **unimolecular nucleophilic substitution (S_N1) reaction** consists of two steps. First, the leaving group leaves in a *heterolysis* step, yielding a carbocation **intermediate**, and then a nucleophile attacks the carbocation in a *coordination* step. (Section 8.1)
- An **overall reaction** is obtained by summing all of the steps in a mechanism. Intermediates do not appear in the overall reaction, just **overall reactants** and **overall products**. (Section 8.1a)
- The reaction free energy diagram of an S_N1 reaction (Fig. 8-2, p. 396) contains two transition states, one for each step. Between the transition states is the **intermediate**, which occurs at a **local minimum** in energy. (Section 8.1a)
- The **unimolecular elimination (E1) reaction** also consists of two steps. First the leaving group leaves, generating a carbocation intermediate, and then H^+ is eliminated with the aid of a base to yield a double bond. (Section 8.2)
- The free energy diagram of an E1 reaction (Fig. 8-3, p. 399), like that of an S_N1 reaction, shows two transition states flanking the local minimum in energy, which represents the carbocation intermediate. (Section 8.2)
- Most of what we know about mechanisms comes from reaction kinetics. An **empirical rate law** illustrates how a reaction rate depends on the concentrations of the reactants. A *proposed mechanism* yields a **theoretical rate law**. Agreement between the theoretical rate law and the empirical rate law lends support to a mechanism. (Section 8.3)
- For S_N2 and E2 reactions, the reaction rate is directly proportional to the concentration of both the nucleophile/base and the substrate. (Section 8.3)
- For S_N1 and E1 reactions, the reaction rate depends only on the concentration of the substrate; it is independent of the concentration of the nucleophile or the base, respectively. (Section 8.3)
- The first step of an S_N1 or E1 reaction (that is, the departure of the leaving group) is the **rate-determining step** of the mechanism. This step is rate-determining because its transition state energy is so high, which makes the step slow. As a result, the rate of the entire reaction is essentially the rate of the first step. (Section 8.3)
- **Transition state theory** relates an elementary step's free energy of activation to the value of its rate constant. (Section 8.4)
- A theoretical rate law can be written for any proposed elementary step of a mechanism, and depends only on the step's reactant species. (Section 8.4)
- In an S_N2 reaction, the nucleophile attacks the substrate only from the side opposite the leaving group, in a so-called **backside attack**. The substituents that remain on the atom being attacked undergo **Walden inversion**, and if the atom is a chiral center, a single stereoisomer is produced, making the S_N2 reaction **stereospecific**. (Section 8.5a)
- If an S_N1 reaction takes place at a chiral center, the products contain a mixture of both stereochemical configurations. (Section 8.5b)
- An E2 reaction is favored by the **anticoplanar** conformation of the substrate, in which the H atom and the leaving group that are eliminated are anti to each other about the C—C bond involved in the reaction. Thus, the E2 reaction is stereospecific. (Section 8.5c)
- Because an E1 reaction takes place in two steps, both *E* and *Z* alkenes are produced. (Section 8.5d)
- Under acidic conditions, strong bases should not appear in a mechanism, and under basic conditions, strong acids should not appear. (Section 8.6a)
- **Intramolecular proton transfer** steps are generally *unreasonable*. Instead, a proton is usually transferred from one part of a molecule to another by a **solvent-mediated proton transfer**. (Section 8.6b)
- **Termolecular** elementary steps are generally *unreasonable* because they require three species to collide at precisely the same time. (Section 8.6c)
- *Carbocation rearrangements* are fast. If a 1,2-hydride shift or a 1,2-methyl shift is energetically favorable, it will generally occur before any other step. (Section 8.6d)
- When an intermediate has resonance structures, any of the resonance structures can be used in the curved arrow notation for the subsequent step. The conversion of one resonance structure to another does not constitute an elementary step. (Section 8.7)

Problems

Problems that are related to synthesis are denoted (SYN).

Sections 8.1 and 8.2 S_N1 and E1 Mechanisms and Free Energy Diagrams

8.1 Draw the complete, detailed S_N1 mechanism for each of the following reactions.

(a)

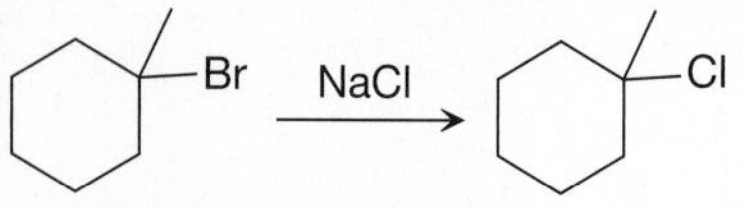

Br
NaCl
Cl

(b)

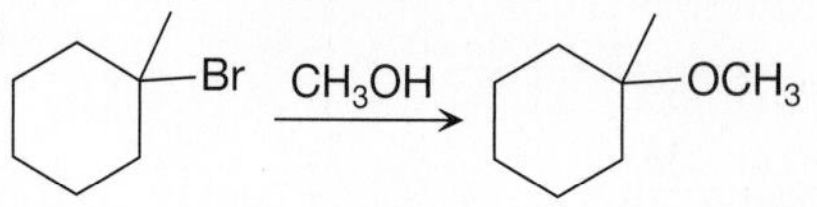

Br
CH_3OH
OCH_3

8.2 Draw the free energy diagram for each of the reactions in Problem 8.1. For each diagram, include and label the overall reactants, overall products, all intermediates, and all transition states.

8.3 Draw the complete, detailed E1 mechanism for each of the following reactions.

(a)

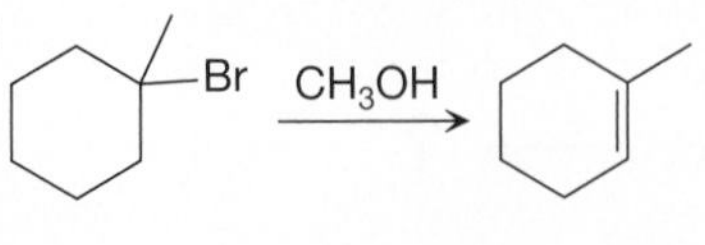

(b)

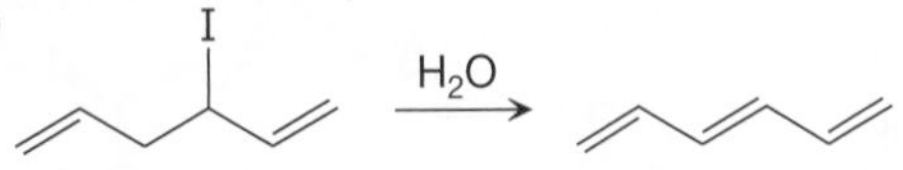

8.4 Draw the free energy diagram for each of the reactions in Problem 8.3. For each diagram, include and label the overall reactants, overall products, all intermediates, and all transition states.

8.5 **(SYN)** For each of these compounds, draw an alkyl halide that can be used to produce it in an S_N1 reaction. Then, determine whether the alkyl halide would need to be treated with water or methanol and draw the corresponding mechanism.

(a)

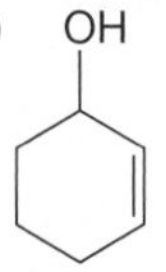

(b)

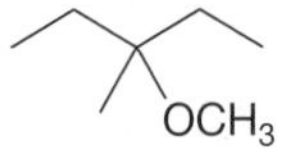

8.6 **(SYN)** For each of these compounds, draw an alkyl halide that can be used to produce it in an E1 reaction. Then, draw the E1 mechanism that would take place when the alkyl halide is treated with water.

(a)

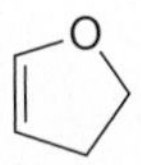

(b)

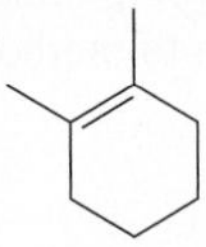

8.7 Draw all possible E1 mechanisms and products involving this alkyl halide and water.

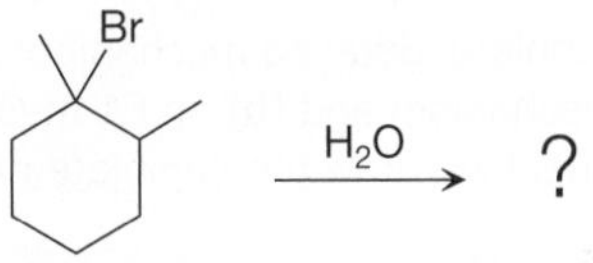

Section 8.3 The Kinetics of S_N2, S_N1, E2, and E1 Reactions

8.8 When benzyl bromide is treated separately with KI and CH_3OH, the substitution products are different but the reaction rates are about the same.

(a) What does this suggest about the mechanism: is it S_N1 or S_N2? Explain.

(b) Draw the complete mechanism (including curved arrows) for the formation of each product.

(c) If the concentration of KI were doubled, what would happen to the rate of the substitution reaction?

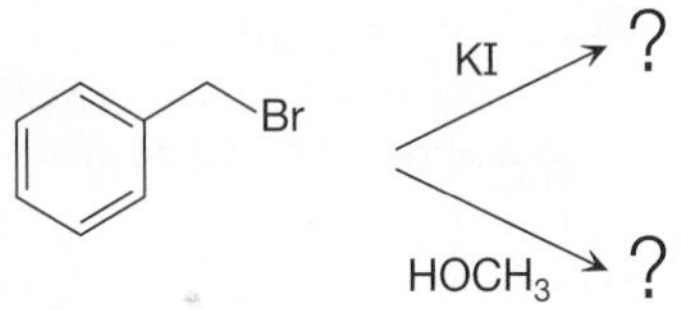

8.9 The initial rates for the following elimination reaction were measured at different concentrations of the substrate and base (water); the data are tabulated in the accompanying table. Do the data suggest an E1 reaction or an E2 reaction?

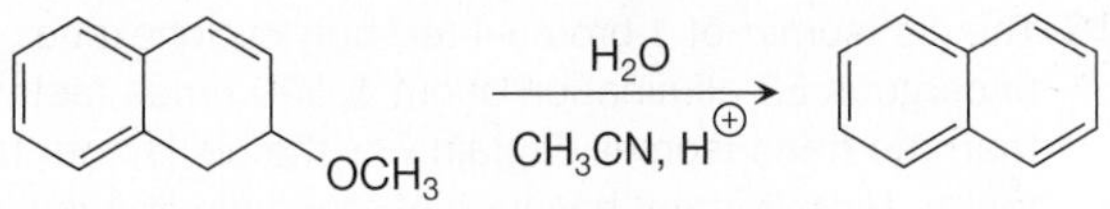

Trial Number	[R—OCH$_3$]	[H$_2$O]	Rate (M/s)
1	0.010 M	0.45 M	9.50×10^{-4}
2	0.020 M	0.45 M	1.85×10^{-3}
3	0.020 M	0.22 M	1.85×10^{-3}

8.10 Write the rate law for the reaction in Problem 8.9.

8.11 The initial rates for the following elimination reaction were measured at different concentrations of the substrate and base; the data are tabulated in the accompanying table. Do the data suggest an E1 reaction or an E2 reaction?

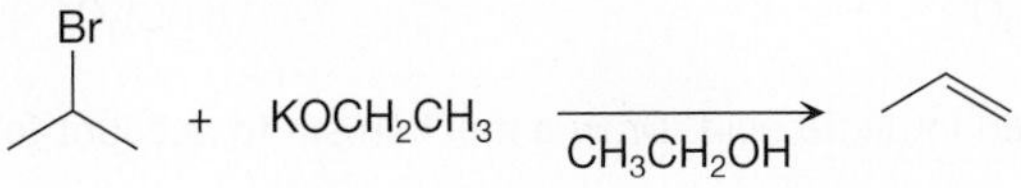

Trial Number	[R—Br]	[KOCH$_2$CH$_3$]	Rate (M/s)
1	1.0 M	1.0 M	2.35×10^{-6}
2	0.50 M	0.50 M	5.9×10^{-7}
3	0.50 M	1.0 M	1.20×10^{-6}

8.12 Write the rate law for the reaction in Problem 8.11.

Section 8.5 Stereochemistry of Nucleophilic Substitution and Elimination Reactions

8.13 Draw the complete, detailed mechanism (including curved arrows) for each of the following reactions occurring by **(a)** an S_N2 mechanism and **(b)** an S_N1 mechanism. Pay attention to stereochemistry.

(1) 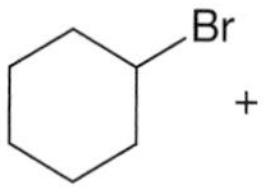
Br
+ NaOH ⟶ ?

(2) 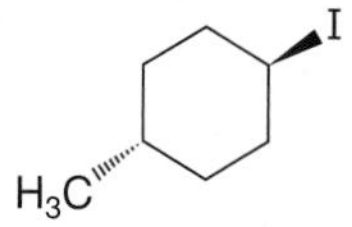
I
H3C
+ NaOH ⟶ ?

(3) 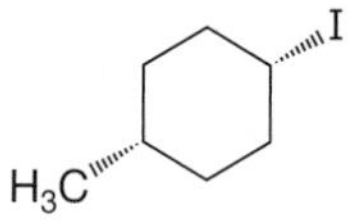
I
H3C
+ NaOH ⟶ ?

(4) 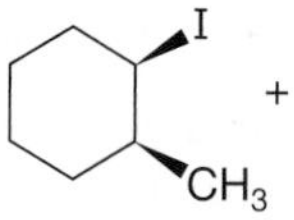
I
CH3
+ KBr ⟶ ?

(5) 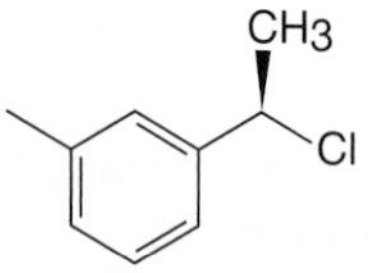
CH3
Cl
+ $NaOCH_3$ ⟶ ?

8.14 Draw the complete, detailed mechanism (including curved arrows) for each of the following reactions occurring by **(a)** an E2 mechanism and **(b)** an E1 mechanism. If more than one possible product can be produced from the same type of mechanism, draw the complete mechanism that leads to each one. Pay attention to stereochemistry.

(1) 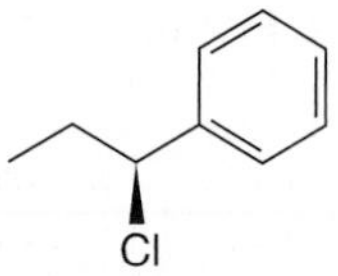
Cl
+ NaOH ⟶ ?

(2) 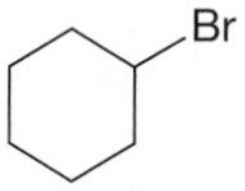
Br
+ NaOH ⟶ ?

(3) 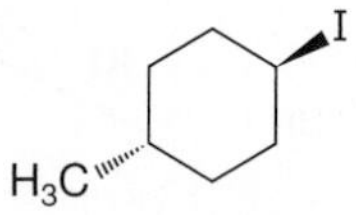
I
H3C
+ $KOC(CH_3)_3$ ⟶ ?

(4) 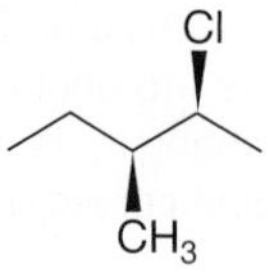
Cl
CH3
+ $NaOCH_3$ ⟶ ?

(5) 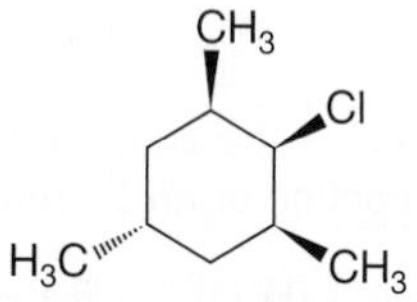
CH3
Cl
H3C
CH3
+ KOH ⟶ ?

(6) 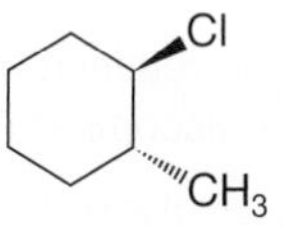
Cl
CH3
+ KOH ⟶ ?

8.15 Which compound, **A** or **B**, would you expect to undergo E2 elimination more readily? Why? *Hint*: Can the H and leaving group attain an anticoplanar conformation in each structure?

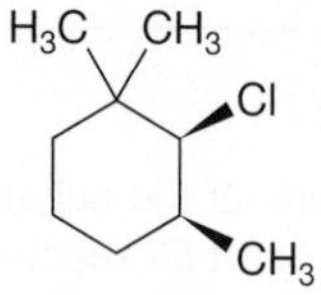
H3C CH3
Cl
CH3
A

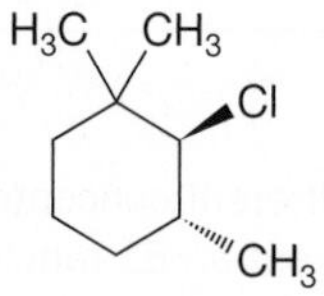
H3C CH3
Cl
CH3
B

8.16 The cis isomer of 1-bromo-4-*tert*-butylcyclohexane undergoes E2 elimination about 1,000 times faster than the trans isomer. Explain why the cis isomer reacts faster. *Hint*: It is *not* because of steric hindrance.

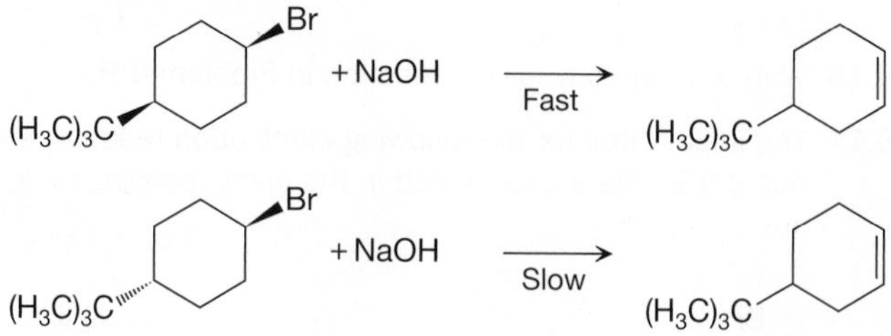
Br
(H3C)3C
+NaOH
Fast
(H3C)3C
Br
(H3C)3C
+NaOH
Slow
(H3C)3C

8.17 Racemization occurs when (*S*)-3,3-dimethylcyclohexanol is dissolved in dilute acid. Draw a mechanism to account for this, including curved arrows.

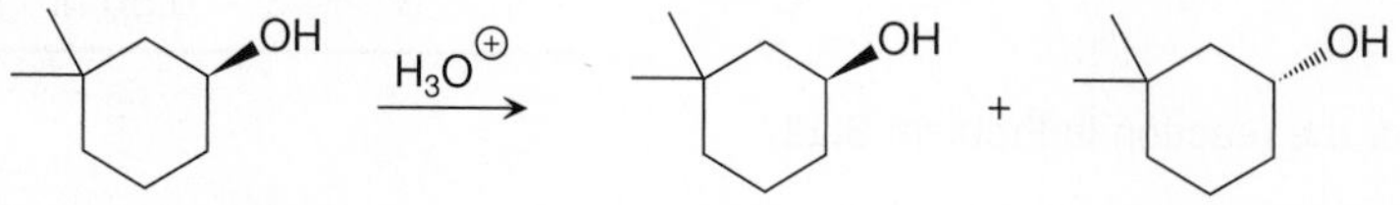
OH
H3O+
OH
+
OH
(S)-3,3-Dimethylcyclohexanol

8.18 Consider the *intramolecular* nucleophilic substitution reaction shown here. Does the stereochemistry of the product suggest an S_N1 or S_N2 mechanism? Draw the complete mechanism for this reaction, including curved arrows.

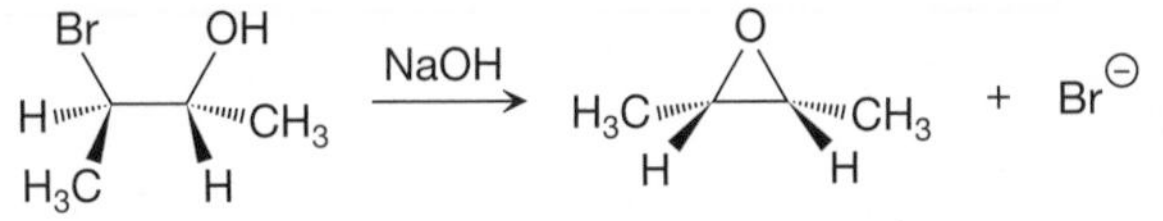

Br
OH
H
CH3
H3C
H
NaOH
O
H3C
CH3
H
H
+ Br⊖

8.19 Consider the elimination reaction shown here, which produces a mixture of diastereomers. From the stereochemistry of this reaction alone, is it possible to tell whether the reaction takes place via an E1 or E2 reaction? Explain.

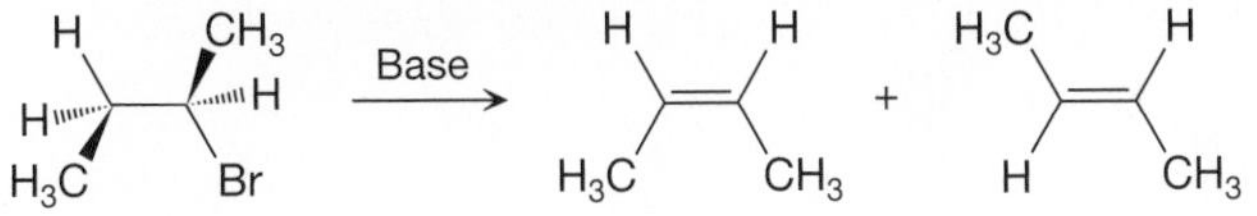

H
CH3
H
H
H3C
Br
Base
H
H
H3C
CH3
+
H3C
H
H
CH3

8.20 Consider the nucleophilic substitution reaction shown here. From the stereochemistry, does it proceed by an S_N1 or S_N2 mechanism? Explain.

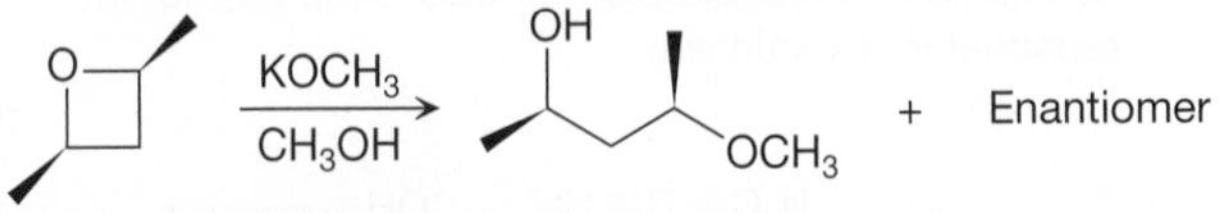

O
KOCH3
CH3OH
OH
OCH3
+ Enantiomer

8.21 (*E*)-Anethole is the major component of anise oil, which is used as an artificial licorice flavoring and has potential antimicrobial and antifungal properties. It can be synthesized from an alkyl halide precursor, as shown here.

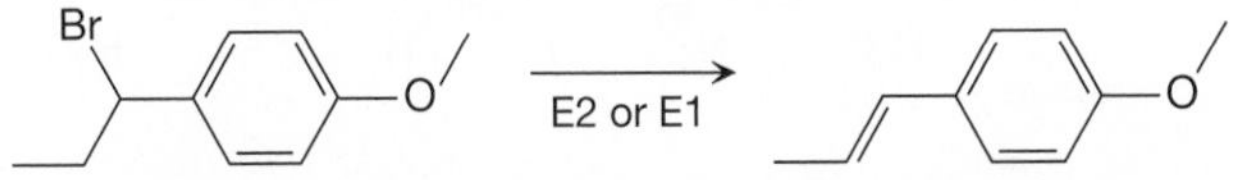

Br
O
E2 or E1
O

(*E*)-Anethole

(a) Will an E2 reaction produce (*E*)-anethole exclusively, or will the reaction produce a mixture of stereoisomers?

(b) Will an E1 reaction produce the pure stereoisomer or a mixture?

(c) For each of these reactions that produces a mixture, which stereoisomer will be produced in greater abundance?

8.22 The following nucleophilic substitution reaction is monitored by measuring the optical rotation of the solution as a function of time. On the basis of the results graphed on the right, suggest whether the reaction takes place by the S_N1 or S_N2 mechanism. *Hint*: Review optical rotation in Chapter 5.

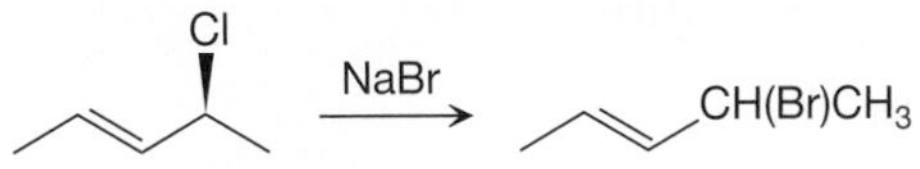

Cl
NaBr
CH(Br)CH3

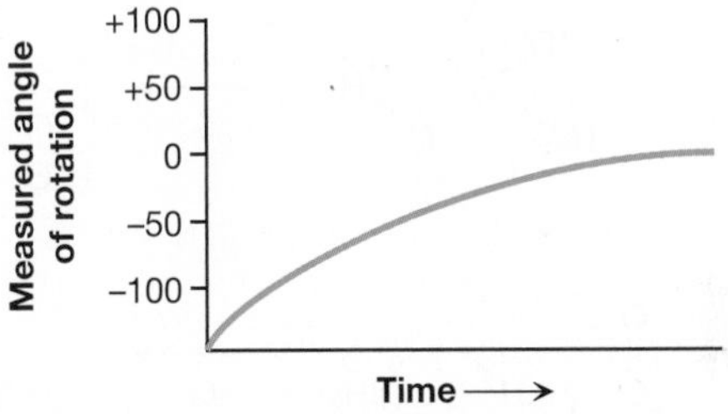

Measured angle of rotation
+100
+50
0
−50
−100
Time ⟶

Sections 8.6 and 8.7 The Reasonableness of Mechanisms

8.23 For each of the following substrates, predict whether a carbocation rearrangement will take place in an S_N1 or E1 mechanism. Explain. Draw the curved arrow notation illustrating the carbocation rearrangement that is likely to occur.

(a)
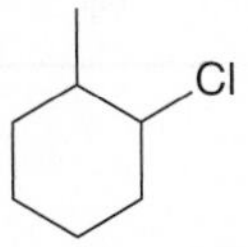

Cl

(b)
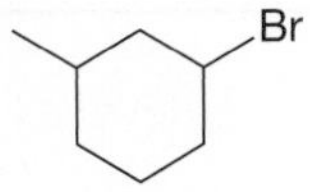

Br

(c)
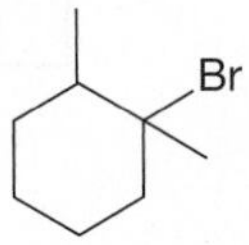

Br

(d)
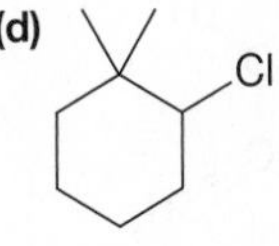

Cl

(e)
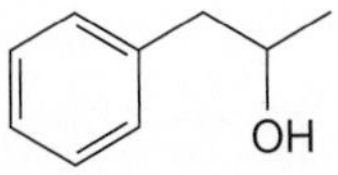

OH

(f)
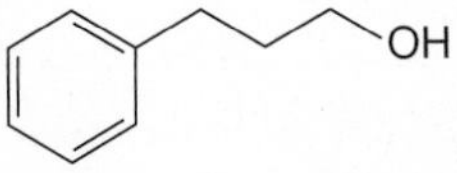

OH

(g)
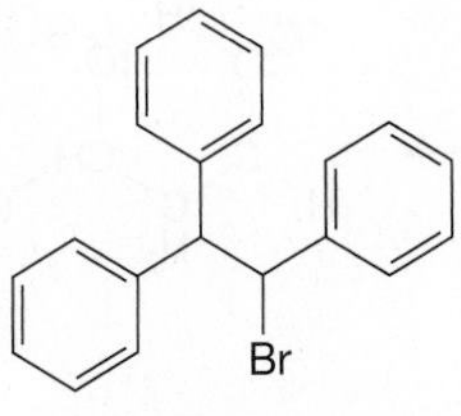

Br

(h)
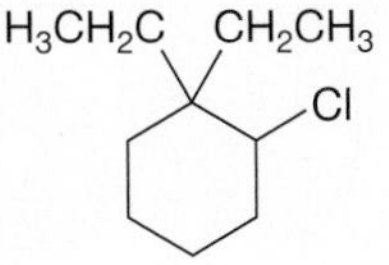

H3CH2C CH2CH3
Cl

(i)
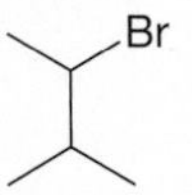

Br

8.24 Consider the *overall* reaction shown in the box, which will be discussed in Chapter 23. Use the rules we learned in this chapter to evaluate whether each step of the proposed mechanism is reasonable. For each step that is *not* reasonable, explain why.

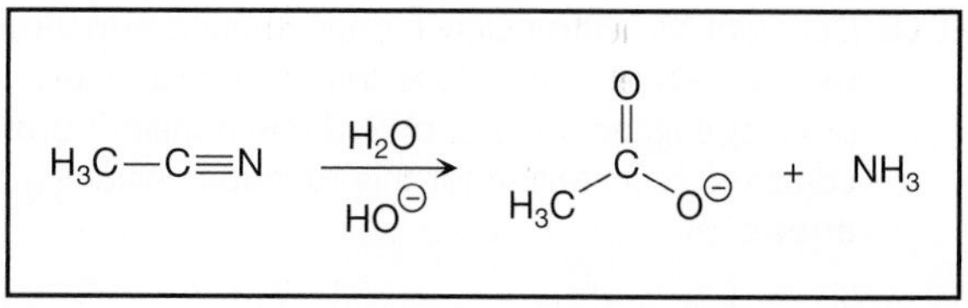

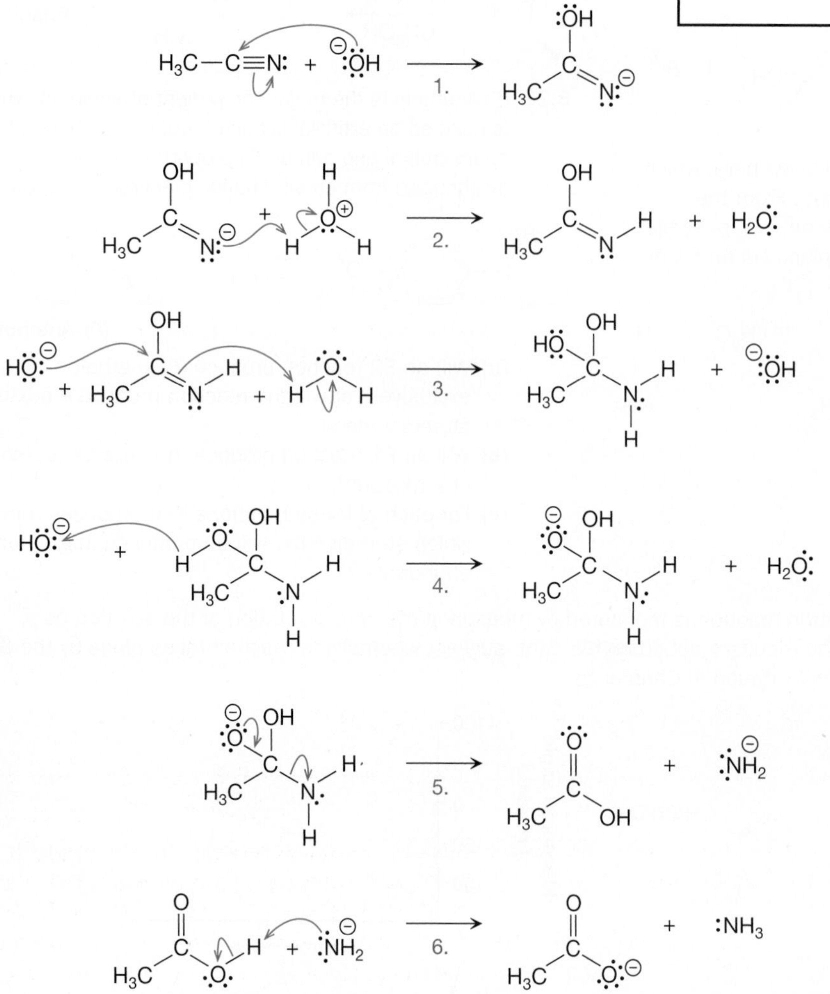

8.25 Consider the *overall* reaction shown in the box, which will be discussed in Chapter 23. Evaluate whether each step of the proposed mechanism is reasonable. For each step that is *not* reasonable, explain why.

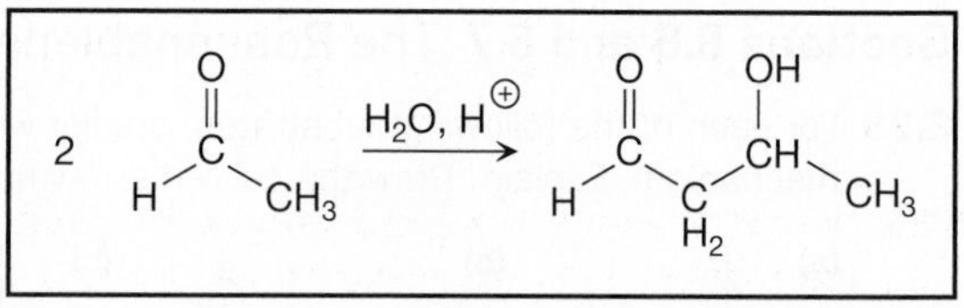

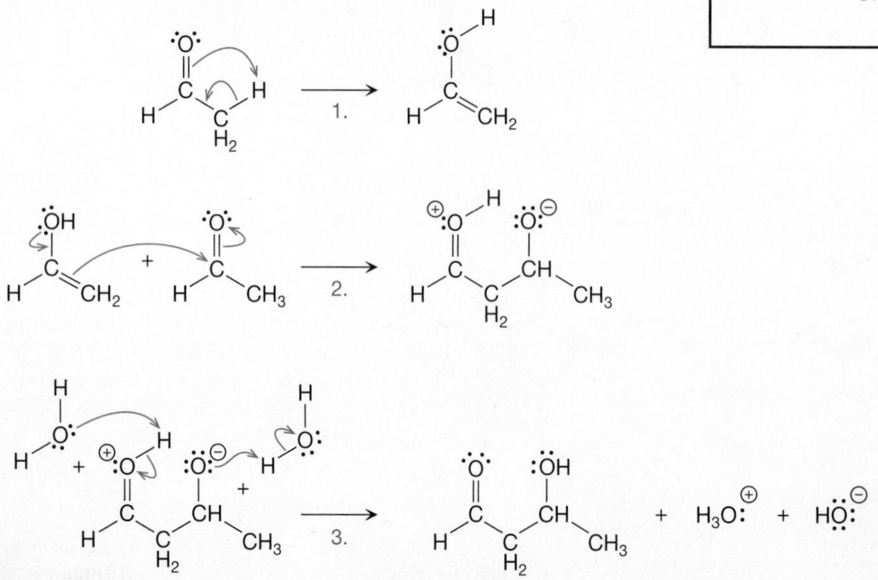

8.26 Consider the nucleophilic substitution reaction shown here, which yields a mixture of constitutional isomers. **(a)** Does this occur by an S_N1 or an S_N2 mechanism? How do you know? **(b)** Propose a mechanism that accounts for the formation of *each* product.

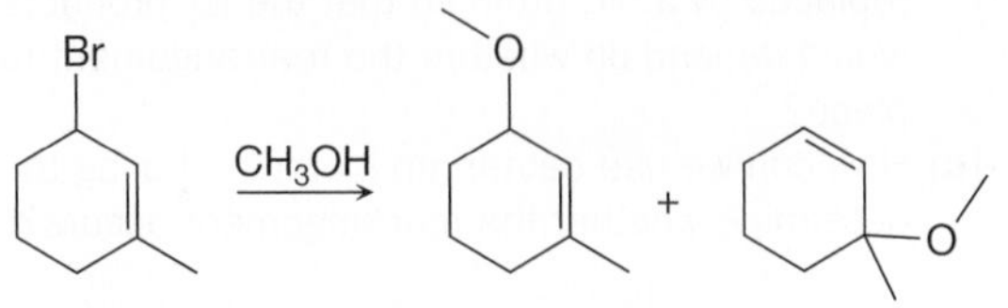
Br
CH_3OH
O
+
O

8.27 Consider the nucleophilic substitution reaction shown here. **(a)** Argue whether this reaction takes place by an S_N1 or an S_N2 reaction. **(b)** Draw the complete mechanism (including curved arrows) for this reaction.

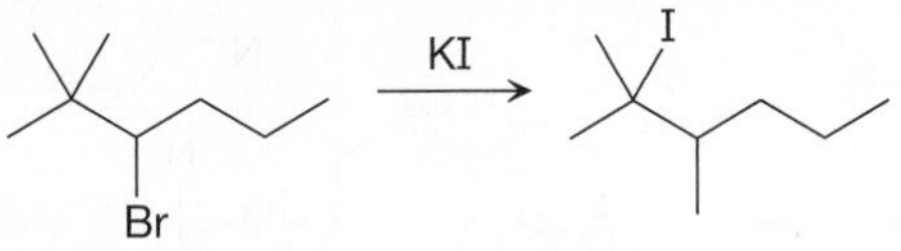
Br
KI
I

8.28 The reaction shown here yields three different nucleophilic substitution products that are constitutional isomers of one another. **(a)** Does this suggest an S_N1 or S_N2 mechanism? **(b)** Draw the mechanism for the formation of each of these products.

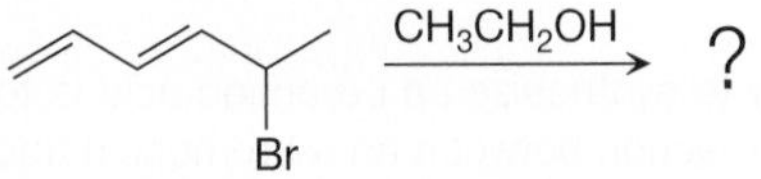
Br
CH_3CH_2OH
?

8.29 The reaction shown here involves a carbocation rearrangement. Draw a complete, detailed mechanism to account for the product. Explain why the carbocation rearrangement is favorable.

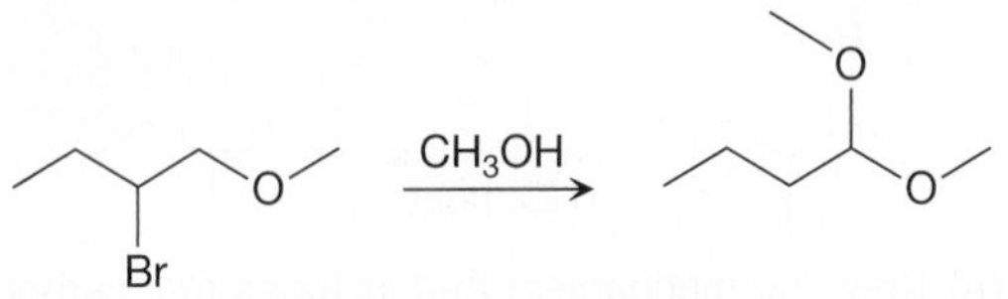
O
Br
CH_3OH
O
O

8.30 One way to synthesize diethyl ether is to heat ethanol in the presence of a strong acid, as shown here. Draw a complete, detailed mechanism for this reaction.

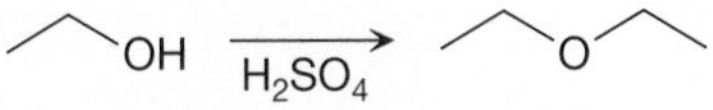
OH
H_2SO_4
O

8.31 Suggest a reasonable mechanism for the reaction shown here.

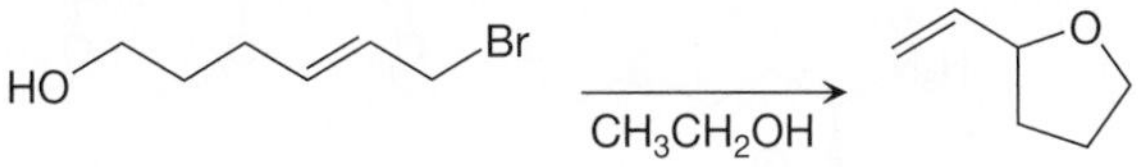
HO
Br
CH_3CH_2OH
O

Integrated Problems

8.32 Consider this E1 reaction. **(a)** Draw a complete, detailed mechanism for the reaction. **(b)** Draw a reaction free energy diagram that agrees with that mechanism, labeling overall reactants, overall products, all transition states, and all intermediates.

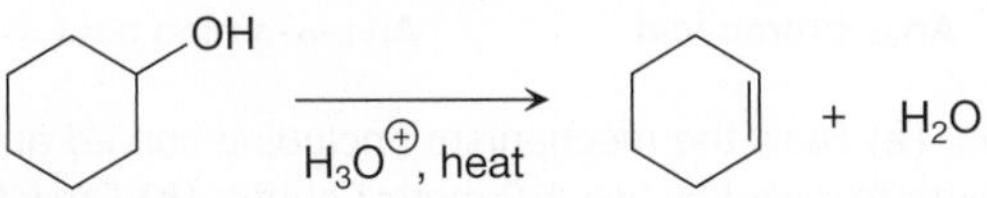
OH
$H_3O^{\oplus}$, heat
+ H_2O

8.33 Draw a reasonable, detailed mechanism that shows this racemization at the α (alpha) carbon. *Note:* The reaction takes place under basic conditions.

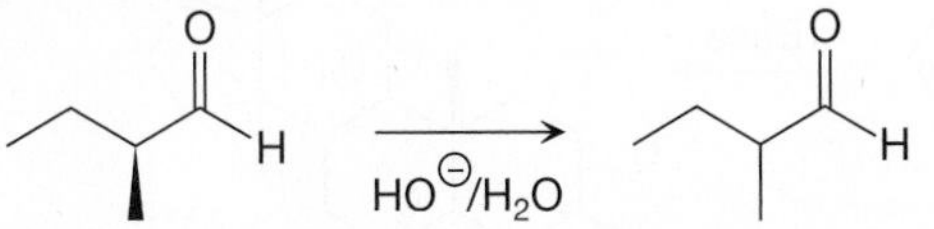
O
H
$HO^{\ominus}/H_2O$
O
H

Racemic mixture

8.34 Draw a reasonable, detailed mechanism that shows this racemization at the α (alpha) carbon. *Note:* The reaction takes place under acidic conditions.

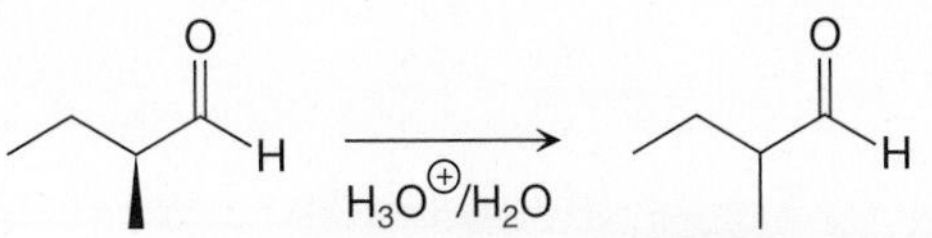
O
H
$H_3O^{\oplus}/H_2O$
O
H

Racemic mixture

8.35 The elimination reaction shown here (top) yields the same alkene product independent of whether it proceeds by the E2 or E1 mechanism. The mechanism by which the reaction proceeds could be determined if the D-labeled substrate shown (bottom) were used instead. *Note:* Deuterium (D) is an isotope of H. They both have one proton and one electron, so they have nearly identical chemical properties, but D, having one additional neutron, is heavier by 1 mass unit.

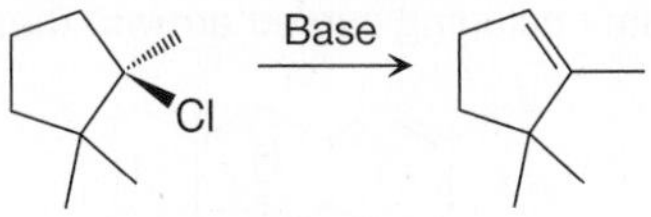
Cl
Base

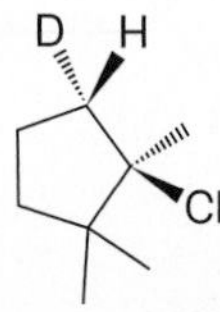
D
H
Cl

(a) Draw the complete mechanism for an E2 reaction involving the D-labeled substrate and predict the major product(s).
(b) Draw the complete mechanism for an E1 reaction involving the D-labeled substrate and predict the major product(s).
(c) What is the molar mass of each product from (a) and (b)?

8.36 According to the rules for reasonable mechanisms, the E1 reaction shown here should undergo a 1,2-hydride shift. However, the same product is produced regardless of whether the rearrangement occurs.

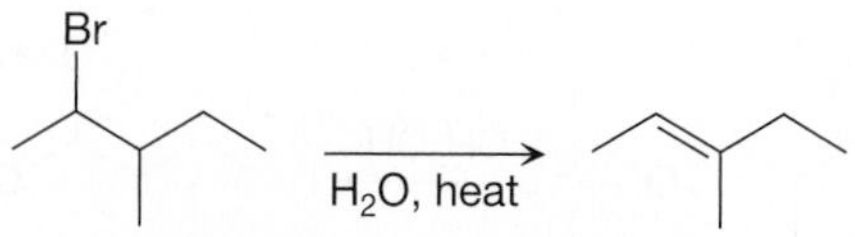
Br
H_2O, heat

(a) Draw the mechanism that includes that carbocation rearrangement.

(b) Draw the mechanism that does not include the rearrangement.

(c) Experimentally, how can we use ^{13}C isotope labeling to determine whether the rearrangement occurs? In other words, can a ^{12}C atom in the substrate be replaced by a ^{13}C atom so that the E1 products would depend on whether the rearrangement takes place?

(d) How can we use deuterium isotope labeling to determine whether the rearrangement occurs?

8.37 (S)-Adenosylmethionine (SAM) is a cosubstrate that is involved in biological methyl group transfers. SAM is believed to be produced by an S_N2 type of reaction between methionine and ATP, as shown here.

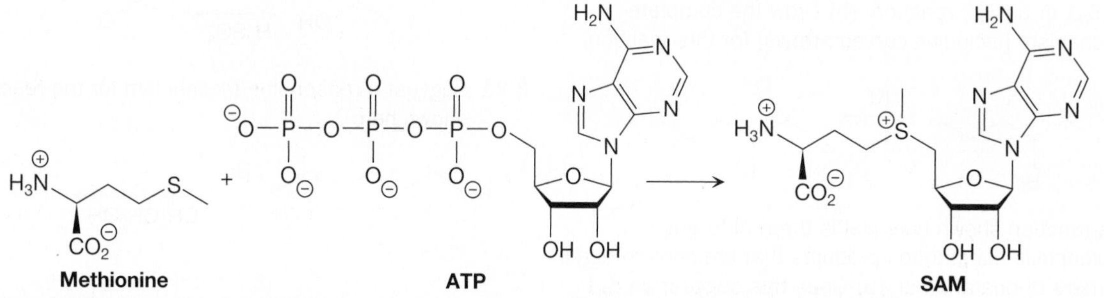

(a) Draw the appropriate curved arrows for this reaction.

(b) Suggest why the reaction takes place with S as the nucleophilic atom instead of one of the negatively charged O atoms on methionine.

8.38 Creatine is a naturally occurring compound that helps provide energy to cells in the body, especially muscle cells. Draw an S_N2 mechanism that shows how creatine is produced from guanidinoacetate and SAM (see Problem 8.37).

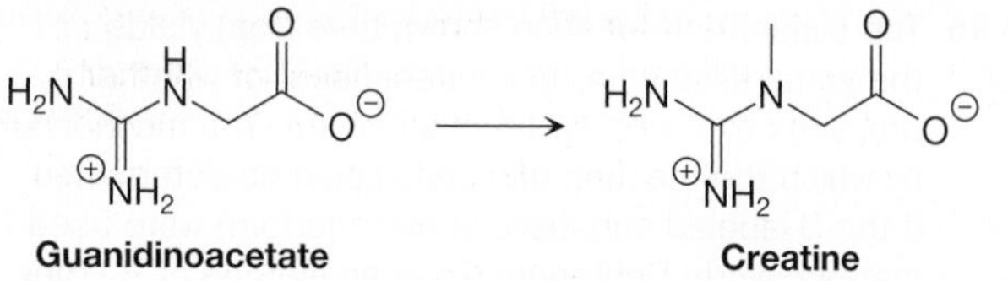

8.39 One way to synthesize an L-α-amino acid is to carry out an S_N2 reaction between an α-bromoacid and ammonia. (The wavy line indicates that the bond could be a dash or a wedge.) Draw the stereoisomer of the α-bromoacid that would be necessary to produce L-alanine, in which the R group is CH_3.

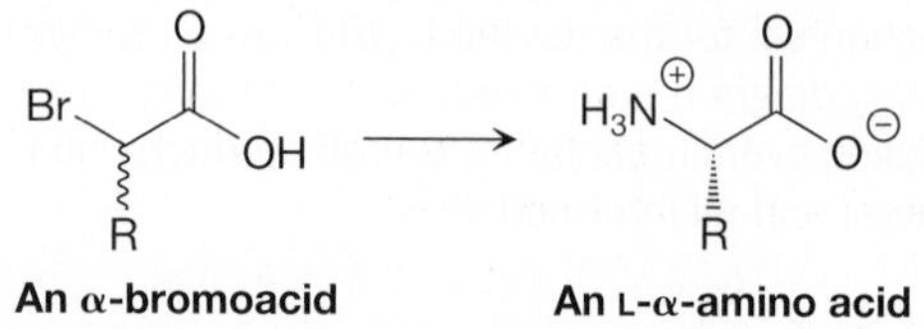

8.40 Structures **A** and **B** are intermediates in the biosynthesis of steroids. **(a)** Draw the mechanism (including curved arrows) that shows how **A** can be converted to **B** through two 1,2-hydride shifts followed by two 1,2-methyl shifts. **(b)** Draw the mechanism (including curved arrows) that shows how **B** is converted to lanosterol.

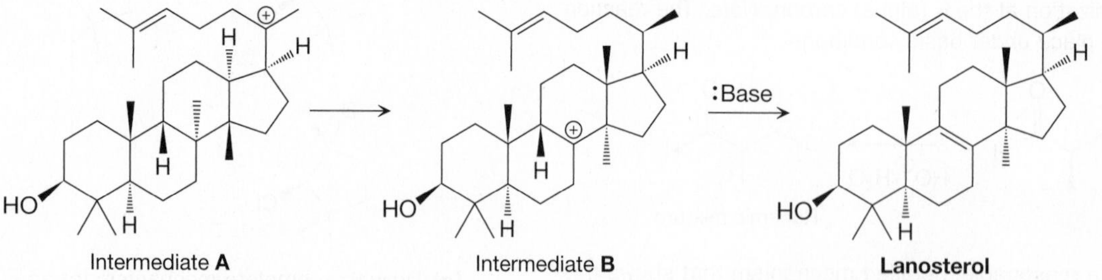

8.41 The reaction shown here is called the pinacol rearrangement. A carbocation rearrangement is believed to be involved. **(a)** Propose a reasonable mechanism for this reaction. **(b)** Suggest why the carbocation rearrangement is favorable.

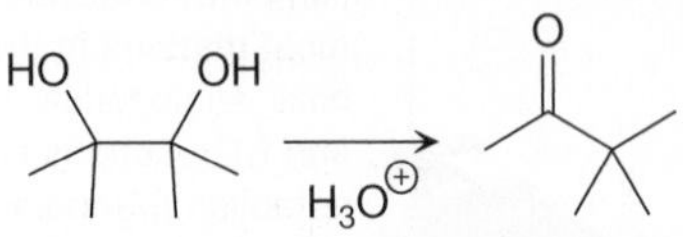
HO
OH
O
$H_3O^{\oplus}$

8.42 Propose a mechanism for the reaction shown here, which produces 1,4-dioxane.

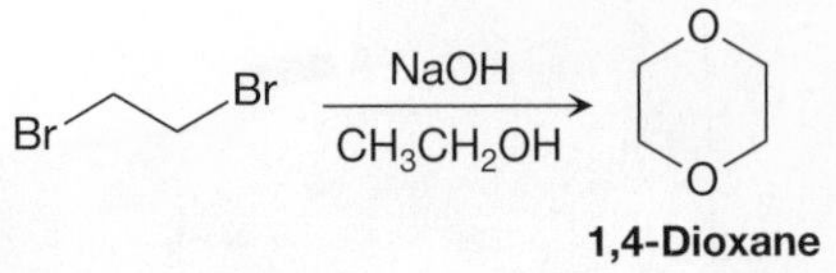
Br
Br
NaOH
CH_3CH_2OH
O
O
1,4-Dioxane

8.43 The specific angle of rotation of (*R*)-2-bromobutane is −23.1°. Treatment of (*R*)-2-bromobutane with potassium bromide produces (*R*)- and (*S*)-2-bromobutane in a racemic mixture, which is optically inactive. The rate at which the product's angle of rotation decreases is directly proportional to the concentration of KBr. Does this suggest that the reaction takes place by an S_N1 or an S_N2 mechanism? Explain.

8.44 A useful rule of thumb in chemical kinetics is that the rate of a reaction roughly doubles for each 10 °C increase in temperature. Use Equation 8-14 (p. 404) to demonstrate this rule of thumb by comparing relative rate constants at 25, 35, and 45 °C. Use 50 kJ/mol for the free energy of activation.

8.45 Propose a mechanism for the reaction shown here, which takes place under conditions that favor an S_N1 reaction.

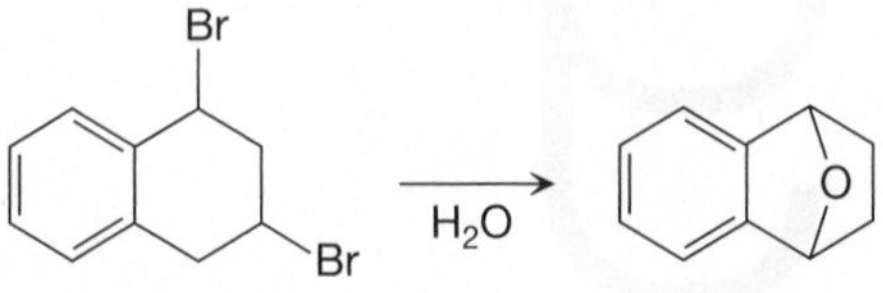
Br
Br
H_2O
O

8.46 Propose a mechanism for the reaction shown here, which takes place under conditions that favor an S_N1 reaction. Based on the mechanism, do you think that the products will be formed in a mixture of stereoisomers?

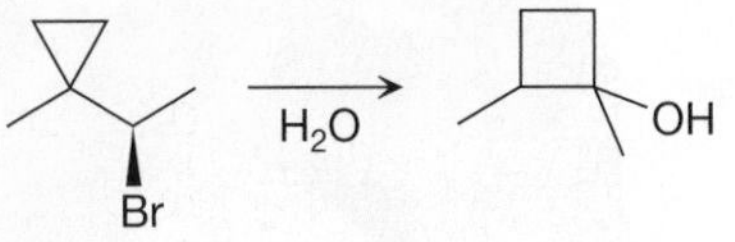
Br
H_2O
OH

8.47 Propose a mechanism for the reaction shown here, which takes place under conditions that favor an E1 reaction.

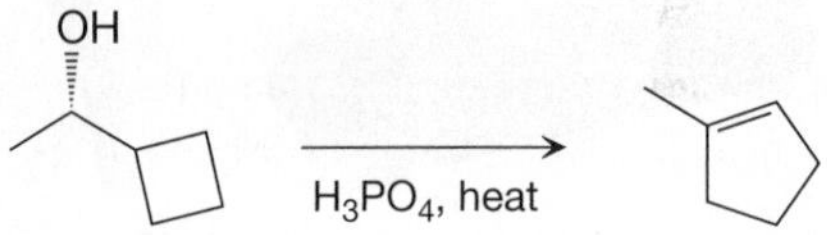
OH
H_3PO_4, heat

8.48 Reactions **A** and **B** take place under the same conditions to convert a methyl ester into a carboxylate anion. A chemist proposes that both reactions proceed by an S_N2 mechanism. To test this hypothesis, the chemist carries out each reaction with oxygen-18 (^{18}O)-labeled hydroxide in ^{18}O-labeled water (i.e., $^{18}OH^-/H_2{}^{18}O$). In the products of reaction **A**, the ^{18}O isotope appeared only in $CH_3CO_2^-$ and not in CH_3OH. In reaction **B**, ^{18}O-labeled methanol was produced. Using these results, argue which reaction (if any) proceeds by the S_N2 mechanism.

A

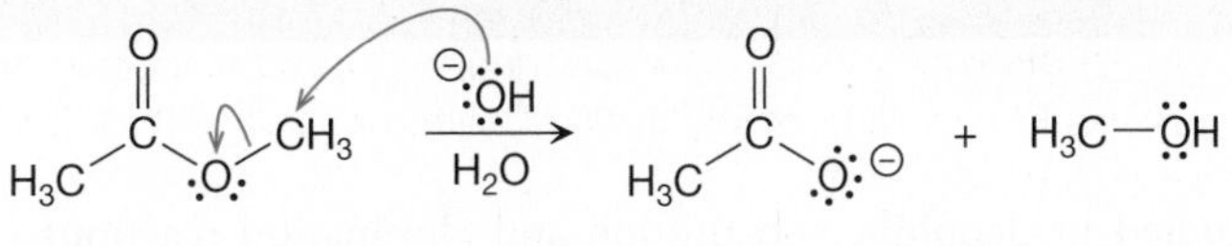
O
C
CH_3
H_3C
O
$:\ddot{O}H$
H_2O
O
C
H_3C
O
+
$H_3C—\ddot{O}H$

B

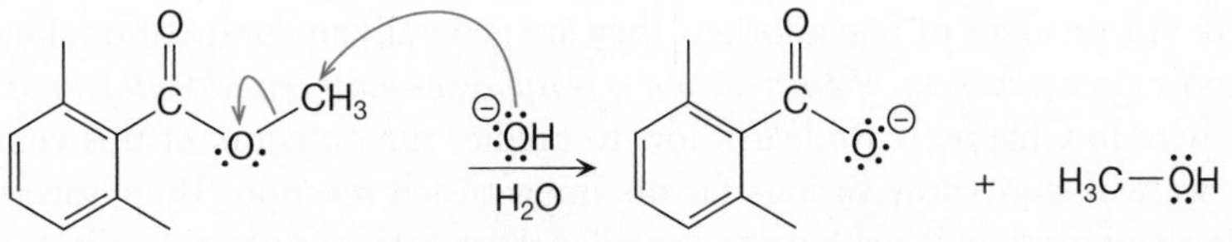
O
C
CH_3
O
$:\ddot{O}H$
H_2O
O
C
O
+
$H_3C—\ddot{O}H$

9

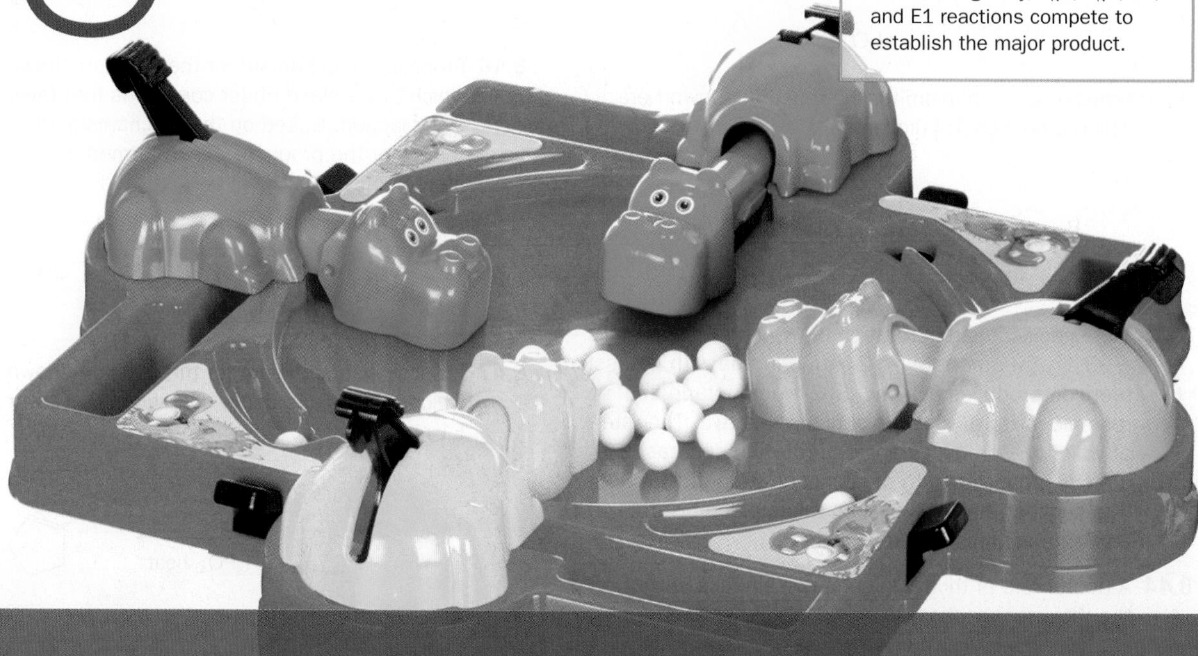

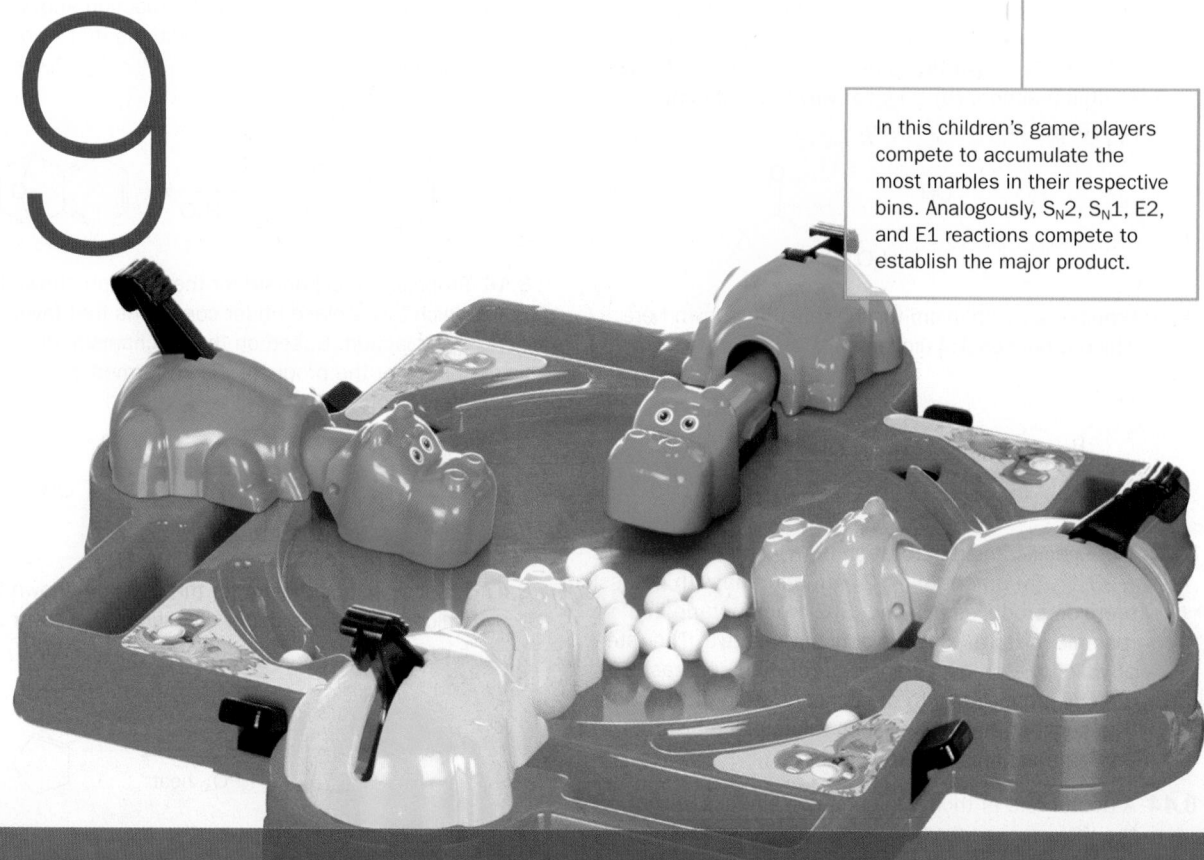

In this children's game, players compete to accumulate the most marbles in their respective bins. Analogously, S_N2, S_N1, E2, and E1 reactions compete to establish the major product.

Competition among S_N2, S_N1, E2, and E1 Reactions

We have studied nucleophilic substitution and elimination reactions extensively in the last two chapters: S_N2 and E2 in Chapter 7, and S_N1 and E1 in Chapter 8. Up to this point, we have considered these four reactions as if they were independent of one another. They are generally in competition, however, so under most circumstances, *if one reaction is feasible, we must consider all four of them*. Therefore, here in Chapter 9 we learn how to predict the outcome of this competition. First we will study how various factors impact each reaction. Then, toward the end of this chapter, we will see how to consider these factors systematically to make our prediction.

Many of the reactions we will encounter in subsequent chapters also involve competitions. The ideas presented here in Chapter 9 pertaining to nucleophilic substitution and elimination reactions will therefore be revisited throughout the book.

Chapter Outline

9.1 Identifying the Competition among S_N2, S_N1, E2, and E1 Reactions

SECTION 9.1 OBJECTIVES

You will be able to:

1. Explain why S_N2, S_N1, E2, and E1 reactions generally compete.
2. Identify which of these reactions exhibits the attacking species acting as a nucleophile versus as a base.

A competition usually exists among S_N2, S_N1, E2, and E1 reactions. In the four reactions shown in Equations 9-1 through 9-4, for example, the reactants are identical but the mechanisms are different, which can lead to different products. These four reactions compete essentially for two reasons:

- S_N2, S_N1, E2, and E1 reactions all involve a substrate containing a *leaving group*.
- Any species that can act as a nucleophile also has the potential to act as a base, and vice versa. To acknowledge this ability to act as either type of species, we will often refer to a nucleophile or a base more generally as an **attacking species**.

Mechanism for the S_N2 reaction in an $S_N2/S_N1/E2/E1$ competition

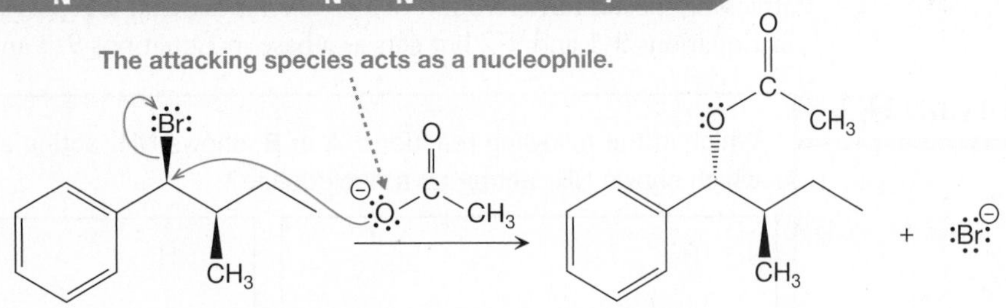

The attacking species acts as a nucleophile.

(9-1)

Mechanism for the S_N1 reaction in an $S_N2/S_N1/E2/E1$ competition

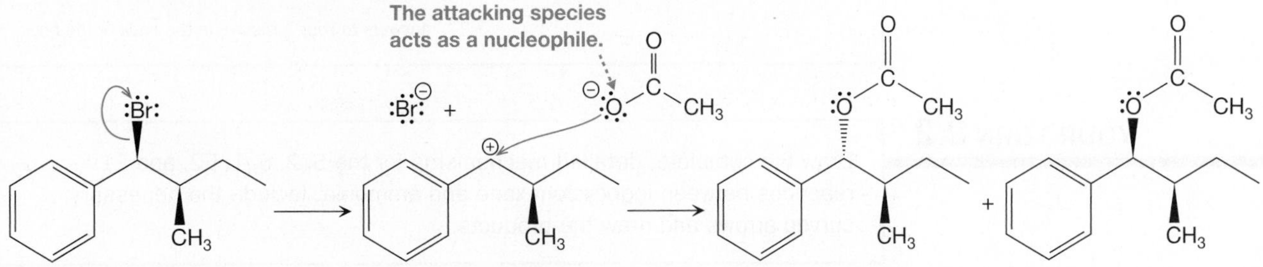

The attacking species acts as a nucleophile.

(9-2)

Mechanism for the E2 reaction in an $S_N2/S_N1/E2/E1$ competition

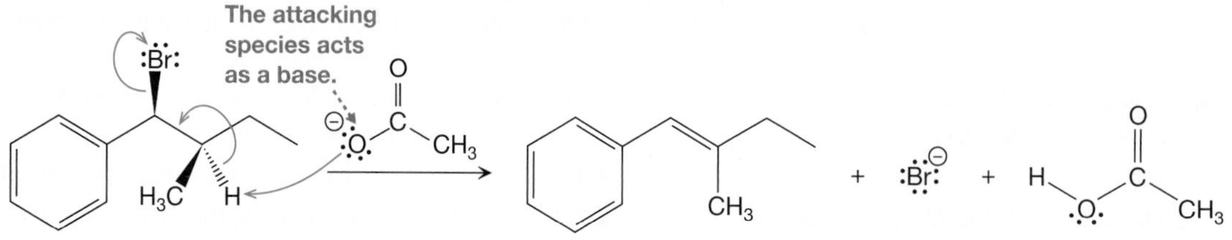

The attacking species acts as a base.

(9-3)

Mechanism for the E1 reaction in an $S_N2/S_N1/E2/E1$ competition

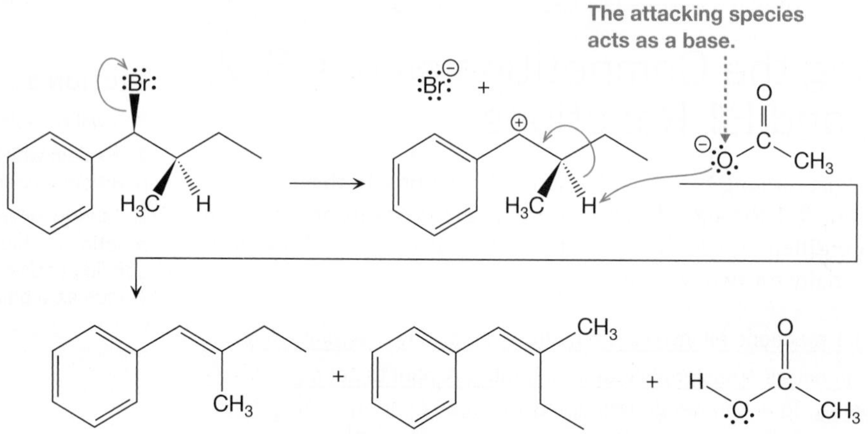

The attacking species acts as a base.

(9-4)

Acting as a nucleophile, an attacking species uses a lone pair of electrons to form a bond to an electron-poor *non-hydrogen atom*. Acting as a base, on the other hand, an attacking species forms a bond to a *proton*. Notice that $CH_3CO_2^-$ acts as a nucleophile in Equations 9-1 and 9-2 but acts as a base in Equations 9-3 and 9-4.

YOUR TURN 9.1

Which of the following reactions, **A** or **B**, shows NH_3 acting as a base, and which shows NH_3 acting as a nucleophile?

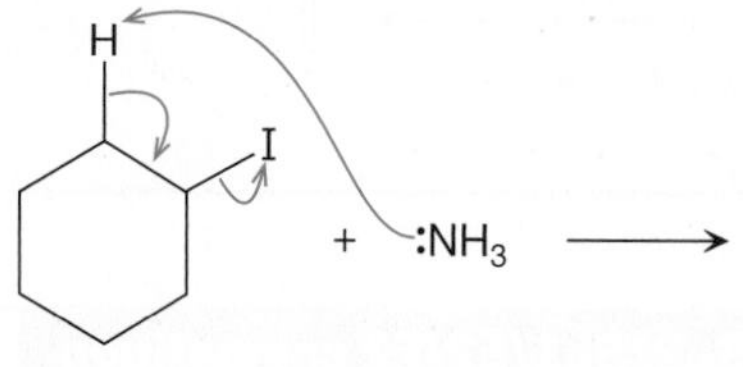

A

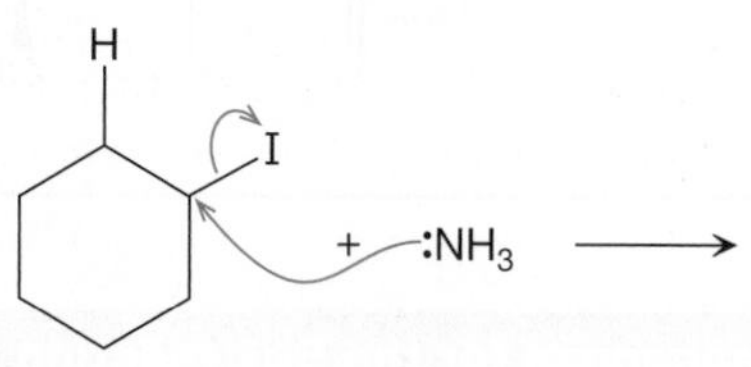

B

Answers to Your Turns are in the back of the book.

YOUR TURN 9.2

Draw the complete, detailed mechanisms for the S_N2, S_N1, E2, and E1 reactions between iodocyclohexane and ammonia. Include the necessary curved arrows and draw the products.

How can we predict the major products of an $S_N2/S_N1/E2/E1$ competition? In general, the relative amount of product formed from each reaction depends on the rate of the reaction. That is to say:

> In a competition among S_N2, S_N1, E2, and E1 reactions, the fastest reaction leads to the major product(s) (see Looking Ahead box).

▸ LOOKING AHEAD

When the outcome of a competition is determined by the relative rates of the reactions, the competition is said to take place under *kinetic control*. In Section 11.3, we will learn that a competition could instead take place under *thermodynamic control*, where the product stabilities dictate the outcome.

As it turns out, there are a variety of factors that control the rates of these reactions. Some factors are dictated by the identities of the attacking species and the substrate. Other factors can be controlled externally, such as the choice of solvent, concentration of the attacking species, and temperature. Thus, to reliably predict the outcome of a competing set of S_N2, S_N1, E2, and E1 reactions, such as the set of reactions in Equations 9-1 through 9-4, we must understand how the various factors control S_N2, S_N1, E2, and E1 reaction rates; these factors are the topics of Sections 9.3 through 9.8. First, however, we devote Section 9.2 to revisiting the rate-determining step of each reaction, so that we are better equipped to navigate the discussions about reaction rates in the sections that follow.

9.2 Rate-Determining Steps Revisited: Simplified Pictures of S_N2, S_N1, E2, and E1 Reactions

SECTION 9.2 OBJECTIVES

You will be able to:

1. Describe how the role of the nucleophile differs in an S_N2 versus an S_N1 reaction.
2. Describe how the role of the base differs in an E2 versus an E1 reaction.

We just learned in Section 9.1 that the outcome of an $S_N2/S_N1/E2/E1$ competition is dictated by the relative rates of the reactions. Moreover, recall from Section 8.3 that the rate of an overall reaction is essentially the same as the rate of the rate-determining step (see Recall box).

◂ RECALL

Section 8.3 used traffic congestion as an analogy for a rate-determining step. When lanes on a freeway are closed, a bottleneck forms and the overall flow of traffic is the same as the flow through the bottleneck. Similarly, an overall reaction rate is the same as the rate of the slow step of the mechanism.

The S_N2 mechanism (Eq. 9-5) consists of just a single step, so that single step must be rate-determining:

Mechanism for the general S_N2 reaction

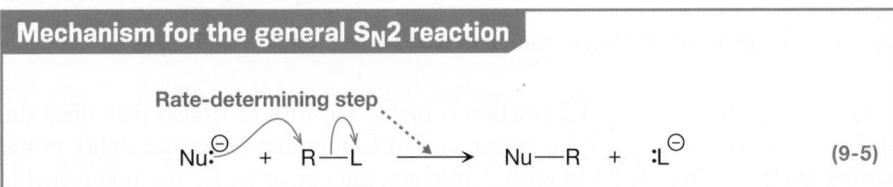

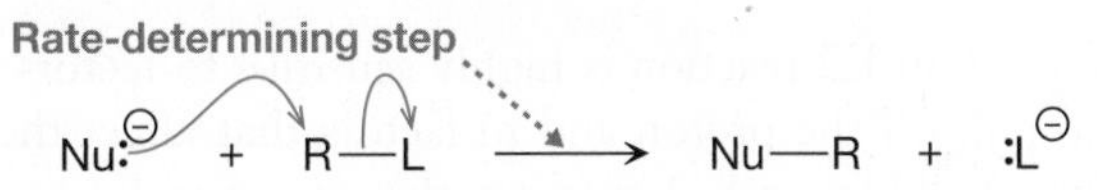

Rate-determining step
Nu:⊖
+
R—L
Nu—R
+
:L⊖

(9-5)

The S_N1 reaction (Eq. 9-6), on the other hand, takes place in two steps. The first step is rate-determining because formation of the carbocation is so difficult:

Mechanism for the general S_N1 reaction

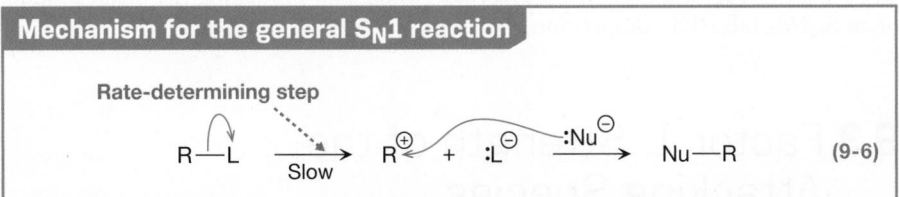

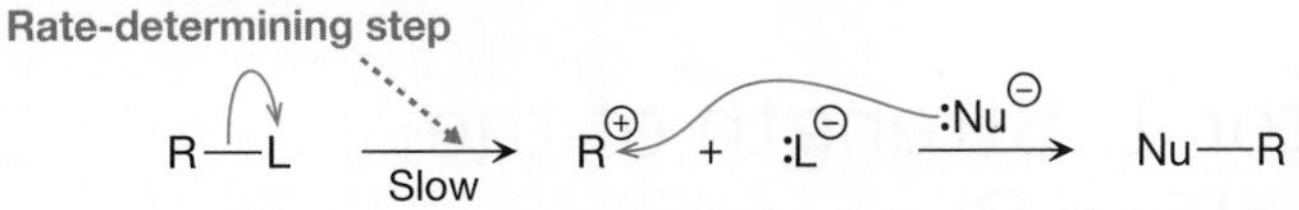

Rate-determining step
R—L
Slow
R⊕
+
:L⊖
:Nu⊖
Nu—R

(9-6)

Because the nucleophile appears in the rate-determining step of an S_N2 reaction but not in the rate-determining step of an S_N1 reaction, we can view the nucleophile as having different roles in the two reactions:

- In an S_N2 reaction, the nucleophile forces the leaving group out.
- In an S_N1 reaction, the nucleophile waits until the leaving group has left.

Consequently, the rate of an S_N2 reaction is highly sensitive to factors that affect the nucleophile's ability to attack the substrate and to factors that affect the ability of the leaving group to depart. The rate of an S_N1 reaction, on the other hand, is highly sensitive only to factors that help the leaving group depart.

Like an S_N2 reaction, an E2 reaction (Eq. 9-7) consists of a single step that must be rate-determining. And as in an S_N1 reaction, the rate-determining step of an E1 reaction (Eq. 9-8) is the first of its two steps:

Mechanism for the general E2 reaction

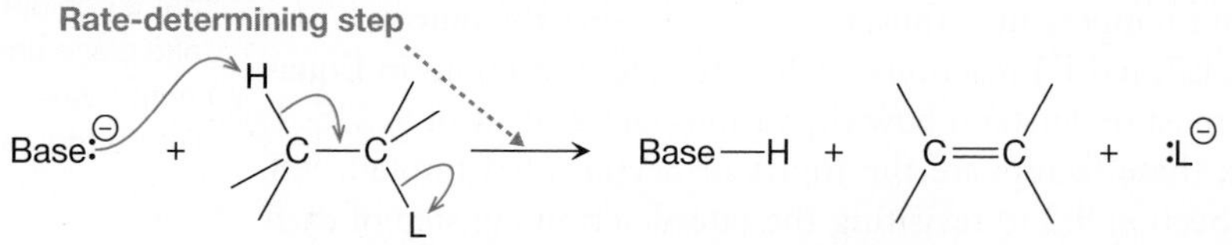

Rate-determining step
Base:
H
C
C
L
Base—H
C=C
:L

(9-7)

Mechanism for the general E1 reaction

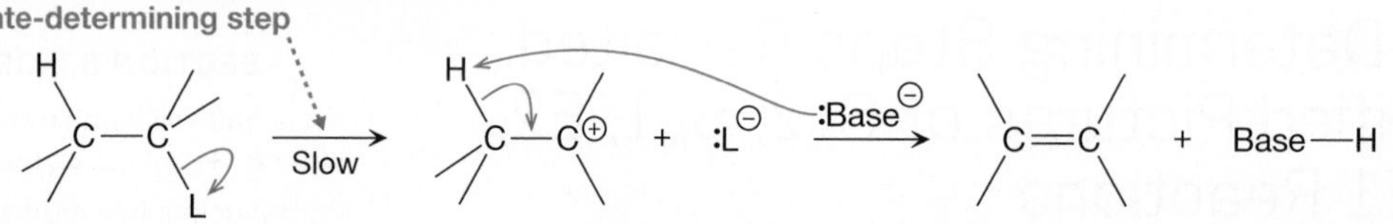

Rate-determining step
H
C
C
L
Slow
:L
:Base
C=C
Base—H

(9-8)

Again, because the base appears in the rate-determining step of an E2 reaction but not in the rate-determining step of an E1 reaction, we can view the base as having different roles in the two reactions:

- In an E2 reaction, the base pulls off the proton, thus forcing the leaving group to leave.
- In an E1 reaction, the base waits until the leaving group has left.

Consequently, the rate of an E2 reaction is highly sensitive to factors that affect the ability of the base to pull off the proton and to factors that affect the ability of the leaving group to leave. And like an S_N1 reaction, the rate of an E1 reaction is highly sensitive only to factors that help the leaving group to depart.

With a general sense of the kinds of things that can affect each reaction rate, let's now examine key factors in some detail in Sections 9.3 through 9.8. Then Section 9.9 will bring these factors together to present a strategy for predicting the major product of an $S_N2/S_N1/E2/E1$ competition.

SECTION 9.3 OBJECTIVES

You will be able to:

1. Distinguish strong nucleophiles from weak nucleophiles and strong bases from weak bases.
2. Predict whether an attacking species will favor an S_N2, S_N1, E2, or E1 reaction from the attacking species' strength as a nucleophile and as a base.
3. Show how a non-nucleophilic carbon can be made strongly nucleophilic by deprotonation.
4. Identify strong, bulky bases and explain why they tend to favor E2 reactions over S_N2.

9.3 Factor 1: Strength of the Attacking Species

Because the S_N2, S_N1, E2, and E1 reactions are sensitive to the attacking species in different ways, the *identity* of the attacking species can play a major role in the outcome of the $S_N2/S_N1/E2/E1$ competition. Here in Section 9.3, we examine how the attacking species affects each of these reactions differently. First we discuss the nature of the attacking species in S_N2 and S_N1 reactions, in which it behaves as a

TABLE 9-1 S_N2 Reaction Rates in DMF for the Reaction:

$$Nu^{\ominus} + CH_3I \longrightarrow NuCH_3 + I^{\ominus}$$

Nucleophile (Nu^-)	H_2O	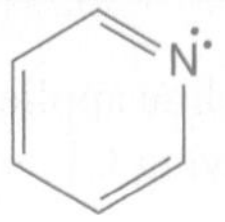	$NCS^{\ominus}$	$Br^{\ominus}$	$Cl^{\ominus}$	$N_3^{\ominus}$	$C_6H_5S^{\ominus}$	$CH_3CO_2^{\ominus}$	$NC^{\ominus}$
Relative (S_N2) Reaction Rate	~0	~0.0005	0.06	1	2	3	12	15	250

S_N2 reaction rate increases

Nucleophile strength increases

nucleophile. Then we turn to E2 and E1 reactions, in which the attacking species behaves as a base.

◂ **RECALL**

In Section 6.4, we saw that $\Delta G^{\circ\ddagger}$ is the difference in free energy between the reactants and the transition state. Section 8.4 showed that reaction rate increases as $\Delta G^{\circ\ddagger}$ becomes smaller because more reactant molecules have sufficient energy to surmount the energy barrier to form products.

9.3a Nucleophile Strength in S_N2 and S_N1 Reactions: An Introduction to the Hammond Postulate

Table 9-1 lists S_N2 reaction rates for various nucleophiles attacking CH_3I in the solvent *N,N*-dimethylformamide (DMF). These rate differences reflect differences in *nucleophile strength*, or **nucleophilicity**:

> The stronger nucleophile promotes a faster S_N2 reaction.

Thus, the relative nucleophilicities of Br^-, Cl^-, and NC^- in the solvent DMF are 1, 2, and 250, respectively. Furthermore, because a smaller energy barrier ($\Delta G^{\circ\ddagger}$) leads to a faster reaction, the energy barrier for an S_N2 reaction must become smaller when the nucleophile is changed from Br^- to Cl^- to NC^- (see Recall box).

To better understand these variations in the size of the S_N2 energy barrier, we turn to the **Hammond postulate**, the ideas of which are summarized in **Figure 9-1**. Notice, in particular, that the energy barrier appears to be smaller when the value of ΔG°_{rxn} is negative (Fig. 9-1a) instead of positive (Fig. 9-1b). This relationship between the energy barrier and ΔG°_{rxn} is generally true when the reacting species undergo similar structural changes. Thus, we arrive at a very useful guideline:

> For two elementary steps that are of the same type (e.g., both S_N2 or both E2), the one with the more negative (or less positive) value of ΔG°_{rxn} tends to have the smaller energy barrier ($\Delta G^{\circ\ddagger}$) and thus tends to be faster.

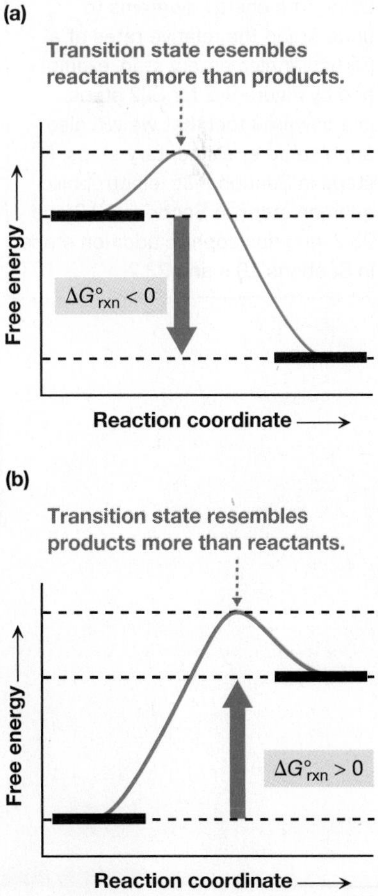
(a)
Transition state resembles reactants more than products.
Free energy
ΔG°rxn < 0
Reaction coordinate
(b)
Transition state resembles products more than reactants.
Free energy
ΔG°rxn > 0
Reaction coordinate

FIGURE 9-1 The Hammond postulate and ΔG°_{rxn} (a) Free energy diagram for an exergonic reaction, showing that the transition state resembles reactants more than it does products, in both energy and structure. (b) Free energy diagram for an endergonic reaction, showing that the transition state resembles products more than it does reactants.

YOUR TURN 9.3

Draw an arrow in Figure 9-1a to indicate $\Delta G^{\circ\ddagger}$ of the exergonic reaction. Do the same for the endergonic reaction in Figure 9-1b. Assuming that the energy diagrams have the same energy scale on the vertical axis, what do you notice?

To see how this guideline applies to S_N2 reactions, consider the reactions in Equations 9-9 and 9-10, involving Cl^- and Br^- as nucleophiles:

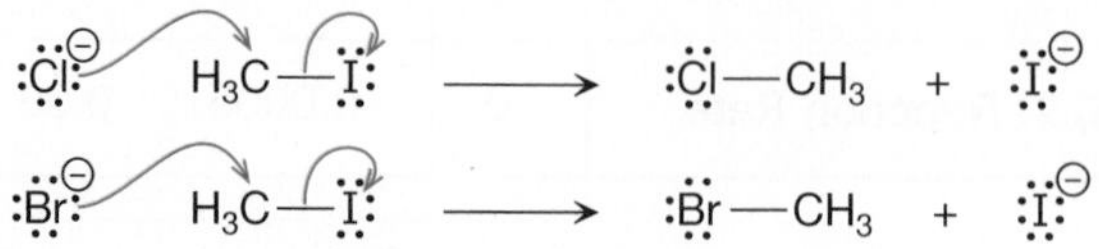

(9-9)

(9-10)

The free energy diagrams for these two reactions are shown together in **Figure 9-2**.

For both reactions, ΔG°_{rxn} is negative because I^- is more stable than either Br^- or Cl^-. (Recall from Section 6.8b that larger atoms can accommodate charges better.) Moreover, Br^- is more stable than Cl^- (Br is larger), making the set of reactants belonging to the blue curve lower in energy than the set of reactants belonging to the red curve. Thus, the reaction involving Cl^- as the nucleophile (shown by the red curve) has the more negative value for ΔG°_{rxn}. According to the guideline just discussed, this corresponds to a smaller $\Delta G^{\circ\ddagger}$ (and a faster rate) for the Cl^- reaction, which agrees with the relative rates we saw in Table 9-1.

YOUR TURN 9.4

Use the values in Table 9-1 to draw a free energy diagram, similar to the one in Figure 9-2, comparing the S_N2 reactions of NC^- with CH_3I and Br^- with CH_3I.

▸ LOOKING AHEAD

Using free energy diagrams to understand the relative rates of a particular elementary step, exemplified by Figure 9-2 for S_N2 steps, is a powerful tool that we will also apply to other elementary steps: E2 steps in Section 9.3c, electrophilic addition steps in Sections 12.3 and 25.2, and nucleophilic addition steps in Sections 18.9 and 23.2.

The comparison of free energy diagrams to understand relative nucleophile strengths is quite helpful in predicting the relative strengths of nucleophiles *not* listed in Table 9-1, including uncharged nucleophiles (see Looking Ahead box). This is explored in Solved Problem 9.1.

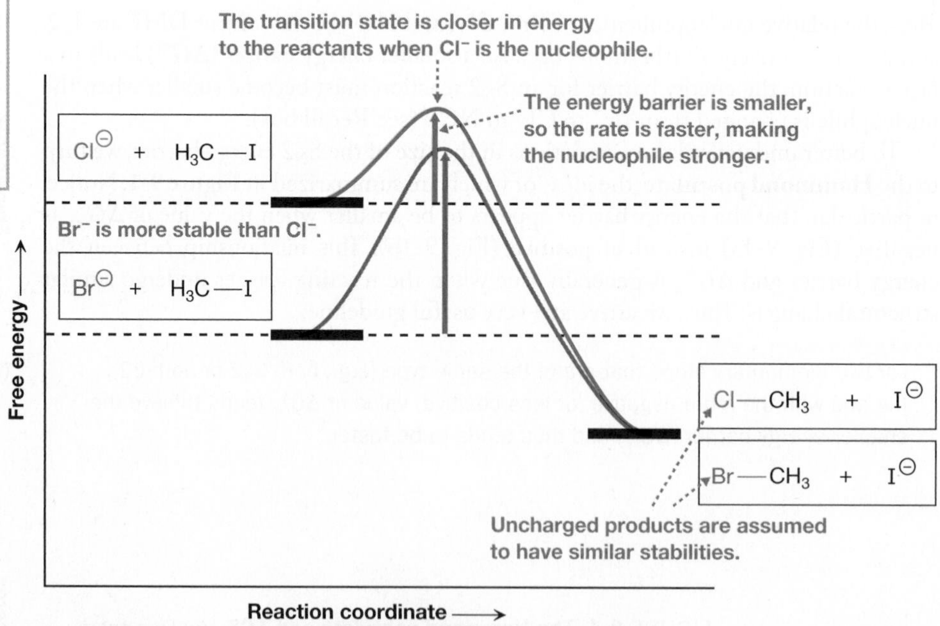

The transition state is closer in energy to the reactants when Cl⁻ is the nucleophile.
The energy barrier is smaller, so the rate is faster, making the nucleophile stronger.
Cl⊖ + H₃C—I
Br⁻ is more stable than Cl⁻.
Br⊖ + H₃C—I
Free energy
Cl—CH₃ + I⊖
Br—CH₃ + I⊖
Uncharged products are assumed to have similar stabilities.
Reaction coordinate

FIGURE 9-2 ΔG°_{rxn} and S_N2 energy barriers Free energy diagrams for the S_N2 reactions of Cl^- (red) and Br^- (blue) with CH_3I. With Cl^- as the nucleophile, the reaction is energetically more favorable. Consequently, the transition state involving Cl^- as the nucleophile lies closer in energy to the reactants than does the transition state involving Br^- as the nucleophile. This corresponds to a smaller energy barrier, and thus a faster reaction, when Cl^- is the nucleophile.

SOLVED PROBLEM **9.1**

How to predict relative strengths of nucleophiles from their structures

Break It Down **Which nucleophile will react faster with CH_3I in an S_N2 reaction: H_2O or H_2S? What does this indicate about their relative nucleophilicities?**

Think	Solve
What are the products of the two reactions?	Add curved arrows for the S_N2 reactions and draw the products. 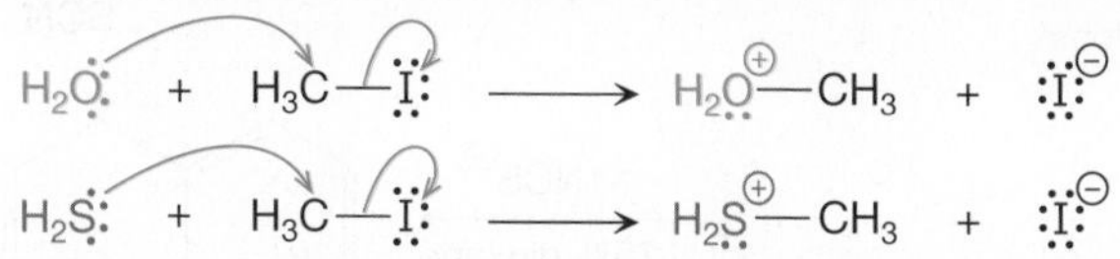
Are the products higher or lower in energy than the reactants? Do the reactants of the two reactions differ significantly in energy? Do the products?	The free energy diagrams for these reactions are given below. Both reactions are endergonic because two new charges are produced. Both sets of reactants are uncharged, so they are placed at the same energy. The set of products from the H_2S reaction is lower in energy than the set of products from the H_2O reaction, because a positive charge is more stable on the larger S atom than it is on the smaller O atom. 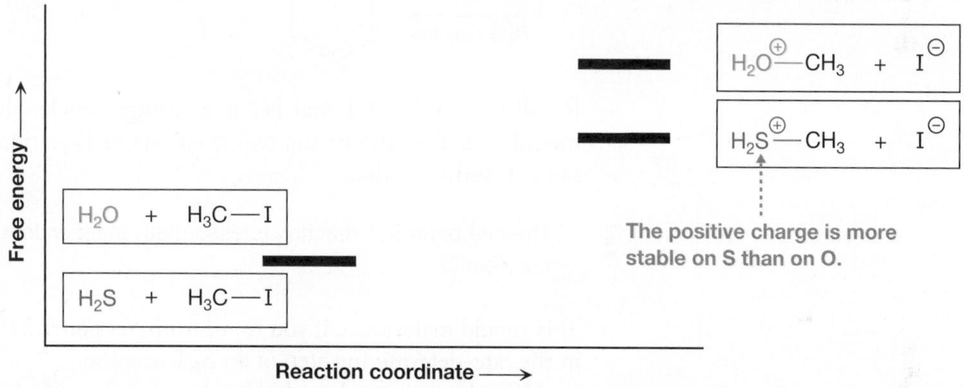 Free energy Reaction coordinate H2O + H3C—I H2S + H3C—I H2O—CH3 + I H2S—CH3 + I The positive charge is more stable on S than on O.
Which reaction has a less positive value for ΔG°_{rxn}, and how should that guide the way you draw the free energy diagrams?	The reaction in which H_2S is the nucleophile (blue curve below) has a less positive value for ΔG°_{rxn} than the reaction in which H_2O is the nucleophile (red curve below). Thus, according to the guideline derived from the Hammond postulate, the reaction involving H_2S has a smaller $\Delta G^{\circ\ddagger}$ and H_2S will react faster, making it a stronger nucleophile than H_2O. 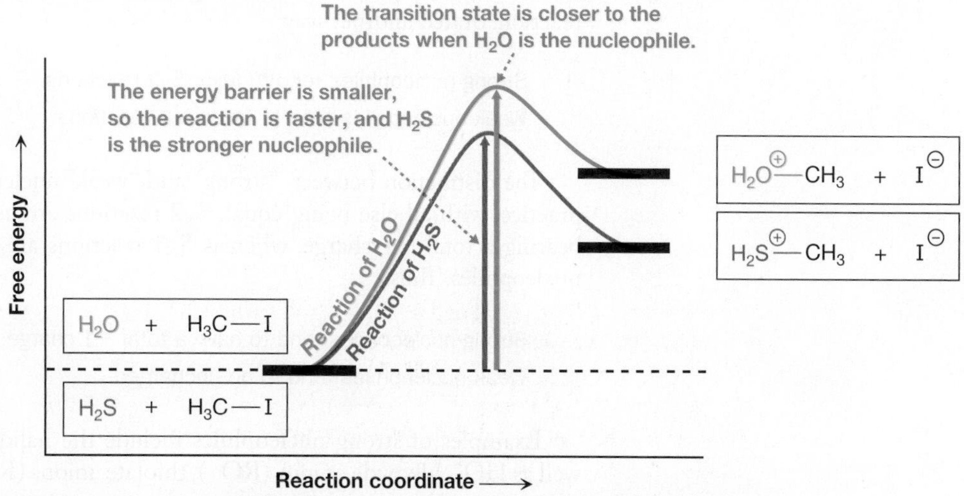 The transition state is closer to the products when H2O is the nucleophile. The energy barrier is smaller, so the reaction is faster, and H2S is the stronger nucleophile. Free energy Reaction of H2O Reaction of H2S Reaction coordinate H2O + H3C—I H2S + H3C—I H2O—CH3 + I H2S—CH3 + I

(continued)

Try It **(a)** For each pair of nucleophiles, predict which will react faster with CH_3I in an S_N2 reaction: (1) CH_3O^- or $CH_3CO_2^-$; (2) H_3N or H_3P. **(b)** Which species in each pair is the stronger nucleophile?

Answers to all Try It exercises can be found in the Solutions Manual.

How does the nucleophile influence the rate of an S_N1 reaction, such as those shown in Equation 9-11a and 9-11b? The substrate in both reactions is chlorodiphenylmethane, but the nucleophile is thiocyanate ion (NCS^-) in Equation 9-11a and azide anion (N_3^-) in Equation 9-11b:

S_N1 reactions

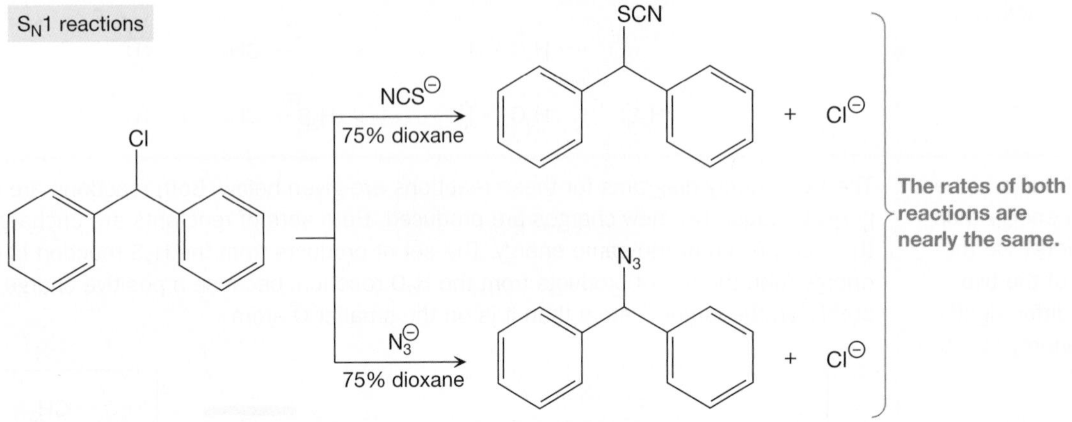

Cl
NCS⊖
75% dioxane
SCN
+ Cl⊖
N3⊖
75% dioxane
N3
+ Cl⊖
The rates of both reactions are nearly the same.

(9-11a)

(9-11b)

Recall from Table 9-1 that N_3^- is a stronger nucleophile than NCS^- by a factor of roughly 50. The rates of the two reactions in Equation 9-11, however, are about the same. It turns out that:

> The rate of an S_N1 reaction is essentially independent of the strength of the nucleophile.

This should make sense if you recall from Section 9.2 that the nucleophile has no role in the rate-determining step of an S_N1 reaction.

What happens to the *relative* rates of S_N2 and S_N1 reactions as the strength of the nucleophile changes? *The rate of an S_N2 reaction increases as the strength of the nucleophile increases, whereas the rate of an S_N1 reaction remains essentially unchanged.* If the nucleophile is strong enough, the S_N2 reaction will be faster than the S_N1 reaction. Conversely, *as the nucleophile becomes weaker, the S_N2 reaction is slowed but the S_N1 reaction is not.* If the nucleophile is weak enough, the S_N2 reaction will be slower than the S_N1 reaction. Stated another way:

- Strong nucleophiles tend to favor S_N2 reactions.
- Weak nucleophiles tend to favor S_N1 reactions.

The distinction between "strong" and "weak" nucleophiles is purely empirical. In practice, with all else being equal, S_N2 reactions are usually favored by nucleophiles bearing a total -1 charge, whereas S_N1 reactions are usually favored by uncharged nucleophiles. Thus:

- Strong nucleophiles tend to have a total -1 charge.
- Weak nucleophiles tend to be uncharged.

Examples of strong nucleophiles include the halide anions Cl^-, Br^-, and I^-, as well as HO^-, alkoxide anions (RO^-), thiolate anions (RS^-), and deprotonated amines

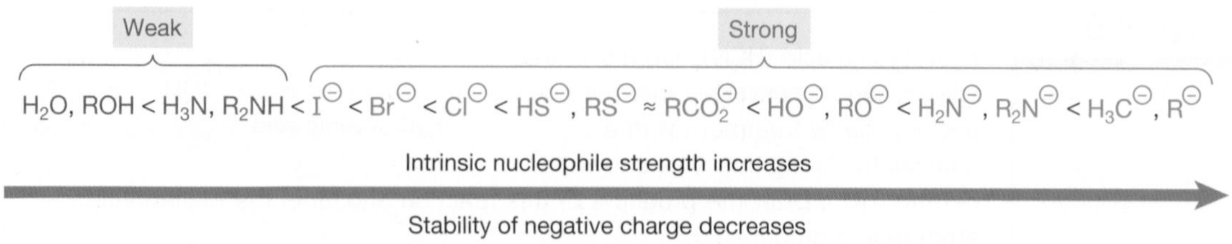
Weak
Strong
H_2O, ROH < H_3N, R_2NH < $I^{\ominus}$ < $Br^{\ominus}$ < $Cl^{\ominus}$ < $HS^{\ominus}$, $RS^{\ominus}$ ≈ $RCO_2^{\ominus}$ < $HO^{\ominus}$, $RO^{\ominus}$ < $H_2N^{\ominus}$, $R_2N^{\ominus}$ < $H_3C^{\ominus}$, $R^{\ominus}$
Intrinsic nucleophile strength increases
Stability of negative charge decreases

FIGURE 9-3 Intrinsic nucleophile strength Uncharged nucleophiles tend to be intrinsically weak, whereas negatively charged nucleophiles tend to be strong.

(R_2N^-), as shown in **Figure 9-3**. Organometallic reagents, which behave as R^-, are strong nucleophiles if the partial negative charge on carbon is sufficiently concentrated. These include alkyllithium (R—Li) and Grignard (R—MgX) reagents. Examples of weak nucleophiles include H_2O, alcohols (ROH), and amines (R_2NH).

YOUR TURN **9.5**

Is H_2P^- a strong nucleophile or a weak nucleophile? Will it favor the S_N2 or the S_N1 mechanism? Explain.

9.3b Generating Carbon Nucleophiles

As we will see in Chapter 11, nucleophilic carbon atoms are often important in synthesis, especially in the formation of carbon–carbon bonds. In uncharged molecules, however, carbon atoms are typically non-nucleophilic for two reasons: (1) They do not possess a lone pair of electrons, and (2) they are rarely considered electron-rich because they are generally bonded to atoms with electronegativities comparable to their own (e.g., hydrogen and other carbon atoms), if not greater (e.g., oxygen, nitrogen, and halogens).

A carbon atom is quite nucleophilic, however, when it bears a −1 formal charge: that is, when it is a *carbanion* (**Figure 9-4**). Carbanions not only are electron-rich but also possess a lone pair of electrons that can be used to form a bond.

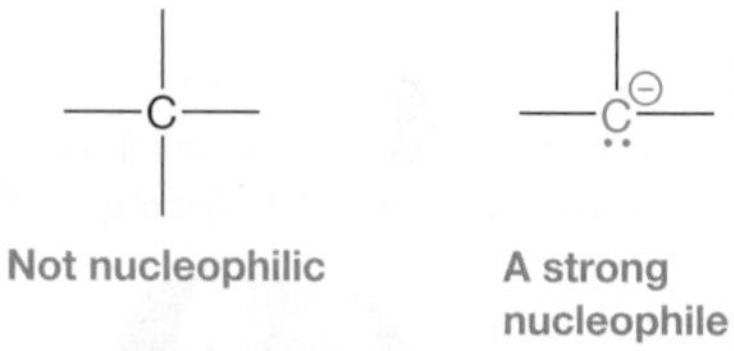
Not nucleophilic
A strong nucleophile

FIGURE 9-4 Carbon nucleophiles An uncharged, tetrahedral C atom (*left*) is not nucleophilic. A carbanion (*right*) is a strong nucleophile because of the negative charge and the lone pair of electrons.

When a nucleophilic carbon is required, it is often convenient to generate a carbanion from an uncharged carbon atom. The simplest way to do so would be to deprotonate the uncharged carbon, but carbon atoms typically do not possess acidic hydrogens. Alkanes, for example, have pK_a values around 50, so they are such weak acids that deprotonation is unfeasible. A terminal alkyne (RC≡C—H), on the other hand, is weakly acidic ($pK_a \approx 25$) and can be deprotonated much more readily (see Recall box).

◂ RECALL

Terminal alkynes are weakly acidic because the alkyne C atom is *sp*-hybridized. Recall from Section 3.9 that an *sp*-hybridized atom has a greater effective electronegativity than its sp^3-hybridized counterpart, so it can better stabilize a negative charge.

After a terminal alkyne is deprotonated (Eq. 9-12a), the resulting **alkynide anion** ($RC{\equiv}C^-$) can behave as a strong nucleophile, as shown in Equation 9-12b. Note the new C—C bond that is formed:

$$R{-}C{\equiv}CH \; + \; NaH \longrightarrow R{-}C{\equiv}C{:}^{\ominus} \; + \; H{-}H \; + \; Na^{\oplus} \qquad (9\text{-}12a)$$

Alkynide anion

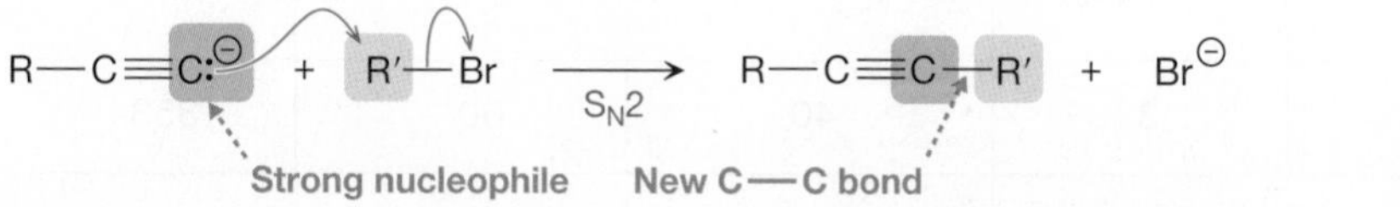
R—C≡C:
R′—Br
SN2
R—C≡C—R′
Br
Strong nucleophile
New C—C bond

(9-12b)

Terminal alkynes are not the only compounds that can be deprotonated to produce strongly nucleophilic carbons. We will discuss other examples in later chapters (see Looking Ahead box).

▸ LOOKING AHEAD

Ketones, R—(C=O)R′, and aldehydes, R—CH=O, have acidic hydrogens on α carbons (i.e., on carbons that are *adjacent* to the C=O group). As we will see in Sections 10.6 and 19.7, these compounds can be deprotonated to generate strong carbon nucleophiles as well.

YOUR TURN 9.6

Hydrocyanic acid (HCN), like a terminal alkyne, can be converted into a carbon nucleophile by treatment with a sufficiently strong base, as shown here for HO^-. Draw the products of this reaction and label the nucleophilic atom that is produced.

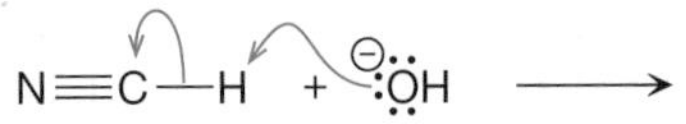

Hydrocyanic acid

YOUR TURN 9.7

Draw the complete, detailed mechanism for the S_N2 reaction that takes place when hex-1-yne is treated with NaH, followed by treatment with bromoethane.

CONNECTIONS 9.1

An apple a day . . . Just don't chew the seeds HCN (Your Turn 9.6) is found naturally in very small concentrations in the pits or seeds of some fruits, such as cherries and apples. The compound has a number of industrial uses, including as a precursor to sodium cyanide, NaCN, which is used in gold and silver mining to separate the metal from the ore.

9.3c Base Strength in E2 and E1 Reactions

Table 9-2 lists the relative rates of E2 reactions with 1,2-dichloroethane as the substrate. These data show that the relative rates of E2 reactions depend on the *strength* of the base:

> The rate of an E2 reaction generally increases as the strength of the base increases (i.e., as the pK_a of the base's conjugate acid increases).

As discussed in Section 9.2, the base has a role in the rate-determining step of an E2 reaction, which is to pull off the proton. The stronger the base, the faster this process can occur.

YOUR TURN 9.8

The pK_a of H_2S is 7.2. Would you expect an E2 reaction involving HS^- to be faster or slower than one involving $CH_3CO_2^-$?

TABLE 9-2 E2 Reaction Rates in H_2O for the Reaction:

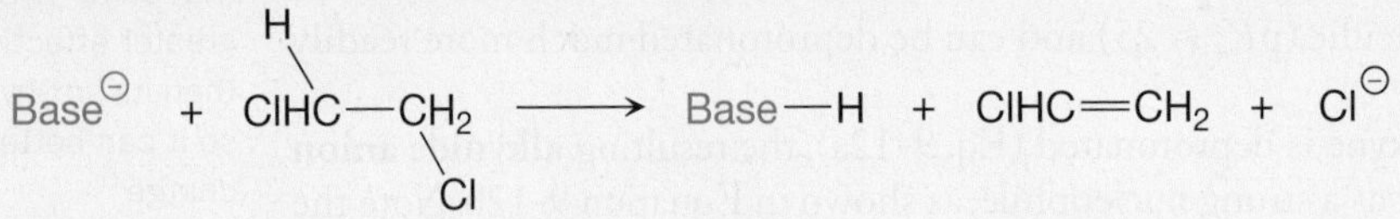

Base	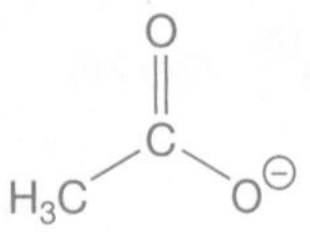		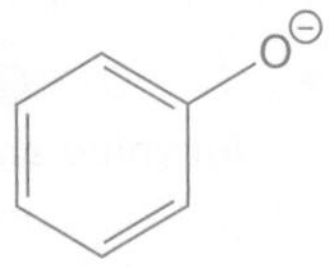	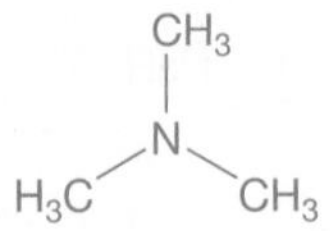	$HO^{\ominus}$
Relative E2 Reaction Rate	1	3	40	60	353
pK_a of Base—H	4.75	5.2	10.0	9.8	14.0

E2 reaction rate increases

Base strength increases

Free energy diagrams can provide insight into how the rate of an E2 reaction depends on the strength of the base. Consider the E2 reactions in Equations 9-13 and 9-14, in which 1,2-dichloroethane is the substrate and acetate anion ($CH_3CO_2^-$) and hydroxide anion (HO^-), respectively, are the bases:

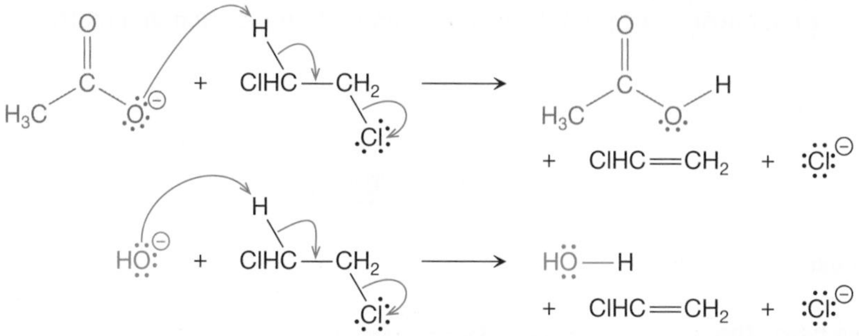

H
O
C
H3C
+ ClHC—CH2
Cl
H3C
+ ClHC═CH2 + :Cl:
HO:
HO—H

(9-13)

(9-14)

The free energy diagrams for these two reactions are shown in **Figure 9-5**. For both reactions, ΔG°_{rxn} is negative, because a negative charge is better stabilized on Cl than it is on O. Also, ΔG°_{rxn} is more negative when HO^- rather than $CH_3CO_2^-$ is the base, because the negative charge is resonance-delocalized in $CH_3CO_2^-$. Thus, using the guideline derived from the Hammond postulate (Section 9.3a), the reaction involving HO^- as the base has a smaller energy barrier and proceeds faster, as confirmed by Table 9-2.

As in S_N2 and S_N1 reactions, there is a stark contrast between the E2 and E1 reactions when it comes to the attacking species:

The rate of an E1 reaction is essentially independent of the strength of the base.

The base does not participate in an E1 reaction until the leaving group has left (i.e., until after the rate-determining step). Thus, because the base does *not* help the leaving group to depart, the strength of the base has little effect on the reaction rate.

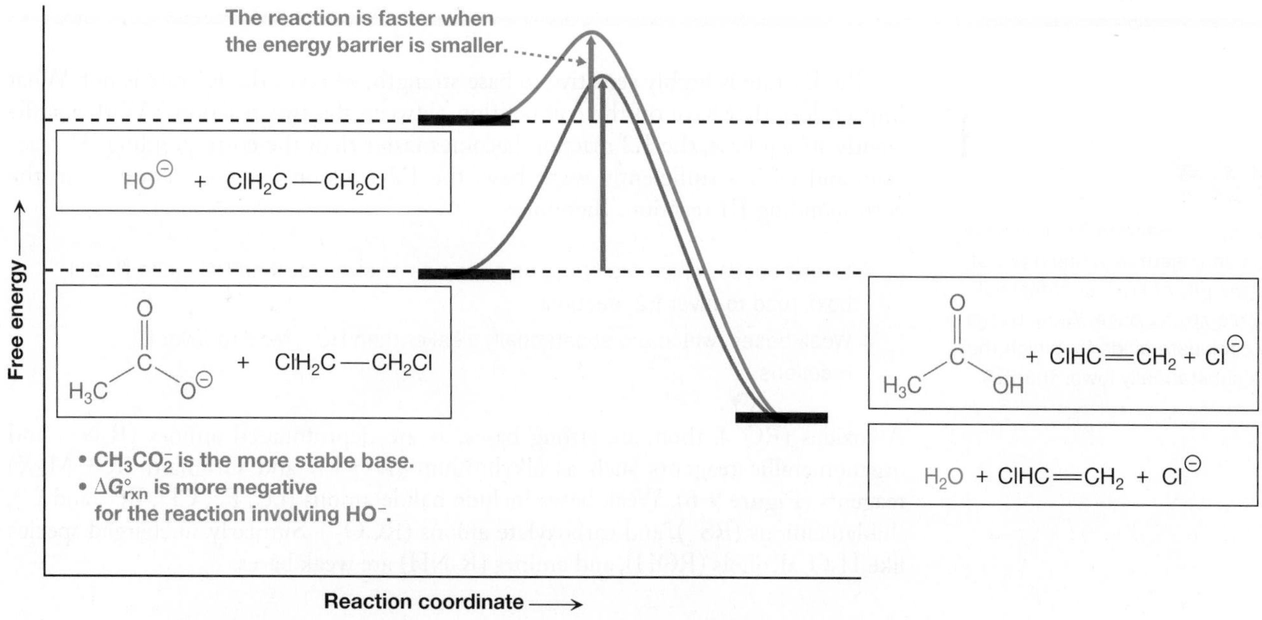

The reaction is faster when the energy barrier is smaller.
HO⊖ + ClH2C—CH2Cl
Free energy
H3C—C(=O)—O⊖ + ClH2C—CH2Cl
• CH3CO2⁻ is the more stable base.
• ΔG°rxn is more negative for the reaction involving HO⁻.
H3C—C(=O)—OH + ClHC═CH2 + Cl⊖
H2O + ClHC═CH2 + Cl⊖
Reaction coordinate

FIGURE 9-5 ΔG°_{rxn} and E2 energy barriers Free energy diagrams for the E2 reactions of HO^- (red) and $CH_3CO_2^-$ (blue) with $ClH_2C—CH_2Cl$ are shown. With HO^- as the base (i.e., with the stronger base), the reaction is energetically more favorable, has a smaller energy barrier, and proceeds faster.

CONNECTIONS 9.2

Bromocyclohexane helps us "see" really small particles

Bromocyclohexane (Solved Problem 9.2) is used as a solvent to match the refractive index of poly(methyl methacrylate) (PMMA). Refractive index matching was used in the acquisition of this high-resolution confocal microscopic image of PMMA microspheres, which have applications in biomedical research, ceramics, cosmetic additives, and self-assembled microfluidic devices.

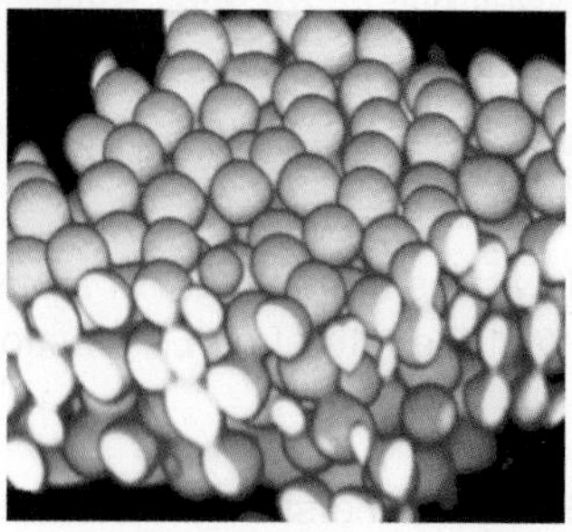

SOLVED PROBLEM **9.2**

How to relate E2 reaction rates to base strength

Break It Down **F. G. Bordwell and S. R. Mrozack carried out the following E2 elimination reaction in dimethyl sulfoxide (DMSO), using a variety of bases.**

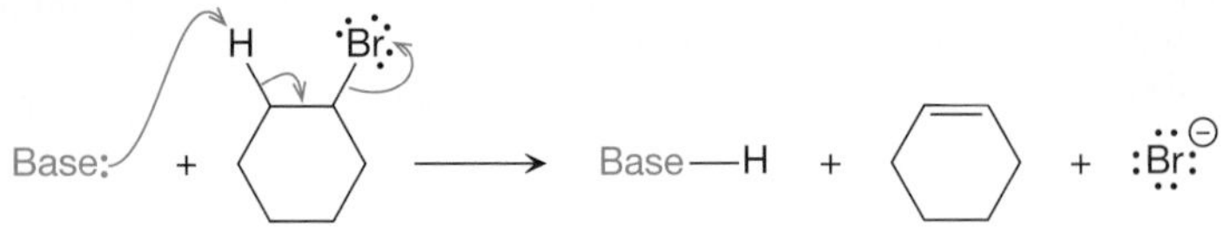

Base:
H
Br
Base—H
Br

Bromocyclohexane

Two of the bases they used, A and B, are shown here. The rate constants with these bases are 5.5×10^{-2} M^{-1} s^{-1} and 1.6×10^{-2} M^{-1} s^{-1}. From the pK_a values shown for each base's conjugate acid, Base—H (measured in DMSO), match each rate constant to the appropriate base.

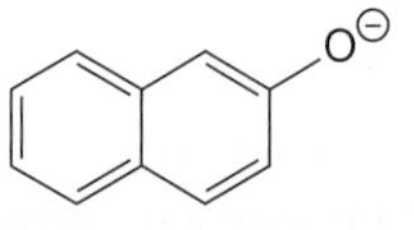

pK_a(Base—H) = 17.1

A

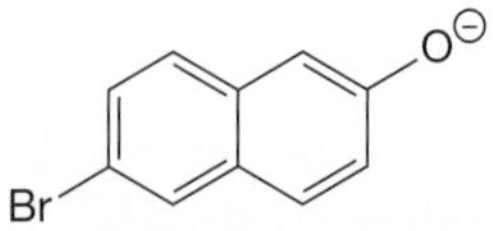

Br

pK_a(Base—H) = 16.2

B

Think	Solve
How does the strength of a base affect the rate of an E2 reaction?	Stronger bases promote faster E2 reactions, so the larger rate constant (5.5×10^{-2} M^{-1} s^{-1}) corresponds to the stronger base and the smaller rate constant (1.6×10^{-2} M^{-1} s^{-1}) corresponds to the weaker base.
How does the strength of a base correspond to the strength of its conjugate acid?	The conjugate acid of anion **A** is weaker (has a higher pK_a) than that of anion **B**, so **A** is the stronger base. Therefore, the rate constant is 5.5×10^{-2} M^{-1} s^{-1} when base **A** is used, and the rate constant is 1.6×10^{-2} M^{-1} s^{-1} when base **B** is used.

Try It Which promotes a faster E2 reaction with bromocyclohexane: **(a)** F^- or HO^-? **(b)** $CH_3CH_2O^-$ or $CF_3CH_2O^-$? Explain your answers.

◂ RECALL

As we saw in Section 8.6, any base whose conjugate acid has a pK_a of ~14 (the pK_a of H_2O) or higher will also be a strong base. Weak bases have conjugate acids for which the pK_a is substantially lower than 14.

The E2 rate is highly sensitive to base strength, whereas the E1 rate is not. What impact does that have on the competition between the two reactions? With a sufficiently strong base, the E2 reaction becomes faster than the corresponding E1 reaction, and with a sufficiently weak base, the E2 reaction becomes slower than the corresponding E1 reaction. Therefore:

- Strong bases, which are about as strong as or stronger than HO^- (see Recall box), tend to favor E2 reactions.
- Weak bases, which are substantially weaker than HO^-, tend to favor E1 reactions.

Alkoxides (RO^-), then, are strong bases, as are deprotonated amines (R_2N^-) and organometallic reagents such as alkyllithium (R—Li) and Grignard (R—MgX) reagents (**Figure 9-6**). Weak bases include halide anions (i.e., F^-, Cl^-, Br^-, and I^-), thiolate anions (RS^-), and carboxylate anions (RCO_2^-). Similarly, uncharged species like H_2O, alcohols (ROH), and amines (R_2NH) are weak bases.

Weak		Strong

$I^- < Br^- < Cl^- < H_2O, ROH < F^- < RCO_2^- < HS^-, RS^- < H_3N, R_2NH < HO^-, RO^- < H_2N^-, R_2N^- < H_3C^-, R^-$

Base strength increases →

Stability of negative charge decreases

FIGURE 9-6 Intrinsic base strength Strong bases are at least as strong as HO^-. Weak bases are significantly weaker than HO^-.

SOLVED PROBLEM **9.3**

How to predict whether a base will favor E1 or E2 reactions

Break It Down Is the phenoxide anion, $C_6H_5O^-$, a strong base or a weak base? Will it tend to favor the E1 or the E2 mechanism?

Think	Solve
What is the pK_a of C_6H_5OH, the conjugate acid of $C_6H_5O^-$? How does this compare to the pK_a of H_2O, the conjugate acid of HO^-?	As listed in Table 6-1 (p. 269), the pK_a values of C_6H_5OH and H_2O are 10.0 and 14, respectively. C_6H_5OH, therefore, is a significantly stronger acid than H_2O.
From these relative pK_a values, is $C_6H_5O^-$ a stronger or weaker base than HO^-? Does that classify $C_6H_5O^-$ as a strong or weak base?	Because C_6H_5OH is a significantly stronger acid than H_2O, $C_6H_5O^-$ is a significantly weaker base than HO^-. Being significantly weaker than HO^-, $C_6H_5O^-$ is classified as a weak base.
Are E1 reactions favored by strong or weak bases? Are E2 reactions favored by strong or weak bases?	E1 reactions are favored by weak bases, whereas E2 reactions are favored by strong bases. $C_6H_5O^-$ will therefore tend to favor the E1 reaction over the E2.

Try It Is NC^- a strong base or a weak base? Will it tend to favor the E1 or the E2 mechanism? Explain. *Hint*: Consult Appendix A.

9.3d Strong, Bulky Bases

According to the guidelines just described, the *tert*-butoxide anion, $(CH_3)_3CO^-$, should be both a strong nucleophile (because it has a full negative charge) and a strong base (because it is stronger than HO^-). Thus, it should favor both S_N2 and E2 reactions. In the competition between substitution and elimination, however, the *tert*-butoxide anion usually favors just E2 products. Why?

The *tert*-butoxide anion tends to favor the E2 reaction over S_N2 because of the bulkiness of the methyl groups surrounding the nucleophilic O^-, as shown in **Figure 9-7a**. That bulkiness makes it difficult for the O^- to form a bond to a C atom and to displace a leaving group in an S_N2 reaction; *steric*

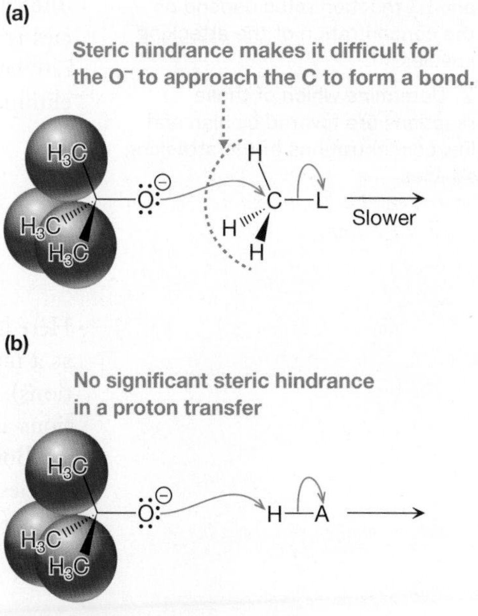

(a)
Steric hindrance makes it difficult for the O⁻ to approach the C to form a bond.
H3C
H3C
H3C
O
H
C
L
H
H
Slower
(b)
No significant steric hindrance in a proton transfer
H3C
H3C
H3C
O
H
A

FIGURE 9-7 Steric hindrance involving the *tert*-butoxide anion (a) Steric hindrance by the CH_3 groups diminishes the nucleophilicity of $(CH_3)_3CO^-$. (b) The basicity of $(CH_3)_3CO^-$ is unaffected because steric hindrance by the CH_3 groups does not come into play; protons are very small and usually well exposed.

hindrance caused by the methyl groups weakens the nucleophile and slows the reaction. The ability of the *tert*-butoxide anion to act as a base, however, is affected very little by steric hindrance, because protons are very small and are usually well exposed. Consequently, protons are pulled off by O^- easily (Fig. 9-7b). In general:

> Strong, bulky bases (such as the *tert*-butoxide anion) tend to favor E2 reactions over S_N2 reactions.

Other common strong, bulky bases include the neopentoxide anion and the anion of lithium diisopropylamide (LDA), shown in **Figure 9-8**.

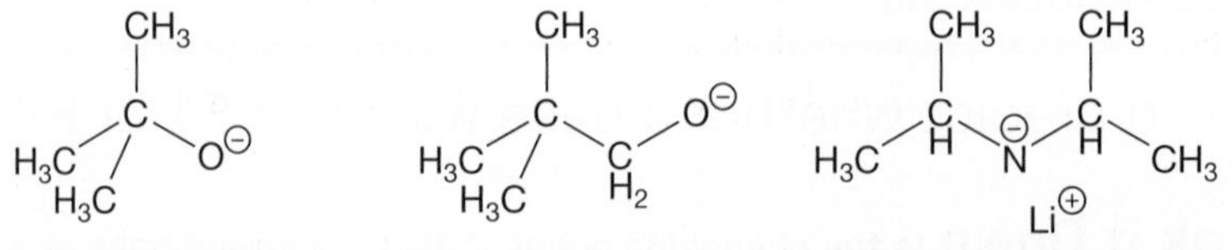

CH3
H3C
H3C
C
O⊖
CH3
H3C
H3C
C
C
H2
O⊖
CH3
CH3
H3C
C
H
N
⊖
C
H
CH3
Li⊕

***tert*-Butoxide anion** **Neopentoxide anion** **Lithium diisopropylamide (LDA)**

FIGURE 9-8 Strong, bulky bases In each case, the bulky alkyl groups attached to the negatively charged atom introduce steric hindrance to weaken the nucleophile.

YOUR TURN 9.9

Rank alkoxide nucleophiles **A–C** in order of increasing S_N2 reaction rate.

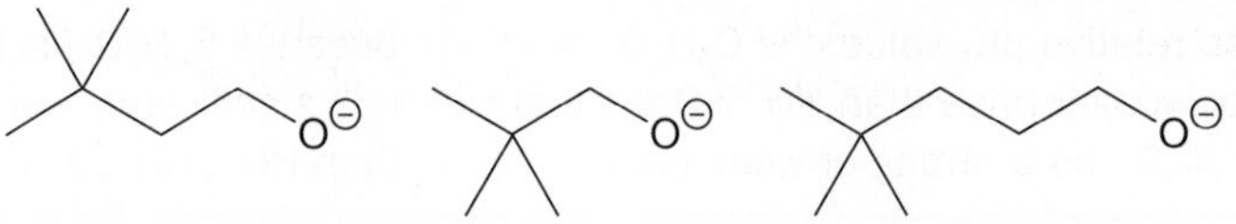

O⊖
O⊖
O⊖

A **B** **C**

SECTION 9.4 OBJECTIVES

You will be able to:

1. Explain how the S_N2, S_N1, E2, and E1 reaction rates depend on the concentration of the attacking species.
2. Determine which of those reactions are favored by high and low concentrations of the attacking species.

9.4 Factor 2: Concentration of the Attacking Species

The dependence of each reaction on the concentrations of substrate and attacking species is summarized in its respective *empirical rate law* (i.e., its experimentally derived rate law). First introduced in Chapter 8, the empirical rate laws for substitution and elimination reactions are shown again in Equations 9-15 through 9-18:

$$S_N2 \text{ Rate} = k_{S_N2}[\text{Att}^-][\text{R—L}] \quad \textbf{(9-15)}$$

$$S_N1 \text{ Rate} = k_{S_N1}[\text{R—L}] \quad \textbf{(9-16)}$$

$$\text{E2 Rate} = k_{E2}[\text{Att}^-][\text{R—L}] \quad \textbf{(9-17)}$$

$$\text{E1 Rate} = k_{E1}[\text{R—L}] \quad \textbf{(9-18)}$$

Here $[\text{Att}^-]$ represents the concentration of the attacking species, whether it is acting as a nucleophile (in the substitution reactions) or as a base (in the elimination reactions). [R—L] is the substrate concentration. The rate constants for the various reactions are different and are therefore denoted as k_{S_N2}, k_{S_N1}, k_{E2}, and k_{E1}.

Both the S_N2 and E2 reaction rates depend on the concentration of the attacking species, $[\text{Att}^-]$, which agrees with our simplified pictures of their rate-determining steps (Section 9.2). In an S_N2 or E2 reaction, the attacking species forces off the leaving group, so with a greater number of attacking species (higher concentration), the rate-determining step occurs more frequently and the rate increases. The S_N1 and E1 reaction rates, on the other hand, are independent of [Att^-], because the attacking species in an S_N1 or E1 reaction must *wait* until the leaving group has departed. In an S_N1 or E1 reaction, a higher concentration of the attacking species simply means more attacking species waiting for the leaving group to come off, but this does not affect the reaction rate.

Because S_N2, S_N1, E2, and E1 reaction rates depend differently on the concentration of the attacking species, the concentration of attacking species can be used to control the outcome of the competition. Raising the concentration of the attacking species high enough can make S_N2 and E2 reaction rates faster than the those of S_N1 and E1 reactions, assuming the attacking species is strong (that is, capable of forcing off the leaving group). Conversely, lowering the concentration of the attacking species could cause the S_N2 and E2 reactions to be slower than S_N1 and E1 reactions. These ideas are summarized as follows:

- A high concentration of a strong nucleophile or base will promote fast S_N2 or E2 reactions, favoring S_N2 or E2 reactions over S_N1 or E1 reactions.
- A low concentration of a strong nucleophile or base will promote slow S_N2 or E2 reactions, leaving the S_N1 or E1 reactions favored over S_N2 or E2 reactions.
- A weak nucleophile or base tends to favor S_N1 or E1 reactions over S_N2 or E2 reactions, regardless of concentration.

In practice, *we may assume that a high concentration of the attacking species is present unless it has been deliberately made dilute.* If the concentration is indeed dilute, this should be indicated in the reaction conditions: for example, $\xrightarrow{\text{dil } Br^-}$.

SOLVED PROBLEM **9.4**

How to determine whether concentration of the attacking species favors S_N2, S_N1, E2, or E1

Break It Down State which reaction(s)—S_N2, S_N1, E2, or E1—are favored by (a) a high concentration of HS^- and (b) a low concentration of HS^-.

Think	Solve
Is HS^- a strong nucleophile or a weak nucleophile? Is it a strong base or a weak base?	We classify HS^- as a strong nucleophile because it possesses a −1 charge. We classify HS^- as a weak base because it is significantly weaker than HO^- (the pK_a of H_2S is 7.2, which is significantly lower than 14, the pK_a of H_2O). HS^- is a significantly weaker base because S can accommodate the negative charge better than O can.
Which reactions are favored by a high concentration of the attacking species? Which are favored by a low concentration of the attacking species?	Because HS^- is a strong nucleophile, a high concentration favors S_N2 over S_N1, while a low concentration of the strong nucleophile favors S_N1 over S_N2. Because HS^- is a weak base, it will favor E1 over E2 regardless of concentration.

Try It For each of the following conditions, state whether an S_N1 or S_N2 reaction is favored and whether an E1 or E2 reaction is favored. **(a)** a high concentration of HO^-; **(b)** a low concentration of HO^-; **(c)** a high concentration of Br^-; **(d)** a low concentration of Br^-; **(e)** a high concentration of $CH_3CO_2^-$; **(f)** a low concentration of $CH_3CO_2^-$.

SECTION 9.5 OBJECTIVES

You will be able to:

1. Determine relative leaving group ability from the leaving group's stability and its base strength.
2. Determine which reactions—S_N2, S_N1, E2, or E1—are feasible, given the identity of the leaving group.
3. Explain why alcohols and ethers are reactive under acidic conditions but not under neutral or basic conditions.

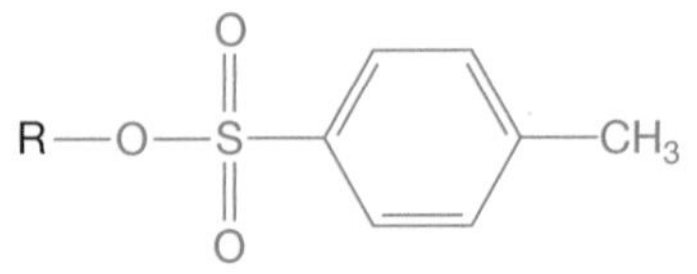

An alkyl tosylate (R—OTs)

FIGURE 9-9 The tosylate leaving group A tosylate group (red), abbreviated OTs, has excellent leaving group ability.

9.5 Factor 3: Leaving Group Ability

A leaving group must leave in the rate-determining step, whether the reaction is S_N2, S_N1, E2, or E1. Not surprisingly, then, the identity of the leaving group has an effect on the rate of each reaction. As shown in Table 9-3, for example, an alkyl tosylate (R—OTs) (**Figure 9-9**) undergoes an S_N2 reaction about 300 times faster than a comparable alkyl chloride (R—Cl). We say, therefore, that the **leaving group ability** of the tosylate anion (TsO^-) in an S_N2 reaction is 300 times greater than that of the chloride anion. More dramatically, Table 9-4 shows that the leaving group ability of TsO^- in an S_N1 reaction is about 10,000 times greater than that of Cl^-! To summarize:

- As the leaving group ability increases, S_N1 and S_N2 reactions become faster.
- S_N1 reactions are more sensitive to leaving group ability than are S_N2 reactions.

We find similar trends with E1 and E2 reactions:

- As the leaving group ability increases, E1 and E2 reactions become faster.
- E1 reactions are more sensitive to leaving group ability than are E2 reactions.

What factors explain these relative leaving group abilities? And why should the reactions have different sensitivities to leaving group ability? We answer these questions here in Section 9.5.

9.5a Leaving Group Ability, Charge Stability, and Base Strength

In all four rate-determining steps of an S_N2/S_N1/E2/E1 competition (Eqs. 9-5 through 9-8, p. 447–448), the leaving group begins as part of the substrate (R—L or R—L^+), and its charge becomes more negative by 1 when it departs as free L^- or L, respectively. Notice that free L^- or L is a product of each rate-determining step. Therefore, as free L^- or L becomes more stable, ΔG°_{rxn} for each rate-determining step

TABLE 9-3 Effects of Leaving Group Ability on Relative Rates for the S_N2 Reaction:

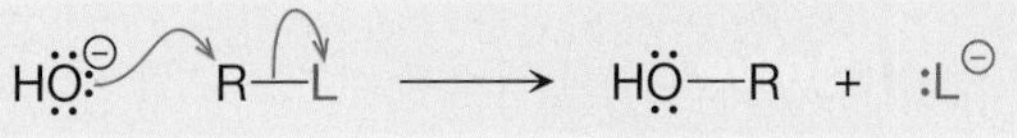

Leaving Group ($L^\ominus$)	$HO^\ominus$, $H_2N^\ominus$, $RO^\ominus$	$F^\ominus$	$Cl^\ominus$	$Br^\ominus$	$I^\ominus$	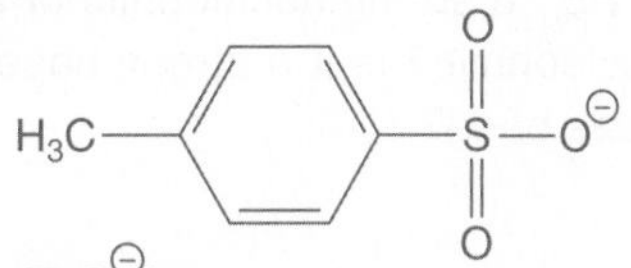 ($TsO^\ominus$)
Relative S_N2 Reaction Rate	~0	0.005	1	50	150	300
pK_a of Conjugate Acid	> 14	3.2	–7	–9	–10	–2.8

S_N2 reaction rate increases

Leaving group ability increases

TABLE 9-4 Effects of Leaving Group Ability on Relative Rates for the S_N1 Reaction:

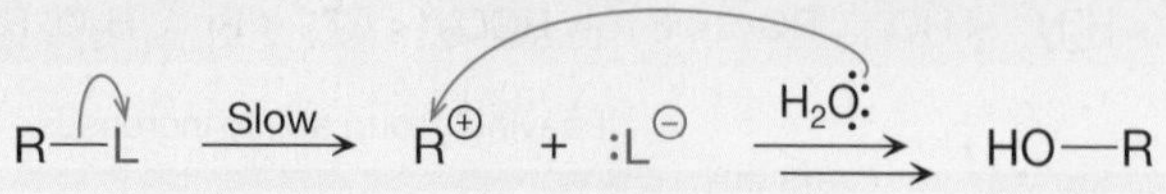

R—L
Slow
R⊕
+ :L⊖
H₂O:
HO—R

Leaving Group ($L^{\ominus}$)	$HO^{\ominus}$, $RO^{\ominus}$, $H_2N^{\ominus}$	$Cl^{\ominus}$	$Br^{\ominus}$	H_2O	$I^{\ominus}$	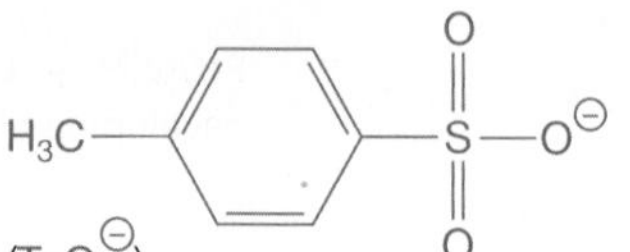 ($TsO^{\ominus}$)	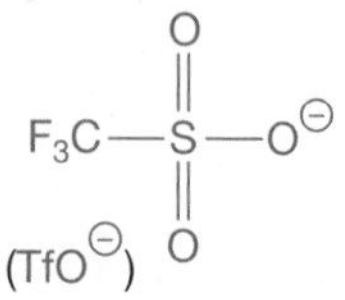 ($TfO^{\ominus}$)
Relative S_N1 Reaction Rate	~0	1	~10	~10	~100	~10,000	~100,000,000
pK_a of Conjugate Acid	> 14	–7	–9	0	–10	–2.8	–13

S_N1 reaction rate increases →

Leaving group ability increases

becomes more negative (or less positive), and as explained in Section 9.3a, the rate of the reaction increases. In other words:

> The more stable the leaving group is in its departed form (free L^- or L), the better its leaving group ability.

For example, H_2O is a much better leaving group than HO^- because water is uncharged. Similarly, Br^- is a much better leaving group than Cl^- because Br is a significantly larger atom (see Recall box).

Why should S_N1 and E1 reactions be more sensitive to leaving group ability than are S_N2 and E2 reactions? S_N1 and E1 reactions are so sensitive because the leaving group must depart on its own in the rate-determining step, as shown in **Figure 9-10a**. By contrast, in an S_N2 or E2 reaction (Fig. 9-10b), leaving group ability is less important because the departure of the leaving group is assisted by the attacking nucleophile or base.

Figure 9-11 (next page) distinguishes leaving groups as *good*, *poor*, or *unsuitable*. A good leaving group is very stable in its form as free L^- or L, so it can come off rather

◂ RECALL

According to the CARDIN-al rule for charge stability discussed in Section 6.9, uncharged species are much more stable than similar charged species, and larger atoms (lower in the periodic table) can better accommodate charges than smaller atoms can.

(a) S_N1/E1

- **Leaving group must leave on its own**
- **Very sensitive to leaving group ability**

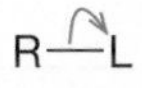

R—L

(b) S_N2/E2

- **Leaving group assisted by attacking species**
- **Not as sensitive to leaving group ability**

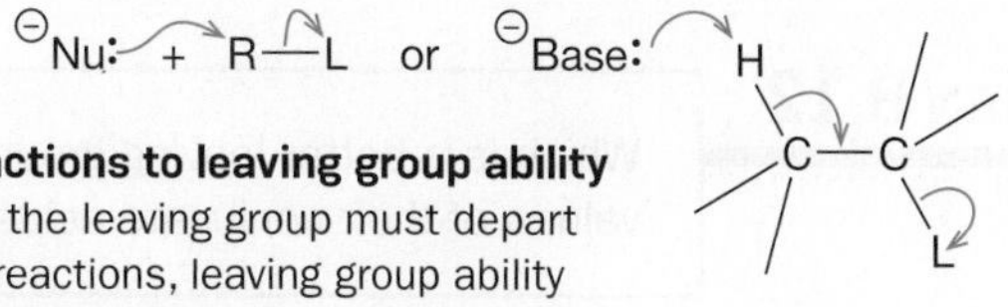

⊖Nu: + R—L or ⊖Base:
H
C—C
L

FIGURE 9-10 Sensitivity of S_N2, S_N1, E2, and E1 reactions to leaving group ability (a) In the rate-determining step of an S_N1 or E1 reaction, the leaving group must depart without assistance from the attacking species. In these reactions, leaving group ability is very important. (b) In the rate-determining step of an S_N2 or E2 reaction, leaving group ability is less important because the attacking species helps the leaving group to depart.

Unsuitable	Poor	Good
$H^{\ominus}$, $H_3C^{\ominus}$ < $H_2N^{\ominus}$ < $HO^{\ominus}$, $RO^{\ominus}$ <	$F^{\ominus}$ < $RCO_2^{\ominus}$ <	$Cl^{\ominus}$ < $Br^{\ominus}$, H_2O, ROH < $I^{\ominus}$ < $MsO^{\ominus}$ < $TsO^{\ominus}$ < $TfO^{\ominus}$

Leaving group ability increases →

Charge stability generally increases

FIGURE 9-11 Leaving group ability Good leaving groups tend to accommodate a developing negative charge rather well. Poor leaving groups do not.

easily from the substrate, either with assistance from the attacking species or on its own. A poor leaving group is less stable as free L^- or L, so it cannot come off easily on its own without assistance from the attacking species. An unsuitable leaving group is much less stable and generally will not come off at all, even with assistance from the attacking species. To summarize:

- With a *good* leaving group, S_N2, S_N1, E2, and E1 reactions are all feasible.
- With a *poor* leaving group, only S_N2 and E2 reactions tend to be feasible.
- With an *unsuitable* leaving group, S_N2, S_N1, E2, and E1 reactions all tend to be unfeasible.

YOUR TURN **9.10**

Which reactions would be feasible—S_N2, S_N1, E2, or E1—if the leaving group were **(a)** H^-? **(b)** H_2O? **(c)** F^-? If none of the reactions are feasible, state so.

Conveniently, relative leaving group abilities correlate rather well with relative base strengths:

Better leaving groups tend to be weaker bases.

This is because weaker bases are more stable (they have less driving force to pick up a proton), and the charge-stability factors that contribute to stabilizing a base are the same factors that contribute to stabilizing a leaving group. Therefore, recalling that weaker bases have stronger conjugate acids, you can quickly identify the better of two leaving groups if you know the pK_a values of their conjugate acids:

The better of two leaving groups is generally the one that has the conjugate acid with lower pK_a value.

YOUR TURN **9.11**

(a) From the pK_a value of its conjugate acid, identify the leaving group in Table 9-4 that is the *weakest base*. **(b)** How does the S_N1 reaction rate involving that leaving group compare with the others? **(c)** To demonstrate, in part, why that leaving group is so stable, draw all of its resonance structures.

YOUR TURN **9.12**

Which is a better leaving group, HCO_2^- or $C_6H_5O^-$? *Hint*: What are the pK_a values of their conjugate acids?

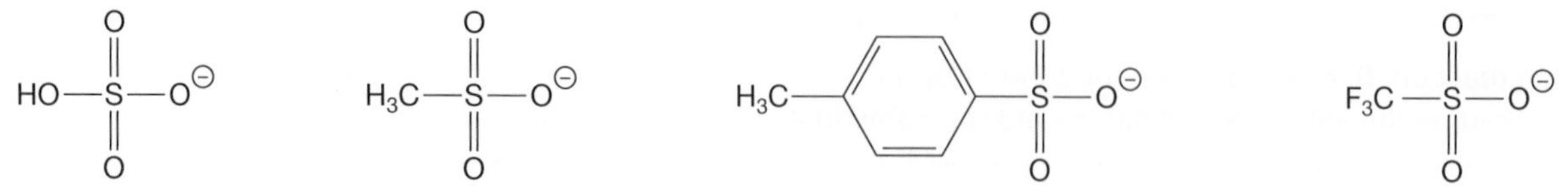
HO—S—O
H3C—S—O
H3C—
—S—O
F3C—S—O

Bisulfate anion | **Methanesulfonate (Mesylate, MsO⁻)** | ***p*-Toluenesulfonate (Tosylate, TsO⁻)** | **Trifluoromethanesulfonate (Triflate, TfO⁻)**

FIGURE 9-12 **Sulfonate leaving groups** The excellent leaving group abilities of the mesylate, tosylate, and triflate groups derive from the same type of resonance and inductive stabilization exhibited by the bisulfate anion, HSO_4^-.

The correlation between base strength and leaving group ability is particularly useful when it comes to identifying good leaving groups:

Good leaving groups are the conjugate bases of strong acids.

HCl, HBr, H_3O^+, and HI are all strong acids, which is consistent with Cl^-, Br^-, H_2O, and I^- being good leaving groups. Moreover, the tosylate anion (TsO^-), the mesylate anion (MsO^-), and the triflate anion (TfO^-), all classified as **sulfonates** (**Figure 9-12**), are structurally very similar to the bisulfate anion (HSO_4^-). HSO_4^- is the conjugate base of sulfuric acid, which is among the strongest acids known, so TsO^-, MsO^-, and TfO^- are among the best leaving groups.

SOLVED PROBLEM **9.5**

How to determine relative E1 and E2 rates from the base and leaving group

Break It Down Which reaction, A–C, will proceed the *fastest* by the E1 mechanism? Which will proceed the *slowest* by the E2 mechanism? (Assume the initial concentrations are the same in each reaction.)

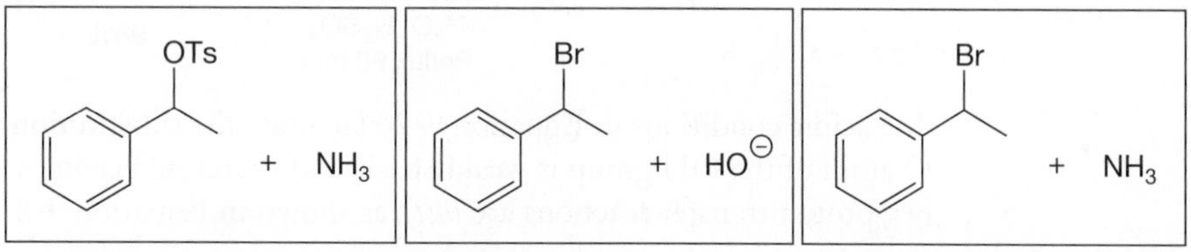
OTs
+ NH3
Br
+ HO
Br
+ NH3

A **B** **C**

Think	Solve
What are the leaving groups? Which one is a better leaving group? What are the bases? Which one is a stronger base?	TsO^- is the leaving group in reaction **A**, whereas Br^- is the leaving group in reactions **B** and **C**. NH_3 is the base in reactions **A** and **C**, whereas HO^- is the base in reaction **B**. The better leaving group is TsO^-, and the stronger base is HO^-.
How are E1 reaction rates affected by leaving group ability and by base strength?	E1 reaction rates are sensitive to leaving group ability but not to base strength. Because TsO^- is a better leaving group than Br^-, reaction **A** will proceed the fastest by the E1 mechanism.
How are E2 reaction rates affected by leaving group ability and by base strength?	E2 reaction rates are sensitive to both leaving group ability and base strength. Because Br^- is a worse leaving group than TsO^- and NH_3 is a weaker base than HO^-, reaction **C** will proceed the slowest by the E2 mechanism.

(continued)

Try It Which reaction, **D–F**, will proceed the *slowest* by the E1 mechanism? Which will proceed the *fastest* by the E2 mechanism? (Assume the initial concentrations are the same in each reaction.)

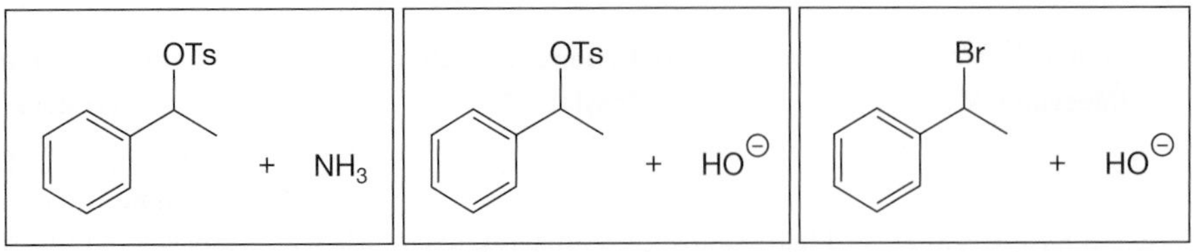

OTs
+ NH3
OTs
+ HO⊖
Br
+ HO⊖

D **E** **F**

9.5b Converting a Poor Leaving Group into a Good Leaving Group

Consider Equation 9-19, in which Br^- is added to butan-1-ol under neutral conditions (i.e., no strong acids or bases present):

OH
+ NaBr
H2O
No reaction

(9-19)

No reaction takes place because the leaving group, which would depart as HO^-, is unsuitable (review Fig. 9-11). Under acidic conditions, however, a reaction does take place, as shown in Equation 9-20:

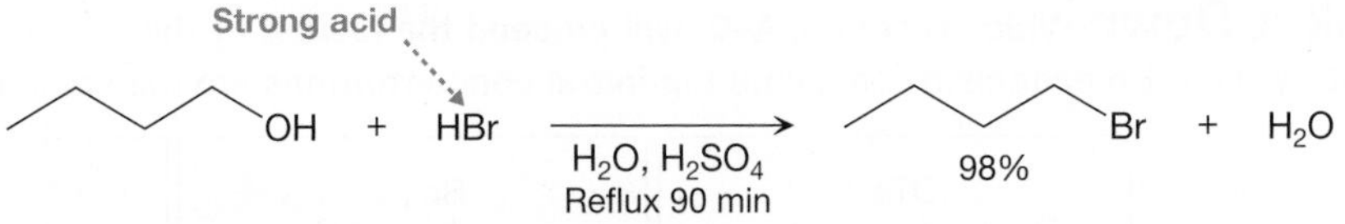

Strong acid
OH
+ HBr
H2O, H2SO4
Reflux 90 min
Br
98%
+ H2O

(9-20)

The acidic conditions in Equation 9-20 facilitate the substitution reaction because the O atom of the OH group is weakly basic and therefore becomes protonated (remember, proton transfer reactions are *fast*), as shown in Equation 9-21:

Mechanism for the S_N2 reaction of an alcohol under acidic conditions (Eq. 9-20)

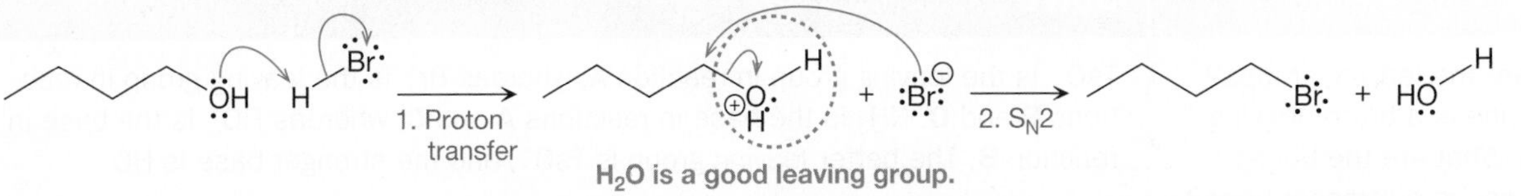

OH
H
Br
1. Proton transfer
H
O
H
+ :Br:
2. SN2
H2O is a good leaving group.
Br
+ HO
H

(9-21)

The leaving group then leaves as H_2O rather than HO^-. Being uncharged, H_2O is much more stable than HO^- and is a *good* leaving group (review Fig. 9-11).

YOUR TURN **9.13**

Circle the potential leaving group in both the reactant and product of the proton transfer reaction shown. Next to each, write the form of the leaving group in which it would depart, and label it as either a good, poor, or unsuitable leaving group.

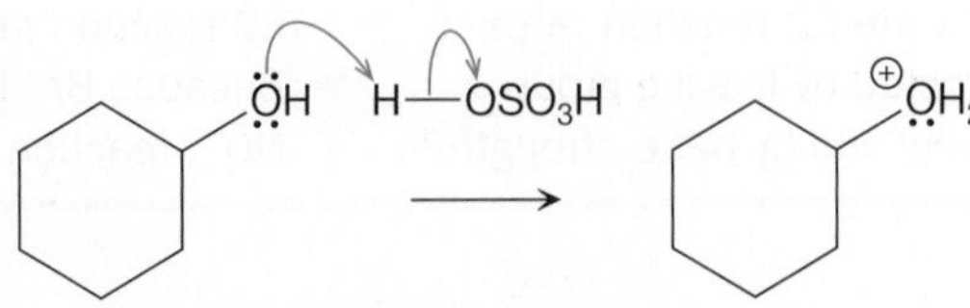

OH
H—OSO3H
⊕OH2

The protonation of ethers works in much the same way. Under neutral conditions (Eq. 9-22), 2-methoxyphenol ($HOC_6H_4OCH_3$) does not undergo nucleophilic substitution or elimination reactions because the leaving group would depart as an RO^- anion, which is an unsuitable leaving group. A reaction does take place, however, under acidic conditions, as shown in Equation 9-23:

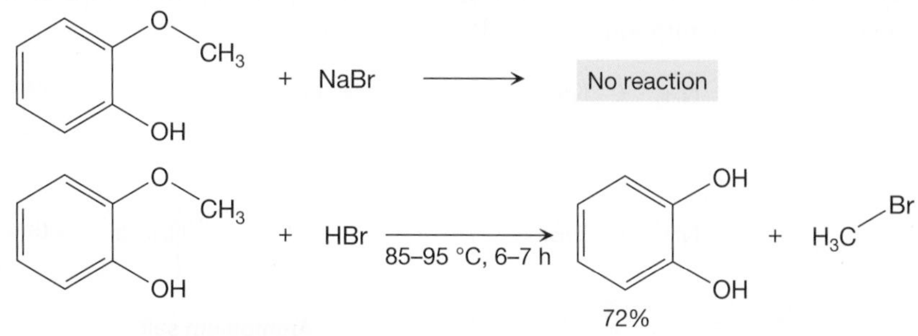

CH3
+ NaBr
No reaction
OH
CH3
+ HBr
85–95 °C, 6–7 h
OH
OH
+ H3C
Br
OH
72%

(9-22)

(9-23)

Just as we saw in Equation 9-21, protonation of the O atom (Eq. 9-24) generates an excellent leaving group: an uncharged and very weakly basic molecule, HOC_6H_4OH. (Although the protonated intermediate could instead be viewed with CH_3OH as the leaving group, we will learn in Section 9.6a that the sp^2-hybridized carbon to which it is attached is unreactive in S_N2 reactions.)

CONNECTIONS 9.3

2-Methoxyphenol: Beverages and plagues 2-Methoxyphenol (Eq. 9-22), commonly called guaiacol, is found in essential oils from a variety of plants and is partly responsible for the flavor of coffee and whiskey. The compound is also one of the pheromones that cause desert locusts to swarm, a crop-destroying phenomenon that has plagued several countries in recent years.

Mechanism for the S_N2 reaction of an ether under acidic conditions (Eq. 9-23)

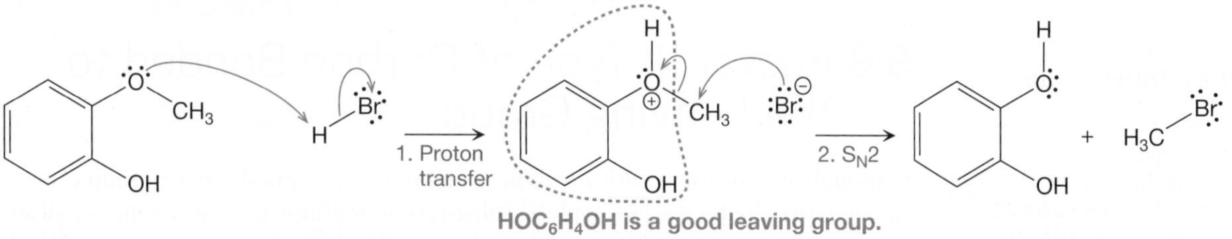

CH3
H
Br
1. Proton transfer
H
CH3
Br
OH
2. SN2
H
OH
+ H3C
Br
HOC6H4OH is a good leaving group.

(9-24)

Generating a good leaving group in this fashion can also facilitate elimination reactions, as shown in the **dehydration** reaction in Equation 9-25:

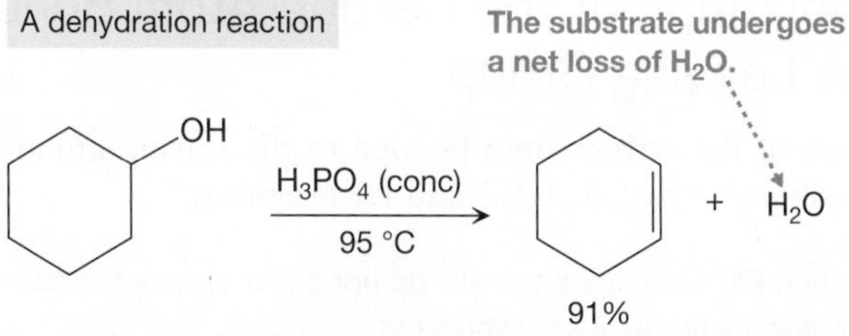

A dehydration reaction
The substrate undergoes a net loss of H2O.
OH
H3PO4 (conc)
95 °C
+ H2O
91%

(9-25)

HO^- would be the leaving group under neutral conditions, but acidic conditions generate a water leaving group, as shown in the mechanism in Equation 9-26:

Mechanism for the dehydration of an alcohol under acidic conditions (Eq. 9-25)

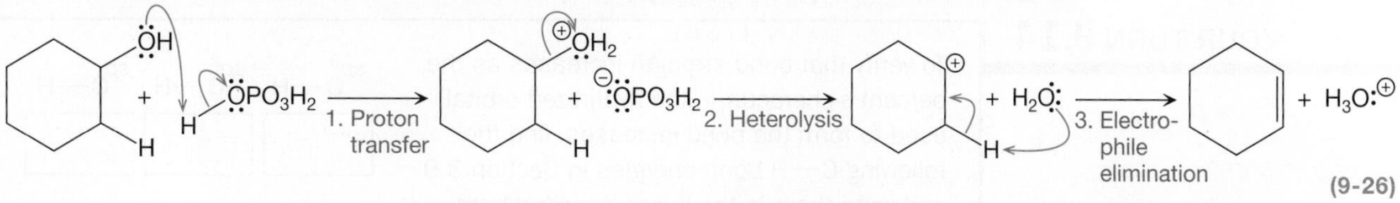

OH
+
H
OPO3H2
1. Proton transfer
H
OH2
+ OPO3H2
2. Heterolysis
+ H2O
H
3. Electrophile elimination
+ H3O

(9-26)

Like alcohols and ethers, amines tend *not* to undergo nucleophilic substitution or elimination reactions under normal conditions (Eq. 9-27). To occur, these reactions would require the departure of a very poor leaving group: namely, H_2N^-, HRN^-, or R_2N^-. Protonation of the mildly basic nitrogen of the amino group would make the leaving group better, but *even under acidic conditions, amines tend not to act as substrates in nucleophilic substitution or elimination reactions.* Instead, the reaction stops at the formation of the ammonium ion (Eq. 9-28):

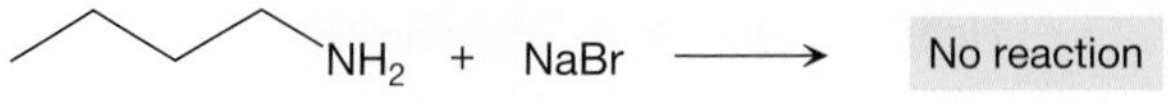

NH2
+
NaBr
No reaction

(9-27)

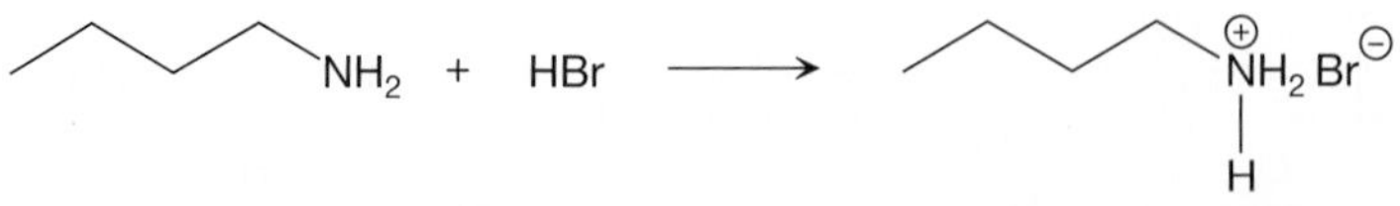

NH2
+
HBr
NH2 Br
H

(9-28)

Ammonium salt
(No S_N2 reaction)

Why do protonated alcohols tend to undergo nucleophilic substitution and elimination reactions but protonated amines do not? Recall from Section 9.5a that good leaving groups are the conjugate bases of strong acids. The leaving group in a protonated alcohol is H_2O, the conjugate base of the *strong* acid H_3O^+. By contrast, the leaving group in a protonated primary amine is NH_3, the conjugate base of the *weak* acid, NH_4^+.

9.6 Factor 4: Type of Carbon Bonded to the Leaving Group

SECTION 9.6 OBJECTIVES

You will be able to:

1. Determine which reactions—S_N2, S_N1, E2, or E1—are feasible on the basis of the type of carbon bonded to the leaving group.
2. Predict relative S_N2, S_N1, E2, and E1 reaction rates from the substrate structure.

Although any substrate with a carbon atom bonded to a good leaving group can *theoretically* participate in a nucleophilic substitution or elimination reaction, not all such reactions are *practical* under normal conditions. The nature of the carbon atom bonded to the leaving group can dramatically influence the outcome of these reactions. Relevant factors include the particular hybridization of the carbon, the number of alkyl groups to which it is bonded, and the proximity of double or triple bonds.

9.6a Hybridization of the Carbon Atom Bonded to the Leaving Group

◂ RECALL

Section 3.9 showed that a hybrid orbital becomes more compact as its *s*-character increases. A more compact hybrid orbital holds electrons closer to its nucleus, so the atom that supplies the hybrid orbital forms shorter and stronger bonds and behaves as if it were more electronegative.

The hybridization of the carbon atom bonded to the leaving group has a dramatic effect on the feasibility of S_N2, S_N1, E2, and E1 reactions:

S_N2, S_N1, E2, and E1 reactions generally do *not* occur unless the carbon atom bonded to the leaving group is sp^3-hybridized.

Why should the carbon atom's hybridization have such an impact? As we saw in Section 3.9, sp^2- and sp-hybridized carbons have more *s*-character than do sp^3-hybridized carbons (see Recall box). With more *s*-character, sp^2- and sp-hybridized carbons form stronger σ bonds, thereby making it more difficult for the leaving group to leave.

YOUR TURN **9.14**

To verify that bond strength increases as the percent *s*-character in the hybridized orbital used to form the bond increases, find the following C—H bond energies in Section 3.9 and write them in the boxes provided here.

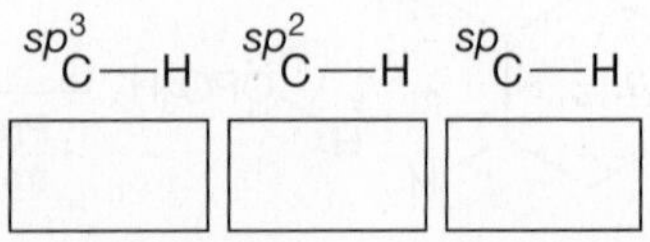

sp3 C—H
sp2 C—H
sp C—H

With greater *s*-character, sp^2- and *sp*-hybridized carbons have higher effective electronegativity values than sp^3-hybridized carbons. Higher effective electronegativity is particularly unfavorable for S_N1 and E1 reactions, in which the carbon gains a positive charge in the rate-determining step (Eq. 9-29a and 9-29b).

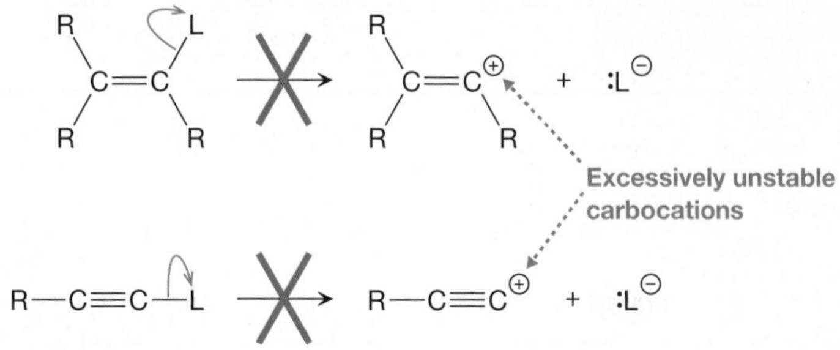

(9-29a)

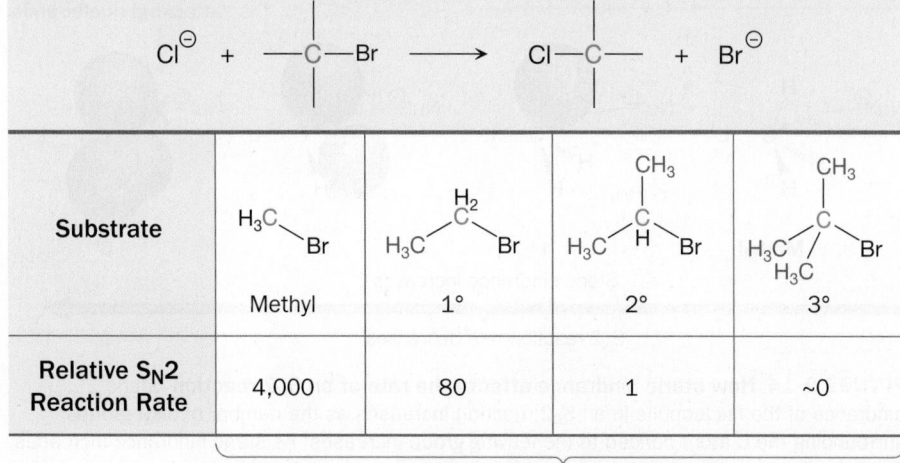

Excessively unstable carbocations

(9-29b)

S_N2 reactions are especially hindered with the leaving group on an *sp*- or sp^2-hybridized carbon due to electrostatic repulsion. As we learned in Section 7.6, C=C and C≡C bonds are relatively electron-rich, so they repel an incoming negatively charged nucleophile (**Figure 9-13**).

> Which carbon atom in the molecule shown here would undergo nucleophilic substitution most readily? Explain.

YOUR TURN **9.15**

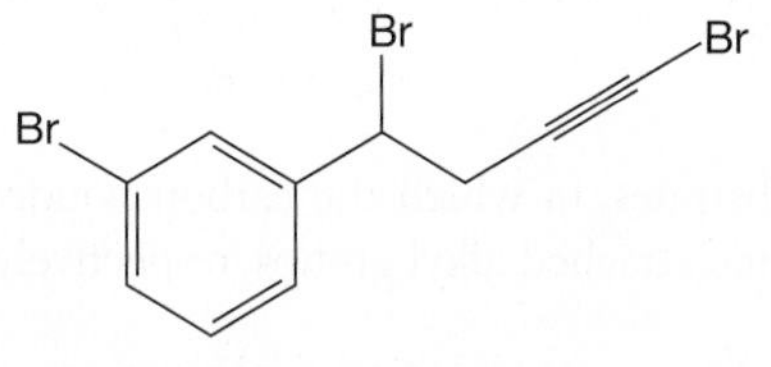

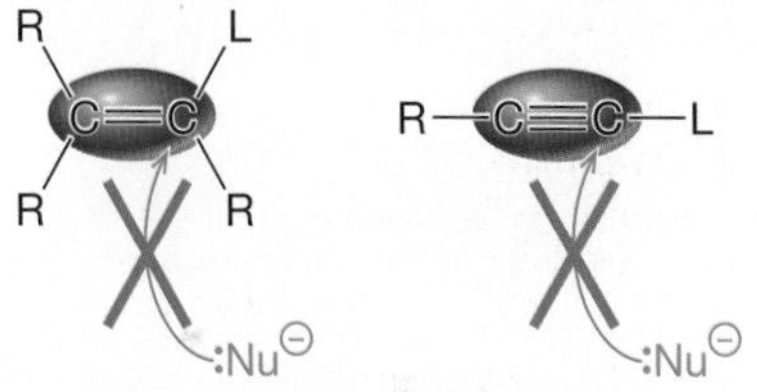

The π electrons in the C=C and C≡C bonds repel negatively charged nucleophiles.

FIGURE 9-13 Electrostatic repulsion between π electrons and a nucleophile When a leaving group is bonded to an alkene or an alkyne carbon, S_N2 reactions are hindered by repulsion between the negatively charged π electron cloud and the incoming nucleophile.

9.6b Number of Alkyl Groups on the Carbon Bonded to the Leaving Group

Even with a good leaving group on an sp^3-hybridized carbon atom, nucleophilic substitution and elimination reactions can be strongly influenced by the number of alkyl groups bonded to that carbon, as shown in Tables 9-5 and Table 9-6. In each table, the relative reaction rates are shown for *methyl*, *primary* (1°), *secondary* (2°), and *tertiary* (3°)

TABLE 9-5 Relative Reaction Rates for the S_N2 Reaction:

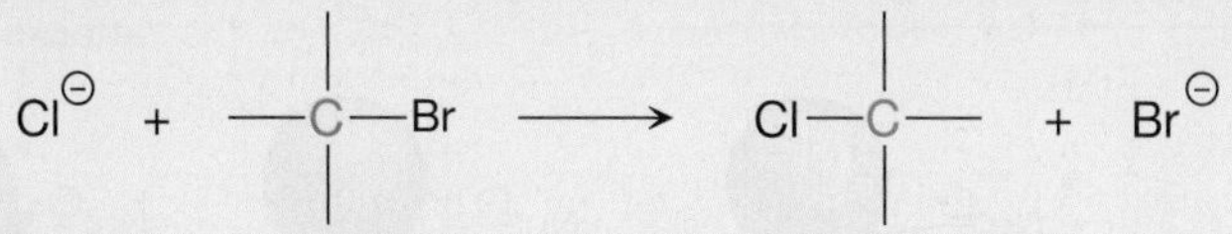

$$Cl^{\ominus} + \overset{|}{\underset{|}{C}}-Br \longrightarrow Cl-\overset{|}{\underset{|}{C}} + Br^{\ominus}$$

Substrate	H₃C—Br	H₃C—C(H₂)—Br	H₃C—CH(CH₃)—Br	(H₃C)(H₃C)C(CH₃)—Br
	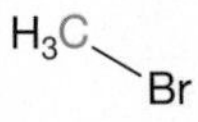 Methyl	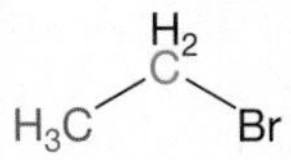 1°	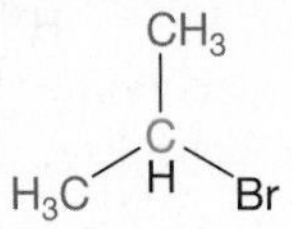 2°	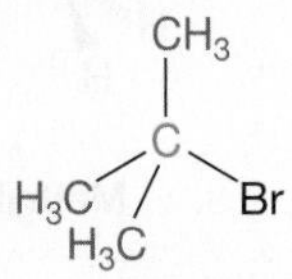 3°
Relative S_N2 Reaction Rate	4,000	80	1	~0

Number of alkyl groups increases

S_N2 reaction rate decreases

TABLE 9-6 Relative Reaction Rates for the S_N1 Reaction:

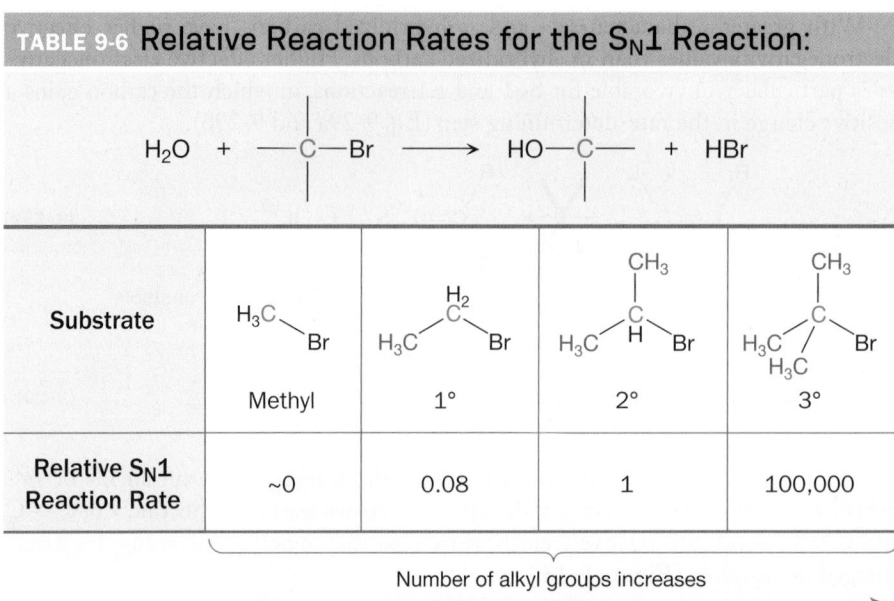

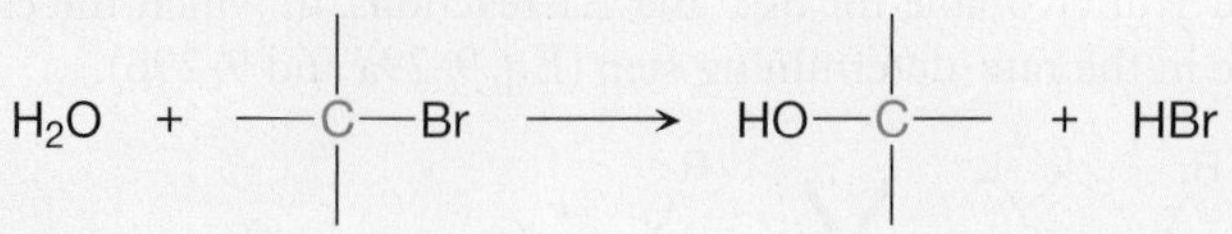

Substrate	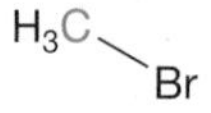 Methyl	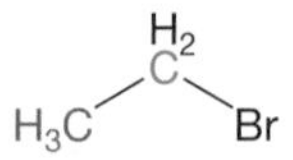 1°	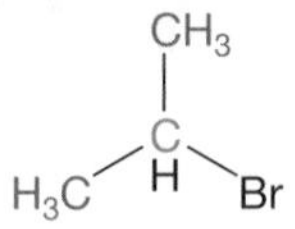 2°	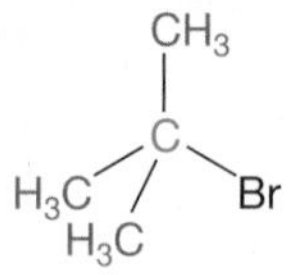 3°
Relative S_N1 Reaction Rate	~0	0.08	1	100,000

Number of alkyl groups increases

S_N1 reaction rate increases

substrates, in which the carbon bonded to the leaving group has zero, one, two, and three attached alkyl groups, respectively. Specifically:

> As the number of alkyl groups on the carbon atom to which the leaving group is bonded increases, the S_N2 reaction rate sharply *decreases* (Table 9-5), whereas the S_N1 reaction rate sharply *increases* (Table 9-6).

To understand why the number of alkyl groups affects reaction rates in these ways, let's revisit their mechanisms. For an S_N2 reaction, recall that the nucleophile *forces off the leaving group*. Each alkyl group surrounding the carbon atom bonded to the leaving group adds *steric hindrance* (**Figure 9-14**), similar to what we saw with the *tert*-butoxide anion, $(CH_3)_3CO^-$, in Section 9.3d. With greater steric hindrance surrounding the C—L carbon in the substrate, it becomes more difficult for the nucleophile to attack

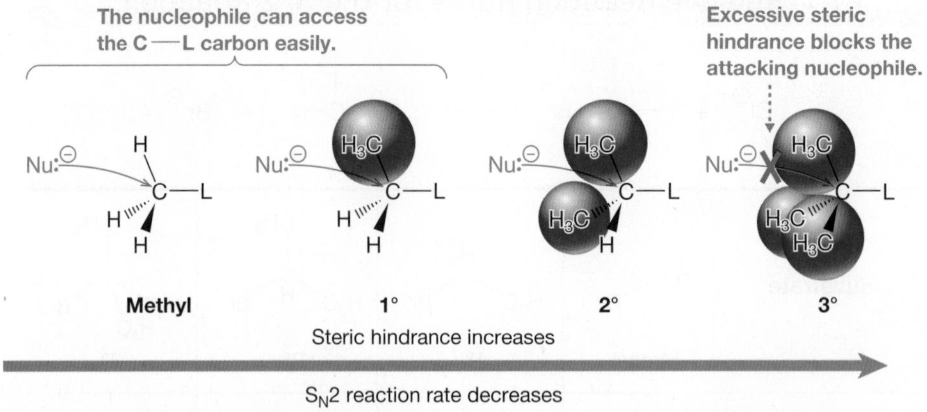
The nucleophile can access the C—L carbon easily.
Excessive steric hindrance blocks the attacking nucleophile.
Methyl
1°
2°
3°
Steric hindrance increases
S_N2 reaction rate decreases

FIGURE 9-14 How steric hindrance affects the rate of an S_N2 reaction Steric hindrance of the nucleophile in an S_N2 reaction increases as the number of alkyl groups surrounding the C atom bonded to the leaving group increases. As steric hindrance increases, the S_N2 reaction rate decreases.

and the S_N2 rate decreases. Importantly, that steric hindrance becomes excessive with three alkyl groups:

S_N2 reactions do not take place for tertiary substrates, $R_3C—L$.

In an S_N1 reaction, the reaction rate is dictated by the ability of the leaving group to leave, so steric hindrance of the nucleophile does not come into play. Instead, *each additional alkyl group, which is electron-donating, stabilizes the carbocation intermediate that is produced and thus helps the leaving group to leave* (**Figure 9-15**). A tertiary substrate reacts the fastest because the carbocation it produces has the maximum number of alkyl groups (three), making it the most stable (see Recall box). Secondary substrates react more slowly because the carbocation that is produced has only two stabilizing alkyl groups. Methyl and primary substrates produce carbocations that are excessively unstable. Consequently:

S_N1 reactions do not take place for methyl substrates ($H_3C—L$) and most primary substrates ($RCH_2—L$).

E1 reaction rates depend on the number of alkyl groups in the same way as S_N1 reaction rates:

The rate of an E1 reaction increases as the number of alkyl groups on the carbon bonded to the leaving group increases.

E1 and S_N1 reaction rates depend on carbocation stability in the same way because they both have *exactly* the same rate-determining step. (See Solved Problem 9.6.) Therefore, like S_N1 reactions:

E1 reactions do not take place for methyl substrates ($H_3C—L$) and most primary substrates ($RCH_2—L$).

◂ RECALL

Section 7.9 explained that alkyl groups attached to C^+ in a carbocation are electron-donating, and thus stabilizing, due to both inductive effects (distortion of electron density through bonds) and hyperconjugation (mixing of filled σ bonding orbitals in an alkyl group with the empty *p* orbital of C^+).

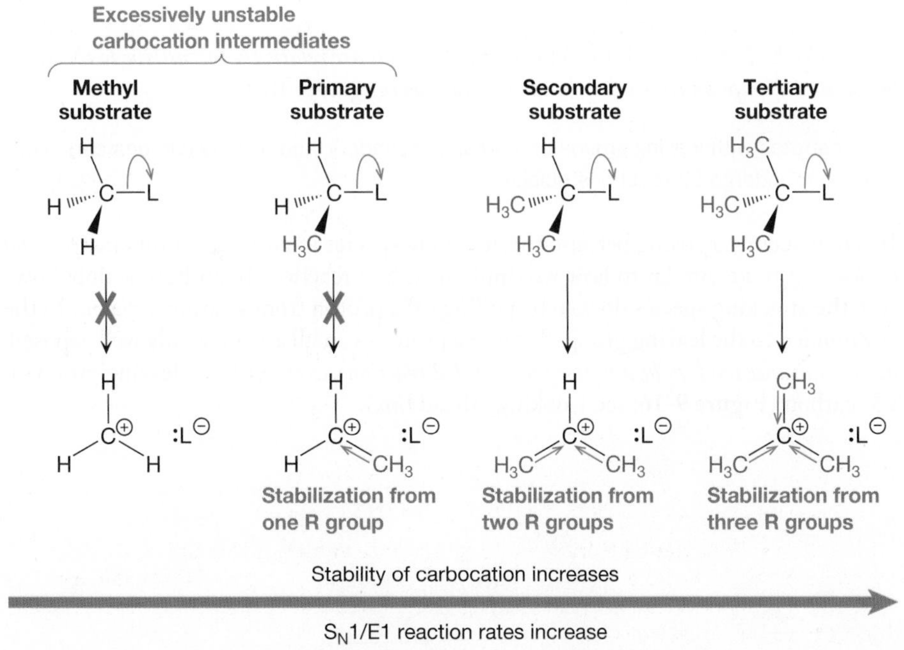
Excessively unstable
carbocation intermediates
Methyl substrate
Primary substrate
Secondary substrate
Tertiary substrate
Stabilization from one R group
Stabilization from two R groups
Stabilization from three R groups
Stability of carbocation increases
SN1/E1 reaction rates increase

FIGURE 9-15 How S_N1 and E1 reaction rates depend on carbocation stability Carbocation stability increases as the number of alkyl groups bonded to the positively charged C of a carbocation increases. In the substrate, therefore, each alkyl group surrounding the C atom bonded to the leaving group increases the rate of S_N1 and E1 reactions.

SOLVED PROBLEM **9.6**

How to determine relative E1 reaction rates from the type of substrate

Break It Down **Which substrate, A or B, undergoes an E1 reaction faster?**

OTs
TsO

A **B**

Think	Solve
Which substrate leads to a more stable carbocation in the E1 rate-determining step?	The two rate-determining steps are shown below. The carbocation formed from substrate **B** is more stable because its additional CH_3 group stabilizes the electron-deficient C^+.

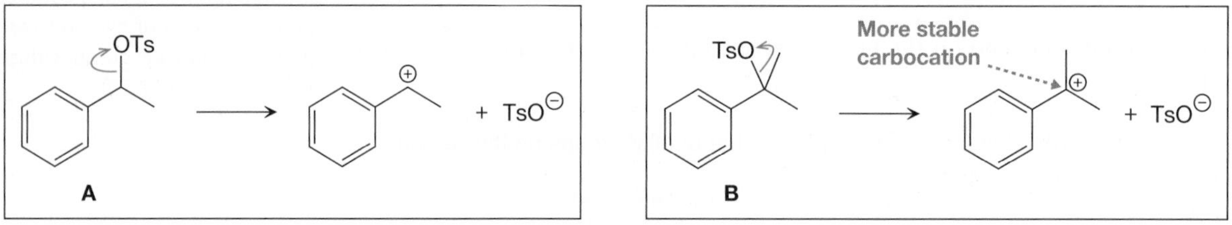
OTs
+ TsO
A
TsO
More stable carbocation
+ TsO
B

How do the relative carbocation stabilities affect the respective E1 reaction rates?	Because each carbocation is a product in the E1 rate-determining step, a more stable carbocation will promote a faster E1 reaction. Therefore, substrate **B** reacts faster by the E1 mechanism.

Try It Which substrate, **C** or **D**, undergoes an E1 reaction faster? Explain.

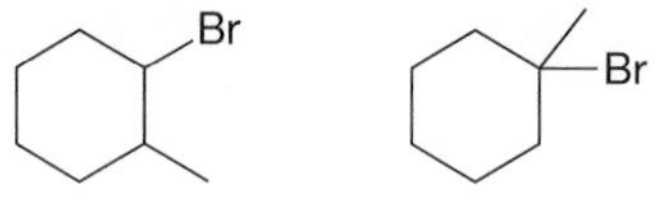
Br
Br

C **D**

Unlike S_N2, S_N1, and E1 reactions, *E2 reactions are relatively insensitive to the number of alkyl groups on the carbon bonded to the leaving group*. That is:

> Substrates with leaving groups on primary, secondary, and tertiary carbons can usually undergo E2 reactions quickly.

▸ LOOKING AHEAD

Although steric hindrance does not dramatically reduce E2 reaction rates, we will see in Section 9.10 that steric hindrance can influence the outcome of competing E2 reactions.

This may seem surprising because the attacking species in an E2 reaction *must force off the leaving group*, similar to how we think of an S_N2 reaction. In an E2 reaction, however, the attacking species does so by pulling off a proton from a carbon *adjacent* to the one bonded to the leaving group. Because a proton is small and generally well exposed, *steric hindrance tends to be a minor factor in E2 reactions*, even with the leaving group on a 3° carbon (**Figure 9-16**; see Looking Ahead box).

Protons are typically well exposed on 1°, 2°, and 3° substrates.

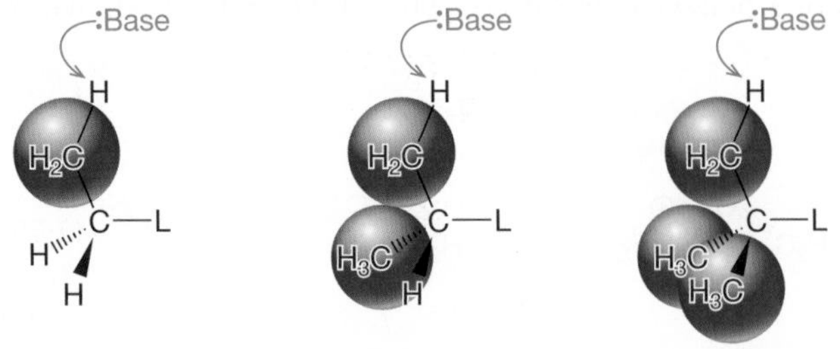
:Base
:Base
:Base
H
H
H
H_2C
H_2C
H_2C
C—L
C—L
C—L
H
H
H
H_3C
H
H_3C
H_3C

FIGURE 9-16 Accessibility of the proton in E2 reactions Unlike in S_N2 reactions, an increase in the number of alkyl groups attached to the carbon bonded to the leaving group does not cause much steric hindrance in E2 reactions. Even with tertiary C atoms, the protons on adjacent C atoms remain well exposed to the base.

TABLE 9-7 Feasibility of S_N2, S_N1, E2, and E1 Reactions[a]

R—L (Type of substrate)	S_N2	S_N1	E2	E1
CH_3—L (methyl)	✓			
RCH_2—L (1°)	✓		✓	
R_2CH—L (2°)	✓	✓	✓	✓
R_3C—L (3°)		✓	✓	✓

[a]A check mark indicates the reaction is feasible; a gray shaded box indicates the reaction is unfeasible.

Table 9-7 summarizes much of the preceding discussion regarding the feasibility of various types of substrates undergoing S_N2, S_N1, E2, and E1 reactions. Specifically, each entry that is shaded represents an unfeasible reaction.[1] This information will be very useful when you are asked to predict the products of an $S_N2/S_N1/E2/E1$ competition, so take the time to review why the reactions are unfeasible in those cases.

YOUR TURN **9.16**

According to Table 9-7, E2 reactions are feasible for substrates in which the leaving group is bonded to a primary, secondary, or tertiary carbon but not for substrates in which the leaving group is bonded to a methyl carbon. Explain why.

YOUR TURN **9.17**

Which substrate, **X**, **Y**, or **Z**, will undergo an S_N2 reaction the fastest? Which will undergo an S_N1 reaction the fastest? Which will undergo an E1 reaction the fastest? Explain.

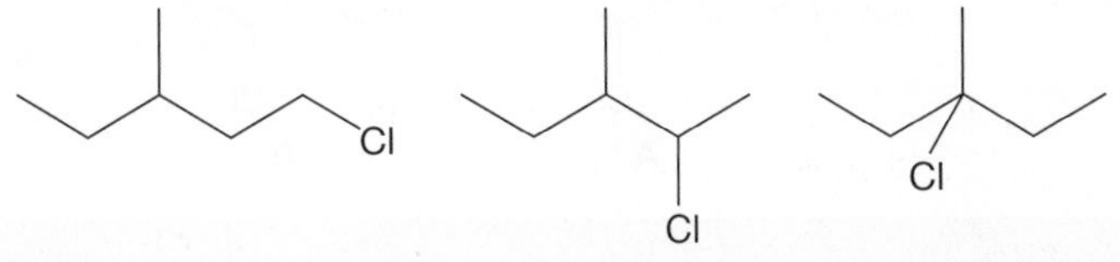
Cl
Cl
Cl

X **Y** **Z**

[1]According to Table 9-7, S_N1 and E1 reactions are feasible for secondary substrates, R_2CH—L, but this is not entirely clear. For a discussion on the matter, see Murphy, T. J. *J. Chem. Educ.* **2009**, *84*(4), 519.

CONNECTIONS 9.4

A shiny protective coat One of the uses of allyl chloride ($CH_2{=}CH{-}CH_2Cl$), a type of allyl halide (Eq. 9-30), is in the manufacture of epoxy resins for protective coatings, like the one on this boat. Allyl chloride is first epoxidized to make epichlorohydrin, which undergoes further conversions to produce a constituent of the resin.

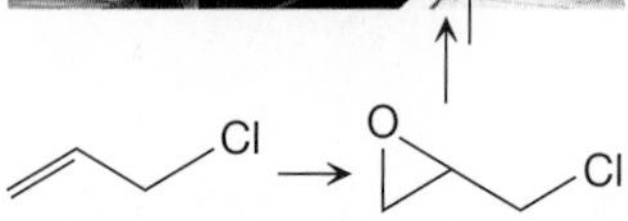

Cl
O
Cl

Allyl chloride **Epichlorohydrin**

An exception to Table 9-7 arises when the reaction involves an **allyl substrate** ($CH_2{=}CH{-}CH_2{-}L$) or a **benzyl substrate** ($C_6H_5{-}CH_2{-}L$), as shown in Equations 9-30 and 9-31:

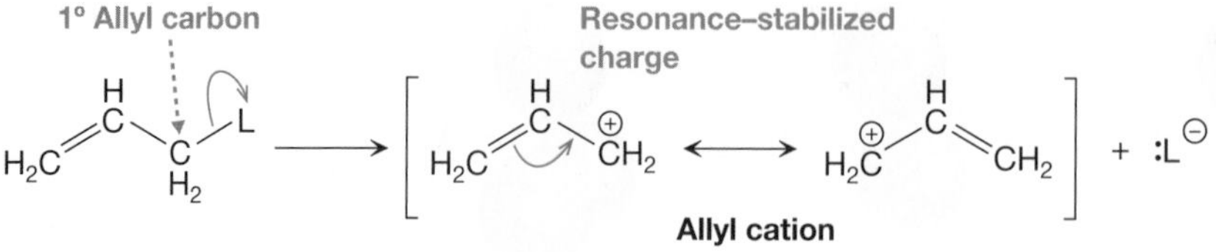

1° Allyl carbon
Resonance-stabilized charge
Allyl cation

(9-30)

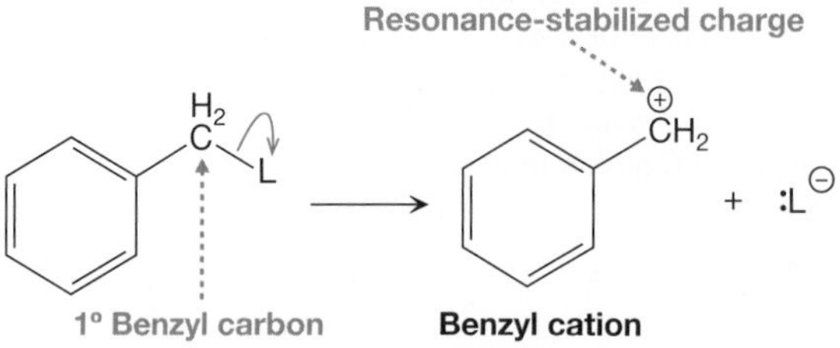

Resonance-stabilized charge
1° Benzyl carbon
Benzyl cation

(9-31)

Normally, S_N1 mechanisms are unavailable to primary substrates because the resulting primary carbocation is too unstable. However, if the leaving group is bonded to a primary allyl or benzyl carbon, then the resulting carbocation is heavily stabilized by resonance:

> If the leaving group is bonded to a primary allyl or benzyl carbon, then both S_N2 and S_N1 reactions are feasible.

YOUR TURN 9.18

Draw all possible resonance structures for the benzyl cation (Eq. 9-31) to illustrate how resonance stabilizes the charge.

SOLVED PROBLEM **9.7**

How to determine the faster S_N1 reaction from the type of substrate

Break It Down **Which substrate, A or B, would undergo an S_N1 reaction faster?**

O
Cl
Cl
A
B

Think

What type of carbocation would substrate **A** produce in the rate-determining step? Is it 1°, 2°, or 3°? Is it stabilized by resonance?

Solve

Substrate **A** would produce a 2° carbocation having two resonance structures. The resonance structure shown on the right is a particularly strong contributor because all of its non-hydrogen atoms have octets.

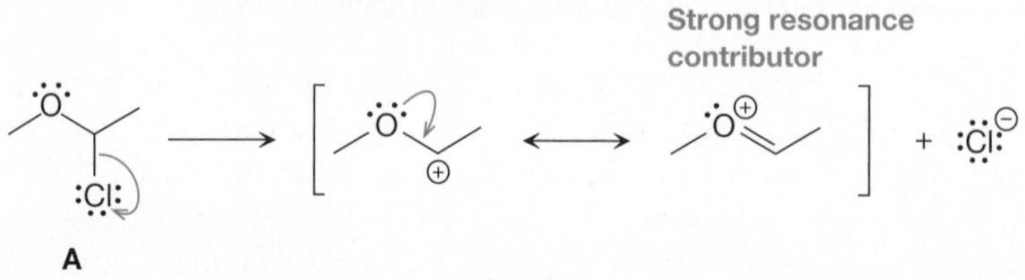

Strong resonance contributor
A

(continued)

What type of carbocation would substrate **B** produce in the rate-determining step? Is it 1°, 2°, or 3°? Is it stabilized by resonance?	Substrate **B** would produce a 2° carbocation having no additional resonance structures. 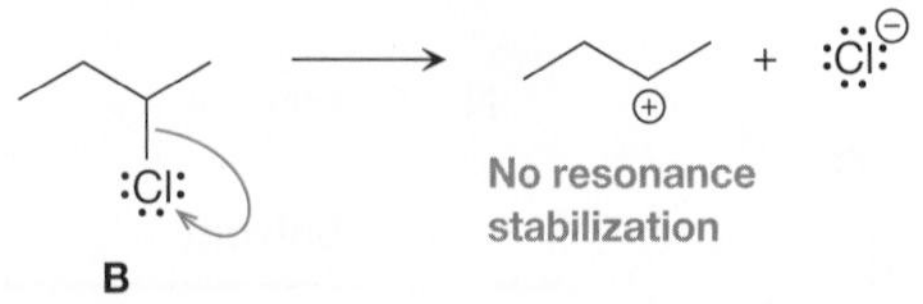
Which carbocation is more stable, and how does that impact the S_N1 reaction rate?	Both carbocations are 2°, but the carbocation produced from substrate **A** is more stable due to resonance. Because it produces the more stable carbocation, substrate **A** would undergo the faster S_N1 rate-determining step, and therefore it would undergo the faster S_N1 reaction.

Try It Which substrate, **C** or **D**, will undergo an E1 reaction faster? Explain.

Br
O
C
Br
D

9.7 Factor 5: Solvent Effects

SECTION 9.7 OBJECTIVES

You will be able to:

1. Determine which reactions—S_N2, S_N1, E2, or E1—are favored by the solvent.
2. Predict relative nucleophile strengths in both protic and aprotic solvents.

S_N2, S_N1, E2, and E1 reactions can take place in a variety of solvents. The solvent must be polar to dissolve the reactants efficiently, given that the reactants are typically polar or ionic. Furthermore, as we learned in Section 2.9, polar solvents can be *protic* (e.g., water and alcohols) because they possess hydrogen-bond donors, or they can be *aprotic* [e.g., dimethyl sulfoxide (DMSO), *N,N*-dimethylformamide (DMF), and acetone] because they do not possess hydrogen-bond donors. Here in Section 9.7, we examine the impact that the choice of solvent has on the competition between S_N2, S_N1, E2, and E1 reactions, as well as on relative nucleophile strengths.

9.7a Protic and Aprotic Solvents and the $S_N2/S_N1/E2/E1$ Competition

Experimental results show that the choice of solvent can have a significant influence on the outcome of nucleophilic substitution and elimination reactions:

- Polar *aprotic* solvents tend to favor S_N2 and E2 reactions.
- Polar *protic* solvents tend to favor S_N1 and E1 reactions.

These effects are illustrated with the data listed in Tables 9-8 and 9-9.

The dramatic impact that the choice of solvent has on S_N2 and S_N1 reactions, an example of a *solvent effect*, is explained partly by solvation of the attacking species. As explained in Section 2.9 (see Recall box), *anions are solvated very strongly by protic solvents* because the large partial positive charge on H in the solvent molecule is well exposed (**Figure 9-17a**, next page). Nucleophiles are therefore stabilized heavily by protic solvents. As we learned in Section 9.3, stabilizing the nucleophile slows an S_N2 reaction but essentially leaves the S_N1 rate unchanged. Aprotic solvents, however, do not solvate anions nearly as strongly because *steric hindrance* keeps the anion away from the positive end of the solvent molecule's dipole (Fig. 9-17b). As a result,

◂ RECALL

Section 2.9 showed that because anions are much more strongly solvated in protic solvents than in aprotic solvents, ionic compounds tend to be much more soluble in protic solvents.

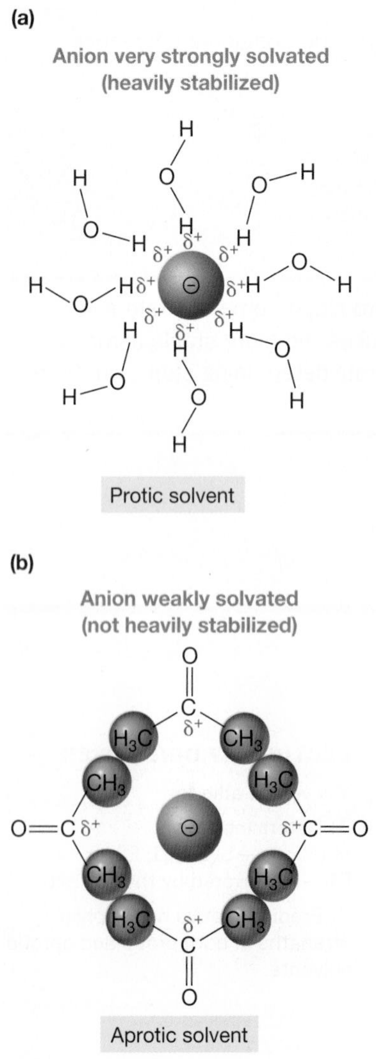
(a)
Anion very strongly solvated
(heavily stabilized)
Protic solvent
(b)
Anion weakly solvated
(not heavily stabilized)
Aprotic solvent

FIGURE 9-17 Comparing solvation of anions in protic and aprotic solvents (a) Solvation of an anion by water, a polar protic solvent. The large concentration of positive charge on a well-exposed hydrogen atom enables water to strongly solvate negative charges. (b) Solvation of an anion by acetone, a polar aprotic solvent. The partial positive end of the net dipole is buried inside the solvent molecule, which severely decreases the ability of acetone to solvate negative charges.

TABLE 9-8 Reaction Rates in Various Solvents for the S_N2 Reaction:

Solvent	Type of Solvent	Relative S_N2 Reaction Rate
CH_3OH	Protic	1
H_2O	Protic	7
$(CH_3)_2S{=}O$, DMSO	Aprotic	1,300
$HCON(CH_3)_2$, DMF	Aprotic	2,800
CH_3CN	Aprotic	5,000

aprotic solvents do not stabilize nucleophiles as much as polar protic solvents do, allowing S_N2 reactions to remain faster than S_N1 reactions. Putting these ideas together:

> Protic solvents (Fig. 9-17a) weaken nucleophiles substantially by solvation; aprotic solvents (Fig. 9-17b) do not.

The strong solvation by polar protic solvents further weakens nucleophiles as a result of the tight "cage" that is formed by the solvent molecules around the nucleophile. To form a bond with a substrate, the nucleophile must first shed some of those solvent molecules.

TABLE 9-9 Reaction Rates in Various Solvents for the S_N1 Reaction:

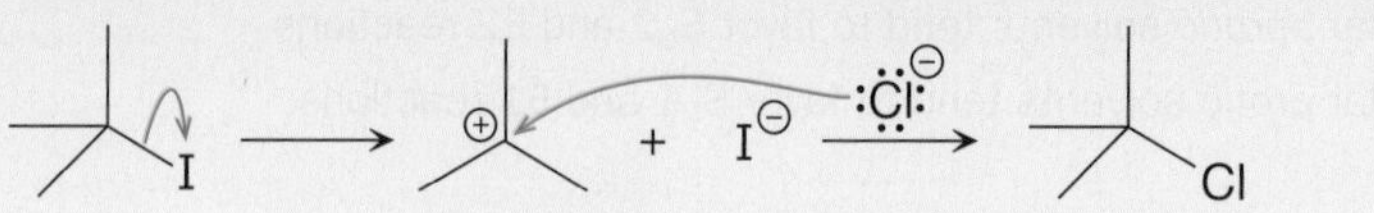

Solvent	Type of Solvent	Relative S_N1 Reaction Rate
CH_3OH	Protic	7,400,000
$HCONH_2$	Protic	1,200,000
$HCON(CH_3)_2$, DMF	Aprotic	12.5
$CH_3CON(CH_3)_2$	Aprotic	1

YOUR TURN 9.19

In which solvent, DMSO or ethanol, does this reaction proceed faster by an S_N1 mechanism? In which solvent does it proceed faster by an S_N2 mechanism? Explain.

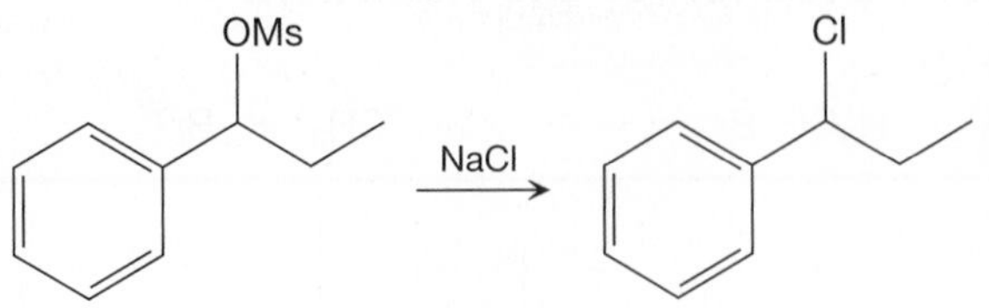
OMs
NaCl
Cl

The solvent effects shown in Tables 9-8 and 9-9 also derive from the different abilities of the solvent to solvate the *leaving group*. Recall that the S_N1 reaction rate is dictated entirely by the departure of the leaving group, which is often negatively charged. In a protic solvent, the anionic leaving group is stabilized heavily by the strong solvation that takes place, but in an aprotic solvent, it is not. Therefore:

A protic solvent (Fig. 9-17a) will dramatically speed up the rate-determining step of an S_N1 reaction by solvating the leaving group; an aprotic solvent (Fig. 9-17b) will not.

The influence of the solvent on the departure of the leaving group does not affect S_N2 reaction rates as greatly because, as we saw in Section 9.5a, S_N2 reactions are less sensitive to leaving group ability.

YOUR TURN 9.20

In which solvent, ethanol or acetone, does this reaction proceed faster by an S_N2 mechanism? Explain.

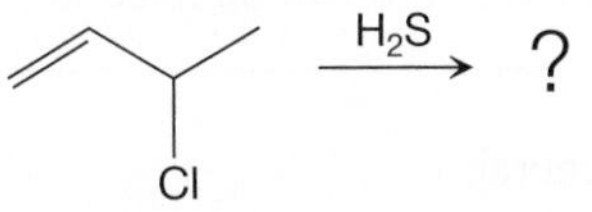
H2S
?
Cl

Similar reasoning explains why protic solvents tend to favor E1 reactions over E2 reactions, while aprotic solvents tend to favor E2 over E1. Strong solvation of the base by a protic solvent weakens the base, thereby slowing the E2 reaction rate. At the same time, protic solvents enhance the ability of the leaving group to leave in the rate-determining step of an E1 reaction. Conversely, aprotic solvents favor E2 reactions over E1 because the base is not weakened as much. The leaving group is slow to depart on its own, moreover, because it is so poorly solvated by the aprotic solvent.

YOUR TURN 9.21

In which solvent, **Y** or **Z**, does the reaction in Your Turn 9.20 proceed faster by the E1 mechanism? Explain.

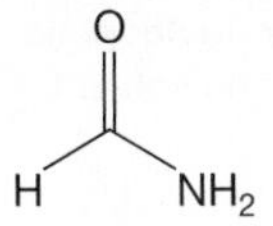
O
H
NH2
Y

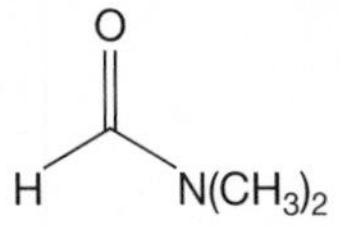
O
H
N(CH3)2
Z

9.7b Relative Nucleophilicities in Protic and Aprotic Solvents

We have just seen that solvation in protic solvents has the effect of weakening nucleophiles substantially. The solvation of anions by protic solvents is so dramatic that it can *reverse* the relative strengths of some nucleophiles. This can be seen in Table 9-10, which lists the S_N2 reaction rates of various nucleophiles in ethanol (a protic solvent).

Note, for example, that the nucleophilicity of Br^- in ethanol is about 30 times greater than that of Cl^- (i.e., 620,000 vs. 23,000). This is contrary to DMF, an aprotic solvent (Table 9-1, p. 449), in which Cl^- is a stronger nucleophile than Br^- (i.e., 2 vs. 1). This reversal occurs in protic solvents because Cl^- is substantially smaller than Br^- (Cl

TABLE 9-10 S_N2 **Reaction Rates in Ethanol for the Reaction:**

$$Nu:^{\ominus} + H_3C{-}Br \longrightarrow Nu{-}CH_3 + Br^{\ominus}$$

Nucleophile	CH_3OH	$F^{\ominus}$	$CH_3CO_2^{\ominus}$	$Cl^{\ominus}$	NH_3	$N_3^{\ominus}$
Relative S_N2 Reaction Rate	1	500	20,000	23,000	320,000	600,000
Nucleophile	$Br^{\ominus}$	$CH_3O^{\ominus}$	$NC^{\ominus}$	Ph_3P	$HS^{\ominus}$	
Relative S_N2 Reaction Rate	620,000	2,000,000	5,000,000	10,000,000	100,000,000	

is above Br in group 7A of the periodic table), which means the negative charge is more concentrated when it is on Cl^-. With a higher concentration of negative charge, Cl^- is solvated much more strongly in a protic solvent, as indicated in **Figure 9-18**. Therefore, protic solvents weaken Cl^- much more than they weaken Br^- as a nucleophile.

YOUR TURN 9.22

Compare Tables 9-1 (p. 449) and 9-10 to find another pair of nucleophiles (other than Cl^- and Br^-) whose *relative* nucleophilicities in ethanol are the reverse of what they are in DMF. What does this observation suggest about which of the two species is more strongly solvated in ethanol?

In general:

We see a reversal of nucleophilicity in protic versus aprotic solvents when both of the following criteria are met:

- The nucleophiles have negative charges localized on an atom (i.e., not resonance delocalized), and
- The atoms bearing the negative charge are in different rows of the periodic table.

This is illustrated further in Solved Problem 9.8.

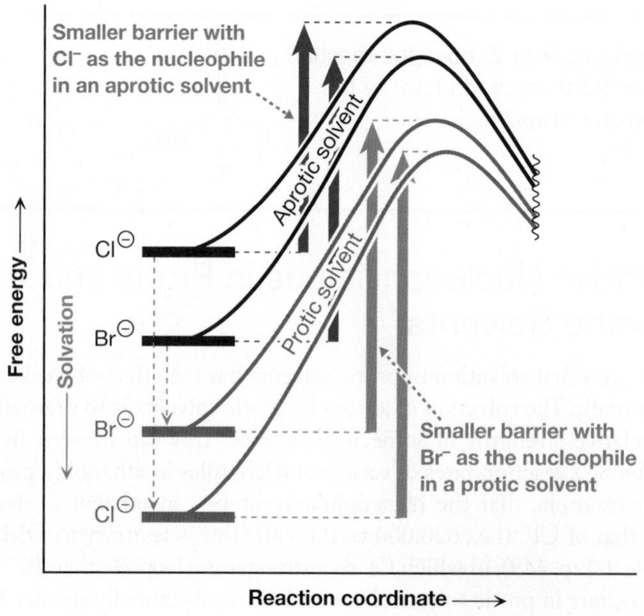

Smaller barrier with
Cl⁻ as the nucleophile
in an aprotic solvent
Aprotic solvent
Protic solvent
Cl⊖
Br⊖
Br⊖
Cl⊖
Free energy
Solvation
Smaller barrier with
Br⁻ as the nucleophile
in a protic solvent
Reaction coordinate

FIGURE 9-18 Solvation and the reversal of nucleophile strengths Cl^- is a stronger nucleophile than Br^- in an aprotic solvent (black curves) because Cl^-, being less stable, undergoes an S_N2 reaction having the smaller energy barrier. In a protic solvent (blue curves), however, Cl^- is solvated (dashed red arrows) much more strongly than Br^-, which results in Br^- undergoing an S_N2 reaction having the smaller energy barrier.

SOLVED PROBLEM **9.8**

How to predict relative nucleophile strength in protic and aprotic solvents

Break It Down **Which nucleophile, HS^- or HO^-, is stronger in DMSO? Which nucleophile is stronger in water?**

Think	Solve
Which is a stronger nucleophile *intrinsically* (i.e., without considerations of solvation)?	To predict the stronger nucleophile without considering solvation, we can apply the method from Section 9.3a in which we compare the energy diagrams of the two nucleophiles undergoing an S_N2 reaction with CH_3I. As shown, HO^- is less stable than HS^- because O is a smaller atom than S. Therefore, HO^- reacts faster and is the stronger nucleophile. 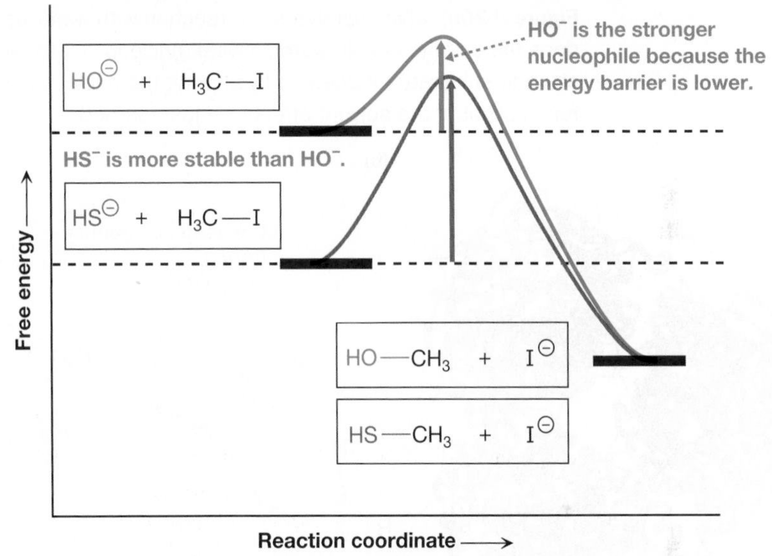
Is DMSO a protic or an aprotic solvent? Should we expect a reversal of nucleophilicities in such a solvent?	DMSO is an aprotic solvent, so solvation is not substantial enough to cause a reversal of nucleophilicities. Therefore, in DMSO, HO^- is a stronger nucleophile than HS^-.
Is water a protic or an aprotic solvent? Do the nucleophiles have a localized negative charge? Are the atoms with the negative charge in different rows of the periodic table?	Water is a protic solvent, so we should expect a reversal of the relative nucleophile strengths if the nucleophiles satisfy the two criteria presented above. The first criterion is satisfied because a negative charge is localized on an atom in both HS^- and HO^-. The second criterion is satisfied, too, because S and O are in different rows of the periodic table. Therefore, we do expect a reversal, in which case HS^- is the stronger nucleophile in water.

HO⊖ + H3C—I
HS⊖ + H3C—I
HS⁻ is more stable than HO⁻.
HO⁻ is the stronger nucleophile because the energy barrier is lower.
HO—CH3 + I⊖
HS—CH3 + I⊖
Free energy
Reaction coordinate

Try It Which nucleophile, F^- or I^-, is stronger in acetone? Which nucleophile is stronger in ethanol? Explain.

The tremendous solvation that occurs in protic solvents causes some negatively charged nucleophiles to be weaker than some uncharged nucleophiles. Notice in Table 9-10, for example, that NH_3 is more than 10 times stronger than Cl^- in ethanol (i.e., 320,000 vs. 23,000), making NH_3 a moderately strong nucleophile. More impressively, triphenylphosphine (Ph_3P) is more than 400 times stronger than Cl^- (i.e., 10,000,000 vs. 23,000).

How an Enzyme Can Manipulate the Reactivity of a Nucleophile and Substrate

Pseudomonas putida PP3, a strain of Gram-negative bacteria, carries out the conversion shown in **Figure 9-19**. The reaction may seem surprising to you, because the Cl substituent is replaced by OH with inversion of configuration, making this an S_N2 reaction. As we learned here in Chapter 9, S_N2 reactions are promoted by strong nucleophiles, so in the laboratory, we might carry out the reaction by treating the substrate with a source of HO^-, such as NaOH. The involvement of HO^-, however, would be unfeasible at physiological pH because a strong base like HO^- would be kept at *very* low concentration. What is the secret of these bacteria?

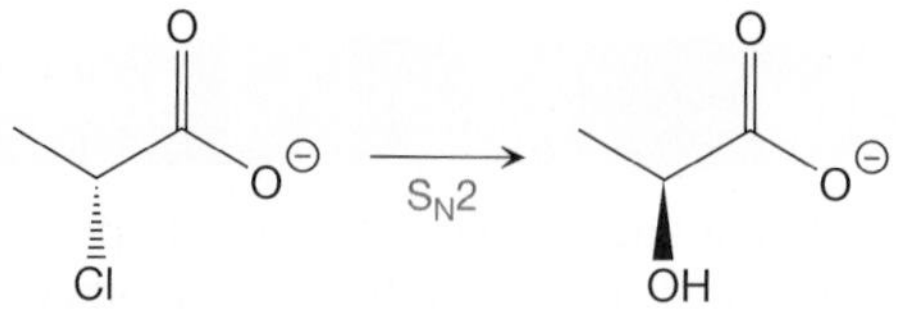

O
O⊖
Cl
SN2
O
O⊖
OH

FIGURE 9-19

The key is an enzyme called haloacid dehalogenase (whose ribbon structure is shown in **Figure 9-20a**), which catalyzes the reaction with *water* as the nucleophile, not HO^-. But how does the enzyme enable water, a weak nucleophile, to facilitate an S_N2 reaction on a secondary chloride substrate? It does so by altering the nucleophile strength and leaving group ability, reminiscent of the solvent effects we just learned.

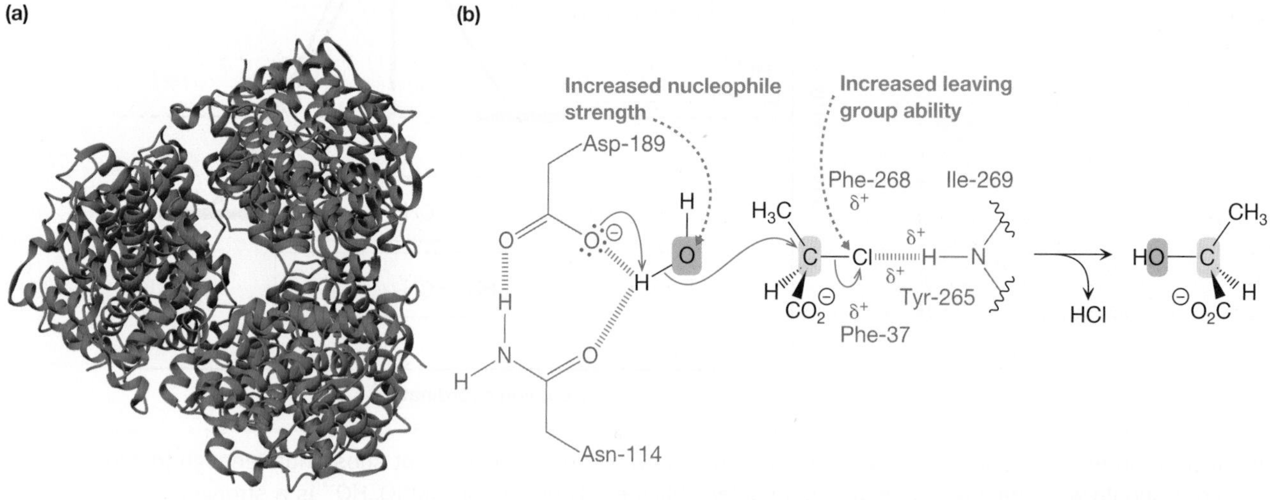

(a)
(b)
Increased nucleophile strength
Increased leaving group ability
Asp-189
Phe-268
Ile-269
δ+
δ+
δ+
Tyr-265
Phe-37
Asn-114
H3C
CO2⊖
HCl
HO
CH3
⊖O2C
H

FIGURE 9-20

As shown in Figure 9-20b, water is initially held in place in the enzyme's active site by hydrogen bonds involving the side groups of the Asp-189 and Asn-114 amino acid residues. Meanwhile, the substrate is situated so that its negatively charged regions benefit from electrostatic attractions to the partially positive H of an amide group from the protein's backbone (Ile-269) and also to the partially positive aromatic hydrogens of the Phe-37, Tyr-265, and Phe-268 residues.

The hydrogen bonding involving water sets up the loss of a proton from water during nucleophilic attack, which adds to the electron density at water's O atom and effectively increases water's nucleophilicity. Simultaneously, the negative charge that develops on Cl during its departure is stabilized by the surrounding partially positive environment, which effectively enhances the leaving group ability. Both of these modes of action together make it easier for the nucleophile to force off the leaving group and facilitate an S_N2 reaction that would otherwise not take place.

The idea of manipulating the reactivities of species involved in a chemical reaction is not unique to haloacid dehalogenase but rather is a common strategy employed by enzymes to deal with various limitations that physiological conditions might bring. This goes a long way toward enzymes being so efficient at carrying out specific reactions vital to an organism.

If we compare nucleophiles with localized negative charges on atoms in the *same row of the periodic table*, then protic solvents do *not* reverse nucleophilicities. In both protic and aprotic solvents, for example, nucleophilicities increase in the order $F^- < CH_3O^- < NC^-$. Even though each ion is solvated quite strongly by the protic solvent, they are not solvated very *differently* from each other because the negatively charged atoms are similar in size.

YOUR TURN 9.23

Solved Problem 9.1 (p. 451) showed, without considering solvation, that H_2S is a stronger nucleophile than H_2O. Would you expect H_2S to be a stronger or weaker nucleophile than H_2O in ethanol? Explain.

9.8 Factor 6: Heat

SECTION 9.8 OBJECTIVES

You will be able to:

1. Explain why elevated temperatures tend to favor elimination reactions over substitution reactions.
2. Identify various notations that specify an elevated temperature for a reaction.

The conditions that favor an S_N2 reaction are similar to the conditions that favor an E2 reaction, so S_N2 and E2 products are often formed together. Similarly, S_N1 and E1 reaction products are often formed together. When substitution and elimination reactions are both favored under a specific set of conditions, it is often possible to influence the outcome by changing the temperature under which the reactions take place. Specifically:

Increasing the temperature of the reaction tends to promote elimination more than substitution.

This effect can be seen in Equations 9-32 and 9-33, in which 2-bromopropane reacts with hydroxide anion at 45 °C and 100 °C, respectively. Substitution and elimination products are formed in roughly equal amounts at the lower temperature, whereas elimination is favored at the higher temperature.

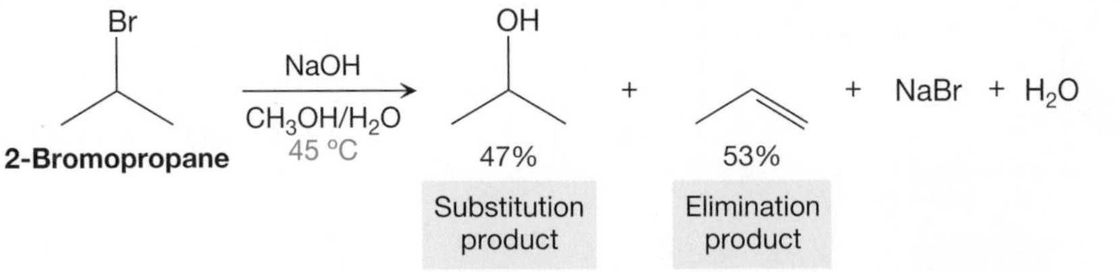
Br
NaOH
CH3OH/H2O
45 °C
2-Bromopropane
OH
47%
Substitution product
53%
Elimination product
+ NaBr + H2O
(9-32)

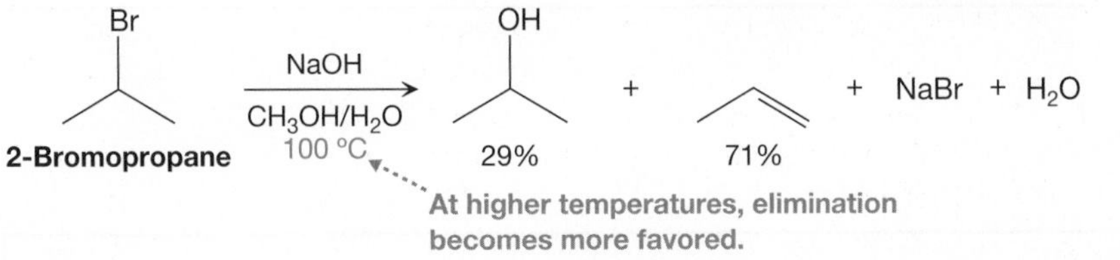
Br
NaOH
CH3OH/H2O
100 °C
2-Bromopropane
OH
29%
71%
+ NaBr + H2O
At higher temperatures, elimination becomes more favored.
(9-33)

This temperature effect can be understood by considering *entropy*, which, as we discussed in Section 2.7, is often thought of as a measure of disorder. More to the point:

The products of an elimination reaction have more entropy (disorder) than the products of a substitution reaction.

We can see this by comparing Equation 9-34a and 9-34b, which shows that two species are produced in a substitution reaction and three species are produced in an elimination reaction. With a greater number of independent species, the atoms that make up the products have greater freedom of movement (disorder).

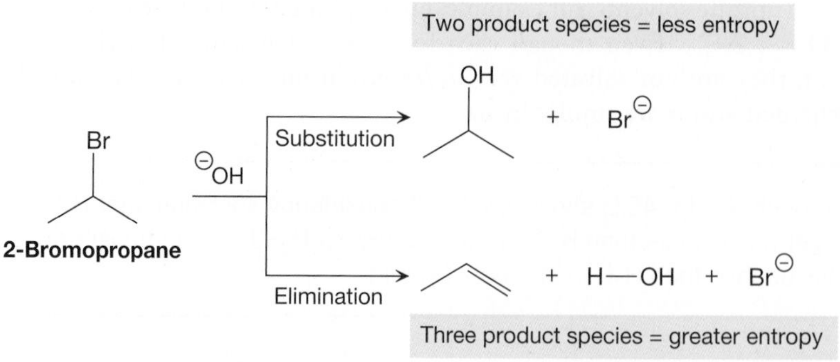

Two product species = less entropy
OH
+ Br⊖
Br
⊖OH
Substitution
2-Bromopropane
+ H—OH + Br⊖
Elimination
Three product species = greater entropy

(9-34a)

(9-34b)

◀ RECALL

Section 6.5 discussed the relationship between standard Gibbs free energy and entropy differences: $\Delta G° = \Delta H° - T\Delta S°$. When $\Delta S°$ is positive, an increase in T will make $\Delta G°$ more negative. In turn, $\Delta G°^{\ddagger}$ becomes smaller and the reaction rate increases.

We turn to entropy to understand the temperature effects in competing substitution and elimination reactions because *heat favors states with greater entropy* (see Recall box). This is why, for example, adding heat to a solid causes the solid to melt and become liquid. The atoms in a liquid have more freedom of movement, and therefore greater entropy, than the atoms in a solid. When heat is added, the state with greater entropy (the liquid) becomes favored. Analogously, adding heat to raise the temperature of a reaction favors the products with greater entropy: the elimination products.

YOUR TURN **9.24**

For the reaction shown here, identify the products that have greater entropy. Label the products of substitution and the products of elimination.

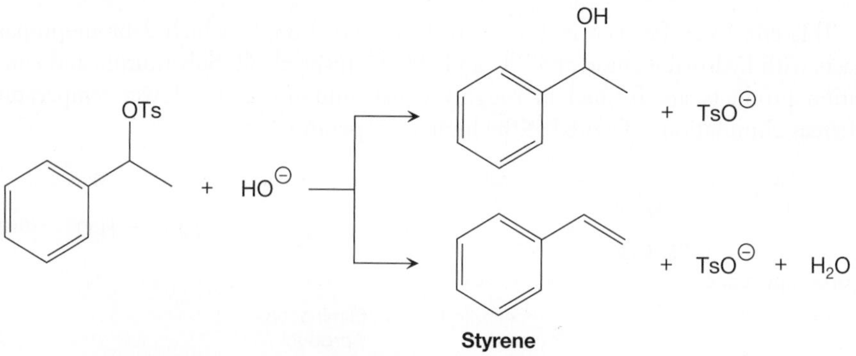

OTs
+ HO⊖
OH
+ TsO⊖
+ TsO⊖ + H2O
Styrene

CONNECTIONS 9.5

Styrene: From coffee cups to coffee beans Styrene (Your Turn 9.24) is the monomer used to make the polymer polystyrene. Polystyrene can be a hard plastic, as is the case with plastic spoons, knives, and forks, or it can be "foamed" to produce coffee cups and takeout containers. Styrene is also found naturally in small quantities in coffee beans and cinnamon.

YOUR TURN **9.25**

Suppose the reaction in Your Turn 9.24 produces a substantial amount of both substitution and elimination products at room temperature. If the temperature at which the reaction is run is raised, then which product will be the major product? If the temperature is lowered, then which product will be the major product?

There are a variety of ways to indicate that a reaction is run at high temperatures. One is simply to write the elevated temperature at which the reaction is run underneath the reaction arrow (e.g., $\xrightarrow[90\ °C]{}$). Alternatively, you can indicate that heat has been added to the reaction mixture by writing either "Heat" or its shorthand notation, Δ, underneath the reaction arrow (e.g., $\xrightarrow[\text{Heat}]{}$ or $\xrightarrow[\Delta]{}$).

9.9 Strategies for Success: Predicting the Outcome of an $S_N2/S_N1/E2/E1$ Competition

SECTION 9.9 OBJECTIVES

You will be able to:

1. Use a systematic method to predict the winning reaction of an $S_N2/S_N1/E2/E1$ competition.
2. Draw the mechanism and the major product for the winning reaction of an $S_N2/S_N1/E2/E1$ competition.

Strategies for Success
Predicting the Outcome of an $S_N2/S_N1/E2/E1$ Competition

We have studied various factors that influence the rates of S_N2, S_N1, E2, and E1 reactions differently. Because these factors generally do not all pull in the same direction, predicting the outcome of the competition between S_N2, S_N1, E2, and E1 reactions is not always clear-cut. The following four steps offer a way to systematically evaluate each of the factors we have examined thus far (Sections 9.3 through 9.8), so that we can reasonably predict the major products:

Step 1: Determine whether an $S_N2/S_N1/E2/E1$ competition is feasible.

- The leaving group should be at least as stable as F^- to be suitable. [Leaving groups that are *unsuitable* include RO^-, HO^-, H_2N^-, CH_3^-, and H^- (Fig. 9-11, p. 462).]
- The leaving group should be bonded to an sp^3-hybridized carbon.
- A recognizable attacking species should be present to act as a nucleophile or base.

Step 2: Rule out reactions that are unfeasible.

- Rule out S_N2 if the substrate is tertiary, since tertiary substrates cause excessive steric hindrance.
- Rule out S_N1 and E1 if the heterolysis products ($R^+ + L^-$) are not sufficiently stabilized. This is the case when:
  - The substrate is primary, unless the resulting carbocation is resonance-stabilized such as allyl or benzyl cations.
  - The solvent is aprotic (e.g., acetone, DMSO, or DMF).
  - The leaving group is poor (e.g., F^- or RCO_2^-).
- Rule out E2 and E1 if there are no β hydrogens (i.e., if there is no arrangement H—C—C—L).

Step 3: Determine which of the remaining reactions are favored by the attacking species.

- S_N2 is favored by a strong nucleophile.
- S_N1 is favored by a weak nucleophile or by a low concentration of a strong nucleophile.
- E2 is favored by a strong base.
- E1 is favored by a weak base or by a low concentration of a strong base.

Step 4: Apply the appropriate tiebreaker to the remaining reactions.

- Tiebreaker for S_N1 and E1 reactions: Determine whether heat is added to the reaction.
  - E1 is favored if heat is added.
  - S_N1 is favored in the absence of added heat.
- Tiebreaker for S_N2 and E2 reactions: Determine whether the attacking species acts better as a base than as a nucleophile.
  - The attacking species acts as a better base, and thus favors E2 over S_N2, if it is bulky (e.g., *tert*-butoxide or LDA) or if it is an extremely strong base (e.g., H^-, H_2N^-, R^-).
  - Otherwise, both S_N2 and E2 remain favored (e.g., HO^-, RO^-).

To illustrate this systematic method, let's try to predict the outcome of the reaction in Equation 9-35:

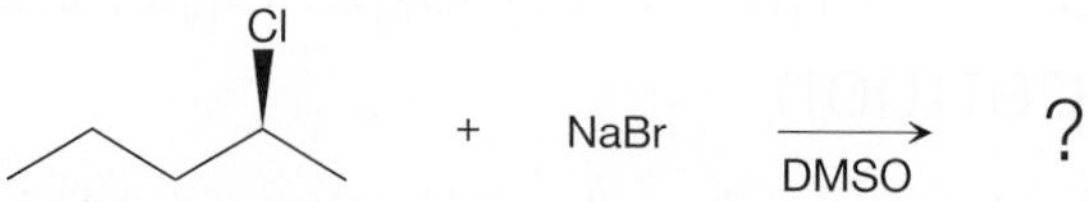

Cl
+ NaBr
DMSO
?

(9-35)

(S)-2-Chloropentane

For Step 1, we see that the leaving group, Cl^-, is suitable and is attached to an sp^3-hybridized carbon. Furthermore, we recognize Br^- as the attacking species, so we do indeed expect an $S_N2/S_N1/E2/E1$ competition. We therefore proceed to Steps 2–4. As we discuss Steps 2–4, it is helpful to construct a diagram, as shown in **Figure 9-21**, to keep track of the results; for each step, the task that we carry out is shown on the left of the figure, and a short explanation is provided on the right.

For Step 2, we cannot rule out any of the reactions from the type of substrate, the leaving group ability, or the absence of β hydrogens. But since the solvent is aprotic, we can rule out S_N1 and E1, indicated by the red Xs in Figure 9-21. This leaves just S_N2 and E2 as candidates.

For Step 3, we note that the attacking species, Br^-, is a strong nucleophile, so it favors S_N2 over S_N1. We keep track of this in Figure 9-21 by circling S_N2. Note, moreover, that Br^- is a weak base, which favors E1 over E2. We would normally circle E1, too, but we have already ruled it out. This leaves S_N2 as the winner.

For Step 4, we would normally apply a tiebreaker. In this case, however, we skip Step 4 because there is no tie; we have already determined from Step 3 that S_N2 is the winning reaction.

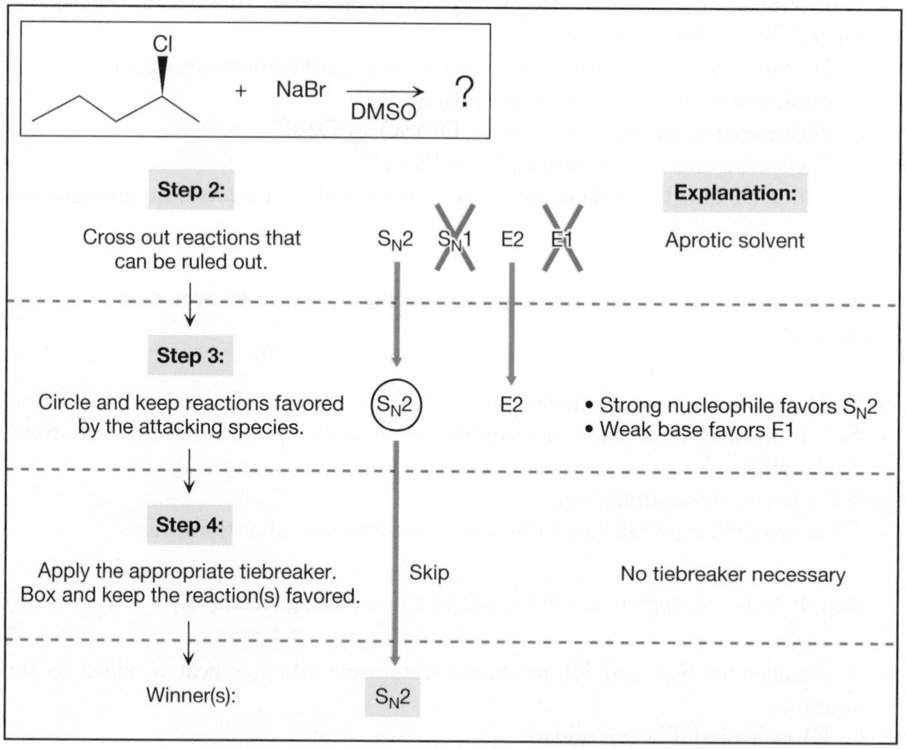

Cl
+ NaBr
DMSO
?
Step 2:
Cross out reactions that can be ruled out.
SN2 SN1 E2 E1
Explanation:
Aprotic solvent
Step 3:
Circle and keep reactions favored by the attacking species.
SN2
E2
• Strong nucleophile favors SN2
• Weak base favors E1
Step 4:
Apply the appropriate tiebreaker. Box and keep the reaction(s) favored.
Skip
No tiebreaker necessary
Winner(s):
SN2

FIGURE 9-21 Applying Steps 2–4 to the reaction in Equation 9-35 Steps 2–4 progress from top to bottom. For each step, the task carried out is shown on the left and a short explanation is provided on the right.

To predict the major product, enter the specific reactants into the general S_N2 mechanism, as is shown in Equation 9-36. Notice that *stereochemistry is important* here, given that the C atom bonded to the leaving group is a chiral center. Backside attack of the nucleophile ensures that the only stereoisomer produced is the one shown, which is (*R*)-2-bromopentane:

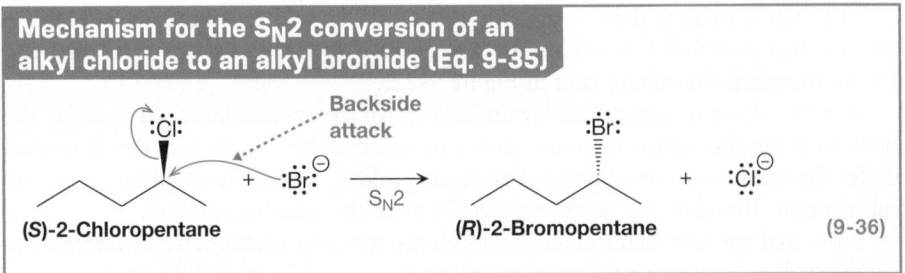

Mechanism for the S_N2 conversion of an alkyl chloride to an alkyl bromide (Eq. 9-35)

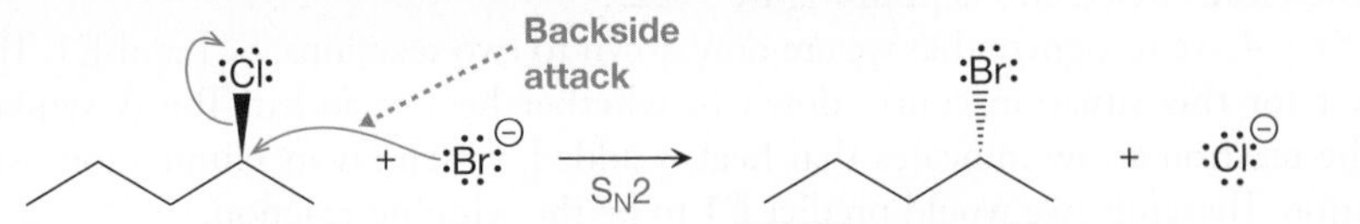

:Cl:
Backside attack
+
:Br:
S_N2
:Br:
+
:Cl:

(*S*)-2-Chloropentane (*R*)-2-Bromopentane (9-36)

Now, let's predict the major product(s) of the reaction in Equation 9-37:

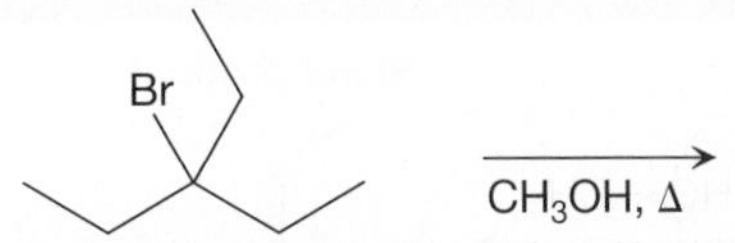

Br
CH_3OH, Δ
?

3-Bromo-3-ethylpentane (9-37)

Again we systematically consider the factors outlined in Steps 1 through 4. For Step 1, we identify Br^- as a suitable leaving group that is attached to an sp^3-hybridized carbon, and we identify CH_3OH as a suitable attacking species. Thus, an $S_N2/S_N1/E2/E1$ competition should take place; such a reaction, in which the solvent is also the attacking species, is called **solvolysis** (where the solvent is responsible for lysis, or bond breaking).

To predict the winner of the competition, we proceed to Steps 2–4 and construct **Figure 9-22** to keep track of the results. For Step 2, we rule out S_N2 because the substrate is tertiary; with three alkyl groups attached to the C—L carbon, excessive steric hindrance prevents the nucleophile from attacking the substrate on the side opposite the leaving group. S_N2 is therefore crossed out in Figure 9-22, leaving us with S_N1, E2, and E1.

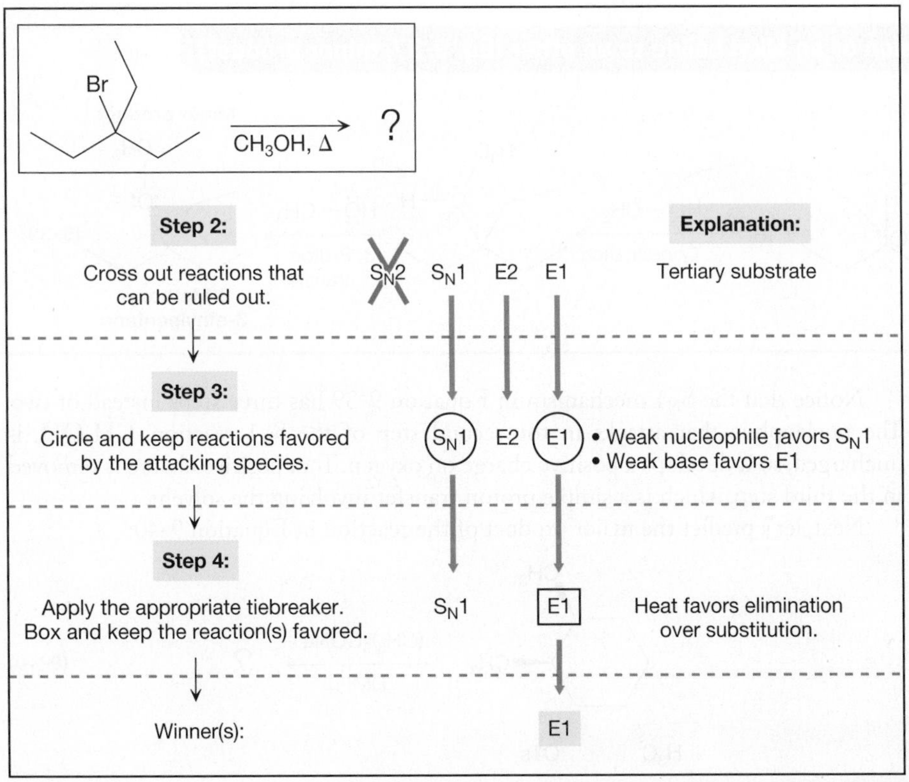

Br
CH_3OH, Δ
?
Step 2:
Cross out reactions that can be ruled out.
S_N2 S_N1 E2 E1
Explanation:
Tertiary substrate
Step 3:
Circle and keep reactions favored by the attacking species.
S_N1 E2 E1
• Weak nucleophile favors S_N1
• Weak base favors E1
Step 4:
Apply the appropriate tiebreaker. Box and keep the reaction(s) favored.
S_N1 E1
Heat favors elimination over substitution.
Winner(s):
E1

FIGURE 9-22 Applying Steps 2–4 to the reaction in Equation 9-37 Steps 2–4 progress from top to bottom. For each step, the task carried out is shown on the left and a short explanation is provided on the right.

For Step 3, we note that the attacking species, CH_3OH, is a weak nucleophile, so it favors S_N1 over S_N2. CH_3OH is also a weak base, so it favors E1 over E2. S_N1 and E1 are therefore circled and kept in Figure 9-22.

For Step 4, we recognize that we are now down to two reactions, S_N1 and E1. The tiebreaker for this situation comes down to whether heat is added. The Δ symbol under the reaction arrow indicates that heat is added, which favors elimination over substitution. Therefore, we would predict E1 to be the winning reaction.

Now that we have determined E1 to be the winning reaction, we can derive the major product by drawing the mechanism, as shown in Equation 9-38:

Mechanism for the E1 conversion of an alkyl halide to an alkene (Eq. 9-37, major product)

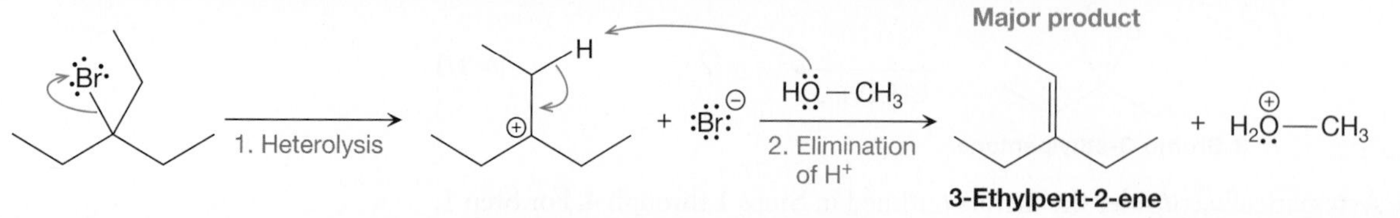

Major product
Br
1. Heterolysis
H
Br
HO—CH3
2. Elimination of H+
H2O—CH3
3-Ethylpent-2-ene

(9-38)

Notice that a proton can be removed from one of three possible carbons in the second step of the mechanism. In this case, all three carbons are chemically equivalent, so removal of any one of them leads to the same alkene product. (In Section 9.10, we will discuss how to predict the major elimination product when such protons are chemically distinct.)

Even though we considered heat to break the tie between substitution and elimination, realize that *heat is a minor factor*; it does not dramatically influence the relative amounts of products. For example, look back to Equations 9-32 and 9-33 (p. 479). When the temperature is raised to 100 °C, elimination is favored over substitution by 71% to 29%. There is still a significant amount of product from substitution, so we say that the substitution product is a *minor product*. Similarly, for the reaction in Equation 9-37, we expect a minor product from the S_N1 reaction, whose mechanism is shown in Equation 9-39:

Mechanism for the S_N1 conversion of an alkyl halide to an ether (Eq. 9-37, minor product)

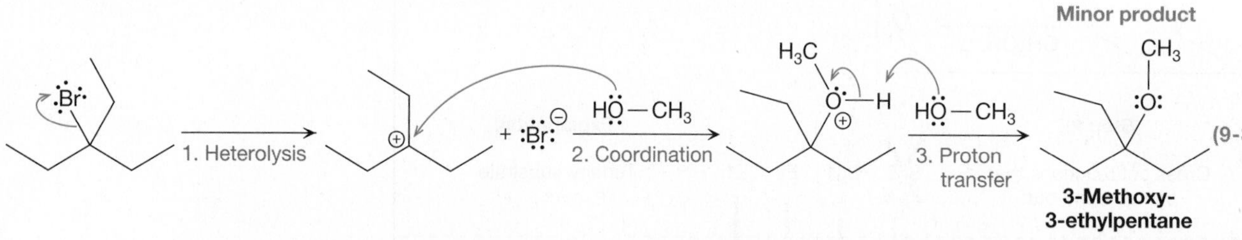

Minor product
Br
1. Heterolysis
Br
HO—CH3
2. Coordination
H3C
O—H
HO—CH3
3. Proton transfer
CH3
:O:
3-Methoxy-3-ethylpentane

(9-39)

Notice that the S_N1 mechanism in Equation 9-39 has three steps instead of two. The nucleophile that attacks in the second step of the S_N1 reaction, CH_3OH, is uncharged, so it develops a positive charge on oxygen. That positive charge is removed in the third step, which is a simple proton transfer involving the solvent.

Next, let's predict the major product of the reaction in Equation 9-40:

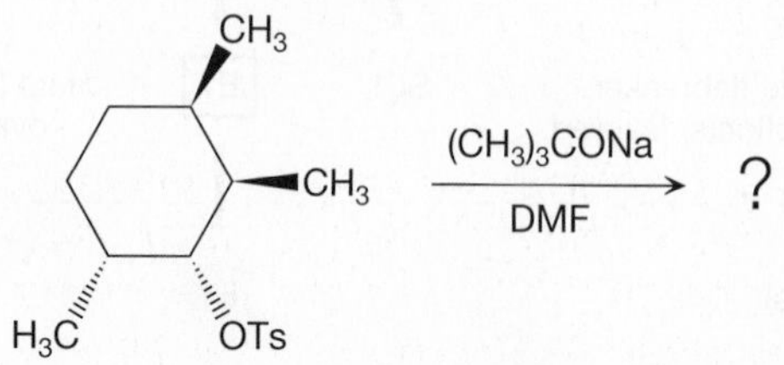

CH3
CH3
H3C
OTs
(CH3)3CONa
DMF
?

(9-40)

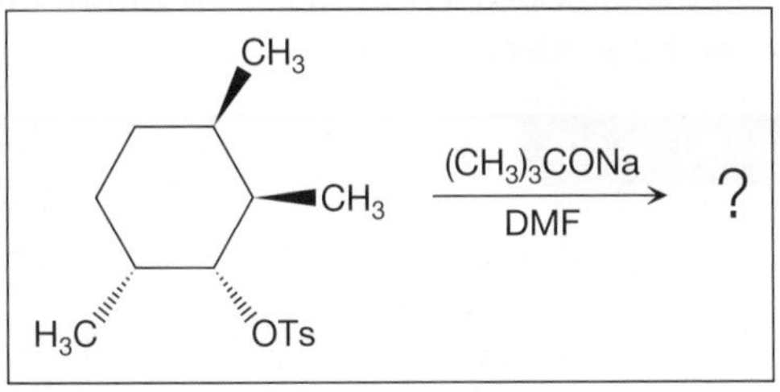

CH3
CH3
H3C
OTs
(CH3)3CONa
DMF
?

Step 2: Cross out reactions that can be ruled out. S_N2 S_N1 E2 E1

Explanation:

Step 3: Circle and keep reactions favored by the attacking species.

Step 4: Apply the appropriate tiebreaker. Box and keep the reaction(s) favored.

Winner(s): E2

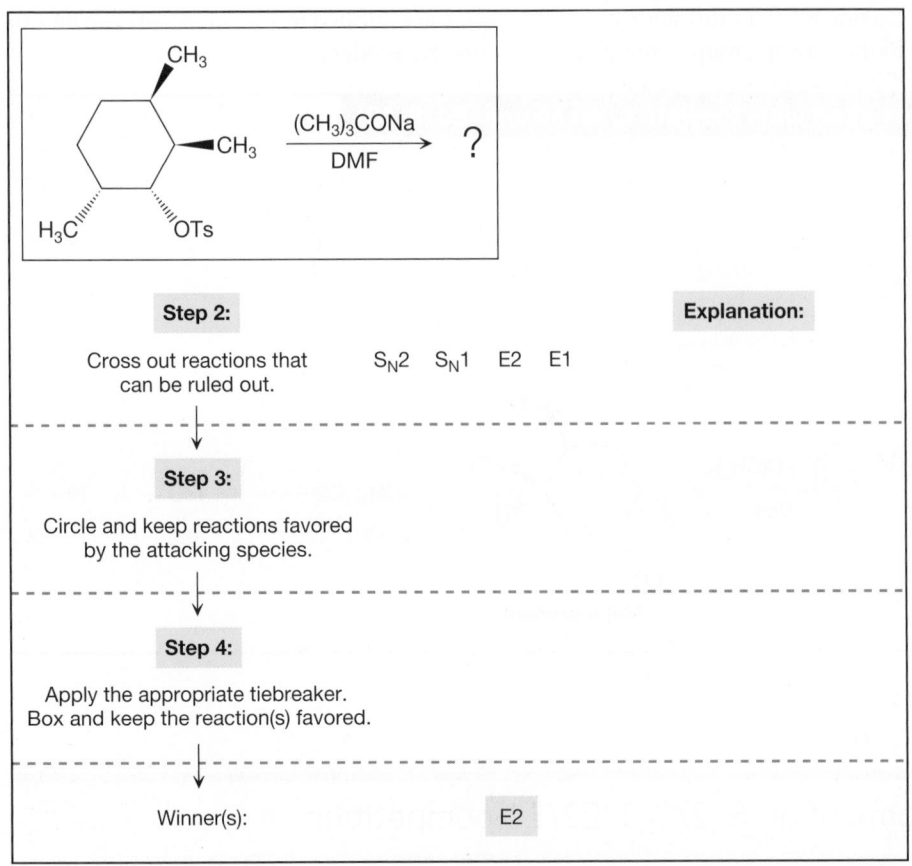

FIGURE 9-23 Applying Steps 2–4 to the reaction in Equation 9-40 Steps 2–4 progress from top to bottom. The tasks are left for you to carry out to complete the figure.

For Step 1, we see that the leaving group, TsO^-, is suitable and is attached to an sp^3-hybridized carbon. We also see that the *tert*-butoxide anion, $(CH_3)_3CO^-$, will serve as the attacking species, so we once again expect an $S_N2/S_N1/E2/E1$ competition to take place and we proceed to Steps 2–4. (**Figure 9-23** lists the steps to be applied, but the rest of the table is left for you to complete as an exercise in Your Turn 9.26.)

For Step 2, we rule out S_N1 and E1 because the solvent, *N,N*-dimethylformamide (DMF), is aprotic, leaving just S_N2 and E2 as options. For Step 3, we identify $(CH_3)_3CO^-$ as a strong nucleophile (because it has a full negative charge) and a strong base (because it is stronger than HO^-). The attacking species therefore favors both S_N2 and E2, so we are still left with these two reactions as candidates.

For Step 4, our goal is to break the tie between S_N2 and E2. The attacking species, $(CH_3)_3CO^-$, is a strong, bulky base, so it will act better as a base than a nucleophile, favoring E2 over S_N2. Therefore, we are left with E2 as the winner.

YOUR TURN **9.26**

Complete Figure 9-23, which summarizes Steps 2–4 for the reaction in Equation 9-40. The relevant information is given in the main text. *Hint*: Use Figures 9-21 and 9-22 as guides.

To determine the major E2 product, notice in the substrate that there is a H atom on each C atom attached to C—OTs. Thus, it may appear that there are two possible E2 products, depending on which of those protons is removed. The E2 reaction is *stereospecific*, however, favoring the anticoplanar conformation of the substrate (review

Section 8.5c). In this substrate, only the proton indicated in Equation 9-41 can be anti to the leaving group, giving rise to only one E2 product:

Mechanism for the E2 conversion of an alkyl tosylate to an alkene (Eq. 9-40)

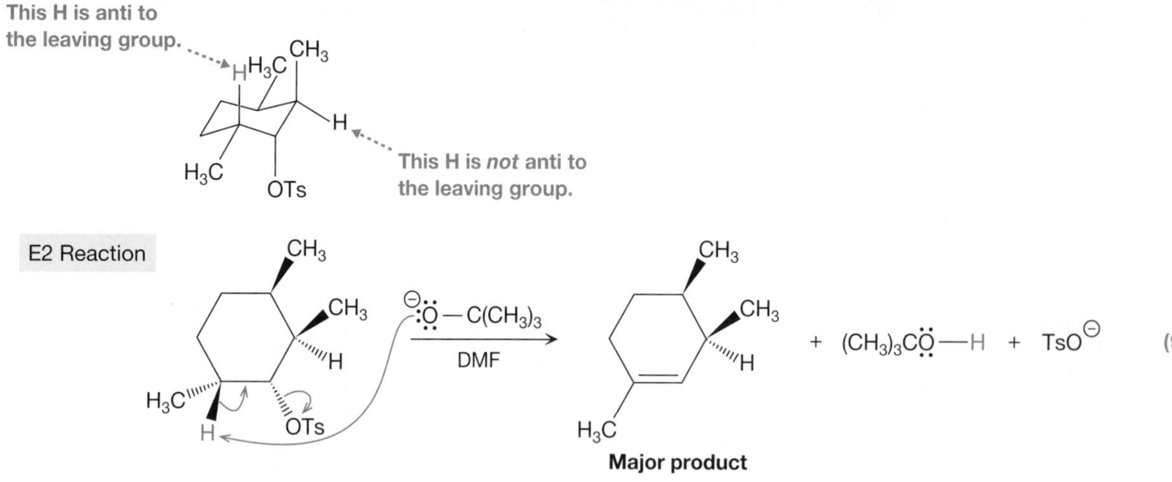

This H is anti to the leaving group.
This H is *not* anti to the leaving group.
E2 Reaction
DMF
+ $(CH_3)_3COH$ + TsO^-
Major product

(9-41)

SOLVED PROBLEM **9.9**

How to predict the outcome of an $S_N2/S_N1/E2/E1$ competition

Break It Down **Draw the complete mechanism and predict the products for the reaction shown here. In this reaction, (*R*)-(bromomethyl-d_1)-benzene is dissolved in methanol.**

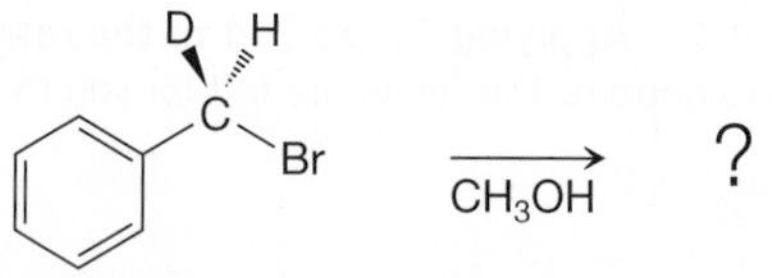

CH_3OH
?

(*R*)-(Bromomethyl-d_1)-benzene

Think	Solve
Step 1: Is there a suitable leaving group on an sp^3-hybridized C? Is there a recognizable attacking species?	The leaving group, Br^-, is suitable because it is more stable than F^-, and it is attached to an sp^3-hybridized C. The attacking species is CH_3OH, which is also the solvent. Therefore, we do expect an $S_N2/S_N1/E2/E1$ competition to take place.
Step 2: What reaction(s) can we rule out, on the basis of type of substrate, solvent, leaving group ability, or the absence of β hydrogens?	The substrate is primary, which normally would lead to an excessively unstable carbocation and rule out S_N1 and E1. However, the substrate is benzylic and the resulting carbocation is resonance-stabilized, so we do not rule out those reactions. There are no β hydrogens, however, so we rule out E2 and E1.
Step 3: Is the attacking species a strong or weak nucleophile? Is it a strong or weak base? Which reactions do these characteristics of the attacking species favor?	The attacking species, CH_3OH, is uncharged and is a weak nucleophile, so it would favor S_N1 over S_N2. CH_3OH is also a much weaker base than HO^-, so it is characterized as a weak base and would favor E1 over E2. We already ruled out E1, however, so S_N1 is the winning reaction.

(continued)

Step 4: What tiebreaker should be applied?	We do not need to apply any tiebreakers because we determined from Step 3 that S_N1 is the winning reaction.
How do you draw the mechanism for the winning reaction?	The mechanism for the S_N1 reaction is shown below. The loss of the leaving group produces an achiral carbocation, so the attack of the nucleophile produces a mixture of enantiomers. The S_N1 product is then deprotonated to yield an uncharged ether.

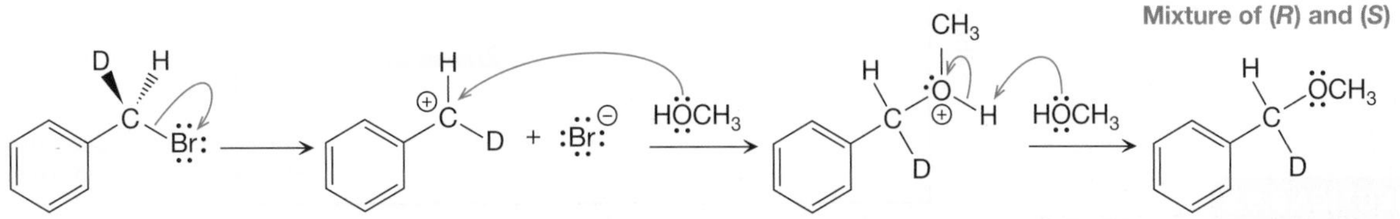

Mixture of (R) and (S)

Try It Predict the major product of the reaction shown in the above exercise when the alkyl bromide is treated with sodium methoxide in acetone.

9.10 Regioselectivity in Elimination Reactions: Alkene Stability and Zaitsev's Rule

SECTION 9.10 OBJECTIVES

You will be able to:

1. Determine the relative stabilities of alkenes from their degree of alkyl substitution.
2. Predict the major alkene product of an elimination reaction when regiochemistry is taken into account.

A substrate can possess two or more distinct hydrogen atoms that can be removed as protons in an elimination reaction, leading to two or more possible alkene products. This is the case for 2-iodohexane undergoing an E2 reaction, as shown in Equation 9-42:

The major product is the more highly substituted alkene.

$$\underset{\textbf{2-Iodohexane}}{\overset{6\ 5\ 4\ 3\ 2\ 1}{CH_3CH_2CH_2CH_2CH(I)CH_3}} \xrightarrow[\substack{CH_3OH \\ 100\ °C}]{CH_3ONa} \underset{\substack{68\% \\ \textbf{Hex-2-ene}}}{CH_3CH_2CH_2CH{=}CHCH_3} + \underset{\substack{16\% \\ \textbf{Hex-1-ene}}}{CH_3CH_2CH_2CH_2CH{=}CH_2} \quad (9\text{-}42)$$

Removing a proton from C-3 produces hex-2-ene, whereas removing a proton from C-1 produces hex-1-ene. With CH_3O^- as the base, the major product is hex-2-ene. This elimination reaction exhibits **regioselectivity**, which is the preference of a reaction to take place at one site within a molecule over another.

Why is hex-2-ene the major product, not hex-1-ene? The answer is that hex-2-ene is more stable than hex-1-ene. Therefore, as shown in **Figure 9-24** (next page), the E2 reaction that produces hex-2-ene has the more negative $\Delta G°_{rxn}$ and the smaller energy barrier. In general:

> The major alkene product of an elimination reaction is the most stable one.

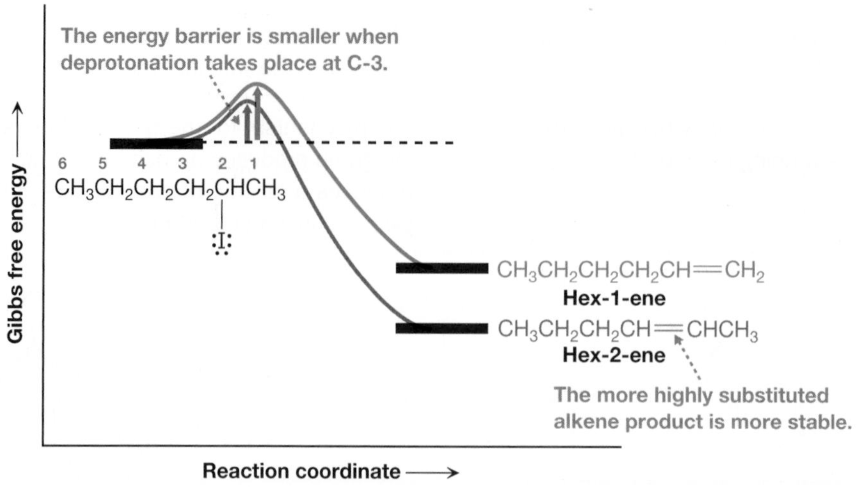
The energy barrier is smaller when deprotonation takes place at C-3.
6 5 4 3 2 1
CH3CH2CH2CH2CHCH3
:I:
CH3CH2CH2CH2CH=CH2
Hex-1-ene
CH3CH2CH2CH=CHCH3
Hex-2-ene
The more highly substituted alkene product is more stable.
Gibbs free energy
Reaction coordinate

FIGURE 9-24 Zaitsev's rule The free energy diagram is shown for the reaction leading to each product in Equation 9-42. The more stable alkene product is hex-2-ene because it is more highly substituted. According to the Hammond postulate, the transition state leading to hex-2-ene is lower in energy than that leading to hex-1-ene, so the energy barrier leading to hex-2-ene is smaller, too.

CONNECTIONS 9.6

Making plastic more fantastic
Hex-1-ene (Eq. 9-42) is used as a comonomer in the production of the polymer polyethylene in order to create varying densities of the plastic for different uses. Small concentrations (less than about 4%) of hex-1-ene are used to produce high-density polyethylene (HDPE), and higher concentrations (up to about 10%) are used to produce linear low-density polyethylene (LLDPE).

Because of the importance of alkene stability in elimination reactions, we need to know how to evaluate the relative stabilities of alkenes. These relative stabilities are summarized in **Figure 9-25**, where two trends stand out:

- Alkene stability increases with a greater number of alkyl groups attached to the C=C bond; that is, with an increasing degree of *alkyl substitution*.
- Trans alkenes are more stable than cis alkenes.

Alkene stability increases as alkyl substitution increases because of *hyperconjugation*, which we will discuss in Section 9.11. Trans isomers are more stable than cis isomers due to *steric strain* (Chapter 4). The bulkiness of the two alkyl substituents causes electrons from those groups to occupy the same space in the cis isomer (**Figure 9-26**), whereas they are on opposite sides of the double bond in the trans isomer. Repulsion of those electrons decreases the stability of the cis isomer.

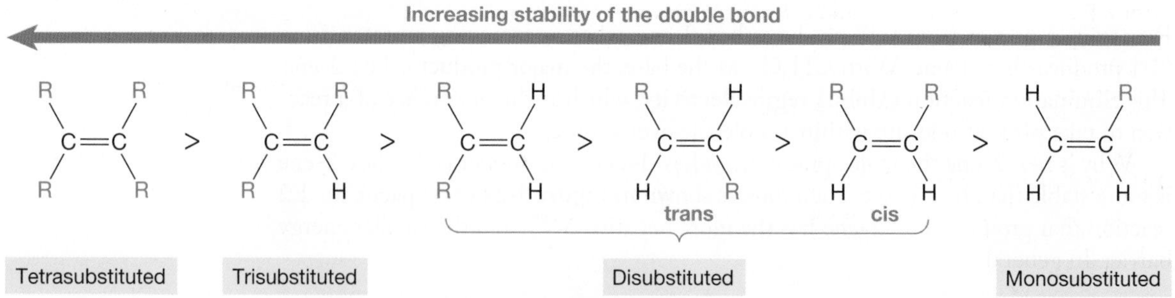
Increasing stability of the double bond
trans
cis
Tetrasubstituted
Trisubstituted
Disubstituted
Monosubstituted

FIGURE 9-25 Trends in alkene stability As the alkyl substitution of the C=C bond increases (right to left), the alkene stability increases. A trans alkene is more stable than its cis counterpart.

FIGURE 9-26 Steric strain in cis alkenes Steric repulsion between the alkyl groups causes (a) the cis isomer of an alkene to be less stable than (b) the trans isomer.

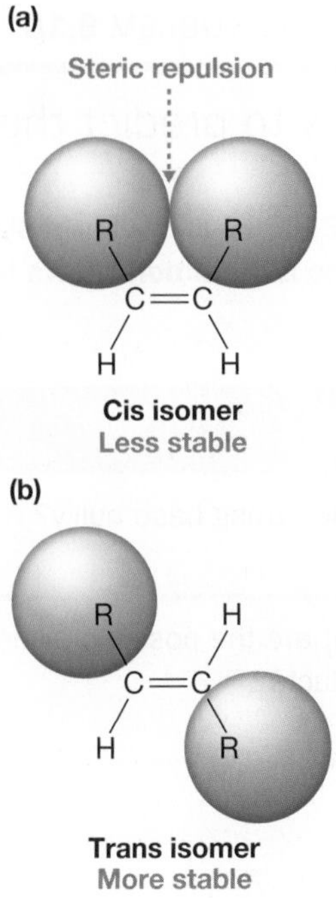

(a)
Steric repulsion
R
R
C=C
H
H
Cis isomer
Less stable
(b)
R
H
C=C
H
R
Trans isomer
More stable

The example in Equation 9-42 dealt with an E2 reaction, but we tend to see the same regiochemistry with E1 reactions, too, such as those in Equation 9-43. A proton on 2-methylbutan-2-ol can be removed from C-1, to produce 2-methylbut-1-ene, or from C-3, to produce 2-methylbut-2-ene. The major product is 2-methylbut-2-ene because, once again, it is the more highly substituted and more stable alkene product.

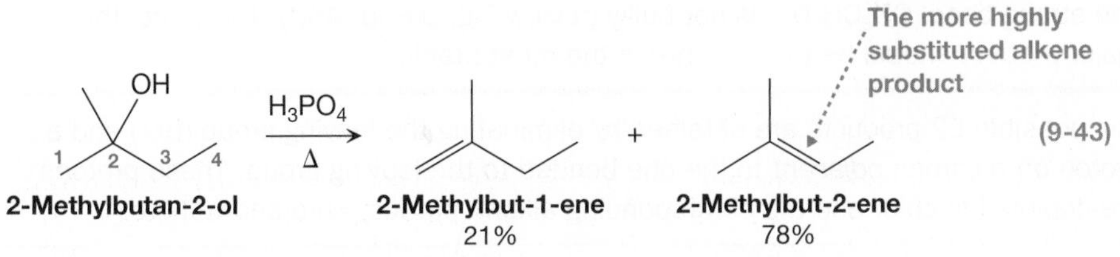

The more highly substituted alkene product
OH
1
2
3
4
H_3PO_4
Δ
+
(9-43)
2-Methylbutan-2-ol
2-Methylbut-1-ene
21%
2-Methylbut-2-ene
78%

Before the elimination mechanisms were fully understood, Alexander M. Zaitsev (1841–1910), a Russian chemist, summarized the regioselectivity of elimination reactions as follows: *The major elimination product is the one produced by deprotonating the carbon atom initially attached to the fewest hydrogen atoms.* Eliminating a proton from the C atom that has the fewest H atoms leads to the most highly alkyl-substituted alkene product, which, we now know, tends to be the most stable. Zaitsev's summary from his empirical observations came to be known as **Zaitsev's rule**, and the most highly substituted alkene product is called the **Zaitsev product**.

YOUR TURN 9.27

For each product in Equation 9-42, circle all of the alkyl groups that are attached to the alkene group and specify the degree of alkyl substitution (i.e., mono, di, tri, tetra, or unsubstituted). Do the same for each product in Equation 9-43.

One noteworthy exception to Zaitsev's rule involves a strong, bulky base, such as the *tert*-butoxide ion, $(CH_3)_3CO^-$. When 2-iodohexane is treated with potassium *tert*-butoxide, the major product is hex-1-ene (Eq. 9-44), which is the *less* highly substituted alkene product; it is called the **anti-Zaitsev product**:

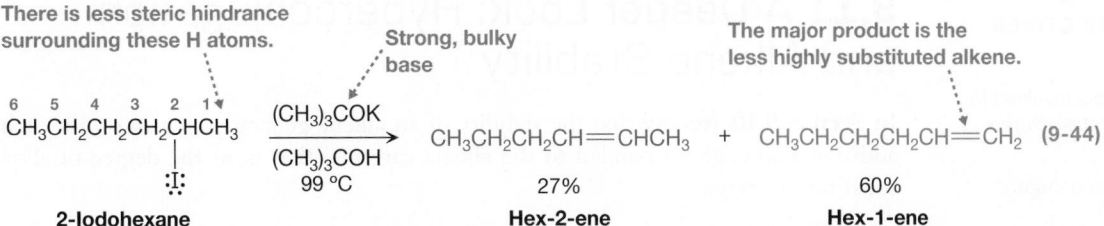

There is less steric hindrance surrounding these H atoms. — Strong, bulky base — The major product is the less highly substituted alkene.

$$\underset{\text{2-Iodohexane}}{\overset{6\;5\;4\;3\;2\;1}{CH_3CH_2CH_2CH_2CH(I)CH_3}} \xrightarrow[\substack{(CH_3)_3COH \\ 99\ ^\circ C}]{(CH_3)_3COK} \underset{\substack{27\% \\ \text{Hex-2-ene}}}{CH_3CH_2CH_2CH{=}CHCH_3} + \underset{\substack{60\% \\ \text{Hex-1-ene}}}{CH_3CH_2CH_2CH_2CH{=}CH_2} \quad (9\text{-}44)$$

Although the H atoms at both C-1 and C-3 are relatively well exposed to the base (Section 9.6b), there is more steric hindrance surrounding those at C-3. Thus, the base, which itself is quite bulky, favors abstraction of the proton at C-1.

SOLVED PROBLEM **9.10**

How to predict the major elimination product, including regiochemistry

Break It Down **Predict the major product of the E2 reaction shown here.**

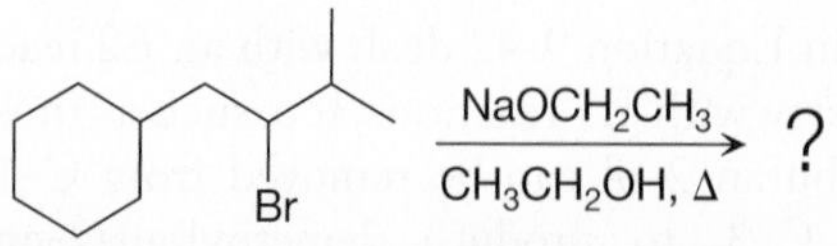

Br
$NaOCH_2CH_3$
CH_3CH_2OH, Δ
?

Think	Solve
Is the strong base bulky?	The strong base, $CH_3CH_2O^-$, is not bulky (review Fig. 9-8, p. 458). Therefore, the major product should be the one that is the most stable.
What are the possible alkene products?	The possible E2 products are obtained by eliminating the leaving group (Br^-) and a proton on a carbon *adjacent* to the one bonded to the leaving group. These protons are depicted in color and the corresponding alkene products are shown here.

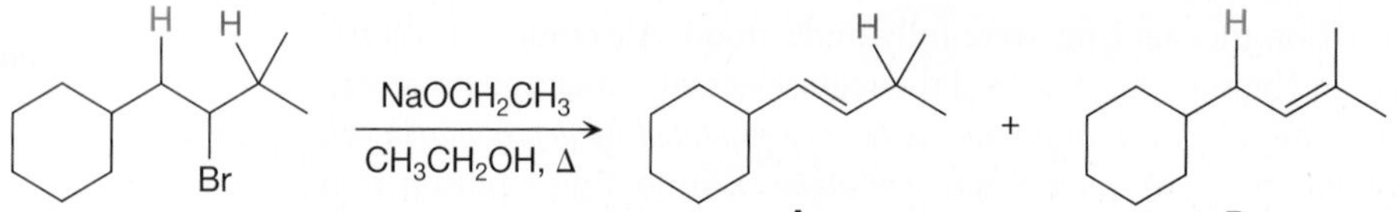

H
H
Br
$NaOCH_2CH_3$
CH_3CH_2OH, Δ
H
+
H

A **B**

Which alkene is more stable?	Alkene **A** is disubstituted and alkene **B** is trisubstituted. Alkene **B**, therefore, is more highly alkyl-substituted and more stable, so it should be the major E2 product.

Try It For each of the following substrates, draw *all* possible E2 products when CH_3ONa is used as the base, and determine which of them is the major product. (Disregard stereochemistry in this case.)

(a)

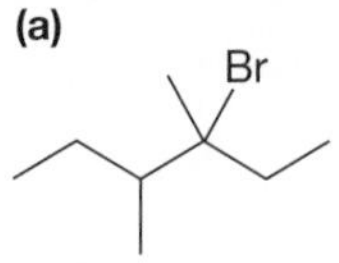

Br

(b)

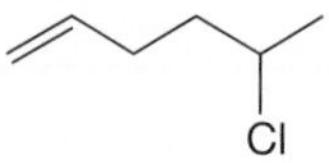

Cl

(c)

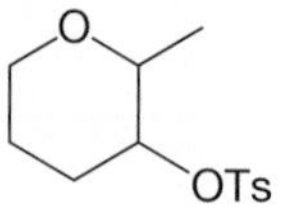

O
OTs

SECTION 9.11 OBJECTIVES

You will be able to:

1. Identify the orbitals involved in hyperconjugation in substituted alkenes.
2. Explain why hyperconjugation stabilizes alkenes.

9.11 A Deeper Look: Hyperconjugation and Alkene Stability

In Section 9.10, we saw that the stability of an alkene generally increases with each additional alkyl group bonded to the alkene carbons (that is, as the degree of alkyl substitution increases):

Alkene stability:

Unsubstituted < Monosubstituted < Disubstituted < Trisubstituted < Tetrasubstituted

This trend can be explained by *hyperconjugation*, which comes about when filled σ bonding molecular orbitals (MOs) mix with an adjacent orbital that is not completely

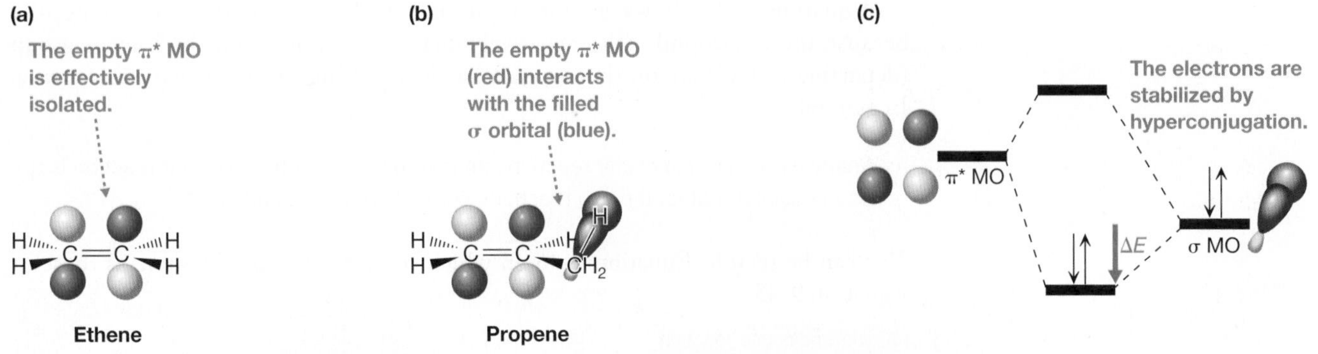

(a)
The empty π* MO is effectively isolated.
H
H
C=C
H
H
Ethene
(b)
The empty π* MO (red) interacts with the filled σ orbital (blue).
H
H
C=C
H
CH2
H
Propene
(c)
The electrons are stabilized by hyperconjugation.
π* MO
ΔE
σ MO

FIGURE 9-27 Hyperconjugation in alkenes (a) In $H_2C{=}CH_2$, the π^* MO does not interact with any adjacent orbitals. (b) In $H_2C{=}CH{-}CH_3$, the empty π^* MO interacts with the filled σ MO of the C—H bond in CH_3. (c) The orbital interaction, an example of hyperconjugation, stabilizes the electrons from the σ MO.

filled (Section 7.9a; see Recall box). In the case of alkenes, the unfilled orbital is the π^* antibonding MO of the C=C bond, and the filled σ bonding MOs are provided by the attached alkyl groups.

To see how an alkene is stabilized by hyperconjugation when an alkyl group is attached to the C=C bond, study **Figure 9-27**. Figure 9-27a shows the π^* antibonding MO from ethene, in which there are no alkyl groups attached to the C=C bond, and Figure 9-27b shows the π^* antibonding MO from propene, which has one attached alkyl group. Without any attached alkyl groups, the π^* antibonding MO in ethene (Fig. 9-27a) does not participate in any orbital mixing. In propene (Fig. 9-27b), on the other hand, notice that a σ bonding orbital from the attached CH_3 group has the appropriate symmetry to mix with the π^* antibonding MO. The result of this orbital mixing, as shown in Figure 9-27c, is the stabilization of those σ C—H electrons.

Figure 9-27c highlights the hyperconjugation that takes place when there is one alkyl group attached to the C=C bond. With each additional alkyl group attached, this type of stabilization increases even further.

◀ **RECALL**

Section 7.9a showed that hyperconjugation in carbocations arises when the filled σ bonding molecular orbitals of an alkyl group attached to C^+ mix with the empty 2*p* orbital of C^+. This mixing lowers the energy of the σ bonding electrons in the attached alkyl groups.

YOUR TURN **9.28**

Hyperconjugation in alkenes can involve σ MOs other than those from C—H bonds. Redraw Figure 9-27b and 9-27c to illustrate the hyperconjugation that takes place in 3,3-dimethylbut-1-ene, $H_2C{=}CH{-}C(CH_3)_3$.

9.12 Intermolecular Reactions versus Intramolecular Cyclizations

SECTION 9.12 OBJECTIVES

You will be able to:

1. Identify when an intramolecular nucleophilic substitution is feasible.
2. Predict the major product from a competition involving intermolecular and intramolecular substitution reactions.

We generally think of a chemical reaction being between two *separate species*: a so-called **intermolecular** reaction (one between molecules). However, a reaction also can occur between functional groups that are part of the *same molecule*, attached at different places on the molecule's backbone; such a reaction is called an ***intra*molecular** reaction.

Equation 9-45 shows an intramolecular S_N2 reaction. It is intramolecular because the nucleophile (the negatively charged O atom) and the leaving group (departing as Cl^-) are on the same molecule, resulting in the formation of a ring. In general:

> Whenever an intramolecular reaction can take place, an intermolecular reaction is also possible; that is, the two reactions compete with each other.

This can be seen in Equation 9-46, in which the reactants are the same as those in Equation 9-45:

An *intramolecular* reaction

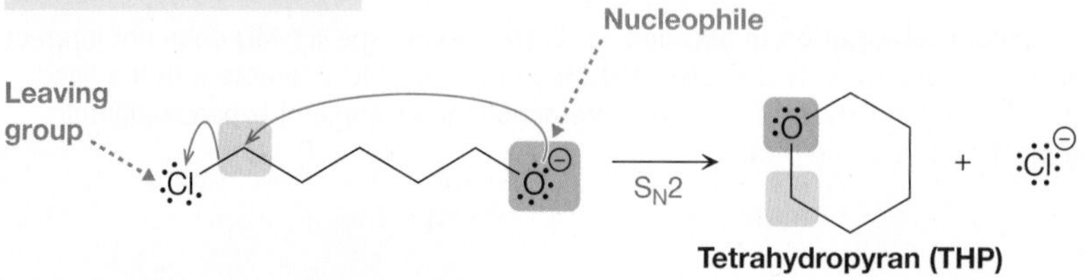
Nucleophile
Leaving group
SN2
Tetrahydropyran (THP)

(9-45)

An *intermolecular* reaction

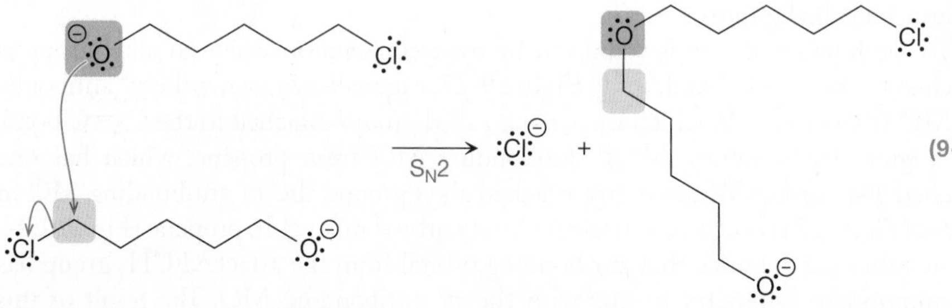
SN2

(9-46)

Which reaction, intramolecular or intermolecular, is the predominant one? Experimentally:

> An *intra*molecular reaction typically "wins out" over its competing intermolecular reaction when the formation of a five- or six-membered ring is possible.

The formation of a five- or six-membered ring is the favored outcome because of the interplay between entropy change and strain during the formation of a ring. For a ring to form, two ends of a chain must form a new bond, which reduces freedom of movement within the molecule. A loss of molecular freedom results in a decrease of entropy (disorder), which is unfavorable. As the chain becomes longer, it becomes less likely for the ends to meet to form a ring; thus, the decrease in entropy becomes more pronounced and the process becomes even less favorable. On the other hand, recall from Section 4.3 that ring strain decreases sharply to zero on going from a three-membered ring to a six-membered ring, and larger rings have a small amount of ring strain. Therefore, as the size of the ring being formed increases from three to six members, the process of forming the ring becomes easier energetically. These opposing factors, entropy and strain energy, reach an optimum in the formation of a five- or six-membered ring.

CONNECTIONS 9.7

Tetrahydropyran: A sweet backbone Derivatives of tetrahydropyran (THP; Eq. 9-45) are used as intermediates in organic synthesis, especially in the protection of alcohol OH functional groups (Chapter 21). In nature, the THP ring system is the basis of cyclic sugars such as glucose.

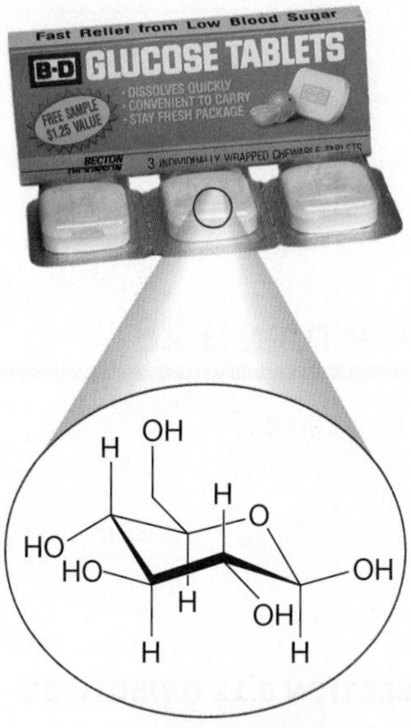
Fast Relief from Low Blood Sugar
B-D GLUCOSE TABLETS
FREE SAMPLE $1.25 VALUE
• DISSOLVES QUICKLY
• CONVENIENT TO CARRY
• STAY FRESH PACKAGE
OH
H
HO
HO
OH
OH
O

Glucose

SOLVED PROBLEM **9.11**

How to predict the outcome of competing intramolecular S_N2 reactions

Break It Down **Two different intramolecular nucleophilic substitution reactions are possible with the substrate shown here. Draw the complete, detailed mechanism that leads to each product. Predict which one is the major product and explain why.**

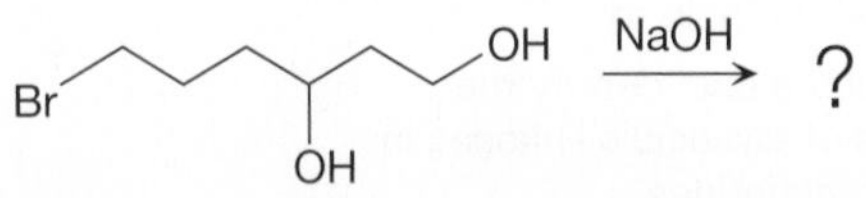

Br
OH
OH
NaOH
?

Think	Solve
Under what conditions does the reaction take place?	The reaction takes place under basic conditions, as indicated by the presence of NaOH.
For an intramolecular nucleophilic substitution reaction under these conditions, what can act as the nucleophile? What can act as the leaving group?	Under basic conditions, deprotonation of an OH group on the organic species would generate a strongly nucleophilic O^- site. The leaving group departs as Br^-.
For each intramolecular nucleophilic substitution reaction, what is the size of the ring that is formed?	The two possible intramolecular nucleophilic substitution reactions are shown below. The first reaction yields a seven-membered ring, whereas the second reaction yields a five-membered ring. Because intramolecular reactions favor the formation of five- and six-membered rings, the second reaction yields the major product.

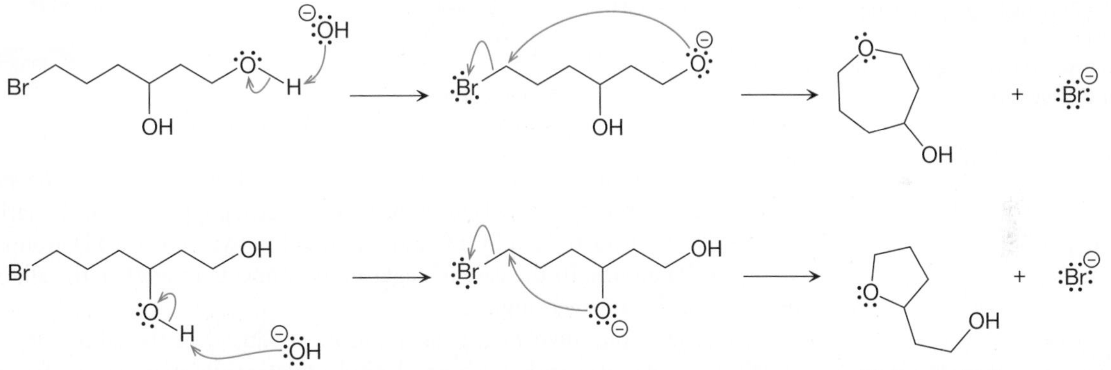

Br
OH
H
OH
Br
OH
O
OH
+
Br
Br
OH
O
H
OH
Br
OH
O
O
OH
+
Br
Major product

Try It What is the major product of the nucleophilic substitution reaction shown here?

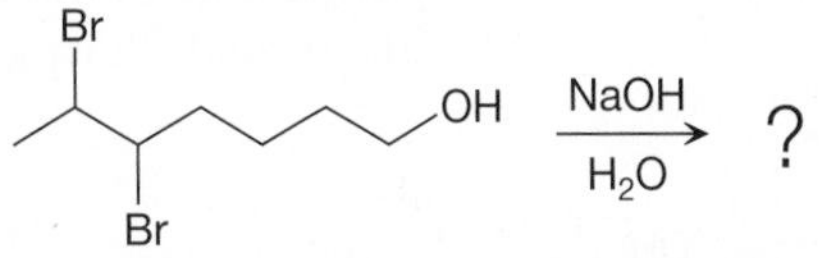

Br
Br
OH
NaOH
H₂O
?

SECTION 9.13 OBJECTIVES

You will be able to:

1. Locate and identify the types of glycosidic linkages in polysaccharides.

2. Draw the mechanism for glycosidation and its reverse reaction, hydrolysis, under acidic conditions.

9.13 Nucleophilic Substitution Reactions and Monosaccharides: The Formation and Hydrolysis of Glycosides

As we saw in previous topics on biomolecules (Sections 1.14b, 4.13, and 5.16), monosaccharides are relatively small carbohydrates and are often shown in their acyclic form. In nature, however, carbohydrates largely exist as more complex structures, such as starch and cellulose, in which numerous simple sugars (frequently many thousands) in their ring forms are connected together. A portion of one such carbohydrate is shown in **Figure 9-28a**. (We will describe these macroscopic structures in greater detail in Chapter 28.)

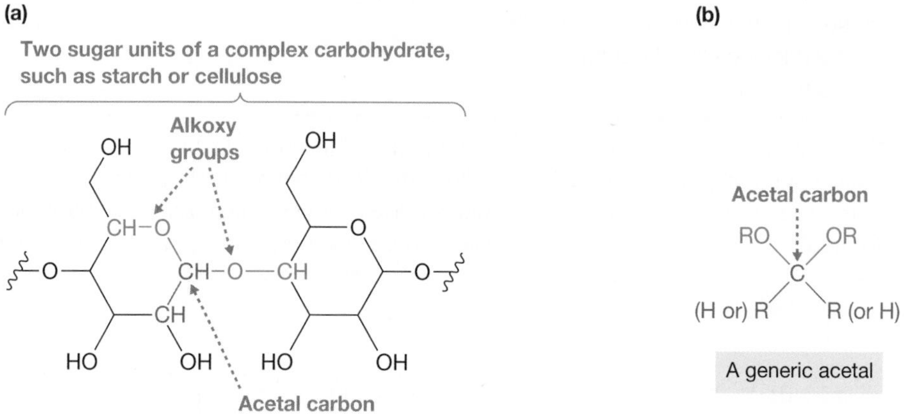
(a)
Two sugar units of a complex carbohydrate, such as starch or cellulose
Alkoxy groups
Acetal carbon
(b)
Acetal carbon
A generic acetal

FIGURE 9-28 Acetal groups in carbohydrates (a) In a complex carbohydrate, one cyclic sugar unit is connected to another by an acetal functional group, highlighted in blue and red. (b) An acetal carbon is bonded to two alkyl (or H) groups and two alkoxy (OR) groups.

As indicated in blue and red, an *acetal* functional group connects the sugar units together. First introduced in Table 1-6, an acetal group (shown in its generic form in Fig. 9-28b) is characterized by a C atom bonded to two alkyl (or H) groups and two alkoxy (OR) groups. In the case of sugar units connected together, the alkoxy groups belong to different sugar units.

An acetal group involving a sugar can be produced in the laboratory simply by treating a monosaccharide with an alcohol under acidic conditions. An example is shown in Equation 9-47, in which β-D-glucose is treated with methanol and hydrochloric acid. In this case, only one alkoxy group in the product belongs to a sugar unit. The second alkoxy group is simply a methoxy group (OCH_3) from the alcohol used.

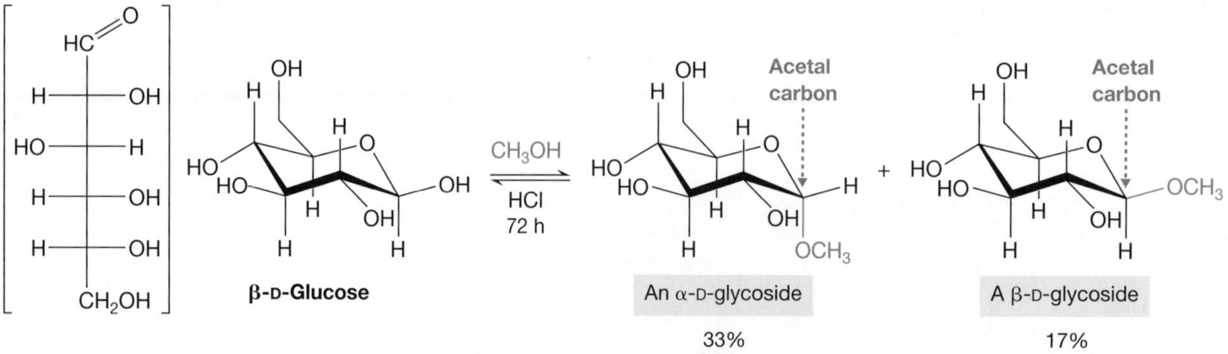
β-D-Glucose
CH_3OH
HCl
72 h
Acetal carbon
An α-D-glycoside
33%
A β-D-glycoside
17%

(9-47)

The products in Equation 9-47, in which OH from a sugar molecule has been replaced by OR, are called **glycosides**. Notice in this **glycosidation** reaction that the products form as a mixture of diastereomers. The first diastereomer, in which the alkoxy group is in the axial position, is designated as α, and the second one, in which the alkoxy group is in the equatorial position, is designated as β. (The α and β designations will be explained in greater detail in Section 19.14.)

To understand why a mixture of diastereomers is produced, study the mechanism of the reaction shown in Equation 9-48:

Mechanism for the glycosidation of a sugar (Eq. 9-47)

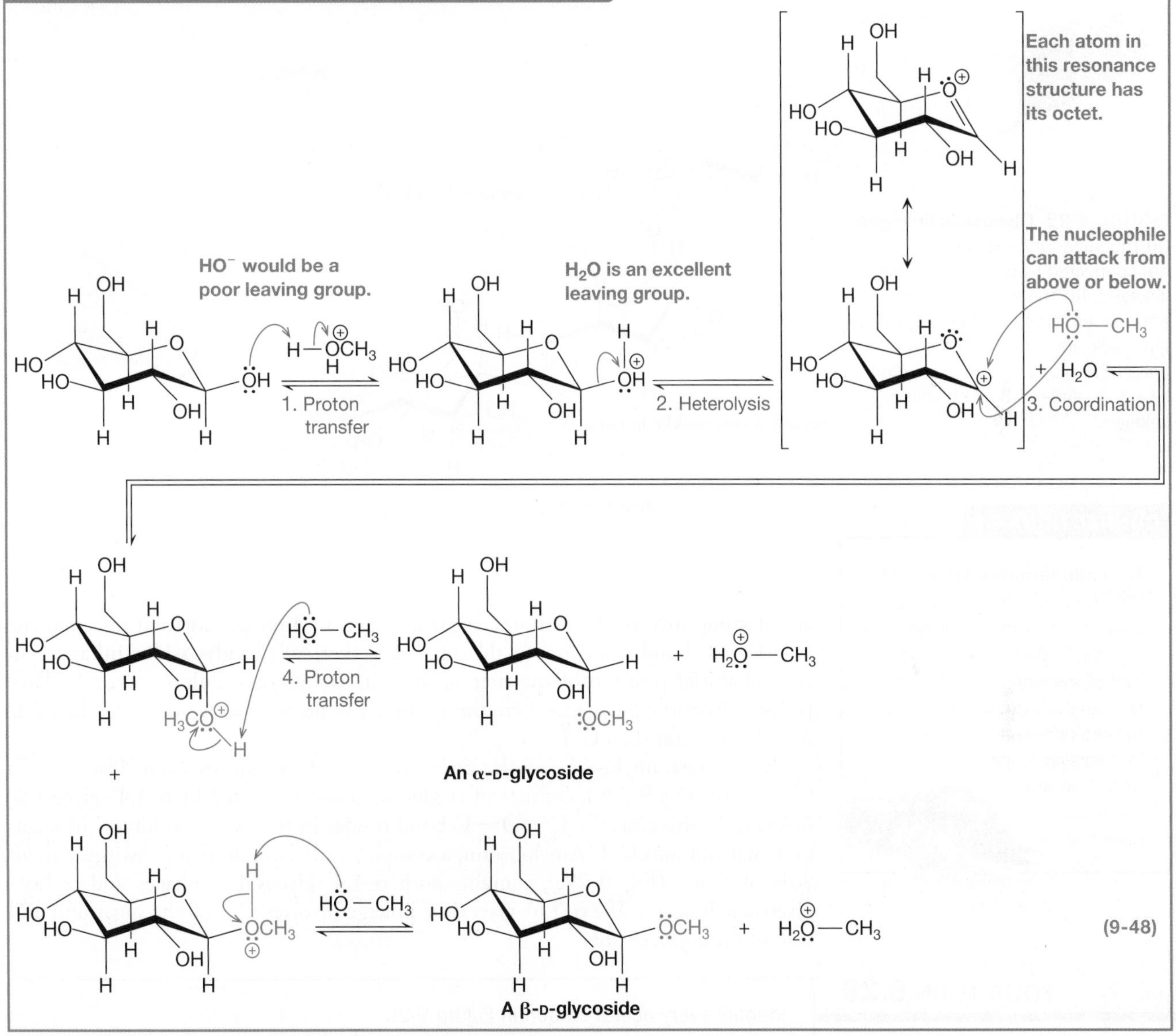

Each atom in this resonance structure has its octet.
The nucleophile can attack from above or below.
HO⁻ would be a poor leaving group.
H_2O is an excellent leaving group.
1. Proton transfer
2. Heterolysis
3. Coordination
4. Proton transfer
An α-D-glycoside
A β-D-glycoside

(9-48)

This glycosidation reaction takes place by an S_N1 mechanism, similar to the one in Equation 9-39 (p. 484). In Step 1, protonation converts the poor HO^- leaving group into a good leaving group, which departs as H_2O in Step 2. The resulting carbocation is stabilized by resonance with the neighboring O atom. In Step 3, the newly formed carbocation is attacked by the methanol nucleophile. As indicated, this can take place on either side of the plane of the carbocation C. Finally, in Step 4, deprotonation removes the positive charge from O.

In nature, complex carbohydrates consisting only of D-glucose subunits can differ by the way in which the acetal groups connect the sugars together (**Figure 9-29**, next page). In cellulose (which makes up about half of wood; Fig. 9-29a), for example, the

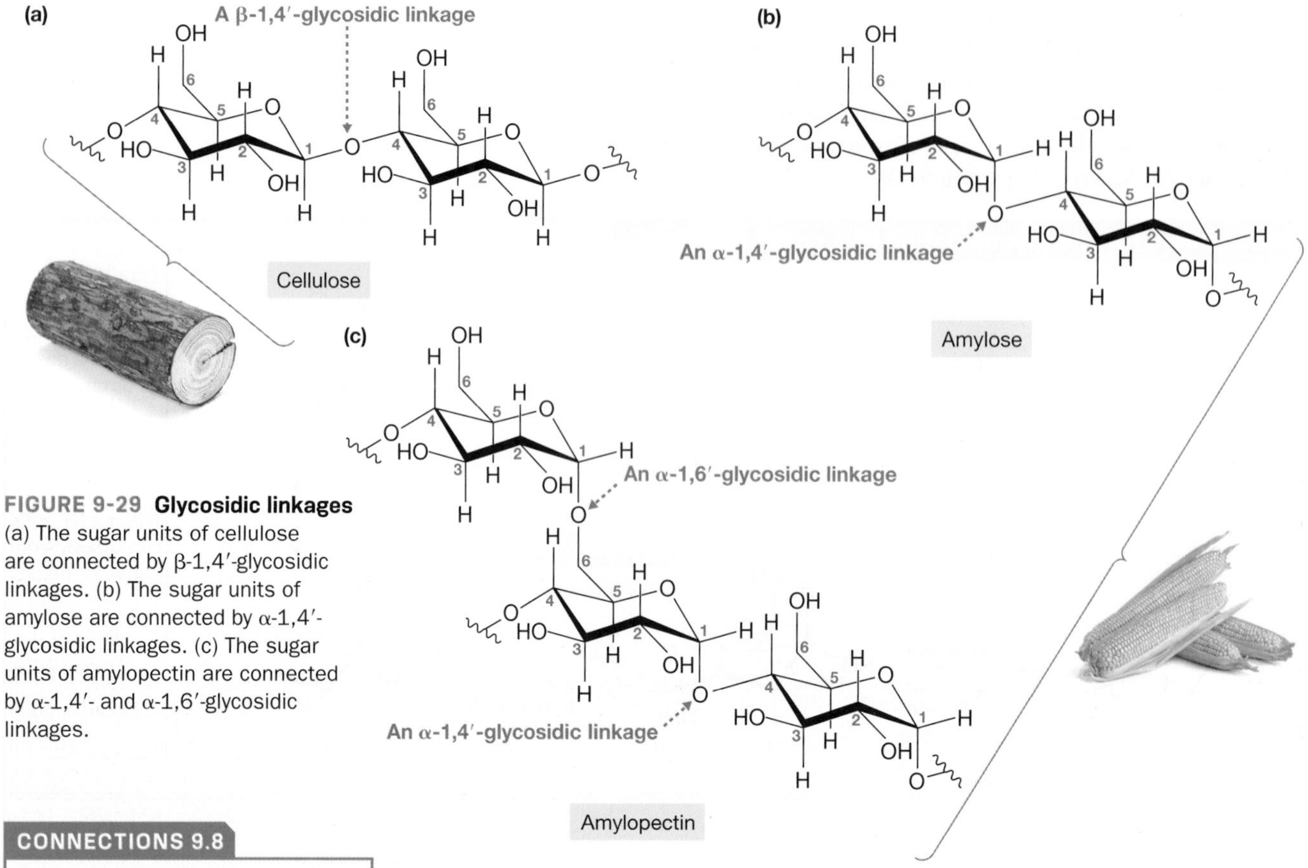
(a)
A β-1,4′-glycosidic linkage
Cellulose
(b)
An α-1,4′-glycosidic linkage
Amylose
(c)
An α-1,6′-glycosidic linkage
An α-1,4′-glycosidic linkage
Amylopectin

FIGURE 9-29 Glycosidic linkages (a) The sugar units of cellulose are connected by β-1,4′-glycosidic linkages. (b) The sugar units of amylose are connected by α-1,4′-glycosidic linkages. (c) The sugar units of amylopectin are connected by α-1,4′- and α-1,6′-glycosidic linkages.

CONNECTIONS 9.8

How can termites eat wood? When termites devour wood, they are after the cellulose (Fig. 9-29) that makes up about half of the wood. Microbes in the termite's gut use enzymes to break down the cellulose into smaller sugar units that are easier to digest.

acetal group involves C-1 on one sugar unit and C-4 on the adjacent one, and the C—O—C bond that connects the sugars together, called a **glycosidic linkage**, is in the equatorial position of the first sugar unit. Therefore, cellulose is said to have β-1,4′-glycosidic linkages, where the prime (′) indicates that C-4 belongs to a different sugar unit than C-1.

By contrast, amylose, a complex carbohydrate that constitutes about 20% of starch (as in corn; Fig. 9-29b), consists of D-glucose units connected by α-1,4′-glycosidic linkages. In this case, the C—O—C bond resides in the axial position of the sugar unit that contains C-1. Amylopectin, a complex carbohydrate that constitutes about 80% of starch (Fig. 9-29c), contains both α-1,4′-glycosidic linkages and α-1,6′-glycosidic linkages. The α-1,6′-glycosidic linkage involves C-1 of one sugar unit and C-6 of the adjacent one.

YOUR TURN 9.29

Identify every acetal carbon in Figure 9-29.

These relatively small structural differences among complex carbohydrates can have a large impact on macroscopic behavior, and therefore they dictate the specific function of the carbohydrate. These consequences will be discussed in greater detail in Chapter 28.

Notice in Equation 9-47 that glycoside formation is reversible, as indicated by the equilibrium arrow. Thus, as shown in Equation 9-49, a glycoside can undergo acid-catalyzed hydrolysis to produce the monosaccharide. The mechanism for this reaction is identical to the one in Equation 9-48, except the roles of water and methanol are reversed; namely, water is the nucleophile and the alcohol is the leaving group in the hydrolysis of a glycoside.

Glycoside hydrolysis

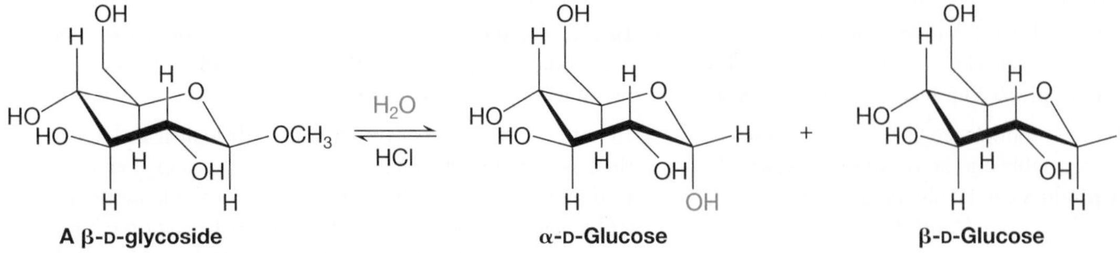
OH
H
H
O
HO
HO
OCH3
H
OH
H
H
A β-D-glycoside
H2O
HCl
α-D-Glucose
+
β-D-Glucose

(9-49)

The stomach provides an acidic environment, so you might think that the breakdown of complex carbohydrates into their monosaccharide subunits would take place in the stomach. Acid hydrolysis is too slow, however, for the body to make use of complex carbohydrates as quick sources of energy. Instead, hydrolysis depends on various enzymes located in the saliva as well as in the small intestine. These enzymes are highly specialized, so that they target only the α-1,4′-glycosidic linkages. As a result, humans can metabolize starches but not cellulose.

Chapter Summary and Key Terms

- S_N2, S_N1, E2, and E1 reactions generally compete with one another. The **attacking species** acts as a nucleophile in S_N2 and S_N1 reactions, whereas it acts as a base in E2 and E1 reactions. The fastest reaction yields the major product. (Section 9.1)
- In the rate-determining step of an S_N2 or E2 reaction, the attacking species can be thought of as forcing off the leaving group. During the rate-determining step of an S_N1 or E1 reaction, the attacking species simply waits. (Section 9.2)
- According to the **Hammond postulate**, the transition state for a reaction resembles reactants more than products if ΔG°_{rxn} is negative, and it resembles products more than reactants if ΔG°_{rxn} is positive. If two elementary steps are of the same type, then the one with the more negative (less positive) value for ΔG°_{rxn} tends to be faster. (Section 9.3a)
- S_N2 reaction rates are highly sensitive to **nucleophilicity**, whereas S_N1 reactions are not. Thus strong nucleophiles (which are typically negatively charged) favor S_N2 reactions, and weak nucleophiles (which are typically uncharged) favor S_N1 reactions. (Section 9.3a)
- E2 reaction rates are highly sensitive to the strength of the attacking base, whereas E1 reactions are not. Thus strong bases (about as strong as HO^- or stronger) favor E2 reactions, and weak bases (substantially weaker than HO^-) favor E1 reactions. (Section 9.3c)
- Nucleophilicity can be weakened significantly by bulky alkyl groups surrounding the nucleophilic site. Base strength, however, is not significantly affected. Therefore, strong, bulky bases favor E2 over S_N2 reactions. (Section 9.3d)
- If a nucleophile is strong, then high concentration favors an S_N2 reaction and low concentration favors an S_N1 reaction. If a base is strong, then high concentration favors an E2 reaction and low concentration favors an E1 reaction. (Section 9.4)
- All four reaction rates are affected by **leaving group ability**. However, S_N1 and E1 reactions are more sensitive to this factor than S_N2 and E2 reactions are. All four reactions are feasible with good leaving groups, whereas poor leaving groups favor S_N2 and E2 reactions only. (Section 9.5)
- Leaving group ability is determined largely by charge stability. The stronger the leaving group's conjugate acid, the better the leaving group. (Section 9.5)
- Substrates with unsuitable leaving groups, such as RO^-, HO^-, H_2N^-, H_3C^-, and H^-, generally cannot undergo any of the four reactions. (Section 9.5)
- Nucleophilic substitution and elimination reactions generally do not occur when leaving groups are on sp^2- or sp-hybridized carbon atoms. (Section 9.6a)
- S_N2, S_N1, and E1 reactions are highly sensitive to the type of carbon to which the leaving group is bonded (i.e., 1°, 2°, or 3°), whereas E2 reactions are not. (Section 9.6b)
  - S_N2 reactions are unfeasible when the leaving group is on a tertiary carbon because steric hindrance is excessive.
  - S_N1 and E1 reactions are unfeasible when the leaving group is on a primary carbon, because the carbocation intermediate is too unstable. Exceptions arise for primary **benzyl substrates** and **allyl substrates**.
  - E2 reactions are feasible for all types of carbons because hydrogen atoms are well exposed.
- *Aprotic solvents* favor S_N2 and E2 reactions; *protic solvents* favor S_N1 and E1 reactions. (Section 9.7)
- Nucleophilicity in a protic solvent is reversed from that in an aprotic solvent when there are dramatic differences in solvation between the two types of solvents. This occurs when both of these criteria are met: (1) The nucleophiles are negatively charged, and (2) the negative charges are localized on atoms in different rows of the periodic table. (Section 9.7b)

- Heat favors elimination over substitution due to the greater *entropy* of the elimination products. **(Section 9.8)**
- The outcome of an $S_N2/S_N1/E2/E1$ competition can be predicted by using a systematic method that considers the various factors controlling the rates of the four reactions. **(Section 9.9)**
- When multiple elimination products are possible, the major product is usually the most stable one, according to **Zaitsev's rule**. The **anti-Zaitsev product** can be obtained when a strong, bulky base like $(CH_3)_3CO^-$ is used. **(Section 9.10)**
- Alkenes are stabilized by alkyl groups attached to the C═C group, as a result of hyperconjugation involving the empty π^* MO from the C═C and filled σ MOs from the attached alkyl groups. **(Section 9.11)**
- **Intramolecular** cyclization reactions are favored over their corresponding **intermolecular** reactions when a five- or six-membered ring can be formed. **(Section 9.12)**
- In nature, cyclic sugars are joined by **glycosidic linkages**, the basis of which is an acetal functional group characterized by the structure RO—C—OR′. In the laboratory, a **glycoside** can be produced from an S_N1 reaction when a monosaccharide reacts with an alcohol under acidic conditions. **(Section 9.13)**

Reaction Tables

This is the first of several end-of-chapter sections in which the reactions from the chapter are summarized in tabular form. For each reaction, the starting compound class, the compound class formed, and the typical reagents and reaction conditions are provided. The sections in which the reaction is discussed are also listed. Similar tables will be provided at the ends of future chapters in which new reactions are encountered.

Two other important features of these tables are noteworthy. First, each entry identifies the key electron-rich and electron-poor species that appear in the mechanism of the reaction (recall from Section 7.1a that these species tend to react with each other). Knowing key electron-rich and electron-poor species for various reactions can help you focus on the mechanisms as you learn new reactions. Second, the reactions are presented in two tables (Tables 9-11 and 9-12), depending on whether the reaction leads to the formation and/or breaking of a carbon–carbon σ bond. Reactions that do *not* are designated as *functional group transformations*, whereas reactions that do are said to *alter the carbon skeleton*. We will discuss the importance of these designations in Chapter 11 in the context of *organic synthesis*.

TABLE 9-11 Functional Group Transformations[a]

	Starting Compound Class	Typical Reagents and Reaction Conditions	Compound Class Formed	Key Electron-Rich Species	Key Electron-Poor Species	Comments	Discussed in Section(s)
(1)	R—CH$_2$—X 1° alkyl halide	NaOH →	R—CH$_2$—OH 1° Alcohol	$HO^{\ominus}$	R—CH$_2$—X (δ^+ on C)	S_N2 reaction	7.2, 8.3, 8.5, 9.9
(2)	R_3C—X 3° alkyl halide	H_2O →	R_3C—OH 3° Alcohol	H_2O	$R_3C^{\oplus}$	S_N1 reaction	7.3, 8.1, 8.3, 8.5, 9.5a, 9.9
(3)	R—O—R Ether	H_2O, $H^{\oplus}$ →	R—OH Alcohol	H_2O	$R^{\oplus}$ or R—$O^{\oplus}$(H)R	S_N1 or S_N2 reaction	7.2, 7.3, 8.1, 8.3, 8.5, 9.5a, 9.9
(4)	R—CH$_2$—X 1° alkyl halide	R′ONa →	R—CH$_2$—O—R′ Ether	$R'O^{\ominus}$	R—CH$_2$—X (δ^+ on C)	S_N2 reaction	7.2, 8.3, 8.5, 9.9

[a] X = Cl, Br, or I.

TABLE 9-11 Functional Group Transformations[a] (continued)

	Starting Compound Class	Typical Reagents and Reaction Conditions	Compound Class Formed	Key Electron-Rich Species	Key Electron-Poor Species	Comments	Discussed in Section(s)
(5)	R–OH Alcohol	H_3PO_4 or H_2SO_4, Δ	R–O–R Ether	ROH	$R^{\oplus}$ or $ROH_2^{\oplus}$	S_N1 or S_N2 reaction	7.2, 7.3, 8.1, 8.3, 8.5
(6)	R–L L = Cl, Br, I, OTs, OMs, or OTf	NaX	R–X Alkyl halide	$X^{\ominus}$	$R{-}CH_2^{\delta+}{-}L$ or $R^{\oplus}$	S_N1 or S_N2 reaction	7.2, 7.3, 8.1, 8.3, 8.5, 9.9
(7)	R–OH Alcohol	HX	R–X Alkyl halide	$X^{\ominus}$	$R^{\oplus}$ or $ROH_2^{\oplus}$	S_N1 or S_N2 reaction	7.2, 7.3, 8.1, 8.3, 8.5, 9.5b
(8)	R–CH(H)–CH(X)–R′ Alkyl halide	$(CH_3)_3CONa$, Δ	R–CH=CH–R′ Alkene	$(CH_3)_3CO^{\ominus}$	R–CH(H)–C$^{\delta+}$H(X)–R′	E2 reaction	7.5, 8.3, 8.5, 9.3d, 9.9
(9)	R–CH(H)–CH(OH)–R′ Alcohol	H_3PO_4 or H_2SO_4, Δ	R–CH=CH–R′ Alkene	H_2O	R–CH(H)–C$^{\oplus}$H–R′	E1 reaction	7.3, 7.6, 8.2, 8.3, 8.5, 9.5a, 9.9

[a]X = Cl, Br, or I.

TABLE 9-12 Reactions That Alter the Carbon Skeleton[a]

	Starting Compound Class	Typical Reagents and Reaction Conditions	Compound Class Formed	Key Electron-Rich Species	Key Electron-Poor Species	Comments	Discussed in Section(s)
(1)	R–C≡C–H Alkyne	1. NaH 2. R′–X	R–C≡C–R′ Alkyne	$R{-}C{\equiv}C{:}^{\ominus}$ Alkynide anion	$R'^{\delta+}{-}X$ Alkyl halide	S_N2 reaction	7.2, 8.3, 8.5, 9.3b, 9.9
(2)	R–X Alkyl halide	NaCN	R–C≡N Nitrile	$N{\equiv}C{:}^{\ominus}$ Cyanide anion	$R^{\delta+}{-}X$ Alkyl halide	S_N2 reaction	7.2, 8.3, 8.5, 9.9

[a]X = Cl, Br, or I.

Problems

Problems that are related to synthesis are denoted (SYN).

Section 9.1 Identifying the Competition among S_N2, S_N1, E2, and E1 Reactions

9.1 When bromocyclohexane is treated with sodium cyanide, the S_N2, S_N1, E2, and E1 reactions compete. Draw the mechanism for each of these four reactions.

9.2 **(SYN)** Suggest an alkyl bromide that can be treated with CH_3SNa to form each of the following products exclusively. By what mechanism should the respective reactions proceed?

(a)

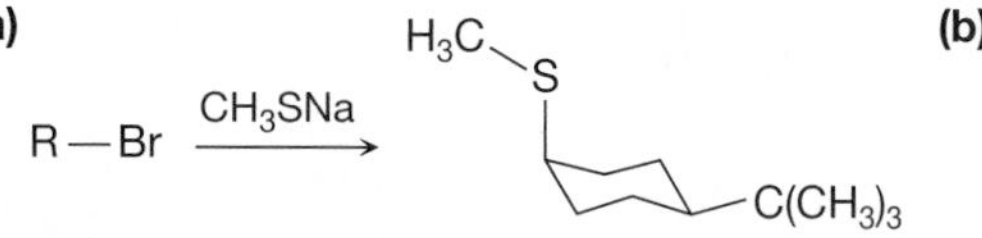
R—Br
CH3SNa
H3C
S
C(CH3)3

(b)

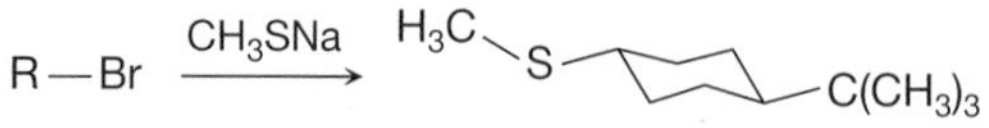
R—Br
CH3SNa
H3C
S
C(CH3)3

9.3 Did the following overall reaction occur by an S_N2, S_N1, E2, or E1 mechanism? How do you know? Draw a complete, detailed mechanism to account for the formation of both products.

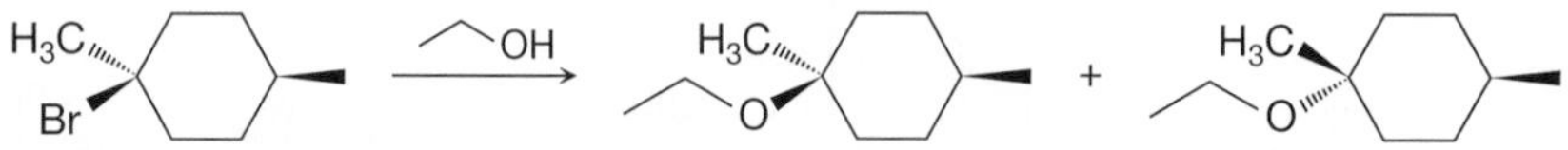
H3C
Br
OH
H3C
O
+
H3C
O

9.4 Did the overall reaction shown here occur by an S_N2, S_N1, E2, or E1 mechanism? How do you know? Draw a complete, detailed mechanism to account for the formation of both products.

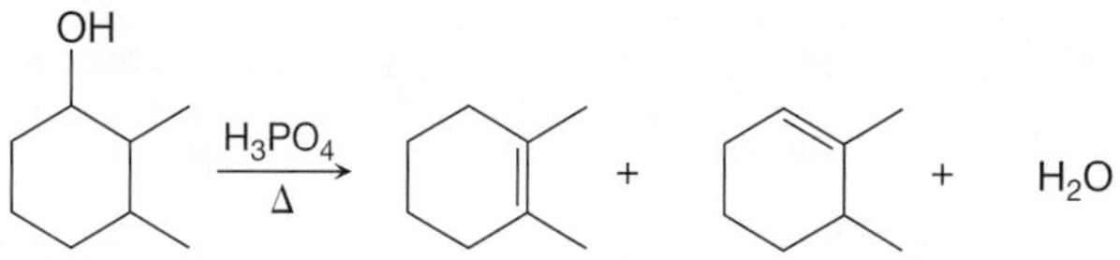
OH
H3PO4
Δ
+
+
H2O

9.5 **(SYN)** The formula of the precursor is given for each of the following reactions. Draw the structure of each precursor, paying attention to stereochemistry, if appropriate.

(a)

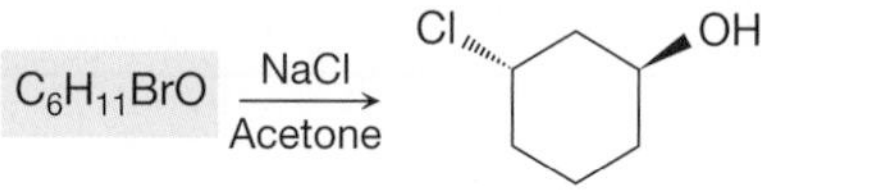
C6H11BrO
NaCl
Acetone
Cl
OH

(b)

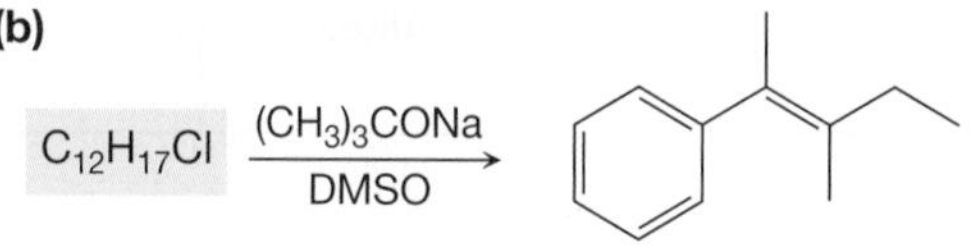
C12H17Cl
(CH3)3CONa
DMSO

Sections 9.3–9.5 Strength and Concentration of the Attacking Species and Leaving Group Ability

9.6 Rank the following bases in order from slowest to fastest E2 reaction rate.

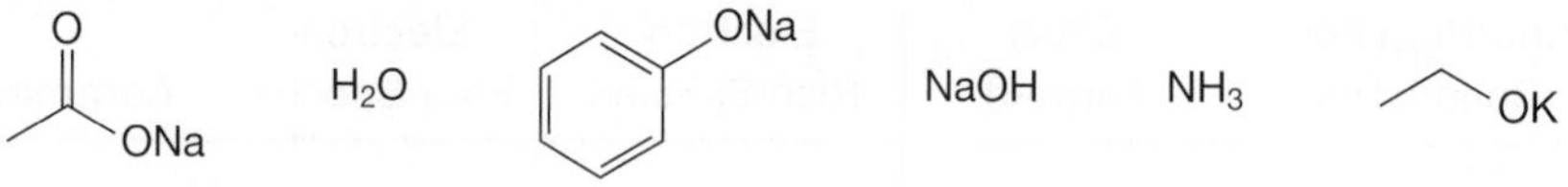
O
ONa
H2O
ONa
NaOH
NH3
OK

A B C D E F

9.7 Rank the following nucleophiles in order from slowest to fastest S_N2 reaction rate when DMSO is the solvent.

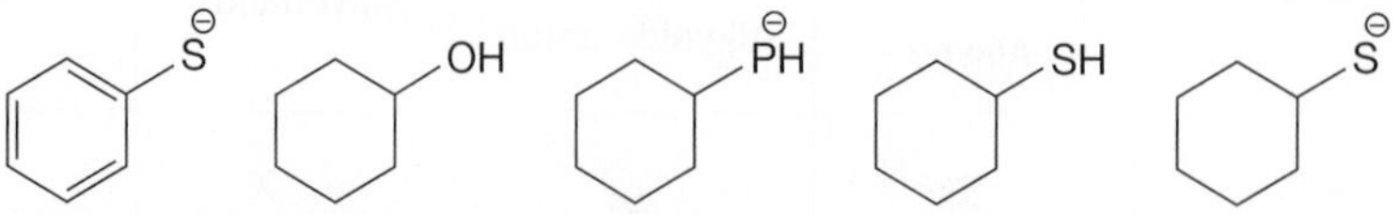
S
OH
PH
SH
S

A B C D E

9.8 **(SYN)** For each S_N2 reaction, draw the missing nucleophile.

(a)
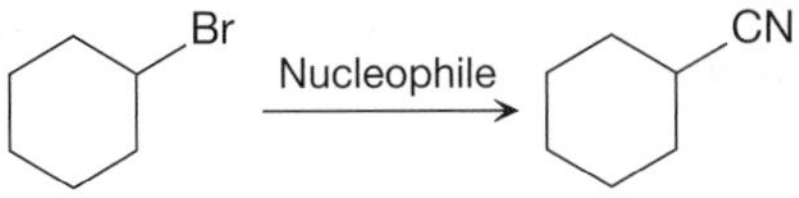
Br
Nucleophile
CN

(b)
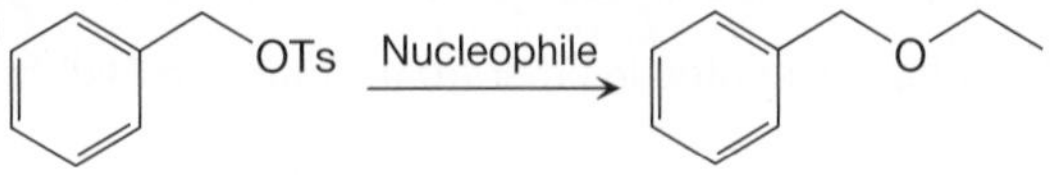
OTs
Nucleophile
O

(c)

Cl
Nucleophile
SCH3

(d)
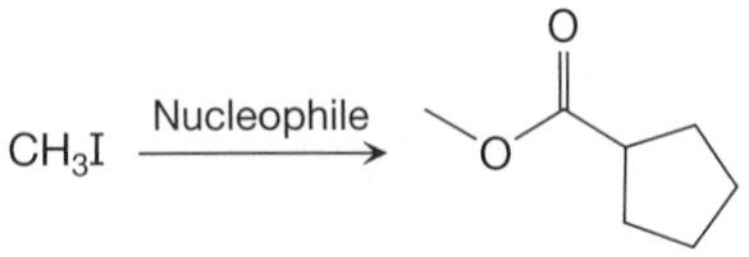
CH3I
Nucleophile
O
O

9.9 **(SYN)** Draw the missing reagents in the following transformation.

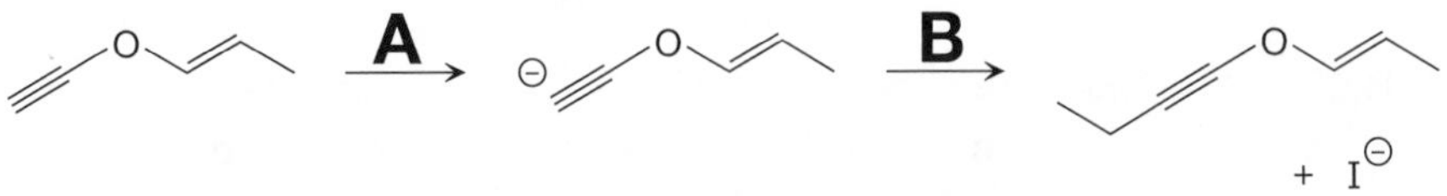
O
A
O
B
O
+ I

9.10 **(SYN)** Show how pent-2-yne can be made from two different alkyl bromides.

9.11 When acetic acid is treated with a strong base, followed by benzyl bromide, a compound is formed whose formula is $C_9H_{10}O_2$. Draw the structure of this product, and draw the mechanism leading to its formation.

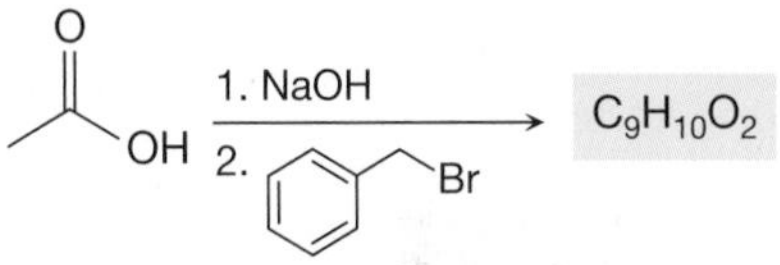
O
OH
1. NaOH
2.
Br
C9H10O2

9.12 When the following deuterium-labeled compound is treated with potassium *tert*-butoxide in DMF, a single product is observed. When the same substrate is heated in the presence of dilute potassium ethoxide in ethanol, a mixture of two products is formed. Provide the complete, detailed mechanism for each reaction and explain these results.

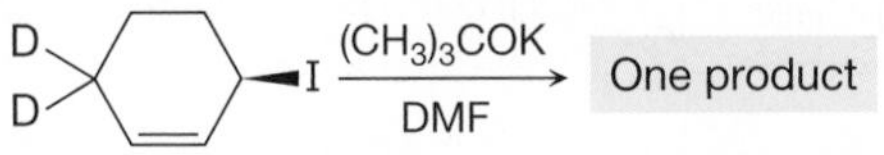
D
D
I
(CH3)3COK
DMF
One product

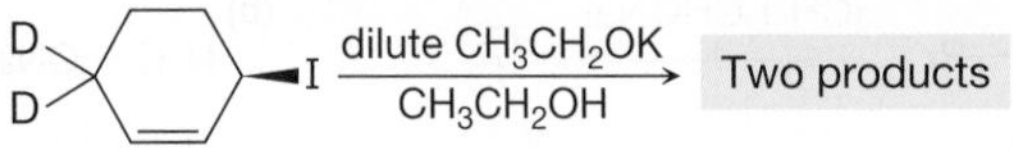
D
D
I
dilute CH3CH2OK
CH3CH2OH
Two products

9.13 Rank the following substrates in order of increasing S_N2 reaction rate.

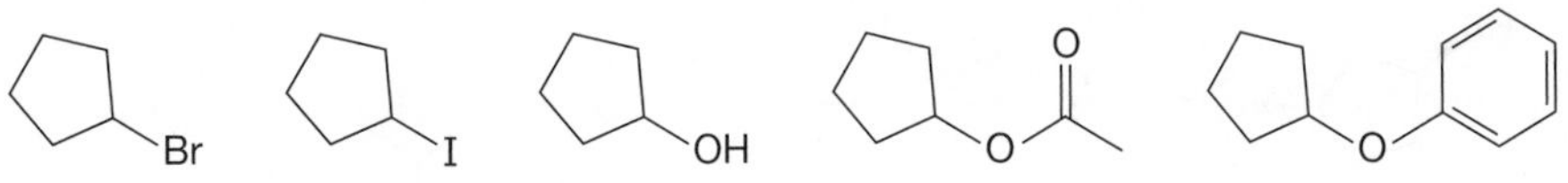
Br
I
OH
O
O
O

A B C D E

9.14 Rank the following substrates in order of increasing E1 reaction rate.

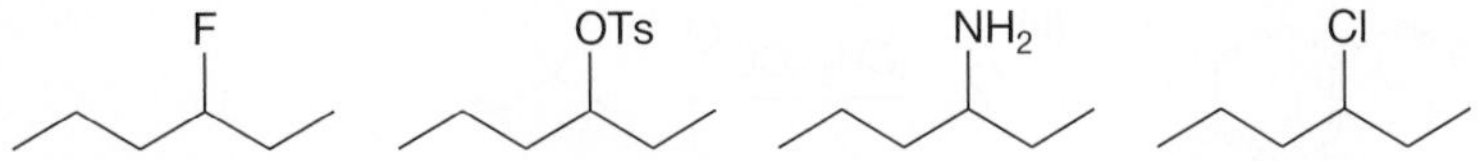
F
OTs
NH2
Cl

A B C D

9.15 Rank the following E2 reactions in order of increasing rate.

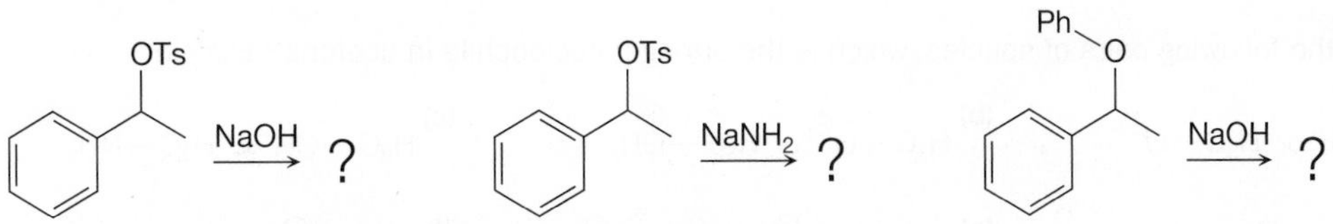
OTs
NaOH
?
OTs
NaNH2
?
Ph
O
NaOH
?

A B C

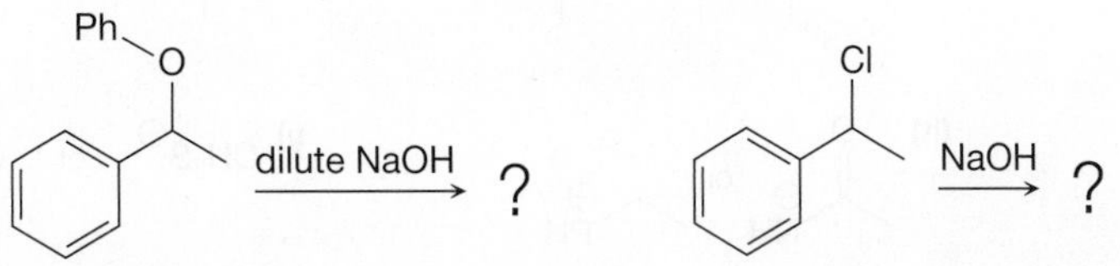
Ph
O
dilute NaOH
?
Cl
NaOH
?

D E

Section 9.6 Type of Carbon Bonded to the Leaving Group

9.16 Rank the following substrates in order from slowest to fastest E1 reaction rate.

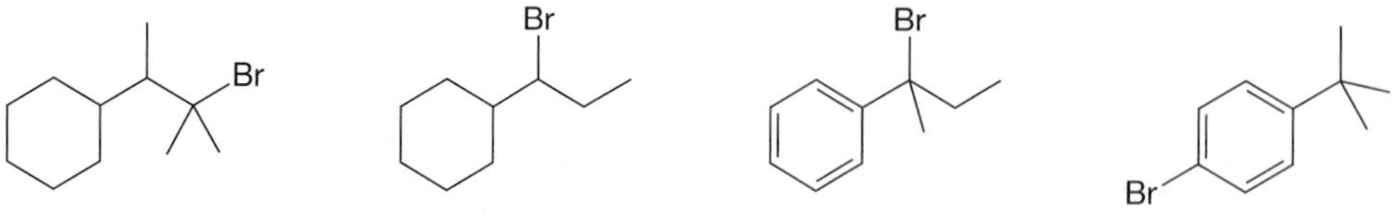

Br
Br
Br
Br

A **B** **C** **D**

9.17 Rank the following substrates in order from slowest to fastest S_N2 reaction rate.

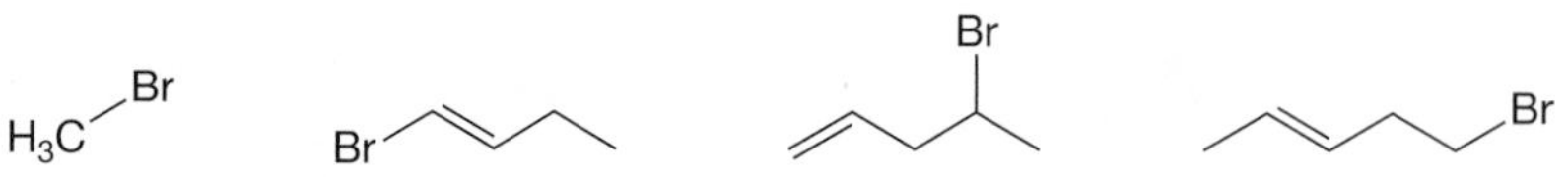

H_3C
Br
Br
Br
Br

A **B** **C** **D**

9.18 Rank the following substrates in order from slowest to fastest S_N1 reaction rate.

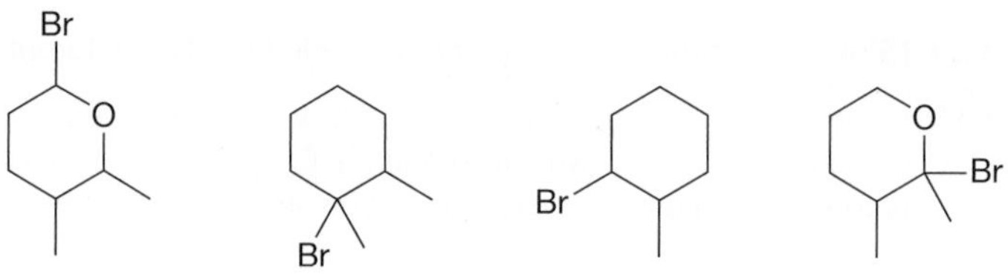

Br
O
Br
Br
O
Br

A **B** **C** **D**

9.19 Both of the following reactions will give the same S_N2 product. Draw the mechanism for each reaction and show the product. Which reaction is more efficient?

(a) $H_3C{-}Br \xrightarrow{(CH_3)_2CHONa} ?$ **(b)** $H_3C{-}ONa \xrightarrow{(CH_3)_2CHBr} ?$

9.20 (SYN) Draw an alkyl halide that could be used as a substrate to carry out each of the following S_N2 reactions.

(a)

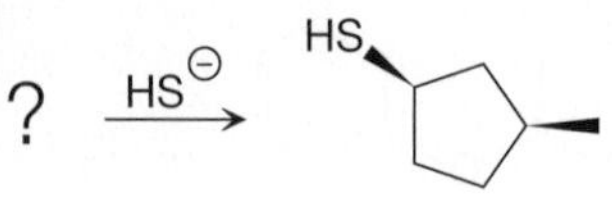

?
$HS^{\ominus}$
HS

(b)

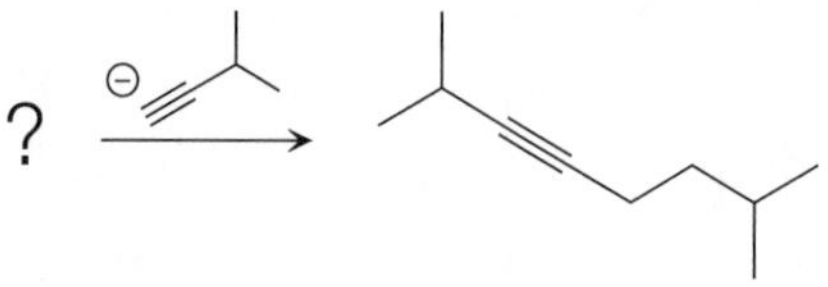

?

9.21 (SYN) Draw an alkyl halide that could be used as a substrate to carry out each of the following E2 reactions.

(a)

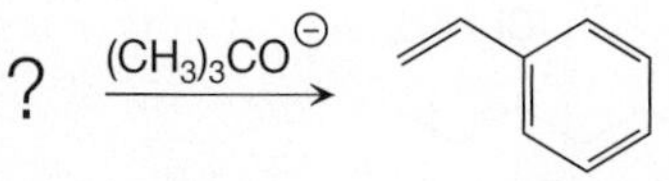

?
$(CH_3)_3CO^{\ominus}$

(b)

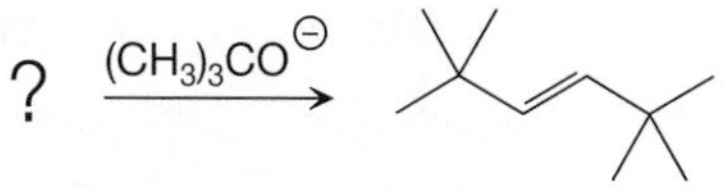

?
$(CH_3)_3CO^{\ominus}$

Sections 9.7 and 9.8 Effects of Solvent and Heat

9.22 For each of the following pairs of species, which is the stronger nucleophile in acetone? Explain.

(a) $H_3C{-}OH$ or $H_3C{-}O^{\ominus}$

(b) $H_3C{-}O^{\ominus}$ or $H_3C{-}\overset{\oplus}{O}H_2$

(c) $H_3C{-}OH$ or $H_3C{-}NH_2$

(d)

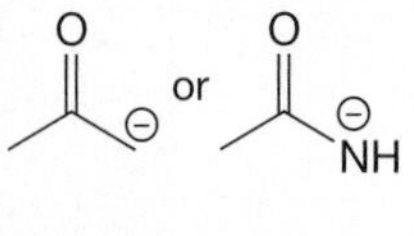

O
O
or
NH

(e)

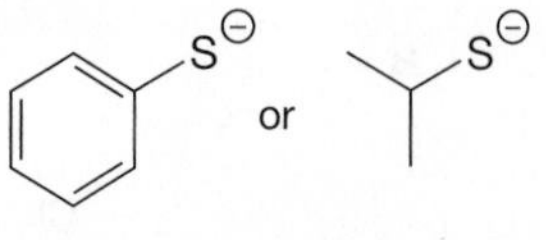

S
or
S

(f)

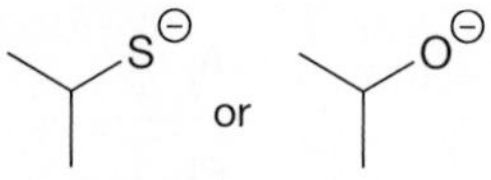

S
or
O

(g)

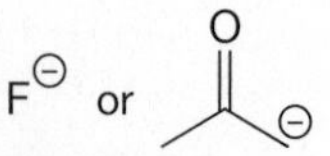

F
or
O

(h)

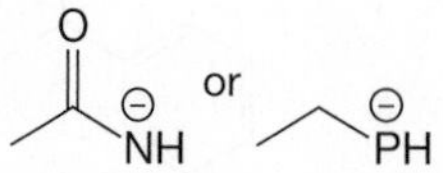

O
NH
or
PH

(i) $CH_3S^{\ominus}$ or $CH_3Se^{\ominus}$

(j) $CH_3Se^{\ominus}$ or $Br^{\ominus}$

9.23 For each of the following pairs of species, which is the stronger nucleophile in ethanol? Explain.

(a) $H_3C—OH$ or $H_3C—O^{\ominus}$

(b) $H_3C—OH$ or $H_3C—NH_2$

(c)

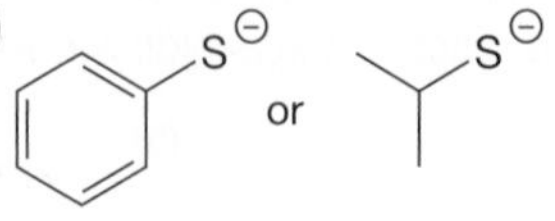

S⊖
or
S⊖

(d)

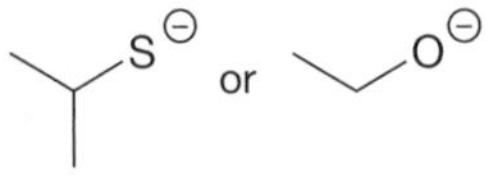

S⊖
or
O⊖

(e) $CH_3S^{\ominus}$ or $CH_3Se^{\ominus}$

(f) $CH_3Se^{\ominus}$ or $Br^{\ominus}$

9.24 (SYN) Which solvent, ethanol or DMSO, would be better to use to carry out the reaction shown here? Why?

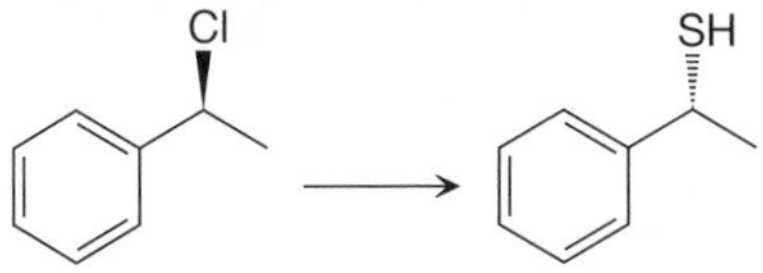

Cl
SH

9.25 (SYN) Which solvent, acetone or *tert*-butyl alcohol, would be better to use to carry out the reaction shown here? Why?

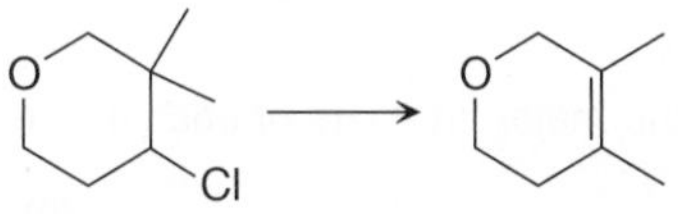

O
Cl
O

9.26 Would heating each of the following reactions increase the yield of the product shown?

(a)

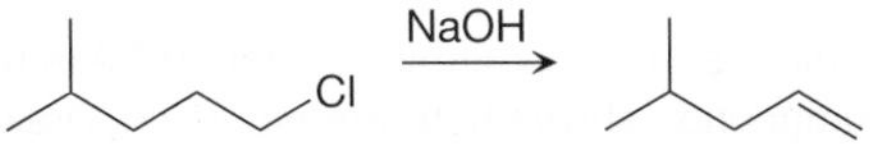

NaOH
Cl

(b)

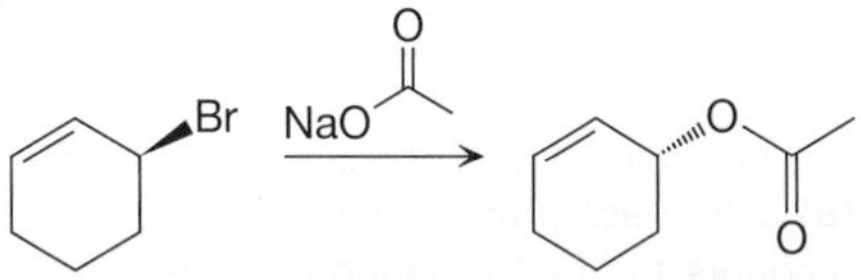

Br
NaO
O
O
O

Sections 9.9, 9.10, and 9.12 Predicting the Outcome of a Competition, Zaitsev's Rule, and Intramolecular versus Intermolecular Reactions

9.27 (SYN) Suggest how each of the reactions shown here could be carried out, focusing in particular on the identity of the nucleophile and the choice of solvent.

(a)

Cl
OCH_3

(b)

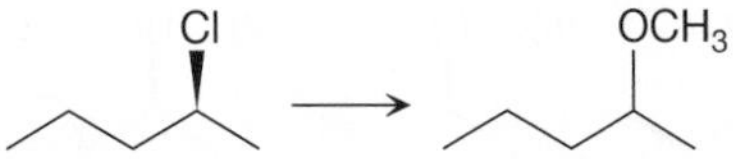

Cl
OCH_3

Racemic

9.28 Provide a complete, detailed mechanism for the reaction shown here.

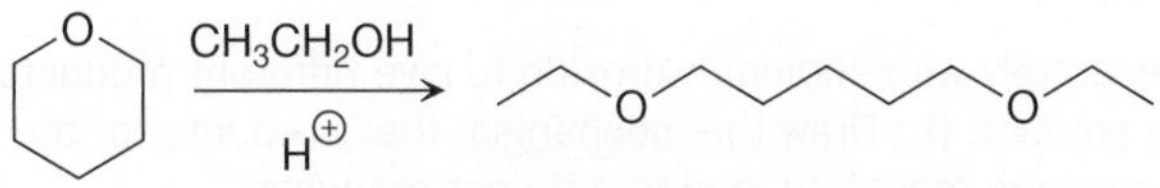

O
CH_3CH_2OH
$H^{\oplus}$
O
O

9.29 For each of the following reactions, provide a complete, detailed mechanism and predict the products, including stereochemistry where appropriate. Determine whether the reaction will yield exclusively one product or a mixture of products. For each reaction that yields a mixture, determine which is the major product.

(a) (S)-3-Chlorooctane $\xrightarrow[\text{DMSO}]{CH_3CH_2OK}$?

(b) (S)-3-Methyl-3-chlorooctane $\xrightarrow[CH_3CH_2OH]{CH_3CH_2OK}$?

(c)

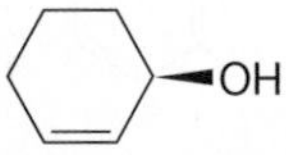

OH

$\xrightarrow[\Delta]{\text{conc } H_3PO_4}$?

(d)

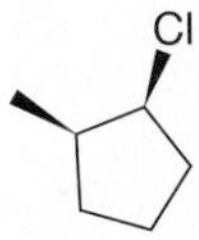

Cl

$\xrightarrow[\text{DMF}]{(CH_3)_3CONa}$?

(e)

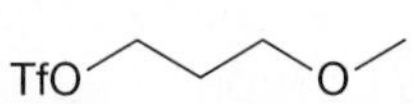

TfO
O

$\xrightarrow[\text{Ethanol}]{NaN_3}$?

(f)

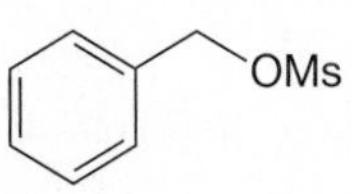

OMs

$\xrightarrow[CH_3CH_2OH]{}$?

9.30 For each of the following reactions, provide a complete, detailed mechanism and predict the products, including stereochemistry where appropriate. Determine whether the reaction will yield exclusively one product or a mixture of products. For each reaction that yields a mixture, determine which is the major product.

(a)
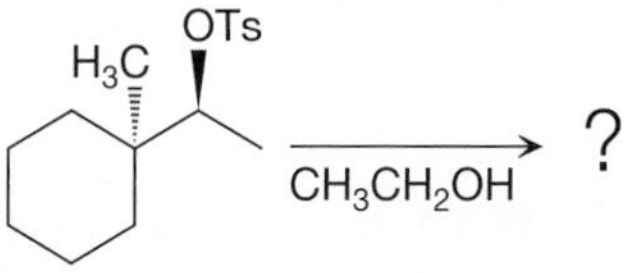
OTs
H_3C
CH_3CH_2OH
?

(b)
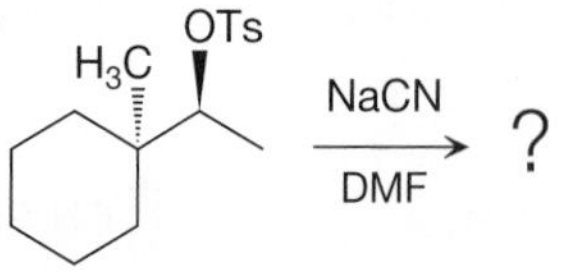
OTs
H_3C
NaCN
DMF
?

(c)
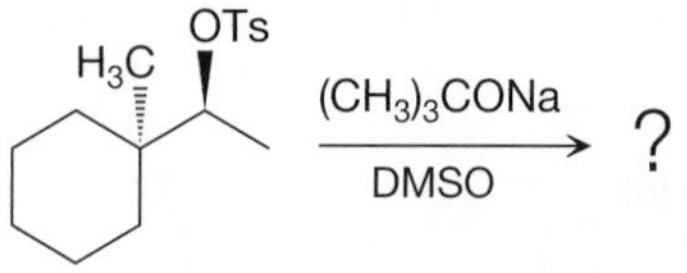
OTs
H_3C
$(CH_3)_3CONa$
DMSO
?

(d)
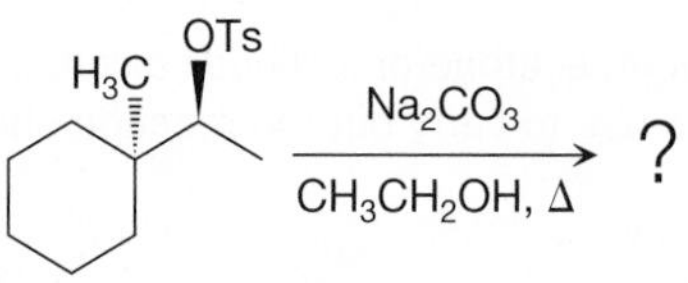
OTs
H_3C
Na_2CO_3
CH_3CH_2OH, Δ
?

(e)
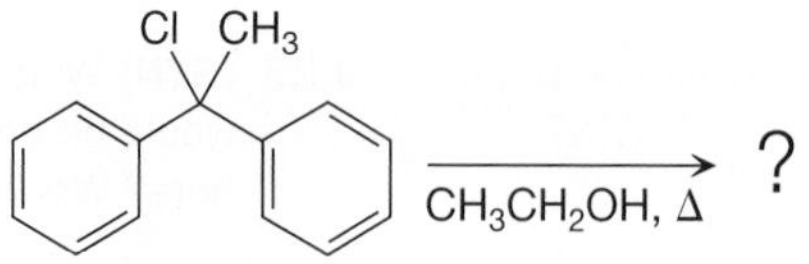
Cl CH_3
CH_3CH_2OH, Δ
?

(f)
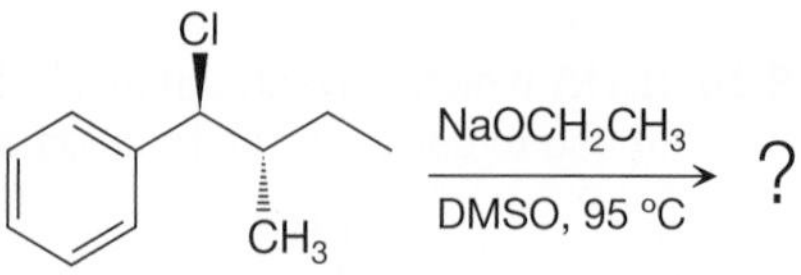
Cl
CH_3
$NaOCH_2CH_3$
DMSO, 95 °C
?

9.31 Predict the major products of each of the following reactions.

(a)
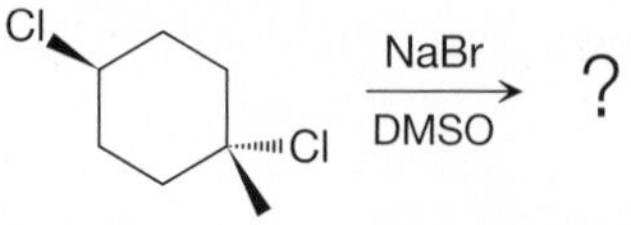
Cl
Cl
NaBr
DMSO
?

(b)
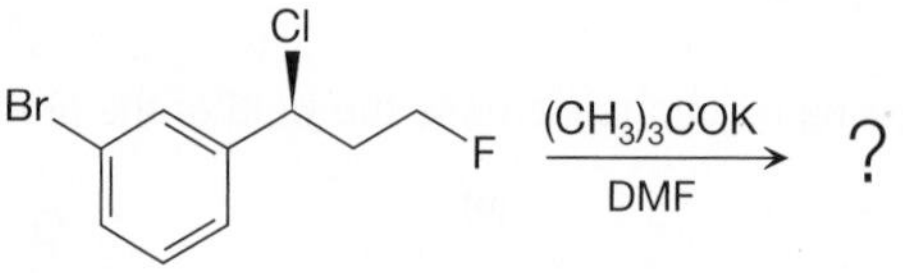
Cl
Br
F
$(CH_3)_3COK$
DMF
?

9.32 The reaction shown here produces two isomers with the formula $C_7H_{11}Br$. **(a)** Draw each product. **(b)** Draw the mechanism that accounts for the formation of each product.

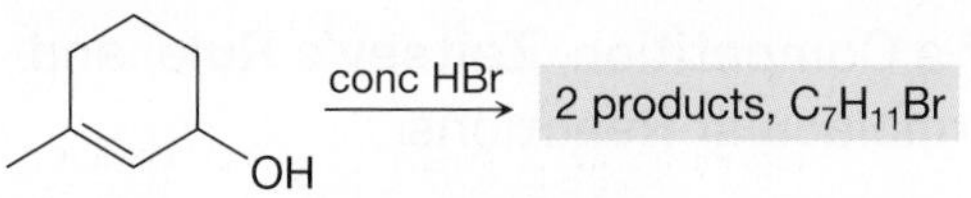
conc HBr
OH
2 products, $C_7H_{11}Br$

9.33 When the reaction mixture in Problem 9.32 is heated, the compounds shown here are produced. Draw the complete, detailed mechanism that accounts for the formation of both of these products.

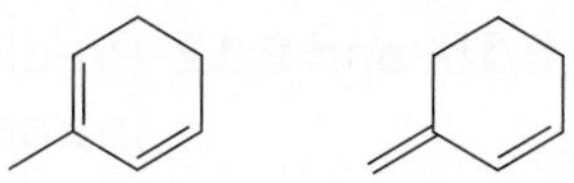

9.34 For each of the following substrates, draw the major E2 product when NaOH is used as the base.

(a)
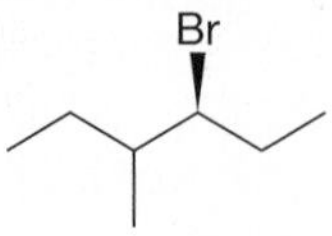
Br

(b)
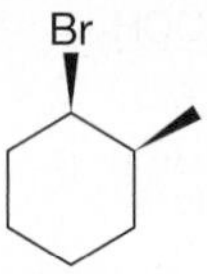
Br

(c)
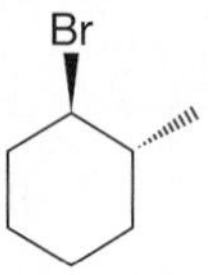
Br

(d)
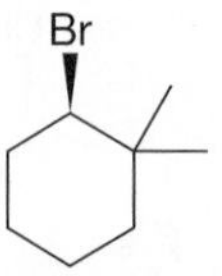
Br

(e)
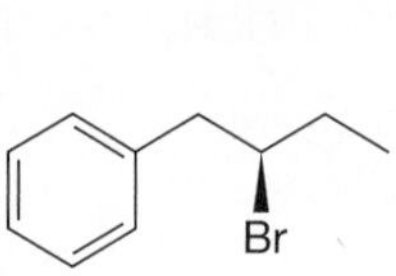
Br

9.35 For each of the substrates in Problem 9.34, draw the major E1 product.

9.36 The following isomers react separately with sodium hydroxide to give different products with the formulas shown. **(a)** Draw the structure of each product. **(b)** Draw the mechanism that accounts for the formation of each of those products. **(c)** Explain why the isomeric reactants lead to different products.

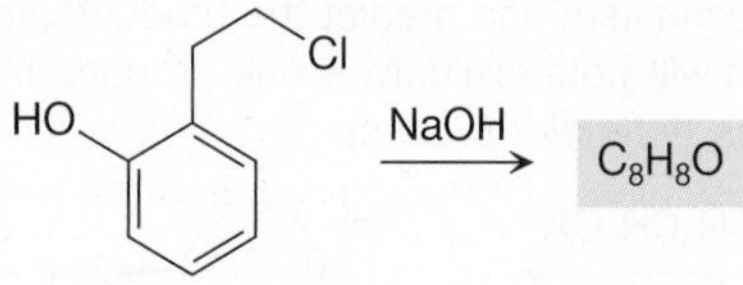
Cl
HO
NaOH
C_8H_8O

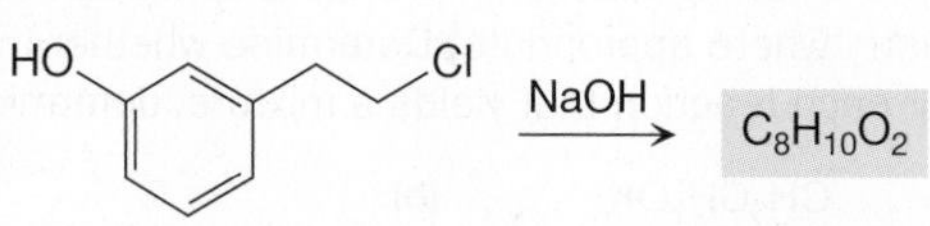
HO
Cl
NaOH
$C_8H_{10}O_2$

9.37 Draw the mechanism for the following reaction.

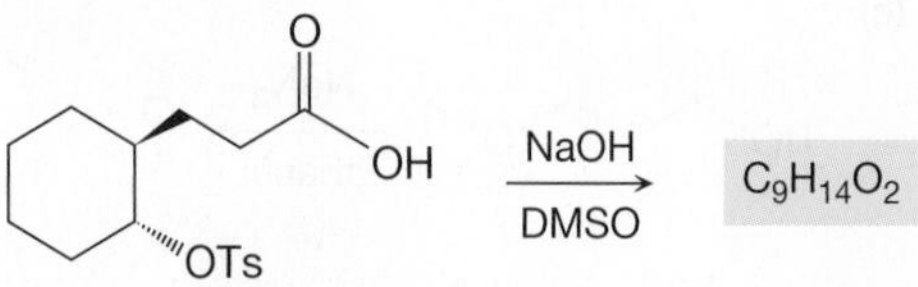
O
OH
OTs
NaOH
DMSO
$C_9H_{14}O_2$

Section 9.13 The Organic Chemistry of Biomolecules

9.38 2,5-Dimethylfuran is a liquid biofuel that can be synthesized from 5-hydroxymethylfurfural (HMF). As shown below, HMF can be synthesized from D-fructose by treatment with sulfuric acid.

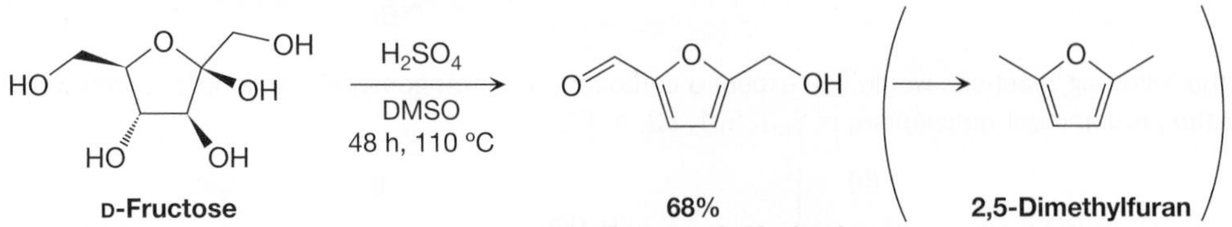

H_2SO_4
DMSO
48 h, 110 °C

D-Fructose — **68% 5-Hydroxymethylfurfural (HMF)** — **2,5-Dimethylfuran**

The mechanism for the formation of HMF from D-fructose is believed to involve the following series of dehydration reactions. Draw the complete, detailed mechanism for each of these dehydration reactions.

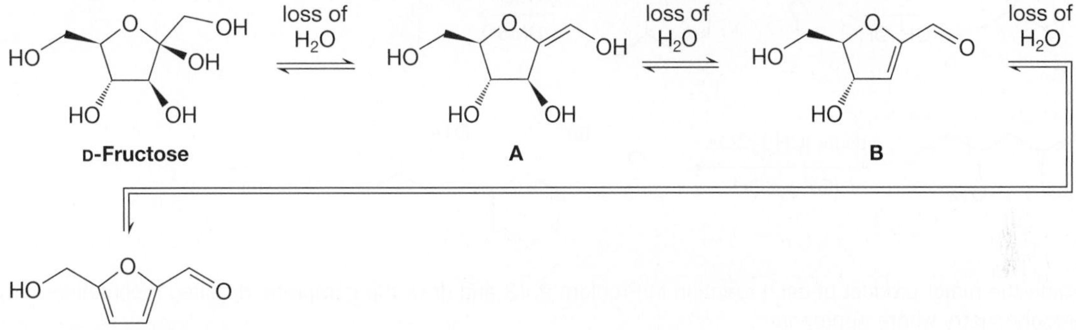

loss of H_2O
loss of H_2O
loss of H_2O
D-Fructose
A
B

5-Hydroxymethylfurfural

9.39 Draw the complete, detailed mechanism and the products for the glycoside formation shown here. Pay attention to stereochemistry.

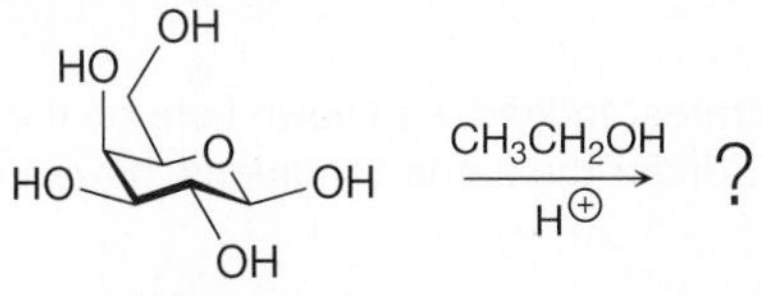

CH_3CH_2OH
$H^{\oplus}$
?

Galactose

9.40 Lactose is a disaccharide in which a glycosidic linkage connects the monosaccharides galactose and glucose. **(a)** Identify the glycosidic linkage and the acetal carbon in lactose. **(b)** What type of glycosidic linkage does lactose have (i.e., is it 1,1′-, 1,2′-, etc., and is it α or β)?

(c) People who are lactose-intolerant are deficient in the enzyme lactase, and therefore they cannot efficiently break down the disaccharide into its monosaccharides. When lactose is treated with aqueous acid, however, this hydrolysis can take place, though relatively slowly. Draw the complete, detailed mechanism and the products of acid-catalyzed hydrolysis of lactose.

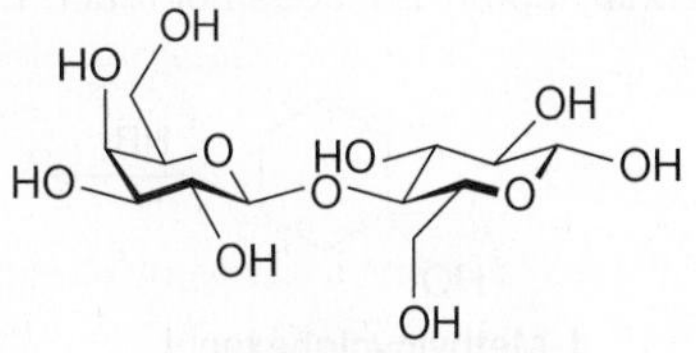

Lactose

9.41 DNA is damaged when a base from the DNA chain is removed after an alkylation has occurred. In a *depurination reaction*, the purine nitrogenous base is displaced from its sugar, as shown in this reaction. Draw the mechanism for this reaction and suggest a reason why it occurs so easily.

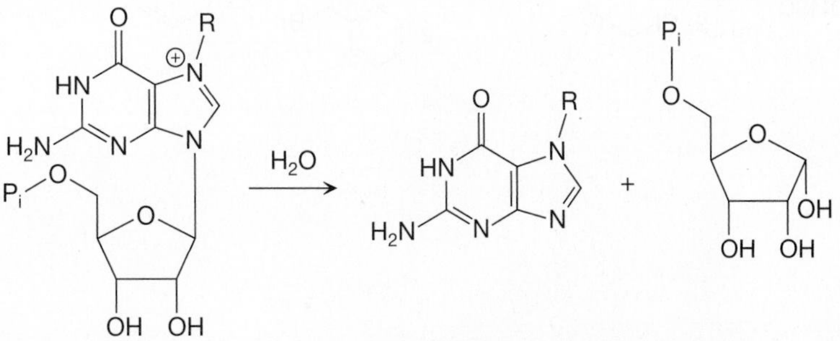

H_2O

Integrated Problems

9.42 Draw the complete, detailed mechanism for the reaction shown here and predict the major products, including stereochemistry.

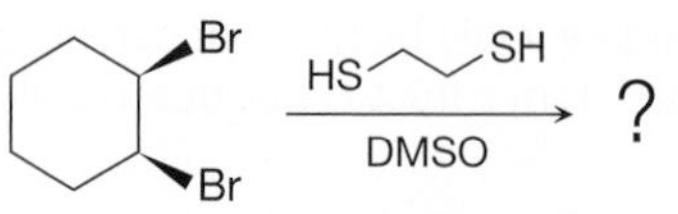
Br
Br
HS SH
DMSO
?

9.43 In which of the following reactions would you expect a carbocation rearrangement? Explain. *Hint*: You will need to figure out whether the predominant mechanism is S_N2, S_N1, E2, or E1.

(a)

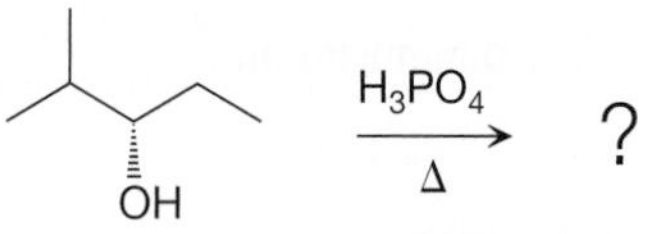
OH
H3PO4
Δ
?

(b)

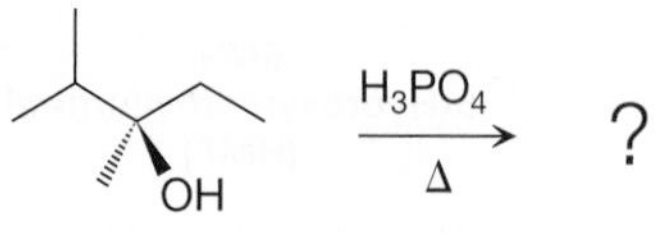
OH
H3PO4
Δ
?

(c)

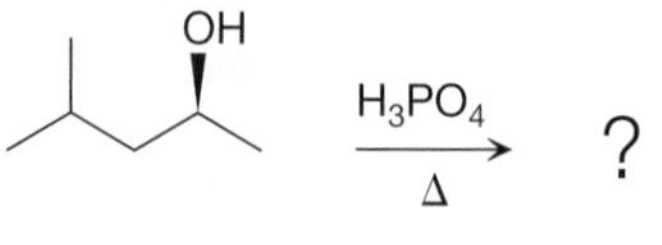
OH
H3PO4
Δ
?

(d)

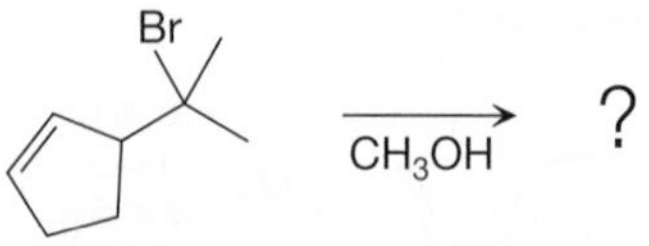
Br
CH3OH
?

(e)

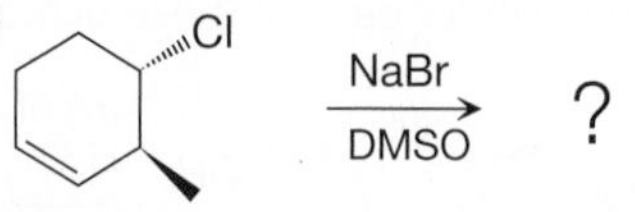
Cl
NaBr
DMSO
?

(f)

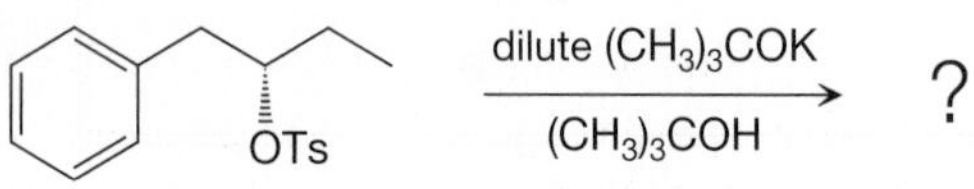
OTs
dilute (CH3)3COK
(CH3)3COH
?

(g)

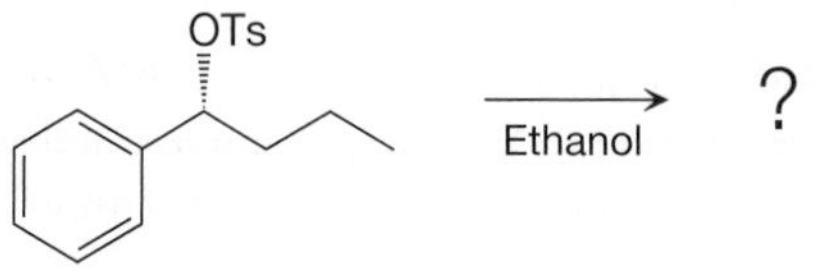
OTs
Ethanol
?

9.44 Determine the major product of each reaction in Problem 9.43 and draw the complete, detailed mechanism. Pay attention to stereochemistry where appropriate.

9.45 The compound shown here is highly unreactive under conditions that favor E2 reactions. Explain why. *Hint*: It may help to build a model of this compound.

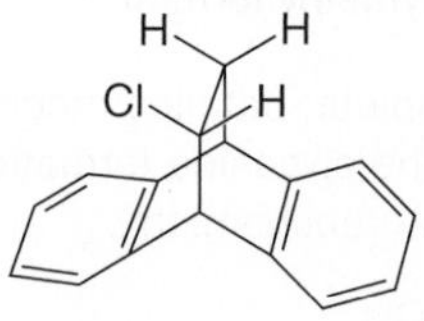
H
H
Cl
H

9.46 We learned in this chapter that S_N1 reactions are favored by tertiary substrates. Indeed, as shown here on the left, 1-methylcyclohexanol reacts readily with HBr to produce the alkyl bromide. Under the same conditions, however, bicyclo[2.2.1]heptan-1-ol does not react. Explain why.

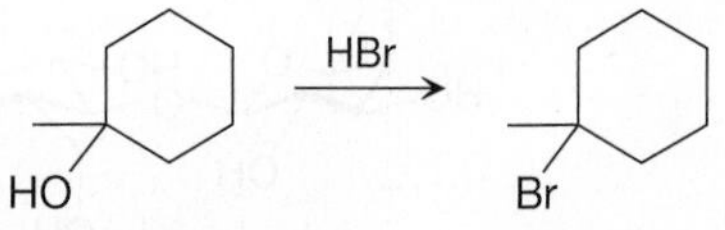
HO
HBr
Br

1-Methylcyclohexanol 94%

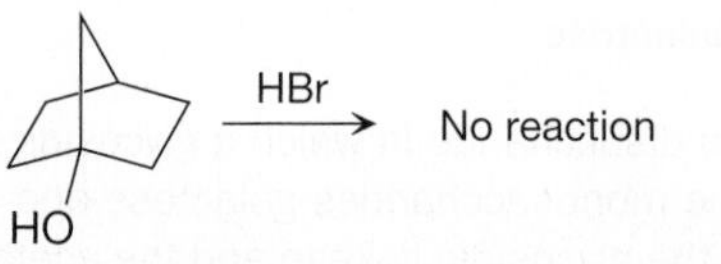
HO
HBr
No reaction

Bicyclo[2.2.1]heptan-1-ol

9.47 Given the following reaction sequence, determine the structures of **A** and **B**, including proper stereochemistry.

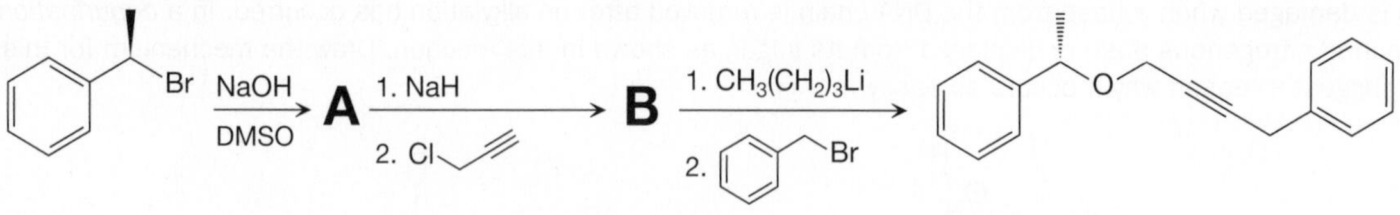
Br
NaOH
DMSO
A
1. NaH
2. Cl
B
1. CH3(CH2)3Li
2.
Br
O

9.48 Suggest why each of the following reactions will *not* occur as indicated.

(a)

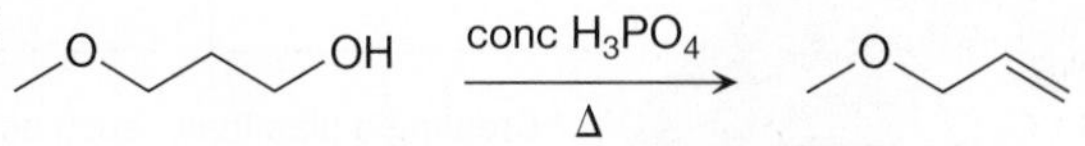
O
OH
conc H_3PO_4
Δ
O

(b)

Cl
Br
NaSH
DMSO
Cl
SH

(c)

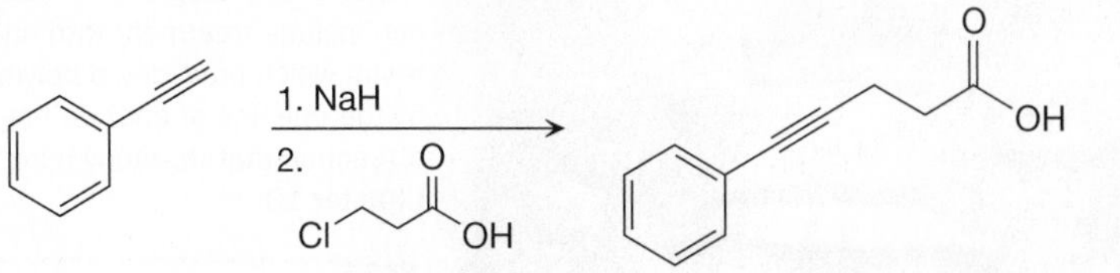
1. NaH
2.
O
Cl
OH
O
OH

(d)

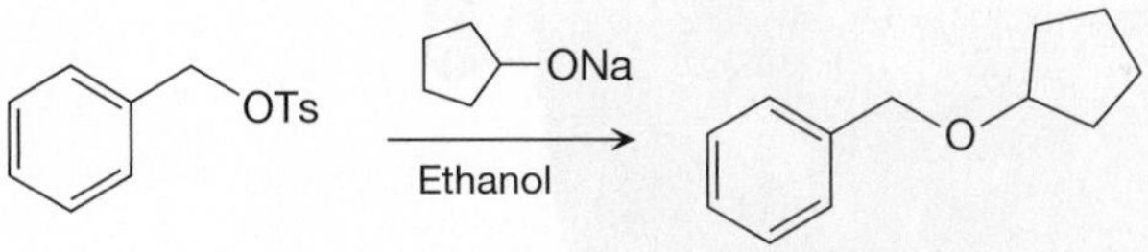
OTs
ONa
Ethanol
O

9.49 A type of hyperconjugation occurs in the F—CH_2—NH^- anion even though there are no double bonds, triple bonds, or empty *p* AOs. Draw the orbital interaction that illustrates the most significant hyperconjugation interaction in this species. *Hint*: What is the HOMO in this species? Which adjacent σ^* orbital is the lowest in energy?

9.50 Draw the orbital interaction that illustrates the hyperconjugation that takes place in propyne.

10

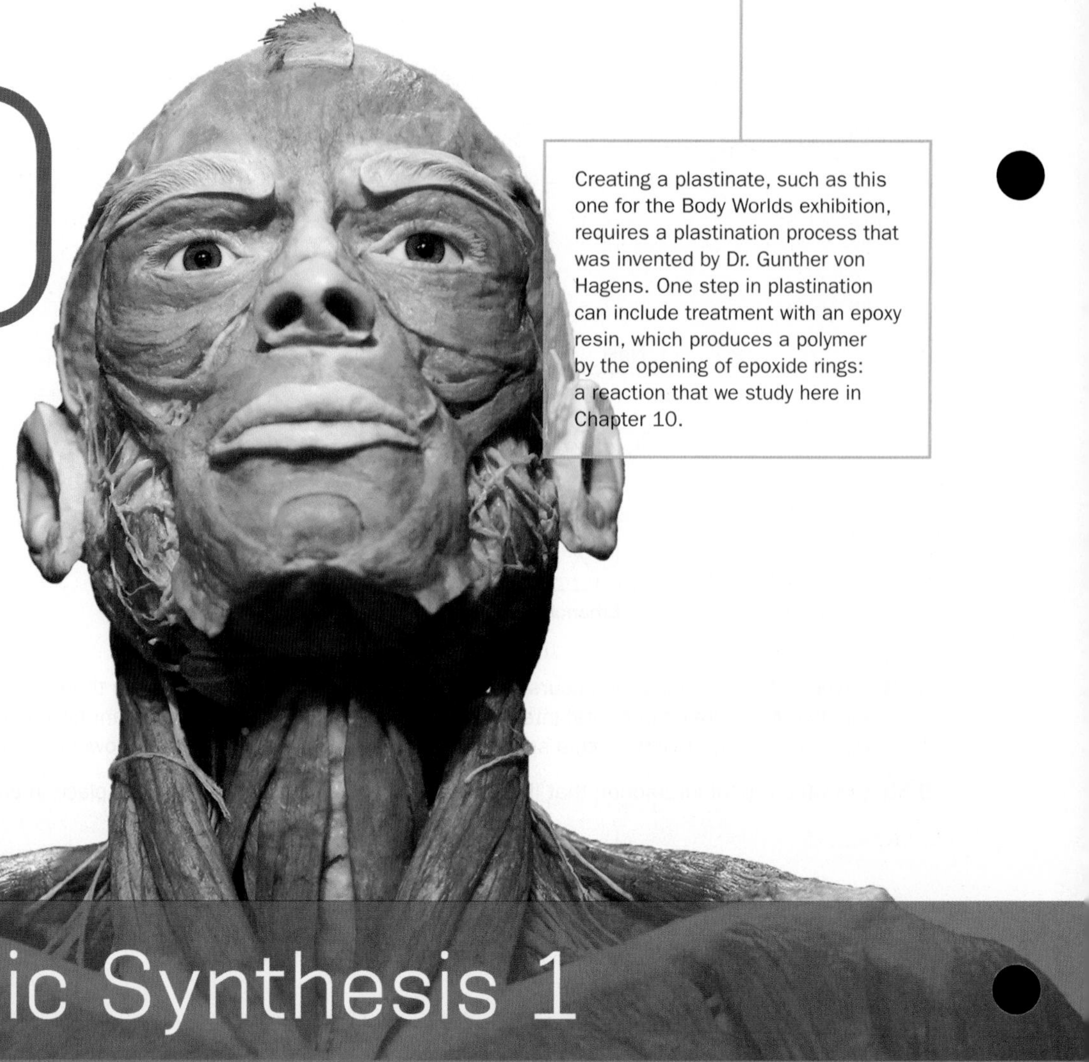

Creating a plastinate, such as this one for the Body Worlds exhibition, requires a plastination process that was invented by Dr. Gunther von Hagens. One step in plastination can include treatment with an epoxy resin, which produces a polymer by the opening of epoxide rings: a reaction that we study here in Chapter 10.

Organic Synthesis 1

Nucleophilic Substitution and Elimination Reactions and Functional Group Transformations

Thus far, our discussions of S_N2, S_N1, E2, and E1 reactions have primarily covered *how* and *why* these reactions occur as they do, and much of our focus has been on their mechanisms. Here in Chapter 10, we revisit those reactions with a different focus: *what* the reactions accomplish. Having a command of the structural changes brought about by various reactions, we can design schemes to string those reactions together in certain ways to make desirable molecules; that is, we can design a *synthesis*.

We begin Chapter 10 with some basic ideas underlying organic synthesis, applying them to the nucleophilic substitution and elimination reactions discussed over the last few chapters. Then, to facilitate the design of more elaborate syntheses, the rest of the chapter will introduce new reactions that are useful in synthesis.

As new reactions are introduced, we will examine the mechanisms by which they take place. You will see that the reactions in this chapter have a common theme: nucleophilic substitution or elimination is at the heart of each mechanism. You'll see that while the *what* of these reactions is new, the *how* and *why* of each reaction

Chapter Outline

involves concepts and mechanisms familiar from the last few chapters. Recognizing these patterns of mechanisms in reactions that might otherwise seem very different can *streamline* and ultimately *simplify* your learning of new reactions. For this reason, it is extremely worthwhile for you to maintain focus on mechanisms as you learn each new reaction.

Chapter 10 represents just the beginning of our treatment of organic synthesis. The concepts of organic synthesis presented in this chapter will be applied to all the reactions we study throughout the rest of the book. Furthermore, Chapters 11 and 21 will present additional concepts of organic synthesis. With each new reaction and each new concept, your mastery of organic synthesis will grow.

10.1 The Language of Organic Synthesis

SECTION 10.1 OBJECTIVES

You will be able to:

1. Describe the goal of a synthesis in terms of the synthetic target and the starting materials
2. Identify synthetic steps and synthetic intermediates in a synthesis

In general, a **synthesis** is the use of particular reactions to make a desirable molecule. To describe aspects of a synthesis reliably and accurately, organic chemists have developed certain terms that we will use throughout this book. First, let's consider the main goal of any synthesis:

> The **target** of a synthesis (or the **synthetic target**) is the molecule we wish to make.

The target may be, for example, a compound with desirable medicinal properties that is produced naturally by a plant or animal. Or the target could be a molecule that promises to have desirable physical or chemical properties but does not yet exist anywhere.

Once we have the target in mind, there is still the question of where to begin:

> The **starting materials** are the compounds that we have available to use at any point in the synthesis.

Starting materials can often be purchased commercially, or they might be obtained from natural sources. Good starting materials tend to be low in cost and are often relatively small in size, and if available from natural sources, they should be obtained in a safe and responsible manner (see Looking Ahead box).

Having defined the *starting materials* and the *target* of a synthesis, we can now offer a more precise definition of a synthesis:

> A *synthesis* is the use of known chemical reactions to convert *starting materials* into the *synthetic target*.

▸ LOOKING AHEAD

The idea of designing syntheses that are safe and environmentally responsible is the basis of *green chemistry*, a topic of Chapter 11.

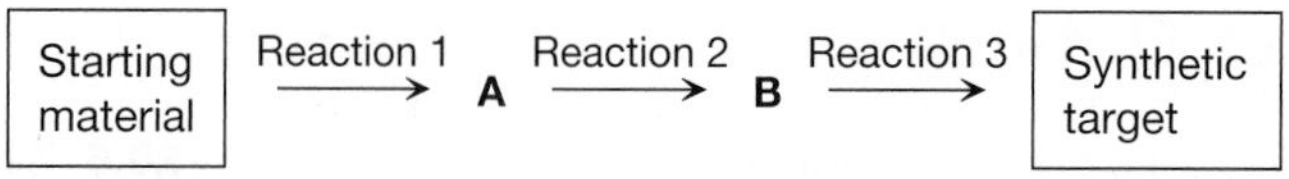
Starting material
Reaction 1
A
Reaction 2
B
Reaction 3
Synthetic target

FIGURE 10-1 A generic multistep synthesis This synthesis indicates that the synthetic target is produced from the starting material in three synthetic steps, and it proceeds through two synthetic intermediates: **A** and **B**.

For any synthesis, the number and types of chemical reactions that are used can vary substantially:

- Each reaction that is used in a synthesis is called a **synthetic step**.
- A compound that is produced in one synthetic step and later used as a reactant in another step is called a **synthetic intermediate**.

For example, **Figure 10-1** represents a synthesis that consists of three synthetic steps (known as a three-step synthesis). In this case, **A** and **B** would be considered synthetic intermediates.

YOUR TURN **10.1**

In the following depiction of a synthesis, how many synthetic steps does it have? How many synthetic intermediates are there?

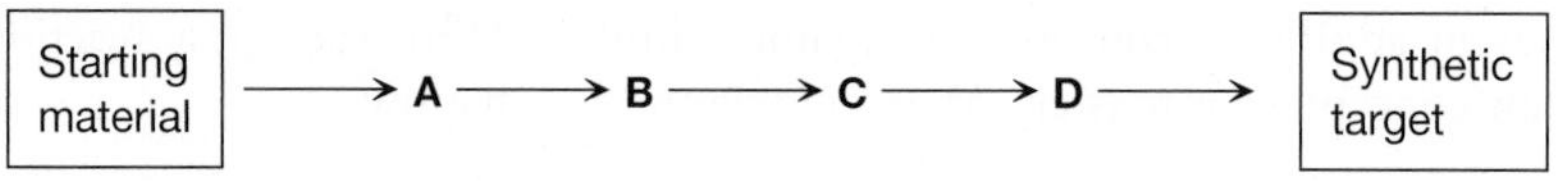
Starting material
A
B
C
D
Synthetic target

Answers to Your Turns are in the back of the book.

We are now ready to consider some of the finer details of a synthesis. Section 10.2 offers some guidelines on how a synthesis should be written.

SECTION 10.2 OBJECTIVES

You will be able to:

1. Distinguish a synthetic step from an elementary step of a mechanism.
2. Properly write a synthetic step to include relevant reagents, reaction conditions, and products.

10.2 Writing the Reactions of an Organic Synthesis

Once a synthesis has been designed, it can be written formally on paper to communicate it to others. When doing so, it is important to keep in mind certain conventions to help ensure that that the synthesis is interpreted in the intended way.

We present in this section three conventions that are routinely applied to writing a synthesis scheme:

Convention 1

Consider a synthesis as an abbreviated recipe. For each synthetic step, write only:

- The overall reactants
- The reagents added
- The reaction conditions
- The overall products

A synthesis should not include the details of any reaction mechanism. Mechanisms help us understand *how* and *why* each reaction takes place as it does, but when you are conveying information about a synthesis to others, the focus should be just on the sequence of actions to be taken in the laboratory to produce the target from the starting material.

Analogously, think about writing a recipe for chocolate chip cookies. To communicate to someone how to make the cookies, it is not important to explain the details of the chemical processes that take place when an egg is heated in the oven. It is important, however, to know that an egg is needed, as well as *when* and *how* to add the egg.

For example, a synthetic step showing how to convert 2-phenyl-2-tosyloxypropane into 2-bromo-2-phenylpropane might be written like this:

Overall reactants   Overall product

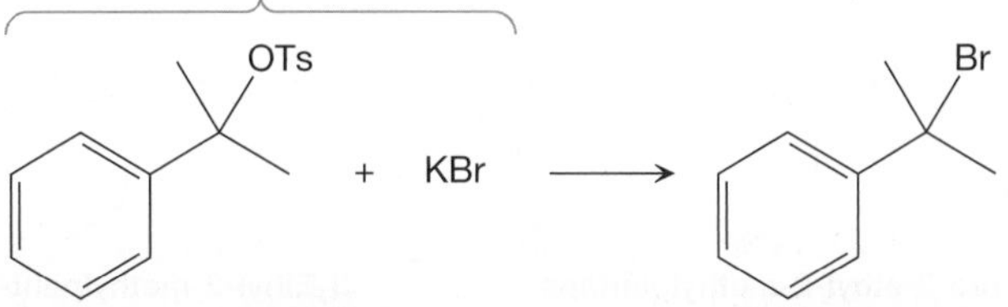
OTs
+ KBr
Br

(10-1)

2-Phenyl-2-tosyloxypropane   **2-Bromo-2-phenylpropane**

This *synthetic step* tells us to combine 2-phenyl-2-tosyloxypropane and potassium bromide and that, when we do, 2-bromo-2-phenylpropane is generated as an overall product. By contrast, the *mechanism* for this reaction, which is S_N1, would be written as follows:

Mechanism for the S_N1 conversion of a tosyloxyalkane to an alkyl halide (Eq. 10-1)

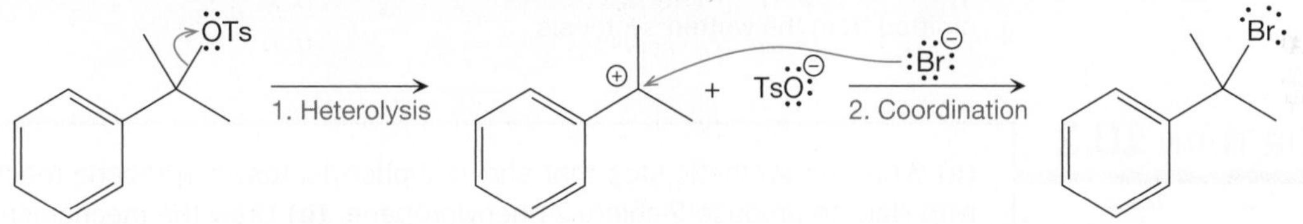
OTs
1. Heterolysis
+ TsO
Br
2. Coordination
Br

(10-2)

Even though KBr dissolves to form K^+ and Br^-, and even though Br^- is the active nucleophile in the mechanism in Equation 10-2, it is inappropriate to write Br^- as a reagent in a synthetic step. Br^- cannot exist in a pure form, due to the charge that it carries, so the synthetic step proposed in Equation 10-3 is technically incorrect:

Not an appropriate *synthetic step* because Br^- does not exist in pure form

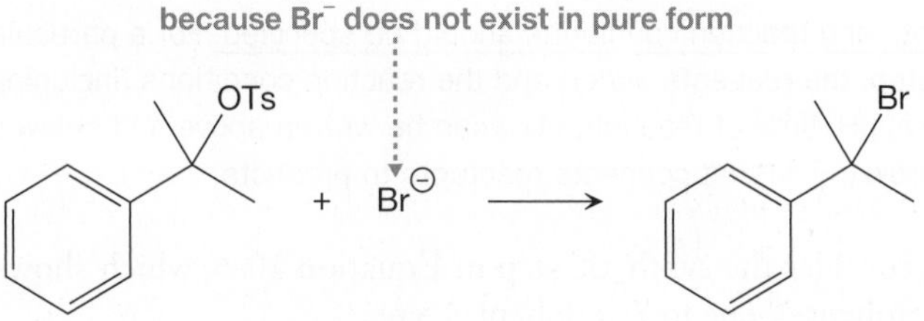
OTs
+ Br
Br

(10-3)

In general:

Reagents must be written in the form in which they can be added, not as they appear in the mechanism.

For this reason, Equation 10-4 is also unacceptable as a synthetic step:

Not an appropriate *synthetic step* because HO^- does not exist on its own

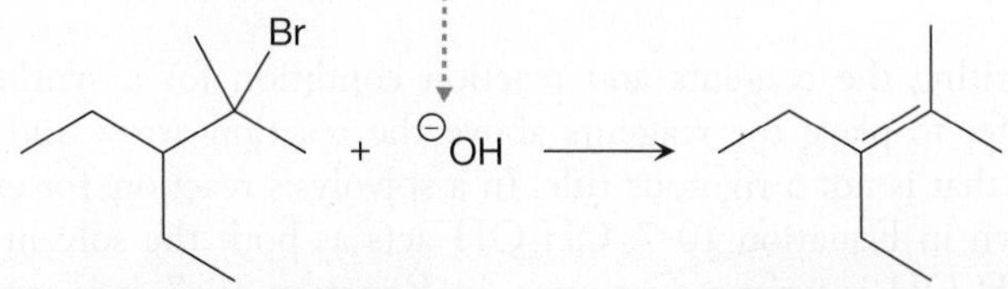
Br
+ OH

(10-4)

2-Bromo-3-ethyl-2-methylpentane   **3-Ethyl-2-methylpent-2-ene**

The hydroxide anion does not exist on its own, so we cannot simply add it in pure form to the reaction mixture. The synthetic step should specify a *source* of the hydroxide anion. Equation 10-5, for example, is an appropriate synthetic step because it indicates that sodium hydroxide can be added to yield the desired product:

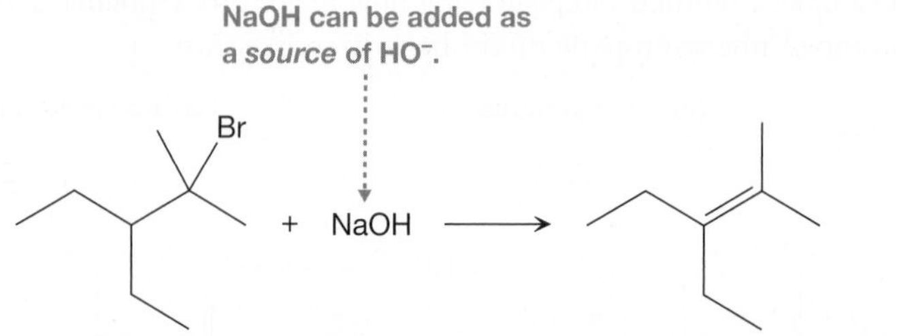
NaOH can be added as
a *source* of HO⁻.
Br
+ NaOH

(10-5)

2-Bromo-3-ethyl-2-methylpentane **3-Ethyl-2-methylpent-2-ene**

Notice in Equations 10-1 and 10-5 that not all of the products are included in the synthesis scheme. The tosylate anion (TsO^-) product has been omitted from Equation 10-1, and the NaBr and H_2O products have been omitted from Equation 10-5. The reason is that TsO^-, NaBr, and H_2O are by-products in which we are not interested. In short:

By-products and leaving groups that are not critical to the synthesis are often omitted from the written synthesis.

YOUR TURN **10.2**

(a) Write the synthetic step that shows 2-phenyl-2-tosyloxypropane reacting with NaCl to produce 2-chloro-2-phenylpropane. **(b)** Draw the mechanism for this reaction.

The second convention for writing synthesis schemes concerns how reagents and reaction conditions are presented:

Convention 2

The reagents and reaction conditions should be specified. For a particular synthetic step, the reagents added and the reaction conditions (including solvent, temperature, pH, time of reaction, etc.) can be written above and below the reaction arrow (⟶) that connects reactants to products.

For example, consider the synthetic step in Equation 10-6, which shows the conversion of 7-chlorohept-1-ene to 7-iodohept-1-ene:

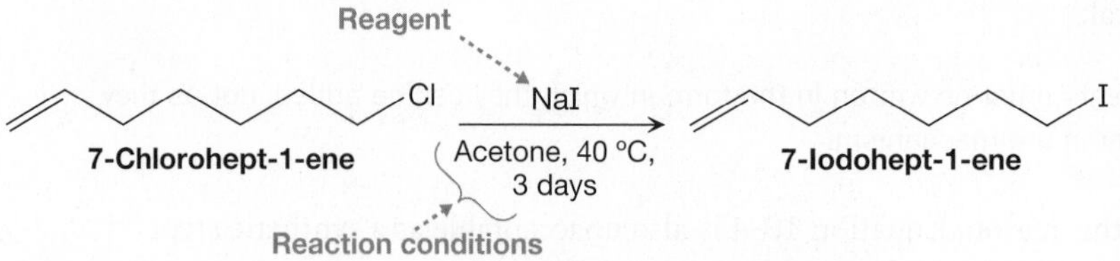
Reagent
Cl
NaI
Acetone, 40 °C,
3 days
I
Reaction conditions

(10-6)

7-Chlorohept-1-ene **7-Iodohept-1-ene**

Sodium iodide is the reagent that is added to 7-chlorohept-1-ene in this synthetic step. Acetone is the solvent, and the reaction is run at an elevated temperature (40 °C) for 3 days.

When writing the reagents and reaction condition for a synthetic step, many chemists prefer to place the reagents above the reaction arrow and the conditions below it, but that is not a rigorous rule. In a solvolysis reaction, for example, such as the one shown in Equation 10-7, CH_3OH acts as both the solvent and a reagent. Therefore, CH_3OH is written just once. In Equation 10-7, it is written below the arrow, but it could instead be written above the arrow:

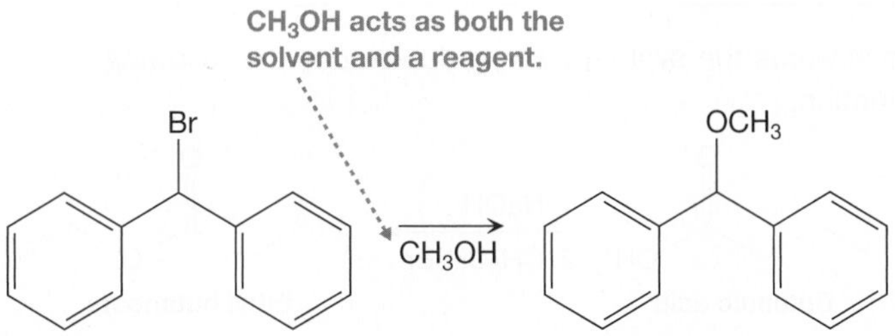
CH3OH acts as both the solvent and a reagent.
Br
OCH3
CH3OH

(10-7)

YOUR TURN **10.3**

Complete the following synthetic step by indicating that water is used both as a reagent and as the solvent and that the reaction is carried out at 70 °C.

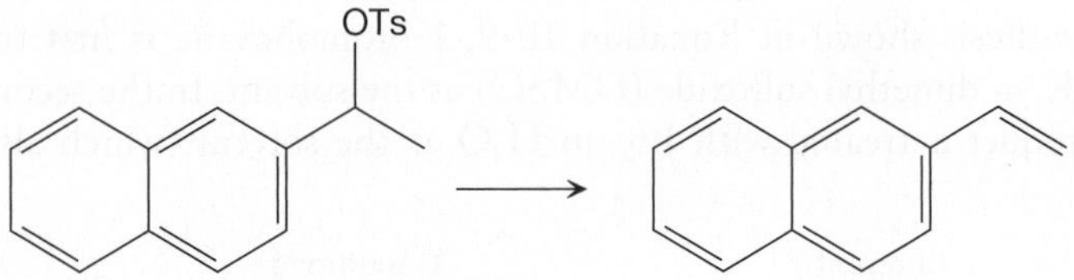
OTs

The third convention for writing syntheses involves shorthand notation for back-to-back synthetic steps:

Convention 3

Use numbers to combine reactions that are customarily carried out sequentially. Each reaction should have its own number, and the reagents and conditions necessary to carry out each reaction can be written above and below the reaction arrow.

This convention is often applied when one of the reactions in the sequence is a proton transfer. It can also be done when the product of a reaction is difficult to isolate and purify. In that case, the next set of reagents can simply be added to the crude product mixture, as long as the components of that mixture do not cause any unwanted side reactions.

An example of numbering sequential synthetic steps above and below the reaction arrow is presented in Equation 10-8, which shows how hex-2-yne can be synthesized from pent-1-yne in a two-step process:

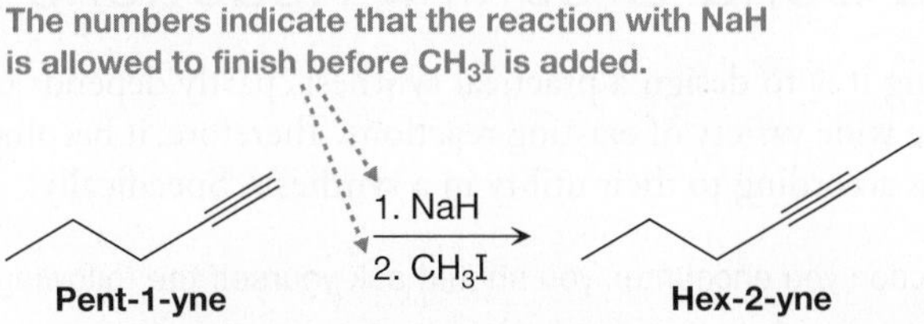
The numbers indicate that the reaction with NaH is allowed to finish before CH3I is added.
1. NaH
2. CH3I
Pent-1-yne
Hex-2-yne

(10-8)

According to this scheme, NaH is added directly to pent-1-yne in the first reaction, in which the terminal alkyne is deprotonated to make the alkynide nucleophile. CH_3I is then added, and the subsequent reaction goes on to produce hex-2-yne.

A critical part of this numbering convention is the following:

In a synthetic step, each reaction that is denoted by a number is understood to finish before the next reagent is added.

For the reaction sequence in Equation 10-8, the deprotonation involving pent-1-yne and sodium hydride is allowed to finish before methyl iodide is added. Therefore, it is possible to carry out the pair of reactions in Equation 10-8 so that the two reagents (NaH and CH_3I) never come into contact with each other.

YOUR TURN **10.4**

Describe in words the synthetic steps depicted in the following transformation.

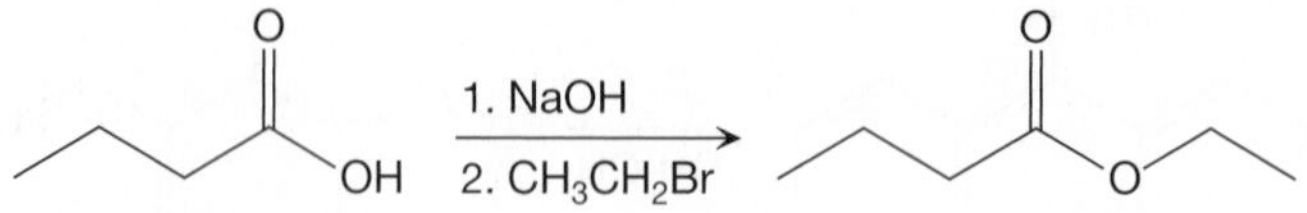
O
OH
1. NaOH
2. CH3CH2Br
O
O

Butanoic acid **Ethyl butanoate**

CONNECTIONS 10.1

Another word for rancid butter Butanoic acid (Your Turn 10.4) is produced when butter turns rancid, giving the butter an unpleasant odor. In fact, the trivial name of butanoic acid is butyric acid, which derives from the Greek word that means butter.

When sequential reactions are numbered, the reaction conditions can be written after the reagent for each numbered step. The reaction conditions are typically separated from the reactant or reagent by either a comma or a slash. For example, in the two-step synthesis shown in Equation 10-9, 1-bromohexane is first treated with $(CH_3)_3COK$, in dimethyl sulfoxide (DMSO) as the solvent. In the second step, the resulting product is treated with Br_2, in H_2O as the solvent (which also acts as a reagent).

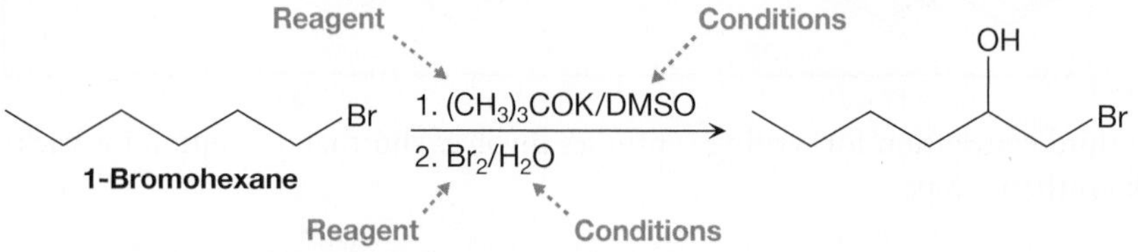
Reagent
Conditions
OH
Br
1. (CH3)3COK/DMSO
2. Br2/H2O
Br
1-Bromohexane
Reagent
Conditions

(10-9)

YOUR TURN **10.5**

Use the numbering convention to write the following sequence of synthetic steps: Pentan-2-ol is treated with HBr, and when that reaction is finished, the product is treated with sodium *tert*-butoxide in DMSO to yield pent-1-ene.

SECTION 10.3 OBJECTIVES

You will be able to:

1. Identify whether a synthetic step is a functional group transformation or one that alters the carbon skeleton.
2. Locate the reaction tables throughout this book, which contain functional group transformations and reactions that alter the carbon skeleton.

10.3 Cataloging Reactions: Functional Group Transformations and Carbon–Carbon Bond-Forming and Bond-Breaking Reactions

How challenging it is to design a practical synthesis partly depends on how familiar you are with the wide variety of existing reactions. Therefore, it becomes important to *catalog* reactions according to their utility in a synthesis. Specifically:

For each reaction you encounter, you should ask yourself the following questions:

- What functional groups in the reactants are involved?
- What functional groups are produced in the products?
- What are the major structural changes that occur?

To help you answer these questions quickly, we have provided reaction summary tables at the end of every chapter in which new reactions are introduced, beginning with Chapter 9. As shown in the example in **Figure 10-2**, each entry in these tables lists the starting compound class, typical reagents and reaction conditions, the compound class formed, and the sections of this book in which the reaction is discussed. Also, to help you apply your understanding of *mechanisms* in synthesis, each entry identifies key electron-rich and electron-poor species, along with the reaction type.

TABLE 9-12 Reactions That Alter the Carbon Skeleton[a]

	Starting Compound Class	Typical Reagents and Reaction Conditions	Compound Class Formed	Key Electron-Rich Species	Key Electron-Poor Species	Comments	Discussed in Section(s)
(1)	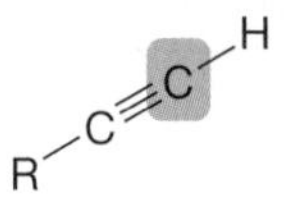 Alkyne	1. NaH → 2. R′–X	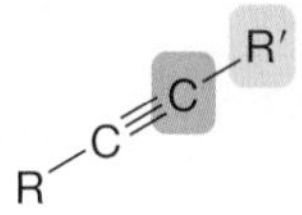 Alkyne	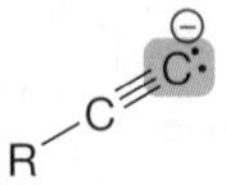 Alkynide anion	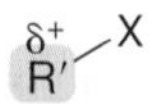 Alkyl halide	S_N2 reaction	7.2, 8.3, 8.5, 9.3b, 9.9

[a]X = Cl, Br, or I.

FIGURE 10-2 An entry from a reaction summary table On the left side of each entry in a reaction summary table, the synthetic step is written. On the right side, key electron-rich and electron-poor species of the mechanism are identified, helpful comments about the reaction are provided, and the book sections in which the reaction is discussed are listed.

In general, two such tables are found at the end of a chapter. One contains **functional group transformations** or **functional group conversions**, which, as their name suggests, simply transform one functional group into another. They do so by leaving alone the **carbon skeleton** (i.e., the bonding arrangement of the carbon atoms). The second table contains reactions that bring about changes in the carbon skeleton. These reactions *require that carbon–carbon σ bonds be broken and/or formed.* (The breaking or formation of a carbon–carbon π bond alone is not considered to be among these reactions, because the σ bond between those atoms remains intact, thereby preserving the carbon skeleton.)

To design a synthesis successfully, you must become very familiar with a variety of reactions. Therefore, take the time now to assess how familiar you are with the reactions we have learned so far, which appear in Table 9-11 (p. 498–499) and Table 9-12 (p. 499); for example, see Your Turn 10.6. For each reaction, you should be able to:

- Specify the reagents and conditions when given the reactant and product.
- Draw the reactant when given the reagents and conditions and the product.

If you encounter difficulty with a particular reaction, make sure to review the sections where the reaction is discussed and study the mechanism.

YOUR TURN 10.6

(a) The synthetic step from Entry 8 of Table 9-11 is shown here, but the reagents and conditions have been omitted (R and R′ are alkyl groups; X = Cl, Br, or I). Write the reagents and conditions that will accomplish this transformation.

(8)

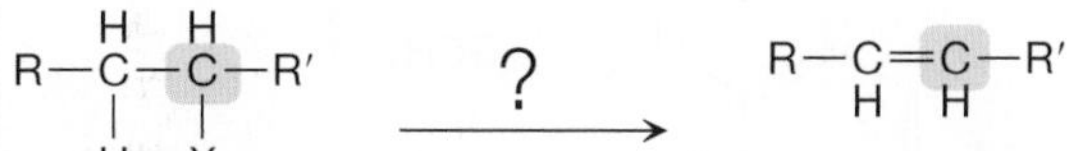
H H
R—C—C—R′
H X
?
R—C=C—R′
H H

Alkyl halide Alkene

(b) The synthetic step from Entry 2 of Table 9-12 is shown here, but the starting compound has been omitted (R is an alkyl group). Draw a starting material that could be used to accomplish this transformation.

(2)

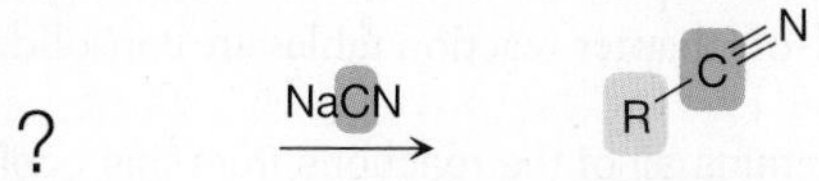
?
NaCN
R
C
N

Nitrile

Equation 10-10 shows the various ways in which functional group conversions and carbon skeleton changes are used in synthesis:

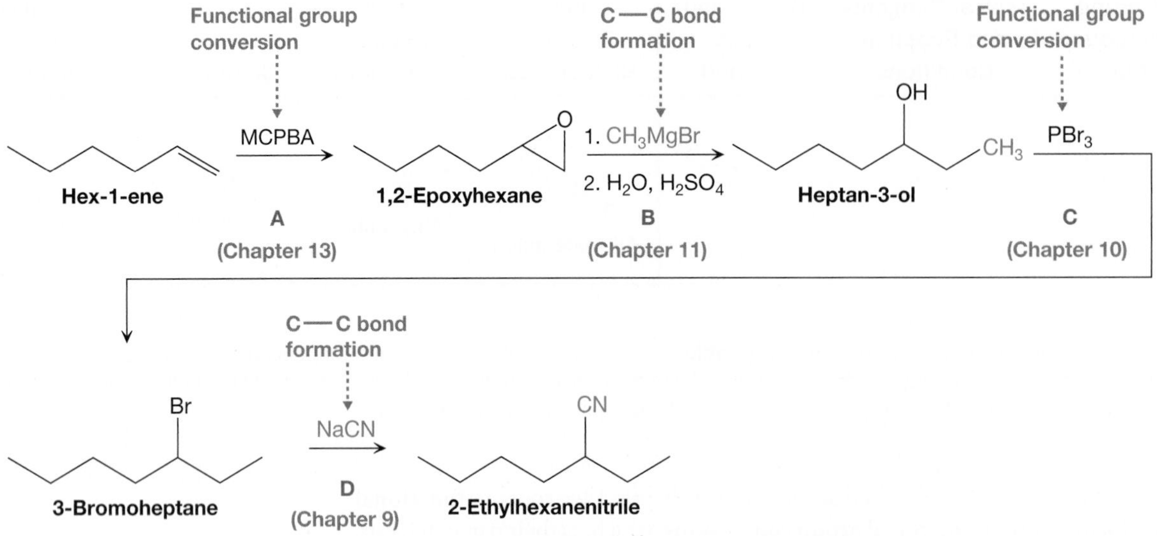

Functional group conversion
C—C bond formation
Functional group conversion
MCPBA
1. CH3MgBr
2. H2O, H2SO4
OH
CH3
PBr3
Hex-1-ene
1,2-Epoxyhexane
Heptan-3-ol
A
(Chapter 13)
B
(Chapter 11)
C
(Chapter 10)
C—C bond formation
Br
NaCN
CN
3-Bromoheptane
D
(Chapter 9)
2-Ethylhexanenitrile

(10-10)

Synthetic steps **A** and **C** do not require any carbon–carbon bonds to form or break and are functional group conversions. Synthetic steps **B** and **D**, on the other hand, are carbon–carbon bond-forming reactions that alter the carbon skeleton. Synthetic step **D** uses a reaction we previously encountered in Chapter 9. The other three synthetic steps, **A–C**, use reactions we will encounter later in this chapter and in the next few chapters.

YOUR TURN 10.7

Label each step in the following synthesis as either a functional group conversion or a reaction that alters the carbon skeleton.

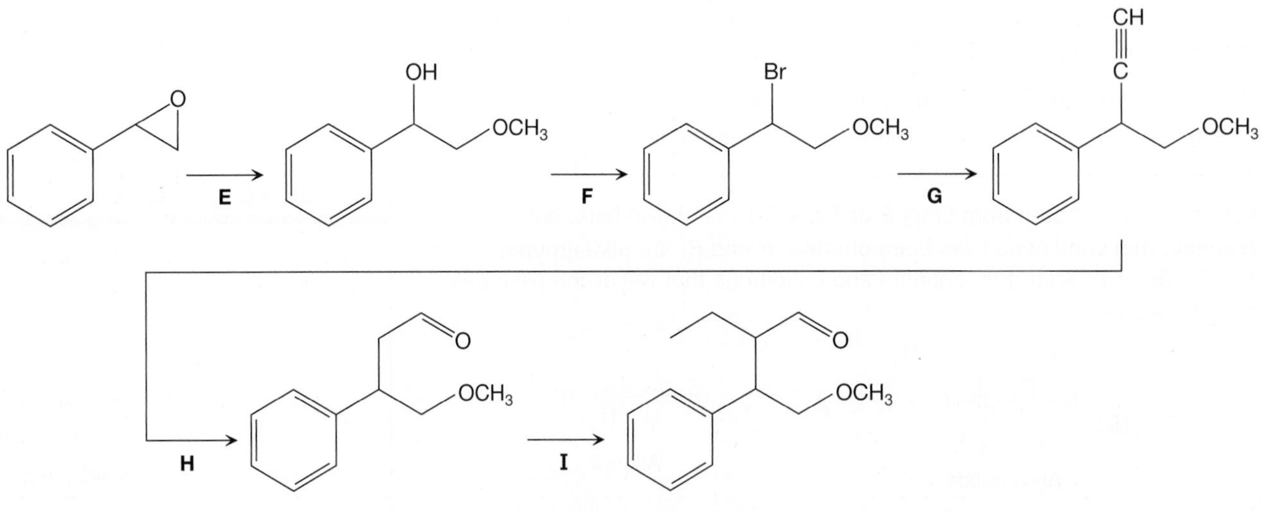

O
OH
OCH3
Br
OCH3
CH
C
OCH3
E
F
G
O
OCH3
O
OCH3
H
I

The reaction tables located at the ends of chapters are convenient to use after you complete the chapter, but as the collection of reactions grows from one chapter to the next, it becomes more helpful to have the reactions together in one place. For ease of reference, these end-of-chapter reaction tables are consolidated in Appendixes C and D.

- Appendix C contains all of the reactions from this book that alter the carbon skeleton.
- Appendix D contains all of the functional group transformations in this book.

The reactions in Appendix D are further grouped into tables according to the functional group that you might be trying to produce.

YOUR TURN 10.8

Use Appendixes C and D to find synthetic steps **A–D** shown in the synthesis scheme in Equation 10-10. For each reaction, identify the table number and the entry number.

10.4 Options and Limitations in Synthesis: Ether Formation by the Williamson Synthesis and Condensation

SECTION 10.4 OBJECTIVES

You will be able to:

1. Use the reaction tables in this book to narrow down your choices for a desired synthetic step.
2. Design a feasible synthesis of an ether that uses a Williamson synthesis or a condensation reaction.
3. Incorporate functional group transformations to produce functional groups required for subsequent steps in a synthesis.

When we have a particular target for a synthesis, we are inherently limited by the reactions that we know. For example, we have learned only two reactions in Chapter 9 that produce an ether: Entries 4 and 5 in Table 9-11 (repeated in **Figure 10-3**). To synthesize an ether, we should consider incorporating one of these reactions. But which reaction?

For some ethers, we could devise a practical synthesis using either of these reactions. For example, Equation 10-11 shows that 1-butoxybutane (dibutyl ether) can be produced from the first reaction shown in Figure 10-3, by treating 1-bromobutane with sodium 1-butoxide:

Williamson ether synthesis

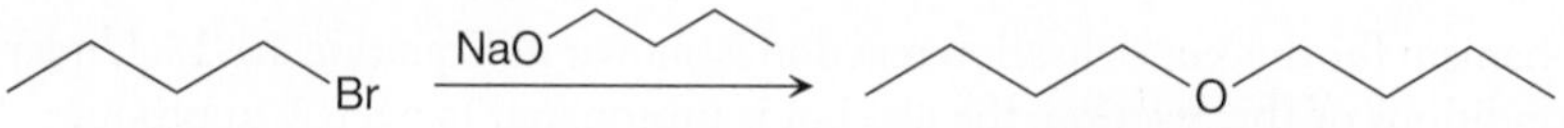

NaO
Br
O

1-Bromobutane → **1-Butoxybutane (Dibutyl ether)** (10-11)

This type of reaction is called a *Williamson ether synthesis*, pioneered by the English chemist Alexander Williamson (1824–1904):

In a **Williamson ether synthesis**, an ether is produced by reacting an alkyl halide with the salt of an alkoxide anion.

FIGURE 10-3 Ether-forming reactions When a synthesis calls for the formation of an ether, these reactions from Table 9-11 could be considered as candidates.

TABLE 9-11 Functional Group Transformations[a]

	Starting Compound Class	Typical Reagents and Reaction Conditions	Compound Class Formed	Key Electron-Rich Species	Key Electron-Poor Species	Comments	Discussed in Section(s)
(4)	$R{-}CH_2{-}X$ 1° Alkyl halide	$R'ONa$ →	$R{-}CH_2{-}O{-}R'$ Ether	$R'O^{\ominus}$	$R{-}CH_2{-}X$ (δ^+ on C)	S_N2 reaction	7.2, 8.3, 8.5, 9.9
(5)	$R{-}OH$ Alcohol	H_3PO_4 or H_2SO_4, Δ →	$R{-}O{-}R$ Ether	ROH	$R^{\oplus}$ or $ROH_2^{\oplus}$	S_N1 or S_N2 reaction	7.2, 7.3, 8.1, 8.3, 8.5

[a] X = Cl, Br, or I.

The alkoxide salt dissolves in solution to form an alkoxide anion (RO^-), which is a strong nucleophile. In the presence of an alkyl halide, an S_N2 reaction then takes place, as shown in the mechanism in Equation 10-12:

Mechanism for the Williamson ether synthesis (Eq. 10-11)

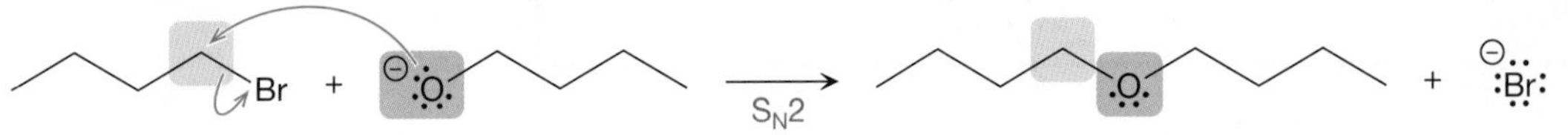

Br
+
S_N2
+

(10-12)

Equation 10-13 shows how the same ether can be produced by the second reaction shown in Figure 10-3. In this case, butan-1-ol is heated in the presence of sulfuric acid:

Condensation reaction

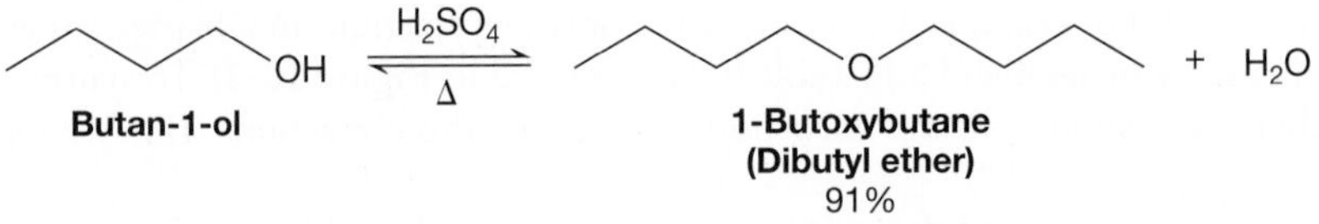

OH
H_2SO_4
Δ
O
+ H_2O
Butan-1-ol
1-Butoxybutane
(Dibutyl ether)
91%

(10-13)

▸ LOOKING AHEAD

Condensation reactions are not limited only to formation of ethers. In Chapter 19, we will study aldol condensation reactions, in which a molecule of water is lost. In Chapter 23, we will study Claisen condensations, in which a molecule of a small alcohol is lost.

Two molecules of the alcohol are joined together and a molecule of water is lost, so this type of reaction is called a *condensation reaction*:

In a **condensation reaction**, two larger molecules are joined at the expense of the loss of a smaller molecule (see Looking Ahead box).

The mechanism for this condensation reaction is shown in Equation 10-14. Under the acidic conditions of the reaction, the alcohol is protonated in Step 1 to produce a good leaving group, H_2O. Then an S_N2 step makes up Step 2, in which a second molecule of the alcohol acts as a nucleophile. Finally, deprotonation in Step 3 produces the uncharged ether:

Mechanism for ether formation by condensation (Eq. 10-13)

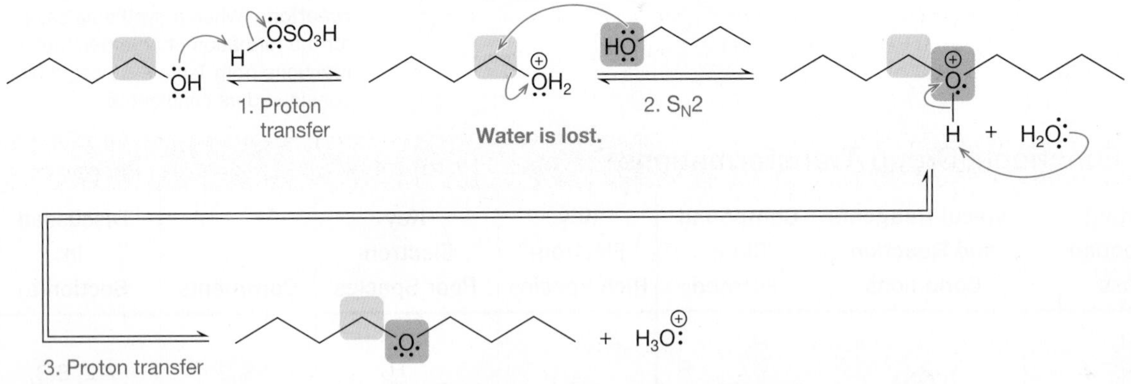

OH
H
OSO_3H
1. Proton transfer
OH_2
Water is lost.
HO
2. S_N2
O
H
+
H_2O
+
H_3O
3. Proton transfer

(10-14)

Mechanism Drawing
Formation of a Symmetric Ether from an Alcohol under Acidic Conditions

The mechanism in Equation 10-14 proceeds by an S_N2 step because the leaving group is on a primary carbon. Even though the conditions of the reaction tend to favor S_N1 (weak nucleophile, excellent leaving group, protic solvent), we learned in Section 9.6b that S_N1 reactions are unfeasible for primary substrates; the primary carbocation that would be formed is too unstable. When the alcohol is secondary or tertiary, on the other hand, an S_N1 reaction becomes more likely (see Your Turn 10.9).

YOUR TURN 10.9

Draw the mechanism for this condensation reaction.

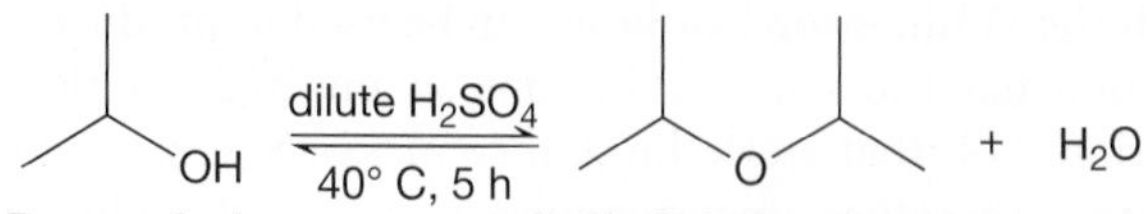
dilute H_2SO_4
40° C, 5 h
OH
O
+ H_2O

Propan-2-ol **2-(1-Methylethoxy)propane (Diisopropyl ether) 96%**

CONNECTIONS 10.2

I scream, you scream, we all scream for butan-1-ol The natural fermentation process of sugars will produce butan-1-ol (Eq. 10-13) in small amounts. Butan-1-ol is used as a flavoring agent in a variety of foods and beverages, including ice cream.

Synthesis of other ethers can be subject to severe limitations that make one method of synthesis much more feasible than the other. For example, suppose we want to synthesize 1-(1-methylethoxy)propane, as shown in Equation 10-15:

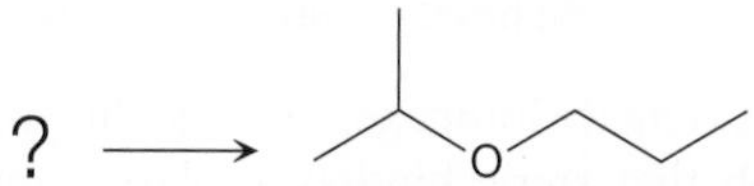
?
O

1-(1-Methylethoxy)propane (Isopropyl propyl ether) (10-15)

This is an *unsymmetric ether* (R^1—O—R^2), in which the two alkyl groups attached to the oxygen atom are different. We might envision carrying out a condensation reaction involving two different alcohols (R^1—OH and R^2—OH), as shown in Equation 10-16:

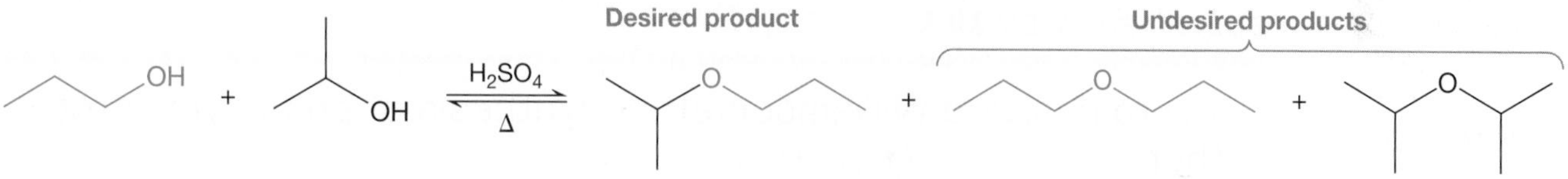
Desired product
Undesired products
OH
+
OH
H_2SO_4
Δ
O
+
O
+
O

(10-16)

Condensation is not a good choice, however, because it would form a mixture of ether products: the desired unsymmetric ether plus two other *symmetric* ethers (R^1—O—R^1 and R^2—O—R^2). The desired ether forms when one alcohol acts as the nucleophile (R^1—OH) and the other alcohol, in its protonated form, acts as the substrate (R^2—OH_2^+). The two symmetric ethers form in competing reactions, in which both the nucleophile and the substrate derive from the *same* alcohol (R^1—OH reacting with R^1—OH_2^+, and R^2—OH reacting with R^2—OH_2^+). For this reason:

Condensation reactions are typically feasible for synthesizing a *symmetric* ether but are often unfeasible for synthesizing an *unsymmetric* ether.

YOUR TURN 10.10

Draw the mechanisms for formation of the first two products in Equation 10-16.

In a Williamson ether synthesis, on the other hand, the alkyl groups of the alkyl halide and the alkoxide anion can be the same or different. Therefore:

Both *symmetric* and *unsymmetric* ethers can be produced by the Williamson ether synthesis.

Equation 10-17, for example, shows how a Williamson ether synthesis can be used to produce 1-(1-methylethoxy)propane:

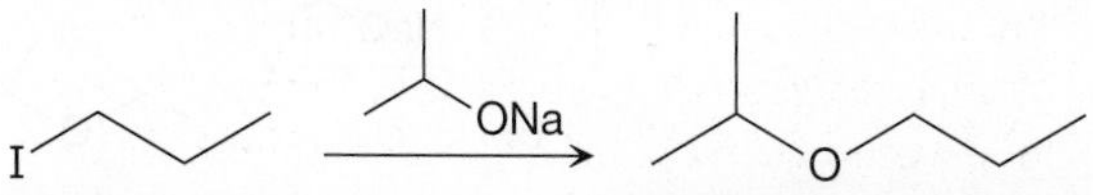
I
ONa
O

1-Iodopropane **1-(1-Methylethoxy)propane (Isopropyl propyl ether)** (10-17)

Only one ether is produced, rather than a mixture of ethers, because only the alkoxide anion can act as the nucleophile and only the alkyl halide can act as the substrate.

Even though the Williamson synthesis can be used to produce a wide variety of ethers, the reaction has the same limitations as any S_N2 reaction. Most notably, recall from Section 9.6b that steric hindrance makes S_N2 reactions unfeasible for tertiary substrates. Therefore, for example, reaction of sodium ethoxide with 2-bromo-2-methylpropane (Equation 10-18) yields essentially no ether product:

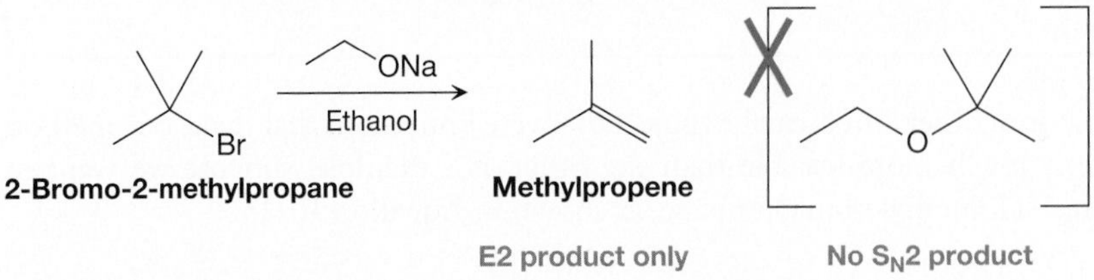

ONa
Ethanol
Br
O
2-Bromo-2-methylpropane
Methylpropene
E2 product only
No S_N2 product

(10-18)

Instead, the major product is methylpropene, which is the product of E2 elimination. (Recall from Section 9.6b that steric hindrance plays a much smaller role in E2 reactions.)

Fortunately, there are two possible choices for the Williamson synthesis of an unsymmetric ether, which differ by the alkyl groups that make up the substrate and alkoxide. If one choice is unfeasible, the other might be feasible (see Solved Problem 10.1).

SOLVED PROBLEM **10.1**

How to design a Williamson ether synthesis of an unsymmetric ether

Break It Down **Devise a Williamson ether synthesis that would produce the ether shown here, which is the intended ether product in Equation 10-18.**

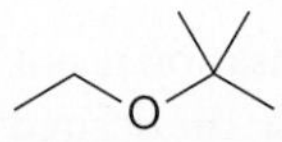

O

Think	Solve
Why is the Williamson synthesis in Equation 10-18 unfeasible?	The Williamson ether synthesis takes place by an S_N2 mechanism. Because the substrate in Equation 10-18, $(CH_3)_3CBr$, is tertiary, steric hindrance will prevent the nucleophile from attacking.
Could a different combination of alkyl halide and alkoxide anion produce the same ether?	A Williamson ether synthesis requires an alkyl halide (R—X) as the substrate and an alkoxide anion ($R'—O^-$) as the nucleophile. In Equation 10-18, R is the *tert*-butyl group and R′ is the ethyl group. The other combination has R as the ethyl group and R′ as the *tert*-butyl group, as shown below.
Is the alternative combination of alkyl halide and alkoxide anion feasible for an S_N2 reaction?	In the Williamson ether synthesis below, the substrate is primary. Primary substrates have very little steric hindrance, so they favor S_N2 reactions. Therefore, this Williamson ether synthesis is feasible. **This is a primary carbon, so the S_N2 reaction is feasible.** 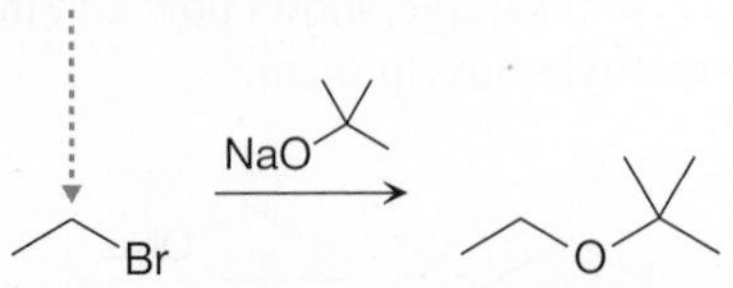 NaO Br O

(continued)

Try It Determine which of the following ethers can be produced from a Williamson ether synthesis. For those that can, show the synthesis that would be successful. If there are two feasible syntheses for a particular ether, determine which one is preferable.

(a)

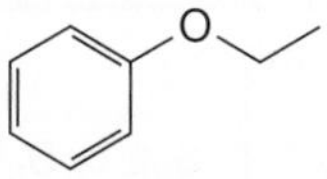
O

(b)

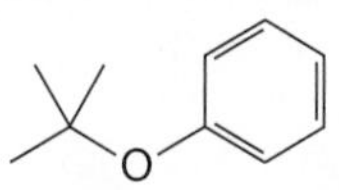
O

(c)

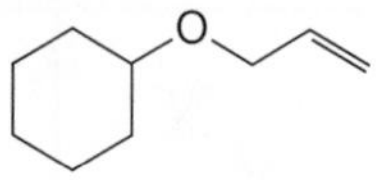
O

Answers to all Try It exercises can be found in the Solutions Manual.

10.4a Expanding Your Options in Synthesis: Functional Group Transformations

Our ability to design a synthesis is limited by the reactions we know. A synthesis can also present challenges when the functional groups that appear in the compounds we have available are not the functional groups required to carry out a necessary synthetic step. In such cases, we can often make use of functional group transformations.

For example, how can we design the synthesis of the unsymmetric ether shown in Equation 10-19, beginning only with alcohols?

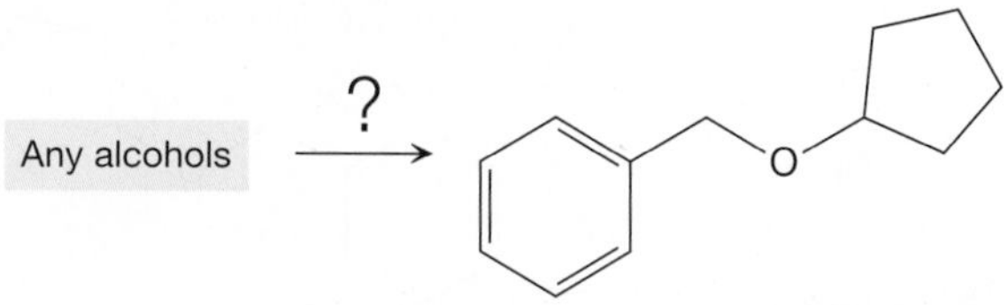
Any alcohols
?
O

(10-19)

To incorporate a Williamson ether synthesis, we could use the following alkyl halide and alkoxide anion:

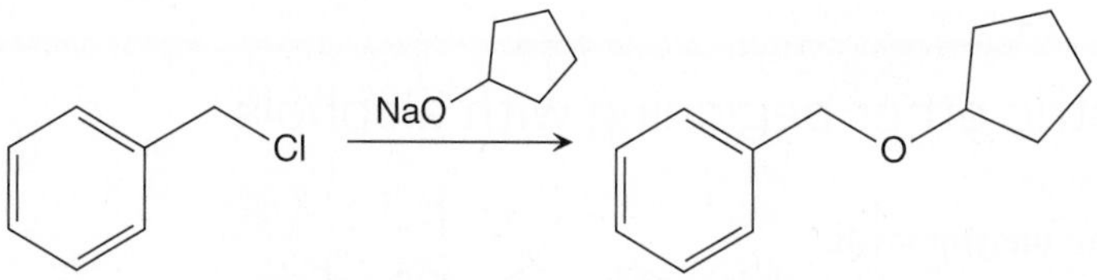
Cl
NaO
O

(10-20)

However, neither of the reactants is an alcohol. Therefore, our new task is to determine how the alkyl halide and alkoxide anion can be produced from alcohols.

To produce the alkyl halide from the corresponding alcohol, consider the functional group transformation shown in Entry 7 of Table 9-11, repeated in **Figure 10-4** (next page; see Looking Ahead box). Specifically, we could treat benzyl alcohol with a strong acid like HCl:

> **▸ LOOKING AHEAD**
>
> Treating an alcohol with concentrated HBr or HCl is not the only way to convert the OH into a halogen. Section 10.5 shows how such a conversion can be carried out with PBr_3 or PCl_3, and Section 23.4 shows how it can be accomplished with $SOCl_2$.

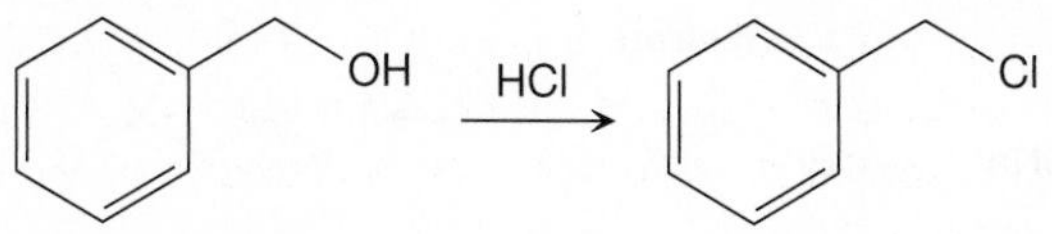
OH
HCl
Cl

(10-21)

To produce the alkoxide anion from an alcohol, we can take advantage of the strategy presented in Section 9.3b for generating strong nucleophiles, which is to carry out a deprotonation. In this case, we can treat cyclopentanol with a powerful base, such as sodium hydride:

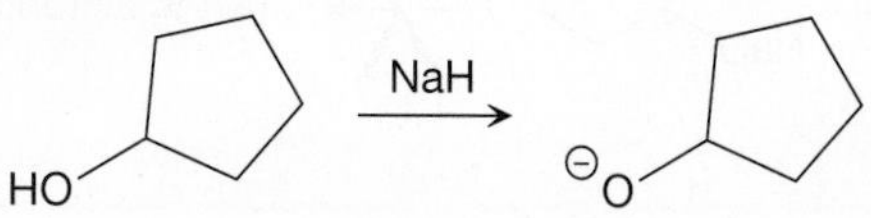
HO
NaH
O

(10-22)

TABLE 9-11 Functional Group Transformations[a]

	Starting Compound Class	Typical Reagents and Reaction Conditions	Compound Class Formed	Key Electron-Rich Species	Key Electron-Poor Species	Comments	Discussed in Section(s)
(7)	R–OH Alcohol	HX ⟶	R–X Alkyl halide	$X^{\ominus}$	$R^{\oplus}$ or $ROH_2^{\oplus}$	S_N1 or S_N2 reaction	7.2, 7.3, 8.1, 8.4, 8.5, 9.5b

[a]X = Cl, Br, or I.

FIGURE 10-4 Formation of an alkyl halide from an alcohol When a synthesis calls for the conversion of an alcohol into an alkyl halide, this reaction from Table 9-11 could be considered as a candidate.

Knowing how to produce the reactants necessary for the desired Williamson synthesis, we can present the entire synthesis together:

Final synthesis

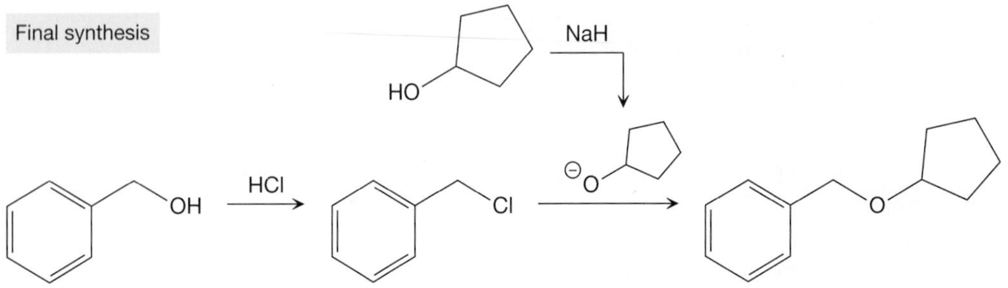
HO
NaH
OH
HCl
Cl
O
O

(10-23)

SOLVED PROBLEM **10.2**

How to synthesize an unsymmetric ether beginning with alcohols

Break It Down Design a synthesis for the unsymmetric ether shown here, beginning with any alcohols.

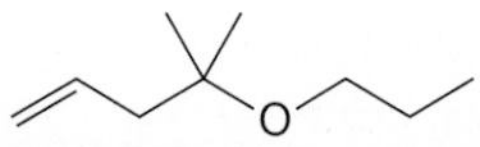
O

Think

What are the two possible combinations of alkyl halide and alkoxide anion for the Williamson synthesis? Which one would be the better choice?

Solve

The two possible combinations are shown below. The second combination is not feasible because no S_N2 reaction would take place with the 3° substrate.

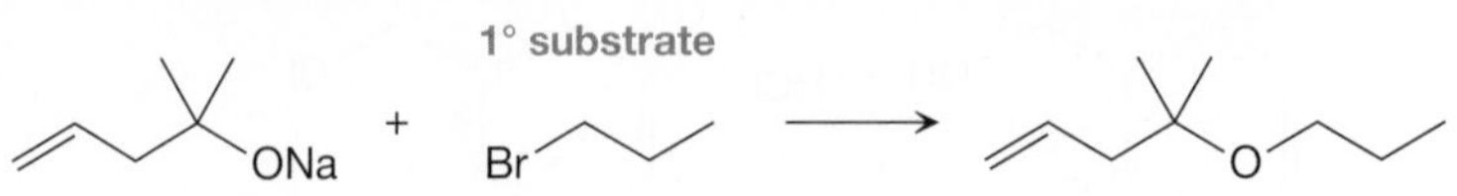
1° substrate
ONa
+
Br
O

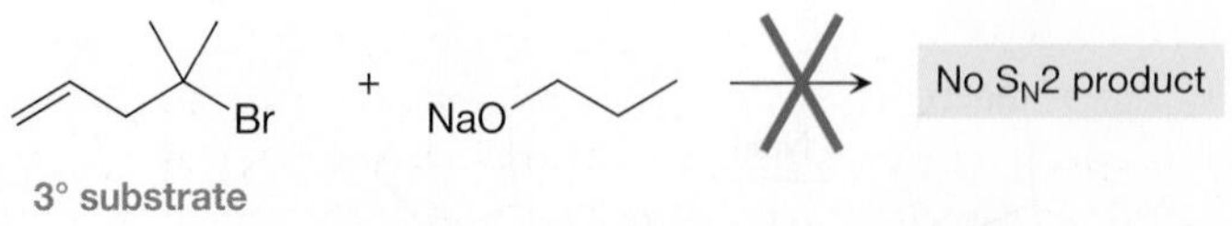
Br
+
NaO
No SN2 product
3° substrate

(continued)

How can the alkoxide anion be produced from an alcohol?	We can deprotonate the corresponding alcohol by using a powerful base to produce the alkoxide anion: 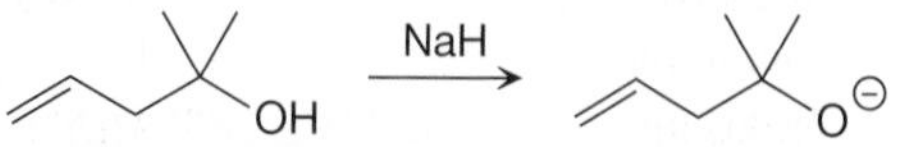 NaH OH O
How can the alkyl halide be produced from an alcohol?	We can use a strong acid like HBr to convert the alcohol into an alkyl bromide, as follows: 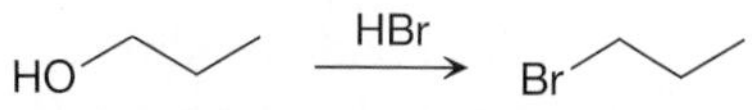 HO HBr Br
How do we put all the steps together to present the complete synthesis?	The final synthesis is shown below. 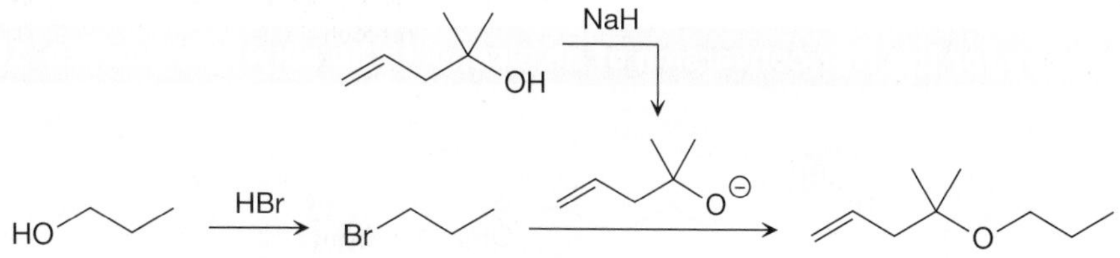 NaH OH HO HBr Br O O

Try It Show how to synthesize the following unsymmetric ether, beginning with any alcohols or phenols.

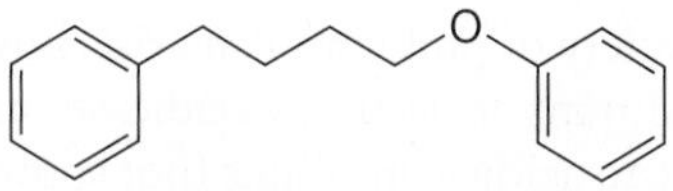
O

Our discussion in this section has been quite specific, dealing with the synthesis of only one type of compound (ethers) and considering just one type of restriction (the starting materials must be alcohols). The takeaway lesson, however, applies broadly:

> Functional group transformations not only are useful in producing functional groups that appear in the target but also can be used to produce functional groups that allow a subsequent synthetic step to occur.

Our ability to design a practical synthesis will improve with each additional functional group transformation we learn. For this reason, we devote the rest of this chapter to introducing more functional group transformations that are useful for synthesis.

We mentioned earlier that all of the new reactions we introduce in this chapter are related by the mechanisms they have in common: nucleophilic substitution or elimination. These mechanistic patterns help *simplify* organic chemistry, so it is worth your while to spend time studying these mechanisms when they are discussed.

10.5 Converting Alcohols into Alkyl Halides: PBr_3 and PCl_3

SECTION 10.5 OBJECTIVES

You will be able to:

1. Draw the mechanism and major product for the reaction of an alcohol with PBr_3 or PCl_3.
2. Explain the advantages of using PBr_3 or PCl_3 for these transformations instead of HBr or HCl.

In Section 10.4a, we saw how useful it can be to convert an alcohol (R—OH) into an alkyl halide, such as an alkyl chloride (R—Cl) or an alkyl bromide (R—Br). This conversion is desirable because HO^- is a rather poor leaving group for nucleophilic substitution and elimination reactions, whereas Br^- and Cl^- are quite good. (Recall that Cl and Br are substantially larger atoms than O and can better stabilize a negative charge.) One way to carry out such a conversion, as we saw in Section 10.4a, is to treat an alcohol with concentrated HCl or HBr. For example, butan-1-ol is converted to 1-bromobutane when treated with concentrated HBr:

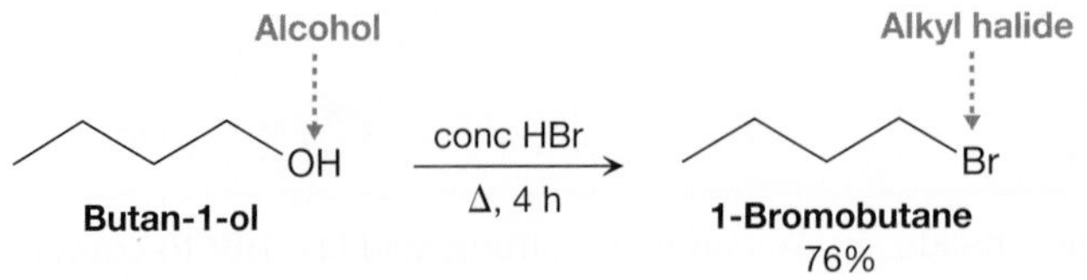
Alcohol
Alkyl halide
OH
conc HBr
Δ, 4 h
Br
Butan-1-ol
1-Bromobutane
76%
(10-24)

Under acidic conditions, a poor leaving group (in this case, HO^-) is converted into a very good leaving group (H_2O), as shown in Step 1 of the mechanism in Equation 10-25. The Br^- that is generated in that step then acts as a nucleophile in Step 2 to displace H_2O. The substrate is primary, so the displacement takes place by an S_N2 step:

Mechanism for the HBr conversion of an alcohol to an alkyl bromide (Eq. 10-24)

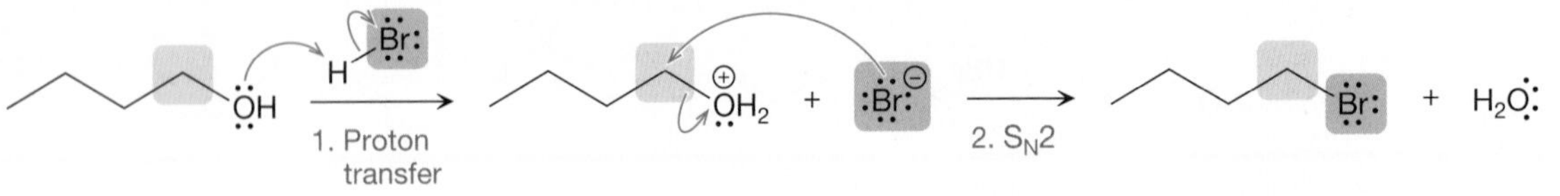
H
Br
OH
1. Proton transfer
OH2
+
Br
2. SN2
Br
+ H2O
(10-25)

◀ RECALL

As we learned in Section 8.5b, when a planar C^+ carbon becomes a chiral center, both the *R* and *S* configurations of the chiral center are produced.

A variety of problems can arise, however, with this type of reaction. For example, the conditions are strongly acidic, so other functional groups in the substrate that are sensitive to acidic conditions (not shown in Eq. 10-24) could react. If the substrate is a secondary or tertiary alcohol, moreover, then these reaction conditions would favor both S_N1 and E1 mechanisms (see Section 9.6b). In that case, the competing E1 reaction would reduce the yield of the intended S_N1 product. Also, because S_N1 reactions proceed through a planar *carbocation intermediate*, the stereochemistry that might exist at the carbon atom bonded to the leaving group would be lost (see top Recall box), as shown in Equation 10-26 (see also Your Turn 10.11):

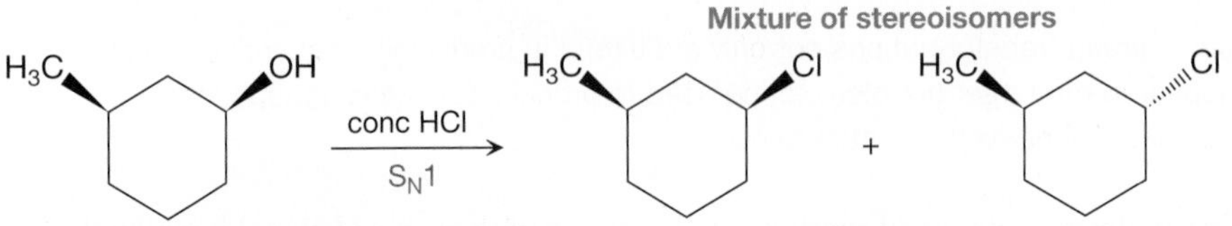
Mixture of stereoisomers
H3C
OH
conc HCl
SN1
H3C
Cl
+
H3C
Cl
(10-26)

YOUR TURN **10.11**

Draw the complete, detailed mechanism for the reaction in Equation 10-26.

◀ RECALL

Section 8.6d showed that 1,2-hydride shifts and 1,2-methyl shifts beat out other competing steps when the resulting carbocation is substantially more stable.

Finally, generating a carbocation means a carbocation rearrangement might be possible (see bottom Recall box), as shown in Equation 10-27 (see also Your Turn 10.12):

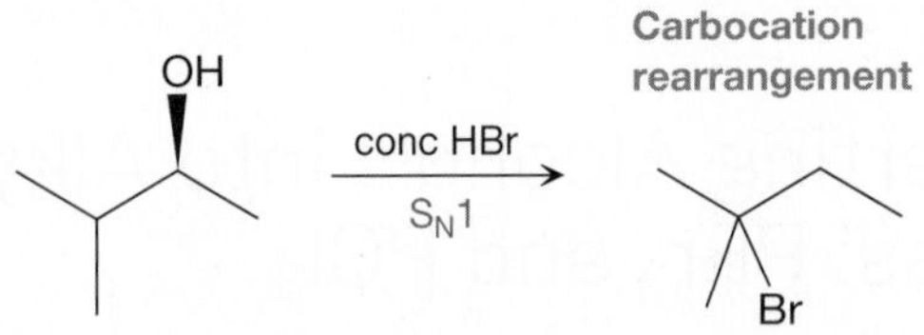
OH
conc HBr
SN1
Carbocation rearrangement
Br
(10-27)

YOUR TURN **10.12**

Draw the complete, detailed mechanism for the reaction in Equation 10-27.

Reagents other than HBr and HCl can be used to convert an alcohol into an alkyl halide. Good choices include phosphorus tribromide, PBr_3 (Eq. 10-28), or phosphorus trichloride, PCl_3 (Eq. 10-29). (Another reagent, $SOCl_2$, is even better than PCl_3, as we will discuss in Chapter 23.)

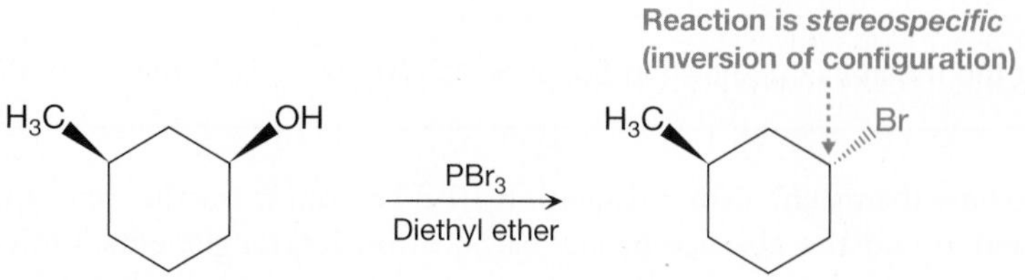
Reaction is *stereospecific*
(inversion of configuration)
H_3C
OH
PBr_3
Diethyl ether
H_3C
Br

(10-28)

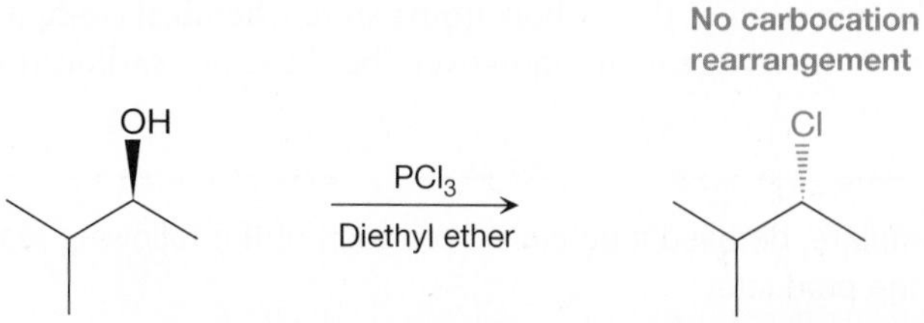
No carbocation
rearrangement
OH
PCl_3
Diethyl ether
Cl

(10-29)

The PBr_3 and PCl_3 reagents have none of the disadvantages that arise from using HBr or HCl:

- PBr_3 and PCl_3 convert an alcohol to an alkyl halide under relatively mild conditions.
- No elimination products are generated.
- The conversion is *stereospecific*. It takes place with *inversion of configuration* at the alcohol carbon atom (see Eq. 10-28).
- No carbocation rearrangements occur (compare Eqs. 10-27 and 10-29).

These observations are explained by the mechanism shown in Equation 10-30, which consists of back-to-back S_N2 steps:

Mechanism for the PBr_3 conversion of an alcohol into an alkyl halide (Eq. 10-28)

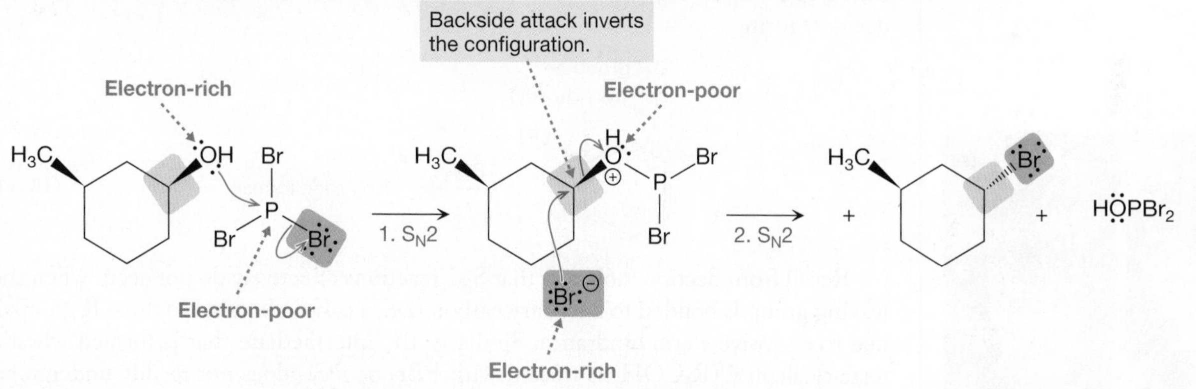
Backside attack inverts
the configuration.
Electron-rich
Electron-poor
H_3C
OH
Br
P
Br
Br
Electron-poor
1. S_N2
H_3C
H
O
P
Br
Br
Br
Electron-rich
2. S_N2
H_3C
Br
+
+
$HOPBr_2$

(10-30)

In Step 1, the O atom of the alcohol is electron-rich and acts as the nucleophile, whereas PBr_3 has an electron-poor P atom and acts as the substrate. In that step, the Br^- anion is the leaving group. In Step 2, the Br^- anion generated in Step 1 acts as the nucleophile and the phosphorus-containing species acts as the substrate. The leaving group is $HOPBr_2$.

Notice that the phosphorus-containing species in Step 2 of the mechanism resembles a protonated alcohol, ROH_2^+ (**Figure 10-5**). The leaving group ($HOPBr_2$) resembles a stable, uncharged H_2O molecule, which is an excellent leaving group.

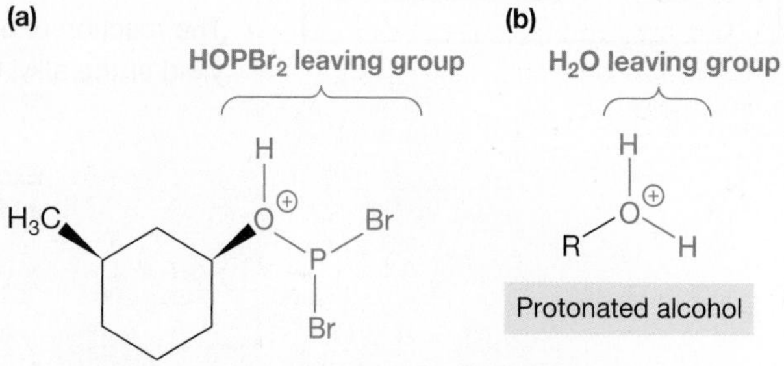
(a)
$HOPBr_2$ leaving group
H
H_3C
O
P
Br
Br
(b)
H_2O leaving group
H
R
O
H
Protonated alcohol

FIGURE 10-5 The $HOPBr_2$ leaving group (a) The $HOPBr_2$ leaving group in Step 2 of Equation 10-30 is highlighted in red. (b) This leaving group resembles the excellent H_2O leaving group in a protonated alcohol.

YOUR TURN **10.13**

Repeat the mechanism shown in Equation 10-30, using PCl_3 instead of PBr_3.

Notice how the mechanism in Equation 10-30 accounts for the stereospecificity of the reaction and the absence of any carbocation rearrangements. Only Step 2 involves breaking or forming bonds to the asymmetric carbon. In that step, the S_N2 attack causes the inversion of the carbon atom's stereochemical configuration. There is no carbocation rearrangement, moreover, because no carbocations are ever generated!

YOUR TURN **10.14**

Draw the complete, detailed mechanism for each of the following reactions and predict the products.

(a)

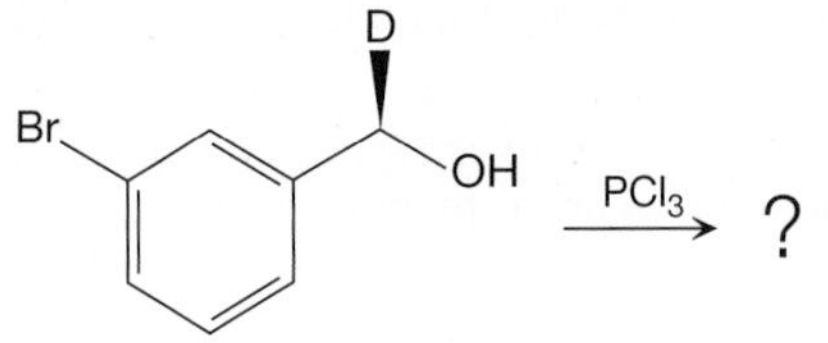
D
Br
OH
PCl3
?

(b)

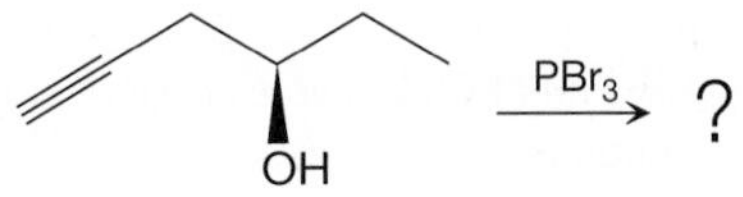
OH
PBr3
?

CONNECTIONS 10.3

PBr_3 and surgical anesthesia

One of the commercial uses of PBr_3 (Eq. 10-28) is in the synthesis of methohexital, marketed as Brevital, which is used as an anesthetic for surgery. The synthetic step that uses PBr_3 is shown here.

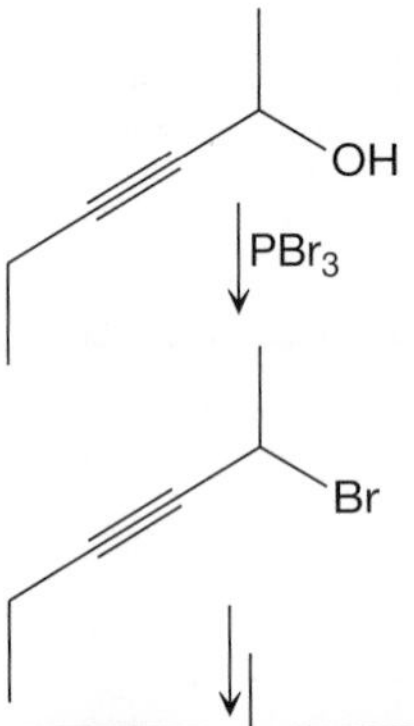
OH
PBr3
Br

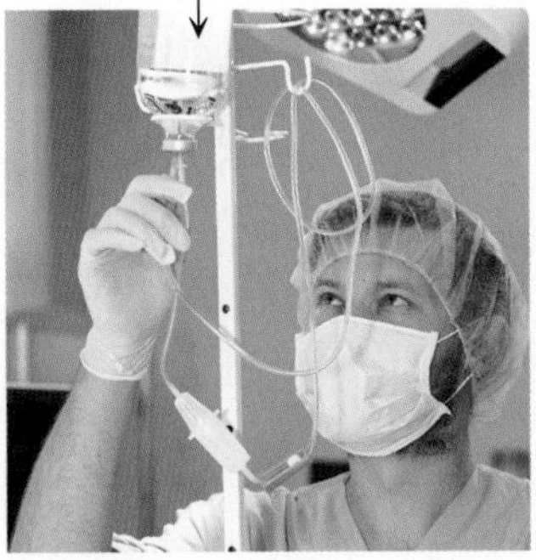

Recall from Section 9.6a that nucleophilic substitution reactions generally do *not* occur when a leaving group is on an sp^2- or sp-hybridized carbon atom. The same is true of these reactions involving phosphorus trihalides:

The conversion of an alcohol into an alkyl halide with PBr_3 or PCl_3 occurs only when the OH group is bonded to an sp^3-hybridized carbon atom.

The OH group in Equation 10-31 is on an sp^2-hybridized C, not sp^3, so the halide does *not* form:

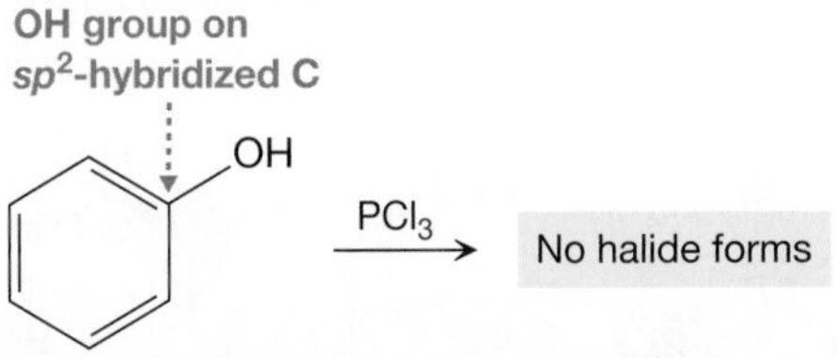
OH group on
sp2-hybridized C
OH
PCl3
No halide forms

(10-31)

Recall from Section 9.6b, too, that S_N2 reactions effectively do not occur when the leaving group is bonded to a tertiary carbon (i.e., a carbon bonded to three R groups), due to excessive steric hindrance. Similarly, the intermediate that is formed when a tertiary alcohol (R_3COH) is treated with PBr_3 or PCl_3 does not readily undergo an S_N2 reaction, though it more feasibly can undergo S_N1. Thus:

The reaction of a tertiary alcohol (R_3COH) with PBr_3 or PCl_3 often gives a poor yield of the alkyl halide.

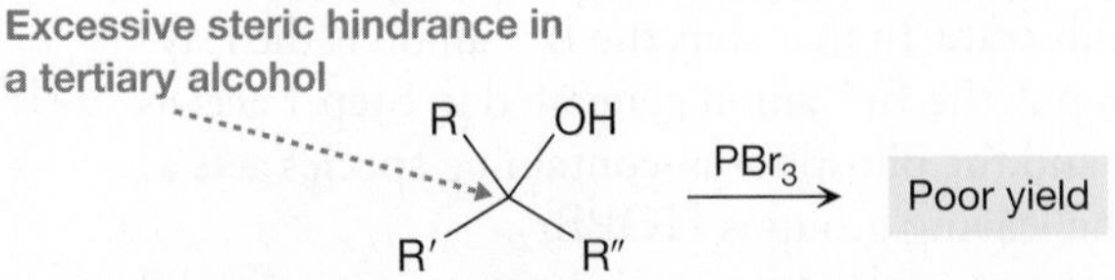
Excessive steric hindrance in
a tertiary alcohol
R
OH
R′
R″
PBr3
Poor yield

(10-32)

As we can see in Solved Problem 10.3, these restrictions on the type of carbon atom bonded to OH make it possible to carry out a selective conversion into the alkyl halide.

SOLVED PROBLEM **10.3**

How to predict the product of an alcohol's reaction with PBr_3

Break It Down **Predict the products of this reaction and draw its complete, detailed mechanism. Pay attention to stereochemistry.**

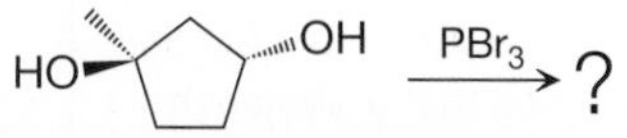

HO
OH
PBr3
?

Think	Solve
What functional groups are present in this molecule, and which, if any, are susceptible to reaction with PBr_3?	PBr_3 targets OH functional groups, and there are two such groups present. The one on the right is on a secondary carbon, and the one on the left is on a tertiary carbon. Because the mechanism (shown below) proceeds by an S_N2 attack, the secondary carbon is prone to reaction but the tertiary carbon is not (due to excessive steric hindrance).
What type of functional group is produced, and how is the stereochemistry of the molecule affected?	PBr_3 will convert the alcohol into an alkyl bromide. Step 2 of the mechanism (shown below) is S_N2, which will reverse the configuration of the carbon atom initially bonded to the OH group. Whereas the C—OH group initially points away, the new C—Br bond points toward you.

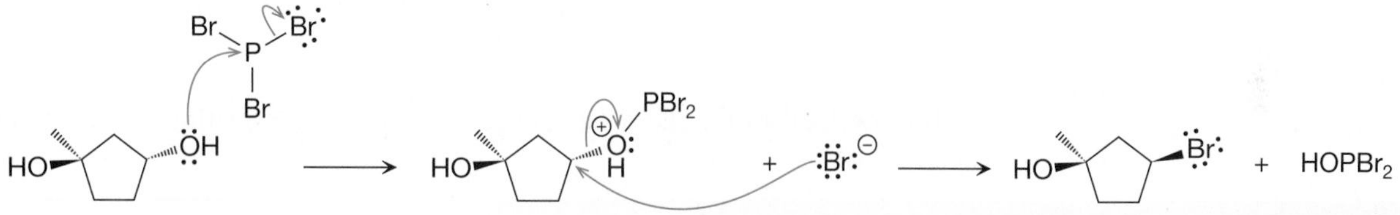

Br
P
Br
Br
HO
OH
PBr2
O
H
+
Br
HO
Br
+
HOPBr2

Try It Which of the following compounds will readily react with PCl_3? For those that will react, **(a)** draw the products, including stereochemistry, and **(b)** draw the complete, detailed mechanism.

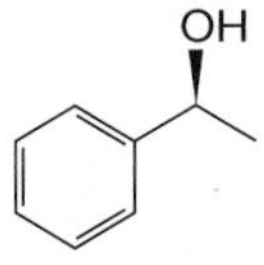

OH

A

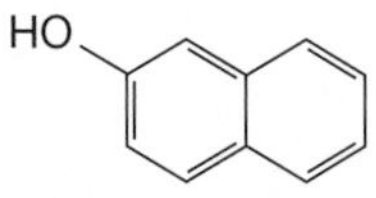

HO

B

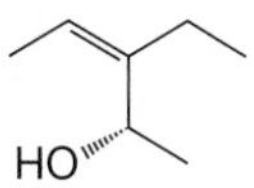

HO

C

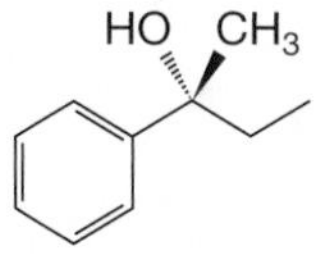

HO
CH3

D

10.6 Halogenation of α Carbons

SECTION 10.6 OBJECTIVES

You will be able to:

1. Draw the mechanism and major product for the α halogenation of a ketone or aldehyde under acidic or basic conditions.
2. Explain why polyhalogenation occurs under basic conditions, whereas monohalogenation occurs under acidic conditions.

So far, we have studied two functional group transformations that convert a poor HO^- leaving group into a good halide leaving group. In this section, we examine reactions that place a halide leaving group on a carbon that does not initially have a leaving group at all. For example, 2-methyl-1-phenylpropan-1-one (Eq. 10-33) has no leaving group. When the ketone is treated with Br_2 under basic conditions, however, a good Br leaving group is placed on the *α* (alpha) carbon (i.e., the carbon that is adjacent to the carbonyl group). In this α halogenation reaction, the *α* hydrogen (attached to the α carbon) has been replaced by Br:

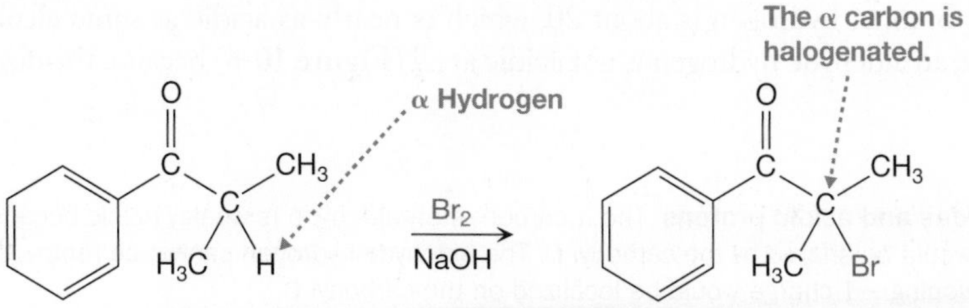

The α carbon is halogenated.
α Hydrogen
O
C
CH3
C
H3C
H
Br2
NaOH
O
C
CH3
C
H3C
Br

(10-33)

▶ LOOKING AHEAD

α Halogenation is not the only reaction that serves to replace an α hydrogen of a ketone or aldehyde with another substituent. In Section 11.3, we will see that α alkylation replaces an α hydrogen with an alkyl group, which makes it a reaction that alters the carbon skeleton.

In general:

> α Halogenation takes place when a ketone or aldehyde with an α hydrogen is treated with a molecular halogen (Cl_2, Br_2, or I_2) under basic conditions.

With a leaving group on the α carbon, subsequent reactions become feasible that would not be possible without the leaving group present (see Looking Ahead box). For example, the α-halogenated product can act as a substrate in a subsequent substitution or elimination reaction:

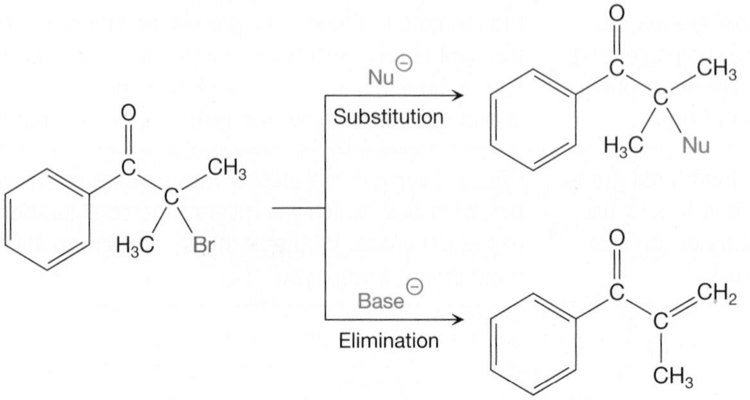

Nu⊖
Substitution
Base⊖
Elimination

(10-34a)

(10-34b)

The mechanism for the α halogenation reaction in Equation 10-33 is shown in Equation 10-35:

Mechanism for α halogenation under basic conditions (Eq. 10-33)

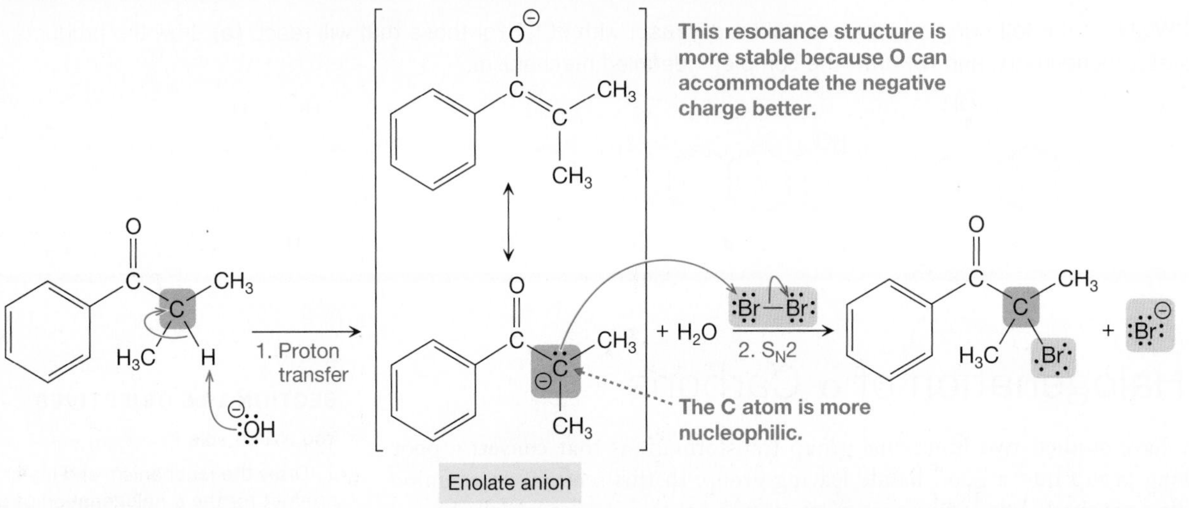

This resonance structure is more stable because O can accommodate the negative charge better.
1. Proton transfer
+ H2O
2. SN2
The C atom is more nucleophilic.
Enolate anion

(10-35)

In Step 1, the base deprotonates the α carbon, producing a nucleophilic enolate anion. In Step 2, the enolate anion attacks the molecular halogen in an S_N2 reaction.

Notice that the enolate anion has two resonance structures, which serve to delocalize the developing −1 charge over the C and O atoms. This charge delocalization is what makes deprotonation of the α carbon feasible; as we saw in Table 6-1 (p. 269), the pK_a of an α hydrogen is about 20, which is nearly as acidic as some alcohols. By contrast, an aldehyde hydrogen is not acidic at all (**Figure 10-6**) because the developing

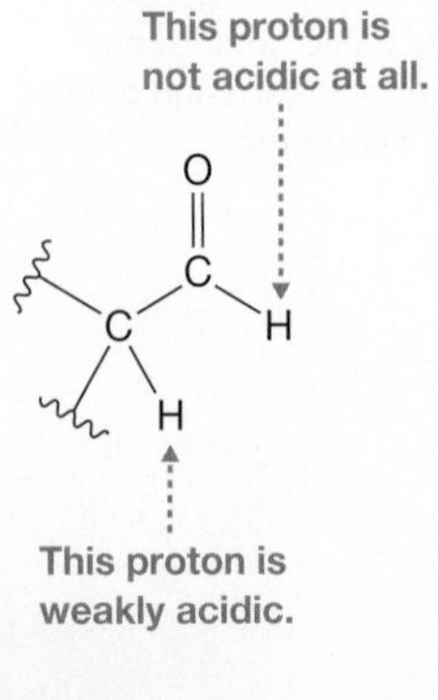

This proton is not acidic at all.
This proton is weakly acidic.

FIGURE 10-6 Aldehydes and acidic protons The α carbon of an aldehyde is weakly acidic because the developing −1 charge would be shared by the carbonyl O. The aldehyde hydrogen cannot be removed by a base because the developing −1 charge would be localized on the carbonyl C.

−1 charge would be localized on the carbonyl C. Therefore, an aldehyde H cannot be removed by a base.

Of the two major resonance structures of an enolate anion, the one that is more stable has the −1 charge on O instead of C, because O is more electronegative. The enolate anion is more nucleophilic at C, however, as indicated in Equation 10-35, analogous to a species like H_3C^- being more nucleophilic than HO^- (Section 9.3a).

Recall from Section 8.7 that when a mechanism involves a species that has resonance structures, we can draw the mechanism using any of those resonance structures. Many organic chemists prefer to show only the most stable resonance structure, in which case the mechanism in Equation 10-35 would instead be drawn like this:

◂ RECALL

As we learned in Section 2.6d, molecules are polarizable because their electron clouds can be distorted relative to the nuclei. Moreover, polarizability generally increases with an increasing number of total electrons in the molecule.

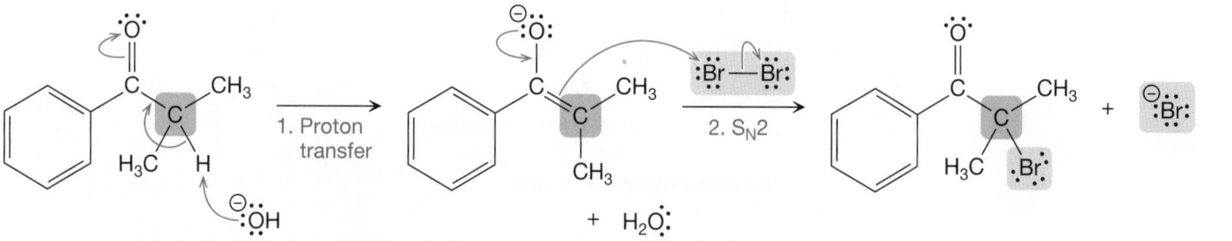

1. Proton transfer
2. S_N2

(10-36)

In this book, however, we will generally use the resonance structure that most clearly portrays how the species reacts. For an enolate anion acting as a nucleophile, therefore, we will generally add the curved arrows to the resonance structure that has the −1 charge on C, as was done in Equation 10-35.

YOUR TURN 10.15

The reaction shown here is similar to that in Equation 10-35. The only difference is the structure of the ketone. Draw its complete, detailed mechanism, including any curved arrows.

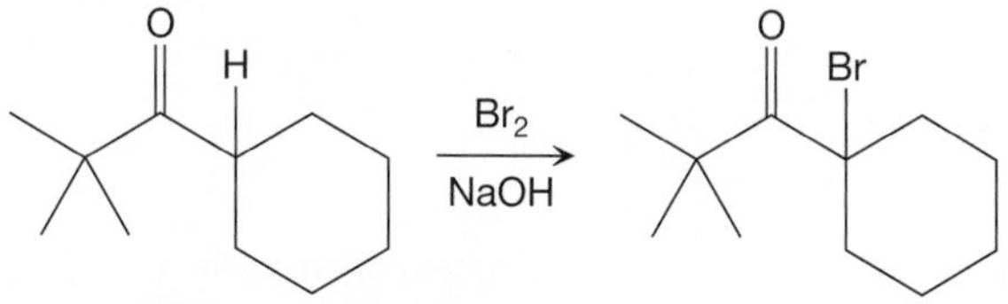

Br_2
NaOH

Why should a nucleophile, such as an enolate anion, attack a molecular halogen?

Halogens like Cl_2, Br_2, and I_2 can behave as substrates in S_N2 reactions in part because they are relatively highly *polarizable* (see Recall box).

Consequently, when an electron-rich species like the enolate anion approaches, the electrons on the halogen molecule are easily repelled, generating a substantial *induced dipole* (**Figure 10-7**). The halogen atom that is nearer the nucleophile, therefore, becomes electron-poor. As a result, a curved arrow can be drawn from the electron-rich nucleophile to the electron-poor halogen atom.

Looking back at the α halogenation mechanism in Equation 10-35 (or Eq. 10-36), notice that the α carbon in the enolate anion is bonded to three groups, whereas it is bonded to four groups in the halogenated product. Therefore, if the α carbon becomes a chiral center when it gains the halogen atom (Step 2), then both the *R* and *S* configurations will be produced. This is the case for the α halogenation reaction shown in Equation 10-37:

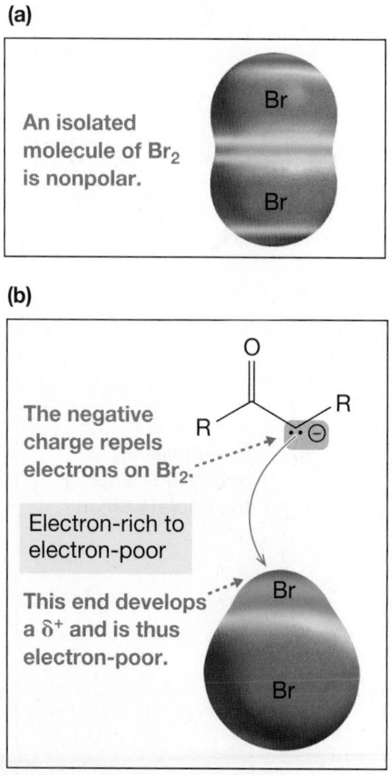

(a)
An isolated molecule of Br_2 is nonpolar.
Br
Br
(b)
The negative charge repels electrons on Br_2.
Electron-rich to electron-poor
This end develops a δ+ and is thus electron-poor.
Br
Br

FIGURE 10-7 Molecular halogens as substrates in nucleophilic substitution (a) An isolated bromine molecule is nonpolar. (b) As the nucleophile approaches, electron repulsion forces electron density around Br_2 to the opposite side, generating an induced dipole. The near side, therefore, becomes electron-poor.

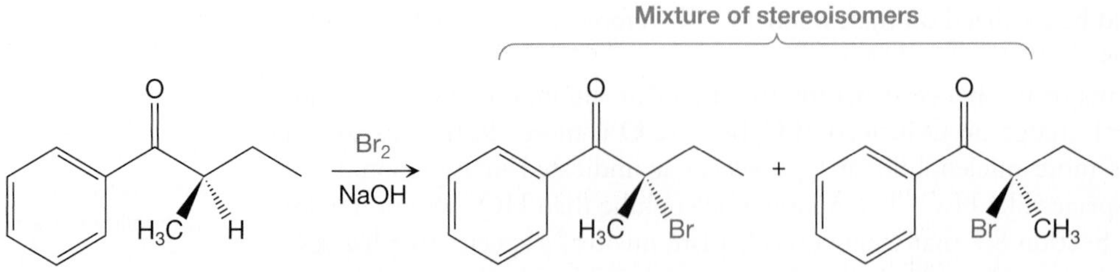
Mixture of stereoisomers
Br2
NaOH
H3C
H
Br
CH3
+

(10-37)

In the α halogenation reactions we have seen so far (Eqs. 10-33 and 10-37), the ketone has only a single α hydrogen. The ketone in Equation 10-38 contains two α hydrogens, and *both* α hydrogens are replaced:

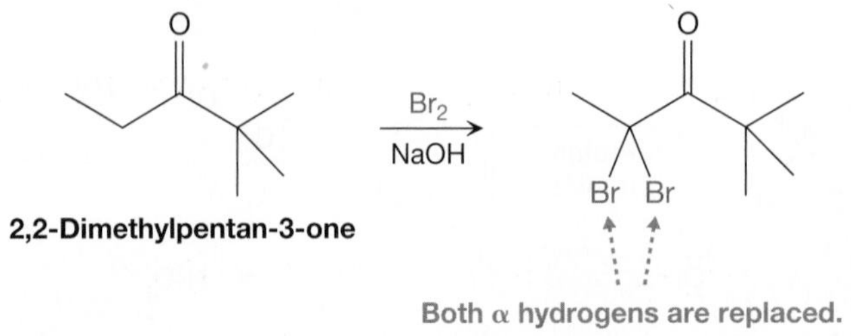
Br2
NaOH
2,2-Dimethylpentan-3-one
Br Br
Both α hydrogens are replaced.

(10-38)

Mechanism Drawing
Polyhalogenation of an α Carbon of a Ketone or Aldehyde under Basic Conditions

Under *basic* conditions, **polyhalogenation** generally occurs, in which every α hydrogen is replaced by a halogen atom.

The mechanism for Equation 10-38 is shown in Equation 10-39; the mechanism for a single α halogenation (Eq. 10-35) essentially occurs twice:

Mechanism for the polyhalogenation of a ketone under basic conditions (Eq. 10-38)

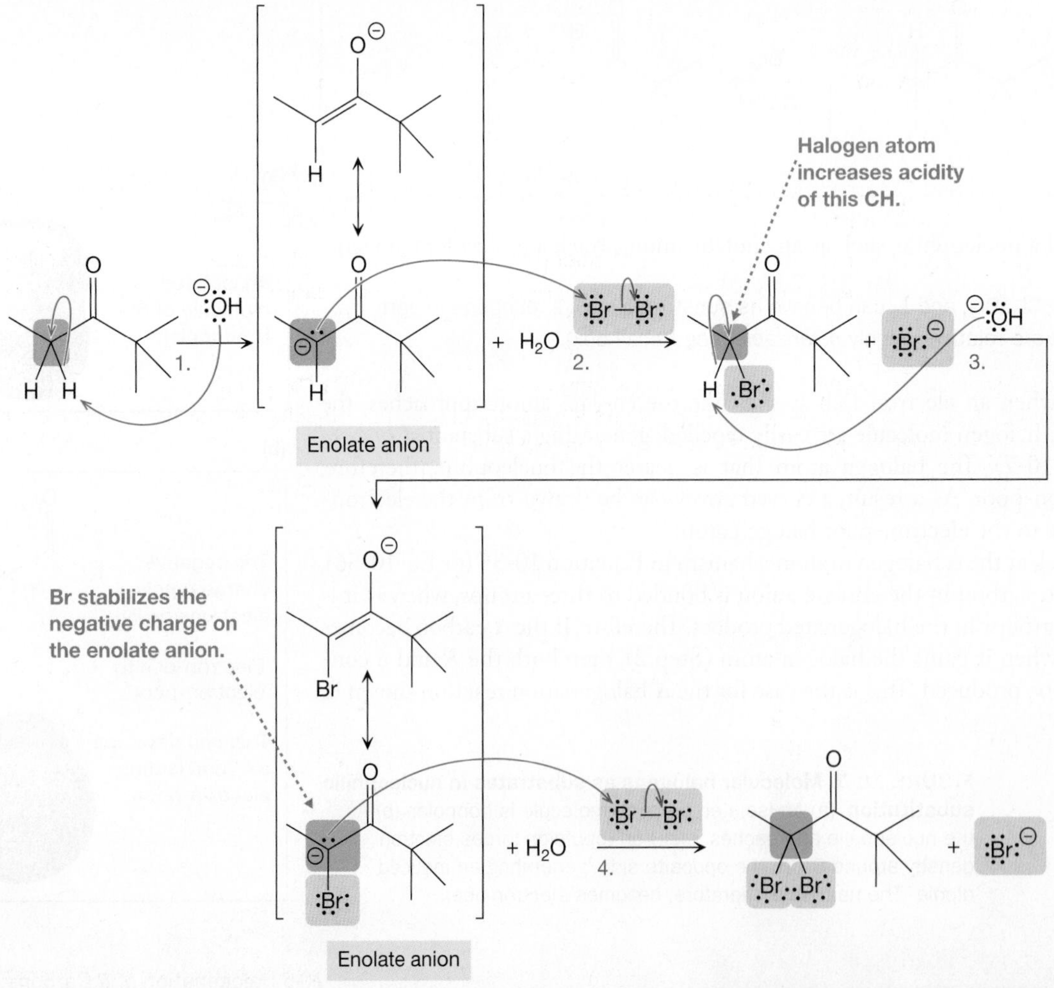
Halogen atom increases acidity of this CH.
Enolate anion
+ H2O
1.
2.
3.
4.
Br stabilizes the negative charge on the enolate anion.
Enolate anion

(10-39)

Under each reaction arrow in the mechanism in Equation 10-39, label the step as either *proton transfer* or S_N2.

YOUR TURN **10.16**

α Halogenation does not stop after a single substitution because *the second halogenation is faster than the first halogenation*. The second α halogenation is faster because addition of the first halogen makes the remaining α hydrogens more acidic. As indicated in Equation 10-39, the halogen's electron-withdrawing ability stabilizes the negative charge that develops in the enolate anion. Therefore, the second enolate is formed more easily than the first.

Which ketone, **A** or **B**, will undergo chlorination faster under basic conditions? Why?

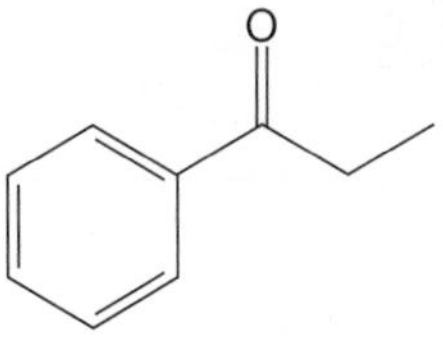

A

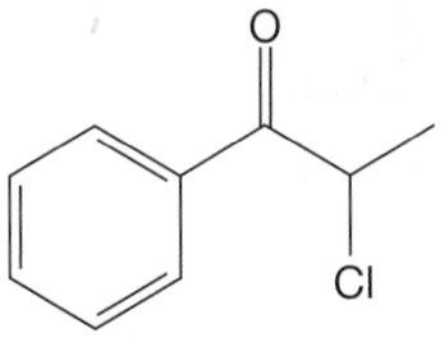
O
Cl

B

YOUR TURN **10.17**

SOLVED PROBLEM **10.4**

How to draw the mechanism and product for polyhalogenation of an α carbon

Break It Down Draw the complete, detailed mechanism for the chlorination of butanal.

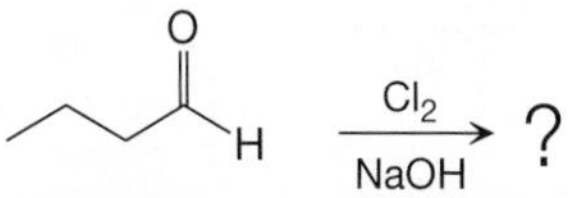
O
H
Cl_2
NaOH
?

Butanal

Think	Solve
In the presence of a strong base, what reaction takes place at an α carbon?	HO^-, a strong base, can deprotonate the α carbon of the aldehyde to produce the enolate anion, as shown in Step 1 of the mechanism on the next page.
How does this affect the chemical properties at the α carbon? What species will the enolate anion attack?	The enolate anion is strongly nucleophilic at the α carbon and will attack a molecule of Cl_2 in an S_N2 step, as shown in Step 2 of the mechanism on the next page. Thus, the α carbon has been halogenated.

(continued)

How many times will such a reaction take place at that α carbon?	This halogenation reaction occurs for each α hydrogen. There are two such α hydrogens, so after the first halogenation, the same pair of steps occurs again to produce the dihalogenated product shown below.

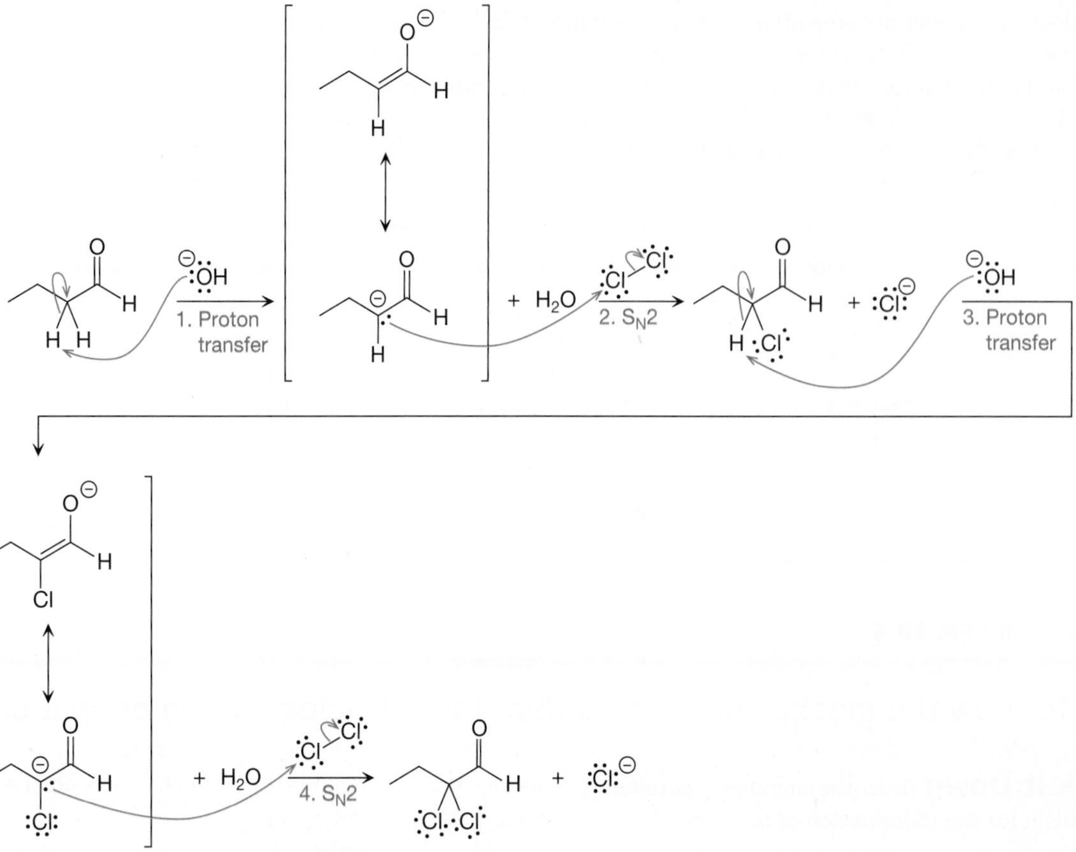

1. Proton transfer
+ H_2O
2. S_N2
3. Proton transfer
+ H_2O
4. S_N2

Try It Draw the complete, detailed mechanism for the iodination of 2,6-dimethylcyclohexanone, which takes place under basic conditions, and predict the major product.

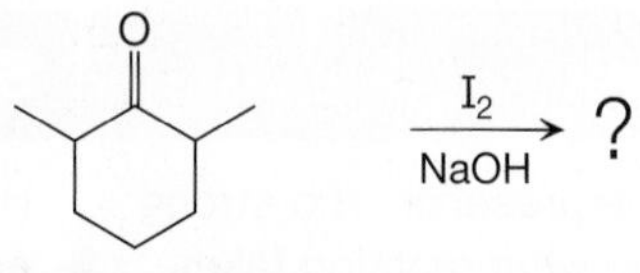

I_2
NaOH
?

2,6-Dimethylcyclohexanone

If polyhalogenation is *not* desired, then we can change the conditions in which the reaction is carried out:

Under *acidic conditions*, only a single α halogenation takes place.

This is exemplified in Equation 10-40, in which the ketone from Equation 10-38 is halogenated in the presence of acetic acid (CH_3CO_2H), abbreviated as HOAc:

Under acidic conditions, halogenation occurs only once.

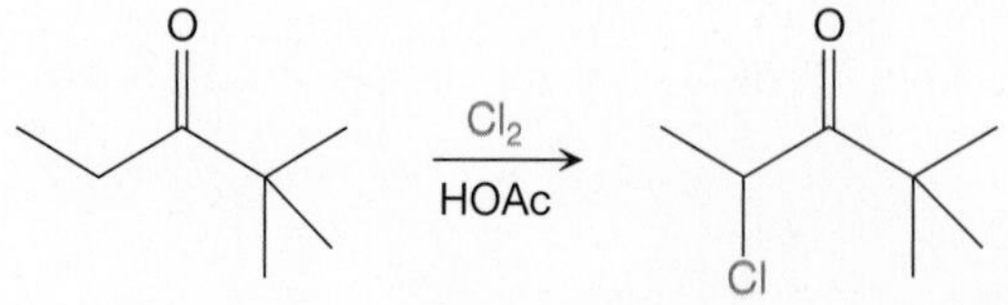

Cl_2
HOAc

(10-40)

Under these conditions, a negatively charged enolate anion cannot exist at any substantial concentration because it is strongly basic (the pK_a of a ketone or aldehyde is ~20). However, the α carbon can still become electron-rich by acid-catalyzed keto–enol tautomerization, as shown in Equation 10-41:

Mechanism for the halogenation of a ketone under acidic conditions (Eq. 10-40)

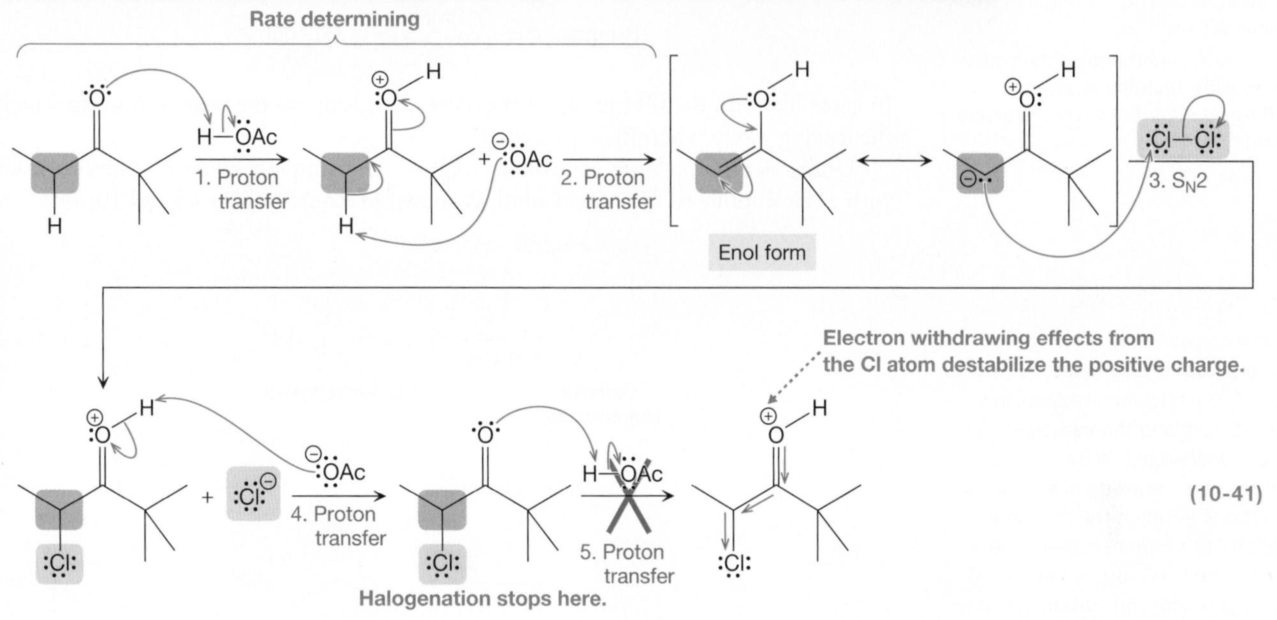

Rate determining
H—ÖAc
1. Proton transfer
2. Proton transfer
Enol form
3. S_N2
Electron withdrawing effects from the Cl atom destabilize the positive charge.
4. Proton transfer
5. Proton transfer
Halogenation stops here.

(10-41)

In the enol form, the α carbon is electron-rich, due to the small contribution by the resonance structure in which a negative charge and a lone pair of electrons are located on the α carbon. As before, one end of the halogen molecule becomes electron-poor when the enol approaches, thus setting up the *electron-rich to electron-poor* driving force for the subsequent nucleophilic substitution.

Why does α halogenation take place only once under acidic conditions? In contrast to what occurs under basic conditions, *α halogenation under acidic conditions becomes slower with each additional halogen*. As indicated in Equation 10-41, formation of the enol (the key nucleophilic species in the mechanism) is rate-determining, and it requires protonation of the carbonyl group. The Cl atom is electron-withdrawing and destabilizes nearby positive charges, so protonating the carbonyl group is more difficult with the Cl present.

Mechanism Drawing
Halogenation of an α Carbon of a Ketone or Aldehyde under Acidic Conditions

YOUR TURN **10.18**

Which ketone, **A** or **B**, will undergo bromination faster under acidic conditions? Why?

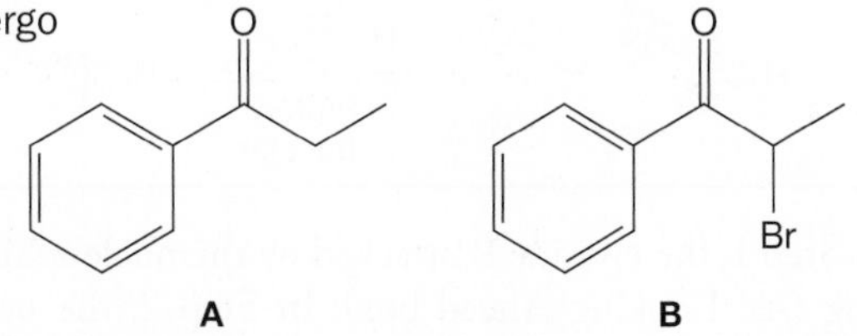

O
O
Br
A
B

YOUR TURN **10.19**

Draw the complete, detailed mechanism for the following iodination under acidic conditions and predict the major product.

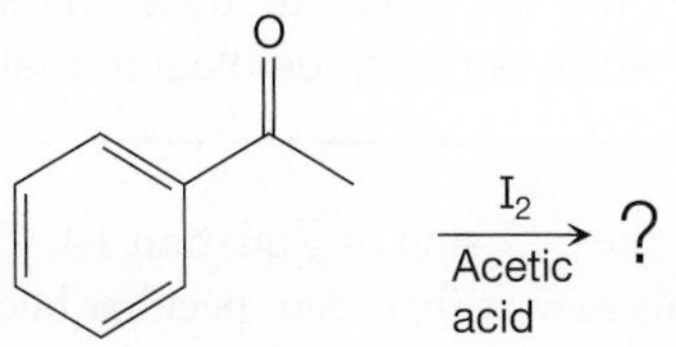

O
I_2
Acetic acid
?

SECTION 10.7 OBJECTIVES

You will be able to:

1. Draw the mechanism and major product, including stereochemistry and regiochemistry, for the reaction of an epoxide with strong and weak nucleophiles.
2. Explain why the regiochemistry of epoxide-opening reactions is different under basic versus acidic conditions.

10.7 Epoxides as Substrates

We have seen how an alcohol can be produced by the simple substitution of a suitable leaving group, such as in the reaction in Equation 10-42:

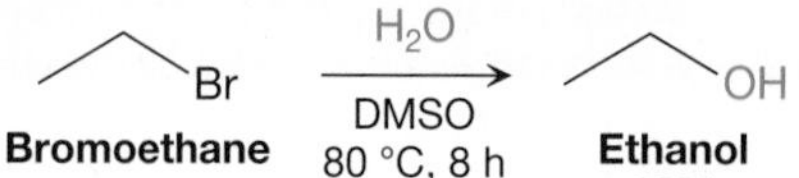

H_2O
Br
OH
DMSO
80 °C, 8 h

Bromoethane → **Ethanol** 88% (10-42)

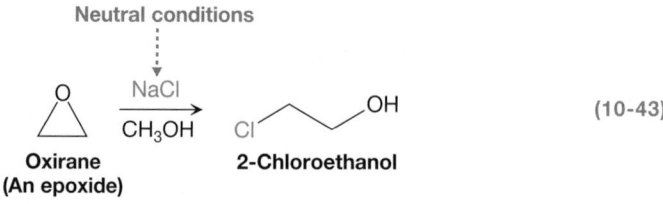

In cases like this, the OH group of the alcohol ends up on the same carbon to which the leaving group was initially attached.

Under neutral or basic conditions, oxirane (the simplest epoxide) can also react with a nucleophile to form an alcohol, as shown in Equations 10-43 and 10-44:

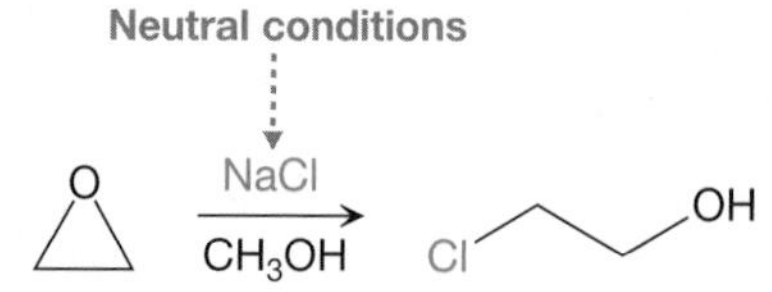

Neutral conditions
O
NaCl
CH_3OH
Cl
OH

Oxirane (An epoxide) → **2-Chloroethanol** (10-43)

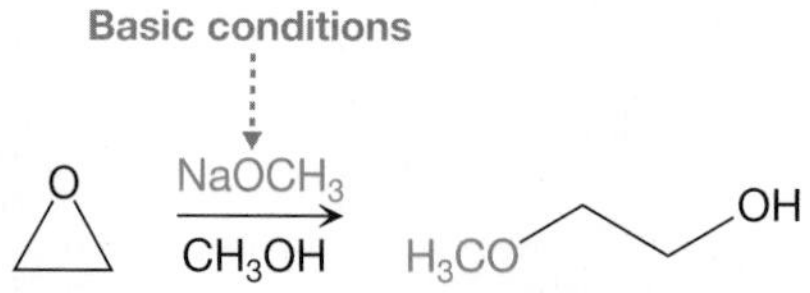

Basic conditions
O
$NaOCH_3$
CH_3OH
H_3CO
OH

Oxirane (An epoxide) → **2-Methoxyethanol** (10-44)

> ▸ **LOOKING AHEAD**
>
> In the epoxide ring-opening reactions shown in Equations 10-43 and 10-44, the nucleophilic atom is a heteroatom and the carbon skeleton is left unchanged. In Section 11.2, we will study epoxide ring-opening reactions in which the attacking species is a carbon nucleophile; these reactions form a new C—C bond and alter the carbon skeleton.

In both cases, the OH group and the nucleophile end up on *adjacent* carbon atoms in the product:

> A 2-substituted alcohol (Sub—C—C—OH) can be produced when an epoxide reacts with a nucleophile.

The mechanism for the reaction in Equation 10-44 is shown in Equation 10-45:

Mechanism for epoxide ring opening by a strong nucleophile under basic conditions (Eq. 10-44)

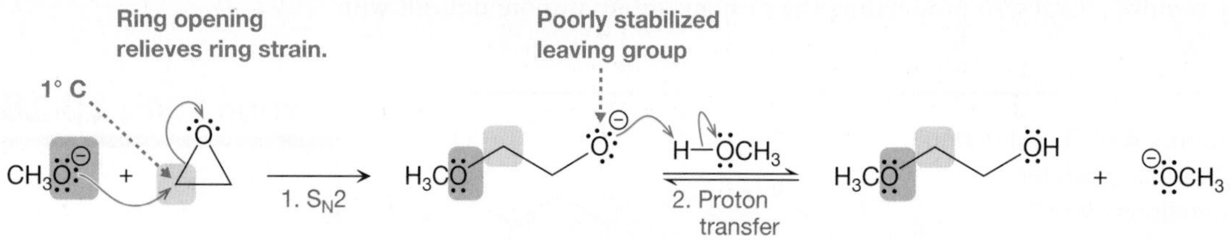

Ring opening relieves ring strain.
Poorly stabilized leaving group
1° C
CH_3O^-
+
1. S_N2
H_3CO
$H—OCH_3$
2. Proton transfer
H_3CO
OH
+
$^-OCH_3$

(10-45)

In Step 1, the epoxide is attacked by the nucleophile in an S_N2 step, which opens the ring (see Looking Ahead box). In Step 2, the negatively charged O atom gains a proton.

YOUR TURN 10.20

> Draw the complete, detailed mechanism for the reaction in Equation 10-43, which is nearly identical to that of Equation 10-44.

In the S_N2 step of Equation 10-45, the leaving group is effectively of the form RO^-. This may at first seem peculiar because, as we learned in Section 9.5, an RO^- leaving group is unsuitable for an S_N2 reaction. However, epoxides are highly strained rings. Therefore:

Epoxides can undergo S_N2 reactions due to the relief of ring strain.

YOUR TURN **10.21**

Determine the missing reagent for the following reaction and draw the complete, detailed mechanism.

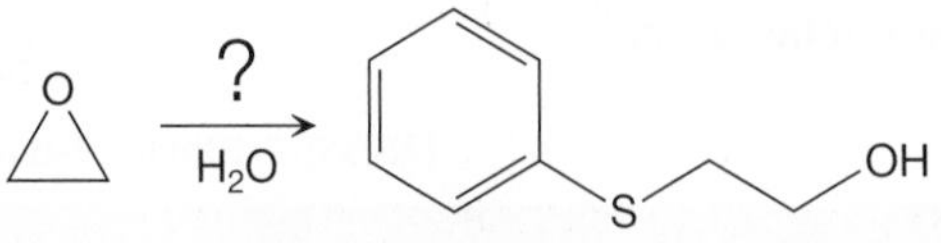

O
?
H_2O
S
OH

Equation 10-46 shows an example in which the reacting epoxide has alkyl groups attached to the carbon atoms of the ring:

The carbon atoms are nonequivalent, and both are chiral centers.

The only substitution product

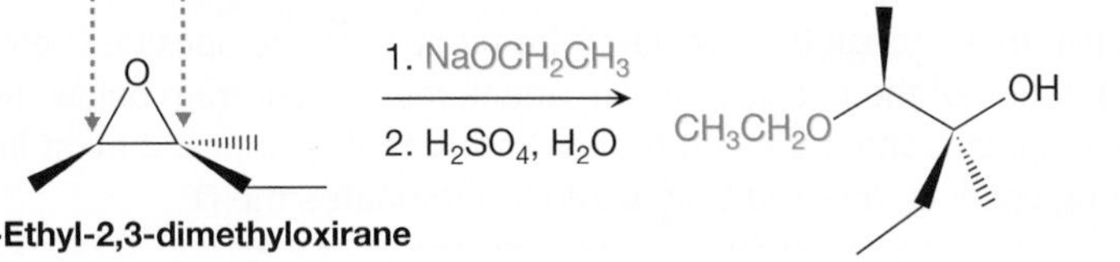

O
1. $NaOCH_2CH_3$
2. H_2SO_4, H_2O
CH_3CH_2O
OH

(10-46)

(2*S*,3*R*)-2-Ethyl-2,3-dimethyloxirane

In this case, the C atoms attached to O are nonequivalent, so different constitutional isomers are possible when the ring opens, depending on which C atom is attacked. Furthermore, the reaction involves attack at a chiral center, so different stereoisomers are imaginable. As shown in Equation 10-46, however, only one substitution product is formed. This is because the ring-opening step is S_N2, and like any S_N2 step: (1) the rate is highly sensitive to steric hindrance and (2) the nucleophile must attack from the side opposite the leaving group (*backside attack*). Therefore:

Under *neutral* or *basic* conditions, a nucleophile attacks an epoxide at the *less highly alkyl-substituted* C atom of the ring, from the side *opposite the O atom*.

The mechanism in Equation 10-47 shows how this rule applies to the reaction in Equation 10-46. Specifically, the C atom on the left is attacked because it has one fewer alkyl group than the one on the right. Moreover, when the nucleophile attacks the C atom from the bottom of the epoxide (as represented in the mechanism), Walden inversion occurs and the remaining groups attached to that C flip upward (see Recall box).

Mechanism highlighting the stereochemistry and regiochemistry of epoxide ring opening under basic conditions (Eq. 10-46)

***Less highly alkyl-substituted* C atom**

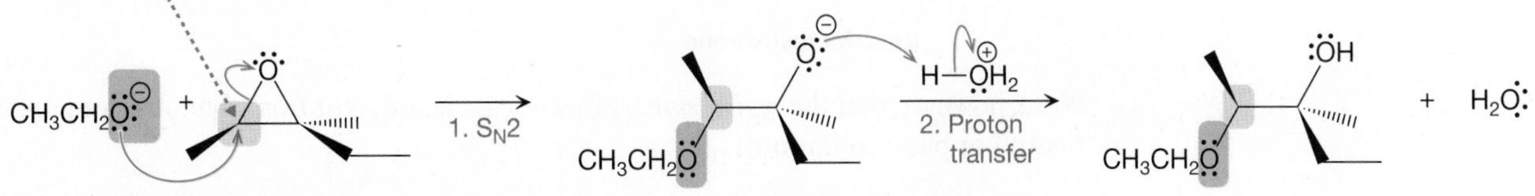

CH_3CH_2O
+
O
1. S_N2
CH_3CH_2O
O
H—OH_2
2. Proton transfer
CH_3CH_2O
OH
+
H_2O

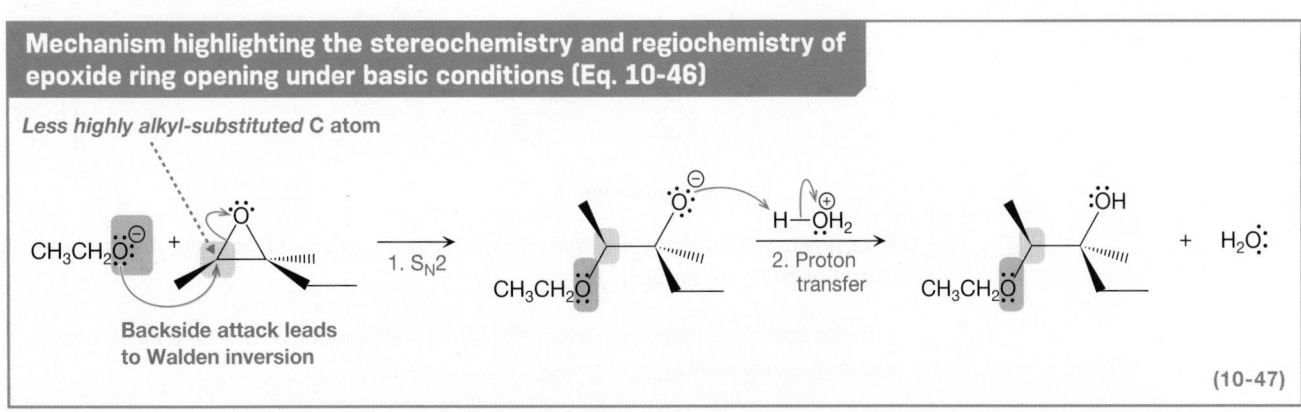

Backside attack leads to Walden inversion

(10-47)

CONNECTIONS 10.4

2-Methoxyethanol: From degreasing to deicing

2-Methoxyethanol (Eq. 10-44) can dissolve a wide variety of compounds, including grease and oils, making it useful as a multipurpose cleaner. It is also used as an additive in airplane deicing solutions.

◀ RECALL

In Section 8.5a, we saw that Walden inversion is analogous to an umbrella flipping inside out. When a nucleophile attacks a C atom in an S_N2 step, the three groups that remain attached to C initially point toward the nucleophile. In the product, those three groups point away from the nucleophile.

Mechanism Drawing
Ring Opening of an Unsymmetric Epoxide under Basic Conditions

SOLVED PROBLEM **10.5**

How to predict the stereochemical and regiochemical outcome of epoxide ring opening under basic conditions

Break It Down Predict the major product of the following reaction. Pay attention to stereochemistry.

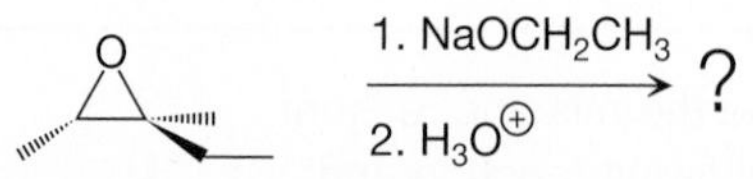

O
1. $NaOCH_2CH_3$
2. $H_3O^{\oplus}$
?

(2*S*,3*S*)-2-Ethyl-2,3-dimethyloxirane

Think	Solve
What is the nucleophile?	When $NaOCH_2CH_3$ dissolves, it will dissociate into Na^+ and $CH_3CH_2O^-$. $CH_3CH_2O^-$ is electron-rich and will act as the nucleophile.
Which C atom of the epoxide ring will the nucleophile attack?	Under basic conditions, the nucleophile will attack the less sterically hindered C of the epoxide ring, which is the one on the left.
From what direction, relative to the epoxide O, must the nucleophile attack? How does that impact stereochemistry?	The nucleophile must attack the epoxide C from opposite the epoxide O atom. With the orientation of the epoxide shown, attack must occur from below the ring. The remaining substituents attached to the C atom that is attacked must flip upward. After ring opening, the acid that is added protonates the O^-.

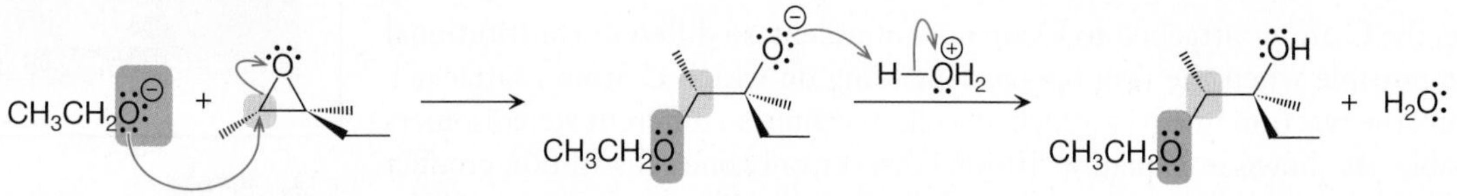

CH_3CH_2O
+
$H-OH_2$
CH_3CH_2O
:OH
CH_3CH_2O
+ H_2O:

Try It Predict the major product for each of the following reactions and draw the complete, detailed mechanisms.

(a)

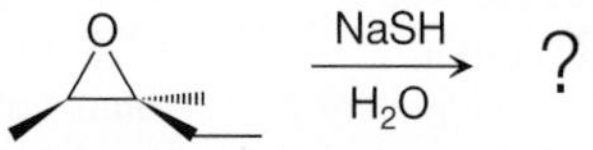

O
NaSH
H_2O
?

(b)

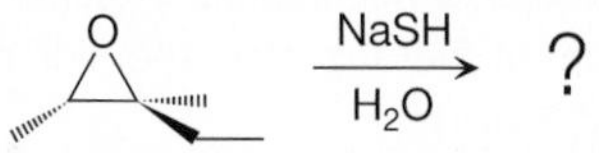

O
NaSH
H_2O
?

The ring opening of epoxides occurs not only under neutral or basic conditions but also under acidic conditions. For example, (*R*)-2-methyloxirane reacts with HBr to form the bromoalcohol shown in Equation 10-48:

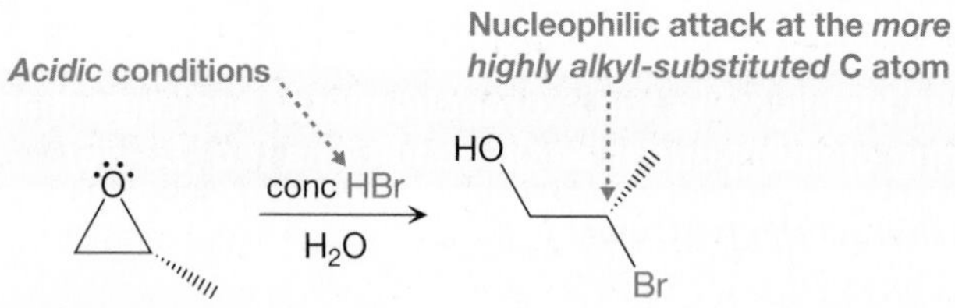

Acidic conditions
Nucleophilic attack at the *more highly alkyl-substituted* C atom
:Ö:
conc HBr
H_2O
HO
Br

(*R*)-2-Methyloxirane

(10-48)

Note, however, that the *regiochemistry* in this case is different from that observed under neutral or basic conditions:

> Under *acidic* conditions, a nucleophile attacks an epoxide at the *more highly alkyl-substituted* C atom.

We can understand this regiochemistry by studying the mechanism shown in Equation 10-49, which is different from the mechanism in Equation 10-45 for neutral or basic conditions:

Mechanism for epoxide ring opening under acidic conditions (Eq. 10-48)

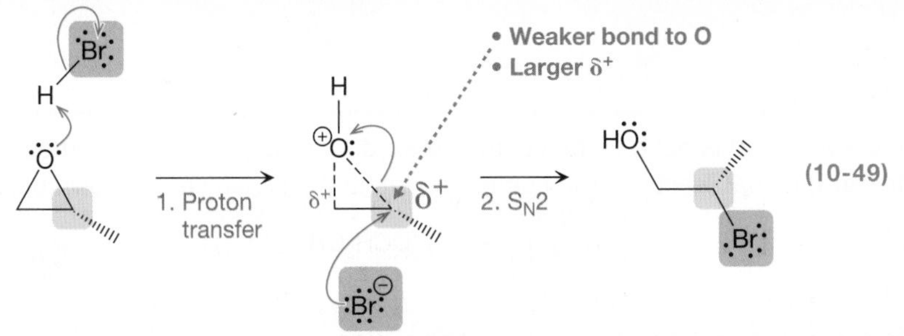

• Weaker bond to O
• Larger δ+
1. Proton transfer
2. S_N2
(10-49)

Mechanism Drawing Ring Opening of an Unsymmetric Epoxide under Acidic Conditions

Prior to the attack of the nucleophile, a fast proton transfer occurs, generating an intermediate with a positive charge on the O atom in the ring.

To help delocalize the positive charge on the protonated O, both C—O bonds *partially* break in the intermediate, indicated by the dashed bonds in Equation 10-49. As a result, both C atoms of the epoxide gain a partial positive charge. The additional alkyl group attached to the C atom on the right is electron-donating and helps stabilize the developing positive charge. Thus, the C—O bond involving the *more highly alkyl-substituted* C atom is broken to a greater extent, which is indicated in **Figure 10-8** by the slightly longer C—O bond length in the protonated form. With the larger partial positive charge generated on the side of the ring with greater alkyl substitution, the nucleophile is attracted more strongly to that side of the ring in the subsequent S_N2 step.

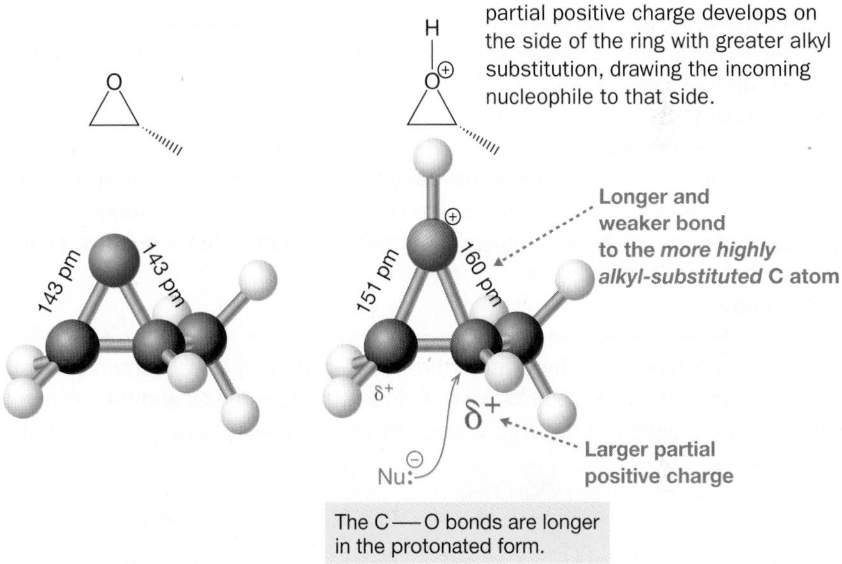

143 pm
143 pm
151 pm
160 pm
Longer and weaker bond to the *more highly alkyl-substituted* C atom
δ+
Nu:
Larger partial positive charge
The C—O bonds are longer in the protonated form.

FIGURE 10-8 Effect of protonation on epoxide C—O bond lengths The C—O bonds in an epoxide (*left*) partially break on protonation (*right*), as shown by the lengthening of the C—O bonds. As a result, both C atoms develop a partial positive charge, but a larger partial positive charge develops on the side of the ring with greater alkyl substitution, drawing the incoming nucleophile to that side.

SOLVED PROBLEM **10.6**

How to predict the product of epoxide ring opening under acidic or neutral/basic conditions

Break It Down **(S)-2-Methyloxirane undergoes a chemical reaction when it is dissolved in ethanol. However, which products are formed depends on whether the reaction takes place under basic or acidic conditions. Draw the complete, detailed mechanism for each reaction and predict the products.**

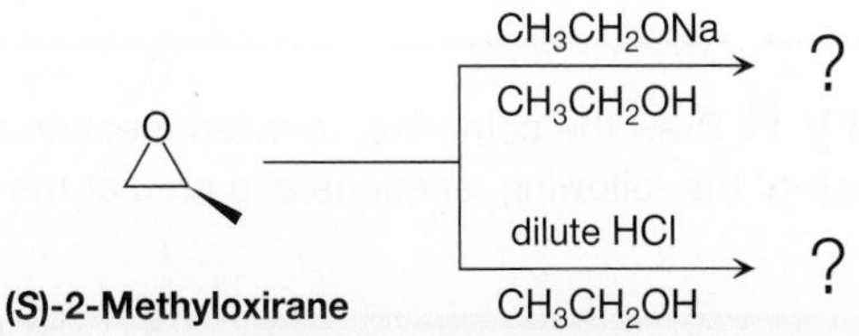

CH_3CH_2ONa
CH_3CH_2OH
?
dilute HCl
CH_3CH_2OH
?
(S)-2-Methyloxirane

Think	Solve
Under basic conditions, what is the nucleophile?	Under basic conditions, the nucleophile is $CH_3CH_2O^-$.

(continued)

Under basic conditions, does steric hindrance or the partial positive charge dictate which epoxide C is attacked?	Under basic conditions, the epoxide O is not protonated, so it remains uncharged when the nucleophile attacks. Therefore, steric hindrance dictates which epoxide C is attacked, not the partial charge on C. The epoxide C on the left is therefore attacked.
Does stereochemistry become an issue under basic conditions?	The C atom that is attacked is not a chiral center, so we do not need to be concerned about stereochemistry for this S_N2 reaction. The complete, detailed mechanism is shown below. 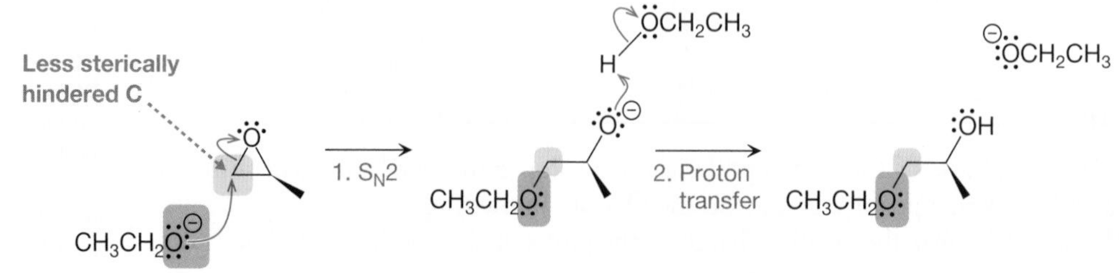Less sterically hindered C 1. S_N2 2. Proton transfer CH_3CH_2O OCH_2CH_3 H OH
Under acidic conditions, what is the nucleophile?	Under acidic conditions, the nucleophile is CH_3CH_2OH.
Under acidic conditions, what factor dictates which epoxide C is attacked?	Under acidic conditions, the epoxide O is first protonated, giving the O atom a +1 charge that becomes shared over the two epoxide C atoms. The epoxide C on the right is more highly alkyl-substituted, so it receives more of that positive charge and is the one attacked by the nucleophile.
Does stereochemistry become an issue under acidic conditions?	The C atom that is attacked is a chiral center, so stereochemistry is an issue. The nucleophile attacks from opposite the epoxide O, and the groups that remain attached to the epoxide C undergo Walden inversion. The complete, detailed mechanism is shown below. 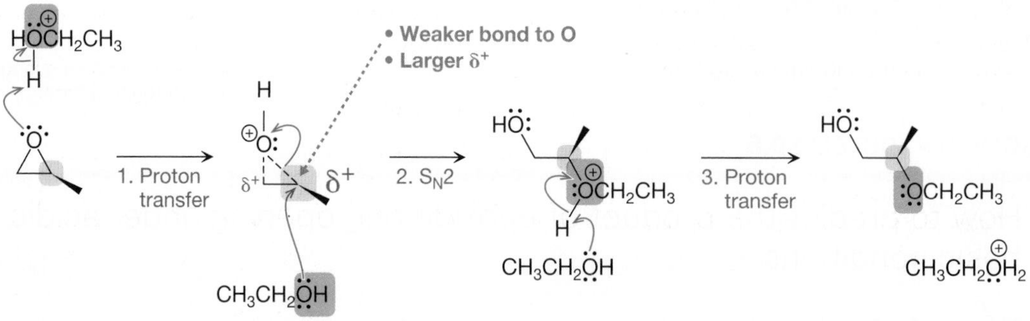• Weaker bond to O • Larger δ+ $HOCH_2CH_3$ 1. Proton transfer 2. S_N2 3. Proton transfer CH_3CH_2OH HO: OCH_2CH_3 $CH_3CH_2OH_2$

Try It Draw the complete, detailed mechanism for each of the following reactions and predict the products.

(a)

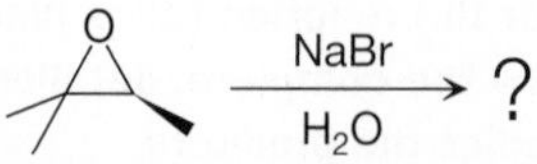
NaBr
H_2O
?

(b)

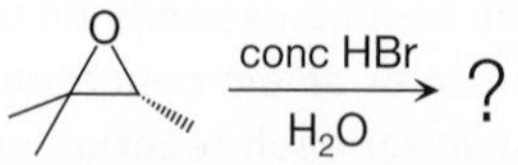
conc HBr
H_2O
?

10.8 Formation of Epoxides by Nucleophilic Substitution

> **SECTION 10.8 OBJECTIVES**
>
> You will be able to:
>
> 1. Show how an epoxide can be synthesized from a halohydrin.
> 2. Explain why such a reaction takes place readily despite the ring strain in an epoxide.

We have seen how valuable epoxides are as substrates in nucleophilic substitution reactions. How can they be formed?

One way to form epoxides is from a **halohydrin**, as shown in Equation 10-50 (see Looking Ahead box):

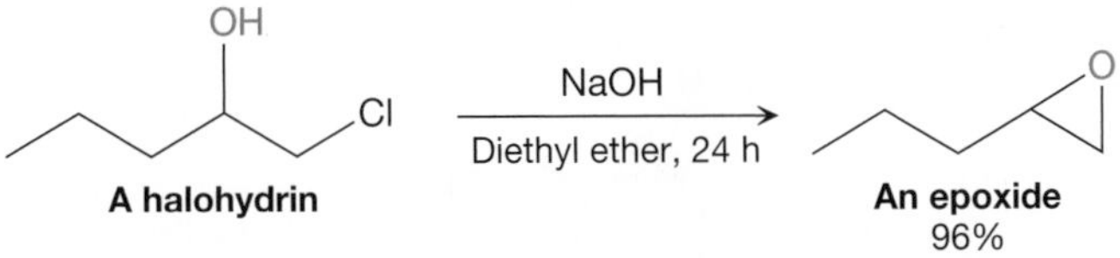

OH
Cl
NaOH
Diethyl ether, 24 h
O
A halohydrin
An epoxide
96%

(10-50)

The mechanism for this reaction is shown in Equation 10-51:

Mechanism for the formation of an epoxide from a halohydrin (Eq. 10-50)

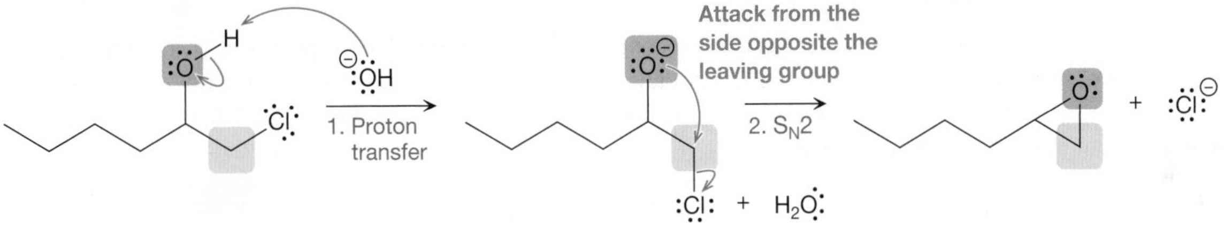

H
1. Proton transfer
Attack from the side opposite the leaving group
2. S_N2
+

(10-51)

In Step 1, the hydroxy group is deprotonated to leave a −1 charge on O, which makes the O strongly nucleophilic. Step 2 is an intramolecular S_N2, which closes the ring to produce the epoxide. Effectively, then, this reaction resembles an intramolecular Williamson ether synthesis.

In Section 9.12, we learned that intramolecular cyclization reactions are favored when a five- or six-membered ring is formed. Why does this reaction form a strained three-membered ring? It has to do with the location of the nucleophilic O^- relative to the leaving group. All S_N2 reactions require the nucleophile to attack from the side opposite the leaving group. The $^-$OC—CCl bond can rotate 360°, and when the O^- and Cl are anti to each other, the O^- is perfectly situated to carry out the backside attack.

> **LOOKING AHEAD**
>
> Halohydrins are not the only starting materials that can be used to form epoxides. In Section 13.5, we will see that epoxides can be produced by treating an alkene with a peroxy acid, RCO_3H.

YOUR TURN 10.22

Draw the mechanism and the product of this reaction.

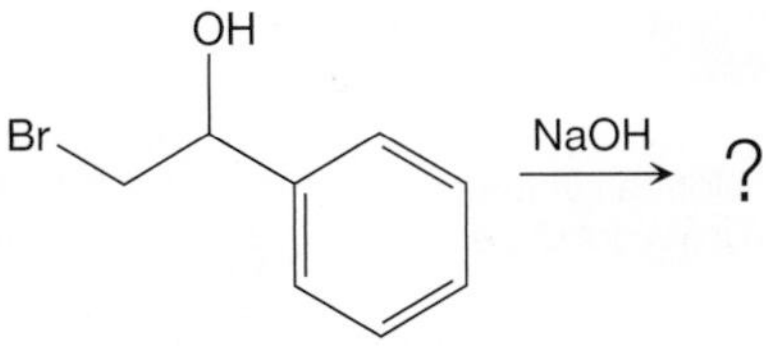

OH
Br
NaOH
?

DNA Alkylation: Causing Cancer and Curing Cancer

DNA bases (adenine, guanine, cytosine, and thymine) contain nucleophilic nitrogen atoms, which is why many halogenated compounds are carcinogenic. The good leaving group ability of a halogen atom can facilitate a nucleophilic substitution reaction (as we will see in Section 10.10), leaving the DNA base *alkylated*, as shown in **Figure 10-9**. Alkylated DNA can still function in its process of replication, though it will do so abnormally, resulting in mutations in the DNA and, ultimately, cancerous cells.

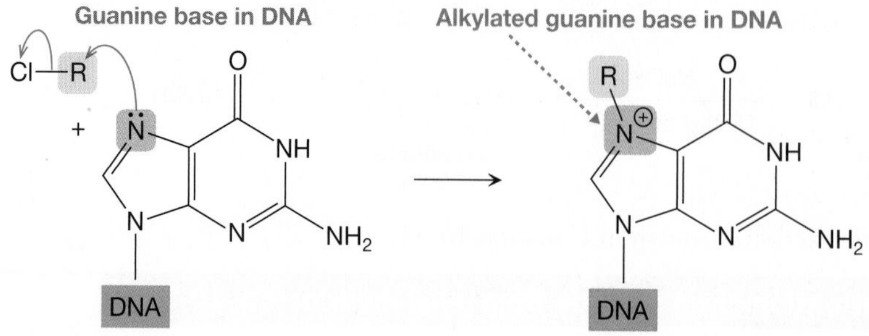
Guanine base in DNA
Alkylated guanine base in DNA
Cl
R
O
N
NH
NH2
DNA

FIGURE 10-9

DNA damage from alkylation can also be used to *treat* cancer. The key is that cancer cells grow and divide more rapidly than normal cells, and thus the cancer cells are more susceptible to mechanisms that damage DNA and impair its function. A number of successful chemotherapeutic drugs, such as mechlorethamine (**Figure 10-10**), have a bis(2-chloroethyl)amino motif to carry out these alkylations.

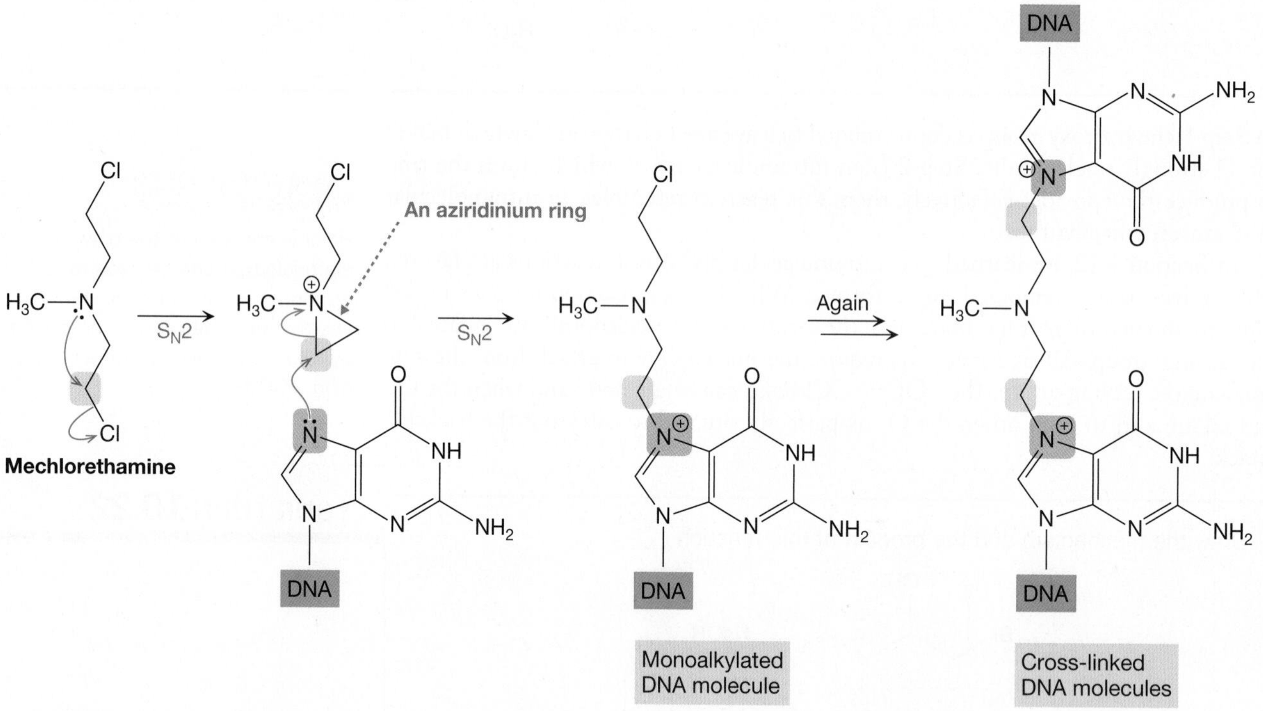
Cl
H3C
N
SN2
An aziridinium ring
Again
Mechlorethamine
O
NH
NH2
DNA
Monoalkylated DNA molecule
Cross-linked DNA molecules

FIGURE 10-10

With a leaving group at two locations, a single molecule of mechlorethamine will alkylate two DNA bases and tether them together, disrupting DNA function even more severely. Each alkylation by mechlorethamine involves the formation of an aziridinium ring followed by ring opening, analogous to epoxide ring formation (Section 10.8) and ring opening (Section 10.7).

Unfortunately, alkylating agents like mechlorethamine cannot differentiate the DNA in cancer cells from the DNA in normal cells. Other cells that grow and divide rapidly, such as cells that grow hair and cells in the epithelial lining of the gastrointestinal tract, will also be targeted. This accounts for some of the side effects associated with chemotherapy, such as hair loss, nausea, vomiting, and diarrhea.

10.9 Diazomethane Formation of Methyl Esters

SECTION 10.9 OBJECTIVES

You will be able to:

1. Draw the mechanism and major product for the reaction of a carboxylic acid with diazomethane.
2. Explain why the leaving group in diazomethane is so good.

Esters, which have the general form RCO_2R', are found extensively in nature. The aromas and flavors of various fruits are in large part attributed to esters, and esters are used widely as flavoring agents in the food industry. Moreover, as we saw in Section 2.10, the ester group is found in fats and oils, as well as many waxes. In Chapters 22 and 23, we will discuss how esters tend to react. Here we ask the question: how can esters be synthesized?

One method is to treat a carboxylic acid with **diazomethane** (CH_2N_2), as shown in Equation 10-52 (see Looking Ahead box). The acidic H atom is replaced by a CH_3 group to produce a methyl ester:

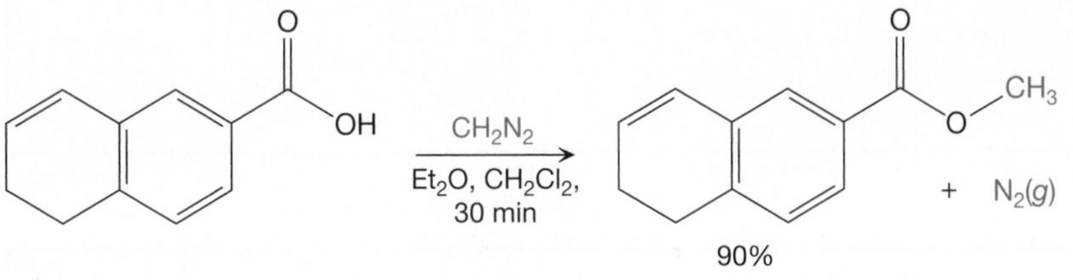

O
OH
CH2N2
Et2O, CH2Cl2,
30 min
O
CH3
O
+ N2(g)
90%

(10-52)

▸ LOOKING AHEAD

Another method of synthesizing esters from carboxylic acids, called the *Fischer esterification reaction*, is presented in Chapter 23. Fischer esterification is much milder and safer than the reaction that uses diazomethane, and it also allows us to produce a wide variety of esters from carboxylic acids.

The mechanism for this reaction consists of a proton transfer followed by a nucleophilic substitution, as shown in Equation 10-53:

Mechanism for the diazomethane formation of a methyl ester (Eq. 10-52)

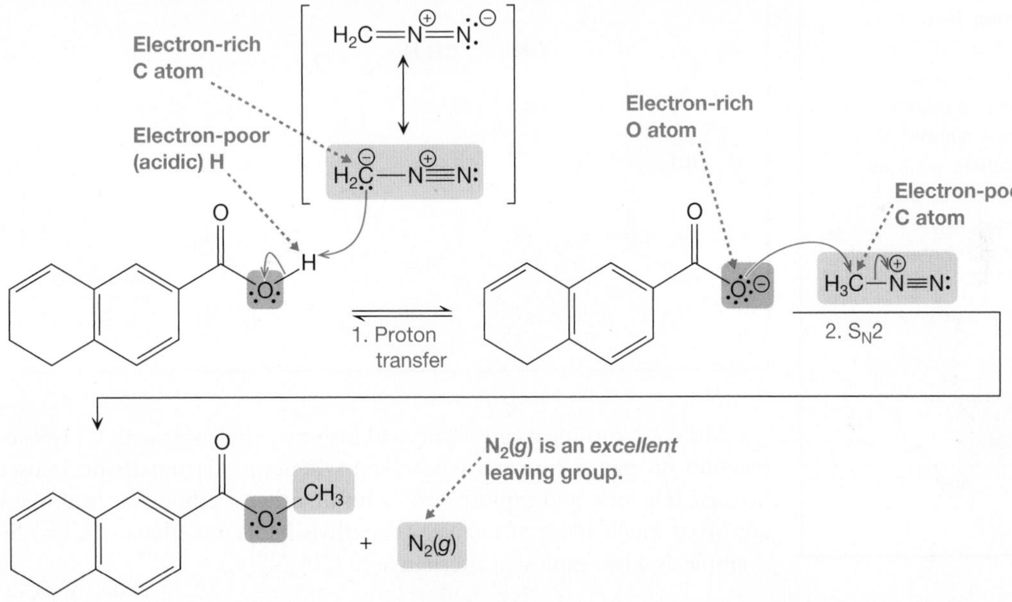

Electron-rich
C atom
Electron-poor
(acidic) H
H2C=N=N:
H2C—N≡N:
1. Proton
transfer
Electron-rich
O atom
Electron-poor
C atom
H3C—N≡N:
2. SN2
CH3
N2(g) is an excellent
leaving group.
+ N2(g)

(10-53)

In Step 1, the C atom of diazomethane is protonated by the acidic proton of the carboxylic acid. The C atom of diazomethane is electron-rich, as indicated by the negative charge that appears on C in one of the resonance structures.

In Step 2 of the mechanism, the carboxylate anion RCO_2^- is electron-rich and acts as the nucleophile in the subsequent S_N2 reaction. The protonated form of diazomethane is electron-poor and acts as the substrate. The leaving group is nitrogen gas, which is an *excellent* leaving group for two reasons:

1. $N_2(g)$ is extremely stable: it is one of the most inert compounds known.
2. It is a gas, so it bubbles out of solution as it is formed, which permanently removes it from the reaction mixture and drives the reaction to completion.

YOUR TURN 10.23

The reaction in the box shows how diazomethane can be used to convert acetic acid into methyl acetate. The mechanism for this reaction is shown below, with the curved arrows omitted. Complete the mechanism by drawing the curved arrows, and under each reaction arrow, label the step as either *proton transfer* or S_N2.

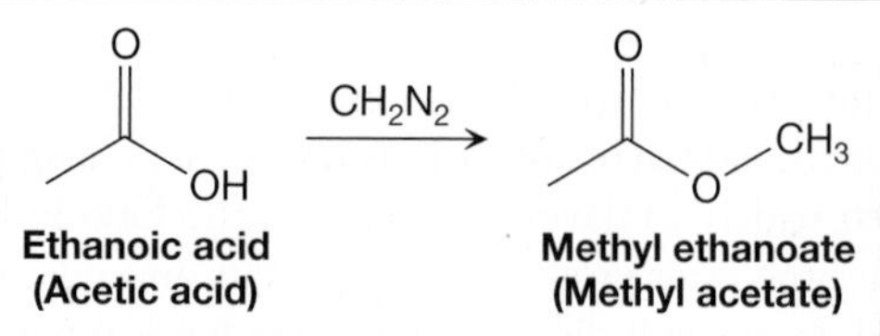

CH2N2
Ethanoic acid
(Acetic acid)
Methyl ethanoate
(Methyl acetate)

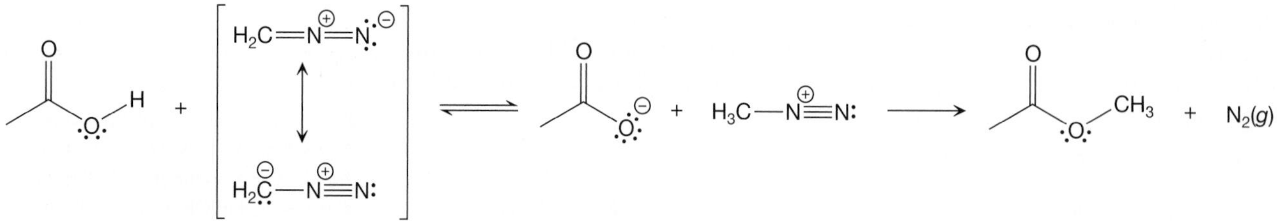

YOUR TURN 10.24

Predict the products of each reaction and provide complete, detailed mechanisms.

(a)

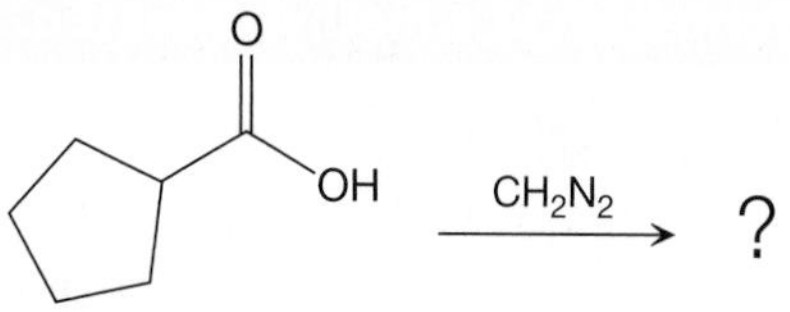

CH2N2
?

(b)

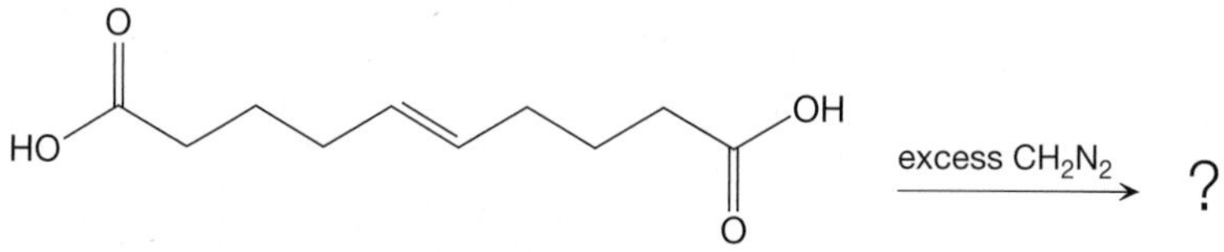

excess CH2N2
?

CONNECTIONS 10.5

Methyl acetate in industry and in the salon Methyl acetate (Your Turn 10.23) is a volatile solvent and is used in fast-drying paints. It can dissolve a number of industrial materials, such as nitrocellulose, resins, fats, and oils, which is why it is a component of many nail polish removers.

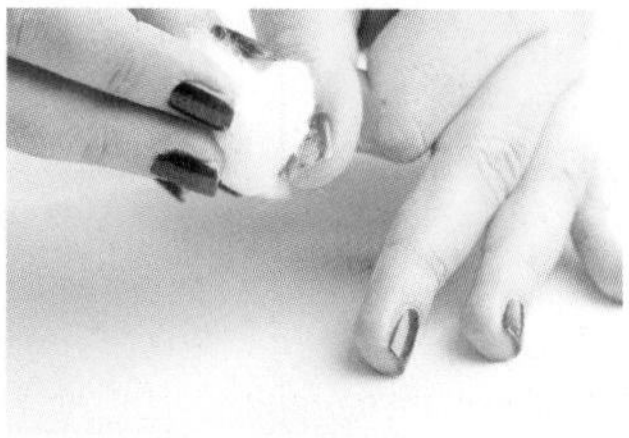

Although turning a carboxylic acid into a methyl ester with CH_2N_2 is a very clean reaction on paper, care must be taken whenever diazomethane is used in the lab because it is toxic and explosive! As a result, other methods for forming methyl esters are often much more attractive. Trimethylsilyldiazomethane [$(CH_3)_3SiCHN_2$], for example, is a less explosive alternative to CH_2N_2.

SECTION 10.10 OBJECTIVES

You will be able to:

1. Draw the mechanism and major product for the alkylation of ammonia or an amine when treated with an alkyl halide.
2. Explain why alkylation reactions are not generally used for synthesizing amines but are effective for making quaternary ammonium salts.

10.10 Amines and Quaternary Ammonium Salts from Alkyl Halides

Amines have a characteristic C—N single bond, and as shown in **Figure 10-11**, they are classified according to the number of alkyl groups attached to N. Primary (1°), secondary (2°), and tertiary (3°) amines have one, two, and three attached alkyl groups, respectively. If four alkyl groups are attached, the N atom has a +1 formal charge and the species is called a **quaternary ammonium ion**.

Amines are abundant in nature; as shown in **Figure 10-12**, the characteristic functional group appears in amino acids, as well as in neurotransmitters like histamine. The functional group also appears in synthetic dyes like methyl orange, and it is common in pharmaceutical drugs like pseudoephedrine (a nasal decongestant marketed as Sudafed).

Some quaternary ammonium compounds have cleansing properties and are found in consumer products like shampoos and detergents. Others are lethal to microbes and are used as disinfectants. Quaternary ammonium ions can be used as phase transfer catalysts (which facilitate the reaction of reagents that are not soluble in the same solvent), and they can serve as synthetic intermediates, as in the Hofmann elimination reaction (Section 10.11).

Amines can be produced from alkyl halides by a nucleophilic substitution reaction. Equation 10-54 shows, in particular, how a primary amine can be produced when an alkyl halide is reacted with ammonia (NH_3):

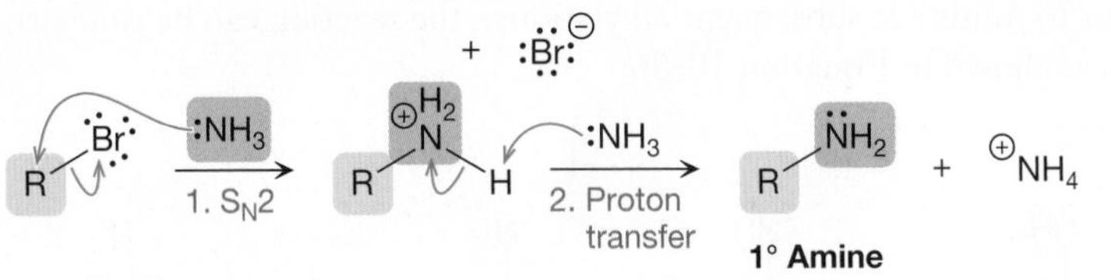

1. S_N2
2. Proton transfer
1° Amine

(10-54)

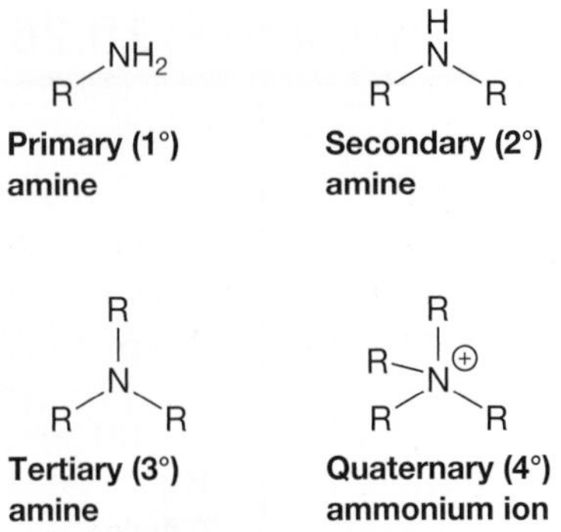

Primary (1°) amine
Secondary (2°) amine
Tertiary (3°) amine
Quaternary (4°) ammonium ion

FIGURE 10-11 Amines and ammonium ions Primary, secondary, and tertiary amines are distinguished by the number of alkyl (R) groups attached to N. An ammonium ion has four R groups attached to N and is positively charged.

Step 1 is an S_N2, in which NH_3 displaces the leaving group. Despite being uncharged, NH_3 is a moderately strong nucleophile. NH_3 is also weakly basic, so in Step 2, the positively charged ammonium ion is deprotonated to yield the uncharged amine. Overall, NH_3 has undergone an **alkylation** to produce a 1° amine.

YOUR TURN **10.25**

Consult Table 9-10 (p. 476) for the relative nucleophilicities of NH_3 and Cl^- in ethanol. Which nucleophile is stronger?

Although amines can be produced by these kinds of alkylation reactions, a major problem can arise because the amine product is nucleophilic. Therefore, when the amine product encounters a molecule of the alkyl halide that has not yet reacted, a second alkylation can take place, as shown in Equation 10-55:

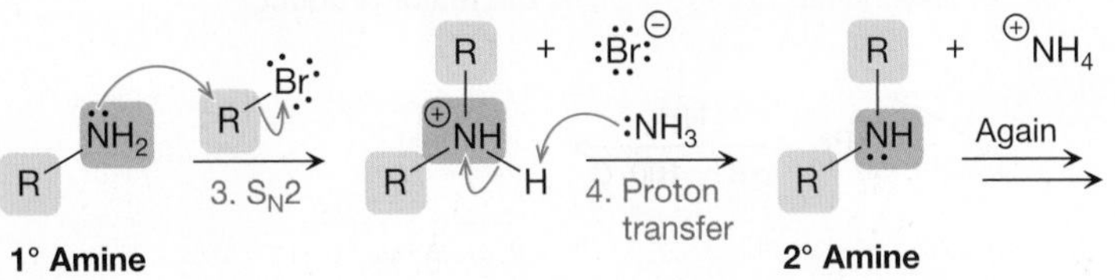

3. S_N2
4. Proton transfer
Again
1° Amine
2° Amine

(10-55)

The result is a mixture of amine products and even some of the quaternary ammonium ion (see Your Turn 10.26 and Looking Ahead box).

▸ LOOKING AHEAD

More effective ways to synthesize amines will be presented in later chapters. Chapter 19 describes how amines can be produced from ketones and aldehydes. Chapter 22 discusses how amines can be produced from amides and introduces the Gabriel synthesis, which produces primary amines from alkyl halides.

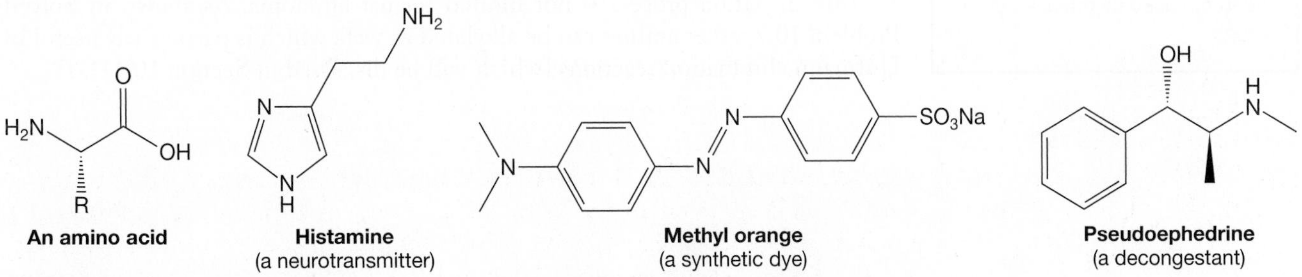

An amino acid
Histamine
(a neurotransmitter)
Methyl orange
(a synthetic dye)
Pseudoephedrine
(a decongestant)

FIGURE 10-12 Examples of amines Amines have a variety of uses in nature and in industry.

YOUR TURN **10.26**

The following mechanism shows how the secondary amine in Equation 10-55 can be alkylated to form a tertiary amine and a quaternary ammonium ion. Draw in the necessary curved arrows, and under each reaction arrow, label the step as either *proton transfer* or S_N2.

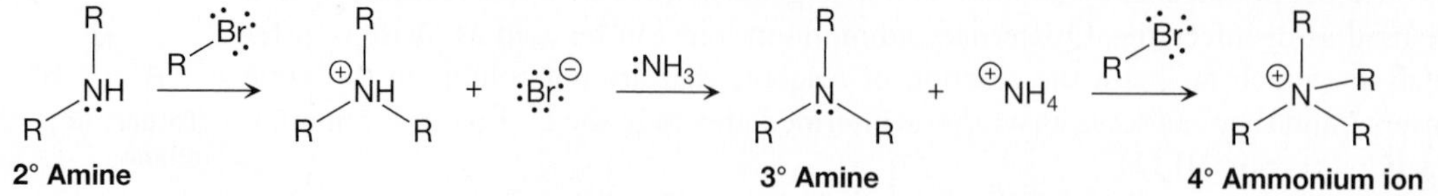

2° Amine
3° Amine
4° Ammonium ion

To help ensure that the alkyl halide reacts with NH_3 instead of an amine product (and thus to minimize subsequent alkylations), the reaction can be run with an excess of NH_3, as shown in Equation 10-56:

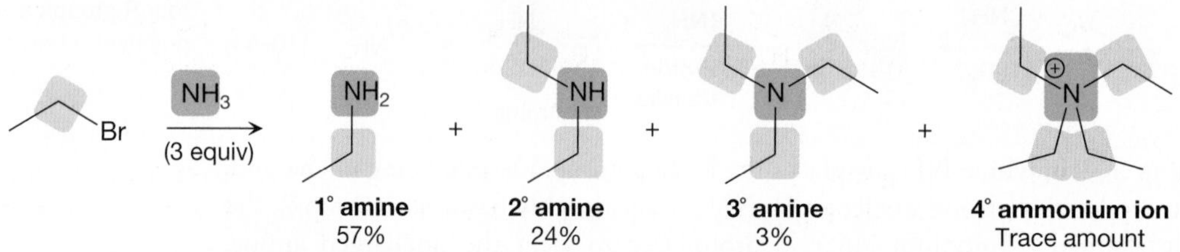

NH3
(3 equiv)
1° amine
57%
2° amine
24%
3° amine
3%
4° ammonium ion
Trace amount

(10-56)

Even with three equivalents of NH_3, however, we still see substantial amounts of undesired products in the mixture. Therefore:

Alkylation is not usually a very effective way to synthesize amines (especially primary amines) from alkyl halides.

Although alkylation is generally a poor method of synthesizing amines, it can be effective in forming quaternary ammonium ions. As shown in Equation 10-57, this can be done simply by adding a large excess of the alkyl halide:

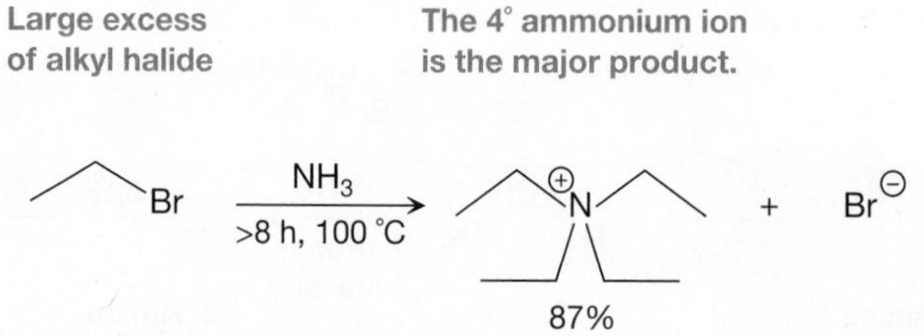

Large excess of alkyl halide
The 4° ammonium ion is the major product.
NH3
>8 h, 100 °C
87%

(10-57)

If desired, the quaternary ammonium ion can be isolated with an anion as a **quaternary ammonium salt**, such as tetraethylammonium bromide, the product in Equation 10-57.

This alkylation process is not limited to just ammonia. As shown in Solved Problem 10.7, other amines can be alkylated as well, which is particularly useful in Hofmann elimination reactions (which will be discussed in Section 10.11).

CONNECTIONS 10.6

Nerve-blocking properties of tetraethylammonium bromide
Tetraethylammonium bromide, $(CH_3CH_2)_4N^+Br^-$ (Eq. 10-57), is a ganglionic blocker that inhibits the transmission of nerve signals in the autonomic nervous system. At one time tetraethylammonium bromide was used in the treatment of high blood pressure, but it has been replaced by other, safer drugs.

SOLVED PROBLEM **10.7**

How to draw the quaternary ammonium ion produced in the alkylation of an amine

Break It Down **Draw the complete, detailed mechanism for the reaction shown here and predict the major product.**

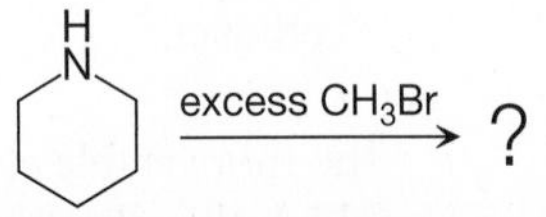

H
N
excess CH_3Br
?

Think	Solve
Which species is electron-rich? Which is electron-poor? What kind of reaction will take place?	The amine is electron-rich at the N atom and can act as a nucleophile. CH_3Br is electron-poor at the C atom and can act as a substrate. An S_N2 reaction will take place, as shown in Step 1 below.
How can the product of Step 1 become uncharged?	The product of Step 1 is a protonated amine and has a weakly acidic proton. Another molecule of the uncharged amine can act as a base in Step 2 to remove the proton and produce an uncharged tertiary amine.
Can the initial uncharged product that is formed react further?	The tertiary amine is also nucleophilic, and there is excess CH_3Br. Therefore, another S_N2 step can occur, as shown in Step 3 below. The product is a quaternary ammonium ion, and it remains charged because it has no acidic protons.

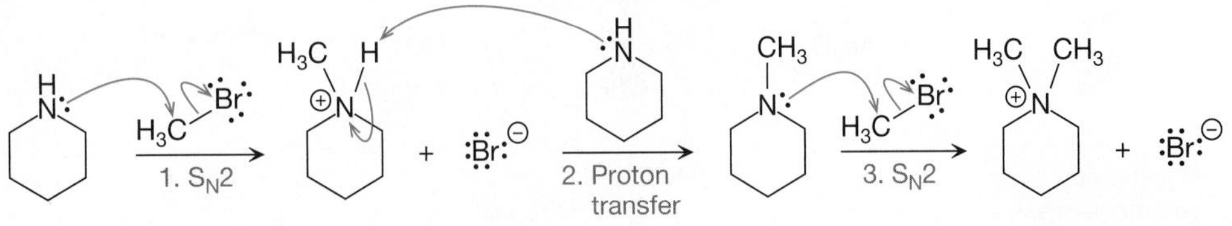

1. S_N2
2. Proton transfer
3. S_N2

Try It Draw the complete, detailed mechanism for the reaction shown here and predict the major product.

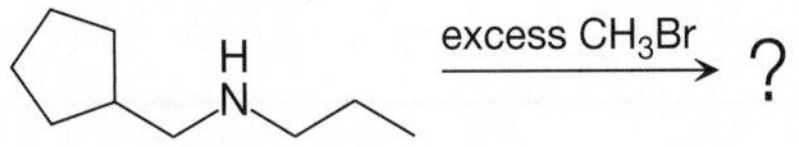

H
N
excess CH_3Br
?

10.11 Hofmann Elimination

SECTION 10.11 OBJECTIVES

You will be able to:

1. Draw the mechanism and major product for the Hofmann elimination.
2. Explain why the major product of Hofmann elimination reactions tends to be the less highly alkyl-substituted alkene.

But-1-ene is produced when butan-2-amine is first treated with excess iodomethane, then treated with silver oxide (Ag_2O), and finally heated:

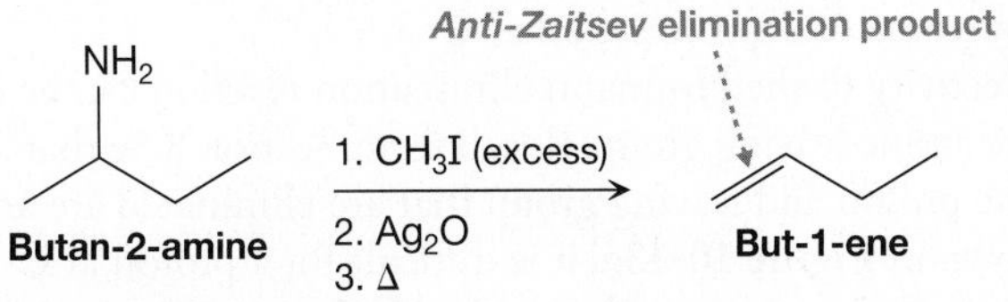

Anti-Zaitsev elimination product
NH_2
1. CH_3I (excess)
2. Ag_2O
3. Δ
Butan-2-amine
But-1-ene

(10-58)

Equation 10-58 is an example of a **Hofmann elimination reaction**. The formation of a C=C double bond strongly suggests that an elimination reaction has occurred in

◂ RECALL

As we saw in Section 9.10, elimination tends to favor the more highly alkyl substituted alkene because alkene stability increases with greater alkyl substitution. Section 9.11 showed that alkyl groups attached to the C=C bond stabilize the alkene by hyperconjugation.

which the leaving group contains the N atom. Two problems, however, must be reconciled: (1) H_2N^- is an unsuitable leaving group for elimination reactions, and (2) the major product is the less alkyl substituted, and therefore the less stable, of two possible elimination products. In other words:

> The major product of Hofmann elimination is the *anti-Zaitsev product* or **Hofmann product.**

The more stable elimination product (i.e., the *Zaitsev product*) would be but-2-ene, in which the alkene group is more highly alkyl-substituted (see Recall box).

The excess CH_3I ensures that the leaving group is not simply H_2N^-, as shown in the mechanism in Equation 10-59:

Mechanism for the Hofmann elimination reaction (Eq. 10-58)

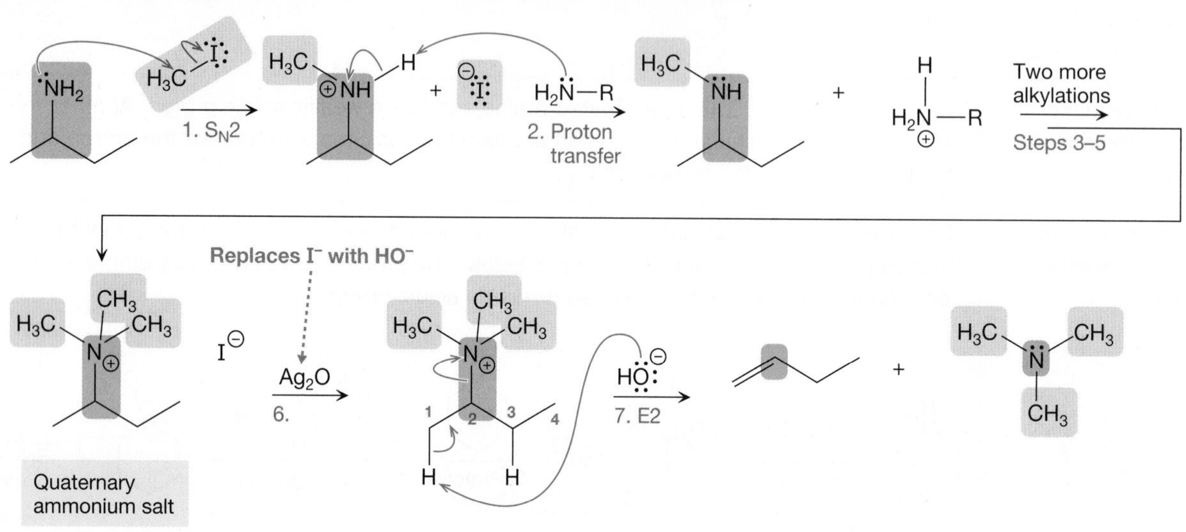

NH2
H3C—I
1. SN2
H3C
⊕NH
H
+
I⊖
H2N—R
2. Proton transfer
H3C
NH
+
H
H2N—R
⊕
Two more alkylations
Steps 3–5
Replaces I⁻ with HO⁻
H3C
CH3
CH3
N⊕
I⊖
Ag2O
6.
Quaternary ammonium salt
1
2
3
4
H
H
HO⊖
7. E2
+
N

(10-59)

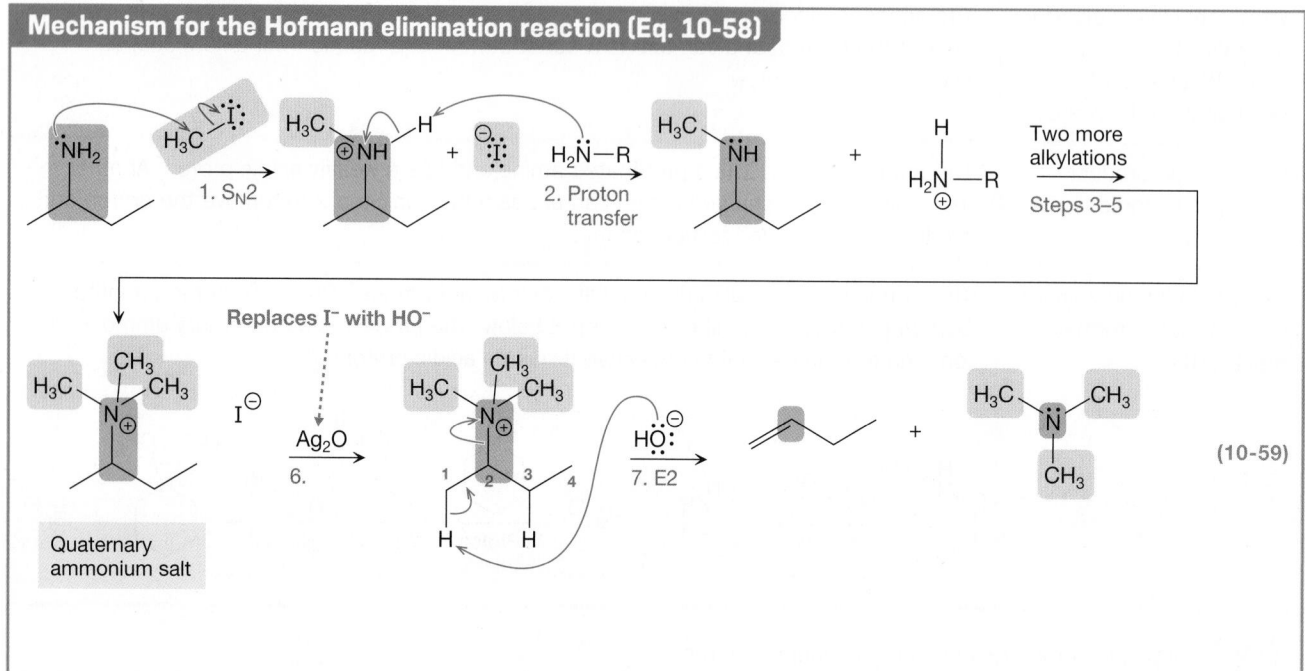

In Steps 1–5, the amine undergoes alkylation to produce the quaternary ammonium salt. Silver oxide is a base, and when it is added, it replaces I^- with HO^-. Then, when heat is supplied, an E2 reaction occurs. Notice that the leaving group is the uncharged amine, $N(CH_3)_3$, instead of the very unstable NH_2^-.

In the final E2 step in Equation 10-59, deprotonation can occur at either C-1 or C-3. Because the major product is but-1-ene, HO^- must have deprotonated at C-1. This is peculiar because, as we learned in Section 9.10, a small, strong base like HO^- typically leads to the more highly alkyl-substituted elimination product, which would have been the outcome of deprotonation at C-3.

The regioselectivity of the Hofmann elimination reaction can be explained by the steric bulk of the amine leaving group. Recall from Section 8.5c that an E2 reaction is favored when the proton and leaving group that are eliminated are anti to each other. However, as shown in **Figure 10-13a**, it is difficult for a proton at C-3 to be oriented anti to the leaving group, because when either C-3 proton is anti, the leaving group and the C-4 methyl group are gauche to each other. This causes steric strain; the molecule instead prefers to have the methyl group anti and both C-3 protons gauche to the leaving group, as depicted in Figure 10-13b. Therefore, elimination involving a proton at C-3 is unlikely. As shown in Figure 10-13c, on the other hand, a H atom on C-1 can be anti to the leaving group without causing excessive steric strain. In this case, elimination is favored.

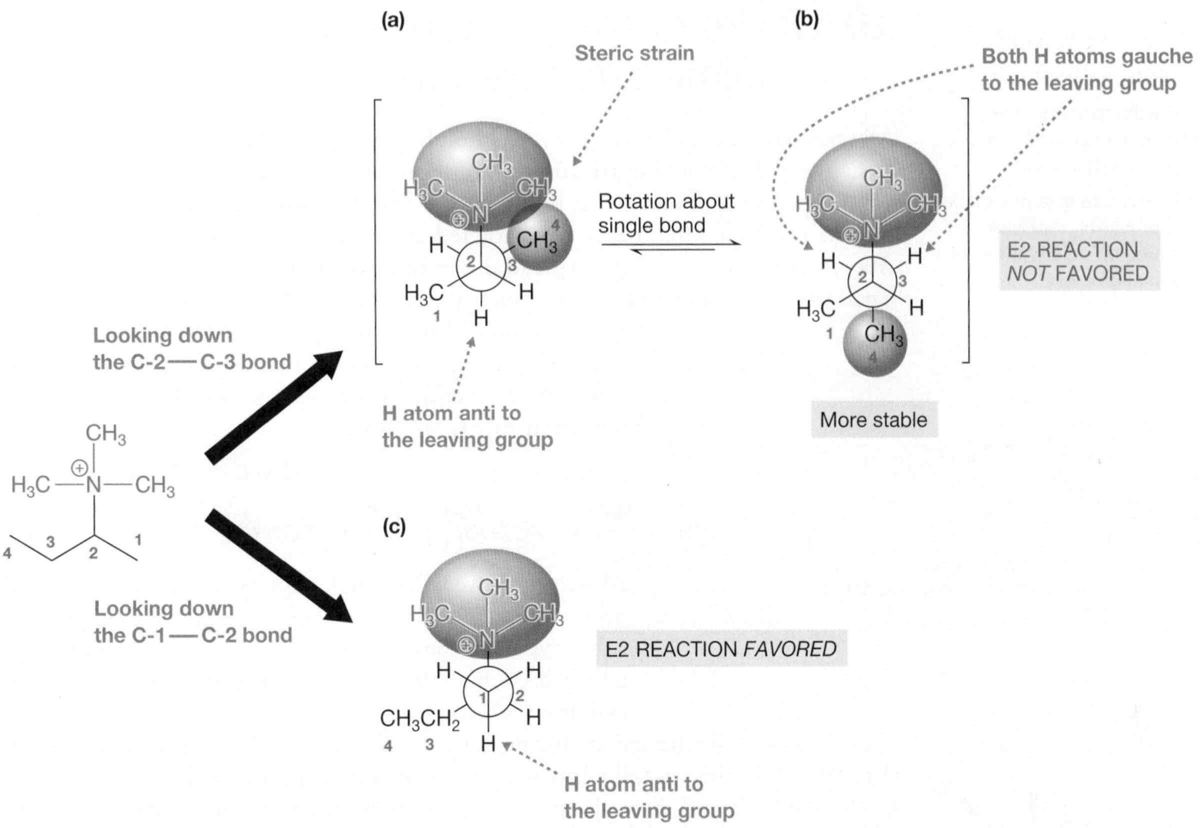

(a)
(b)
Steric strain
Both H atoms gauche to the leaving group
Rotation about single bond
E2 REACTION NOT FAVORED
Looking down the C-2—C-3 bond
H atom anti to the leaving group
More stable
Looking down the C-1—C-2 bond
(c)
E2 REACTION FAVORED
H atom anti to the leaving group

FIGURE 10-13 Regioselectivity in Hofmann elimination reactions Newman projections looking down the C-2—C-3 bond (*top*) and the C-1—C-2 bond (*bottom*) of the tetraalkylammonium ion are shown on the left. (a) Conformation necessary for formation of the Zaitsev product, where the H on C-3 is anti to the amine leaving group. In this conformation, there is substantial steric strain between the C-4 methyl group and the leaving group. (b) The more stable conformation is the one in which the C-4 methyl group is anti to the leaving group. This conformation does not favor the E2 reaction because the H and the amine leaving group are not in the anticoplanar conformation. (c) A H atom is anti to the leaving group and no substantial steric strain exists, so an E2 reaction favors elimination of a proton on C-1.

YOUR TURN 10.27

2-Methylpentan-3-amine undergoes complete alkylation to give the quaternary ammonium ion shown below in the middle.

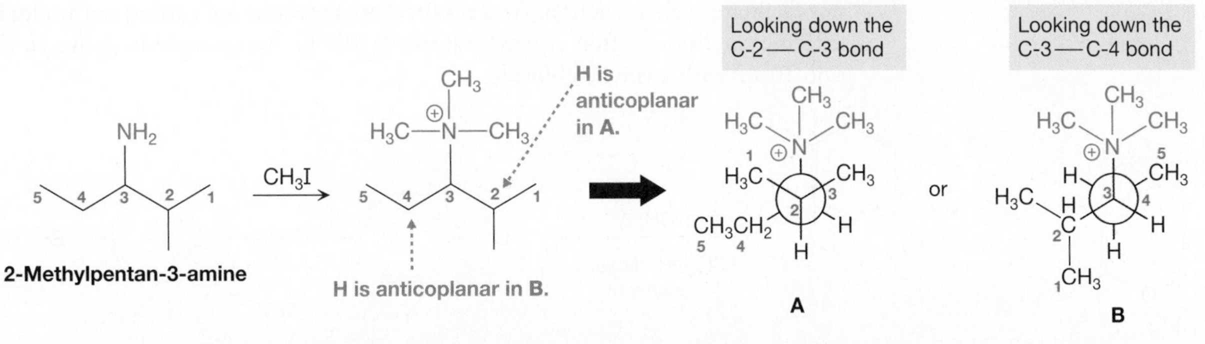

Looking down the C-2—C-3 bond
Looking down the C-3—C-4 bond
2-Methylpentan-3-amine
H is anticoplanar in A.
H is anticoplanar in B.
or
A
B

As indicated in the graphic, the leaving group on C-3 can be anti to the H atom on C-2 (shown in the Newman projection in **A**) or anti to a H atom on C-4 (shown in **B**).

(a) In the Newman projections, label the H atoms that are anti to the leaving group.

(b) Identify and label all sources of steric strain along the C-2—C-3 bond in **A** and the C-3—C-4 bond in **B**. Label the conformation with the least steric strain.

(c) Draw the major product formed when the quaternary ammonium ion is treated with Ag_2O and then heated.

SECTION 10.12 OBJECTIVES

You will be able to:

1. Draw the mechanism and major product for the conversion of a vinylic halide or a dihalide into an alkyne.
2. Explain why the use of a powerful base like NaH or $NaNH_2$ in these reactions requires an acid workup to recover a terminal alkyne.

10.12 Generating Alkynes by Elimination Reactions

Alkynes have a characteristic C≡C bond. Some naturally occurring alkynes are bioactive. Falcarinol (**Figure 10-14a**), for example, is found in carrots and acts as a natural pesticide. The C≡C bond is also found in some pharmaceutical drugs, such as norethynodrel, formerly marketed as an oral contraceptive (Fig. 10-14b). Alkynes, moreover, have widespread use in industry and in synthesis. For example, recall from Section 9.3b that a terminal alkyne, RC≡CH, is weakly acidic and can be deprotonated by a strong base. The resulting alkynide anion is a strong nucleophile that can be used in a subsequent S_N2 reaction to produce a new C—C bond, as shown in Equation 10-60:

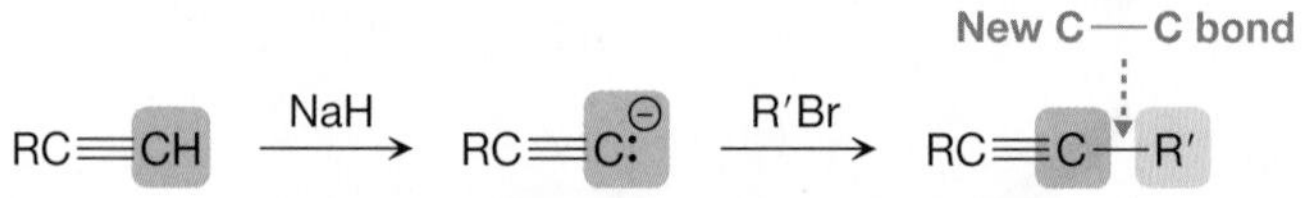

New C—C bond
RC≡CH
NaH
RC≡C:⊖
R′Br
RC≡C—R′

(10-60)

Moreover, as we will see in Chapters 12 and 13, the C≡C group can undergo functional group conversions to produce other types of compounds, such as alkenes, ketones, and aldehydes. For all these reasons, it is important to be able to synthesize alkynes.

(a)

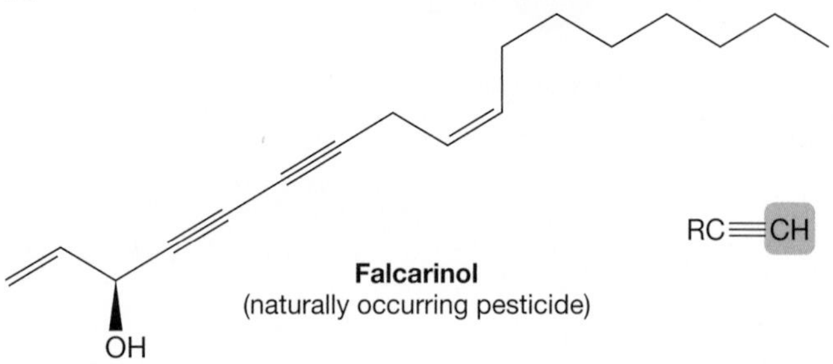

OH

Falcarinol
(naturally occurring pesticide)

(b)

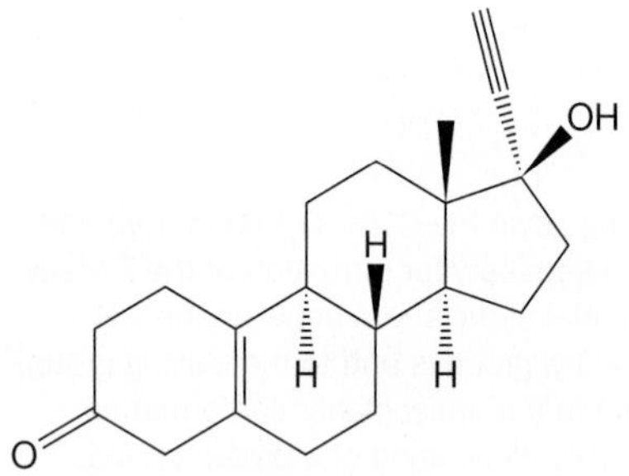

OH
H
H
H
O

Norethynodrel
(formerly used in oral contraception)

FIGURE 10-14 Biologically active alkynes (a) Falcarinol is naturally occurring pesticide. (b) Norethynodrel was used as an oral contraceptive.

One way to synthesize an alkyne is by carrying out an E2 elimination reaction (Eq. 10-61). In this case, the leaving group is in a *vinylic* position (i.e., attached to a C═C double bond). As with the other E2 reactions we have examined, a proton and a leaving group are required on adjacent atoms:

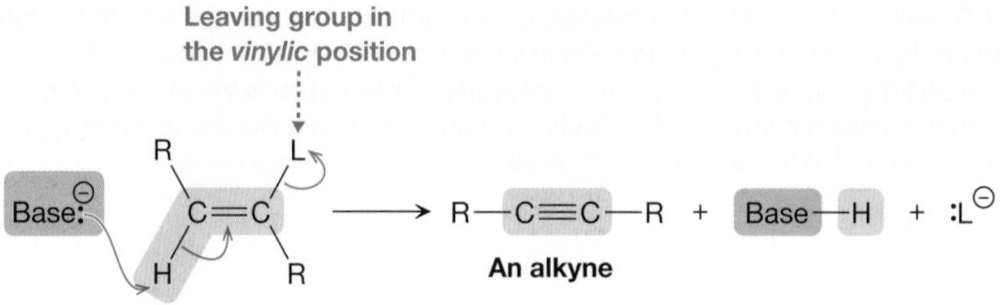

Leaving group in the *vinylic* position
Base:⊖
R
L
C═C
H
R
R—C≡C—R
An alkyne
+ Base—H + :L⊖

(10-61)

Because the leaving group is attached to an sp^2-hybridized C, these vinylic substrates are quite resistant to nucleophilic substitution and elimination reactions (Section 9.6a). Under normal conditions, therefore, even a strong base such as HO^- does not facilitate such a reaction. As a result, these reactions are carried out under more extreme conditions, often at temperatures >200 °C. An example is shown in Equation 10-62 with a vinylic chloride:

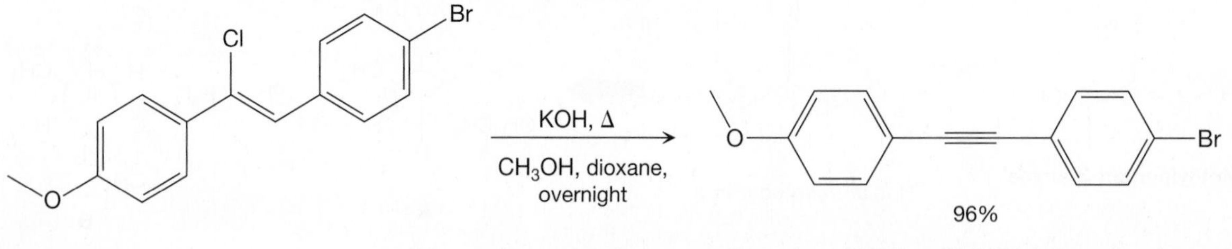

Cl
Br
O
KOH, Δ
CH3OH, dioxane, overnight
O
Br
96%

(10-62)

If a *much* stronger base is used, such as NaH or $NaNH_2$, then the elimination can take place without extreme temperatures. An example is shown in Equation 10-63, which takes place at room temperature:

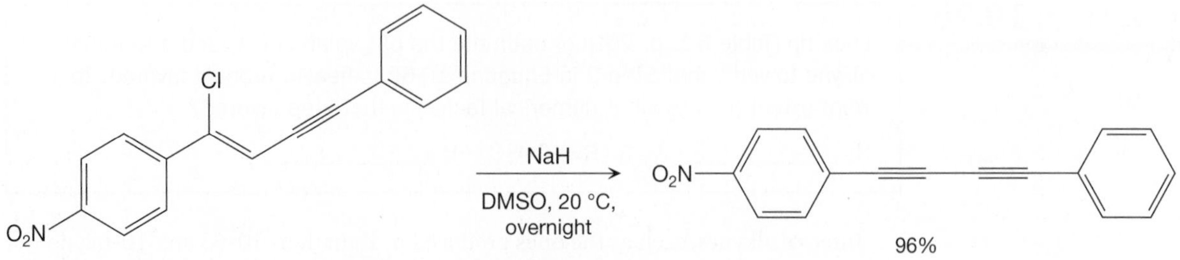

Cl
NaH
DMSO, 20 °C, overnight
O2N
96%

(10-63)

When a very strong base like NaH or $NaNH_2$ is used and the elimination product is a terminal alkyne, as in Equation 10-64, we typically add an acid after allowing the elimination reaction to finish. When such a follow-up addition of acid is carried out to recover the desired products, it is called an **acid workup**:

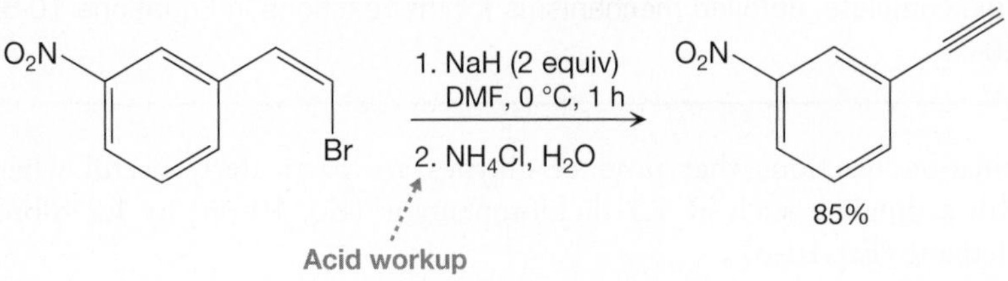

O2N
Br
1. NaH (2 equiv)
DMF, 0 °C, 1 h
2. NH4Cl, H2O
Acid workup
85%

(10-64)

We can see why the acid workup is necessary by studying the mechanism in Equation 10-65:

Mechanism for the formation of a terminal alkyne from a vinylic halide (Eq. 10-64)

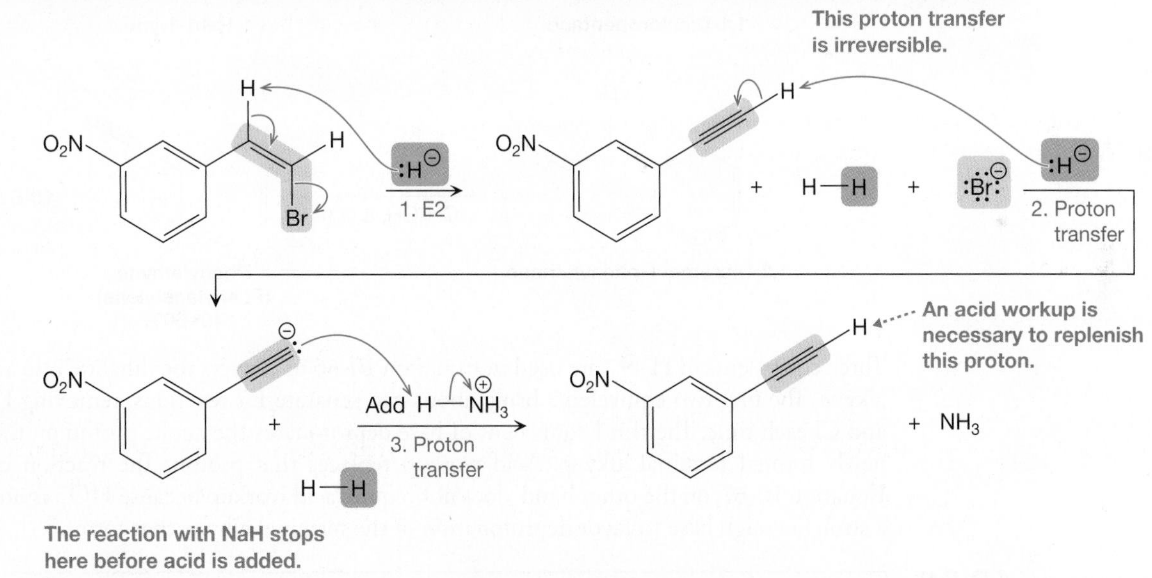

This proton transfer is irreversible.
H
O2N
Br
:H⊖
1. E2
+ H—H +
:Br:⊖
2. Proton transfer
An acid workup is necessary to replenish this proton.
Add H—NH3⊕
3. Proton transfer
+ NH3
H—H
The reaction with NaH stops here before acid is added.

(10-65)

In Step 1, the powerful H^- base encounters the vinylic halide and the resulting E2 elimination forms the uncharged terminal alkyne. However, the reaction does not stop there. In Step 2, the terminal alkyne just produced encounters another H^- and is very quickly deprotonated to make the alkynide anion. That proton transfer is heavily product-favored because the pK_a of H_2 (the conjugate acid of H^-) is substantially higher than that of a terminal alkyne (see Your Turn 10.28). The reaction stops there, so an acid workup is carried out to replace that proton on the terminal C atom and recover the desired uncharged product.

Mechanism Drawing
Formation of a Terminal Alkyne from a Vinylic Halide

YOUR TURN 10.28

Look up (Table 6-1, p. 269) or estimate the pK_a values of H_2 and a terminal alkyne to verify that Step 2 in Equation 10-65 is heavily product-favored. To what extent (i.e., by what numerical factor) is that step favored?

H_2 ______________ R—C≡C—H ______________

Internal alkynes, such as the ones produced in Equations 10-63 and 10-62, do not contain an acidic proton. Therefore, the mechanisms for those reactions would not include the proton transfer steps that appear in Equation 10-65; that is why those reactions do not require an acid workup (see Your Turn 10.29).

YOUR TURN 10.29

Draw the complete, detailed mechanisms for the reactions in Equations 10-62 and 10-63.

Elimination reactions that produce alkynes are particularly useful when we begin with a dihalide such as 1,1-dichloropentane (Eq. 10-66) or 1,2-dibromo-1-phenylethane (Eq. 10-67):

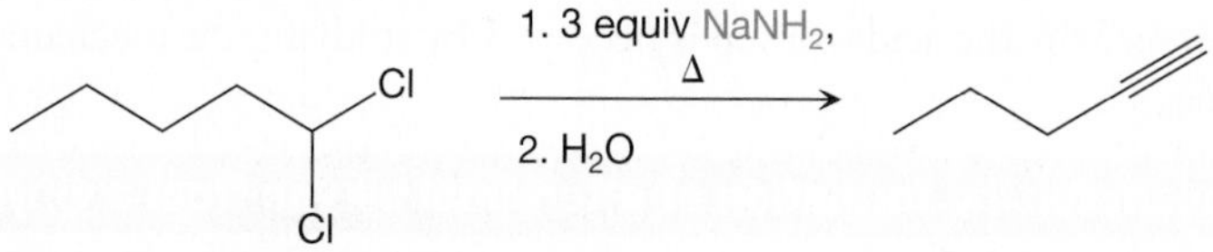

Cl
Cl
1. 3 equiv $NaNH_2$, Δ
2. H_2O

1,1-Dichloropentane Pent-1-yne (10-66)

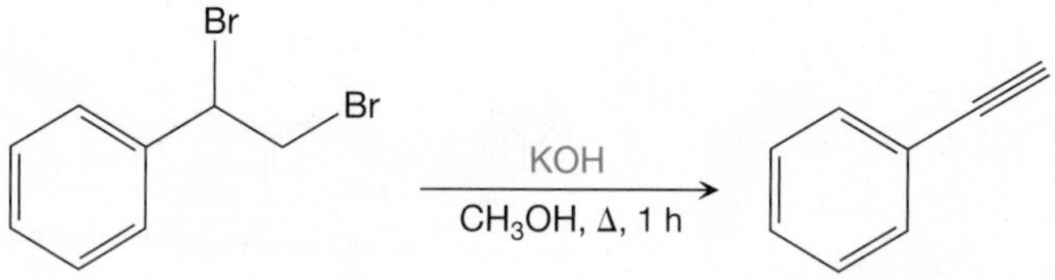

Br
Br
KOH
CH_3OH, Δ, 1 h

1,2-Dibromo-1-phenylethane Phenylethyne (Phenylacetylene) 40–50% (10-67)

Three equivalents of H_2N^- are used in Equation 10-66 to convert the dihalide into an alkyne. The first two equivalents bring about two separate E2 reactions, removing H and Cl each time. The third equivalent of base deprotonates the acidic proton on the newly formed terminal alkyne. Acid workup replaces that proton. The reaction in Equation 10-67, on the other hand, does not require acid workup because HO^- is not a strong enough base to favor deprotonation of the terminal alkyne that forms.

YOUR TURN 10.30

Draw the complete, detailed mechanisms for the reactions in Equations 10-66 and 10-67.

YOUR TURN 10.31

Predict the major product of each of the following reactions and draw their complete, detailed mechanisms.

(a)

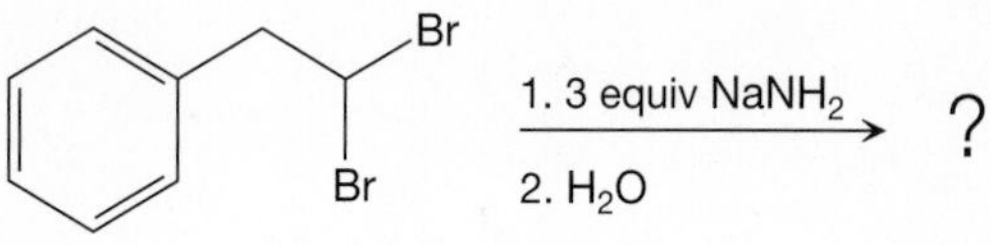

Br
Br
1. 3 equiv $NaNH_2$
2. H_2O
?

(b)

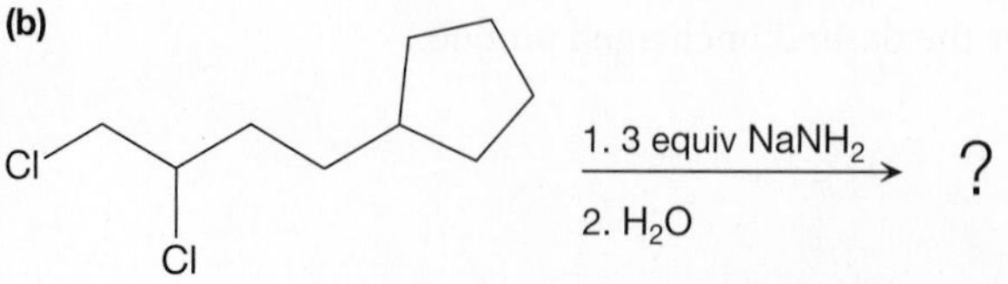

Cl
Cl
1. 3 equiv $NaNH_2$
2. H_2O
?

Chapter Summary and Key Terms

- A **synthesis** scheme is an abbreviated recipe that tells how **starting materials** are converted into a particular **target**. (Section 10.1)
- In each **synthetic step**, only the reactants, reagents added, reaction conditions, and products are included. Reagents and reaction conditions can be written above and below the reaction arrow. (Section 10.2)
- Reactions that form and/or break C—C σ bonds alter the **carbon skeleton**, whereas **functional group conversions** do not. (Section 10.3)
- Under basic conditions, the **Williamson ether synthesis** can be used to synthesize either symmetric or unsymmetric ethers by an S_N2 reaction between an alkoxide anion ($R'O^-$) and an alkyl halide (RX). (Section 10.4)
- Under acidic conditions, a **condensation** reaction can be used to synthesize a symmetric ether from an alcohol. (Section 10.4)
- Phosphorus tribromide (PBr_3) and phosphorus trichloride (PCl_3) convert primary and secondary alcohols into alkyl halides *stereospecifically* by back-to-back S_N2 reactions. The configuration of the alkyl halide is opposite that of the initial alcohol. (Section 10.5)
- **α Halogenation** may occur at an α carbon of aldehydes and ketones under either acidic or basic conditions. The reaction stops after just a single halogenation under acidic conditions, whereas multiple halogenations occur under basic conditions. (Section 10.6)
- **Epoxides** are three-membered ring ethers that can be opened in an S_N2 reaction to relieve substantial ring strain. Under neutral or basic conditions, a nucleophile attacks the less highly alkyl-substituted carbon of the epoxide ring. Under acidic conditions, the nucleophile attacks the more highly alkyl-substituted carbon of the ring. (Section 10.7)
- An epoxide can be produced from a **halohydrin** (X—C—C—OH) under basic conditions. The hydroxyl group is deprotonated, and the strongly nucleophilic O^- then displaces the halide leaving group in an S_N2 step. (Section 10.8)
- **Diazomethane** (CH_2N_2) converts a carboxylic acid (RCO_2H) into a methyl ester (RCO_2CH_3). After an initial proton transfer, an S_N2 reaction occurs, displacing $N_2(g)$ as the leaving group. (Section 10.9)
- Ammonia and amines undergo **alkylation** when treated with an alkyl halide that has a good leaving group. Multiple alkylations tend to occur because the product amine is also nucleophilic. Alkylation of ammonia is a poor method to synthesize a primary amine, but it is an effective way of generating a **quaternary ammonium salt**. (Section 10.10)
- The **Hofmann elimination reaction** converts an amine to an alkene. (Section 10.11)
    - The reaction proceeds with *anti-Zaitsev* regiochemistry to produce the less highly alkyl-substituted alkene, called the **Hofmann product**.
    - The alkylation stage of the reaction converts the amine with a poor leaving group into a tetraalkylammonium ion that has a moderately good leaving group.
- A *vinylic* halide can undergo an E2 reaction to produce an alkyne. Because the leaving group is attached to an sp^2-hybridized carbon, these reactions require strong bases and often elevated temperatures. (Section 10.12)
    - When a very powerful base such as H^- or H_2N^- is used and the alkyne product is terminal, a subsequent rapid deprotonation produces the alkynide anion. An **acid workup** replenishes the proton to yield the uncharged alkyne. (Section 10.12)

Reaction Table

The reactions introduced in this chapter are all functional group transformations and are collected in Table 10-1.

TABLE 10-1 Functional Group Transformations[a]

	Starting Compound Class	Typical Reagents and Reaction Conditions	Compound Class Formed	Key Electron-Rich Species	Key Electron-Poor Species	Comments	Discussed in Section
(1)	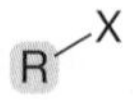 **Alkyl halide**	NaOR′ →	 **Ether (symmetric or unsymmetric)**	$R'O^{\ominus}$	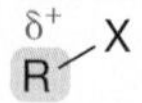	Williamson ether synthesis, S_N2	10.4
(2)	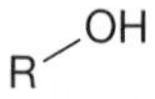 **Alcohol**	H_2SO_4 → Δ	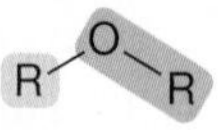 **Ether (symmetric)**	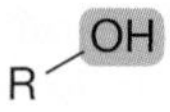	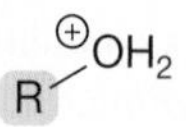	S_N1 or S_N2 (dehydration)	10.4
(3)	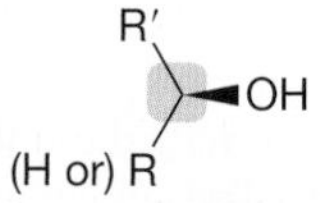 **1° or 2° alcohol**	PBr_3 →	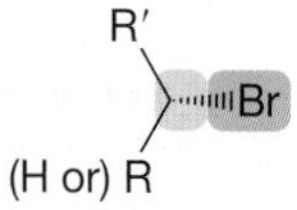 **1° or 2° alkyl halide**	$Br^{\ominus}$	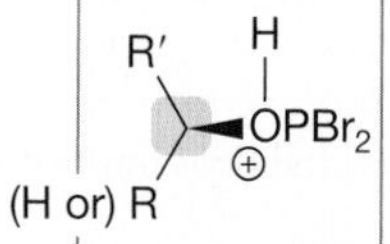	Back-to-back S_N2 reactions	10.5
(4)	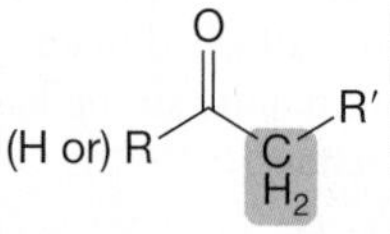 **Ketone or aldehyde**	X_2 → NaOH	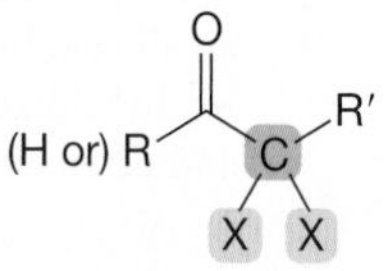 **α-Halogenated ketone or aldehyde**	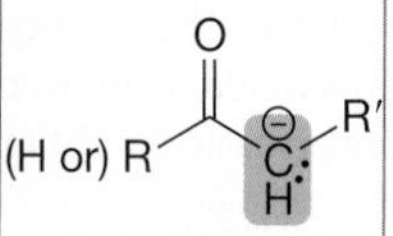 **Enolate anion**	$\overset{\delta^+}{X}$—$\overset{\delta^-}{X}$	Multiple S_N2 reactions	10.6
(5)	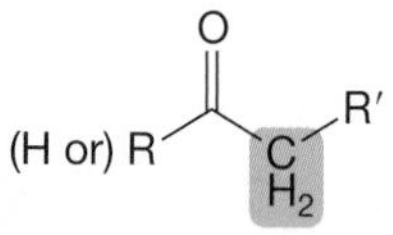 **Ketone or aldehyde**	X_2 → Acid	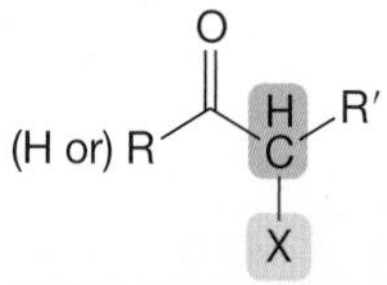 **α-Halogenated ketone or aldehyde**	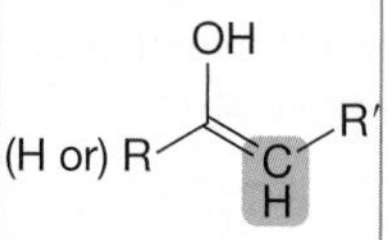 **Enol**	$\overset{\delta^+}{X}$—$\overset{\delta^-}{X}$	Single S_N2 reaction	10.6
(6)	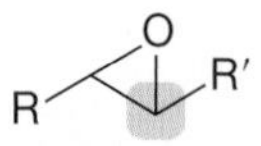 **Epoxide**	$:Nu^{\ominus}$ → Neutral or basic	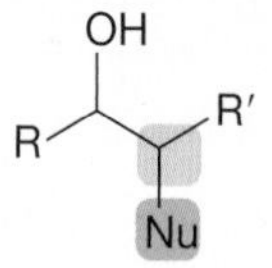 **Alcohol (2-substituted)**	$:Nu^{\ominus}$	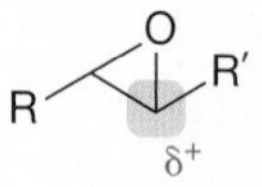	S_N2	10.7
(7)	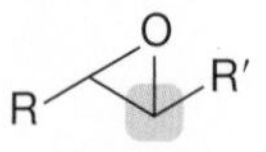 **Epoxide**	H—Nu → Acidic	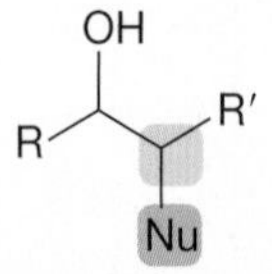 **Alcohol (2-substituted)**	$:Nu^{\ominus}$	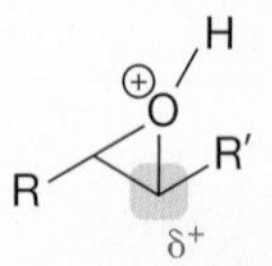	S_N2	10.7

[a]X = Cl, Br, or I.

(continued)

TABLE 10-1 Functional Group Transformations[a] (continued)

	Starting Compound Class	Typical Reagents and Reaction Conditions	Compound Class Formed	Key Electron-Rich Species	Key Electron-Poor Species	Comments	Discussed in Section
(8)	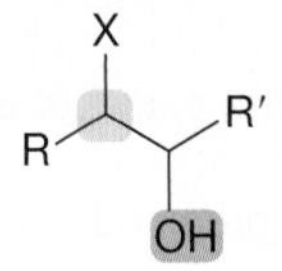 Halohydrin	NaOH →	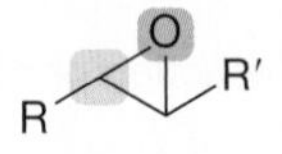 Epoxide	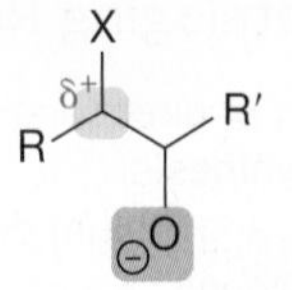		Intramolecular S_N2	10.8
(9)	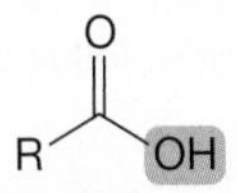 Carboxylic acid	CH_2N_2 →	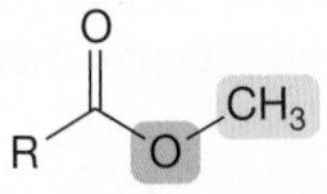 Methyl ester	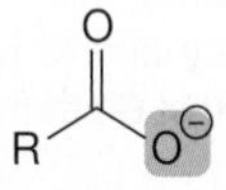 Carboxylate anion	$H_3C—N_2^{\oplus}$	S_N2	10.9
(10)	R—X 1° alkyl halide	1 equiv of NH_3 →	R—NH_2 + other amines 1° amine	NH_3	δ^+ R—X	S_N2 reaction (Not useful in synthesis)	10.10
(11)	R—NH_2 Amine	excess R′—X →	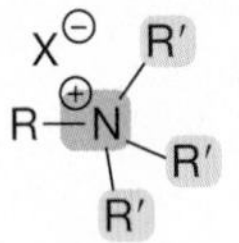 Quaternary ammonium salt	R—NH_2	δ^+ R′—X	Multiple S_N2 reactions	10.10
(12)	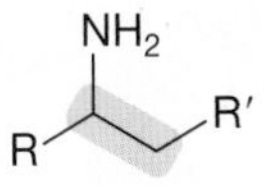 Amine	1. CH_3I (excess) → 2. Ag_2O 3. Δ	 Alkene	$^{\ominus}OH$	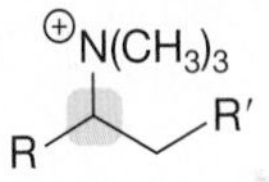	Hofmann elimination, E2	10.11
(13)	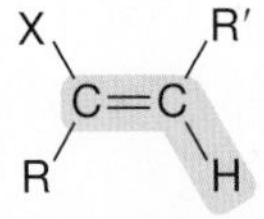 Vinylic halide	$NaNH_2$ or NaH or NaOH, Δ →	R—C≡C—R′ Internal alkyne	$^{\ominus}NH_2$ or $^{\ominus}H$ or $^{\ominus}OH$	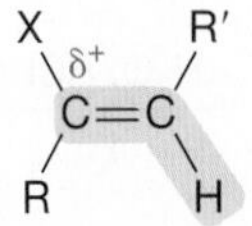	E2	10.12
(14)	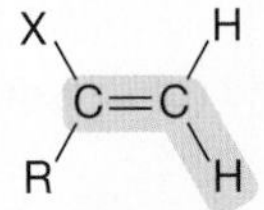 Vinylic halide	1. $NaNH_2$ or NaH → 2. H_2O	R—C≡CH Terminal alkyne	$^{\ominus}NH_2$ or $^{\ominus}H$	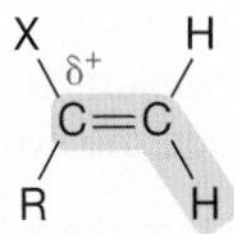	E2	10.12
(15)	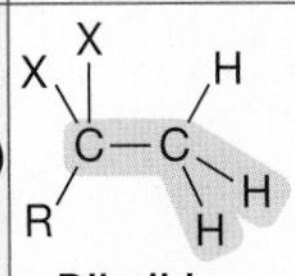 Dihalide	$NaNH_2$ or NaH or NaOH, Δ →	R—C≡C—R′ Internal alkyne	$^{\ominus}NH_2$ or $^{\ominus}H$ or $^{\ominus}OH$	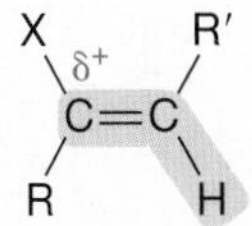	Back-to-back E2	10.12
(16)	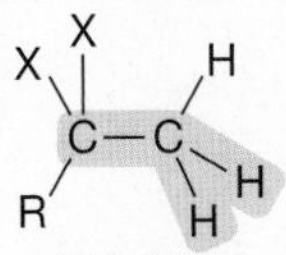 Dihalide	1. $NaNH_2$ or NaH → 2. H_2O	R—C≡CH Terminal alkyne	$^{\ominus}NH_2$ or $^{\ominus}H$	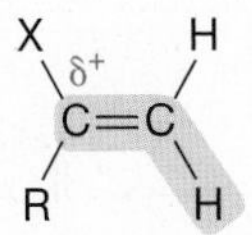	Back-to-back E2	10.12

[a]X = Cl, Br, or I.

Problems

Problems that are related to synthesis are denoted (SYN).

Sections 10.1–10.3 The Language of Organic Synthesis, Writing Syntheses, and Cataloging Reactions

10.1 Each of the following is a set of directions for carrying out a reaction or sequence of reactions. Rewrite each set of directions in the form of a synthesis.

(a) To 2-ethylcyclohexanone, add lithium diisopropylamide, and when that reaction has finished, add bromoethane to yield 2,6-diethylcyclohexanone.

(b) Add molecular bromine to 2,2-dimethylcyclohexanone in the presence of acetic acid to yield 6-bromo-2,2-dimethylcyclohexanone. To the resulting mixture, add sodium cyanide to yield 6-cyano-2,2-dimethylcyclohexanone.

(c) Treat pent-4-ynoic acid with diazomethane to produce methyl pent-4-ynoate. Next, add sodium hydride, followed by (bromomethyl)benzene, to yield methyl 6-phenylhex-4-ynoate.

10.2 Convert each synthesis scheme into words that can be used as instructions in the laboratory, similar to what you see in Problem 10.1.

(a)

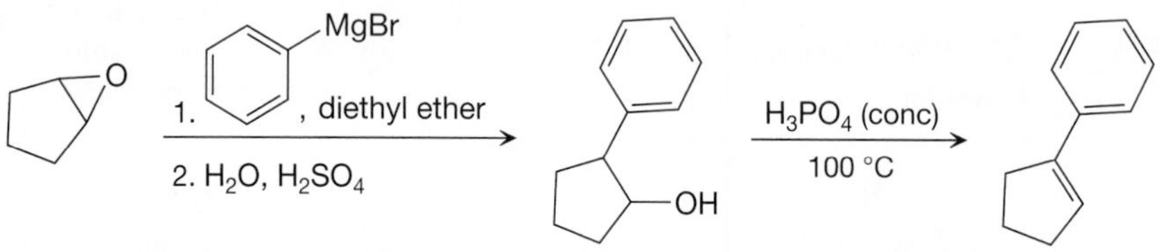

O
MgBr
1. , diethyl ether
2. H_2O, H_2SO_4
OH
H_3PO_4 (conc)
100 °C

(b)

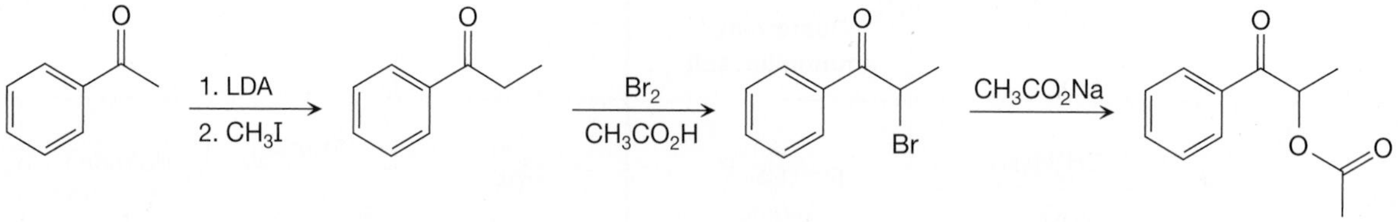

O
1. LDA
2. CH_3I
Br_2
CH_3CO_2H
Br
CH_3CO_2Na

(c)

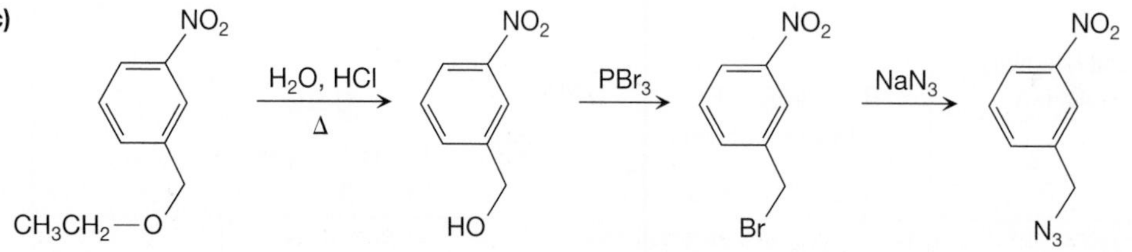

NO_2
$CH_3CH_2—O$
H_2O, HCl
Δ
HO
PBr_3
Br
NaN_3
N_3

10.3 For each synthesis in Problem 10.2, **(a)** identify the target, **(b)** identify each synthetic intermediate, and **(c)** determine how many synthetic steps the synthesis has.

10.4 Determine whether each of the following syntheses requires a reaction that alters the carbon skeleton.

(a)

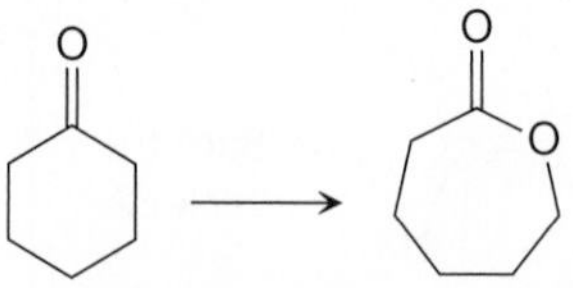

O

(b)

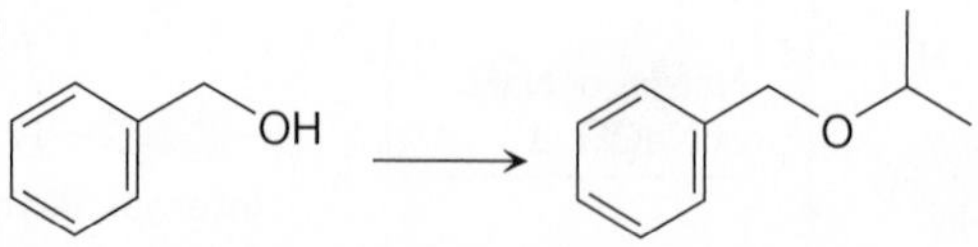

OH
O

(c)

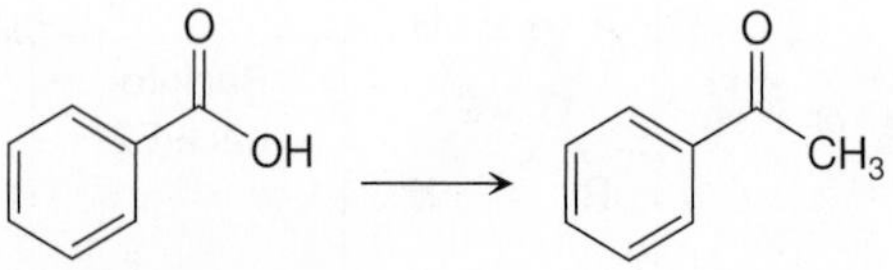

O
OH
CH_3

(d)

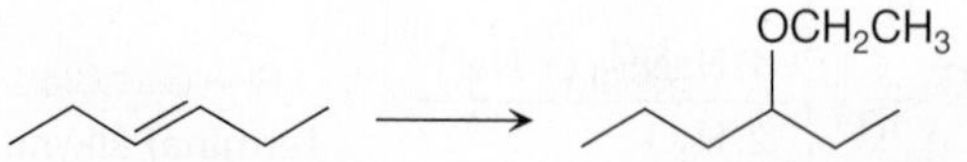

OCH_2CH_3

(e)

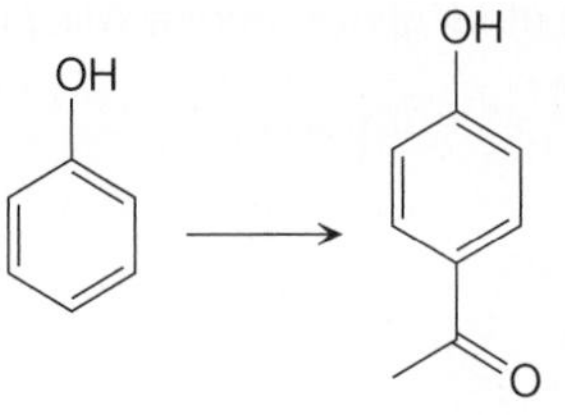

(f)

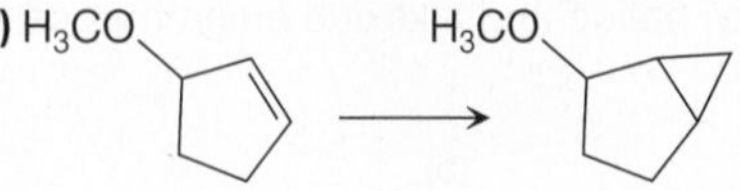

(g)

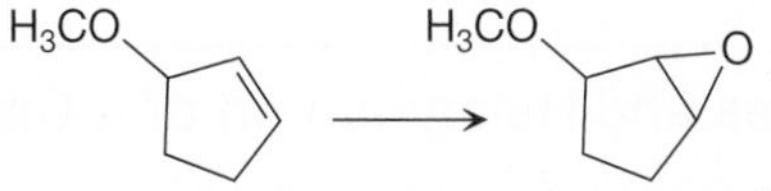

(h)

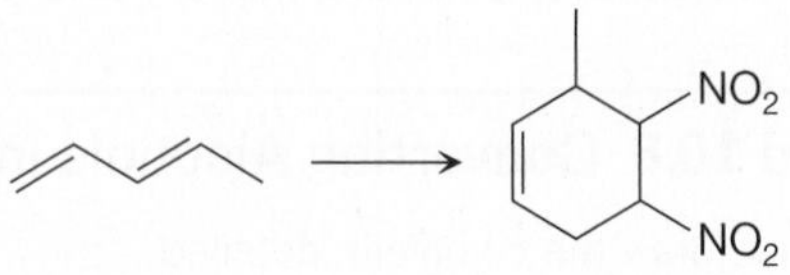

10.5 Rewrite each of the following mechanisms as a synthetic step.

(a)

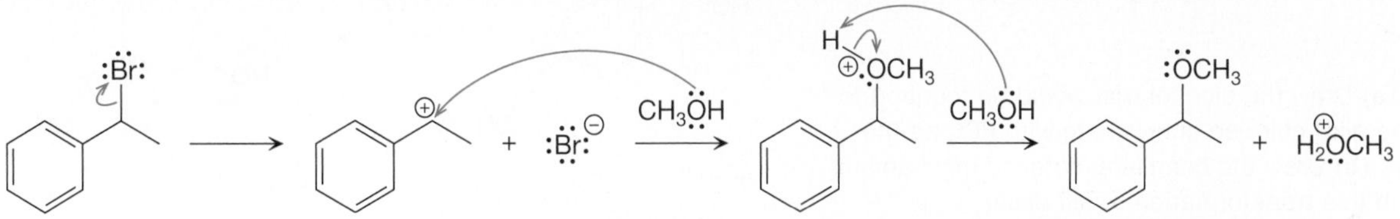

(b)

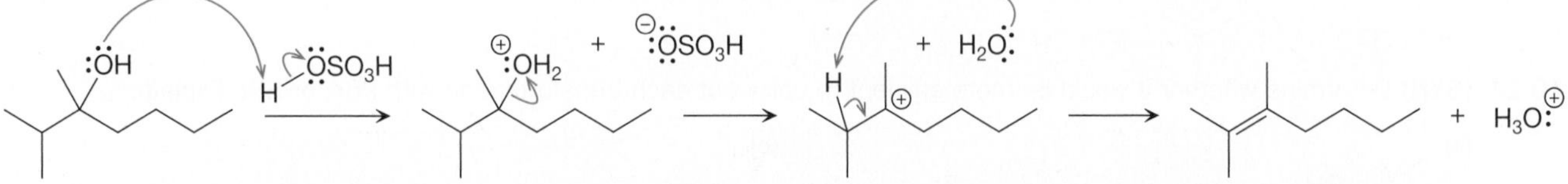

Section 10.4 Ether Formation and Functional Group Transformations in Synthesis

10.6 Draw a complete, detailed mechanism for the reaction shown here.

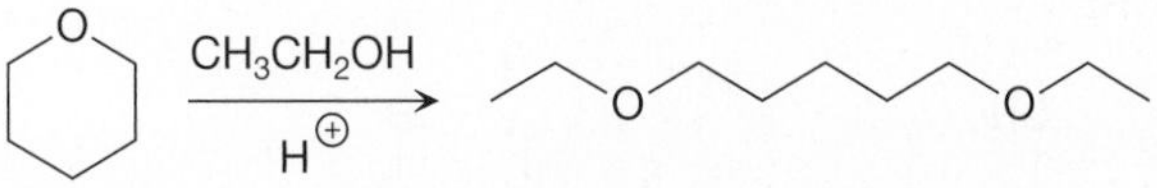

10.7 A student wanted to prepare (1-ethylpropoxy)cyclopentane by heating cyclopentanol and pentan-3-ol under acidic conditions. On carrying out the reaction, however, the student found that there were three ethers produced, each containing 10 carbon atoms. One of the ethers was (1-ethylpropoxy)cyclopentane. Draw the structures of the other two ethers and draw the complete, detailed mechanisms showing how all three ethers are produced.

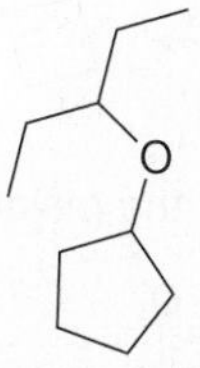

(1-Ethylpropoxy)cyclopentane

10.8 **(SYN)** Consider each of these reactions, in which an ether is produced by condensation from a reactant having the blue shaded molecular formula. Draw a reasonable structure for each reactant.

(a)

(b)

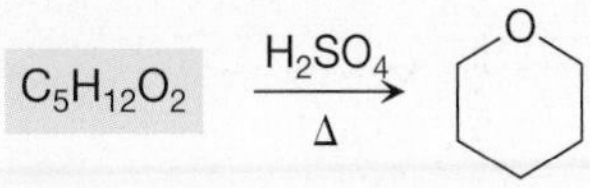

(c)

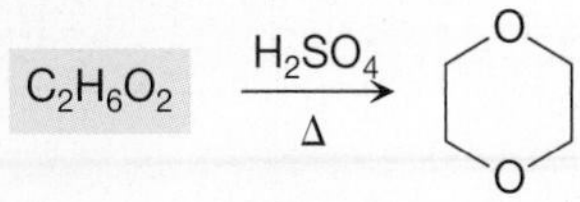

10.9 **(SYN)** Draw an alkyl halide and alkoxide anion that can be used to synthesize each ether shown from a Williamson ether synthesis reaction.

(a)

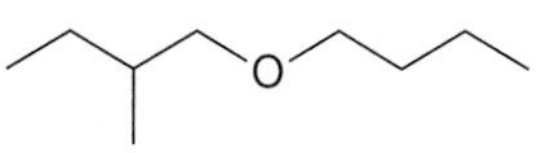

O

(b)

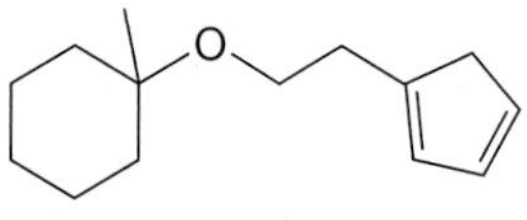

O

(c)

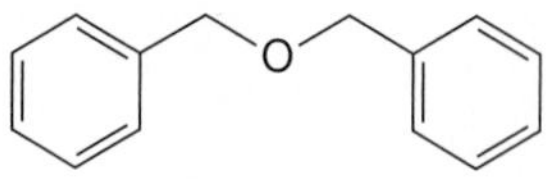

O

10.10 **(SYN)** Repeat Problem 10.9 beginning with any alcohols.

Sections 10.5 and 10.6 Converting Alcohols into Alkyl Halides and Halogenation of α Carbons

10.11 For each reaction, draw the complete, detailed mechanism and the major product.

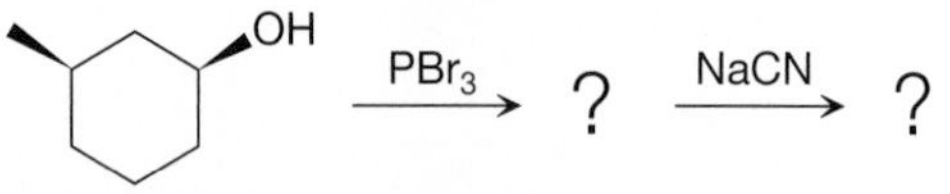

OH
PBr3
?
NaCN
?

10.12 **(SYN)** **(a)** Draw the alcohol that would be required to form the alkyl chloride shown here with PCl_3 as the reagent. **(b)** Draw the complete, detailed mechanism by which this transformation would occur.

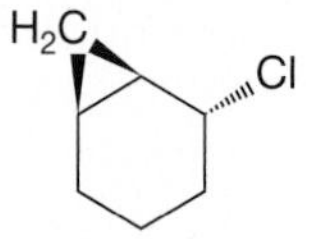

H2C
Cl

10.13 **(SYN)** Show how to carry out the transformation shown and draw the complete, detailed mechanism for that reaction.

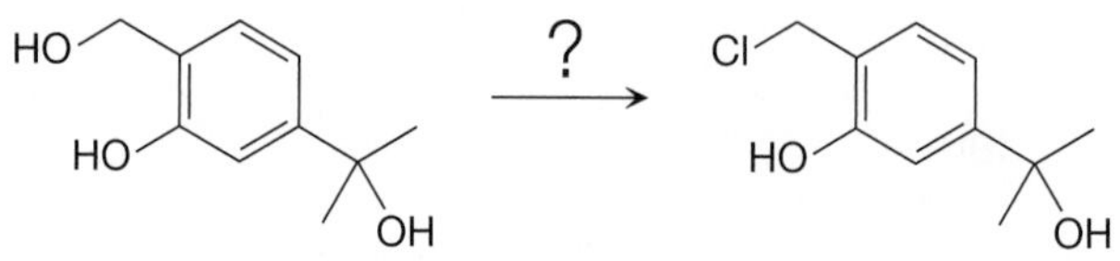

HO
HO
OH
?
Cl
HO
OH

10.14 **(SYN)** Determine whether it would be more efficient to carry out each transformation with PBr_3 or HBr. Explain.

(a)

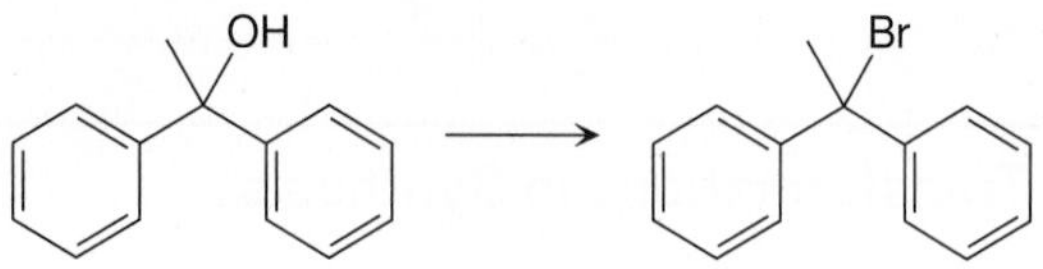

OH
Br

(b)

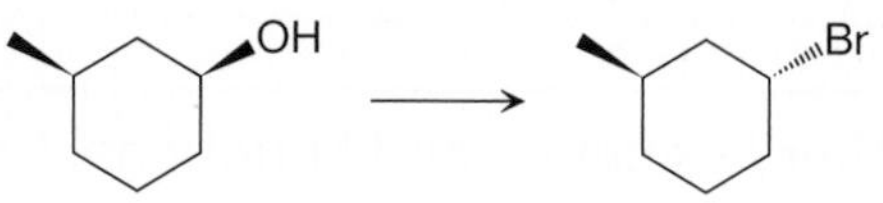

OH
Br

(c)

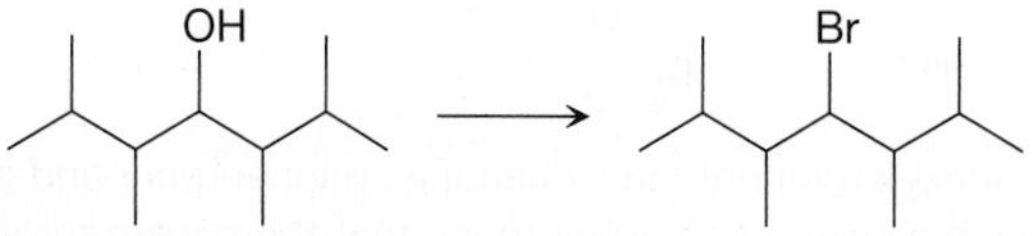

OH
Br

10.15 **(SYN)** Draw the compound having the formula $C_9H_{16}O$ that would produce the alkyl halide shown when treated with PCl_3.

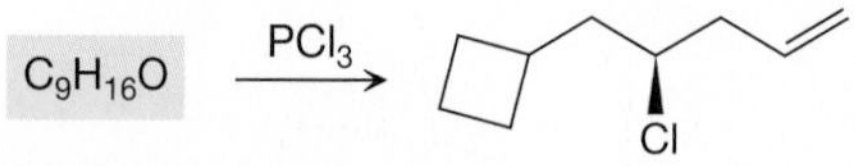

C9H16O
PCl3
Cl

10.16 Draw the complete, detailed mechanism and predict the major product(s) for each of the following reactions.

(a)

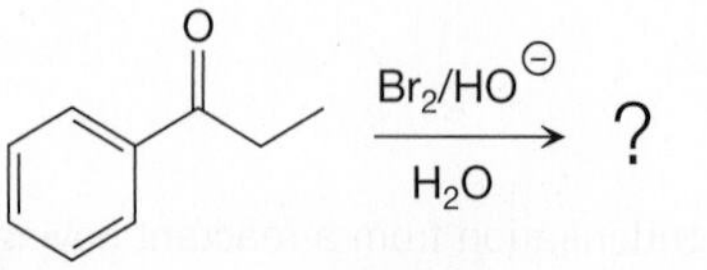

O
Br2/HO⊖
H2O
?

(b)

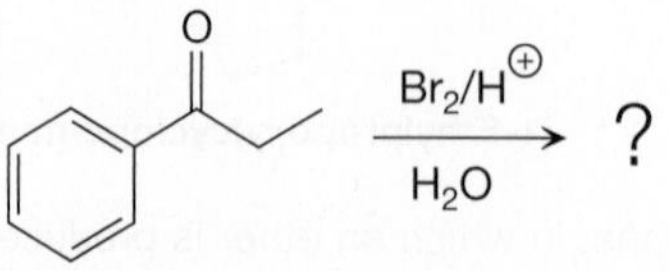

O
Br2/H⊕
H2O
?

10.17 Halogenation readily takes place at an α carbon of a ketone or aldehyde under basic conditions if the halogen is Cl_2, Br_2, or I_2. Explain why it does *not* readily take place with F_2.

10.18 (SYN) Show how each of these halogenated ketones and aldehydes can be synthesized from a ketone or aldehyde.

(a)

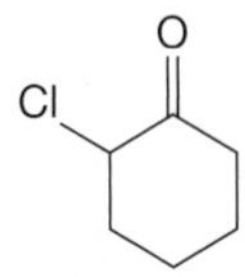

O
Cl

(b)

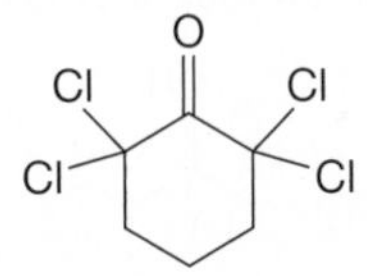

O
Cl
Cl
Cl
Cl

(c)

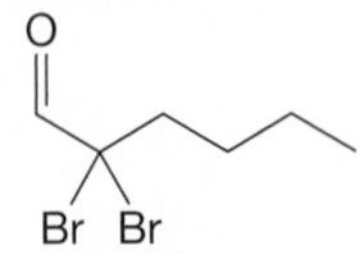

O
Br Br

(d)

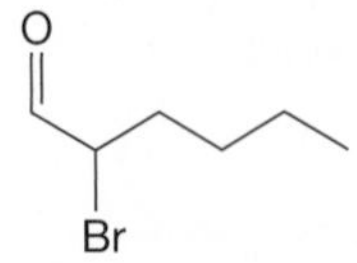

O
Br

Sections 10.7 and 10.8 Reactions Involving Epoxides

10.19 For each reaction, draw the complete, detailed mechanism and the major product.

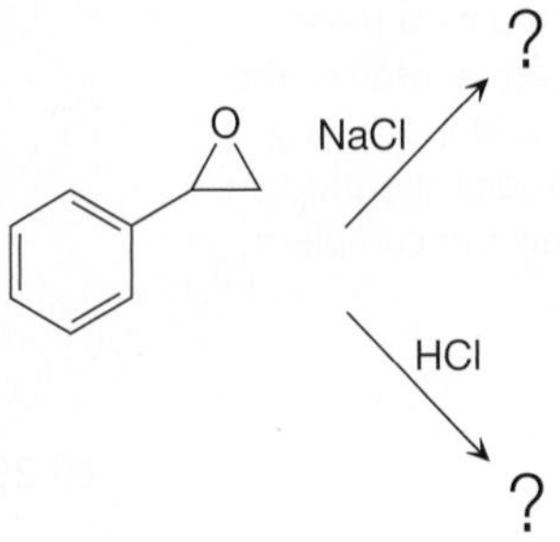

O
NaCl
?
HCl
?

10.20 Draw the product for each of the following reactions.

(a)

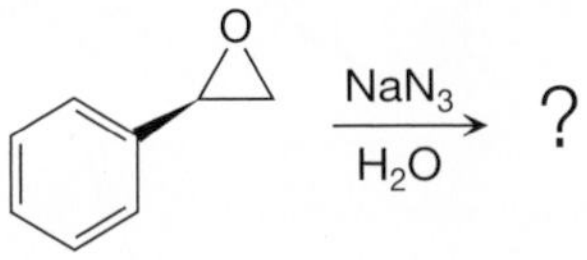

O
NaN3
H2O
?

(b)

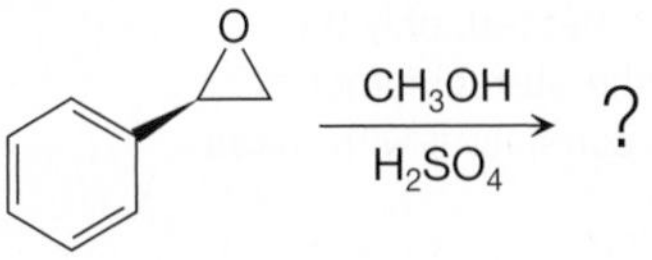

O
CH3OH
H2SO4
?

(c)

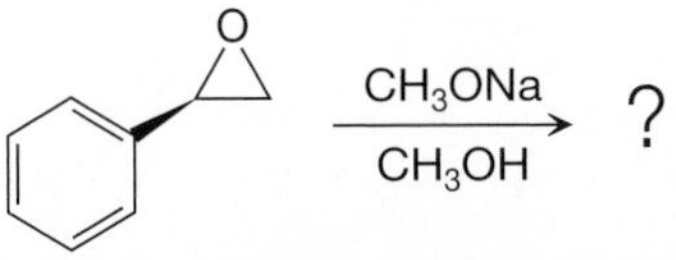

O
CH3ONa
CH3OH
?

(d)

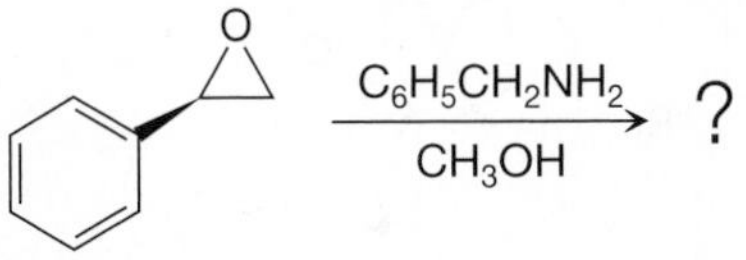

O
C6H5CH2NH2
CH3OH
?

10.21 As discussed in Section 7.1b, reagents like $NaBH_4$ and $LiAlH_4$ can be simplified to just H^-. With this in mind, draw the mechanism for each of the following reactions.

(a)

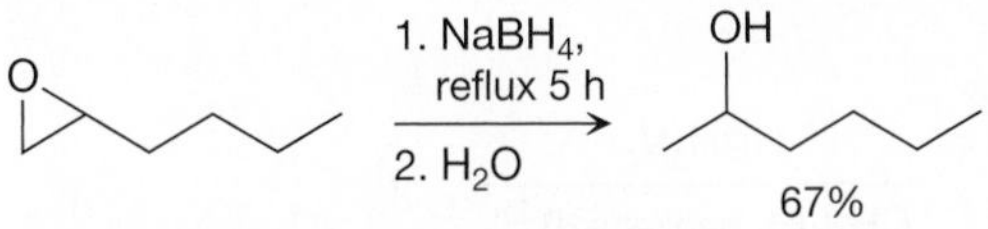

O
1. NaBH4,
reflux 5 h
2. H2O
OH
67%

(b)

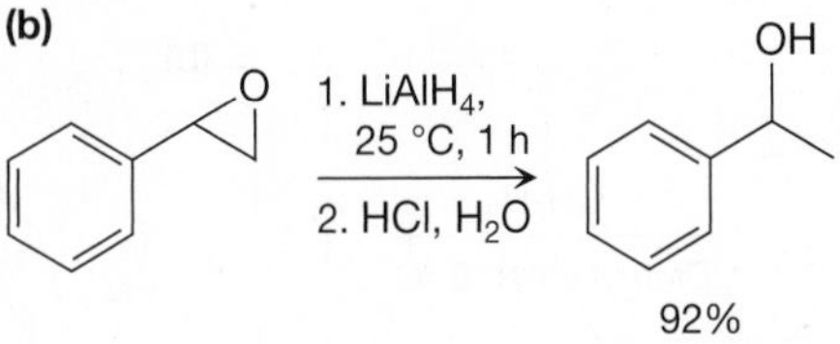

O
1. LiAlH4,
25 °C, 1 h
2. HCl, H2O
OH
92%

10.22 (SYN) Show how each of these alcohols can be synthesized from an epoxide. (*Hint*: See Problem 10.21.) If there is more than one epoxide from which the alcohol can be produced, choose the one that would give the highest yield.

(a)

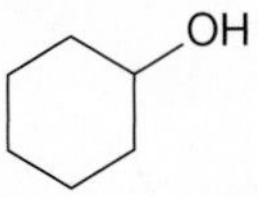

OH

(b)

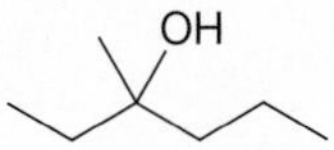

OH

(c)

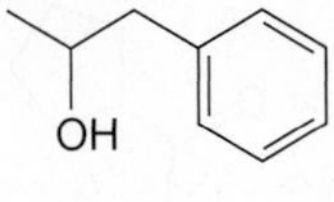

OH

10.23 In the protonated epoxide shown here, which C—O bond would you expect to be longer? Why?

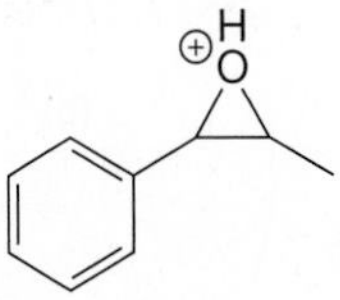

H
O

10.24 Draw the complete, detailed mechanism for the reaction shown here, and explain why nucleophilic attack takes place predominantly at the epoxide carbon that is attached to the vinyl group.

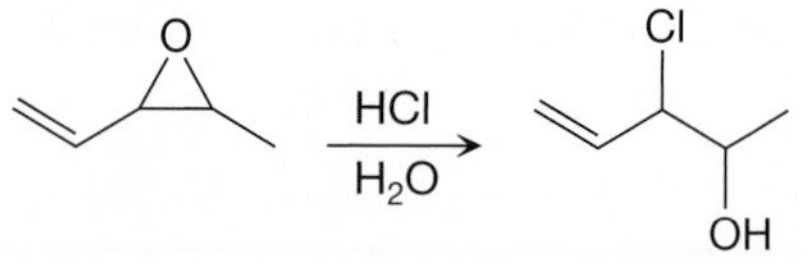
O
HCl
H_2O
Cl
OH

63%

10.25 An *aziridine* is a compound that contains a three-membered ring consisting of two carbon atoms and a nitrogen atom. Because of the strain in the ring, it behaves similarly to an epoxide. Predict the product of the reaction shown here and draw the complete, detailed mechanism.

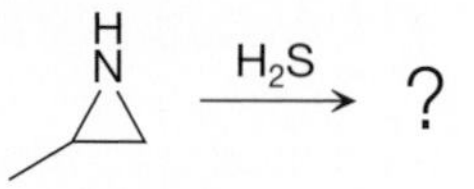
H
N
H_2S
?

10.26 One stereoisomer of 2,6-dibromocyclohexanol is labeled with a ^{13}C isotope (indicated by an asterisk) at one of the C atoms bonded to Br. When this compound is treated with a strong base and heated, only the product shown is formed. Draw the stereoisomer of 2,6-dibromocyclohexanol that is consistent with these results. Explain.

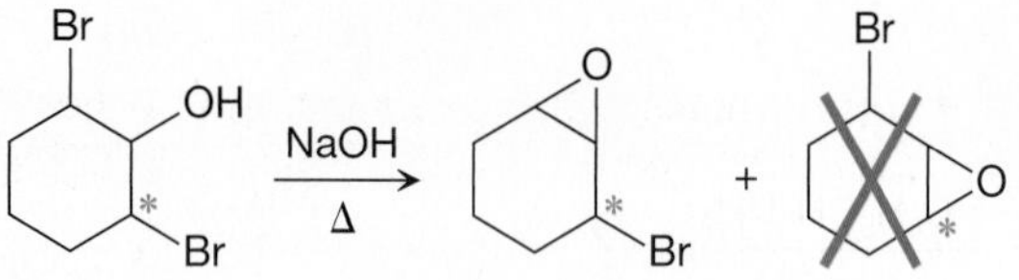
Br
OH
Br
NaOH
Δ
O
Br
+
Br
O

10.27 Draw and name the stereoisomer of 3-bromobutan-2-ol that, on heating in the presence of sodium hydroxide, will produce an epoxide that is achiral.

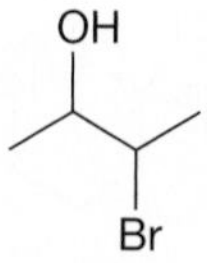
OH
Br

3-Bromobutan-2-ol

10.28 A student attempted to synthesize an epoxide according to the reaction scheme shown here, but no epoxide was formed. Explain why. *Hint*: It may be helpful to build a model of the reactant molecule.

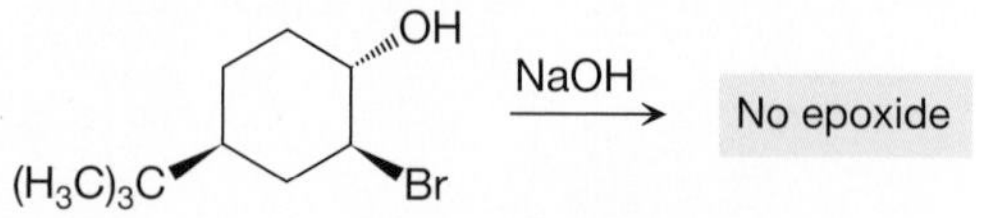
OH
$(H_3C)_3C$
Br
NaOH
No epoxide

10.29 **(SYN)** Show how each of these epoxides can be made from a halohydrin. Pay attention to stereochemistry.

(a)

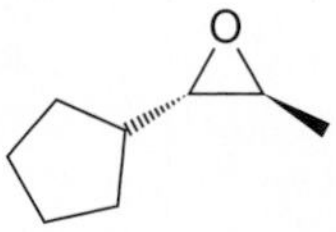

(b)

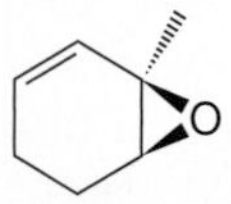

(c)

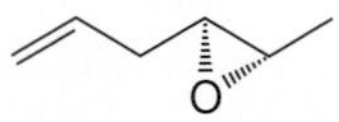

Section 10.9 Diazomethane Formation of Methyl Esters

10.30 Predict the products for each of the following reactions and draw the complete, detailed mechanisms.

(a)

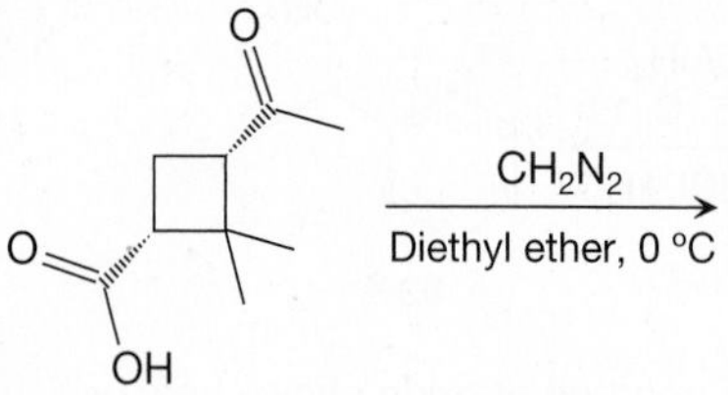
CH_2N_2
Diethyl ether, 0 °C
?

(b)

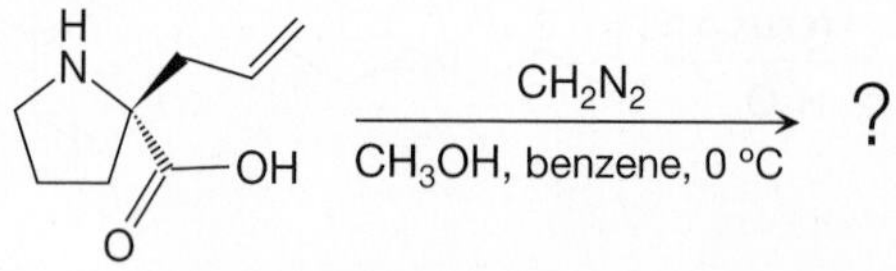
CH_2N_2
CH_3OH, benzene, 0 °C
?

10.31 **(SYN)** Draw the structure of the carboxylic acid that can be reacted with diazomethane to form each of the following compounds.

(a)

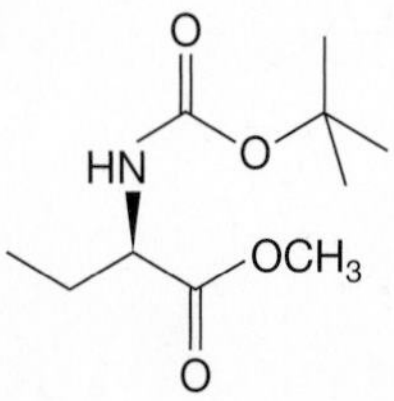
HN
OCH_3

(b)

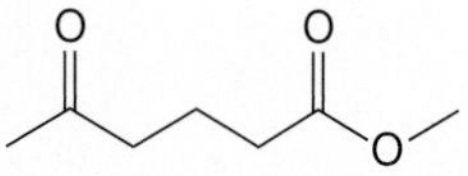

(c)

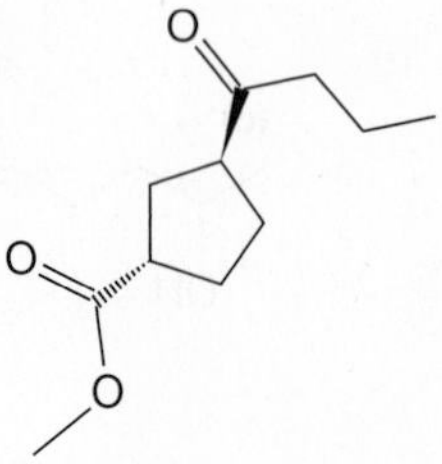

10.32 A compound, $C_2H_2O_4$, reacts with excess diazomethane to produce $C_4H_6O_4$. Draw the structure of each compound.

$$C_2H_2O_4 \xrightarrow{CH_2N_2\text{ (excess)}} C_4H_6O_4$$

10.33 The pK_a of a compound, $C_6H_{12}O_2$, is measured to be 25. Do you expect this compound to react with diazomethane? Explain.

Section 10.10 Amines and Quaternary Ammonium Salts from Alkyl Halides

10.34 Draw the complete, detailed mechanism for the reaction shown here and give the major product.

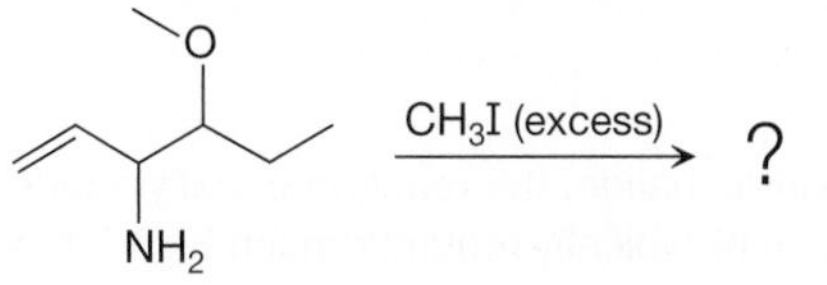

O
CH_3I (excess)
?
NH_2

10.35 **(SYN)** Draw the reactant of this reaction, whose formula is $C_{10}H_{16}ClN$.

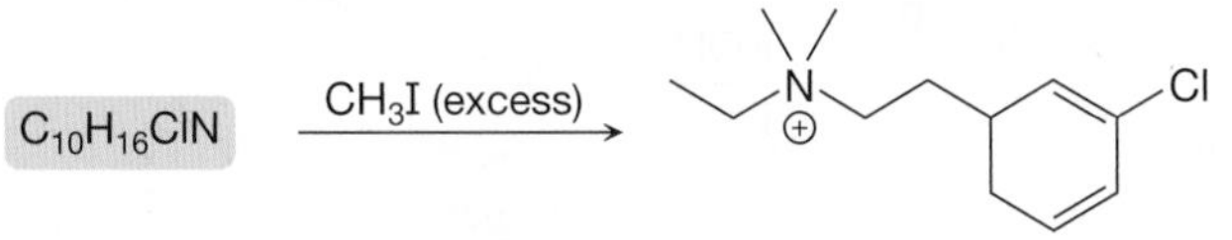

$C_{10}H_{16}ClN$
CH_3I (excess)
N
Cl

10.36 **(SYN)** Suggest a reagent that can be used to carry out the transformation shown here and draw the complete, detailed mechanism for the reaction.

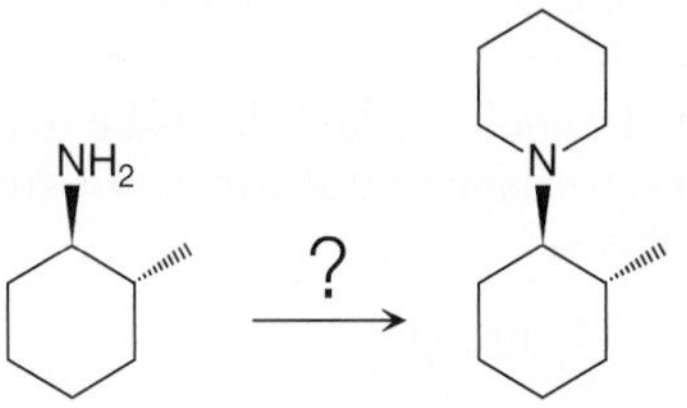

NH_2
?
N

10.37 Draw the complete, detailed mechanism for the reaction shown here and draw the major product.

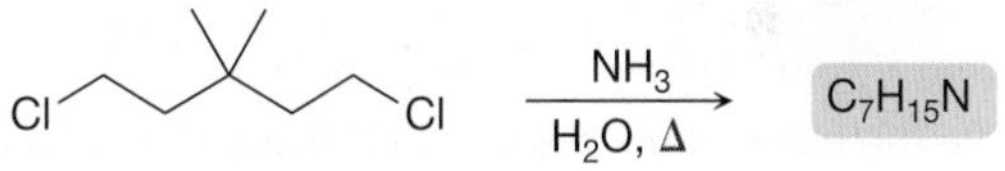

Cl
Cl
NH_3
H_2O, Δ
$C_7H_{15}N$

Section 10.11 Hofmann Elimination

10.38 For the reaction shown here, draw the complete, detailed mechanism and major product.

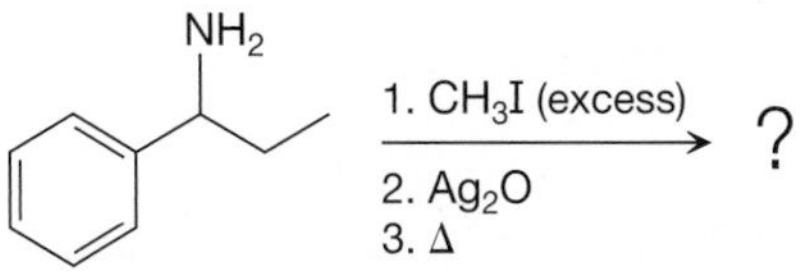

NH_2
1. CH_3I (excess)
2. Ag_2O
3. Δ
?

10.39 The Hofmann elimination reaction shown here is significantly slower than one involving pentan-3-amine. Explain why. *Hint*: You may want to build a molecular model of this molecule and the intermediates formed in the mechanism.

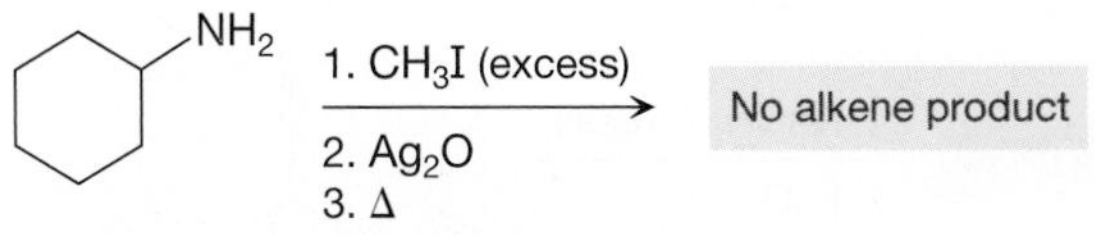

NH_2
1. CH_3I (excess)
2. Ag_2O
3. Δ
No alkene product

10.40 Draw the complete, detailed mechanism for the reaction shown here.

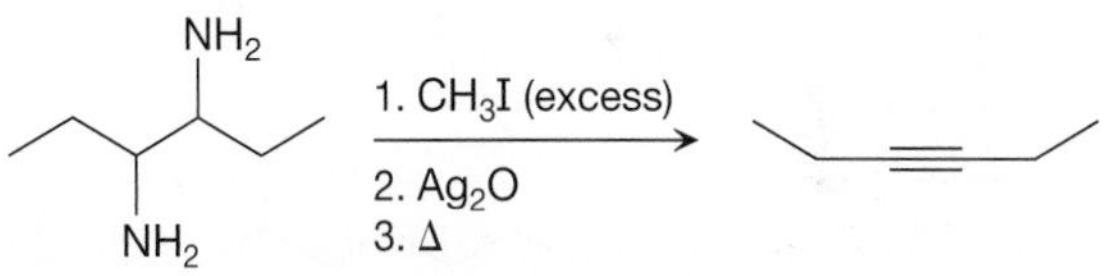

NH_2
NH_2
1. CH_3I (excess)
2. Ag_2O
3. Δ

10.41 Under conditions that favor Hofmann elimination, *N*-ethylhexan-3-amine can lead to three different alkene products. Draw the complete, detailed mechanism that leads to each alkene product and predict the major product.

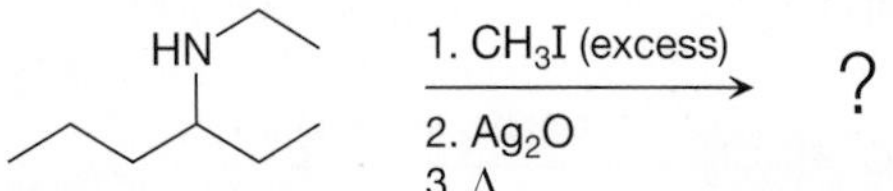

HN
1. CH_3I (excess)
2. Ag_2O
3. Δ
?

***N*-Ethylhexan-3-amine**

10.42 **(SYN)** An amine, whose formula is $C_9H_{13}N$, was treated first with excess iodomethane and then with silver oxide and was finally heated. When the product mixture was analyzed, two isomeric alkenes were found, as indicated here, along with trimethylamine. Draw the structure of the initial amine.

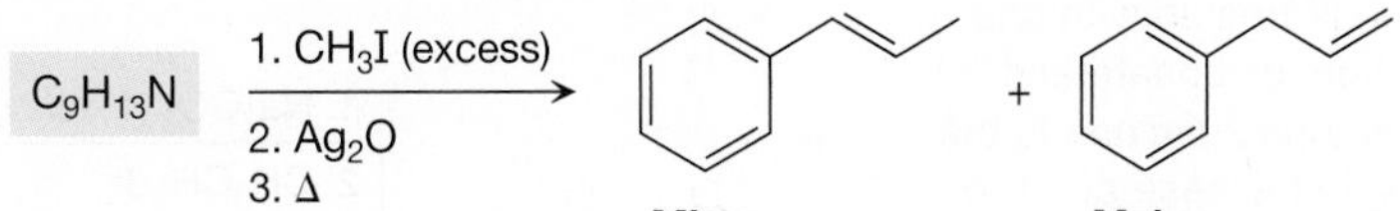

$C_9H_{13}N$
1. CH_3I (excess)
2. Ag_2O
3. Δ
+

Minor **Major**

10.43 What are the structures of **A** and **B** in the following reaction sequence?

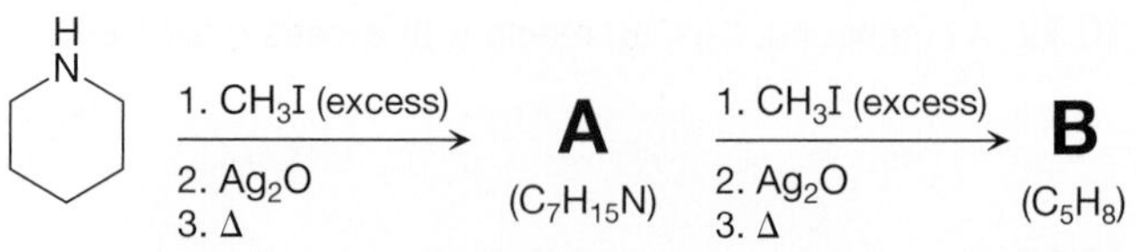

1. CH_3I (excess)
2. Ag_2O
3. Δ
A
($C_7H_{15}N$)
1. CH_3I (excess)
2. Ag_2O
3. Δ
B
(C_5H_8)

Section 10.12 Generating Alkynes by Elimination Reactions

10.44 For each reaction, draw the complete, detailed mechanism and the major product.

(a)

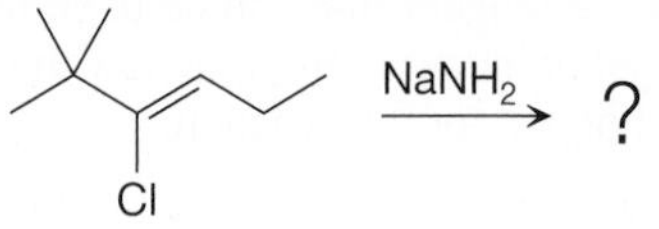

$NaNH_2$
?
Cl

(b)

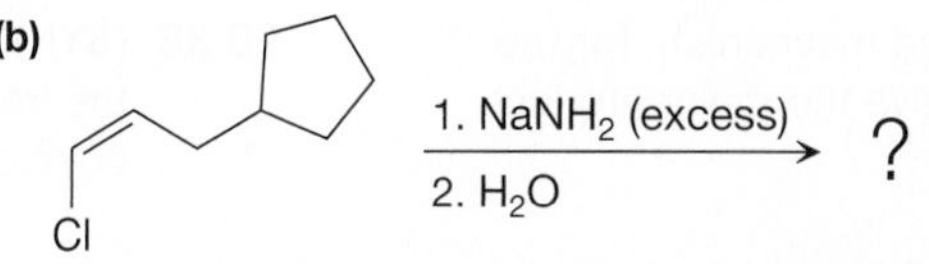

1. $NaNH_2$ (excess)
2. H_2O
?
Cl

10.45 When hydroxide is used as the base to carry out an E2 reaction on a vinylic halide, the reaction usually needs to be heated significantly. As shown below, such a reaction involving the *E* isomer typically requires much higher temperatures. Why is this so?

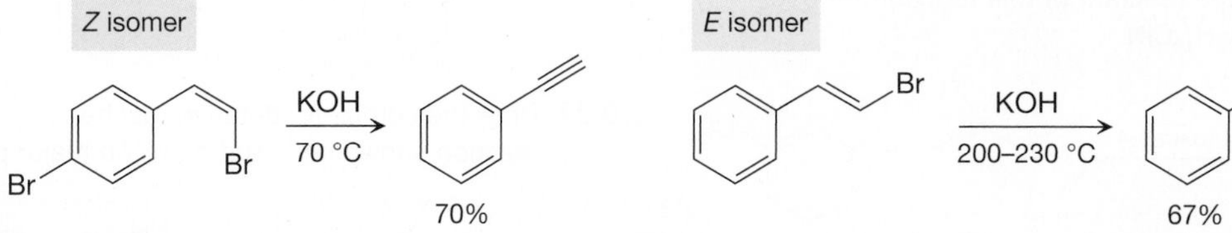

Z isomer
KOH
70 °C
Br
Br
70%
E isomer
Br
KOH
200–230 °C
67%

10.46 In the elimination of a vicinal dihalide to yield an internal alkyne, two equivalents of $NaNH_2$ are required: one for each equivalent of HX that is eliminated. When the product is a terminal alkyne, however, three equivalents of $NaNH_2$ are required. Explain why.

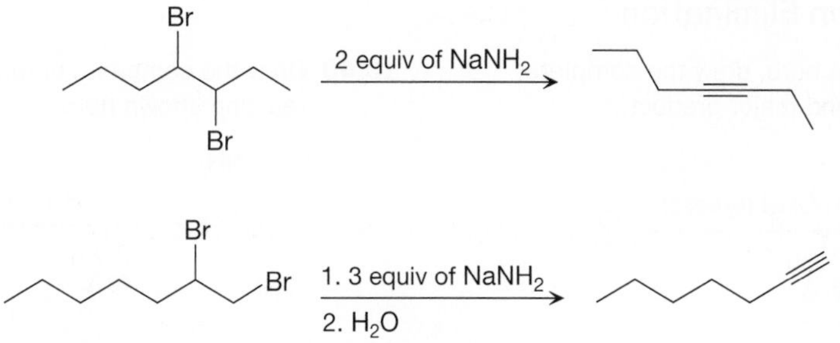

Br
Br
2 equiv of $NaNH_2$
Br
Br
1. 3 equiv of $NaNH_2$
2. H_2O

10.47 Elimination occurs when (*Z*)-3-bromohex-3-ene is treated with $NaNH_2$. Under the same conditions, 1-bromocyclohexene undergoes elimination much more sluggishly. Explain why.

10.48 **(SYN)** Draw the starting compound for each of the following reactions.

(a)

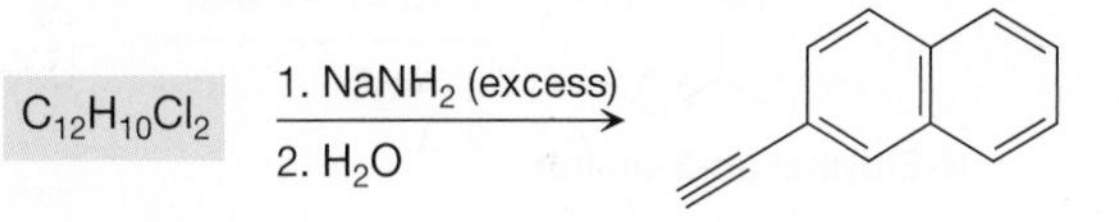

$C_{12}H_{10}Cl_2$
1. $NaNH_2$ (excess)
2. H_2O

(b)

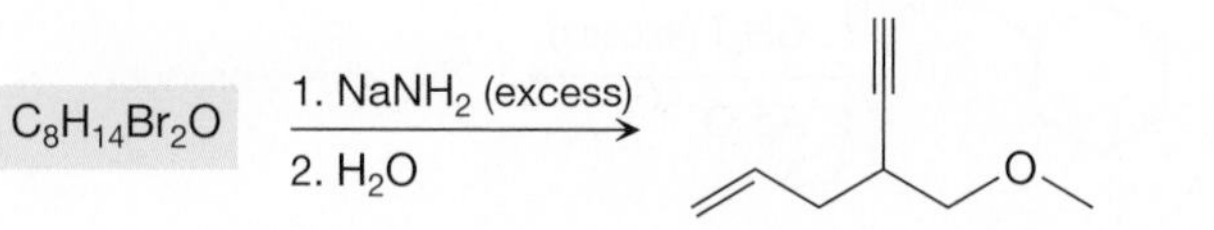

$C_8H_{14}Br_2O$
1. $NaNH_2$ (excess)
2. H_2O
O

Integrated Problems

10.49 When pentane-2,4-dione is treated with one molar equivalent of sodium carbonate and bromoethane, 3-ethylpentane-2,4-dione is the major product. If $NaNH_2$ is the base and two molar equivalents are used, however, then heptane-2,4-dione is the major product. Explain these observations.

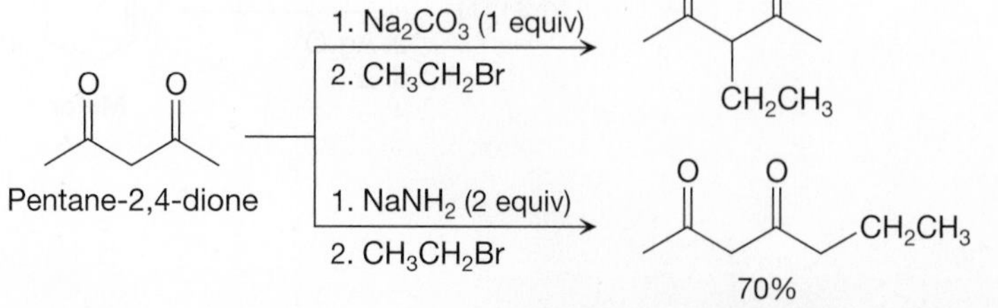

O
O
Pentane-2,4-dione
1. Na_2CO_3 (1 equiv)
2. CH_3CH_2Br
CH_2CH_3
1. $NaNH_2$ (2 equiv)
2. CH_3CH_2Br
CH_2CH_3
70%

10.50 **(SYN)** Show how to synthesize the following ether, beginning with any alkyl halide.

10.51 **(SYN)** Propose how to carry out the transformation shown here. *Hint*: It may take more than a single reaction.

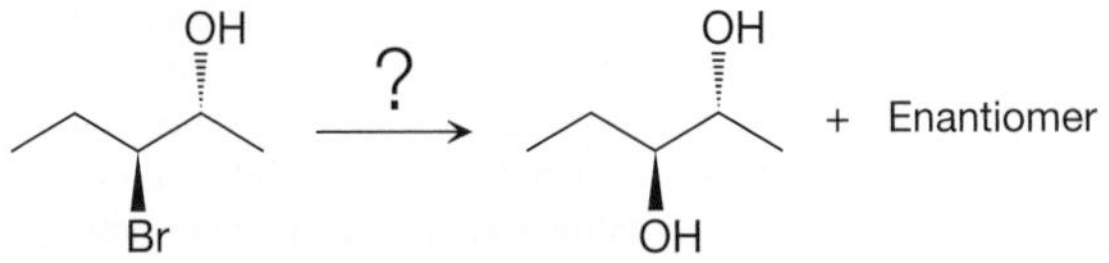
OH
?
OH
+ Enantiomer
Br
OH

10.52 When oxirane is treated with NaOH, an S_N2 reaction predominantly occurs, thus opening the ring. Given that conditions favoring an S_N2 reaction also generally favor an E2 reaction, we can also write an E2 mechanism that opens the ring. The E2 reaction, however, does *not occur* readily. Why not? *Hint*: It may help to build a molecular model of the epoxide.

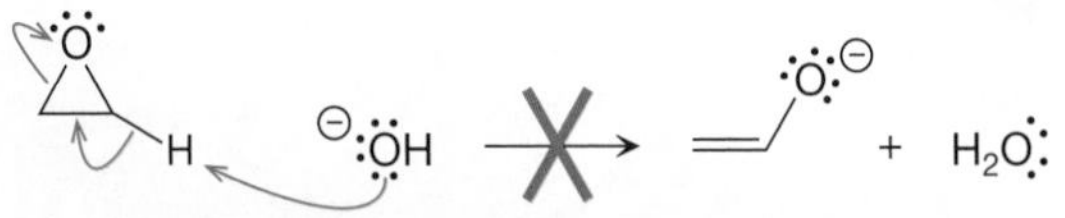

10.53 Draw a mechanism to account for the formation of the product in the reaction shown here. *Hint*: Under these conditions, the deprotonation of a propargylic (C≡C—CH) carbon is an equilibrium that is reactant-favored.

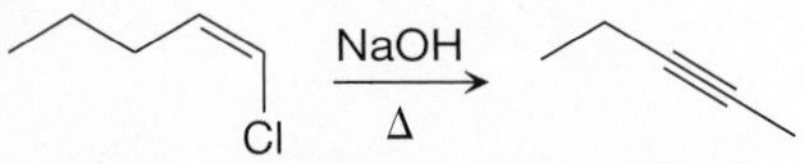
NaOH
Δ
Cl

10.54 Draw a mechanism to account for the formation of each product in the following reaction. *Hint*: Under these conditions, the deprotonation of a propargylic (C≡C—CH) carbon is an equilibrium that is reactant-favored.

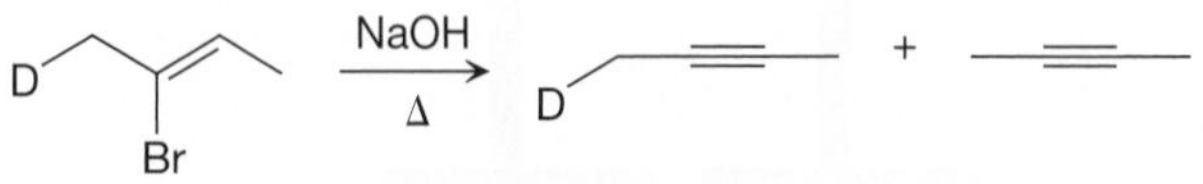
D
Br
NaOH
Δ
D
+

10.55 **(SYN)** The reaction in Problem 10.7 produces a mixture of ethers rather than the desired ether exclusively. Starting with cyclopentanol and pentan-3-ol (the same two alcohols given in Problem 10.7), show the sequence of reactions that would need to be carried out to produce (1-ethylpropoxy)cyclopentane as the exclusive ether.

10.56 When the following 2,3-epoxyalcohol is dissolved in aqueous base, an equal mixture of the two compounds shown is produced. Draw a complete, detailed mechanism for this reaction.

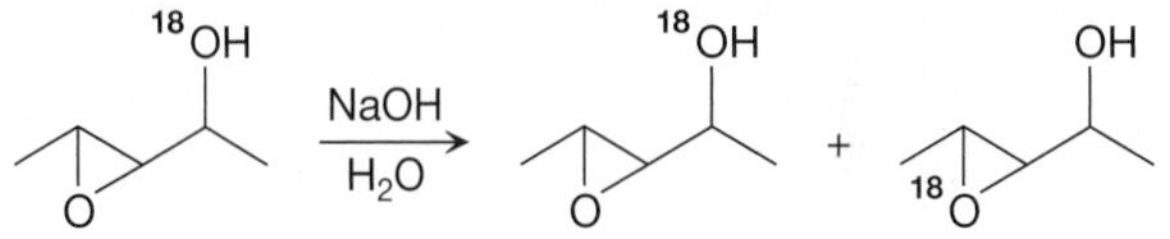
NaOH
H2O
+

10.57 **(SYN)** Show how you would carry out the following transformations. *Hint*: Each transformation may require more than one reaction.

(a)

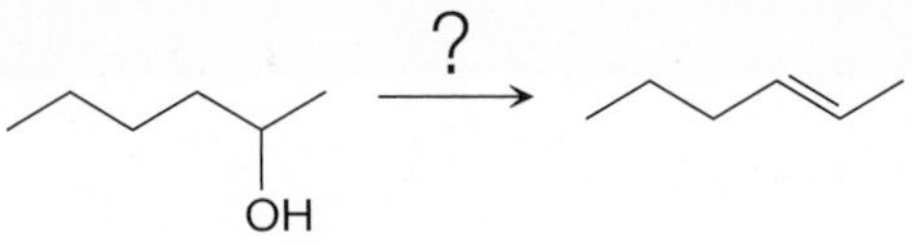

(b)

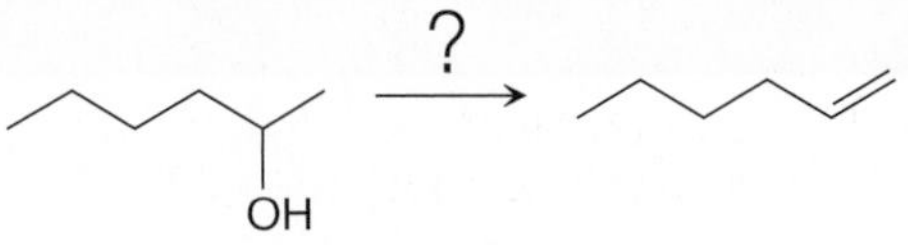

10.58 Determine the structures of compounds **A–F** in the following sequence of reactions.

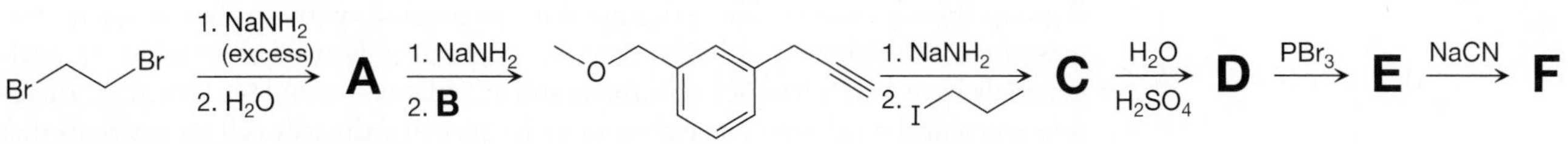
1. NaNH2 (excess)
2. H2O
A
1. NaNH2
2. B
1. NaNH2
2.
C
H2O
H2SO4
D
PBr3
E
NaCN
F

10.59 Determine the structures of compounds **G–L** in the following sequence of reactions.

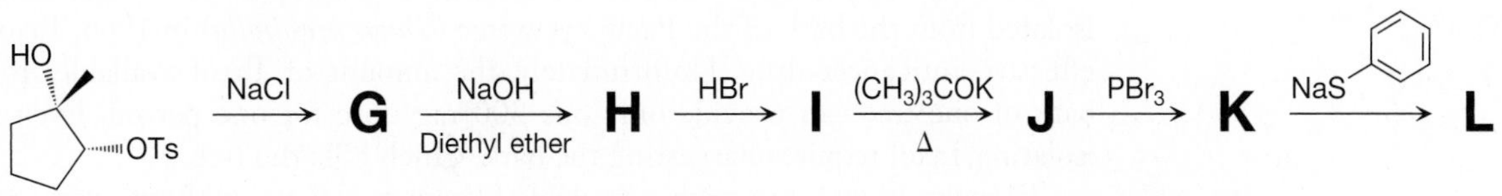
HO
OTs
NaCl
G
NaOH
Diethyl ether
H
HBr
I
(CH3)3COK
Δ
J
PBr3
K
NaS
L

11

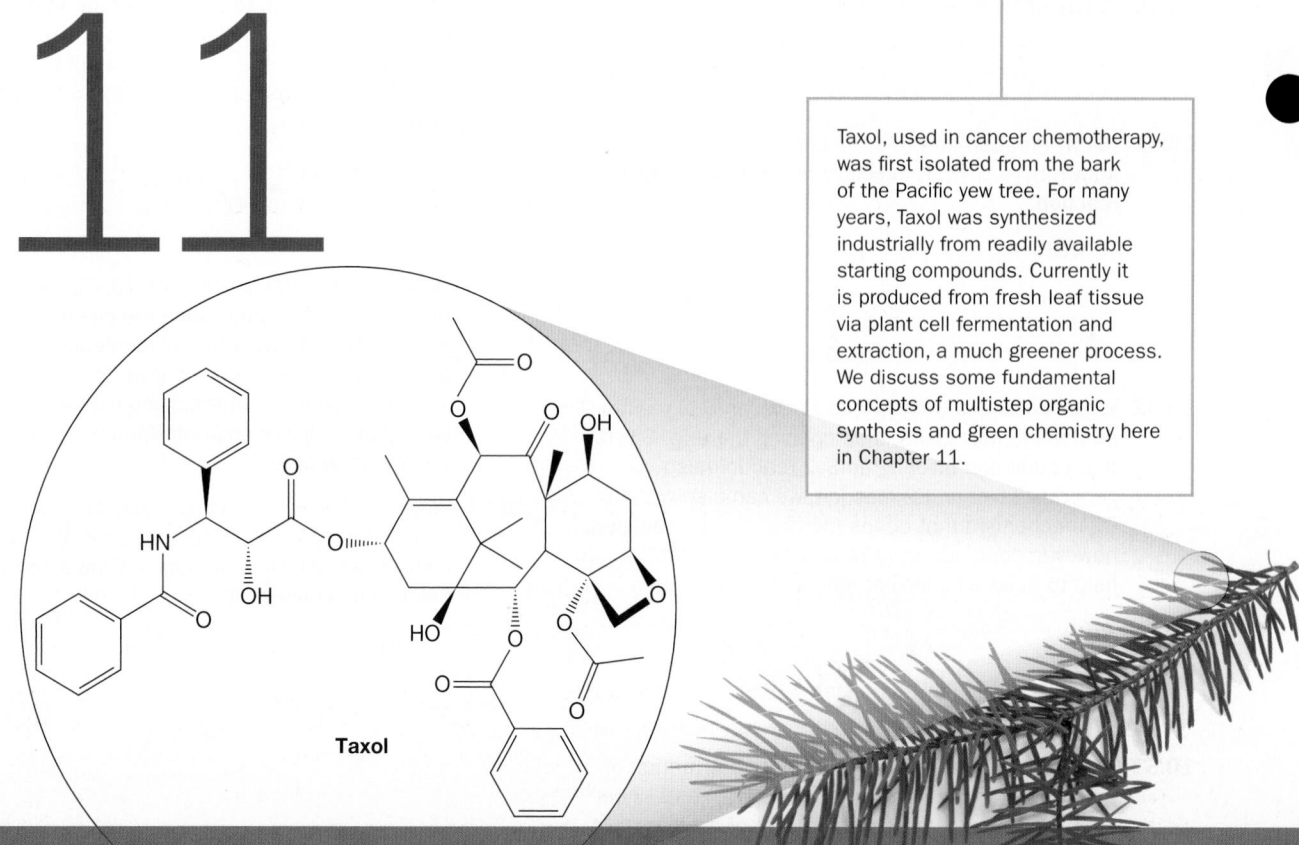

Taxol, used in cancer chemotherapy, was first isolated from the bark of the Pacific yew tree. For many years, Taxol was synthesized industrially from readily available starting compounds. Currently it is produced from fresh leaf tissue via plant cell fermentation and extraction, a much greener process. We discuss some fundamental concepts of multistep organic synthesis and green chemistry here in Chapter 11.

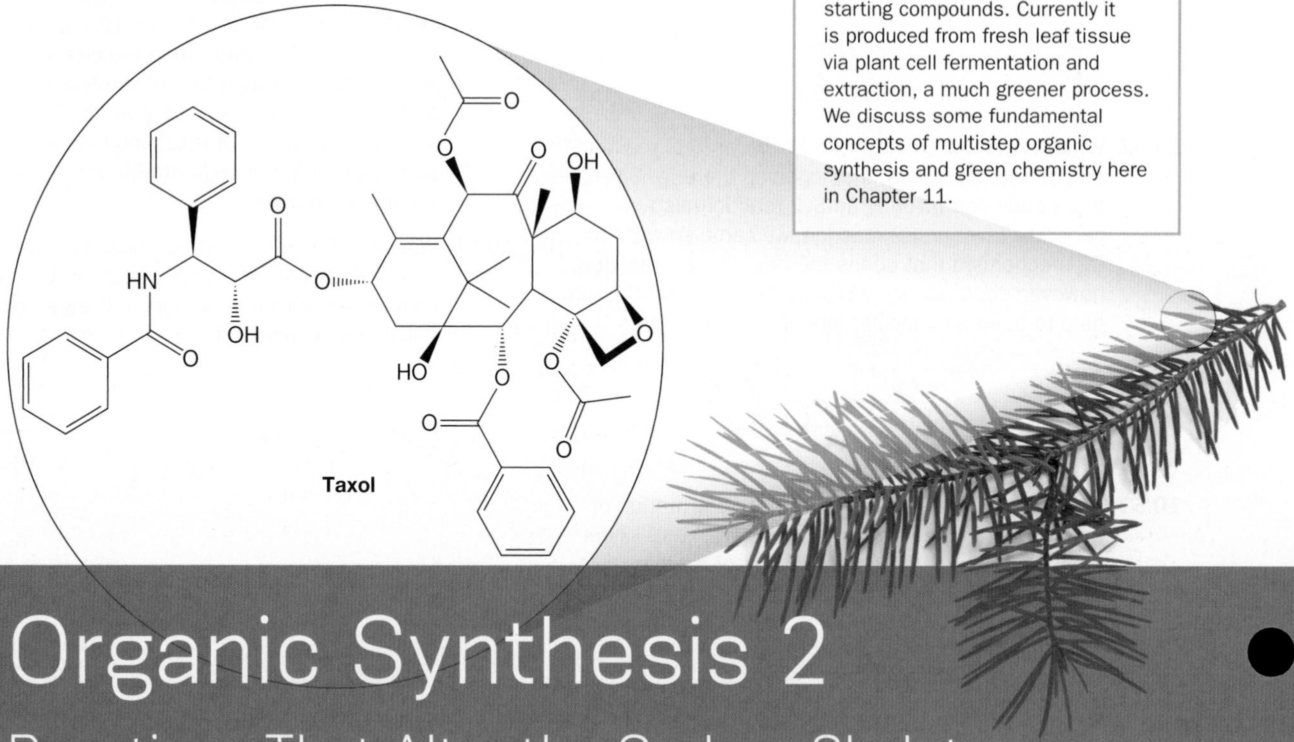
Taxol

Organic Synthesis 2

Reactions That Alter the Carbon Skeleton, and Designing Multistep Syntheses

In Chapter 10, we introduced some general ideas surrounding organic synthesis, but our discussions were limited mainly to *functional group transformations*. Functional group transformations are very important to organic synthesis, but synthetic targets often have elaborate carbon skeletons, whereas readily available starting materials generally have only a handful of carbons and are relatively simple in structure. Therefore, a practical synthesis of an elaborate molecule will ordinarily call for reactions that *alter the carbon skeleton*: that is, reactions that form or break C—C σ bonds.

Consider Taxol, whose structure is shown at the top of this page. Originally isolated from the bark of the Pacific yew tree (*Taxus brevifolia*) in 1966, Taxol is an effective anticancer drug. Unfortunately, the amount of Taxol available from the bark of one tree can provide only one 300-mg dose for one person. Even worse, isolating Taxol requires harvesting the bark, which kills the tree.

To make Taxol more readily available to cancer patients without overharvesting the Pacific yew to the point of extinction, organic chemists began efforts to synthesize Taxol. In 1994, Robert A. Holton (b. 1944) of Florida State University devised the first route for synthesizing Taxol from commercially available starting materials. This synthesis, which was the culmination of 12 years of work, consisted of 46 synthetic steps. As you can imagine from Taxol's elaborate structure, several of those

Chapter Outline

steps involve reactions that alter the carbon skeleton, particularly reactions that form carbon–carbon bonds. (Since then, other schemes to synthesize Taxol have been designed with somewhat fewer steps.)

Here in Chapter 11, we explore some of the strategies for devising a multistep synthesis. We begin by revisiting the carbon–carbon bond-forming reactions we have previously encountered. In doing so, we introduce a strategy called *retrosynthetic analysis* to help us determine which known reactions might be feasible to use in a synthesis, especially reactions that alter the carbon skeleton. Then we will learn some new reactions that form carbon–carbon bonds, which will give us more opportunities to practice retrosynthetic analysis. Finally, we will discuss *green chemistry*, which describes a responsible approach to designing and carrying out a synthesis, especially as it pertains to taking care of our planet.

As was the case with the new reactions introduced in Chapter 10, the new reactions introduced here in Chapter 11 are all related by their mechanisms; at the heart of each one is a nucleophilic substitution, the same type of mechanism we have been studying for the last few chapters. Therefore, as you learn these new reactions, focus on these mechanistic patterns that *simplify* organic chemistry.

SECTION 11.1 OBJECTIVES

You will be able to:

1. Explain what a transform is, and effectively carry out transforms on carbon–carbon bond-forming reactions introduced in previous chapters.
2. Use retrosynthetic analysis to design a synthesis that incorporates carbon–carbon bond-forming reactions from previous chapters.

11.1 Reactions That Alter the Carbon Skeleton and Retrosynthetic Analysis

We have mentioned that reactions that alter the carbon skeleton are key tools of synthesis. Only two such reactions have been introduced in this book so far; they are found in Table 9-12 (repeated below). As you can see, both reactions form a carbon–carbon bond, and both proceed through an S_N2 mechanism.

TABLE 9-12 Reactions That Alter the Carbon Skeleton[a]

	Starting Compound Class	Typical Reagents and Reaction Conditions	Compound Class Formed	Key Electron-Rich Species	Key Electron-Poor Species	Comments	Discussed in Section(s)
(1)	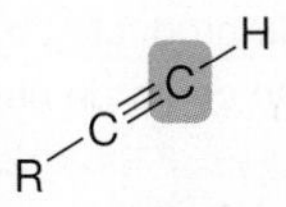 Alkyne	1. NaH 2. R′–X	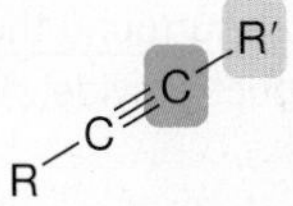 Alkyne	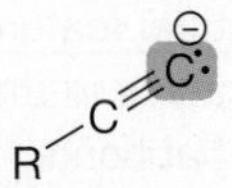 Alkynide anion	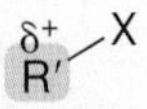 Alkyl halide	S_N2 reaction	7.2, 8.3, 8.5, 9.3b, 9.9
(2)	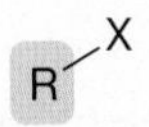 Alkyl halide	NaCN	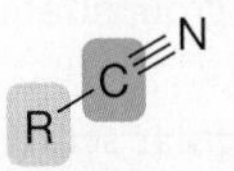 Nitrile	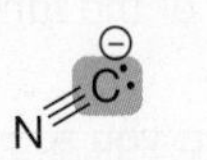 Cyanide anion	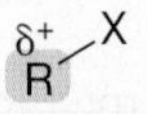 Alkyl halide	S_N2 reaction	7.2, 8.3, 8.5, 9.9

[a]X = Cl, Br, or I.

Equation 11-1 gives a specific example of the general reaction in Entry 1 of Table 9-12, which is *alkylation* of a terminal alkyne:

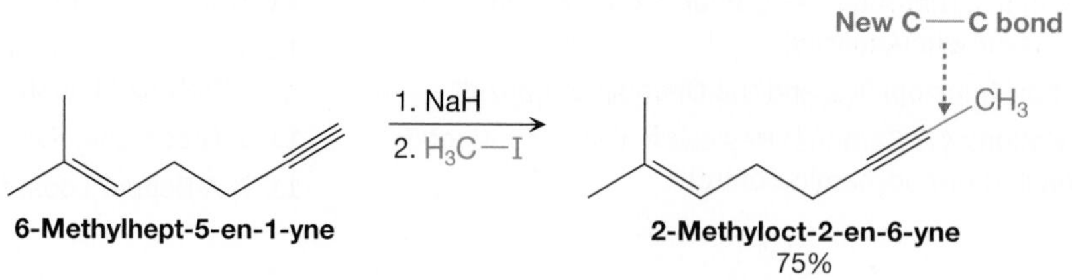
New C—C bond
1. NaH
2. $H_3C—I$
CH_3
6-Methylhept-5-en-1-yne
2-Methyloct-2-en-6-yne
75%

(11-1)

The mechanism for this reaction is shown in Equation 11-2. In Step 1, the powerful hydride base (H^-) deprotonates the terminal alkyne to yield an alkynide anion. The alkynide anion is a strong nucleophile, and in Step 2, it undergoes an S_N2 reaction with CH_3I:

Mechanism for the alkylation of a terminal alkyne (Eq. 11-1)

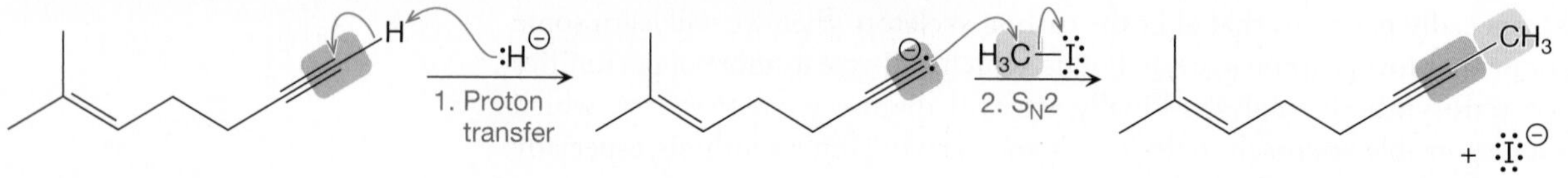
1. Proton transfer
2. S_N2
CH_3

(11-2)

A specific example of the general reaction in Entry 2 of Table 9-12 is given in Equation 11-3:

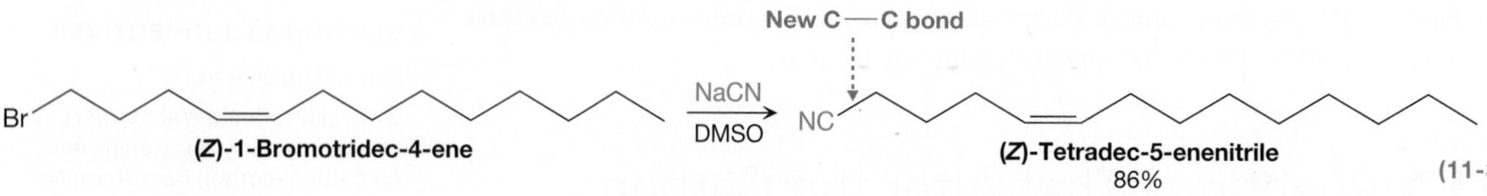
New C—C bond
Br
NaCN
DMSO
NC
(Z)-1-Bromotridec-4-ene
(Z)-Tetradec-5-enenitrile
86%

(11-3)

The mechanism for this reaction, shown in Equation 11-4, consists of just one S_N2 elementary step:

Mechanism for the conversion of an alkyl halide into a nitrile (Eq. 11-3)

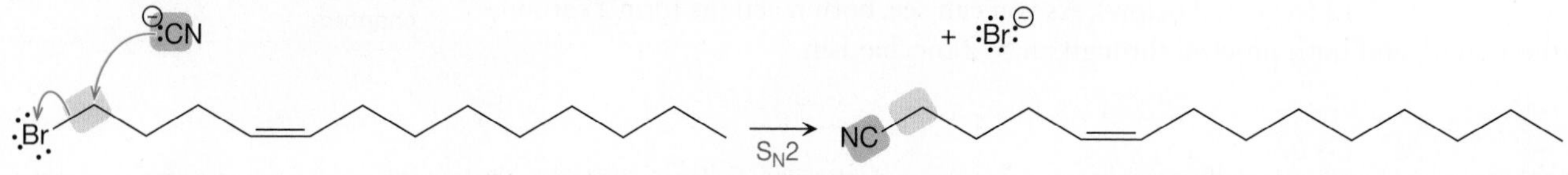
CN
Br
S_N2
NC
Br

(11-4)

To know that one of these carbon–carbon bond-forming reactions could be incorporated into a synthesis, you need to be familiar with two aspects of each reaction:

Important Aspects of a C—C Bond-Forming Reaction

1. The structural features that surround the new C—C bond in the product. These features in the product provide *clues* as to which reaction could be used to make that bond.
2. The reactants, or **precursors**, that would be necessary to carry out that reaction. In particular, you should be keenly aware of the identities and relative locations of the functional groups required in the precursors.

Therefore, when you see a particular set of features surrounding a C—C bond in the target, you will quickly be able to draw the precursors for a reaction that could make that bond.

For example, consider the general reaction in Entry 1 of Table 9-12. As shown in Equation 11-5, the new C—C bond in the product involves one C atom (red screen) that is part of a C≡C triple bond and another C atom (blue screen) that is sp^3-hybridized and is part of an alkyl group:

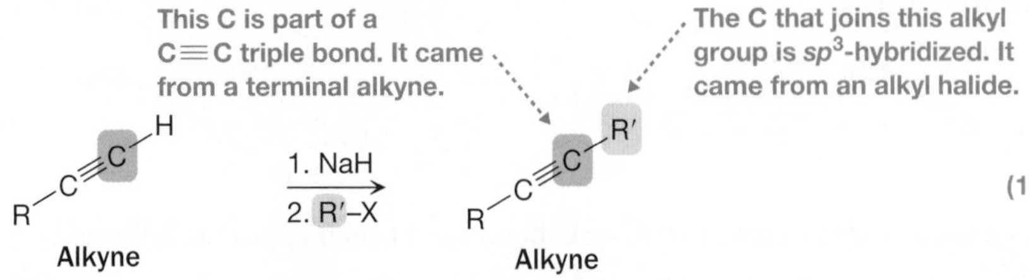
This C is part of a C≡C triple bond. It came from a terminal alkyne.
The C that joins this alkyl group is sp³-hybridized. It came from an alkyl halide.
1. NaH
2. R′–X
Alkyne
Alkyne

(11-5)

To form such a bond, one precursor would be a terminal alkyne and the other precursor would be an alkyl halide.

The idea of drawing precursors for a reaction that can accomplish desired features in a target is formalized (and streamlined) by what is called a **transform**, which can be thought of as the *undoing* of a synthetic step. Once we have a reaction in mind that will produce a particular feature of a target, we determine the necessary precursors and then draw an open arrow (⟹) *from the target to the precursors*:

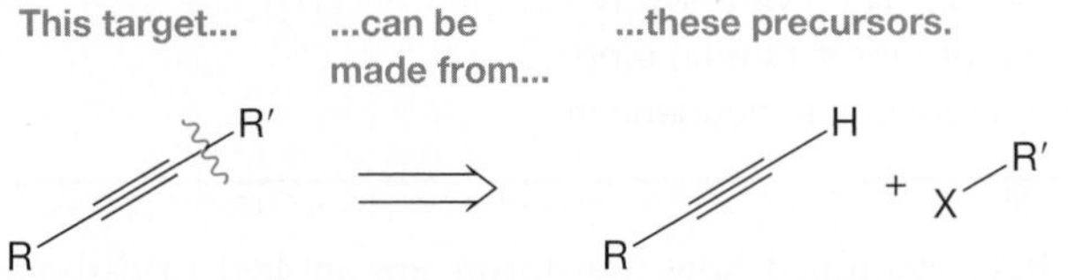
This target...
...can be made from...
...these precursors.

(11-6)

The open arrow is called a **retrosynthetic arrow** because it points to the materials that would come *beforehand* in a synthesis. As indicated above, it is helpful to think of the retrosynthetic arrow as saying "can be made from." Thus the transform in Equation 11-6 can be read: "The new C—C bond in the target *can be made from* a terminal alkyne and an alkyl halide." The squiggly red line drawn across the C—C bond is a convention used to help us keep track of the bond that needs to be made from the precursors.

In Equation 11-7, we apply a transform to the general reaction in Entry 2 of Table 9-12:

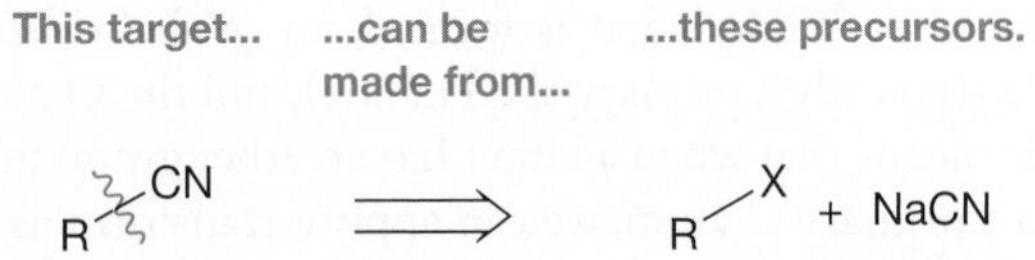
This target...
...can be made from...
...these precursors.
+ NaCN

(11-7)

In this case, the transform tells us "The new C—C bond in the target *can be made from* an alkyl halide and sodium cyanide."

YOUR TURN 11.1

Complete each of these transforms. *Hint*: Use Equations 11-1 and 11-3 as guides.

(a)

(b)

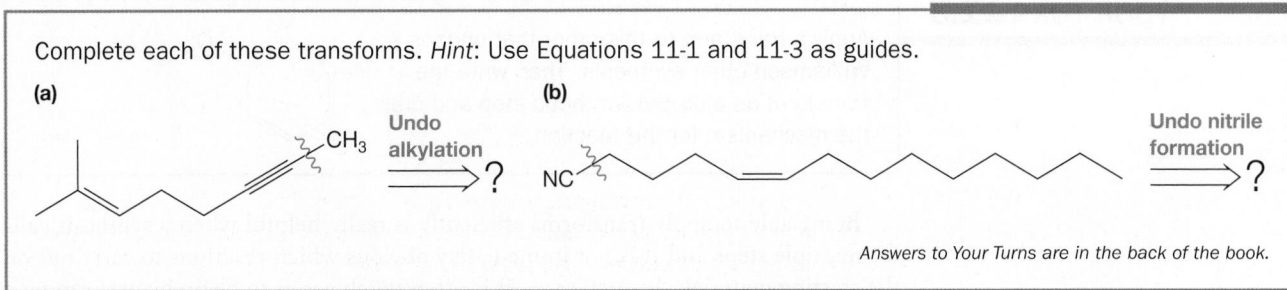

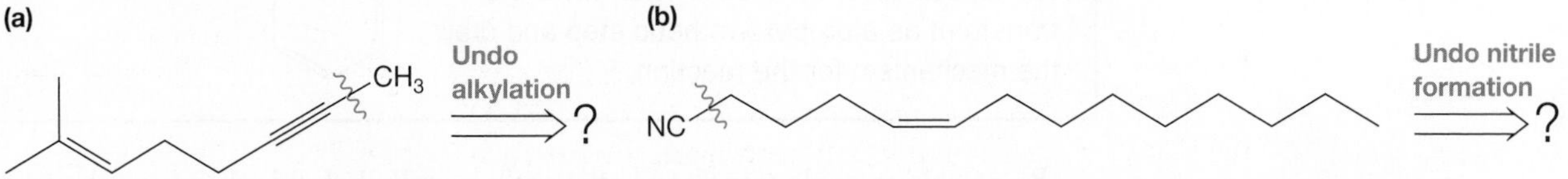
Undo alkylation
?
Undo nitrile formation
?

Answers to Your Turns are in the back of the book.

Frequently a target has more than one feature to consider when transforms are applied, in which case there could be more than one possible set of precursors. For example, Your Turn 11.1a indicates one way to apply a transform that undoes alkylation of a terminal alkyne (Entry 1 of Table 9-12). However, as indicated in Equation 11-8, there is another C—C bond on the other side of the triple bond that could also be the product of an alkylation reaction. Therefore, we could apply the following transform instead:

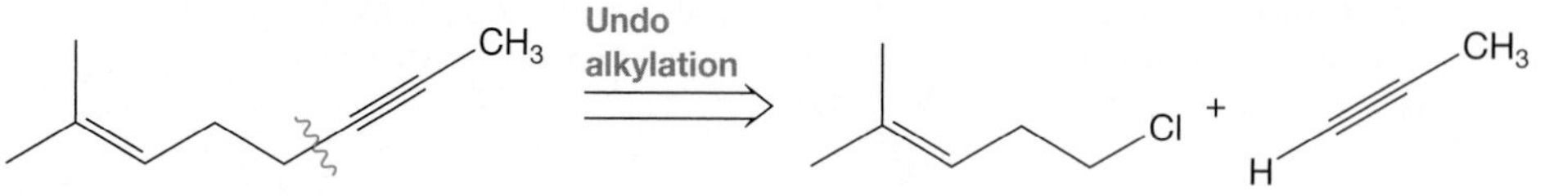

CH3
Undo
alkylation
Cl
+
CH3
H

(11-8)

The synthetic step to make that C—C bond might then appear as follows:

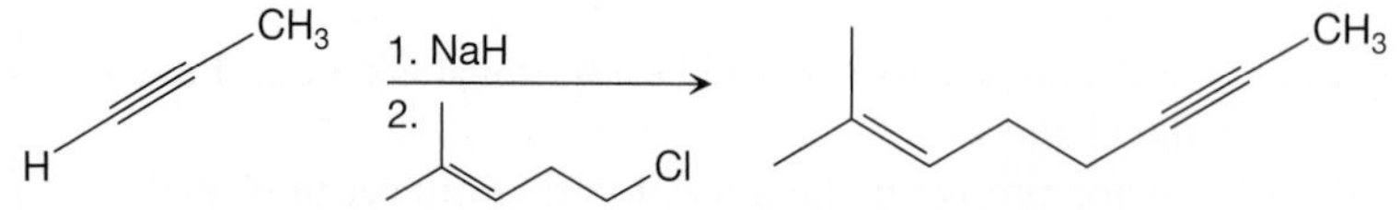

CH3
H
1. NaH
2.
Cl
CH3

(11-9)

YOUR TURN **11.2**

Apply two different transforms to the following alkyne that would undo an alkylation reaction. Then write each transform as a proper synthetic step and draw each reaction's mechanism.

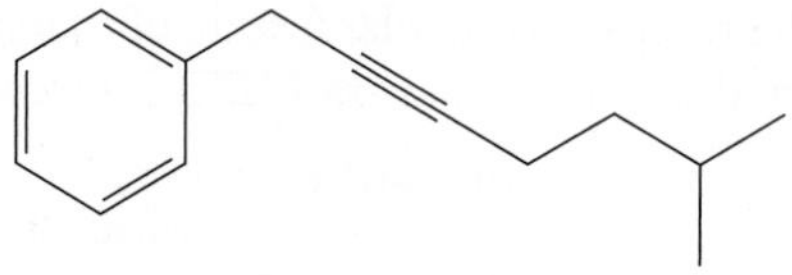

So far we have examined how transforms are applied to carbon–carbon bond-forming reactions. Let's now see how they can be applied to functional group transformations. Consider the Williamson ether synthesis (Entry 4 from Table 9-11):

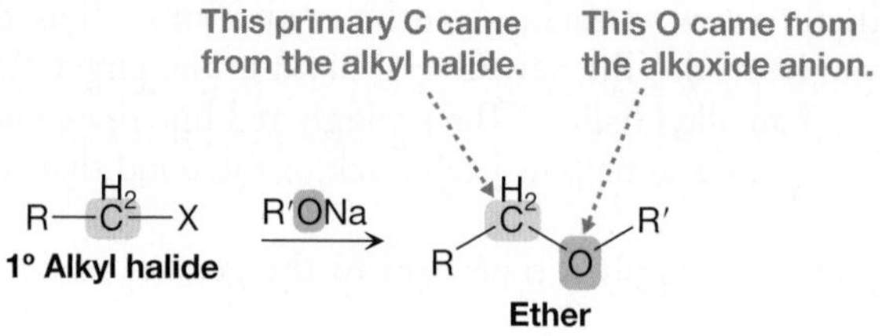

This primary C came from the alkyl halide.
This O came from the alkoxide anion.
R—C—X
H2
1° Alkyl halide
R′ONa
R
H2
C
O
R′
Ether

(11-10)

As indicated, in the C—O bond that is formed, an sp^3-hybridized C atom comes from an alkyl halide (typically a primary alkyl halide), and the O atom comes from an alkoxide anion. This means that when a target has an ether group in which the oxygen atom is attached to a primary C atom, we can apply a transform as follows:

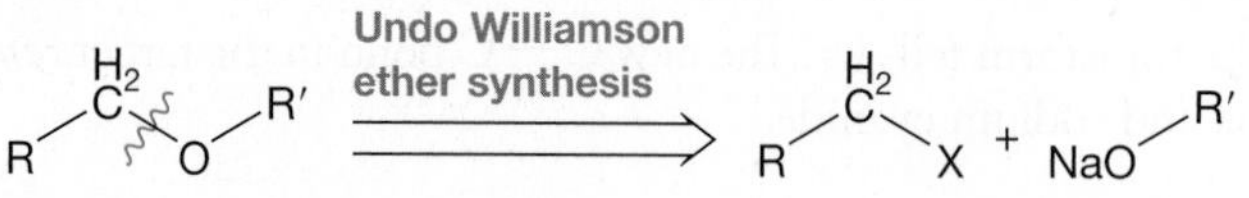

H2
C
R
O
R′
Undo Williamson
ether synthesis
H2
C
R
X
+
NaO
R′

(11-11)

YOUR TURN **11.3**

Apply a transform to this ether that undoes a Williamson ether synthesis. Then write the transform as a proper synthetic step and draw the mechanism for the reaction.

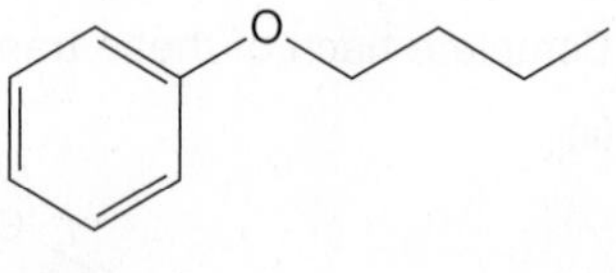

O

Being able to apply transforms efficiently is really helpful when a synthesis calls for multiple steps and it is not immediately obvious which reactions to carry out on the starting materials. In such cases, it is often much easier to begin by performing a **retrosynthetic analysis**, a process that helps in the design of a multistep synthesis:

Steps in a Retrosynthetic Analysis

1. Examine the target for a feature that could be made from a known reaction.
2. Apply a transform that *undoes* the reaction you have in mind, in order to determine the precursors of that reaction.
3. Examine each precursor for a feature that could be made from a known reaction.
4. For each precursor, apply a transform that undoes the reaction you have in mind.
5. Continue applying transforms until you arrive at starting materials.

Retrosynthetic analysis is essential to the field of organic synthesis. The concept of retrosynthetic analysis was developed in the first half of the 20th century, but some of the most significant advances came in the 1960s when Elias J. Corey (b. 1928) of Harvard University applied it to design complex synthesis schemes. This changed the face of organic synthesis and helped earn Professor Corey the Nobel Prize in Chemistry in 1990.

To begin to appreciate the usefulness of retrosynthetic analysis, let's design the synthesis that is called for in Equation 11-12. Specifically, we are asked to show how 1-methoxypent-2-yne can be synthesized from starting compounds that contain three or fewer carbons. (The two reaction arrows suggest that the synthesis might require more than one synthetic step.)

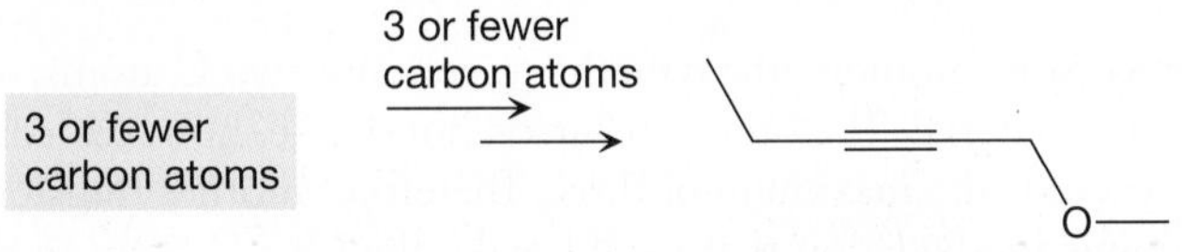
3 or fewer carbon atoms
3 or fewer carbon atoms
O
1-Methoxypent-2-yne

(11-12)

Because the target contains a continuous chain of five C atoms, and the compounds we may use as our starting materials can contain at most three C atoms, the synthesis of 1-methoxypent-2-yne must contain at least one reaction that forms a C—C bond.

Notice that the target contains a C≡C triple bond, and that triple bond is joined to an alkyl group on the left. Therefore, we can apply a transform that undoes alkylation, as follows:

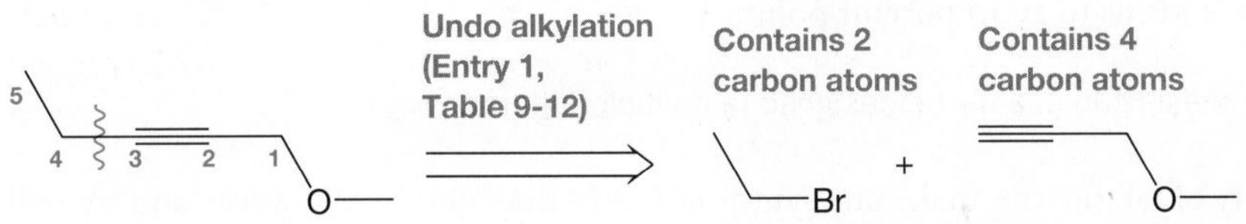
Undo alkylation (Entry 1, Table 9-12)
Contains 2 carbon atoms
Contains 4 carbon atoms
5
4
3
2
1
O
Br
+
O
Bromoethane **3-Methoxyprop-1-yne**

(11-13)

The alkyl halide precursor contains two C atoms, and the other precursor, 3-methoxyprop-1-yne, is a terminal alkyne.

Of those two precursors, only bromoethane is acceptable for our starting material, because it contains three or fewer C atoms. 3-Methoxyprop-1-yne contains four C atoms, so it cannot be used as a starting material. Instead, we must apply a transform to dissect it into smaller precursors.

Because 3-methoxyprop-1-yne contains a C—O—C group characteristic of ethers, we can apply a transform that undoes a Williamson ether synthesis:

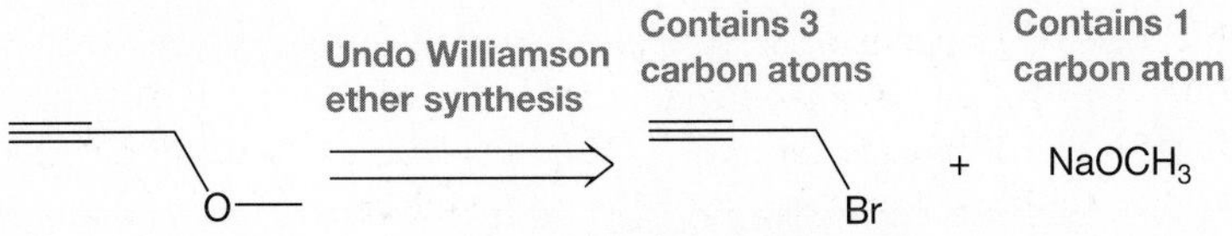
Undo Williamson ether synthesis
Contains 3 carbon atoms
Contains 1 carbon atom
O
Br
+
NaOCH3

(11-14)

Both of these precursors now contain three or fewer carbons and can be used as starting materials.

What remains to complete the synthesis is to reverse the transforms to present them as proper synthetic steps, as shown in Equation 11-15:

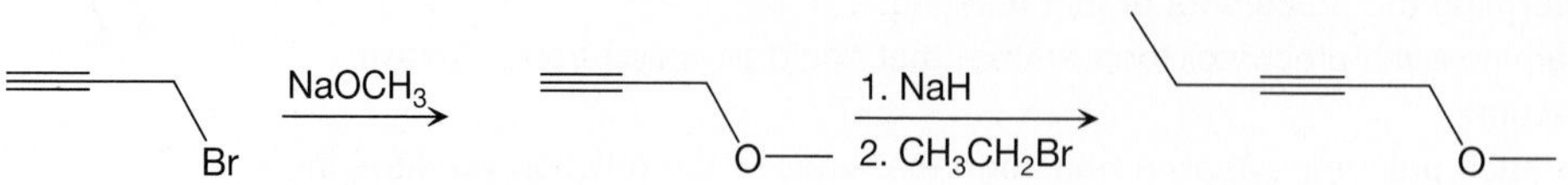

$NaOCH_3$
Br
1. NaH
2. CH_3CH_2Br
O

(11-15)

Consider that each of the previous transforms could have been applied in a different way. For example, whereas in Equation 11-13 the transform was applied to the C-3—C-4 bond, we could instead begin by applying the transform to the C-1—C-2 bond to the right of the triple bond. This is shown in the first transform in Equation 11-16:

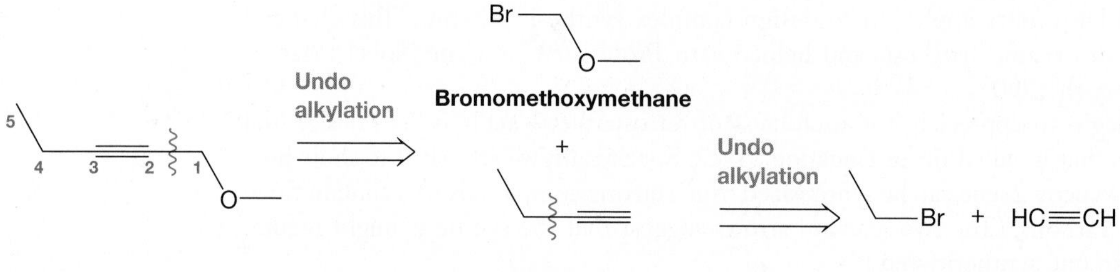

Br
O
Undo alkylation
Bromomethoxymethane
+
Undo alkylation
5
4
3
2
1
Br + HC≡CH
But-1-yne

(11-16)

One of the precursors, bromomethoxymethane, contains two C atoms, so it is acceptable as a starting material. The other precursor, but-1-yne, however, contains four C atoms, which exceeds the maximum of three. Therefore, another transform is applied, this time undoing an alkylation that would make the C—C bond to the left of the triple bond. The two precursors for that transform each have two C atoms, so both of them are acceptable as starting materials. The synthesis can then be written as shown in Equation 11-17:

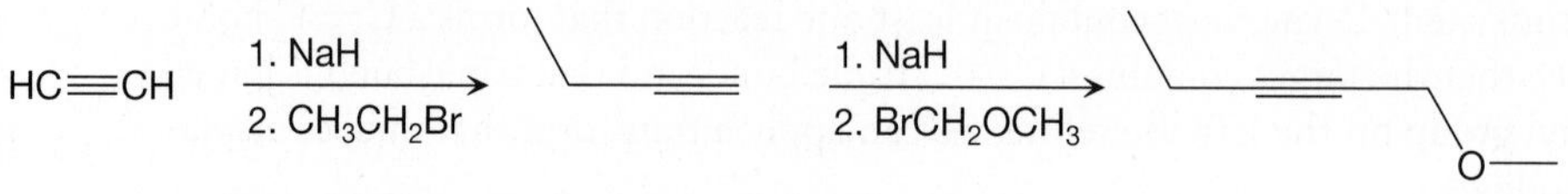

HC≡CH
1. NaH
2. CH_3CH_2Br
1. NaH
2. $BrCH_2OCH_3$
O

(11-17)

This leads us to an important point:

A synthesis can usually be designed in multiple different ways.

A variety of factors can make one synthesis better than another, however, and we will touch upon several of these factors in our continued discussion of synthesis here in Chapter 11 and in Chapter 21.

YOUR TURN **11.4**

Show how to carry out the transform in Equation 11-14 by undoing a Williamson ether synthesis that would make the other O—C bond, and modify the synthesis in Equation 11-15 accordingly.

SOLVED PROBLEM **11.1**

How to design a synthesis that calls for the formation of a C—C bond

Break It Down **Propose a way to carry out the synthesis shown here.**

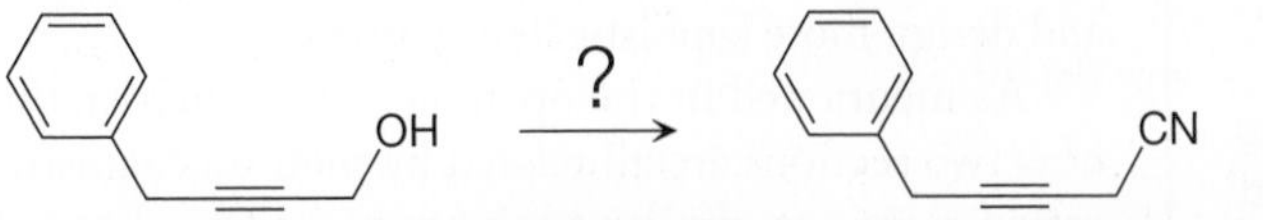

OH
?
CN

Think	Solve
Will a C—C bond-forming reaction be necessary?	Yes. Notice that the C—OH bond must become a C—CN bond instead.
How do we apply a transform to undo that C—C bond-forming reaction?	As we saw in the transform in Equation 11-7 (p. 565), a new C—CN bond in the target could be made from an alkyl halide and sodium cyanide. We can apply the same kind of transform here. 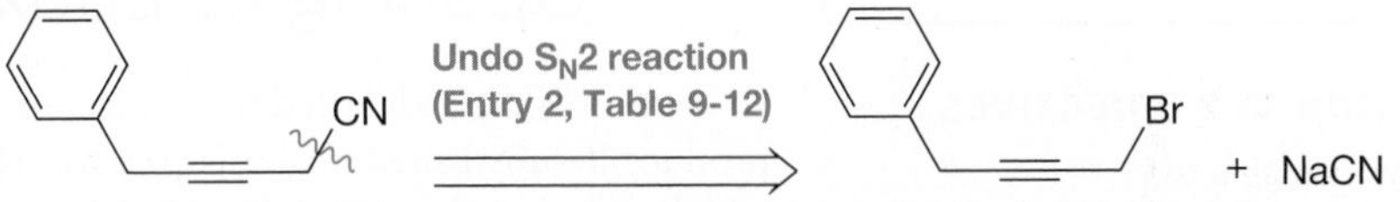 CN Undo S_N2 reaction (Entry 2, Table 9-12) Br + NaCN
Can the precursor be made from the starting material? Would the desired change require a functional group transformation or a reaction that alters the carbon skeleton?	The precursor from the first transform is a primary alkyl bromide and the starting material is an alcohol. To make the alkyl bromide from the alcohol would require a functional group transformation, so we should consider functional group transformations we have studied so far (Table 9-11 on pp. 498–499 and Table 10-1 on pp. 552–553). Entry 3 of Table 10-1 shows that an alkyl bromide can be made from the corresponding alcohol and PBr_3, as shown in the following transform. 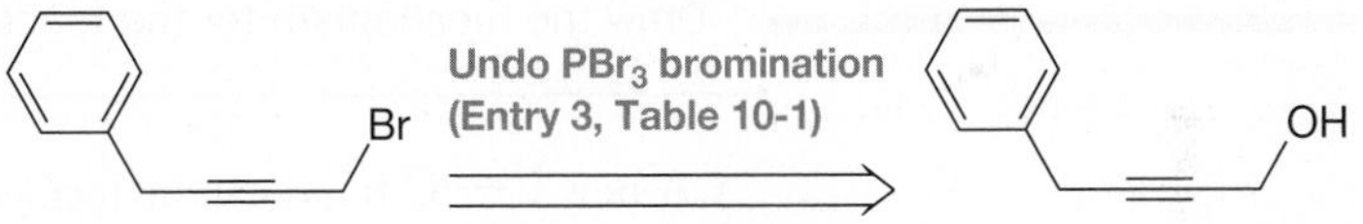 Br Undo PBr_3 bromination (Entry 3, Table 10-1) OH
With the retrosynthetic analysis complete, how is the synthesis written?	To present the synthesis, reverse each transform and apply the necessary reagents. The final synthesis is shown below. 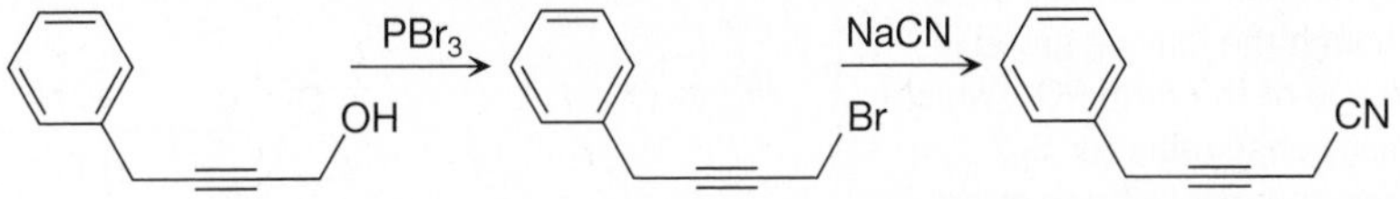 OH PBr_3 Br NaCN CN

Try It Propose a synthesis of pent-2-yne from compounds containing two or fewer carbons.

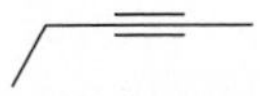

Pent-2-yne

Answers to all Try It exercises can be found in the Solutions Manual.

CONNECTIONS 11.1

Bundle up!
3-Hydroxypropanenitrile (Eq. 11-19) is a precursor to acrylonitrile, a monomer of polyacrylonitrile. Polyacrylonitrile is spun into a synthetic fiber that is marketed as Orlon and is commonly used to make knitted clothing.

We have seen that reactions that alter the carbon skeleton are really important in synthesis, and we have seen how helpful retrosynthetic analysis can be when designing a multistep synthesis. Our discussions about these topics have been rather limited, however, because only two reactions that alter the carbon skeleton have been presented so far. Sections 11.2 and 11.3 will introduce additional carbon–carbon bond-forming reactions and their mechanisms, expanding our ability to perform retrosynthetic analyses and design more sophisticated syntheses.

As mentioned in the opening of this chapter, the new reactions introduced in the next two sections are all related by their mechanisms; they are all nucleophilic substitution reactions, similar to the ones we have been studying in the previous chapters. Pay attention to the patterns that emerge in these mechanisms to avoid what might otherwise seem to be an overwhelming number of different organic reactions. The more you maintain your focus on mechanisms, the more simplified organic chemistry becomes.

11.2 Carbon Nucleophiles and the Opening of Epoxides

SECTION 11.2 OBJECTIVES

You will be able to:

1. Identify nucleophiles that open an epoxide ring to form a new C—C bond.
2. Apply transforms to the products of those reactions to determine feasible precursors.

In Section 10.7, we learned that nucleophiles can attack epoxides to open the ring and produce 2-substituted alcohols (see top Recall box). One example we previously saw, which is repeated in Equation 11-18, involves CH_3O^- as the nucleophile:

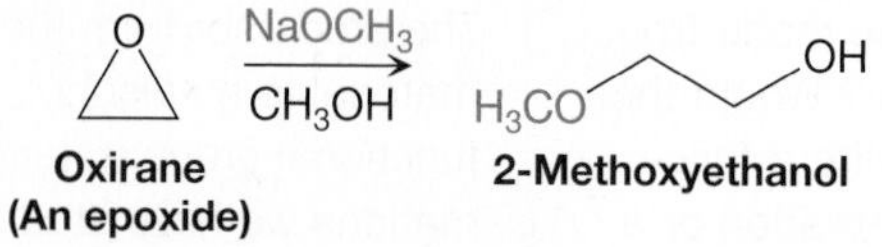

O
NaOCH3
CH3OH
OH
H3CO
Oxirane
(An epoxide)
2-Methoxyethanol

(11-18)

YOUR TURN 11.5

Draw the mechanism for the reaction in Equation 11-18.

◂ RECALL

The key step in epoxide ring-opening reactions is an S_N2 step. Even though the leaving group in that step is of the form RO^-, which is normally unsuitable for S_N2 reactions, the relief of ring strain compensates to drive the reaction forward.

A new C—C bond can be formed when a carbon nucleophile is used to open an epoxide ring. For example, Equations 11-19 and 11-20 show an epoxide reacting with the cyanide anion (NC^-) and an alkynide anion ($RC{\equiv}C^-$), respectively; both are nucleophiles that we have previously seen react in S_N2 reactions:

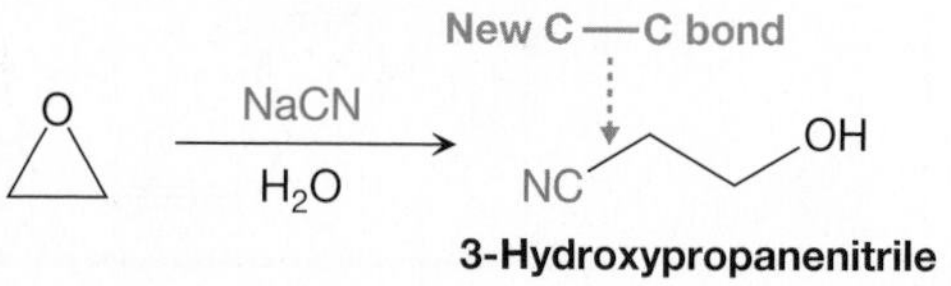

New C—C bond
O
NaCN
H2O
OH
NC
3-Hydroxypropanenitrile

(11-19)

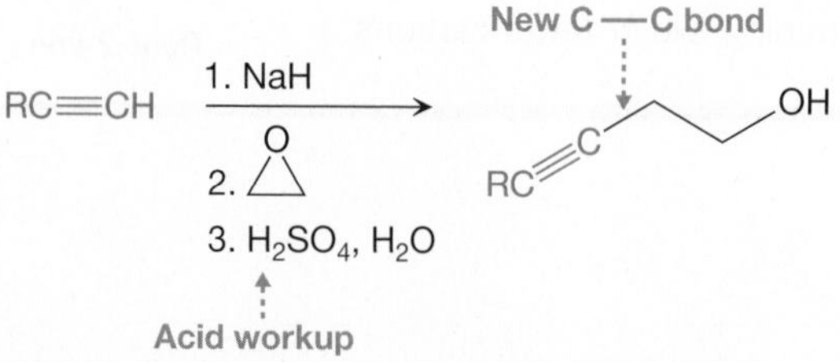

New C—C bond
RC≡CH
1. NaH
O
2.
3. H2SO4, H2O
Acid workup
C
RC
OH

(11-20)

◂ RECALL

As we saw in Section 10.12, an acid workup is often incorporated when the overall product of an organic reaction is negatively charged and basic. When an acid is added, the negatively charged product picks up a proton to become uncharged.

The mechanism for the reaction in Equation 11-20 is shown in Equation 11-21. Step 1 is deprotonation of the terminal alkyne to produce the alkynide anion nucleophile. In Step 2, which is an S_N2 step, the alkynide anion attacks the epoxide to open the ring. Step 3 is an acid workup to produce the uncharged product (see bottom Recall box).

Mechanism for the opening of an epoxide by an alkynide anion (Eq. 11-20)

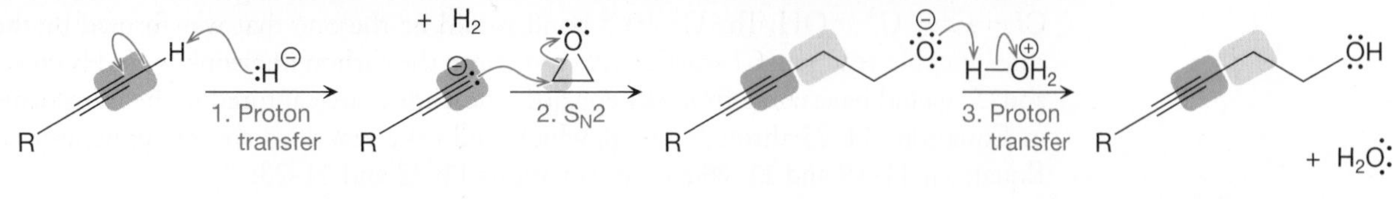
+ H2
1. Proton transfer
2. SN2
3. Proton transfer
+ H2O

(11-21)

YOUR TURN **11.6**

Draw the mechanism for the reaction in Equation 11-19.

As discussed in Section 7.1b, *organometallic compounds* such as alkyllithium reagents (R—Li) and Grignard reagents (R—MgX) can be simplified to just R:⁻. Therefore, these organometallic reagents can behave as carbon nucleophiles, and as shown in Equations 11-22 and 11-23, they will react with epoxides to open the ring:

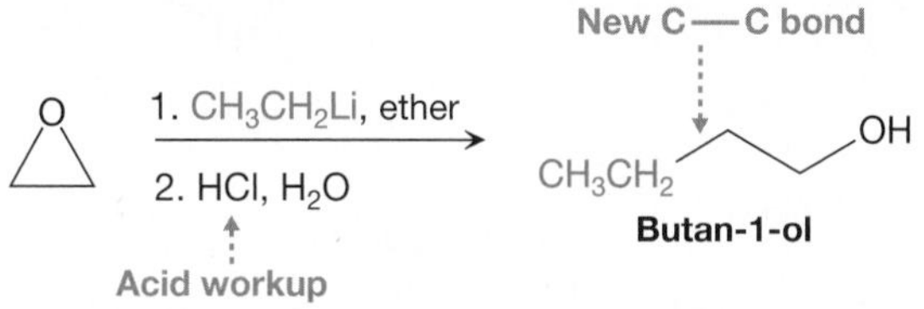
New C—C bond
1. CH3CH2Li, ether
2. HCl, H2O
Acid workup
CH3CH2
OH
Butan-1-ol

(11-22)

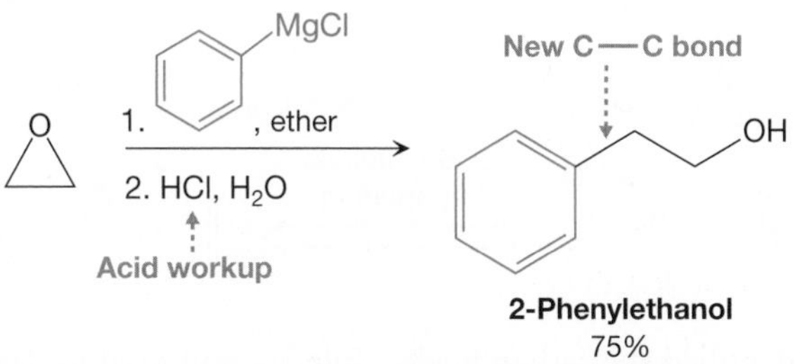
MgCl
1. , ether
2. HCl, H2O
Acid workup
New C—C bond
OH
2-Phenylethanol
75%

(11-23)

The mechanism for the reaction in Equation 11-23 is shown in Equation 11-24. In Step 1, the simplified representation of the Grignard reagent, $C_6H_5^-$, attacks the epoxide ring in an S_N2 step. The resulting alkoxide anion is protonated in Step 2 when the acid is added:

CONNECTIONS 11.2

Stop and smell the ... 2-phenylethanol
2-Phenylethanol (Eq. 11-23) is found in the extracts of certain flowers, such as rose, carnation, and geranium. This makes it useful in the perfume industry.

Mechanism for the opening of an epoxide by a Grignard reagent (Eq. 11-23)

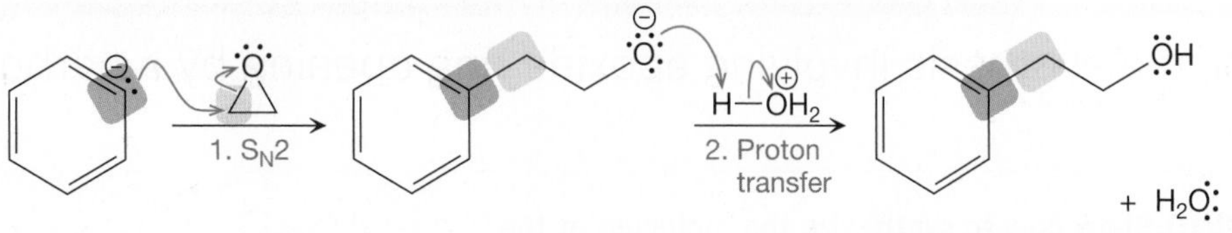
1. SN2
2. Proton transfer
+ H2O

(11-24)

YOUR TURN **11.7**

Draw the mechanism for the reaction in Equation 11-22.

11.2a Using Epoxides to Form C—C Bonds in Synthesis

As discussed in Section 11.1, carbon–carbon bond-forming reactions like the ones just presented are valuable in organic synthesis. To know whether one of these reactions should be considered for a synthesis, we need to recognize the feature that characterizes each of the products, which is a bonding arrangement of the form $C^1—C^2—C^3—OH$. The $C^1—C^2$ bond would be the one that was formed by the ring-opening reaction, C^1 would have come from the carbon nucleophile, and both C^2 and C^3 would have come from the epoxide. These ideas are captured in the transforms in Equations 11-25 through 11-28, which undo the reactions we saw previously in Equations 11-19 and 11-20 and in Equations 11-22 and 11-23:

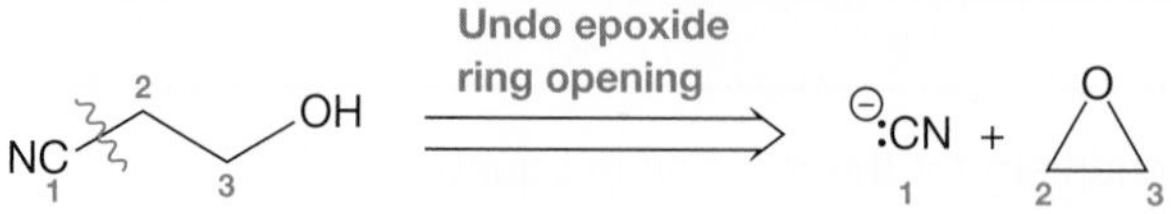
Undo epoxide
ring opening

(11-25)

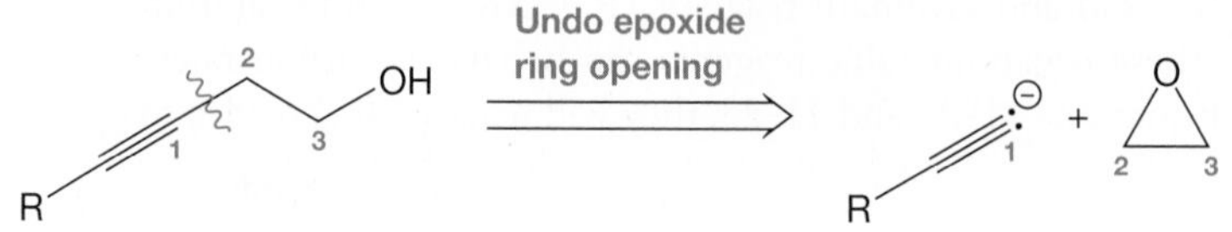
Undo epoxide
ring opening

(11-26)

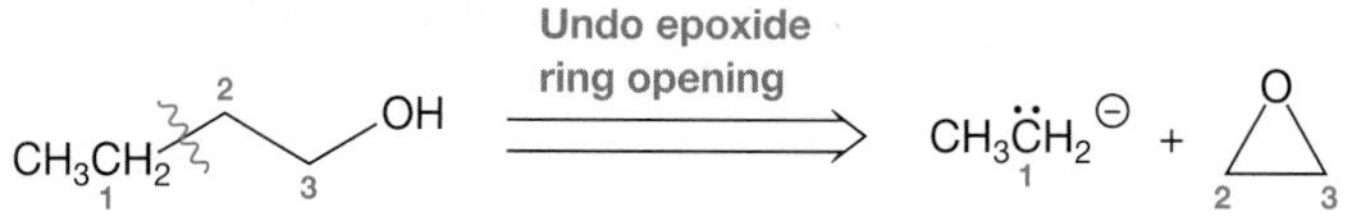
Undo epoxide
ring opening

(11-27)

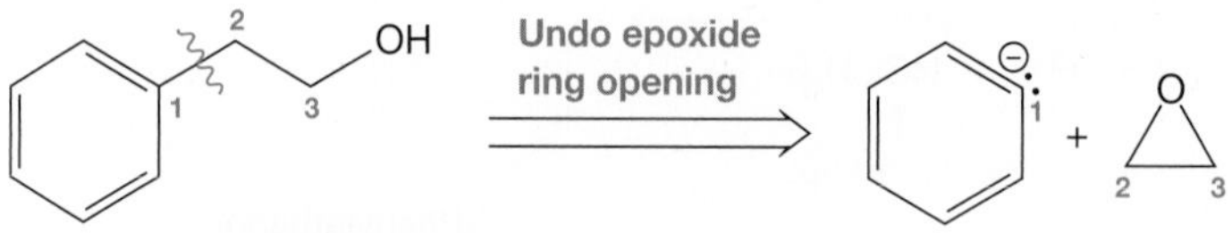
Undo epoxide
ring opening

(11-28)

Once we have identified the carbon nucleophile, we still need to determine the precursor from which it could have come. For example, NC^- could have come from directly adding NaCN, $RC{\equiv}C^-$ could have come from deprotonating $RC{\equiv}CH$, and $CH_3CH_2^-$ and $C_6H_5^-$ could have come from directly adding the corresponding organometallic reagent: R—Li or R—MgX.

SOLVED PROBLEM **11.2**

How to design a synthesis involving epoxide ring opening by a carbon nucleophile

Break It Down **Show how to synthesize the molecule at the right, beginning with compounds that contain four or fewer carbons.**

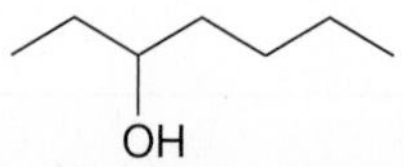

Think	Solve
Does the target have the bonding arrangement C—C—C—OH? How many of these bonding arrangements are there?	There are two such bonding arrangements, highlighted here: 

(continued)

How can we apply transforms to undo an epoxide ring-opening reaction?

For the first bonding arrangement, we can apply the following transform:

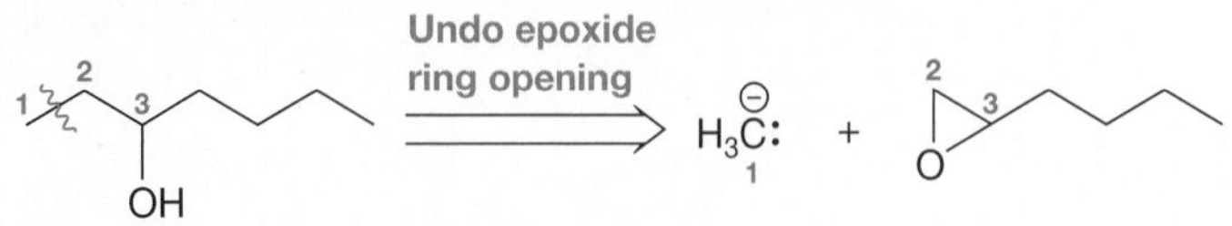

Undo epoxide ring opening
OH

For the second bonding arrangement, we can apply the following transform:

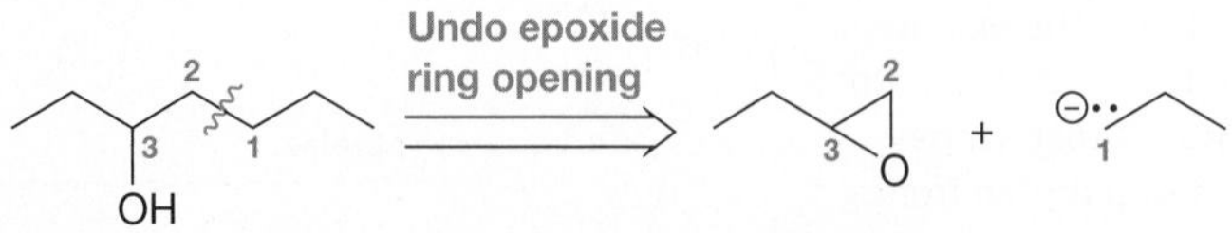

Undo epoxide ring opening
OH

Considering the restrictions for the starting materials, which transform would be the better choice? How can you turn that transform into a synthetic step?

Given that the starting materials must have four or fewer carbons, the second transform would be the better choice. The second transform has precursors with four carbons and three carbons, whereas the first transform has precursors with one carbon and six carbons.

To write the synthetic step, we can choose $CH_3CH_2CH_2MgBr$ as the source of the carbon nucleophile:

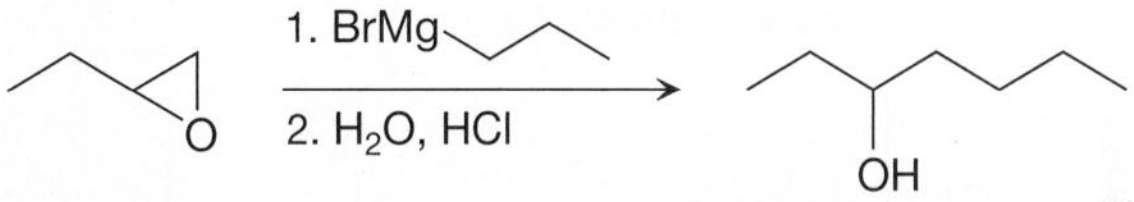

1. BrMg
2. H2O, HCl
OH

Try It Show how to synthesize the molecule at the right, beginning with compounds containing six or fewer carbons.

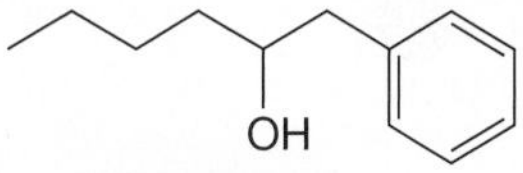

OH

11.3 Alkylation of α Carbons: Regioselectivity and Kinetic versus Thermodynamic Control

SECTION 11.3 OBJECTIVES

You will be able to:

1. Draw the mechanism and predict the products for α alkylation of a ketone or aldehyde.
2. Apply transforms to the products of α alkylation reactions to determine feasible precursors.
3. Recognize whether a reaction is reversible or irreversible, and connect this idea to a competition taking place under thermodynamic control or kinetic control.
4. Predict the regiochemistry of α alkylation on the basis of whether the deprotonation step is reversible or irreversible.

No reaction occurs when an aldehyde (RCH═O) or ketone (R_2C═O) is treated with an alkyl halide alone:

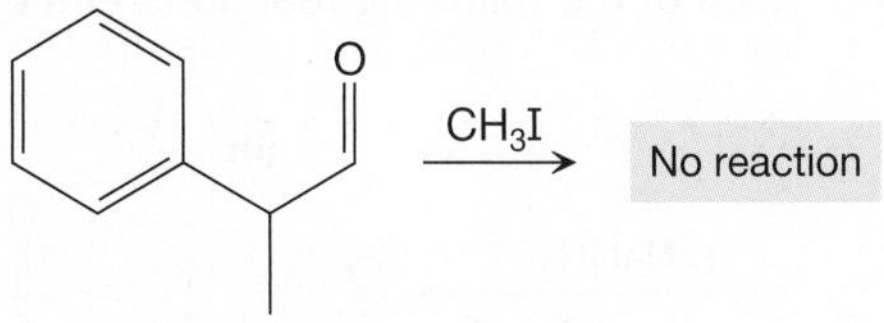

O
CH3I
No reaction

(11-29)

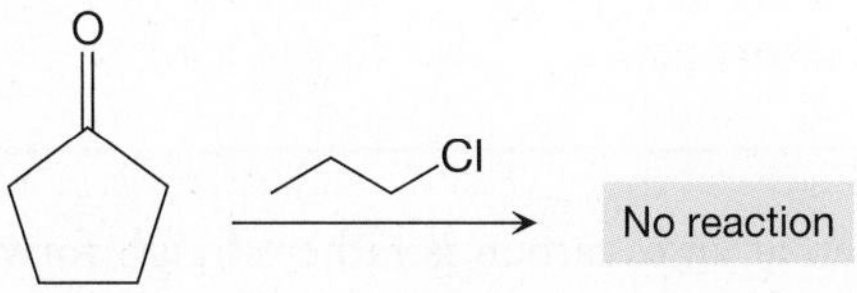

O
Cl
No reaction

(11-30)

When a strong base like sodium hydride (NaH) or sodium amide ($NaNH_2$) is added first, however, *alkylation* can take place at the *α carbon* (i.e., at the C atom adjacent to the C═O group). Examples are shown in Equations 11-31 and 11-32, and in each case, you can see that a new C—C bond is formed:

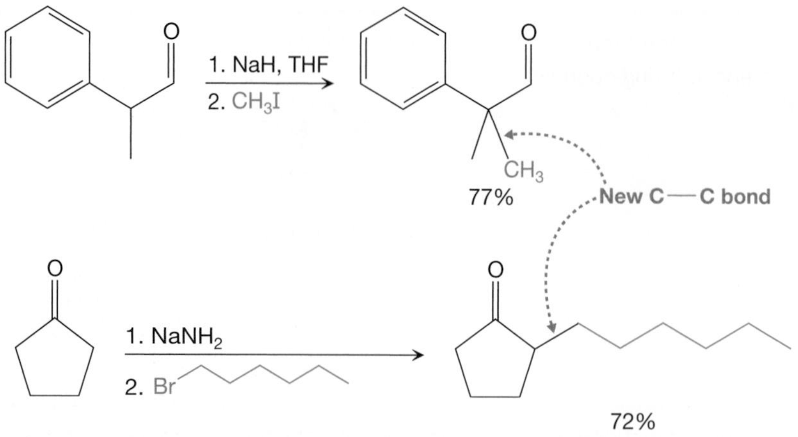
1. NaH, THF
2. CH_3I
CH_3
77%
New C—C bond
1. $NaNH_2$
2. Br
72%

(11-31)

(11-32)

◀ RECALL

An α hydrogen is weakly acidic, but an aldehyde hydrogen is not acidic at all (Section 10.6). The enolate anion produced on loss of a proton from an α carbon is resonance-stabilized. Loss of a proton from a carbonyl carbon would result in an unstable localized −1 charge on the carbonyl C.

The general mechanism for these reactions, shown in Equation 11-33, is a proton transfer step followed by an S_N2 step:

Mechanism for the alkylation of an α carbon (Eqs. 11-31 and 11-32)

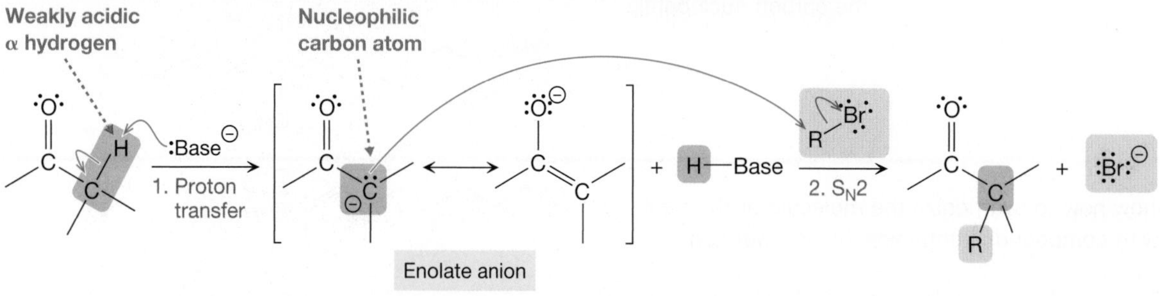
Weakly acidic
α hydrogen
Nucleophilic
carbon atom
:Base
1. Proton
transfer
H—Base
2. S_N2
Enolate anion

(11-33)

Just as we saw for α halogenation under basic conditions (Section 10.6), a base is necessary to convert the uncharged ketone or aldehyde into an enolate anion, which is strongly nucleophilic at the α carbon (see Recall box).

YOUR TURN 11.8

Draw the complete, detailed mechanism, including curved arrows, for the reactions in Equations 11-31 and 11-32. *Hint*: Use Equation 11-33 as a guide.

YOUR TURN 11.9

Predict the product of each of the following reactions and draw their complete mechanisms.

(a)

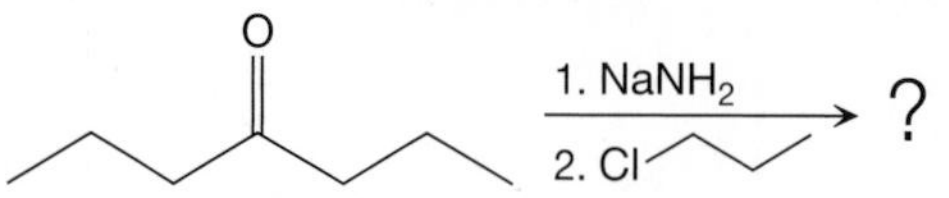
1. $NaNH_2$
2. Cl
?

(b)

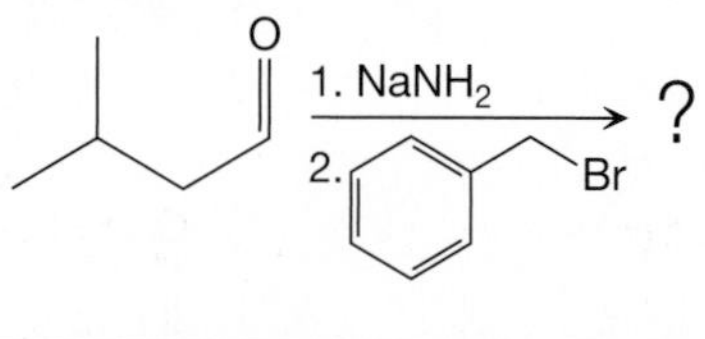
1. $NaNH_2$
2.
Br
?

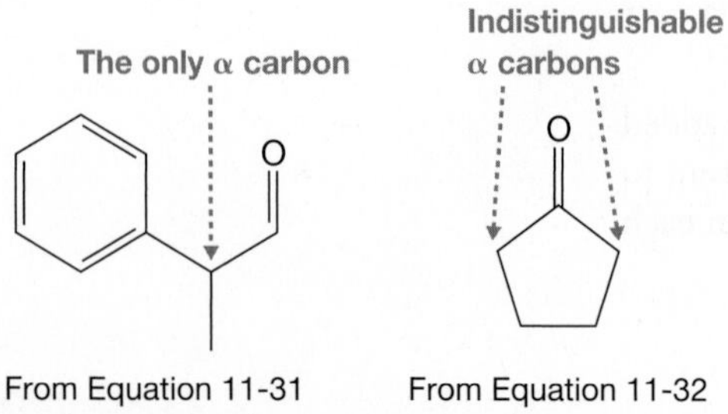
The only α carbon
Indistinguishable
α carbons
From Equation 11-31
From Equation 11-32

Alkylation at an α carbon is rather straightforward if there is only one distinct type of α carbon to consider. This is the case for the aldehyde in Equation 11-31, which contains only one α carbon. It is also the case for the symmetric ketone in Equation 11-32, because the two α carbons are indistinguishable (**Figure 11-1**).

FIGURE 11-1 Species with only one type of α carbon Regiochemistry is not an issue in α alkylation of these species.

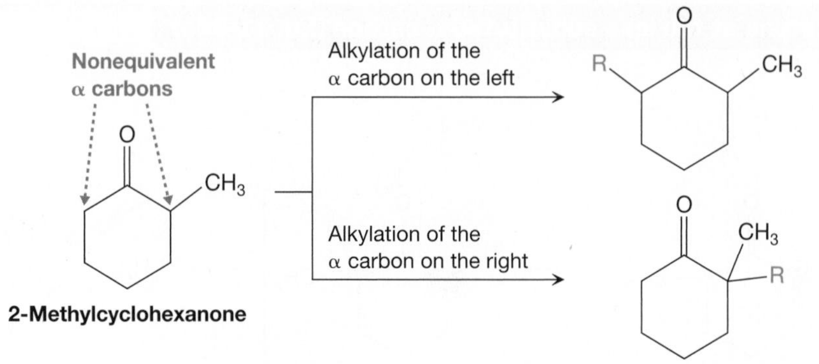

Nonequivalent
α carbons
O
CH3
2-Methylcyclohexanone
Alkylation of the
α carbon on the left
Alkylation of the
α carbon on the right
R
CH3
R

FIGURE 11-2 Regiochemistry in α alkylation 2-Methylcyclohexanone has two nonequivalent α carbons, so α alkylation can produce different constitutional isomers.

Many ketones, however, such as 2-methylcyclohexanone, are unsymmetric; the α carbons are nonequivalent, so alkylation of the different C atoms leads to different products (**Figure 11-2**). *Regioselectivity*, therefore, is a concern for alkylation of ketones that have distinct α carbons. In Section 11.3a, we will discuss how this regiochemistry can be controlled. Then, in Section 11.3b, we will examine how to incorporate these kinds of reactions in synthesis.

11.3a Regioselectivity in α Alkylations

When a ketone has two nonequivalent α carbons, we can often control regiochemistry by the choice of base and reaction conditions, as shown in Equation 11-34:

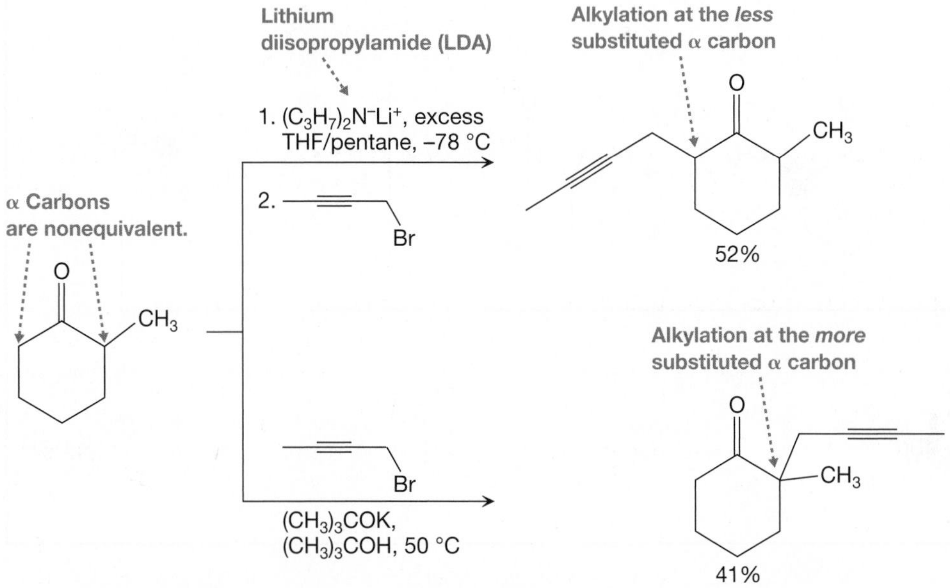

Lithium
diisopropylamide (LDA)
1. (C3H7)2N−Li+, excess
THF/pentane, −78 °C
2.
Br
Alkylation at the less
substituted α carbon
52%
α Carbons
are nonequivalent.
CH3
Br
(CH3)3COK,
(CH3)3COH, 50 °C
Alkylation at the more
substituted α carbon
CH3
41%

(11-34a)

(11-34b)

Controlling Regiochemistry in α Alkylations

- Lithium diisopropylamide (LDA) at low temperatures causes alkylation to occur at the *less* substituted α carbon of a ketone.
- Alkoxide bases (RO^-) cause alkylation to occur at the *more* substituted α carbon of a ketone.

The mechanism for the reaction in Equation 11-34a is shown in Equation 11-35, and the mechanism for the reaction in Equation 11-34b is shown in Equation 11-36. The difference between the two mechanisms is which α carbon is deprotonated. LDA favors deprotonation of the less substituted α carbon, whereas RO^- favors deprotonation of the more substituted α carbon.

Mechanism for the alkylation of a ketone at the less substituted α carbon (Eq. 11-34a)

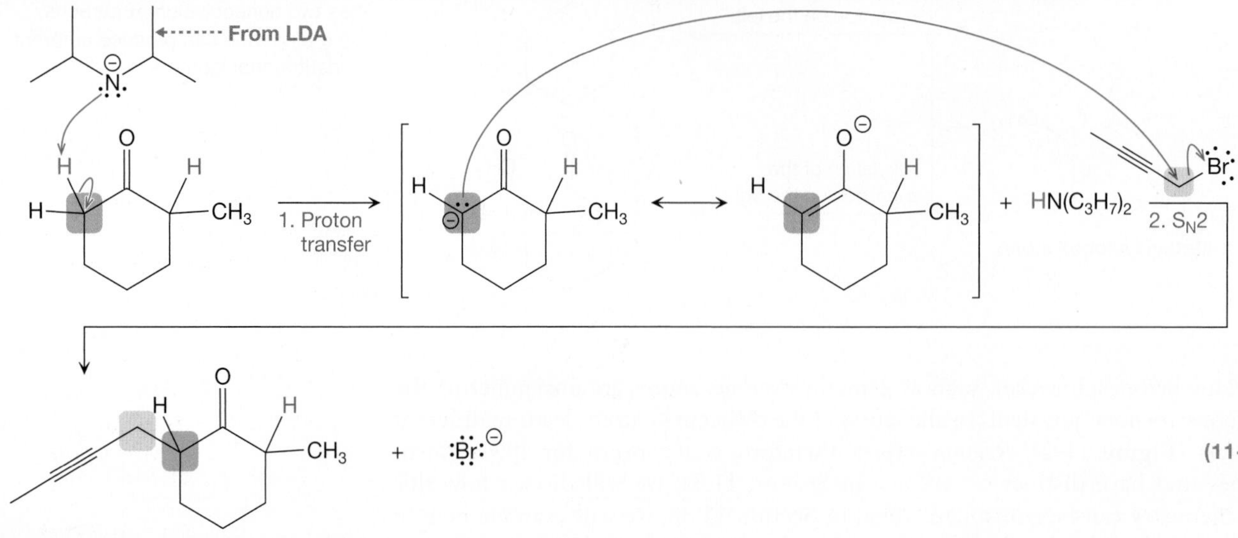
From LDA
1. Proton transfer
+ HN(C3H7)2
2. SN2
CH3
Br

(11-35)

Mechanism Drawing
Regioselective Alkylation of an α Carbon of a Ketone Using LDA

Mechanism for the alkylation of a ketone at the more substituted α carbon (Eq. 11-34b)

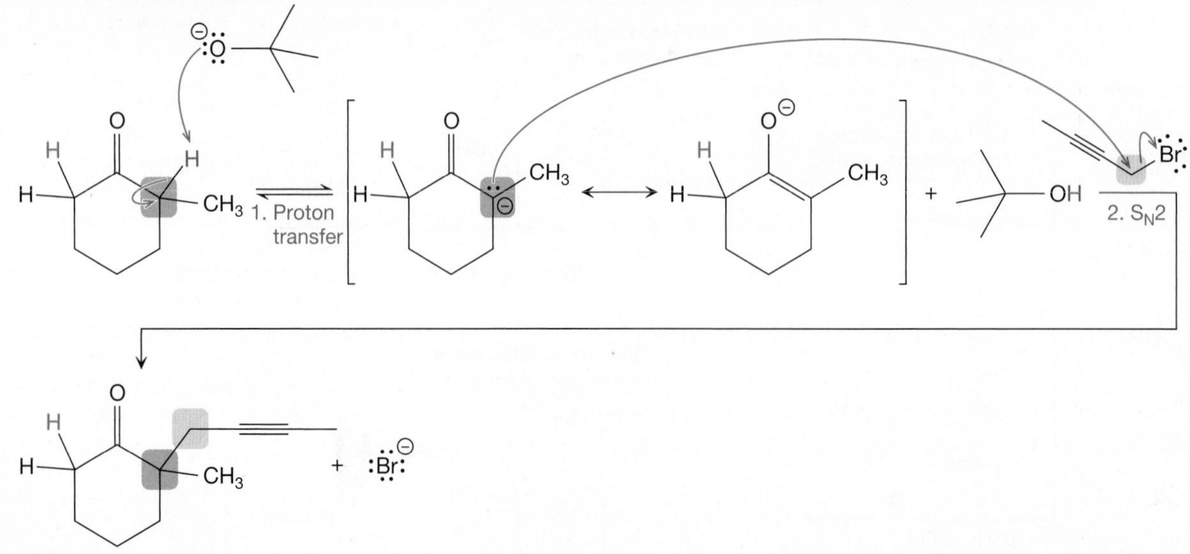
1. Proton transfer
2. SN2
OH
CH3
Br

(11-36)

Mechanism Drawing
Regioselective Alkylation of an α Carbon of a Ketone Using a Bulky Alkoxide Base

◂ RECALL

Section 6.2 showed that the favored side of a proton transfer reaction is *opposite* the stronger acid (lower pK_a), by a factor of 10 for each unit of difference in pK_a between the two acids. As we saw in Section 6.4, the favored side of the reaction has the lower standard Gibbs free energy and is more stable.

Why do LDA and RO^- favor deprotonation at different α carbons? It is *not* a matter of one base being much bulkier than the other; notice in Equation 11-34a and 11-34b that both bases (LDA and the *tert*-butoxide anion) are quite bulky. Rather, it results mainly from LDA being a *much* stronger base than the *tert*-butoxide anion.

As we can see from the relevant pK_a values in **Figure 11-3a**, deprotonation with LDA favors the product side heavily. This means that the products are much more stable than the reactants (see Recall box). Consequently, as the energy diagram indicates, the energy barrier for the reverse reaction is very large, which makes the reverse reaction excessively slow. Effectively, the reaction takes place only in the forward direction, so we say that the deprotonation is **irreversible**. We indicate the reaction is irreversible by drawing a one-directional reaction arrow, called an *irreversible reaction arrow* (⟶).

By contrast, as shown in Figure 11-3b, deprotonation of an α carbon with an alkoxide anion as the base slightly favors the reactant side. Therefore, the energy

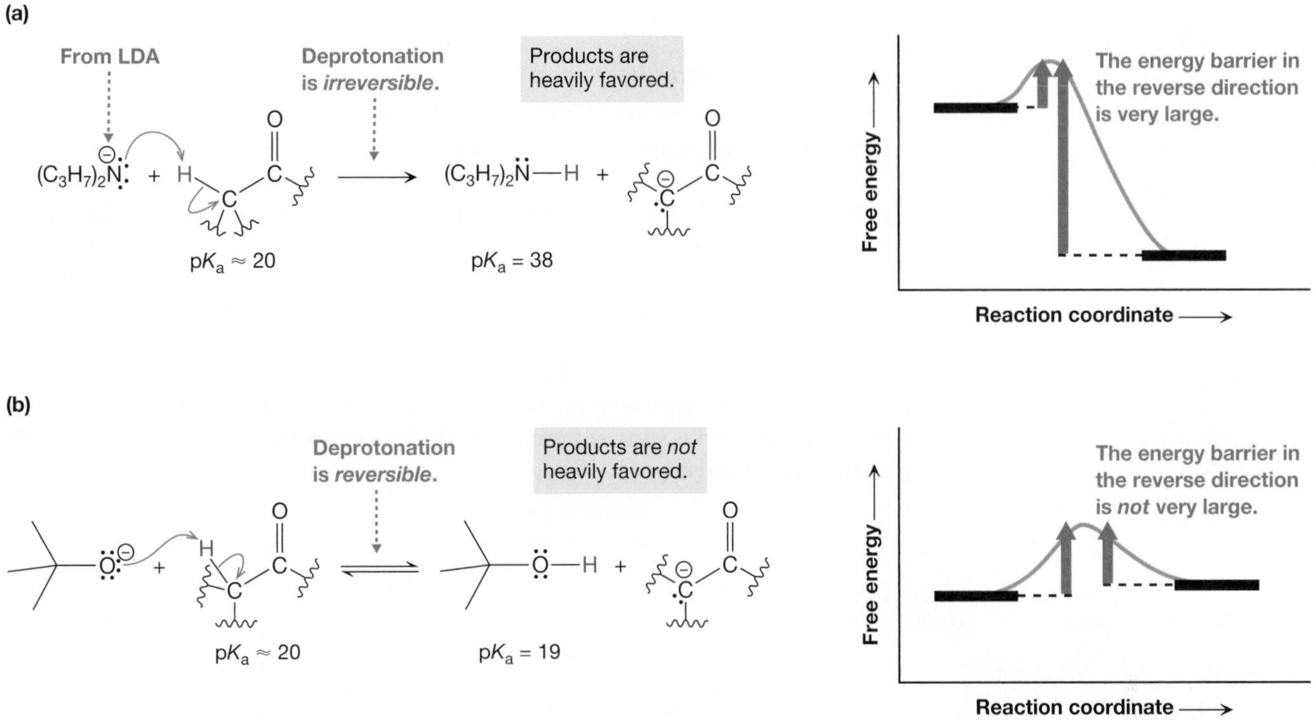
(a)
From LDA
Deprotonation is *irreversible.*
Products are heavily favored.
$(C_3H_7)_2N$
$(C_3H_7)_2N$—H
pK_a ≈ 20
pK_a = 38
The energy barrier in the reverse direction is very large.
Free energy
Reaction coordinate
(b)
Deprotonation is *reversible.*
Products are *not* heavily favored.
pK_a ≈ 20
pK_a = 19
The energy barrier in the reverse direction is *not* very large.
Free energy
Reaction coordinate

FIGURE 11-3 Reversibility in Deprotonation of an α Carbon (a) Deprotonation of an α carbon is irreversible when LDA is the base. The pK_a values indicate that the product side is heavily favored. Therefore, the products are much more stable than the reactants, and the energy barrier in the reverse direction is excessively large. (b) Deprotonation of an α carbon is reversible when *tert*-butoxide is the base. The pK_a values indicate that the reactant side is slightly favored and that the reactants and products have similar stabilities. Therefore, the reverse reaction does not have an excessively large energy barrier, and it can proceed at a reasonable rate.

barrier in the reverse direction is not very large, so the reaction in the reverse direction will take place at a reasonable rate. In this case, the reaction is **reversible**, and we indicate this by drawing a two-directional reaction arrow ($\rightleftharpoons$) that we call a *reversible reaction arrow*.

How does reversibility impact the outcome of a competition among reactions? Study Equation 11-37, which represents competing *reversible* reactions to produce two different products, labeled Product 1 and Product 2. Each product, once it is produced, can react in the reverse direction to regenerate the reactants, and then can react in the forward direction to produce the *other* product. Effectively, Product 1 and Product 2 are in equilibrium. As with any equilibrium, the species that is the most stable ends up being present in the greatest abundance, regardless of how fast it is produced. The competition is said to take place under **thermodynamic control**.

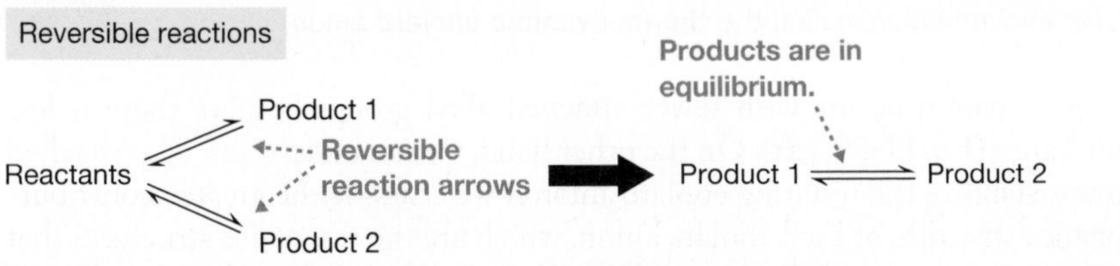
Reversible reactions
Products are in equilibrium.
Product 1
Reversible reaction arrows
Reactants
Product 2
Product 1
Product 2
(11-37)

Now consider Equation 11-38, which represents competing *irreversible* reactions. In this case, each product is effectively permanent once it is produced. Therefore, the product that accumulates the fastest will be present in the greatest abundance when the reaction is complete, regardless of how stable that product is. This kind of competition is said to take place under **kinetic control**.

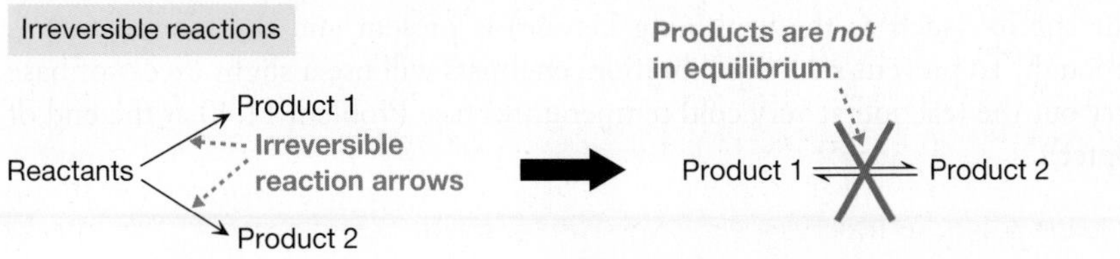
Irreversible reactions
Products are *not* in equilibrium.
Product 1
Irreversible reaction arrows
Reactants
Product 2
Product 1
Product 2
(11-38)

The main lesson from Equations 11-37 and 11-38 is as follows:

A competition generally takes place under:

- *kinetic control* when the competing reactions are *irreversible*.
- *thermodynamic control* when the competing reactions are *reversible*.

Applying this idea to the deprotonation of α carbons, we can say that the deprotonation of a ketone takes place under kinetic control when LDA is used as the base (because the deprotonation is irreversible), and it takes place under thermodynamic control when an alkoxide anion is used as the base (because the deprotonation is reversible).

There is one more piece to the puzzle as to how the choice of base dictates the regiochemistry of α alkylation: In the deprotonation step to produce the enolate anion, which enolate anion is formed faster, and which one is more stable? Equation 11-39 provides these answers:

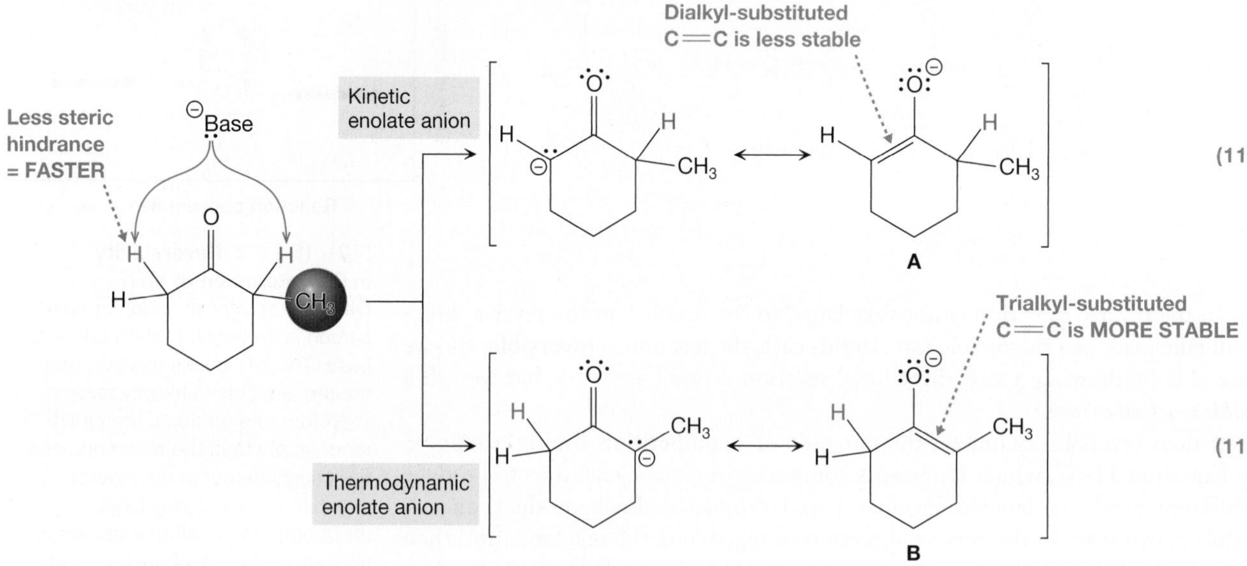

Dialkyl-substituted C=C is less stable
Less steric hindrance = FASTER
Base
Kinetic enolate anion
Thermodynamic enolate anion
A
Trialkyl-substituted C=C is MORE STABLE
B

(11-39a)

(11-39b)

- Deprotonation of a ketone at the less substituted α carbon is *faster*, leading to the **kinetic enolate anion**.
- Deprotonation of a ketone at the more substituted α carbon produces the *more stable* enolate anion, called the **thermodynamic enolate anion**.

◄ RECALL

Section 9.10 showed that the stability of an alkene increases with greater alkyl substitution. Section 9.11 explained that alkyl groups attached to the C=C bond stabilize the alkene via hyperconjugation.

Faster deprotonation occurs with fewer attached alkyl groups because there is less steric hindrance (Eq. 11-39, left). On the other hand, we can understand why attached alkyl groups stabilize the resulting enolate anion if we examine the greater-contributing resonance structure of each enolate anion, which are the resonance structures that have the negative charge on O instead of C (Eq. 11-39a and 11-39b, right). Notice that each of those resonance structures, labeled **A** and **B**, has a C=C double bond. That C=C double bond is more substituted in **B** and, as we learned in Section 9.10, is more stable (see Recall box).

Even when a powerful base such as LDA is used to produce the kinetic enolate anion, the kinetic and thermodynamic enolate anions can still equilibrate over time if an acidic species (such as the beginning ketone) is present and the temperature is warm enough. To prevent such equilibration, chemists will use a slight excess of base and carry out the reaction at very cold temperatures (see Problem 11.40 at the end of the chapter).

SOLVED PROBLEM **11.3**

How to predict the major product of α alkylation of an unsymmetric ketone

Break It Down (a) Predict the major product for the reaction shown here and draw the complete, detailed mechanism. (b) What would the major product be if the base were $NaOC(CH_3)_3$ instead?

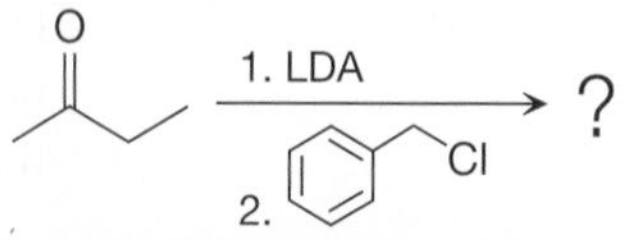

O
1. LDA
?
2.
Cl

Think	Solve
Are the two α carbons equivalent?	The ketone is unsymmetric, so the two α carbons are nonequivalent. The one on the left is part of a CH_3 group, and the one on the right is part of a CH_2 group. Thus, the product will depend on which carbon is alkylated.
What does LDA do? How does it differentiate between the two α carbons?	LDA is a very strong base that will deprotonate α carbons *irreversibly*. Therefore, the two α carbons will be deprotonated in a competition that takes place under *kinetic control*, favoring the enolate anion that is formed the fastest. Such a kinetic enolate anion comes from deprotonating the less highly alkyl-substituted α carbon on the left.
How does the resulting enolate anion react with the alkyl halide?	The enolate anion is strongly nucleophilic at the α carbon, so it will attack the alkyl halide in an S_N2 step, as shown below.

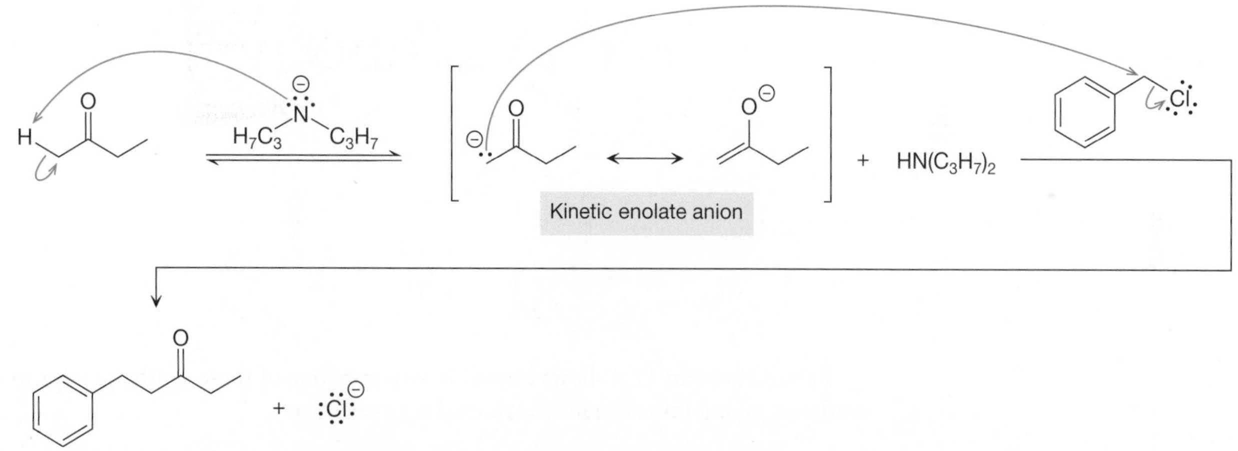

H
O
N
H7C3
C3H7
O
O
Kinetic enolate anion
+
HN(C3H7)2
Cl
O
+
Cl

How does $NaOC(CH_3)_3$ differentiate between the two α carbons of the ketone?	$NaOC(CH_3)_3$ will deprotonate α carbons *reversibly*. Therefore, the two α carbons will be deprotonated in a competition that takes place under *thermodynamic control*, favoring the more stable enolate anion. Such a thermodynamic enolate anion comes from deprotonating the more highly alkyl-substituted α carbon on the right. The resulting alkylated ketone is shown here. 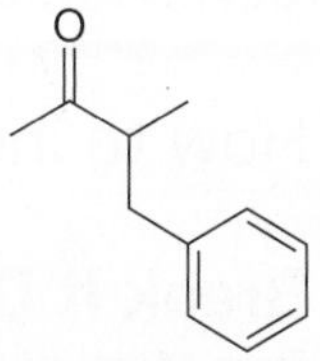

Try It (a) Draw the complete mechanism for this reaction and predict the major product. **(b)** Do the same for the reaction in which $KOC(CH_3)_3$ is used as the base instead of LDA.

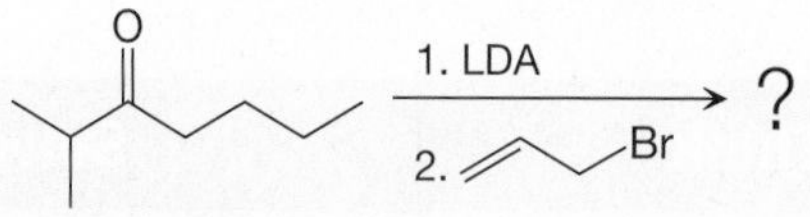

O
1. LDA
?
2.
Br

11.3b Using α Alkylations in Synthesis

α Alkylations are valuable carbon–carbon bond-forming reactions, and to use them effectively when designing a synthesis, we must be able to apply transforms that undo these reactions. We know that the outcome of α alkylation is the formation of a new C—C bond that attaches an alkyl group to an α carbon, as shown on the left in Equation 11-40. Therefore, we draw the red squiggly line through that bond to indicate that that is the bond we need to form:

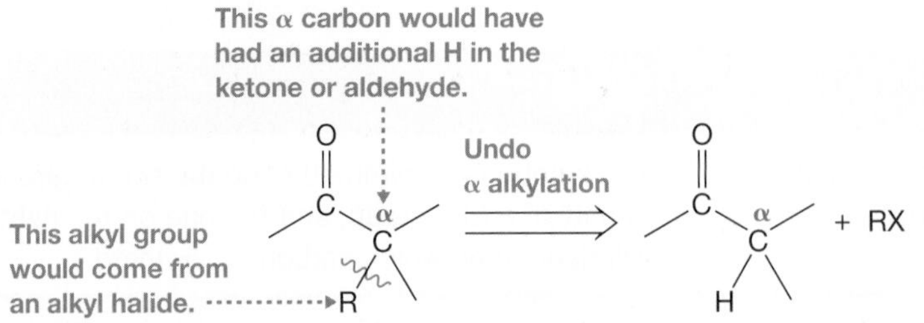
This α carbon would have had an additional H in the ketone or aldehyde.
Undo α alkylation
This alkyl group would come from an alkyl halide.
O
C
α
R
H
+ RX
(11-40)

Examining the mechanism we previously saw in Equation 11-33 (p. 574), we can see that the alkyl group would have come from an alkyl halide (RX) and the α carbon would have had an additional attached hydrogen in the ketone or aldehyde precursor. This allows us to draw the precursors on the right in Equation 11-40.

Once we have the precursors established, we can write the synthetic step as shown in either Equation 11-41 or 11-42, depending on whether we want the initial deprotonation to take place under kinetic control or thermodynamic control:

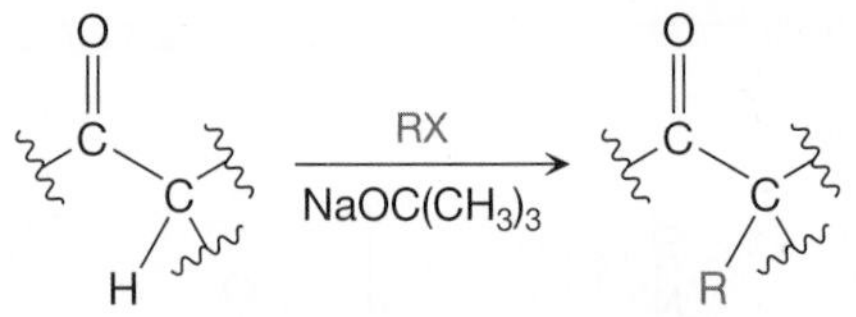
RX
NaOC(CH3)3
O
C
H
R
(11-41)

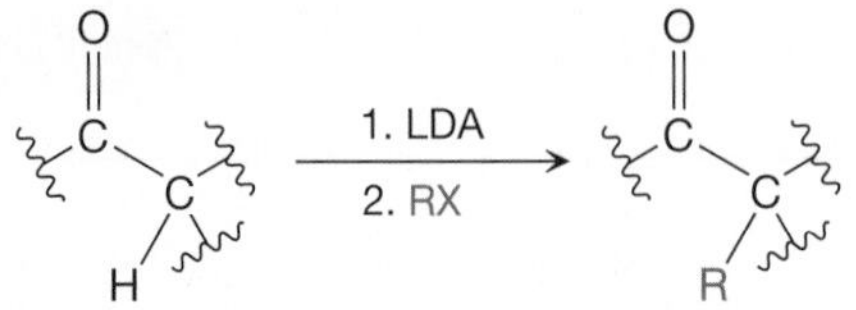
1. LDA
2. RX
O
C
H
R
(11-42)

Solved Problem 11.4 shows how to incorporate one of these synthetic steps into a synthesis, taking into account the desired regiochemistry.

SOLVED PROBLEM **11.4**

How to incorporate an α alkylation into a synthesis regioselectively

Break It Down **Show how to synthesize the following compound from starting materials that contain seven or fewer carbons.**

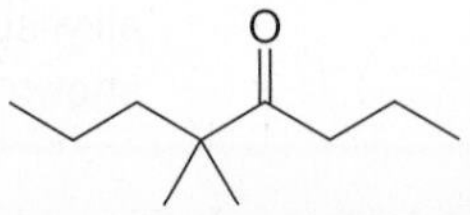

Think	Solve
Will a C—C bond need to be made? What reaction can be used to make that bond?	The carbon backbone of the target has 10 carbons, whereas our starting materials are limited to seven carbons, so a C—C bond will need to be made. Each α carbon in the target has at least one attached alkyl group, so we can consider using α alkylation to make the C—C bond.

(continued)

Which C—C bond should be the one made? How do we apply the appropriate transform to determine the precursors?

Our synthesis requires adding at least three carbons, so we should consider attaching a three-carbon piece. The α carbon on the left is attached to a propyl group, so as shown here, we can apply a transform that undoes the formation of that bond.

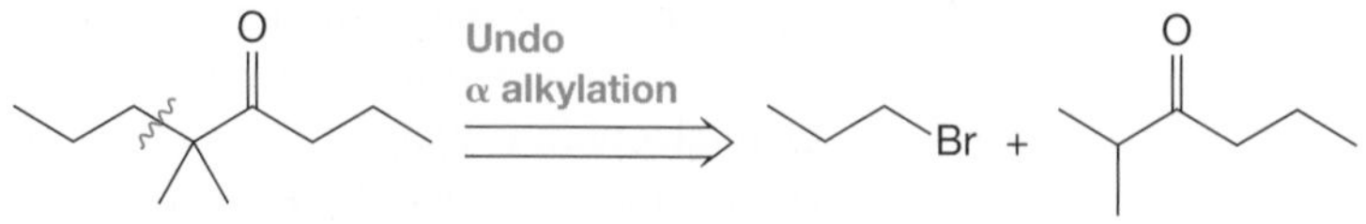
O
Undo
α alkylation
Br +
O

When we write the synthetic step, is regiochemistry a concern? How do we control the regiochemistry?

The ketone precursor is unsymmetric and has two nonequivalent α carbons. The one on the left has two attached alkyl groups, and the one on the right has one attached alkyl group. Our synthesis calls for alkylation of the more substituted α carbon, so we choose a base that will deprotonate the ketone reversibly and under thermodynamic control. The *tert*-butoxide anion will accomplish this.

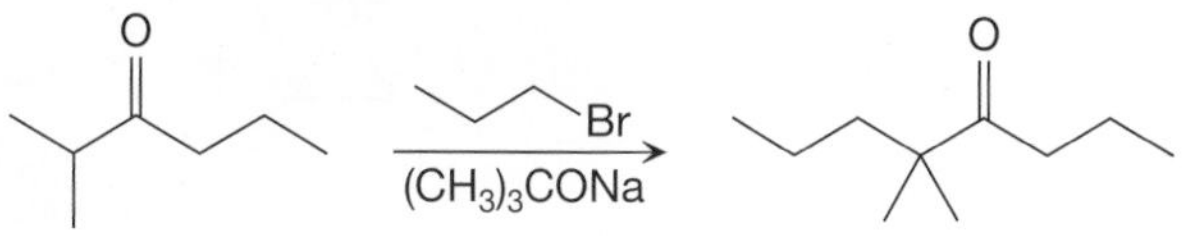
O
Br
(CH3)3CONa
O

Try It Show how to synthesize the following compound from starting materials that contain seven or fewer carbons.

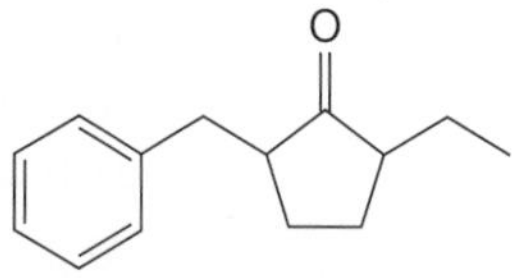
O

11.4 Synthetic Traps

SECTION 11.4 OBJECTIVES

You will be able to:

1. Explain what synthetic traps are and how they come about.
2. Identify synthetic traps when they arise from a retrosynthetic analysis.

When we apply a transform that undoes a particular reaction, we tend to focus just on the specific changes that we *want* to occur. When we restrict our thinking in this way, we can encounter a **synthetic trap**, in which some factor we have temporarily overlooked prevents the reaction from occurring in the *forward* direction as planned.

For example, suppose our target on the left of Equation 11-43 must be synthesized from starting materials containing three or fewer carbons. We can apply a transform that undoes epoxide ring opening (review Eq. 11-26), in which case the precursors on the right of Equation 11-43 would be required:

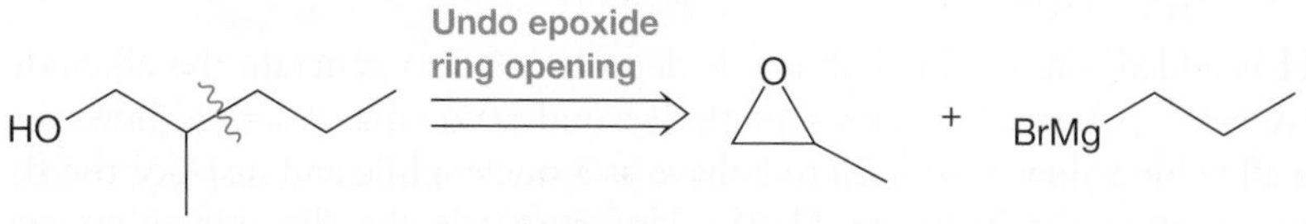
Undo epoxide
ring opening
HO
O
+
BrMg

(11-43)

However, we encounter a problem when we try to run the reaction in the forward direction. The Grignard reagent is a strong base, so when it reacts with the epoxide ring, it attacks the less highly alkyl-substituted (less sterically hindered) carbon (see Section 10.7). Therefore, as shown in Equation 11-44, the wrong product is synthesized:

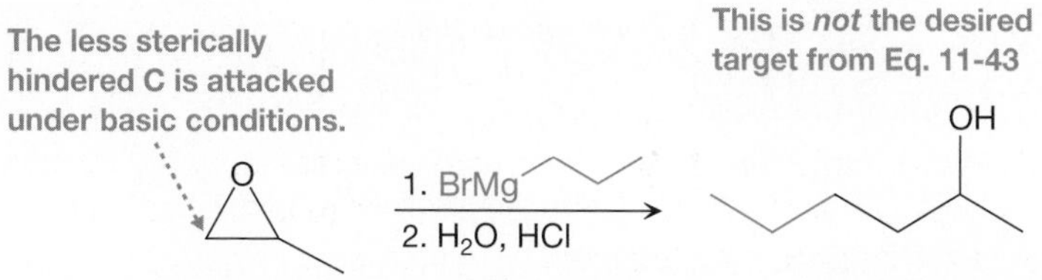
The less sterically
hindered C is attacked
under basic conditions.
This is not the desired
target from Eq. 11-43
O
1. BrMg
2. H2O, HCl
OH

(11-44)

YOUR TURN **11.10**

Draw the complete mechanism for the reaction in Equation 11-44.

To produce the desired target, the nucleophile would have to attack the more highly alkyl-substituted carbon of the epoxide. In Section 10.7, we saw examples of nucleophiles attacking the more highly alkyl-substituted carbon under acidic conditions, in which case the epoxide O is protonated and carries a +1 formal charge. However, this strategy will not work for our synthesis either. As shown in Equation 11-45, the strongly basic Grignard reagent will instead rapidly deprotonate the epoxide O:

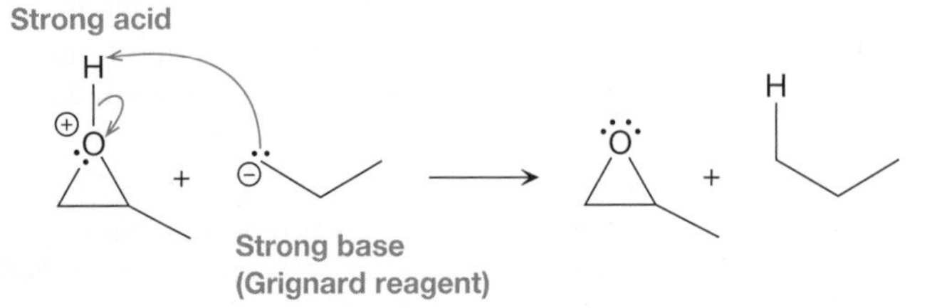

Strong acid
Strong base
(Grignard reagent)

(11-45)

The synthetic trap we just examined is a result of regiochemistry that prevents us from being able to make the desired product. Regiochemistry applies to other reactions, too, so keep this type of synthetic trap in mind whenever you propose to use a particular reaction in a synthesis:

Always make sure the regiochemistry of a proposed synthetic step will lead to the intended product.

Another example of a synthetic trap is presented in the transform proposed in Equation 11-46, which undoes alkylation of a terminal alkyne (review Eq. 11-6, p. 565):

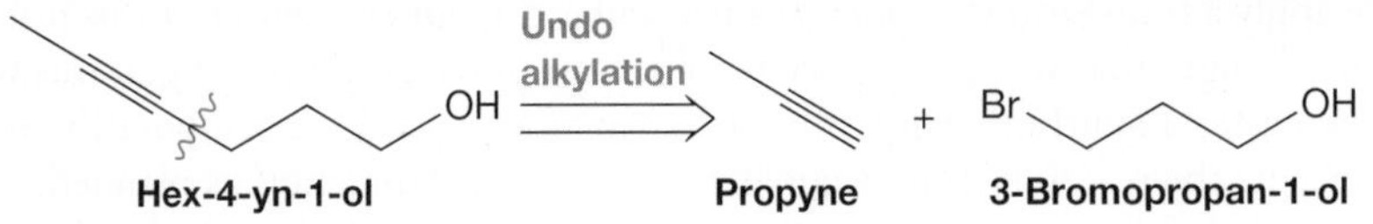

Undo
alkylation
Hex-4-yn-1-ol
Propyne
3-Bromopropan-1-ol

(11-46)

In the forward direction, this synthetic step would appear as follows:

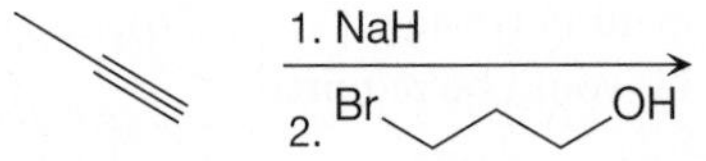

1. NaH
2.

(11-47)

When NaH is added, the terminal alkyne is deprotonated to generate the alkynide anion, $CH_3C{\equiv}C^-$. A problem arises in the second sequential reaction, however, because the alkynide anion is *intended* to behave as a nucleophile and displace the Br leaving group, as shown in Equation 11-48a. Unfortunately, the alkynide anion can also behave as a strong base to deprotonate the OH group, as shown in Equation 11-48b. Because proton transfer reactions tend to be much faster than nucleophilic substitution reactions (Section 8.6a), the reaction in Equation 11-48b dominates, and the synthesis does not proceed as intended:

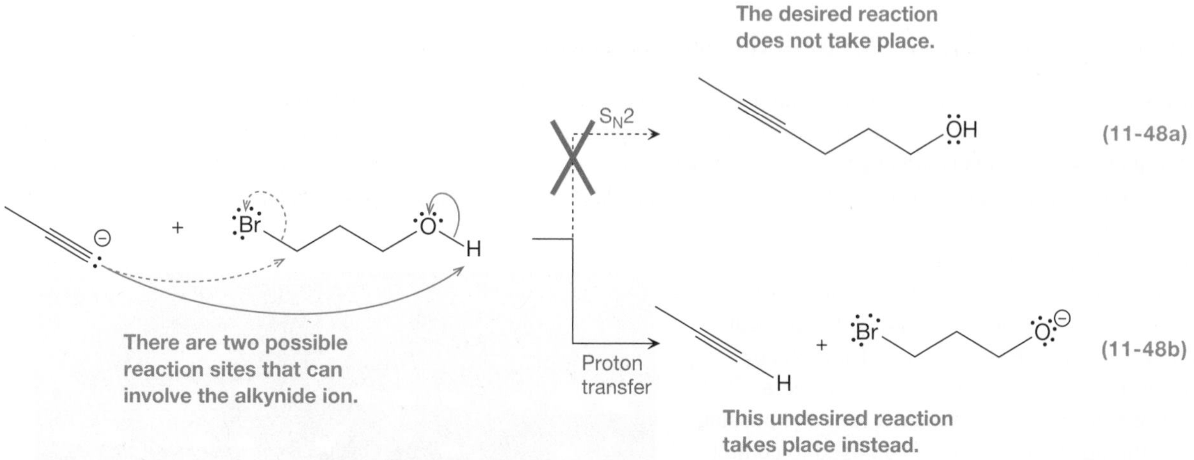
The desired reaction does not take place.
SN2
OH
(11-48a)
Br
O
H
There are two possible reaction sites that can involve the alkynide ion.
Proton transfer
H
Br
O
(11-48b)
This undesired reaction takes place instead.

The synthetic trap we just discussed arises because there is *more than one reactive functional group* in the proposed synthetic step. In the case at hand, this leads to an undesired reaction, which is an important lesson to keep in mind:

Whenever you propose a synthetic step in a synthesis, check for other functional groups that would react.

We have seen two examples of synthetic traps in this section. The *potential* for a synthetic trap, however, exists whenever we apply a transform. If we encounter a synthetic trap, our synthesis needs to be altered in some way to ensure it leads successfully to the synthesis of our intended target. Sometimes a synthetic trap can be circumvented with minor changes to the synthesis scheme, perhaps simply by reordering the steps. In other cases, a specialized reaction might be required to avoid the synthetic trap, many of which we will learn in the chapters to come. Sometimes, however, there will be no apparent way around a synthetic trap, forcing us to search for an altogether different synthetic route. As you gain more experience with organic synthesis, and as you learn more reactions in subsequent chapters, you will be better equipped to make these kinds of decisions. For now, we just focus on identifying synthetic traps so that we can avoid them.

YOUR TURN 11.11

For each of the following proposed transforms, determine whether it leads to a synthetic trap (i.e., it will not proceed as planned in the forward direction). Explain your reasoning.

(a)

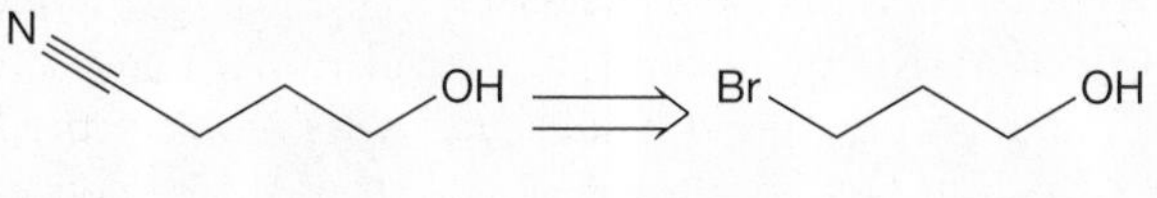
N
OH
Br
OH

(b)

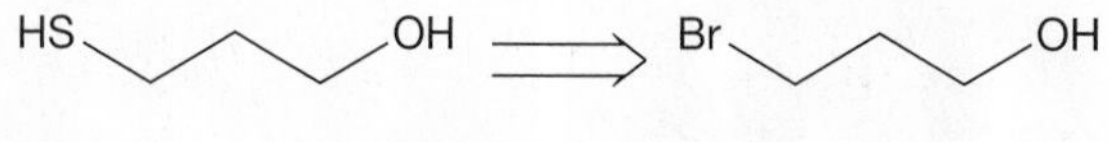
HS
OH
Br
OH

(c)

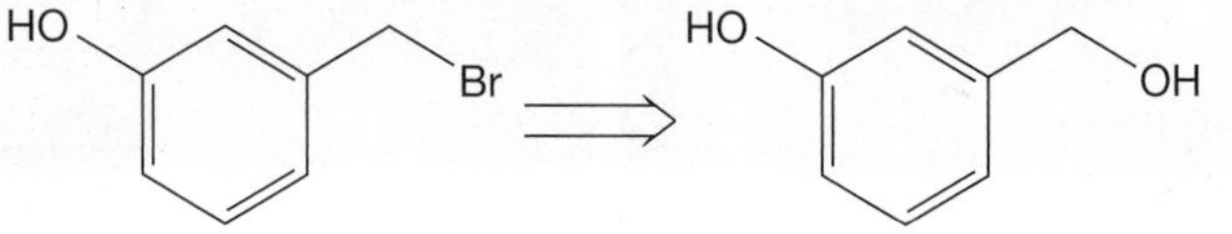
HO
Br
HO
OH

(d)

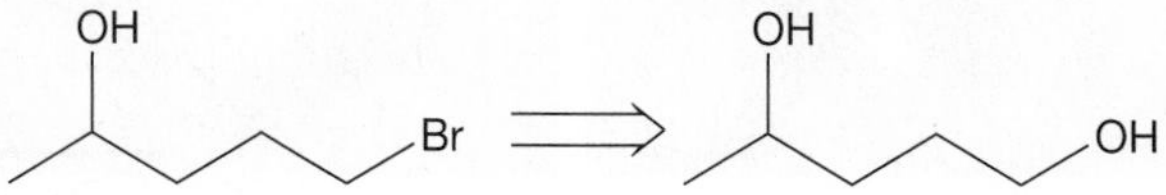
OH
Br
OH
OH

(e)

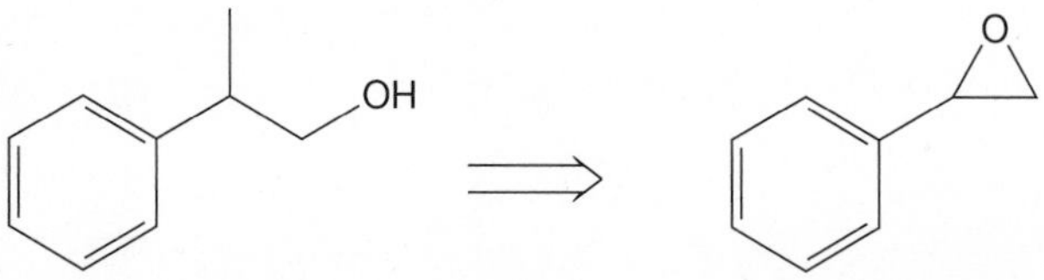
OH
O

(f)

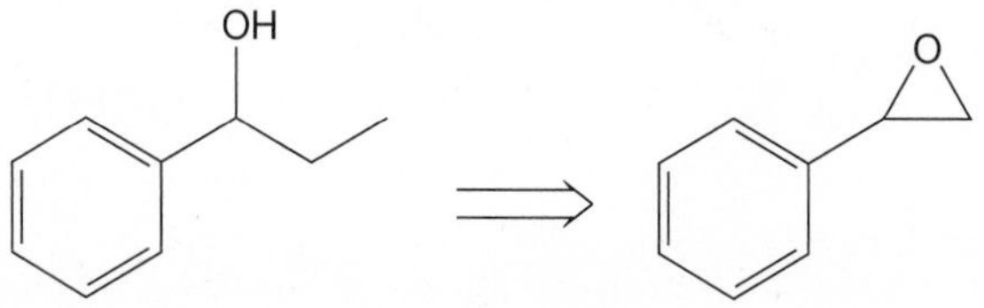
OH
O

Manipulating Atoms One at a Time: Single-Molecule Engineering

As we have seen in Chapter 10 and here in Chapter 11, the basic strategy of organic synthesis is to use known reactions in precise sequences to construct a particular target. Despite its tremendous success, traditional organic synthesis is limited by the specific structural changes that reactions can bring about, as illustrated in our discussion of *synthetic traps* here in Section 11.4. Are there ways around these limitations? Perhaps.

In 1989, Don Eigler and Erhard Schweizer, working for IBM, used scanning tunneling microscopy (STM) to move 35 xenon atoms on a nickel surface to spell out the company's acronym (**Figure 11-4**). STM works by positioning a very small metal tip narrowly above a sample surface (typically within about 1 nm) and passing a voltage to the tip. That voltage can be used to control the interaction between the STM tip and an individual atom on the sample surface, thereby giving the STM the ability to move atoms.

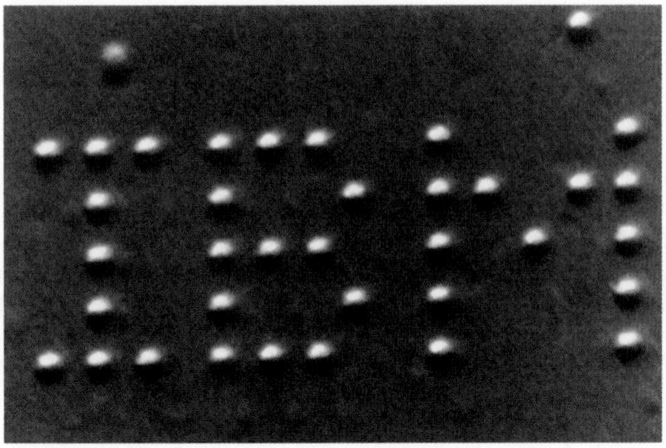

FIGURE 11-4

Using STM to spell out the IBM acronym with atoms is admittedly a novel application. The technology has tremendous potential, however, for creating nanostructures with valuable functions. In recent years, the technology has even been applied toward organic molecules. In early 2016, for example, Leo Gross and co-workers, working at IBM Research—Switzerland, reported using single-atom manipulation to carry out the transformation shown in **Figure 11-5**. After depositing the initial dibromo compound on a copper surface, they applied 1.6 V to the STM tip to remove the first Br atom and 3.3 V to remove the second one. Then, applying 1.7 V, they carried out a retro-Bergman cyclization to produce the final product, 3,4-benzocyclodeca-3,7,9-triene-1,5-diyne, which belongs to a class of compounds called enediynes. Some enediynes are used as anticancer antibiotics.

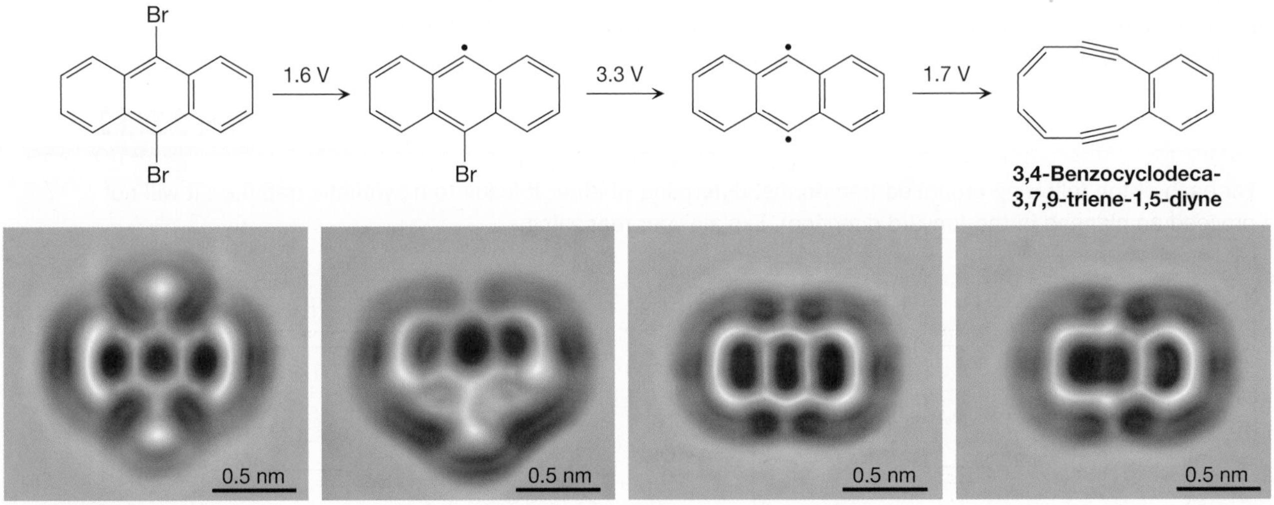
Br
Br
1.6 V
Br
3.3 V
1.7 V
3,4-Benzocyclodeca-3,7,9-triene-1,5-diyne
0.5 nm
0.5 nm
0.5 nm
0.5 nm

FIGURE 11-5

11.5 Strategies for Success: Improving Your Proficiency with Solving Multistep Syntheses

SECTION 11.5 OBJECTIVES

You will be able to:

1. Construct your own synthesis problems.
2. Use the synthesis problems constructed by a study partner to improve your proficiency with solving synthesis problems.

Strategies for Success Improving Your Proficiency with Solving Multistep Syntheses

Your success in solving multistep syntheses will depend on your mastery of various reactions and on your ability to carry out a retrosynthetic analysis. Developing these skills requires practice, and there are several end-of-chapter problems, here and in later chapters, that will help you become more proficient. In addition to working end-of-chapter problems, one of the best ways to improve is to *construct your own synthesis problems*:

Constructing Your Own Synthesis Problem

1. Choose a starting compound. It should have a relatively small number of carbon atoms and also have a functional group you know can participate in a reaction we have studied.
2. Choose a reaction to carry out in the forward direction on that starting compound. Keep track of any relevant reagents and conditions, and determine the product, paying attention to regiochemistry and stereochemistry.
3. Choose a reaction to carry out in the forward direction on the major product of the first reaction. Again, determine the second reaction's major product, and keep track of relevant reagents, reaction conditions, regiochemistry, and stereochemistry.
4. Continue this process through two or three reactions. As you improve with synthesis problems, you should feel comfortable making these four or five reactions long, or longer.
5. Write the synthesis problem. Treat the product of the final reaction as the target, and ask how the target can be produced from the starting compound.

For example, to apply Step 1, let's choose the ether below as the starting compound, and for Step 2, let's choose a hydrolysis to convert it into an alcohol (Section 9.5b):

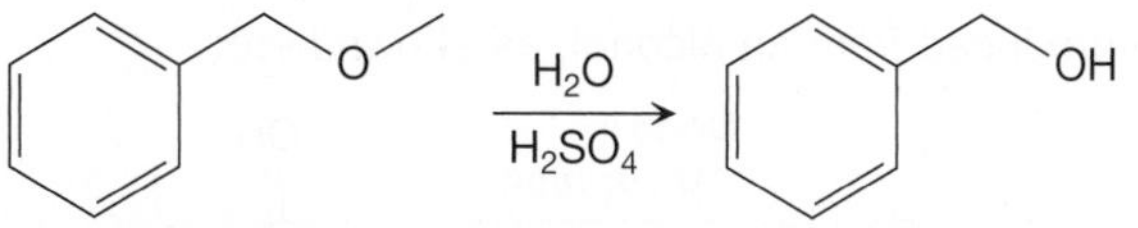
O
H_2O
H_2SO_4
OH

(11-49)

For Step 3, we could convert the alcohol into an alkyl halide using PBr_3 (Section 10.5):

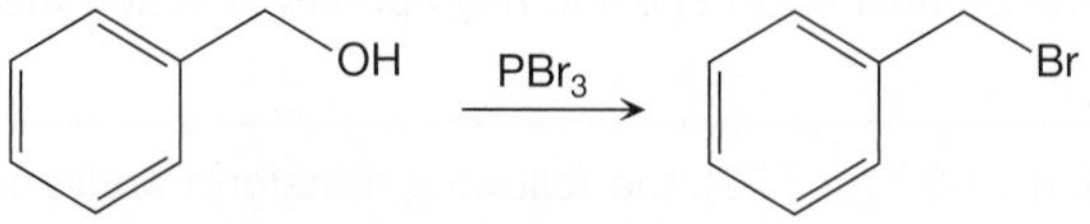
OH
PBr_3
Br

(11-50)

Let's carry out one more reaction for Step 4, in which the alkyl halide participates in alkylation of a terminal alkyne (Section 9.3b):

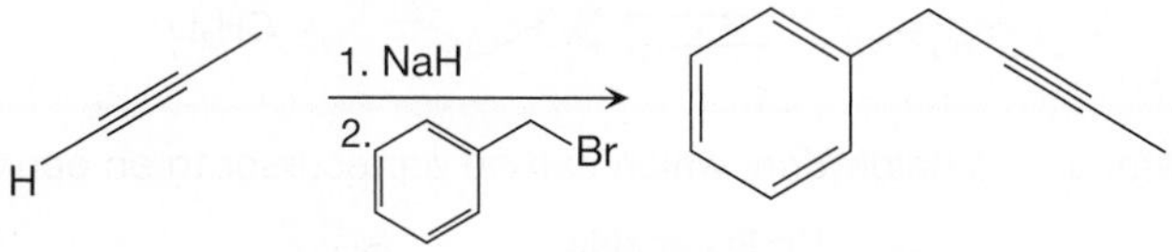
H
1. NaH
2.
Br

(11-51)

For Step 5, treat the final product as the target, and ask how to synthesize it from the starting material, as follows:

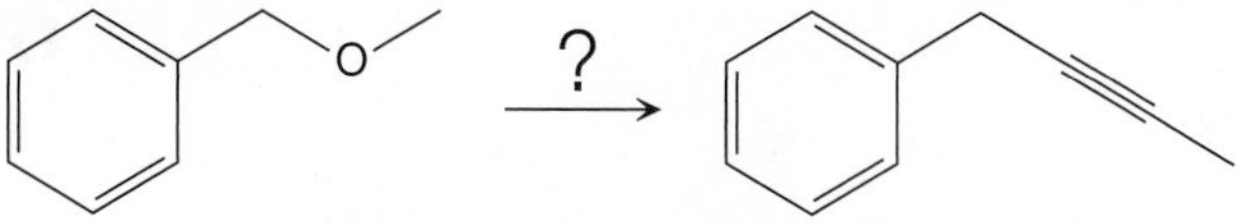
O
?

(11-52)

Using this procedure to construct synthesis problems will help you become more familiar with the reactions you have previously encountered. In turn, the more familiar you are with those reactions, the better you will be able to solve synthesis problems.

To improve your skills even more when it comes to solving synthesis problems, it is helpful to work with a study partner. Each of you can construct separate synthesis problems and then swap. To solve the problem your study partner gave you, apply the retrosynthetic analysis strategies presented here in Chapter 11. When you finish, check with your partner to see if your solution agrees with the reaction scheme your partner used to construct the problem. If your solution does not line up with the reaction scheme your partner used, work together to see if one solution is flawed. Or perhaps both are good!

As you learn new reactions throughout this book, revisit this exercise of constructing your own synthesis problems and swapping with a partner. Each time you do, you and your partner are sure to become more proficient in solving multistep syntheses.

SOLVED PROBLEM **11.5**

How to improve your proficiency with solving multistep syntheses

Break It Down Suppose your study partner constructed the following synthesis problem and gave it to you to solve. Design a synthesis that could be used to carry out the transformation.

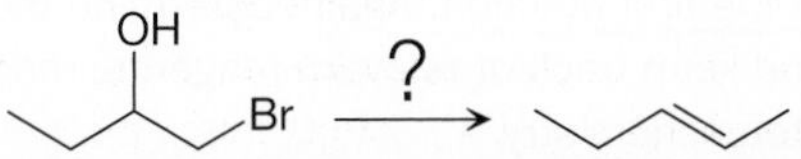

OH
Br
?

Think	Solve
Does a C—C bond-forming reaction need to be used? Are you familiar with a reaction that will produce an alkene?	The target's backbone has five carbons, but the starting material has just four carbons. Therefore, a C—C bond-forming reaction should be used. To this point, however, we have not learned such a reaction that will produce an alkene.
What functional group could be converted into an alkene? Could that functional group be the product of a C—C bond-forming reaction?	An alkene can be produced from an alcohol, as shown here: 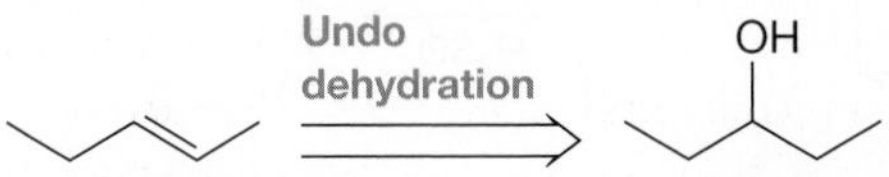 Undo dehydration OH An alcohol can be the product of an epoxide ring-opening reaction that forms a C—C bond.
How do we apply a transform that would undo that C—C bond-forming reaction?	According to Equation 11-27 (p. 572), the following transform would undo an epoxide ring-opening reaction: 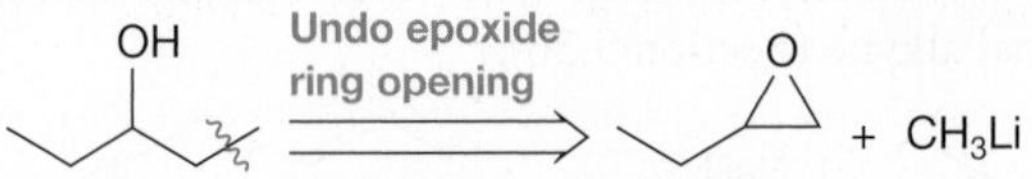 OH Undo epoxide ring opening O + CH$_3$Li
Can the epoxide be made from the starting material?	The starting material is a halohydrin, which can be a precursor to an epoxide: 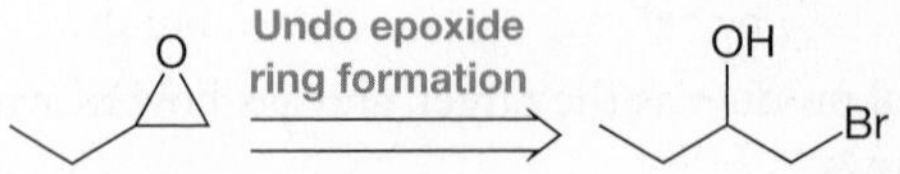 O Undo epoxide ring formation OH Br

(continued)

Having completed the retrosynthetic analysis, how can we write the synthesis?	The synthesis is written by reversing the transforms and supplying the necessary reagents, as shown below.

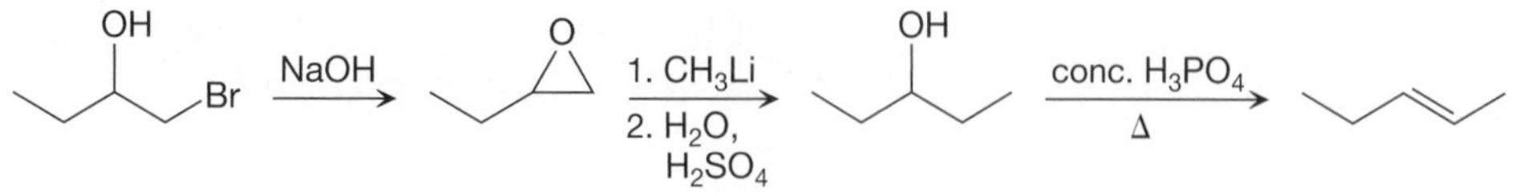

OH
Br
NaOH
O
1. CH_3Li
2. H_2O, H_2SO_4
OH
conc. H_3PO_4
Δ

Try It Suppose your study partner constructed the following synthesis problem and gave it to you to solve. Design a synthesis that could be used to carry out the transformation.

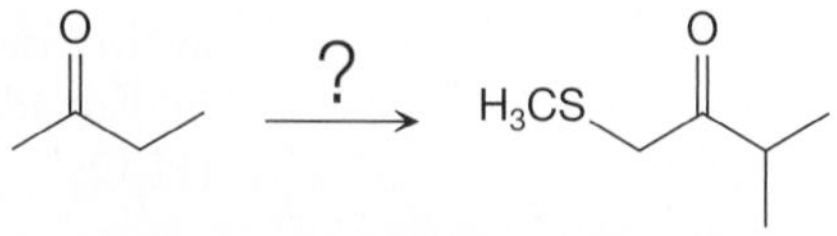

O
?
H_3CS
O

11.6 Green Chemistry

SECTION 11.6 OBJECTIVES

You will be able to:

1. Describe what green chemistry is, in general terms, and why it is important.
2. Explain why, in green chemistry, the use of reagents and solvents that are toxic or otherwise unsafe should be avoided.
3. Compute the percent atom economy of a reaction, and on that basis, determine the better of two syntheses.

Over the last century or more, organic synthesis has offered numerous benefits to our society, including safer and more effective medicines, better crop protection, enhanced energy production and storage, and new materials for consumer products. Unfortunately, considerations for the environment were often an afterthought, and by the middle of the 20th century, the adverse effects of the chemical industry on the environment were apparent. Acid rain was polluting our waters and destroying our forests, "holes" had developed in our ozone layer, and compounds linked to cancer were in common use. The field of *green chemistry* evolved in the 1990s to begin tackling these issues.

Green chemistry is a set of guiding principles established to help prevent various forms of pollution and other hazards. Rather than focusing on the proper handling of materials after a synthesis has been carried out, the goal of green chemistry is to *avoid* the production and accumulation of hazardous materials in the first place. Green chemistry drives the innovation of new chemical reactions, new techniques, and new technologies, which are generally known as **green alternatives.**

There are 12 distinct principles of green chemistry, which we encourage you to look up on the American Chemical Society's website. A thorough discussion of all 12 principles is beyond the scope this book. Here, we focus instead on some of the overarching ideas and how they apply to a handful of reactions encountered in previous chapters. Later chapters of this book will present additional asides on green chemistry in special boxes (like the one appearing here in the margin), which highlight aspects of green chemistry pertaining to new reactions we will encounter.

GREEN CHEMISTRY

Reactions appearing in later chapters that are relevant to green chemistry will be identified in boxes that contain this symbol.

11.6a Less Toxic Reagents and Solvents

Even when proper safety precautions are taken, there is still some risk that the compounds used in a synthesis will be released into the environment or that the people involved in the synthesis will be exposed to those compounds. In light of this, green chemistry emphasizes that it is better to use less toxic, or even nontoxic, reagents and solvents whenever possible to minimize adverse effects.

Consider, for example, α bromination of a ketone, introduced in Section 10.6:

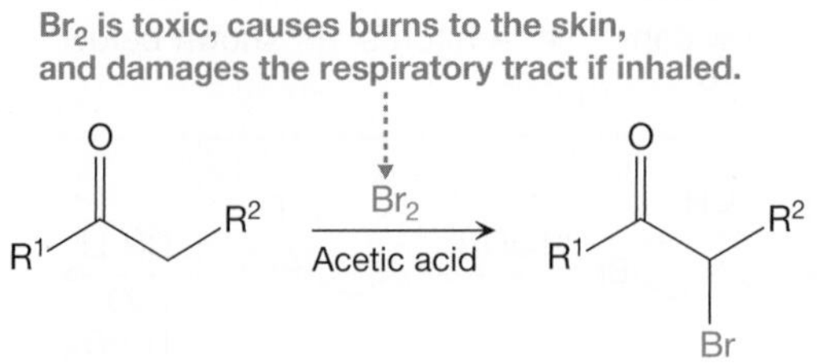
Br2 is toxic, causes burns to the skin,
and damages the respiratory tract if inhaled.
Br2
Acetic acid

(11-53)

As indicated above, molecular bromine (Br_2) is a rather hazardous compound. To avoid direct handling of Br_2, we can employ other reactions, such as the one shown in Equation 11-54 that uses aqueous solutions of HBr and hydrogen peroxide (H_2O_2):

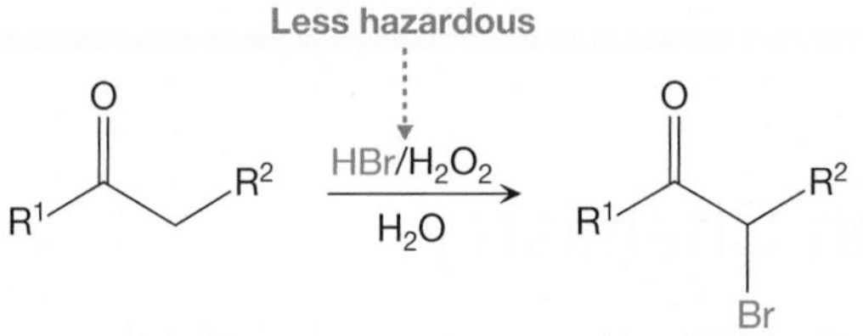
Less hazardous
HBr/H2O2
H2O

(11-54)

Aqueous HBr and H_2O_2 are hazardous as well, but they are generally considered to be safer to use than Br_2. Therefore, the reaction in Equation 11-54 can be considered a *green alternative*.

Solvents are also of great concern, especially because they are typically used in large amounts in chemical reactions. We first encountered choices of solvent in Section 9.7a, where we learned that protic solvents like water or ethanol favor S_N1 and E1 reactions, whereas aprotic solvents like *N,N*-dimethylformamide (DMF) favor S_N2 and E2 reactions. Therefore, if an S_N2 reaction is required for a synthesis, such as the one in Equation 11-55, you might at first consider using an aprotic solvent:

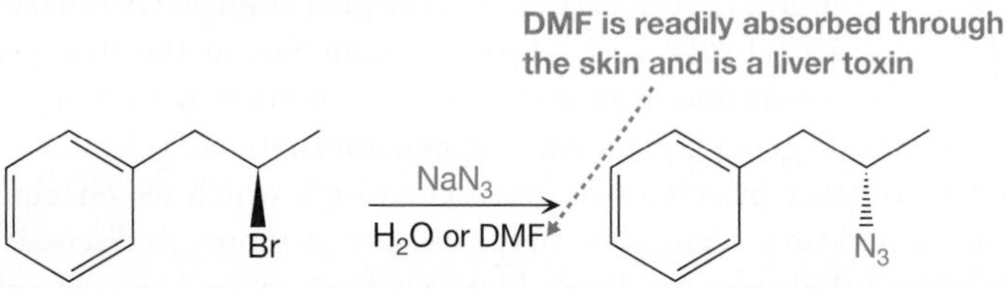
DMF is readily absorbed through
the skin and is a liver toxin
NaN3
H2O or DMF

(11-55)

In this case, however, an S_N2 reaction would take place in either water or DMF because the azide anion (N_3^-) is a strong nucleophile. As noted, however, there are significant hazards associated with DMF, so water would be the greener choice.

YOUR TURN **11.12**

Recall from Section 9.7a that S_N2 reactions are promoted by aprotic solvents, such as dimethyl sulfoxide (DMSO) or DMF. All else being equal, which solvent should you use? *Hint*: You can search the Internet to learn about each solvent's toxicity.

11.6b Safer Synthesis Routes

Sometimes a synthesis can be green in terms of the by-products and other waste that it produces but should be avoided if it poses a high risk for accidents, including fires and explosions. Consider the conversion of a carboxylic acid into a methyl ester in Equation 11-56, which was discussed in Section 10.9:

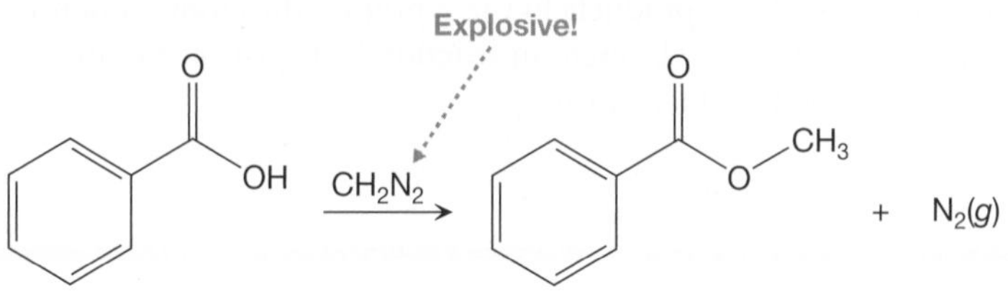

Explosive!
O
OH
CH_2N_2
O
CH_3
O
+ $N_2(g)$

(11-56)

In this case, the only by-product is $N_2(g)$, which is nontoxic. However, diazomethane is *explosive* and should be avoided if there are safer alternatives. As we will learn in Chapter 23, the esterification reaction in Equation 11-56 can be accomplished in a much safer way, using methanol and a catalytic amount of acid (Eq. 11-57):

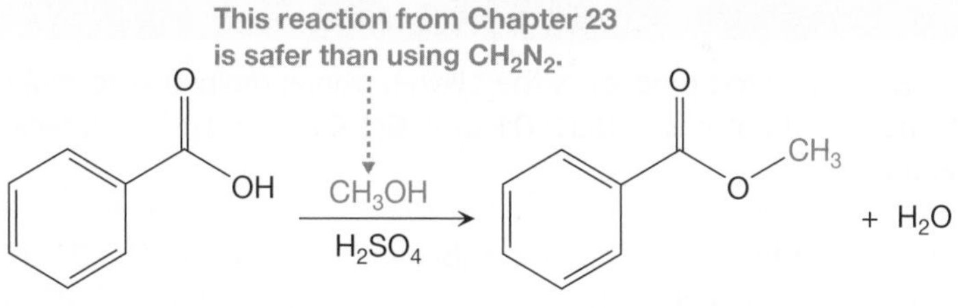

This reaction from Chapter 23
is safer than using CH_2N_2.
O
OH
CH_3OH
H_2SO_4
O
CH_3
O
+ H_2O

(11-57)

11.6c Minimize By-products and Other Waste

For any reagents used in a synthesis, there is risk of release into the environment as well as human exposure. The same is true for any by-products and other accumulated waste. Therefore, green chemistry places value on incorporating as much of the starting material into the desired products as possible. One way to do so is to maximize the percent yield (which we will discuss in Section 11.7). Even if a reaction proceeds with 100% yield, however, it can still be quite wasteful. Consider, for example, the elimination reaction to produce an alkyne:

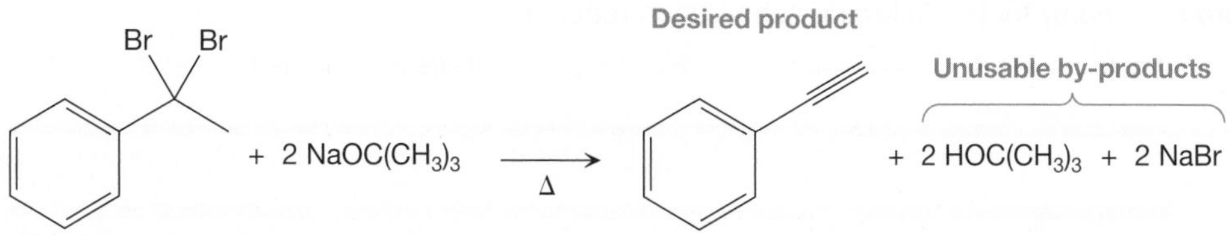

Br Br
+ 2 $NaOC(CH_3)_3$
Δ
Desired product
Unusable by-products
+ 2 $HOC(CH_3)_3$ + 2 NaBr

(11-58)

The alcohol and NaBr by-products are unusable in the synthesis and would probably be discarded. These by-products represent a significant amount of material that would go to waste.

By contrast, consider the following epoxide ring-opening reaction:

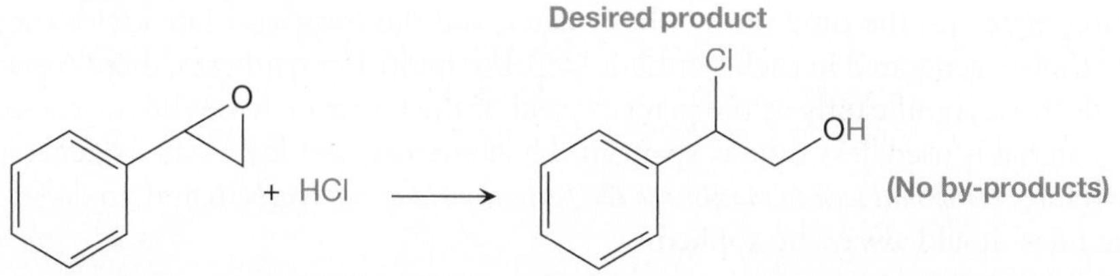

O
+ HCl
Desired product
Cl
OH
(No by-products)

(11-59)

In this case, *all* of the material that reacts ends up in the desired product. If the reaction were to proceed with 100% yield, then *none* of the starting materials would go to waste. Inherently, then, this reaction is more *efficient* than the one in Equation 11-58.

This type of inherent efficiency of a reaction is called **percent atom economy**, calculated according to Equation 11-60:

$$\%\ \text{Atom economy} = \frac{\text{Mass of atoms in the desired product}}{\text{Mass of atoms in all reagents}} \times 100\% \qquad (11\text{-}60)$$

When the numerator and denominator are the same, as is the case for the epoxide ring-opening reaction in Equation 11-59, the atom economy is 100%. On the other hand, if there are unusable by-products in the synthesis, the atom economy falls below 100%. This is the case for the elimination reaction in Equation 11-58, as we can see more explicitly in Solved Problem 11.6.

SOLVED PROBLEM **11.6**

How to calculate a reaction's percent atom economy

Break It Down **Compute the percent atom economy of the elimination reaction shown in Equation 11-58.**

Think	Solve
What is the desired product? What is the mass of its atoms?	In Equation 11-58, the desired product is the alkyne, whose molecular formula is C_8H_6. The total mass of its atoms is 8(12.01 u) + 6(1.01 u) = 102.14 u (where u indicates mass units).
What is the mass of all the reactant atoms?	The molecular formula of the dibromide is $C_8H_8Br_2$ and its mass is 8(12.01 u) + 8(1.01u) + 2(79.90 u) = 263.96 u. The mass for each formula unit of $NaOC(CH_3)_3$ is 1(40.00 u) + 1(16.00 u) + 4(12.01 u) + 9(1.01 u) = 113.13 u, so the mass for two formula units of the base would be 226.26 u. Therefore, the total mass of all the reactant atoms is 263.96 u + 226.26 u = 490.22 u.
How do we calculate the percent atom economy from these values?	Substituting 102.14 u for the numerator in Equation 11-60, and substituting 490.22 u for the denominator, we obtain: $$\%\text{ Atom economy} = \frac{102.14\text{ u}}{490.22\text{ u}} \times 100\% = 20.84\%$$

Try It Compute the percent atom economy for the following substitution reaction.

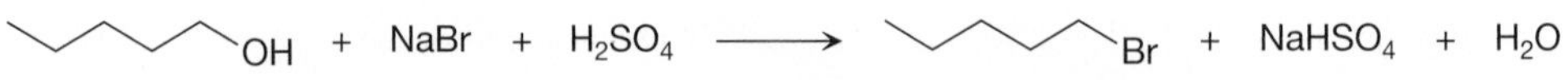

OH
+ NaBr + H_2SO_4
Br
+ $NaHSO_4$ + H_2O

SECTION 11.7 OBJECTIVES

You will be able to:

1. Compute the percent yield for a linear or convergent synthesis, given the percent yield of each synthetic step.
2. Determine which of two or more syntheses is preferred, on the basis of percent yield.

11.7 A Deeper Look: Considerations of Percent Yield

A number of factors contribute to the cost of a synthesis, such as the purchase price of the starting materials, the time the synthesis takes, and the costs associated with the disposal of waste generated in each synthetic step. For multistep syntheses, these costs typically decrease significantly as the percent yield of the target increases because less starting material is used, less time is spent in the laboratory, and less waste is generated. Therefore, *we should seek to maximize the percent yield of the synthesis* and, to do so, two basic rules should always be applied:

Maximizing the Percent Yield for a Synthesis

- The number of steps in a synthesis scheme should be minimized.
- Each step in the synthesis should proceed with the highest possible percent yield.

These rules are essentially an outcome of how percent yield is computed for a **linear synthesis** (i.e., a synthesis composed of sequential steps): *For a linear synthesis, the overall percent yield is equal to the product of the yields of the individual steps.* For example, compare a three-step linear synthesis to one that is six steps long, and suppose that each individual step in both syntheses proceeds with an 80% yield of product (which is often considered quite good). The three-step synthesis will have an *overall* yield of $(0.80) \times (0.80) \times (0.80) = (0.80)^3 = 0.51$, or 51%, whereas the six-step synthesis will have an overall yield of 26%. Thus, the synthesis with the fewer number of steps has the greater yield, consistent with the first rule.

YOUR TURN 11.13

Show how 26% was obtained as the overall yield for the six-step synthesis.

Now consider another pair of syntheses, each of which consists of three steps. Suppose that each step in the first synthesis proceeds with a 90% yield, to give an overall yield of $(0.90) \times (0.90) \times (0.90) = 0.73$, or 73%. Suppose, in the second synthesis, that each step proceeds with a 70% yield, so the overall yield is $(0.70) \times (0.70) \times (0.70) = 0.34$, or 34%. Thus, as suggested in rule 2, the first synthesis has the higher overall yield because each of its steps has a higher yield than the individual steps in the second synthesis.

Table 11-1 illustrates how dramatically the overall yield of a synthesis can change with the number of steps and the yield of each step. The published syntheses of natural products commonly consist of 15–30 steps, with overall yields of <5%! In the synthesis of Taxol highlighted in the opening of this chapter (p. 562), considered a triumph at the time, the overall yield was <2%.

YOUR TURN 11.14

Calculate the percent yield of the following seven-step synthesis that converts the starting material **S** into the target **T**.

$$\mathbf{S} \xrightarrow[90\%]{} \mathbf{A} \xrightarrow[81\%]{} \mathbf{B} \xrightarrow[85\%]{} \mathbf{C} \xrightarrow[98\%]{} \mathbf{D} \xrightarrow[82\%]{} \mathbf{E} \xrightarrow[72\%]{} \mathbf{F} \xrightarrow[94\%]{} \mathbf{T}$$

TABLE 11-1 How Overall Yield Is Affected by the Number and Yield of Individual Steps in a Synthesis

Number of Steps	Yield per Step	Overall Yield
5	90%	59%
5	80%	33%
5	70%	17%
10	90%	35%
10	80%	11%
10	70%	2.8%
20	90%	12%
20	80%	1.2%
20	70%	0.08%

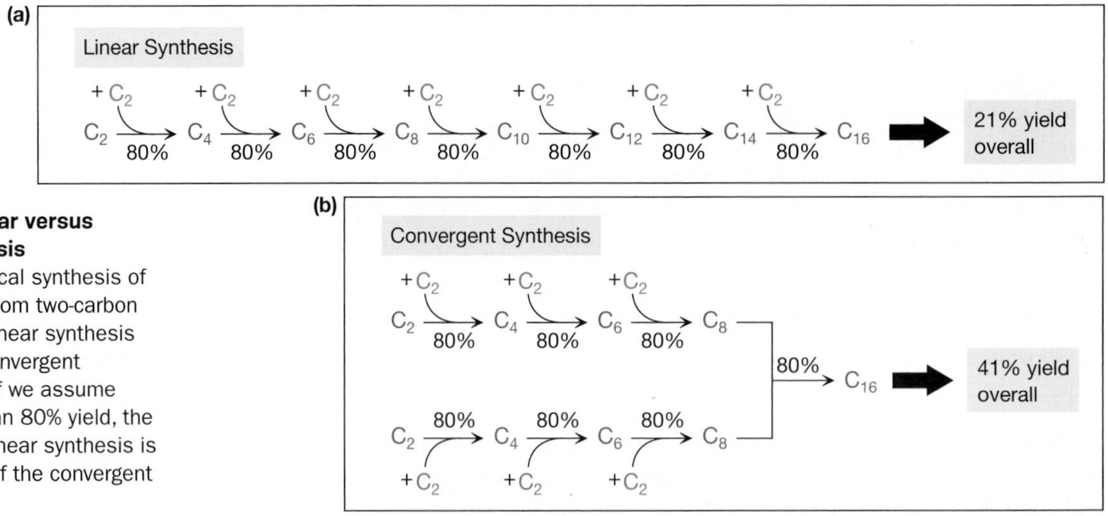
(a)
Linear Synthesis
+C2
C2
80%
C4
C6
C8
C10
C12
C14
C16
21% yield overall
(b)
Convergent Synthesis
C2
C4
C6
C8
80%
C16
41% yield overall
+C2

FIGURE 11-6 Linear versus convergent synthesis schemes Hypothetical synthesis of a 16-carbon target from two-carbon pieces, using (a) a linear synthesis scheme and (b) a convergent synthesis scheme. If we assume that each step has an 80% yield, the overall yield of the linear synthesis is 21%, whereas that of the convergent synthesis is 41%.

So far, we have considered percent yield in a *linear synthesis* only. In a **convergent synthesis**, portions of a target molecule are synthesized separately and are assembled together at a later stage:

> In general, the yield of a multistep synthesis is higher if a target can be produced from a *convergent synthesis* instead of a linear one.

To demonstrate this point, consider **Figure 11-6**. Both Figure 11-6a and 11-6b depict an overly simplified synthesis of a target that contains 16 carbons (where it is assumed that our only carbon source contains two carbons). In Figure 11-6a, we see a *linear synthesis* where two carbons are added at a time. Seven steps are required, and if we assume an 80% yield for each step, then the overall yield would be $(0.80)^7 = 0.21 = 21\%$. Figure 11-6b depicts a *convergent synthesis*, where two eight-carbon pieces are connected together in the final step, with each of those pieces having been constructed separately from our two-carbon source. Reaching the final target still requires seven separate steps, but the longest branch of the synthesis is only four steps, so the overall yield would be $(0.80)^4 = 0.41 = 41\%$. This is roughly twice the yield from the linear synthesis!

Consider Schemes 1 and 2 shown here, both of which produce the same eight-carbon target. For each synthesis scheme, **(a)** determine whether it is linear or convergent, and **(b)** compute the overall percent yield assuming that each synthetic step proceeds with a 90% yield.

Scheme 1

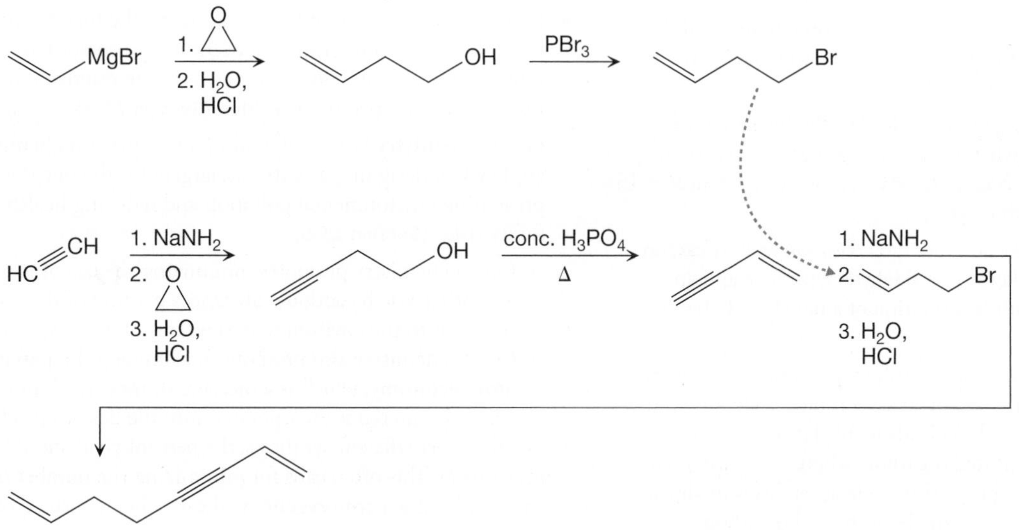
MgBr
1.
O
2. H_2O, HCl
OH
PBr_3
Br
HC
CH
1. $NaNH_2$
2. O
3. H_2O, HCl
OH
conc. H_3PO_4
Δ
1. $NaNH_2$
2.
Br
3. H_2O, HCl

Scheme 2

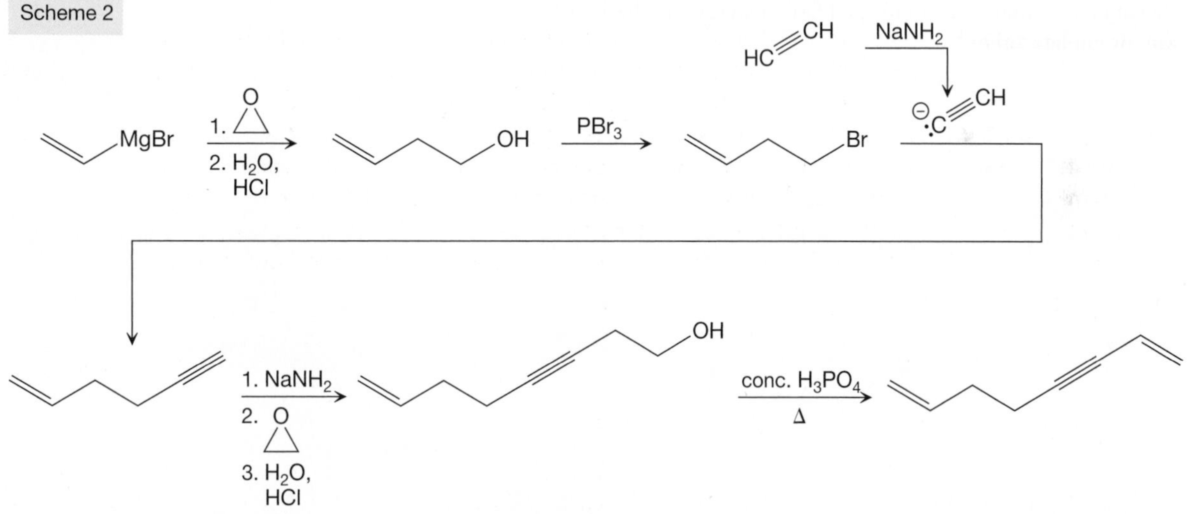
MgBr
1.
O
2. H_2O, HCl
OH
PBr_3
Br
HC
CH
$NaNH_2$
C
CH
1. $NaNH_2$
2. O
3. H_2O, HCl
OH
conc. H_3PO_4
Δ

Chapter Summary and Key Terms

- Reactions that alter the carbon skeleton are important because synthetic targets often have carbon frameworks that are more elaborate than the starting materials. (Section 11.1)
- **Retrosynthetic analysis** streamlines the process of designing an organic synthesis. **Transforms** are applied to the target molecule to arrive at smaller or simpler **precursors**, and the cycle is repeated on the precursors until a suitable starting material is reached. (Section 11.1)
- Epoxide ring-opening reactions lead to the formation of a new C—C bond when the attacking species is a carbon nucleophile, such as NC^-, $RC{\equiv}C^-$, or R^- (e.g., from R—Li or R—MgBr). (Section 11.2)
- A ketone or aldehyde can undergo *alkylation* at an α carbon by treatment of the ketone or aldehyde with base and an alkyl halide. The result is formation of a new C—C bond. (Section 11.3)
    - When a ketone has nonequivalent α carbons, regiochemistry is an issue. The use of a very strong base like lithium diisopropylamide (LDA) leads to alkylation at the less highly alkyl-substituted α carbon, whereas the use of an alkoxide base like the *tert*-butoxide anion leads to alkylation at the more highly alkyl-substituted α carbon.
    - The deprotonation of a ketone by LDA is **irreversible** and the competition takes place under **kinetic control**. The less substituted α carbon is deprotonated faster and leads to the **kinetic enolate anion**.
    - The deprotonation of a ketone by an alkoxide (RO^-) base is **reversible** and the competition takes place under **thermodynamic control**. The enolate anion produced by deprotonating the more substituted α carbon is more stable and is the **thermodynamic enolate anion**.
- Some transforms cannot be carried out in the forward direction. These **synthetic traps** can occur if a precursor has multiple reactive functional groups or if one reactive functional group has two reactive sites. (Section 11.4)
- **Green chemistry** is a set of guiding principles for chemists to apply when designing a synthesis, largely for the purpose of preventing environmental pollution and reducing health and safety risks. (Section 11.6)
    - Green chemistry promotes minimizing the use of toxic and otherwise hazardous substances because of the risk of release into the environment as well as human exposure.
    - Green chemistry also promotes maximizing the **percent atom economy**, which is a measure of how much of the starting material is incorporated into the desired product.
- For the most efficient synthesis, the percent yield should be maximized. This often calls for minimizing the number of steps and using a **convergent** synthesis scheme instead of a **linear synthesis**. (Section 11.7)

Reaction Table

All of the reactions introduced in this chapter alter the carbon skeleton; they are collected in Table 11-2.

TABLE 11-2 Reactions That Alter the Carbon Skeleton[a]

	Starting Compound Class	Typical Reagents and Reaction Conditions	Compound Class Formed	Key Electron-Rich Species	Key Electron-Poor Species	Comments	Discussed in Section
(1)	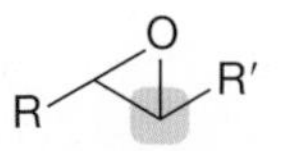 Epoxide	NaCN, H_2O	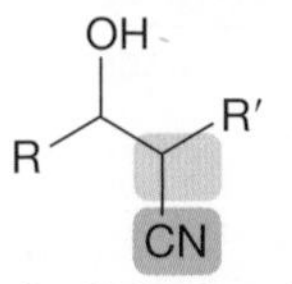 Nitrile (β-hydroxy)	$NC^{\ominus}$	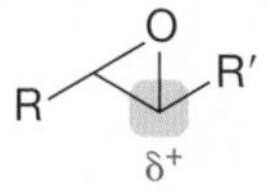	S_N2	11.2
(2)	R″C≡CH Alkyne (terminal)	1. NaH 2.  3. $H_3O^{\oplus}$	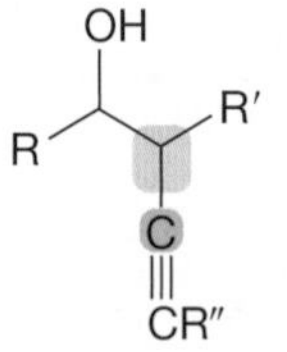 Alcohol (3-Alkyn-1-ol)	R″C≡$C^{\ominus}$	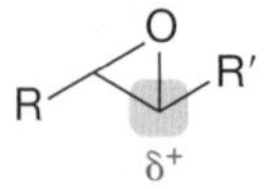	S_N2	11.2
(3)	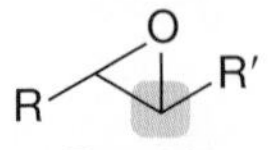 Epoxide	1. R″–Li or R″–MgX 2. $H_3O^{\oplus}$	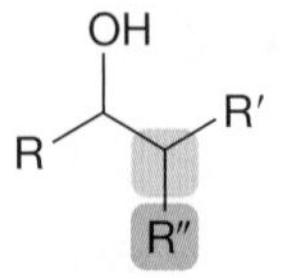 Alcohol	$R''^{\ominus}$	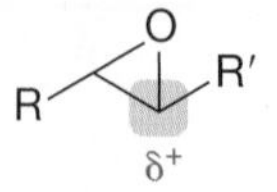	S_N2	11.2
(4)	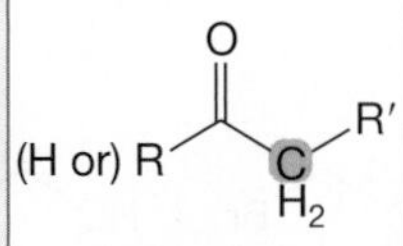 Ketone or aldehyde	1. $Base^{\ominus}$ 2. R″–X	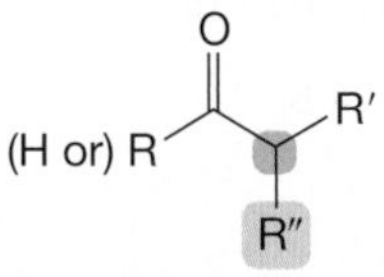 α-Alkylated ketone or aldehyde	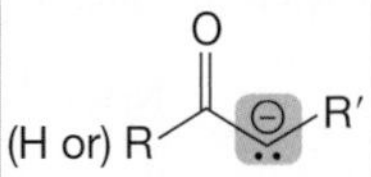 Enolate anion	δ^+ R″–X Alkyl halide	S_N2	11.3

[a]X = Cl, Br, or I.

Problems

Problems that are related to synthesis are denoted (SYN).

Sections 11.1 and 11.2 Reactions That Alter the Carbon Skeleton, Retrosynthetic Analysis, and Opening of Epoxides

11.1 Show how a retrosynthetic analysis might be constructed for each synthesis presented here.

(a)

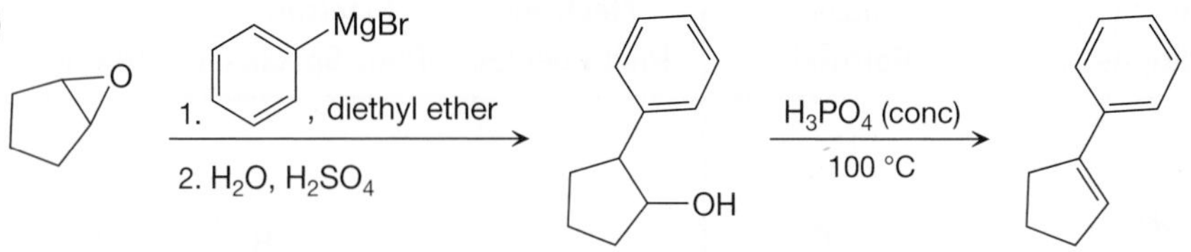
O
MgBr
1. , diethyl ether
2. H_2O, H_2SO_4
OH
H_3PO_4 (conc)
100 °C

(b)

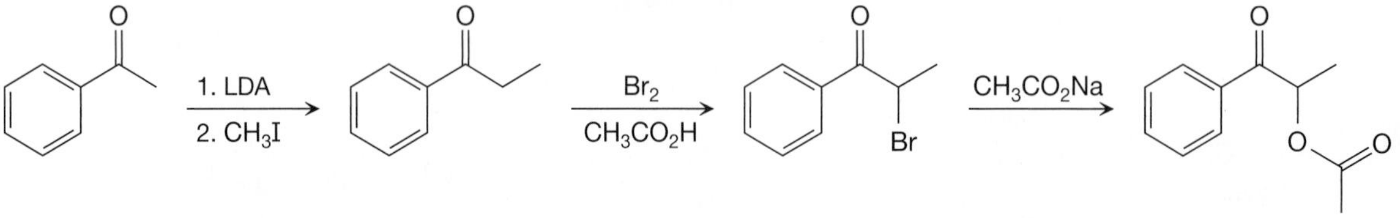
O
1. LDA
2. CH_3I
Br_2
CH_3CO_2H
Br
CH_3CO_2Na

(c)

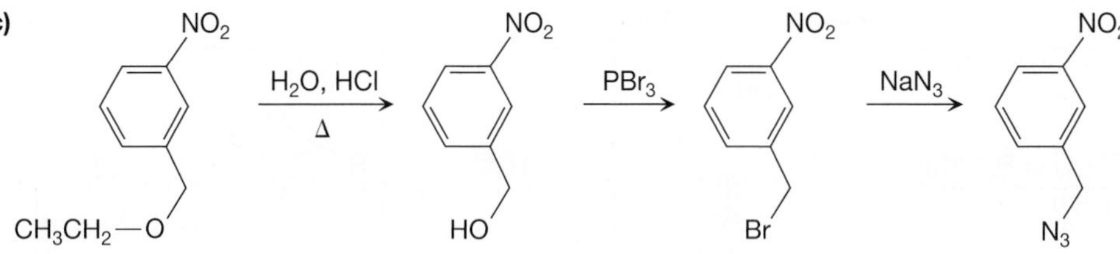
NO_2
CH_3CH_2—O
H_2O, HCl
Δ
HO
PBr_3
Br
NaN_3
N_3

11.2 Rewrite each of these transforms as a synthetic step in the forward direction, including reagents and any special reaction conditions. *Hint*: You may wish to consult Table 10-1 on pp. 552–553.

(a)

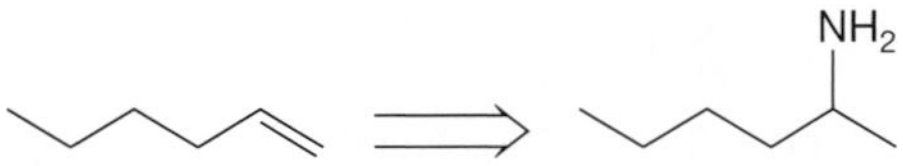
NH_2

(b)

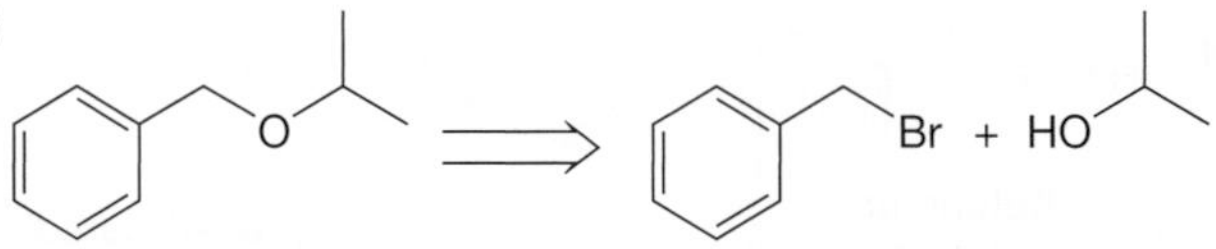
O
Br + HO

(c)

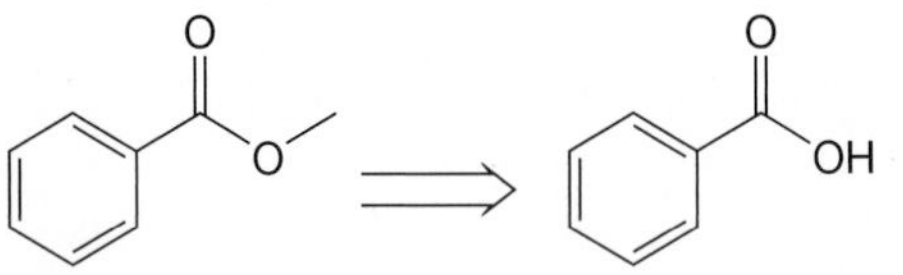
O
OH

(d)

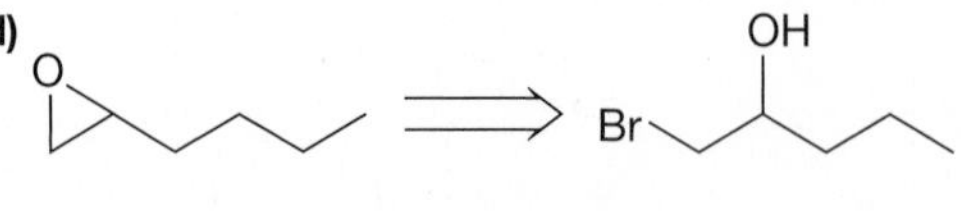
O
Br
OH

11.3 Rewrite each of these transforms as a synthetic step in the forward direction, including reagents and any special reaction conditions. *Hint*: You may wish to consult Table 9-12 on p. 499.

(a)

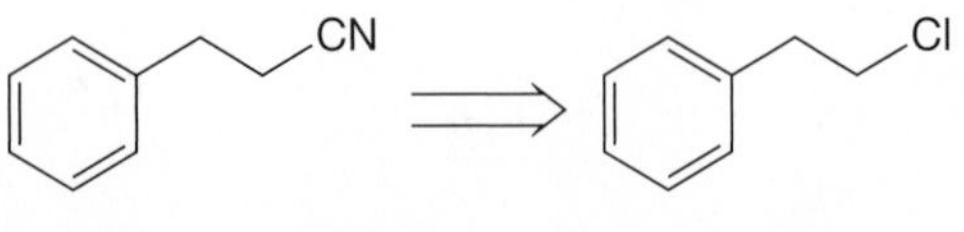
CN
Cl

(b)

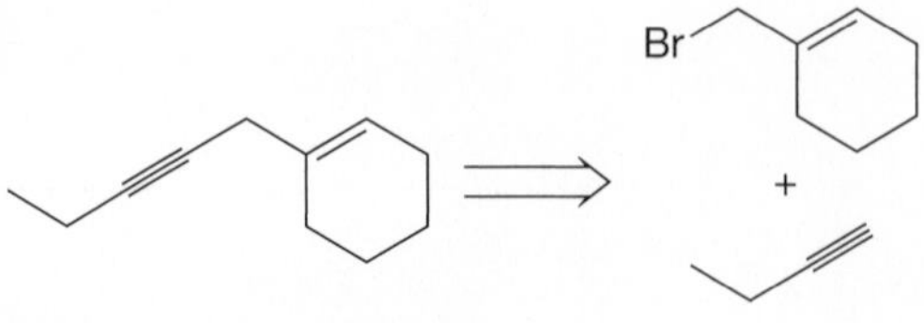
Br
+

11.4 Rewrite each of these transforms as a synthetic step in the forward direction, including reagents and any special reaction conditions. *Hint*: You may wish to consult Table 11-2 on p. 595.

(a)

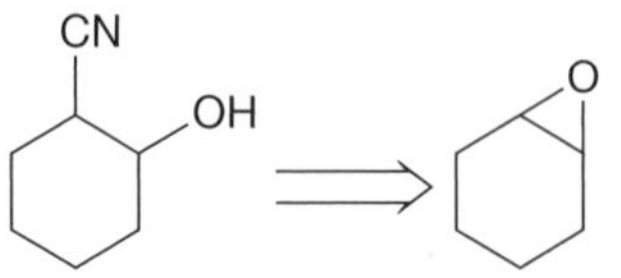
CN
OH
O

(b)

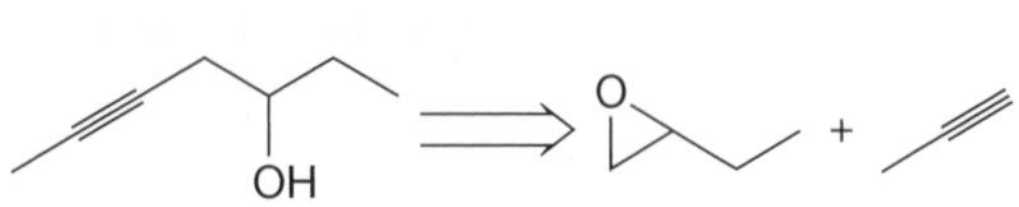
OH
O
+

11.5 **(SYN)** Draw the precursors for each of the following transforms.

(a)

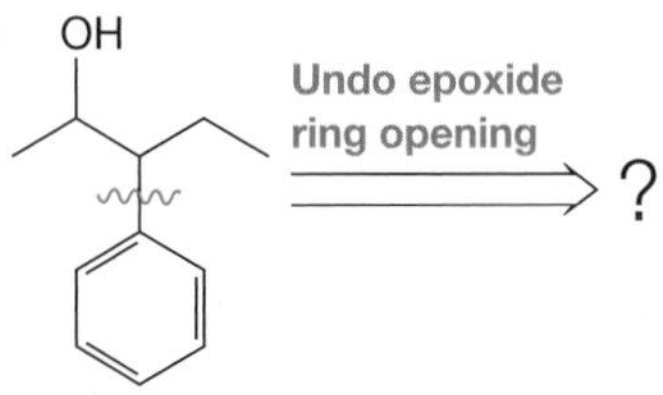
OH
Undo epoxide
ring opening
?

(b)

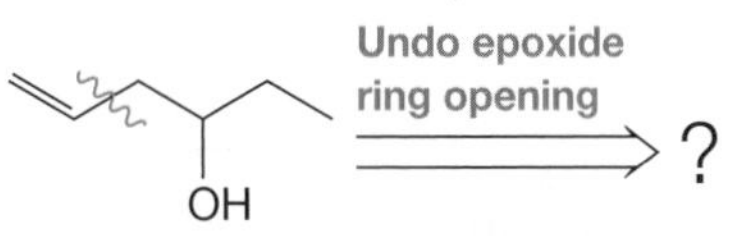
Undo epoxide
ring opening
OH
?

(c)

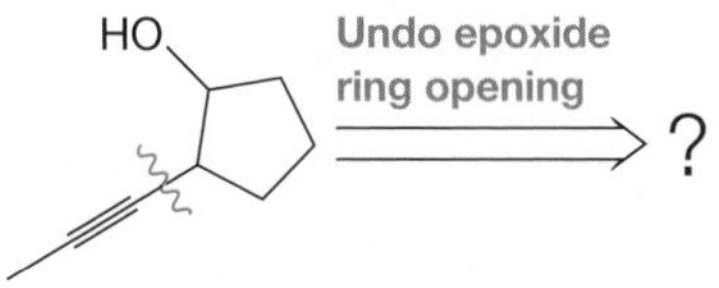
HO
Undo epoxide
ring opening
?

11.6 Recall from Section 10.7 that epoxide ring-opening reactions are stereospecific. Draw the mechanism and predict the product of each of the following reactions, paying attention to stereochemistry.

(a)

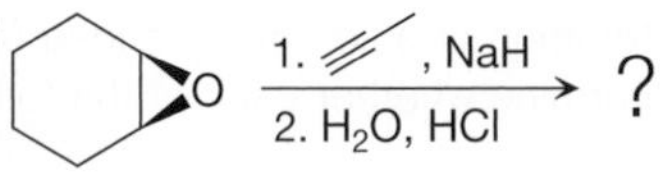
O
1. , NaH
2. H2O, HCl
?

(b)

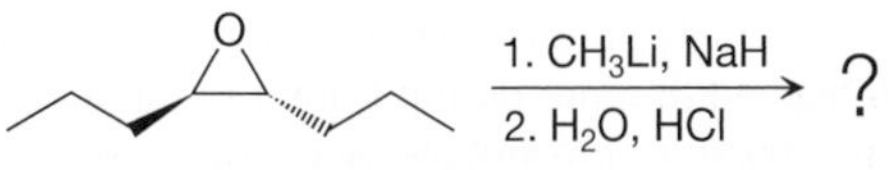
O
1. CH3Li, NaH
2. H2O, HCl
?

11.7 **(SYN)** Draw the precursors for each of the following transforms, paying attention to stereochemistry. *Hint*: See Problem 11.6.

(a)

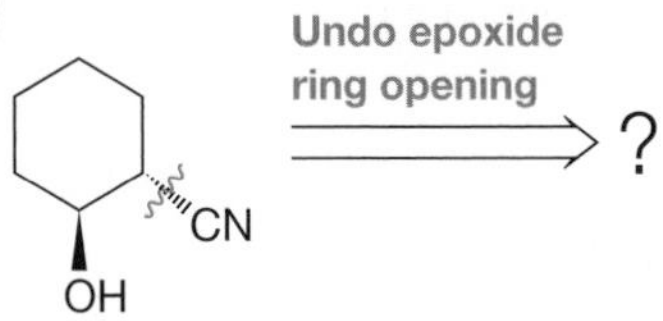
Undo epoxide
ring opening
?
CN
OH

(b)

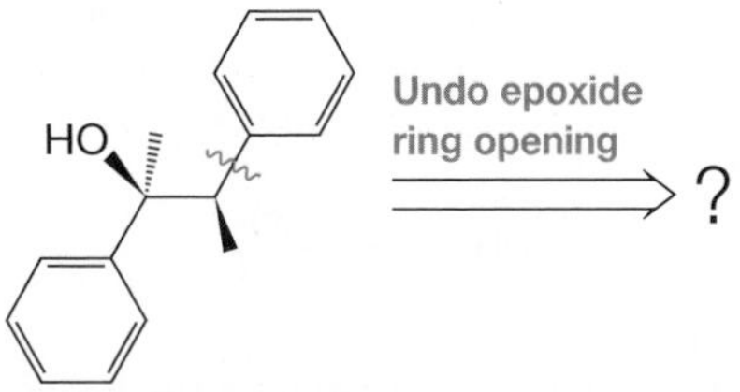
HO
Undo epoxide
ring opening
?

11.8 **(SYN)** Show how the following compounds can be synthesized from the indicated carbon sources (starting materials that add carbons to the target).

(a) Compounds containing seven or fewer carbons

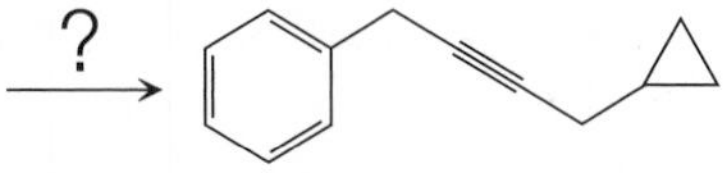
?

(b) Compounds containing four or fewer carbons

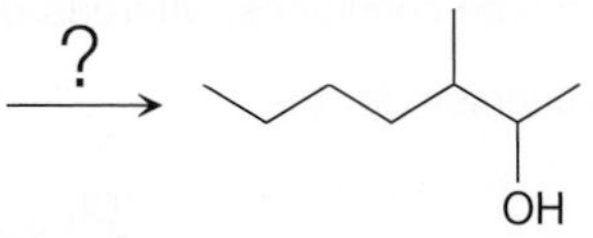
?
OH

Section 11.3 Alkylation of α Carbons: Regioselectivity and Kinetic versus Thermodynamic Control

11.9 Draw the mechanism and the major product for each of the following reactions.

(a)

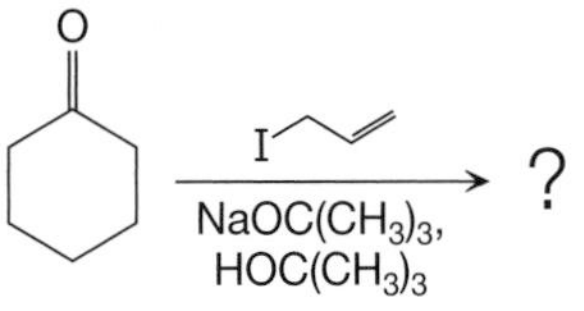
I
NaOC(CH3)3,
HOC(CH3)3
?

(b)

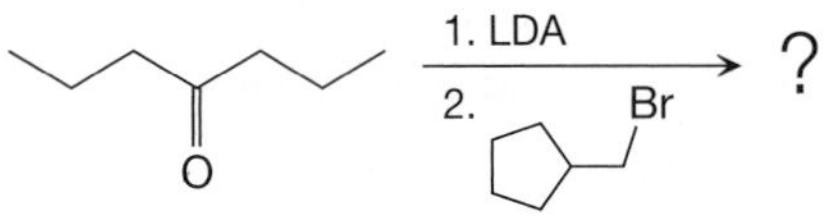
1. LDA
2.
Br
?

(c)

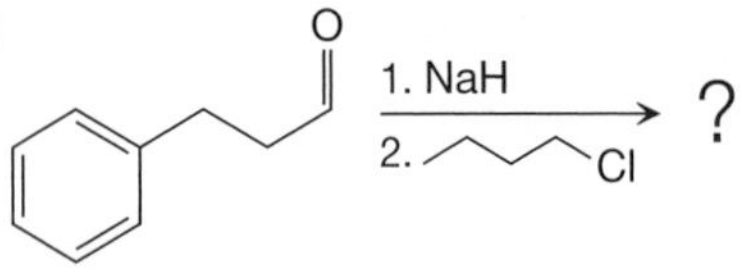
1. NaH
2.
Cl
?

11.10 Draw the mechanism and the major product for each of the following reactions.

(a)

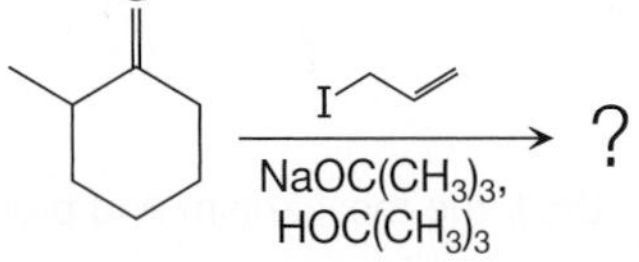
I
NaOC(CH3)3,
HOC(CH3)3
?

(b)

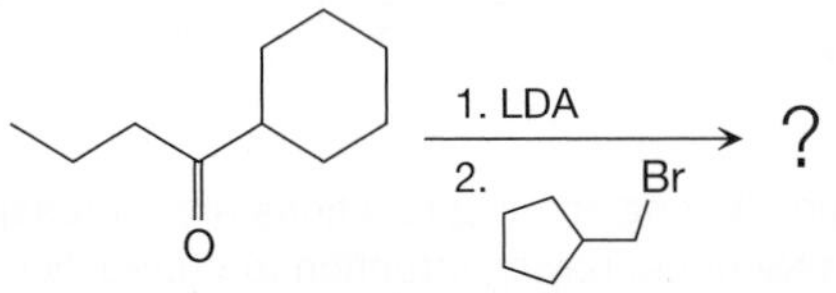
1. LDA
2.
Br
?

11.11 This chapter discussed the reversibility of reactions as it pertains to the deprotonation of a ketone. The idea of reversibility can, however, be applied to other proton transfer reactions, too. Determine whether each of the following proton transfer reactions is reversible or irreversible, and explain your reasoning.

(a)

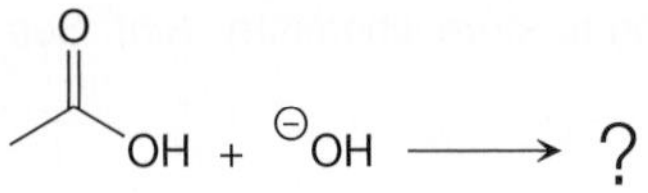
OH
OH
?

(b)

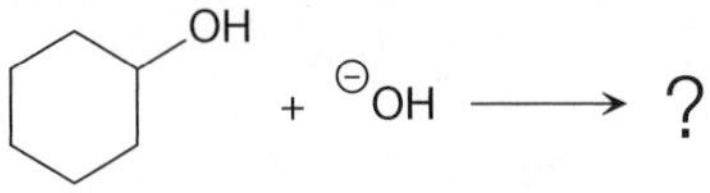
OH
OH
?

(c)

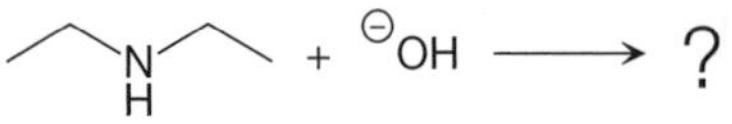
N
H
OH
?

11.12 Show how the following compounds can be synthesized from the indicated carbon sources (starting materials that add carbons to the target).

(a) Compounds containing four or fewer carbons

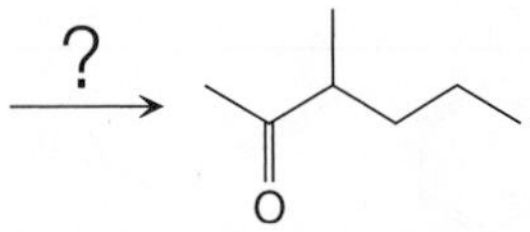
?

(b) Compounds containing seven or fewer carbons

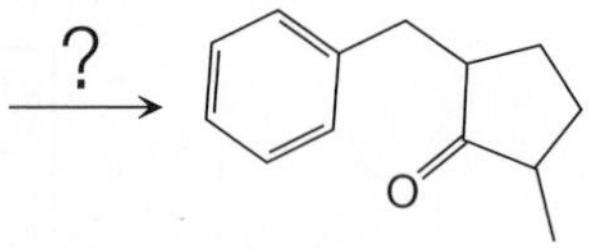
?

11.13 An α carbon of a ketone or aldehyde can be alkylated or halogenated under basic conditions. Recall that multiple halogenations take place under these conditions, whereas polyalkylation is generally not a concern. Suggest why.

11.14 Draw the complete, detailed mechanism for the reaction shown here.

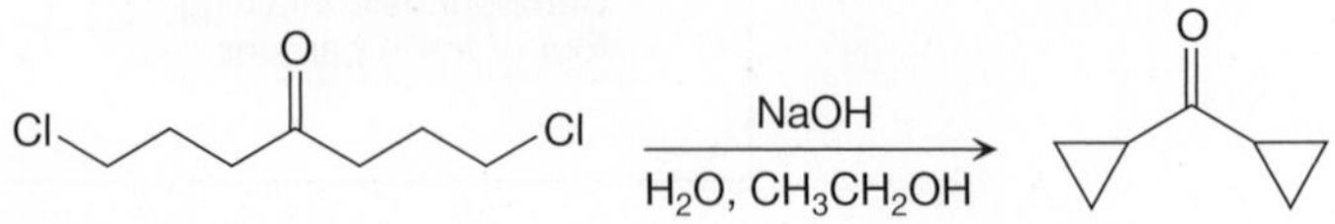
Cl
Cl
NaOH
H2O, CH3CH2OH

11.15 Amides are moderately acidic at the N atom, so they can be alkylated in a fashion that is quite similar to alkylation of ketones and aldehydes. Predict the product of the reaction shown here and draw its complete, detailed mechanism.

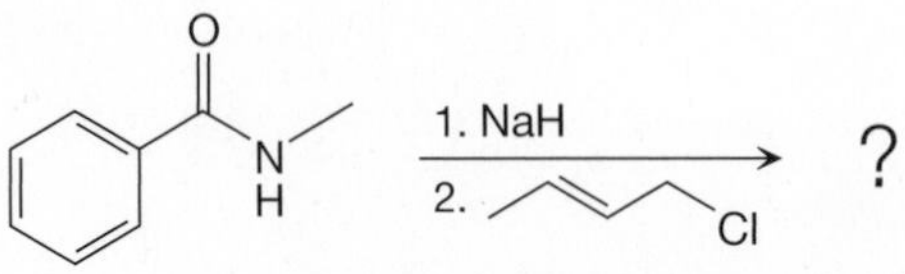
N
H
1. NaH
2.
Cl
?

Section 11.4 Synthetic Traps

11.16 Determine whether each of the following proposed transforms represents a synthetic trap (i.e., it will not proceed as planned in the forward direction). Explain your reasoning.

(a) 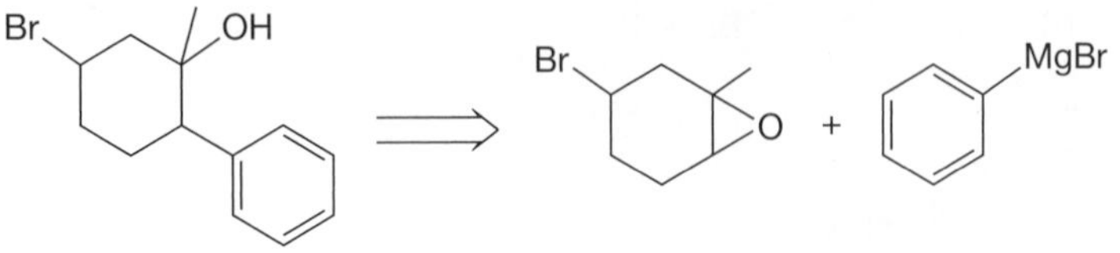
Br
OH
Br
O
+
MgBr

(b) 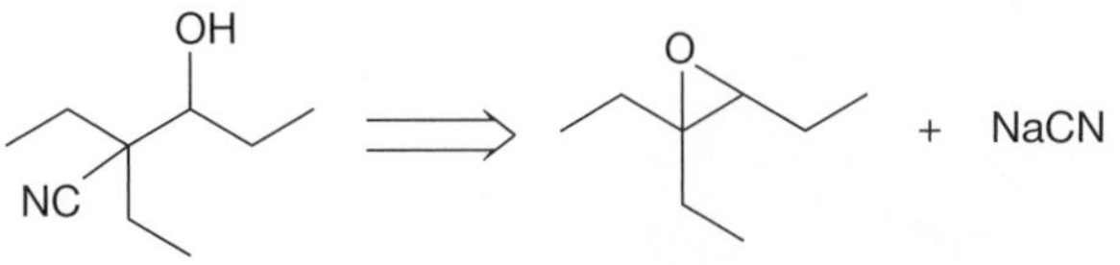
OH
NC
O
+ NaCN

11.17 Determine whether each of the following proposed transforms represents a synthetic trap (i.e., it will not proceed as planned in the forward direction). Explain your reasoning.

(a) 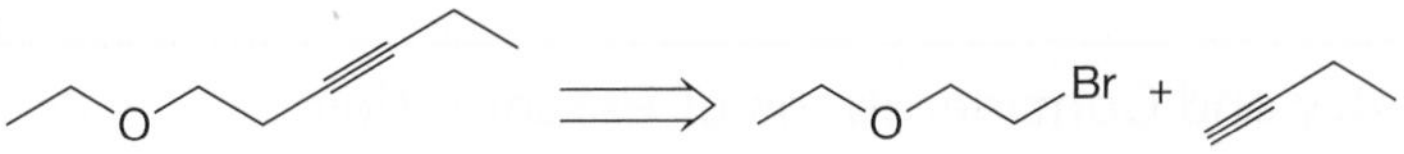
O
O
Br +

(b) 
O
O
+ CH3I

(c) 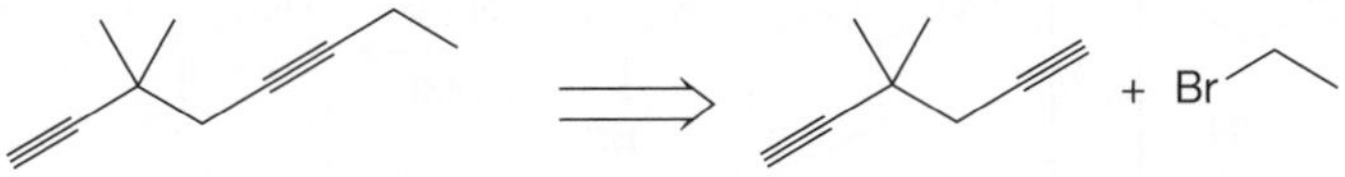
+ Br

11.18 Determine whether each of the following proposed transforms represents a synthetic trap (i.e., it will not proceed as planned in the forward direction). Explain your reasoning.

(a) 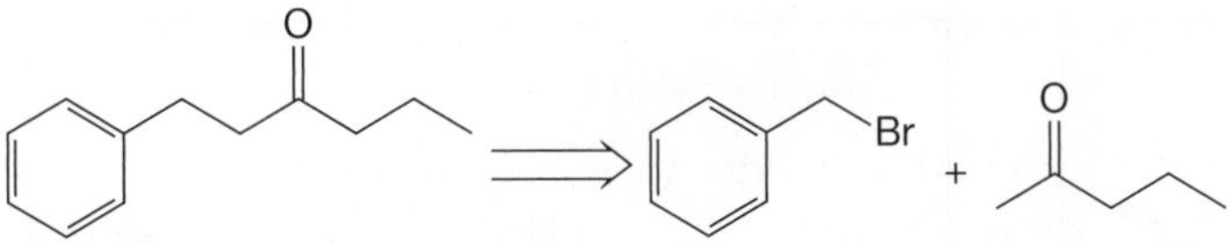
O
Br
+
O

(b) 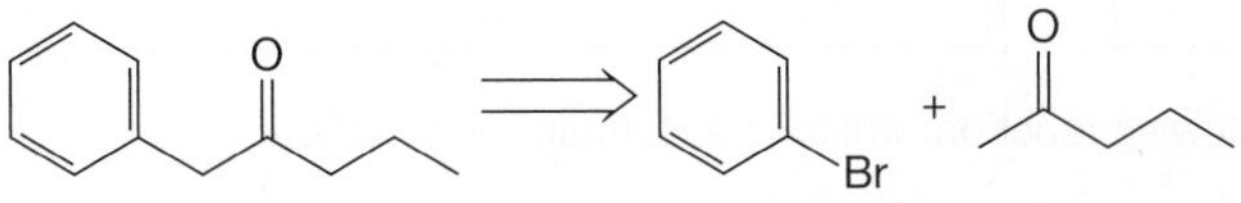
O
+
O
Br

(c) 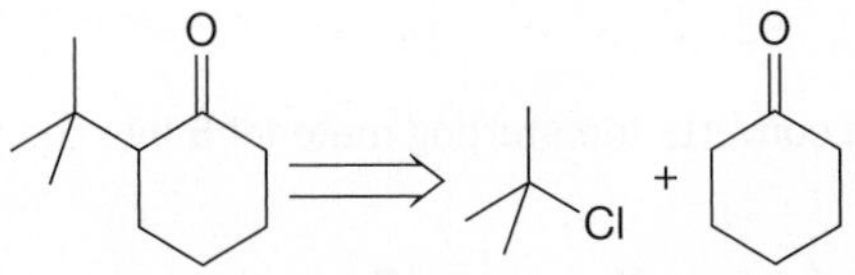
O
O
+
Cl

11.19 Determine whether each of the following proposed transforms represents a synthetic trap (i.e., it will not proceed as planned in the forward direction). Explain your reasoning.

(a)

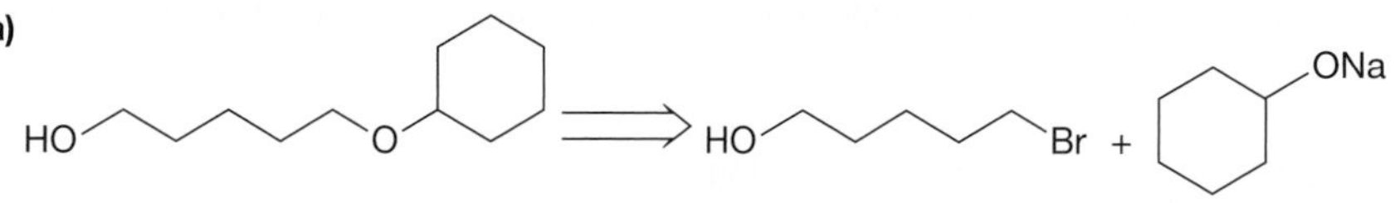
HO
O
HO
Br +
ONa

(b)

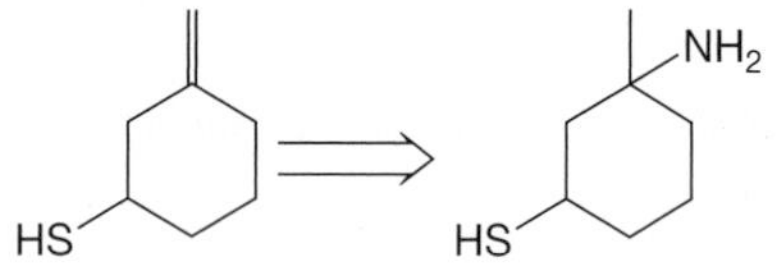
HS
HS
NH2

(c)

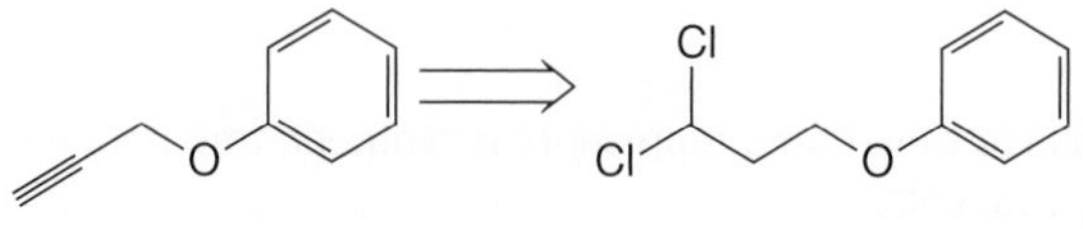
O
Cl
Cl
O

Sections 11.6 and 11.7 Green Chemistry and Considerations of Percent Yield

11.20 Which of the following synthetic steps would be considered more green? *Hint*: Consider searching the Internet to determine the toxicity and other hazards of the compounds that are involved.

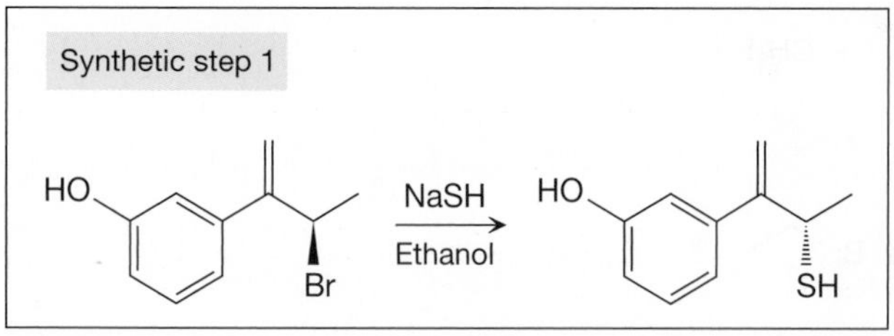
Synthetic step 1
HO
Br
NaSH
Ethanol
HO
SH

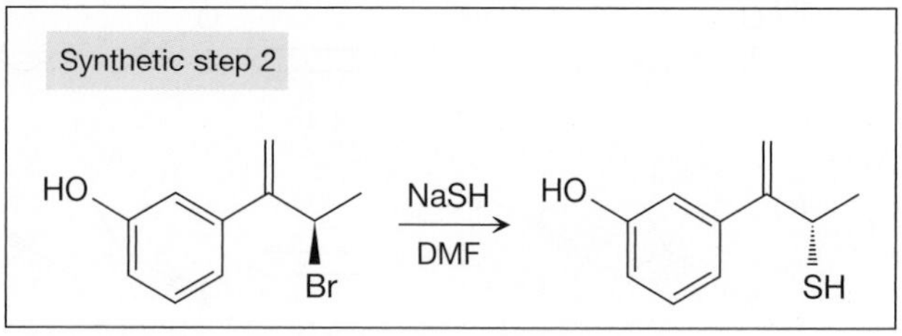
Synthetic step 2
HO
Br
NaSH
DMF
HO
SH

11.21 Which of the following synthetic steps would be considered more green? *Hint:* Consider searching the Internet to determine the toxicity and other hazards of the compounds that are involved.

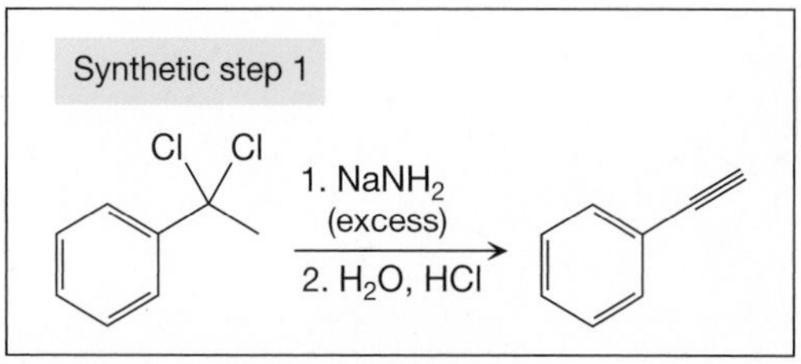
Synthetic step 1
Cl Cl
1. NaNH2
(excess)
2. H2O, HCl

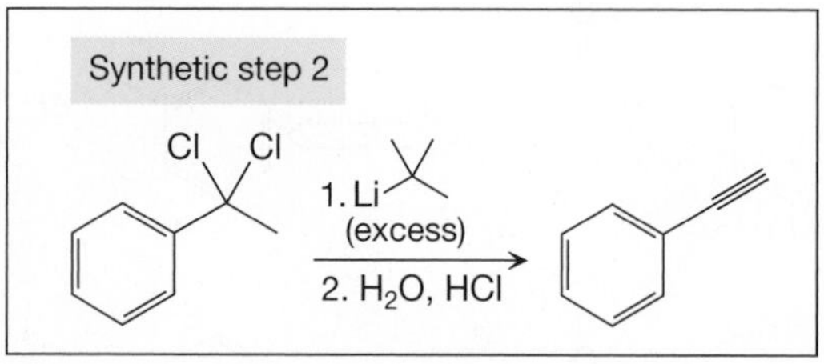
Synthetic step 2
Cl Cl
1. Li
(excess)
2. H2O, HCl

11.22 Compute the percent atom economy for the following reaction, which is a Hofmann elimination.

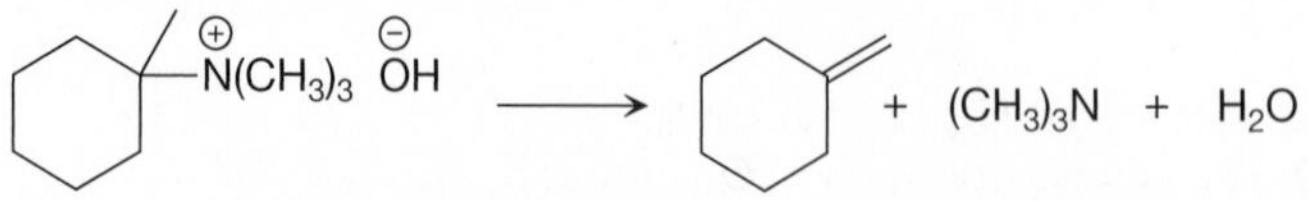
N(CH3)3 OH
+ (CH3)3N + H2O

11.23 Determine whether this generic synthesis scheme, which converts the starting material **S** into the target **T**, is linear or convergent and compute the overall percent yield.

$$\mathbf{S} \xrightarrow[59\%]{V} \mathbf{A} \xrightarrow[78\%]{W} \mathbf{B} \xrightarrow[92\%]{X} \mathbf{C} \xrightarrow[66\%]{Y} \mathbf{D} \xrightarrow[85\%]{Z} \mathbf{T}$$

11.24 Determine whether the generic synthesis scheme at the right, which converts the starting material **S** into the target **T**, is linear or convergent and compute the overall percent yield.

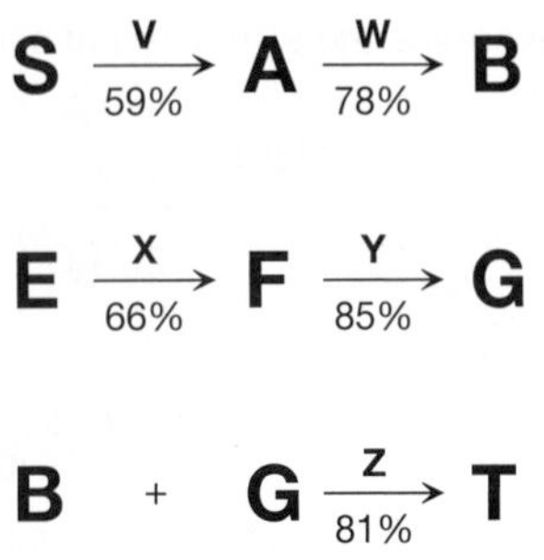
S
V
59%
A
W
78%
B
E
X
66%
F
Y
85%
G
B + G
Z
81%
T

11.25 Compute the *overall* percent yield of the following proposed synthesis. The percent yield of each synthetic step or sequence of steps is provided above the appropriate reaction arrow.

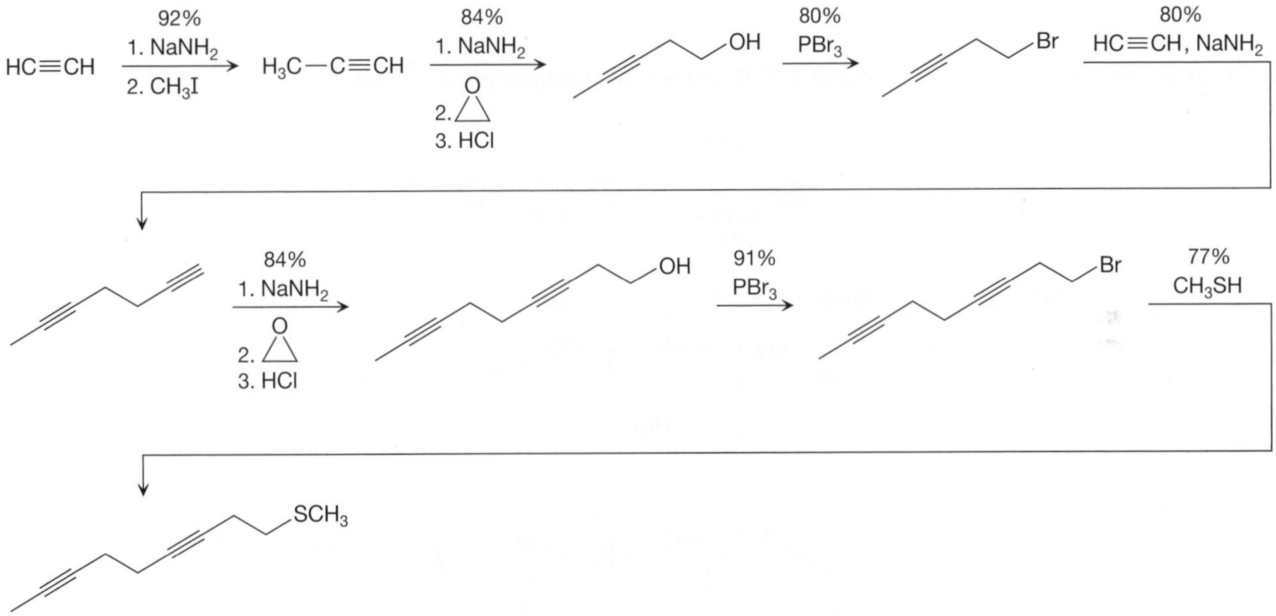
92%
1. NaNH₂
2. CH₃I
HC≡CH
H₃C—C≡CH
84%
1. NaNH₂
2.
3. HCl
OH
80%
PBr₃
Br
80%
HC≡CH, NaNH₂
84%
1. NaNH₂
2.
3. HCl
OH
91%
PBr₃
Br
77%
CH₃SH
SCH₃

11.26 The proposed synthesis in Problem 11.25 is a *linear* scheme. Using the same starting compounds and the same types of reactions shown in the proposed synthesis, construct a *convergent* synthesis that might produce the same target in a higher yield.

Integrated Problems

11.27 Draw the mechanism for this reaction.

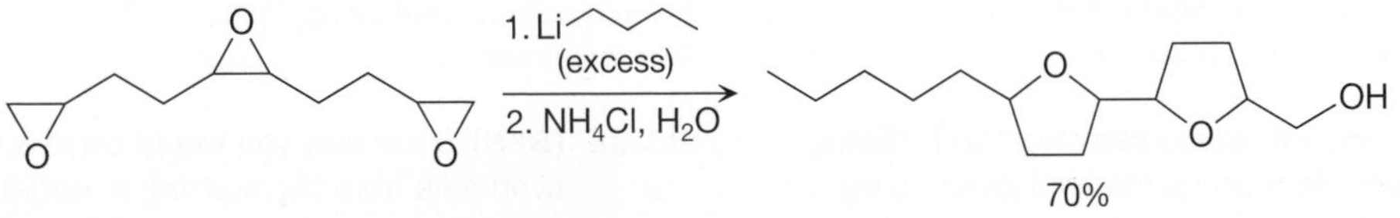
1. Li
(excess)
2. NH₄Cl, H₂O
OH
70%

11.28 Draw the mechanism for the following reaction and predict the major product. *Hint*: Under what conditions are intramolecular reactions favored over intermolecular reactions?

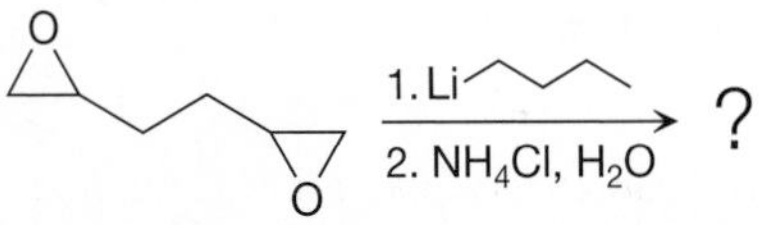
1. Li
2. NH₄Cl, H₂O
?

11.29 Oxetane is a four-membered-ring ether. As shown here, oxetane will react with a powerful nucleophile like a Grignard reagent.

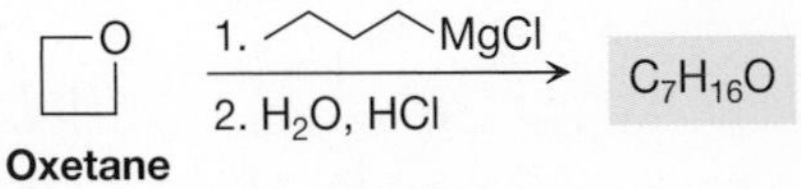
1. MgCl
2. H₂O, HCl
C₇H₁₆O

Oxetane

(a) Draw the complete mechanism and product for the above reaction.

(b) If tetrahydrofuran (THF) is treated with a Grignard reagent, no reaction occurs. Explain why oxetane reacts but THF does not.

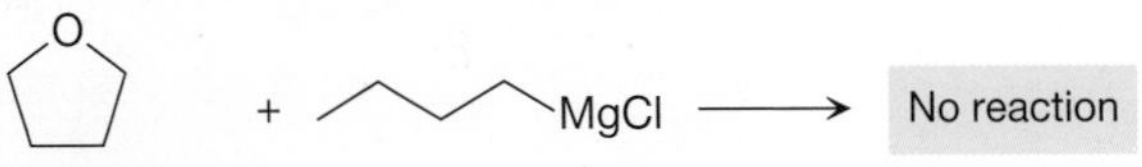
+
MgCl
No reaction

Tetrahydrofuran (THF)

11.30 Determine the structures of compounds **A**, **B**, **C**, and **D** in the following reaction sequences.

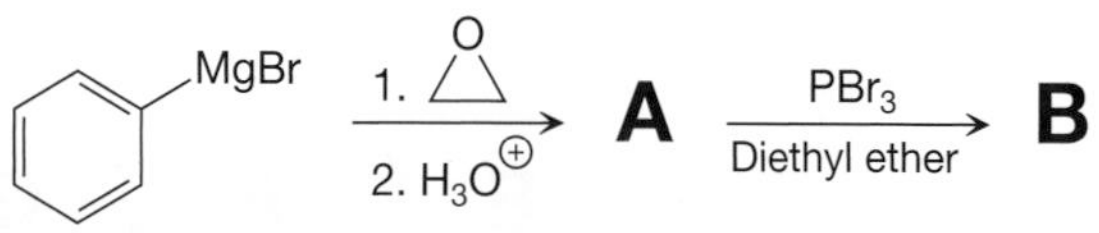
MgBr
1. O (epoxide)
2. $H_3O^{\oplus}$
A
PBr_3
Diethyl ether
B

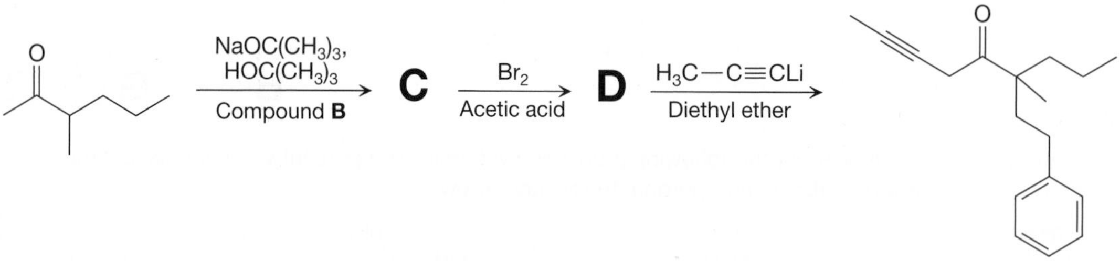
O
$NaOC(CH_3)_3$,
$HOC(CH_3)_3$
Compound B
C
Br_2
Acetic acid
D
$H_3C-C\equiv CLi$
Diethyl ether
O

11.31 Determine the structures of compounds **E**, **F**, **G**, and **H** in the following reaction sequence.

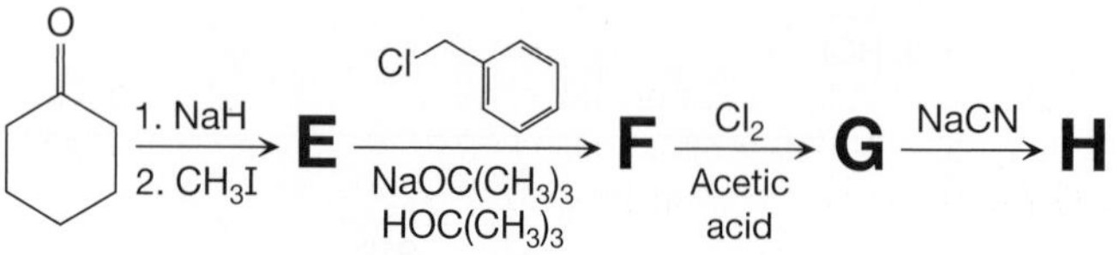
O
1. NaH
2. CH_3I
E
Cl
$NaOC(CH_3)_3$
$HOC(CH_3)_3$
F
Cl_2
Acetic acid
G
NaCN
H

11.32 Determine the structures of compounds **I**, **J**, **K**, and **L** in the following reaction sequences.

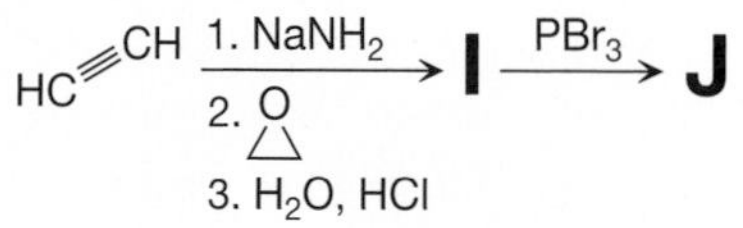
HC≡CH
1. $NaNH_2$
2. O (epoxide)
3. H_2O, HCl
I
PBr_3
J

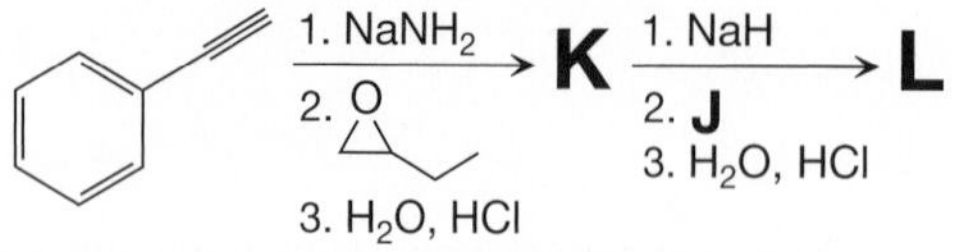
1. $NaNH_2$
2. O (epoxide)
3. H_2O, HCl
K
1. NaH
2. J
3. H_2O, HCl
L

11.33 **(SYN)** Show how hept-2-yne can be made from two different alkyl bromides.

11.34 **(SYN)** Show how you would synthesize each of the following compounds from the materials specified.

(a)

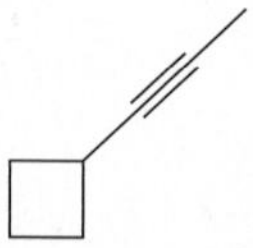

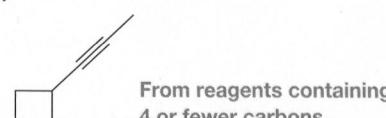

From reagents containing 4 or fewer carbons

(b)

From reagents containing 5 or fewer carbons

11.35 **(SYN)** Show how you would carry out the following synthesis from the starting material given, using any other compound containing, at most, one carbon atom.

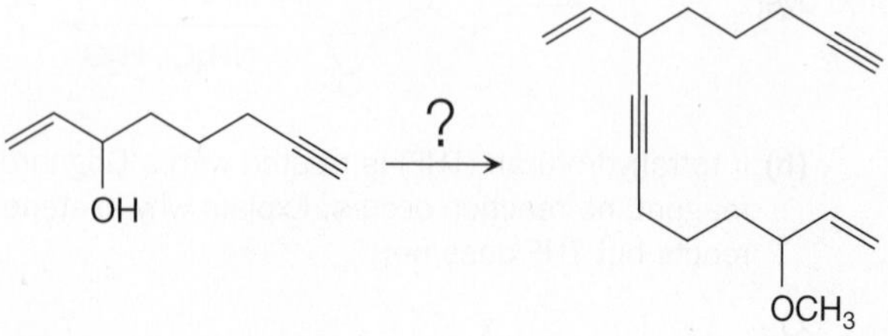
OH
?
OCH_3

11.36 **(SYN)** Show how you would carry out the following synthesis from the starting material given, plus propyne, and any other inorganic reagents (i.e., reagents containing no carbon).

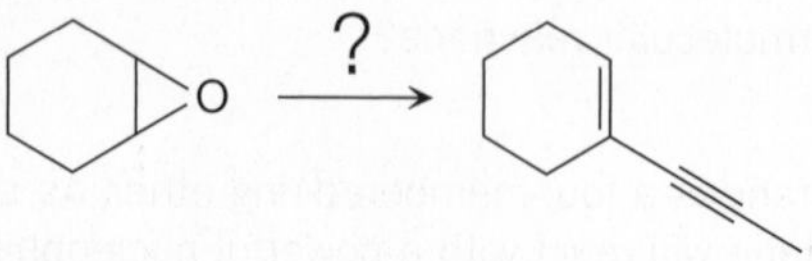
O
?

11.37 (SYN) Show how you would carry out each of the following syntheses.

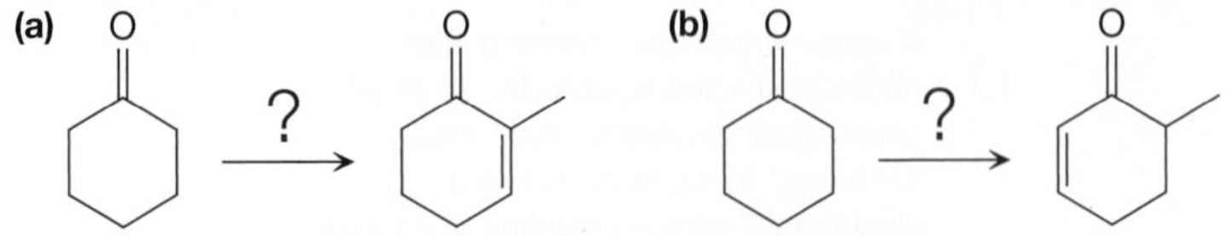

(a)
O
?
O
(b)
O
?
O

11.38 Show how the following compound can be synthesized from the indicated carbon sources (starting materials that add carbons to the target).

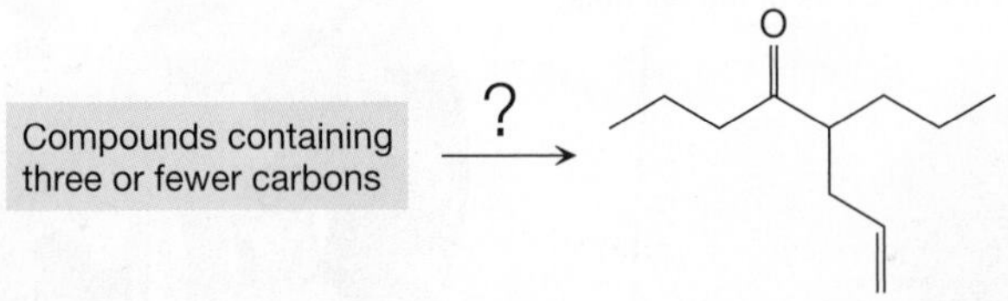

Compounds containing three or fewer carbons
?
O

11.39 Show how the following compound can be synthesized from the indicated carbon sources (starting materials that add carbons to the target).

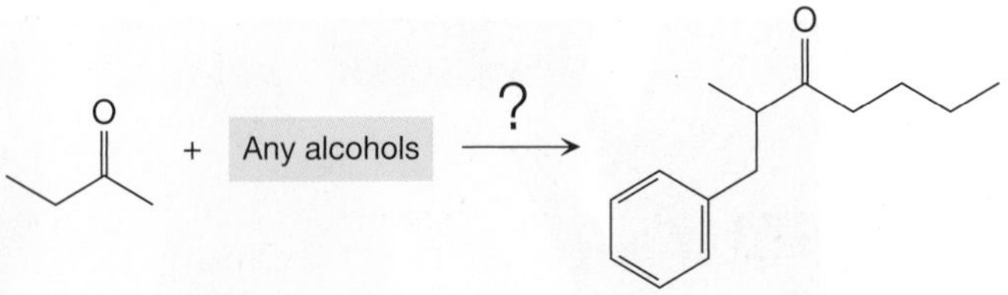

O
+
Any alcohols
?
O

11.40 In Section 11.3a, we learned that the deprotonation of a ketone will favor the kinetic enolate anion when LDA is used as the base. In these situations, excess LDA is typically used, and the reaction is run at a very low temperature (e.g., −78 °C). **(a)** Why is LDA used in excess? **(b)** Why must the temperature be kept low?

12

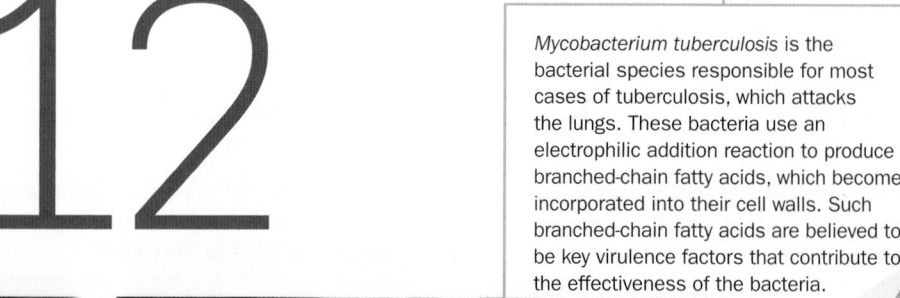

Mycobacterium tuberculosis is the bacterial species responsible for most cases of tuberculosis, which attacks the lungs. These bacteria use an electrophilic addition reaction to produce branched-chain fatty acids, which become incorporated into their cell walls. Such branched-chain fatty acids are believed to be key virulence factors that contribute to the effectiveness of the bacteria.

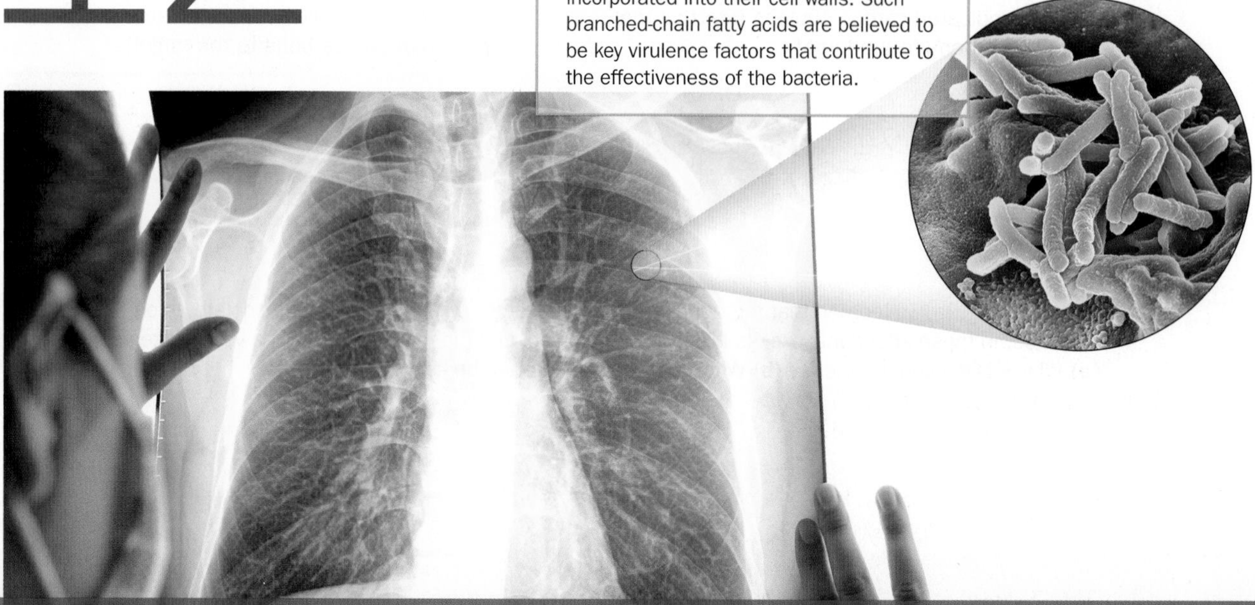

Electrophilic Addition to Nonpolar π Bonds 1

Addition of a Brønsted Acid

In the last several chapters, we have seen that bond formation is frequently driven by the flow of electrons from an electron-rich species to an electron-poor species. In the reactions we have examined in depth so far, the electron-rich species, acting as a nucleophile or base, typically possesses an atom that has a partial or full negative charge and a lone pair of electrons. In such cases, those electrons are the ones used to form the new bond.

Here in Chapter 12 and later in Chapter 13, we discuss **electrophilic addition reactions**, whose mechanisms contain an *electrophilic addition step* (or a variation of it). Recall from Section 7.6 that the electrons used to form a new bond in an electrophilic addition step originate from a nonpolar π bond, such as the C═C double bond of an alkene or the C≡C triple bond of an alkyne. These bonds are relatively electron-rich because several electrons are confined to the region between two atoms (**Figure 12-1a**). Thus:

> Alkenes and alkynes tend to behave as nucleophiles and react with electrophiles (i.e., with electron-poor species).

Chapter Outline

Two other factors contribute to the reactivity of the π electrons of a nonpolar double or triple bond, compared to an analogous single bond:

1. π Electrons are, on average, located farther away from a molecule's nuclei than σ electrons are, as shown in Figure 12-1b. Therefore, π electrons are more accessible spatially.
2. As indicated in Figure 12-1c, π electrons are higher in energy, and thus they are less stable than σ electrons. Consequently:

> It is easier to break the π bond of a double bond than the σ bond of an analogous single bond.

We examine a variety of electrophilic addition reactions here in Chapter 12 and in Chapter 13. The complexity of these reactions can vary greatly. Some are stepwise additions, whose mechanisms consist of two or more steps, while others are concerted, taking place in a single step. Some result in the formation of rings. Given the complexity that electrophilic addition reactions can have, we begin with the addition of a Brønsted acid (HA) to an alkene, a prototype of electrophilic addition reactions. We then explore the intricacies of other electrophilic addition mechanisms (see Looking Ahead box).

▸ LOOKING AHEAD

Alkenes can undergo addition reactions other than the electrophilic addition reactions presented in this chapter and in Chapter 13. In Chapter 26, we will explore cycloaddition mechanisms involving alkenes, which describe the Diels–Alder reaction and oxidative cleavage reactions.

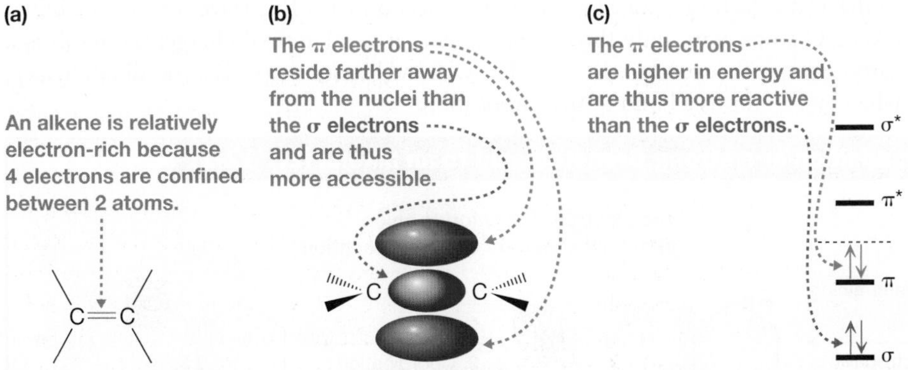

(a)
An alkene is relatively electron-rich because 4 electrons are confined between 2 atoms.
C=C
(b)
The π electrons reside farther away from the nuclei than the σ electrons and are thus more accessible.
C
C
(c)
The π electrons are higher in energy and are thus more reactive than the σ electrons.
σ*
π*
π
σ

FIGURE 12-1 Relative reactivity of π electrons (a) The nonpolar π bond is relatively electron-rich because multiple electrons are confined to the region between two atoms. In general, π electrons are more reactive than σ electrons because (b) π electrons are more easily accessed spatially and (c) π electrons are higher in energy.

SECTION 12.1 OBJECTIVES

You will be able to:

1. Draw the mechanism for the addition of a Brønsted acid to an alkene and predict the major product.
2. Draw an energy diagram for the addition of a Brønsted acid to an alkene and identify the rate-determining step.

12.1 The General Electrophilic Addition Mechanism: Addition of a Strong Brønsted Acid to an Alkene

Equation 12-1 shows an electrophilic addition reaction in which cyclohexene reacts with HCl, a strong Brønsted acid, to produce chlorocyclohexane, the **adduct** (i.e., the addition product). As we can see, one alkene carbon forms a new bond to H, and the other one forms a new bond to Cl. The HCl molecule is said to *add across* the C=C double bond. Similarly, in the reaction in Equation 12-2, H_2SO_4 adds across the C=C double bond in 2,3-dimethylbut-2-ene:

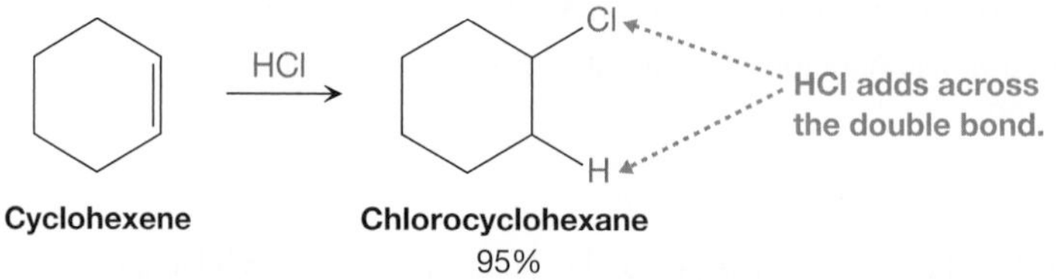

HCl
Cl
HCl adds across the double bond.
H
Cyclohexene
Chlorocyclohexane
95%

(12-1)

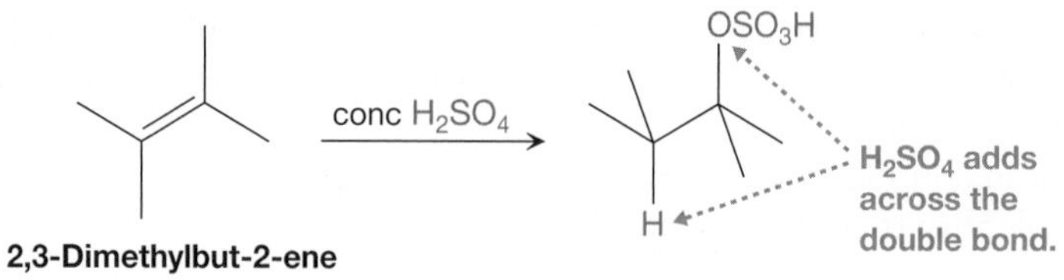

conc H_2SO_4
OSO_3H
H_2SO_4 adds across the double bond.
H
2,3-Dimethylbut-2-ene

(12-2)

YOUR TURN **12.1**

Describe what takes place in the following reaction:

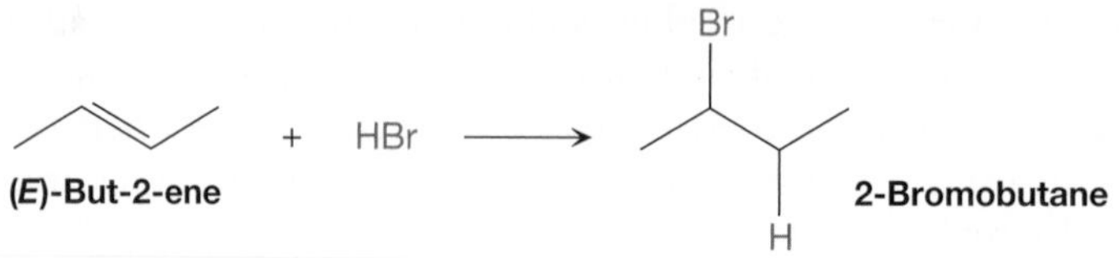

Br
+ HBr
(E)-But-2-ene
H
2-Bromobutane

Answers to Your Turns are in the back of the book.

The reactions shown in Equations 12-1 and 12-2 take place by the two-step mechanism presented in Equation 12-3 for the addition of HCl. Step 1 is an electrophilic addition step, in which a pair of electrons from the electron-rich π bond forms a bond to the acid's electron-poor H atom (review Section 7.6). This leaves one of the initial alkene C atoms with only three bonds, giving it a +1 formal charge; the result is a carbocation. Cl^- is produced as the H—Cl bond breaks. Step 2 is a coordination step, whereby Cl^- forms a bond to the carbocation:

Mechanism Drawing
Addition of a Brønsted Acid to an Alkene

Mechanism for the electrophilic addition of a strong Brønsted acid to an alkene (Eq. 12-1)

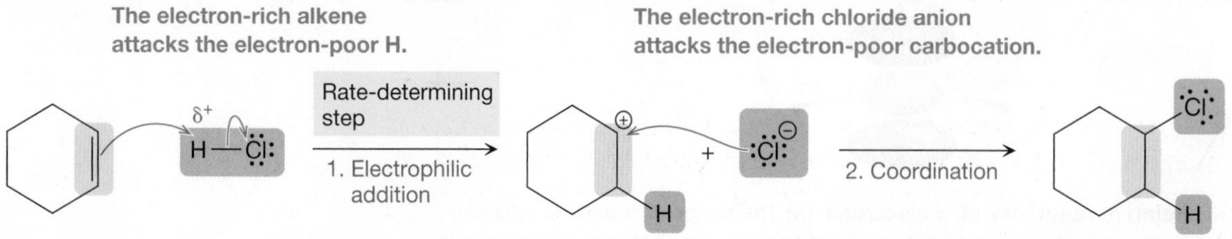

The electron-rich alkene attacks the electron-poor H.
The electron-rich chloride anion attacks the electron-poor carbocation.
Rate-determining step
δ+
H—Cl:
1. Electrophilic addition
+
H
:Cl:
2. Coordination
H

(12-3)

YOUR TURN 12.2

The mechanism for the electrophilic addition reaction in Equation 12-2 is as follows, but the curved arrows have been omitted:

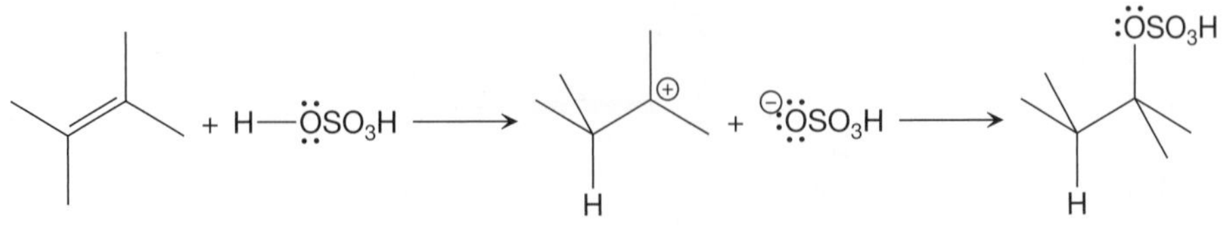

:ÖSO3H
+ H—ÖSO3H
+ :ÖSO3H
H
H

Supply the missing curved arrows and write the name of each elementary step below the appropriate reaction arrow. Also, label the appropriate electron-rich and electron-poor sites in each step.

YOUR TURN 12.3

Draw the complete, detailed mechanism and predict the major product for each of the following reactions. You may ignore stereochemistry in these cases.

(a) **(b)**
(c) **(d)**

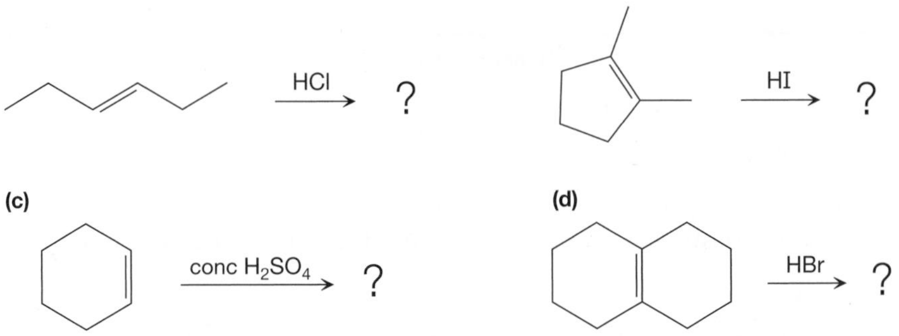

HCl
?
HI
?
conc H2SO4
?
HBr
?

As indicated in Equation 12-3:

> In an electrophilic addition of a Brønsted acid to an alkene, the rate-determining step is Step 1, addition of the H^+ electrophile.

Step 1 is rate-determining because it has such a high-energy transition state, as shown in the free energy diagram in **Figure 12-2** (next page), which makes the step inherently slow. We expect the transition state to be really high in energy because, according to the Hammond postulate (see Recall box), the transition state should be similar in energy to the carbocation intermediate. The high energy of the intermediate, in turn, is due to both the lack of an octet on C and the creation of two charges.

Figure 12-2 also shows that the product of an electrophilic addition reaction is typically more stable than the reactants. Thus:

> In general, electrophilic addition reactions are energetically quite favorable.

These reactions tend to be favorable because, as shown in **Figure 12-3**, a σ bond and a π bond from the reactants are broken, and two σ bonds are formed in the products. Effectively, there is a tradeoff of a π bond for a σ bond, and as we saw in Figure 12-1, the electrons of a σ bond are usually lower in energy.

◀ RECALL

According to the Hammond postulate, discussed in Section 9.3a, the transition state of an elementary step is similar to the product, both in structure and energy, if the step is endothermic. If the step is exothermic, then the transition state is similar in structure and energy to the reactant.

FIGURE 12-2 Reaction energy diagram for electrophilic addition of a strong acid to an alkene The intermediates are much higher in energy than the reactants or products, due to the lack of an octet on C and the presence of two charges. The transition state of the first step is higher in energy than that of the second step, which makes the first step rate-determining.

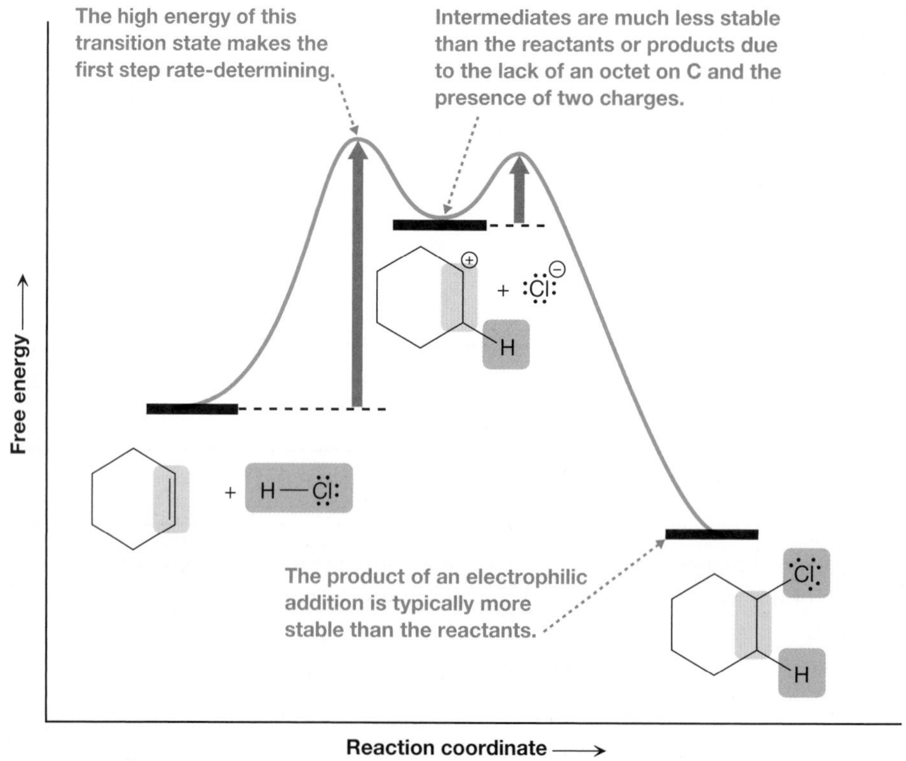

The high energy of this transition state makes the first step rate-determining.
Intermediates are much less stable than the reactants or products due to the lack of an octet on C and the presence of two charges.
Free energy
+ H—Cl:
+ :Cl:
H
The product of an electrophilic addition is typically more stable than the reactants.
Cl
H
Reaction coordinate

FIGURE 12-3 Driving force for electrophilic addition A σ bond and a π bond (shown in red) are lost, and two σ bonds (shown in blue) are gained. Because the electrons of a σ bond are usually lower in energy, the products are typically more stable.

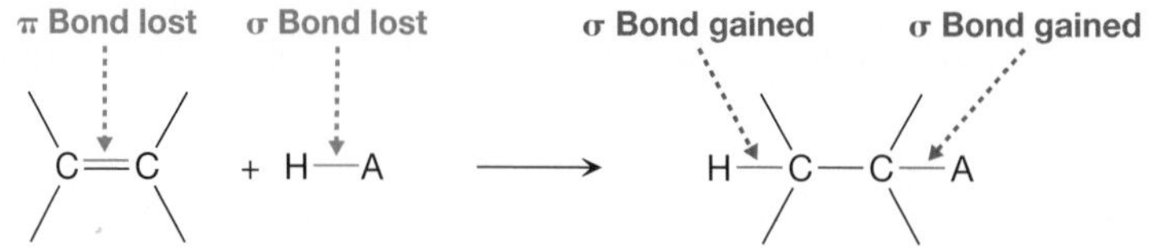

π Bond lost
σ Bond lost
σ Bond gained
σ Bond gained
C=C
+ H—A
H—C—C—A

SOLVED PROBLEM **12.1**

How to predict the relative rates of electrophilic addition to alkenes

Break It Down Which alkene, A or B, will react faster with HCl?

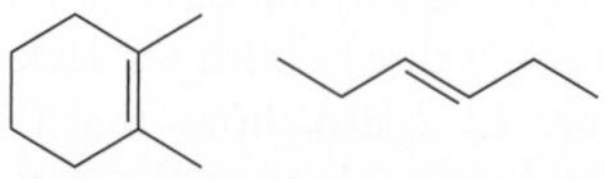

A **B**

Think	Solve
What is the rate-determining step for the reaction of an alkene with HCl?	The mechanism consists of the two steps shown in Equation 12-3, for which the rate-determining step is Step 1, addition of the proton to produce a carbocation intermediate.

(continued)

What are the carbocation intermediates produced on protonation of **A** and **B**?	The steps for addition of a proton to **A** and **B** are shown here. 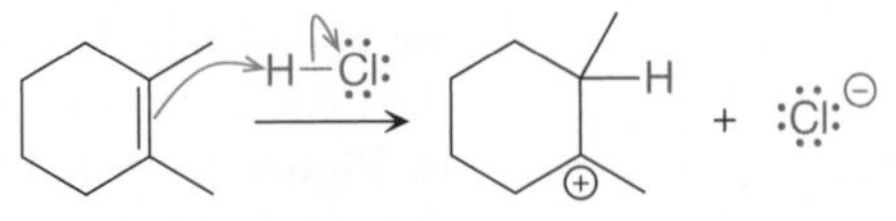 **A** 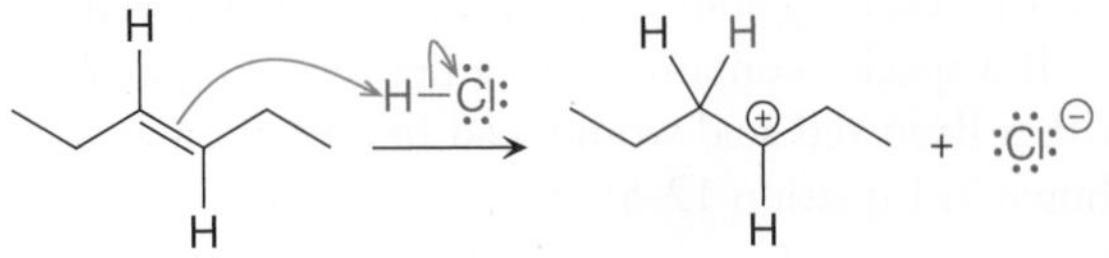 **B**
Which carbocation is more stable? How does that impact the overall rate of the reaction?	The carbocation produced from **A** is tertiary, whereas the one produced from **B** is secondary. Because each alkyl group attached to C^+ is electron-donating, the carbocation produced from **A** is more stable. Thus, protonation of **A** has the smaller energy barrier and is faster, making the overall reaction rate for **A** faster than for **B**.

Try It Which alkene, **C** or **D**, will react faster with HCl?

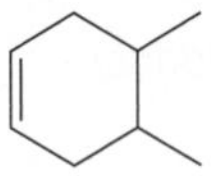

C

$H_2C{=}CH_2$

D

Answers to all Try It exercises can be found in the Solutions Manual.

12.2 Benzene Rings Do Not Readily Undergo Electrophilic Addition of Brønsted Acids

SECTION 12.2 OBJECTIVES

You will be able to:

1. Distinguish a C═C bond characteristic of an alkene from C═C bonds that characterize an aromatic ring.
2. Predict the product when a Brønsted acid reacts with a compound containing both an aromatic ring and a C═C bond characteristic of an alkene.

The Lewis structure of benzene, C_6H_6, has three carbon–carbon double bonds. We might therefore expect benzene to undergo electrophilic addition with a Brønsted acid, HA, similar to the reactions we have just seen. As indicated in Equation 12-4, however, these reactions do *not* take place:

Brønsted acids do *not* add to benzene.

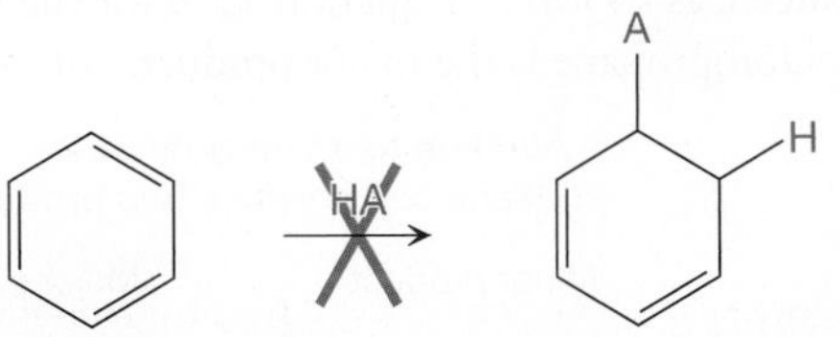

Benzene

(12-4)

In general:

Brønsted acids do *not* add across a C═C double bond in benzene.

Brønsted acids do not add to benzene because the π electrons of benzene are too heavily stabilized. The source of this stability is a phenomenon called *aromaticity*, a

The π electrons in benzene are heavily stabilized by electron delocalization.

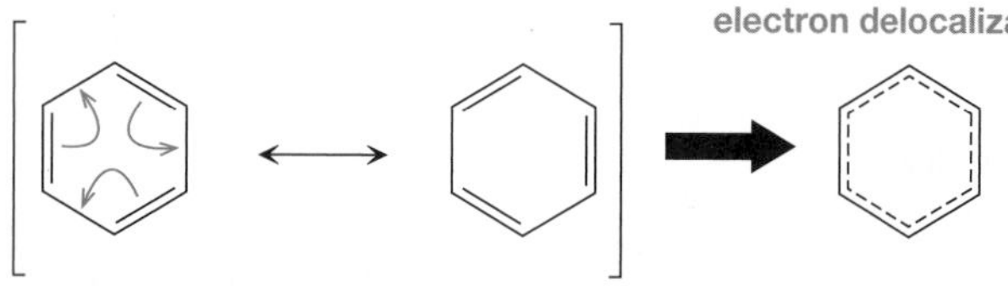

FIGURE 12-4 Stability of benzene Contribution by the resonance structures (*left*) leads to the resonance hybrid (*right*), in which benzene's π electrons are delocalized entirely around the ring.

topic of Chapter 14. Although we will not fully discuss aromaticity here, it is helpful to know that, due to its aromaticity, the six π electrons around the benzene ring are completely delocalized, just as we would expect in the hybrid of benzene's two resonance structures shown in **Figure 12-4**. If HA were to add across one of the C=C double bonds, as in Equation 12-4, such cyclic delocalization of the π electrons would cease to exist, and the resulting stabilization would be destroyed.

If a species contains both a benzene ring *and* a separate C=C bond, treatment with a Brønsted acid would lead to a reaction at the separate C=C double bond, as shown in Equation 12-5:

HBr adds across this C=C double bond.

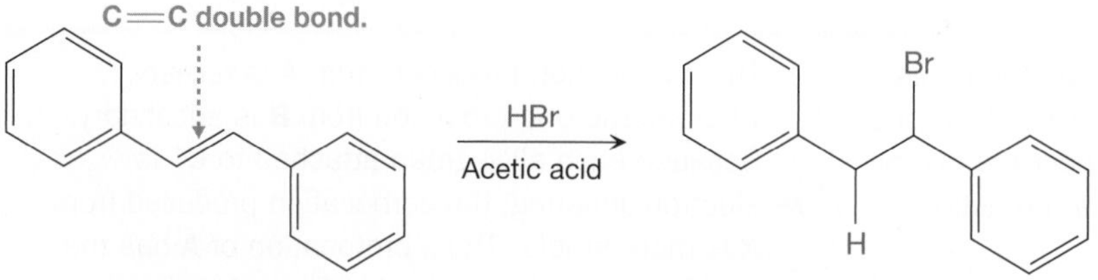
HBr
Acetic acid
Br
H

1,2-Diphenylethene — (1-Bromo-2-phenylethyl)benzene (12-5)

YOUR TURN **12.4**

Draw the mechanism and the product for the following reaction.

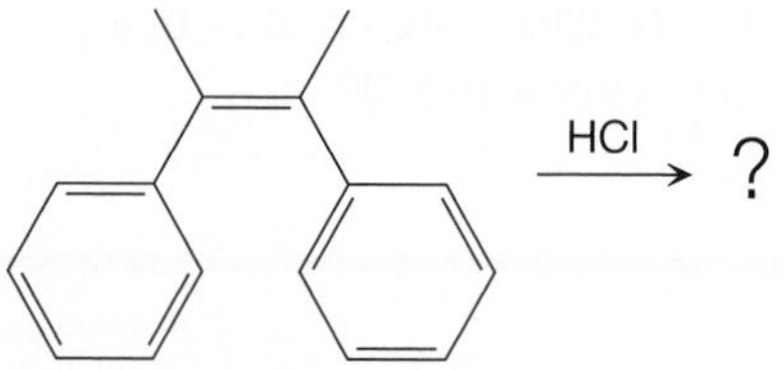
HCl
?

SECTION 12.3 OBJECTIVES

You will be able to:

1. Determine whether regiochemistry will be an issue when an alkene undergoes electrophilic addition.
2. Predict the major product of electrophilic addition to an alkene with regiochemistry taken into account.

12.3 Regiochemistry: Production of the More Stable Carbocation and Markovnikov's Rule

In the addition of a Brønsted acid across a double bond, the proton can bond to one of two possible carbon atoms. In each reaction we have examined so far, the alkene has been *symmetric* (i.e., the groups attached to one of the alkene carbons are identical to the groups attached to the other), so the same adduct is produced regardless of which alkene carbon gains the proton. With an *unsymmetric* alkene, on the other hand, two constitutional isomers can be produced, as shown in Equation 12-6 for the reaction of propene with HCl. In this case, 2-chloropropane is the major product, not 1-chloropropane:

Addition to an unsymmetric alkene can produce two products.

Minor product — Major product

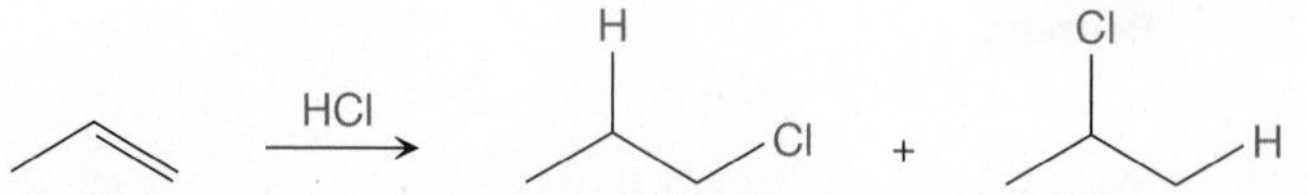
HCl
H
Cl
+
Cl
H

Propene — 1-Chloropropane — 2-Chloropropane 61% (12-6)

Why is 2-chloropropane the major product in Equation 12-6? Recall from Section 12.1 that the overall product of an electrophilic addition reaction is significantly more stable than the overall reactants. Consequently:

> Electrophilic addition reactions tend to be irreversible and generally take place under *kinetic control* (see top Recall box).

As with any kinetically controlled set of competing reactions, the major product is the one that is produced the *fastest*. Because the first step of the mechanism (formation of the carbocation intermediate) is the rate-determining step of the overall reaction (Section 12.1), the major product comes from the *carbocation intermediate* that is produced most rapidly.

◂ RECALL

Section 11.3 explained that when the products of a reaction are much lower in energy than the reactants, the rate in the reverse direction is very slow, making the reaction irreversible. A competition of irreversible reactions is kinetically controlled because the various products do *not* equilibrate.

With this in mind, let's examine **Figure 12-5**, which shows the free energy diagrams for the formation of 1-chloropropane (minor product; red curve) and 2-chloropropane (major product; blue curve) from propene. The carbocation intermediate produced by the addition of H^+ to C-1 (blue curve) is *secondary*, so it is lower in energy than the *primary* carbocation intermediate produced by the addition of H^+ to C-2 (red curve). Because the two carbocations are produced from the same type of elementary step, production of the secondary carbocation involves a smaller energy barrier and is faster (see bottom Recall box); the secondary carbocation therefore leads to the major product, consistent with Equation 12-6.

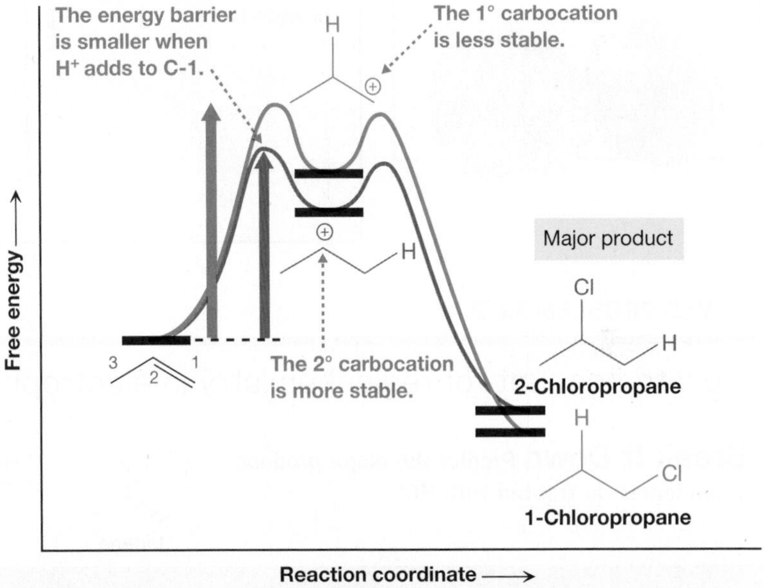

The energy barrier is smaller when H⁺ adds to C-1.
The 1° carbocation is less stable.
Major product
The 2° carbocation is more stable.
2-Chloropropane
1-Chloropropane
Free energy
Reaction coordinate

FIGURE 12-5 Regiochemistry and relative energy barriers in electrophilic addition Electrophilic addition of HCl to propene to form 2-chloropropane is represented by the blue curve, whereas formation of 1-chloropropane via the same reaction is represented by the red curve. The faster rate of the reaction shown in blue is consistent with a smaller energy barrier, which, in turn, is consistent with a more stable carbocation intermediate.

The lesson illustrated in Figure 12-5 can be generalized as follows:

> The major product of electrophilic addition of a Brønsted acid to an alkene is the one that proceeds through the *more stable* carbocation intermediate.

Applying this idea to the addition of HBr to 1-methylcyclohexene (Eq. 12-7), we can see why the major product is the one in which the proton has added to C-2 and Br^- has added to C-1 (see Your Turn 12.5). Moreover, this concept allows us to *predict* the major products of other electrophilic addition reactions of Brønsted acids to alkenes, like the one in Solved Problem 12.2.

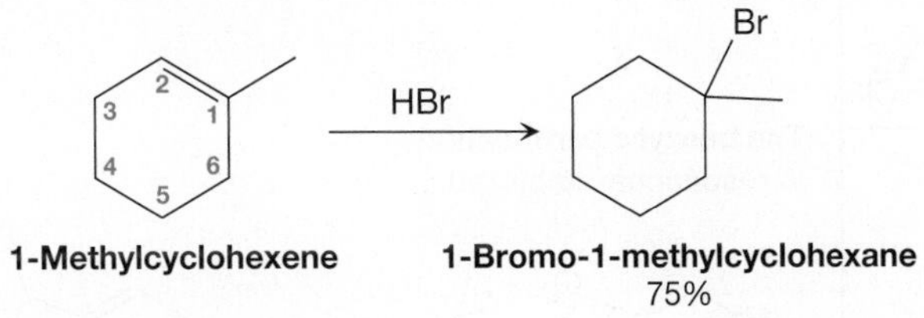

HBr
Br
1-Methylcyclohexene
1-Bromo-1-methylcyclohexane
75%

(12-7)

◂ RECALL

Section 9.3a showed that, for two elementary steps of the same type, the one with the more negative (or less positive) value of ΔG°_{rxn} tends to have the smaller energy barrier ($\Delta G^{\circ\ddagger}$) and thus tends to be faster.

YOUR TURN **12.5**

The free energy diagrams for the reactions that produce the isomeric adducts in Equation 12-7 are shown here. Complete the diagram by drawing the carbocation intermediates in the appropriate boxes provided.

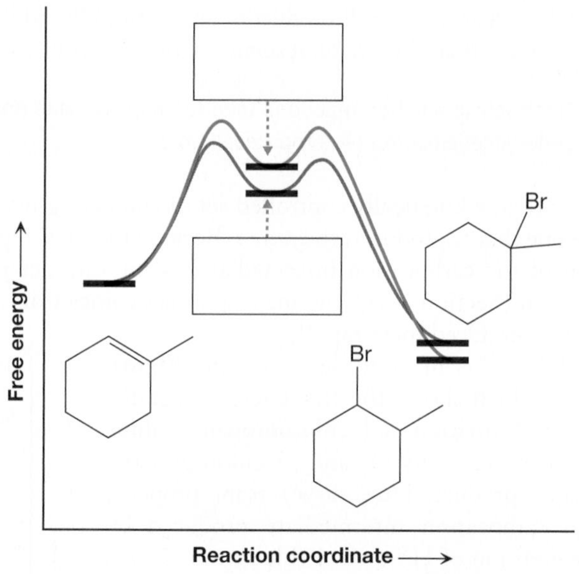

Br
Br
Free energy
Reaction coordinate

CONNECTIONS 12.1

Keeping your fruit looking good Indene (Solved Problem 12.2) is used in industry to make coumarone–indene resin, which is applied as an edible, protective coating to citrus fruits and apples.

SOLVED PROBLEM **12.2**

How to account for regiochemistry in electrophilic addition to an alkene

Break It Down Predict the major product when indene is treated with HCl.

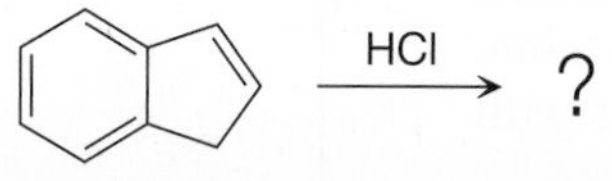

HCl
?
Indene

Think	Solve
Which C=C double bond will undergo electrophilic addition?	The rightmost C=C double bond is the one that will undergo electrophilic addition. The others make up an aromatic ring similar to benzene and are much too stable to react under these conditions.
What are the *possible* products and the corresponding carbocation intermediates from which they are produced?	The two possible products of HCl addition differ by which C atom gains the H^+ and which gains the Cl^-, as shown below. Carbocation **A** is produced when a proton adds to the top carbon of the C=C bond, and carbocation **B** is produced when a proton adds to the bottom carbon.

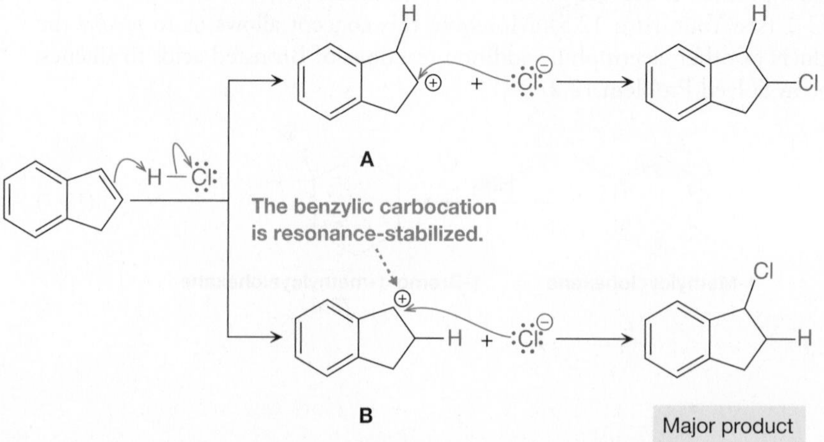

H
H
Cl
A
The benzylic carbocation is resonance-stabilized.
Cl
H
H
B
Major product

(continued)

Which carbocation intermediate is more stable?	As indicated above, carbocation **B** is benzylic and therefore is resonance-stabilized, giving it significantly greater stability than carbocation **A**. Thus, the product that derives from **B** is the major product.

Try It Draw the detailed mechanism for the reaction of each compound with HCl and predict the major product.

(a)

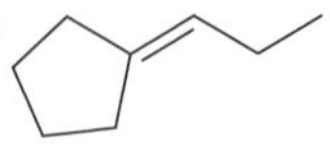

(b)

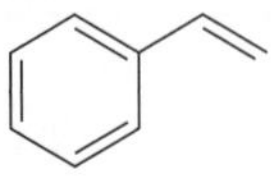

(c)

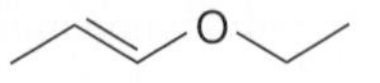
O

(d)

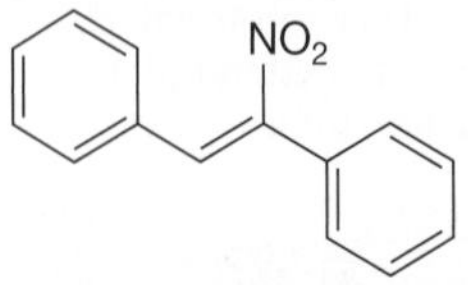
NO_2

Before the mechanism for electrophilic addition reactions was known, the Russian chemist Vladimir Markovnikov (1838–1904) made the following generalization to describe the reaction's regioselectivity: *The addition of a hydrogen halide to an alkene favors the product in which the proton adds to the alkene carbon that is initially bonded to the greater number of hydrogen atoms.* Thus, the H^+ forms a bond to C-1 when HCl adds to propene (Eq. 12-6, p. 610); C-1 is initially bonded to two H atoms, whereas C-2 is initially bonded to only one H atom.

We now know that Markovnikov's generalization is just the outcome of the reaction favoring the more stable carbocation intermediate. Nonetheless, his generalization has come to be known as **Markovnikov's rule**, and the type of regioselectivity it describes is called **Markovnikov addition** (see Looking Ahead box).

▸ LOOKING AHEAD

In Chapter 13, we will encounter examples of electrophilic addition reactions with regioselectivity that is opposite to what would be predicted by Markovnikov's rule: so-called *anti-Markovnikov addition*. Such mechanisms do not involve carbocation intermediates at all.

12.4 Carbocation Rearrangements

SECTION 12.4 OBJECTIVES

You will be able to:

1. Predict when the addition of a Brønsted acid to an alkene will involve a carbocation rearrangement.
2. Draw the mechanism for electrophilic addition reactions that involve carbocation rearrangements.

When 3-methylbut-1-ene is treated with hydrochloric acid (Eq. 12-8), significant amounts of both 2-chloro-3-methylbutane and 2-chloro-2-methylbutane are produced:

The production of this adduct involves a carbocation rearrangement.

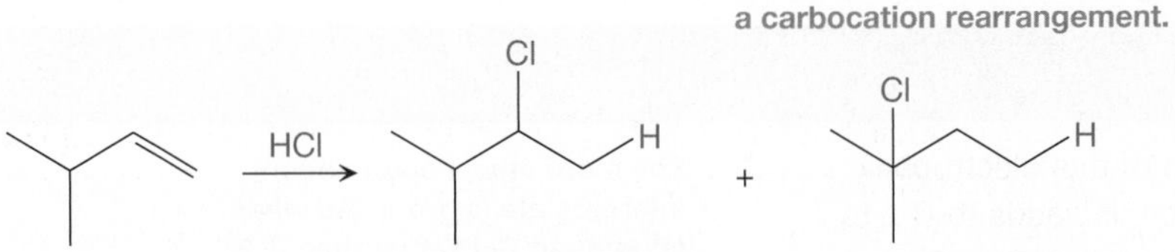
HCl
Cl
H
+
Cl
H

(12-8)

3-Methylbut-1-ene | **2-Chloro-3-methylbutane** 45% | **2-Chloro-2-methylbutane** 45%

2-Chloro-3-methylbutane is the product of a normal Markovnikov addition of HCl across the C=C double bond. Specifically, H^+ adds to C-1 of the alkene and Cl^- adds to the adjacent, secondary C. On the other hand, in 2-chloro-2-methylbutane, Cl^- appears to have attached to a C atom that was not initially part of the double bond.

As is the case with any mechanism that proceeds through a carbocation intermediate:

> Electrophilic addition of a Brønsted acid across a C=C double bond is susceptible to carbocation rearrangements.

Recall from Section 8.6d that carbocation rearrangements are fast! In this case, a 1,2-hydride shift can account for the formation of 2-chloro-2-methylbutane, as shown in the mechanism in Equation 12-9. This 1,2-hydride shift converts a

Mechanism Drawing
Addition of a Brønsted Acid to an Alkene, with Carbocation Rearrangement

secondary carbocation into an even more stable tertiary carbocation prior to the attack of the Cl^- nucleophile:

Mechanism for the addition of a hydrogen halide to an alkene, with carbocation rearrangement (Eq. 12-8)

The terminal C is protonated to produce a 2° instead of a 1° carbocation intermediate.

A carbocation rearrangement transforms the 2° carbocation into an even more stable 3° one.

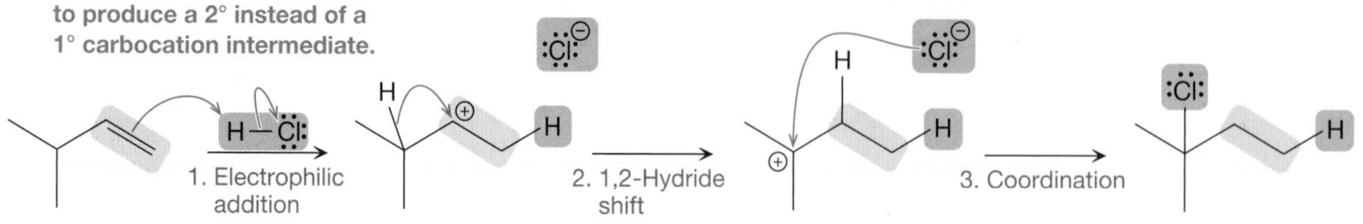

H—Cl:
1. Electrophilic addition
:Cl:
H
2. 1,2-Hydride shift
3. Coordination

(12-9)

YOUR TURN **12.6**

The following carbocation will rearrange after it is produced. Draw the curved arrow notation for that rearrangement and draw the resulting carbocation.

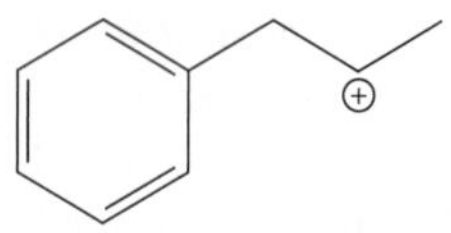

Recall that 1,2-methyl shifts also take place quickly, so they can appear in the mechanism of an electrophilic addition reaction, too. An example is illustrated in Solved Problem 12.3.

SOLVED PROBLEM **12.3**

How to predict carbocation rearrangements in electrophilic addition

Break It Down **Draw the complete, detailed mechanism and predict the major product of the reaction shown here.**

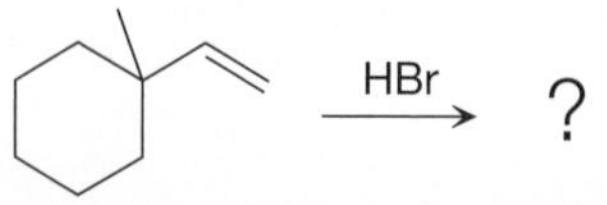

HBr
?

Think	Solve
To which C will the H^+ attach?	In the first step of this electrophilic addition reaction, H^+ adds to C-1 to produce a secondary carbocation intermediate, as shown here. (Addition of H^+ to C-2 would instead produce a less stable primary carbocation intermediate.)
Can that secondary carbocation intermediate undergo a 1,2-hydride shift or a 1,2-methyl shift to attain greater stability?	The secondary carbocation intermediate rapidly converts to an even more stable tertiary one by a 1,2-methyl shift in Step 2, as shown here.

The more stable carbocation intermediate is produced when H^+ adds to C-1 rather than C-2.

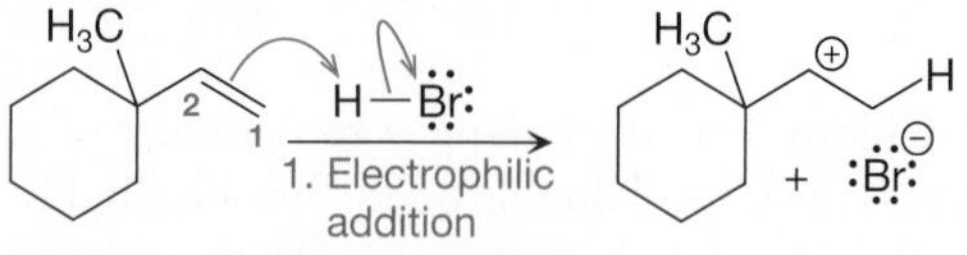

H_3C
2
1
H—Br:
1. Electrophilic addition
H_3C
H
+ :Br:

The 2° carbocation intermediate transforms into an even more stable 3° one by a 1,2-methyl shift.

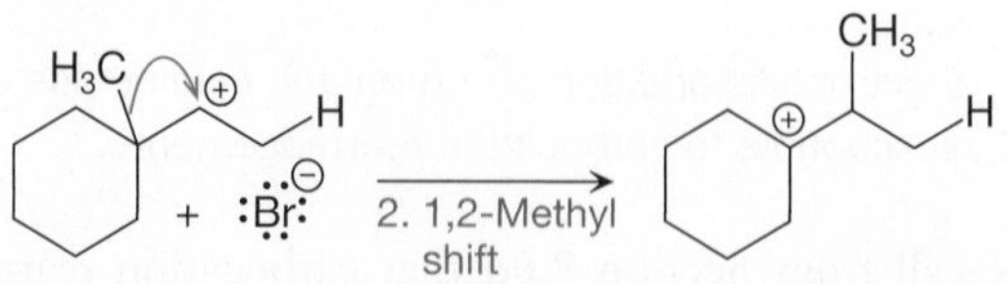

H_3C
H
+ :Br:
2. 1,2-Methyl shift
CH_3
H

(continued)

What elementary step completes the reaction?	After the carbocation rearrangement, coordination of Br^- in Step 3 completes the reaction. The full mechanism is shown below.

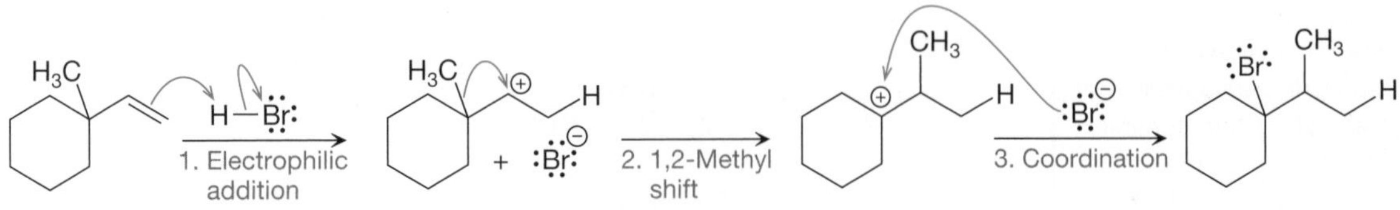

H_3C
H—Br:
1. Electrophilic addition
H_3C
H
+ :Br:
2. 1,2-Methyl shift
CH_3
H
:Br:
3. Coordination
:Br:
CH_3
H

Try It Draw the complete, detailed mechanism for each of the following reactions and predict the major product.

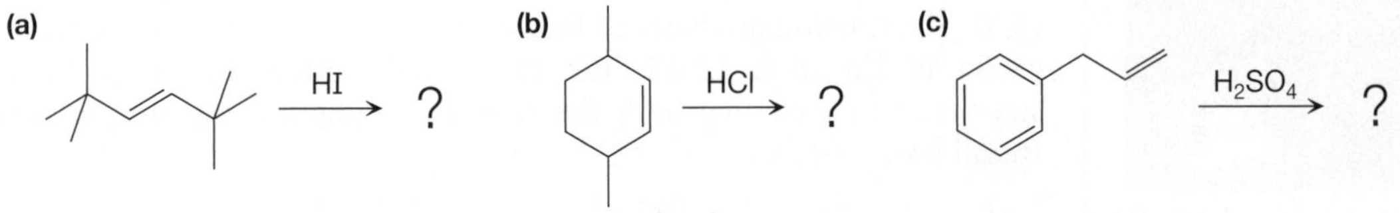

(a)
HI
?
(b)
HCl
?
(c)
H_2SO_4
?

12.5 Stereochemistry in the Addition of a Brønsted Acid to an Alkene

SECTION 12.5 OBJECTIVES

You will be able to:

1. Identify when stereochemistry is an issue in the addition of a strong acid to an alkene.
2. Draw the stereoisomers that are produced when a strong acid adds to an alkene.

In an electrophilic addition reaction involving an alkene, both alkene carbons, which are initially planar, become tetrahedral in the product. It is possible, therefore, for new chiral centers to be produced during the course of the reaction. In these cases, stereochemistry becomes an issue. For example, in the reaction shown previously in Equation 12-5 (shown again in Eq. 12-10), a single chiral center is formed, so each product molecule is chiral. Because the starting material and the conditions under which the reaction takes place are achiral, a racemic mixture of enantiomers is produced:

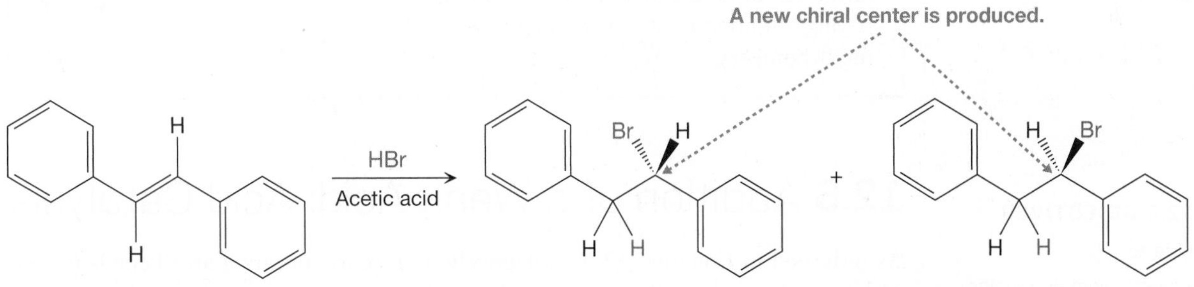

A new chiral center is produced.
H
H
HBr
Acetic acid
Br
H
H H
+
H
Br
H H
Racemic mixture of products

1,2-Diphenylethene

(12-10)

YOUR TURN 12.7

In the electrophilic addition reaction shown previously in Solved Problem 12.2 (p. 612), the major product has gained a chiral center. Mark that chiral center with an asterisk.

CONNECTIONS 12.2

Treating clothes and cancer
1,2-Diphenylethene (stilbene, Eq. 12-10), provides the framework for several useful derivatives. One derivative is used as an optical brightener in some laundry detergents. Some naturally occurring stilbene derivatives have the potential to treat cancer.

Equation 12-11 shows an example of an electrophilic addition reaction in which two new chiral centers are produced:

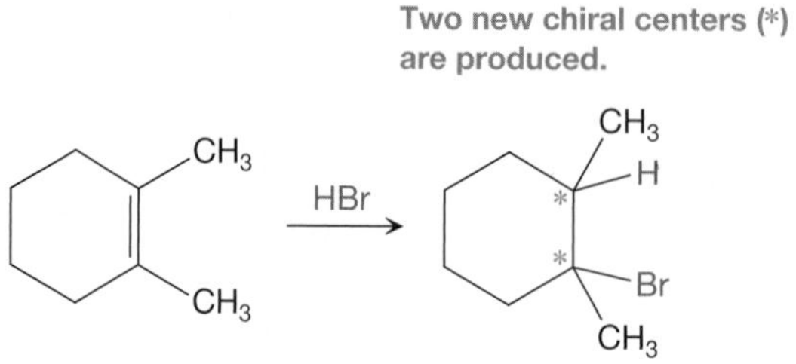
Two new chiral centers (*) are produced.
CH3
CH3
HBr
CH3
H
Br
CH3

(12-11)

Four ($2^n = 2^2 = 4$) stereoisomers of the product exist: (*R*,*R*), (*R*,*S*), (*S*,*R*), and (*S*,*S*). The reaction produces all four of those stereoisomers, as shown in the mechanism in Equation 12-12. The two chiral centers are generated in separate steps, and in each step both the *R* and *S* configurations are produced (see top Recall box, p. 617).

Mechanism for the addition of a hydrogen halide to an alkene, including stereochemistry (Eq.12-11)

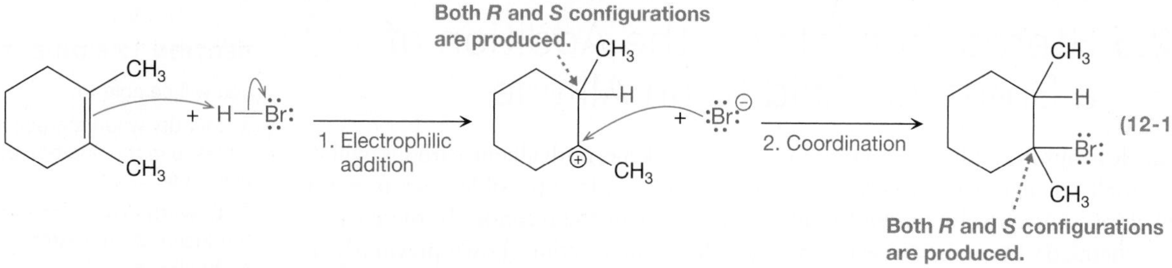
CH3
CH3
H—Br:
1. Electrophilic addition
Both R and S configurations are produced.
CH3
H
CH3
:Br:
2. Coordination
CH3
H
Br:
CH3
Both R and S configurations are produced.

(12-12)

YOUR TURN **12.8**

Draw the complete mechanism for the formation of all products in this reaction, paying attention to stereochemistry and regiochemistry.

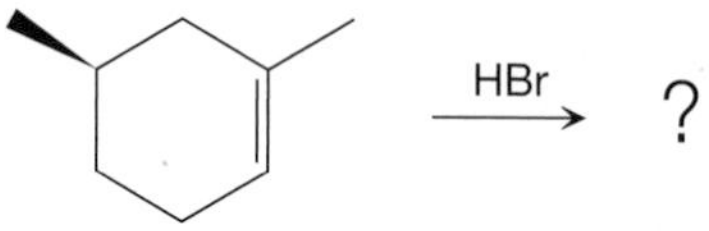
HBr
?

SECTION 12.6 OBJECTIVES

You will be able to:

1. Draw the mechanism and major product for the acid-catalyzed addition of a weak acid to an alkene.
2. Explain why no reaction between an alkene and a weak acid takes place in the absence of a strong acid catalyst.

12.6 Addition of a Weak Acid: Acid Catalysis

As indicated in Equation 12-13, effectively no reaction occurs if an alkene is treated with water (a weak acid) under neutral conditions:

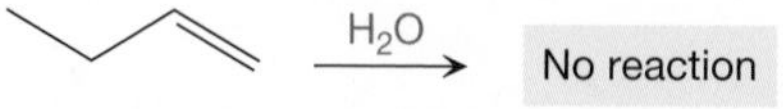
H2O
No reaction

(12-13)

With water as the acid, the first step of the general mechanism for electrophilic addition of a Brønsted acid to an alkene (Eq. 12-3, p. 606) is too unfavorable to take place at a reasonable rate. The first step not only would produce a carbocation but also would produce HO^-, in which the negative charge is relatively poorly stabilized. (See Your Turn 12.9.)

YOUR TURN **12.9**

Draw the hypothetical two-step mechanism just mentioned, in which water adds across the double bond in Equation 12-13 according to the mechanism shown in Equation 12-3 (p. 606). Identify the HO^- intermediate. Why is this mechanism unfeasible, whereas the same mechanism with HCl as the acid is feasible?

Equation 12-14, on the other hand, shows the following:

The addition of water to an alkene takes place readily in the presence of a strong acid (such as sulfuric acid) to produce an alcohol.

Equation 12-14 is an example of an **acid-catalyzed hydration reaction**:

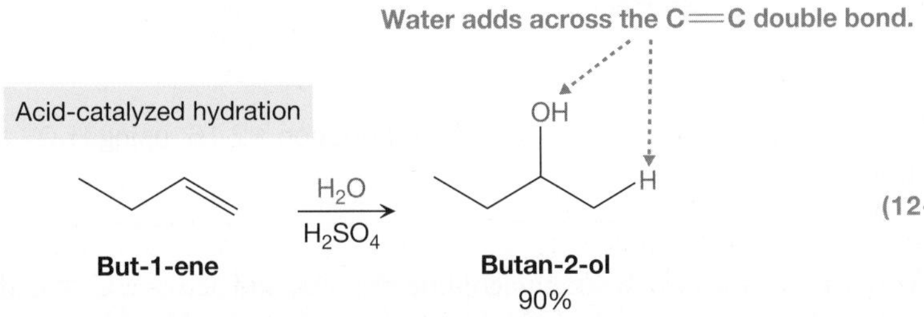

Water adds across the C=C double bond.
Acid-catalyzed hydration
OH
H
H_2O
H_2SO_4
But-1-ene
Butan-2-ol
90%

(12-14)

◂ RECALL

As we learned in Section 8.5b, the conversion of a planar carbon into a chiral center generally produces both the *R* and *S* configurations. Because the carbon begins with its three bonds lying in a plane, the formation of the fourth bond can take place on either side of that plane.

The mechanism for the hydration reaction is shown in Equation 12-15. Due to the leveling effect (see bottom Recall box), H_2SO_4 dissociates essentially entirely in water to produce H_3O^+ as the acid. Being a strong Brønsted acid, H_3O^+ can protonate the alkene to produce a carbocation intermediate, as illustrated in Step 1. Notice that the proton adds to the terminal C to yield the more stable carbocation intermediate. In Step 2, that carbocation intermediate is attacked by H_2O, a weak nucleophile. A final deprotonation in Step 3 removes the positive charge from the adduct, yielding an uncharged product. Step 3 also regenerates H_3O^+, a reactant in Step 1. Therefore, H_3O^+ speeds up the reaction but is not consumed overall: characteristics required of a **catalyst**.

◂ RECALL

The leveling effect, discussed in Section 6.2a, states that the strongest acid that can exist in solution is the protonated solvent. Any acid that is stronger than the protonated solvent will donate its proton to the solvent, thereby producing more of the protonated solvent.

Mechanism for the acid-catalyzed hydration of an alkene (Eq. 12-14)

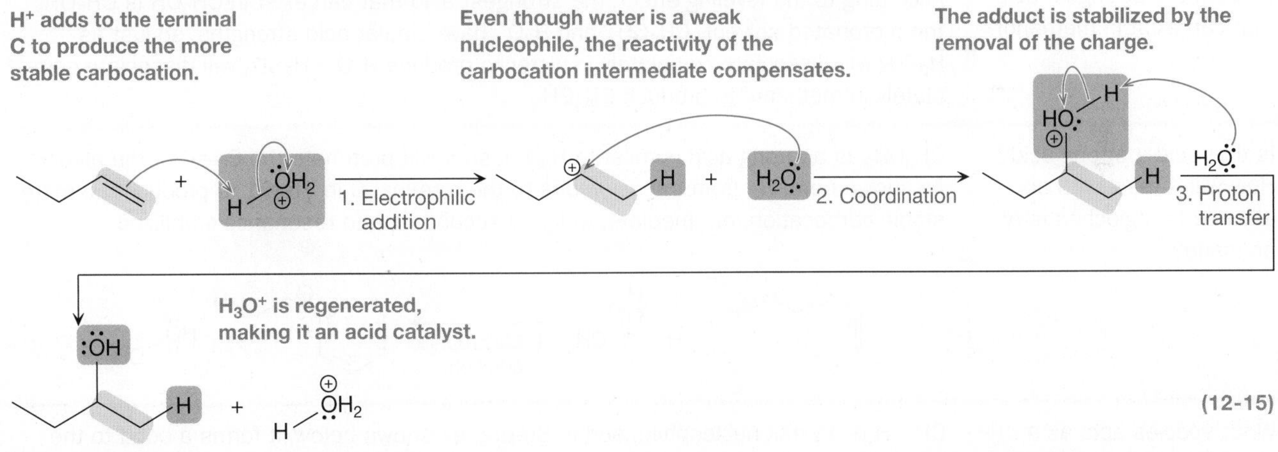

H⁺ adds to the terminal C to produce the more stable carbocation.
Even though water is a weak nucleophile, the reactivity of the carbocation intermediate compensates.
The adduct is stabilized by the removal of the charge.
1. Electrophilic addition
2. Coordination
3. Proton transfer
H_3O^+ is regenerated, making it an acid catalyst.

(12-15)

Notice that H_2SO_4 appears in both Equations 12-14 and 12-2 (p. 606), but the two reactions have different outcomes. H_2O adds across the double bond in Equation 12-14, whereas H_2SO_4 adds across the double bond in Equation 12-2. In Equation 12-2, H_2SO_4 is shown to be *concentrated*, so very little water is present. In that case, H_2SO_4 acts as the strong acid and HSO_4^- is the nucleophile. In Equation 12-14, on the other hand, water is the solvent and is present in high concentration, so H_3O^+ acts as the strong acid and H_2O is the nucleophile.

Mechanism Drawing
Acid-catalyzed Hydration of an Alkene

HCl is another strong acid that dissociates essentially entirely in water to produce H_3O^+ as the acid, but HCl is generally *not* used to catalyze the hydration of an alkene. The Cl^- that is produced on dissociation in water is a strong nucleophile, much stronger than HSO_4^-. Consequently, a substantial amount of the alkyl chloride (the product of HCl addition) tends to form, as shown in Equation 12-16:

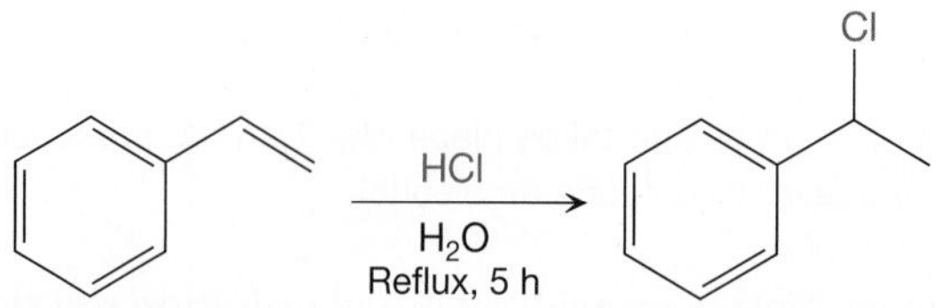

Cl
HCl
H_2O
Reflux, 5 h

(12-16)

Ethenylbenzene (Styrene) **(1-Chloroethyl)benzene** 96%

YOUR TURN **12.10**

Draw the mechanism for the reaction in Equation 12-16, using H_3O^+ as the strong acid.

Water is not the only weak nucleophile that can add across a C=C double bond by acid catalysis. When an alcohol adds, as shown in Solved Problem 12.4, it is called an **acid-catalyzed alkoxylation reaction.**

SOLVED PROBLEM **12.4**

How to draw the mechanism and products for acid-catalyzed alkoxylation

Break It Down **Draw the complete, detailed mechanism for this reaction and predict the products.**

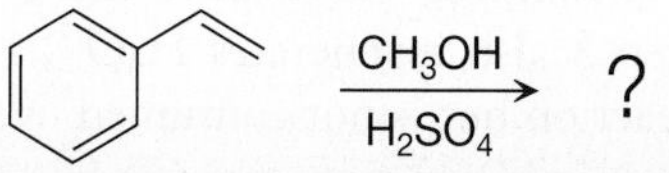

CH_3OH
H_2SO_4
?

Think	Solve
What is the strongest acid that can exist in methanol?	According to the leveling effect, the strongest acid that can exist in CH_3OH is $CH_3OH_2^+$, the protonated solvent. $CH_3OH_2^+$ and H_3O^+ have similar acid strengths, so just as H_2SO_4 will dissociate completely in water to produce H_3O^+, H_2SO_4 will dissociate completely in methanol to produce $CH_3OH_2^+$.
Is that acid a strong acid? How will it react with an alkene? Is regiochemistry an issue?	$CH_3OH_2^+$ is a strong acid (similar to H_3O^+), so it will protonate the C=C of the alkene. As shown here, H^+ from the acid adds to the terminal C in Step 1 to produce the more stable carbocation intermediate, which is secondary and resonance-stabilized.

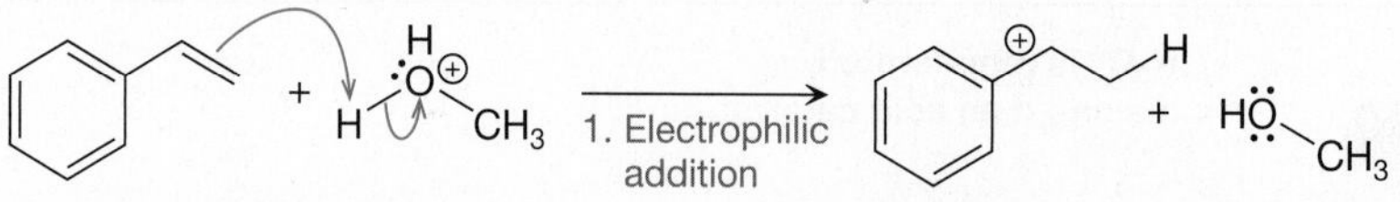

H
H
CH_3
1. Electrophilic addition
H
HO
CH_3

Think	Solve
What species acts as a nucleophile? Is the product charged?	CH_3OH is a weak nucleophile, and in Step 2, as shown below, it forms a bond to the positively charged C. In Step 3, CH_3OH acts as a base to remove a proton from the positively charged adduct.

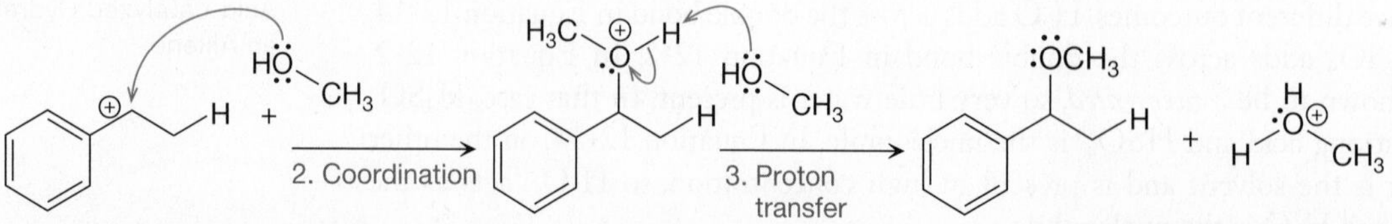

HO
CH_3
H
2. Coordination
H_3C
H
HO
CH_3
H
3. Proton transfer
OCH_3
H
H
H
CH_3

Think	Solve
How does this mechanism compare to the one in Equation 12-15?	This mechanism is essentially identical to the one in Equation 12-15. Here CH_3OH acts as the nucleophile instead of water, so an ether is produced instead of an alcohol.

(continued)

Try It Draw the complete, detailed mechanism for each of the following reactions and predict the products.

(a)

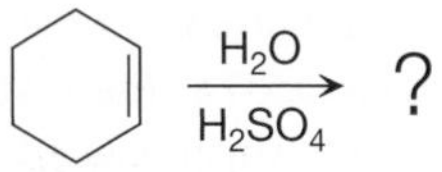

H2O
H2SO4
?

(b)

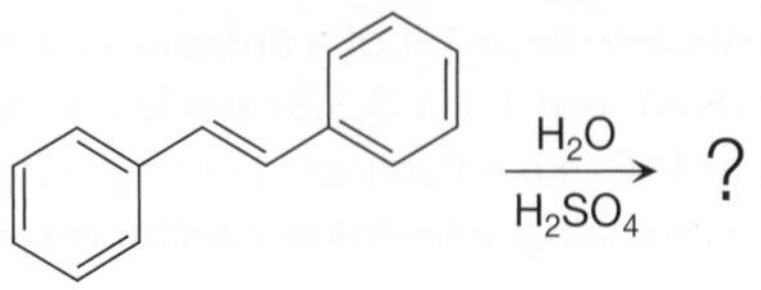

H2O
H2SO4
?

(c)

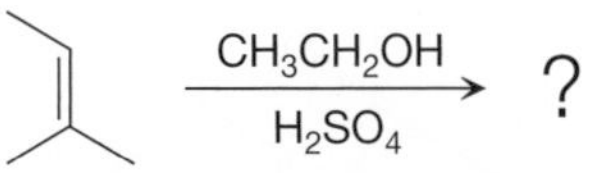

CH3CH2OH
H2SO4
?

(d)

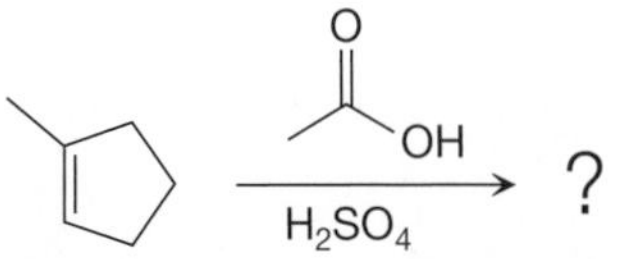

O
OH
H2SO4
?

CBD Oil Giving False-Positive Tests for THC: An Outcome of Electrophilic Addition

Tetrahydrocannabinol (THC, **Figure 12-6a**) and cannabidiol (CBD, Fig. 12-6b) are both produced naturally by cannabis plants. THC is the principal psychoactive compound in marijuana; as of 2021, it remains a federal crime to possess, buy, or sell marijuana, although it is legal for recreational use by adults in at least 15 states. CBD, on the other hand, became federally legal when the 2018 Farm Bill was signed into law, and it is now available in stores across the United States in a variety of consumer products. There is some evidence that CBD has significant health benefits, and it is *not* believed to be psychoactive.

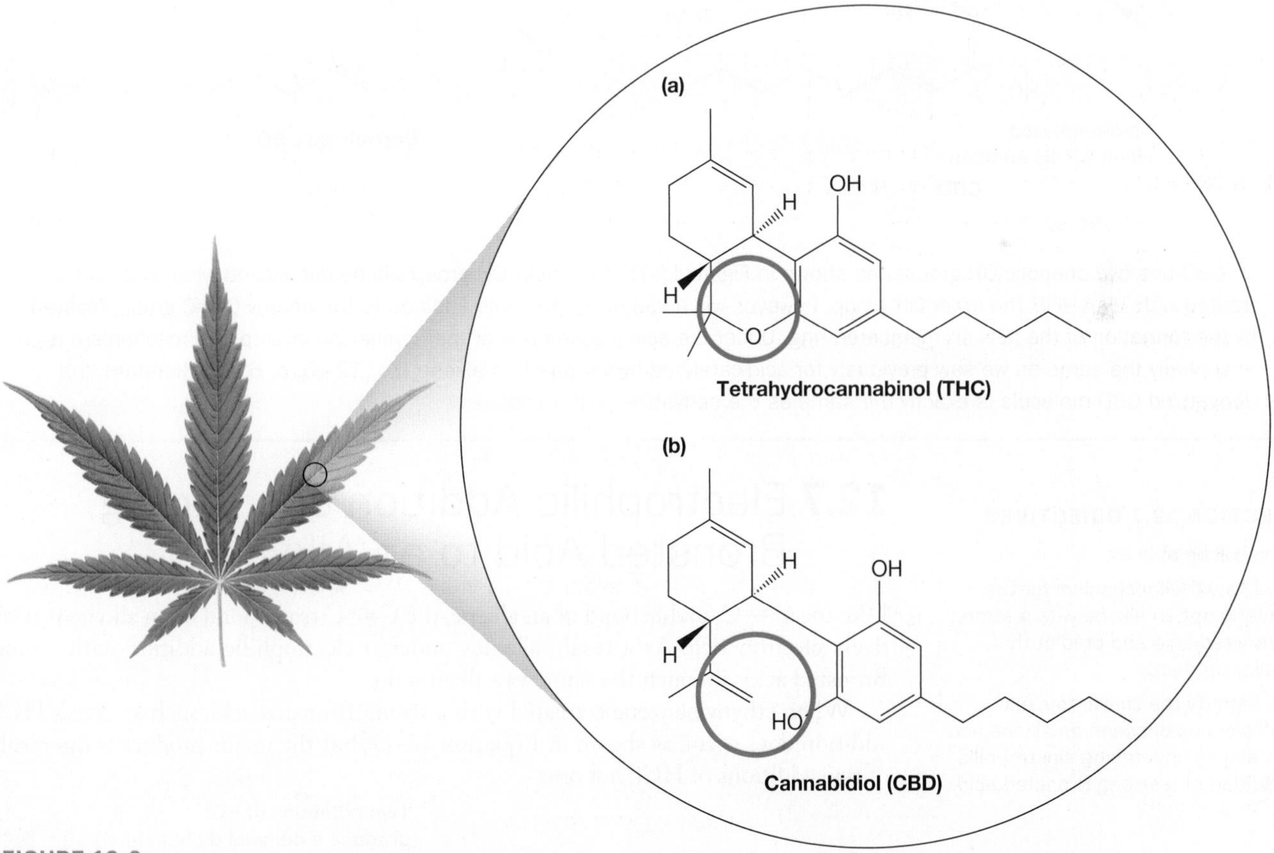

(a)
OH
H
H
O
Tetrahydrocannabinol (THC)
(b)
H
OH
H
HO
Cannabidiol (CBD)

FIGURE 12-6

As you can see in Figure 12-6, THC and CBD are very similar in structure, differing only in the portions circled in red. The molecules are not exactly the same, however, so they can indeed be distinguished with a variety of laboratory methods. Nevertheless, a common forensic drug testing method tends to mistake the presence of CBD for THC, in which case a person using products containing CBD could falsely test positively for THC.

(continued)

CBD Oil Giving False-Positive Tests for THC *(continued)*

Such false-positive tests are the result of a derivatization step in this method, where a sample is treated with trifluoroacetic anhydride (TFAA) and 1,1,1,3,3,3-hexafluoroisopropanol (HFIP). The purpose of the derivatization is to convert the phenolic OH of THC into a fluorinated ester group, as shown in **Figure 12-7a**. The resulting THC derivative is easier to detect in a gas chromatography–mass spectrometry (GC-MS) instrument, which is used in a subsequent step.

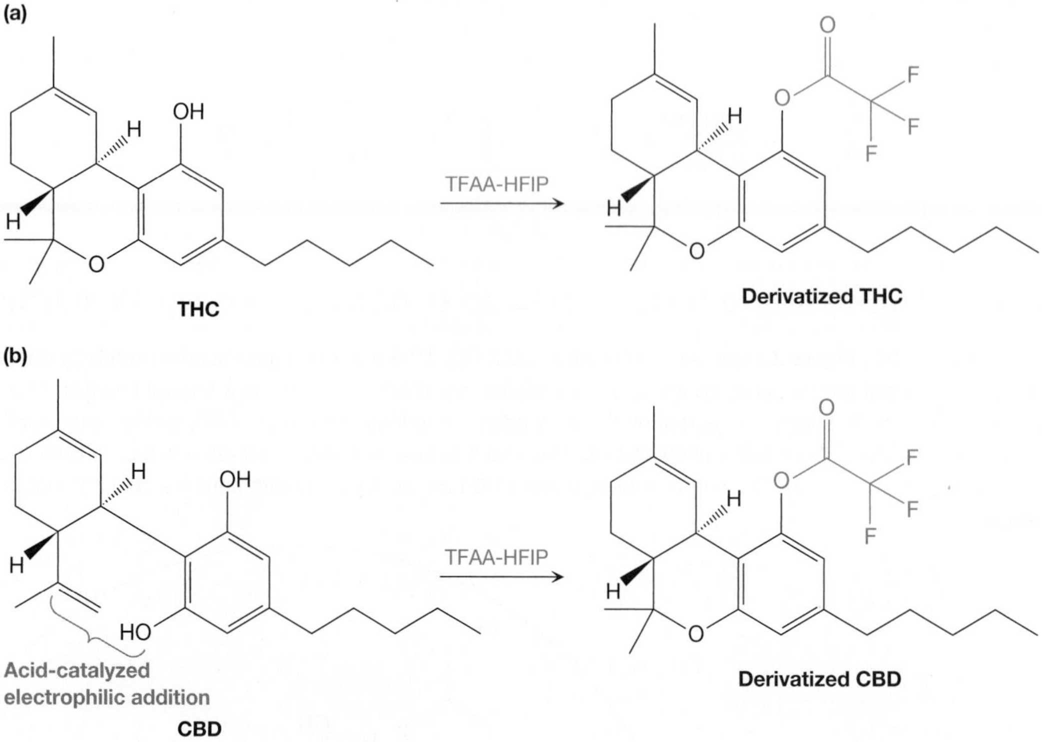

(a)
OH
H
H
TFAA-HFIP
O
THC
O
O
F
F
F
H
H
O
Derivatized THC
(b)
H
OH
H
HO
TFAA-HFIP
Acid-catalyzed electrophilic addition
CBD
O
O
F
F
F
H
H
O
Derivatized CBD

FIGURE 12-7

CBD has two phenolic OH groups. As shown in Figure 12-7b, the upper OH group will be derivatized when CBD is treated with TFAA-HFIP. The lower OH group, however, will undergo electrophilic addition to the nearby C═C group, favored by the formation of the new six-membered ring. Under the acidic conditions of the derivatization step, the mechanism is essentially the same as we saw previously for acid-catalyzed hydration of an alkene (Eq. 12-15, p. 617). Therefore, the derivatized CBD molecule is exactly the same as the derivatized THC molecule.

SECTION 12.7 OBJECTIVES

You will be able to:

1. Draw the mechanism for the reaction of an alkyne with a strong Brønsted acid and predict the major product.
2. Identify the similarities and differences between an alkene and an alkyne undergoing electrophilic addition of a strong Brønsted acid.

12.7 Electrophilic Addition of a Strong Brønsted Acid to an Alkyne

Like the C═C double bond of an alkene, the C≡C triple bond of an alkyne is relatively electron-rich. As a result, alkynes undergo electrophilic addition with strong Brønsted acids in much the same way alkenes do.

When ethynylbenzene is treated with a strong Brønsted acid, such as excess HCl, addition does occur, as shown in Equation 12-17, but the major product is the result of two additions of HCl, not one:

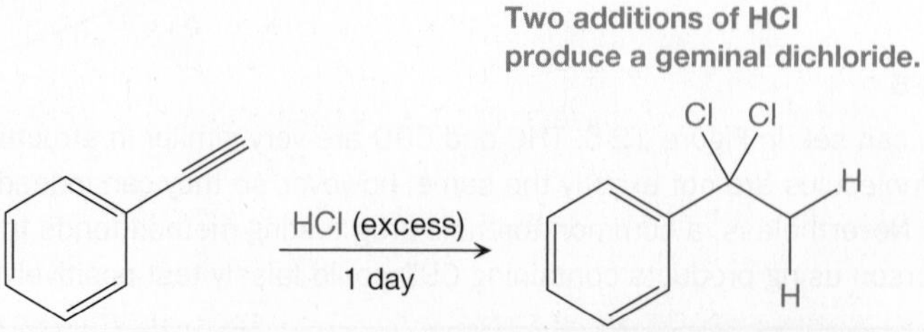

Two additions of HCl produce a geminal dichloride.
Cl Cl
H
H
HCl (excess)
1 day

Ethynylbenzene → 1,1-Dichloro-1-phenylethane, 82% (12-17)

In general:

The reaction of an alkyne with a hydrogen halide produces a **geminal dihalide** as the major product, in which both halogen atoms appear on the same carbon.

The mechanism shown in Equation 12-18 accounts for the formation of a geminal dihalide product:

Mechanism for the addition of a hydrogen halide to an alkyne to produce a geminal dihalide (Eq. 12-17)

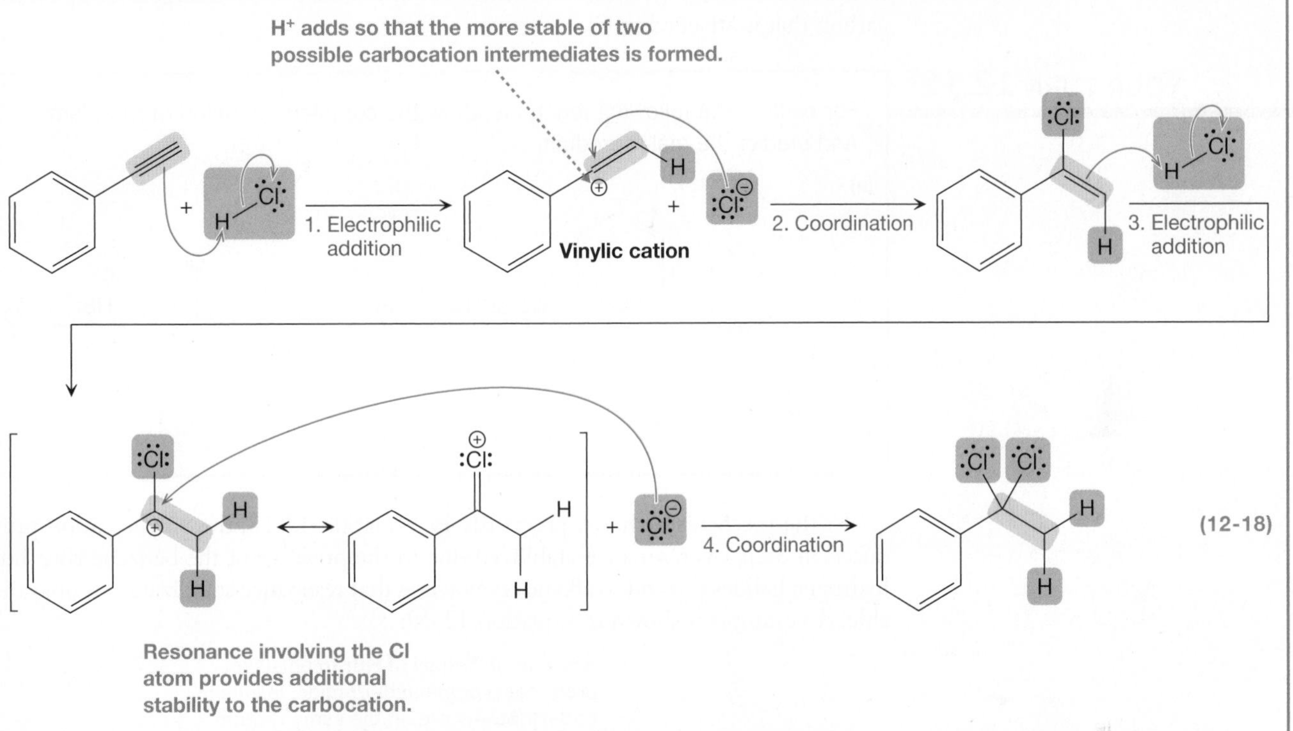

H⁺ adds so that the more stable of two possible carbocation intermediates is formed.
1. Electrophilic addition
Vinylic cation
2. Coordination
3. Electrophilic addition
4. Coordination
Resonance involving the Cl atom provides additional stability to the carbocation.
(12-18)

Step 1 is electrophilic addition of H^+ to the C≡C triple bond, producing a vinylic cation ($C{=}C^+$). Just as we saw with alkenes, H^+ adds so as to produce the more stable carbocation. In this case, the proton adds to the terminal C, so the resulting carbocation is secondary and is stabilized by resonance involving the benzene ring. In Step 2, Cl^- attacks the positively charged C in a coordination step to produce a vinylic chloride (C═C—Cl). That vinylic chloride, however, reacts further because it contains a C═C double bond, to which another H^+ adds in Step 3. Finally, in Step 4, a second Cl^- undergoes coordination with the carbocation to produce the geminal dichloride, which is the major product in Equation 12-17.

Mechanism Drawing
Addition of a Brønsted Acid to an Alkyne to Produce a Geminal Dilhalide

YOUR TURN 12.11

Draw the resonance structures of the vinylic cation in Equation 12-18 to show the delocalization of the positive charge over the benzene ring (and thus to explain the regiochemistry of the first addition).

The major product is the result of two additions, not one, because the second addition is easier than the first. It is easier because the carbocation produced in the rate-determining step of the second addition (Step 3) is more stable than the one produced in the rate-determining step of the first addition (Step 1).

The greater stability of the carbocation produced in Step 3 comes from two main factors:

1. Effective electronegativity. An alkene C is sp^2-hybridized, so it has a lower effective electronegativity than an alkyne C, which is sp-hybridized (Section 3.9).

The alkene C, therefore, handles the positive charge better than an alkyne C (Section 6.8c).

2. Resonance involving the lone pair from Cl. As shown in Step 3 of Equation 12-18, the positive charge generated in the vinylic cation is resonance-delocalized onto the Cl atom that added in Step 2. Without the Cl atom present, this resonance stabilization would be unavailable to the carbocation produced in Step 1.

This kind of resonance involving the Cl atom also helps ensure that both Cl atoms add to the same C of the initial alkyne. In Step 3 of Equation 12-18, the proton adds to the carbon that is *not* attached to the Cl atom, so the positive charge ends up on the carbon that is attached to Cl.

YOUR TURN 12.12

For each of the following reactions, draw the complete, detailed mechanism and predict the major product.

(a)

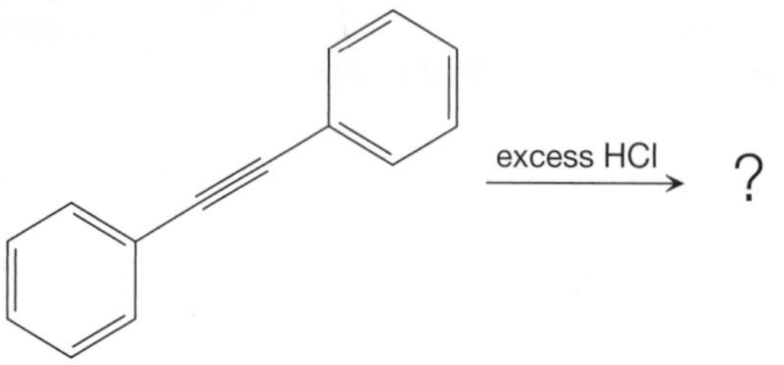
excess HCl
?

(b)

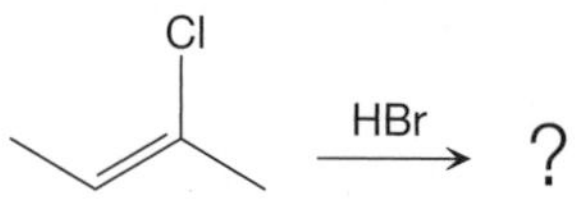
Cl
HBr
?

In the mechanism shown previously in Equation 12-18, the vinylic cation produced in Step 1 is resonance-stabilized due to the presence of the benzene ring, but hydrogen halides can add to alkynes even when that resonance stabilization is unavailable. An example is shown in Equation 12-19:

Addition of 2 equiv of HBr to an alkyne produces a *geminal* dibromide, in which both Br atoms are on the same C atom.

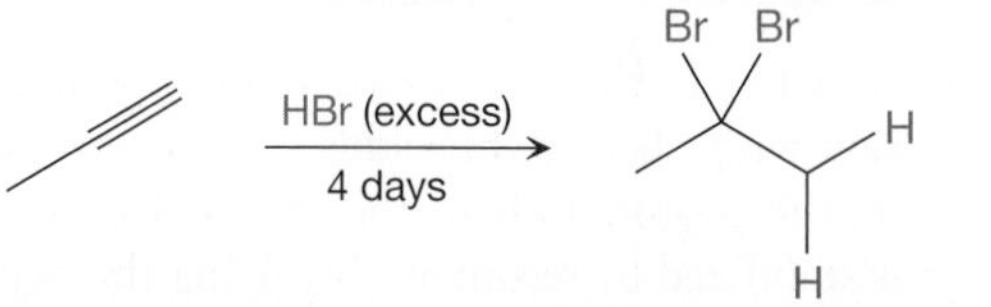
HBr (excess)
4 days
Br
Br
H
H

Propyne **2,2-Dibromopropane** 100% (12-19)

The mechanism for this reaction is believed to be slightly different, however, because the addition of a proton to the alkyne would produce a vinylic cation with a *localized* positive charge, making the species too high in energy. Instead, to avoid making the vinylic cation, Br^- attacks a π complex of the acid with the alkyne, as shown in Equation 12-20:

A π complex of the acid with the alkyne

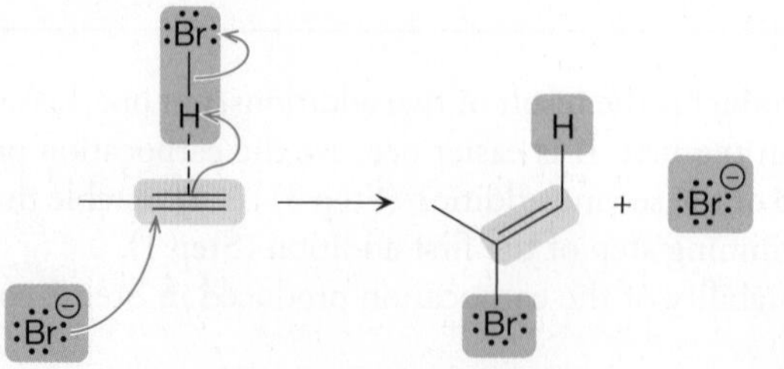
:Br:
H
:Br:
H
+
:Br:
:Br:

(12-20)

The vinylic halide product then continues with the addition of a second equivalent of HBr, just as we saw in Steps 3 and 4 of Equation 12-18.

CONNECTIONS 12.3

Propyne: From rocket fuel to searing meat Propyne (Eq. 12-19) has been researched for potential use as a rocket fuel for low-Earth orbits. Propyne is also a component of a gas mixture called MAPP, which chefs prefer as the fuel when they use a blowtorch to sear meat.

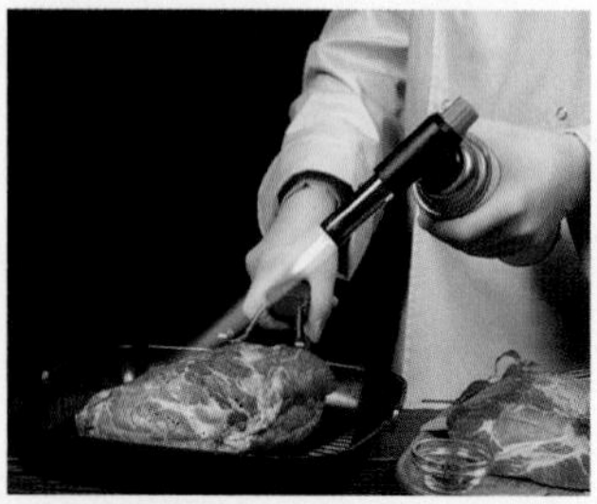

12.8 Acid-Catalyzed Hydration of an Alkyne: Synthesis of a Ketone

SECTION 12.8 OBJECTIVES

You will be able to:

1. Draw the mechanism showing how a ketone is produced when an alkyne is treated with water under acidic conditions.
2. Explain why an aldehyde is not produced from the acid-catalyzed hydration of an alkyne.

Recall from Section 12.6 that, under acidic conditions, water adds across the double bond of an alkene to produce an alcohol. It makes sense, therefore, that an alkyne would react in a similar way under the same conditions. Indeed, Equation 12-21 shows that a reaction does take place. However:

Acid-catalyzed hydration of an alkyne produces a ketone, not an alcohol.

Acid-catalyzed hydration of an alkyne produces a ketone.

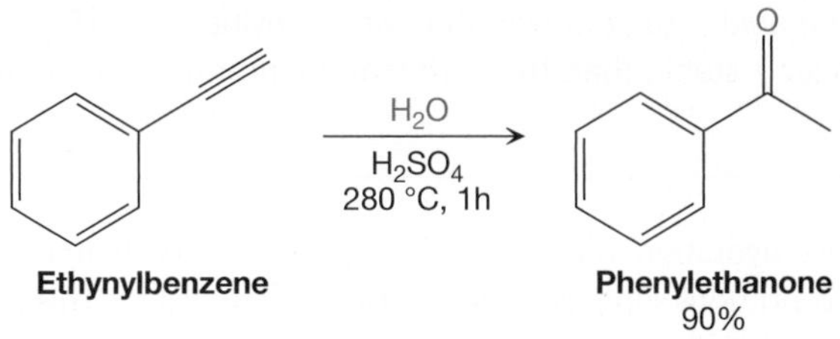

H_2O
H_2SO_4
280 °C, 1h
Ethynylbenzene
Phenylethanone
90%

(12-21)

Mechanism Drawing
Acid-catalyzed Hydration of an Alkyne

The mechanism for Equation 12-21 is shown in Equation 12-22:

Mechanism for the acid-catalyzed hydration of an alkyne (Eq. 12-21)

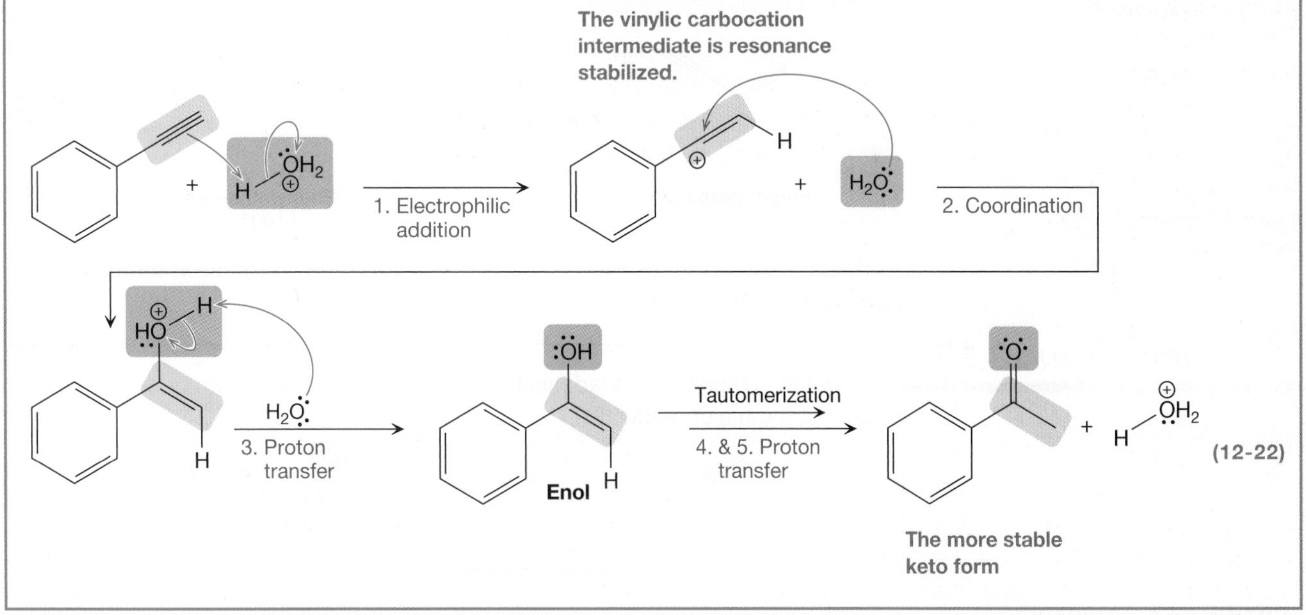

The vinylic carbocation intermediate is resonance stabilized.
1. Electrophilic addition
2. Coordination
3. Proton transfer
Tautomerization
4. & 5. Proton transfer
Enol
The more stable keto form
(12-22)

Steps 1–3 are the same as the ones that make up the mechanism for the acid-catalyzed hydration of an alkene, shown previously in Equation 12-15 (p. 617). The product of Step 3 is an *enol* (see Recall box). Under these acidic conditions, the enol rapidly tautomerizes to the more stable *keto* form in two steps (Steps 4 and 5), which are both proton transfers (see Your Turn 12.13).

Note two important aspects of this reaction:

1. The product is a ketone, not an aldehyde. The ketone product is dictated by Step 1, in which H^+ adds preferentially to the terminal C to give the more stable carbocation intermediate. Water then adds to the internal C atom in the second step. For an aldehyde to form, the proton would need to add to the internal C atom in the first step, but that would produce the less stable carbocation intermediate (see Your Turn 12.14).

◂ RECALL

As discussed in Section 7.10, keto and enol forms are tautomers that are in rapid equilibrium in solution, and their interconversion is called keto–enol tautomerization. In most cases, the equilibrium favors the keto form because it has a greater total bond strength than the enol form does.

2. <u>The reaction is run at very high temperatures.</u> The addition of H^+ in the first step of the mechanism produces a vinylic carbocation intermediate; as was discussed in Section 12.7, this intermediate is rather unstable. The first step, therefore, has a very large energy barrier when H_3O^+ is the acid, which can be surmounted with large amounts of added heat.

YOUR TURN 12.13

Draw the mechanism for the tautomerization (Steps 4 and 5) in Equation 12-22. *Hint*: Review Section 7.10.

YOUR TURN 12.14

Draw the carbocation intermediate that must be generated to produce an aldehyde from the acid-catalyzed hydration of ethynylbenzene (Eq. 12-21). Explain why it is less stable than the carbocation intermediate shown in Equation 12-22.

The acid-catalyzed hydration in Equation 12-21 can occur without extreme temperatures if the reaction conditions support an acid stronger than H_3O^+. This is the case when the alkyne is treated with trifluoromethanesulfonic acid (CF_3SO_3H, also known as triflic acid, TfOH) in 2,2,2-trifluoroethanol (CF_3CH_2OH), as shown in Equation 12-23:

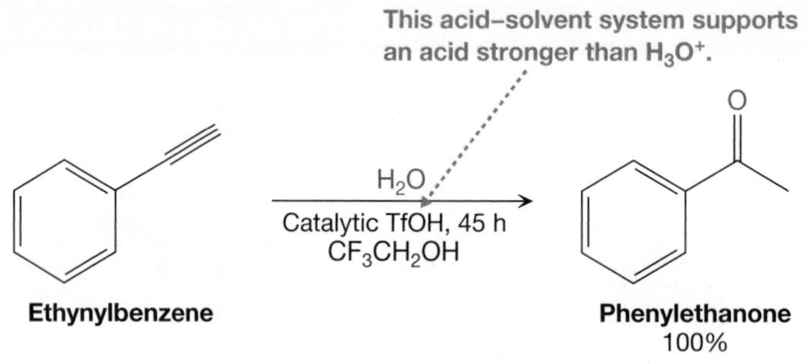
This acid–solvent system supports an acid stronger than H_3O^+.
O
H_2O
Catalytic TfOH, 45 h
CF_3CH_2OH
Ethynylbenzene
Phenylethanone
100%

(12-23)

▸ LOOKING AHEAD

In Chapter 13, we will see that water can add to an alkyne in the presence of a mercury(II) catalyst, Hg^{2+}, instead of a Brønsted acid catalyst. The presence of the mercury(II) catalyst, however, changes the mechanism.

In this case, the stronger acid makes the first step of the mechanism more favorable (see Looking Ahead box).

YOUR TURN 12.15

Draw the complete, detailed mechanism for the reaction shown here and predict the major product.

H_2O
Catalytic TfOH
CF_3CH_2OH
?

SECTION 12.9 OBJECTIVES

You will be able to:

1. Identify when a Brønsted acid can undergo 1,2-addition and 1,4-addition to a diene.
2. Draw the mechanism for 1,2-addition and 1,4-addition of a Brønsted acid to a conjugated diene, and draw the resulting adducts.

12.9 Electrophilic Addition of a Brønsted Acid to a Conjugated Diene: 1,2-Addition and 1,4-Addition

A molecule such as buta-1,3-diene is said to have **conjugated** double bonds because the two double bonds are separated by another bond (in this case, a single bond). A conjugated diene such as buta-1,3-diene is electron-rich, much like the previous alkenes we have studied in this chapter, so it undergoes electrophilic addition with a Brønsted acid such as HCl:

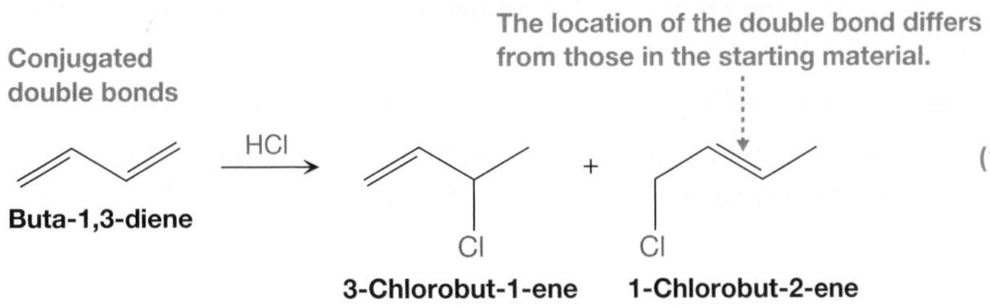
Conjugated double bonds
The location of the double bond differs from those in the starting material.
HCl
Buta-1,3-diene
Cl
Cl
3-Chlorobut-1-ene
1-Chlorobut-2-ene
(12-24)

Notice that the reaction of buta-1,3-diene with HCl yields a mixture of isomeric products. One product, 3-chlorobut-1-ene, appears to be as expected because the H^+ and Cl^- have added across one of the double bonds with Markovnikov regiochemistry. The other product, 1-chlorobut-2-ene, cannot be produced simply by the addition of HCl across one of the double bonds, because the double bond in the product is in a different location than either of the double bonds in the reactant species.

Both reaction products are produced from the same general mechanism, as shown in Equation 12-25a and 12-25b. In Step 1, H^+ adds to a π bond, and in Step 2, the Cl^- anion attacks the newly formed carbocation intermediate in a coordination step:

CONNECTIONS 12.4

Buta-1,3-diene: Outfitting you and your car Buta-1,3-diene (Eq. 12-24) is a precursor of polybutadiene, which is a synthetic rubber used to manufacture tires. Buta-1,3-diene is also converted into adiponitrile, an important precursor in the manufacture of nylon-6,6 synthetic fibers found in swimwear, carpets, parachutes, and many other products.

Mechanism for 1,2- and 1,4-addition of a Brønsted acid to a conjugated diene (Eq. 12-24)

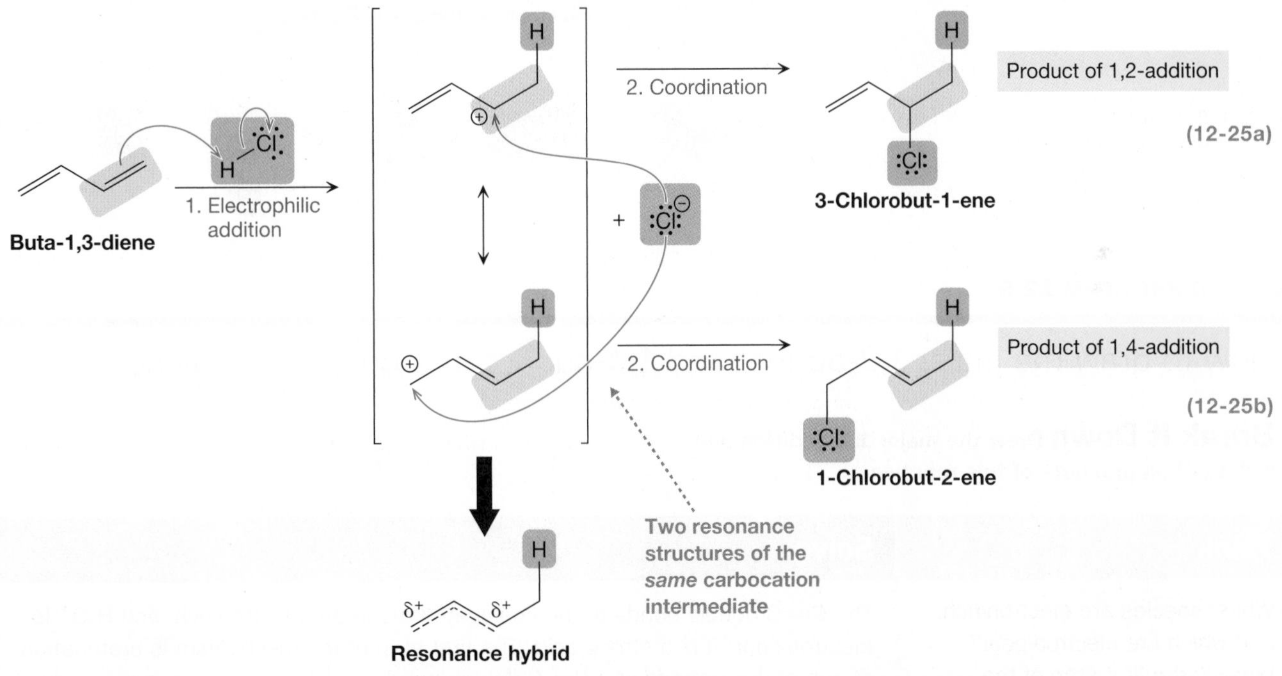
H
:Cl:
Buta-1,3-diene
1. Electrophilic addition
2. Coordination
+ :Cl:
Two resonance structures of the *same* carbocation intermediate
Resonance hybrid
δ+
δ+
3-Chlorobut-1-ene
Product of 1,2-addition
(12-25a)
1-Chlorobut-2-ene
Product of 1,4-addition
(12-25b)

Both products are produced from the *same carbocation intermediate*. As indicated in Equation 12-25, this intermediate has two resonance structures: one with the positive charge on C-1 and one with the positive charge on C-3. In the resonance hybrid, therefore, each of those two C atoms bears a partial positive charge, so each can be attacked by Cl^-. Attack on C-3 (Eq. 12-25a) yields 3-chlorobut-1-ene, whereas attack on C-1 (Eq. 12-25b) yields 1-chlorobut-2-ene.

Mechanism Drawing
Addition of a Brønsted Acid to a Conjugated Diene

The H^+ and Cl^- that added to the diene to produce 3-chlorobut-1-ene are separated by two C atoms, making it the product of **1,2-addition**. On the other hand, 1-chlorobut-2-ene is the product of **1,4-addition** because the H^+ and Cl^- that added to the diene are separated by four C atoms.

YOUR TURN **12.16**

Which of the products shown here results from 1,2-addition, and which results from 1,4-addition?

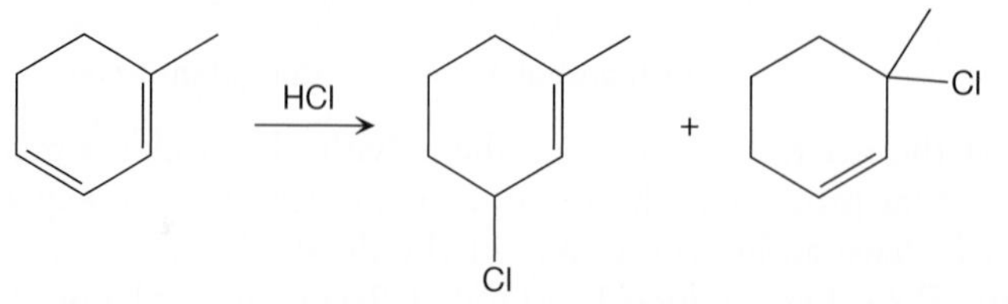

HCl
+
Cl
Cl

Addition of the proton in the first step of the mechanism occurs to give *the more stable carbocation intermediate*, just as we saw previously in the electrophilic addition to propene (Eq. 12-6, p. 610). The carbocation intermediate shown in Equation 12-25, which is produced by the addition of H^+ to a terminal C, is *resonance-stabilized*, and it goes on to form the major 1,2-adduct and 1,4-adduct. If one of the internal C atoms were to gain the H^+ instead, then the positive charge in the resulting carbocation would be *localized* on a primary C, as shown in Equation 12-26:

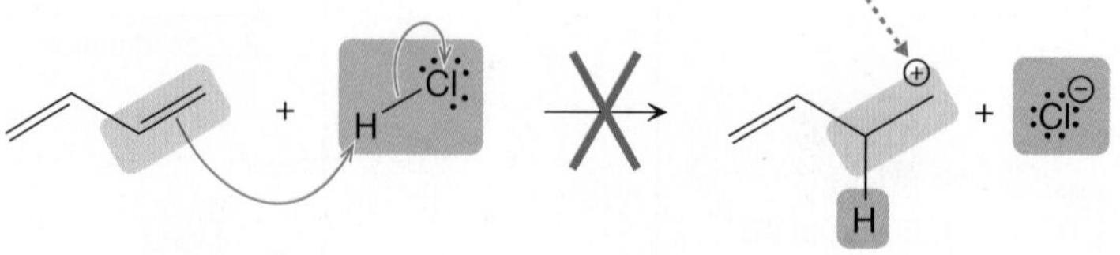

This carbocation intermediate is not as stable as the one in Eq. 12-25.
+
H
Cl
+
Cl
H

(12-26)

SOLVED PROBLEM **12.5**

How to draw the major 1,2-adduct and 1,4-adduct of a conjugated diene

Break It Down **Draw the major 1,2-addition and 1,4-addition products of this reaction.**

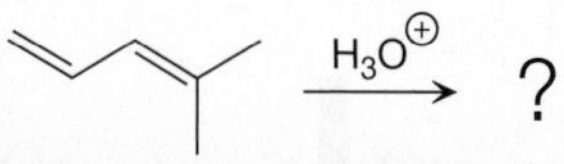

H3O
?

Think	Solve
Which species are electron-rich, and which are electron-poor? What is the first step of the mechanism?	The C═C double bonds of the conjugated diene are electron-rich, and H_3O^+ is electron-poor; it is a strong acid. The first step of the mechanism is protonation of one of the carbons of a C═C double bond.
How many distinct carbocation intermediates are possible from protonation of a double bond?	Either carbon atom of a C═C double bond can gain a proton. There are two distinct C═C double bonds, so there are four possible carbocation intermediates that can be produced, labeled **A–D** below.

(continued)

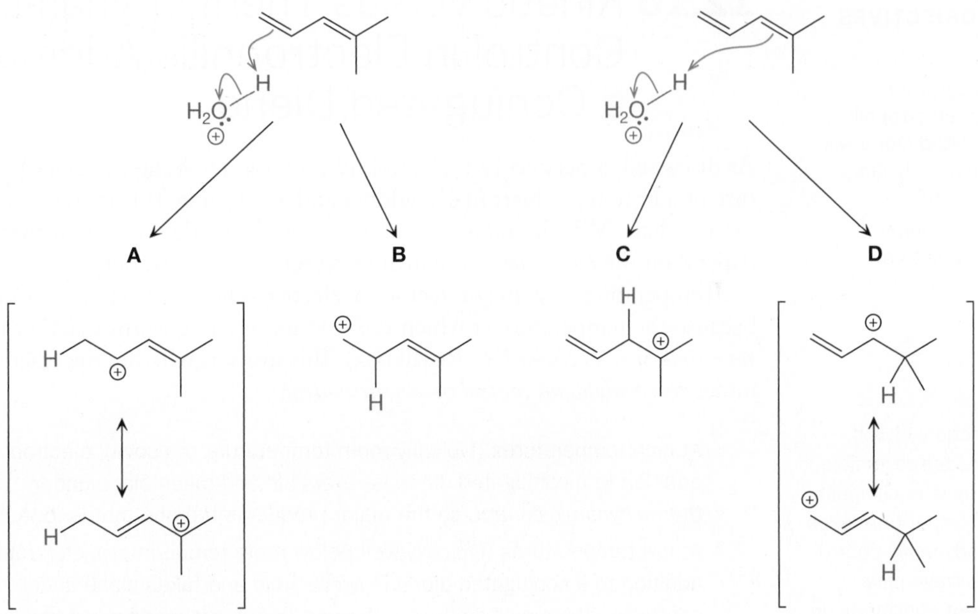

H
H_2O
A
B
C
D
H

The positive charge is resonance-delocalized over 2° and 3° C atoms.

The positive charge is resonance-delocalized over 2° and 1° C atoms.

Which carbocation intermediate is the most stable?	Intermediates **A** and **D** are more stable than **B** and **C** due to resonance delocalization of the positive charge. Intermediate **A** is more stable than **D** (and is the most stable of all four) because its positive charge is shared on a tertiary C atom.
What species can be produced on nucleophilic attack of the most stable carbocation intermediate?	Beginning with carbocation **A**, the 1,2-addition and 1,4-addition products are obtained by attack of the nucleophile, H_2O, on the carbon atoms sharing the positive charge. The outcomes are shown below.

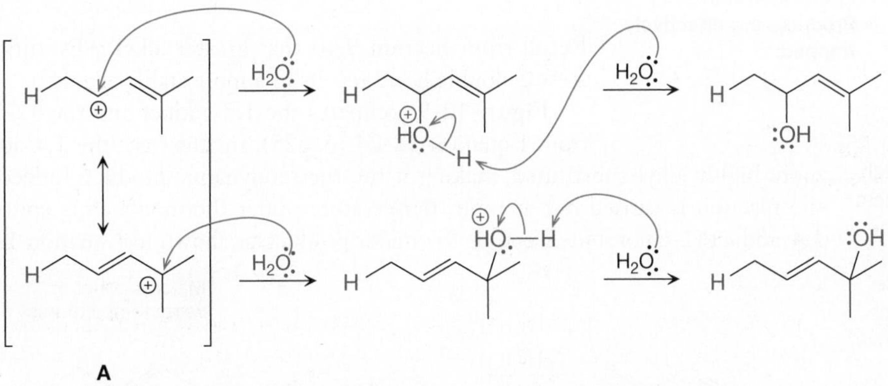

H_2O
HO
H
OH
A

1,2-Addition product

1,4-Addition product

Try It Draw the complete, detailed mechanism for the formation of the major 1,2-addition and 1,4-addition products of this reaction.

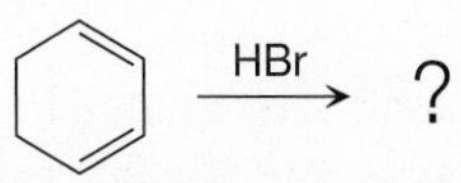

HBr
?

SECTION 12.10 OBJECTIVES

You will be able to:

1. Explain why temperature determines whether electrophilic addition to a conjugated diene will take place under thermodynamic control or kinetic control.
2. Predict the major product of electrophilic addition to a conjugated diene.

12.10 Kinetic versus Thermodynamic Control in Electrophilic Addition to a Conjugated Diene

As discussed in Section 12.9, electrophilic addition to buta-1,3-diene produces a mixture of addition products (a 1,2-adduct and a 1,4-adduct) from the same carbocation intermediate. Which adduct is the major product? The answer to that question can depend on the *temperature* at which the reaction is carried out.

Temperature is a major factor in electrophilic addition to a conjugated diene because the temperature at which the reaction is run governs whether the reaction is *reversible* or *irreversible* (see Recall box). This impacts whether the reaction takes place under *thermodynamic control* or *kinetic control*:

◂ RECALL

As discussed in Section 11.3, if competing reactions are reversible, their products will be in equilibrium, in which case the competition takes place under thermodynamic control. If the reactions are irreversible, their products will not equilibrate, in which case the competition takes place under kinetic control.

- At high temperatures (typically room temperature or above), electrophilic addition to a conjugated diene is *reversible* and takes place under *thermodynamic control*, so the major product is the one that is lowest in energy.
- At low temperatures (typically well below room temperature), electrophilic addition to a conjugated diene is *irreversible* and takes place under *kinetic control*, so the major product is the one that is produced most rapidly.

As **Figure 12-8** shows, high temperatures give the products enough energy to cross over the energy barrier in the reverse direction to re-form the reactants. At low temperatures, the products have insufficient energy to overcome the energy barrier, so they remain essentially permanently once they are formed.

With this understanding, we can predict the major product of electrophilic addition to a conjugated diene if we know which adduct is formed more quickly (the kinetic product) and which one is more stable (the thermodynamic product):

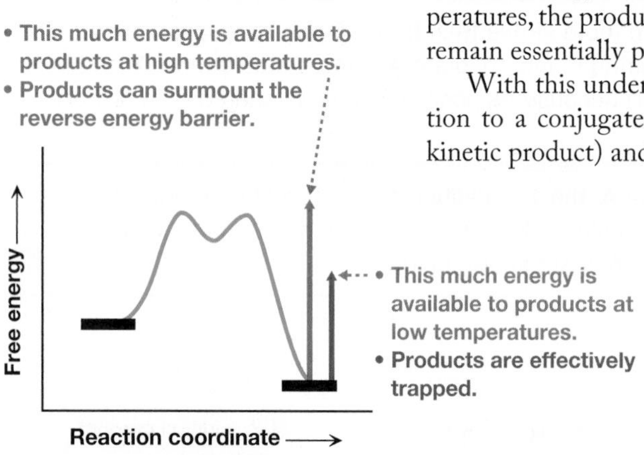

• This much energy is available to products at high temperatures.
• Products can surmount the reverse energy barrier.
Free energy
• This much energy is available to products at low temperatures.
• Products are effectively trapped.
Reaction coordinate

FIGURE 12-8 Effect of temperature on reversibility At high temperatures (red arrow), the products have enough energy to cross over the energy barrier, making the reaction reversible. At low temperatures (blue arrow), the products have insufficient energy to cross over, so the reaction is irreversible.

The *thermodynamic product* of electrophilic addition to a conjugated diene is generally the one in which the remaining C═C bond is the most highly alkyl-substituted. This could be either the 1,2-adduct or the 1,4-adduct.

Recall from Section 9.10 that greater alkyl substitution of a C═C double bond results in a more stable alkene.

Figure 12-9 compares the 1,2-adduct and the 1,4-adduct from Equation 12-24 (p. 625). In this case, the 1,4-adduct is more highly alkyl-substituted, making it the thermodynamic product. Indeed, when the reaction is carried out at room temperature under thermodynamic control, the 1,4-adduct (1-chlorobut-2-ene) is the major product, as shown in Equation 12-27:

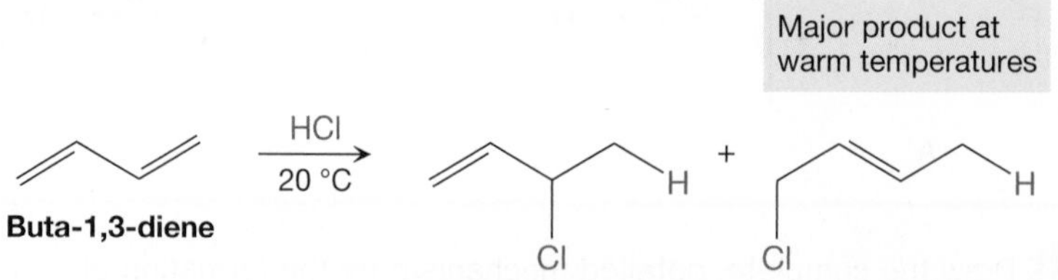

Major product at warm temperatures
HCl
20 °C
H
Cl
+
H
Cl

(12-27)

Buta-1,3-diene

3-Chlorobut-1-ene
25% of adduct mixture

1-Chlorobut-2-ene
75% of adduct mixture

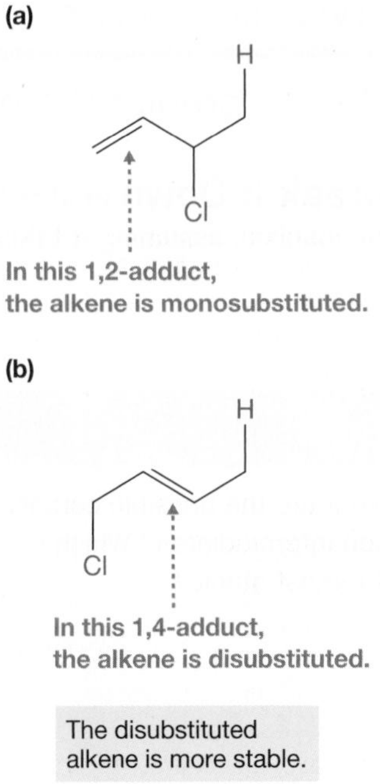
(a)
H
Cl
In this 1,2-adduct,
the alkene is monosubstituted.
(b)
H
Cl
In this 1,4-adduct,
the alkene is disubstituted.
The disubstituted
alkene is more stable.

FIGURE 12-9 Stability of the 1,2-adduct and the 1,4-adduct (a) The 1,2-adduct and (b) the 1,4-adduct of Equation 12-24 are shown. The 1,4-adduct is more stable because its double bond is more highly substituted.

In contrast:

> The *kinetic product* of electrophilic addition to a conjugated diene is generally the 1,2-adduct.

The 1,2-adduct is the kinetic product due to the *location* of Cl^- at the instant it is formed from the first step of the mechanism. For example, on addition of H^+ to buta-1,3-diene, Cl^- appears closer to C-2 than to C-4 (Eq. 12-28):

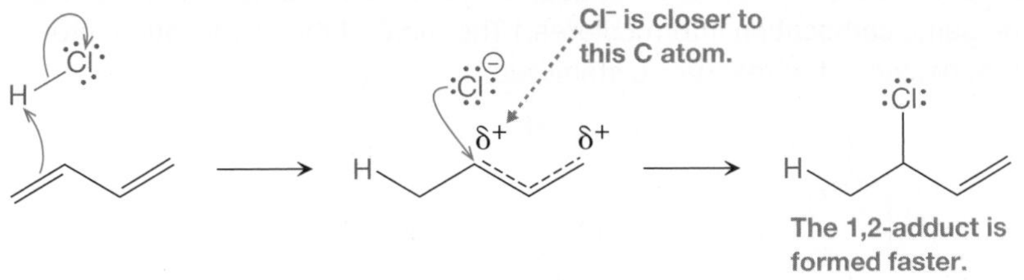
Cl⁻ is closer to
this C atom.
H
Cl
δ+
δ+
The 1,2-adduct is
formed faster.

(12-28)

C-2 and C-4 both develop a partial positive charge and attract Cl^-, but the attraction is greater for C-2 because the distance is shorter. Thus, the energy barrier is smaller and the rate is faster when Cl^- attacks C-2. At cold temperatures and under kinetic control, therefore, the 1,2-adduct is the major product:

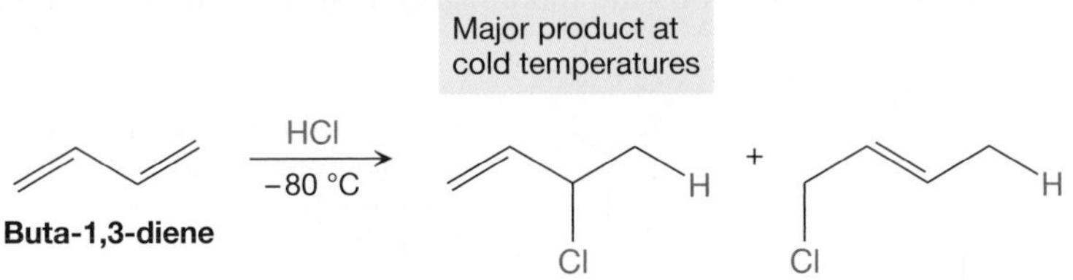
Major product at
cold temperatures
HCl
−80 °C
H
H
Cl
Cl

(12-29)

Buta-1,3-diene

3-Chlorobut-1-ene
80% of adduct mixture

1-Chlorobut-2-ene
20% of adduct mixture

YOUR TURN **12.17**

Identify the thermodynamic product and the kinetic product in the following electrophilic addition reaction.

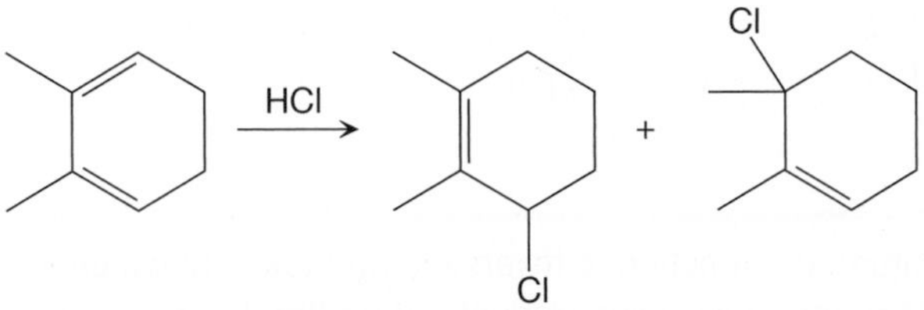
HCl
Cl
Cl

SOLVED PROBLEM **12.6**

How to predict the outcome of electrophilic addition to a conjugated diene

Break It Down **Predict the major product of this reaction and draw its mechanism, assuming it takes place at (a) room temperature and (b) −80 °C.**

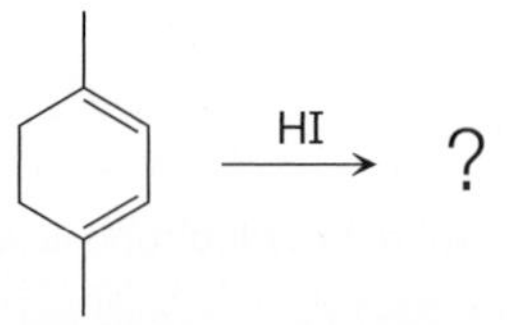

HI
?

Think

What are the possible carbocation intermediates? Which is the most stable?

Solve

Two carbocations can be produced if the π bond at the top is used to form a bond to H^+. (Because the diene is symmetric, addition of H^+ to the bottom π bond would produce the same carbocation intermediates.) The more stable carbocation intermediate is **A**, because it is resonance-stabilized.

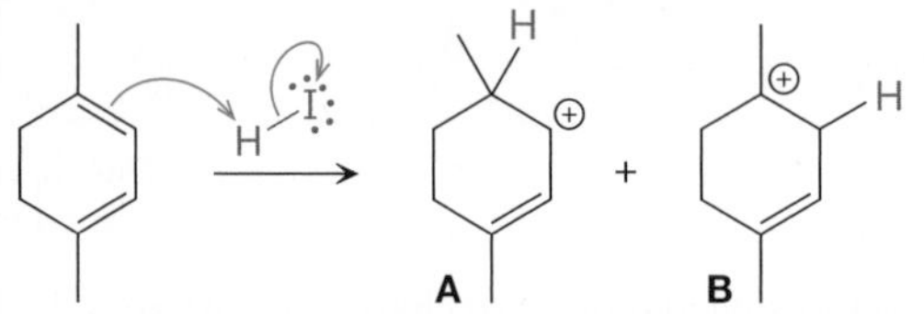

H
I
H
A
B

Think

What adducts can be produced on nucleophilic attack of the most stable carbocation intermediate? Which adduct is the kinetic product, and which is the thermodynamic product?

Solve

Adding I^- yields the 1,2-adduct and the 1,4-adduct, as shown below. The 1,2-adduct is generally the kinetic product. The 1,2-adduct is also the thermodynamic product in this case, because it has the more highly alkyl-substituted C=C bond.

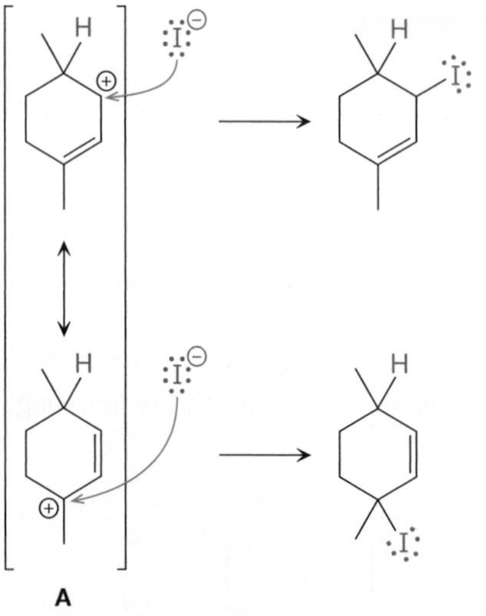

H
I
H
I
A

The 1,2-adduct is formed faster (kinetic product) and is also the more stable alkene (thermodynamic product).

The 1,4-adduct

Think

At room temperature, will the major product be the kinetic or thermodynamic product?

Solve

At room temperature, the reaction is reversible and takes place under thermodynamic control. Therefore, the major product will be the thermodynamic product, which is the 1,2-adduct.

Think

At −80 °C, will the major product be the kinetic or thermodynamic product?

Solve

At −80 °C, the reaction is irreversible and takes place under kinetic control. Therefore, the major product will be the kinetic product, which is the 1,2-adduct.

Try It Determine the major thermodynamic and kinetic products in the reaction shown here and draw the complete, detailed mechanism for the formation of each.

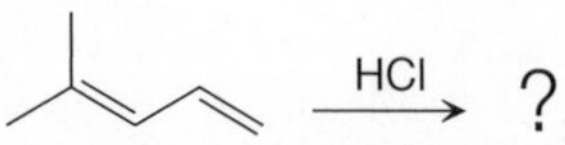

HCl
?

12.11 Organic Synthesis: Additions of Brønsted Acids to Alkenes and Alkynes

SECTION 12.11 OBJECTIVES

You will be able to:

1. Apply a transform to the reactions in which a Brønsted acid adds to an alkene or alkyne.
2. Design a synthesis that incorporates reactions in which a Brønsted acid adds to an alkene or alkyne.

We have studied a variety of reactions in Chapter 12 in which a Brønsted acid adds to an alkene or alkyne. We have focused primarily on their mechanisms, which allows us to understand how and why those reactions take place as they do. Here in Section 12.11, we turn our attention to incorporating those reactions in syntheses.

Recall from Section 11.1 that retrosynthetic analysis helps us determine whether a particular reaction should be considered in a given synthesis. A key part of retrosynthetic analysis is identifying a structural feature in the target that could be the result of a known reaction and then applying a transform (i.e., *undoing* that reaction) to determine the precursors.

For example, we have seen that an alkyl halide can be produced when a strong acid like HCl or HBr adds across the C=C double bond of an alkene (Section 12.1). We have also seen that an alcohol or an ether can be produced when H_2O or ROH adds across a C=C double bond under acidic conditions (Section 12.6). Therefore, when our target is an alkyl halide or an alcohol, we could consider applying one of these transforms:

Br
Undo addition of HBr

Alkyl halide

(12-30)

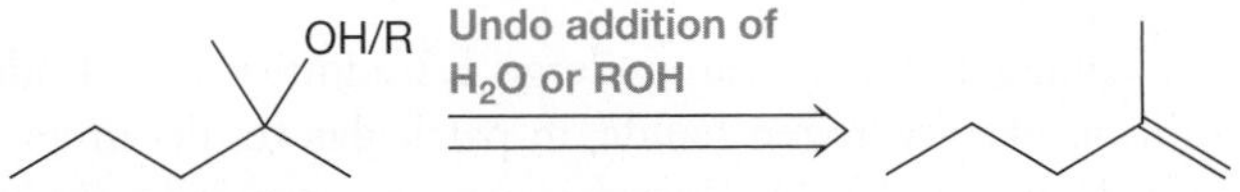

OH/R
Undo addition of H_2O or ROH

Alcohol or Ether

(12-31)

YOUR TURN 12.18

Show how each of the following compounds can be synthesized from two different alkenes.

(a)

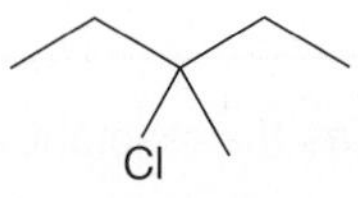

Cl

(b)

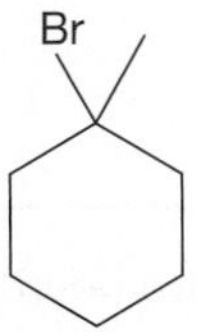

Br

(c)

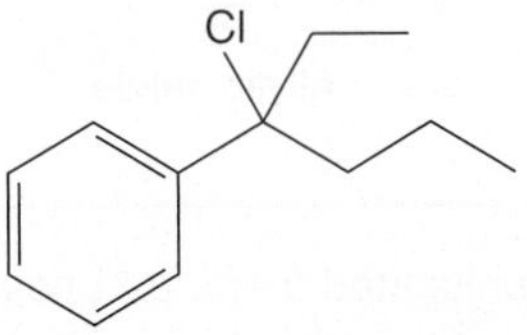

Cl

YOUR TURN 12.19

Show how each of the following compounds can be produced from an alkene.

(a)

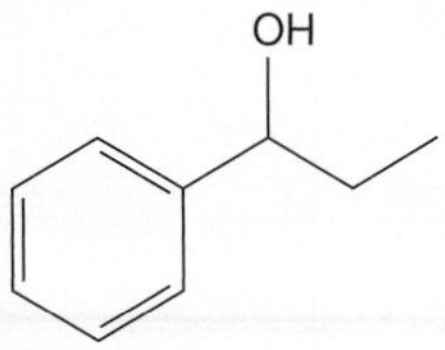

OH

(b)

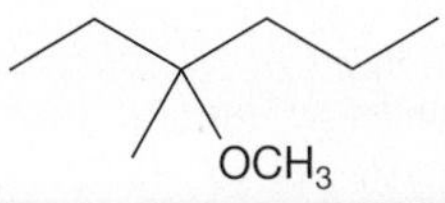

OCH_3

(c)

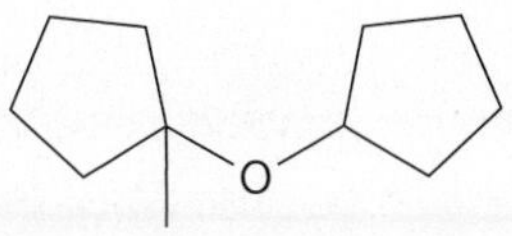

O

Moreover, we learned that alkynes tend to react with strong acids like HCl and HBr to produce geminal dihalides (Section 12.7), and we learned that alkynes can undergo hydration to produce ketones (Section 12.8). Therefore, when our target is a geminal dihalide or a ketone, we might consider an alkyne as a precursor, as shown in Equations 12-32 and 12-33:

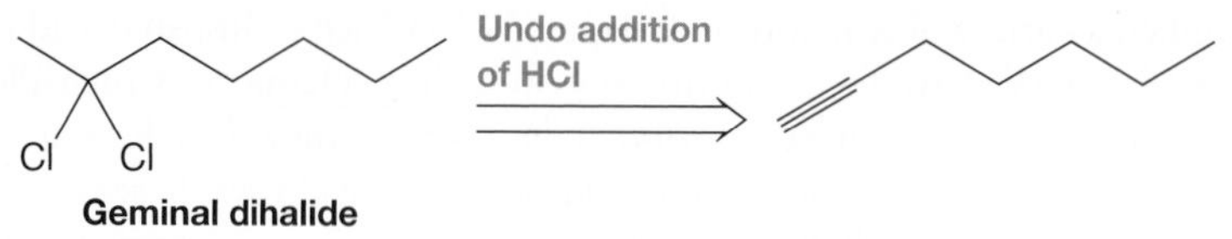

Undo addition
of HCl
Cl
Cl
Geminal dihalide

(12-32)

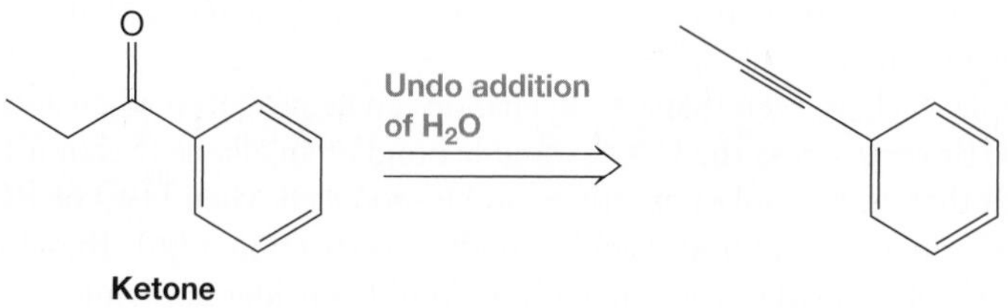

O
Undo addition
of H_2O
Ketone

(12-33)

YOUR TURN **12.20**

Show how to synthesize each of the following compounds from an alkyne.

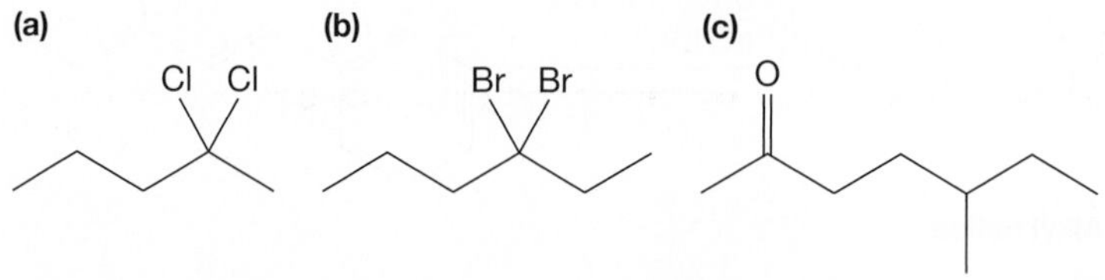

(a)
Cl Cl
(b)
Br Br
(c)
O

Finally, we saw that a conjugated diene can undergo 1,2-addition or 1,4-addition (Section 12.9). 1,4-Addition of a hydrogen halide, in particular, results in an allylic halide, such as the one in Equation 12-34. Therefore, we can consider a conjugated diene as a precursor if our target is an allylic halide:

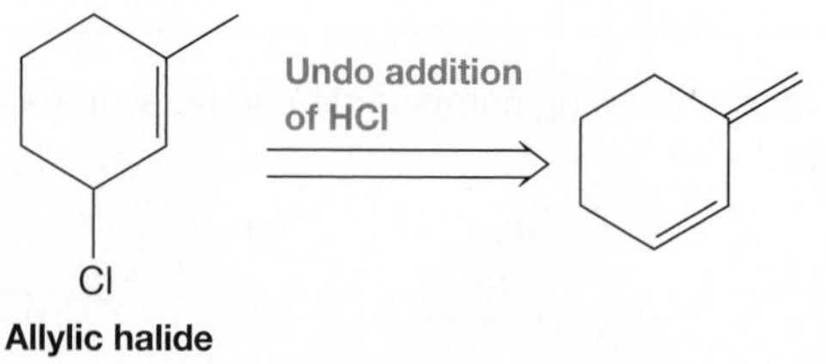

Undo addition
of HCl
Cl
Allylic halide

(12-34)

YOUR TURN **12.21**

Draw a conjugated diene that could have been used as the reactant for this reaction.

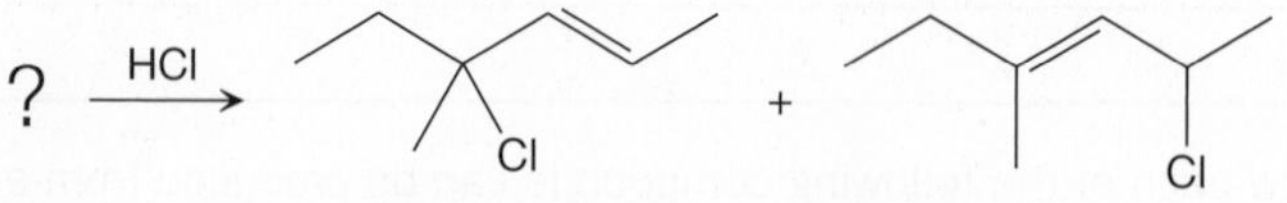

?
HCl
Cl
+
Cl

If you have command of all of these transforms, as well as transforms that undo reactions we have learned from previous chapters, then solving a synthesis problem like the one in Solved Problem 12.7 can become straightforward.

SOLVED PROBLEM **12.7**

How to design a synthesis involving electrophilic addition reactions

Break It Down Show how to carry out the following synthesis.

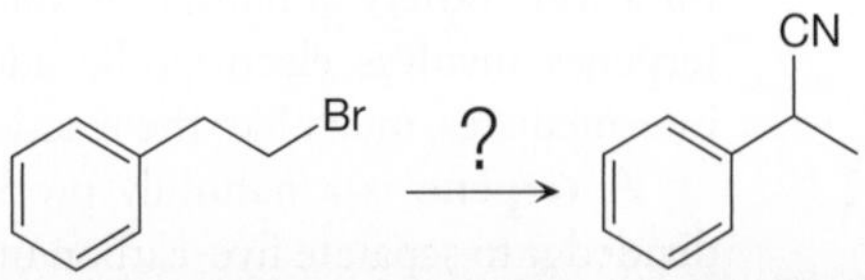
Br
?
CN

Think	Solve
Must a C—C bond be formed? What reaction can be used?	A C—C bond must be formed to join the CN group. This can be the result of an S_N2 reaction, in which case the precursor would be an alkyl halide. 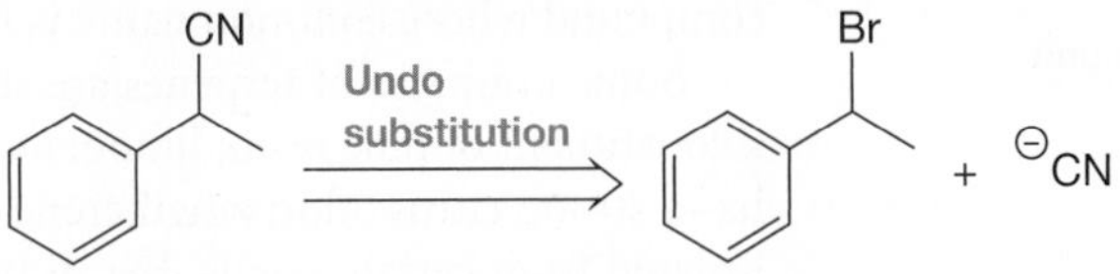 CN Undo substitution Br + ⊖CN
From what precursor could the alkyl halide be formed?	An alkyl halide can be formed from an alkene, as we saw in Equation 12-30. 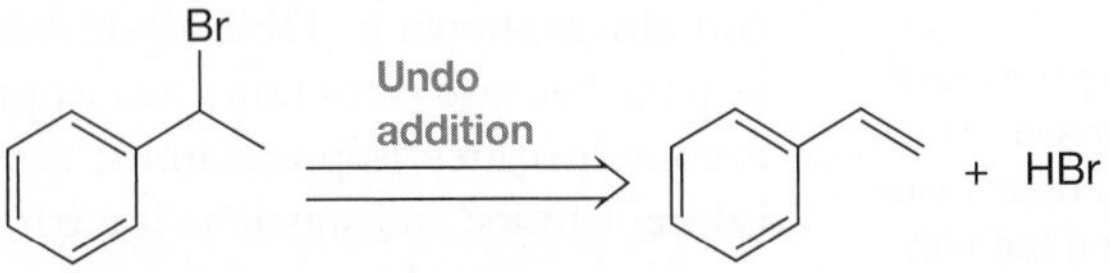 Br Undo addition + HBr
Can the alkene be produced from the starting material?	Yes, the alkene can be produced if the starting material were to undergo elimination. 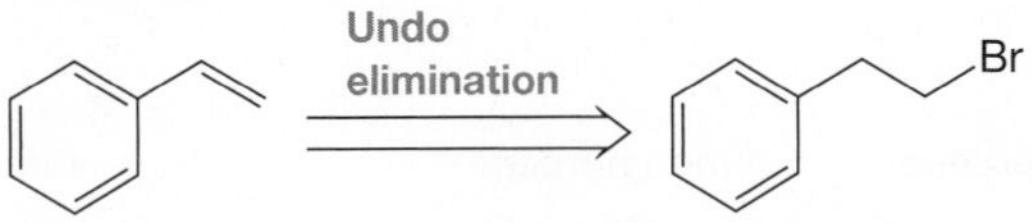 Undo elimination Br
How do we write the final synthesis?	To write the synthesis, we reverse the transforms from the retrosynthetic analysis and we add the necessary reagents, as shown below. 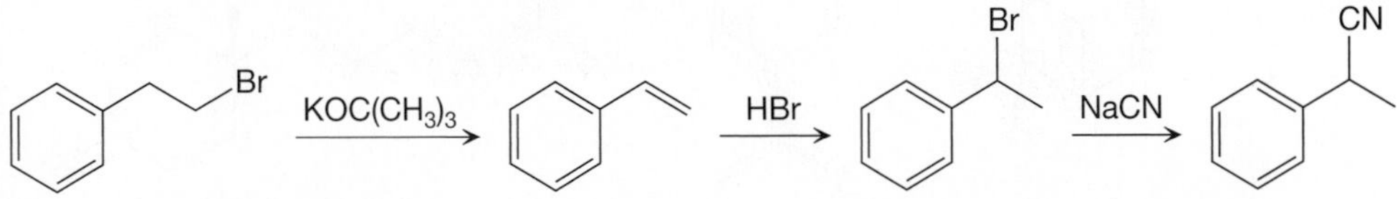 Br KOC(CH3)3 HBr Br NaCN CN

Try It Show how to carry out the following synthesis.

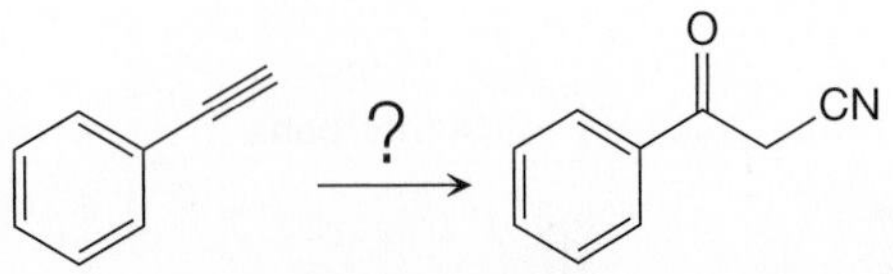
?
O
CN

THE ORGANIC CHEMISTRY OF BIOMOLECULES

12.12 Terpenes and Their Biosynthesis: Carbocation Chemistry in Nature

SECTION 12.12 OBJECTIVES

You will be able to:

1. Characterize a terpene on the basis of its structure.
2. Identify isopentyl diphosphate as the building block for the biosynthesis of terpenes.
3. Show how the biosynthesis of terpenes incorporates electrophilic addition reactions and carbocation intermediates.

Section 2.10 discussed how lipids are biological molecules that are soluble in organic solvents but are insoluble in water. One important class of lipids, called *terpenes*, accounts for a wide variety of natural products. As we will see in this section, the biosynthesis of terpenes involves electrophilic addition reactions that proceed through carbocation intermediates, much like the reactions discussed in the previous sections of this chapter.

A **terpene** is a naturally produced hydrocarbon whose carbon backbone can be divided into separate five-carbon units called **isoprene units**, as shown in **Figure 12-10**:

- In a terpene, every carbon atom is part of an isoprene unit.
- No carbon atom of a terpene is part of more than one isoprene unit.

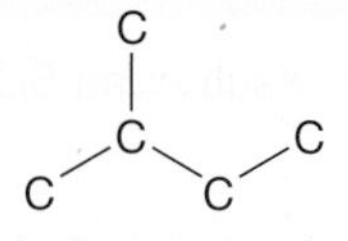

An isoprene unit

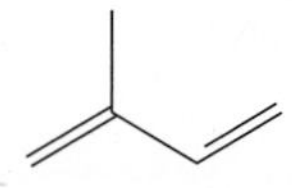

2-Methylbuta-1,3-diene (Isoprene)

FIGURE 12-10 The isoprene unit An isoprene unit (*top*) consists of five carbons, in which four carbons make up a continuous chain and the fifth carbon establishes a branch from that chain. The isoprene molecule (*bottom*) has the same connectivity.

They are called isoprene units because they resemble 2-methylbuta-1,3-diene, the compound whose common name is isoprene.

Some examples of terpenes are shown in **Figure 12-11**. α-Pinene, for example, is a constituent of pine resin; limonene, which can be isolated from the rinds of lemons, has a strong citrus odor; zingiberene is a component of ginger oil; and cembrene A is isolated from certain corals. Recall from Section 2.10c that squalene is the precursor to lanosterol, from which all steroids are derived.

Terpenes are classified according to the number of pairs of isoprene units they contain, as shown in Table 12-1. According to these definitions, α-pinene is a monoterpene because it contains two isoprene units; zingiberene is a sesquiterpene because it contains three isoprene units; cembrene A is a diterpene because it contains four isoprene units; and squalene is a triterpene because it contains six isoprene units.

Many natural products are produced from chemical modifications to terpenes, in which the carbon backbone is altered or atoms other than just carbon or hydrogen are introduced. All of these modified compounds are called **terpenoids**. Some terpenoids

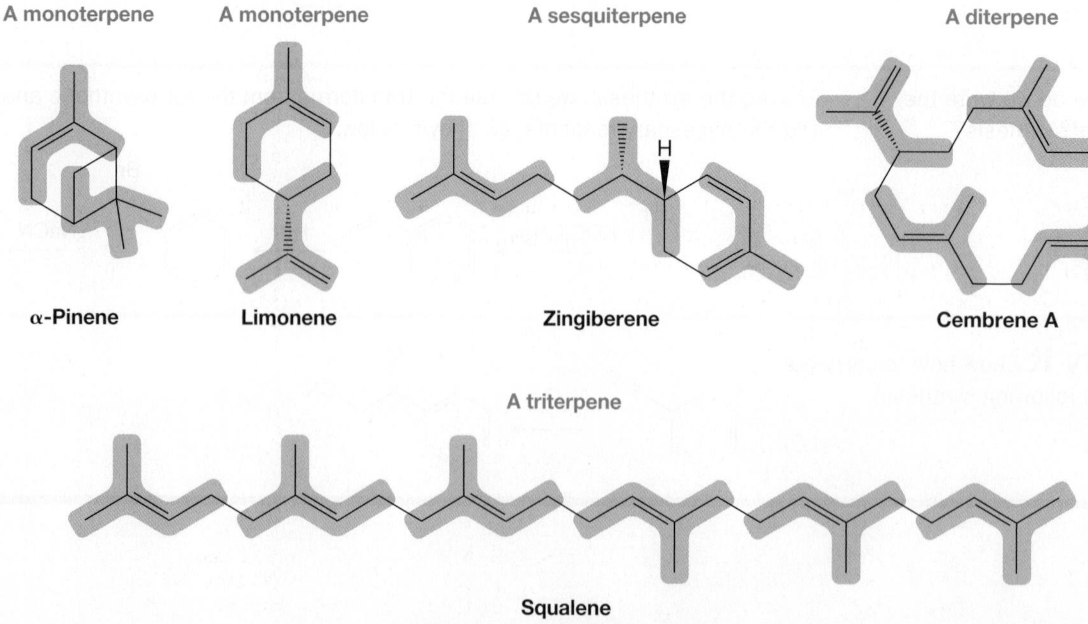
A monoterpene
A monoterpene
A sesquiterpene
A diterpene
H
α-Pinene
Limonene
Zingiberene
Cembrene A
A triterpene
Squalene

FIGURE 12-11 Examples of terpenes The natural sources of these terpenes are described in the text. Isoprene units are highlighted in red.

TABLE 12-1 Classification of Terpenes

	Monoterpene	Sesquiterpene	Diterpene	Triterpene
Number of pairs of isoprene units	1	$1\frac{1}{2}$	2	3
Number of isoprene units	2	3	4	6
Number of carbons	10	15	20	30

are shown in **Figure 12-12**, including menthol (obtained from mint oil), geraniol (a main constituent of rose oil), and retinal (involved in the chemistry of vision).

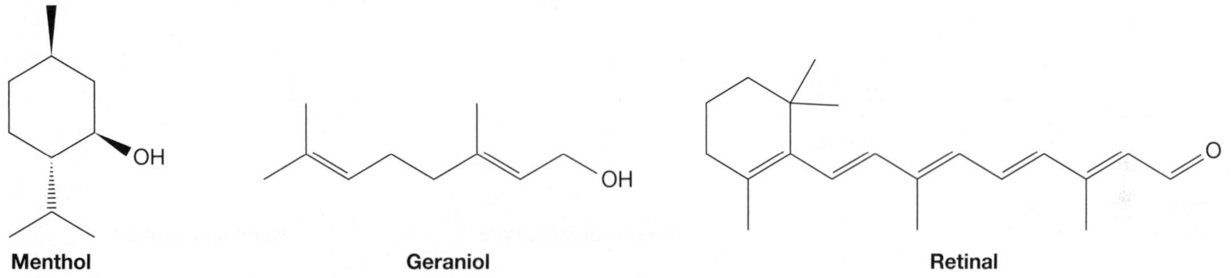

OH
OH
O
Menthol
Geraniol
Retinal

FIGURE 12-12 Examples of terpenoids Terpenoids are derived from chemical modifications of terpenes.

Terpenes have identifiable isoprene units because terpene biosynthesis uses isopentenyl diphosphate as a building block, which itself is produced in several steps from acetic acid (Eq. 12-35). As you can see, isopentenyl diphosphate has the same carbon structure as the fundamental isoprene unit.

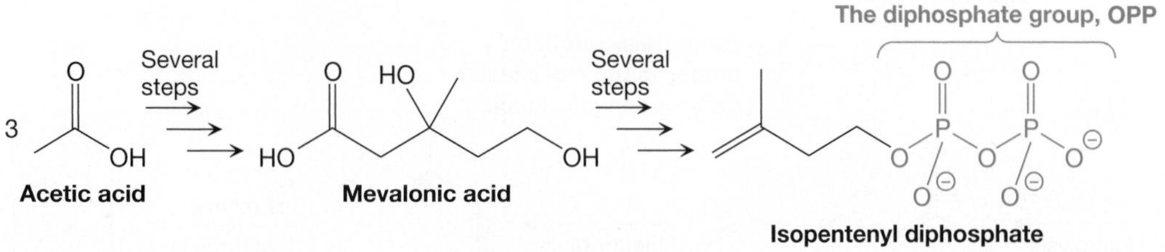

The diphosphate group, OPP
3
Several steps
Acetic acid
Mevalonic acid
Isopentenyl diphosphate

(12-35)

As mentioned earlier, terpene biosynthesis involves reactions that proceed through carbocation intermediates. Such carbocation chemistry is made possible by two features of isopentenyl diphosphate: (1) the C=C double bond and (2) the diphosphate group (OPP), which has good leaving group ability. For example, as shown in Equation 12-36, isopentenyl diphosphate can react with an enzyme (a protein catalyst), isomerizing to dimethylallyl diphosphate:

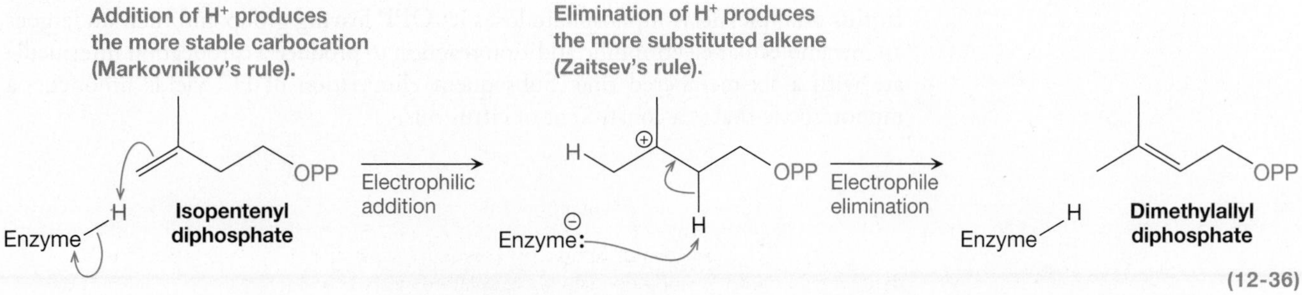

Addition of H+ produces the more stable carbocation (Markovnikov's rule).
Elimination of H+ produces the more substituted alkene (Zaitsev's rule).
OPP
Enzyme
Isopentenyl diphosphate
Electrophilic addition
Electrophile elimination
Dimethylallyl diphosphate

(12-36)

The first step is electrophilic addition of a proton to produce a carbocation intermediate, and the second step is the elimination of a different proton. Notice that the electrophilic addition step produces the more stable carbocation intermediate, thus adhering to Markovnikov's rule (Section 12.3), and that the elimination step produces the more substituted alkene product, consistent with Zaitsev's rule (Section 9.10).

Equation 12-37 shows how a C—C bond can be formed in the biosynthesis of terpenes and terpenoids:

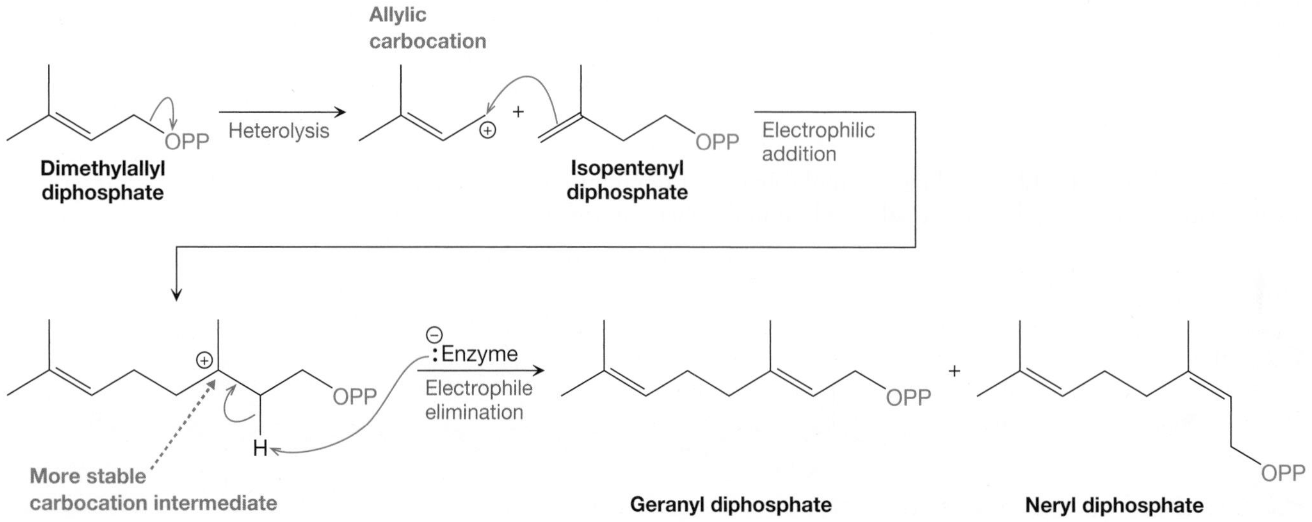

Allylic carbocation
OPP
Heterolysis
OPP
Electrophilic addition
Dimethylallyl diphosphate
Isopentenyl diphosphate
OPP
:Enzyme
Electrophile elimination
H
More stable carbocation intermediate
OPP
OPP
Geranyl diphosphate
Neryl diphosphate

(12-37)

First, dimethylallyl diphosphate loses its OPP group in a heterolysis step, resulting in an allylic carbocation. The allylic carbocation then reacts with isopentenyl diphosphate in an electrophilic addition step, producing another carbocation intermediate, which now contains 10 carbon atoms. Subsequent elimination of H^+ produces geranyl diphosphate and neryl diphosphate, which are *E*/*Z* isomers.

Equation 12-38 shows how a final terpene can be produced from an alkyl diphosphate precursor:

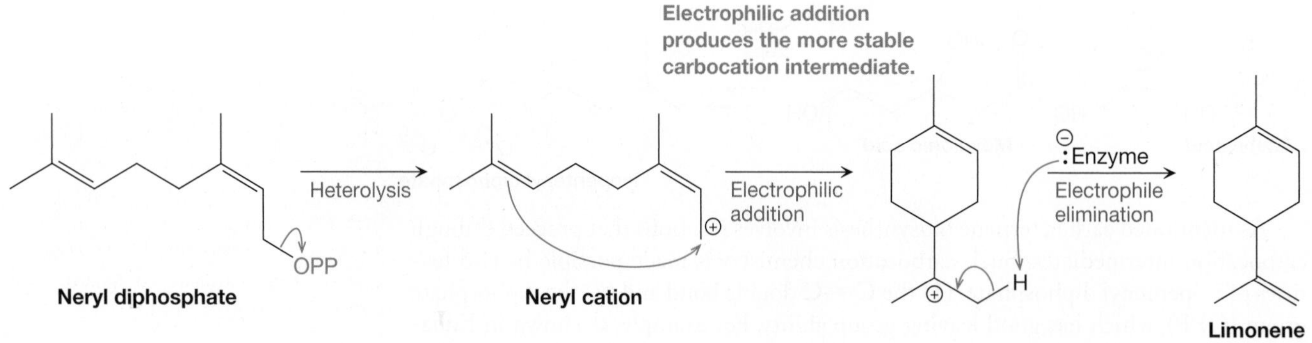

Electrophilic addition produces the more stable carbocation intermediate.
Heterolysis
Electrophilic addition
:Enzyme
Electrophile elimination
OPP
H
Neryl diphosphate
Neryl cation
Limonene

(12-38)

In this example, neryl diphosphate loses its OPP leaving group and then undergoes an intramolecular electrophilic addition reaction to produce a carbocation intermediate with a six-membered ring. Subsequent elimination of H^+ yields limonene, a monoterpene that is a constituent of citrus oils.

Equation 12-39 shows how a terpenoid can be biosynthesized:

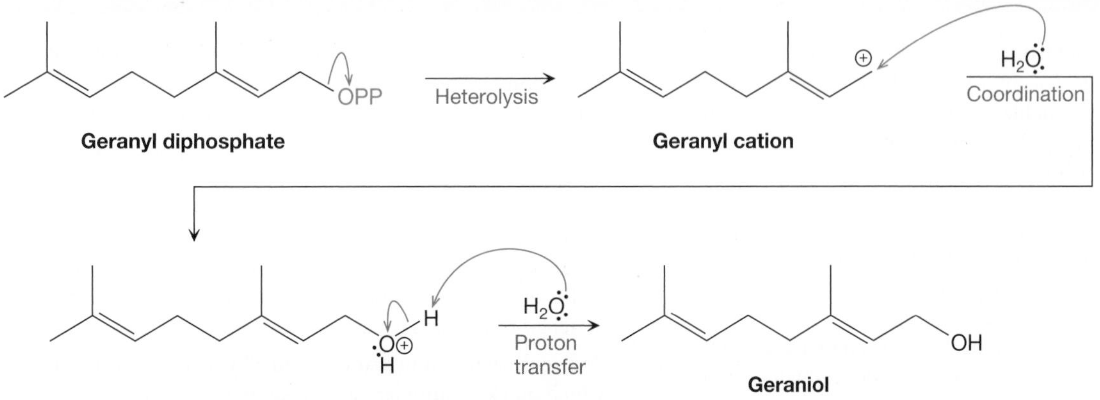

OPP
Heterolysis
Geranyl diphosphate
Geranyl cation
$H_2\ddot{O}$:
Coordination
H
$\ddot{O}\oplus$
H
$H_2\ddot{O}$:
Proton transfer
OH
Geraniol

(12-39)

In this case, geranyl diphosphate undergoes an S_N1 reaction with water as the nucleophile to produce geraniol, found in oils of rose and geranium plants.

These examples of terpene biosynthesis illustrate key aspects of the chemistry used in the biosynthesis of tens of thousands of known terpenes and terpenoids (see Looking Ahead box). You can apply these ideas to other examples in the following Your Turn exercises, as well as in problems at the end of the chapter.

YOUR TURN 12.22

Draw the mechanism for the formation of farnesyl diphosphate (shown here) from the geranyl cation (Eq. 12-39).

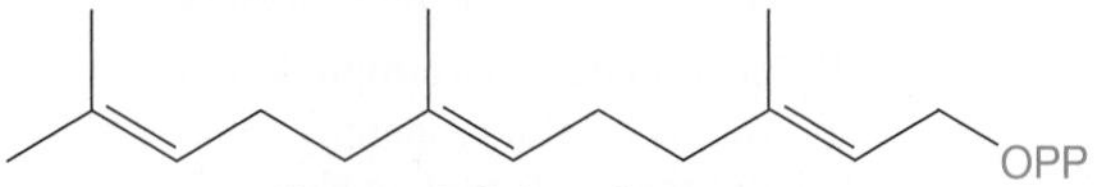

OPP

Farnesyl diphosphate

YOUR TURN 12.23

Neryl diphosphate can react with water to produce α-terpineol and terpin hydrate, terpenoids that are found in natural oils. Draw the mechanism for each of these reactions.

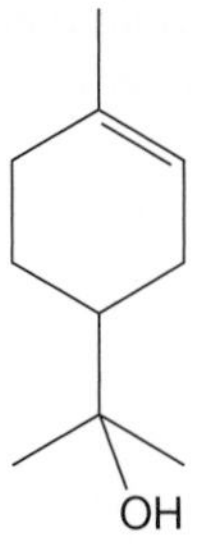

OH

α-Terpineol

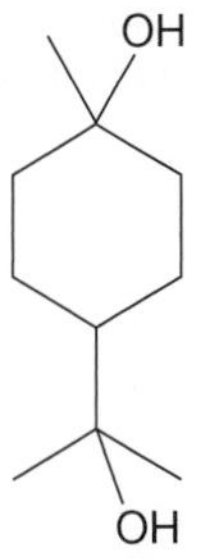

OH
OH

Terpin hydrate

▸ LOOKING AHEAD

In Section 30.4, we will see that the chemistry of terpene biosynthesis is integral in the biosynthesis of cholesterol. Cholesterol has multiple important roles in the body: it is a structural component of cell membranes, it is a signaling molecule, and it is a precursor of steroid hormones.

Chapter Summary and Key Terms

- In an **electrophilic addition reaction** between an alkene and a strong Brønsted acid such as HCl or HBr, the Brønsted acid adds across a C=C double bond in two steps: (1) the proton adds to one carbon and (2) the newly formed conjugate base adds to the other carbon. The product of such a reaction is called the **adduct**. (Section 12.1)
  - In these electrophilic addition reactions, the nonpolar π bond of an alkene is relatively electron-rich and acts as a nucleophile, whereas the proton of the Brønsted acid is electron-poor and acts as an electrophile.
  - The rate-determining step in the addition of a Brønsted acid to an alkene is addition of the proton, which is Step 1 of the general mechanism.
- Benzene does not undergo electrophilic addition with Brønsted acids, because the π electrons of benzene are too heavily stabilized. (Section 12.2)
- **Markovnikov's rule** describes the regiochemistry of addition of a Brønsted acid to an unsymmetric alkene. The regiochemistry is established by Step 1 of the mechanism (protonation of the C=C bond), which favors the production of the more stable carbocation intermediate. (Section 12.3)
- Because the mechanism for addition of a Brønsted acid to an alkene proceeds through a carbocation intermediate, electrophilic addition reactions are susceptible to carbocation rearrangements. (Section 12.4)
- Stereochemistry applies to electrophilic addition reactions involving alkenes if one of the alkene carbons becomes a chiral center in the product. If the starting alkene is achiral, then any chiral products are typically produced as a racemic mixture of enantiomers. (Section 12.5)
- Weak Brønsted acids, such as water and alcohols, can add across the double bond of an alkene under acid catalysis. When water adds, the reaction is called an **acid-catalyzed hydration reaction**. When an alcohol adds, the reaction is called an **acid-catalyzed alkoxylation reaction.** (Section 12.6)
- An alkyne can undergo the electrophilic addition of two equivalents of a Brønsted acid to produce a **geminal dihalide**, in which two halogen atoms are attached to the same carbon. In the addition of the second equivalent of the acid, the carbocation intermediate that is produced is resonance-stabilized if the positive charge appears on the carbon atom already attached to the halogen atom. (Section 12.7)
- The acid-catalyzed hydration of an alkyne produces an enol, which quickly tautomerizes to a ketone. (Section 12.8)
- A **conjugated** diene undergoes electrophilic addition via **1,2-addition** and **1,4-addition**, producing a mixture of products. Both mechanisms involve precisely the same carbocation intermediate, in which the positive charge is resonance-delocalized over two carbon atoms. (Section 12.9)
- Electrophilic addition to a conjugated diene takes place under kinetic control at cold temperatures and under thermodynamic control at warm temperatures. The 1,2-adduct is typically the kinetic product. The thermodynamic product could be either the 1,2-adduct or the 1,4-adduct, depending on which one has the more stable C=C. (Section 12.10)
- To incorporate an electrophilic addition reaction into a synthesis, it is helpful to identify features of a molecule that could make it the product of an electrophilic addition reaction. Thus, a transform can be applied to a target to arrive at the appropriate precursors. (Section 12.11)
- A **terpene** is a natural product for which all carbons can be divided into separate **isoprene units**. A **terpenoid** is derived from chemical modifications of a terpene. (Section 12.12)

Reaction Table

The reactions introduced in this chapter are all functional group transformations; they are collected in Table 12-2.

TABLE 12-2 Functional Group Transformations[a]

	Starting Compound Class	Typical Reagents and Reaction Conditions	Compound Class Formed	Key Electron-Rich Species	Key Electron-Poor Species	Comments	Discussed in Section(s)
(1)	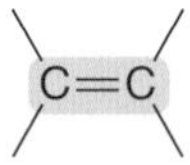 Alkene	HX →	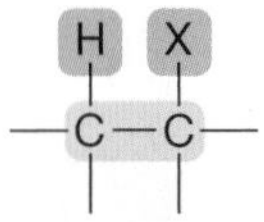 Alkyl halide	$:\ddot{X}:^{\ominus}$	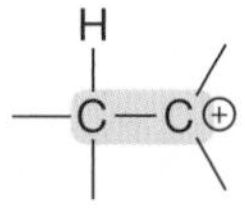	Markovnikov addition	12.1
(2)	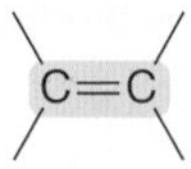 Alkene	H_2O → $H^{\oplus}$	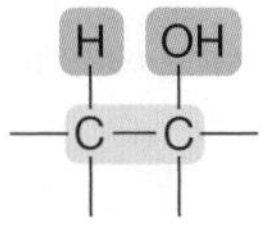 Alcohol	$H_2\ddot{O}:$	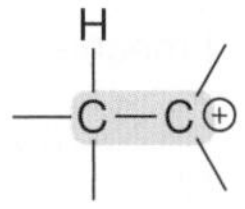	Markovnikov addition, acid catalysis	12.6
(3)	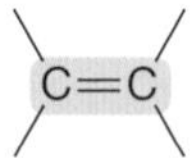 Alkene	ROH → $H^{\oplus}$	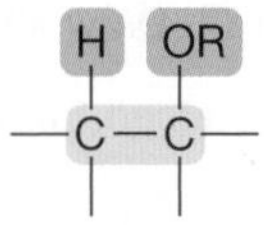 Ether	$R\ddot{O}H$	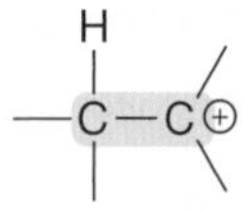	Markovnikov addition, acid catalysis	12.6
(4)	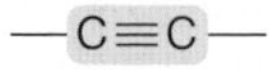 Alkyne	HX (1 equiv) →	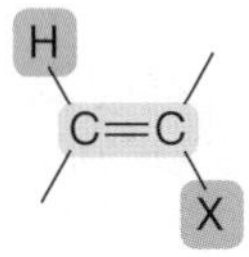 Vinylic halide	$:\ddot{X}:^{\ominus}$	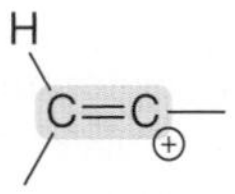	Markovnikov addition, predominantly trans; not useful for synthesis	12.7
(5)	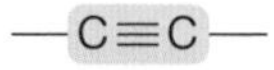 Alkyne	HX (2 equiv) →	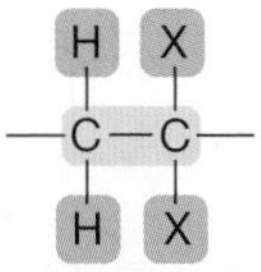 Geminal dihalide	$:\ddot{X}:^{\ominus}$	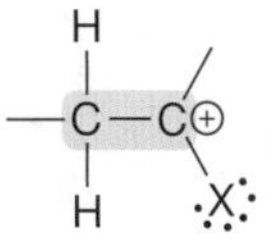	Markovnikov addition twice	12.7
(6)	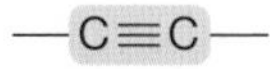 Alkyne	H_2O → H_2SO_4, Δ or TfOH, CF_3CH_2OH	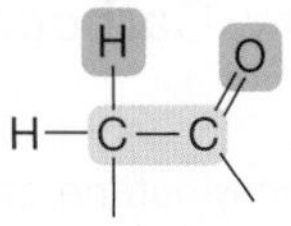 Ketone	$H_2\ddot{O}:$	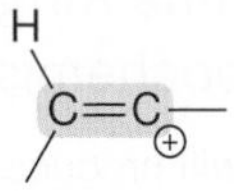	Markovnikov addition of H_2O, keto–enol tautomerization	12.8
(7)	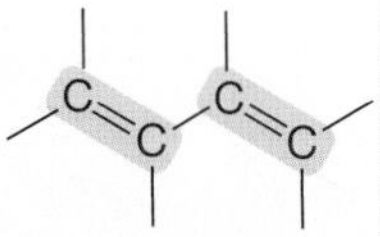 Conjugated diene	HX (1 equiv), cold →	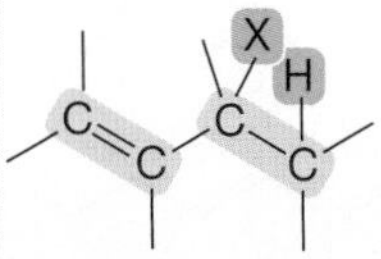 Allylic halide (1,2-adduct)	$:\ddot{X}:^{\ominus}$	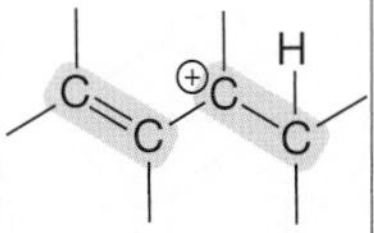	Kinetic control; 1,2-addition	12.9, 12.10
(8)	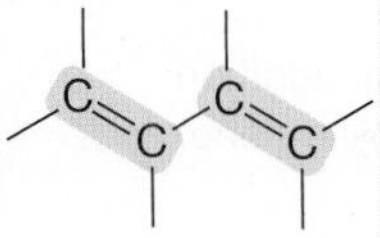 Conjugated diene	HX (1 equiv), warm →	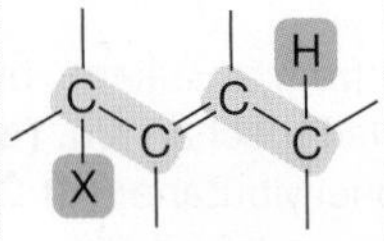 Allylic halide (1,4-adduct)	$:\ddot{X}:^{\ominus}$	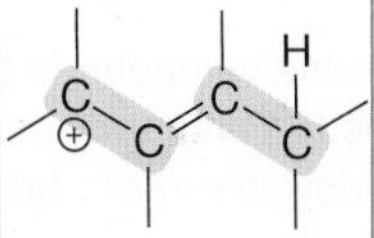	Thermodynamic control; 1,4-addition	12.9, 12.10

[a]X = Cl, Br, or I.

Problems

Problems that are related to synthesis are denoted (SYN).

Section 12.1 The General Electrophilic Addition Mechanism: Strong Brønsted Acids

12.1 Cyclohexene can react with hydrogen halides, HX, to yield the various halocyclohexanes, $C_6H_{11}X$. Rank HF, HCl, HBr, and HI in order from slowest reaction rate to fastest. Explain. *Hint*: What is the rate-determining step?

12.2 Rank alkenes **A–D** in order from slowest rate of electrophilic addition of HCl to fastest. Explain. *Hint*: What is the rate-determining step?

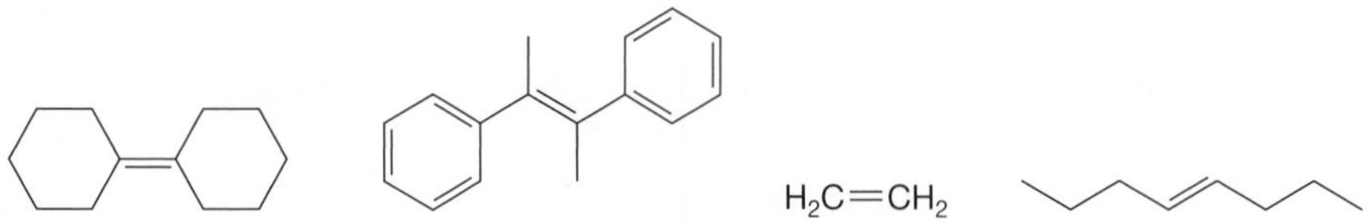
H2C=CH2

A **B** **C** **D**

12.3 Draw the complete, detailed mechanism for each of the following reactions, including the major organic product.

(a) 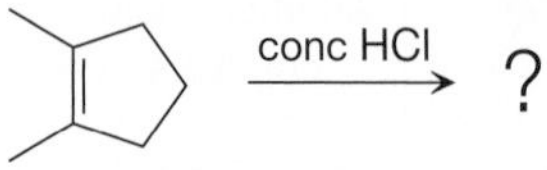
conc HCl
?

(b) 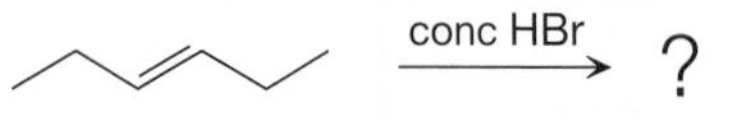
conc HBr
?

(c) 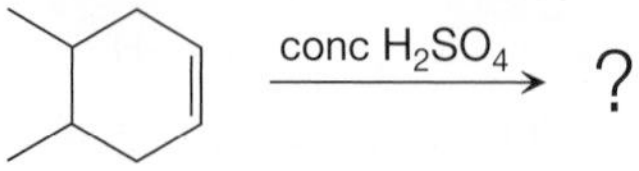
conc H2SO4
?

12.4 A compound C_5H_8 is treated with excess HCl to produce C_5H_9Cl. Draw all possible structures for the initial compound.

12.5 **(SYN)** Show how each of the following compounds can be produced from an alkene.

(a) 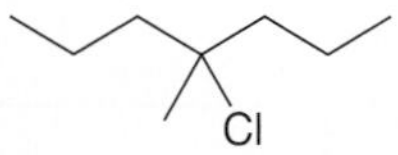
Cl

(b) 
Br

(c) 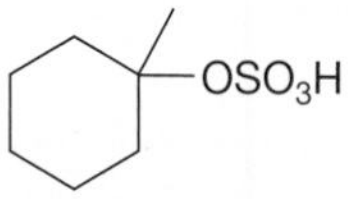
OSO3H

12.6 **(SYN)** Each of the following deuterated bromoalkanes can be produced by treating an alkene with deuterium bromide (DBr). Draw the corresponding alkenes that could have been used. *Hint*: Deuterium, D, has essentially the same chemical behavior as hydrogen, H.

(a) 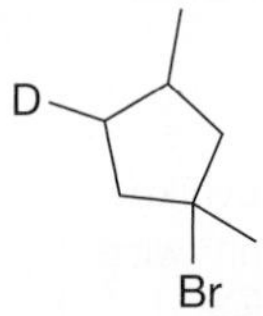
D
Br

(b) 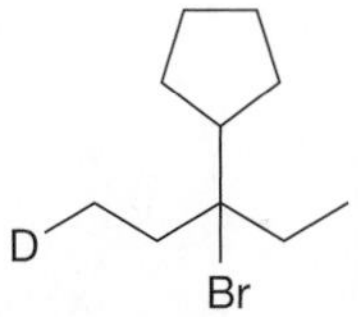
D
Br

(c) 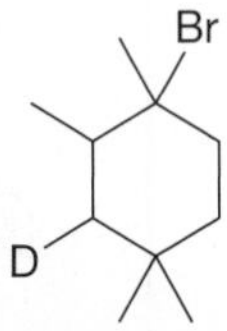
Br
D

(d) 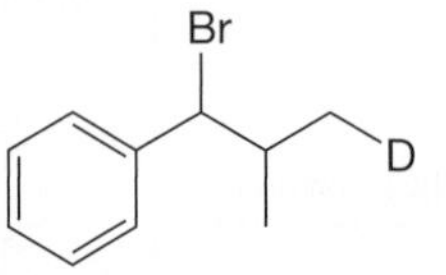
Br
D

Sections 12.2–12.5 Benzene Rings, Regiochemistry, Carbocation Rearrangements, and Stereochemistry

12.7 Which of the alkenes **E–I** will produce 2-chloro-3-methyl-2-phenylbutane as the major product when treated with HCl? Explain.

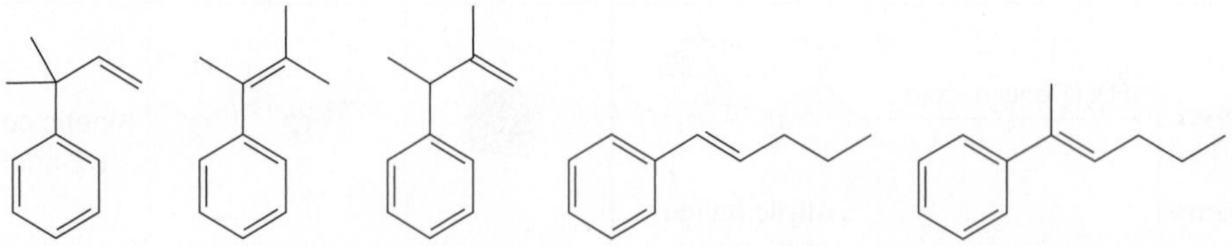

E **F** **G** **H** **I**

12.8 **(SYN)** Each of the following compounds can be produced from an alkene, by a single electrophilic addition reaction. Write that reaction and draw its complete, detailed mechanism. **(a)** 4-chloro-1,2-dimethylcyclohexane; **(b)** 1-chloro-1,2-dimethylcyclohexane; **(c)** 1-bromo-1,1-diphenylbutane; **(d)** 2,2-dichloropentane

12.9 Draw the complete, detailed mechanism and predict the major product for each of the following reactions.

(a)

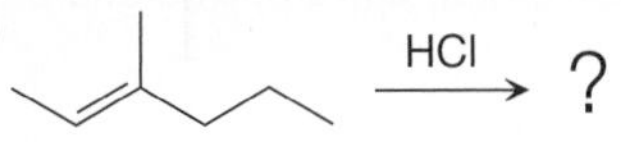
HCl
?

(b)

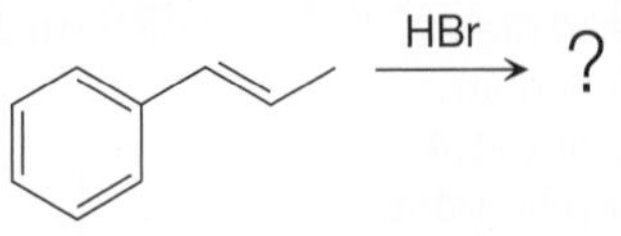
HBr
?

12.10 Draw the complete, detailed mechanism and predict the major product for each of the following reactions.

(a)

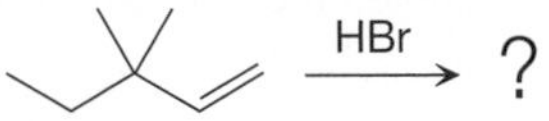
HBr
?

(b)

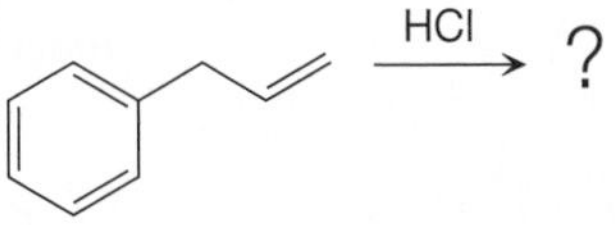
HCl
?

12.11 (SYN) Show how each of the following compounds can be produced from an alkene.

(a)

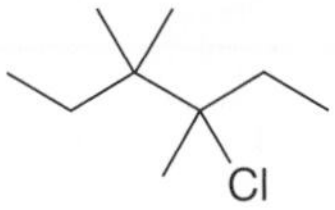
Cl

(b)

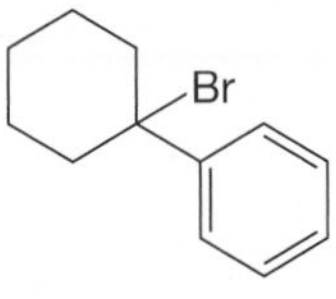
Br

(c)

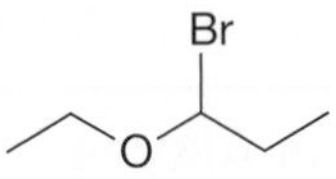
Br
O

12.12 Treatment of (*R*)-4-chlorocyclohexene with HCl produces a mixture of four products. Draw the mechanism that accounts for the formation of each product, and identify which products are optically active.

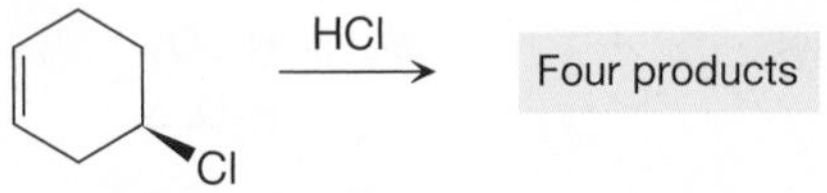
HCl
Four products
Cl

12.13 Draw the complete, detailed mechanism for the addition of HCl to dihydropyran and predict the major product.

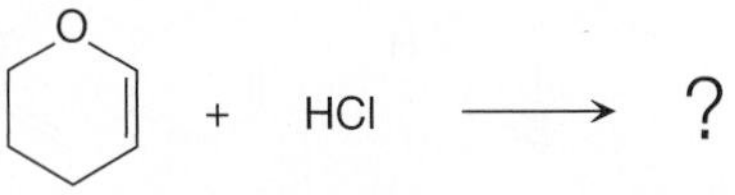
O
+ HCl
?

12.14 When penta-1,4-diene is heated in the presence of HCl, the major product is 1-chloropent-2-ene. Draw the complete, detailed mechanism that accounts for this reaction.

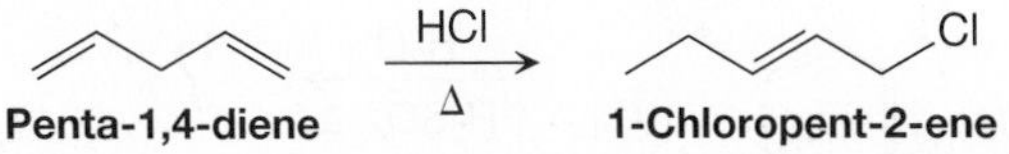
HCl
Δ
Cl

Penta-1,4-diene **1-Chloropent-2-ene**

12.15 The regiochemistry in the electrophilic addition reaction shown here does not adhere to the original generalization put forth by Markovnikov. Draw the complete, detailed mechanism for this reaction and explain its regiochemistry.

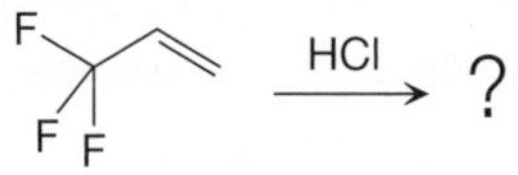
F
F F
HCl
?

12.16 Draw the complete, detailed mechanism and predict the major product for the following reaction.

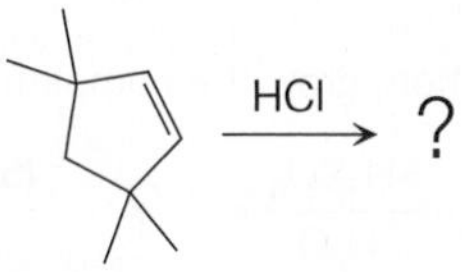
HCl
?

12.17 In the biosynthesis of aromatic amino acids, erythrose 4-phosphate undergoes electrophilic addition to phosphoenolpyruvate (PEP). Draw the products of this step, paying particular attention to regiochemistry.

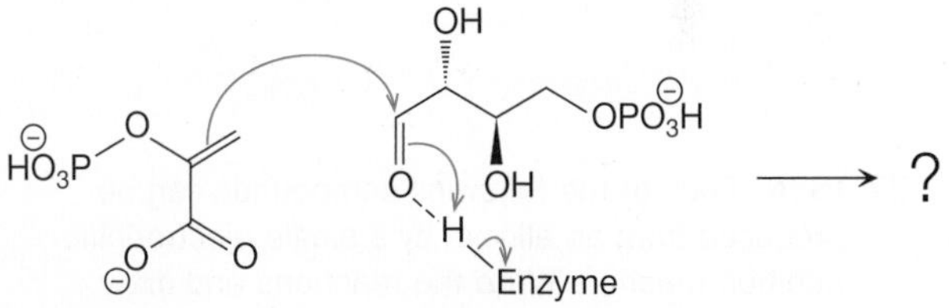
OH
OPO3H
HO3P
O
OH
H
O
O
Enzyme
?

Phosphoenolpyruvate (PEP) **Erythrose 4-phosphate**

Section 12.6 Addition of a Weak Acid: Acid Catalysis

12.18 Draw the mechanism and predict the major product for each of the following reactions.

(a)

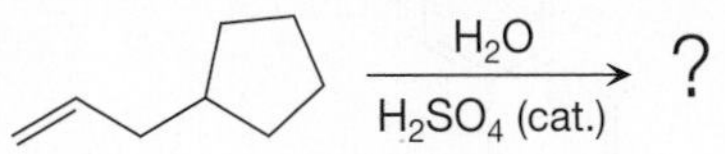
H2O
H2SO4 (cat.)
?

(b)

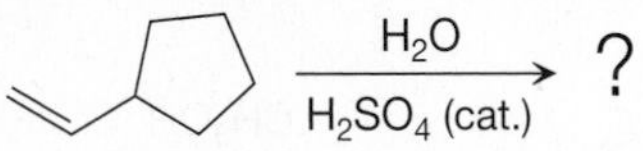
H2O
H2SO4 (cat.)
?

(c)

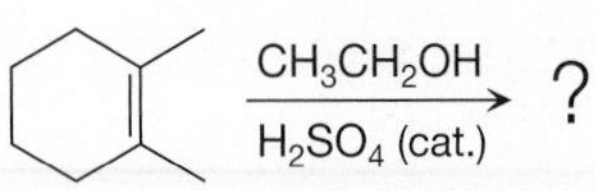
CH3CH2OH
H2SO4 (cat.)
?

(d)

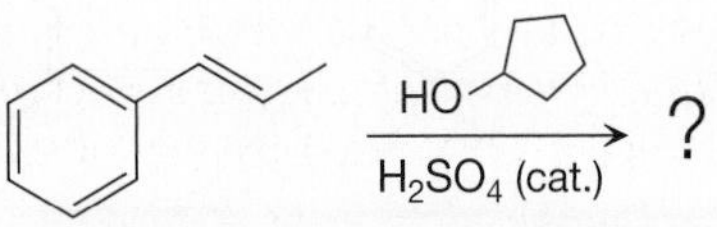
HO
H2SO4 (cat.)
?

12.19 **(SYN)** Each of the following compounds can be produced from an alkene, by a single electrophilic addition reaction. Write that reaction and draw its complete, detailed mechanism. **(a)** pentan-2-ol; **(b)** 3-methylpentan-3-ol; **(c)** 1-methoxy-1,4-dimethylcyclohexane; **(d)** (1-ethoxypropyl)benzene

12.20 **(SYN)** Show how to synthesize each of these compounds from an alkene.

(a)
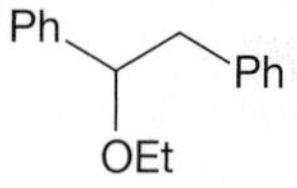
Ph
Ph
OEt

(b)
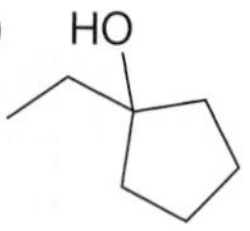
HO

12.21 **(SYN)** Show how 1-methylcyclohexanol can be produced from two *different* alkenes.

12.22 Draw the complete, detailed mechanism for the addition of hexan-3-ol to dihydropyran and predict the major product.

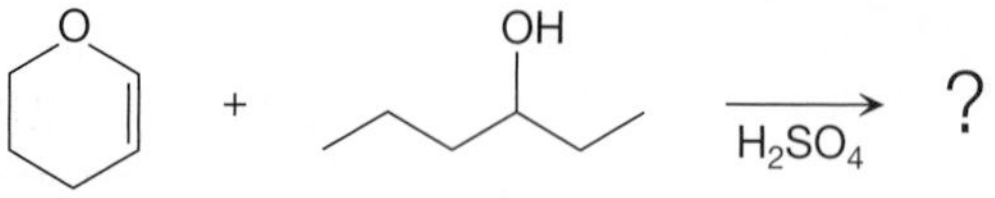
O
+
OH
H2SO4
?

12.23 Draw the complete, detailed mechanism for this reaction.

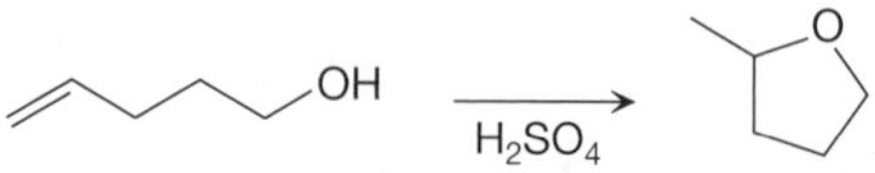
OH
H2SO4
O

Sections 12.7 and 12.8 Electrophilic Addition to an Alkyne

12.24 For each reaction, draw the complete, detailed mechanism and the major product.

(a)
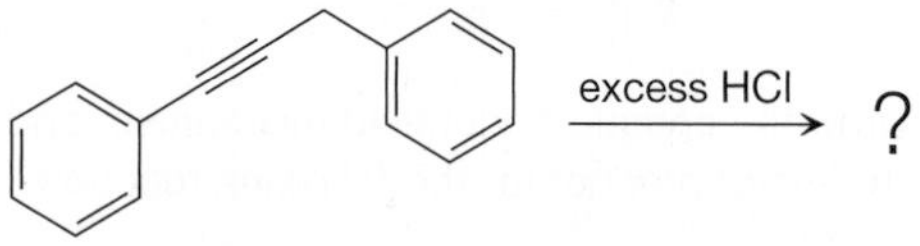
excess HCl
?

(b)
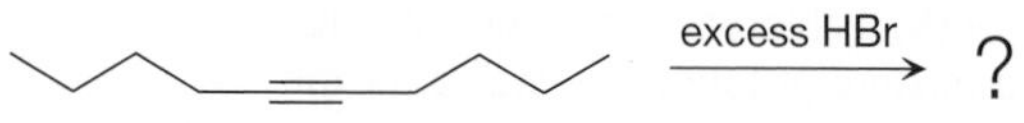
excess HBr
?

12.25 For each reaction, draw the complete, detailed mechanism and the major product.

(a)
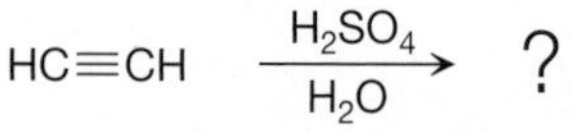
HC≡CH
H2SO4
H2O
?

(b)
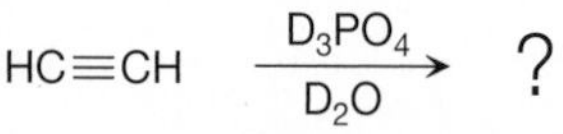
HC≡CH
D3PO4
D2O
?

(c)

H2SO4
H2O, Δ
?

12.26 **(SYN)** Each of the following compounds can be produced from an alkyne, by electrophilic addition. Write the reactions and draw complete, detailed mechanisms.

(a) (1,1-Dichloro-2-cyclopentylethyl)benzene **(b)** 3,3-Dibromohexane **(c)**
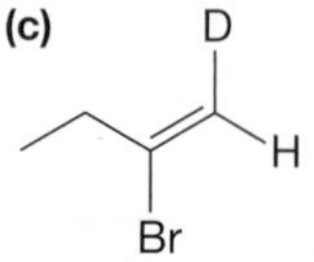
D
H
Br

(d)
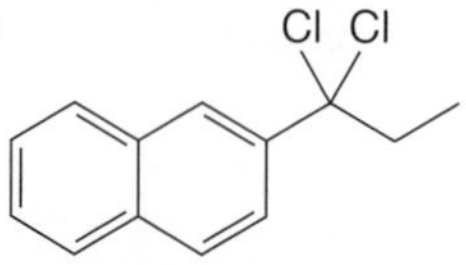
Cl Cl

12.27 **(SYN)** Each of the following compounds can be produced from an alkyne, by a single electrophilic addition reaction. Write the reactions and draw complete, detailed mechanisms.

(a)
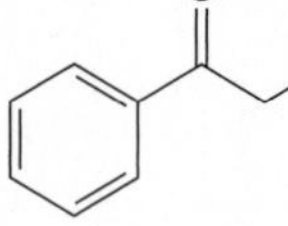
O

(b)
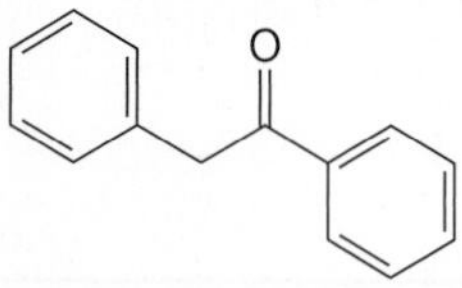
O

12.28 The acid-catalyzed hydration of the internal alkyne shown here leads to only a single adduct. Draw the product and explain why a mixture of adducts is not produced.

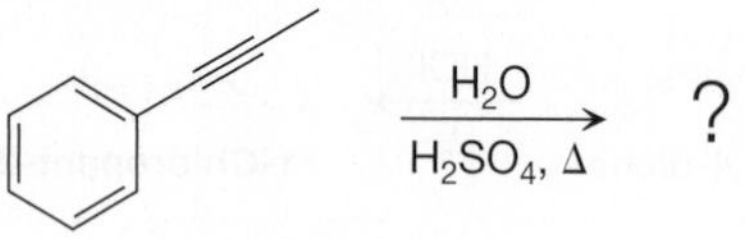
H2O
H2SO4, Δ
?

12.29 Draw the complete, detailed mechanism for this reaction. TsOH is *p*-toluenesulfonic acid, a strong acid.

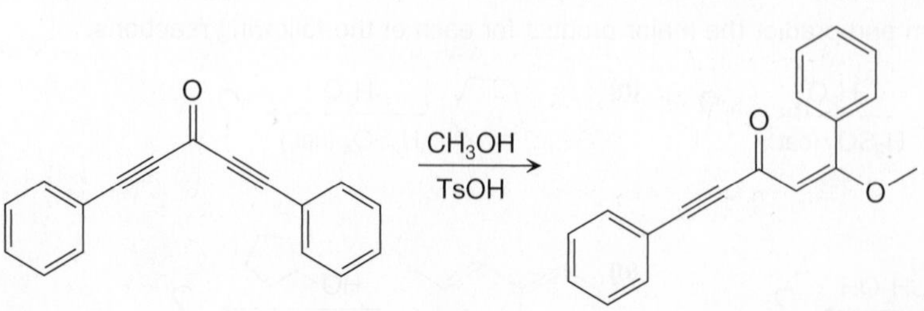
O
CH3OH
TsOH
O
O

Sections 12.9 and 12.10 Electrophilic Addition to a Conjugated Diene; Kinetic versus Thermodynamic Control

12.30 Which product is the result of 1,2-addition and which one is the result of 1,4-addition?

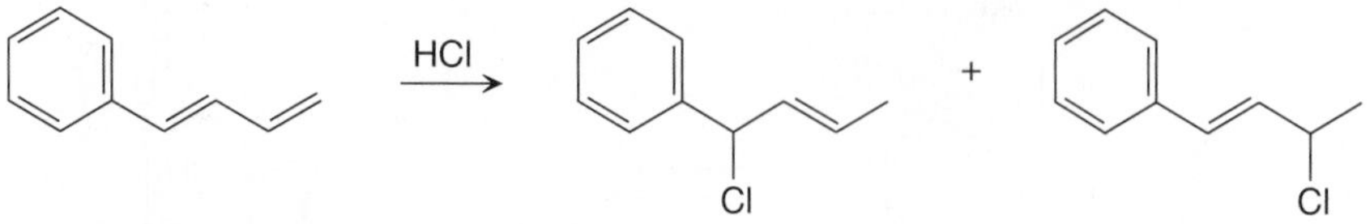

HCl
+
Cl
Cl

12.31 Consider the addition of HBr shown here.

(a) Draw all four carbocation intermediates possible from protonation of the diene and identify the most stable one.

(b) Draw both halogenated products formed by attack of Br^- on that carbocation.

(c) Which of those products would you expect to be formed in the greatest amount at low temperatures?

(d) Which would you expect to be formed in the greatest amount at high temperatures?

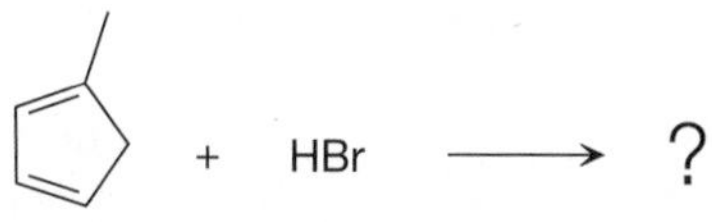

+
HBr
?

12.32 Consider the addition of HBr shown here.

(a) There are three carbocation intermediates possible from the protonation of this triene. Draw all three of them and identify the most stable one.

(b) Draw all halogenated products formed by attack of Br^- on the most stable carbocation.

(c) Which of those products would you expect to be formed in the greatest amount at low temperatures?

(d) Which would you expect to be formed in the greatest amount at high temperatures?

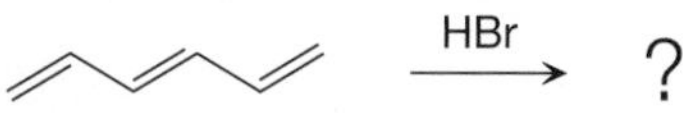

HBr
?

12.33 The addition of HBr to buta-1,3-diene results in 1,2-addition at cold temperatures and 1,4-addition at warm temperatures. If the 1,2-adduct is first formed at cold temperatures and then warmed up, the 1,4-adduct is formed, as shown here. Draw a mechanism for this isomerization.

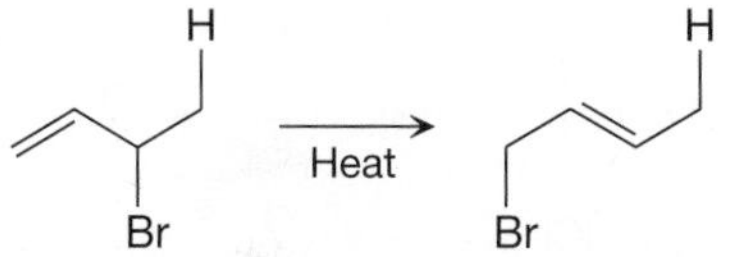

H
Heat
H
Br
Br

1,2-Adduct **1,4-Adduct**

12.34 **(SYN)** Draw the starting material that is used to synthesize this compound.

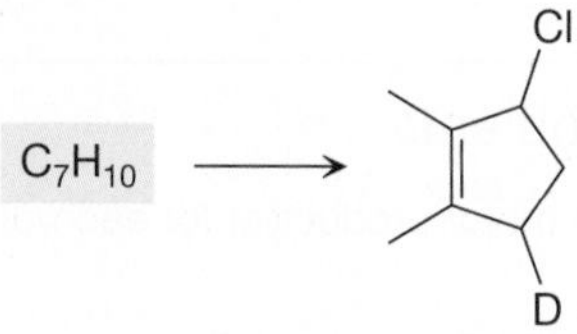

C_7H_{10}
Cl
D

Section 12.12 The Organic Chemistry of Biomolecules

12.35 α-Terpineol, a naturally occurring monoterpene alcohol, isomerizes to 1,8-cineole and 1,4-cineole when treated with acid. Draw a complete, detailed mechanism to account for the formation of each product.

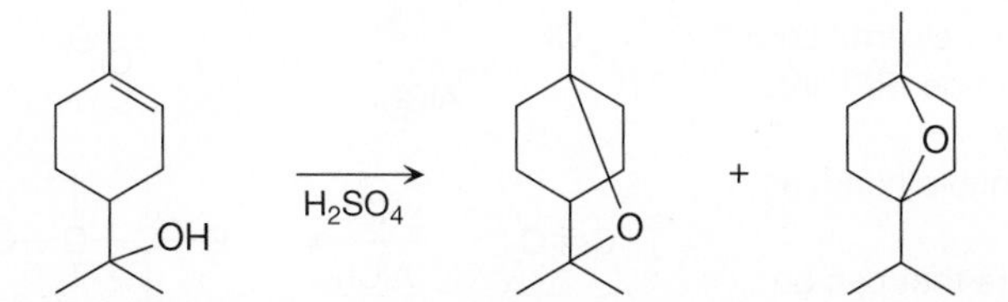

OH
H_2SO_4
O
+
O

α-Terpineol **1,8-Cineole** **1,4-Cineole**

12.36 Draw the mechanism for how α-pinene is biosynthesized from geranyl diphosphate.

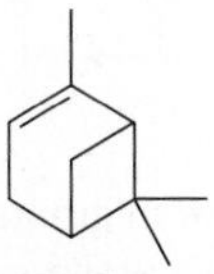

α-Pinene

12.37 Draw the mechanism for how γ-curcumene is biosynthesized from farnesyl diphosphate.

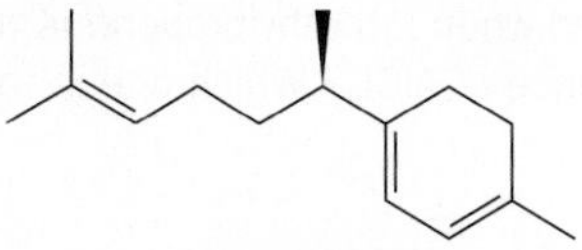

γ-Curcumene

12.38 As mentioned in the chapter, all naturally occurring steroids are derived from lanosterol. In the biosynthesis of lanosterol, squalene (a triterpene) undergoes an epoxidation, followed by an epoxide ring opening, to produce carbocation **A**. As indicated, carbocation **A** subsequently undergoes three electrophilic addition steps to produce the protosterol cation, which has the fused ring system that is characteristic of all steroids. Draw each electrophilic addition step and its curved arrow notation explicitly.

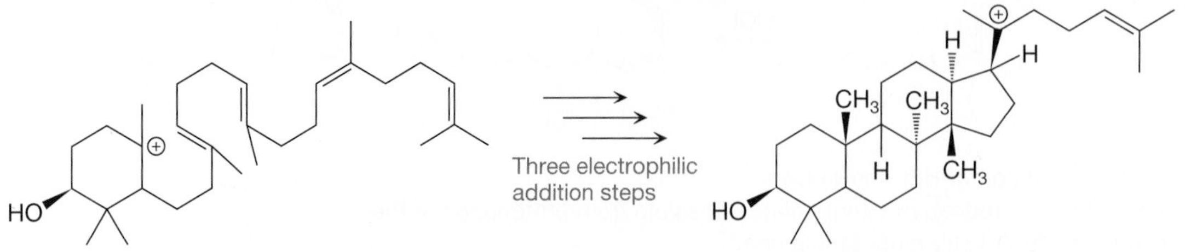

HO
Three electrophilic
addition steps
CH3
H
HO

A **Protosterol cation**

12.39 In the biosynthesis of lanosterol (see Problem 12.38), the protosterol cation is converted to carbocation **B**, which, as shown here, eliminates H^+ to produce lanosterol. The conversion of the protosterol cation to carbocation **B** involves four sequential carbocation rearrangements. Draw each of these carbocation rearrangements and the corresponding curved arrow notation explicitly.

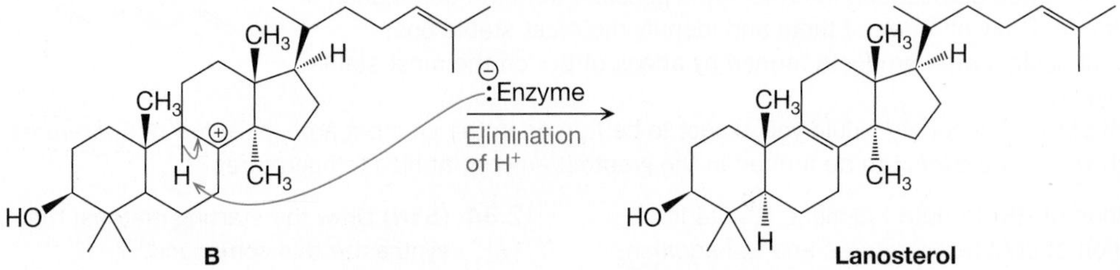

CH3
H
:Enzyme
Elimination
of H+
HO

B **Lanosterol**

Integrated Problems

12.40 Predict the major product(s) for each of the following reactions.

(a) 4-Chlorobut-1-ene + HBr ⟶ ?

(b) 1-Chlorobut-1-ene + HBr ⟶ ?

(c) 4,4-Dimethylcyclopentene + H_2O, H^+ ⟶ ?

(d) Propyne + 2 HCl ⟶ ?

(e) Cyclopentylethene $\xrightarrow{H_3O^+}$?

12.41 **(SYN)** Show how you would carry out each of the following transformations. *Hint*: Two or more separate reactions may be required.

(a)

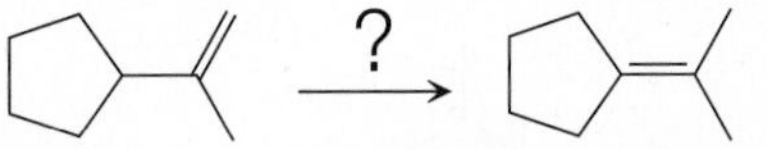

(b)

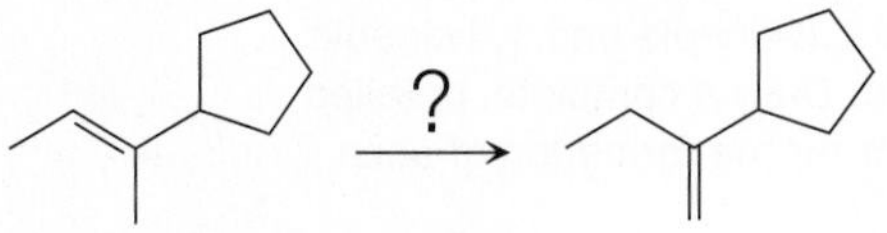

12.42 As will be discussed in greater detail in Chapter 24, $AlCl_3$ is a powerful Lewis acid that effectively catalyzes the dissociation of an alkyl chloride, RCl, into its respective ions, R^+ and Cl^-, as shown in the first reaction.

(a) Propose a mechanism for the addition of RCl across a double bond, as shown in the second reaction.

(b) Using that mechanism, what are the two possible isomers that can be formed when 2-methylpropene is treated with 2-chloropropane in the presence of $AlCl_3$? Which one is the major product? Explain.

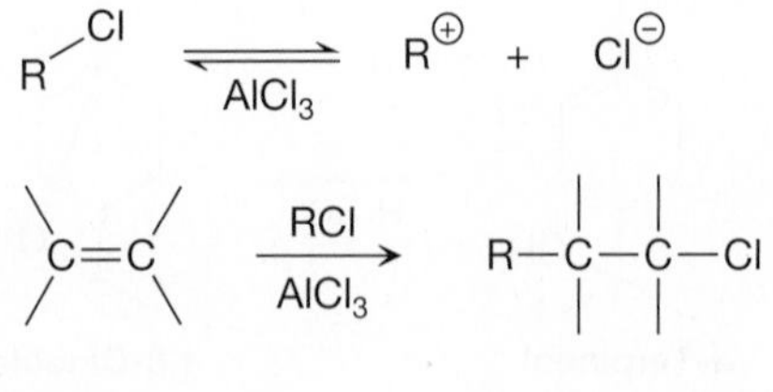

Cl
R
AlCl3
R
+
Cl
C=C
RCl
AlCl3
R—C—C—Cl

12.43 As will be discussed in Chapters 27 and 28, a polymer is a very large molecule that contains many repeating units called monomers. The first reaction shows, for example, how styrene reacts to form polystyrene. The reaction is *initiated* by the electrophilic addition of H^+ from an acid like sulfuric acid, which generates an initial carbocation. Afterward, that carbocation behaves as an electrophile in the presence of another molecule of styrene, resulting in yet another carbocation. This reaction can repeat many thousands of times to build up the polymer. With this in mind, draw a detailed mechanism that illustrates initiation of the polymerization reaction and addition of the first two monomers, as shown in the second reaction.

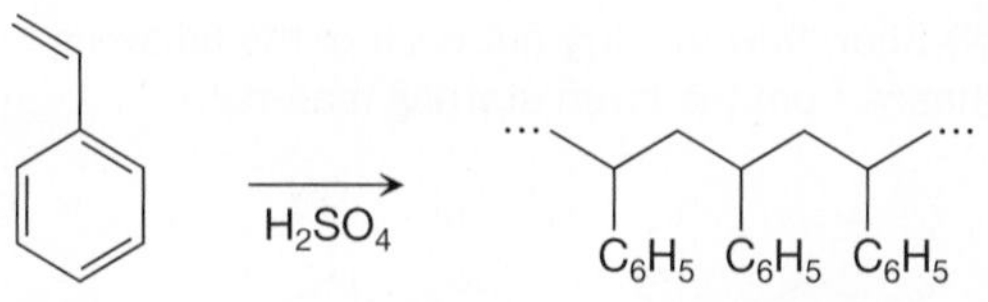

H_2SO_4
C_6H_5 C_6H_5 C_6H_5

Styrene **Polystyrene**

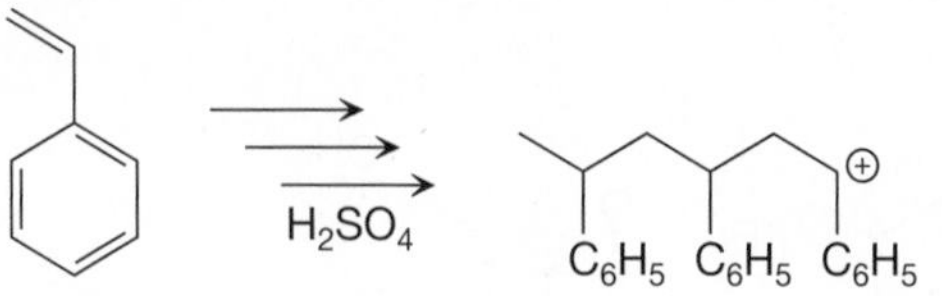

H_2SO_4
C_6H_5 C_6H_5 C_6H_5

12.44 Treatment of but-1-en-3-yne with HBr produces 4-bromobuta-1,2-diene, which is an allene. Draw the complete, detailed mechanism for this reaction.

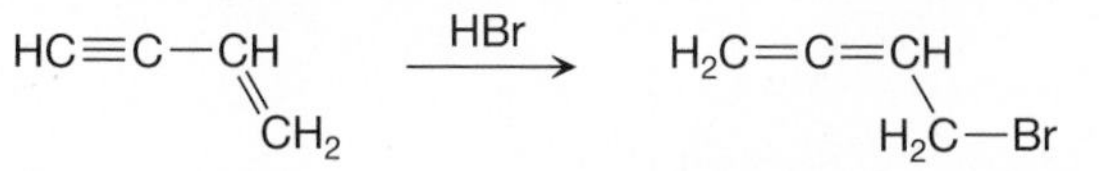

HC≡C—CH
CH_2
HBr
H_2C=C=CH
H_2C—Br

But-1-en-3-yne **4-Bromobuta-1,2-diene**

12.45 Propose a mechanism for the reaction shown here, in which HCl adds to hepta-1,6-diene.

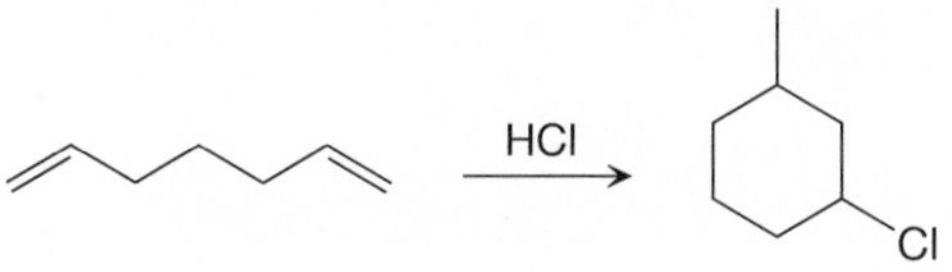

HCl
Cl

12.46 Propose a reasonable mechanism that would account for the reaction shown here.

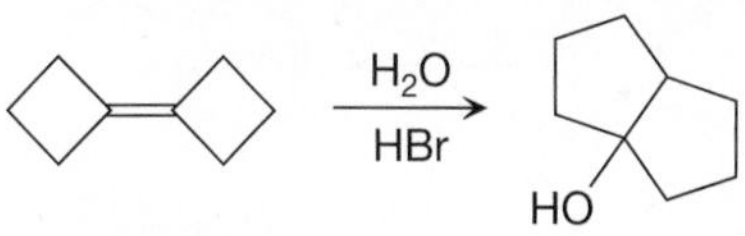

H_2O
HBr
HO

12.47 In the following reaction, both carbon atoms that make up the reactive C=C group are tertiary. Why does the reaction exhibit the regiochemistry shown?

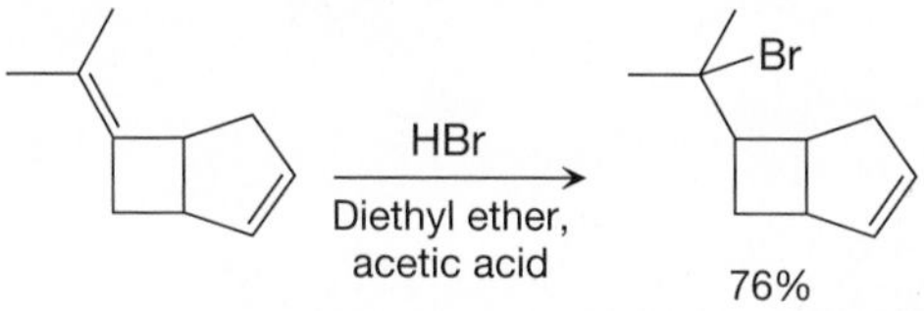

HBr
Diethyl ether, acetic acid
Br
76%

12.48 Determine the structures of compounds **A** through **D** in the following reaction scheme:

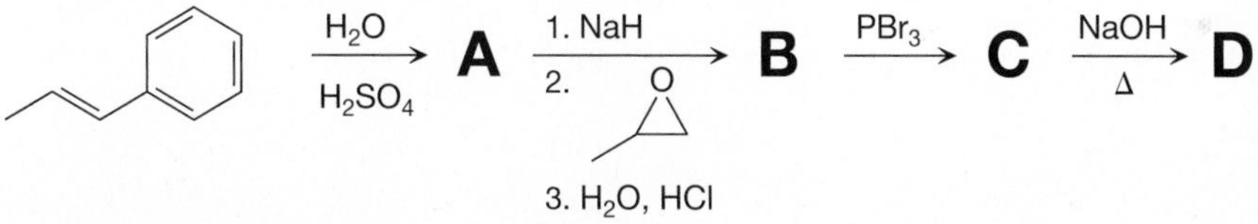

H_2O
H_2SO_4
A
1. NaH
2.
O
3. H_2O, HCl
B
PBr_3
C
NaOH
Δ
D

12.49 Determine the structures of compounds **E** through **I** in the following reaction scheme:

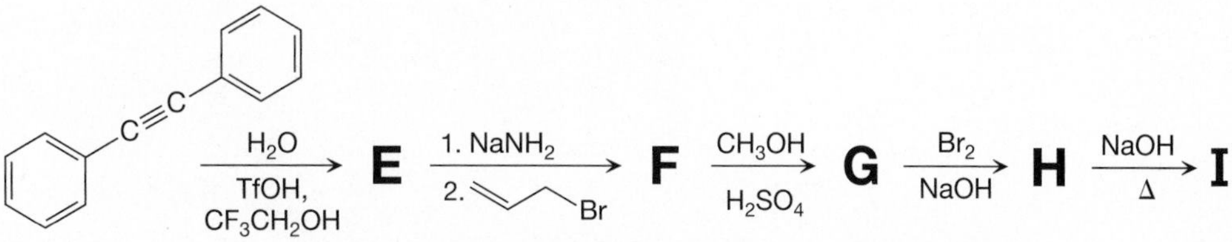

C≡C
H_2O
TfOH, CF_3CH_2OH
E
1. $NaNH_2$
2.
Br
F
CH_3OH
H_2SO_4
G
Br_2
NaOH
H
NaOH
Δ
I

12.50 Determine the structures of compounds **J** through **N** in the following reaction scheme:

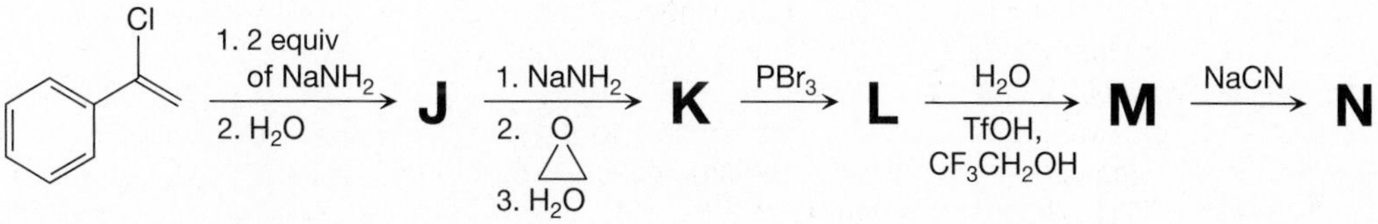

Cl
1. 2 equiv of $NaNH_2$
2. H_2O
J
1. $NaNH_2$
2. O
3. H_2O
K
PBr_3
L
H_2O
TfOH, CF_3CH_2OH
M
NaCN
N

12.51 **(SYN)** Show how to carry out each of the following syntheses from the given starting material.

(a)

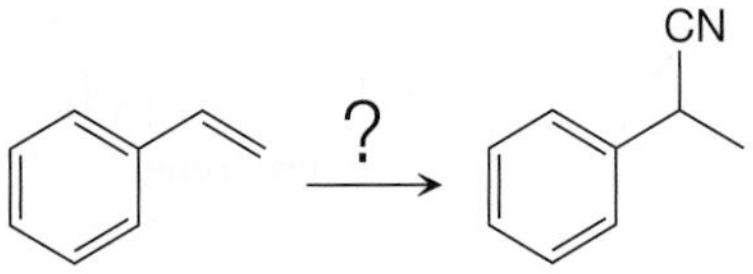

(b)

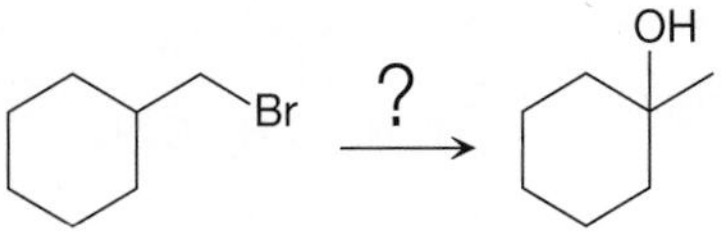

(c)

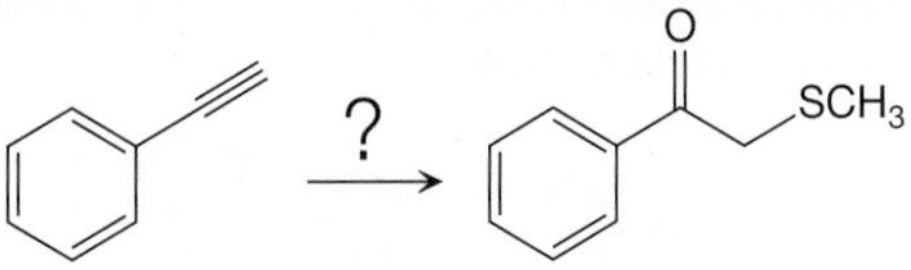

(d)

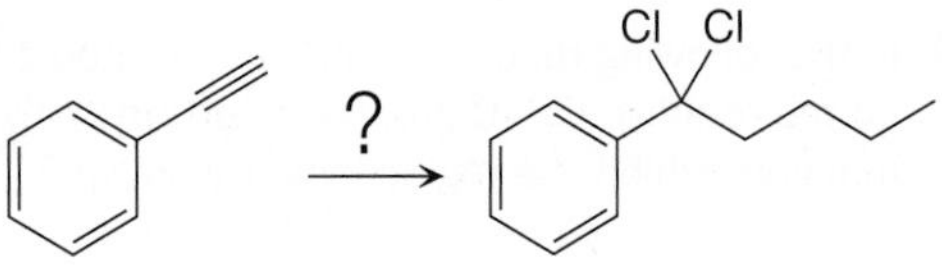

12.52 **(SYN)** Show how to carry out each of the following syntheses from the given starting materials.

(a)

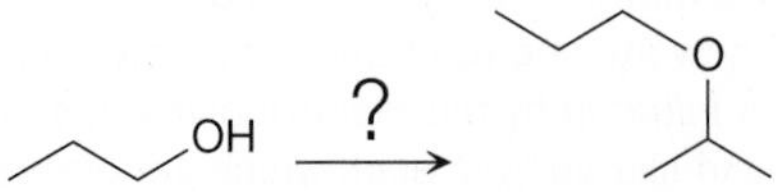

(b)

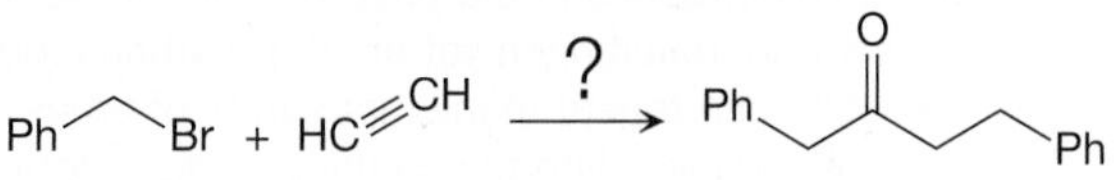

Benzo[*a*]pyrene, found in cigarette smoke, is classified as a procarcinogen because it is a *precursor* to the specific compound that is directly responsible for causing cancer: (+)-benzo[*a*]pyrene-7,8-dihydrodiol-9,10-epoxide (**A**). In the body, the conversion of benzo[*a*]pyrene into **A** involves two epoxidation reactions, analogous to the ones we will learn about here in Chapter 13. Once formed, **A** can react with DNA and distort the double helix, which interferes with the normal process by which DNA is copied, thus inducing mutations.

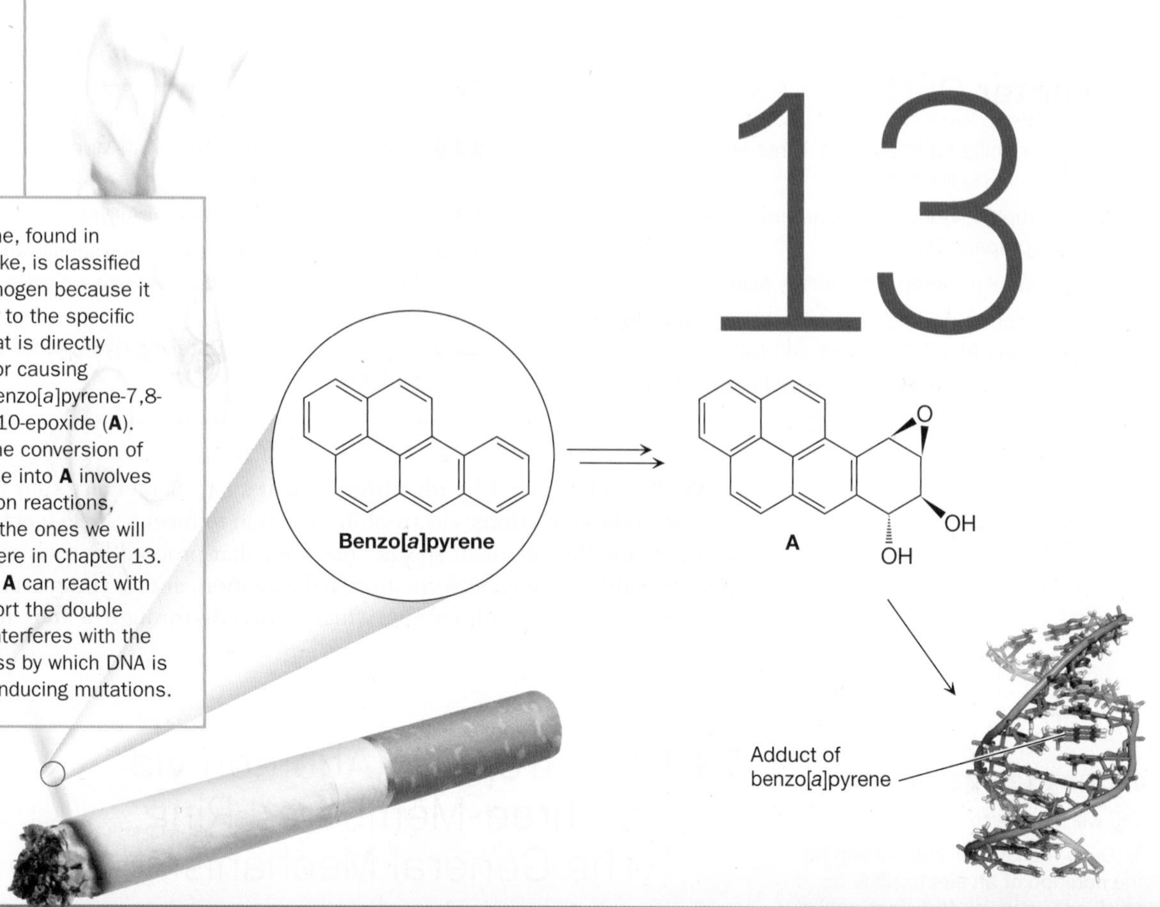

Benzo[a]pyrene
O
OH
A
OH
Adduct of benzo[a]pyrene

13

Electrophilic Addition to Nonpolar π Bonds 2

Reactions Involving Cyclic Transition States

Chapter 12 discussed reactions in which a Brønsted acid adds across a C═C double bond of an alkene or a C≡C triple bond of an alkyne. In those reactions, the π bond of the alkene or alkyne is relatively electron-rich, whereas the proton (H^+) from the Brønsted acid is electron-poor. Consequently, the proton acts as an electrophile and is picked up by the alkene or alkyne to produce a carbocation intermediate, which has the potential to rearrange. Then, that carbocation intermediate is attacked by a nucleophile.

Here in Chapter 13, we will see that species other than protons can act as electrophiles and thus can add to an alkene or alkyne as well. Examples include molecular halogens like Cl_2 and Br_2, peroxy acids (RCO_3H), carbenes (R_2C:), and borane (BH_3). Unlike the electrophilic addition of a Brønsted acid, all of these reaction mechanisms involve a step whose transition state is cyclic. Proceeding through a cyclic transition state avoids the formation of a carbocation intermediate and therefore significantly affects the outcomes of the reactions, both regiochemically and stereochemically.

Chapter Outline

We begin Chapter 13 with a brief look at a key elementary step that is involved in some of these reactions: electrophilic addition to form a three-membered ring. We then examine the details of specific reactions that proceed by such a step, including carbene addition, epoxide formation, halogenation, and oxymercuration. Following that, we examine hydroboration, which proceeds through a four-membered-ring transition state.

SECTION 13.1 OBJECTIVES

You will be able to:

1. Draw the general mechanism for the addition of an electrophile to an alkene, in which the electrophilic atom has a lone pair of electrons.
2. Account for the stereochemistry in electrophilic addition to an alkene, in which the electrophilic atom has a lone pair of electrons.

13.1 Electrophilic Addition via a Three-Membered Ring: The General Mechanism

The mechanisms of all the electrophilic addition reactions we saw in Chapter 12 include a step in which a carbocation is produced. Recall that this step is generally highly unfavorable, due in large part to the loss of an octet on a C atom, as indicated in Equation 13-1:

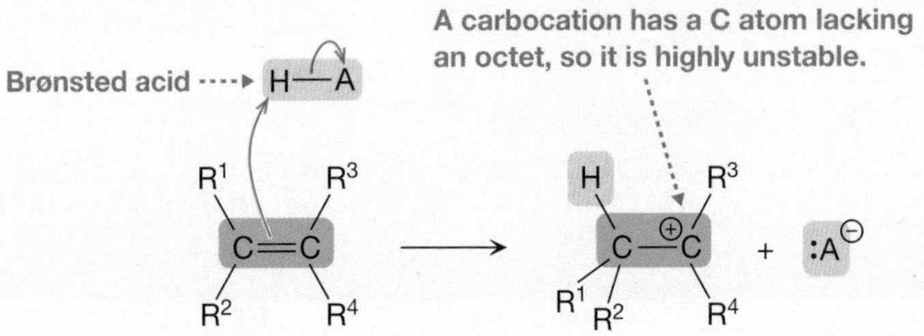

A carbocation has a C atom lacking an octet, so it is highly unstable.
Brønsted acid
H—A
R1
R3
C=C
R2
R4
H
R3
C—C
R1
R2
R4
+ :A

(13-1)

However, if the electrophilic atom on the electrophile has a lone pair of electrons, then addition can take place in a way that avoids losing an octet. This is illustrated in Equation 13-2, in which E: represents a generic electrophile that possesses a lone pair of electrons:

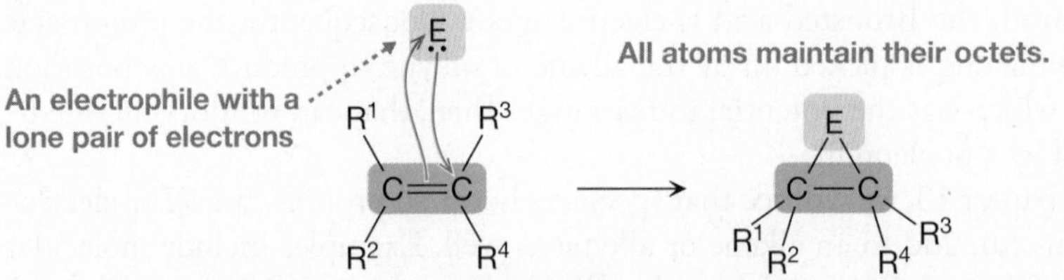

All atoms maintain their octets.
An electrophile with a lone pair of electrons
E
R1
R3
C=C
R2
R4
E
C—C
R1
R2
R3
R4

(13-2)

In this step, two new E—C σ bonds are formed simultaneously to produce a three-membered ring. One of those bonds is formed by the electrons from the initial carbon–carbon π bond, and the other is formed by the lone pair of electrons from the electrophile.

In the cyclic structure in Equation 13-2, how many bonds does each highlighted C atom have? How many bonds does each highlighted C atom have in the carbocation in Equation 13-1? How do those numbers compare to the number of bonds each C atom has in the initial alkene?

Answers to Your Turns are in the back of the book.

YOUR TURN **13.1**

Notice in Equation 13-2 that as the alkene reacts, two C atoms rehybridize from sp^2 to sp^3, so *stereochemistry* can be an issue. In such cases, stereochemistry is governed by the following rules:

Stereochemistry for the Addition of E: to a C═C Double Bond

- The cis/trans relationship in the alkene is conserved for the groups attached to the C═C bond. Groups that are on the same side of the double bond in the reactant must end up on the same side of the plane of the three-membered ring in the product.
- If the cyclic product is chiral, then a mixture of stereoisomers is produced. A racemic mixture of enantiomers is produced if the original alkene and other reagents are achiral; otherwise, an unequal mixture of stereoisomers is produced (see Recall box).

◂ RECALL

The appearance of new chiral centers can lead to the production of a meso compound (see Your Turn 13.2). Recall from Section 5.5a that a compound is meso if it has at least two chiral centers and also has a plane of symmetry, which makes the compound achiral.

These rules are exemplified by Equation 13-3:

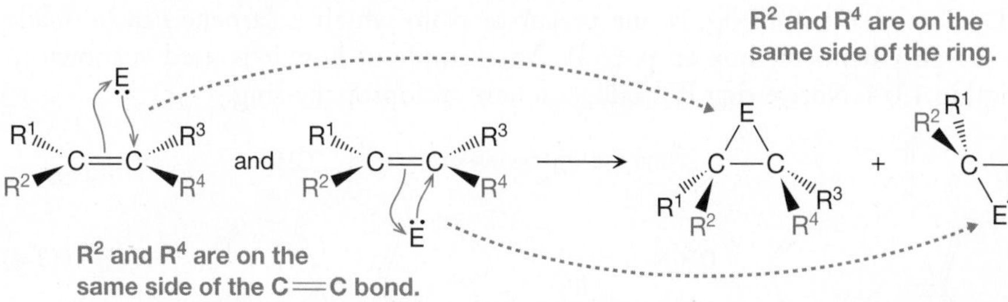

R² and R⁴ are on the same side of the ring.
and
R² and R⁴ are on the same side of the C═C bond.

(13-3)

Stereochemistry is conserved in reactions that proceed by the mechanism in Equation 13-3 because both C—E bonds are formed to the same face of the alkene *simultaneously* to form the ring. Once the ring is formed, the substituents attached to the ring are locked in place. Moreover, stereoisomers are produced because, as shown in Equation 13-3, the electrophile can approach either face of the alkene.

YOUR TURN **13.2**

Match each curved arrow notation, **A** or **B**, with the appropriate set of products, **X** or **Y**. Will the set of products **Y** be produced as a racemic mixture?

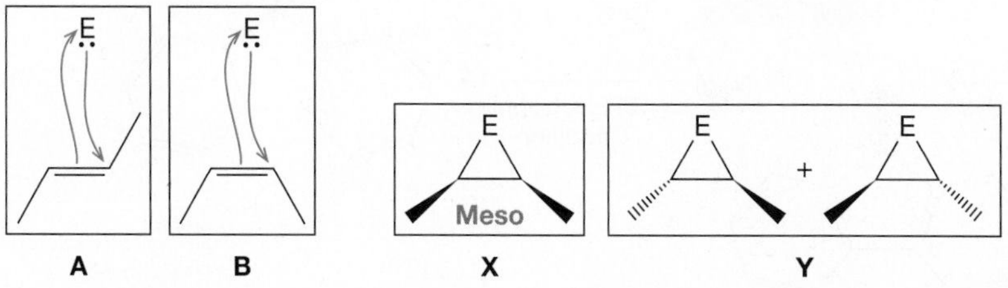

Meso
A
B
X
Y

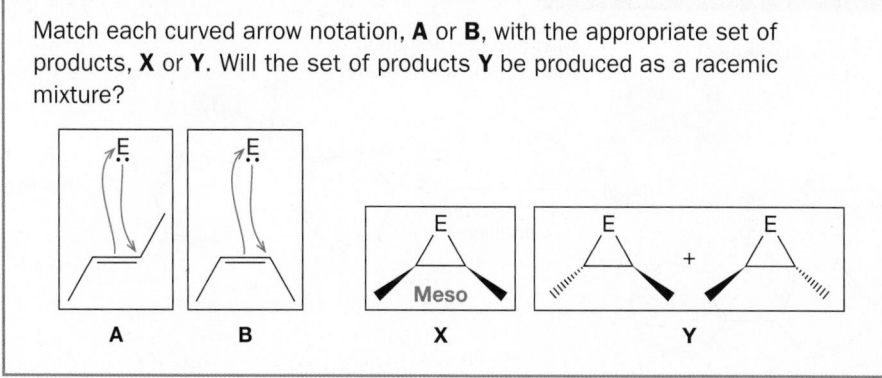

Having examined this elementary step in a generic fashion, let's now turn our attention toward four specific types of reaction whose mechanisms include that step.

SECTION 13.2 OBJECTIVES

You will be able to:

1. Draw the mechanism for the cyclopropanation of an alkene with diazomethane.
2. Predict the product of such a reaction, including stereochemistry.

13.2 Electrophilic Addition of Carbenes: Formation of Cyclopropane Rings

Mechanistically, the simplest of the reactions we discuss here in Chapter 13 occurs between an alkene and a *carbene*. A **carbene** is a species containing a carbon atom that has two bonds and a lone pair of electrons,[1] as shown in **Figure 13-1**. Because it has three total electron groups, that C atom lacks an octet and is sp^2-hybridized; the lone pair of electrons occupies a hybrid orbital, leaving the p orbital empty. Thus, these carbenes resemble carbocations and are generally *highly* electron-poor. Unlike a carbocation, however, the electron-poor C atom of a carbene has a formal charge of 0.

YOUR TURN 13.3

Using the method we learned in Chapter 1, count the number of valence electrons assigned to the carbene C in Figure 13-1. How does that number compare to carbon's group number? From those two numbers, what is the calculated formal charge on the carbene C?

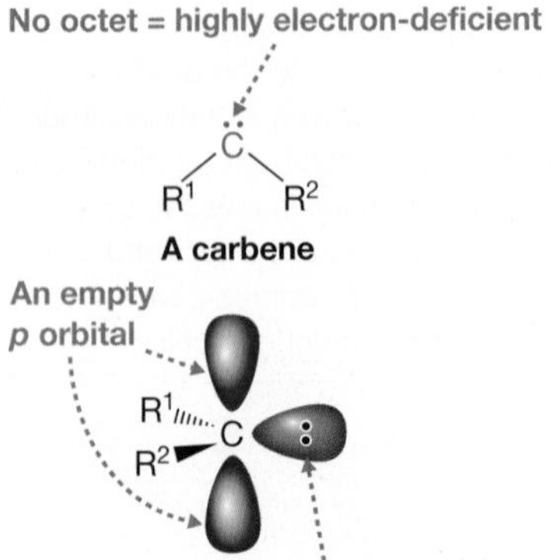

No octet = highly electron-deficient
C
R1
R2
A carbene
An empty
p orbital
R1
C
R2
The lone pair occupies
an sp2 hybrid orbital.

FIGURE 13-1 A generic carbene (*Top*) A carbene is characterized by a C atom with two bonds and a lone pair of electrons. Even though the C atom is uncharged, carbenes are typically highly electrophilic due to the lack of an octet. (*Bottom*) Carbenes are sp^2-hybridized. The lone pair occupies an sp^2 hybrid orbital, whereas the p orbital is empty.

Most carbenes are highly reactive, so they typically have very short lifetimes and cannot be isolated. In these cases, *we cannot simply add a carbene as a reagent*. Instead:

Highly reactive carbenes must be generated in situ (i.e., "on site") from precursors that can be added as reagents.

Diazomethane, CH_2N_2, is one precursor from which a carbene can be made (see Green Chemistry box on p. 652). An example of how it is used is shown in Equation 13-4. Notice that it produces a new cyclopropane ring:

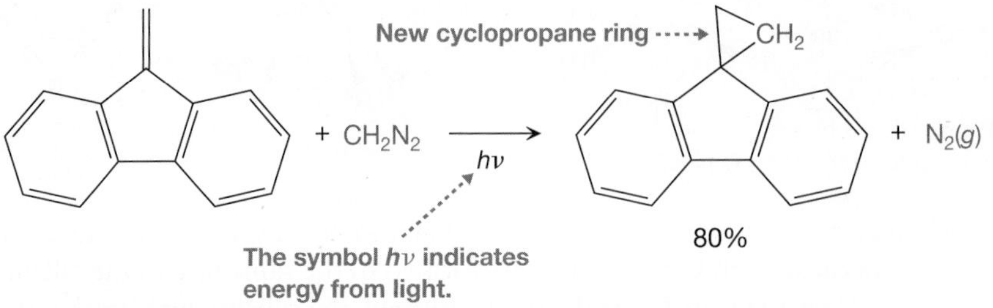

New cyclopropane ring
CH2
+ CH2N2
hν
+ N2(g)
80%
The symbol hν indicates
energy from light.

(13-4)

The complete mechanism for this reaction is shown in Equation 13-5:

Mechanism for the cyclopropanation of an alkene (Eq. 13-4)

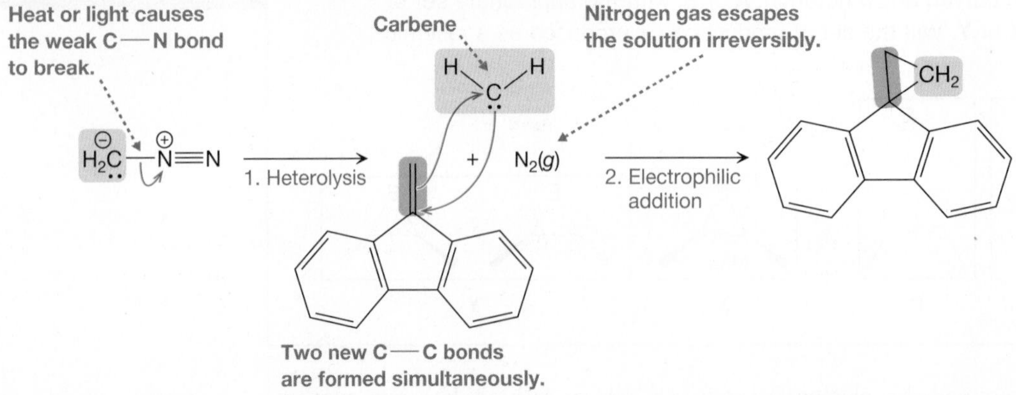

Heat or light causes
the weak C—N bond
to break.
H2C—N≡N
1. Heterolysis
Carbene
H
H
C
+
N2(g)
Nitrogen gas escapes
the solution irreversibly.
2. Electrophilic
addition
CH2
Two new C—C bonds
are formed simultaneously.

(13-5)

[1] These are called *singlet carbenes* when the nonbonding electrons occupy the same orbital. In a *triplet carbene*, one nonbonding electron is in each of two separate orbitals. In this book, we discuss only singlet carbenes.

In Step 1, the C—N bond in diazomethane is broken when sufficient energy is absorbed, and H_2C: is produced. The energy required for that step could come from a photon of light (as indicated in Equation 13-4 by the notation $h\nu$),[2] or it could come from added heat by warming the reaction mixture. Even though H_2C: is highly unstable, Step 1 is helped by the production of $N_2(g)$, an excellent leaving group that escapes the reaction mixture *irreversibly* (see top Recall box). In Step 2, H_2C: reacts with the alkene to generate the three-membered ring by the same mechanism as in Equation 13-2.

◂ RECALL

Section 10.9 showed how CH_2N_2 is used to convert a carboxylic acid into a methyl ester, relying on the excellent leaving group ability of $N_2(g)$.

YOUR TURN **13.4**

Draw the complete, detailed mechanism for the reaction shown here and predict the major products.

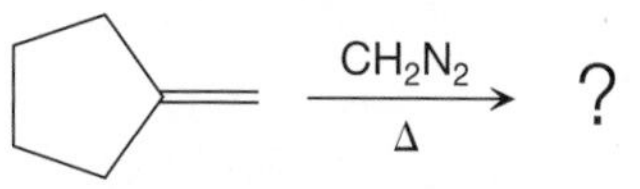

CH2N2
Δ
?

13.3 Epoxide Formation with Peroxy Acids

SECTION 13.3 OBJECTIVES

You will be able to:

1. Draw the mechanism for the formation of an epoxide from the reaction of an alkene with a peroxy acid.
2. Predict the major product for epoxide formation reactions with peroxy acids, including stereochemistry.

Sections 10.7 and 11.2 showed how useful epoxides can be in carrying out certain functional group transformations and reactions that form a new C—C bond. One method of synthesizing epoxides is to react an alkene with a **peroxy acid** (RCO_3H), also called a *peracid*. Examples of such **epoxidation reactions** are shown in Equations 13-6 and 13-7, where ***m*-chloroperbenzoic acid (MCPBA)** is the peroxy acid:

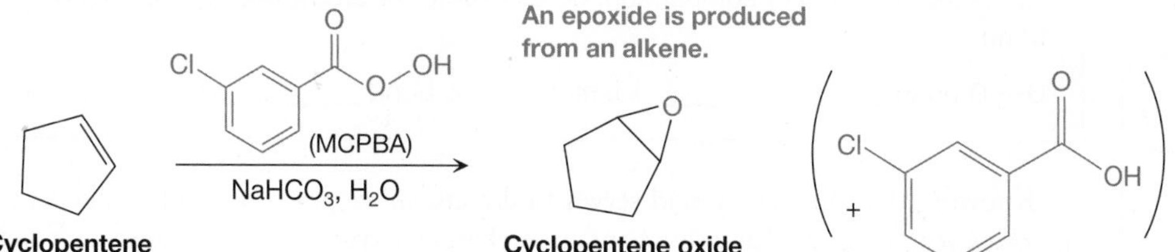

An epoxide is produced from an alkene.
Cl
O
OH
(MCPBA)
NaHCO3, H2O
O
Cl
O
OH
+
Cyclopentene
Cyclopentene oxide
90%

(13-6)

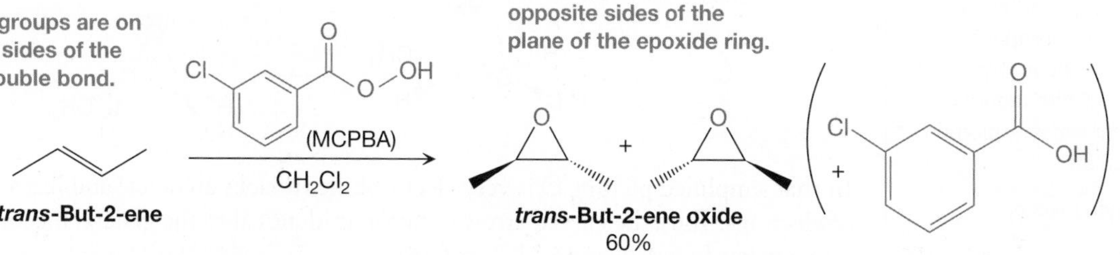

The CH3 groups are on opposite sides of the C=C double bond.
The CH3 groups are on opposite sides of the plane of the epoxide ring.
Cl
O
OH
(MCPBA)
CH2Cl2
O
+
O
Cl
O
OH
+
trans-But-2-ene
trans-But-2-ene oxide
60%

(13-7)

Synthesizing epoxides in this way is advantageous because the reaction conditions are relatively mild and many alkenes are common or easily synthesized, but other methods are also possible (see bottom Recall box).

◂ RECALL

Section 10.8 showed how an epoxide can be produced from an intramolecular S_N2 reaction, such as the example shown here.

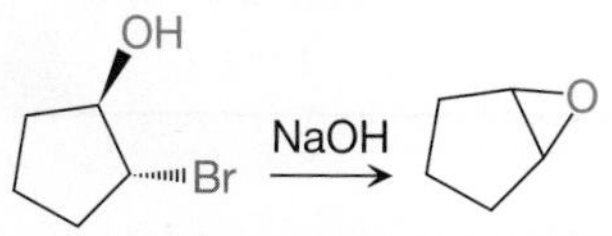

OH
Br
NaOH
O

[2]In the notation $h\nu$, h is Planck's constant and ν (Greek letter nu) is the photon frequency, and the product of these values is the photon's energy.

The mechanism for these epoxidation reactions is shown in Equation 13-8. Notice that it takes place in a single step; that is, the reaction is *concerted*:

Mechanism for the epoxidation of an alkene (Eq. 13-7)

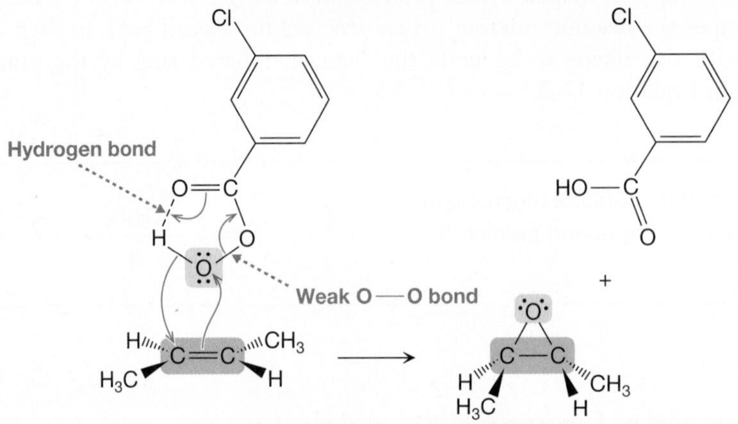

Cl
Hydrogen bond
O
C
H
O
O
Weak O—O bond
H
C=C
CH$_3$
H$_3$C
H
Cl
HO—C
O
+
O
C—C
H
CH$_3$
H$_3$C
H

(13-8)

Mechanism Drawing
Epoxidation of an Alkene Using a Peroxyacid

The O atom of the OH group is the one transferred to the alkene because both of its original covalent bonds are relatively weak. The O—O single bond is inherently very weak. An O—H bond is normally quite strong, but in this case the O's bond to H is weakened by the internal hydrogen bond involving the OH and the carbonyl O atom.

YOUR TURN **13.5**

Verify that the O—O single bond is weak by looking up its average value (Table 1-2, p. 10). For comparison, do the same for an average C—C single bond.

O—O bond ______________ kJ/mol C—C bond ______________ kJ/mol

GREEN CHEMISTRY
Although the formation of carbene from diazomethane (Eq. 13-4) can lead to a good yield of the cyclopropane-containing product, the reaction is of rather limited use in synthesis because diazomethane is explosive and requires extreme caution in the laboratory. A safer way to produce a cyclopropane ring from an alkene is with the Simmons–Smith reaction, whose mechanism is explored in Problem 13.39.

Simmons–Smith reaction

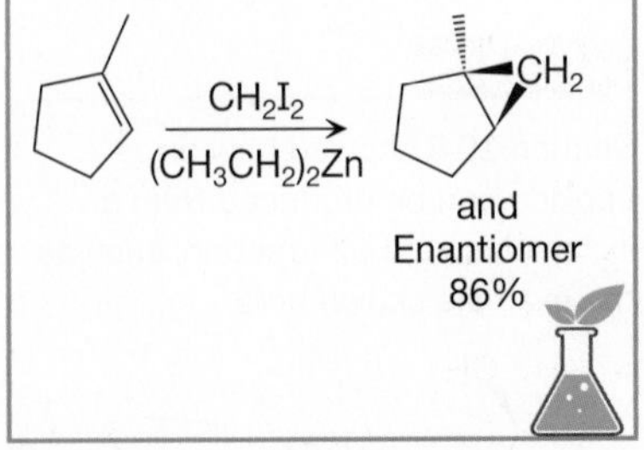

CH_2I_2
$(CH_3CH_2)_2Zn$
CH$_2$
and
Enantiomer
86%

Knowing that the peroxy acid serves to donate an oxygen atom to the alkene, we can *think of* a peroxy acid as a source of an uncharged oxygen atom, as shown in Equation 13-9:

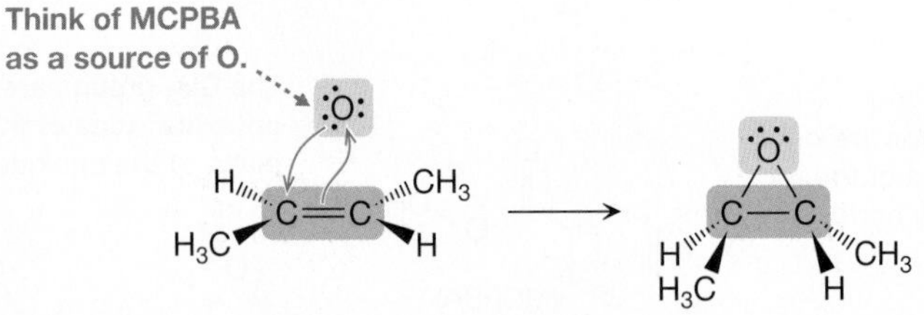

Think of MCPBA
as a source of O.
O
H
C=C
CH$_3$
H$_3$C
H
O
C—C
H
CH$_3$
H$_3$C
H

(13-9)

In that simplified picture, O is very electrophilic (it lacks an octet) and has a lone pair of electrons. Thus, the curved arrow notation is identical to the general mechanism we saw previously in Equation 13-2 (p. 648).

Because epoxidation takes place in a single step, the stereochemical requirements presented in Section 13.1 apply. As shown previously in Equation 13-7, for example, stereochemistry is conserved, so the trans relationship of the CH_3 groups about the C=C double bond in the reactants establishes a trans relationship about the plane of the epoxide ring in the products. Furthermore, because the products are chiral, a mixture of stereoisomers is produced.

Draw the complete, detailed mechanism for the reaction shown here and predict the major product(s), paying particular attention to the stereochemistry.

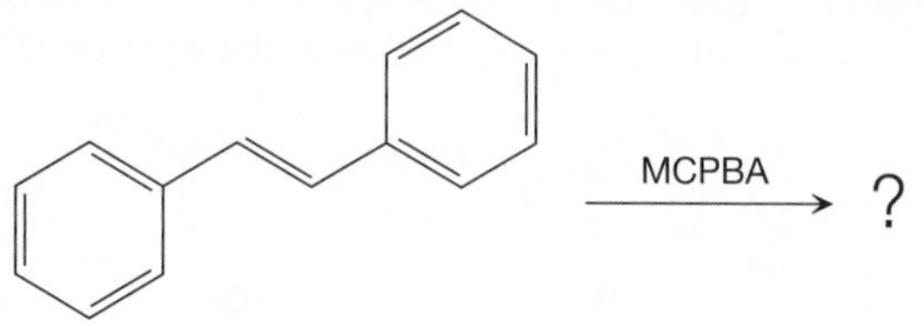

MCPBA
?

YOUR TURN **13.6**

Because an epoxide readily undergoes ring opening (Section 10.7), the product of an epoxidation reaction is often used as a synthetic intermediate, as exemplified in Solved Problem 13.1.

SOLVED PROBLEM **13.1**

How to incorporate an epoxidation reaction in a synthesis

Break It Down **Identify the missing compounds A–C.**

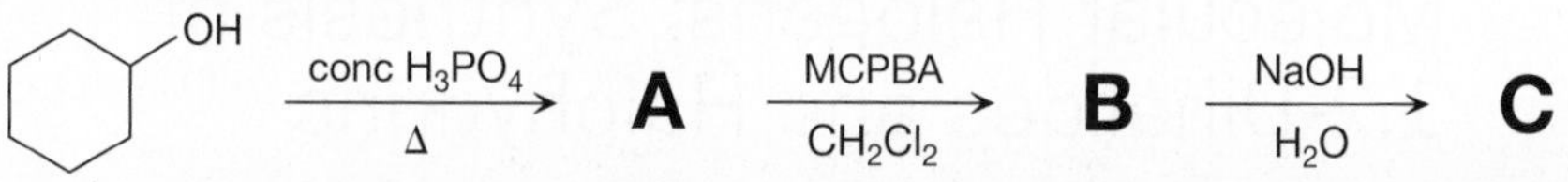

OH
conc H_3PO_4
Δ
A
MCPBA
CH_2Cl_2
B
NaOH
H_2O
C

Think	Solve
In the first reaction, what happens to the OH group in the presence of a strong acid? How does that change the nature of the OH group? What types of reactions are made possible, and how do we consider various factors to determine the winning reaction?	The strong acid will protonate the OH group to make it OH_2^+, an excellent leaving group. Thus, the protonated alcohol can act as a substrate in an $S_N2/S_N1/E2/E1$ competition. The winning reaction is E1 because the attacking species is weak, the leaving group is excellent, the solvent is protic, and heat favors elimination over substitution (review Section 9.9). This is an acid-catalyzed dehydration to form an alkene, **A**. 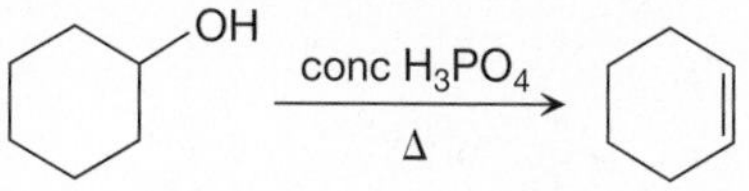 **A**
For the second reaction, what type of functional group does **A** contain? How will it react with a peroxy acid?	Compound **A** is an alkene. As discussed in this section, MCPBA (a peroxy acid) will react with the alkene to produce an epoxide, **B**. 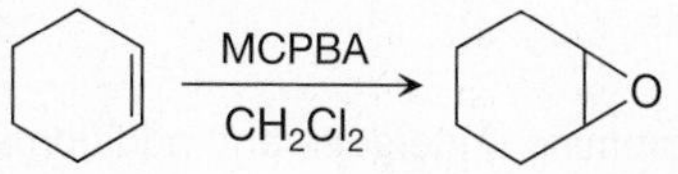 **A** **B**

OH
conc H_3PO_4
Δ
MCPBA
CH_2Cl_2
O

(continued)

GREEN CHEMISTRY

Peroxy acids such as MCBPA are convenient reagents to produce an epoxide from an alkene. One problem, however, is that these reactions suffer from a low percent atom economy. As we can see in Equations 13-6 and 13-7, a fairly massive carboxylic acid by-product tends to go to waste. A variety of much more efficient epoxidation reactions that use catalysts have been developed. One such reaction uses polyoxometalate-supported gold nanoparticles (Au/BaPOM) as catalysts and uses molecular oxygen as the reactant.

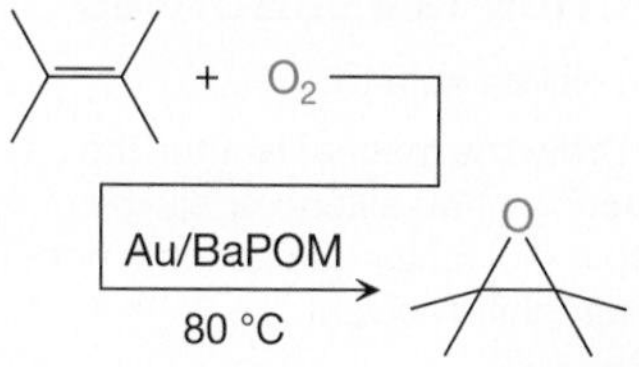

+ O_2
Au/BaPOM
80 °C
O

CONNECTIONS 13.1

Making their mark with cyclohexane-1,2-diol
Cyclohexane-1,2-diol (compound **C** in Solved Problem 13.1) is found in castoreum, an excretion by North American beavers that is used to mark their territories by scent.

In the third reaction, what acts as the nucleophile? What acts as the substrate?

In the third reaction, HO^- acts as the nucleophile to open the epoxide in an S_N2 reaction and produce the *trans*-1,2-diol, **C**. The trans stereochemistry is governed by the attack of the nucleophile from the side of the ring opposite the epoxide O.

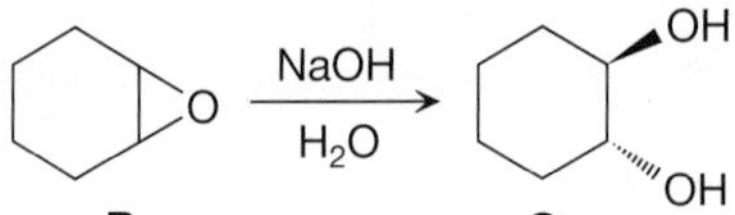

O
NaOH
H_2O
OH
OH

B **C** and Enantiomer

Try It Identify the missing compounds **D–F**.

Br
$NaOCH_3$
Δ
D
MCPBA
E
1. CH_3MgBr
2. H_3O^+
F

Answers to all Try It exercises can be found in the Solutions Manual.

SECTION 13.4 OBJECTIVES

You will be able to

1. Draw the mechanism for the reaction of an alkene or alkyne with a molecular halogen in a non-nucleophilic solvent.
2. Draw the mechanism for the reaction of a molecular halogen with an alkene in a nucleophilic solvent.
3. Predict the major products when a molecular halogen adds to an alkene or alkyne, including regiochemistry and stereochemistry.

13.4 Electrophilic Addition Involving Molecular Halogens: Synthesis of 1,2-Dihalides and Halohydrins

Like carbenes and peroxy acids, molecular halogens such as Cl_2 and Br_2 can react with an alkene to produce a three-membered ring. Unlike what we observe with carbenes and peroxy acids, however, the three-membered ring produced from a molecular halogen is an unstable intermediate and reacts further. In Section 13.4a, we will see how this intermediate leads to the formation of a *1,2-dihalide* (i.e., a *vicinal dihalide*), and in Section 13.4b, we will see how it leads to the formation of a *halohydrin*.

13.4a Synthesis of 1,2-Dihalides

When cyclohexene is treated with molecular bromine (Br_2) in tetrachloromethane (CCl_4), also called carbon tetrachloride, a racemic mixture of *trans*-1,2-dibromocyclohexane is produced, as shown in Equation 13-10:

Anti addition of Br_2

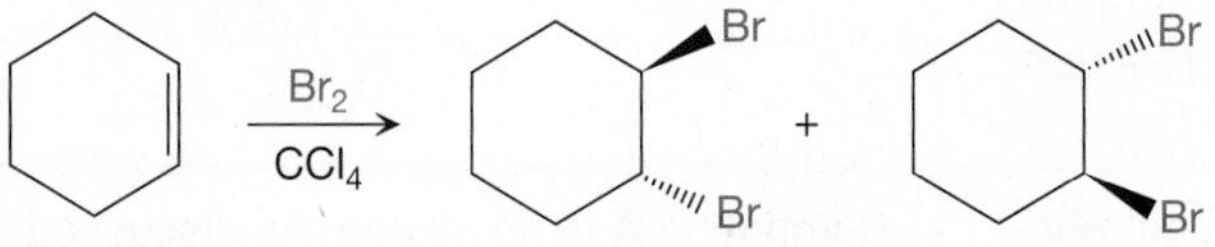

Br_2
CCl_4
Br
Br
+
Br
Br

Cyclohexene ***trans*-1,2-Dibromocyclohexane** 59% **(13-10)**

GREEN CHEMISTRY CCl_4 is the solvent for the reaction in Equation 13-10 because it is non-nucleophilic. A nucleophilic solvent such as water would lead to the production of a halohydrin instead (discussed in Section 13.4b). However, CCl_4 is toxic, causes ozone depletion in the stratosphere, and is a suspected carcinogen. One green alternative to this reaction uses a 5:1 ratio of NaBr:$NaBrO_3$ as the source of bromine, with acetic acid as the solvent. Acetic acid is significantly less toxic than CCl_4.

In other words:

Molecular bromine undergoes anti addition across a C═C double bond.

Although an isolated Br_2 molecule does not possess an electron-poor atom, the Br_2 molecule becomes *polarized* as the electron-rich π bond approaches. Thus, one of the Br atoms becomes electron-poor; that is, Br_2 becomes an electrophile (see top Recall box, p. 655), as illustrated in **Figure 13-2**.

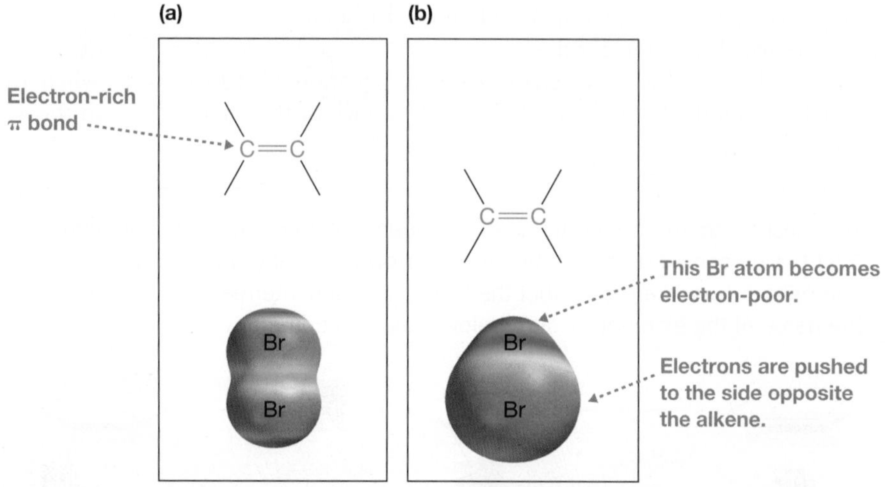

(a)
(b)
Electron-rich
π bond
C=C
C=C
Br
Br
Br
Br
This Br atom becomes
electron-poor.
Electrons are pushed
to the side opposite
the alkene.

FIGURE 13-2 The electrophilic nature of a molecular halogen in the presence of an alkene (a) When isolated from other species, Br_2 is not electron-poor. (b) As the electron-rich alkene approaches the Br_2 molecule, electrons on Br_2 are repelled to the side opposite the alkene, temporarily generating an electron-poor site on the Br atom closer to the alkene. Subsequent flow of electrons takes place between the electron-rich alkene and the electron-poor Br atom.

◂ RECALL

The electrophilic nature of Br_2 was discussed in the context of α-halogenation reactions of ketones and aldehydes (Section 10.6). In an α-halogenation reaction, an enol or an enolate anion is the nucleophile. In the addition of Br_2 to an alkene, the alkene is the nucleophile.

To account for the stereochemistry of the reaction in Equation 13-10, the mechanism must *not* proceed through a carbocation intermediate; otherwise, both syn and anti addition would take place (see bottom Recall box). Instead, as shown in Equation 13-11, the mechanism proceeds through a **bromonium ion intermediate** (possessing a positively charged bromine atom), which is produced in Step 1:

◂ RECALL

Chiral centers are produced in separate steps when an electrophilic addition to an alkene proceeds through a carbocation intermediate (Section 12.5). In that case, each step produces both *R* and *S* configurations, and if both C=C carbons become chiral centers, the product mixture will contain the (*R*,*R*), (*R*,*S*), (*S*,*R*), and (*S*,*S*) stereoisomers.

Mechanism for the bromination of an alkene: Formation of one of two possible enantiomers (Eq. 13-10)

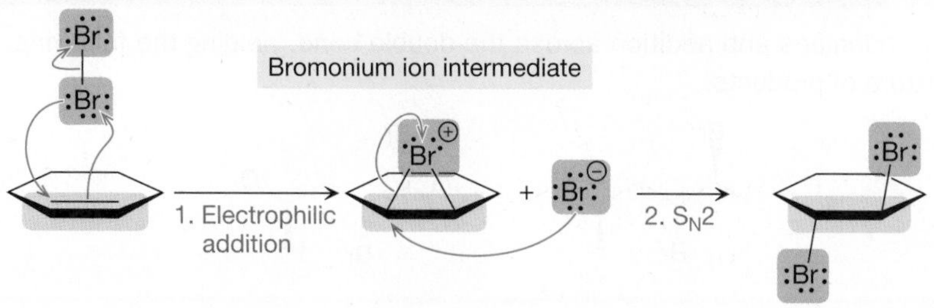

:Br:
:Br:
Bromonium ion intermediate
Br
+
:Br:
1. Electrophilic
addition
2. S_N2
:Br:
:Br:

(13-11)

The curved arrow from the π bond to Br represents the flow of electrons from an electron-rich site to an electron-poor site. Similar to the general reaction in Equation 13-2, a lone pair of electrons on Br forms a bond back to one of the alkene C atoms to avoid breaking the C atom's octet, resulting in a three-membered ring. In this case, the ring consists of two C atoms and one Br atom. Simultaneously, the weak Br—Br bond breaks, and one of the atoms leaves as Br^-.

Step 2 of the mechanism is an S_N2 step: The Br^- ion produced in Step 1 acts as the nucleophile, and the positively charged Br atom in the ring becomes the leaving group. This is exactly the same step we saw in the opening of a protonated epoxide ring in Section 10.7, where a positively charged oxygen atom behaves as the leaving group.

Notice in Equation 13-11 that the S_N2 step (Step 2) is precisely what requires the two Br atoms to be anti to each other in the product. As explained in Section 8.5a, the nucleophile in an S_N2 reaction must attack from the side *opposite the leaving group* (opposite the Br^+ in this case).

The mechanism in Equation 13-11 shows Br_2 approaching from the top face of the alkene, which accounts for the formation of one enantiomer when Br^- attacks the carbon on the left. The other enantiomer in Equation 13-10 can form when Br_2 approaches from the bottom face, followed by attack of the same carbon on the left (see Your Turn 13.7).

YOUR TURN 13.7

The mechanism for the formation of the enantiomer not shown in Equation 13-11 is presented here, but the curved arrows are not drawn. Draw the appropriate curved arrows, label the bromonium ion intermediate, and write the name of the elementary step below each reaction arrow.

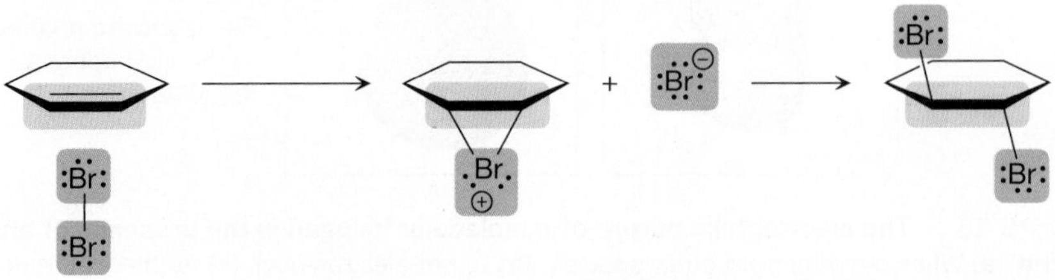

:Br:
:Br:
Br
+
:Br:
:Br:
:Br:

SOLVED PROBLEM 13.2

How to draw the mechanism and the products for the bromination of an alkene

Break It Down Predict the products of the reaction shown here. Do you expect the product mixture to be optically active? Why or why not?

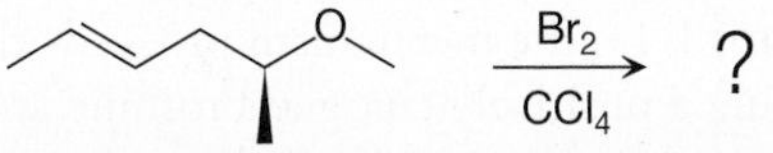

O
Br_2
CCl_4
?

Think	Solve
What reaction takes place between Br_2 and an alkene? How do you take stereochemistry into account?	Br_2 undergoes anti addition across the double bond, yielding the following mixture of products. 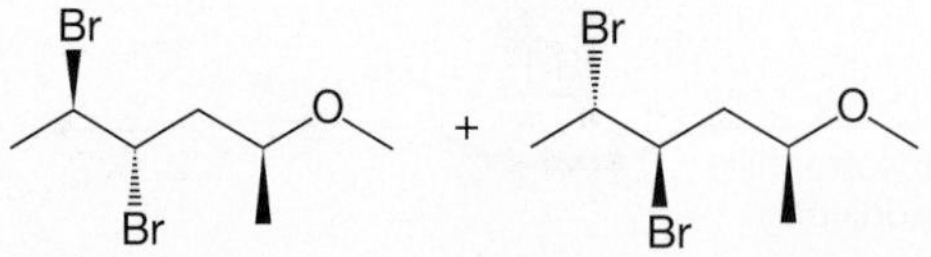
Are the product molecules chiral? Is each optically active?	Each of the product molecules is chiral. Therefore, each is optically active.
How are the product molecules related? How does that impact the optical activity of the product mixture?	The product molecules are diastereomers. Therefore, they are formed in unequal amounts, and they do not have equal and opposite values of $[\alpha]_D^{20}$. As a result, the product solution will be optically active.

Br
O
Br
+
Br
O
Br

Try It Draw the product(s) that would be produced from reacting each of the following compounds with molecular bromine in carbon tetrachloride. Will the product mixture be optically active?

(a) (b) (c) (d)

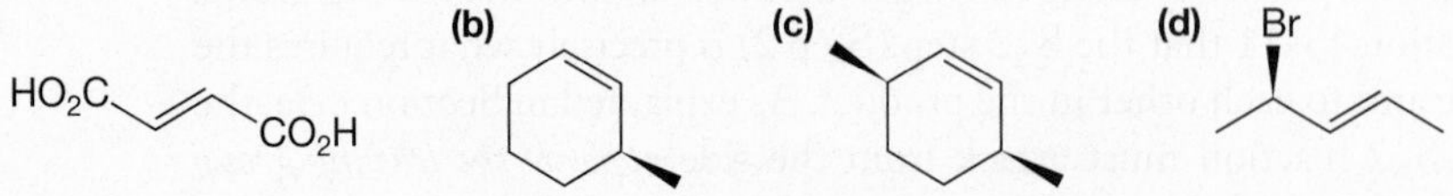

HO_2C
CO_2H
Br

Like Br_2, molecular chlorine (Cl_2) adds to alkenes to produce vicinal dichlorides. For simple alkenes, such as the one shown in Equation 13-12, Cl_2 adds anti to the double bond, just as we saw when Br_2 adds to an alkene. To explain this stereochemistry, the mechanism for chlorination must proceed through a **chloronium ion intermediate** (Your Turn 13.8) instead of a carbocation intermediate. (Some exceptions exist for the chlorination stereochemistry; see Problem 13.38 at the end of the chapter.)

Anti addition of Cl_2

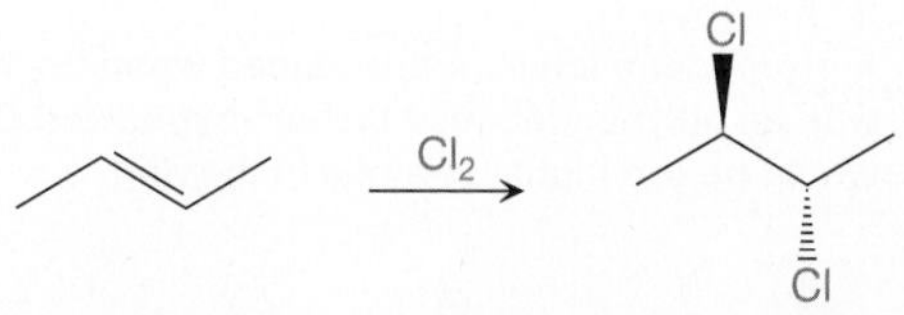

Cl
Cl_2
Cl

(13-12)

***trans*-But-2-ene** **(*meso*)-2,3-Dichlorobutane** 73%

YOUR TURN 13.8

The mechanism for the reaction in Equation 13-12 is shown below, but the curved arrows have been omitted. Complete the mechanism by adding the curved arrows and write the name of each elementary step under the appropriate reaction arrow. Label the chloronium ion intermediate.

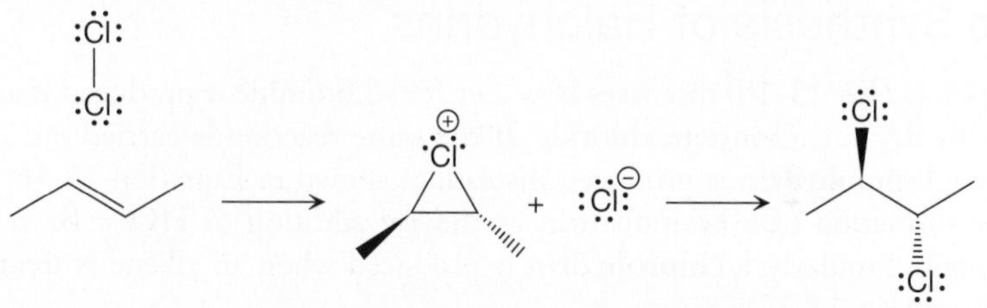

:Cl:
:Cl:
Cl
+
:Cl:
:Cl:
:Cl:

Molecular fluorine (F_2) and iodine (I_2) react with alkenes as well. These reactions are not as useful in organic synthesis, however, because F_2 reacts explosively with alkenes, whereas the reaction with I_2 is energetically unfavorable (see Looking Ahead box). Therefore, we will not discuss these reactions any further.

▸ LOOKING AHEAD

The relative reactivities for molecular halogens in the halogenation of alkenes is the same as that for radical halogenations of alkanes, discussed in Chapter 27. Namely, for radical halogenation, the order of reactivity is $F_2 > Cl_2 > Br_2 > I_2$; whereas F_2 reacts explosively, I_2 reacts very slowly.

Br_2 and Cl_2 add to alkynes in much the same way that they add to alkenes. For example, oct-1-yne reacts with *one equivalent* of Br_2 to yield 1,2-dibromooct-1-ene (Eq. 13-13) and with *excess* Br_2 to yield the tetrabromide (Eq. 13-14):

One equivalent of Br_2 adds both anti and syn to the C≡C bond.

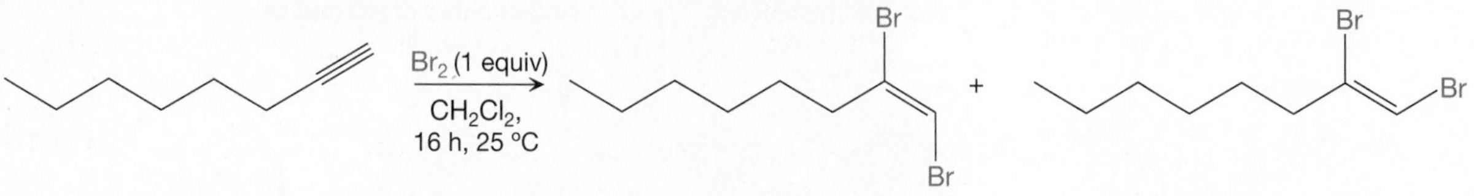

Br_2 (1 equiv)
CH_2Cl_2,
16 h, 25 °C
Br
Br
+
Br
Br

(13-13)

Oct-1-yne **(*E*)-1,2-Dibromooct-1-ene** 65% **(*Z*)-1,2-Dibromooct-1-ene** 19%

Two equivalents of Br_2 add to an alkyne.

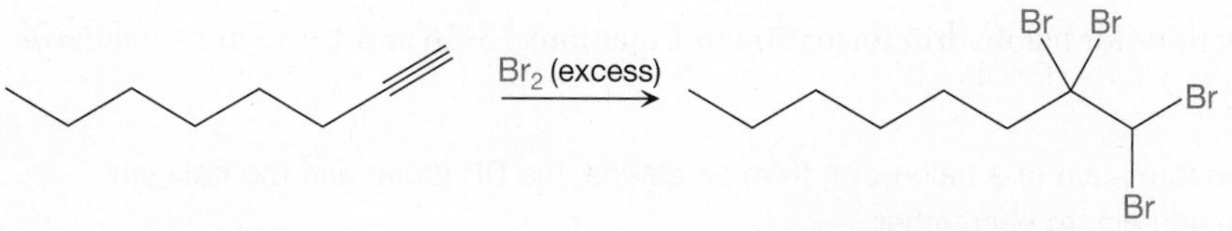

Br_2 (excess)
Br Br
Br
Br

(13-14)

Oct-1-yne **1,1,2,2-Tetrabromooctane**

Notice in Equation 13-13 that a mixture of both E and Z isomers is formed. In other words:

Br_2 adds to an alkyne by both syn and anti addition.

This means that the reaction proceeds through a carbocation-like intermediate instead of a bromonium ion intermediate; otherwise, only anti addition would take place to produce the E isomer exclusively. To understand why, consider the bromonium ion intermediate that would be formed from an alkyne:

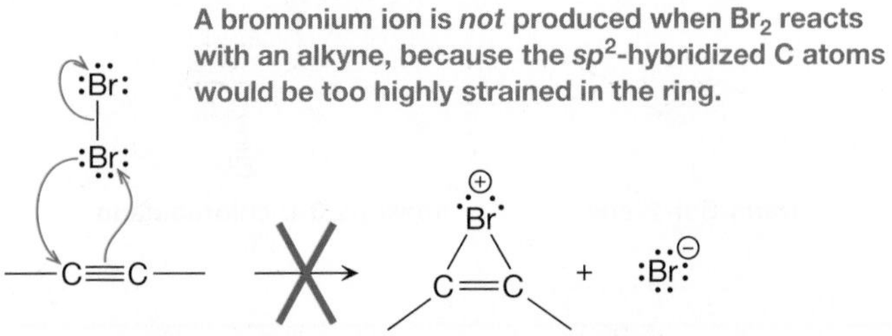

A bromonium ion is *not* produced when Br2 reacts with an alkyne, because the *sp*2-hybridized C atoms would be too highly strained in the ring.
:Br:
:Br:
C≡C
Br
C=C
+
:Br:

(13-15)

The resulting three-membered ring would consist of two sp^2-hybridized C atoms, whose ideal angles are 120°. Because the actual angles are near 60°, far from the ideal angles, that ring would be too highly strained.

13.4b Synthesis of Halohydrins

Section 13.4a (Eq. 13-10) discusses how a vicinal dibromide is produced if an alkene reacts with Br_2 in carbon tetrachloride. If the same reaction is carried out in water, however, a **bromohydrin** is produced instead, as shown in Equation 13-16. We can view the formation of a bromohydrin as the *net* addition of HO—Br across the double bond. Similarly, a **chlorohydrin** is produced when an alkene is treated with Cl_2 in water (Eq. 13-17):

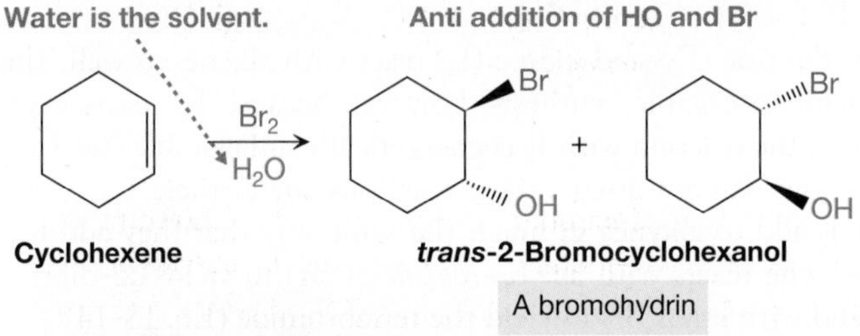

Water is the solvent.
Anti addition of HO and Br
Br2
H2O
Br
OH
+
Br
OH
Cyclohexene
trans-2-Bromocyclohexanol
A bromohydrin

(13-16)

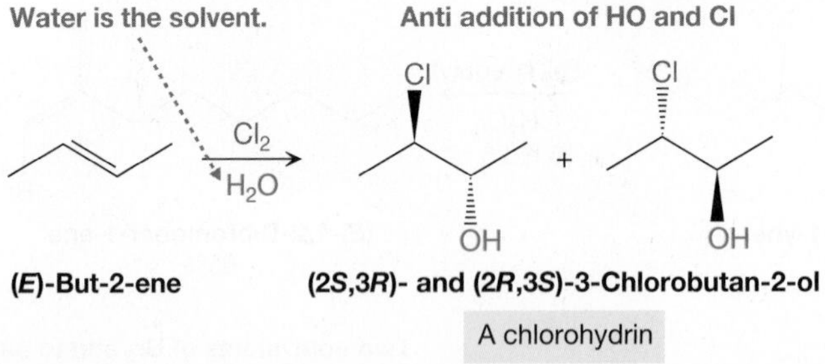

Water is the solvent.
Anti addition of HO and Cl
Cl2
H2O
Cl
OH
+
Cl
OH
(*E*)-But-2-ene
(2*S*,3*R*)- and (2*R*,3*S*)-3-Chlorobutan-2-ol
A chlorohydrin

(13-17)

The reactions for halohydrin formation in Equations 13-16 and 13-17 are *stereospecific*. Namely:

In the formation of a halohydrin from an alkene, the OH group and the halogen atom add anti to each other.

This stereochemistry is the same as in the addition of Br_2 or Cl_2 across a double bond (recall Eqs. 13-10 and 13-12), strongly suggesting that *halohydrin formation proceeds through a halonium ion intermediate*, as illustrated in the mechanism in Equation 13-18:

Mechanism for the formation of a halohydrin from an alkene (Eq. 13-16)

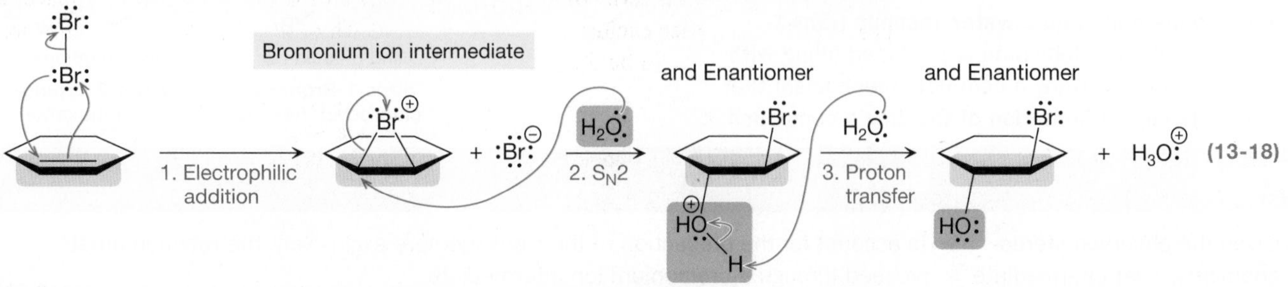
Bromonium ion intermediate
and Enantiomer
and Enantiomer
1. Electrophilic addition
2. SN2
3. Proton transfer
(13-18)

The first two steps are essentially the same as the ones in Equation 13-11, in which Br_2 adds to an alkene. Step 1 is an electrophilic addition that produces the bromonium ion intermediate, and Step 2 is an S_N2 step that opens the ring. In contrast to the mechanism in Equation 13-11, however, the ring-opening in Step 2 involves H_2O as the nucleophile instead of Br^-. Finally, in Step 3, a proton transfer produces the uncharged bromohydrin.

It might seem counterintuitive that H_2O acts as the nucleophile in Step 2, even though the much stronger nucleophile Br^- is present in solution. Water is the solvent, however, and is therefore quite abundant, whereas Br^- is produced in Step 1 of the mechanism and is therefore maintained at much lower concentrations. Consequently, the bromonium ion intermediate is much more likely to encounter a molecule of H_2O than Br^-.

With CCl_4 as the solvent instead, we saw that Br^- is the nucleophile that attacks the bromonium ion intermediate (Eq. 13-11). Even though CCl_4 is much more abundant than Br^-, CCl_4 is a non-nucleophilic solvent.

YOUR TURN 13.9

The mechanism for the reaction in Equation 13-17 is shown here, but the curved arrows have been omitted. Complete the mechanism by drawing in the curved arrows, and write the name of each elementary step below the appropriate reaction arrow.

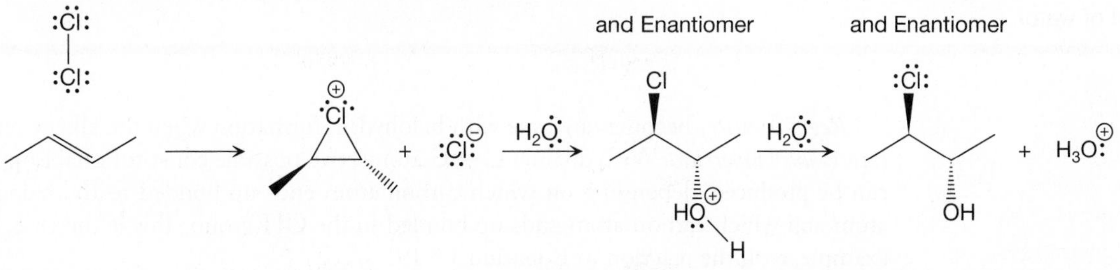
and Enantiomer
and Enantiomer

YOUR TURN 13.10

Draw the complete, detailed mechanism leading to the formation of the second enantiomer shown in Equation 13-16, which is not shown explicitly in Equation 13-18.

SOLVED PROBLEM **13.3**

How to predict the product of a reaction involving a bromonium ion

Break It Down **When the reaction in Equation 13-16 is carried out in an aqueous NaCl solution instead of pure water, racemic *trans*-1-bromo-2-chlorocyclohexane is produced along with the bromohydrin. Draw a complete mechanism that accounts for the formation of the dihalo compound.**

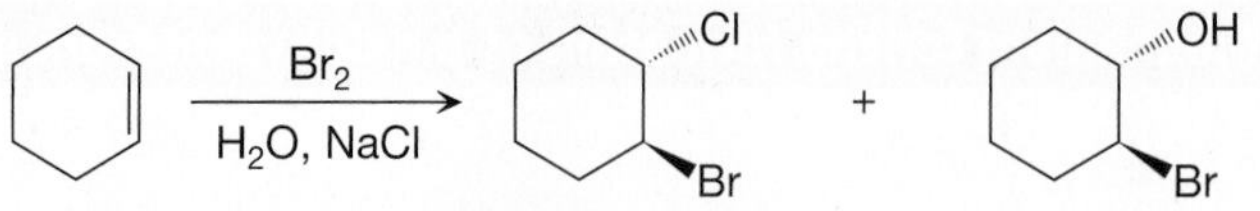

Br2
H2O, NaCl
Cl
Br
+
OH
Br

and Enantiomer — ***trans*-1-Bromo-2-chlorocyclohexane**

and Enantiomer — ***trans*-2-Bromo-cyclohexanol**

Think	Solve
Given the observed stereochemistry, what intermediate must be produced?	To account for the production of the trans isomers exclusively, the reaction must proceed through a bromonium ion intermediate.
In the formation of that intermediate, what species is electron-rich? What species is electron-poor?	In the formation of the bromonium ion, the alkene is relatively electron-rich and one of the bromine atoms from Br_2 is relatively electron-poor. A curved arrow is drawn from the C=C bond to the electrophilic Br, and a lone pair of electrons on that Br is used to form another bond to close the ring. 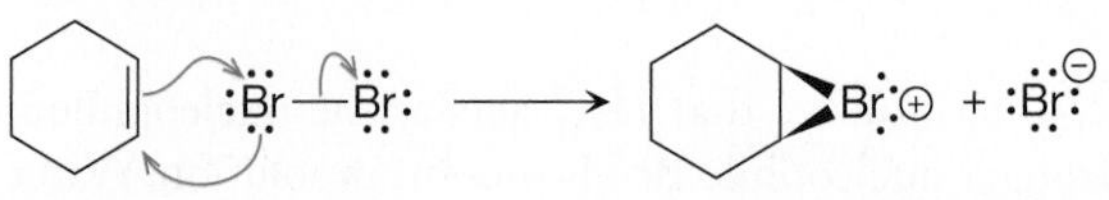
What acts as the nucleophile in the formation of the chlorine-containing product? How is the stereochemistry of the product established?	Cl^- must be the nucleophile that opens the bromonium ion intermediate to form the chlorine-containing product, as illustrated. Cl^- attacks the bromonium ion from opposite the Br leaving group, resulting in the trans relationship between the Cl and Br substituents in the product. 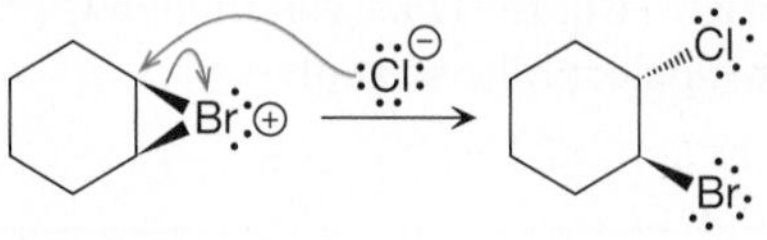 and Enantiomer

Try It Draw the complete, detailed mechanism of the reaction in Equation 13-16, assuming it was carried out in ethanol instead of water.

Regiochemistry becomes an issue with halohydrin formation when the alkene reactant is *unsymmetrical*. With distinct C=C atoms, two possible constitutional isomers can be produced, depending on which carbon atom ends up bonded to the halogen atom and which carbon atom ends up bonded to the OH group. This is the case, for example, with the reaction in Equation 13-19:

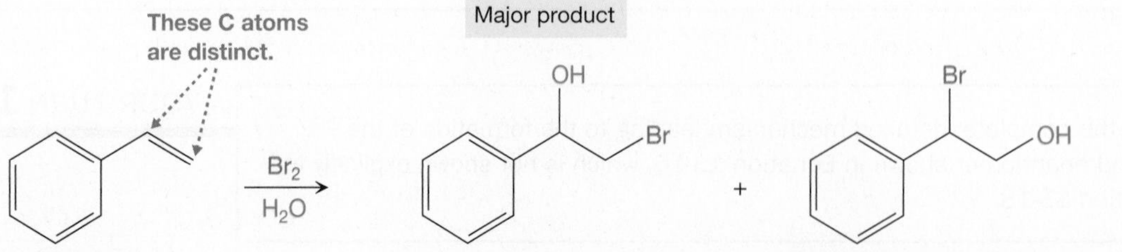

These C atoms are distinct.
Major product
OH
Br
Br2
H2O
+
Br
OH

Phenylethene — **2-Bromo-1-phenylethan-1-ol** 78% — **2-Bromo-2-phenylethan-1-ol** (13-19)

Why is the first of these products the major product? The answer can be understood by studying the mechanism, which is presented in Equation 13-20:

Mechanism for the formation of a bromohydrin, including regiochemistry (Eq. 13-19)

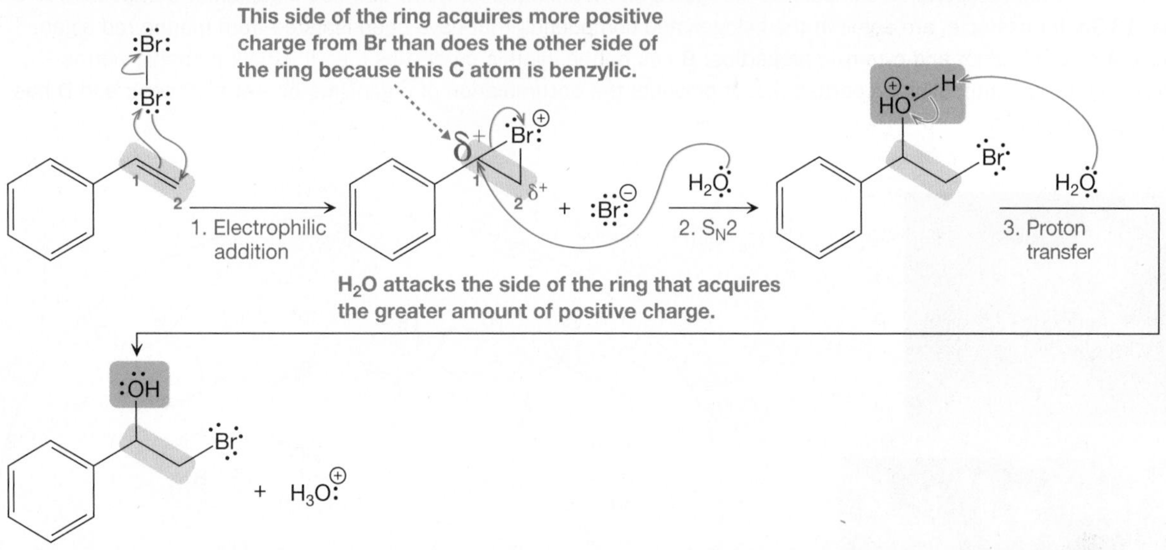
This side of the ring acquires more positive charge from Br than does the other side of the ring because this C atom is benzylic.
1. Electrophilic addition
2. S_N2
3. Proton transfer
H_2O attacks the side of the ring that acquires the greater amount of positive charge.

(13-20)

The specific isomer that is formed is dictated by Step 2 of the mechanism: namely, nucleophilic attack by water. Although attack can occur at either C atom of the three-membered ring, attack is favored at C-1 instead of C-2. The strained three-membered ring becomes more stable by sharing some of the positive charge from Br^+ onto C-1 and C-2, but C-1 picks up more of that positive charge; being benzylic and secondary, C-1 can accommodate a positive charge better than C-2 (see Recall box). Thus, the nucleophile is attracted more to C-1.

Mechanism Drawing
Addition of HOX to an Unsymmetric Alkene

YOUR TURN 13.11

Draw a complete, detailed mechanism for the reaction shown here and predict the major product, paying careful attention to both regiochemistry and stereochemistry.

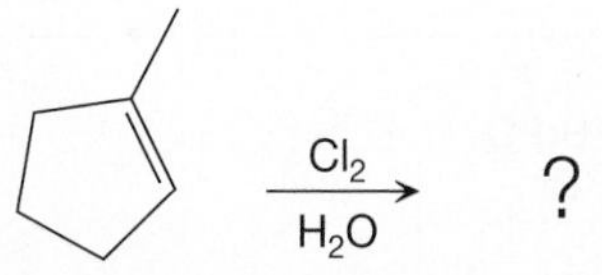
Cl_2
H_2O
?

◂ RECALL

In Section 10.7, we saw that a nucleophile attacks a protonated epoxide ring at the carbon atom that can better handle a positive charge, just as we see for a bromonium ion. Both a protonated epoxide and a bromonium ion have a three-membered ring consisting of two carbons and a positively charged heteroatom.

13.5 Oxymercuration–Reduction: Addition of Water

Recall from Chapter 12 that water can undergo acid-catalyzed addition to an alkene or alkyne, producing an alcohol or ketone, respectively. In the first step of the mechanism, H^+ adds to one of the alkene or alkyne carbons to produce the more stable carbocation intermediate (i.e., Markovnikov regiochemistry), and then H_2O attacks the carbocation in a coordination step. One drawback of these reactions, however, is that carbocation rearrangements are also possible. An example is shown in Equation 13-21:

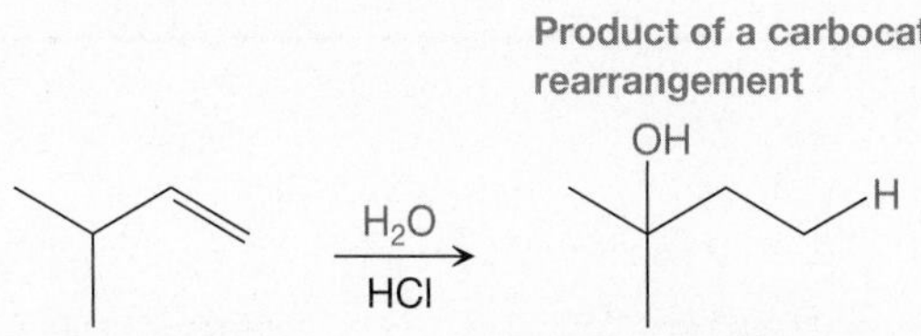
Product of a carbocation rearrangement
OH
H
H_2O
HCl

3-Methylbut-1-ene → 2-Methylbutan-2-ol (13-21)

SECTION 13.5 OBJECTIVES

You will be able to:

1. Draw the mechanism for the oxymercuration–reduction of an alkene or alkyne.
2. Predict the major product for the oxymercuration–reduction of an alkene or alkyne, including regiochemistry.

Halogenated Metabolites: True Sea Treasures

Natural products isolated from marine organisms have a wide range of potential applications in medicine and beyond. Of particular interest are halogenated compounds that serve as metabolites for many of these organisms. Compounds **A–D** in **Figure 13-3a**, for example, are some of the halogenated compounds that have been isolated from marine red algae. Compound **A** has antitumor and cytotoxic properties; **B** has antihelminthic properties (i.e., it expels parasitic worms from the body); **C** has antifouling properties (i.e., it prevents the accumulation of organisms on wet surfaces); and **D** has antimicrobial properties.

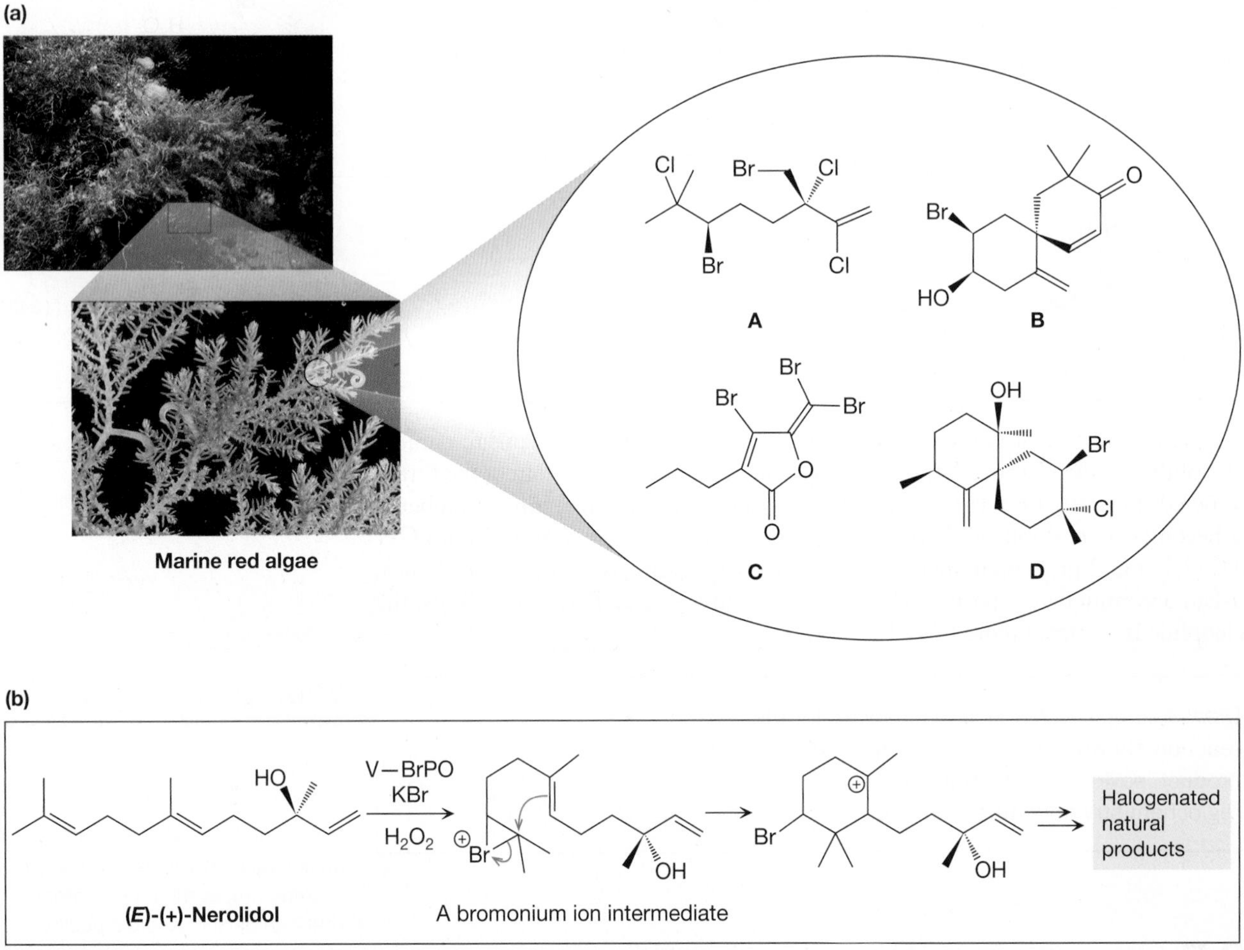

(a)
Marine red algae
Cl
Br
Cl
Br
Cl
A
Br
HO
O
B
Br
Br
Br
O
O
C
OH
Br
Cl
D
(b)
HO
V−BrPO
KBr
H_2O_2
Br
OH
Br
OH
Halogenated natural products
(E)-(+)-Nerolidol
A bromonium ion intermediate

FIGURE 13-3

J. N. Carter-Franklin and A. Butler, from the University of California, Santa Barbara, have shown that the biosynthesis of these halogenated metabolites probably involves a bromonium ion intermediate, much like we see in the bromination of alkenes here in Chapter 13. Production of the bromonium ion intermediate in these biosynthetic pathways, however, does not involve molecular Br_2. Rather, an alkene is believed to react with Br^+, which is produced from Br^- (an abundant ion in seawater) in the presence of hydrogen peroxide (H_2O_2), catalyzed by the enzyme vanadium bromoperoxidase (V-BrPO). Br^- undergoes a two-electron oxidation in the active site of the enzyme to make Br^+ (or its equivalent), which then adds to the C=C double bond. In many cases, the opening of the three-membered ring results in a new ring of carbons, as shown with (*E*)-(+)-nerolidol in Figure 13-3b.

Draw the mechanism that accounts for the formation of the product in Equation 13-21.

YOUR TURN **13.12**

Oxymercuration–reduction (also called **oxymercuration–demercuration**) offers another way to add water across a double bond, an example of which is shown in Equation 13-22. The alkene is first treated with mercury(II) acetate, $Hg(OAc)_2$, in a water–tetrahydrofuran (THF) solution, and that is followed by reduction with sodium borohydride:

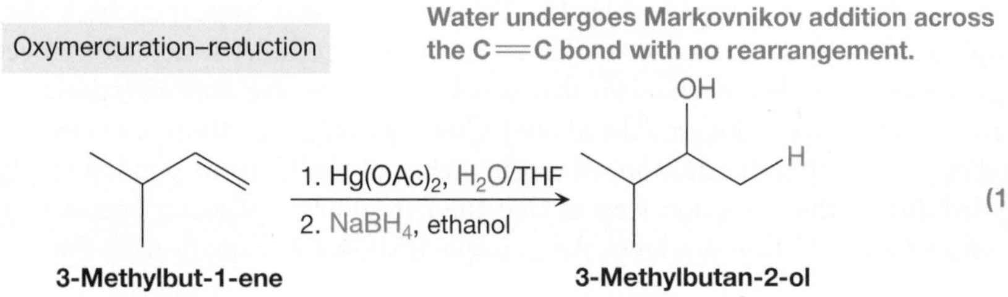

Oxymercuration–reduction
Water undergoes Markovnikov addition across the C═C bond with no rearrangement.
OH
H
1. Hg(OAc)2, H2O/THF
2. NaBH4, ethanol
3-Methylbut-1-ene
3-Methylbutan-2-ol

(13-22)

Two aspects of this reaction are noteworthy:

Key Aspects of Oxymercuration–Reduction Reactions

- The product is the one expected from the Markovnikov addition of H_2O. That is, the OH group forms a bond to the carbon atom that can better stabilize a positive charge.
- Rearrangement generally does *not* take place.

To better understand these outcomes, study the mechanism shown in Equation 13-23:

Mechanism Drawing Oxymercuration-reduction of an Alkene

Mechanism for the oxymercuration–reduction of an alkene (Eq. 13-22)

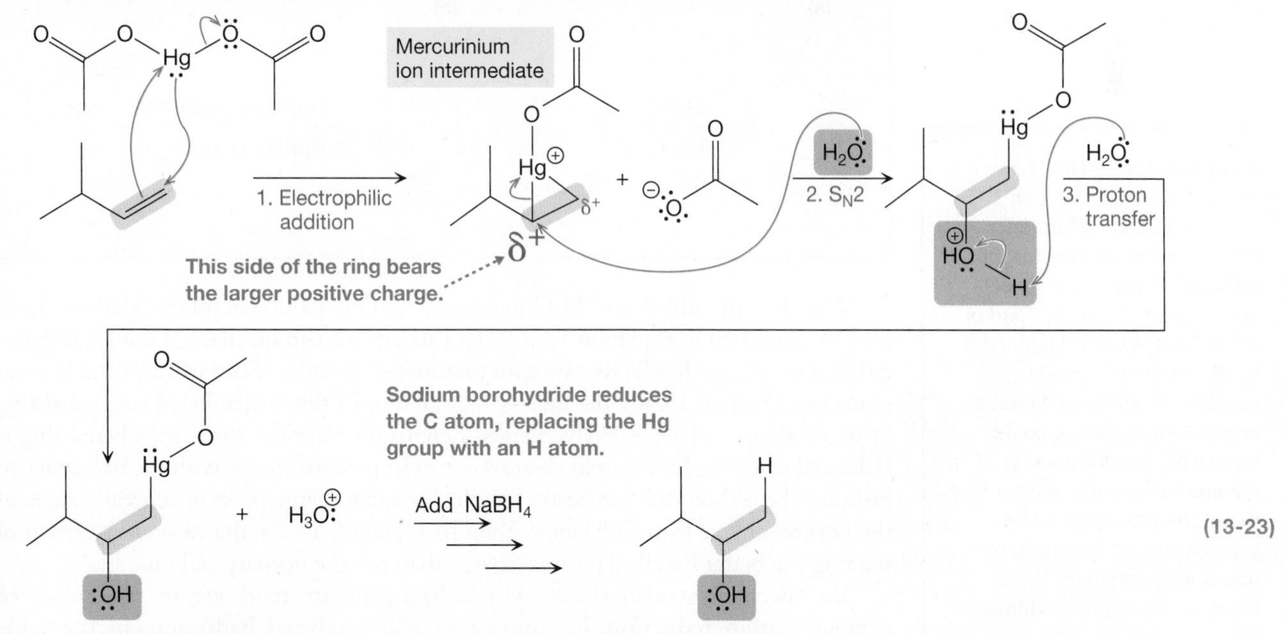

Mercurinium ion intermediate
1. Electrophilic addition
This side of the ring bears the larger positive charge.
2. SN2
3. Proton transfer
Sodium borohydride reduces the C atom, replacing the Hg group with an H atom.
Add NaBH4

(13-23)

The first three steps of the mechanism are identical to those in the formation of a halohydrin, shown previously in Equation 13-20. In Step 1, the Hg atom is electron-poor, given that it is bonded to two highly electronegative O atoms. It is therefore attacked by the electron-rich double bond, and simultaneously a lone pair of electrons on Hg forms a bond to C to produce the three-membered ring. The result is a **mercurinium ion intermediate**, which is analogous to the bromonium (or chloronium) ion intermediate we encountered previously. In Step 2 of the mechanism, H_2O acts as a nucleophile to open the three-membered ring, and in Step 3, the positively charged O atom is deprotonated.

Reduction occurs when sodium borohydride ($NaBH_4$) is added, in which the Hg-containing substituent is replaced by H. Although this may appear to be a simple nucleophilic substitution reaction with H^- as the nucleophile, it actually proceeds through a more complex mechanism that is believed to involve *radicals* (species with unpaired electrons; see Looking Ahead box). Consequently, even though oxymercuration takes place with anti addition, stereochemistry of the C atom bonded to Hg is scrambled during the reduction step so that the net addition of water occurs to give both syn and anti addition products. An example is shown in Equation 13-24:

▸ LOOKING AHEAD

The chemistry of radicals will be discussed in Chapter 27. Radicals have an unpaired electron, so they tend to be highly reactive intermediates. Furthermore, the mechanisms in which radicals participate tend to be quite different from mechanisms involving only species for which all electrons are paired.

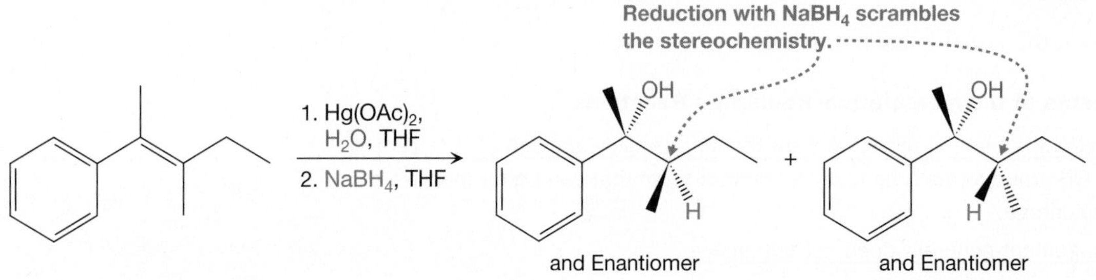

Reduction with $NaBH_4$ scrambles the stereochemistry.
1. $Hg(OAc)_2$, H_2O, THF
2. $NaBH_4$, THF
OH
H
+
OH
H
and Enantiomer
and Enantiomer

(13-24)

YOUR TURN **13.13**

Draw a detailed mechanism for each of the following reactions and identify the major products.

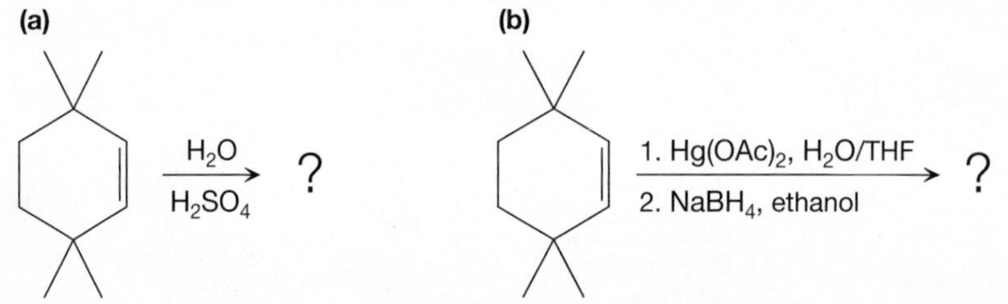

(a)
H_2O
H_2SO_4
?
(b)
1. $Hg(OAc)_2$, H_2O/THF
2. $NaBH_4$, ethanol
?

GREEN CHEMISTRY As discussed here in Section 13.5, oxymercuration–reduction reactions are valuable for the addition of water or alcohols across a C═C double bond or a C≡C triple bond. Mercury(II) acetate and other mercury(II) compounds are toxic, however, and chronic exposure could lead to permanent damage of the central nervous system. It is therefore preferable, when possible, to use less toxic or nontoxic reagents for these kinds of electrophilic addition reactions. For example, as we saw in Section 12.6, a strong acid like H_2SO_4 can be used to catalyze such additions.

Why does the addition of H_2O in oxymercuration–reduction follow Markovnikov's rule? As indicated in Equation 13-23, H_2O attacks the carbon that has the greater partial positive charge. Just as we saw with protonated epoxides (Section 10.7) and bromonium ions (Section 13.4b), the mercurinium ion has a three-membered ring consisting of two carbons and a positively charged heteroatom, and the three-membered ring is stabilized when the heteroatom shares some of its positive charge with the two attached carbons. The carbon that can better handle a positive charge picks up a greater share of the positive charge from the heteroatom. In Equation 13-23, the secondary carbon of the ring can better handle a positive charge than can the primary carbon.

The mechanism also shows why rearrangements tend *not* to take place in oxymercuration–reduction, in contrast to acid-catalyzed hydration. In the acid-catalyzed hydration of an alkene, a *full* positive charge develops on C in the carbocation intermediate, whereas only a *partial* positive charge develops on C in the mercurinium ion intermediate of the oxymercuration reaction. With a smaller concentration of positive charge on C in a mercurinium ion, a rearrangement would not lead to as much of an increase in stability compared to a carbocation.

YOUR TURN 13.14

Draw the complete mechanism and the major product for the following reaction.

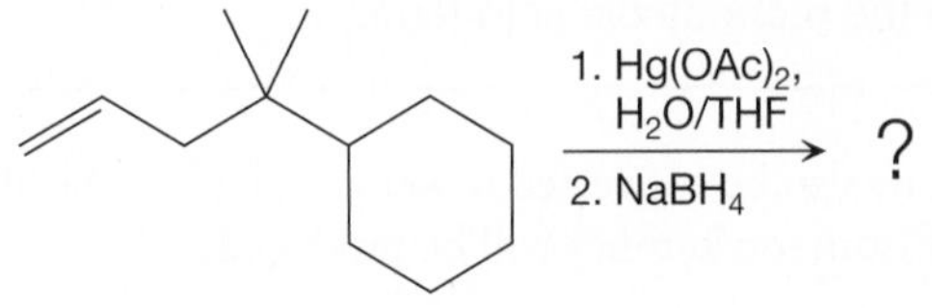
1. $Hg(OAc)_2$, H_2O/THF
2. $NaBH_4$
?

Alkynes, too, can undergo Markovnikov addition of water by oxymercuration. However, as we saw with the acid-catalyzed hydration of an alkyne (Section 12.8), an unstable enol is produced initially. Subsequent tautomerization converts the enol into the more stable keto form:

Hydration of an alkyne leads to an initial enol, which tautomerizes to the more stable keto form.

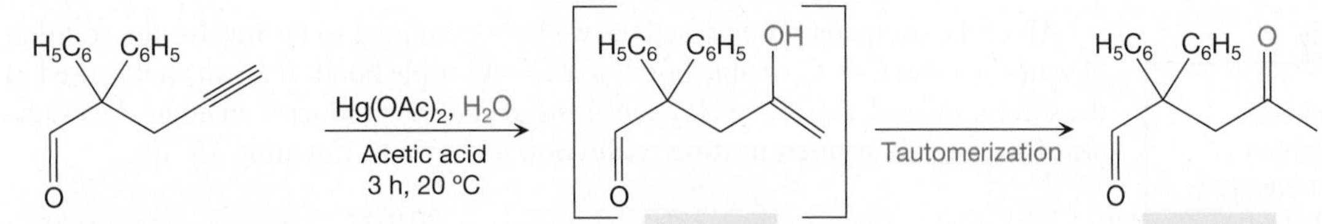
H_5C_6 C_6H_5
O
$Hg(OAc)_2$, H_2O
Acetic acid
3 h, 20 °C
OH
Tautomerization

2,2-Diphenylpent-4-ynal Enol form Keto form

4-Oxo-2,2-diphenylpentanal
55%

(13-25)

The oxymercuration reaction in Equation 13-25 does not require reduction with $NaBH_4$ to remove the mercury(II) substituent. Instead, as shown in Equation 13-26, the mercurinium ion intermediate opens to produce a mercuric enol, which, after it tautomerizes to a mercuric ketone, is hydrolyzed by water to produce the enol in Equation 13-25:

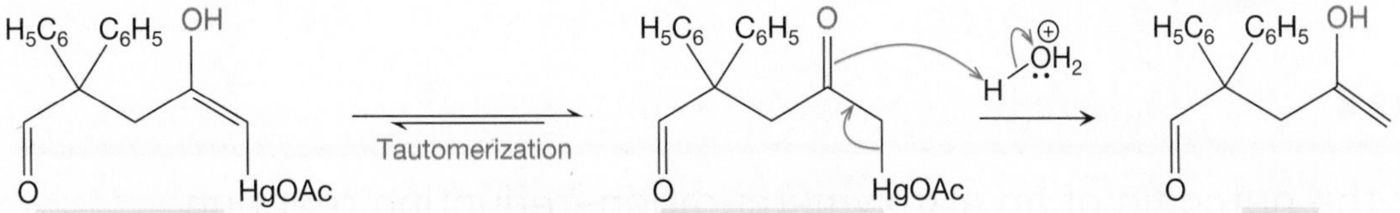
H_5C_6 C_6H_5
OH
O
HgOAc
Tautomerization
H
$\overset{+}{O}H_2$

Mercuric enol Mercuric ketone Enol

(13-26)

Mercury(II) acetate is not the only source of Hg^{2+} used for oxymercuration reactions. Equations 13-27 and 13-28 show examples in which $HgCl_2$ and $HgSO_4$ are used instead:

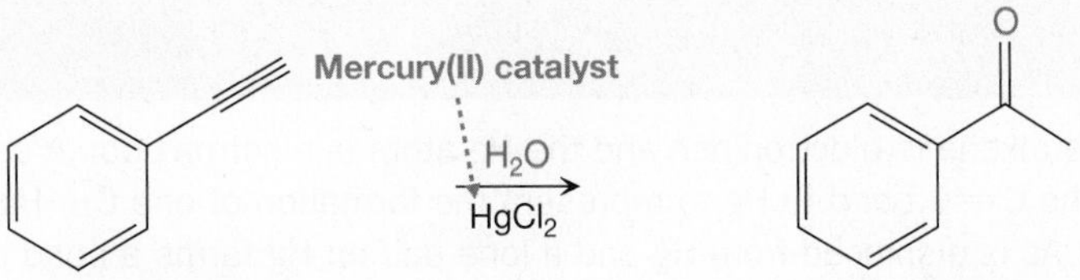
Mercury(II) catalyst
H_2O
$HgCl_2$
O

Phenylethyne **Phenylethanone**
82%

(13-27)

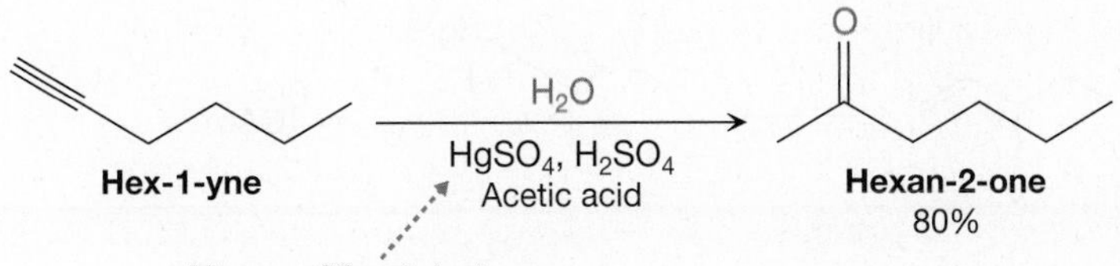
H_2O
$HgSO_4$, H_2SO_4
Acetic acid
O

Hex-1-yne **Hexan-2-one**
80%

Mercury(II) catalyst

(13-28)

YOUR TURN 13.15

Equations 13-27 and 13-28 show the overall products of hydration of the alkynes. For each reaction, draw the enol that is produced prior to tautomerization to the more stable keto form.

Internal alkynes can also be converted to ketones. Unless the alkyne is symmetric, however, a mixture of isomeric ketones will be produced:

Hydration of an unsymmetric internal alkyne leads to a mixture of isomeric ketones.

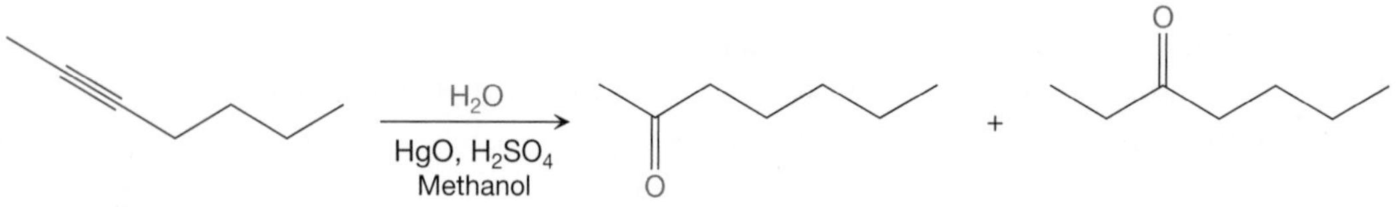

O
H_2O
HgO, H_2SO_4
Methanol
O
+

Hept-2-yne **Heptan-2-one** ~67% **Heptan-3-one** ~33% (13-29)

> **CONNECTIONS 13.2**
>
> **What do bees and cheese have in common?** Heptan-2-one (Eq. 13-29) is believed to be used as an anesthetic by honeybees when they bite small insects and larvae that enter the hive. It is also responsible for the odor of gorgonzola cheese.
>
> 

All of the oxymercuration reactions we have examined so far involve the addition of water across a C=C double bond or a C≡C triple bond. If an alcohol is used as the solvent instead, then R—OH adds instead and the product is an ether. An example of such an **alkoxymercuration–reduction** is shown in Equation 13-30:

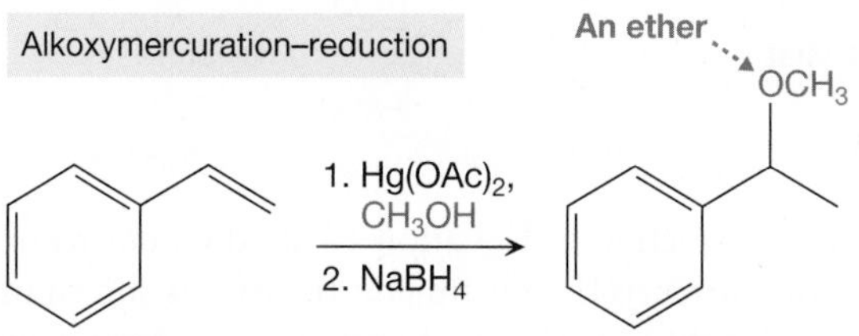

Alkoxymercuration–reduction
An ether
OCH_3
1. $Hg(OAc)_2$, CH_3OH
2. $NaBH_4$

93% (13-30)

SOLVED PROBLEM 13.4

How to predict the outcome of an alkoxymercuration–reduction reaction

Break It Down **Draw the complete, detailed mechanism for the alkoxymercuration part of this reaction and predict the major product.**

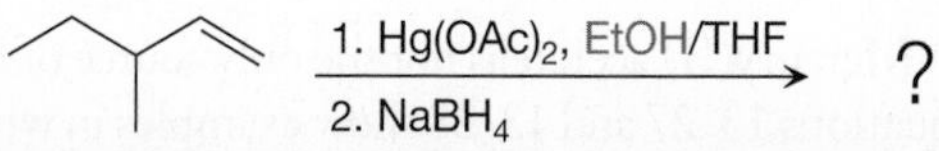

1. $Hg(OAc)_2$, EtOH/THF
2. $NaBH_4$
?

Think	Solve
When the alkene reacts with $Hg(OAc)_2$, what species is electron-rich? What species is electron-poor? Is there a lone pair on the electron-poor atom?	The C=C bond of the alkene is electron-rich and the Hg atom is electron-poor. A curved arrow is drawn from the C=C bond to Hg to represent the formation of one C—Hg bond. Simultaneously, one OAc is displaced from Hg and a lone pair on Hg forms a bond to the second carbon of the C=C bond, resulting in a mercurinium ion intermediate. 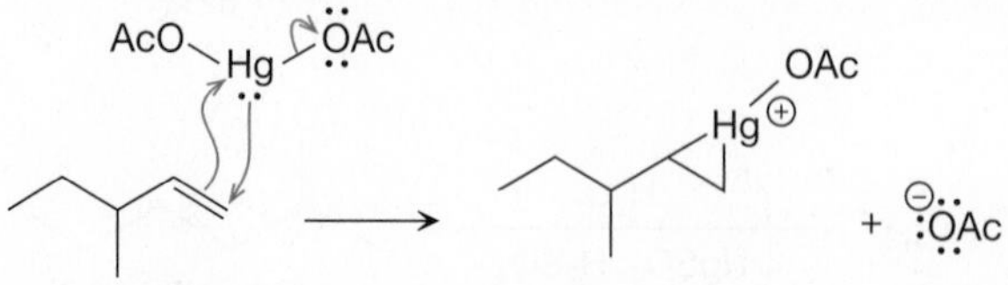

AcO
Hg
OAc
OAc
Hg
+
OAc

What nucleophile reacts with the intermediate? How is the regiochemistry of that step determined?

Ethanol (EtOH) is the nucleophile that attacks the mercurinium ion intermediate. Two possible C atoms can be attacked to open the ring. The C atom on the left is more likely to be attacked by ethanol because that C (which can better handle a positive charge due to the attached alkyl group) picks up a greater partial positive charge from Hg^+.

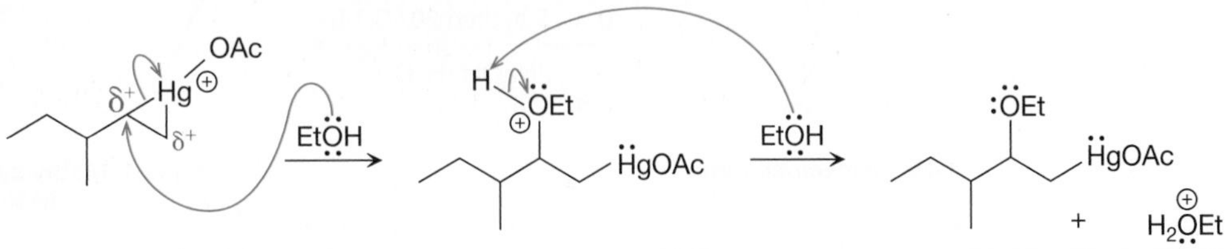

OAc
δ+
Hg
δ+
EtÖH
H
ÖEt
HgOAc
EtÖH
:ÖEt
HgOAc
+
H2ÖEt

Is a carbocation rearrangement likely to occur?

Like oxymercuration–reduction, alkoxymercuration–reduction doesn't involve the production of a carbocation, so no rearrangement is expected.

What is the role of $NaBH_4$?

$NaBH_4$ replaces the mercury-containing substituent with H.

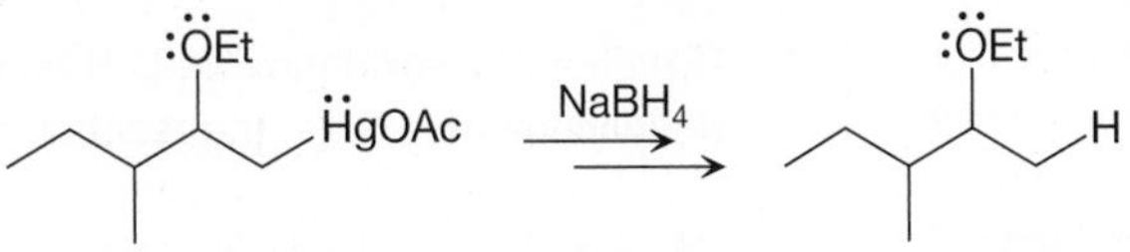

:ÖEt
HgOAc
NaBH4
:ÖEt
H

Try It Predict the product of this reaction.

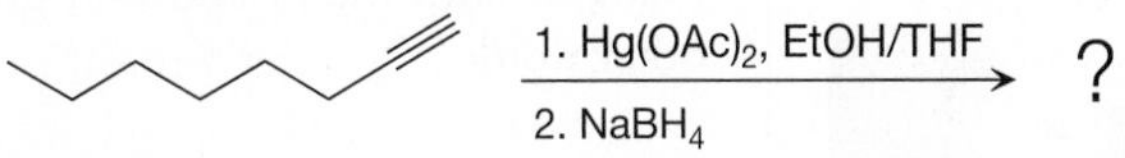

1. Hg(OAc)2, EtOH/THF
2. NaBH4
?

13.6 Hydroboration–Oxidation: Anti-Markovnikov Syn Addition of Water to an Alkene

SECTION 13.6 OBJECTIVES

You will be able to:

1. Draw the mechanism for the hydroboration–oxidation of an alkene.
2. Predict the major product of the hydroboration–oxidation of an alkene, including stereochemistry and regiochemistry.

So far, we have covered two reactions that serve to add water across a carbon–carbon double or triple bond: *acid-catalyzed hydration* (Chapter 12), which proceeds through a carbocation intermediate; and *oxymercuration–reduction* (Section 13.5), which proceeds through a cyclic mercurinium ion intermediate, thereby avoiding carbocation rearrangements. Both of these reactions add water in a *Markovnikov* fashion, in which the carbon atom that gains the OH group is the one that is better able to stabilize a positive charge. Also, neither of these reactions is stereospecific; in each case, a mixture of stereoisomers from both syn and anti addition is produced.

Hydroboration–oxidation provides a third way to add water across a nonpolar π bond, as shown in Equations 13-31 and 13-32. In each case, the alkene first undergoes **hydroboration**, in which borane, BH_3 (from either $BH_3 \cdot THF$ or B_2H_6), adds across the double bond. The product is then *oxidized* with a basic solution of hydrogen peroxide, H_2O_2:

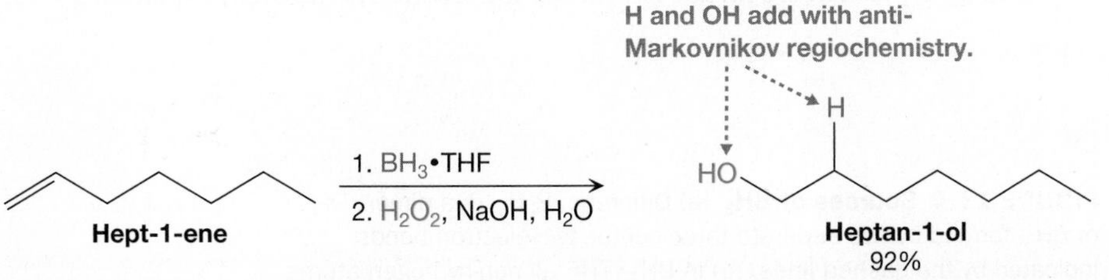

H and OH add with anti-Markovnikov regiochemistry.
H
HO
1. BH3•THF
2. H2O2, NaOH, H2O
Hept-1-ene
Heptan-1-ol
92%

(13-31)

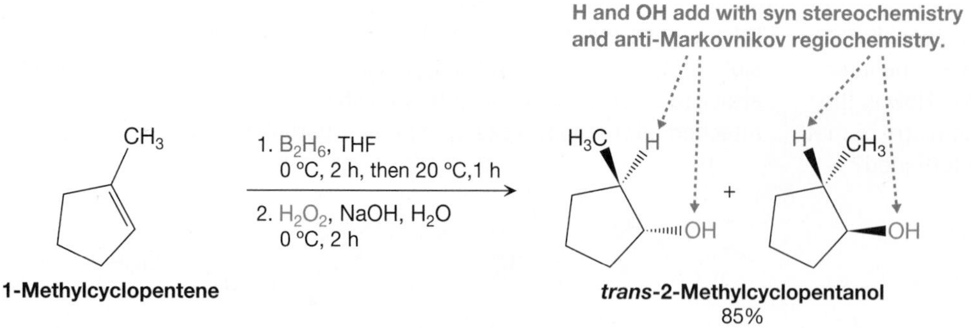
H and OH add with syn stereochemistry and anti-Markovnikov regiochemistry.
CH3
1. B2H6, THF
0 °C, 2 h, then 20 °C,1 h
2. H2O2, NaOH, H2O
0 °C, 2 h
H3C
H
OH
H
CH3
OH
1-Methylcyclopentene
trans-2-Methylcyclopentanol
85%

(13-32)

CONNECTIONS 13.3

Studying the heart Heptan-1-ol (Eq. 13-31) is used in cardiac electrophysiology, which deals with understanding the electrical activities of the heart. Specifically, heptan-1-ol uncouples gap junctions, which are densely packed protein channels that allow the cells to contract in unison.

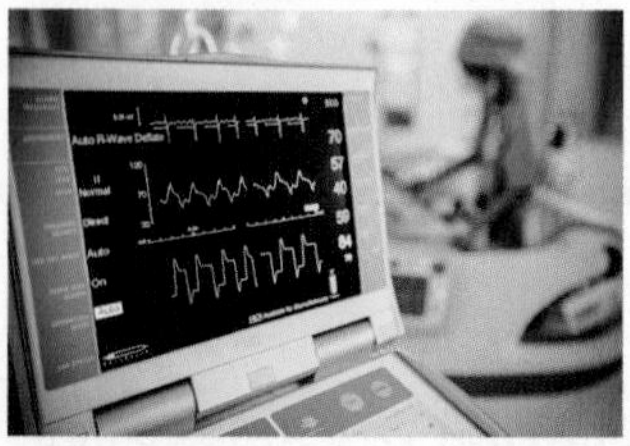

Notice the regiochemistry exhibited by these reactions. Specifically, in both Equations 13-31 and 13-32, addition of OH is favored at the alkene C atom that can *least* stabilize a positive charge: namely, a primary C atom in Equation 13-31 and a secondary C atom in Equation 13-32. This is opposite to what we see with Markovnikov regiochemistry exhibited by acid-catalyzed hydration and oxymercuration–reduction. That is:

Hydroboration–oxidation adds H and OH to an alkene with **anti-Markovnikov regiochemistry**. Thus, the reaction is said to undergo **anti-Markovnikov addition**.

Notice also that hydroboration–oxidation is stereospecific. In Equation 13-32, for example, both the H and OH groups add to the same face of the alkene's plane. In other words:

In hydroboration–oxidation, an alkene undergoes *syn addition* of H and OH.

To understand these aspects of hydroboration–oxidation reactions, we must understand their mechanisms. First, we will study the mechanism of hydroboration in Section 13.6a, and then we will examine the mechanism of the subsequent oxidation in Section 13.6b.

13.6a Hydroboration: Addition of BH_3 across a C═C Double Bond

In the hydroboration of an alkene, borane (BH_3) effectively adds across the C═C double bond; H adds to one C atom, and BH_2 adds to the other C atom. Borane is highly unstable, however, because the central B atom does not have an octet. Therefore, BH_3 cannot be isolated. Instead, in its pure form it exists as a gaseous dimer, **diborane (B_2H_6)**, in which two H atoms constitute a bridge between the B atoms (shown in **Figure 13-4a**). Those H atoms are involved in what are called **three-center, two-electron bonds**. Although these bonds provide some stability, B_2H_6 remains highly reactive; it is both *toxic* and *explosive*. A more stable variation of BH_3 is sold commercially as a one-to-one complex with tetrahydrofuran, denoted $BH_3 \cdot THF$ (shown in Fig. 13-4b), where THF acts as a Lewis base to give the B atom its octet. Similarly, a one-to-one complex between BH_3 and dimethyl sulfide (DMS; $CH_3—S—CH_3$), denoted $BH_3 \cdot DMS$, can be used as a source of borane.

The partial mechanism for the hydroboration reaction is shown in Equation 13-33:

(a)

A 3-center, 2-electron bond provides some stability to the B atoms.

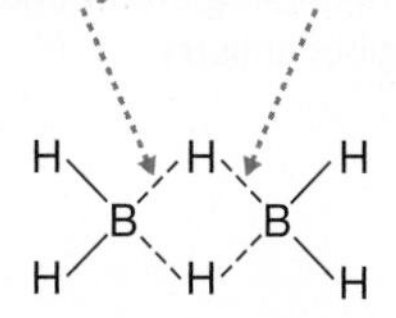

Diborane, B_2H_6

(b)

Coordination of THF to BH_3 provides some stability by giving B an octet.

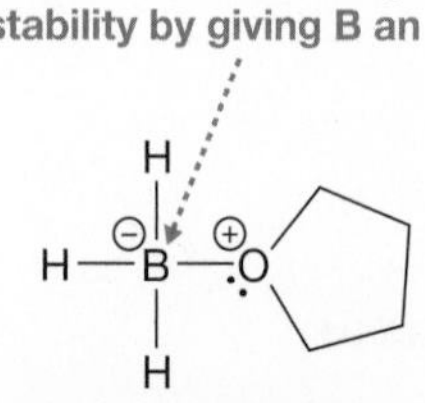

Borane–THF complex ($BH_3 \cdot THF$)

FIGURE 13-4 Sources of BH_3 (a) Diborane, B_2H_6, is a dimer of BH_3, formed by two separate three-center, two-electron bonds indicated by the dashed lines. (b) In $BH_3 \cdot THF$, all non-hydrogen atoms have an octet.

Partial mechanism for the hydroboration of an alkene (Eq. 13-32)

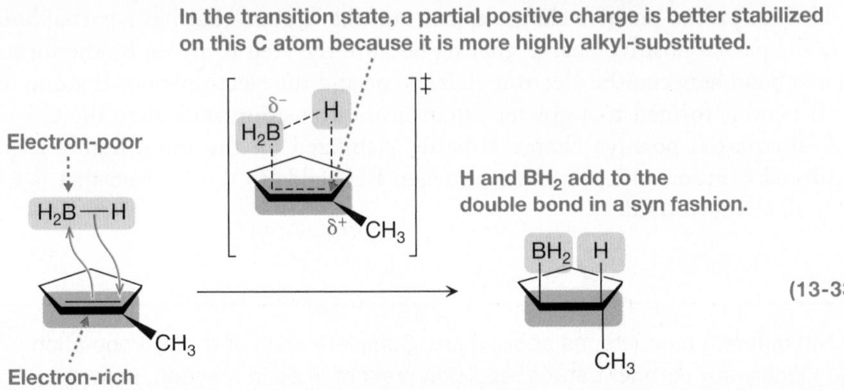
In the transition state, a partial positive charge is better stabilized on this C atom because it is more highly alkyl-substituted.
Electron-poor
H₂B—H
Electron-rich
CH₃
‡
δ⁻
H₂B
H
δ⁺
CH₃
H and BH₂ add to the double bond in a syn fashion.
BH₂
H
CH₃

(13-33)

Mechanism Drawing
Hydroboration of an Alkene

It is driven primarily by the flow of electrons from the electron-rich π bond to the electron-poor boron atom of BH_3. Similar to the mechanisms of other reactions in this chapter, this reaction avoids the formation of a highly unstable carbocation by simultaneously forming a bond back to the second C atom of the double bond. In hydroboration, however, this second bond to C comes from electrons originally part of a B—H bond in BH_3 rather than from a lone pair (compare Eq. 13-33 with Eq. 13-2, p. 648). Overall, two bonds are broken and two bonds are formed in a *concerted* fashion (that is, without the formation of intermediates).

According to Equation 13-33, hydroboration is both *stereospecific* and *regioselective*:

Stereochemistry and Regiochemistry in the Hydroboration of an Alkene

- The H and BH_2 groups add to the C═C bond in a syn fashion.
- The H atom primarily adds to the C with the greater number of alkyl groups, whereas the BH_2 group adds to the C with the lesser number of alkyl groups.

Both of these properties are explained by the concerted nature of hydroboration. Syn addition of H and BH_2 is an outcome of the C—H and the C—BH_2 bonds forming simultaneously to the same face of the C═C bond. Moreover, with no charged intermediates formed, charge stability does not provide as much of a driving force as it does in other reactions we have seen in this chapter and Chapter 12. Consequently, *steric hindrance* plays a more significant role:

When BH_3 adds to an alkene, *steric repulsion* directs the larger group, BH_2, to the carbon atom with the lesser number of alkyl groups, where there is more room.

Equation 13-34 shows the steric repulsion that would occur if the BH_2 group were to add to the more substituted alkene carbon:

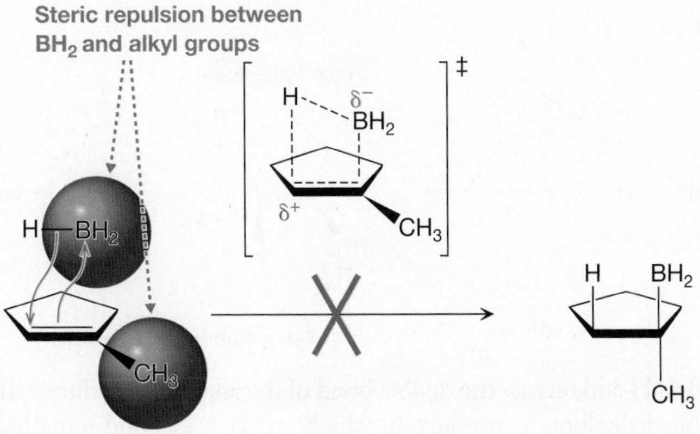
Steric repulsion between BH₂ and alkyl groups
H—BH₂
CH₃
‡
H
δ⁻
BH₂
δ⁺
CH₃
H
BH₂
CH₃

(13-34)

CONNECTIONS 13.4

Fueling the future Borane can form a complex with ammonia: $BH_3 \cdot NH_3$. This borane–ammonia complex is being studied as an air-stable form of hydrogen storage, which can have a wide variety of energy applications, including a source of H_2 gas for fuel cells in automobiles.

Shell
Hydrogen

Even though no formal charges appear, charge stability is also a factor in the regioselectivity of hydroboration. In the transition states shown in Equations 13-33 and 13-34, a *partial* positive charge appears on the C atom that has a partial bond to H. The partial positive charge appears because the step is driven by the formation of a bond between the electron-rich alkene and the electron-poor B atom; the C—B bond is formed to a greater extent in the transition state than the C—H bond. The partial positive charge is better stabilized on the more highly alkyl-substituted C atom, which is achieved when BH_2 adds to the C atom that is less highly alkyl-substituted.

YOUR TURN 13.16

Borane can add to propene to produce two different products, as shown here. Complete each of the hydroboration steps by adding the curved arrows. Also identify any pertinent steric repulsion present in each reaction, as well as the partial charges that develop in the transition state (similar to Eqs. 13-33 and 13-34), and determine which reaction is favored.

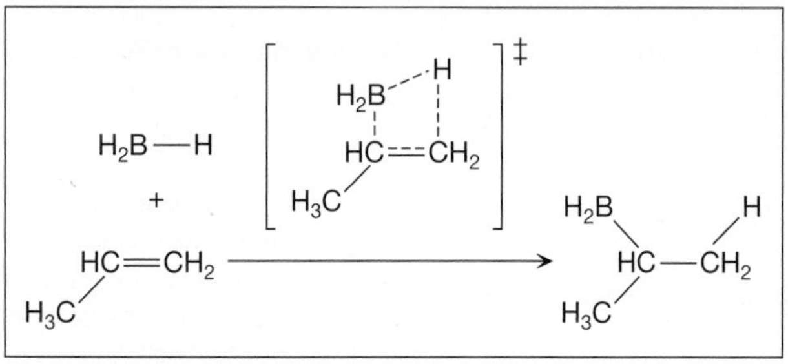

H2B—H
+
H3C
HC=CH2
H2B
H
HC==CH2
‡
H2B
H
HC—CH2
H3C
H—BH2
+
HC=CH2
H3C
H
BH2
HC==CH2
‡
H
BH2
HC—CH2
H3C

The product of hydroboration is an **alkylborane**, R—BH_2, as shown in Equation 13-35a:

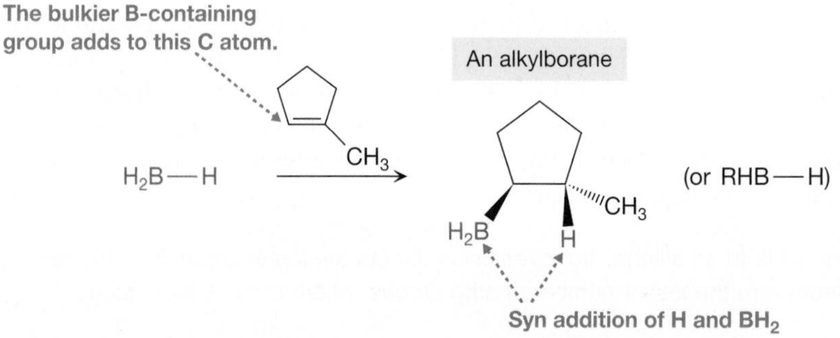

The bulkier B-containing group adds to this C atom.
An alkylborane
H2B—H
CH3
CH3
H2B
H
(or RHB—H)
Syn addition of H and BH2

(13-35a)

That alkylborane has two B—H bonds remaining, and one of these bonds can react with an additional unreacted alkene, as shown in Equation 13-35b:

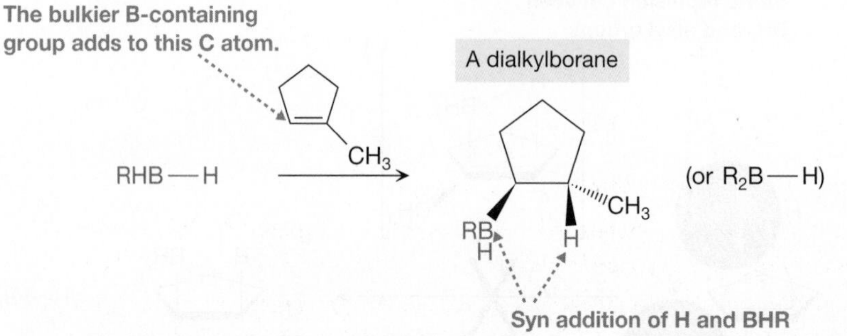

The bulkier B-containing group adds to this C atom.
A dialkylborane
RHB—H
CH3
CH3
RB
H
H
(or R2B—H)
Syn addition of H and BHR

(13-35b)

That is, RHB—H adds across the double bond of the alkene to produce a **dialkylborane**, R_2B—H. This dialkylborane product, in which one B—H bond remains, in turn adds across yet another equivalent of the unreacted alkene to produce a **trialkylborane,** R_3B, as shown in Equation 13-35c:

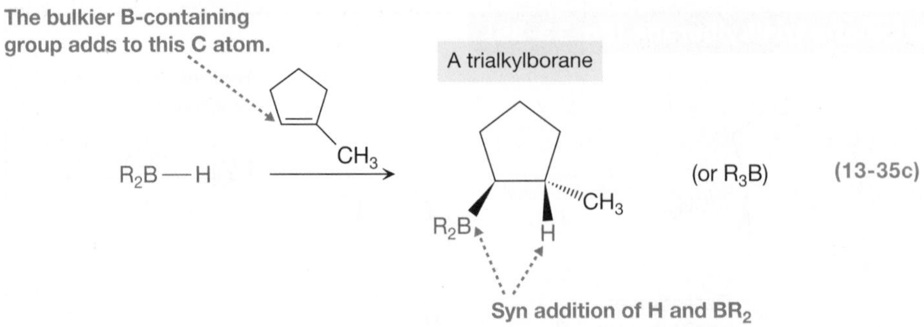

The bulkier B-containing group adds to this C atom.
A trialkylborane
R_2B-H
CH_3
CH_3
R_2B
H
(or R_3B)
(13-35c)
Syn addition of H and BR_2

As with the addition of BH_3, *each of these is a syn addition, and the bulkier B-containing portion adds preferentially to the less sterically hindered alkene C atom.* Once the trialkylborane is formed, it is then treated with a basic solution of hydrogen peroxide to convert it to the alcohol, as discussed in Section 13.6b.

YOUR TURN 13.17

Draw the detailed mechanism for the formation of the monoalkylborane in the reaction shown here. Also draw the trialkylborane that is ultimately produced.

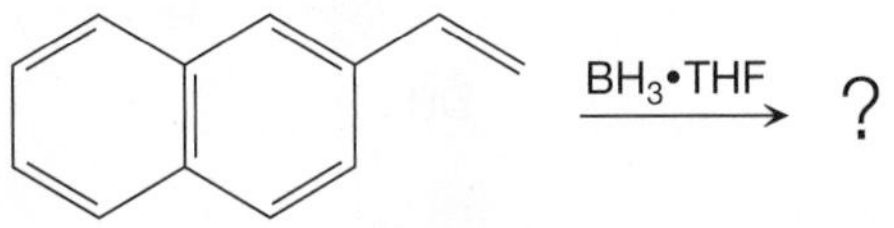

BH_3•THF
?

13.6b Oxidation of the Trialkylborane: Formation of the Alcohol

Equations 13-31 and 13-32 (pp. 667–668) show that after an alkene has undergone hydroboration, treatment with a basic solution of H_2O_2 produces the alcohol. We can now see from Equation 13-35 in the previous section that the actual species that undergoes oxidation is a trialkylborane. The net reaction is shown in Equation 13-36 (each R group in blue has the carbon structure shown in black):

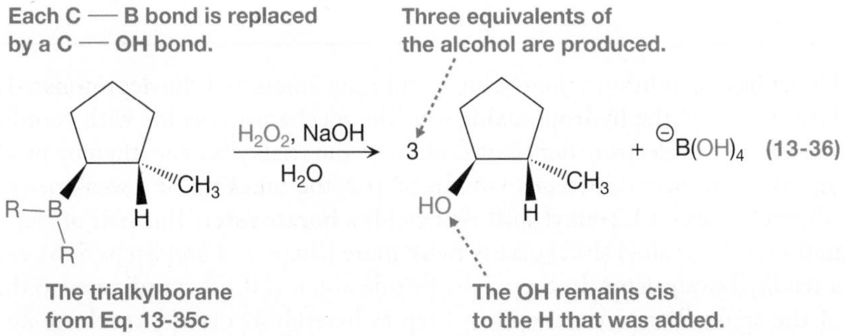

Each C — B bond is replaced by a C — OH bond.
Three equivalents of the alcohol are produced.
H_2O_2, NaOH
H_2O
3
CH_3
CH_3
R—B
R
H
HO
H
+ $^{\ominus}B(OH)_4$
(13-36)
The trialkylborane from Eq. 13-35c
The OH remains cis to the H that was added.

Note the following features of this oxidation:

Oxidation of a Trialkylborane

- Each of the three C—B bonds is replaced by a C—OH bond. Thus, three equivalents of the alcohol are produced.
- The configuration at each C atom bonded to B remains unchanged. Thus, the OH group in the product is syn to the hydrogen atom added from the previous hydroboration reaction.

These aspects of the oxidation reaction can be better understood by studying the partial mechanism, which is shown in Equation 13-37:

Partial mechanism for the oxidation of a trialkylborane (Eq. 13-36)

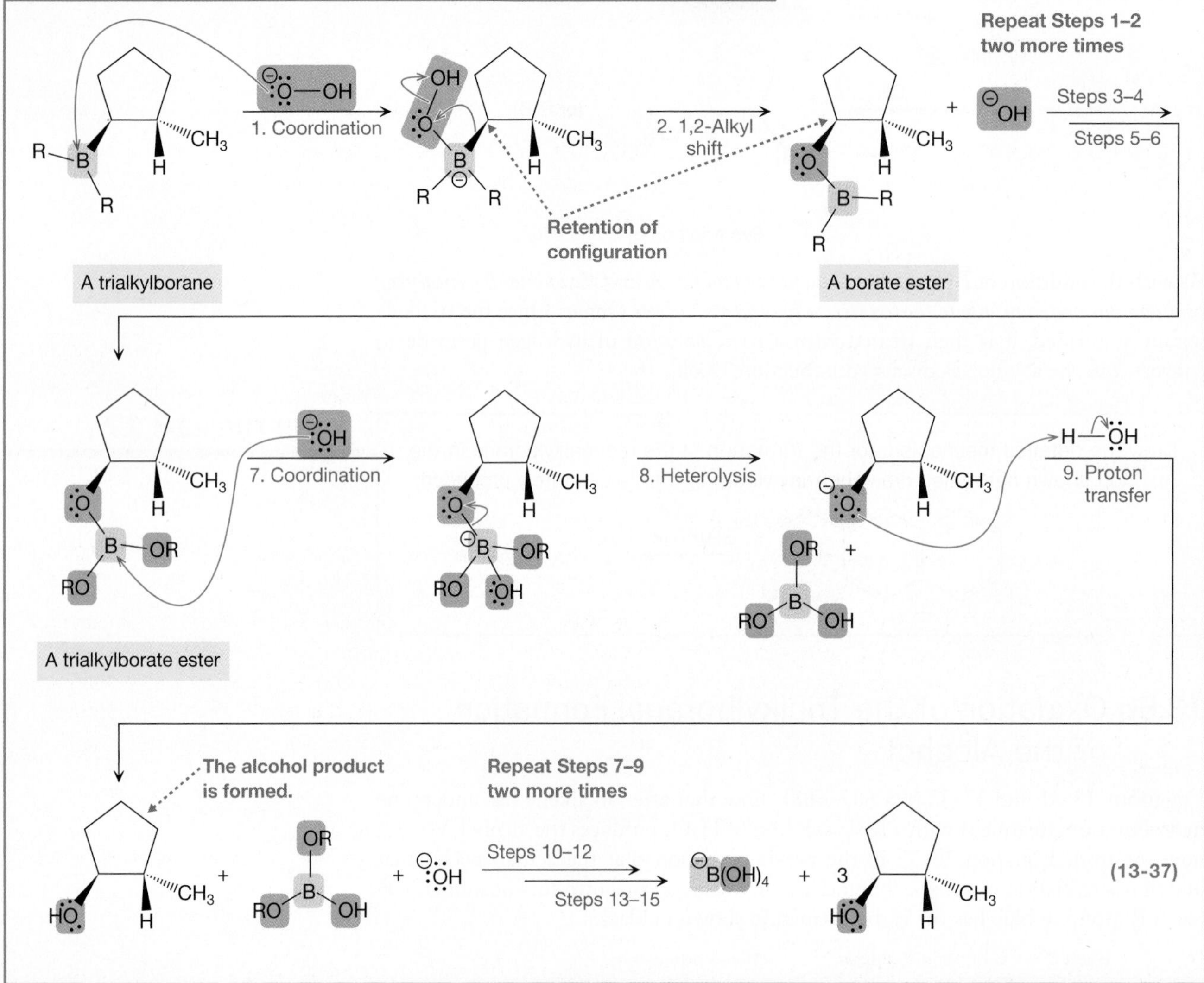

Repeat Steps 1–2 two more times
1. Coordination
2. 1,2-Alkyl shift
Retention of configuration
Steps 3–4
Steps 5–6
A trialkylborane
A borate ester
7. Coordination
8. Heterolysis
9. Proton transfer
A trialkylborate ester
The alcohol product is formed.
Repeat Steps 7–9 two more times
Steps 10–12
Steps 13–15

(13-37)

Under basic conditions, there is an equilibrium amount of the deprotonated peroxide, HOO^-, called the **hydroperoxide ion**. The mechanism begins with coordination of HOO^- to the electron-deficient B atom of the trialkylborane, thereby producing an unstable tetrahedral intermediate. In Step 2, the breaking of a weak peroxide bond (O—O) drives a 1,2-alkyl shift that yields a **borate ester**. This pair of steps (coordination and 1,2-alkyl shift) occurs twice more (Steps 3–4 and Steps 5–6), resulting in a **trialkylborate ester**. In Step 7, hydroxide anion (HO^-) coordinates to the B atom of the trialkylborate ester, and in Step 8, heterolysis occurs to release an alkoxide anion (RO^-) leaving group. In Step 9, the strongly basic alkoxide anion gains a proton from H_2O to produce the first equivalent of the final alcohol. This trio of steps (coordination, heterolysis, and proton transfer) is then repeated twice (Steps 10–12 and Steps 13–15) to produce two more equivalents of the alcohol.

With this mechanism, we can now see how conversion of the trialkylborane to the alcohol takes place with retention of configuration. The critical step is Step 2, where a C—B bond breaks at the same time a C—O bond forms. Because of geometric constraints during this *concerted* process, the O-containing group simply assumes the position that was originally occupied by the B-containing group.

YOUR TURN 13.18

Draw the complete detailed mechanism of the reaction that takes place when the product of the reaction in Your Turn 13.17 is treated with a basic solution of hydrogen peroxide.

SOLVED PROBLEM **13.5**

How to predict the product for the hydroboration–oxidation of an alkene

Break It Down Consider the following reaction. (a) Draw the first step of the hydroboration mechanism, including stereochemistry, and then draw the trialkylborane product, similar to the representation in Equation 13-35c. (b) Draw the product that is formed from the oxidation step.

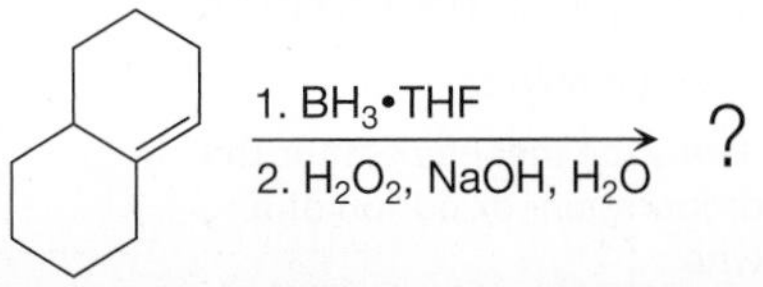

1. BH_3•THF
2. H_2O_2, NaOH, H_2O
?

Think	Solve
What is the preferred orientation when BH_3 approaches the C=C bond?	Two ways BH_3 can approach the C=C bond are shown here. The first approach is favored because the bulkier BH_2 group is away from the more sterically hindered C atom. 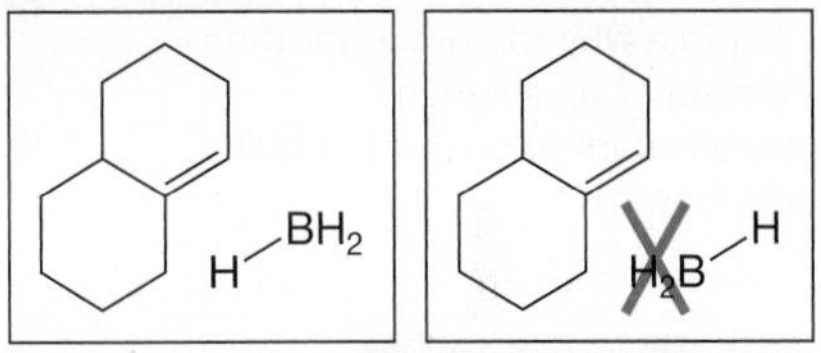
In the hydroboration reaction, what species is electron-rich and what species is electron-poor? Is a carbocation formed? What is the stereochemistry of this step?	The C=C bond of the alkene is electron-rich and the B atom of BH_3 is electron-poor, so a curved arrow is drawn from the C=C bond to the B atom. A C—B bond is formed, and to avoid the production of a carbocation, an H—B bond breaks and the H forms a bond to the other C atom from the C=C bond. The H and BH_2 add syn to each other to produce the alkylborane. 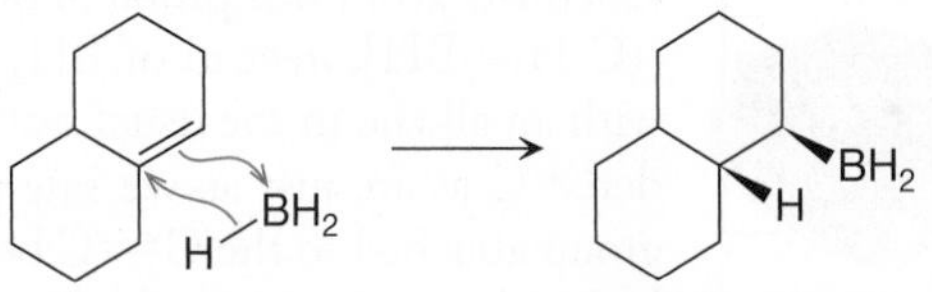 and Enantiomer
In the alkylborane that is produced, how many B—H bonds are there? How does that differ from the trialkylborane that is made?	In the alkylborane, two B—H bonds remain. To form the trialkylborane, each B—H bond is replaced by B—R, where R is an alkyl group that has the same carbon structure as in the alkylborane. 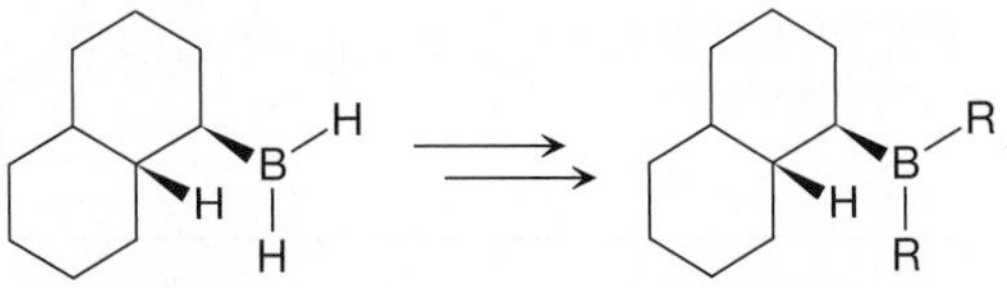 and Enantiomer and Enantiomer
In the oxidation step, what group replaces each B-containing group attached to C? What is the stereochemistry of this step?	Each C—B bond is replaced with C—OH, and the stereochemical configuration at each C is retained. The first replacement is shown below, treating the trialkylborane as R—BR_2. The product is an alcohol. 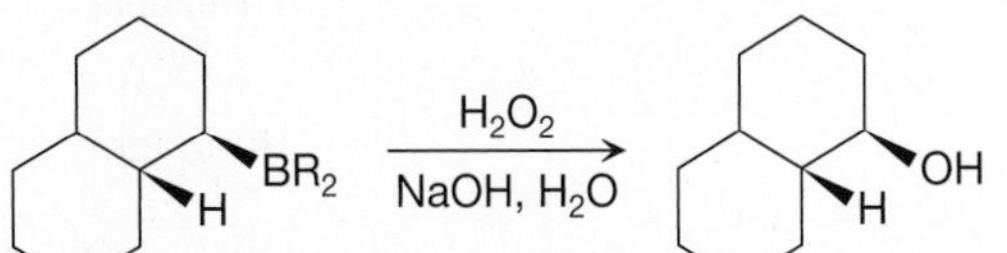 and Enantiomer and Enantiomer

(continued)

Try It Consider the following reaction. **(a)** Draw the first step of the hydroboration mechanism, including stereochemistry, and then draw the trialkylborane product, similar to the representation in Equation 13-35c. **(b)** Draw the product that is formed from the oxidation step.

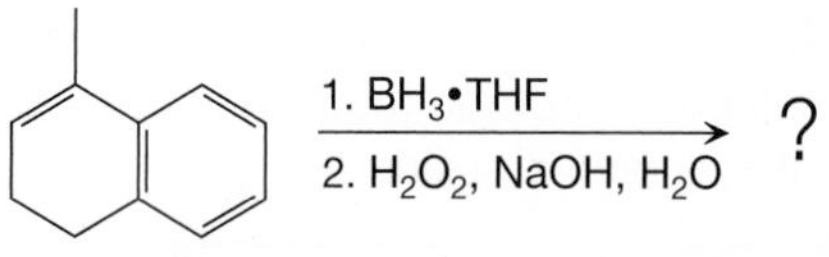
1. BH_3•THF
2. H_2O_2, NaOH, H_2O
?

SECTION 13.7 OBJECTIVES

You will be able to

1. Draw the mechanism for the hydroboration–oxidation of an alkyne.
2. Predict the major product in the hydroboration–oxidation of an alkyne, including regiochemistry.
3. Explain why the hydroboration–oxidation of an alkyne is generally carried out with a bulky dialkylborane.

CONNECTIONS 13.5

Meat lovers appreciate hexanal Hexanal (Eq. 13-39) is an oxidation product of linoleic acid and is thought to be partly responsible for the distinct flavor of cooked meats.

13.7 Hydroboration–Oxidation of Alkynes

The addition of BH_3 to an alkyne takes place in much the same way as it does to an alkene, with BH_2 adding to the less sterically hindered carbon and H adding to the more sterically hindered one (Eq. 13-38). A C=C double bond remains after the first addition of BH_3, however, and if that C=C bond is terminal, a second hydroboration takes place readily. As a result, such a reaction would lead to a mixture of products, making it a fairly useless reaction.

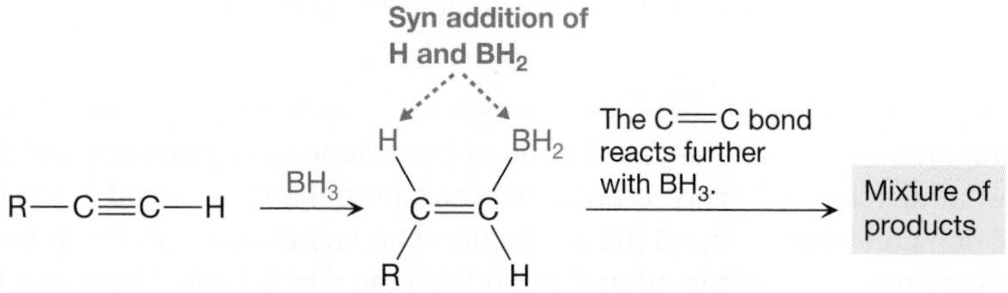
Syn addition of H and BH_2
R—C≡C—H
BH_3
H
BH_2
C=C
R
H
The C=C bond reacts further with BH_3.
Mixture of products

(13-38)

Chemists avoid this problem by using a bulky dialkylborane, such as **disiamylborane** [$(C_5H_{11})_2BH$], instead of BH_3, as shown in Equation 13-39. Disiamylborane reacts with an alkyne in the usual way, with the R_2B group adding to the less sterically hindered C atom, just as we saw previously in Equation 13-35c. With the bulky R_2B group attached to the C=C bond, *a second addition of disiamylborane does not occur*, so hydroboration stops at the alkene stage:

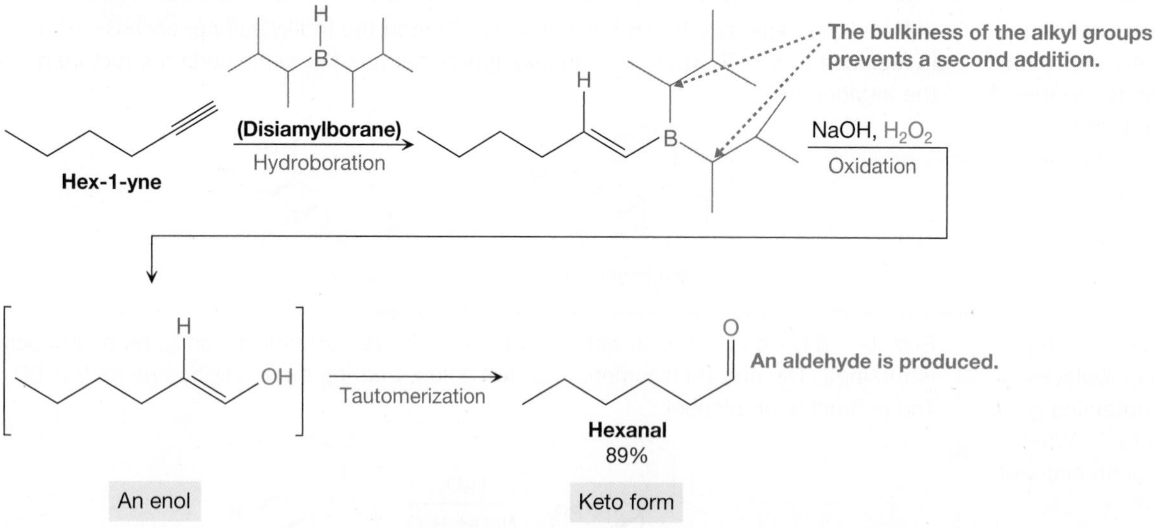
H
B
Hex-1-yne
(Disiamylborane)
Hydroboration
H
B
The bulkiness of the alkyl groups prevents a second addition.
NaOH, H_2O_2
Oxidation
H
OH
Tautomerization
O
An aldehyde is produced.
Hexanal
89%
An enol
Keto form

(13-39)

Subsequent oxidation with a basic solution of H_2O_2 converts the R_2B substituent on the alkene into an OH group, similar to Equation 13-36. In this case, however, the product is an *enol*, which tautomerizes to the more stable keto form.

Disiamylborane is not the only bulky dialkylborane used to carry out these kinds of conversions. Other examples include **dicyclohexylborane** and **9-borabicyclo[3.3.1]nonane (9-BBN)**, as shown in **Figure 13-5**.

As we can see from Equation 13-39:

> Hydroboration–oxidation is a useful way to convert a *terminal alkyne* into an aldehyde.

This reaction can also be used to convert an internal alkyne into a ketone, but a mixture of products results unless the alkyne is symmetric.

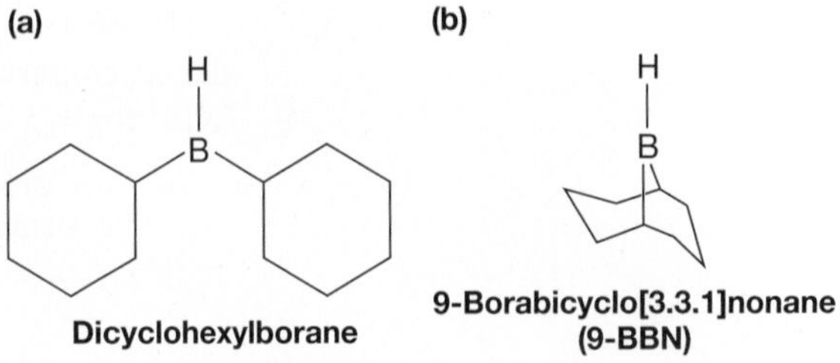

(a)
(b)
H
B
H
B
Dicyclohexylborane
9-Borabicyclo[3.3.1]nonane (9-BBN)

FIGURE 13-5 Bulky dialkylboranes (a) Dicyclohexylborane and (b) 9-borabicyclo[3.3.1]nonane (9-BBN) add just once to a terminal alkyne.

YOUR TURN 13.19

Alkyne **A** is treated with disiamylborane followed by a basic solution of H_2O_2. The overall product is an aldehyde. Draw the structures of the initial alkyne **A** and intermediate **B**.

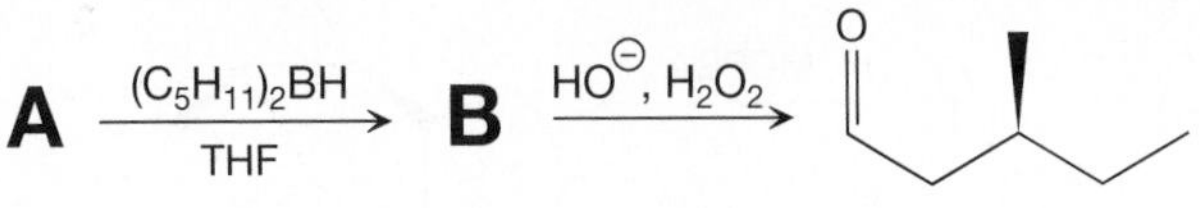

A
(C5H11)2BH
THF
B
HO⊖, H2O2
O

13.8 Organic Synthesis: Using Electrophilic Addition Reactions That Proceed through a Cyclic Transition State

SECTION 13.8 OBJECTIVES

You will be able to:

1. Apply transforms to the electrophilic addition reactions we have learned in this chapter to determine potential precursors for a target.
2. Incorporate electrophilic addition reactions from this chapter into syntheses.

This chapter has introduced a variety of electrophilic addition reactions whose mechanisms involve a cyclic transition state. Having spent the bulk of this chapter focusing on the mechanisms for these reactions, we now turn to how these reactions are used in synthesis. In particular, we stress the importance of being able to apply transforms to these reactions to determine possible precursors, which will help you carry out retrosynthetic analyses more efficiently.

Section 13.2 described how an alkene can react with a carbene (produced in situ from diazomethane) to form a cyclopropane ring, which conserves the stereochemistry about the C=C bond. When our target contains a cyclopropane ring that contains a CH_2 group, we can therefore consider applying a transform like this one:

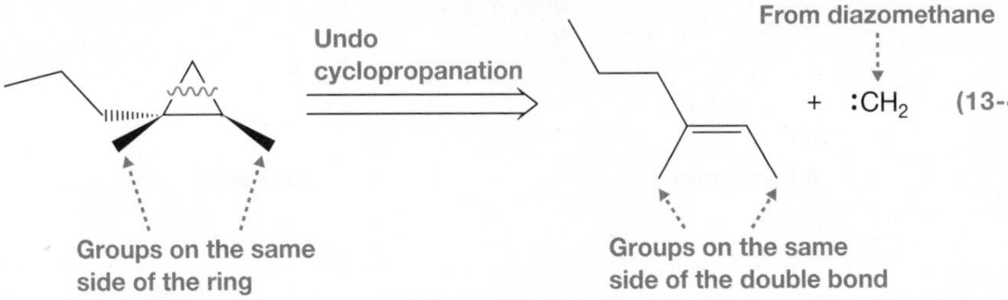

Undo cyclopropanation
From diazomethane
+ :CH2
Groups on the same side of the ring
Groups on the same side of the double bond

(13-40)

YOUR TURN 13.20

Show how each of the following compounds can be produced from an alkene.

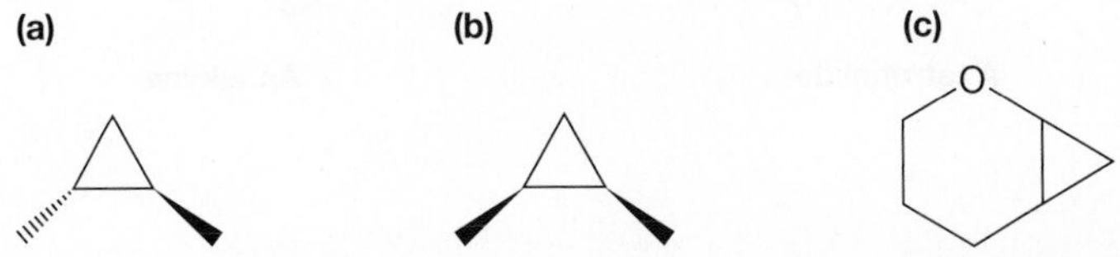

(a)
(b)
(c)
O

In Section 13.3, we learned that peroxy acids like MCPBA will epoxidize an alkene, conserving the stereochemistry in the process. Therefore, when an epoxide is called for in a synthesis, we can apply this transform:

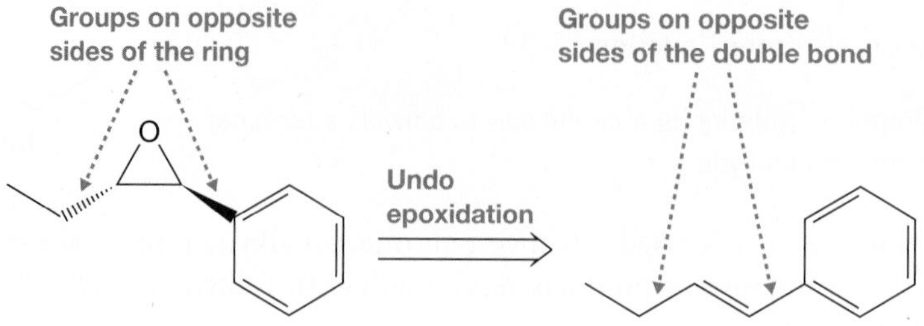

Groups on opposite sides of the ring
O
Undo epoxidation
Groups on opposite sides of the double bond

An epoxide | An alkene

(13-41)

YOUR TURN 13.21

What alkene can be epoxidized with MCPBA to yield the following compound?

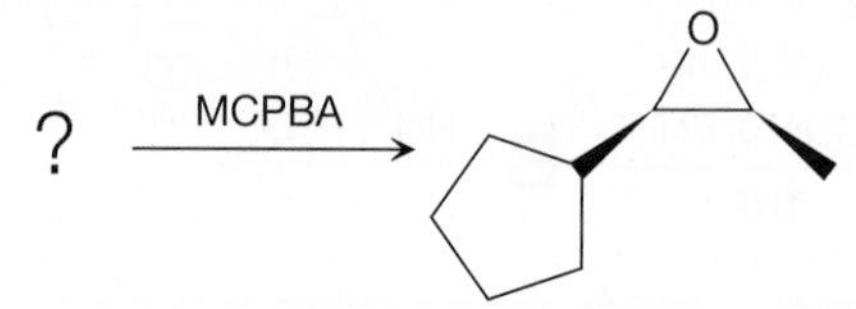

?
MCPBA
O

In Section 13.4, we studied reactions that proceed through bromonium and chloronium ion intermediates. Recall that, in the absence a nucleophilic solvent, Br_2 or Cl_2 will add anti across the C=C bond of an alkene. In water (a nucleophilic solvent), however, a halohydrin is formed, resulting from the anti addition of OH and a halogen atom across the C=C bond. Molecular halogens will also add across the C≡C triple bond of an alkyne to produce a tetrahalide. Therefore, if we see one of these features in our target, we can consider the corresponding transform:

Br
Undo Br2 addition
Br

A vicinal dihalide | An alkene

(13-42)

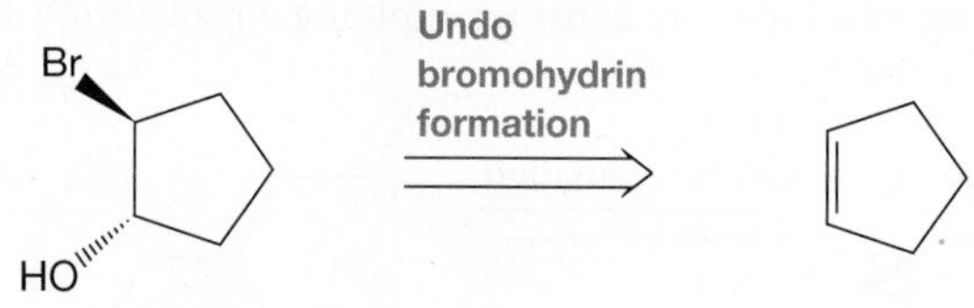

Br
Undo bromohydrin formation
HO

A halohydrin | An alkene

(13-43)

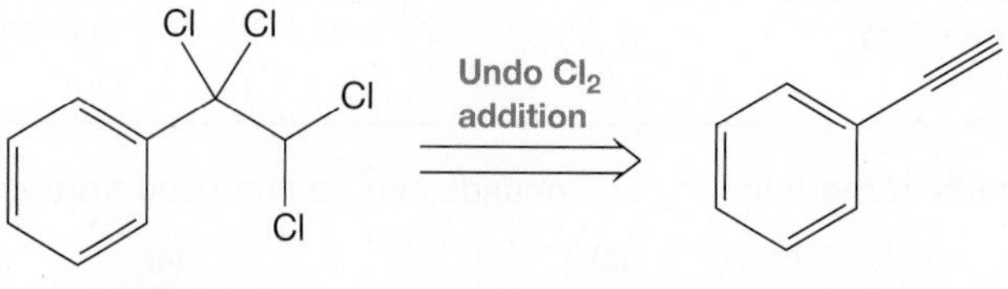

Cl Cl
Cl
Cl
Undo Cl2 addition

A tetrahalide | An alkyne

(13-44)

YOUR TURN **13.22**

Show how each of these compounds can be produced from an alkene or an alkyne.

(a)

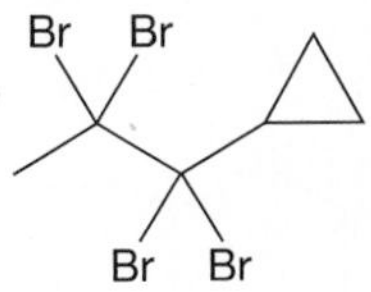
Br
Br
Br
Br

(b)

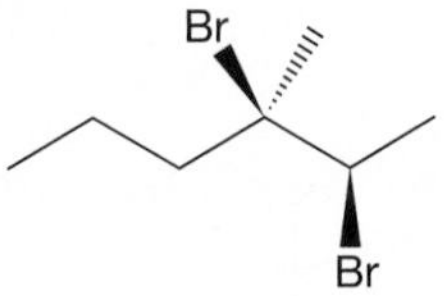
Br
Br

(c)

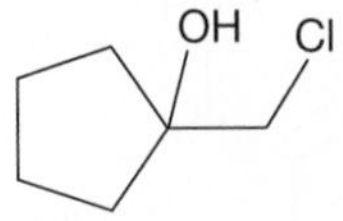
OH
Cl

Finally, two reactions were presented in this chapter that add water across a C=C double bond or a C≡C triple bond: oxymercuration–reduction in Section 13.5 and hydroboration–oxidation in Sections 13.6 and 13.7. Oxymercuration–reduction results in the Markovnikov addition of water to convert an alkene into an alcohol or an alkyne into a ketone, all while avoiding carbocation rearrangements. Hydroboration–oxidation results in the syn addition of water, with anti-Markovnikov regiochemistry, to convert an alkene into an alcohol or a terminal alkyne into an aldehyde. Therefore, we can apply the following transforms:

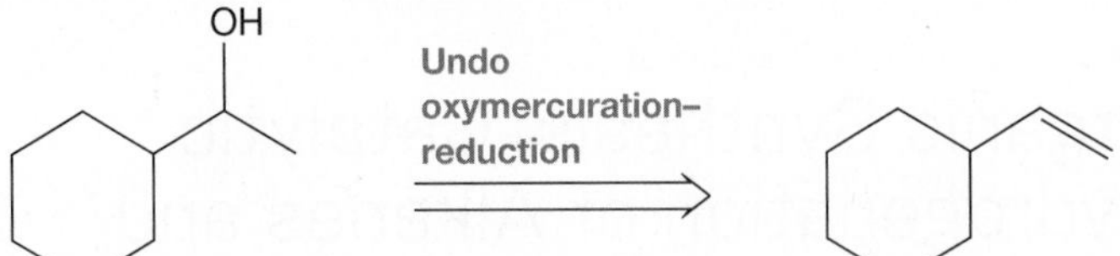
OH
Undo
oxymercuration–
reduction

An alcohol — An alkene (13-45)

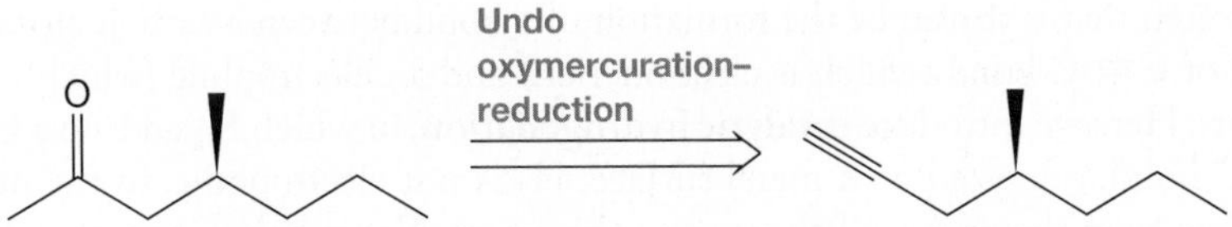
O
Undo
oxymercuration–
reduction

A ketone — An alkyne (13-46)

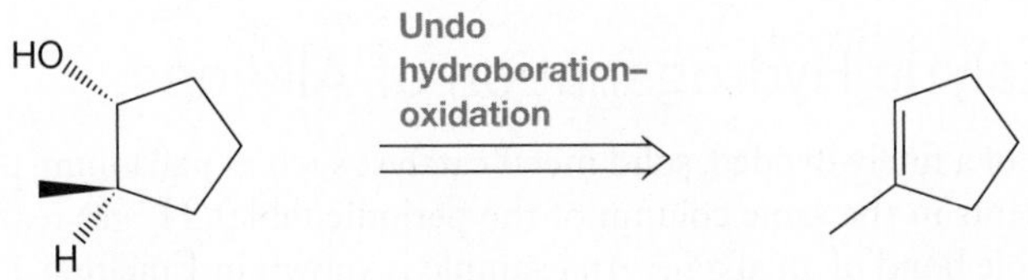
HO
H
Undo
hydroboration–
oxidation

An alcohol — An alkene (13-47)

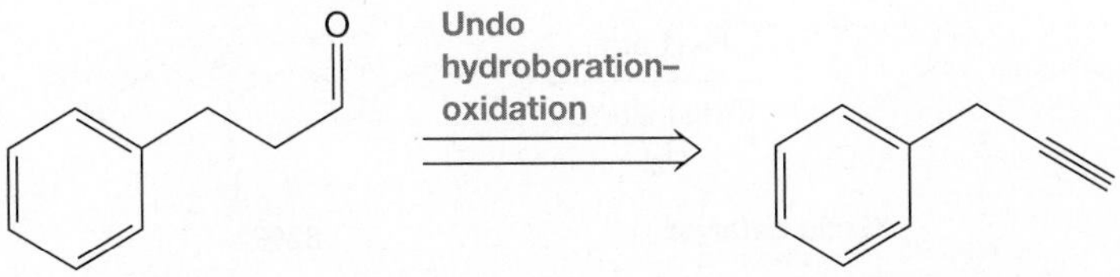
O
Undo
hydroboration–
oxidation

An aldehyde — A terminal alkyne (13-48)

YOUR TURN 13.23

Provide the reagents necessary to carry out each of the following transformations.

(a)

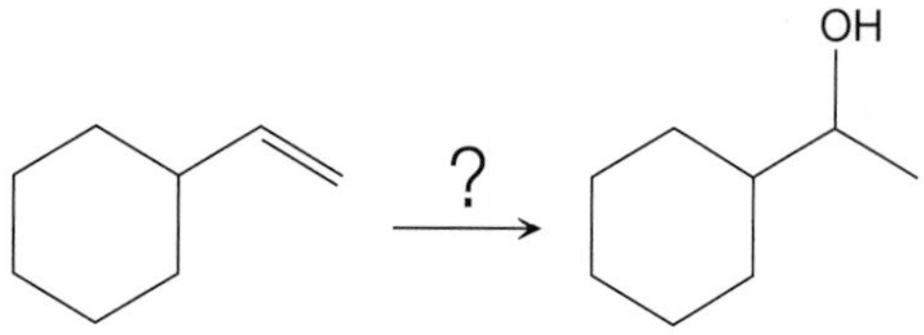

?
OH

(b)

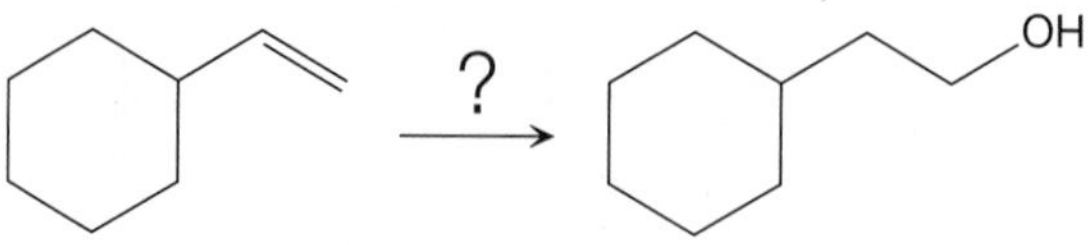

?
OH

(c)

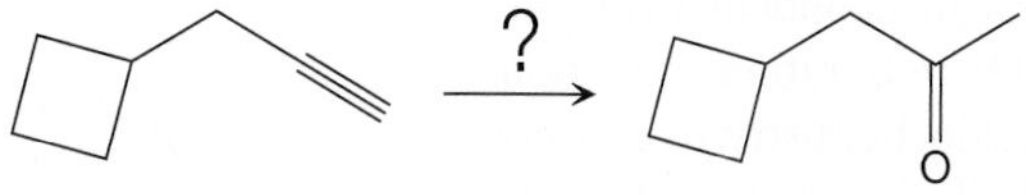

?
O

(d)

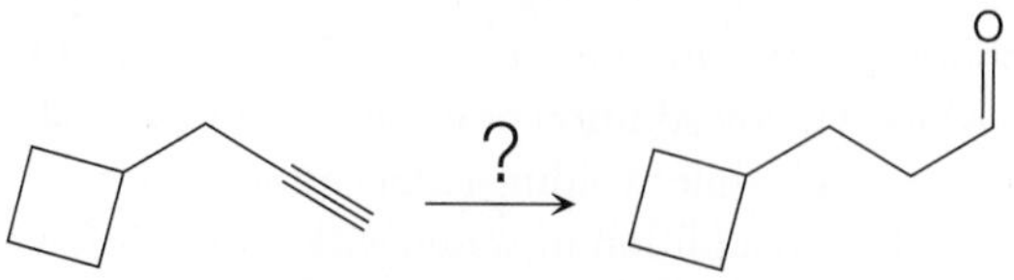

?
O

SECTION 13.9 OBJECTIVES

You will be able to:

1. Explain the role of the metal catalyst in catalytic hydrogenation of an alkene or alkyne.
2. Explain the role of a poisoned catalyst in catalytic hydrogenation of an alkyne.
3. Predict the major product from catalytic hydrogenation of an alkene or alkyne, including stereochemistry.

13.9 Organic Synthesis: Catalytic Hydrogenation of Alkenes and Alkynes

The reactions presented in Chapters 12 and 13 are related by their mechanisms; each has a key step that is driven by the formation of a bond between a carbon atom from a C=C or C≡C bond (which is electron-rich) and an electrophile (which is electron-poor). Here we introduce **catalytic hydrogenation**, in which H_2 adds to a C=C or C≡C bond, catalyzed on a metal surface. H_2 is not electrophilic, so the mechanism differs from the ones we have seen to this point. Nevertheless, we present catalytic hydrogenation here in Chapter 13 because it is such a useful reaction in synthesis.

13.9a Catalytic Hydrogenation of Alkenes

In the presence of a finely divided, solid metal catalyst such as palladium, platinum, or nickel (all elements in the same column of the periodic table), H_2 gas readily adds to the C=C double bond of an alkene. An example is shown in Equation 13-49:

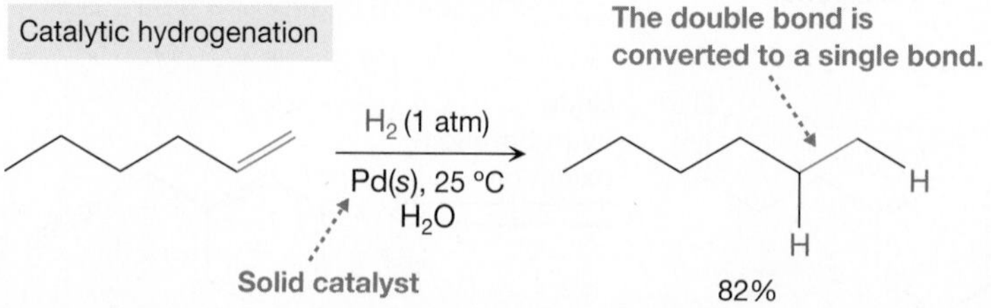

Catalytic hydrogenation
The double bond is converted to a single bond.
H2 (1 atm)
Pd(s), 25 °C
H2O
Solid catalyst
H
H
82%

(13-49)

Notice, in particular:

Catalytic hydrogenation using a platinum, palladium, or nickel metal catalyst converts the C=C double bond of an alkene to a C—C single bond.

The metal catalyst in the above reaction is called a **heterogeneous catalyst** because it exists in a different phase from the rest of the reaction mixture. The catalyst used during catalytic hydrogenation is *an insoluble solid*, suspended (by stirring or shaking) in a solution that contains both hydrogen and the organic substance to be hydrogenated.

The detailed mechanism for catalytic hydrogenation is relatively complex. A simplified picture is shown in **Figure 13-6**. Initially, the hydrogen and the alkene adsorb onto the surface of the catalyst, as shown in Figure 13-6a through 13-6c. As that occurs, the H—H single bonds are effectively broken, producing individual H atoms that reside on the metal surface. Similarly, adsorption of the alkene partially breaks the π bond of the C=C double bond. Eventually, an adsorbed H atom encounters an adsorbed alkene, and the first of two C—H bonds is formed (Fig. 13-6d). Very shortly after the first C—H bond forms, the second C—H bond is formed through a similar process (Fig. 13-6e). As each C—H bond is formed, the corresponding C atom is released from the metal surface. Because the reaction takes place at the metal's surface, using a finely divided catalyst dramatically increases the surface area of the metal and, hence, the rate of the reaction.

YOUR TURN **13.24**

Draw the product of each of the following reactions.

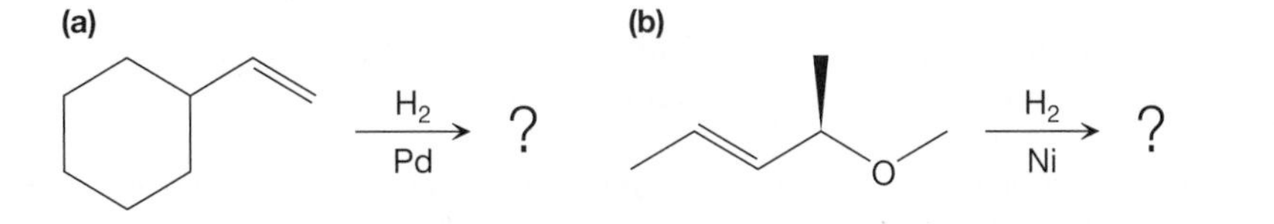

(a)
H_2
Pd
?
(b)
O
H_2
Ni
?

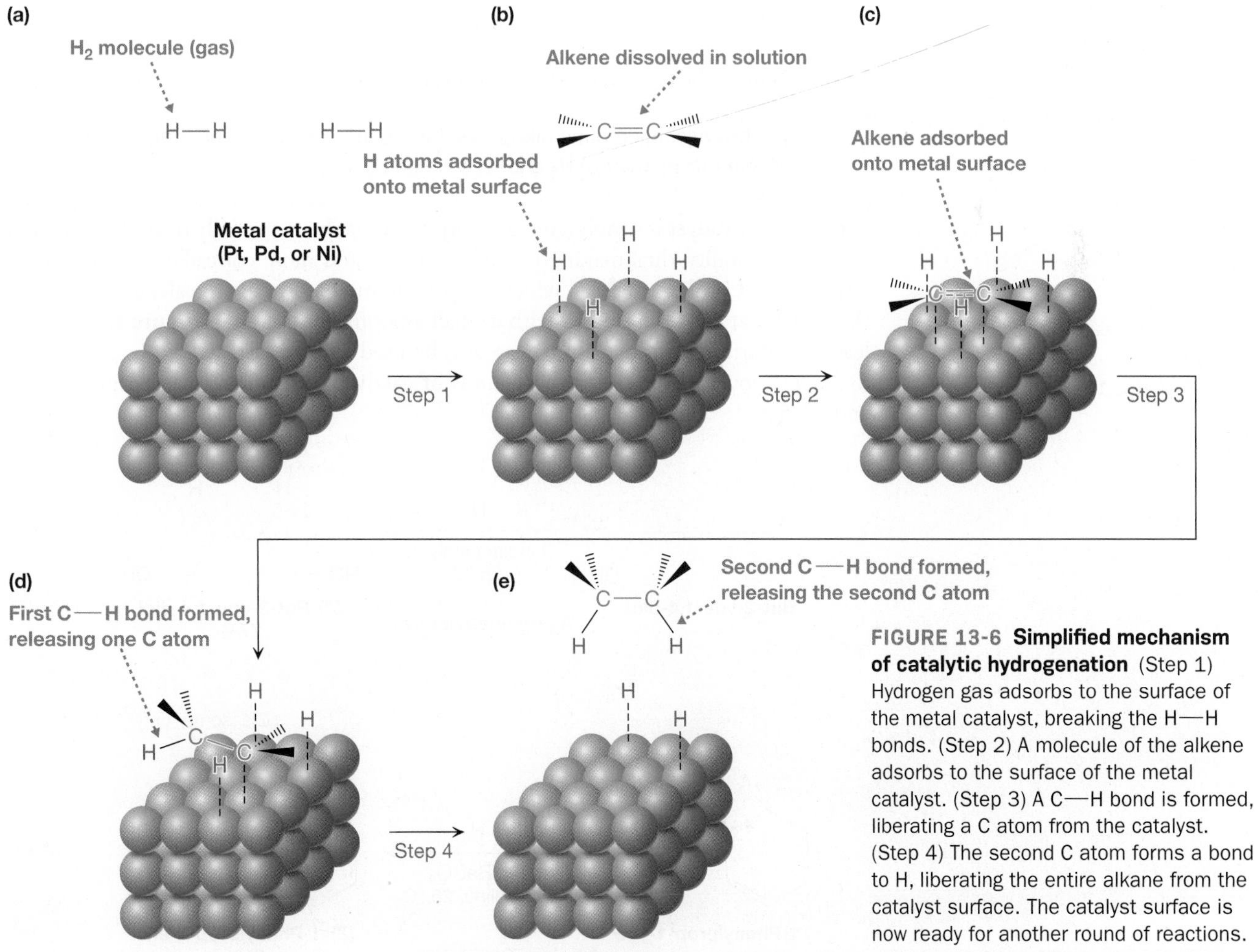

(a)
H_2 molecule (gas)
H—H
H—H
Metal catalyst
(Pt, Pd, or Ni)
Step 1
(b)
Alkene dissolved in solution
C=C
H atoms adsorbed
onto metal surface
H
H
H
H
Step 2
(c)
Alkene adsorbed
onto metal surface
H
H
H
C=C
H
Step 3
(d)
First C—H bond formed,
releasing one C atom
H
H
H
C
C
H
Step 4
(e)
C—C
H
H
Second C—H bond formed,
releasing the second C atom
H
H

FIGURE 13-6 Simplified mechanism of catalytic hydrogenation (Step 1) Hydrogen gas adsorbs to the surface of the metal catalyst, breaking the H—H bonds. (Step 2) A molecule of the alkene adsorbs to the surface of the metal catalyst. (Step 3) A C—H bond is formed, liberating a C atom from the catalyst. (Step 4) The second C atom forms a bond to H, liberating the entire alkane from the catalyst surface. The catalyst surface is now ready for another round of reactions.

13.9b Catalytic Hydrogenation of Alkynes: Poisoned Catalysts

The C≡C triple bond of an alkyne can undergo catalytic hydrogenation because it, too, contains carbon–carbon π bonds (see Looking Ahead box). Similar to alkenes, the addition of H_2 removes a π bond and causes the total number of bonds between the alkyne carbons to decrease by one. Thus, an alkyne is converted to an alkene, as shown in brackets:

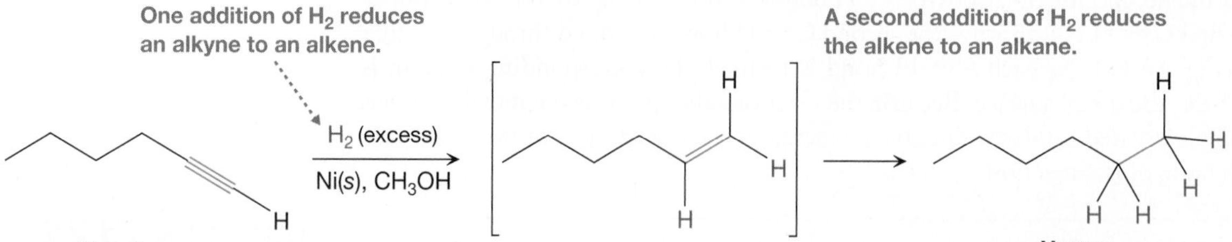

One addition of H2 reduces an alkyne to an alkene.
A second addition of H2 reduces the alkene to an alkane.
H2 (excess)
Ni(s), CH3OH
H

Hex-1-yne **Hexane** 85% (13-50)

The alkene that is produced is susceptible to catalytic hydrogenation, as indicated in Equation 13-50 and as we saw in Section 13.9a. Therefore:

- If equimolar amounts of H_2 and an alkyne react under normal conditions, we run the risk of producing a mixture of the alkene and alkane products: a generally undesirable result.
- If *excess* H_2 is present, then an alkyne will be converted completely to the alkane.

▸ **LOOKING AHEAD**

Alkenes and alkynes are not the only types of compounds that can undergo catalytic hydrogenation. Section 20.3 will discuss the catalytic hydrogenation of other types of compounds, such as aldehydes, ketones, nitriles, and amides.

If the alkene is the desired product, however:

Catalytic hydrogenation of an alkyne can be stopped at the alkene stage by using a stoichiometric amount of H_2 and a *poisoned catalyst*.

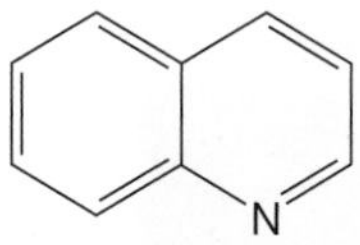

N

FIGURE 13-7 **Quinoline**

A **poisoned catalyst** is simply a metal catalyst that has been specially treated to decrease its catalytic ability, thus making possible a slower and more controlled reaction. One example is **Lindlar catalyst**, which is palladium deposited on calcium carbonate ($CaCO_3$) that has been treated with a small amount of quinoline (**Figure 13-7**) and a lead salt. Barium sulfate ($BaSO_4$) can also be used instead of $CaCO_3$. Representative hydrogenation reactions with these kinds of catalysts are shown in Equations 13-51 and 13-52:

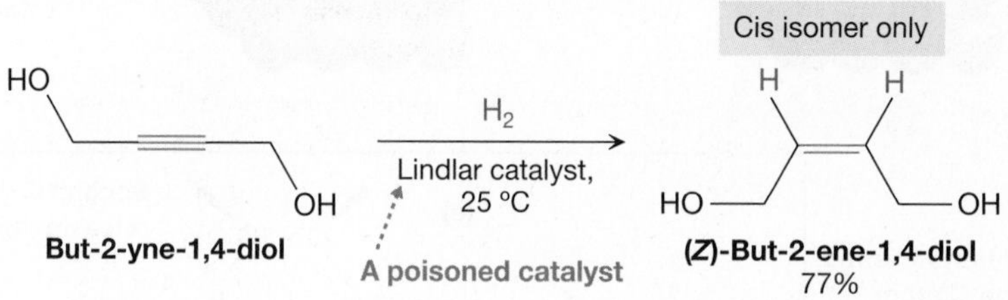

Cis isomer only
HO
OH
H2
Lindlar catalyst, 25 °C
A poisoned catalyst
H
H
HO
OH

But-2-yne-1,4-diol **(Z)-But-2-ene-1,4-diol** 77% (13-51)

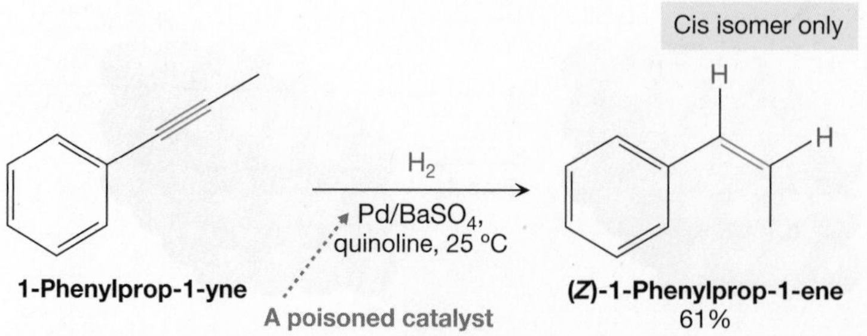

Cis isomer only
H2
Pd/BaSO4, quinoline, 25 °C
A poisoned catalyst
H
H

1-Phenylprop-1-yne **(Z)-1-Phenylprop-1-ene** 61% (13-52)

Equations 13-51 and 13-52 show that catalytic hydrogenation takes place *stereoselectively*:

> The reduction of an alkyne to an alkene by catalytic hydrogenation favors production of the cis isomer over the trans isomer.

This stereoselectivity can be understood from the simplified picture of the mechanism we saw previously in Figure 13-6 (p. 679). After the first H atom adds to one C of the multiple bond (Fig. 13-6d), the second H atom adds to the other C (Fig. 13-6e) before any significant changes occur in the orientation of the molecule. Thus, the individual H atoms end up on the same side of the newly formed C═C double bond; the H atoms add in a syn fashion (see Looking Ahead box).

▸ LOOKING AHEAD

In Chapter 27, we will discuss hydrogenation reactions that add H atoms in an anti fashion and thus convert alkynes into trans alkenes. Those reactions proceed by mechanisms that involve radical intermediates (species with unpaired electrons), the theme of Chapter 27.

YOUR TURN 13.25

Which of the following molecules **A–C** could be produced from an alkyne if a poisoned catalyst were used?

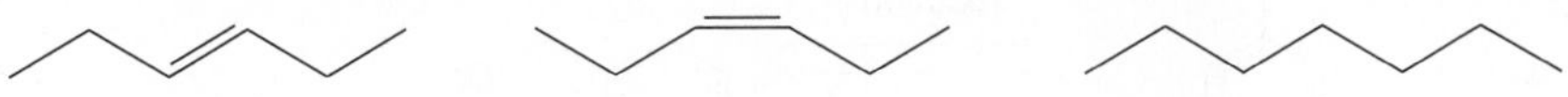

A **B** **C**

YOUR TURN 13.26

In Equation 13-52, why are the double bonds in the starting material unaffected by hydrogenation?

SOLVED PROBLEM **13.6**

How to design a synthesis that calls for the formation of a C—C bond

Break It Down Outline a synthesis of (*Z*)-1-phenylhept-2-ene from (bromomethyl)benzene and any hydrocarbon (i.e., a compound containing only C and H).

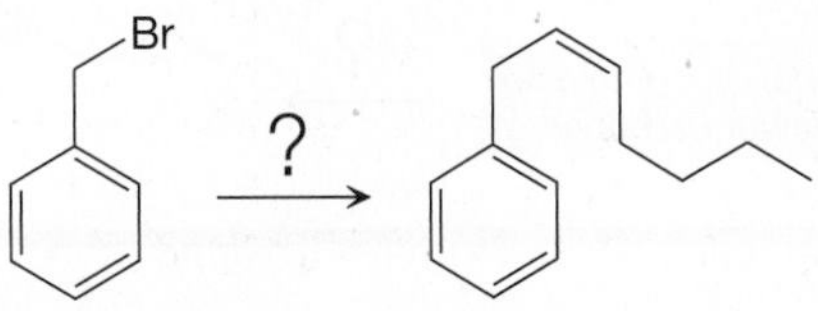

Br
?

(Bromomethyl)benzene (Benzyl bromide) **(*Z*)-1-Phenylhept-2-ene**

Think	Solve
Does this synthesis require a carbon–carbon bond-forming reaction? If so, have you learned a carbon–carbon bond-forming reaction that leaves a C═C bond in the product?	This synthesis requires the formation of the highlighted carbon–carbon bond below. However, we have not learned a reaction that forms such a bond and leaves a C═C bond in the product. 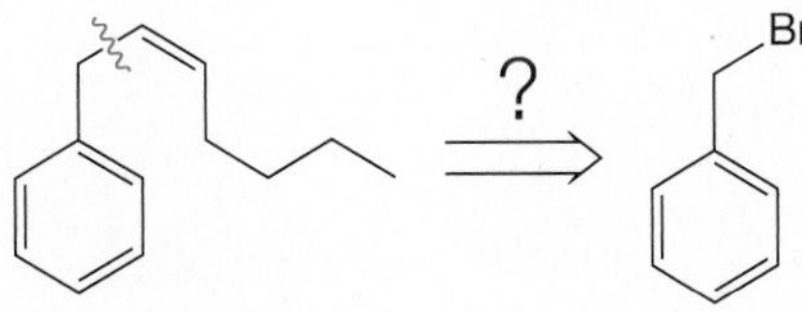

(continued)

Can the cis C═C bond be produced from another functional group?	The cis C═C bond can be produced from the C≡C bond of an alkyne if the alkyne is treated with a poisoned catalyst. This transform is shown here. 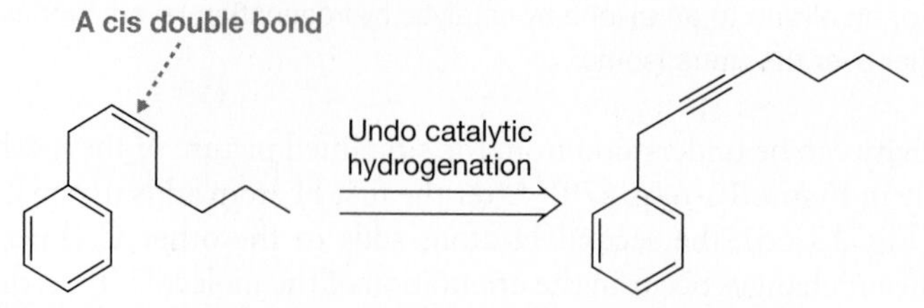 A cis double bond Undo catalytic hydrogenation
Can you recall a carbon–carbon bond-forming reaction that leaves a C≡C triple bond in the product?	Chapter 11 describes the alkylation of a terminal alkyne, an S_N2 reaction in which a C—C single bond forms between an alkyne C and a primary tetrahedral C. 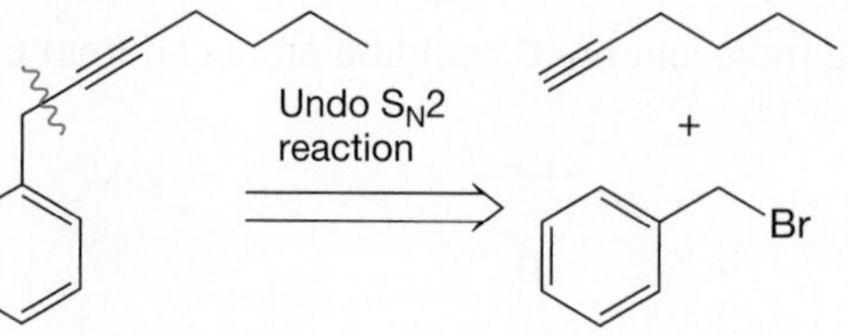 Undo S_N2 reaction + Br
Having completed the retrosynthetic analysis, how can we write the final synthesis?	To write the final synthesis, we reverse the transforms and add the appropriate reagents, as shown below. 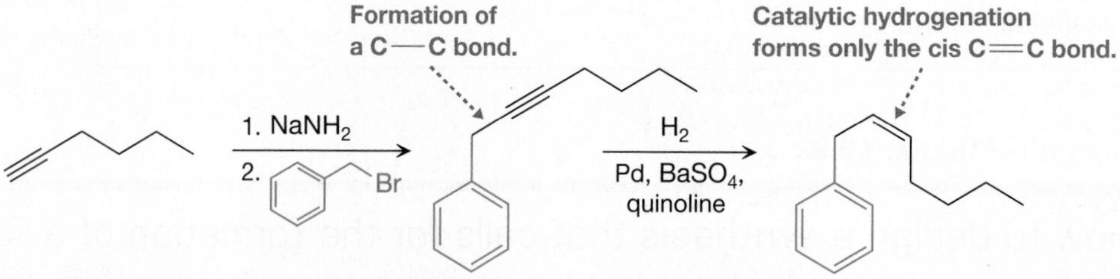 Formation of a C—C bond. Catalytic hydrogenation forms only the cis C═C bond. 1. $NaNH_2$ 2. Br H_2 Pd, $BaSO_4$, quinoline

Try It Show how to carry out the following synthesis.

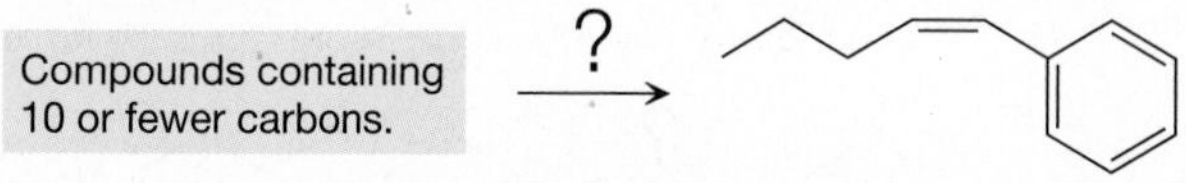
Compounds containing
10 or fewer carbons.
?

Trans Fats in Your Diet

The U.S. Food and Drug Administration requires all food packaging to list the amount of *trans fat* per serving because dietary trans fats are associated with increased risk of heart disease and certain types of cancer. As discussed in Section 2.10a, a fat or oil is a triglyceride (a triester of glycerol), which has three long-chain carbon tails that can vary in length and in the number of C=C double bonds present. In a trans fat, at least one of the alkyl chains contains a C=C double bond in the trans configuration, as shown in **Figure 13-8**.

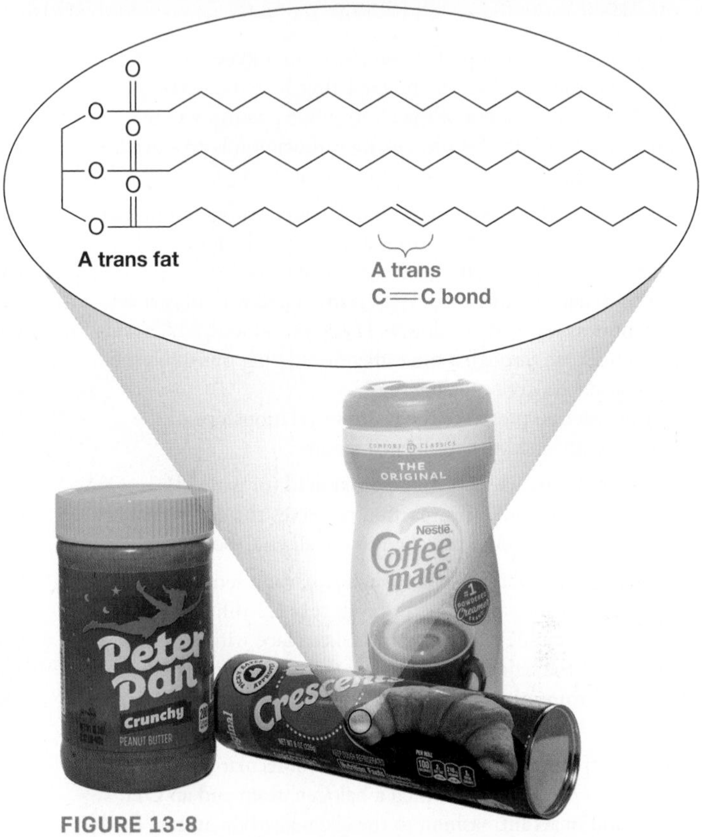
A trans fat
A trans C=C bond
Peter Pan
Crunchy
PEANUT BUTTER
Nestlé
Coffee mate
THE ORIGINAL

FIGURE 13-8

The bulk of dietary trans fats comes from an industrial process called the *partial hydrogenation of oil*. Naturally occurring oils are liquids at room temperature because they are unsaturated, containing C=C double bonds that are predominantly in the cis configuration (Section 4.14). In partial hydrogenation, the oil is treated with hydrogen gas and a metal catalyst and undergoes catalytic hydrogenation (the same reaction presented in Section 13.9) until a specified percentage of the C=C double bonds remain. Because it has fewer C=C double bonds, the resulting partially hydrogenated oil becomes a solid with long shelf life, which are desired properties for many packaged foods. Some of the C=C double bonds that remain, however, are converted from the cis configuration to the more stable trans configuration. This cis/trans isomerization is made possible because the mechanism for catalytic hydrogenation (Fig. 13-6) is *reversible* until the second hydrogen has been added.

Consider the mechanism shown in **Figure 13-9**, which begins with a C=C double bond in the cis configuration. Steps 1 and 2 result in the addition of H to one of the carbons, at which point the carbons are connected by a single bond. After rotation of the C—C single bond by 120°, Steps 2 and 1 can proceed in the reverse direction to re-form the C=C double bond, now in the trans configuration.

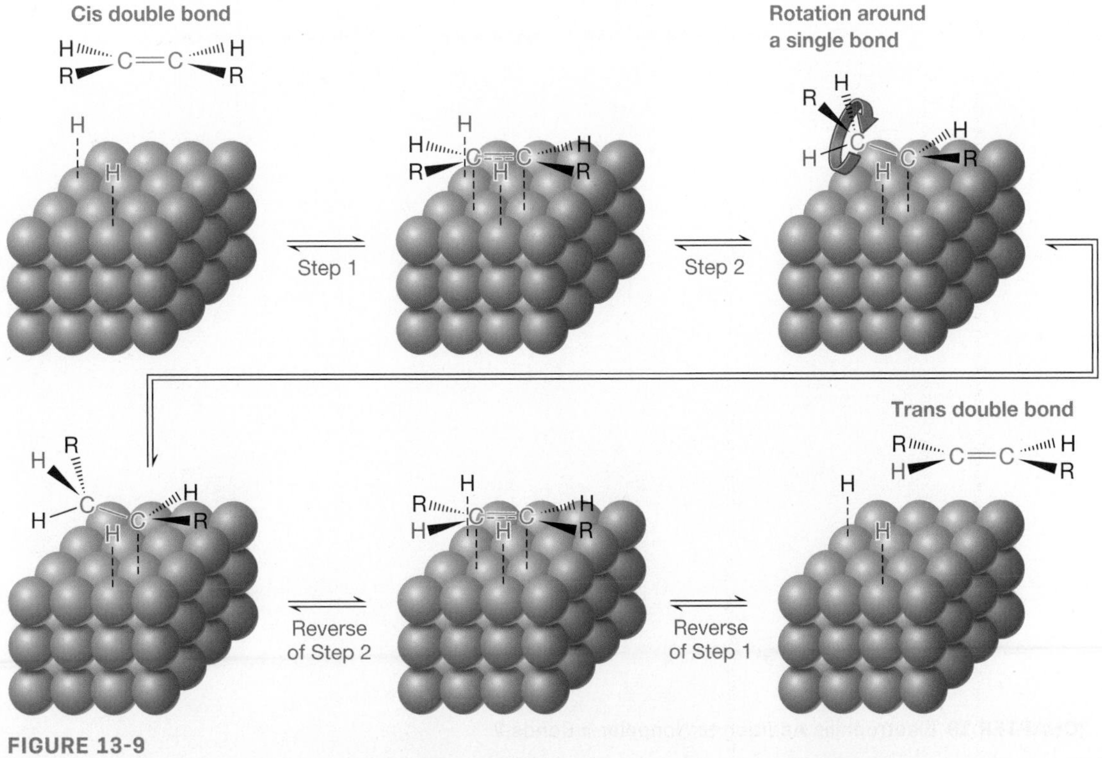
Cis double bond
Rotation around a single bond
Step 1
Step 2
Trans double bond
Reverse of Step 2
Reverse of Step 1

FIGURE 13-9

Chapter Summary and Key Terms

- Addition of an electrophile to an alkene or alkyne tends to proceed through a three-membered-ring transition state if the electron-poor atom of the electrophile possesses a lone pair of electrons. In this process, no carbocation is produced. **(Section 13.1)**
- A **carbene** is characterized by an uncharged carbon atom that possesses a lone pair of electrons and is typically produced in situ from an appropriate precursor. **(Section 13.2)**
  - When diazomethane (CH_2N_2) is irradiated with ultraviolet light or is warmed in solution, H_2C: is produced, which adds to an alkene through a three-membered-ring transition state to produce a cyclopropane ring.
  - This reaction preserves the cis/trans relationships of the groups attached to the alkene carbons.
- Treatment of an alkene with a **peroxy acid** (or peracid) produces an epoxide. This reaction preserves the cis/trans relationships of the groups attached to the alkene. **(Section 13.3)**
- In a non-nucleophilic solvent (such as carbon tetrachloride), Br_2 or Cl_2 adds to an alkene to produce a 1,2-dihalide (or vicinal dihalide). This reaction takes place with anti addition of the halogens, signifying the initial production of a **bromonium** or **chloronium ion intermediate**. **(Section 13.4a)**
- In water, treatment of an alkene with a molecular halogen produces a *halohydrin*, in which a halogen atom and an OH group add in an anti fashion to the alkene carbon atoms. The OH group ends up on the carbon that can better handle a positive charge. **(Section 13.4b)**
- **Oxymercuration–reduction** proceeds through a **mercurinium ion intermediate** and results in the addition of water to an alkene or alkyne with Markovnikov regiochemistry. Carbocation rearrangements do *not* occur in such reactions. **(Section 13.5)**
- In a **hydroboration–oxidation reaction**, H—OH adds to an alkene in a syn fashion, with **anti-Markovnikov regiochemistry**, to produce an alcohol. **(Section 13.6)**
  - The hydroboration step involves the addition of BH_3 to the alkene to produce a **trialkylborane** and proceeds through a four-membered-ring transition state. **(Section 13.6a)**
  - The oxidation step converts the trialkylborane to the alcohol, with retention of configuration. **(Section 13.6b)**
- A single hydroboration–oxidation of an alkyne produces an enol that tautomerizes into a ketone or an aldehyde. To ensure that an alkyne undergoes only a single hydroboration, a bulky dialkylborane is used, such as **disiamylborane**, **dicyclohexylborane**, or **9-borabicyclo[3.3.1]nonane (9-BBN)**. **(Section 13.7)**
- **Catalytic hydrogenation** takes place when an alkene or alkyne is treated with H_2 in the presence of a metal catalyst such as Pt, Pd, or Ni. In these reactions, H_2 adds across the C=C double bond or the C≡C triple bond. **(Section 13.9)**
  - Catalytic hydrogenation of an alkene produces an alkane. **(Section 13.9a)**
  - Catalytic hydrogenation of an alkyne produces an alkane when excess H_2 is used. If a **poisoned catalyst** is used, such as **Lindlar catalyst**, then the reaction can be used to produce a cis alkene. **(Section 13.9b)**

Reaction Tables

Functional group transformations introduced in this chapter are collected in Table 13-1, and reactions introduced in this chapter that alter the carbon skeleton are collected in Table 13-2.

TABLE 13-1 Functional Group Transformations[a]

	Starting Compound Class	Typical Reagents and Reaction Conditions	Compound Class Formed	Key Electron-Rich Species	Key Electron-Poor Species	Comments	Discussed in Section(s)
(1)	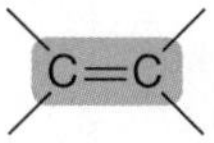 Alkene	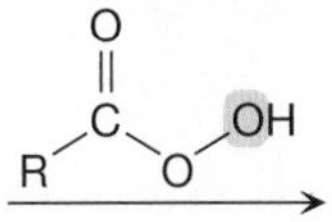	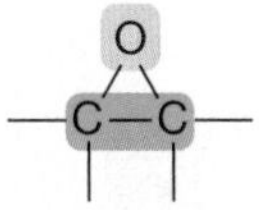 Epoxide	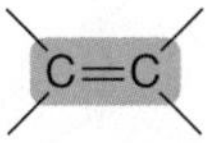	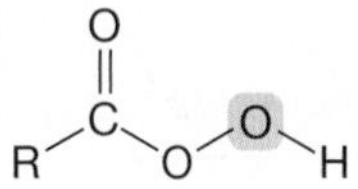	Conservation of cis/trans configuration	13.3
(2)	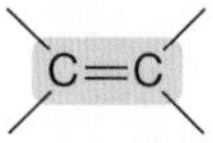 Alkene	$\xrightarrow[CCl_4]{X_2}$	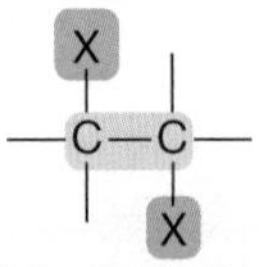 Vicinal dihalide	$:\ddot{X}:^{\ominus}$	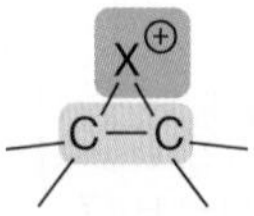	Anti addition	13.4a
(3)	 Alkyne	$\xrightarrow[CCl_4]{X_2\ 2\ equiv}$	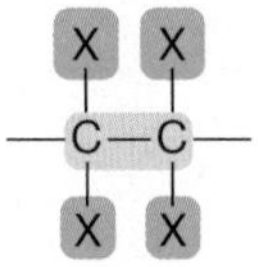 1,1,2,2-Tetrahalide	$:\ddot{X}:^{\ominus}$	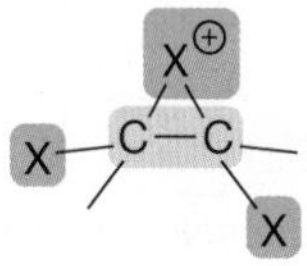	2 equiv of halogen	13.4a
(4)	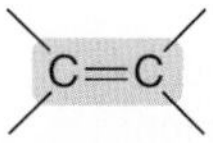 Alkene	$\xrightarrow[H_2O]{X_2}$	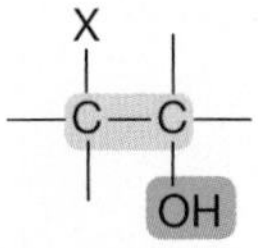 Halohydrin	$H_2\ddot{O}:$	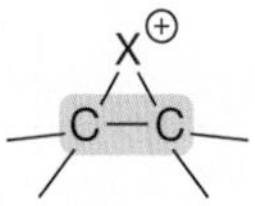	OH ends up on more substituted carbon; anti addition	13.4b
(5)	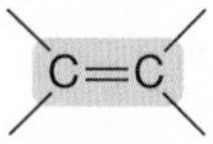 Alkene	1. $Hg(OAc)_2$, H_2O → 2. $NaBH_4$	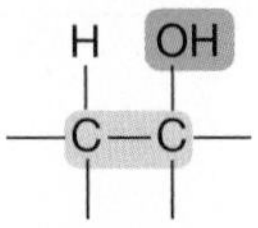 Alcohol	$H_2\ddot{O}:$	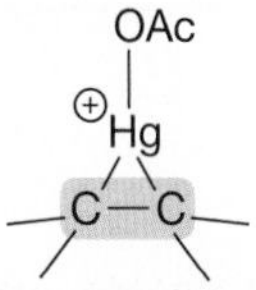	Markovnikov addition of water; no carbocation rearrangements	13.5

[a]X = Cl or Br.

(continued)

TABLE 13-1 Functional Group Transformations[a] (continued)

	Starting Compound Class	Typical Reagents and Reaction Conditions	Compound Class Formed	Key Electron-Rich Species	Key Electron-Poor Species	Comments	Discussed in Section(s)
(6)	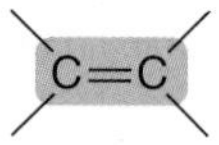 Alkene	1. B_2H_6 or BH_3•THF → 2. H_2O_2, NaOH, H_2O	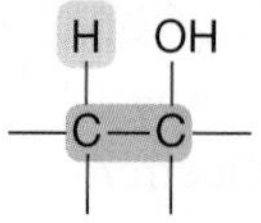 Alcohol	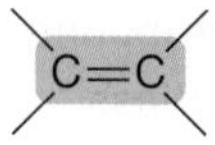	BH_3	Anti-Markovnikov syn addition of water	13.6
(7)	—C≡C— Alkyne	$Hg(OAc)_2$, H_2O →	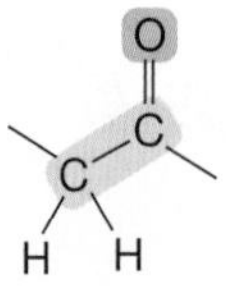 Ketone	$H_2\ddot{O}$:	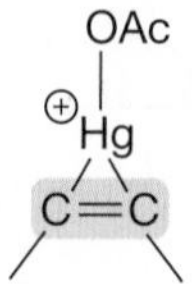	Markovnikov addition of water	13.5
(8)	—C≡C— Alkyne	1. $(C_5H_{11})_2BH$ → 2. H_2O_2, NaOH, H_2O	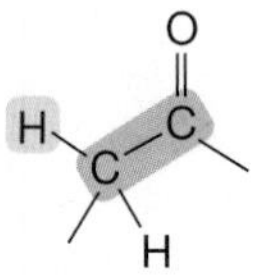 Ketone or aldehyde	—C≡C—	$(C_5H_{11})_2BH$	Anti-Markovnikov addition of water	13.7
(9)	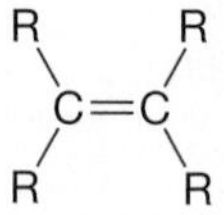 Alkene	H_2 → Pt, Pd, or Ni	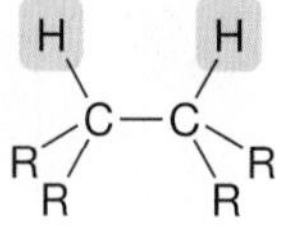 Alkane			Catalytic hydrogenation	13.9a
(10)	R—C≡C—R Alkyne	H_2 → Lindlar catalyst	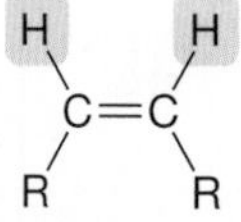 *cis*-Alkene			Catalytic hydrogenation; poisoned catalyst	13.9b

[a]X = Cl or Br.

TABLE 13-2 Reactions That Alter the Carbon Skeleton

	Starting Compound Class	Typical Reagents and Reaction Conditions	Compound Class Formed	Key Electron-Rich Species	Key Electron-Poor Species	Comments	Discussed in Section(s)
(1)	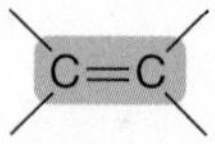 Alkene	CH_2N_2 → Δ or *hν*	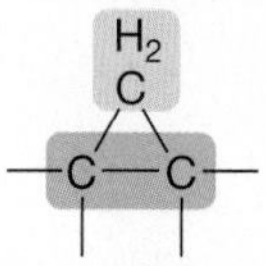 Cyclopropane ring	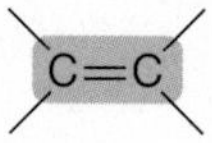	$:CH_2$	Syn addition; retention of cis/trans configuration; not very useful in synthesis	13.2

Problems

Problems that are related to synthesis are denoted (SYN).

Section 13.2 Electrophilic Addition of Carbenes: Formation of Cyclopropane Rings

13.1 Draw the mechanism for the reaction that would take place when each of the following compounds is treated with CH_2N_2 and irradiated with ultraviolet light.

(a) (*R*)-1,6-Dimethylcyclohexene

(b) 

(c) 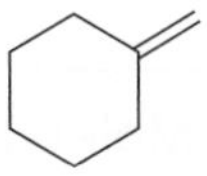

(d) 

(e) 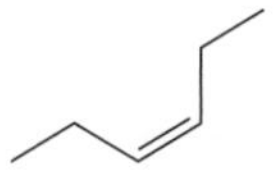

13.2 **(SYN)** The high reactivity of carbenes can facilitate the synthesis of some unusual compounds. Show how each of the following can be synthesized from acyclic compounds.

(a) 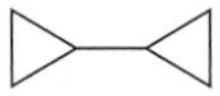

(b) 

13.3 **(SYN)** Show how each of these compounds can be produced from an alkene. In each case, include the alkene, the reagents, and any special reaction conditions. Pay attention to stereochemistry.

(a) 

(b) 

(c) 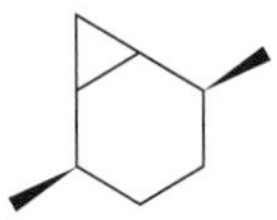

(d) 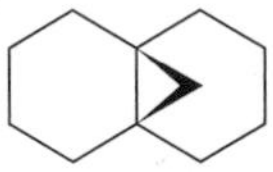

13.4 **(SYN)** Draw the alkyne that, when treated with diazomethane and irradiated with ultraviolet light, will produce the compound shown here, and draw the complete mechanism for the reaction.

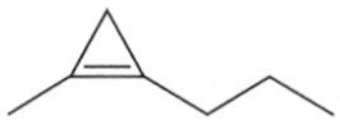

13.5 Draw the mechanism for this reaction.

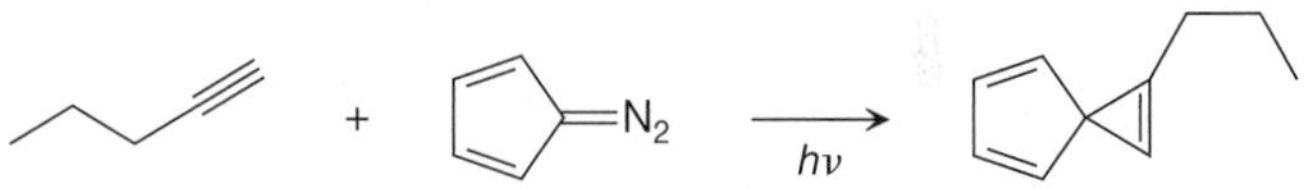
+
N_2
$h\nu$

55%

13.6 Draw all stereoisomers that can be produced in this reaction.

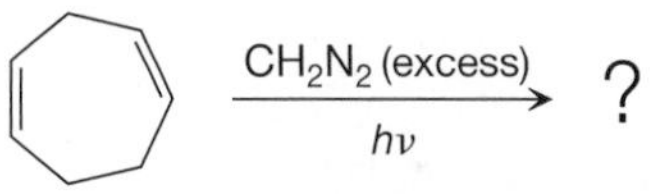
CH_2N_2 (excess)
$h\nu$
?

Section 13.3 Epoxide Formation with Peroxy Acids

13.7 For each reaction, draw the complete mechanism and the major product(s), paying attention to stereochemistry.

(a)

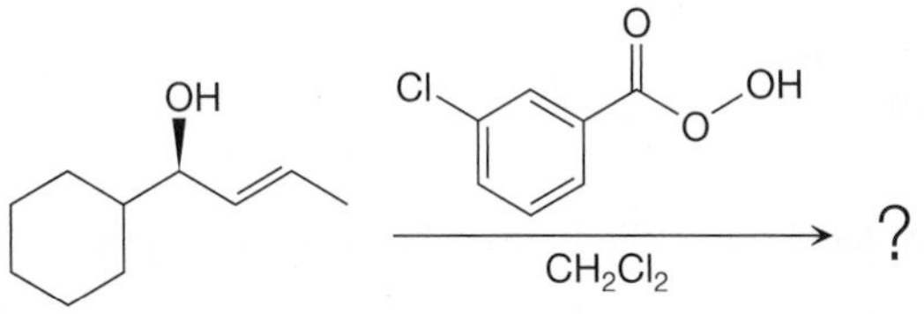
OH
Cl
O
OH
O
CH_2Cl_2
?

(b)

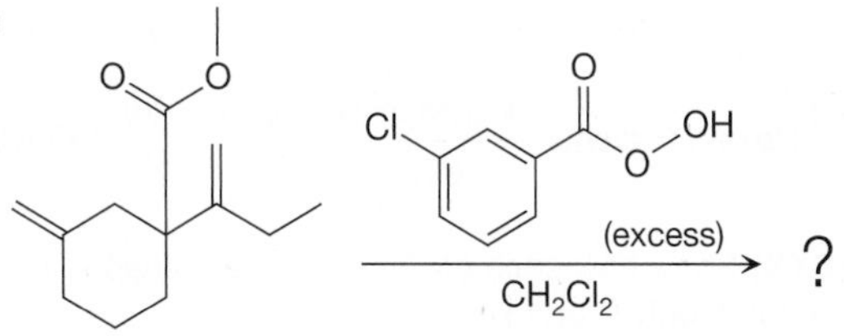
O
O
Cl
O
OH
O
(excess)
CH_2Cl_2
?

13.8 **(SYN)** Show how each epoxide can be produced from an alkene.

(a) 

(b) 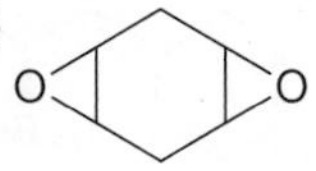

(c) 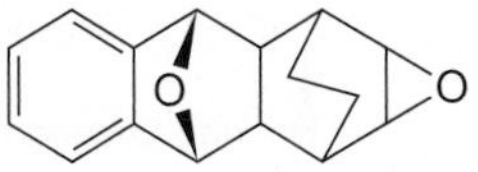

13.9 Draw the complete mechanism for the following reaction.

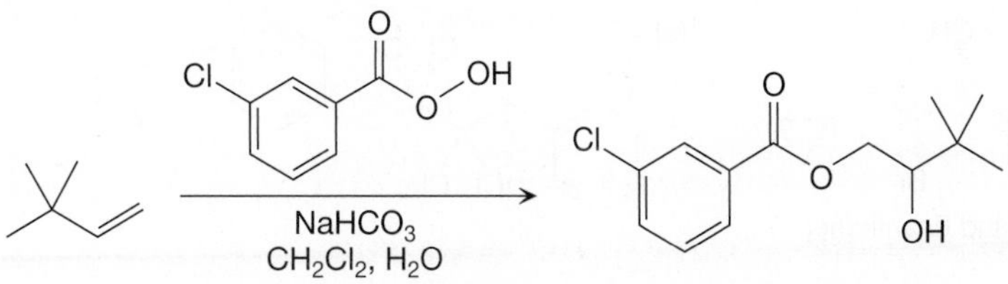
O
Cl
OH
O
$NaHCO_3$
CH_2Cl_2, H_2O
O
Cl
O
OH

13.10 When cyclohexene is treated with *m*-chloroperbenzoic acid and H_2O, *trans*-cyclohexane-1,2-diol is produced. Propose a mechanism for this reaction that accounts for the observed stereochemistry. *Hint*: Recall what a peroxy acid does to an alkene.

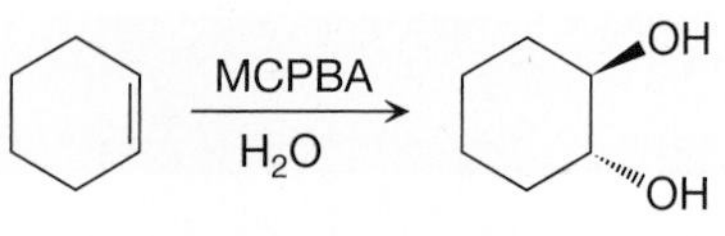
MCPBA
H2O
OH
OH
and Enantiomer

13.11 Why do you think the epoxidation reaction shown here favors the C=C bond on the left?

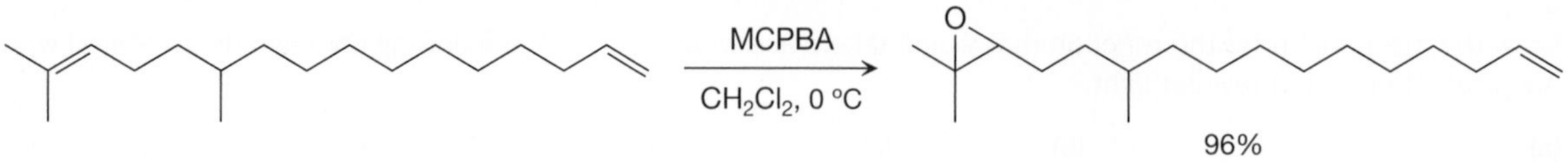
MCPBA
CH2Cl2, 0 °C
O
96%

Section 13.4 Electrophilic Addition Involving Molecular Halogens: Synthesis of 1,2-Dihalides and Halohydrins

13.12 Br_2 undergoes electrophilic addition to maleic anhydride as shown here. Explain why this reaction is much slower than the analogous reaction with cyclopentene.

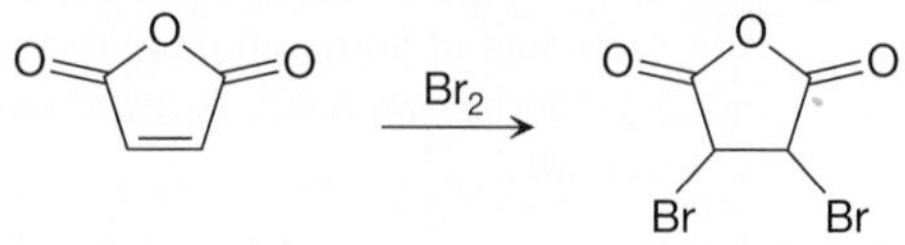
O
O
O
Br2
O
O
O
Br
Br

13.13 The electrophilic addition of Br_2 to several alkenes was examined. Explain why the relative reaction rates are as follows:

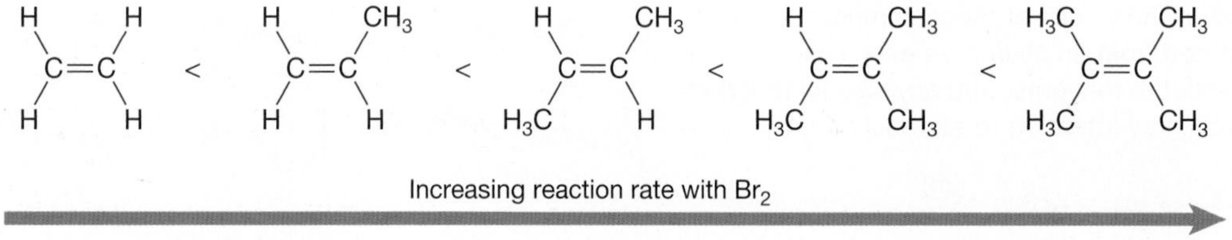
Increasing reaction rate with Br2

13.14 For each of the following reactions, draw a complete, detailed mechanism and predict the major products, paying close attention to regiochemistry and stereochemistry.

(a) 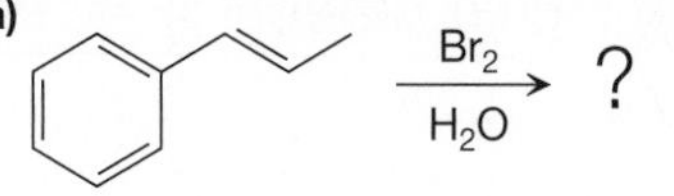
Br2
H2O
?

(b) 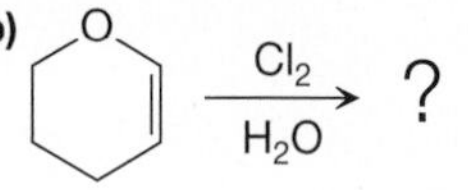
O
Cl2
H2O
?

13.15 For each of the following reactions, draw a complete, detailed mechanism and predict the major products.

(a) 2-Methylbut-2-ene $\xrightarrow[CCl_4]{Br_2}$?

(b) 2-Methylbut-2-ene $\xrightarrow[H_2O]{Br_2}$?

(c) Hexa-1,5-diene $\xrightarrow[CCl_4]{Cl_2\text{ (excess)}}$?

(d) 3-Ethylpent-1-yne $\xrightarrow[CCl_4]{Br_2\text{ (excess)}}$?

13.16 **(SYN)** Show how each of the following compounds can be synthesized from a hydrocarbon (i.e., a compound that contains only C and H).

(a) 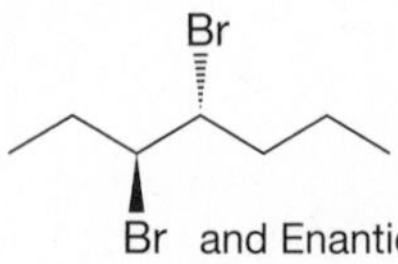
Br
Br
and Enantiomer

(b) 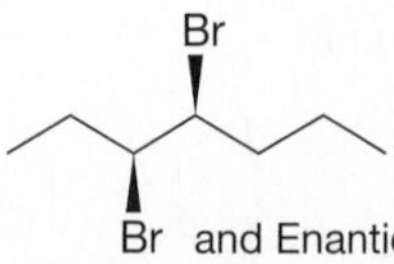
Br
Br
and Enantiomer

(c) 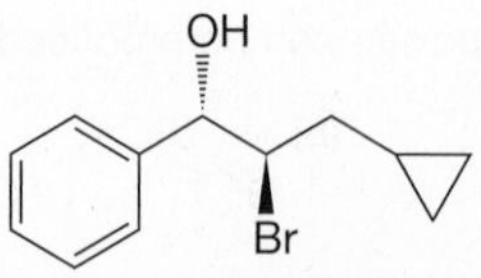
OH
Br
and Enantiomer

(d) 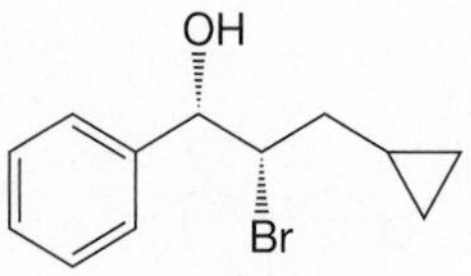
OH
Br
and Enantiomer

(e) 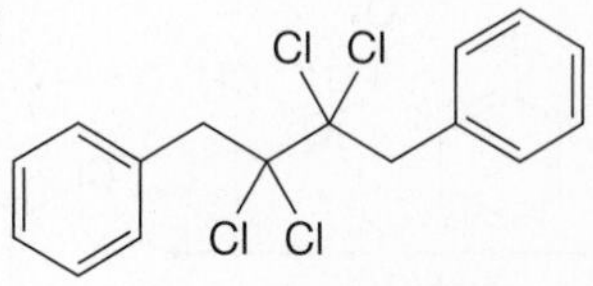
Cl Cl
Cl Cl

13.17 Bromination can occur in a 1,4-fashion across conjugated double bonds, as shown here for cyclohexa-1,3-diene:

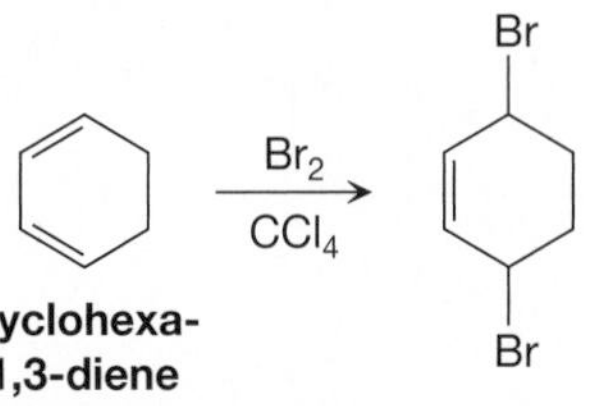
Br
Br_2
CCl_4
Br

Cyclohexa-1,3-diene

One mechanism that has been proposed involves a five-membered ring, bromonium ion intermediate, as shown below. **(a)** According to this mechanism, what should the stereochemistry be for the products: all cis, all trans, or a mixture of cis and trans? **(b)** Experimental observations show that both cis and trans products are formed. Does this support or discredit the proposed mechanism?

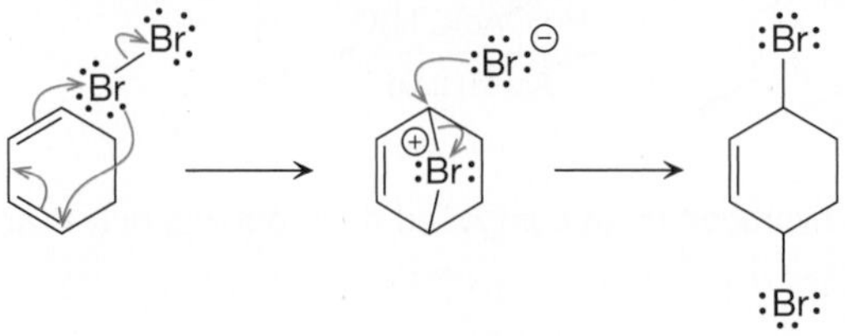
:Br:
:Br
:Br:
:Br:
:Br:
:Br:

13.18 Propose a mechanism for the following reaction that accounts for the observed stereochemistry.

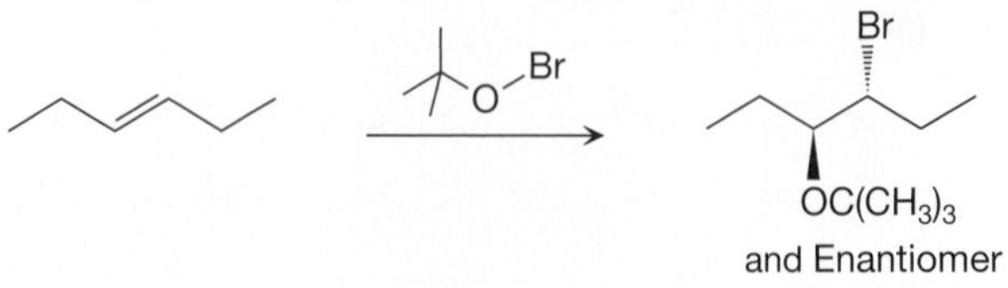
Br
O
Br
$OC(CH_3)_3$
and Enantiomer

13.19 A student attempted a bromination of the double bond in pent-4-en-1-ol, but ended up with the following cyclic ether instead. Propose a mechanism for the formation of this product.

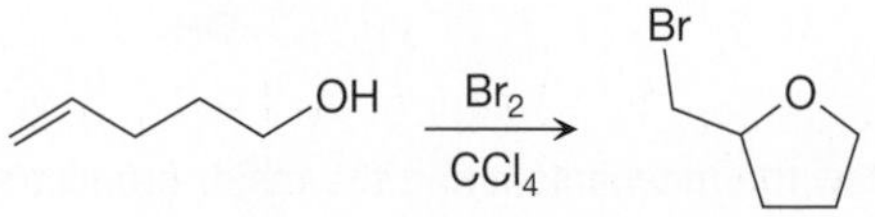
OH
Br_2
CCl_4
Br
O

13.20 Iodine monochloride (ICl) is a mixed halogen that adds to an alkene by the same mechanism by which bromination takes place. With that in mind, propose a mechanism for the following reaction, and use that mechanism to predict the products, paying attention to both *regiochemistry* and *stereochemistry*. *Hint*: In ICl, one atom is more electrophilic than the other.

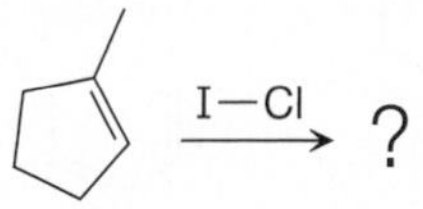
I—Cl
?

Section 13.5 Oxymercuration–Reduction: Addition of Water

13.21 Draw the mechanism and the major product(s) for each of the following reactions.

(a) Cyclopentylethene $\xrightarrow{H_3O^{\oplus}}$?

(b) Cyclopentylethene $\xrightarrow[\text{2. NaBH}_4\text{, ethanol}]{\text{1. Hg(OAc)}_2\text{, H}_2\text{O}}$?

(c)

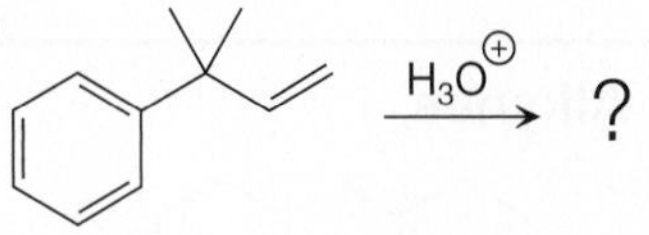
$H_3O^{\oplus}$
?

(d)

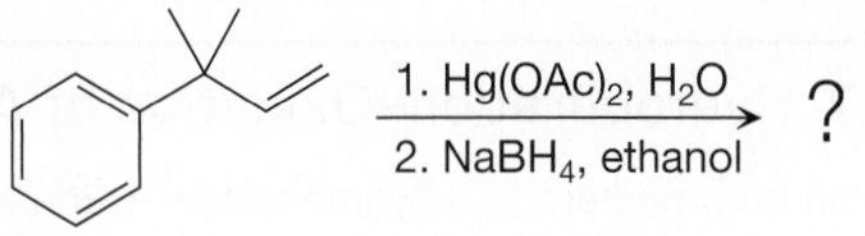
1. $Hg(OAc)_2$, H_2O
2. $NaBH_4$, ethanol
?

13.22 **(SYN)** Show how to make each compound from an alkene.

(a)

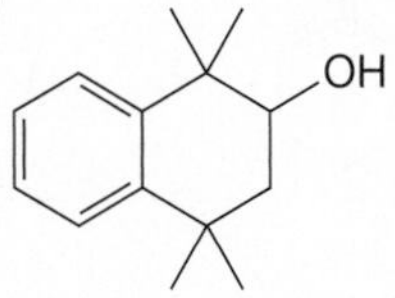
OH

(b)

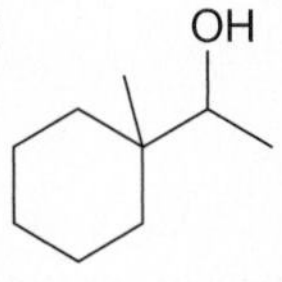
OH

13.23 Which of these transformations would be the result of acid-catalyzed hydration, and which would be the result of oxymercuration–reduction?

(a)

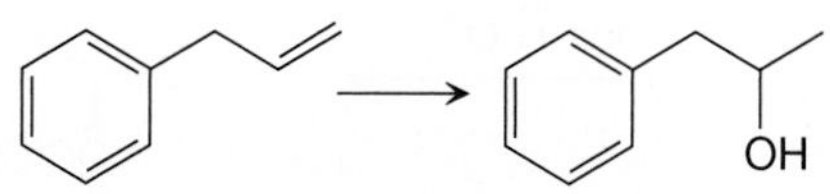
OH

(b)

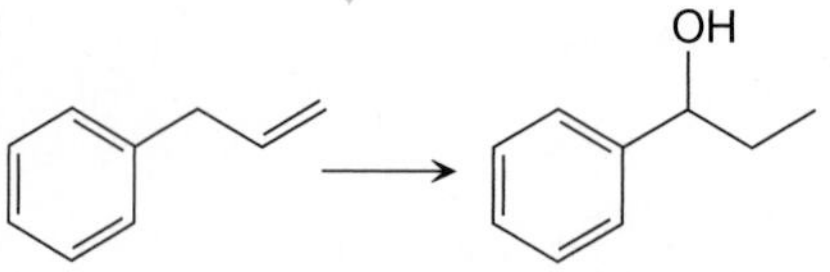
OH

(c)

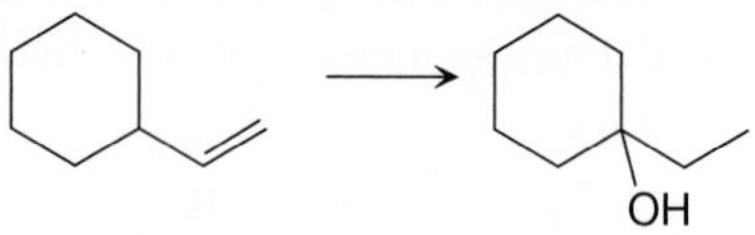
OH

(d)

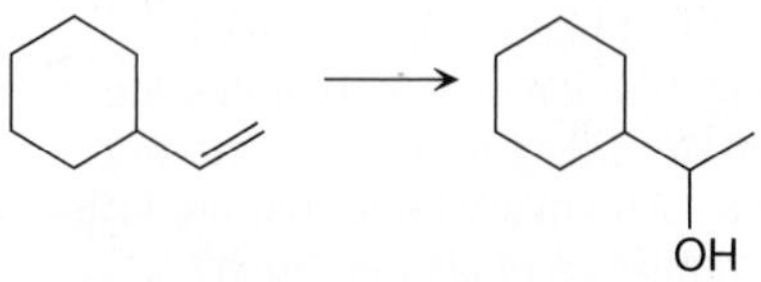
OH

13.24 Draw the mechanism and the major product(s) for each of the following reactions.

(a)

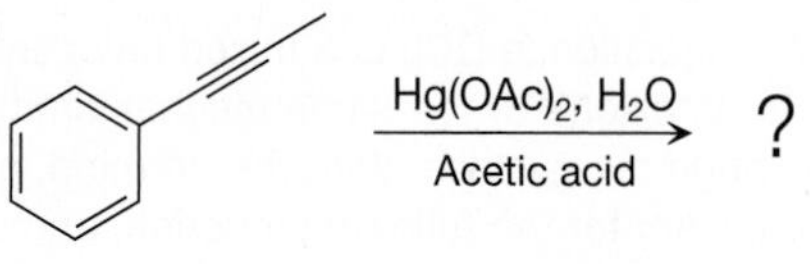
Hg(OAc)2, H2O
Acetic acid
?

(b)

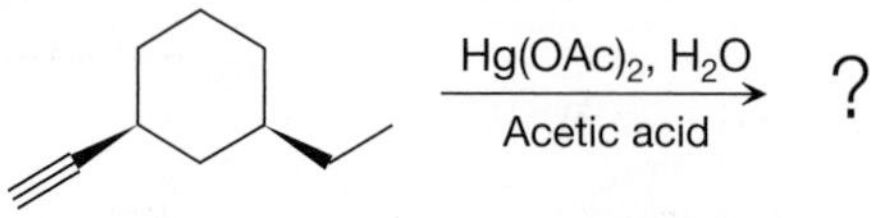
Hg(OAc)2, H2O
Acetic acid
?

13.25 **(SYN)** Show how to synthesize each of these compounds from a hydrocarbon (a compound that contains only C and H).

(a)

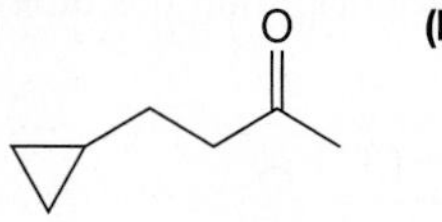
O

(b)

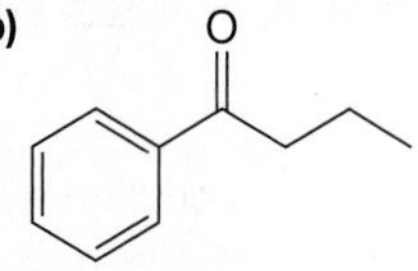
O

13.26 In the following oxymercuration–reduction reaction, H adds to the more highly substituted C atom, which might appear to violate Markovnikov's rule. Explain why this reaction exhibits this regiochemistry.

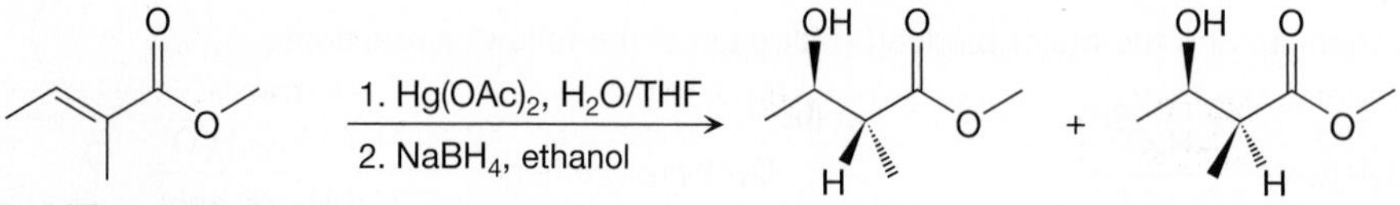
O
O
1. Hg(OAc)2, H2O/THF
2. NaBH4, ethanol
OH O
O
H
+
OH O
O
H

Methyl (*E*)-2-methylbut-2-enoate

and Enantiomer

and Enantiomer

Sections 13.6 and 13.7 Hydroboration–Oxidation of Alkenes and Alkynes

13.27 This trialkylborane is an intermediate in a hydroboration–oxidation reaction. Draw the alcohol that is produced on treatment with a basic solution of H_2O_2.

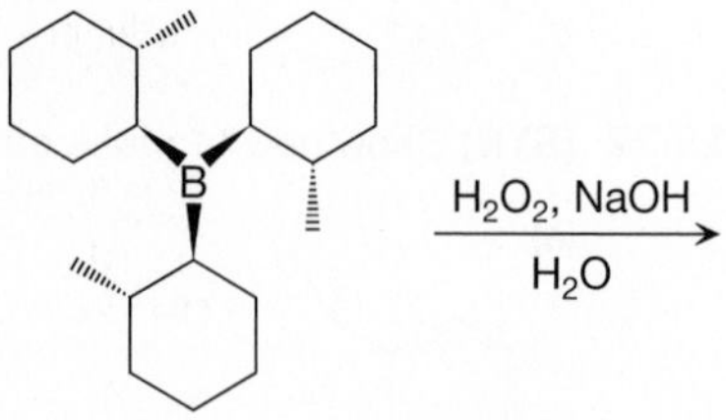
B
H2O2, NaOH
H2O

13.28 Draw the mechanism and the major product(s) for each of the following reactions.

(a)

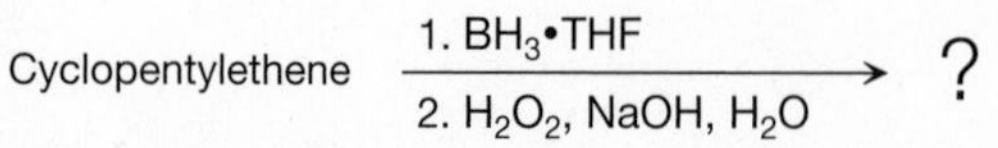
Cyclopentylethene
1. BH3•THF
2. H2O2, NaOH, H2O
?

(b)

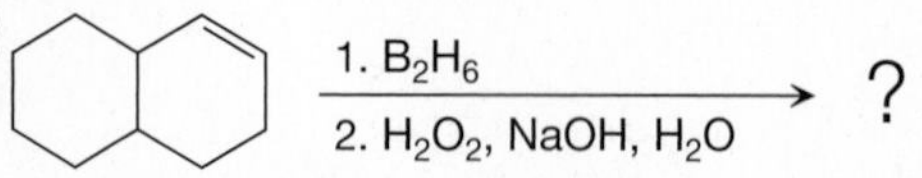
1. B2H6
2. H2O2, NaOH, H2O
?

(c)

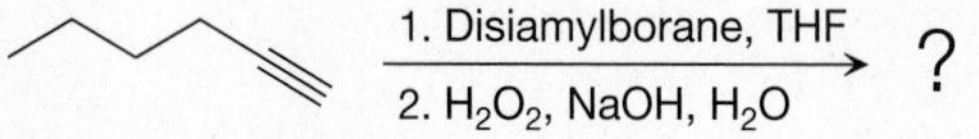
1. Disiamylborane, THF
2. H2O2, NaOH, H2O
?

(d)

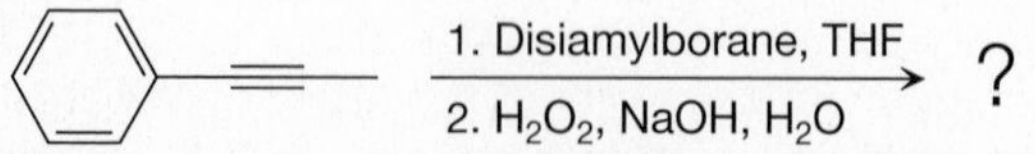
1. Disiamylborane, THF
2. H2O2, NaOH, H2O
?

13.29 **(SYN)** Show how each of these compounds can be produced from an alkene or alkyne. Draw the appropriate alkene or alkyne, and include any necessary reagents and special reaction conditions.

(a)
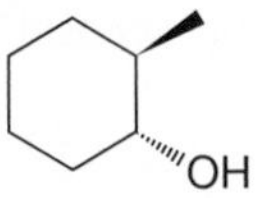
OH

(b)
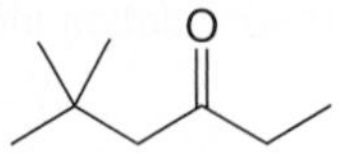
O

(c)
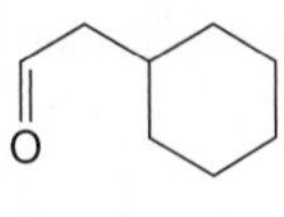
O

(d)
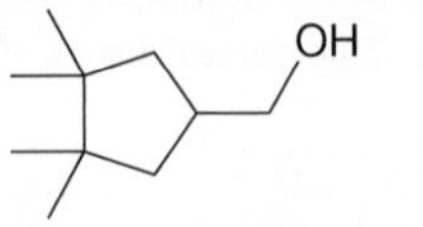
OH

13.30 **(SYN)** Hydroboration–oxidation can be carried out with deuterated forms of the reagents and solvent. For example, $BD_3 \cdot THF$ can be used instead of $BH_3 \cdot THF$, and D_2O could be used instead of H_2O. With this in mind, show how each of the following compounds can be produced from an alkene.

(a)
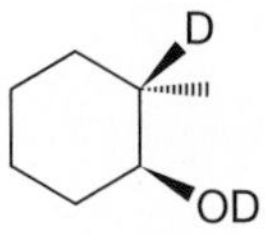
D
OD

(b)
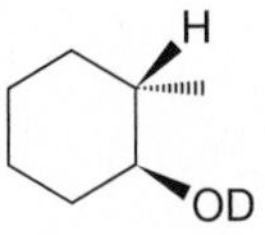
H
OD

(c)
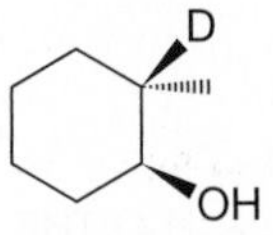
D
OH

13.31 Predict the product of the reaction shown here.

Buta-1,3-diene $\xrightarrow[\text{2. NaOH, } H_2O_2, H_2O]{\text{1. } BH_3 \bullet THF \text{ (excess)}}$?

Section 13.9 Catalytic Hydrogenation

13.32 Draw the product of each of the following reactions.

(a)
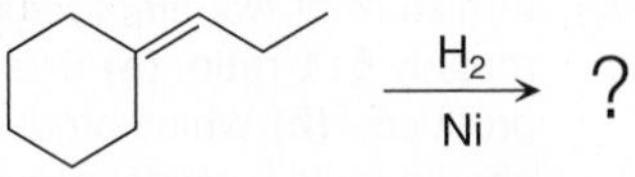
H2
Ni
?

(b)
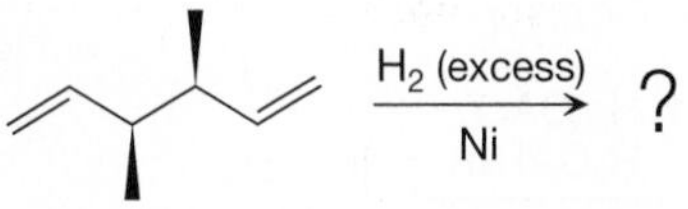
H2 (excess)
Ni
?

13.33 **(SYN)** Draw three different reactants that could be used for this reaction.

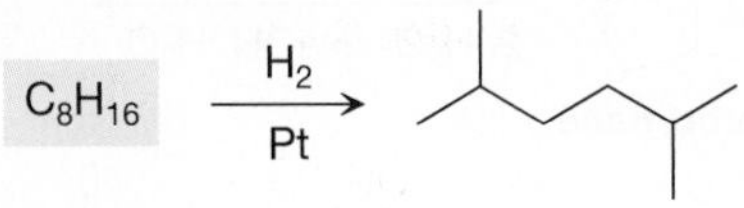
C8H16
H2
Pt

13.34 **(SYN)** Draw the compound that undergoes catalytic hydrogenation to produce 2,2-dimethylbutane.

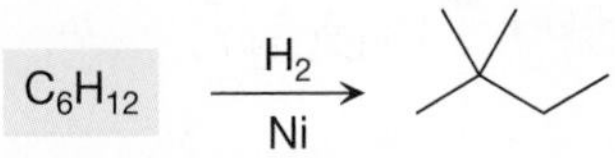
C6H12
H2
Ni

13.35 **(SYN)** When a reactant with the formula C_6H_8 is treated with excess H_2 in the presence of a Ni catalyst, C_6H_{12} is produced. Draw the reactant and the product.

$C_6H_8 \xrightarrow[\text{Ni}]{H_2 \text{ (excess)}} C_6H_{12}$

13.36 Draw the product of each of the following reactions.

(a)
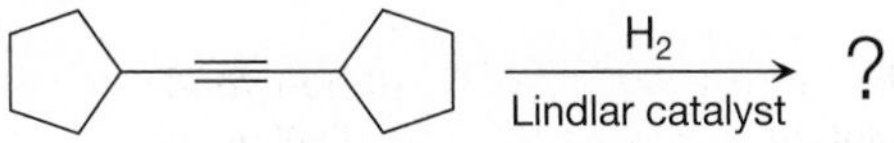
H2
Lindlar catalyst
?

(b)
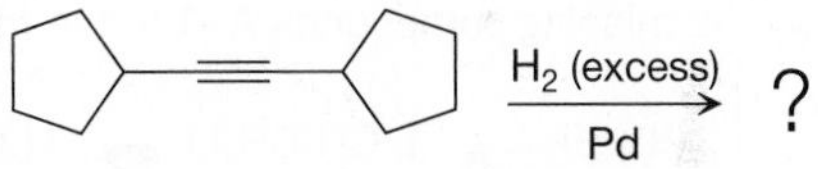
H2 (excess)
Pd
?

(c)
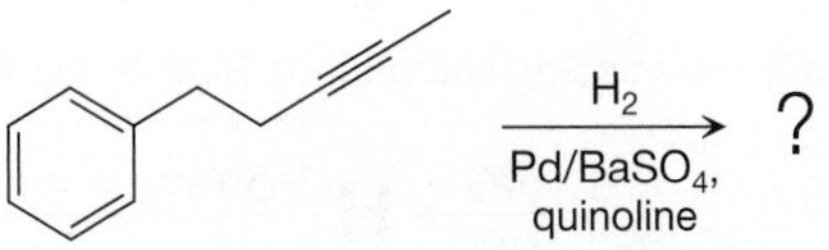
H2
Pd/BaSO4,
quinoline
?

13.37 Show how to produce each of these compounds from an alkyne.

(a)
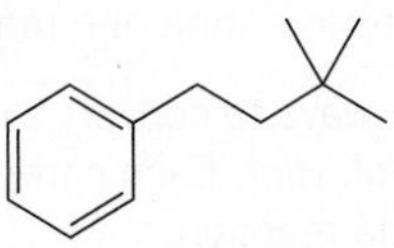

(b)
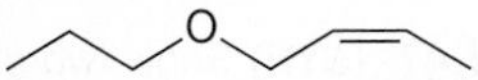
O

Integrated Problems

13.38 In Section 13.4, we learned that Cl_2 undergoes anti addition to an alkene such as but-2-ene. Under similar conditions, Cl_2 undergoes both syn and anti addition to (*E*)-1-phenylprop-1-ene to produce the isomers shown here, plus their enantiomers. **(a)** Draw the mechanism to account for this mixture of products. **(b)** Explain why the mechanism for 1-phenylprop-1-ene is different from the one for but-2-ene.

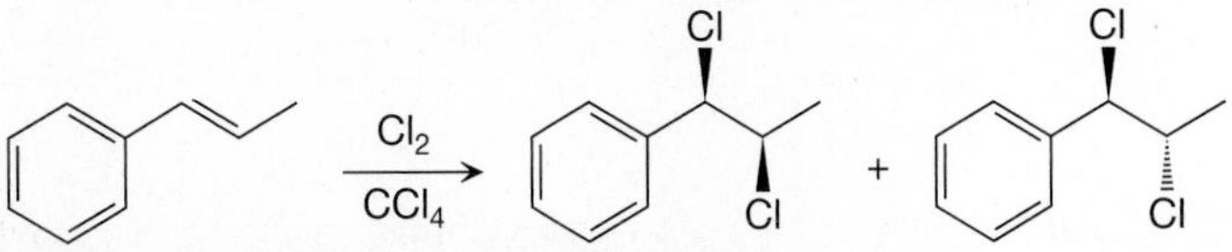
Cl2
CCl4
Cl
Cl
+
Cl
Cl

13.39 Section 13.2 mentions that the Simmons–Smith reaction produces a cyclopropane ring from an alkene. Diiodomethane (CH_2I_2) is treated with a source of zinc to produce the Simmons–Smith reagent (ICH_2ZnI), which reacts with the alkene in a single elementary step. Complete the mechanism shown here by adding the necessary curved arrows for this elementary step. *Hint*: The curved arrow notation is very similar to that for epoxidation involving a peroxy acid.

H2
C
I
Zn
I
CH2
Zn
I
I

Simmons–Smith reagent and Enantiomer

13.40 When benzene is treated with diazomethane and irradiated with light, cyclohepta-1,3,5-triene is produced. Propose a mechanism for this reaction.

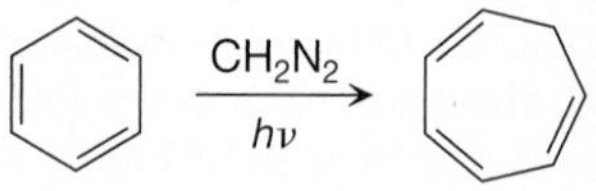

CH2N2
hν

13.41 Draw the mechanism for Step 1 in the following reaction.

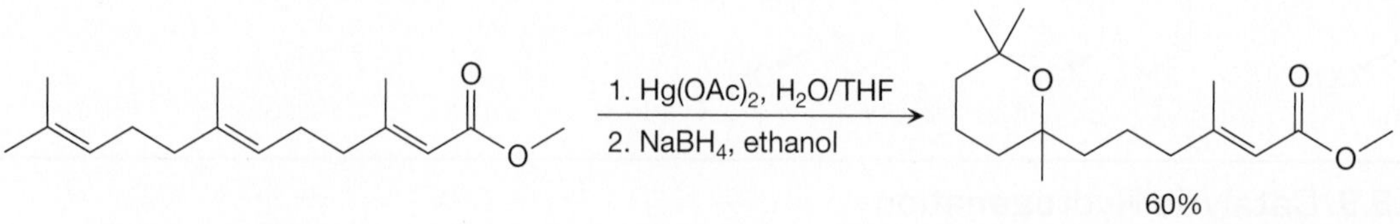

1. Hg(OAc)2, H2O/THF
2. NaBH4, ethanol
60%

13.42 Draw the mechanism for Step 1 in the following reaction.

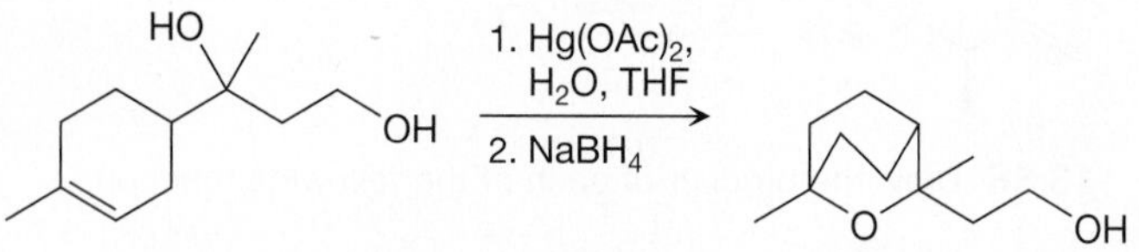

HO
OH
1. Hg(OAc)2, H2O, THF
2. NaBH4
O
OH

13.43 When norbornene undergoes hydroboration–oxidation, a mixture of two stereoisomers is produced in a roughly 6:1 ratio. **(a)** Draw both of these isomeric products. **(b)** Which product is favored? *Hint*: You should build a model of norbornene and consider the transition state leading to each product.

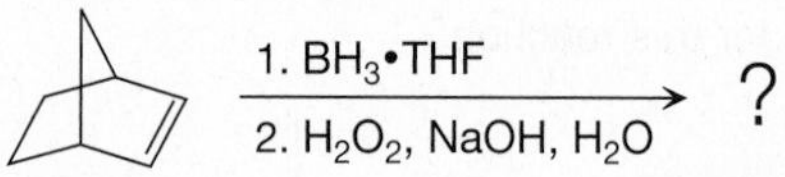

1. BH3•THF
2. H2O2, NaOH, H2O
?

Norbornene

13.44 Supply the missing compounds **A–G** in the following sequence of reactions.

MCPBA
A
1. CH3CH2Li
2. H3O⊕
B
H3O⊕
Δ
C
MCPBA
D
NaBr
CH3CH2OH
E
NaOH
Δ
F
CH2N2
hν
G

13.45 Supply the missing compounds **H–M** in the following synthesis scheme.

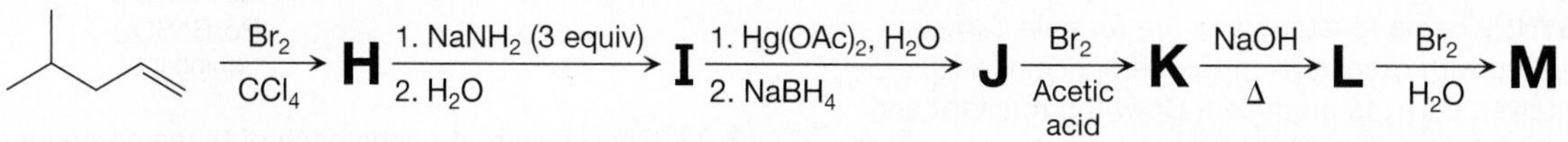

Br2
CCl4
H
1. NaNH2 (3 equiv)
2. H2O
I
1. Hg(OAc)2, H2O
2. NaBH4
J
Br2
Acetic acid
K
NaOH
Δ
L
Br2
H2O
M

13.46 **(SYN)** Propose how to convert hex-1-yne to **(a)** 2,2-dibromohexane and **(b)** 1,2-dibromohexane. *Hint*: Each conversion might require carrying out more than one reaction.

13.47 **(SYN)** Show two different ways to convert 2-methylbut-2-ene to 3-bromo-2-methylbutan-2-ol. *Hint*: Each conversion might require carrying out more than one reaction.

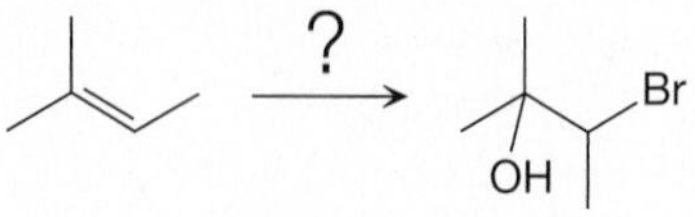

?
Br
OH

14

Graphene aerogel, which is approximately seven times lighter than air, rests on the petals of a flower. The material, whose fundamental structural motif is graphene (molecular chicken wire made entirely of carbon; see p. 5), is mechanically strong and electrically conductive, giving it a wide range of potential applications. What makes graphene conductive is the conjugation of its *p* orbitals, a topic discussed here in Chapter 14.

Conjugation and Aromaticity

Chapter 3 introduced valence bond (VB) theory, a model that describes the orbitals that hold valence electrons in a molecule or molecular ion. For example, recall that valence bond theory describes a single bond as a σ bond, the result of two half-filled orbitals (*s* orbitals or hybrid orbitals) overlapping along the bonding axis. A double bond, on the other hand, is made up of one σ bond and one π bond, and a triple bond is made up of one σ bond and two π bonds; each π bond is the result of two *p* orbitals overlapping on opposite sides of the bonding axis.

Although valence bond theory accounts for a number of important characteristics of molecular structure, it does not adequately describe species with electrons that are *delocalized* by resonance. To account for such electron delocalization, we introduce the concept of *conjugation* among *p* orbitals. We will then apply the idea of conjugation to account for *aromaticity*, an important property of cyclic species that impacts molecular structure and stability.

Toward the end of this chapter, we will discuss how conjugation of *p* orbitals applies to molecular orbital (MO) theory. Section 3.10 introduced MO theory, expanding the ideas of valence bond theory to account for certain aspects of molecular structure and stability that valence bond theory cannot explain, such as the existence of unoccupied orbitals in a molecule. We will examine, in particular, how conjugation impacts the shapes and energies of the π molecular orbitals that are made when *p* orbitals mix.

What we learn about conjugation and aromaticity here in Chapter 14 will be very useful in upcoming chapters. In Chapters 16 and 17, you will see how aspects

Chapter Outline

of spectroscopy (the study of how molecules interact with light) rely on conjugation and aromaticity. Additionally, you will learn in Chapter 18 how conjugation can significantly affect the reactivity of particular species and the outcomes of chemical reactions in which they take part, and in Chapters 24 and 25 we will study reactions of aromatic species.

SECTION 14.1 OBJECTIVES

You will be able to:

1. Draw the *p* orbital contribution to the π system of the allyl cation and other species that exhibit the same kind of resonance.
2. Draw the *p* orbital contribution to the π system of buta-1,3-diene and other species that have conjugated double bonds.
3. Explain what is required for *p* orbitals to be conjugated.
4. Explain how the conjugation of *p* orbitals relates to electron delocalization via resonance and the stabilization of a species.
5. Use resonance structures and resonance hybrids to determine the atoms and electrons that contribute to the same π system.

14.1 The Allyl Cation and Buta-1,3-diene: Resonance and the Conjugation of *p* Orbitals in Acyclic π Systems

We just mentioned that valence bond theory is unable to account for the resonance delocalization of electrons. As an example, consider the allyl cation shown in Equation 14-1. The allyl cation has two resonance structures, which is an outcome of the atom lacking an octet (C^+) adjacent to the multiple bond (C=C):

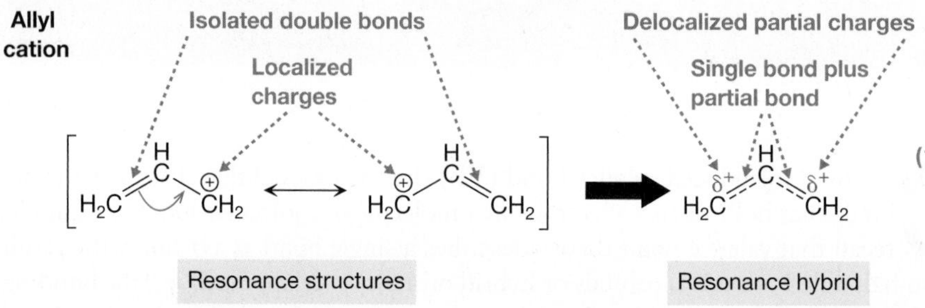

Allyl cation
Isolated double bonds
Localized charges
Delocalized partial charges
Single bond plus partial bond
H_2C
H
C
CH_2
δ+
Resonance structures
Resonance hybrid

(14-1)

Recall from Section 1.10 that each resonance structure is hypothetical; the actual structure is described by the *resonance hybrid*, which is a weighted average of the resonance structures. Therefore, as shown above, the two electrons of the π bond are delocalized over the two carbon–carbon bonding regions, making both carbon–carbon bonds equivalent; both are intermediate between a single bond and a double bond. Furthermore, the positive charge of the allyl cation is delocalized over the two terminal carbons in the resonance hybrid.

How does valence bond theory fail to describe these aspects of resonance delocalization? To answer this question, study **Figure 14-1**, which shows the *p* orbitals that are contributed to the allyl cation's valence bond picture. Each carbon is sp^2-hybridized and, as shown in Figure 14-1a, contributes one valence *p* orbital (see Recall box). For the allyl cation to have a total charge of +1, we can envision the allyl cation being constructed from two uncharged carbons and one positively charged carbon; this is why one electron occupies the *p* orbital contributed by the left and middle carbons (uncharged carbons) and the carbon on the right contributes an empty *p* orbital (C^+). As indicated in Figure 14-1a, two half-filled *p* orbitals overlap on opposite sides of the bonding axis (π overlap), resulting in a π bond (Fig. 14-1b). Such a valence bond

◂ RECALL

Section 3.4 showed that the valence shell of an sp^2-hybridized carbon has three hybrid orbitals occupying a plane and one unhybridized *p* orbital perpendicular to that plane. For an uncharged C, which has four valence electrons, each valence orbital contains one electron. For a C^+, the *p* orbital is empty.

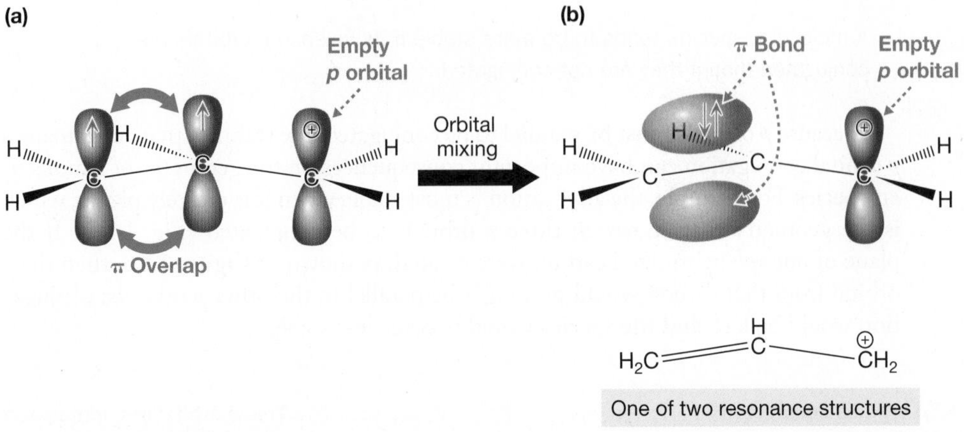
(a)
Empty
p orbital
π Overlap
Orbital
mixing
(b)
π Bond
Empty
p orbital
One of two resonance structures

FIGURE 14-1 Valence bond picture of one resonance structure of the allyl cation (a) The two uncharged C atoms (left and center) each contribute a valence *p* orbital that contains one electron, and C^+ (right) contributes an empty *p* orbital. (b) The two half-filled *p* orbitals overlapping on opposite sides of the bonding axis (π overlap) produce a π bond (shown in orange). One empty *p* orbital (shown in blue) remains associated with the C^+.

picture suggests a double bond between the left and center carbons, which corresponds to one resonance structure of the allyl cation (the first resonance structure in Eq. 14-1), not the resonance hybrid.

YOUR TURN 14.1

Redraw Figure 14-1 to depict the second resonance structure in Equation 14-1.

Answers to Your Turns are in the back of the book.

The example illustrated in Figure 14-1 can be generalized:

Valence bond theory accounts for features of bonding in individual resonance structures, but it does not account for the delocalization of electrons in a resonance hybrid.

This shortcoming arises because valence bond theory considers just the overlap between *pairs* of orbitals contributed by adjacent atoms.

To account for electron delocalization, and thus to overcome this shortcoming of valence bond theory, special consideration must be given to the overlap among *multiple p* orbitals simultaneously:

***p* Orbital Conjugation and π Systems**

- Simultaneous overlap among *p* orbitals occurs when the *p* orbitals are all parallel to each other and are on sequential atoms, forming what are called **conjugated** *p* orbitals.
- A set of conjugated *p* orbitals represents a single **π system** of orbitals.
- Electrons occupying a particular π system are delocalized over all the atoms that contribute *p* orbitals to that π system.

As shown in **Figure 14-2**, for example, all three *p* orbitals of the allyl cation are conjugated, representing a single π system. The two π electrons in that system are therefore delocalized over both carbon–carbon bonding regions, in agreement with the resonance hybrid we saw previously in Equation 14-1.

Recall from Section 1.10 that the resonance delocalization of electrons stabilizes a species. With the understanding that resonance delocalization is made possible by *p* orbital conjugation, we arrive at the following generalization:

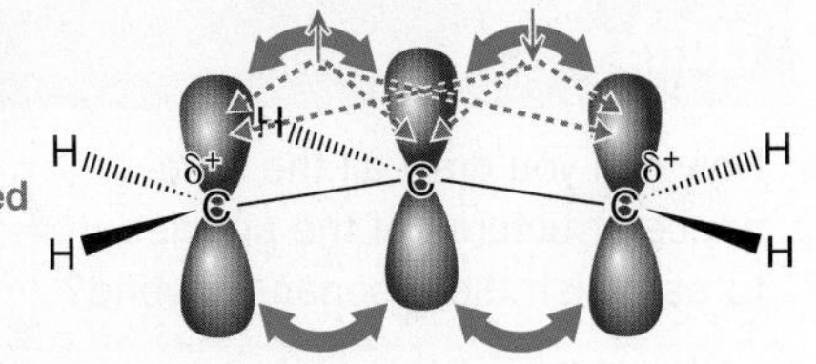
These three p orbitals are conjugated and undergo simultaneous π overlap.
The two π electrons in this π system are delocalized over all three carbons.

FIGURE 14-2 Conjugation of *p* orbitals in the allyl cation All three *p* orbitals are conjugated because they are located on sequential atoms and are all parallel. Because all three *p* orbitals contribute to a single π system, the two π electrons in that system are delocalized over all three carbons.

A molecular species tends to be more stable if its valence *p* orbitals are conjugated than if they are not conjugated.

Because *p* orbitals must be parallel to be conjugated, the stability that accompanies *p* orbital conjugation can have important consequences on the geometry of a molecular species. For example, the allyl cation is most stable when it is entirely planar, which is the geometry that allows all three *p* orbitals to be conjugated (Fig. 14-2). If the plane of one sp^2-hybridized carbon were rotated, as shown in **Figure 14-3**, then the *p* orbital from that carbon would no longer be parallel to the other *p* orbitals; conjugation would be lost, and the species would become less stable.

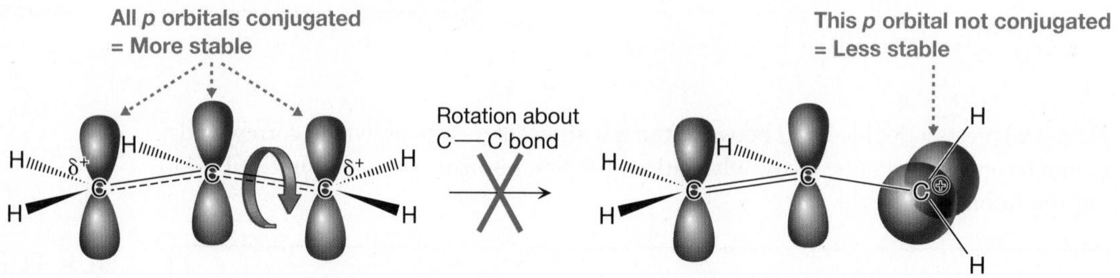

All p orbitals conjugated
= More stable
Rotation about
C—C bond
This p orbital not conjugated
= Less stable
δ+
δ+
H
C

FIGURE 14-3 Conjugation and planarity (*Left*) The allyl cation is most stable when it is entirely planar, because all three *p* orbitals are conjugated. (*Right*) If the plane of one carbon is perpendicular to the other two, conjugation is lost and the species is less stable.

The takeaway lessons from the allyl cation provide a really convenient way to use ideas of resonance to make conclusions about *p* orbital conjugation in a species:

Using Rules of Resonance to Identify π Systems and π Electrons

- In a resonance hybrid, each atom over which electrons are delocalized contributes a *p* orbital to the same π system.
- The number of electrons in a π system is the same as the number of electrons that are delocalized in the resonance hybrid. You can count the electrons by interconverting resonance structures in such a way that all the atoms that contribute a *p* orbital to the π system are involved.

These ideas are applied in Solved Problem 14.1.

SOLVED PROBLEM **14.1**

How to identify a π system and its electrons from a resonance hybrid

Break It Down Which atoms in the hexa-1,3-dienyl cation contribute a *p* orbital to the same π system? How many electrons are in that π system?

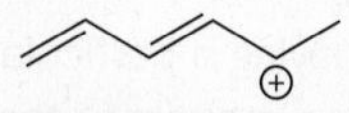

Hexa-1,3-dienyl cation

Think	Solve
How can you draw all the resonance structures of the species to establish the resonance hybrid?	The species has three resonance structures, as shown below. We draw the resonance hybrid as a blend of all three resonance structures.

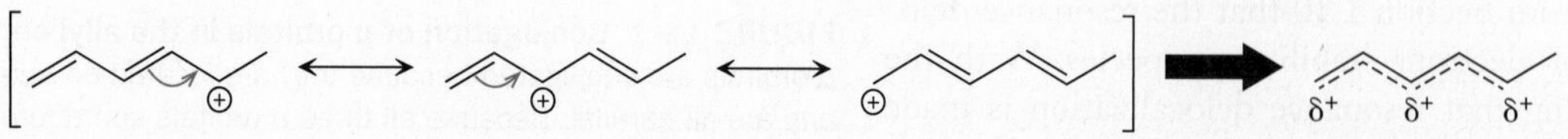

δ+
δ+
δ+

(continued)

In the resonance hybrid, over which atoms do we see electrons delocalized? Which atoms, therefore, contribute a *p* orbital to the π system?	Notice that electrons are delocalized over the first five carbons on the left, so each of those carbons contributes a *p* orbital to the same π system. The rightmost carbon does *not* contribute a *p* orbital to the π system because that carbon is not involved in electron delocalization.
How can you use electron movement in drawing resonance structures to indicate all of the π electrons in a given π system?	Draw two resonance structures that are related by moving electrons over every atom that contributes a *p* orbital to the π system. For the hexa-1,3-dienyl cation, this requires moving four electrons, as shown below on the left. Therefore, the π system contains four π electrons, as shown below on the right.

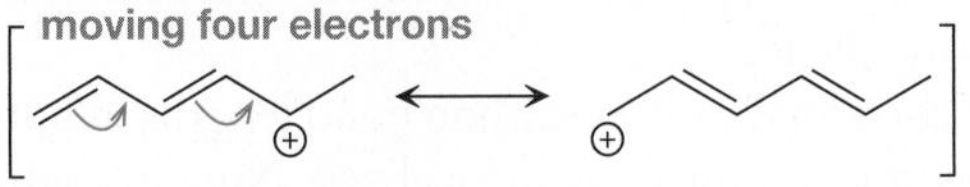

These resonance structures are related by moving four electrons

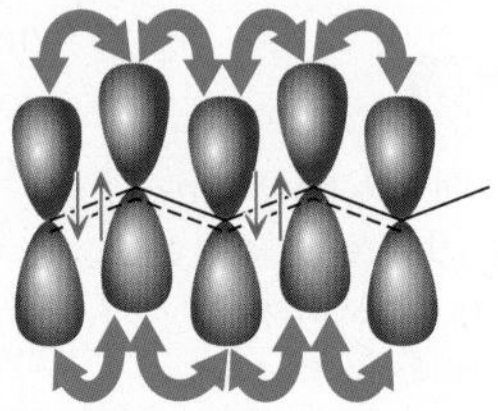

These five *p* orbitals are conjugated.
Four electrons occupy this π system.

Try It Which atoms in the octa-1,3,5-trienyl cation contribute a *p* orbital to the same π system? How many electrons are in that π system?

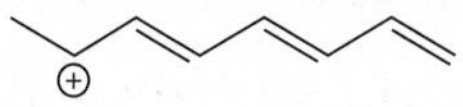

Octa-1,3,5-trienyl cation

Answers to all Try It exercises can be found in the Solutions Manual.

Unlike the allyl cation, buta-1,3-diene ($H_2C{=}CH{-}CH{=}CH_2$) does not have an atom lacking an octet adjacent to a multiple bond, so it does not exhibit the same kind of resonance. Nevertheless, conjugation explains two key features of buta-1,3-diene shown in **Figure 14-4**: (1) Even though the central C—C bond can rotate, its rotation is hindered and the molecule favors an entirely planar geometry, and (2) the C=C

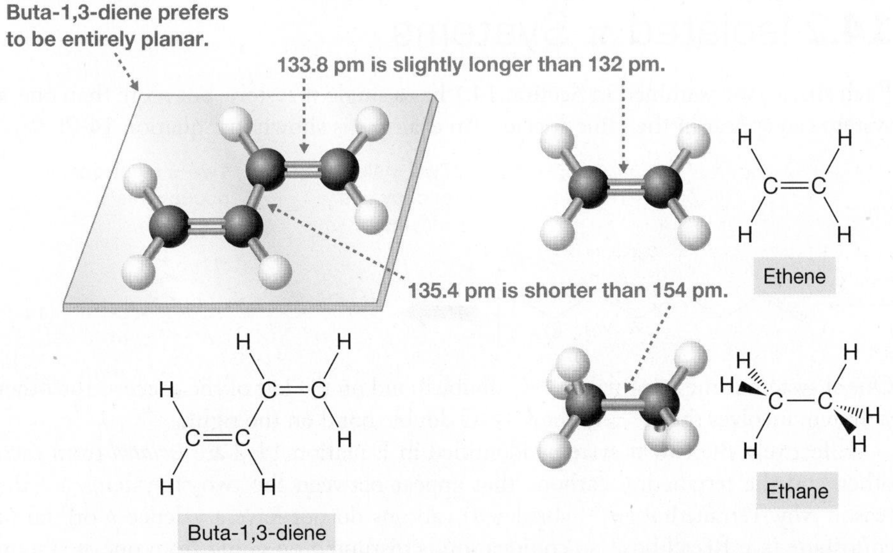

Buta-1,3-diene prefers to be entirely planar.
133.8 pm is slightly longer than 132 pm.
135.4 pm is shorter than 154 pm.
Ethene
Ethane
Buta-1,3-diene

FIGURE 14-4 Bond lengths and planar geometry of buta-1,3-diene Buta-1,3-diene favors an entirely planar geometry. The C—C single bond in buta-1,3-diene is significantly shorter than the corresponding single bond in ethane. Both C=C double bonds in buta-1,3-diene are slightly longer than the corresponding double bond in ethene.

CONNECTIONS 14.1

Buta-1,3-diene: Helping bring ideas to life Buta-1,3-diene (Fig. 14-4) is used to make synthetic polymers such as acrylonitrile butadiene styrene (ABS), a plastic commonly used in 3-D printers.

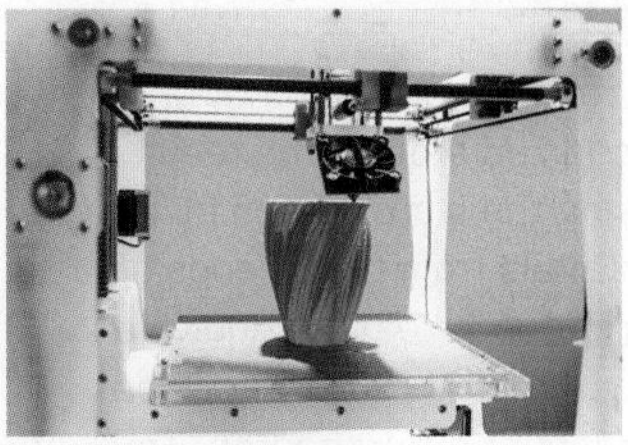

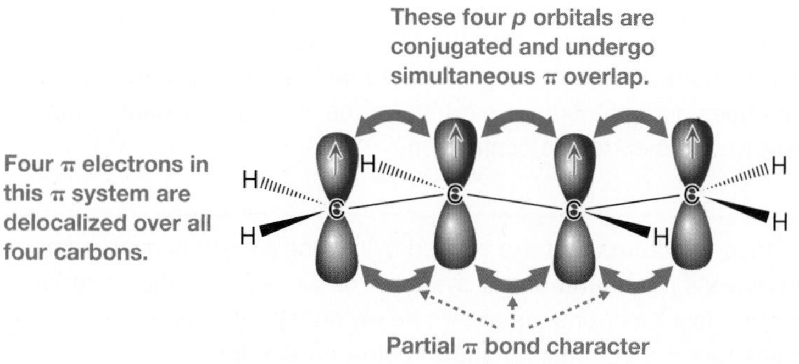
These four p orbitals are conjugated and undergo simultaneous π overlap.
Four π electrons in this π system are delocalized over all four carbons.
Partial π bond character

FIGURE 14-5 Conjugation of *p* orbitals in buta-1,3-diene All four *p* orbitals are conjugated and contribute to a single π system. Four π electrons in that π system are delocalized over all four carbons. The electron density from the four π electrons is distributed over all three carbon–carbon bonding regions.

double bonds of buta-1,3-diene are longer than normal, whereas the C—C single bond is shorter than normal (see Looking Ahead box).

To understand those features of buta-1,3-diene, consider the role that the valence *p* orbitals play. Each carbon atom is sp^2-hybridized and is uncharged, so as shown in **Figure 14-5**, each carbon contributes one valence *p* orbital that contains a single electron. For those *p* orbitals to remain parallel and thus conjugated, which provides stabilization to the molecule, the bonds from all four carbons must lie in the same plane.

▸ LOOKING AHEAD

In Chapter 18, we will see how conjugation can impact the reactivity of a carbonyl (C═O) group. Chapter 26 discusses the Diels–Alder reaction, which requires a conjugated diene as one of the reactants.

To understand the abnormal carbon–carbon bond lengths in buta-1,3-diene, recall that conjugation allows π electrons to be delocalized. Note in Figure 14-5 that the π system extends over all four carbon atoms, so the four π electrons are delocalized over the three carbon–carbon bonding regions. Therefore, instead of the four π electrons localized in two terminal C═C double bonds (as the Lewis structure in Fig. 14-4 would suggest), all three carbon–carbon bonds have π bond character. The additional π bond character between the two central carbons results in a shorter C—C single bond than normal. Conversely, the π bond character between each pair of outer carbons is reduced, which results in longer C═C double bonds than normal.

YOUR TURN 14.2

Which molecule, **A** or **B**, has the longer C═O bond? Explain your reasoning.

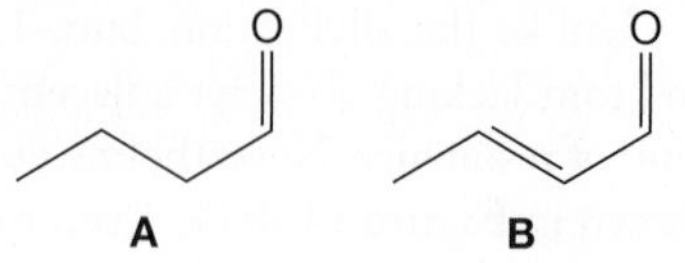
O
O
A
B

SECTION 14.2 OBJECTIVES

You will be able to:

1. Identify π systems that are separated by tetrahedral carbons.
2. Explain why a triple bond must contribute to two separate π systems.

14.2 Isolated π Systems

Each species we examined in Section 14.1 has a single π system, but more than one π system can appear in the same species. An example is shown in Equation 14-2:

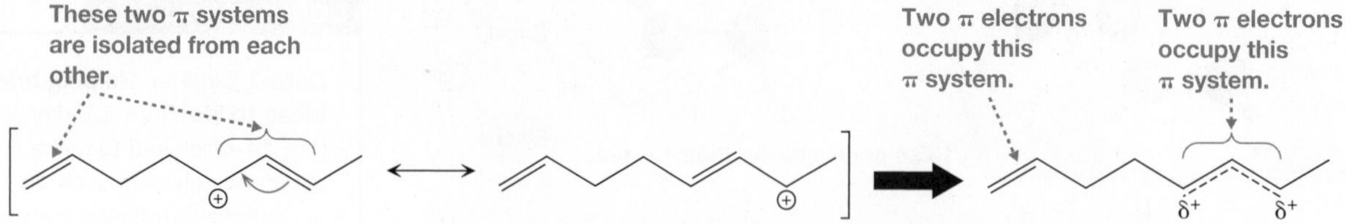
These two π systems are isolated from each other.
Two π electrons occupy this π system.
Two π electrons occupy this π system.
δ+
δ+

(14-2)

One π system is the terminal C═C double bond on the left of the species. The other π system involves the C^+ and the C═C double bond on the right.

Effectively, the two π systems identified in Equation 14-2 are *isolated* from each other, and the tetrahedral carbons that appear between the two π systems are the reason why. Tetrahedral (sp^3-hybridized) carbons do not have a valence *p* orbital to contribute (see Recall box), so conjugation is disrupted on going from one π system to the other, as shown in **Figure 14-6**. In general:

◂ RECALL

Section 3.2 showed that an sp^3-hybridized atom is the result of mixing the *s* orbital and all three *p* orbitals from the valence shell, which produces four equivalent hybrid orbitals pointing to the corners of a tetrahedron. Thus, no *p* orbitals remain.

> Tetrahedral carbons disrupt conjugation, so π systems appearing on either side of a tetrahedral carbon are effectively isolated from each other.

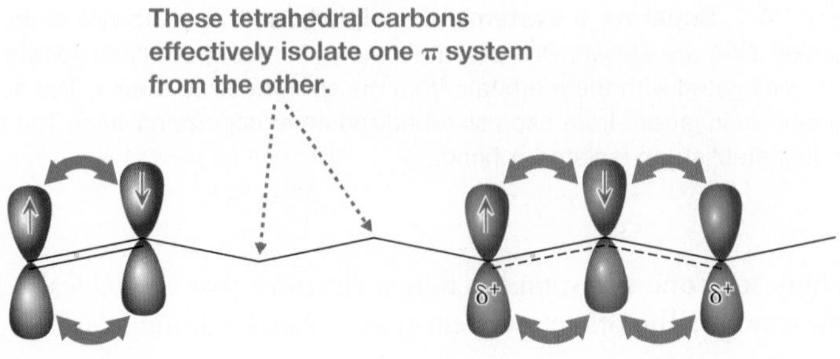
These tetrahedral carbons effectively isolate one π system from the other.
δ+
δ+

FIGURE 14-6 π Systems isolated by tetrahedral carbons The two π systems of the species in Equation 14-2 are isolated because the tetrahedral carbons between them do not contribute *p* orbitals. Therefore, conjugation among the *p* orbitals is disrupted on going from one π system to the other.

YOUR TURN 14.3

How many π systems does this species have? How many π electrons are in each π system?

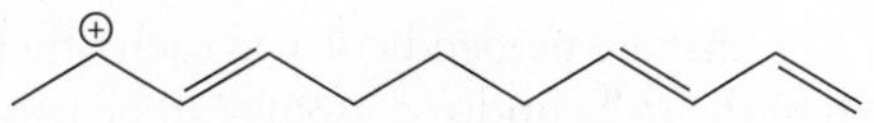

> ◂ **RECALL**
>
> Section 9.10 explained that alkene stability increases as the number of alkyl groups attached to the C═C bond increases. Therefore, all else being equal, E2 reactions tend to favor the more highly alkyl-substituted alkene product.

Because conjugation increases stability, the outcomes of chemical reactions can vary depending upon whether the π systems involved are conjugated or isolated. For example, two different alkene products can be produced from the E2 reaction in Equation 14-3 (see Recall box); the new double bond is conjugated in one product and isolated in the other. The product in which the new double bond is conjugated is more stable and is therefore the major product:

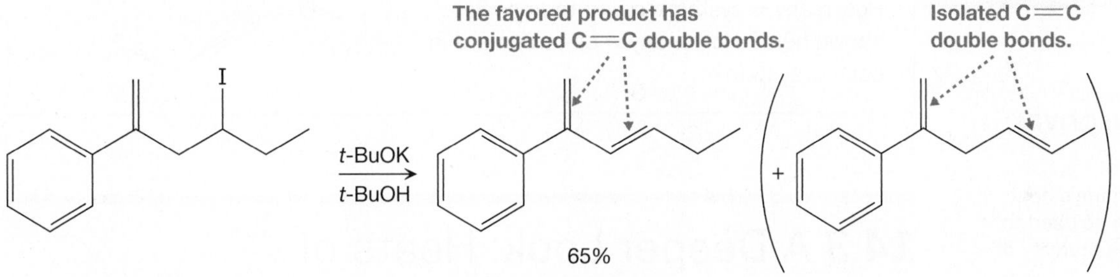
The favored product has conjugated C═C double bonds.
Isolated C═C double bonds.
I
t-BuOK
t-BuOH
+
65%

(14-3)

The quantitative difference in stability between conjugated double bonds and isolated double bonds can be determined from heats of hydrogenation, a topic we will examine in more detail in Section 14.3.

YOUR TURN 14.4

Draw the two possible E2 products of this reaction. Which product is favored? Why?

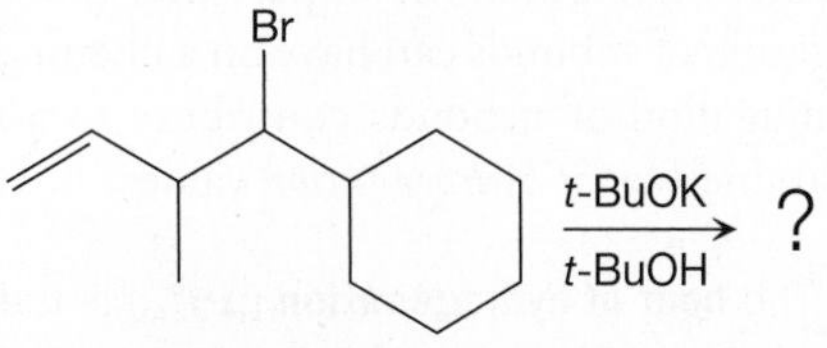
Br
t-BuOK
t-BuOH
?

The species depicted in Equation 14-4 has two separate π systems, even though it has no tetrahedral carbons:

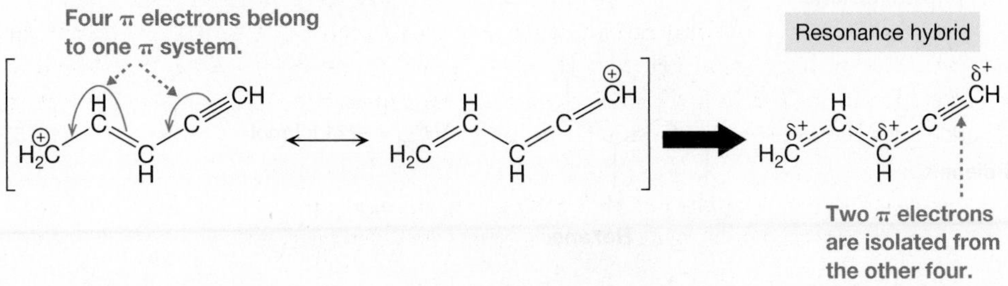
Four π electrons belong to one π system.
Resonance hybrid
Two π electrons are isolated from the other four.

(14-4)

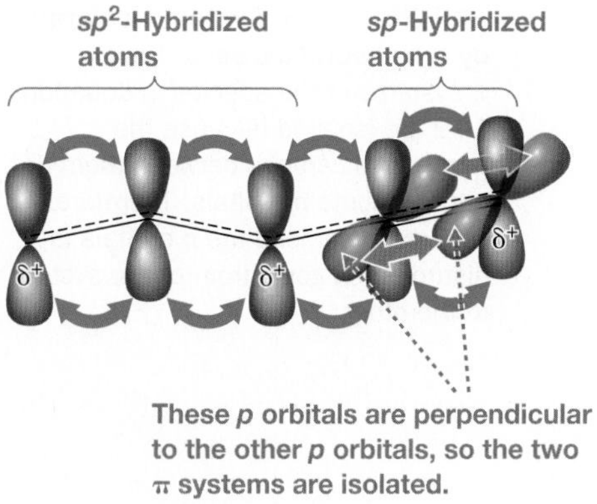

sp^2-Hybridized atoms
sp-Hybridized atoms
δ+
δ+
δ+
δ+
These p orbitals are perpendicular to the other p orbitals, so the two π systems are isolated.

FIGURE 14-7 Separate π systems of a triple bond The p orbitals of the species in Equation 14-4 are shown. One p orbital (shown in blue) from each sp-hybridized atom is conjugated with the p orbitals from the sp^2-hybridized atoms. The second p orbital (shown in green) from each sp-hybridized atom is perpendicular. The two green p orbitals establish an isolated π bond.

As indicated, one π system has four π electrons that are delocalized over five carbon atoms. The other π system is an isolated π bond, consisting of two π electrons.

The orbital picture in **Figure 14-7** shows why the species in Equation 14-4 has an isolated π bond. The three carbons on the left are sp^2-hybridized and each contributes one p orbital. The two carbons on the right are linear and sp-hybridized (see top Recall box), so each of those carbons has two p orbitals that are perpendicular to each other. Only one p orbital (shown in blue) from each of the sp-hybridized atoms can be parallel to, and therefore conjugated with, the p orbitals from the sp^2-hybridized atoms. The remaining two p orbitals (shown in green), which are perpendicular, overlap to form a separate π bond. The lesson in Figure 14-7 can be summarized as follows:

At most one π bond from a given triple bond can contribute to a particular π system.

◂ RECALL

Section 3.5 shows that an sp-hybridized atom results from mixing the valence s orbital with one of the three valence p orbitals. Thus, two equivalent hybrid orbitals are produced, and the two p orbitals that are left over remain perpendicular to each other.

YOUR TURN 14.5

How many π systems are in the species shown here? How many π electrons are in each π system?

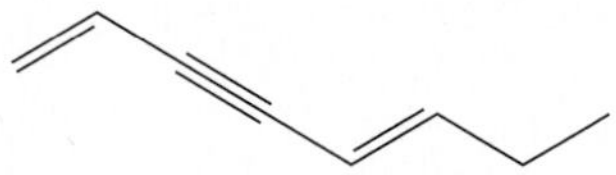

SECTION 14.3 OBJECTIVES

You will be able to:

1. Explain why an alkene's heat of hydrogenation can be used to determine the relative stability of the alkene.
2. Use heats of hydrogenation to determine the magnitude of stabilization associated with the conjugation of double bonds.

14.3 A Deeper Look: Heats of Hydrogenation and the Stability of Conjugated π Bonds

In Section 14.2, we distinguished conjugated π bonds from isolated π bonds, and we further highlighted the impact that the additional stability that comes from the conjugation of π bonds can have on a chemical reaction. How much stabilization does the conjugation of π bonds contribute to a molecule? To answer this question, we will examine *heat of hydrogenation* values:

The **heat of hydrogenation** (ΔH°_{hyd}) is the enthalpy change that accompanies the addition of H_2 to an unsaturated species (see bottom Recall box).

◂ RECALL

Section 13.9 introduced catalytic hydrogenation reactions that add H_2 across the C═C double bond of an alkene or the C≡C bond of an alkyne. These reactions are catalyzed by a metal catalyst, such as Ni, Pd, or Pt.

For example, consider the hydrogenation reactions in Equations 14-5 and 14-6, in which two different hexadienes are hydrogenated to produce exactly the same compound, hexane:

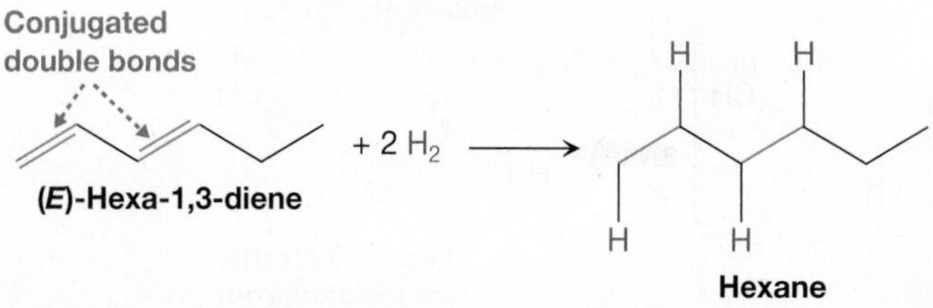

Conjugated double bonds
(*E*)-Hexa-1,3-diene
+ 2 H2
H
H
H
H
Hexane

$\Delta H^\circ_{hyd} = -221$ kJ/mol **(14-5)**

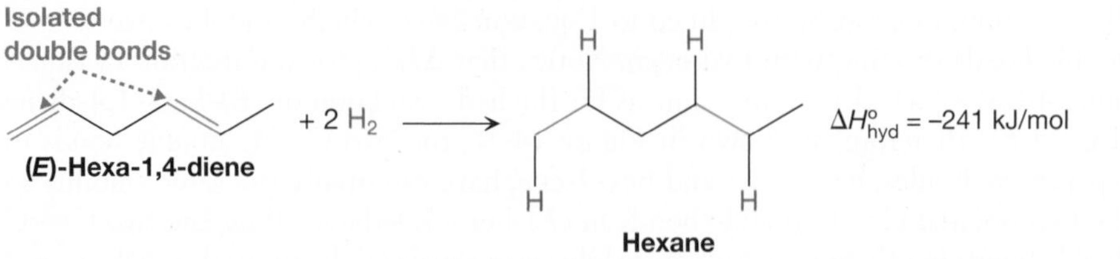
Isolated double bonds
+ 2 H2
H
H
H
H
ΔH°hyd = −241 kJ/mol
(E)-Hexa-1,4-diene
Hexane

(14-6)

Both of these reactions can be simplified to Equation 14-7, in which two C═C double bonds react with H_2, producing two C—C single bonds and four C—H single bonds:

$$2\ \mathrm{C{=}C} \ + \ 2\ H_2 \longrightarrow 2\ \mathrm{C{-}C} \ + \ 4\ \mathrm{C{-}H} \qquad (14\text{-}7)$$

However, ΔH°_{hyd} for the two reactions differs significantly. Whereas the hydrogenation of (*E*)-hexa-1,3-diene releases 221 kJ/mol, the hydrogenation of (*E*)-hexa-1,4-diene releases 241 kJ/mol. Because (*E*)-hexa-1,3-diene releases less heat when it undergoes hydrogenation, it must be lower in energy than (*E*)-hexa-1,4-diene, as indicated in **Figure 14-8a** and 14-8b. Specifically, the π system of (*E*)-hexa-1,3-diene is more stable by 241 kJ/mol − 221 kJ/mol = 20 kJ/mol. We can therefore say that conjugation provides about 20 kJ/mol additional stabilization to (*E*)-hexa-1,3-diene (see Recall box).

◀ RECALL

Using heat of hydrogenation values to establish relative stabilities of π systems is very similar to using heat of combustion values to establish relative amounts of ring strain, discussed in Section 4.4. In both cases, the less stable (higher energy) molecule releases a greater amount of heat.

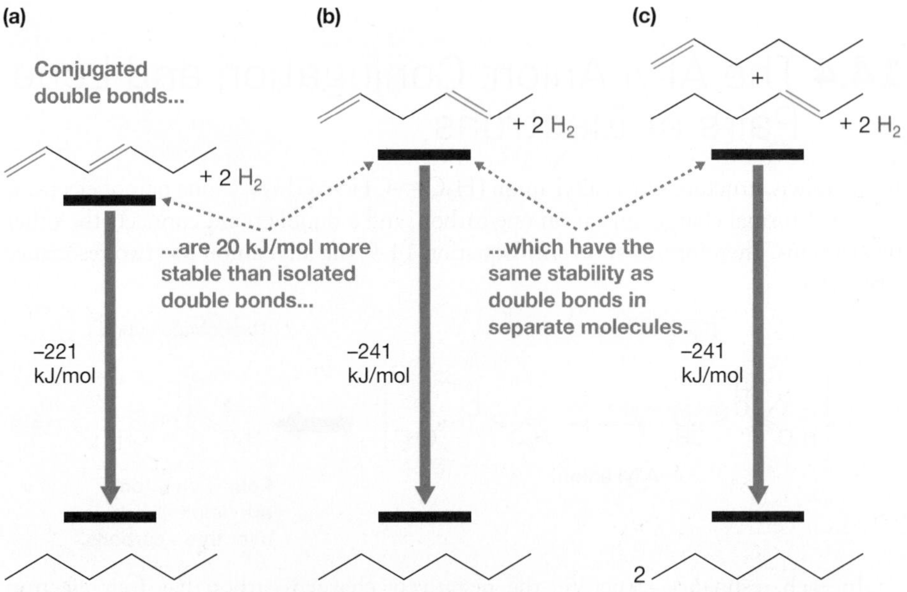
(a)
(b)
(c)
Conjugated double bonds...
+ 2 H2
+ 2 H2
+
+ 2 H2
...are 20 kJ/mol more stable than isolated double bonds...
...which have the same stability as double bonds in separate molecules.
−221 kJ/mol
−241 kJ/mol
−241 kJ/mol
2

FIGURE 14-8 Stabilization of conjugated double bonds Energy diagrams are shown for the hydrogenation of (a) two conjugated double bonds in (*E*)-hexa-1,3-diene, (b) two isolated double bonds in (*E*)-hexa-1,4-diene, and (c) two double bonds in separate molecules of hex-1-ene and (*E*)-hex-2-ene. All three reactions are exothermic. The double bonds in (*E*)-hexa-1,3-diene are stabilized by conjugation, so less heat is released when they undergo hydrogenation.

Do the isolated π systems in (*E*)-hexa-1,4-diene exhibit any special stabilization? To answer this question, let's examine the reaction in Equation 14-8, in which the C═C double bond in hex-1-ene and the C═C double bond in (*E*)-hex-2-ene each undergo hydrogenation to produce hexane:

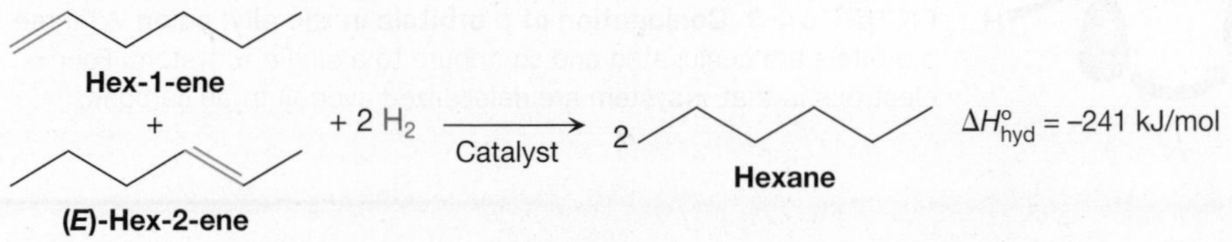
Hex-1-ene
+
+ 2 H2
Catalyst
2
Hexane
ΔH°hyd = −241 kJ/mol
(E)-Hex-2-ene

(14-8)

This reaction, too, can be simplified to Equation 14-7, which describes two C=C double bonds reacting with hydrogen. Notice that ΔH°_{hyd} for the reaction in Equation 14-8 is −241 kJ/mol, the same as for the hydrogenation of (*E*)-hexa-1,4-diene (Eq. 14-6). Therefore, as shown in Figure 14-8c, the two C=C double bonds in separate molecules, hex-1-ene and hex-2-ene, have essentially the same stability as the two isolated C=C double bonds in (*E*)-hexa-1,4-diene. Thus, the two C=C double bonds in (*E*)-hexa-1,4-diene exhibit no special stabilization; they behave as if they are truly isolated from each other.

YOUR TURN **14.6**

Using the heats of hydrogenation given, determine whether the double bonds are more stable in cycloocta-1,3-diene or cycloocta-1,5-diene and by how much.

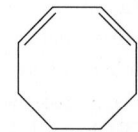

Cycloocta-1,3-diene ΔH°_{hyd} = −210 kJ/mol

Cycloocta-1,5-diene ΔH°_{hyd} = −227 kJ/mol

SECTION 14.4 OBJECTIVES

You will be able to:

1. Draw the *p* orbital contribution to the π system of the allyl anion and other species that exhibit the same kind of resonance.
2. Use resonance structures and resonance hybrids to determine whether lone pairs of electrons belong to a π system.

14.4 The Allyl Anion: Conjugation and Lone Pairs of Electrons

In the Lewis structure of the allyl anion ($H_2C{=}CH{-}CH_2^-$), a lone pair of electrons and a −1 formal charge appear on one carbon, and a double bond connects the other two carbons. Therefore, as shown in Equation 14-9, the allyl anion has two resonance structures:

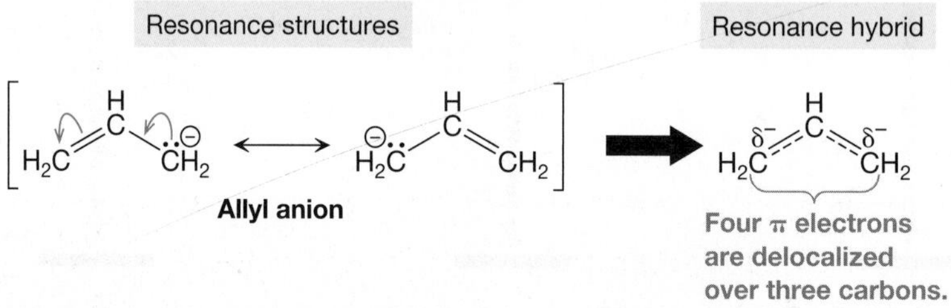

Resonance structures
Resonance hybrid
H
H₂C
CH₂
δ−
Allyl anion
Four π electrons are delocalized over three carbons.

(14-9)

In each resonance structure, the negatively charged carbon has four electron groups (three single bonds and a lone pair), suggesting a tetrahedral electron geometry and sp^3 hybridization. Notice in the resonance hybrid, however, that all three carbons are involved in electron delocalization. Therefore, each carbon must contribute a valence *p* orbital to the same π system, which occurs if all three carbons are sp^2-hybridized (**Figure 14-9**). Moreover, because converting one resonance structure of the allyl anion into the other requires moving four electrons, we can see that the allyl anion's π system has four π electrons.

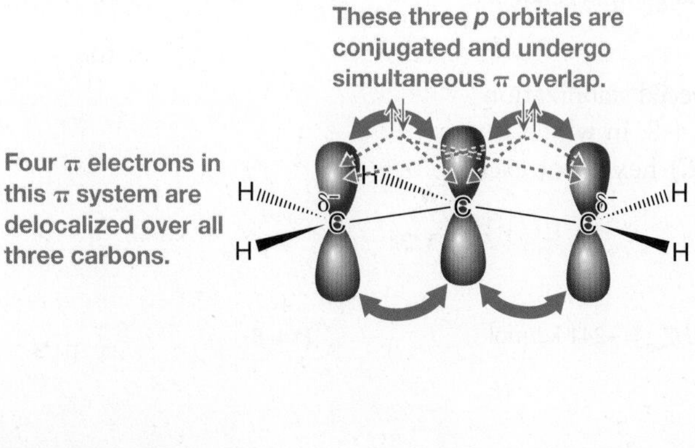

These three p orbitals are conjugated and undergo simultaneous π overlap.
Four π electrons in this π system are delocalized over all three carbons.
H
C
δ−

FIGURE 14-9 Conjugation of *p* orbitals in the allyl anion All three *p* orbitals are conjugated and contribute to a single π system. Four π electrons in that π system are delocalized over all three carbons.

YOUR TURN 14.7

How many π systems are in the species shown here? How many π electrons are in each π system?

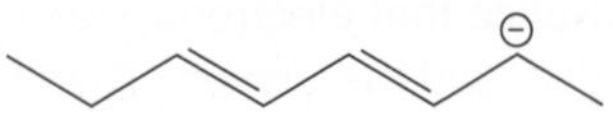

The acetaldehyde enolate anion in Equation 14-10 is an example in which an atom involved in resonance (specifically, the oxygen atom) has more than one lone pair of electrons:

Resonance structures — Resonance hybrid

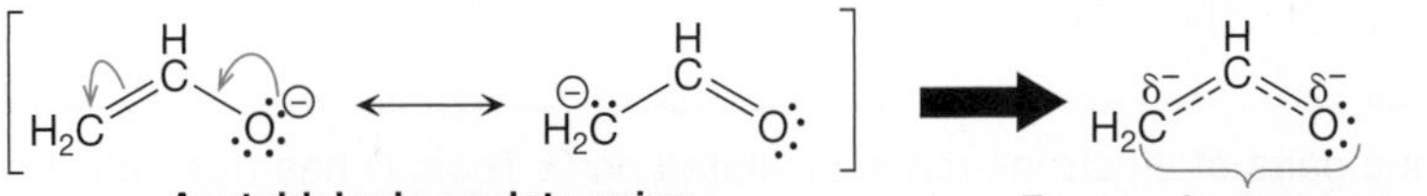

(14-10)

Acetaldehyde enolate anion

Four π electrons are delocalized over two carbons and one oxygen.

Both carbons and the oxygen are involved in resonance, so each of those atoms must contribute a valence *p* orbital to the same π system. Therefore, as shown in **Figure 14-10**, all three atoms are sp^2-hybridized. Moreover, like the allyl anion, the acetaldehyde enolate anion has four π electrons in its π system.

The electron movement in Equation 14-10 indicates that the oxygen contributes one lone pair of electrons to the acetaldehyde enolate anion's π system. Therefore, as shown in Figure 14-10, the other two lone pairs occupy sp^2 hybrid orbitals that are perpendicular to (and therefore isolated from) the π system of orbitals. In general:

> An atom can contribute at most one lone pair of electrons to a particular π system.

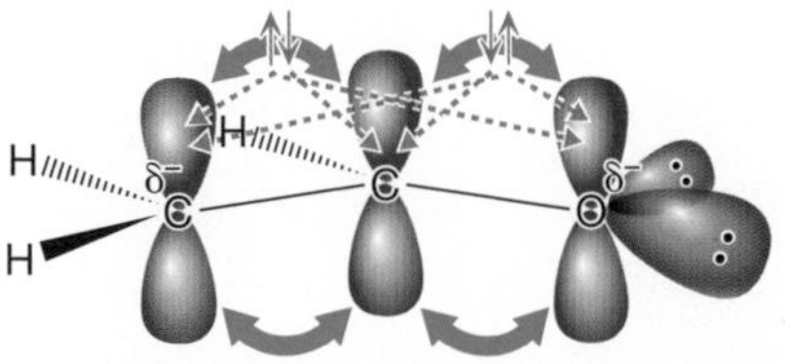

These lone pairs of electrons are localized in hybrid orbitals that are perpendicular to the π system.

FIGURE 14-10 Conjugation of *p* orbitals in the acetaldehyde enolate anion All three *p* orbitals are conjugated and contribute to a single π system (shown in blue). The oxygen contributes one lone pair of electrons to the π system, giving the π system a total of four π electrons. The other two lone pairs of electrons on oxygen occupy sp^2 hybrid orbitals (shown in purple) that are perpendicular to the π system, so those two lone pairs remain localized on oxygen and isolated from the π system.

SOLVED PROBLEM 14.2

How to use resonance structures to identify lone pairs in a π system

Break It Down How many π systems does this species have? How many π electrons does each π system contain? What types of orbitals do the lone pairs occupy?

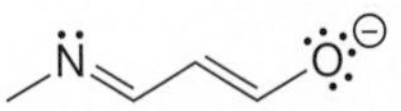

Think	Solve
How can you draw all the resonance structures of the species to establish the resonance hybrid?	The species has three resonance structures, as shown below. We draw the resonance hybrid as a blend of all three resonance structures.

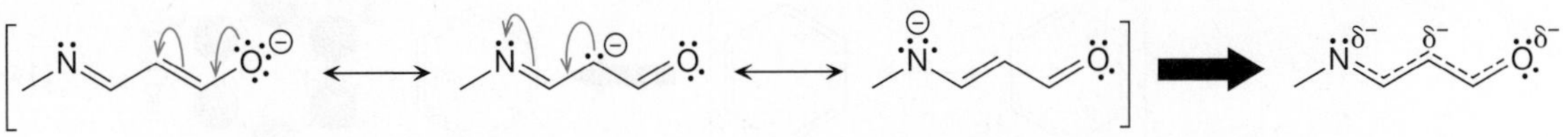

(continued)

Over which atoms in the resonance hybrid are electrons delocalized? Which atoms, therefore, contribute a *p* orbital to the π system?	Notice that electrons are delocalized over five atoms: three carbons, the nitrogen, and the oxygen. Therefore, each of those atoms contributes a *p* orbital to a single π system.
How many electrons are moved to go from one resonance structure to another, such that all atoms that contribute a *p* orbital are involved?	To involve all five atoms that contribute a *p* orbital to the π system, we can draw two resonance structures that are related by moving six electrons, as shown below on the left. Therefore, the π system contains six π electrons. 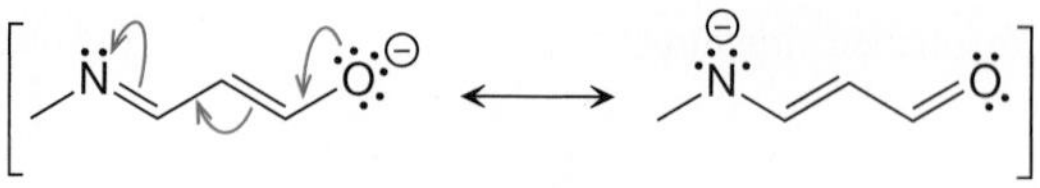
In that electron movement, how many lone pairs on O are left alone? Is the lone pair on N moved? What hybrid orbitals are available to hold the electrons that are not moved?	Two lone pairs of electrons remain isolated on O. Thus, O has three electron groups (two lone pairs and the bonding group to C), making it sp^2-hybridized; the lone pairs on O occupy sp^2 hybrid orbitals. The lone pair on N is not involved in resonance, so it remains isolated on N. Thus, N has three electron groups (one lone pair and a bonding group to each of two C atoms), making it sp^2-hybridized as well; the lone pair on N occupies an sp^2 hybrid orbital. 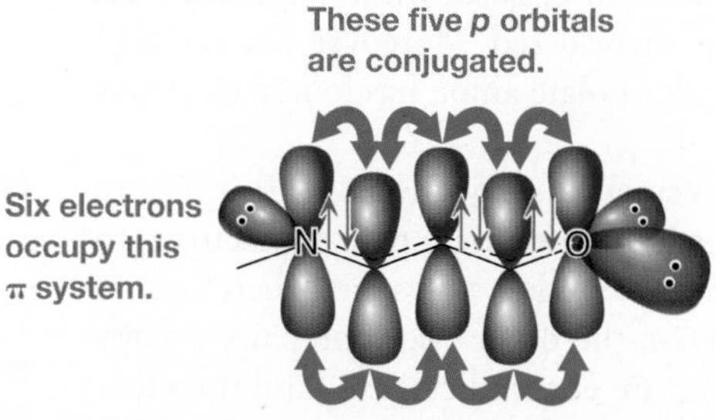 These five *p* orbitals are conjugated. Six electrons occupy this π system. N O

Try It How many π systems does this species have? How many π electrons does each π system contain? What types of orbitals do the lone pairs occupy?

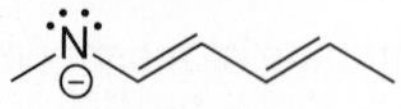

SECTION 14.5 OBJECTIVES

You will be able to:

1. Distinguish a cyclic π system from an acyclic π system on the basis of *p* orbital contribution.
2. Identify benzene as an aromatic compound and cyclobutadiene as an antiaromatic compound.
3. Explain how the stability of a species' cyclic π system corresponds to whether the species is aromatic, antiaromatic, or nonaromatic.

14.5 Cyclic π Systems: Benzene as an Aromatic Compound, and Cyclobutadiene as an Antiaromatic Compound

So far, all of the π systems we have dealt with are acyclic. However, resonance can also occur in which all the atoms of a ring are involved. Benzene is a common example. The benzene ring consists of alternating single and double bonds, so as shown in Equation 14-11, we can draw two resonance structures:

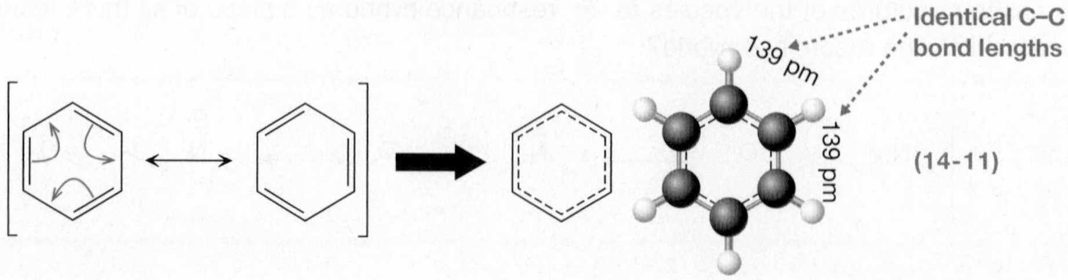
Identical C–C bond lengths
139 pm
139 pm

(14-11)

Benzene

Because the electron delocalization involves all the carbon atoms, each carbon contributes a *p* orbital to the same π system, as shown in **Figure 14-11**. All of the *p* orbitals are conjugated in a complete ring, so benzene has a **cyclic π system**. Moreover, six electrons are shifted to convert the first resonance structure into the second, so we can see that the π system contains six π electrons.

The delocalization of electrons around the entire ring of benzene has important consequences. As shown previously in Equation 14-11, for instance, the molecule is highly symmetric: Benzene is entirely planar, and all six carbon–carbon bonds are equivalent. Perhaps more importantly, from a chemical standpoint:

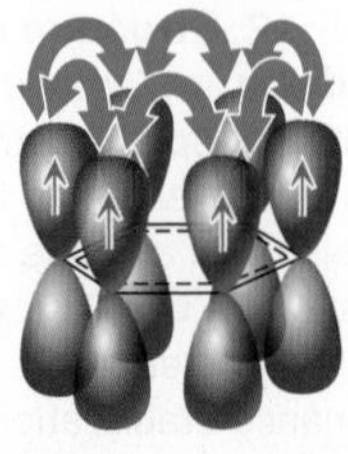

FIGURE 14-11 Cyclic π system of benzene Converting one resonance structure in Equation 14-11 to the other involves all six carbon atoms and requires shifting six electrons. Therefore, each carbon atom contributes a *p* orbital to the same π system, and that π system has six π electrons.

> Benzene's system of π electrons is unusually *stable*.

You can gain a feel for how stable benzene is by comparing Equations 14-12 and 14-13:

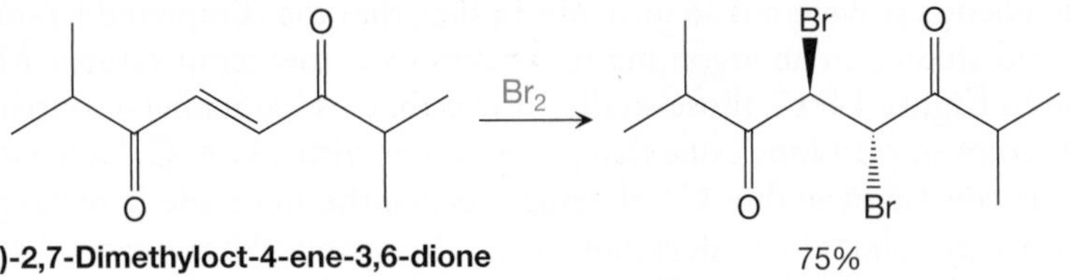

O
O
Br₂
Br
O
Br
O
(E)-2,7-Dimethyloct-4-ene-3,6-dione
75%

(14-12)

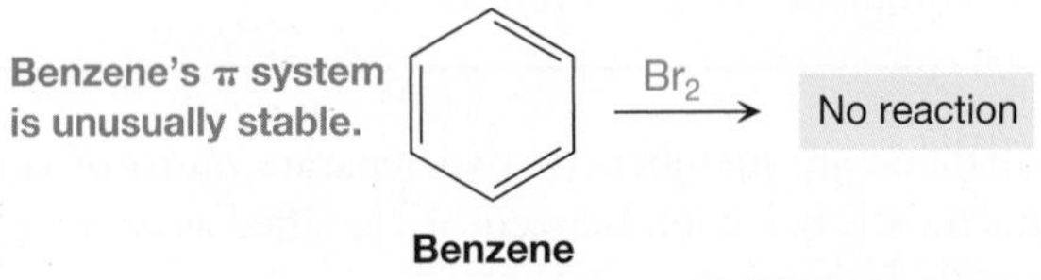

Benzene's π system
is unusually stable.
Br₂
No reaction
Benzene

(14-13)

In Equation 14-12, Br_2 adds across the C=C double bond of (*E*)-2,7-dimethyloct-4-ene-3,6-dione, according to the mechanism we learned in Section 13.4a. As shown in Equation 14-13, on the other hand, no reaction occurs with benzene under the same conditions. Both (*E*)-2,7-dimethyloct-4-ene-3,6-dione and benzene have three conjugated double bonds that make up the π system, but benzene's π system is *much* more stable.

Equation 14-14 presents further evidence of the stability of benzene's π system. $FeBr_3$ is a strong Lewis acid catalyst that enables Br_2 to react with benzene, but rather than addition, benzene undergoes substitution to preserve the π system (see Looking Ahead box):

▸ LOOKING AHEAD

The substitution reaction shown in Equation 14-14 is an example of *electrophilic aromatic substitution*, which we will discuss in greater detail in Chapters 24 and 25.

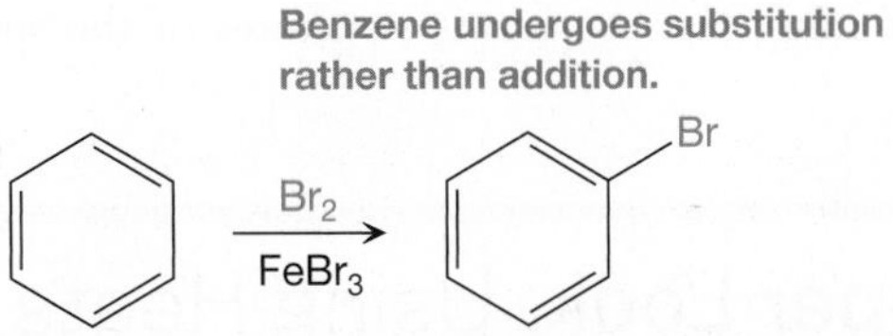

Benzene undergoes substitution
rather than addition.
Br
Br₂
FeBr₃

(14-14)

The unusual stability of benzene can be explained, in part, by resonance delocalization of the π electrons. The two resonance structures of benzene (shown previously in Eq. 14-11) are equivalent; they are called **Kekulé structures** after the German chemist, August Kekulé (1829–1896), who proposed them. Recall from Section 1.10 that a species having equivalent resonance structures tends to be highly stabilized.

Resonance does not fully explain benzene's unusual stability, however. If it did, then we should expect a similar stability in the π system of cyclobutadiene (see margin). Just like benzene, cyclobutadiene's ring consists of alternating single and double bonds.

Cyclobutadiene

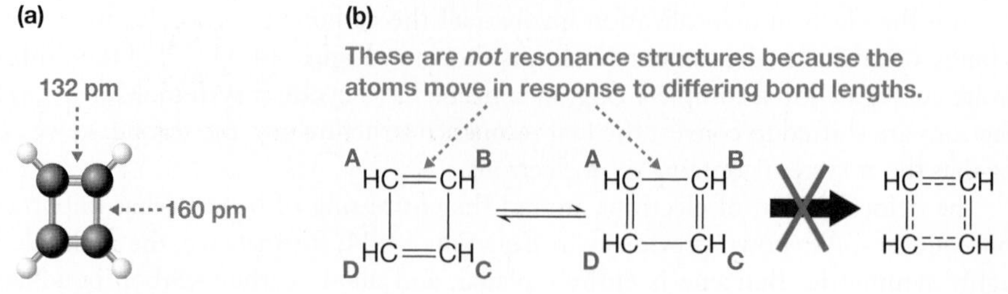
(a)
132 pm
160 pm
(b)
These are *not* resonance structures because the atoms move in response to differing bond lengths.
A
B
HC=CH
HC=CH
D
C
HC—CH
HC—CH
HC==CH
HC==CH

FIGURE 14-12 Structure of cyclobutadiene (a) Cyclobutadiene has two different bond lengths, one that is characteristic of a C=C double bond and one that is characteristic of a C—C single bond. (b) Cyclobutadiene does not enjoy the same resonance stabilization that benzene does.

Unlike benzene, however:

Cyclobutadiene's π system of π electrons is unusually *unstable*.

Cyclobutadiene's π system is so unstable, in fact, that the compound has only been isolated and studied in an argon matrix at extremely low temperatures. Moreover, as shown in **Figure 14-12**, those studies reveal that cyclobutadiene consists of *two different carbon–carbon bonds*: one that is consistent with a C=C double bond and one that is consistent with a C—C single bond; the molecule is rectangular! In other words, cyclobutadiene does not exist as a symmetric resonance hybrid like benzene does, but rather it equilibrates between two different structures.

YOUR TURN 14.8

Compare the carbon–carbon bond lengths in ethane and ethene (see Fig. 14-4, p. 697) to those in cyclobutadiene. What do you notice?

Benzene and cyclobutadiene are members of two separate *classes* of compounds that exhibit different characteristic behavior. Benzene is classified as *aromatic*, whereas cyclobutadiene is *antiaromatic*. In general:

- **Aromatic** compounds have cyclic π systems that are unusually *stable*.
- **Antiaromatic** compounds have cyclic π systems that are unusually *unstable*.
- All other compounds are classified as **nonaromatic** (i.e., as neither unusually stable nor unusually unstable).

▸ LOOKING AHEAD

Experimental evidence that a species is aromatic can be obtained by employing various types of spectroscopy. In Chapter 16, we will see how aromatic compounds can be identified by infrared spectroscopy, and in Chapter 17, we will learn how to identify such compounds by nuclear magnetic resonance spectroscopy.

There are a variety of other aromatic and antiaromatic species aside from benzene and cyclobutadiene. How can we determine whether a species is aromatic, antiaromatic, or nonaromatic? Section 14.6 describes how heats of hydrogenation can be used to make such determinations. Section 14.7 describes how these determinations can be made by examining just the Lewis structures of the species (see Looking Ahead box).

14.6 A Deeper Look: Using Heats of Hydrogenation to Determine Aromaticity

SECTION 14.6 OBJECTIVES

You will be able to:

1. Use heats of hydrogenation to show that benzene's π system is especially stable and cyclobutadiene's π system is especially unstable.
2. Determine whether a species is aromatic, antiaromatic, or nonaromatic on the basis of its heat of hydrogenation.

In Section 14.5, we learned that benzene has an unusually stable π system and is aromatic, whereas cyclobutadiene has an unusually unstable π system and is antiaromatic. Here we show how heats of hydrogenation can be used to quantify the stabilization in benzene's π system and the destabilization in cyclobutadiene's π system.

First, let's consider benzene's π system. As Equation 14-15 shows, the three C=C double bonds in benzene undergo hydrogenation with H_2, which produces cyclohexane. Similarly, three C=C double bonds in separate molecules of cyclohexene will undergo hydrogenation to produce cyclohexane, as shown in Equation 14-16. Even though three

C═C double bonds are hydrogenated in both cases, the reaction is 150 kJ/mol less exothermic for the double bonds in benzene (−206 kJ/mol vs. −356 kJ/mol):

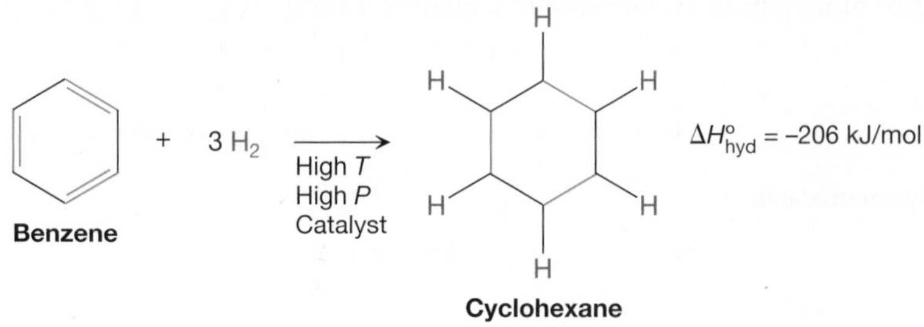

Benzene
+ 3 H2
High T
High P
Catalyst
H
Cyclohexane
ΔH°hyd = −206 kJ/mol

(14-15)

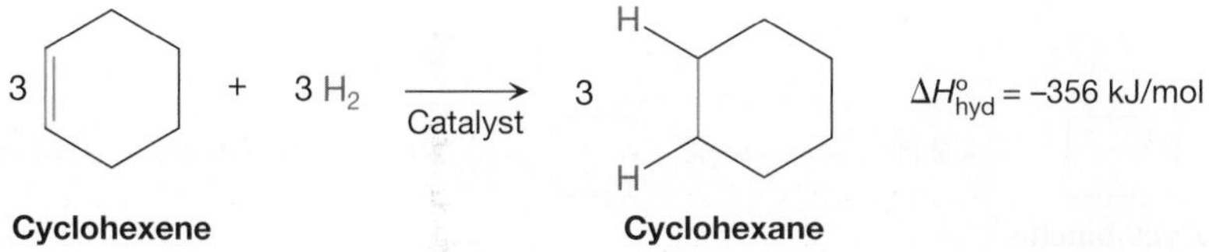

3
+ 3 H2
Catalyst
3
H
Cyclohexene
Cyclohexane
ΔH°hyd = −356 kJ/mol

(14-16)

Thus, as shown in the energy diagram in **Figure 14-13a**, benzene's π system is more stable by about 150 kJ/mol. This substantial "extra" stability, sometimes called benzene's *resonance energy*, is much more than can be attributed to the normal conjugation of double bonds, such as in hexa-1,3-diene (~20 kJ/mol; Fig. 14-8, p. 701); it is instead attributed to benzene's *aromaticity*.

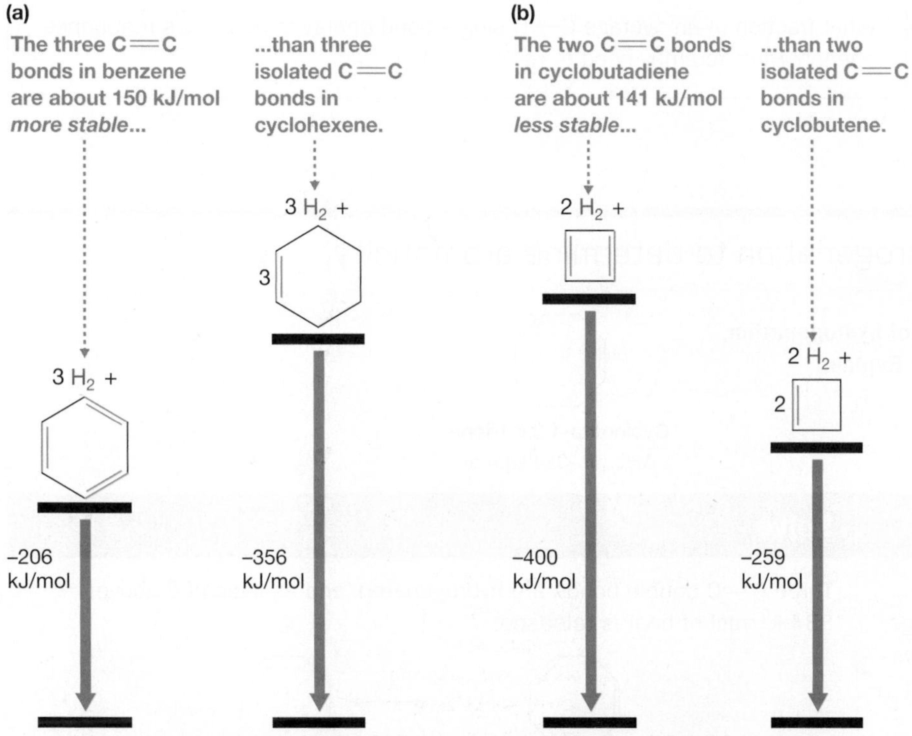

(a)
The three C═C bonds in benzene are about 150 kJ/mol more stable...
...than three isolated C═C bonds in cyclohexene.
(b)
The two C═C bonds in cyclobutadiene are about 141 kJ/mol less stable...
...than two isolated C═C bonds in cyclobutene.
3 H2 +
3 H2 +
3
2 H2 +
2 H2 +
2
−206 kJ/mol
−356 kJ/mol
−400 kJ/mol
−259 kJ/mol

FIGURE 14-13 The stability of benzene and the instability of cyclobutadiene
(a) Energy diagrams for the hydrogenation of three conjugated double bonds in benzene and of three isolated double bonds in cyclohexene. The hydrogenation of benzene releases 150 kJ/mol less heat, indicating that benzene's π system is stabilized by about 150 kJ/mol. (b) Energy diagrams for the hydrogenation of two conjugated double bonds in cyclobutadiene and of two isolated double bonds in cyclobutene. The hydrogenation of cyclobutadiene releases 141 kJ/mol more heat, indicating that cyclobutadiene's π system is destabilized by about 141 kJ/mol.

How can we use heats of hydrogenation to assess the stability of cyclobutadiene? Compare the hydrogenation of cyclobutadiene in Equation 14-17 with the hydrogenation of two molecules of cyclobutene in Equation 14-18:

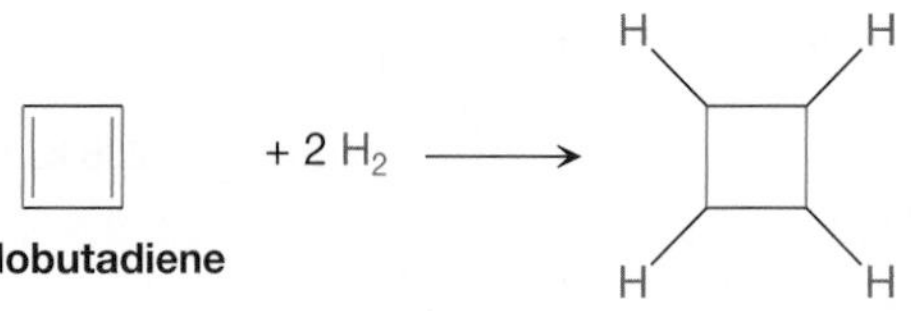

Cyclobutadiene → Cyclobutane $\Delta H^{\circ}_{hyd} = -400$ kJ/mol **(14-17)**

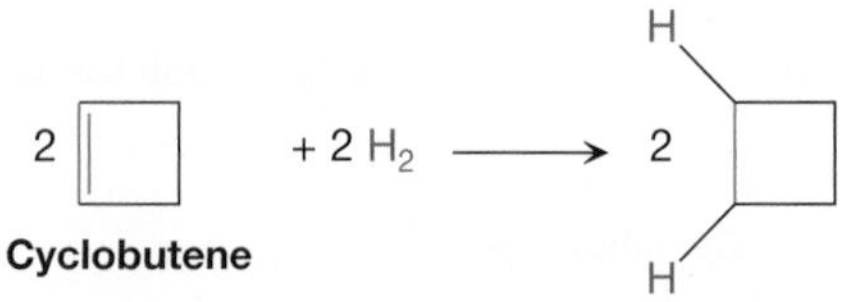

Cyclobutene → Cyclobutane $\Delta H^{\circ}_{hyd} = -259$ kJ/mol **(14-18)**

In both cases, two C═C bonds are converted into C—C single bonds, but ΔH°_{hyd} is 141 kJ/mol more exothermic when the double bonds are part of cyclobutadiene. Therefore, as shown in Figure 14-13b, the π system of cyclobutadiene is *destabilized* by about 141 kJ/mol. Such destabilization is a reflection of cyclobutadiene being *antiaromatic*.

YOUR TURN **14.9**

What fraction of an average C—C single bond energy is benzene's resonance energy? *Hint*: You may need to review Section 1.4.

SOLVED PROBLEM **14.3**

How to use heats of hydrogenation to determine aromaticity

Break It Down From its heat of hydrogenation, is cycloocta-1,3,6-triene aromatic? Explain.

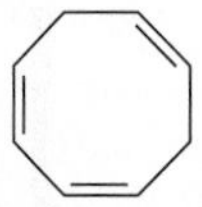

Cycloocta-1,3,6-triene
$\Delta H^{\circ}_{hyd} = -334$ kJ/mol

Think	Solve
How many C═C double bonds are hydrogenated in the complete hydrogenation of cycloocta-1,3,6-triene? How much heat is released?	Three C═C double bonds are hydrogenated, and as indicated above, 334 kJ/mol of heat is released. 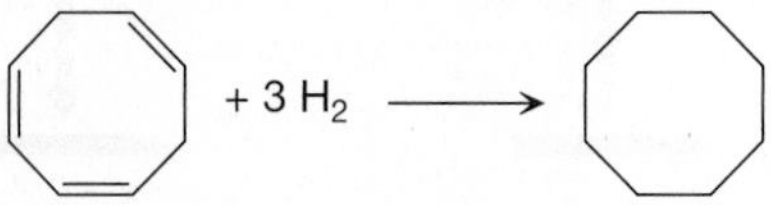
How much heat is released in the hydrogenation of three isolated C═C bonds instead?	According to Equation 14-16, 356 kJ/mol of heat is released when three isolated C═C bonds in cyclohexene are hydrogenated. Even though cycloocta-1,3,6-triene has an eight-membered ring, we can use the heat of hydrogenation of cyclohexene (six-membered ring) for comparison because cyclohexene and cyclooctene will have very similar heats of hydrogenation.

(continued)

How do the two heats of hydrogenation compare? Are the three C=C bonds more stable in cycloocta-1,3,6-triene or in separate molecules of cyclohexene? By how much?	When the three C=C bonds are part of cycloocta-1,3,6-triene, 22 kJ/mol less heat is released. Therefore, the three C=C bonds in cycloocta-1,3,6-triene are more stable by about 22 kJ/mol.
Is the magnitude of the additional stability what you would expect of an aromatic compound?	We previously saw that benzene's resonance stabilization is about 150 kJ/mol. The 22 kJ/mol of stabilization in cycloocta-1,3,6-triene is much smaller, suggesting that the compound is nonaromatic. In fact, the 22 kJ/mol of stabilization in cycloocta-1,3,6-triene is similar to the 20 kJ/mol of stabilization identified in (*E*)-hexa-1,3-diene (Fig. 14-8, p. 701), and can be attributed to two double bonds being conjugated.

Try It From their heats of hydrogenation (ΔH°_{hyd}), predict whether each compound shown here is aromatic, antiaromatic, or nonaromatic.

(a)

Cyclopenta-1,3-diene
$\Delta H^\circ_{hyd} = -211$ kJ/mol

(b)

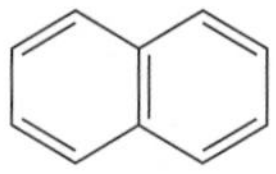

Naphthalene
$\Delta H^\circ_{hyd} = -318$ kJ/mol

14.7 Hückel's Rules: Assessing Aromaticity Using Lewis Structures

SECTION 14.7 OBJECTIVES

You will be able to:

1. Use the rules of resonance to identify a cyclic π system and to determine the number of electrons it contains.
2. Apply Hückel's rules to predict whether a species is aromatic, antiaromatic, or nonaromatic.

Section 14.6 showed how heats of hydrogenation can be used to assess whether a compound is aromatic, antiaromatic, or nonaromatic. It is far more convenient, however, to make this kind of determination from a species' Lewis structure. **Hückel's rules** for aromaticity allow us to do so (see Looking Ahead box). These rules were proposed by the German physicist and physical chemist Erich Hückel (1896–1980):

Hückel's Rules for Aromaticity

- If a species possesses a π system consisting of *p* orbitals that are fully conjugated around a ring, then the species is:
  - *Aromatic* if the cyclic π system contains an odd number of pairs of electrons: 1 pair = 2 electrons, 3 pairs = 6 electrons, 5 pairs = 10 electrons, and so on. These numbers of electrons are called **Hückel numbers**.
  - *Antiaromatic* if the cyclic π system contains an even number of pairs of electrons: 2 pairs = 4 electrons, 4 pairs = 8 electrons, 6 pairs = 12 electrons, and so on. These numbers of electrons are called **anti-Hückel numbers**.
- All other species are *nonaromatic*.

▸ LOOKING AHEAD

Hückel's rules for aromaticity are based on patterns that are observed in the molecular orbital energy diagrams for cyclic π systems. We will discuss those patterns in more detail in Section 14.8.

Keep in mind that, for a ring of *p* orbitals to be fully conjugated, *the atoms that contribute those orbitals must lie entirely in the same plane*. Also, you might find it helpful to know that the Hückel numbers correspond to $4n + 2$ electrons, where n is any integer ≥ 0, and the anti-Hückel numbers correspond to $4n$ electrons, where n is any integer ≥ 1.

Figure 14-14 (next page) shows how Hückel's rules apply to benzene, cyclobutadiene, and hexa-1,3,5-triene. Both benzene and cyclobutadiene have a fully conjugated ring of *p* orbitals because every carbon atom lies in the same plane and contributes a *p* orbital. Benzene's π system contains six π electrons (2 π electrons for each of the three π bonds), which is a Hückel number, whereas cyclobutadiene's π system contains four π electrons (2 π bonds), which is an anti-Hückel number. Thus benzene is *aromatic*, whereas cyclobutadiene is *antiaromatic*. In hexa-1,3,5-triene, on the other hand, the π system is acyclic. Therefore, even though the π system contains six π electrons, the molecule is *nonaromatic*.

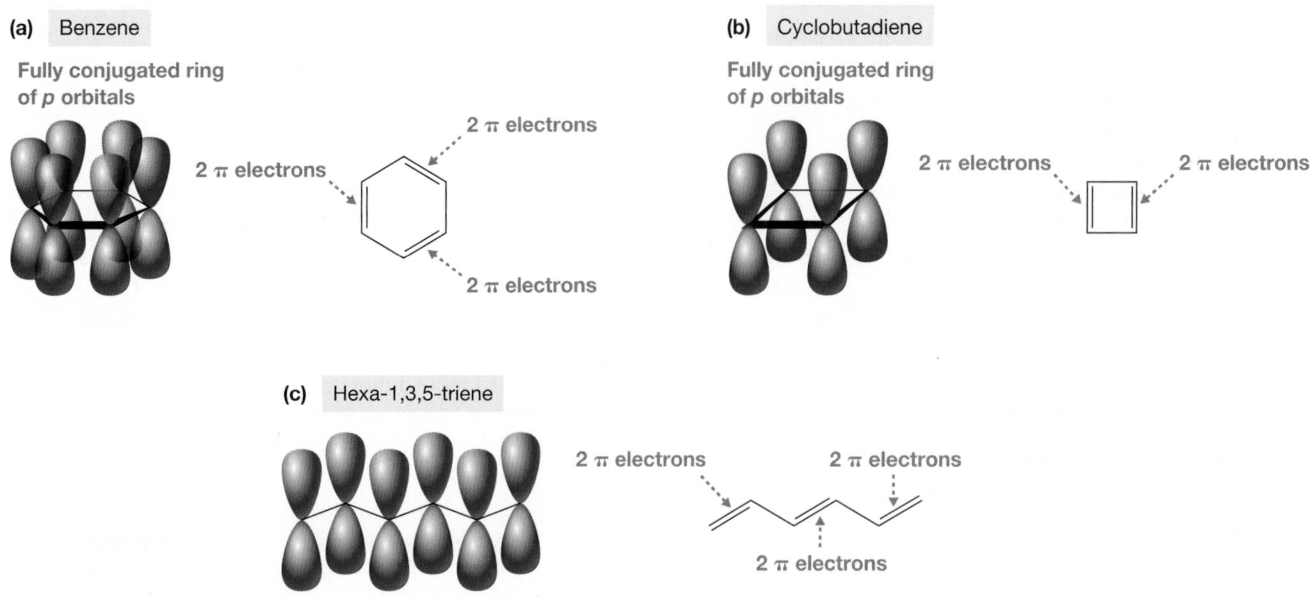
(a) Benzene
Fully conjugated ring of p orbitals
2 π electrons
2 π electrons
2 π electrons
(b) Cyclobutadiene
Fully conjugated ring of p orbitals
2 π electrons
2 π electrons
(c) Hexa-1,3,5-triene
2 π electrons
2 π electrons
2 π electrons

FIGURE 14-14 Benzene, cyclobutadiene, hexa-1,3,5-triene, and Hückel's rules (a) Benzene is aromatic because it has a cyclic π system that is fully conjugated and is occupied by six electrons (a Hückel number). (b) Cyclobutadiene is antiaromatic because it has a cyclic π system that is fully conjugated and is occupied by four electrons (an anti-Hückel number). (c) Hexa-1,3,5-diene is nonaromatic because it has an acyclic π system, despite having six π electrons.

When we apply Hückel's rules to other species, it can be really helpful to take advantage of the connections between resonance and conjugated π systems discussed in Section 14.1:

- Each atom over which electrons are delocalized by resonance contributes a valence *p* orbital to the same π system, and all of those *p* orbitals are conjugated.
- The number of electrons occupying that π system is the same as the number of electrons that are delocalized by resonance.

Combining these ideas with Hückel's rules, we can use the following method to quickly determine whether a species is aromatic, antiaromatic, or nonaromatic:

Using Rules of Resonance to Help Predict Aromaticity

1. Draw curved arrows to represent electron movement via resonance.
   a. Try to maximize the number of electrons being moved at once.
   b. Try to move the electrons around a complete ring.
2. Determine whether the species has a cyclic π system.
   a. If the electron movement represented by the curved arrows in Step 1 involves all the atoms in a ring and the ring is planar, then the species has a cyclic π system and you need to count the number of electrons in the π system (Step 3).
   b. Otherwise, the species does not have a cyclic π system and must be *nonaromatic*.
3. Count the number of π electrons. Use the curved arrows you drew in Step 1.
   a. If the curved arrows correspond to a Hückel number of electrons (an odd number of pairs), then the species is *aromatic*.
   b. If the curved arrows correspond to an anti-Hückel number of electrons (an even number of pairs), then the species is *antiaromatic*.
   c. Otherwise, the species is *nonaromatic*. (This case would require unpaired electrons, which we deal with in Chapter 27.)

Figure 14-15 shows how these steps are applied to benzene, cyclobutadiene, and hexa-1,3,5-triene, which we have already established are aromatic, antiaromatic, and nonaromatic, respectively (review Fig. 14-14).

(a)

(b)

(c)

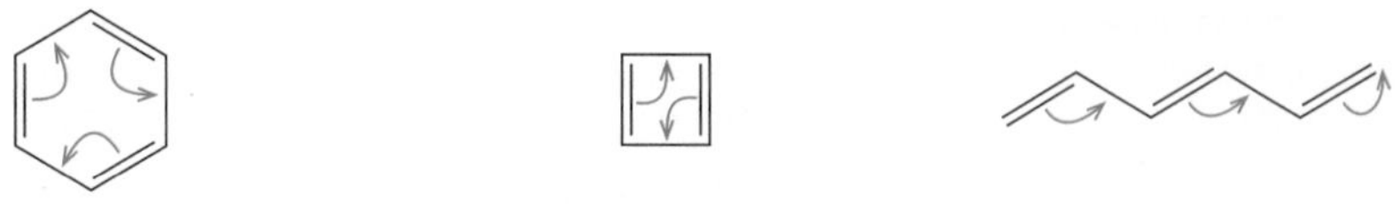

Benzene

Step 1: Maximum electron movement is depicted by the curved arrows.
Step 2: All six atoms of the ring are involved and the ring is planar, so the π system is cyclic.
Step 3: The curved arrows represent six electrons, a Hückel number, so the species is *aromatic*.

Cyclobutadiene

Step 1: Maximum electron movement is depicted by the curved arrows.
Step 2: All four atoms of the ring are involved and the ring is planar, so the π system is cyclic.
Step 3: The curved arrows represent four electrons, an anti-Hückel number, so the species is *antiaromatic*.

Hexa-1,3,5-triene

Step 1: Maximum electron movement is depicted by the curved arrows.
Step 2: All six atoms are involved, but the atoms do not make a ring, so the π system is acyclic and the species is *nonaromatic*.

FIGURE 14-15 Using rules of resonance to assess aromaticity (a) Benzene has a cyclic π system that is occupied by six electrons, so it is aromatic. (b) Cyclobutadiene has a cyclic π system that is occupied by four electrons, so it is antiaromatic. (c) Hexa-1,3,5-triene has an acyclic π system, so it is nonaromatic.

Figure 14-16 offers examples of **heterocyclic aromatic compounds,** so named because they have a heteroatom as part of the ring. In all three cases, the curved arrows show electron movement involving every atom of the ring and the ring is planar, so all three compounds have cyclic π systems. Furthermore, each π system contains six electrons (as shown by the three curved arrows). Six is a Hückel number, so all three of these compounds are aromatic.

Notice in Figure 14-16a that the curved arrows depicting the electron movement for pyridine do not include the lone pair of electrons on N. This is in agreement with the orbital picture of pyridine, which shows the lone pair occupying an sp^2 hybrid orbital that is perpendicular to (and isolated from) the π system. By contrast, the lone pair on N in pyrrole (Fig. 14-16b) is included in the electron movement. As pyrrole's

CONNECTIONS 14.2

S'more pyridine? Pyridine (Fig. 14-16a) is an important compound in numerous chemical applications, which is why roughly 100,000 tons of it are produced annually. It is used as a solvent, as a precursor in the synthesis of certain herbicides and pesticides, and as a starting material for pyridinium chlorochromate (PCC), which is a specialized oxidizing agent (Section 20.5a). Pyridine is not found much in nature, but one natural source is the marshmallow plant, the roots of which were once commonly used in the recipe for marshmallows.

(a) Six electrons occupy this cyclic π system.

(b) Six electrons occupy this cyclic π system.

(c) Six electrons occupy this cyclic π system.

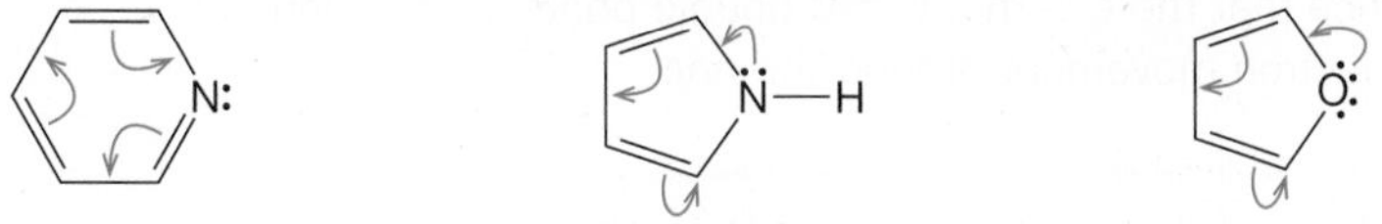
N:
N—H
O:

Pyridine

Pyrrole

Furan

The lone pair is isolated from the π system.

The lone pair resides in a *p* orbital and is therefore part of the π system.

This lone pair is part of the π system.

This lone pair is isolated from the π system.

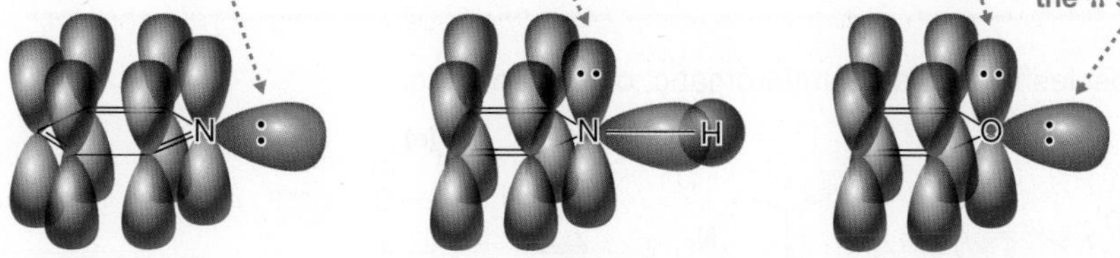
N
N
H
O

FIGURE 14-16 Heterocyclic aromatic compounds Each compound has a cyclic π system that contains six electrons, so each is aromatic. (a) The lone pair in pyridine is isolated on N. (b) The lone pair in pyrrole is part of the cyclic π system. (c) Of the two lone pairs on oxygen in furan, one is part of the cyclic π system, whereas the other is isolated on oxygen.

FIGURE 14-17 Ions and aromaticity (a) The cyclopentadienyl anion has a cyclic π system that contains six electrons, so it is aromatic. (b) The cycloheptatrienyl cation has a cyclic π system that contains six electrons, so it is aromatic. (c) The cyclopropenyl anion has a cyclic π system that contains four electrons, so it is antiaromatic.

(a) Six electrons occupy this cyclic π system = *Aromatic*

(b) Six electrons occupy this cyclic π system = *Aromatic*

(c) Four electrons occupy this cyclic π system = *Antiaromatic*

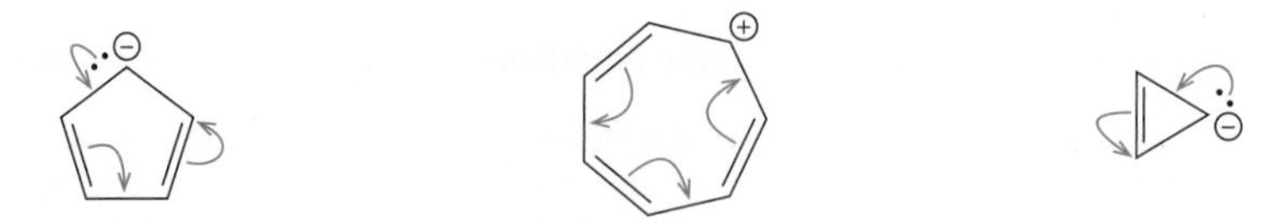

Cyclopentadienyl anion | **Cycloheptatrienyl cation** | **Cyclopropenyl anion**

CONNECTIONS 14.3

A double shot of furan? Furan (Fig. 14-16c) is found in foods that have been heat-processed because it is produced when some natural components undergo thermal degradation. It is found, for example, in foods that are canned and jarred, as well as in espresso coffee.

orbital picture shows, the N—H bond uses one of nitrogen's sp^2 hybrid orbitals, leaving the lone pair free to join the π system. Finally, note in Figure 14-16c that a curved arrow is drawn from just one of the two lone pairs on O in furan. The corresponding orbital picture for furan shows one lone pair is involved in the π system and the other is isolated in an sp^2 hybrid orbital.

Molecular ions, too, can be aromatic or antiaromatic. In the examples shown in **Figure 14-17**, the curved arrows involve every atom of the ring and the rings are planar, so each species has a cyclic π system. The cyclopentadienyl anion and the cycloheptatrienyl cation each have six π electrons, which makes them aromatic. The cyclopropenyl anion, by contrast, has four π electrons, making it antiaromatic.

SOLVED PROBLEM **14.4**

How to determine the aromaticity of a species with lone pairs

Break It Down Determine whether this species is aromatic, antiaromatic, or nonaromatic. You may assume that the molecule is planar.

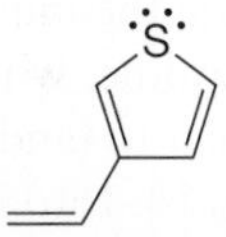

Think	Solve
Can you draw curved arrows to represent the movement of electrons completely around the ring?	These curved arrows represent the movement of electrons around the ring. Notice that the external C═C double bond is left alone to achieve electron movement around the ring. 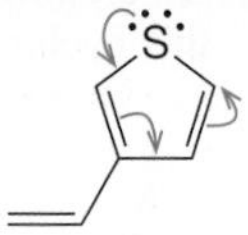
Does the molecule have a cyclic π system?	The ring is planar and all of the atoms of the ring are involved in the electron movement drawn, so the molecule does have a cyclic π system.
How many electrons are in that π system?	The three curved arrows represent the movement of six electrons, so the cyclic π system has six electrons. Six is a Hückel number, so the molecule is aromatic. Note that, for the ring to be aromatic, the external C═C double bond is effectively treated as a separate π system.

Try It Determine whether each of these species is aromatic, antiaromatic, or nonaromatic.

(a) (b) (c) (d) (e)

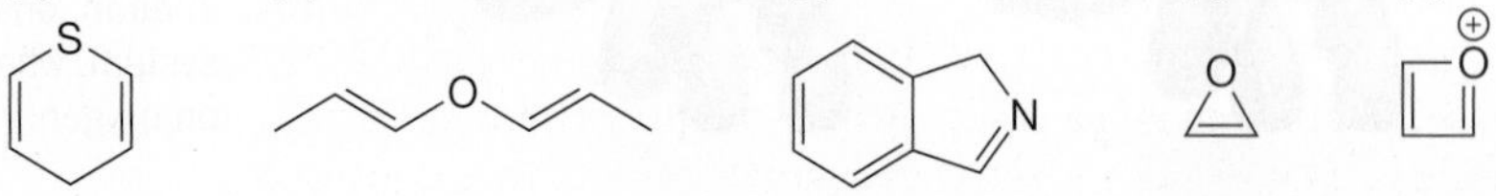

14.7a Aromaticity in Larger Rings: [*n*]Annulenes

Benzene and cyclobutadiene (the prototypical aromatic and antiaromatic compounds, respectively) are *monocyclic* (one-ring) hydrocarbons with C═C and C—C bonds alternating around the ring. These molecules belong to a class of compounds collectively called *annulenes*. All annulenes have the same general formula $(CH)_n$, as shown in **Figure 14-18a**; they are commonly named **[*n*]annulenes**, where *n* is an even number that denotes the number of carbon atoms in the ring. For example, cyclobutadiene (Fig. 14-18b) is [4]annulene and benzene (Fig. 14-18c) is [6]annulene.

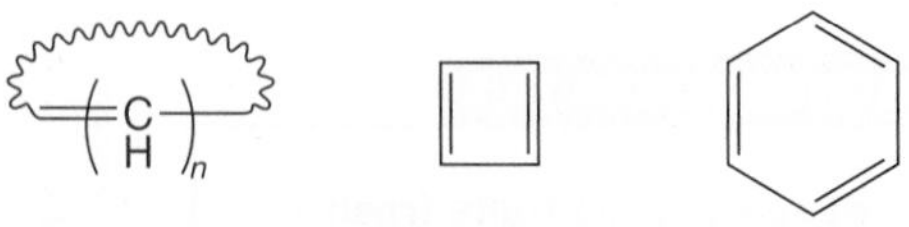

(a)
(b)
(c)
C
H
n
[n]Annulene
Cyclobutadiene
[4]Annulene
Benzene
[6]Annulene

FIGURE 14-18 [*n*]Annulenes (a) An [*n*]annulene is a cyclic compound consisting entirely of alternating C═C and C—C bonds, with the general formula $(CH)_n$. (b) Cyclobutadiene is an annulene with four carbons, making it [4]annulene. (c) Benzene is an annulene with six carbons, making it [6]annulene.

[*n*]Annulenes of any size can be drawn, and we can apply Hückel's rules to determine whether a particular [*n*]annulene should be aromatic, antiaromatic, or nonaromatic. When doing so, however, we must take geometry into account; recall that Hückel's rules require aromatic and antiaromatic rings to be entirely planar. With this in mind, consider cycloocta-1,3,5,7-tetraene (**Figure 14-19a**), which is also called [8]annulene. According to Hückel's rules, [8]annulene should be antiaromatic if it were planar. This would give it a fully conjugated, cyclic π system, and it has eight π electrons, which is an anti-Hückel number. Because of the instability associated with antiaromaticity, however, [8]annulene resists planarity; the ring is large enough and flexible enough to allow the molecule to become nonplanar (something that is not achievable by much smaller rings). Specifically, the most stable conformation of [8]annulene is *tub-shaped* (Fig. 14-19b), in which the *p* orbitals are not all parallel to one another (Fig. 14-19c), and are therefore not fully conjugated. Thus, [8]annulene is better characterized as nonaromatic.

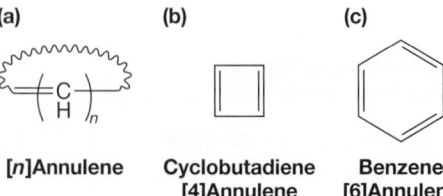

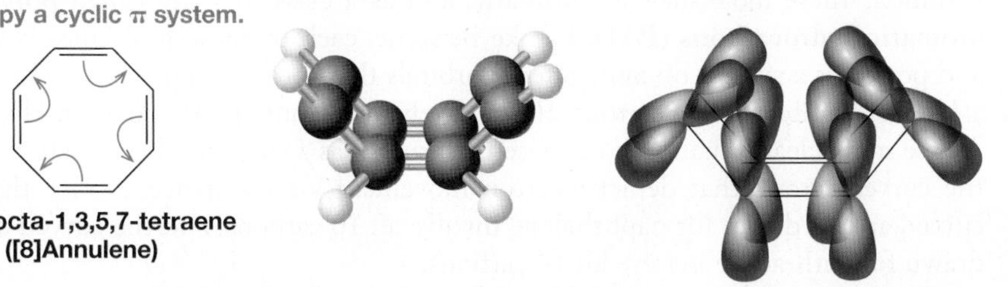

(a)
If the ring were planar, then 8 electrons would occupy a cyclic π system.
(b)
Tub-shaped conformation
(c)
The p orbitals are not fully conjugated around the ring.
Cycloocta-1,3,5,7-tetraene ([8]Annulene)

FIGURE 14-19 Cycloocta-1,3,5,7-tetraene ([8]annulene) (a) Line structure of [8]annulene. The curved arrows indicate that the molecule would have a cyclic π system if all of the C atoms in the ring were coplanar. (b) Ball-and-stick model of [8]annulene, showing that the molecule is tub-shaped rather than planar. (c) In the tub shape, the *p* orbitals do not make a fully conjugated ring, so the compound is nonaromatic.

CONNECTIONS 14.4

A natural source of cycloocta-1,3,5,7-tetraene Cycloocta-1,3,5,7-tetraene (Fig. 14-19) is produced by a species of fungus in the genus *Gliocladium* that lives within the tree *Eucryphia cordifolia*. The compound can be used to synthesize polyacetylene, a conductive organic polymer.

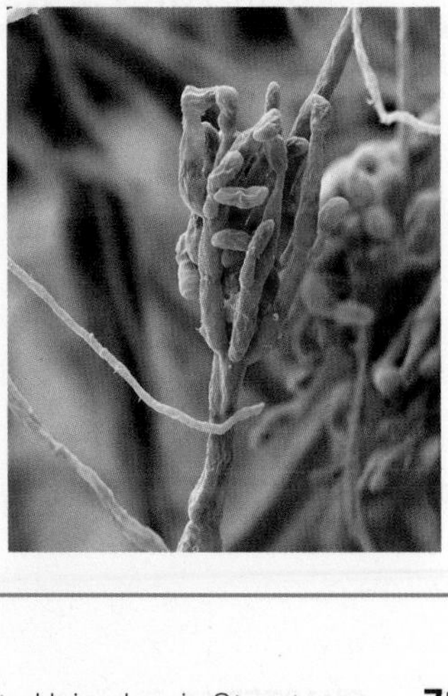

Like benzene, [10]annulene, [14]annulene, and [18]annulene each have a Hückel number of π electrons: 10, 14, and 18, respectively. Therefore, if the rings can be made and are planar, these molecules should all be aromatic, but that is not always the case. As it turns out, [10]annulene is unstable, while [14]annulene and [18]annulene are stable. This idea is explored further in Problem 14.39 at the end of the chapter.

14.7b Aromaticity and Multiple Rings

Polycyclic compounds, which are compounds with two or more rings, can be aromatic. Biphenyl (**Figure 14-20a**, next page) is a somewhat straightforward example, consisting of two separate benzene rings connected by a single bond. Although the two rings are conjugated to each other, each π system forms its own ring with six π

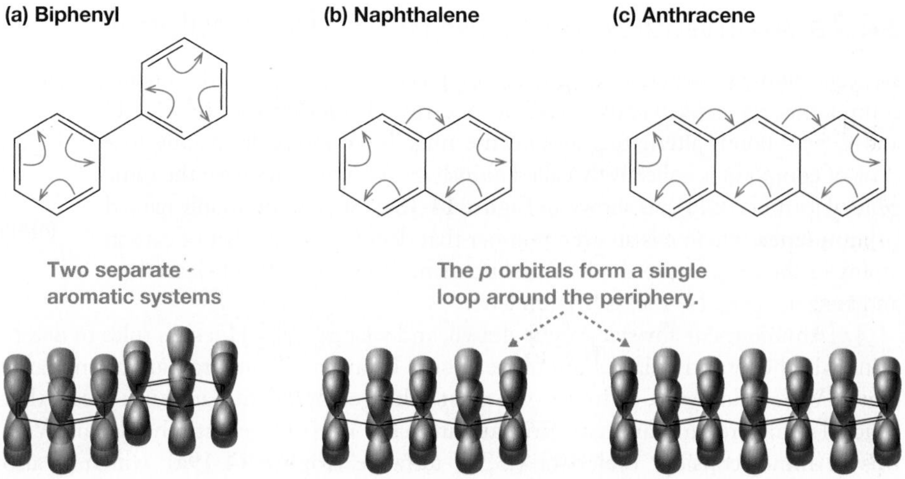

(a) Biphenyl
(b) Naphthalene
(c) Anthracene
Two separate aromatic systems
The p orbitals form a single loop around the periphery.

FIGURE 14-20 Aromaticity in polycyclic compounds (a) Biphenyl can be viewed as two independent aromatic systems, given that the *p* orbitals form two different closed loops. (b) Naphthalene and (c) anthracene, on the other hand, have *p* orbitals that form one complete ring around the periphery. The curved arrows depicting electron movement in resonance also suggest that biphenyl consists of two π systems, whereas naphthalene and anthracene each have one π system.

electrons. Therefore, each essentially behaves as an independent aromatic system. Notice that the curved arrows depicting electron movement via resonance also suggest two independently behaving π systems.

Naphthalene (Fig. 14-20b) and anthracene (Fig. 14-20c) contain two and three **fused rings**, respectively; the rings are considered fused because they have bonds in common. These molecules are aromatic, and as a class they are called **polycyclic aromatic hydrocarbons (PAHs)**. Like benzene, each of these molecules is planar and possesses a system of conjugated *p* orbitals that form a single loop and contain a Hückel number of π electrons. Respectively, they contain 10 and 14 π electrons. To see more clearly that each of these molecules has a single cyclic π system, study the curved arrows that depict electron movement via resonance. Notice that the curved arrows drawn for naphthalene involve all 10 carbons, and the curved arrows drawn for anthracene involve all 14 carbons.

The Lewis structures of PAHs can be misleading. In the Lewis structures of naphthalene and anthracene given in Figure 14-20, the C=C double bonds appear to make up a single ring. However, in other resonance structures, the locations of the double bonds might suggest otherwise. Your Turn 14.10 has you explore this idea.

CONNECTIONS 14.5

Keeping citrus fruits fresh Biphenyl (Fig. 14-20a) is used as a citrus fruit preservative because of its ability to prevent the growth of molds and fungi.

CONNECTIONS 14.6

Anthracene's role in selecting the next pope Anthracene (Fig. 14-20c) has insecticidal and fungicidal properties and has been used as a wood preservative. It is also used to make the mixture (along with potassium perchlorate and sulfur) that is burned to produce black smoke from the chimney of the Sistine Chapel, indicating that a new pope has not yet been chosen.

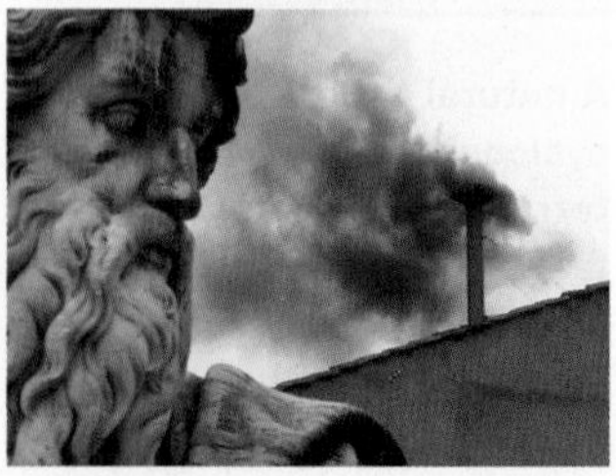

YOUR TURN **14.10**

In the resonance structures of naphthalene and anthracene in Figure 14-20, the double bonds appear to make one ring around the outside of the molecules. Draw a resonance structure of each compound such that the double bonds trace out *two* separate rings. Do these resonance structures have an effect on the locations of the *p* orbitals in Figure 14-20?

SOLVED PROBLEM **14.5**

How to determine the aromaticity of a polycyclic hydrocarbon

Break It Down **Is the compound shown here aromatic, antiaromatic, or nonaromatic? Explain.**

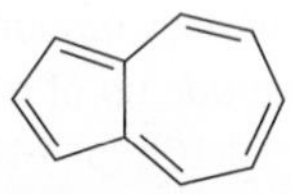

Think	Solve
Does the molecule contain a cyclic π system? How can you tell?	When we draw curved arrows that depict moving the maximum number of electrons via resonance, as shown here, all 10 carbons are involved. 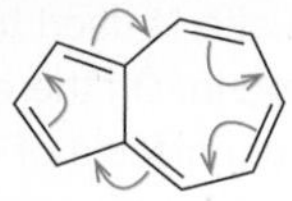 Those 10 carbons make a complete ring, and the molecule is planar, so the molecule has a cyclic π system.
Does the orbital picture support the conclusion about the existence of a cyclic π system?	Each C atom is sp^2-hybridized and contributes a *p* orbital. In the orbital picture for this compound, those *p* orbitals make a single loop, which establishes a cyclic π system. 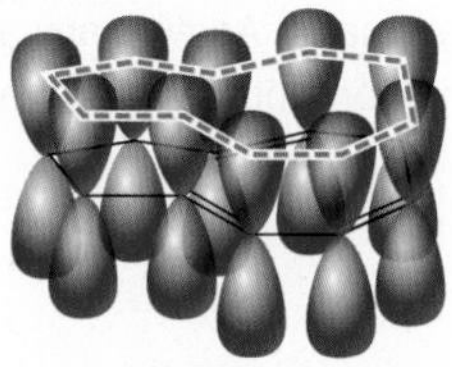
How many electrons does that π system contain? Is that a Hückel number or an anti-Hückel number?	Five curved arrows were drawn above, representing 10 π electrons in the cyclic π system. Ten is a Hückel number, so the molecule is aromatic.

Try It Are the compounds shown here aromatic, antiaromatic, or nonaromatic? Explain.

(a)

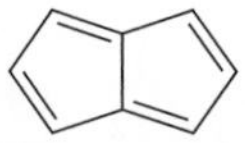

(b)

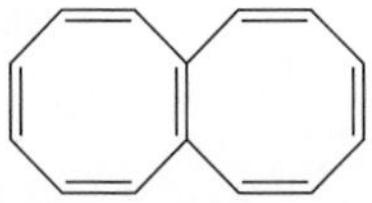

(c)

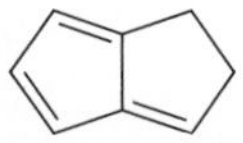

14.8 A Deeper Look: Molecular Orbital Theory, Conjugation, and Aromaticity

SECTION 14.8 OBJECTIVES

You will be able to:

1. Draw the MOs and the MO energy diagram for both acyclic and cyclic π systems.
2. Use the MO energy diagram of a cyclic π system to determine whether a species is aromatic, antiaromatic, or nonaromatic.

We have seen how conjugation among *p* atomic orbitals (AOs) can be applied to account for the resonance delocalization of electrons and how it helps us identify aromatic and antiaromatic species. Conjugation involves mixing AOs from different atoms, which, as discussed in Sections 3.10 and 3.11, produces molecular orbitals (MOs): in this case, π MOs. To this point in Chapter 14, we have yet to consider MO theory in the production of π MOs from conjugated *p* AOs. However, MO theory provides a deeper understanding of the relative stabilities of π systems. Moreover, π systems of MOs play key roles in some chemical processes. For example, Chapter 16 discusses the role that π MOs have in ultraviolet–visible spectroscopy.

Aromaticity Helping Us Breathe: A Look at Hemoglobin

Hemoglobin is the protein responsible for carrying oxygen from our lungs to the tissues that need it. In humans and other mammals, the most common type of hemoglobin has four subunits that are associated noncovalently, and each subunit has an embedded heme group (**Figure 14-21**). It is this heme group that is directly responsible for binding and releasing O_2 molecules.

A heme group is made up of a *porphyrin*, which has a planar, cyclic arrangement of four pyrrole-type rings (see Fig. 14-16b, p. 711), covalently bonded to each other by single-carbon bridges. At the center of the porphyrin is an iron atom in the +2 oxidation state. The iron atom has six sites available for coordination in an essentially octahedral geometry, and four of those sites are occupied by the N atoms of the porphyrin ring, all in the same plane. On one side of that plane, a fifth coordination site is used to covalently bond the iron to a N atom in the side chain of a histidine residue of the protein. On the other side of that plane, the sixth coordination site is used to temporarily bind a molecule of O_2 for transport.

The geometry about the iron atom is vital to the proper functioning of the heme group, and the rigidity of the porphyrin ensures the proper geometry. Where does this rigidity come from? Notice that the porphyrin contains a ring (highlighted in red) consisting entirely of sp^2-hybridized atoms, and each of those atoms contributes a valence *p* orbital to make a fully conjugated cyclic π system. Furthermore, there are 18 electrons (a Hückel number) occupying that π system, indicating that the porphyrin is aromatic. As with any aromatic species, planarity is heavily favored to maximize the overlap among the contributing *p* orbitals.

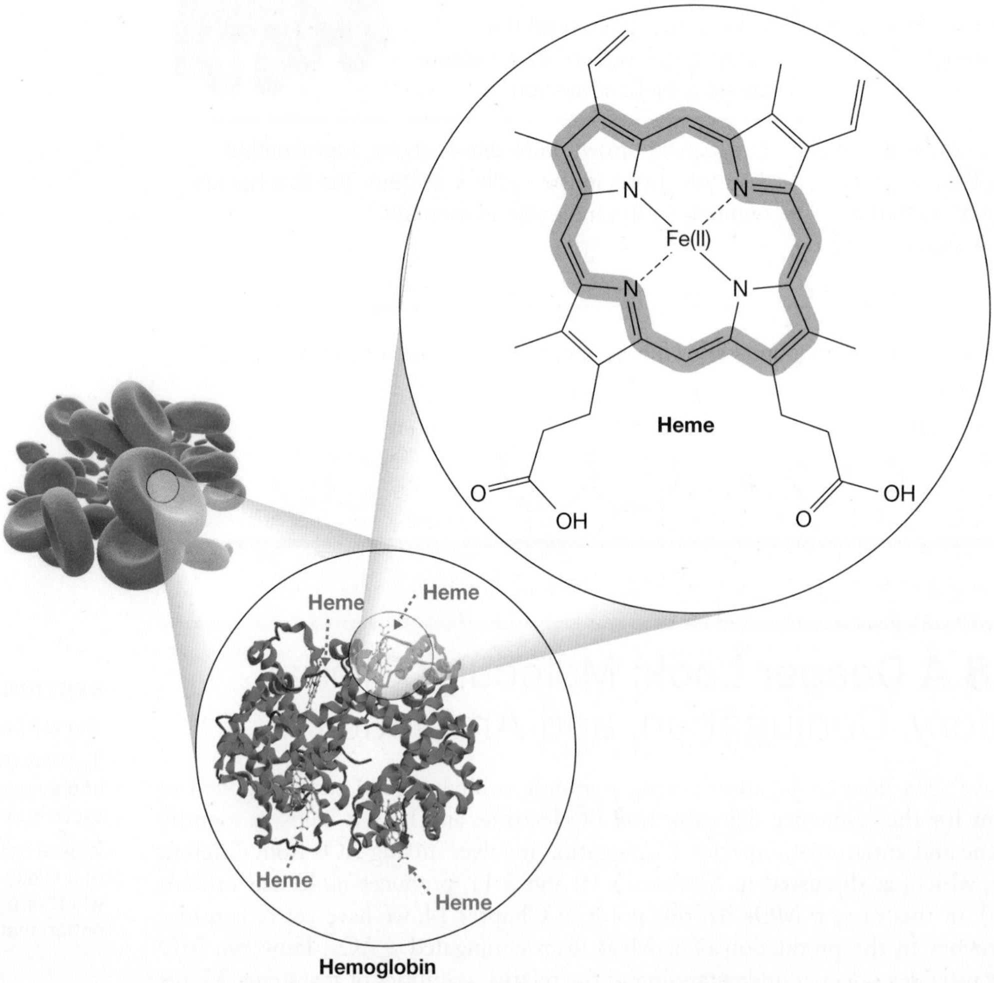

N
N
N
N
Fe(II)
Heme
O
OH
OH
O
Heme
Heme
Heme
Heme
Hemoglobin

FIGURE 14-21

Chapter 26 shows how π MOs make up the frontier molecular orbitals (FMOs, see Interchapter C) for the Diels–Alder reaction, a very useful reaction in synthesis.

Here in Section 14.8, we apply MO theory to the mixing of conjugated *p* AOs. We will begin with acyclic π systems in Section 14.8a, and then we will discuss cyclic π systems and aromaticity in Section 14.8b.

14.8a MO Theory and Acyclic π Systems: The Allyl Cation and Buta-1,3-Diene

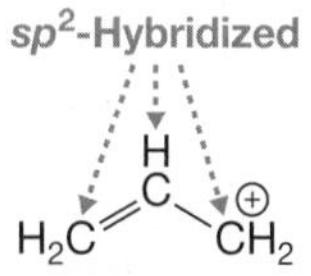

sp^2-Hybridized
H
C
H_2C
CH_2

Allyl cation

Recall from Section 14.1 that each carbon of the allyl cation is sp^2-hybridized, so each carbon contributes a valence *p* AO. Those three *p* AOs are conjugated, overlapping on opposite sides of the bonding axes, and will mix to produce new π MOs. But what do those π MOs look like, and how do the *p* AOs mix to form them?

To answer these questions, let's first review some of the main ideas of MO theory presented in Section 3.10:

Principles of Molecular Orbital Theory

- The number of molecular orbitals (MOs) will be equal to the number of atomic orbitals (AOs) that are mixed.
- Different MOs are produced when the contributed AOs have different phase combinations.
- *Constructive interference* occurs in regions of space where AOs overlap with the same phase; it leads to a build-up of the resulting MO and a lowering in energy.
- *Destructive interference* occurs in regions of space where AOs overlap with opposite phases; it leads to a diminishing of the resulting MO and a rise in energy.
- A *node* appears where there is complete cancellation of the resulting MO; there is zero probability of an electron in a particular orbital existing at a node.

We can then use the following systematic method for deriving the MOs of any acyclic π system, which focuses on the number and location of nodes:

Deriving the Molecular Orbitals of an Acyclic π System

1. Draw the lowest-energy π MO, π_1. Here all contributing *p* AOs have the same phase. Only constructive interference takes place, so mixing produces no new nodes in the π_1 MO.
2. Draw the next lowest-energy π MO, π_2. For this MO, the *p* AO contributions will lead to one new node on mixing. *The phases of the contributing p AOs must change on crossing the node.*
3. Draw the next lowest-energy π MO, π_3. In this case, the *p* AO contributions will lead to two new nodes on mixing.
4. Continue the pattern. The number of nodes will continue to increase for each remaining π MO of the system.

Because the above method focuses on the nodes, it is helpful to know the following rule for adding nodes:

For a symmetric molecular species, the nodes must be placed symmetrically.

- If there is an odd number of new nodes for a particular π MO, then one node must appear at the center of the species.
- For any node located on one half of the species, there must be a corresponding node located on the other half of the species, so each node in the pair is the same distance from the center of the species.

FIGURE 14-22 **π MOs of the allyl cation** (*Bottom*) Derivation of the π_1 MO. The three contributing *p* AOs (left) have the same phase, and the resulting π_1 MO (right) has no new nodes. (*Middle*) Derivation of the π_2 MO. One nodal plane goes through the central carbon, so the *p* AO on that atom cannot contribute to π_2. (*Top*) Derivation of the π_3 MO. Two nodal planes are placed symmetrically about the central carbon.

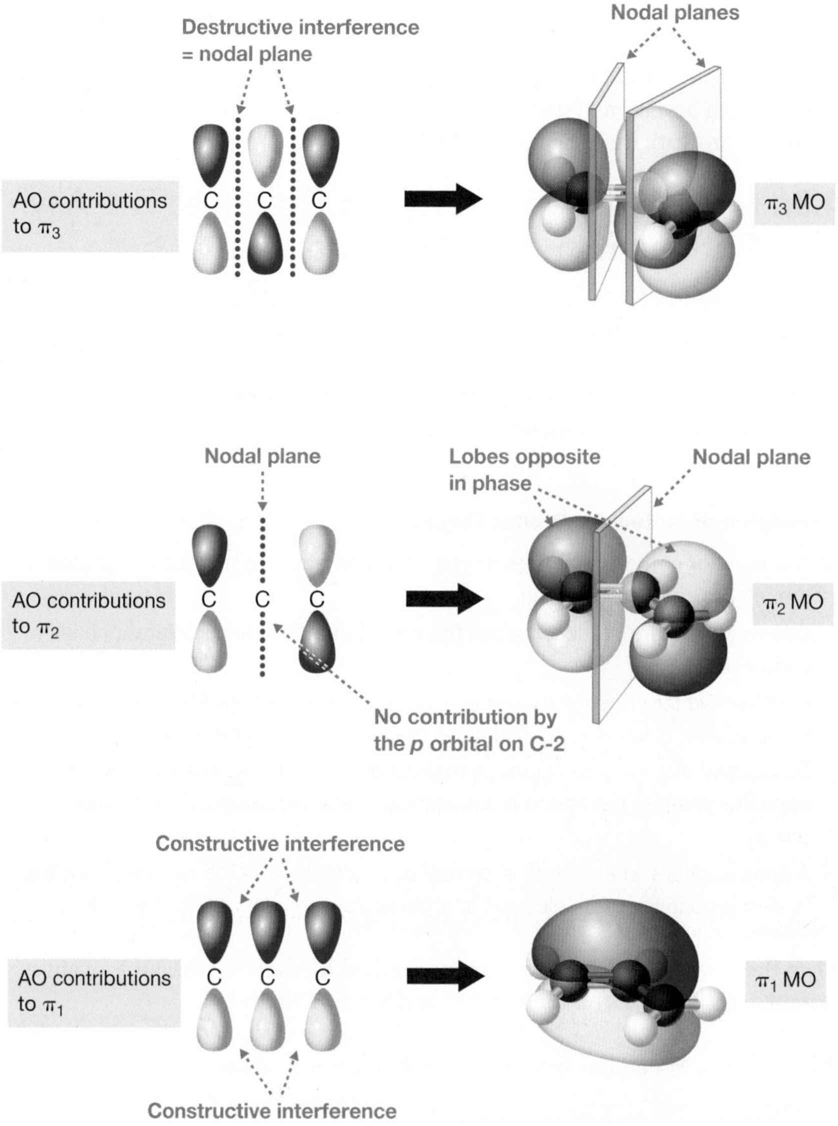

Destructive interference
= nodal plane
Nodal planes
AO contributions to π_3
C C C
π_3 MO
Nodal plane
Lobes opposite in phase
Nodal plane
AO contributions to π_2
C C C
π_2 MO
No contribution by the *p* orbital on C-2
Constructive interference
AO contributions to π_1
C C C
π_1 MO
Constructive interference

With these ideas in mind, we can derive the π_1, π_2, and π_3 MOs of the allyl *cation*, as shown in **Figure 14-22**. In each case, the *p* AO contributions are shown on the left, and the resulting MO, after constructive and destructive interference have been taken into account, is shown on the right.

Notice that the π_1 and π_3 MOs have contributions from all three *p* AOs, but only the *p* AOs on the terminal carbons contribute to the π_2 MO. The π_2 MO has no contribution from the central carbon's *p* AO because the central atom lies in the nodal plane, where there is no probability of finding an electron occupying π_2.

When we know how the contributed *p* AOs interact by constructive or destructive interference in π_1, π_2, and π_3, the relative energies of these three MOs can be established, as shown in the energy diagram in **Figure 14-23**. Each region of constructive interference results in a lowering of energy and can therefore be viewed as a **bonding interaction**. Conversely, each region of destructive interference results in a rise in energy and can be viewed as an **antibonding interaction**. Notice that π_1 is the result of two bonding interactions, so it is stabilized relative to the *p* AOs and is a bonding MO. By contrast, π_3 is the result of two antibonding interactions, so it is destabilized relative to the *p* AOs and is an antibonding MO; we therefore denote it π_3^*. π_2 exhibits no substantial bonding or antibonding interactions among its

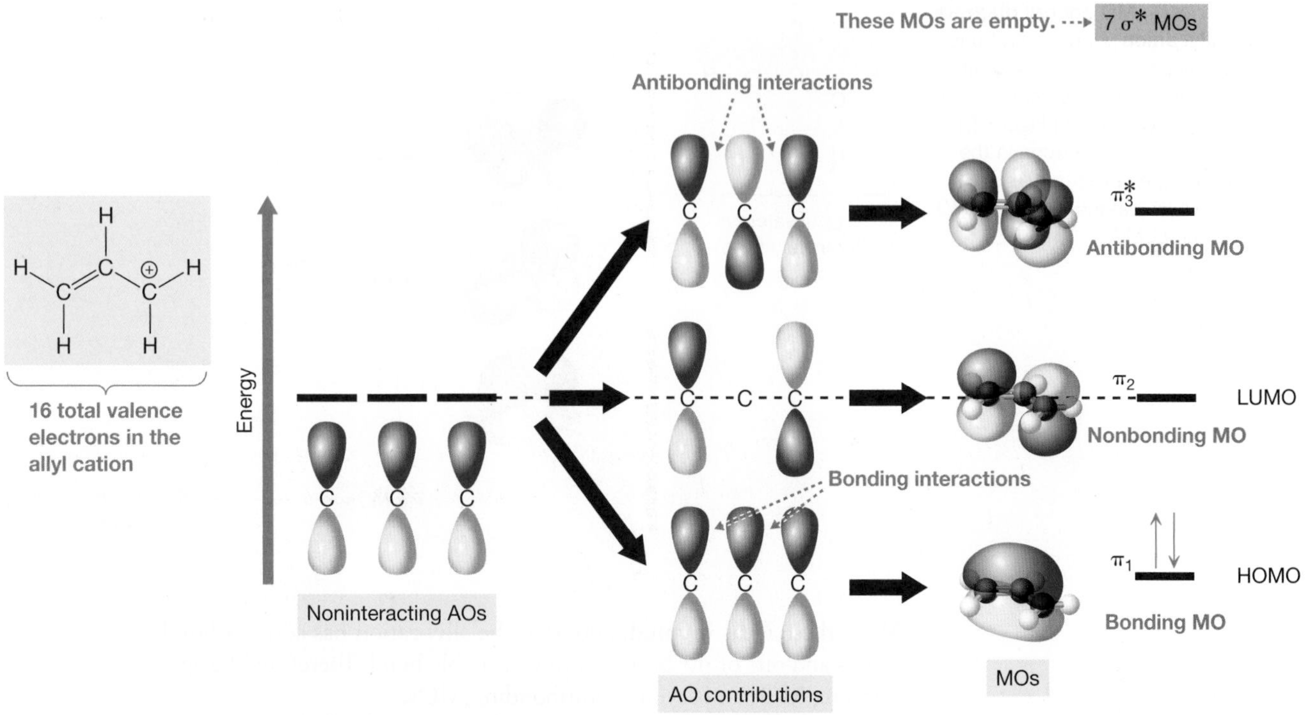

These MOs are empty.
7 σ* MOs
Antibonding interactions
16 total valence electrons in the allyl cation
Energy
Noninteracting AOs
AO contributions
MOs
π3*
Antibonding MO
π2
LUMO
Nonbonding MO
Bonding interactions
π1
HOMO
Bonding MO
14 electrons occupy these MOs.
7 σ MOs

FIGURE 14-23 MO energy diagram for the allyl cation The lowest-energy π MO, π_1, is an outcome of two bonding interactions among the contributing *p* AOs; π_1 is thus a bonding MO. The π_2 MO does not exhibit substantial bonding or antibonding interactions among the contributing *p* AOs, so the result is a nonbonding MO. The highest-energy π MO, π_3, is an outcome of two antibonding interactions among the contributing *p* AOs; π_3 is thus an antibonding MO and is labeled π_3^*. The allyl cation has two π electrons, which fill π_1 only, so π_1 is the HOMO and π_2 is the LUMO.

contributing *p* AOs, so its energy is roughly the same as that of the *p* AOs, and it is a nonbonding MO.

YOUR TURN **14.11**

In Figure 14-23, indicate the location of every nodal plane perpendicular to the bond axes in each MO. (Try to do so without looking at the previous diagrams.)

Notice in Figure 14-23 that the number of bonding interactions decreases, and the number of antibonding interactions increases, as the number of nodes increases. We therefore arrive at a very useful generalization:

As the number of nodes in a MO increases, so does the MO energy.

We have constructed the three π MOs of the allyl cation. Let's now add the MOs of σ symmetry to Figure 14-23. To do so, let's first recall these main ideas of MO energy diagrams discussed in Section 3.11b:

Principles of Molecular Orbital Energy Diagrams

- Each σ bond in a Lewis structure represents a pair of electrons occupying a σ bonding MO.
- There is one σ* antibonding MO for each σ bonding MO.
- The σ MOs tend to be lower in energy than the π MOs, whereas the σ* MOs tend to be higher in energy than the π* MOs.

FIGURE 14-24 MO energy diagram for the allyl anion All three carbons are sp^2-hybridized, so the molecular orbitals produced are the same as the ones for the allyl cation in Figure 14-23. The 18 valence electrons in the allyl anion fill the seven σ MOs, π_1, and π_2, in which case π_2 is the HOMO and π_3 is the LUMO.

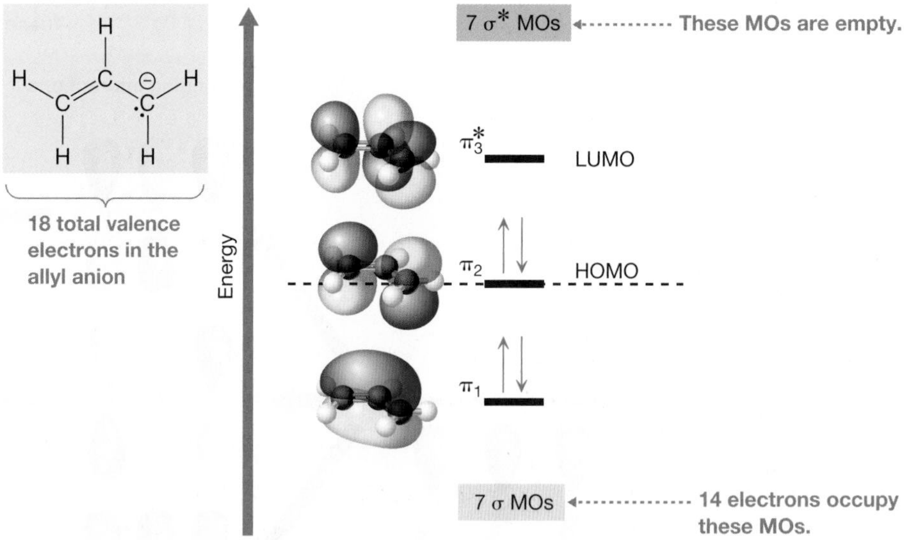

18 total valence electrons in the allyl anion
Energy
7 σ* MOs
These MOs are empty.
LUMO
HOMO
7 σ MOs
14 electrons occupy these MOs.

With these ideas in mind, note that the allyl cation has seven σ bonds: the six single bonds and one of the bonds from the double bond. Therefore, the species has seven σ bonding MOs and seven σ* antibonding MOs.

Finally, we can add the valence electrons to the energy diagram. As we can see from the Lewis structure in Figure 14-23, the allyl cation has 16 total valence electrons. The first 14 electrons fill the seven σ bonding MOs, and the final two electrons fill the π_1 MO. Therefore, π_1 is the highest occupied molecular orbital (HOMO) and π_2 is the lowest unoccupied molecular orbital (LUMO).

The MO energy diagram for the allyl *anion* is shown in **Figure 14-24**. All three carbons are sp^2-hybridized, so the MOs for the allyl anion are the same as the ones for the allyl cation (Fig. 14-23). The allyl anion has 18 valence electrons, which is two more than the allyl cation has; the additional two electrons fill the π_2 MO. Thus, π_2 is the HOMO and π_3 is the LUMO.

YOUR TURN **14.12**

Draw the MO picture and the MO energy diagram for the allyl *radical* ($H_2C{=}CH{-}CH_2^{\bullet}$), which has one unpaired electron. Identify the HOMO and the LUMO. (All carbon atoms are sp^2-hybridized.)

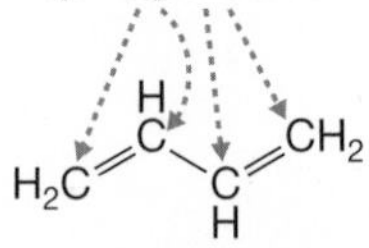

sp²-Hybridized

Buta-1,3-diene

We can apply a similar strategy to describe the π MOs of buta-1,3-diene. As we saw earlier, each carbon is sp^2-hybridized and contributes a valence *p* AO. With an all-planar conformation of the molecule, the four *p* AOs are *conjugated* and they interact simultaneously to form *four MOs of π symmetry*.

The MO energy diagram for buta-1,3-diene is shown in **Figure 14-25**. As with the allyl cation, the π MOs of buta-1,3-diene differ in the number of nodal planes perpendicular to the bonding axes:

Molecular Orbitals of Buta-1,3-diene

- π_1 MO: All of the *p* AOs have the same phase, so no additional nodes are produced on mixing. There are three bonding interactions from the contributing *p* AOs, so π_1 is a bonding MO and is the lowest-energy MO in the π system.
- π_2 MO: One node is added, which appears at the center of the molecule. The *p* AO contributions to π_2 lead to two bonding interactions and one antibonding interaction, so π_2 is a bonding MO but is not as stable as π_1.
- π_3^* MO: Two nodes are added. π_3^* is an antibonding MO and is higher in energy than π_2 because its contributing *p* AOs lead to two antibonding interactions and only one bonding interaction.

- π_4^* MO: Three nodes are added. Its contributing *p* AOs exhibit no bonding interactions and three antibonding interactions, making π_4^* the highest-energy MO.

YOUR TURN 14.13

For the AO contributions of each MO in Figure 14-25, label all regions that represent bonding interactions and all regions that represent antibonding interactions.

YOUR TURN 14.14

The drawing shown here indicates the *p* AO contribution to a single MO of π symmetry. Locate the regions that represent bonding interactions and antibonding interactions. How many are there of each? Will the contributions of the *p* AOs in this fashion produce a bonding, nonbonding, or antibonding MO? Explain.

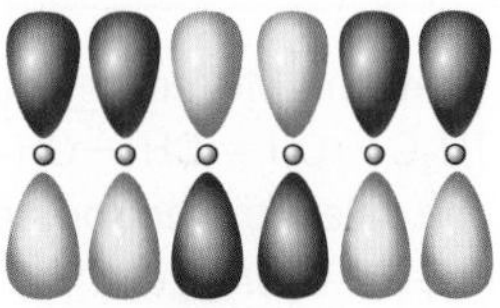

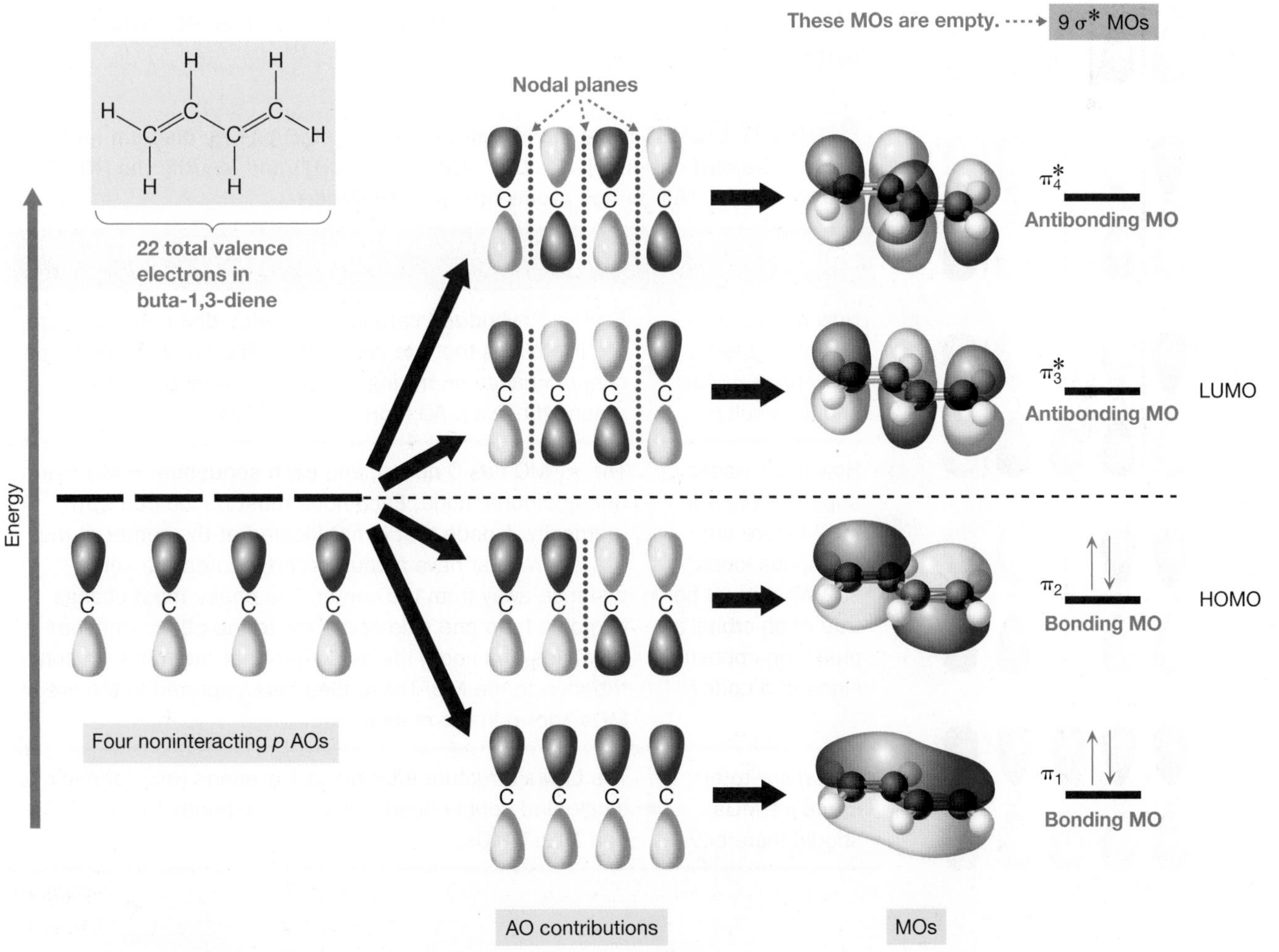
These MOs are empty.
9 σ* MOs
22 total valence electrons in buta-1,3-diene
Nodal planes
Energy
Four noninteracting p AOs
π4*
Antibonding MO
π3*
Antibonding MO
LUMO
π2
Bonding MO
HOMO
π1
Bonding MO
AO contributions
MOs
18 electrons occupy these MOs.
9 σ MOs

FIGURE 14-25 MO energy diagram for buta-1,3-diene The π_1 MO is an outcome of three bonding interactions among the contributing *p* AOs, so the result is a bonding MO. The π_2 MO is an outcome of two bonding interactions and one antibonding interaction, so the result is a bonding MO. The π_3^* MO is an outcome of one bonding interaction and two antibonding interactions, so the result is an antibonding MO. The π_4^* MO is an outcome of three antibonding interactions, so the result is an antibonding MO.

There are nine total σ MOs for buta-1,3-diene: one for each of the seven single bonds shown in the Lewis structure and one from each of the two double bonds. There are also nine total σ^* MOs, one for each σ bonding MO. Just as with the allyl cation, the σ MOs are lower in energy than the π MOs, and the σ^* MOs are higher in energy than the π^* MOs.

The Lewis structure of buta-1,3-diene indicates a total of 22 total valence electrons. The first 18 of those electrons fill the nine σ MOs. The remaining four electrons fill π_1 and π_2, whereas π_3^* and π_4^* are empty. Therefore, π_2 is the HOMO, and π_3 is the LUMO.

YOUR TURN **14.15**

Draw the MO energy diagram for the butadienyl dication, $[H_2C{-}CH{=}CH{-}CH_2]^{2+}$, similar to the one in Figure 14-25. Draw in all of the valence electrons and identify the HOMO and the LUMO. *Note*: All carbons are sp^2-hybridized.

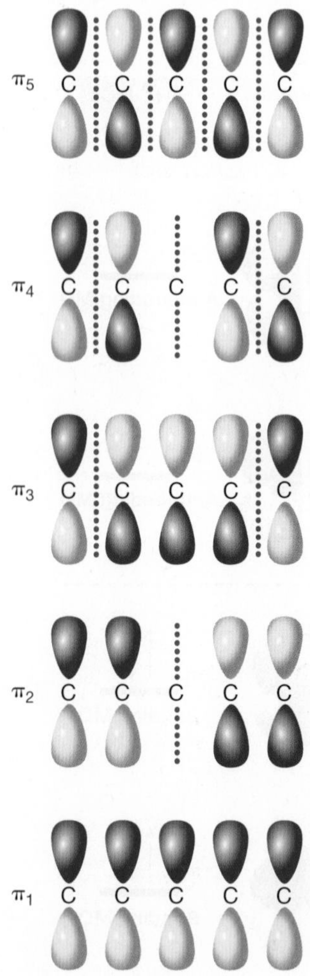

π5
C C C C C
π4
C C C C C
π3
C C C C C
π2
C C C C C
π1
C C C C C

SOLVED PROBLEM **14.6**

How to draw the MO energy diagram for a species with an acyclic π system

Break It Down Draw the MO picture and the MO energy diagram for the penta-1,3-dienyl cation ($H_2C{=}CH{-}CH{=}CH{-}CH_2^+$) and identify the HOMO and the LUMO. (All carbon atoms are sp^2-hybridized.)

Think	Solve
How many *p* AOs are conjugated? How many π MOs should result?	Each sp^2-hybridized carbon contributes one *p* AO, so there are five *p* AOs that are conjugated. The number of orbitals cannot change on mixing, so the simultaneous overlap among the five *p* AOs forms five π MOs.
How many nodes appear in each π MO? Where are the nodes located? What must be true of an orbital's phase on opposite sides of a node?	The π_1 MO has 0 nodes, and each sequential π MO has one additional node. Each node must be located symmetrically. A node that is not located at the center of the π system must have a counterpart located the same distance away from the center. The phase must change on going from one side of a node to the other; when an atom lies in a node, the *p* AO from that atom has no contribution to the MO. These ideas are captured in the five π MOs shown in the margin here.
How many total σ and σ^* MOs should there be?	The Lewis structure indicates 11 σ bonds (one for each single and double bond), which corresponds to 11 σ MOs and 11 σ^* MOs.

(continued)

How do you determine whether a π MO is bonding, nonbonding, or antibonding? How do the π MO energies compare to the σ MO energies?	The π_1 and π_2 MOs have more bonding interactions than antibonding interactions, so they are both bonding MOs. The π_3 MO has the same number of bonding and antibonding interactions (two of each), so it is a nonbonding MO. The π_4 and π_5 MOs have more antibonding interactions than bonding interactions, so they are both antibonding MOs. The energies of the π MOs tend to be in between those of the σ MOs.
How many total valence electrons are there, and how should they be arranged in the orbitals?	There are 26 total valence electrons in the penta-1,3-dienyl cation. As shown here, the first 22 fill the 11 σ MOs, the next two fill π_1, and the final two fill π_2. Therefore, π_2 is the HOMO and π_3 is the LUMO.

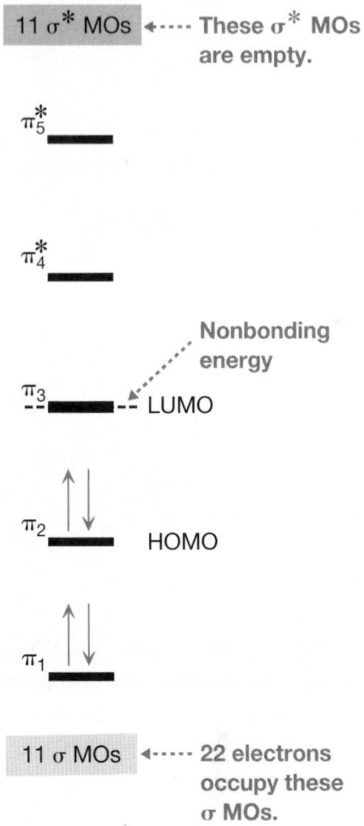

11 σ* MOs
These σ* MOs are empty.
π5*
π4*
Nonbonding energy
π3
LUMO
π2
HOMO
π1
11 σ MOs
22 electrons occupy these σ MOs.

Try It Draw the MO picture and the MO energy diagram for the penta-1,3-dienyl anion ($H_2C{=}CH{-}CH{=}CH{-}CH_2^-$) and identify the HOMO and the LUMO. (All carbon atoms are sp^2-hybridized.)

14.8b MO Theory and Cyclic π Systems: Benzene and Cyclobutadiene

In benzene, all six carbons are sp^2-hybridized, so there are six unhybridized *p* AOs fully conjugated around the ring (**Figure 14-26a**). The simultaneous interactions among benzene's *p* AOs produce six MOs of π symmetry.

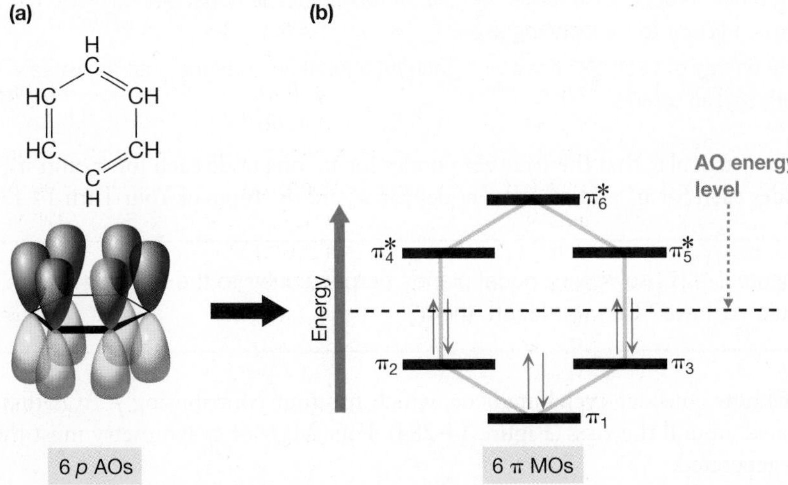

(a)
(b)
6 p AOs
Energy
AO energy level
π6*
π4*
π5*
π2
π3
π1
6 π MOs

FIGURE 14-26 Energy diagram for the π MOs of benzene (a) The six *p* AOs of benzene. (b) Energy levels of the six π MOs of benzene and their occupancy by the six π electrons. The dashed line represents the energy of the unhybridized *p* AOs.

The relative energies of MOs in a cyclic π system follow a pattern described by the **Frost method**, developed by the American chemist Arthur A. Frost (1909–2002):

The Frost Method for Energies of Cyclic π MOs

1. Draw a regular polygon that represents the cyclic compound's line structure. Orient one vertex of the polygon directly downward.
2. Add the nonbonding energy. Draw a dashed horizontal line through the center of the polygon, which represents the energy of the noninteracting *p* AOs.
3. Place the energies of the π MOs. Draw a short, solid horizontal line at each vertex of the polygon. Each line represents the energy of a π MO.

Figure 14-26b shows how the Frost method is applied to benzene. Benzene has a single π MO (π_1), which is lowest in energy. At a somewhat higher energy, there are the π_2 and π_3 MOs; these two MOs are **degenerate orbitals** because they have identical energies. A second pair of degenerate orbitals, π_4^* and π_5^*, is found at a higher energy level, and π_6^* has the highest energy. Benzene's six π electrons fill the lowest-energy π MOs first: namely π_1, π_2, and π_3.

YOUR TURN **14.16**

In Figure 14-26b, label each of the six MOs as either *bonding*, *nonbonding*, or *antibonding*. Also, identify each *pair* of degenerate orbitals. Then, indicate the number and relative energies of the MOs of σ symmetry, similar to Figures 14-23, 14-24, and 14-25, and identify both the HOMO and LUMO.

Figure 14-27 shows how each of benzene's π MOs is produced from the contributing *p* AOs. As we have seen before, these MOs differ in the phases of the contributing *p* AOs, which impacts the number and locations of the nodes that appear on mixing. More specifically, the nodes that appear establish the following patterns:

Nodes in Cyclic π Systems

- Each pair of degenerate MOs has the same number of nodal planes perpendicular to the bonding axes.
- The energy of each MO rises with each additional nodal plane, just as we saw with acyclic π MOs.

Notice, in particular, that there are zero nodes for π_1, one node each for π_2 and π_3, and two nodes each for π_4^* and π_5^*. (The nodes for π_6^* are the topic of Your Turn 14.17.)

YOUR TURN **14.17**

In Figure 14-27, how many nodal planes perpendicular to the bonding axes should π_6^* have? Can you locate them?

Let's now consider cyclobutadiene, which has four contributing *p* AOs that are conjugated around the ring (**Figure 14-28a**). Four MOs of π symmetry must therefore be generated.

To obtain the relative energies of cyclobutadiene's π MOs, we again use the Frost method. As shown in Figure 14-28b, the compound's square line structure is oriented so that one vertex is pointed downward. The horizontal dashed line through the center of the square represents the nonbonding energy, and each of the four vertices represents the energy of a π MO (π_1, π_2, π_3, and π_4^*).

According to Figure 14-28b, the four π electrons in cyclobutadiene occupy π_1, π_2, and π_3. The π_1 MO is completely filled, whereas π_2 and π_3 contain only one electron each. The two highest-energy electrons occupy different MOs due to *Hund's rule*

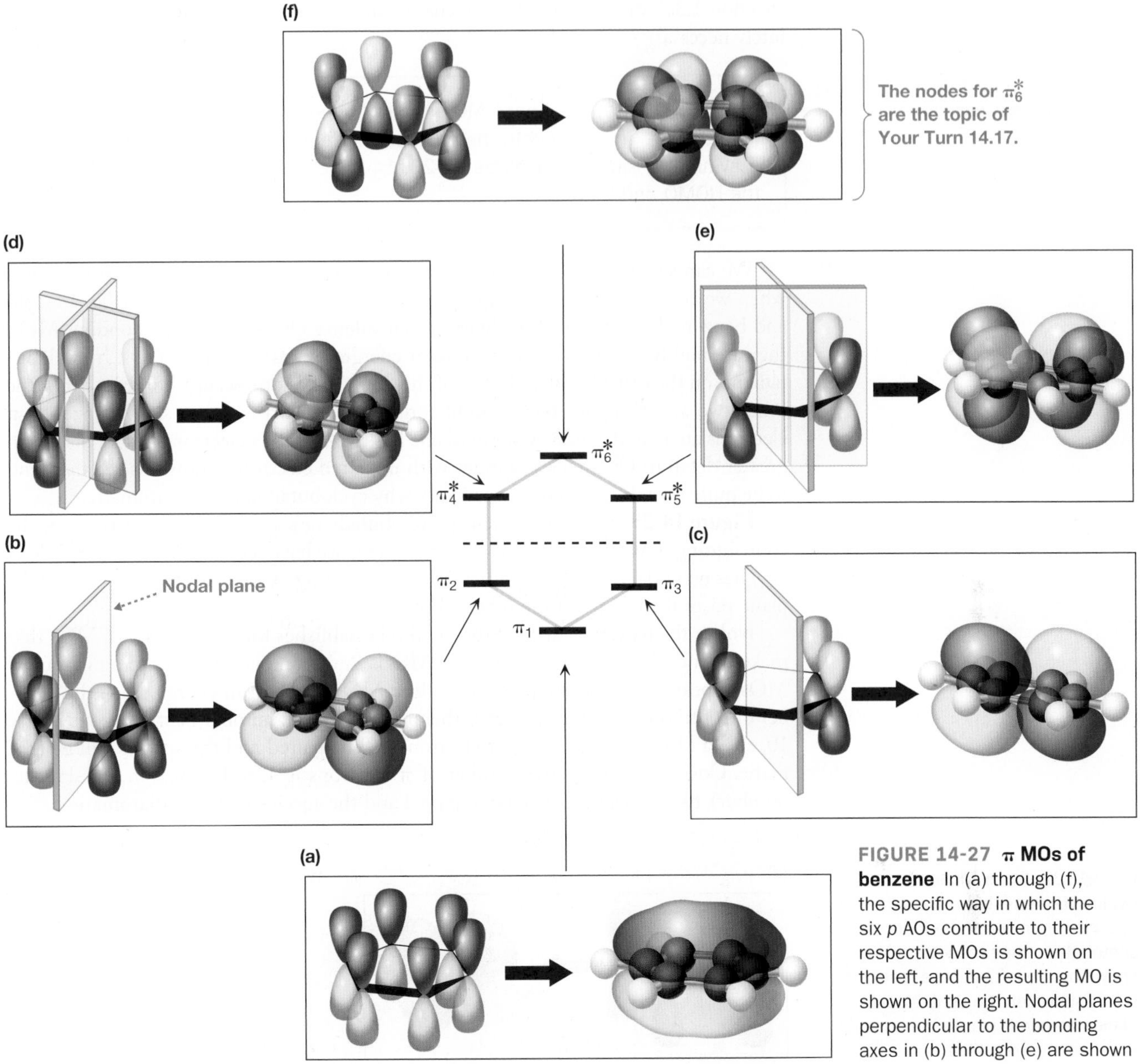
(f)
The nodes for π_6^* are the topic of Your Turn 14.17.
(d)
(e)
π_6^*
π_4^*
π_5^*
(b)
Nodal plane
(c)
π_2
π_3
π_1
(a)

FIGURE 14-27 π MOs of benzene In (a) through (f), the specific way in which the six *p* AOs contribute to their respective MOs is shown on the left, and the resulting MO is shown on the right. Nodal planes perpendicular to the bonding axes in (b) through (e) are shown in blue.

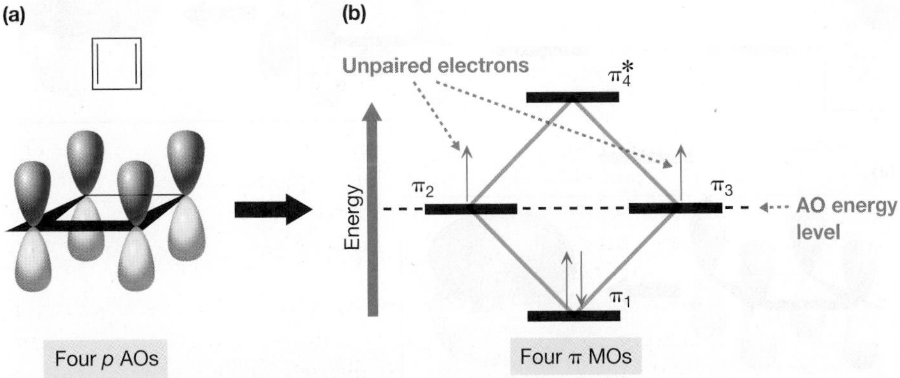
(a)
(b)
Unpaired electrons
π_4^*
Energy
π_2
π_3
AO energy level
π_1
Four *p* AOs
Four π MOs

FIGURE 14-28 Energy diagram for the π MOs of square cyclobutadiene (a) Four unhybridized *p* AOs on the C atoms of cyclobutadiene. (b) Energy diagram of the four π MOs of cyclobutadiene. The dashed line represents the energy of the unhybridized *p* AOs.

(Section 1.3c): orbitals of the same energy are not doubly occupied unless it is absolutely necessary.

YOUR TURN 14.18

In Figure 14-28b, label each MO as either bonding, antibonding, or nonbonding. Then, indicate the number and relative energies of the MOs of σ symmetry, similar to Figures 14-23, 14-24, and 14-25, and identify both the HOMO and LUMO.

We can see why cyclobutadiene's π system is so much less stable than benzene's when we compare the MO energy diagrams of square cyclobutadiene (Fig. 14-28b) and benzene (Fig. 14-26b). In benzene, all valence electrons occupy bonding MOs; they are highly stabilized relative to their energies in unhybridized AOs. In cyclobutadiene, on the other hand, only two of the four π electrons occupy bonding MOs; the other two are in higher-energy nonbonding MOs. Furthermore, all of benzene's π electrons are paired, while cyclobutadiene has two *unpaired* electrons. As we discuss in greater detail in Chapter 27, species with unpaired electrons, known as *radicals*, tend to be quite unstable, which is principally why cyclobutadiene is antiaromatic.

Figure 14-29 shows how each of cyclobutadiene's π MOs is produced from the contributing *p* AOs. As with the other π systems we have seen, the lowest-energy MO (π_1) has no nodal planes perpendicular to the bonding axes, and each additional nodal plane raises the energy of the other MOs.

Notice the pattern that the Frost method establishes for the energies of MOs that make up a cyclic π system: a single π MO is lowest in energy, and the remaining π MOs appear as degenerate pairs (a single π MO is highest in energy when the number of contributing *p* AOs is even). Therefore, when the number of π electrons is 2, 6, 10, etc. (a Hückel number), all π electrons will be paired and the species will be aromatic. Conversely, when the number of π electrons is 4, 8, 12, etc. (an anti-Hückel number), two π electrons will be unpaired and the species will be antiaromatic.

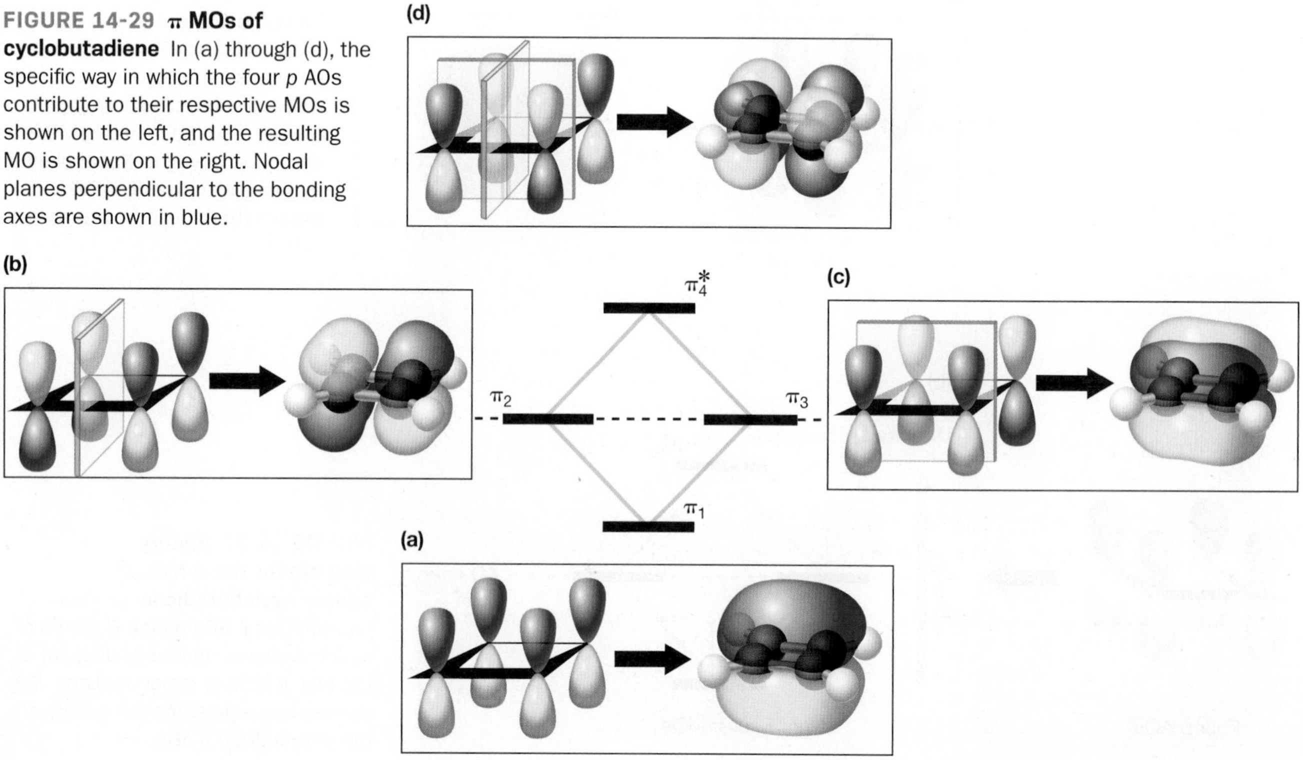

(d)
(b)
(c)
(a)
π_4^*
π_2
π_3
π_1

FIGURE 14-29 π MOs of cyclobutadiene In (a) through (d), the specific way in which the four *p* AOs contribute to their respective MOs is shown on the left, and the resulting MO is shown on the right. Nodal planes perpendicular to the bonding axes are shown in blue.

SOLVED PROBLEM **14.7**

How to use MO energy diagrams to predict aromaticity

Break It Down From the characteristics of its MO energy diagram, would you expect the cyclopropenyl cation to be aromatic, antiaromatic, or nonaromatic? Explain.

Cyclopropenyl cation

Think	Solve
Does the Frost method apply to this species?	All three carbons are planar and are sp^2-hybridized, so each carbon contributes a valence *p* AO to establish a cyclic π system. Therefore, the Frost method applies.
What polygon should you draw and how should it be oriented? How do you locate the nonbonding energy?	The line structure is a triangle. We therefore draw a triangle so one vertex points downward. The energy of the noninteracting *p* AOs (that is, the nonbonding energy) is represented by the center of the triangle and is indicated by a horizontal dashed line. 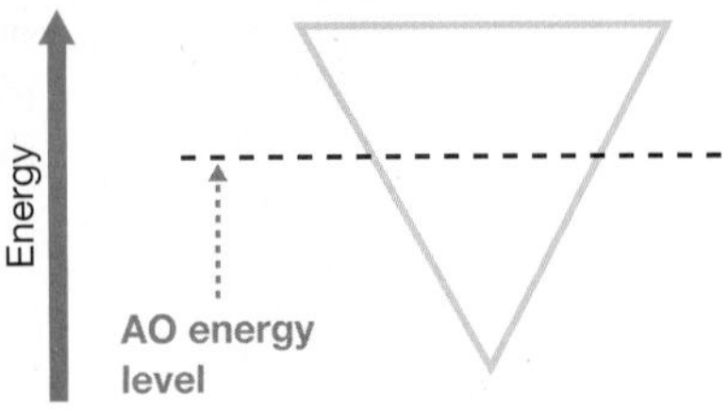 Energy AO energy level
How do you locate the energies of the π MOs?	The π MOs are located at the vertexes of the triangle. π_1 is lowest in energy; it is below the nonbonding energy and thus is a bonding MO. π_2 and π_3 will appear above the nonbonding energy level, so they are antibonding MOs. 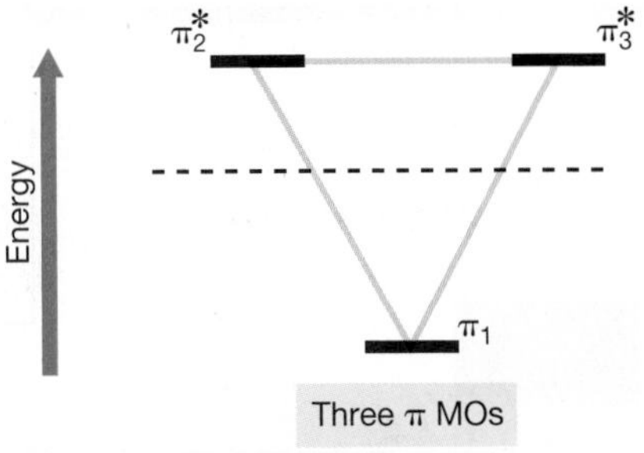 Energy π_2^* π_3^* π_1 Three π MOs
How many π electrons are there, and how should they fill the π MOs?	There are two π electrons, represented by the double bond in the line structure. These electrons fill the lowest energy MO, the π_1 MO. 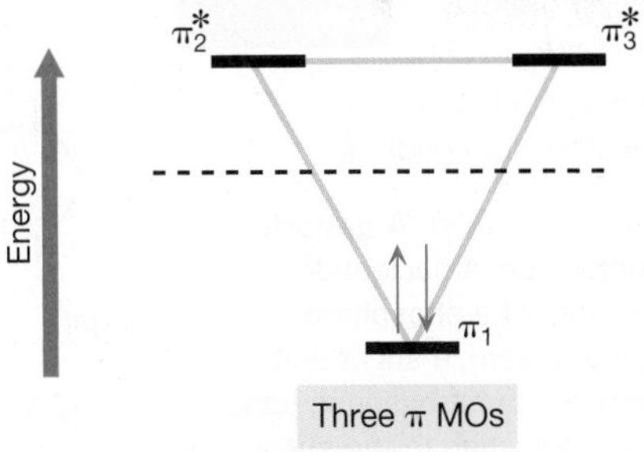 Energy π_2^* π_3^* π_1 Three π MOs
How do the electron energies and pairings relate to aromaticity?	All π electrons are paired and they occupy a bonding MO. Therefore, the species should be aromatic.

Try It From the characteristics of its MO diagram, do you think the cyclopropenyl anion is aromatic, antiaromatic, or nonaromatic? Explain.

Cyclopropenyl anion

SECTION 14.9 OBJECTIVES

You will be able to

1. Demonstrate that all nitrogenous bases in nucleic acids are aromatic and explain the benefit of such aromaticity.
2. Describe the role of hydrogen bonding in the complementarity among nitrogenous bases.

14.9 Aromaticity and DNA

Our discussion of aromaticity thus far has been limited to a few prototypical molecules. In this section, we examine how aromaticity affects the structure and properties of deoxyribonucleic acid (DNA).

Recall from Section 1.14c that each nucleic acid strand of DNA consists of a long chain of nucleotides (**Figure 14-30**). One strand is distinguished from another by the specific sequence of nitrogenous bases attached to the sugar–phosphate backbone. The four nitrogenous bases found in DNA are guanine (G), adenine (A), cytosine (C), and thymine (T), shown in **Figure 14-31**.

The ring system of each nitrogenous base consists of atoms that have planar geometries and are sp^2-hybridized. Thus, each nitrogenous base has a fully conjugated, cyclic system of p orbitals. Additionally, each π system contains a Hückel number of electrons: 10 π electrons for guanine and adenine and 6 π electrons for cytosine and thymine. These π electrons are highlighted in red in the structures in Figure 14-31. According to Hückel's rules (Section 14.7), then:

All nitrogenous bases in nucleic acids are aromatic.

YOUR TURN 14.19

Draw a resonance structure of guanine and of adenine such that, in a subsequent electron movement via resonance, 10 electrons could simultaneously be shifted around a single ring of atoms. As we learned in Section 14.5, this would indicate that 10 electrons occupy a single, cyclic π system. Do the same for cytosine and thymine to show 6 electrons in a single, cyclic π system.

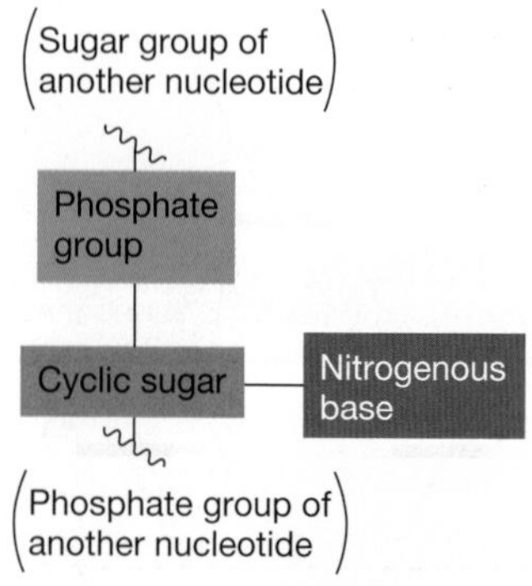
Sugar group of another nucleotide
Phosphate group
Cyclic sugar
Nitrogenous base
Phosphate group of another nucleotide

FIGURE 14-30 A generic nucleotide A nucleotide consists of a phosphate group (green), a sugar unit (red), and a nitrogenous base (blue) attached to the sugar. The backbone of a nucleic acid strand is made up of alternating phosphate and sugar units.

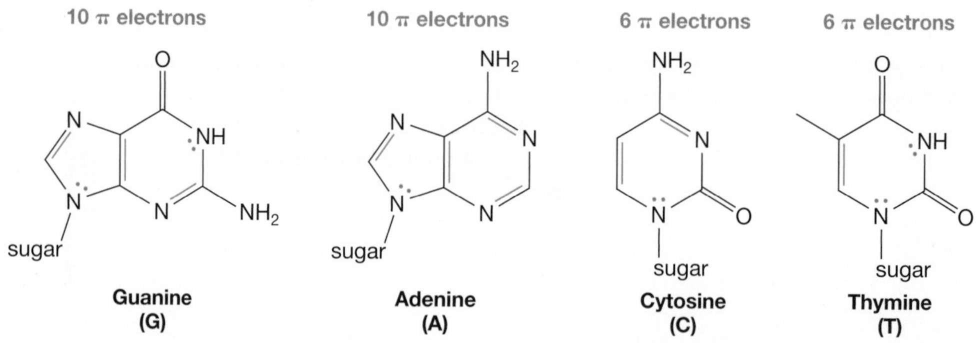
10 π electrons
10 π electrons
6 π electrons
6 π electrons
sugar
Guanine (G)
Adenine (A)
Cytosine (C)
Thymine (T)

FIGURE 14-31 DNA nitrogenous bases and aromaticity The ring system of each nitrogenous base is entirely made of sp^2-hybridized atoms and is planar. Each cyclic π system is occupied by a Hückel number of π electrons (shown in red).

The aromatic nature of the nitrogenous bases in DNA has much to do with the molecule's remarkable ability to store a great deal of genetic information. To appreciate the role of aromaticity in DNA, consider first the general structure of DNA, shown in **Figure 14-32**. DNA consists of two nucleic acid strands, wrapped around each other to form a *double helix*. The nitrogenous bases from each nucleic acid point toward

FIGURE 14-32 **General structure of DNA** DNA consists of two nucleic acid strands that are wrapped around each other in a double helix structure. The sugar–phosphate backbones of the strands define a cylinder, inside which the nitrogenous bases are located. The strands have *complementary* sequences of nitrogenous bases: that is, adenine in one strand is matched with thymine in the other, and guanine in one strand is matched with cytosine in the other.

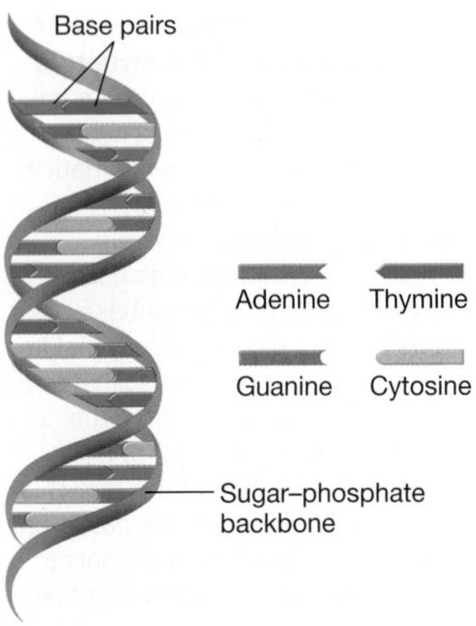

Base pairs
Adenine
Thymine
Guanine
Cytosine
Sugar–phosphate backbone

the center of the cylinder that is created by joining the two sugar–phosphate backbones. The base pairing is highly specific:

- Guanine in one strand of DNA is matched with cytosine in the other.
- Adenine in one strand of DNA is matched with thymine in the other.

The two strands in DNA are thus **complementary**, with a significant consequence: *The sequence of nitrogenous bases in one nucleic acid strand dictates the sequence in the other.*

The G–C/A–T base pairing is heavily favored because the two strands are held together relatively strongly by hydrogen bonding between the nitrogenous bases, as shown in **Figure 14-33**. Figure 14-33a shows that guanine has two hydrogen-bond donors and one hydrogen-bond acceptor that are ideally located to establish hydrogen bonds with two acceptors and one donor on cytosine. Thus, guanine and cytosine form three hydrogen bonds. Similarly, adenine and thymine form two hydrogen bonds, as shown in Figure 14-33b.

Importantly, the G–C base pair has about the same width (i.e., from one sugar unit to the other) as the A–T base pair. This allows the diameter of the DNA double helix to remain essentially constant. G–G and A–A base pairs are wider, whereas C–C and T–T base pairs are narrower, so the inclusion of these self-pairings would make DNA's diameter uneven, ultimately compromising the hydrogen bonding between the two strands.

YOUR TURN **14.20**

The G–T base pair has about the same width as the G–C base pair. How many hydrogen bonds would be formed in the G–T base pair? How does that number compare to number of hydrogen bonds for the G–C base pair shown in Figure 14-33?

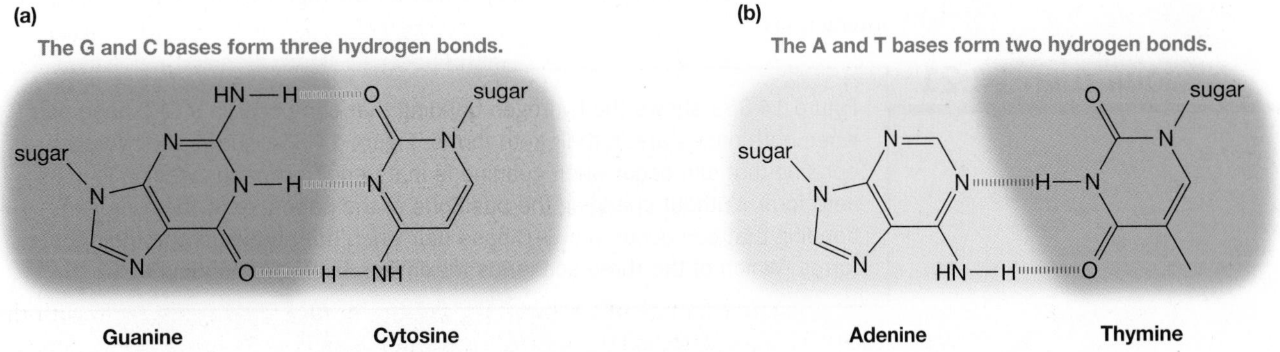

(a)
The G and C bases form three hydrogen bonds.
HN—H
O
sugar
N
sugar
N
N—H
N
N
O
H—NH
Guanine
Cytosine
(b)
The A and T bases form two hydrogen bonds.
O
sugar
N
sugar
N
N
H—N
N
N
HN—H
O
Adenine
Thymine

FIGURE 14-33 **Complementarity among nitrogenous bases** (a) G and C bases are complementary and (b) A and T bases are complementary because each hydrogen-bond donor in one nitrogenous base is aligned with a hydrogen-bond acceptor in the other.

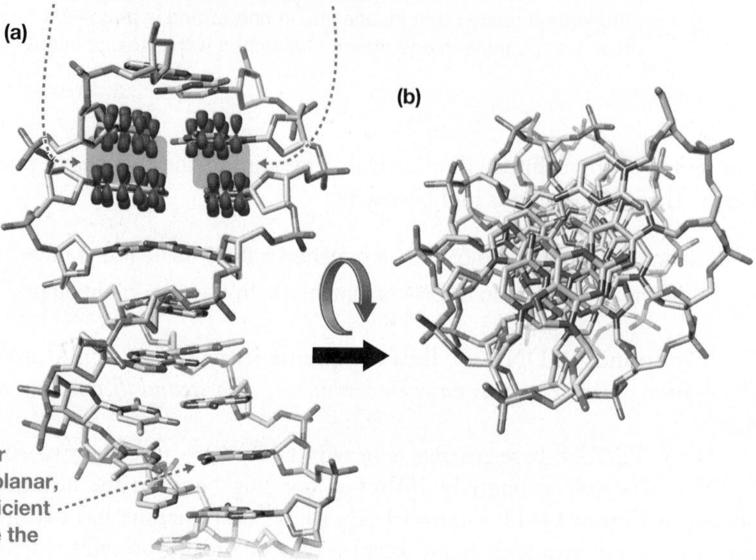
π Stacking takes place inside the double helix, whereby the orbitals from the π system of one base pair overlap with those from another.
(a)
(b)
Each base pair is essentially planar, making for efficient packing inside the double helix.

FIGURE 14-34 Consequences of aromaticity on the DNA structure (a) DNA double helix shown from the side. Each base pair is essentially planar, stemming from the aromaticity of each nitrogenous base and the hydrogen bonding between complementary nitrogenous bases. The planar geometry of the base pairs allows them to pack efficiently inside the double helix and also facilitates π stacking, which arises from the overlap among the *p* AOs. (b) DNA double helix shown from the top. This view shows the nitrogenous bases on top of one another, which enhances the stability from the π stacking that takes place.

Figure 14-34a illustrates the advantages that the aromaticity of the nitrogenous bases offers DNA. First, aromaticity causes the base pairs to be planar. As discussed in Section 14.7, aromatic rings favor a planar structure, as this maximizes the overlap of the *p* orbitals that make up the π system. Hydrogen bonding essentially locks complementary planar bases into the same plane. Consequently, DNA base pairs "stack" within the interior of the DNA helix, much like sheets of paper, which keeps steric crowding to a minimum. Such highly efficient packing of nitrogenous bases allows DNA to store a large amount of genetic information in relatively little space.

Another advantage afforded by the aromaticity of the nitrogenous bases is the stability it provides to the DNA double helix. Because nitrogenous bases are stacked on top of one another, the *p* orbitals from the aromatic system of one nitrogenous base overlap with the *p* orbitals from another nitrogenous base attached to an adjacent sugar, setting up a stabilizing interaction called **π stacking** (Fig. 14-34a). Individually, these interactions are relatively weak, but the *sum* of these interactions along the entire length of DNA provides significant stability. In the top-down view of the DNA double helix in Figure 14-34b, you can see the high density of these π stacking interactions.

YOUR TURN **14.21**

Figure 14-33a shows the hydrogen bonding that can occur in a G–C base pair when both bases are in their keto forms. Figure 14-35a shows the hydrogen bonding that can occur when guanine is in its enol form and cytosine is in its keto form. Without changing the positions of the bases, draw the hydrogen bonding that can occur in a G–C base pair when both bases are in their enol forms. Which of the three scenarios maximizes hydrogen bonding?

The Discovery of DNA's Structure

James Watson (b. 1928), an American biologist, and Francis Crick (1916–2004), a British physicist, published their historic paper on the structure of DNA in 1953. Watson and Crick had two important pieces of information with which to work. One was the *parity relationship* among the nitrogenous bases: the discovery by the American chemist Erwin Chargaff (1905–2002, Austro-Hungarian-born) that, in DNA, the ratio of guanine to cytosine is 1:1 and the ratio of adenine to thymine is also 1:1. The second key piece of information came from X-ray diffraction images of DNA taken in the laboratory of Rosalind Franklin (1920–1958), a British biophysicist, which suggested that the structure was helical.

Watson and Crick used physical models to determine how the base pairing could occur. However, they were working with the incorrect structures for guanine and thymine; they assumed these bases were more stable in their enol forms than in their keto forms (**Figure 14-35**) because, like benzene, each enol form has a ring of alternating single and double bonds. In their enol forms, however, the number of hydrogen bonds guanine and cytosine can make with their complementary bases is reduced. The enol form of guanine can form only two hydrogen bonds with cytosine, and the enol form of thymine can form only one hydrogen bond with adenine.

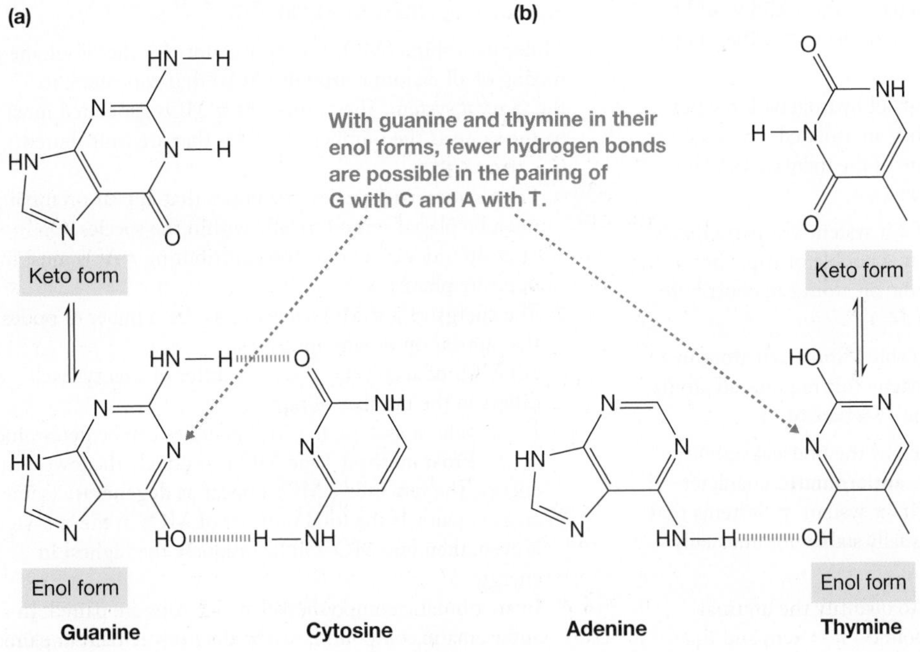
(a)
(b)
With guanine and thymine in their enol forms, fewer hydrogen bonds are possible in the pairing of G with C and A with T.
Keto form
Enol form
Keto form
Enol form
Guanine
Cytosine
Adenine
Thymine

FIGURE 14-35

Fortunately, Jerry Donohue (1920–1985), an American chemist, was studying at Cambridge on a six-month grant and was sharing an office with Crick and Watson. Donohue had expertise with small organic molecules and suggested that guanine and thymine were more stable in their keto forms. This suggestion turned out to be the final piece of the puzzle that Crick and Watson needed to elucidate the structure of DNA.

Even though Rosalind Franklin's X-ray results were vital to the elucidation of DNA's structure, she did not receive proper credit. One of Franklin's colleagues, Maurice Wilkins (1916–2004), a British biophysicist, showed Watson her X-ray diffraction image without her knowledge. Watson, Crick, and Wilkins were awarded the 1962 Nobel Prize in Physiology or Medicine. Sadly, Franklin died of ovarian cancer in 1958 before the Nobel Prize was awarded.

Chapter Summary and Key Terms

- The valence bond (VB) picture of a species that has resonance structures does not account for resonance delocalization of electrons. Instead, a VB picture corresponds to one resonance structure. **(Section 14.1)**
- Valence *p* orbitals are **conjugated** if they are on adjacent atoms and are parallel. A set of conjugated *p* orbitals establishes a **π system**, and electrons occupying a π system are understood to be delocalized over the atoms that contribute to the π system. **(Section 14.1)**
- A species tends to be more stable when its valence *p* orbitals are conjugated. **(Section 14.1)**
- π Systems are isolated if they are separated by a tetrahedral carbon or if they are perpendicular to each other. A triple bond can contribute two of its four electrons to a π system. **(Section 14.2)**
- The **heat of hydrogenation** (ΔH°_{hyd}) for an alkene or alkyne is the enthalpy change that accompanies the addition of H_2 across the C═C bond of an alkene or the C≡C bond of an alkyne. **(Section 14.3)**
- π Bonds tend to have smaller heats of hydrogenation when they are conjugated than when they are isolated. The smaller heat of hydrogenation is a measure of the increased stability that conjugation provides. **(Section 14.3)**
- A lone pair of electrons is part of a π system if it participates in resonance with π electrons from a double or triple bond. At most one lone pair of electrons from an atom can contribute to a particular π system. **(Section 14.4)**
- In a **cyclic π system**, a valence *p* orbital from each atom in a ring contributes to the same π system; this requires all atoms of the ring to lie in the same plane. **(Section 14.5)**
- Benzene is **aromatic**, characterized by the unusual stability of its π system. Cyclobutadiene is **antiaromatic**, characterized by the unusual instability of its π system. π Systems that are **nonaromatic** are neither unusually stable nor unusually unstable. **(Section 14.5)**
- Heats of hydrogenation are used to quantify the unusual stabilization of an aromatic compound's π system and the unusual destabilization of an antiaromatic compound's π system. **(Section 14.6)**
- **Hückel's rules** can predict whether a species is aromatic, antiaromatic, or nonaromatic. **(Section 14.7)**
  - A species is *aromatic* if it has a cyclic π system occupied by a **Hückel number** (an odd number of pairs) of electrons.
  - A species is *antiaromatic* if it has a cyclic π system occupied by an **anti-Hückel number** (an even number of pairs) of electrons.
  - Otherwise, a species is *nonaromatic*.
- A cyclic π system can be identified if all the atoms of a ring are involved in resonance. The number of π electrons in that system is the same as the number of electrons shifted via resonance, such that all atoms of the ring are involved. **(Section 14.7)**
- Heteroatoms can be part of an aromatic ring, giving rise to **heterocyclic aromatic compounds**. In these rings, the heteroatoms can contribute a lone pair of electrons to achieve a Hückel number of π electrons. **(Section 14.7)**
- Ions follow the same rules that Hückel outlined and can therefore be aromatic, antiaromatic, or nonaromatic. **(Section 14.7)**
- Hückel's rules apply to **[*n*]annulenes** that can be formed and are planar. **(Section 14.7a)**
- **Polycyclic aromatic hydrocarbons (PAHs)** generally have a single π system, although their Lewis structures show them as separate rings. **(Section 14.7b)**
- Molecular orbital (MO) theory accounts for the simultaneous mixing of all *p* atomic orbitals (AOs) that contribute to the same π system. The number of π MOs generated must be the same as the number of *p* AOs that are contributed. **(Section 14.8)**
  - For a symmetric species, the nodes that appear on mixing must be placed symmetrically within the species. On opposite sides of a node, the contributing *p* AOs must have opposite phases.
  - The energy of a π MO increases as the number of nodes that appear on mixing increases.
  - All MOs of an acyclic π system differ in energy; each differs in the number of nodes.
  - For a cyclic π system, the MO energies can be determined by the **Frost method**. One MO is uniquely the lowest in energy. The remaining MOs appear as **degenerate** (same energy) pairs. If the total number of MOs in the π system is even, then one MO will be uniquely the highest in energy.
  - In an aromatic compound, all π electrons are paired. In an antiaromatic compound, two π electrons remain unpaired.
- The nitrogenous bases of nucleic acids are aromatic and planar, which enables DNA to store a large amount of genetic information in a small space. **(Section 14.9)**
- The two strands of DNA have complementary nucleotide sequences, whereby guanine in one strand pairs with cytosine in the other, and adenine in one strand pairs with thymine in the other. This complementarity among the nucleotides maximizes the number of hydrogen bonds between nucleotides and maintains a constant diameter of the DNA double helix. **(Section 14.9)**

Problems

Sections 14.1, 14.2, and 14.4 Resonance and Conjugation in Acyclic π Systems; Isolated π Systems

14.1 How many total π electrons are in the molecule shown here? In how many separate π systems do they reside? How many π electrons are in each π system?

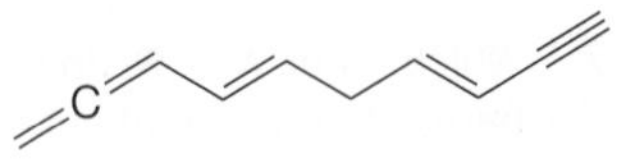
C

14.2 Carotenes are naturally occurring pigments that are responsible for the orange color of carrots and sweet potatoes. Two common forms are α-carotene and β-carotene, as shown below. For each molecule, determine the number of π systems and the number of π electrons in each system.

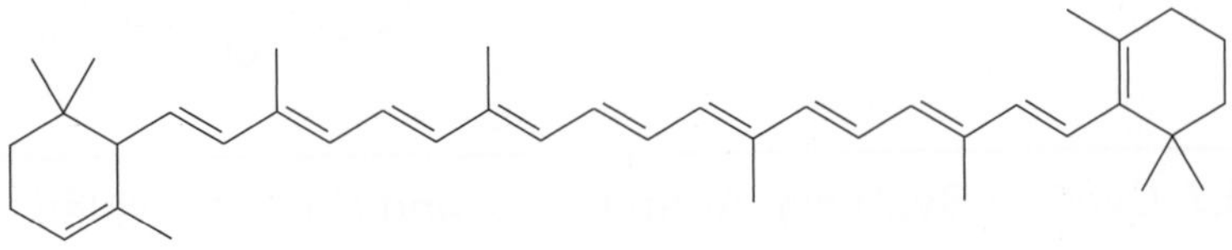

α-Carotene

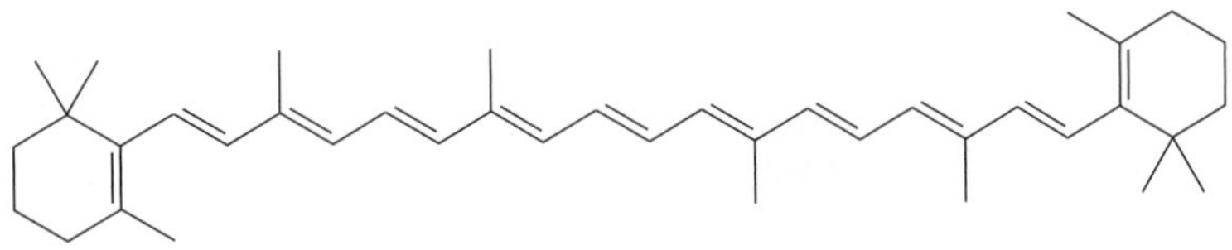

β-Carotene

14.3 How many total π electrons are in each molecule shown here? In how many separate π systems do they reside? How many π electrons are in each π system?

(a) **(b)** **(c)**

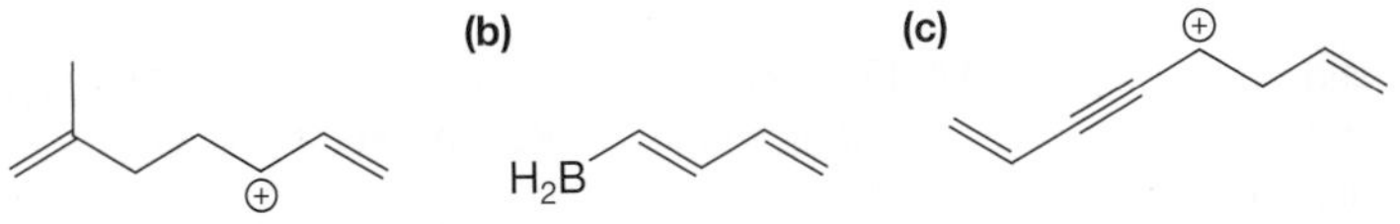
H_2B

14.4 How many total π electrons are in each molecule shown here? In how many separate π systems do they reside? How many π electrons are in each π system?

(a) **(b)** **(c)** **(d)**

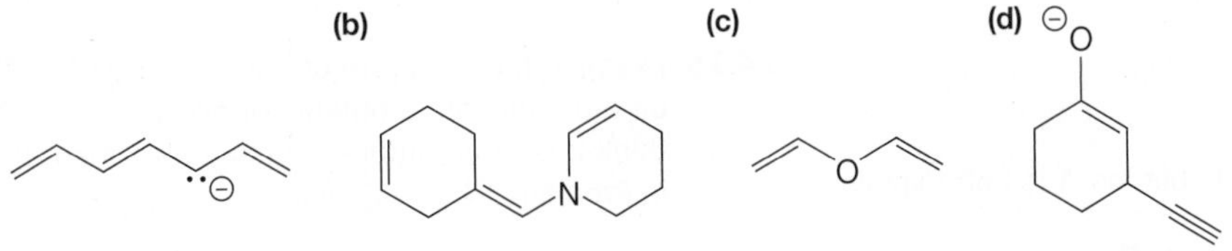
N
O
O

14.5 As we will learn in Chapter 16, molecules that have extensive conjugation tend to have color. With that in mind, explain why phenolphthalein, an indicator commonly used in acid/base titrations, is clear under acidic conditions but is pink when it is deprotonated under moderately basic conditions.

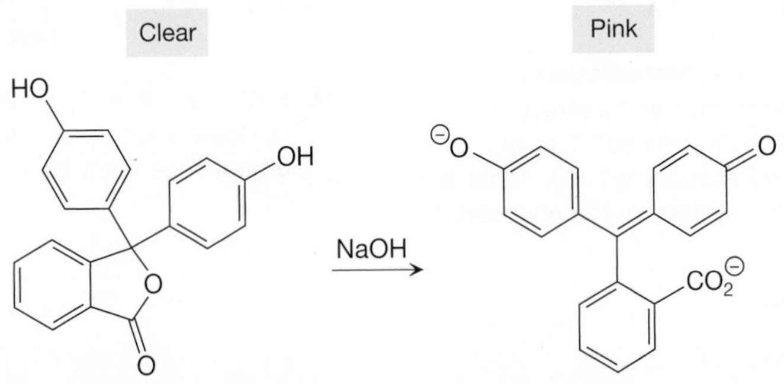
Clear
Pink
HO
OH
O
O
NaOH
O
O
$CO_2^{\ominus}$

Phenolphthalein
pH < 8

pH 9–13

14.6 Although the hypothetical molecule shown here has alternating single and double bonds, those double bonds are not considered to be conjugated. Why not?

14.7 Which ether, **A** or **B**, do you expect to have a larger barrier to rotation about the C—O bond? Why?

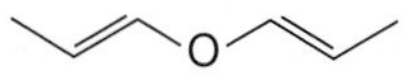

A

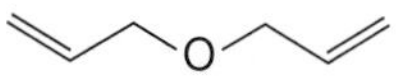

B

14.8 Predict the major product of the following E2 reaction. Explain.

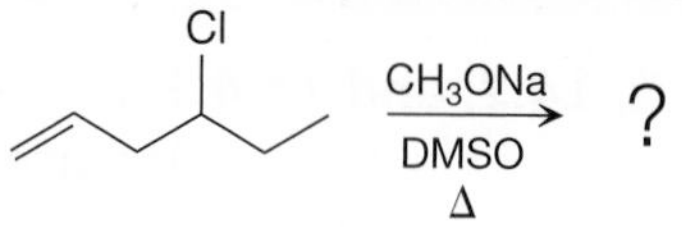

Cl
CH_3ONa
DMSO
Δ
?

14.9 There are two possible E2 products for the following reaction, as shown. Which do you think is the major product? Why?

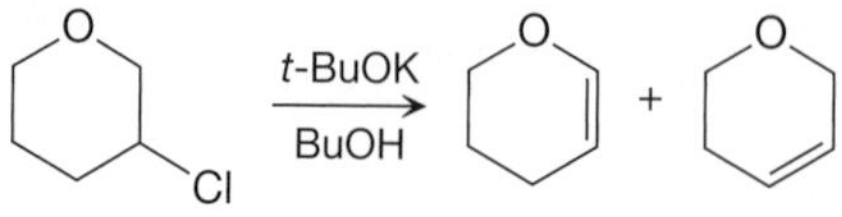

O
Cl
t-BuOK
BuOH
+

Sections 14.5 and 14.7 Cyclic π Systems, Aromaticity, and Hückel's Rules

14.10 Determine whether each of the following species is aromatic, antiaromatic, or nonaromatic. Explain. *Hint*: Don't forget the lone pairs.

(a)

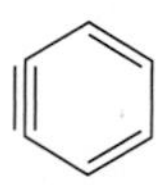

All carbons lie in the same plane.

(b)

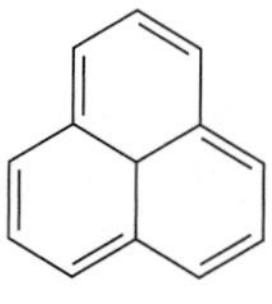

All sp^2 carbons lie in the same plane.

(c)

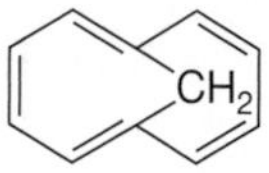

CH_2

All sp^2 carbons lie in the same plane.

(d)

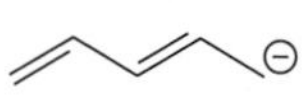

All carbons lie in the same plane.

(e)

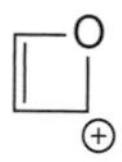

O

All non–H atoms lie in the same plane.

(f)

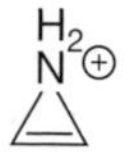

H_2
N

All non–H atoms lie in the same plane.

(g)

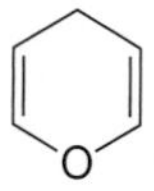

O

All non–H atoms lie in the same plane.

14.11 [16]Annulene can accommodate both cis and trans double bonds in the ring, as shown here. Suggest whether [16]annulene should be aromatic, antiaromatic, or nonaromatic. Explain.

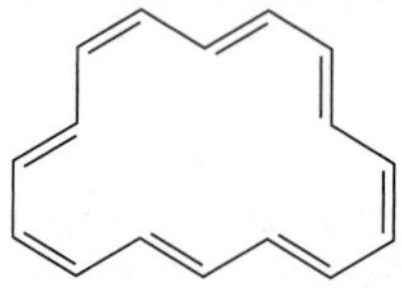

14.12 The tropylium ion is aromatic, but ion **A** is not. Explain.

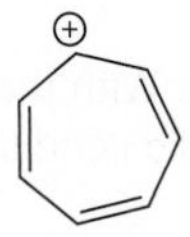

The tropylium ion

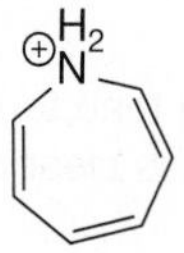

H_2
N

A

14.13 Pyrene has been determined experimentally to be aromatic. At first glance, however, its structure appears to break Hückel's rule. How so? Can you explain why pyrene exhibits aromaticity? *Hint*: What are the characteristics of the π system on the periphery of the molecule?

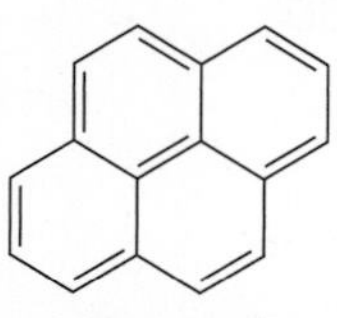

Pyrene

14.14 Examine the structure of B_3N_3. Should it be aromatic, antiaromatic, or nonaromatic? Explain.

B
N
N
B
B
N

14.15 Examine the structure of borazine, $B_3H_6N_3$. Should it be aromatic, antiaromatic, or nonaromatic? Do you think it is more stable or less stable than B_3N_3 shown in Problem 14.14? Explain.

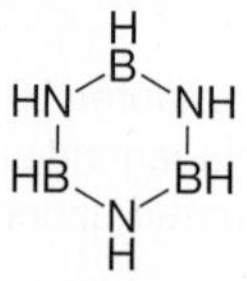

H
B
HN
NH
HB
BH
N
H

Borazine

14.16 Each N atom in B_3N_3, shown in Problem 14.14, contains a lone pair of electrons. In what kind of orbital does each lone pair reside?

14.17 Coronene is a polycyclic aromatic hydrocarbon. **(a)** How many total π electrons does it have? **(b)** Is that number consistent with the fact that the compound is aromatic? Explain.

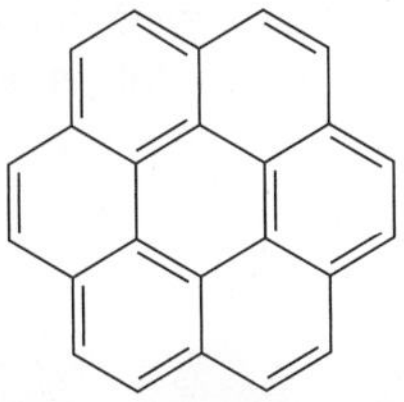

Coronene

14.18 Most dianions of hydrocarbons are very unstable. However, if cyclooctatetraene is treated with potassium, the cyclooctatetraenyl dianion is readily formed via a redox reaction. **(a)** Explain why $C_8H_8^{2-}$ is easy to make. **(b)** As we saw in Figure 14-19b (p. 713), cyclooctatetraene is tub-shaped. What do you think the geometry of $C_8H_8^{2-}$ is? Explain.

Sections 14.3 and 14.6 Heats of Hydrogenation, Conjugation, and Aromaticity

14.19 Rank the following in order of increasingly exothermic heat of hydrogenation. Explain.

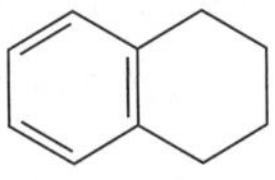

A

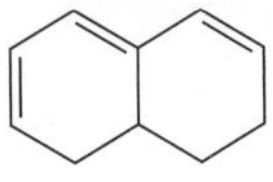

B

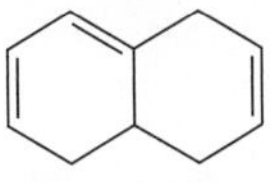

C

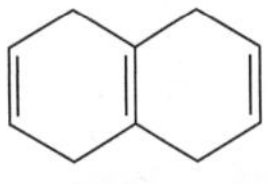

D

14.20 Which of the following amines do you expect to have the more exothermic heat of hydrogenation? Explain.

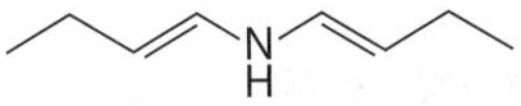

N
H

E

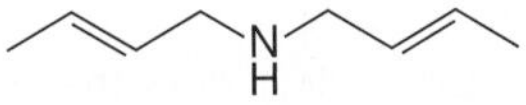

N
H

F

14.21 Toluene and 5-methylenecyclohexa-1,3-diene are isomers, but they have very different heats of hydrogenation. Explain why.

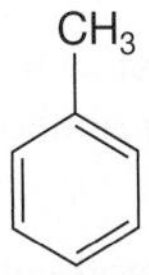

CH3

Toluene
$\Delta H^\circ_{hyd} = -204.8$ kJ/mol

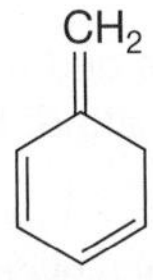

CH2

5-Methylenecyclohexa-1,3-diene
$\Delta H^\circ_{hyd} = -351.4$ kJ/mol

14.22 Molecules **G** and **H** are isomers of each other, and they have the same number of C=C double bonds. Which one has the more exothermic heat of hydrogenation? Why?

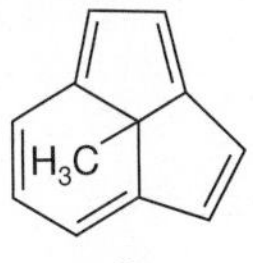

H3C

G

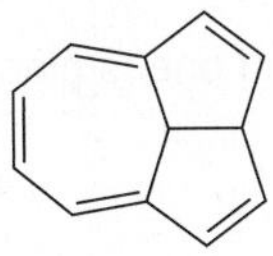

H

14.23 On the basis of the heats of hydrogenation given, determine whether oxirene is aromatic, antiaromatic, or nonaromatic.

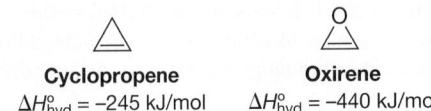

Cyclopropene
$\Delta H^\circ_{hyd} = -245$ kJ/mol

O

Oxirene
$\Delta H^\circ_{hyd} = -440$ kJ/mol

14.24 On the basis of the heat of hydrogenation given, determine whether cycloocta-1,3,5,7-tetraene is aromatic, antiaromatic, or nonaromatic.

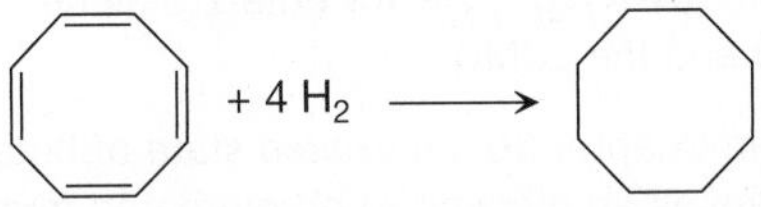

+ 4 H2

$\Delta H^\circ_{hyd} = -423.7$ kJ/mol

14.25 On the basis of the heat of hydrogenation given, determine whether tropone is aromatic, antiaromatic, or nonaromatic.

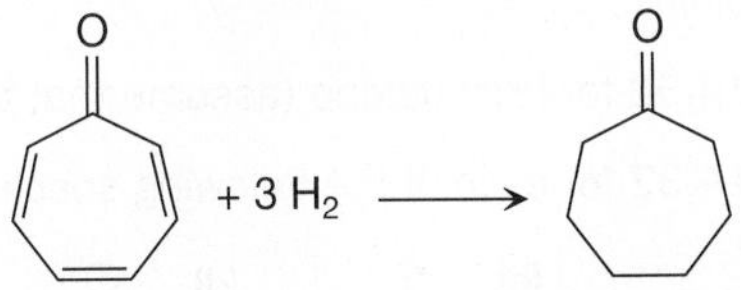

O
+ 3 H2
O

$\Delta H^\circ_{hyd} = -282.5$ kJ/mol

Tropone **Cycloheptanone**

Section 14.8 MO Theory, Conjugation, and Aromaticity

14.26 The following are three of the π MOs for the heptatrienyl cation. For each MO, **(a)** determine the number of nodal planes perpendicular to the bonding axes and rank them in order of increasing energy; **(b)** draw the *p* AO contributions on each C atom that would give rise to the MO; **(c)** identify each internuclear region as having either a *bonding* or an *antibonding* interaction; and **(d)** based on your answer to part (c), determine whether each MO is *bonding*, *nonbonding*, or *antibonding*.

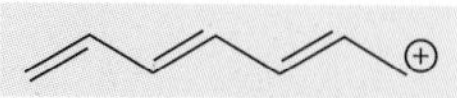

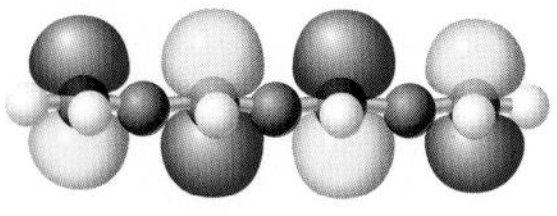

I

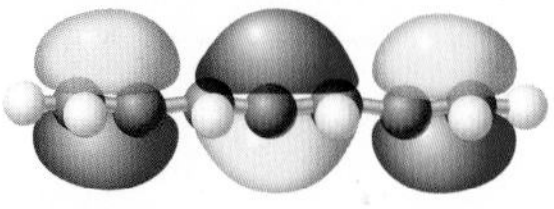

J

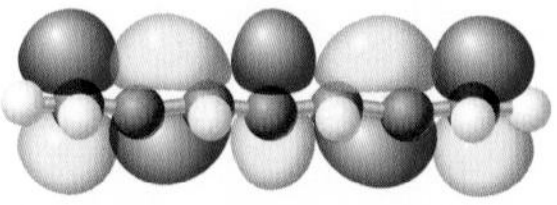

K

14.27 The following are three of the π MOs of octa-1,3,5,7-tetraene. Repeat Problem 14.26 for these orbitals.

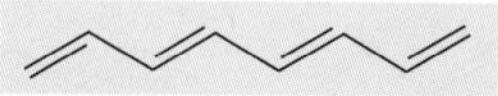

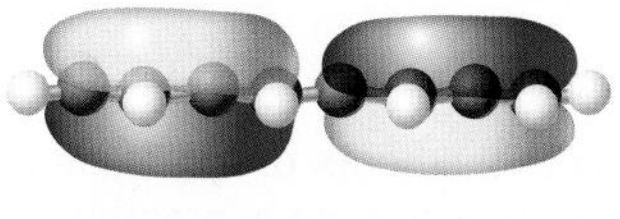

L

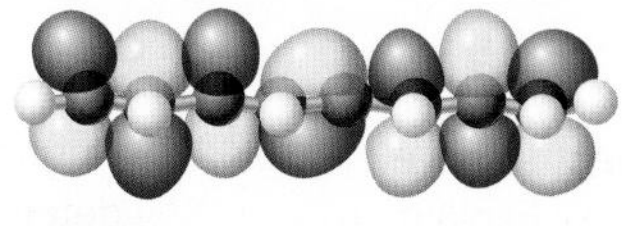

M

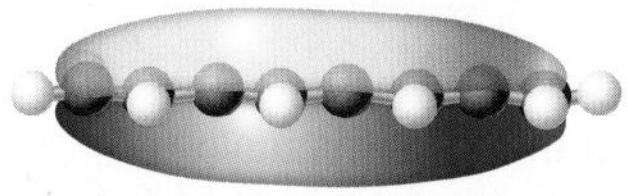

N

14.28 For the hepta-1,3,5-trienyl cation ($H_2C{=}CH{-}CH{=}CH{-}CH{=}CH{-}CH_2^+$), draw the π MOs and the MO energy diagram, similar to what is shown in Solved Problem 14.6 for the penta-1,3-dienyl cation (pp. 722–723). Identify each MO as either bonding, nonbonding, or antibonding. Label the HOMO and the LUMO.

14.29 For the hepta-1,3,5-trienyl anion ($H_2C{=}CH{-}CH{=}CH{-}CH{=}CH{-}CH_2^-$), draw the π MOs and the MO energy diagram, similar to what is shown in Solved Problem 14.6 for the penta-1,3-dienyl cation (pp. 722–723). Identify each MO as either bonding, nonbonding, or antibonding. Label the HOMO and the LUMO.

14.30 For hexa-1,3,5-triene ($H_2C{=}CH{-}CH{=}CH{-}CH{=}CH_2$), draw the π MOs and the MO energy diagram, similar to what is shown in Figure 14-25 (p. 721) for buta-1,3-diene. Identify each MO as either bonding, nonbonding, or antibonding. Label the HOMO and the LUMO.

14.31 As we will learn in Chapter 16, an *excited state* of buta-1,3-diene can be achieved when the molecule absorbs a photon of light, which causes an electron to be promoted from a lower energy MO to a higher energy MO. If the molecule absorbs the minimum energy possible from such a photon absorption, in which MOs would the π electrons reside?

14.32 Draw the π MO energy diagram for [10]annulene, similar to those in Figures 14-26 and 14-28 (pp. 723 and 725). Fill up the orbitals with the appropriate number of π electrons. From this diagram, should [10]annulene be aromatic or antiaromatic? Explain.

14.33 Repeat Problem 14.32 for [8]annulene (assume that the molecule is planar).

14.34 Repeat Problem 14.32 for each of the following species (assume that each one is planar).

(a)

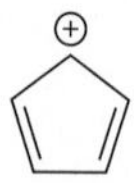

(b)

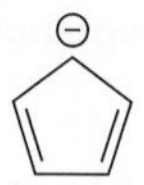

(c)

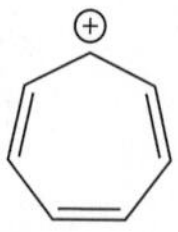

(d)

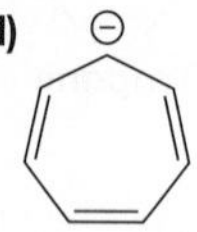

Section 14.9 The Organic Chemistry of Biomolecules

14.35 A strand of nucleic acid is defined by its sequence of nucleotides: A, C, T, and G. How many different sequences are possible for a nucleic acid that is 200 nucleotides long? How does that number compare to the estimated number of atoms in the universe, which is approximately 10^{80}?

14.36 Figure 14-33a (p. 729) shows how hydrogen bonding reflects the complementarity of guanine to cytosine. Draw the optimal alignment for the interaction between guanine and adenine. How many simultaneous hydrogen bonds exist in that interaction?

14.37 One nucleic acid strand in a particular segment of DNA has the following nucleotide sequence: CGGATACATTTGC. In the same segment of DNA, what is the sequence of nucleotides in the other strand?

14.38 Doxorubicin, shown here, is an important chemotherapy drug used to treat a variety of cancers, including bladder cancer, breast cancer, and certain forms of leukemia. Doxorubicin works by binding to DNA in such a way that a portion of it penetrates the DNA double helix, in a process called *intercalation*. During transcription (the process that forms RNA), portions of the DNA strands are temporarily separated, and then the base pairs are reconnected. With bound doxorubicin, however, the double helix does not re-form properly after the strands are separated, which disrupts replication (the process that forms an identical copy of DNA). Which portion of doxorubicin do you think intercalates into the DNA double helix, and why do you think it has little difficulty doing so?

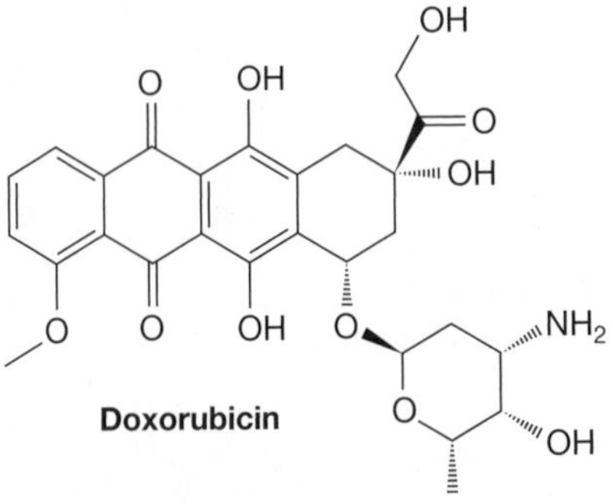

Doxorubicin

Integrated Problems

14.39 According to Hückel's rules, [10]annulene should be aromatic, but both of the geometric isomers shown here are unstable. Explain why.

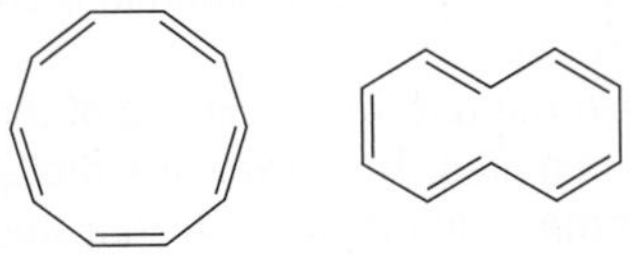

14.40 Which ketone, **O** or **P**, do you think has the more stable π system? Why? *Hint*: Consider various resonance structures of each species.

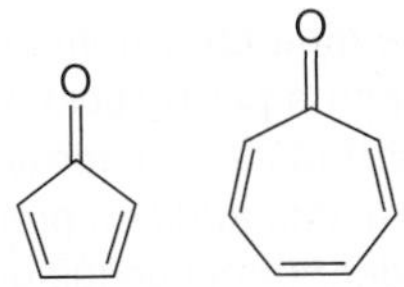

O **P**

14.41 The molecule shown here has quite a large dipole, as indicated in its electrostatic potential map. Explain why. *Hint*: Consider various resonance structures.

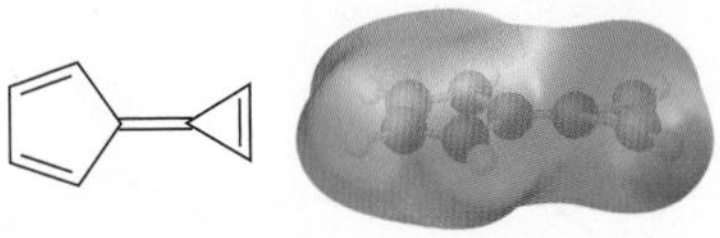

14.42 Based on your answer to Problem 14.41, do you think the compound shown here should have a significant dipole? If so, in which direction does it point?

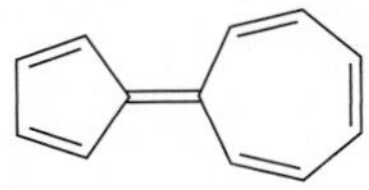

14.43 Using your knowledge of aromaticity, explain the difference in the magnitudes of the dipoles of compounds **Q** and **R**. *Hint*: Consider various resonance structures.

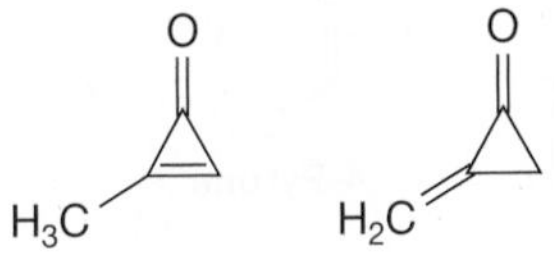

4.87 D **Q** 3.41 D **R**

14.44 Bromobenzene is insoluble in water, but 7-bromocyclohepta-1,3,5-triene is water-soluble. Explain why. *Hint*: In order for compounds to have dramatic differences in solubility, do you think the type of intermolecular forces between each compound and water can be the same?

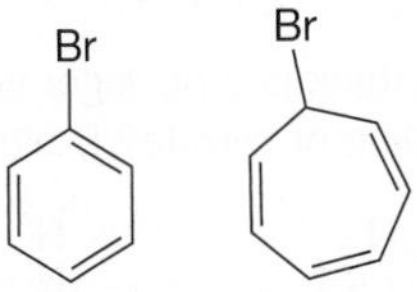

Insoluble Soluble

14.45 Rank compounds **S–W** in order of decreasing acid strength, from lowest pK_a to highest pK_a. Explain.

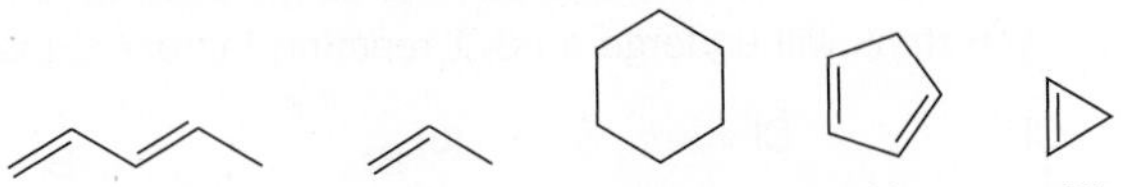

S **T** **U** **V** **W**

14.46 Which cation, **X** or **Y**, do you think is the stronger acid? Why?

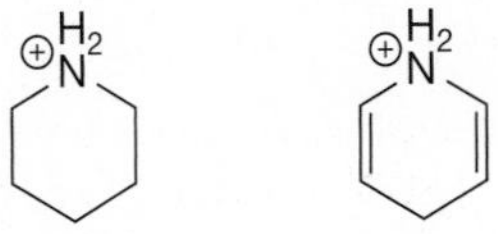

X **Y**

14.47 The most basic site is indicated for each molecule below. Explain these observations.

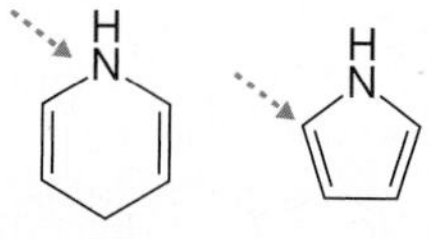

A B

14.48 Identify the most basic site in imidazole and explain your reasoning.

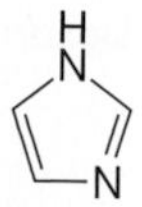

Imidazole

14.49 Which O atom of 4-pyrone do you think is more basic? Explain.

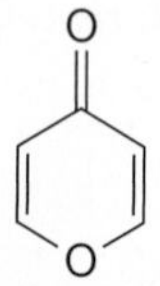

4-Pyrone

14.50 For each of the following pairs of molecules, which do you think should have the more acidic hydrogen α to the carbonyl group? Explain why.

(a)

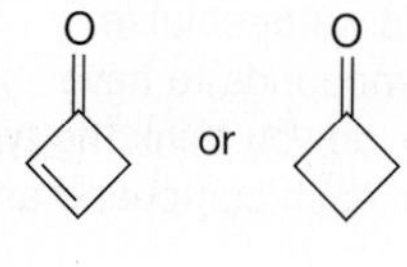

C D

(b)

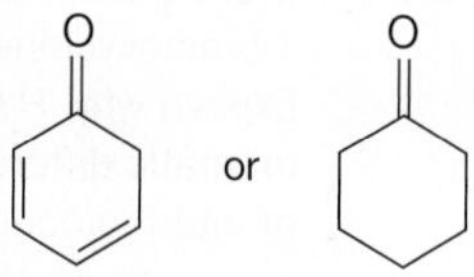

E F

14.51 Which do you think is a stronger nucleophile in an S_N2 reaction: pyridine or pyrrole? Explain.

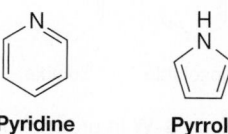

Pyridine **Pyrrole**

14.52 For each of the following pairs of substrates, which do you think will undergo an S_N1 reaction faster? Explain.

(a)

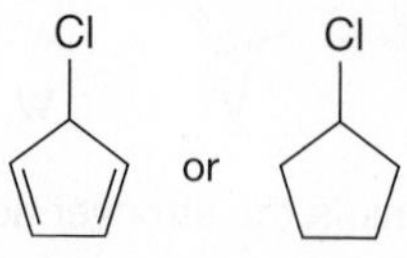

G H

(b)

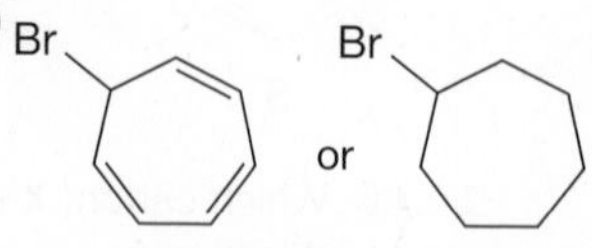

I J

14.53 Which compound, **K** or **L**, do you think undergoes dehydration more quickly? Why?

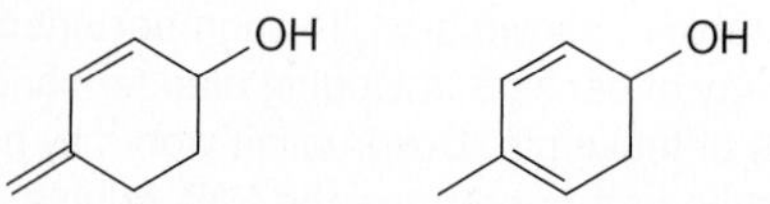

K **L**

14.54 Treatment of propadiene with hydrogen bromide produces 2-bromopropene as the major product. This suggests that the more stable carbocation intermediate is produced by the addition of a proton to a terminal carbon rather than to the central carbon.

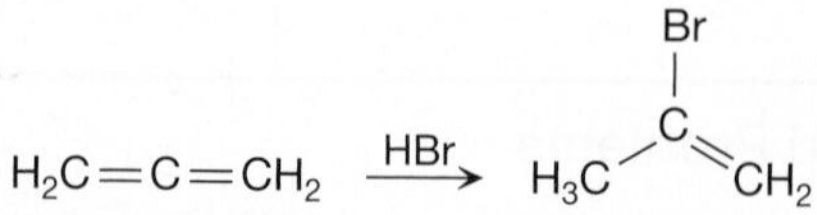

$H_2C{=}C{=}CH_2$
HBr
H_3C
Br
C
CH_2

Propadiene **2-Bromopropene**

(a) Draw both carbocation intermediates that can be produced by the addition of a proton to propadiene.

(b) Explain the relative stabilities of those intermediates. *Hint*: Draw the orbital picture of the intermediates and consider whether the CH_2 groups in propadiene are in the same plane.

14.55 Alkynes behave quite like alkenes when it comes to carbene addition. For example, a carbene can add to an alkyne to yield a cyclopropene, as shown here. Alkynes behave differently from alkenes, however, when treated with a peroxy acid. Whereas an alkene would be converted into an epoxide by the addition of an oxygen atom, this addition product is not observed for alkynes under normal conditions. Suggest why. *Hint*: Pay special attention to the lone pairs.

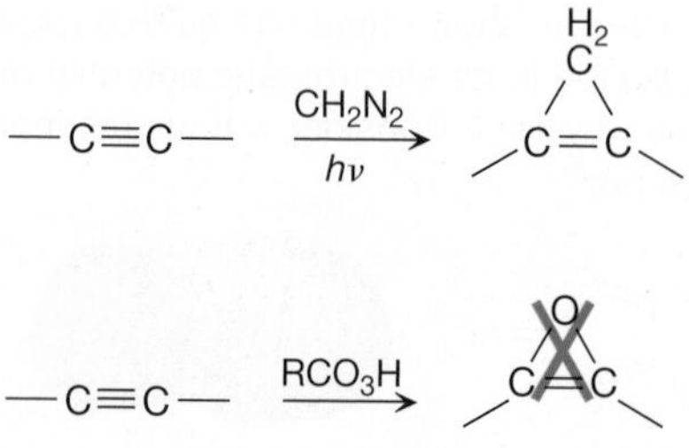

CH_2N_2
$h\nu$
RCO_3H

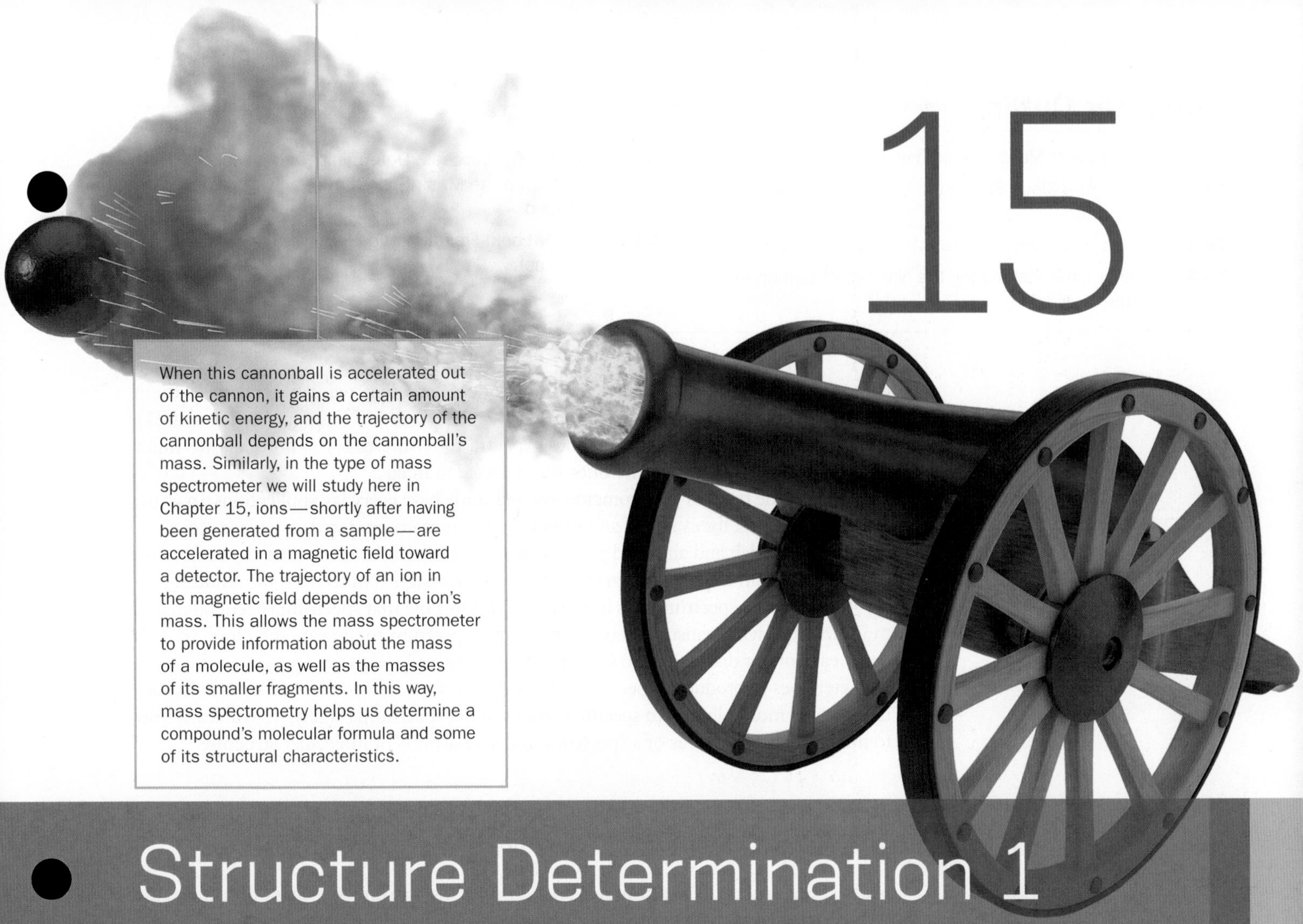

When this cannonball is accelerated out of the cannon, it gains a certain amount of kinetic energy, and the trajectory of the cannonball depends on the cannonball's mass. Similarly, in the type of mass spectrometer we will study here in Chapter 15, ions—shortly after having been generated from a sample—are accelerated in a magnetic field toward a detector. The trajectory of an ion in the magnetic field depends on the ion's mass. This allows the mass spectrometer to provide information about the mass of a molecule, as well as the masses of its smaller fragments. In this way, mass spectrometry helps us determine a compound's molecular formula and some of its structural characteristics.

15

Structure Determination 1

Mass Spectrometry

By now you have seen the structures of many hundreds of molecules throughout this book. What guarantee do you have that those structures are accurate? When organic chemistry was a relatively immature field, chemists would derive molecular structure by measuring a compound's physical properties and by carrying out different reactions designed to provide information about the presence and relative positions of specific functional groups. As you might imagine, these processes were quite painstaking and often unreliable.

Today, much of our knowledge about chemical structure comes from specialized instruments called *spectrometers*. In a typical analysis using a spectrometer, a *spectrum* is generated, and features of that spectrum are correlated with certain characteristics of molecular structure. Therefore, in the field of organic chemistry, interpreting the features of such spectra becomes a valuable skill.

There are many different types of spectrometers; the ones we focus on in this book are the ones most widely used to characterize organic molecules. Here in Chapter 15, we introduce *mass spectrometers* and the interpretation of the spectra they generate, called *mass spectra*. Chapter 16 discusses the spectra generated by *infrared (IR) spectrometers* and *ultraviolet–visible (UV–vis) spectrometers*, and Chapter 17 deals with the spectra generated by *nuclear magnetic resonance (NMR) spectrometers*.

Acquiring and interpreting these kinds of spectra are particularly important in the context of synthesis. Those spectra often help us to identify newly discovered

Chapter Outline

compounds in nature (so-called natural products) so that we can synthesize them from simpler compounds in the laboratory (as described in Chapters 10, 11, and 21). Additionally, we routinely rely on these spectra to ensure that the products we make in the laboratory are in fact the ones we *intended* to make.

Some of the types of spectrometers we will study have everyday applications. In criminal investigations, for example, an unknown substance encountered at a crime scene can be brought to a lab and analyzed by a spectrometer. Often the identity of the compound (or at least certain important characteristics) can be assigned in seconds or minutes.

To interpret a spectrum, it is important to know how that spectrum is generated and to understand what causes certain features in a spectrum to appear. Therefore, we will begin each of our discussions in Chapters 15–17 with a brief overview of what the spectrometer does to produce a spectrum. We will then study how certain structural characteristics of a molecule lead to specific features in the spectrum. Finally, we will learn how to interpret those features of a spectrum to derive aspects of molecular structure.

SECTION 15.1 OBJECTIVES

You will be able to:

1. Explain how a mass spectrum is generated by an electron impact ionization mass spectrometer.
2. Describe what information is contained in a mass spectrum.

15.1 An Overview of Mass Spectrometry

Mass spectrometry is a technique used to gain insight into the mass of a molecule and the fragments that compose it. As we mentioned briefly in the introduction to this chapter, a sample's *mass spectrum* is produced by a mass spectrometer, and we aim to interpret the mass spectrum to determine aspects of molecular structure.

Let's begin by exploring one way a mass spectrum is generated, as shown in **Figure 15-1a**. A small sample (typically on the order of ≤1 μL of a dilute solution) of a compound M is injected into the spectrometer, where it is immediately vaporized.

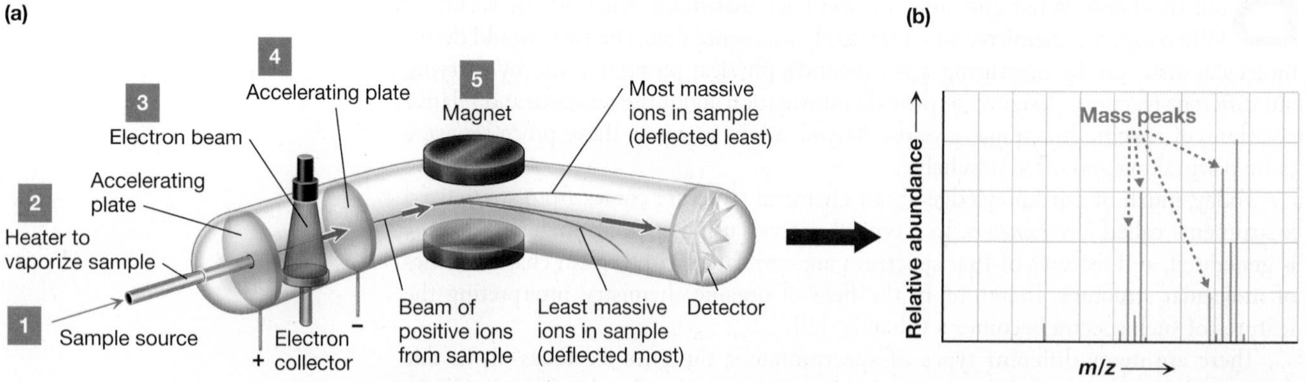

(a)
(b)
4
Accelerating plate
5
Magnet
Most massive ions in sample (deflected least)
3
Electron beam
Accelerating plate
2
Heater to vaporize sample
1
Sample source
Electron collector
+
−
Beam of positive ions from sample
Least massive ions in sample (deflected most)
Detector
Mass peaks
Relative abundance ⟶
m/z ⟶

FIGURE 15-1 Generating a mass spectrum (a) Schematic of a mass spectrometer. An injected sample (1) is converted to vapor (2) and passed through a beam of highly energetic electrons (3). Collisions with the electrons generate positively charged ions of the entire molecule and of its fragments. These ions are accelerated (4) through a magnet (5) that separates them on the basis of their mass and charge. As the ions impact the detector, a signal is registered. Varying the magnetic field allows the spectrometer to measure the relative abundance of charged particles with different mass-to-charge ratios. (b) A generic mass spectrum. Each bar is a mass peak that depicts the relative abundance of an ion with a particular m/z value.

This process of *vaporization* is depicted in Equation 15-1, where $M(\ell)$ represents a liquid solution of M and $M(g)$ represents its gaseous state:

$$M(\ell) \longrightarrow M(g) \quad (15\text{-}1)$$

Once vaporized, the gaseous molecules, $M(g)$, drift through a beam of fast-moving electrons and undergo *electron impact ionization* (Eq. 15-2). In **electron impact ionization (EI)**, an electron from the beam impacts a molecule of $M(g)$, and the collision knocks off an electron from $M(g)$ to produce a gaseous **molecular ion, $M^{\dot{+}}(g)$**. The positive charge appears because a negatively charged electron was lost, and the dot indicates an unpaired electron left behind. As will be explained in greater detail in Chapter 27, a species with an unpaired electron is called a *radical* (see Looking Ahead box), so $M^{\dot{+}}(g)$ is more properly called a **radical cation**.

▸ **LOOKING AHEAD**

In Chapter 27, you will learn that radicals tend to be highly unstable and typically appear as reactive intermediates in various mechanisms, including conversion of alkanes into alkyl halides, polymerization of alkenes to produce plastics, autooxidation of fatty acids, and decomposition of stratospheric ozone.

$$M(g) \xrightarrow[\text{Ionization}]{\text{Electron beam}} e^- + M^{\dot{+}}(g) \xrightarrow[\text{Fragmentation}]{} Fg_1^{+}(g) + Fg_2^{\bullet}(g) + \cdots \quad (15\text{-}2)$$

Electron impact ionization is a highly energetic process, enough to cause bonds in the molecular ion to break. Therefore, as shown in Equation 15-2, some molecular ions will undergo **fragmentation** to produce lighter species, called fragments; these fragments are depicted as $Fg_1^{+}(g)$ and $Fg_2^{\bullet}(g)$. Notice that some fragments are charged, while others are uncharged. We will discuss fragmentation in greater detail later in this chapter.

Ions that are formed in the mass spectrometer, both $M^{\dot{+}}(g)$ and fragment ions, can be guided toward the spectrometer's detector through a curved tube by using a magnetic field to bend the ion's path. How much a given ion's path is bent depends on the strength of the magnetic field that is applied and the **mass-to-charge ratio (*m*/*z*)** of the particle. Thus, when the magnetic field is set to a particular strength, only ions of a specific *m*/*z* value can reach the detector. Ions with *m*/*z* different from that value will collide with the wall of the tube and will be destroyed before reaching the detector: ions that are too light will be deflected too much, whereas those that are too massive will not be deflected enough.

YOUR TURN 15.1

In Figure 15-1, paths are shown for three different ions. Suppose the magnetic field strength is set to allow the molecular ion to reach the detector. At that magnetic field strength, which of the other two paths could represent a fragment ion?

Answers to Your Turns are in the back of the book.

The detector is designed to keep track of the number of charged species that collide with it; this number is converted into what is called the **relative abundance** of the ion. The greater the number of charged species detected, the greater the ion's relative abundance. If multiple ions are produced with different values of *m*/*z*, then the magnetic field strength can be varied to determine the relative abundance at *each* *m*/*z*. A **mass spectrum** (Fig. 15-1b) presents this information as a bar graph with *m*/*z* on the *x* axis (where *m* is in atomic mass units, u) and the relative abundance on the *y* axis; each bar is called a **mass peak**.

The process represented in Figure 15-1 is not the only one that can be used to generate a mass spectrum. A variety of other types of mass spectrometers exist as well, each using its own particular method for generating a mass spectrum. All types of mass spectrometers, however, must (1) produce gaseous ions from an uncharged sample, (2) separate ions by their *m*/*z* values, and (3) detect the relative abundance of ions having a particular value of *m*/*z*. It is worth noting, in particular, that modern instruments use a *quadrupole* (four charged poles) to separate ions, which causes the ions to move in a spiral path, rather than a bent path.

SECTION 15.2 OBJECTIVES

You will be able to:

1. Identify the $M^{\ddagger}$ peak in a mass spectrum if you know the identity of the compound.
2. Identify the base peak in a mass spectrum.
3. Use the nitrogen rule to determine whether a particular molecular mass suggests an odd or even number of nitrogen atoms.

15.2 Features of a Mass Spectrum, the Nitrogen Rule, and Fragmentation

When a mass spectrometer uses electron impact to ionize a compound (Eq. 15-2), the mass spectrum is more properly called an *electron ionization (EI) mass spectrum*. Furthermore, the charge (z) on each ion that is produced by electron ionization is typically +1. In that case, m/z is simply m. That is:

> The x axis of an EI mass spectrum can usually be interpreted as the mass of each ion detected.

In turn, the mass of each ion is just the mass of the atoms that make it up, because the mass of the electron that was lost from the uncharged molecule is negligible.

All of the mass spectra we deal with in this book are EI mass spectra, and we will refer to them from now on simply as mass spectra. The mass spectrum of hexane, for example, is shown in **Figure 15-2**; all relative abundances are relative to the tallest peak, called the **base peak**, whose value is assigned 100%. The mass of hexane (C_6H_{14}) is 86 u (or 86 g/mol), so the peak representing the molecular ion, $M^{+\bullet}$, is found at $m/z = 86$. In general:

> The $M^{+\bullet}$ peak of a mass spectrum is taken to be the compound's molecular mass.

The molecular mass of a compound can help us determine the compound's molecular formula, because the molecular mass equals the sum of the masses of its individual atoms. (In Figure 15-2, the base peak is at $m/z = 57$, which is *not* the same as the $M^{+\bullet}$ peak, but don't be surprised if they are the same in mass spectra of some other compounds.)

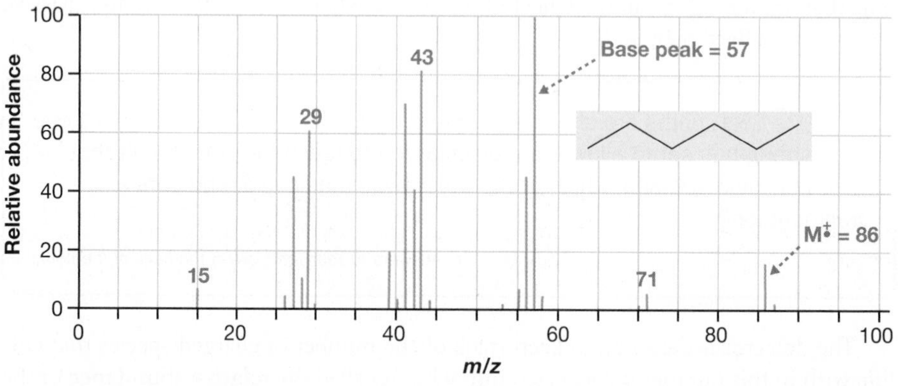

100
80
60
40
20
0
Relative abundance
43
29
15
71
Base peak = 57
M+• = 86
0
20
40
60
80
100
m/z

FIGURE 15-2 Mass spectrum of hexane The $M^{+\bullet}$ peak and the base peak are identified. The values of m/z for selected peaks are provided above the peaks.

The value of the $M^{+\bullet}$ peak can also provide insight into whether the compound contains nitrogen, based on the **nitrogen rule**:

> **The Nitrogen Rule**
>
> - A compound containing an odd number of nitrogen atoms typically has an odd molecular mass.
> - A compound containing an even number of nitrogen atoms, or no nitrogen atoms at all, typically has an even molecular mass.

For example, NH_3 contains a single nitrogen atom and its mass is 17 u, whereas ethane (H_3CCH_3) and hydrazine (H_2NNH_2) contain zero and two nitrogen atoms, respectively, and have masses of 30 and 32 u, respectively.

YOUR TURN 15.2

Compute the molecular mass of *N*,*N*-dimethylacetamide, CH_3–CO–N(CH_3)$_2$. Do the same for diazomethane, CH_2N_2. Are these values consistent with the nitrogen rule?

Section 15.1 explained how electron impact ionization provides sufficient energy to break bonds, resulting in fragmentation. In a molecule such as hexane, several different bonds can be broken; therefore, there are several different *fragmentation pathways*. Three of the fragmentation pathways that involve the breaking of carbon–carbon bonds are shown in **Figure 15-3**.

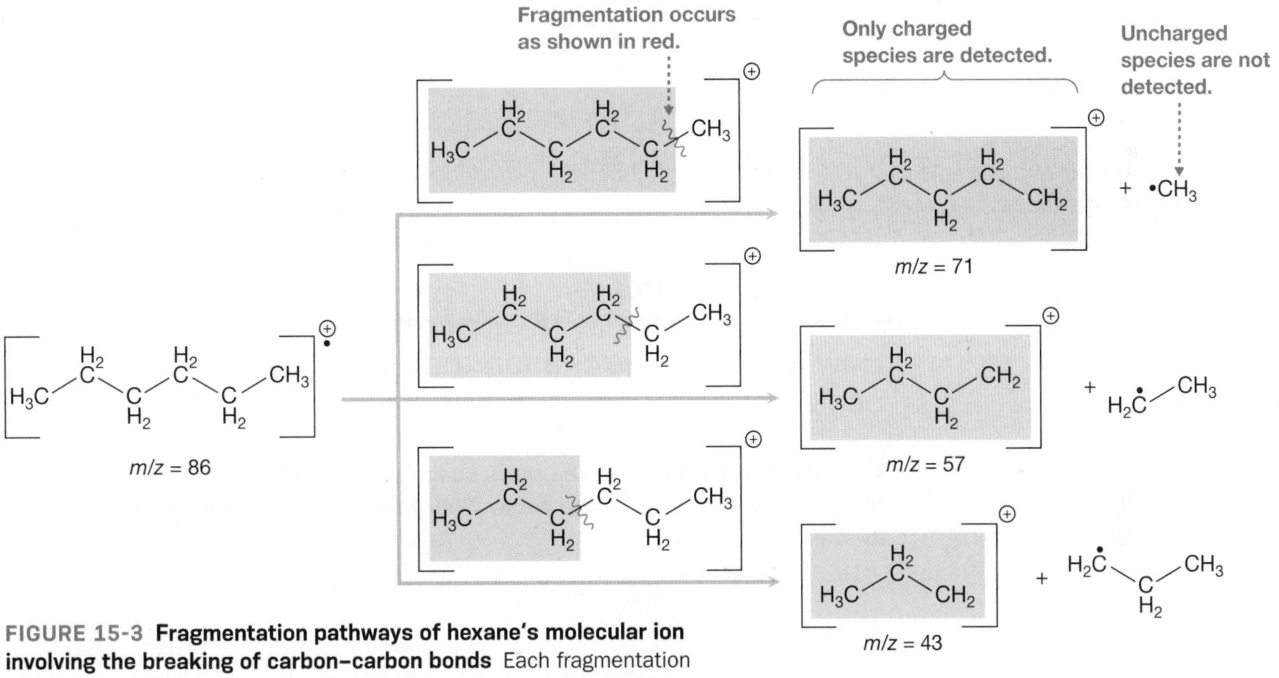

Fragmentation occurs as shown in red.
Only charged species are detected.
Uncharged species are not detected.
m/z = 86
m/z = 71
m/z = 57
m/z = 43

FIGURE 15-3 Fragmentation pathways of hexane's molecular ion involving the breaking of carbon–carbon bonds Each fragmentation produces a cation and an uncharged species, ensuring that the total charge after fragmentation, +1, is the same as it was before fragmentation.

When a molecular ion undergoes fragmentation, there must be conservation of charge. As indicated in Figure 15-3, a molecular ion whose charge is +1 invariably fragments into one species bearing a +1 charge and another that is uncharged. *Only the charged fragments (fragment ions) can be detected in mass spectrometry!*

Each fragment ion in Figure 15-3 appears in hexane's mass spectrum, and each is indicated in Figure 15-2. Thus, if we understand fragmentation pathways, then the fragment peaks that appear can help us to determine molecular structure.

Fragmentation pathways can be quite complex; notice that many more ion peaks appear in the spectrum of hexane than just those presented in Figure 15-3. The complexity of fragmentation processes arises, in part, because the pathways involve very high-energy radical species in the gas phase. A more in-depth discussion of fragmentation in mass spectrometry will be presented in Section 15.6.

YOUR TURN 15.3

Hexane's molecular ion can undergo the following two fragmentation pathways not shown in Figure 15-3:

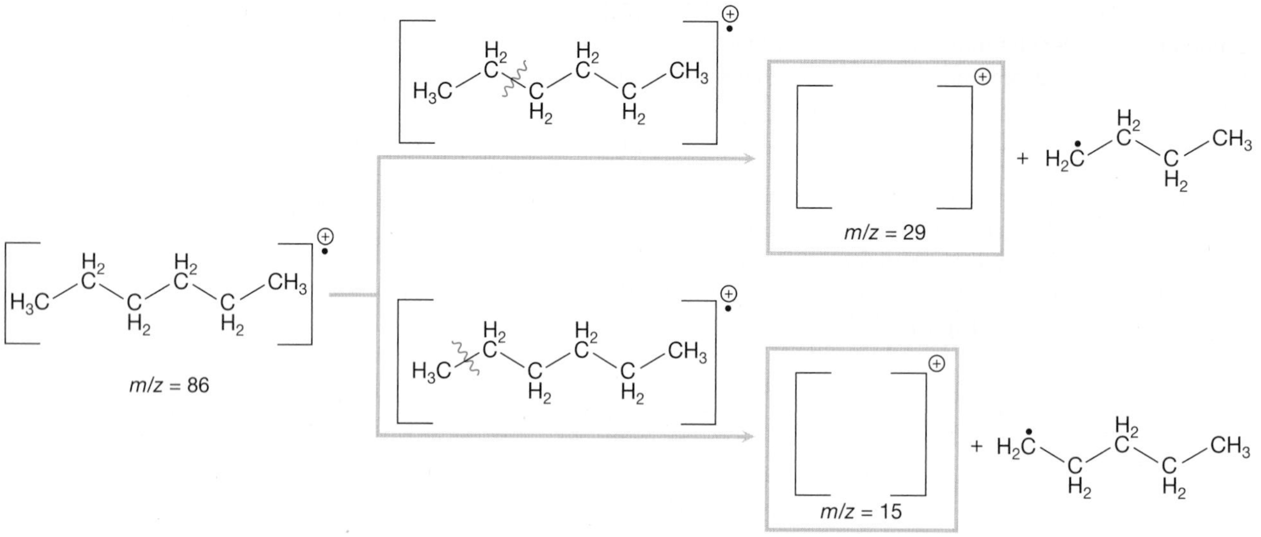

m/z = 86
m/z = 29
m/z = 15

Both pathways involve the breaking of a C—C bond. In the brackets provided, draw the appropriate structures for the two fragment ions.

SOLVED PROBLEM **15.1**

How to determine the ion that correspond to a mass peak

Break It Down Using the mass spectrum of ethylbenzene provided, identify the $M^{+\bullet}$ peak and the base peak. What is the formula of the ion responsible for the base peak?

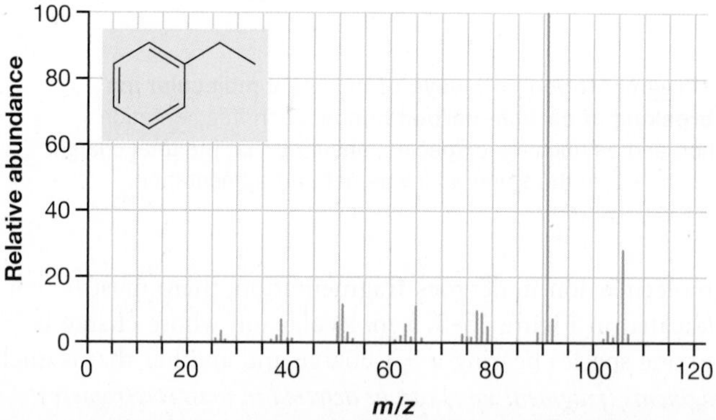

Relative abundance
m/z

Think	Solve
What is the molecular mass of ethylbenzene? What corresponding mass peak could be assigned as $M^{+\bullet}$?	The molecular formula is C_8H_{10}, so the molecular mass is 8(12 u) + 10(1 u) = 106 u. We therefore assign the mass peak at *m/z* = 106 to be the $M^{+\bullet}$ peak.
At what *m/z* is the base peak?	The base peak is defined as the tallest mass peak, which is normalized to 100%. The base peak for ethylbenzene is found at *m/z* = 91.

(continued)

How much lighter is the base peak than $M^{\cdot+}$? What bond could have been broken to produce the corresponding fragment ion?	The base peak ($m/z = 91$) is 15 u lighter than the $M^{\cdot+}$ peak ($m/z = 106$ u). Therefore, the fragment ion that represents the base peak would be produced on loss of a $\cdot CH_3$ group from $M^{\cdot+}$, as shown below.

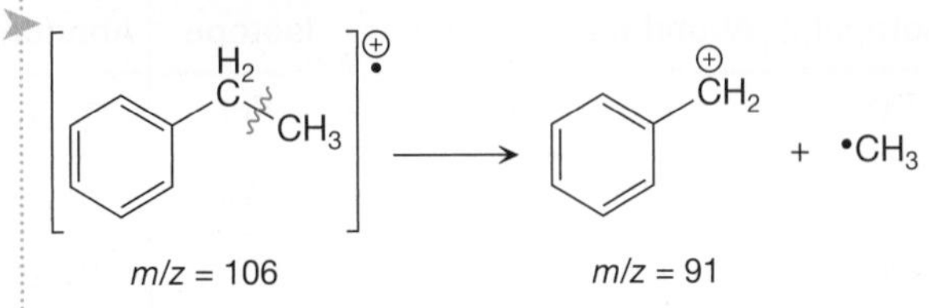

H2
C
CH3
CH2
+ •CH3
m/z = 106
m/z = 91

Try It Using the mass spectrum of 2,2-dimethylpropanenitrile provided, identify the $M^{\cdot+}$ peak. What is the structure of the ion responsible for the peak at $m/z = 68$?

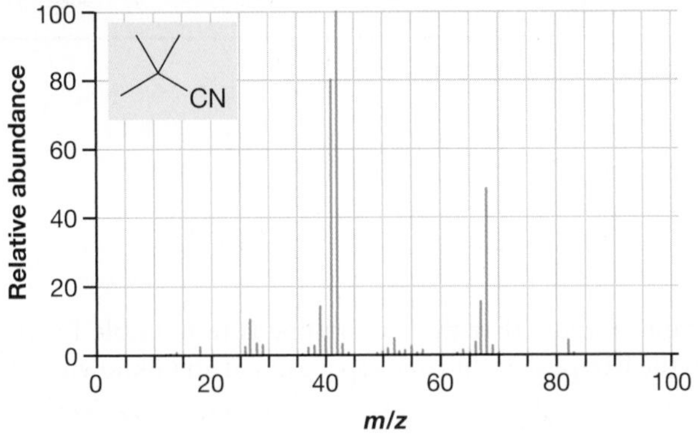

CN
Relative abundance
100
80
60
40
20
0
0
20
40
60
80
100
m/z

Answers to all Try It exercises can be found in the Solutions Manual.

15.3 Isotopes and Mass Spectra: M + 1 and M + 2 Peaks

SECTION 15.3 OBJECTIVES

You will be able to:

1. Explain the origin of an M + 1 peak or an M + 2 peak in a mass spectrum.
2. Use the M + 1 peak to help identify the $M^{\cdot+}$ peak in a mass spectrum of an unknown compound.
3. Identify and use an M + 2 peak in a mass spectrum to determine whether the molecule contains Br or Cl.

Although the $M^{\cdot+}$ peak of hexane appears at $m/z = 86$, there is a small peak at $m/z = 87$ in Figure 15-2 (p. 742), too. A peak in a mass spectrum that is 1 u heavier than the $M^{\cdot+}$ peak is known as the **M + 1 peak**.

YOUR TURN 15.4

Label the M + 1 peak in Figure 15-2 (p. 742). Also identify and label the M + 1 peak in the mass spectrum of ethylbenzene in Solved Problem 15.1.

◂ RECALL

Atoms are designated as isotopes if they have the same number of protons but they differ in the number of neutrons. A heavy isotope of an atom is one that contains more neutrons than the atom's most common isotope.

The M + 1 peak represents a molecular ion containing a heavy isotope (see Recall box). Hexane contains only carbon and hydrogen atoms, so in this case it must be due to the appearance of either an atom of ^2H (deuterium) or ^{13}C. According to Table 15-1, however, the natural abundance of ^2H is negligible, whereas that of ^{13}C is about 1.1%, so hexane's M + 1 peak must be due primarily to an ion that contains five ^{12}C atoms, one ^{13}C atom, and 14 ^1H atoms; the molecular formula of such an ion is $[^{12}C_5{}^{13}C_1{}^1H_{14}]^{\cdot+}$, and its mass is 5(12 u) + 1(13 u) + 14(1 u) = 87 u, the same as the m/z value for the M + 1 peak.

YOUR TURN 15.5

Write the molecular formula for the ion corresponding to the M + 1 peak in the mass spectrum of ethylbenzene in Solved Problem 15.1.

TABLE 15-1 Relative Isotopic Abundance of Naturally Occurring Elements Common in Organic Molecules

Element	Most Abundant Isotope	Abundance	Heavy Isotope(s)	Abundance[a]	Element	Most Abundant Isotope	Abundance	Heavy Isotope(s)	Abundance[a]
Carbon	^{12}C	98.90%	^{13}C	1.10%	Chlorine	^{35}Cl	75.77%	^{37}Cl	24.23%
Hydrogen	^{1}H	99.985%	^{2}H (D)	0.015%	Bromine	^{79}Br	50.69%	^{81}Br	49.31%
Nitrogen	^{14}N	99.634%	^{15}N	0.366%	Sulfur	^{32}S	95.02%	^{33}S	0.75%
Oxygen	^{16}O	99.76%	^{17}O	0.038%				^{34}S	4.21%
			^{18}O	0.20%	Silicon	^{28}Si	92.23%	^{29}Si	4.67%
								^{30}Si	3.10%

[a]Abundances shown in red are the heavy isotopes most likely to be observable in a mass spectrum.

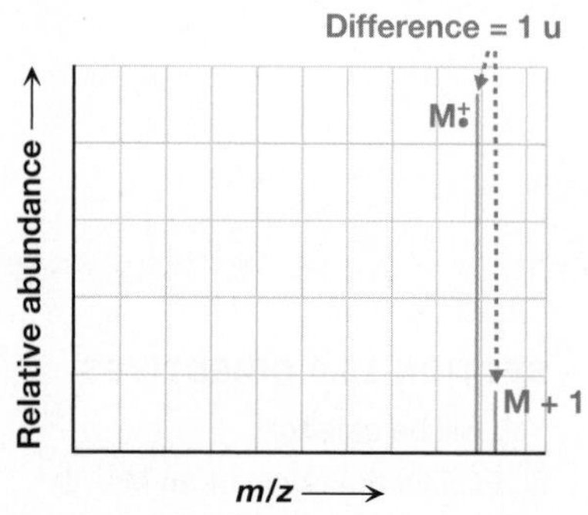
Difference = 1 u
M+·
M + 1
Relative abundance
m/z

FIGURE 15-4 Identifying $M^{+\cdot}$ and M + 1 peaks

It is important to know that the ^{13}C isotope is responsible for the M + 1 peak, especially when the $M^{+\cdot}$ peak in the mass spectrum of an unknown compound is being assigned:

For small- and medium-sized organic molecules, the $M^{+\cdot}$ and M + 1 peaks are often identified as the two peaks with the highest mass (farthest to the right) in the spectrum (**Figure 15-4**).

- The two peaks are separated by 1 u.
- The M + 1 peak is generally much smaller than the $M^{+\cdot}$ peak.

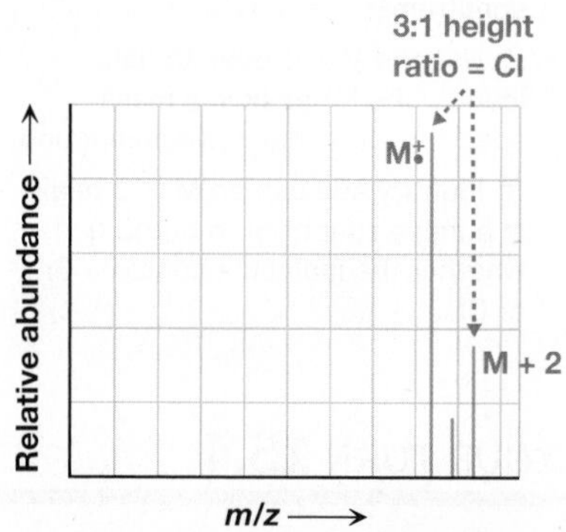
3:1 height
ratio = Cl
M+·
M + 2
Relative abundance
m/z

FIGURE 15-5 Characteristic $M^{+\cdot}$ and M + 2 peaks indicating Cl

Some elements have relatively abundant isotopes that are 2 u heavier than their most common isotopes. Table 15-1 highlights four such elements: chlorine, bromine, sulfur, and silicon. Thus, the appearance of a mass peak 2 u higher than the $M^{+\cdot}$ peak, called an **M + 2 peak**, may indicate the presence of one of these elements.

The M + 2 peak for chlorine or bromine can be easy to spot in a mass spectrum because their heavy isotopes are particularly abundant: the relative abundance for the heavy isotope of chlorine (^{37}Cl) is 24.23%, and the heavy isotope of bromine (^{81}Br) has a relative abundance of 49.31%. Moreover, chlorine and bromine each have a characteristic ratio for the relative abundances of the light versus heavy isotopes: For chlorine, the abundances of ^{35}Cl and ^{37}Cl (75.77% and 24.23%) establish a ratio of roughly 3:1, and for bromine, the abundances of ^{79}Br and ^{81}Br (50.69% and 49.31%) establish a ratio of about 1:1. Therefore:

- If $M^{+\cdot}$ and M + 2 peaks appear in a mass spectrum in a 3:1 ratio, the molecule likely contains a Cl atom (**Figure 15-5**).
- If $M^{+\cdot}$ and M + 2 peaks appear in a mass spectrum in a 1:1 ratio, the molecule likely contains a Br atom (**Figure 15-6**).

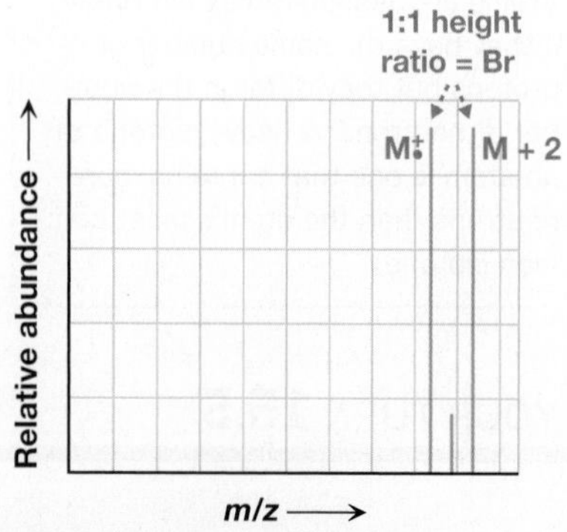
1:1 height
ratio = Br
M+·
M + 2
Relative abundance
m/z

FIGURE 15-6 Characteristic $M^{+\cdot}$ and M + 2 peaks indicating Br

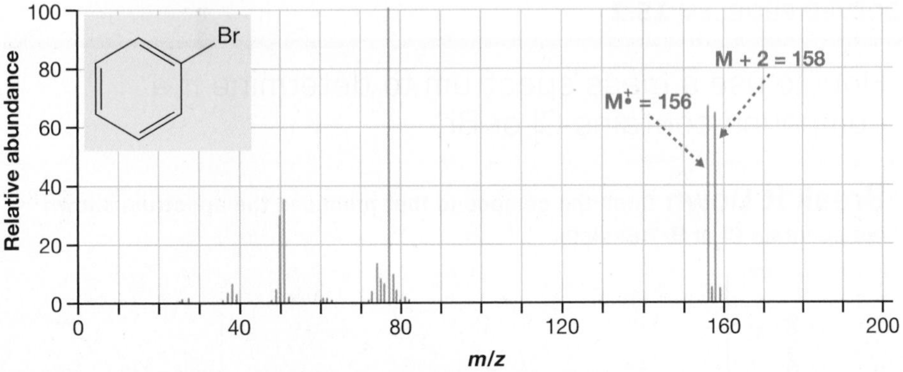
Br
M + 2 = 158
M$^{+\cdot}$ = 156
Relative abundance
m/z

FIGURE 15-7 Mass spectrum of bromobenzene The M$^{+\cdot}$ and M + 2 peaks correspond to molecular ions with ^{79}Br and ^{81}Br isotopes, respectively.

For example, notice in the mass spectrum of bromobenzene (C_6H_5Br; **Figure 15-7**) that the M$^{+\cdot}$ peak and the M + 2 peak have roughly equal intensities. The M$^{+\cdot}$ peak represents the molecular ion $[C_6H_5Br]^{+\cdot}$ that contains the ^{79}Br isotope, whereas the M + 2 peak represents the molecular ion $[C_6H_5Br]^{+\cdot}$ that contains the ^{81}Br isotope.

YOUR TURN 15.6

The molecular formula for the ion that gives rise to the M$^{+\cdot}$ peak in Figure 15-7 can be written as $[C_6H_5{}^{79}Br]^{+\cdot}$. (a) Write the molecular formula for the ion that gives rise to the M + 2 peak. (b) Calculate the molecular masses of both ions. How do those masses compare to the *m*/*z* values for the M$^{+\cdot}$ and M + 2 peaks in the spectrum? (c) What molecular formula (including isotope designations) would account for the small peak at *m*/*z* = 157? What formula would account for the small peak at *m*/*z* = 159?

Fragment ions that contain a bromine atom also appear as pairs of mass peaks of roughly equal magnitude, which differ by 2 in their values of *m*/*z*. We can see these fragment ions in the mass spectrum of 1-bromo-4-(1-methylethyl)benzene, shown in **Figure 15-8**.

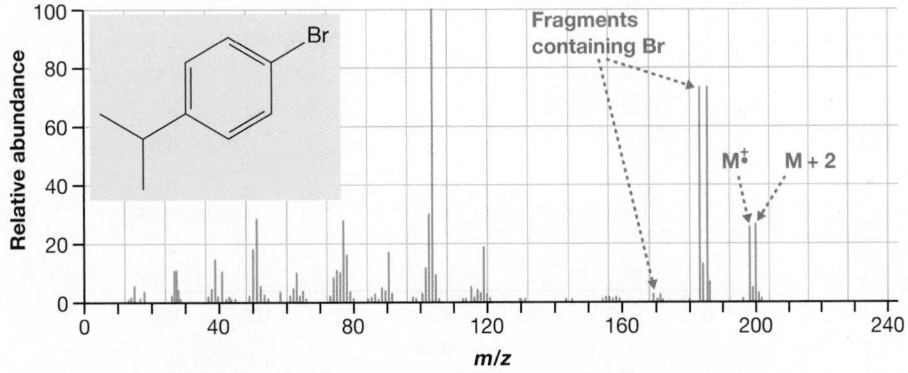
Br
Fragments containing Br
M$^{+\cdot}$
M + 2
Relative abundance
m/z

FIGURE 15-8 Mass spectrum of 1-bromo-4-(1-methylethyl)benzene Two fragments containing Br are indicated, as evidenced by pairs of peaks of roughly equal intensity, differing by two units of *m*/*z*.

SOLVED PROBLEM **15.2**

How to use a mass spectrum to determine if a compound contains Cl or Br

Break It Down Does the compound that produced the spectrum shown here contain Cl or Br? Explain.

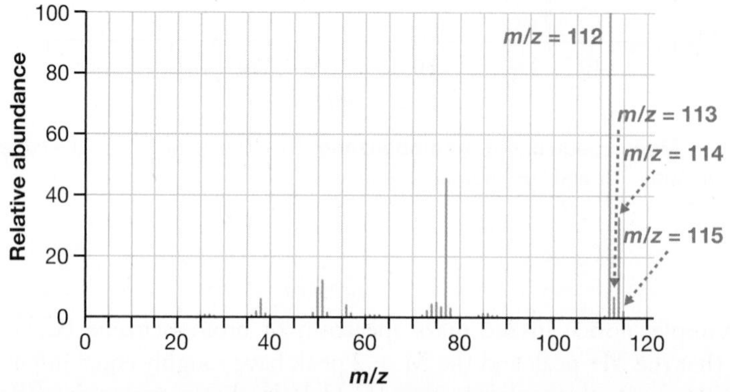

100
80
60
40
20
0
Relative abundance
m/z = 112
m/z = 113
m/z = 114
m/z = 115
0
20
40
60
80
100
120
m/z

Think	Solve
Where are the $M^{\dot{+}}$ and M + 2 peaks in the spectrum?	At the high-mass end of the spectrum, there are substantial peaks at $m/z = 112$ and $m/z = 114$. The $M^{\dot{+}}$ peak has $m/z = 112$, and the M + 2 peak has $m/z = 114$.
What is the ratio of the intensities for the $M^{\dot{+}}$ and M + 2 peaks?	The $M^{\dot{+}}$ peak's relative abundance is 100%. That of the M + 2 peak is about 33%. These values establish a ratio that is roughly 3 : 1.
Is the ratio of intensity characteristic of either Cl or Br?	The 3 : 1 ratio of the $M^{\dot{+}}$ and M + 2 peak intensities is characteristic of chlorine, so the compound likely contains Cl. If the compound were to contain bromine, we would expect a 1 : 1 ratio of the $M^{\dot{+}}$ and M + 2 peak intensities.

Try It Does the compound that produced the spectrum shown here contain Cl or Br? Explain.

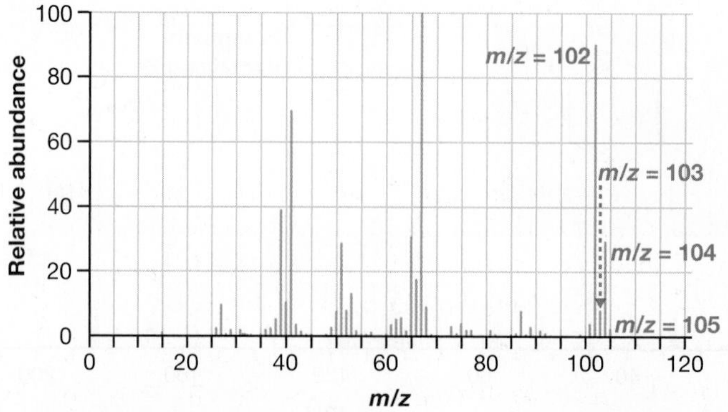

100
80
60
40
20
0
Relative abundance
m/z = 102
m/z = 103
m/z = 104
m/z = 105
0
20
40
60
80
100
120
m/z

15.4 A Deeper Look: Estimating the Number of Carbon Atoms from the M + 1 Peak

SECTION 15.4 OBJECTIVES

You will be able to:

1. Explain why the relative intensity of the M + 1 peak increases as the number of carbon atoms in the molecule increases.
2. Use the M + 1 peak intensity to estimate the number of carbon atoms a molecule has.

In Section 15.3, we learned that the presence of the ^{13}C isotope in a molecule gives rise to an M + 1 peak in the mass spectrum, and the M + 1 peak can help us identify the $M^{+\bullet}$ peak. In this section, we will also see that the *intensity* of the M + 1 peak relative to the intensity of the $M^{+\bullet}$ peak can be very useful.

In the mass spectrum of hexane (Fig. 15-2, p. 742), for example, the relative intensity of the M + 1 peak is 1.0% and that of the $M^{+\bullet}$ peak is 15.5%. The ratio of these two intensities is (1.0)/(15.5) = 0.065, or 6.5%. Consider, now, the mass spectrum of dodecane, $C_{12}H_{26}$, which is shown in **Figure 15-9**. The relative intensity of the M + 1 peak is 0.8%, and that of the $M^{+\bullet}$ peak is 5.9%. The ratio of these intensities is (0.8)/(5.9) = 0.136, or 13.6%. In other words:

> The ratio of M + 1 peak intensity to $M^{+\bullet}$ peak intensity increases as the number of carbon atoms in the molecule increases.

The M + 1 intensity increases when the molecule contains more carbons because of the increased likelihood that the molecular ion contains a ^{13}C isotope.

CONNECTIONS 15.1

Fueling the skies Dodecane (Fig. 15-9) is a substitute for traditional jet fuels because of its relatively high molecular mass and its relatively low hydrogen-to-carbon ratio.

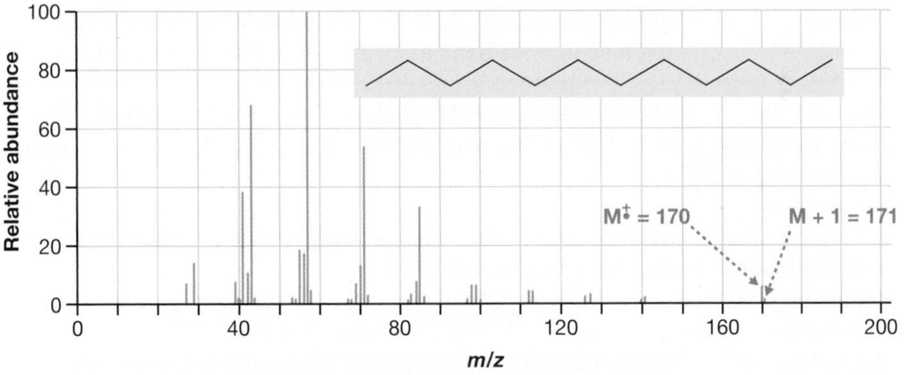

100
80
60
40
20
0
Relative abundance
$M^{+\bullet}$ = 170
M + 1 = 171
0
40
80
120
160
200
m/z

FIGURE 15-9 Mass spectrum of dodecane, $C_{12}H_{26}$ The $M^{+\bullet}$ and M + 1 peaks are labeled.

The intensity of the M + 1 peak can be used to *estimate* the number of carbon atoms, according to Equation 15-3:

$$\text{Number of C atoms} \approx \frac{\text{Intensity of M + 1}}{\text{Intensity of } M^{+\bullet}} \times \frac{100\%}{1.1\%} \qquad (15\text{-}3)$$

The value of 1.1% appears in the equation because that is the probability that a given carbon atom is ^{13}C (Table 15-1, p. 746). Part of the reason that Equation 15-3 can only be used as an estimate is that atoms other than carbon, such as hydrogen and nitrogen, have isotopes that contribute a small amount to the M + 1 peak.

YOUR TURN 15.7

Use Equation 15-3 to verify that hexane has six carbons and dodecane has 12.

SOLVED PROBLEM **15.3**

How to use the M + 1 peak to estimate the number of carbons in a compound

Break It Down **Estimate the number of carbon atoms in the compound that produced the following mass spectrum.**

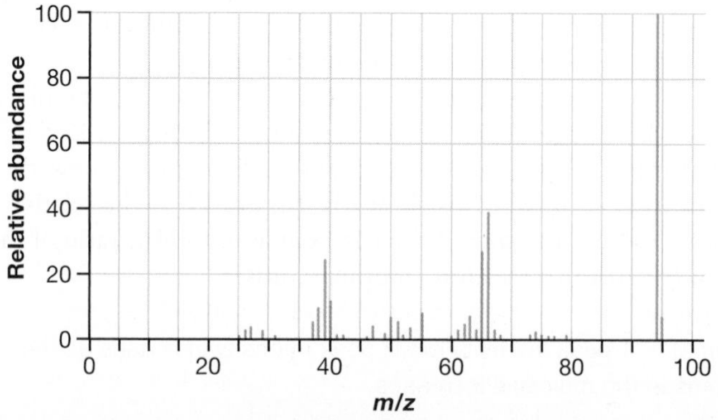

100
80
60
40
20
0
Relative abundance
0
20
40
60
80
100
m/z

Think	Solve
Where are the $M^{+\bullet}$ and M + 1 peaks?	To find the $M^{+\bullet}$ and the M + 1 peaks, look for a pair of peaks separated by 1 u at the high-mass end of the spectrum. The more intense peak at m/z = 94 is the $M^{+\bullet}$ peak, whereas the less intense peak at m/z = 95 is the M + 1 peak.
What are the relative intensities of those two peaks?	The intensity of the $M^{+\bullet}$ peak is 100%. The intensity of the M + 1 peak is approximately 7%.
What equation should be used to estimate the number of carbons?	According to Equation 15-3: $$\text{\# C atoms} \approx \frac{7\%}{100\%} \times \frac{100\%}{1.1\%} = 6.4$$ We therefore estimate that the compound has about six carbons.

Try It Estimate the number of carbon atoms present in the compound that produced the following mass spectrum.

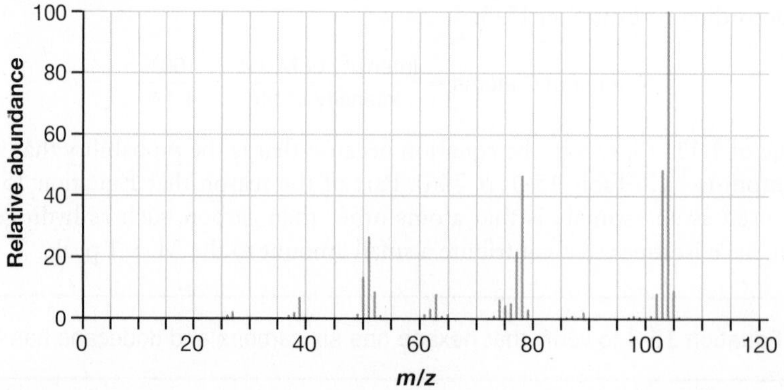

100
80
60
40
20
0
Relative abundance
0
20
40
60
80
100
120
m/z

15.5 Strategies for Success: Determining a Molecular Formula from the Mass Spectrum of an Organic Compound

SECTION 15.5 OBJECTIVES

You will be able to:

1. Use a mass spectrum to determine the molecular mass of an unknown compound and identify whether the compound contains N, Br, or Cl.
2. Derive a reasonable molecular formula of a compound given its mass, number of carbons, and whether the compound contains N, Br, or Cl.

Strategies for Success
Determining a Molecular Formula from the Mass Spectrum of an Organic Compound

One of the fundamental pieces of information you can obtain from a mass spectrum is a compound's molecular mass. Knowing the molecular mass, along with other information from the mass spectrum, you can often derive an organic compound's formula. You will eventually develop a strategy for interpreting mass spectra that works best for you, but for now we'll apply the following method:

Using a Mass Spectrum to Determine a Reasonable Molecular Formula

1. Assign the $M^{+\bullet}$ peak. If the m/z value of the $M^{+\bullet}$ peak is not already given, try to assign it as follows:
   a. At the high-mass end of the spectrum, look for two major peaks separated by 2 u in their m/z values. If you can locate this pattern, then the lower of the two m/z values is likely the $M^{+\bullet}$ peak and the higher one is the M + 2 peak.
   b. If no M + 2 peak is apparent, then find the two highest-mass peaks whose m/z values differ by 1 u. If the lower-mass peak is significantly more intense, it is likely the $M^{+\bullet}$ peak and the higher-mass peak is the M + 1 peak.
2. Record the number of C atoms. If the number of C atoms is not given, estimate the number by plugging the intensities of the $M^{+\bullet}$ and M + 1 peaks into Equation 15-3 (p. 749). (Remember that this number is just an *estimate*.)
3. Determine if the molecule contains any heteroatoms (i.e., atoms other than carbon or hydrogen).
   a. Does the nitrogen rule suggest the presence of any nitrogen atoms?
   b. If an M + 2 peak is present, do the relative intensities of the $M^{+\bullet}$ and M + 2 peaks suggest the presence of Br or Cl?
4. Compute the remaining mass. Subtract the masses of the ^{12}C atoms you determined in Step 2, and the masses of the heteroatoms you determined in Step 3, from the molecular mass.
5. Determine whether H atoms can account for the remaining mass.
   a. If so, then you have a complete molecular formula that could be feasible.
   b. If the number of H atoms is unreasonably high, then consider adding another non-hydrogen atom (such as C, O, or F) to the formula and repeat Step 5.

Let's apply this strategy to determine the molecular formula of Unknown 1 from its mass spectrum, which is presented in **Figure 15-10**.

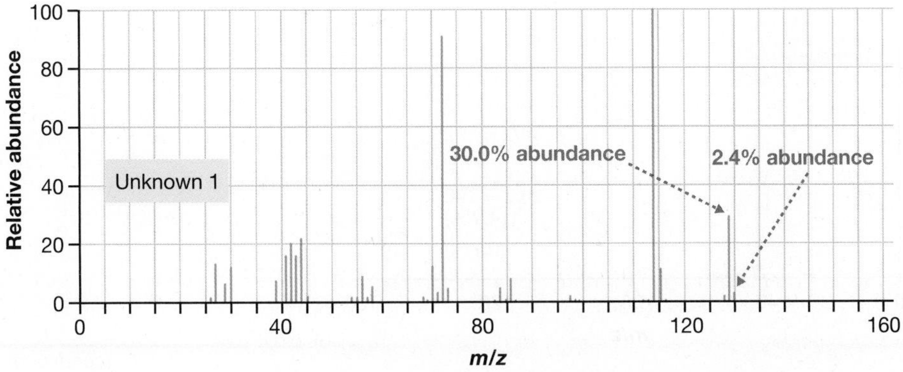
Relative abundance
100
80
60
40
20
0
Unknown 1
30.0% abundance
2.4% abundance
0
40
80
120
160
m/z

FIGURE 15-10 Mass spectrum of Unknown 1

Step 1. We are not given the $M^{+\bullet}$ peak, but notice that the two highest-mass peaks are at $m/z = 129$ and $m/z = 130$, and the peak at $m/z = 129$ is significantly more intense. We therefore assign $m/z = 129$ to the $M^{+\bullet}$ peak and $m/z = 130$ to the M + 1 peak, in which case the molecular mass of Unknown 1 is 129 u.

Step 2. Plugging the intensities of the $M^{+\bullet}$ and M + 1 peaks into Equation 15-3 produces a value of

$$\#\text{ C atoms} \approx \left(\frac{2.4\%}{30.0\%}\right) \times \left(\frac{100.0\%}{1.1\%}\right) = 7.3$$

This suggests the compound has seven carbons.

Step 3. For Step 3a, the nitrogen rule suggests that the molecule has an odd number of N atoms. Step 3b can be skipped because the spectrum does not contain an M + 2 peak.

Step 4. Subtracting the mass of seven ^{12}C atoms (weighing 84 u) from the molecular mass of 129 u leaves us with 45 u that must be accounted for by non-carbon atoms. We must also subtract the mass of an odd number of N atoms (since the nitrogen rule suggests there is an odd number of N atoms). But how many? If we assume that the compound contains three N atoms (weighing 42 u), the remaining mass of 3 u could be accounted for by three H atoms. However, it's unlikely that a compound containing seven C atoms and three N atoms would have just three H atoms. It would be more reasonable to assume that Unknown 1 contains just one N atom, leaving a mass of 31 u yet to be accounted for.

◀ RECALL

In Section 4.11 we learned that the number of hydrogen atoms in a saturated molecule can be calculated from the formula: # of H atoms = $2n + 2 +$ (# of N atoms) − (# of halogen atoms).

Step 5. The remaining mass of 31 u cannot come only from hydrogen because 31 H atoms exceeds that of a completely saturated molecule containing seven C atoms and one N atom (see Recall box). We can more confidently conclude that the molecule contains another heteroatom, such as O or F. Formulas that are consistent with this mass spectrum could therefore be $C_7H_{15}NO$ or $C_7H_{12}NF$.

YOUR TURN **15.8**

To confirm that it would be unreasonable for Unknown 1 to contain 31 H atoms, calculate the number of H atoms in a saturated molecule with seven C atoms and one N atom.

SOLVED PROBLEM **15.4**

How to use a mass spectrum to determine the molecular mass of a compound

Break It Down **Unknown 2 has the mass spectrum shown here. Propose a molecular formula for this compound.**

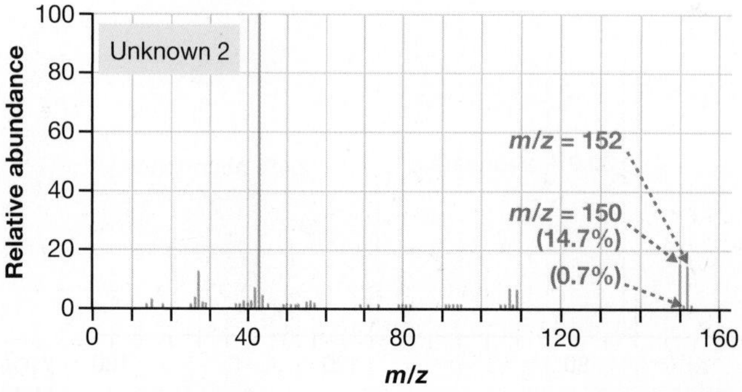

Unknown 2
m/z = 152
m/z = 150
(14.7%)
(0.7%)
Relative abundance
100
80
60
40
20
0
0
40
80
120
160
m/z

(continued)

Think	Solve
Step 1: Are there two significant peaks separated by 2 u at the high-mass end of the spectrum?	At the high-mass end of the spectrum, the peaks at $m/z = 150$ and $m/z = 152$ are separated by 2 u. We can thus identify the $M^{+\bullet}$ peak at $m/z = 150$ and M + 2 at $m/z = 152$.
Step 2: How many C atoms are in Unknown 2?	The number of carbons is not given, so we estimate the number using Equation 15-3: $$\#\text{ C atoms} \approx \frac{0.7\%}{14.7\%} \times \frac{100\%}{1.1\%} = 4.3$$ Therefore, we estimate Unknown 2 contains four C atoms.
Step 3: Does $M^{+\bullet}$ have an odd or even mass? What are the relative intensities of the $M^{+\bullet}$ and M + 2 peaks?	$M^{+\bullet}$ has an even mass (150 u), so Unknown 2 should contain either no nitrogens or an even number of them. The $M^{+\bullet}$ and M + 2 peaks have nearly the same intensities, suggesting that Unknown 2 contains Br.
Step 4: What mass remains after we account for the atoms in Steps 2 and 3?	After accounting for the four C atoms (48 u) from Step 2 and the ^{79}Br atom from Step 3 (79 u), the remaining mass is: 150 u − 48 u − 79 u = 23 u. Nitrogen atoms cannot account for the remaining mass because the mass of the lowest even number of N atoms would be 2, and 2(14 u) = 28 u. Thus, the mass of the minimum number of N atoms would exceed the remaining mass of 23 u.
Step 5: Can the remaining mass be accounted for by just H atoms?	Assuming H atoms account for the remaining mass of 23 u, 23 H atoms would be required. But a compound with just four C atoms cannot accommodate 23 H. Therefore, Unknown 2 must have another non-hydrogen atom, such as an O or F atom. Possible molecular formulas include C_4H_7BrO and C_4H_4BrF.

Try It Unknown 3 has the mass spectrum shown here. Propose a molecular formula for this compound.

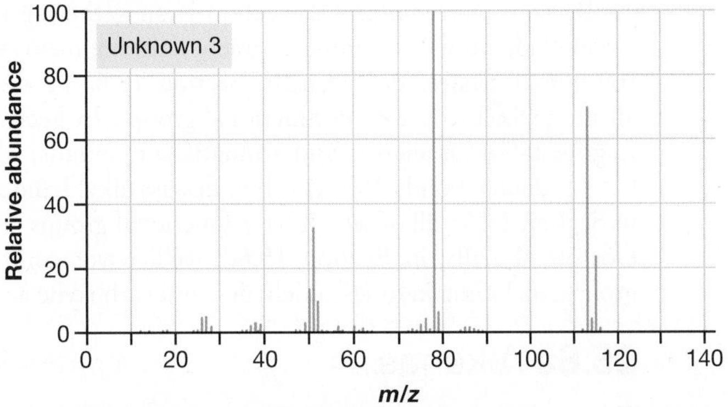

Unknown 3
Relative abundance
100
80
60
40
20
0
0
20
40
60
80
100
120
140
m/z

15.6 A Deeper Look: Fragmentation Pathways in Mass Spectrometry

SECTION 15.6 OBJECTIVES

You will be able to

1. Predict the more likely fragmentation pathway from the stabilities of the fragment ions.
2. Draw common fragmentation pathways for alkenes, aromatics, compounds that contain heteroatoms with lone pairs, and carbonyl-containing compounds.

To this point in Chapter 15, we have interpreted mass spectra primarily to determine the molecular mass of the compound that produces the spectrum. Doing so largely involves identifying the $M^{+\bullet}$ peak, as well as various M + 1 and M + 2 isotope peaks. Other fragment peaks that appear in a mass spectrum and their relative intensities carry important information about a molecule's structure as well. **Fragmentation pathways**, which are the chemical processes responsible for producing fragment ions, depend on the structure of the molecule and its functional

Mass Spectrometry, *CSI*, and *Grey's Anatomy*

CRIME SCENE DO NOT

FIGURE 15-11

Mass spectrometry is not just an analytical tool in chemistry; it can help investigators solve crimes (**Figure 15-11**) and can help doctors identify and treat cancer.

Investigating a crime involving explosives is often challenging when the explosive has been nearly entirely consumed. But a mass spectrum of the residue that is produced can help investigators trace the explosive back to its origin. When investigators suspect arson, they can use mass spectrometry to analyze partially charred wood for the presence of trace amounts of an accelerant such as gasoline, kerosene, or mineral spirits. And scientists are looking into the possibility of using mass spectrometry as evidence that can place a criminal at the scene of a crime. In their 2010 study, A. Curran, P. Prada, and K. Furton showed that human scent can be analyzed by mass spectrometry to produce a unique bar code of an individual's "primary odor" compounds, making it possible to identify an individual by the odor that they leave behind.

In medicine, mass spectrometry can help diagnose brain tumors. Detecting tumors is difficult, in part, because there are over 125 different kinds, and pathologists don't always agree on their diagnoses. To help identify a tumor, a spectrum produced by compounds removed from a tissue sample can be compared to a library of spectra generated from various types of tumors. Perhaps more interestingly, researchers are finding that a patient's breath can be analyzed by mass spectrometry to diagnose the specific type and stage of lung cancer with remarkable accuracy. And other breath tests are being developed for breast and colon cancers.

groups. Here in Section 15.6, we explore some fragmentation pathways and how they are helpful in interpreting mass spectra.

Because our focus in this section is on gathering structural information about a compound, we will examine characteristic fragmentation pathways for a variety of compound classes. We begin in Section 15.6a by discussing the fragmentation of alkanes, which contain no functional groups. In Section 15.6b, we will consider the fragmentation of alkenes and aromatic compounds, whose Lewis structures contain C=C double bonds. We will then discuss alkyl halides, amines, ethers, and alcohols in Section 15.6c, all of which have functional groups containing a singly bonded heteroatom. Finally, in Section 15.6d, we'll cover compounds that contain carbonyl groups, including ketones, aldehydes, and carboxylic acids.

15.6a Alkanes

The mass spectrum of hexane (**Figure 15-12**) was previously discussed in Section 15.2.

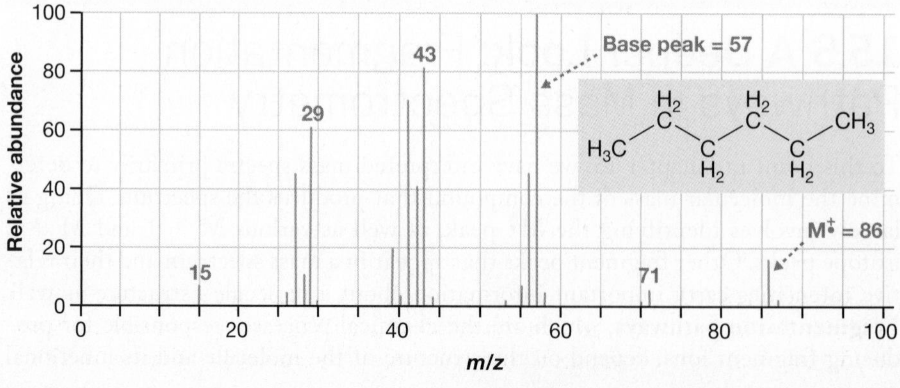
Relative abundance
100
80
60
40
20
0
0
20
40
60
80
100
m/z
15
29
43
71
Base peak = 57
M+· = 86
H2 C
H3C
C H2
CH3

FIGURE 15-12 Mass spectrum of hexane The $M^{+\cdot}$ and base peaks are indicated. The values of *m/z* for selected peaks are indicated above the peaks.

The $M^{\dot{+}}$ peak appears at $m/z = 86$, which corresponds to the molecular mass of hexane. Because the molecular ion can be produced by the loss of an electron from any one of hexane's many σ bonds, the molecular ion is ambiguously represented by placing square brackets around the parent molecule, along with a dot and a positive charge to indicate a radical cation:

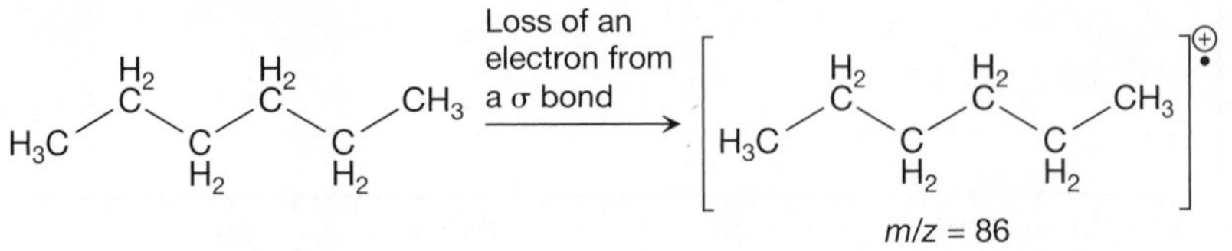
Loss of an electron from a σ bond
m/z = 86
(15-4)

Several key fragment peaks in the spectrum can also be identified at m/z values of 71, 57, 43, 29, and 15; as we saw in Figure 15-3 (p. 743), these fragments correspond to breaking of the various C—C bonds in hexane. For example, the base peak (i.e., the most intense mass peak) at $m/z = 57$ corresponds to breaking of the C-2—C-3 bond to produce both a butyl cation and an ethyl radical:

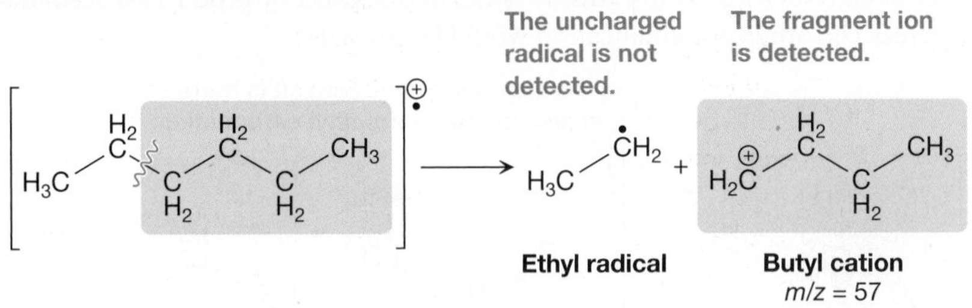
The uncharged radical is not detected.
The fragment ion is detected.
Ethyl radical
Butyl cation
m/z = 57
(15-5)

The peak at $m/z = 15$ corresponds to breaking of the C-1—C-2 bond to produce a methyl cation and a pentyl radical:

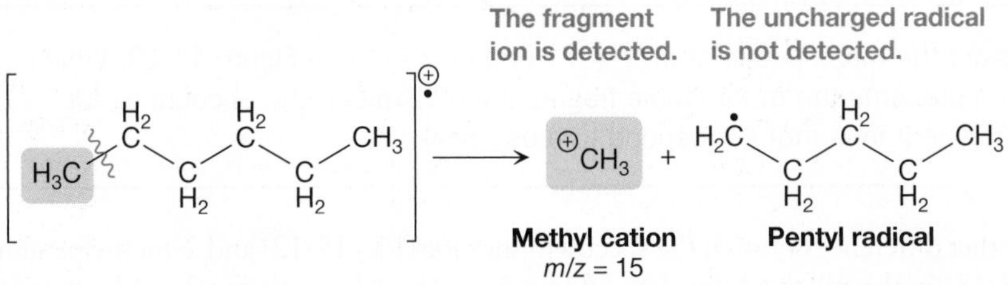
The fragment ion is detected.
The uncharged radical is not detected.
Methyl cation
m/z = 15
Pentyl radical
(15-6)

Because the peak at $m/z = 57$ is substantially more intense than the one at $m/z = 15$, we know that the fragmentation pathway in Equation 15-5 is much more likely than the one in Equation 15-6. Why is this? In general:

A fragmentation pathway becomes more likely as the stability of the fragment ion produced by that pathway increases.

Notice that the fragment ion in Equation 15-5 is a primary carbocation, which is more stable than the methyl cation in Equation 15-6.

YOUR TURN 15.9

Will the fragmentation shown here more likely produce a mass peak at $m/z = 43$ or $m/z = 57$? Explain.

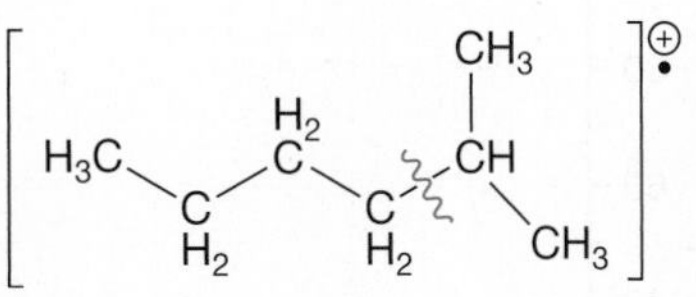

Knowing that fragment ion stability governs the likelihood of a fragmentation pathway can be very useful, particularly for distinguishing isomers by mass spectrometry. Consider 2-methylpentane, whose mass spectrum is shown in **Figure 15-13**.

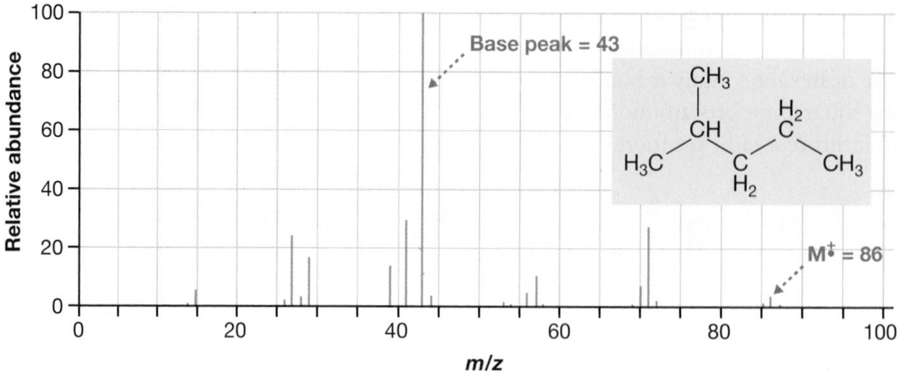

Relative abundance
m/z
Base peak = 43
M+• = 86

FIGURE 15-13 Mass spectrum of 2-methylpentane The values of m/z for the $M^{+\bullet}$ and base peaks are indicated above the peaks.

The $M^{+\bullet}$ peak appears at $m/z = 86$, the same as in the mass spectrum of hexane. The base peak for 2-methylpentane, however, is at $m/z = 43$, whereas the base peak for hexane is at $m/z = 57$. The fragmentation that accounts for the base peak at $m/z = 43$ is shown in Equation 15-7. This pathway is favored because it produces a secondary cation, whereas the other potential cation would be primary:

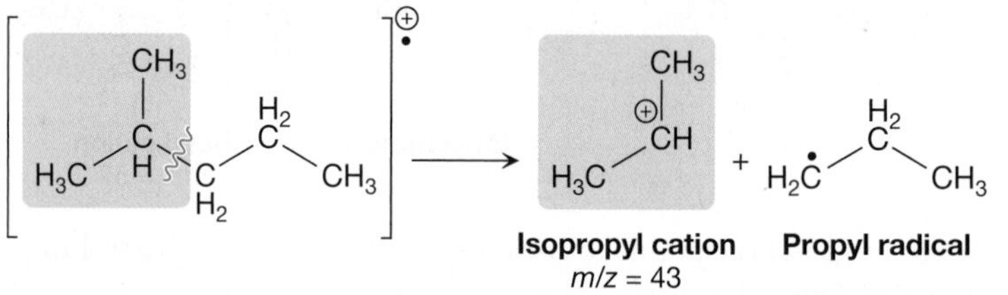

The secondary carbocation is more stable than a primary or methyl carbocation.
Isopropyl cation
m/z = 43
Propyl radical

(15-7)

YOUR TURN 15.10

Consider the mass peaks at $m/z = 71$ and $m/z = 29$ in Figure 15-13. Which peak represents the more stable fragment ion? Explain why, accounting for the fragment ions that correspond to those peaks.

Another difference between the spectra for hexane (Fig. 15-12) and 2-methylpentane (Fig. 15-13) is the relative size of the $M^{+\bullet}$ peaks: The $M^{+\bullet}$ peak for 2-methylpentane is much smaller than the one for hexane. Thus, fragmentation is more likely for the molecular ion of 2-methylpentane because, with additional branching, fragment ions that are more stable can be produced. With even more branching, as in 2,2-dimethylbutane (**Figure 15-14**), the $M^{+\bullet}$ peak essentially disappears entirely:

If a fragment ion is sufficiently stable, then the $M^{+\bullet}$ peak can essentially disappear entirely from a compound's mass spectrum.

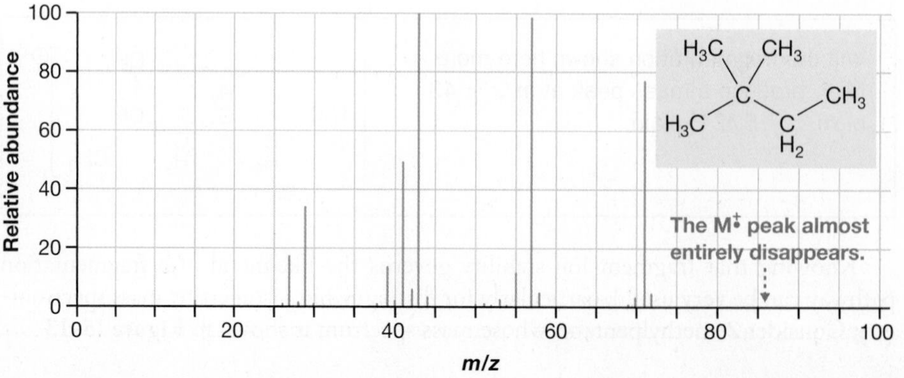

Relative abundance
m/z
The M+• peak almost entirely disappears.

FIGURE 15-14 Mass spectrum of 2,2-dimethylbutane The $M^{+\bullet}$ peak is almost entirely absent from the spectrum, because the significant branching of the alkyl chain means that fragmentation gives rise to relatively highly stable fragment ions.

15.6b Alkenes and Aromatic Compounds

The π electrons of alkenes and aromatic compounds are relatively high in energy, so one of them is usually ejected in the ionization process to produce the molecular ion. An example is shown for hex-2-ene in Equation 15-8:

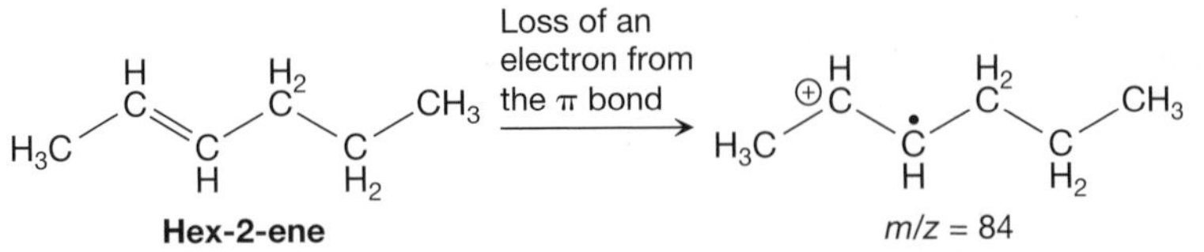

Loss of an electron from the π bond
Hex-2-ene
m/z = 84

(15-8)

Because of the relatively well-defined nature of an alkene's molecular ion, fragmentation pathways for alkenes tend to be clear-cut. In fact:

> An alkene's molecular ion tends to expel an alkyl radical from an allylic carbon, producing an allylic cation of the form C=C—C$^+$.

For example, Equation 15-9 shows that the molecular ion of hex-2-ene can expel an ethyl radical to produce a resonance-stabilized 2-butenyl cation (see Looking Ahead box):

▸ LOOKING AHEAD

The fragmentation pathway shown in Equation 15-9 involves the participation of an unpaired electron. Chapter 27, which deals with radical reactions, will introduce curved arrow notation to describe the movement of unpaired electrons in such elementary steps.

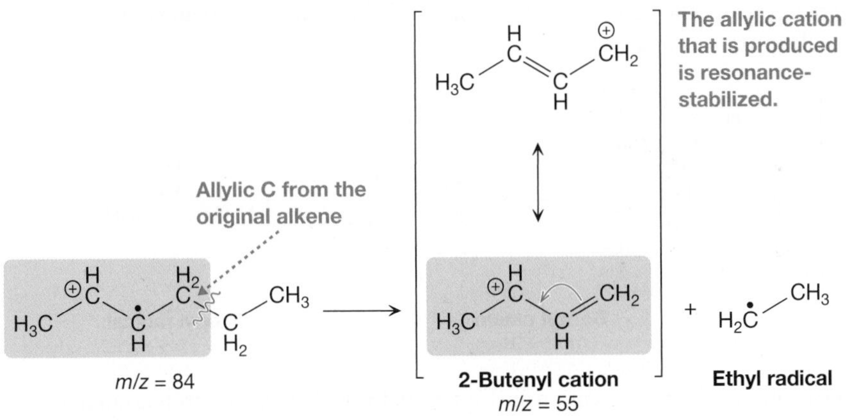

The allylic cation that is produced is resonance-stabilized.
Allylic C from the original alkene
m/z = 84
2-Butenyl cation
m/z = 55
Ethyl radical

(15-9)

The driving force for this process is the stability gained by resonance delocalization of the positive charge in the resulting allylic cation. This fragmentation pathway is the most likely one for the molecular ion of hex-2-ene because the base peak in the mass spectrum of hex-2-ene (**Figure 15-15**) is found at $m/z = 55$, which corresponds to the 2-butenyl cation in Equation 15-9.

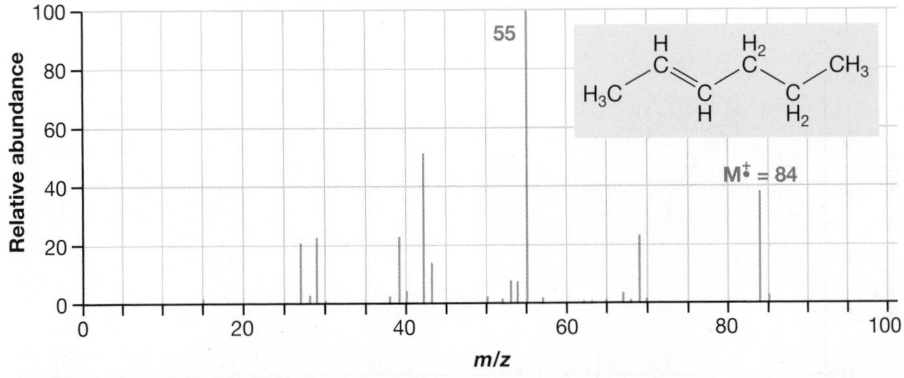

Relative abundance
100
80
60
40
20
0
55
M⁺̇ = 84
0
20
40
60
80
100
m/z

FIGURE 15-15 Mass spectrum of hex-2-ene The $M^{+\cdot}$ peak appears at $m/z = 84$. Loss of an ethyl radical produces a resonance-stabilized allylic cation that gives rise to the base peak at $m/z = 55$.

YOUR TURN 15.11

Hex-1-ene undergoes ionization and fragmentation to expel a propyl radical, as shown here. Draw the allyl cation that is also produced.

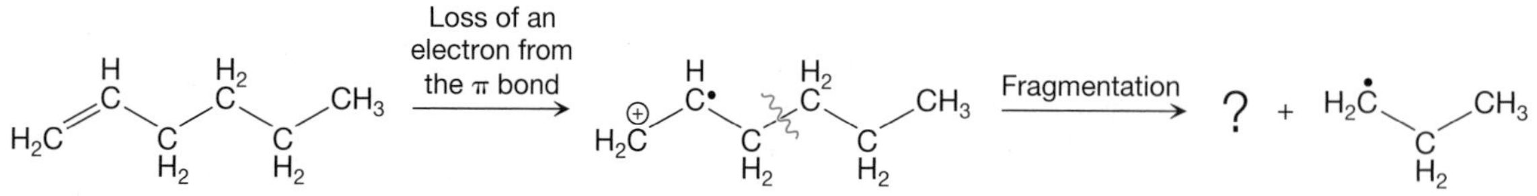
Loss of an electron from the π bond
Fragmentation
?

◄ RECALL

According to Hückel's rules (Section 14.7), a compound is aromatic if it has a cyclic π system that is planar and contains an odd number of pairs of electrons. A benzene ring and the tropylium ion are both aromatic because they are planar and their cyclic π systems each contain six electrons (three pairs).

Similar fragmentations are observed for aromatic compounds (see Recall box):

The molecular ion of an alkylbenzene tends to expel an alkyl radical from a benzylic carbon, producing a benzylic cation.

The mass spectrum of butylbenzene is shown in **Figure 15-16**. The molecular ion, produced by the loss of a π electron, gives rise to the peak at $m/z = 134$. Loss of a propyl radical from the benzylic carbon (Eq. 15-10) produces the benzyl cation, whose mass peak appears at $m/z = 91$:

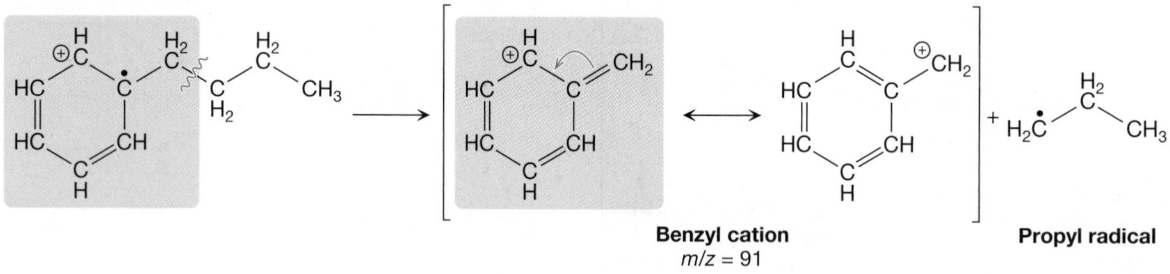
Benzyl cation
m/z = 91
Propyl radical

(15-10)

In the gas phase, the benzyl cation in Equation 15-10 is believed to rearrange to the **tropylium ion** (Eq. 15-11), which has an aromatic seven-membered ring:

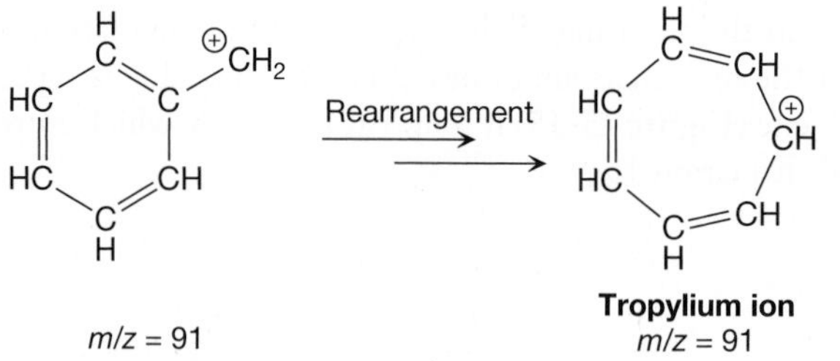
Rearrangement
m/z = 91
Tropylium ion
m/z = 91

(15-11)

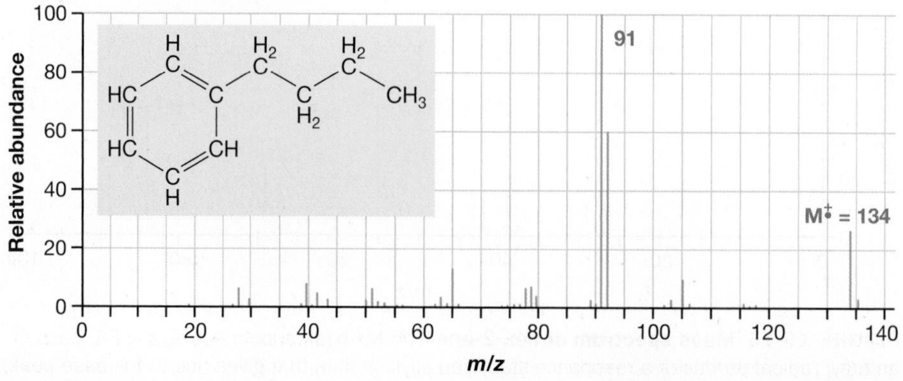
Relative abundance
m/z
91
M⁺• = 134
0
20
40
60
80
100
120
140

FIGURE 15-16 Mass spectrum of butylbenzene The $M^{+\bullet}$ peak appears at $m/z = 134$. Loss of a propyl radical produces a resonance-stabilized benzyl cation that gives rise to the base peak at $m/z = 91$.

YOUR TURN **15.12**

Draw all resonance structures and the resonance hybrid for both the tropylium ion and the benzyl cation. How many resonance structures of each cation exhibit aromaticity in the ring? Which does this suggest is the more stable cation?

15.6c Alkyl Halides, Amines, Ethers, and Alcohols

Many functional groups contain *heteroatoms* (atoms other than carbon or hydrogen) that can play major roles in fragmentation pathways and, therefore, help govern the fragmentation patterns observed in a mass spectrum. In mass spectrometry, one of the most important features of a heteroatom is its lone pair of electrons. As nonbonding electrons, lone pairs are typically the least tightly bound electrons in the molecule. Therefore:

In the ionization of a molecule containing a heteroatom, a lone-pair electron is generally the most likely electron lost to produce the molecular ion, $M^{+\bullet}$.

Loss of a nonbonding electron from the Cl atom in 2-chloro-2-methylbutane produces the molecular ion with m/z = 106, as shown in Equation 15-12:

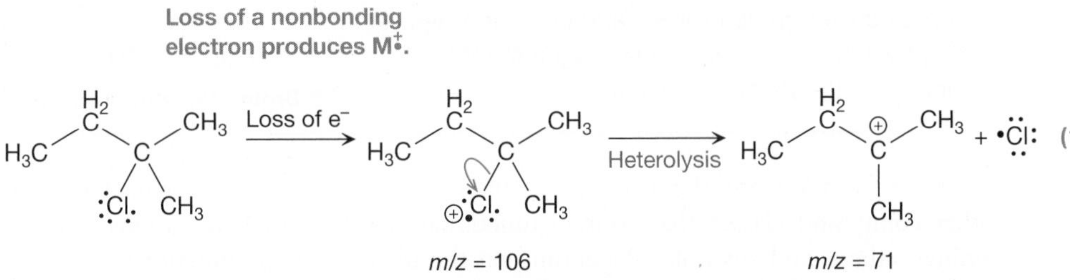

Loss of a nonbonding electron produces M+•.
Loss of e⁻
Heterolysis
m/z = 106
m/z = 71

(15-12)

The peak corresponding to $M^{+\bullet}$ does not appear in the spectrum in **Figure 15-17**, however, because fragmentation takes place too readily. One fragmentation pathway, shown in Equation 15-12, is heterolysis of the C—Cl bond, producing an alkyl cation fragment with m/z = 71.

Another common fragmentation pathway is *α cleavage*:

α Cleavage is the elimination of an alkyl group from the carbon atom bonded to the heteroatom.

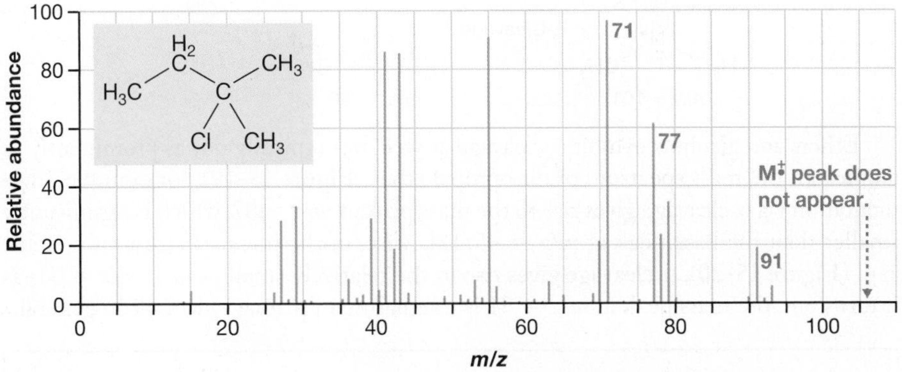

Relative abundance
m/z
71
77
91
M+• peak does not appear.

FIGURE 15-17 Mass spectrum of 2-chloro-2-methylbutane The $M^{+\bullet}$ peak, which would appear at m/z = 106, is absent. The masses of other significant fragment ions are labeled above their corresponding peaks.

There are two α cleavage pathways for the molecular ion of 2-chloro-2-methylbutane, as shown in Equations 15-13 and 15-14, accounting for mass peaks at $m/z = 91$ and $m/z = 77$:

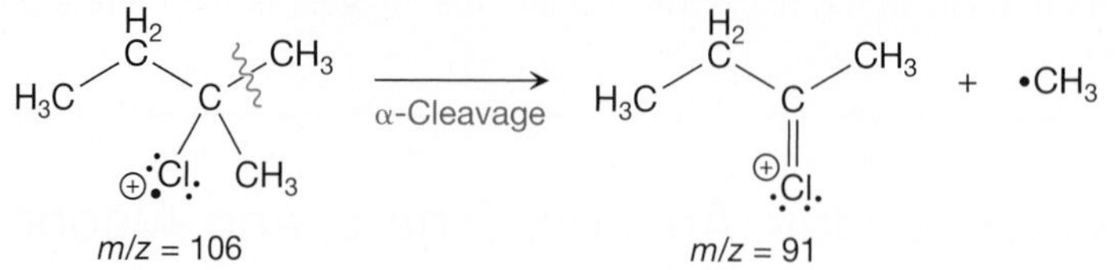
α-Cleavage
m/z = 106
m/z = 91
+ •CH3

(15-13)

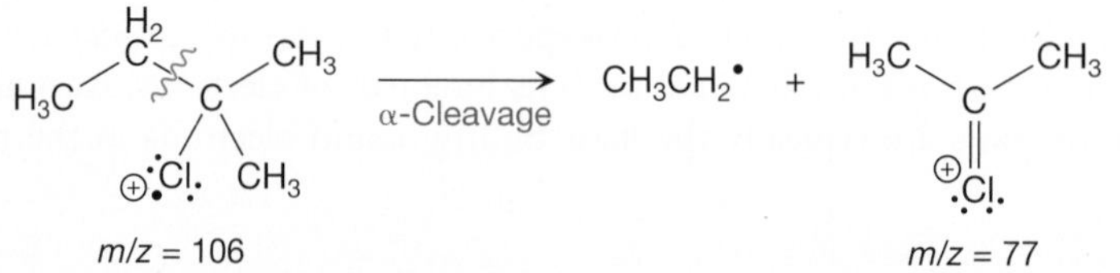
α-Cleavage
CH3CH2• +
m/z = 106
m/z = 77

(15-14)

Notice that, in the resonance structure shown for each fragment ion, *all non-hydrogen atoms have an octet*, which provides a substantial driving force for each process.

YOUR TURN **15.13**

For the compound shown here, draw the fragment ion produced on heterolysis and on α cleavage. At what values of m/z will those fragment ions appear in the mass spectrum?

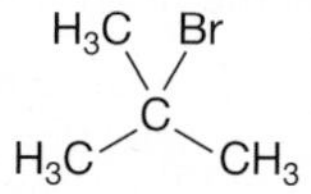

2-Bromo-2-methylpropane

These two fragmentation pathways, heterolysis and α cleavage, are characteristic of other compound classes that contain functional groups with heteroatoms, such as amines, ethers, and alcohols. Depending on the identity of the functional group, as well as the specific structure of the compound, one of these fragmentation pathways can be highly favored over the other.

α Cleavage is very common for amines, typically leading to the fragment ion that corresponds to the base peak. This is the case for *N,N*,2-trimethylpropan-2-amine, whose mass spectrum is shown in **Figure 15-18**. The molecular ion appears at $m/z = 101$. Loss of a CH_3 group via α cleavage (Eq. 15-15) produces the fragment ion giving rise to the base peak at $m/z = 86$:

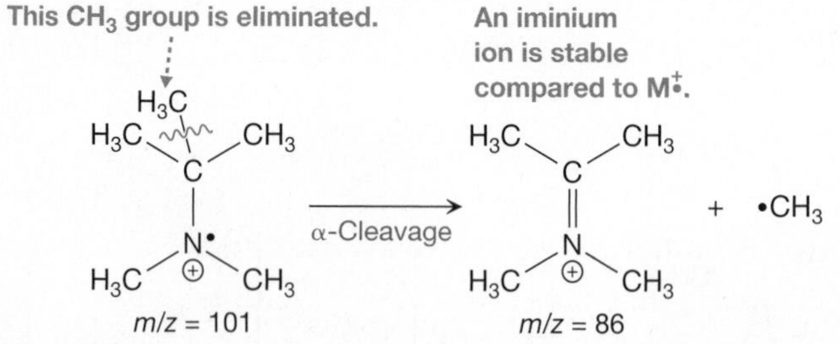
This CH3 group is eliminated.
An iminium ion is stable compared to M+•.
α-Cleavage
+ •CH3
m/z = 101
m/z = 86

(15-15)

Ethers and alcohols exhibit α cleavage as well, but typically not as prominently as amines. In the mass spectrum of diisopropyl ether (**Figure 15-19**), for example, fragmentation via α cleavage gives rise to the mass peak at $m/z = 87$, which is significantly smaller than the base peak at $m/z = 45$. Likewise, in the mass spectrum of pentan-1-ol (**Figure 15-20**), α cleavage gives rise to the relatively small peak at $m/z = 31$; as it turns out, the mass peak at $m/z = 31$ is a signature of primary alcohols in general.

YOUR TURN **15.14**

Draw the fragment ion produced on α cleavage of diisopropyl ether's molecular ion that accounts for the mass peak at $m/z = 87$.

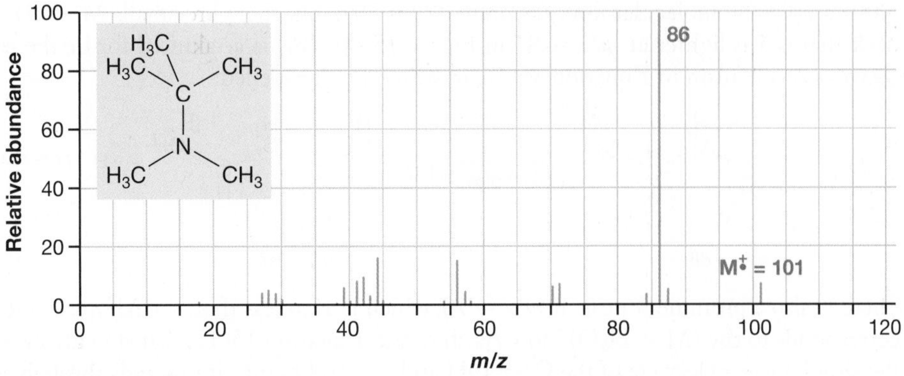
Relative abundance
100
80
60
40
20
0
0
20
40
60
80
100
120
m/z
86
M+• = 101
H3C
H3C
CH3
C
N
H3C
CH3

FIGURE 15-18 Mass spectrum of *N,N*,2-trimethylpropan-2-amine The $M^{+\bullet}$ peak appears at $m/z = 101$ and is relatively small. The base peak at $m/z = 86$ corresponds to a fragment ion produced by α cleavage of the molecular ion.

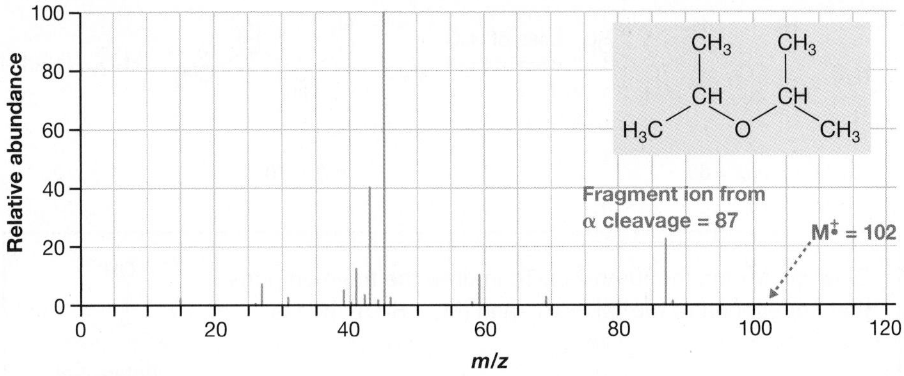
Relative abundance
100
80
60
40
20
0
0
20
40
60
80
100
120
m/z
CH3
CH3
CH
CH
H3C
O
CH3
Fragment ion from
α cleavage = 87
M+• = 102

FIGURE 15-19 Mass spectrum of diisopropyl ether The $M^{+\bullet}$ peak appears at $m/z = 102$. The peak at $m/z = 87$ corresponds to a fragment ion produced by α cleavage of the molecular ion.

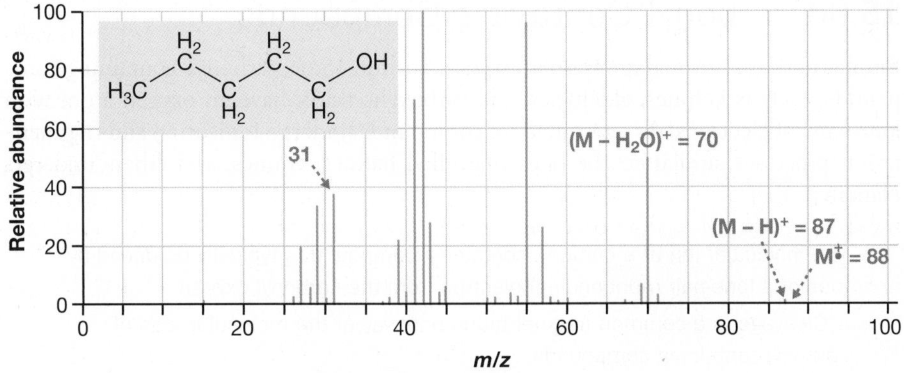
Relative abundance
100
80
60
40
20
0
0
20
40
60
80
100
m/z
H2
H2
C
C
OH
H3C
C
C
H2
H2
31
(M – H2O)+ = 70
(M – H)+ = 87
M+• = 88

FIGURE 15-20 Mass spectrum of pentan-1-ol The $M^{+\bullet}$ peak would appear at $m/z = 88$, but is absent. The peak at $m/z = 31$ corresponds to loss of an alkyl radical from $M^{+\bullet}$ via α cleavage. The peak at $m/z = 70$ corresponds to loss of water from the molecular ion. The peak at $m/z = 87$ corresponds to a fragment ion produced by loss of a hydrogen atom.

YOUR TURN 15.15

It was just stated that a mass peak at $m/z = 31$ is characteristic of primary alcohols. Draw the fragment ions produced on α cleavage of the molecular ions of pentan-1-ol and hexan-1-ol. What do you notice?

There are two other fragmentation pathways characteristic of an alcohol:

An alcohol's molecular ion will typically undergo:

- Loss of a hydrogen atom to give rise to an $(M - H)^+$ peak that is 1 u lighter than the molecular ion.
- Loss of a water molecule to give rise to an $(M - H_2O)^+$ peak that is 18 u lighter than the molecular ion.

For example, the molecular ion of pentan-1-ol is 88 u, but there is a small $(M - H)^+$ peak that is 1 u lighter at $m/z = 87$ in Figure 15-20. This is accounted for by the α cleavage mechanism in Equation 15-16, in which H• is expelled:

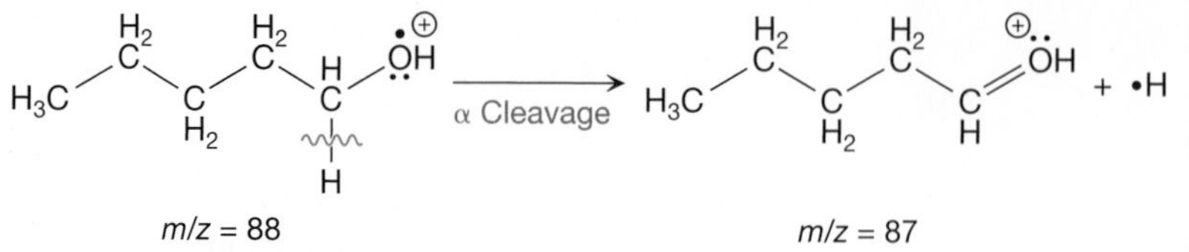

α Cleavage
+ •H
m/z = 88
m/z = 87

(15-16)

There is also a prominent peak at $m/z = 70$, which is 18 u less than the $M^{+\bullet}$ peak and corresponds to the $(M - H_2O)^+$ ion. As shown in Equation 15-17, that step involves the simultaneous cleavage of the C^α—OH and C^γ—H bonds; it proceeds through a five-membered-ring transition state, which does not suffer from excessive strain or loss of entropy:

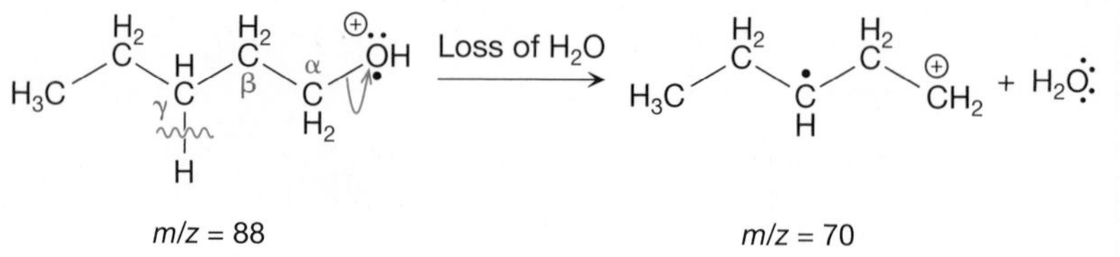

Loss of H2O
m/z = 88
m/z = 70

(15-17)

YOUR TURN **15.16**

Draw the $M^{+\bullet}$ ion for butan-2-ol. Then draw the fragment ions that correspond to the $(M - H)^+$ and $(M - H_2O)^+$ peaks.

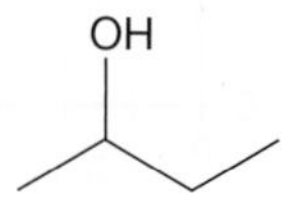

Butan-2-ol

15.6d Carbonyl-Containing Compounds

Similar to the functional groups discussed in Section 15.6c, carbonyl-containing compounds, such as ketones, aldehydes, and carboxylic acids, have an oxygen atom with lone pairs of electrons. As a result, these compounds undergo ionization and fragmentation processes similar to the ones that alkyl halides, amines, and ethers undergo. Namely:

- The molecular ion of a carbonyl-containing compound is typically produced by loss of a lone-pair (nonbonding) electron from the carbonyl oxygen.
- α Cleavage is a common fragmentation pathway of the molecular ions of carbonyl-containing compounds.

▸ LOOKING AHEAD

The acylium ion appears as an intermediate in the Friedel–Crafts acylation reaction, a very useful reaction for synthesis that we will discuss in Section 24.5.

Equation 15-18, for example, shows that hexan-2-one undergoes ionization to produce the molecular ion with $m/z = 100$ (**Figure 15-21**):

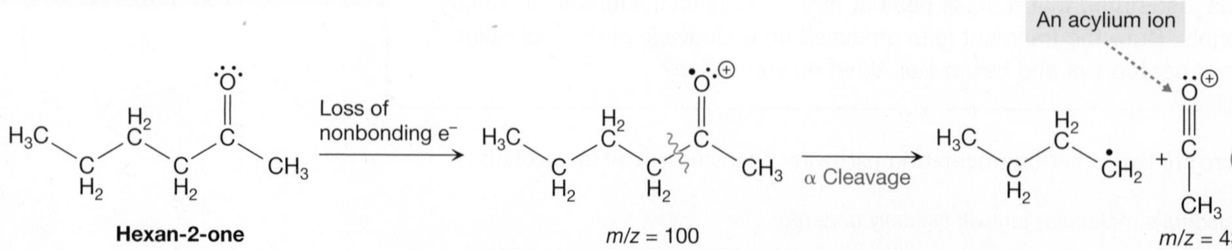

An acylium ion
Loss of nonbonding e⁻
α Cleavage
Hexan-2-one
m/z = 100
m/z = 43

(15-18)

Subsequent α cleavage can expel a butyl radical from the carbonyl carbon to produce a relatively stable *acylium ion* (see Looking Ahead box), giving rise to the base peak at $m/z = 43$. Alternatively, α cleavage of a methyl radical produces the ion corresponding to the peak at $m/z = 85$.

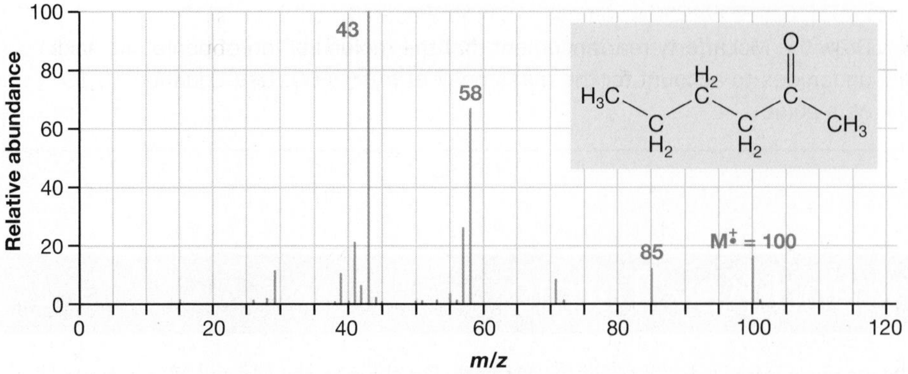

Relative abundance
m/z
43
58
85
M+• = 100
H3C, C H2, C H2, C, O, CH3

FIGURE 15-21 Mass spectrum of hexan-2-one The $M^{+\bullet}$ peak appears at $m/z = 100$. The peaks at $m/z = 43$ and $m/z = 85$ correspond to fragment ions produced on α cleavage of the molecular ion. The mass peak at $m/z = 58$ corresponds to a fragment ion produced by a McLafferty rearrangement.

YOUR TURN 15.17

Draw the fragmentation pathway that gives rise to the peak at $m/z = 85$ in the mass spectrum of hexan-2-one (Fig. 15-21). Use Equation 15-18 as a guide.

In addition to α cleavage, there is another fragmentation pathway characteristic of carbonyl-containing compounds, called a *McLafferty rearrangement*. An example is shown in Equation 15-19:

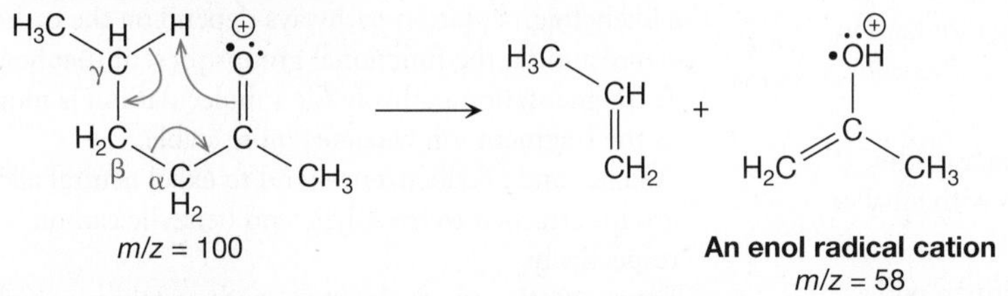

McLafferty rearrangement
m/z = 100
An enol radical cation
m/z = 58

(15-19)

In a **McLafferty rearrangement**, the molecular ion of a carbonyl-containing compound undergoes the cyclic movement of six electrons to produce an enol radical cation and an alkene.

This fragmentation pathway is named after Professor Fred W. McLafferty (b. 1923). As shown in Equation 15-19, a hydrogen on the γ carbon shifts to the carbonyl O atom, and the bond joining the α and β carbons is broken. In the case of hexan-2-one's molecular ion, the McLafferty rearrangement produces an enol radical cation of acetone, giving rise to the mass peak at $m/z = 58$ in Figure 15-21.

The McLafferty rearrangement is not limited to just ketones; it is characteristic of several compound classes containing the carbonyl group, including aldehydes, carboxylic acids, esters, and amides. For example, the molecular ion of pentanoic acid undergoes a McLafferty rearrangement, giving rise to the mass peak at $m/z = 60$ in **Figure 15-22**.

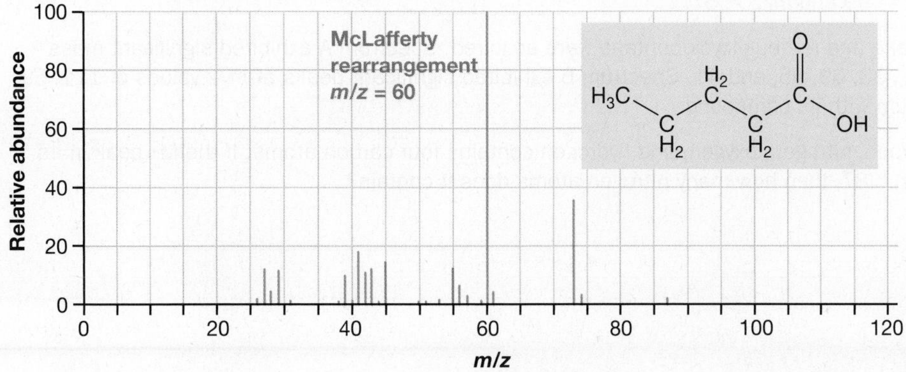

Relative abundance
m/z
McLafferty rearrangement
m/z = 60

FIGURE 15-22 Mass spectrum of pentanoic acid The mass peak at $m/z = 60$ corresponds to a fragment ion produced by a McLafferty rearrangement.

YOUR TURN **15.18**

Draw the McLafferty rearrangement that the molecular ion of pentanoic acid undergoes to account for the mass peak at $m/z = 60$. Use Equation 15-19 as a guide.

Chapter Summary and Key Terms

- In a **mass spectrometer**, a sample in the gas phase is ionized, and the **mass-to-charge ratio (*m*/*z*)** and **relative abundance** of the resulting ions are measured. **(Section 15.1)**
- A **mass spectrum** plots the relative abundance of gaseous ions against the mass-to-charge ratio. **(Section 15.1)**
- **Electron impact ionization (EI)** knocks off an electron from a molecule of the sample to produce the **molecular ion, $M^{+\cdot}(g)$**, and it also provides enough energy to cause the molecular ion to undergo **fragmentation**. **(Section 15.1)**
- The most intense (tallest) peak in a mass spectrum is called the **base peak**. **(Section 15.2)**
- For a mass spectrum generated by electron impact ionization, the charge of each ion produced is typically +1, so the value of *m*/*z* is equal to the ion's mass. **(Section 15.2)**
- A molecule's mass can be determined from the *m*/*z* of the molecular ion. Fragmentation gives rise to peaks with smaller *m*/*z* values. **(Section 15.2)**
- According to the **nitrogen rule**, a compound with an odd number of nitrogen atoms has an odd molecular mass, and a compound with zero or an even number of nitrogen atoms has an even molecular mass. **(Section 15.2)**
- The presence of ^{13}C gives rise to an **M + 1 peak** that is typically much smaller than the $M^{+\cdot}$ peak. **(Section 15.3)**
- The presence of bromine or chlorine can be identified by the intensity of an **M + 2 peak** peak relative to the intensity of the $M^{+\cdot}$ peak. For chlorine, the $M^{+\cdot}$ and M + 2 peak intensities have a 3 : 1 ratio, and for bromine the ratio is 1 : 1. **(Section 15.3)**
- The intensity of the M + 1 peak relative to that of the $M^{+\cdot}$ peak is proportional to the number of carbons in the molecule. An estimate of the total number of carbon atoms in a molecule can be computed from that ratio. **(Section 15.4)**
- The molecular formula for an unknown compound can be determined from key pieces of information obtained from its mass spectrum: the molecular mass; the number of carbon atoms; and the presence of N, Cl, or Br. **(Section 15.5)**
- The likely fragmentation pathways depend on the carbon structure and on the functional groups present **(Section 15.6)**
  - A fragmentation pathway for a molecular ion is more likely as the fragment ion becomes more stable.
  - Alkenes and alkylbenzenes tend to expel neutral alkyl groups attached to the allylic and benzylic carbon, respectively.
  - Fragmentation via **α cleavage** tends to take place when a molecule has a functional group with a lone pair of electrons.
  - Alcohols tend to exhibit mass peaks that result from the loss of H or of H_2O.
  - Fragmentation via a **McLafferty rearrangement** is observed for molecules that contain a carbonyl group and a hydrogen bonded to a γ carbon.

Problems

Sections 15.2–15.4 The Nitrogen Rule, Fragmentation, and Isotopes

15.1 At what value of *m*/*z* would the $M^{+\cdot}$ peak appear for 2,2,3,3-tetramethylbutane? Draw the fragment ions that would account for mass peaks at $m/z = 99$ and $m/z = 57$.

15.2 Mass spectra of butylcyclopentane and *tert*-butylcyclopentane were acquired. Spectrum A exhibited significant mass peaks at *m*/*z* values of 126, 97, 83, 69, 55, and 41. Spectrum B exhibited significant peaks at *m*/*z* values of 111, 69, 57, and 41. Match each spectrum with its compound.

15.3 A compound containing only carbon, nitrogen, oxygen, and hydrogen contains four carbon atoms. If the $M^{+\cdot}$ peak in its mass spectrum appears at $m/z = 87$, then how many nitrogen atoms does it contain?

15.4 **(a)** Draw the structures of the species that correspond to each peak **A**–**E** in the following mass spectrum of heptane. **(b)** Identify the $M^{+\bullet}$ peak, the M + 1 peak, and the base peak.

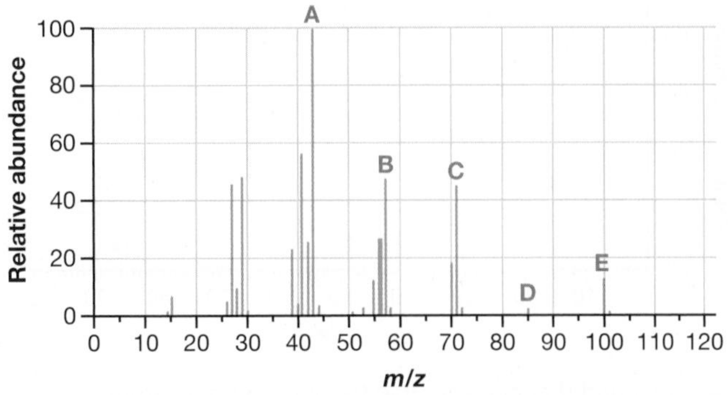

A
B
C
D
E
Relative abundance
100
80
60
40
20
0
0 10 20 30 40 50 60 70 80 90 100 110 120
m/z

15.5 Compounds **X** and **Y** both produce mass spectra in which the $M^{+\bullet}$ peak appears at $m/z = 122$. In the spectrum of compound **X**, the relative intensity of the $M^{+\bullet}$ peak is 83.2% and that of the M + 1 peak is 6.7%. In the mass spectrum of compound **Y**, the analogous intensity values are 16.9% and 1.6%. Which compound contains more carbon atoms?

15.6 Is the compound giving rise to the mass spectrum shown here more likely to contain bromine or chlorine? Explain.

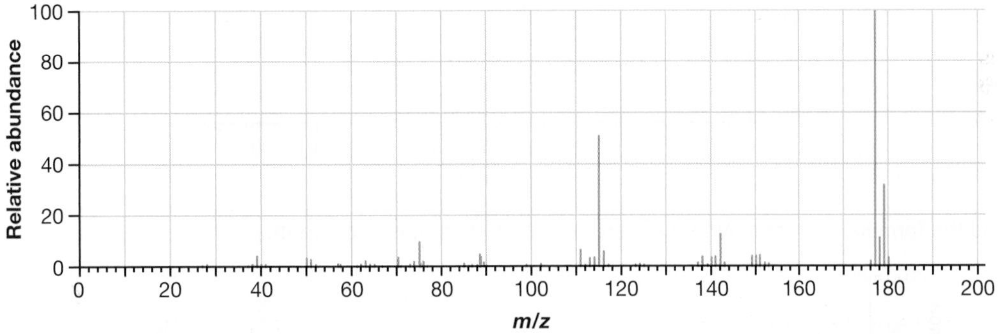

Relative abundance
100
80
60
40
20
0
0 20 40 60 80 100 120 140 160 180 200
m/z

15.7 Coronene is made of only carbon and hydrogen. In its mass spectrum, the base peak, which is also the $M^{+\bullet}$ peak, appears at $m/z = 300$. At $m/z = 301$ and $m/z = 302$, two peaks appear with relative intensities of 24% and 4%, respectively. Explain why the spectrum exhibits a significant M + 2 peak even though the molecule has no heteroatoms.

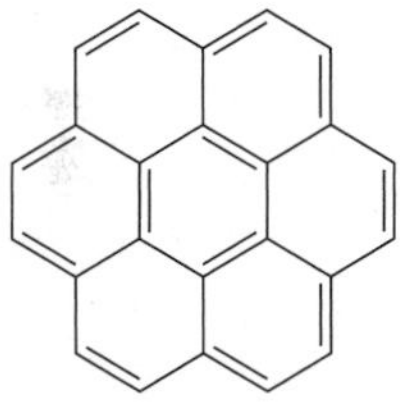

Coronene

Section 15.5 Determining a Molecular Formula from the Mass Spectrum

15.8 Determine the formula of a compound that can produce this mass spectrum.

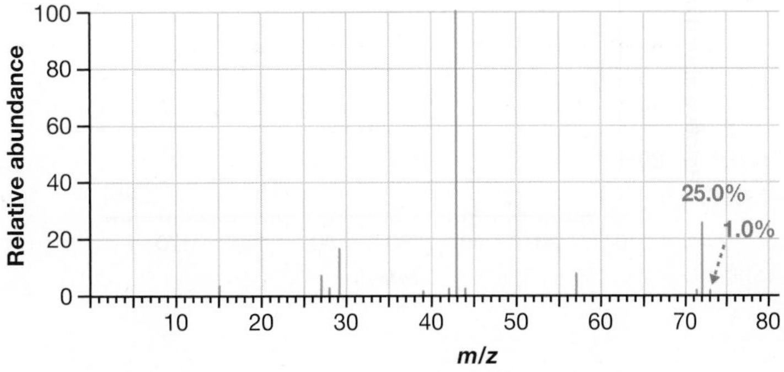

25.0%
1.0%
Relative abundance
100
80
60
40
20
0
10 20 30 40 50 60 70 80
m/z

15.9 Determine the formula of a compound that can produce this mass spectrum.

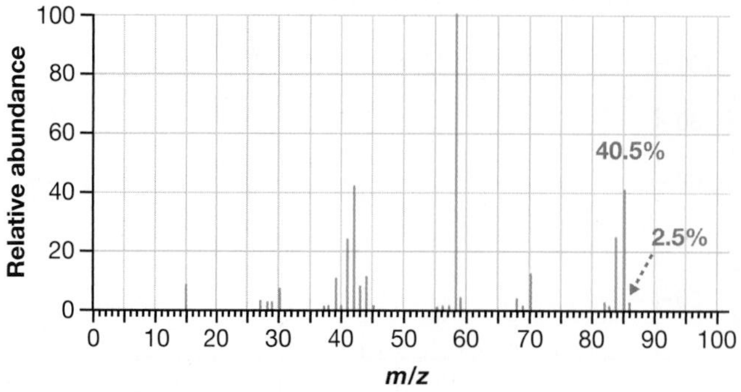
Relative abundance
100
80
60
40
20
0
40.5%
2.5%
0 10 20 30 40 50 60 70 80 90 100
m/z

15.10 Determine the formula of a compound that can give rise to this mass spectrum.

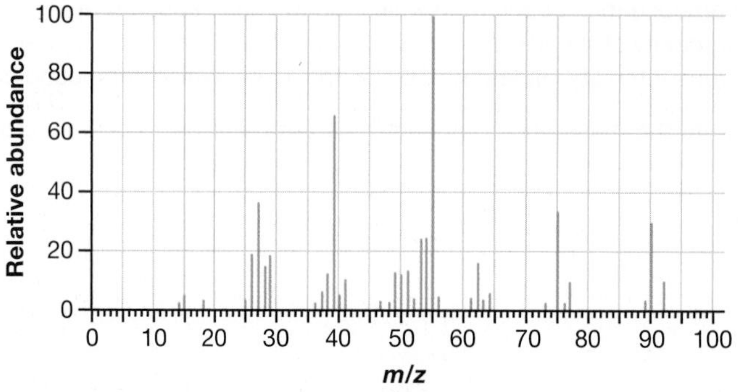
Relative abundance
100
80
60
40
20
0
0 10 20 30 40 50 60 70 80 90 100
m/z

15.11 Determine the formula of a compound that can give rise to this mass spectrum.

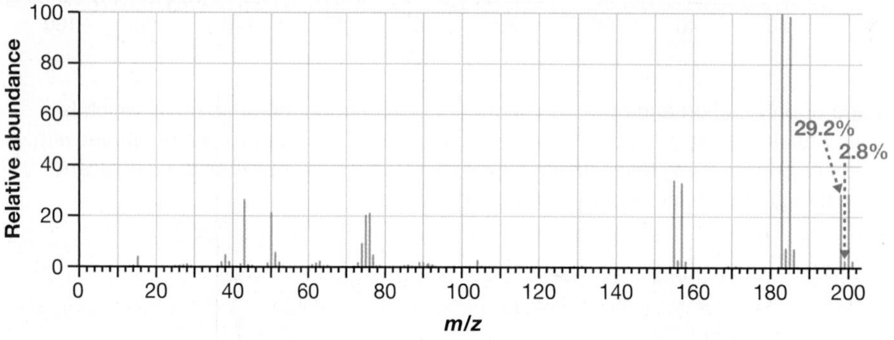
Relative abundance
100
80
60
40
20
0
29.2%
2.8%
0 20 40 60 80 100 120 140 160 180 200
m/z

15.12 Determine the formula of a compound that can give rise to this mass spectrum.

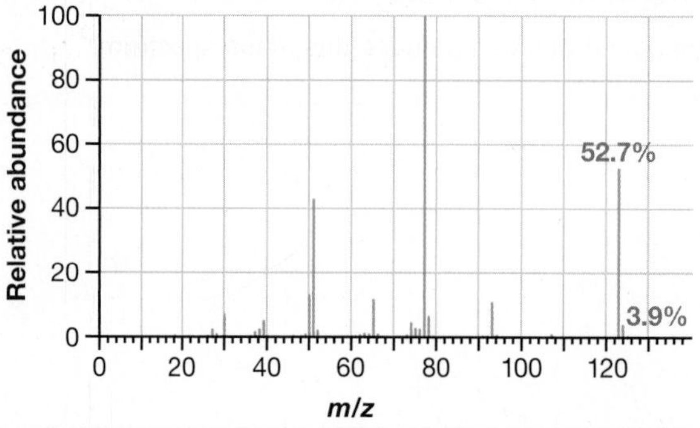
Relative abundance
100
80
60
40
20
0
52.7%
3.9%
0 20 40 60 80 100 120
m/z

15.13 A compound, which is made up of carbon and only one other element, generates the following mass spectrum. Determine a reasonable formula for this compound.

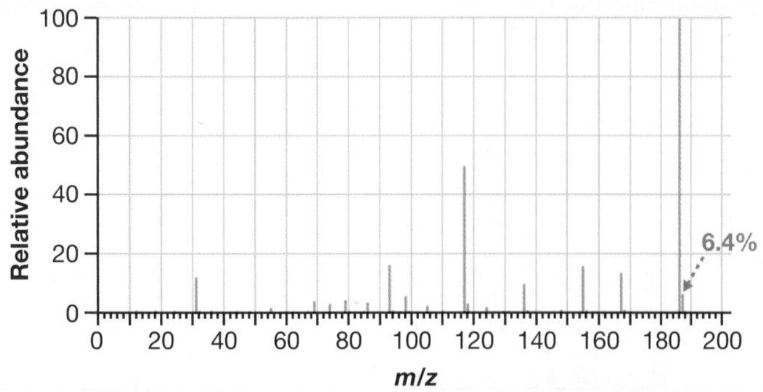

Relative abundance
100
80
60
40
20
0
6.4%
0
20
40
60
80
100
120
140
160
180
200
m/z

Section 15.6 Fragmentation Pathways

15.14 The base peak in the mass spectrum of an alkane, C_7H_{16}, appears at $m/z = 57$. Draw a molecule that is consistent with these data.

15.15 A peak appears at $m/z = 83$ in the mass spectrum of hept-3-ene. Show how the fragmentation of hept-3-ene's molecular ion produces the ion that gives rise to this peak. Why do you think the peak at $m/z = 83$ is smaller than the one at $m/z = 69$?

15.16 The mass spectrum of an alkene, C_8H_{16}, exhibits a peak at $m/z = 41$. Draw two isomers that are consistent with these data.

15.17 Mass spectra were acquired for 1,4-diethylbenzene and 1-methyl-4-propylbenzene. The base peak of spectrum A is at $m/z = 105$ and that of spectrum B is at $m/z = 119$. Match each spectrum to its compound.

15.18 The mass spectrum of an amine ($C_6H_{15}N$) exhibits a base peak at $m/z = 30$. Which of the following amines **A–C** could give rise to that mass spectrum?

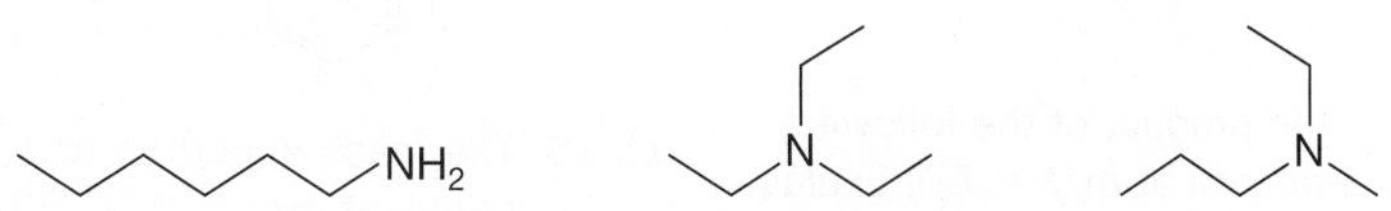

NH2
N
N

A **B** **C**

15.19 The mass spectrum of an alcohol ($C_5H_{12}O$) exhibits a base peak at $m/z = 59$. Is the alcohol most likely pentan-1-ol, pentan-2-ol, or pentan-3-ol? Explain.

15.20 The mass spectrum of a ketone ($C_7H_{14}O$) exhibits a base peak at $m/z = 57$. Is the ketone most likely heptan-2-one, heptan-3-one, or heptan-4-one? Explain.

15.21 The base peak in the mass spectrum of hexanamide appears at $m/z = 59$. Draw the ion that corresponds to this mass peak, and show how it is produced from the molecular ion.

15.22 A mass peak at $m/z = 59$ appears in the mass spectrum of an amide, $C_5H_{11}NO$. Draw the structure of a molecule that is consistent with this result.

Integrated Problems

15.23 Use Table 15-1 (p. 746) to determine the type of heteroatom present in the molecule that generated this mass spectrum.

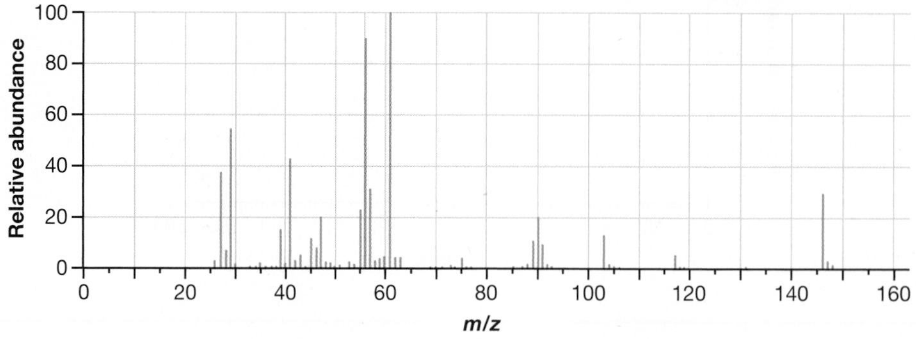

Relative abundance
100
80
60
40
20
0
0
20
40
60
80
100
120
140
160
m/z

15.24 When the following reaction is carried out with oxygen-18-labeled water under acidic conditions, a product is formed whose mass spectrum exhibits an $M^{\dot{+}}$ peak at m/z = 76. Draw the mechanism for this reaction.

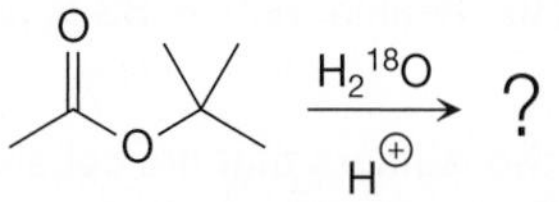

O
O
H2 18O
H⊕
?

15.25 In the mass spectrum of the product of the following reaction, the base peak appears at m/z = 57. Explain this outcome.

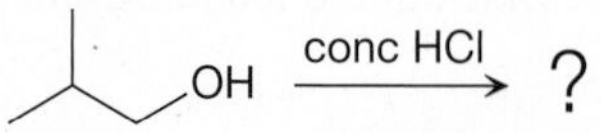

OH
conc HCl
?

15.26 In the mass spectrum of the product of the following reaction, the base peak appears at m/z = 57. Explain this outcome.

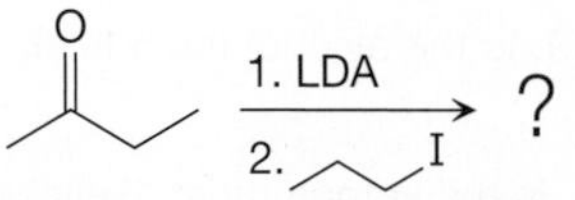

O
1. LDA
2.
I
?

15.27 The mass spectrum of the major product of the following reaction has a major mass peak at m/z = 57. Explain this outcome.

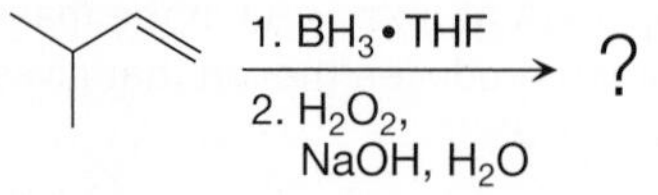

1. BH3 • THF
2. H2O2,
NaOH, H2O
?

15.28 The major product of the following reaction has a mass spectrum in which the base peak appears at m/z = 105. Explain this outcome.

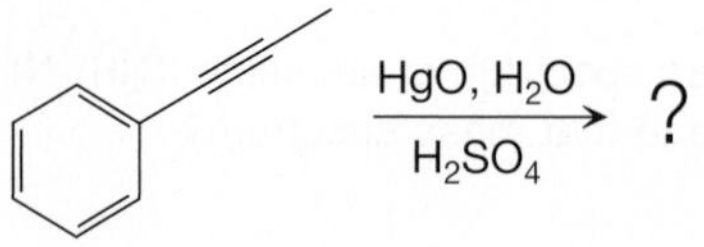

HgO, H2O
H2SO4
?

15.29 The mass spectrum of 1,4-dibromobenzene has mass peaks at m/z = 234, 236, and 238. Explain the m/z values for these mass peaks, and predict their relative intensities.

15.30 A compound that has the following mass spectrum can react with up to two molar equivalents of $H_2(g)$ in the presence of a Ni catalyst. Draw a reasonable structure for this compound.

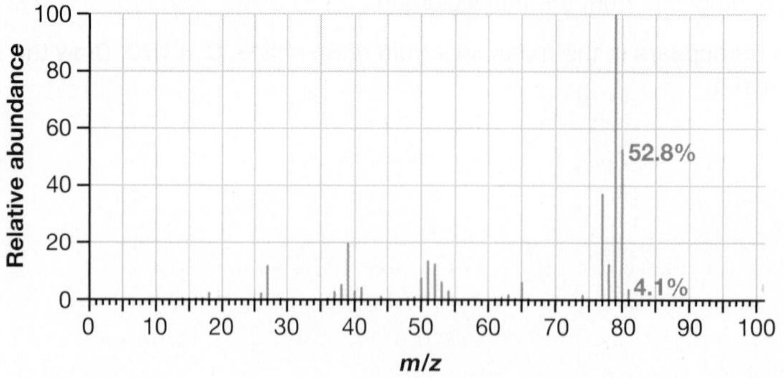

Relative abundance
100
80
60
40
20
0
52.8%
4.1%
0
10
20
30
40
50
60
70
80
90
100
m/z

16

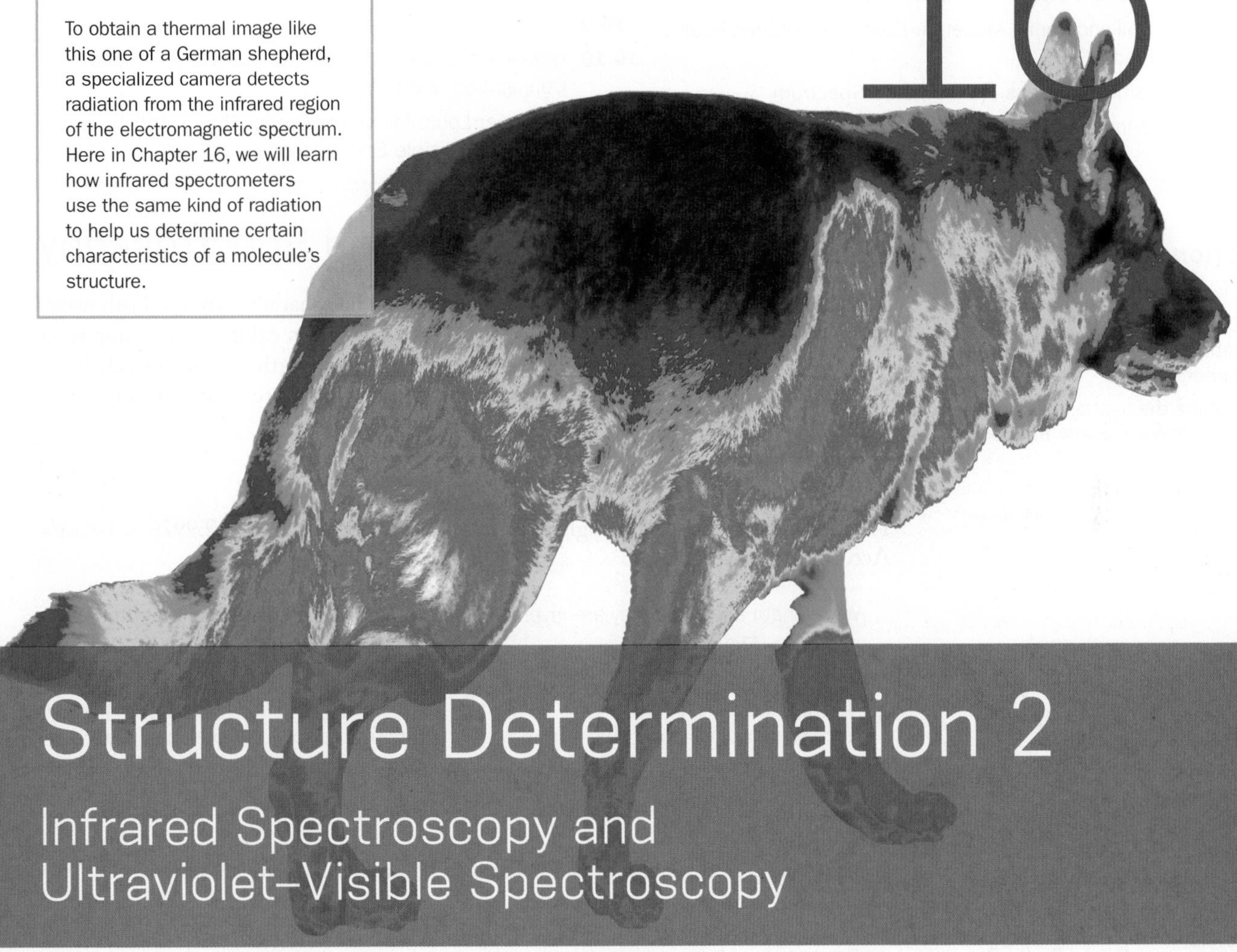

To obtain a thermal image like this one of a German shepherd, a specialized camera detects radiation from the infrared region of the electromagnetic spectrum. Here in Chapter 16, we will learn how infrared spectrometers use the same kind of radiation to help us determine certain characteristics of a molecule's structure.

Structure Determination 2

Infrared Spectroscopy and Ultraviolet–Visible Spectroscopy

Chapter 15 explained that mass spectrometry can be used to determine aspects of a molecule's structure. In a mass spectrometer, a vaporized sample is ionized, and the mass-to-charge ratios and relative abundances of the resulting ions are measured.

Another really valuable tool for determining aspects of molecular structure is **spectroscopy**: the study of the interaction of electromagnetic radiation (i.e. photons) with matter. There are several types of spectroscopy, but we will focus on just three types in this book. Here in Chapter 16 we will learn about *infrared spectroscopy* and *ultraviolet–visible spectroscopy*, and in Chapter 17 we will study *nuclear magnetic resonance spectroscopy*. For each type of spectroscopy, we will first learn the principles behind how a spectrum is generated, and then we will learn how to interpret features of the spectrum to obtain structural characteristics of the molecule.

Chapter Outline

SECTION 16.1 OBJECTIVES

You will be able to:

1. Describe how electromagnetic radiation behaves as both waves and photons.
2. Outline the relationship between a photon's wavelength, frequency, and energy.
3. Explain how an infrared spectrum is acquired and how to recognize an absorption peak in the spectrum.

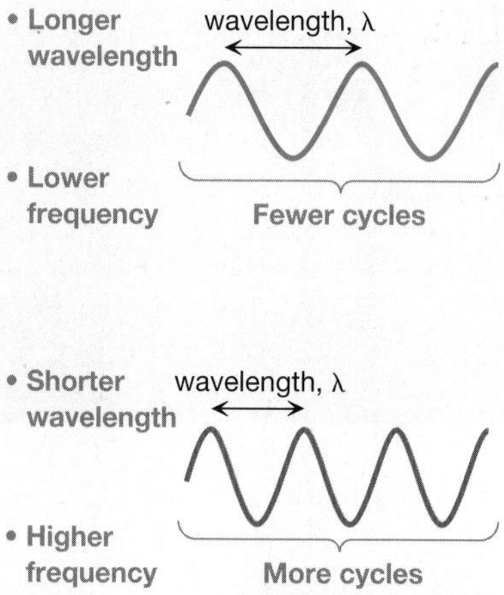

• Longer wavelength
wavelength, λ
• Lower frequency
Fewer cycles
• Shorter wavelength
wavelength, λ
• Higher frequency
More cycles

FIGURE 16-1 Inverse relationship between wavelength and frequency

16.1 An Overview of Infrared Spectroscopy

Electromagnetic radiation is a form of energy that has characteristics of both waves and particles. Behaving as a wave, electromagnetic radiation exhibits oscillating electric and magnetic fields that can be assigned a **wavelength** (λ, the Greek letter lambda) and a **frequency** (ν, the Greek letter nu), which are related according to Equation 16-1:

$$c = \lambda\nu \quad \text{or} \quad \nu = \frac{c}{\lambda} \tag{16-1}$$

Here c stands for the speed of light, which is a universal constant: $c = 2.9979 \times 10^8$ m/s. According to this equation:

> Wavelength and frequency are *inversely* related: As one increases, the other must decrease (**Figure 16-1**).

Behaving as a particle, electromagnetic radiation exists as *photons*. Each photon has a characteristic energy that depends only on its frequency (or wavelength), according to Equation 16-2:

$$E_{\text{photon}} = h\nu_{\text{photon}} = \frac{hc}{\lambda_{\text{photon}}} \tag{16-2}$$

E_{photon} is the energy of a *single* photon, and h is **Planck's constant** (6.626×10^{-34} J·s). Thus:

> The energy of a given photon is *directly* proportional to its frequency: As one increases, so does the other.

The electromagnetic spectrum is divided into regions, as shown in **Figure 16-2**. You are probably most familiar with the visible region, which our eyes detect as colors. The wavelengths of the visible region extend from about 380 nm (violet) to about 740 nm (red).

In **infrared (IR) spectroscopy**, we examine the interaction of a sample with radiation from the IR region of the electromagnetic spectrum (other types of radiation are used for other types of spectroscopy). Infrared radiation, which includes wavelengths from ~800 to ~10^6 nm (1 mm), is invisible to our eyes, but we can feel it as warmth. Infrared radiation that emanates from lamps is used at fast-food restaurants to keep your food warm, and it is responsible for the heat you feel when you stand several meters away from a campfire, or when sunlight shines on your face.

The general setup of a modern IR spectrometer is shown in **Figure 16-3**. A beam of IR radiation (1) from a range of wavelengths (typically about 2500–25,000 nm) is directed toward a beam splitter (2), which transmits half the beam and reflects the other half. The transmitted portion of the beam proceeds toward a fixed mirror (3), and the reflected portion is guided toward a movable mirror (4). Those mirrors completely reflect the two halves of the beam back toward the splitter, and the split beams

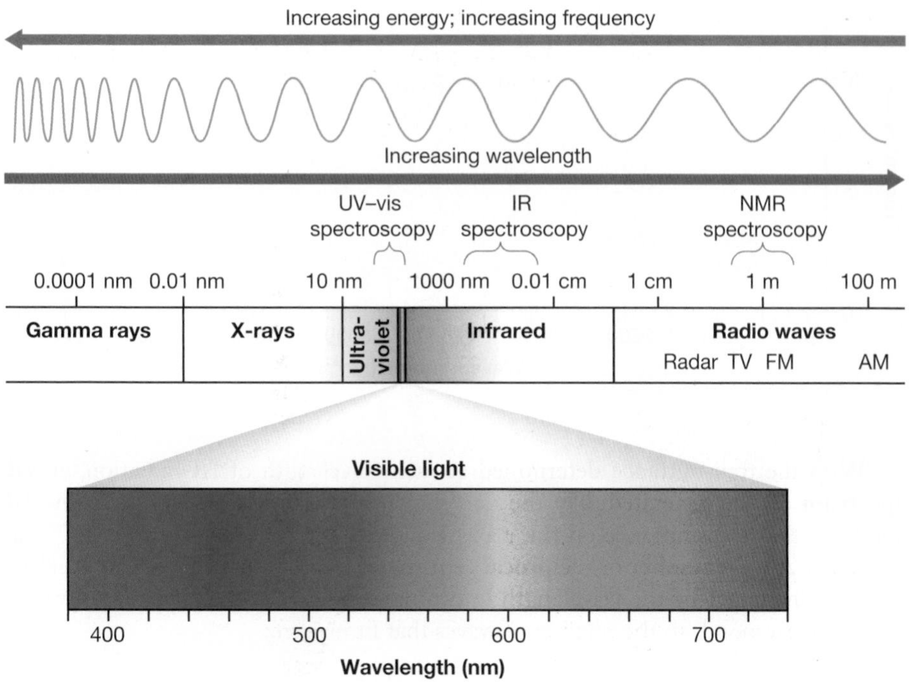

Increasing energy; increasing frequency
Increasing wavelength
UV–vis spectroscopy
IR spectroscopy
NMR spectroscopy
0.0001 nm
0.01 nm
10 nm
1000 nm
0.01 cm
1 cm
1 m
100 m
Gamma rays
X-rays
Ultra-violet
Infrared
Radio waves
Radar
TV
FM
AM
Visible light
400
500
600
700
Wavelength (nm)

FIGURE 16-2 The electromagnetic spectrum Different types of spectroscopy use different wavelengths of electromagnetic radiation.

CONNECTIONS 16.1

Infrared thermometers Infrared thermometers focus the IR radiation emanating from your body onto a component called a thermopile that absorbs the energy. As the thermopile warms up, it produces a voltage that is converted to a temperature readout.

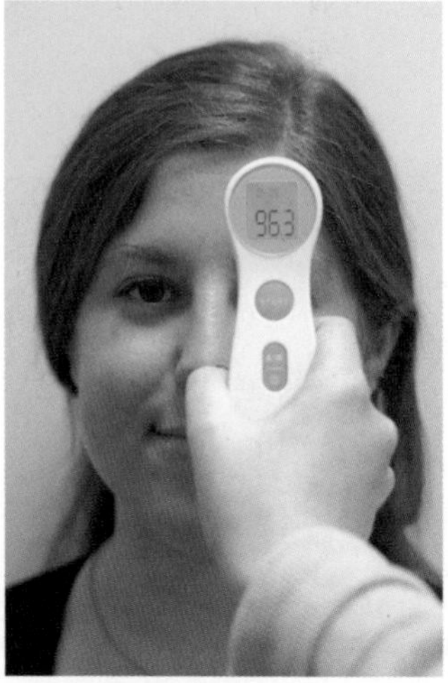

are recombined (5). The recombined beam then travels through the sample (6) and is detected (7).

At the detector, the measured intensity increases and decreases very quickly over time because, over time, the moving mirror changes the way that the waves build up or cancel out (constructive and destructive interference) when the split beams are recombined. By applying a mathematical algorithm to that fluctuating intensity, a computer determines the intensity at each wavelength of radiation (I_{detected}), which is compared to the intensity at that wavelength from the laser source (I_{source}). Measuring I_{detected} and I_{source} allows the **transmittance (%*T*)** to be computed for each wavelength, according to Equation 16-3:

$$\%T = \frac{I_{\text{detected}}}{I_{\text{source}}} \times 100\% \qquad \textbf{(16-3)}$$

Although intensity is a quantity that has units such as watts (W), these units cancel when I_{detected} is divided by I_{source}.

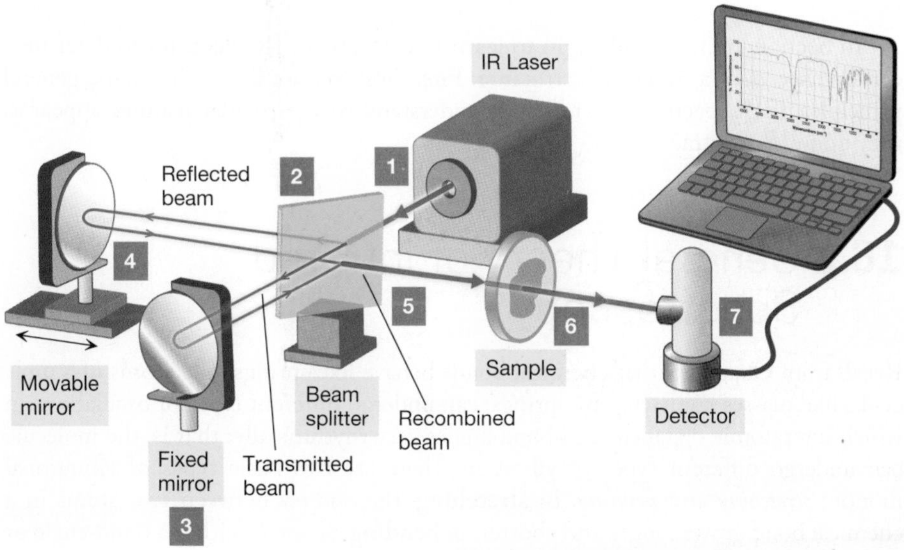

IR Laser
Reflected beam
2
1
4
5
6
7
Movable mirror
Sample
Beam splitter
Recombined beam
Detector
Fixed mirror
Transmitted beam
3

FIGURE 16-3 Setup of an infrared spectrometer A beam of IR radiation from a laser source (1) is directed toward a beam splitter (2). Half the beam continues through the splitter toward a fixed mirror (3). The other half is reflected toward a movable mirror (4). The two split beams are recombined (5) and travel through the sample (6) to the detector (7).

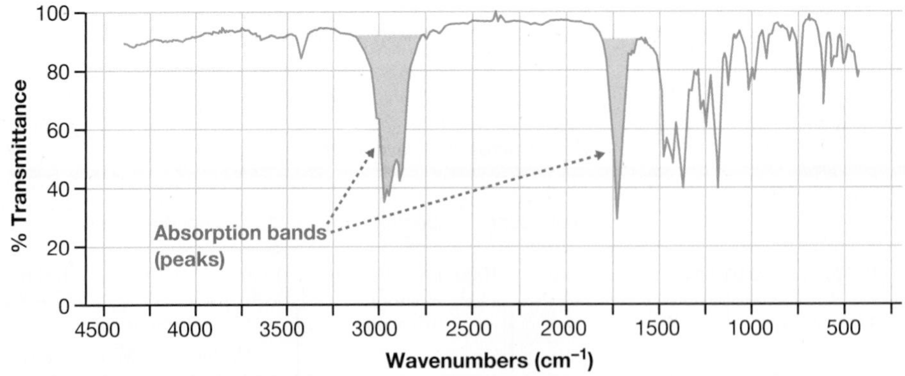
100
80
60
40
20
0
% Transmittance
Absorption bands
(peaks)
4500
4000
3500
3000
2500
2000
1500
1000
500
Wavenumbers (cm⁻¹)

FIGURE 16-4 An infrared spectrum Transmittance on the *y* axis is plotted against wavenumbers (cm^{-1}) on the *x* axis. Near the baseline at the top of the spectrum, most of the IR radiation at a particular frequency makes it through the sample to the detector. Absorption bands (or peaks) appear as dips from the top for frequencies of IR radiation that are absorbed by the sample.

With the transmittance determined at each wavelength of IR radiation, an **IR spectrum** can be generated, like the one shown in **Figure 16-4**. Notice in the IR spectrum that transmittance on the *y* axis is plotted against *wavenumbers* (cm^{-1}) on the *x* axis. A **wavenumber** or **reciprocal centimeter** is a unit of frequency; it is calculated by dividing 1 by the wavelength in centimeters (Eq. 16-4). Physically, a wavenumber corresponds to the number of waves that fit in 1 cm:

$$\text{wavenumbers (in cm}^{-1}) = \frac{1}{\text{wavelength (in cm)}} \qquad \textbf{(16-4)}$$

For historical reasons, wavenumbers increase from right to left along the *x* axis. Commonly, the frequency range in an IR spectrum is from ~400 to ~4000 cm^{-1}.

At frequencies where the transmittance is near 100% (i.e., the baseline), most of the IR radiation makes it through the sample to the detector. Dips in the transmittance represent frequencies of IR radiation that are being absorbed by the sample, so less radiation makes it to the detector. Each such dip is called an **absorption band** or a **peak**. A **strong absorption** is one whose transmittance is near zero (near the bottom of the spectrum), and a **weak absorption** is one whose transmittance is near 100% (near the top of the spectrum). In Figure 16-4, for example, two peaks are highlighted: one at 2961 cm^{-1} and the other at 1717 cm^{-1}.

YOUR TURN 16.1

Two peaks are highlighted in Figure 16-4. Draw arrows to identify two more peaks in that spectrum and estimate their frequencies in wavenumbers.

Answers to Your Turns are in the back of the book.

In Section 16.3, we will begin to learn how to use an IR spectrum to determine certain aspects of a molecule's structure. First, however, we'll examine some general principles of IR spectroscopy, to better understand why particular features appear as they do in IR spectra.

SECTION 16.2 OBJECTIVES

You will be able to:

1. Describe what happens to a molecule's vibrational energy when an IR photon is absorbed.
2. Explain how IR absorption frequencies relate to vibrational frequencies for a molecule.
3. Characterize types of molecular vibration as either stretching or bending.

16.2 General Theory of Infrared Spectroscopy

Recall from Chapter 1 that chemical bonds behave like springs. The atoms of a molecule, like masses connected by springs, can undergo different types of oscillations in which interatomic distances and bond angles vary rhythmically: that is, the molecule can undergo different types of vibration. There are two basic types of vibrational motion: *stretching* and *bending*. In **stretching**, the *distance* between two atoms in a chemical bond grows longer and shorter; in **bending**, an *angle* (either a bond angle or a dihedral angle) becomes larger and smaller.

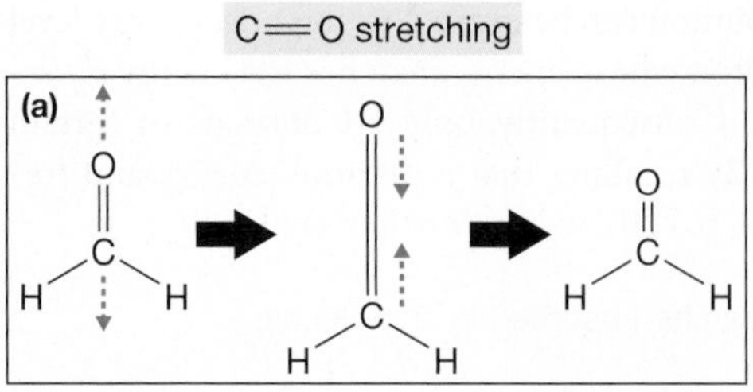
C═O stretching
(a)
O
C
H
H
O
C
H
H
O
C
H
H

FIGURE 16-5 Types of vibration Various types of vibration are shown for a molecule of formaldehyde. (a) The C═O bond stretches and compresses. (b) Both C—H bonds stretch and compress in unison. (c) While one C—H bond stretches, the other compresses. (d) The H—C—H bond angle closes and opens. (e) The two H atoms and the O atom shift downward and upward. *Note*: The magnitudes of displacement are exaggerated for illustration.

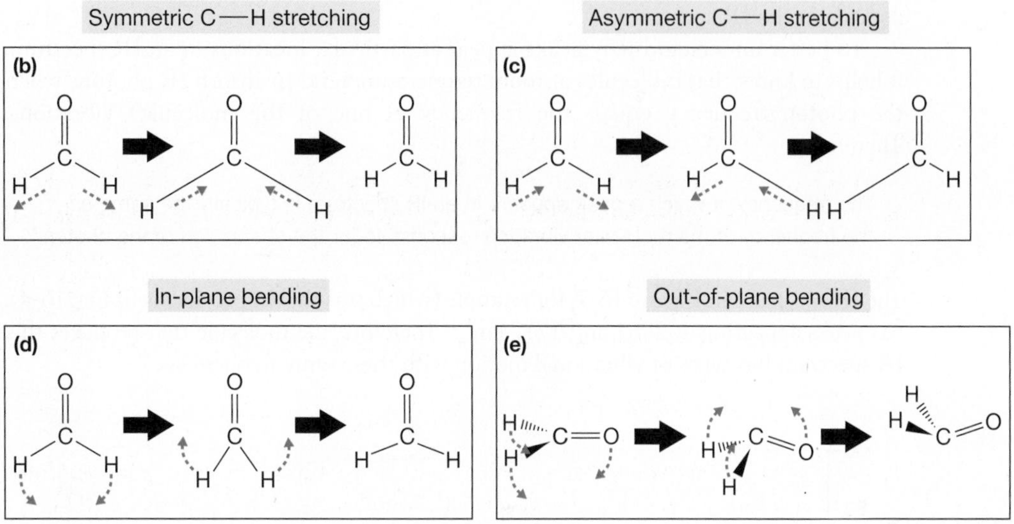
Symmetric C—H stretching
Asymmetric C—H stretching
(b)
(c)
In-plane bending
Out-of-plane bending
(d)
(e)

Figure 16-5 shows several modes of vibration that take place simultaneously in a molecule of formaldehyde ($H_2C{=}O$). The carbonyl (C═O) group undergoes a stretching vibration, as indicated in Figure 16-5a. The C—H bonds can also undergo stretching vibrations, but not independently of each other: two bonds can undergo **symmetric stretching** (Fig. 16-5b) in which the bonds lengthen and shorten together, as well as **asymmetric stretching** (Fig. 16-5c) in which one bond lengthens while the other bond shortens. Two types of bending modes are also shown for formaldehyde: **in-plane** bending (Fig. 16-5d) in which the moving atoms remain in the same plane, and **out-of-plane bending** (Fig. 16-5e) in which the atoms periodically occupy the same plane.

◂ RECALL

When we say that only certain amounts of vibrational energy are allowed, we are saying that each type of vibrational motion is *quantized*. Similarly, as discussed in Section 3.10, electron energies are quantized: each electron is allowed to occupy only certain orbitals with specific energies.

YOUR TURN 16.2

Shown here is another type of vibration that formaldehyde

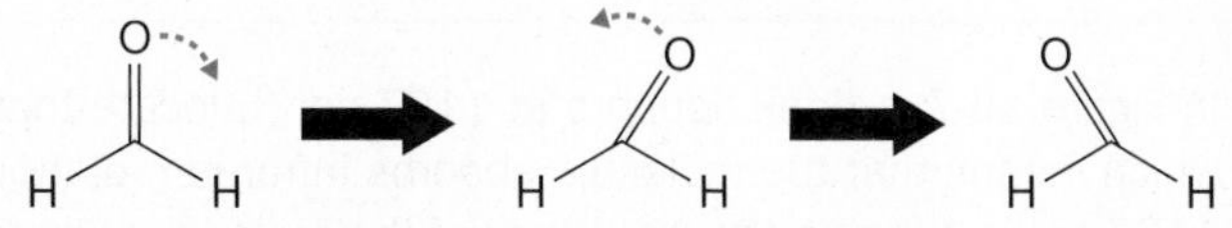

undergoes, one that is not shown in Figure 16-5. Classify this motion as symmetric stretching, asymmetric stretching, or bending.

For each type of vibration, only certain amounts of energy are allowed (see Recall box). This idea is captured in **Figure 16-6**, which represents the energy levels that are available for one type of vibration within a molecule. At room temperature, that vibration is typically likely to be found in its lowest energy state, or the *ground*

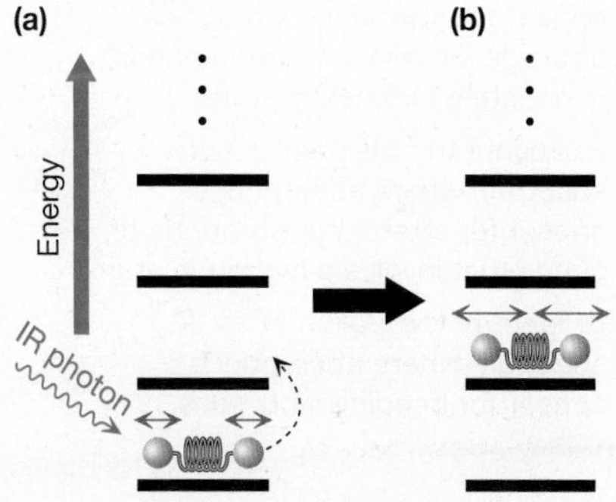
(a)
(b)
Energy
IR photon

FIGURE 16-6 Absorption of an infrared photon The horizontal lines represent the energy levels available to a particular type of vibration. (a) The vibration is in the lowest energy level. The vibration can be promoted to the next energy level when the molecule absorbs a photon that matches the energy difference between the two levels. (b) After absorption of the photon, the vibration is in the next higher energy level.

state, represented by Figure 16-6a. The vibration can be excited to the next energy level (Fig. 16-6b) if the molecule absorbs a photon whose energy matches the energy *difference* between the two levels of vibration. Consequently, only IR photons of certain energies can be absorbed by a molecule. By recalling that a photon's energy and frequency are directly proportional (Eq. 16-2, p. 770), we can further say:

Only IR photons of certain frequencies can be absorbed by a molecule.

At each frequency for which photons are absorbed, transmittance decreases and a peak appears in the IR spectrum.

To better understand why peaks appear at particular locations in an IR spectrum, it helps to know that molecules at room temperature tend to absorb IR photons when the photon frequency equals the frequency of one of the molecule's vibrations. Therefore:

The frequency at which a peak appears in an IR spectrum is typically the same as the frequency of the molecular vibration responsible for the absorption of the photon.

The IR spectrum in **Figure 16-7**, for example (which was shown previously in Fig. 16-4), has peaks appearing at 2961 and 1717 cm^{-1}. Therefore, the molecule that produces this IR spectrum has types of vibrational motion with these same frequencies.

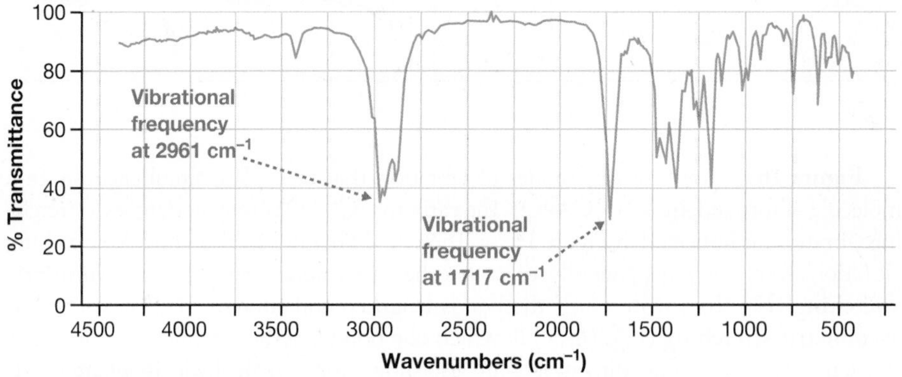

100
80
60
40
20
0
% Transmittance
Vibrational frequency at 2961 cm⁻¹
Vibrational frequency at 1717 cm⁻¹
4500
4000
3500
3000
2500
2000
1500
1000
500
Wavenumbers (cm⁻¹)

FIGURE 16-7 Infrared absorption peaks and vibrational frequencies Each peak corresponds to a vibration of the molecule having the same frequency.

YOUR TURN **16.3**

In Figure 16-7, a peak appears at 1167 cm^{-1} (locate that peak for yourself), which means that the molecule absorbs infrared radiation at a frequency of 1167 cm^{-1}. What is the frequency of the molecular vibration responsible for that absorption? Explain.

SECTION 16.3 OBJECTIVES

You will be able to:

1. Distinguish the regions of an IR spectrum where absorptions appear for stretching vibrations of single, double, and triple bonds connecting two heavy atoms.
2. Locate the region of an IR spectrum where absorptions appear for stretching vibrations of bonds that involve a hydrogen atom.
3. Identify the region of an IR spectrum where absorptions appear for bending vibrations.

16.3 Location of Peaks in an Infrared Spectrum

One of the greatest advantages of IR spectroscopy is that the frequency of a particular type of vibration does not change dramatically from one molecule to another. Thus:

Each type of vibration is typically found within a characteristic range of frequencies.

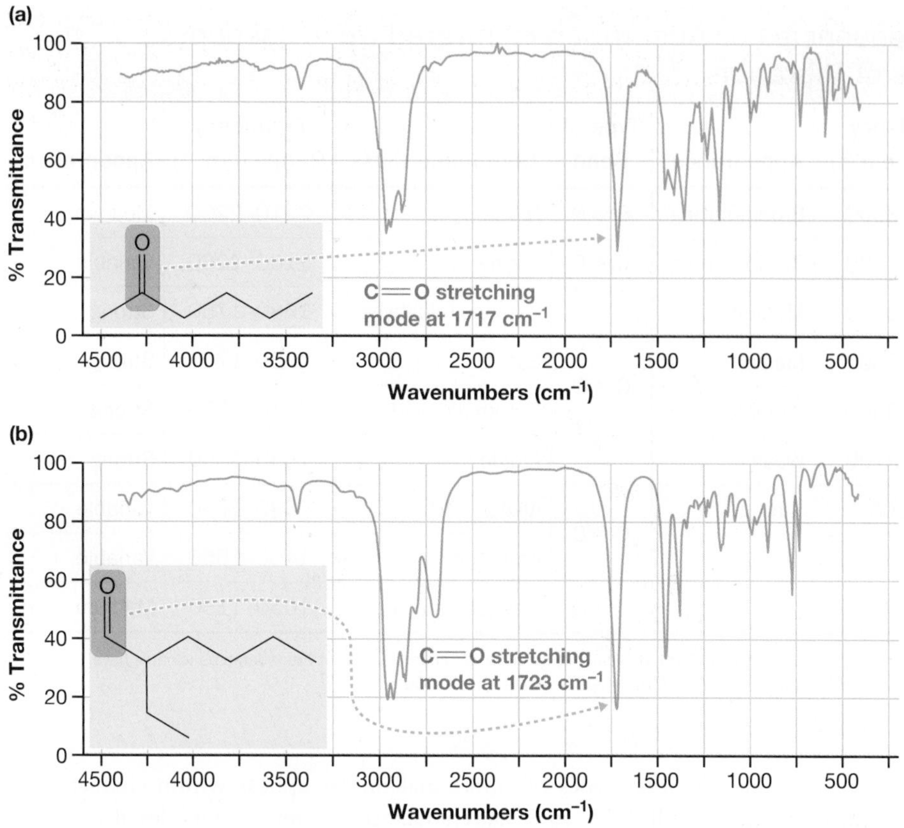
(a)
% Transmittance
C═O stretching mode at 1717 cm⁻¹
Wavenumbers (cm⁻¹)
(b)
% Transmittance
C═O stretching mode at 1723 cm⁻¹
Wavenumbers (cm⁻¹)

FIGURE 16-8 Characteristic absorption frequency of the C═O stretching mode of vibration The IR spectra of (a) hexan-2-one and (b) 2-ethylhexanal are shown. Although the molecules belong to different compound classes (hexan-2-one is a ketone and 2-ethylhexanal is an aldehyde), the absorptions corresponding to the C═O stretching modes are quite similar.

For example, compare the IR spectra of hexan-2-one and 2-ethylhexanal, shown in **Figure 16-8**. Each compound contains a C═O bond: hexan-2-one as part of a ketone and 2-ethylhexanal as part of an aldehyde. Even though the molecules belong to different compound classes, the absorptions corresponding to the C═O stretching frequencies are quite similar, appearing at 1717 and 1723 cm^{-1}, respectively.

Knowing that absorptions by certain vibrations appear within characteristic frequency ranges, we can use IR spectroscopy to obtain structural information about a molecule. For example, on the basis of the spectra in Figure 16-8, we can safely say that, in the IR spectrum of an unknown compound, the appearance of a strong, sharp peak around 1720 cm^{-1} strongly suggests that the compound contains a carbonyl (C═O) group.

YOUR TURN 16.4

Benzaldehyde, whose IR spectrum is shown here, contains a C═O bond. Identify the absorption that corresponds to the C═O bond.

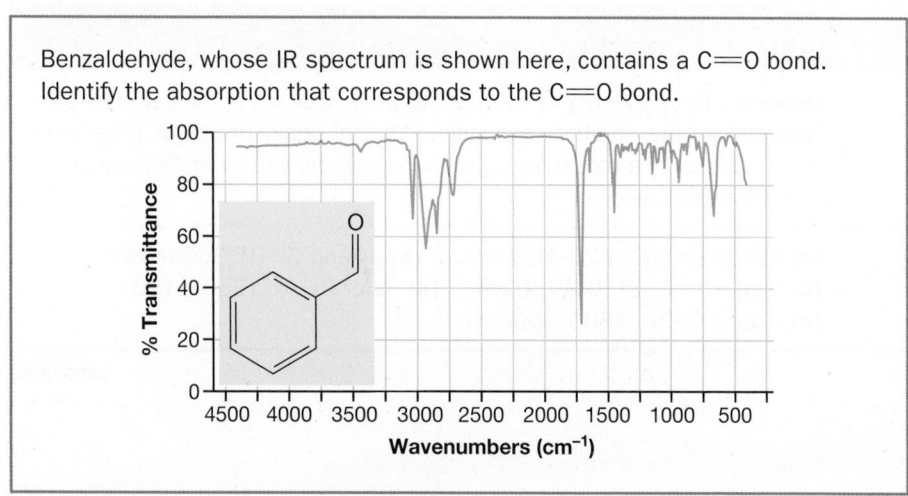

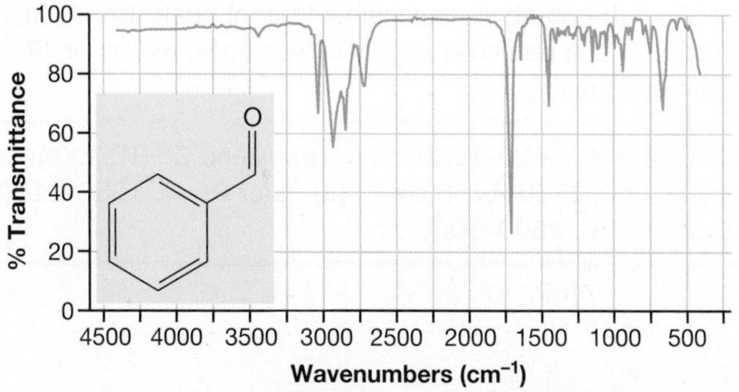
% Transmittance
Wavenumbers (cm⁻¹)

TABLE 16-1 **Characteristic Frequencies of Absorption in Infrared Spectroscopy: Stretching Modes of Vibration**

Type of Bond	Compound Class	Frequency Range (cm^{-1})	Appearance[a]	Type of Bond	Compound Class	Frequency Range (cm^{-1})	Appearance[a]
O—H	Alcohol and phenol	3200–3600	Broad, strong	C≡N	Nitrile	2210–2260	Medium
	Carboxylic acid	2500–3200	Broad, strong	C≡C	Alkyne	2100–2260	Variable
N—H	Amine	3300–3500	Medium	C=O	Ketones/aldehydes	1680–1750	Strong
	Amide	3350–3500	Medium		Esters	1730–1750	Strong
C—H	Alkane	2800–3000	Variable		Carboxylic acid	1710–1780	Strong
	Alkene	3000–3100	Weak		Amide	1630–1690	Strong
	Alkyne	~3300	Strong	C=C	Alkene	1620–1680	Variable
	Aldehyde	2720 and 2820	Strong		Aromatic	1450–1550	Variable
				C—O	Alcohol, ester, ether	1050–1150	Medium

[a]Peak intensities are characterized as *strong* (%*T* near 0%), *medium* (%*T* near 50%), or *weak* (%*T* near 100%); absorptions that are labeled as *variable* have intensities that depend on the molecule. Peak widths are characterized as *broad* if the range is greater than ~200 cm^{-1}.

Absorptions for other types of vibrational modes appear within characteristic frequency ranges as well. Table 16-1 lists characteristic stretching modes of vibration. (We examine some bending modes of vibration in Section 16.8). Notice that the frequencies of these stretching modes range from ~1000 to ~3500 cm^{-1} (bending modes generally occur from ~500 to ~1500 cm^{-1}).

SOLVED PROBLEM **16.1**

How to predict the locations of peaks in an IR spectrum

Break It Down **Use Table 16-1 to estimate the frequencies where IR absorption peaks would appear for each of the stretching vibrations indicated.**

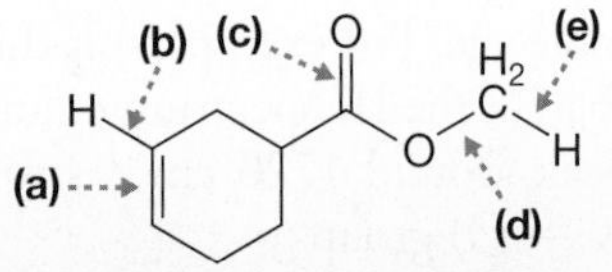
(a)
(b)
(c)
(d)
(e)
H
O
O
H_2
C
H

Think	Solve
How does the frequency for a particular IR peak relate to a molecule's vibrations?	Generally, the frequency at which an IR peak appears is the same as the frequency of the vibration responsible for that peak. Therefore, if we know the frequency of a particular vibration, we should expect an IR peak at that same frequency.
Find each type of bond and the corresponding vibrational frequency in Table 16-1.	**(a)** Alkene C=C, 1620–1680 cm^{-1}; **(b)** alkene C—H, 3000–3100 cm^{-1}; **(c)** ester C=O, 1730–1750 cm^{-1}; **(d)** ester C—O, 1050–1150 cm^{-1}; **(e)** alkane C—H, 2800–3000 cm^{-1}.

(continued)

Try It For each of the following molecules, estimate the frequencies where IR absorption peaks would appear for the stretching vibrations indicated.

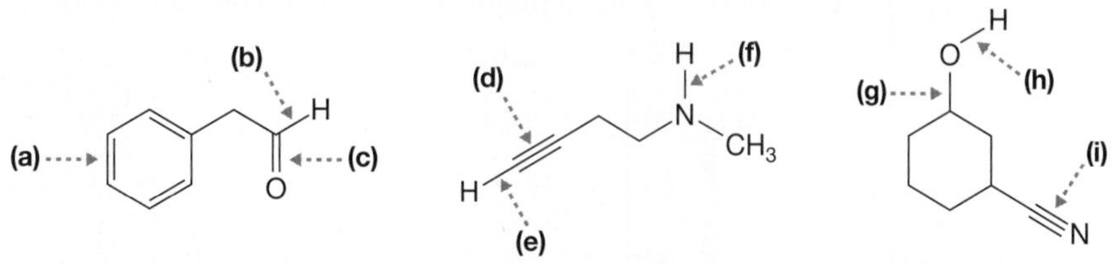

(a)
(b)
H
(c)
O
(d)
H
(e)
H
(f)
N
CH3
(g)
O
H
(h)
(i)
N

Answers to all Try It exercises can be found in the Solutions Manual.

There are a number of trends in Table 16-1 worth noting. One defines the major regions in which absorptions appear. These regions, shown in **Figure 16-9**, are as follows:

The Major Regions in an IR Spectrum

- Absorptions from stretching vibrations of Q—H bonds (where Q is a "heavy" atom such as C, N, or O) occur in the region between ~2500 and 4000 cm^{-1}.
- Absorptions from stretching vibrations of triple bonds (C≡C or C≡N) appear between 2000 and 2500 cm^{-1}.
- Absorptions from stretching vibrations of double bonds appear between ~1500 and 2000 cm^{-1}.
- Absorptions from stretching vibrations of single bonds between two heavy atoms appear between ~1000 and 1500 cm^{-1}.
- Absorptions from bending vibrations appear below 1500 cm^{-1}.

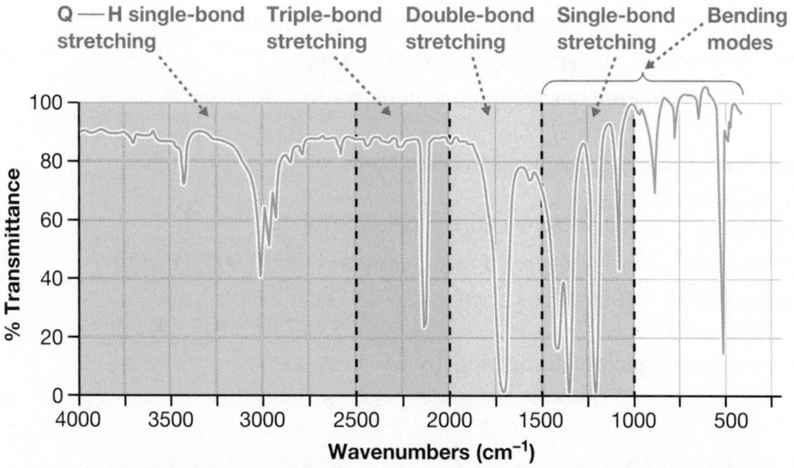

Q—H single-bond stretching
Triple-bond stretching
Double-bond stretching
Single-bond stretching
Bending modes
100
80
60
40
20
0
% Transmittance
4000
3500
3000
2500
2000
1500
1000
500
Wavenumbers (cm−1)

FIGURE 16-9 Major regions of absorption in infrared spectroscopy Absorptions corresponding to the stretching frequencies of O—H, N—H, and C—H bonds appear between 2500 and 4000 cm^{-1}. Those for triple bonds generally appear between 2000 and 2500 cm^{-1}. Those for double bonds generally appear between 1500 and 2000 cm^{-1}. Those for single bonds not involving hydrogen appear between 1000 and 1500 cm^{-1}. Absorptions corresponding to bending modes appear below 1500 cm^{-1}.

YOUR TURN **16.5**

The infrared spectrum of an unknown compound is shown here. Determine whether the molecule (a) contains a hydrogen atom attached to a heavy atom (C, N, or O); (b) has a double bond; and (c) has a triple bond.

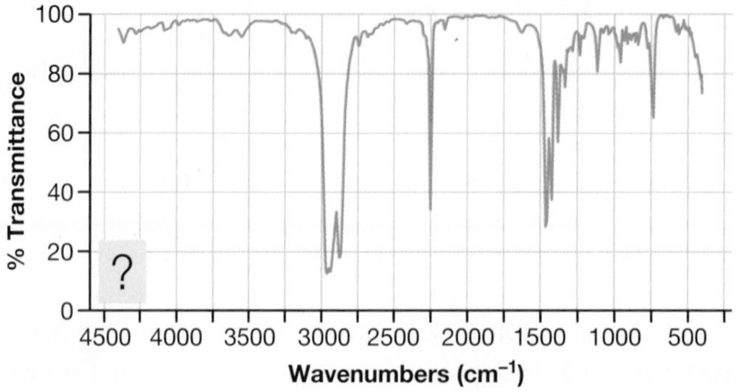

100
80
60
40
20
0
% Transmittance
?
4500 4000 3500 3000 2500 2000 1500 1000 500
Wavenumbers (cm⁻¹)

The region below ~1400 cm^{-1} is called the **fingerprint region**. Numerous peaks typically appear in this region, even for relatively simple molecules, and many of those peaks overlap. Therefore, we focus primarily on identifying absorptions above ~1400 cm^{-1}. Suffice it to say, however, that the collection of peaks in a fingerprint region is unique for each molecular species, just as every human has unique fingerprints.

YOUR TURN **16.6**

What types of vibrations are primarily responsible for IR peaks in the fingerprint region?

Two other trends that are useful to know involve bonds between hydrogen and a heavy atom—that is, absorptions that appear in the region above 2500 cm^{-1}. First, there is a periodic-table trend for these stretching frequencies:

- C—H stretches appear between ~2700 and 3300 cm^{-1}.
- N—H stretches appear around 3300–3500 cm^{-1}.
- Alcohol O—H stretches creep up a bit higher to ~3600 cm^{-1}.

Second, there is a trend involving hybridization for C—H stretches:

- Alkane (sp^3) C—H stretches appear below 3000 cm^{-1}.
- Alkene (sp^2) C—H stretches appear between ~3000 and 3100 cm^{-1}.
- Alkyne (sp) C—H stretches appear at ~3300 cm^{-1}.

These trends are explained in Section 16.4.

SECTION 16.4 OBJECTIVES

You will be able to:

1. Explain why the IR absorptions for stretching vibrations of bonds between two heavy atoms have frequencies that increase in the order: single < double < triple.
2. Account for the very high frequencies of IR absorptions for stretching vibrations of bonds involving hydrogen.
3. Explain why the IR absorption for a C—H stretching vibration depends on the hybridization of carbon.

16.4 The Ball-and-Spring Model for Explaining Infrared Peak Locations

To interpret an IR spectrum, you must be able to determine the types of bonds represented by individual IR peaks. Table 16-1 (p. 776) shows these correlations for several IR peaks, but why should those peaks appear at the frequencies they do? To begin to answer this question, recall that an IR peak's frequency is generally equal to the frequency of the molecular vibration that is responsible for producing the peak. Therefore, if we understand the factors that control the vibrational frequencies of molecules, we can make sense out of the information in Table 16-1.

FIGURE 16-10 Vibrational frequency, mass, and spring stiffness (a) Masses connected by a spring undergo vibration. (b) With a lighter mass, the vibrational frequency increases. (c) With a stiffer (stronger) spring, the vibrational frequency increases, too.

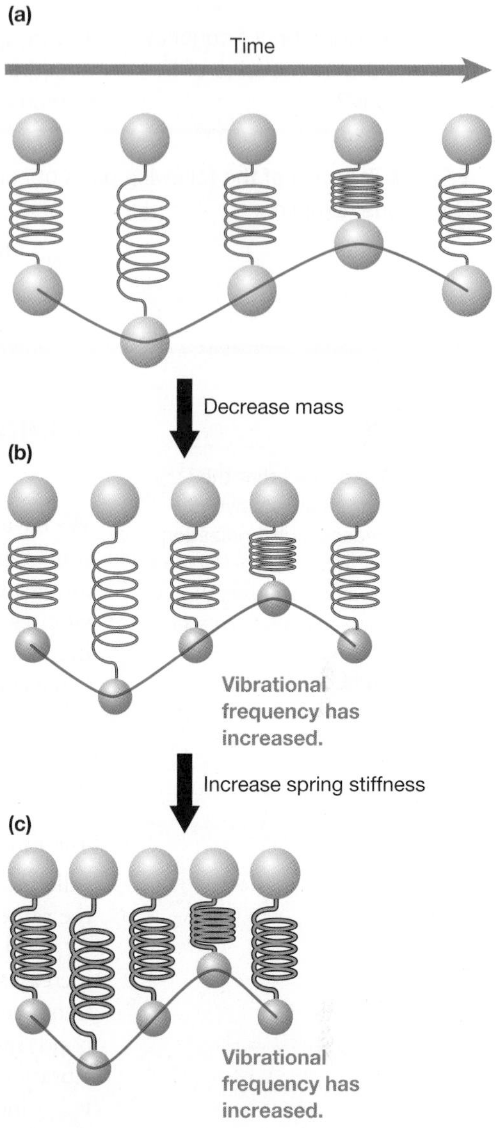
(a)
Time
Decrease mass
(b)
Vibrational frequency has increased.
Increase spring stiffness
(c)
Vibrational frequency has increased.

We simplify the picture of molecular vibrations by considering the *ball-and-spring model*, which treats bonds simply as springs and treats atoms simply as balls with particular masses (**Figure 16-10**). Two major variables impact the vibrational frequency in this model: the *masses* of the balls and the *spring stiffness* (how much the spring resists being stretched or compressed). More specifically:

For a ball-and-spring model, vibrational frequency increases
- as the masses decrease (Fig. 16-10, a → b).
- as the stiffness of the spring increases (Fig. 16-10, b → c).

The dependence of the ball-and-spring's frequency on mass explains why C—H, N—H, and O—H stretches have such high frequencies: The H atom is *very light*. The dependence of the ball-and-spring's frequency on spring stiffness explains why the vibrational frequency between atoms of comparable mass decreases in the order: triple bonds > double bonds > single bonds. Triple bonds tend to be stronger and stiffer than double bonds, just as double bonds tend to be stronger and stiffer than single bonds.

The generalization about spring stiffness also accounts for the relationship between the C—H stretching frequency and the hybridization of C. We learned in Section 3.9 (see Recall box, p. 780) that the C—H bond strength increases as the *s*-character of the C atom's hybridization increases: alkane (sp^3) C—H < alkene (sp^2) C—H < alkyne (sp) C—H. The stretching frequency for these bonds increases in the same order.

SOLVED PROBLEM **16.2**

How to use the ball-and-spring model to predict relative IR frequencies

Break It Down Deuterium (D), an isotope of hydrogen, has roughly twice the mass of hydrogen, but the two have nearly identical chemical properties. A C—H bond, therefore, has essentially the same strength as a C—D bond. Which vibrational mode, a C—H stretch or a C—D stretch, absorbs at a higher frequency in the IR region? Explain.

Think	Solve
Considering the ball-and-spring model, is the spring stiffness the same for the two cases? If not, how does spring stiffness control vibrational frequency?	The ball-and-spring model associates bond strength with spring stiffness. If C—H and C—D bonds are essentially identical in strength, each one's spring stiffness must be about the same, too. Spring stiffness, therefore, does not come into play.
Are the masses the same? If not, how do differences in mass control vibrational frequency?	The masses are substantially different, as D has roughly twice the mass as H. Because D is proportionally much heavier than H, a C—D vibration has a substantially lower frequency than a C—H vibration.

(continued)

How does vibrational frequency relate to the frequencies of IR absorptions?	The frequency of vibration is the same as the IR photon frequency that can be absorbed, so a C—D stretch must absorb lower-frequency photons than a C—H stretch.

Try It For each of the following pairs of compounds, indicate which CN stretching mode absorbs the higher-frequency IR photons. Explain.

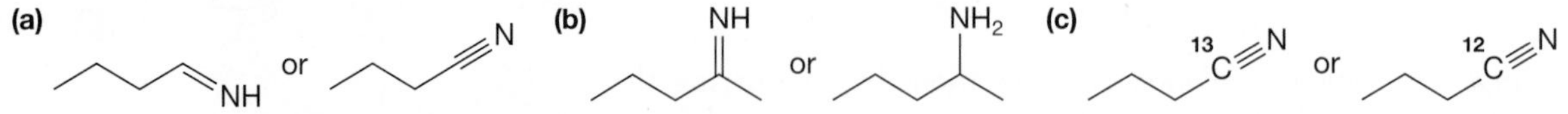

(a)
NH
or
N
(b)
NH
or
NH2
(c)
13
C
N
or
12
C
N

◀ RECALL

Section 3.9 explained that the *s*-character of an atom's hybrid orbitals increases as hybridization goes from sp^3 to sp^2 to sp. Because *s* orbitals are more compact than *p* orbitals in the same shell, greater *s*-character leads to shorter and stronger bonds.

16.4a A Deeper Look: Hooke's Law and IR Spectroscopy

We have applied a simple ball-and-spring model to explain the relative frequencies for some types of stretching vibrations. You might remember from physics that the behavior of such a system is described by **Hooke's law**. According to Hooke's law, the spring vibrates at a particular frequency (ν_{spring}) that depends on the masses (m_1 and m_2) of the objects connected to the spring (in this case, the two atoms) and on the spring's **force constant (*k*)**, as shown in Equation 16-5:

$$\nu_{spring} = \sqrt{\frac{k}{\left(\frac{m_1 m_2}{m_1 + m_2}\right)}} = \sqrt{\frac{k}{\mu}} \qquad (16\text{-}5)$$

The force constant is often thought of as the spring stiffness. The quantity $\frac{m_1 m_2}{(m_1 + m_2)}$ is called the **reduced mass (μ)**. When one mass increases while the other mass remains the same, the reduced mass increases, too.

Notice that the force constant, *k*, is in the numerator, so ν_{spring} increases as *k* increases. This agrees with the trend we observed previously about the vibrational frequency involving two heavy atoms bonded together: the strength and stiffness of bonds increases in the order single bonds < double bonds < triple bonds, and so does vibrational frequency. Notice, too, that since the reduced mass μ is in the denominator, ν_{spring} increases as μ decreases. Again this agrees with our previous observation that the vibrational frequency increases when the masses are lighter.

In addition to using the ball-and-spring model to reproduce qualitative trends, we can apply the model quantitatively. For example, let's first compare the O—H and O—C stretching frequencies, which involve atoms of very different masses. If we assume that the two bonds have the same bond strength (in actuality, the O—H bond is about 25% stronger), then we would take their spring constants to be the same. Their reduced masses, on the other hand, are very different:

$$\mu_{O\text{-}H} = \frac{(16\ u)(1\ u)}{16\ u + 1\ u} = \frac{16\ u^2}{17\ u} = 0.94\ u \qquad \mu_{O\text{-}C} = \frac{(16\ u)(12\ u)}{16\ u + 12\ u} = \frac{192\ u^2}{28\ u} = 6.9\ u$$

The ratio of the two frequencies would then be calculated as follows:

$$\frac{\nu_{O\text{-}H\ (Hooke)}}{\nu_{O\text{-}C\ (Hooke)}} = \sqrt{\frac{\left(\frac{k}{\mu_{O\text{-}H}}\right)}{\left(\frac{k}{\mu_{O\text{-}C}}\right)}} = \sqrt{\frac{\mu_{O\text{-}C}}{\mu_{O\text{-}H}}} = \sqrt{\frac{6.9\ u}{0.94\ u}} = 2.7$$

This ratio is not very different than the one calculated from the actual frequencies listed in Table 16-1. If we use 3400 cm^{-1} for the midrange of an alcohol O—H and 1100 cm^{-1} for the midrange of an alcohol O—C, we calculate:

$$\frac{\nu_{\text{O-H (actual)}}}{\nu_{\text{O-C (actual)}}} = \frac{3400\ \text{cm}^{-1}}{1100\ \text{cm}^{-1}} = 3.1$$

Now let's compare the O—C and O=C stretching frequencies, for which μ is taken to be the same but k is substantially different. If we assume that k is proportional to the respective average bond strengths (720 kJ/mol for C=O and 351 kJ/mol for C—O), then Hooke's law would predict the ratio of the two frequencies to be:

$$\frac{\nu_{\text{O=C (Hooke)}}}{\nu_{\text{O-C (Hooke)}}} = \sqrt{\frac{\left(\frac{k_{\text{O=C}}}{\mu}\right)}{\left(\frac{k_{\text{O-C}}}{\mu}\right)}} = \sqrt{\frac{(\text{constant})(720\ \text{kJ/mol})}{(\text{constant})(351\ \text{kJ/mol})}} = 1.4$$

Again, this ratio is not very different than the one calculated from the actual frequencies listed in Table 16-1. Using 1715 cm^{-1} for the midrange of a ketone/aldehyde O=C and 1100 cm^{-1} for the midrange of an alcohol O—C, we calculate:

$$\frac{\nu_{\text{O=C (actual)}}}{\nu_{\text{O-C (actual)}}} = \frac{1715\ \text{cm}^{-1}}{1100\ \text{cm}^{-1}} = 1.6$$

YOUR TURN **16.7**

(a) Using Hooke's law and the simple ball-and-spring model, estimate the ratio of the C—H and C—D stretching frequencies. **(b)** The actual alkane C—D stretching frequency is roughly 2150 cm^{-1}. How does the estimate from the ball-and-spring model compare to the actual ratio of the two frequencies?

16.5 Intensities of Peaks in an Infrared Spectrum

SECTION 16.5 OBJECTIVES

You will be able to:

1. Explain why the IR absorptions for some bonds are intense and others are not.
2. Describe how the symmetry of an alkene or alkyne controls the absorption intensity of a C=C or C≡C stretch.

As shown in Table 16-1 (p. 776), some absorptions have characteristically strong intensities, whereas others are typically weak. Still others are variable, depending on the specific molecules in which they are found. What explains the intensity of a given absorption peak? Quantum mechanics tells us that a photon is more likely to be absorbed if a particular vibrational mode causes oscillations in the magnitude or orientation of the molecule's dipole. In turn, dipole oscillations tend to be more pronounced for a stretching vibration when the bond is polar. Therefore:

- A stretching mode of vibration involving a highly polar bond (such as C=O or O—H) tends to have a strong IR absorption.
- A stretching mode of vibration involving a nonpolar bond (such as C=C) tends to have a:
  - weak or nonexistent IR absorption if the two portions connected by the bond are similar.
  - medium intensity IR absorption if the two portions connected by the bond are dissimilar.

To illustrate the second point, examine the IR spectra of hept-1-ene and hept-3-ene in **Figure 16-11** (next page). In the IR spectrum of hept-1-ene (Fig. 16-11a), the C=C stretching band at 1643 cm^{-1} is moderately intense because the two portions of the molecule connected by the C=C bond (i.e., the CH_2 and C_6H_{12} portions) are rather dissimilar. The C=C stretch is essentially absent in the spectrum of hept-3-ene (Fig. 16-11b), however, because the C_3H_6 and C_4H_8 portions connected by the C=C bond are quite similar.

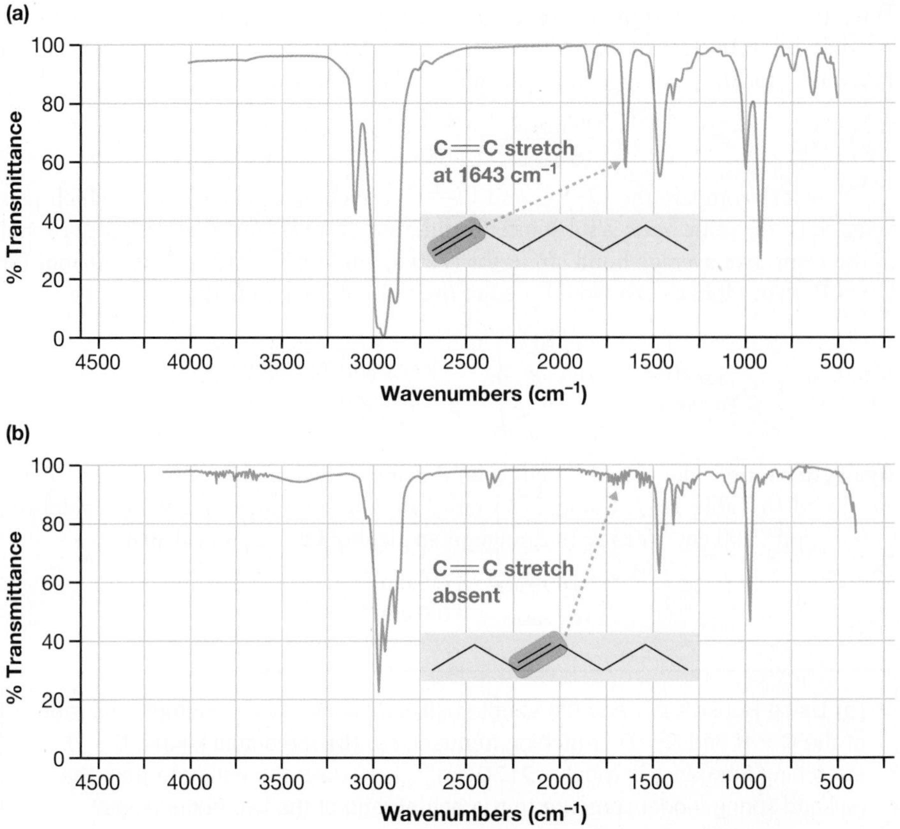

(a)
% Transmittance
C=C stretch
at 1643 cm⁻¹
Wavenumbers (cm⁻¹)
(b)
C=C stretch
absent

FIGURE 16-11 Molecular symmetry and intensity of stretching absorptions (a) IR spectrum of hept-1-ene, illustrating the presence of the C=C stretching band. Because of the considerable lack of symmetry about the C=C double bond, the absorption is moderately intense. (b) IR spectrum of hept-3-ene. The C=C stretching band is essentially absent because of the greater symmetry about the C=C double bond.

YOUR TURN 16.8

Based on the intensities of the C=C stretching bands, match each of the compounds shown here with its IR spectrum.

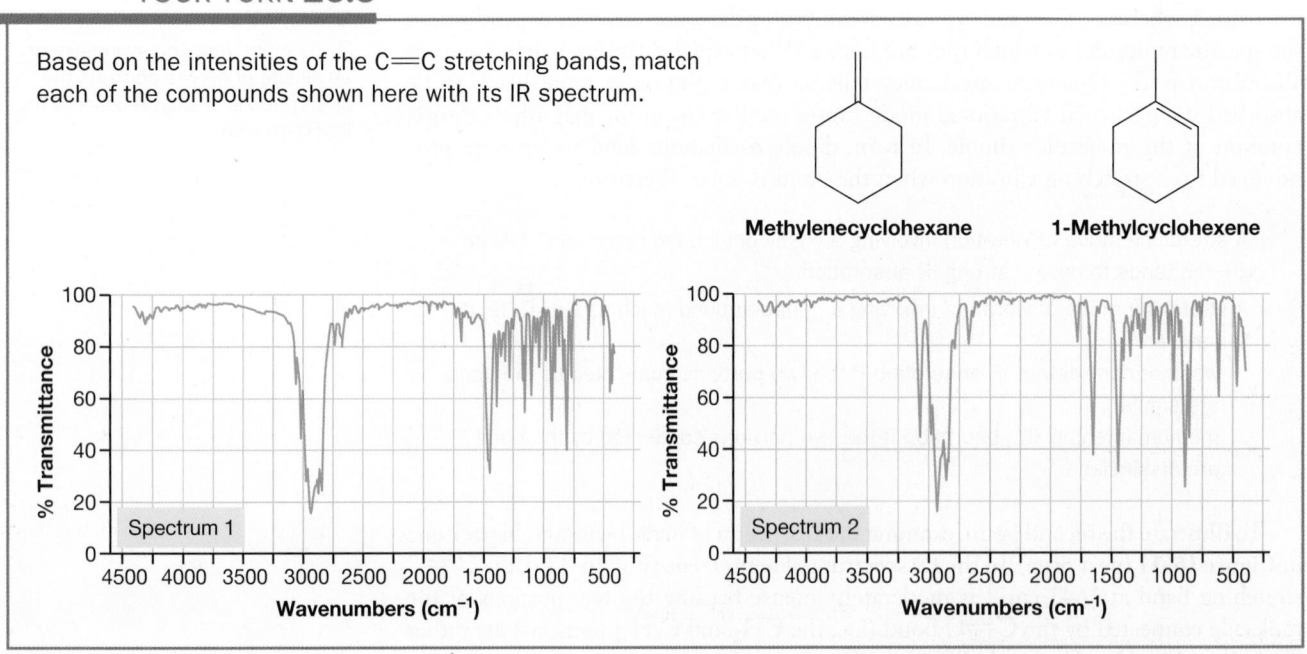

Methylenecyclohexane **1-Methylcyclohexene**

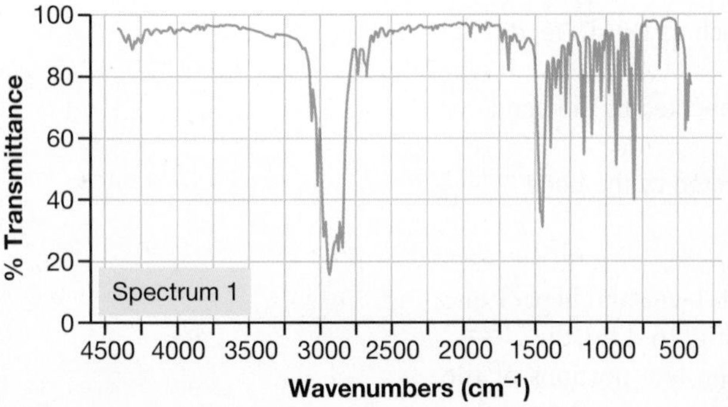

% Transmittance
Spectrum 1
Wavenumbers (cm⁻¹)

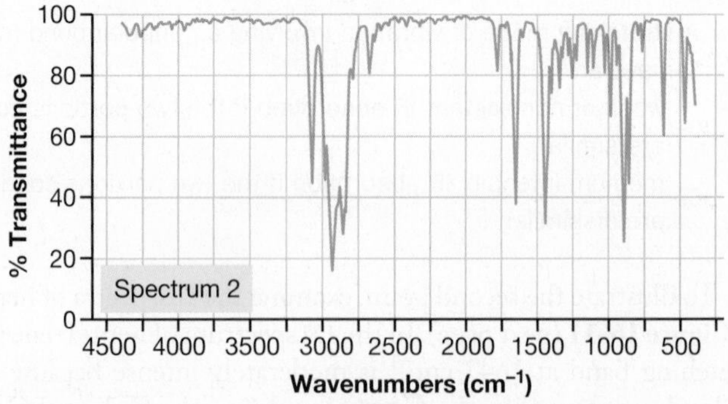

% Transmittance
Spectrum 2
Wavenumbers (cm⁻¹)

16.6 Some Important Infrared Stretches

SECTION 16.6 OBJECTIVES

You will be able to:

1. Quickly identify prominent absorptions in an IR spectrum, such as O—H and C═O stretches.
2. Use appropriate IR absorption peaks to distinguish an alcohol from a carboxylic acid, an NH group from an NH_2 group, an alkene from an aromatic ring, an alkyne from a nitrile, and an aldehyde from a ketone.

Even a simple organic molecule can have dozens of peaks in its IR spectrum. To interpret an IR spectrum, where should we begin? It is usually best to begin by looking for the presence or absence of peaks in the region above ~1400 cm^{-1} (i.e., above the fingerprint region), where absorptions appear for several characteristic stretching vibrations. The region above ~1400 cm^{-1} is generally uncrowded, making it relatively easy to spot important peaks. Then, if the information provided by the spectrum above ~1400 cm^{-1} needs to be clarified, we can look for the presence or absence of specific peaks in the fingerprint region.

The sections that follow will help you identify and interpret several of these peaks, which, in turn, will help you determine aspects of a molecule's structure.

16.6a The O—H Stretch

Among the easiest IR absorption bands to spot are those associated with the OH stretch. OH stretching bands are intense and are usually rather broad, often extending well above 3000 cm^{-1}. For example, OH stretching bands are evident in the IR spectra of cyclohexanol (**Figure 16-12**) and 3,3-dimethylbutanoic acid (**Figure 16-13**).

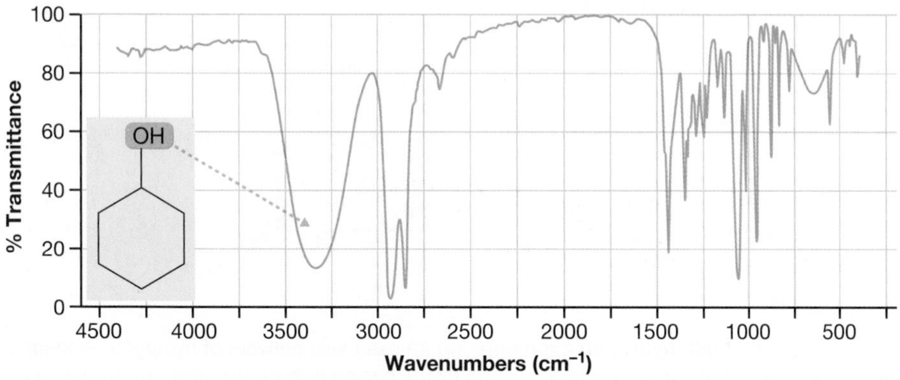

100
80
60
40
20
0
% Transmittance
OH
4500
4000
3500
3000
2500
2000
1500
1000
500
Wavenumbers (cm⁻¹)

FIGURE 16-12 IR spectrum of cyclohexanol Notice the broad OH stretching band centered at ~3350 cm^{-1}.

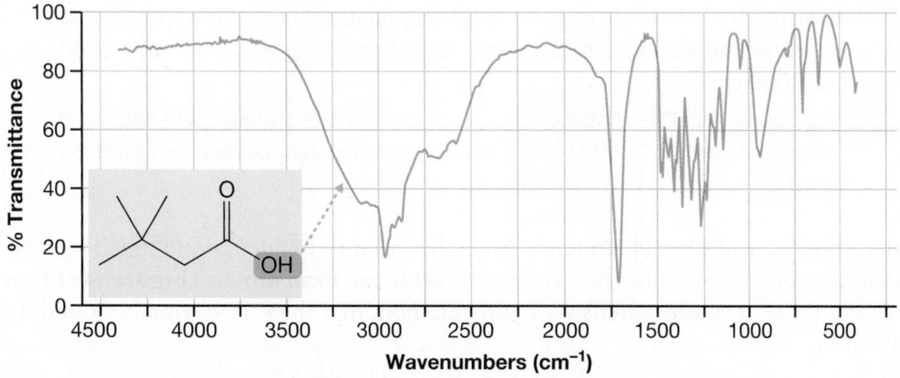

100
80
60
40
20
0
% Transmittance
O
OH
4500
4000
3500
3000
2500
2000
1500
1000
500
Wavenumbers (cm⁻¹)

FIGURE 16-13 IR spectrum of 3,3-dimethylbutanoic acid Notice the broad OH stretching band centered at ~3000 cm^{-1}.

YOUR TURN **16.9**

Determine whether the compound that generated this IR spectrum has an OH group. Explain.

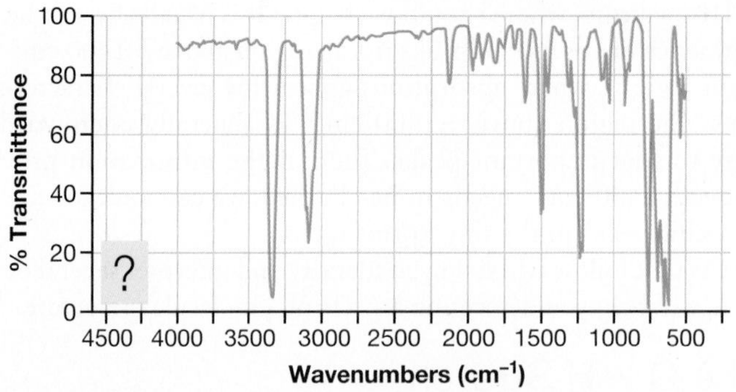
100
80
60
40
20
0
% Transmittance
?
4500 4000 3500 3000 2500 2000 1500 1000 500
Wavenumbers (cm^{-1})

The broadening of an OH stretching band is due to hydrogen bonding involving the OH groups of the sample (**Figure 16-14**). A network of hydrogen bonding in a sample facilitates a rapid exchange of hydrogen atoms from one OH group to another, since each OH hydrogen atom is already partially bonded to two different oxygen atoms. This process gives rise to a lot of variation in the O—H bond strengths. Thus, a wide range of O—H stretching frequencies overlap in the spectrum, resulting in what appears to us as a single broad peak.

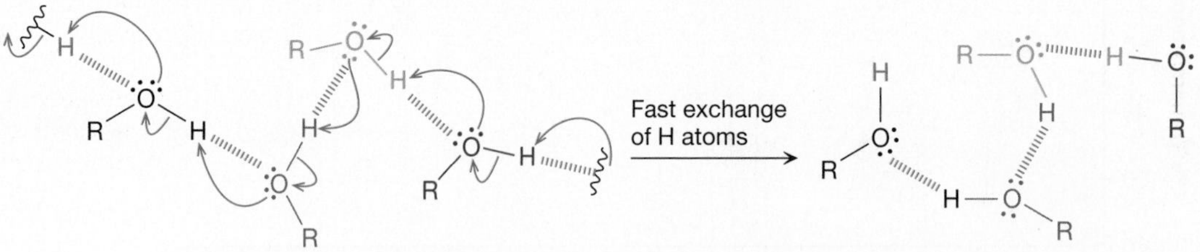
Fast exchange
of H atoms

FIGURE 16-14 Rapid hydrogen exchange (a) An extensive network of hydrogen bonding facilitates rapid hydrogen exchange, indicated by the curved arrows. (b) After the exchange, the hydrogen atoms are in different environments than where they began.

Notice that the OH stretching bands in Figures 16-12 and 16-13 are markedly different:

- An alcohol O—H stretching band is typically centered near 3300 cm^{-1} and is usually well-separated from the alkane C—H stretching bands between 2800 and 3000 cm^{-1}.
- A carboxylic acid O—H stretching band is centered at around 3000 cm^{-1} and can extend down to ~2500 cm^{-1}, thus overlapping the alkane C—H stretching bands.

A carboxylic acid O—H stretch is generally lower in frequency and much broader than that of an alcohol because carboxylic acids can form dimers (**Figure 16-15**) in which there is more extensive hydrogen bonding than is normally found in alcohols.

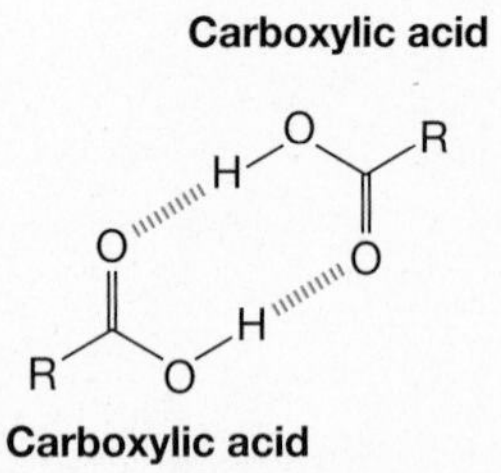
Carboxylic acid
Carboxylic acid

FIGURE 16-15 Carboxylic acid dimer Two molecules of a carboxylic acid are bound together by relatively strong hydrogen bonding.

Which of the following isomers, **A** or **B**, is consistent with the IR spectrum provided? Explain.

A

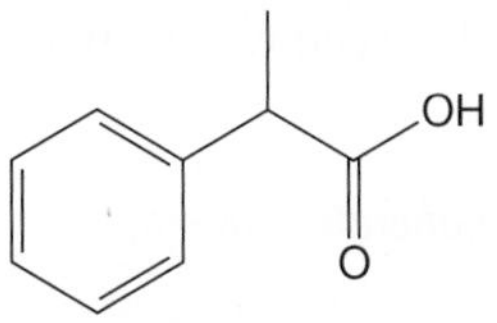
OH
O

B

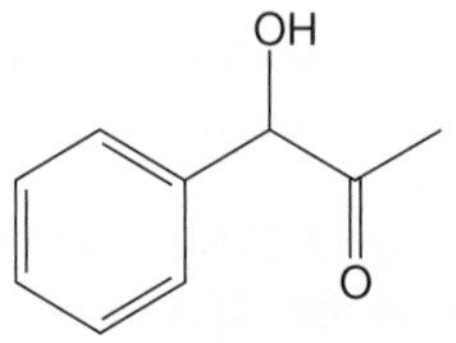
OH
O

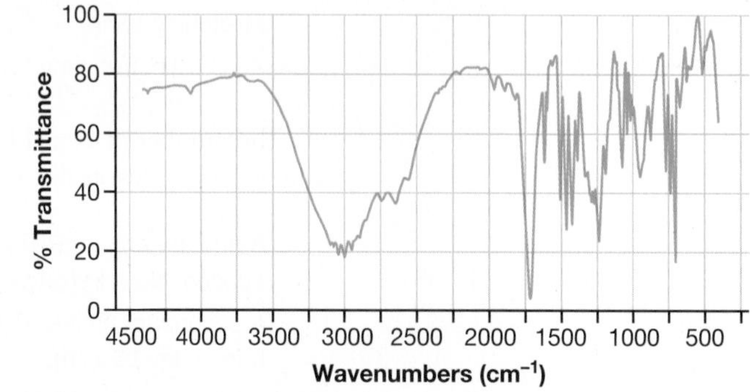
% Transmittance
100
80
60
40
20
0
4500 4000 3500 3000 2500 2000 1500 1000 500
Wavenumbers (cm⁻¹)

An O—H stretching band in an IR spectrum can also indicate the presence of an impurity such as water or an alcohol; these solvents are often difficult to eliminate entirely from a sample. This is the case with the IR spectrum of 2,5-dimethyltetrahydrofuran shown in **Figure 16-16**. No OH group appears in the molecule, but a weak, broad absorption appears around 3500 cm^{-1}. If the compound itself were to contain an OH group, that peak would be *much* more intense, as we saw in Figures 16-12 and 16-13.

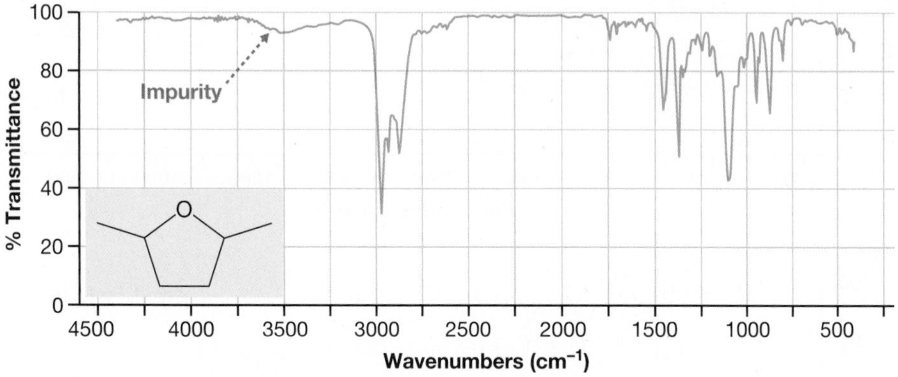
% Transmittance
100
80
60
40
20
0
Impurity
O
4500 4000 3500 3000 2500 2000 1500 1000 500
Wavenumbers (cm⁻¹)

FIGURE 16-16 Infrared spectrum of 2,5-dimethyltetrahydrofuran Because the compound itself does not contain an OH group, the weak, broad absorption near 3500 cm^{-1} must indicate the presence of an impurity, such as water or an alcohol.

If a sample is contaminated with a *substantial* amount of water or an alcohol solvent, then the OH absorption can be intense, making it difficult to determine whether the OH group is an impurity or is part of the compound itself. For reasons like this, it is usually important to remove solvents (and other contaminants) from a sample as completely as possible before acquiring the spectrum.

YOUR TURN **16.11**

The IR spectrum of hept-3-ene shown in Figure 16-11b (p. 782) exhibits a water or alcohol impurity. Identify that peak.

16.6b The N—H Stretch

Bands representing N—H stretches from an amine or amide share many similarities with those of O—H stretches, including being generally easy to identify:

- N—H stretching bands appear between 3300 and 3500 cm^{-1}.
- Hydrogen bonding involving N—H bonds usually causes these bands to be moderately broad.

There are often noticeable differences between N—H and O—H absorption bands, because N—H bonds are less polar and tend to undergo weaker hydrogen bonding:

- The intensity of an N—H stretching band is usually less than that of an O—H stretching band.
- An N—H stretching band is usually not as broad as an O—H one.

The number of N—H peaks can be used to distinguish between various types of amines or amides, as illustrated in **Figure 16-17**:

- A primary amine (RNH_2) or amide ($RCONH_2$) exhibits two separate (but closely spaced) N—H stretching bands (Fig. 16-17a).
- A secondary amine (R_2NH) or amide (RCONHR) exhibits one N—H stretching band (Fig. 16-17b).
- A tertiary amine (R_3N) or amide ($RCONR_2$) does not exhibit any N—H stretching bands (Fig. 16-17c).

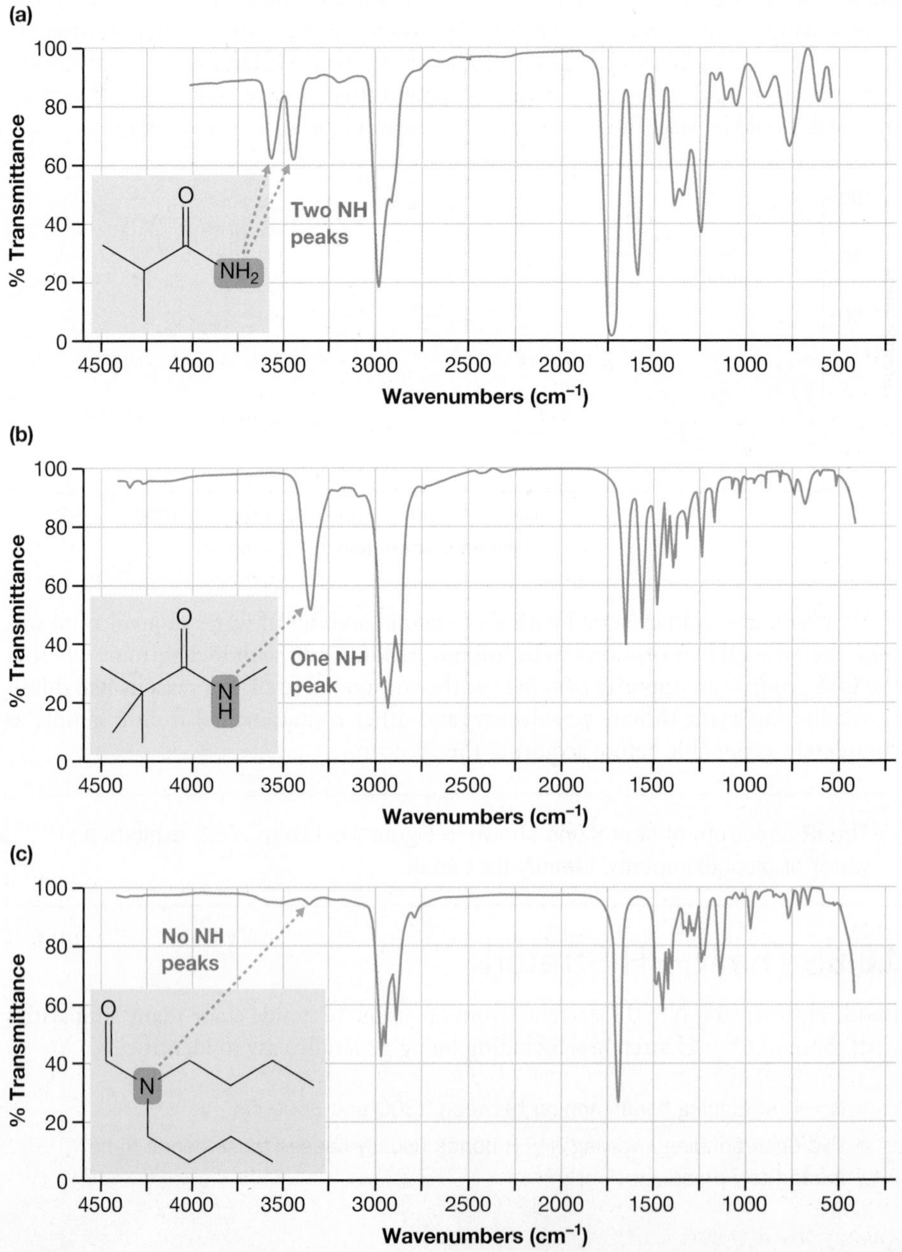

(a)
% Transmittance
Two NH peaks
Wavenumbers (cm⁻¹)
(b)
One NH peak
(c)
No NH peaks

FIGURE 16-17 N—H stretching bands in infrared spectra
IR spectra are shown for (a) 2-methylpropanamide, a primary amide; (b) *N*-methyl-2,2-dimethylpropanamide, a secondary amide; and (c) *N*,*N*-dibutylformamide, a tertiary amide.

Two N—H stretching bands appear for a primary amine or amide because an NH_2 group has two different modes of vibration involving the two N—H bonds: symmetric stretching and asymmetric stretching (**Figure 16-18**). A secondary amine or amide has just one N—H bond and therefore just one type of vibration, while a tertiary amine or amide has no N—H bonds and thus no N—H stretching bands.

YOUR TURN 16.12

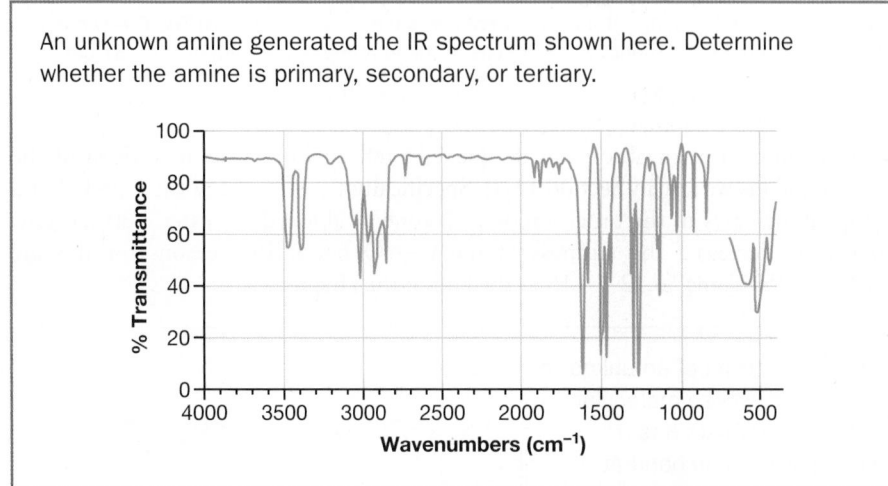

An unknown amine generated the IR spectrum shown here. Determine whether the amine is primary, secondary, or tertiary.

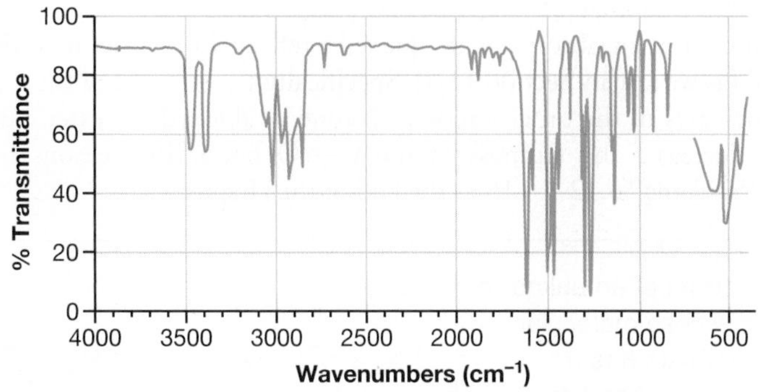

100
80
60
40
20
0
% Transmittance
4000
3500
3000
2500
2000
1500
1000
500
Wavenumbers (cm⁻¹)

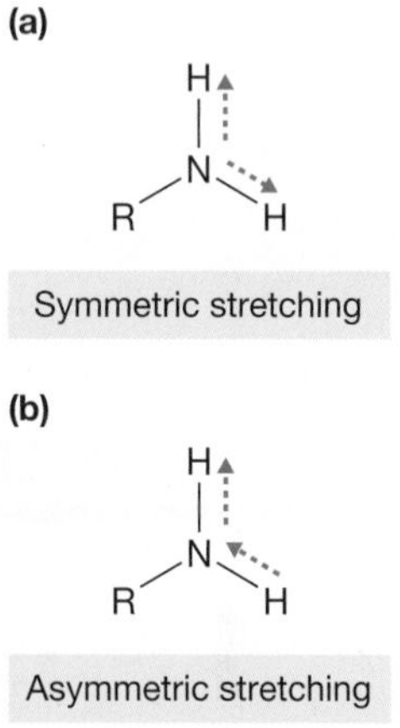

(a)
H
N
R
H
Symmetric stretching
(b)
H
N
R
H
Asymmetric stretching

FIGURE 16-18 N—H stretching vibrations in a primary amine or amide (a) In symmetric stretching, both N—H bonds stretch and compress together. (b) In asymmetric stretching, one N—H bond lengthens while the other one shortens.

16.6c The Carbonyl (C=O) Stretch

The carbonyl group (C=O) is found in many classes of compounds, including simple ketones and aldehydes, carboxylic acids, esters, and amides. A carbonyl stretching absorption is quite strong and the band is relatively narrow, usually making it very easy to spot.

Given the variety of compound classes that contain a carbonyl group, we find a moderately large range of frequencies at which the carbonyl stretching absorption can appear, generally between 1600 and 1800 cm^{-1}. Within that range, however, the C=O stretching absorption tends to appear at frequencies that are somewhat characteristic of the compound class to which the C=O group belongs:

For each of the following compound classes, the C=O stretch typically appears in the corresponding range:

- Ester 1730–1750 cm^{-1}
- Aldehyde 1720–1740 cm^{-1}
- Ketone 1710–1730 cm^{-1}
- Amide 1630–1690 cm^{-1}

Moreover, *conjugation* can have a significant impact on the location of a C=O stretch (see Recall box):

When a C=O group is conjugated to a C=C or C≡C bond, the frequency of the C=O absorption is typically lowered by 20–40 cm^{-1}.

In 4-methylpentan-2-one (**Figure 16-19a**, next page), the C=O bond is *not* conjugated and its absorption appears at 1721 cm^{-1}. For 4-methylpent-3-en-2-one (Fig. 16-19b), however, the conjugated C=C double bond lowers the C=O frequency to 1690 cm^{-1}.

CONNECTIONS 16.2

Going for gold 4-Methylpentan-2-one (Fig. 16-19), more commonly called methyl isobutyl ketone (MIBK), is used to extract gold and silver from aqueous cyanide solutions as part of an analytical technique used during certain mining processes.

◂ RECALL

Double bonds are *conjugated* when they are separated by one bond. In Section 14.1, we learned that the four π electrons that make up a pair of conjugated double bonds are part of the same π system.

(a) (b)

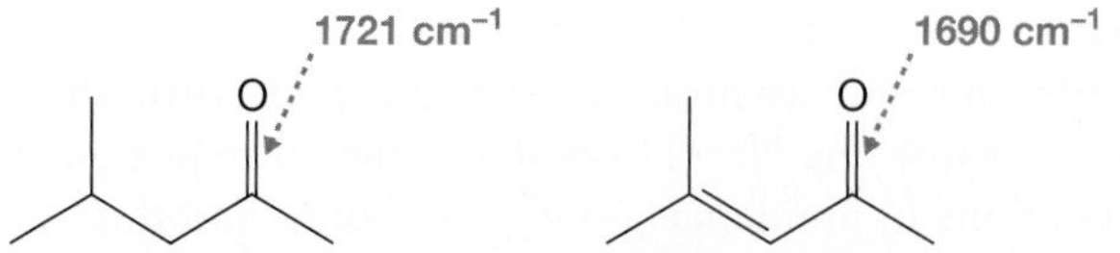
1721 cm⁻¹
O
1690 cm⁻¹
O

4-Methylpentan-2-one 4-Methylpent-3-en-2-one

FIGURE 16-19 Effect of conjugation on C═O stretching frequencies (a) The C═O bond is isolated and absorbs at a characteristic frequency for ketones. (b) The C═O bond is conjugated with the C═C bond, which results in the lowering of the frequency by 31 cm^{-1}.

These differences in absorption frequencies reflect differences in *stiffness* of the C═O bond (as we saw in Section 16.4). Specifically, the stiffness of the C═O bond in general increases in the order amide < ketone < aldehyde < ester. Furthermore, conjugation decreases the stiffness of the C═O bond. The reasons for this are explored in Problems 16.12–16.15 at the end of the chapter.

YOUR TURN **16.13**

The IR spectrum of an unknown compound, whose molecular formula is $C_9H_{10}O$, has a strong absorption band at 1686 cm^{-1}. Which of these compounds is consistent with that spectrum? Explain.

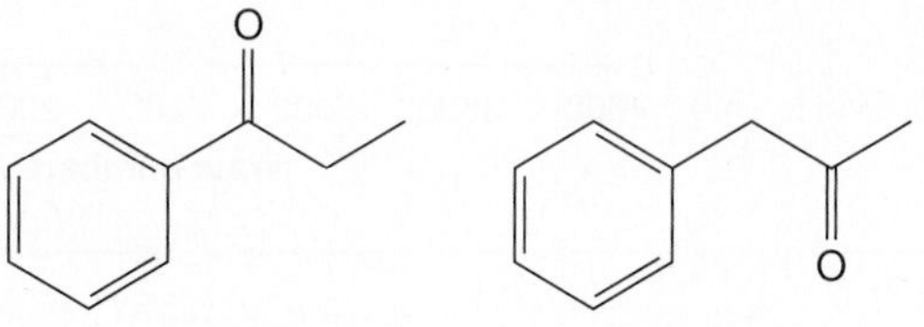
O
O

C **D**

CONNECTIONS 16.3

1-Phenylpropan-2-one in stimulants 1-Phenylpropan-2-one (compound **D** in Your Turn 16.13), commonly called phenylacetone, is used to manufacture amphetamine and methamphetamine, stimulants that are used to treat obesity and attention deficit hyperactivity disorder (ADHD). Amphetamine and methamphetamine are addictive drugs, however, so phenylacetone is tightly controlled by the U.S. Food and Drug Administration (FDA).

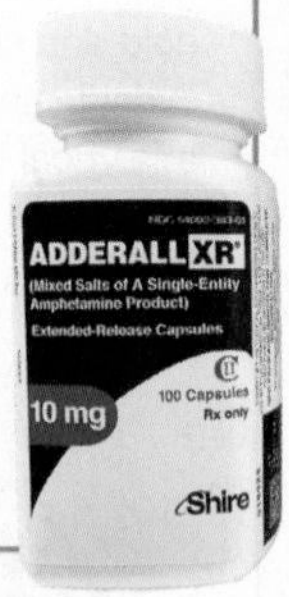
ADDERALL XR
(Mixed Salts of A Single-Entity Amphetamine Product)
Extended-Release Capsules
10 mg
100 Capsules
Rx only
Shire

16.6d The C═C Stretch

Alkenes and aromatic rings both contain C═C double bonds in their Lewis structures, but their C═C stretching bands appear differently in an IR spectrum:

- An alkene C═C stretch generally appears as a single peak in the range 1620–1680 cm^{-1}. (Review Fig. 16-11a, p. 782.)
- Aromatic C═C stretches generally appear as two or three peaks in the range 1450–1600 cm^{-1}. (See **Figure 16-20**.)

An alkene C═C stretch can sometimes be difficult to identify in an IR spectrum for two reasons. First, an alkene C═C stretch can appear in the same region as some C═O stretches, in which case the absorption by the C═C stretch can be obscured. Second, in some highly symmetric alkenes, such as *trans*-hept-3-ene, the C═C stretch has very little absorption (review Fig. 16-11b, p. 782).

Absorptions from aromatic C═C stretches, on the other hand, tend to be distinct and are often prominent. In Figure 16-20a, for example, three peaks are present between roughly 1450 and 1600 cm^{-1} and two of them are relatively intense; in Figure 16-20b, two peaks appear in that range, one of which is relatively intense.

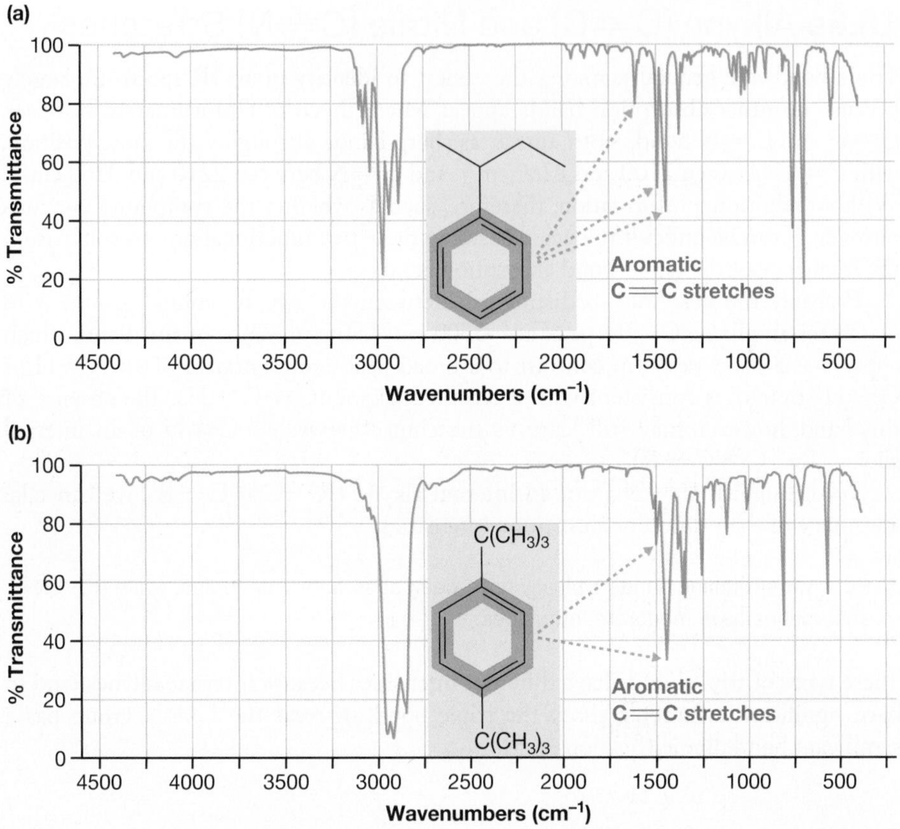

(a)
% Transmittance
Wavenumbers (cm^{-1})
Aromatic
C=C stretches
(b)
% Transmittance
C(CH$_3$)$_3$
C(CH$_3$)$_3$
Wavenumbers (cm^{-1})
Aromatic
C=C stretches

FIGURE 16-20 Aromatic C=C stretches Bands that appear around 1600, 1500, and just below 1500 cm^{-1} are characteristic of aromatic C=C stretches. (a) All three bands are present in the spectrum of *sec*-butylbenzene. (b) Two of the three bands are present in the spectrum of 1,4-di-*tert*-butylbenzene.

YOUR TURN 16.14

Match isomers **E** and **F** with the correct IR spectrum. Explain.

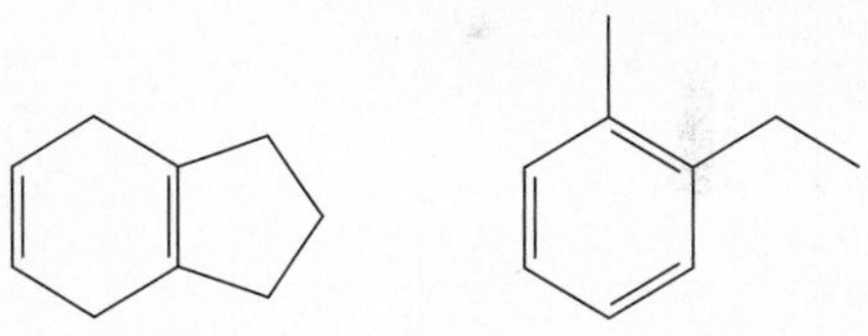

E **F**

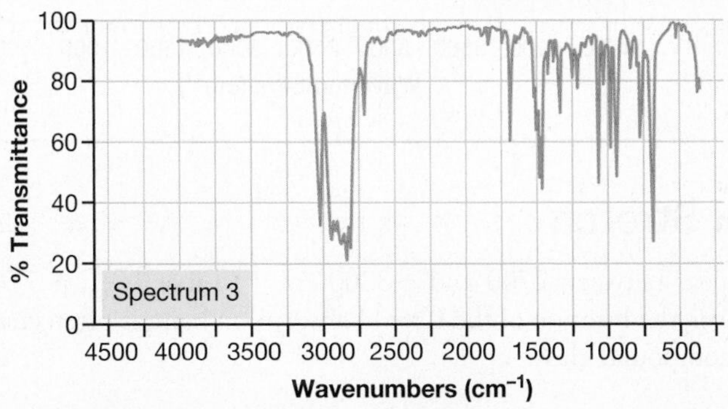

% Transmittance
Spectrum 3
Wavenumbers (cm^{-1})

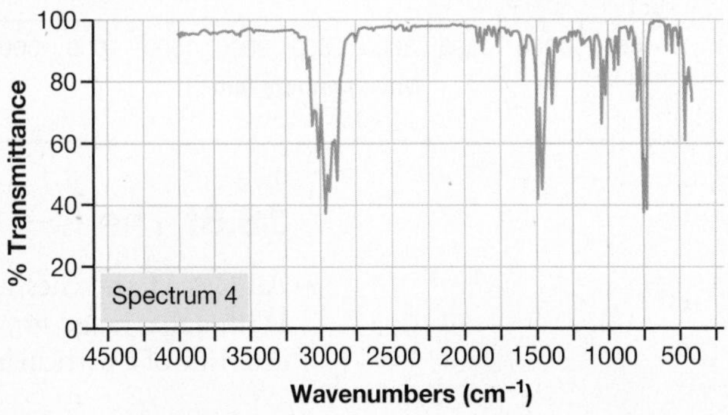

% Transmittance
Spectrum 4
Wavenumbers (cm^{-1})

16.6e Alkyne (C≡C) and Nitrile (C≡N) Stretches

Triple bonds are generally among the easiest to identify in an IR spectrum, largely because no other absorption bands appear where they do. Unfortunately, however, C≡C and C≡N bonds both appear as sharp bands at roughly the same position, with C≡C between 2100 and 2260 cm^{-1} and C≡N between 2210 and 2260 cm^{-1}. Without additional information, therefore, such as whether the compound contains nitrogen, it can be difficult to decide between these two functional groups solely from the frequency of the triple-bond absorption band.

Probably the best way to distinguish between the two functional groups is to search for an alkyne C—H peak at ~3300 cm^{-1}. The presence of this band, which appears as a *sharp* peak (in contrast to a broad peak representative of an N—H or O—H stretch), is consistent with a terminal alkyne (C≡C—H). The absence of this band, however, may still leave us the choice between a C≡N or an internal alkyne (R—C≡C—R).

To distinguish C≡N from an internal alkyne (R—C≡C—R), we can take advantage of their different absorption intensities:

> RC≡CR stretching bands typically have weak absorption intensities, while RC≡N absorptions have moderate intensities.

These types of triple bonds have different intensities because internal alkynes tend to have significant symmetry about the triple bond, whereas the C≡N group has a significant bond dipole (Section 16.5).

YOUR TURN 16.15

(a) Identify which of these two spectra corresponds to a nitrile and which corresponds to an alkyne. **(b)** Is the alkyne most likely internal or terminal? Explain.

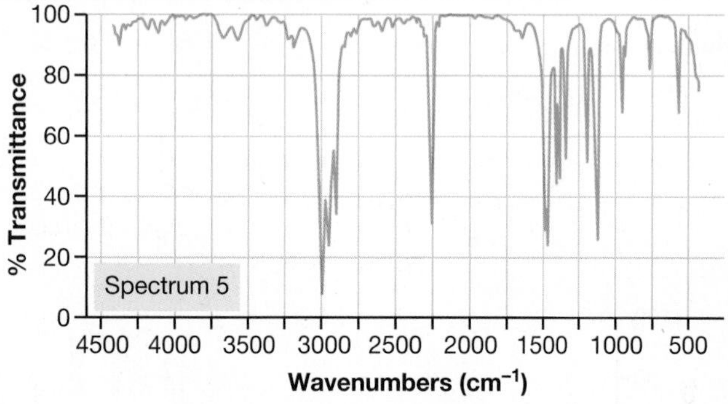
100
80
60
40
20
0
% Transmittance
Spectrum 5
4500 4000 3500 3000 2500 2000 1500 1000 500
Wavenumbers (cm⁻¹)

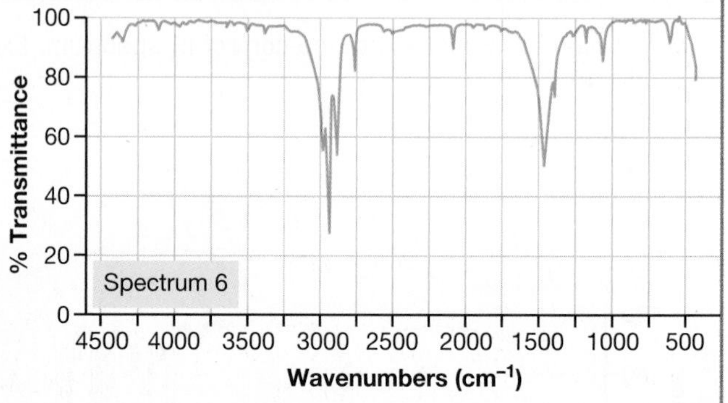
100
80
60
40
20
0
% Transmittance
Spectrum 6
4500 4000 3500 3000 2500 2000 1500 1000 500
Wavenumbers (cm⁻¹)

16.6f The C—H Stretch

All C—H stretches appear between 2700 and ~3300 cm^{-1} (Table 16-1, p. 776). Within that range, however, the location of the C—H absorption band is often characteristic of a particular compound class:

- Alkyne C—H, ~3300 cm^{-1} (moderate intensity)
- Alkene C—H, 3000–3100 cm^{-1} (variable intensity)
- Aromatic C—H, 3000–3100 cm^{-1} (variable intensity)
- Alkane C—H, 2800–3000 cm^{-1} (variable intensity)
- Aldehyde C—H, two peaks, ~2720 and ~2820 cm^{-1} (moderate intensity)

Often, the presence or absence of one of these C—H absorption bands can help you narrow your choice of compounds when another region of the spectrum is difficult to

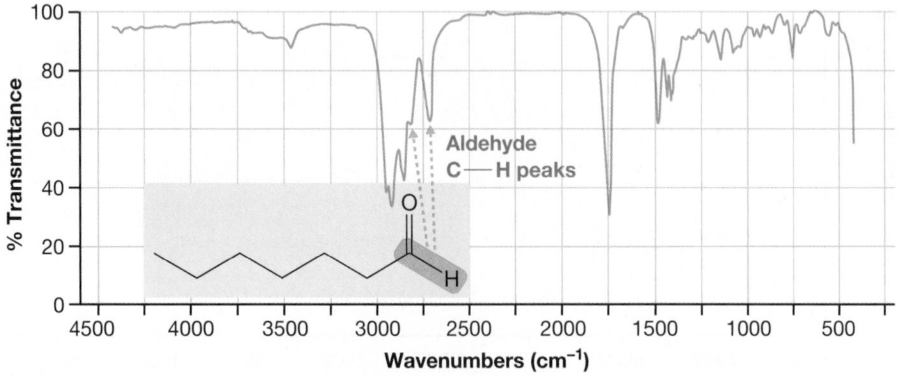
% Transmittance
Wavenumbers (cm^{-1})
Aldehyde C—H peaks
O
H

FIGURE 16-21 Infrared spectrum of heptanal Notice the aldehyde C—H stretching peaks at ~2820 and ~2720 cm^{-1}. The one at ~2820 cm^{-1} is partly obscured by the alkane C—H band.

CONNECTIONS 16.4

Diagnosing lung cancer

Heptanal (Fig. 16-21) is being studied as a biomarker for lung cancer because it can be detected in the breath or urine of patients with lung cancer.

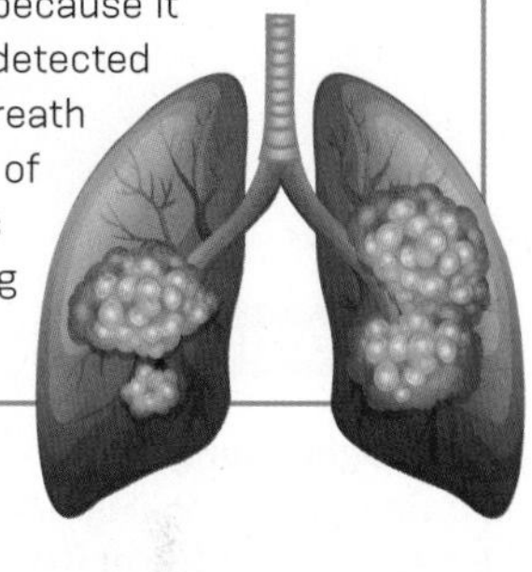

interpret unambiguously. For example, a C═O stretch appearing in an IR spectrum at 1720 cm^{-1} could be consistent with either a ketone or an aldehyde. If you also see peaks at 2720 and 2820 cm^{-1}, however, then the compound is almost certainly an aldehyde, as you can see in the IR spectrum for heptanal (**Figure 16-21**). As another example, if you are uncertain as to whether an IR spectrum exhibits a C═C stretch, you should examine the 3000–3100 cm^{-1} region to see if there is evidence of an alkene C—H stretch. This idea is explored in Your Turn 16.16.

YOUR TURN **16.16**

Does Spectrum 7 or Spectrum 8 more likely correspond to a compound that contains a C═C double bond? Explain.

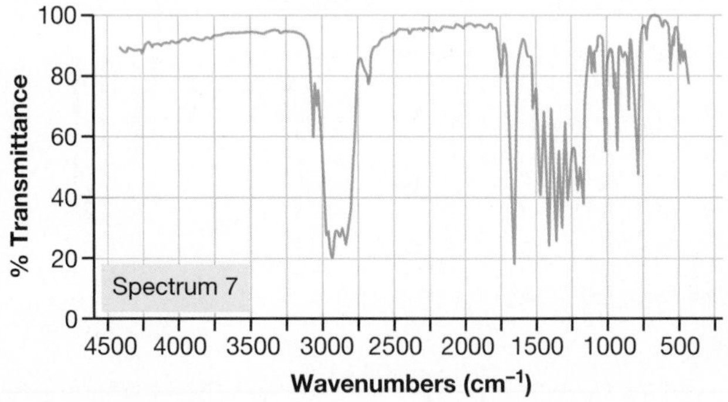
% Transmittance
Spectrum 7
Wavenumbers (cm^{-1})

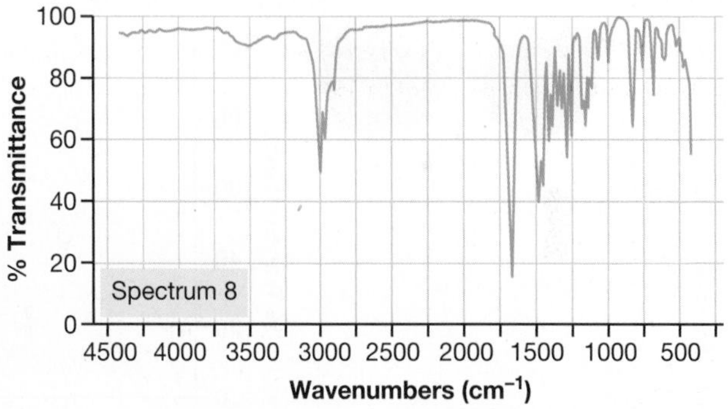
% Transmittance
Spectrum 8
Wavenumbers (cm^{-1})

Alkane C—H stretches, which appear between 2800 and 3000 cm^{-1}, are so commonplace in organic molecules that they are generally *not* useful in structure elucidation. Trying to use these bands to determine a structure is like trying to identify a car from its tires.

The alkane C—H stretching band is perhaps most useful when it is low in intensity or absent altogether:

The relative intensity of the alkane C—H band decreases as the relative number of alkane C—H bonds in the molecule decreases.

For example, 2-ethylhexan-1-ol has 17 C—H bonds, making the C—H stretching band even more intense than the O—H stretch (**Figure 16-22a**, next page). In the IR spectrum of ethanol (Fig. 16-22b), on the other hand, the alkane C—H stretching band is less intense than the O—H stretch because there are only five alkane C—H bonds. Diphenylmethanone (benzophenone) has no alkane C—H bonds at all. Its IR spectrum (Fig. 16-22c), therefore, has no absorption band between 2800 and 3000 cm^{-1}.

FIGURE 16-22 Relative intensities of the alkane C—H bands IR spectra are shown for (a) 2-ethylhexan-1-ol, (b) ethanol, and (c) diphenylmethanone. As the number of alkane C—H bonds decreases, so does the intensity of the alkane C—H absorption band.

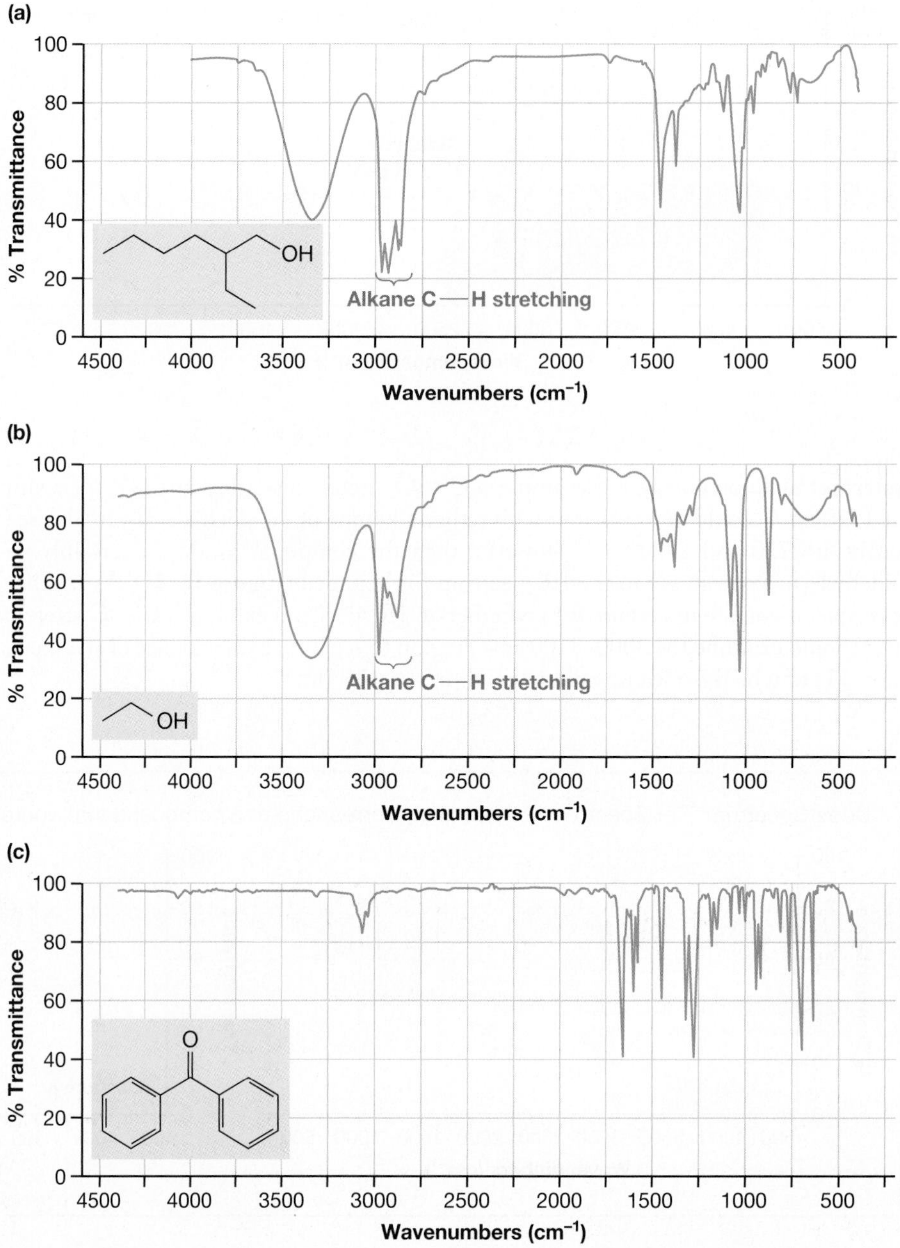

(a)
100
80
60
40
20
0
% Transmittance
OH
Alkane C—H stretching
4500
4000
3500
3000
2500
2000
1500
1000
500
Wavenumbers (cm^{-1})
(b)
OH
Alkane C—H stretching
Wavenumbers (cm^{-1})
(c)
O
Wavenumbers (cm^{-1})

CONNECTIONS 16.5

Tougher sunglasses
Benzophenone (Fig. 16-22c) absorbs ultraviolet (UV) light and is used as a curing agent in the manufacturing of cellulose acetate sunglasses. Curing is a process that hardens the plastic after it is poured into a mold.

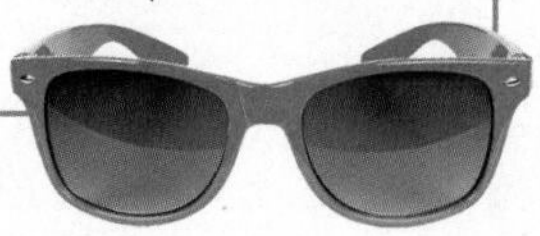

YOUR TURN **16.17**

In Figure 16-22c, indicate where alkane C—H stretching bands would normally appear.

SECTION 16.7 OBJECTIVES

You will be able to

1. Analyze an IR spectrum to systematically determine aspects of a molecule's structure.
2. Combine the analysis of an IR spectrum with information from other sources, such as a molecular formula, to determine a reasonable molecular structure.

Strategies for Success
Structure Elucidation Using IR Spectroscopy

16.7 Strategies for Success: Structure Elucidation Using Infrared Spectroscopy

Interpreting an IR spectrum requires practice applying the concepts we have learned so far. For this reason, the IR spectra of three unknown compounds are presented in Sections 16.7a through 16.7c, and we take the time to analyze them to obtain

1. Identify peaks above ~1400 cm^{-1}
   - These peaks tell you whether certain bonds are present.
   - Look especially for the presence or absence of peaks highlighted in Section 16.6: O—H, N—H, C═O, C═C, C≡C, C≡N, C—H.

2. Consider functional groups that have more than one type of bond identified in Step 1.
   - For example:
   - (C═O) + (O—H) = carboxylic acid?
   - (C═O) + (N—H) = amide?
   - (C═O) + (C—H at 2720 & 2820 cm^{-1}) = aldehyde?
   - (C═C) + (C—H at ~3050 cm^{-1}) = alkene or aromatic ring?
   - (C≡C) + (C—H at ~3300 cm^{-1}) = terminal alkyne?

3. Look for special characteristics of absorption peaks identified in Step 1.
   - Is the O—H absorption consistent with an alcohol or a carboxylic acid? (Section 16.6a)
   - Is the N—H absorption consistent with NH or NH_2? (Section 16.6b)
   - Does the frequency of the C═O absorption suggest a carboxylic acid or ester? A ketone or aldehyde? An amide? (Section 16.6c)
   - Does the C═C absorption suggest an alkene or an aromatic ring? (Section 16.6d)
   - Does the absorption for the triple bond suggest C≡C or C≡N ? (Section 16.6e)
   - Is the alkane C—H absorption noticeably weak? What does that suggest? (Section 16.6f)

4. Establish whether a C═O bond is conjugated.
   - To have a conjugated C═O bond, there must also be a C═C as part of an alkene or an aromatic ring.
   - Conjugation typically lowers the C═O frequency by 20 – 40 cm^{-1}. (Section 16.6c)

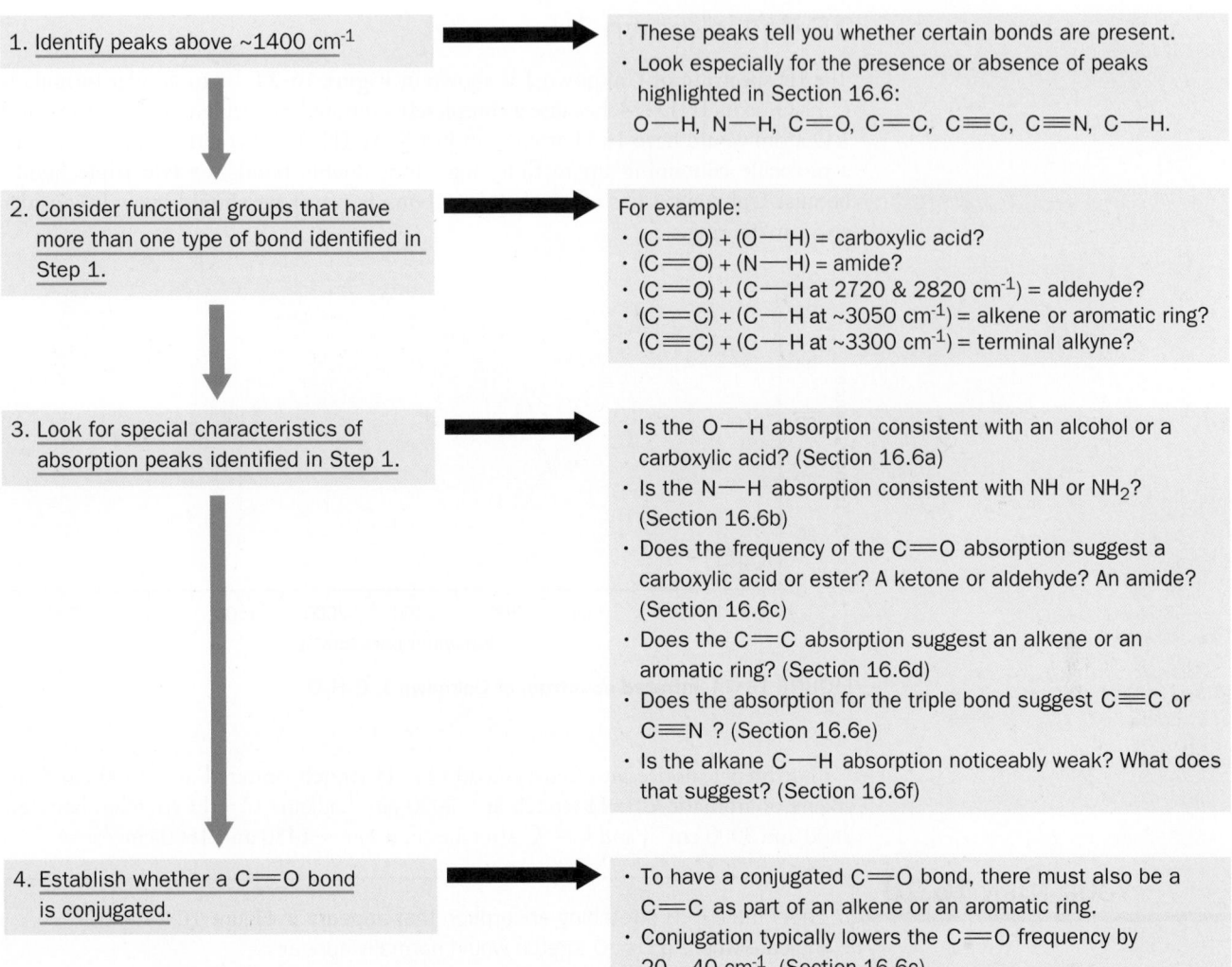

FIGURE 16-23 Steps for interpreting an infrared spectrum Follow-up information for each step is provided on the right.

structural information. While there are many ways to analyze an IR spectrum, we will apply a systematic method consisting of the steps outlined in **Figure 16-23**.

Even after extracting all of the information from an IR spectrum, you will be unable to completely determine the compound's structure without significant additional information, such as the molecular formula or results from other forms of spectroscopy. IR spectra allow you to determine the types of bonds and functional groups present, but they provide little structural information beyond that. Therefore, if you are given the formula of the compound that generated the IR spectrum, take full advantage of it. For example, if there is a single O atom in the formula and the IR spectrum indicates a C═O stretch, the compound *cannot* be a carboxylic acid or ester; those types of compounds each require two O atoms.

Given the molecular formula, you should also calculate the molecule's index of hydrogen deficiency (IHD; Section 4.11), which tells you how many double bonds, triple bonds, and rings the molecule can have (see Recall box). The IHD can therefore supplement your findings from the steps in Figure 16-23. For example, if the IHD = 0, the compound cannot contain C═O, C═C, C≡C, or C≡N bonds. As another example, if the IHD ≤ 3, the compound cannot contain a benzene ring, which would require an IHD of 4 (three double bonds and a ring).

◂ RECALL

Section 4.11 showed that the number of H atoms in a saturated molecule is (# of H atoms) = $2n$ + 2 + (# of N atoms) − (# of halogen atoms), and IHD is calculated as half the number of H atoms missing from the saturated molecule.

16.7a Unknown 1

The IR spectrum of Unknown 1 is shown in **Figure 16-24**. Its molecular formula is C_7H_8O, so its IHD is 4, because a completely saturated molecule with 7 C atoms and 1 O atom would have 16 H atoms, not just 8. An IHD of 4 could be the outcome of a molecule containing up to four rings, four double bonds, or two triple bonds; because Unknown 1 has relatively few carbons, however, we should strongly consider an aromatic ring.

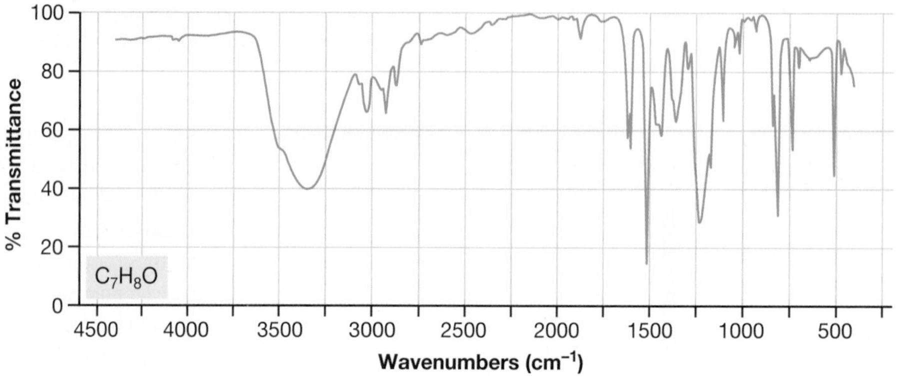

100
80
60
40
20
0
% Transmittance
C_7H_8O
4500
4000
3500
3000
2500
2000
1500
1000
500
Wavenumbers (cm^{-1})

FIGURE 16-24 Infrared spectrum of Unknown 1, C_7H_8O

For Step 1, notice an intense, broad O—H stretch centered at ~3300 cm^{-1}, an alkene or aromatic C—H stretch at ~3050 cm^{-1}, alkane C—H stretches between 2800 and 3000 cm^{-1}, and C=C stretches between ~1450 and 1600 cm^{-1}.

YOUR TURN 16.18

Label the O—H stretching absorption that appears in Figure 16-24 and indicate where a C=O stretch would normally appear.

For Step 2, notice the absorption around 3050 cm^{-1}, which belongs to an alkene or aromatic C—H stretch, and notice the absorptions between ~1450 and 1600 cm^{-1}, which belong to C=C stretches. For Step 3, we should establish whether the C=C stretch is consistent with an alkene or aromatic ring. An alkene typically exhibits one peak above ~1620 cm^{-1}, whereas an aromatic ring typically exhibits two or three peaks in the 1450–1600 cm^{-1} range. In this case, we appear to have an aromatic ring. With the IHD of 4 that we previously calculated, this could indicate a benzene ring.

YOUR TURN 16.19

In Figure 16-24, label the aromatic C—H stretching bands and all three bands corresponding to aromatic C=C stretches.

Continuing with Step 3, notice that alkane C—H peaks are present between 2800 and 3000 cm^{-1}, but their intensity is low (much less than the O—H band), suggesting that there are relatively few alkane C—H bonds. A relatively low number of alkane C—H bonds would be consistent with six out of the seven C atoms being part of an aromatic ring.

YOUR TURN 16.20

Identify the alkane C—H stretching band in Figure 16-24.

For Step 4, we would normally ask whether a C=O bond that is present is conjugated to a C=C bond. However, because there is no evidence of a C=O bond, we can skip Step 4 in this case.

At this stage, we know that the compound has a benzene ring (which accounts for six carbons and the entire IHD of 4) and an OH group. Given that the molecular formula is C_7H_8O, we still need to account for one more carbon atom. Four structures that fit these criteria are shown in **Figure 16-25**.

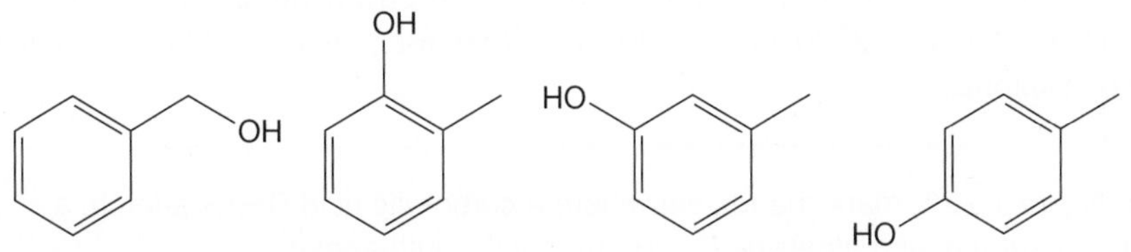

OH
OH
HO
HO

G H I J

FIGURE 16-25 Possible structures for Unknown 1, C_7H_8O

YOUR TURN **16.21**

The molecule shown here has a molecular formula of C_7H_8O. Determine whether it is consistent with the IR spectrum for Unknown 1 (Fig. 16-24).

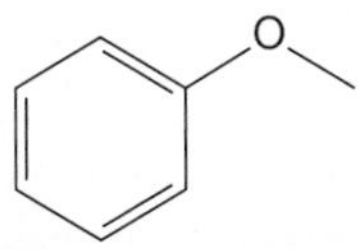

O

Our analysis of Unknown 1 is an excellent example of the limitations of IR spectroscopy. Specific absorption bands in an IR spectrum provide structural information about only *pieces* of a molecule. Frequently, there are multiple ways those pieces can be put together and you will not have sufficient information from the spectrum to converge on a single structure.

16.7b Unknown 2

The IR spectrum of Unknown 2 (molecular formula $C_8H_{14}O$) is shown in **Figure 16-26**. We begin again with determining the compound's IHD. A completely saturated molecule with 8 C and 1 O would have 18 H, not 14, so Unknown 2 has an IHD of 2. Thus, Unknown 2 could have one triple bond, two double bonds, two rings, or a double bond and a ring.

For Step 1 (Fig. 16-23, p. 793), notice the following stretching absorption bands: alkene or aromatic C—H at ~3050 cm^{-1}, alkane C—H stretches between 2800 and 3000 cm^{-1}, a C=O stretch at 1682 cm^{-1}, and a C=C stretch at 1617 cm^{-1}.

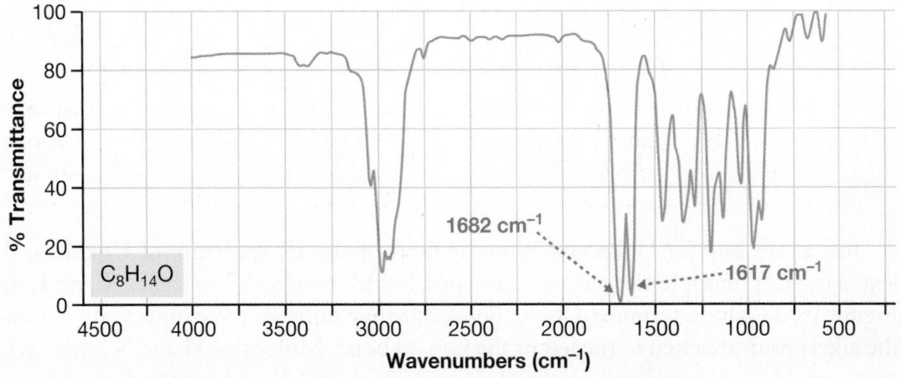

100
80
60
40
20
0
% Transmittance
C8H14O
1682 cm−1
1617 cm−1
4500
4000
3500
3000
2500
2000
1500
1000
500
Wavenumbers (cm−1)

FIGURE 16-26 Infrared spectrum of Unknown 2, $C_8H_{14}O$

YOUR TURN **16.22**

In Figure 16-26, label the stretching absorptions we identified for Step 1.

For Step 2, let's consider the compound class in which the C═O bond might be involved. We can rule out a carboxylic acid or ester because these require two O atoms each, but the formula we were given has just one. We can also rule out an amide because the formula has no N atoms. Furthermore, there are no O—H or N—H stretches in the IR spectrum, which might have supported a carboxylic acid or amide. We can also rule out an aldehyde because the spectrum doesn't exhibit aldehyde C—H stretches at ~2720 and ~2820 cm^{-1}. Therefore, the C═O bond is probably part of a ketone.

YOUR TURN **16.23**

In Figure 16-26, mark the regions where a carboxylic acid O—H stretch, a N—H stretch, and aldehyde C—H stretches would appear.

Continuing with Step 2, notice the absorption at ~3050 cm^{-1}, which could belong to an alkene or aromatic C—H stretch, and the one at 1617 cm^{-1}, which belongs to a C═C stretch.

For Step 3, the frequency of the C═C stretch at 1617 cm^{-1} suggests an alkene rather than an aromatic ring. Evidence for aromatic C═C bonds would have appeared as two or three peaks in the 1450–1600 cm^{-1} region. Furthermore, we can rule out an aromatic ring because the IHD is only 2.

YOUR TURN **16.24**

In Figure 16-26, circle the region where multiple C═C stretch absorptions would appear if the molecule contained an aromatic ring.

For Step 4, notice that a C═O stretch indicating a ketone normally appears at ~1720 cm^{-1}, but in this case it appears at 1682 cm^{-1}. This suggests that the C═O and C═C bonds are conjugated.

Knowing that the molecule is a conjugated ketone, the general structure for Unknown 2 is C—C(═O)—C═C. But we still have four carbon atoms and 14 hydrogen atoms to add. The remaining carbon atoms must be sp^3-hybridized (the entire IHD of 2 has already been accounted for) and they can be added to either side of the C═O bond, as shown in **Figure 16-27**. In molecules **K** and **L**, all of the remaining carbon atoms were added to the left side of the C═O bond, and in molecules **M** and **N** some of the carbon atoms were added to the right side.

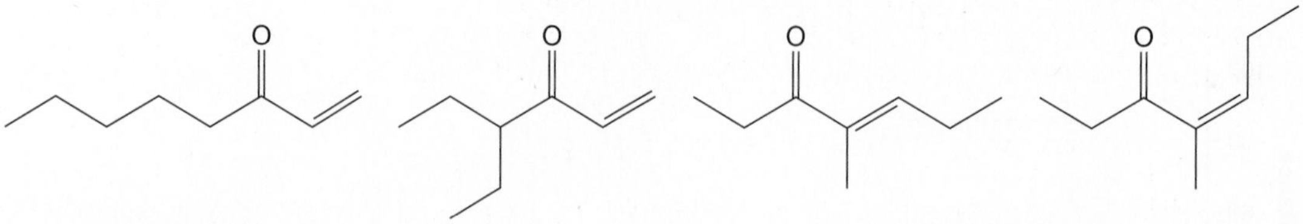

O
O
O
O

K **L** **M** **N**

FIGURE 16-27 Possible structures for Unknown 2, $C_8H_{14}O$

Just as we saw for Unknown 1, our analysis of the IR spectrum of Unknown 2 leaves us with multiple isomers as candidates. Notice that both molecules **K** and **L** in Figure 16-27 have a terminal C═C bond, but they differ in the connectivity within the alkyl group attached to the left of the C═O bond. Molecules **M** and **N** both have an internal C═C bond and are diastereomers; the C═C bond has the *E* configuration in **M** and has the *Z* configuration in **N**.

SOLVED PROBLEM **16.3**

How to draw isomers that are consistent with an IR spectrum

Break It Down **Draw another possible structure that is consistent with the IR spectrum in Figure 16-26.**

Think	Solve
What is the basic structure required from our previous analysis of the IR spectrum?	The basic structure requires that the C═O bond is part of a ketone and is conjugated to a C═C bond: 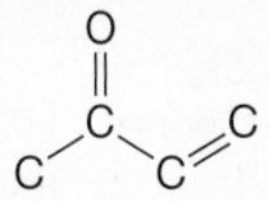
What atoms must be added to the basic structure to complete the molecule? Do we need to increase the IHD?	The basic structure accounts for four C atoms and one O atom, and exhibits an IHD of 2, so we still need to add four C atoms and 14 H atoms. The molecular formula we were given ($C_8H_{14}O$) has an IHD of 2, the same as the basic structure, so we cannot add any double bonds, triple bonds, or rings.
How can we add those atoms without repeating one of the structures in Figure 16-27?	Similar to molecules **K** and **L** in Figure 16-27, we can add the remaining carbons to the left side of the carbonyl group, as shown in molecule **O**. Alternatively, similar to molecules **M** and **N** in Figure 16-27, we can add carbons to the right side of the carbonyl group, as shown in molecule **P**. 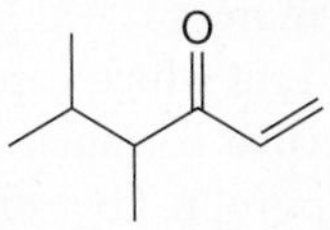 **O** 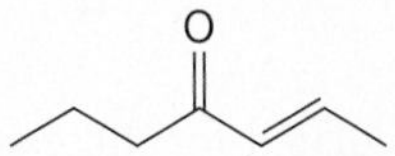 **P**

Try It Draw two additional structures consistent with the IR spectrum in Figure 16-26, each of which is different from molecules **K** through **P**.

16.7c Unknown 3

The IR spectrum for Unknown 3 (molecular formula $C_7H_{13}NO$) is shown in **Figure 16-28**. Again we begin by determining the IHD, which is 2. The molecule could therefore have up to two double bonds, two rings, or a triple bond.

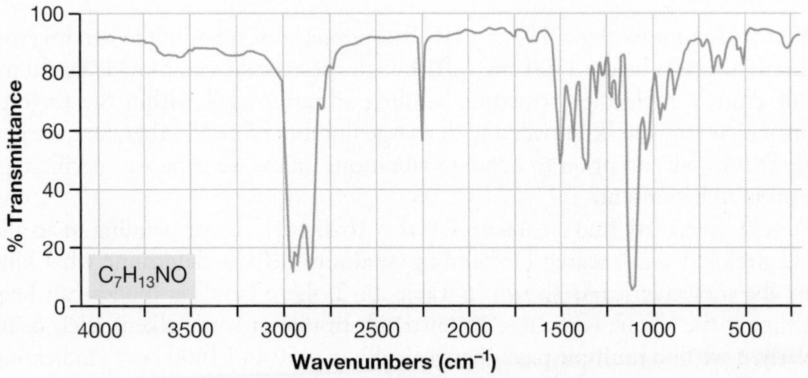
100
80
60
40
20
0
% Transmittance
C7H13NO
4000
3500
3000
2500
2000
1500
1000
500
Wavenumbers (cm−1)

FIGURE 16-28 Infrared spectrum of Unknown 3, $C_7H_{13}NO$

YOUR TURN **16.25**

Calculate the IHD of $C_7H_{13}NO$ on your own. Is that consistent with Unknown 3 having an IHD of 2?

For Step 1, there is an absorption around 2800–3000 cm^{-1}, corresponding to alkane C—H bonds. There is also a sharp peak at ~2250 cm^{-1}, which is where we would expect a C≡C or C≡N to appear.

For Step 2, notice that there is no alkyne C—H stretch at ~3300 cm^{-1}, so we can rule out a terminal alkyne. Therefore, if the molecule has a C≡C bond, it must be internal.

YOUR TURN **16.26**

Label the stretching bands in Figure 16-28 that we identified in Step 1. Also, indicate where an alkyne C—H stretch would have appeared.

For Step 3, notice that the peak at ~2250 cm^{-1} is moderately intense, which suggests that the triple bond is C≡N. If the triple bond were instead of the form RC≡CR, we would expect the intensity to be rather weak.

We can skip Step 4 because the IR spectrum does not indicate a C=O.

So far, we have determined that $C_7H_{13}NO$ has an IHD of 2, and it has a C≡N bond. Because the C≡N bond accounts for the entire IHD required by the molecular formula, all of the remaining bonds must be single bonds, and there can be no rings. But we have yet to determine the functional group associated with the O atom. The O atom cannot be part of a C=O group or an O—H group because the IR spectrum does not have absorptions that would indicate the presence of those bonds. Furthermore, a C=O bond would require increasing the IHD by 1, in which case the total IHD would exceed what we calculated for the given molecular formula. The only remaining possibility is for the O atom to be part of an ether group, C—O—C. Two possibilities for Unknown 3 are shown in **Figure 16-29**.

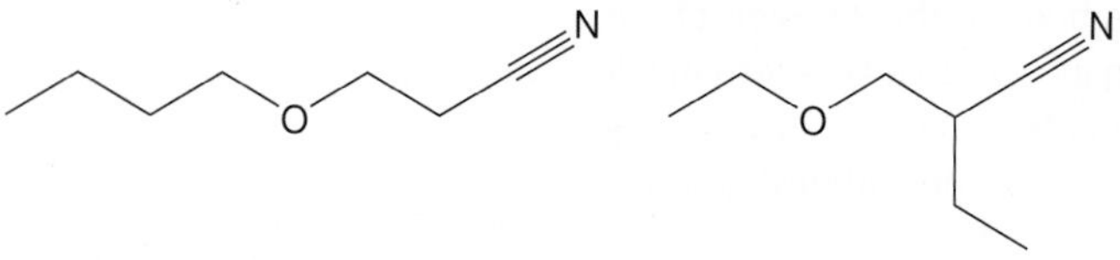

N
O
N
O

Q R

FIGURE 16-29 Possible structures for Unknown 3, $C_7H_{13}NO$

YOUR TURN **16.27**

Draw another molecule of $C_7H_{13}NO$ that is consistent with the IR spectrum in Figure 16-28.

SECTION 16.8 OBJECTIVES

You will be able to

1. Explain why you should avoid analysis of the fingerprint region of an IR spectrum unless you expect certain peaks there.
2. Use IR absorptions for bending vibrations to distinguish the type of substitution on a benzene ring or the substitution pattern about the C=C bond of an alkene.

16.8 A Deeper Look: Infrared Bending Vibrations

Recall from Figure 16-9 (p. 777) that IR absorptions corresponding to bending modes of vibration appear below 1500 cm^{-1}. Although these peaks can provide useful information about a molecule's structure, bending vibrations fall within the fingerprint region, which tends to be crowded with a large number of peaks. Therefore, we generally don't turn our attention to bending vibrations unless we expect a specific type of absorption to be present.

For example, if we find an absorption at ~1620 cm^{-1}, corresponding to an alkene C=C stretch, we can search for bending modes to help us determine what kind of alkene the molecule is. As shown in Table 16-2, these bending modes can help us determine if the alkene is mono-, di-, or trisubstituted or if the alkene is cis or trans. Similarly, if we find multiple peaks between about 1450 and 1600 cm^{-1}, indicating an aromatic C=C, we could look for bending modes to help us determine if the

Infrared Spectroscopy and the Search for Extraterrestrial Life

Our culture is obsessed with extraterrestrial life. Even though we have yet to find any hard evidence that extraterrestrial life exists, we continue to invest significant time and resources looking for it. One way this is done by the SETI (Search for Extraterrestrial Intelligence) Institute is to use radio telescopes to detect radio waves emanating from deep space. The data collected are then analyzed for patterns that might suggest the radio waves were produced by intelligent life.

But radio telescopes are not the only tool used to search for life on other planets; IR spectroscopy is a pivotal tool in this quest as well. Researchers record IR spectra of the atmospheres of distant planets, looking for absorbances characteristic of gases generally believed to be conducive to life. The IR spectrum of Earth's atmosphere shown in **Figure 16-30**, for example, reveals the presence of H_2O, CO_2, CH_4, and O_3 (ozone).

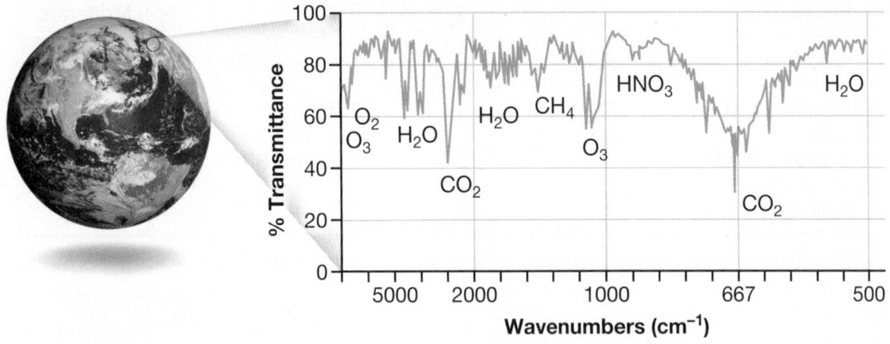
100
80
60
40
20
0
% Transmittance
O2
O3
H2O
CO2
H2O
CH4
O3
HNO3
CO2
H2O
5000
2000
1000
667
500
Wavenumbers (cm−1)

FIGURE 16-30

Of these gases, researchers are particularly interested in the existence of O_3. Ozone not only is produced from atmospheric O_2 (which sustains life) but also provides an important layer of protection from harmful UV radiation.

Whereas an IR spectrum can indicate whether an atmosphere might be able to support life, researchers believe that the detection of IR radiation in the range of 750–1000 nm (13,000–10,000 cm^{-1}) would provide more direct evidence of life. That's because, on Earth, photosynthetic plants tend to reflect IR radiation in that range with relatively high efficiency.

compound has a monosubstituted benzene ring, or if it has an ortho-, meta-, or para-disubstituted benzene ring.

To see how this might work, consider the spectra of *sec*-butylbenzene and 1,4-di-*tert*-butylbenzene shown previously in Figure 16-20 (p. 789). The low-frequency portions of these two spectra are repeated in **Figure 16-31**. Notice the relatively strong

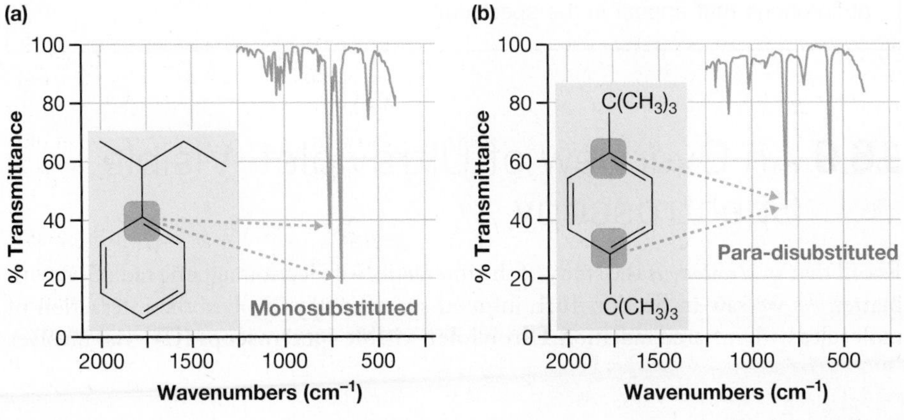
(a)
100
80
60
40
20
0
% Transmittance
Monosubstituted
2000
1500
1000
500
Wavenumbers (cm−1)
(b)
C(CH3)3
C(CH3)3
Para-disubstituted
% Transmittance
2000
1500
1000
500
Wavenumbers (cm−1)

FIGURE 16-31 Determining substitution patterns from bending vibrations The low-frequency portions of the IR spectra in Figure 16-20 (p. 789) are repeated here. (a) *sec*-Butylbenzene, which is monosubstituted, has two relatively strong bending modes at 730 and 759 cm^{-1}. (b) 1,4-Di-*tert*-butylbenzene, which is para-disubstituted, has a single bending mode at 833 cm^{-1}.

TABLE 16-2 Characteristic Frequencies of Absorption in Infrared Spectroscopy: C—H Bending Modes of Vibration

Type of Bond	Number of Bands	Frequency Range (cm^{-1})	Appearance[a]
R—CH═CH_2	2	910 and 990 (two peaks)	Strong
R_2C═CH_2	1	890	Strong
RCH═CHR (cis)	1	660–730	Strong
RCH═CHR (trans)	1	970	Strong
R_2C═CHR	1	815	Moderate
Aromatic (monosubstituted)	2	700 and 750	Strong
Aromatic (ortho)	1	750	Strong
Aromatic (meta)	2	780 and 880	Strong
Aromatic (para)	1	830	Strong

[a]Peak intensities are characterized as *strong* (%*T* near 0%), *medium* (%*T* near 50%), or *weak* (%*T* near 100%).

absorptions at 730 and 759 cm^{-1} in the spectrum of *sec*-butylbenzene (Fig. 16-31a), which represent the bending modes of a monosubstituted benzene, consistent with Table 16-2. In the spectrum of 1,4-di-*tert*-butylbenzene (Fig. 16-31b), the bending mode at 833 cm^{-1} indicates a para-disubstituted benzene, again consistent with Table 16-2.

When you are analyzing the IR spectrum of an unknown compound, bending absorptions can be particularly valuable when multiple structures are consistent with the stretching absorptions in the spectrum. For example, see Your Turns 16.28 and 16.29.

YOUR TURN 16.28

Our previous analysis of the stretching absorptions in Figure 16-24 (p. 794) showed that Unknown 1 could be any of the molecules in Figure 16-25 (p. 795). Which of those molecules are consistent with the bending absorptions that appear in the spectrum?

YOUR TURN 16.29

Our previous analysis of the stretching absorptions in Figure 16-26 (p. 795) showed that Unknown 2 could be any of the molecules in Figure 16-27 (p. 796). Which of those molecules are consistent with the bending absorptions that appear in the spectrum?

SECTION 16.9 OBJECTIVES

You will be able to:

1. Describe how an ultraviolet–visible spectrum is acquired.
2. Identify absorption peaks in a UV-vis spectrum.

16.9 An Overview of Ultraviolet–Visible Spectroscopy

Recall that *spectroscopy* is the study of the interaction of electromagnetic radiation with matter. As we saw in Section 16.1, infrared spectroscopy involves the interaction of molecules with infrared radiation. **Ultraviolet–visible spectroscopy (UV–vis)** involves

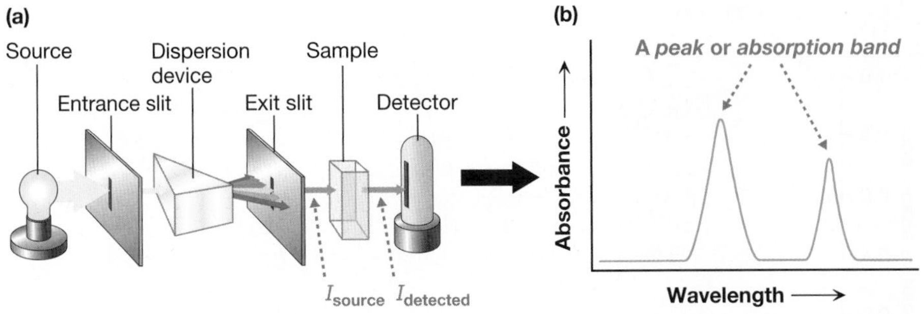
(a)
Source
Dispersion device
Sample
Entrance slit
Exit slit
Detector
I_{source} $I_{detected}$
(b)
A peak or absorption band
Absorbance
Wavelength

FIGURE 16-32 Ultraviolet–visible spectroscopy (a) General schematic of a UV–vis spectrophotometer. Specific wavelengths of light are selected to enter a sample. The intensity of light entering the sample is I_{source}, whereas the intensity of light that exits the sample and is detected by the detector is $I_{detected}$. (b) A generic UV–vis spectrum, in which wavelength is plotted on the *x* axis and absorbance is plotted on the *y* axis.

radiation from the ultraviolet and visible regions of the electromagnetic spectrum (Fig. 16-2, p. 771). The visible region is the light we can see with our eyes, which includes wavelengths from ~380 to ~740 nm. UV radiation (or UV light) has shorter wavelengths than visible light and contains the harmful radiation associated with sunburns and skin cancer.

In a typical UV–vis spectroscopy experiment (**Figure 16-32a**), a range of wavelengths (usually 200–800 nm) is sent through the sample. The intensity of light that reaches the detector ($I_{detected}$) is measured separately for each wavelength and is compared to that wavelength's intensity from the light source (I_{source}). Transmittance at each wavelength is computed as we saw previously (Eq. 16-3, p. 771), and is then converted to **absorbance (A)** according to Equation 16-6:

$$A = -\log\left(\frac{I_{detected}}{I_{source}}\right) = -\log\left(\frac{\%T}{100}\right) \quad (16\text{-}6)$$

Finally, a **UV–vis spectrum** is produced by plotting absorbance on the *y* axis against wavelength on the *x* axis, as shown for a generic case in Figure 16-32b.

Notice that the peaks in a UV–vis spectrum grow from the bottom up. This is different from the peaks we saw in IR spectra, which appear as dips down from the top. The peaks appear differently in the two types of spectra because of the relationship between absorbance and transmittance that was given in Equation 16-6:

Absorbance increases as transmittance decreases.

YOUR TURN **16.30**

Which scenario corresponds to a greater proportion of light absorbed by a sample: **(a)** $\%T = 20\%$ or $\%T = 40\%$? **(b)** $A = 0.500$ or $A = 0.750$?

16.10 Ultraviolet–Visible Spectra and Molecular Structure: Conjugation and Lone Pairs

SECTION 16.10 OBJECTIVES

You will be able to:

1. Describe how the wavelength of the longest-wavelength UV–vis absorption changes as conjugation increases or when a lone pair of electrons is present.
2. Explain how compounds that absorb in the visible region acquire characteristic colors.
3. Describe how UV–vis spectroscopy can be used for quantitative measurements.

An important aspect of any kind of spectroscopy is interpreting how certain peaks in a spectrum correlate with particular structural characteristics of a molecule. Multiple absorption peaks can appear in a UV–vis spectrum, depending on the molecule, but in this book we will primarily focus on the one that has longest wavelength. More specifically, we will focus on the wavelength of maximum absorption, called λ_{max} (pronounced lambda-max), for the longest-wavelength peak. For example, in the UV–vis spectrum of buta-1,3-diene shown in **Figure 16-33** (next page), the longest-wavelength absorption has its λ_{max} at 217 nm (notice that no other peaks appear at longer wavelengths).

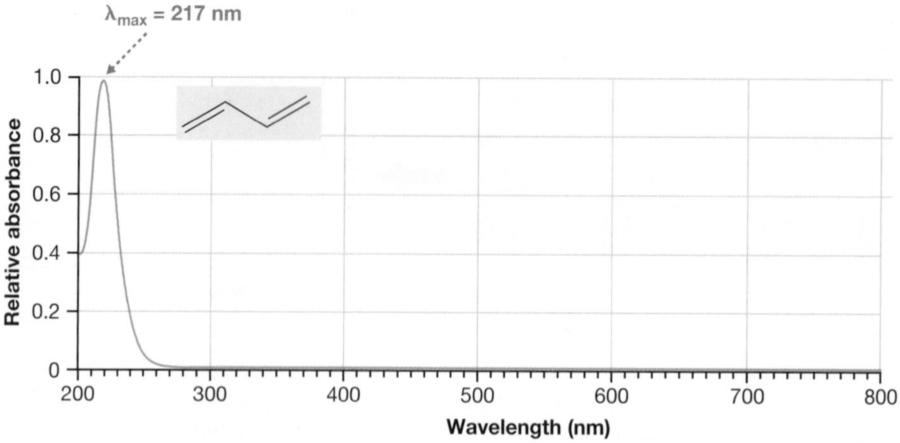

λmax = 217 nm
Relative absorbance
1.0
0.8
0.6
0.4
0.2
0
200
300
400
500
600
700
800
Wavelength (nm)

FIGURE 16-33 Ultraviolet–visible spectrum of buta-1,3-diene Relative absorbance is plotted against wavelength. The wavelength of maximum absorption, λ_{max}, is 217 nm.

Table 16-3 shows the λ_{max} of the longest-wavelength absorption for several molecules. The range is wide, from ~161 nm (in the UV region) to >450 nm (in the visible region).

To gain insight into the widely varying λ_{max} values in Table 16-3, it helps to know what happens to a molecule when a UV–vis photon is absorbed. Unlike IR photons, which increase a molecule's vibrational energy when they are absorbed (Section 16.2), the energy of a UV–vis photon is taken up by one of the molecule's *electrons* (we will investigate this in greater depth in Section 16.11). With this in mind, we can look for ways that the λ_{max} values in Table 16-3 depend on the nature of the electrons within the molecule.

Notice the significance of π electrons in Table 16-3:

- Molecules that contain only σ bonds (e.g., alkanes and cycloalkanes) do not absorb in the UV or visible regions; their longest-wavelength λ_{max} is much too short.
- Molecules that contain at least one π bond (e.g., ethene or hex-1-ene) have a longest-wavelength λ_{max} greater than about ~160 nm.

CONNECTIONS 16.6

What's in your soft drink? *trans*-Penta-1,3-diene (Table 16-3) is produced in soft drinks and energy drinks that contain the preservative sorbic acid when a spoilage yeast, such as *Saccharomyces cerevisiae*, degrades sorbic acid.

ROCKSTAR
REVOLT
MONSTER
ENERGY
ENERGY DRINK

Furthermore, of the molecules that have π bonds, *λ_{max} for the longest-wavelength absorption depends heavily on the extent of conjugation.* For example, the λ_{max} of $H_2C{=}CH_2$ and the λ_{max} of cyclohexene, both molecules that contain an isolated double bond, are similar at 161 and 182 nm, respectively. The values for λ_{max} of *cis*-penta-1,3-diene and cyclopentadiene, both molecules that contain two conjugated double bonds, are similar, too, but they are located at 223 and 239 nm, respectively. In general:

The value of the longest-wavelength λ_{max} increases as the extent of conjugation increases.

YOUR TURN 16.31

Examine the compounds in Table 16-3 that contain only carbon and hydrogen. Determine which ones have just one π bond making up the largest π system. What is the range of values for their longest-wavelength λ_{max}? Repeat this exercise for all the compounds that have two conjugated π bonds making up the largest π system, then three conjugated π bonds, and finally four conjugated π bonds.

Notice, too, the impact the presence of a *lone pair of electrons* has on the longest-wavelength λ_{max}. For example, compare formaldehyde ($H_2C{=}O$) and ethene

TABLE 16-3 λ_{max} **for the Longest-Wavelength Ultraviolet–Visible Absorptions of a Variety of Organic Compounds**[a]

Compound	λ_{max} (nm)	Compound	λ_{max} (nm)	Compound	λ_{max} (nm)
Alkanes and cycloalkanes	<150				
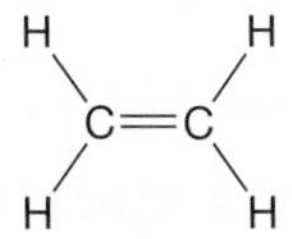 Ethene	161	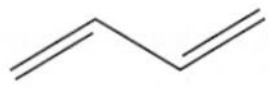 Buta-1,3-diene	217	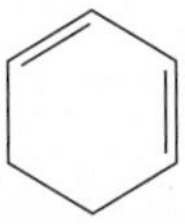 Cyclohexa-1,3-diene	256
 Hex-1-ene	177	 *cis*-Penta-1,3-diene	223	 Hexa-1,3,5-triene	274
 Penta-1,4-diene	178	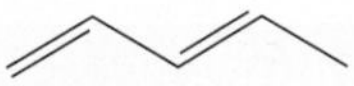 *trans*-Penta-1,3-diene	223.5	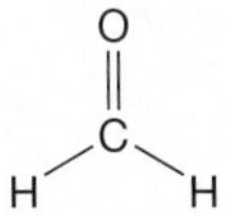 Methanal (Formaldehyde)	280
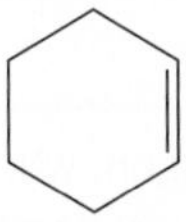 Cyclohexene	182	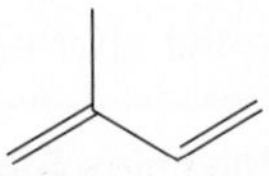 2-Methylbuta-1,3-diene (Isoprene)	224	 Octa-1,3,5,7-tetraene	290
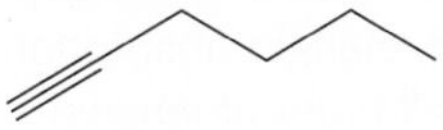 Hex-1-yne	185	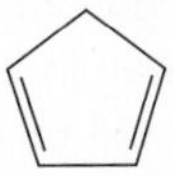 Cyclopentadiene	239	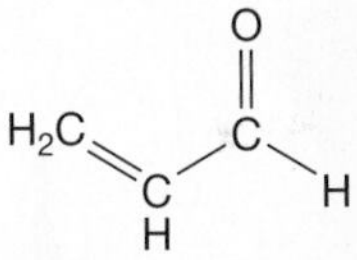 Propenal (Acrolein)	340
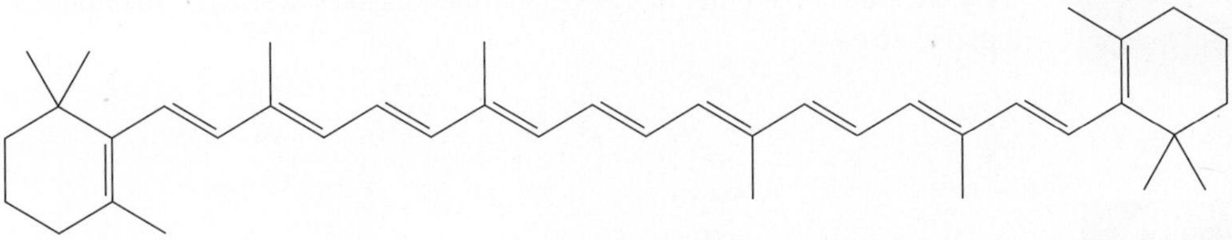 β-Carotene					455

[a]Values <200 nm are measured in the vapor phase to avoid absorption by a cuvette, solvent, or air.

($H_2C{=}CH_2$). Both molecules have just one π bond, but formaldehyde, which has lone pairs of electrons on O, has a much longer λ_{max} (280 vs. 161 nm). Similarly, propenal ($H_2C{=}CH{-}CH{=}O$) and buta-1,3-diene each have two conjugated double bonds. Propenal, however, has lone pairs of electrons and has a much longer λ_{max} (340 vs. 217 nm). In general:

> The longest-wavelength λ_{max} tends to be much longer for a species that has a lone pair of electrons than a similar species that has no lone pairs.

YOUR TURN **16.32**

(a) Considering the trend observed for just the hydrocarbons in Table 16-3, estimate λ_{max} for the longest-wavelength absorption of deca-1,3,5,7,9-pentaene ($C_{10}H_{12}$). **(b)** Considering the trend for the carbonyl-containing compounds, estimate λ_{max} for the longest-wavelength absorption of penta-2,4-dienal ($H_2C{=}CH{-}CH{=}CH{-}CH{=}O$).

SOLVED PROBLEM **16.4**

How to predict relative λ_{max} values for UV–vis spectra

Break It Down Rank these species in order of the λ_{max} for their longest-wavelength absorptions.

N
N

S **T** **U** **V**

Think	Solve
Which species have π bonds?	Molecules **S**, **T**, and **V** have π bonds, whereas **U** has only σ bonds. Therefore, the longest-wavelength absorption will be the shortest for **U**.
Which species have lone pairs?	Molecules **S** and **V** have a lone pair on nitrogen, whereas **T** has no lone pairs. Therefore, the longest-wavelength absorption for **T** will be shorter than the ones for **S** and **V**.
What is the extent of conjugation in each species?	The double bonds are isolated in **S**, whereas they are conjugated in **V**. Therefore, the longest-wavelength absorption in **V** will be longer than in **S**. The overall order of longest-wavelength absorptions is as follows: **U** < **T** < **S** < **V**.

Try It Predict the order of the λ_{max} for the longest-wavelength absorptions in these species.

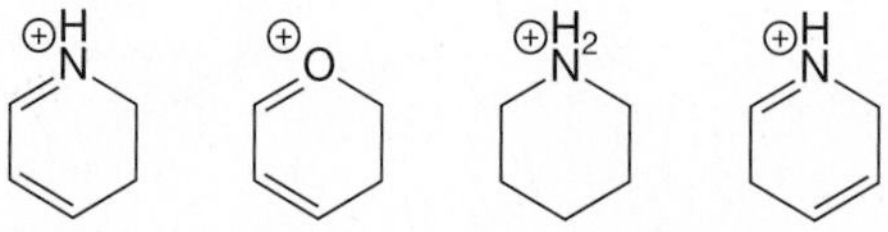

⊕H
N
⊕
O
⊕H2
N
⊕H
N

W **X** **Y** **Z**

(a)

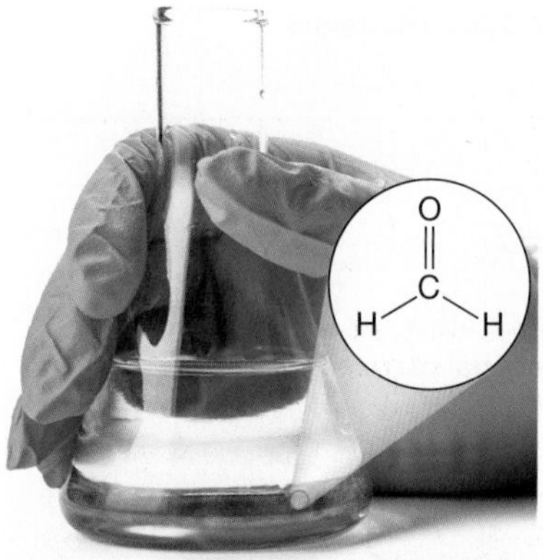

O
C
H
H

(b)

FIGURE 16-34 Ultraviolet–visible absorption and color
(a) Formaldehyde is colorless because it absorbs in the UV portion of the spectrum. (b) Absorption by β-carotene in the visible portion of the electromagnetic spectrum gives carrots their characteristic color.

16.10a UV–Vis Absorption and Color

Liquid formaldehyde is colorless (**Figure 16-34a**), whereas β-carotene, the compound responsible for the color of carrots, is orange (Fig. 16-34b). What makes these compounds so different in color?

White light is a mixture of all wavelengths (colors) from the visible spectrum (about 400–700 nm), and when a compound absorbs a particular visible wavelength, our eyes will detect the absence of that wavelength as a characteristic color. With this in mind, notice in Table 16-3 (p. 803) that formaldehyde's longest-wavelength absorption is at 280 nm, which is in the UV region of the spectrum. Therefore, all the colors of white light pass through formaldehyde and reach our eye, so the white light appears unaffected.

β-Carotene, on the other hand, absorbs at 455 nm, which is in the visible part of the spectrum. Therefore, when white light impinges on the compound, the 455-nm light will not reach our eye, giving the appearance of a color that is nonwhite.

Why, specifically, should β-carotene appear orange? When a particular color of light is removed from the spectrum, our eye registers the *complementary* color. In the case of β-carotene, 455-nm light is blue and its complementary color is orange, as illustrated in **Figure 16-35**, a color wheel in which complementary colors are located on opposite sides.

YOUR TURN **16.33**

Crystal violet is a dye that is used as a pH indicator. At a pH of −1, a solution of the dye absorbs at 420 nm. What color does that solution appear?
Hint: Use Figure 16-2 (p. 771) to determine the color to which 420 nm roughly corresponds.

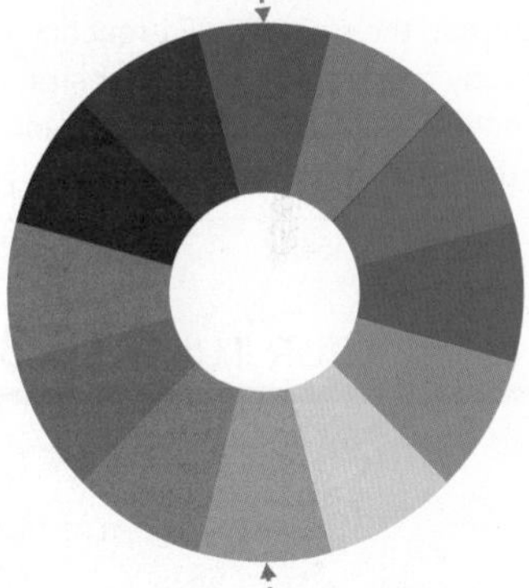
β-Carotene absorbs in this blue region.
Our eye registers the complementary color, which is orange.

FIGURE 16-35 Complementary colors of visible light
Complementary colors of visible light are found on opposite sides of this color wheel. When a particular color of light is removed from white light, the human eye registers the complementary color.

16.10b UV–Vis Spectroscopy in Quantitative Measurements

While UV–vis spectra can help elucidate the structure of a molecular species, chemists typically rely on other methods to determine a species' structure. Mass spectrometry (Chapter 15), infrared spectroscopy (Sections 16.1–16.8), and nuclear magnetic resonance spectroscopy (Chapter 17) all provide more structural information than UV–vis spectroscopy. For this reason:

The most common use of UV–vis spectroscopy is to *quantify the amount* of one or more compounds present in solution.

Using UV–vis spectroscopy to quantify a substance draws on the **Beer–Lambert law** (Eq. 16-7), which you may have encountered in general chemistry:

$$A = \varepsilon l C \qquad (16\text{-}7)$$

The Beer–Lambert law states that absorbance, A, is directly proportional to (1) the concentration, C, of the species responsible for absorbing light; (2) the length, l, of the sample through which the light travels; and (3) the **molar absorptivity** (ε, the Greek letter epsilon), also called the *extinction coefficient*, an experimentally derived quantity that is characteristic of a given species at a given wavelength of radiation.

The Beer–Lambert law takes the form it does because the amount of light that a sample absorbs is proportional to the number of light-absorbing molecules the light encounters as it travels through the sample. The number of light-absorbing molecules, in turn, increases with both C and l. The molar absorptivity reflects *the probability that light of a given wavelength will be absorbed when it encounters light-absorbing molecules.*

YOUR TURN **16.34**

If increasing the wavelength of light causes the molar absorptivity of a sample to decrease by a factor of 3, what happens to the measured absorbance?

In a quantitative experiment using UV–vis spectroscopy, the path length (l) will be held constant; it's typically a standard length such as 1.0 cm. A particular λ will be chosen to monitor, so the molar absorptivity (ε) will be constant, too. Therefore:

In a quantitative experiment using UV–vis spectroscopy, the measured absorbance (A) is directly proportional to the concentration (C) of the light-absorbing molecules.

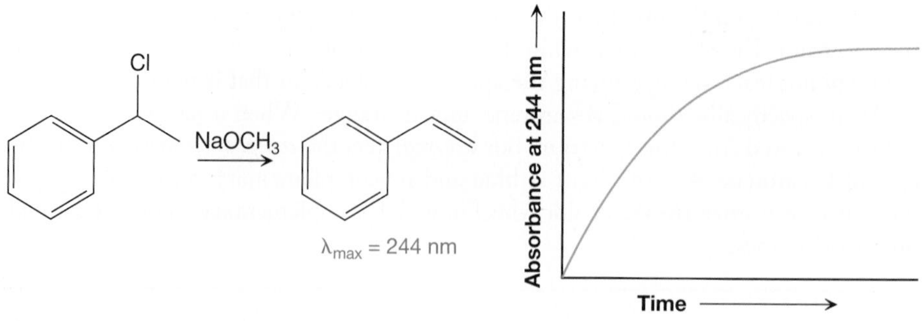

Cl
NaOCH$_3$
λ_{max} = 244 nm
Absorbance at 244 nm
Time

FIGURE 16-36 Ultraviolet–visible spectroscopy and kinetics The kinetics of the elimination reaction on the left can be investigated by monitoring the absorbance at the product's λ_{max} as a function of time. As shown on the right, as the concentration of the product increases, so does the absorbance.

◂ RECALL

In Section 8.3, we learned that the overall reaction rate of an E2 reaction depends on the concentrations of both the base and the substrate. By contrast, the rate of an E1 reaction is directly proportional to the substrate concentration only; it is *independent* of the base concentration.

Using UV–vis spectroscopy for quantitative measurements is particularly valuable in kinetics experiments, where relative reactant and/or product concentrations (i.e., absorbance at λ_{max}) are monitored over time. Suppose, for example, we want to determine whether the elimination reaction shown in **Figure 16-36** takes place by the E2 or E1 mechanism. The product has a λ_{max} of 244 nm, so as the reaction progresses, the absorbance at that wavelength increases. Because absorbance is directly proportional to concentration, the initial reaction rate is simply the change in absorbance divided by time. Therefore, if the concentration of the base, $NaOCH_3$, is doubled and the absorbance at 244 nm that is measured over an initial period also doubles, we can conclude that the reaction proceeds by the E2 mechanism, not the E1 (see top Recall box).

YOUR TURN **16.35**

For the reaction in Figure 16-36, suppose that the concentration of the base is doubled and the absorbance at 244 nm that is measured over an initial period remains unchanged. What would we conclude about the mechanism? Explain.

SECTION 16.11 OBJECTIVES

You will be able to:

1. Articulate the type of electron transition that corresponds to the longest-wavelength UV–vis absorption.
2. Explain why the wavelength of absorption increases as the extent of π conjugation increases, and decreases substantially when a lone pair of electrons is present.

16.11 A Deeper Look: Molecular Orbital Theory and Ultraviolet–Visible Spectroscopy

In Section 16.10, we mentioned that the energy of an absorbed UV–vis photon is taken up by an electron. Knowing that electrons in a molecule must reside in molecular orbitals (MOs) and that each MO has a very specific energy:

The absorption of a UV–vis photon causes an electron transition from a lower-energy MO to a higher-energy MO.

For a given species, a variety of such electron transitions are possible, each requiring a different photon energy. Recall, however, that our focus in Section 16.10 was on the longest-wavelength λ_{max}, which corresponds to the lowest energy transition possible (recall from Eq. 16-2 that a photon's energy and wavelength are inversely proportional). As shown in **Figure 16-37**, for a species in its ground state electron configuration:

◂ RECALL

Section 3.10 showed that the highest-energy MO that contains an electron is the HOMO. The lowest-energy MO that is empty is the LUMO.

The longest-wavelength λ_{max} corresponds to the transition of an electron from the highest occupied molecular orbital (HOMO) to the lowest unoccupied molecular orbital (LUMO), called the **HOMO–LUMO transition** (see bottom Recall box).

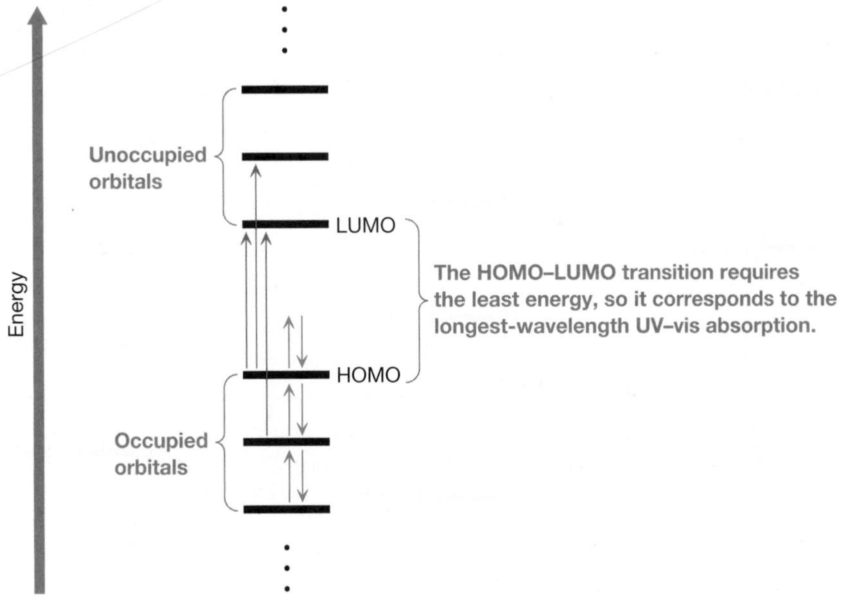

Energy
Unoccupied orbitals
LUMO
The HOMO–LUMO transition requires the least energy, so it corresponds to the longest-wavelength UV–vis absorption.
HOMO
Occupied orbitals

FIGURE 16-37 Electron transitions in ultraviolet–visible spectroscopy In UV–vis spectroscopy, the absorption of a photon typically corresponds to the promotion of an electron from an occupied MO to an unoccupied one. These electron transitions are represented by the blue arrows.

YOUR TURN **16.36**

In Figure 16-37, draw arrows to represent five more electron transitions involving the six MOs that are given. How do the energies of the transitions you drew correspond to the energy required for the HOMO–LUMO transition?

Knowing that the HOMO–LUMO transition corresponds to the longest-wavelength λ_{max}, we can begin to explain the trends we observed in Section 16.10. For example, recall that *the longest-wavelength λ_{max} tends to be much longer for species that contain a π bond than for species that contain only σ bonds*. Thus:

Species containing π bonds tend to have a smaller difference in energy between the HOMO and LUMO than species containing only σ bonds.

This observation is supported by the MO energy diagrams for ethane and ethene shown in **Figure 16-38** (next page), which we first derived in Sections 3.11a and 3.11b. For ethane (Fig. 16-38a), a molecule that contains only σ bonds, the HOMO is a σ bonding MO and the LUMO is a σ* antibonding MO. Therefore, the HOMO–LUMO transition is a **$\sigma \rightarrow \sigma^*$ transition** (pronounced "sigma-to-sigma-star"). Ethene (Fig. 16-38b), on the other hand, contains a π bond, so the HOMO is the π bonding MO and the LUMO is the π* antibonding MO. Ethene's HOMO–LUMO transition is therefore a **$\pi \rightarrow \pi^*$ transition** (pronounced "pi-to-pi-star"). As we can see, the $\pi \rightarrow \pi^*$ transition requires less energy (i.e., a longer-wavelength photon) than the $\sigma \rightarrow \sigma^*$ transition.

We also learned in Section 16.10 that *the longest-wavelength λ_{max} increases as the extent of conjugation in the molecule increases*. Thus:

As the extent of conjugation in a molecule increases, the energy difference between the HOMO and LUMO decreases.

We can see this trend explicitly by comparing the MO energy diagrams of ethene (Fig. 16-38b), buta-1,3-diene (Fig. 16-38c), and hexa-1,3,5-triene (Fig. 16-38d). Specifically, as discussed in Section 14.8a, a π system that exhibits more extensive conjugation contains a greater number of π MOs (see Recall box). As that number of π MOs increases, the HOMO and LUMO become more similar in energy.

◀ RECALL

Section 14.8 showed that, for a set of conjugated π bonds, all contributed *p* AOs mix to produce one π system of MOs. Because the number of orbitals is conserved on mixing, the number of π MOs making up a π system increases as the number of conjugated double bonds increases.

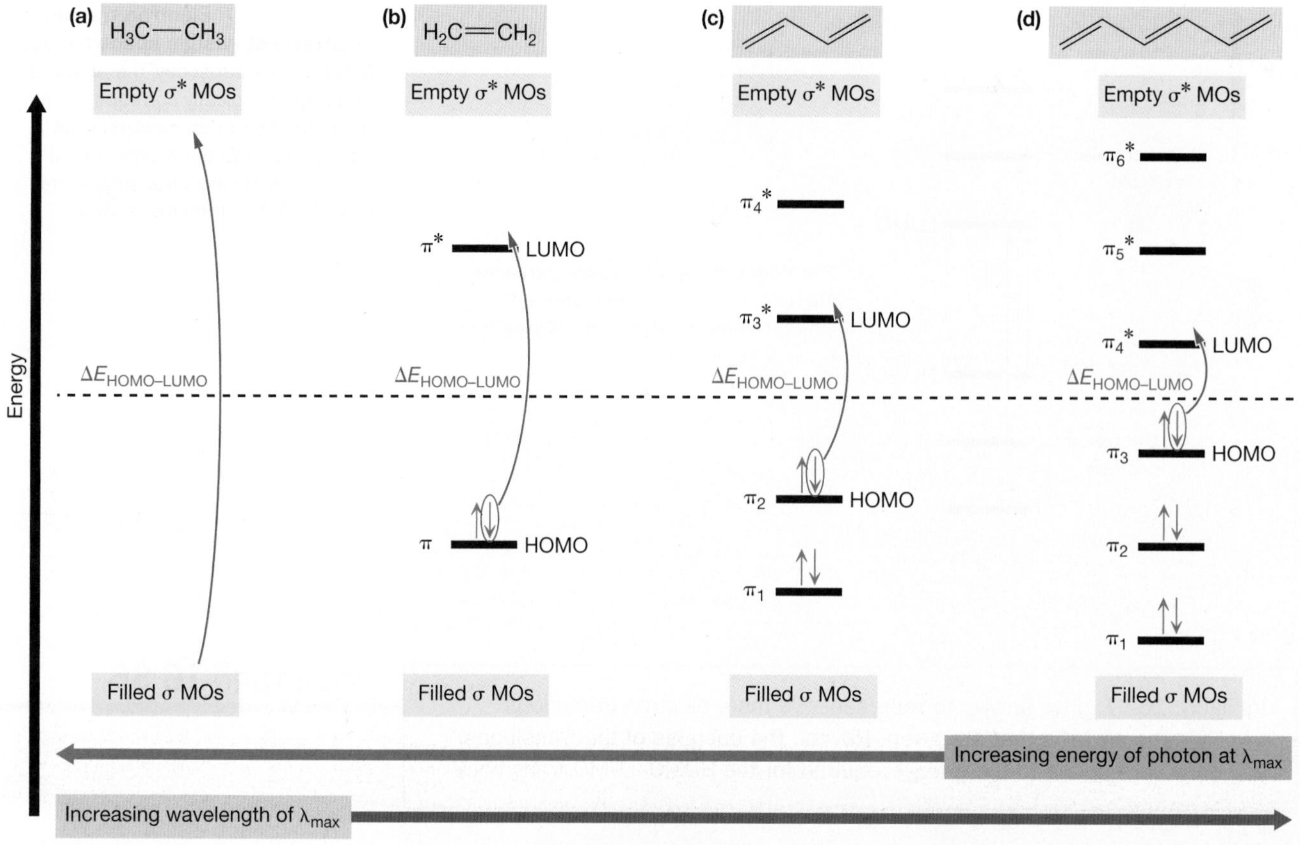

(a)
$H_3C—CH_3$
(b)
$H_2C=CH_2$
(c)
(d)
Empty σ* MOs
Empty σ* MOs
Empty σ* MOs
Empty σ* MOs
π6*
π4*
π*
LUMO
π5*
π3*
LUMO
π4*
LUMO
Energy
ΔE HOMO–LUMO
ΔE HOMO–LUMO
ΔE HOMO–LUMO
ΔE HOMO–LUMO
π3
HOMO
π2
HOMO
π
HOMO
π2
π1
π1
Filled σ MOs
Filled σ MOs
Filled σ MOs
Filled σ MOs
Increasing energy of photon at λmax
Increasing wavelength of λmax

FIGURE 16-38 Conjugation and HOMO–LUMO transitions Molecular orbital energy diagrams are shown for the π MOs of (a) ethane, (b) ethene, (c) buta-1,3-diene, and (d) hexa-1,3,5-triene. As conjugation of the π MOs increases, the HOMO–LUMO energy difference ($\Delta E_{\text{HOMO–LUMO}}$) decreases, so the value of λ_{max} must increase.

◂ RECALL

In the MO–VB model for molecules (Section 3.11), a lone pair of electrons occupies an orbital that was contributed by just one AO; that orbital is not the result of mixing. Therefore, the energy of an orbital containing a lone pair is similar to the AO energies, and it is defined as nonbonding.

Finally, we learned in Section 16.10 that *the longest-wavelength λ_{max} tends to be substantially longer when a lone pair of electrons is present*. Thus:

> The energy between the HOMO and LUMO tends to be smaller for species that possess a lone pair of electrons.

We can see why this is true by examining the energy diagrams of ethene and formaldehyde ($H_2C=O$) in **Figure 16-39**.

In formaldehyde, the HOMO is a nonbonding MO (i.e., *not* a π MO), which holds a lone pair of electrons on O (see Recall box). Therefore, the HOMO–LUMO transition is from the nonbonding orbital to the π* orbital, so it is called an **n → π* transition** (pronounced "n-to-pi-star"). Notice that formaldehyde's nonbonding orbitals are intermediate in energy between the π and π* MOs (Fig. 16-39b). Therefore, the n → π* transition requires substantially *less* energy than the π → π* transition (Fig. 16-39a).

YOUR TURN 16.37

How does the energy of the HOMO–LUMO transition for $H_2C=NH$ compare to that for $H_2C=CH_2$? Explain.

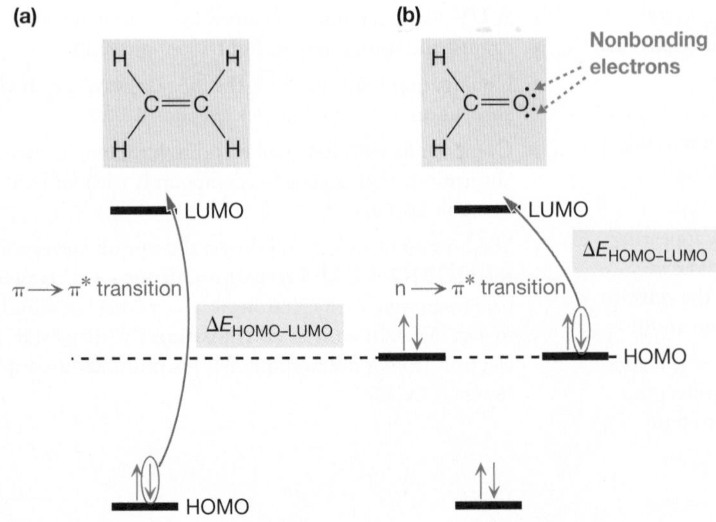
(a)
H
H
C=C
H
H
LUMO
π ⟶ π* transition
ΔE HOMO–LUMO
HOMO
(b)
H
C=O
H
Nonbonding
electrons
LUMO
ΔE HOMO–LUMO
n ⟶ π* transition
HOMO

FIGURE 16-39 Nonbonding electrons and HOMO–LUMO transitions Molecular orbital energy diagrams are shown for (a) ethene and (b) formaldehyde. The presence of the nonbonding electrons on O significantly decreases the HOMO–LUMO energy difference ($\Delta E_{\text{HOMO–LUMO}}$).

CONNECTIONS 16.7

A molecule that is out of this world Methanimine, $H_2C{=}NH$ (Your Turn 16.37), has been detected in distant galaxies. This is significant because methanimine is viewed as a possible precursor to amino acids, so its existence in distant galaxies supports the idea that life can exist elsewhere in the universe.

Chapter Summary and Key Terms

- **Spectroscopy** is the study of how electromagnetic radiation interacts with matter.
- Electromagnetic radiation behaves as both a wave and a particle. As a wave, it exhibits frequency (ν) and wavelength (λ): $\nu = c/\lambda$. As a particle, each photon contains a certain amount of energy: $E_{\text{photon}} = h\nu_{\text{photon}}$. **(Section 16.1)**
- In **infrared (IR) spectroscopy**, a range of frequencies of infrared radiation is sent through a sample, and the amount of radiation absorbed at each frequency is measured. **(Section 16.1)**
- In an IR spectrum, **transmittance** (the fraction of incident light that passes through a sample) is plotted against IR frequency, in units of **wavenumbers (cm^{-1})**. Peaks appear as dips down from the top. **(Section 16.1)**
- Absorption of an IR photon excites a particular type of vibration within a molecule. Absorption occurs when the frequency of the photon equals the frequency of that vibration. **(Section 16.2)**
  - In a **stretching** vibration, the distance between two atoms in a chemical bond grows longer and shorter.
  - In a **bending** vibration, an angle becomes larger and smaller.
- The highest-frequency vibrations in an organic molecule are those of Q—H bonds (where Q is a heavy atom like C, N, or O), because H is very light. **(Sections 16.3 and 16.4)**
- For a bond between two heavy atoms, the vibrational frequency depends on the strength and stiffness of the bond. Thus, vibrational frequency decreases in the order triple bond > double bond > single bond. Vibrational frequency also decreases in the order alkyne (*sp*) C—H > alkene (sp^2) C—H > alkane (sp^3) C—H. **(Sections 16.3 and 16.4)**
- The ball-and-spring model, which treats molecules as masses connected by springs, accounts for several of the trends for peak locations in IR spectra. **Hooke's law** mathematically relates the frequency of vibration to the spring's **force constant (k)** and the **reduced mass (μ)** of the masses connected by the spring. **(Section 16.4)**
- The intensity of an IR stretching absorption increases, in general, as the magnitude of the dipole undergoing vibration increases. Thus, polar bonds such as C=O and O—H tend to have strong IR absorptions, whereas symmetric C=C bonds tend to have weak absorptions. **(Section 16.5)**
- The O—H stretch typically appears as a broad absorption due to extensive hydrogen bonding. **(Section 16.6a)**
- The N—H stretch appears as two peaks for a primary amide or amine and one peak for a secondary amide or amine. No N—H peaks appear for a tertiary amide or amine. **(Section 16.6b)**
- The C=O stretch of an amide is lower in frequency than that of a ketone or aldehyde, whereas an ester's C=O stretch is at a higher frequency than that of a ketone or aldehyde. Conjugation of a C=O bond tends to lower the absorption frequency by ~20–40 cm^{-1}. **(Section 16.6c)**
- The C=C stretch of an alkene generally appears above 1620 cm^{-1}, whereas that of an aromatic ring usually appears as two or three peaks in the 1450–1600 cm^{-1} range. **(Section 16.6d)**
- A C≡N stretching absorption is usually more intense than a C≡C stretching absorption, due to the greater bond dipole of C≡N. **(Section 16.6e)**

- The intensity of an alkane C—H stretching band (2800–3000 cm^{-1}) is indicative of the number of C—H bonds that contribute to it. **(Section 16.6f)**
- IR spectra can be analyzed systematically to uncover structural information about an unknown compound. It is best to begin by analyzing the stretching absorptions above 1400 cm^{-1}. **(Section 16.7)**
- Bending modes of vibration are low in frequency, appearing below 1500 cm^{-1}. Absorptions that are characteristic of bending modes of vibration can help distinguish the substitution pattern of an alkene or aromatic ring. **(Section 16.8)**
- In **UV–vis spectroscopy**, a range of wavelengths of UV and visible light is sent through a sample. At each wavelength, the percent transmittance is measured and converted to **absorbance (*A*)**, where $A = -\log\left(\frac{\%T}{100}\right)$. **(Section 16.9)**
- A **UV–vis spectrum** is obtained by plotting absorbance against the wavelength of light. **(Section 16.9)**
- Conjugation tends to cause the longest-wavelength UV–vis absorption to become longer. **(Section 16.10)**
- Compounds with lone pairs tend to have longer-wavelength absorptions than analogous compounds without lone pairs. **(Section 16.10)**
- The longest-wavelength UV–vis absorption corresponds to the **HOMO–LUMO transition**. In a **$\pi \rightarrow \pi^*$ transition** ("pi-to-pi-star"), an electron from a π MO is promoted to a π^* MO. In an **$n \rightarrow \pi^*$ transition** ("n-to-pi-star"), an electron from a nonbonding MO is promoted to a π^* MO. **(Section 16.11)**

Problems

Sections 16.1–16.3 and 16.5 Infrared Spectroscopy and Peak Locations and Intensities

16.1 In the following three compounds, estimate the IR stretching frequency for each lettered bond.

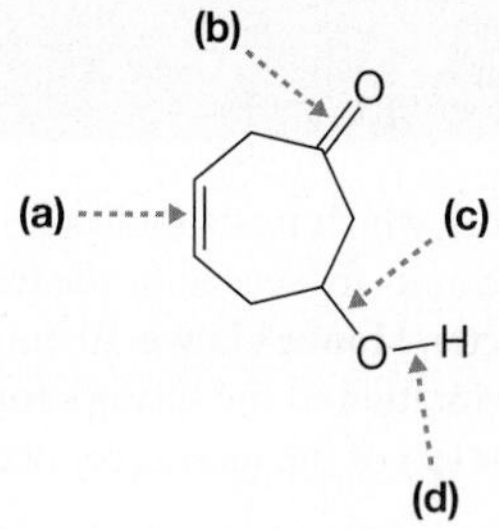
(a)
(b)
(c)
(d)
O
O—H
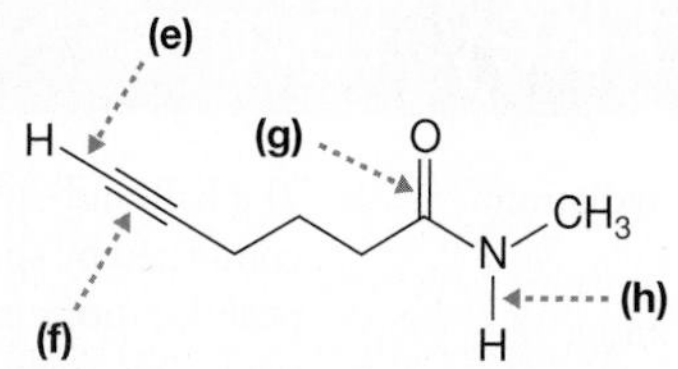
(e)
(f)
(g)
(h)
H
O
N
CH3
H
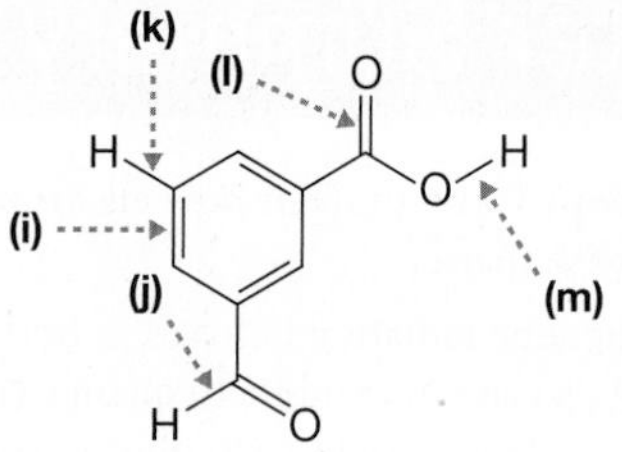
(i)
(j)
(k)
(l)
(m)
H
O
H
H
O

16.2 What differences in the IR spectra of the reactant and product would enable you to tell that each of the following reactions took place?

(a)
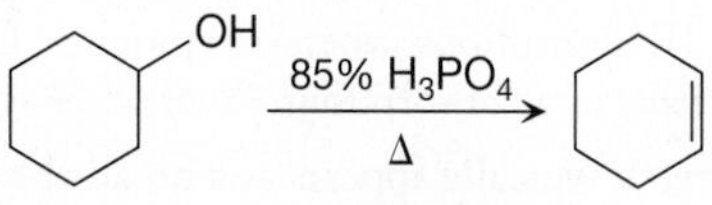
OH
85% H3PO4
Δ

(b)
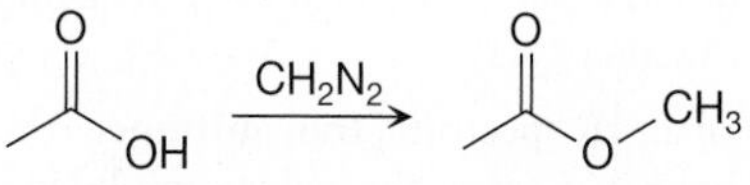
O
OH
CH2N2
O
O
CH3

(c)
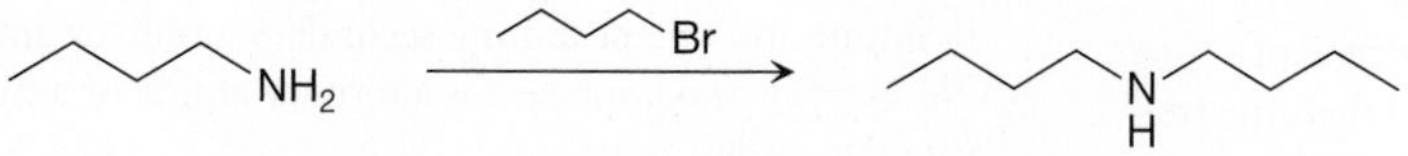
NH2
Br
N
H

(d)
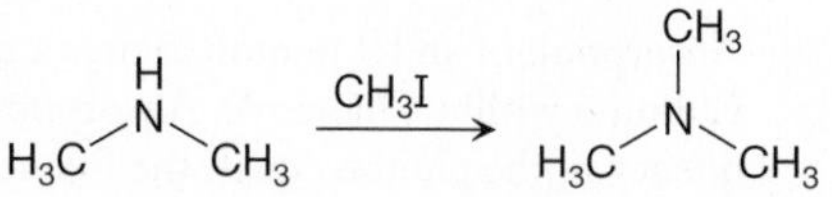
H
N
H3C
CH3
CH3I
CH3
N
H3C
CH3

(e)
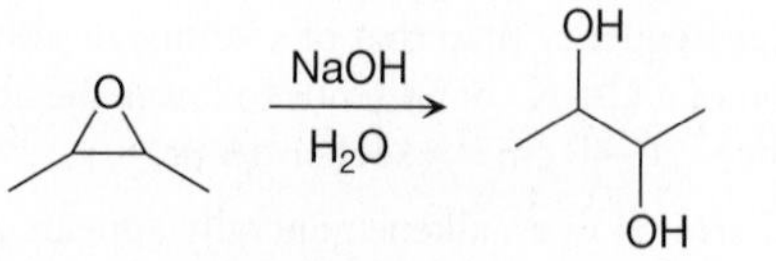
O
NaOH
H2O
OH
OH

(f)
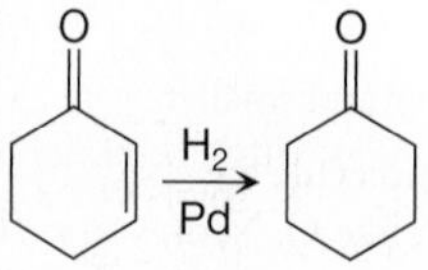
O
H2
Pd
O

(g)
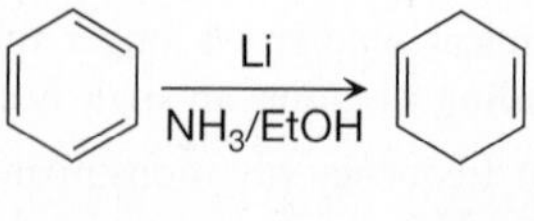
Li
NH3/EtOH

(h)
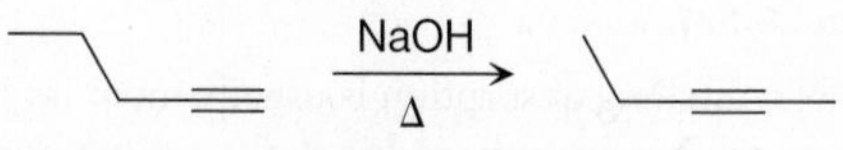
NaOH
Δ

(i)
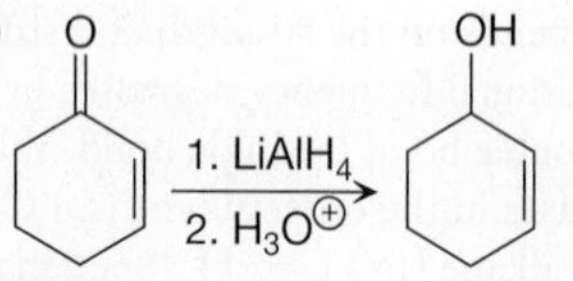
O
1. LiAlH4
2. H3O⊕
OH

16.3 How could you use IR spectroscopy to distinguish between compounds **A** and **B**?

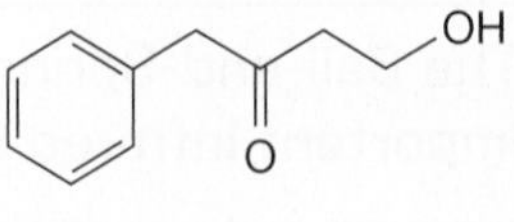
OH
O

A

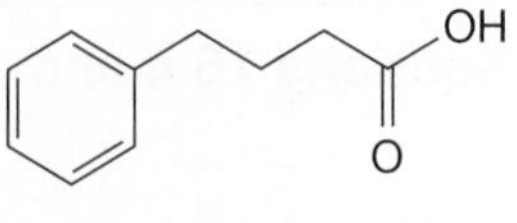
OH
O

B

16.4 The compound that generated this IR spectrum has a ketone C═O bond, an alkene C═C bond, and alkene C—H bonds. **(a)** Identify the peaks in the spectrum that correspond to these bonds. **(b)** Does the compound contain an OH group? How do you know?

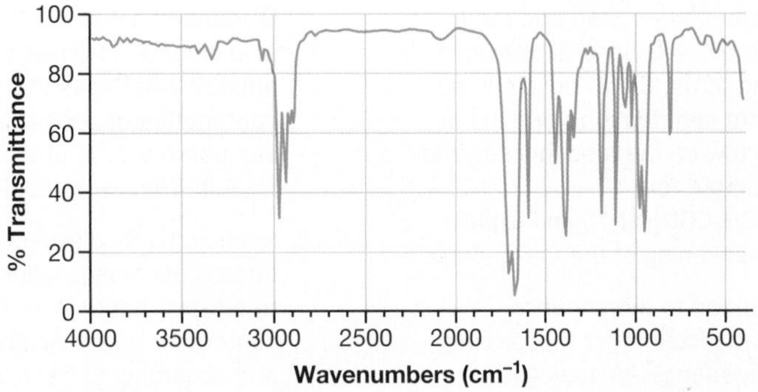
100
80
60
40
20
0
% Transmittance
4000
3500
3000
2500
2000
1500
1000
500
Wavenumbers (cm⁻¹)

16.5 The compound that generated this IR spectrum has an alcohol O—H bond and alkane C—H bonds. **(a)** Identify the peaks in the spectrum that correspond to these bonds. **(b)** Does the compound contain a C═O bond, a C≡N bond, or a C═C bond? How do you know?

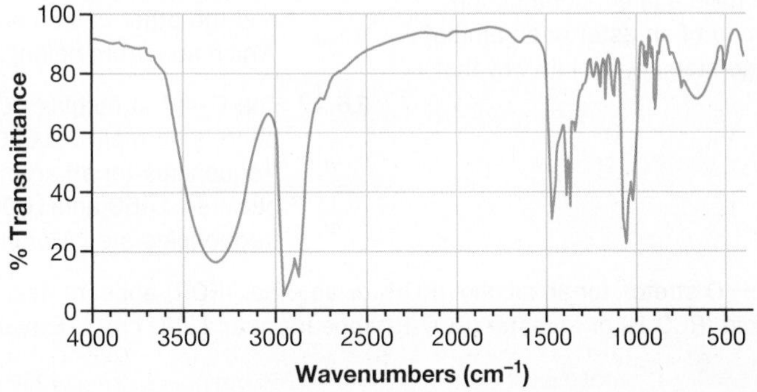
100
80
60
40
20
0
% Transmittance
4000
3500
3000
2500
2000
1500
1000
500
Wavenumbers (cm⁻¹)

16.6 Sketch the IR spectrum that each compound would produce. Have the *x* axis range from 400 to 4000 cm^{-1} and pay attention to each absorption's frequency, breadth, and intensity.

(a)

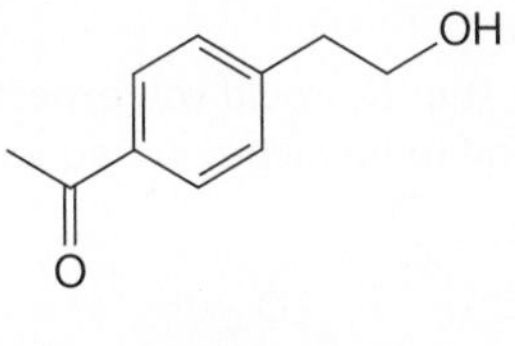
OH
O

(b)

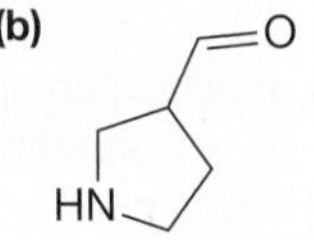
O
HN

(c)

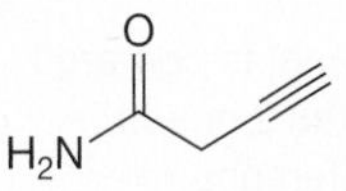
O
H2N

(d)

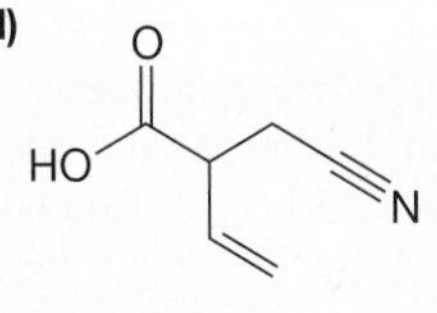
O
HO
N

16.7 In which compound, **C** or **D**, would you expect the C═C stretching absorption to be more intense? Explain.

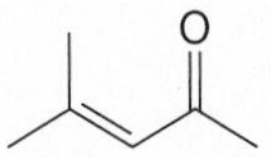
O

C

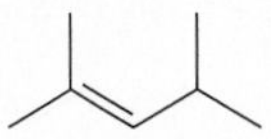

D

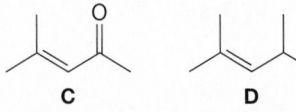

16.8 The stretching frequencies for C═N and C—N bonds are not given in Table 16-1. **(a)** What would you estimate the frequencies of these vibrations to be? **(b)** Do you think these absorptions will be intense or weak?

16.9 The nitro group (NO_2) has two characteristic absorptions for its stretching vibrations: one represents a symmetric stretch and the other an asymmetric stretch. **(a)** Depict these two stretching vibrations similar to the way Figure 16-5 (p. 773) shows the CH_2 stretches. **(b)** Do you think these absorptions will be intense or weak?

16.10 The Lewis structure of carbon monoxide, CO, is best represented with a triple bond connecting the two atoms. At what approximate frequency would you expect carbon monoxide to absorb IR radiation?

Sections 16.4 and 16.6 The Ball-and-Spring Model for Explaining Infrared Peak Locations and Important Infrared Stretches

16.11 In which compound would you expect the C═O bond to absorb at the higher frequency: **E** or **F**? Explain.

O
^{18}O

E **F**

16.12 Section 16.6c discusses how the frequency of the C═O stretch for an amide is lower than it is for a ketone, suggesting that the C═O bond is weaker in an amide. This weakening of the C═O bond can be explained by the significant contribution from one of its resonance structures toward the resonance hybrid. Draw that resonance structure for *N,N*-dimethylacetamide [$CH_3CON(CH_3)_2$] and explain how it accounts for the weakening of the C═O bond.

16.13 Problem 16.12 calls attention to a resonance structure of an amide that accounts for the lowering of the C═O stretching frequency. An analogous resonance structure can be drawn for an ester. **(a)** Draw that resonance structure for methyl acetate ($CH_3CO_2CH_3$). **(b)** Given that an ester's C═O stretching frequency is higher than an amide's, does that resonance structure have a larger contribution toward the resonance hybrid of an ester or an amide? Using arguments of charge stability, explain why that should be so.

16.14 The carbonyl stretch of acetyl chloride (CH_3COCl) is found at 1806 cm^{-1}. Is the C═O bond in an acid chloride stronger or weaker than the one in an amide? What does this suggest about the resonance contribution of a lone pair on Cl in an acid chloride compared to that of the lone pair on N in an amide? Explain. *Hint*: See Problems 16.12 and 16.13.

16.15 Section 16.6c discusses how the frequency of a C═O stretch decreases when the C═O bond is conjugated to a C═C bond. Draw the pertinent resonance contributor of a conjugated carbonyl (C═C—C═O), and according to the resulting resonance hybrid, explain why the frequency decreases.

16.16 A student acquires the IR spectra of the isomers cyclohepta-1,3-diene and 3-methylcyclohexa-1,4-diene. One spectrum has an absorption band at 1648 cm^{-1} and the other has an absorption band at 1618 cm^{-1}. Which spectrum belongs to which compound?

16.17 The C═C stretching frequency of an isolated C═C bond is normally ~1620 cm^{-1}. The C═C stretching frequencies for an aromatic ring are typically found between 1450 and 1600 cm^{-1}. Explain why the frequencies are lower in an aromatic ring.

16.18 In an IR spectrum, the C—O stretch for an alcohol (ROH) or an ether (ROR) appears near 1050 cm^{-1}, but the C—O stretch for a carboxylic acid (RCO_2H) or an ester (RCO_2R) appears near 1250 cm^{-1}. Explain why.

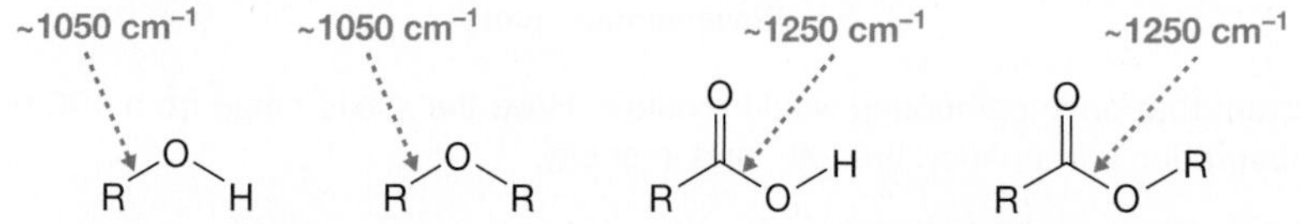

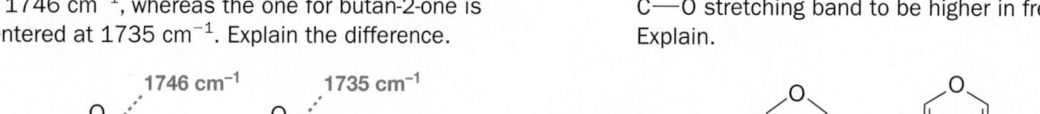

~1050 cm^{-1}
~1050 cm^{-1}
~1250 cm^{-1}
~1250 cm^{-1}
R O H
R O R
R O O H
R O O R

16.19 The C═O stretching frequency for butanal is centered at 1746 cm^{-1}, whereas the one for butan-2-one is centered at 1735 cm^{-1}. Explain the difference.

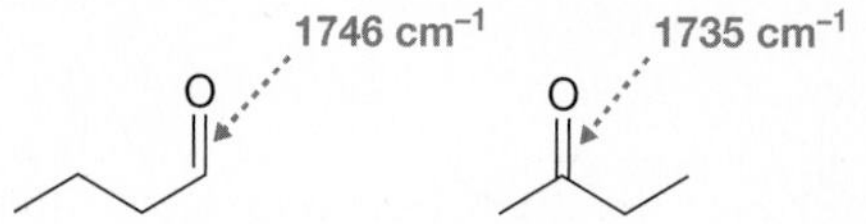

1746 cm^{-1}
1735 cm^{-1}
O
O

16.20 In which compound, **G** or **H**, would you expect the C—O stretching band to be higher in frequency? Explain.

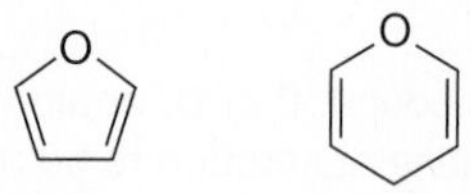

O
O

G **H**

16.21 The IR spectra for cyclohexanone and cyclobutanone are shown. In which compound is the C═O bond stronger? How do you know?

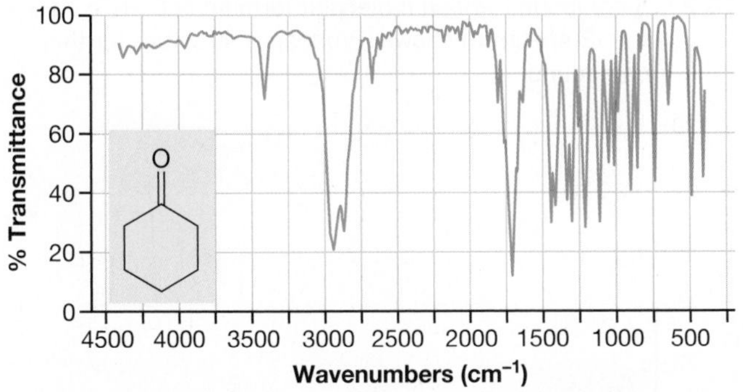

100
80
60
40
20
0
% Transmittance
O
4500 4000 3500 3000 2500 2000 1500 1000 500
Wavenumbers (cm⁻¹)

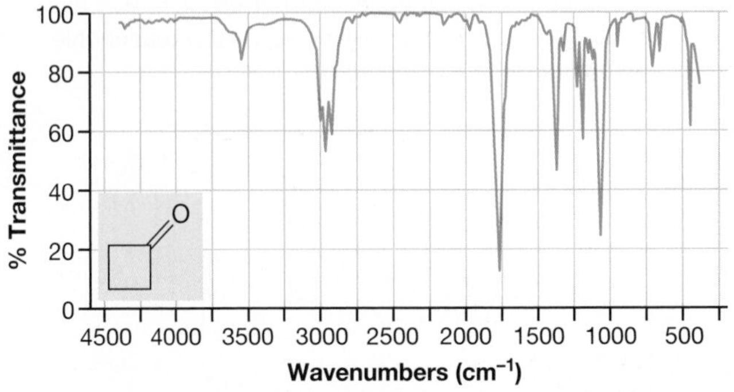

100
80
60
40
20
0
% Transmittance
O
4500 4000 3500 3000 2500 2000 1500 1000 500
Wavenumbers (cm⁻¹)

16.22 Which compound, **I** or **J**, do you expect to exhibit the lower C═O stretching frequency? Explain.

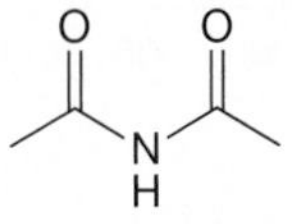

O
O
N
H

I

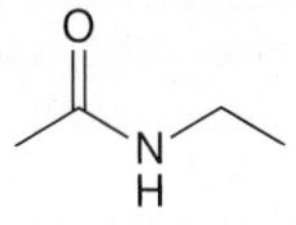

O
N
H

J

16.23 Sodium acetate has a strong, sharp IR peak appearing at 1569 cm^{-1}, as shown in the spectrum here. To what kind of stretching mode does this band correspond? Why is its frequency so different from that of an ester?

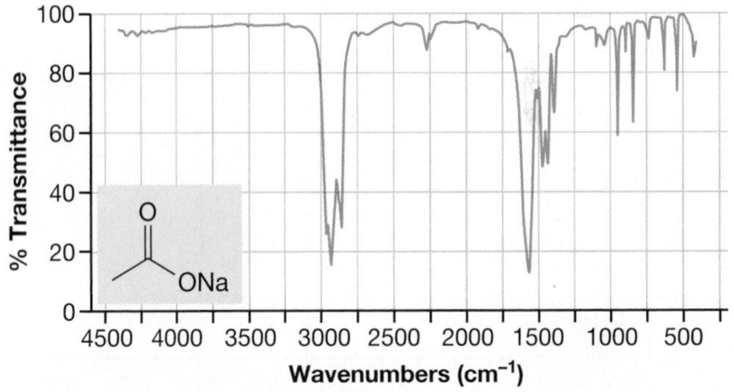

100
80
60
40
20
0
% Transmittance
O
ONa
4500 4000 3500 3000 2500 2000 1500 1000 500
Wavenumbers (cm⁻¹)

16.24 Based on the relative intensities of the alkane C—H absorption bands, match compounds **K**–**M** with Spectra 1–3.

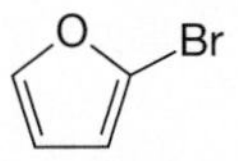

O
Br

K

O

L

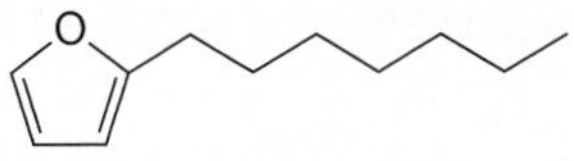

O

M

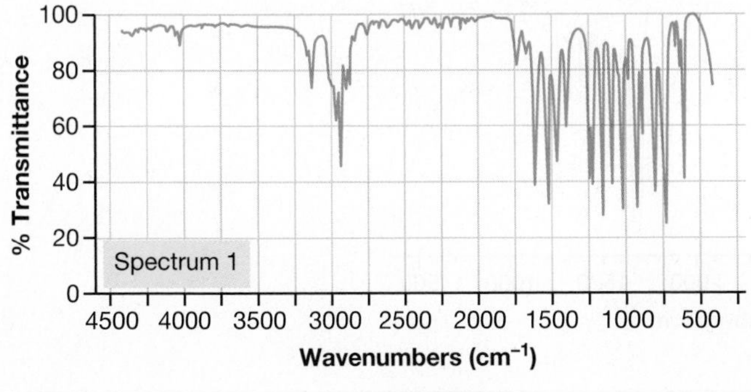

100
80
60
40
20
0
% Transmittance
Spectrum 1
4500 4000 3500 3000 2500 2000 1500 1000 500
Wavenumbers (cm⁻¹)

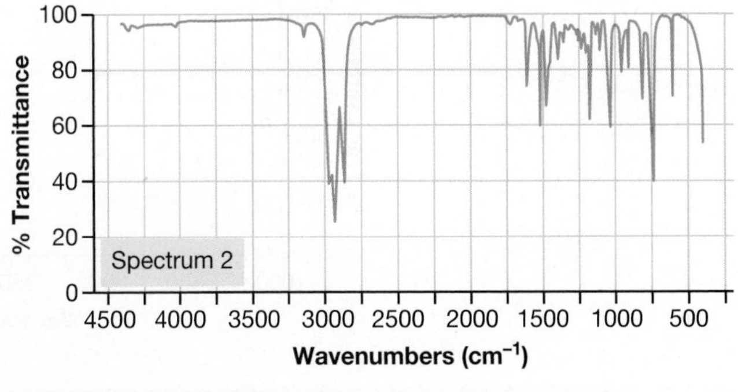

100
80
60
40
20
0
% Transmittance
Spectrum 2
4500 4000 3500 3000 2500 2000 1500 1000 500
Wavenumbers (cm⁻¹)

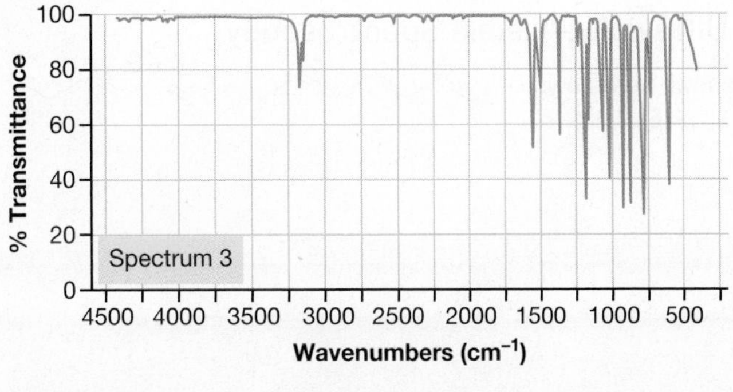

100
80
60
40
20
0
% Transmittance
Spectrum 3
4500 4000 3500 3000 2500 2000 1500 1000 500
Wavenumbers (cm⁻¹)

Section 16.7 Structure Elucidation Using Infrared Spectroscopy

16.25 A compound whose molecular formula is C_6H_7N has the IR spectrum shown here. Suggest a reasonable structure for this compound.

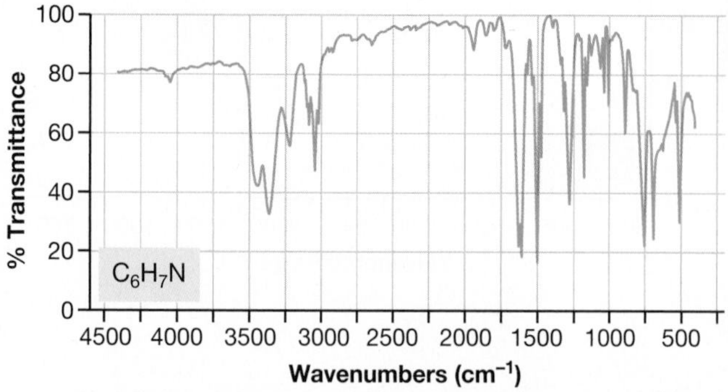
100
80
60
40
20
0
% Transmittance
C6H7N
4500 4000 3500 3000 2500 2000 1500 1000 500
Wavenumbers (cm⁻¹)

16.27 A compound whose molecular formula is $C_3H_2O_2$ has the IR spectrum shown. Propose a structure for this compound.

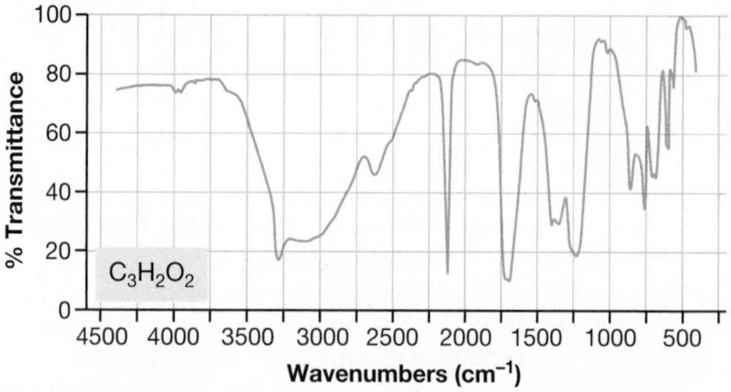
100
80
60
40
20
0
% Transmittance
C3H2O2
4500 4000 3500 3000 2500 2000 1500 1000 500
Wavenumbers (cm⁻¹)

16.26 A compound whose molecular formula is C_8H_8O has the IR spectrum shown. Suggest a reasonable structure for this compound.

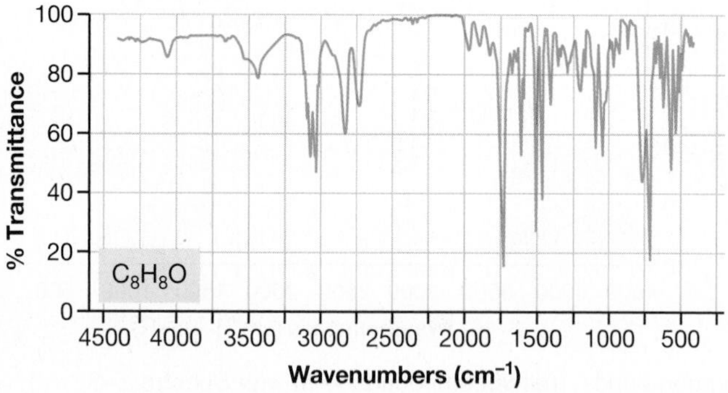
100
80
60
40
20
0
% Transmittance
C8H8O
4500 4000 3500 3000 2500 2000 1500 1000 500
Wavenumbers (cm⁻¹)

16.28 A compound whose molecular formula is $C_{13}H_{10}O$ has the IR spectrum shown. Suggest a reasonable structure for this compound.

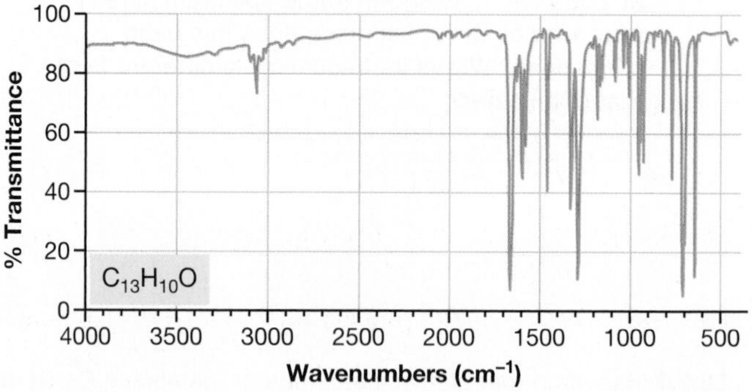
100
80
60
40
20
0
% Transmittance
C13H10O
4000 3500 3000 2500 2000 1500 1000 500
Wavenumbers (cm⁻¹)

16.29 A compound whose molecular formula is C_5H_9NO has the IR spectrum shown. Suggest a reasonable structure for this compound.

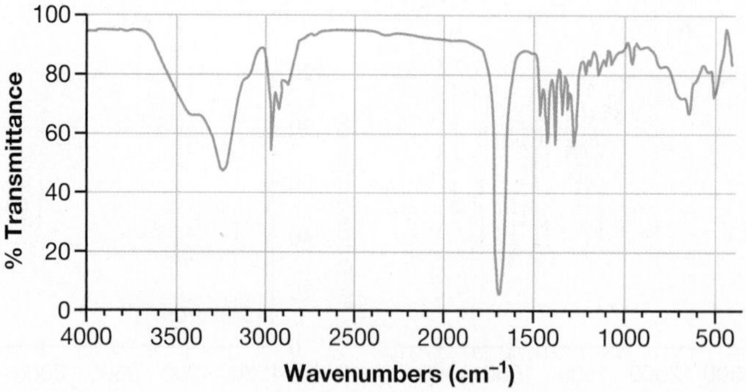
100
80
60
40
20
0
% Transmittance
4000 3500 3000 2500 2000 1500 1000 500
Wavenumbers (cm⁻¹)

Sections 16.9 and 16.10 Ultraviolet–Visible Spectroscopy

16.30 Which of the compounds shown here do you expect to have the longer λ_{max}? Explain.

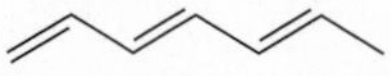

16.31 Naturally occurring carotene primarily exists in two different forms, called α-carotene and β-carotene. Which has the longer-wavelength UV–vis absorption? Explain.

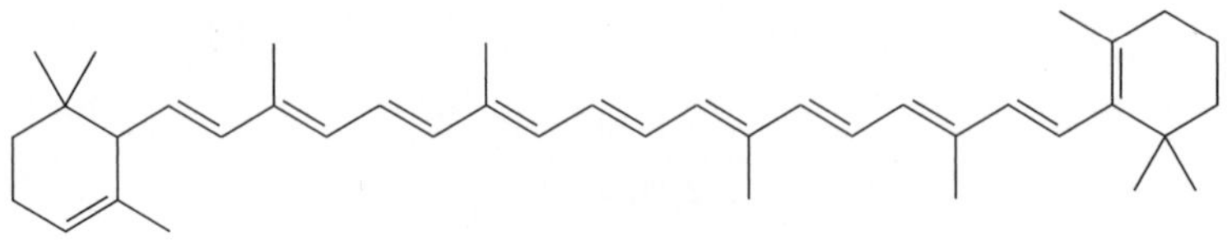

α-Carotene

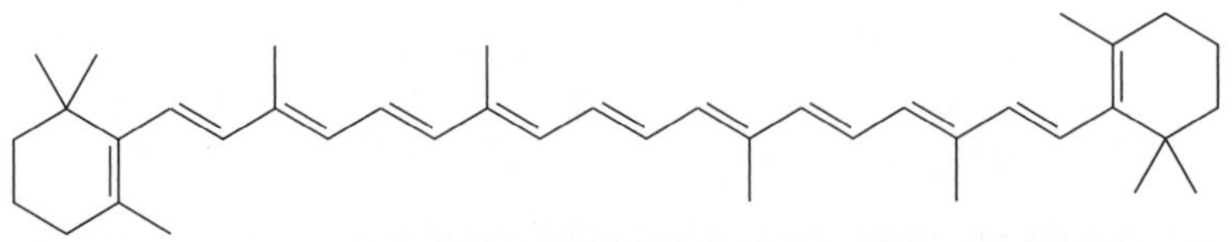

β-Carotene

16.32 In the UV–vis spectrum of buta-1,2-diene ($CH_3CH{=}C{=}CH_2$), the longest-wavelength absorption appears at 178 nm. Compare this to the longest-wavelength absorption in buta-1,3-diene (see Table 16-3, p. 803) and explain the significant difference.

16.33 The longest-wavelength λ_{max} for an unknown compound, C_7H_{10}, is determined to be 247 nm. Which of these compounds could the unknown be?

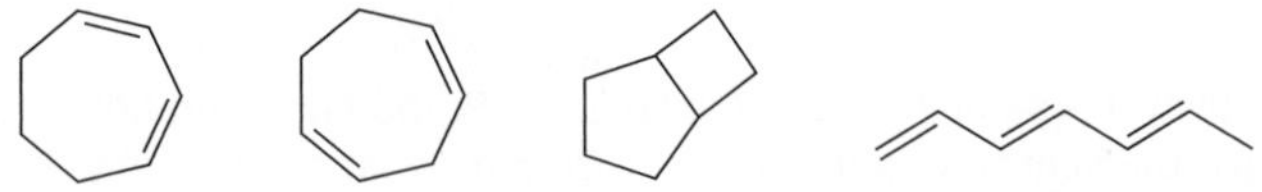

N O P Q

16.34 An unknown compound has the formula C_5H_6. Its longest-wavelength UV–vis absorption is centered at 215 nm. Draw four isomers that are consistent with these results.

16.35 A compound whose formula is C_7H_{12} is known to have a six-membered ring. In its UV–vis spectrum, the longest-wavelength λ_{max} appears at 191 nm. Draw four isomers that are consistent with these results.

16.36 Phenolphthalein is often used as an indicator in acid–base titration experiments because its color depends on the pH of the solution. When the solution is acidic or near neutral (pH < 8), it is colorless. Under mildly basic conditions (pH 9–13), the solution is red. Under strongly basic conditions (pH > 14), the solution is colorless again. Given the following structures of phenolphthalein under the various pH conditions indicated, explain the color dependence on pH.

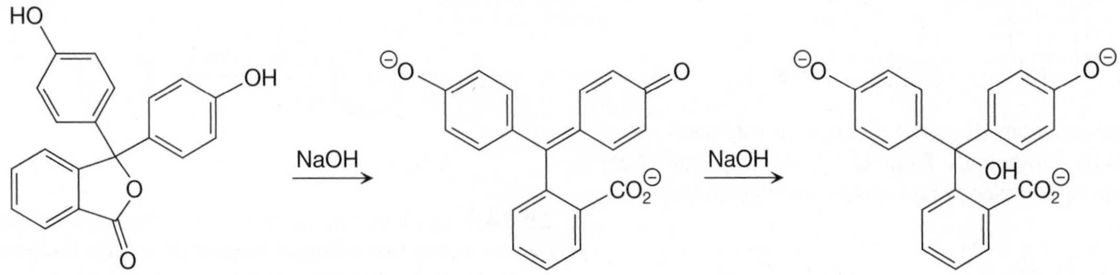
HO
OH
O
O
NaOH
O
O
CO2
NaOH
O
O
OH
CO2

Phenolphthalein
pH < 8

pH 9–13

pH > 14

16.37 Which compound has the longer-wavelength λ_{max}: propyne or acetonitrile ($CH_3C{\equiv}N$)? Explain.

16.38 Suggest how UV–vis spectroscopy could be used to determine whether each of the following reactions actually took place. Explain your reasoning.

(a)

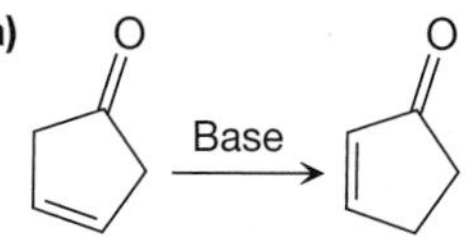
Base

(b)

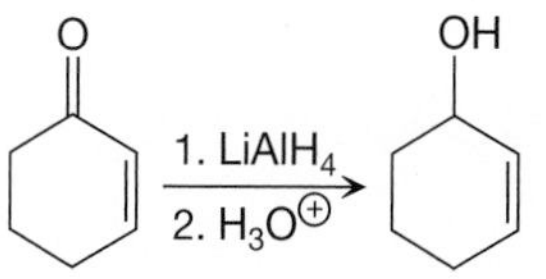
1. $LiAlH_4$
2. $H_3O^{\oplus}$

(c)

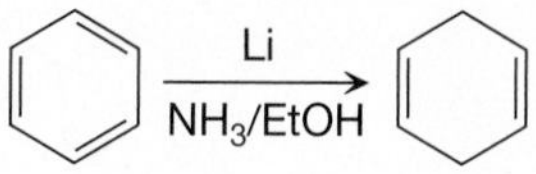
Li
NH_3/EtOH

(d)

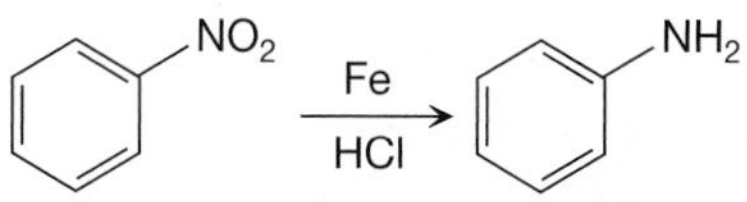
NO_2
Fe
HCl
NH_2

(e)

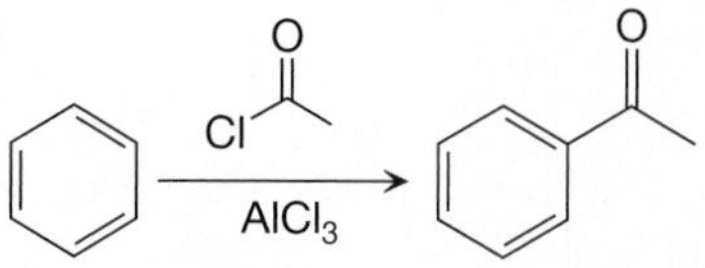
Cl
$AlCl_3$

16.39 In Section 6.2b, we saw that the pK_a of an acid is equal to the pH of the solution at which half the acid has dissociated into its conjugate base. UV–vis spectroscopy can be used to measure the relative concentrations involved if the acid or conjugate base absorbs UV–vis light. With this in mind, suppose that a particular acid has a λ_{max} of 312 nm. The plot here shows the absorbance at 312 nm as a function of pH. What is the pK_a of the acid?

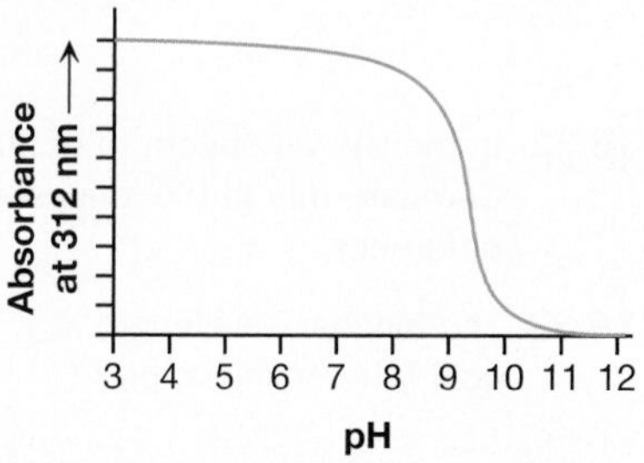
Absorbance at 312 nm
3 4 5 6 7 8 9 10 11 12
pH

16.40 Calculate the molar absorptivity if a sample's absorbance is 0.78, the concentration of the sample is 6.00×10^{-6} M, and the length of the sample the light travels through is 1.00 cm. What are the units?

Integrated Problems

16.41 IR spectroscopy does not distinguish very well between isomers **R** and **S**. Explain why. How could UV–vis spectroscopy be used to distinguish between them?

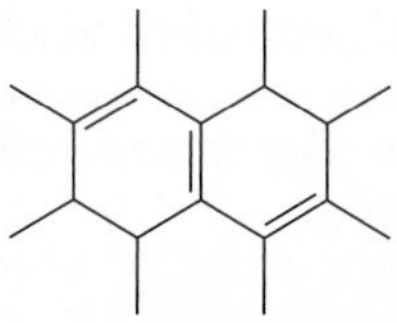

R

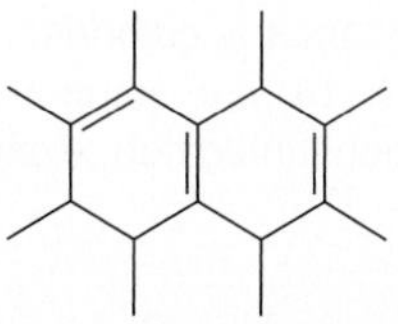

S

16.42 IR spectroscopy does not distinguish very well between compounds **T** and **U**. Explain why. How could UV–vis spectroscopy be used to distinguish between them?

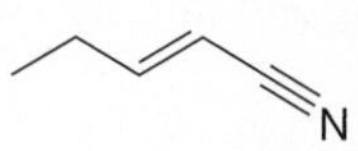
N

T

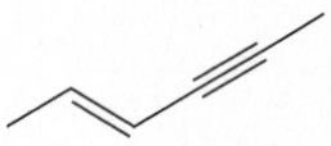

U

16.43 Consider the reaction shown here. For a particular concentration of HCl, the absorbance at 244 nm measured over an initial period decreases from 0.60 to 0.50. When the concentration of HCl is doubled, the absorbance measured at the end of that same period is 0.40. What can you conclude about whether HCl is involved in the rate-determining step? Explain.

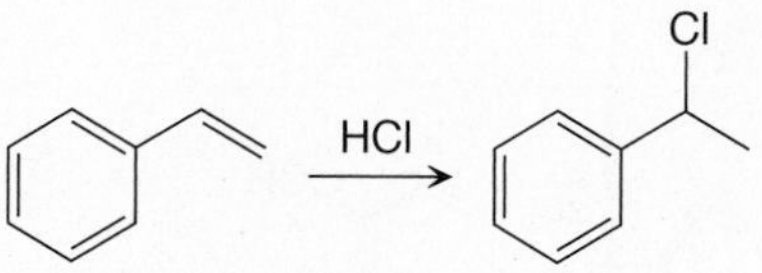
HCl
Cl

λ_{max} = 244 nm

16.44 A student ran the reaction shown here separately using two different bases: once with NaOH and again with LDA, $LiN(C_3H_7)_2$. When NaOH was used, the organic product's UV–vis spectrum had a λ_{max} of ~220 nm. When LDA was used, the product's spectrum had a λ_{max} of ~180 nm. In both cases, the formula of the organic product was C_7H_{10}. Explain.

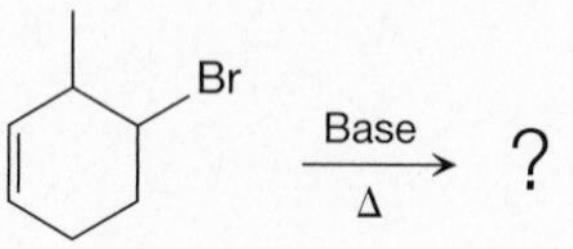
Br
Base
Δ
?

16.45 Match each IR spectrum provided with either compound **V**, **W**, or **X**.

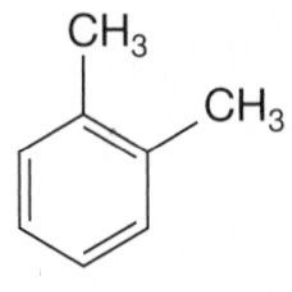

CH3
CH3

V

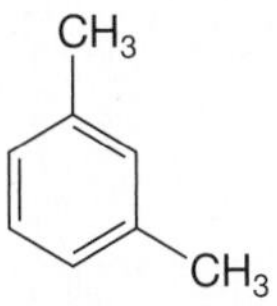

CH3
CH3

W

CH3
CH3

X

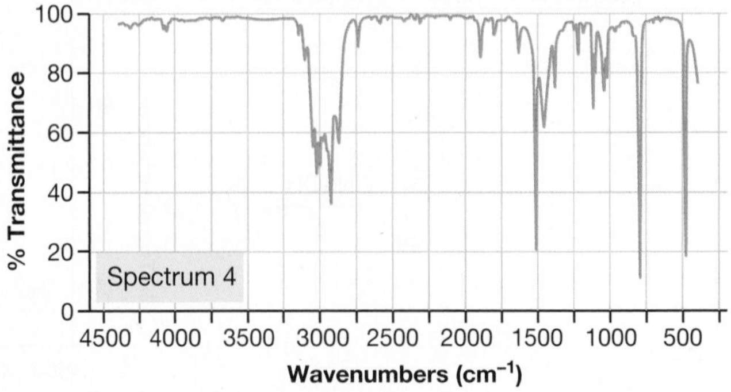

% Transmittance
Spectrum 4
Wavenumbers (cm⁻¹)

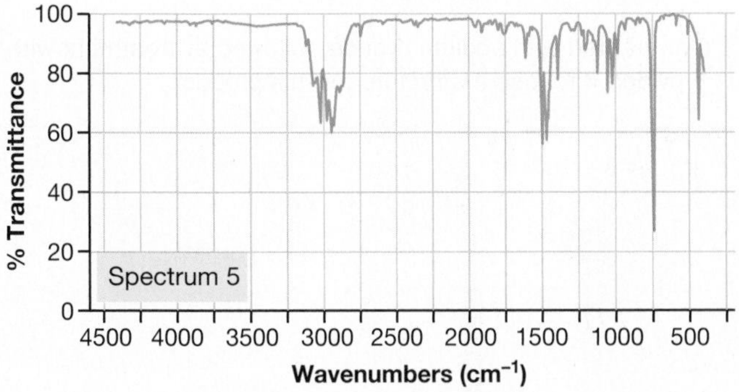

% Transmittance
Spectrum 5
Wavenumbers (cm⁻¹)

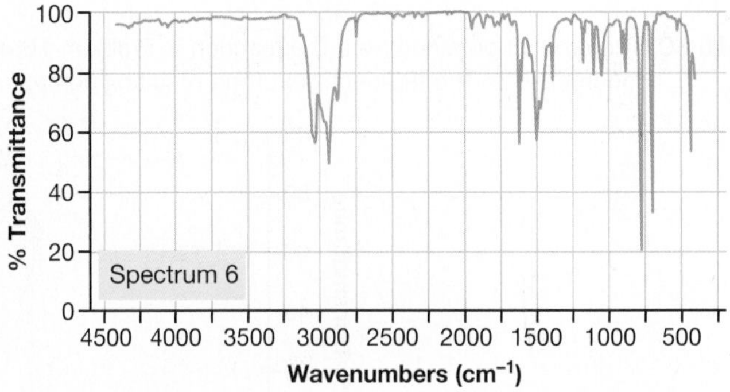

% Transmittance
Spectrum 6
Wavenumbers (cm⁻¹)

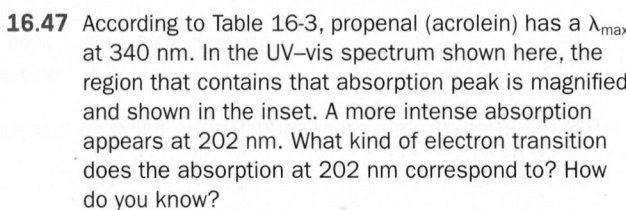

16.46 A compound whose molecular formula is $C_5H_{10}O$ has the IR spectrum shown. The compound's pK_a is >40. Propose a structure for this compound that is consistent with these data.

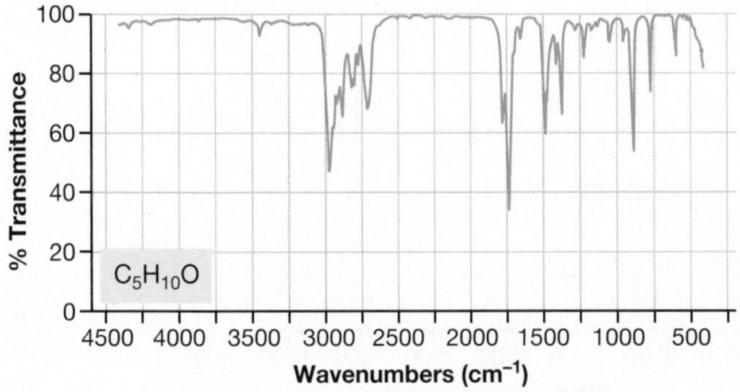

% Transmittance
C5H10O
Wavenumbers (cm⁻¹)

16.47 According to Table 16-3, propenal (acrolein) has a λ_{max} at 340 nm. In the UV–vis spectrum shown here, the region that contains that absorption peak is magnified and shown in the inset. A more intense absorption appears at 202 nm. What kind of electron transition does the absorption at 202 nm correspond to? How do you know?

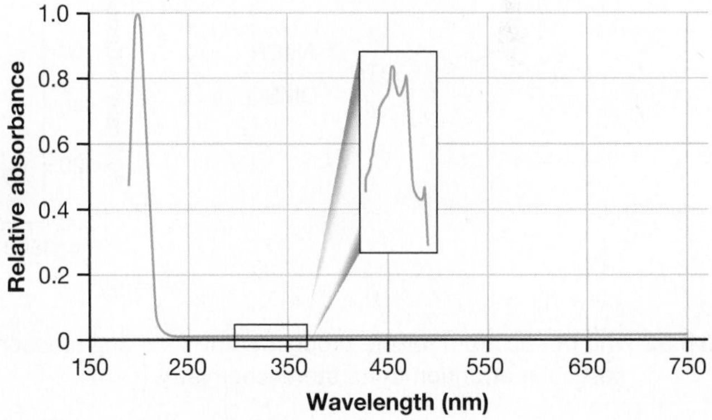

Relative absorbance
Wavelength (nm)

16.48 In the UV–vis spectrum of benzene, the absorption that corresponds to the HOMO–LUMO transition occurs at 184 nm. How does this compare to the corresponding electron transition in hexa-1,3,5-triene (see Table 16-3)? Explain why there is a significant difference.

16.49 When 1,2-dibromo-1-phenylethane is heated with sodium hydroxide, a compound with the IR spectrum shown here is produced. Propose a structure for this product.

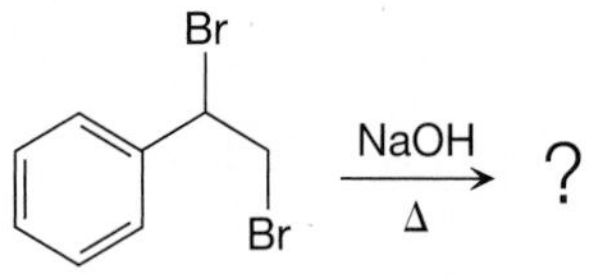
Br
Br
NaOH
Δ
?

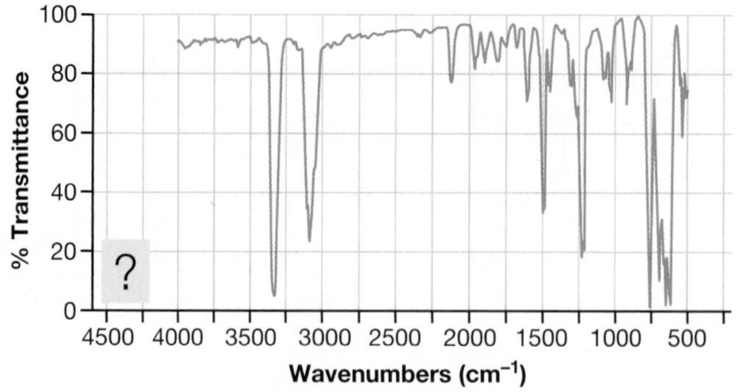
% Transmittance
Wavenumbers (cm^{-1})
?

16.50 The product obtained from the reaction in Problem 16.49 is then treated with sodium hydride, followed by treatment with iodomethane. The IR spectrum of the resulting compound is provided. Propose a structure for this product.

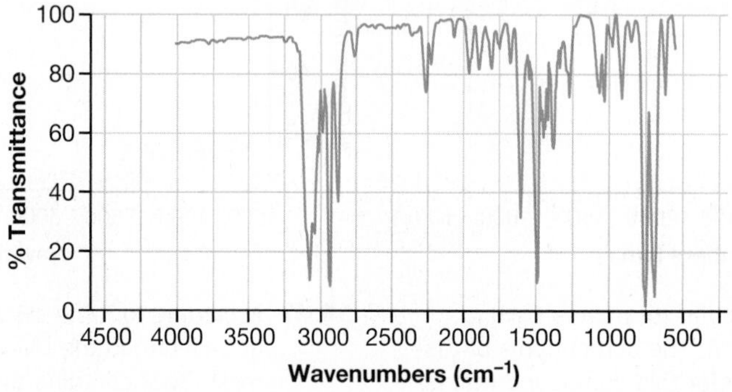
% Transmittance
Wavenumbers (cm^{-1})

16.51 The IR spectrum for the product of the following reaction is shown. Propose a structure for this compound.

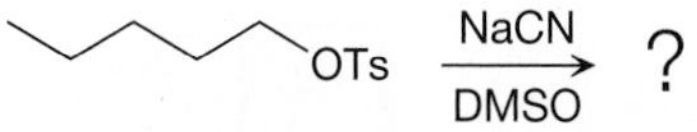
OTs
NaCN
DMSO
?

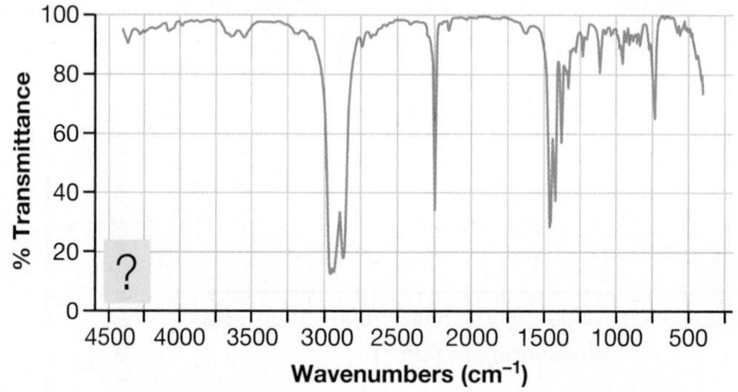
% Transmittance
Wavenumbers (cm^{-1})
?

16.52 The IR spectrum for the product of the following reaction is shown. Propose a structure for this compound, paying particular attention to its stereochemistry.

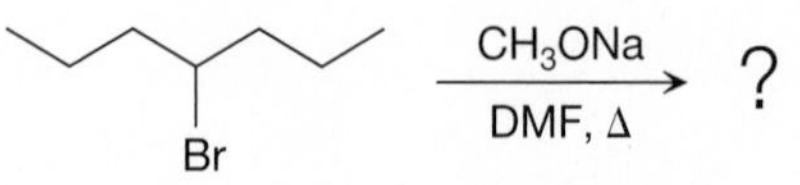
Br
CH_3ONa
DMF, Δ
?

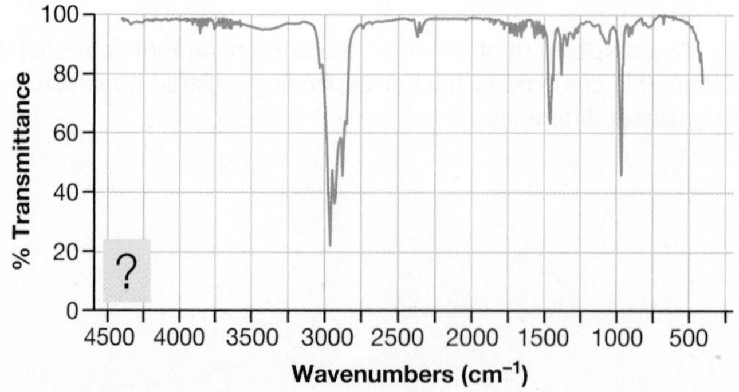
% Transmittance
Wavenumbers (cm^{-1})
?

16.53 Based on your answer to Problem 16.21, in which compound, cyclohexanone or cyclobutanone, is there greater s character in the σ bond between C and O? Explain your answer.

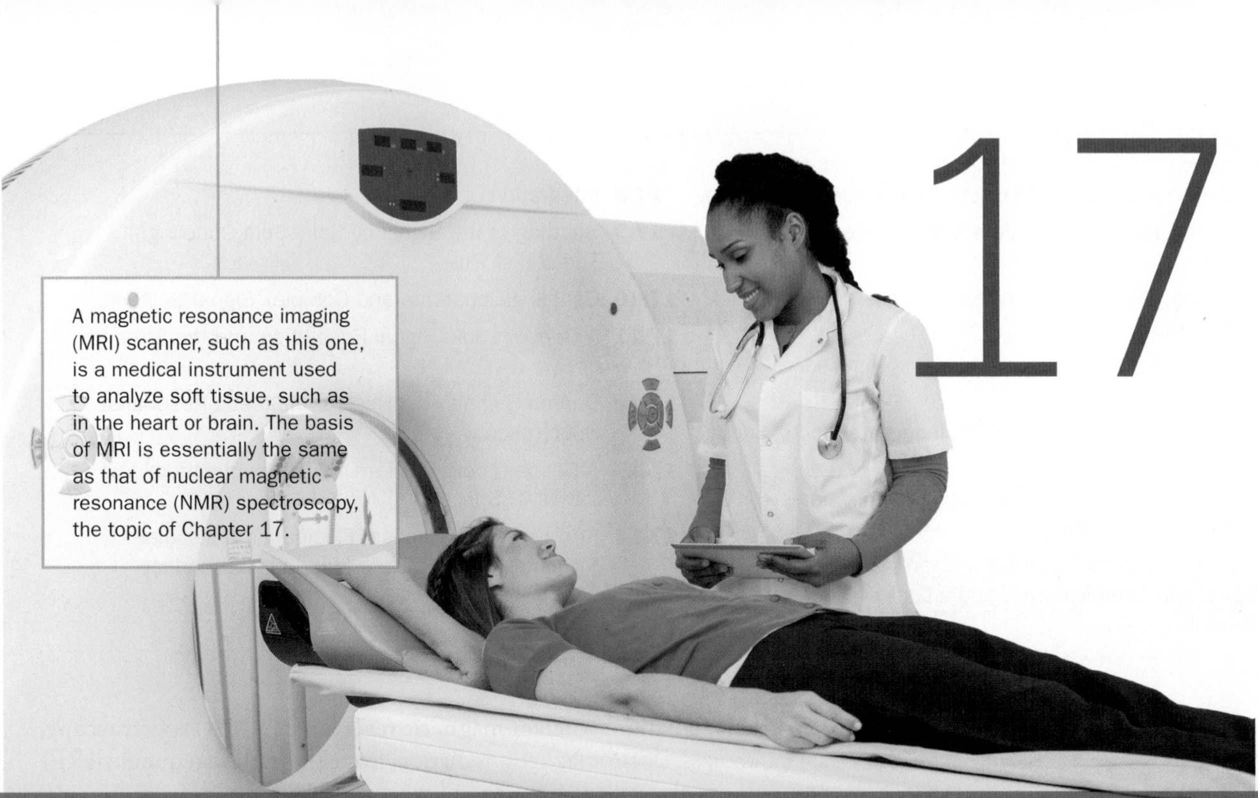

A magnetic resonance imaging (MRI) scanner, such as this one, is a medical instrument used to analyze soft tissue, such as in the heart or brain. The basis of MRI is essentially the same as that of nuclear magnetic resonance (NMR) spectroscopy, the topic of Chapter 17.

17

Structure Determination 3

Nuclear Magnetic Resonance Spectroscopy

Chapter 16 discussed infrared (IR) spectroscopy and ultraviolet–visible (UV–vis) spectroscopy. Here in Chapter 17, we continue the discussion of spectroscopy, focusing on *nuclear magnetic resonance (NMR) spectroscopy*.

Because of the kind of information it provides, NMR spectroscopy is generally considered the single most powerful tool in organic chemistry for the elucidation of molecular structure. NMR spectroscopy can tell us about the number of distinct types of hydrogen and carbon atoms in a given molecule, as well as each atom's specific environment. This, in turn, allows us to determine the *connectivity* of atoms within the molecule. By comparison, IR spectroscopy provides relatively little information about connectivity, and UV–vis spectroscopy provides even less.

Understanding NMR spectroscopy, however, requires a grasp of principles that are somewhat more complex than those underlying IR or UV–vis spectroscopy. Moreover, an NMR spectrum often has more features to analyze than a typical IR or UV–vis spectrum, so interpreting an NMR spectrum is somewhat more involved. For these reasons, we devote an entire chapter to NMR spectroscopy.

17.1 An Overview of Nuclear Magnetic Resonance Spectroscopy

SECTION 17.1 OBJECTIVES

You will be able to:

1. Explain how an NMR spectrometer acquires a spectrum.
2. Describe the quantities plotted in an NMR spectrum.

Recall from Chapter 16 that IR spectroscopy and UV–vis spectroscopy are characterized by the kind of radiation that they use. IR spectroscopy uses radiation from the infrared region of the electromagnetic spectrum, whereas UV–vis spectroscopy uses

Chapter Outline

ultraviolet and visible radiation. **Nuclear magnetic resonance (NMR) spectroscopy**, on the other hand, uses electromagnetic radiation from the **radio frequency (RF)** region of the spectrum, also called *radio waves* (review Fig. 16-2, p. 771).

You are probably familiar with RF radiation from its use in communication technology, including AM and FM radio signals and wireless network connections for computers. Photons in this region are less energetic than those in the IR or UV–vis regions, encompassing frequencies between roughly 3 Hz and 3×10^{11} Hz (i.e., wavelengths between 100,000 km and 1 mm). Most modern NMR spectrometers, however, work in the relatively narrow region between about 10^7 and 10^9 Hz (i.e., wavelengths between 30 m and 30 cm).

A typical setup for an NMR experiment is shown in **Figure 17-1a**. A solution containing a small amount of the sample (on the order of 5 mg), dissolved in a

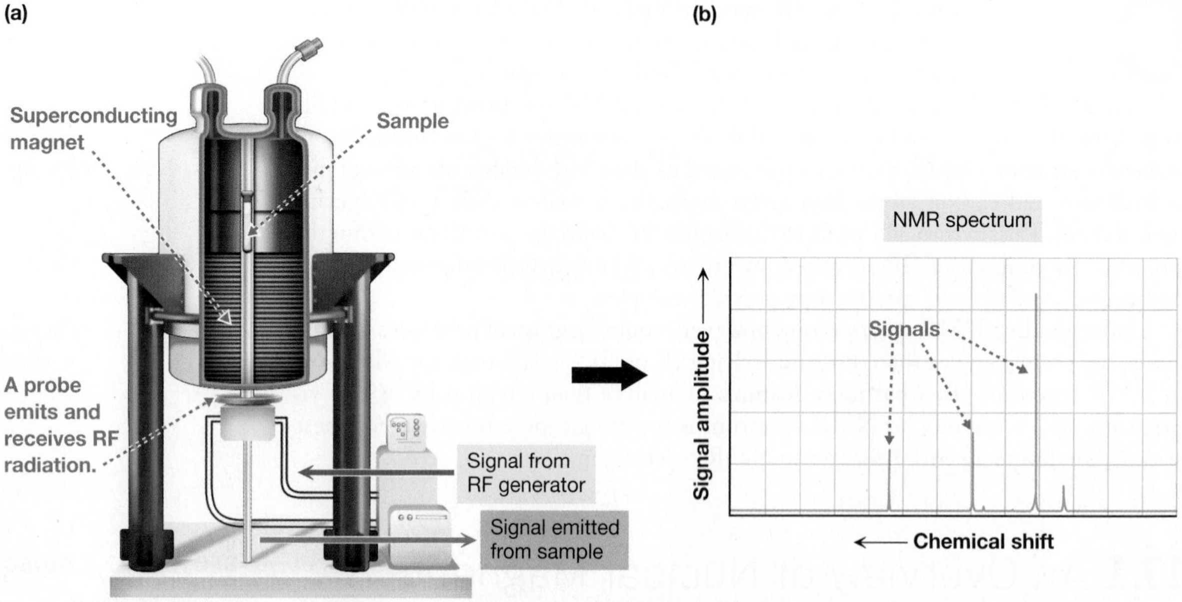

(a)
Superconducting magnet
Sample
A probe emits and receives RF radiation.
Signal from RF generator
Signal emitted from sample
(b)
NMR spectrum
Signal amplitude
Signals
Chemical shift

FIGURE 17-1 Typical nuclear magnetic resonance experiment (a) A modern superconducting NMR spectrometer. A sample is placed in the hollow bore of a superconducting magnet. An NMR probe irradiates the sample with RF radiation and detects RF signals emitted by the sample. (b) The RF radiation emitted by the sample is recorded and converted into an NMR spectrum, in which amplitude is plotted against chemical shift.

deuterated solvent such as $CDCl_3$ (to be described further in Section 17.7), is placed in a glass tube. The tube is lowered into the hollow bore of a superconducting magnet, where it is irradiated with a short pulse (several microseconds) of RF radiation emitted from an NMR probe. The probe delivers a range of frequencies produced by an RF generator, and as in any spectroscopic experiment, we want to obtain a *spectrum* that can tell us which of those frequencies are absorbed and how strong each absorption is.

The general setup for NMR spectroscopy differs from the typical setup for IR or UV–vis spectroscopy in two major ways. The first is the use of a superconducting magnet, which subjects the sample to a very strong **external magnetic field (B_{ext})**. The second is in the way that each absorbed frequency is detected. In IR spectroscopy and UV–vis spectroscopy, transmittance at a particular frequency or wavelength is obtained by comparing the intensity of radiation that has passed through the sample, $I_{detected}$, to the intensity of radiation from a source, I_{source} (review Eq. 16-3, p. 771).

By contrast, most NMR spectrometers take advantage of the fact that a portion of the RF radiation absorbed by the sample at each frequency is *re-emitted* at the same frequency. The magnitude of the oscillating RF radiation re-emitted from the sample is recorded over a period of a few seconds and is digitized, producing what is called a **free induction decay (FID)**. Many FIDs are typically acquired and are averaged to improve the quality, after which a mathematical algorithm, called a **Fourier transform**, decomposes the FID into its individual frequencies, called **signals**. The *amplitude* of each signal is proportional to the amount of radiation that was originally absorbed. Thus, the recorded signals are converted automatically into a spectrum analogous to other spectra we have seen, in which relative absorbance is plotted on the *y* axis, against a characteristic of radiation on the *x* axis (Fig. 17-1b). In this case, the *x* axis of the NMR spectrum is **chemical shift** (abbreviated as δ, the Greek letter delta), which is a measure of *relative frequency*. Chemical shift represents how much a particular signal frequency differs from the frequency of a reference compound. (We discuss chemical shift in greater detail in Sections 17.5 and 17.6.)

With this overview of NMR spectroscopy in mind, we ask the following questions:

- Why must a large magnetic field be applied to the sample?
- Why are only certain frequencies of RF radiation absorbed by a given sample?
- How can an NMR spectrum be used to interpret molecular structure?

We will answer these questions in the sections that follow.

17.2 Nuclear Spin and the Nuclear Magnetic Resonance Signal

SECTION 17.2 OBJECTIVES

You will be able to:

1. Explain why a sample must be placed in an external magnetic field to acquire an NMR spectrum.
2. Describe what happens to a nucleus when it absorbs an RF photon.

In an NMR experiment, the sample is placed in a strong magnetic field because:

> Without being subjected to a strong magnetic field, a sample does not absorb RF radiation and therefore cannot produce an NMR spectrum.

Why is this?

Acquiring an NMR spectrum depends on a strong magnetic field because of *nuclear spin*. **Nuclear spin** describes the state of atomic nuclei that generates a small magnetic field, the same kind of magnetic field that would be produced from a spinning charge. The most common example is the nucleus of a ^{1}H atom (i.e., a proton), whose spin is analogous to that of an electron. Just as an electron can assume one of two spin states (see Recall box), a proton can also exist in one of two spin states:

◂ RECALL

Section 1.3c discussed the Pauli exclusion principle, which states that two electrons in the same orbital must not have the same spin. Because only two spin states exist for an electron, no more than two electrons can occupy the same orbital.

> A proton has a spin of $+\frac{1}{2}$ or $-\frac{1}{2}$ au, which corresponds to the **α spin state** or the **β spin state**, respectively.

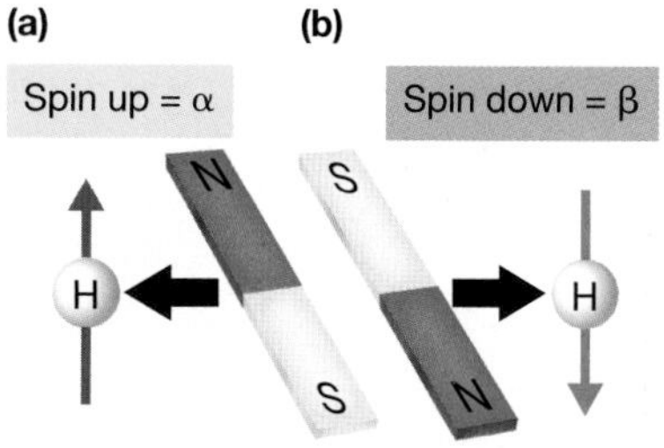
(a)
(b)
Spin up = α
Spin down = β
N
S
S
N
H
H

FIGURE 17-2 Spin states and magnetic dipoles of the hydrogen nucleus (a) The α spin state, also called spin-up. (b) The β spin state, also called spin-down.

Because nuclear spin generates a small magnetic field and a proton can assume one of two spin states:

> Protons can generate a magnetic dipole in one of two ways, and thus each proton behaves as a tiny bar magnet, with a north and a south pole.

These nuclei are thus often represented as arrows, indicating the direction in which their magnetic dipoles point (**Figure 17-2**).

When there is no external magnetic field present, there is no energy difference between the α and β spin states, so a proton is equally likely to be in either state (**Figure 17-3**, left). Moreover, the magnetic dipoles of the protons point in random directions. The situation is similar to what we would observe if we were to grab several bar magnets and toss them onto the floor. Unless two magnets lie close enough to affect each other, they will end up with random orientations.

In the presence of an external magnetic field (B_{ext}), however, the situation is different. Each nucleus with spin has its average magnetic dipole aligned parallel to B_{ext}. As shown on the right in Figure 17-3:

> - When nuclei are exposed to B_{ext}, the magnetic dipoles of nuclei in the α spin state become aligned *with* B_{ext}, whereas the dipoles of nuclei in the β spin state become aligned *against* it.
> - In these orientations, the energy of the α spin state is slightly lower than the energy of the β spin state.
> - The difference in energy between the α and β spin states, ΔE_{spin}, is directly proportional to B_{ext}: As B_{ext} increases, so does ΔE_{spin}.

This energy difference is like being in a canoe on a river, in which the river's current is analogous to B_{ext}: Paddling with the current requires less energy than paddling against it. Moreover, it is even more difficult to paddle against the current when the current becomes stronger. (A more quantitative treatment of ΔE_{spin} is provided in Section 17.7.)

Typical values of ΔE_{spin} correspond to photon energies from the RF region of the electromagnetic spectrum. Therefore, a nucleus in the α spin state can absorb an RF photon and be promoted to the β spin state in a so-called **spin flip** (**Figure 17-4**). When a nucleus in the β spin state relaxes back to the α spin state, it emits RF radiation that we detect as an NMR signal.

We can now understand why an NMR spectrum cannot be acquired in the absence of B_{ext}. As we saw in Figure 17-3, the α and β spin states of a proton have exactly the

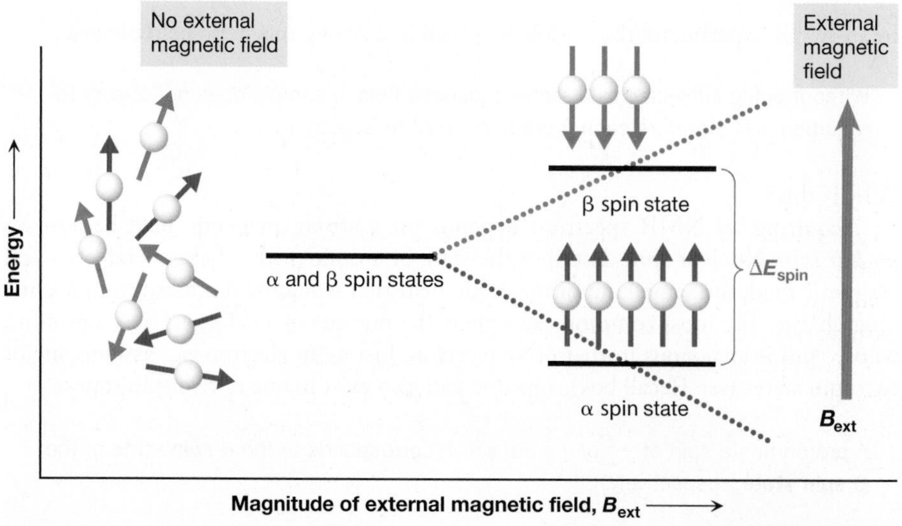
No external magnetic field
External magnetic field
Energy
α and β spin states
β spin state
α spin state
ΔE_{spin}
B_{ext}
Magnitude of external magnetic field, B_{ext}

FIGURE 17-3 Effect of an external magnetic field on nuclear spin states (*Left*) In the absence of an external magnetic field, the α and β spin states are at exactly the same energy, and the nuclear magnetic dipoles are oriented in random directions. (*Right*) In the presence of an external magnetic field, represented by the green arrow, the α spins align with the external magnetic field and the β spins align against it. This makes the energy of the α spin state slightly lower than that of the β spin state, by a difference ΔE_{spin}.

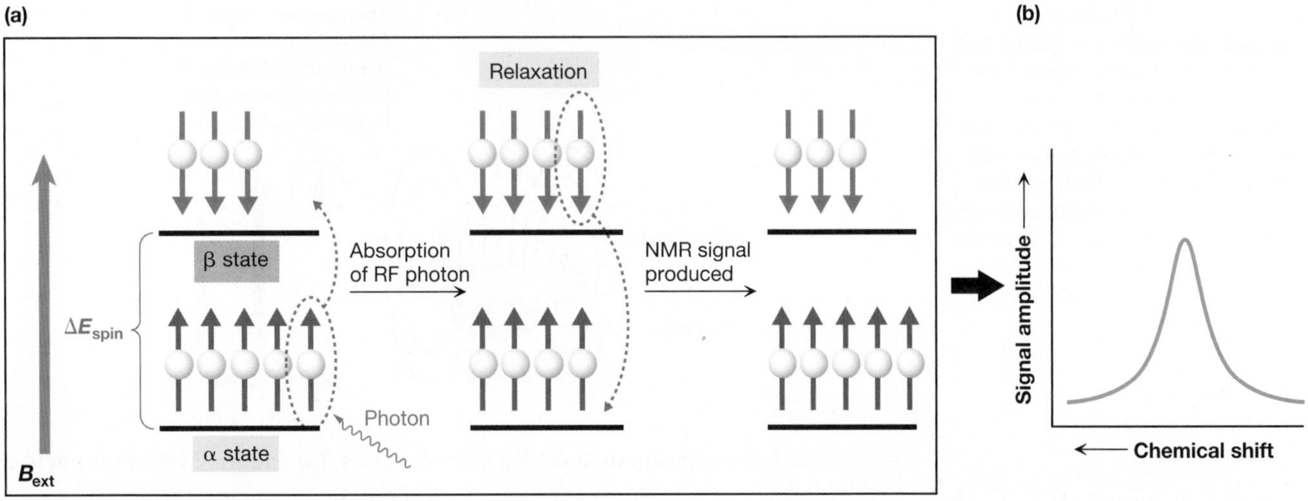
(a)
Relaxation
β state
α state
ΔE_{spin}
B_{ext}
Absorption of RF photon
Photon
NMR signal produced
(b)
Signal amplitude
Chemical shift

FIGURE 17-4 A spin flip in NMR spectroscopy (a) Several protons in an external magnetic field. An incoming photon is absorbed by one of the nuclei in the α spin state, promoting it to the β spin state. When a nucleus relaxes back to the α spin state, a signal is produced. (b) A spectrum is obtained by plotting signal amplitude versus the frequency of radiation detected.

same energy in the absence of B_{ext}. Under these circumstances, there is no higher-energy spin state to which a nucleus can be promoted, so no RF photon can be absorbed.

Most of this chapter focuses on **proton NMR spectroscopy** (or **^{1}H NMR spectroscopy**), in which the RF radiation used causes spin flips in the nuclei of hydrogen atoms. NMR spectroscopy, however, can also be used to probe other nuclei that possess spin, which are called **NMR-active nuclei**. In general:

> A nucleus is NMR-active and can be studied with NMR spectroscopy if it has an odd number of protons, or an odd number of neutrons, or both.

This is consistent with ^{1}H being NMR-active, because its nucleus has just one proton (an odd number). ^{2}H (D, deuterium) is NMR-active, too, because its nucleus has one proton and one neutron (both odd numbers). In addition, the carbon-13 (^{13}C) nucleus, which has six protons (an even number) and seven neutrons (an odd number), is NMR-active, but the carbon-12 (^{12}C) nucleus, which has six protons and six neutrons (both even numbers), is not (see Recall box).

Many other nuclei are NMR-active, including ^{14}N, ^{15}N, ^{17}O, ^{19}F, and ^{31}P. Organic molecules are principally composed of hydrogen and carbon, however, so we will discuss only ^{1}H NMR spectroscopy (Sections 17.3 through 17.11) and ^{13}C NMR spectroscopy (Sections 17.12 and 17.13).

◂ RECALL

The atomic number of an atom is defined as the number of protons in the nucleus (Section 1.3a). The mass number of an atom is the total number of protons and neutrons that make up the nucleus, and it is written at the top-left corner of the atomic symbol.

17.3 Shielding, Chemical Distinction, and the Number of NMR Signals

SECTION 17.3 OBJECTIVES

You will be able to:

1. Describe the origin of the shielding of protons and explain why chemically distinct protons generate different NMR signals.
2. Identify chemically distinct protons in a molecule.

All protons in a molecule typically do *not* absorb at the same frequency; if they did, then every spectrum would consist of just one signal, in which case we would be unable to use NMR spectroscopy to determine aspects of molecular structure. Protons in the same molecule can absorb at different frequencies because of the electron cloud that surrounds each nucleus. Like any moving charges, the electrons that make up that cloud experience a force from B_{ext}, which causes the electrons to move in a circular path, as shown in **Figure 17-5** (next page).

The moving electrons create their own magnetic field lines, and at the nucleus, those magnetic field lines result in a **local magnetic field (B_{loc})** that is in the opposite direction of B_{ext}. The sum of the two magnetic fields is the **effective magnetic field (B_{eff})** that is felt by the nucleus, according to Equation 17-1:

$$B_{eff} = B_{ext} + B_{loc} \quad (17\text{-}1)$$

FIGURE 17-5 **Shielding of the nucleus** The external magnetic field (B_{ext}, thick green arrow) causes the electrons surrounding the nucleus to move in a circular path (thick red arrow). The moving electrons create their own magnetic field lines (thin blue arrows). At the nucleus, the local magnetic field (B_{loc}, thick blue arrow) opposes B_{ext}, which reduces the effective magnetic field (B_{eff}) felt by the nucleus.

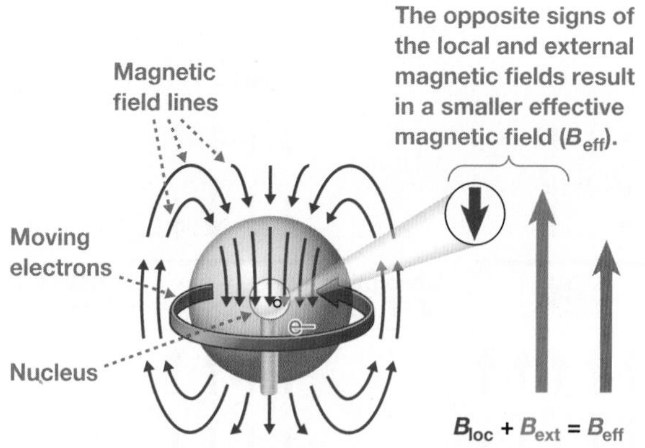

Magnetic field lines
The opposite signs of the local and external magnetic fields result in a smaller effective magnetic field (B_{eff}).
Moving electrons
Nucleus
$B_{loc} + B_{ext} = B_{eff}$

B_{loc} and B_{ext} have opposite signs, so B_{eff} is smaller than B_{ext}, and we say that the nucleus is **shielded**.

The extent of shielding for a particular nucleus, and therefore B_{eff}, depends on the surrounding electrons and atoms within the molecule—that is, on the **chemical environment** of the nucleus. Protons that are in identical chemical environments, which are called **homotopic** or **chemically equivalent**, have the same B_{eff}. On the other hand, protons that are in different chemical environments, which are called **heterotopic** or **chemically distinct**, will each have a different B_{eff}. As we saw previously in Figure 17-3 (p. 822), protons that are exposed to different magnetic fields will absorb photons at different frequencies. Putting these ideas together, we arrive at one of the most important rules for ^{1}H NMR spectroscopy:

Each chemically distinct type of hydrogen atom in a molecule gives rise to an individual signal in a proton NMR spectrum.

How can we tell by looking at a molecular structure whether two protons are in different chemical environments and are therefore distinct? One way is to look for a unique point of reference within the molecule and determine how close the protons are to that reference point:

If two protons are located at different distances from a unique point of reference within a molecule, then those protons are chemically distinct and give rise to two separate ^{1}H NMR signals.

Consider propynoic acid ($HO_2C—C{\equiv}CH$, **Figure 17-6**), which has two protons total. There are several unique points of reference, but let's choose the terminal C atom of the triple bond. The proton on the right is closer to that C atom than is the proton on the left, so the protons are distinct. Consequently, the molecule generates two signals in the ^{1}H NMR spectrum, as shown in Figure 17-6: one around 11.2 ppm and the other around 3.0 ppm (the unit ppm stands for "parts per million," which is discussed

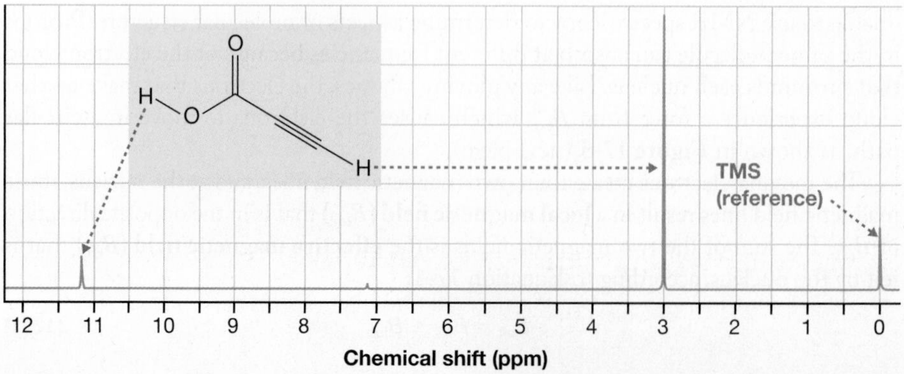

TMS
(reference)
12
11
10
9
8
7
6
5
4
3
2
1
0
Chemical shift (ppm)

FIGURE 17-6 **^{1}H NMR spectrum of propynoic acid** The two signals on the left correspond to the protons in propynoic acid, indicating that propynoic acid has two chemically distinct protons. The signal at 0 ppm corresponds to TMS, the reference compound.

in Section 17.7). Note a third signal in the spectrum appears at 0 ppm, but it is not generated from the sample. Instead, it is due to a small amount of **tetramethylsilane (TMS)** [$(CH_3)_4Si$], which is added to the sample to provide a reference signal.

YOUR TURN **17.1**

On the basis of the positions of the two signals in Figure 17-6, do you think that the protons in TMS are equivalent to any of the protons in propynoic acid? Explain.

Answers to Your Turns are in the back of the book.

As another example, let's consider 3-bromoprop-1-yne (shown in **Figure 17-7**), which has three protons total. If we choose the Br atom as our unique point of reference, then we can see that the protons labeled B are closer to that reference point than is proton A. Therefore, protons A and B are distinct. The two protons labeled B, on the other hand, are the same distance from the Br atom and are equivalent. Therefore, the molecule has two distinct types of protons, and as shown in the ^{1}H NMR spectrum in **Figure 17-8**, two signals are generated.

Proton A is farther from the Br atom than protons B are, so proton A is distinct from protons B.

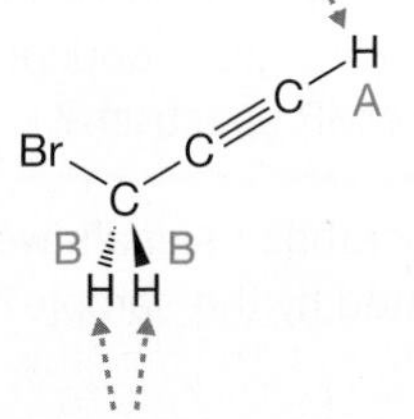

Br
C
C
C
H
A
B
B
H H

The two protons B are the same distance from the Br atom, so they are not distinct from each other; they are equivalent.

FIGURE 17-7 Chemically distinct protons in 3-bromoprop-1-yne

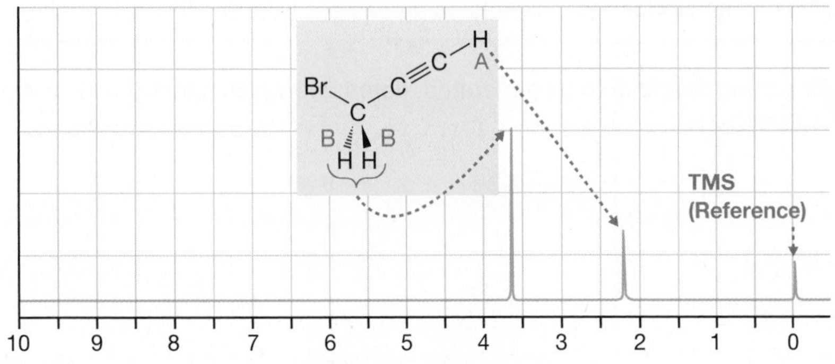

Br
C
C
C
H
A
B
B
H H
TMS
(Reference)
10
9
8
7
6
5
4
3
2
1
0
Chemical shift (ppm)

FIGURE 17-8 **^{1}H NMR spectrum of 3-bromoprop-1-yne** The two signals on the left correspond to the protons in 3-bromoprop-1-yne, indicating that the molecule has two chemically distinct protons. The signal at 0 ppm corresponds to TMS, the reference compound.

SOLVED PROBLEM **17.1**

How to match a molecule to its ^{1}H NMR spectrum from the number of signals

Break It Down Considering the number of ^{1}H NMR signals that should be generated, determine which spectrum (1 or 2) was produced by dichloroacetic acid, shown here.

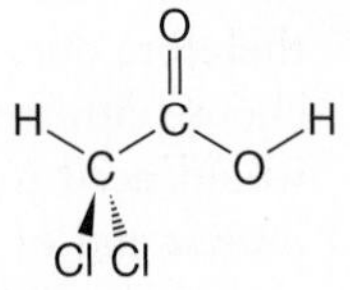

O
H
C
C
O
H
Cl Cl

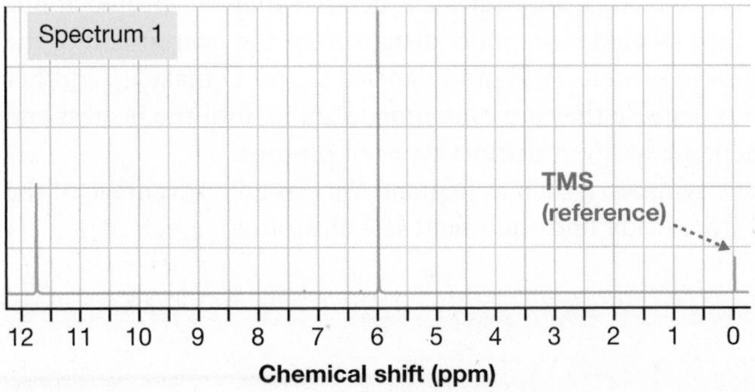

Spectrum 1
TMS
(reference)
12
11
10
9
8
7
6
5
4
3
2
1
0
Chemical shift (ppm)

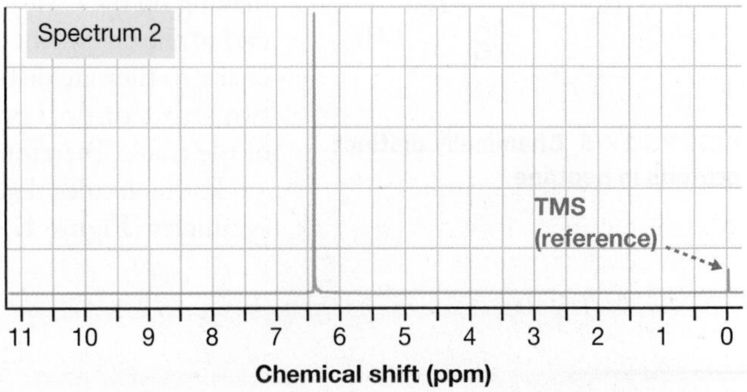

Spectrum 2
TMS
(reference)
11
10
9
8
7
6
5
4
3
2
1
0
Chemical shift (ppm)

(continued)

Think	Solve
Is there a unique point of reference in Cl_2CHCO_2H?	There are multiple points of reference that are unique. Let's choose the O atom at the very right. 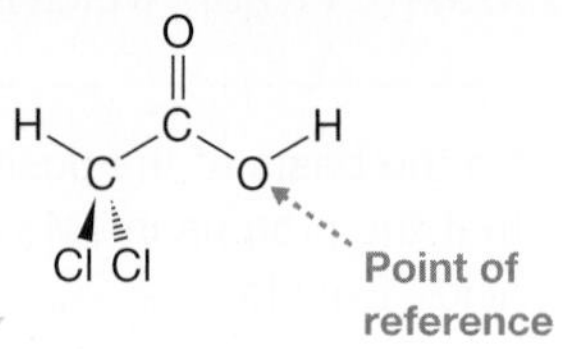 Point of reference
Are the protons the same distance from that point of reference?	The proton on the right is closer to the O, whereas the proton on the left is farther away. Therefore, the two protons are distinct.
How many signals appear in each proton NMR spectrum?	Spectrum 1 has three signals, appearing at 0, 6.0, and 11.8 ppm. Spectrum 2 has two signals, appearing at 0 and 6.4 ppm.
Which of those signals were generated by the sample?	The signal at 0 ppm in each spectrum corresponds to added TMS, so two signals in Spectrum 1 were generated by the sample, and one signal in Spectrum 2 was generated by the sample.
How many signals should each distinct type of proton produce?	Each distinct type of proton should produce one signal. Therefore, dichloroacetic acid should produce two signals, in agreement with Spectrum 1.

Try It Considering the number of ^1H NMR signals that should be generated, determine which spectrum (3 or 4) was produced by methoxypropan-2-one, $CH_3OCH_2C(=O)CH_3$.

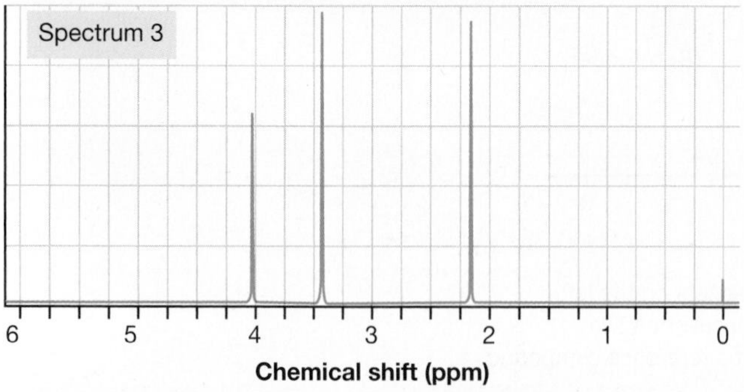
Spectrum 3
6
5
4
3
2
1
0
Chemical shift (ppm)

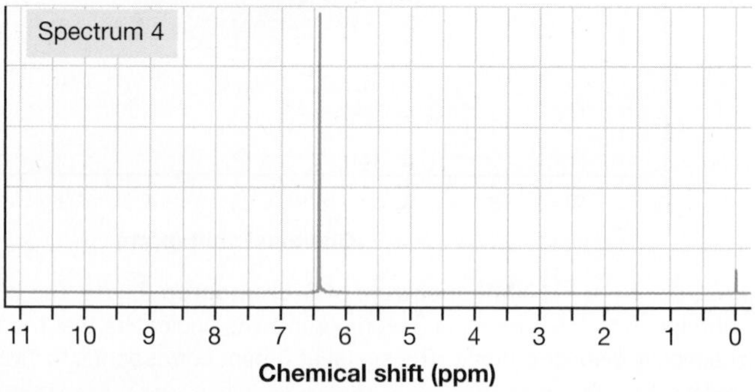
Spectrum 4
11
10
9
8
7
6
5
4
3
2
1
0
Chemical shift (ppm)

Answers to all Try It exercises can be found in the Solutions Manual.

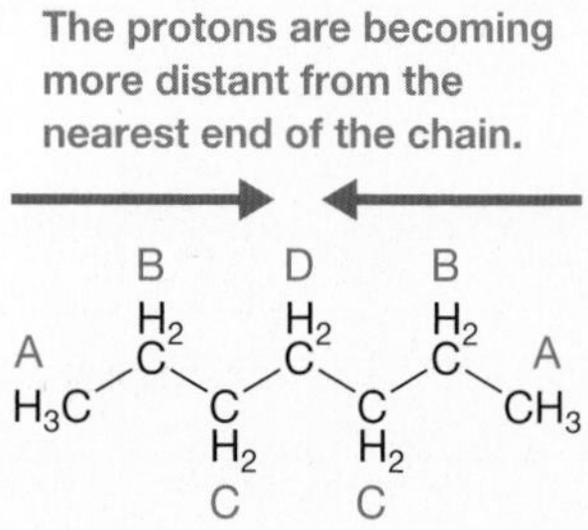
The protons are becoming more distant from the nearest end of the chain.
B D B
A A
C C

FIGURE 17-9 Chemically distinct protons in heptane

Next let's consider heptane (**Figure 17-9**), which is a symmetric molecule and therefore does not have a unique point of reference. For example, we could equally choose either end of the chain as a reference point. To account for this symmetry, we would need to modify our question to ask how close each set of protons is to the *nearest* end of the chain. By asking this question, we conclude that the six protons making up the CH_3 groups, labeled A, are equivalent because they are located at one end of the chain. The protons labeled B are more distant from the nearest end of the chain, so they are distinct from protons A. Protons labeled C and D make up another two sets of distinct protons because they are even more distant from the nearest end of the chain. Therefore, heptane has four distinct types of protons.

For molecules that have symmetry, such as heptane, we can take advantage of the symmetry (**Figure 17-10**) to quickly find equivalent sets of protons:

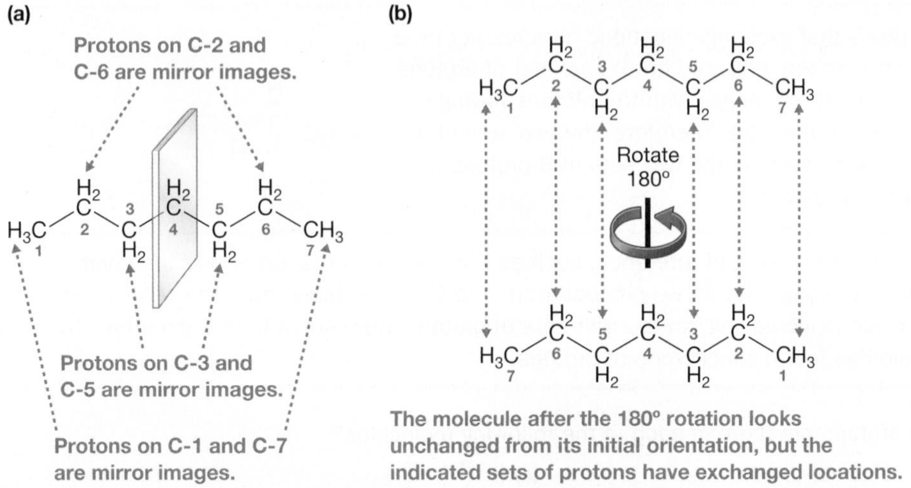
(a)
Protons on C-2 and C-6 are mirror images.
Protons on C-3 and C-5 are mirror images.
Protons on C-1 and C-7 are mirror images.
(b)
Rotate 180°
The molecule after the 180° rotation looks unchanged from its initial orientation, but the indicated sets of protons have exchanged locations.

FIGURE 17-10 Symmetry and the chemical equivalence of nuclei (a) The protons on C-1 and C-7 are mirror images of each other, so they are equivalent. The same is true for the protons on C-2 and C-6, as well as the protons on C-3 and C-5. (b) On rotating the heptane molecule 180°, the molecule looks unchanged, but the protons on C-1 and C-7 exchanged locations, making those protons equivalent. The same is true for the protons on C-2 and C-6, as well as the protons on C-3 and C-5.

CONNECTIONS 17.1

Seaweed and skin care

Dichloroacetic acid (Solved Problem 17.1) occurs naturally in the seaweed *Asparagopsis taxiformis*. It is used in skin peels for cosmetic treatments and tattoo removal and is used in the treatment of warts. It has also been studied, with little success, as a cancer treatment.

Symmetry and the Chemical Equivalence of Nuclei

Two atoms must be chemically equivalent in *either* of these two cases:

- The atoms are mirror images with respect to a plane of symmetry of the molecule (illustrated in Fig. 17-10a).
- A rotation of the entire molecule causes the atoms to appear in different locations, but the molecules before and after rotation look identical (illustrated in Fig. 17-10b).

SOLVED PROBLEM **17.2**

How to use symmetry to identify equivalent protons

Break It Down How many distinct types of protons are there in the following molecule?

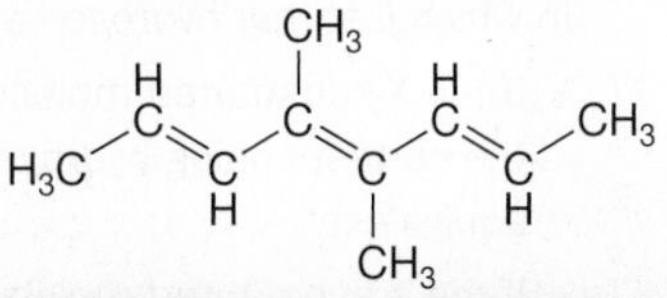

Think	Solve
Does the molecule have a plane of symmetry? Can the molecule be rotated to exchange the locations of some protons without affecting the appearance of the molecule?	When we rotate the molecule 180° in the plane of the page, as shown here, some protons exchange locations, but the molecule appears to be unchanged. 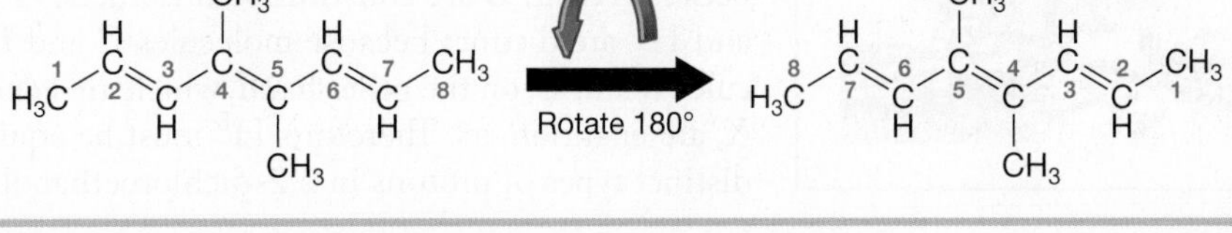

(continued)

Which protons exchanged locations as a result of that rotation? What does that tell you about those protons?	The protons that exchange locations as a result of the above rotation are indicated here. Each set of protons A–D on the left exchanges with the protons having the same label on the right. Therefore, the two sets of A protons are equivalent, the two sets of B protons are equivalent, and so on. 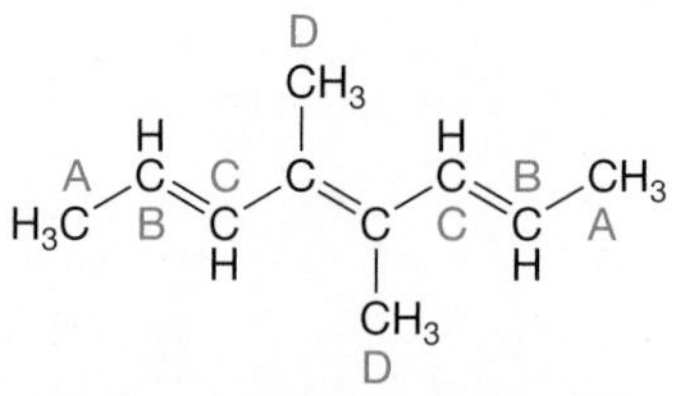
How can you determine whether protons A–D are distinct?	We can choose a point of reference, such as the carbon on the left end of the chain (attached to protons A). As we proceed from A to D, the distance from the nearest end of the chain is increasing, so the four sets of protons are distinct from each other. The molecule has four distinct types of protons.

Try It How many distinct types of protons are there in each of the following molecules?

(a)

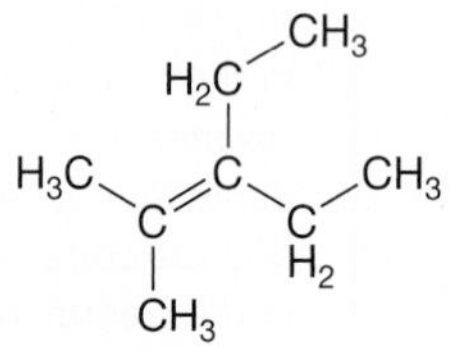

(b)

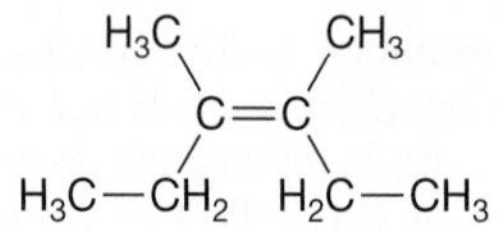

(c)

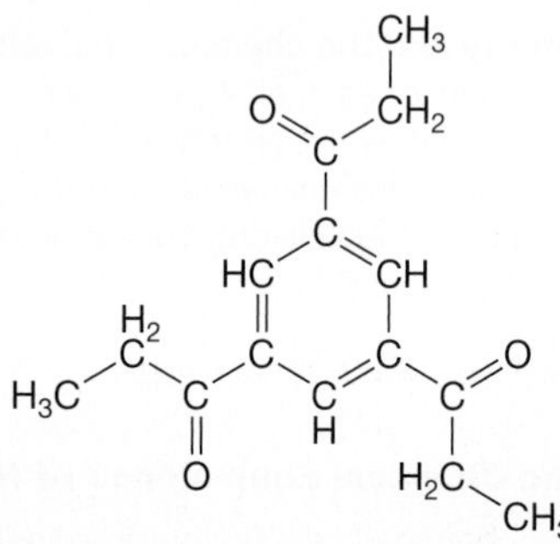

Strategies for Success
The Chemical Distinction Test

17.3a Strategies for Success: The Chemical Distinction Test

We just discussed how to identify distinct protons by examining their chemical environments. Another way is to apply the **chemical distinction test**, which takes advantage of our knowledge of isomers:

The Chemical Distinction Test for Hydrogen Atoms

For each hydrogen atom in question, draw the complete structure of the molecule in which *just that hydrogen atom* is replaced by an imaginary atom, X.

- If the X-substituted molecules are either *identical* or *enantiomers*, then the corresponding hydrogen atoms in the original molecule are *chemically equivalent*.
- If the X-substituted molecules are either *constitutional isomers* or *diastereomers*, then the corresponding hydrogen atoms in the original molecule are *chemically distinct*.

Let's apply this chemical distinction test to the protons in 2,2-dichloroethanol (**Figure 17-11**). Molecules **A** and **B** are generated by replacing H^A and H^B with X; because **A** and **B** are constitutional isomers, H^A and H^B are distinct. Similarly, H^C and H^D are distinct because molecules **C** and **D** are constitutional isomers. Molecules **B** and **C**, on the other hand, which are generated by replacing H^B and H^C with X, are enantiomers. Therefore, H^B must be equivalent to H^C. In all, there are three distinct types of protons in 2,2-dichloroethanol.

CONNECTIONS 17.2

Facilitating indoor plumbing
Chloroethene (Solved Problem 17.3), more commonly called vinyl chloride, is used to make poly(vinyl chloride), or PVC, which is widely used in pipes and fittings for plumbing.

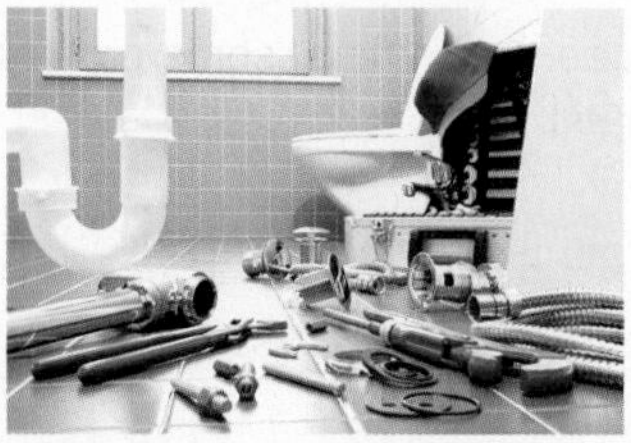

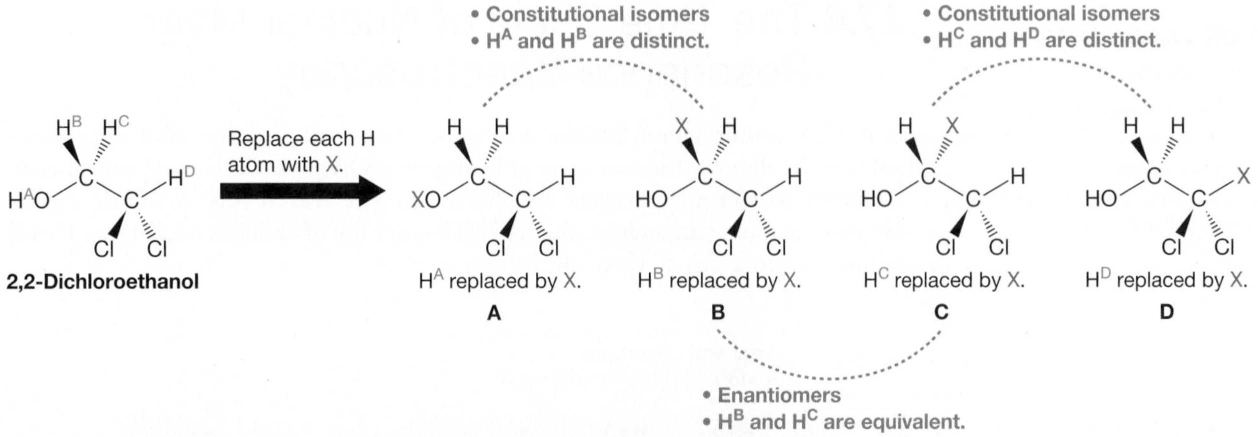
• Constitutional isomers
• H^A and H^B are distinct.
• Constitutional isomers
• H^C and H^D are distinct.
Replace each H atom with X.
2,2-Dichloroethanol
H^A replaced by X.
A
H^B replaced by X.
B
H^C replaced by X.
C
H^D replaced by X.
D
• Enantiomers
• H^B and H^C are equivalent.

FIGURE 17-11 Applying the chemical distinction test to 2,2-dichloroethanol

SOLVED PROBLEM **17.3**

How to apply the chemical distinction test to a molecule

Break It Down Use the chemical distinction test to determine how many chemically distinct H atoms there are in chloroethene, $H_2C{=}CHCl$.

Think	Solve
What molecules are generated by substituting each H atom by X?	Replacing proton H^A, H^B, or H^C with X generates molecules **A**, **B**, or **C**, respectively. 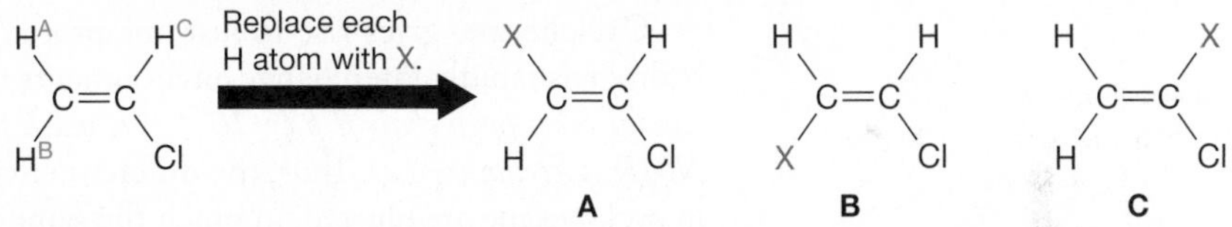 Replace each H atom with X. A B C
What are the relationships between those molecules?	Molecules **A** and **B** are cis/trans isomers, which makes them diastereomers. The connectivity of molecule **C** is different from the connectivity of **A** or **B**, so **C** is a constitutional isomer of **A** and **B**.
What do the relationships among the X-substituted molecules tell you about the protons that were replaced by X?	Because **A** and **B** are diastereomers, the two protons that were replaced (H^A and H^B) are distinct. Because **C** is a constitutional isomer of **A** and **B**, H^C must be distinct from H^A and H^B. There are three distinct protons in the original molecule.

Try It Use the chemical distinction test to determine how many types of chemically distinct H atoms there are in each of the following molecules.

(a)
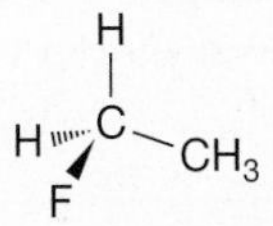

(b)
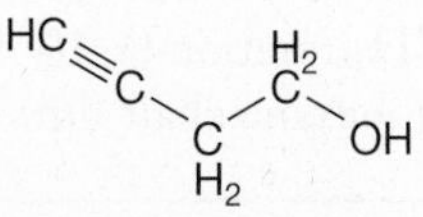

(c)
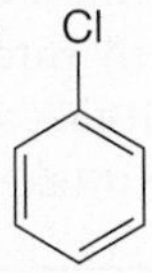

(d)
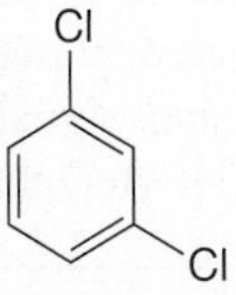

(e)
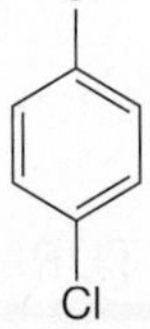

(f)
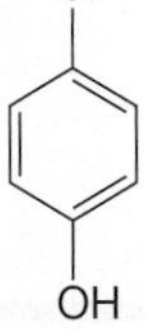

SECTION 17.4 OBJECTIVES

You will be able to:

1. Give the approximate time it takes to acquire an NMR spectrum.
2. Explain why protons that interchange positions rapidly within a molecule will give rise to the same signal.

◄ RECALL

In Section 4.7, we learned that a substituent on a cyclohexane ring encounters more steric strain in an axial position than in an equatorial position. Chair flips, which occur through partial C—C bond rotations, interconvert axial and equatorial positions.

17.4 The Time Scale of Nuclear Magnetic Resonance Spectroscopy

In its chair conformation, cyclohexane has two types of hydrogens: axial and equatorial (see Recall box). The two types of hydrogen atoms are in different chemical environments, so you might expect cyclohexane to give rise to two ^1H NMR signals. However, at room temperature, the ^1H NMR spectrum of cyclohexane (**Figure 17-12**) exhibits only one signal. How can we explain this?

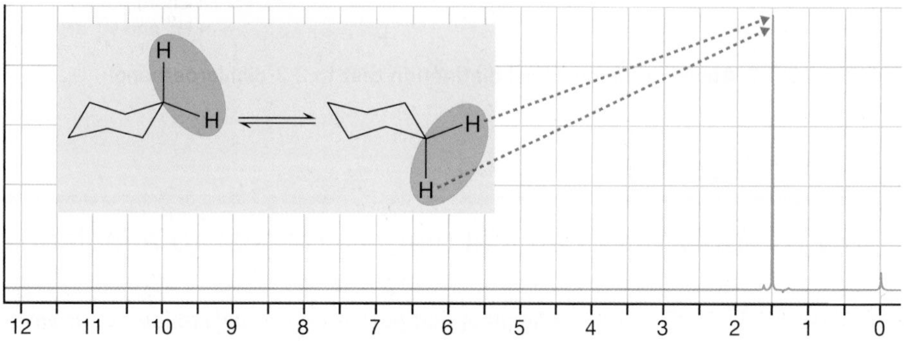

Axial and equatorial
H atoms rapidly interconvert.
H
H
H
H
12
11
10
9
8
7
6
5
4
3
2
1
0
Chemical shift (ppm)

FIGURE 17-12 ^{1}H NMR spectrum of cyclohexane The axial and equatorial H atoms give rise to the same signal because they rapidly interconvert by a chair flip.

Cyclohexane gives rise to just one proton signal because the axial and equatorial hydrogens rapidly interchange environments through chair flips. More specifically, *the time it takes for a chair flip (~10^{-5} s) is much shorter than the time it takes to acquire an NMR spectrum (~1 s)*. Thus, the different environments of the interchanging protons in cyclohexane are blurred, in much the same way that a camera blurs objects that are moving too quickly. The NMR signal, as a result, reflects the *average* proton environment of each proton during its chair flip. (At low temperatures, however, two signals can be observed; see Problem 17.4 at the end of the chapter.)

This phenomenon is not limited to just cyclohexane. In general:

> If protons in different chemical environments interchange rapidly, then they give rise to the same NMR signal that reflects the *average* of those environments.

Another example involves acetic acid, CH_3CO_2H, whose proton NMR spectrum (**Figure 17-13**) exhibits two signals. One signal is from the carboxyl H and the other is from the CH_3 protons. In the conformation shown in the figure, the CH_3 protons are not all the same distance away from the carbonyl O atom, so they might not appear to be in the same chemical environment. However, because the CH_3 protons interchange positions rapidly through rotation of the CH_3 group, they all give rise to the *same* signal. The time it takes for that CH_3 rotation (~10^{-10} s) is even shorter (much shorter) than the time it takes for a cyclohexane chair flip.

YOUR TURN 17.2

Explain why the CH_3 protons in molecule **A** generate two ^{1}H NMR signals but the CH_3 protons in **B** generate just one signal.

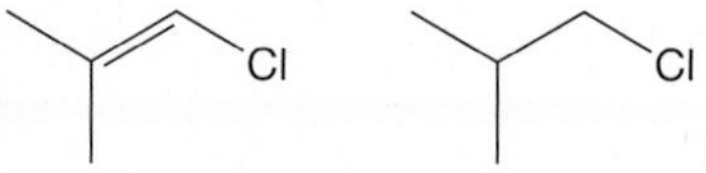

Cl
Cl

A **B**

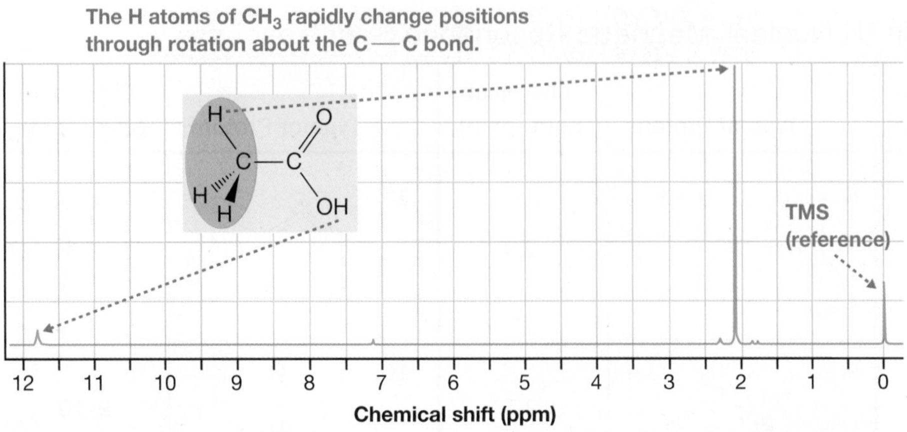
The H atoms of CH_3 rapidly change positions through rotation about the C—C bond.
H
O
C
C
H
H
OH
TMS (reference)
12
11
10
9
8
7
6
5
4
3
2
1
0
Chemical shift (ppm)

FIGURE 17-13 ^{1}H NMR spectrum of acetic acid The three H atoms of CH_3 give rise to the same signal because they rapidly interchange positions by rotation of the CH_3 group.

17.5 Characteristic Chemical Shifts, Inductive Effects, and Magnetic Anisotropy

SECTION 17.5 OBJECTIVES

You will be able to:

1. Explain how and why chemical shift is related to the extent of deshielding for a proton.
2. Describe how deshielding can result from inductive effects and from magnetic anisotropy.
3. Give an approximate chemical shift value for a proton on the basis of the functional group with which the proton is associated.

As Section 17.3 explained, protons in different chemical environments give rise to different signals in an NMR spectrum; the signals appear at *different chemical shifts*. Table 17-1, which lists chemical shifts observed in ^{1}H NMR spectroscopy, shows that a proton's chemical shift is governed largely by the identity of the surrounding atoms and the types of bonds:

Most chemical shifts for *protons* are found in the range 0–12 ppm.

YOUR TURN 17.3

Identify two different types of protons in Table 17-1 whose signals appear at *higher* chemical shifts and two types that appear at *lower* chemical shifts relative to the protons in $ClCH_3$.

To understand the characteristic chemical shift of each type of proton in Table 17-1, recall from Section 17.3 that the effective magnetic field (B_{eff}) felt by a particular proton depends on the extent to which the proton is *shielded* by the surrounding electrons. If the extent of shielding for a proton is decreased, meaning that the proton is **deshielded**, then B_{eff} increases. As shown in **Figure 17-14**, an increase in B_{eff} causes an increase in the energy separation between the α and β spin states (ΔE_{spin}). In turn, the proton will absorb a higher-frequency photon, and the chemical shift will increase, too. Putting these ideas together:

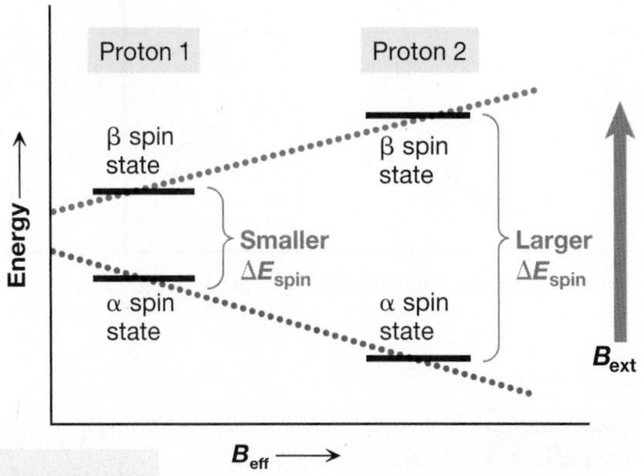
Proton 1
Proton 2
β spin state
β spin state
Smaller ΔE_{spin}
Larger ΔE_{spin}
α spin state
α spin state
Energy
B_{ext}
B_{eff}

FIGURE 17-14 B_{eff} and ΔE_{spin} As the effective magnetic field (B_{eff}) felt by a proton increases, so does the energy difference (ΔE_{spin}) between the α and β spin states.

The chemical shift of a proton will increase as the extent of deshielding increases.

The more deshielded a proton is (i.e., more positive chemical shift; farther to the left in the spectrum), the more the signal is said to be shifted **downfield**. Conversely, the less deshielded a proton is, the more the signal is said to be shifted **upfield**.[1]

[1]The terms *downfield* and *upfield* originate from older types of NMR spectrometers, in which a sample was irradiated with a fixed frequency of RF radiation, and the magnetic field was adjusted to make ΔE_{spin} equal E_{photon}. The more positive a proton's chemical shift, the stronger the magnetic field that was required, and vice versa.

TABLE 17-1 Chemical Shifts in ¹H Nuclear Magnetic Resonance Spectroscopy

Type of Proton	Chemical Shift (ppm)	Type of Proton	Chemical Shift (ppm)	Type of Proton[a]	Chemical Shift (ppm)
1. 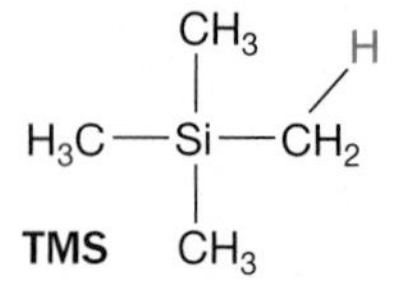CH3 H H3C—Si—CH2 TMS CH3	0	8. 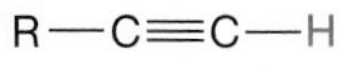R—C≡C—H	2.4	15. 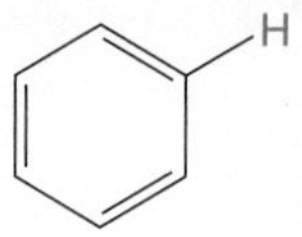H	7.3
2. 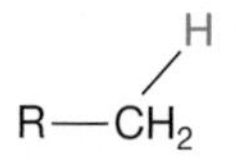H R—CH2	0.9	9. 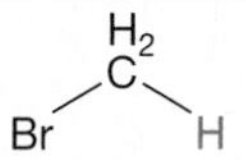H2 C Br H	2.7	16. 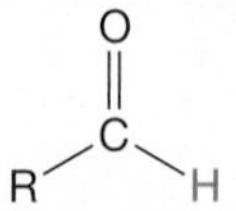O C R H	9–10
3. 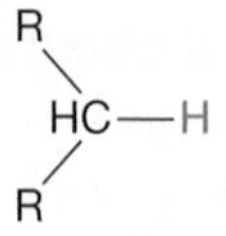R HC—H R	1.3	10. 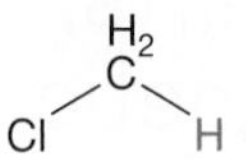H2 C Cl H	3.1	17. 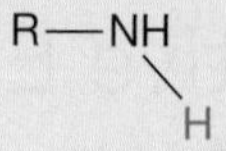R—NH H	1.5–4
4. 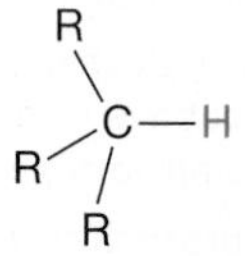R C—H R R	1.4	11. 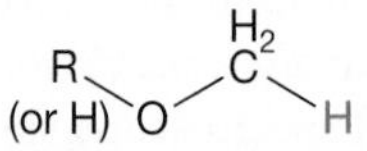H2 R C (or H) O H	3.3	18. 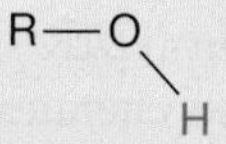R—O H	2–5
5. 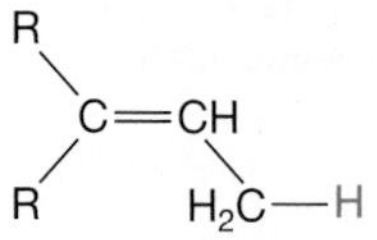R C═CH R H2C—H	1.7	12. 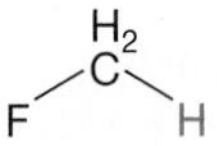H2 C F H	4.1	19. 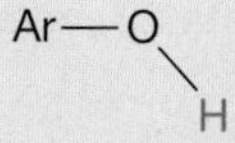Ar—O H	4–7
6. 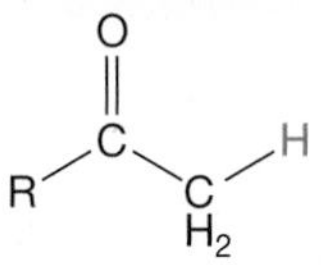O C H R C H2	2.1	13. 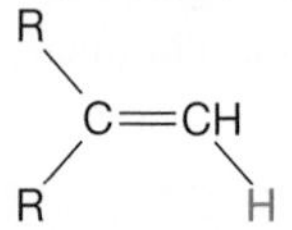R C═CH R H	4.7	20. 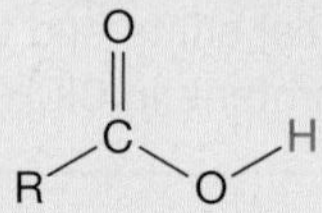O C H R O	10–12
7. 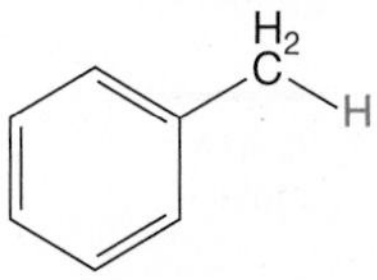H2 C H	2.3	14. 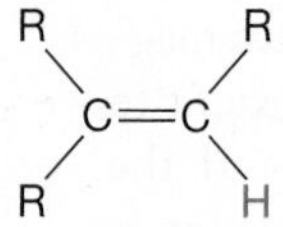R R C═C R H	5.3		

[a]Protons in shaded boxes undergo hydrogen bonding.

◂ RECALL

Section 6.8e explained that inductive effects are the outcome of electron density being distorted through covalent bonds. Electron density is distorted toward electron-withdrawing groups, such as highly electronegative atoms, and away from electron-donating groups, such as alkyl groups.

Two major factors influence the extent to which a hydrogen nucleus is deshielded: *inductive effects* (see Recall box) and *magnetic anisotropy*. We will study how these factors impact chemical shift in Sections 17.5a and 17.5b.

17.5a Inductive Effects

The role of inductive effects on chemical shift can be seen by comparing Entries 2 and 12 in Table 17-1 (RCH_2—H and FCH_2—H, respectively). In Entry 2, no significantly electronegative atoms are present and the proton has a very low chemical shift of 0.9 ppm. In Entry 12, the C atom to which the H atom is attached is itself bonded to a highly electronegative F atom. The presence of that F atom causes a substantial downfield shift of the proton's signal, to 4.1 ppm. A similar phenomenon occurs with other highly electronegative atoms. In general, then:

A proton's signal is shifted downfield (i.e., to a higher chemical shift value) by nearby electronegative atoms.

This downfield shift occurs because electronegative atoms are inductively *electron-withdrawing*, so they remove electron density from the nearby proton. Consequently, the shielding that those electrons provide is diminished; the proton is *deshielded*.

The extent of this inductive deshielding depends, in part, on the electronegativity of the nearby atom. Notice in Table 17-1, for example, that the chemical shifts of the protons in FCH_3 appear downfield from those in $ClCH_3$. The F atom is more electronegative than Cl, so it more powerfully deshields the CH_3 protons.

YOUR TURN **17.4**

In which compound will the proton chemical shift be greater, CH_3Br or CH_3I? Explain.

17.5b Magnetic Anisotropy

Magnetic anisotropy is the second factor that affects B_{eff}. The word *anisotropy* derives from Greek (*anisos* = unequal; *tropos* = way) and refers to a characteristic that is directionally dependent. **Magnetic anisotropy**, in particular, describes a magnetic field that is nonuniform and, as we will see, is responsible for the large chemical shifts in aromatic compounds and alkenes. The protons in benzene (C_6H_6), for example, have a chemical shift of 7.3 ppm, and the protons attached to the C═C bond in hex-3-ene ($CH_3CH_2CH{=}CHCH_2CH_3$) have a chemical shift of 5.3 ppm. Inductive effects cannot explain such a large downfield shift because benzene and hex-3-ene contain no highly electronegative atoms.

To gain a better understanding of magnetic anisotropy, let's examine the π system of benzene, which contains six electrons. As shown in **Figure 17-15**, those π electrons occupy regions of space that look like two donuts on either side of the ring's plane. Because electrons are charged particles, B_{ext} forces the π electrons of benzene to move in a circular path parallel to the plane of the ring (Fig. 17-15a). Such a circular movement of electrons, called **ring current**, creates a separate local magnetic field (B_{loc}), represented by the blue arrows in Figure 17-15b. Notice that the H atoms in benzene sit where B_{loc} produced by the ring current is in the same direction as B_{ext}. The hydrogen nuclei of benzene therefore feel a greater total magnetic field (i.e., B_{eff} is increased) and are deshielded.

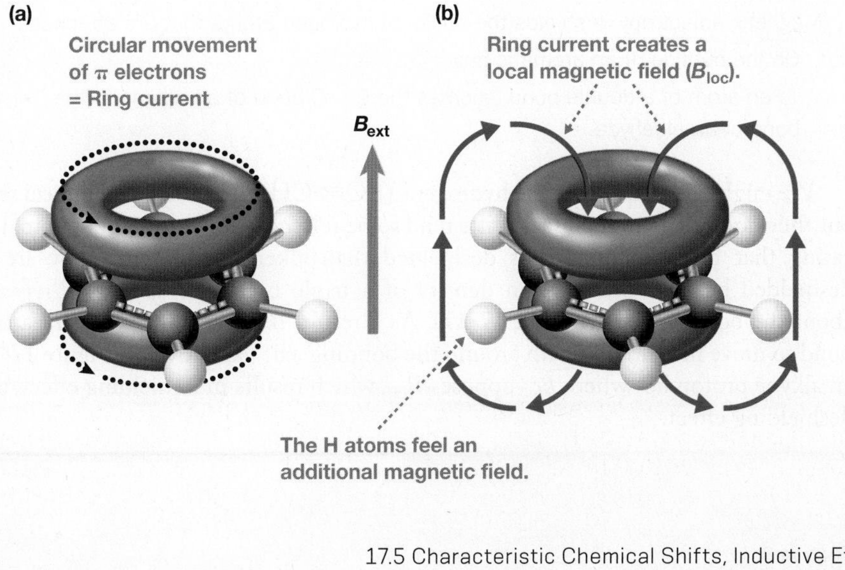

(a)
Circular movement
of π electrons
= Ring current
B_ext
(b)
Ring current creates a
local magnetic field (B_loc).
The H atoms feel an
additional magnetic field.

FIGURE 17-15 Deshielding of hydrogens in benzene (a) B_{ext} forces the π electrons of benzene to move in a circular trajectory above and below the plane of the ring, creating a ring current (indicated by black dotted arrows). (b) The ring current gives rise to a local magnetic field (shown by blue arrows) that is in the same direction as B_{ext} at the location of the hydrogen atoms. The hydrogen nuclei are therefore deshielded, so much so that their signal appears well downfield of TMS.

YOUR TURN 17.5

Which of the indicated protons will experience a larger B_{eff}? Explain.

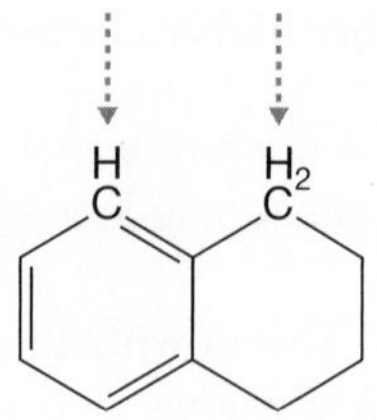

H
C
H2
C

Just like the H atoms in benzene, vinylic H atoms (C═C—H) in alkenes are substantially deshielded due to magnetic anisotropy. Although the π electron density for the C═C double bond is not donut-shaped, the π electrons still undergo a coherent circular motion on either side of the molecular plane, causing an increase in B_{eff} where the vinylic H atoms sit (**Figure 17-16**).

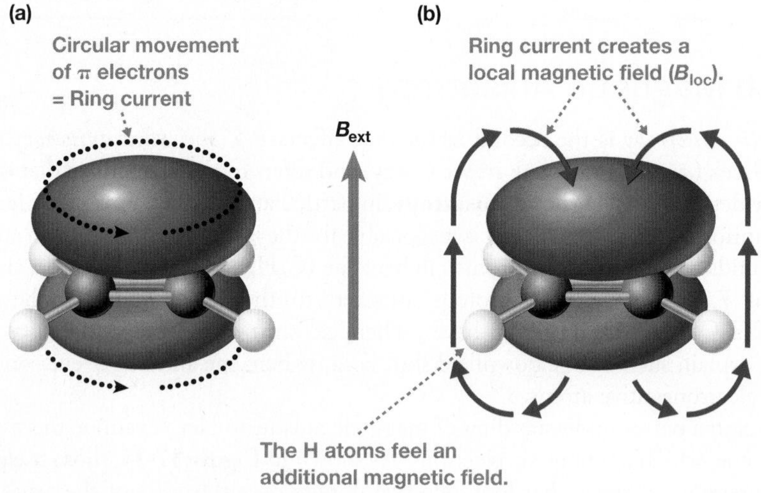

(a)
Circular movement of π electrons = Ring current
B_{ext}
(b)
Ring current creates a local magnetic field (B_{loc}).
The H atoms feel an additional magnetic field.

FIGURE 17-16 Deshielding of vinylic hydrogens (a) B_{ext} forces the π electrons of a double bond to move in a circular trajectory above and below the plane of the double bond, creating a ring current (indicated by black dotted arrows). (b) The ring current gives rise to a local magnetic field (shown by blue arrows) that is in the same direction as B_{ext} at the location of the hydrogen atoms. The hydrogen nuclei are therefore deshielded.

The specific examples of magnetic anisotropy we just examined can be generalized:

Magnetic anisotropy deshields the nuclei of hydrogen atoms that are attached:

- On the outside of an aromatic ring.
- To an atom of a double bond, such as the C═C bond of an alkene or the C═O bond of an aldehyde.

We might also expect alkyne hydrogens (RC≡CH) to have high chemical shifts, but they do not. Their chemical shifts tend to be relatively low, around 2.4 ppm, indicating that they are much less deshielded than alkene hydrogens. They are less deshielded because the electron density of a triple bond has *cylindrical symmetry* about the bonding axis (**Figure 17-17**). As a result, B_{ext} causes electrons in a triple bond to move in a circular path around the bonding axis. As shown in Figure 17-17b, an alkyne proton lies where B_{loc} opposes B_{ext}, which results in a shielding effect, not a deshielding effect.

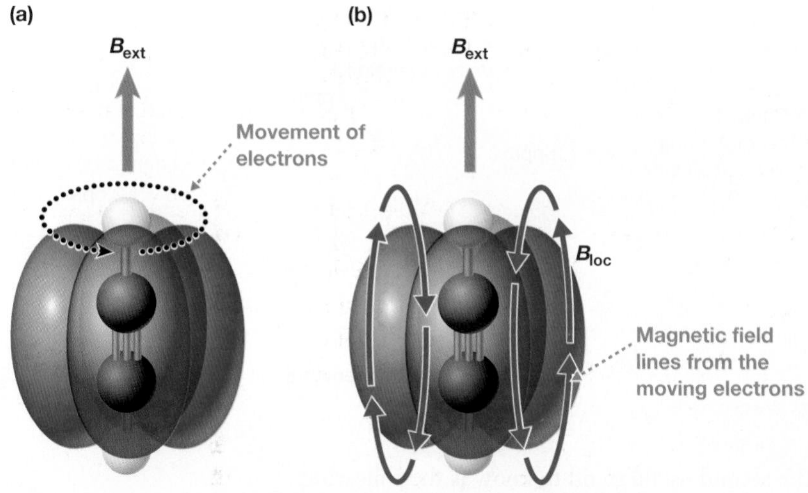
(a)
(b)
B_ext
B_ext
Movement of electrons
B_loc
Magnetic field lines from the moving electrons

FIGURE 17-17 Cylindrical symmetry of a triple bond The two π bonds of ethyne (HC≡CH) are shown. The electron density of a triple bond has cylindrical symmetry about the bonding axis. When placed in a magnetic field, the motion of those electrons, indicated by a black dotted arrow in (a), generates magnetic field lines shown by blue arrows in (b), which shield the hydrogen nuclei.

YOUR TURN 17.6

Which of the indicated protons experiences a greater B_{eff}? Explain.

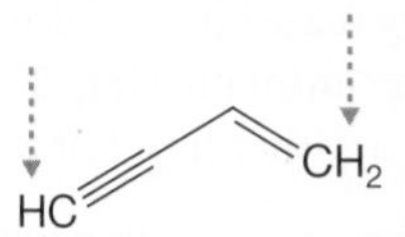
HC
CH2

SECTION 17.6 OBJECTIVES

You will be able to:

1. Derive the impact on chemical shift of a C—H proton by an attached substituent.
2. Use those substituent effects to estimate the chemical shift value of a C—H proton.

17.6 Strategies for Success: Predicting Approximate Chemical Shift Values

Table 17-1 provides chemical shifts of representative protons, but it is not an exhaustive list. How do we deal with protons in molecules that don't closely match the ones in the table?

We can take advantage of two useful trends. The first trend can be stated as follows:

The effects that cause deshielding are essentially additive.

For example, notice how the chemical shifts in **Figure 17-18** increase with each additional Cl atom attached to carbon.

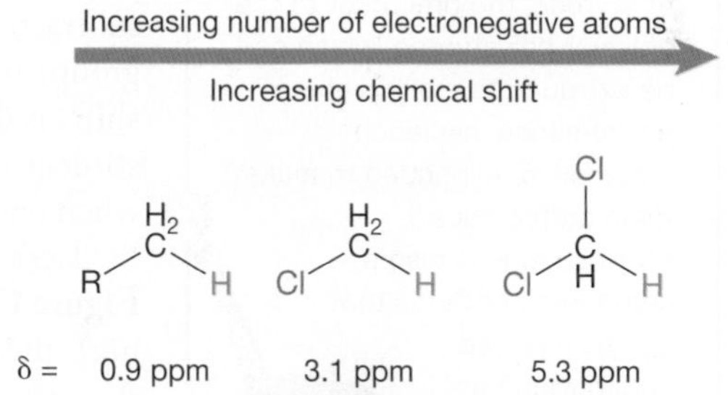
Increasing number of electronegative atoms
Increasing chemical shift
δ = 0.9 ppm
3.1 ppm
5.3 ppm

FIGURE 17-18 Additivity of inductive effects in chemical shifts

YOUR TURN 17.7

For each pair of indicated protons, determine the one that will have the higher chemical shift.

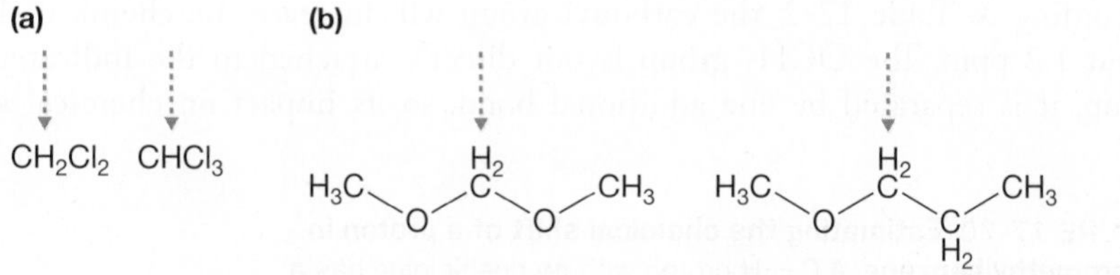
(a)
(b)
CH2Cl2 CHCl3

Strategies for Success Predicting Approximate Chemical Shift Values

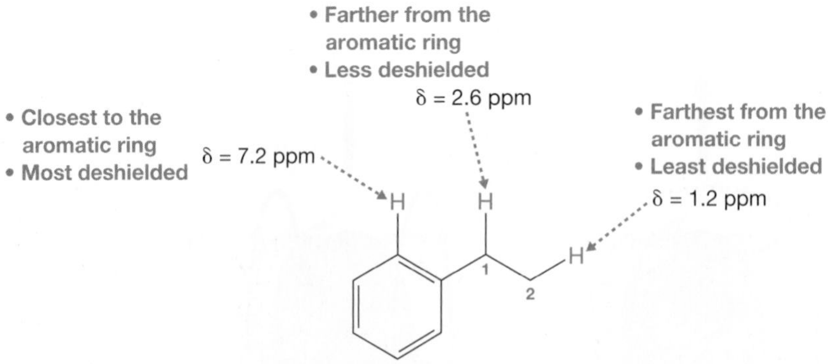
• Closest to the aromatic ring
• Most deshielded
δ = 7.2 ppm
• Farther from the aromatic ring
• Less deshielded
δ = 2.6 ppm
• Farthest from the aromatic ring
• Least deshielded
δ = 1.2 ppm
H
H
H
1
2

Ethylbenzene

FIGURE 17-19 Dependence of chemical shift on distance As a proton becomes more distant from the benzene ring, chemical shift rapidly decreases.

The second useful trend to know is the following:

Deshielding effects fall off very rapidly with distance.

In the case of ethylbenzene, shown in **Figure 17-19**, notice how the chemical shift decreases from 7.2 to 2.6 ppm when the proton becomes one bond farther away from the aromatic ring. The chemical shift decreases again from 2.6 to 1.2 ppm when there is another bond of separation.

YOUR TURN 17.8

Rank the sets of protons A–C in order from lowest to highest chemical shift.

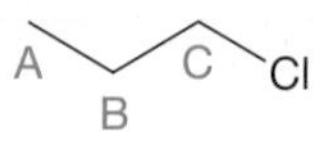
A
B
C
Cl

CONNECTIONS 17.3

Helping to keep your coffee and your homes warm
Ethylbenzene (Fig. 17-19) is used primarily in the production of styrene, the precursor to the polymer polystyrene, which can be extruded to make high-performance insulation materials or expanded to make foam coffee cups. Ethylbenzene is also a component of fluids that can be injected underground as part of a process to recover natural gas.

How can we use the above trends to estimate the value of a chemical shift that does not match a representative proton in Table 17-1? First we need to know what numeric values to assign to various substituent effects. As shown in Table 17-2, we can derive the effect a substituent (Sub) has on the chemical shift of a C—H proton by subtracting 0.9 ppm (the chemical shift of R—CH_3 protons, where R is an alkyl group) from the chemical shift of Sub—CH_3. The difference in the two chemical shifts is due to additional deshielding by Sub. Second, we need to know that the substituent effects in Table 17-2 are reduced to approximately 20% of the listed values when one additional bond separates the substituent from the C—H proton.

Let's use this information to estimate the chemical shift of the indicated proton in **Figure 17-20**. Without the attached C_6H_5 and Cl substituents (i.e., with no deshielding), the proton's chemical shift would be about 0.9 ppm (Table 17-1, Entry 2). According to Table 17-2, the aromatic substituent should increase the chemical shift by 1.4 ppm, and the Cl substituent should increase it by another 2.2 ppm, resulting in a chemical shift of 0.9 + 1.4 + 2.2 = 4.5 ppm. This estimate agrees well with the actual chemical shift measured experimentally, which is 4.6 ppm.

As an example that takes into account the falloff of deshielding effects with distance, let's estimate the chemical shift of the protons indicated in **Figure 17-21**. Again, we begin with 0.9 ppm, the approximate chemical shift with no deshielding. According to Table 17-2, the carbonyl group will increase the chemical shift by about 1.2 ppm. The OCH_3 group is not directly attached to the indicated CH_2 group; it is separated by one additional bond, so its impact on chemical shift is

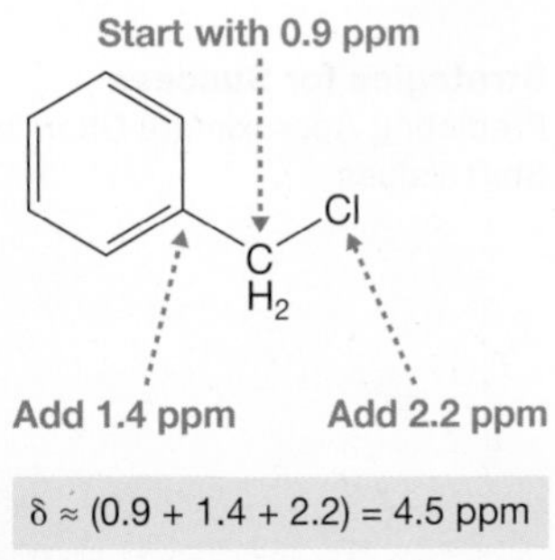
Start with 0.9 ppm
C
H2
Cl
Add 1.4 ppm
Add 2.2 ppm
δ ≈ (0.9 + 1.4 + 2.2) = 4.5 ppm

FIGURE 17-20 Estimating the chemical shift of a proton in chloromethylbenzene A C—H proton with no deshielding has a chemical shift of about 0.9 ppm. Table 17-2 shows that the impact of a benzene ring on the chemical shift of a C—H proton is about 1.4 ppm, and the impact of a Cl atom is about 2.2 ppm.

TABLE 17-2 Substituent Effects on Chemical Shift of C—H Protons

Substituent (Sub)	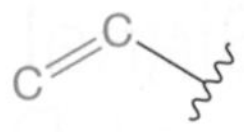	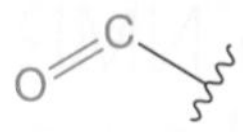	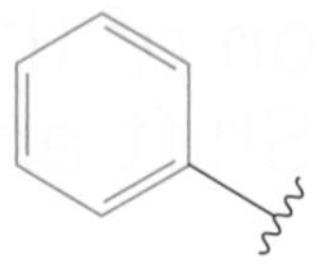	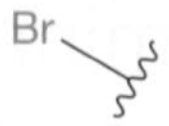	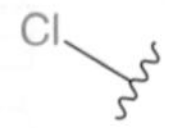	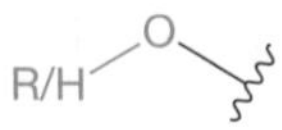	
δ of Sub—CH_3	1.7 ppm	2.1 ppm	2.3 ppm	2.7 ppm	3.1 ppm	3.3 ppm	4.1 ppm
− δ of R—CH_3	− 0.9 ppm	− 0.9 ppm	− 0.9 ppm	− 0.9 ppm	− 0.9 ppm	− 0.9 ppm	− 0.9 ppm
= Substituent effect	**= 0.8 ppm**	**= 1.2 ppm**	**= 1.4 ppm**	**= 1.8 ppm**	**= 2.2 ppm**	**= 2.4 ppm**	**= 3.2 ppm**

roughly 20% of the 2.4 ppm value in Table 17-2. We thus estimate the overall chemical shift to be 0.9 + 1.2 + 0.2(2.4) = 2.6 ppm. The actual chemical shift measured experimentally is 2.7 ppm.

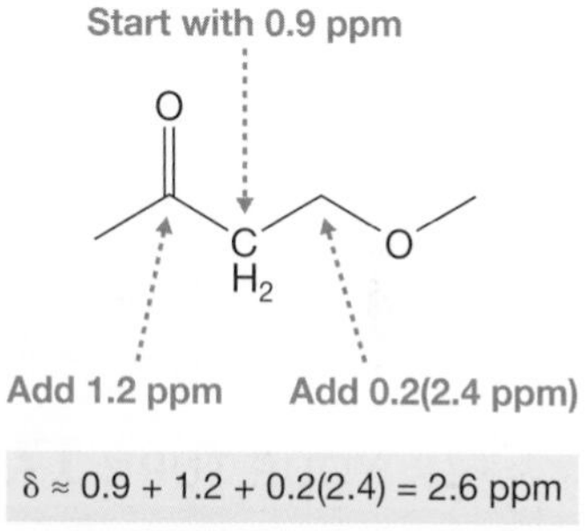

Start with 0.9 ppm
Add 1.2 ppm
Add 0.2(2.4 ppm)
δ ≈ 0.9 + 1.2 + 0.2(2.4) = 2.6 ppm

FIGURE 17-21 Estimating the chemical shift of a proton in 4-methoxybutan-2-one A C—H proton with no deshielding has a chemical shift of about 0.9 ppm. Table 17-2 shows that the impact of a carbonyl group on the chemical shift of a C—H proton is about 1.2 ppm. The OCH_3 group is one bond away from the CH_2 carbon, so it will have about 20% of the 2.4 ppm impact listed in Table 17-2.

SOLVED PROBLEM **17.4**

How to use substituent effects to estimate the chemical shift of a proton

Break It Down Estimate the value of the chemical shift for the indicated proton.

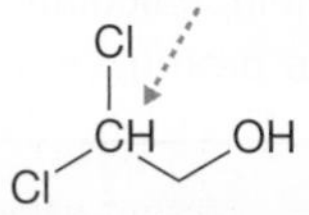

Think	Solve
What would the chemical shift be for that proton if there were no deshielding?	Without deshielding, the chemical shift would be about 0.9 ppm, which is what we observe for protons of the type R—CH_3.
By how much does each attached Cl increase the chemical shift? How many attached Cl atoms are there?	According to Table 17-2, each attached Cl should increase the chemical shift by about 2.2 ppm. There are two attached Cl atoms, so they should increase the chemical shift by 2(2.2 ppm) = 4.4 ppm.
What would the impact of the OH group be if it were attached to the C—H carbon? How do we account for the additional bond of separation?	According to Table 17-2, the OH group would increase the chemical shift by 2.4 ppm if it were attached to the C—H carbon. However, because it is one additional bond removed, the impact is roughly 0.2(2.4 ppm) = 0.5 ppm. Putting all of the impacts together, we arrive at 0.9 + 4.4 + 0.5 = 5.8 ppm. The actual chemical shift measured experimentally is 5.7 ppm.

Try It Estimate the value of the chemical shift for the indicated protons.

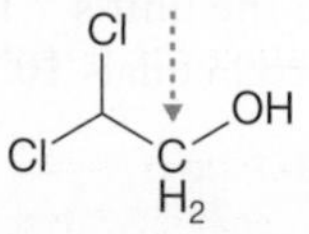

SECTION 17.7 OBJECTIVES

You will be able to:

1. Convert a proton's signal frequency relative to tetramethylsilane into chemical shift and vice versa.
2. Explain why signal frequency depends on the external magnetic field strength but chemical shift does not.

17.7 A Deeper Look: A Quantitative Examination of the NMR Signal and Chemical Shift and a Look at Deuterated Solvents

Section 17.2 described how the α and β spin states of a proton develop different energies when placed in an external magnetic field, B_{ext}. Equation 17-2 shows how that energy difference (ΔE_{spin}) for a *bare* proton (i.e., one that has no shielding) depends on B_{ext}:

$$\Delta E_{\text{spin, bare proton}} = \frac{\gamma h B_{ext}}{2\pi} \qquad (17\text{-}2)$$

Here, B_{ext} is in units of **tesla (T)**, the SI unit for the strength of a magnetic field; h is Planck's constant (6.626×10^{-34} J·s); and γ (the Greek letter gamma) is the **gyromagnetic ratio**, a measure of how sensitive the nuclear spin state energies are to an applied magnetic field. Each nucleus that has spin has a characteristic value for the gyromagnetic ratio; for a proton, its value is $2.67512 \times 10^{8}\ T^{-1}\ s^{-1}$.

In a typical NMR experiment, values of ΔE_{spin} are on the order of 10^{-25} J (see Your Turn 17.9), which is about 0.01% of the thermal energy available at room temperature. Therefore, nuclei in the lower-energy α spin state are in small excess, but that excess is significant.

YOUR TURN 17.9

A common magnetic field strength of modern NMR instruments is 7.046 T. In this magnetic field, calculate the energy difference between the α and β spin states of a bare proton.

For an NMR signal to be produced, a nucleus must absorb photons whose energy matches ΔE_{spin}. Recalling the relationship $E_{photon} = h\nu_{photon}$ (Eq. 16-2, p. 770) and substituting the relationship from Equation 17-2 for a bare proton, we see that the frequency of the absorbed photon is proportional to B_{ext}:

$$E_{photon} = \Delta E_{\text{spin, bare proton}}$$

$$h\nu_{photon} = \frac{\gamma h B_{ext}}{2\pi}$$

$$\nu_{photon} = \frac{\gamma B_{ext}}{2\pi} \qquad (17\text{-}3)$$

Like any NMR signal, the signal that would be produced by such a bare proton, called the **operating frequency (ν_{op})** of the spectrometer, must be equal to the frequency of the absorbed photon. Therefore, substituting ν_{op} for ν_{photon} in Equation 17-3, we obtain:

$$\nu_{op} = \frac{\gamma B_{ext}}{2\pi} \qquad (17\text{-}4)$$

Because the gyromagnetic ratio (γ) is a constant, ν_{op} is directly proportional to B_{ext}. Thus, ν_{op} is constant for a given magnetic field strength. If the strength of the spectrometer's magnet is 7.046 T, for example, then ν_{op} is calculated as follows:

$$\nu_{op} = \frac{(2.67512 \times 10^{8}\ T^{-1}\ s^{-1})(7.046\ T)}{2(3.14159)} = 3.000 \times 10^{8}\ s^{-1}$$

Alternatively, because the unit s^{-1} is equivalent to the unit hertz (Hz), and because 1 MHz (i.e., megahertz) equals 10^{6} Hz, a spectrometer with a 7.046-T magnet has an operating frequency of 300 MHz. We say that the spectrometer is a 300-MHz instrument.

YOUR TURN 17.10

What is the operating frequency of an NMR spectrometer using a magnet whose strength is 11.74 T? Give your answer in units of megahertz.

In a molecule, protons are not bare. Rather, the protons are shielded to various extents and will feel an effective magnetic field, B_{eff}, that is slightly different from B_{ext}. The signal frequency for such a proton is denoted ν_{sample}.

As we described earlier, *chemical shift* is a measure of the extent to which a signal's frequency differs from that of a reference compound, tetramethylsilane (TMS). Formally, chemical shift, in units of *parts per million (ppm)*, is defined by the mathematical expression in Equation 17-5:

$$\text{Chemical shift (ppm)} = \frac{\nu_{sample} - \nu_{TMS}}{\nu_{op}} \times 10^6 \qquad (17\text{-}5)$$

The frequencies ν_{sample} and ν_{op} were defined previously, and ν_{TMS} is the frequency of the signal from the protons in TMS. All of these frequencies are in units of hertz.

Chemical shift is plotted on the *x* axis of an NMR spectrum instead of frequency, because signal frequency depends on B_{ext}. Therefore, signal frequency can vary from one NMR instrument to the next, depending on the strength of its magnet. By contrast, a proton's *chemical shift is independent of* B_{ext}, because the operating frequency that appears in the denominator of Equation 17-5 has the same dependence on magnetic field strength as the frequency terms in the numerator. The magnetic field dependence thus cancels out:

A proton's chemical shift is the same regardless of the NMR instrument used to measure it.

YOUR TURN 17.11

Suppose that the signal of a specific hydrogen nucleus appears 2200 Hz higher than that of the protons in TMS. If the NMR spectrometer uses a 7.046-T magnet, what is the chemical shift of that proton?

Now that we have studied the NMR signal more closely, we can better understand why an NMR spectrum is typically acquired from a solution in which the sample is dissolved in a deuterated solvent, such as deuterochloroform ($CDCl_3$), deuterium oxide (D_2O), or acetone-d_6 (CD_3—CO—CD_3). These solvents contain deuterium (D, or ^2H), which is NMR-active (Section 17.2), so the solvents will produce NMR signals. This is not a concern, however, because the gyromagnetic ratio of D is $0.41065 \times 10^8\ T^{-1}\ s^{-1}$, which is very different from that of a proton, $2.67512 \times 10^8\ T^{-1}\ s^{-1}$. Therefore, the deuterium signals will have very different frequencies from protons and will not appear in a ^1H NMR spectrum.

Deuterated solvents typically contain a small percentage of the ^1H analog, which will produce a solvent peak in the spectrum. $CDCl_3$, for example, contains a small percentage of $CHCl_3$, whose proton's chemical shift is about 7.2 ppm. Consequently, a ^1H NMR spectrum acquired with $CDCl_3$ as the solvent will often exhibit a signal there. (Can you find evidence that $CDCl_3$ was used to acquire the spectrum in Fig. 17-13 on page 831?)

SECTION 17.8 OBJECTIVES

You will be able to:

1. Explain how the integration values for proton signals relate to the numbers of protons contributing to those signals.
2. Describe the different ways that integration values can be presented in an NMR spectrum.

17.8 Integration of Signals

One of the most important features of NMR spectrometers is their ability to compute the *area under an absorption peak*, called the **integration** of the signal. Signal integration is important because:

> The area under an absorption peak is proportional to the number of protons that generate that peak.

In modern instruments, the integration is done digitally, and the results can be displayed in a variety of ways.

One way to display the integration is as an **integral trace** superimposed on the spectrum, as shown by the blue line in **Figure 17-22**. The integral trace for a single peak resembles a stairstep, and the size of that stairstep is proportional to the total area under the peak. Therefore:

> The more the stairstep of an integral trace rises for a particular signal, the greater the number of protons that contribute to that signal.

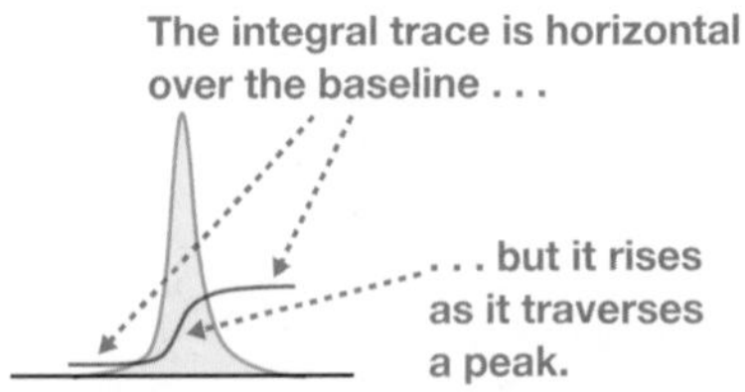

The integral trace is horizontal over the baseline . . .
. . . but it rises as it traverses a peak.

FIGURE 17-22 An integral trace A proton signal is represented by the orange peak. The blue stair-step line is the integral trace, which represents the cumulative area under the peak (represented by the shading) going from left to right.

With this in mind, consider the ^{1}H NMR spectrum of 1,4-dimethylbenzene (*p*-xylene) shown in **Figure 17-23**. The integral trace is drawn in blue. The signal at 2.3 ppm represents the six CH_3 protons, and the signal at 7.1 ppm represents the four aromatic protons. The ratio of these numbers of protons is 6 : 4, or 1.5 : 1, which is essentially the same as the ratio of the stair-step sizes.

CONNECTIONS 17.4

Stay hydrated and stay green 1,4-Dimethylbenzene (Fig. 17-23), also called *p*-xylene, is used as a precursor to terephthalic acid, which is a starting material for poly(ethylene terephthalate), or PET, the plastic used to make this water bottle. PET is completely recyclable and is the world's most recycled plastic, so make sure your water bottles find their way to the recycling bin!

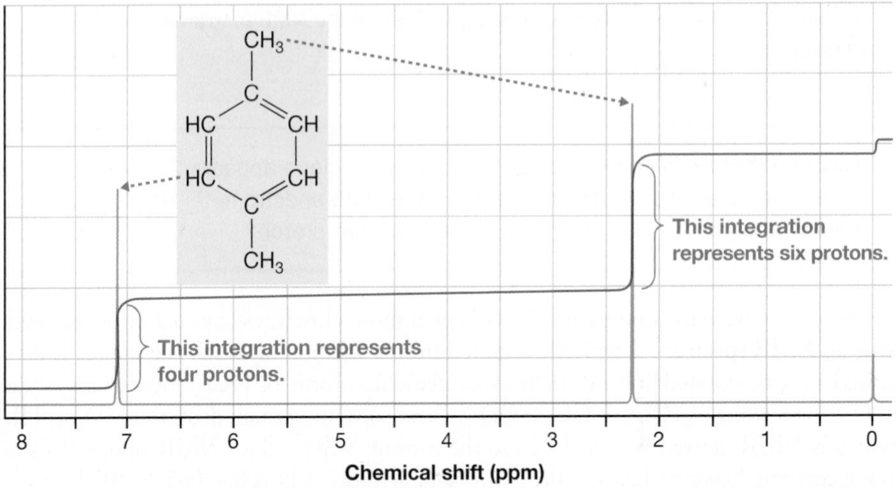

CH3
C
HC
CH
HC
CH
C
CH3
This integration represents six protons.
This integration represents four protons.
8
7
6
5
4
3
2
1
0
Chemical shift (ppm)

FIGURE 17-23 ^{1}H NMR spectrum of 1,4-dimethylbenzene The integral trace, shown in blue, indicates that the ratio of CH_3 hydrogens (signal at 2.3 ppm) to aromatic hydrogens (signal at 7.1 ppm) is 1.5 : 1.

YOUR TURN **17.12**

Which signal in this proton NMR spectrum represents the greatest number of protons? Which signal represents the fewest? Roughly how many times more protons contribute to the former signal than to the latter?

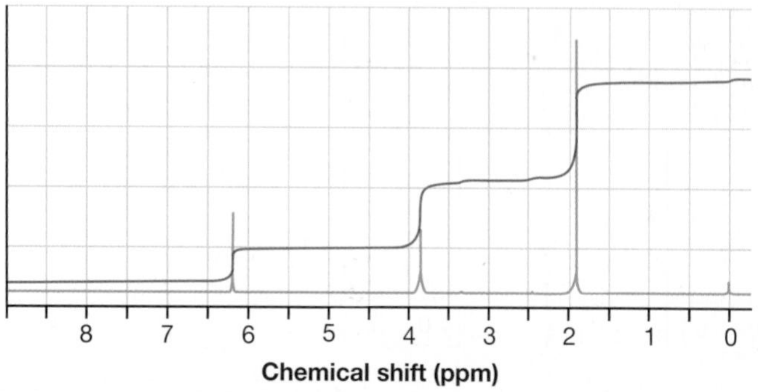

8
7
6
5
4
3
2
1
0
Chemical shift (ppm)

Often it is convenient to convert the output from integration to the smallest set of whole-number ratios, because the number of hydrogen atoms each signal represents *must* be a whole number. The actual number of hydrogen atoms each signal represents is either the same as that in the ratio or a multiple of it. For example, suppose that an NMR spectrum contains three signals and the stair-step sizes measure 10 mm, 10 mm, and 15 mm, respectively. We can divide each size by the smallest number, yielding 1:1:1.5. The smallest set of whole number ratios is double that, or 2:2:3. The actual numbers of hydrogen atoms contributing to each signal could be 2, 2, and 3; or 4, 4, and 6; or 6, 6, and 9; and so on.

In spectral problems involving NMR, the smallest set of whole number ratios is sometimes given to you. If the integration is from a proton NMR spectrum, it is common to place an H after the numbers. A specific signal might be said to have an integration of 1 H, 2 H, 3 H, and so on.

YOUR TURN **17.13**

If the molecule giving the spectrum in Your Turn 17.12 contains a total of six protons, then how many protons does each signal represent? What if the molecule contains a total of 12 protons instead?

17.9 Splitting of the Signal by Spin–Spin Coupling: The *N* + 1 Rule

SECTION 17.9 OBJECTIVES

You will be able to:

1. Describe what spin–spin coupling is and explain how it enables a proton's signal to be split according to the *N* + 1 rule.
2. Explain why OH and NH protons tend not to be involved in signal splitting.
3. Use the splitting pattern of a proton signal to determine the number of coupled protons.

1,1,2-Trichloroethane (Cl_2CHCH_2Cl) has only two chemically distinct H atoms, so its ^1H NMR spectrum (**Figure 17-24**, next page) exhibits two signals. Notice in the magnifications, however, that each signal is *split* into more than one peak. Why does this happen, and how can we predict these splitting patterns? We answer these questions here in Section 17.9.

FIGURE 17-24 Proton NMR spectrum of 1,1,2-trichloroethane The signal at δ ≈ 4.0 ppm is split into a doublet, and the one at δ ≈ 5.8 ppm is split into a triplet. Magnifications (insets) show these splitting patterns more clearly.

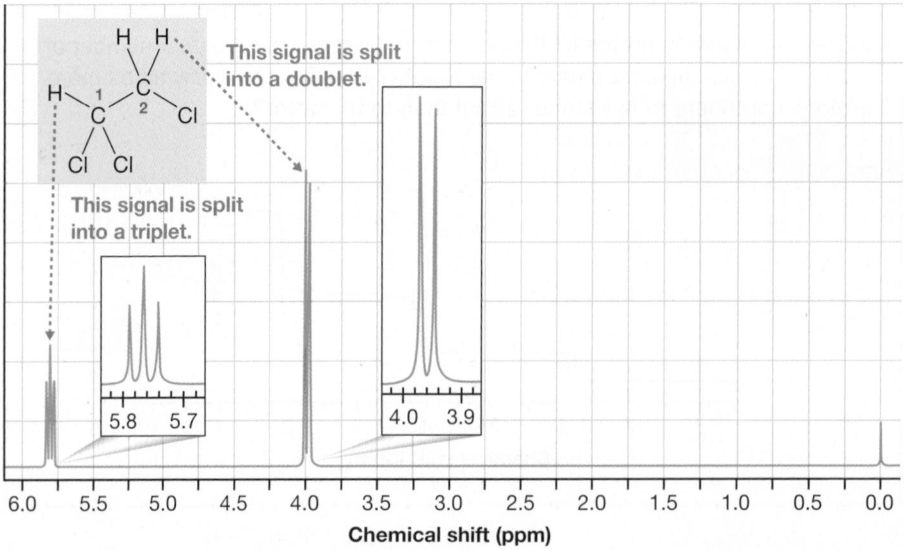

H H
H
C
C
Cl
Cl Cl
1
2
This signal is split into a doublet.
This signal is split into a triplet.
5.8 5.7
4.0 3.9
6.0 5.5 5.0 4.5 4.0 3.5 3.0 2.5 2.0 1.5 1.0 0.5 0.0
Chemical shift (ppm)

17.9a Spin–Spin Coupling and the $N + 1$ Rule

The **signal splitting** just illustrated in Figure 17-24 occurs because every proton behaves like a tiny bar magnet that can be in either the α spin state or the β spin state. The magnetic field experienced by any particular proton (i.e., B_{eff}) can therefore be altered by the magnetic fields of nearby protons, and these alterations can affect the proton's apparent chemical shift. In these situations, protons are said to interact with each other through **spin–spin coupling**, and the protons involved are said to be **coupled** to each other. In general:

> Protons that are coupled are chemically distinct from each other and are generally separated by three or fewer single bonds.

(In some cases, protons that are separated by more than three bonds can exhibit coupling, as shown in Section 17.10.)

Relatively simple splitting patterns like the ones in Figure 17-24 can be predicted by the **$N + 1$ rule**:

The $N + 1$ Rule for Signal Splitting

If proton A is coupled only to proton B and there are N equivalent protons B, then

- Proton A has N coupled protons.
- The signal from proton A will be split into $N + 1$ peaks.

It is important to keep in mind that N is not the number of protons responsible for generating a particular signal, but rather it is the number of *coupled* protons.

Various types of splitting patterns that arise from the $N + 1$ rule are summarized in Table 17-3. When there are zero, one, two, three, or four coupled protons, the signal appears as a **singlet (s)**, **doublet (d)**, **triplet (t)**, **quartet (q)**, or **quintet (qn)**, respectively. With a significantly greater number of coupled protons, the splitting pattern is described as a **multiplet (m)**.

TABLE 17-3 Common Splitting Patterns and Relative Peak Heights

Number of Coupled Protons, N	Number of Peaks in Splitting Pattern, $N + 1$	Description of Splitting Pattern	Relative Peak Heights
0	1	Singlet (s)	1
1	2	Doublet (d)	1:1
2	3	Triplet (t)	1:2:1
3	4	Quartet (q)	1:3:3:1
4	5	Quintet (qn)	1:4:6:4:1
Several	Several	Multiplet (m)	

Notice how the splitting patterns in Figure 17-24 are consistent with the $N + 1$ rule. The H that is bonded to C-1 has two coupled protons (the H atoms bonded to C-2), so $N = 2$ and $N + 1 = 3$. Therefore, the signal that arises from the proton on C-1 ($\delta \approx 5.8$ ppm) is a triplet. The H atoms that are bonded to C-2 have one coupled proton (the lone H bonded to C-1), so $N = 1$ and $N + 1 = 2$ for the corresponding signal ($\delta \approx 4.0$), giving rise to a doublet.

YOUR TURN **17.14**

In Figure 17-24, circle the proton(s) responsible for splitting the signal at around 4.0 ppm, and draw a box around the proton(s) responsible for splitting the signal at around 5.8 ppm.

YOUR TURN **17.15**

How many protons are coupled to the one that gives rise to each of the signals shown here? Explain.

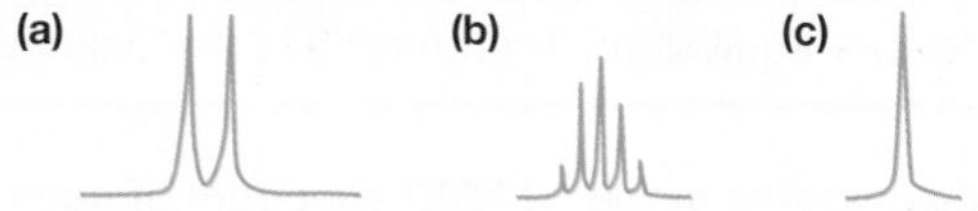
(a)
(b)
(c)

According to the $N + 1$ rule, the protons that are responsible for splitting a signal must be distinct from the protons that give rise to the signal. In other words:

Chemically equivalent protons do not show the effects of being coupled together.

This is why the four H atoms of 1,4-dimethylbenzene (**Figure 17-25**) give rise to a singlet (Fig. 17-23, p. 840). If the adjacent protons split each other's signals, then the ^{1}H NMR spectrum would be quite a bit more complex.

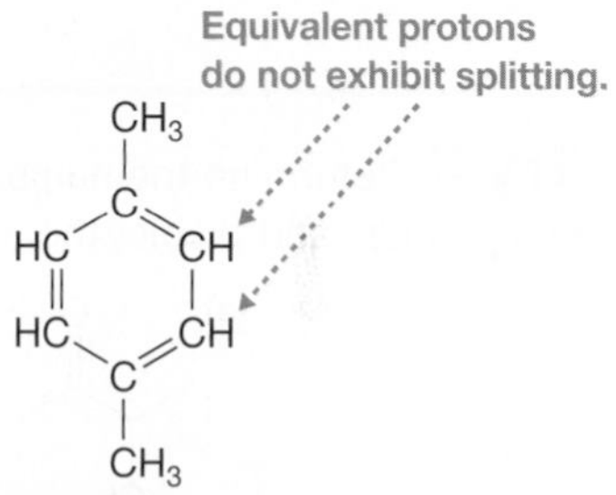
Equivalent protons do not exhibit splitting.
CH3
C
HC
CH
HC
CH
C
CH3

1,4-Dimethylbenzene

FIGURE 17-25 **Chemical equivalence and proton coupling** The two indicated CH protons are close enough to be coupled and to exhibit signal splitting, but they do not because they are equivalent.

SOLVED PROBLEM **17.5**

How to use signal splitting to identify a compound

Break It Down An unknown compound produces a ^{1}H NMR spectrum that has just two signals, each of which is a singlet. Which of compounds 1–4 could the unknown be?

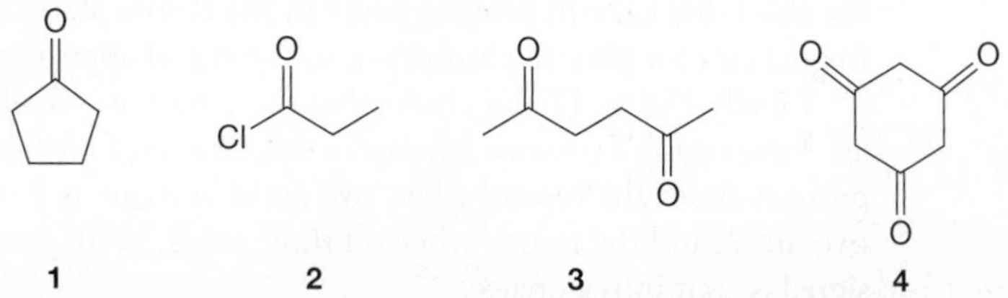
O
O
Cl
O
O
O
O
O

1 **2** **3** **4**

Think	Solve
How many chemically distinct protons are indicated by the spectrum?	Because the spectrum has two signals, the compound must have two chemically distinct protons.

(continued)

Which of compounds 1–4 exhibit that number of distinct protons?

The distinct types of protons are indicated by different letters below. Compounds **1**, **2**, and **3** are candidates because they each have two distinct types of protons. Compound **4** has just one type of proton, so it is ruled out.

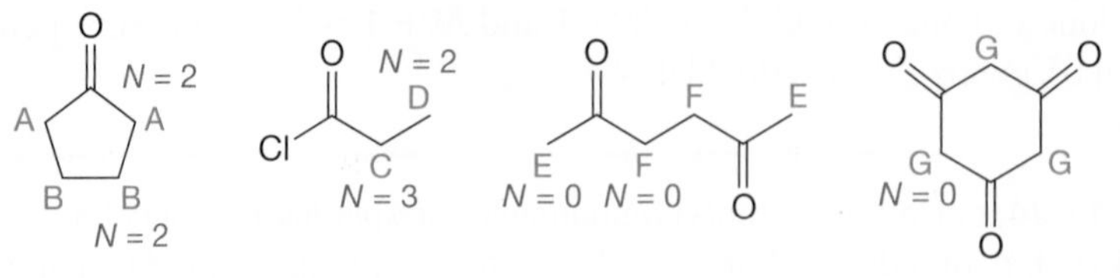

O
N = 2
A
A
B
B
N = 2
O
N = 2
D
Cl
C
N = 3
O
F
E
E
F
N = 0
N = 0
O
O
G
O
G
G
N = 0
O

1 **2** **3** **4**

In those compounds, can any protons be coupled to other protons?

The NMR signals are both singlets, so the protons giving rise to those signals must not be coupled to other protons. Compound **1** is ruled out because protons A and B are coupled. Compound **2** is ruled out because protons C and D are coupled. In compound **3**, protons E and F are *not* coupled because they are four bonds away from each other. Each pair of protons F are within three bonds of each other, but they cannot be coupled to each other because they are equivalent. Therefore, **3** is the unknown compound.

Try It Determine the number of signals that would be generated in the ^{1}H NMR spectrum of each of the following compounds, and predict the splitting pattern of each signal.

(a) **(b)** **(c)** **(d)**

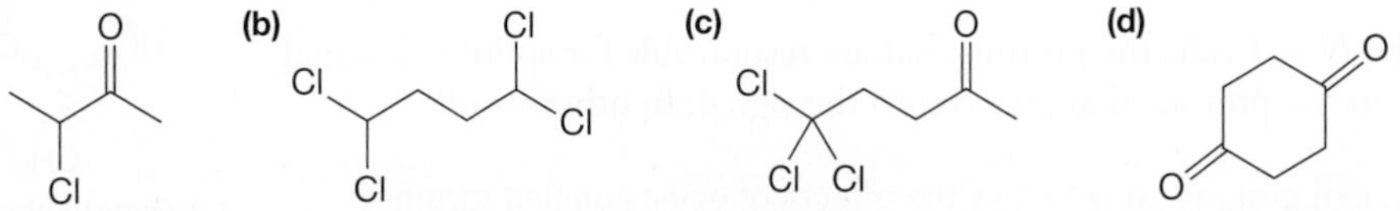

O
Cl
Cl
Cl
Cl
Cl
O
Cl
Cl
Cl
O
O

The origin of the $N + 1$ rule can be understood by considering the various magnetic fields (B_{loc}) generated by a set of protons responsible for splitting a particular signal. In **Figure 17-26a**, for example, the proton that generates the signal (shown in black) is coupled to one proton (shown in red). Therefore, there are two possible values for B_{loc} from that coupled proton: one due to the coupled proton in the α spin state and the other due to the coupled proton in the β spin state. Therefore, there are two possible frequencies for photon absorption, and the signal appears as a doublet.

Figure 17-26b deals with two coupled protons (shown in red and blue). There are three possible values for B_{loc} from those coupled protons: one due to both protons being in the α spin state, the second due to one proton being α and the other β, and the third due to both protons being in the β spin state. Thus, there are three possible frequencies for photon absorption, so the signal appears as a triplet.

Finally, Figure 17-26c shows that there are four possible values for B_{loc} when there are three coupled protons (shown in red, blue, and green): one when all three coupled protons are α, the second when two are α and one is β, the third when one is α and two are β, and the fourth when all three are β. With four possible values for B_{loc}, the signal is split into a quartet.

Notice in Table 17-3 (p. 842) that the peaks in each splitting pattern appear in characteristic *height ratios*. The peak heights of a doublet are in a 1:1 ratio, those of a triplet are in a 1:2:1 ratio, and those of a quartet are in a 1:3:3:1 ratio. These patterns arise because the α and β spin states are essentially equally likely for a proton, and the height of each peak reflects the number of ways the spins of the coupled protons can produce the same B_{loc}. For the coupled protons in Figure 17-26c (quartet), for example, notice that there is just one way to have all three coupled protons α, three ways to have a net of one α, three ways to have a net of one β, and one way to have all three β. This matches the 1:3:3:1 height ratio characteristic of a quartet.

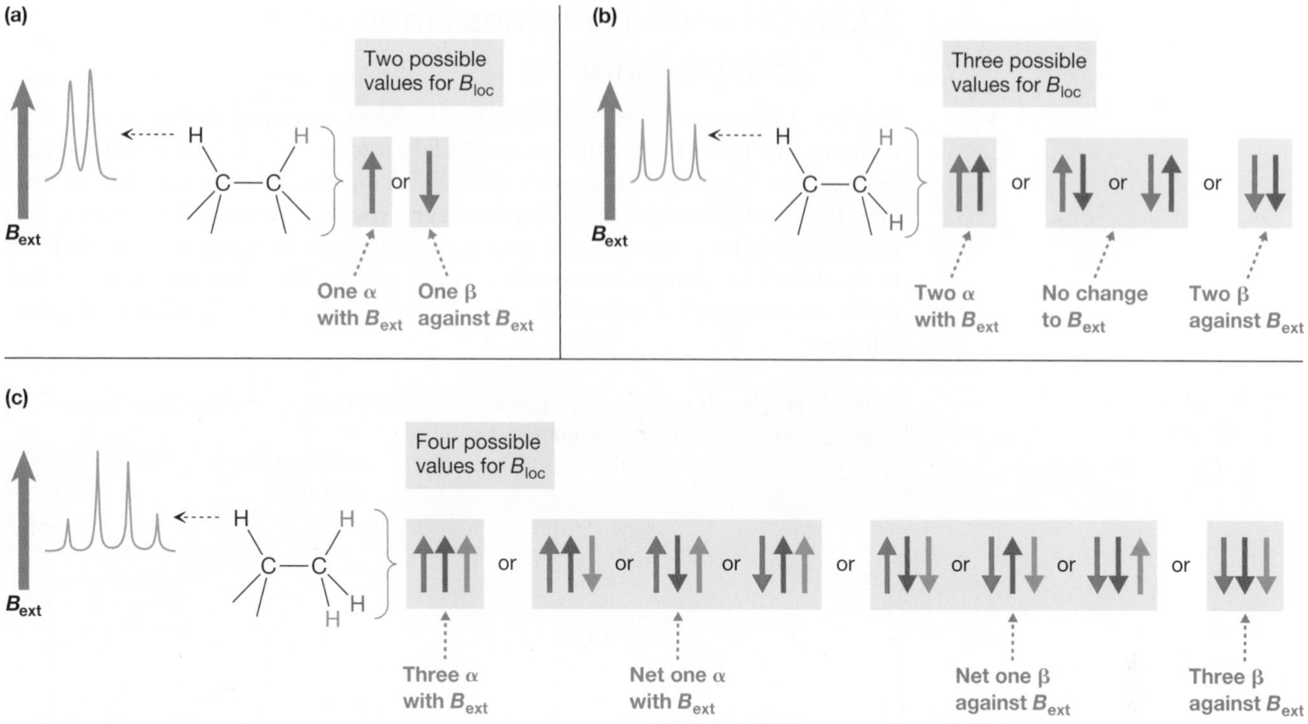

(a)
Two possible values for B_{loc}
B_{ext}
or
One α with B_{ext}
One β against B_{ext}
(b)
Three possible values for B_{loc}
B_{ext}
or
Two α with B_{ext}
No change to B_{ext}
Two β against B_{ext}
(c)
Four possible values for B_{loc}
B_{ext}
or
Three α with B_{ext}
Net one α with B_{ext}
Net one β against B_{ext}
Three β against B_{ext}

FIGURE 17-26 The origin of signal splitting In each case, our focus is on the signal from the proton shown in black, on the left end of the molecule, being split by the coupled proton(s) shown in color, on the right end of the molecule. (a) One coupled proton gives rise to two possible values for B_{loc}, so the signal is split into a doublet. (b) Two coupled protons give rise to three possible values for B_{loc}, so the signal is split into a triplet. (c) Three coupled protons give rise to four possible values for B_{loc}, so the signal is split into a quartet.

The height ratios for signal splitting form a pattern known as **Pascal's triangle** (**Figure 17-27**). The first and last number in each row is 1. Each of the remaining numbers in a particular row is the sum of the two closest numbers in the row above it. For example, consider the relative peak heights for a quintet, 1 : 4 : 6 : 4 : 1. As shown in Figure 17-27, 4 is the sum of 1 and 3, the two closest numbers in the previous line, and 6 is the sum of the two 3s that appear in the line above it.

SOLVED PROBLEM **17.6**

How to determine the peak height ratios in signal splitting

Break It Down **In what ratios would the peaks of a sextet (a signal with six peaks) appear?**

Think	Solve
For Pascal's triangle, what should the first and last numbers be?	The first and last numbers should be 1. That's because there is only one way for all coupled protons to have α spin or β spin.
How are the remaining numbers derived from the line above it in Pascal's triangle?	We sum each adjacent pair of numbers from the line representing a quintet: 1 + 4 = 5, 4 + 6 = 10, 6 + 4 = 10, and 4 + 1 = 5. Therefore, the ratios are 1:5:10:10:5:1.

Try It In what ratios would the peaks of a septet (a signal with seven peaks) appear?

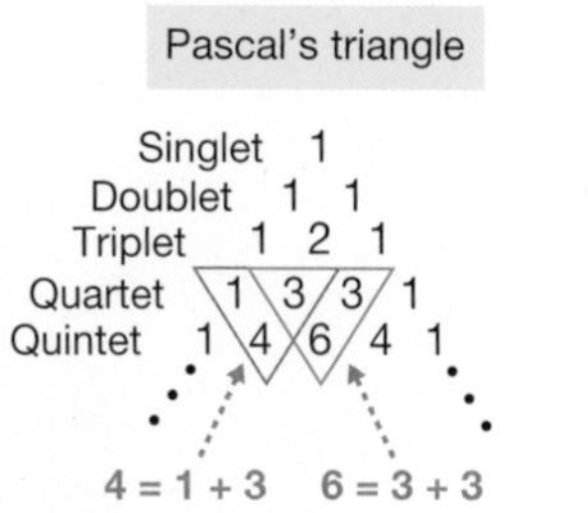

Pascal's triangle
Singlet 1
Doublet 1 1
Triplet 1 2 1
Quartet 1 3 3 1
Quintet 1 4 6 4 1
4 = 1 + 3
6 = 3 + 3

FIGURE 17-27 Pascal's triangle The numbers in each row correspond to the height ratios in various splitting patterns.

17.9b OH and NH Protons Often Do Not Exhibit Coupling

The $N + 1$ rule seems to be violated in the ^1H NMR spectrum of ethanamine, which is shown in **Figure 17-28**. The amino (NH_2) protons ($\delta \approx 3.7$ ppm) and the CH_2 protons ($\delta \approx 2.7$ ppm) don't appear to be coupled together, even though they are separated by only three bonds. The NH_2 protons give rise to a broad singlet, so they appear to be uncoupled to any protons. Moreover, the CH_2 protons appear to be coupled only to the three CH_3 protons, making the signal a quartet. This phenomenon is not limited to ethanamine, but rather it occurs commonly with protons bonded to oxygen or nitrogen:

O—H and N—H protons often give rise to broad singlets, and thus they do not appear to couple to other protons.

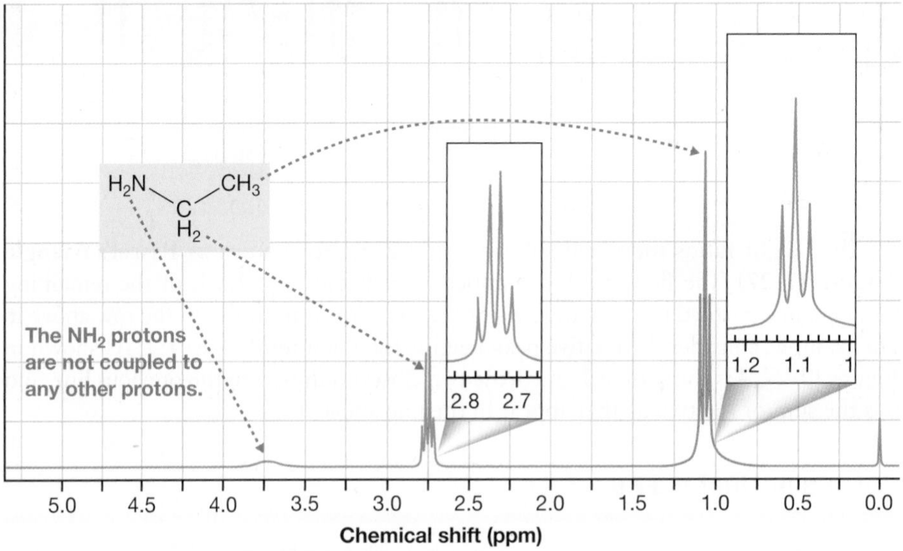

H_2N
CH_3
C
H_2
The NH_2 protons are not coupled to any other protons.
2.8 2.7
1.2 1.1 1
5.0 4.5 4.0 3.5 3.0 2.5 2.0 1.5 1.0 0.5 0.0
Chemical shift (ppm)

FIGURE 17-28 Proton NMR spectrum of ethanamine The NH_2 protons and the CH_2 protons do not appear to be coupled together.

O—H and N—H protons tend not to exhibit coupling because of rapid *proton exchange*, which we first encountered in Section 16.6a. Protons on nitrogen and oxygen undergo extensive hydrogen bonding, and thus can hop rapidly from one nitrogen or oxygen atom to another. This proton exchange is usually much faster than the time it takes to acquire an NMR spectrum, so the signal that we observe reflects the *average* environment from all the molecules on which it spends time, resulting in an unsplit singlet. Moreover, protons bonded to oxygen or nitrogen have less well-defined chemical environments than protons bonded to carbon, so they tend to absorb a larger range of frequencies, which also broadens their signals.

We can take advantage of this proton exchange to identify O—H or N—H signals. If a sample is treated with D_2O, the O—H and N—H protons in that sample are rapidly replaced by D (i.e., by ^2H), whose signals do not appear in ^1H NMR spectra (Section 17.7). Thus, the intensities of the O—H and N—H signals decrease dramatically or disappear entirely.

YOUR TURN **17.16**

What similarities would you expect between proton NMR spectra of compounds **A** and **B**? What differences would you expect? How would each spectrum be affected by the addition of D_2O?

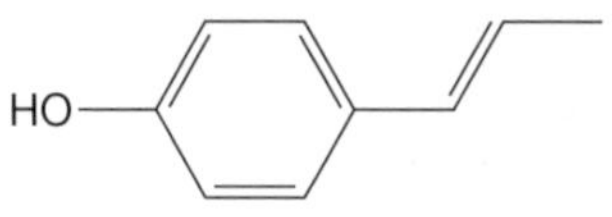

HO

A

O

B

17.10 Coupling Constants and Complex Signal Splitting

SECTION 17.10 OBJECTIVES

You will be able to:

1. Determine a proton signal's coupling constant from the NMR spectrum.
2. Use coupling constants to determine which signals in a ^{1}H NMR spectrum represent coupled protons and to identify what types of protons are coupled.
3. Describe the origin of complex signal splitting and use coupling constants to derive a complex splitting pattern.

In Section 17.9, we saw that signals are split as a result of the various local magnetic fields (B_{loc}) generated from the spins of coupled protons. Each peak in a split signal represents a slightly different frequency being detected. The frequency *difference* between any pair of adjacent peaks in a split signal is called the **coupling constant (*J*)**, which has units of hertz. Coupling constants can be helpful because their values are characteristic of the kinds of protons that are involved in coupling, as shown in Table 17-4.

Moreover, coupling constants can be used to interpret a ^{1}H NMR spectrum if you remember the following:

Signals of protons that are coupled together exhibit the same coupling constant.

This is because the energetic effects of one magnetic dipole on a second are the same as the energetic effects of the second magnetic dipole on the first. For example, the

TABLE 17-4 Commonly Encountered Coupling Constants

Relationship between Protons	Coupling Constant, *J* (Hz)	Relationship between Protons	Coupling Constant, *J* (Hz)	Relationship between Protons	Coupling Constant, *J* (Hz)
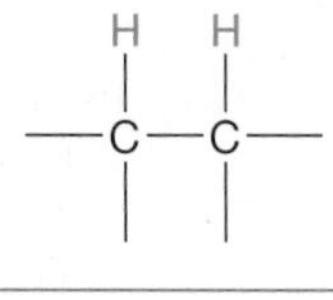	6–9	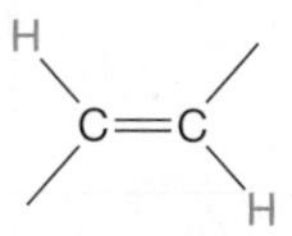	13–18	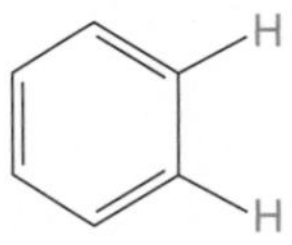	6–9
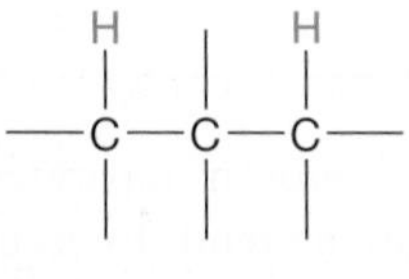	~0	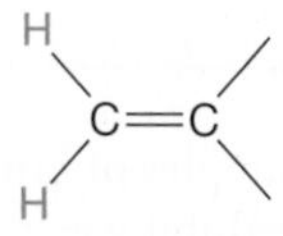	1–3	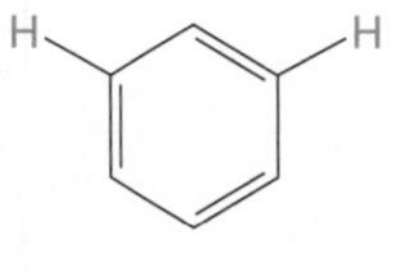	1–3
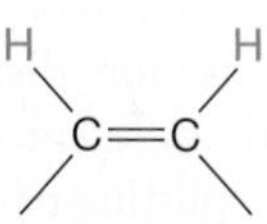	7–12	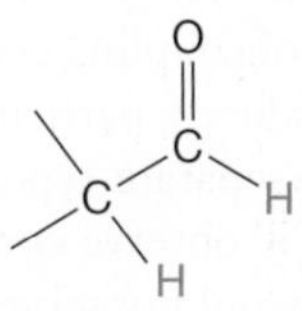	1–3	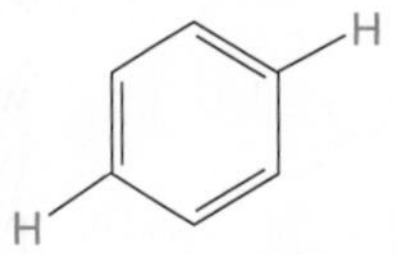	0–1

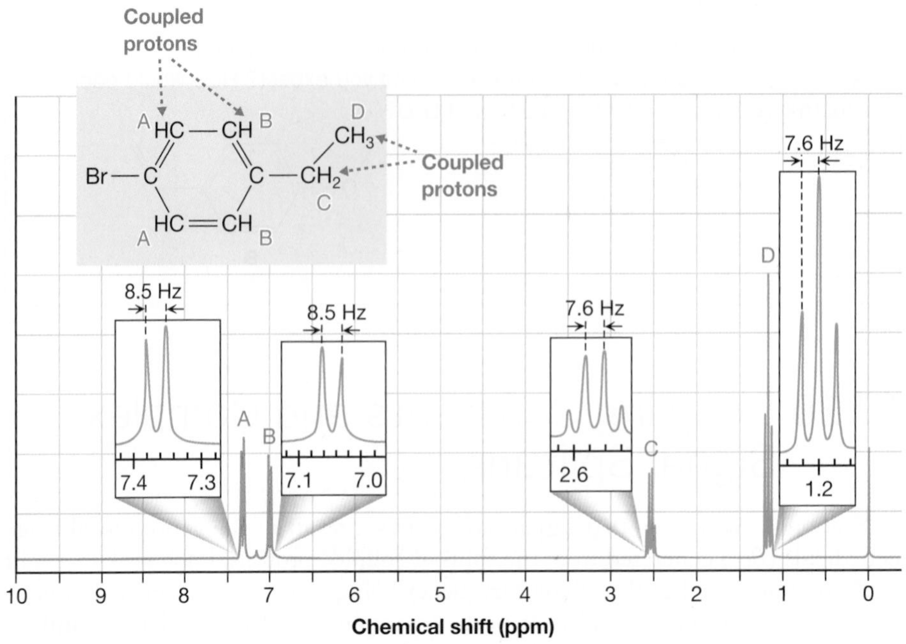
Coupled
protons
A HC—CH B
D
CH3
Br—C
C—CH2
Coupled
protons
C
HC=CH
A
B
8.5 Hz
7.4 7.3
8.5 Hz
7.1 7.0
7.6 Hz
2.6
7.6 Hz
1.2
A
B
C
D
10 9 8 7 6 5 4 3 2 1 0
Chemical shift (ppm)

FIGURE 17-29 Proton NMR spectrum of 1-bromo-4-ethylbenzene Protons A and B are coupled together, and their signals have the same apparent coupling constant (i.e., $J = 8.5$ Hz). Protons C and D are coupled together, too, and their signals have the same coupling constant (i.e., $J = 7.6$ Hz).

spectrum of 1-bromo-4-ethylbenzene (**Figure 17-29**) has four distinguishable signals. Protons A and B are coupled together, so their signals have the same coupling constant, which is 8.5 Hz. (In actuality, the coupling constants that describe signals A and B are more complicated because of long-range coupling, described later in this section.) Similarly, protons C and D are coupled together, and the coupling constant for both signals is 7.6 Hz.

YOUR TURN **17.17**

In the ^{1}H NMR spectrum shown here, identify each pair of signals that represent coupled protons.

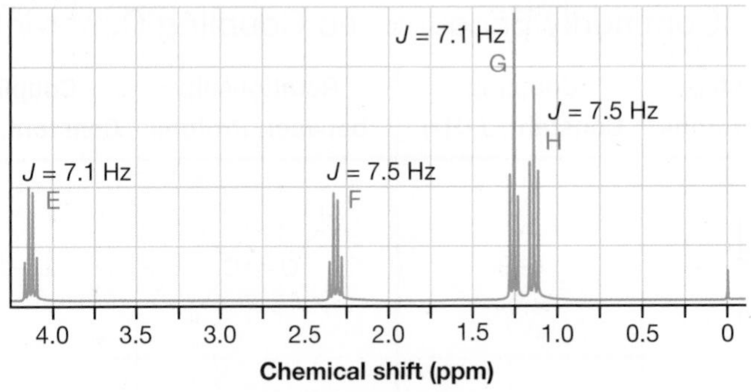
J = 7.1 Hz
G
J = 7.5 Hz
H
J = 7.1 Hz
E
J = 7.5 Hz
F
4.0 3.5 3.0 2.5 2.0 1.5 1.0 0.5 0
Chemical shift (ppm)

Table 17-4 lists two examples of **long-range coupling** in which protons separated by more than three bonds exhibit weak coupling. Long-range coupling tends to occur when the protons are connected by a rigid carbon framework, established by π bonds.

One important aspect of coupling constants is the splitting that we tend to observe when the protons that produce a particular signal are coupled to two or more distinct types of protons. If those separate types of coupling have sufficiently different coupling constants, then we will observe **complex splitting**, in which the splitting pattern is different from what we would observe if all coupled protons were equivalent.

Consider the ^{1}H NMR spectrum of bromoethene ($H_2C{=}CHBr$) shown in **Figure 17-30**. Bromoethene has three chemically distinct types of protons, and each is coupled to the other two. H^A is coupled to H^B by a coupling constant of 1.8 Hz, H^B

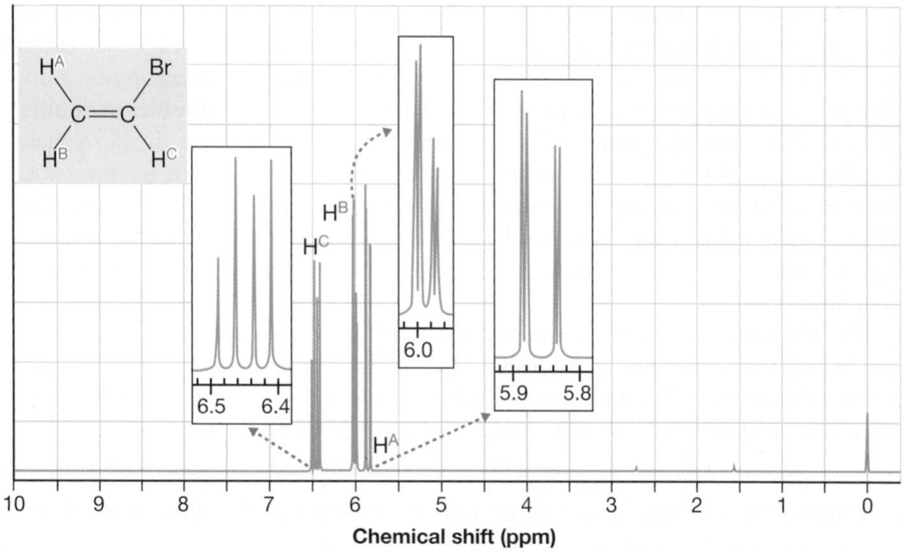

H^A
Br
C=C
H^B
H^C
6.5
6.4
6.0
5.9
5.8
10
9
8
7
6
5
4
3
2
1
0
Chemical shift (ppm)

FIGURE 17-30 Proton NMR spectrum of bromoethene The spectrum would be less complicated if H^A and H^B were equivalent.

is coupled to H^C by a coupling constant of 7.1 Hz, and H^A is coupled to H^C by a coupling constant of 14.9 Hz. Notice that the splitting for all three signals is more complex than a simple singlet, doublet, triplet, etc.

To understand how these complex splitting patterns arise, it helps to view the coupling to each chemically distinct proton *one at a time* and to construct what is called a **splitting diagram**. An example of a splitting diagram for the H^B proton ($\delta = 5.97$ ppm) is shown in **Figure 17-31**.

Figure 17-31a considers first the splitting of the H^B signal by proton H^C (coupling constant = 7.1 Hz), which would cause the unsplit signal (Fig. 17-31a, top) to be split

FIGURE 17-31 Splitting diagram for proton B in bromoethene (a) The signal from proton B is split first by proton C and then by proton A. (b) The signal from proton B is split first by proton A and then by proton C. The peak locations in the resulting doublet of doublets are independent of the order in which we think about the splitting taking place.

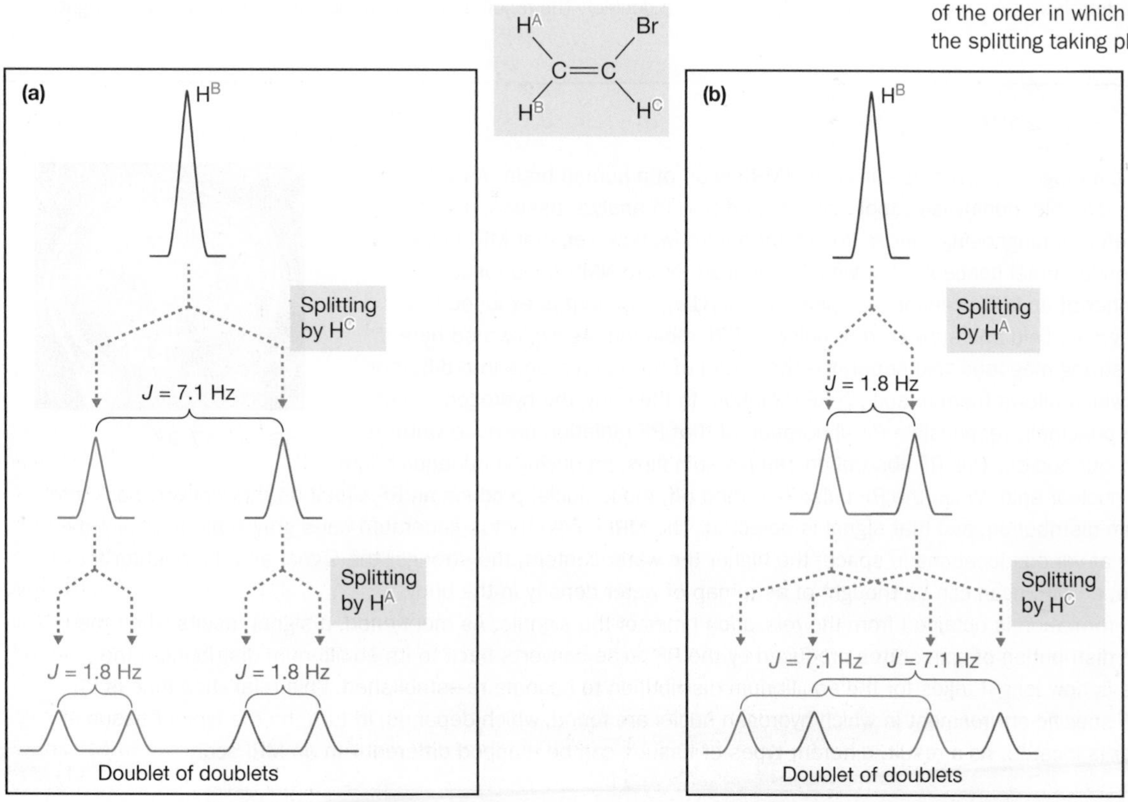

(a)
H^B
Splitting by H^C
J = 7.1 Hz
Splitting by H^A
J = 1.8 Hz
J = 1.8 Hz
Doublet of doublets
H^A
Br
C=C
H^B
H^C
(b)
H^B
Splitting by H^A
J = 1.8 Hz
Splitting by H^C
J = 7.1 Hz
J = 7.1 Hz
Doublet of doublets

into a doublet of peaks separated by 7.1 Hz (Fig. 17-31a, middle). Now, if we take into account the coupling between H^B and H^A (coupling constant = 1.8 Hz), then each of the peaks in the doublet brought about by the first coupling is split again into a doublet, this time with the peaks separated by 1.8 Hz. The result is a **doublet of doublets** (Fig. 17-31a, bottom), which is what we observe in the spectrum for the H^B signal.

The same splitting pattern, a doublet of doublets, is obtained if we reverse the order in which we perform the splitting. As shown in Figure 17-31b, the signal from H^B is first split by H^A, and the resulting peaks are then split by H^C. It is generally easier, however, to construct these splitting diagrams by working in order from largest coupling constant to smallest.

For the same reasons, the signals of H^A and H^C are each a doublet of doublets. H^B and H^C separately split the signal from H^A into a doublet. Likewise, H^A and H^B separately split the signal from H^C into a doublet. These splitting patterns can be seen in the insets for the two signals in Figure 17-30 at δ = 5.85 and 6.45 ppm.

YOUR TURN **17.18**

Construct a splitting diagram for H^A in bromoethene. Do the same for H^C. (The relevant coupling constants are provided in the text.)

Another example of complex splitting appears in the ^1H NMR spectrum of butanal, $CH_3CH_2CH_2CH{=}O$. The signal for the protons on C-2 is shown in **Figure 17-32**. The two protons on C-3 split the C-2 protons into a triplet. Separately, the aldehyde proton on C-1 splits the signal for the protons on C-2 into a doublet. The result is six peaks in a 1:1:2:2:1:1 height ratio, or a **triplet of doublets**.

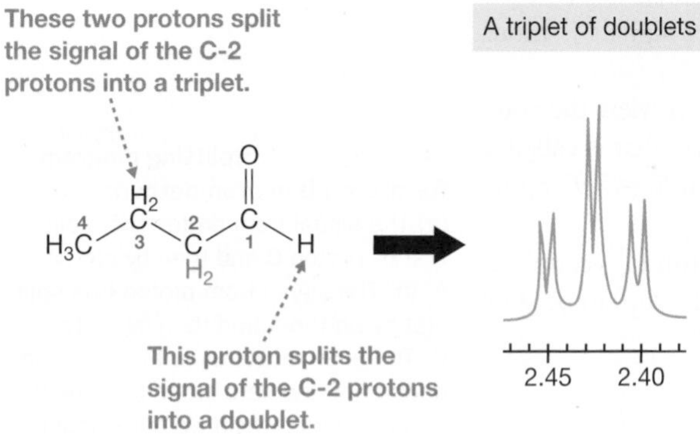

These two protons split the signal of the C-2 protons into a triplet.
This proton splits the signal of the C-2 protons into a doublet.
A triplet of doublets
2.45
2.40

FIGURE 17-32 Origin of a triplet of doublets The signal from the protons on C-2 (shown in red) is split by the protons on C-3 into a triplet, and each of the three peaks is separately split by the proton on C-1 into a doublet. The result is a triplet of doublets, as shown on the right.

Magnetic Resonance Imaging

Figure 17-33 is a magnetic resonance imaging (MRI) scan of a human brain. As you may know, MRI is a valuable, noninvasive tool used in medicine to analyze tissues, and it is particularly useful for diagnosing cancer. You might not know, however, that MRI is based on the same fundamental concepts that we have applied toward NMR spectroscopy.

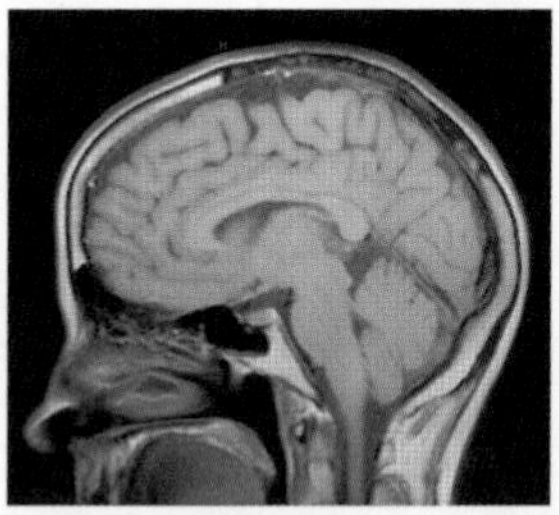

FIGURE 17-33

In the chamber of an MRI scanner (see photo on p. 819), a patient is exposed to a very strong magnetic field and subjected to pulses of RF radiation. As we learned here in Chapter 17, a strong magnetic field separates the nuclei of hydrogen atoms into different energy levels, which allows them to absorb RF radiation. In the body, the hydrogen atoms from water are principally responsible for absorption of that RF radiation because water is so abundant in our bodies. This RF absorption causes spin flips, producing a nonequilibrium distribution of nuclear spin. When the RF pulse is turned off, those nuclei produce an RF signal as they convert back into their equilibrium distribution, and that signal is detected. The MRI image that is generated uses gray scale to depict the signal intensity at various locations in space: the higher the water content, the stronger the signal and the brighter the spot. Therefore, an MRI scan can be thought of as a map of water density in the body.

Additional information is obtained from the *relaxation times* of the signals. As mentioned, a signal results when the nonequilibrium distribution of spin states produced by the RF pulse converts back to its equilibrium distribution; the relaxation time is how long it takes for the equilibrium distribution to become re-established. This relaxation time is affected by the specific environment in which hydrogen nuclei are found, which depends, in turn, on the type of tissue in which the water is located. As a result, different types of tissues can be mapped differently in an MRI scan.

How would you describe the splitting pattern for the CH_2 proton signal in propanal? Sketch the signal, which should be similar to the one in Figure 17-32.

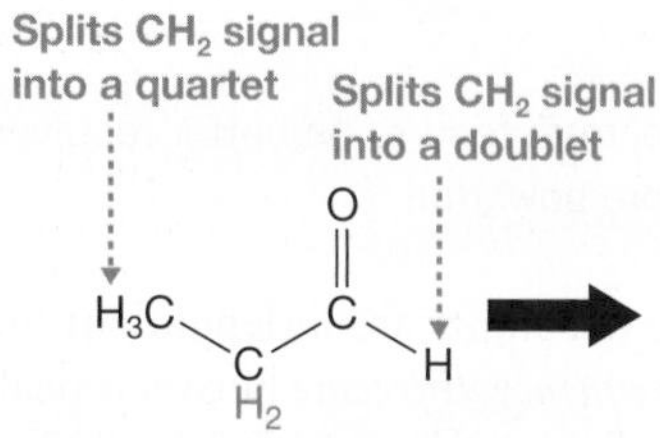

Splits CH2 signal into a quartet
Splits CH2 signal into a doublet
O
H3C
C
C
H
H2

YOUR TURN **17.19**

CONNECTIONS 17.5

Greener coatings Propanal (Your Turn 17.19) is used to synthesize trimethylolethane, $CH_3C(CH_2OH)_3$, which is important in the manufacture of alkyd resins. Alkyd resins have use as coatings, especially wood coatings, and are considered greener than coatings like polyurethane.

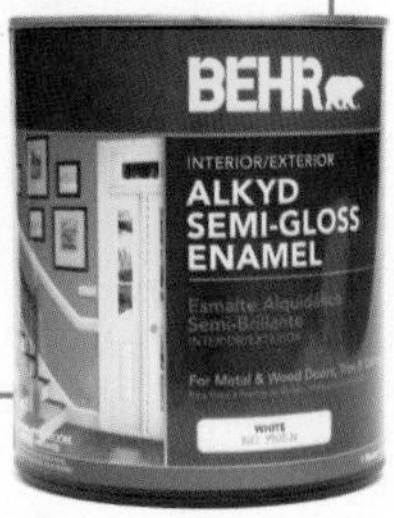

BEHR
INTERIOR/EXTERIOR
ALKYD
SEMI-GLOSS
ENAMEL

17.11 A Deeper Look: Signal Resolution and the Strength of B_{ext}

SECTION 17.11 OBJECTIVES

You will be able to:

1. Explain why a greater B_{ext} results in a greater separation between signals.

Figure 17-34 shows the ^{1}H NMR spectrum of hexan-3-one taken with a 90-MHz spectrometer (Fig. 17-34a) and a 300-MHz spectrometer (Fig. 17-34b). Based on the structure of hexan-3-one, the two sets of CH_3 hydrogens are chemically distinct and should give rise to two different signals, each a triplet. However, the spectrum taken with the 90-MHz spectrometer does not clearly show this. Instead, the two

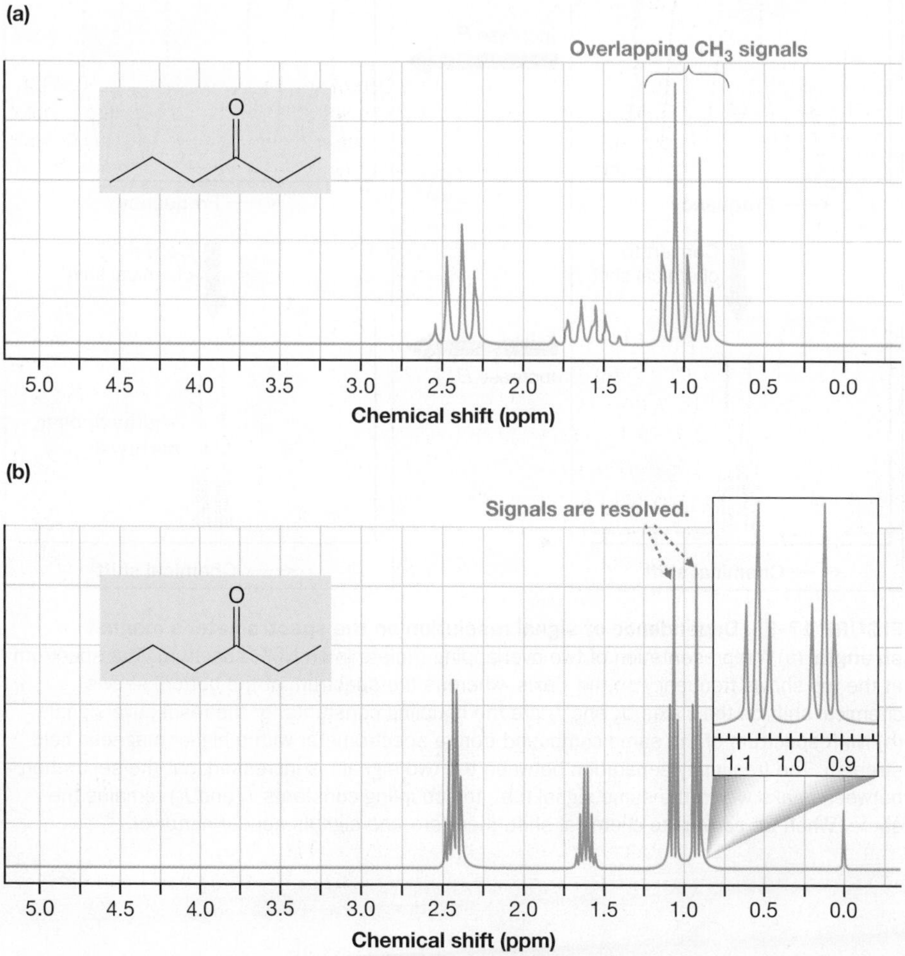

(a)
Overlapping CH3 signals
O
5.0
4.5
4.0
3.5
3.0
2.5
2.0
1.5
1.0
0.5
0.0
Chemical shift (ppm)
(b)
Signals are resolved.
O
1.1
1.0
0.9
5.0
4.5
4.0
3.5
3.0
2.5
2.0
1.5
1.0
0.5
0.0
Chemical shift (ppm)

FIGURE 17-34 Proton NMR spectra of hexan-3-one (a) Spectrum taken with a 90-MHz spectrometer. (b) Spectrum taken with a 300-MHz spectrometer. The stronger magnet resolves the signals much better.

signals overlap and are therefore not **resolved** from each other. In cases such as this, interpreting the spectrum can be a more formidable task. The spectrum taken with the 300-MHz spectrometer, on the other hand, clearly shows two distinct triplets.

The 90-MHz and 300-MHz ^{1}H NMR spectra of hexan-3-one demonstrate the following important point:

> The signals in an NMR spectrum tend to be better resolved as the magnet of the spectrometer becomes more powerful.

This is because the coupling constants are independent of B_{ext}. Therefore, regardless of the strength of B_{ext}, the *frequency difference* between peaks of a split signal remains unchanged. By contrast, recall from Figure 17-3 (p. 822) that, for an unsplit signal, increasing B_{ext} causes an increase in ΔE_{spin} and hence an increase in the signal frequency.

With these two concepts in mind, let's examine **Figure 17-35** to see how the spectrometer's magnet strength affects the quality of the spectrum. At the top of Figure 17-35a, two unresolved signals are plotted, with frequency on the x axis. As the strength of the magnet increases, the centers of the two signals move apart

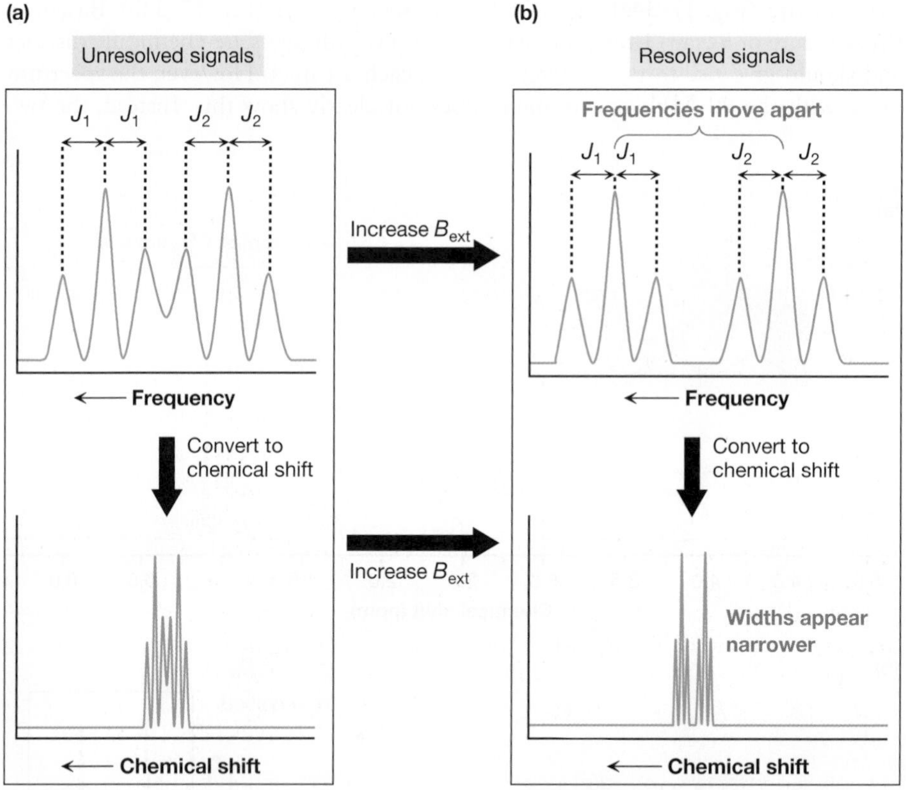

(a)
(b)
Unresolved signals
Resolved signals
J1 J1 J2 J2
Frequencies move apart
J1 J1 J2 J2
Increase Bext
Frequency
Frequency
Convert to chemical shift
Convert to chemical shift
Increase Bext
Widths appear narrower
Chemical shift
Chemical shift

FIGURE 17-35 Dependence of signal resolution on the spectrometer's magnet strength (a) A representation of two overlapping triplets in an NMR spectrum. The spectrum at the top shows frequency on the x axis, whereas the spectrum at the bottom shows chemical shift on the x axis. J_1 and J_2 are the coupling constants for the respective signals. (b) NMR spectrum of the same compound from a spectrometer with a higher magnetic field strength. The frequency separation between the two signals is increased, but the separation between peaks within the same signal (i.e., the coupling constants J_1 and J_2) remains the same. When we convert to chemical shift, therefore, the signals appear narrower.

(Fig. 17-35b, top), but the frequency separation between peaks of each triplet remains essentially the same. Thus, the signals are resolved from each other.

Recall that to convert signal frequencies to chemical shifts (which are independent of the instrument's magnet strength), we must divide those frequencies by the instrument's *operating frequency* (Eq. 17-5, p. 839). This is shown at the bottom of Figure 17-35. When we do this, the signal width (in units of parts per million) becomes narrower with the stronger magnet.

17.12 Carbon Signals: ^{13}C Nuclear Magnetic Resonance Spectroscopy

SECTION 17.12 OBJECTIVES

You will be able to:

1. Describe the origin of a carbon signal in ^{13}C NMR spectroscopy.
2. Determine the number of distinct carbon atoms in a molecule and the number of carbon signals the molecule would generate.
3. Give an approximate chemical shift value for a carbon on the basis of the functional group with which the carbon is associated.
4. Explain why all carbon signals appear as singlets.

We have focused so far on ^{1}H NMR spectroscopy, but the nucleus of the ^{13}C isotope (which contains six protons and seven neutrons) can have spin states of $+\frac{1}{2}$ and $-\frac{1}{2}$ au, too, just like ^{1}H. As a result, ^{13}C nuclei can absorb radiation in the RF region when placed in a strong magnetic field, and thus they can produce a ^{13}C NMR spectrum. Just as ^{1}H NMR spectroscopy provides valuable information about the environments of *hydrogen* atoms in a molecule, **^{13}C NMR spectroscopy** provides valuable information about the environments of *carbon* atoms in a molecule. This section is dedicated to explaining some of the details of ^{13}C NMR spectroscopy and to interpreting ^{13}C NMR spectra.

17.12a The ^{13}C NMR Signal

Because the ^{1}H and ^{13}C nuclei each have the same available spin states, the two types of spectroscopy have a variety of characteristics in common. In ^{13}C NMR spectroscopy, however, the frequency of the RF radiation that is used to irradiate a sample is significantly lower than in ^{1}H NMR spectroscopy, because the gyromagnetic ratio (γ) of a ^{13}C nucleus is about one-fourth that of a proton. This ensures that proton signals do not appear on carbon spectra, and vice versa.

One of the challenges of ^{13}C NMR spectroscopy is the low natural abundance of the ^{13}C isotope, which is only 1.1%; the remaining 98.9% of carbon is ^{12}C, which is NMR-inactive because it has an even number of protons (six) and an even number of neutrons (six). Because most carbon atoms in a sample are NMR inactive, ^{13}C NMR spectroscopy tends to suffer from poor signal strength, yielding noisy spectra like the ^{13}C NMR spectrum of 1-chloropropane shown in **Figure 17-36a** (next page). Obtaining a good-quality spectrum in ^{13}C NMR spectroscopy often requires averaging a large number of spectra (sometimes thousands) acquired from the same sample. Figure 17-36b shows the improvement that this kind of averaging can produce.

Just as a ^{1}H NMR spectrum can tell us the number of chemically distinct protons in a molecule, a ^{13}C NMR spectrum can tell us the number of chemically distinct carbons:

Each chemically distinct type of carbon atom produces one ^{13}C NMR signal.

As you can see in Figure 17-36b, three ^{13}C NMR signals appear in the spectrum of 1-chloropropane, signifying three chemically distinct carbon atoms. The peak at 0 ppm is due to TMS, which is added as a reference.

Similar to ^{1}H NMR spectroscopy, signals from the solvent typically appear in ^{13}C NMR spectra. In Figure 17-36b, for example, the three closely spaced peaks at 77 ppm are due to the carbon signal from the solvent, $CDCl_3$.

FIGURE 17-36
^{13}C NMR spectrum of 1-chloropropane
(a) Without signal averaging.
(b) With signal averaging.

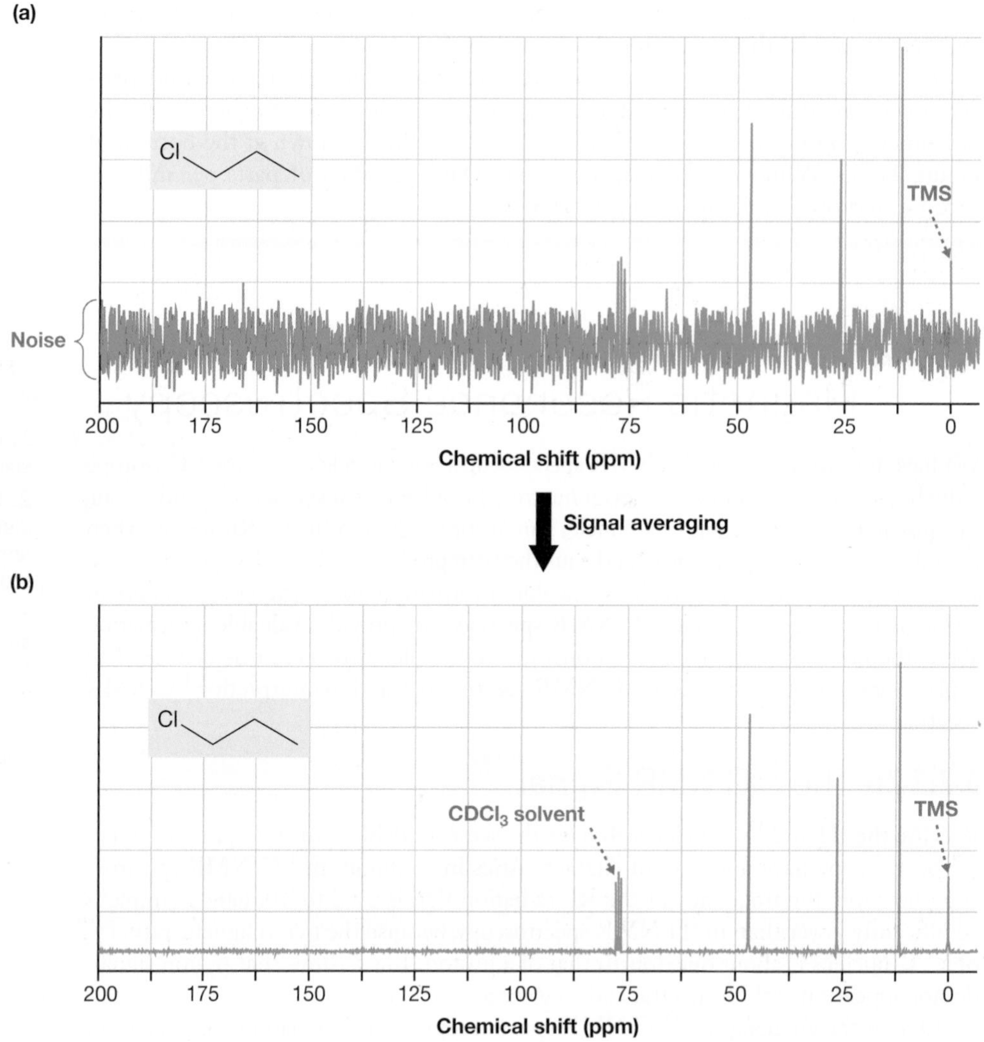
(a)
Cl
TMS
Noise
200 175 150 125 100 75 50 25 0
Chemical shift (ppm)
Signal averaging
(b)
Cl
CDCl3 solvent
TMS
200 175 150 125 100 75 50 25 0
Chemical shift (ppm)

YOUR TURN **17.20**

How many chemically distinct carbon atoms are in the compound that generates the following ^{13}C NMR spectrum? (The signal at 77 ppm is from the solvent, $CDCl_3$.)

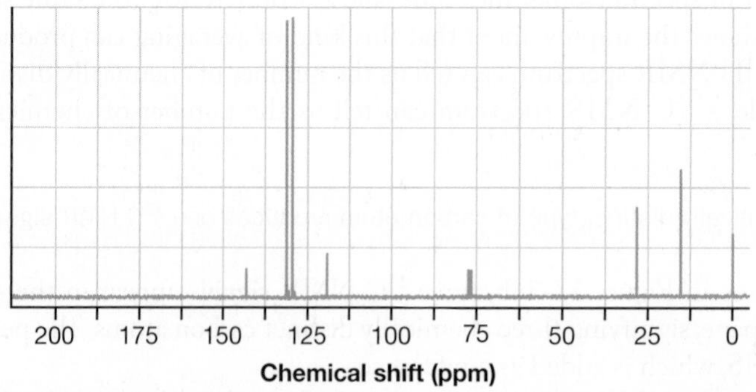
200 175 150 125 100 75 50 25 0
Chemical shift (ppm)

To determine the number of chemically distinct carbon atoms in a molecule, we can apply strategies similar to those used to determine the number of chemically distinct protons. For example, we can compare the locations of C atoms relative to a unique point of reference (Section 17.3). An example is shown in Solved Problem 17.7.

Alternatively, we could apply the chemical distinction test (Section 17.3a), in which we first substitute an imaginary atom X for each carbon atom and then determine the isomeric relationships among the X-substituted products.

SOLVED PROBLEM **17.7**

How to identify chemically distinct carbons in a molecular structure

Break It Down How many ^{13}C NMR signals would you expect for this molecule?

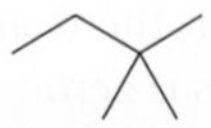

Think	Solve
Is there a unique point of reference in the molecule?	As our unique point of reference, we can choose the carbon at C-4. 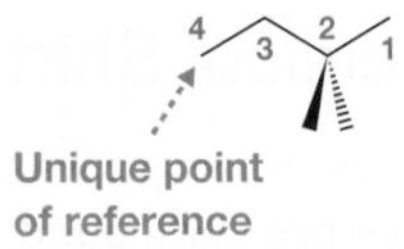 4 3 2 1 Unique point of reference
Are C-1, C-2, C-3, and C-4 different distances from the point of reference?	C-1, C-2, C-3, and C-4 are located at different distances from the point of reference, so all four are distinct carbons.
Are there any planes of symmetry or rotations that make some carbon atoms equivalent?	The three methyl groups attached to C-2 rapidly interchange locations as a result of single-bond rotation about the C-2—C-3 single bond. Therefore, the three methyl carbons attached to C-2 are equivalent. 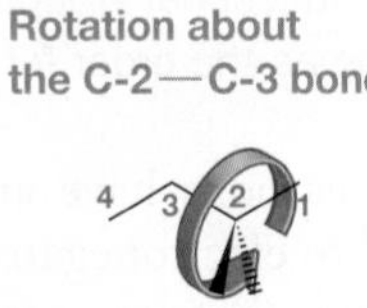 Rotation about the C-2—C-3 bond 4 3 2 1
How many distinct carbon atoms are there in all?	There are four distinct carbons, as indicated by the letters A–D. 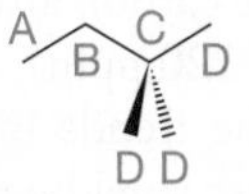 A B C D D D

Try It How many ^{13}C NMR signals would you expect for the molecule shown here? Explain.

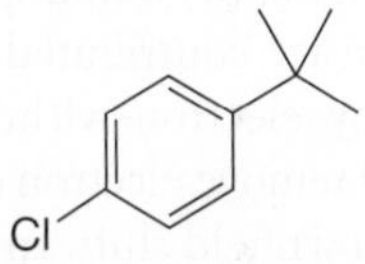
Cl

17.12b Signal Splitting in ^{13}C NMR Spectroscopy

Because ^{13}C nuclei have spin, they undergo coupling with other nearby nuclei that have spin, such as protons or other ^{13}C nuclei. However, under the conditions that the spectra are acquired, we do not observe signal splitting. In other words:

> In most of the ^{13}C NMR spectra you will encounter, every carbon signal will appear as a singlet.

In the ^{13}C NMR spectrum of 1-chloropropane in Figure 17-36 (p. 854), for example, all three signals appear as singlets.

We do not observe coupling between two ^{13}C nuclei because the natural abundance of ^{13}C is so low. With ^{13}C making up approximately 1 out of every 100 carbon atoms, there is only about a 1% chance that a given ^{13}C nucleus being detected will be adjacent to another ^{13}C nucleus.

We do not observe the splitting of a carbon signal by attached protons because *broadband decoupling* is typically used to essentially "turn off" the coupling between ^{13}C and ^{1}H nuclei. **Broadband decoupling** is a procedure that continuously sends a specific range of RF radiation through the sample, forcing all protons to flip back and forth rapidly between the α and β spin states. Therefore, the average magnetic field each proton produces is zero.

Broadband decoupling is helpful because it causes the signal intensity to increase, which helps with the interpretation of the spectrum. A disadvantage, however, is that we lose valuable information about the number of protons attached to each carbon. This information can be obtained in other ways, however, such as with DEPT spectroscopy (see Section 17.13).

17.12c Chemical Shifts in ^{13}C NMR Spectroscopy

As in ^{1}H NMR spectroscopy, ^{13}C absorptions are reported as chemical shifts, with TMS as the reference compound (its carbon atom is assigned a chemical shift of 0 ppm).

Chemical shifts for a variety of carbon atoms are listed in Table 17-5. Notice that their range is different from that for protons (review Table 17-1, p. 832):

Whereas the chemical shifts in ^{1}H NMR generally range from 0 to 12 ppm, those for carbon atoms generally range from 0 to 220 ppm.

Despite the different values for ^{1}H and ^{13}C chemical shifts:

The order of the functional groups for ^{13}C NMR chemical shifts in Table 17-5 is roughly the same as the order for ^{1}H NMR chemical shifts in Table 17-1.

Saturated alkane carbons have among the lowest chemical shifts (10–45 ppm). Carbons attached to electronegative atoms (as in hydroxy, halo, and amino groups) have chemical shifts that are somewhat farther downfield (25–70 ppm), followed by the carbon atoms of alkenes and aromatics (105–150 ppm) and carbonyl carbons (160–220 ppm).

The trends in chemical shift are the same for both carbon and proton signals because shielding and deshielding phenomena affect both types of nuclei in roughly the same way. Sigma (σ) bonding electrons shield the carbon nucleus, and the greater the electron density contributed by those electrons, the more the carbon nucleus is shielded. Nearby electron-withdrawing substituents (such as halogen, oxygen, or nitrogen atoms) remove electron density from the carbon atom, thereby deshielding it. The result is a downfield shift. In addition, ring current from aromatic rings or double bonds adds to the magnetic field experienced by the carbon atom, resulting, once again, in a downfield shift.

CONNECTIONS 17.6

Making surfactants and amphetamines Benzyl chloride (Your Turn 17.22) is used in a wide variety of organic syntheses because of how easily its Cl substituent can be replaced in S_N2 or S_N1 reactions. In particular, benzyl chloride can be used in the synthesis of a number of pharmaceuticals, including amphetamines. Benzyl chloride sales are therefore monitored by the U.S. Drug Enforcement Agency.

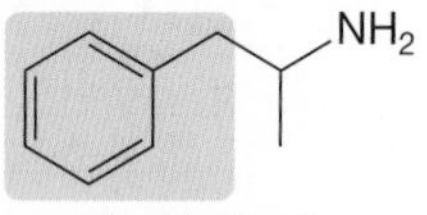
NH2

Amphetamine

YOUR TURN **17.21**

Identify two pairs of carbon atoms in Table 17-5 whose chemical shifts are in the same order as the chemical shifts of the analogous protons in Table 17-1 (p. 832). For each type of carbon and hydrogen nucleus you select, identify the major sources of deshielding.

TABLE 17-5 ^{13}C Nuclear Magnetic Resonance Chemical Shifts

Type of Carbon	Chemical Shift (ppm)	Type of Carbon	Chemical Shift (ppm)	Type of Carbon	Chemical Shift (ppm)
1. 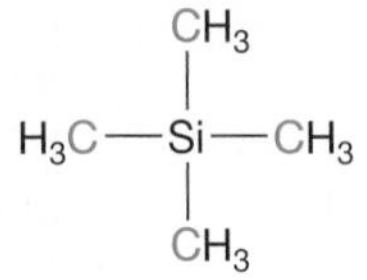	0	6. 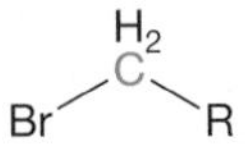	25–35	11. 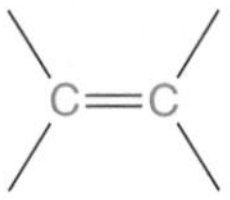	105–150
2. $R-CH_3$	10–25	7. 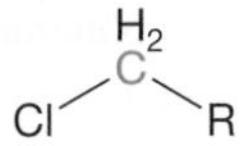	35–55	12. 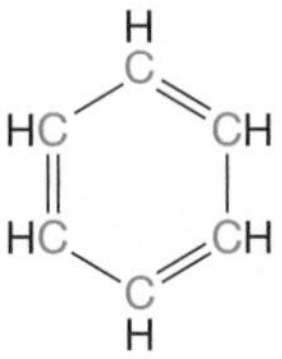	128
3. 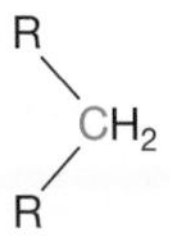	20–45	8. 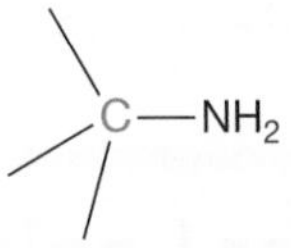	35–40	13. 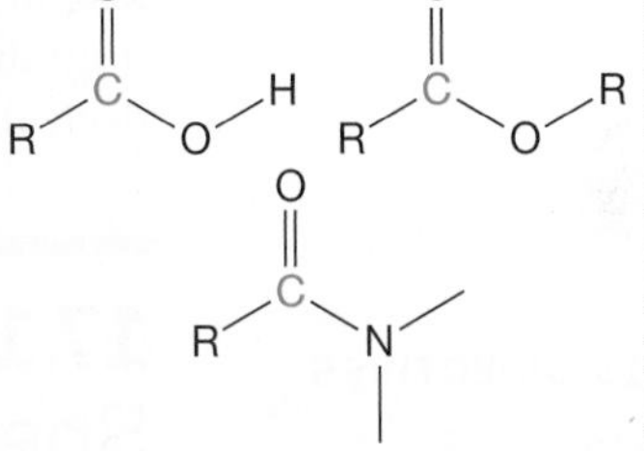	160–185
4. 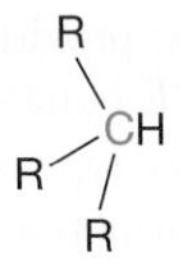	25–45	9. 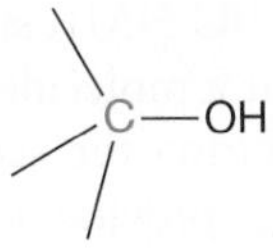	55–70	14. 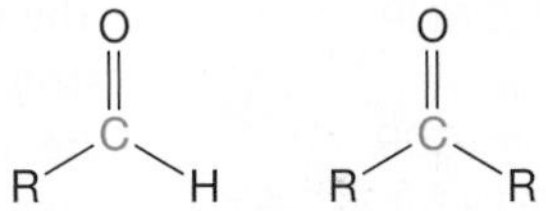	190–220
5. 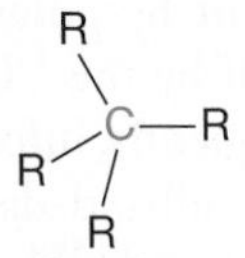	30–35	10. $R-C\equiv C-R$	65–85		

YOUR TURN **17.22**

Predict which C atom in benzyl chloride would have the highest chemical shift. Explain.

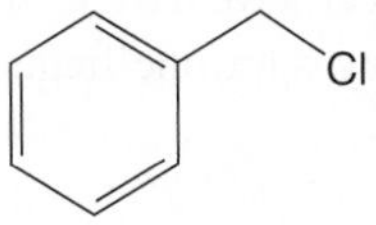
Cl

17.12d Integration of ^{13}C NMR Signals

The ^{13}C NMR spectrum of 2-methylbutanal (**Figure 17-37**, next page) shows five signals, each of which is different in height. If the number of carbon atoms contributing to each signal were proportional to the area, then all five peaks would have essentially the same height, because each signal represents exactly one carbon atom in the molecule. However:

In typical ^{13}C NMR spectra, the area under a peak is *not* proportional to the number of carbon atoms contributing to that peak.

FIGURE 17-37 ^{13}C NMR spectrum of 2-methylbutanal Although one carbon atom contributes to each signal, the heights of the signals differ markedly.

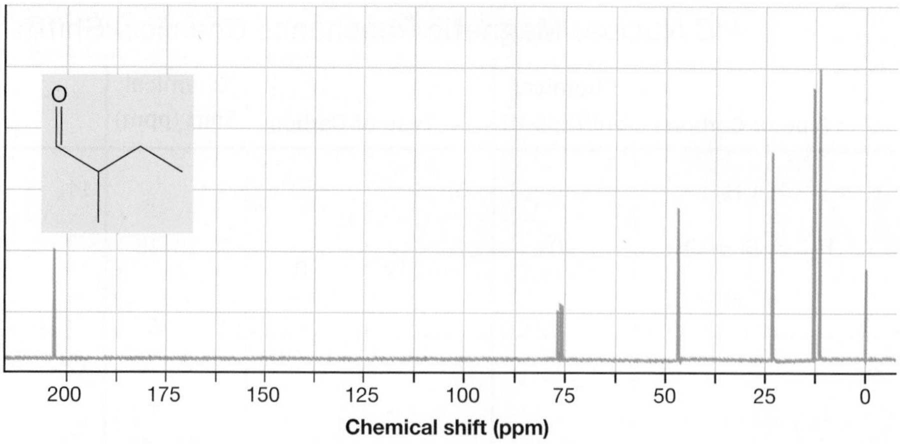
O
200
175
150
125
100
75
50
25
0
Chemical shift (ppm)

The poor correlation between the area under a ^{13}C NMR peak and the number of carbons can be attributed to broadband decoupling. Broadband decoupling tends to magnify each carbon signal through what is called the *nuclear Overhauser effect.* That magnification differs for different types of carbon atoms, so the integration is of relatively little value in ^{13}C NMR spectroscopy.

SECTION 17.13 OBJECTIVES

You will be able to:

1. Describe the type of information provided by DEPT ^{13}C NMR spectroscopy.
2. Use a COSY or HETCOR spectrum to determine which nuclei are coupled.

17.13 A Deeper Look: DEPT ^{13}C NMR Spectroscopy and 2-D NMR Spectra

The types of ^{1}H NMR and ^{13}C NMR spectra we have studied so far provide valuable structural information about a molecule. If specific sequences of RF radiation pulses are applied to the sample during the acquisition process, then other types of spectra can be constructed, which provide even richer structural information about a molecule.

For example, a technique called **distortionless enhancement by polarization transfer (DEPT)** produces spectra in which the signals given off by the ^{13}C nuclei depend on the number of protons attached to those carbons. Frequently, information from DEPT spectroscopy is simply summarized in the normal broadband-decoupled ^{13}C NMR spectrum, as shown in **Figure 17-38** for the C, CH, CH_2, and CH_3 carbons of ethylbenzene.

NMR spectrometers can also produce a variety of *two-dimensional (2-D) spectra.* The spectra we have seen to this point in the chapter are all one-dimensional (1-D) because they have one frequency axis (the *x* axis). The second axis (the *y* axis) corresponds to

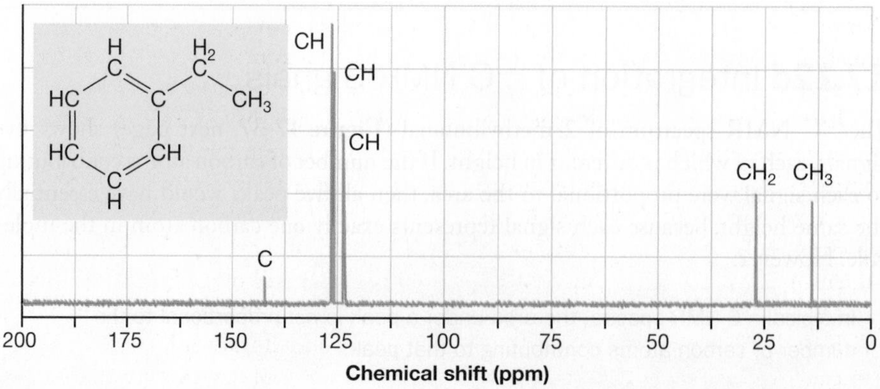
H
C
H2
C
HC
C
CH3
HC
CH
C
H
CH
CH
CH
C
CH2
CH3
200
175
150
125
100
75
50
25
0
Chemical shift (ppm)

FIGURE 17-38 Broadband-decoupled ^{13}C NMR spectrum of ethylbenzene Results from a DEPT experiment have been provided for the individual peaks in the spectrum.

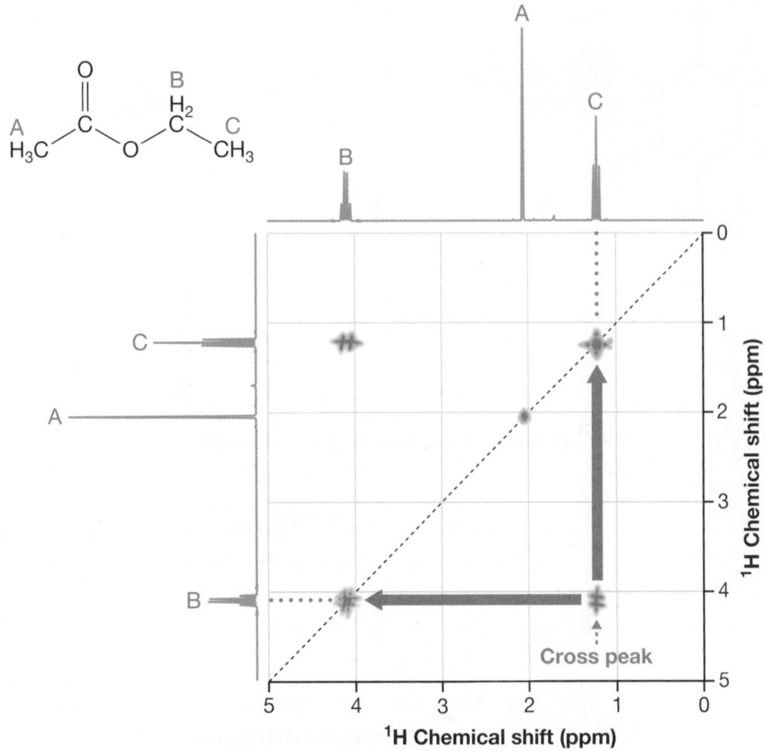

A
B
H2
C
H3C
O
CH3
Cross peak
0
1
2
3
4
5
1H Chemical shift (ppm)
1H Chemical shift (ppm)

FIGURE 17-39 COSY spectrum of ethyl ethanoate The 1-D ^{1}H NMR spectrum is shown on the *x* and *y* axes. The thick red arrows originating from the cross peak below the diagonal show that the protons that produce the signal at 1.3 ppm (vertical arrow) are coupled to the protons that produce the signal at 4.1 ppm (horizontal arrow).

amplitude. In a **2-D NMR spectrum**, there are two frequency axes (the *x* and *y* axes), and the third axis (the *z* axis) corresponds to amplitude.

One common type of 2-D NMR spectrum comes from **homonuclear correlation spectroscopy (COSY)**, an example of which is shown for ethyl ethanoate in **Figure 17-39**. In the COSY spectrum, the 1-D proton NMR spectrum is shown on both the *x* and *y* axes. The peaks that appear on the diagonal (black dashed line) are the same peaks that appear in each 1-D spectrum. The peaks that appear off the diagonal, called *cross peaks*, indicate which protons are coupled. In Figure 17-39, thick red arrows are drawn vertically and horizontally from the cross peak appearing below the diagonal. The vertical arrow corresponds to the protons that produce signal C (1.3 ppm), and the horizontal arrow corresponds to the protons that produce signal B (4.1 ppm). We can therefore conclude that protons B and C are coupled, in agreement with the structure shown.

Another common type of 2-D NMR spectrum comes from **heteronuclear correlation (HETCOR) spectroscopy**, an example of which is shown for diethyl phthalate in **Figure 17-40** (next page). In this HETCOR spectrum, the 1-D ^{13}C NMR spectrum is shown on the *x* axis and the 1-D ^{1}H NMR spectrum is shown on the *y* axis. Each cross peak provides information about which protons are attached to which carbons. For example, thick red arrows drawn in Figure 17-40 indicate that the carbons that produce signal E in the carbon spectrum (vertical arrow) are attached to the protons that produce signal E in the proton spectrum (horizontal arrow). We can verify that this is indeed the case by examining the structure of the molecule.

Two-dimensional NMR spectra from COSY and HETCOR spectroscopy become much more important in structure elucidation when the molecules are more complex than the ones given in the examples here, such as proteins. Moreover, there are a variety of 2-D NMR techniques other than COSY and HETCOR, each of which provides distinct information about molecular connectivity. Three- and four-dimensional experiments can even be carried out, and still other NMR techniques can be used to determine how close nuclei are in space rather than through bonds. With all of the structural information that can be acquired from NMR spectroscopy, you can see why NMR spectroscopy is such a powerful tool in structure elucidation.

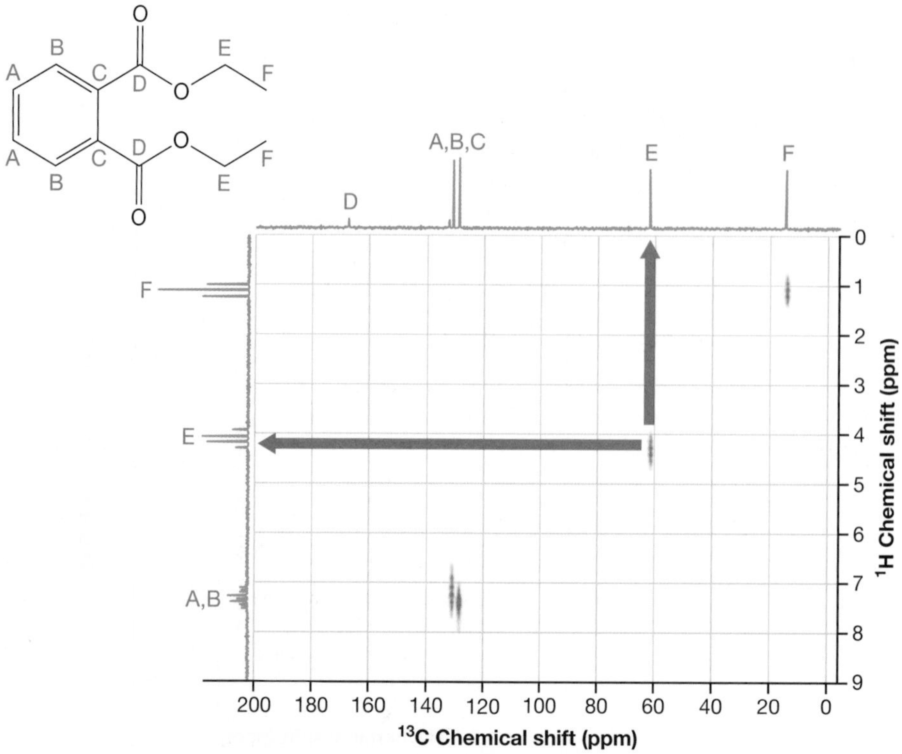
A
B
C
D
O
E
F
A,B,C
E
F
D
F
E
A,B
200
180
160
140
120
100
80
60
40
20
0
^{13}C Chemical shift (ppm)
0
1
2
3
4
5
6
7
8
9
^{1}H Chemical shift (ppm)

FIGURE 17-40 HETCOR spectrum of diethyl phthalate The 1-D ^{13}C NMR spectrum is shown on the *x* axis, and the 1-D ^{1}H NMR spectrum is shown on the *y* axis. The thick red arrows originating from the cross peak show that the carbons that produce the signal around 65 ppm (vertical arrow) are attached to the protons that produce the signal around 4.2 ppm (horizontal arrow).

17.14 Strategies for Success: Elucidating Molecular Structure Using Nuclear Magnetic Resonance Spectroscopy

SECTION 17.14 OBJECTIVES

You will be able to:

1. Use a systematic method to derive molecular fragments by interpreting ^{1}H NMR and ^{13}C NMR signals.
2. Assemble those fragments to obtain a complete structure for a molecule.

Strategies for Success
Elucidating Molecular Structure Using Nuclear Magnetic Resonance Spectroscopy

To this point in Chapter 17, we have dealt with various aspects of NMR spectra somewhat independently of one another. Each aspect of an NMR spectrum tells us a certain amount of information about the structure of the compound that produced the spectrum:

Information Obtained by ^{1}H NMR Spectroscopy

- Number of signals: The total number of signals gives you the number of chemically distinct types of protons.
- Chemical shift: A signal's chemical shift tells you whether aromatic rings, double bonds, or electronegative atoms are near the protons responsible for that signal.
- Integration: The integration of each signal tells you the number of protons responsible for that signal.
- Splitting pattern: A signal's splitting pattern tells you the number of neighboring protons that are distinct from the protons responsible for that signal.

Information Obtained by ^{13}C NMR Spectroscopy

- Number of signals: The total number of signals gives you the number of chemically distinct types of carbons.
- Chemical shift: A signal's chemical shift tells you whether aromatic rings, double bonds, or electronegative atoms are near the carbon atoms responsible for that signal.

To derive a more complete picture of a molecule's structure, individual pieces of information available in an NMR spectrum must be brought together, much like you would fit pieces of a jigsaw puzzle together. Section 17.14a shows how you can bring this information together when interpreting a ^{1}H NMR spectrum, and Section 17.14b does the same for the interpretation of a ^{13}C NMR spectrum. A systematic method of analysis can be applied to both types of spectra. As you gain experience interpreting NMR spectra, you will learn how to make adjustments and settle on a strategy that works best for you.

17.14a Unknown 1: Interpreting a ^{1}H NMR Spectrum

It helps to be methodical in your approach to analyzing a ^{1}H NMR spectrum. To do so, you can use the following sequence of steps:

Steps for Interpreting a ^{1}H NMR Spectrum

1. Determine the number of proton signals.
2. Examine each signal:
   a. Analyze the chemical shift. What kinds of aromatic rings, double bonds, or electronegative atoms, if any, does the chemical shift suggest might be nearby? Can you use the molecular formula or information from other spectra to provide insight into the presence of electronegative atoms or double bonds?
   b. Consider the relative integration. If you know the total number of protons in the molecule (for example, from the molecular formula), can you determine how many protons each signal represents?
   c. Interpret the splitting pattern. What does it say about the number of neighboring protons (distinct from the ones responsible for the signal)?
3. Build molecular fragments. Combine the information from Step 2 to build fragments that have multiple carbon atoms. These are your puzzle pieces.
4. Assemble the identified molecular fragments. Think of it as fitting puzzle pieces together. The complete molecule must be consistent with every aspect of the ^{1}H NMR spectrum.

Let's apply these steps to interpret the ^{1}H NMR spectrum shown in **Figure 17-41**, which is generated from a compound (Unknown 1) having the formula $C_{10}H_{12}O_2$.

For Step 1, the spectrum appears to have at least four signals: one at $\delta \approx 1.1$ ppm, one at $\delta \approx 1.8$ ppm, one at $\delta \approx 4.2$ ppm, and a set of signals between $\delta \approx 7.4$ and 8.1 ppm. Therefore, there are at least four distinct types of protons.

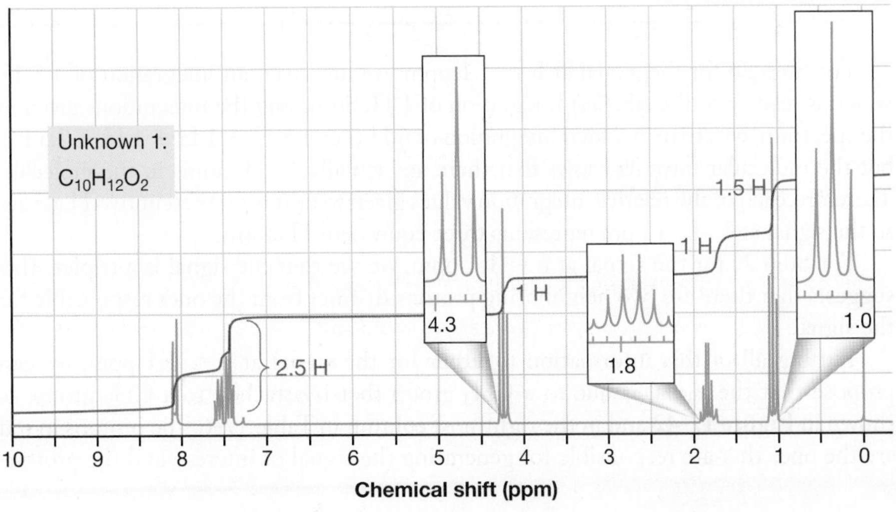

Unknown 1:
$C_{10}H_{12}O_2$
2.5 H
4.3
1 H
1.8
1 H
1.5 H
1.0
10 9 8 7 6 5 4 3 2 1 0
Chemical shift (ppm)

FIGURE 17-41 ^{1}H **NMR spectrum of Unknown 1, with the formula** $C_{10}H_{12}O_2$

TABLE 17-6 Summary of Information from Figure 17-41

	STEP 2a		STEP 2b		STEP 2c		STEP 3
Entry	Chemical Shift (ppm)	Nearby Double Bonds or EN Atoms?	Relative Integration	Number of Protons	Splitting Pattern	Number of Neighboring Distinct H	Molecular Fragment
1	~1.1	None	1.5	3	Triplet	2	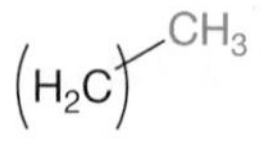
2	~1.8	None	1	2	Sextet	5	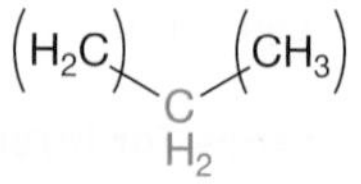
3	~4.2	H—C—O	1	2	Triplet	2	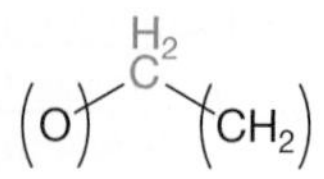
4	~7.4–8.1	H—Aromatic	2.5	5	Complex	?	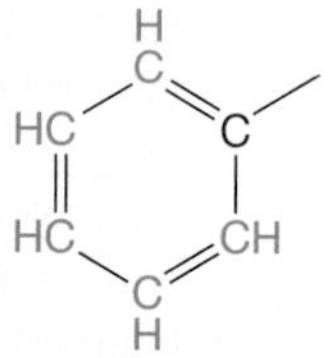

To organize our thoughts as we work through Steps 2 and 3, let's construct a table that has a row for each signal, as shown in Table 17-6. For Step 2a for the signal at $\delta \approx 1.1$ ppm (Entry 1), we can say that the protons are not immediately attached to a double bond, nor are those protons on a C atom that is attached to an electronegative (EN) atom. These scenarios would have required chemical shifts that are significantly higher.

YOUR TURN 17.23

According to Table 17-1 (p. 832), what is the lowest chemical shift you should expect to observe for a proton that is attached to a double bond or is on a carbon attached to an electronegative atom? How does that value compare to the chemical shift of $\delta \approx 1.1$ ppm in Entry 1 of Table 17-6?

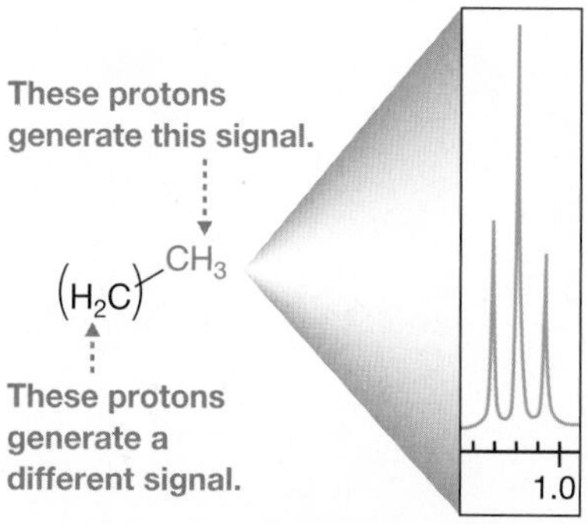
These protons generate this signal.
These protons generate a different signal.
1.0

FIGURE 17-42 Molecular fragment consistent with the $\delta \approx 1.1$ ppm signal in Figure 17-41

For Step 2b for the signal at $\delta \approx 1.1$ ppm, we are given an integration of 1.5 H, which is relative to the smallest integration of 1 H. Summing the integrations given in the spectrum, we arrive at a total integration of 6 H (i.e., 1.5 H + 1 H + 1 H + 2.5 H), but the molecular formula shows that there are actually 12 H atoms in the molecule. Therefore, each of the relative integration values given to us must represent two H atoms, so the signal at $\delta \approx 1.1$ ppm represents three equivalent H atoms.

For Step 2c for the signal at $\delta \approx 1.1$ ppm, we see that the signal is a triplet. This suggests that there are two neighboring protons distinct from the ones responsible for the signal.

Putting all of this information together for the signal at $\delta \approx 1.1$ ppm, we can propose that the signal is due to a CH_3 group that is attached to a CH_2 group, as shown in **Figure 17-42** and in the rightmost column in Table 17-6. The protons in red are the ones that are responsible for generating the signal of interest, and the protons on the neighboring group in black and in the parentheses are responsible for generating *another* signal.

Let's now move to the signal at $\delta \approx 1.8$ ppm, the information for which is summarized in Entry 2 of Table 17-6. What does the low chemical shift tell us? As before, the protons responsible for this signal are not directly attached to an atom that is part of a double bond. Furthermore, the carbon atom that possesses those protons cannot be attached to an electronegative atom. The relative integration of 1 H tells us that the signal represents two protons, and the apparent sextet splitting pattern (six peaks) tells us that there are five neighboring protons. Putting this information together, we can propose that the signal is due to a CH_2 group that is bonded to a CH_3 group on one side and a CH_2 group on the other; this is shown in **Figure 17-43** and at the right of Entry 2 in Table 17-6.

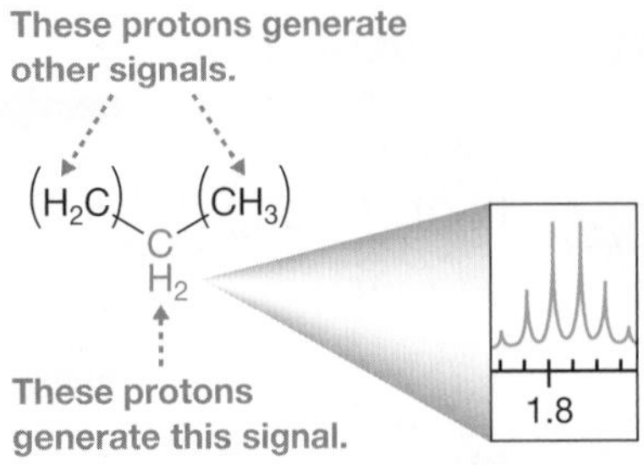
These protons generate other signals.
(H_2C)
(CH_3)
C
H_2
These protons generate this signal.
1.8

FIGURE 17-43 Molecular fragment consistent with the $\delta \approx 1.8$ ppm signal in Figure 17-41

The signal at $\delta \approx 4.2$ ppm (Entry 3 in Table 17-6) is consistent with a proton on a carbon that has an attached electronegative atom. According to the molecular formula, the electronegative atom would need to be oxygen. The relative integration of 1 H tells us that the signal represents two protons, and because the signal is split into a triplet, there must be two neighboring protons. As shown in **Figure 17-44** and at the right in Table 17-6, this signal can be from a CH_2 group that is bonded to O on one side and a CH_2 group on the other.

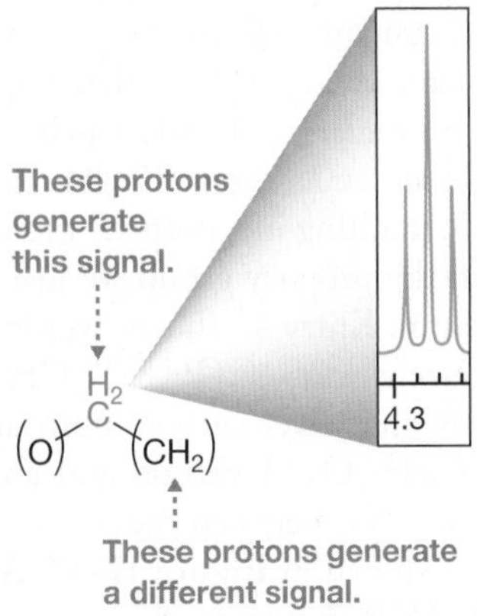
These protons generate this signal.
H_2
C
(O)
(CH_2)
4.3
These protons generate a different signal.

FIGURE 17-44 Molecular fragment consistent with the $\delta \approx 4.2$ ppm signal in Figure 17-41

YOUR TURN 17.24

> In Table 17-1 (p. 832), what is the normal chemical shift of a proton that is part of a fragment H—C—O in an ether or alcohol? How does that compare to the chemical shift in Entry 3 of Table 17-6? What could be the source of that difference in chemical shift?

The final set of signals between $\delta \approx 7.4$ and 8.1 ppm is consistent with aromatic protons, as shown in Entry 4 of Table 17-6. The relative integration of 2.5 H tells us that there are five such protons, which would be consistent with a monosubstituted benzene, as shown in the rightmost column and in **Figure 17-45**. Because these signals appear at different chemical shifts and complex splitting is apparent, we will analyze the splitting pattern later.

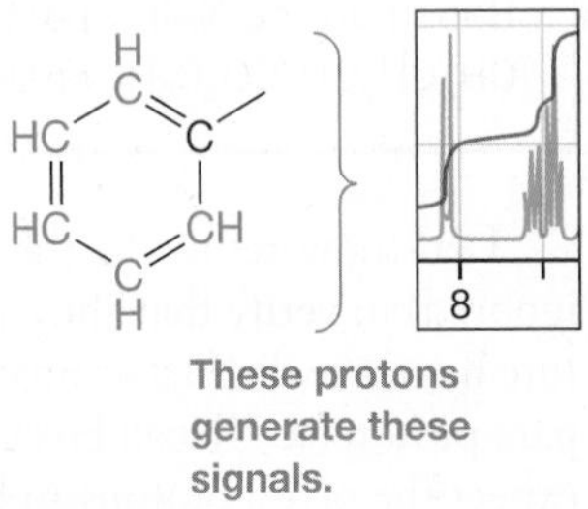
H
C
HC
C
HC
CH
C
H
8
These protons generate these signals.

FIGURE 17-45 Molecular fragment consistent with signals between $\delta \approx 7.4$ and 8.1 ppm in Figure 17-41

YOUR TURN 17.25

> In Table 17-1 (p. 832), what is the normal chemical shift of a proton in benzene? How does that compare to the chemical shifts in Entry 4 of Table 17-6? What could be the source of those differences in chemical shift?

Step 4 asks us to consider how to assemble the proposed molecular fragments to complete the entire molecule. Let's try to connect fragments like you would connect

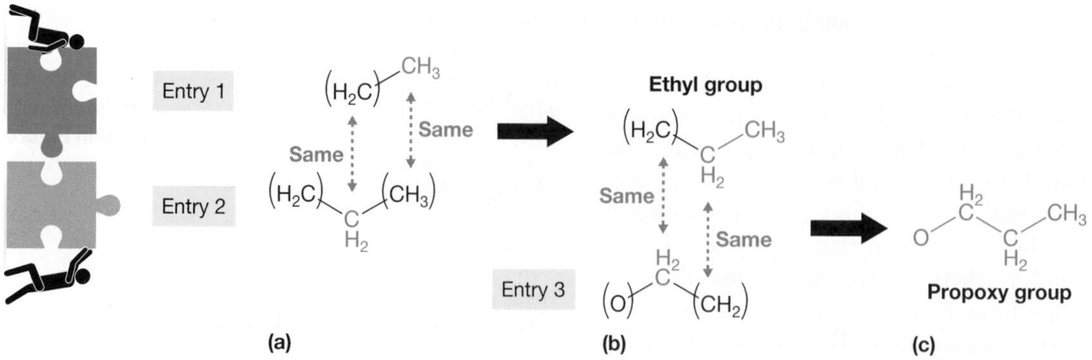

Entry 1
Entry 2
Same
Same
Ethyl group
Same
Same
Entry 3
Propoxy group
(a)
(b)
(c)

FIGURE 17-46 Assembling identified molecular fragments from the ^{1}H NMR spectrum in Figure 17-41

pieces of a puzzle. For each possible connection, look for identical portions in two different fragments, where the portion is inside parentheses in one fragment and not inside parentheses in the other fragment. For example, as shown in **Figure 17-46a**, fragments in Entries 1 and 2 can be connected to produce an ethyl group (Fig. 17-46b). Then, as shown in Figure 17-46b, the ethyl group can be connected to the fragment in Entry 3, resulting in a propoxy group as shown in Figure 17-46c.

Can the propoxy group we just derived be attached directly to the benzene ring fragment in Entry 4? The answer is no because the resulting molecule would be propoxybenzene, $C_6H_5OCH_2CH_2CH_3$, which has the formula $C_9H_{12}O$; propoxybenzene has one fewer carbon atom and one fewer oxygen than the formula we were given, $C_{10}H_{12}O_2$. A carbon and an oxygen could, however, be added as a carbonyl group (C═O) between the propoxy group and the benzene ring, giving propyl benzoate, as shown in **Figure 17-47**. All aspects of propyl benzoate are consistent with the ^{1}H NMR spectrum.

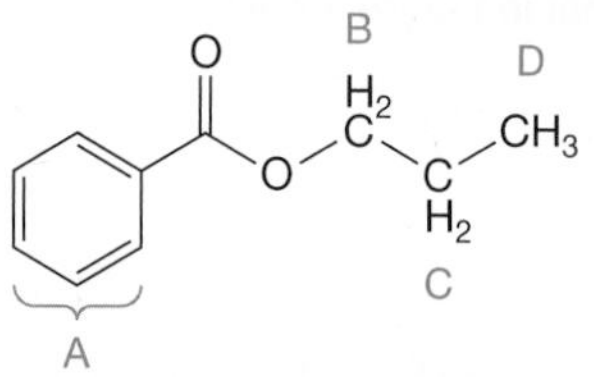

A
B
C
D

Unknown 1: $C_{10}H_{12}O_2$

FIGURE 17-47 Complete structure of Unknown 1

YOUR TURN **17.26**

Write A, B, C, or D above the signals in Figure 17-41 to match up with each chemically distinct H atom in propyl benzoate.

YOUR TURN **17.27**

Based on the NMR spectrum in Figure 17-41, can Unknown 1 be $CH_3CH_2CH_2CO_2C_6H_5$ or $CH_3CH_2OCH_2(C{=}O)C_6H_5$? Why or why not?

Let's now return to the features of the aromatic signals (which we temporarily ignored) to verify that they agree with our completed structure. The completed structure has three distinct aromatic protons: two ortho protons, two meta protons, and one para proton (see Recall box). Because they are closest to the carbonyl group, we would expect the ortho protons to be deshielded the most. This is consistent with the peaks at $\delta = 8.1$ ppm, which have the highest chemical shift and an integration of 1 H, representing two protons. The meta and para protons must therefore give rise to the overlapping peaks centered at ~7.5 ppm, which have an integration of ~1.5 H, representing three protons.

◂ RECALL

Interchapter B (Section B.3a) explained that substituents on a benzene ring are ortho to each other if they have 1,2 relative positioning (i.e., are attached to adjacent carbons); they are meta if they have 1,3 relative positioning; and they are para if they have 1,4 relative positioning.

17.14b Unknown 2: Interpreting a ^{13}C NMR Spectrum

As with the interpretation of a ^{1}H NMR spectrum, it is helpful to approach a ^{13}C NMR spectrum by using a systematic sequence of steps:

Steps for Interpreting a ^{13}C NMR Spectrum

1. Determine the number of carbon signals. Can you compare the number of signals to the number of carbons in the molecular formula to determine whether there are equivalent carbons?
2. Analyze the chemical shift of each signal. What kinds of aromatic rings, double bonds, or electronegative atoms, if any, does that chemical shift suggest might be nearby? Can you use the molecular formula or information from other spectra to provide insight into the presence of aromatic rings, double bonds, or electronegative atoms?
3. Build molecular fragments. Use the information from Step 2, as well as information from other sources (e.g., ^{13}C DEPT spectroscopy), to build molecular fragments with multiple carbon atoms. These are your puzzle pieces.
4. Assemble the identified molecular fragments. Think of it as fitting puzzle pieces together. The complete molecule must be consistent with every aspect of the ^{13}C NMR spectrum.

Let's consider the ^{13}C NMR and IR spectra for Unknown 2 ($C_5H_{12}O$), shown in **Figure 17-48**. Notice that the ^{13}C NMR spectrum also provides the results from DEPT spectroscopy (Section 17.13), which indicates the type of carbon generating each signal: C, CH, CH_2, or CH_3.

For Step 1, the ^{13}C spectrum has three signals: one at $\delta \approx 26$ ppm, one at $\delta \approx 33$ ppm, and one at $\delta \approx 73$ ppm (remember that the signal at 77 ppm is from the $CDCl_3$ solvent and the one at 0 ppm is from the TMS reference). Thus, only three of the five total C atoms in Unknown 2 are distinct. This means that two of the C atoms are equivalent to others in the molecule.

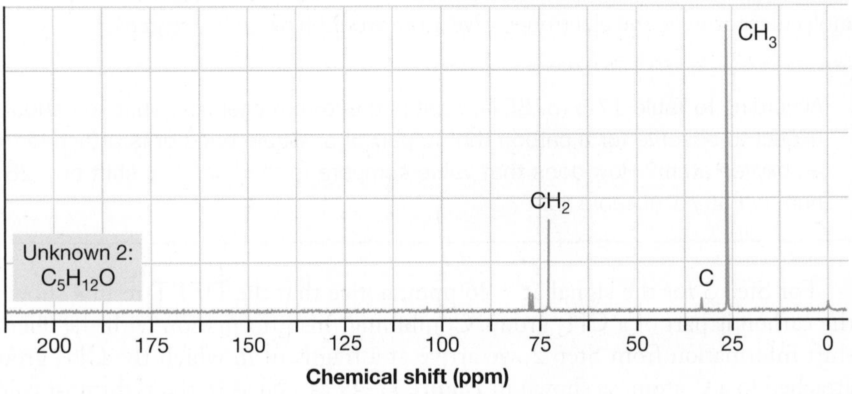

CH3
CH2
C
Unknown 2:
C5H12O
200
175
150
125
100
75
50
25
0
Chemical shift (ppm)

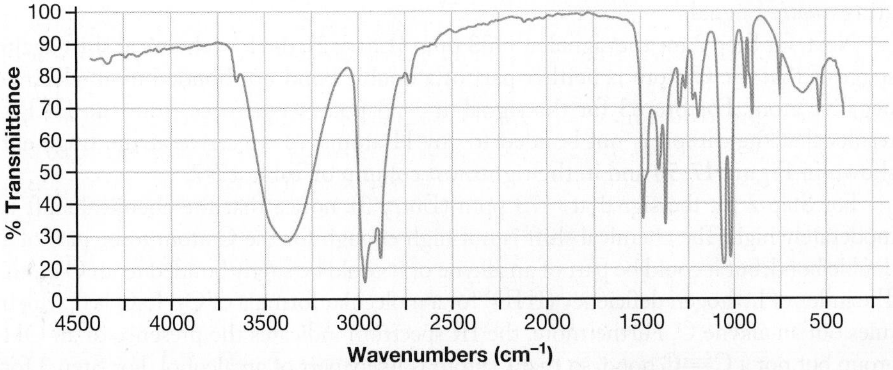

% Transmittance
100
90
80
70
60
50
40
30
20
0
4500
4000
3500
3000
2500
2000
1500
1000
500
Wavenumbers (cm−1)

FIGURE 17-48 **^{13}C NMR and IR spectra of Unknown 2, with the formula $C_5H_{12}O$**

TABLE 17-7 Summary of Information from Figure 17-48

	STEP 2		STEP 3	
Entry	Chemical Shift (ppm)	Nearby Double Bonds or EN Atoms?	DEPT Spectrum	Molecular Fragment
1	~26	None	CH_3	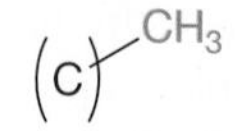
2	~33	None	C	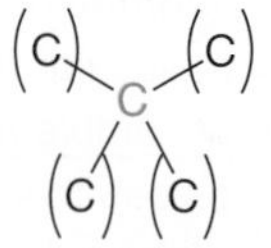
3	~73	C—O	CH_2	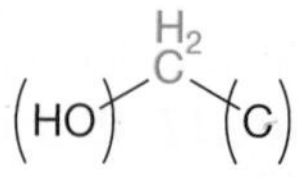

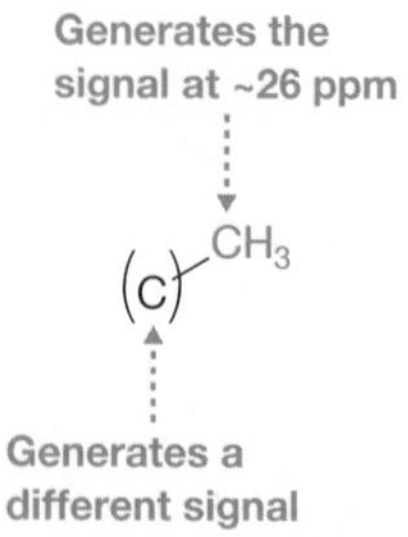

Generates the signal at ~26 ppm
CH3
(C)
Generates a different signal

FIGURE 17-49 Molecular fragment consistent with the δ ≈ 26 ppm signal in Figure 17-48

As we did for the ^{1}H NMR spectrum of Unknown 1 in Section 17.14a, let's construct a table (Table 17-7) to organize our thoughts for Steps 2 and 3, with a separate row for each signal. We begin with the signal at ~26 ppm (Entry 1). For Step 2, the chemical shift is quite low and suggests that the carbon responsible for generating that signal is not part of a double bond or attached to an electronegative atom (from the molecular formula, the electronegative atom would have to be oxygen).

YOUR TURN 17.28

According to Table 17-5 (p. 857), what is the lowest chemical shift you should expect to observe for a carbon that is part of a double bond or is attached to an oxygen atom? How does that value compare to the chemical shift of ~26 ppm in Entry 1 of Table 17-7?

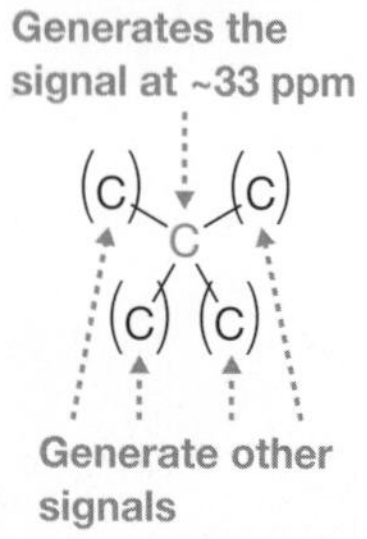

Generates the signal at ~33 ppm
(C)
(C)
C
(C)
(C)
Generate other signals

FIGURE 17-50 Molecular fragment consistent with the δ ≈ 33 ppm signal in Figure 17-48

For Step 3 for the signal at ~26 ppm, notice that the DEPT results show that the carbon is part of a CH_3 group. Combining this information with the chemical shift information from Step 2, we arrive at a fragment in which the CH_3 group is attached to a C atom, as shown in **Figure 17-49** as well as in the rightmost column in Table 17-7. The carbon shown in red is responsible for generating the signal of interest, and the carbon shown in black and in parentheses is responsible for generating *another* signal.

Next, for Step 2 for the signal at ~33 ppm (Entry 2), the low chemical shift again suggests that the C atom is neither part of a double bond nor bonded to an electronegative atom. For Step 3 for the signal at ~33 ppm, we can see from the DEPT results that the carbon is not bonded to any H atoms, so we arrive at the fragment shown in **Figure 17-50** and in the rightmost column of Table 17-7.

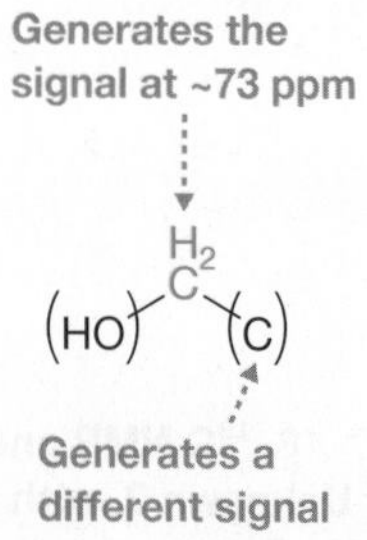

Generates the signal at ~73 ppm
H2
C
(HO)
(C)
Generates a different signal

FIGURE 17-51 Molecular fragment consistent with the δ ≈ 73 ppm signal in Figure 17-48

For Step 2 for the signal at ~73 ppm (Entry 3), notice that the chemical shift is moderately high. The chemical shift is not high enough for the C atom to be part of a double bond, but it could be part of an alkyne or it could be singly bonded to an O atom. The index of hydrogen deficiency (IHD) for a molecular formula of $C_5H_{12}O$ is 0, which rules out an alkyne C. Furthermore, the IR spectrum indicates the presence of an OH group but not a C≡C bond, so that C atom is likely part of an alcohol. For Step 3 for the signal at ~73 ppm, the DEPT results show that the C atom is part of a CH_2 group, suggesting the fragment shown in **Figure 17-51** and at the far right of Entry 3.

YOUR TURN 17.29

Use Table 17-5 (p. 857) to verify that a chemical shift of ~73 ppm is consistent with an alkyne carbon or a carbon that is singly bonded to O but is inconsistent with a carbon that is part of a double bond.

YOUR TURN 17.30

Identify the IR band in Figure 17-48 that indicates an OH group. In addition, identify where you would expect to see absorptions corresponding to a C≡C and an alkyne C—H stretch if these groups were present.

For Step 4, we now try to assemble the fragments listed in Table 17-7, as shown in **Figure 17-52**. The red C atom in Entry 2 must be bonded to four other C atoms. One of them could be the red CH_3 group from Entry 1, as shown in Figure 17-52a. When we connect those pieces, we arrive at the larger fragment shown Figure 17-52b. If that fragment is connected to the one from Entry 3, we derive the even larger fragment shown in Figure 17-52c, in which the two C atoms in parentheses are not yet fully characterized.

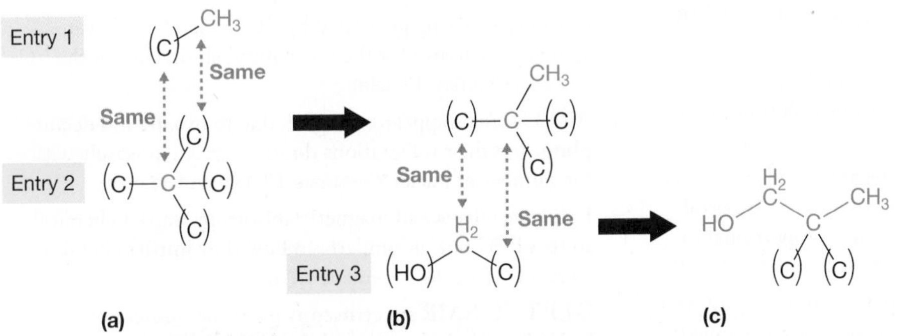

Entry 1
Same
Same
Entry 2
Same
Same
Entry 3
(a)
(b)
(c)

FIGURE 17-52 Assembling identified molecular fragments from the ^{13}C NMR spectrum in Figure 17-48

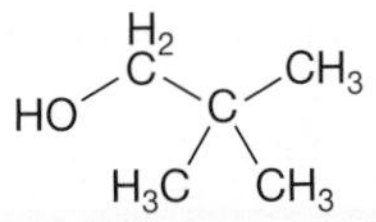

Unknown 2: $C_5H_{12}O$

FIGURE 17-53 Complete structure of Unknown 2

Each of the C atoms in parentheses in the partial structure in Figure 17-52c must be equivalent to other carbons that have already been added. Otherwise, we would have more than three distinct carbons. We can achieve such equivalence by making each of those final two carbons part of a CH_3 group, in which case all three CH_3 groups would be equivalent. The final structure is shown in **Figure 17-53**.

Chapter Summary and Key Terms

- In **nuclear magnetic resonance (NMR) spectroscopy**, a sample is placed in a strong **external magnetic field (B_{ext})** and irradiated with radiation from the **radio frequency (RF)** portion of the electromagnetic spectrum. The re-emitted frequencies are recorded as a **free induction decay (FID)**, and multiple FIDs are averaged before a **Fourier transform** is applied to obtain the separate NMR signals. An NMR spectrum plots the intensity of each signal emitted by the sample against *chemical shift*, a quantity related to relative frequency. (Section 17.1)
- Absorption of an RF photon causes a nucleus to undergo a **spin flip**. In **^{1}H NMR spectroscopy**, the nuclei that undergo spin flips are those of hydrogen atoms (protons, ^{1}H); in **^{13}C NMR spectroscopy**, carbon-13 nuclei undergo spin flips. (Section 17.2)
- Signal frequency depends on the identity of the nucleus and increases with increasing B_{ext}, due to an increasing energy separation between nuclear spin states. (Section 17.2)
- Atoms are **chemically distinct** when they are located differently with respect to a unique reference point within the

molecule; that is, they reside in different **chemical environments**. Chemically distinct nuclei differ in the extent to which they are **shielded** from B_{ext} and thus generate signals at different frequencies. (Section 17.3)

- If nuclei in different chemical environments rapidly interchange positions, they tend to give rise to the same averaged signal. (Section 17.4)
- **Chemical shift** is a measure of a signal's frequency relative to the signal frequency generated by a reference compound such as **tetramethylsilane (TMS)**. (Section 17.5)
- Nearby electron-withdrawing groups **deshield** nuclei inductively, thereby increasing the chemical shift of the nuclei. Nearby π electrons from double bonds deshield nuclei via **magnetic anisotropy**. (Section 17.5)
- Deshielding from inductive effects and from magnetic anisotropy is additive and falls off rapidly with distance. A group that is separated from a nucleus by more than two bonds has little effect on the chemical shift of that nucleus. (Section 17.6)
- Chemical shift is a relative frequency difference between a signal of interest and a reference signal; the frequency difference is relative to the **operating frequency (ν_{op})** of the NMR spectrometer. (Section 17.7)
- The signal frequency of a nucleus depends on the magnetic field strength of the spectrometer, but chemical shift does not. (Section 17.7)
- The **integration** of an NMR signal is the area under the peaks in the spectrum and is graphically represented as an **integral trace**. In a ^{1}H NMR spectrum, integration is proportional to the number of protons giving rise to that signal. (Section 17.8)
- The signal from one set of protons is split when those protons are **coupled** to other protons. In general, protons are coupled when they are chemically distinct and are separated by three or fewer bonds. Protons that are separated by more than three bonds can undergo weak **long-range coupling** when they are separated by a rigid framework of π bonds. (Sections 17.9a and 17.10)
- According to the **$N + 1$ rule**, the signal generated by a set of protons will be split into $N + 1$ peaks when N protons are coupled to the protons that generate the signal. The relative intensities of those peaks are described by **Pascal's triangle**. (Section 17.9a)
- Protons on oxygen or nitrogen tend to exhibit none of the effects of coupling, appearing instead as broad singlets. (Section 17.9b)
- The **coupling constant (J)** of an NMR signal is the difference in frequency between adjacent peaks belonging to the same split signal. Signals of protons that are coupled together have the same coupling constant. (Section 17.10)
- A proton signal can exhibit **complex splitting** if the proton is coupled to two or more protons that are not equivalent to each other. These splitting patterns can be derived from a **splitting diagram**. (Section 17.10)
- Coupling constants are independent of B_{ext}, so signals become better resolved with increasing B_{ext}. (Section 17.11)
- Carbon signals are generated by ^{13}C nuclei. Signal averaging compensates for the low natural abundance of the ^{13}C nucleus. (Section 17.12a)
- All ^{13}C signals appear as singlets due to **broadband decoupling**, and their integrations do *not* correlate precisely with the number of nuclei. (Sections 17.12b and 17.12d)
- Inductive effects and magnetic anisotropy impact chemical shifts of ^{13}C nuclei, similarly to how they impact chemical shifts of ^{1}H nuclei. (Sections 17.12c)
- **DEPT ^{13}C NMR spectroscopy** gives the number of hydrogen atoms on each carbon. **2-D NMR spectra** like **COSY** and **HETCOR** provide information about which nuclei are coupled. (Section 17.13)

Problems

Sections 17.3 and 17.4 Chemical Distinction, the Number of NMR Signals, and the Time Scale of NMR Spectroscopy

17.1 For each of the following molecules, determine how many signals should appear in its ^{1}H NMR spectrum.

(a)
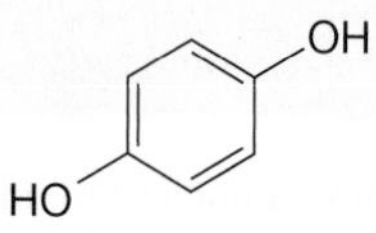
(b)
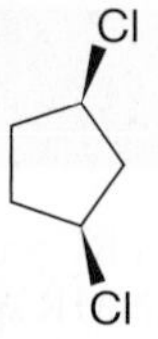
(c)
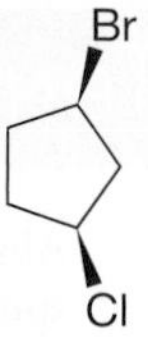
(d)
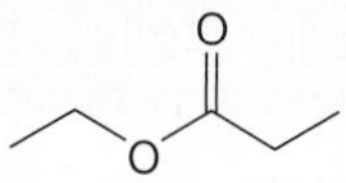
(e)
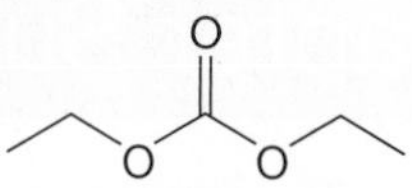
(f)
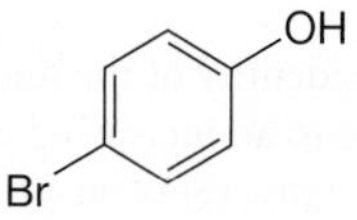
(g)
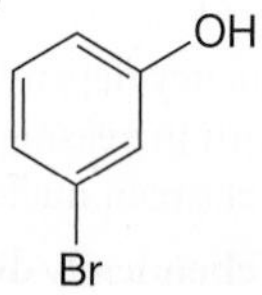
(h)
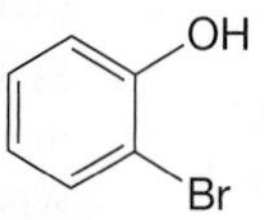
(i)
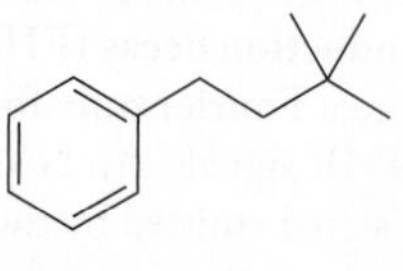

17.2 A compound gives rise to two signals in its ^{1}H NMR spectrum. Which of compounds **A–D** can it be? Explain.

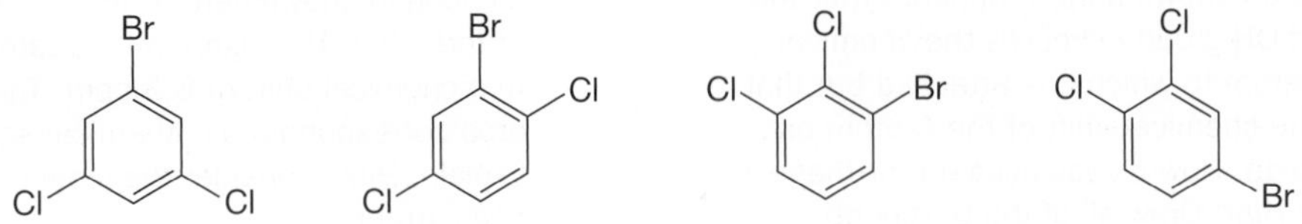

Br
Cl
Cl
Br
Cl
Cl
Cl
Cl
Br
Cl
Cl
Br

A **B** **C** **D**

17.3 At room temperature, *N,N*-dimethylformamide, $HCON(CH_3)_2$, has three ^{1}H NMR signals, appearing at 2.9, 3.0, and 8.0 ppm. As the temperature is increased, the two signals at 2.9 and 3.0 ppm merge into one signal. Explain. *Hint*: Consider the resonance structures of the compound.

17.4 Cyclohexane-d_{11} (C_6HD_{11}) exhibits one signal in its ^{1}H NMR spectrum at room temperature. Two signals appear in the spectrum, however, when the temperature is lowered significantly, as shown here. Explain why this happens.

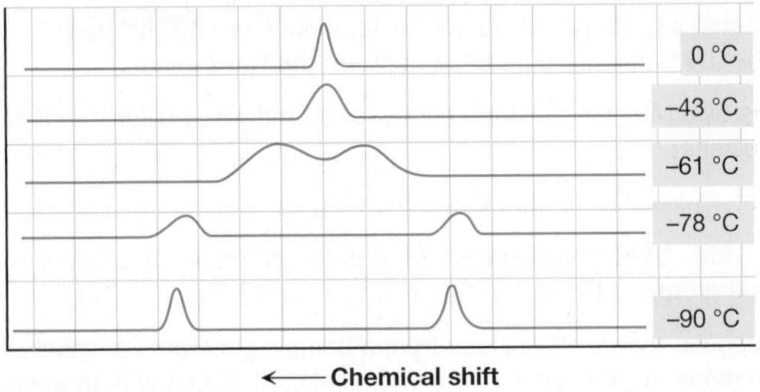

0 °C
–43 °C
–61 °C
–78 °C
–90 °C
Chemical shift

17.5 At room temperature, the ^{1}H NMR spectrum of all-*cis*-1,2,3,4,5,6-cyclohexanehexacarboxylic acid exhibits two signals for the H atoms directly bonded to the ring. Explain why. *Hint*: Draw its chair conformation explicitly.

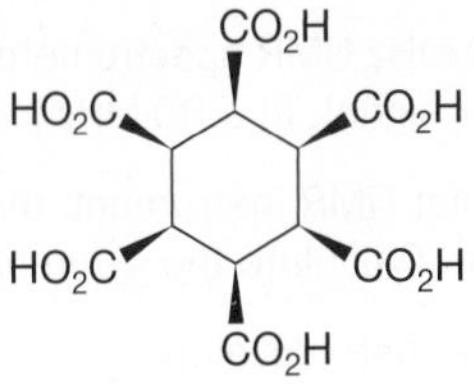

CO2H
HO2C
CO2H
HO2C
CO2H
CO2H

Sections 17.5 and 17.6 Chemical Shift, Shielding, and Deshielding

17.6 Rank protons A–C in order of increasing chemical shift.

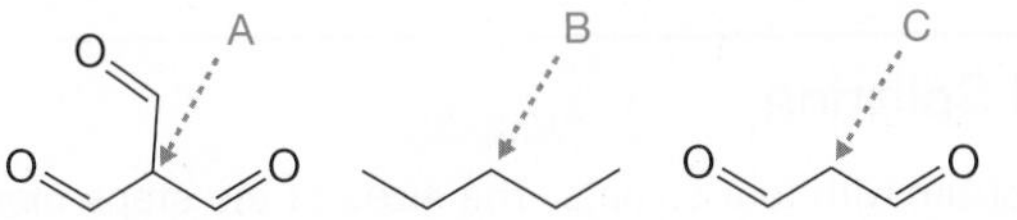

A
B
C
O
O
O
O
O

17.7 Rank protons D–H in order from largest chemical shift to smallest.

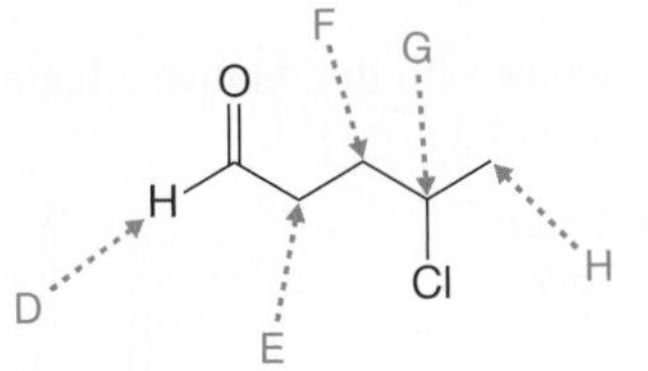

F
G
O
H
Cl
H
D
E

17.8 Rank protons I–M in order from largest chemical shift to smallest.

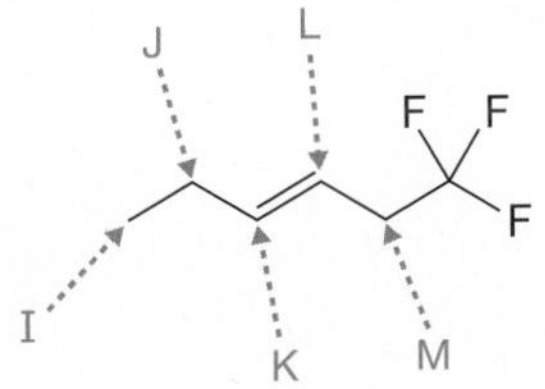

J
L
F
F
F
I
K
M

17.9 Explain why TMS has a lower chemical shift than its carbon analog dimethylpropane, $(CH_3)_4C$.

17.10 Estimate the ^{1}H NMR chemical shift for the protons on C-2 in the following compound.

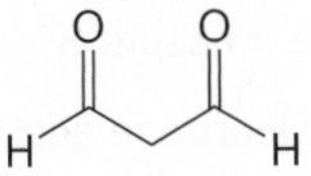

O
O
H
H

17.11 How would the ^{1}H NMR spectra of compounds **E** and **F** differ?

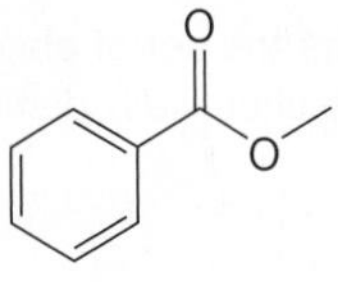

O
O

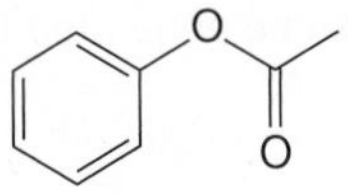

O
O

E **F**

17.12 The chemical shifts of two carbon atoms are given for the molecules shown here. It appears that the addition of the OH group *increases* the chemical shift of the C atom to which it is attached but that it *decreases* the chemical shift of the C atom on the opposite side. How do you account for these observations? *Hint*: Draw all of the pertinent resonance structures.

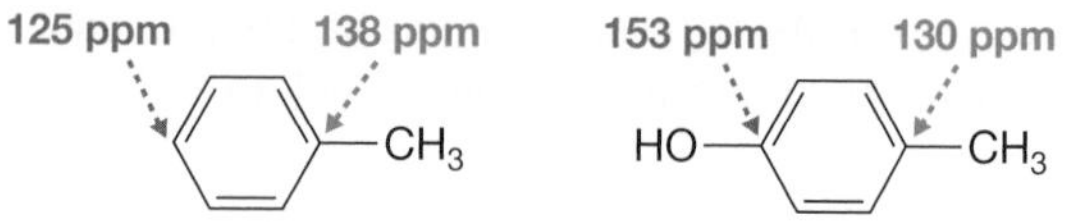
125 ppm
138 ppm
CH3
153 ppm
130 ppm
HO
CH3

17.13 Two signals appear in the ^1H NMR spectrum of the compound shown here. One has twice the integration of the other. The signal with greater area corresponds to a chemical shift of 9.3 ppm. The signal with less area corresponds to a chemical shift of −2.9 ppm. Explain. *Hint*: Consider the magnetic field lines from ring current.

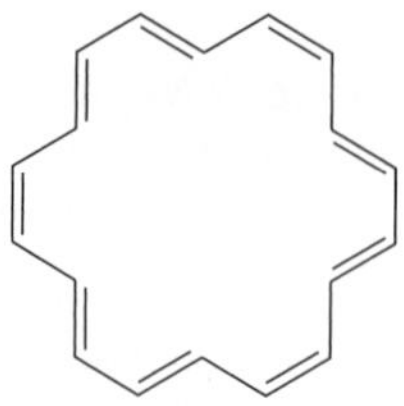

Sections 17.7 and 17.11 A Quantitative Examination of the NMR Signal

17.14 When a 300-MHz NMR spectrometer is used, one of the proton signals produced from a compound is 150 Hz higher than another signal. In a 90-MHz instrument, what would be the frequency difference between the two signals?

17.15 For a particular NMR instrument, the operating frequency is 300 MHz for ^1H NMR spectroscopy and 75 MHz for ^{13}C NMR spectroscopy. Calculate the gyromagnetic ratio for a ^{13}C nucleus.

17.16 In 2015, scientists developed a 1020-MHz NMR instrument. Calculate the strength of the magnet.

17.17 Suppose that a proton's chemical shift is 2.4 ppm in a 300-MHz NMR spectrometer. What is the difference between the signal frequency of that proton and the signal frequency of a proton in TMS?

17.18 Using the NMR instrument described in Problem 17.15, suppose that a ^{13}C nucleus from a sample generates a signal whose frequency is 11,250 Hz higher than that from the carbons in TMS. What is the chemical shift of that carbon atom from the sample?

17.19 A compound generates two ^1H NMR signals. The frequency of the first signal is 450 Hz higher than that of the signal from TMS, whereas the frequency of the second signal is 755 Hz higher than that of TMS. Which signal corresponds to the protons that are shielded to a greater extent? Explain.

Sections 17.8 and 17.10 Signal Integration and Signal Splitting

17.20 A compound, whose formula is $C_{11}H_{14}$, produces a ^1H NMR spectrum with four signals. The sizes of the steps made by the integral trace measure 37, 9, 26, and 52 mm. How many protons give rise to each signal?

17.21 Both 1,4-dimethylbenzene and 1,3,5-trimethylbenzene produce a ^1H NMR spectrum that has two signals. In which spectrum do the signal integrations have a 1:3 ratio?

17.22 Suppose that the ^1H NMR spectrum of a compound, $C_5H_{12}O$, exhibits five signals with the relative integration 1:5:5:20:30. What can you say about the signal with the relative integration of 1?

17.23 A ^1H NMR spectrum exhibits the set of absorption peaks shown here. Can those peaks be generated by one chemically distinct type of proton? Why or why not?

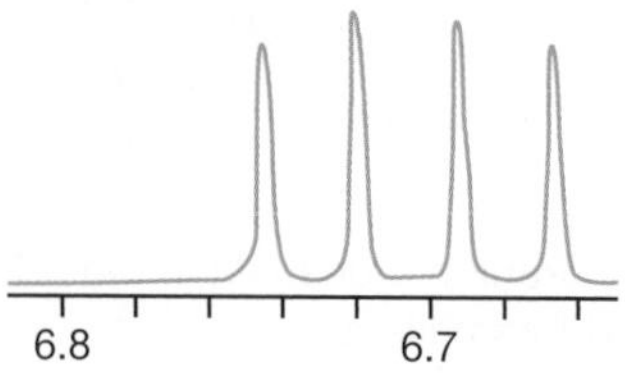
6.8
6.7

17.24 Determine the splitting pattern for each type of H highlighted in the following molecules. (You can ignore long-range coupling in this case.)

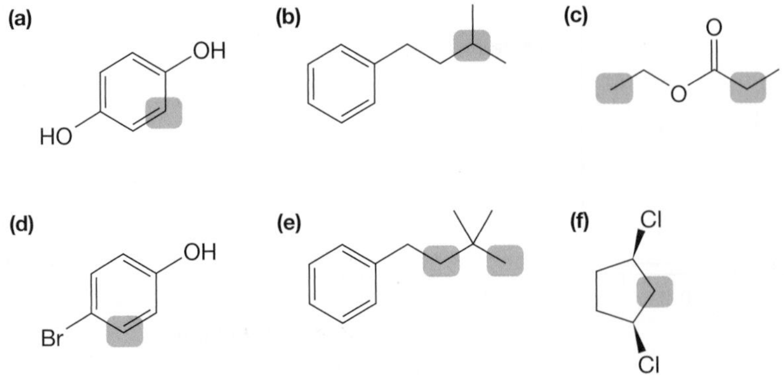

(a)
OH
HO
(b)
(c)
O
O
(d)
OH
Br
(e)
(f)
Cl
Cl

17.25 Suppose that a sextet appears in a ^{1}H NMR spectrum. Is it possible for the protons that produce the signal to be coupled to protons that are all equivalent to each other? Explain.

17.26 Draw the splitting pattern that would be observed for proton B, highlighted here. The coupling constant between protons A and B is about 7 Hz, whereas the coupling constant between protons B and C is about 16 Hz.

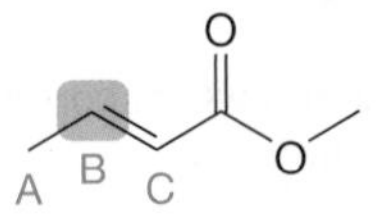

O
O
A
B
C

17.27 Based on the splitting pattern, how many total protons are coupled to the proton that gave rise to the signal shown here?

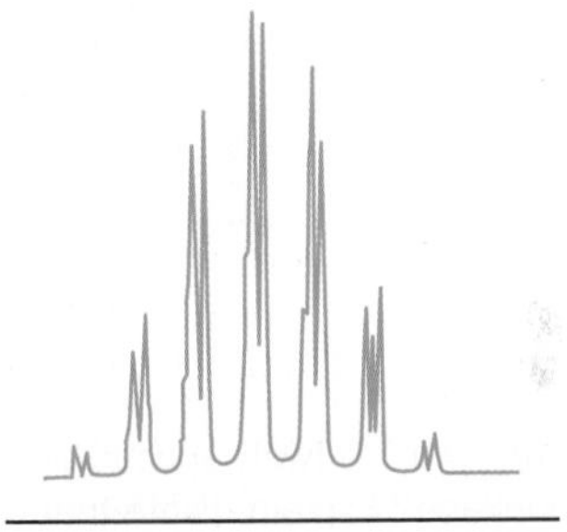

Chemical shift (ppm)

17.28 Using the ^{1}H NMR spectrum provided, along with the relative frequencies of absorption noted in hertz, determine which signal or signals represent protons coupled to the protons with δ = 4.1 ppm.

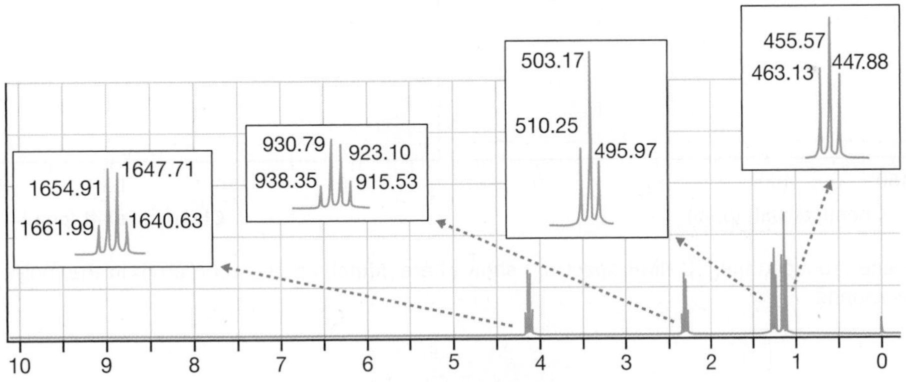

1654.91
1647.71
1661.99
1640.63
930.79
923.10
938.35
915.53
503.17
510.25
495.97
455.57
463.13
447.88
10
9
8
7
6
5
4
3
2
1
0
Chemical shift (ppm)

Section 17.12 ^{13}C NMR Spectroscopy

17.29 For each of the molecules shown in Problem 17.1, determine how many signals should appear in its ^{13}C NMR spectrum.

17.30 Rank carbons A–E from lowest ^{13}C chemical shift to highest.

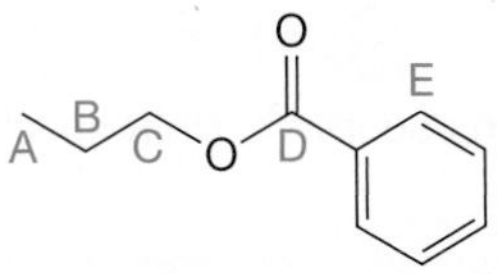

O
A
B
C
O
D
E

17.31 Rank carbons F–I from lowest ^{13}C chemical shift to highest.

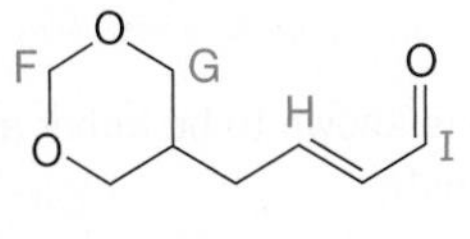

F
O
G
O
H
O
I

17.32 ^{13}C NMR spectra of three isomers of C_8H_{18} are provided. Match each spectrum to one of the following compounds: octane; 2,5-dimethylhexane; and 4-methylheptane. (Remember that the signal at ~77 ppm is due to the solvent.)

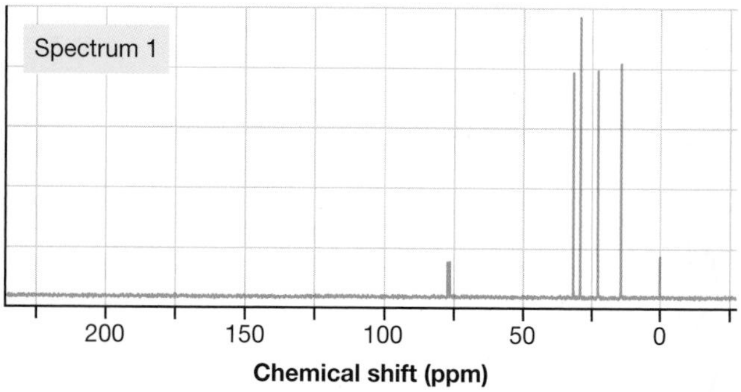

Spectrum 1
200
150
100
50
0
Chemical shift (ppm)

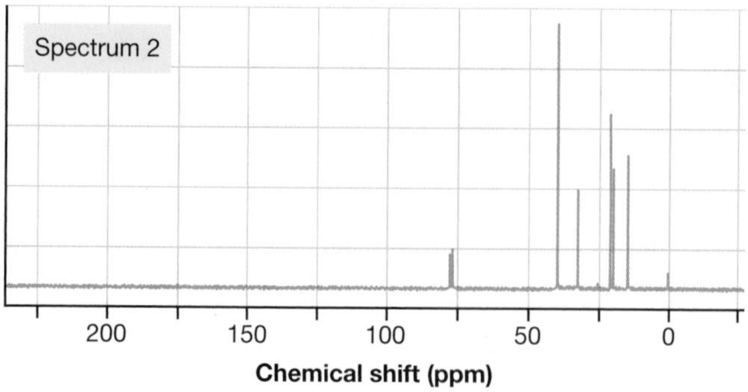

Spectrum 2
200
150
100
50
0
Chemical shift (ppm)

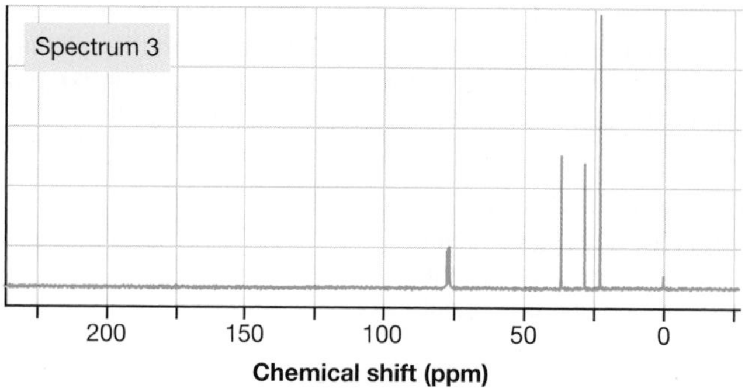

Spectrum 3
200
150
100
50
0
Chemical shift (ppm)

17.33 Which of the two ^{13}C NMR spectra shown here corresponds to chlorocyclohexane and which corresponds to iodocyclohexane? Explain. (Note that each spectrum contains signals from impurities.)

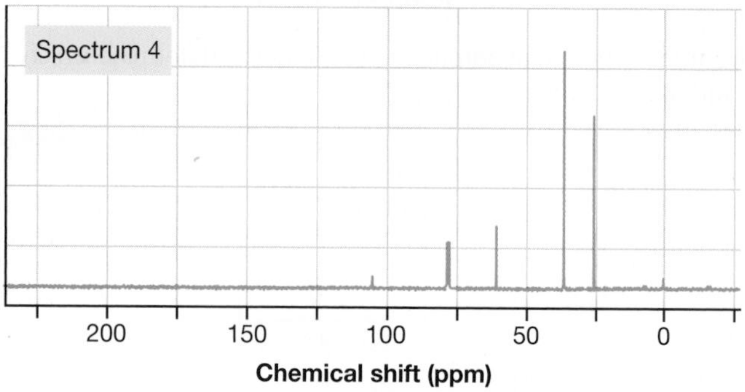

Spectrum 4
200
150
100
50
0
Chemical shift (ppm)

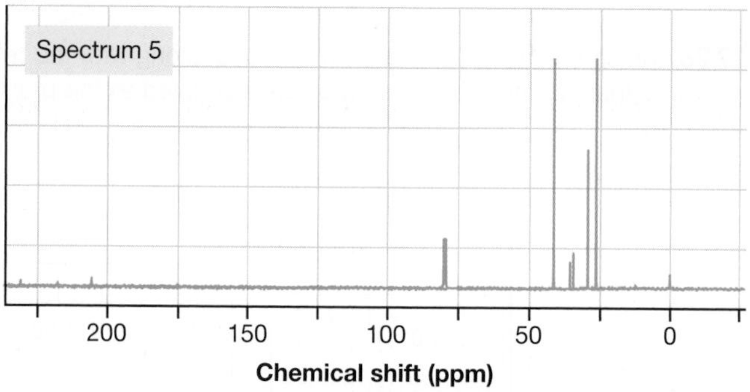

Spectrum 5
200
150
100
50
0
Chemical shift (ppm)

17.34 1-Chloropropane produced the ^{13}C NMR spectrum shown here. Match each carbon atom in the molecule to the signal to which it corresponds.

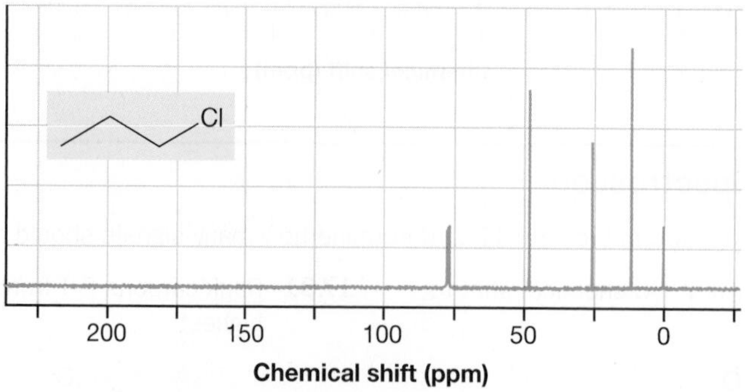

Cl
200
150
100
50
0
Chemical shift (ppm)

17.35 A compound is known to be either a ketone or an ester. Explain how you could use its ^{13}C NMR spectrum to determine which is correct.

Section 17.14 Structure Elucidation Using NMR Spectroscopy

17.36 A compound whose formula is $C_9H_{18}O$ produces a ^1H NMR spectrum that contains only one signal: namely, a singlet that appears at 1.25 ppm. What is the structure of the compound?

17.37 Determine the structure of the compound $C_6H_{10}O$ whose ^1H NMR spectrum is shown here.

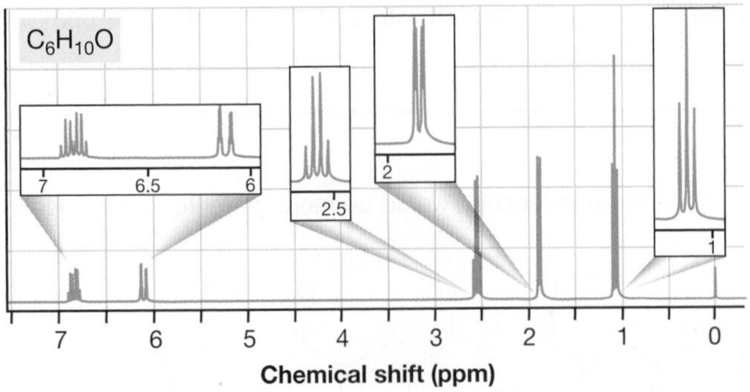

C6H10O
7
6.5
6
2.5
2
1
7 6 5 4 3 2 1 0
Chemical shift (ppm)

17.38 Determine the structure of the compound $C_7H_{14}O_2$ whose ^1H NMR spectrum is shown here.

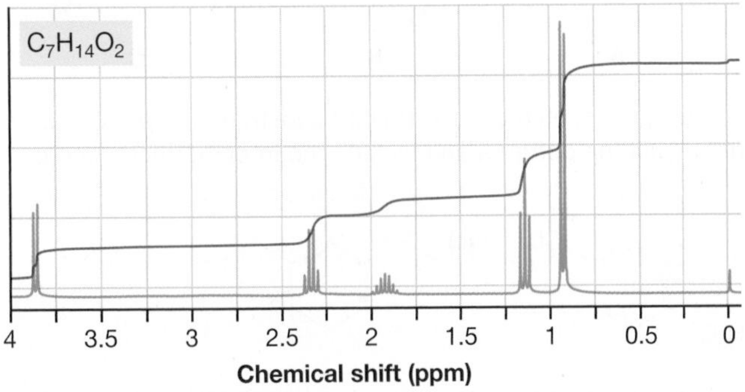

C7H14O2
4 3.5 3 2.5 2 1.5 1 0.5 0
Chemical shift (ppm)

17.39 Determine the structure of the compound $C_4H_9NO_2$ whose ^1H NMR spectrum is shown here.

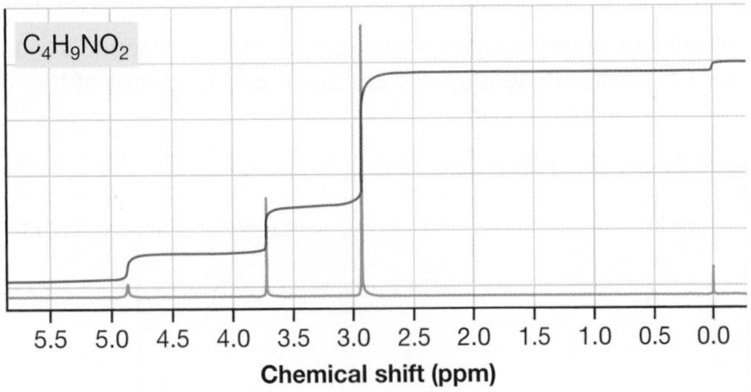

C4H9NO2
5.5 5.0 4.5 4.0 3.5 3.0 2.5 2.0 1.5 1.0 0.5 0.0
Chemical shift (ppm)

17.40 Determine the structure of the compound $C_{10}H_{14}$ whose ^{13}C NMR spectrum is shown here.

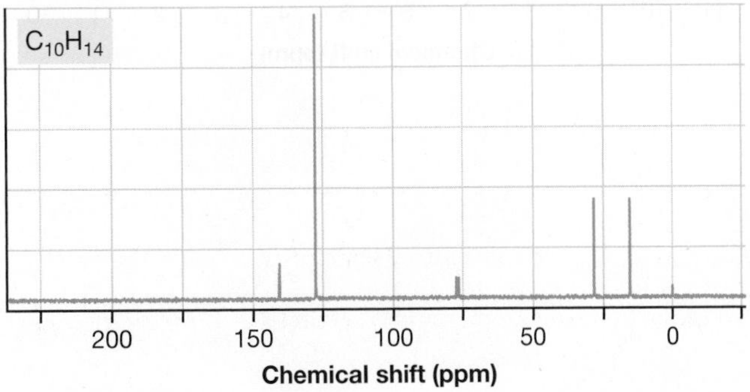

C10H14
200 150 100 50 0
Chemical shift (ppm)

17.41 An unknown compound has the formula $C_9H_{10}O_2$. Four signals appear in its ^1H NMR spectrum: (1) a singlet, $\delta = 2.3$ ppm, 6 H; (2) a doublet, $\delta = 7.0$ ppm, 2 H; (3) a triplet, $\delta = 7.2$ ppm, 1 H; and (4) a very broad singlet, $\delta = 12.9$ ppm, 1 H. Six signals appear in its ^{13}C NMR spectrum at $\delta = 19.4, 127.2, 128.5, 133.6, 135.3$, and 170.9 ppm. Propose a structure for this compound.

17.42 An unknown compound has the formula $C_8H_{10}O$. There are four distinct signals in its ^1H NMR spectrum: (1) a doublet, $\delta = 1.4$ ppm, 3 H; (2) a singlet, $\delta = 2.4$ ppm, 1 H; (3) a quartet, $\delta = 4.8$ ppm, 1 H; and (4) overlapping signals, $\delta = 7.2$–7.4 ppm, 5 H. When the sample is treated with D_2O, the signal at 2.4 ppm disappears. Propose a structure for this compound.

Integrated Problems

17.43 Which method, ^1H NMR or ^{13}C NMR spectroscopy, would be more suitable for distinguishing among compounds **A**, **B**, and **C**? Explain.

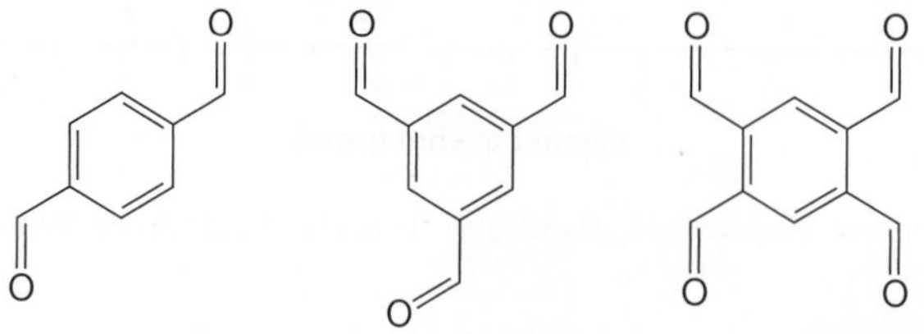

A **B** **C**

17.44 For each of the following compounds, sketch both a ^1H NMR spectrum and a ^{13}C NMR spectrum. In the ^1H NMR spectrum, pay attention to the splitting patterns and include the integral trace. (You can ignore long-range coupling in this case.)

(a) 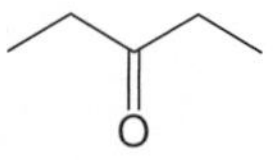 **(b)** 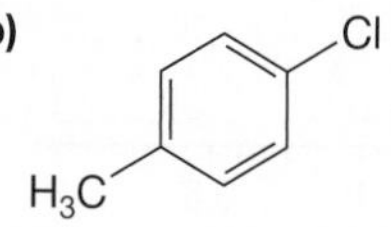
Cl
H3C
(c) 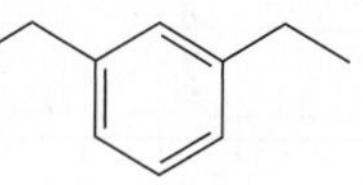

17.45 A compound has a formula of $C_{19}H_{16}$. Five signals appear in its ^{13}C NMR spectrum: one at 57 ppm and the remaining four between 126 and 144 ppm. In its ^1H NMR spectrum, an unresolved multiplet (15 H) appears between 6.9 and 7.44 ppm, and a singlet (1 H) appears at 5.5 ppm. What is the structure of this compound?

17.46 The ^1H NMR spectrum of an unknown compound is shown here. In the compound's mass spectrum, the $M^{\ddagger}$ peak appears at $m/z = 92$. An M + 2 peak, whose intensity is roughly one-third that of the $M^{\ddagger}$ peak, also appears. Draw the structure of this compound.

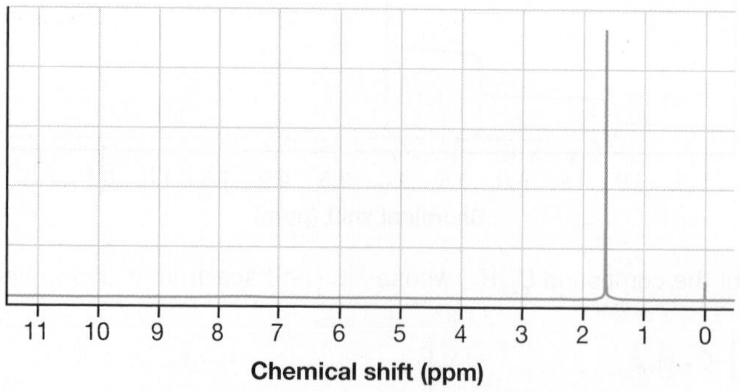
11
10
9
8
7
6
5
4
3
2
1
0
Chemical shift (ppm)

17.47 The formula of a compound is $C_9H_{10}O_3$. Use the IR, ^1H NMR, and ^{13}C NMR spectra provided to determine its structure.

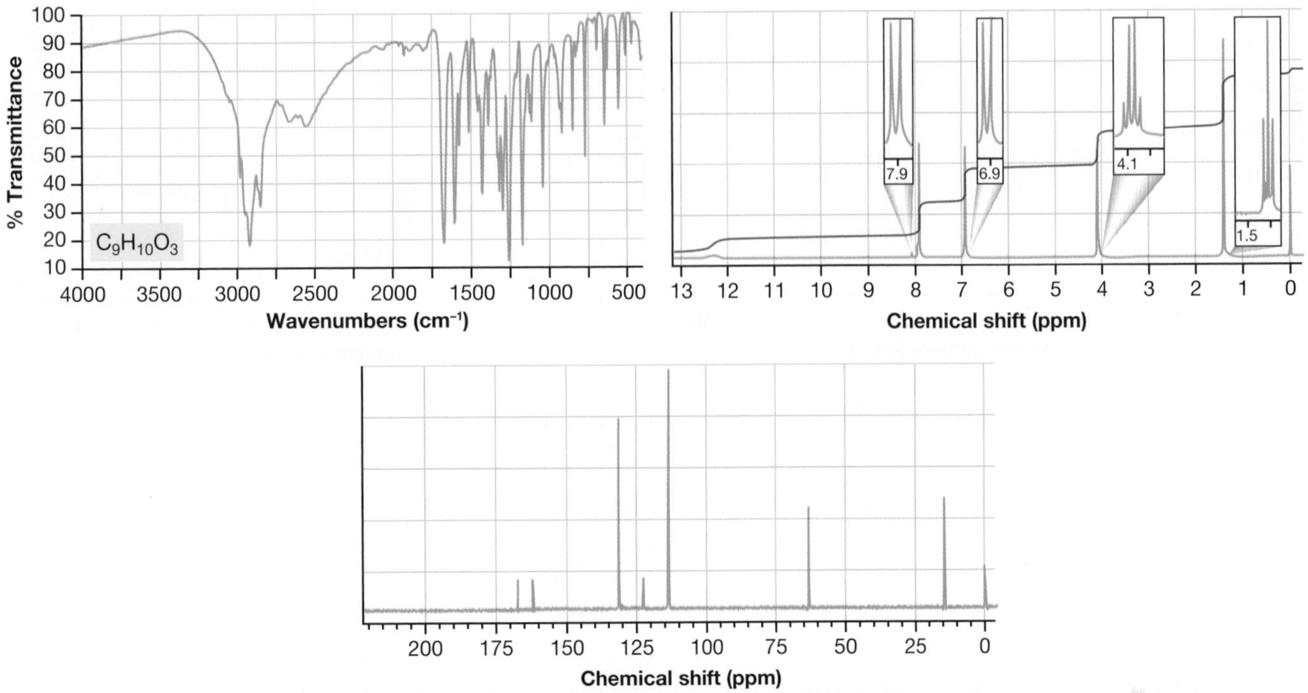

% Transmittance
C9H10O3
Wavenumbers (cm⁻¹)
7.9
6.9
4.1
1.5
Chemical shift (ppm)
Chemical shift (ppm)

17.48 The formula of a compound is C_9H_8O, and its IR and ^1H NMR spectra are provided. If its ^{13}C NMR spectrum has seven signals, then what is the compound's structure?

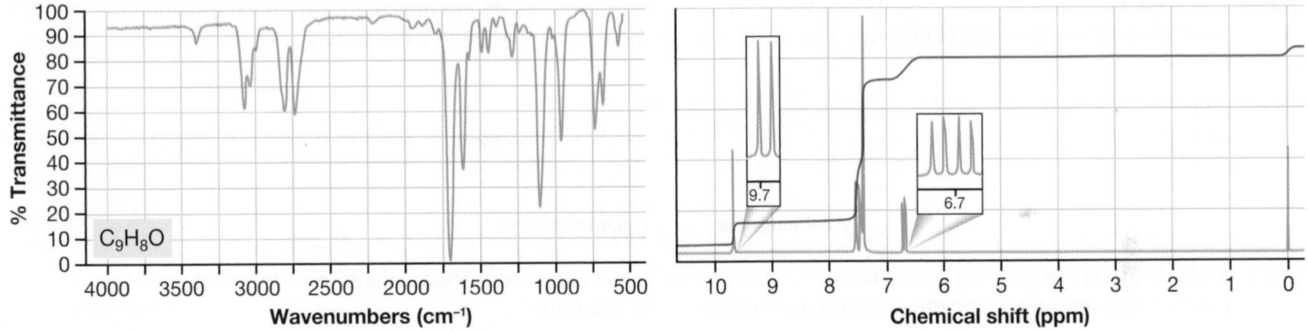

% Transmittance
C9H8O
Wavenumbers (cm⁻¹)
9.7
6.7
Chemical shift (ppm)

17.49 A compound with the formula $C_4H_{10}O_2$ has the following IR, ^1H NMR, and ^{13}C NMR spectra. Determine the structure of the compound.

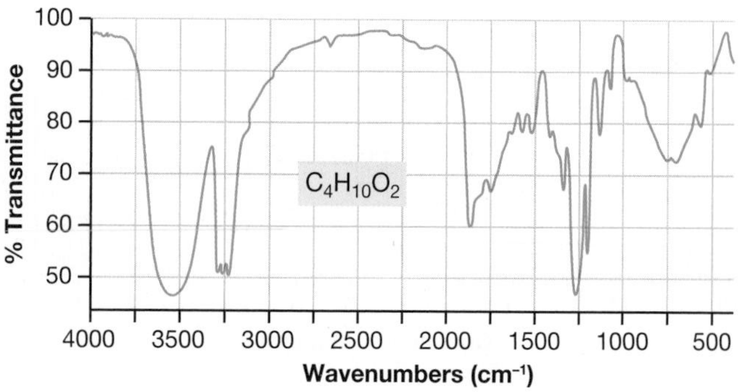

% Transmittance
100
90
80
70
60
50
C4H10O2
4000 3500 3000 2500 2000 1500 1000 500
Wavenumbers (cm-1)

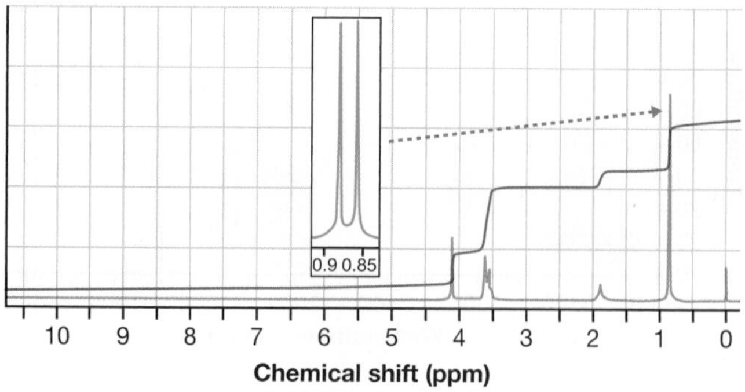

0.9 0.85
10 9 8 7 6 5 4 3 2 1 0
Chemical shift (ppm)

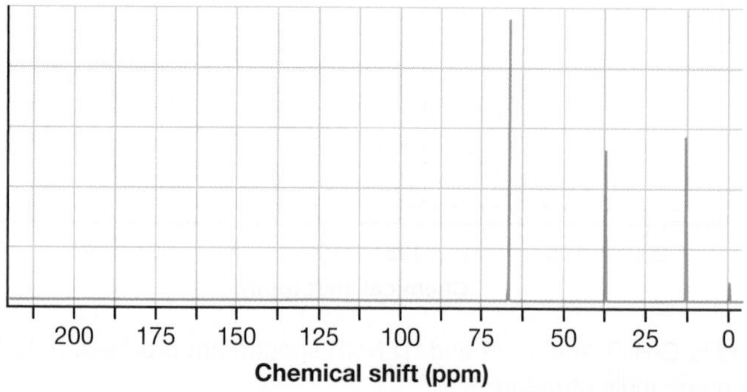

200 175 150 125 100 75 50 25 0
Chemical shift (ppm)

17.50 The chemical shifts of the α protons on cyclohexanone and cyclobutanone are indicated. **(a)** Which α carbon has greater effective electronegativity? **(b)** Explain why, using arguments of *s*-character and *p*-character.

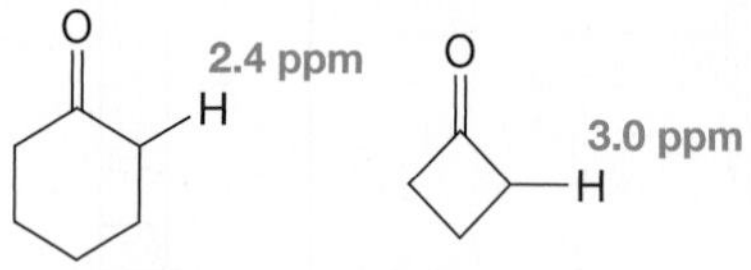

2.4 ppm
3.0 ppm

Cyclohexanone Cyclobutanone

17.51 A student runs the reaction shown here and obtains the ^1H NMR spectrum shown. Determine the product of the reaction and draw the complete, detailed mechanism of the reaction.

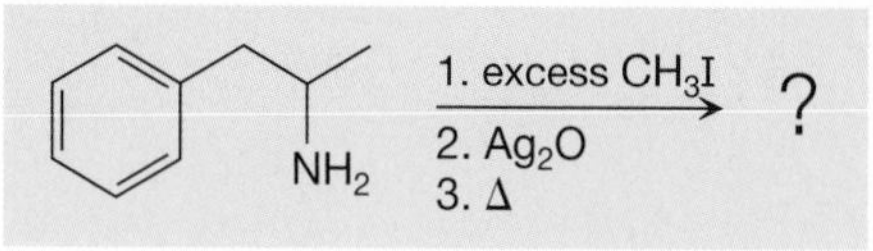

NH2
1. excess CH3I
2. Ag2O
3. Δ
?

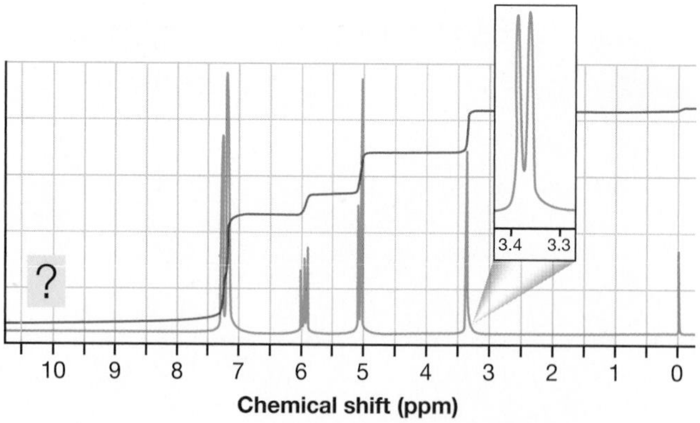

?
3.4 3.3
10 9 8 7 6 5 4 3 2 1 0
Chemical shift (ppm)

17.52 An alcohol was treated with HBr, yielding a mixture of 1-bromopent-2-ene and 3-bromopent-1-ene. The ^{1}H and ^{13}C NMR spectra of the starting alcohol are given here. Determine the structure of the starting alcohol and draw a complete, detailed mechanism to account for each of the products.

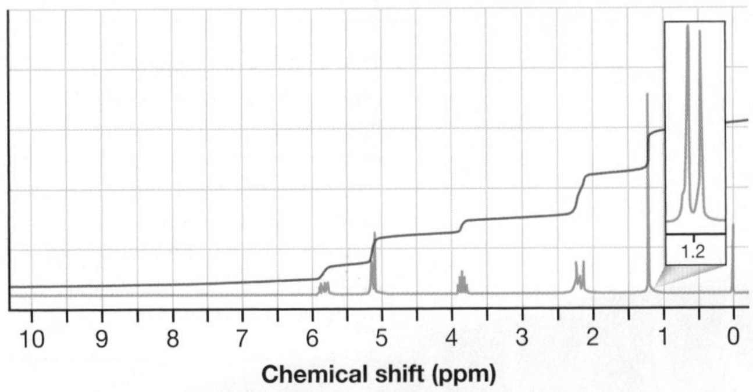

1.2
10 9 8 7 6 5 4 3 2 1 0
Chemical shift (ppm)

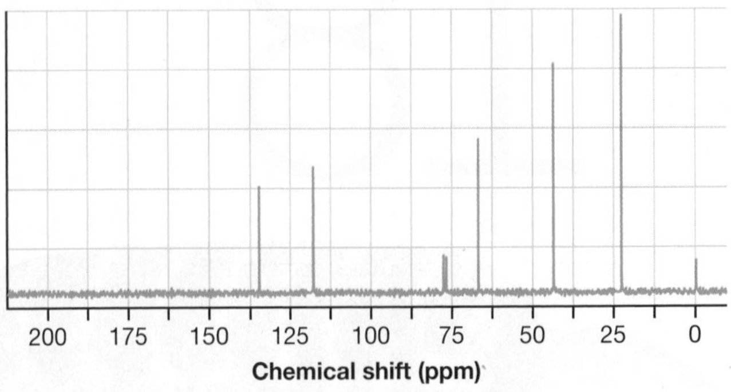

200 175 150 125 100 75 50 25 0
Chemical shift (ppm)

17.53 An alcohol was treated with concentrated sulfuric acid and heated. The product that was obtained had the following IR, ^{1}H NMR, and ^{13}C NMR spectra. **(a)** Determine the structure of the alcohol. **(b)** Draw a complete, detailed mechanism for the reaction that took place.

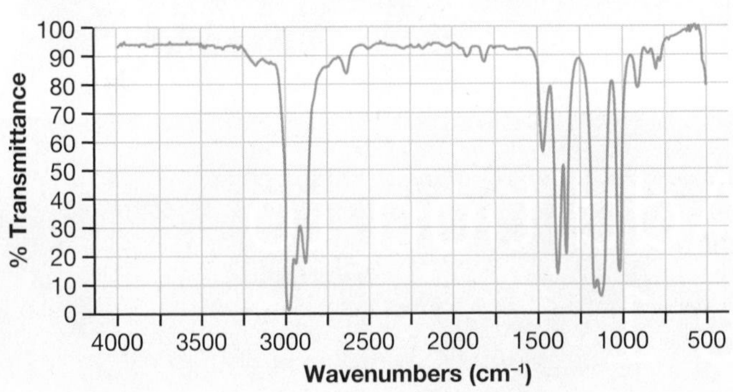

% Transmittance
100 90 80 70 60 50 40 30 20 10 0
4000 3500 3000 2500 2000 1500 1000 500
Wavenumbers (cm⁻¹)

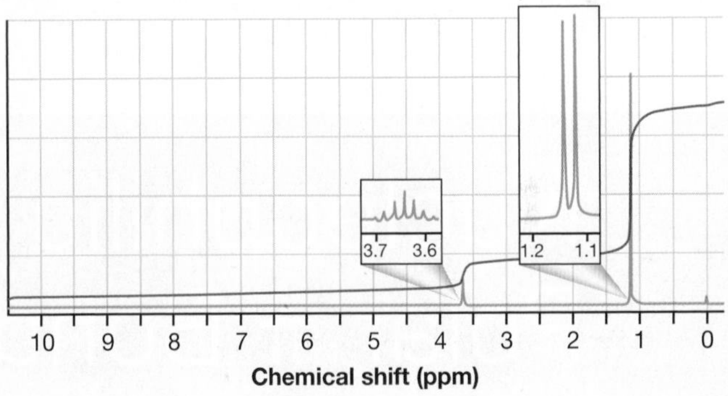

3.7 3.6
1.2 1.1
10 9 8 7 6 5 4 3 2 1 0
Chemical shift (ppm)

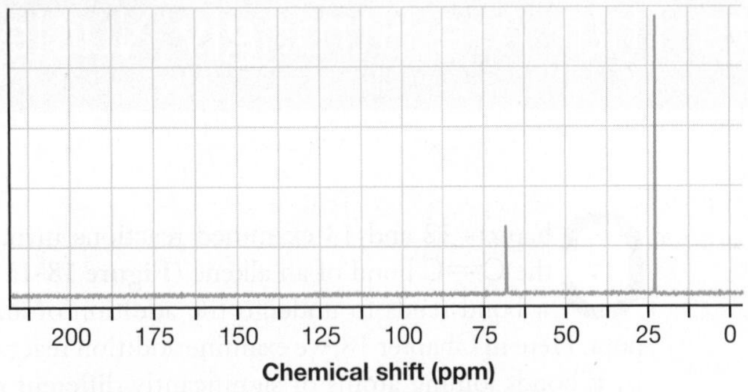

200 175 150 125 100 75 50 25 0
Chemical shift (ppm)

18

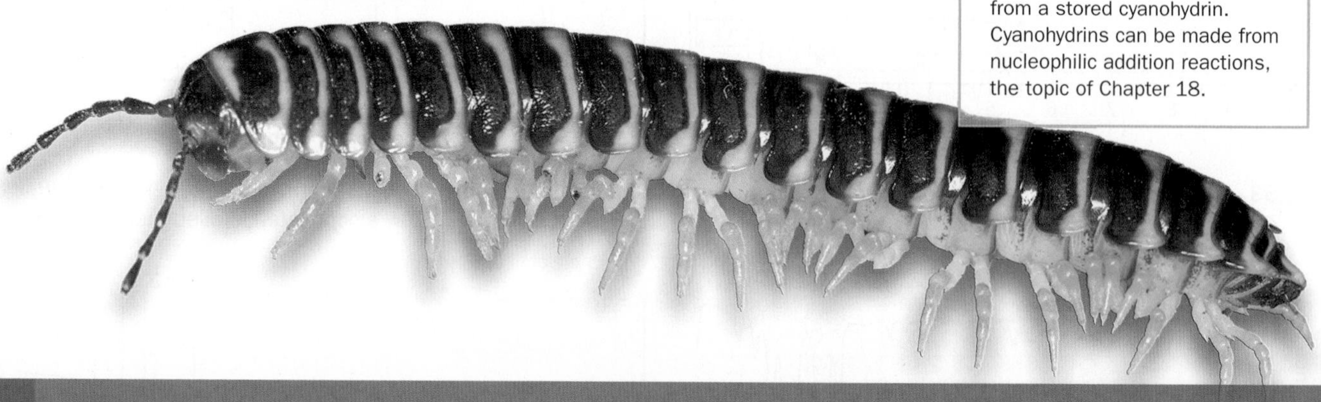

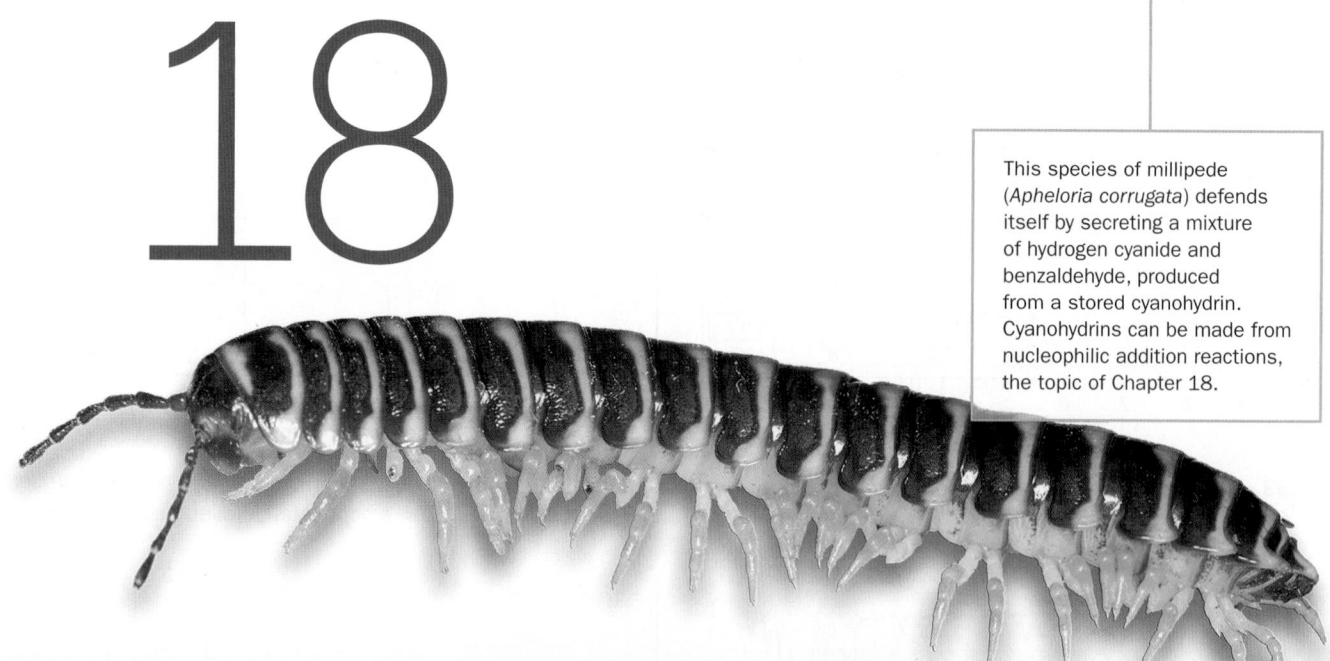

This species of millipede (*Apheloria corrugata*) defends itself by secreting a mixture of hydrogen cyanide and benzaldehyde, produced from a stored cyanohydrin. Cyanohydrins can be made from nucleophilic addition reactions, the topic of Chapter 18.

Nucleophilic Addition to Polar π Bonds 1

Reagents That Are Strongly Nucleophilic

Chapters 12 and 13 examined reactions involving nonpolar π bonds, such as the C═C bond of an alkene (**Figure 18-1a**). Being electron-rich, a *nonpolar* π bond tends to undergo the addition of an electrophile, which is electron-poor. Here in Chapter 18, we examine addition reactions involving *polar* π bonds (that is, π bonds joining atoms of significantly different electronegativity), represented as C═Y in Figure 18-1b. Unlike in an alkene, a polar π bond has an atom that is relatively electron-poor (i.e., electrophilic), so it tends to undergo the addition of a nucleophile, which is electron-rich. These **nucleophilic addition reactions** are some of the most important reactions in organic chemistry, and they are integral in a variety of biological reactions, too.

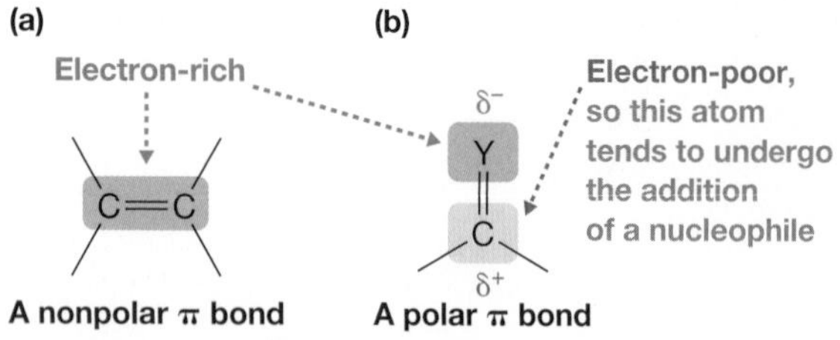
(a)
(b)
Electron-rich
δ−
Y
C═C
C
δ+
Electron-poor, so this atom tends to undergo the addition of a nucleophile
A nonpolar π bond
A polar π bond

FIGURE 18-1 Nonpolar and polar π bonds (a) A nonpolar π bond is relatively electron-rich, so it tends to undergo the addition of an electrophile. (b) A polar π bond, where Y is more electronegative than C, has an electron-poor C atom that tends to undergo the addition of a nucleophile.

A polar π bond appears in several compound classes, as shown in **Figure 18-2**. Far and away, *the most common polar π bond that participates in nucleophilic addition reactions is the one in the carbonyl (C═O) group.* Carbonyl groups are present in ketones ($R_2C{=}O$), aldehydes (RCH═O), carboxylic acids (RCO_2H), esters (RCO_2R), amides ($RCONR_2$), acid halides (RCOX), and acid anhydrides (RCO_2COR). Of these, we focus primarily on ketones and aldehydes here in Chapter 18 and also in Chapter 19. The carbonyl group in the remaining compound classes behaves somewhat differently because of a *leaving group* attached to the carbonyl C (shown in red type in Fig. 18-2); we will study such compounds in

Chapter Outline

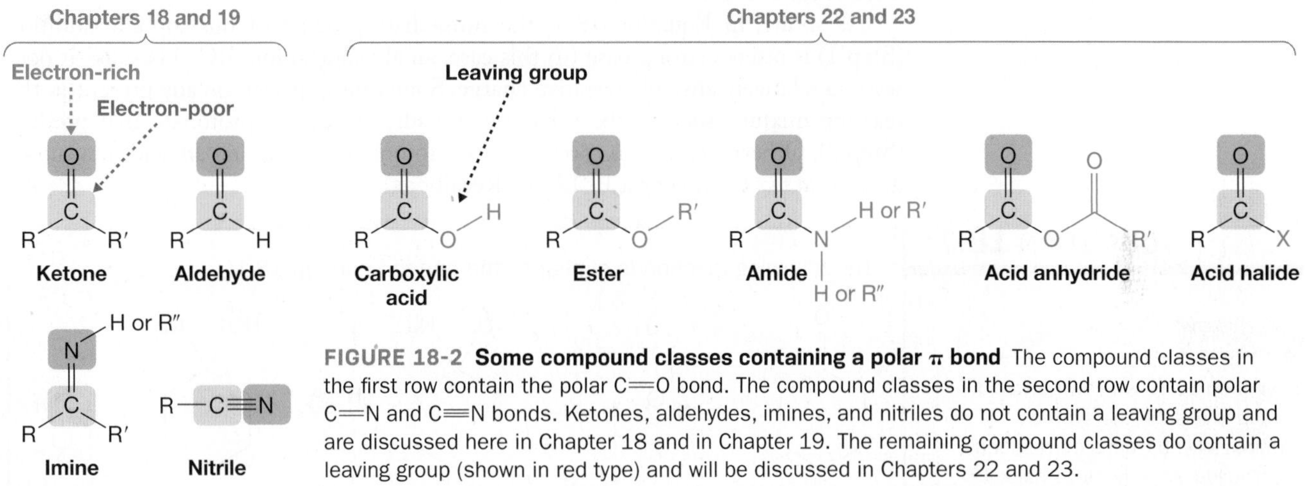

Chapters 18 and 19
Chapters 22 and 23
Electron-rich
Electron-poor
Leaving group
Ketone
Aldehyde
Carboxylic acid
Ester
Amide
Acid anhydride
Acid halide
H or R′
H or R″
Imine
Nitrile

FIGURE 18-2 Some compound classes containing a polar π bond The compound classes in the first row contain the polar C═O bond. The compound classes in the second row contain polar C═N and C≡N bonds. Ketones, aldehydes, imines, and nitriles do not contain a leaving group and are discussed here in Chapter 18 and in Chapter 19. The remaining compound classes do contain a leaving group (shown in red type) and will be discussed in Chapters 22 and 23.

Chapters 22 and 23. Although they are less common, other polar π bonds encountered in organic molecules, such as the C═N bond in imines and the C≡N bond in nitriles, react similarly to the carbonyl group in ketones and aldehydes, so they are also discussed here in Chapter 18.

We have divided nucleophilic addition reactions into two types, according to the nature of the reagent that is responsible for supplying the nucleophile: (1) the reagent itself is strongly nucleophilic, or (2) the reagent is weakly nucleophilic or non-nucleophilic. When the reagent itself is strongly nucleophilic, the mechanism for the nucleophilic addition reaction tends to be simpler; we discuss these kinds of reactions here in Chapter 18. When the reagent is weakly nucleophilic or non-nucleophilic, base or acid catalysis is used to speed up the reaction for it to occur at a reasonable rate; such reactions tend to have more complex mechanisms and will be discussed in Chapter 19.

SECTION 18.1 OBJECTIVES

You will be able to:

1. Draw the general mechanism for the addition of a strong nucleophile to a polar π bond to produce an uncharged product.
2. Account for stereochemistry when a nucleophile adds to a polar π bond.

18.1 An Overview of the General Mechanism: Addition of Strong Nucleophiles

As we saw in Chapter 7, a nucleophile tends to form a bond with the atom at the positive end of a *polar π bond*. Whereas the nucleophile is relatively electron-rich, the partially positive (δ^+) atom of the π bond is relatively electron-poor. An example with a generic strong nucleophile (Nu^-) and a ketone is shown in Equation 18-1:

General mechanism for nucleophilic addition to a polar π bond

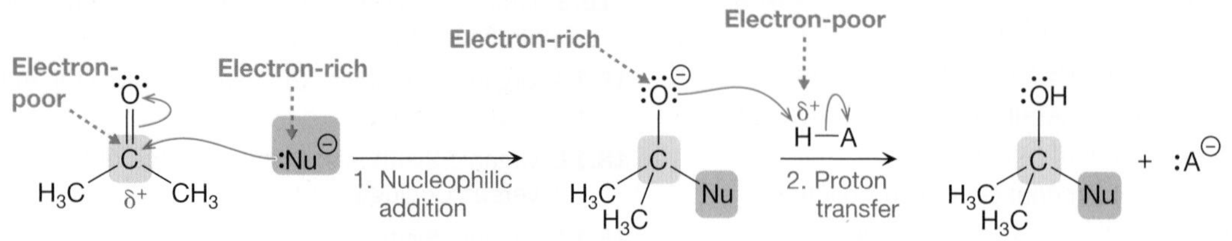

Electron-poor
Electron-rich
Electron-rich
Electron-poor
1. Nucleophilic addition
2. Proton transfer

(18-1)

To avoid exceeding the octet on the C atom attacked by the nucleophile, the π bond is broken and the pair of electrons from the π bond becomes a lone pair on the more electronegative O atom.

As shown in Equation 18-1, the immediate product of nucleophilic addition (Step 1) is often a strong base (in this case, an alkoxide anion, RO^-) because it possesses a relatively unstable negative charge. Sometimes, species already present in the reaction mixture, such as the solvent, are acidic enough to protonate that product (Step 2). Otherwise, we can carry out this protonation by adding an acid in a subsequent *acid workup* (Section 10.12; see Recall box).

YOUR TURN **18.1**

The following reaction is similar to the one in Equation 18-1:

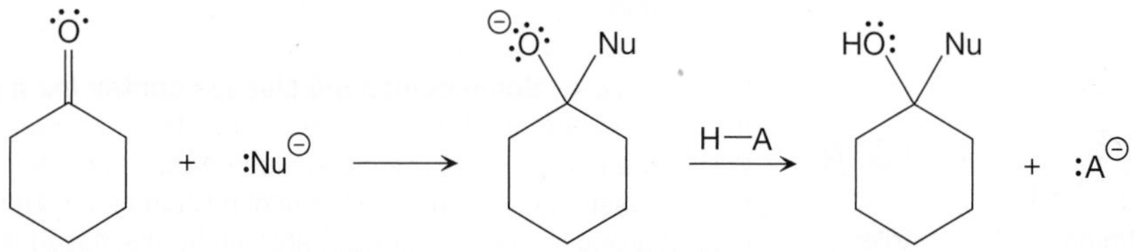

Label each reacting species as either "electron-rich" or "electron-poor," draw in the appropriate curved arrows, and under each reaction arrow, name the type of elementary step involved.

Answers to Your Turns are in the back of the book.

◂ RECALL

In Section 10.12 we saw how *acid workup* is used in the synthesis of a terminal alkyne from a corresponding dihalide. After back-to-back E2 steps, the initial terminal alkyne RC≡CH is immediately deprotonated to produce $RC{\equiv}C^-$, and acid workup replenishes the proton to produce RC≡CH.

SOLVED PROBLEM **18.1**

How to apply the general mechanism for a nucleophilic addition reaction

Break It Down **Draw the complete, detailed mechanism and predict the product for the reaction of 3-methylbutanal shown here.**

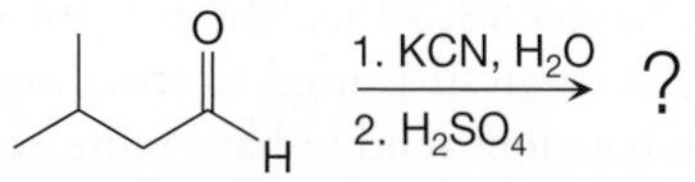

1. KCN, H_2O
2. H_2SO_4
?

3-Methylbutanal

Think	Solve
What nucleophile is generated when KCN dissolves in water?	KCN is ionic, so it dissolves in water as K^+ and ^-CN ions. ^-CN has a localized negative charge on C and is a strong nucleophile.
Which atom will the nucleophile attack? Which bond will break as a result?	Being a strong nucleophile, ^-CN will attack the electron-poor carbonyl carbon, breaking the π bond of the double bond, as shown in the first step below.

(continued)

What acid exists when H_2SO_4 is dissolved in water? What is the role of the acid?	H_2SO_4 dissolves in water to produce H_3O^+. The O^- that results from the first step is protonated by the acid, as shown in the second step below.

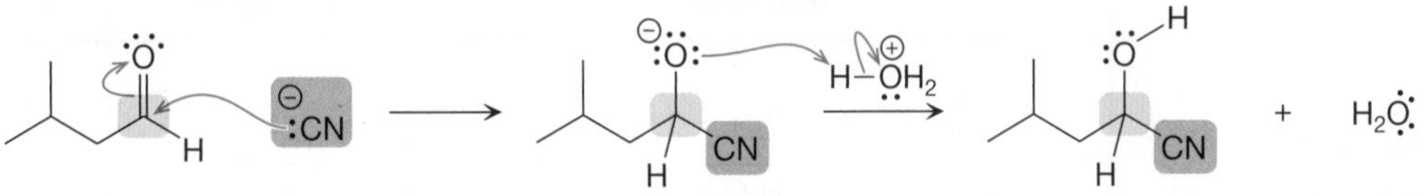

:CN
CN
H
H–OH₂
CN
H
+ H₂O

Try It Draw the complete, detailed mechanism for the reaction shown here and draw the product.

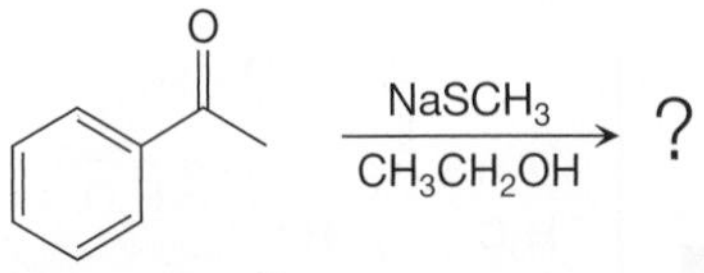

O
NaSCH₃
CH₃CH₂OH
?

Answers to all Try It exercises can be found in the Solutions Manual.

Stereochemistry must be accounted for in nucleophilic addition when the carbon atom that is attacked becomes an asymmetric carbon in the product. An example is shown in Equation 18-2:

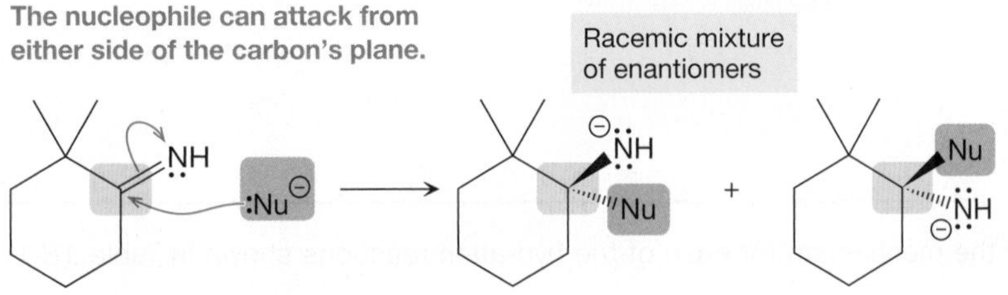

The nucleophile can attack from either side of the carbon's plane.
Racemic mixture of enantiomers
NH
:Nu
NH
Nu
+
Nu
NH

(18-2)

An imine

Because the C atom of the polar π bond has a planar electron geometry, a nucleophile can attack from either side of the plane. In this case, the reactants and the environment are achiral, so the product mixture will contain equal amounts of the *R* and *S* enantiomers: it will be a racemic mixture (Section 8.5b).

YOUR TURN 18.2

The reaction in Solved Problem 18.1 results in a new asymmetric carbon. Identify that atom and draw both stereoisomers that would be produced.

18.2 Substituent Effects: Relative Reactivity of Ketones and Aldehydes in Nucleophilic Addition

SECTION 18.2 OBJECTIVES

You will be able to:

1. Rank ketones and aldehydes in order of their rates of nucleophilic addition, as well as the extent to which the reactions are product-favored.
2. Explain how the reactivity of ketones and aldehydes depends on the alkyl groups attached to the carbonyl carbon.

Ketones and aldehydes exhibit very similar chemical behavior because they are rather similar structurally, but the nucleophilic addition reactions they undergo are noticeably different, both thermodynamically and kinetically:

> Nucleophilic attack at a carbonyl carbon tends to be more energetically favorable and faster for aldehydes than for ketones.

These points are exemplified in Table 18-1, which presents both equilibrium and rate data for the conversion of three different carbonyl compounds to their *hydrates* (two OH groups bonded to the same C) under basic conditions.

CONNECTIONS 18.1

What do beer, chicken, and pesticides have in common? 3-Methylbutanal (Solved Problem 18.1), commonly called isovaleraldehyde, is a flavor component described as having a cheesy or malt flavor. It is found in a variety of foods and beverages, including cheese, beer, chicken, and fish. 3-Methylbutanal is also used as feedstock in the manufacture of some pesticides.

TABLE 18-1 Extent and Rate of Carbonyl Hydration in Ketones and Aldehydes

Reaction	Relative Rate Constant[a]	Percent Hydrate at Equilibrium[b]
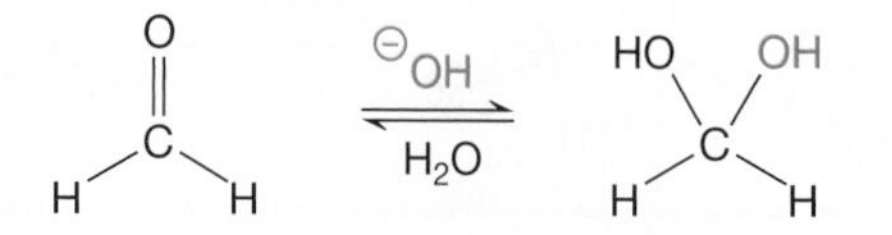	3×10^6	>99.9%
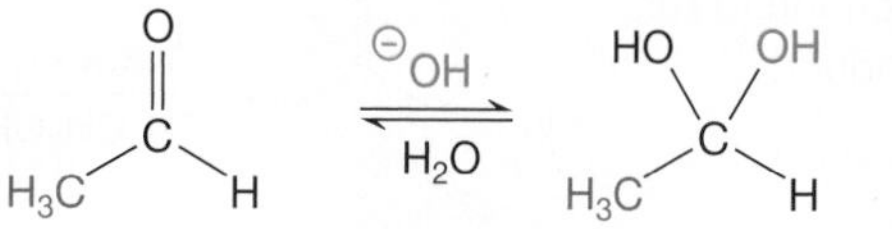	5×10^4	57%
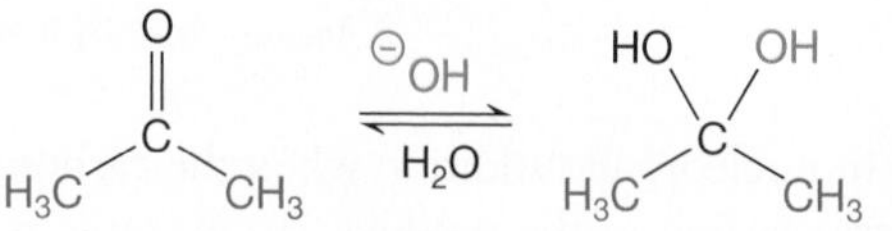	1	<1%

[a]The rate of hydration is determined in water.
[b]The extent of hydration at equilibrium is determined in methanol.

YOUR TURN **18.3**

Draw the mechanism for each of the hydration reactions shown in Table 18-1.

Notice in Table 18-1 that both the rate of hydration and the extent of hydration at equilibrium are greater for the aldehydes than for the ketone. Both of these results can be explained in part by steric effects associated with the bulky alkyl groups of the ketone, as shown in **Figure 18-3**. In a ketone, the *steric repulsion* from the two alkyl groups on the carbonyl carbon (Fig. 18-3a, left) makes it more difficult for the nucleophile to attack. Furthermore, the bulky alkyl groups in the hydrate product (Fig. 18-3a, right) overlap with the bulky OH groups, generating *steric strain* and decreasing stability. An aldehyde (Fig. 18-3b), on the other hand, has at most one alkyl group bonded to the carbonyl carbon, so both of these steric effects are diminished.

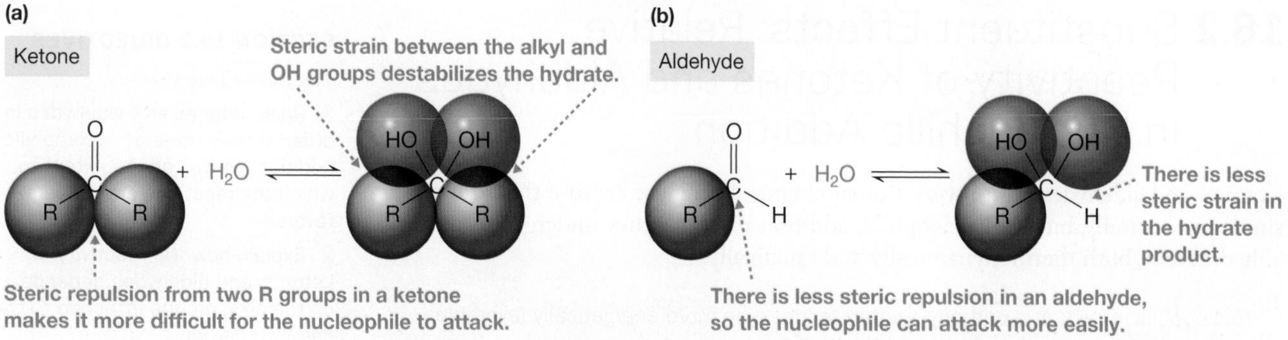
(a)
Ketone
Steric strain between the alkyl and OH groups destabilizes the hydrate.
Steric repulsion from two R groups in a ketone makes it more difficult for the nucleophile to attack.
(b)
Aldehyde
There is less steric strain in the hydrate product.
There is less steric repulsion in an aldehyde, so the nucleophile can attack more easily.

FIGURE 18-3 Steric effects in nucleophilic addition (a) In a ketone, steric repulsion by each bulky alkyl group (left) makes it more difficult for a nucleophile to attack. Steric strain in the hydrate product (right) decreases stability. (b) In an aldehyde, there is at most one bulky alkyl group, so steric effects are decreased.

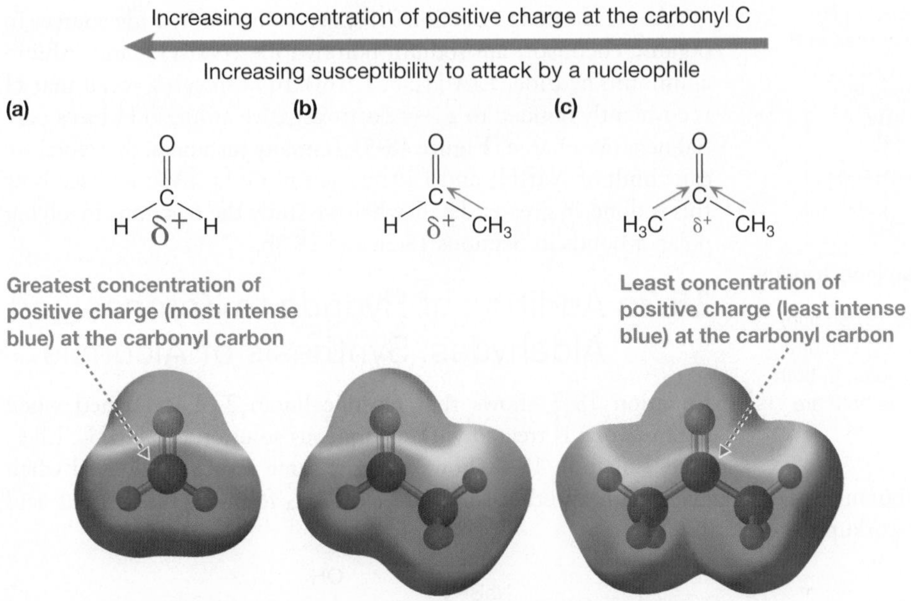
Increasing concentration of positive charge at the carbonyl C
Increasing susceptibility to attack by a nucleophile
(a)
(b)
(c)
Greatest concentration of positive charge (most intense blue) at the carbonyl carbon
Least concentration of positive charge (least intense blue) at the carbonyl carbon

FIGURE 18-4 Inductive effects in nucleophilic addition Electrostatic potential maps of (a) formaldehyde, (b) acetaldehyde, and (c) acetone are shown. Additional alkyl groups bonded to the carbonyl carbon decrease its concentration of positive charge by donating electron density, making it less reactive.

Aldehydes are more reactive than ketones, too, because ketones are stabilized more by *inductive effects*, as illustrated in **Figure 18-4**. Recall from Section 6.6e that alkyl groups are electron-donating, so they decrease the concentration of positive charge at the carbonyl carbon. With less concentration of positive charge at that carbon, the carbonyl group is less susceptible to attack by a nucleophile bearing excess negative charge.

YOUR TURN **18.4**

Which imine, **A**, **B**, or **C**, has the greatest concentration of positive charge at the C=N carbon, and which has the least concentration of positive charge? Which imine is the most reactive? Which is the least reactive?

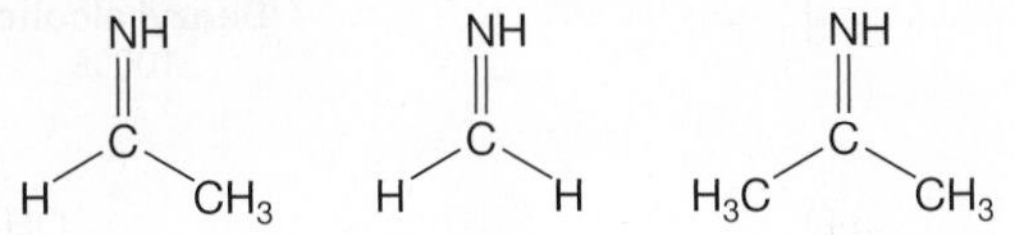

A **B** **C**

18.3 Reactions of Hydride Reagents: $LiAlH_4$, $NaBH_4$, and NaH

SECTION 18.3 OBJECTIVES

You will be able to:

1. Draw the mechanism and the major product for the reaction of $LiAlH_4$ or $NaBH_4$ with ketones, aldehydes, imines, and nitriles.
2. Explain why protic solvents like water and alcohols can be used for reactions involving $NaBH_4$ but not $LiAlH_4$.
3. Explain why NaH is a powerful base but a poor nucleophile.

Recall that the hydride anion, $H{:}^-$, is a hydrogen atom with an extra electron (it is usually further abbreviated to H^-). Unlike such species as Cl^- and HO^-, however, H^- does not exist on its own at any appreciable concentration in solution because it is extremely reactive, both as a nucleophile and as a base; it even reacts with many common solvents. H^- is so reactive because it is small in size and its nucleus is only moderately electronegative, so it does not accommodate the negative charge well.

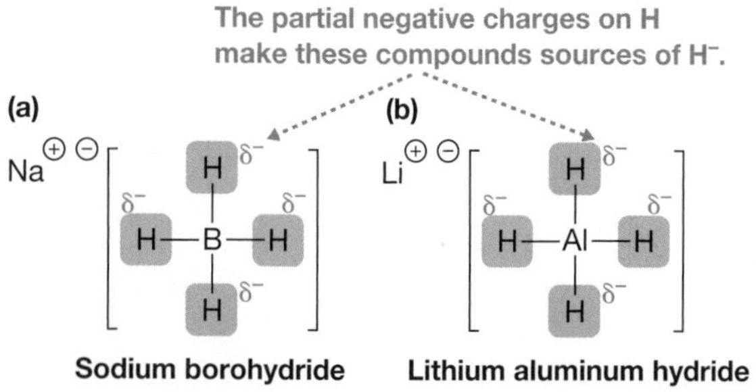
The partial negative charges on H make these compounds sources of H⁻.
(a)
(b)
Na
Li
H
B
Al
δ⁻
Sodium borohydride
Lithium aluminum hydride

FIGURE 18-5 Common hydride sources (a) Sodium borohydride consists of Na^+ and BH_4^- ions. (b) Lithium aluminum hydride consists of Li^+ and AlH_4^- ions. In both anions, H bears a partial negative charge, so both are sources of hydride ions, H^-.

As we learned in Section 7.1b, two common hydride sources in organic chemistry are sodium borohydride ($NaBH_4$) and lithium aluminum hydride ($LiAlH_4$, or LAH). In both cases, recall that H is covalently bonded to a less electronegative atom, so H has a partial negative charge (**Figure 18-5**). In many instances, therefore, we can think of $NaBH_4$ and $LiAlH_4$ as simply H^-. We will see how this is done, in greater detail, when we study the reactions involving polar π bonds in Sections 18.3a and 18.3b.

18.3a Addition of Hydride to Ketones and Aldehydes: Synthesis of Alcohols

Equation 18-3 shows that racemic butan-2-ol is formed when butan-2-one is treated with an aqueous solution of $NaBH_4$. Likewise, Equation 18-4 shows that the same result is achieved when butan-2-one is refluxed with an ether solution of $LiAlH_4$ followed by aqueous acid workup:

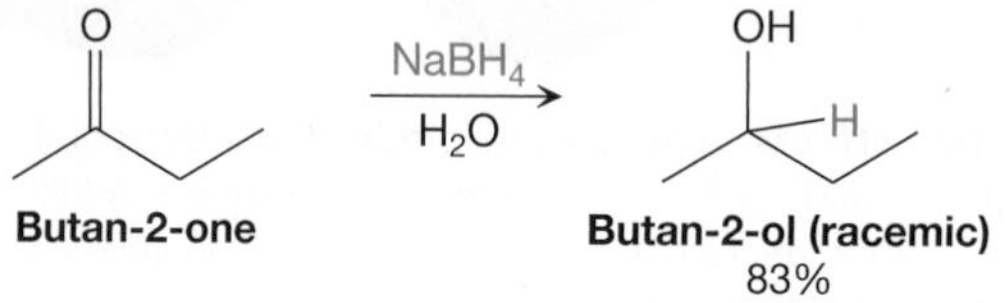
O
NaBH₄
H₂O
OH
H
Butan-2-one
Butan-2-ol (racemic)
83%

(18-3)

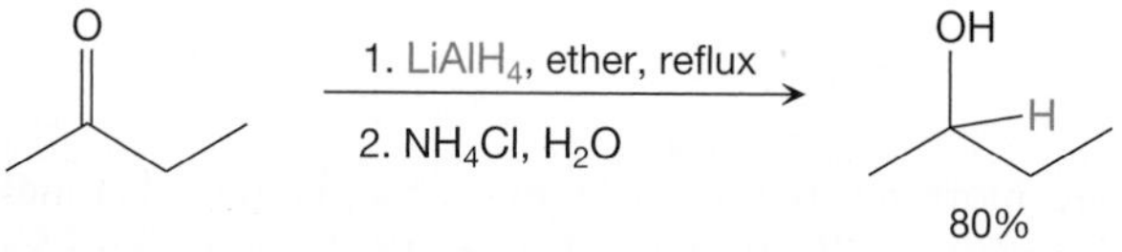
O
1. LiAlH₄, ether, reflux
2. NH₄Cl, H₂O
OH
H
80%

(18-4)

▸ LOOKING AHEAD

The reactions in Equations 18-3 through 18-6 are *reduction* reactions because the organic species overall gains a bond to H and loses a bond to O. Chapter 20 will discuss reduction reactions more broadly, along with the reverse reactions, known as *oxidation* reactions.

Similar reactions, shown in Equations 18-5 and 18-6, convert benzaldehyde to phenylmethanol (see Looking Ahead box):

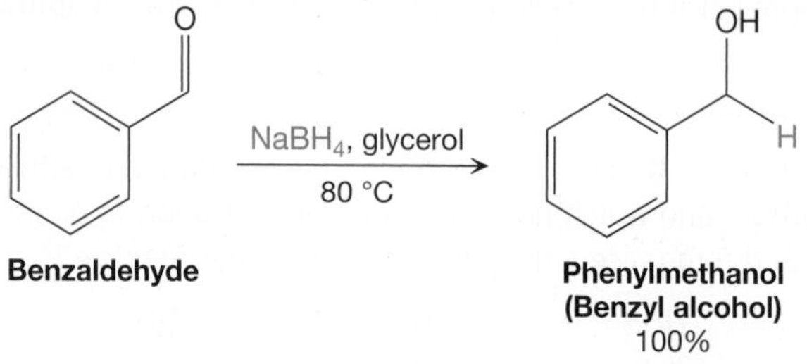
O
NaBH₄, glycerol
80 °C
OH
H
Benzaldehyde
Phenylmethanol
(Benzyl alcohol)
100%

(18-5)

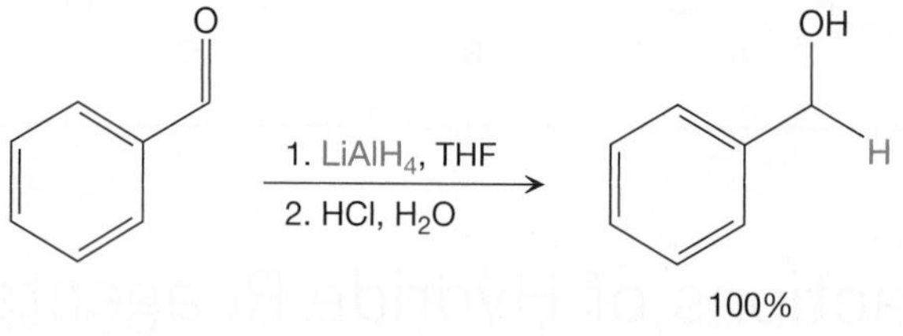
O
1. LiAlH₄, THF
2. HCl, H₂O
OH
H
100%

(18-6)

In general, $NaBH_4$ or $LiAlH_4$ can be used to convert:

- a ketone to a 2° alcohol.
- an aldehyde to a 1° alcohol.

The simplified mechanism for Equation 18-3, in which $NaBH_4$ serves as the hydride source, is shown in Equation 18-7:

Simplified mechanism for the reaction of $NaBH_4$ with a ketone (Eq. 18-3)

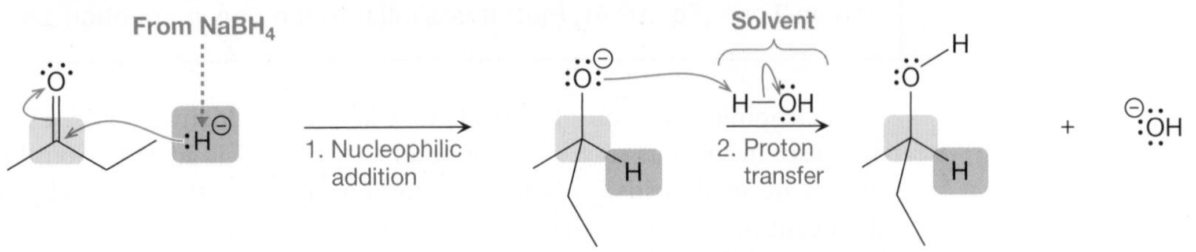
From $NaBH_4$
1. Nucleophilic addition
Solvent
2. Proton transfer

(18-7)

In Step 1, H^- undergoes nucleophilic addition to the carbonyl group to produce the strongly basic alkoxide anion. In Step 2, water (the solvent that is already present) protonates the alkoxide anion to produce the final alcohol product.

The simplified mechanism for Equation 18-6, in which $LiAlH_4$ serves as the hydride source, is shown in Equation 18-8. It is essentially identical to Equation 18-7, in which $NaBH_4$ is used. The difference is that the reaction with $LiAlH_4$ occurs in ether, which is not acidic, so the proton transfer in Step 2 does not occur until the acid is added separately.

Simplified mechanism for the reaction of $LiAlH_4$ with an aldehyde (Eq. 18-6)

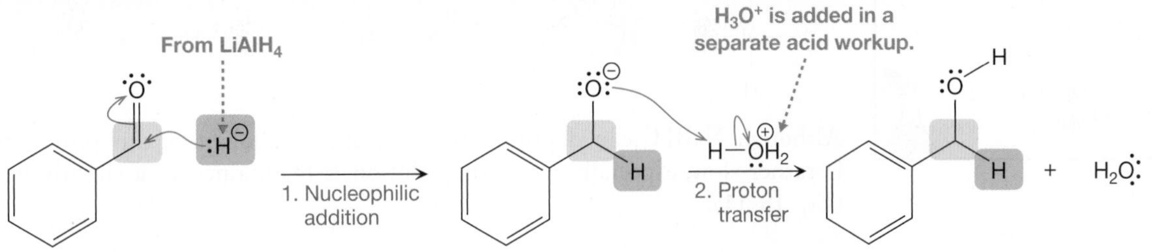
From $LiAlH_4$
1. Nucleophilic addition
H_3O^+ is added in a separate acid workup.
2. Proton transfer

(18-8)

YOUR TURN 18.5

Draw the simplified mechanisms for the reactions involving the ketone in Equation 18-4 and the aldehyde in Equation 18-5. *Hint*: Use Equations 18-7 and 18-8 as your guide.

Because H^- cannot exist on its own, a more complete, detailed mechanism must show the nucleophilic attack as a *hydride transfer*. That is, the H atom's bond to either B or Al must be broken at the same time the C—H bond is formed. This is illustrated in Equation 18-9 for the reaction of $NaBH_4$ with butan-2-one (Eq. 18-3):

Detailed mechanism for the hydride transfer from BH_4^- to a ketone (Eq. 18-3)

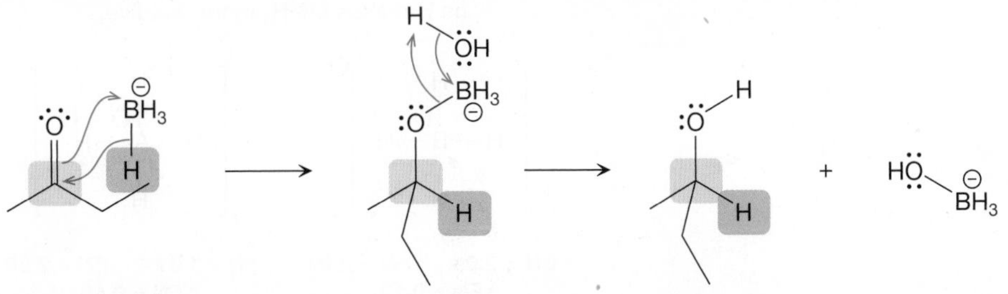

(18-9)

The more complete, detailed mechanism for the $LiAlH_4$ reaction with butan-2-one is very similar (see Your Turn 18.6). In the interest of simplicity, however, we will generally work with the simplified mechanisms depicted in Equations 18-7 and 18-8.

YOUR TURN 18.6

Draw the complete, detailed mechanism for the reaction of $LiAlH_4$ with butan-2-one (Eq. 18-4). *Hint*: It is similar to the one in Equation 18-9.

Nucleophilic addition of $NaBH_4$ to a ketone or aldehyde (Eqs. 18-3 and 18-5) takes place in solvents such as water or an alcohol. This is advantageous because these solvents are weak acids, so both the addition of H^- to the carbonyl group and the subsequent protonation can occur in the same synthetic step.

Nucleophilic addition involving $LiAlH_4$, on the other hand, cannot take place in water or alcohol because $LiAlH_4$ is too reactive:

$LiAlH_4$ is much more reactive than $NaBH_4$.

GREEN CHEMISTRY
Although a ketone or aldehyde can be converted to an alcohol by using either $NaBH_4$ or $LiAlH_4$, the greener choice is $NaBH_4$. $NaBH_4$ is greener because there is essentially no risk of explosion and its solvent (water or alcohol) is less toxic than the ether solvent typically required for $LiAlH_4$.

The hydride from $LiAlH_4$ deprotonates the weakly acidic proton from water and alcohols very quickly (Eq. 18-10), producing hydrogen gas. The reaction is so exothermic that the hydrogen can ignite, causing an explosion!

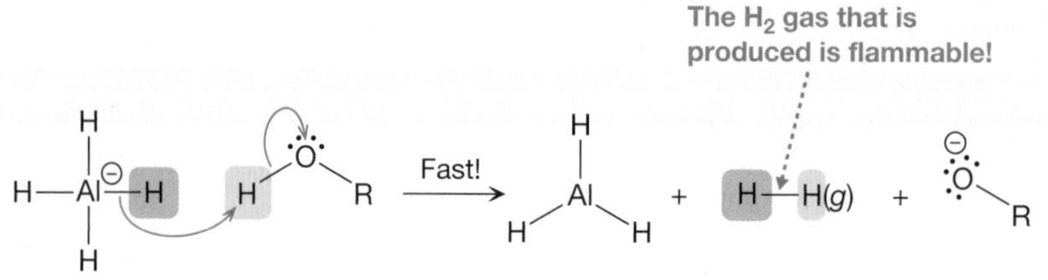

The H₂ gas that is produced is flammable!
Fast!
H(g)

(18-10)

Although $NaBH_4$ can deprotonate water and alcohols, too, this proton transfer is rather slow, especially when the solution is maintained at a slightly basic pH (Eq. 18-11):

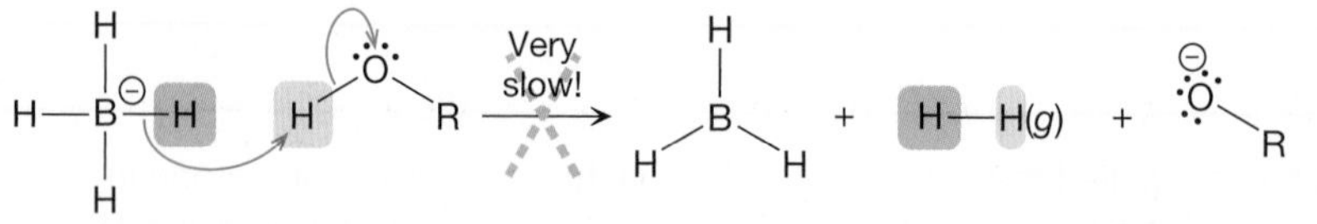

Very slow!
H(g)

(18-11)

$LiAlH_4$ is more reactive than $NaBH_4$ because, as shown in **Figure 18-6**, the electronegativity (EN) of aluminum (1.61) is substantially lower than that of boron (2.04), and both are lower than hydrogen (2.20). As a result, H has a partial negative charge in both the Al—H and the B—H bonds, but the electronegativity *difference* (ΔEN) is greater in the case of Al, giving H a higher concentration of negative charge in $LiAlH_4$ than in $NaBH_4$. As we learned in Chapter 6, a higher concentration of charge like this in $LiAlH_4$ makes it less stable and thus more reactive.

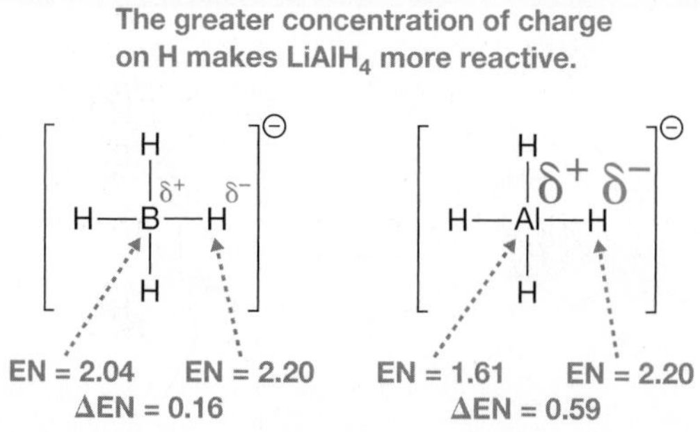

The greater concentration of charge on H makes LiAlH₄ more reactive.
EN = 2.04
EN = 2.20
ΔEN = 0.16
EN = 1.61
EN = 2.20
ΔEN = 0.59

FIGURE 18-6 Relative reactivities of $NaBH_4$ and $LiAlH_4$ The Al—H bond is more polar than the B—H bond, so the H atoms in $LiAlH_4$ bear a larger concentration of negative charge, making $LiAlH_4$ a more reactive source of H^-.

SOLVED PROBLEM **18.2**

How to draw the mechanism and products for a hydride addition reaction

Break It Down **Predict the major organic product of the reaction shown here.**

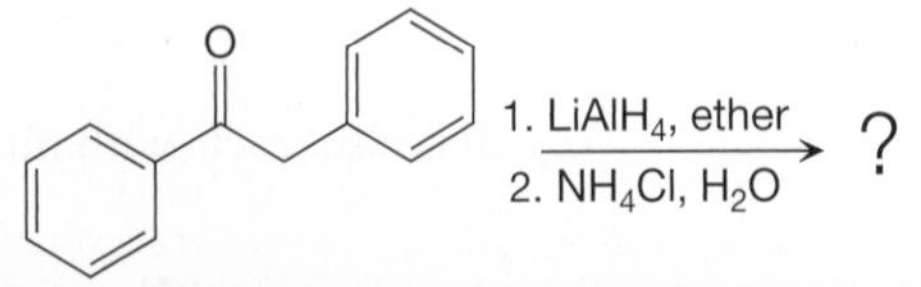
O
1. $LiAlH_4$, ether
2. NH_4Cl, H_2O
?

Think	Solve
How can $LiAlH_4$ be simplified for drawing the mechanism? How will it react with the ketone?	$LiAlH_4$ can be simplified to just the hydride anion, H^-, which will behave as a nucleophile when it reacts with the ketone. As shown in Step 1 below, H^- will add to the C atom of the carbonyl group.
How does NH_4Cl dissolve in solution? What species will react with the product from the first step?	NH_4Cl is ionic and will dissolve as NH_4^+ and Cl^- in solution. The product of Step 1 is a strongly basic alkoxide anion, and NH_4^+ is weakly acidic, so NH_4^+ will protonate the alkoxide anion in Step 2 below.
Why must the reaction with $LiAlH_4$ be complete before NH_4Cl is added?	$LiAlH_4$ is very reactive as a base. Therefore, if NH_4Cl is added along with $LiAlH_4$, then $LiAlH_4$ will react with NH_4^+ instead of the ketone.

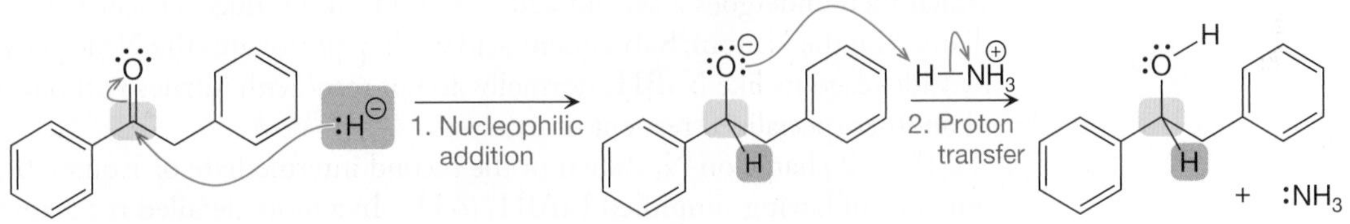
:H
1. Nucleophilic addition
H
H—NH3
2. Proton transfer
H
H
+ :NH3

Try It Predict the major organic product in each of these reactions.

(a)

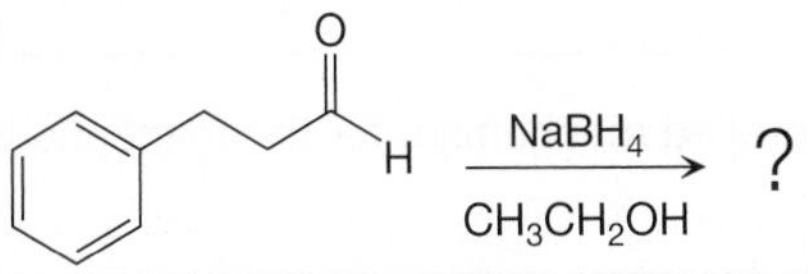
O
H
NaBH4
CH3CH2OH
?

(b)

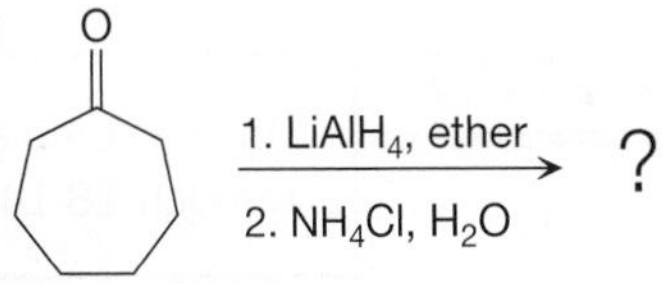
O
1. LiAlH4, ether
2. NH4Cl, H2O
?

18.3b Addition of Hydride to Imines and Nitriles: Synthesis of Amines and Imines

Compound classes with polar π bonds other than the carbonyl group react with hydride reagents in much the same way. An imine, for example, reacts with $NaBH_4$ or $LiAlH_4$ to form an amine, as shown in Equations 18-12 and 18-13, respectively. As explained earlier, methanol, a weakly acidic solvent, is suitable for the reaction with $NaBH_4$, but the reaction with $LiAlH_4$ must take place in a solvent that has no acidic protons, such as ether.

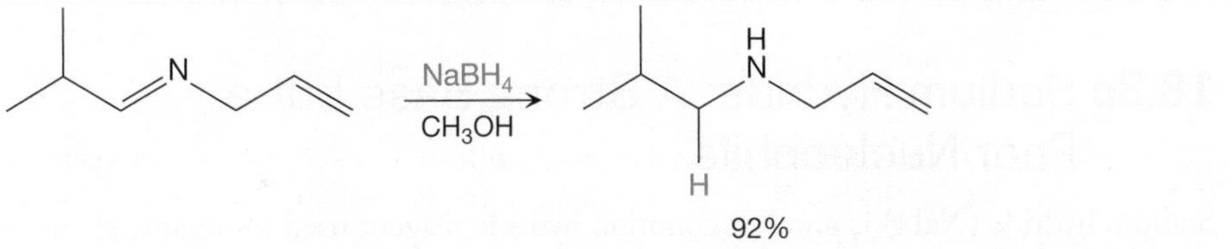
N
NaBH4
CH3OH
H
N
H
92%

(18-12)

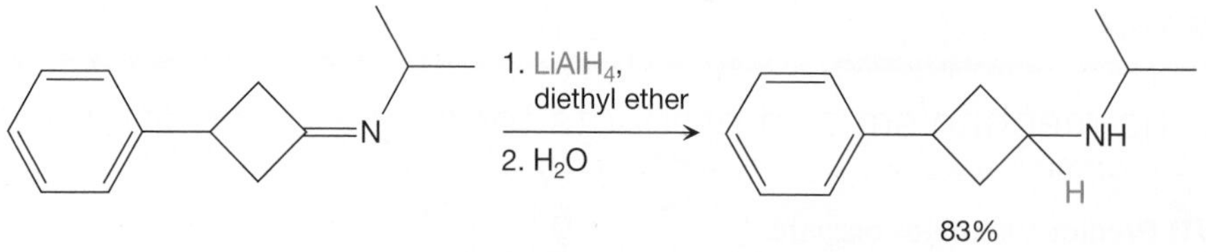

1. $LiAlH_4$,
diethyl ether
2. H_2O
N
NH
H
83%

(18-13)

$LiAlH_4$ also reacts with nitriles to primary amines, as shown in Equation 18-14:

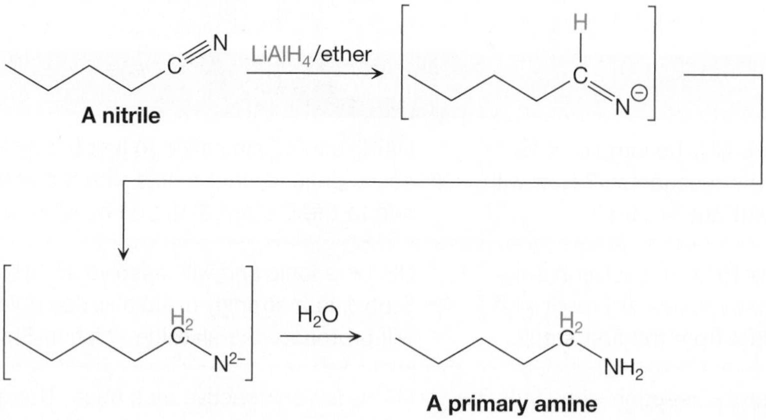

N
C
$LiAlH_4$/ether
A nitrile
H
C
N
H_2
C
N^{2-}
H_2O
H_2
C
NH_2
A primary amine

(18-14)

The first addition of H^- yields a negatively charged intermediate with a C=N bond, which then undergoes a second addition of H^- to produce a species that resembles a dianion on the N atom. Subsequent acid workup protonates the N atom twice. Weaker hydride reagents like $NaBH_4$ normally do not react with nitriles without the presence of another specialized reagent or catalyst.

The −2 charge on N, shown in the second intermediate of Equation 18-14, is an outcome of having simplified $LiAlH_4$ to H^-. In a more detailed mechanism in which $LiAlH_4$ is not simplified (see Your Turn 18.7), each H^- addition is more accurately treated as a hydride transfer from Al to C, similar to what was shown in Equation 18-9. Simultaneously, N forms a bond to Al, which provides significant stabilization.

YOUR TURN **18.7**

Draw a complete, detailed mechanism for the reactions in Equations 18-12 through 18-14.

YOUR TURN **18.8**

Predict the major organic product and draw the mechanism for each of the following reactions.

(a)

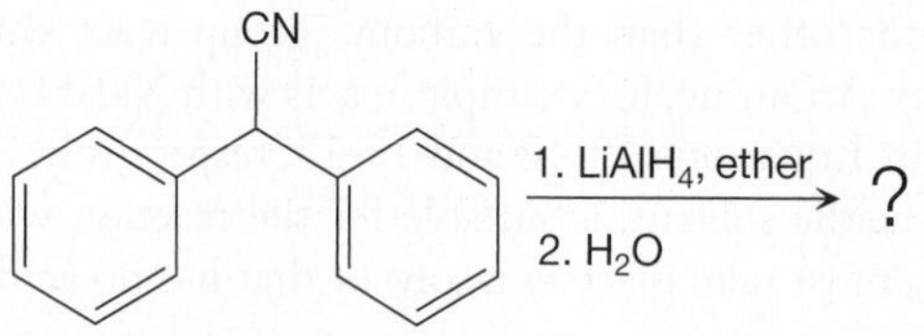

CN
1. $LiAlH_4$, ether
2. H_2O
?

(b)

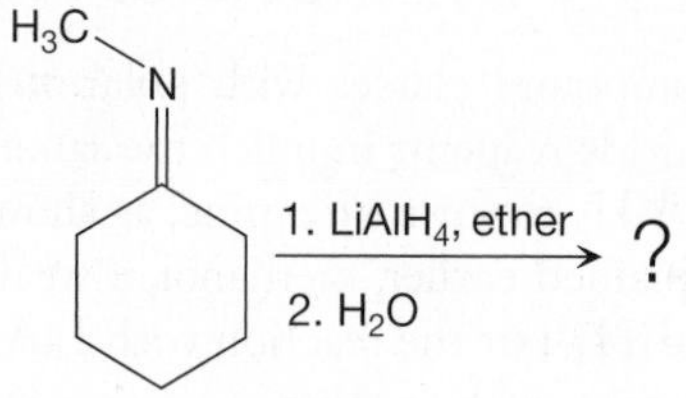

H_3C
N
1. $LiAlH_4$, ether
2. H_2O
?

18.3c Sodium Hydride: A Strong Base but a Poor Nucleophile

Sodium hydride (NaH) is another common hydride reagent used in organic chemistry. Sodium hydride is a powerful base, so it is often a good choice for reactions that require the deprotonation of a weakly acidic proton, such as the Williamson ether synthesis (Section 10.4) or the α alkylation of a ketone or aldehyde (Section 11. 3; see Recall box).

Even though NaH is a source of hydride, it behaves differently from $NaBH_4$ and $LiAlH_4$:

> Sodium hydride, NaH, is a very strong base but a poor nucleophile.

Whereas $NaBH_4$ and $LiAlH_4$ favor the addition of H^- to the carbonyl group of a ketone or aldehyde, NaH will instead favor deprotonation to yield the enolate anion *quantitatively* (i.e., in 100% yield), as shown in Equation 18-15a. Addition to the carbonyl group (Eq. 18-15b) does not occur:

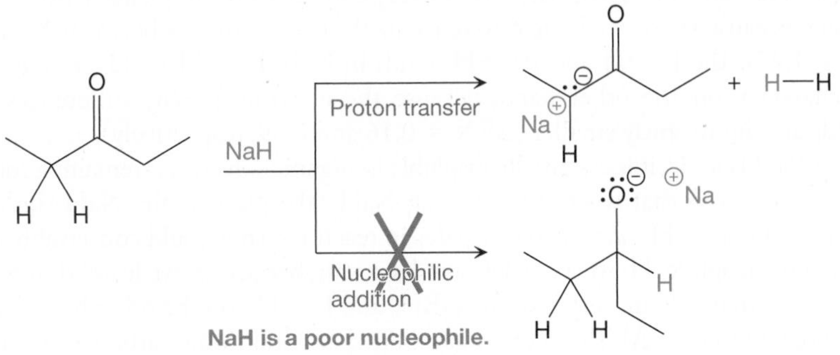

Proton transfer
NaH
Nucleophilic addition
NaH is a poor nucleophile.
+ H—H

(18-15a)

(18-15b)

◂ RECALL

In a Williamson ether synthesis (Section 10.4), NaH deprotonates an alcohol to produce an alkoxide anion. In α alkylation (Section 11.3), NaH deprotonates an α carbon to produce an enolate anion. In both cases, the strong nucleophile that is produced subsequently undergoes S_N2 with an alkyl halide.

SOLVED PROBLEM **18.3**

How to determine the product of a reaction that incorporates NaH

Break It Down Predict the major product of the reaction shown here.

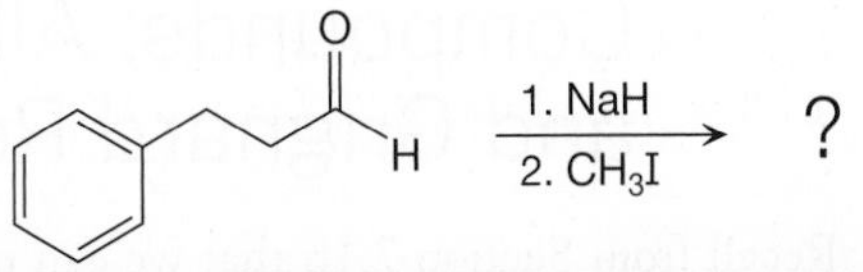

1. NaH
2. CH_3I
?

Think	Solve
Will the hydride anion from NaH act as a base or as a nucleophile?	NaH is a strong base but a poor nucleophile, so it will deprotonate the most acidic site.
Which atom will H^- attack?	The only site that is acidic is the α carbon of the carbonyl group, where the pK_a is about 19. Recall from Section 10.6 that an aldehyde hydrogen attached directly to the carbonyl group is not acidic at all. Deprotonation is shown in Step 1 below.
How will the resulting species behave in the presence of CH_3I?	The resulting species, an enolate anion, is strongly nucleophilic at the α carbon, so it will attack CH_3I in an S_N2 step, as shown below.

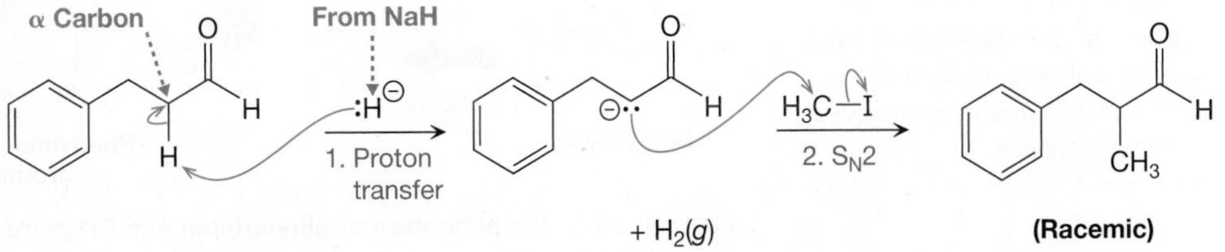

α Carbon
From NaH
1. Proton transfer
+ $H_2(g)$
2. S_N2
(Racemic)

(continued)

Try It Predict the major organic product in each of the following reactions.

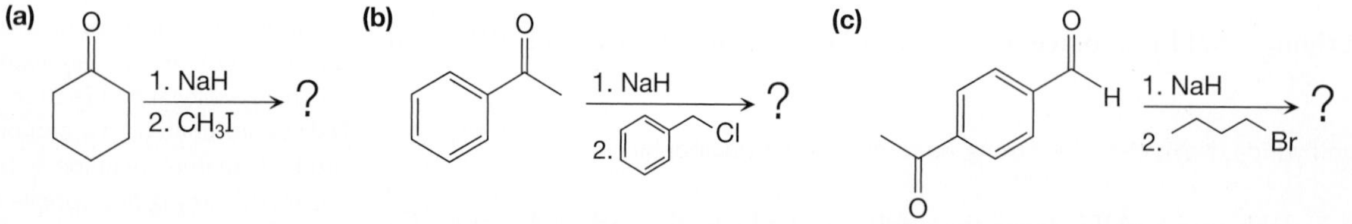
(a)
O
1. NaH
2. CH_3I
?
(b)
O
1. NaH
2.
Cl
?
(c)
O
H
1. NaH
2.
Br
?
O

NaH behaves differently from $NaBH_4$ or $LiAlH_4$ because NaH is an *ionic* hydride, consisting of Na^+ and H^- ions, whereas $NaBH_4$ and $LiAlH_4$ are *covalent* hydrides. NaH is ionic because there is a large difference in electronegativities between Na and H ($\Delta EN = 1.27$). The B—H and Al—H bonds in $NaBH_4$ and $LiAlH_4$ have more covalent character, on the other hand, because the electronegativity differences in those bonds are significantly smaller ($\Delta EN = 0.16$ and 0.59, respectively).

Because NaH is ionic, it is essentially insoluble in organic solvents; it remains a solid. It is therefore believed that reactions involving NaH take place at the NaH surface. Under these conditions, H^- *directly* participates in reactions, so it could conceivably act as a base or a nucleophile. However, it acts as a base only, because as we learned in Section 8.6a, proton transfers are very fast. In $NaBH_4$ and $LiAlH_4$, on the other hand, H is covalently bonded to B or Al. The B or Al atom forms a bond to the carbonyl O at the same time H^- is transferred to the carbonyl C (review Eq. 18-9, p. 885), so the B or Al atom effectively *guides* H^- toward the carbonyl C to act as a nucleophile.

SECTION 18.4 OBJECTIVES

You will be able to:

1. Draw the mechanism and the major product for the reaction of an alkyllithium reagent or a Grignard reagent with ketones, aldehydes, imines, and nitriles.
2. Explain why protic solvents like water and alcohols should be avoided for reactions involving these organometallic reagents.

18.4 Reactions of Organometallic Compounds: Alkyllithium Reagents and Grignard Reagents

Recall from Section 7.1b that we can usually treat organometallic compounds such as Grignard reagents (RMgX) and alkyllithium reagents (RLi) as alkyl anions, $:R^-$ (**Figure 18-7**; see Looking Ahead box).

The poorly stabilized charge on C enables alkyllithium and Grignard reagents to behave both as *strong bases* and as *strong nucleophiles*. For example, both alkyllithium reagents and Grignard reagents react rapidly with water in substantially exothermic proton transfer reactions (Eqs. 18-16 and 18-17) to produce an alkane and HO^-. The

▸ LOOKING AHEAD

Section 20.6 will show how alkyllithium reagents and Grignard reagents are synthesized by treating an alkyl halide with solid lithium or magnesium, respectively. Section 21.1a will describe how these conversions represent a charge reversal at the carbon, which is useful in designing multistep syntheses.

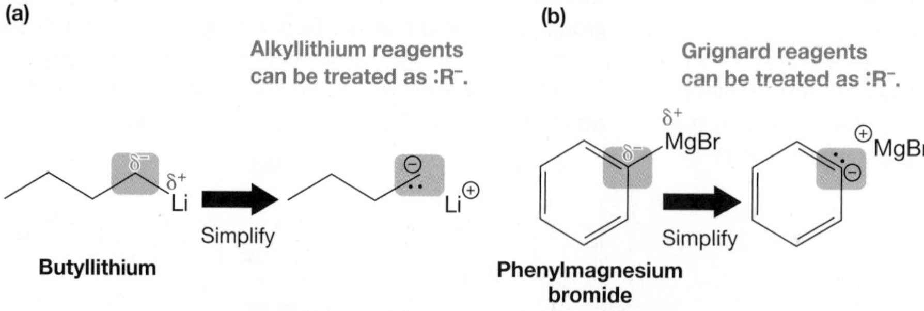
(a)
Alkyllithium reagents can be treated as :R⁻.
δ−
δ+
Li
Simplify
Li
Butyllithium
(b)
Grignard reagents can be treated as :R⁻.
δ+
MgBr
δ−
MgBr
Simplify
Phenylmagnesium bromide

FIGURE 18-7 Simplification of alkyllithium and Grignard reagents (a) An alkyllithium reagent has a polar covalent C—Li bond, which can be simplified to $C:^-$ and Li^+. (b) A Grignard reagent has a polar C—MgBr bond, which can be treated as $C:^-$ and $(MgBr)^+$.

products are much more stable because the negative charge is transferred from a C atom to a more electronegative O atom:

Li
H_2O
H
+
$^{\ominus}OH$
+
$Li^{\oplus}$

(18-16)

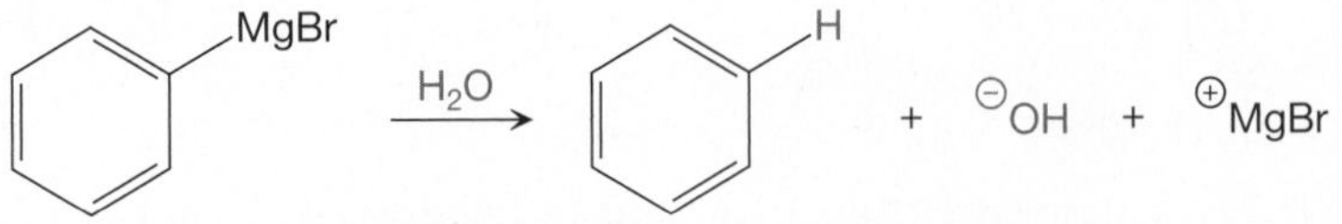

MgBr
H_2O
H
+
$^{\ominus}OH$
+
$^{\oplus}MgBr$

(18-17)

Although these organometallic reagents react as if they are R^-, they are not truly ionic. When they are dissolved in solution, free R^- does not exist. Instead, think of them as *R^- donors*, in much the same way that we view $LiAlH_4$ and $NaBH_4$ as H^- donors. The reaction that takes place is an R^- transfer from the metal atom to the proton of the acid, as shown for butyllithium in Equation 18-18:

Mechanism for an alkyllithium reagent acting as a base (Eq. 18-16)

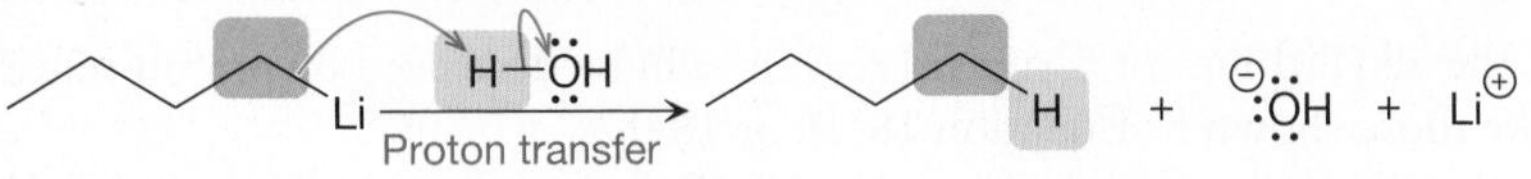

Li
H—ÖH
Proton transfer
H
+
:ÖH
+
$Li^{\oplus}$

(18-18)

Add the curved arrows to show an R^- transfer mechanism for the Grignard reagent in Equation 18-17, similar to the mechanism shown in Equation 18-18 for an alkyllithium reagent.

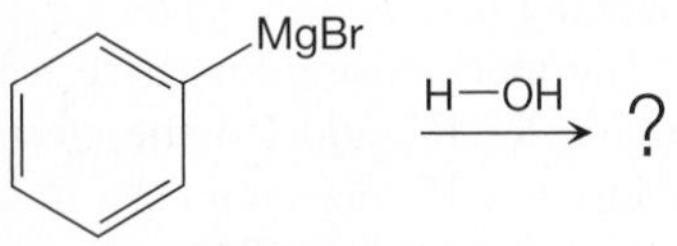

MgBr
H—OH
?

Even though alkyllithium and Grignard reagents are strong bases, they do not deprotonate at the α carbon of a polar π bond. Instead:

When R—Li or R—MgX reacts with a compound containing a polar π bond, R^- acts as a nucleophile.

R^- acts as a nucleophile in these reactions because the electron-rich atom of the polar π bond (O or N) coordinates with the electron-poor metal atom during the R^- transfer, similar to what we saw with $NaBH_4$ and $LiAlH_4$. Thus, R^- is effectively guided to the electron-poor C of the polar π bond to act as a nucleophile. This nucleophilic behavior of R^- is exemplified with a ketone in Equation 18-19 and with a nitrile in Equation 18-20. When a Grignard reagent adds in as a nucleophile, it is called a **Grignard reaction**.

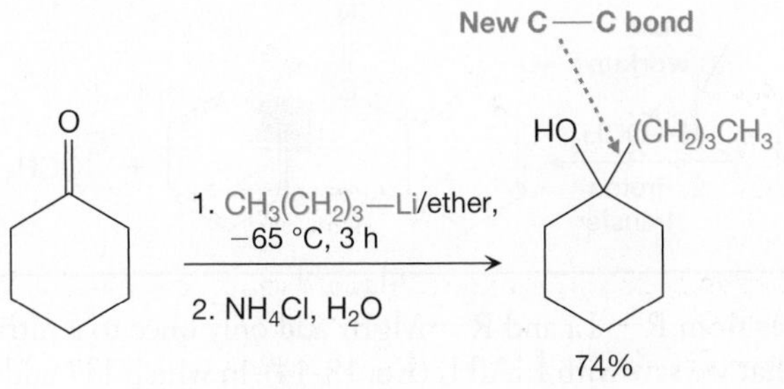

New C—C bond
O
HO
$(CH_2)_3CH_3$
1. $CH_3(CH_2)_3$—Li/ether, −65 °C, 3 h
2. NH_4Cl, H_2O
74%

(18-19)

CONNECTIONS 18.2

The production of polyisoprene rubber

Butyllithium (Eq. 18.16) is a very powerful base and nucleophile. One of its uses industrially is to initiate polymerization in the production of some types of rubber, such as polyisoprene, which is the type of rubber used to make the gloves shown. Butyllithium and other alkyllithium reagents are pyrophoric, meaning they ignite on contact with air, so they are typically stored in a hydrocarbon solvent.

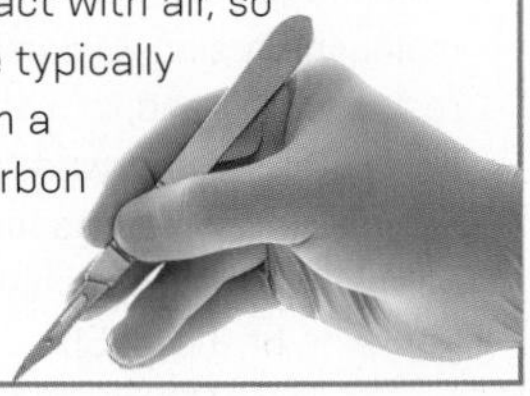

YOUR TURN **18.9**

GREEN CHEMISTRY Grignard reactions traditionally require substantial amounts of ether solvents, which are not environmentally friendly. Green alternatives include reactions that take place in water, such as this one, which facilitates the addition of acetylenic nucleophiles to benzaldehyde:

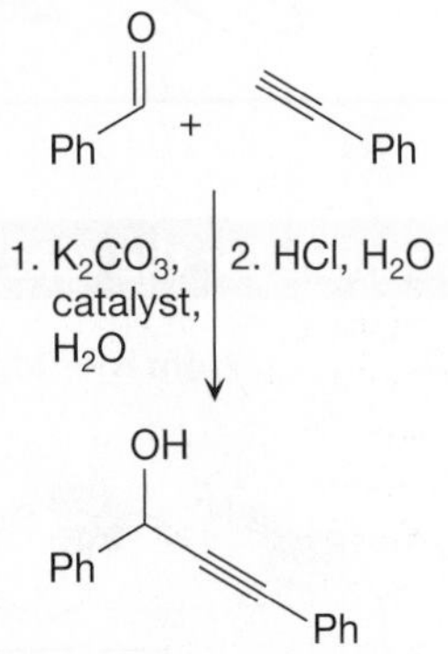

O
Ph
+
Ph
1. K_2CO_3, catalyst, H_2O
2. HCl, H_2O
OH
Ph
Ph

Here, the catalyst is a three-component system of $RuCl_3$, $In(OAc)_3$, and morpholine.

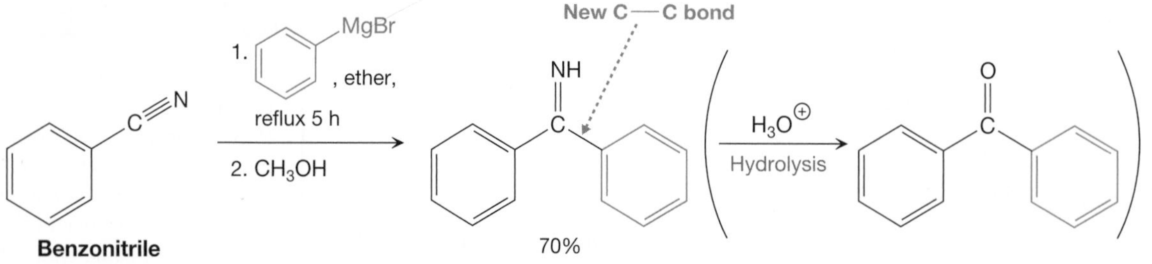

Benzonitrile
1. MgBr, ether, reflux 5 h
2. CH_3OH
New C—C bond
NH
70%
$H_3O^{\oplus}$
Hydrolysis
O

(18-20)

CONNECTIONS 18.3

Kitsch in the kitchen

Benzonitrile (Eq. 18-20) is a precursor to benzoguanamine, which is used to manufacture melamine resins. Melamine resins were used to make the first plastic dinnerware and laminate countertops (such as Formica) found in fashionable kitchens of the 1950s.

A new C—C bond is formed in both of these reactions! As we learned in Chapter 11, reactions that alter the carbon framework are distinct from functional group transformations and are, therefore, special.

In both Equations 18-19 and 18-20, the nucleophilic addition takes place in ether, followed by workup with a proton source:

> In the step in which R—Li or R—MgX acts as an R^- nucleophile, it is vitally important to keep the reaction free of any acidic compounds, such as water or alcohols.

Otherwise, the alkyllithium or Grignard reagent will be destroyed by proton transfer reactions like those shown in Equation 18-16 or 18-17.

Notice also that the workup in Equation 18-20 is carried out with methanol. If it is carried out with H_3O^+ instead, then the imine that is produced from nucleophilic addition is hydrolyzed to the analogous carbonyl (C═O) compound (a ketone in this case) as shown in the parentheses. This reaction will be discussed in greater detail in Chapter 19.

The mechanisms for these reactions are shown in Equations 18-21 and 18-22. Specifically, R^- adds to the electron-poor atom of the polar π bond. Once again, because free R^- does not exist in solution, each mechanism would be more accurately shown as a transfer of R^-:

Mechanism for the reaction of an alkyllithium reagent with a ketone (Eq. 18-19)

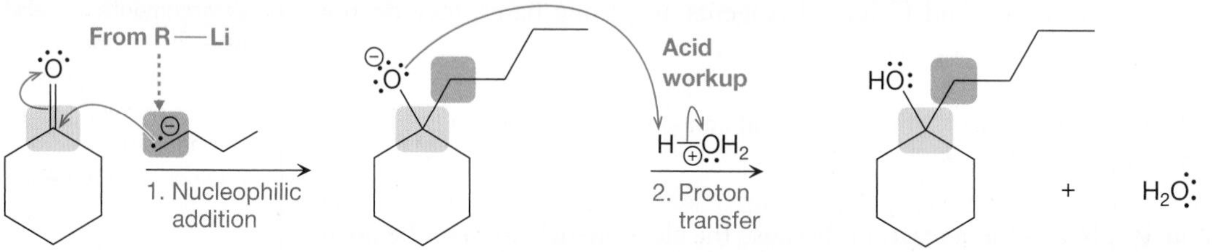

From R—Li
1. Nucleophilic addition
Acid workup
$H—OH_2$
2. Proton transfer
HO:
+
H_2O:

(18-21)

Mechanism for the reaction of a Grignard reagent with a nitrile (Eq. 18-20)

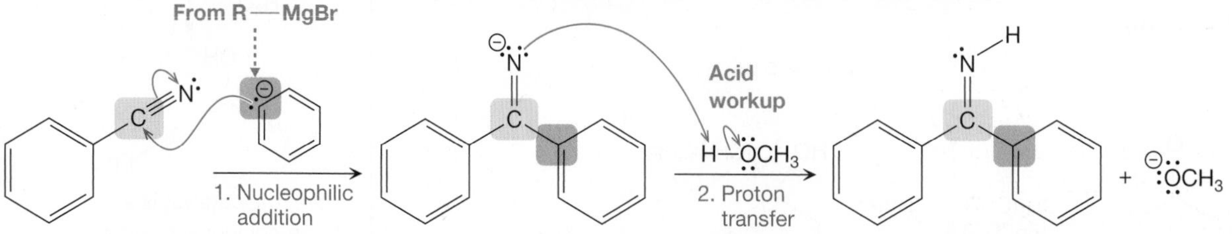

From R—MgBr
1. Nucleophilic addition
Acid workup
$H—OCH_3$
2. Proton transfer
H
+
$:OCH_3$

(18-22)

The R^- nucleophiles from R—Li and R—MgBr add only once to a nitrile carbon. This is in contrast to what we saw with $LiAlH_4$ (Eq. 18-14), in which H^- adds twice. In other words, these R^- nucleophiles are not strong enough to generate the effective −2 formal charge on nitrogen that is a necessary outcome of a second nucleophilic addition.

SOLVED PROBLEM **18.4**

How to draw the mechanism and product for a Grignard reaction

Break It Down Predict the major product of the reaction shown here.

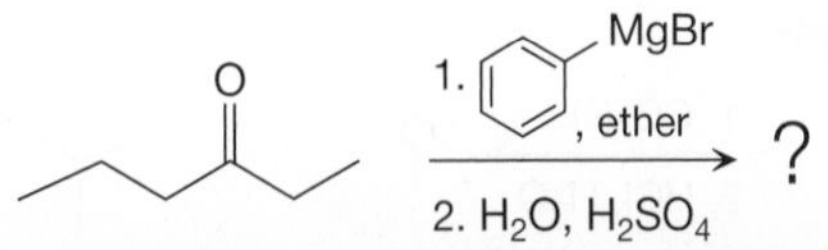
O
MgBr
1.
, ether
2. H2O, H2SO4
?

Think	Solve
How can we simplify the Grignard reagent to an R$^-$ nucleophile?	The C_6H_5MgBr Grignard reagent can be treated simply as $C_6H_5^-$.
Which atom will the R$^-$ nucleophile attack?	$C_6H_5^-$ will undergo nucleophilic addition at the carbonyl carbon, as shown in the first step below.
What is the role of the acid?	As shown in the second step below, the aqueous acid (H_3O^+) is added in an acid workup to protonate the strongly basic O$^-$ generated in the first step.

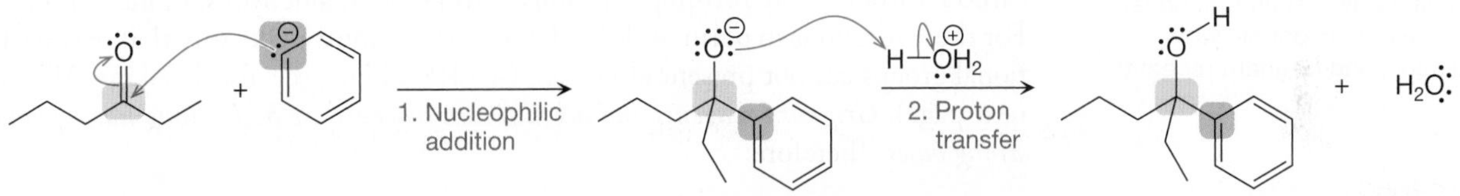
1. Nucleophilic addition
2. Proton transfer
H
+
H2O

Try It Predict the major organic product in each of the following reactions.

(a)

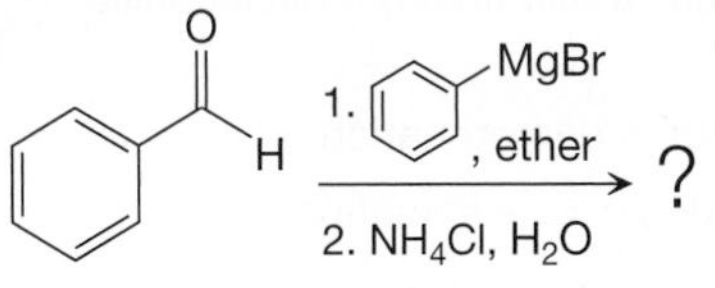
O
H
MgBr
1.
, ether
2. NH4Cl, H2O
?

(b)

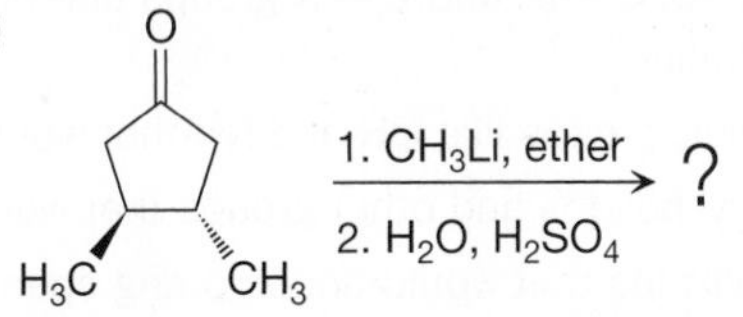
O
H3C
CH3
1. CH3Li, ether
2. H2O, H2SO4
?

(c)

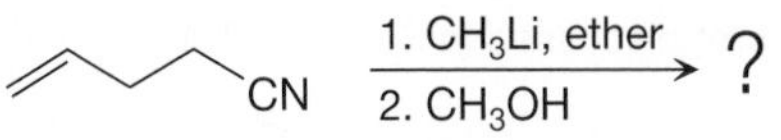
CN
1. CH3Li, ether
2. CH3OH
?

Although CO_2 is a nonpolar compound overall, each C=O bond is highly polar, and the central carbon atom is quite electron-poor and susceptible to nucleophilic attack. Thus, Grignard reagents can add to CO_2 in what is called a **carboxylation** reaction (Eq. 18-23). As with any Grignard reaction, a new C—C bond is formed:

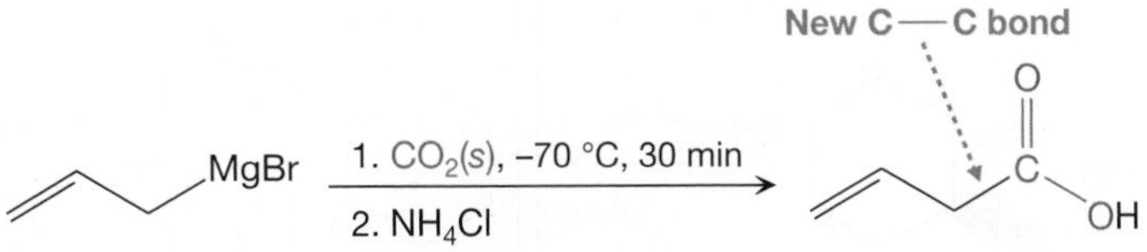
New C—C bond
MgBr
1. CO2(s), –70 °C, 30 min
2. NH4Cl
O
C
OH

(18-23)

The immediate product of carboxylation, a carboxylate anion, is subsequently protonated through an acid workup to yield a carboxylic acid. Because CO_2 is a gas at room temperature, carrying out this reaction requires either bubbling CO_2 through an ether solution of the Grignard reagent or pouring the ether solution of the Grignard reagent over dry ice (which is solid CO_2).

YOUR TURN **18.10**

Draw the complete, detailed mechanism for the reaction in Equation 18-23.

YOUR TURN **18.11**

Predict the major organic product in each of the following reactions.

(a)

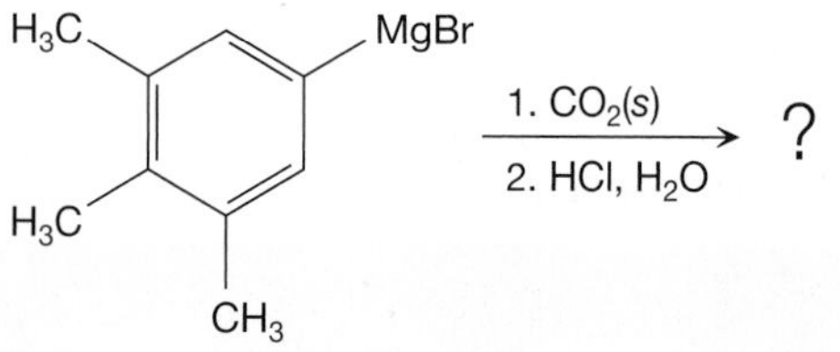

H3C
MgBr
H3C
CH3
1. CO2(s)
2. HCl, H2O
?

(b)

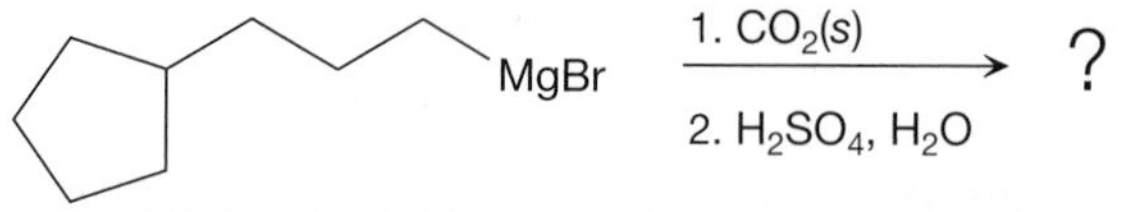

MgBr
1. CO2(s)
2. H2SO4, H2O
?

SECTION 18.5 OBJECTIVES

You will be able to:

1. Identify functional groups that are incompatible for a desired reaction involving an alkyllithium or Grignard reagent.
2. Explain why certain functional groups are incompatible with alkyllithium and Grignard reagents.

18.5 Compatibility of Functional Groups in Reactions Involving Alkyllithium and Grignard Reagents

In Section 18.4, we saw how Grignard reagents and alkyllithium reagents undergo carbon–carbon bond-forming reactions with ketones, aldehydes, imines, and nitriles. For these reactions to occur as desired, however, we must make sure that reactive functional groups are not present elsewhere (see Recall box; see also Looking Ahead box, next page). *Grignard reagents and alkyllithium reagents are both strong nucleophiles and strong bases.* Therefore:

◂ RECALL

The idea of a reactive functional group elsewhere in a molecule interfering with a desired reaction is an example of a *synthetic trap*, which we first discussed in Section 11.4.

To carry out a desired nucleophilic addition of R—Li or R—MgX at a particular C═O, C═N, or C≡N bond, avoid these *incompatible* groups:

- C═O, C═N, and C≡N groups elsewhere that would undergo nucleophilic addition
- Acidic groups like OH and NH that would undergo deprotonation
- Alkyl halides and other groups that would undergo E2 elimination
- Epoxides that would undergo ring opening

In each case in **Figure 18-8**, for example, the highlighted functional group is incompatible with the desired reaction. Notice that the incompatible functional group

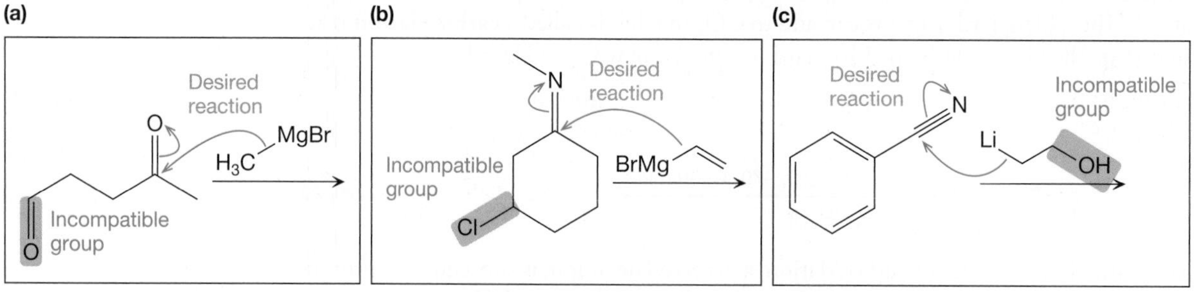

(a)
Desired reaction
MgBr
H3C
Incompatible group
(b)
Desired reaction
N
Incompatible group
BrMg
Cl
(c)
Desired reaction
N
Incompatible group
Li
OH

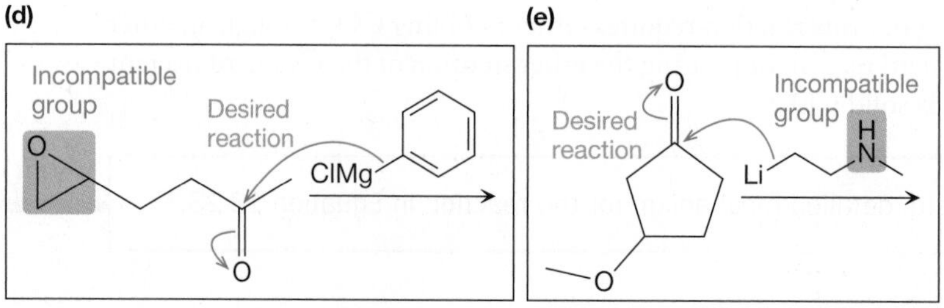

(d)
Incompatible group
Desired reaction
ClMg
O
(e)
Desired reaction
Incompatible group
H
N
Li
O

FIGURE 18-8 Functional groups that are incompatible with reactions involving R—MgX or R—Li The highlighted functional groups in (a)–(e) would interfere with the desired nucleophilic addition reactions.

could be in the species containing the polar π bond (Figure 18-8a, 18-8b, and 18-8d) or in the organometallic reagent (Figure 18-8c and 18-8e):

Functional groups that are not susceptible to deprotonation or to nucleophilic attack are generally compatible with the desired nucleophilic addition reactions. For example, a C═C group in an alkene (Fig. 18-8b), an aromatic ring (Fig. 18-8d), and an ether group (Fig. 18-8e) are all compatible with nucleophilic addition.

The compatibility of functional groups also applies to the solvent. This is why, as we learned in Section 18.4, ethers are the solvents of choice when carrying out reactions involving Grignard and alkyllithium reagents. Other common solvents, like alcohols and acetone, have incompatible functional groups.

▸ LOOKING AHEAD

When functional groups are incompatible with a desired chemical reaction, the desired reaction may be carried out using a *protecting group*. As Section 21.2b will explain, protecting groups work by temporarily converting the incompatible functional group into a different, unreactive functional group.

YOUR TURN 18.12

Determine which of these reactions will take place without interference from an incompatible functional group.

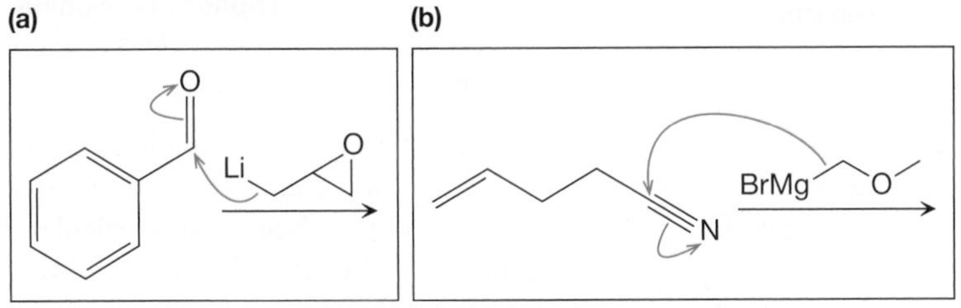

(a)
O
Li
O
(b)
BrMg
O
N

18.6 Wittig Reagents and the Wittig Reaction: Synthesis of Alkenes

SECTION 18.6 OBJECTIVES

You will be able to:

1. Describe a Wittig reagent and why it behaves as a strong carbon nucleophile.
2. Draw the mechanism and the products for reaction of a Wittig reagent with a ketone or aldehyde, and incorporate such a reaction in a synthesis.

Wittig reagents (pronounced VIT-tig), named after the German chemist Georg Wittig (1897–1987), are an important class of compounds used to synthesize alkenes. A Wittig reagent (**Figure 18-9**) is characterized by a C—P bond in which the C atom bears a −1 formal charge and the P atom bears a +1 formal charge.

A Wittig reagent is an *ylide* (pronounced IH-lid), which is characterized by adjacent charged atoms that each have a complete octet of electrons. More specifically, because the +1 charge is on P, a Wittig reagent is also called a **phosphonium ylide**. As indicated:

> The −1 charge on C makes a Wittig reagent strongly nucleophilic at the C atom.

Normally, a structure with adjacent positive and negative charges is the weaker contributor of two resonance structures; the stronger contributor is usually the one in which the atoms are connected by a double bond and each atom has a zero formal

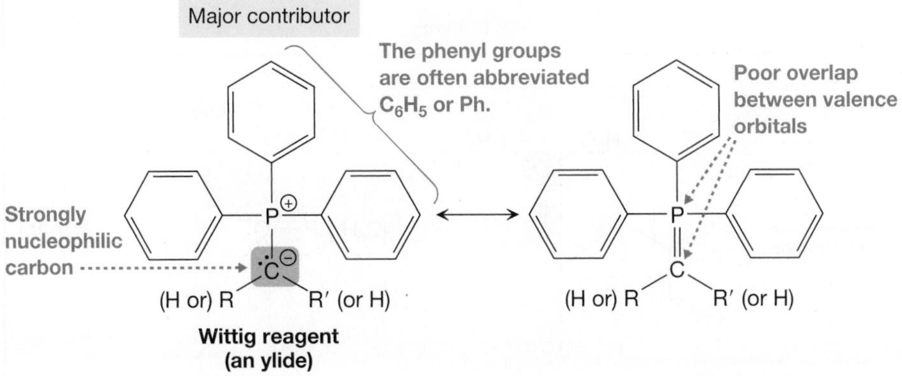

Major contributor
The phenyl groups are often abbreviated C6H5 or Ph.
Poor overlap between valence orbitals
Strongly nucleophilic carbon
P
C
(H or) R
R′ (or H)
Wittig reagent (an ylide)

FIGURE 18-9 Wittig reagents A Wittig reagent, also called a phosphonium ylide, is strongly nucleophilic at the C^- site. The structure on the left is the major resonance contributor because the C═P π bond in the structure on the right is weak, requiring orbitals from different shells.

charge. In the case of a Wittig reagent, however, the C=P resonance structure is the *weaker* contributor, because the π bond of a C=P bond would require the interaction of orbitals from different valence shells: the second shell on carbon and the third shell on phosphorus. This results in a weak interaction and, consequently, little stabilization relative to the atomic orbital energies, leaving the $^{+}$P—C:$^{-}$ structure as the more accurate representation.

The primary importance of Wittig reagents is in their reaction with ketones and aldehydes: so-called **Wittig reactions**. An example is shown in Equation 18-24:

Wittig reaction

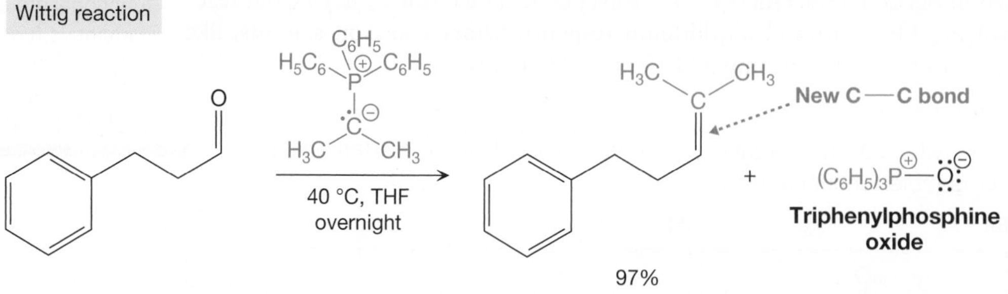

C_6H_5
H_5C_6
C_6H_5
P
C
H_3C
CH_3
O
40 °C, THF
overnight
H_3C
CH_3
C
New C—C bond
+
$(C_6H_5)_3P$—O
Triphenylphosphine
oxide
97%

(18-24)

As we can see from this example, a Wittig reaction results in the joining of two carbon-containing groups by a C=C bond: one group comes from the Wittig reagent and the second comes from the ketone or aldehyde. Notice, in particular, that the newly formed C=C bond is between the original carbonyl carbon and the original P—C carbon. In other words:

In a Wittig reaction, the C=O bond of a ketone or aldehyde is converted into a C=C bond.

The mechanism for the Wittig reaction in Equation 18-24 is shown in Equation 18-25. In Step 1, the strongly nucleophilic C atom of the Wittig reagent attacks the electrophilic carbonyl C atom, yielding a **betaine** (pronounced BEE-ta-een), a species in which a positive and a negative charge are separated by two uncharged atoms. Step 2 is a coordination step, in which a bond is formed between the negatively charged O atom and the positively charged P atom. This results in an **oxaphosphetane** that contains a four-membered ring; due to the strain, this ring falls apart into the alkene and triphenylphosphine oxide shown in Step 3.

Mechanism Drawing
Wittig Reaction

Mechanism for a Wittig reaction (Eq. 18-24)

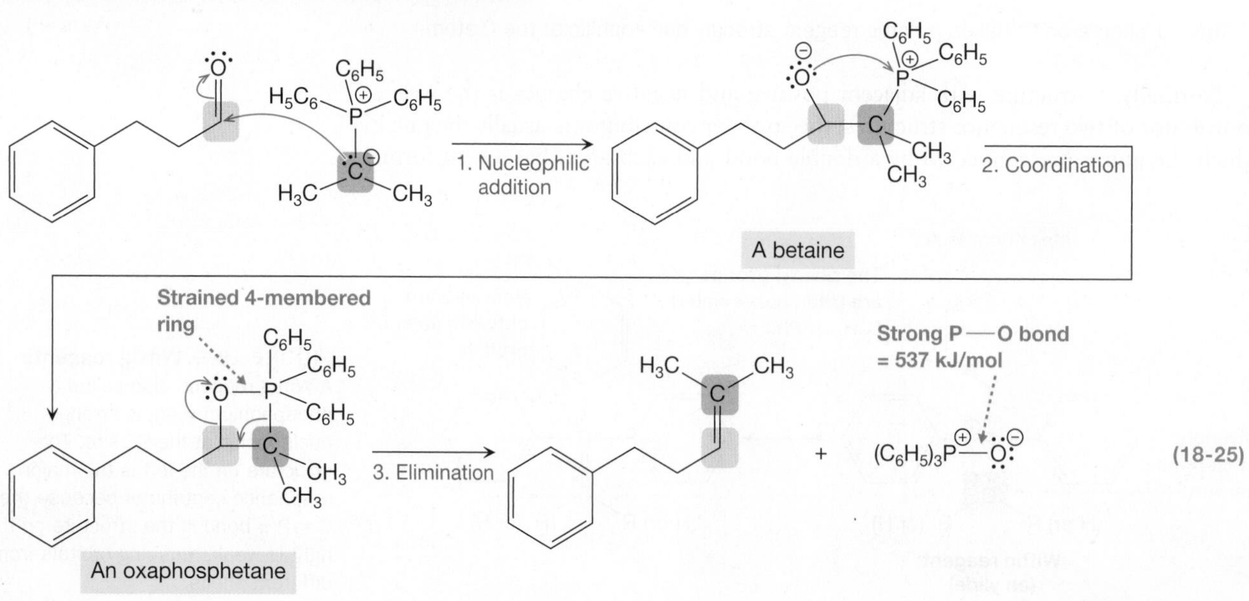

O
C_6H_5
H_5C_6
C_6H_5
P
C
H_3C
CH_3
1. Nucleophilic
addition
O
C_6H_5
C_6H_5
P
C_6H_5
C
CH_3
CH_3
2. Coordination
A betaine
Strained 4-membered
ring
C_6H_5
C_6H_5
O
P
C_6H_5
C
CH_3
CH_3
3. Elimination
An oxaphosphetane
H_3C
CH_3
C
Strong P—O bond
= 537 kJ/mol
+
$(C_6H_5)_3P$—O

(18-25)

The first two steps of the Wittig reaction are driven by the principle of *electron-rich to electron-poor*. The last step, however, is driven primarily by the formation of the very strong $^{+}P—O^{-}$ bond, whose bond energy is 537 kJ/mol, significantly stronger than typical single bonds (see Recall box).

For many Wittig reactions, the oxaphosphetane forms in one step rather than two. Which mechanism occurs depends on a number of variables, including the solvent and the structure of the Wittig reagent. (If the oxaphosphetane forms in a single step, the step would be called cycloaddition, the topic of Chapter 26.)

If *E*/*Z* isomerism exists about the C=C bond in the Wittig product, then a mixture of the two diastereomers is produced, as shown in Equation 18-26:

◀ RECALL

As we saw in Table 1-2 (p. 10), the average C—C bond energy is 339 kJ/mol and the average C—H bond energy is 418 kJ/mol.

A Wittig reaction produces a mixture of *Z* and *E* isomers.

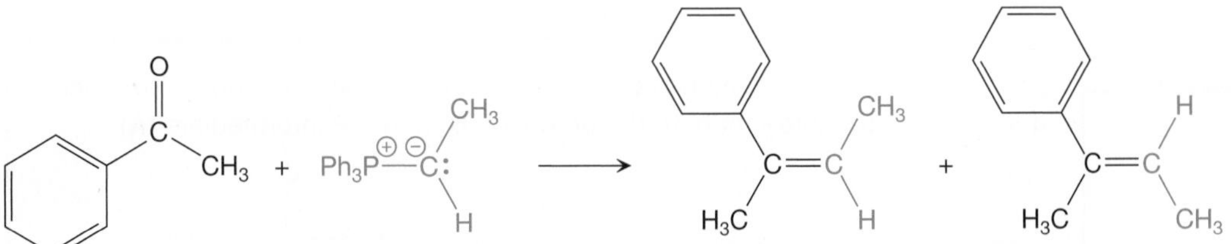

O
C
CH3
+
Ph3P
C:
CH3
H
CH3
C=C
H3C
H
+
H
C=C
H3C
CH3

(18-26)

(*Z*)-2-Phenylbut-2-ene **(*E*)-2-Phenylbut-2-ene**

This stereochemistry is explained by the first step of the mechanism, in which either face of the carbonyl-containing compound can be attacked. Often, one diastereomer is heavily favored over the other, but predicting which one is favored is beyond the scope of our discussion.

YOUR TURN 18.13

Draw the complete, detailed mechanism for the reaction shown here and predict the major organic product(s). Pay attention to stereochemistry.

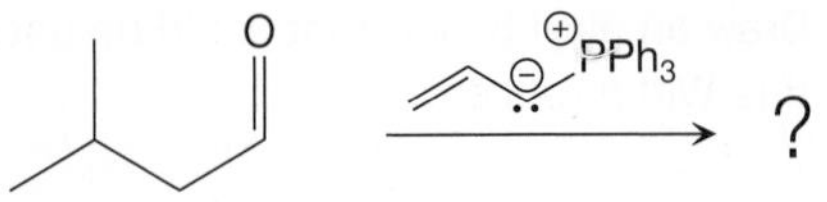

O
PPh3
?

18.7 Generating Wittig Reagents

SECTION 18.7 OBJECTIVES

You will be able to:

1. Show how to synthesize a Wittig reagent from an alkyl halide.
2. Explain the limitations of synthesizing a Wittig reagent.

One reason Wittig reactions are so useful is that Wittig reagents can be generated from common precursors: namely, alkyl halides. As shown in Equation 18-27, the Wittig reagent in Equation 18-24 can be synthesized from 2-bromopropane:

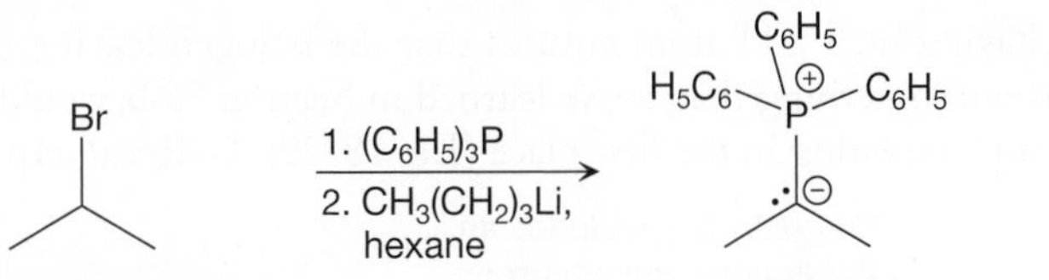

Br
1. (C6H5)3P
2. CH3(CH2)3Li,
hexane
C6H5
H5C6
C6H5
P

(18-27)

2-Bromopropane 56%

The alkyl halide is first treated with triphenylphosphine, $P(C_6H_5)_3$ or PPh_3, and the product of that reaction is treated with a very strong base such as butyllithium.

The mechanism for this reaction is shown in Equation 18-28:

Mechanism for the synthesis of a Wittig reagent (Eq. 18-27)

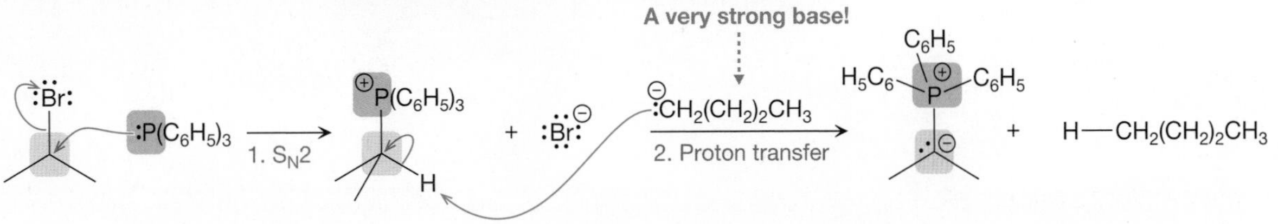

A very strong base!
:Br:
:P(C6H5)3
1. SN2
P(C6H5)3
H
+ :Br:
:CH2(CH2)2CH3
2. Proton transfer
C6H5
H5C6
C6H5
P
+
H—CH2(CH2)2CH3

(18-28)

Step 1 is an S_N2 reaction in which the nucleophile is $P(C_6H_5)_3$ and the leaving group is the halide anion. There is a positive charge on the P atom of the organic product of Step 1. Although $P(C_6H_5)_3$ is uncharged, it is a good nucleophile because the P atom in the product can accommodate the positive charge rather well, due to both its large size (being in the third row of the periodic table) and its modest electronegativity (EN = 2.19).

Step 2 of Equation 18-28 is deprotonation by the alkyllithium species. A *very* strong base such as an alkyllithium is necessary because deprotonation occurs at a carbon atom, and unlike deprotonation from the α carbon of a ketone or aldehyde, the negative charge that develops in the Wittig reagent is *not* resonance-delocalized. Therefore, many of the bases capable of deprotonating a ketone or aldehyde would not be strong enough in this case.

YOUR TURN 18.14

Draw the complete, detailed mechanism for the reaction sequence shown here and provide structures for both the products (**B**) and the intermediate (**A**).

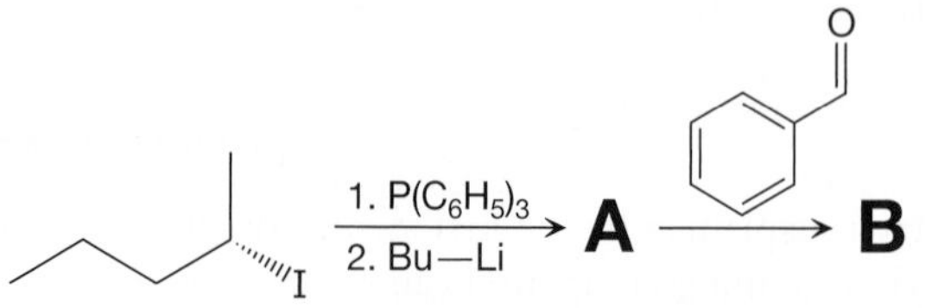

I
1. P(C6H5)3
2. Bu—Li
A
O
B

YOUR TURN 18.15

Draw an alkyl halide that could be used to synthesize this Wittig reagent.

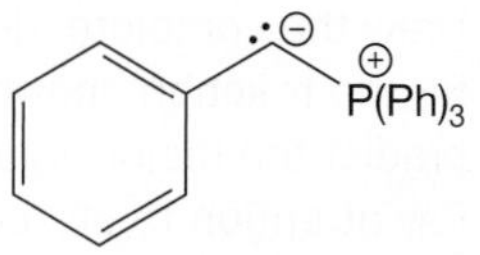

P(Ph)3

◂ RECALL

Steric hindrance of the nucleophile in an S_N2 reaction increases as the number of alkyl groups surrounding the C atom bonded to the leaving group increases. As steric hindrance increases, the S_N2 reaction rate decreases (Fig. 9-14, p. 468).

The C atom that is deprotonated in the proton transfer step in Equation 18-28 is the one that was originally bonded to the leaving group in the alkyl halide precursor. Therefore:

For an alkyl halide to be a suitable precursor for a Wittig reagent, the C atom bonded to the leaving group must possess at least one H.

Moreover, having such a H atom ensures that the halogen leaving group is not on a tertiary carbon: something that, as we learned in Section 9.6b, would prevent the S_N2 reaction from happening in the first place (Eq. 18-29; see Recall box):

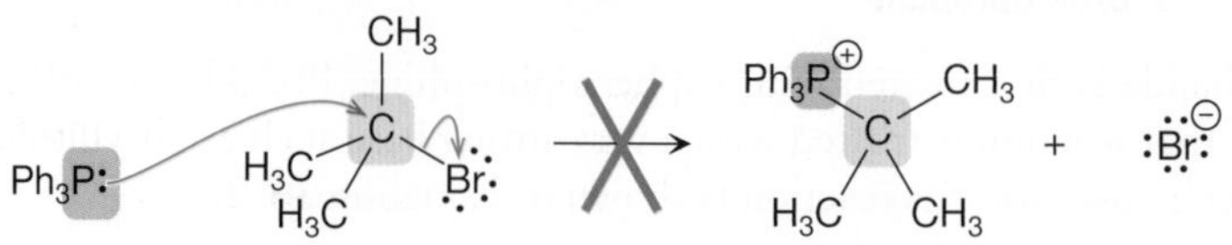

A 3° substrate precludes an
SN2 reaction from occurring.
CH3
Ph3P:
H3C
H3C
C
Br:
Ph3P
CH3
C
H3C
CH3
+
:Br:

(18-29)

SOLVED PROBLEM **18.5**

How to devise a multistep synthesis that incorporates a Wittig reaction

Break It Down **Show how you could synthesize oct-4-ene, using butanal as your only source of carbon.**

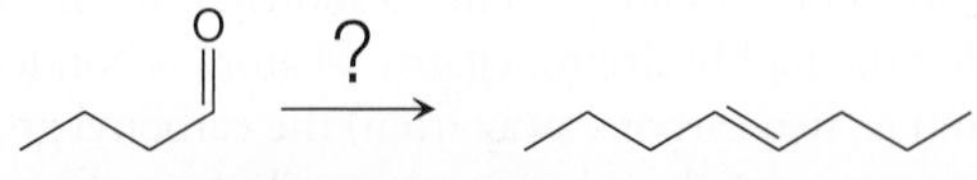

Think	Solve
Can the target be the product of a Wittig reaction? What would the precursors be?	The target is an alkene, so it can be the product of a Wittig reaction. As shown in the following transform, one C atom of the C═C bond could have been part of a C═O bond in one precursor, and the other C could have been part of a Wittig reagent as the other precursor.
What alkyl halide could be the precursor to that Wittig reagent? How could that alkyl halide be made from the starting aldehyde?	As shown below, the Wittig reagent can be made from the corresponding alkyl halide. The alkyl halide could be made from the alcohol, which could be produced from the aldehyde.
How do you report the final synthesis?	To report the final synthesis, we reverse the retrosynthetic analysis and add the proper reagents and reaction conditions, as shown below.

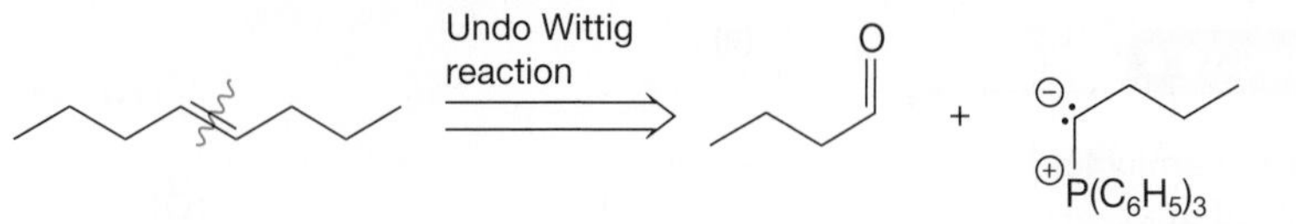

Undo Wittig reaction
O
+
$P(C_6H_5)_3$

Wittig reagent

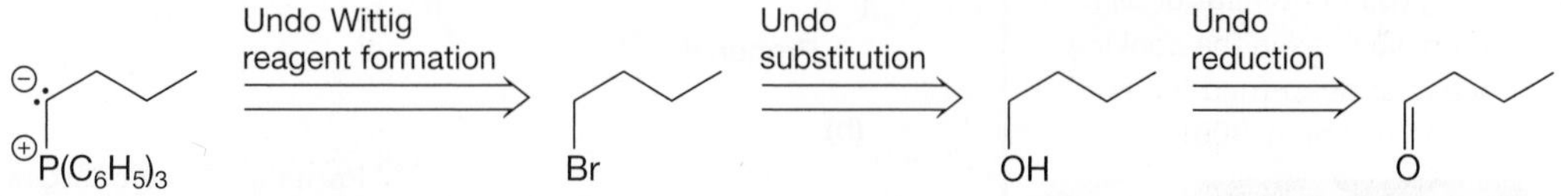

Undo Wittig reagent formation
Undo substitution
Undo reduction
$P(C_6H_5)_3$
Br
OH
O

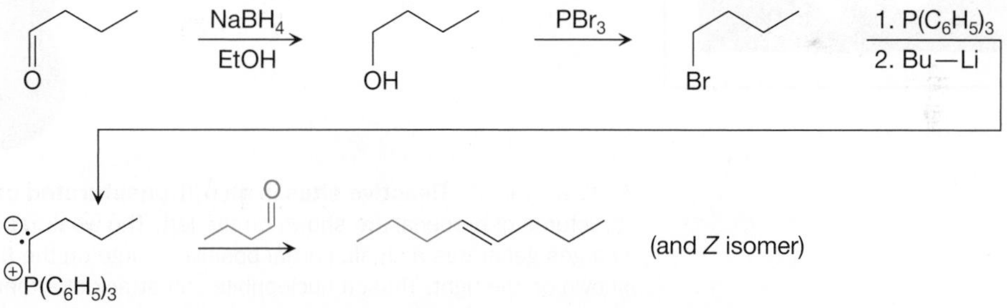

$NaBH_4$
EtOH
PBr_3
1. $P(C_6H_5)_3$
2. Bu—Li
O
OH
Br
$P(C_6H_5)_3$
(and *Z* isomer)

Try It Show how you could carry out the synthesis shown here, beginning with benzaldehyde and using any other reagents necessary. *Hint*: For an unsymmetric alkene, can the C═C double bond be made in more than one way?

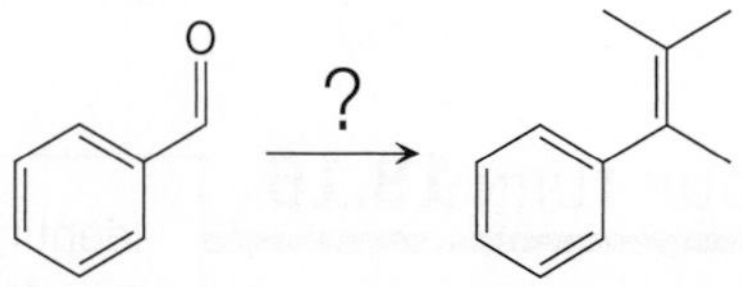

SECTION 18.8 OBJECTIVES

You will be able to:

1. Identify the two electrophilic sites in a conjugated ketone or aldehyde.
2. Draw the mechanism and product for the 1,2-addition and 1,4-addition of a nucleophile to a conjugated ketone or aldehyde.
3. Predict the major product in the competition between 1,2-addition and 1,4-addition of a nucleophile to a conjugated ketone or aldehyde, and explain these observations.

18.8 Direct Addition versus Conjugate Addition

When a C═C double bond is conjugated to a C═O bond, as in propenal (**Figure 18-10**), the species is called an **α,β-unsaturated carbonyl compound**. Two electron-poor sites are present, as shown. One of those sites is the carbonyl C atom, given that the highly electronegative O atom is bonded to it, and the other is the C atom *beta* to (i.e., two carbons away from) the carbonyl group. We can see why this is so by examining one of the resonance contributors of propenal, which places a formal negative charge on the O atom and a formal positive charge on the β C atom (Fig. 18-10a). Although this resonance contributor is somewhat weak due to the charges present, its contribution to the resonance hybrid places a small but significant partial positive charge on the β C atom, as indicated in the electrostatic potential map in Figure 18-10b.

CONNECTIONS 18.4

Fried food and herbicides? Propenal (Fig. 18-10a), commonly called acrolein, is used as an herbicide to control algae and aquatic weeds in irrigation canals. It is produced when glycerol from fat or oil is burned, such as in the cooking process of deep-fried foods (see the box on p. 906).

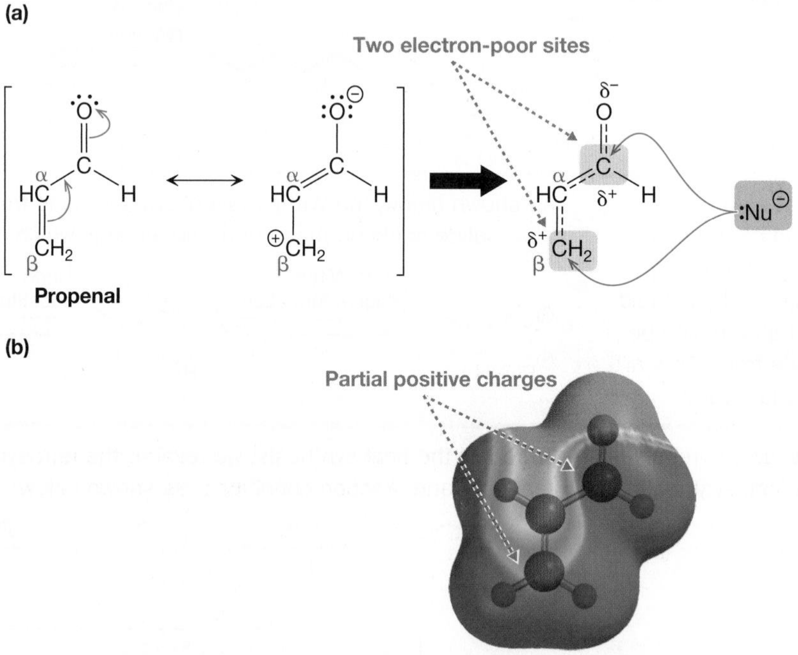

(a)
Two electron-poor sites
α
HC
C
H
O
CH₂
β
Propenal
δ⁻
δ⁺
:Nu
(b)
Partial positive charges

FIGURE 18-10 Reactive sites in an α,β-unsaturated carbonyl compound (a) Resonance structures of propenal are shown on the left. The weak resonance contributor with separated charges generates a small, partial positive charge on the β carbon in the resonance hybrid, shown on the right. Thus, a nucleophile can attack at either the carbonyl carbon or the β carbon. (b) An electrostatic potential map of propenal, showing the partial positive charge (blue) on both the carbonyl carbon and the β carbon.

YOUR TURN **18.16**

Identify the two electron-poor sites in cyclohex-2-en-1-one, shown here, and label the α and β carbons.

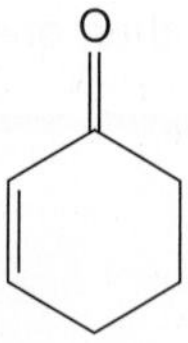

O

Cyclohex-2-en-1-one

Given these *two electrophilic sites* in an α,β-unsaturated carbonyl compound, nucleophiles in general can attack at two positions: either at the carbonyl carbon itself (Eq. 18-30) or at the **β carbon** (Eq. 18-31).

Mechanism Drawing
Direct Addition of a Nucleophile to a Conjugated Aldehyde

Mechanism for direct addition (1,2-addition) to an α,β-unsaturated carbonyl

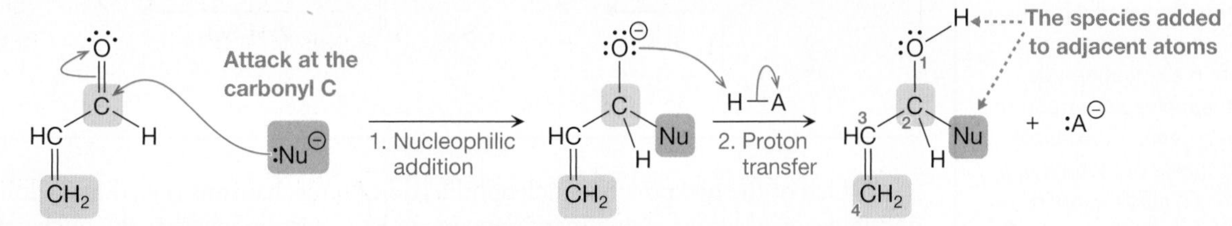

Attack at the carbonyl C
:Nu
1. Nucleophilic addition
H—A
2. Proton transfer
The species added to adjacent atoms
+ :A

(18-30)

Mechanism for conjugate addition (1,4-addition) to an α,β-unsaturated carbonyl

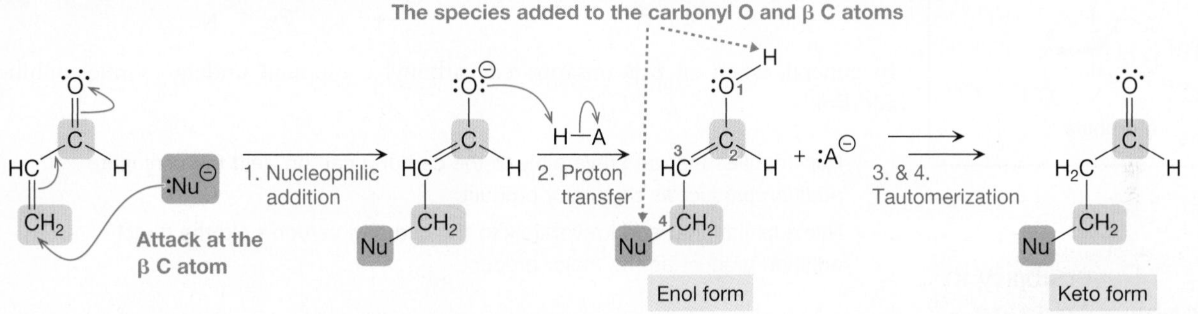

The species added to the carbonyl O and β C atoms
:Nu
Attack at the β C atom
1. Nucleophilic addition
H—A
2. Proton transfer
+ :A
3. & 4. Tautomerization
Enol form
Keto form

(18-31)

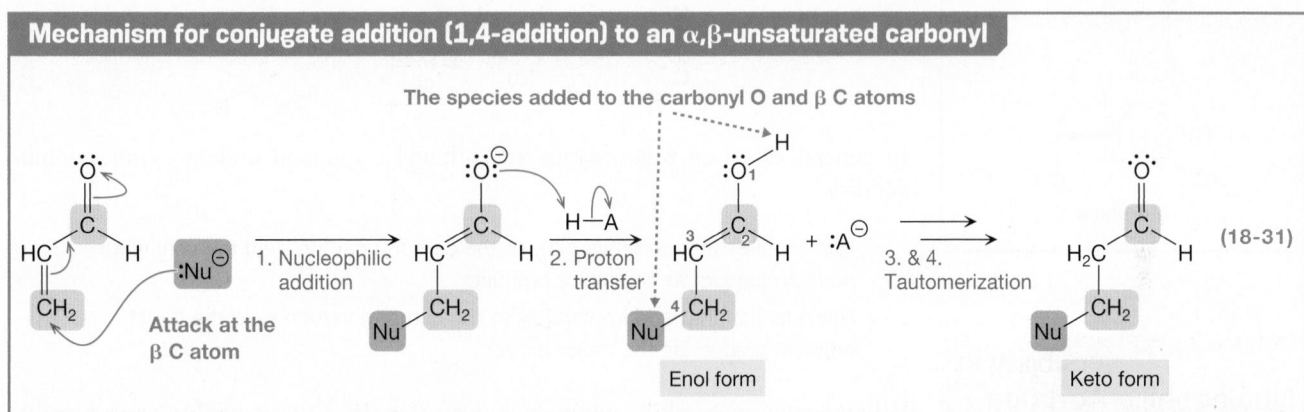

Attack of the nucleophile at the carbonyl carbon is called *1,2-addition*, or **direct addition**, because after protonation in Step 2, species have added to adjacent atoms, which is a 1,2-positioning. Attack at the β C atom, on the other hand, is called *1,4-addition*, or **conjugate addition**, because after protonation in Step 2, species have added to atoms separated by three bonds, which is a 1,4-positioning. Direct addition and conjugate addition are analogous to 1,2-addition and 1,4-addition of electrophiles to conjugated dienes (Section 12.9).

Mechanism Drawing
Conjugate Addition of a Nucleophile to a Conjugated Aldehyde

Notice in Equation 18-31 that the 1,4-addition product is an enol. As we saw in Section 7.10, this enol form will rapidly tautomerize to generate the more stable keto form as the major product (see Recall box and Your Turn 18.17).

YOUR TURN **18.17**

Draw the mechanism that converts the enol in Equation 18-31 into its keto form. *Hint*: Review Section 7.10. You may assume basic conditions.

◂ RECALL

Section 7.10 showed that keto and enol forms exist in equilibrium and that the keto form is typically the more stable form. Conversion of one form to the other involves back-to-back proton transfers, and the order in which those steps occur is dictated by whether the conditions are acidic or basic.

If a carbon nucleophile adds by conjugate addition, thereby forming a carbon–carbon bond, the process is called a **Michael reaction** or **Michael addition**, after the American chemist Arthur Michael (1853–1942). Over the years, however, the term *Michael reaction* has evolved into a generic description of conjugate additions involving any nucleophile.

YOUR TURN **18.18**

Draw the complete 1,2-addition and 1,4-addition mechanisms for each of the reactions shown here.

(a)

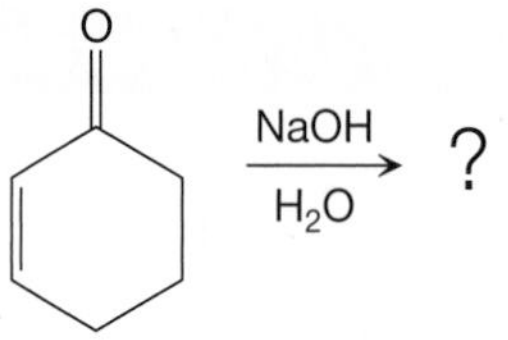

(b)

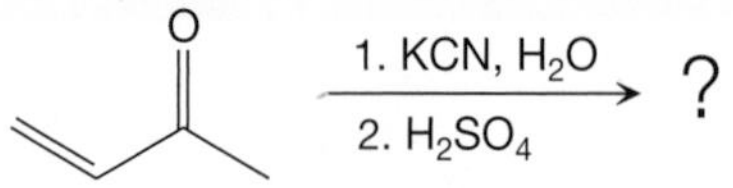

CONNECTIONS 18.5

Fighting pain Cyclohex-2-en-1-one (Your Turn 18.16) is a useful starting material for the synthesis of pharmaceuticals that contain six-membered rings in the molecular structure. It has been used, for example, in the synthesis of morphine, a powerful pain medication in the opiate family.

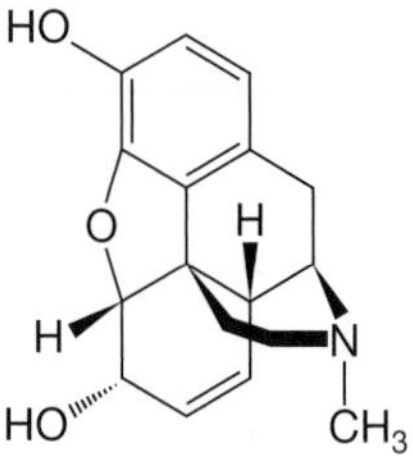

Morphine

Which of the two possible nucleophilic addition mechanisms (i.e., direct addition or conjugate addition) is dominant depends in large part on whether the nucleophile adds to the carbonyl carbon reversibly or irreversibly (Eq. 18-32):

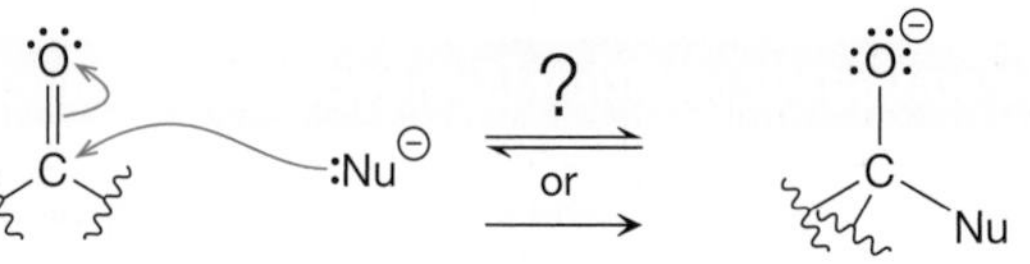

(18-32)

In general, when an α,β-unsaturated carbonyl compound undergoes nucleophilic addition:

- Nucleophiles that add reversibly to the carbonyl carbon yield the conjugate addition product as the major product.
- Nucleophiles that add irreversibly to the carbonyl carbon yield the direct addition product as the major product.

Whether the nucleophilic addition in Equation 18-32 is reversible or irreversible depends on the charge stability that each side of the reaction exhibits: *Nucleophilic addition tends to be irreversible if the negative charge that develops in the adduct is substantially better stabilized than it is in the nucleophile.* In practice, these situations are limited to ones in which the nucleophile has the negative charge located on a carbon or hydrogen atom, and the negative charge is not stabilized by resonance or inductive effects. Therefore:

- Nucleophilic addition to a carbonyl carbon tends to be irreversible when it involves a very strong R^- or H^- nucleophile.
- Otherwise, the nucleophilic addition tends to be reversible.

These ideas are summarized in Table 18-2.

For example, $C_6H_{11}MgBr$ (in which $C_6H_{11}^-$ is the nucleophile) adds irreversibly to a carbonyl C atom, so the major product is from direct addition (Eq. 18-33):

The major product is from 1,2-addition.

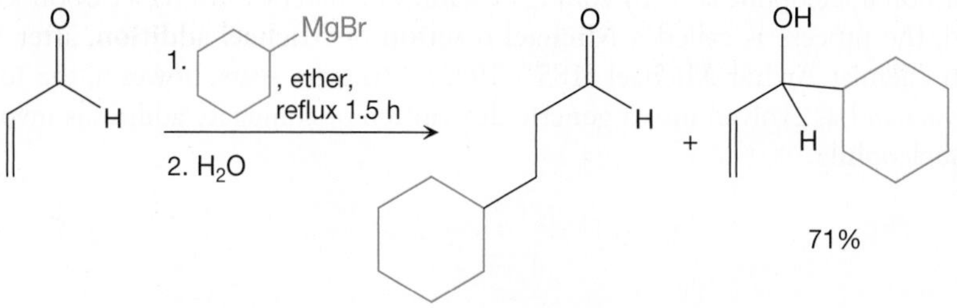
71%

(18-33)

On the other hand, CH_3O^- adds reversibly, so the major nucleophilic addition product is from conjugate addition (Eq. 18-34):

TABLE 18-2 Reversibility in Nucleophilic Addition

Nucleophiles That Add *Reversibly*	Nucleophiles That Add *Irreversibly*
$HO^{\ominus}$, $RO^{\ominus}$	R—MgBr (:$R^{\ominus}$)
$H_2N^{\ominus}$, $R_2N^{\ominus}$	R—Li (:$R^{\ominus}$)
$Cl^{\ominus}$, $Br^{\ominus}$, $I^{\ominus}$	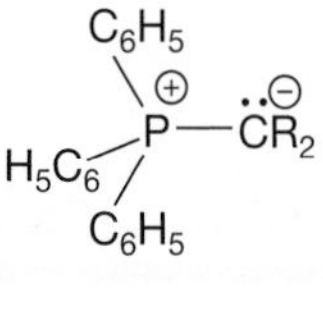
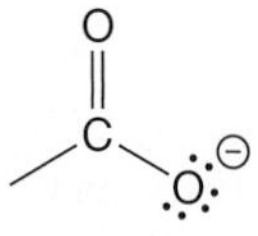	$LiAlH_4$ (:$H^{\ominus}$)
N≡C:$^{\ominus}$	$NaBH_4$ (:$H^{\ominus}$)
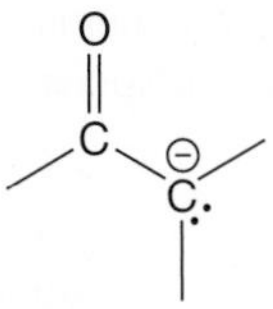	

The major product is from 1,4-addition.

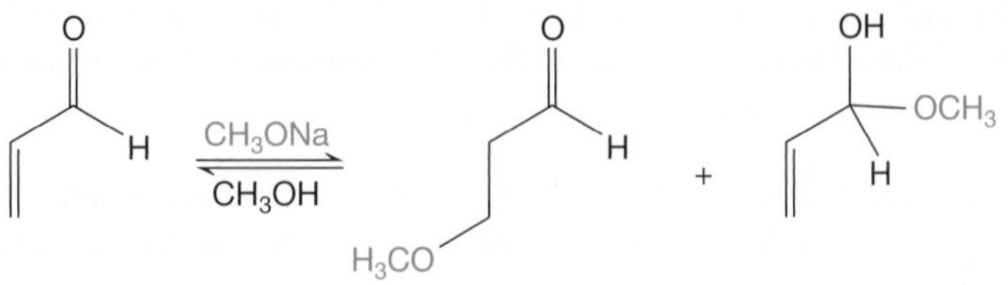

O
H
CH3ONa
CH3OH
O
H
H3CO
+
OH
OCH3
H

80%

(18-34)

SOLVED PROBLEM **18.6**

How to predict the outcome of direct addition versus conjugate addition

Break It Down **Draw the mechanism that leads to the major product for the following reaction.**

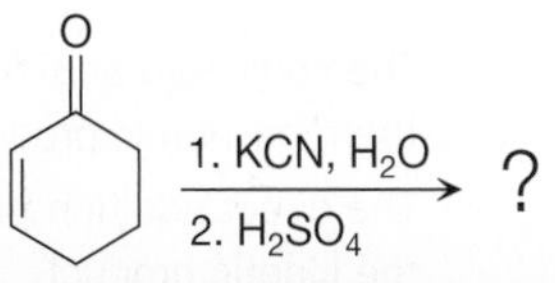

O
1. KCN, H2O
2. H2SO4
?

Think	Solve
What is the nucleophile? Can the nucleophile attack more than one electrophilic site?	The nucleophile is NC^-. The ketone is α,β-unsaturated, so the nucleophile can attack the carbonyl carbon in 1,2-addition or the β carbon in 1,4-addition.
Is the addition to the carbonyl carbon reversible or irreversible? Will that favor 1,2-addition or 1,4-addition?	According to Table 18-2, the addition of NC^- to the carbonyl carbon is reversible. Therefore, the major product will be from 1,4-addition.
In 1,4-addition, where will the nucleophile attack? Where will the proton add?	In 1,4-addition, the nucleophile will attack the β carbon and the resulting negatively charged oxygen is protonated, as shown in the first two steps below.
Is the immediate product of 1,4-addition stable? Will it rearrange?	The immediate product is an enol and will undergo tautomerization to produce the more stable keto form, as shown below.

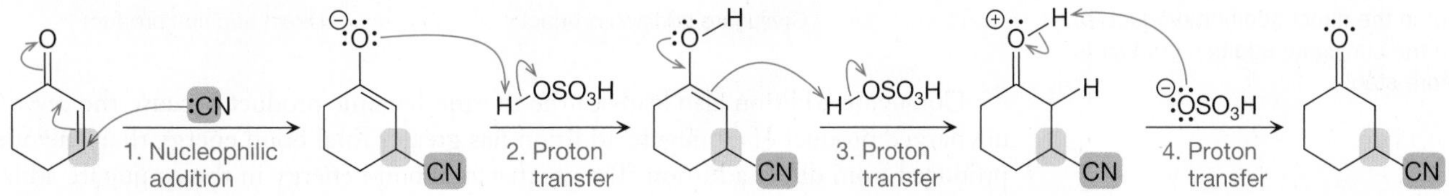

:CN
1. Nucleophilic addition
CN
H–OSO3H
2. Proton transfer
CN
H–OSO3H
3. Proton transfer
H
CN
:OSO3H
4. Proton transfer
CN

Try It Draw the major product for the reaction between cyclohex-2-en-1-one and each of the nucleophiles in **(a)–(e)**, and draw the mechanism that leads to each of those products. You may assume an acid workup, if necessary.

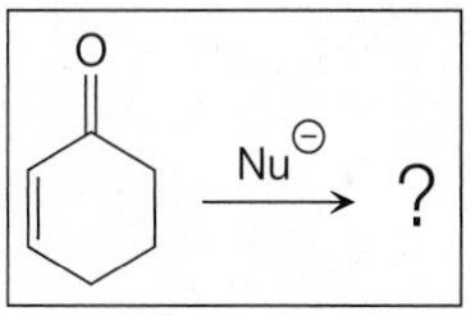

O
Nu
?

(a) CH_3SNa

(b)

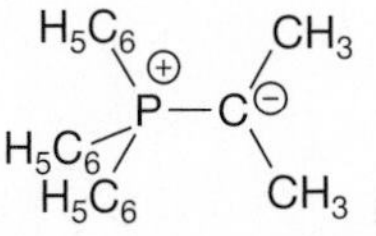

H5C6
CH3
P
C
H5C6
H5C6
CH3

(c)

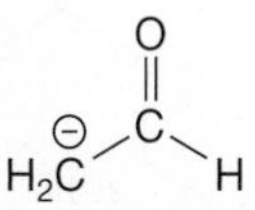

O
C
H2C
H

(d)

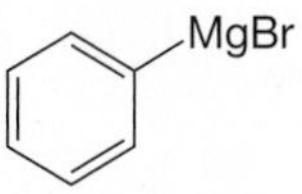

MgBr

(e) $LiAlH_4$

◀ RECALL

Section 12.10 showed that the addition of an electrophile to a conjugated diene takes place reversibly at warm temperatures to favor the thermodynamic product, and it takes place irreversibly at cold temperatures to favor the kinetic product.

Why does regioselectivity involving 1,2-addition versus 1,4-addition depend on whether the nucleophile adds reversibly to the carbonyl carbon atom? As we saw with electrophilic addition to conjugated dienes (Section 12.10; see Recall box), reversibility of nucleophilic addition governs whether the competition takes place under thermodynamic or kinetic control (Section 11.3):

- If the nucleophile adds reversibly, then the reaction takes place under thermodynamic control and the major product is the thermodynamic product (i.e., the one that is more stable).
- If the nucleophile adds irreversibly, then the reaction takes place under kinetic control and the major product is the kinetic product (i.e., the one that is produced more rapidly).

To apply these ideas to nucleophilic addition, we need to know which product is the thermodynamic product and which is the kinetic product. Generally speaking:

- The conjugate addition product is the one that is more stable, making it the thermodynamic product.
- The direct addition product is the one that is produced more rapidly, making it the kinetic product.

The conjugate addition product is more stable in part because of charge stability. Notice from Equation 18-31 that the immediate product of conjugate addition is an enolate anion, which, as shown in **Figure 18-11a**, has a resonance-stabilized negative charge. The direct addition product (Eq. 18-30) shown in Figure 18-11b, on the other hand, has an isolated negative charge and is therefore less stable.

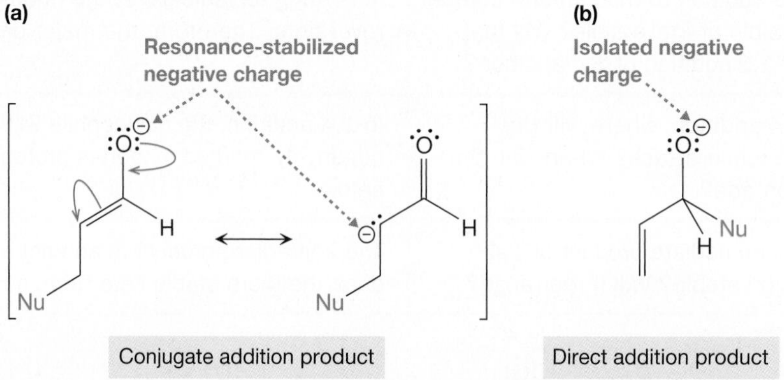

(a)
Resonance-stabilized negative charge
H
Nu
Conjugate addition product
(b)
Isolated negative charge
Nu
H
Direct addition product

FIGURE 18-11 Charge stability and direct addition versus conjugate addition The negative charge produced on nucleophilic addition is resonance-delocalized in the conjugate addition product (a) but not in the direct addition product (b), so the conjugate addition product is more stable.

Conjugate addition also leads to the thermodynamic product because the *overall* uncharged product of conjugate addition has greater total bond energy than the one produced from direct addition. The greater total bond energy in the conjugate addition product comes primarily from the type of double bond present. As shown in **Figure 18-12**, the conjugate addition product (Fig. 18-12a) has a C═O double bond, which, on average, is 101 kJ/mol stronger than the C═C double bond in the direct addition product (Fig. 18-12b).

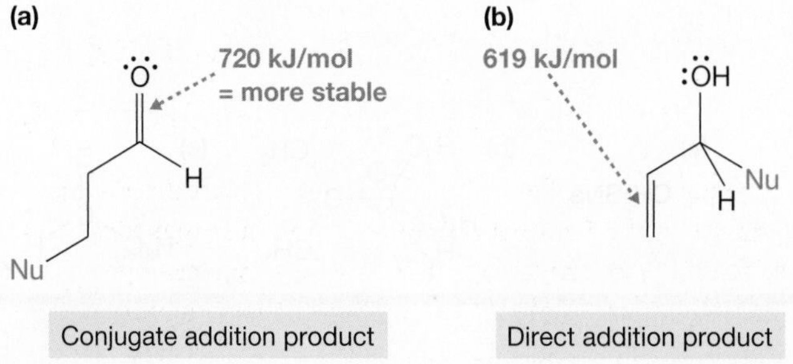

(a)
720 kJ/mol
= more stable
H
Nu
Conjugate addition product
(b)
619 kJ/mol
:ÖH
Nu
H
Direct addition product

FIGURE 18-12 Bond energies and direct addition versus conjugate addition The overall product of conjugate addition (a) is more stable than the overall product of direct addition (b), primarily because the average C═O double bond is much stronger than the average C═C double bond.

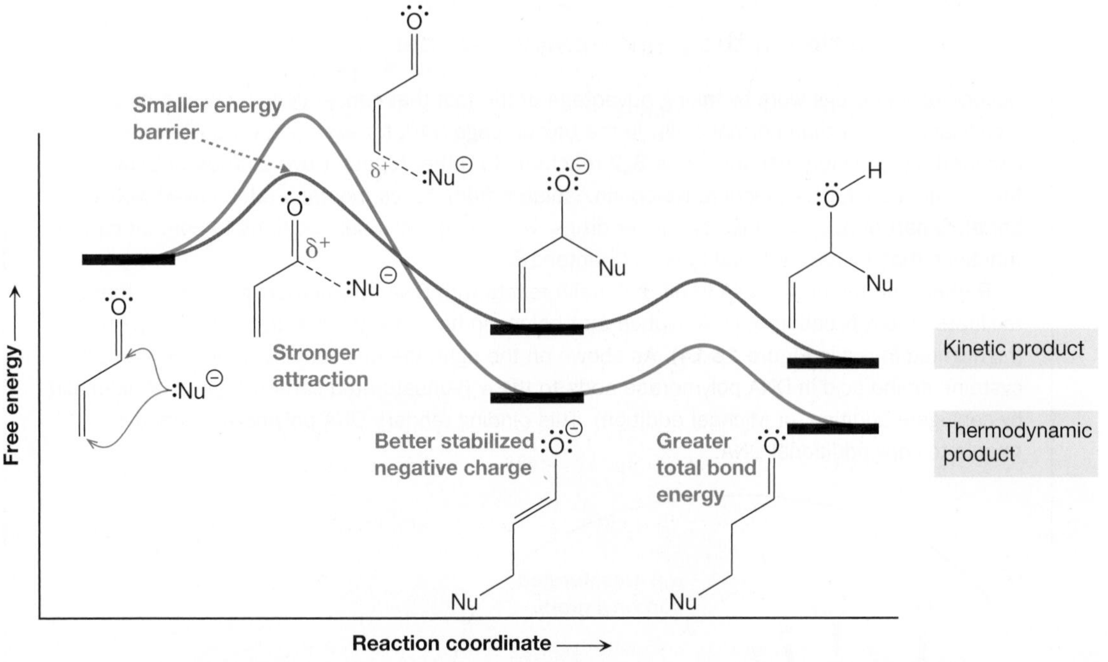

Smaller energy barrier
Stronger attraction
Better stabilized negative charge
Greater total bond energy
Kinetic product
Thermodynamic product
Free energy
Reaction coordinate

FIGURE 18-13 Direct addition versus conjugate addition of a generic nucleophile to propenal The blue curve represents direct addition (Eq. 18-30), whereas the red curve represents conjugate addition (Eq. 18-31). The energy barrier is lower for direct addition because, in the transition state, the nucleophile is attracted more strongly to the carbonyl carbon than to the β carbon. Thus, direct addition gives the kinetic product. The more stable product is formed from conjugate addition, so conjugate addition gives the thermodynamic product.

If the direct addition product is the kinetic product, then it must be formed faster, which means the path to form it has a smaller activation energy (**Figure 18-13**). 1,2-Addition has the smaller energy barrier because of the greater concentration of positive charge on the carbonyl C atom than on the β C atom. Therefore, in the initial stages of nucleophilic attack, the nucleophile is better stabilized by its attraction to the carbonyl C atom than by its attraction to the β C atom.

YOUR TURN **18.19**

Which product of the following nucleophilic addition reaction is the *thermodynamic product* and which is the *kinetic product*?

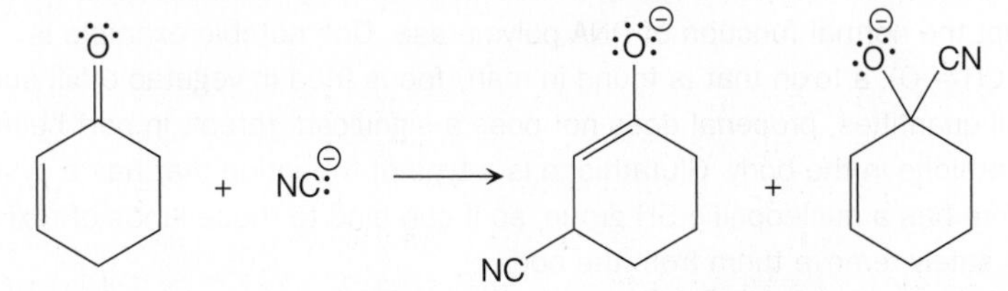

18.9 Lithium Dialkylcuprates and the Selectivity of Organometallic Reagents

SECTION 18.9 OBJECTIVES

You will be able to:

1. Identify the nucleophilic carbon in a lithium dialkylcuprate.
2. Predict the major product from the reaction of a lithium dialkylcuprate with a conjugated ketone or aldehyde, and draw the mechanism for these reactions.
3. Design syntheses that incorporate the addition of a lithium dialkylcuprate to a conjugated ketone or aldehyde.

Organocopper reagents, also called organocuprates, constitute an important class of organometallic compounds. Among the most common organocuprates are **lithium dialkylcuprates**, R_2CuLi, sometimes referred to as **Gilman reagents** (after the American chemist Henry Gilman, 1893–1986). As with other organometallic reagents, the carbon atoms of lithium dialkylcuprates are electron-rich, because carbon (EN = 2.55)

Michael Addition in the Fight against Cancer

Several cancer drugs work by taking advantage of the fact that cancer cells grow and divide significantly faster than normal cells. In the box on page 540, for example, we saw how one cancer drug, mechlorethamine, uses S_N2 reactions to tether together two strands of DNA, thereby disrupting DNA function. Helenalin, isolated from *Arnica montana* (also called wolf's bane), is part of another class of cancer drugs, which uses Michael additions to combat cancer: reactions that we have studied here in Chapter 18.

Rather than target the DNA itself, helenalin reacts with DNA polymerase, an enzyme that facilitates the replication of DNA. Notice that helenalin has an α,β-unsaturated carbonyl group (highlighted in red in **Figure 18-14**). As shown on the right, the nucleophilic thiol (SH) group of a cysteine amino acid in DNA polymerase adds to the α,β-unsaturated carbonyl group of helenalin by conjugate addition (or Michael addition). This binding renders DNA polymerase inactive, unable to copy additional DNA.

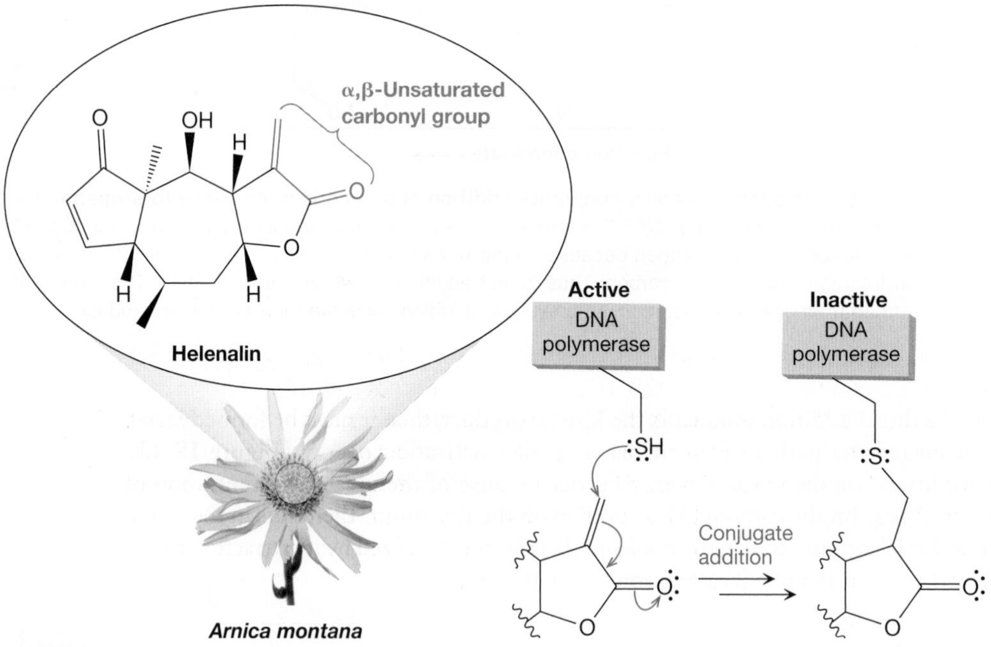
α,β-Unsaturated
carbonyl group
Helenalin
Active
DNA
polymerase
Inactive
DNA
polymerase
Conjugate
addition
Arnica montana

FIGURE 18-14

Cancer drugs like helenalin are not the only α,β-unsaturated carbonyl compounds that can enter the body to disrupt the normal function of DNA polymerase. One notable example is propenal ($H_2C{=}CH{-}CH{=}O$), a toxin that is found in many foods fried in vegetable oil, such as french fries. In small quantities, propenal does not pose a significant threat, in part because of the presence of glutathione in the body. Glutathione is a type of tripeptide that has a cysteine amino acid, and therefore has a nucleophilic SH group, so it can bind to these kinds of toxins by conjugate addition and safely remove them from the body.

has a higher electronegativity than copper (EN = 1.90). As a result, these reagents, too, can be treated as simply R^-.

Lithium dialkylcuprates are much less reactive than either alkyllithium reagents (RLi) or Grignard reagents (RMgX). Largely, this is because the C—Cu bond is significantly less polar than either the R—Mg bond or the R—Li bond, as shown in **Figure 18-15**. Because the electronegativity of Cu (1.90) is greater than that of Mg (1.31) or Li (0.98), R_2CuLi has the smallest concentration of negative charge on C.

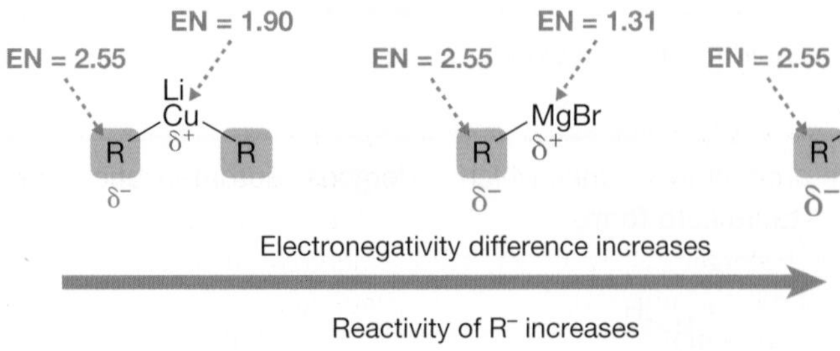
EN = 2.55
EN = 1.90
Li
Cu
δ+
R
R
δ−
EN = 2.55
EN = 1.31
MgBr
δ+
R
δ−
EN = 2.55
EN = 0.98
Li
δ+
R
δ−
Electronegativity difference increases
Reactivity of R⁻ increases

FIGURE 18-15 Relative reactivities of organometallic reagents As the electronegativity of the metal atom in the C—metal bond decreases, the electronegativity difference between the metal and C atoms increases, resulting in a larger partial negative charge on C and greater reactivity.

Unlike alkyllithium and Grignard reagents, lithium dialkylcuprates tend *not* to undergo direct addition to a polar π bond:

> When an α,β-unsaturated carbonyl compound is treated with R_2CuLi, R^- adds almost exclusively at the β carbon by conjugate addition.

An example is shown in Equation 18-35:

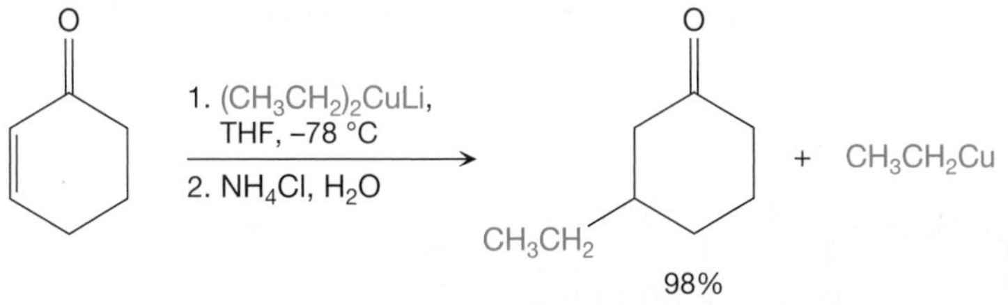
O
1. (CH₃CH₂)₂CuLi,
THF, −78 °C
2. NH₄Cl, H₂O
O
CH₃CH₂
98%
+ CH₃CH₂Cu
(18-35)

The reason for this regioselectivity is not precisely known because the specific mechanism for the reaction of lithium dialkylcuprates is not fully understood. However, chemists generally believe that the species that initially attacks as a nucleophile is *not* R^-. Instead, a key step is the reversible binding of R_2Cu^- to the C=C double bond, followed by the transfer of the alkyl group. As we have seen previously with nucleophiles that add reversibly to the carbonyl carbon, the reversible nature of the initial binding may explain the tendency of organocopper reagents to react by conjugate addition instead of direct addition.

SOLVED PROBLEM **18.7**

How to predict the outcome when R_2CuLi reacts with a conjugated ketone or aldehyde

Break It Down Predict the major product of the reaction shown here.

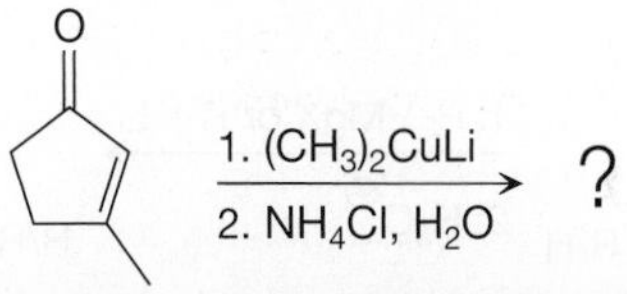
O
1. (CH₃)₂CuLi
2. NH₄Cl, H₂O
?

Think	Solve
How can we simplify the lithium dialkylcuprate as an R^- nucleophile?	This lithium dialkylcuprate has two H_3C—Cu bonds, so we can think of it as a source of H_3C^-.
Will it add predominantly by direct addition or conjugate addition?	Lithium dialkylcuprates tend to add by conjugate addition rather than direct addition, as shown in the mechanism below.

(continued)

What role does NH_4^+ play after the addition of R^- is complete?	NH_4^+ acts as the acid in the acid workup step.
Is the immediate product stable, or does it rearrange?	The immediate product is an enol, which undergoes tautomerization to produce the more stable keto form.

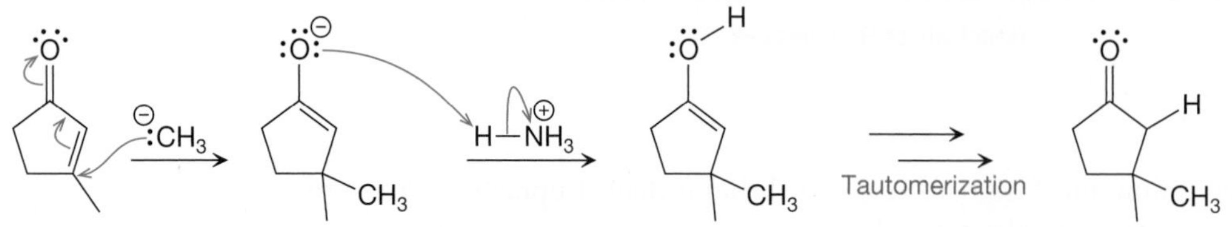

:CH3
H—NH3
CH3
CH3
Tautomerization
H
CH3

Try It Predict the major product of each of the following reactions.

(a)

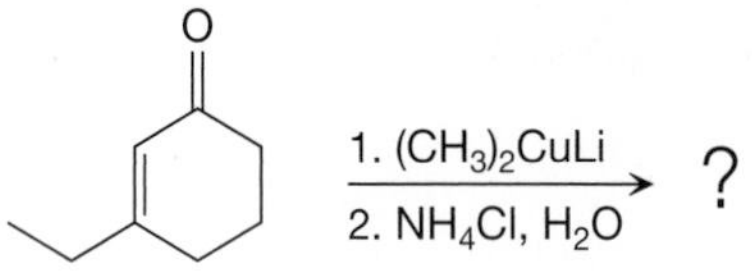

O
1. (CH3)2CuLi
2. NH4Cl, H2O
?

(b)

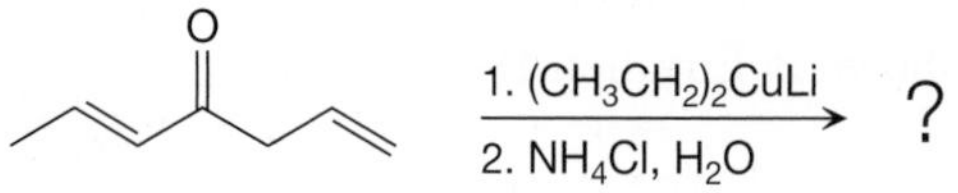

O
1. (CH3CH2)2CuLi
2. NH4Cl, H2O
?

(c)

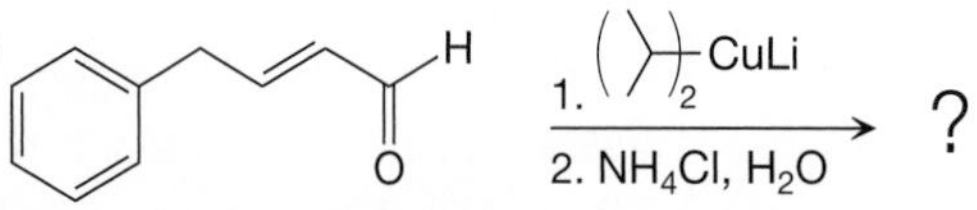

H
O
CuLi
1.
2
2. NH4Cl, H2O
?

SECTION 18.10 OBJECTIVES

You will be able to:

1. Identify alcohols as potential products of reactions involving Grignard or alkyllithium reagents.
2. Effectively carry out transforms of Grignard or alkyllithium reactions in a retrosynthetic analysis.

18.10 Organic Synthesis: Grignard and Alkyllithium Reactions in Synthesis

One of the most important reactions in organic synthesis is the one between a carbonyl compound (such as a ketone or aldehyde) and either a Grignard or an alkyllithium reagent. As shown in Equation 18-36, these reactions are important for two main reasons:

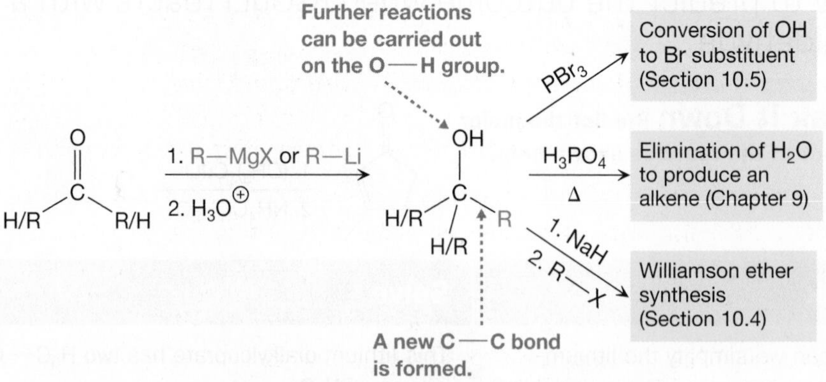

Further reactions can be carried out on the O—H group.
O
C
H/R
R/H
1. R—MgX or R—Li
2. H3O+
OH
C
H/R
R
H/R
A new C—C bond is formed.
PBr3
Conversion of OH to Br substituent (Section 10.5)
H3PO4
Δ
Elimination of H2O to produce an alkene (Chapter 9)
1. NaH
2. R—X
Williamson ether synthesis (Section 10.4)

(18-36)

First, they are carbon–carbon bond-forming reactions, so they can play a key role in constructing the desired carbon skeleton of a target compound. Second, an OH group is generated at one of the carbon atoms joined by the new bond, so we can use the characteristic reactivity of the OH group to carry out further changes at that carbon. Some reactions involving the OH group of the alcohol are shown in Equation 18-36.

Because of the utility of Grignard and alkyllithium reactions in synthesis, it is important to be able to undo these reactions comfortably in your mind to execute transforms efficiently in a retrosynthetic analysis. These transforms can be carried out on essentially any alcohol by disconnecting the bond between the alcohol carbon and an adjacent carbon, as shown in Equation 18-37:

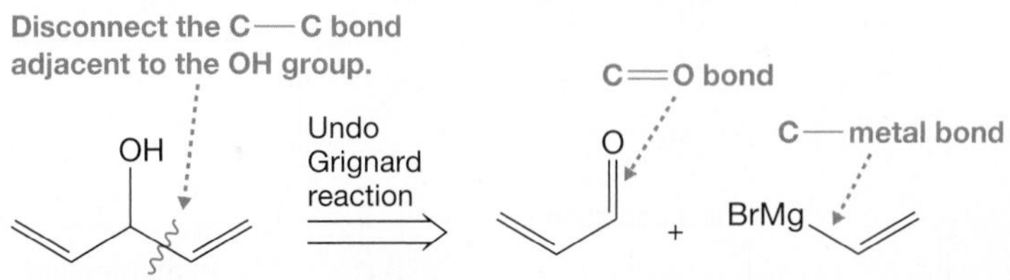

Disconnect the C—C bond adjacent to the OH group.
C=O bond
Undo Grignard reaction
OH
O
C—metal bond
BrMg
+

(18-37)

One precursor is a ketone or an aldehyde, whose carbonyl group contains the alcohol C atom from the target. In the other precursor, the second C atom from the disconnected bond is bonded to the metal atom.

Because the target alcohol in Equation 18-37 is symmetric, disconnecting the other C—C bond involving the alcohol carbon would give us the same precursor. With other alcohols, however, disconnecting different C—C bonds can give us different precursors. An example is shown in Equation 18-38, in which the alcohol carbon is involved in three different C—C bonds:

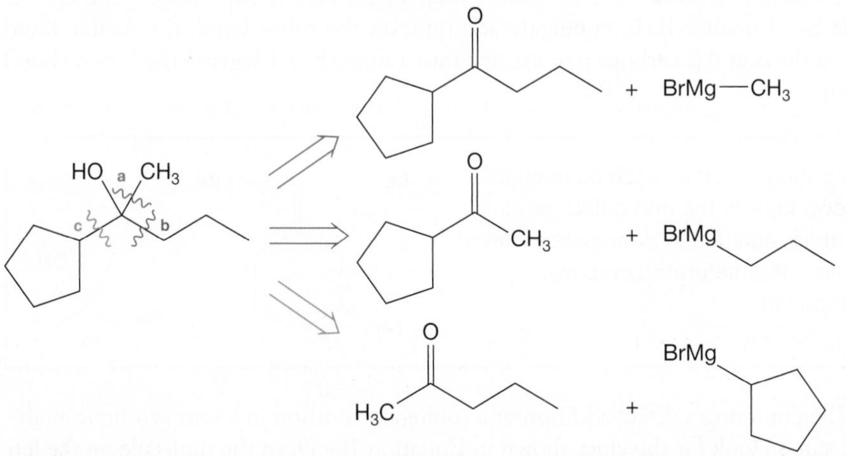

HO
a
CH_3
b
c
O
+ BrMg—CH_3
CH_3
+ BrMg
H_3C
+
BrMg

(18-38a)
(18-38b)
(18-38c)

Disconnecting the C—C bond indicated by the wavy line labeled a, b, or c yields the precursors shown in Equation 18-38a, 18-38b, or 18-38c, respectively.

Having the choice of which C—C bond to disconnect may at first seem daunting. With practice, however, carrying out these kinds of transforms will become quite straightforward, and you will appreciate the options that the Grignard reaction affords.

YOUR TURN 18.20

Rewrite the three transforms in Equation 18-38 as three different syntheses.

YOUR TURN 18.21

Show how this compound can be synthesized from two different alkyllithium reagents.

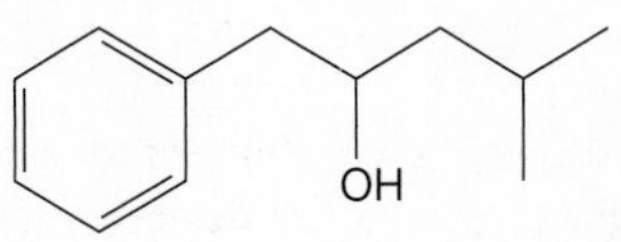

OH

SECTION 18.11 OBJECTIVES

You will be able to:

1. Distinguish targets that could be the outcome of direct addition to a ketone or aldehyde from targets that could be the outcome of conjugate addition.
2. Effectively carry out transforms of direct addition and conjugate addition in a retrosynthetic analysis.

18.11 Organic Synthesis: Considerations of Direct Addition versus Conjugate Addition

As we saw in Section 18.8, a nucleophile can attack an α,β-unsaturated carbonyl compound at either the carbonyl carbon, yielding the direct addition product (Eq. 18-39a), or the β carbon, yielding the conjugate addition product (Eq. 18-39b):

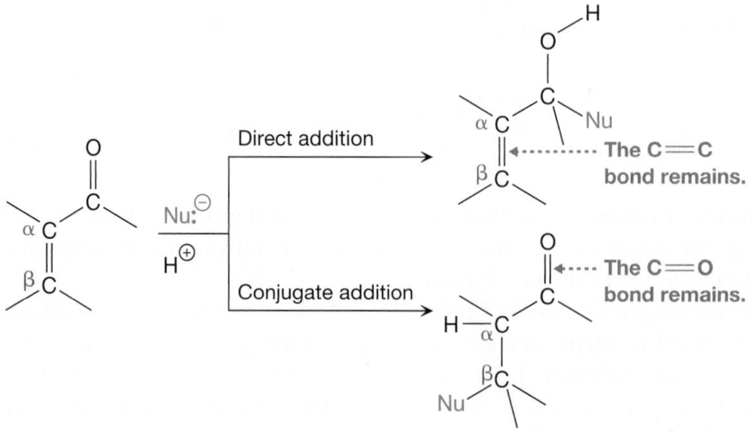

Direct addition
Nu:⊖
H⊕
Conjugate addition
The C=C bond remains.
The C=O bond remains.

(18-39a)

(18-39b)

Direct addition converts the carbonyl group to an OH group, leaving the C=C double bond unaltered. In conjugate addition, on the other hand, the double bond between the α and β carbons is converted into a single bond, leaving the C=O bond unaltered.

YOUR TURN 18.22

Determine whether each compound shown here is the immediate product of direct addition or conjugate addition to an α,β-unsaturated carbonyl compound.

(a) **(b)**

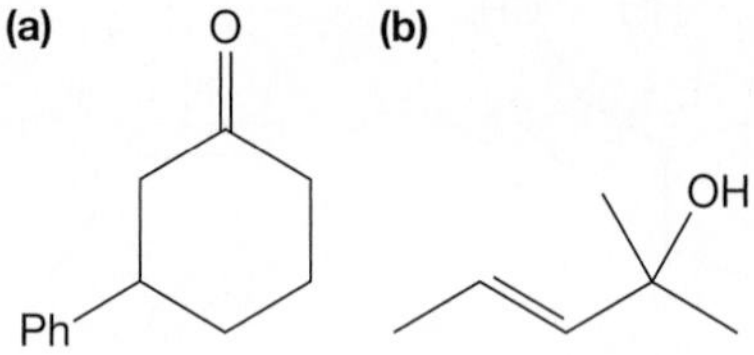

When undoing a direct addition or a conjugate addition in a retrosynthetic analysis, be sure to look for the clues shown in Equation 18-39. In the molecule on the left in Equation 18-40, for example, notice that the cyano group is beta to the C=O bond. Thus, the target can be generated by conjugate addition, in which NC^- attacks the β carbon:

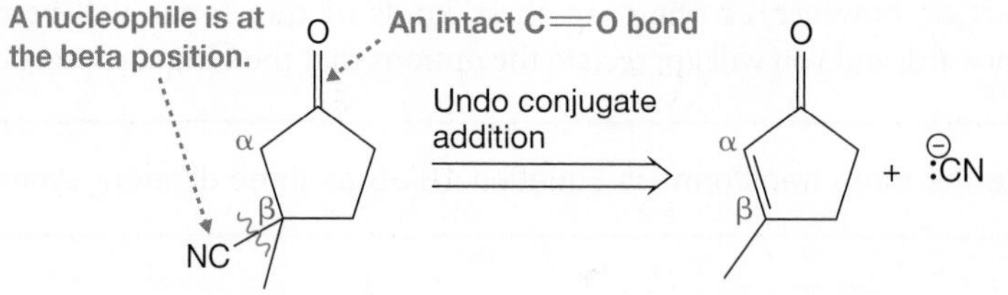

A nucleophile is at the beta position.
An intact C=O bond
Undo conjugate addition

(18-40)

In the forward direction, the synthetic step might appear as in Equation 18-41:

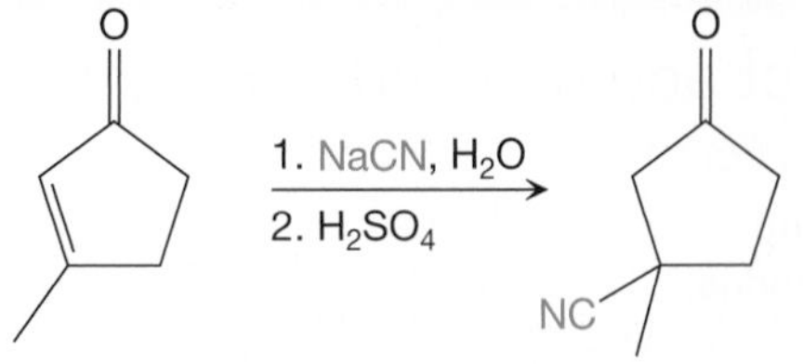

O
1. NaCN, H_2O
2. H_2SO_4
O
NC

(18-41)

In the molecule on the left in Equation 18-42, notice the C=C double bond adjacent to the OH group. This provides a clue that the bond may be the result of direct addition, with H^- as the nucleophile:

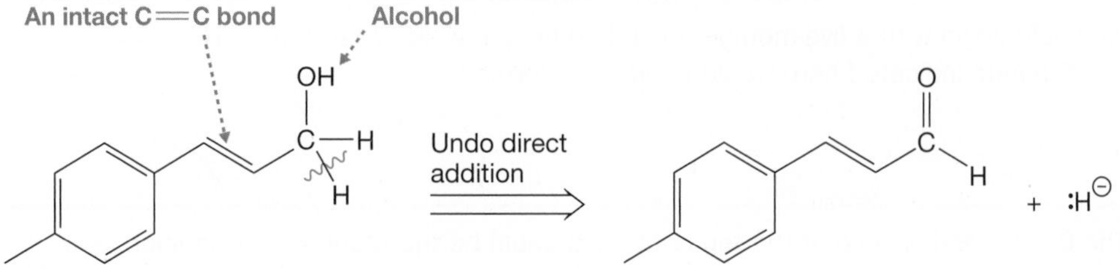

An intact C=C bond
Alcohol
OH
C—H
H
Undo direct
addition
O
C
H
+ :H⊖

(18-42)

Thus, the forward reaction might appear as in Equation 18-43:

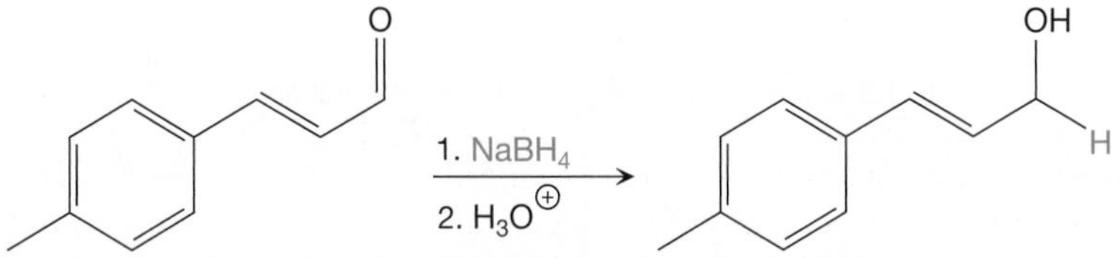

O
1. NaBH₄
2. H₃O⊕
OH
H

(18-43)

If a particular retrosynthetic analysis suggests the use of an R^- nucleophile in the forward direction, then we must also consider regioselectivity. Suppose, for example, that we carry out the transform in Equation 18-44, for which the precursors on the right are an α,β-unsaturated ketone and an R^- nucleophile:

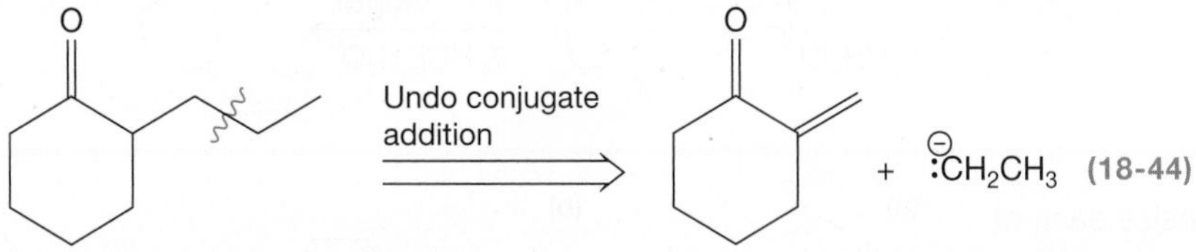

O
Undo conjugate
addition
O
+ ⊖:CH₂CH₃

(18-44)

In the forward direction, the R^- nucleophile can take a variety of forms, such as an alkyllithium reagent (RLi), a Grignard reagent (RMgX), or a lithium dialkylcuprate (R_2CuLi). We want the nucleophile to attack at the β carbon, however, so we should choose a lithium dialkylcuprate, which leads almost exclusively to the conjugate addition product. Thus, the forward reaction would appear as in Equation 18-45:

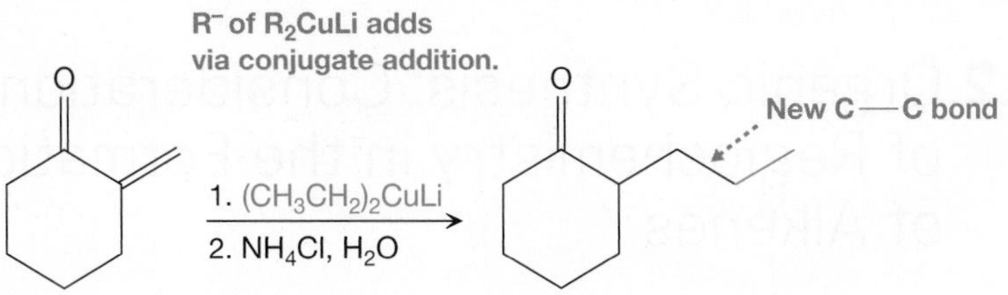

R⁻ of R₂CuLi adds
via conjugate addition.
O
1. (CH₃CH₂)₂CuLi
2. NH₄Cl, H₂O
O
New C—C bond

(18-45)

SOLVED PROBLEM **18.8**

How to design a synthesis involving direct addition and conjugate addition

Break It Down **Show how to synthesize the compound shown here, using compounds containing five or fewer carbons.**

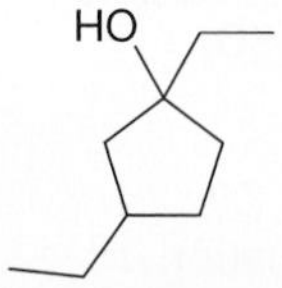

HO

Think	Solve
Do any C—C bonds need to be formed?	We could begin with a five-membered carbon ring, in which case the C—C bonds indicated here would need to be formed. 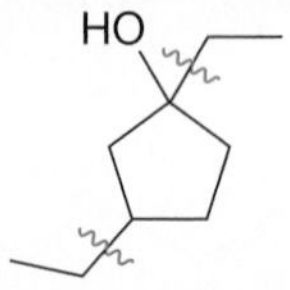
Do any structural features in the target indicate that a 1,2-addition or 1,4-addition would need to take place?	The C—C bond formed at the top of the ring could be the result of 1,2-addition, and the C—C bond formed at the bottom of the ring could be the result of 1,4-addition. These ideas are captured in the retrosynthetic analysis below. 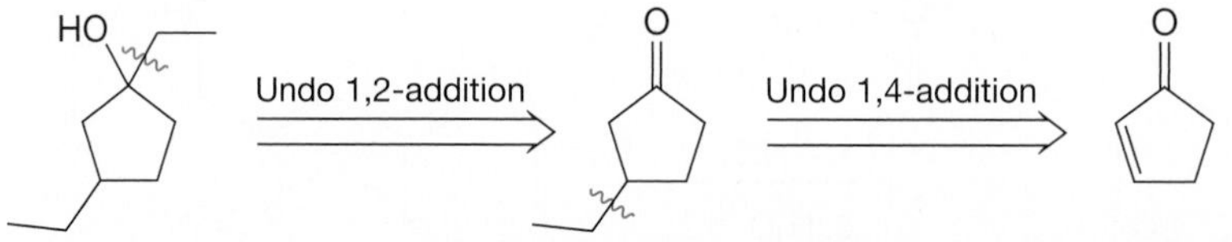
What organometallic reagent could be used to carry out the 1,4-addition? The 1,2-addition?	As shown in the synthesis below, a lithium dialkylcuprate could be used to carry out the 1,4-addition, and a Grignard reagent could be used to carry out the 1,2-addition. 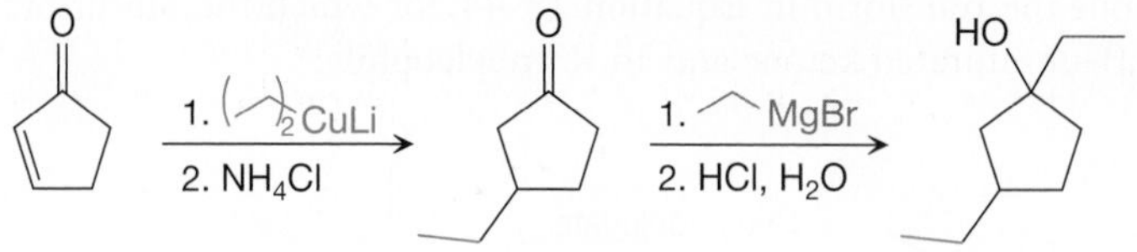

HO
HO
Undo 1,2-addition
O
Undo 1,4-addition
O
O
1. CuLi
2. NH4Cl
O
1. MgBr
2. HCl, H2O
HO

Try It Show how you would synthesize each of these molecules from hex-4-en-3-one.

(a)

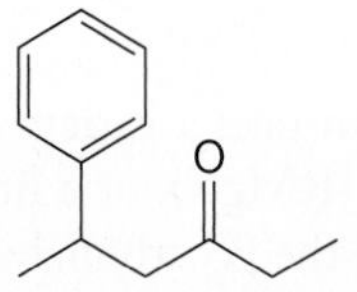

O

(b)

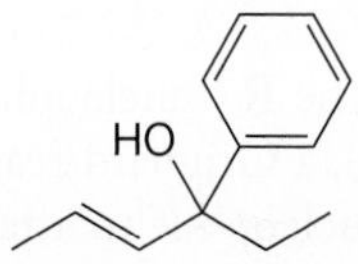

HO

SECTION 18.12 OBJECTIVES

You will be able to:

1. Effectively incorporate a Wittig reaction into a synthesis.
2. Explain the advantages and disadvantages of using Wittig reactions and elimination reactions in the synthesis of an alkene.

18.12 Organic Synthesis: Considerations of Regiochemistry in the Formation of Alkenes

In Section 18.6, we learned that alkenes can be synthesized by the Wittig reaction. In Chapters 8–10, we also saw examples of alkene formation by E1 and E2 reactions. The Wittig reaction is generally regarded as the more synthetically useful reaction, however, due to its regiospecificity:

> In a Wittig reaction, a C═C double bond forms precisely at the location of the initial C═O bond in the ketone or aldehyde.

E1 and E2 reactions, on the other hand, typically form a mixture of alkene isomers, and occasionally the desired isomer is the minor product.

Suppose, for example, that we want to synthesize 1-cyclopentylpent-1-ene. As shown in Equation 18-46, this can be accomplished straightforwardly by the Wittig reaction:

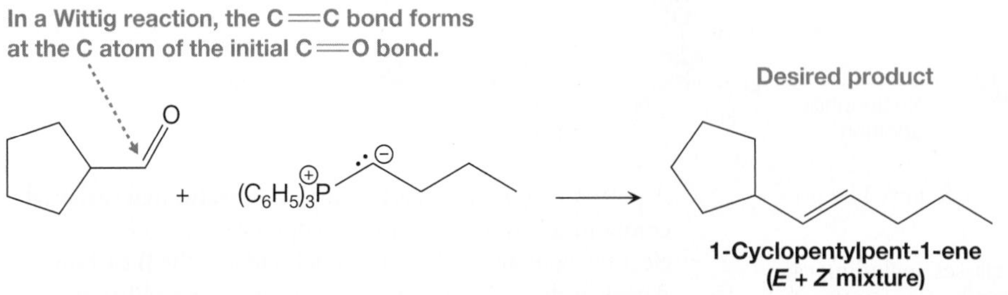
In a Wittig reaction, the C=C bond forms at the C atom of the initial C=O bond.
Desired product
$(C_6H_5)_3P$
1-Cyclopentylpent-1-ene
(*E* + *Z* mixture)

(18-46)

However, attempting to synthesize this compound by an elimination reaction is problematic. One possible precursor is 1-bromo-1-cyclopentylpentane, as shown in Equation 18-47, but the major product is the undesired trisubstituted alkene:

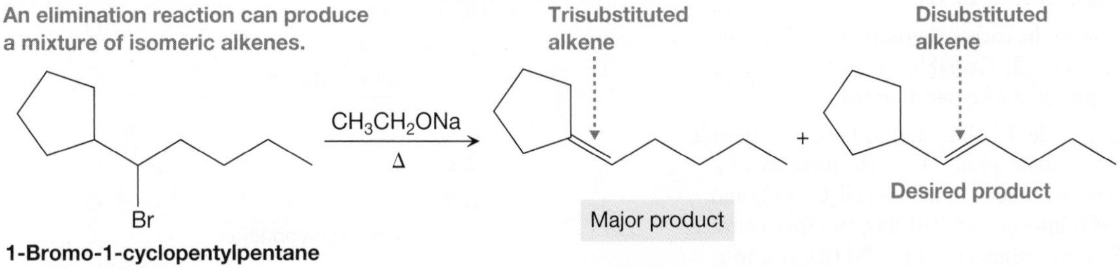
An elimination reaction can produce a mixture of isomeric alkenes.
Trisubstituted alkene
Disubstituted alkene
CH_3CH_2ONa
Δ
Br
1-Bromo-1-cyclopentylpentane
Major product
Desired product

(18-47)

According to Zaitsev's rule (Section 9.10), elimination favors the more substituted alkene. In this case, the desired product is the less substituted alkene, which is disubstituted.

A similar problem arises if 2-bromo-1-cyclopentylpentane is used as the precursor. As shown in Equation 18-48, both possible elimination products are disubstituted alkenes, so a significant amount of each will be produced:

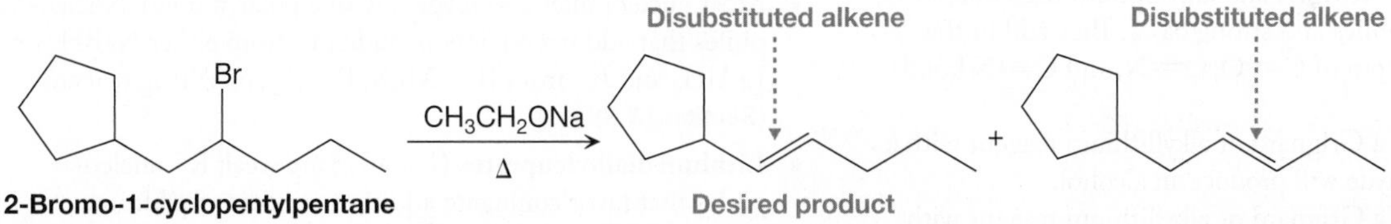
Disubstituted alkene
Disubstituted alkene
Br
CH_3CH_2ONa
Δ
2-Bromo-1-cyclopentylpentane
Desired product

(18-48)

The main lesson from these examples is that, when given the option of using either a Wittig reaction or an elimination reaction to synthesize an alkene, a Wittig reaction is usually the better choice to maximize percent yield of the desired product.

GREEN CHEMISTRY Even though Wittig reactions are superior to E1 or E2 reactions with regard to percent yield, E1 and E2 reactions are generally the greener option. Wittig reactions suffer from low atom economy due to the high-molecular-weight byproduct, $(C_6H_5)_3PO$, whose molecular mass is 278 g/mol. Wittig reactions also suffer because the synthesis of a Wittig reagent requires an alkyllithium base, which is pyrophoric and requires an organic solvent such as ether or hexane.

Chapter Summary and Key Terms

- The general mechanism for the addition of a strong, negatively charged nucleophile (Nu^-) to a *polar π bond* consists of two steps:

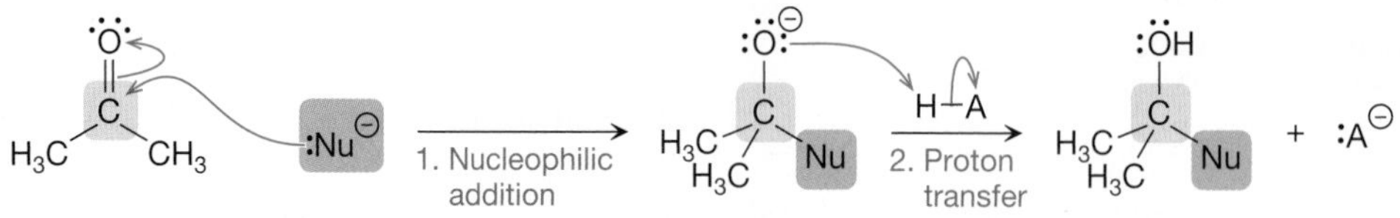

1. Nucleophilic addition
2. Proton transfer

Nucleophilic attack occurs in the first step, followed by protonation. (Section 18.1)

- Some carbonyl-containing compound classes, including carboxylic acids (RCO_2H), esters (RCO_2R), amides ($RCONR_2$), acid chlorides ($RCOCl$), and acid anhydrides (RCO_2COR), have a leaving group attached to the carbonyl carbon. As such, the reactivities of these compound classes differ from those of ketones and aldehydes. (Section 18.1)
- Nucleophilic addition to the carbonyl group of an aldehyde tends to be more energetically favorable and faster than addition to the carbonyl group of a ketone. (Section 18.2)
- Lithium aluminum hydride ($LiAlH_4$) and sodium borohydride ($NaBH_4$) are sources of nucleophilic H^- in the presence of a polar π bond. Both reagents convert ketones ($R_2C{=}O$) and aldehydes ($RCH{=}O$) into alcohols (ROH), and they convert imines ($R_2C{=}NR$) into amines ($R_2CH{-}NHR$). A nitrile (RCN) can be converted into a primary amine (RCH_2NH_2) by $LiAlH_4$ but not by $NaBH_4$. (Sections 18.3a and 18.3b)
- $LiAlH_4$ is a very strong base, so it is incompatible with protic solvents like water and alcohols. (Section 18.3a)
- Sodium hydride (NaH) is an ionic hydride, and thus a strong base, but it is not nucleophilic. (Section 18.3c)
- Grignard reagents ($RMgX$) and alkyllithium reagents (RLi) are strong nucleophiles and strong bases. They add to the electron-poor C atom of C=O, C=N, and C≡N bonds. (Section 18.4)
  - The reaction of a Grignard or alkyllithium reagent with a ketone or aldehyde will produce an alcohol.
  - The reaction of a Grignard or alkyllithium reagent with CO_2 is a **carboxylation** reaction that will produce a carboxylic acid.
  - The reaction of a Grignard or alkyllithium reagent with an imine will produce an amine, and a reaction involving a nitrile will produce an imine.
- Functional groups that are acidic or are susceptible to nucleophilic attack tend to interfere with desired reactions involving Grignard and alkyllithium reagents. (Sections 18.4 and 18.5)
- A **Wittig reagent**, also called a **phosphonium ylide**, is characterized by a $^+P{-}C{:}^-$ bond and is strongly nucleophilic at the negatively charged carbon atom. In a **Wittig reaction**, the phosphonium ylide undergoes nucleophilic addition to the C=O bond of a ketone or aldehyde, and after subsequent elimination, an alkene is formed. (Section 18.6)
- A Wittig reagent is synthesized by treating an alkyl halide with Ph_3P, followed by a very strong base such as an alkyllithium reagent. (Section 18.7)
- A polar π bond that is part of an **α,β-unsaturated carbonyl compound** is susceptible to nucleophilic attack at both the electron-poor atom of the polar π bond and the **β carbon**. Attack at the carbonyl carbon yields the **direct addition** (or *1,2-addition*) product, whereas attack at the β carbon yields the **conjugate addition** (or *1,4-addition*) product. (Section 18.8)

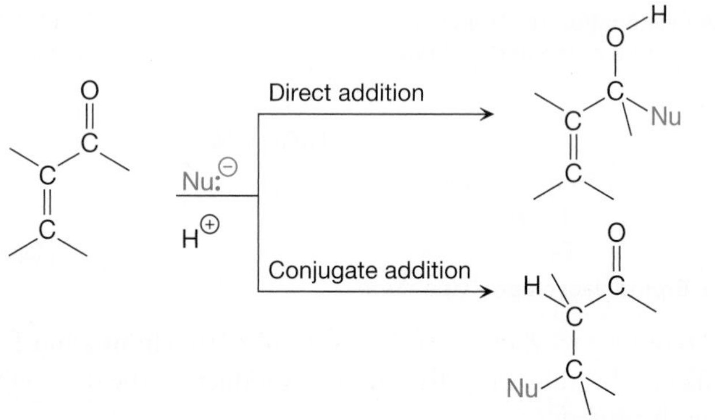

Direct addition
Conjugate addition

- Direct addition to an α,β-unsaturated polar π bond is favored if the nucleophile adds *irreversibly* to the polar π bond. Otherwise, conjugate addition is favored. (Section 18.8)
- Most nucleophiles add reversibly to a polar π bond. Nucleophiles that add irreversibly include H^- from either $NaBH_4$ or $LiAlH_4$ and R^- from $R{-}MgX$, $R{-}Li$, or Wittig reagents. (Section 18.8)
- **Lithium dialkylcuprates** (R_2CuLi) are weak R^- nucleophiles that favor conjugate addition over direct addition. (Section 18.9)
- The reaction of a Grignard or alkyllithium reagent with a ketone or aldehyde is useful in synthesis because a new C—C bond is formed, and the product is an alcohol that can be used for further reactions. (Section 18.10)
- The products of direct addition and conjugate addition to an α,β-unsaturated ketone or aldehyde have distinct features. In direct addition, the C=O group is converted into a C—OH group and the C=C bond remains. In conjugate addition, the C=C bond is converted into a C—C bond and the C=O bond remains. (Section 18.11)
- When the target of a synthesis calls for a new C=C bond, Wittig reactions are generally better choices than E1 or E2 reactions because Wittig reactions are regiospecific. (Section 18.12)

Reaction Tables

Functional group transformations introduced in this chapter are collected in Table 18-3, and reactions introduced in this chapter that alter the carbon skeleton are collected in Table 18-4.

TABLE 18-3 Functional Group Transformations

	Starting Compound Class	Typical Reagents and Reaction Conditions	Compound Class Formed	Key Electron-Rich Species	Key Electron-Poor Species	Comments	Discussed in Section
(1)	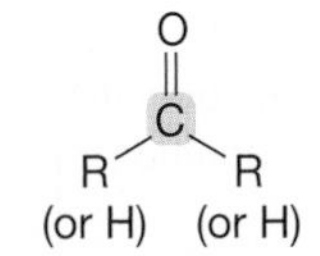 Ketone or aldehyde	1. $NaBH_4$ or $LiAlH_4$ 2. H_2O, H_2SO_4	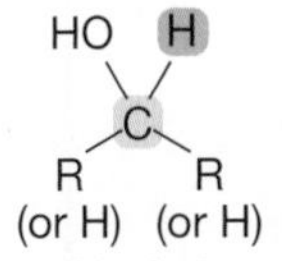 Alcohol	$:H^{\ominus}$ Hydride anion	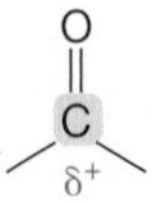	Nucleophilic addition	18.3
(2)	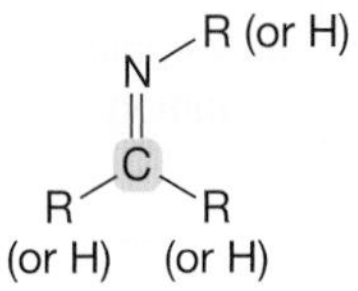 Imine	1. $LiAlH_4$ 2. H_2O	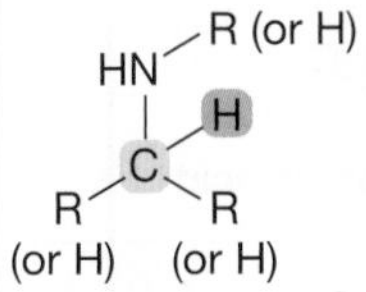 Amine	$:H^{\ominus}$ Hydride anion	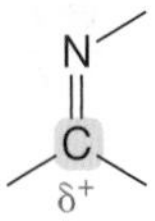	Nucleophilic addition	18.3
(3)	R—C≡N Nitrile	1. $LiAlH_4$ 2. H_2O	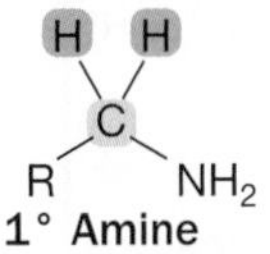 1° Amine	$:H^{\ominus}$ Hydride anion	δ^+ —C≡N	Sequential nucleophilic additions	18.3
(4)	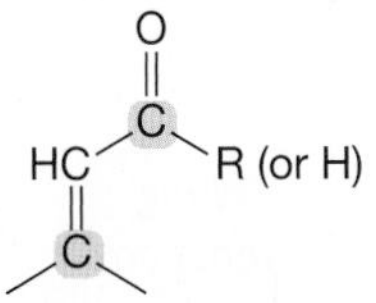 α,β-Unsaturated ketone or aldehyde	1. $NaBH_4$ or $LiAlH_4$ 2. NH_4Cl, H_2O	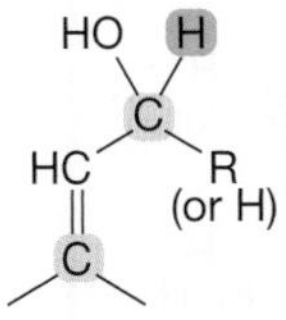 Alcohol	$:H^{\ominus}$ Hydride anion	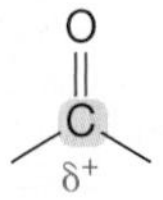	Nucleophilic addition	18.8
(5)	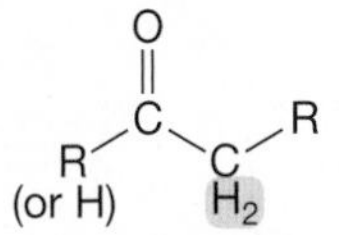 Ketone or aldehyde	NaH	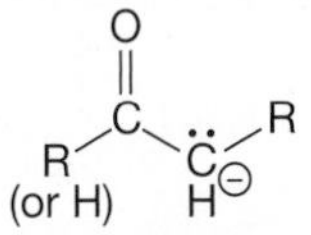 Enolate anion	$:H^{\ominus}$ Hydride anion	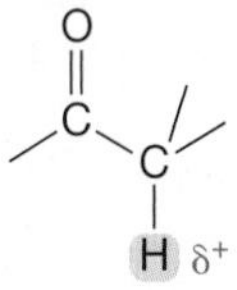	Proton transfer	18.3
(6)	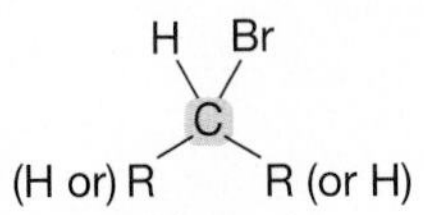 Alkyl halide	1. $P(C_6H_5)_3$ 2. R–Li	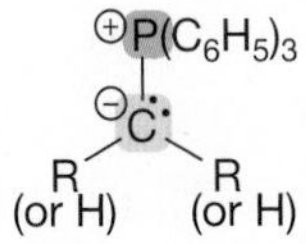 Wittig reagent	δ^- $:P(C_6H_5)_3$ Triphenylphosphine	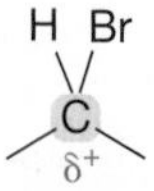	S_N2 followed by proton transfer	18.6

TABLE 18-4 Reactions That Alter the Carbon Skeleton

	Starting Compound Class	Typical Reagents and Reaction Conditions	Compound Class Formed	Key Electron-Rich Species	Key Electron-Poor Species	Comments	Discussed in Section
(1)	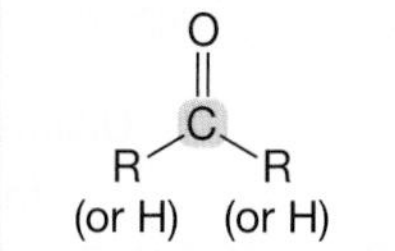 Ketone or aldehyde	1. R′—Li or R′—MgX 2. H_2O, H_2SO_4	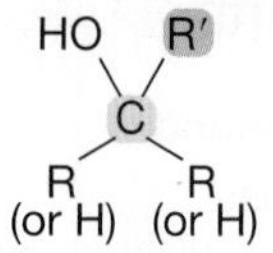 Alcohol	:R′⊖	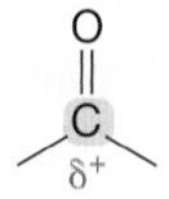	Nucleophilic addition	18.4
(2)	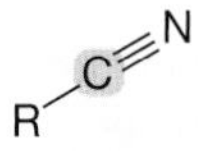 Nitrile	1. R′—MgX 2. CH_3OH	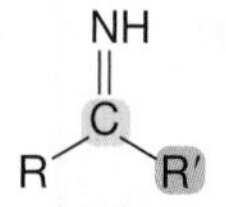 Imine	:R′⊖	$R-\overset{\delta+}{C}\equiv N$	Nucleophilic addition	18.4
(3)	 Grignard reagent	1. $CO_2(s)$ 2. H_2O, H_2SO_4	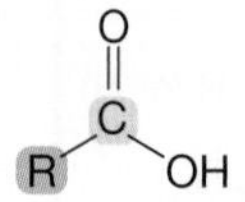 Carboxylic acid	:R⊖	$O=\overset{\delta+}{C}=O$	Nucleophilic addition	18.4
(4)	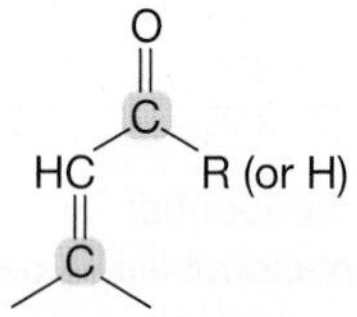 α,β-Unsaturated ketone or aldehyde	1. R'_2CuLi, THF 2. NH_4Cl, H_2O	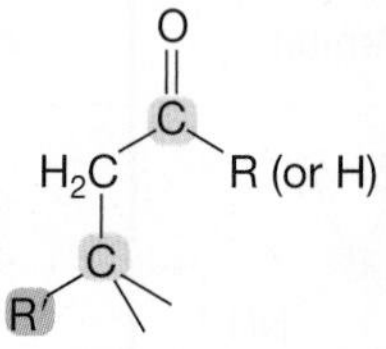 Ketone or aldehyde	:R′⊖	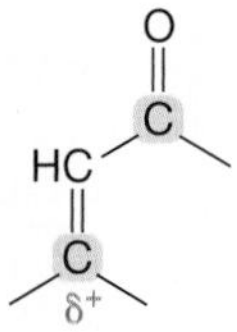	Conjugate nucleophilic addition	18.9
(5)	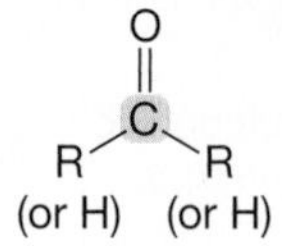 Ketone or aldehyde	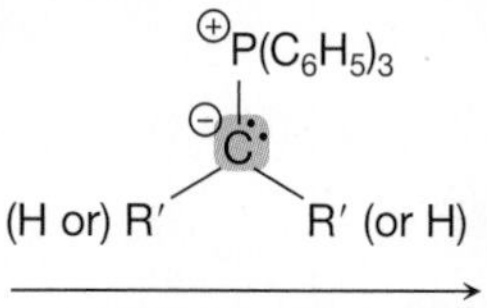 Wittig reagent	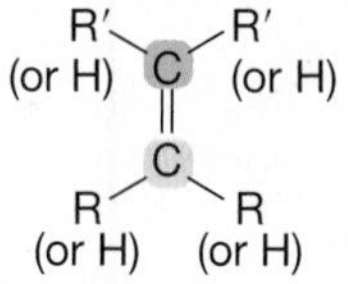 Alkene	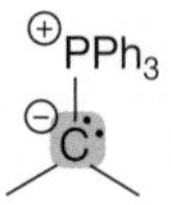	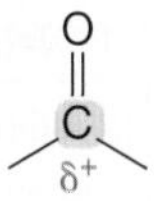	Wittig reaction	18.6

Problems

Problems that are related to synthesis are denoted (SYN).

Sections 18.1 and 18.2 Addition of Strong Nucleophiles and Substituent Effects

18.1 For each pair of compounds, which compound has the polar π bond that will undergo nucleophilic addition more rapidly? Why?

(a)

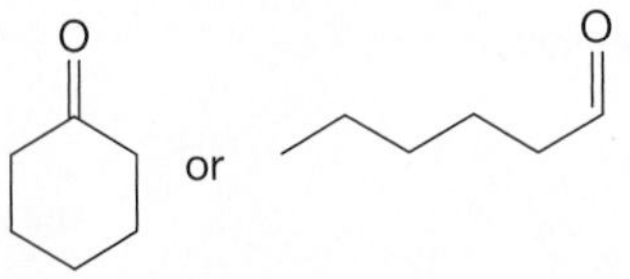

(b)

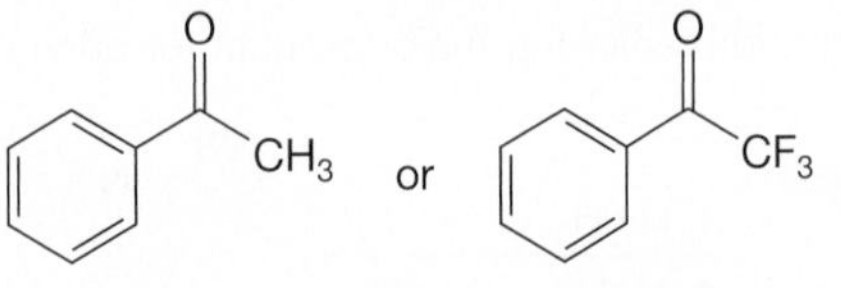

(c)

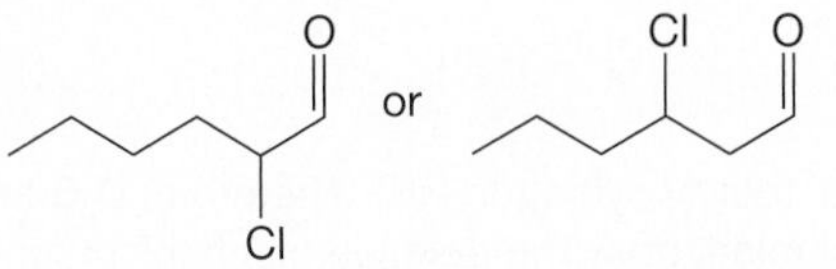

(d) $Cl_3C-C\equiv N$ or $H_3C-C\equiv N$

18.2 Compounds **A** and **B** are both ketones. Which one would you expect to undergo hydration to a greater extent? Explain.

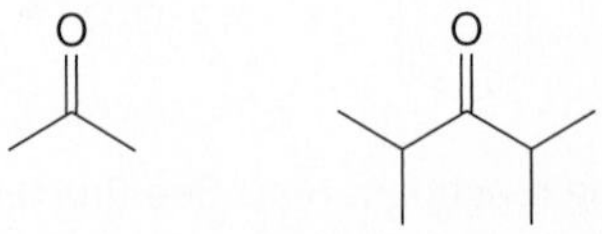

A **B**

18.3 Chloral, $Cl_3CCH{=}O$, forms a very stable hydrate called chloral hydrate, a potent sedative. When it is dissolved in water, essentially 100% of chloral is hydrated. In contrast, the extent of hydration for ethanal (acetaldehyde) is much smaller (see Table 18-1, p. 882). Explain why.

18.4 Unlike most hydrates, the hydrate of cyclopropanone is stable and can be isolated. Explain why this hydrate is stable.

18.5 Draw the mechanism for each of the following reactions.

(a)

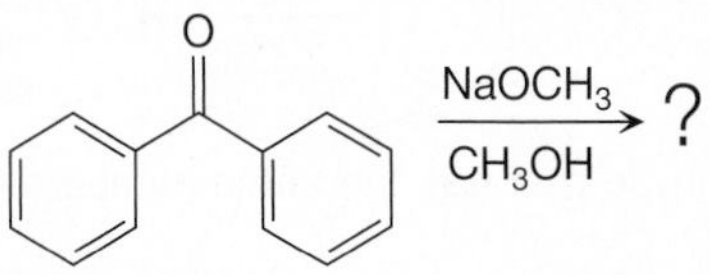

(b)

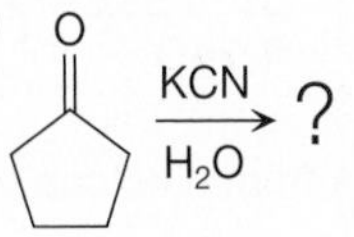

(c)

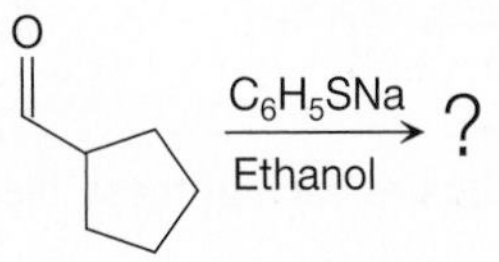

18.6 Draw the mechanism for the following reaction.

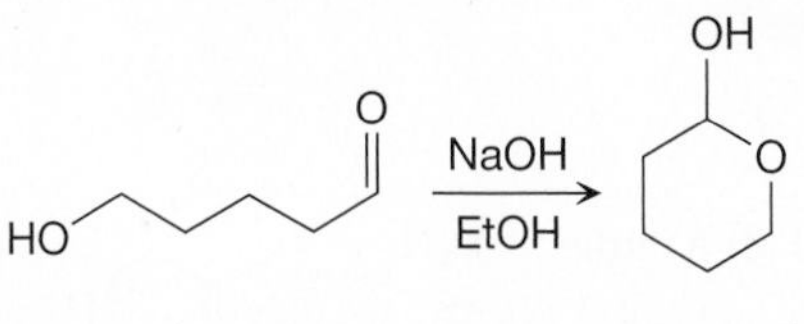

18.7 The treatment of a nitrile with cyanide yields an α-aminomalononitrile, as shown here in the reaction. Provide a detailed mechanism for this reaction.

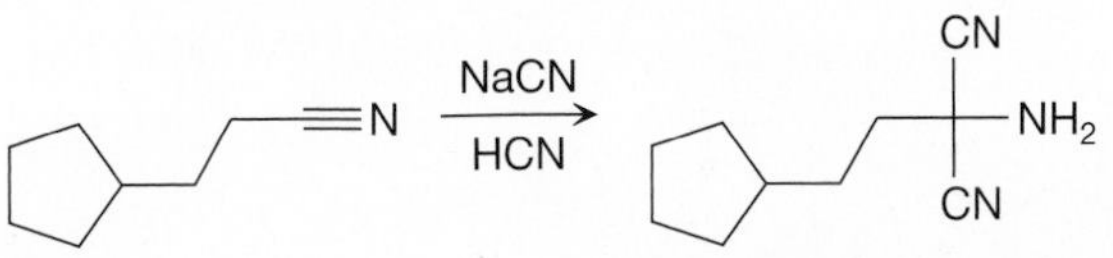

An α-aminomalononitrile

18.8 **(SYN)** Draw the ketone or aldehyde and the nucleophile that would be required to form each of these species.

(a)

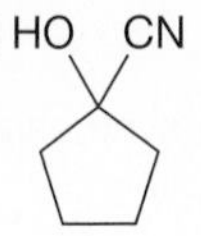

(b)

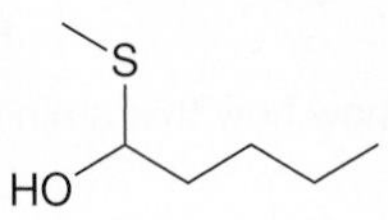

Section 18.3 Reactions of Hydride Agents

18.9 Draw the mechanism and predict the major product for each of the following reactions.

(a)
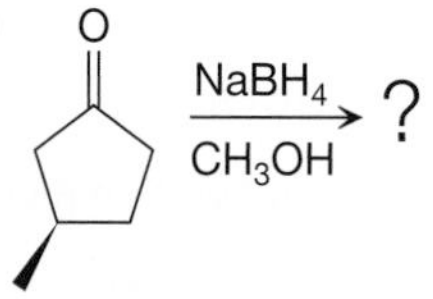
O
NaBH4
CH3OH
?

(b)
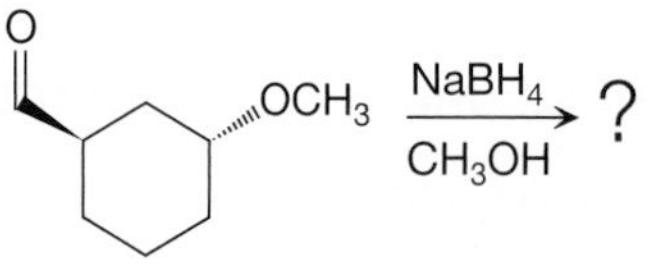
O
OCH3
NaBH4
CH3OH
?

(c)
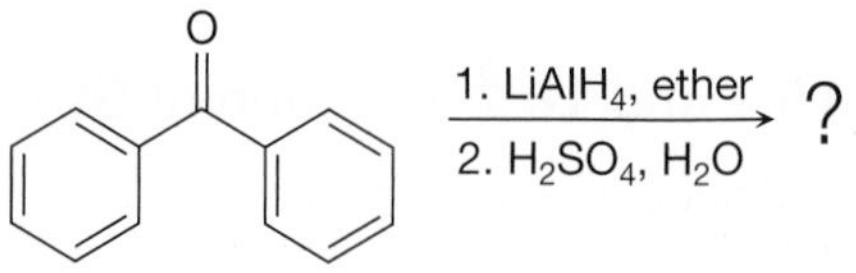
O
1. LiAlH4, ether
2. H2SO4, H2O
?

18.10 Draw the mechanism and predict the major product for each of the following reactions.

(a)
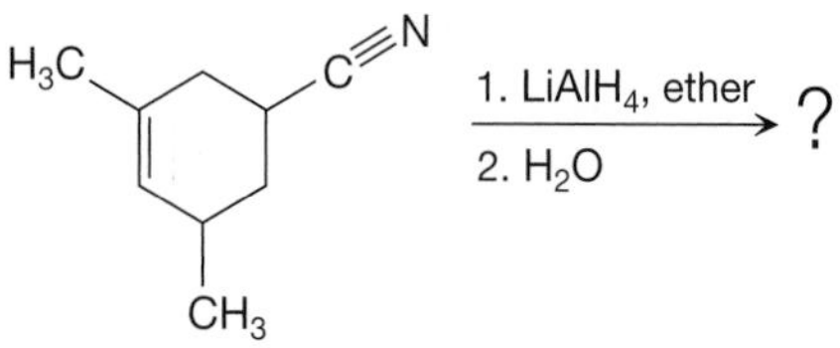
H3C
C≡N
CH3
1. LiAlH4, ether
2. H2O
?

(b)
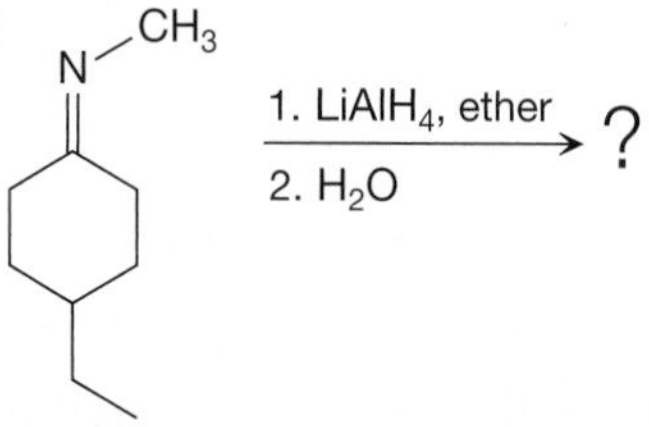
N
CH3
1. LiAlH4, ether
2. H2O
?

(c)
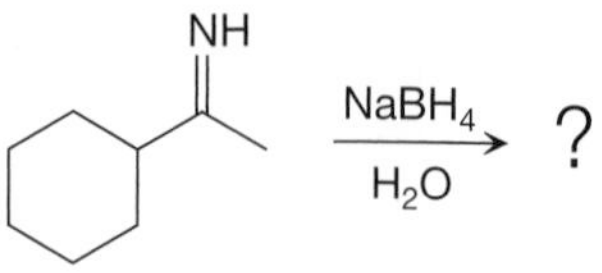
NH
NaBH4
H2O
?

18.11 The chemical behavior of deuterium (D or ^{2}H) is essentially identical to that of hydrogen (^{1}H). Therefore, D_2O behaves the same as H_2O, and $LiAlD_4$ behaves the same as $LiAlH_4$. With this in mind, draw the detailed mechanism for each of the following reactions. Using that mechanism, predict the reaction products in each case.

(a)
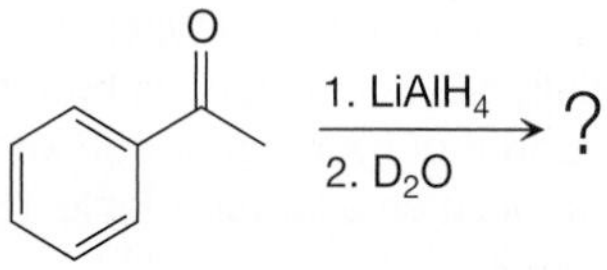
O
1. LiAlH4
2. D2O
?

(b)
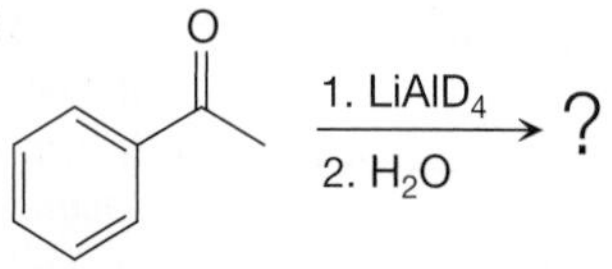
O
1. LiAlD4
2. H2O
?

(c)
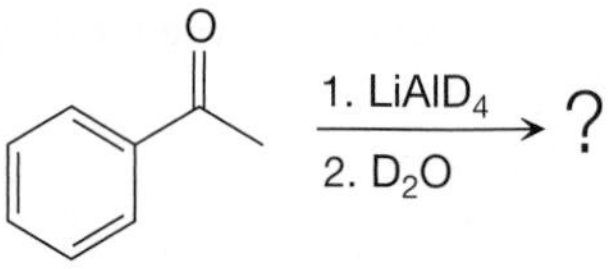
O
1. LiAlD4
2. D2O
?

18.12 Draw the mechanism and the major organic product for each of the following reactions. *Hint*: See Problem 18.11.

(a)
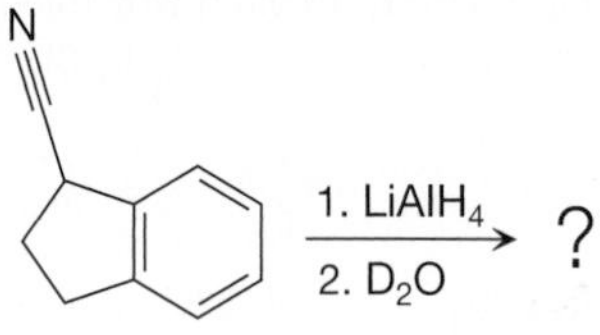
N
1. LiAlH4
2. D2O
?

(b)
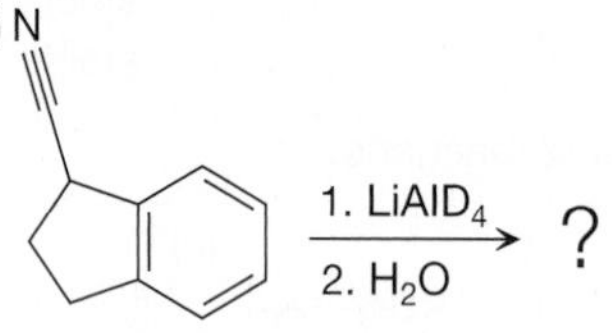
N
1. LiAlD4
2. H2O
?

(c)
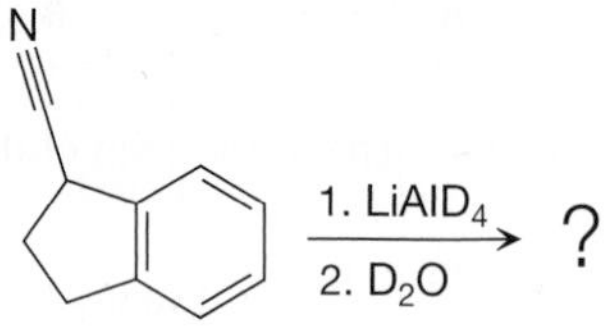
N
1. LiAlD4
2. D2O
?

18.13 (SYN) Show how to synthesize each of these alcohols from a ketone or aldehyde that has the same number of carbons as the alcohol.

(a)
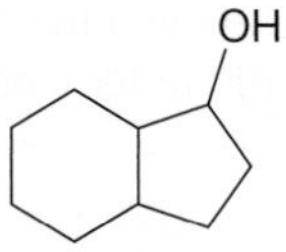
OH

(b)

HO

(c)
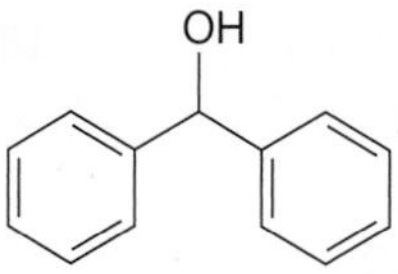
OH

18.14 (SYN) Show how this amine can be synthesized from (a) an imine and (b) a nitrile.
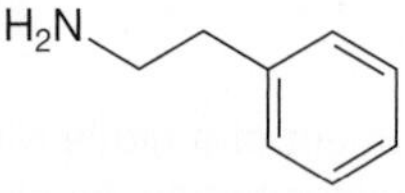
H2N

18.15 (SYN) Show how each of these deuterium-labeled alcohols can be synthesized from a ketone or an aldehyde. *Hint*: See Problem 18.11.

(a)
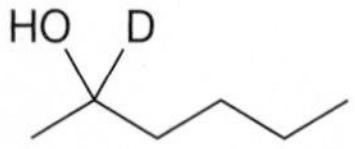
HO
D

(b)
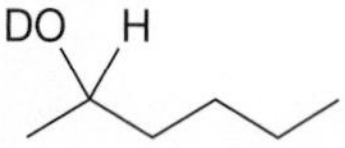
DO
H

(c)
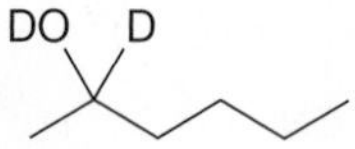
DO
D

18.16 Draw the mechanism and predict the major product for the reaction shown here.
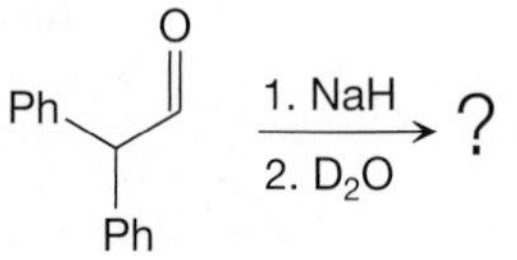
O
Ph
Ph
1. NaH
2. D2O
?

18.17 Draw the mechanism and predict the major product for each of the following reactions.

(a) 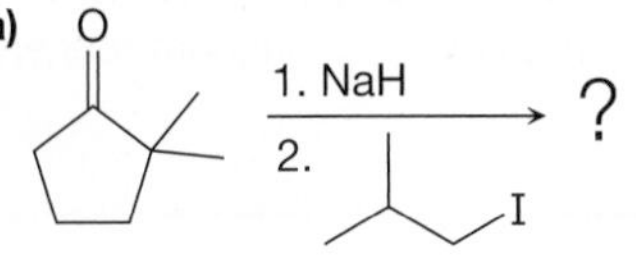
1. NaH
2.
I
?

(b) 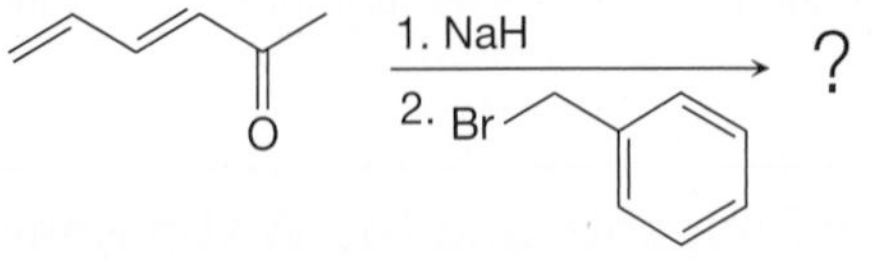
O
1. NaH
2. Br
?

18.18 (SYN) Show how to carry out each of the following transformations.

(a) 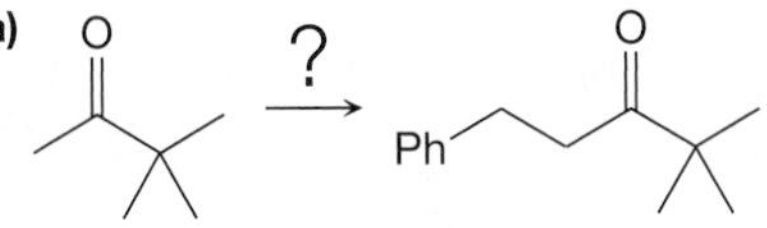
O
?
O
Ph

(b) 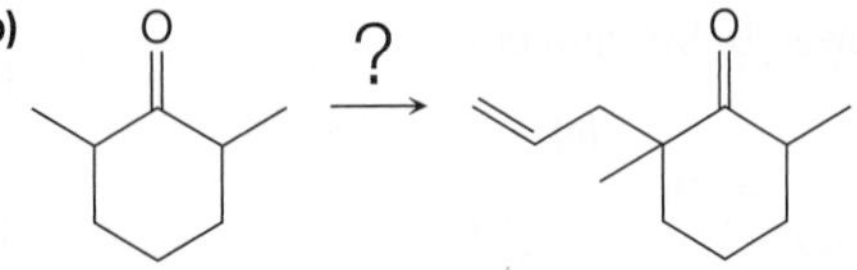
O
?
O

Sections 18.4 and 18.5 Reactions of Alkyllithium Reagents and Grignard Reagents

18.19 Draw the mechanism and predict the major product for each of the following reactions.

(a) 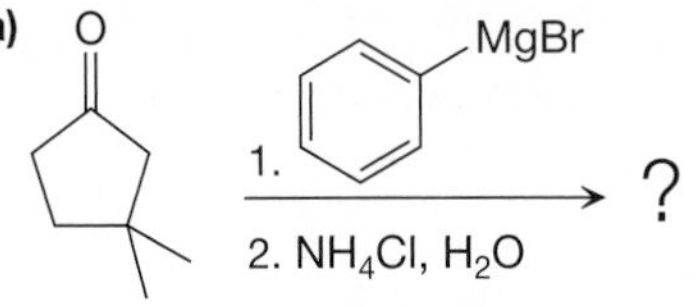
O
MgBr
1.
2. NH_4Cl, H_2O
?

(b) 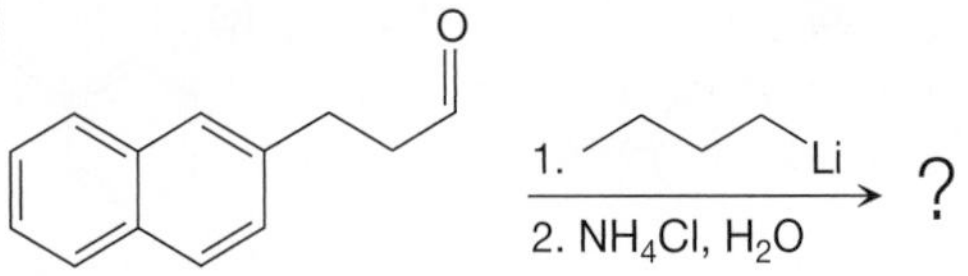
O
1.
Li
2. NH_4Cl, H_2O
?

(c) CH_3MgBr $\xrightarrow[\text{2. } H_2O,\ HCl]{\text{1. } CO_2(s)}$?

18.20 Draw the mechanism and predict the major product for each of the following reactions.

(a) 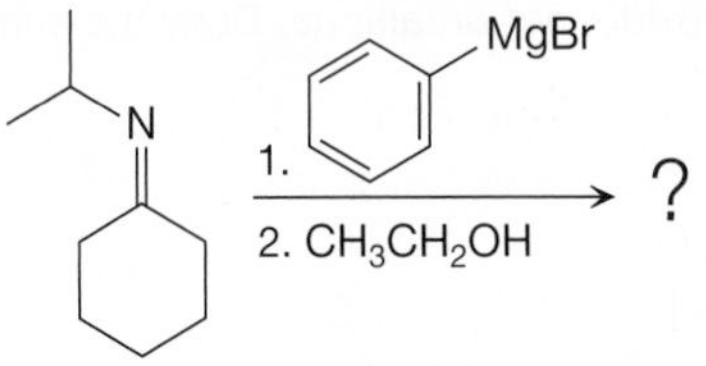
N
MgBr
1.
2. CH_3CH_2OH
?

(b) 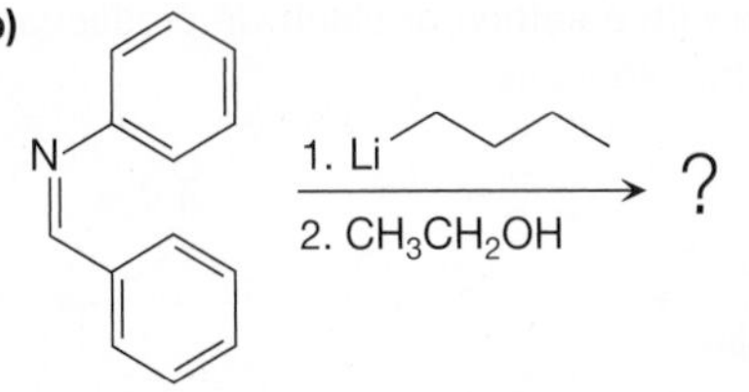
N
1. Li
2. CH_3CH_2OH
?

(c) 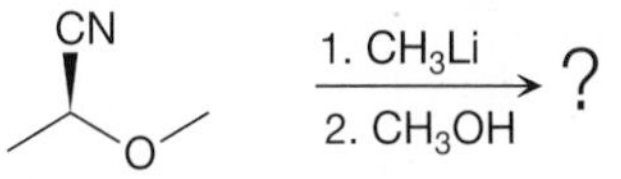
CN
O
1. CH_3Li
2. CH_3OH
?

18.21 The chemical behavior of deuterium (D or ^2H) is essentially identical to that of hydrogen (^1H). Therefore, D_2O behaves the same as H_2O, and CD_3Li behaves the same as CH_3Li. With this in mind, draw the detailed mechanism of each of the following reactions. Using that mechanism, predict the reaction products in each case.

(a) 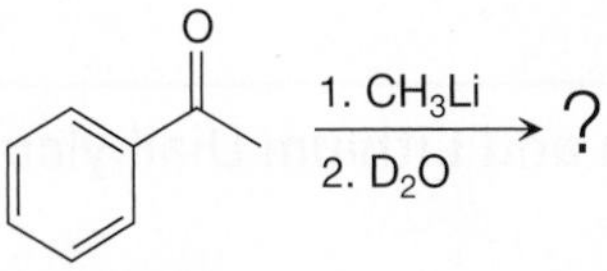
O
1. CH_3Li
2. D_2O
?

(b) 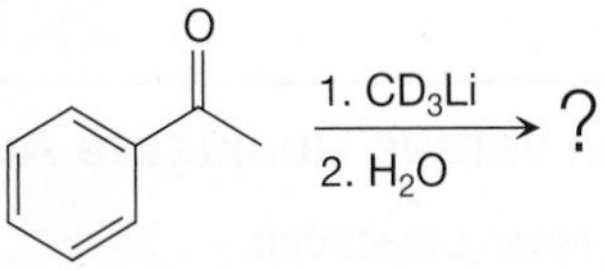
O
1. CD_3Li
2. H_2O
?

(c) 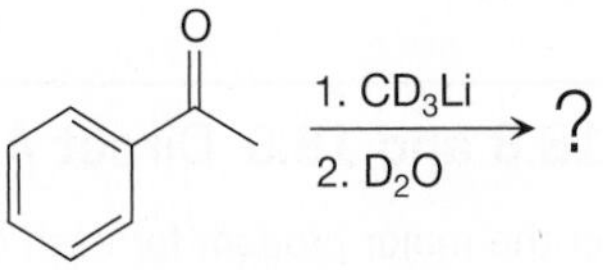
O
1. CD_3Li
2. D_2O
?

18.22 (SYN) Propose three different syntheses of the alcohol shown here, each using a different Grignard reagent.

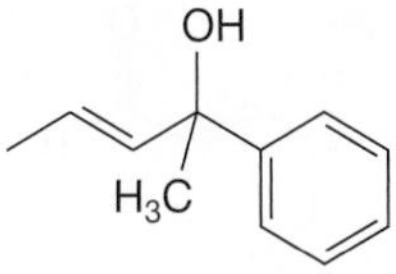
OH
H_3C

18.23 (SYN) Show how to carry out each of the following transformations.

(a) 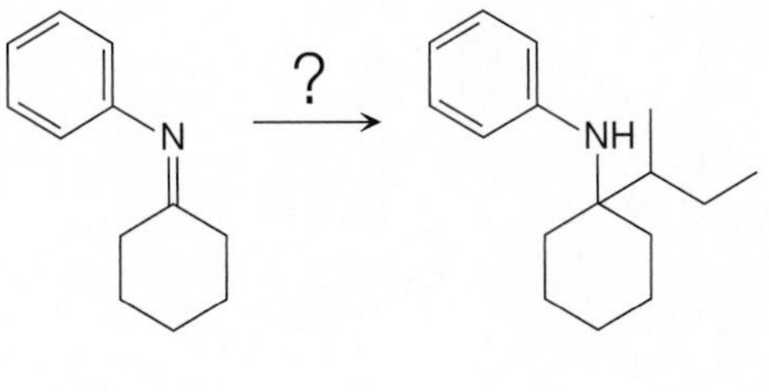
N
?
NH

(b) 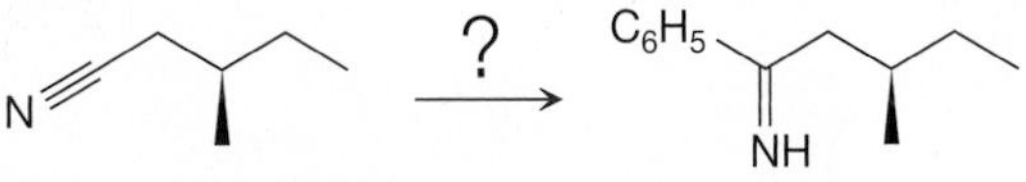
N
?
C_6H_5
NH

18.24 Alkyllithium and Grignard reagents are highly reactive with protic solvents (e.g., water and alcohols), so they require aprotic solvents (e.g., ethers). Acetone is an aprotic solvent that can be used in nucleophilic substitution and elimination reactions, but it cannot be used as a solvent for reactions involving alkyllithium and Grignard reagents. Explain why.

Sections 18.6 and 18.7 Wittig Reagents and the Wittig Reaction

18.25 Draw the complete mechanism that takes place when each of the following species is treated first with triphenylphosphine, followed by butyllithium.

(a)
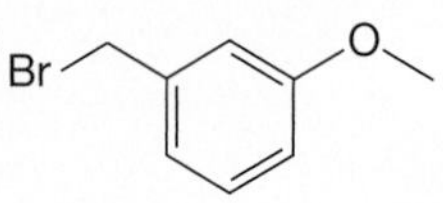

Br
O

(b)
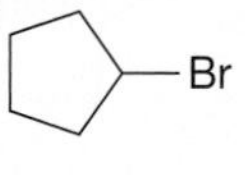

Br

(c)
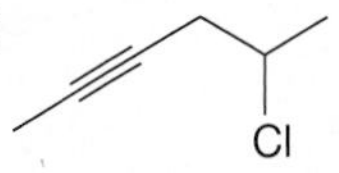

Cl

18.26 **(SYN)** Show how to synthesize each of these species from an alkyl halide.

(a)
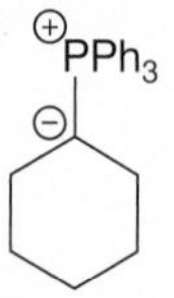

PPh3

(b)
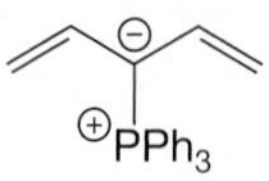

PPh3

(c)
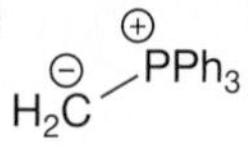

PPh3
H2C

18.27 Draw the complete mechanism for the reaction between benzaldehyde and each of the species from Problem 18.26.

18.28 **(SYN)** Show how to synthesize each of the following compounds from an alkyl halide and a ketone or aldehyde.

(a)
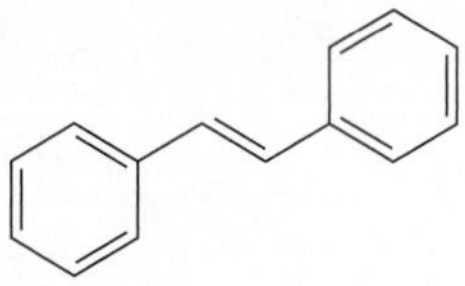

(b)
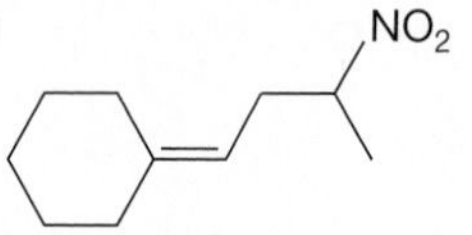

NO2

(c)
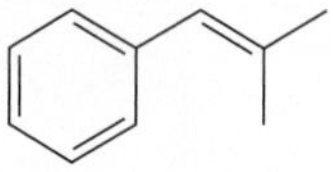

18.29 This chapter discusses how a phosphonium ylide is produced from an alkyl halide, and how such a phosphonium ylide reacts with a ketone or aldehyde to produce an alkene. *Sulfonium ylides* can also be produced from alkyl halides, as shown here, but their reaction with a ketone or aldehyde produces an epoxide, not an alkene. Draw the complete mechanism for each reaction in this sequence.

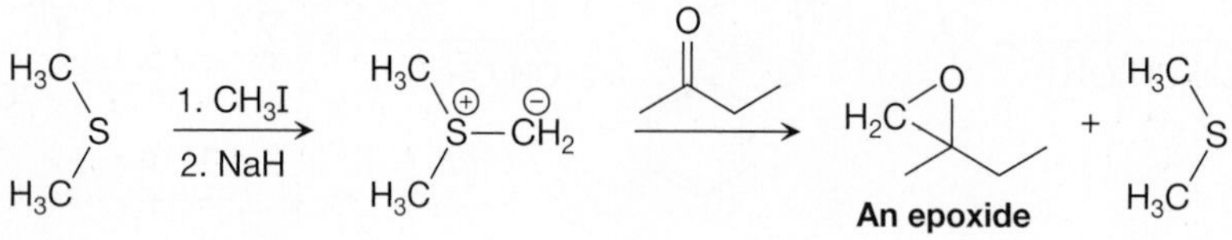

H3C
S
H3C
1. CH3I
2. NaH
S—CH2
O
H2C
+
An epoxide

18.30 The reaction of a phosphonium ylide with a ketone or aldehyde produces an alkene, but as shown in Problem 18.29, the reaction of a sulfonium ylide produces an epoxide. Explain why. *Hint*: What is the major driving force for the Wittig reaction to produce an alkene? The $^{+}S—O^{-}$ bond energy in dimethyl sulfoxide is 362 kJ/mol.

Sections 18.8 and 18.9 Direct Addition versus Conjugate Addition and Lithium Dialkylcuprates

18.31 Predict the major product for each of the following reactions.

(a)
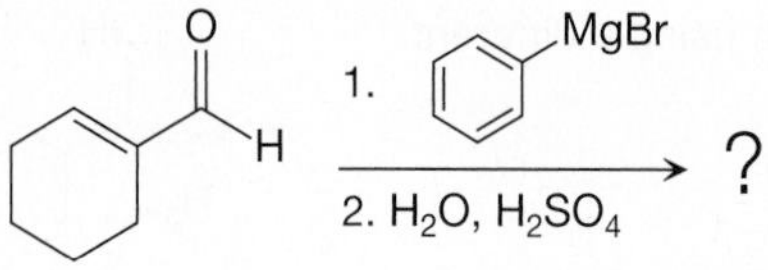

O
H
1. MgBr
2. H2O, H2SO4
?

(b)
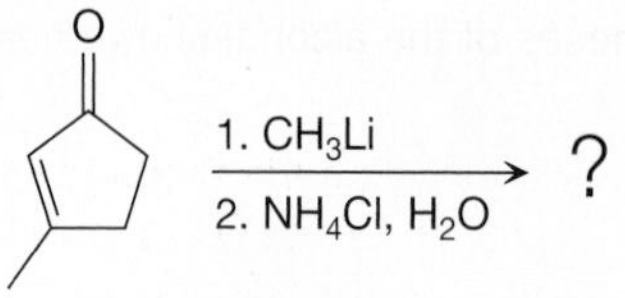

O
1. CH3Li
2. NH4Cl, H2O
?

(c)
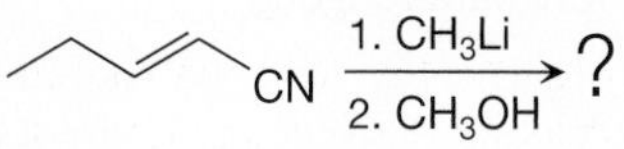

CN
1. CH3Li
2. CH3OH
?

18.32 Which of the following nucleophiles will add *reversibly* to a polar π bond? Which will add *irreversibly*?

(a) 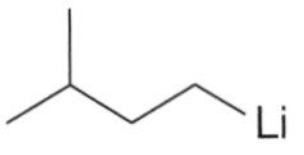
Li

(b) 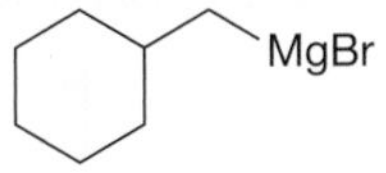
MgBr

(c) 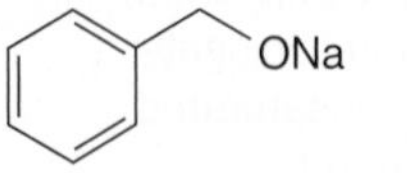
ONa

(d) 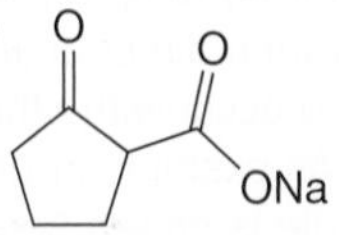
O
O
ONa

(e) 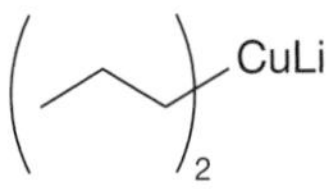
CuLi
2

(f) 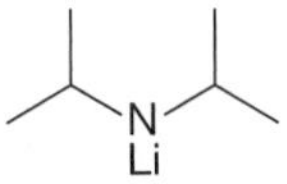
N
Li

(g) H_2O

(h) 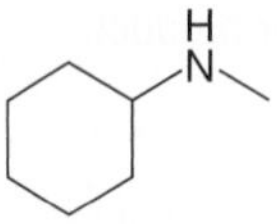
H
N

(i) 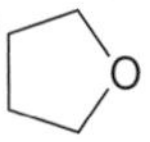
O

(j) 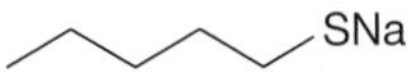
SNa

(k) 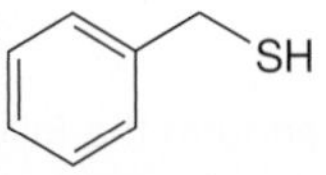
SH

18.33 Draw the mechanism and predict the major product for each of the following reactions.

(a) 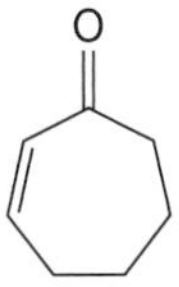
O
1. KCN, H_2O; 2. H_2SO_4 → ?

(b) 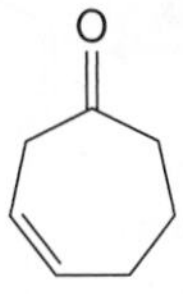
O
1. KCN, H_2O; 2. H_2SO_4 → ?

(c) 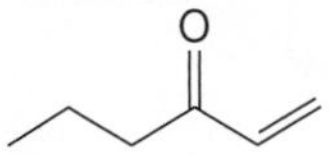
O
1. CH_3MgBr, ether; 2. NH_4Cl, H_2O → ?

(d) 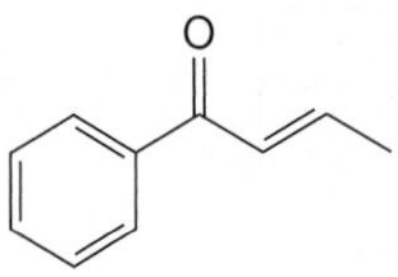
O
1. 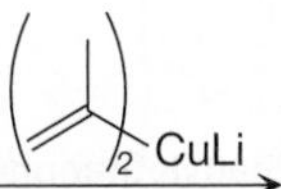
2
CuLi
2. NH_4Cl, H_2O → ?

(e) 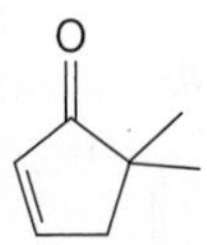
O
1. CH_3CH_2SNa, ethanol; 2. NH_4Cl, H_2O → ?

18.34 **(SYN)** Show two different syntheses for the compound shown here, one with $(CH_3)_2CuLi$ as a reagent and the other with $(CH_3CH_2)_2CuLi$.

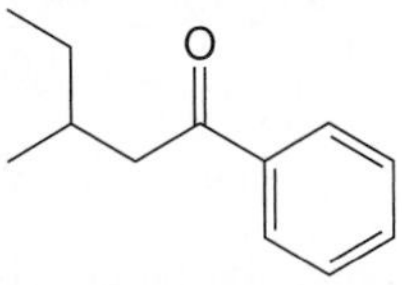
O

18.35 The conjugate addition of $NaBH_4$ to an α,β-unsaturated carbonyl compound occurs to a small extent, but when it does, it results in two sequential nucleophilic additions. The conjugate addition of a lithium dialkylcuprate (R_2CuLi), on the other hand, results in only a single nucleophilic addition. Explain.

18.36 Draw the complete, detailed mechanism for the reaction shown here. (See Problem 18.35.)

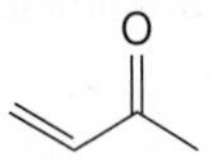
O
$NaBH_4$ / Ethanol →
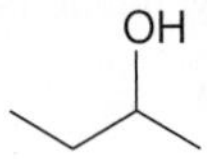
OH

Integrated Problems

18.37 When this conjugated ketone is treated with CH_3MgBr followed by an acid workup, 86% of the product is from direct addition and 14% is from conjugate addition. When CH_3Li is used instead, >99% of the product is from direct addition and <1% is from conjugate addition. Explain why CH_3Li is more selective toward direct addition.

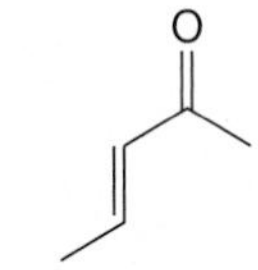
O

18.38 Both $NaBH_4$ and $LiAlH_4$ favor direct addition to an α,β-unsaturated carbonyl over conjugate addition, but their selectivities differ. Which of these hydride reducing agents would be more selective toward direct addition? Why?

18.39 Although thus far we have examined conjugate addition only as it pertains to carbonyl compounds, competition between direct addition and conjugate addition can also occur with other α,β-unsaturated polar π bonds. An example involving an α,β-unsaturated nitrile is shown here. Predict whether the reaction will favor direct addition or conjugate addition, and draw the major product.

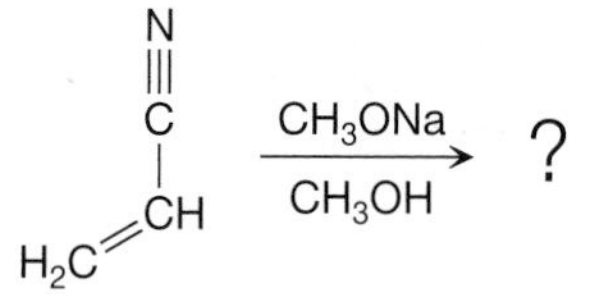

N
C
CH
H_2C
CH_3ONa
CH_3OH
?

18.40 Predict the major product of the reaction shown here. *Hint*: See Problem 18.39.

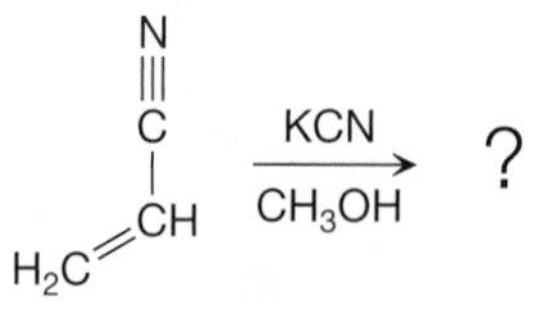

N
C
CH
H_2C
KCN
CH_3OH
?

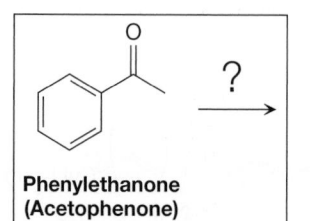

18.41 (SYN) Provide the reagents necessary to perform the following transformation.

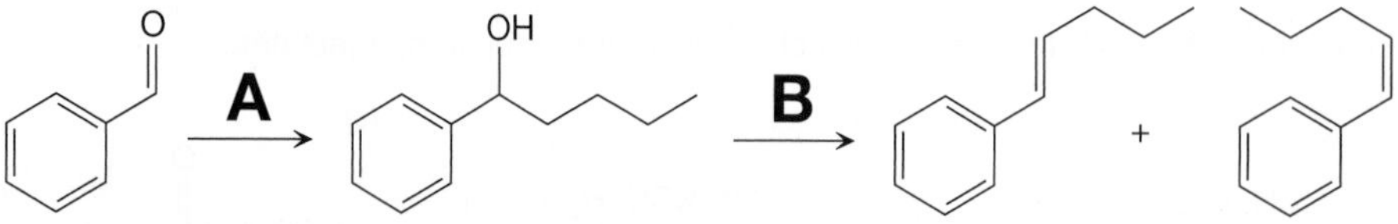

O
A
OH
B
+

18.42 (SYN) Show how you would synthesize each of the following from phenylethanone (acetophenone), using any reagents necessary. *Hint*: Each synthesis may require more than one synthetic step.

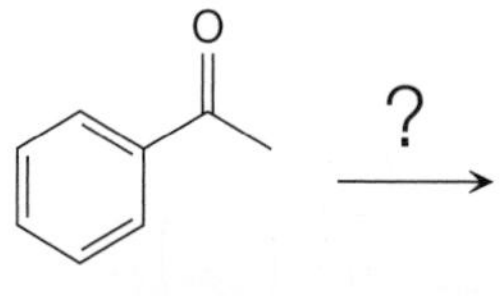

O
?

Phenylethanone (Acetophenone)

(a)

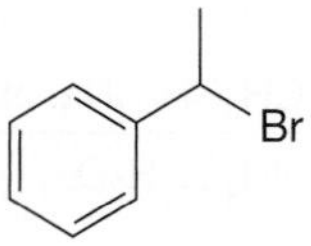

Br

(b)

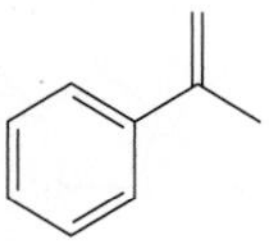

(c)

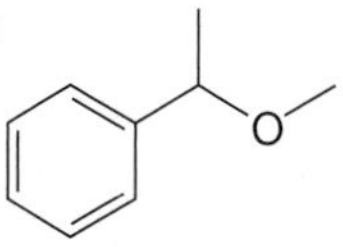

O

18.43 Predict the major organic product and draw the complete, detailed mechanism for each of the following reactions.

(a)

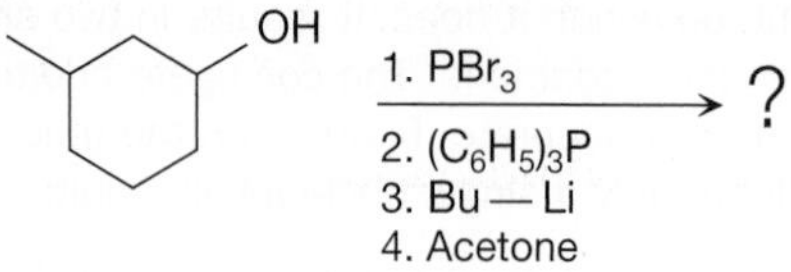

OH
1. PBr_3
2. $(C_6H_5)_3P$
3. Bu—Li
4. Acetone
?

(b)

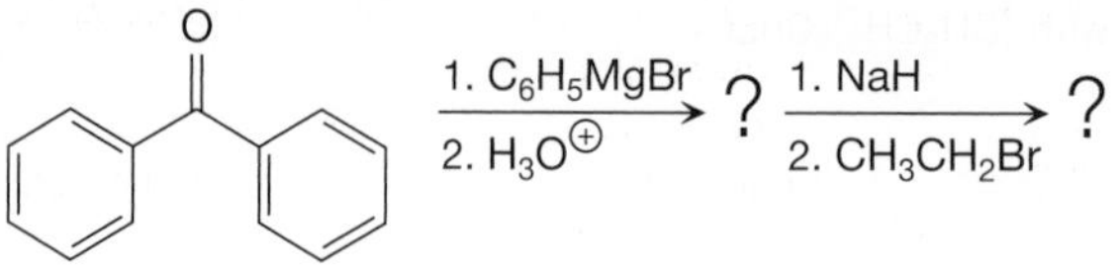

O
1. C_6H_5MgBr
2. $H_3O^{\oplus}$
?
1. NaH
2. CH_3CH_2Br
?

18.44 When carbon disulfide (S=C=S) is treated with an alcohol in the presence of base, the product is a xanthate salt. If an alkyl halide is also present, a xanthate ester is formed. Propose a mechanism for each of these reactions.

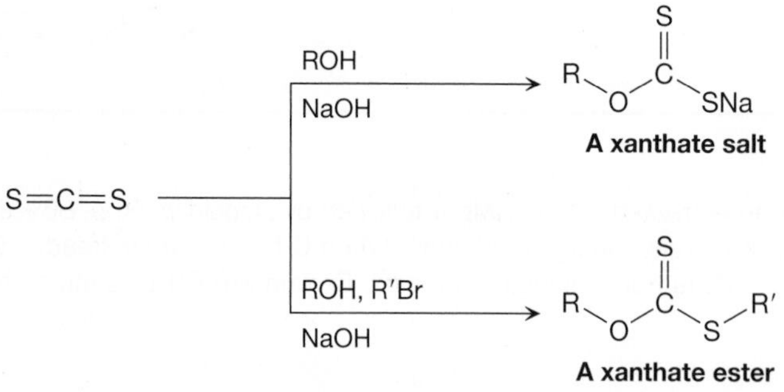

S=C=S
ROH
NaOH
S
R
C
O
SNa
A xanthate salt
ROH, R′Br
NaOH
S
R
C
O
S
R′
A xanthate ester

18.45 Phenylmagnesium bromide reacts with sulfur dioxide to produce a reactive intermediate, which, on further reaction with CH_3Br, produces methyl phenyl sulfone. Propose a mechanism for this reaction, and propose a structure for the reactive intermediate.

MgBr
SO2
THF, –78° C
?
CH3Br
O
CH3
S
O

18.46 An α,β-unsaturated ketone reacts with a conjugated Wittig reagent to produce a relatively highly strained bicyclic compound. Draw the complete, detailed mechanism for this reaction. (A key intermediate has been provided.)

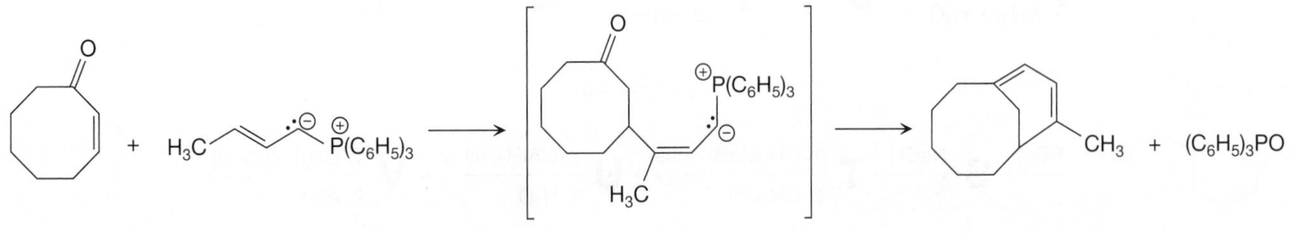
O
+ H3C
P(C6H5)3
O
P(C6H5)3
H3C
CH3 + (C6H5)3PO

18.47 The reaction shown here is an example of the Corey–Chaykovsky aziridination reaction. Draw its complete, detailed mechanism. *Hint*: See Problem 18.29.

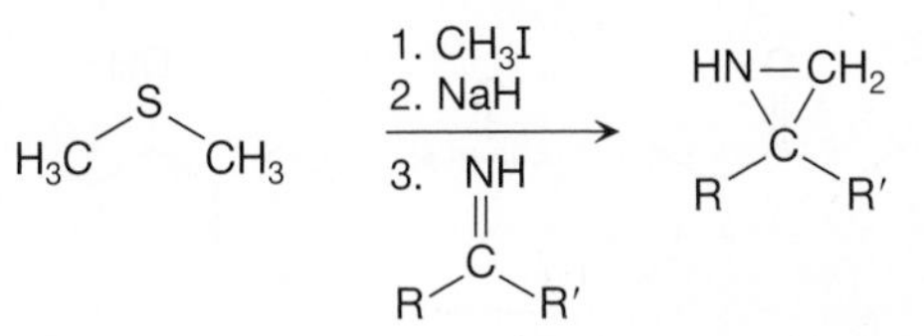
S
H3C
CH3
1. CH3I
2. NaH
3. NH
C
R
R′
HN—CH2
C
R
R′

18.48 The following is an example of the Corey–Chaykovsky cyclopropanation reaction. Draw its complete, detailed mechanism. *Hint*: See Problem 18.29.

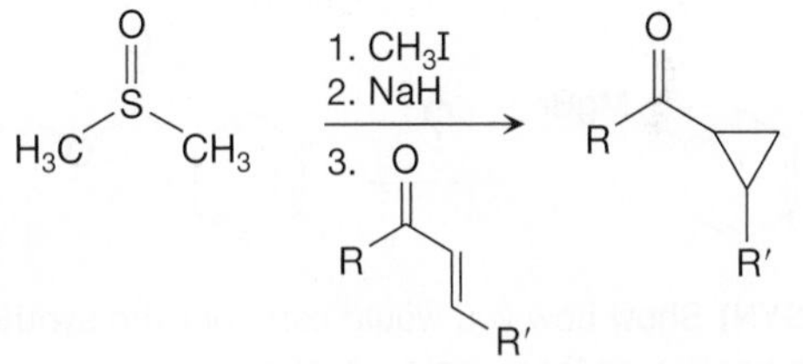
O
S
H3C
CH3
1. CH3I
2. NaH
3. O
R
R′
O
R
R′

18.49 Although a Wittig reagent can be prepared from 5-bromo-1,3-cyclopentadiene in the usual way, that Wittig reagent is unreactive toward ketones or aldehydes.

(a) Draw the complete mechanism showing the formation of the Wittig reagent.

(b) Explain why that Wittig reagent does not undergo nucleophilic addition with ketones or aldehydes.

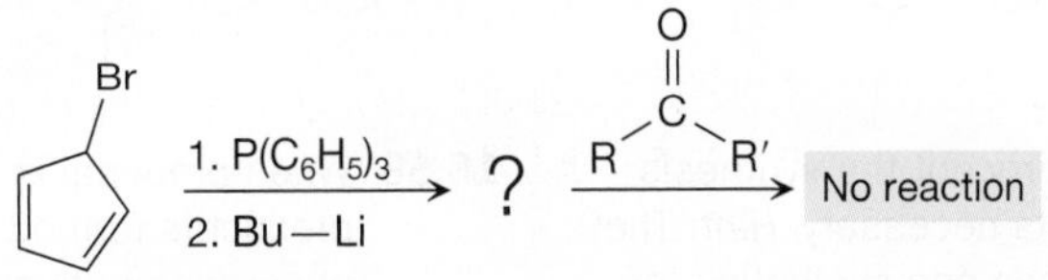
Br
1. P(C6H5)3
2. Bu—Li
?
O
C
R
R′
No reaction

18.50 Determine the structures of compounds **A–J** in the following reaction sequences.

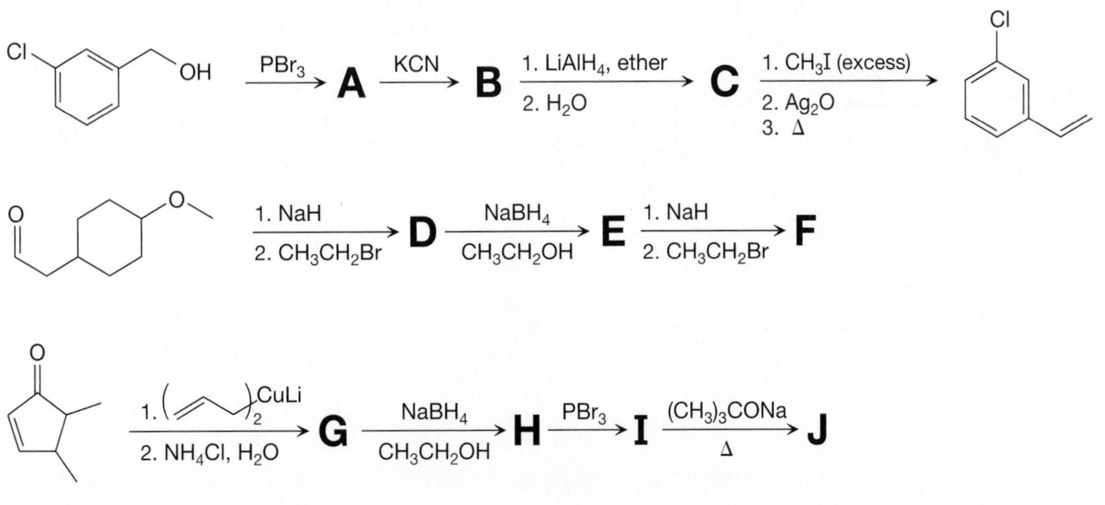
Cl
OH
PBr3
A
KCN
B
1. LiAlH4, ether
2. H2O
C
1. CH3I (excess)
2. Ag2O
3. Δ
Cl
O
O
1. NaH
2. CH3CH2Br
D
NaBH4
CH3CH2OH
E
1. NaH
2. CH3CH2Br
F
O
CuLi
2. NH4Cl, H2O
G
NaBH4
CH3CH2OH
H
PBr3
I
(CH3)3CONa
Δ
J

18.51 Determine the structures of compounds **K–V** in the following reaction sequences.

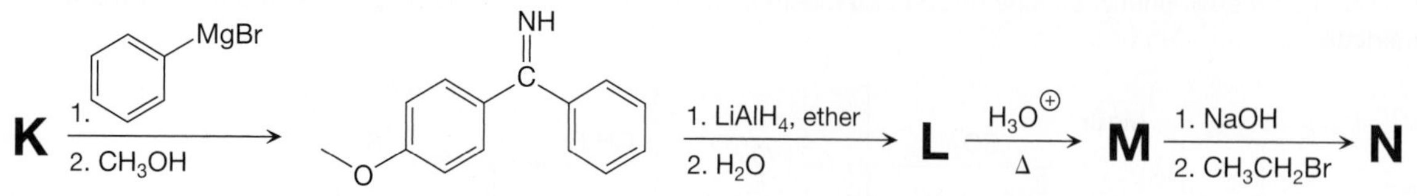

K
1. MgBr
2. CH_3OH
NH
C
O
1. $LiAlH_4$, ether
2. H_2O
L
$H_3O^{\oplus}$
Δ
M
1. NaOH
2. CH_3CH_2Br
N

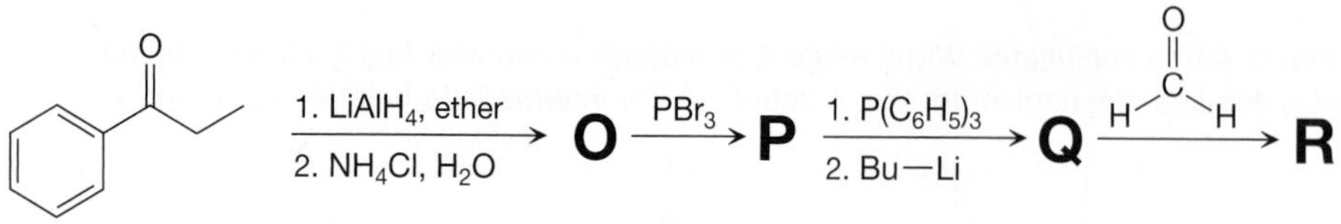

O
1. $LiAlH_4$, ether
2. NH_4Cl, H_2O
O
PBr_3
P
1. $P(C_6H_5)_3$
2. Bu—Li
Q
O
C
H
H
R

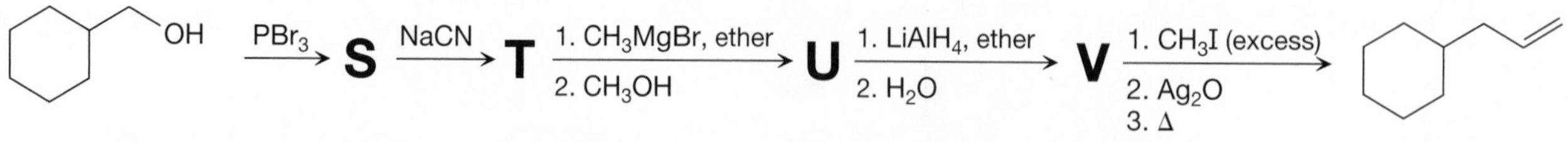

OH
PBr_3
S
NaCN
T
1. CH_3MgBr, ether
2. CH_3OH
U
1. $LiAlH_4$, ether
2. H_2O
V
1. CH_3I (excess)
2. Ag_2O
3. Δ

18.52 **(SYN)** Show how you would carry out the synthesis shown here, using any reagents necessary. *Hint*: The synthesis may require more than one synthetic step.

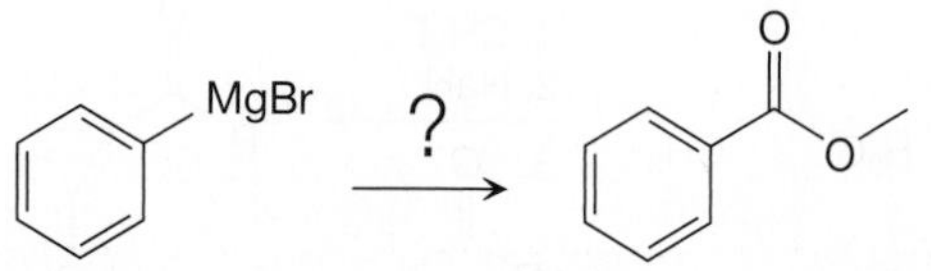

MgBr
?
O
O

18.53 **(SYN)** Show how you would carry out the synthesis shown here, using any reagents necessary. *Hint*: The synthesis may require more than one synthetic step.

O
?
OH

18.54 **(SYN)** Show how you would carry out the synthesis shown here, using any reagents necessary. *Hint*: The synthesis may require more than one synthetic step.

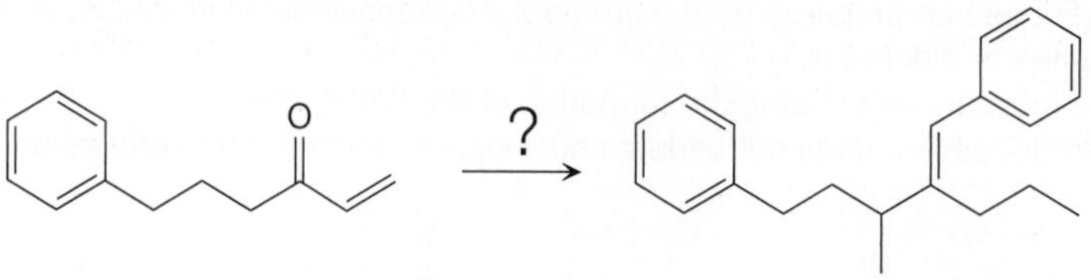

O
?

18.55 **(SYN)** Show how you would carry out the synthesis shown here, using any reagents necessary. *Hint*: The synthesis may require more than one synthetic step.

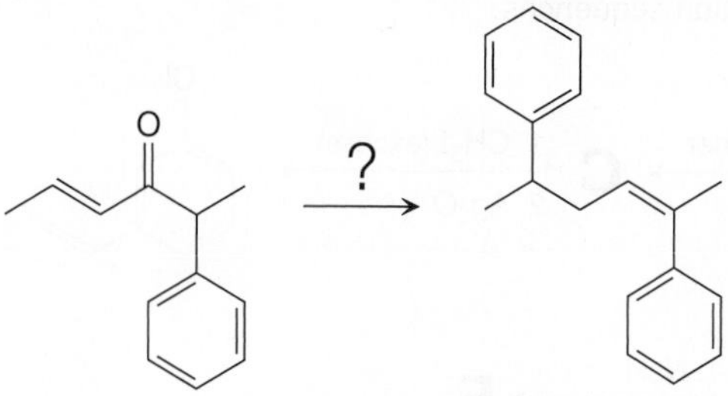

O
?

18.56 When propenal is treated with sodium acetylide, a product is formed whose IR spectrum exhibits a broad absorption between 3200 and 3600 cm^{-1} but shows no absorption near 1700 cm^{-1}. **(a)** Draw the structure of the product. **(b)** Argue whether the nucleophile adds *reversibly* or *irreversibly* to the carbonyl group.

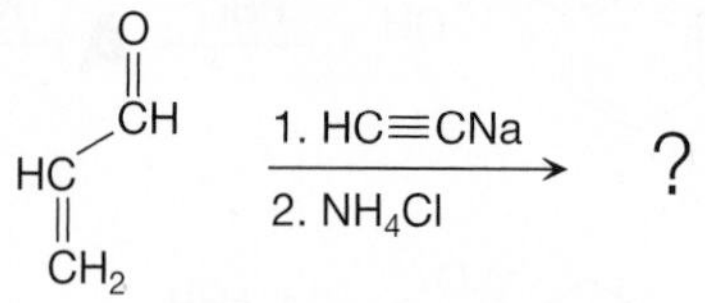

O
CH
HC
CH_2
1. HC≡CNa
2. NH_4Cl
?

18.57 When 5-bromopentanal is treated with sodium borohydride, a compound is produced whose ^{13}C NMR spectrum is shown here. In its IR spectrum, no absorption bands appear near 1700 cm^{-1} or above 3000 cm^{-1}. Propose a mechanism to account for the formation of this product.

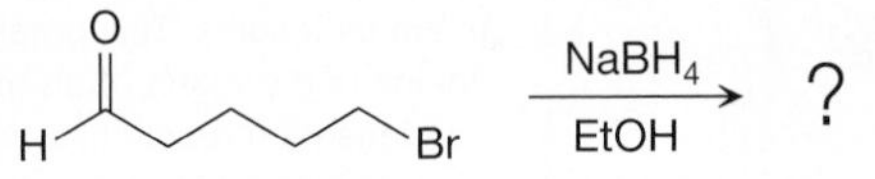

NaBH4
EtOH
?

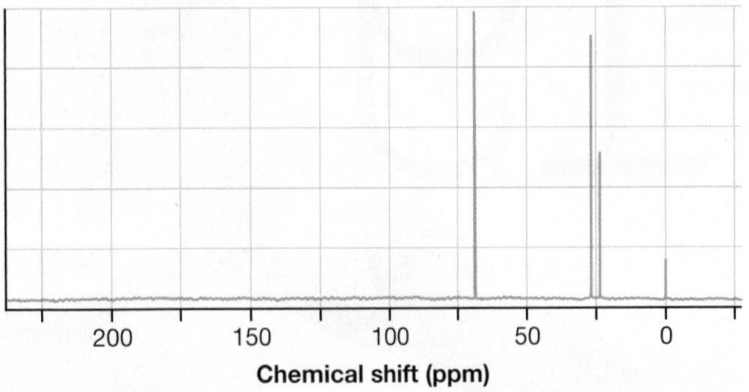

200
150
100
50
0
Chemical shift (ppm)

18.58 Lithium dimethylcuprate reacts with the β-alkynyl carbonyl shown in the following reaction. The IR spectrum of the product is shown, and the ^{1}H NMR spectrum has the following four signals: 1.9 ppm, 3 H; 2.1 ppm, 3 H; 2.2 ppm, 3 H; and 6.1 ppm, 1 H. What is the structure of the product?

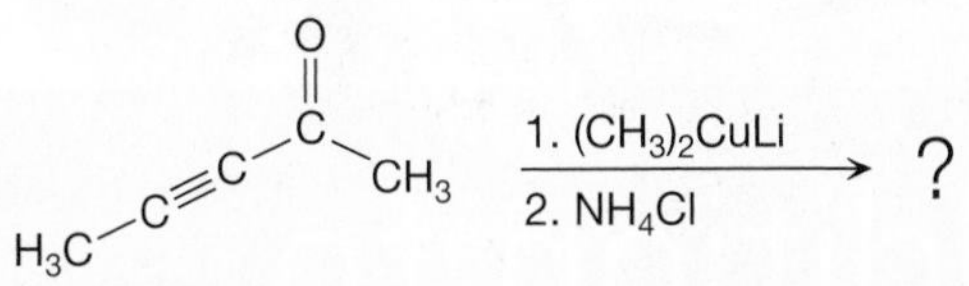

1. (CH3)2CuLi
2. NH4Cl
?

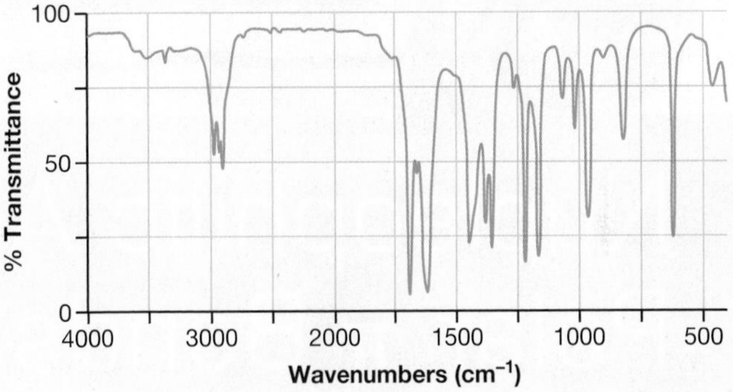

100
50
0
% Transmittance
4000
3000
2000
1500
1000
500
Wavenumbers (cm−1)

18.59 When phenyl-5-bromopentanone is treated with triphenylphosphine, followed by base, a compound is produced whose formula is $C_{11}H_{12}$. Its ^{13}C NMR spectrum has nine signals, six of which appear between 120 and 140 ppm and three of which appear below 50 ppm. For this reaction, draw the complete, detailed mechanism as well as the major organic product.

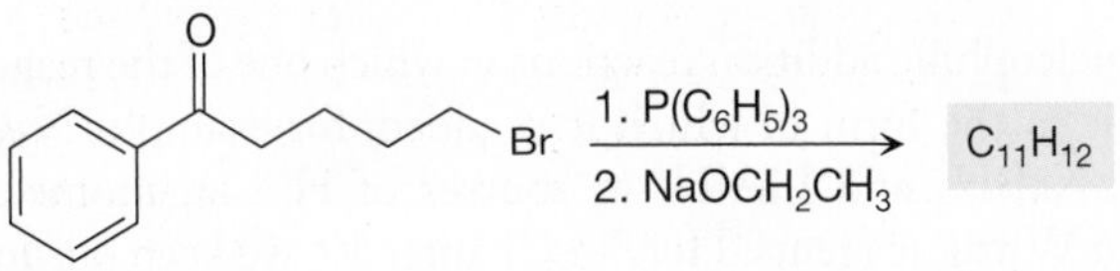

1. P(C6H5)3
2. NaOCH2CH3
C11H12

18.60 The reaction shown here produces a compound, $C_{10}H_{21}N$, whose IR spectrum exhibits no peaks between 1500 and 2000 cm^{-1}. Draw the complete mechanism for this reaction.

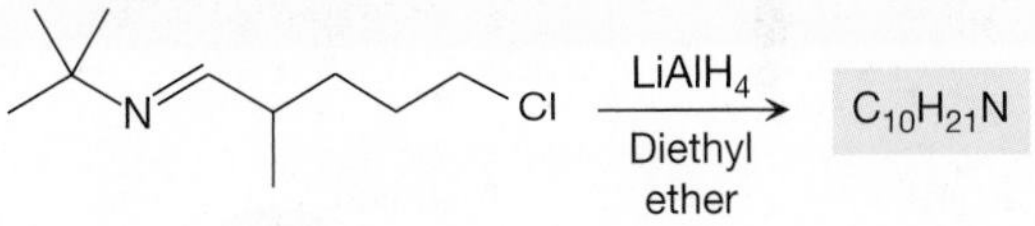

LiAlH4
Diethyl ether
C10H21N

19

Skin can resume its original shape after being stretched in part because of elastin, a protein that exhibits cross-linked bonding between its long-chain molecules. This cross-linking is the result of an aldol condensation reaction, a type of nucleophilic addition reaction we examine here in Chapter 19.

Nucleophilic Addition to Polar π Bonds 2

Reagents That Are Weakly Nucleophilic or Non-nucleophilic, and Acid and Base Catalysis

Chapter 18 discussed nucleophilic addition reactions in which one of the reagents is *strongly* nucleophilic in the form in which it is added: for example, NaOH as a source of HO^-, $NaBH_4$ and $LiAlH_4$ as sources of H^-, organometallic reagents as sources of R^-, and Wittig reagents. Here in Chapter 19, we keep our focus on nucleophilic addition, but now we examine reactions for which the reagent that is added is either *weakly* nucleophilic or *non-nucleophilic*. Such reactions generally require catalysis by a strong acid or a strong base, which slightly alters the nucleophilic addition mechanism we saw in Chapter 18 to provide a lower-energy route to forming products. Of these reactions, we spend the greatest amount of time on the *aldol reaction*, because it is one of the most important and versatile reactions in organic synthesis.

SECTION 19.1 OBJECTIVES

You will be able to:

1. Draw the mechanism for addition of a weak nucleophile to a polar π bond under neutral, acidic, or basic conditions.
2. Explain why addition of a weak nucleophile to a polar π bond can be catalyzed under basic or acidic conditions.

19.1 Weak Nucleophiles as Reagents: Acid and Base Catalysis

Thus far, we have dealt mainly with nucleophilic addition reactions in which the reagent that supplies the nucleophile is itself strongly nucleophilic. In general, those nucleophiles have an atom that bears a full negative charge or (in the case of hydride reagents and organometallic reagents) can be treated *as if* one of their atoms bears a full negative

Chapter Outline

charge. As we saw in Chapters 8–11, however, a variety of *uncharged* species can act as nucleophiles, including water, alcohols (ROH), amines (RNH_2), thiols (RSH), and phosphines (RPH_2). These nucleophiles can also add to polar π bonds.

Equation 19-1 shows that ethanol, a weak nucleophile, can add to the C=O group of butan-2-one under neutral conditions to produce a **hemiacetal**, a compound in which a carbon atom is bonded to both an OH group and an OR group:

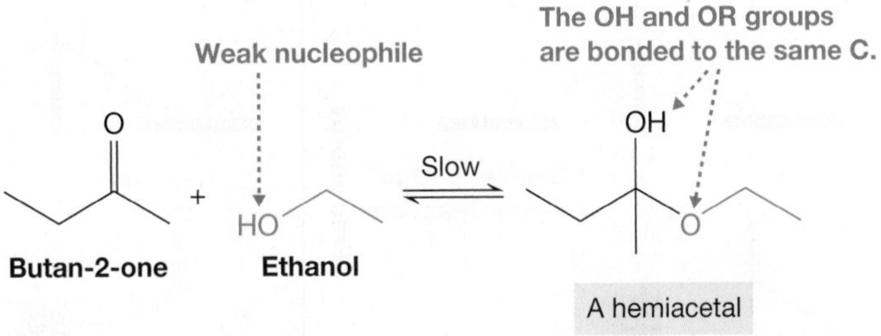

Weak nucleophile
The OH and OR groups are bonded to the same C.
O
HO
Slow
OH
O
Butan-2-one
Ethanol
A hemiacetal

(19-1)

The mechanism for this reaction is shown in Equation 19-2. In Step 1, the weak nucleophile attacks the carbonyl carbon of the ketone to produce a species with a +1 formal charge on one oxygen and a −1 formal charge on the other oxygen. Steps 2 and 3 are proton transfers that leave each oxygen uncharged. The alcohol is shown as the acid in Step 2 and as the base in Step 3 because it is in much greater abundance than any other acids or bases present.

Mechanism for hemiacetal formation under neutral conditions (Eq. 19-1)

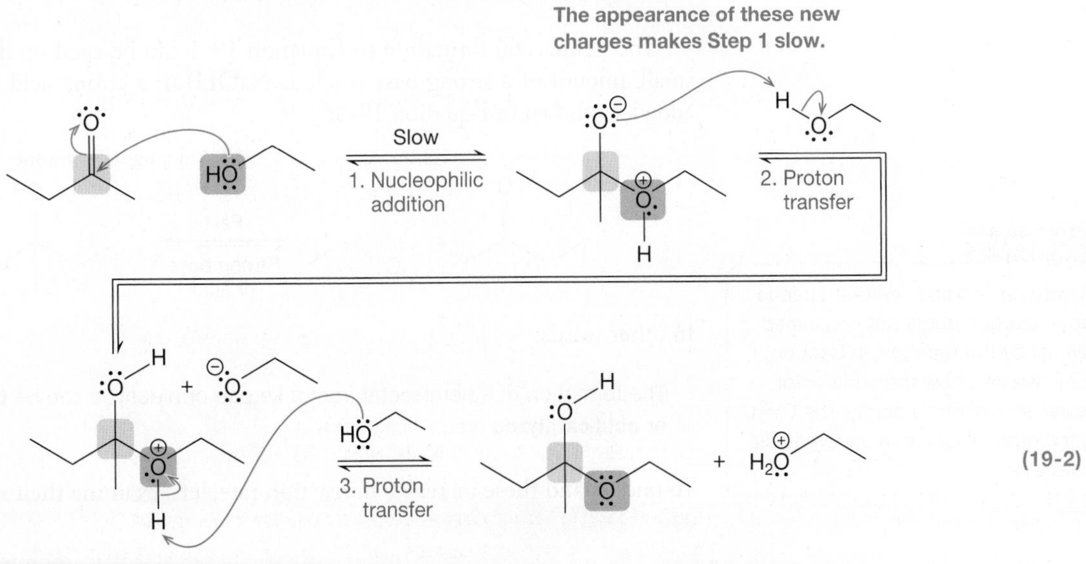

The appearance of these new charges makes Step 1 slow.
Slow
1. Nucleophilic addition
2. Proton transfer
3. Proton transfer
HO
H
H₂O

(19-2)

YOUR TURN 19.1

Draw the mechanism and the hemiacetal product for the following reaction.

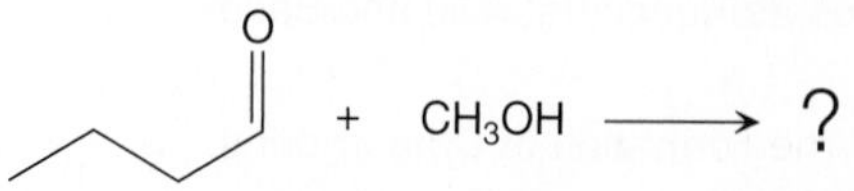

O
+ CH_3OH
?

Answers to Your Turns are in the back of the book.

Notice that the hemiacetal formation in Equation 19-1 is slow. This is because *two new charges are produced* when the nucleophile adds in Step 1 of the mechanism, which, as we can see in **Figure 19-1a**, results in a large energy barrier.

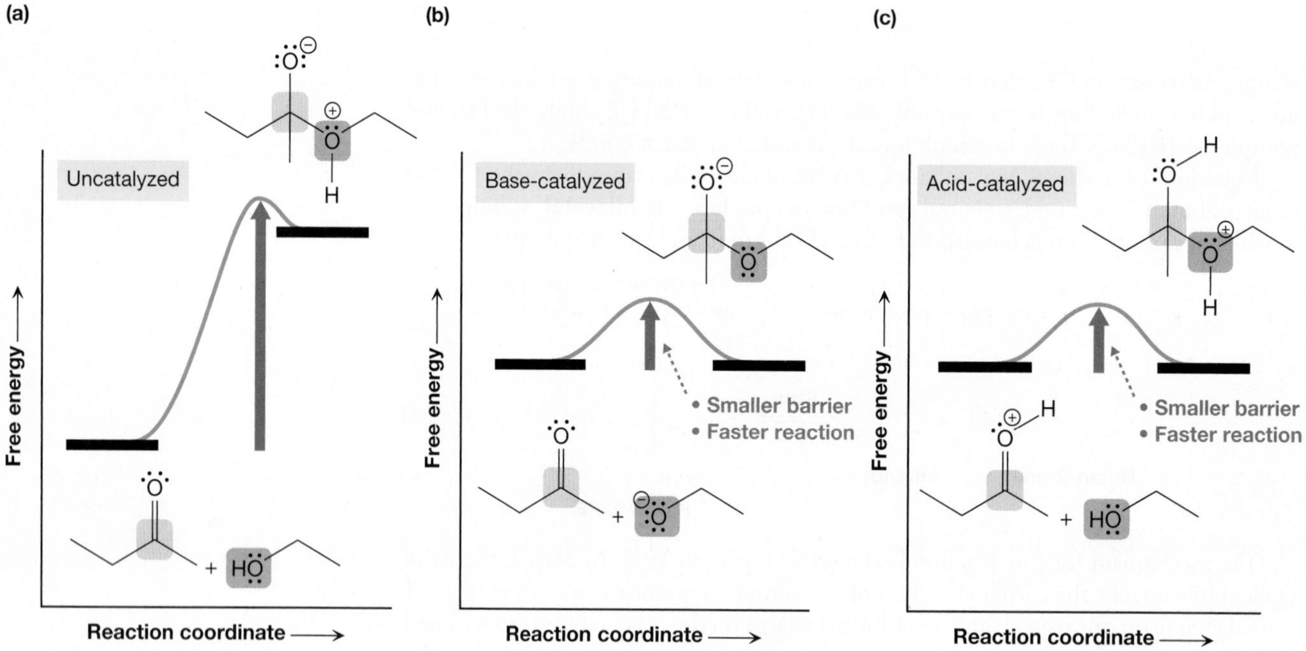

(a)
(b)
(c)
Uncatalyzed
Base-catalyzed
Acid-catalyzed
Free energy
Reaction coordinate
• Smaller barrier
• Faster reaction
HO
H

FIGURE 19-1 Nucleophilic addition and acid/base catalysis Free energy diagrams are shown for the nucleophilic addition steps of (a) the uncatalyzed mechanism in Equation 19-2, (b) the base-catalyzed mechanism in Equation 19-4, and (c) the acid-catalyzed mechanism in Equation 19-5. For the uncatalyzed mechanism, the production of two additional charges results in a larger energy barrier and a slower reaction.

The hemiacetal formation in Equation 19-1 can be sped up dramatically when a small amount of a strong base (such as NaOH) or a strong acid (such as H_2SO_4) is added, as shown in Equation 19-3:

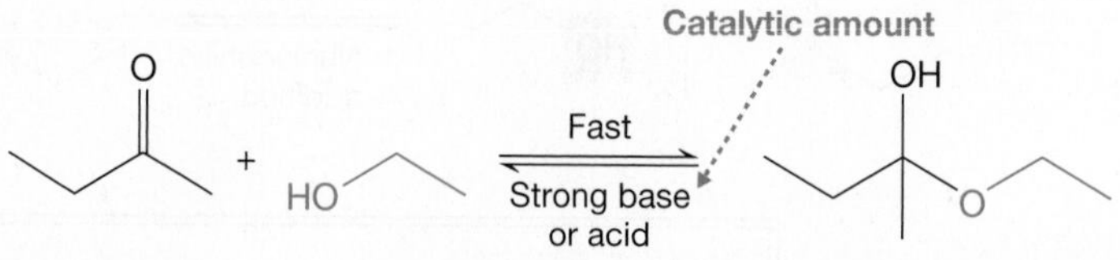

Catalytic amount
O
+
HO
Fast
Strong base
or acid
OH
O

(19-3)

In other words:

The formation of a hemiacetal from a ketone or aldehyde can be **base-catalyzed** or **acid-catalyzed** (see Recall box).

To understand these increases in reaction rate, let's examine their mechanisms.

◂ RECALL

A *catalyst* is a species that speeds up a reaction but is not consumed overall by the reaction. In Section 12.6, we saw how the addition of water and alcohols across the C═C bond of an alkene can undergo acid catalysis.

The mechanism for the base-catalyzed reaction is shown in Equation 19-4; because the reaction takes place under basic conditions, no strong acids should appear (see Recall box).

Mechanism Drawing
Base-catalyzed Nucleophilic Addition of a Weak Nucleophile to a Ketone

Mechanism for base-catalyzed hemiacetal formation (Eq. 19-3)

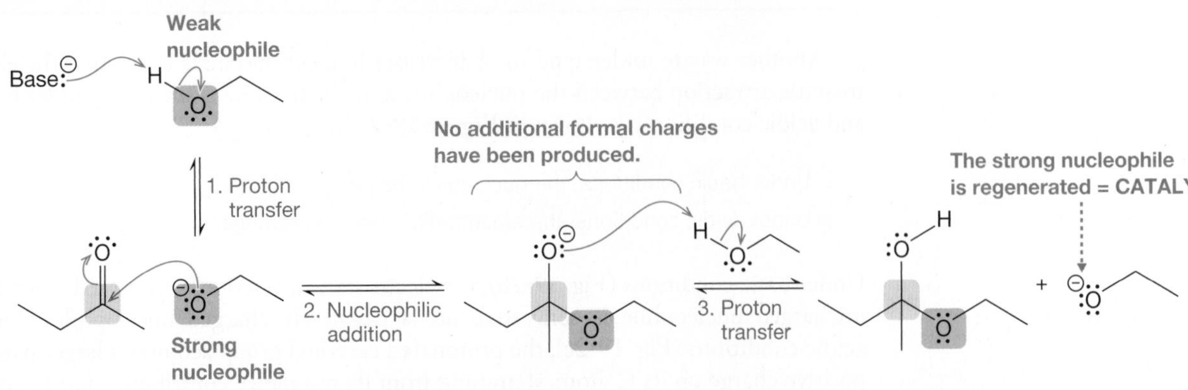
Weak
nucleophile
Base:
1. Proton
transfer
Strong
nucleophile
2. Nucleophilic
addition
No additional formal charges
have been produced.
3. Proton
transfer
The strong nucleophile
is regenerated = CATALYST.

(19-4)

The alcohol (ROH) is very abundant, so, according to the leveling effect (Section 6.2a), the strongest base that can exist in solution is the deprotonated alcohol, RO^-, produced in Step 1. RO^-, a strong nucleophile, adds to the C=O carbon in Step 2, and the resulting species is protonated by ROH in Step 3. Notice that the RO^- nucleophile is regenerated in Step 3, so it can be used again in Step 2. Because it is responsible for increasing the reaction rate but is not consumed overall, RO^- is the *catalyst*.

In the acid-catalyzed mechanism in Equation 19-5, no strongly basic species should appear. The protonated alcohol (ROH_2^+) is the strongest acid that can exist in solution, and the mechanism begins with ROH_2^+ protonating the carbonyl O atom in Step 1. The nucleophile attacks in Step 2, and deprotonation in Step 3 produces the uncharged product. Similar to the base-catalyzed mechanism, the strong acid (ROH_2^+) is regenerated in Step 3, making it a catalyst that can be used again in Step 1.

◂ RECALL

Section 8.6a explained that strong acids should not appear in mechanisms for reactions that take place under basic conditions, and strong bases should not appear under acidic conditions. A feature such as H—O^+ indicates a strong acid, whereas O^- and N^- are features that indicate strong bases.

Mechanism for acid-catalyzed hemiacetal formation (Eq. 19-3)

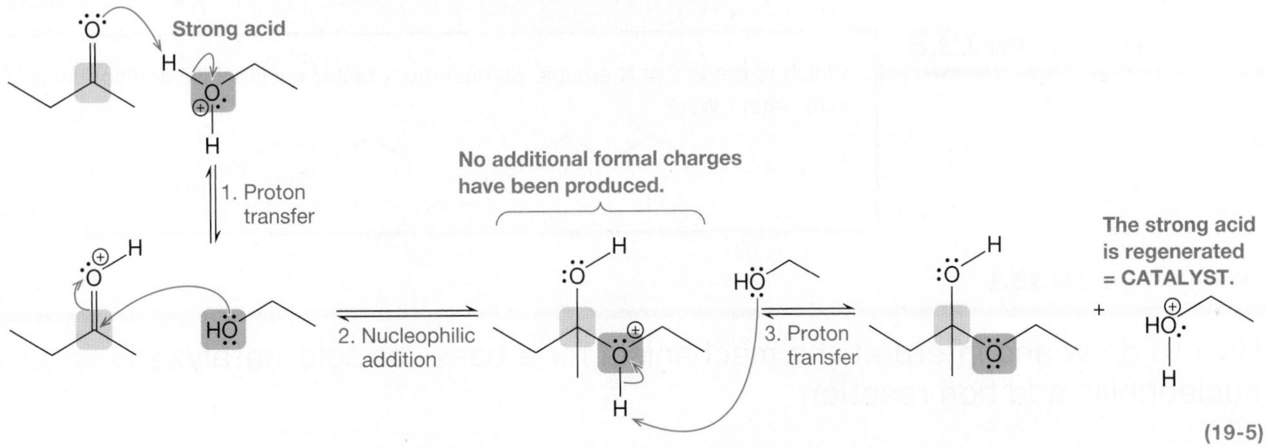
Strong acid
1. Proton
transfer
2. Nucleophilic
addition
No additional formal charges
have been produced.
3. Proton
transfer
The strong acid
is regenerated
= CATALYST.

(19-5)

The reaction rate dramatically increases under basic or acidic conditions because the nucleophilic addition step produces *no additional formal charges*. Therefore, the energy barrier for the nucleophilic addition step is much lower, as we can see in Figure 19-1b (basic conditions) and Figure 19-1c (acidic conditions).

Mechanism Drawing
Acid-catalyzed Nucleophilic Addition of a Weak Nucleophile to a Ketone

YOUR TURN 19.2

At each stage of the mechanism in Equations 19-2, 19-4, and 19-5, count the total *number* of charges that exist, not the total charge (e.g., one positive charge and one negative charge should be counted as two charges). What do you notice?

Another way to understand these increases in reaction rate is to see that the electrostatic attraction between the nucleophile and electrophile is increased under basic and acidic conditions, as shown in **Figure 19-2**. That is:

- Under basic conditions, the nucleophile becomes stronger.
- Under acidic conditions, the electrophile becomes stronger.

Under basic conditions (Fig. 19-2b), the electrostatic attraction is increased when the uncharged nucleophile is converted into a negatively charged nucleophile. Under acidic conditions (Fig. 19-2c), the protonated carbonyl group acquires a larger partial positive charge on its C atom, stemming from its resonance contributor, and the carbonyl group is said to be *activated* toward nucleophilic attack.

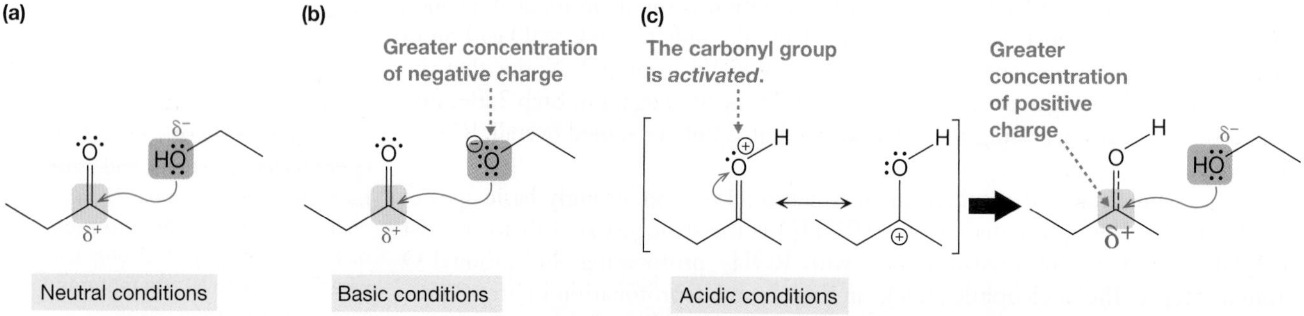

(a)
(b)
(c)
Greater concentration of negative charge
The carbonyl group is *activated*.
Greater concentration of positive charge
Neutral conditions
Basic conditions
Acidic conditions

FIGURE 19-2 Nucleophile and electrophile strength under various conditions (a) The electrostatic attraction between the nucleophile and electrophile is weakest under neutral conditions. (b) Under basic conditions, the nucleophile acquires a full negative charge. (c) Under acidic conditions, the partial positive charge on the carbonyl C atom increases due to the second resonance contributor.

YOUR TURN 19.3

Which of these C≡N groups will undergo a faster nucleophilic addition step with water? Why?

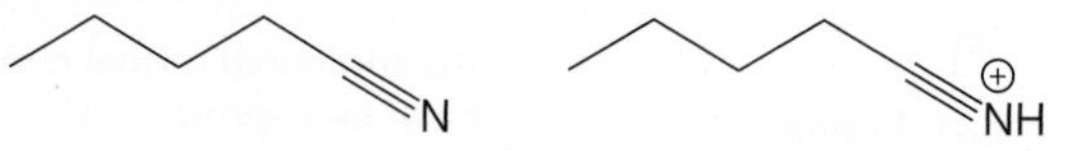

SOLVED PROBLEM 19.1

How to draw and interpret the mechanism for a base- or acid-catalyzed nucleophilic addition reaction

Break It Down Recall from Chapter 18 that water can add to a ketone or aldehyde to form a *hydrate*, according to the balanced equation shown here. Draw the mechanism for this reaction under (a) neutral and (b) basic conditions. Under which conditions do you think this hydration reaction will proceed faster? Why?

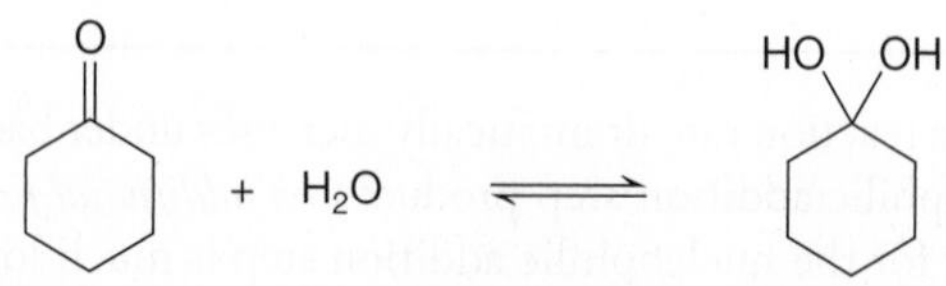

+ H_2O

Cyclohexanone **Cyclohexanone hydrate**

(continued)

Think	Solve
Under neutral conditions, what will act as the nucleophile? As the acid? As the base?	Under neutral conditions, H_2O acts as the nucleophile, the acid, and the base, as shown in the mechanism below. Neutral conditions 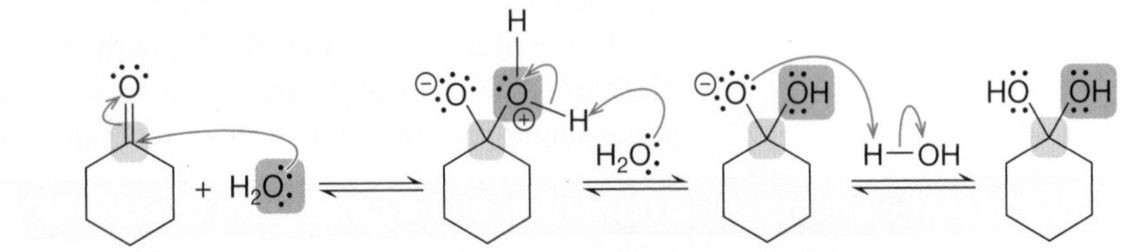
Under basic conditions, what will act as the nucleophile? As the acid? As the base?	Under basic conditions, HO^- will act as the nucleophile and the base, whereas H_2O will act as the acid. The mechanism is shown below. Basic conditions 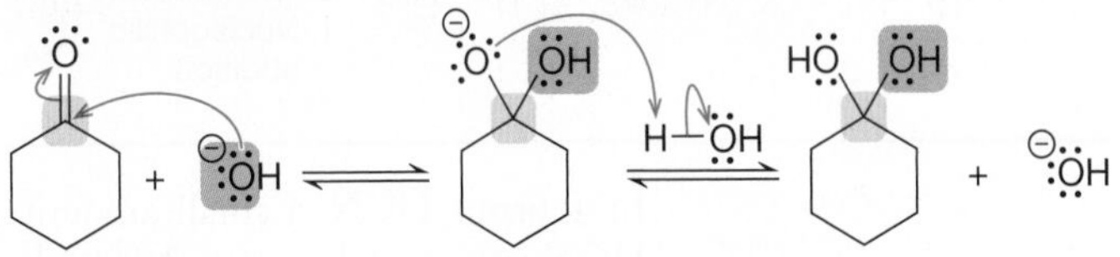
How do the total numbers of charges compare before and after the nucleophilic addition step in each mechanism?	Under neutral conditions, the nucleophilic addition step increases the total number of charges by two, whereas the total number of charges remains the same under basic conditions. Thus, nucleophilic addition is faster under basic conditions.

H
H
H₂O:
H—OH
HO
OH

OH
H—OH
HO
OH

Try It Draw the mechanism for the hydration of cyclohexanone under acidic conditions, and argue whether this reaction should be faster or slower than the corresponding hydration under neutral conditions.

Answers to all Try It exercises can be found in the Solutions Manual.

19.2 Addition of HCN: The Formation of Cyanohydrins

SECTION 19.2 OBJECTIVES

You will be able to:

1. Draw the mechanism for cyanohydrin formation.
2. Explain why cyanohydrin formation is catalyzed by NC^- or HO^-.

When a ketone or aldehyde is treated with aqueous hydrocyanic acid (HCN), the product is a **cyanohydrin**, in which an OH group and a cyano (CN) group are bonded to the same carbon atom. An example is shown in Equation 19-6:

A cyanohydrin   An α-hydroxy acid

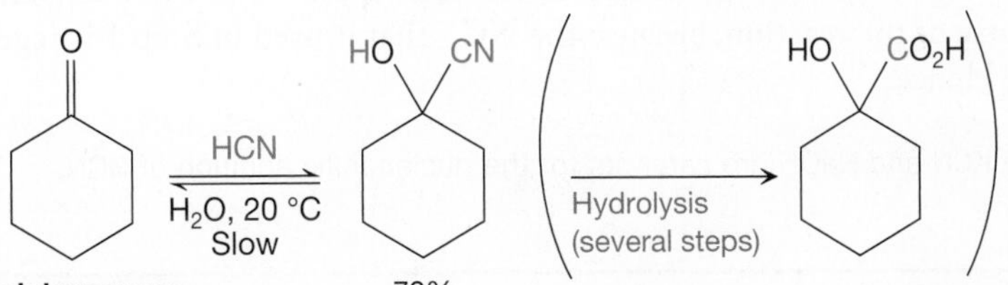

O
HO
CN
HO
CO₂H
HCN
H₂O, 20 °C
Slow
Hydrolysis
(several steps)

(19-6)

Cyclohexanone   70%

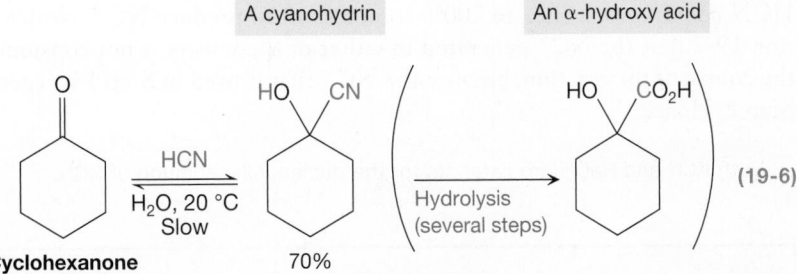

Cyanohydrin formation is important for two reasons. First, it is another valuable *carbon–carbon bond-forming reaction*, giving us an additional way to construct carbon backbones. Second, the C≡N functional group is readily transformed into CO_2H by a *hydrolysis* reaction (discussed in Chapter 23). The overall product is an

An α-hydroxy acid

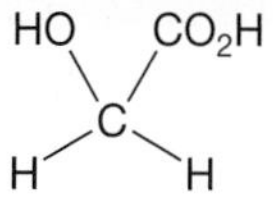

HO
CO_2H
C
H
H

FIGURE 19-3 Glycolic acid Glycolic acid is an α-hydroxy acid used to treat some skin ailments.

α-hydroxy acid. Not only are these compounds useful in synthesis, but some α-hydroxy acids, such as glycolic acid (**Figure 19-3**), are used to treat a variety of skin ailments.

In the overall reaction of HCN with the carbonyl group, the cyano group adds to the carbonyl carbon and a hydrogen adds to the carbonyl oxygen. This reaction occurs according to the mechanism shown in Equation 19-7:

Mechanism for the uncatalyzed formation of a cyanohydrin (Eq. 19-6)

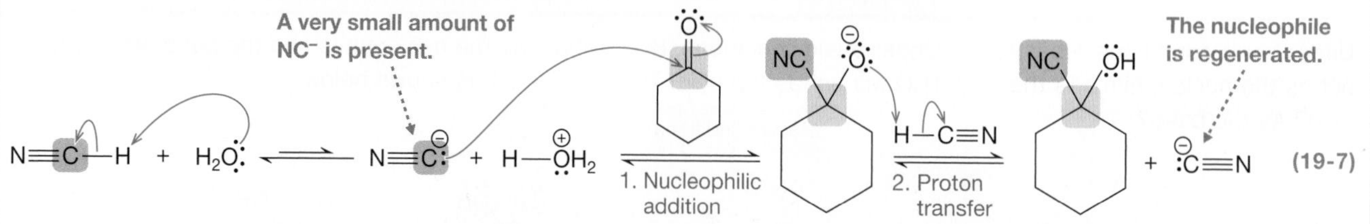

A very small amount of NC^- is present.
The nucleophile is regenerated.
1. Nucleophilic addition
2. Proton transfer

(19-7)

In aqueous HCN, a small amount of the cyanide anion (NC^-) is present because HCN ($pK_a = 9.2$) is a weak acid. In Step 1 of the ensuing reaction, NC^- attacks the carbonyl group, generating a negative charge on the O atom, and in Step 2, that O atom is protonated.

The equilibrium proton transfer between HCN and water (Eq. 19-7) heavily favors reactants, so only a small amount of NC^- is generated. In fact, only about 0.001% of HCN molecules dissociate into NC^- and H_3O^+. As a result, HCN reacts quite slowly with the carbonyl carbon under normal conditions, even though NC^- is a very good nucleophile.

The reaction can be sped up dramatically by adding a small amount of either KCN or a strong base such as NaOH (Eq. 19-8):

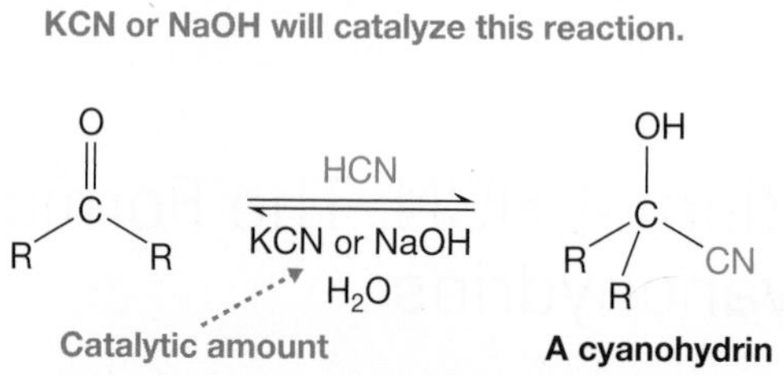

KCN or NaOH will catalyze this reaction.
HCN
KCN or NaOH
H_2O
Catalytic amount
A cyanohydrin

(19-8)

> **GREEN CHEMISTRY**
> Although forming cyanohydrins is very synthetically useful, it is important to know that HCN and KCN are extremely toxic. Making matters worse, HCN boils slightly above room temperature and is effectively a gas. Proper precautions must be taken to handle these compounds safely.

The reaction rate increases because the addition of either KCN or NaOH increases the concentration of NC^- present in solution. KCN is an ionic compound that dissociates into K^+ and NC^- in water, while the HO^- from NaOH deprotonates HCN *quantitatively* (i.e., to 100% completion) to produce NC^-. Notice in Equation 19-7 that the NC^- generated in either of these ways is not consumed during the course of the reaction, because the NC^- that is used in Step 1 is regenerated in Step 2. Hence:

Both KCN and NaOH are *catalysts* for the nucleophilic addition of HCN.

YOUR TURN **19.4**

Use the appropriate pK_a values (Appendix A) to verify that the equilibrium between HCN and H_2O (Eq. 19-7) heavily favors the reactants, whereas HO^- (Eq. 19-8) quantitatively deprotonates HCN.

YOUR TURN **19.5**

Draw the complete, detailed mechanism and predict the products for each of the following reactions.

(a)

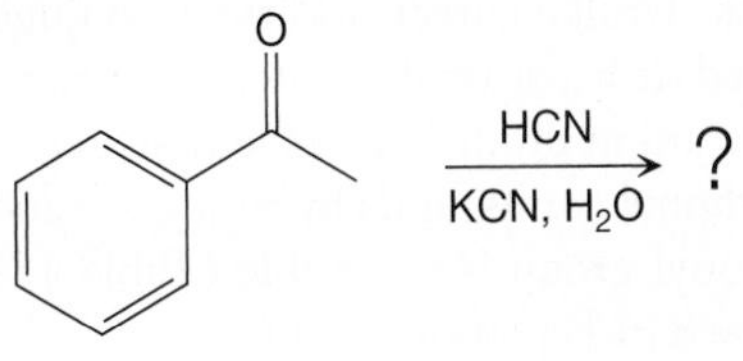
O
HCN
KCN, H_2O
?

(b)

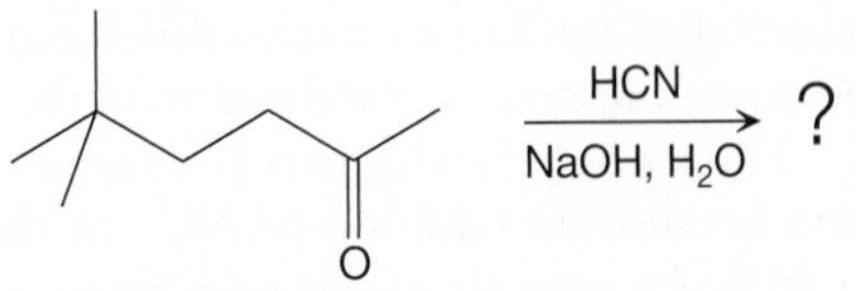
HCN
NaOH, H_2O
?
O

19.3 Direct Addition versus Conjugate Addition of Weak Nucleophiles and HCN

SECTION 19.3 OBJECTIVES

You will be able to:

1. Draw the mechanisms for 1,2-addition and 1,4-addition of a weak nucleophile to a conjugated polar π bond.
2. Explain why such reactions tend to favor 1,4-addition.

Like negatively charged nucleophiles, uncharged nucleophiles can attack α,β-unsaturated carbonyls at two locations: at the carbonyl carbon to give the direct addition product (i.e., the 1,2-addition product) and at the β carbon to give the conjugate addition product (i.e., the 1,4-addition product). In general:

Uncharged nucleophiles heavily favor conjugate addition over direct addition.

An example with ethanethiol (CH_3CH_2SH) as the nucleophile is shown in Equation 19-9:

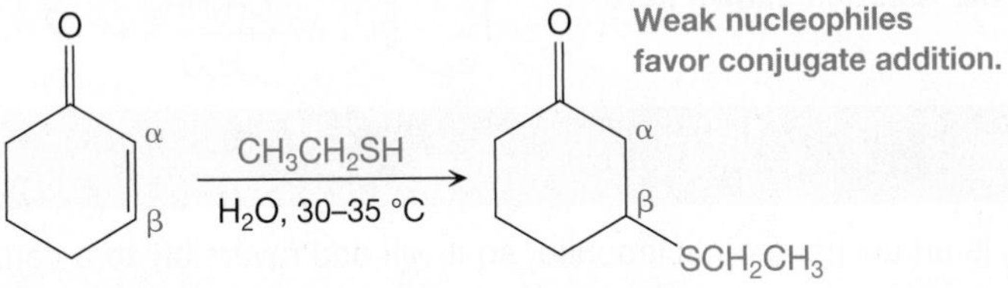
O
α
β
CH_3CH_2SH
H_2O, 30–35 °C
O
α
β
SCH_2CH_3
Weak nucleophiles favor conjugate addition.

Cyclohex-2-enone 95% (19-9)

The mechanism for this reaction is shown in Equation 19-10:

Mechanism for the 1,4-addition of an uncharged nucleophile (Eq. 19-9)

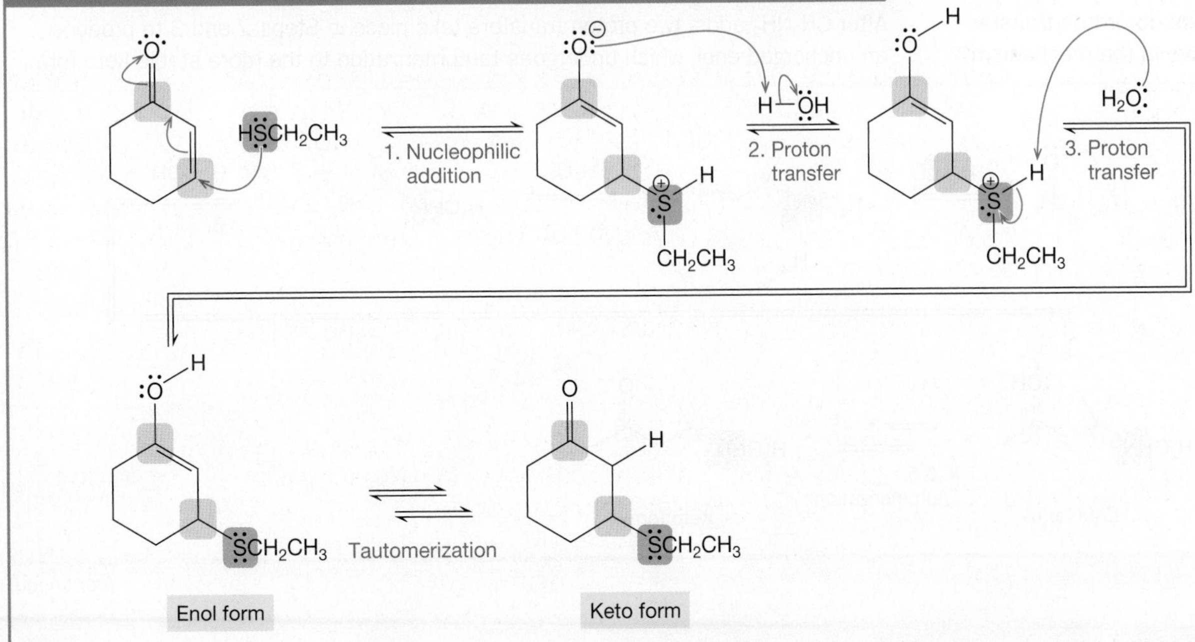
$HSCH_2CH_3$
1. Nucleophilic addition
H–OH
2. Proton transfer
CH_2CH_3
H_2O
3. Proton transfer
CH_2CH_3
SCH_2CH_3
Tautomerization
SCH_2CH_3
Enol form
Keto form

(19-10)

Uncharged nucleophiles favor conjugate addition because Step 1 of the mechanism, the nucleophilic addition step, is *reversible*, so it takes place under *thermodynamic control* (Section 18.8).

Frequently, the addition of uncharged nucleophiles to α,β-unsaturated carbonyl compounds does not require acidic conditions. Unlike direct addition, conjugate addition of uncharged nucleophiles can proceed at a reasonable rate, in large part because of resonance stabilization in the enolate anion produced in the first step.

HCN similarly adds to α,β-unsaturated carbonyl compounds by conjugate addition because the addition of NC^- to the carbonyl group is reversible (Table 18-2, p. 902). An example of one such reaction is shown in Equation 19-11:

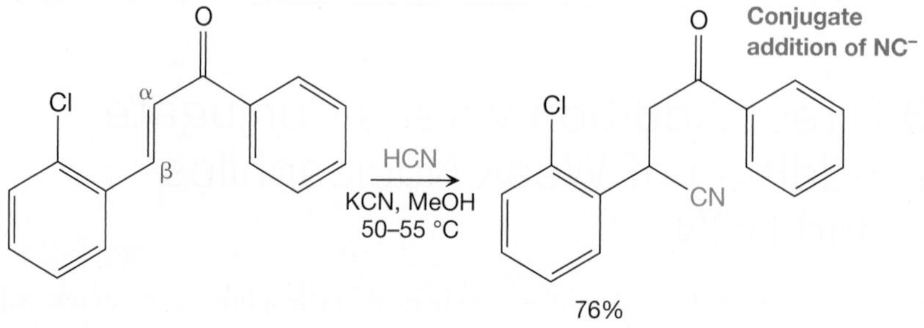

O
Cl
α
β
HCN
KCN, MeOH
50–55 °C
O
Conjugate addition of NC⁻
Cl
CN
76%

(19-11)

SOLVED PROBLEM **19.2**

How to draw the mechanism and product for the addition of an uncharged nucleophile to an α,β-unsaturated ketone or aldehyde

Break It Down **Predict the product of the reaction shown here and draw its complete, detailed mechanism.**

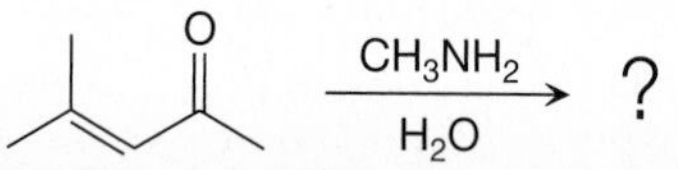

O
CH₃NH₂
H₂O
?

Think	Solve
Does CH_3NH_2 add to the carbonyl group reversibly or irreversibly?	CH_3NH_2 is an uncharged nucleophile, so it will add reversibly to a carbonyl group.
Will this favor direct addition or conjugate addition?	Because CH_3NH_2 adds reversibly, conjugate addition will be favored. This is shown in Step 1 below.
What roles do proton transfer steps have in the mechanism?	After CH_3NH_2 adds, two proton transfers take place in Steps 2 and 3 to produce an uncharged enol, which undergoes tautomerization to the more stable keto form.

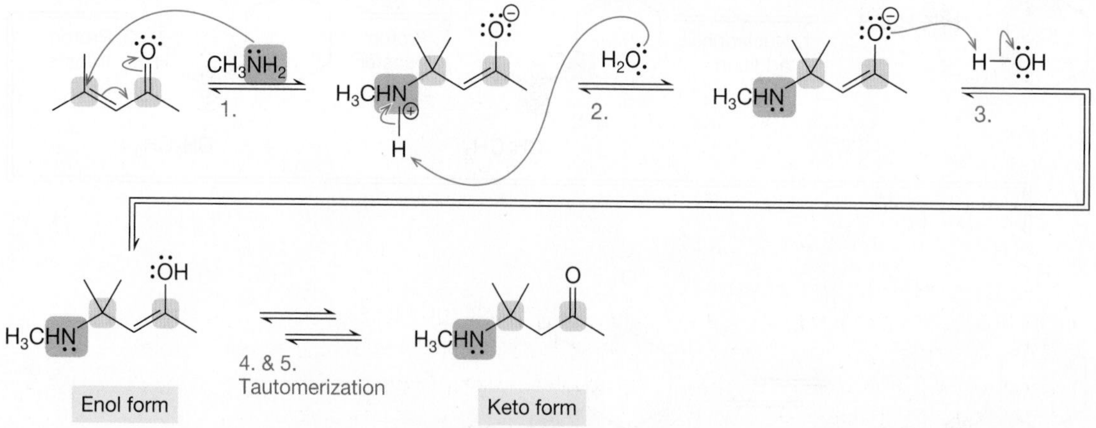

:O:
CH₃NH₂
1.
:O:
H₃CHN
H
H₂O:
2.
:O:
H₃CHN
H—OH
3.
:OH
H₃CHN
4. & 5.
Tautomerization
O
H₃CHN
Enol form
Keto form

(continued)

Try It Predict the major product and draw the complete, detailed mechanism for each of the reactions shown here.

(a)

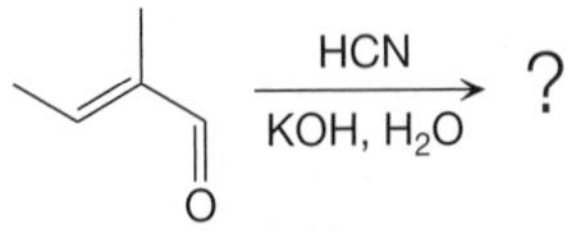
HCN
KOH, H_2O
?

(b)

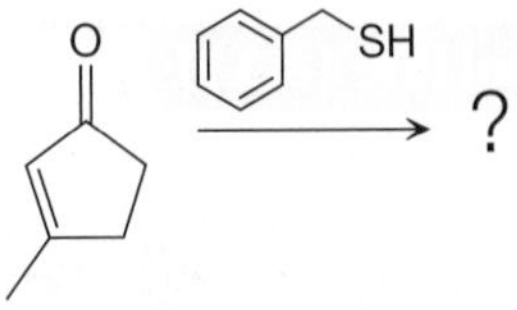
SH
?

(c)

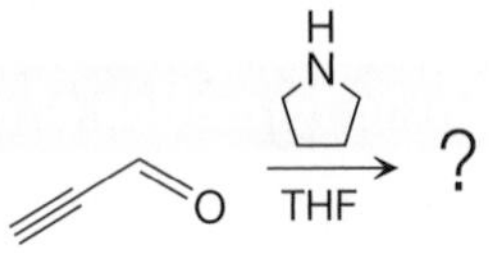
THF
?

19.4 Formation and Hydrolysis of Acetals, Imines, and Enamines

SECTION 19.4 OBJECTIVES

You will be able to:

1. Draw the mechanisms for the formation and hydrolysis of acetals, imines, and enamines.
2. Explain why the hydrolysis of an acetal, imine, or enamine can take place under acidic conditions but not under basic conditions.

In Section 19.1, we saw that weak nucleophiles can add to polar π bonds. Frequently, the immediate product of these reactions can react further under the conditions used for nucleophilic addition. We examine some of those further reactions here in Section 19.4, which result in the formation of acetals, imines, and enamines from ketones or aldehydes. We also examine the *hydrolysis* of acetals, imines, and enamines, which is simply the reverse of each formation reaction.

19.4a Formation and Hydrolysis of Acetals

In Equation 19-1 (p. 927), we saw that a *hemiacetal* forms when a ketone or aldehyde is treated with an alcohol, and in Equation 19-3 (p. 928), we saw that the reaction is catalyzed under either basic or acidic conditions:

> If an aldehyde or ketone is treated with a *large excess* of an alcohol under *acidic* conditions, then the hemiacetal produced from nucleophilic addition reacts further to form an *acetal*, in which two alkoxy (RO) groups are bonded to the same carbon.

The overall reaction, shown in Equation 19-12 using pentanal as an example, is reversible:

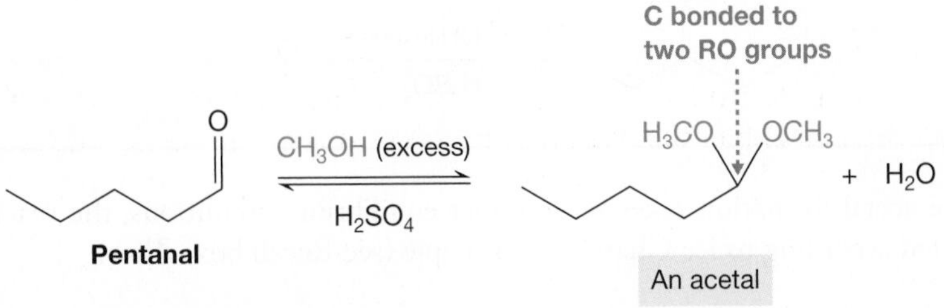
C bonded to two RO groups
CH_3OH (excess)
H_2SO_4
H_3CO
OCH_3
+ H_2O
Pentanal
An acetal

(19-12)

CONNECTIONS 19.1

Flavor and durability Pentanal (Eq. 19-12) has a slightly fruity, nutlike flavor and, like many aldehydes, finds use as a flavoring agent. It is also used to accelerate the vulcanization process for rubber. Rubber in its natural state is a liquid, and vulcanization transforms it into a durable, solid form.

YOUR TURN 19.6

Draw the acetal that would be produced in Equation 19-12 if propanol ($CH_3CH_2CH_2OH$) were used instead of methanol.

The complete mechanism for this acetal formation reaction is shown in Equation 19-13. The first three steps are identical to the acid-catalyzed nucleophilic addition in Equation 19-5 (p. 929). That is, the C=O group is protonated in Step 1, which *activates* it toward nucleophilic addition by the weak ROH nucleophile in Step 2. In Step 3, deprotonation produces the uncharged hemiacetal. The remaining steps essentially make up an S_N1 reaction. In Step 4, protonation of the OH group generates a good H_2O

Mechanism Drawing Acid-catalyzed Formation of an Acetal

leaving group, which departs in Step 5 to produce a resonance-stabilized carbocation. That carbocation is subsequently attacked by another ROH nucleophile in Step 6, and the proton transfer in Step 7 results in the uncharged acetal.

Mechanism for the formation of an acetal (Eq. 19-12)

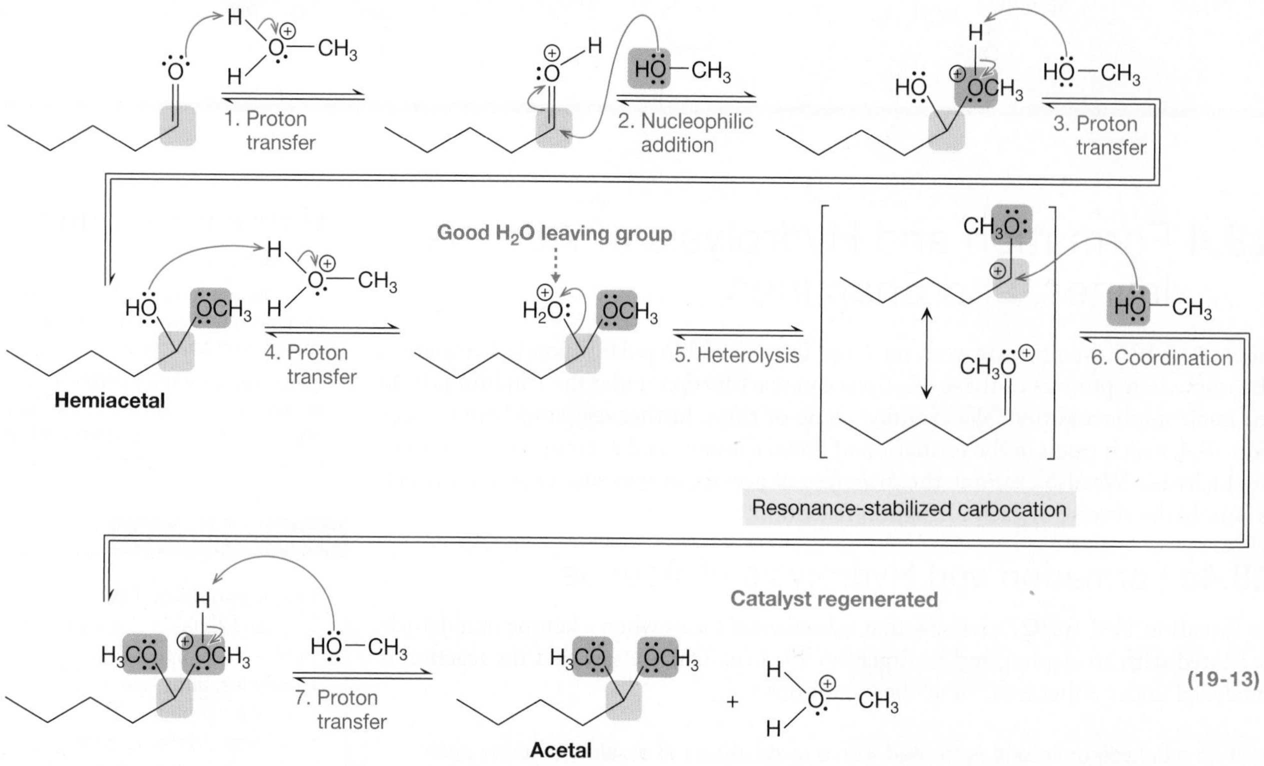

1. Proton transfer
2. Nucleophilic addition
3. Proton transfer
Hemiacetal
4. Proton transfer
Good H2O leaving group
5. Heterolysis
6. Coordination
Resonance-stabilized carbocation
7. Proton transfer
Catalyst regenerated
Acetal

(19-13)

YOUR TURN **19.7**

Draw the mechanism and major product for the following reaction (use Eq. 19-13 as a guide). In the completed mechanism, identify the hemiacetal, the acetal, and the steps that make up an S_N1 reaction.

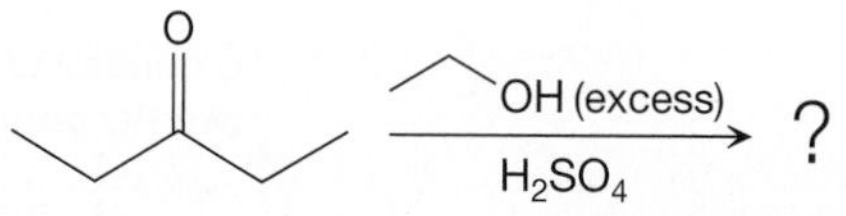

OH (excess)
H2SO4
?

◀ **RECALL**

According to Le Châtelier's principle (Section 6.2b), a reaction at equilibrium will shift toward products if reactants are added or if products are removed. Conversely, the equilibrium will shift toward reactants if products are added or if reactants are removed.

Because acetal formation takes place under equilibrium conditions, the reaction can be shifted according to Le Châtelier's principle (see Recall box). Thus:

While formation of the acetal product is favored by using excess alcohol (a reactant), the reverse reaction is favored by using excess water (a product; see Eq. 19-12 again) under acidic conditions.

This is exemplified in Equation 19-14, whose mechanism is precisely the reverse of that in Equation 19-13:

The mechanism for this reaction is the reverse of the one in Eq. 19-13.

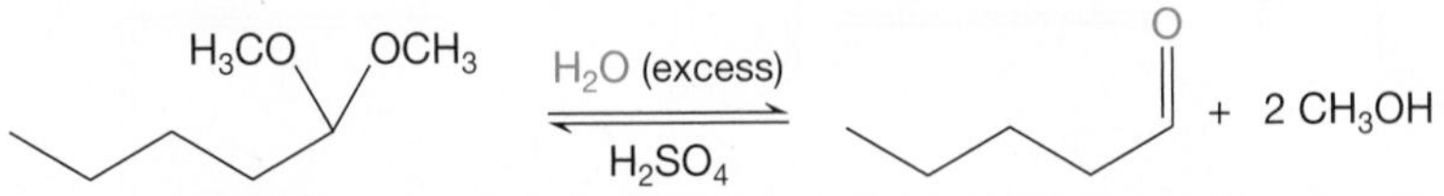

H_3CO
OCH_3
H_2O (excess)
H_2SO_4
O
+ 2 CH_3OH

(19-14)

An acetal

Equation 19-14 is a **hydrolysis** reaction, because the addition of water results in the breaking of the C—OCH_3 bonds.

YOUR TURN **19.8**

Draw the complete, detailed mechanism for the reaction in Equation 19-14.

Equation 19-15 shows that a *cyclic acetal* can form if the two nucleophilic OH groups are part of the same molecule (see Looking Ahead box). In this case, 1,2-ethanediol (ethylene glycol) is used, and the product side is favored as a result of the five-membered ring that is formed (review Section 9.12).

1,2-Ethanediol (Ethylene glycol)

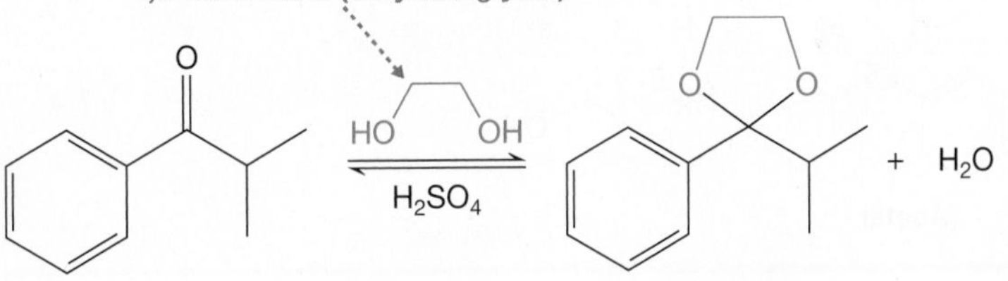

O
HO
OH
H_2SO_4
O
O
+ H_2O

(19-15)

A cyclic acetal

▸ LOOKING AHEAD

Acetals are unreactive toward nucleophiles and bases, and they form reversibly. Therefore, as discussed in Section 21.2b, acetals make good *protecting groups* for ketones and aldehydes. Cyclic acetals like the one in Equation 19-15 are common protecting groups because they are easily produced.

SOLVED PROBLEM **19.3**

How to draw the mechanism for cyclic acetal formation

Break It Down **Draw a complete, detailed mechanism for the reaction in Equation 19-15.**

Think	Solve
What steps produce the hemiacetal?	Steps 1–3 below show how the hemiacetal forms. The carbonyl O is protonated in Step 1, followed by nucleophilic addition of the diol in Step 2, and then deprotonation in Step 3.
How does the leaving group form? After the leaving group leaves from the hemiacetal, what will most reasonably act as the nucleophile in the next step?	Protonation of the OH group in Step 4 produces a good H_2O leaving group, and in Step 5, the leaving group leaves. Step 6 is nucleophilic attack. In Equation 19-13, a second molecule of the alcohol acts as the nucleophile. In this case, the step takes place intramolecularly to form the favorable five-membered ring. The deprotonation in Step 7 completes the mechanism.

(continued)

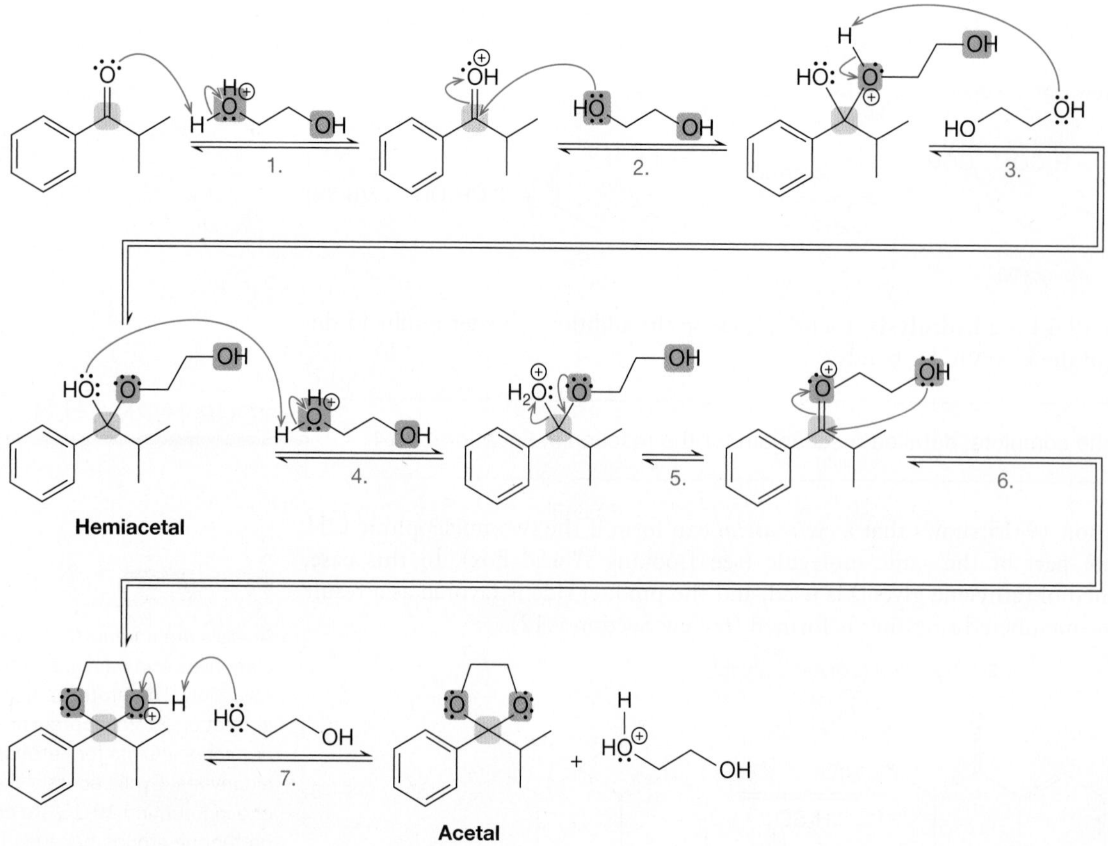
1.
2.
3.
4.
5.
6.
7.
Hemiacetal
Acetal

Try It Draw a complete, detailed mechanism for the following reaction, and predict the major product.

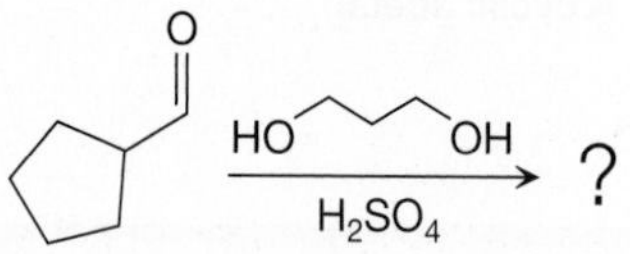
HO
OH
H₂SO₄
?

Although a hemiacetal can form under either basic or acidic conditions (review Eq. 19-3, p. 928), the story is somewhat different for acetal formation:

> A ketone or aldehyde readily forms an acetal under *acidic* conditions but not under *basic* conditions.

Acetals do not form under basic conditions because the nucleophilic substitution that would convert the hemiacetal to the acetal would require the leaving group to be HO^- (Eq. 19-16). As we learned in Section 9.5a, HO^- is an unsuitable leaving group for an S_N1 or S_N2 reaction.

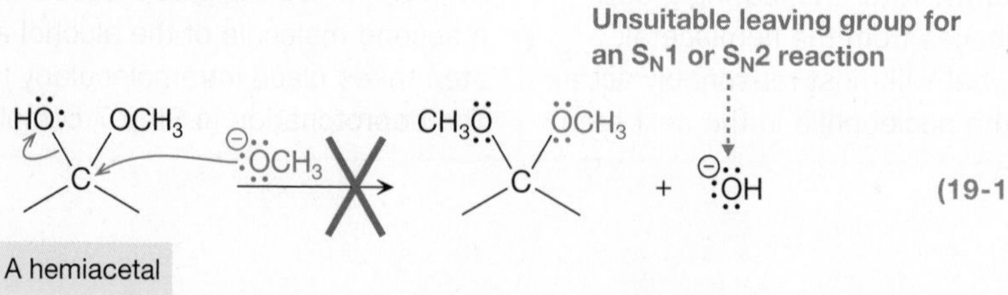
Unsuitable leaving group for an SN1 or SN2 reaction
A hemiacetal

(19-16)

Similarly, acetals can undergo hydrolysis under acidic conditions. However:

Acetals do *not* undergo hydrolysis under basic conditions.

As shown in Equation 19-17, this would require an alkoxide (RO^-) leaving group, which is unsuitable for S_N1 or S_N2 reactions.

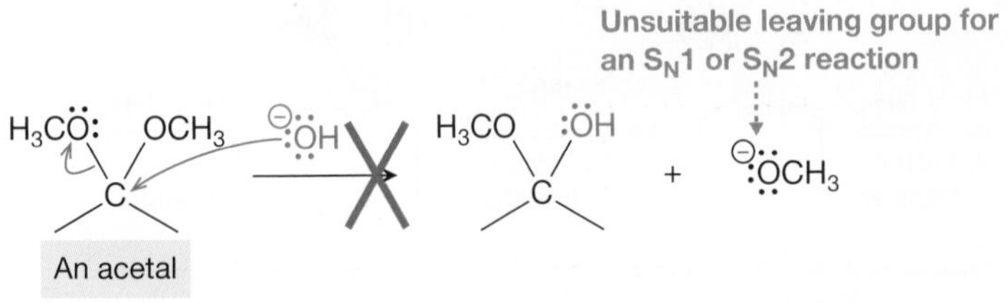

Unsuitable leaving group for an S_N1 or S_N2 reaction
An acetal

(19-17)

YOUR TURN **19.9**

Draw the mechanism and product for each of these reactions. If no reaction will occur, write NR.

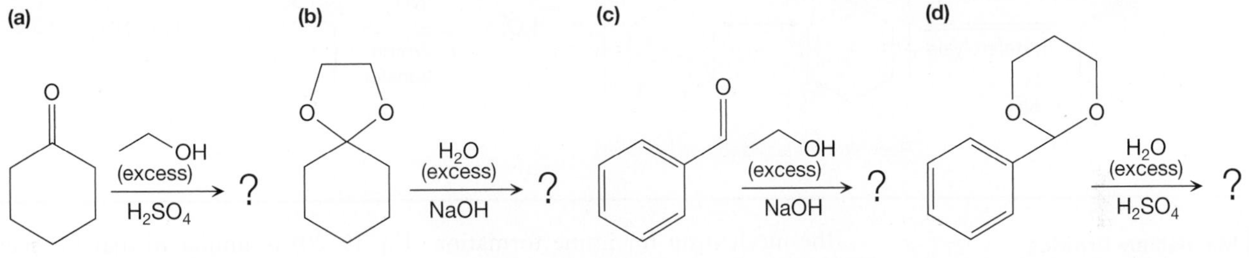

(a)
(b)
(c)
(d)
(excess)
H_2SO_4
H_2O (excess)
NaOH
(excess)
NaOH
H_2O (excess)
H_2SO_4

19.4b Formation and Hydrolysis of Imines and Enamines

Ammonia (NH_3) and amines (RNH_2) are uncharged nucleophiles that can add reversibly to carbonyl groups of ketones and aldehydes. When a small amount of a strong acid is added (i.e., under mildly acidic conditions), as shown in Equations 19-18 and 19-19, the product is an **imine**, sometimes referred to as a **Schiff base**, which has a characteristic C=N double bond.

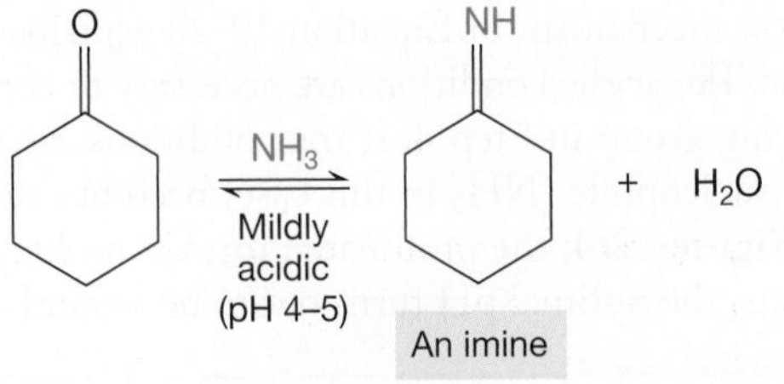

NH_3
Mildly acidic (pH 4–5)
+ H_2O
An imine

(19-18)

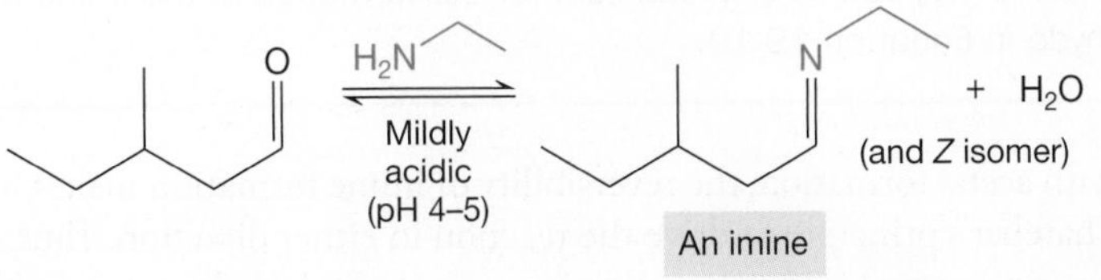

Mildly acidic (pH 4–5)
+ H_2O
(and *Z* isomer)
An imine

(19-19)

The complete mechanism for the formation of an imine from a ketone is shown in Equation 19-20:

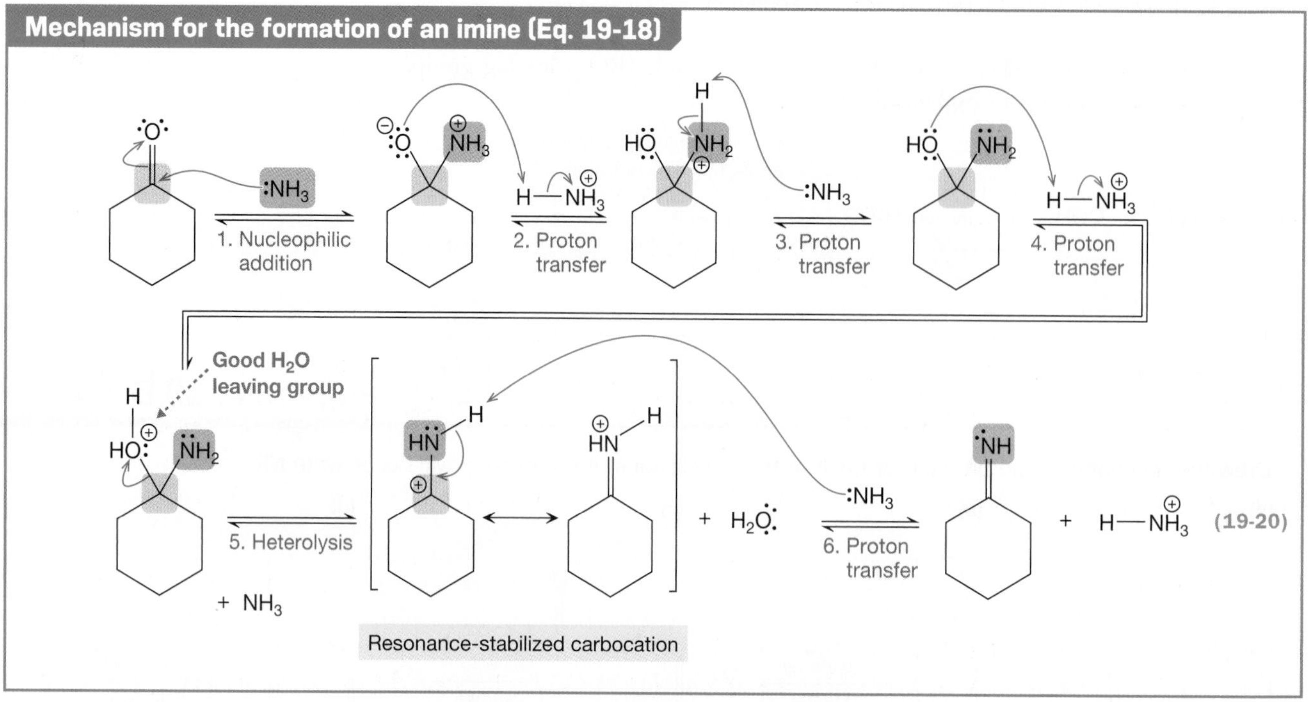

Mechanism for the formation of an imine (Eq. 19-18)
:NH3
1. Nucleophilic addition
H—NH3
2. Proton transfer
:NH3
3. Proton transfer
H—NH3
4. Proton transfer
Good H2O leaving group
5. Heterolysis
+ NH3
+ H2O:
:NH3
6. Proton transfer
H—NH3
(19-20)
Resonance-stabilized carbocation

Mechanism Drawing
Acid-catalyzed Formation of an Imine

The mechanism for imine formation (Eq. 19-20) is similar to that for acetal formation (Eq. 19-13, p. 936). One difference between the mechanisms is the step in which the nucleophile adds. In acetal formation, the weak ROH nucleophile adds in Step 2, after the carbonyl group has been activated. In imine formation, on the other hand, the nucleophile adds in Step 1 because NH_3 is a stronger nucleophile than ROH, and the weakly acidic conditions don't substantially activate the carbonyl group.

The mechanisms for acetal formation and imine formation also differ in Step 6. In imine formation, the N is deprotonated, thus completing the second step of an E1 mechanism (Section 8.2). In acetal formation, an analogous deprotonation is unavailable, because the O that is attached to the C^+ is not bonded to any hydrogen atoms.

The imine formation mechanism in Equation 19-20 explains why the conditions need to be *mildly* acidic. The acidic conditions are necessary to convert the OH group into a good water leaving group in Step 4. If the conditions are too acidic, however, then the weakly basic nucleophile (NH_3 in this case) becomes essentially 100% protonated, as shown in **Figure 19-4**; the protonated form is no longer nucleophilic. To balance these two effects, the optimal pH turns out to be around 4–5.

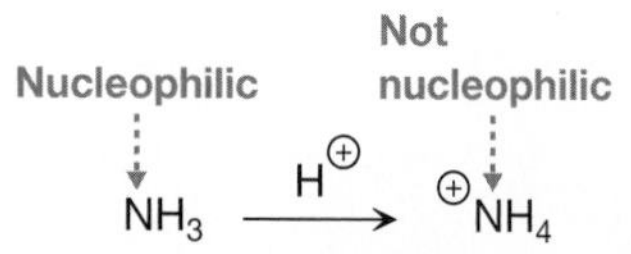

Nucleophilic
Not nucleophilic
NH3
H+
+NH4

FIGURE 19-4 Ionization state and nucleophilicity

YOUR TURN **19.10**

Draw the complete, detailed mechanism for the formation of the imine from the aldehyde in Equation 19-19.

Just as with acetal formation, the reversibility of imine formation makes it possible to use Le Châtelier's principle to drive the reaction in either direction. Thus:

An imine can be *hydrolyzed* by treating it with excess water under acidic conditions (Eq. 19-21).

Under acidic conditions, an imine is hydrolyzed.

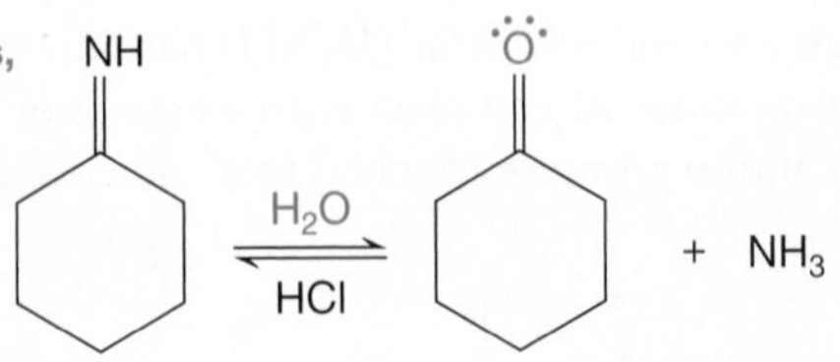

NH
H_2O
HCl
O
+ NH_3

(19-21)

SOLVED PROBLEM **19.4**

How to draw the mechanism for imine hydrolysis

Break It Down **Draw the complete, detailed mechanism for the hydrolysis reaction in Equation 19-21.**

Think	Solve
How is the C═N bond affected under the strongly acidic conditions?	Under strongly acidic conditions, the N atom becomes protonated, as shown in Step 1 below. This activates the C═N bond toward nucleophilic attack.
What acts as the nucleophile?	The nucleophile is water, which attacks the C═N carbon in Step 2.
What acts as the leaving group? How are proton transfer steps incorporated before and after the leaving group leaves?	Steps 3 and 4 are proton transfers, which serve to stabilize the nucleophile that just added in and to convert the NH_2 group into an NH_3 leaving group. After NH_3 leaves in Step 5, the deprotonation in Step 6 produces the final ketone.

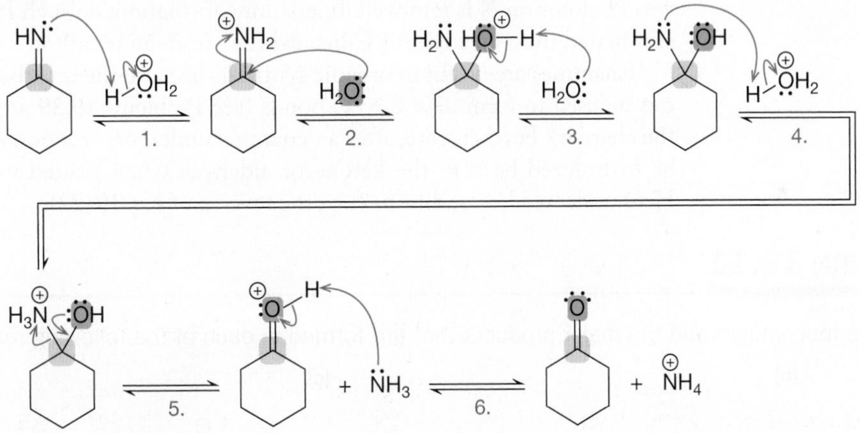

HN
H
OH_2
1.
NH_2
H_2O
2.
H_2N
HO
H
H_2O
3.
H_2N
OH
H
OH_2
4.
H_3N
OH
5.
O
H
+ NH_3
6.
O
+ NH_4

Try It The imine product in Equation 19-19 will undergo hydrolysis when treated with aqueous sulfuric acid. Draw the complete, detailed mechanism and product for this hydrolysis reaction.

Based on the overall reactions in Equations 19-18 and 19-19, *imine formation requires at least two hydrogens on the nucleophilic N atom.* One of those hydrogens is removed in Step 3 of the mechanism (Eq. 19-20), and the other is removed in Step 6. Thus:

> Only NH_3 and primary amines (RNH_2) can form imines on reaction with ketones or aldehydes.

Although a secondary amine (R_2NH) has only one hydrogen on nitrogen and thus cannot form an imine, it can react with a ketone or aldehyde to produce an **enamine**, in which an amino group is attached to an alkene carbon (Eq. 19-22):

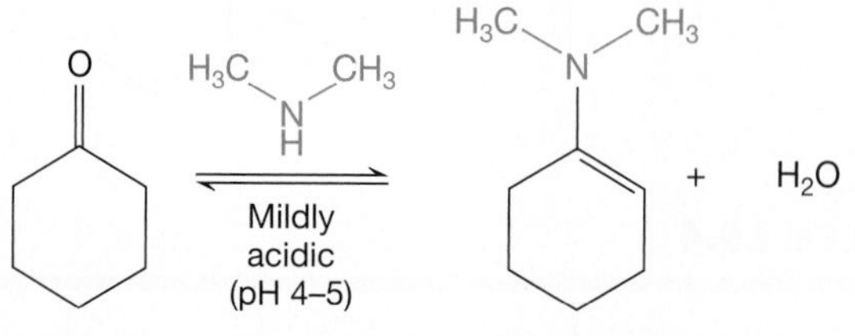

O
H3C CH3
N
H
Mildly
acidic
(pH 4–5)
H3C CH3
N
+ H2O

(19-22)

An enamine

The mechanism for enamine formation (Eq. 19-23) is identical to the mechanism for imine formation (Eq. 19-20) through the first five steps:

Mechanism for enamine formation (Eq. 19-22)

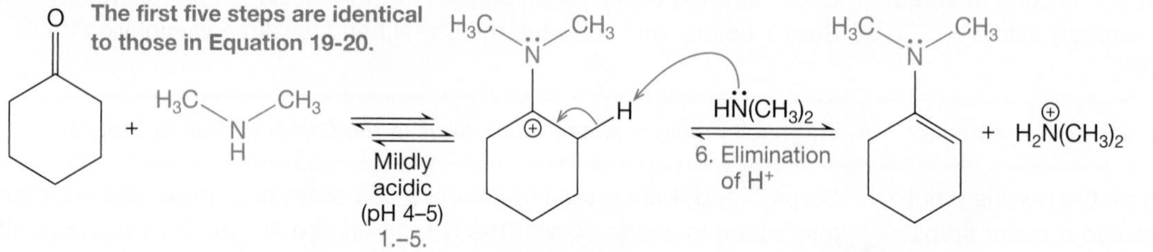

The first five steps are identical to those in Equation 19-20.
O
+
H3C CH3
N
H
Mildly
acidic
(pH 4–5)
1.–5.
H3C CH3
N
H
HN(CH3)2
6. Elimination
of H+
H3C CH3
N
+ H2N(CH3)2

(19-23)

The only difference is in the last step. In imine formation (Eq. 19-20), the second of two H atoms on N is removed. In enamine formation, no such H exists, so a proton is eliminated from an adjacent C instead (i.e., from an α carbon).

Enamines are useful in organic synthesis because the α carbon is nucleophilic and can be used to form new C—C bonds (see Problems 19.39 and 19.40 at the end of the chapter). Furthermore, after an enamine undergoes reaction at the α carbon, it can be hydrolyzed back to the ketone or aldehyde when treated with large amounts of H_2O under acidic conditions (i.e., the reverse of Eq. 19-22).

YOUR TURN 19.11

Draw the complete mechanism and the major products that are formed in each of the following reactions.

(a)

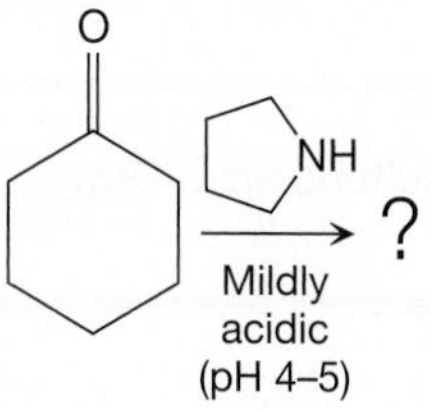

O
NH
?
Mildly
acidic
(pH 4–5)

(b)

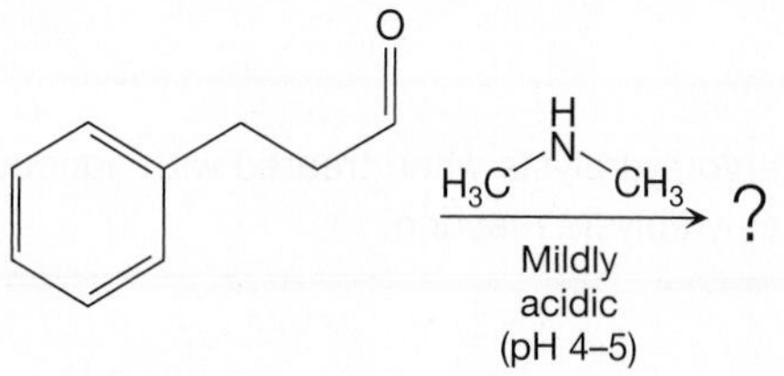

O
H
N
H3C CH3
?
Mildly
acidic
(pH 4–5)

(c)

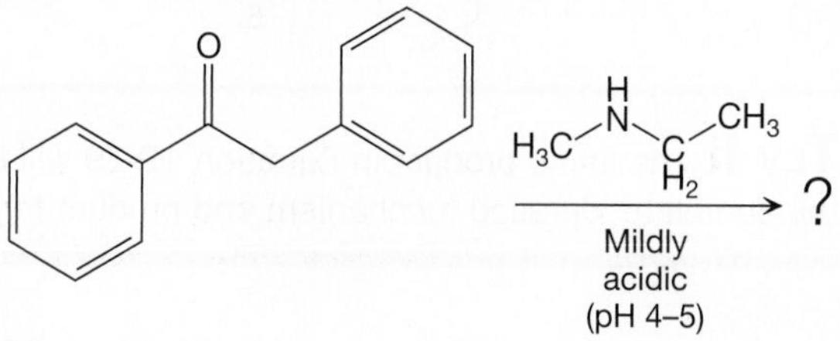

O
H
N
H3C C CH3
H2
?
Mildly
acidic
(pH 4–5)

Imine Formation and Hydrolysis in Biochemical Reactions

Because of the relative ease with which imines can be formed and hydrolyzed, as we have seen here in Section 19.4b, some biochemical processes incorporate imines (or their protonated forms, iminium ions) as a means by which to bind an aldehyde or ketone to a protein for a subsequent reaction. This is integral in the chemistry of vision, as shown in **Figure 19-5**.

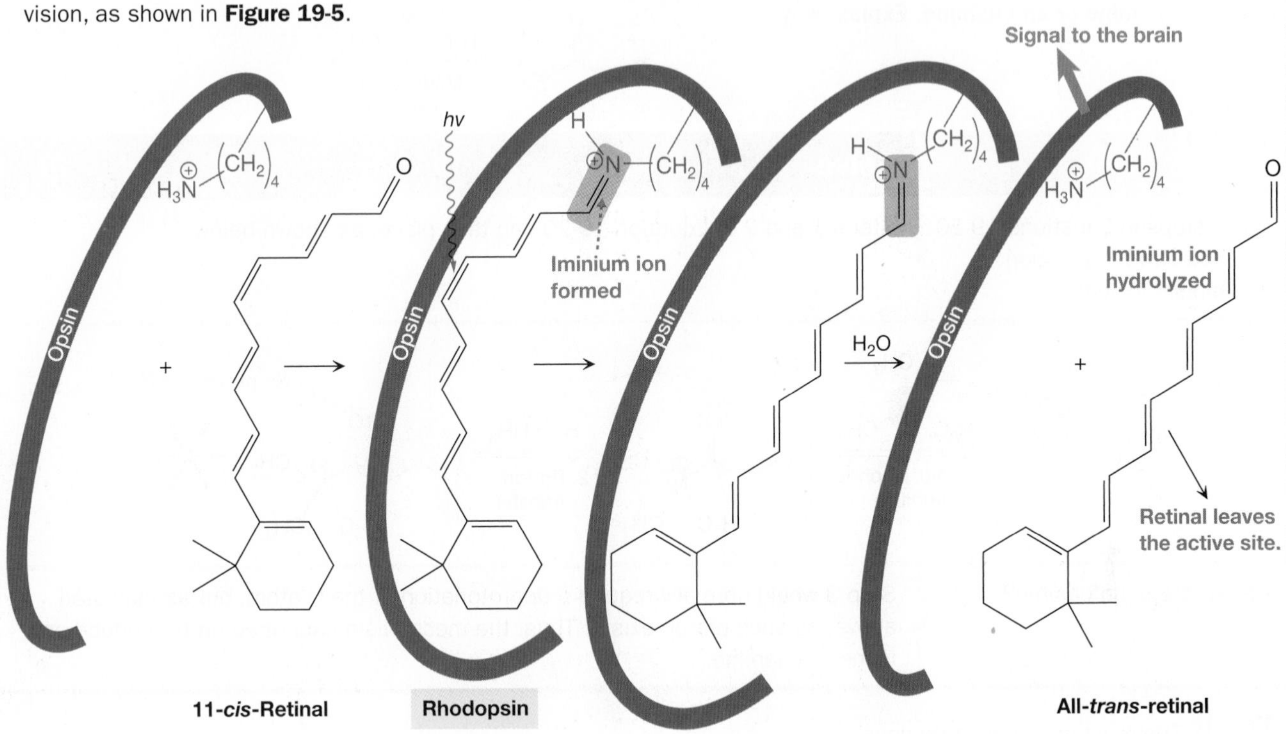

Signal to the brain
hv
Iminium ion formed
Iminium ion hydrolyzed
H_2O
Opsin
Retinal leaves the active site.
11-*cis*-Retinal
Rhodopsin
All-*trans*-retinal

FIGURE 19-5

The retina in the back of the eye is lined with millions of photoreceptor cells called rods and cones. In cones, the protein opsin binds 11-*cis*-retinal in its active site by forming an iminium ion between the two, producing what is called rhodopsin. Formation of the iminium ion involves the HC=O group from retinal and the NH_3^+ from the side chain of a lysine residue in opsin. Then, when light strikes rhodopsin, the cis double bond is very quickly converted to trans, which triggers the hydrolysis of the iminium ion. All-*trans*-retinal is ejected and an electrical signal is sent to the brain. Through a series of enzyme-catalyzed steps, the trans form is then recycled back to the cis form.

Another example involves pyridoxal phosphate (PLP), a derivative of vitamin B_6 (OP represents the phosphate group), as shown in **Figure 19-6**.

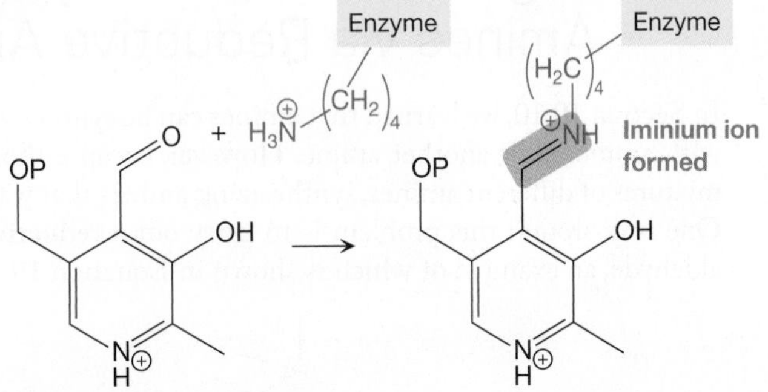

Enzyme
Enzyme
Iminium ion formed
OP
OH

Pyridoxal phosphate (PLP)

FIGURE 19-6

Many enzymatic reactions are PLP-dependent, relying on the formation of an iminium ion between the HC=O group of free PLP and the NH_3^+ group from a lysine residue in the enzyme. Bound PLP can then facilitate a variety of different reactions involving amino acids, including racemization, decarboxylation, transamination, and nucleophilic substitution reactions.

SOLVED PROBLEM **19.5**

How to determine whether a ketone or aldehyde can form an imine or enamine

Break It Down **The reaction shown here does *not* form an imine or an enamine. Explain why.**

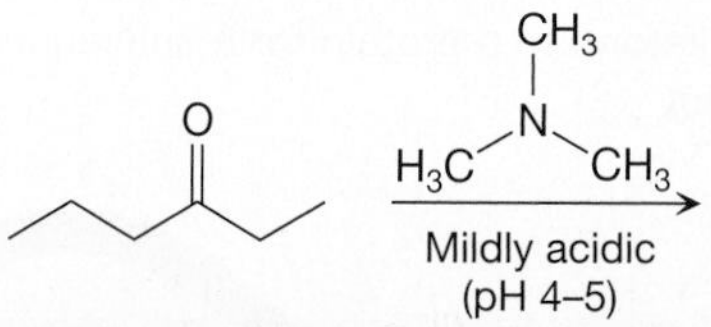

O
CH_3
N
H_3C
CH_3
Mildly acidic
(pH 4–5)

Think	Solve
Which steps in Equations 19-20 or 19-23 can the reaction mechanism include?	Steps 1 and 2 of Equation 19-20 can take place, as shown below.

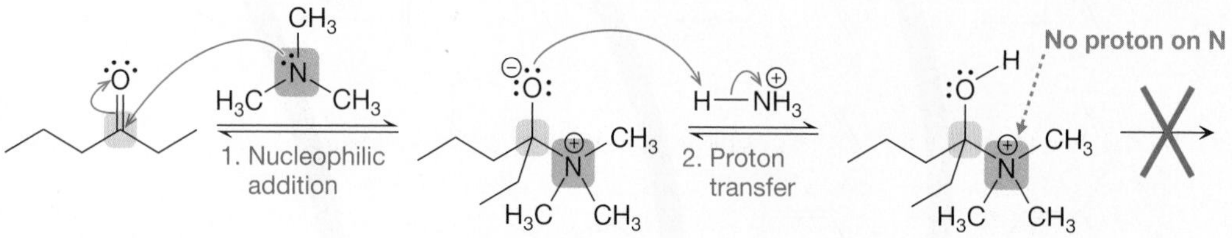

CH_3
H_3C
CH_3
1. Nucleophilic
addition
CH_3
H_3C
CH_3
H—NH_3
2. Proton
transfer
No proton on N
H
CH_3
H_3C
CH_3

Think	Solve
Are any steps unfeasible?	Step 3 would normally require a deprotonation of the N atom, but as indicated above, no such proton exists. Thus, the mechanism cannot go on to produce an imine or enamine.

Try It The reaction shown here does *not* form an imine or enamine. Explain why.

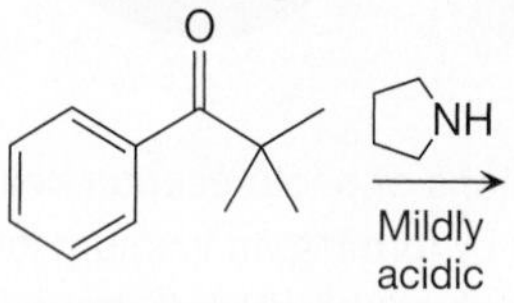

O
NH
Mildly
acidic

SECTION 19.5 OBJECTIVES

You will be able to:

1. Draw the mechanism and product for reductive amination of a ketone or aldehyde.
2. Show how to use a reductive amination in synthesis.

19.5 Organic Synthesis: Synthesizing Amines via Reductive Amination

In Section 10.10, we learned that amines can be synthesized by treating an alkyl halide with ammonia or another amine. However, because those reactions tend to produce mixtures of different amines, synthesizing amines that way is generally not very useful. One way around this problem is to carry out a **reductive amination** of a ketone or aldehyde, an example of which is shown in Equation 19-24:

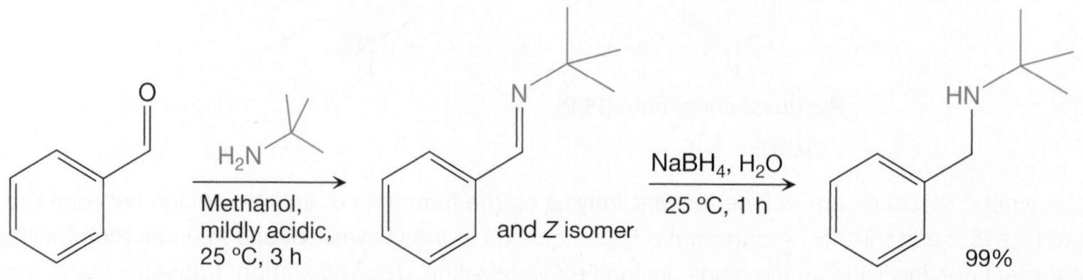

O
H_2N
Methanol,
mildly acidic,
25 °C, 3 h
N
and *Z* isomer
$NaBH_4$, H_2O
25 °C, 1 h
HN
99%

(19-24)

In this case, the aldehyde is first treated with an amine to produce an imine, just as we learned in Section 19.4b. Then $NaBH_4$ is added to reduce the imine to the amine (review Section 18.3b; see Your Turn 19.12). Notice N of the amine is located precisely where the carbonyl O was.

YOUR TURN 19.12

Draw the mechanism for the conversion of the imine into the amine in Equation 19-24.

In the example shown (Eq. 19-24), a primary amine (RNH_2) is used to produce a secondary amine (R_2NH), proceeding through an imine intermediate. If ammonia (NH_3) were used instead, an imine would still be produced as an intermediate, but the product would be a primary amine (see Your Turn 19.13).

YOUR TURN 19.13

For the reaction shown here, draw the intermediate imine and the product.

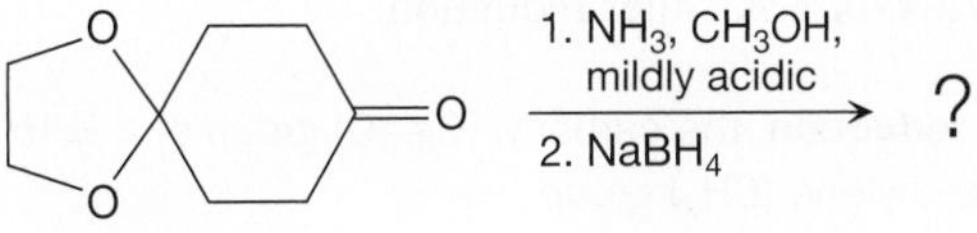

O
O
O
1. NH3, CH3OH, mildly acidic
2. NaBH4
?

In Equation 19-24, $NaBH_4$ is not added until after the imine formation has come to completion. Imine formation takes place under slightly acidic conditions, which would neutralize $NaBH_4$ (see Recall box). A clever solution to this problem is to use $NaBH_3CN$ instead, as shown in Equation 19-25:

◀ RECALL

Section 18.3a explained that $NaBH_4$ is weakly basic and will persist for a substantial time in a neutral solvent like water or an alcohol. If the solution is acidic, however, then H^- from $NaBH_4$ will be protonated to form $H_2(g)$.

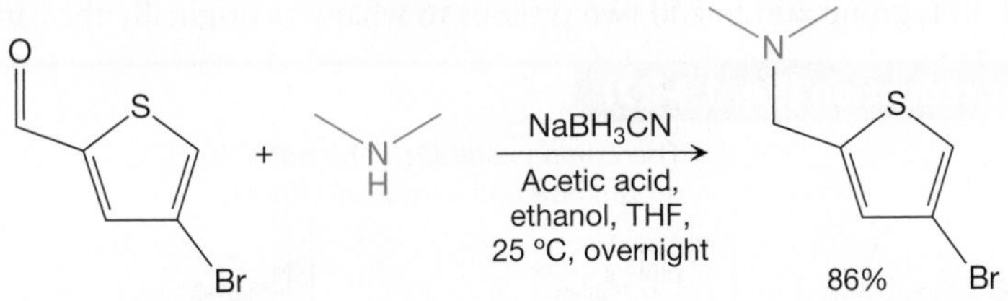

O
S
Br
+
N
H
NaBH3CN
Acetic acid, ethanol, THF, 25 °C, overnight
N
S
86%
Br

(19-25)

The partial mechanism for this reaction is shown in Equation 19-26. $NaBH_3CN$ is a source of hydride, but the electron-withdrawing CN group makes it less basic, allowing it to remain intact under the mildly acidic reaction conditions.

Partial mechanism for reductive amination (Eq. 19-25)

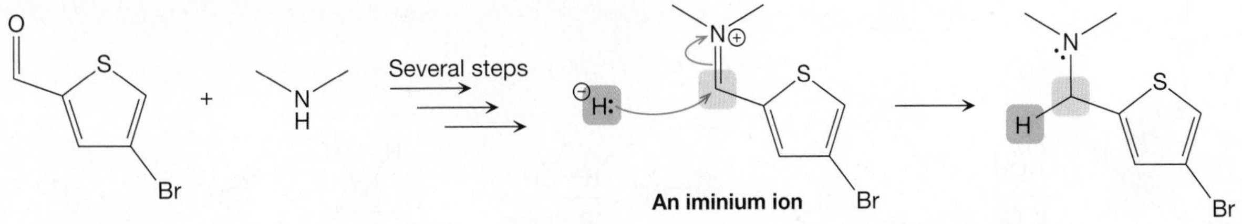

O
S
Br
+
N
H
Several steps
H:
N
S
An iminium ion
Br
N
H
S
Br

(19-26)

YOUR TURN 19.14

Show how to synthesize each of these amines from a ketone or aldehyde.

(a)

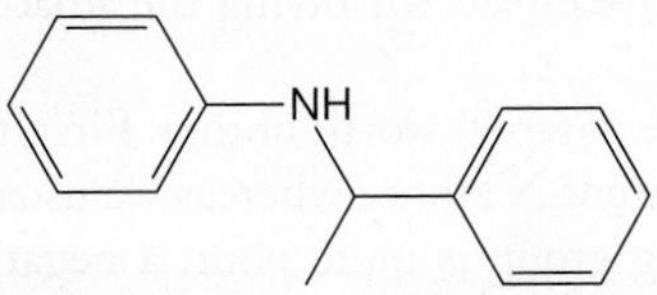

NH

(b)

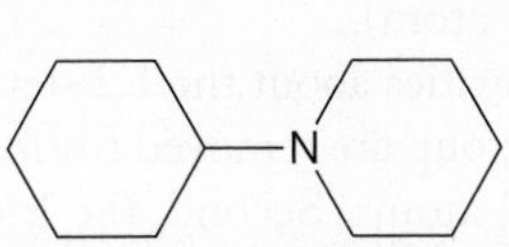

N

(c)

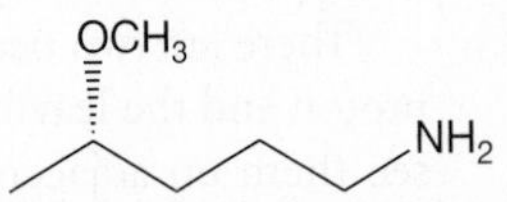

OCH3
NH2

19.6 The Wolff–Kishner Reduction

SECTION 19.6 OBJECTIVES

You will be able to:

1. Draw the mechanism and product for a Wolff-Kishner reduction.
2. Show how to use a Wolff-Kishner reduction in synthesis.

When cyclopropylethanone is treated with hydrazine ($H_2N{-}NH_2$) under mildly acidic conditions, followed by heating in the presence of a strong base, ethylcyclopropane is produced, as shown in Equation 19-27:

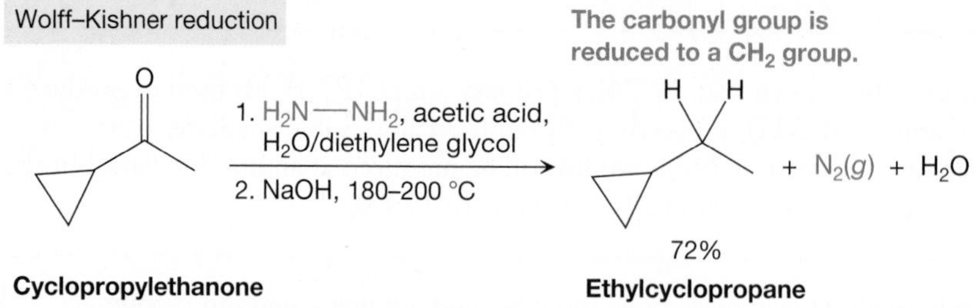

Wolff–Kishner reduction
The carbonyl group is reduced to a CH2 group.
1. H2N—NH2, acetic acid, H2O/diethylene glycol
2. NaOH, 180–200 °C
+ N2(g) + H2O
72%
Cyclopropylethanone
Ethylcyclopropane

(19-27)

This is an example of a Wolff–Kishner reduction:

> In a **Wolff–Kishner reduction**, the carbonyl (C=O) group of a ketone or aldehyde is converted to a methylene (CH_2) group.

The partial mechanism for the Wolff–Kishner reduction is shown in Equation 19-28. Because each N atom of hydrazine possesses two H atoms, the first several steps (Steps 1–6) are analogous to those for imine formation in Equation 19-20. The result is a **hydrazone**, characterized by the $C{=}N{-}NH_2$ group. The four steps that occur after the hydrazone has formed (Steps 7–10) serve to remove two protons from the remaining NH_2 group and to add two protons to what was originally the carbonyl C.

Partial mechanism for the Wolff–Kishner reduction (Eq. 19-27)

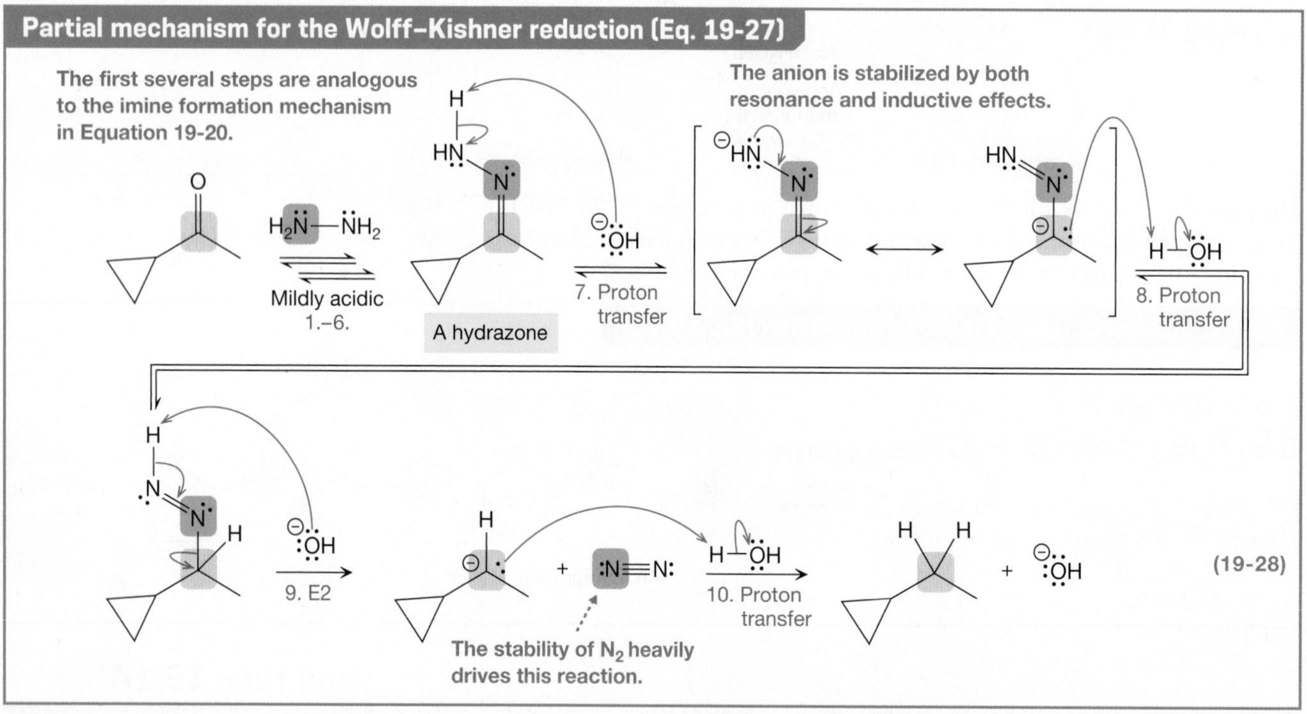

The first several steps are analogous to the imine formation mechanism in Equation 19-20.
Mildly acidic
1.–6.
A hydrazone
7. Proton transfer
The anion is stabilized by both resonance and inductive effects.
8. Proton transfer
9. E2
10. Proton transfer
The stability of N2 heavily drives this reaction.

(19-28)

Notice in Step 7 that HO^- deprotonates a N atom. HO^- is not normally a strong enough base to do this, but the resulting conjugate base is stabilized by resonance (involving the adjacent double bond) and by inductive effects (involving the adjacent electron-withdrawing N atom).

There are two peculiarities about the E2 step (i.e., Step 9) worth noting. First, the proton and the leaving group are removed from adjacent N atoms, whereas we usually see them on adjacent C atoms. Second, the leaving group is quite poor: a negative charge becomes localized on a C atom. Normally this would prevent an E2 reaction from occurring, but the formation of $N_2(g)$ is a substantial driving force. Not only is $N_2(g)$ very stable but also, being a gas, it leaves the reaction system once it is formed. This makes the overall reaction *irreversible*, which, according to Le Châtelier's principle, helps drive the formation of products (see Recall box).

The Wolff–Kishner reduction in Equation 19-27 is carried out in two sequential steps: first the hydrazone forms under mildly acidic conditions, and then the hydrazone reacts to form the methylene group under basic conditions. Conveniently, the hydrazone can form under basic conditions, too. Therefore, Wolff–Kishner reductions are frequently carried out in a single step, simply by treating the ketone or aldehyde with hydrazine under strongly basic conditions and high temperature, as shown in Equation 19-29:

◂ RECALL

Section 10.9 showed how $N_2(g)$ acts as a leaving group when diazomethane (CH_2N_2) reacts with a carboxylic acid to produce a methyl ester. In Section 13.2, we saw how $N_2(g)$ acts as a leaving group when an alkene is treated with diazomethane to produce a cyclopropane ring.

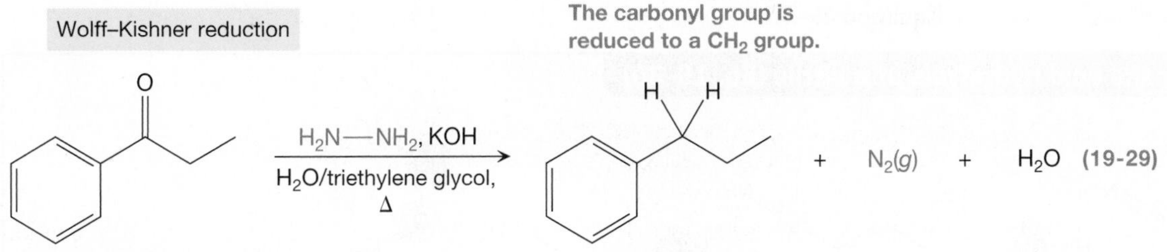
Wolff–Kishner reduction
The carbonyl group is reduced to a CH_2 group.
$H_2N—NH_2$, KOH
H_2O/triethylene glycol, Δ
+ $N_2(g)$ + H_2O

(19-29)

1-Phenylpropan-1-one **Propylbenzene** 82%

YOUR TURN 19.15

Draw the complete, detailed mechanism and predict the product for each of the following reactions.

(a)

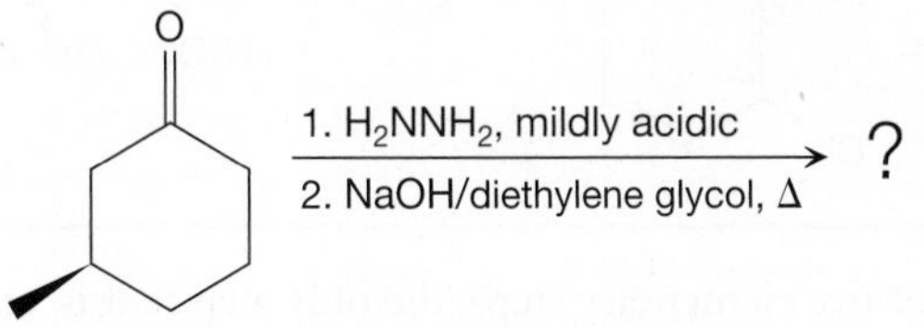
1. H_2NNH_2, mildly acidic
2. NaOH/diethylene glycol, Δ
?

(b)

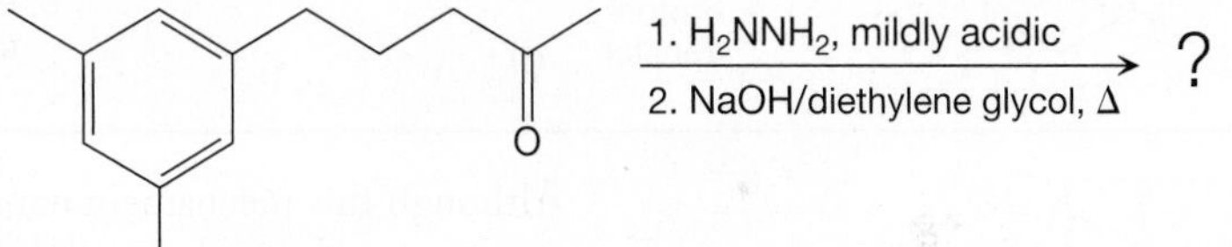
1. H_2NNH_2, mildly acidic
2. NaOH/diethylene glycol, Δ
?

19.7 Hydrolysis of Nitriles

SECTION 19.7 OBJECTIVES

You will be able to:

1. Draw the mechanism that shows how a nitrile undergoes hydrolysis under acidic or basic conditions to produce an amide.
2. Explain why the hydrolysis of a nitrile can take place under acidic or basic conditions.

Section 19.4 discussed the hydrolysis of acetals and imines. Nitriles (R—C≡N), too, can undergo hydrolysis, as shown in Equations 19-30 and 19-31:

The treatment of a nitrile with water under either acidic or basic conditions produces a primary amide, R—CO—NH_2.

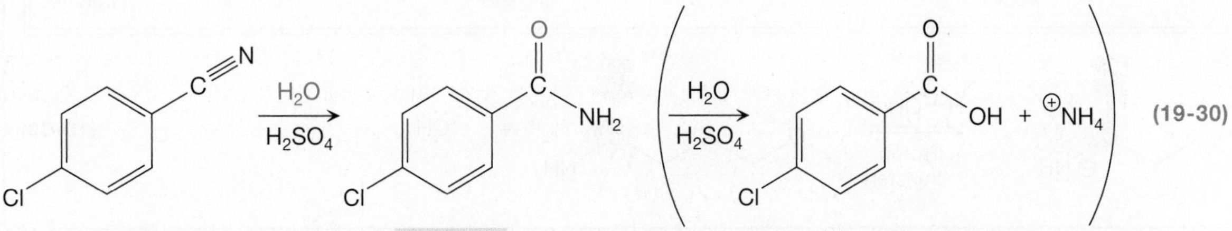
H_2O
H_2SO_4
NH_2
H_2O
H_2SO_4
OH + $^{\oplus}NH_4$

(19-30)

An amide

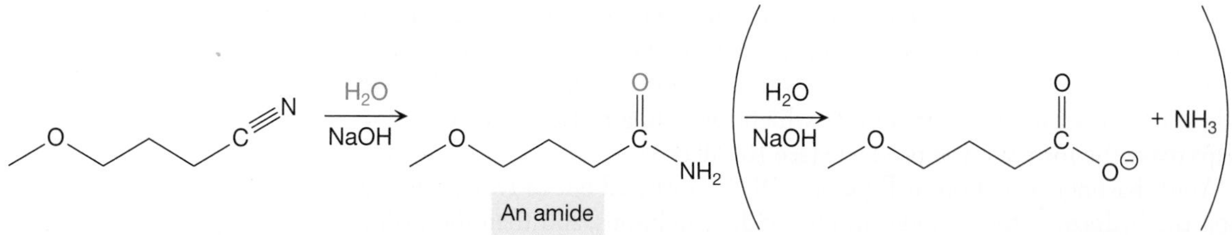
H2O
NaOH
An amide
H2O
NaOH
+ NH3
(19-31)

To isolate the amide, the reaction must be monitored carefully because, as shown in parentheses in the two equations, the amide can easily undergo further hydrolysis to produce a carboxylic acid. (Such amide hydrolysis reactions will be described in detail in Chapters 22 and 23.)

The mechanism for the hydrolysis of a nitrile under acidic conditions is shown in Equation 19-32:

Mechanism for the acid hydrolysis of a nitrile (Eq. 19-30)

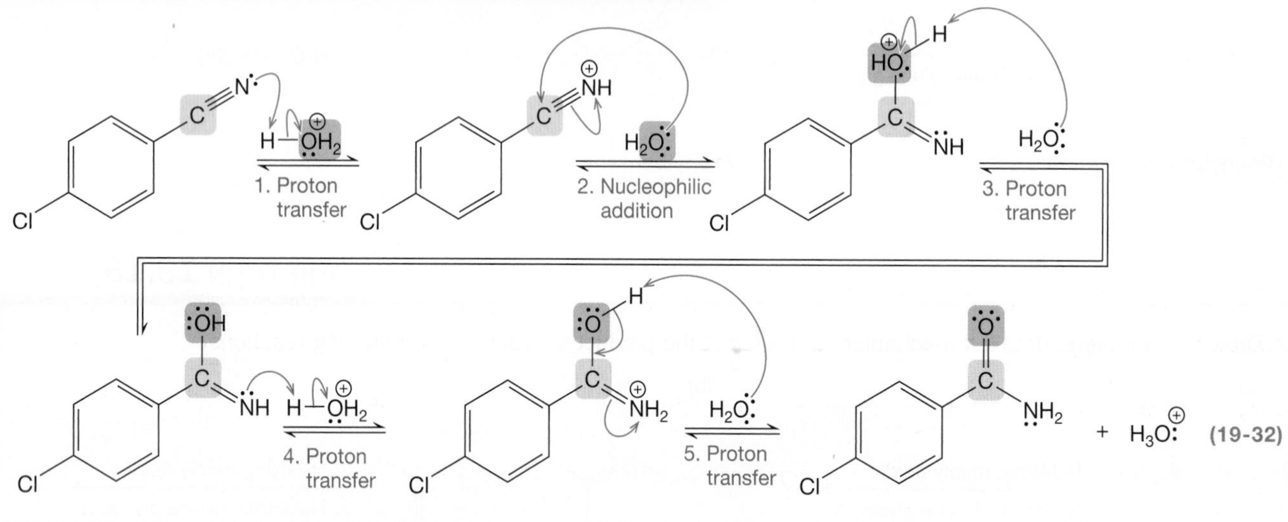
1. Proton transfer
2. Nucleophilic addition
3. Proton transfer
4. Proton transfer
5. Proton transfer
(19-32)

Although this mechanism consists of five elementary steps, the only step that is *not* a proton transfer is the nucleophilic addition step (Step 2). The four proton transfer steps add protons to N and remove them from O, so *no strongly basic species appear in the mechanism*; this is a necessary condition for a reaction taking place under acidic conditions.

The mechanism for the hydrolysis of a nitrile under basic conditions is shown in Equation 19-33:

Mechanism for the base hydrolysis of a nitrile (Eq. 19-31)

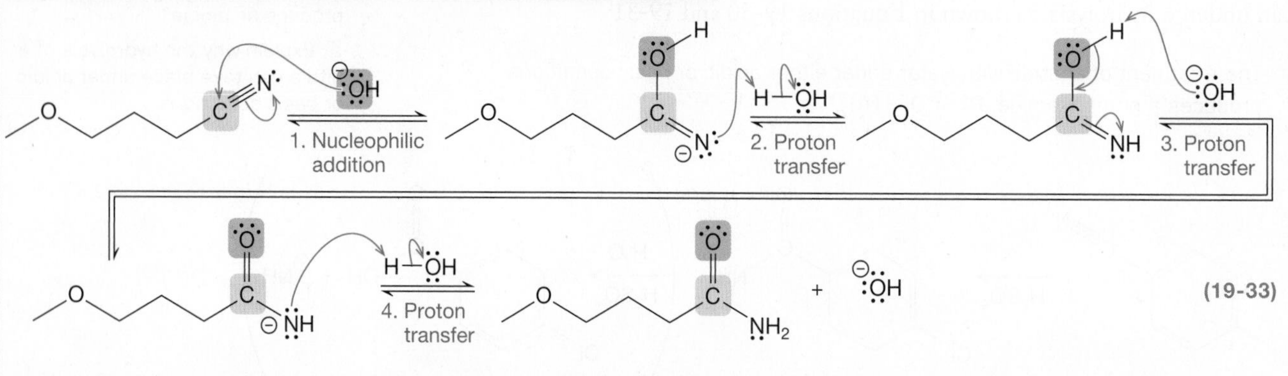
1. Nucleophilic addition
2. Proton transfer
3. Proton transfer
4. Proton transfer
(19-33)

As in hydrolysis under acidic conditions, the only step that is not a proton transfer is the nucleophilic addition step (Step 1 in this case). Similar to the acid-catalyzed mechanism, the proton transfer steps in Equation 19-33 serve to add protons to N and remove one from O. Because the reaction takes place under basic conditions, these proton transfer steps allow the reaction to take place without generating any strongly acidic species.

YOUR TURN **19.16**

Draw the complete, detailed mechanism and predict the major organic product of each of these reactions.

(a)

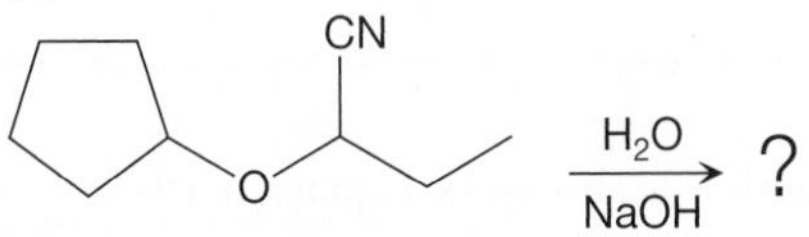

CN
O
H_2O
NaOH
?

(b)

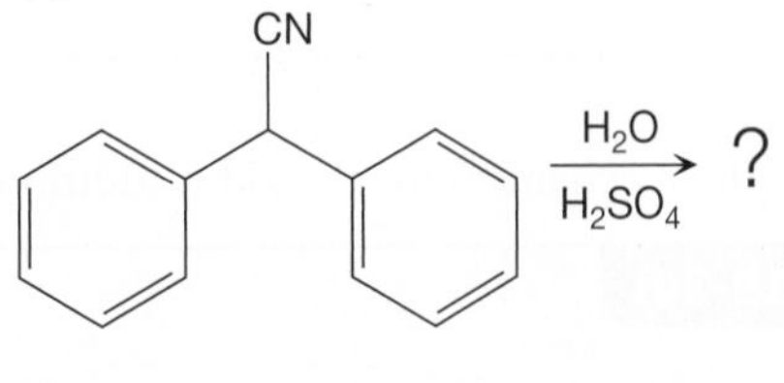

CN
H_2O
H_2SO_4
?

SECTION 19.8 OBJECTIVES

You will be able to:

1. Draw the mechanism and product for an aldol addition.
2. Identify a target as a possible product of an aldol addition.

19.8 Enolate Nucleophiles: Aldol Additions

Nearly all of the acid- and base-catalyzed nucleophilic addition reactions we have encountered thus far are ones in which the nucleophilic atom is a heteroatom such as nitrogen, oxygen, or sulfur. Reactions that involve carbon nucleophiles, however, are among the most important reactions in organic synthesis. These include aldol reactions, which we will examine throughout the rest of the chapter.

When ethanal (acetaldehyde, $CH_3CH{=}O$) is treated with sodium hydroxide (Eq. 19-34), the product is 3-hydroxybutanal, a compound containing a four-carbon chain:

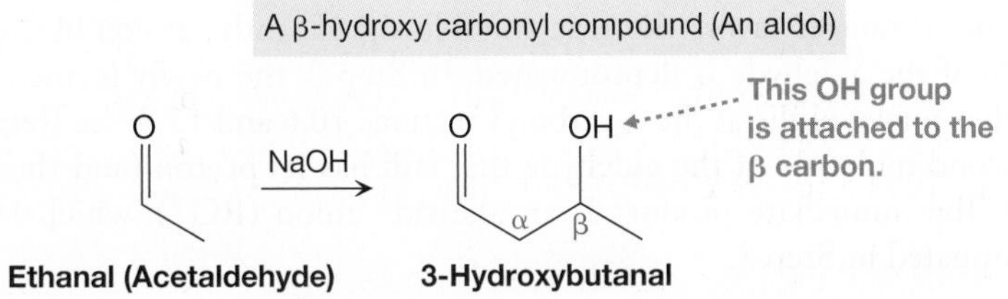

A β-hydroxy carbonyl compound (An aldol)
This OH group is attached to the β carbon.
O
NaOH
O
OH
α
β
Ethanal (Acetaldehyde)
3-Hydroxybutanal

(19-34)

Because the product contains both a CH═O group (characteristic of an aldehyde) and an O—H group (characteristic of an alcohol), it is called an **aldol**, and the reaction that forms it is called an **aldol addition**.

Aldol reactions are particularly important because they form a new C—C bond. Notice, too, that the carbonyl and the hydroxyl groups in the product are separated by two carbon atoms; the molecule is therefore classified as a **β-hydroxy carbonyl compound**, which is the general form of any aldol addition product:

Every aldol addition produces a β-hydroxy carbonyl compound.

CONNECTIONS 19.2

What else is in cigarette smoke? 3-Hydroxybutanal (Eq. 19-34) is a component of cigarette smoke and is also a hypnotic. The substance was once used in medicine as a sedative.

GREEN CHEMISTRY Aldol addition reactions are highly efficient since they have 100% atom economy (review Section 11.6); every atom in the two equivalents of the aldehyde reactant appears in the aldol product.

YOUR TURN 19.17

Which of the following compounds could be the product of an aldol addition reaction? Explain.

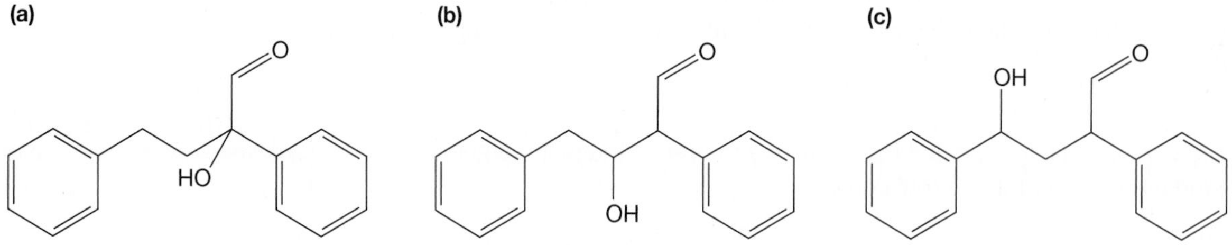
(a)
(b)
(c)
O
HO
O
OH
OH
O

The mechanism for the aldol addition reaction is shown in Equation 19-35:

Mechanism for aldol addition (Eq. 19-34)

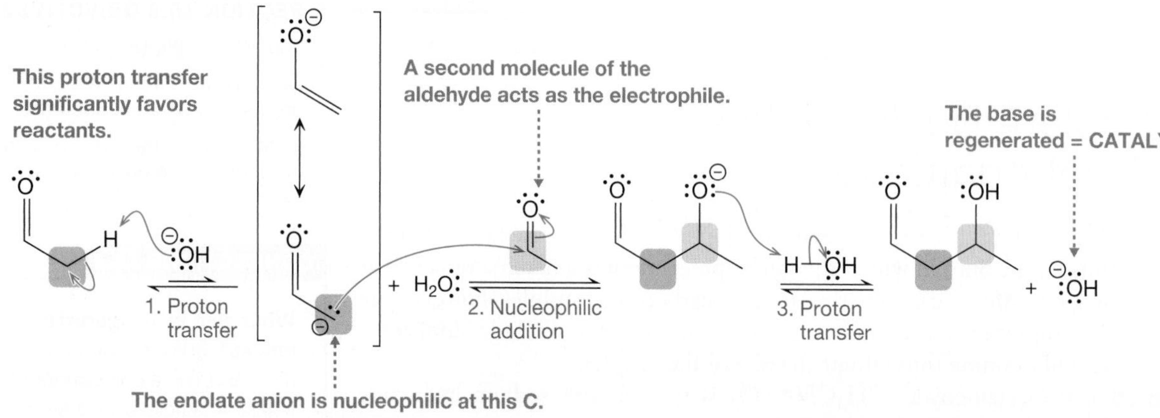
This proton transfer significantly favors reactants.
A second molecule of the aldehyde acts as the electrophile.
The base is regenerated = CATALYST.
H
:OH
1. Proton transfer
+ H₂O:
2. Nucleophilic addition
H—OH
3. Proton transfer
+ :OH
The enolate anion is nucleophilic at this C.

(19-35)

Mechanism Drawing Self-aldol Addition Involving an Aldehyde

In Step 1, HO^- *reversibly* deprotonates the α carbon to yield an enolate anion. In fact, that proton transfer favors the reactant side significantly; at equilibrium, only about 0.01% of the aldehyde is deprotonated. In Step 2, the newly formed enolate anion, which is nucleophilic at the α carbon (Sections 10.6 and 11.3; see Recall box), attacks a second molecule of the aldehyde that still has its proton (and therefore is uncharged). The immediate product is an alkoxide anion (RO^-), which is subsequently protonated in Step 3.

YOUR TURN 19.18

Use the appropriate pK_a values to verify that the proton transfer in Step 1 of the mechanism in Equation 19-35 significantly favors the reactant side.

◂ RECALL

Sections 10.6 and 11.3 showed that an enolate anion can act as a nucleophile in an S_N2 reaction. In α halogenation, the α carbon of an enolate anion attacks a molecular halogen (Cl_2, Br_2, or I_2), and in α alkylation, the α carbon attacks an alkyl halide.

The nucleophilic addition step in Equation 19-35 is *reversible*, too (recall Table 18-2, p. 902). Therefore, the overall aldol reaction is reversible.

SOLVED PROBLEM **19.6**

How to draw the mechanism and product for an aldol addition reaction

Break It Down **Draw the complete, detailed mechanism for the reaction shown here, and use the mechanism to predict the products.**

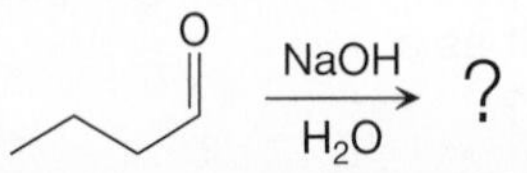

O
NaOH
?
H_2O

Think	Solve
What is the role of NaOH?	NaOH acts as a base to reversibly deprotonate the α carbon of the aldehyde to produce a small concentration of the enolate anion. This is shown in Step 1 below.
What becomes the nucleophile? What is the electrophile?	The enolate anion acts as the nucleophile and an uncharged molecule of the aldehyde acts as the electrophile. This nucleophilic addition step is shown in Step 2 below. Protonation in Step 3 completes the mechanism to produce an aldol product.

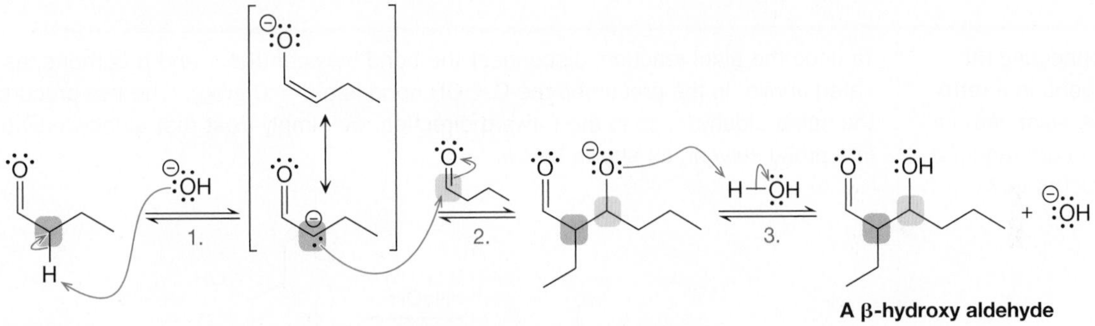

H
:OH
1.
2.
H—OH
3.
:OH
+ :OH

A β-hydroxy aldehyde

Try It Draw the complete, detailed mechanism for the reaction shown here and predict the product.

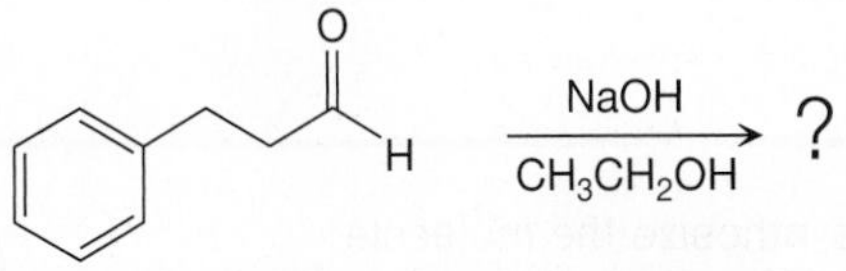

O
H
NaOH
CH_3CH_2OH
?

Aldol reactions can be catalyzed by acid, too. Exploring the mechanism for this reaction is left as an exercise at the end of this chapter (see Problem 19.25).

Once a synthetic target has been identified as the product of an aldol addition, you should be able to determine the appropriate precursors. Solved Problem 19.7 takes you through this exercise.

SOLVED PROBLEM **19.7**

How to identify the precursors of an aldol addition

Break It Down **Show how to synthesize the molecule shown here using an aldol reaction.**

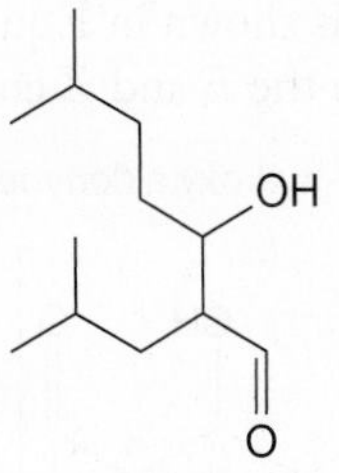

OH
O

(continued)

Think	Solve
Can you identify the portion of the molecule that characterizes it as a β-hydroxy aldehyde?	The α and β carbons of the C=O group are labeled in the structure below on the left. An OH group is attached to the β carbon, so the molecule is indeed a β-hydroxy aldehyde. 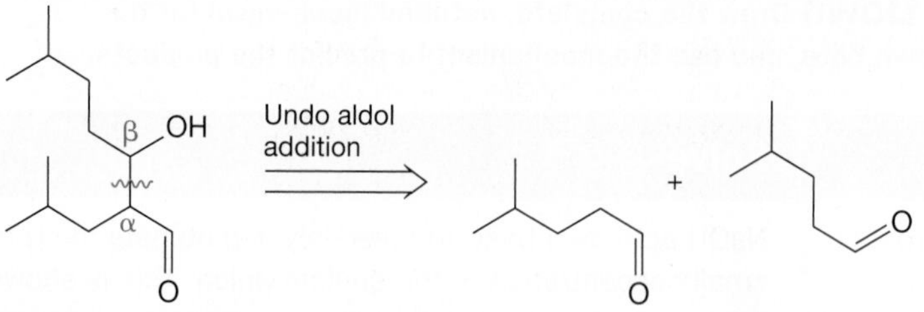 β OH α O Undo aldol addition + O O
Which carbons of the β-hydroxy aldehyde have been joined in the aldol addition?	The aldol addition mechanism in Equation 19-35 (p. 950) shows that the bond between the α and β carbons in the aldol product is the new carbon–carbon bond that is formed. This is indicated above on the left.
On disconnecting the C^{α}—C^{β} bond in a retrosynthesis, what carbon backbones are required in the precursors?	To undo the aldol reaction, disconnect the bond between the α and β carbons, as indicated above. In the precursor, the C—OH bond is a C=O group. The two precursors are the same aldehyde, so in the forward direction, we simply treat that aldehyde with NaOH in a protic solvent, as shown below. 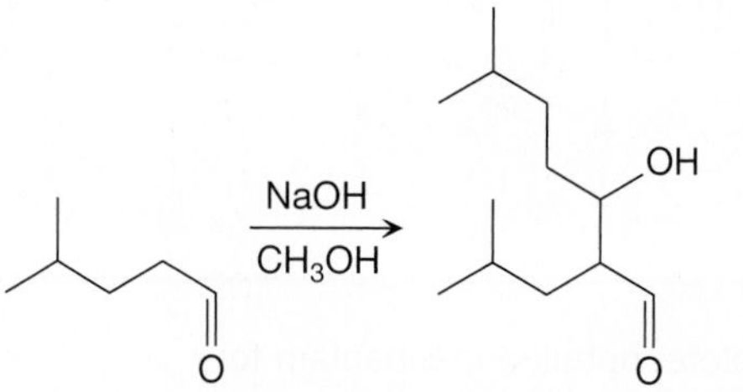 NaOH CH_3OH OH O O

Try It Show how to synthesize the molecule shown here using an aldol reaction.

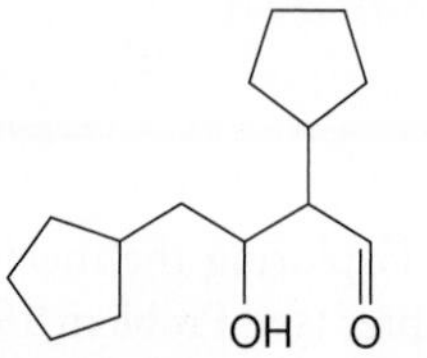

OH
O

SECTION 19.9 OBJECTIVES

You will be able to:

1. Draw the mechanism and product for an aldol condensation reaction.
2. Identify a target as a possible product of an aldol condensation.

19.9 Aldol Condensations

As we saw in Section 19.8, a β-hydroxy aldehyde is the immediate product of an aldol addition. If the reaction is heated, however, then *dehydration* occurs: Water is eliminated from the β-hydroxy aldehyde, giving the overall product a C=C double bond. An example is shown in Equation 19-36, which takes place under basic conditions to produce both the *E* and *Z* configurations of the new C=C bond:

A β-hydroxy aldehyde An α,β-unsaturated aldehyde

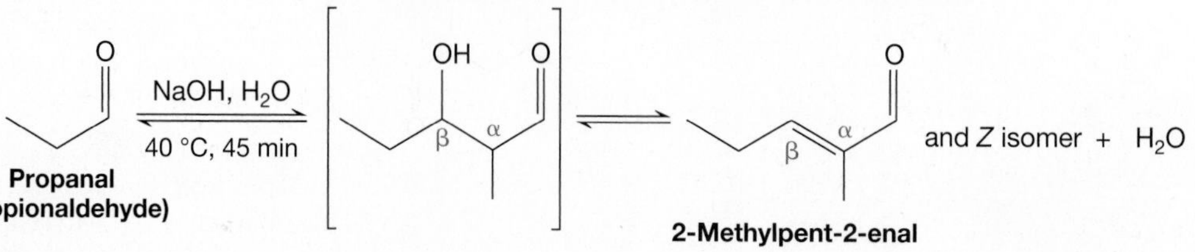

O
NaOH, H_2O
40 °C, 45 min
OH
O
β
α
O
β
α
and *Z* isomer + H_2O

(19-36)

Propanal (Propionaldehyde)

2-Methylpent-2-enal
93%

This overall reaction, in which an aldol addition is followed by dehydration, is called an **aldol condensation**. Recall that a *condensation* reaction is one in which two larger molecules bond together with the elimination of a smaller molecule; in this case, that smaller molecule is H_2O (see Recall box).

YOUR TURN 19.19

To see that Equation 19-36 is truly a condensation reaction, count the total number of C, H, and O atoms in two molecules of the reactant and do the same for the organic product molecule shown. How do they compare?

◂ RECALL

Section 10.4 showed how a symmetric ether can be produced from the condensation of two alcohol molecules under acidic conditions: 2 ROH → R—O—R + H_2O.

The newly formed C═C double bond appears between the α and β carbons of the aldehyde in Equation 19-36, so the product is called an *α,β-unsaturated aldehyde*. In general:

The product of an aldol condensation is an α,β-unsaturated carbonyl compound.

Under basic conditions, dehydration of a β-hydroxy aldehyde takes place by an **E1cb mechanism**, which stands for *elimination, unimolecular, conjugate base* (Eq. 19-37):

Mechanism for E1cb elimination

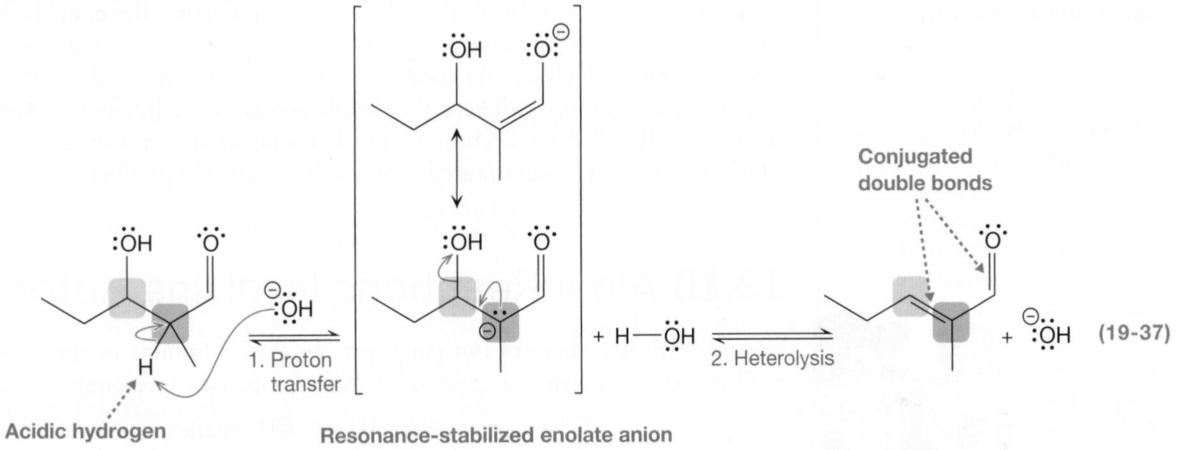
:ÖH
:Ö:
:ÖH
1. Proton transfer
H
Acidic hydrogen
Resonance-stabilized enolate anion
+ H—ÖH
2. Heterolysis
Conjugated double bonds
+ :ÖH
(19-37)

Because of the enhanced acidity at the α carbon, Step 1 is a proton transfer, generating a resonance-stabilized enolate anion. In Step 2, the HO^- leaving group departs to yield the overall product.

The E1cb mechanism might at first seem to contradict the general rule we encountered for elimination reactions in Section 9.9, which states that an HO^- leaving group is generally unsuitable for E1 and E2 reactions. An E1cb mechanism is not strictly an E1 or E2 mechanism, however, so the general rule is not broken. Moreover, the poor leaving group ability of HO^- is partly compensated for by the stability that arises from the conjugation between the C═C and C═O double bonds in the overall product.

Mechanism Drawing
Dehydration of an Aldol Product under Basic Conditions: An E1cb Mechanism

YOUR TURN 19.20

Dehydration occurs if 3-hydroxybutanal is heated under basic conditions, but no dehydration occurs when pent-4-en-2-ol is subjected to the same conditions. Explain.

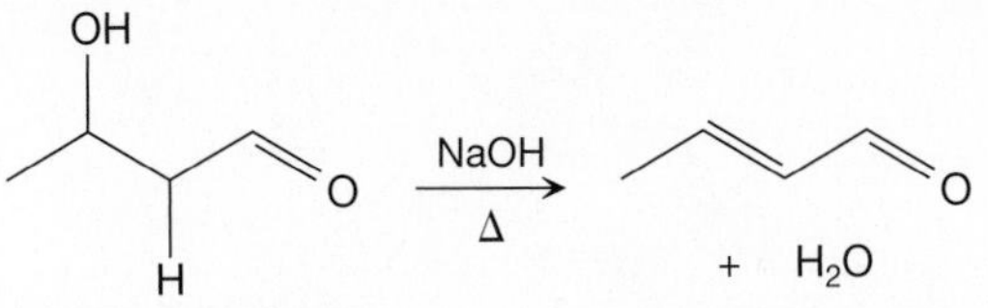
OH
O
H
NaOH
Δ
O
+ H_2O

3-Hydroxybutanal

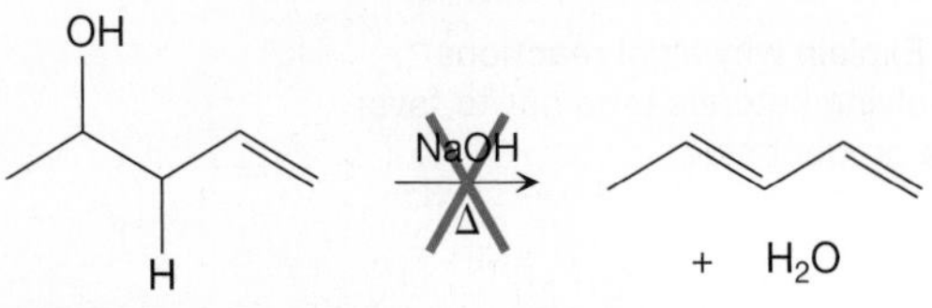
OH
H
NaOH
Δ
+ H_2O

Pent-4-en-2-ol

Dehydration of an aldol product can also take place under acidic conditions, again producing an α,β-unsaturated aldehyde (Eq. 19-38):

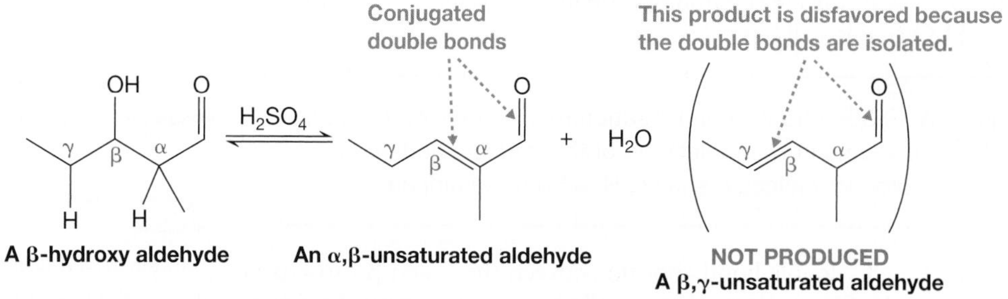
Conjugated double bonds
This product is disfavored because the double bonds are isolated.
OH
O
γ
β
α
H
H
H_2SO_4
+ H_2O
A β-hydroxy aldehyde
An α,β-unsaturated aldehyde
NOT PRODUCED
A β,γ-unsaturated aldehyde

(19-38)

Unlike the E1cb mechanism, which takes place under basic conditions, dehydration under acidic conditions proceeds by an E1 mechanism, just as we learned in Chapter 9 (Eq. 9-26, p. 465).

YOUR TURN 19.21

Draw the complete mechanism that shows the formation of the α,β-unsaturated aldehyde in Equation 19-38.

CONNECTIONS 19.3

Quick-drying inks 4-Hydroxy-4-methylpentan-2-one (Eq. 19-39), also called diacetone alcohol, is a component of gravure printing inks. In gravure printing, the image to be printed is engraved onto a cylinder of a rotary printing press. The cylinder draws up the ink and transfers it to a substrate, such as the consumer product label shown here, so the inks need to flow easily and dry quickly.

DOUBLE CHOCOLATE
Nesquik
Nestlé

Notice in Equation 19-38 that, depending on whether the α or the γ proton is eliminated, dehydration could produce either the α,β-unsaturated aldehyde or the β,γ-unsaturated aldehyde. As indicated, the double bonds in the α,β-unsaturated aldehyde are *conjugated*, whereas the double bonds in the β,γ-unsaturated aldehyde are *isolated*. Recall from Section 14.1 that conjugation is a source of stabilization, which is why the α,β-unsaturated aldehyde is the favored product.

19.10 Aldol Reactions Involving Ketones

Ketones with α hydrogens can participate in aldol additions in the same way that aldehydes do, as shown in Equation 19-39 for propanone (acetone):

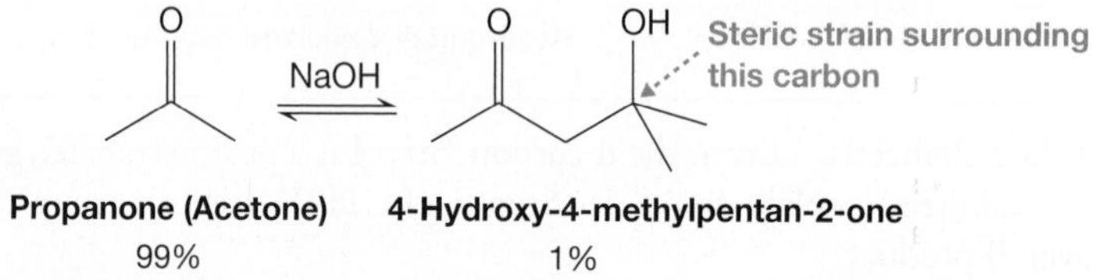
O
NaOH
O
OH
Steric strain surrounding this carbon
Propanone (Acetone)
99%
4-Hydroxy-4-methylpentan-2-one
1%

(19-39)

YOUR TURN 19.22

Label the α and β carbons in the product of Equation 19-39. Is it a β-hydroxy carbonyl compound?

SECTION 19.10 OBJECTIVES

You will be able to:

1. Draw the mechanism and product for an aldol reaction of a ketone.
2. Explain why aldol reactions involving ketones tend not to favor the product side.

The mechanism for the aldol addition of a ketone, shown in Equation 19-40, is identical to the one for the reaction involving only aldehydes, shown previously in Equation 19-35:

Mechanism for the aldol addition of a ketone (Eq. 19-39)

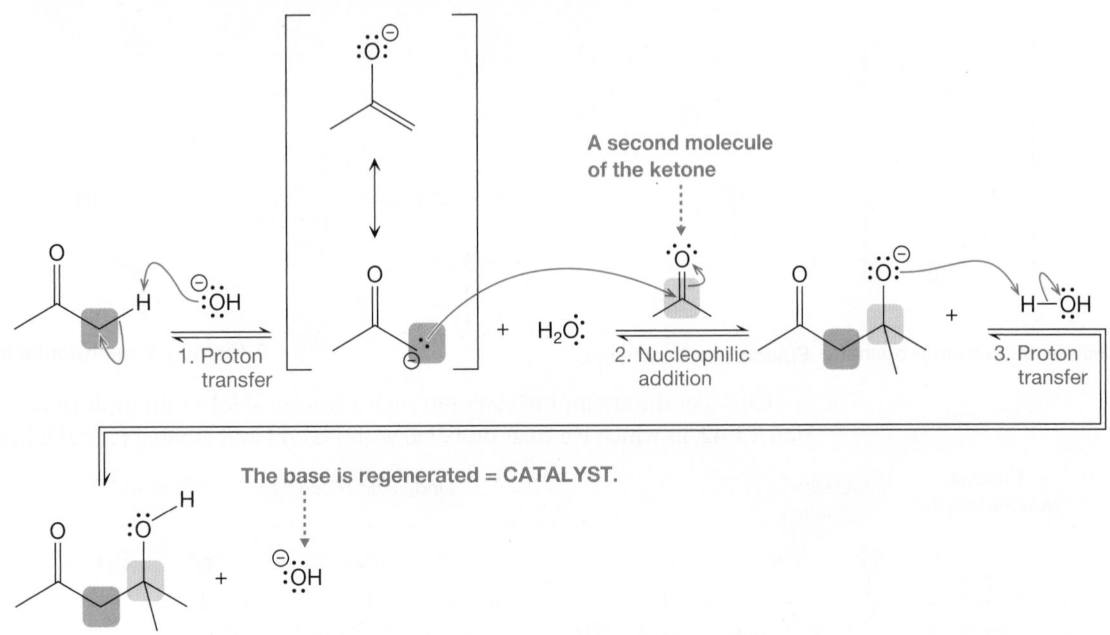

A second molecule of the ketone
1. Proton transfer
2. Nucleophilic addition
3. Proton transfer
The base is regenerated = CATALYST.

(19-40)

Looking back at Equation 19-39, notice that the aldol product forms in only 1% yield at equilibrium. In general:

> An aldol addition reaction between ketones tends to form very little product at equilibrium.

The reaction involving ketones is unfavorable in part because the product has considerable steric strain. Additionally, the electron-donating effects from a ketone's alkyl groups diminish the concentration of positive charge on the carbonyl carbon, making it less susceptible to nucleophilic attack (see Recall box).

Because aldol additions involving ketones generally favor reactants, chemists must manipulate the equilibrium using Le Châtelier's principle to achieve a reasonable yield. Although we will not discuss the details here, one way to do so is to remove the aldol product as it is formed. Alternatively, we can carry out the condensation reaction, which generally makes the α,β-unsaturated ketone product in good yield.

◂ RECALL

The factors that disfavor aldol additions involving ketones—steric strain and electron-donating effects by the attached alkyl groups—also make the hydration of a ketone less favorable than the hydration of an aldehyde (Section 18.2).

19.11 Crossed Aldol Reactions

The aldol additions we have examined thus far have been **self-aldol additions** involving a *single* aldehyde or ketone, so that the nucleophilic enolate anion is derived from the same aldehyde or ketone it attacks. In a **crossed aldol reaction**, on the other hand, a nucleophilic enolate anion is generated from a *different* aldehyde or ketone than the one that is attacked. For example, Equation 19-41 shows the enolate anion of propanal attacking an uncharged molecule of ethanal (acetaldehyde), yielding 3-hydroxy-2-methylbutanal:

SECTION 19.11 OBJECTIVES

You will be able to:

1. Identify crossed aldol reactions that produce a mixture of aldol products and explain why such reactions are not synthetically useful.
2. Show how a synthetically useful crossed aldol reaction can be carried out if one aldehyde has no α hydrogens or if a very strong base is used.

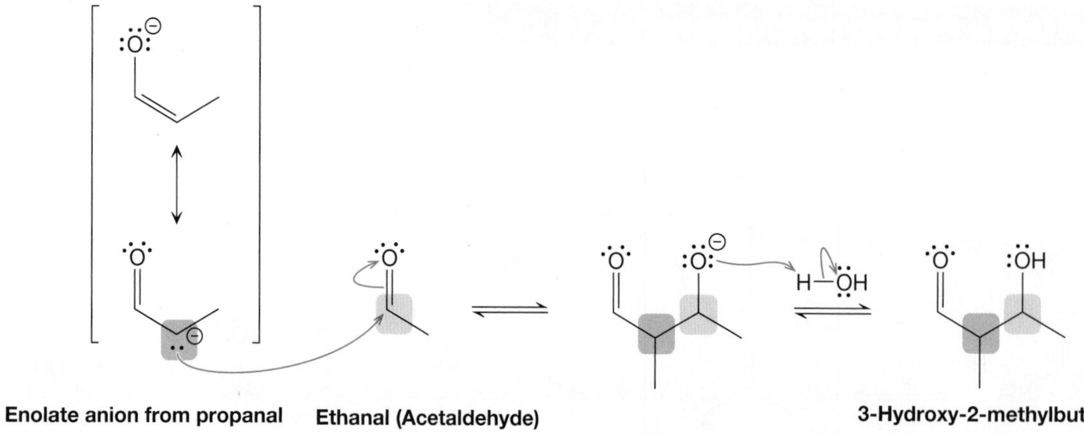

H—OH
Enolate anion from propanal
Ethanal (Acetaldehyde)
3-Hydroxy-2-methylbutanal

(19-41)

Consider the attempt to carry out such a crossed aldol addition, as shown in Equation 19-42, in which we treat propanal with NaOH and ethanal (acetaldehyde):

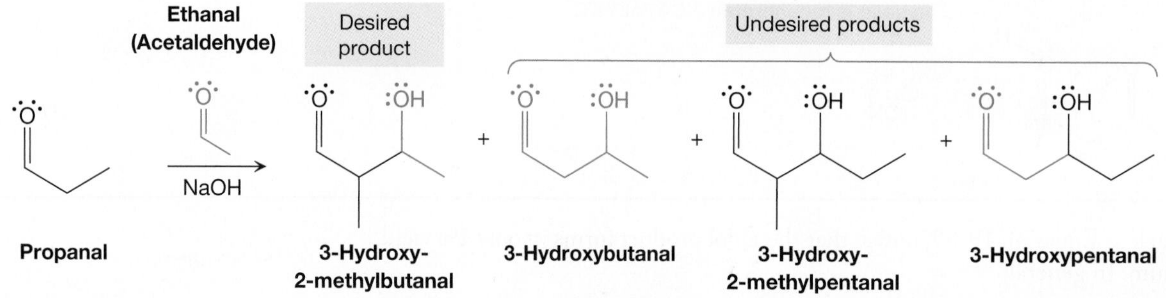

Ethanal (Acetaldehyde)
Desired product
Undesired products
NaOH
Propanal
3-Hydroxy-2-methylbutanal
3-Hydroxybutanal
3-Hydroxy-2-methylpentanal
3-Hydroxypentanal

(19-42)

The hope is that the base will deprotonate propanal and the resulting enolate anion will attack ethanal to produce 3-hydroxy-2-methylbutanal. Indeed, the desired product is formed, as shown in the equation, but so are three other aldol products. Not only does this lower the yield of the reaction, but the four products are difficult to separate due to their similar physical properties. Consequently, this kind of reaction is *not* synthetically useful. Equation 19-43 shows why four aldol products are formed in the above reaction:

GREEN CHEMISTRY
Colin L. Raston and Janet L. Scott (*Green Chem.* **2000**, *2*, 49–52) showed that efficient crossed aldol reactions can be carried out free of solvent, simply by grinding solid reagents together with NaOH. By avoiding the use of solvents, the amount of waste can be dramatically reduced.

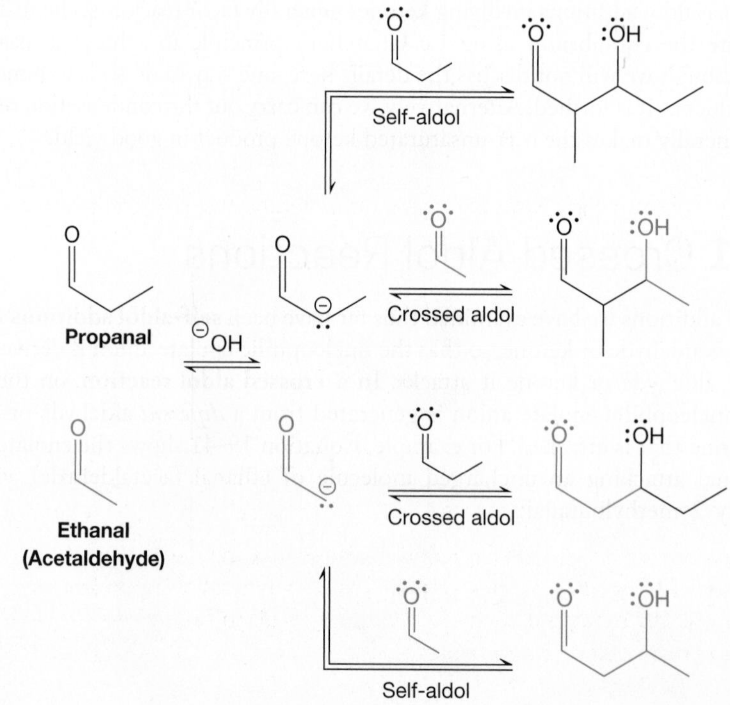

Self-aldol
Propanal
OH
Crossed aldol
Crossed aldol
Ethanal (Acetaldehyde)
Self-aldol

(19-43a)
(19-43b)
(19-43c)
(19-43d)

The problem arises because deprotonation of an α hydrogen by NaOH is somewhat unfavorable since an aldehyde ($pK_a \approx 19$) is a weaker acid than water ($pK_a = 14.0$), the conjugate acid of HO^-. Thus, at any given time throughout the reaction, a significant concentration of HO^- exists. When the second aldehyde is added, it can be deprotonated to a small extent by the remaining HO^-. As a result, the enolate anions from *both* aldehydes are present at the same time, and each enolate anion can attack either of the two different uncharged aldehydes. Thus, four different pairings of an enolate anion with an uncharged aldehyde are possible, and each gives rise to a different aldol product. Two of the products are from *self-aldol reactions* (Eq. 19-43a and 19-43d), and two are from *crossed aldol reactions* (Eq. 19-43b and 19-43c).

YOUR TURN **19.23**

Draw the complete, detailed mechanism for the reaction in Equation 19-43c.

One way around this complication is to use an aldehyde that has no α hydrogens, such as methanal (formaldehyde), benzaldehyde, or dimethylpropanal (**Figure 19-7**).

If an aldehyde *with* α hydrogens is added slowly to a basic solution of an aldehyde *without* α hydrogens, primarily one aldol product is formed.

An example is shown in Equation 19-44, in which cinnamaldehyde is produced:

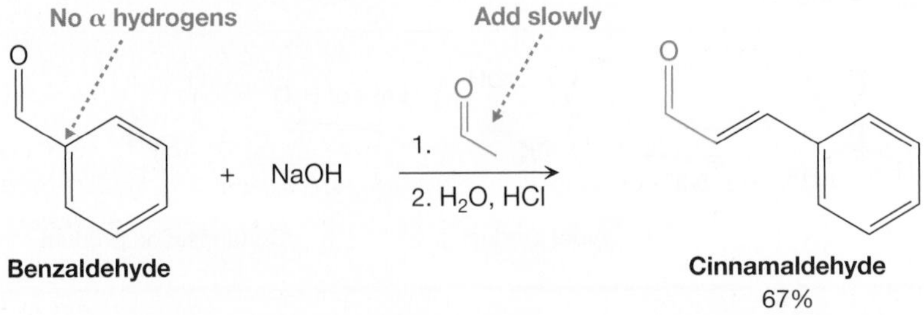
No α hydrogens
Add slowly
+ NaOH
1.
2. H_2O, HCl
Benzaldehyde
Cinnamaldehyde
67%

(19-44)

Benzaldehyde has no α hydrogens, so it cannot be deprotonated by NaOH and does *not* form an enolate anion. In contrast to Equation 19-42, therefore, only one enolate anion is present at any given time. Moreover, if acetaldehyde (which has α hydrogens) is added *slowly*, we avoid a buildup of the uncharged aldehyde and thus minimize the amount of product from the self-aldol reaction between acetaldehyde and its own enolate anion.

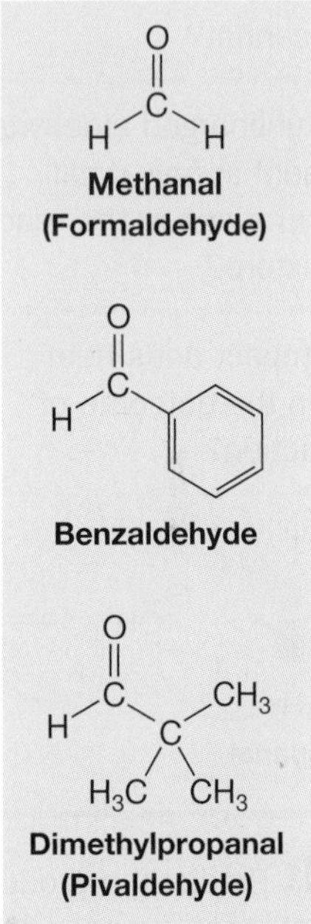
Methanal
(Formaldehyde)
Benzaldehyde
Dimethylpropanal
(Pivaldehyde)

FIGURE 19-7 Aldehydes with no α hydrogens These aldehydes do not form enolate anions, so they can be used effectively in crossed aldol reactions.

YOUR TURN **19.24**

Which of the following ketones or aldehyde would be the best choice to use for a crossed aldol reaction with butanal?

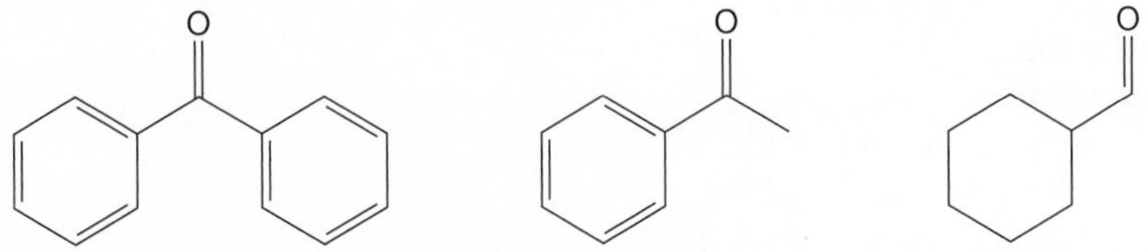

A **B** **C**

For practice with crossed aldol reactions, take the time to work through Solved Problems 19.8 and 19.9 and their corresponding Try It exercises. Solved Problem 19.8 deals with predicting the product of a crossed aldol reaction, and Solved Problem 19.9 helps you design a crossed aldol reaction for synthesis.

CONNECTIONS 19.4

A little spice to life As its name suggests, cinnamaldehyde (Eq. 19-44) gives cinnamon its characteristic flavor and odor. It is the principal component of the essential oil from cinnamon bark.

SOLVED PROBLEM **19.8**

How to predict the product of a crossed aldol condensation

Break It Down Predict the product of the reaction shown here, in which propanal is added slowly to a basic solution of formaldehyde.

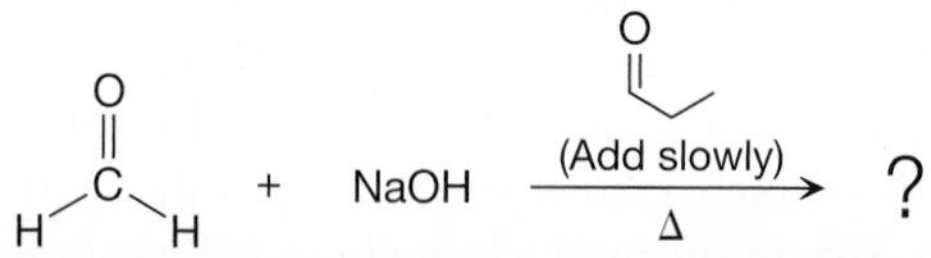

NaOH
(Add slowly)
Δ
?

Think	Solve
Which aldehyde can form an enolate anion and which cannot?	Formaldehyde has no α hydrogens, so it cannot form an enolate anion. Thus, the only enolate nucleophile that is present is derived from propanal, as shown in Step 1 below.
Which uncharged aldehyde is present in only small concentrations in the reaction mixture?	Because propanal is added slowly, there is never a substantial concentration of it in its uncharged form, so the major reaction occurs between the propanal enolate anion and formaldehyde. This is shown in Steps 2 and 3 below.
What impact does heat have on the outcome of the reaction?	Because the reaction is heated (denoted by the symbol Δ), dehydration leads to the condensation product. Under basic conditions, this dehydration follows the E1cb mechanism (Steps 4 and 5).

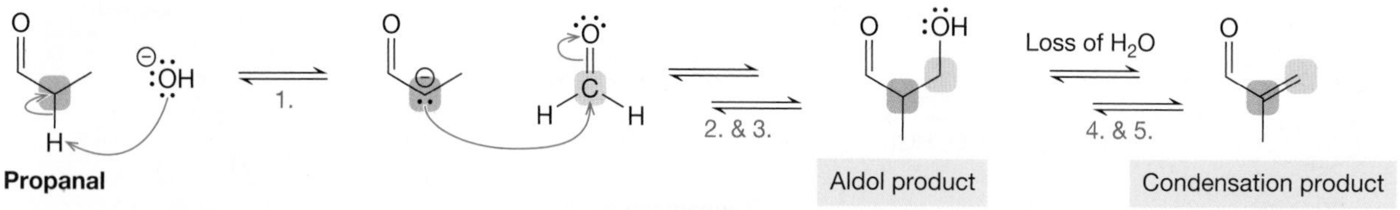

1.
2. & 3.
Loss of H_2O
4. & 5.
Propanal
Aldol product
Condensation product

Try It Predict the product of the reaction shown here, in which phenylethanal is added slowly to a basic solution of dimethylpropanal.

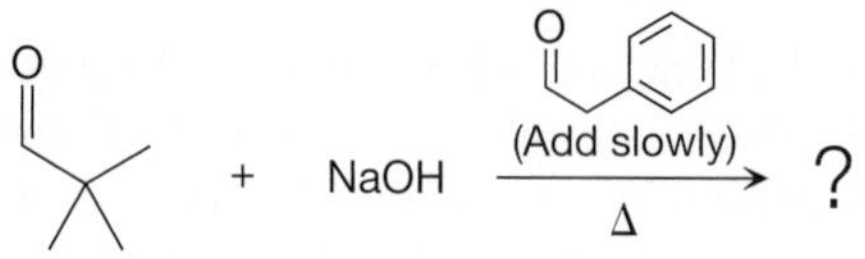

NaOH
(Add slowly)
Δ
?

SOLVED PROBLEM **19.9**

How to determine the precursors for a crossed aldol reaction

Break It Down Show how to synthesize the molecule shown here using an aldol condensation.

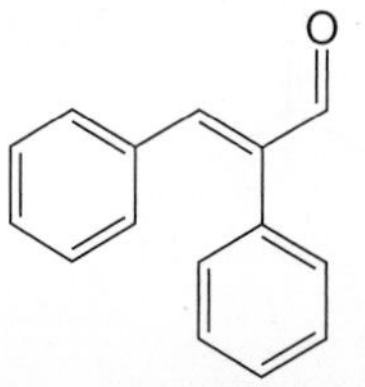

Think	Solve
What portion of the molecule characterizes it as an α,β-unsaturated carbonyl compound?	The carbons that are α and β to the C=O group are labeled in the first structure below.

(continued)

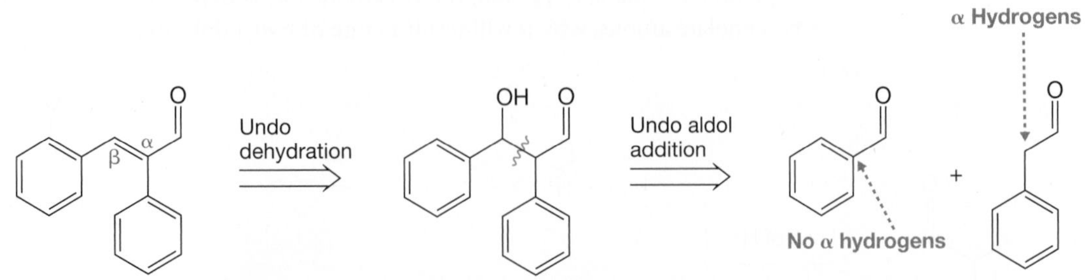
α Hydrogens
O
β
α
Undo
dehydration
OH O
Undo aldol
addition
O
O
+
No α hydrogens

From what β-hydroxy carbonyl compound could it have been generated?	The target is an α,β-unsaturated aldehyde, so it can be the product of dehydrating the second structure above, which is a β-hydroxy aldehyde.
On applying a transform to that β-hydroxy carbonyl compound to undo an aldol addition, which C—C bond should be disconnected?	To apply a transform that undoes an aldol addition, we must disconnect the bond between the α and β carbons, as indicated in the second structure above. The precursors are shown above on the right. Notice that the two aldehyde precursors are different, so a crossed aldol reaction would be required.
To carry out a crossed aldol reaction, can you take advantage of one precursor lacking α protons?	One of the required precursors is benzaldehyde, which has no α protons. Therefore, to carry out the crossed aldol reaction, benzaldehyde can be treated with the base, and the second aldehyde can be added slowly, as shown below. 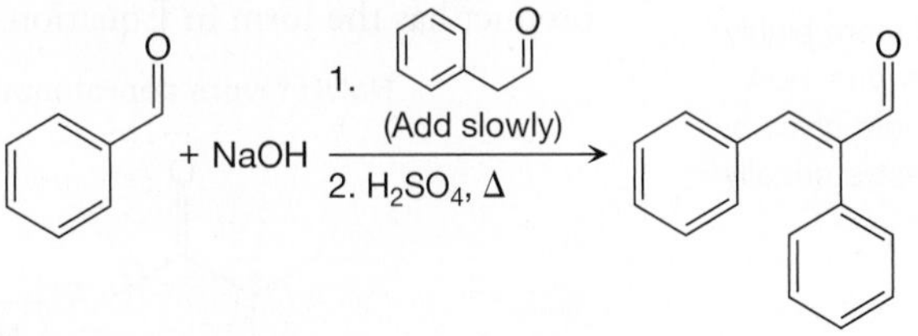 O + NaOH 1. O (Add slowly) 2. H2SO4, Δ O

Try It Show how to synthesize the molecule shown here using an aldol reaction.

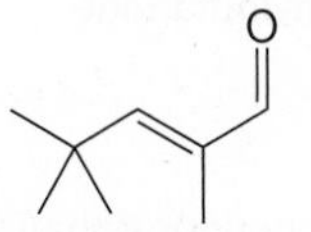
O

A second way to carry out a crossed aldol reaction selectively is to use a very strong base such as lithium diisopropylamide (LDA) to generate the enolate anion, as shown in Equation 19-45:

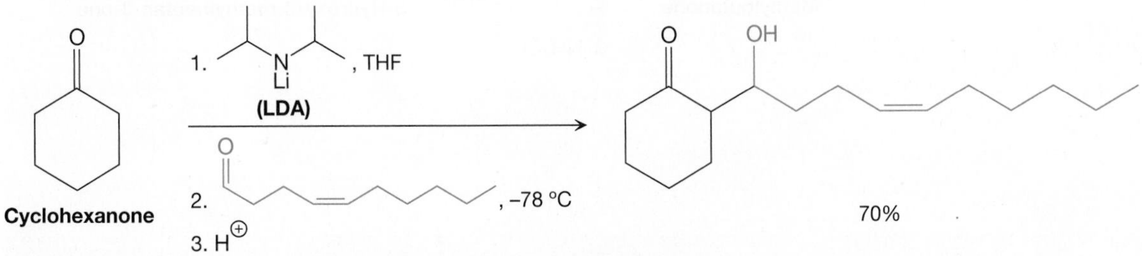
O
Cyclohexanone
1.
N
Li
, THF
(LDA)
2.
O
, –78 °C
3. H⊕
O
OH
70%

(19-45)

Because LDA is a very strong base, it deprotonates the α carbon rapidly, quantitatively, and irreversibly. Therefore, essentially 100% of the cyclohexanone is converted to its enolate anion prior to the addition of the second carbonyl-containing compound. In this way, only one enolate anion is available to react in the second step of the synthesis.

In an aldol reaction involving ketones, regiochemistry becomes a concern when the ketone (e.g., methylbutanone) has two chemically distinct α carbons. As shown in

Equation 19-46a and 19-46b, the α carbon that is deprotonated will lead to one of two enolate anions, which will result in one of two aldol products:

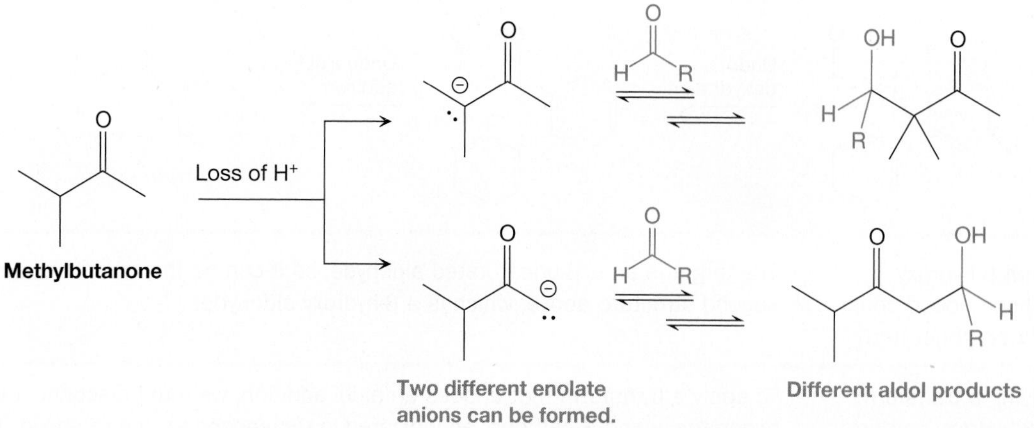

Loss of H^+
Methylbutanone
Two different enolate anions can be formed.
Different aldol products

(19-46a)

(19-46b)

◀ RECALL

◀ RECALL

Section 11.3 showed that a ketone will be deprotonated reversibly by NaOH and irreversibly by excess LDA at very low temperature (e.g., −78 °C). Thus, NaOH favors the *thermodynamic enolate anion* by deprotonating the more highly alkyl-substituted α carbon. LDA favors the *kinetic enolate anion* by deprotonating the least sterically hindered α carbon.

Fortunately, as we learned in Section 11.3, the choice of base can often control which enolate anion is predominantly formed (see Recall box), allowing us to control the regiochemistry of these kinds of aldol reactions. For example, Equation 19-47 shows that if NaOH is the base, then deprotonation is favored at the more substituted α carbon and the major aldol product has the form that appears in Equation 19-46a. If excess LDA is the base and the temperature is kept very low (Eq. 19-48), however, then deprotonation is favored at the less substituted α carbon and the major aldol product has the form in Equation 19-46b.

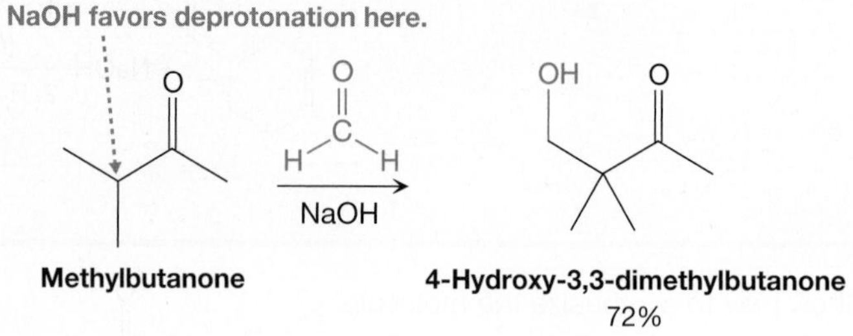

NaOH favors deprotonation here.
NaOH
Methylbutanone
4-Hydroxy-3,3-dimethylbutanone
72%

(19-47)

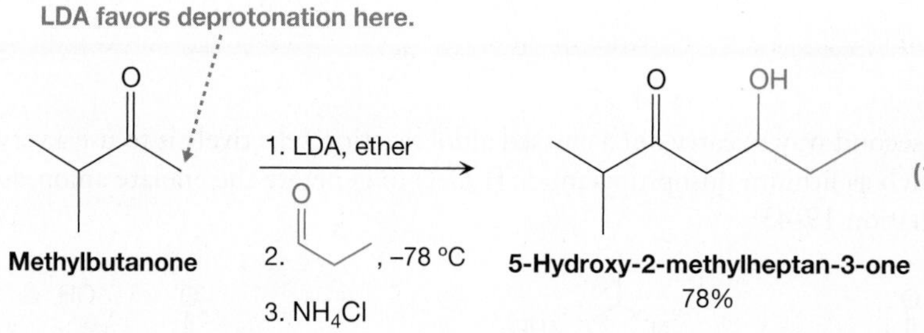

LDA favors deprotonation here.
1. LDA, ether
2. , −78 °C
3. NH_4Cl
Methylbutanone
5-Hydroxy-2-methylheptan-3-one
78%

(19-48)

YOUR TURN **19.25**

In each of the following boxes, write the base that would accomplish the respective aldol reaction.

(a)

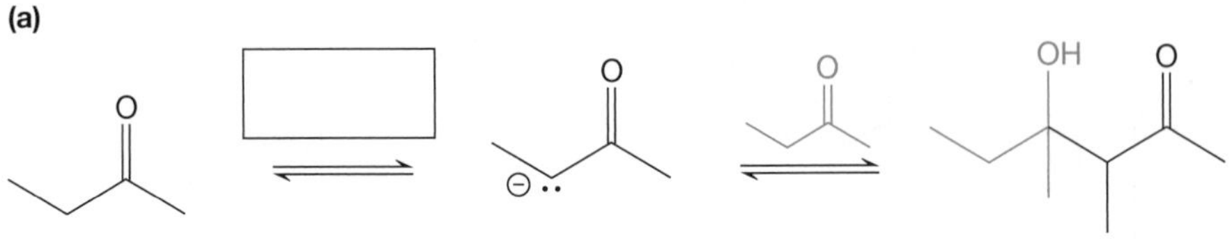

(b)

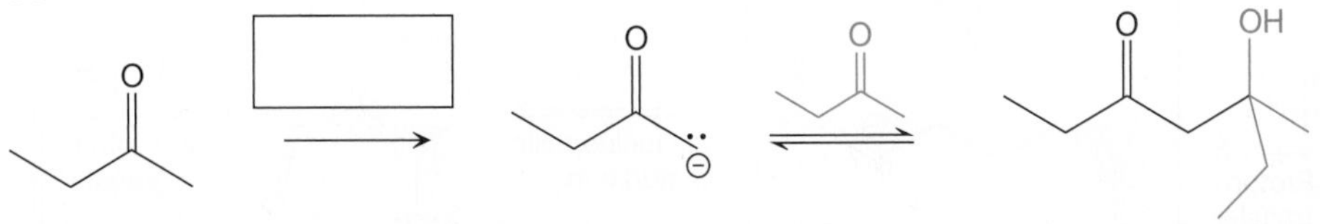

19.12 Intramolecular Aldol Reactions

SECTION 19.12 OBJECTIVES

You will be able to:

1. Identify compounds that can undergo an intramolecular aldol reaction.
2. Predict the major product of an intramolecular aldol reaction on the basis of the size of the ring that is formed and whether the carbonyl group that is attacked is characteristic of a ketone or aldehyde.

If a molecule has two carbonyl groups, as in hexanedial (Eq. 19-49), then an *intramolecular* aldol reaction (i.e., one between different parts of the same molecule) is possible. The result is the formation of a *ring*:

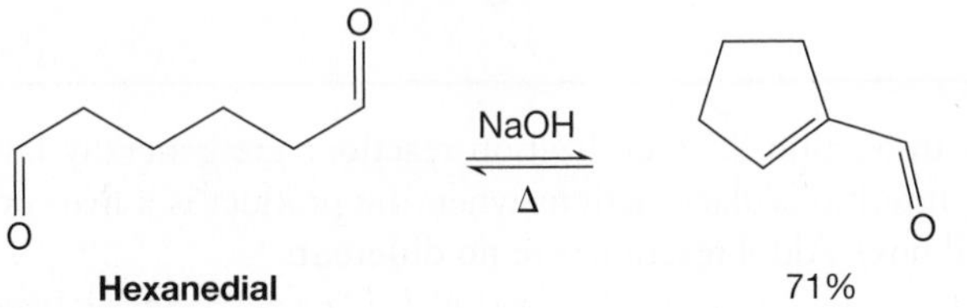

NaOH
Δ
Hexanedial
71%

(19-49)

YOUR TURN **19.26**

Identify the structural features in the product of Equation 19-49 that characterize it as the product of an aldol condensation.

Mechanism Drawing
Aldol Condensation Forming a Ring

The mechanism for this reaction, shown in Equation 19-50, is identical to the mechanism for an aldol condensation that occurs between two separate aldehyde molecules:

Mechanism for an intramolecular aldol condensation reaction (Eq. 19-49)

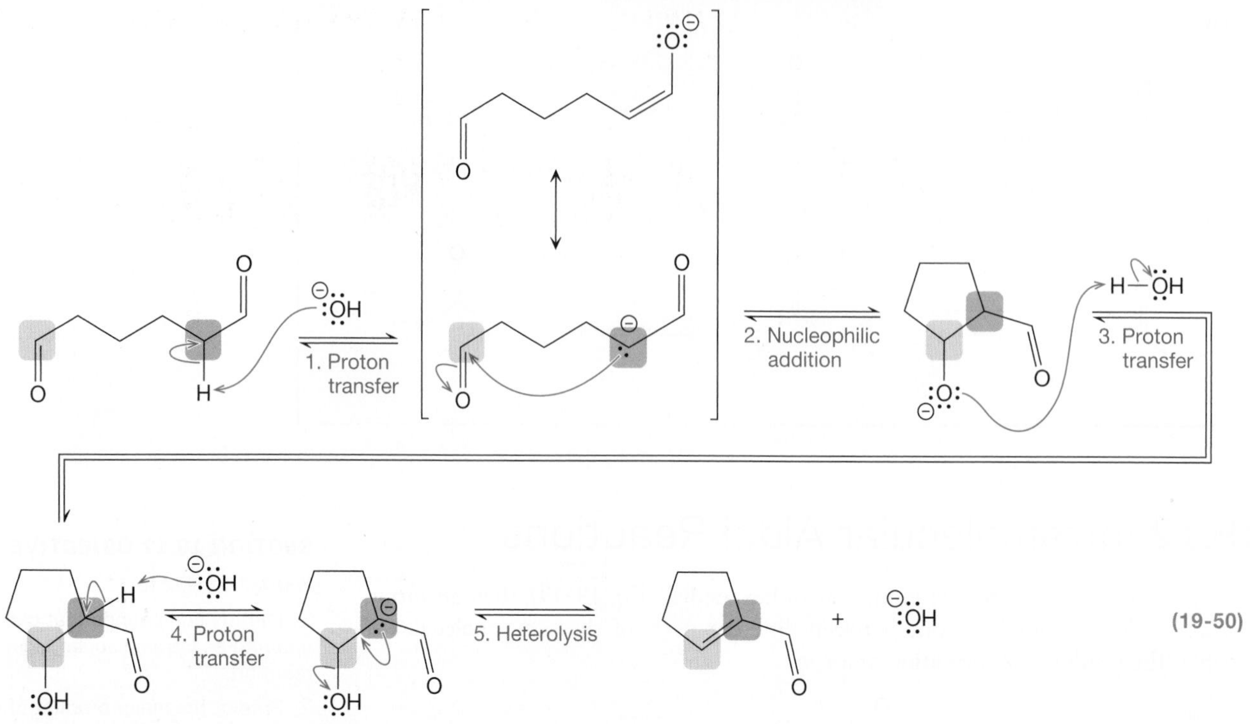

1. Proton transfer
2. Nucleophilic addition
3. Proton transfer
4. Proton transfer
5. Heterolysis

(19-50)

◂ RECALL

Section 9.12 explained that the formation of a five- or six-membered ring optimizes the balance between ring strain and entropy. Small rings are disfavored because they are highly strained, whereas large rings are disfavored because their formation requires a substantial decrease in entropy.

As we saw in Section 9.12, cyclization reactions are generally favored over their corresponding intermolecular reactions when the product is a five- or six-membered ring (see Recall box). Aldol reactions are no different:

Intramolecular aldol reactions are favored when five- or six-membered rings are formed.

By contrast, pentanedial (Eq. 19-51) and octanedial (Eq. 19-52) do *not* favor intramolecular aldol reactions because their aldol products would possess four- and seven-membered rings, respectively:

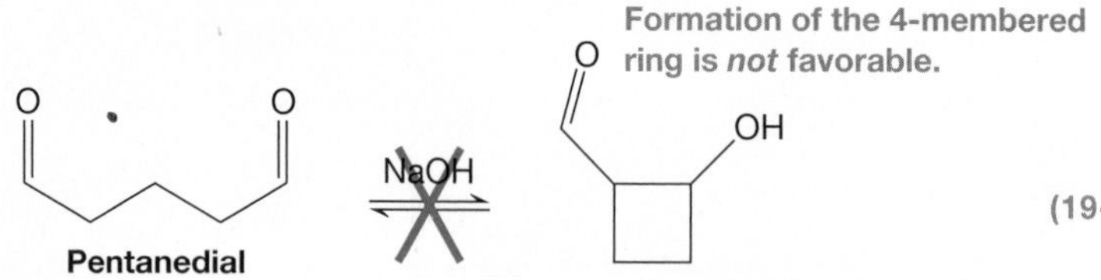

Formation of the 4-membered ring is *not* favorable.
NaOH
Pentanedial

(19-51)

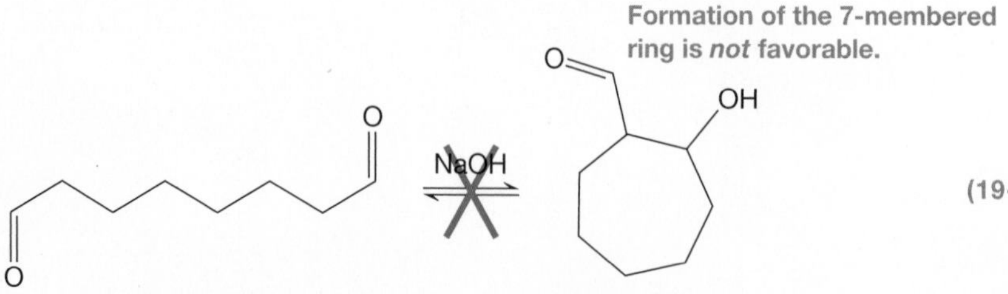

Formation of the 7-membered ring is *not* favorable.
NaOH
Octanedial

(19-52)

YOUR TURN **19.27**

The intramolecular aldol reaction involving heptanedial is favorable. Draw the mechanism for this reaction, along with the major product formed. Explain why the reaction is favorable.

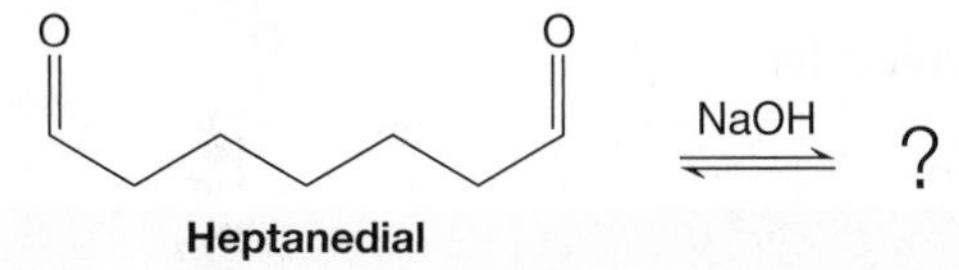

O
O
NaOH
?
Heptanedial

Equation 19-53 shows a dicarbonyl compound that can form three different enolate anions, in which case we can envision three different cyclic aldol products:

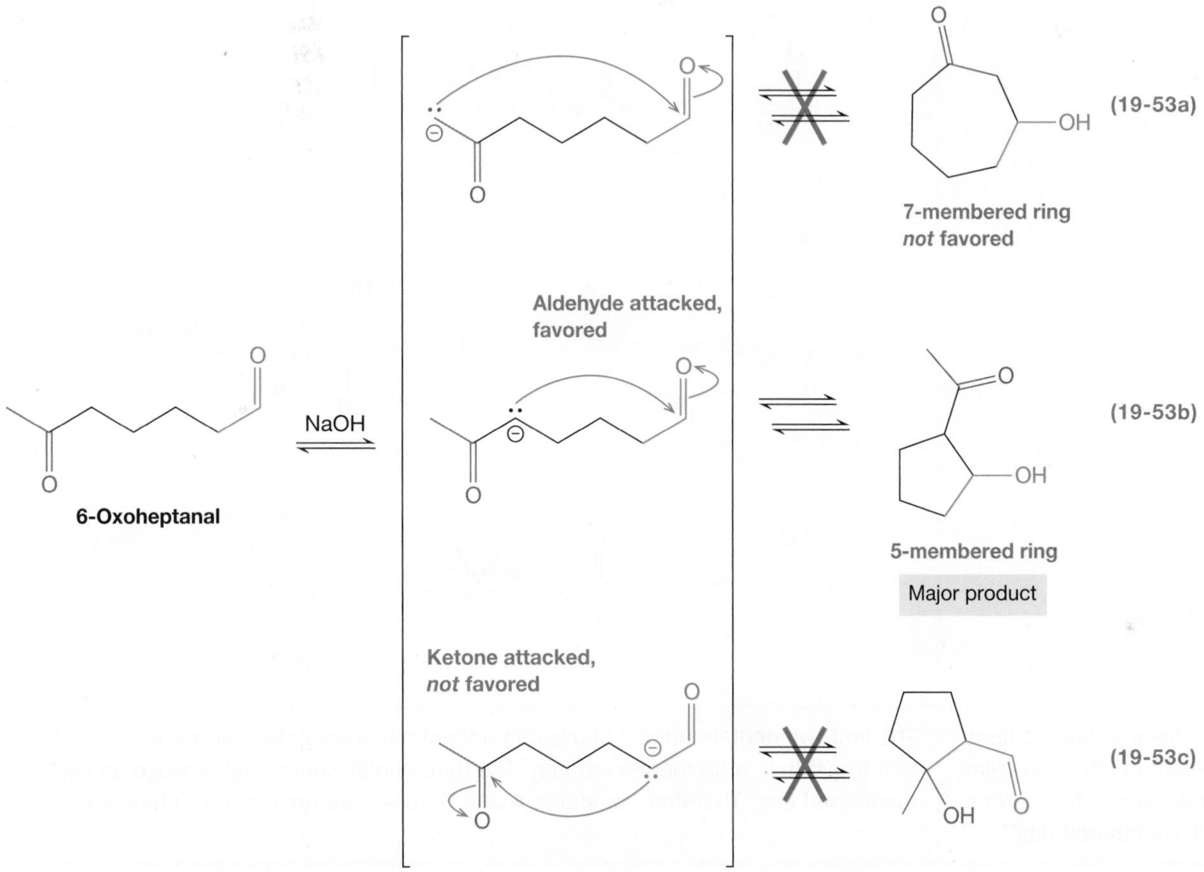

O
OH
(19-53a)
7-membered ring
not favored
Aldehyde attacked,
favored
NaOH
6-Oxoheptanal
OH
(19-53b)
5-membered ring
Major product
Ketone attacked,
not favored
OH
(19-53c)

The product in Equation 19-53b is heavily favored over the others. The aldol product in Equation 19-53a is not favored because it forms a seven-membered ring, whereas the reactions in Equation 19-53b and 19-53c both form five-membered rings. The major difference between the two reactions that form five-membered rings is in the carbonyl group that is attacked: In Equation 19-53b, the carbonyl C is attached to one alkyl group, characteristic of an aldehyde, whereas in Equation 19-53c, it is attached to two alkyl groups, characteristic of a ketone. Recall from Section 19.10 that addition to a ketone is generally less favorable than addition to an aldehyde.

SOLVED PROBLEM **19.10**

How to draw the mechanism and product for an intramolecular aldol reaction

Break It Down **Draw the complete, detailed mechanism for the reaction shown here and predict the major product.**

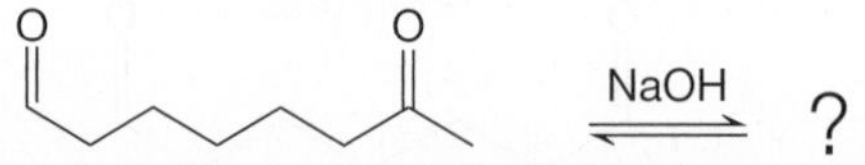

NaOH
?

Think	Solve
What enolate anions can be formed?	The three possible enolate anions resulting from deprotonation of an α proton and their corresponding aldol products are shown below on the left. **Ketone attacked** 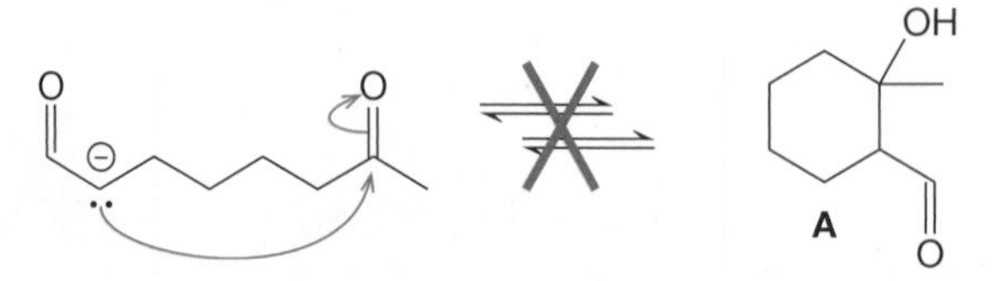 OH A **Aldehyde attacked** 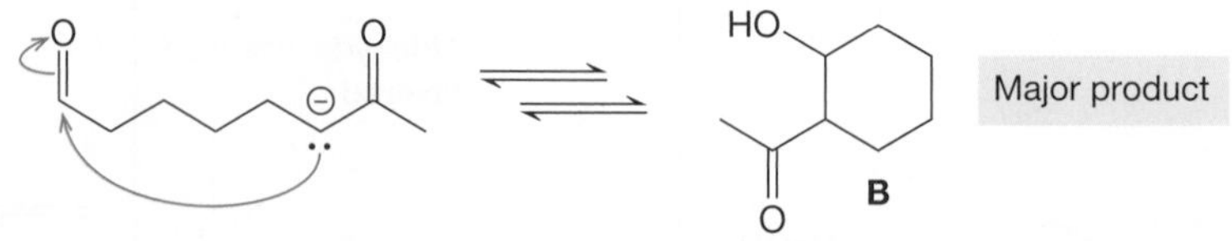 HO B Major product **8-membered ring** 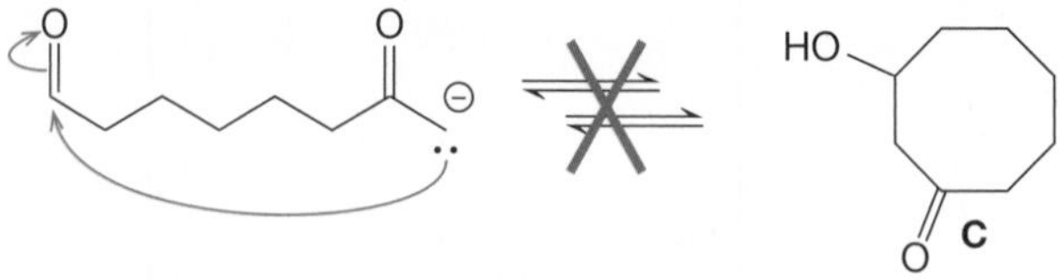 HO C
Which of those enolate anions can undergo an intramolecular nucleophilic addition to form a five- or six-membered ring?	The first two enolate anions above can undergo an intramolecular nucleophilic addition to produce a six-membered ring. The third enolate anion will produce an eight-membered ring. Therefore, products **A** and **B** above are favored over product **C**.
In those nucleophilic additions, what kind of carbonyl group is attacked: a ketone or an aldehyde?	To produce **A** and **B**, the carbonyl groups that are attacked are characteristic of a ketone and an aldehyde, respectively. Because aldehydes are preferentially attacked, product **B** is favored.

Try It Predict the major product of the reaction shown here.

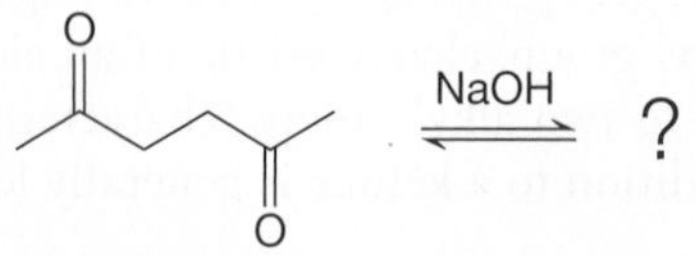

NaOH
?

19.13 The Robinson Annulation

SECTION 19.13 OBJECTIVES

You will be able to:

1. Draw the mechanism and product for a Robinson annulation.
2. Predict whether a Robinson annulation is feasible on the basis of the structures of the carbonyl-containing reactants.

As we learned in Chapter 4, six-membered rings are the most abundant in natural products due to their relative stability. Synthetic methods for constructing six-membered rings are therefore of great value. Sir Robert Robinson (1886–1975), an English chemist, developed one such reaction, which has since become known as the **Robinson annulation** (*annulation* means "ring formation"). An example is shown in Equation 19-54:

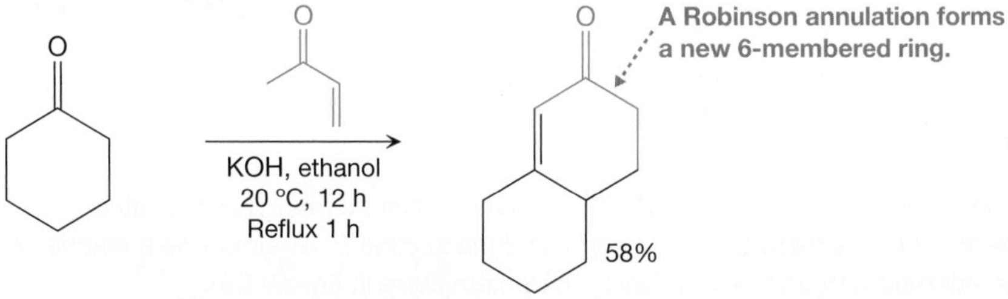

A Robinson annulation forms a new 6-membered ring.
KOH, ethanol
20 °C, 12 h
Reflux 1 h
58%

(19-54)

A Robinson annulation is essentially the conjugate addition of an enolate anion (also called a *Michael reaction*; Section 18.8) followed by an intramolecular aldol condensation (i.e., aldol addition plus dehydration), as shown in the partial mechanism in Equation 19-55:

Partial mechanism for Robinson annulation (Eq. 19-54)

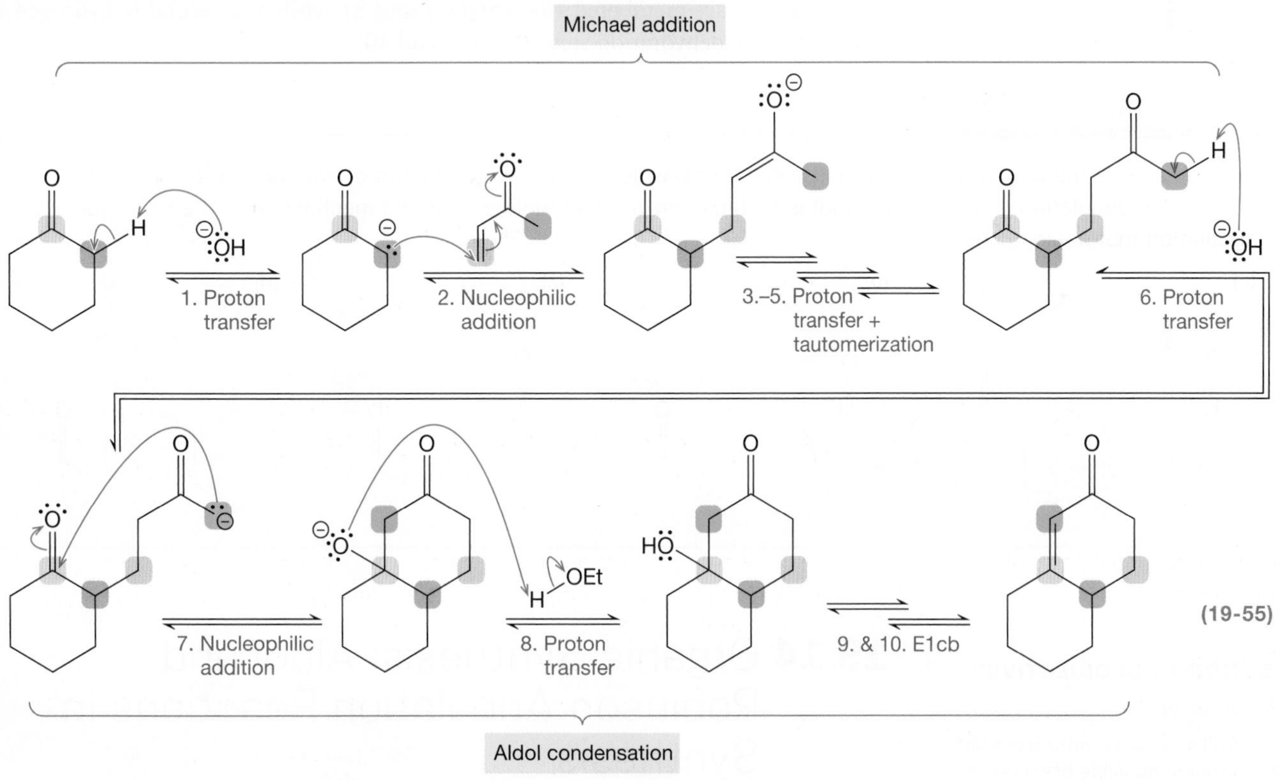

Michael addition
1. Proton transfer
2. Nucleophilic addition
3.–5. Proton transfer + tautomerization
6. Proton transfer
7. Nucleophilic addition
8. Proton transfer
9. & 10. E1cb
Aldol condensation

(19-55)

YOUR TURN 19.28

Complete the partial mechanism for the Robinson annulation by adding missing steps 3–5, 9 and 10 in Equation 19-55.

For these back-to-back reactions to take place, the reactants of a Robinson annulation must have the general form shown in Equation 19-56:

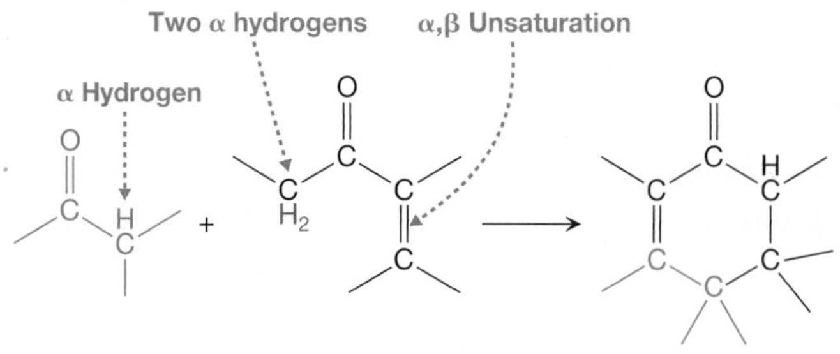

Two α hydrogens
α,β Unsaturation
α Hydrogen

(19-56)

In particular:

1. One of the reactants of a Robinson annulation must be an α,β-unsaturated ketone (black structure in Eq. 19-56), and the second must simply be a ketone or aldehyde with an acidic α hydrogen (red structure in Eq. 19-56).
2. The α,β-unsaturated carbonyl compound must have two acidic α hydrogens (shown in Eq. 19-56 in blue).

The first requirement ensures that an enolate nucleophile can be formed and conjugate addition can take place (Steps 1–5 in Eq. 19-55). The second requirement ensures that the subsequent intramolecular aldol condensation can take place: Deprotonation of the first α hydrogen generates the enolate nucleophile (Step 6) that leads to the formation of a six-membered ring (Steps 7 and 8), while the second α hydrogen is removed in the dehydration steps (Steps 9 and 10).

YOUR TURN **19.29**

On the basis of the requirements just listed in the box, which of the following pairs of reactants are suitable for a Robinson annulation? For each pair that is suitable, draw the complete, detailed mechanism of the Robinson annulation that could occur.

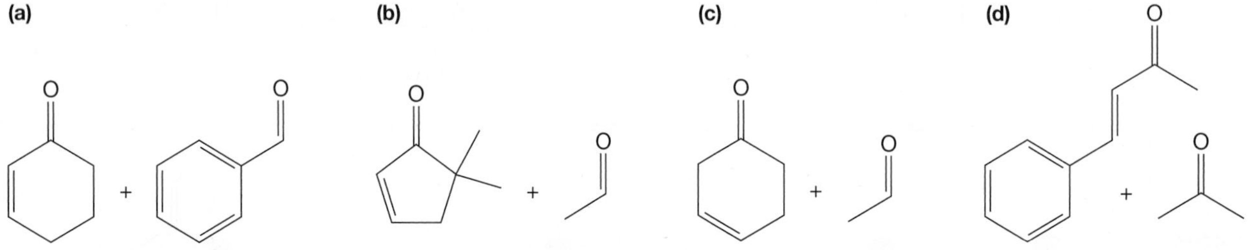

(a)
(b)
(c)
(d)

SECTION 19.14 OBJECTIVES

You will be able to:

1. Effectively carry out a transform to determine possible precursors for an aldol addition, an aldol condensation, or a Robinson annulation.
2. Incorporate aldol and Robinson annulation reactions in a synthesis.

19.14 Organic Synthesis: Aldol and Robinson Annulation Reactions in Synthesis

Aldol reactions are valuable tools in organic synthesis because they form carbon–carbon bonds and because the compounds they involve, ketones and aldehydes, are quite common. Thus, aldol reactions can be used to produce compounds with a wide variety of structures. In Section 19.12, for example, we saw that aldol reactions can form rings. Perhaps more impressively, aldol reactions can be used to link two compounds with elaborate carbon frameworks, as shown in Equation 19-57, which makes up one of the steps in a synthesis of epothilone B, an anticancer agent:

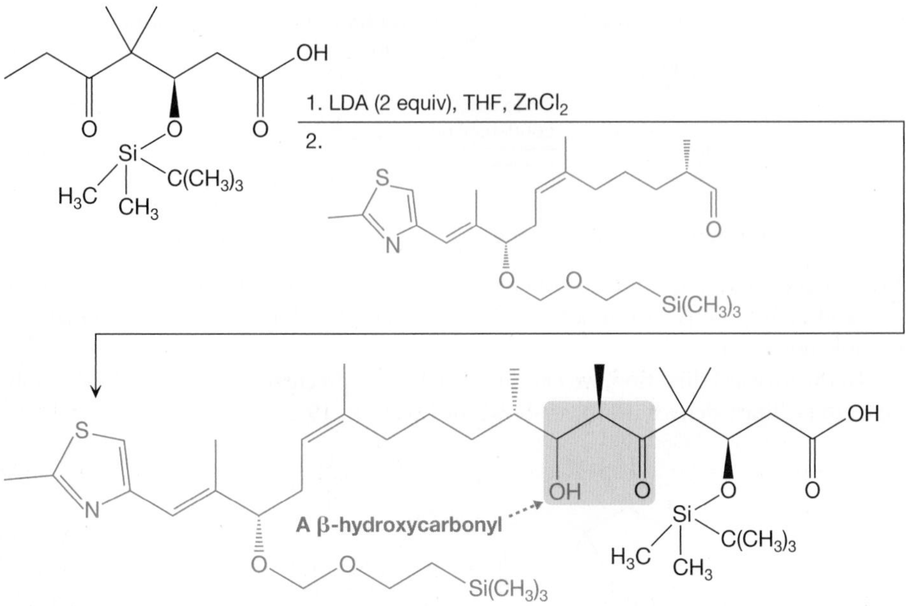

OH
1. LDA (2 equiv), THF, $ZnCl_2$
2.
Si
$C(CH_3)_3$
H_3C
CH_3
S
N
O
$Si(CH_3)_3$
OH
A β-hydroxycarbonyl

(19-57)

Because of the utility of aldol reactions in synthesis, it is important to be able to efficiently carry out transforms that undo aldol reactions, as part of a retrosynthetic analysis. When doing so, the following guidelines should help:

- The product of an aldol addition is a β-hydroxy carbonyl compound, and the product of an aldol condensation is an α,β-unsaturated carbonyl compound.
- The new C—C bond that is formed in an aldol reaction appears between the α and β carbons in the product, so a transform that undoes an aldol reaction involves disconnecting that bond.
- In constructing the precursors to an aldol reaction, the β carbon from the aldol product receives a C═O bond.

These guidelines are illustrated in the two generic transforms illustrated in **Figure 19-8**.

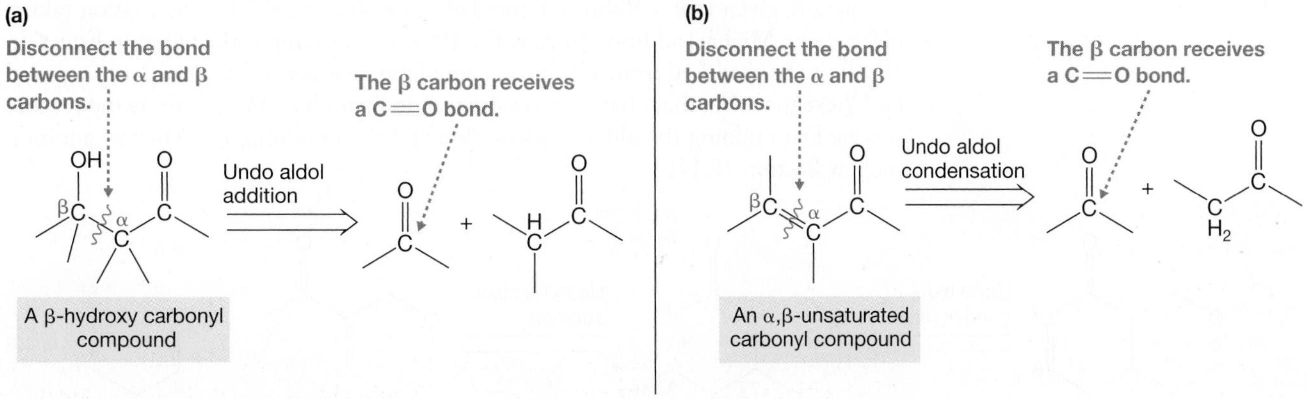

(a)
Disconnect the bond between the α and β carbons.
The β carbon receives a C═O bond.
Undo aldol addition
A β-hydroxy carbonyl compound
(b)
Disconnect the bond between the α and β carbons.
The β carbon receives a C═O bond.
Undo aldol condensation
An α,β-unsaturated carbonyl compound

FIGURE 19-8 Retrosynthesis involving aldol reactions To carry out a transform that undoes (a) an aldol addition or (b) an aldol condensation, disconnect the α and β carbons and add a C═O bond to the β carbon.

Suppose, for example, that our target compound is 5,5-dimethylcyclopent-2-enone, which is an α,β-unsaturated ketone (Eq. 19-58):

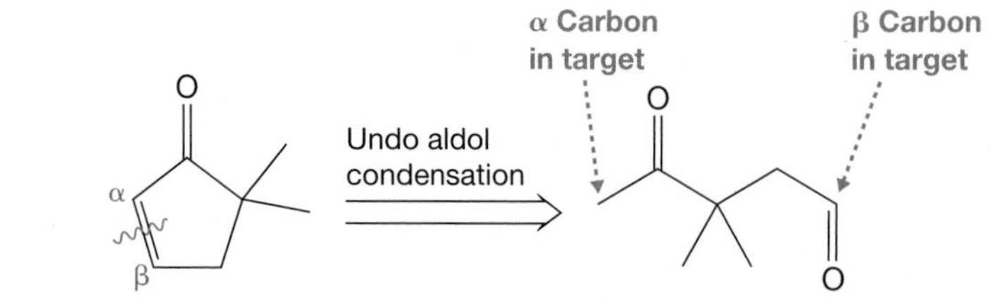
α Carbon in target
β Carbon in target
Undo aldol condensation
α
β
5,5-Dimethylcyclopent-2-enone
3,3-Dimethyl-4-oxopentanal

(19-58)

We can undo an aldol condensation by disconnecting the bond indicated by the wavy line and giving the β carbon a C=O bond. Thus, 3,3-dimethyl-4-oxopentanal is a suitable precursor.

In the forward direction, we can simply treat the precursor with NaOH and apply heat (to facilitate dehydration), as shown in Equation 19-59:

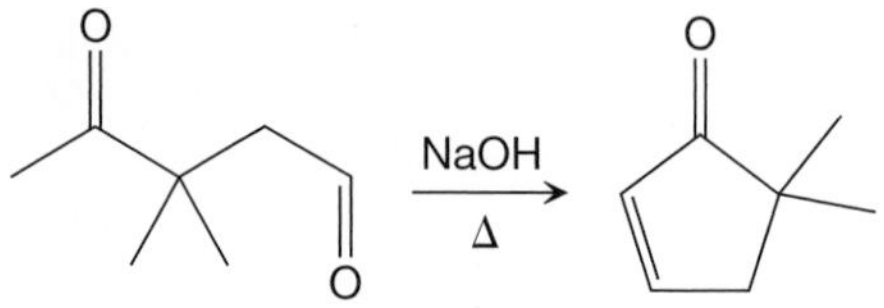
NaOH
Δ

(19-59)

YOUR TURN **19.30**

Show how to synthesize the following compounds using either an aldol addition or an aldol condensation.

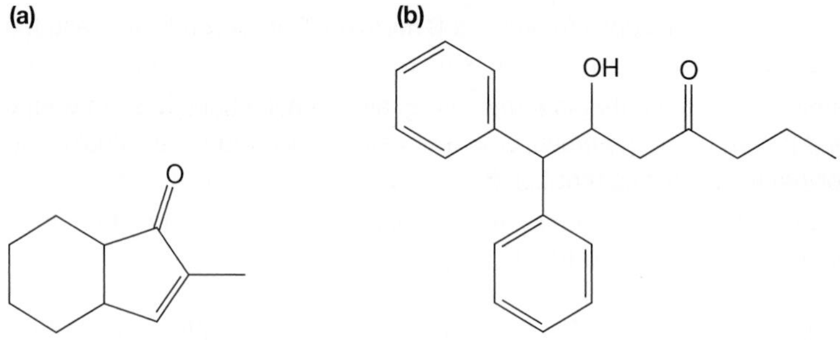
(a)
(b)
OH
O

The guidelines above are useful also in determining the precursors for a Robinson annulation, given that a Robinson annulation involves an aldol condensation taking place after a Michael addition (review Eq. 19-55). For example, the target in Equation 19-60 can be produced from a Robinson annulation because it has an α,β-unsaturated cyclohexenone ring that characterizes the reaction's product. We can draw the precursors by first undoing the aldol condensation and then undoing the Michael addition (review Section 18.11).

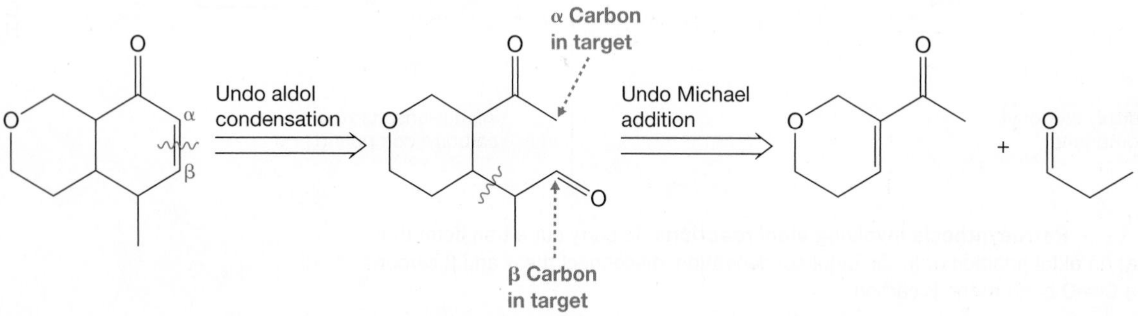
α Carbon in target
Undo aldol condensation
Undo Michael addition
β Carbon in target
α
β
+

(19-60)

To carry out the Robinson annulation, the precursors would simply need to be heated under basic conditions:

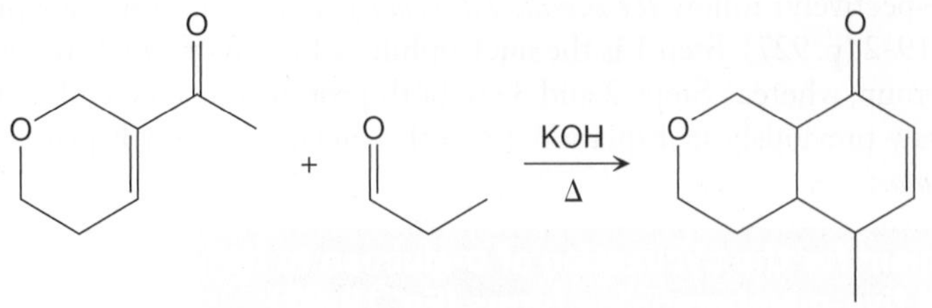

KOH
Δ

(19-61)

YOUR TURN **19.31**

Show how to synthesize each of the following compounds using a Robinson annulation.

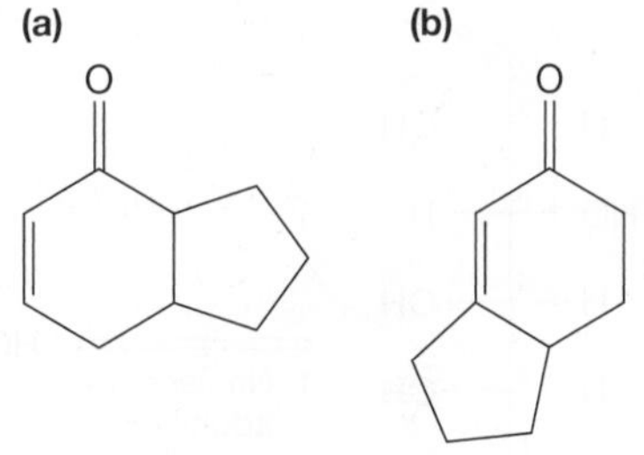

(a)
(b)

THE ORGANIC CHEMISTRY OF BIOMOLECULES

19.15 Ring Opening and Ring Closing of Monosaccharides

SECTION 19.15 OBJECTIVES

You will be able to:

1. Show how the cyclization of a monosaccharide leads to the formation of both the α and β anomers of the sugar.
2. Name a cyclic monosaccharide given its structure, and draw the structure of a monosaccharide given its name.

In Section 1.14b, we showed that a monosaccharide can have both open-chain and cyclic forms. In aqueous solution, the various forms equilibrate, as shown in Equations 19-62 and 19-63 for D-glucose and D-ribose, respectively:

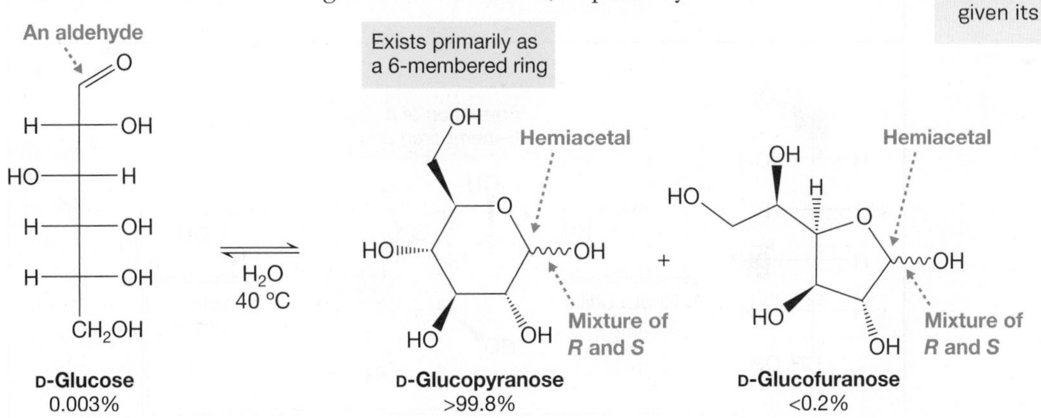

An aldehyde
Exists primarily as a 6-membered ring
Hemiacetal
Hemiacetal
H₂O 40 °C
Mixture of R and S
Mixture of R and S
D-Glucose 0.003%
D-Glucopyranose >99.8%
D-Glucofuranose <0.2%

(19-62)

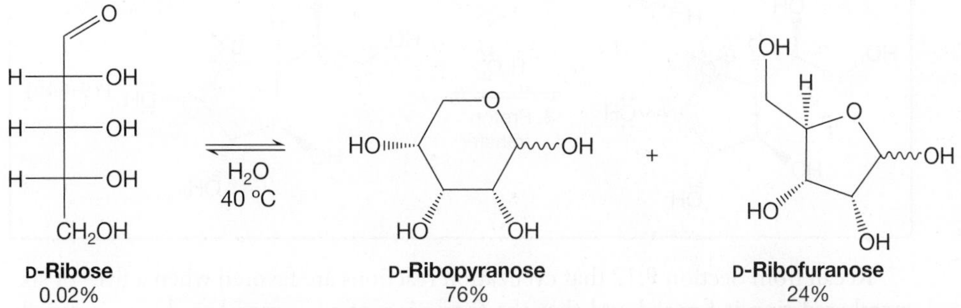

H₂O 40 °C
D-Ribose 0.02%
D-Ribopyranose 76%
D-Ribofuranose 24%

(19-63)

Notice that each cyclic form has a hemiacetal group. Therefore, the mechanisms showing how D-glucose cyclizes to its six- and five-membered rings (Eq. 19-64a and 19-64b, respectively) follow *the hemiacetal formation mechanism* we saw previously in Equation 19-2 (p. 927). Step 1 is the nucleophilic addition of a hydroxyl group to the carbonyl group, whereas Steps 2 and 3 are both proton transfers. Unlike the mechanism we saw previously in Equation 19-2, the mechanisms in Equation 19-64 are *intramolecular*:

Mechanism for the cyclization of D-glucose to its six- and five-membered ring forms (Eq. 19-62)

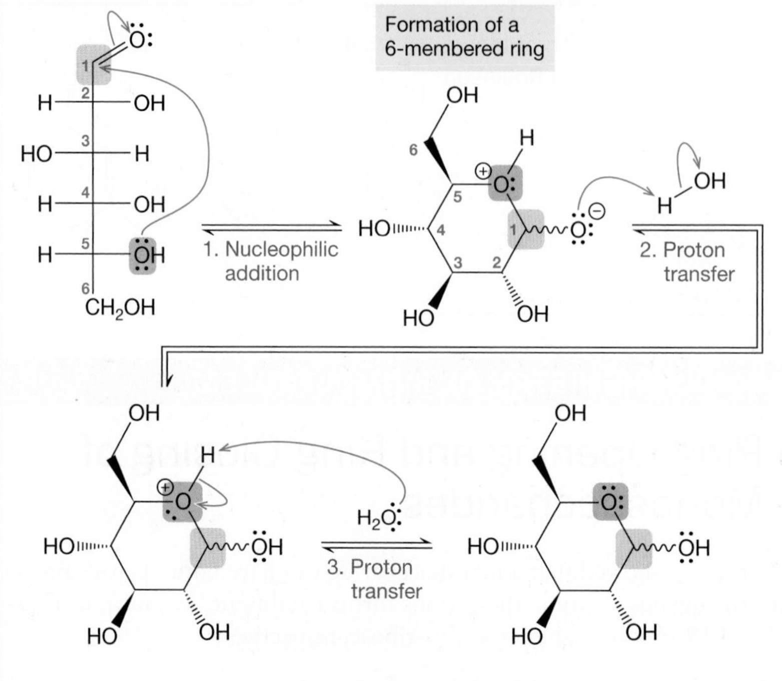

Formation of a 6-membered ring
1. Nucleophilic addition
2. Proton transfer
3. Proton transfer

(19-64a)

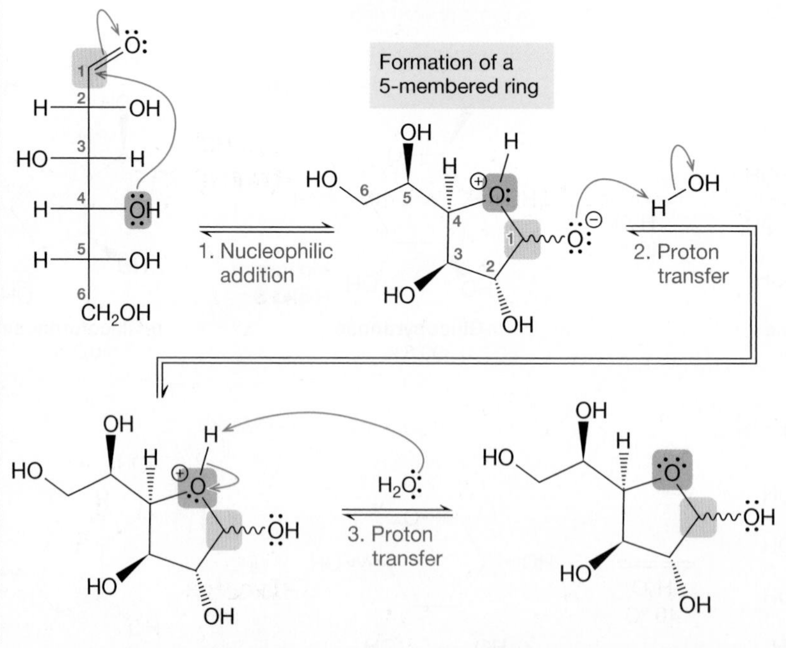

Formation of a 5-membered ring
1. Nucleophilic addition
2. Proton transfer
3. Proton transfer

(19-64b)

Recall from Section 9.12 that cyclization reactions are favored when a five- or six-membered ring is formed and that the formation of a six-membered ring is usually favored over a five-membered ring. As we can see in Equations 19-62 and 19-63, this is no different for the cyclization of monosaccharides. Specifically:

- At equilibrium, monosaccharides typically favor their five- and six-membered ring forms over their open-chain forms.
- The six-membered ring form is generally favored over the five-membered ring form.

Specific nomenclature has been developed to distinguish the five- and six-membered ring forms from each other, as well as from the open-chain form. Under this system, the monosaccharide's name (review Sections 4.13 and 5.16) is modified by inserting an "o" followed by either "pyran" or "furan" prior to the *ose* suffix, depending on ring size:

- A monosaccharide that has cyclized to a six-membered ring is designated as a **pyranose**.
- A monosaccharide that has cyclized to a five-membered ring is designated as a **furanose**.

Thus, as indicated previously in Equation 19-62, the cyclic form of D-glucose that has a six-membered ring is called D-glucopyranose, and the one that has a five-membered ring is called D-glucofuranose. The corresponding cyclic forms of D-ribose are D-ribopyranose and D-ribofuranose (Eq. 19-63).

Looking back at the reactions in Equations 19-62 and 19-63, notice that the carbonyl carbon of the monosaccharide becomes a *new asymmetric carbon* as a result of the cyclization. As with any reaction in which a new asymmetric atom is generated, a mixture of stereoisomers is produced, one having the *R* configuration at the new asymmetric atom and the other having the *S* configuration. This is why that C—O bond is denoted with a wavy line (〰), not a dash or a wedge.

As we can see in Equation 19-64a, the new asymmetric carbon is produced in Step 1, the nucleophilic addition step. In this step, the OH group can attack the carbonyl C atom from either side of that atom's plane, shown in Equation 19-65a and 19-65b for the formation of D-glucopyranose:

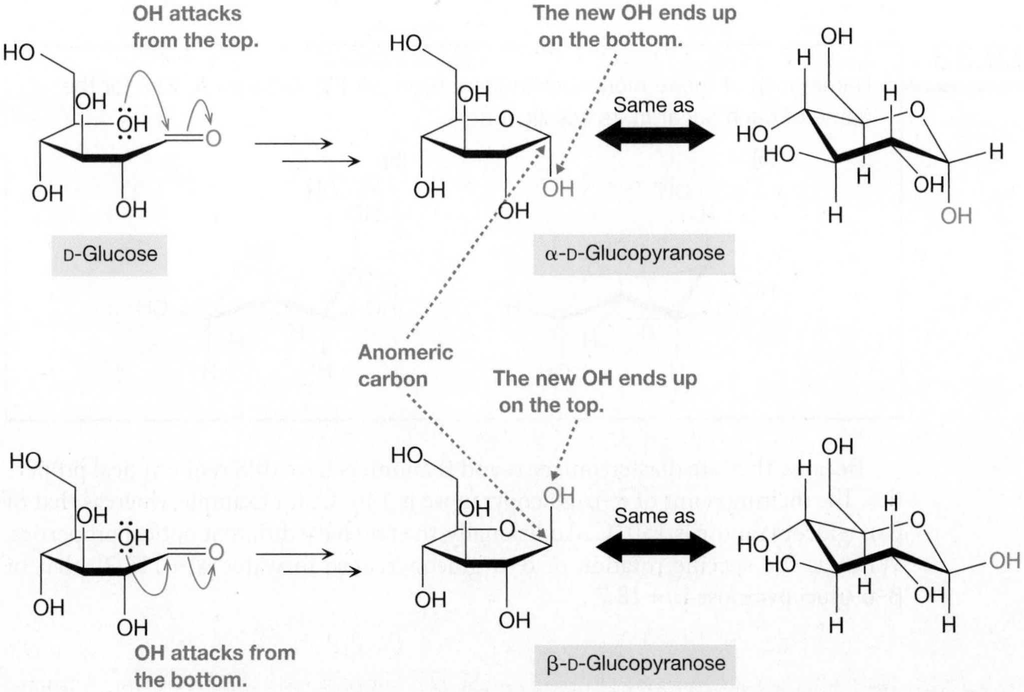

OH attacks from the top.
The new OH ends up on the bottom.
Same as
D-Glucose
α-D-Glucopyranose
Anomeric carbon
The new OH ends up on the top.
Same as
OH attacks from the bottom.
β-D-Glucopyranose

(19-65a)

(19-65b)

FIGURE 19-9 Anomers of monosaccharides (a) In an α anomer, the anomeric OH is on the side of the ring opposite the CH_2OH group. (b) In a β anomer, the anomeric OH is on the same side of the ring as the CH_2OH group.

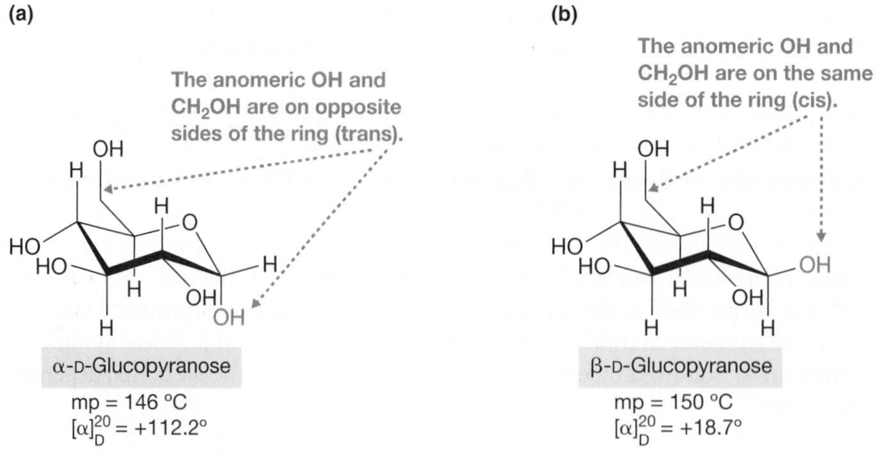

(a)
The anomeric OH and CH2OH are on opposite sides of the ring (trans).
OH
H
H
O
HO
HO
H
H
OH
OH
H
α-D-Glucopyranose
mp = 146 °C
[α]20D = +112.2°
(b)
The anomeric OH and CH2OH are on the same side of the ring (cis).
OH
H
H
O
HO
HO
OH
H
OH
H
H
β-D-Glucopyranose
mp = 150 °C
[α]20D = +18.7°

The two stereoisomers differ in configuration at just one of the asymmetric carbons, so they are *diastereomers* of each other. In carbohydrate chemistry, they are more specifically called **anomers** of each other, and the carbon atom that differs in stereochemical configuration (the one that is part of the carbonyl group in the open-chain form) is called the **anomeric carbon**. One anomer is designated the α anomer and the other is the β anomer (**Figure 19-9**).

- In the **α anomer** of a cyclic monosaccharide, the anomeric OH and the CH_2OH substituents are trans to each other (located on opposite sides of the ring).
- In the **β anomer**, the two substituents are cis to each other (located on the same side of the ring).

YOUR TURN **19.32**

(a) Draw the Haworth projections of α-D-ribofuranose and β-D-ribofuranose.
(b) Draw the mechanisms that show how each anomer is produced from the acyclic form of the monosaccharide.

YOUR TURN **19.33**

Name each of these monosaccharides. (Consult Fig. 5-55 on p. 252 for the name of each sugar in its acyclic form.)

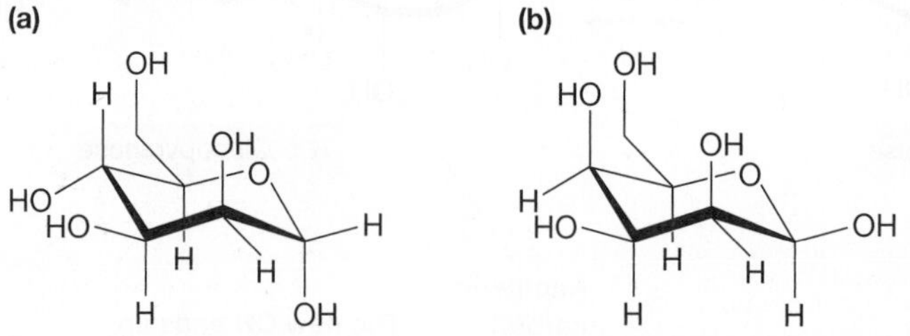

(a)
OH
H
OH
O
HO
HO
H
H
H
H
OH
(b)
OH
HO
OH
O
H
HO
OH
H
H
H
H

Because they are diastereomers, α and β anomers have different physical properties. The melting point of α-D-glucopyranose is 146 °C, for example, whereas that of β-D-glucopyranose is 150 °C. Additionally, the two have different optical properties. Whereas the specific rotation of α-D-glucopyranose in water is +112.2°, that of β-D-glucopyranose is +18.7°.

Chapter Summary and Key Terms

- Nucleophilic addition of a weak nucleophile to a polar π bond is typically slow. If the nucleophilic atom has a weakly acidic proton, *base catalysis* can increase the rate of the reaction by converting the weak nucleophile into a strong one. Alternatively, *acid catalysis* can increase the reaction rate by making the polar π bond more electrophilic: that is, by *activating* the polar π bond. (Section 19.1)
- A **cyanohydrin** can be formed by addition of HCN to the carbonyl group of a ketone or aldehyde, and the reaction can be catalyzed by the addition of a strong base or NC^-. (Section 19.2)
- When a weak nucleophile adds to an α,β-unsaturated polar π bond, conjugate addition is generally favored over direct addition. (Section 19.3)
- Acetals, **imines**, and **enamines** can be formed reversibly from ketones or aldehydes under acidic conditions. Formation of each of these products is favored (according to Le Châtelier's principle) if there is an excess of the respective nucleophile. (Sections 19.4a and 19.4b)
- Acetals, imines, and enamines can be hydrolyzed to ketones or aldehydes under acidic conditions using an excess of water. (Sections 19.4a and 19.4b)
- In a **reductive amination**, an amine is produced by first converting a ketone or aldehyde to an imine and then reducing the imine to the amine. (Section 19.5)
- The C=O group of a ketone or aldehyde can be converted to a methylene (CH_2) group via the **Wolff–Kishner reduction**, in which the ketone or aldehyde is first treated with hydrazine (H_2NNH_2), followed by heating under basic conditions. (Section 19.6)
- A nitrile can undergo hydrolysis under acidic or basic conditions to produce an amide. (Section 19.7)
- When treated with a strong base, a ketone or aldehyde can react in an **aldol addition**, resulting in a **β-hydroxy carbonyl compound**. Under these basic conditions, an enolate anion acts as a nucleophile. (Sections 19.8 and 19.10)
- Heating an aldol reaction facilitates an **aldol condensation**, in which the β-hydroxy carbonyl product undergoes dehydration to yield an α,β-unsaturated carbonyl compound. (Section 19.9)
- Aldol reactions involving ketones tend to be unfavorable, and thus require exploiting Le Châtelier's principle to drive the reaction toward products. (Section 19.10)
- A **crossed aldol reaction** forms a carbon–carbon bond between two different carbonyl compounds. These reactions are not synthetically useful if they form a mixture of aldol products. (Section 19.11)
- A crossed aldol reaction can be synthetically useful if one of the carbonyl-containing reactants possesses no α hydrogens. Alternatively, a crossed aldol reaction can be synthetically useful if it involves a ketone that is first deprotonated quantitatively by a very strong base like LDA. (Section 19.11)
- An intramolecular aldol reaction is favored if it forms a five- or six-membered ring. Intramolecular reactions involving the attack of an aldehyde C=O are favored over ones involving the attack of a ketone C=O. (Section 19.12)
- The **Robinson annulation** produces a six-membered ring from two separate carbonyl compounds, one of which is an α,β-unsaturated carbonyl compound. This reaction consists of a conjugate addition to the α,β-unsaturated carbonyl compound, followed by an intramolecular aldol condensation. (Section 19.13)
- When an aldol reaction is undone to identify precursors, a C^{α}—C^{β} bond is disconnected and the β carbon from the aldol product receives a C=O bond. (Section 19.14)
- At equilibrium, monosaccharides typically favor their five- and six-membered ring forms over their open-chain forms. The cyclic forms of these sugars can exist as either of two diastereomers called **anomers**. (Section 19.15)

Reaction Tables

Functional group transformations introduced in this chapter are collected in Table 19-1, and reactions introduced in this chapter that alter the carbon skeleton are collected in Table 19-2.

TABLE 19-1 Functional Group Conversions

	Starting Compound Class	Typical Reagents and Reaction Conditions	Compound Class Formed	Key Electron-Rich Species	Key Electron-Poor Species	Comments	Discussed in Section
(1)	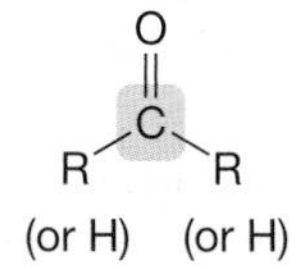 Ketone or aldehyde	H—Nu → Strong base; Nu = OR, SR, NR_2	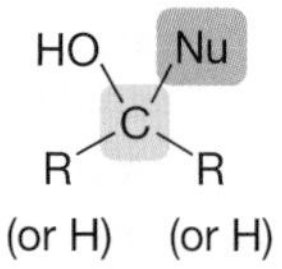	$Nu:^{-}$	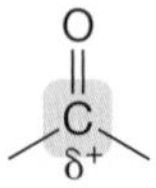	Base-catalyzed nucleophilic addition	19.1
(2)	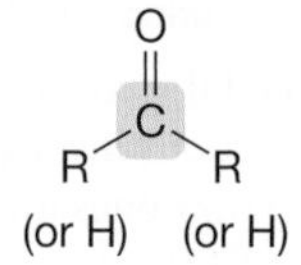 Ketone or aldehyde	H—Nu → Strong acid; Nu = OR, SR, NR_2	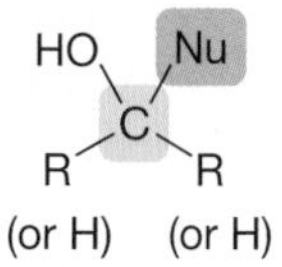	H—$\overset{\delta-}{Nu}$:	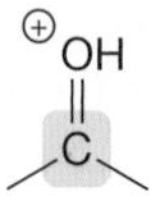	Acid-catalyzed nucleophilic addition	19.1
(3)	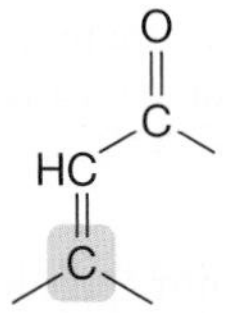 α,β-Unsaturated ketone or aldehyde	H—Nu →; Nu = OR, SR, NR_2	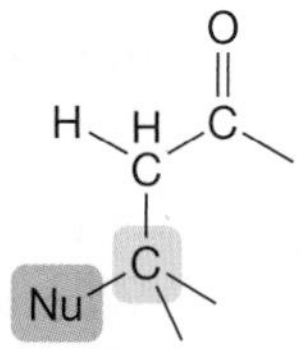	H—$\overset{\delta-}{Nu}$:	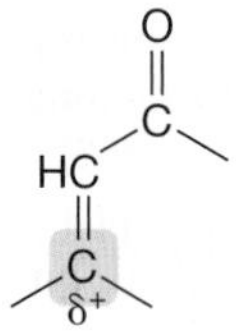	Conjugate nucleophilic addition	19.3
(4)	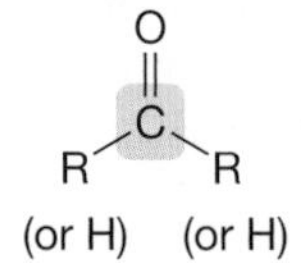 Ketone or aldehyde	R′OH (excess) → H_2SO_4	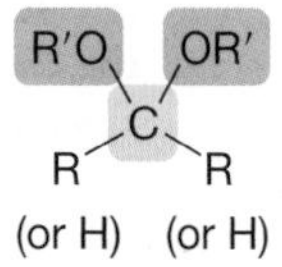 Acetal	R′—$\overset{\delta-}{\ddot{O}H}$	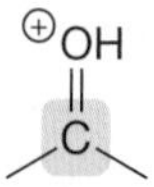	Nucleophilic addition, then S_N1	19.4a
(5)	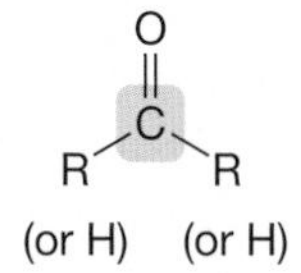 Ketone or aldehyde	Ammonia or 1° amine; NH_3 or $R'NH_2$ (excess) → Mildly acidic	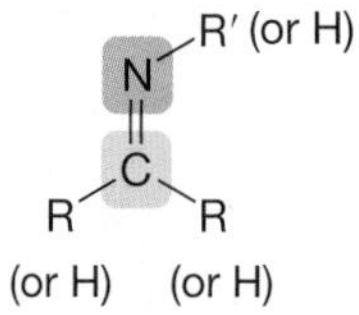 Imine	R′—$\overset{\delta-}{\ddot{N}H_2}$	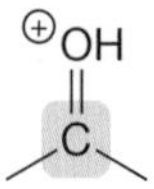	Nucleophilic addition, then E1	19.4b
(6)	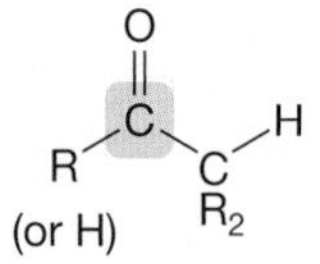 Ketone or aldehyde	2° Amine; R'_2NH (excess) → Mildly acidic	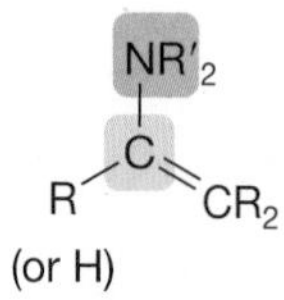 Enamine	$\overset{\delta-}{R'_2\ddot{N}H}$	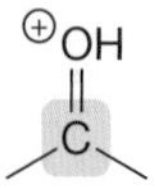	Nucleophilic addition, then E1	19.4b

TABLE 19-1 Functional Group Conversions (continued)

	Starting Compound Class	Typical Reagents and Reaction Conditions	Compound Class Formed	Key Electron-Rich Species	Key Electron-Poor Species	Comments	Discussed in Section
(7)	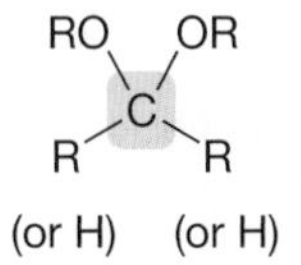 **Acetal**	H_2O (excess), H_2SO_4	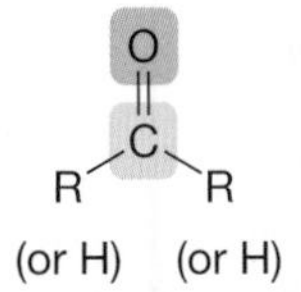 **Ketone or aldehyde**	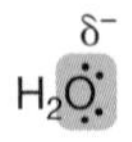	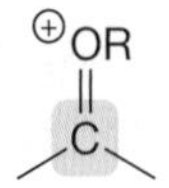	S_N1, then E1	19.4a
(8)	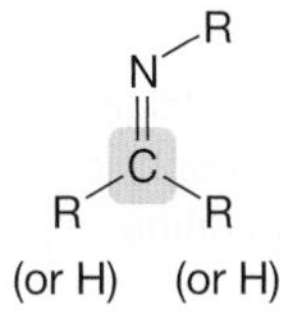 **Imine**	H_2O (excess), HCl	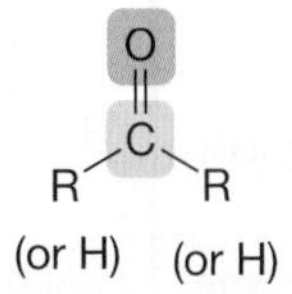 **Ketone or aldehyde**	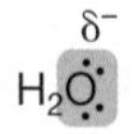	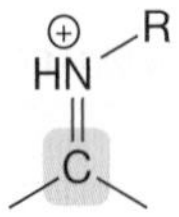	Nucleophilic addition, then E1	19.4b
(9)	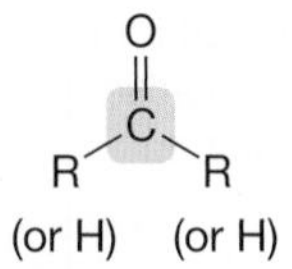 **Ketone or aldehyde**	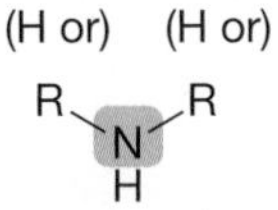 $NaBH_4$	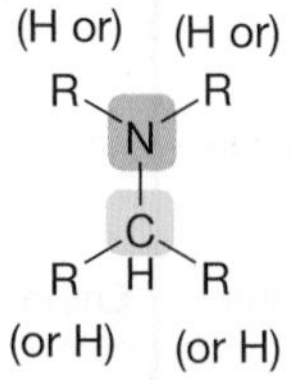 **Amine**	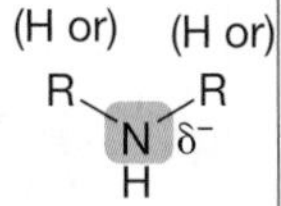	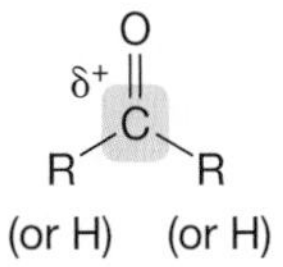	Reductive amination: imine formation, then reduction	19.5
(10)	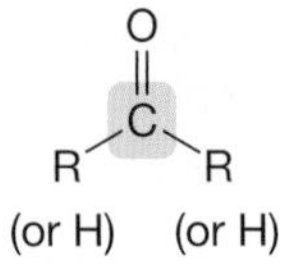 **Ketone or aldehyde**	1. H_2N-NH_2, mildly acidic 2. KOH/diethylene glycol, Δ or H_2N-NH_2 KOH/H_2O, diethylene glycol, Δ	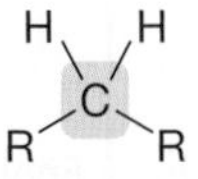 **Alkane**	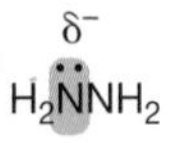	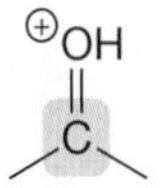	Wolff–Kishner reduction: nucleophilic addition, then E1, then E2	19.6
(11)	R—C≡N **Nitrile**	H_2O (1 equiv), H_2SO_4 or NaOH	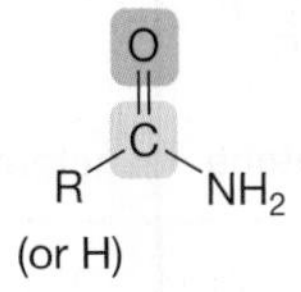 **Amide**	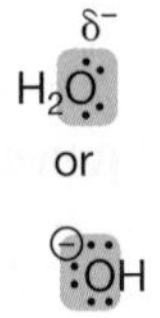	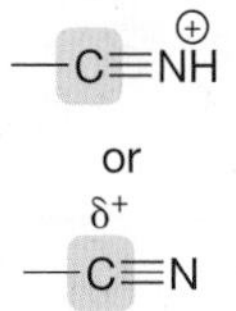	Nucleophilic addition	19.7
(12)	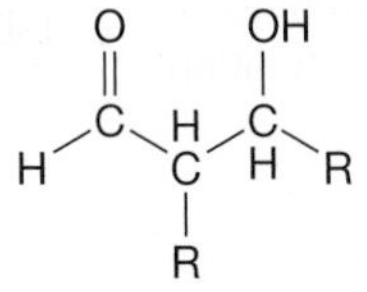 **β-Hydroxy carbonyl compound**	H_2SO_4 or NaOH, Δ	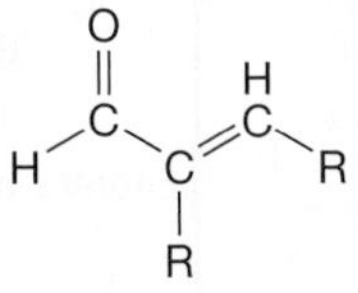 **α,β-Unsaturated carbonyl compound**	–	–	E1 or E1cb	19.9

TABLE 19-2 Reactions That Alter the Carbon Skeleton

	Starting Compound Class	Typical Reagents and Reaction Conditions	Compound Class Formed	Key Electron-Rich Species	Key Electron-Poor Species	Comments	Discussed in Section
(1)	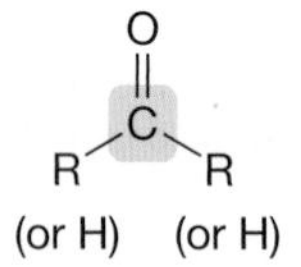 Ketone or aldehyde	H—CN; NaOH or KCN →	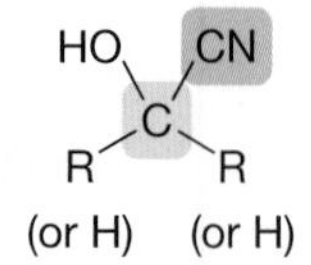 Cyanohydrin	NC:⁻	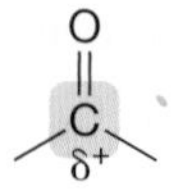	Nucleophilic addition	19.2
(2)	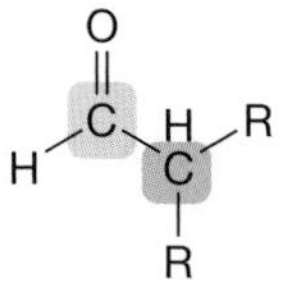 Aldehyde	NaOH →	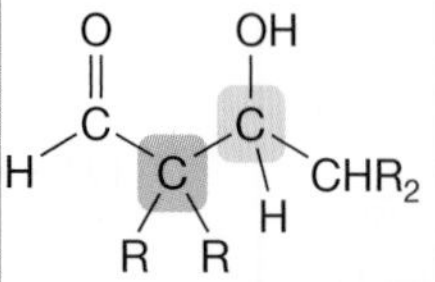 β-Hydroxy aldehyde	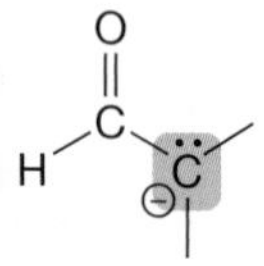 Enolate anion	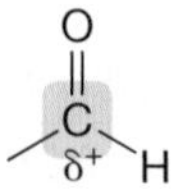	Aldol addition; nucleophilic addition	19.8
(3)	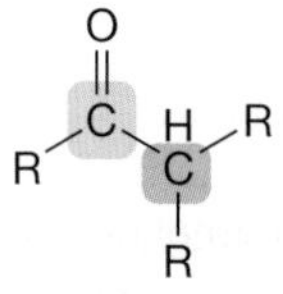 Ketone	NaOH →	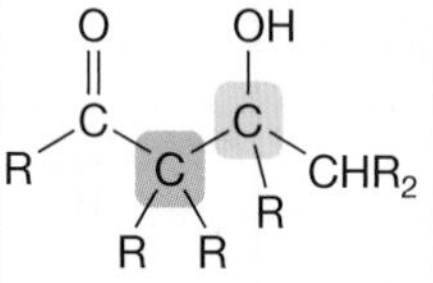 β-Hydroxy ketone	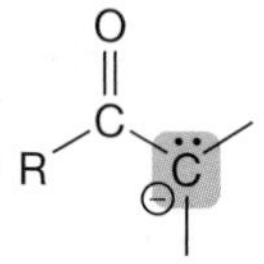 Enolate anion	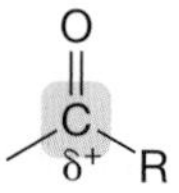	Aldol addition; nucleophilic addition	19.10
(4)	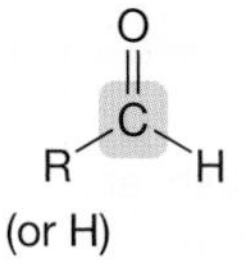 Aldehyde	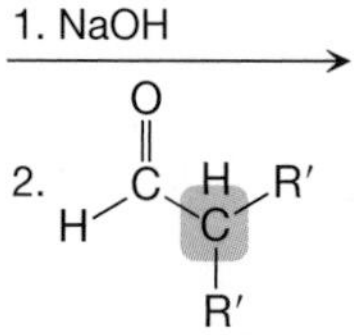	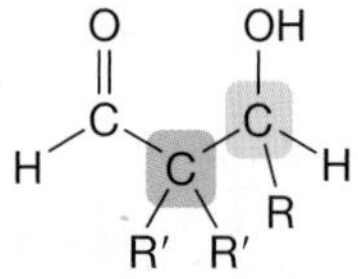 β-Hydroxy aldehyde	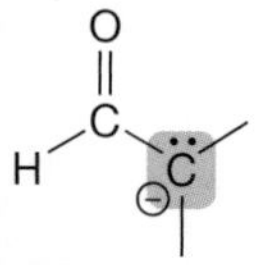 Enolate anion	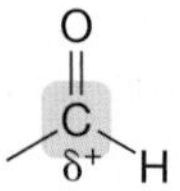	Crossed aldol addition; nucleophilic addition	19.11
(5)	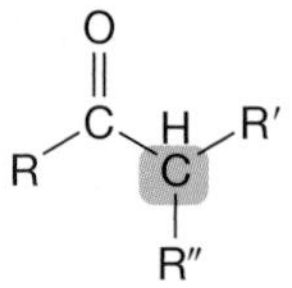 Ketone	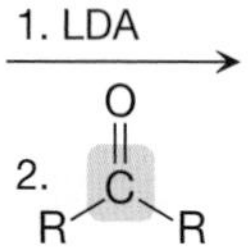	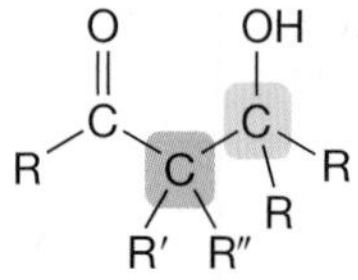 β-Hydroxy ketone	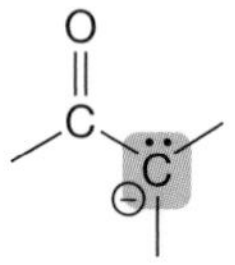 Enolate anion	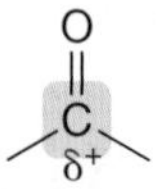	Crossed aldol addition; nucleophilic addition	19.11
(6)	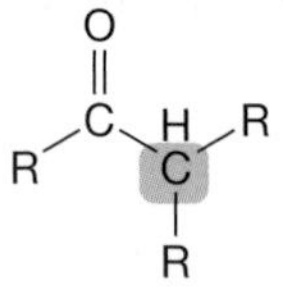 Ketone	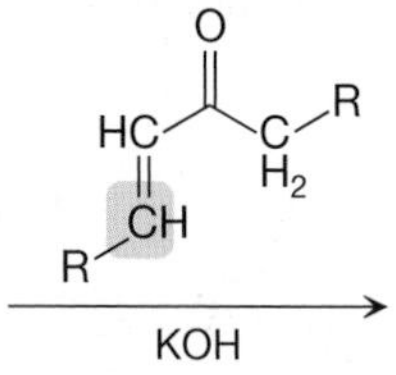	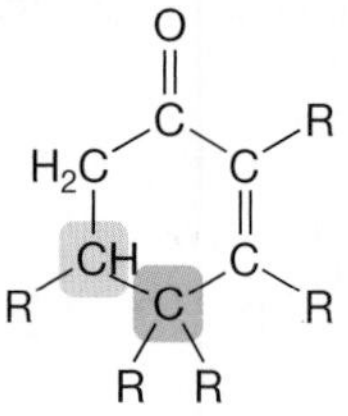	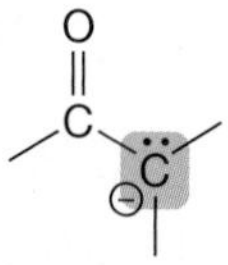 Enolate anion	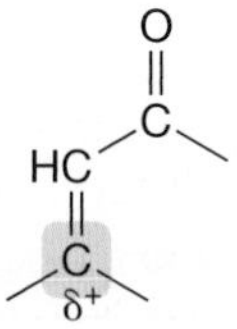	Robinson annulation	19.13

Problems

Problems that are related to synthesis are denoted (SYN).

Sections 19.1–19.3 Weakly Nucleophilic and Non-nucleophilic Reagents: Acid and Base Catalysis

19.1 Draw the complete, detailed mechanism for the reaction shown here under **(a)** basic and **(b)** acidic conditions.

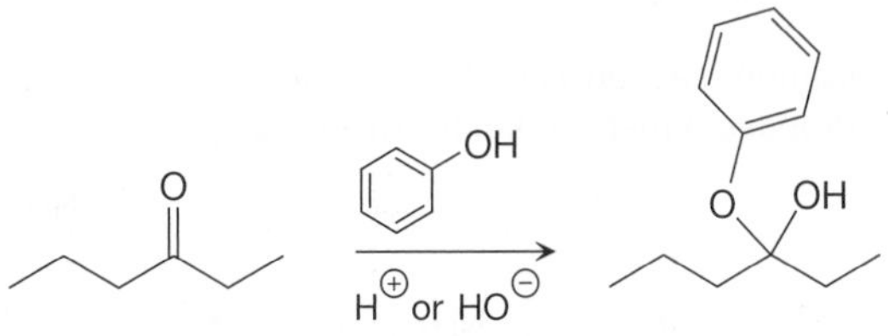

O
OH
OH
O
H⊕ or HO⊖

19.2 Draw the mechanism and product for each reaction shown.

(a)

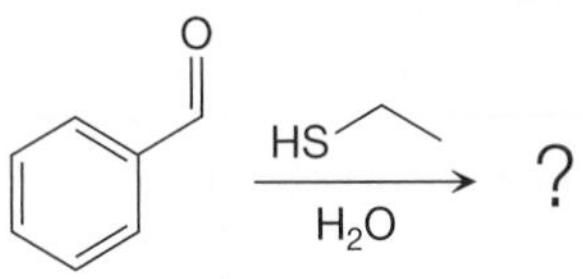

O
HS
H₂O
?

(b)

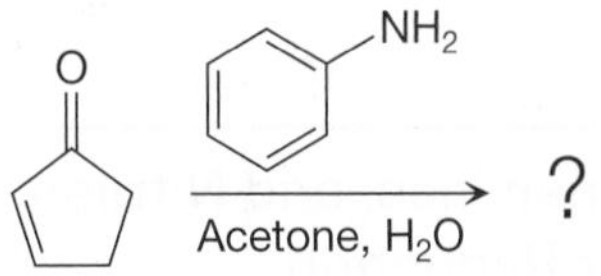

O
NH₂
Acetone, H₂O
?

19.3 Draw the mechanism and product for each reaction in Problem 19.2 when they are catalyzed by **(a)** base and **(b)** acid.

19.4 Draw the mechanism and product for each reaction shown.

(a)

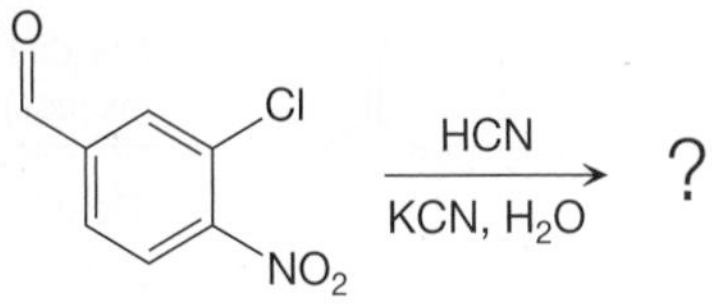

O
Cl
NO₂
HCN
KCN, H₂O
?

(b)

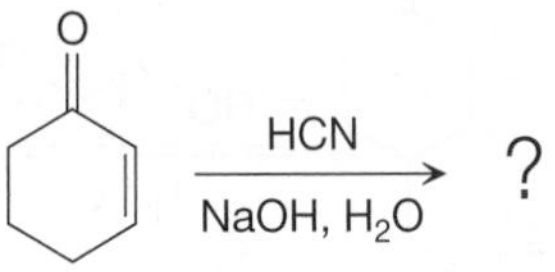

O
HCN
NaOH, H₂O
?

19.5 When acetone is dissolved in either a slightly basic or a slightly acidic solution of oxygen-18-labeled water ($H_2{}^{18}O$), the product of the reaction is oxygen-18-labeled acetone, $(CH_3)_2C{=}{}^{18}O$. This is a form of an isotopic exchange reaction between acetone and water. Provide mechanisms to account for this reaction in **(a)** basic solution and **(b)** acidic solution. *Hint*: Is the addition of the nucleophile reversible or irreversible?

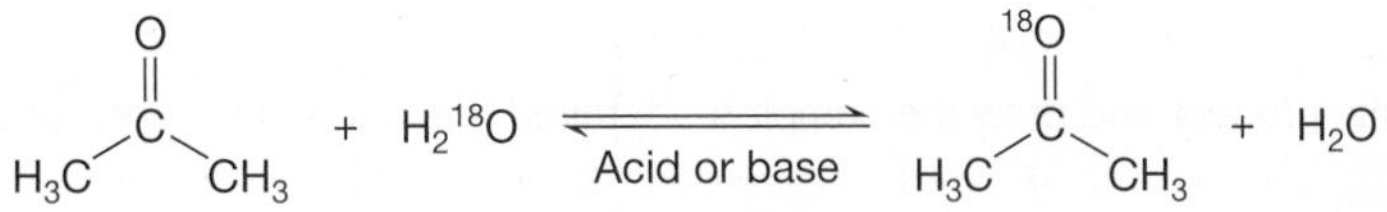

O
C
H₃C
CH₃
+ H₂¹⁸O
Acid or base
¹⁸O
C
H₃C
CH₃
+ H₂O

19.6 Explain why the reaction in Problem 19.5 proceeds dramatically more slowly under neutral conditions than under either acidic or basic conditions.

19.7 A carbamate can be prepared by treating an isocyanate with an alcohol, as shown here. This type of reaction is used to synthesize polyurethanes: polymers that have a wide variety of industrial applications, such as surface sealants, high-performance adhesives, and synthetic fibers. Propose a mechanism for this transformation.

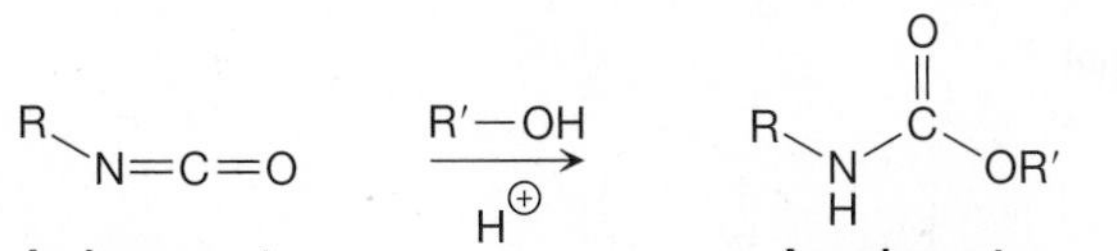

R
N=C=O
R′—OH
H⊕
O
C
R
N
H
OR′

An isocyanate

A carbamate
(Substituted urethane)

19.8 An imino ester is formed when a nitrile is treated with an alcohol in the presence of *dry* HCl (i.e., without H_2O), followed by treatment with a weak base such as sodium bicarbonate. Propose a mechanism for this reaction.

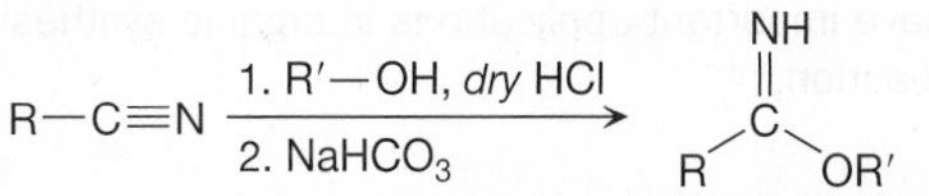

R—C≡N
1. R′—OH, dry HCl
2. NaHCO₃
NH
C
R
OR′

An imino ester

19.9 Draw the complete, detailed mechanism for the reaction shown here, which produces an amidine (a nitrogen analog to an ester).

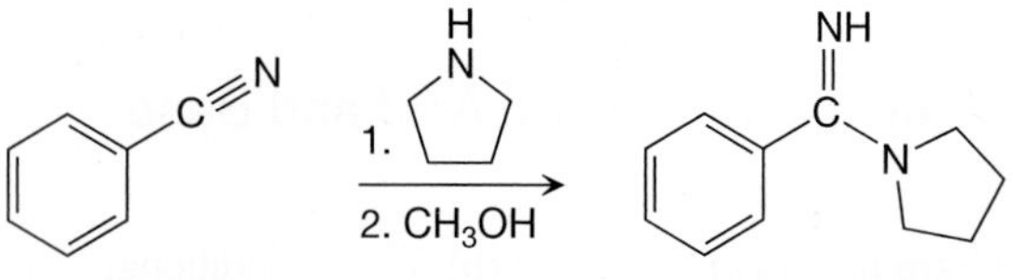
1. pyrrolidine
2. CH_3OH

Benzonitrile **An amidine**

19.10 **(SYN)** After consulting Problem 19.9, suggest how the amidine shown here can be synthesized from benzonitrile, $C_6H_5C{\equiv}N$. *Hint*: More than one synthetic step may be necessary.

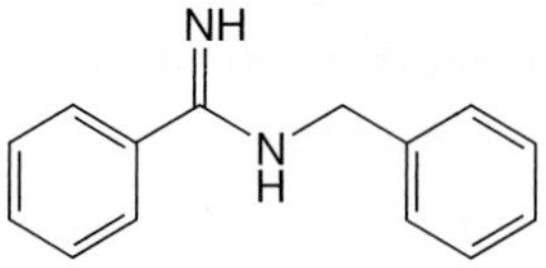

An amidine

19.11 Pentanedinitrile undergoes a cyclization reaction when treated with ammonia under weakly acidic conditions, as shown here. The product is an imidine. Propose a mechanism for this reaction.

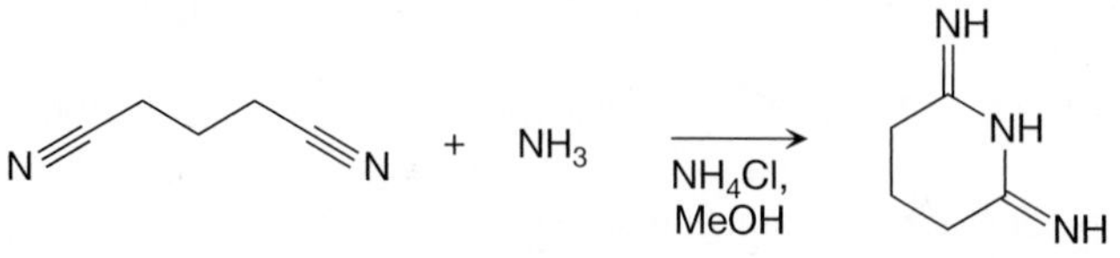
+ NH_3
NH_4Cl, MeOH

An imidine

Sections 19.4–19.7 Acetals, Imines, Enamines, and Nitriles; Reductive Amination; and Wolff–Kishner Reduction

19.12 Predict the major organic product and draw the complete, detailed mechanism for each of the following reactions.

(a)

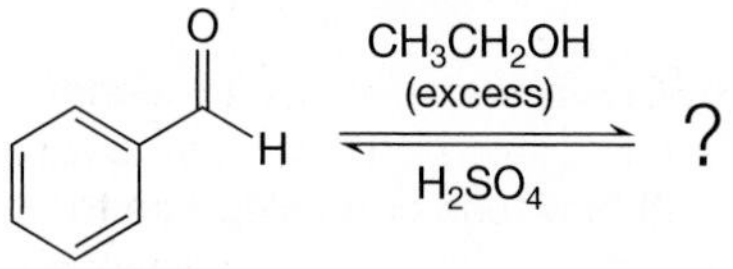
CH_3CH_2OH (excess)
H_2SO_4
?

(b)

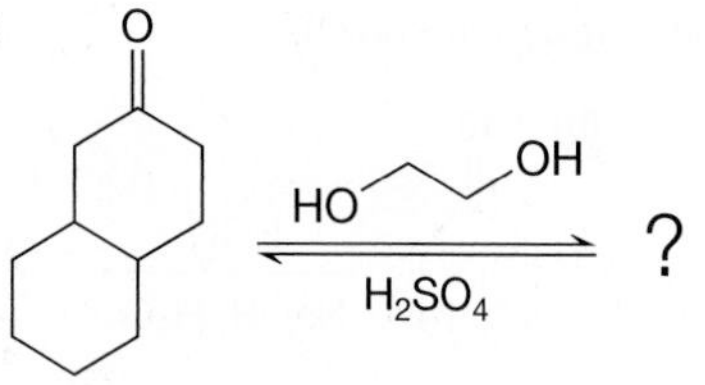
H_2SO_4
?

(c)

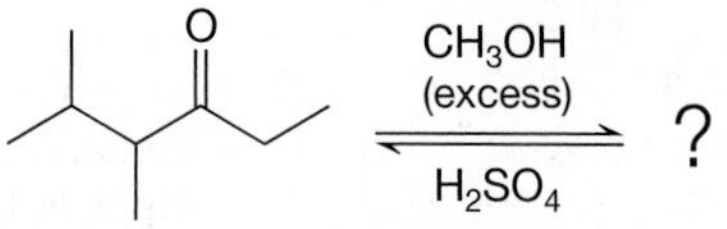
CH_3OH (excess)
H_2SO_4
?

(d)

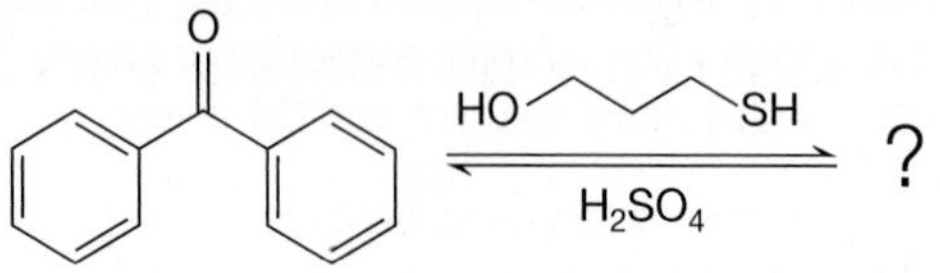
H_2SO_4
?

(e)

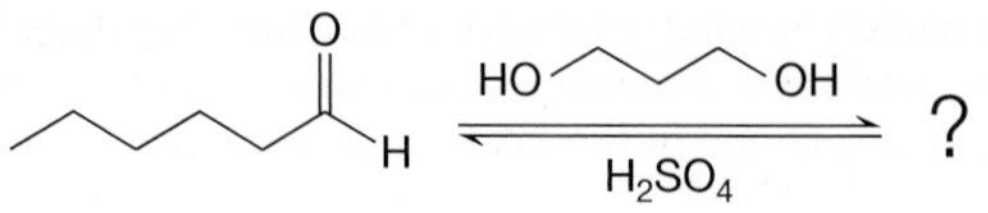
H_2SO_4
?

19.13 Predict the major organic product and draw the complete, detailed mechanism for each of the following reactions.

(a)

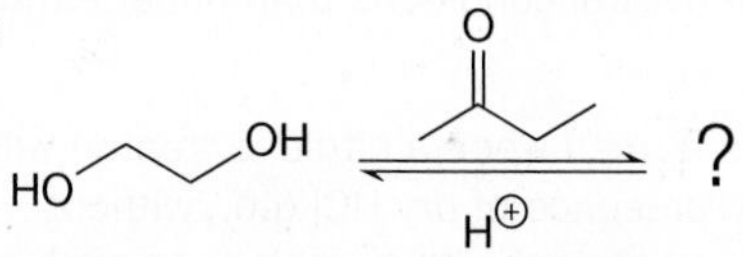
$H^{\oplus}$
?

(b)

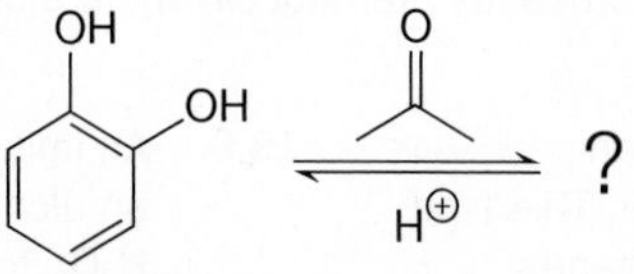
$H^{\oplus}$
?

(c)

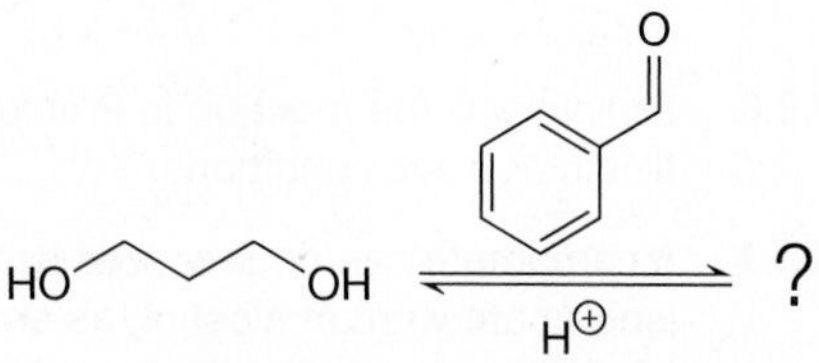
$H^{\oplus}$
?

19.14 The sulfur analog of an acetal, called a *thioacetal*, can be produced when a ketone or aldehyde is treated with a thiol (RSH) under acidic conditions. When propane-1,3-dithiol is used, a 1,3-dithiane is produced, as shown here. Dithianes have important applications in organic synthesis. Draw the complete, detailed mechanism for this 1,3-dithiane formation reaction.

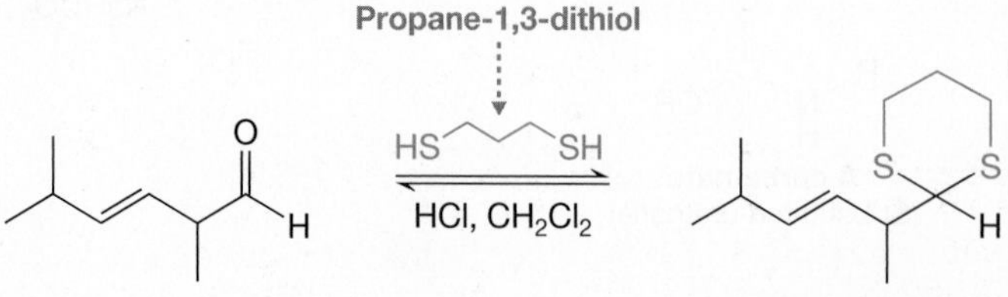
Propane-1,3-dithiol
HCl, CH_2Cl_2

A 1,3-dithiane

19.15 Predict the major product and draw the complete, detailed mechanism for each of the following reactions.

(a)

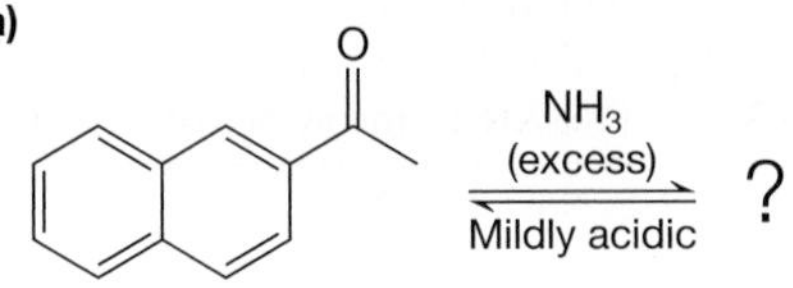

NH3
(excess)
Mildly acidic
?

(b)

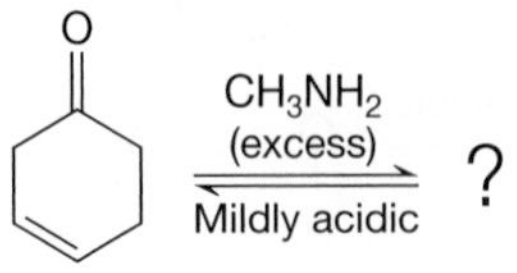

CH3NH2
(excess)
Mildly acidic
?

(c)

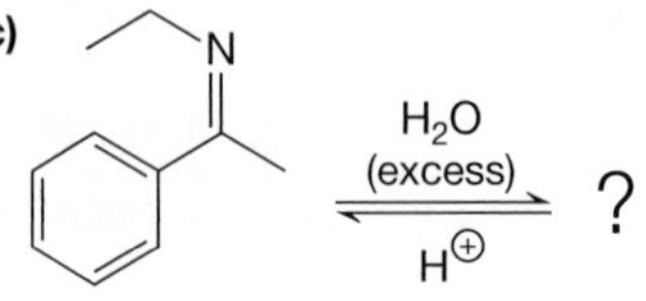

N
H2O
(excess)
H⊕
?

(d)

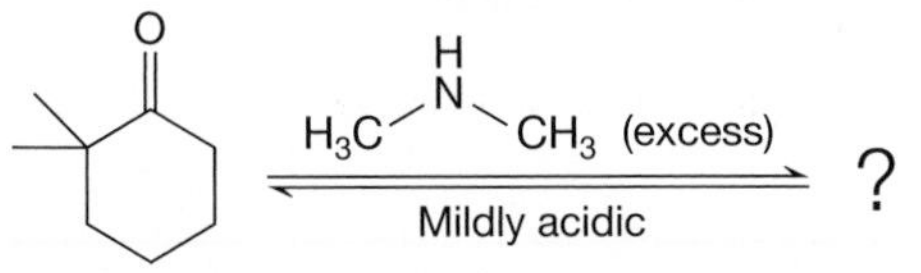

H3C-NH-CH3 (excess)
Mildly acidic
?

(e)

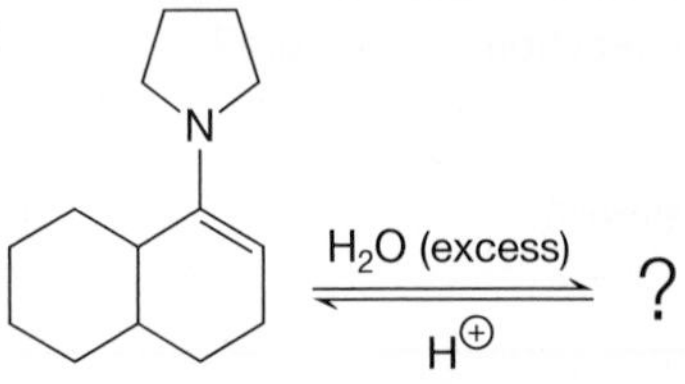

N
H2O (excess)
H⊕
?

19.16 Predict the major product and draw the complete, detailed mechanism for each of the following reactions.

(a)

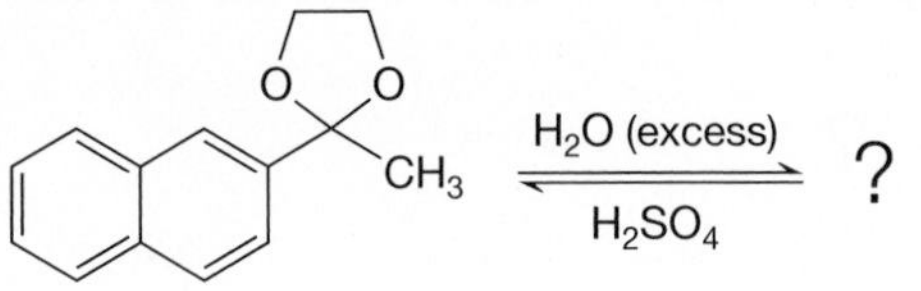

CH3
H2O (excess)
H2SO4
?

(b)

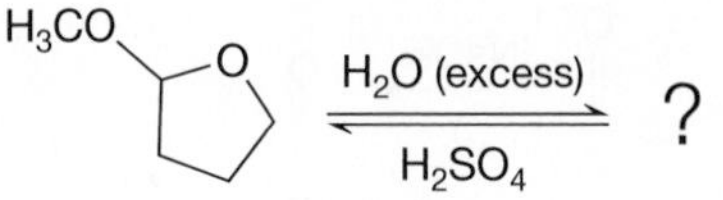

H3CO
H2O (excess)
H2SO4
?

(c)

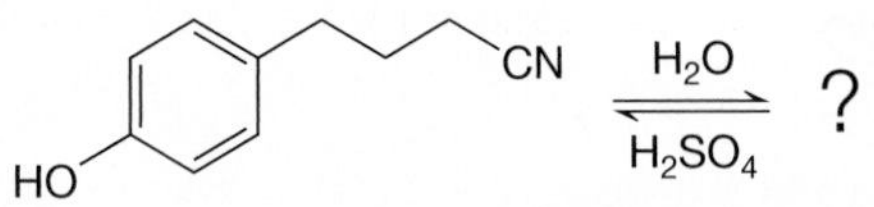

HO
CN
H2O
H2SO4
?

(d)

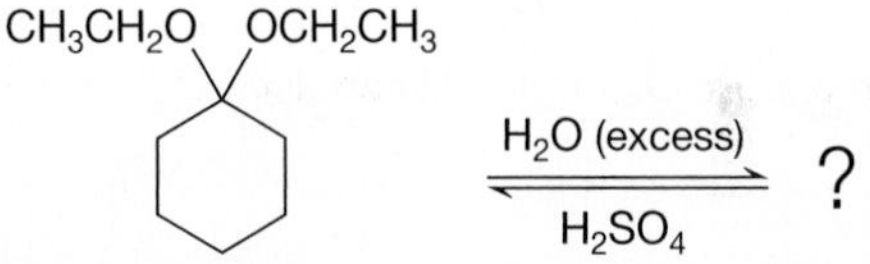

CH3CH2O OCH2CH3
H2O (excess)
H2SO4
?

19.17 An isonitrile is an unusual species that has the form R—$^{+}$N≡C^{-}. When an isonitrile is treated with water, an *N*-alkylformamide is formed, as shown here. Propose a mechanism for this reaction.

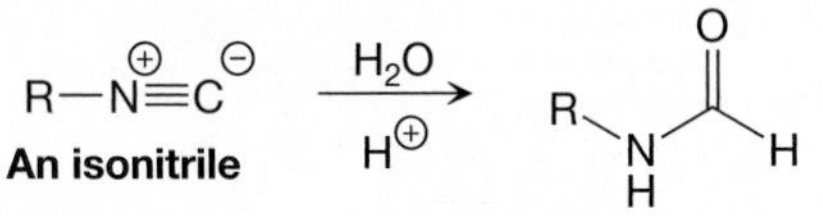

R—N≡C
H2O
H⊕

An isonitrile

An *N*-alkylformamide

19.18 The mechanism for formation of an acetal from a ketone or aldehyde (Eq. 19-13, p. 936) is very similar to the mechanism for formation of an imine (Eq. 19-20, p. 940). As was explained in this chapter, the formation of an imine from a ketone or aldehyde is generally carried out at a pH of about 4 or 5. Under more strongly acidic conditions, the rate of imine formation slows down dramatically, as shown below. The rate of acetal formation, however, does not slow down under such strongly acidic conditions. Explain why.

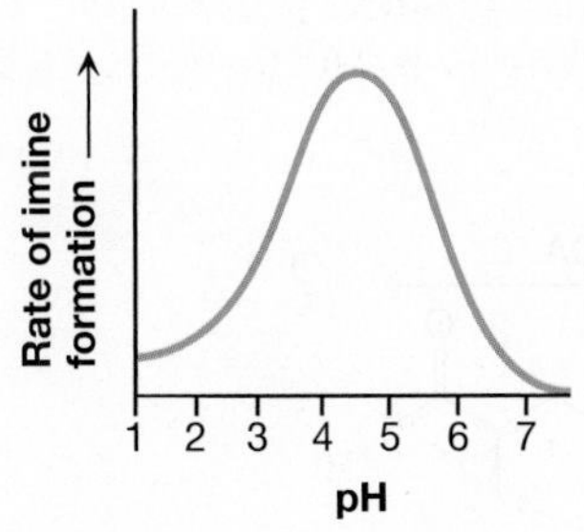

Rate of imine formation
1 2 3 4 5 6 7
pH

19.19 Hydroxylamine, H_2NOH, has both an OH functional group and an NH_2 functional group, so it can feasibly undergo reaction with a ketone or an aldehyde to produce either an acetal or an imine-like compound called an oxime. **(a)** Draw each of these mechanisms for the reaction of hydroxylamine with acetone. **(b)** Which is the major product? *Hint*: Which step decides the outcome?

19.20 Draw the complete, detailed mechanism for the reaction shown here and, using the mechanism, predict the major product. *Hint*: TsOH is a strong acid.

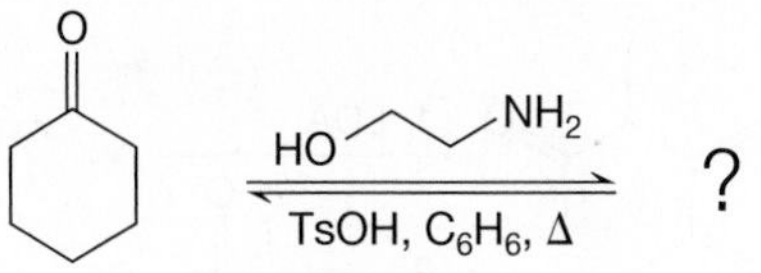

HO
NH2
TsOH, C6H6, Δ
?

19.21 Predict the major product and draw the complete, detailed mechanism for each of the following reactions.

(a)

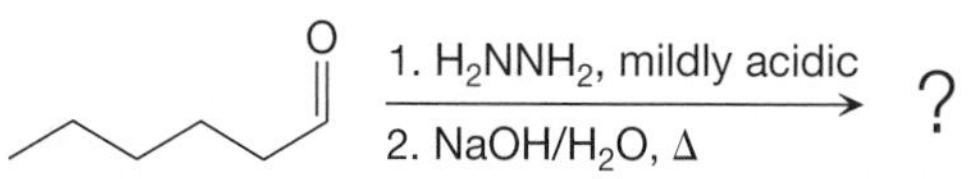
O
1. H_2NNH_2, mildly acidic
2. NaOH/H_2O, Δ
?

(b)

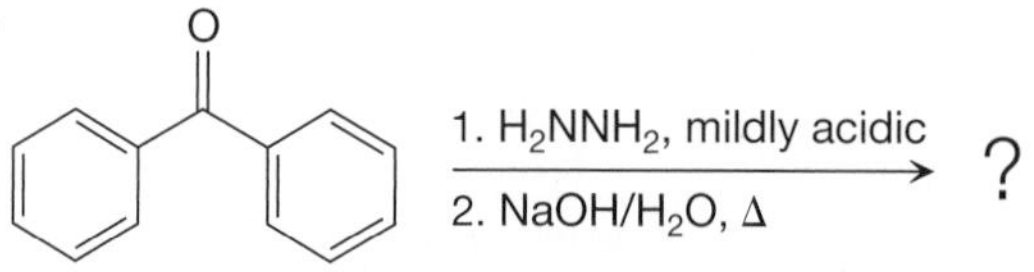
O
1. H_2NNH_2, mildly acidic
2. NaOH/H_2O, Δ
?

19.22 **(SYN)** What carbonyl-containing compound could be used as a reactant in the reaction shown here?

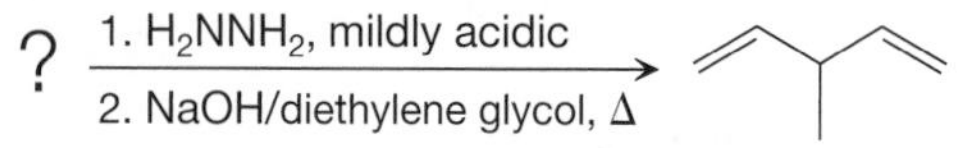
?
1. H_2NNH_2, mildly acidic
2. NaOH/diethylene glycol, Δ

19.23 **(SYN)** Draw three different ketone or aldehyde precursors that could be used to produce hexane via a Wolff–Kishner reduction.

Sections 19.8–19.13 Aldol and Robinson Annulation Reactions

19.24 Draw the complete, detailed mechanism and predict the major organic product for each of the following reactions.

(a)

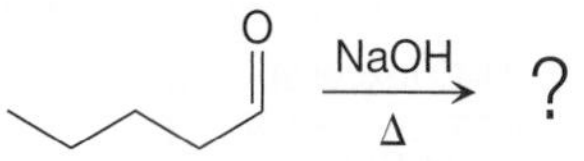
O
NaOH
Δ
?

(b)

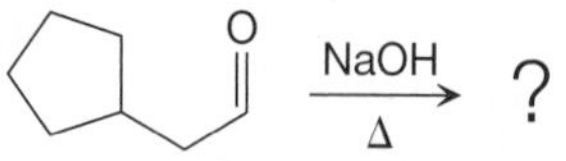
O
NaOH
Δ
?

(c)

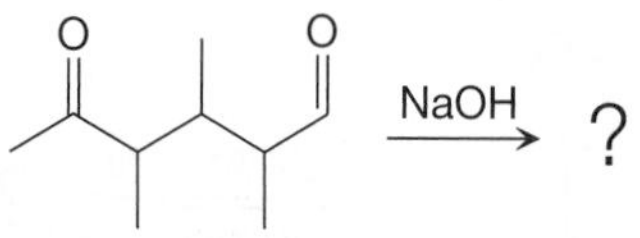
O
O
NaOH
?

(d)

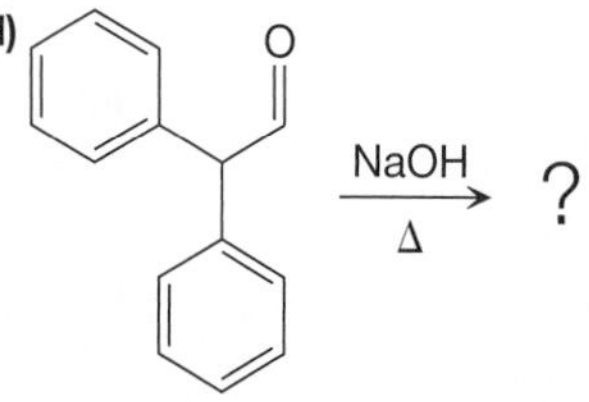
O
NaOH
Δ
?

19.25 Draw the mechanism for the aldol addition reaction shown here, which is catalyzed by acid. *Hint*: Under acidic conditions, can an enolate anion act as a nucleophile?

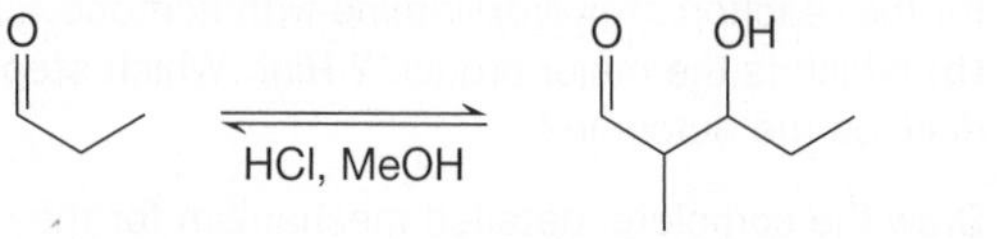
O
O
OH
HCl, MeOH

Propanal **3-Hydroxy-2-methylpentanal**

19.26 Which compound, **A** or **B**, will produce more aldol product at equilibrium? Why?

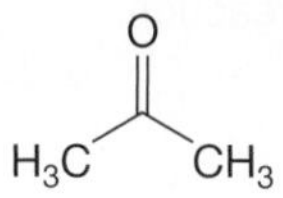
O
H_3C
CH_3

A

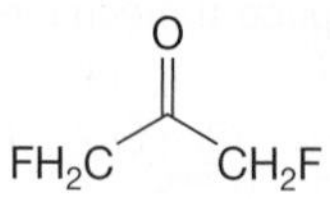
O
FH_2C
CH_2F

B

19.27 Draw a complete, detailed mechanism and predict the major product for each of the following reactions.

(a)

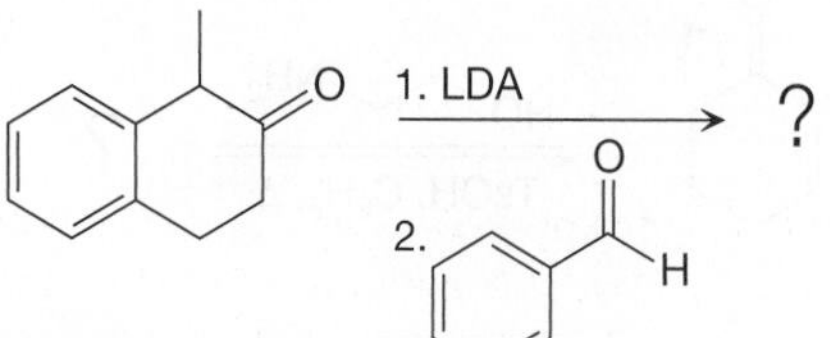
O
1. LDA
2.
O
H
?

(b)

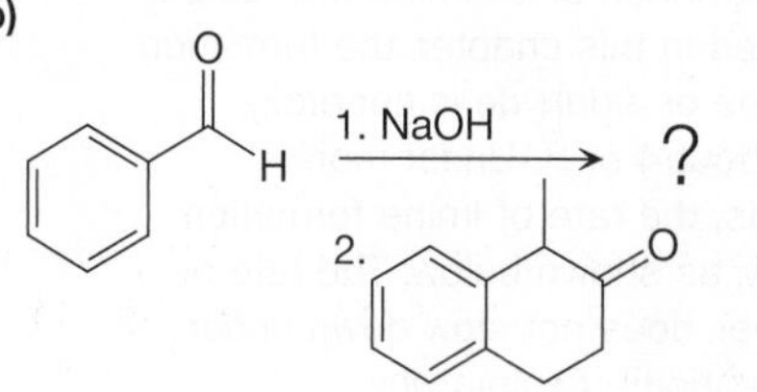
O
H
1. NaOH
2.
O
?

(c)

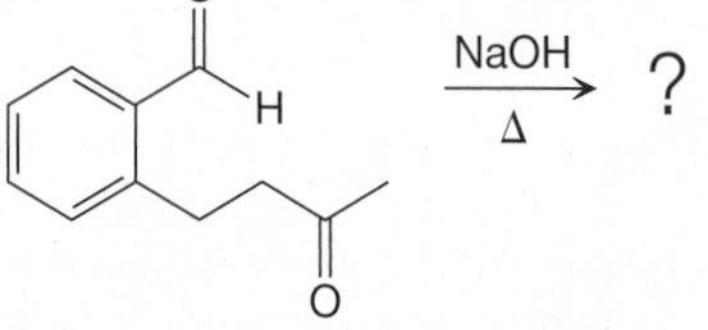
O
H
O
NaOH
Δ
?

(d)

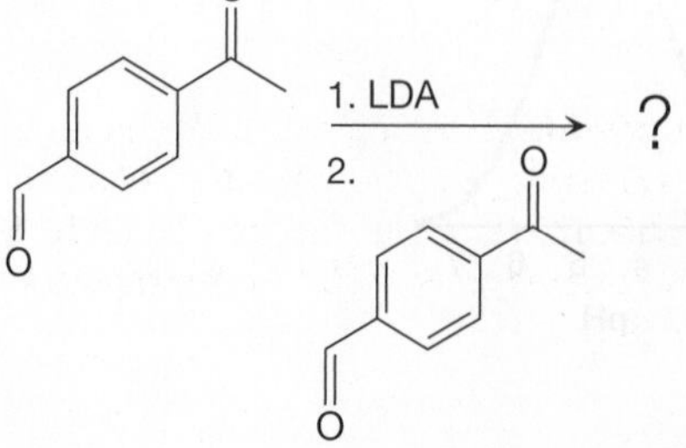
O
O
1. LDA
2.
O
O
?

19.28 **(SYN)** Show how to synthesize each of the following, using cyclopentanone as one of the reagents.

(a)

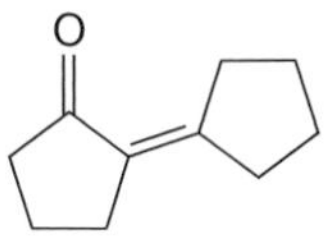

(b)

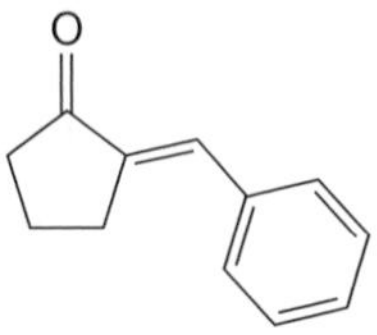

(c)

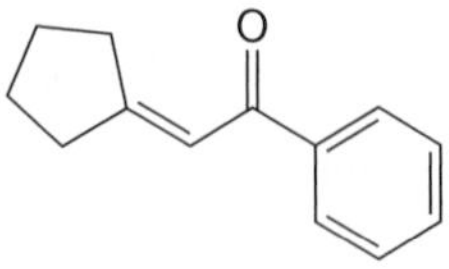

(d)

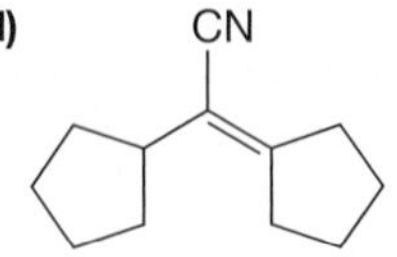

(e)

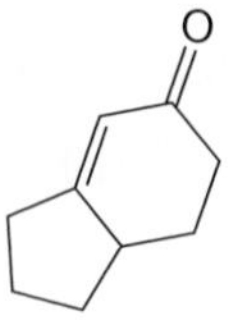

19.29 The crossed aldol reaction shown here can be carried out using a weak base such as pyridine. **(a)** Draw the complete, detailed mechanism for this reaction. **(b)** Explain why a relatively weak base can be used.

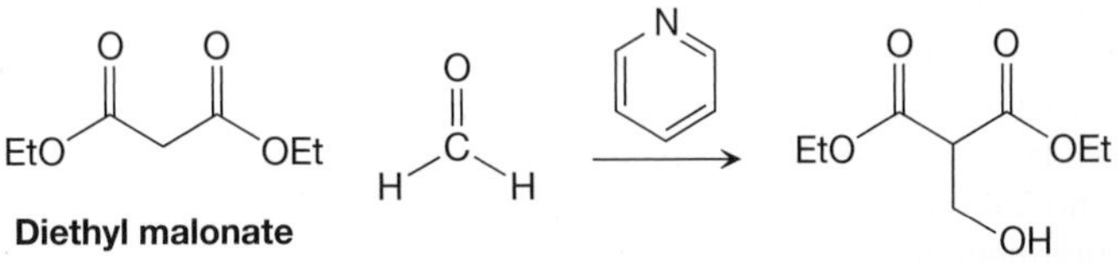

Diethyl malonate

Section 19.15 The Organic Chemistry of Biomolecules

19.30 Draw Haworth projections for each of the following molecules: **(a)** α-D-allopyranose, **(b)** β-D-allopyranose, **(c)** α-D-allofuranose, and **(d)** β-D-allofuranose. (Consult Fig. 5-55 on p. 252 for the structure of each sugar in its acyclic form.)

19.31 Name each of the following cyclic sugars. (Consult Fig. 5-55 for the name of each sugar in its acyclic form.)

(a)

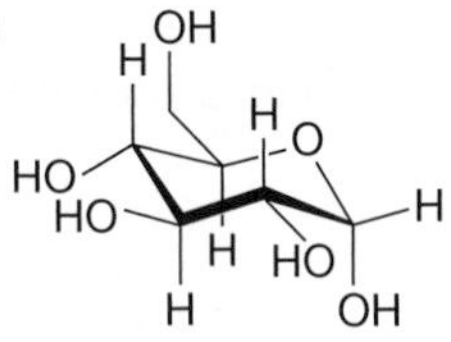

(b)

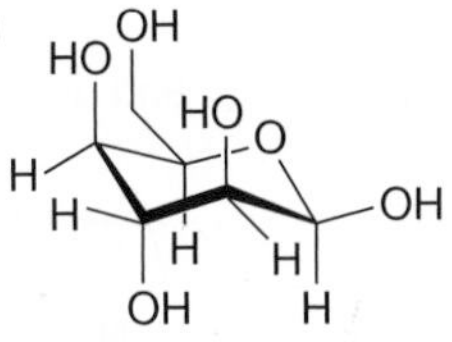

(c)

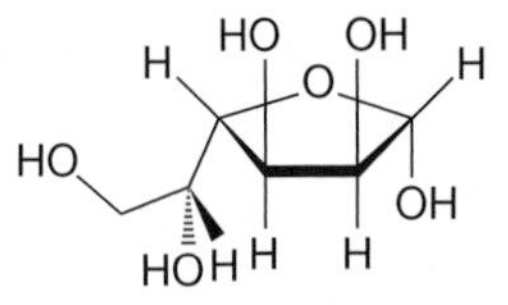

19.32 Identify the anomeric carbon in each molecule in Problems 19.30 and 19.31.

19.33 The acyclic form of D-talose is shown here as its Fischer projection. Identify the anomeric carbon.

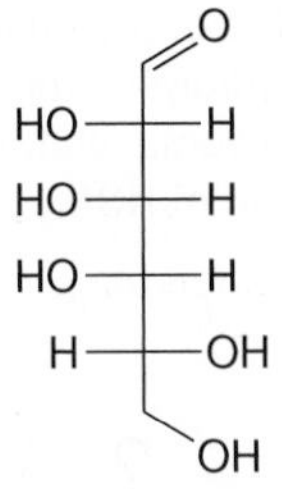

D-Talose

19.34 Draw the mechanism that shows how α-D-allopyranose converts to β-D-allopyranose under acidic conditions.

19.35 Draw the mechanism that shows how α-D-allopyranose converts to α-D-allofuranose under acidic conditions.

19.36 The specific rotation of α-D-mannopyranose is +29.3°, and that of β-D-mannopyranose is −16.3°. When either anomer is dissolved in water, the specific rotation slowly changes to +14.5° because the anomers interconvert to arrive at an equilibrium. This change in optical rotation is called *mutarotation*. The specific rotation of the mixture depends on the fraction of the mixture that each anomer makes up, according to the following equation:

$$[\alpha]^{20}_{\text{D,mixture}} = \{[\alpha]^{20}_{\text{D,anomer 1}}\}(\text{fraction anomer 1}) + \{[\alpha]^{20}_{\text{D,anomer 2}}\}(\text{fraction anomer 2})$$

Knowing that the fractions of the anomers must add up to 1, calculate the relative amounts of the two anomers at equilibrium.

19.37 At equilibrium, D-galactose exists almost exclusively in its α and β pyranose forms. Aqueous solutions are freshly prepared for the α and β forms, both at the same concentration and temperature. The solution of the α form rotates plane-polarized light +150.7°, whereas the solution of the β form rotates the light +52.8°. Over time, both solutions have the same measured rotation of +80.2°. How much of the equilibrated solution does each form account for? *Hint*: See Problem 19.36.

Integrated Problems

19.38 Predict the major product(s) of each of the following reactions.

(a)

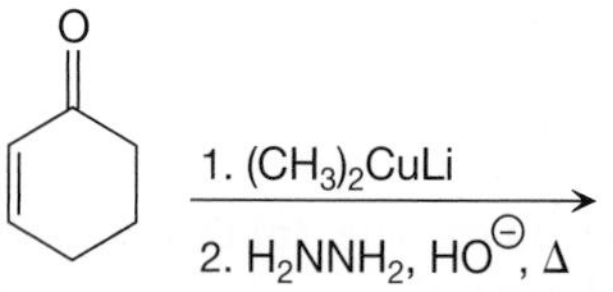

1. $(CH_3)_2CuLi$
2. H_2NNH_2, $HO^{\ominus}$, Δ
?

(b)

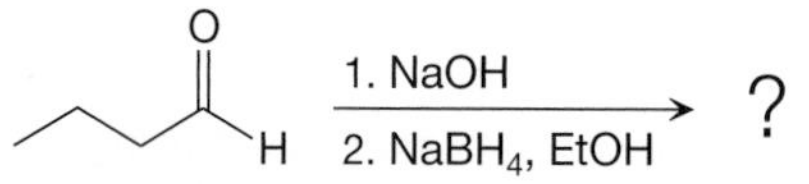

1. NaOH
2. $NaBH_4$, EtOH
?

19.39 An enamine, $R_2C{=}C{-}NR_2$, behaves as a nucleophile in much the same way that an enolate anion does. This is because an enamine has resonance structures similar to those observed for an enolate anion, as shown in the box. With this in mind, draw the complete mechanism for the following reaction and provide the structure of the missing intermediate.

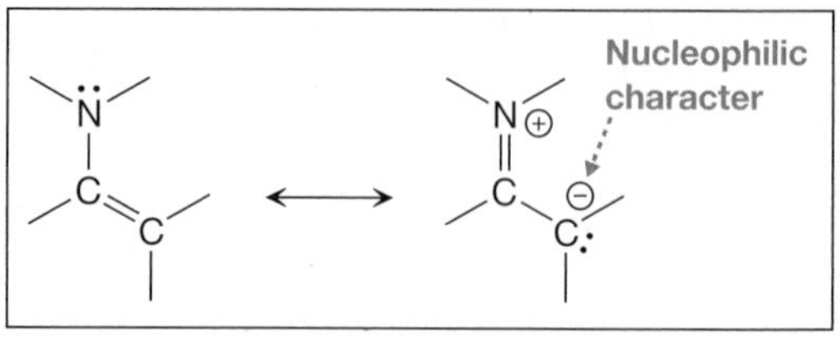

Nucleophilic character

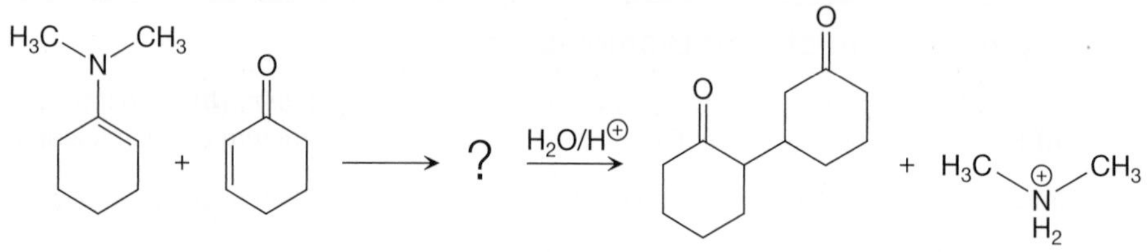

H_3C CH_3 N
+
?
$H_2O/H^{\oplus}$
+ H_3C CH_3 $\overset{\oplus}{N}H_2$

19.40 For each sequence of reactions, draw the complete, detailed mechanism and predict the major product. *Hint*: See Problem 19.39.

(a)

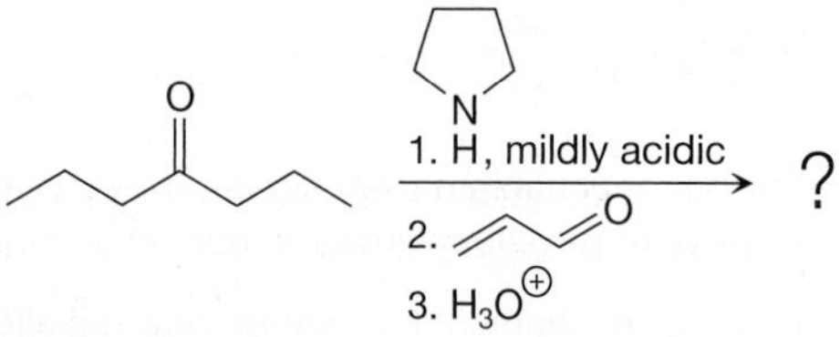

1. H, mildly acidic
2.
3. $H_3O^{\oplus}$
?

(b)

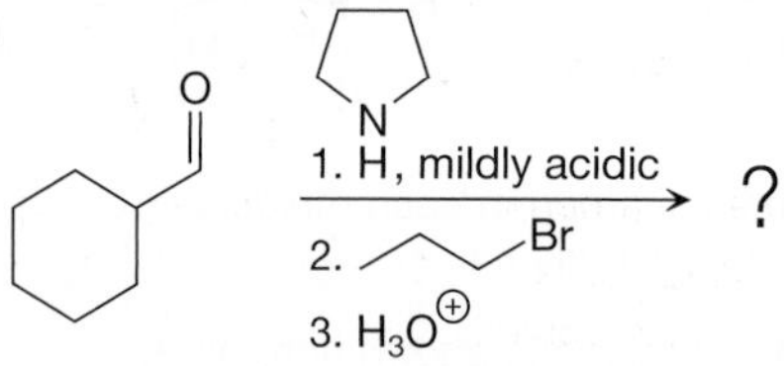

1. H, mildly acidic
2. Br
3. $H_3O^{\oplus}$
?

19.41 This reaction shows that a secondary nitro compound can be hydrolyzed to a ketone on treatment with aqueous sulfuric acid. Propose a mechanism for this reaction.

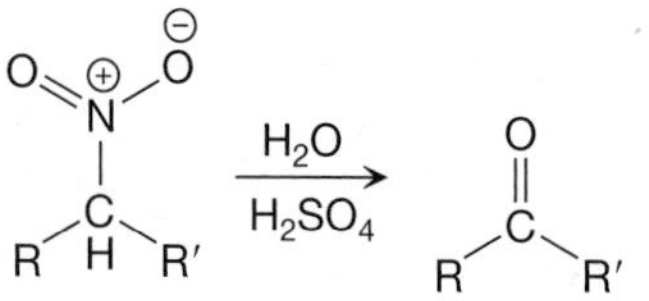

H_2O
H_2SO_4

19.42 Draw a complete, detailed mechanism for the following reaction.

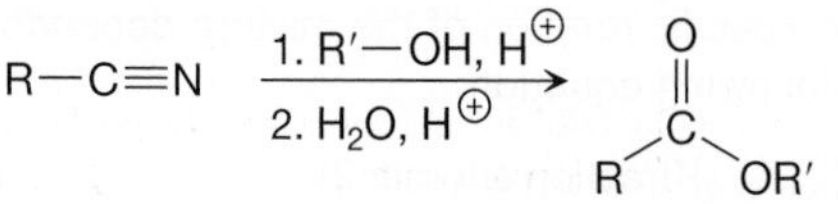

R—C≡N
1. R′—OH, $H^{\oplus}$
2. H_2O, $H^{\oplus}$

19.43 This reaction shows that an aldol-type reaction can be performed with a deprotonated imine as the nucleophile. On hydrolysis, the product is the normal β-hydroxy carbonyl compound. Notice that LDA is used as the base instead of HO^-.

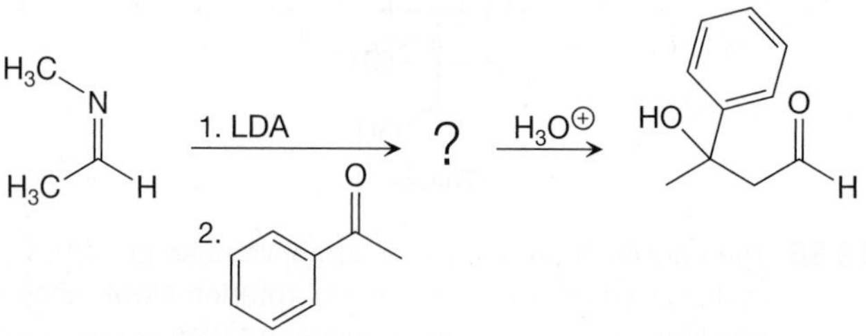

1. LDA
2.
?
$H_3O^{\oplus}$

(a) Explain why HO^- cannot be used as a base for this reaction.

(b) Provide a detailed mechanism for this reaction, including the structure of the intermediate species not shown.

19.44 The α proton of a nitroalkane is weakly acidic and has a pK_a of about 10. With this in mind, draw the mechanism for the following reaction.

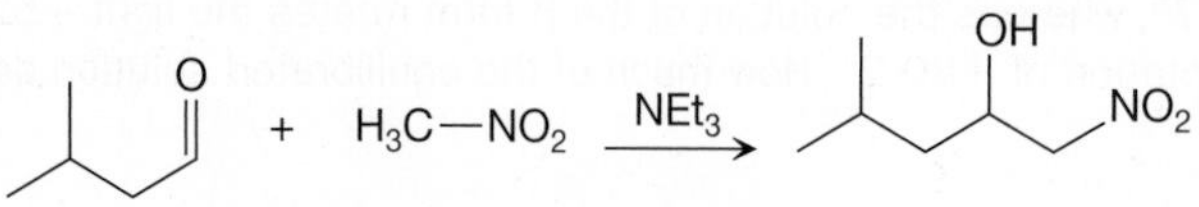

+ $H_3C{-}NO_2$
NEt_3

19.45 The α proton of a nitrile is weakly acidic and has a pK_a of about 25. With this in mind, draw the mechanism for the following reaction.

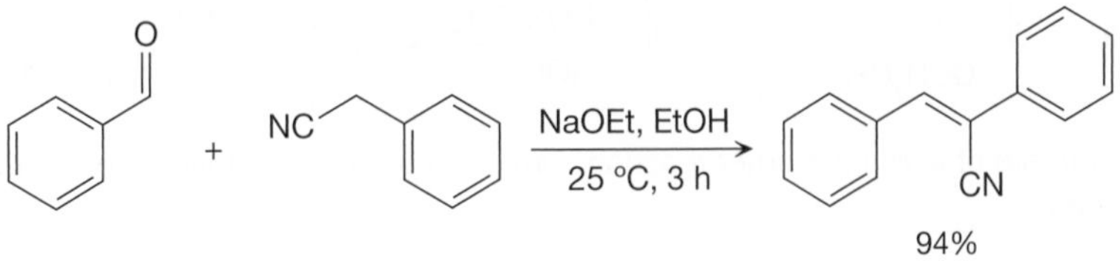
NC
+
NaOEt, EtOH
25 °C, 3 h
CN

94%

19.46 Treatment of a nitrile with base, followed by acid hydrolysis, yields a β-keto nitrile, as shown here. Provide a detailed mechanism for this reaction. *Hint*: See Problem 19.45.

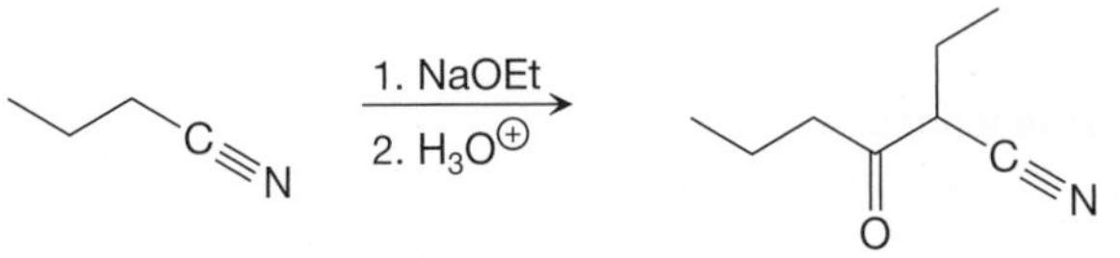
1. NaOEt
2. $H_3O^{\oplus}$

19.47 Draw the mechanism and product for the following reaction. *Hint*: See Problem 19.45.

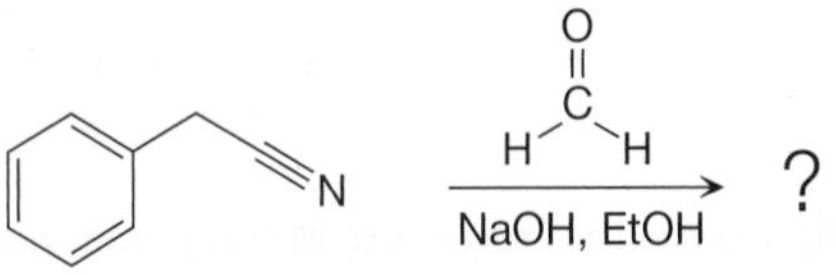
NaOH, EtOH
?

19.48 When benzaldehyde is treated with a catalytic amount of KCN, the benzoin condensation occurs. Draw a complete, detailed mechanism for this reaction. *Hint*: The reaction does not take place without the presence of NC^-.

An α-hydroxy ketone

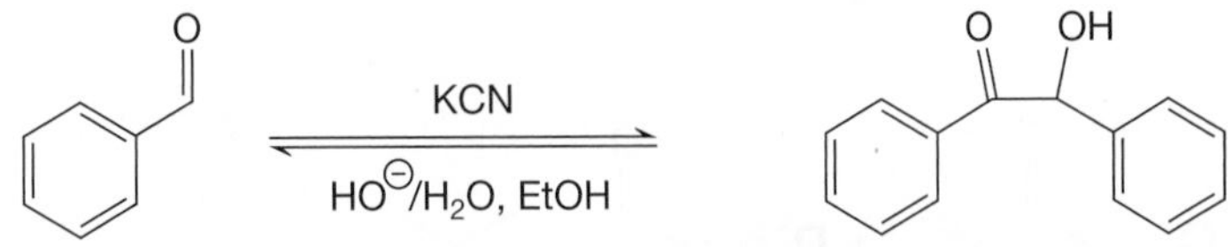
KCN
$HO^{\ominus}/H_2O$, EtOH

Benzaldehyde

2-Hydroxy-1,2-diphenylethanone (Benzoin)
88%

19.49 No reaction occurs when benzaldehyde and propenenitrile (acrylonitrile) are combined. In the presence of a catalytic amount of NaCN, however, the reaction shown here takes place. Draw a complete, detailed mechanism to account for these results. *Hint*: See Problem 19.48.

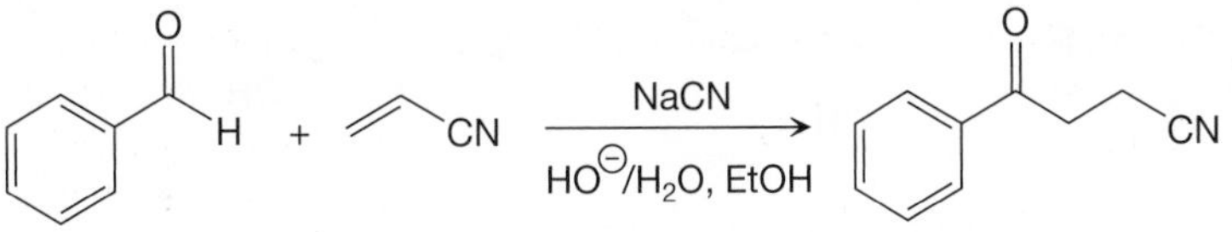
NaCN
$HO^{\ominus}/H_2O$, EtOH

19.50 The following reaction is believed to proceed through the intermediate shown. Draw the complete, detailed mechanism that leads to the formation of that intermediate.

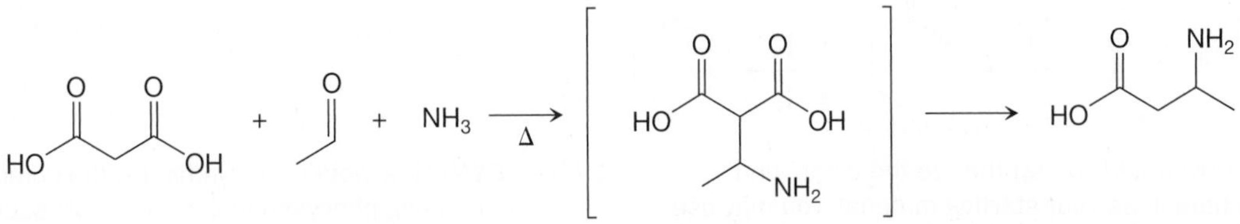
NH_3
Δ

19.51 When a 1,5-diketone is treated with acid, a 2,6-dialkylpyran is produced, as shown here. Propose a mechanism for this reaction.

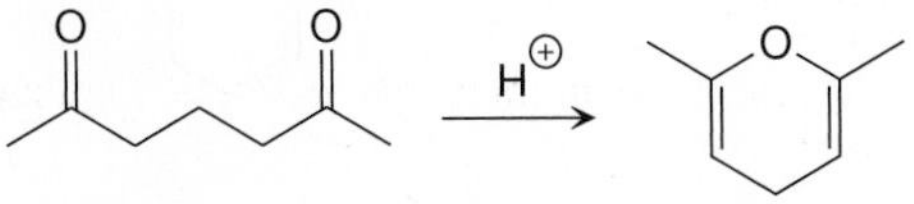

19.52 When an α,β-unsaturated carbonyl is treated with H_2O_2 under basic conditions, the C=C double bond is epoxidized, as shown here. Propose a mechanism for this reaction.

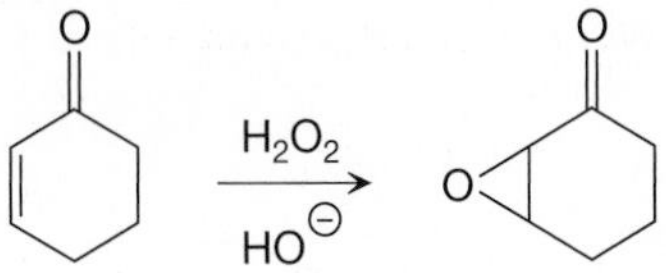
H_2O_2
$HO^{\ominus}$

19.53 The following transformation is an example of a Darzens reaction. Draw its complete, detailed mechanism.

19.54 The following is an example of a Wittig–Horner reaction. Draw its complete, detailed mechanism. *Hint*: A key intermediate is provided.

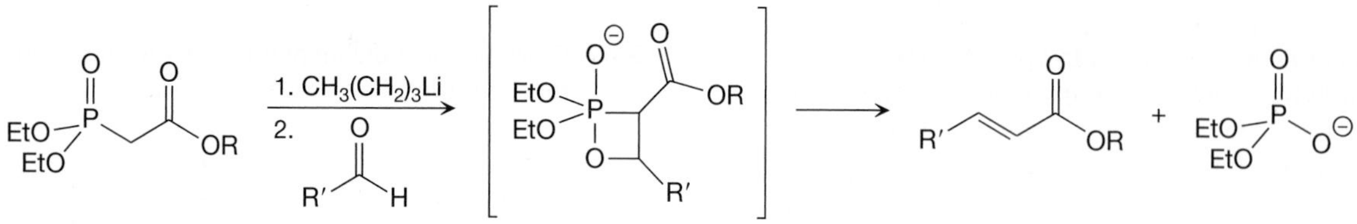

19.55 **(SYN)** Provide the reagent(s) missing from each of the following reactions.

(a)

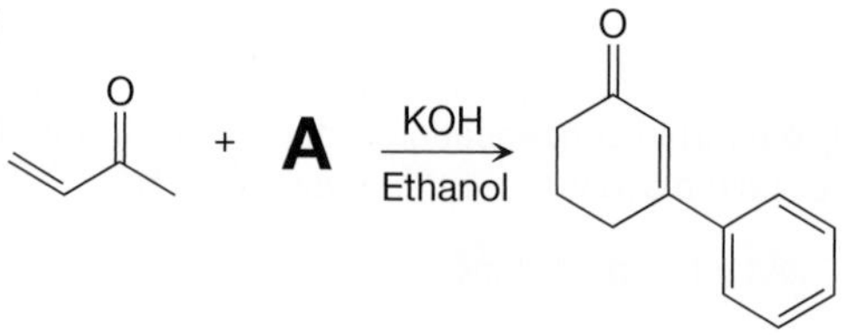

(b)

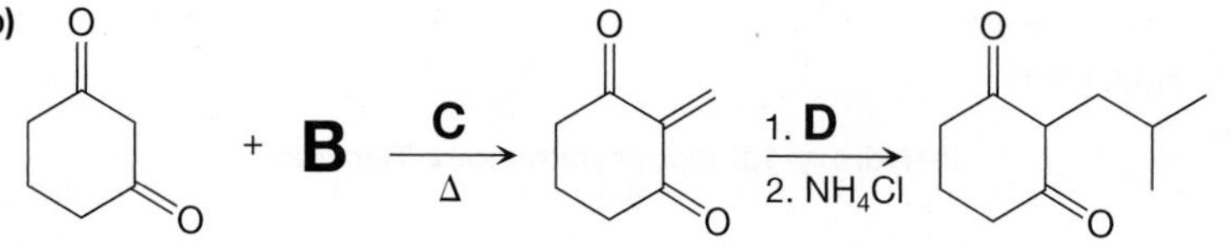

(c)

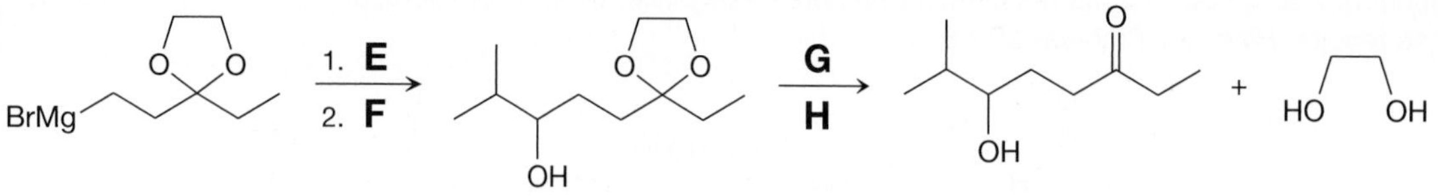

(d)

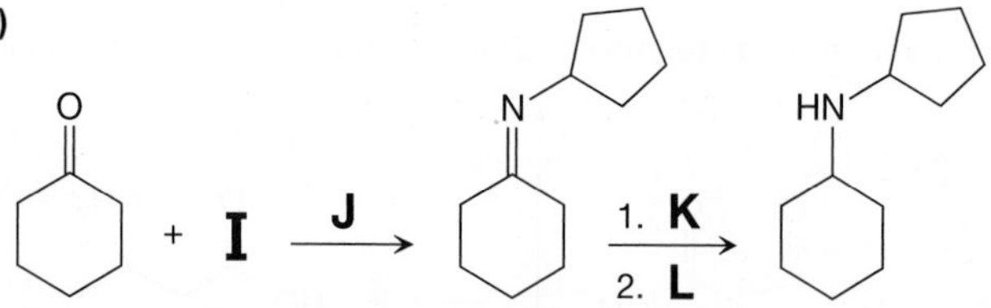

19.56 **(SYN)** How would you synthesize the compound shown here if, as your starting material, you may use any organic reagents that contain exactly two carbon atoms and any inorganic reagents?

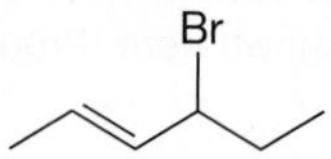

19.57 **(SYN)** How would you synthesize the compound shown here using phenylethanal as your only source of carbon atoms? You may ignore stereochemistry in this case.

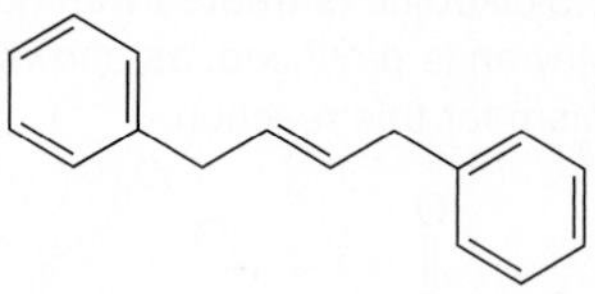

19.58 (SYN) How would you synthesize 2-methylhexane from hex-4-en-3-one and any other reagents necessary?

19.59 (SYN) Using butanal as your only source of carbons, show how to synthesize *N*-butylbutan-1-amine.

19.60 (SYN) Using only compounds containing three or fewer carbons, show how to synthesize 2,3-dimethylpentan-1-amine.

19.61 A compound with formula $C_{10}H_{14}O$ has the IR, ^{1}H NMR, and ^{13}C NMR spectra shown here. The DEPT spectra reveal that the seven carbon signals farthest upfield are produced from CH_2 carbons. $C_{10}H_{14}O$ can be synthesized using an aldol condensation reaction, simply by heating a compound C_5H_8O in the presence of NaOH. **(a)** Provide the structures of C_5H_8O and $C_{10}H_{14}O$. **(b)** Provide the mechanism for the reaction that is described.

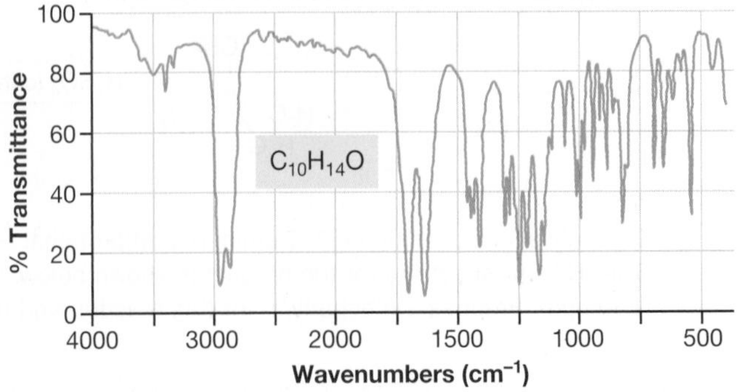

100
80
60
40
20
0
% Transmittance
C10H14O
4000
3000
2000
1500
1000
500
Wavenumbers (cm−1)

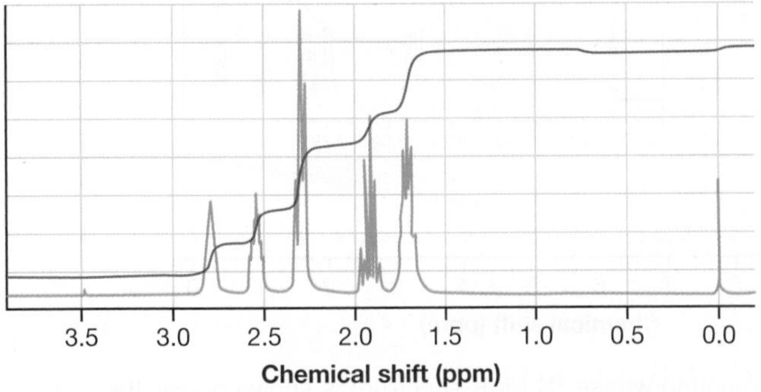

3.5
3.0
2.5
2.0
1.5
1.0
0.5
0.0
Chemical shift (ppm)

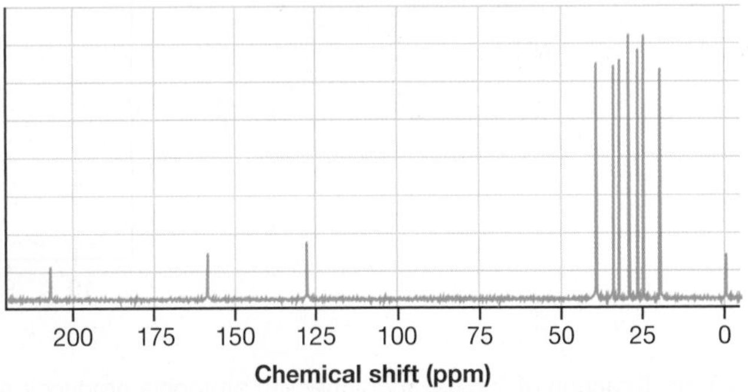

200
175
150
125
100
75
50
25
0
Chemical shift (ppm)

19.62 When but-2-enal is treated with 3-phenylpropenal in the presence of a strong base, a compound is formed whose formula is $C_{13}H_{12}O$. In its ^{1}H NMR spectrum, one signal has a chemical shift around 10 ppm, several overlapping signals have chemical shifts between 7 and 9 ppm, and several other overlapping signals have chemical shifts between 5 and 6 ppm. Integration of those sets of signals gives a 1:5:6 ratio.
(a) What is the structure of the product?
(b) Draw a complete, detailed mechanism that accounts for the formation of the product.

19.63 When treated with acid, hexane-2,5-dione forms a compound with the formula C_6H_8O. The ^{1}H NMR spectrum of the product is shown below. A key intermediate is shown. Identify the structure of the product and propose a mechanism for this reaction.

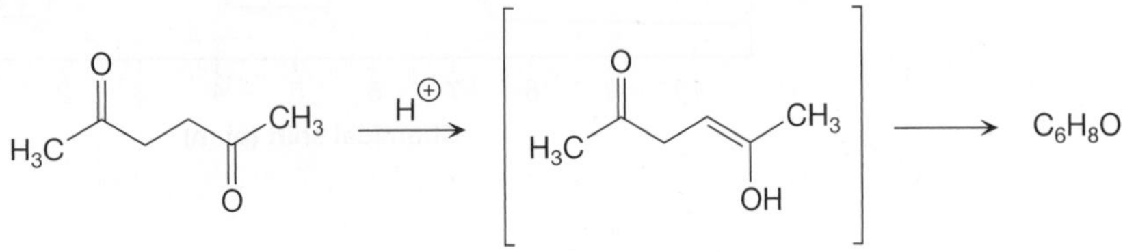

O
H3C
CH3
O
H⊕
O
H3C
CH3
OH
C6H8O

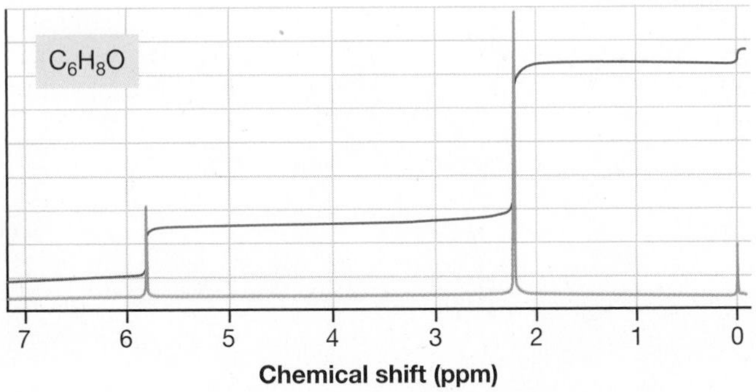

C6H8O
7
6
5
4
3
2
1
0
Chemical shift (ppm)

19.64 When acetonitrile is treated with concentrated sulfuric acid and *tert*-butanol, followed by water, a product is formed whose ^{1}H NMR spectrum exhibits the following three signals: singlet, 1.3 ppm, 9 H; singlet, 2.0 ppm, 3 H; and broad singlet, 8.2 ppm, 1 H. Its IR spectrum exhibits one broad absorption of medium intensity, between 3300 and 3500 cm^{-1}, and a narrow, intense absorption near 1650 cm^{-1}. A key intermediate is shown. Draw the structure of the product, and draw the complete, detailed mechanism for the reaction.

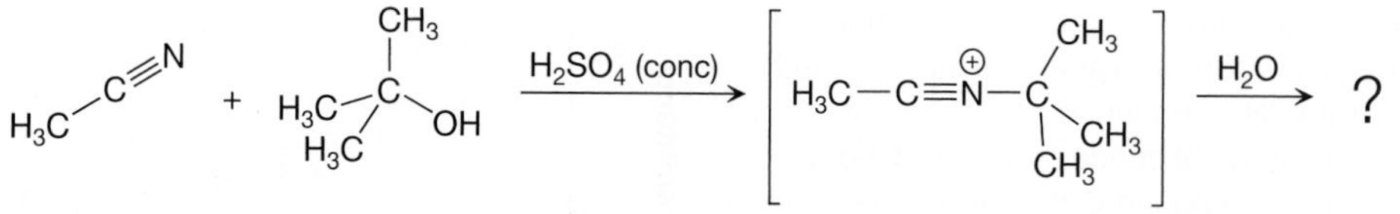

H3C
C≡N
+
CH3
H3C
C
H3C
OH
H2SO4 (conc)
H3C—C≡N—C
CH3
CH3
CH3
H2O
?

19.65 In mildly acidic conditions, 3-(2-aminophenyl)propenal reacts to form a compound whose molecular weight is 129 g/mol. The ^{1}H NMR spectrum for the product is shown below. Its ^{13}C NMR spectrum contains nine peaks, all between 120 and 150 ppm. Propose a mechanism for this reaction and draw the product.

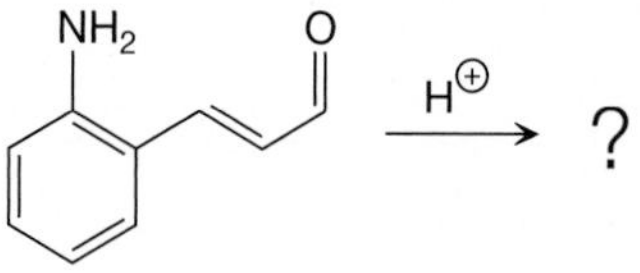

NH2
O
H⊕
?

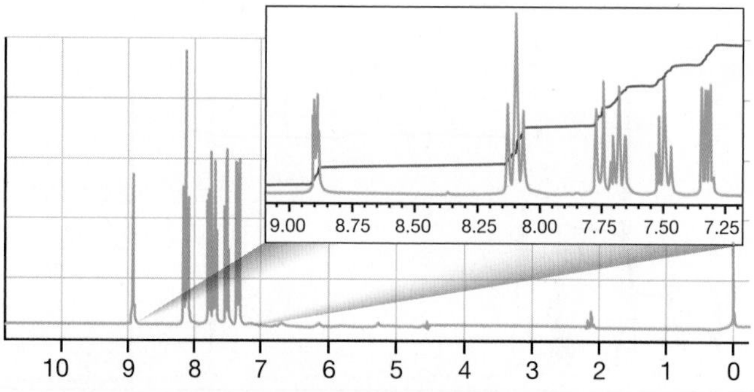

9.00
8.75
8.50
8.25
8.00
7.75
7.50
7.25
10
9
8
7
6
5
4
3
2
1
0
Chemical shift (ppm)

19.66 Reaction of 2,5-hexanedione with ammonia produces a compound whose ^{1}H NMR spectrum is shown below. Its ^{13}C NMR spectrum exhibits three signals. Draw the complete, detailed mechanism leading to the formation of that product.

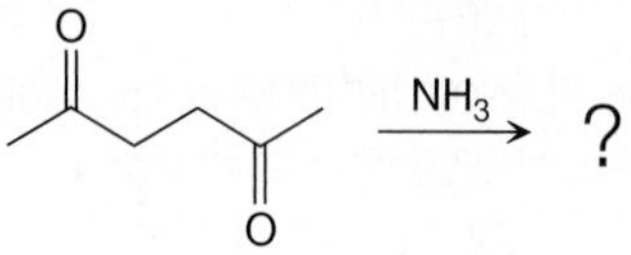

O
O
NH3
?

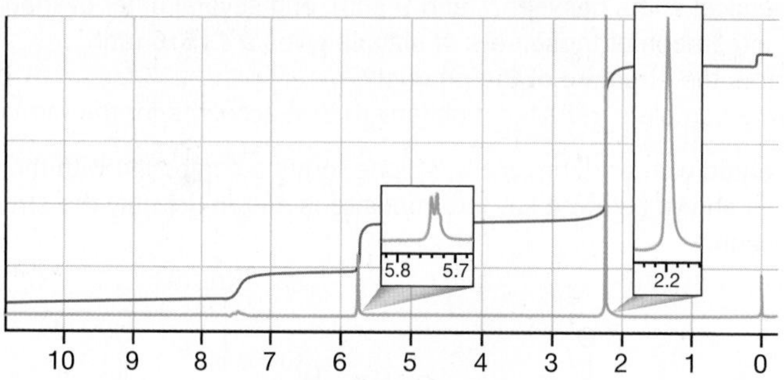

5.8
5.7
2.2
10
9
8
7
6
5
4
3
2
1
0
Chemical shift (ppm)

20

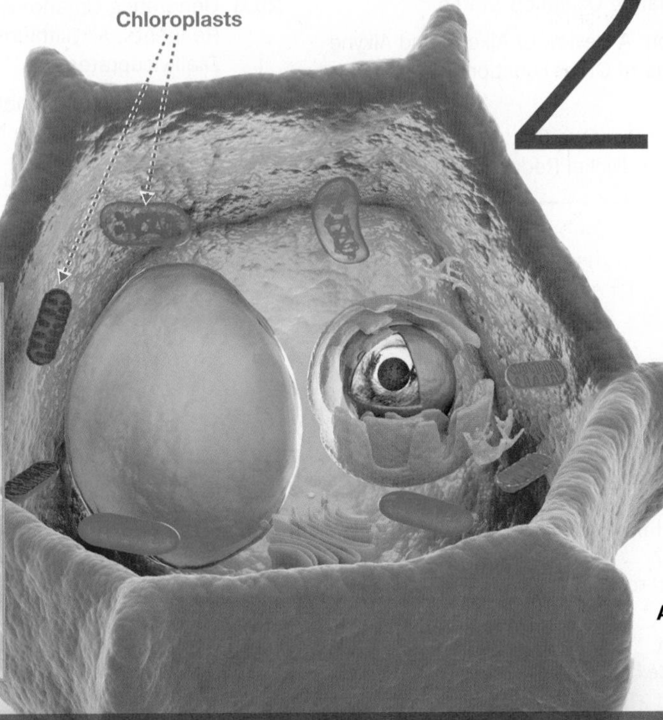
Chloroplasts
A plant cell

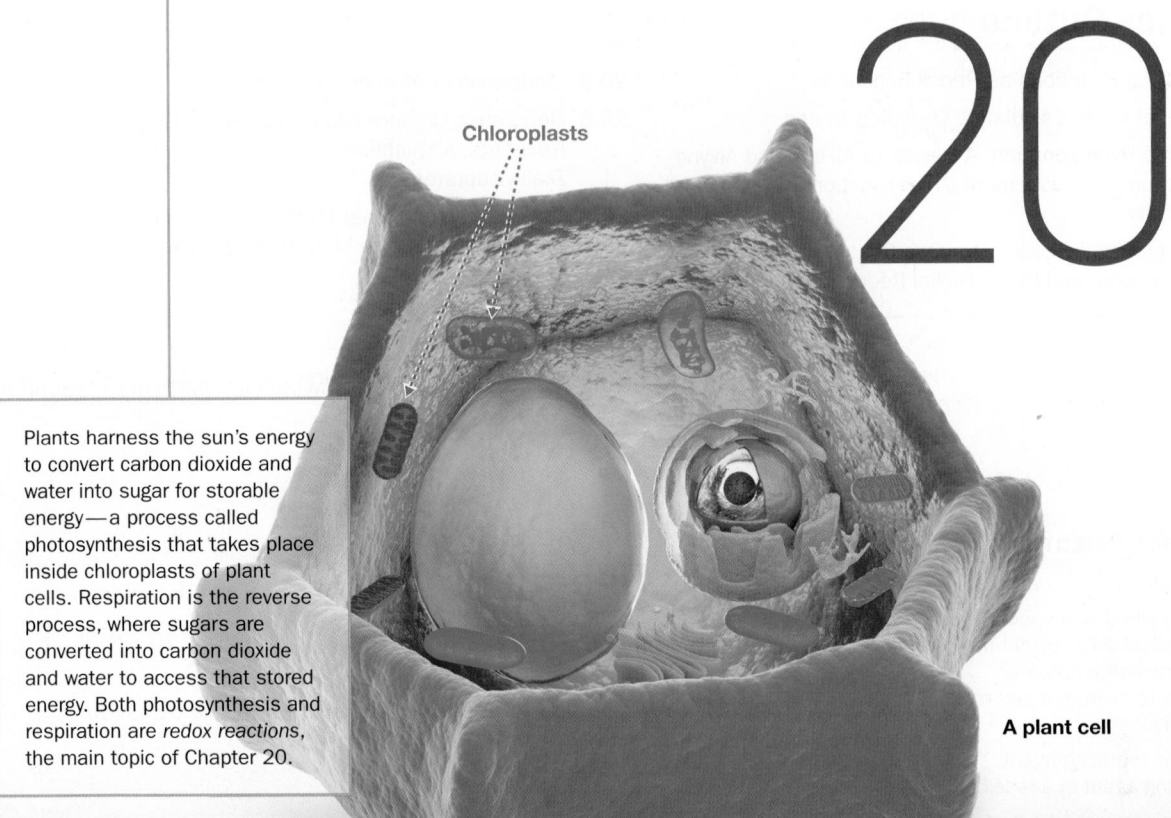

Plants harness the sun's energy to convert carbon dioxide and water into sugar for storable energy—a process called photosynthesis that takes place inside chloroplasts of plant cells. Respiration is the reverse process, where sugars are converted into carbon dioxide and water to access that stored energy. Both photosynthesis and respiration are *redox reactions*, the main topic of Chapter 20.

Redox Reactions; Organometallic Reagents and Their Reactions

To this point in the book, we have classified reactions primarily by the actions that take place among the *nuclei* of the reactant species. For example, we use the term *proton transfer* to describe a reaction in which a Brønsted acid donates a proton to a Brønsted base. An *addition* is a reaction that joins nuclei that were initially separated, whereas an *elimination* is the opposite. In a *substitution*, one or more nuclei in a given species are replaced.

Reactions can also be classified as *reduction–oxidation (redox) reactions* if there is a transfer of electrons from one species to another. We begin Chapter 20 by learning how to determine whether a reaction is a redox, and we will see that some of the reactions we have previously studied are examples. We will also learn some new redox reactions that are quite valuable for synthesis.

Some of the most useful redox reactions involve organometallic reagents—not only reactions in which organometallic reagents are produced, but also reactions that organometallic reagents undergo. Therefore, here in Chapter 20, we will learn how to synthesize some familiar organometallic reagents, such as Grignard reagents (RMgX), alkyllithium reagents (RLi), and lithium dialkylcuprates (R_2CuLi). We will also learn

Chapter Outline

some new reactions involving organometallic species, which are particularly useful in generating new carbon–carbon bonds.

SECTION 20.1 OBJECTIVES

You will be able to:

1. Determine whether a species undergoes reduction or oxidation by keeping track of a carbon atom's bonds to hydrogen and to electronegative atoms.
2. Identify the reducing agent or the oxidizing agent in a redox reaction.

20.1 Identifying Reactions as Redox Reactions

You may have learned in general chemistry that a **redox reaction**, which stands for reduction–oxidation, is a reaction that involves a transfer of electrons from one species to another. A redox reaction can be identified by changes in the *oxidation states* of atoms involved in the reaction.

A species:

- undergoes **reduction** and becomes **reduced** if the oxidation state of one or more of its atoms decreases (becomes more negative); or
- undergoes **oxidation** and becomes **oxidized** if the oxidation state of one or more of its atoms increases (becomes more positive).

To apply these definitions directly, we must be able to determine an atom's oxidation state, and in Section 20.2 we will learn how to do so. Alternatively, we can reliably identify organic species that are reduced or oxidized by applying the following rules, which can be far more convenient:

- An organic species tends to become *reduced* when it gains C—H bonds or loses C—EN bonds (where EN is an atom that is more electronegative than carbon).
- An organic species tends to become *oxidized* when it gains C—EN bonds or loses C—H bonds.

For example, consider the reactions in Equations 20-1 and 20-2 (previously presented in Chapter 18), in which hydride adds to a ketone or aldehyde:

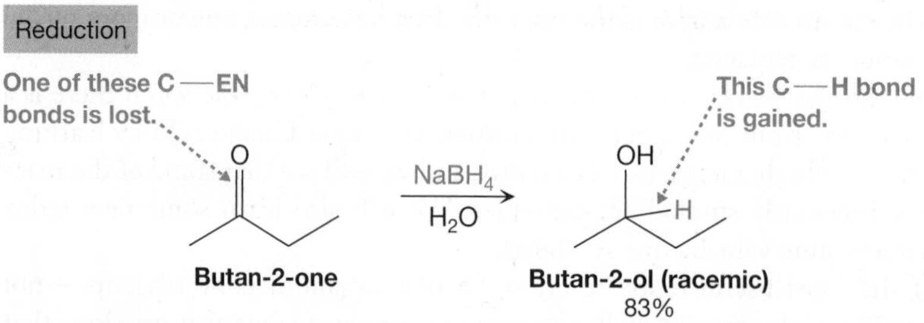

Reduction
One of these C—EN bonds is lost.
This C—H bond is gained.
O
NaBH4
H2O
OH
H
Butan-2-one
Butan-2-ol (racemic)
83%

(20-1)

Reduction

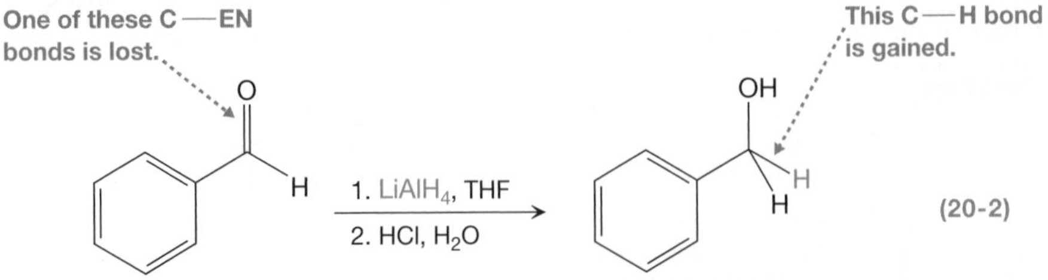

One of these C—EN bonds is lost.
This C—H bond is gained.
O
H
OH
H
H
1. LiAlH$_4$, THF
2. HCl, H$_2$O

(20-2)

Benzaldehyde

Phenylmethanol (Benzyl alcohol)
100%

In both cases, notice that the ketone or aldehyde gains a C—H bond and loses one C—O bond. Therefore, the ketone in Equation 20-1 is reduced, as is the aldehyde in Equation 20-2.

When a reduction occurs, it is helpful to identify the **reducing agent**, which we can think of as the species that is responsible for causing the reduction. In Equation 20-1, $NaBH_4$ is the reducing agent; when H^- from $NaBH_4$ adds to the carbonyl carbon, the ketone gains a C—H bond and loses a C—O bond (see Your Turn 20.1). For this reason, $NaBH_4$ is more generally called a *hydride reducing agent*, and the reaction in Equation 20-1 is an example of a *hydride reduction*. Similarly, $LiAlH_4$ is the reducing agent for the hydride reduction in Equation 20-2.

YOUR TURN **20.1**

Draw the mechanism for the reaction in Equation 20-1. In which step of the mechanism does the number of C—H bonds increase and the number of C—O bonds decrease? Repeat this exercise for the reaction in Equation 20-2.

Answers to Your Turns are in the back of the book.

YOUR TURN **20.2**

Hydride reductions are not limited to ketones and aldehydes. Draw the product of the following reaction, and show that the nitrile undergoes reduction. *Hint*: Review Section 18.3b.

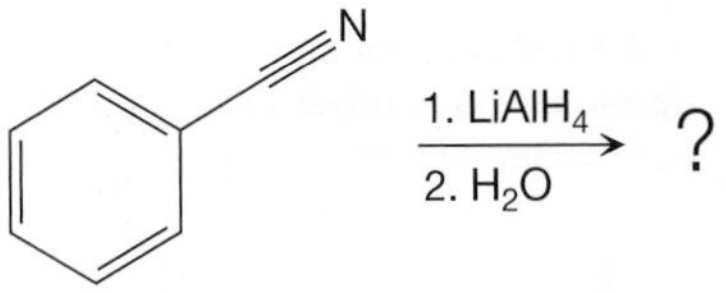

N
1. LiAlH$_4$
2. H$_2$O
?

Hydride reductions are not the only type of reaction in which an organic species is reduced. Consider the catalytic hydrogenation reaction shown in Equation 20-3, first presented in Section 13.9. Notice that two new C—H bonds form to the carbon atoms that make up the initial C=C bond. Therefore, these hydrogenation reactions are also reductions.

Reduction

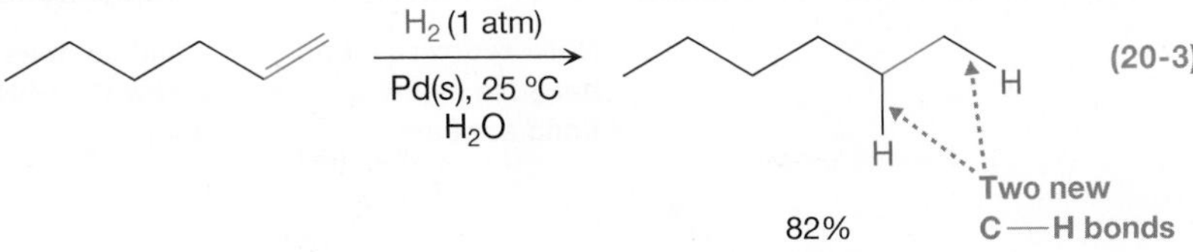

H$_2$ (1 atm)
Pd(s), 25 °C
H$_2$O
H
H
Two new C—H bonds
82%

(20-3)

Another reduction reaction we have previously encountered is the Wolff–Kishner reduction (Section 19.6), such as the one in Equation 20-4. In this case, both C—O bonds of the carbonyl group are lost, and two C—H bonds are gained.

Reduction

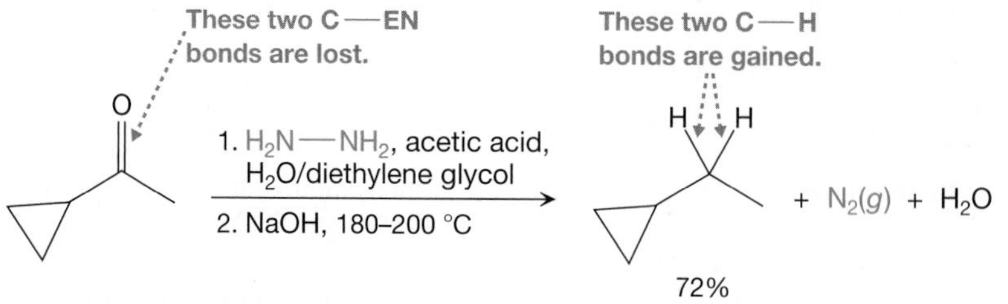

These two C—EN bonds are lost.
These two C—H bonds are gained.
O
H
H
1. $H_2N—NH_2$, acetic acid, H_2O/diethylene glycol
2. NaOH, 180–200 °C
+ $N_2(g)$ + H_2O
72%

Cyclopropylethanone **Ethylcyclopropane**

(20-4)

One type of oxidation reaction is epoxidation, which we first encountered in Section 13.3. As we can see in the example in Equation 20-5, two new C—O bonds are formed to the carbon atoms of the initial C═C bond:

Oxidation

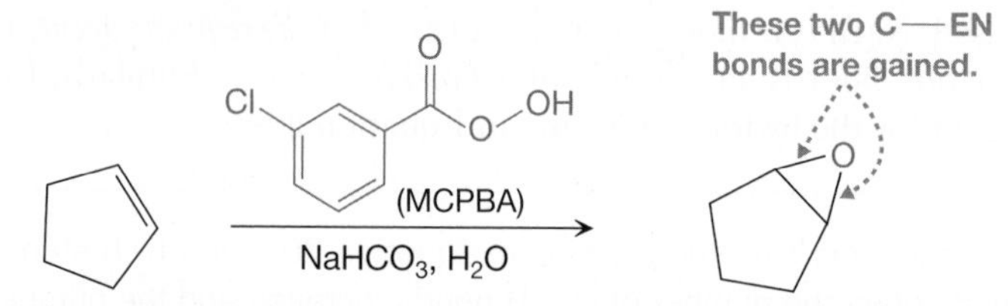

These two C—EN bonds are gained.
Cl
O
O
OH
(MCPBA)
$NaHCO_3$, H_2O
O

Cyclopentene **Cyclopentene oxide** 90%

(20-5)

Just as a reducing agent can be viewed as the species responsible for causing a reduction, an **oxidizing agent** can be viewed as the species responsible for causing an oxidation. For the oxidation in Equation 20-5, the peroxy acid (RCO_3H) is the oxidizing agent; it is the species that donates the oxygen atom involved in the new C—O bonds.

In addition to recognizing reactions as reductions or oxidations, it is also important to recognize when a reaction is *not* a redox reaction at all. For example, consider the nucleophilic substitution in Equation 20-6:

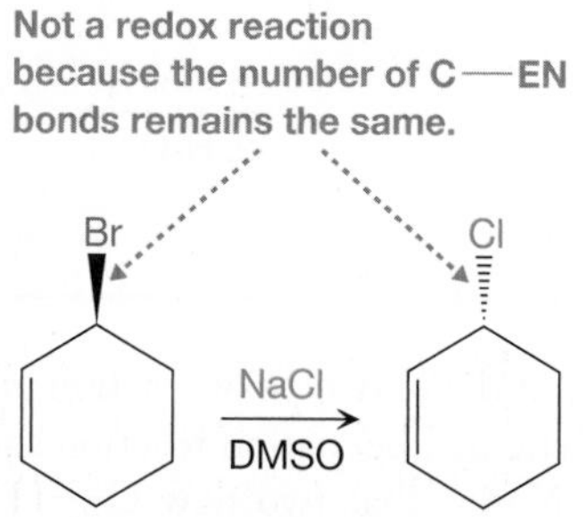

Not a redox reaction because the number of C—EN bonds remains the same.
Br
Cl
NaCl
DMSO

(20-6)

The only change to the bonding is the replacement of a C—Br bond with a C—Cl bond. Both Br and Cl are more electronegative than carbon, so the number of C—EN bonds remains unchanged, and the reaction is not a redox.

Equation 20-7 shows the addition of H_2O across a C═C double bond:

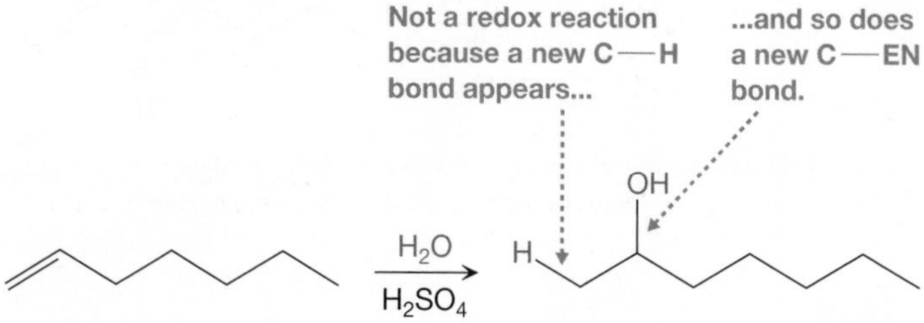

Not a redox reaction because a new C—H bond appears...
...and so does a new C—EN bond.
OH
H_2O
H_2SO_4
H

(20-7)

Even though the reaction produces a new C—H bond and a new C—EN bond, it is *not* a redox reaction. In general:

> When a particular functional group gains (or loses) the same number of C—H and C—EN bonds, the reaction is not classified as a redox.

SOLVED PROBLEM **20.1**

How to identify a reduction or oxidation from changes in C—H and C—EN bonds

Break It Down Determine whether the following acetal formation is a redox reaction. If it is, then does the transformation represent an oxidation or a reduction?

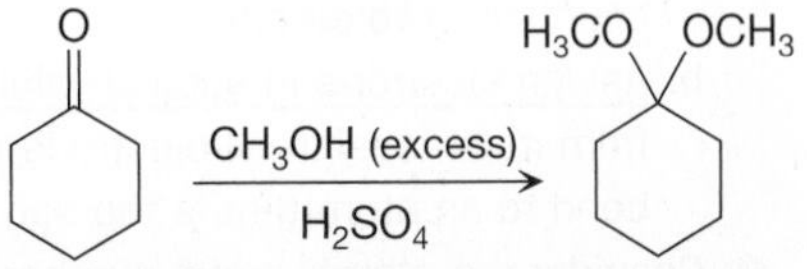
O
H3CO OCH3
CH3OH (excess)
H2SO4

Think	Solve
Does the organic species gain or lose any C—H bonds?	All of the C—H bonds that are initially part of cyclohexanone remain intact in the acetal product. Also, all of the C—H bonds in CH_3OH remain intact in the product. Therefore, the reaction does not change the number of C—H bonds.
Does the organic species gain or lose any C—EN bonds?	As shown here, two C—EN bonds make up the C=O bond in the ketone reactant. In the acetal product, the carbon that was the initial carbonyl carbon has two C—EN bonds: specifically, the two C—O bonds. Therefore, the reaction does not change the number of C—EN bonds. 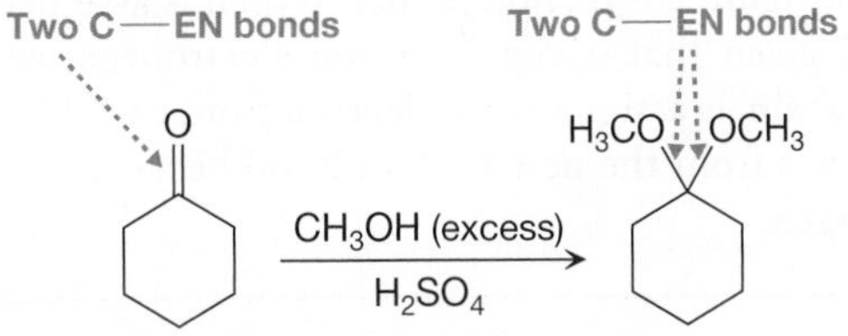 Two C—EN bonds Two C—EN bonds O H3CO OCH3 CH3OH (excess) H2SO4
What can we conclude from the number of C—H and C—EN bonds in the reactant and product?	Because there is no change to the number of C—H or C—EN bonds in the reaction, this transformation is not a redox reaction.

Try It Determine whether the following alkene bromination is a redox reaction. If it is, then does the transformation represent an oxidation or a reduction?

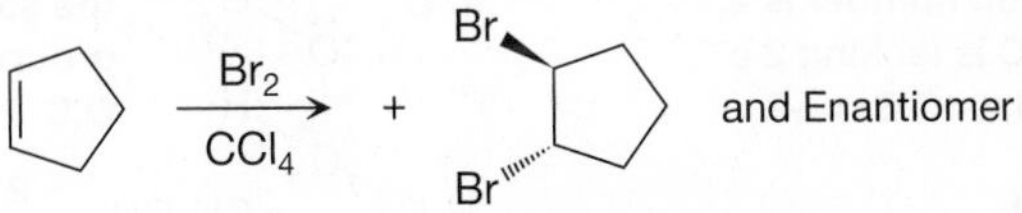
Br2
CCl4
Br
Br
+
and Enantiomer

Answers to all Try It exercises can be found in the Solutions Manual.

SECTION 20.2 OBJECTIVES

You will be able to:

1. Calculate the oxidation state of any atom in a species.
2. Keep track of changes in oxidation states to determine whether a species undergoes reduction or oxidation.

20.2 A Deeper Look: Calculating Oxidation States

In Section 20.1, we learned how to identify reduction and oxidation reactions by keeping track of the number of C—H and C—EN bonds (where EN represents an atom that is more electronegative than carbon). That method works because **oxidation state** represents the charge of an atom calculated according to the following rules:

Calculating an atom's oxidation state, O.S. (see Fig. 20-1)

1. Count the valence electrons on the atom in question.
   a. Assign lone pairs of electrons. Each lone pair of electrons on an atom counts as two electrons.
   b. Assign electrons in each covalent bond. For a bond to an atom different from itself, assign all electrons to the more electronegative atom. For a bond to an atom that is the same as itself, divide the electrons equally.
2. Consider the atom's group number. The group number is the number of valence electrons the atom would need to be uncharged.
3. Determine the excess or deficiency of electrons.
   a. If the number of assigned valence electrons equals the group number, the oxidation state is 0.
   b. For each excess valence electron, add −1 to the oxidation state.
   c. For each valence electron that is lacking, add +1 to the oxidation state.

◂ RECALL

Calculating an atom's oxidation state (O.S.) is similar to calculating its formal charge (F.C.; Section 1.9). Whereas F.C. calculations have us divide electrons in a covalent bond equally to the two atoms involved, O.S. calculations have us assign all electrons to the more electronegative atom.

In essence, this method to calculate oxidation states treats all bonds between different atoms as ionic rather than covalent (see Recall box).

Figure 20-1 illustrates how the oxidation state is calculated for the highlighted C atom in butan-2-one (Fig. 20-1a) and butan-2-ol (Fig. 20-1b), which are the reactant and product from Equation 20-1, respectively. In Figure 20-1a, notice that all four electrons of the C═O bond are assigned to oxygen because oxygen is more electronegative than carbon. The carbon atom is assigned one electron from each of the two C—C bonds because those bonds connect two of the same atom.

In Figure 20-1b, notice that oxygen is assigned both electrons from the O—C bond, given that oxygen is more electronegative than carbon. The carbon atom, once again, is assigned one electron from each C—C bond. It is also assigned both electrons from the new C—H bond because carbon is more electronegative than hydrogen.

YOUR TURN 20.3

Determine the oxidation state of the oxygen atom in Figure 20-1a and 20-1b.

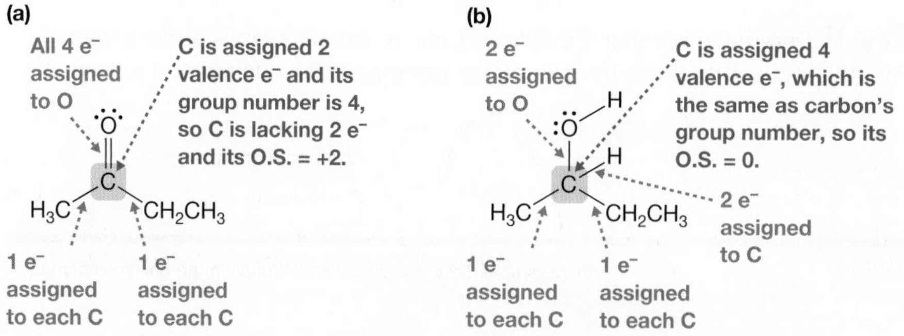

(a)
All 4 e⁻ assigned to O
C is assigned 2 valence e⁻ and its group number is 4, so C is lacking 2 e⁻ and its O.S. = +2.
H3C
CH2CH3
1 e⁻ assigned to each C
1 e⁻ assigned to each C
(b)
2 e⁻ assigned to O
C is assigned 4 valence e⁻, which is the same as carbon's group number, so its O.S. = 0.
2 e⁻ assigned to C
H3C
CH2CH3
1 e⁻ assigned to each C
1 e⁻ assigned to each C

FIGURE 20-1 Determining an atom's oxidation state (a) The carbonyl carbon (highlighted in blue) is assigned two valence electrons (one from each C—C bond), which is two fewer than its group number of 4, so its O.S. = +2. (b) The alcohol carbon (highlighted in blue) is assigned one electron from each C—C bond, and because it is more electronegative than hydrogen, it is also assigned the two electrons from the C—H bond. Carbon therefore has four total valence electrons, which is the same as its group number, so its O.S. = 0.

From the results in Figure 20-1a and 20-1b, we can now reexamine the reaction from Equation 20-1 to see that the carbonyl carbon in butan-2-one undergoes a change in oxidation state:

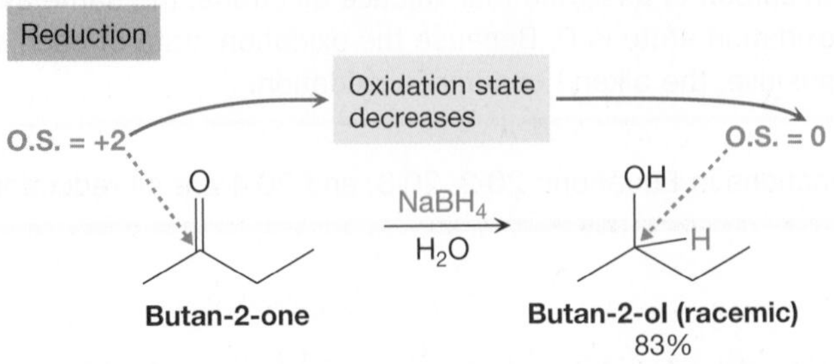
Reduction
Oxidation state decreases
O.S. = +2
O.S. = 0
NaBH4
H2O
Butan-2-one
Butan-2-ol (racemic)
83%

(20-8)

More specifically, the carbonyl carbon's oxidation state *decreases* from +2 to 0, so butan-2-one is indeed undergoing reduction.

SOLVED PROBLEM **20.2**

How to calculate oxidation states to identify a reduction or oxidation

Break It Down **The epoxidation reaction from Equation 20-5 is repeated here. Use oxidation states to verify that the alkene undergoes oxidation in this reaction.**

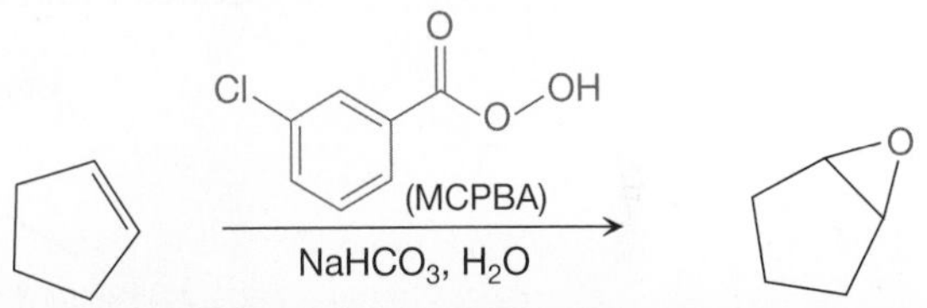
(MCPBA)
NaHCO3, H2O

Think	Solve
In the alkene, which atoms undergo changes in bonding?	Only the carbon atoms of the C═C bond undergo bonding changes, so those are the only atoms whose oxidation states could change.
In the alkene reactant, how many lone pairs are on each of those carbons? How many valence electrons are assigned to each carbon from its C═C, C—C, and C—H bonds?	As shown here on the left, each carbon is assigned two of the four electrons from the C═C bond and one of the two electrons from the C—C bond. Each carbon is also assigned both electrons of the C—H bond because carbon is more electronegative than hydrogen. Therefore, each carbon is assigned a total of five valence electrons. 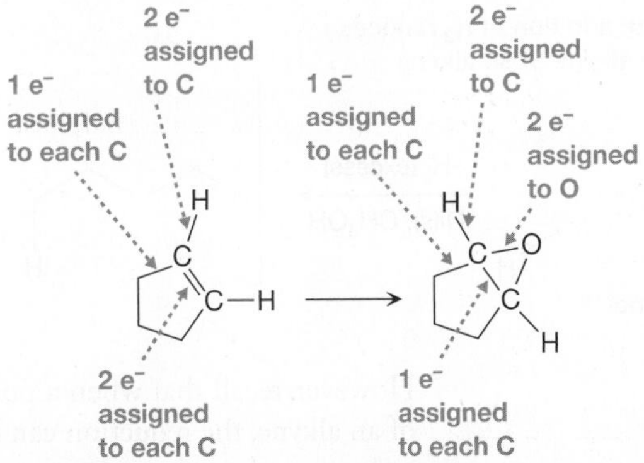
In the epoxide product, how do we assign valence electrons to those carbon atoms?	As shown above on the right, each carbon is assigned one electron from each of its two C—C bonds and both electrons from its C—H bond. The carbon is not assigned any electrons from its C—O bond because oxygen is more electronegative than carbon. Therefore, each carbon is assigned a total four valence electrons.

2 e⁻ assigned to C
1 e⁻ assigned to each C
2 e⁻ assigned to each C
2 e⁻ assigned to C
1 e⁻ assigned to each C
2 e⁻ assigned to O
1 e⁻ assigned to each C

(continued)

How do you calculate each carbon's oxidation state from the number of its assigned valence electrons?	In the alkene, each carbon of the C═C bond is assigned five valence electrons, which is one more than carbon's group number of 4, so the oxidation state is −1. In the epoxide, each carbon is assigned four valence electrons, the same as its group number, so the oxidation state is 0. Because the oxidation state of each carbon becomes more positive, the alkene undergoes oxidation.

Try It Use oxidation states to verify that the reactions in Equations 20-2, 20-3, and 20-4 are all reductions.

SECTION 20.3 OBJECTIVES

You will be able to:

1. Predict the catalytic hydrogenation product of an alkene, alkyne, aldehyde, ketone, nitrile, and amide.
2. Incorporate a selective catalytic hydrogenation in a synthesis.

20.3 Catalytic Hydrogenation: A Review of Alkene and Alkyne Reductions, Reductions of Other Functional Groups, and Selectivity

In Section 13.9, we learned that an alkene can undergo catalytic hydrogenation when treated with $H_2(g)$ and a metal catalyst such as Ni, Pt, or Pd:

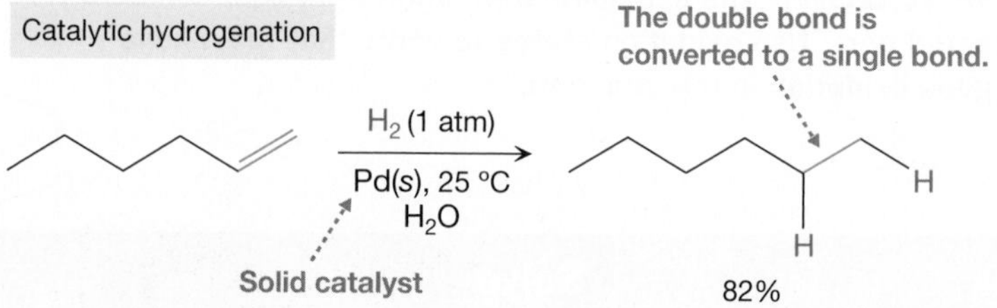
Catalytic hydrogenation
The double bond is converted to a single bond.
H2 (1 atm)
Pd(s), 25 °C
H2O
Solid catalyst
H
H
82%

(20-9)

From our earlier discussions here in Chapter 20, we also know that the alkene undergoes *reduction* in this type of reaction.

YOUR TURN 20.4

Draw the product when cyclohexene is treated with $H_2(g)$ in the presence of Pt.

When an alkyne undergoes complete hydrogenation, as shown in Equation 20-10, it is reduced to an alkane:

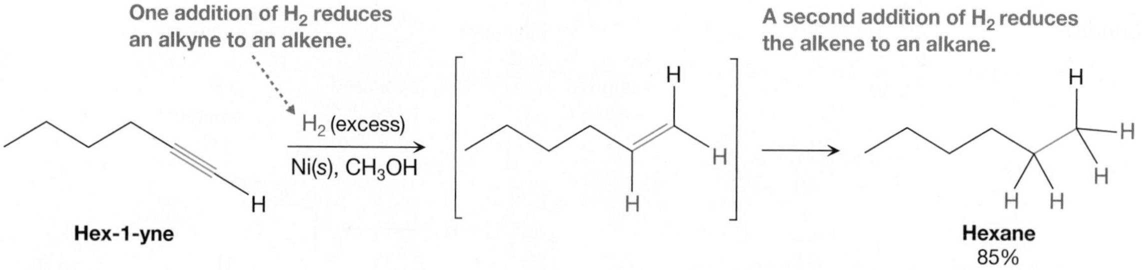
One addition of H2 reduces an alkyne to an alkene.
A second addition of H2 reduces the alkene to an alkane.
H2 (excess)
Ni(s), CH3OH
H
Hex-1-yne
Hexane
85%

(20-10)

◀ RECALL

As we saw in Section 13.9, a poisoned catalyst is used to slow the reaction so the reduction can be stopped after just the first addition. In such cases, both H atoms add to the same side of the C═C bond to produce a cis alkene.

However, recall that when a poisoned catalyst is used for the catalytic hydrogenation of an alkyne, the reduction can be stopped at the cis alkene stage (see Recall box):

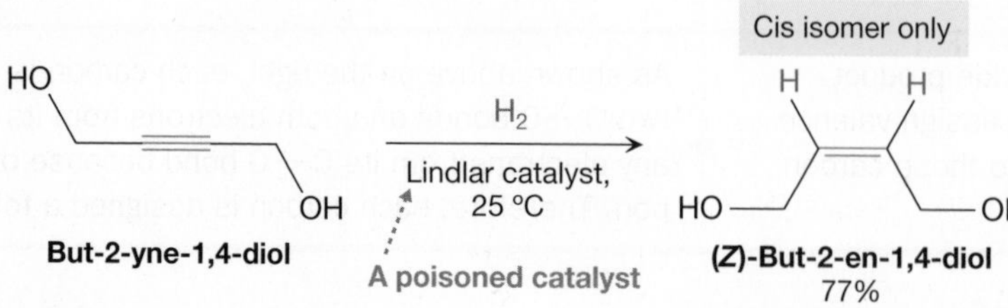
Cis isomer only
HO
OH
H2
Lindlar catalyst,
25 °C
A poisoned catalyst
But-2-yne-1,4-diol
(Z)-But-2-en-1,4-diol
77%

(20-11)

TABLE 20-1 Reduction of Various Functional Groups via Catalytic Hydrogenation

Reactant	Reaction Conditions	Product
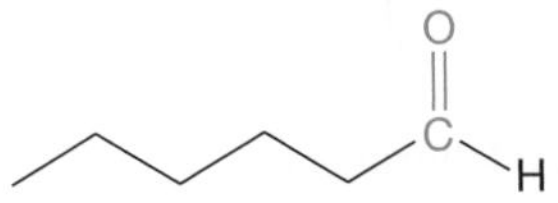 Aldehyde	H_2 → Pt, 20 °C, 1 atm	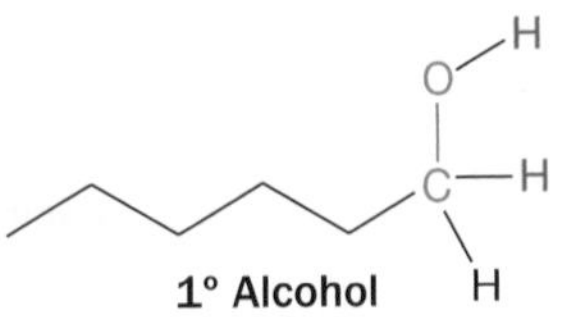 1° Alcohol
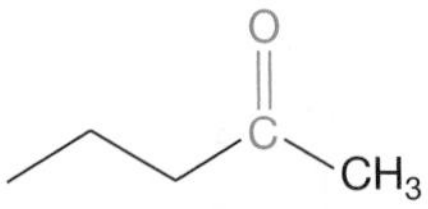 Ketone	H_2 → Rh, 50 °C, 3 atm	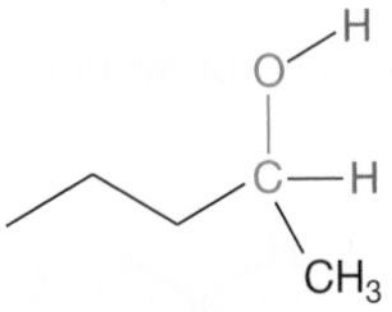 2° Alcohol
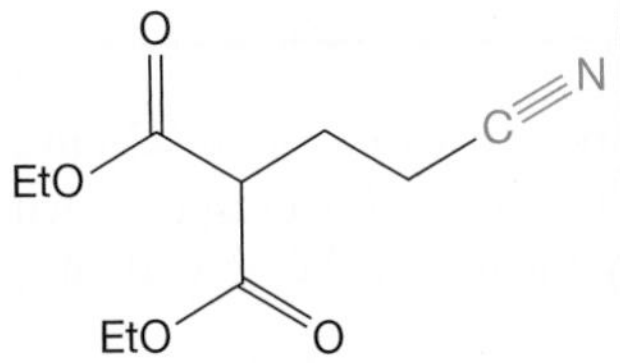 Nitrile	H_2 → Raney Ni, 80 °C, 75 atm	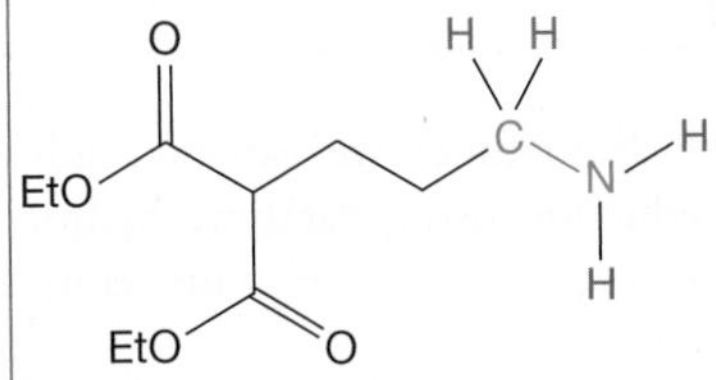 1° Amine
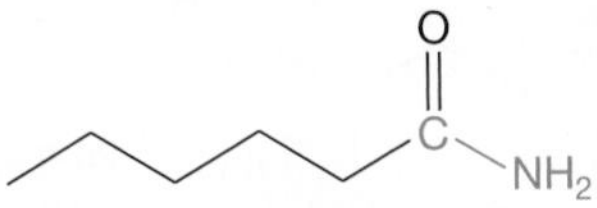 1° Amide	1 equiv H_2 → Pt, 250 °C, 200 atm (<50% yield)	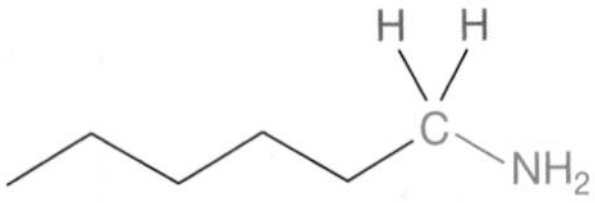 1° Amine

Catalytic hydrogenation is not limited to the reduction of alkenes and alkynes. As Table 20-1 shows, a variety of other functional groups can be reduced using catalytic hydrogenation, too, though not with equal ease. Pay particular attention to the typical experimental conditions required.

Notice, in particular, that with Pt as the catalyst:

> The reduction of an aldehyde takes place under mild conditions that are similar to the conditions for reduction of an alkene or alkyne.

Other functional groups are more difficult to reduce, and their reactions generally proceed with poorer yields. This is particularly true for the reduction of amides to amines, because the product amine poisons (i.e., deactivates) the metal catalyst. If you try to force the reaction by increasing the temperature or pressure of H_2, then the risk of unwanted side reactions increases (see Looking Ahead box).

▸ LOOKING AHEAD

In Section 22.6 we will see how $LiAlH_4$ can be used to reduce amides to amines in good yield.

Because the catalytic hydrogenation of various functional groups can require very different reaction conditions, we can often use catalytic hydrogenation to carry out a *selective* reduction. More to the point, alkenes, alkynes, and aldehydes are reduced under mild conditions, so:

> The functional groups that characterize alkenes, alkynes, and aldehydes can be selectively reduced when functional groups that characterize ketones, nitriles, and amides are also present.

An example of selective reduction is shown in Equation 20-12:

Catalytic hydrogenation selectively reduces an alkene's C=C relative to a ketone's C=O.

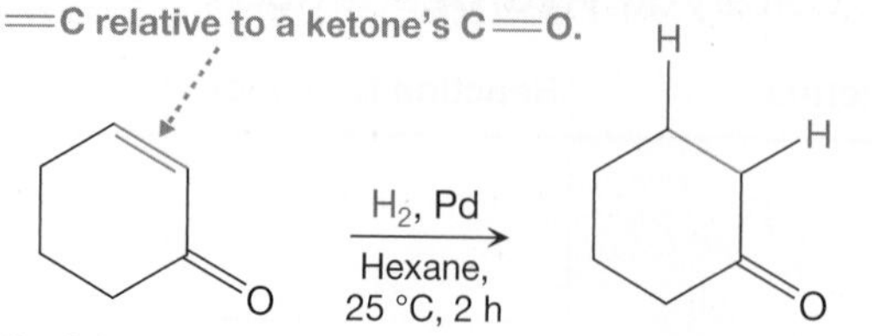

H
H
O
H_2, Pd
Hexane,
25 °C, 2 h
O

Cyclohex-2-enone **Cyclohexanone** 99% (20-12)

YOUR TURN 20.5

Show how you would carry out this synthesis.

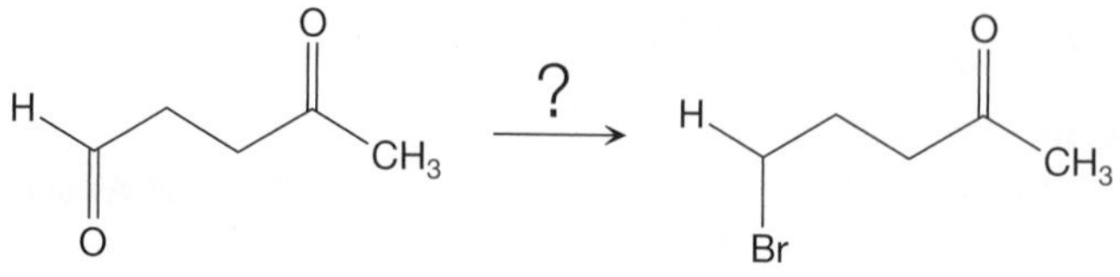

O
H
CH3
O
?
O
H
CH3
Br

> **CONNECTIONS 20.1**
>
> **When life gives you lemons** Limonene (Eq. 20-13) is a monoterpene that occurs naturally in the rinds of lemons and other citrus fruits, contributing to their distinctive aromas. The compound is used as a fragrance additive in consumer products, is sold as a dietary supplement, and is also a natural insecticide.

Sometimes we can take advantage of steric hindrance to carry out a selective reduction using catalytic hydrogenation. Equation 20-13 shows, for example, that treating limonene with one equivalent of H_2 reduces only the terminal C=C double bond:

The less sterically hindered C=C double bond is selectively reduced.

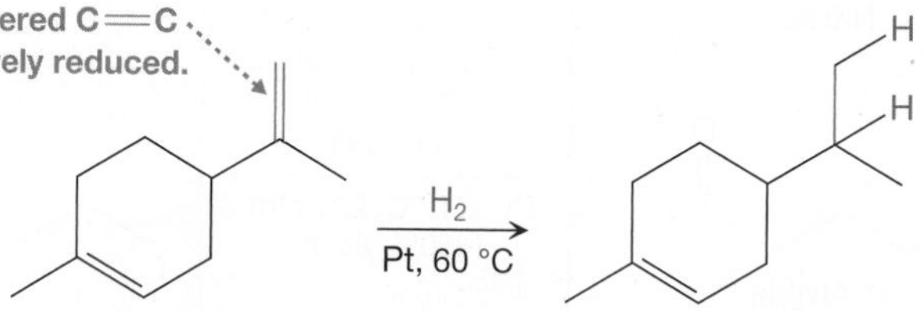

H_2
Pt, 60 °C
H
H

Limonene 97% (20-13)

The terminal C=C bond is less substituted, so it is less sterically hindered. In general:

> Catalytic hydrogenation is more favored at a less sterically hindered multiple bond than at a more sterically hindered one.

With more steric bulk surrounding the double bond, it is more difficult for the alkene to adsorb to the surface of the metal catalyst—a critical step in catalytic hydrogenation (review Fig. 13-6c, p. 679).

YOUR TURN 20.6

There are two possible syn addition products in the catalytic hydrogenation of α-pinene, **A** and **B**, but one of them is formed exclusively. Which one? Why?

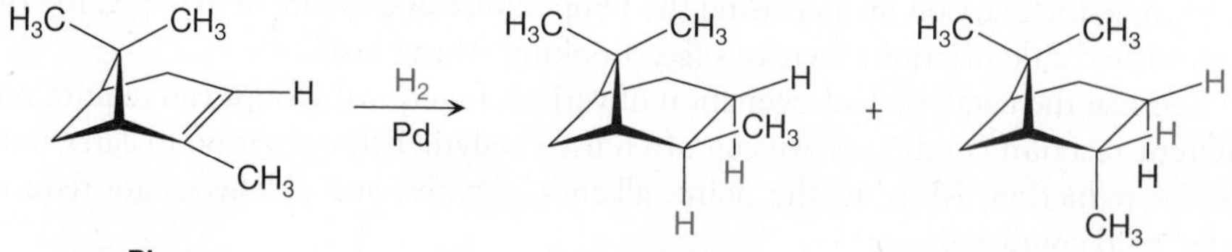

H3C
CH3
H
CH3
H_2
Pd
H3C
CH3
H
CH3
H
H
+
H3C
CH3
H
H
H
CH3

α-Pinene **A** **B**

20.4 Reactions That Reduce C═O to CH_2: Wolff–Kishner, Clemmensen, and Raney-Nickel Reductions

SECTION 20.4 OBJECTIVES

You will be able to:

1. Predict the product when a ketone or aldehyde undergoes a Wolff–Kishner, Clemmensen, or Raney-nickel reduction.
2. Incorporate a Wolff–Kishner, Clemmensen, or Raney-nickel reduction in a synthesis in a way that avoids unwanted side reactions.

In Section 19.6, we learned that a **Wolff–Kishner reduction** will convert the carbonyl (C═O) group of a ketone or aldehyde into a methylene (CH_2) group (see Recall box):

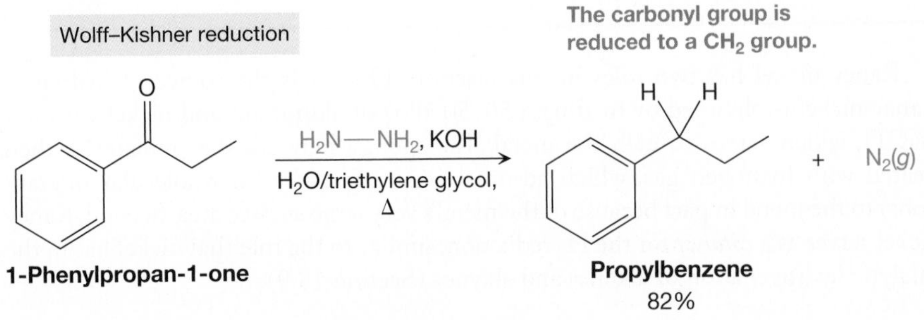
Wolff–Kishner reduction
The carbonyl group is reduced to a CH2 group.
O
H H
H2N—NH2, KOH
H2O/triethylene glycol, Δ
+ N2(g) + H2O
1-Phenylpropan-1-one
Propylbenzene
82%

(20-14)

Earlier in this chapter, we verified that such a reaction indeed results in the reduction of the ketone or aldehyde.

The Wolff–Kishner reduction is not the only reaction that reduces the C═O group of a ketone or aldehyde to a CH_2 group. The **Clemmensen reduction**, named after Danish chemist Erik Christian Clemmensen (1876–1941), accomplishes this transformation, too. An example of a Clemmensen reduction is shown in Equation 20-15:

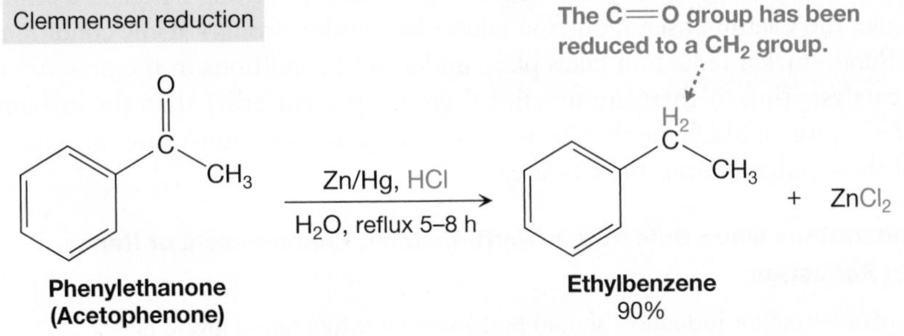
Clemmensen reduction
The C═O group has been reduced to a CH2 group.
O
C
CH3
Zn/Hg, HCl
H2O, reflux 5–8 h
H2
C
CH3
+ ZnCl2
Phenylethanone
(Acetophenone)
Ethylbenzene
90%

(20-15)

◂ RECALL

Section 19.6 explained that in a Wolff–Kishner reduction, hydrazine (H_2NNH_2) reacts with the carbonyl group of a ketone or aldehyde to produce a hydrazone, characterized by a C═N—N group. Heating the hydrazone under basic conditions eliminates $N_2(g)$ to generate the CH_2 group in the product.

The Clemmensen reduction uses a **zinc amalgam**, which is an alloy (blend) of zinc and mercury. The ketone or aldehyde is refluxed (i.e., continually evaporated and recondensed under heat) with the amalgam in a concentrated HCl solution. HCl is the source of the protons that form bonds to the carbonyl C. The zinc metal acts as a reducing agent; it is oxidized on going from elemental Zn, or Zn(0), to Zn(+2) represented by $ZnCl_2$ in Equation 20-15. As the reaction proceeds, the metal dissolves into solution as an ion, which is why it is called a **dissolving metal reduction** (see Looking Ahead box).

A third reaction that reduces the carbonyl group of a ketone or aldehyde to a methylene group is the **Raney-nickel reduction**, developed by Murray Raney (1885–1966), a mechanical engineer. An example is shown in Equation 20-16:

▸ LOOKING AHEAD

In Chapter 27, we will see how an alkyne can be reduced to a trans alkene by a dissolving metal reduction that involves radical intermediates, species that contain unpaired electrons.

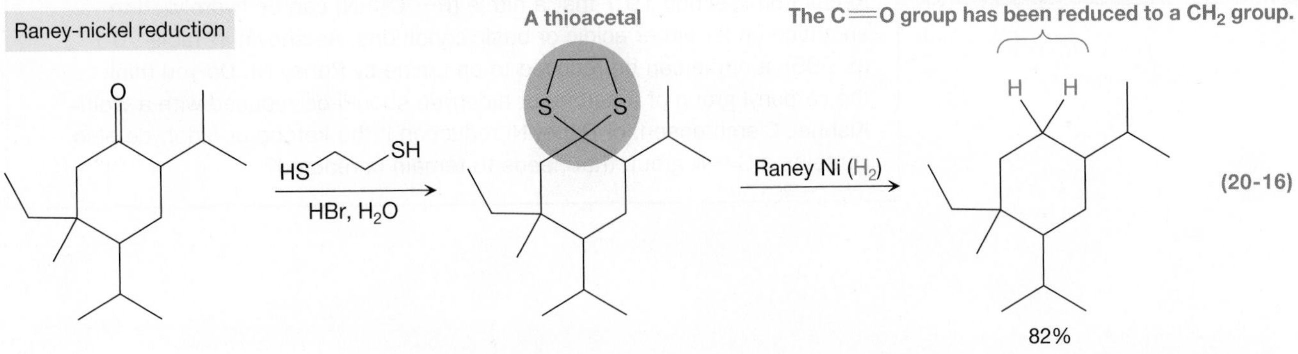
Raney-nickel reduction
A thioacetal
The C═O group has been reduced to a CH2 group.
O
HS SH
HBr, H2O
S S
Raney Ni (H2)
H H
82%

(20-16)

In a Raney-nickel reduction, the ketone or aldehyde is first converted to a *thioacetal* by treatment with a thiol under acidic conditions. A thioacetal is analogous to an acetal, but with sulfur atoms in place of oxygen atoms, and the mechanism for the formation of the thioacetal is the same as the mechanism for acetal formation introduced in Section 19.4a (see Your Turn 20.7). Subsequent treatment with **Raney nickel** converts the thioacetal group into a methylene group.

YOUR TURN 20.7

Draw the mechanism for the formation of the thioacetal in Equation 20-16.

GREEN CHEMISTRY Raney nickel (Eq. 20-16) is very reactive and will ignite spontaneously on contact with atmospheric oxygen, so it must be kept under an inert liquid or an inert gas. For this reason, Wolff–Kishner and Clemmensen reductions are often preferred over Raney-nickel reductions when all else is equal.

Raney nickel has two roles in this reaction. First, it is the source of hydrogen. Raney nickel is obtained by treating a 50:50 alloy of aluminum and nickel with hot NaOH, which serves to etch the metal. The spongy network that remains is then treated with hydrogen gas, which adsorbs (accumulates by intermolecular interactions) to the metal in part because of the metal's very large surface area. Second, Raney nickel serves as a *catalyst* for the H_2 reduction, similar to the role that nickel has in the catalytic hydrogenation of alkenes and alkynes (Section 13.9).

20.4a Limitations of the Wolff–Kishner, Clemmensen, and Raney-Nickel Reductions

The Wolff–Kishner, Clemmensen, and Raney-nickel reactions reduce the carbonyl group of a ketone or aldehyde to a methylene group, but notice in Equations 20-14, 20-15, and 20-16 that the three reactions take place under different conditions. The Wolff–Kishner reduction takes place with HO^-, which is a strong base and a strong nucleophile; the Clemmensen reduction takes place under strongly acidic conditions; and the Raney-nickel reduction takes place under mild conditions in the presence of a metal catalyst. Thus, if there are functional groups present other than the carbonyl group of a ketone or aldehyde that we want to reduce, then we must carefully choose which of these reduction reactions to use.

Considerations when Selecting a Wolff–Kishner, Clemmensen, or Raney-Nickel Reduction

- The Wolff–Kishner reduction should be avoided if a functional group is present that is susceptible to reaction under basic conditions or with strong nucleophiles.
- The Clemmensen reduction should be avoided if a functional group is present that is susceptible to reaction under acidic conditions.
- The Raney-nickel reduction should be avoided if a functional group is present that is susceptible to reaction with nucleophilic thiols (RSH) or with H_2 in the presence of a metal catalyst.

YOUR TURN 20.8

Recall from Section 19.7 that a nitrile (R—C≡N) can be hydrolyzed to an amide under either acidic or basic conditions. As shown in Table 20-1 (p. 995), a nitrile can be reduced to an amine by Raney Ni. Do you think the carbonyl group of a ketone or aldehyde should be reduced with a Wolff–Kishner, Clemmensen, or Raney-Ni reduction if the ketone or aldehyde also contains a C≡N group that needs to remain unreacted?

SOLVED PROBLEM **20.3**

How to determine whether a Wolff–Kishner, Clemmensen, or Raney-nickel reduction is appropriate to use

Break It Down **Which reduction reaction(s)—the Wolff–Kishner, Clemmensen, or Raney nickel—can be used to carry out the following transformation?**

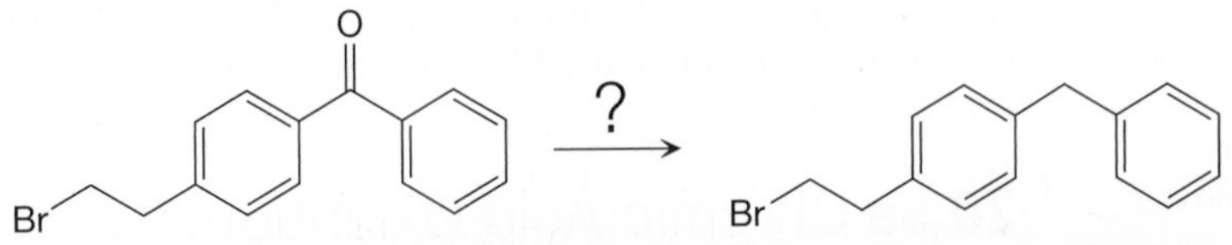

Think	Solve
What is the desired transformation? What functional groups do we want to leave unchanged?	The intention is to reduce the carbonyl group characterizing a ketone to a methylene (CH_2) group. The C—Br group characterizing an alkyl halide should be left alone, and so should the two aromatic rings.
Will the conditions for a Wolff–Kishner reduction cause the C—Br group or an aromatic ring to react?	HO^- and hydrazine (H_2NNH_2) are both nucleophiles that would cause an S_N2 reaction at the C—Br group. Furthermore, HO^- is a strong base that would cause an E2 reaction involving the C—Br group. Therefore, a Wolff–Kishner reduction should be avoided.
Will the conditions for a Clemmensen reduction cause the C—Br group or an aromatic ring to react?	Neither the C—Br group nor the aromatic rings are susceptible to reaction with HCl, so the Clemmensen reduction could be used for this transformation.
Will the conditions for a Raney-nickel reduction cause the C—Br group or an aromatic ring to react?	Although an alkene would be reduced under the catalytic hydrogenation conditions (H_2 and nickel), the aromatic rings are unreactive. However, the thiol (RSH) that would be used is nucleophilic and would cause an S_N2 reaction at the C—Br group. Therefore, a Raney-nickel reduction should be avoided.

Try It Which reduction reaction(s)—the Wolff–Kishner, Clemmensen, or Raney nickel—can be used for each of the following transformations?

(a)

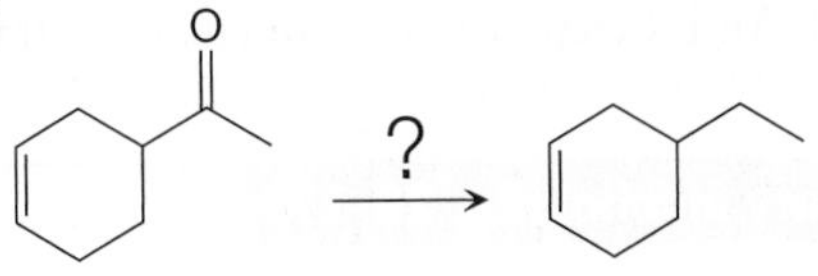

(b)

(c)

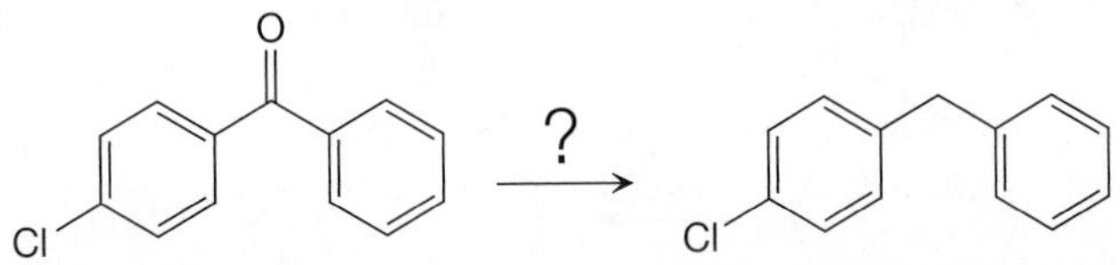

SECTION 20.5 OBJECTIVES

You will be able to:

1. Predict the product when an alcohol or aldehyde is treated with an oxidizing agent such as chromic acid, pyridinium chlorochromate (PCC), or potassium permanganate.
2. Explain why the absence of water is important when PCC is used to oxidize a primary alcohol to an aldehyde.
3. Incorporate the oxidation of an alcohol or an aldehyde into a synthesis.

20.5 Oxidations of Alcohols and Aldehydes

We have discussed a variety of reduction reactions so far, including hydride reductions involving $NaBH_4$ and $LiAlH_4$, as well as catalytic hydrogenation.

To have greater flexibility in designing a synthesis, however, it is important to be able to carry out oxidation reactions as well. As we learned in Section 20.1, these oxidations can be done by carrying out reactions that increase the number of C—EN bonds (where EN represents an atom that is more electronegative than carbon) or decrease the number of C—H bonds. We present two types of oxidizing agents that can be used for these kinds of reactions: *chromic acid* and *potassium permanganate*.

20.5a Chromic Acid Oxidation

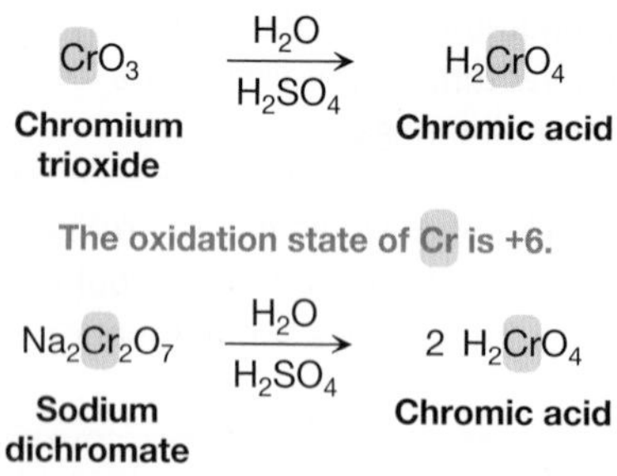

CrO_3
H_2O
H_2SO_4
H_2CrO_4
Chromium trioxide
Chromic acid
The oxidation state of Cr is +6.
$Na_2Cr_2O_7$
H_2O
H_2SO_4
2 H_2CrO_4
Sodium dichromate
Chromic acid

FIGURE 20-2 Chromium oxidizing agents CrO_3, $Na_2Cr_2O_7$, and H_2CrO_4 all contain Cr(+6). H_2CrO_4 is produced from either CrO_3 or $Na_2Cr_2O_7$ by treatment with aqueous acid.

Chromic acid (H_2CrO_4) is prepared by dissolving either chromium trioxide (CrO_3) or sodium dichromate ($Na_2Cr_2O_7$) in an acidic aqueous solution (**Figure 20-2**). A molecule of water adds to the starting material in both reactions. Furthermore, the oxidation state of chromium is +6 in all three forms: CrO_3, $Na_2Cr_2O_7$, and H_2CrO_4.

A chromic acid oxidation, also called a **Jones oxidation** after the Welsh organic chemist Sir Ewart Jones (1911–2002), is the oxidation of a primary or secondary alcohol with chromic acid acting as the oxidizing agent. An example is shown in Equation 20-17, in which cyclooctanol is oxidized to cyclooctanone:

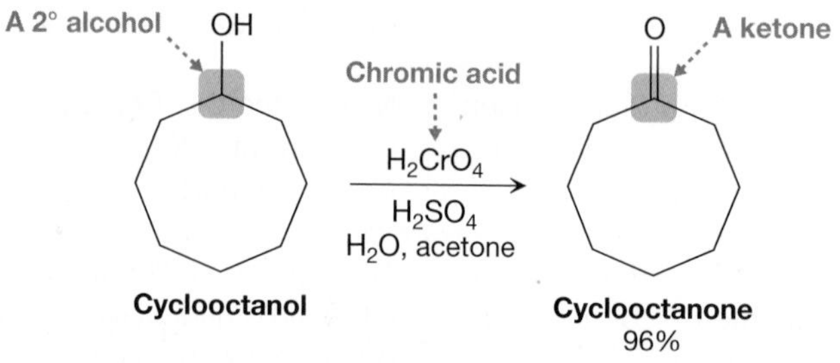

A 2° alcohol
OH
Chromic acid
H_2CrO_4
H_2SO_4
H_2O, acetone
O
A ketone
Cyclooctanol
Cyclooctanone
96%

(20-17)

In general:

Chromic acid oxidizes a secondary alcohol to a ketone.

The mechanism for this reaction is believed to involve a **chromate ester** as a key intermediate, shown in Equation 20-18. An E2 step on the chromate ester then produces the ketone.

Partial mechanism for the chromic acid oxidation of a secondary alcohol (Eq. 20-17)

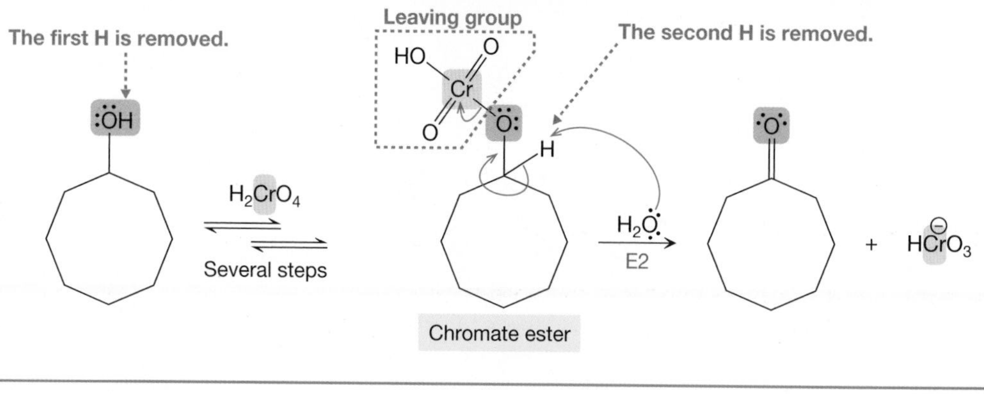

The first H is removed.
:ÖH
H_2CrO_4
Several steps
Leaving group
HO
O
Cr
O
Ö:
H
The second H is removed.
Chromate ester
$H_2\ddot{O}$:
E2
:Ö:
+
$HCrO_3^-$

(20-18)

Notice in Equation 20-18 that two H atoms must be removed: one from the OH group and one from the adjacent C atom. Therefore:

Oxidation by H_2CrO_4 requires an OH group that is attached to a C atom bonded to at least one H atom.

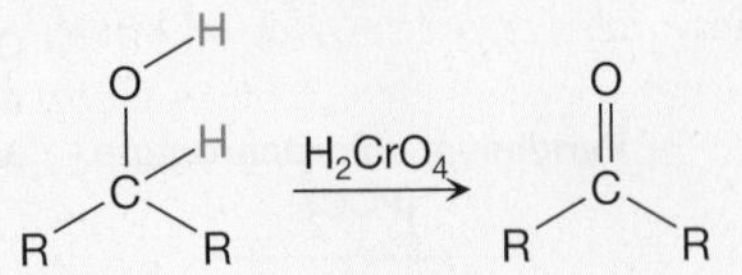

Note that the tertiary alcohol in Equation 20-19 is *not* oxidized when treated with chromic acid because the indicated carbon has no additional bond to a H atom:

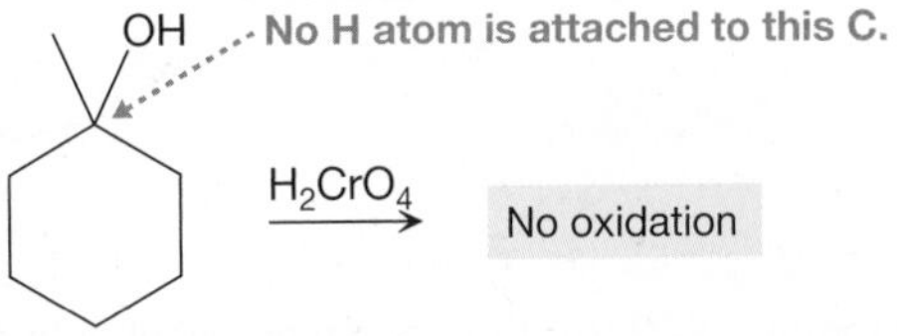

OH
No H atom is attached to this C.
H2CrO4
No oxidation

(20-19)

A primary alcohol, on the other hand, *is* oxidizable because the alcohol carbon is bonded to at least one hydrogen. An example is shown in Equation 20-20:

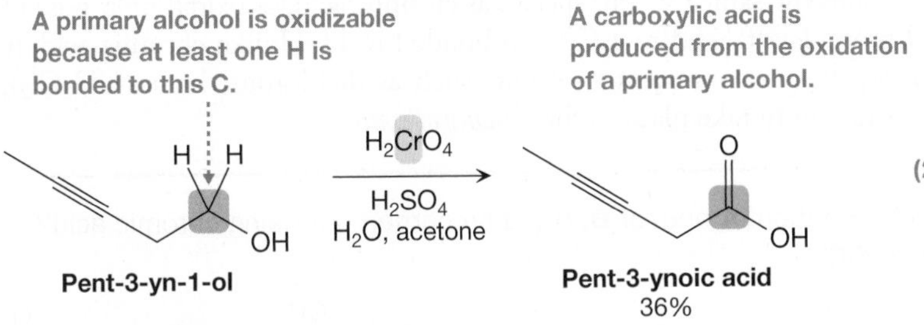

A primary alcohol is oxidizable because at least one H is bonded to this C.
A carboxylic acid is produced from the oxidation of a primary alcohol.
H2CrO4
H2SO4
H2O, acetone
Pent-3-yn-1-ol
Pent-3-ynoic acid
36%

(20-20)

The oxidation product, a carboxylic acid, is different from the ketone obtained in the oxidation of a secondary alcohol.

Chromic acid oxidizes a primary alcohol to a carboxylic acid.

◂ RECALL

A hydrate is characterized by the HO—C—OH group. In Section 18.2, we saw that a hydrate forms by nucleophilic addition to the carbonyl group of the ketone or aldehyde. In Section 19.1, we saw that such reactions can be catalyzed by acid or base.

As shown in Equation 20-21, an aldehyde is initially produced when the H atoms on adjacent C and O atoms are removed. Water is present in solution, however, so the aldehyde equilibrates with its *hydrate* (see Recall box). In that hydrate, an OH is attached to CH, which allows a second oxidation to take place.

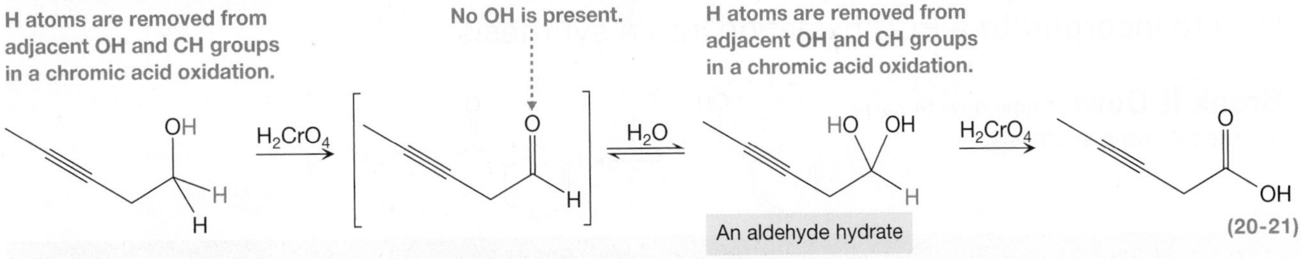

H atoms are removed from adjacent OH and CH groups in a chromic acid oxidation.
No OH is present.
H atoms are removed from adjacent OH and CH groups in a chromic acid oxidation.
H2CrO4
H2O
H2CrO4
An aldehyde hydrate

(20-21)

YOUR TURN 20.9

Draw the mechanism that shows the conversion of the aldehyde in Equation 20-21 into the hydrate. *Hint*: Notice that the reaction takes place under acidic conditions.

GREEN CHEMISTRY

Compounds that contain Cr(+6), such as H_2CrO_4 and PCC, are toxic and carcinogenic. When possible, greener oxidizing agents should be used. For example, the *Swern oxidation* can be used to oxidize primary and secondary alcohols to aldehydes and ketones, respectively, similar to the outcomes with PCC.

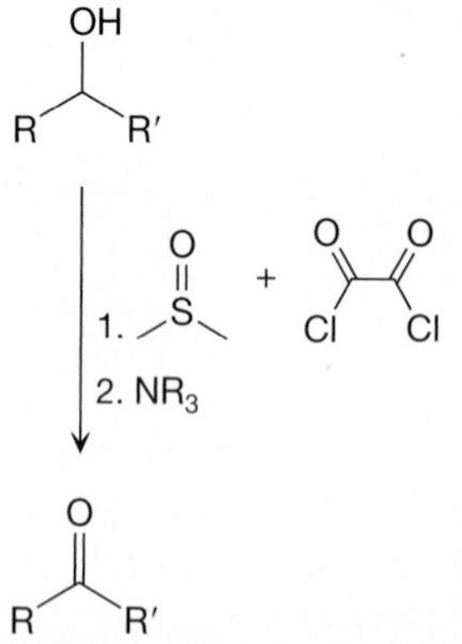
OH
R
R′
1.
2. NR₃
O
S
+
O
O
Cl
Cl
O
R
R′

Given the role that water plays in the oxidation of a primary alcohol to a carboxylic acid, the oxidation would have to stop at the aldehyde stage in the absence of water. Chromic acid cannot be used in such an oxidation, however, because water is required to produce chromic acid in the first place (see Fig. 20-2). Instead, as Equation 20-22 shows, **pyridinium chlorochromate (PCC)** can be used as the oxidizing agent:

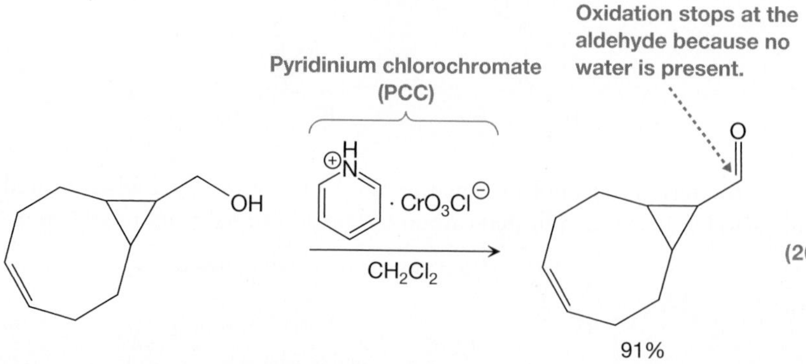
Oxidation stops at the aldehyde because no water is present.
Pyridinium chlorochromate (PCC)
OH
H
N
· CrO₃Cl
CH₂Cl₂
O
91%

(20-22)

Pyridinium chlorochromate (PCC) oxidizes a primary alcohol to an aldehyde and a secondary alcohol to a ketone.

PCC contains the same Cr(+6) species as chromic acid, so oxidation is possible when an OH group is attached to a C atom bonded to H. Unlike chromic acid, however, PCC is soluble in nonaqueous solvents such as dichloromethane (CH_2Cl_2), which allows oxidation to take place in the *absence of water*.

YOUR TURN **20.10**

Which oxidation, **A** and/or **B**, could be carried out using chromic acid? Using PCC?

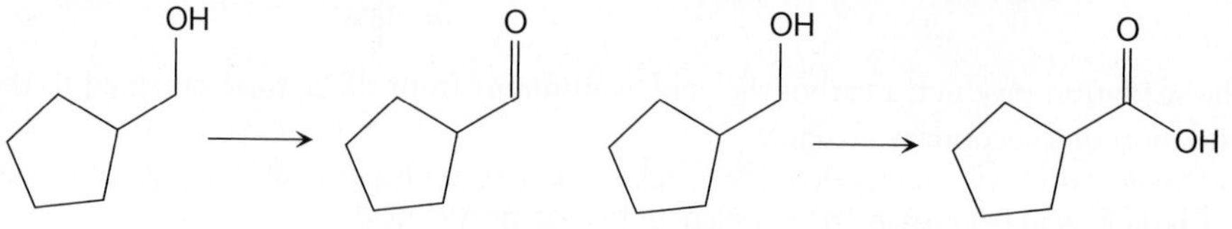
OH
O
OH
O
OH

A **B**

SOLVED PROBLEM **20.4**

How to incorporate a PCC oxidation into a synthesis

Break It Down Show how to carry out the following synthesis.

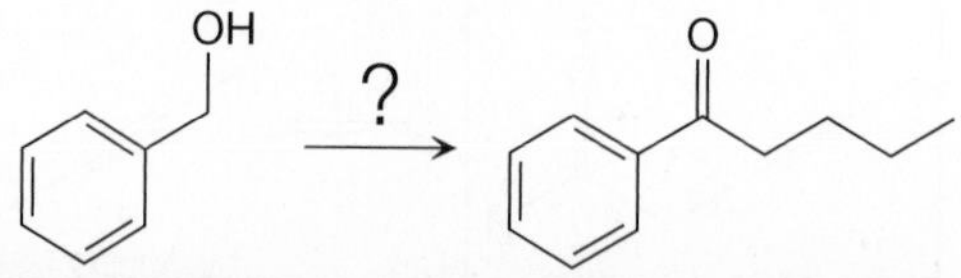
OH
?
O

Think	Solve
Does the synthesis require the formation of a C—C bond? Which C—C bond?	The C—C bond indicated must be formed. 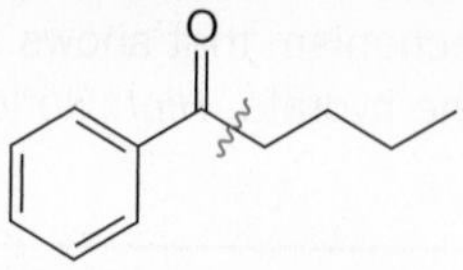 O

(continued)

Have we learned a reaction that will form such a bond and leave us with a ketone? If not, can the ketone be produced from the product of another carbon–carbon bond-forming reaction?

None of the reactions we have learned will form a bond between a carbonyl carbon and an α carbon and leave us with a ketone. However, the ketone could be produced from the oxidation of the corresponding alcohol, as shown below. That alcohol, in turn, could be the product of a Grignard reaction that would form the C—C bond.

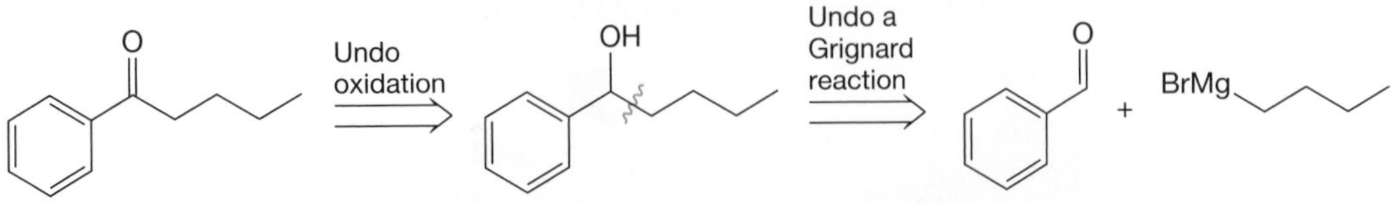
O
Undo oxidation
OH
Undo a Grignard reaction
O
BrMg
+

How can the aldehyde be produced from the starting alcohol?

Benzaldehyde can be made from benzyl alcohol by an oxidation reaction.

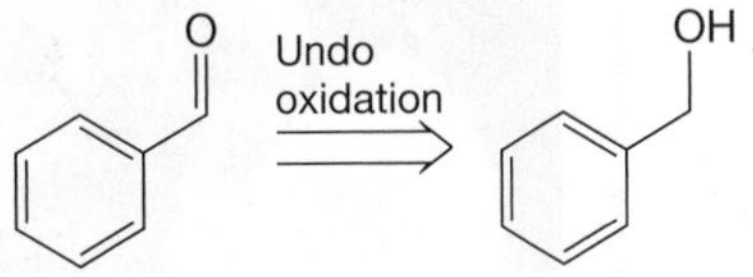
O
Undo oxidation
OH

How can you report the synthesis in the forward direction? What oxidizing agents would be appropriate?

The complete synthesis is shown below. There are two oxidations of alcohols required in this synthesis. The first is an oxidation to an aldehyde, which requires the absence of water and thus requires PCC as the oxidizing agent. The second is an oxidation to a ketone, which can take place in water, thus allowing us to use H_2CrO_4 as the oxidizing agent.

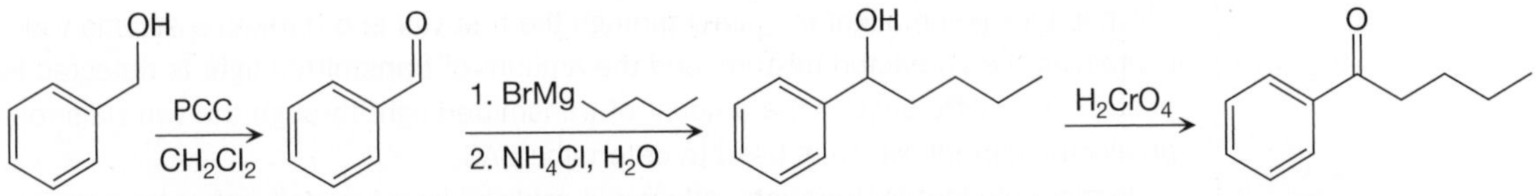
OH
PCC
CH2Cl2
O
1. BrMg
2. NH4Cl, H2O
OH
H2CrO4
O

Try It Show how to carry out this synthesis using the indicated Grignard reagent and the alcohol as starting materials.

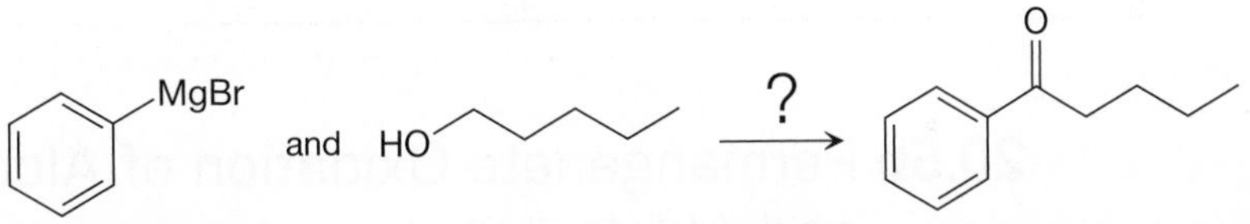
MgBr
and HO
?
O

Chromic Acid Oxidation and the Breathalyzer Test

According to the National Highway Traffic Safety Administration, more than 10,500 people died in drunk-driving crashes in the United States in 2018. It is no wonder, then, that there are strict laws against driving under the influence of alcohol, which each state defines as having a blood alcohol content (BAC) above 0.08%. Law enforcement officers can measure the BAC of a suspected drunk driver using a Breathalyzer test, the basis of which is the same chromic acid oxidation reaction presented here in Chapter 20.

POLICE

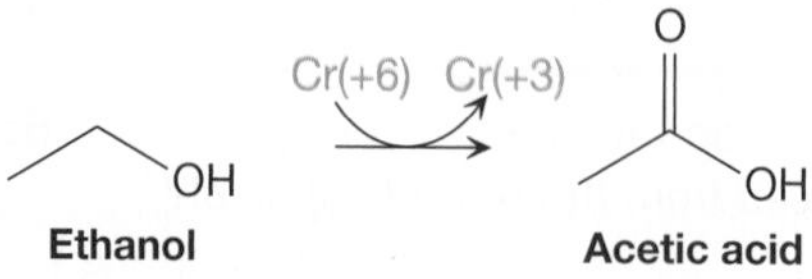
OH
Cr(+6) Cr(+3)
O
OH
Ethanol
Acetic acid

FIGURE 20-3

To carry out a Breathalyzer test, a person blows into a mouthpiece, and a fixed volume of breath is collected (**Figure 20-3**, left). The glass neck of a test vial is broken, and the breath sample is forced into that vial. The test vial contains a mixture of $K_2Cr_2O_7$ and H_2SO_4 (i.e., H_2CrO_4), so any ethanol from the breath is quickly oxidized to acetic acid (Fig. 20-3, right). Cr(+6), which is bright orange, is simultaneously reduced to Cr(+3), which is blue-green. Light is shined through the test vial and through a second vial containing the unreacted mixture, and the amount of transmitted light is detected by photocells. A difference in the amount of transmitted light through the two vials results in an electric current, which is used to determine BAC.

In more modern instruments, ethanol is oxidized by a fuel cell rather than by chromic acid. Oxidation at the anode produces acetic acid, protons, and electrons, and the protons travel to the cathode, where atmospheric oxygen is reduced to water. The electric current that is produced is converted to a BAC reading.

20.5b Permanganate Oxidation of Alcohols and Aldehydes

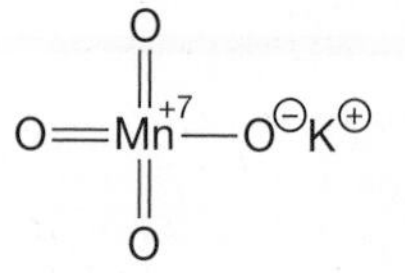
O
O=Mn—O⊖K⊕
+7
O

Potassium permanganate

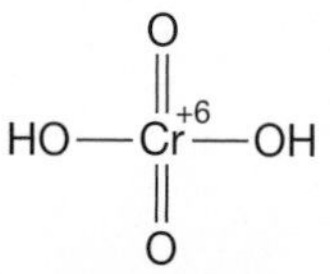
O
HO—Cr—OH
+6
O

Chromic acid

FIGURE 20-4 **$KMnO_4$ and H_2CrO_4** These oxidizing agents are similar structurally, and each has a metal atom in a high, positive oxidation state.

Potassium permanganate ($KMnO_4$) is another common oxidizing agent; it is an ionic compound consisting of the potassium cation, K^+, and the permanganate anion, MnO_4^-. Structurally, MnO_4^- resembles H_2CrO_4 (**Figure 20-4**). In both compounds, a central metal atom is bonded to four O atoms, thus giving the metal atom a high, positive oxidation state: namely, +7 for MnO_4^- and +6 for H_2CrO_4.

Like chromic acid, potassium permanganate can be used to oxidize alcohols, as shown in Equations 20-23 and 20-24:

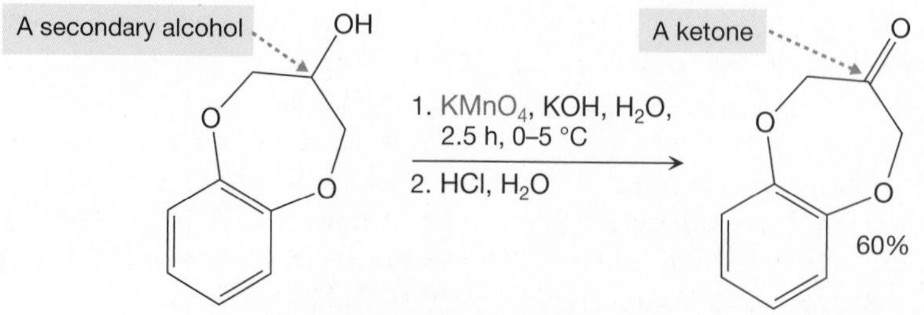
A secondary alcohol
OH
A ketone
O
O
O
1. KMnO4, KOH, H2O,
2.5 h, 0–5 °C
2. HCl, H2O
O
O
60%

(20-23)

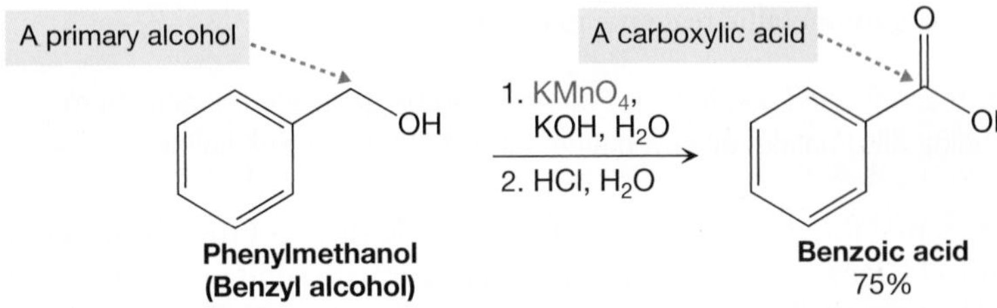
A primary alcohol
A carboxylic acid
OH
1. KMnO4, KOH, H2O
2. HCl, H2O
OH
O
Phenylmethanol
(Benzyl alcohol)
Benzoic acid
75%

(20-24)

More generally:

When treated with a basic solution of potassium permanganate ($KMnO_4$), followed by acid workup:

- Primary alcohols and aldehydes are oxidized to carboxylic acids.
- Secondary alcohols are oxidized to ketones.

These are the same outcomes we see with H_2CrO_4 as the oxidizing agent. It might therefore seem that $KMnO_4$ and H_2CrO_4 are completely interchangeable, but they are not.

H_2CrO_4 is more selective than $KMnO_4$.

As will be discussed in Chapters 24 and 26, $KMnO_4$ can oxidize a variety of compounds in addition to alcohols and aldehydes, including alkenes, alkynes, and alkylbenzenes. As a result, chromic acid's greater selectivity makes it the oxidizing agent of choice when these other groups are present.

GREEN CHEMISTRY

$KMnO_4$ is less toxic than H_2CrO_4, so $KMnO_4$ is sometimes the preferred oxidizing agent. Greener alternatives that don't involve heavy metals have been developed, which can also oxidize primary alcohols to carboxylic acids. The example below incorporates $NaClO_2$ and NaClO (bleach).

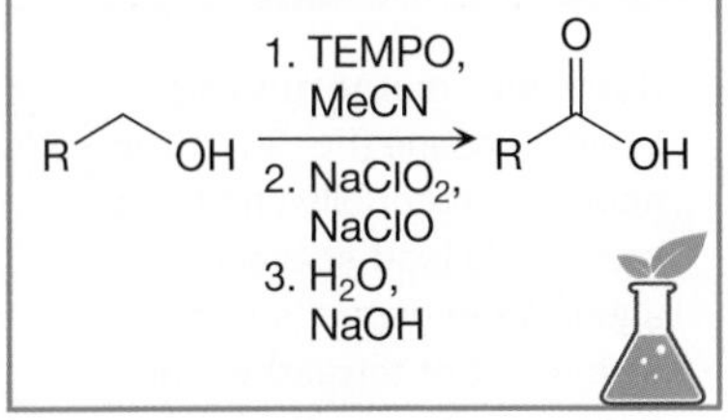
R
OH
1. TEMPO, MeCN
2. NaClO2, NaClO
3. H2O, NaOH
R
OH
O

YOUR TURN **20.11**

What are the structures of **A** and **B** in the following sequence of reactions?

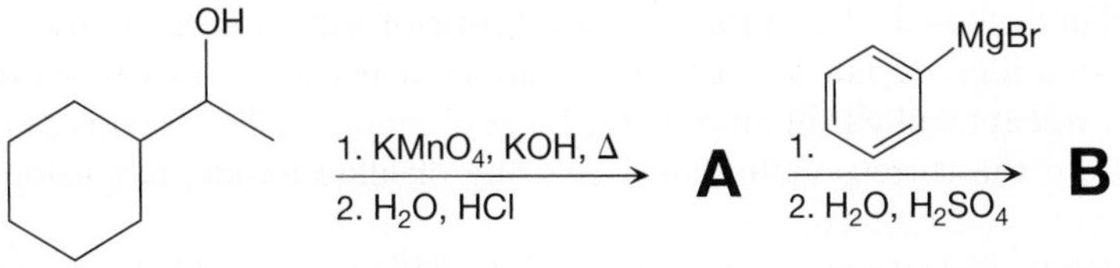
OH
1. KMnO4, KOH, Δ
2. H2O, HCl
A
1. MgBr
2. H2O, H2SO4
B

20.6 Generating Organometallic Reagents: Grignard Reagents, Alkyllithium Reagents, and Lithium Dialkylcuprates

SECTION 20.6 OBJECTIVES

You will be able to:

1. Show how a Grignard reagent, an alkyllithium reagent, or a lithium dialkylcuprate can be synthesized from an alkyl halide.
2. Explain how the conversion of an alkyl halide into one of these organometallic species involves a reduction of the alkyl halide.

We have seen how organometallic reagents such as Grignard reagents (RMgX), alkyllithium reagents (RLi), and lithium dialkylcuprates (R_2CuLi) are used in a variety of reactions. Because metals have low electronegativities, the dipole of the C—Metal bond points toward carbon. The carbon atom is therefore electron-rich and nucleophilic, allowing organometallic species to behave as carbon nucleophiles (R^-) to form valuable new C—C bonds. For example, we have seen that Grignard and alkyllithium reagents can attack epoxide carbons to open the ring (Section 11.2), and we have seen these reagents undergo nucleophilic addition to the carbonyl group of a ketone or aldehyde (Section 18.4). R^- from a lithium dialkylcuprate favors conjugate addition to an α,β-unsaturated ketone or aldehyde (Section 18.9). Grignard reagents and alkyllithium reagents are very strong R^- bases, too, which is why alkyllithium reagents are commonly used to deprotonate a very weakly acidic C—H proton in the formation of a Wittig reagent (Section 18.7).

How are these organometallic reagents made? Conveniently:

Both Grignard reagents and alkyllithium reagents can be generated directly from the corresponding alkyl halide, alkenyl halide, alkynyl halide, or aryl halide.

Equation 20-25 shows, for example, that an aryl bromide such as bromobenzene can be converted into a Grignard reagent simply by treating it with solid magnesium in an ether solvent such as tetrahydrofuran (THF). Similarly, Equation 20-26 shows that an alkyllithium reagent (RLi) can be synthesized from an alkyl bromide by treating it with solid lithium in ether.

CONNECTIONS 20.2

Keep your motor running
Bromobenzene (Eq. 20-25) is added to motor oils and fuels to act as a lead-scavenging agent. Lead deposits form as a result of tetraethyl lead added to gasoline to improve engine performance. Tetraethyl lead was banned in the United States in 1996 for vehicles used on the road, but it can still be used for aircraft and marine engines.

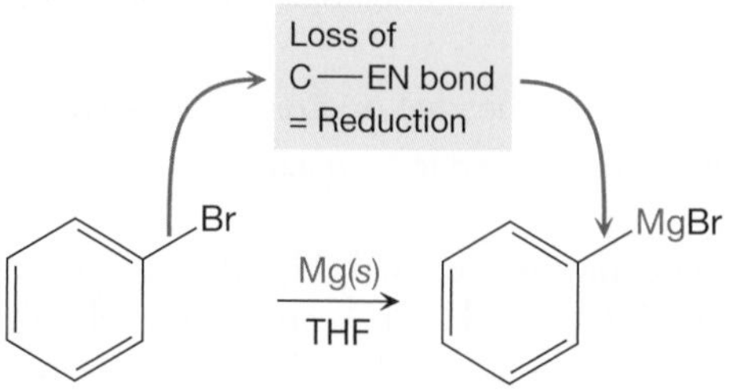
Loss of
C—EN bond
= Reduction
Br
MgBr
Mg(s)
THF
A Grignard reagent (20-25)

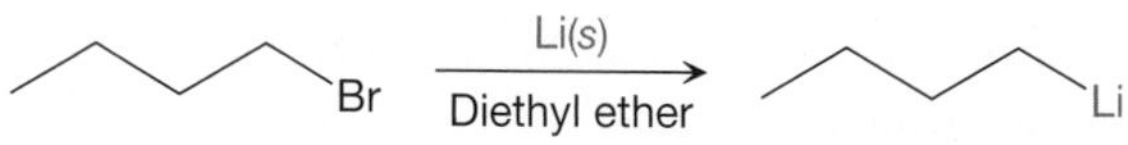
Br
Li(s)
Diethyl ether
Li
An alkyllithium reagent (20-26)

Notice that the aryl or alkyl halide undergoes *reduction* in both of these reactions. As indicated, carbon's bond to an electronegative atom (bromine in this case) is lost, and taking its place is a metal atom whose electronegativity is lower than that of carbon; we learned in Section 20.1 that this is characteristic of reduction reactions.

Alkyl bromides are not the only alkyl halides that can be used to synthesize a Grignard reagent or alkyllithium reagent. Those organometallic reagents can be synthesized from the corresponding alkyl chloride or alkyl iodide, too, using similar procedures.

A lithium dialkylcuprate is not generated directly from an alkyl halide, but rather is produced from the corresponding alkyllithium species by using cuprous iodide (CuI), as shown in Equation 20-27:

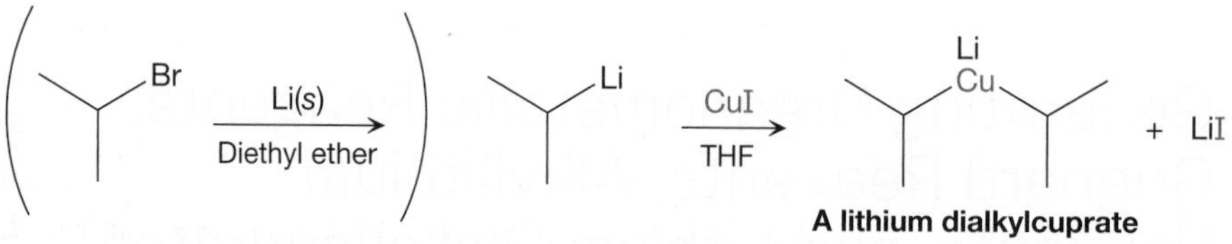
Br
Li(s)
Diethyl ether
Li
CuI
THF
Li
Cu
+ LiI
A lithium dialkylcuprate (20-27)

The conversion of the alkyllithium species into the lithium dialkylcuprate is a type of **transmetalation** reaction, so called because one metal in the C—Metal bond is exchanged for another.

YOUR TURN 20.12

Draw the product of each of the following reactions.

(a)

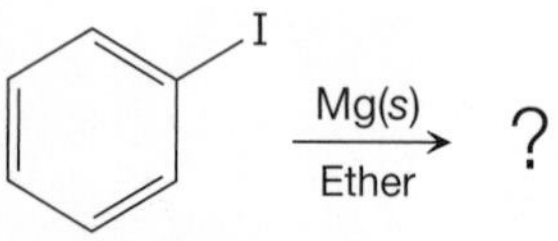
I
Mg(s)
Ether
?

(b)

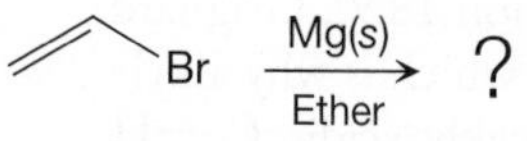
Br
Mg(s)
Ether
?

(c)

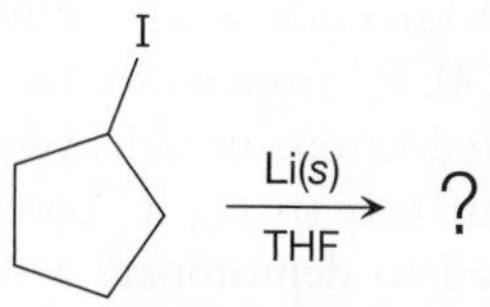
I
Li(s)
THF
?

(d)

Product from (c) $\xrightarrow[\text{THF}]{\text{CuI}}$?

Show how to synthesize each of the following organometallic compounds from an alkyl, alkenyl, or aryl halide.

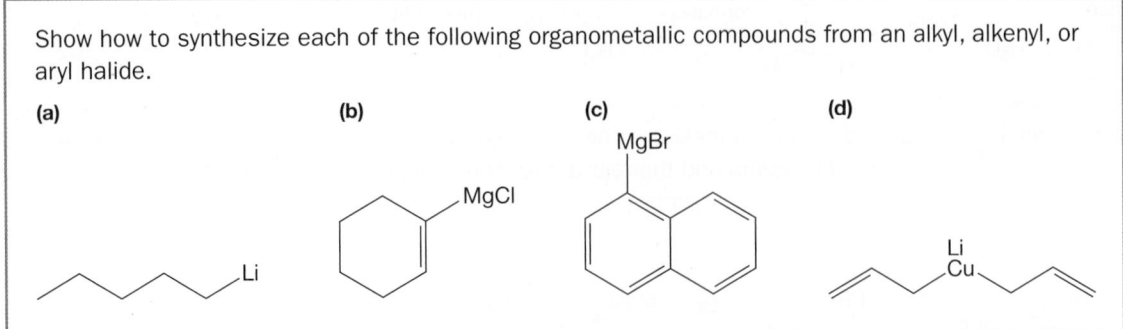

(a)

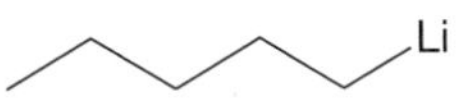
Li

(b)

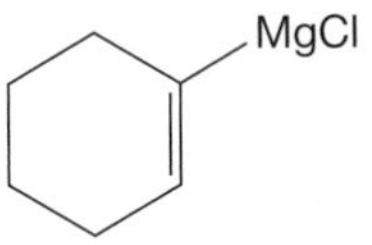
MgCl

(c)

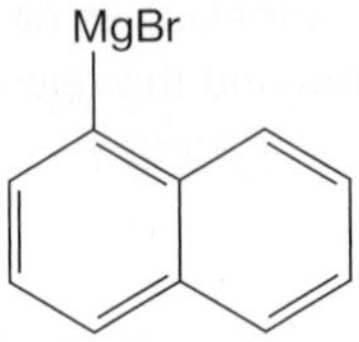
MgBr

(d)

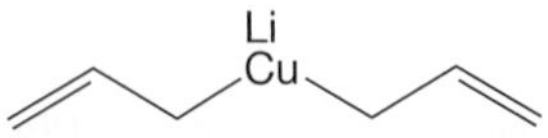
Li
Cu

SOLVED PROBLEM **20.5**

How to carry out a synthesis that requires making an organometallic reagent

Break It Down Using formaldehyde ($H_2C{=}O$) as your only source of carbon, show how you would synthesize propan-1-ol.

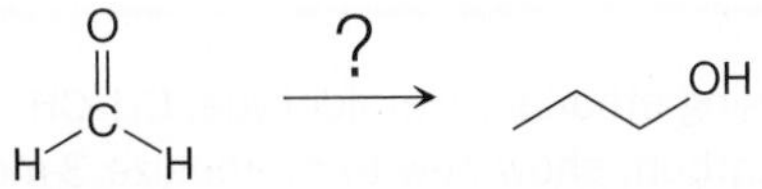
O
C
H
H
?
OH

Methanal (Formaldehyde) **Propan-1-ol**

Think	Solve
Do C—C bonds have to be formed in the synthesis?	Yes; because the target has a chain of three carbons and the only source of carbon is formaldehyde, both C—C bonds must be formed in the synthesis.
What reaction can form a C—C bond and leave us with an alcohol?	A Grignard reaction can accomplish this. Therefore, as shown here, we can carry out a transform that undoes a Grignard reaction. Formaldehyde, the starting material, is one precursor. The other precursor is a Grignard reagent, which becomes our new target. 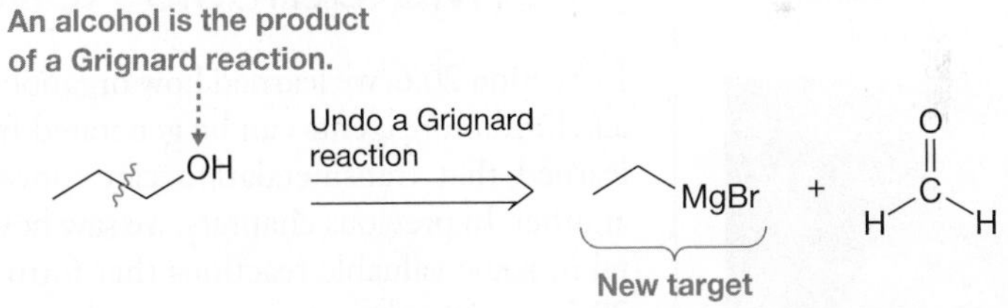
What precursor would be required to generate the Grignard reagent? How can that precursor be produced?	As shown below, the Grignard reagent can be made from the corresponding alkyl halide, and the alkyl halide can be produced from ethanol. Therefore, our goal now is to synthesize ethanol from the starting material. 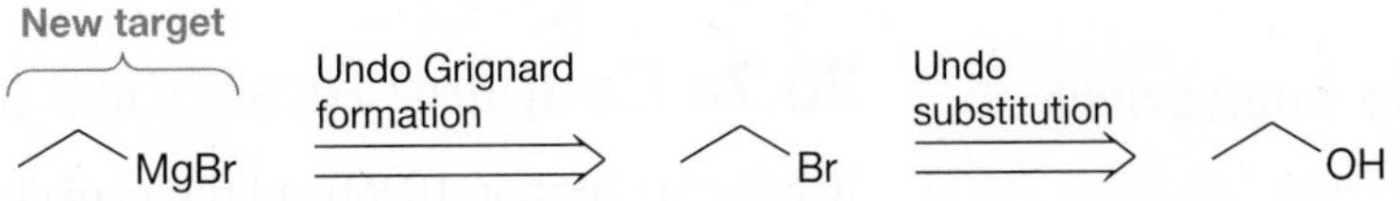
What reaction can be used to form the C—C bond in ethanol? How could the required precursors be synthesized from the starting material?	As shown below, ethanol could be made from another Grignard reaction. The required Grignard reagent can be generated from CH_3Br, and CH_3Br can be synthesized from the starting material.

An alcohol is the product of a Grignard reaction.
OH
Undo a Grignard reaction
MgBr
+
O
C
H
H
New target

New target
MgBr
Undo Grignard formation
Br
Undo substitution
OH

(continued)

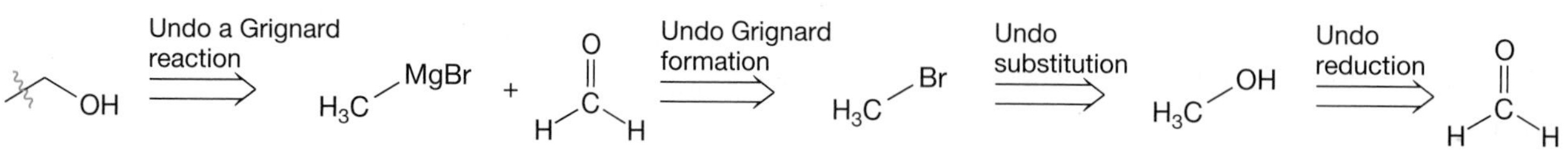
Undo a Grignard reaction
MgBr
Undo Grignard formation
Br
Undo substitution
OH
Undo reduction

How do you report the final synthesis?	To report the final synthesis, we need to begin with the starting material and include the required reagents and the relevant reaction conditions, as shown below.

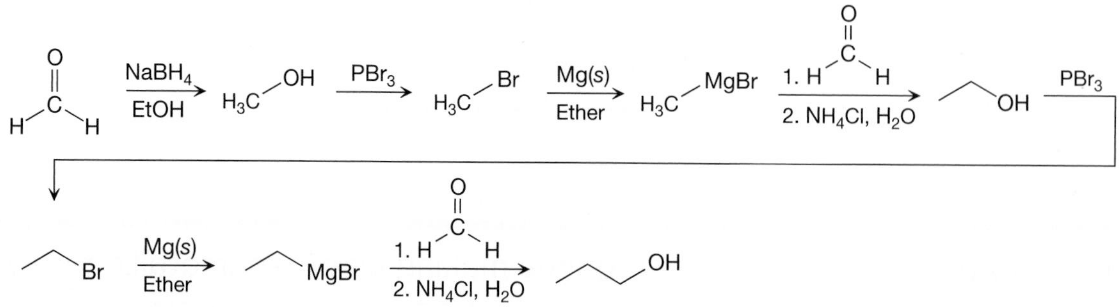
NaBH4
EtOH
PBr3
Mg(s)
Ether
1. H
2. NH4Cl, H2O
PBr3
Mg(s)
Ether
MgBr
1. H
2. NH4Cl, H2O
OH

Try It Using ethanal (acetaldehyde, $CH_3CH{=}O$) as your only source of carbon, show how to synthesize 3-methylpentan-3-ol.

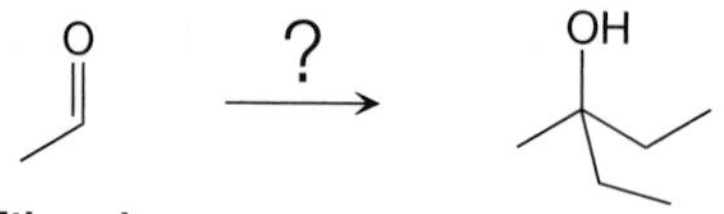
?
OH

Ethanal (Acetaldehyde) **3-Methylpentan-3-ol**

CONNECTIONS 20.3

Tackling anxiety

3-Methylpentan-3-ol (Solved Problem 20.5, Try It) is a precursor to emylcamate, a drug that was once used to treat anxiety and tension.

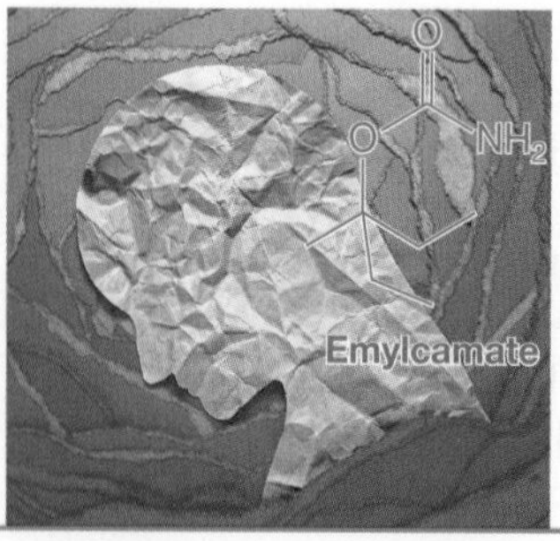
NH2
Emylcamate

20.7 Useful Reactions That Form Carbon–Carbon Bonds: Coupling and Alkene Metathesis Reactions

SECTION 20.7 OBJECTIVES

You will be able to:

1. Identify conditions for coupling and alkene metathesis reactions.
2. Incorporate coupling and alkene metathesis reactions in a synthesis.

In Section 20.6, we learned how organometallic species such as Grignard reagents and alkyllithium reagents can be generated from the reduction of an alkyl halide. We also learned that transmetalation can convert one type of organometallic species into another. In previous chapters, we saw how such organometallic species are instrumental in some valuable reactions that form new carbon–carbon bonds. Here in Section 20.7, we introduce some new carbon–carbon bond-forming reactions that rely on organometallic species, too, either as reagents or as intermediates. Namely, we will introduce *coupling reactions* and *alkene metathesis*. As we learned in Section 11.1, reactions that form new C—C bonds are valuable in constructing the carbon skeleton of a synthetic target.

20.7a Coupling Reactions Involving Organocuprates

Recall from Section 18.9 that lithium dialkylcuprates (R_2CuLi) act as relatively weak R^- nucleophiles in the conjugate addition to α,β-unsaturated aldehydes, ketones, and other polar π bonds. As shown in Equation 20-28, lithium dialkylcuprates also react with alkyl halides:

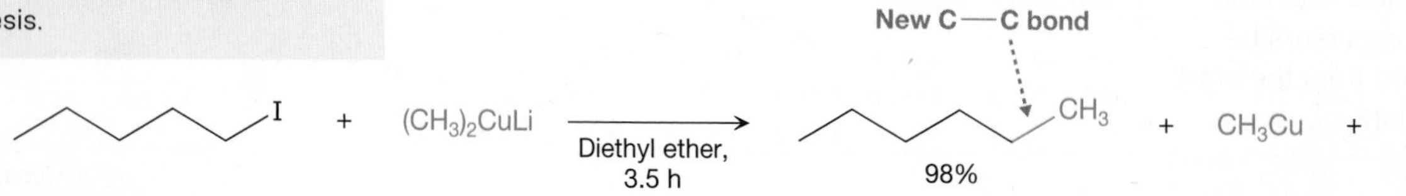
New C—C bond
I
(CH3)2CuLi
Diethyl ether, 3.5 h
CH3
98%
CH3Cu
LiI

(20-28)

In this reaction, two alkyl groups are joined together, one from the alkyl halide and the other from the dialkylcuprate, so these types of reactions are called **coupling reactions**.

Coupling reactions such as the one in Equation 20-28 can involve a wide variety of alkyl halides and organocuprates:

In the coupling reaction $R{-}X + R'_2CuLi \longrightarrow R{-}R'$,

- R from the alkyl halide can be a methyl, primary, or secondary alkyl group; a vinylic group; or an aryl group.
- R′ from the dialkylcuprate can be an alkyl, vinylic, or aryl group.
- The halogen X can be Cl, Br, or I.

Examples illustrating some of these variations are shown in Equations 20-29 and 20-30.

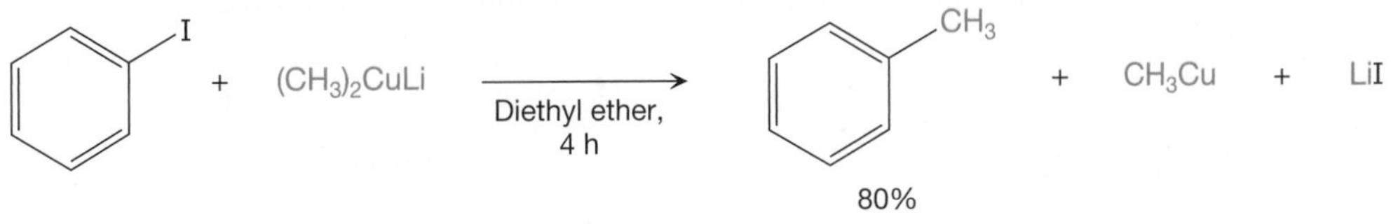

I
+ (CH3)2CuLi
Diethyl ether, 4 h
CH3
80%
+ CH3Cu + LiI

(20-29)

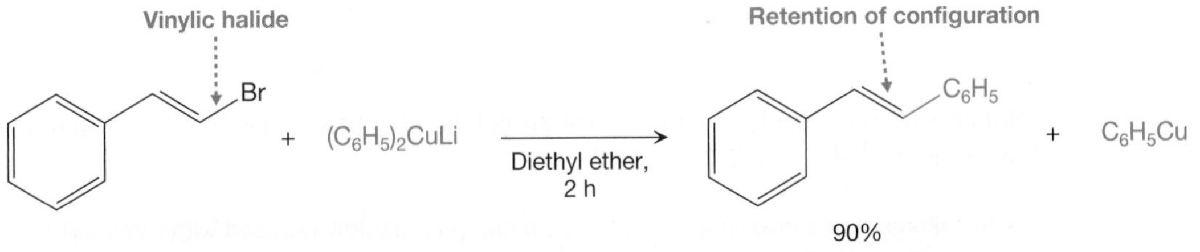

Vinylic halide
Br
+ (C6H5)2CuLi
Diethyl ether, 2 h
Retention of configuration
C6H5
90%
+ C6H5Cu + LiBr

(20-30)

Notice in Equation 20-30 that when R—X is a vinylic halide, the R′ group from R'_2CuLi assumes the position originally occupied by the halogen atom. Therefore:

Coupling reactions between R—X and R'_2CuLi are *stereospecific*, taking place with *retention of configuration* about the C═C bond of a vinylic halide.

YOUR TURN 20.14

Draw the major organic product for each of the following reactions.

(a)

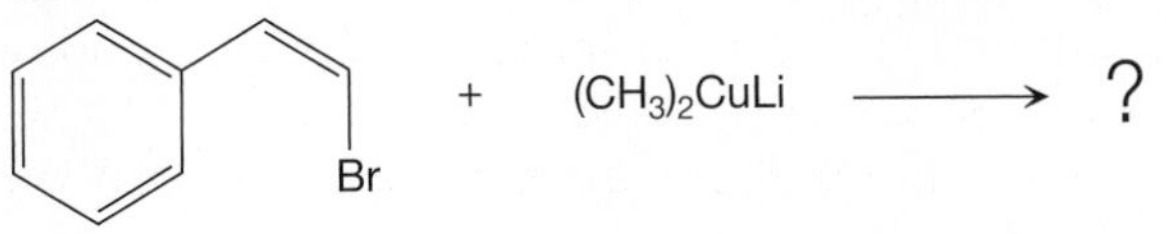

Br
+ (CH3)2CuLi
?

(b)

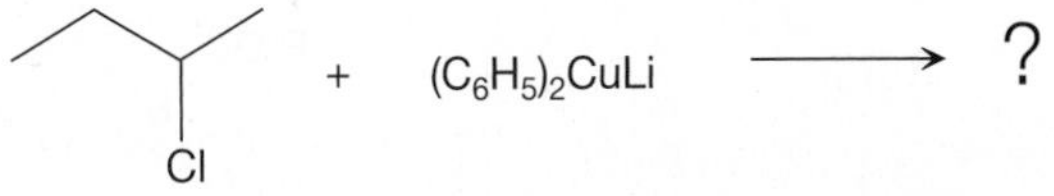

Cl
+ (C6H5)2CuLi
?

20.7b Palladium-Catalyzed Coupling Reactions

The organocuprate coupling reactions we examined in Section 20.7a are not the only type of coupling reactions used in organic synthesis. Numerous others have been developed, involving a range of metal atoms. We study two other coupling reactions here in Section 20.7b, both of which involve palladium: the *Suzuki reaction* and the *Heck reaction*. These reactions have found such widespread utility in organic synthesis that Akira Suzuki (b. 1930) and Richard F. Heck (1931–2015), the pioneers of the reactions, shared the Nobel Prize in Chemistry 2010 along with Ei-ichi Negishi (1935–2021).

There are several variations of the **Suzuki reaction**, but in the general reaction, a vinylic or aryl halide is treated with an organoboron compound and a palladium catalyst (PdL_n) under basic conditions:

Suzuki Coupling Reaction

$$R{-}X + R'{-}B(OR'')_2 \xrightarrow[\text{Base}]{PdL_n} R{-}R'$$

- R from RX can be a vinylic or aryl group.
- R′ from the boron-containing compound can be an alkyl, vinylic, or aryl group.
- X can be Cl, Br, or I.

In the palladium catalyst, PdL_n, L represents any of a variety of ligands coordinated to the Pd metal center.

An example of the Suzuki reaction is shown in Equation 20-31.

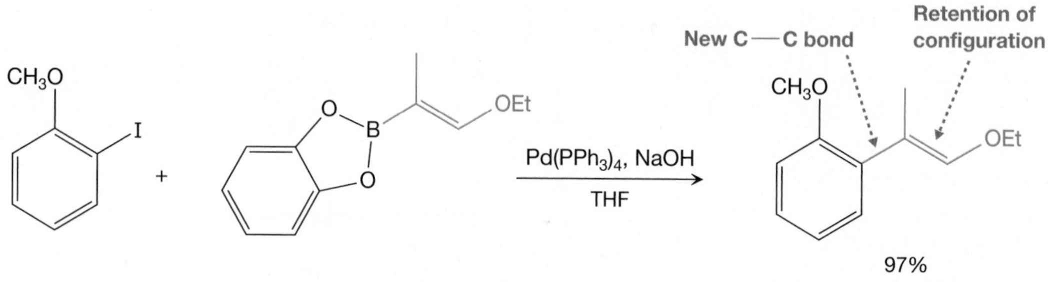

CH3O
I
+
O
B
O
OEt
Pd(PPh3)4, NaOH
THF
New C—C bond
Retention of configuration
CH3O
OEt
97%

(20-31)

Notice that the Suzuki reaction is stereospecific, much like the coupling reactions involving dialkylcuprates.

Suzuki reactions involving possible *E*/*Z* isomerism usually proceed with *retention of configuration*.

An abbreviated mechanism for the general Suzuki reaction is shown in Equation 20-32, highlighting four major steps. Step 1 is oxidative addition, where the Pd metal atom is oxidized as it essentially inserts between the R and X groups of the vinylic or aryl halide. In Step 2, the hydroxide anion displaces the halide leaving group. Meanwhile, another hydroxide anion coordinates with the $R'B(OR'')_2$ compound, which increases the nucleophilicity of R′ and facilitates the transmetalation in Step 3. Finally, reductive elimination occurs in Step 4 to create the new R—R′ bond and regenerate the PdL_n catalyst for another cycle.

Abbreviated mechanism for the Suzuki reaction (Eq. 20-31)

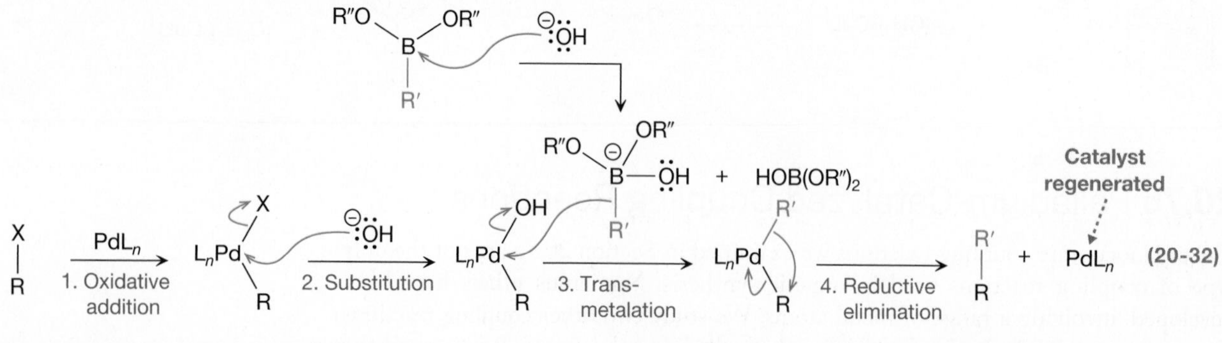

R″O
OR″
B
R′
:ÖH
OR″
R″O
B—ÖH
+
HOB(OR″)2
R′
Catalyst regenerated
X
R
PdLn
1. Oxidative addition
LnPd
X
R
:ÖH
2. Substitution
LnPd
OH
R
3. Trans-metalation
LnPd
R′
R
4. Reductive elimination
R′
R
+
PdLn

(20-32)

Similar to the Suzuki reaction, the **Heck reaction** can couple one vinylic or aryl group to another. An example is shown in Equation 20-33:

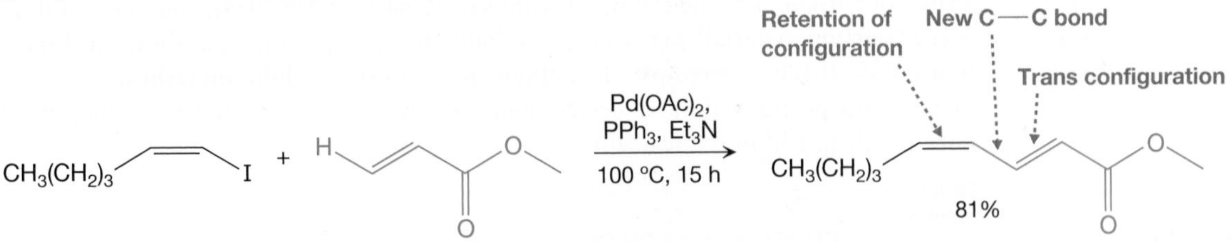
Retention of configuration
New C—C bond
Trans configuration
$CH_3(CH_2)_3$
I
+
H
O
O
$Pd(OAc)_2$, PPh_3, Et_3N
100 °C, 15 h
$CH_3(CH_2)_3$
81%
O
O

(20-33)

The general characteristics of a Heck reaction are as follows:

Heck Coupling Reaction

$$R{-}X + H{-}R' \xrightarrow[\text{Base}]{PdL_2} R{-}R' + H{-}X$$

- R from RX can be a vinylic or aryl group.
- R′ from H—R′ can be a vinylic or aryl group.
- X can be Cl, Br, or I.

In essence, R from R—X replaces H from H—R′.

The stereochemistry of the Heck reaction can be summarized as follows:

- If the R—X halide in a Heck reaction is vinylic, the configuration about the double bond is retained.
- If H—R′ is vinylic and has an attached substituent (Sub) at the opposite end of the C═C, then R and Sub will be trans to each other in the product.

Both of these aspects of stereochemistry are illustrated in Equation 20-33.

The abbreviated mechanism for the Heck reaction is shown in Equation 20-34, which highlights four main steps. Step 1 is oxidative addition of the PdL_2 catalyst to R—X. In Step 2, the double bond inserts between the Pd and R groups, temporarily converting the double bond to a single bond. Then, in Step 3, the double bond is re-formed in an elimination, and the organic product is produced. Step 4 regenerates the PdL_2 catalyst in a reductive elimination involving the amine base.

Abbreviated mechanism for the Heck reaction (Eq. 20-33)

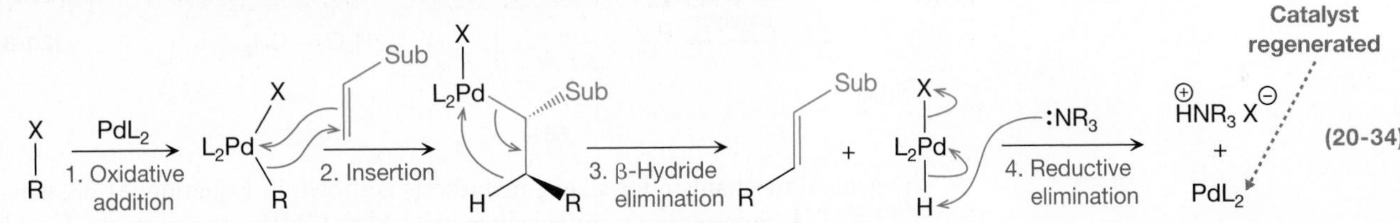
Catalyst regenerated
X
R
PdL_2
1. Oxidative addition
L_2Pd
X
R
Sub
2. Insertion
X
L_2Pd
Sub
H
R
3. β-Hydride elimination
Sub
R
+
X
L_2Pd
H
:NR_3
4. Reductive elimination
$H\overset{+}{N}R_3\ X^{-}$
+
PdL_2

(20-34)

YOUR TURN **20.15**

Draw the major organic product for each of the following reactions.

(a)

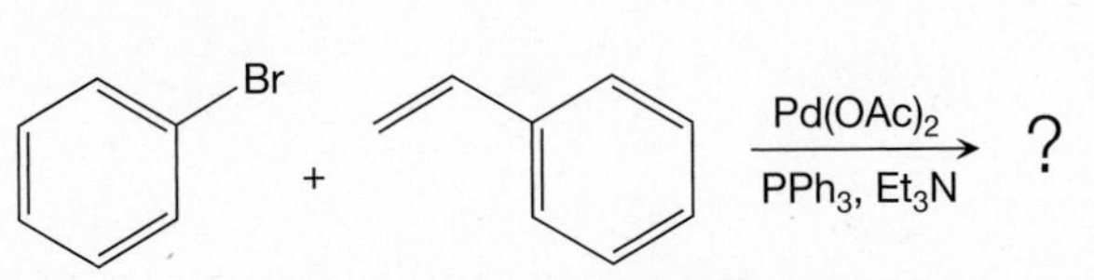
Br
+
$Pd(OAc)_2$
PPh_3, Et_3N
?

(b)

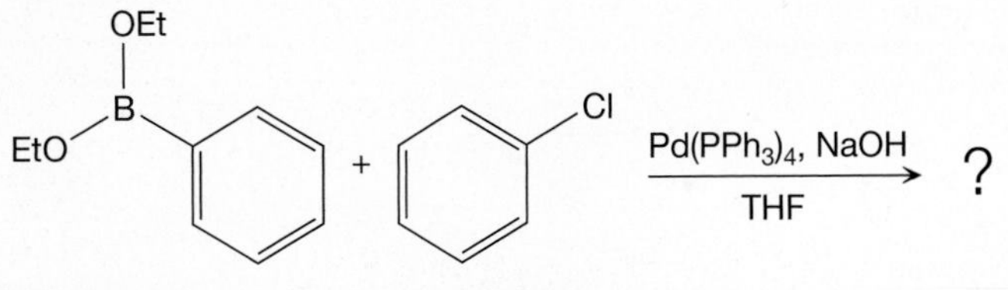
OEt
B
EtO
+
Cl
$Pd(PPh_3)_4$, NaOH
THF
?

20.7c Alkene Metathesis

When dec-4-ene is treated with a **Grubbs catalyst** (**Figure 20-5**), a mixture of dec-4-ene (starting material), oct-4-ene, and dodec-6-ene is produced, as shown in Equation 20-35. This is an example of an **alkene metathesis** or **olefin metathesis** reaction, in which the portions of the molecules joined by the C═C bond in the products were not initially joined in the reactant.

$$\underset{\textbf{Dec-4-ene}}{CH_3(CH_2)_2CH{=}CH(CH_2)_4CH_3} \underset{4\ h}{\overset{\text{Grubbs catalyst}}{\rightleftharpoons}} \underbrace{\underset{\textbf{Oct-4-ene}}{CH_3(CH_2)_2CH{=}CH(CH_2)_2CH_3} + \underset{\textbf{Dodec-6-ene}}{CH_3(CH_2)_4CH{=}CH(CH_2)_4CH_3}}_{\substack{\text{Mixture of } E \text{ and } Z \text{ isomers} \\ 39\%}} \quad \textbf{(20-35)}$$

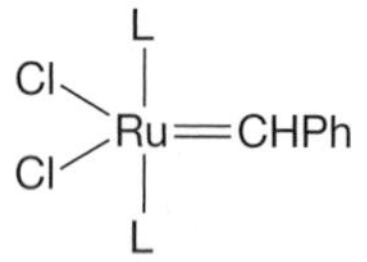

L
Cl
Ru═CHPh
Cl
L

FIGURE 20-5 The general structure of a Grubbs catalyst Grubbs catalysts can vary in their ligands (L) but generally have in common a ruthenium–carbene bond (Ru═C) and two chloride ligands.

Alkene metathesis reactions generally take place under equilibrium conditions, as indicated in Equation 20-35. In such cases, the yield tends to be relatively low because the product alkenes have thermodynamic stabilities similar to that of the reactant alkene.

As is the case with any chemical equilibrium, Le Châtelier's principle can be exploited by removing products as they form. For a reaction like the one in Equation 20-35, where the products form as a mixture of liquids, this can be cumbersome and quite challenging. If the reactants are terminal alkenes, however, as in Equation 20-36, then one of the products is ethene, which is a gas that escapes the system as it forms. The reaction is then effectively irreversible.

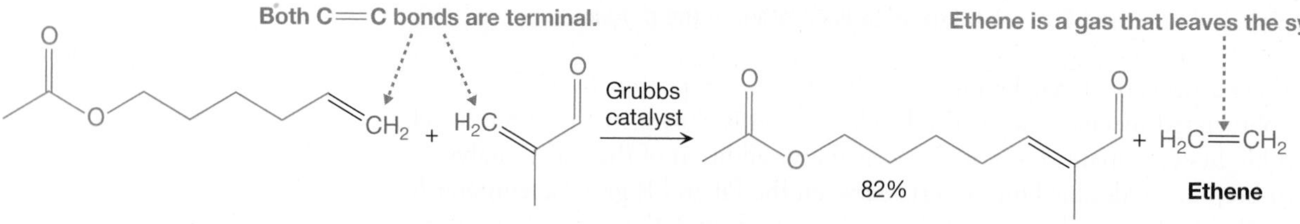

Both C═C bonds are terminal.
Ethene is a gas that leaves the system.
O
O
CH2
H2C
O
Grubbs
catalyst
O
O
O
82%
+ H2C═CH2
Ethene

(20-36)

The irreversible nature of alkene metathesis when ethene is produced can be exploited to form a new ring from a compound containing two terminal C═C bonds. An example of this **ring-closing metathesis** is shown in Equation 20-37:

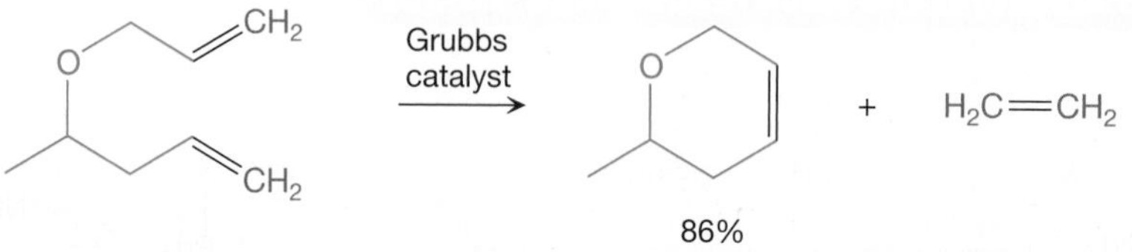

CH2
O
CH2
Grubbs
catalyst
O
86%
+
H2C═CH2

(20-37)

The general mechanism for alkene metathesis is shown in Equation 20-38, where R—CH═CH_2 represents a terminal alkene and M═CHPh represents the Grubbs catalyst (M is the $RuCl_2L_2$ portion of it). In Step 1, the Grubbs catalyst adds to the original alkene to produce a four-membered ring. In Step 2, the ring opens to produce a species in which M is doubly bonded to one of the fragments from the original alkene, represented as M═CH—R. The same two steps repeat in Steps 3 and 4, this time involving M═CH—R instead of the Grubbs catalyst.

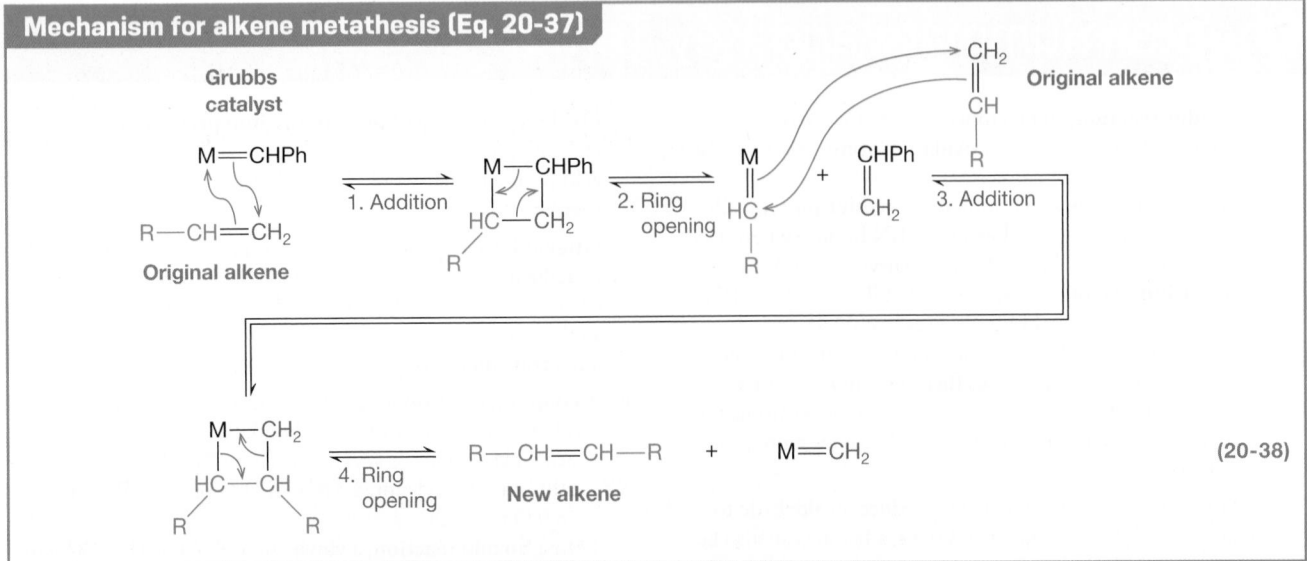

Mechanism for alkene metathesis (Eq. 20-37)

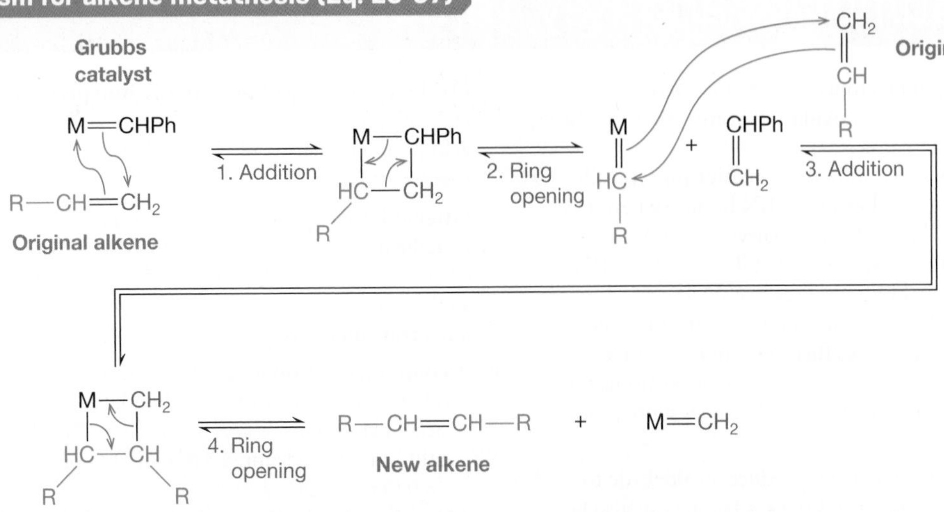

Grubbs catalyst
M=CHPh
R—CH=CH2
Original alkene
1. Addition
M—CHPh
HC—CH2
R
2. Ring opening
M
HC
R
+
CHPh
CH2
CH2
CH
R
Original alkene
3. Addition
M—CH2
HC—CH
R
R
4. Ring opening
R—CH=CH—R
New alkene
+
M=CH2

(20-38)

The mechanism in Equation 20-38 shows explicitly how one alkene product, R—CH=CH—R, is produced. The other alkene product of this reaction, $H_2C{=}CH_2$ (not shown in Eq. 20-38), is produced from the same mechanism, the difference being the relative orientations of the original alkene and the Grubbs catalyst in Step 1. To produce $H_2C{=}CH_2$, the CH_2 group must be oriented on the same end as M, and the CH—R group must be oriented on the same end as CHPh.

YOUR TURN 20.16

Draw the major organic products that would be formed when each of the following is treated with Grubbs catalyst.

(a)

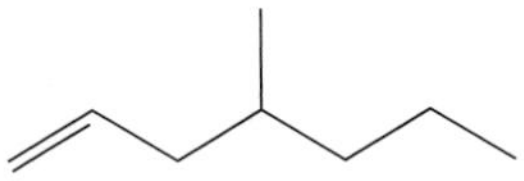

(b)

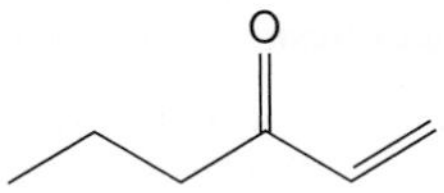

O

(c)

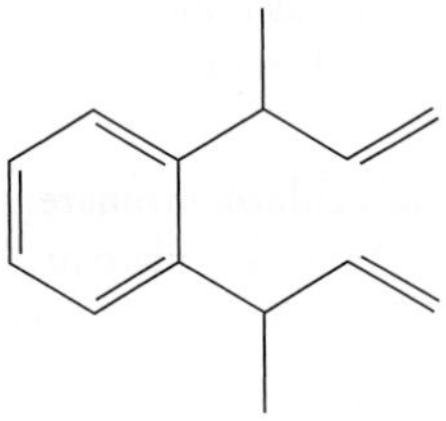

Chapter Summary and Key Terms

- In a **redox reaction**, some atoms that are involved in the reaction undergo a change in **oxidation state**. (Sections 20.1 and 20.2)
  - An organic species that undergoes **reduction** typically gains C—H bonds or loses C—EN bonds (where EN is an atom that is more electronegative than C). In an **oxidation**, the organic species typically gains C—EN bonds or loses C—H bonds. (Section 20.1)
  - A species that undergoes reduction has atoms for which the oxidation state decreases (becomes more negative), whereas a species that undergoes oxidation has atoms for which the oxidation state increases (becomes more positive). (Section 20.2)
- Catalytic hydrogenation will readily reduce an aldehyde to an alcohol. Under moderate conditions, a ketone can also be reduced to an alcohol, and under more extreme conditions, other compounds such as nitriles and amides can be reduced. (Section 20.3)
- Catalytic hydrogenation is selective toward alkenes, alkynes, and aldehydes. (Section 20.3)
- The **Wolff–Kishner reduction**, the **Clemmensen reduction**, and the **Raney-nickel reduction** reduce the carbonyl (C═O) group of a ketone or aldehyde to a methylene (CH_2) group. These reactions take place under basic, acidic, and catalytic hydrogenation conditions, respectively, so care must be taken to avoid unwanted side reactions at other functional groups in the molecule. (Section 20.4)
- **Chromic acid** (H_2CrO_4) will oxidize a primary alcohol to a carboxylic acid or a secondary alcohol to a ketone. (Section 20.5a)
- Oxidation of a primary alcohol by **pyridinium chlorochromate (PCC)** stops at the aldehyde because the reaction takes place in the absence of water. (Section 20.5a)
- Oxidation of an alcohol by **potassium permanganate** ($KMnO_4$) produces the same ketone and carboxylic acid products that would be produced by chromic acid. (Section 20.5b)
- Grignard reagents or alkyllithium reagents can be generated by reducing the corresponding alkyl halide using magnesium or lithium, respectively. Lithium dialkylcuprates can be generated from the corresponding alkyllithium reagent by carrying out a **transmetalation** using CuI. (Section 20.6)
- A **coupling reaction** joins one alkyl, vinylic, or aryl group to another, forming a new C—C bond. (Section 20.7a)
  - An alkyl, vinylic, or aryl halide (R—X) will react with a lithium dialkylcuprate (R'_2CuLi) to produce R—R′. (Section 20.7a)
  - In a **Suzuki reaction**, a vinylic or aryl halide (R—X) will react with an organoboron compound [R′—B(OR″)$_2$] under basic conditions in the presence of a palladium catalyst to produce R—R′. (Section 20.7b)
  - In a **Heck reaction**, the R group from a vinylic or aryl halide (R—X) will replace a vinylic or aryl H from H—R′ to produce R—R′ when treated with a palladium catalyst under basic conditions. (Section 20.7b)
- An **alkene metathesis** occurs when one or more alkenes are treated with **Grubbs catalyst**, which contains a Ru═C bond. In the product of an alkene metathesis, the fragments that are joined by a double bond were initially part of a double bond to other fragments in the reactant. These reactions are particularly useful when the reactants are terminal alkenes. When the reaction produces a new ring, it is called a **ring-closing metathesis**. (Section 20.7c)

Reaction Tables

Functional group transformations introduced in this chapter are collected in Table 20-2, and reactions introduced in this chapter that alter the carbon skeleton are collected in Table 20-3.

TABLE 20-2 Functional Group Transformations[a]

	Starting Compound Class	Typical Reagents and Reaction Conditions	Compound Class Formed	Comments	Discussed in Section(s)
(1)	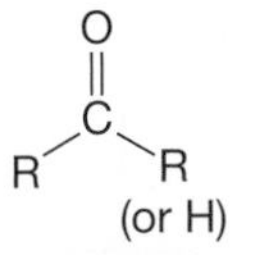 **Ketone or aldehyde**	H_2 → Pt, Pd, or Ni	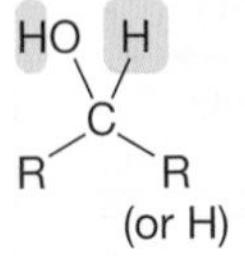 **Alcohol**	Catalytic hydrogenation	20.3
(2)	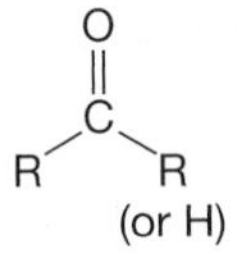 **Ketone or aldehyde**	Zn/Hg, HCl → H_2O, reflux	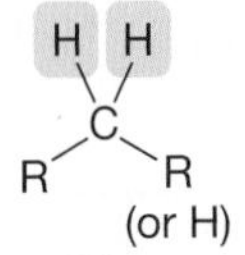 **Alkane**	Clemmensen reduction	20.4
(3)	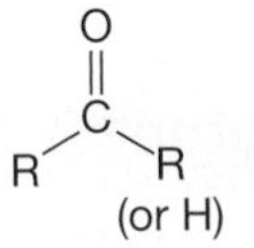 **Ketone or aldehyde**	1. $HSCH_2CH_2SH$, $H^{\oplus}$ → 2. Raney Ni (H_2)	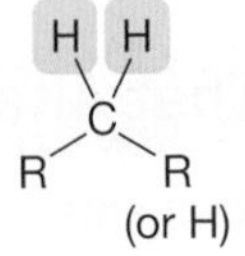 **Alkane**	Raney-nickel reduction	20.4
(4)	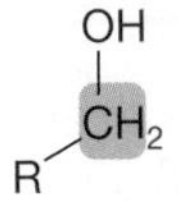 **1° Alcohol**	H_2CrO_4 → or 1. $KMnO_4$, KOH → 2. H_2O, HCl	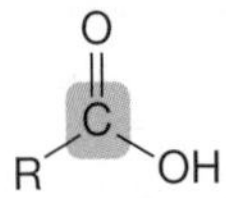 **Carboxylic acid**	Oxidation	20.5a, 20.5b
(5)	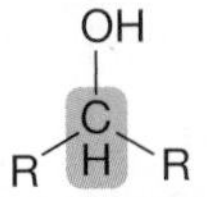 **2° Alcohol**	H_2CrO_4 → or $KMnO_4$, KOH →	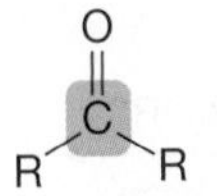 **Ketone**	Oxidation	20.5a, 20.5b
(6)	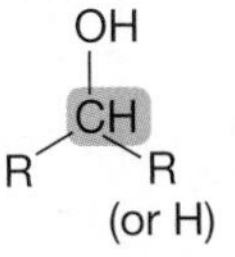 **1° or 2° Alcohol**	PCC →	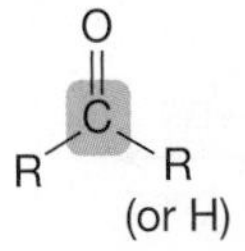 **Aldehyde or ketone**	Oxidation	20.5a, 20.5b

[a]X = Cl, Br, or I.

(continued)

TABLE 20-2 Functional Group Transformations[a] (continued)

	Starting Compound Class	Typical Reagents and Reaction Conditions	Compound Class Formed	Comments	Discussed in Section(s)
(7)	R–X **Alkyl halide**	$\xrightarrow[\text{Ether}]{\text{Mg(s)}}$	R–MgX **Grignard reagent**	Dissolving metal reduction	20.6
(8)	R–X **Alkyl halide**	$\xrightarrow[\text{Ether}]{\text{Li(s)}}$	R–Li **Alkyllithium reagent**	Dissolving metal reduction	20.6
(9)	R–Li **Alkyllithium reagent**	$\xrightarrow[\text{Ether}]{\text{CuI}}$	R–Cu(Li)–R **Lithium dialkylcuprate**	Transmetalation	20.6

[a]X = Cl, Br, or I.

TABLE 20-3 Reactions That Alter the Carbon Skeleton[a]

	Starting Compound Class	Typical Reagents and Reaction Conditions	Compound Class Formed	Comments	Discussed in Section
(1)	R–X **Alkyl, vinylic, or aryl halide**	$\xrightarrow{R'_2CuLi}$	R–R′	Coupling reaction	20.7a
(2)	R–X **Vinylic or aryl halide**	$\xrightarrow[\text{PdL}_n\text{, base}]{R'-B(OR'')_2}$	R–R′	Suzuki reaction	20.7b
(3)	R–X **Vinylic or aryl halide**	$\xrightarrow[\text{PdL}_2\text{, base}]{H-R'}$	R–R′	Heck reaction	20.7b
(4)	R—CH═CH_2 **Terminal alkene**	Grubbs catalyst ⟶	R—CH═CH—R **Alkene**	Alkene metathesis	20.7c

[a]X = Cl, Br, or I.

Problems

Problems that are related to synthesis are denoted (SYN).

Sections 20.1 and 20.2 Identifying Reactions as Redox Reactions; Oxidation States

20.1 Shown here is the conversion of an imine into an amine—a reaction we learned in Section 18.3. Determine whether the imine undergoes reduction, oxidation, or neither.

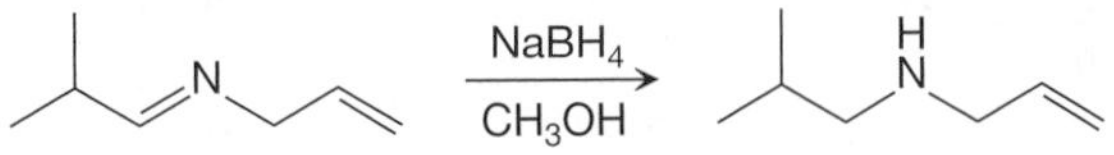

N
$NaBH_4$
CH_3OH
H
N

20.2 In this reaction, an R^- nucleophile adds to the carbonyl group of a ketone. Determine whether the ketone undergoes reduction, oxidation, or neither.

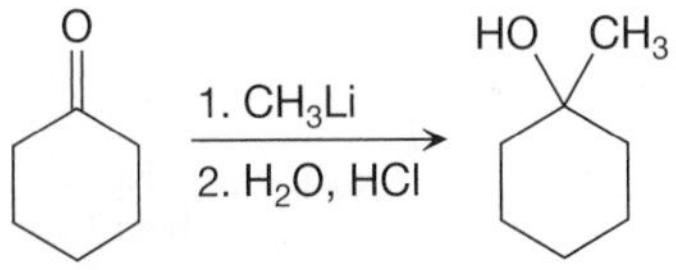

O
1. CH_3Li
2. H_2O, HCl
HO
CH_3

20.3 In Section 13.5, we learned that oxymercuration–reduction converts an alkene into an alcohol by adding water across the C═C bond in a Markovnikov fashion. In the second stage of such a transformation, the oxymercuration product is treated with sodium borohydride, as shown here. Argue that the oxymercuration product undergoes reduction in this reaction.

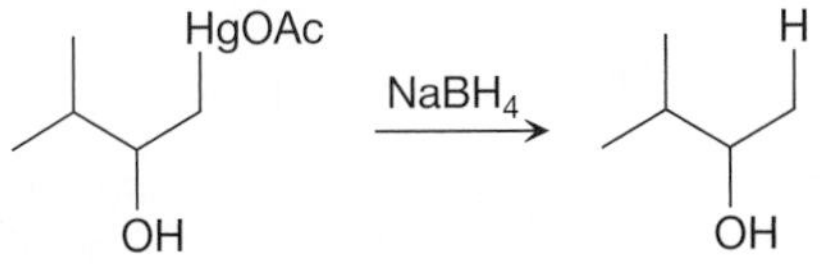

HgOAc
OH
$NaBH_4$
H
OH

20.4 In Section 13.6, we learned that hydroboration–oxidation converts an alkene into an alcohol by adding water across the C═C bond in an anti-Markovnikov fashion. In the second stage of such a transformation, the hydroboration product is treated with a basic solution of hydrogen peroxide, as shown below. Argue that the hydroboration product undergoes oxidation in this reaction.

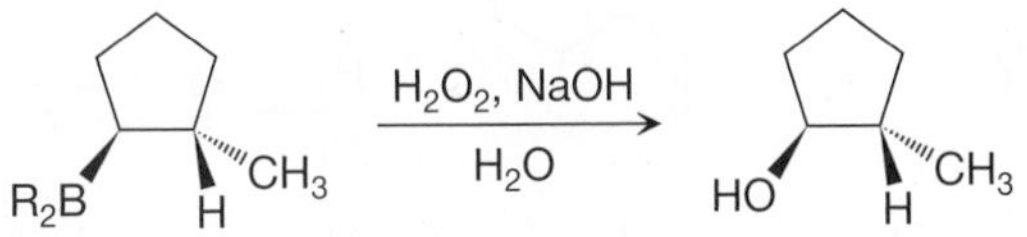

R_2B
H
CH_3
H_2O_2, NaOH
H_2O
HO
H
CH_3

20.5 In Section 20.1, we learned that an increase in the number of C—H bonds in a species typically characterizes a reduction of that species. However, when an organometallic species acts as a base to pick up a proton, such as in the example below, the organometallic species is *not* reduced. Explain why.

$$H_3C{-}Li \;+\; H{-}OCH_2CH_3 \longrightarrow H_3C{-}H \;+\; Li^{\oplus}\,{}^{\ominus}OCH_2CH_3$$

20.6 You may recall from general chemistry that, in a redox reaction, the reducing agent is the species that is oxidized, whereas the oxidizing agent is the species that is reduced. **(a)** Identify the reducing agents in Equations 20-1, 20-2, and 20-4 and argue that they are indeed oxidized. **(b)** Identify the oxidizing agent in Equation 20-5 and argue that it is indeed reduced.

Section 20.3 Catalytic Hydrogenation

20.7 Why do you think the acyclic C═C bond is selectively reduced in this reaction?

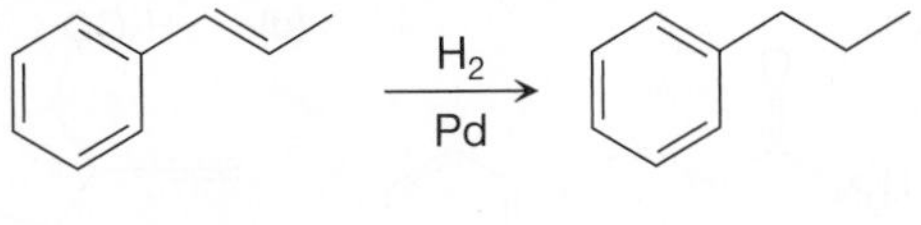

H_2
Pd

20.8 Draw the product of each of the following reactions.

(a)

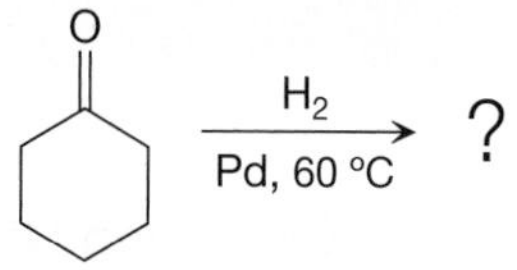
O
H2
Pd, 60 °C
?

(b)

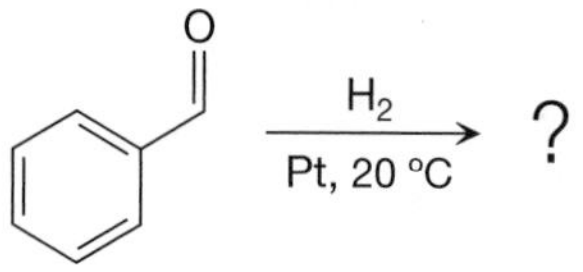
O
H2
Pt, 20 °C
?

(c)

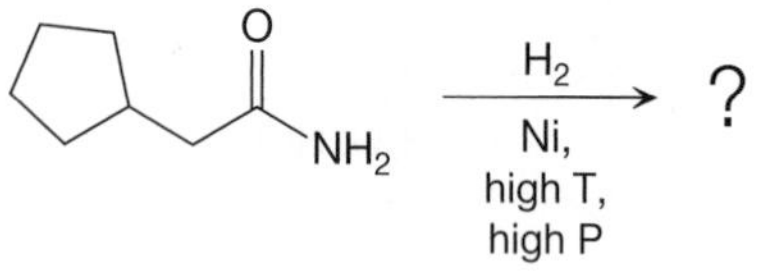
O
NH2
H2
Ni,
high T,
high P
?

(d)

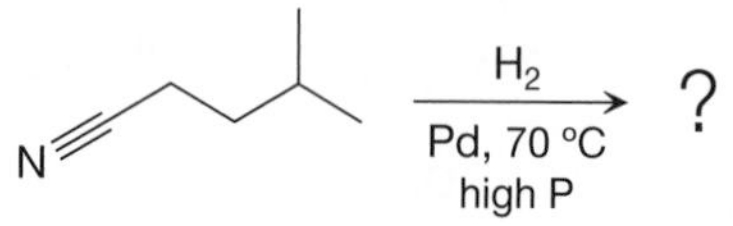
N
H2
Pd, 70 °C
high P
?

20.9 **(SYN)** Draw the starting material for each of the following transformations.

(a)

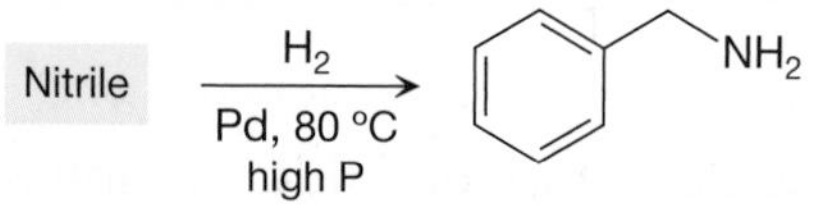
Nitrile
H2
Pd, 80 °C
high P
NH2

(b)

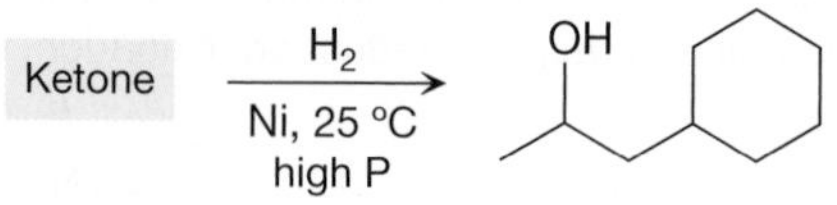
Ketone
H2
Ni, 25 °C
high P
OH

(c)

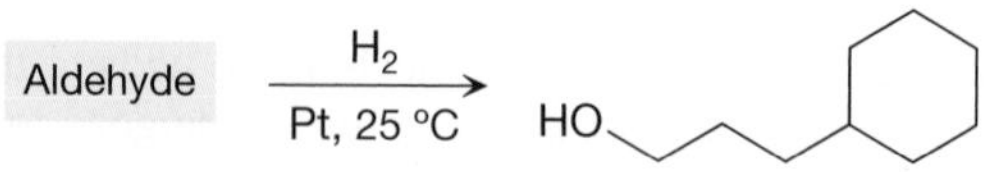
Aldehyde
H2
Pt, 25 °C
HO

20.10 Predict the product for each of the following reactions. Unless otherwise indicated, you may assume that one molar equivalent of H_2 reacts.

(a)

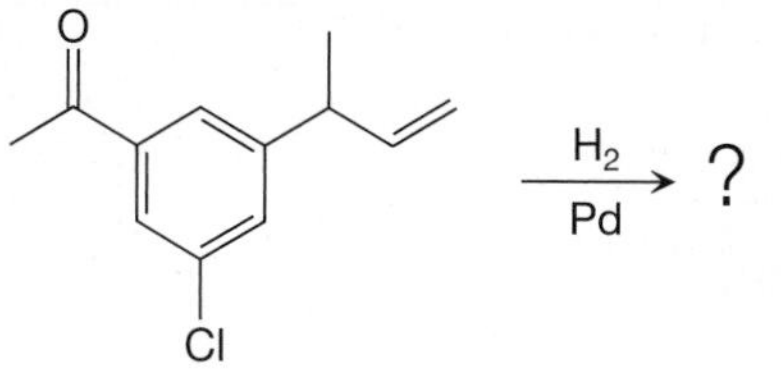
O
Cl
H2
Pd
?

(b)

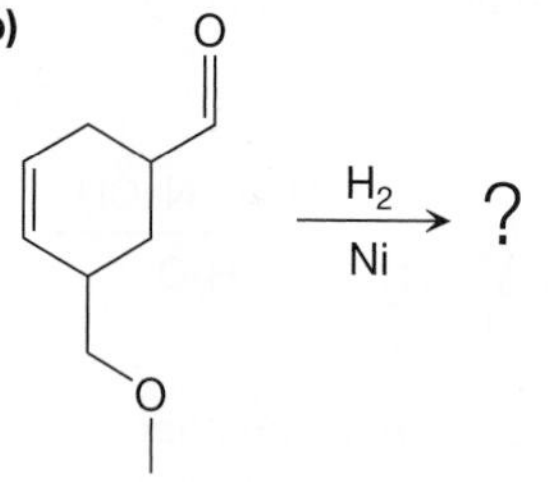
O
O
H2
Ni
?

(c)

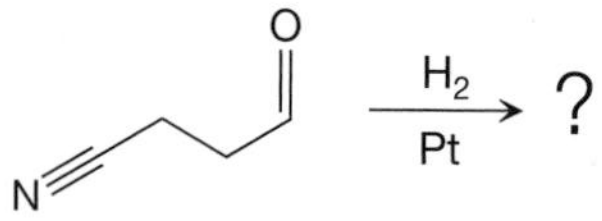
O
N
H2
Pt
?

(d)

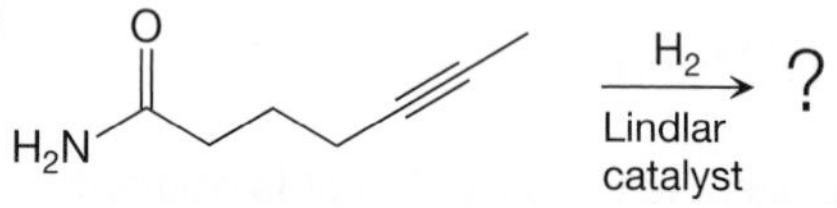
O
H2N
H2
Lindlar
catalyst
?

(e)

O
H2N
H2 (excess)
Pd
?

20.11 **(SYN)** Show how to carry out each of the following transformations.

(a)

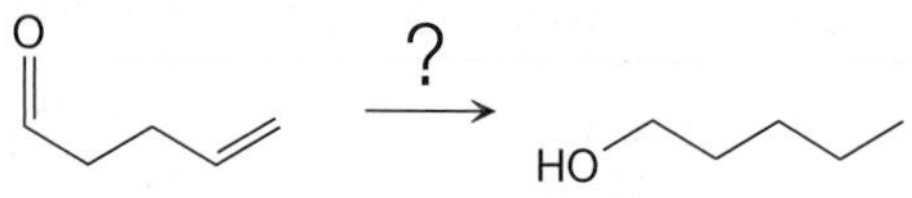
O
?
HO

(b)

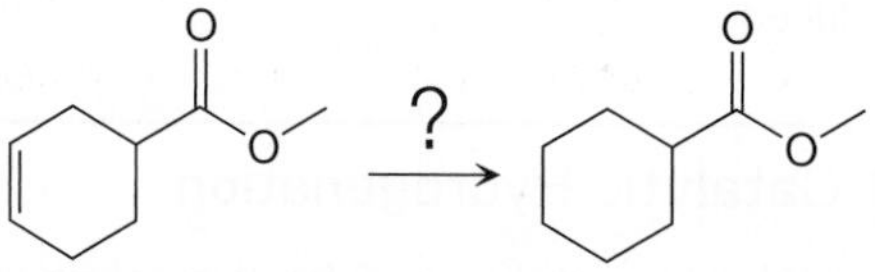
O
O
?
O
O

(c)

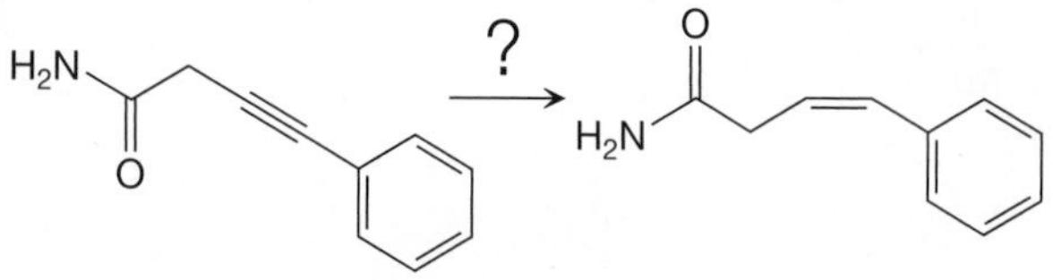
H2N
O
?
O
H2N

(d)

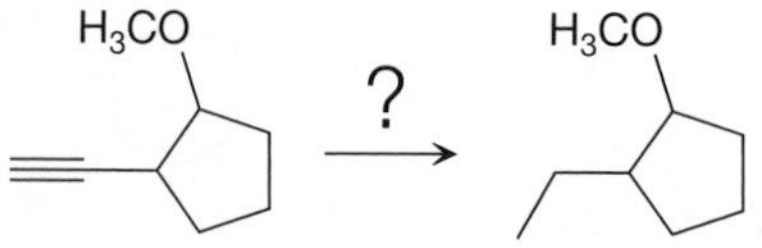
H3CO
?
H3CO

Section 20.4 Reactions That Reduce C=O to CH_2

20.12 Predict the product of each of the following reactions.

(a)

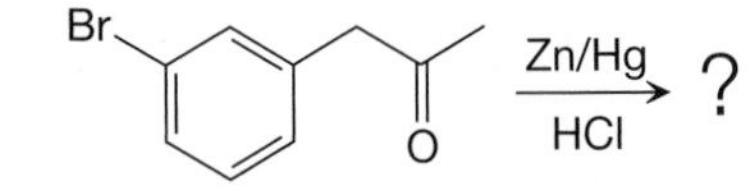
Br
O
Zn/Hg
HCl
?

(b)

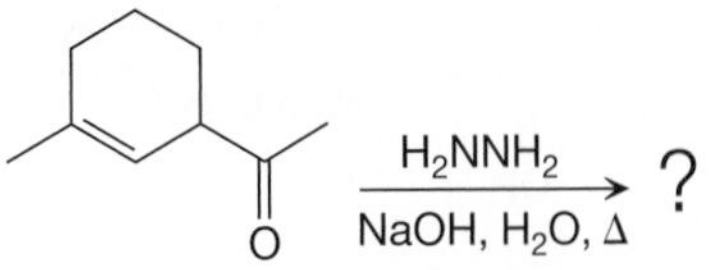
O
H_2NNH_2
NaOH, H_2O, Δ
?

(c)

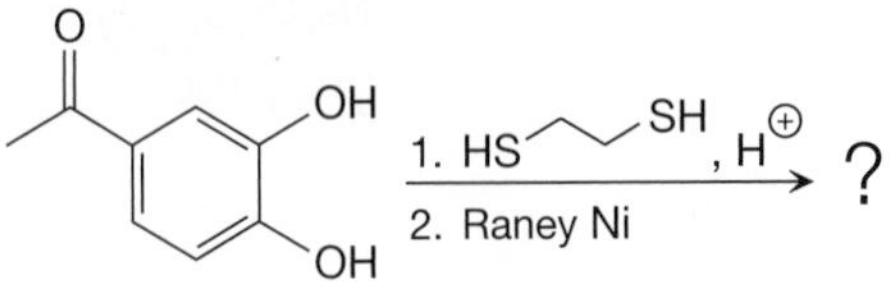
O
OH
OH
1. HS⁀⁀SH, $H^{\oplus}$
2. Raney Ni
?

20.13 (SYN) Show how to carry out each of the following transformations.

(a)

O
?

(b)

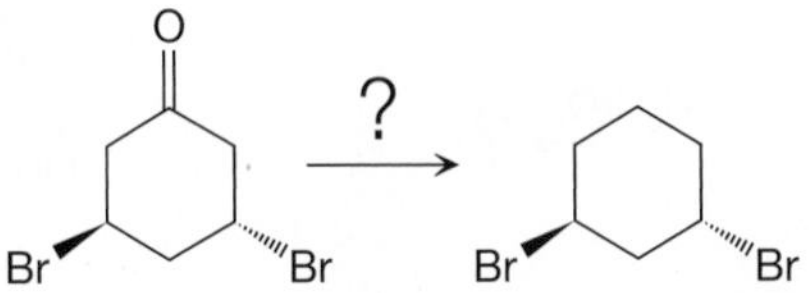
O
?
Br
Br
Br
Br

(c)

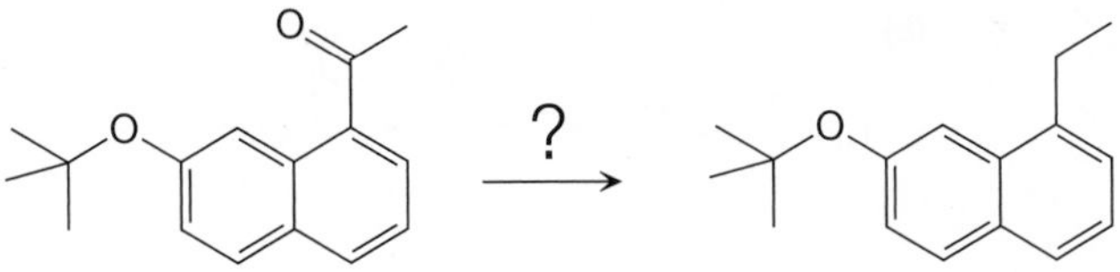
O
O
?
O

20.14 (SYN) Show how to carry out this transformation using $(CH_3CH_2CH_2)_2CuLi$ as your only other carbon source.

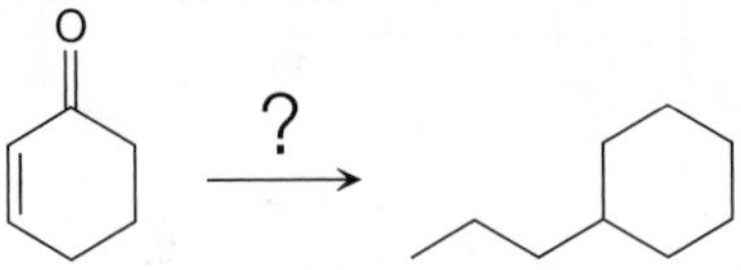
O
?

20.15 (SYN) Draw two different compounds having the formula C_8H_8O that could be used as the starting material for this transformation.

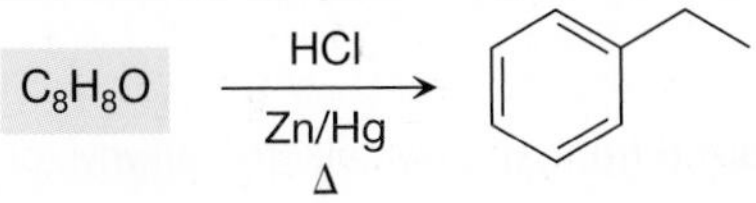
C_8H_8O
HCl
Zn/Hg
Δ

20.16 (SYN) How many different compounds with the formula $C_{10}H_{18}O$ could be used as the starting material for this reaction? Draw each one that is possible.

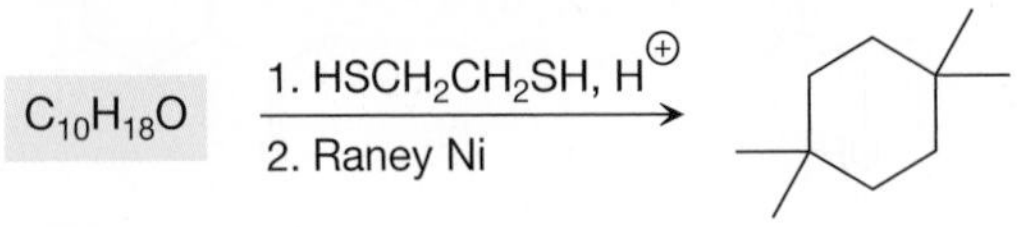
$C_{10}H_{18}O$
1. $HSCH_2CH_2SH$, $H^{\oplus}$
2. Raney Ni

Section 20.5 Oxidations of Alcohols and Aldehydes

20.17 (SYN) Draw the starting compound with the indicated formula that could be used for each of the following transformations.

(a)

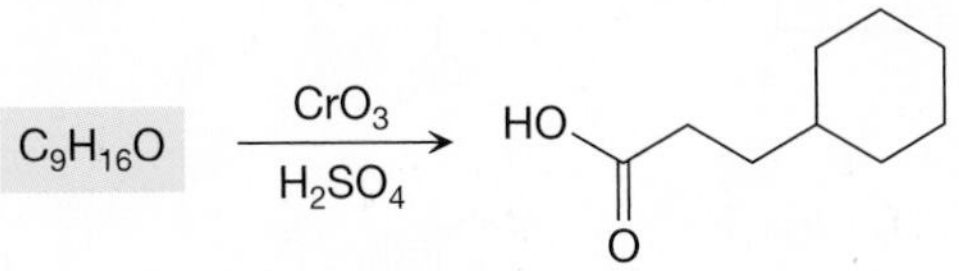
$C_9H_{16}O$
CrO_3
H_2SO_4
HO
O

(b)

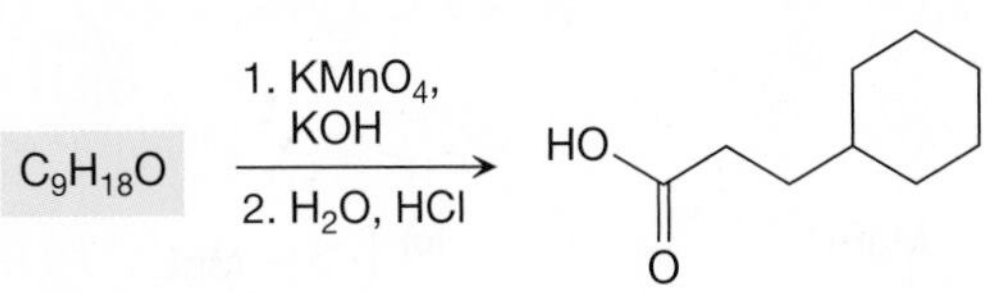
$C_9H_{18}O$
1. $KMnO_4$, KOH
2. H_2O, HCl
HO
O

(c)

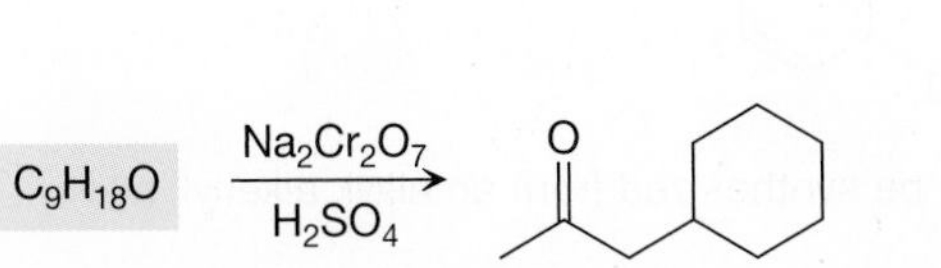
$C_9H_{18}O$
$Na_2Cr_2O_7$
H_2SO_4
O

(d)

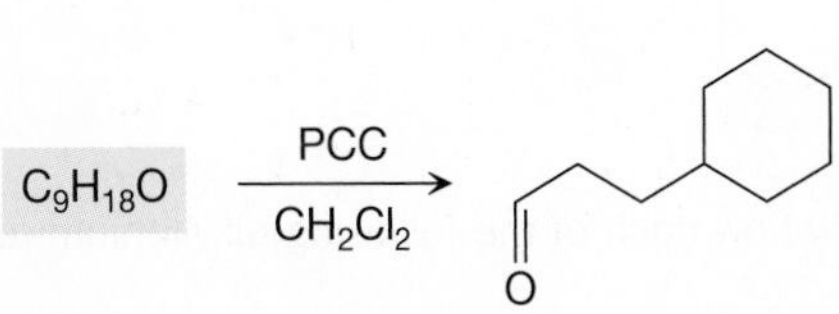
$C_9H_{18}O$
PCC
CH_2Cl_2
O

20.18 Predict the product of each of the following reactions.

(a)
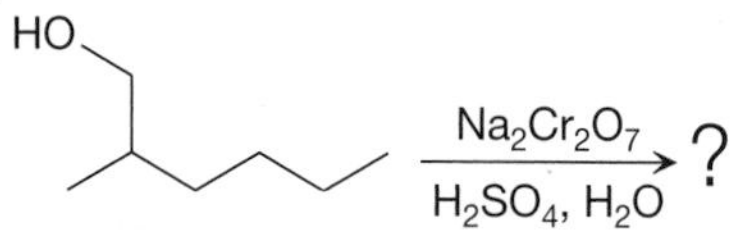

(b)
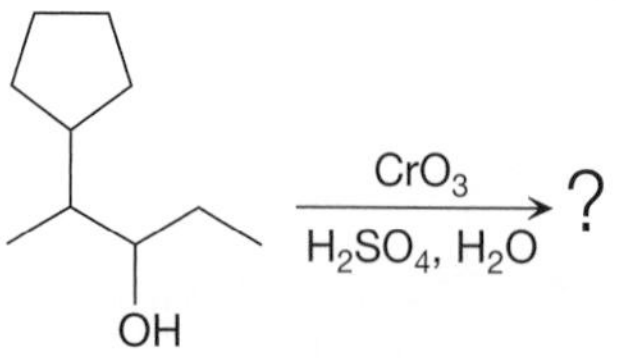

(c)
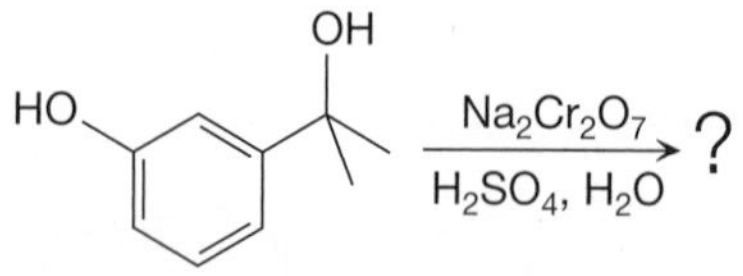

(d)
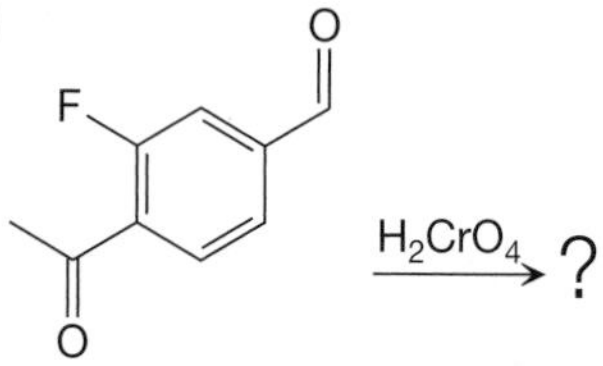

(e)
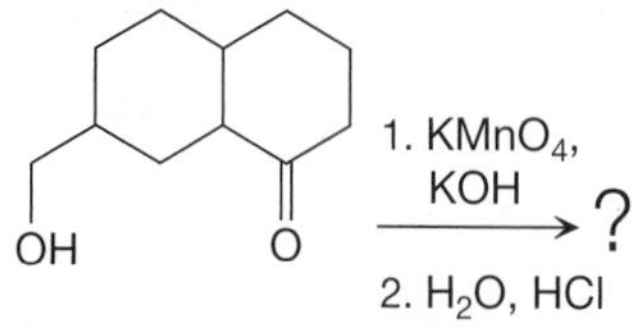

(f)
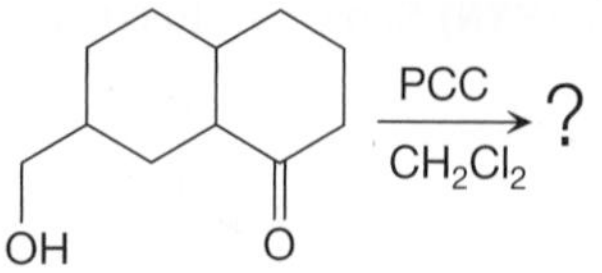

20.19 **(SYN)** Show how to carry out each of the following transformations.

(a)
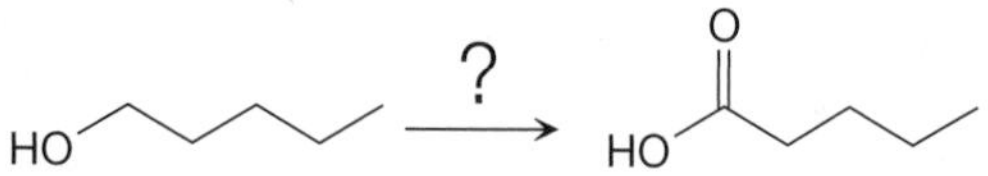

(b)
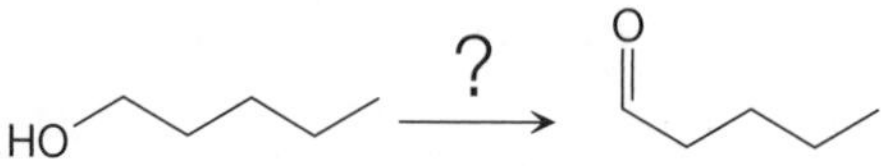

(c)
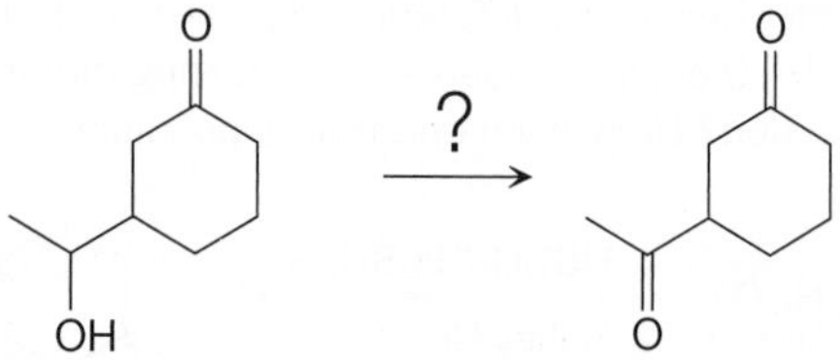

(d)
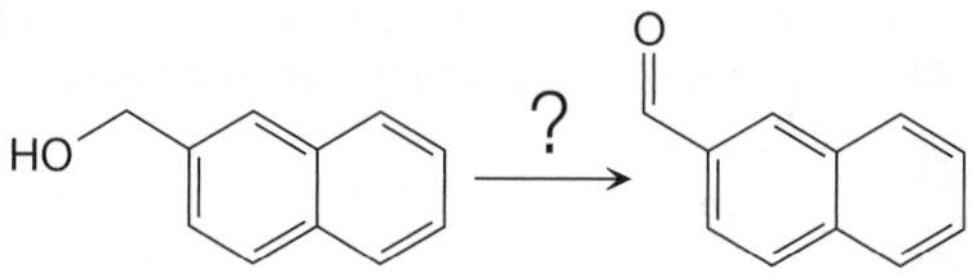

20.20 Draw the structure of a diol having the formula $C_7H_{16}O_2$ that will not react when treated with sodium dichromate under acidic conditions.

Diol = $C_7H_{16}O_2$ $\xrightarrow[H_2SO_4]{Na_2Cr_2O_7}$ No reaction

Section 20.6 Generating Organometallic Reagents

20.21 **(SYN)** Show how each of the following Grignard reagents can be synthesized from an alkyl, alkenyl, alkynyl, or aryl halide.

(a)
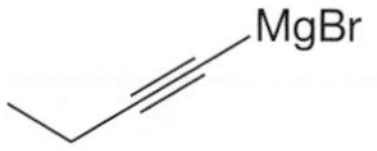

(b)
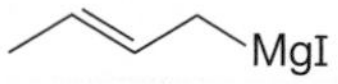

(c)
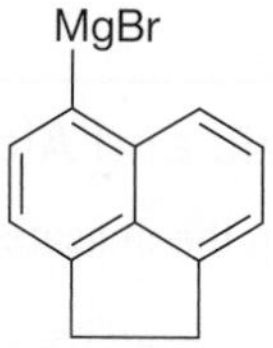

(d)

(e)
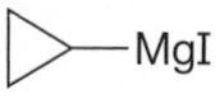

(f)
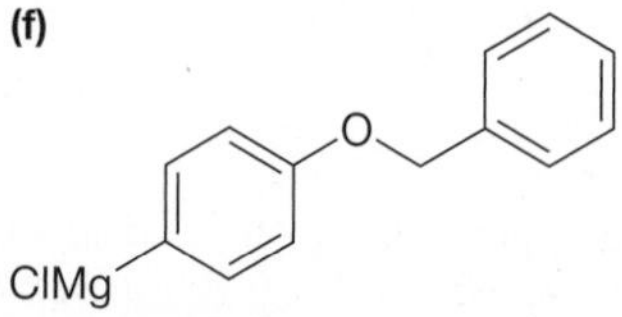

20.22 **(SYN)** Show how each of the following alkyllithium reagents can be synthesized from an alkyl, alkenyl, alkynyl, or aryl halide.

(a)

(b)
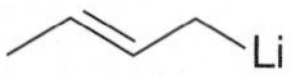

(c)
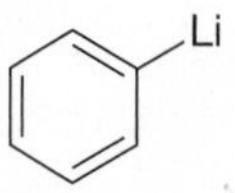

(d)
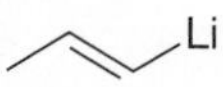

20.23 **(SYN)** Show how each of the following lithium dialkylcuprate reagents can be synthesized from an alkyl, alkenyl, alkynyl, or aryl halide.

(a) 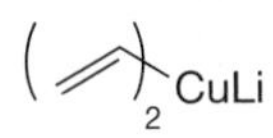
(b) 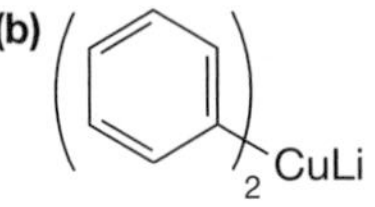
(c) 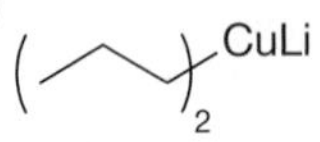
(d) 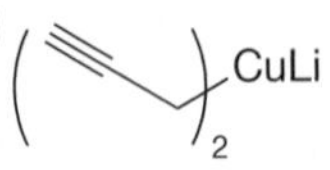

20.24 Draw the organometallic compound that would be produced by each of the following reactions.

(a) 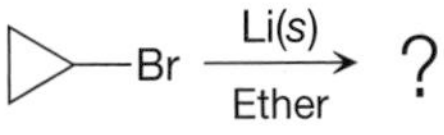
(b) 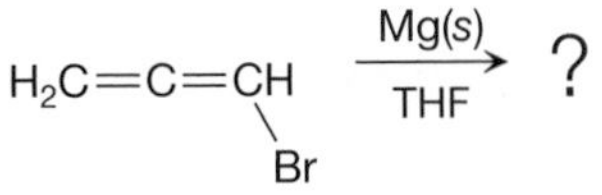
(c) 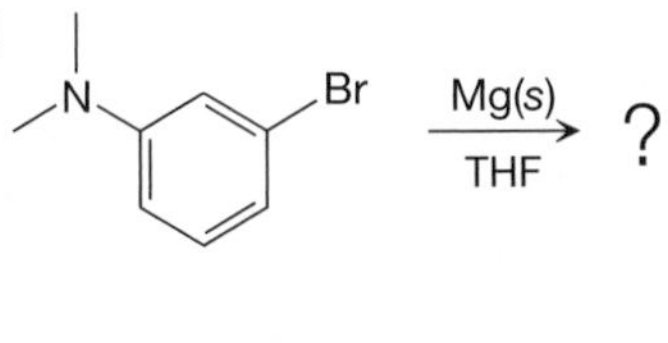
(d) 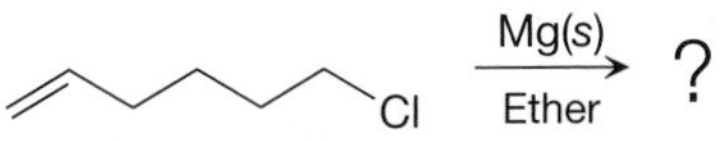
(e) 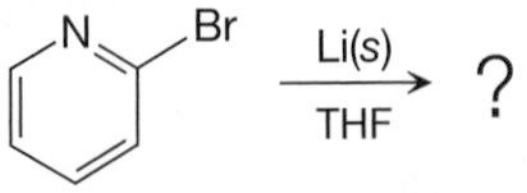

20.25 Draw the organometallic compound that would be produced by each of the following reactions.

(a) 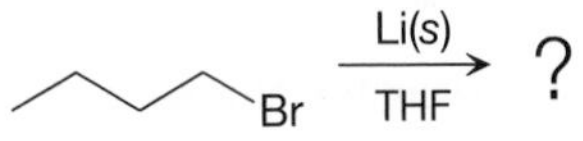
(b) 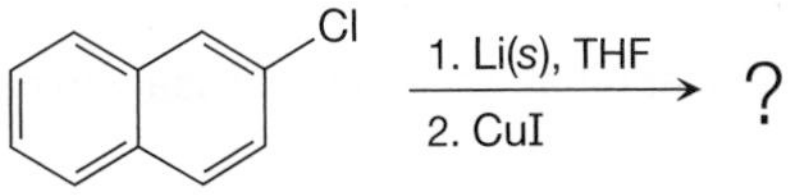

20.26 Explain why a Grignard reagent will not form when this compound is treated with magnesium. 

Section 20.7 Coupling and Alkene Metathesis Reactions

20.27 Draw the major organic products for each of the following reactions. If no reaction occurs, state so.

(a) 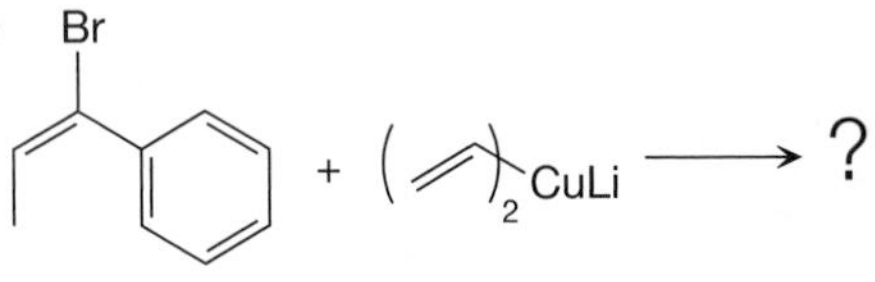
(b) 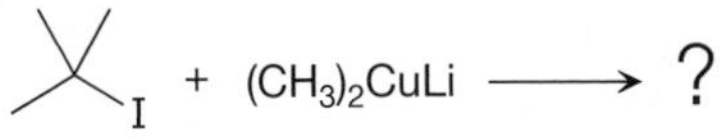
(c) 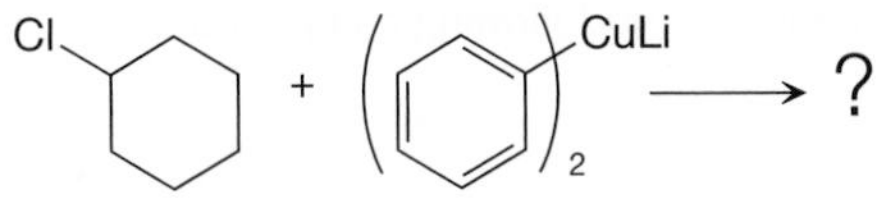
(d) 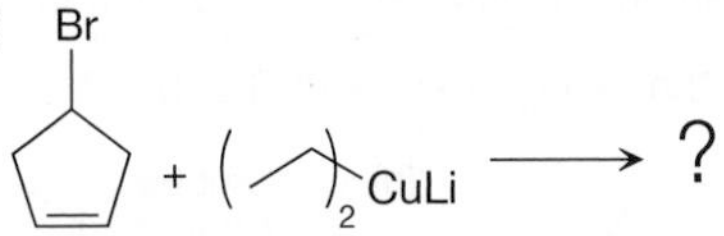

20.28 **(SYN)** Draw the missing lithium dialkylcuprate that would be necessary to carry out each of the following transformations.

(a) 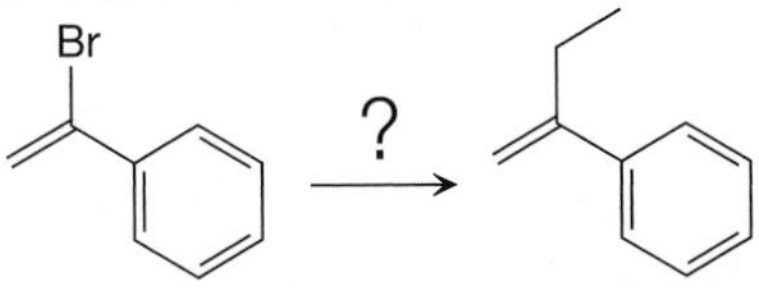
(b) 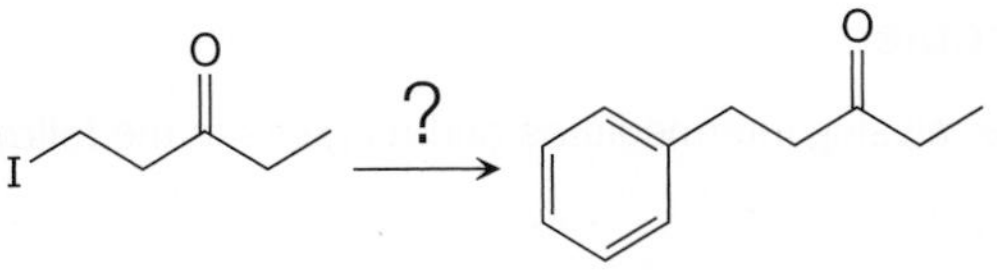

20.29 Can a Suzuki reaction be used to produce the single bond between the two phenyl rings in biphenyl, $C_6H_5—C_6H_5$? Can a Heck reaction be used? In each case, what would the precursors be?

20.30 Draw the major organic products for each of the following reactions.

(a)

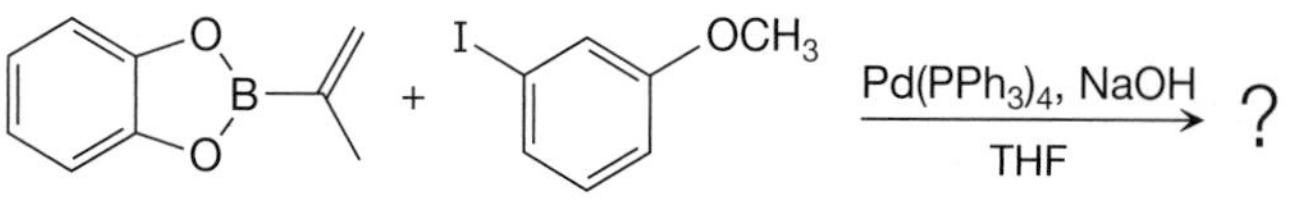

Pd(PPh3)4, NaOH
THF

(b)

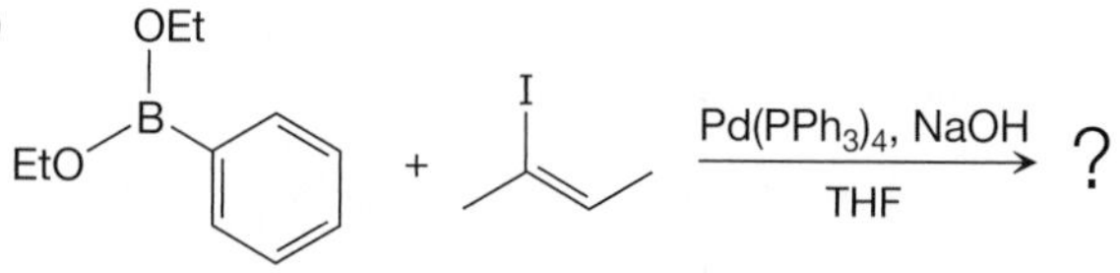

Pd(PPh3)4, NaOH
THF

(c)

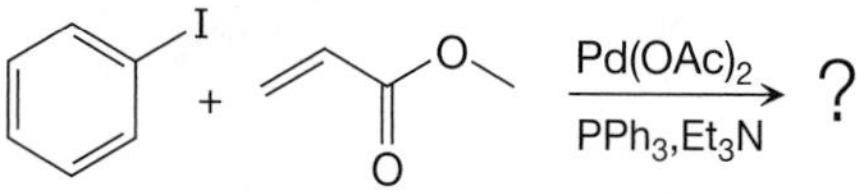

Pd(OAc)2
PPh3,Et3N

(d)

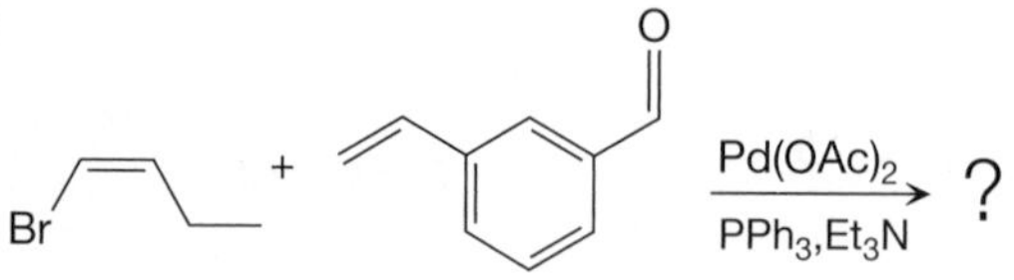

Pd(OAc)2
PPh3,Et3N

20.31 Draw the major organic product for each for the following reactions.

(a)

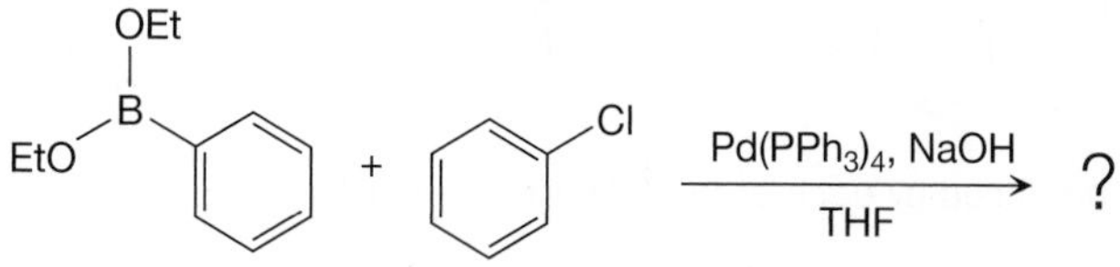

Pd(PPh3)4, NaOH
THF

(b)

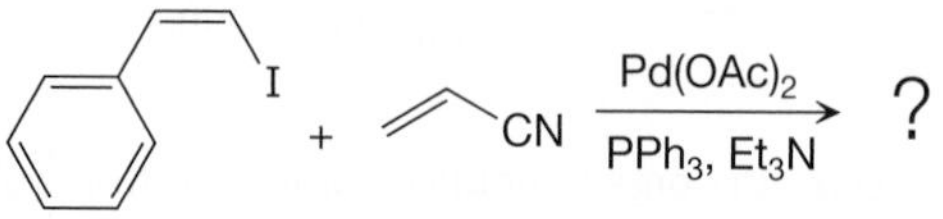

Pd(OAc)2
PPh3, Et3N

20.32 (SYN) Draw the missing reactant that would be necessary to carry out each of the following transformations.

(a)

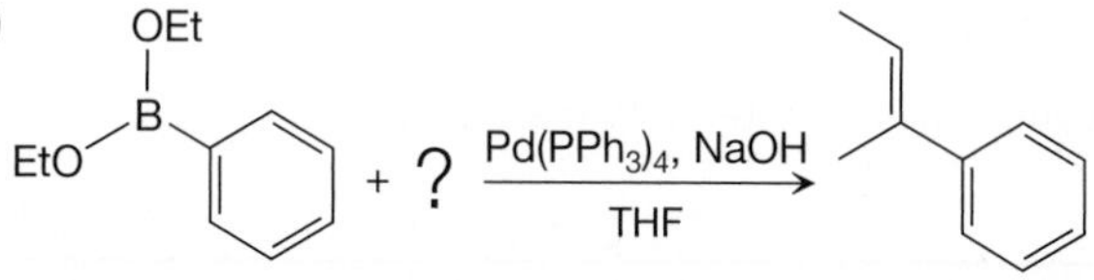

Pd(PPh3)4, NaOH
THF

(b)

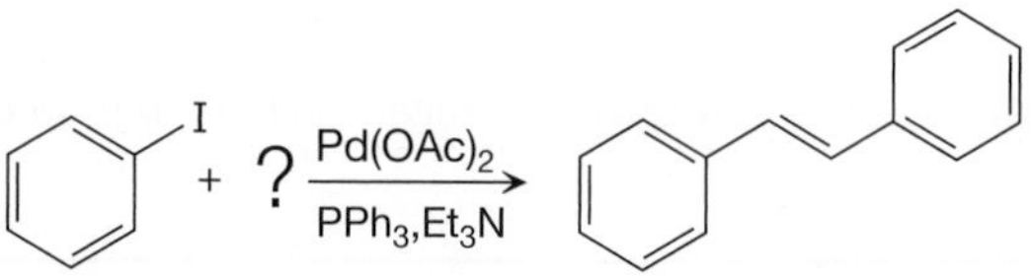

Pd(OAc)2
PPh3,Et3N

20.33 Draw the major organic products for each of the following reactions.

(a)

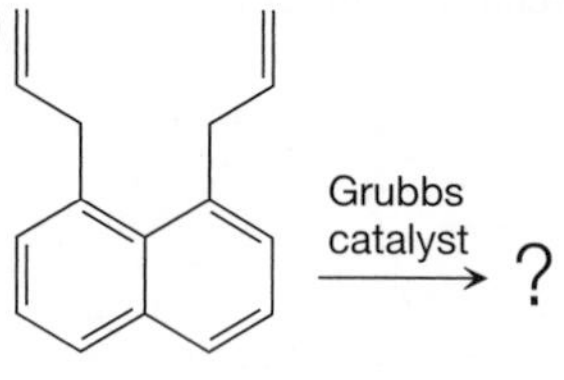

Grubbs
catalyst

(b)

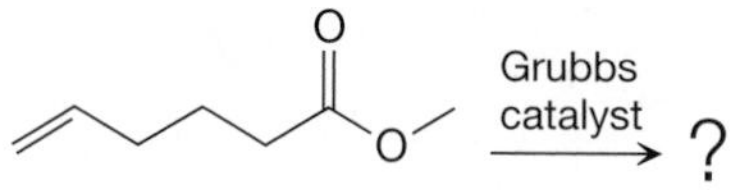

Grubbs
catalyst

20.34 Modify the mechanism in Equation 20-38 (p. 1013) to show how $H_2C{=}CH_2$ is produced.

20.35 (SYN) Draw a diene that would react with Grubbs catalyst to produce each of the following compounds.

(a)

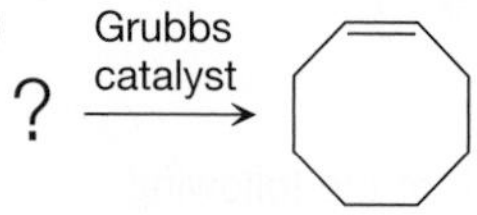

Grubbs
catalyst

(b)

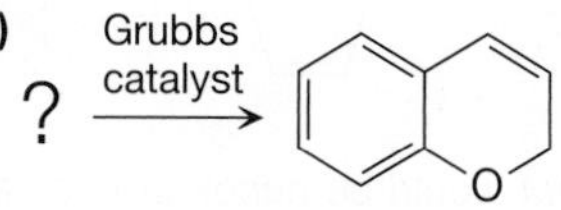

Grubbs
catalyst

Integrated Problems

20.36 Supply the missing intermediates and reagents in the following synthesis.

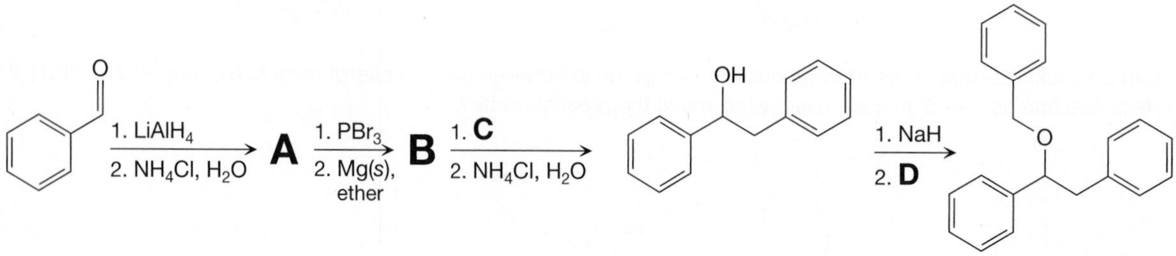

1. LiAlH4
2. NH4Cl, H2O
A
1. PBr3
2. Mg(s), ether
B
1. C
2. NH4Cl, H2O
OH
1. NaH
2. D

20.37 Supply the missing intermediates and reagents in the following synthesis.

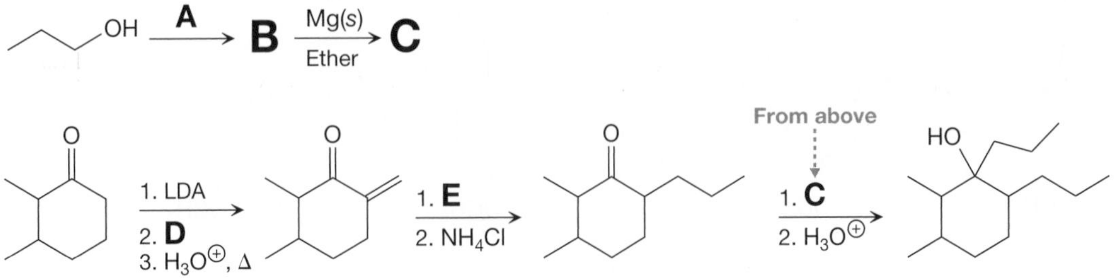
OH
A
B
Mg(s)
Ether
C
O
1. LDA
2. D
3. $H_3O^{\oplus}$, Δ
1. E
2. NH_4Cl
From above
1. C
2. $H_3O^{\oplus}$
HO

20.38 Provide the missing intermediates and reagents in the synthesis shown here.

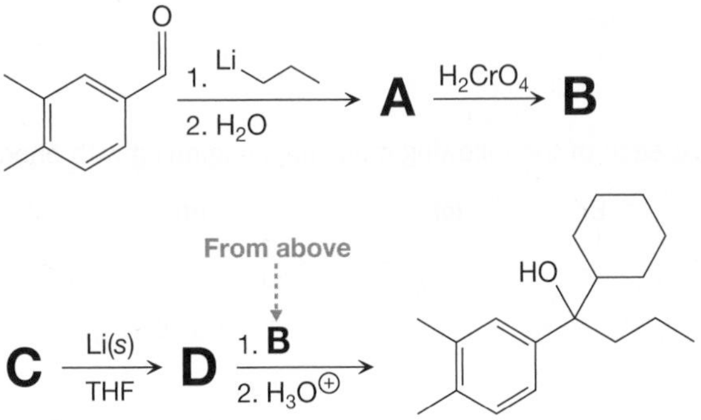
O
1. Li
2. H_2O
A
H_2CrO_4
B
From above
HO
C
Li(s)
THF
D
1. B
2. $H_3O^{\oplus}$

20.39 Provide the missing intermediates and final product in the following synthesis.

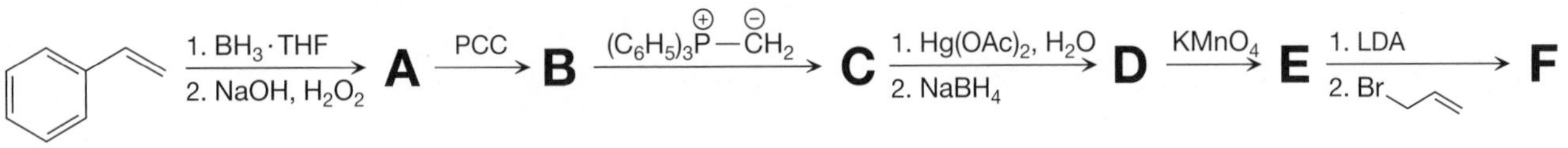
1. $BH_3 \cdot THF$
2. NaOH, H_2O_2
A
PCC
B
$(C_6H_5)_3\overset{\oplus}{P}-\overset{\ominus}{C}H_2$
C
1. $Hg(OAc)_2$, H_2O
2. $NaBH_4$
D
$KMnO_4$
E
1. LDA
2. Br
F

20.40 Provide the missing intermediates and final product in the following synthesis.

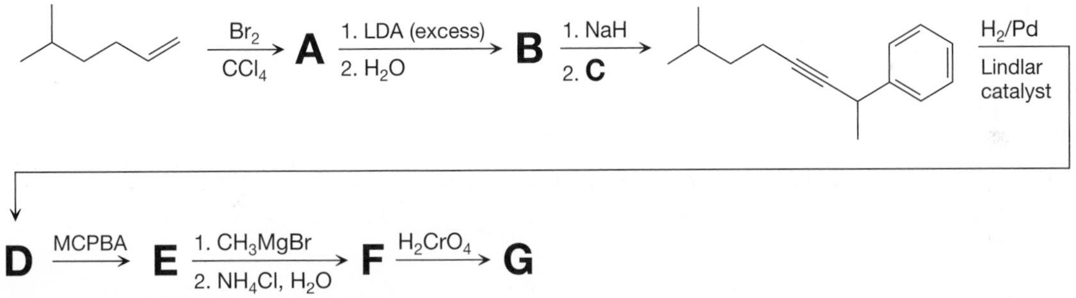
Br_2
CCl_4
A
1. LDA (excess)
2. H_2O
B
1. NaH
2. C
H_2/Pd
Lindlar catalyst
D
MCPBA
E
1. CH_3MgBr
2. NH_4Cl, H_2O
F
H_2CrO_4
G

20.41 **(SYN)** Using acetone, any alcohol with six or fewer carbons, and any inorganic reagents necessary, show how to synthesize each of the following compounds.

(a)

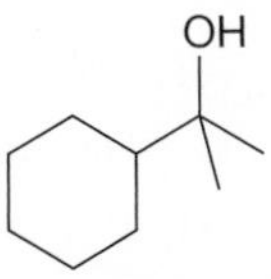
OH

(b)

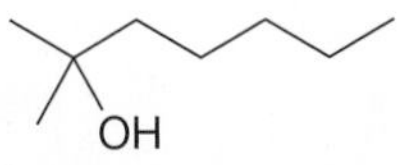
OH

(c)

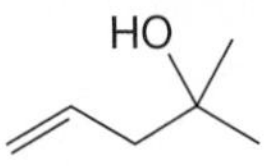
HO

(d)

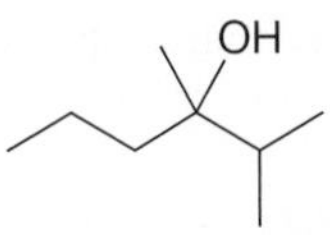
OH

20.42 Show how you would synthesize 4-phenylbutan-1-ol from bromobenzene, using oxirane, , as your only other source of carbon.

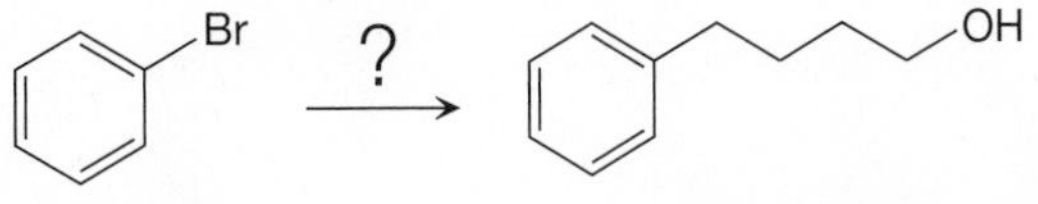
Br
?
OH

Bromobenzene **4-Phenylbutan-1-ol**

20.43 (SYN) Show how to carry out each of the following syntheses, using any reagents necessary. *Hint*: In each case, the carbonyl group of a ketone or aldehyde is entirely removed.

(a)

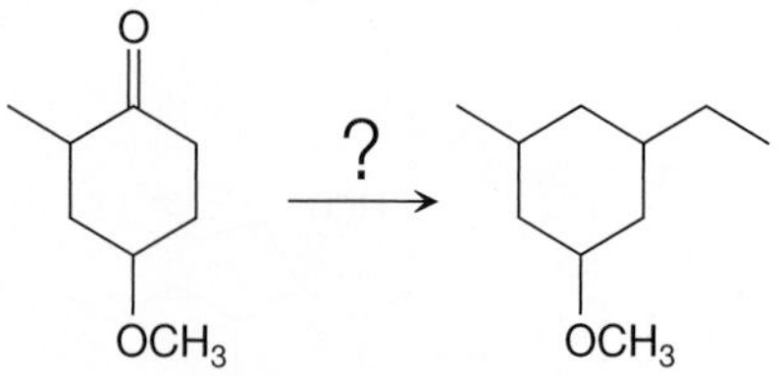

(b)

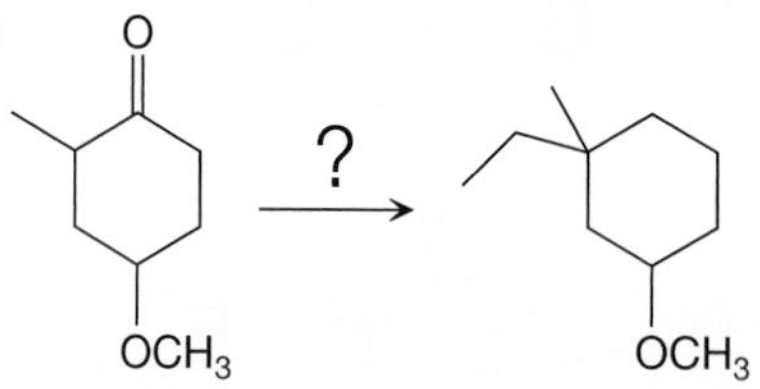

(c)

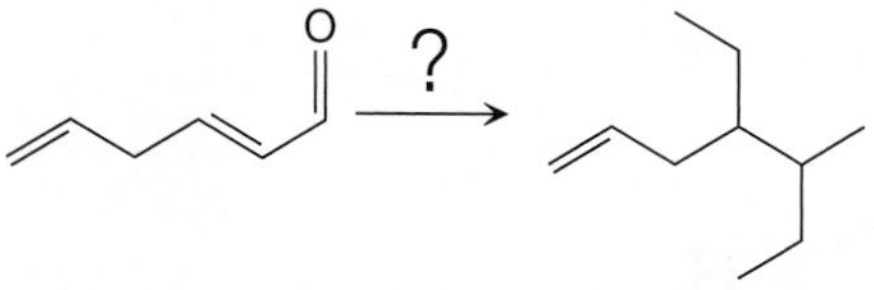

20.44 (SYN) Show how to synthesize each of the following molecules beginning with phenylmethanol (benzyl alcohol).

(a)

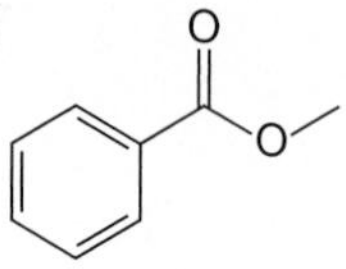

(b)

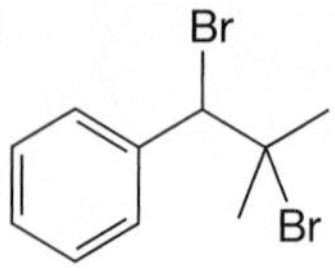

(c)

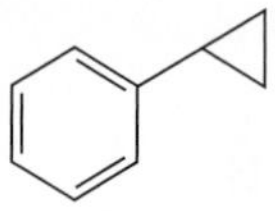

(d)

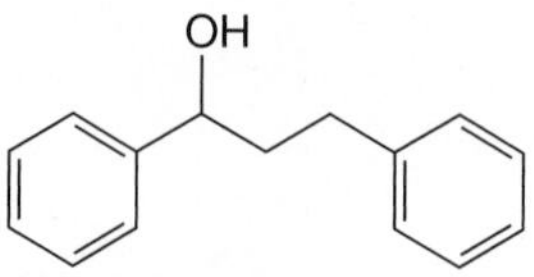

21

When oxygen is scarce, these goldfish perform ethanol fermentation to avoid the buildup of toxic levels of lactic acid. In ethanol fermentation, an enzyme called pyruvate decarboxylase is involved in converting pyruvate into acetaldehyde, and a key step in that conversion effectively changes an electrophilic carbon into a nucleophilic one. Such a reversal of electrophilic/nucleophilic character is called *umpolung*, and as we will see here in Chapter 21, it can be used as a strategy in organic synthesis.

Organic Synthesis 3

Intermediate Topics in Synthesis Design

Chapters 10 and 11 introduced the basics of organic synthesis, focusing on how to construct a molecule with the appropriate carbon skeleton and how to convert one functional group into another. Now that we have gained experience with even more reactions, we continue our discussion of organic synthesis, exploring some higher-level topics that will allow us to synthesize more elaborate target molecules.

Much of our focus in Chapter 21 is geared toward things that are helpful to consider when a synthesis calls for the formation of a new carbon–carbon bond. Carbon–carbon bonds typically form between carbon atoms with opposite charges, but we are often faced with the challenge of forming these bonds between carbon atoms that are initially of like charge. Therefore, we begin with a strategy to accomplish this. Next, we focus on clues in a target molecule that help us determine the types of carbon–carbon bond-forming reactions that should be considered in a synthesis. We also consider ways to tackle a synthesis in which these kinds of clues do not exist.

Another focus of Chapter 21 is on ways to circumvent *synthetic traps* (see Recall box). Specifically, we discuss the use of *selective reagents* to carry out reactions that target one functional group over another. We also discuss strategies for keeping functional groups intact by using *protecting groups*.

◂ RECALL

In Section 11.4, we learned that a synthetic trap arises when the conditions necessary for a desired reaction at one site within a molecule will cause an undesired reaction at another site.

Chapter Outline

SECTION 21.1 OBJECTIVES

You will be able to:

1. Identify reactions in which umpolung takes place, and use umpolung as a synthesis strategy when considering how to form a new carbon–carbon bond.
2. Use the relative positioning of heteroatoms in a target as a clue to help determine which carbon–carbon bond-forming reaction should be considered in a synthesis.
3. Design syntheses that incorporate the removal of a functional group after a carbon–carbon bond has been formed.

21.1 Considerations When a Synthesis Calls For a New Carbon–Carbon Bond

In Chapter 11 we stressed the importance of reactions that alter the carbon skeleton and, in particular, reactions that form carbon–carbon bonds. So far, about 20 such carbon–carbon bond-forming reactions have been presented. When a synthesis calls for the formation of a carbon–carbon bond, how do we know which of these reactions might be appropriate to use? Once we decide on a particular carbon–carbon bond-forming reaction to use, what issues should we consider in our effort to convert the starting materials into the necessary precursors for that reaction? These questions are tackled here in Section 21.1.

21.1a Umpolung in Organic Synthesis: Forming Bonds between Carbon Atoms Initially Bearing Like Charge

In Section 7.1, we learned that a bond can form between two atoms when one atom bears a partial or full negative charge (and thus is electron-rich, or nucleophilic) and the other bears a partial or full positive charge (making it electron-poor, or electrophilic). This general idea is applicable to a wide variety of bond-forming reactions, including those that form carbon–carbon bonds. Consider, for example, the reaction in Equation 21-1:

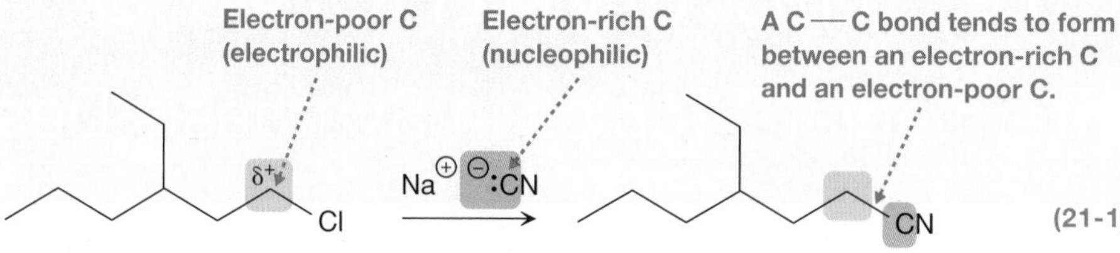

Electron-poor C (electrophilic)
Electron-rich C (nucleophilic)
A C—C bond tends to form between an electron-rich C and an electron-poor C.
δ+
Cl
Na⊕ ⊖:CN
CN

(21-1)

The bond that is formed involves the carbon atom from NC^- and the carbon atom attached to C-1 in the alkyl halide. The NC^- carbon bears a full negative charge, whereas the alkyl halide carbon bears a partial positive charge.

Because carbon–carbon bond-forming reactions usually involve oppositely charged carbon atoms, a problem arises when we want to form a bond between two carbon atoms bearing like charges. For example, Equation 21-2 shows that no bond readily forms between the carbonyl C atom of a ketone and the C atom attached to Br in an alkyl bromide. This is because both C atoms are attached to atoms with relatively high electronegativities (O and Br, respectively), so both bear partial positive charges.

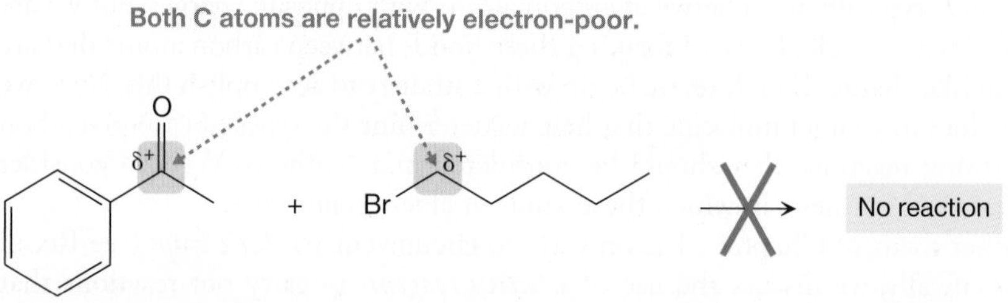

Both C atoms are relatively electron-poor.
O
δ+
δ+
+
Br
No reaction

(21-2)

One way to form a bond between two carbons of like charge is to carry out a separate reaction that first reverses the charge (or *polarity*) at one of the carbons. Thus, one carbon atom would become electron-rich while the other would remain electron-poor. Reversing a charge at a particular atom, a strategy called **umpolung** (a German term meaning "polarity reversal"), is common practice in organic synthesis. In fact, we have already encountered some reactions in which umpolung takes place. For example, as we learned in Section 20.6, we can convert the alkyl halide in Equation 21-3 into an organometallic species such as a Grignard reagent:

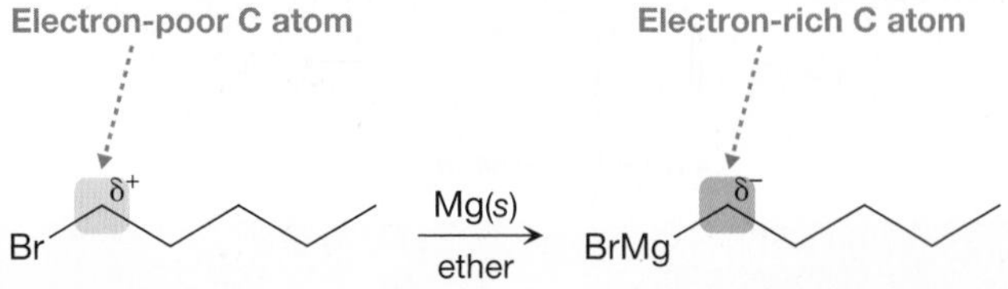
Electron-poor C atom
Electron-rich C atom
Br
Mg(s)
ether
BrMg

(21-3)

Notice that the carbon atom that was electron-poor in the alkyl halide becomes electron-rich in the Grignard reagent (see top Recall box). In a subsequent Grignard reaction, the Grignard reagent can react with the ketone to form a new carbon–carbon bond:

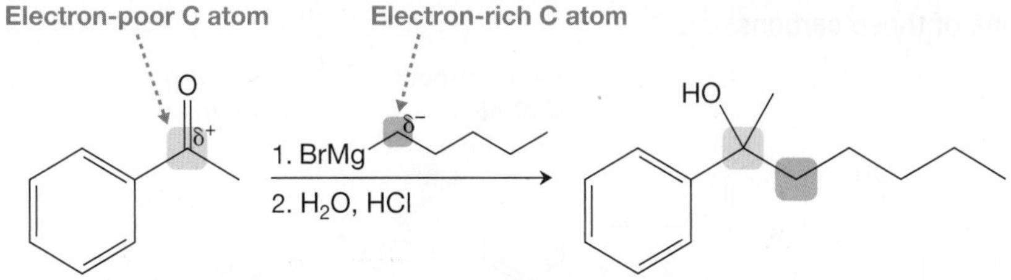
Electron-poor C atom
Electron-rich C atom
O
1. BrMg
2. H2O, HCl
HO

(21-4)

◂ RECALL

Although Grignard and other organometallic reagents have C—Metal covalent bonds, we learned in Section 7.1b that such compounds can be simplified to carbanions in which the C atom bears a lone pair of electrons and a −1 formal charge.

Another example of umpolung is the conversion of an alkyl halide into a Wittig reagent (see bottom Recall box), which was first presented in Section 18.7:

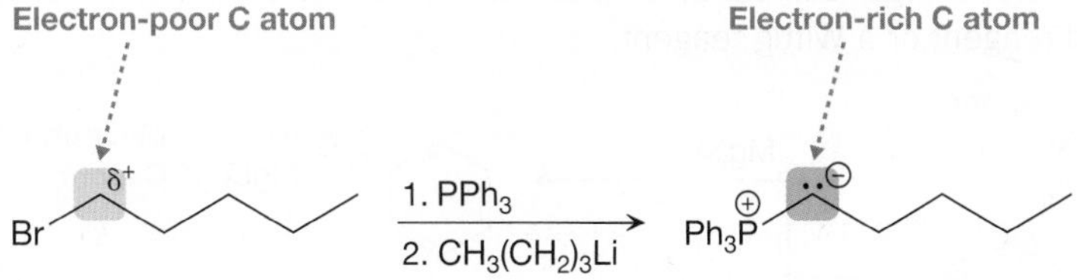
Electron-poor C atom
Electron-rich C atom
Br
1. PPh3
2. CH3(CH2)3Li
Ph3P

(21-5)

◂ RECALL

Section 18.6 showed that Wittig reagents are characterized by a C—P bond in which the C atom bears a −1 formal charge and a lone pair and the P atom bears a +1 formal charge. Thus, a Wittig reagent is strongly nucleophilic at the C atom.

We can then carry out a subsequent Wittig reaction with the ketone to form a new carbon–carbon bond:

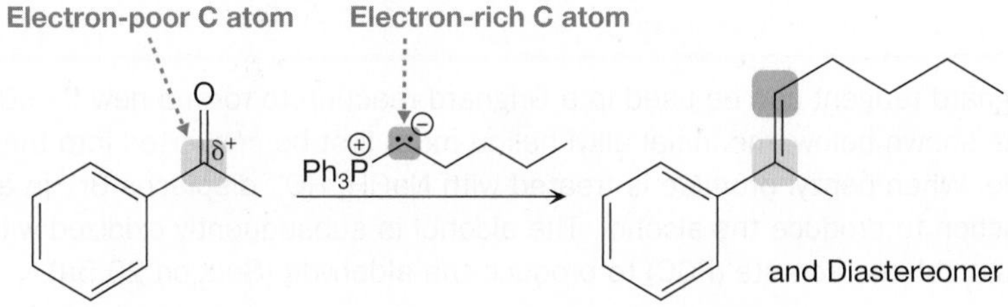
Electron-poor C atom
Electron-rich C atom
O
Ph3P
and Diastereomer

(21-6)

YOUR TURN 21.1

For each reaction, write either δ^+ or δ^- next to the C atom bonded to the halogen in the reactant and the C atom bonded to the metal atom in the product. Argue whether umpolung has taken place in each reaction.

(a)

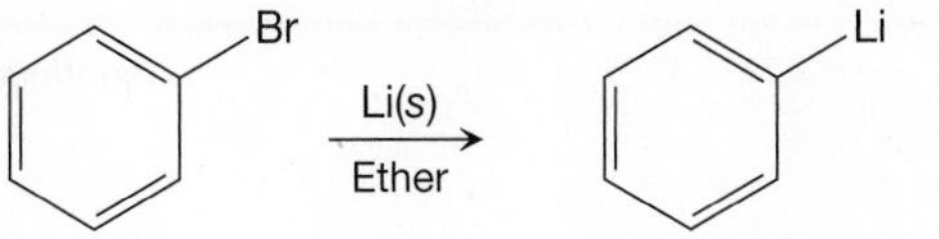
Br
Li(s)
Ether
Li

(b)

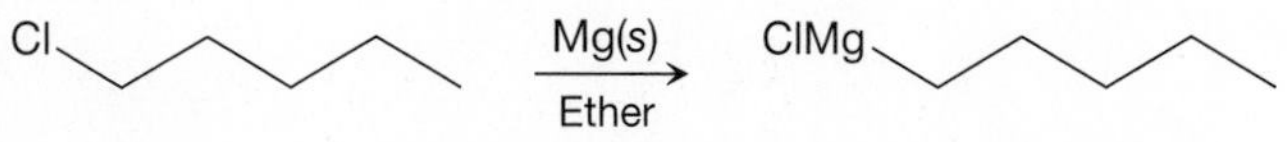
Cl
Mg(s)
Ether
ClMg

Answers to Your Turns are in the back of the book.

SOLVED PROBLEM **21.1**

How to incorporate umpolung in a synthesis that requires a new C—C bond

Break It Down Show how to carry out the following synthesis, using benzyl bromide as your only carbon source.

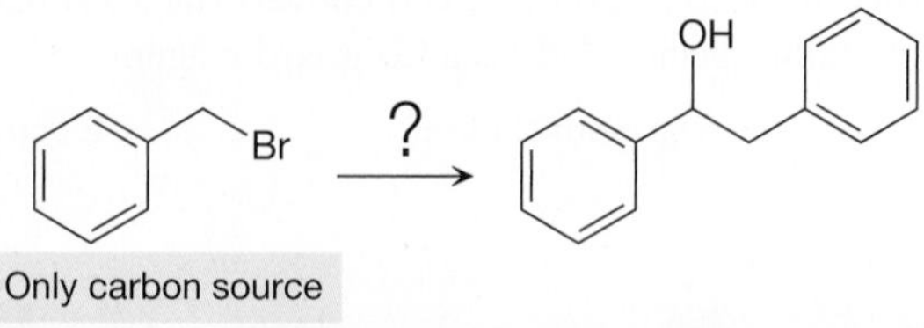

Br
?
OH
Only carbon source

Think	Solve
In the starting material, which carbon atom(s) must be involved in the new C—C bond? Should umpolung be considered to form that C—C bond?	Because benzyl bromide is the only carbon source, the new C—C bond must involve two benzylic carbons, as shown here. Both benzylic carbons are electron-poor in the starting material, so umpolung should be considered for charge reversal at one of those carbons. 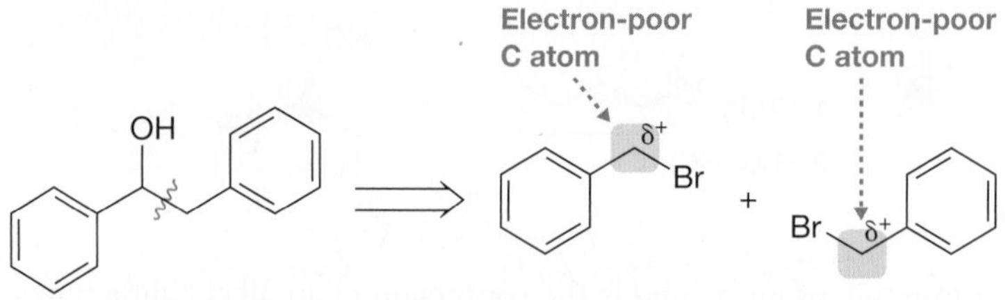
What reactions will carry out charge reversal of an alkyl halide carbon?	As shown here, charge reversal takes place when we convert the alkyl halide into a Grignard reagent or a Wittig reagent. 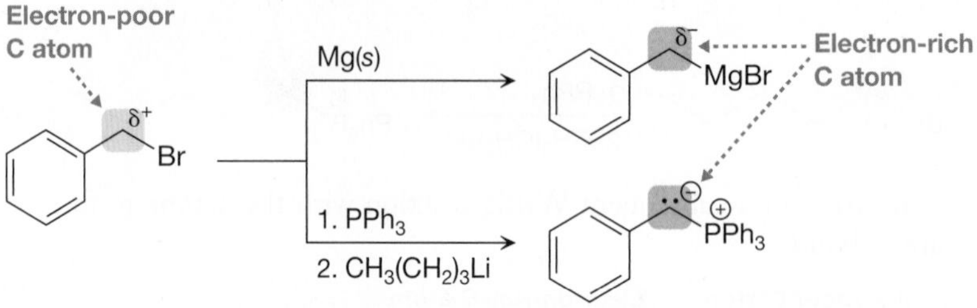
To carry out an appropriate C—C bond-forming reaction, what are the necessary precursors? Once the product is formed, does it need to undergo further changes?	The Grignard reagent can be used in a Grignard reaction to form a new C—C bond. As shown below, the initial alkyl halide must first be converted into the aldehyde. When benzyl bromide is treated with NaOH, HO^- displaces Br^- in an S_N2 reaction to produce the alcohol. The alcohol is subsequently oxidized with pyridinium chlorochromate (PCC) to produce the aldehyde (Section 20.5a).

OH
Electron-poor C atom
δ+
Br
+
Electron-poor C atom
Br
δ+
Electron-poor C atom
δ+
Br
Mg(s)
δ−
MgBr
Electron-rich C atom
1. PPh3
2. CH3(CH2)3Li
PPh3

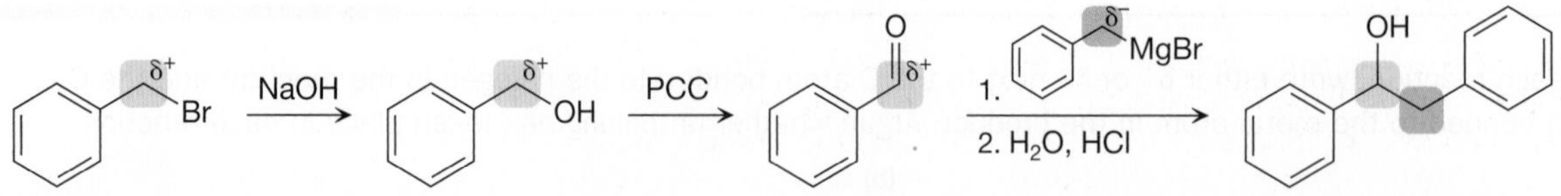

δ+
Br
NaOH
δ+
OH
PCC
O
δ+
δ−
MgBr
1.
2. H2O, HCl
OH

(continued)

Alternatively, as shown here, the Wittig reagent can be used in a Wittig reaction to form a new C=C bond (Section 18.6). The product is an alkene that can subsequently undergo acid-catalyzed hydration to produce the target (Section 12.6).

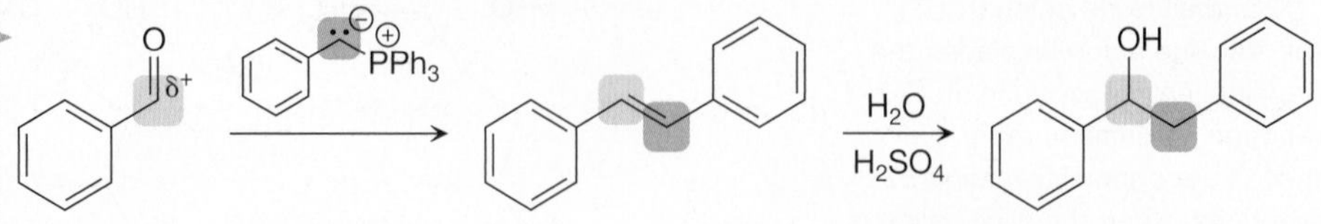

O
δ+
PPh3
H2O
H2SO4
OH

Try It Show how to carry out the following synthesis, using benzaldehyde as your only carbon source.

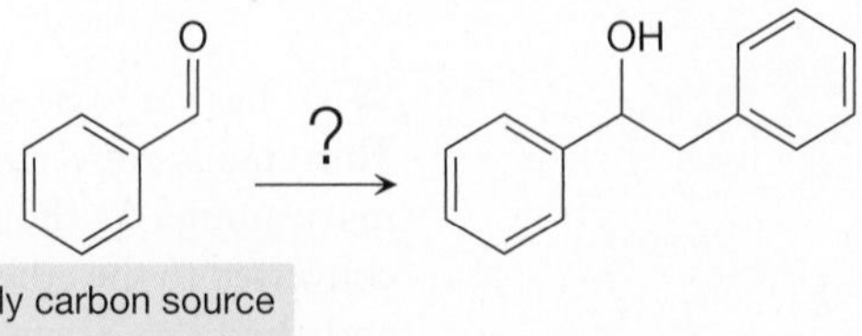

O
?
OH
Only carbon source

Answers to all Try It exercises can be found in the Solutions Manual.

21.1b Relative Positioning of Heteroatoms in Carbon–Carbon Bond-Forming Reactions

Carbon–carbon bond-forming reactions are important in organic synthesis because they allow us to alter the carbon framework of a particular molecule. In many of those reactions, heteroatoms in the product are left with very specific relative locations along the carbon skeleton. Therefore, the relative positioning of heteroatoms in a target can give us a clue as to which C—C bond-forming reactions we might use in the synthesis.

Consider, for example, the formation of a *cyanohydrin*, shown in Equation 21-7:

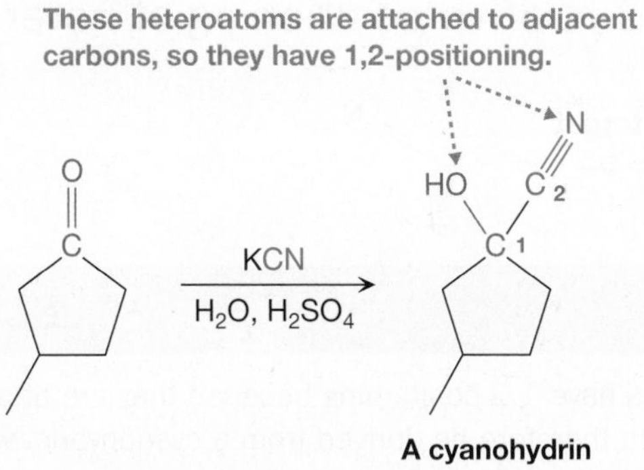

These heteroatoms are attached to adjacent carbons, so they have 1,2-positioning.
O
C
KCN
H2O, H2SO4
HO
N
C 2
C 1

A cyanohydrin

(21-7)

A C—C bond is formed between the cyanide C and the carbonyl C. Notice, in particular, that the two heteroatoms in the product (N and O atoms) are attached to C atoms that are *adjacent* to each other. In other words, the heteroatoms have **1,2-positioning** relative to each other along the carbon backbone.

Knowing that this reaction produces a compound with 1,2-positioning of the resulting heteroatoms is particularly useful when our target molecule is *not* a cyanohydrin but still has heteroatoms with 1,2-positioning. Suppose, for example, that we want to carry out the following synthesis, starting from the ketone given:

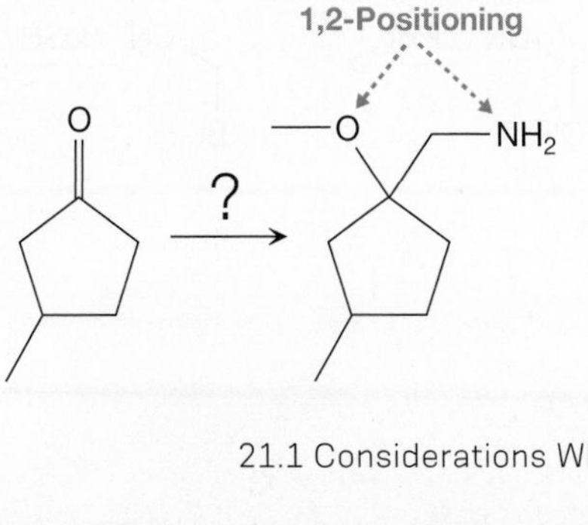

1,2-Positioning
O
?
O
NH2

(21-8)

◂ RECALL

A *Williamson ether synthesis* (Section 10.4) involves an alkyl halide (RX) and alkoxide anion ($R'O^-$); the alkoxide anion displaces the bromide leaving group in an S_N2 reaction. Williamson ether syntheses are optimal (avoiding E2 reactions) when the alkyl halide is primary or methyl.

◂ RECALL

As we saw in Section 18.3b, $LiAlH_4$ adds 2 equiv of H^- to the C atom of the C≡N bond to produce an intermediate with an effective −2 charge on N. Subsequent acid workup converts the N^{2-} to the uncharged NH_2 group.

The O and N atoms in the target have 1,2-positioning along the carbon backbone, so we could consider a cyanohydrin as a synthetic intermediate, as shown in the following retrosynthetic analysis:

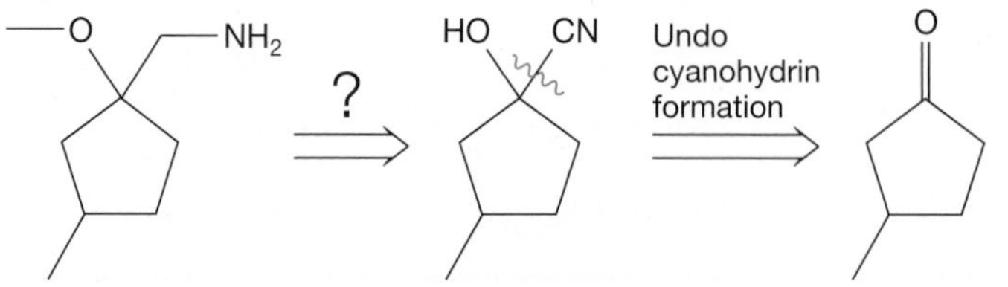

NH2
?
HO
CN
Undo
cyanohydrin
formation
O
A cyanohydrin

(21-9)

What has yet to be solved is the conversion of the cyanohydrin to the target molecule. This entails converting the O—H to the ether and converting the C≡N to a primary amine. As shown in the reaction scheme in Equation 21-10, the O—H can be converted to the ether using a Williamson synthesis (Section 10.4; see top Recall box), and the C≡N can be converted to the primary amine by reduction with $LiAlH_4$ (Section 18.3b; see bottom Recall box):

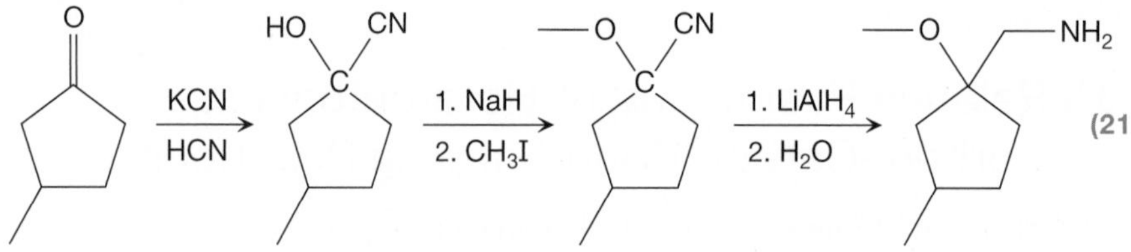

O
KCN
HCN
HO
CN
C
1. NaH
2. CH3I
O
CN
1. LiAlH4
2. H2O
NH2
A cyanohydrin

(21-10)

SOLVED PROBLEM **21.2**

How to synthesize a target with 1,2-relative positioning of heteroatoms

Break It Down **Show how to synthesize the target shown here, beginning with propanal, $CH_3CH_2CH{=}O$.**

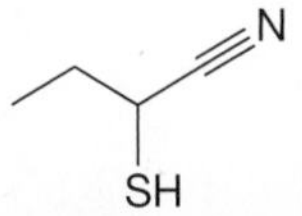

N
SH

Think	Solve
Does the target have 1,2-positioning of the heteroatoms, which could result from the formation of a carbon–carbon bond?	The N and S heteroatoms have 1,2-positioning because they are attached to adjacent C atoms. The target might therefore be derived from a cyanohydrin, which could be made from propanal, as shown in the following retrosynthetic analysis. 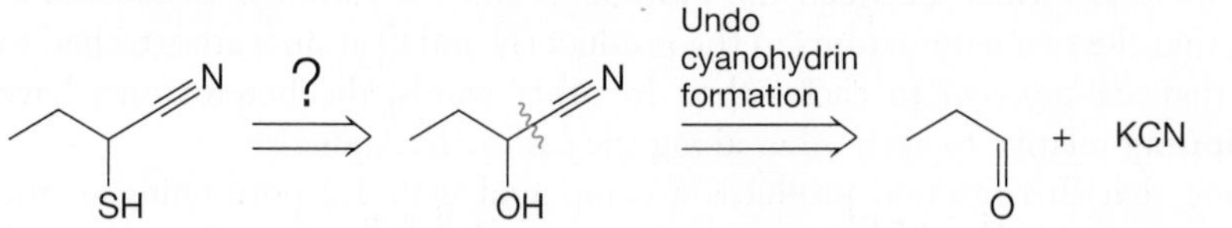
How could the target be made from the cyanohydrin?	To convert the OH group to an SH group, the cyanohydrin could first be treated with PBr_3 (Section 10.5), followed by NaSH, as shown in the following synthesis. 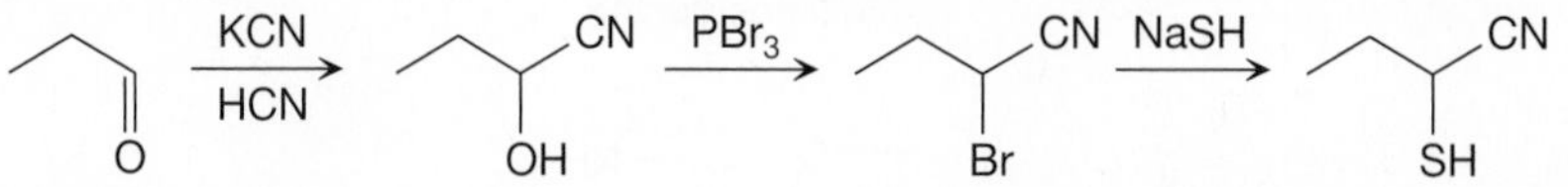

N
?
SH
OH
Undo
cyanohydrin
formation
O
+ KCN
KCN
HCN
CN
PBr3
Br
NaSH

(continued)

Try It Show how to synthesize this target, using compounds with seven or fewer carbon atoms.

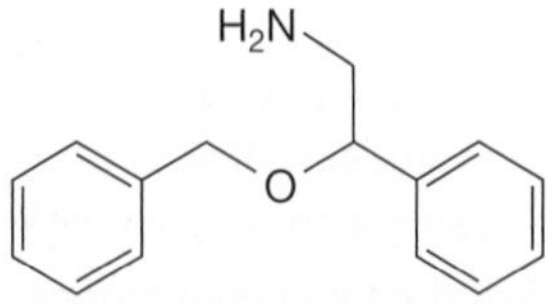

Cyanohydrin formation is not the only carbon–carbon bond-forming reaction that results in heteroatoms having a specific relative positioning along the carbon backbone. Table 21-1 shows other such reactions that we have encountered previously, whose products have heteroatoms with 1,2-, 1,3-, 1,4-, and 1,5-positioning.

YOUR TURN 21.2

For each entry in Table 21-1, number the carbon atoms in the chains of the respective products so that the numbers assigned to the carbon atoms attached to the heteroatoms agree with the relative positioning listed. *Hint*: The C-1 and C-2 carbons are not necessarily the atoms that are highlighted.

TABLE 21-1 Relative Positioning of Heteroatoms in Reactions That Form Carbon–Carbon Bonds

Relative Positioning	Product Formed	Electron-Rich Reactant	Electron-Poor Reactant	Discussed in Section
1,2	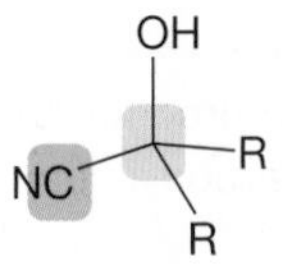 Cyanohydrin	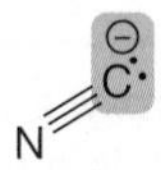 Cyanide anion	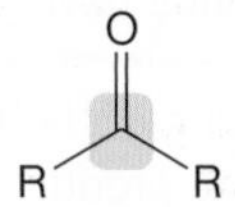 Ketone/ aldehyde	19.1a
1,3	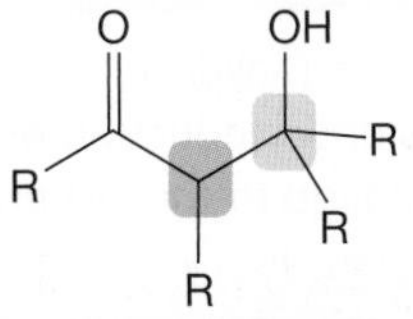 β-Hydroxy ketone/ aldehyde	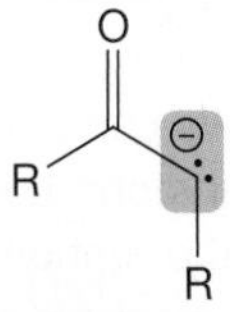 Enolate ion	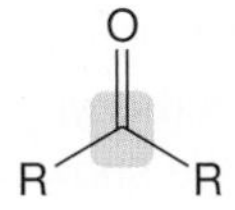 Ketone/ aldehyde	19.7
1,4	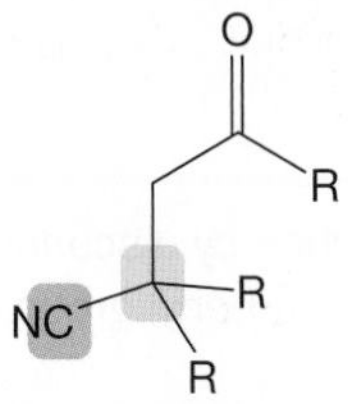 β-Cyano ketone/ aldehyde	 Cyanide anion	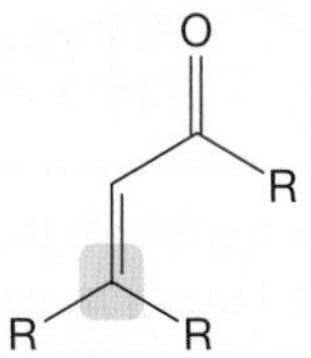 α,β-Unsaturated ketone/aldehyde	19.2
1,5	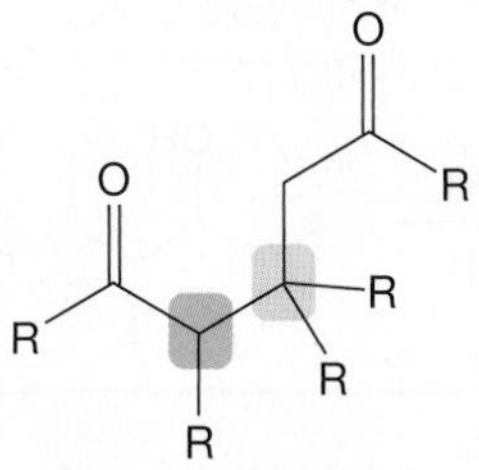 1,5-Dicarbonyl compound	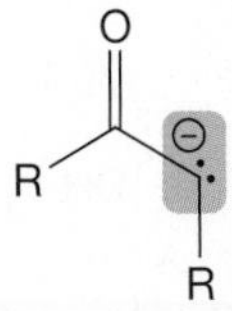 Enolate ion	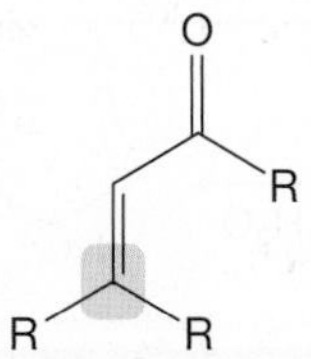 α,β-Unsaturated ketone/aldehyde	19.12

The choices available in Table 21-1 allow us to apply the following strategy:

- If the heteroatoms in a target have 1,2-, 1,3-, 1,4-, or 1,5-positioning and the synthesis calls for a carbon–carbon bond-forming reaction, you should consider using a corresponding reaction from Table 21-1.
- If the functional groups in the target don't match the ones produced from the carbon–carbon bond-forming reaction, then consider implementing functional group transformations after the carbon–carbon bond has been formed.

An example is shown in Solved Problem 21.3.

SOLVED PROBLEM **21.3**

How to design a synthesis by considering relative positions of heteroatoms

Break It Down Show how you can synthesize 2-methylpentane-1,3-diol from compounds containing five or fewer carbons.

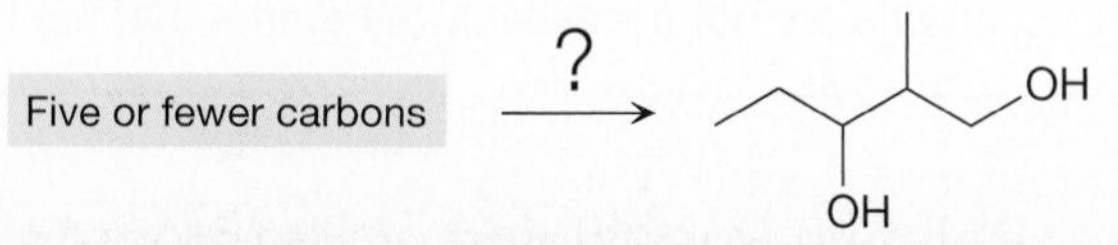

Five or fewer carbons
?
OH
OH

Think	Solve
Will a carbon–carbon bond-forming reaction be necessary?	A carbon–carbon bond-forming reaction is needed because the target's carbon skeleton contains six carbons bonded together, while the synthesis calls for starting with compounds having five or fewer carbons.
What is the relative positioning of the heteroatoms in the target? Which reaction from Table 21-1 should you consider?	The 1,3-positioning of the two hydroxyl groups in the product suggests using an aldol reaction, the product of which is a β-hydroxy carbonyl compound.
Is the target the same as the product of the carbon–carbon bond-forming reaction?	The target is a 1,3-diol, which could be made from a β-hydroxy carbonyl compound by reducing the carbonyl group. We can undo a hydride reduction on either of the two OH groups. We show this transform below applied to the OH group on C-3. (See the Try It exercise for the other option.)

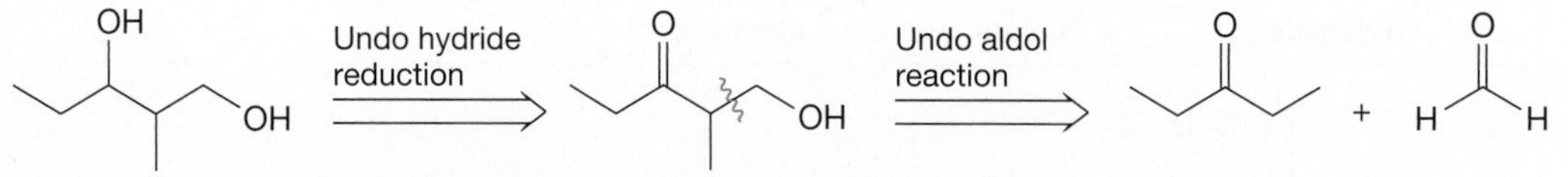

OH
OH
Undo hydride reduction
O
OH
Undo aldol reaction
O
+
O
H
H

Think	Solve
From what precursors could the β-hydroxy carbonyl compound be made?	We can apply a transform that undoes an aldol reaction by disconnecting the bond between the carbons that are alpha and beta to the carbonyl group (Section 19.14). This is shown in the second transform above.
How do we report the final synthesis?	To report the final synthesis, begin with the starting materials and write the appropriate reagents for each synthetic step.

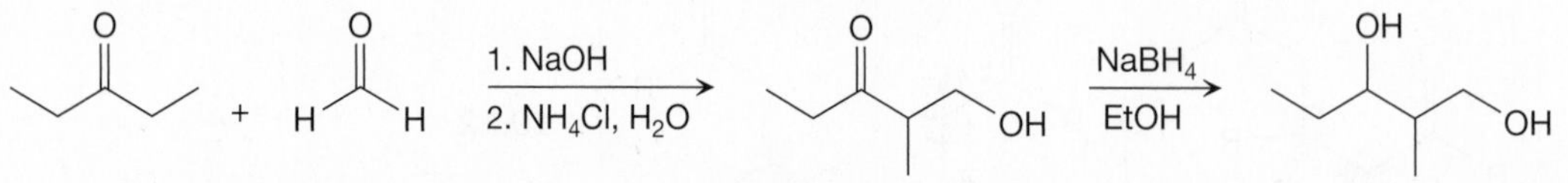

O
+
O
H
H
1. NaOH
2. NH_4Cl, H_2O
O
OH
$NaBH_4$
EtOH
OH
OH

Try It Show how you can synthesize 2-methylpentane-1,3-diol from compounds containing three or fewer carbons.

21.1c Reactions That Remove a Functional Group Entirely from a Molecule

When we design a synthesis, we typically begin by looking for structural features in the target that suggest we use certain reactions. We saw in Section 21.1b, for example, that reactions in Table 21-1 might be incorporated into a synthesis when a target requiring a carbon–carbon bond-forming reaction exhibits a specific relative positioning of heteroatoms. Frequently, however, a synthesis will call for a carbon–carbon bond-forming reaction, but the target doesn't contain functional groups that suggest which carbon–carbon bond-forming reaction we should use. In such cases, the synthesis might be carried out by first forming the relevant carbon–carbon bond and then removing a functional group to produce the target molecule.

One reaction that removes a functional group is catalytic hydrogenation of an alkene, which we first learned in Section 13.9 (see Recall box):

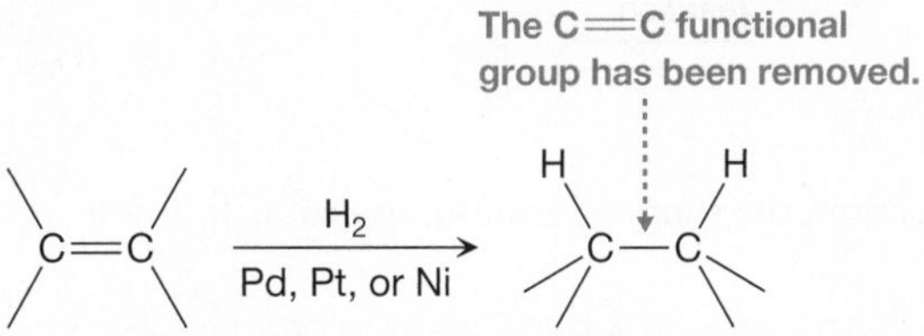
The C=C functional group has been removed.
H_2
Pd, Pt, or Ni

(21-11)

Other reactions that remove a functional group include the Wolff–Kishner reduction (Section 19.5), the Clemmensen reduction (Section 20.4), and the Raney-nickel reduction (Section 20.4). In each of these cases, the carbonyl group of a ketone or aldehyde is removed:

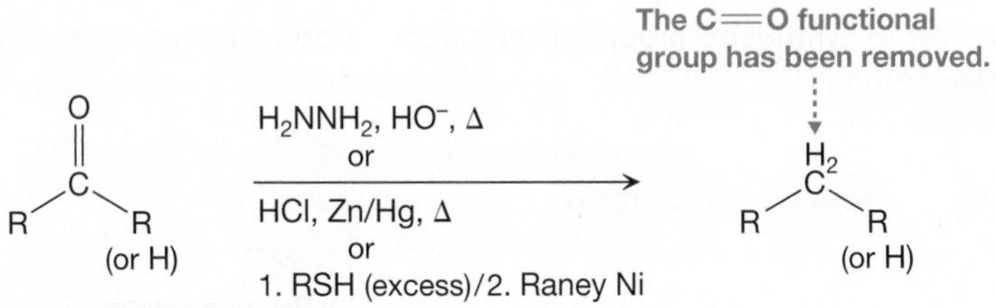
The C=O functional group has been removed.
H_2NNH_2, HO^-, Δ
or
HCl, Zn/Hg, Δ
or
1. RSH (excess)/2. Raney Ni
(or H)
(or H)

(21-12)

For example, suppose we want to synthesize propylbenzene from carbon sources that contain eight or fewer carbons:

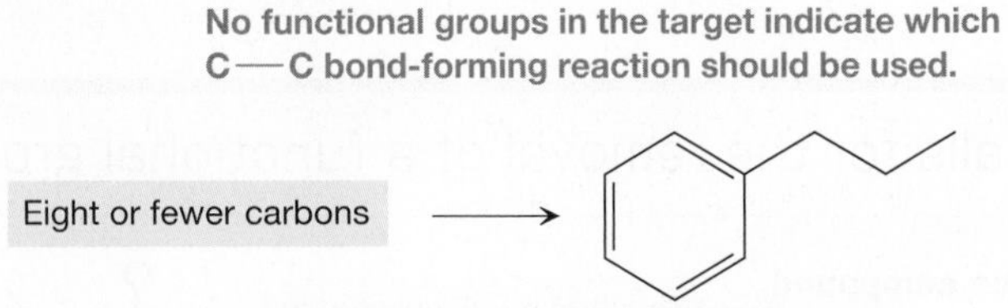
No functional groups in the target indicate which C—C bond-forming reaction should be used.
Eight or fewer carbons

(21-13)

Propylbenzene

The backbone of the target has nine carbons, so a carbon–carbon bond must be formed. But which one? The target doesn't have the functional groups we would expect to see in the product of any carbon–carbon bond-forming reaction we have studied so far. We could imagine, however, forming the carbon–carbon bond first and then using one of the reactions just listed to remove a carbonyl group. In that case, the target might be derived from the ketone shown in Equation 21-14, which could be the product of a carbon–carbon bond-forming reaction: in this case, an alkylation of the ketone's α carbon.

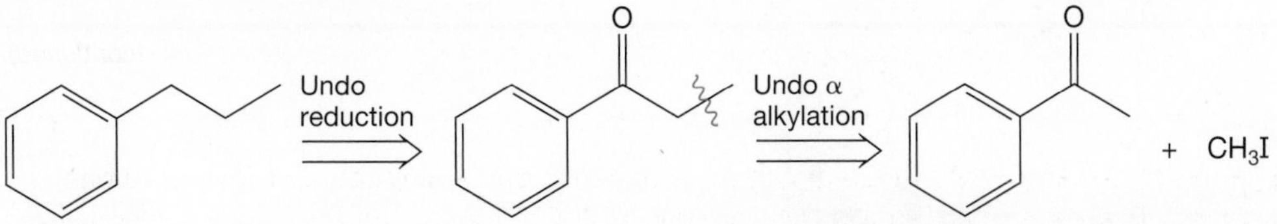
Undo reduction
Undo α alkylation
+ CH_3I

(21-14)

RECALL

Catalytic hydrogenation (Section 13.9) takes place on the surface of a metal catalyst that has bound H atoms. When an alkene or alkyne adsorbs to the metal, a C=C or C≡C π bond effectively breaks. C—H σ bond formation occurs when the adsorbed alkene or alkyne encounters a surface-bound H atom.

We might then report the synthesis as follows:

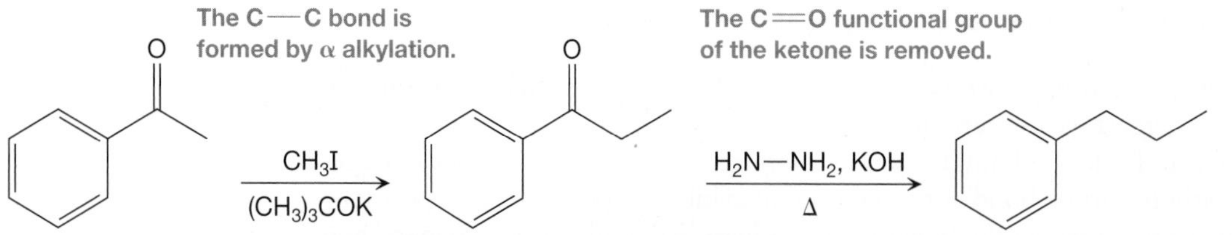

The C—C bond is formed by α alkylation.
The C=O functional group of the ketone is removed.
CH_3I
$(CH_3)_3COK$
$H_2N—NH_2$, KOH
Δ

(21-15)

Alternatively, instead of converting a C=O group into a CH_2 group, we could consider catalytic hydrogenation to remove a C=C group after the new carbon–carbon bond is formed. For example, as shown in the retrosynthetic analysis in Equation 21-16, the target could be made from the alkene, and the C=C bond could be the result of a Wittig reaction:

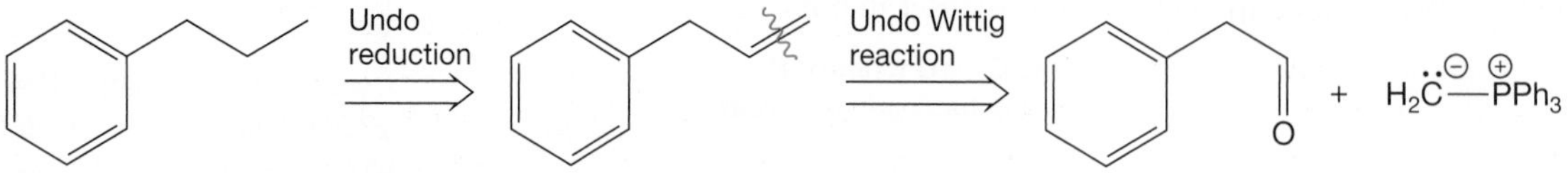

Undo reduction
Undo Wittig reaction
O
+ $H_2\ddot{C}^{\ominus}—\overset{\oplus}{P}Ph_3$

(21-16)

In the forward direction, the synthesis might appear as follows:

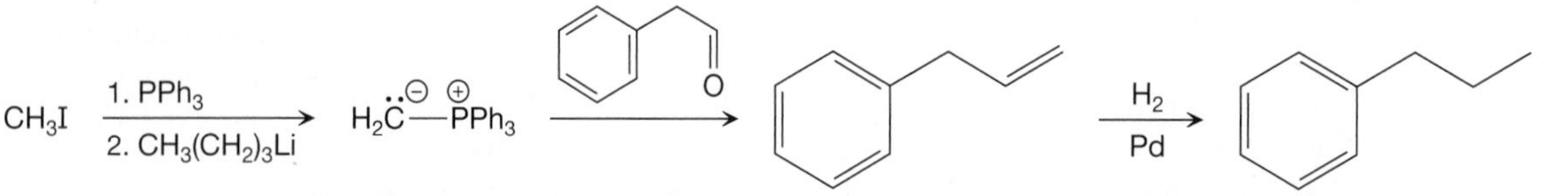

CH_3I
1. PPh_3
2. $CH_3(CH_2)_3Li$
$H_2\ddot{C}^{\ominus}—\overset{\oplus}{P}Ph_3$
O
H_2
Pd

(21-17)

YOUR TURN **21.3**

Show how to synthesize propylbenzene from carbon sources containing seven or fewer carbons.

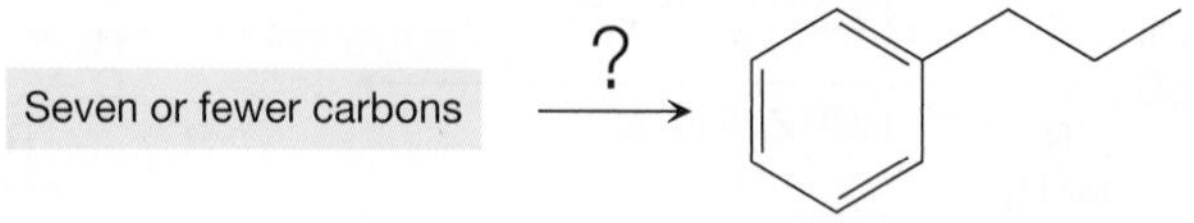

Seven or fewer carbons
?

Propylbenzene

SOLVED PROBLEM **21.4**

How to design a synthesis that calls for the removal of a functional group

Break It Down Show how to synthesize this compound, beginning with an α,β-unsaturated ketone or aldehyde that contains six carbons.

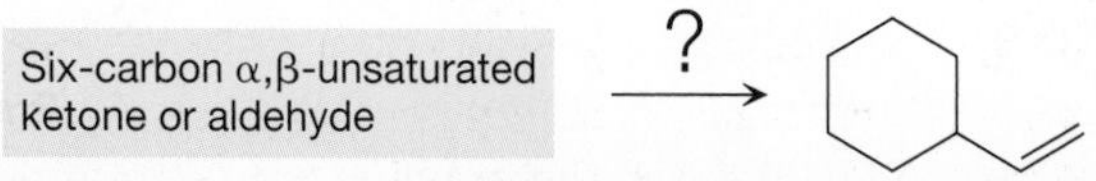

Six-carbon α,β-unsaturated ketone or aldehyde
?

Think	Solve
Which carbon–carbon bond could be formed in the synthesis?	To synthesize the eight-carbon target from a six-carbon starting material, the carbon–carbon bond indicated here could be formed. 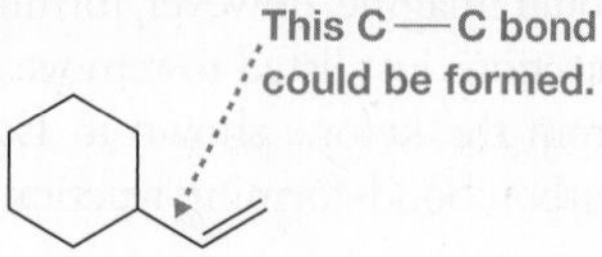 This C—C bond could be formed.

(continued)

When that carbon–carbon bond is formed in a reaction involving an α,β-unsaturated carbonyl compound, what functional group should appear in the product? Where?

Conjugate addition to an α,β-unsaturated carbonyl compound takes place at the carbon atom that is beta to the carbonyl carbon, and in the product of such a reaction, the carbonyl group remains. However, no carbonyl group is present in the target. Therefore, in the precursor to the target, we could envision the carbonyl group present, as shown in the retrosynthesis here.

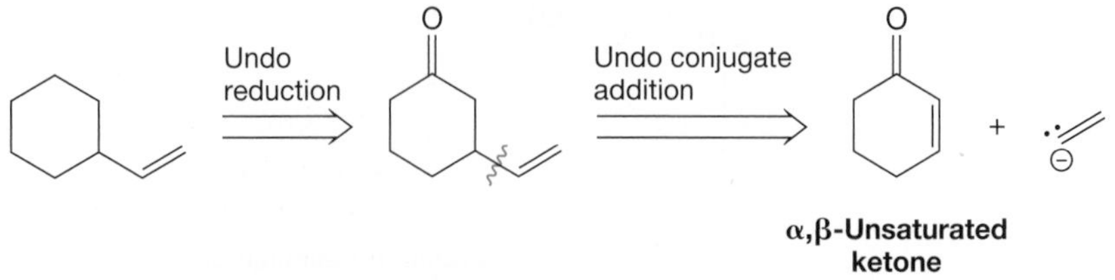
Undo reduction
Undo conjugate addition
α,β-Unsaturated ketone

To ensure conjugate addition of the R^- nucleophile, what organometallic reagent is appropriate? Which carbonyl reduction should you use?

As shown in the synthesis here, a lithium dialkylcuprate should be used to ensure conjugate addition to form the C—C bond (Section 18.9). To reduce the carbonyl group to a methylene group, we should use a Wolff–Kishner reduction. We should avoid a Clemmensen reduction because the acidic conditions would cause the C=C group to react, and we should avoid a Raney-nickel reduction because it would reduce the C=C bond.

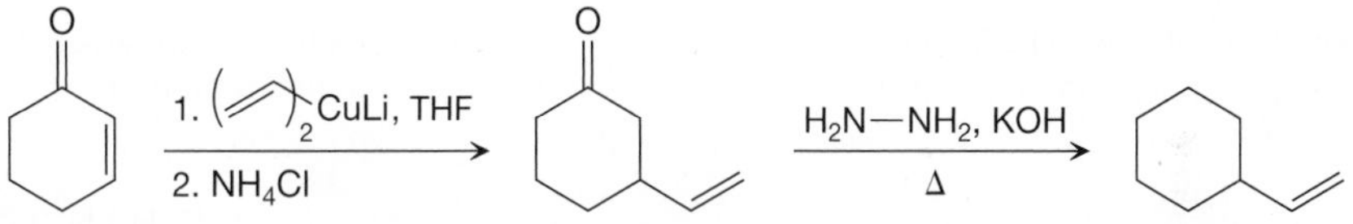
1. ( )2CuLi, THF
2. NH_4Cl
$H_2N—NH_2$, KOH
Δ

Try It Show three different syntheses of this compound, each starting from a different α,β-unsaturated ketone that has 10 or fewer carbon atoms.

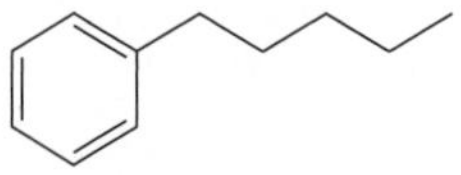

21.2 Avoiding Synthetic Traps: Selective Reagents and Protecting Groups

SECTION 21.2 OBJECTIVES

You will be able to:

1. Incorporate selective reagents and selective reactions effectively in a synthesis.
2. Identify when a functional group should be protected in a synthetic step.
3. Design syntheses that call for the protection of a carbonyl group in a ketone or aldehyde or for the protection of a hydroxyl group in an alcohol.

As we saw in Section 11.4, a *synthetic trap* arises when a specific transform in a retrosynthesis would lead to an undesired reaction in the *forward* direction. Generally, synthetic traps arise when a functional group we want to leave alone is, in fact, **labile** under the reaction conditions: that is, the functional group is reactive and readily undergoes a chemical transformation.

We can overcome many of the difficulties presented by synthetic traps in one of two ways: (1) by using a *selective reagent* (Section 21.2a) or (2) by using a *protecting group* (Section 21.2b). As discussed in the following sections, both of these strategies exploit differences in reactivity among functional groups.

21.2a Selective Reagents

When two or more outcomes are possible for a given reaction, the actual result often depends on the specific reagents that are used and the specific reaction conditions. In these situations, a reaction that can be chosen to facilitate one outcome over another is called a **selective reaction**, and a reagent that is responsible for such selectivity is called a **selective reagent**.

We first encountered an example of a selective reaction in Chapter 9, in the context of the competition between nucleophilic substitution and elimination reactions. Even though S_N2 and E2 reactions tend to compete with each other, given that strong nucleophiles are often strong bases, we can choose specific reagents to selectively favor one reaction over another. For example, Cl^- favors the S_N2 reaction (Eq. 21-18a), whereas the *tert*-butoxide anion selectively favors the E2 reaction (Eq. 21-18b):

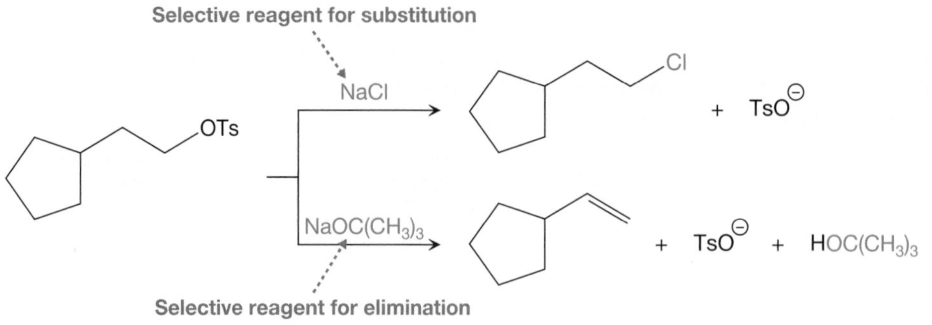
Selective reagent for substitution
NaCl
OTs
Cl
+ TsO⊖
NaOC(CH3)3
+ TsO⊖ + HOC(CH3)3
Selective reagent for elimination

(21-18a)

(21-18b)

> **◀ RECALL**
>
> In α alkylation of a ketone or aldehyde (Section 11.3), the α carbon is deprotonated to make a strongly nucleophilic enolate anion, which then attacks a substrate in an S_N2 step. Deprotonation takes place under kinetic control with LDA and under thermodynamic control with *tert*-butoxide.

We saw another example of selective reagents in Section 11.3, when we discussed alkylations at the α carbons of ketones and aldehydes. Recall, as shown in Equation 21-19a, that lithium diisopropylamide (LDA) is a base that irreversibly deprotonates ketones and aldehydes, so LDA is selective for alkylation at the *less* substituted α carbon. By contrast (Eq. 21-19b), $KOC(CH_3)_3$ deprotonates ketones and aldehydes reversibly, so it is selective for alkylation at the *more* substituted α carbon (see Recall box).

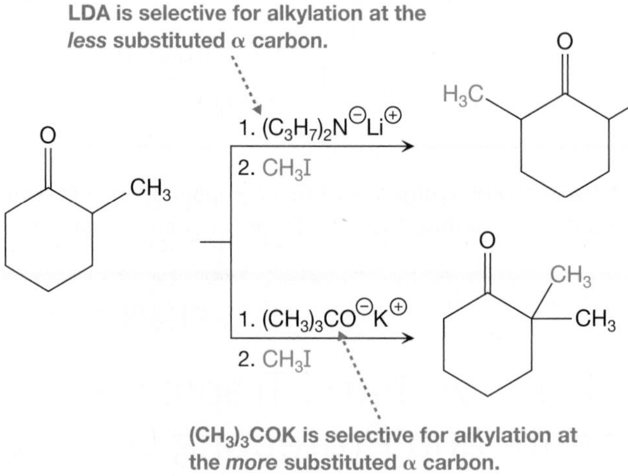
LDA is selective for alkylation at the less substituted α carbon.
O
CH3
1. (C3H7)2N⊖Li⊕
2. CH3I
H3C
CH3
1. (CH3)3CO⊖K⊕
2. CH3I
CH3
CH3
(CH3)3COK is selective for alkylation at the more substituted α carbon.

(21-19a)

(21-19b)

Nucleophilic addition to α,β-unsaturated carbonyl compounds presents us with another case of selectivity in reactions. Recall from Sections 18.8 and 18.9 that very strong nucleophiles like Grignard reagents (RMgX) selectively add to the carbonyl carbon in a *direct addition* or 1,2-addition (Eq. 21-20a). Weaker nucleophiles like lithium dialkylcuprates (R_2CuLi), on the other hand, selectively add to the β carbon in a *conjugate addition* or 1,4-addition (Eq. 21-20b):

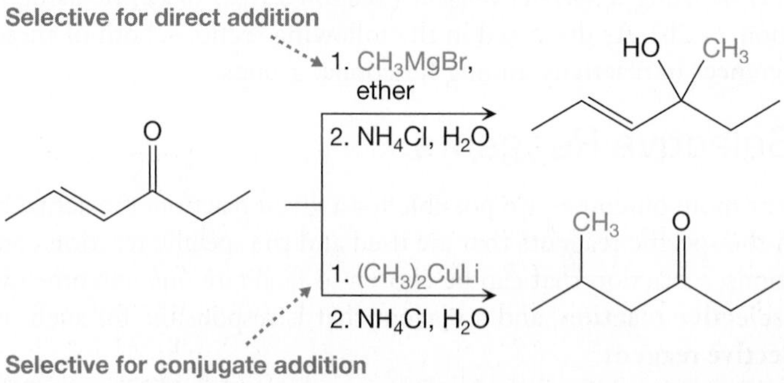
Selective for direct addition
1. CH3MgBr, ether
2. NH4Cl, H2O
HO
CH3
O
1. (CH3)2CuLi
2. NH4Cl, H2O
CH3
O
Selective for conjugate addition

(21-20a)

(21-20b)

The selective reactions presented here in Section 21.2a are far from exhaustive; rather, they are intended simply to introduce the concept and to demonstrate how selective reactions can be used to plan a synthesis. As we continue to learn more reactions, we will find several more opportunities for designing syntheses that take advantage of selectivity.

SOLVED PROBLEM **21.5**

How to incorporate a selective reaction into a synthesis

Break It Down **Show how you would carry out the synthesis shown here, using any reagents necessary.**

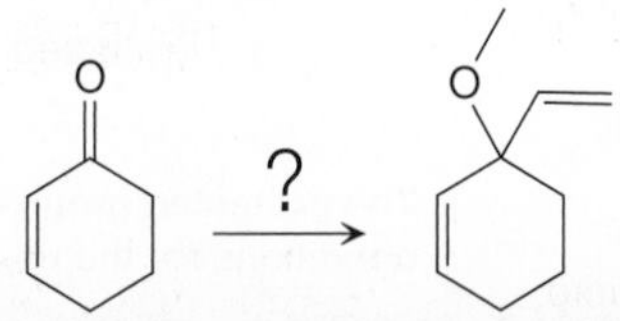

Think	Solve
When a C—C bond forms to the carbonyl carbon of an α,β-unsaturated ketone, what functional group is produced?	To form a C—C bond to the carbonyl carbon, an R⁻ nucleophile can add to the C═O bond, which will convert the C═O group to C—OH after acid workup. The target has an ether group instead of C—OH, so we can begin the retrosynthetic analysis by undoing a Williamson ether synthesis. Then we can disconnect the R⁻ nucleophile in the second transform.

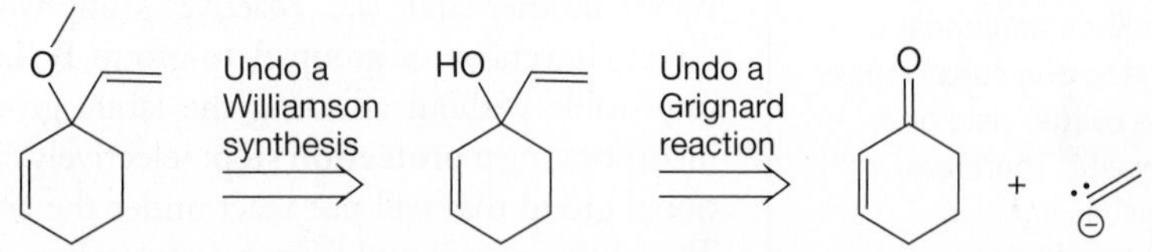

Undo a Williamson synthesis
HO
Undo a Grignard reaction
O
+

Think	Solve
What type of R⁻ nucleophile will selectively add by direct addition to the carbonyl group rather than conjugate addition?	A Grignard reagent will selectively add by direct addition, as shown in the synthesis here. Then, we can carry out the Williamson ether synthesis by treating the alcohol with a powerful base followed by an alkyl halide.

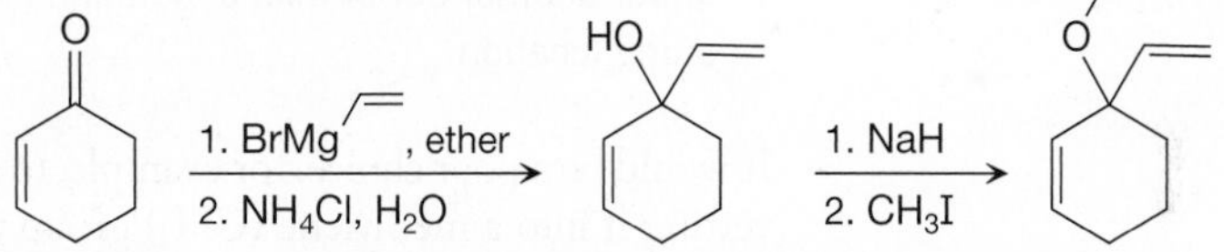

O
1. BrMg , ether
2. NH_4Cl, H_2O
HO
1. NaH
2. CH_3I
O

Try It Show how you would carry out the synthesis shown here, using any reagents necessary.

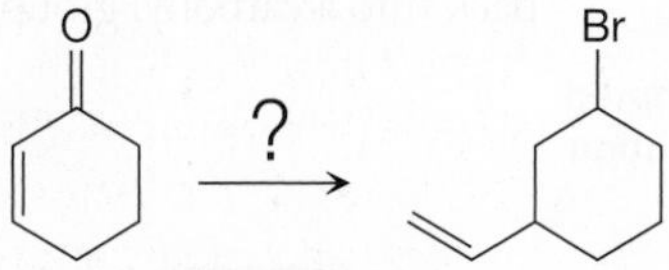

O
?
Br

21.2b Protecting Groups

Selective reagents (Section 21.2a) make it possible to exploit differences in the reactivity of functional groups when we want one group in a molecule to react but leave another alone. There are times, however, when this is unfeasible: when a step in a synthesis may require the use of a reagent that would react with two or more functional groups. In situations like these, we may be able to use a **protecting group** to temporarily make one or more functional groups unreactive under the specific conditions our desired reaction calls for. After making the desired change in the molecule, we must be able to remove the protecting group and restore the original functional group.

Here we focus primarily on protection of the carbonyl group in ketones and aldehydes, as well as protection of the hydroxyl group in alcohols. The use of protecting

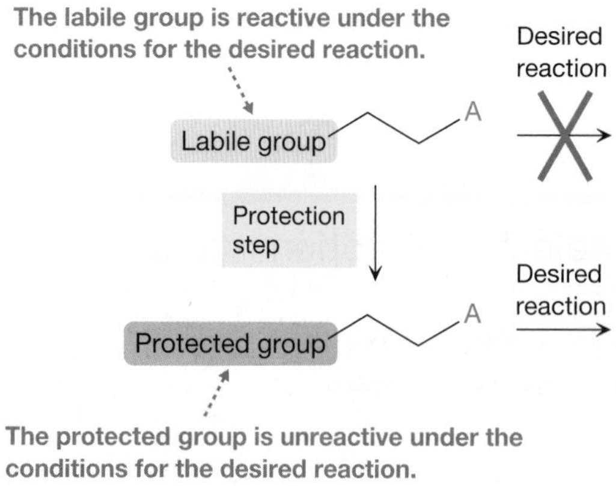

The labile group is reactive under the conditions for the desired reaction.
Desired reaction
Labile group
A
Labile group
B
Protection step
Deprotection step
Desired reaction
Protected group
A
Protected group
B
The protected group is unreactive under the conditions for the desired reaction.

FIGURE 21-1 General strategy for using a protecting group The starting material (*top left*) cannot be converted to the target (*top right*) directly, because the labile group would also react under those conditions. A protection step is carried out to convert the labile group into a different group (*bottom left*) that is unreactive under the conditions that convert group A to group B. Next, the desired reaction is carried out to convert group A to group B (*bottom right*), and a final deprotection step converts the protected group back into the original labile group (*top right*).

> **GREEN CHEMISTRY** Notice in Figure 21-1 that using a protecting group in a synthesis requires a minimum of two additional synthetic steps: one to protect and another to deprotect. Each additional synthetic step can substantially reduce the overall yield and increase waste. Therefore, when all else is equal, a transformation that incorporates a selective reaction is preferred over one that requires a protecting group.

groups has become a mature subdiscipline of organic synthesis, and several authors have published books in this area. Suffice it to say that many different functional groups can be protected in a variety of ways, and often there are several factors to consider when choosing a particular protecting group.

The general use of a protecting group is outlined in **Figure 21-1**. Suppose we have a molecule with a functional group A that we want to convert to another functional group B, but another labile (i.e., reactive) group would also be changed in the process. That is, direct conversion of group A to group B (i.e., the top reaction in Fig. 21-1) would be impossible without affecting the labile group. We can work around this problem by incorporating a **protection step**: selectively changing the labile group into another functional group that will not react under the conditions that convert group A to group B. The labile group is said to be *protected* when it is in the unreactive form. After the desired reaction is carried out, the original labile group can be restored in a **deprotection step**.

Reversibility is important in reactions that add a protecting group:

> A good protecting group is unreactive under one set of conditions but is *removable* under another set of mild conditions to restore the original functional group at the same location.

It would be a poor choice, for example, to protect the carbonyl group of a ketone by converting it into a methylene (CH_2) group using the Clemmensen reduction (Eq. 21-21), because we do not know any reactions that would allow us to convert that CH_2 group back into a carbonyl group selectively:

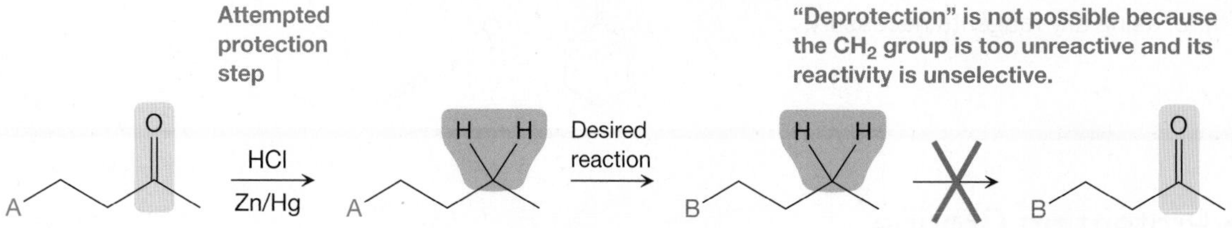

Attempted protection step
"Deprotection" is not possible because the CH2 group is too unreactive and its reactivity is unselective.
O
A
HCl
Zn/Hg
H
H
A
Desired reaction
H
H
B
B
O

(21-21)

21.2b.1 Protection of the C=O Group in Ketones and Aldehydes

Ketones and aldehydes are most often protected by converting them to *acetals*, as shown in Equation 21-22:

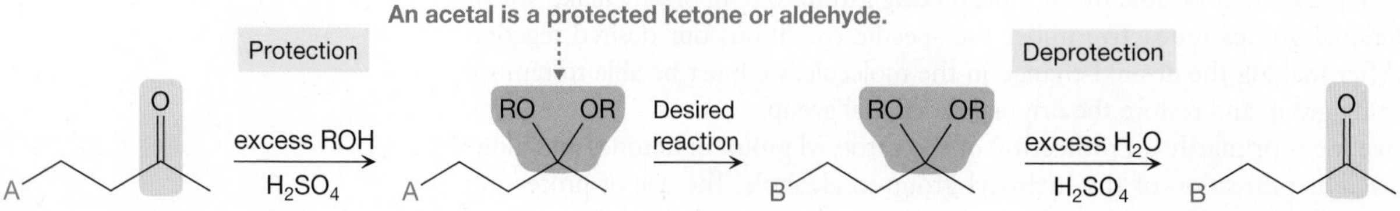

An acetal is a protected ketone or aldehyde.
Protection
Deprotection
O
A
excess ROH
H2SO4
RO
OR
A
Desired reaction
RO
OR
B
excess H2O
H2SO4
O
B

(21-22)

An acetal has the form RO—C—OR, where one C is involved in two C—O—C groups, each resembling an ether:

Acetals, like ethers, are resistant to strong bases and strong nucleophiles (Section 9.5b). They are also resistant to oxidizing and reducing agents.

An acetal can be formed by reacting a ketone or aldehyde with excess alcohol under acidic conditions (Section 19.4a). Fortunately, the C=O group of a ketone or aldehyde can be recovered by hydrolysis under mildly acidic conditions (see Recall box).

A commonly used alcohol in protecting ketones and aldehydes is ethane-1,2-diol (**ethylene glycol**), which has the formula $HOCH_2CH_2OH$ (Eq. 21-23):

◀ RECALL

As we saw in Section 19.4a, the acid-catalyzed formation of an acetal from a ketone or aldehyde is reversible, and H_2O is formed as a product. Therefore, according to Le Châtelier's principle, the ketone or aldehyde is favored when an acetal is treated with excess H_2O under acidic conditions.

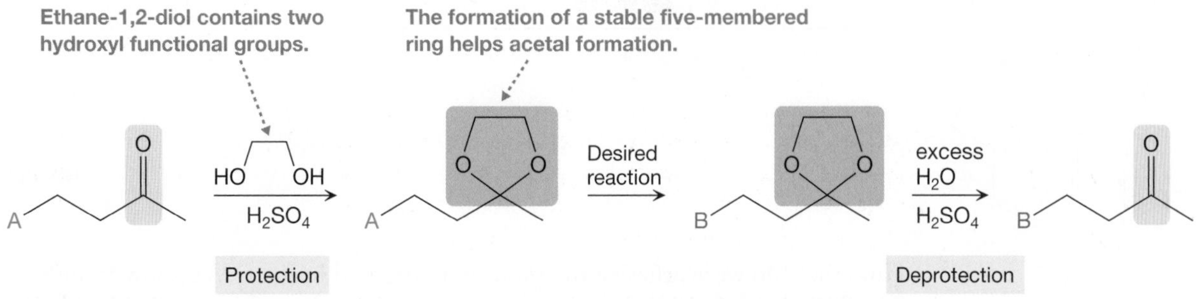

Ethane-1,2-diol contains two hydroxyl functional groups.
The formation of a stable five-membered ring helps acetal formation.
HO OH
H2SO4
Desired reaction
excess H2O
H2SO4
A
B
Protection
Deprotection

(21-23)

Ethylene glycol is a popular protecting group in part because it has two hydroxyl groups on the same molecule, so only one molar equivalent is needed to protect a carbonyl group (rather than the two molar equivalents that would be required if a monoalcohol were used). Additionally, the acetal that it produces consists of a five-membered ring, which is relatively stable and thus favors the formation of the acetal.

YOUR TURN 21.4

In the reaction shown here, circle the protected carbonyl group and draw the compound that would be produced when it is deprotected.

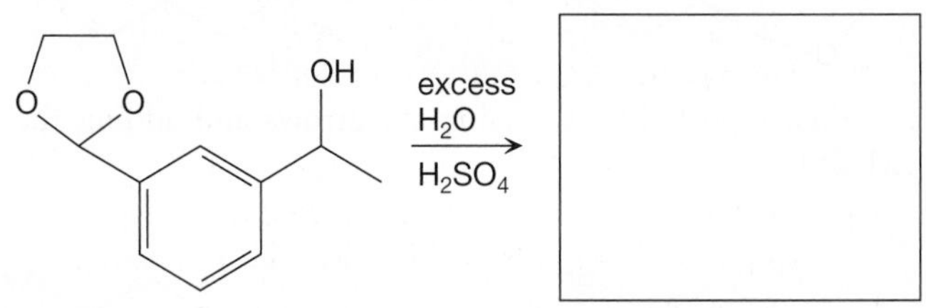

OH
excess
H2O
H2SO4

To see how such a protecting group might be used, let's propose a way to carry out the synthesis in Equation 21-24:

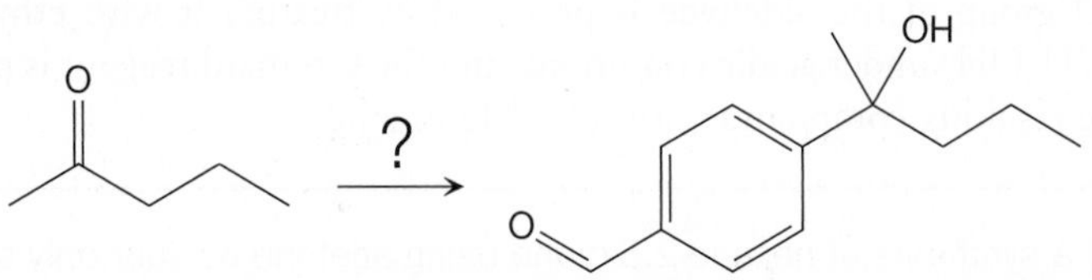

?
OH

(21-24)

The product has an OH group characteristic of an alcohol, so it may appear at first that we can arrive back at the starting material through a transform that undoes a Grignard reaction, as shown in Equation 21-25:

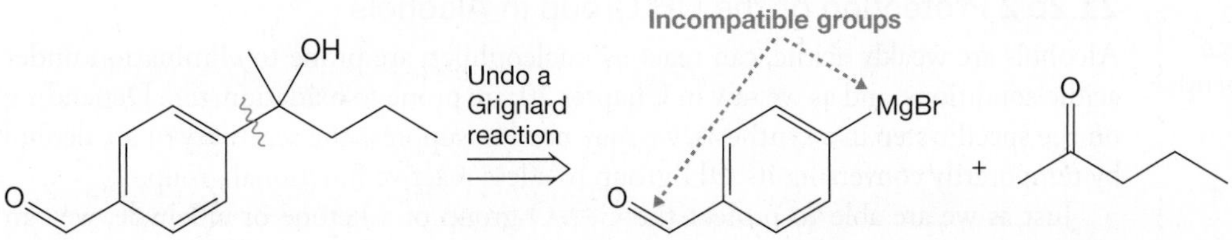

Incompatible groups
OH
Undo a Grignard reaction
MgBr
+

(21-25)

Notice, however, that the proposed Grignard reagent has a carbonyl group, which (as discussed in Section 18.5) is incompatible with Grignard reagents (see Recall box at the bottom of this page). To work around this incompatibility, instead envision using a Grignard reagent in which that carbonyl group is protected, as shown in Equation 21-26:

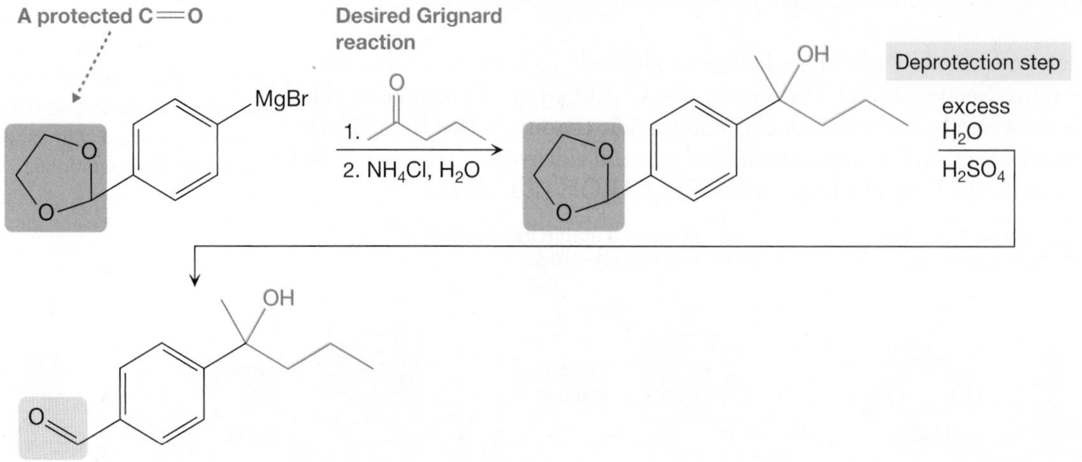

A protected C=O
Desired Grignard reaction
MgBr
1.
2. NH4Cl, H2O
OH
Deprotection step
excess H2O
H2SO4
O

(21-26)

How, then, do we synthesize the protected Grignard reagent? We know from Section 20.6 that a Grignard reagent is produced from an analogous alkyl halide. To avoid the presence of a C=O group on the Grignard reagent, the C=O must be protected prior to the addition of Mg, so the retrosynthetic analysis would appear as shown in Equation 21-27:

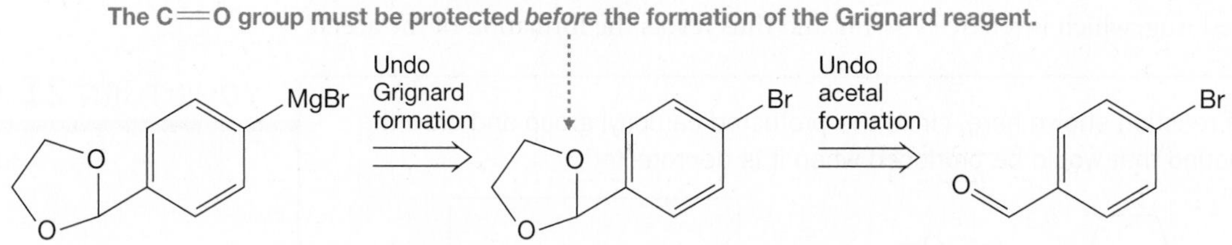

The C=O group must be protected *before* the formation of the Grignard reagent.
MgBr
Undo Grignard formation
Br
Undo acetal formation
Br
O

(21-27)

The synthesis is then reported by reversing the arrows and adding the appropriate reagents (Eq. 21-28):

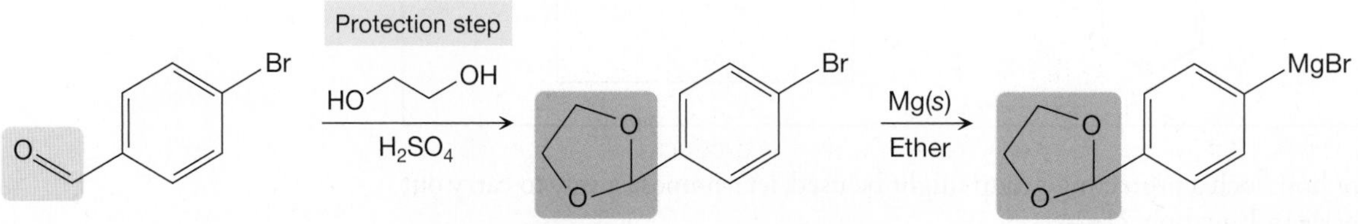

Protection step
Br
HO
OH
H2SO4
Br
Mg(s)
Ether
MgBr
O

(21-28)

The C=O group of the aldehyde is protected by treating it with ethylene glycol ($HOCH_2CH_2OH$) under acidic conditions, and the Grignard reagent is produced by treating the resulting compound with solid Mg in ether.

YOUR TURN 21.5

Propose a synthesis of hexane-2,5-dione using acetone as your only source of carbon. *Hint*: Consider how you might use a protecting group.

◂ **RECALL**

As we learned in Section 18.5, Grignard reagents are incompatible with groups that would react with the Grignard reagent: acidic groups that undergo deprotonation, carbonyl groups that undergo nucleophilic addition, epoxides that undergo ring opening, and alkyl halides that undergo E2 reactions.

21.2b.2 Protection of the OH Group in Alcohols

Alcohols are weakly acidic, can react as nucleophiles, are prone to elimination under acidic conditions, and as we saw in Chapter 20, are prone to oxidation, too. Depending on the specific step in a synthesis, we may need to suppress the reactivity of an alcohol by temporarily converting its OH group to a less reactive functional group.

Just as we are able to protect the C=O group of a ketone or aldehyde, we can protect the OH group of an alcohol in the form of an *ether* or *acetal*. Table 21-2 shows

TABLE 21-2 Protecting Groups for Alcohols

	Protection Step	Comments	Deprotection Step	Comments
(1)	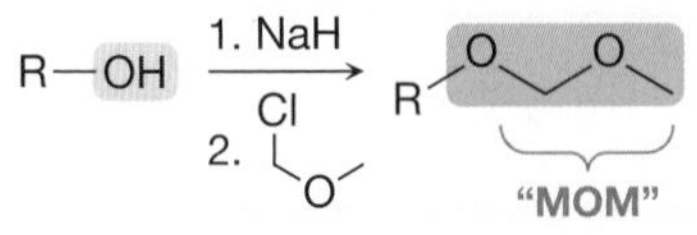 methoxymethyl ether	Williamson ether synthesis (basic conditions, Section 10.4). The product is an acetal.	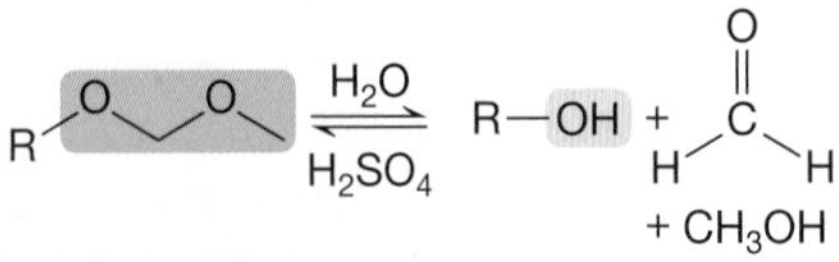	S_N1 hydrolysis (acidic conditions, Section 9.5b)
(2)	Dihydropyran (DHP) 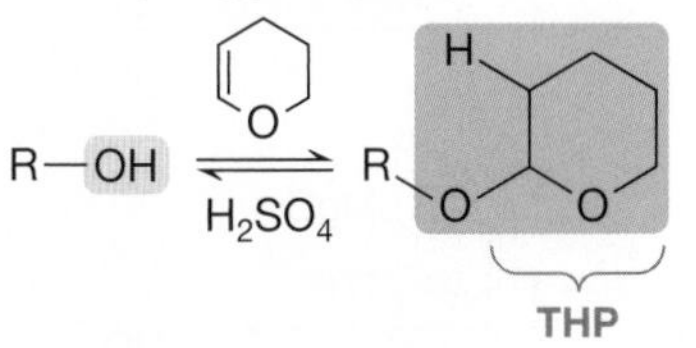 tetrahydropyranyl ether	Electrophilic addition of ROH to the alkene (acidic conditions, Section 12.6). The product is an acetal.	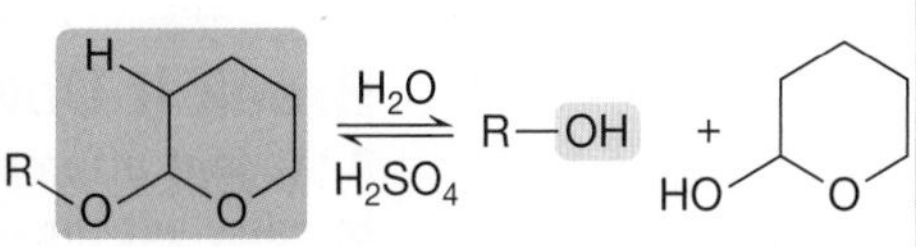	S_N1 hydrolysis (acidic conditions, Section 9.5b)
(3)	*tert*-Butyldimethylsilyl chloride (TBDMS—Cl) 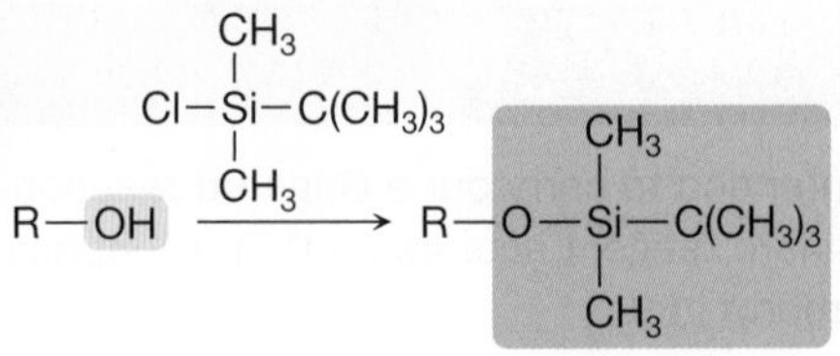 R—O—TBDMS	The product is a silyl ether, characterized by a C—O—Si group.	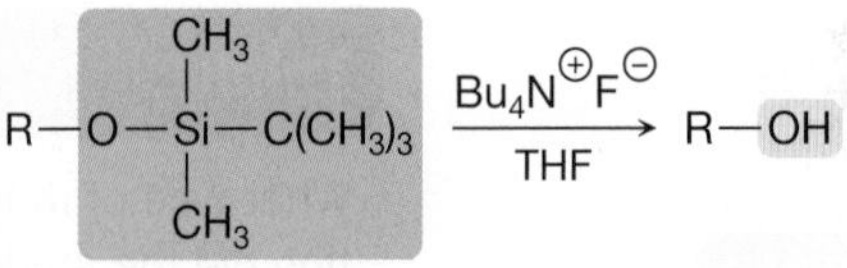	Substitution reaction in which F^- is the nucleophile and RO^- leaves

three ways to carry out these protection steps, as well as their corresponding deprotection steps.

For Entries 1 and 2, the protection step produces an acetal, but this occurs by different reactions. In Entry 1, the protection step is a Williamson ether synthesis, whereas in Entry 2 it is an acid-catalyzed addition of the alcohol to the alkene. For Entry 3, the protection step involves an S_N2 reaction to produce a silyl ether, characterized by a C—O—Si group. Like a regular ether, a silyl ether is unreactive under basic conditions.

YOUR TURN 21.6

Identify the acetal carbon in Entries 1 and 2 in Table 21-2.

The deprotection steps in Entries 1 and 2 are acid-catalyzed hydrolysis reactions. In Entry 3, the deprotection step is a nucleophilic substitution reaction in which F^- attacks the Si atom. The leaving group is RO^-, which is usually an unsuitable leaving group for substitution reactions, but the Si—F bond that is formed is very strong and thus compensates; its bond energy is 553 kJ/mol, making it about 30% stronger than a C—C single bond!

Even though there are multiple options available to protect an alcohol, they are not always interchangeable. You must consider whether the conditions required for the protection and deprotection of the OH group will interfere with functional groups elsewhere in the molecule. For example, Entry 1 in Table 21-2 calls for basic conditions in the protection step and acidic aqueous conditions in the deprotection step, so that would be a poor choice if other groups in the molecule react under basic or acidic conditions.

Entry 2 would be a poor choice if you need to avoid acidic conditions, and Entry 3 should be avoided if the molecule has other sites that are nucleophilic or will react with F^-.

YOUR TURN 21.7

Draw the complete, detailed mechanism for both the protection step and the deprotection step of Entries 1 and 2 in Table 21-2.

SOLVED PROBLEM **21.6**

How to design a synthesis that calls for protecting an alcohol's OH group

Break It Down

A student attempted to carry out the following reaction on 3-hydroxypropanal, but it did not work. Suggest why, and propose a synthesis route that would circumvent this problem.

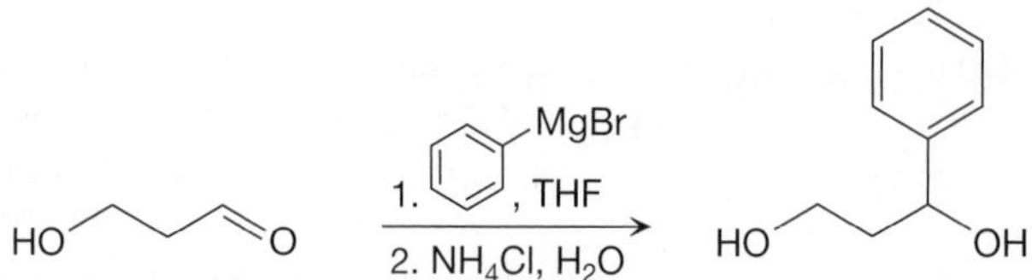
HO
O
1. MgBr, THF
2. NH4Cl, H2O
HO
OH

3-Hydroxypropanal (Reuterin)

Think	Solve
What type of reaction did the student intend to carry out?	The student intended to carry out a Grignard reaction, in which the Grignard reagent acts as an R^- nucleophile to add to the carbonyl group.
What undesired reaction can take place, and what functional group would that involve?	Grignard reagents are not only strong nucleophiles but also very strong bases. In this case, the Grignard reagent can deprotonate the weakly acidic OH group on the hydroxy aldehyde, as shown.

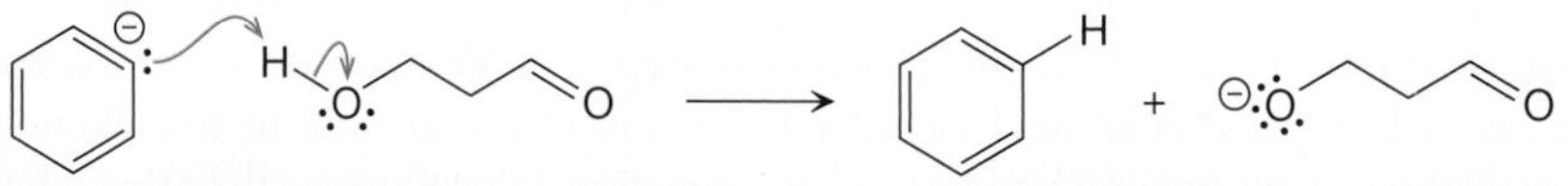
H
O
O
H
+
O
O

Think	Solve
How can the OH group be protected? How can it be deprotected?	As shown below, the OH group can be protected with dihydropyran (DHP), which leaves alone the C═O group under acidic conditions. Once the Grignard reaction is complete, the product can be deprotected. Because the workup step of the Grignard reaction requires acidic conditions, the acid workup and deprotection can occur together. (Note that an O—TBDMS protecting group would also have been feasible.)

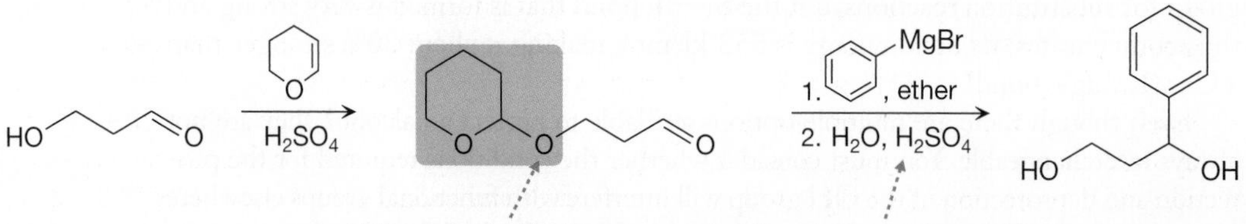
HO
O
O
H2SO4
O
O
O
1. MgBr, ether
2. H2O, H2SO4
HO
OH
THP-protected OH group
Acid workup and deprotection

(continued)

CONNECTIONS 21.1

3-Hydroxypropanal's probiotic properties

3-Hydroxypropanal (Solved Problem 21.6), also called reuterin, is an antimicrobial compound produced by *Lactobacillus reuteri*, a species of probiotic bacteria found in the gut of humans and other mammals. Reuterin is believed to play a part in the health benefits of these bacteria.

ONCE DAILY
True Release
Nature's Way
Primadophilus
Reuteri
pearls
TRUE POTENCY SYNERGY BLEND
ACTIVE PROBIOTIC
DIGESTION & IMMUNITY
60 SOFTGELS

Try It Show how you would carry out the synthesis shown here.

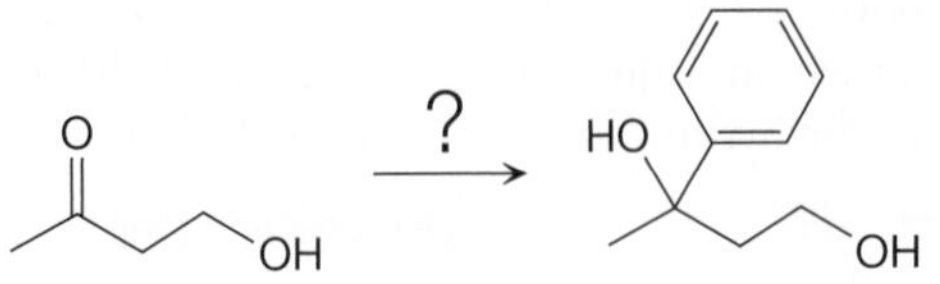

O
OH
?
HO
OH

Protecting Groups in DNA Synthesis

Oligonucleotides are relatively short strands of DNA, with lengths on the order of 10–100 nucleotides (i.e., A, C, T, and G). They have a number of important applications in molecular biology, including DNA sequencing and synthesis of artificial genes. Consequently, it is important to synthesize oligonucleotides in an efficient and accurate way. As it turns out, protecting groups play a major role in these syntheses, as shown in the simplified scheme in **Figure 21-2**.

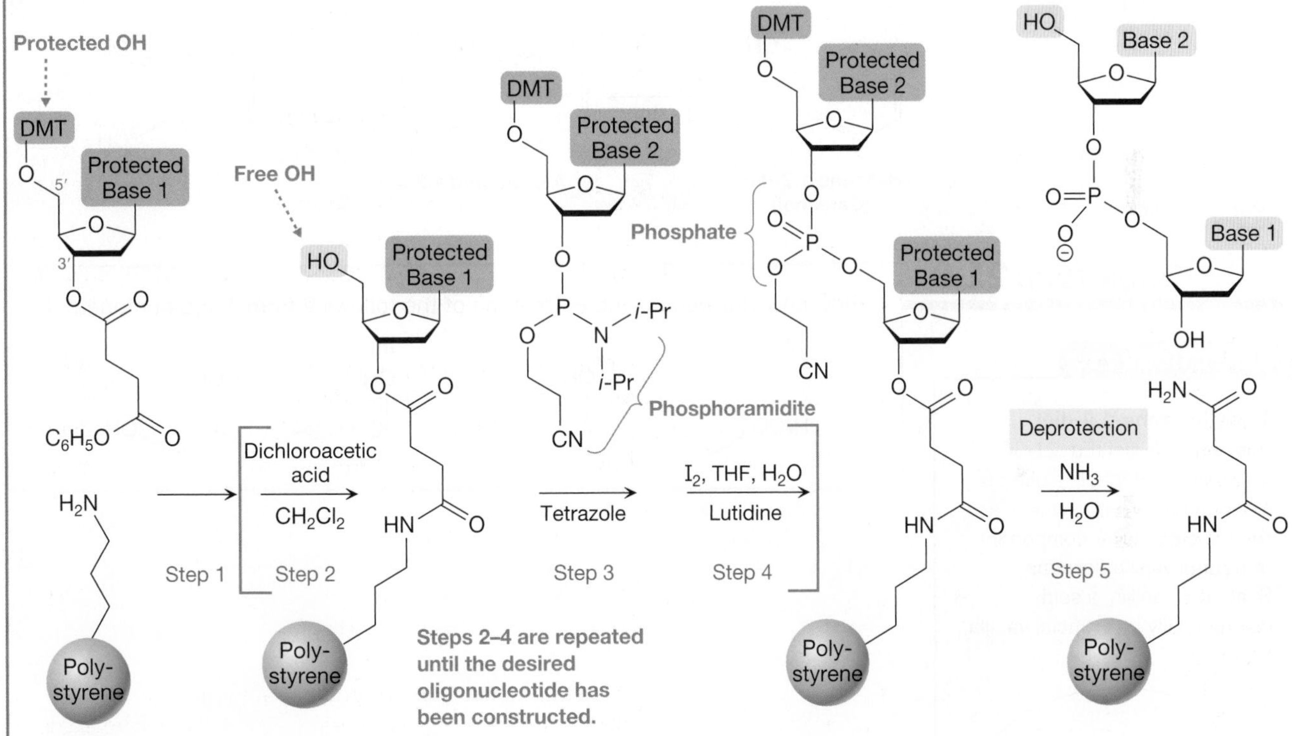

Protected OH
DMT
Protected Base 1
Free OH
HO
Protected Base 1
DMT
Protected Base 2
Phosphate
Protected Base 2
Protected Base 1
Phosphoramidite
i-Pr
CN
C_6H_5O
H_2N
Dichloroacetic acid
CH_2Cl_2
Tetrazole
I_2, THF, H_2O
Lutidine
Deprotection
NH_3
H_2O
Step 1
Step 2
Step 3
Step 4
Step 5
Base 2
Base 1
OH
Poly-styrene
Steps 2–4 are repeated until the desired oligonucleotide has been constructed.

FIGURE 21-2

Protecting groups are necessary because each nucleotide has multiple possible reactive sites, including the 5′-OH and the 3′-OH groups of each sugar unit and the NH_2 group of adenine, guanine, and cytosine bases. By using protecting groups appropriately, we can ensure that the correct groups are free to react at any given time, so that the DNA chain grows in a specific way.

The synthesis consists of the five distinct steps shown in Figure 21-2. Step 1 connects the 3′-end of the first nucleoside (i.e., base linked to a sugar) to a support, such as polystyrene, by an amide linkage. Notice that the 5′-OH and the NH_2 group of the base (in the case of A, G, and C) are initially protected. The 5′-OH is protected as a 4,4′-dimethoxytrityl (DMT) ether, and the NH_2 group of the base is protected as an amide. In Step 2, the 5′-OH is deprotected, making it available to react. In Step 3, that 5′-OH connects to the P atom of a phosphoramidite group [characterized by $(RO)_2PNR_2$] at the 3′-end of a second protected nucleoside, and the oxidation in Step 4 produces a phosphate group. Steps 2–4 are repeated to add more nucleosides, and once the desired chain has been constructed, Step 5 deprotects all the groups and releases the DNA chain from the silica support.

Just as the carbonyl group of a ketone or aldehyde can react with a diol to produce a cyclic acetal (a protected form of the carbonyl group), the same reaction can protect diols. For example, both 1,2-diols and 1,3-diols can be protected with acetone [$(CH_3)_2C{=}O$], as shown in Equations 21-29 and 21-30, respectively. As usual, deprotection takes place by hydrolysis, which requires dilute aqueous acid.

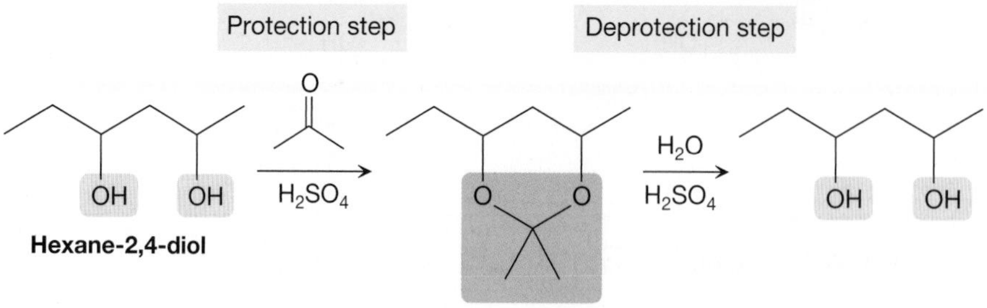
Protection step
Deprotection step
O
OH
OH
H_2SO_4
O
O
H_2O
H_2SO_4
OH
OH

Hexane-2,4-diol

A protected 1,3-diol

(21-29)

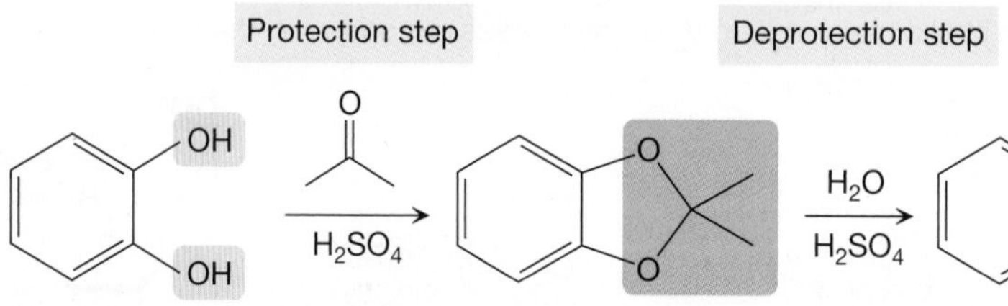
Protection step
Deprotection step
OH
OH
O
H_2SO_4
O
O
H_2O
H_2SO_4
OH
OH

Benzene-1,2-diol (Catechol)

A protected 1,2-diol

(21-30)

YOUR TURN **21.8**

Show how you would synthesize each of the following from 1,2,5-pentanetriol.

(a)

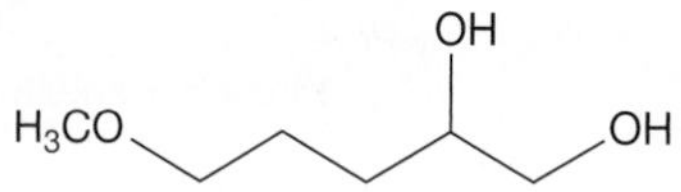
OH
H_3CO
OH

(b)

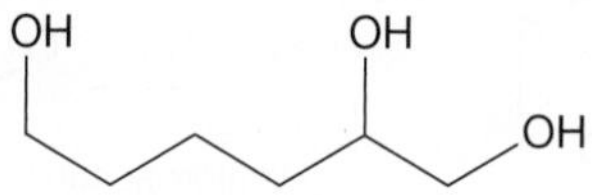
OH
OH
OH

CONNECTIONS 21.2

Tasty benzene-1,2-diol
Benzene-1,2-diol (Eq. 21-30), also called catechol, is used to manufacture vanillin, which is the principal flavor component of natural vanilla flavoring. Synthetic vanillin is sold commercially as artificial vanilla flavoring.

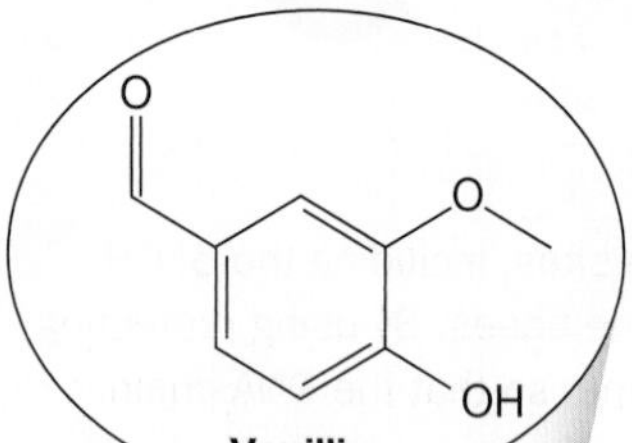
O
O
OH

Vanillin

VANILLA
FLAVOR
PREMIUM

Chapter Summary and Key Terms

- The formation of a bond between two carbon atoms is a problem when the atoms are of like charge. To circumvent such a problem, we can first carry out a reaction that reverses the charge (polarity) of one atom by a process called **umpolung**. Examples of umpolung include the conversion of an alkyl halide into an organometallic species or a Wittig reagent. **(Section 21.1a)**
- Many carbon–carbon bond-forming reactions leave heteroatoms with very specific relative positioning. Thus, target molecules that exhibit such relative positioning provide clues as to which of those reactions should be considered in a synthesis. **(Section 21.1b)**
- If a synthesis requires the formation of a new carbon–carbon bond but the target does not exhibit a specific relative positioning of heteroatoms, then the synthesis may require a reaction that removes a functional group entirely from a molecule. **(Section 21.1c)**
  - The C=C functional group of an alkene or the C≡C functional group of an alkyne can be removed by catalytic hydrogenation.
  - Reactions that remove the C=O functional group of a ketone or aldehyde include the *Wolff–Kishner reduction*, the *Clemmensen reduction*, and the *Raney-nickel reduction*.
- If two or more reactive functional groups appear in a molecule, we can often carry out a reaction at just one of those groups by using either a *selective reagent* or a *protecting group*. **(Section 21.2)**
  - A **selective reagent** favors reaction with one functional group over another. **(Section 21.2a)**
  - A **protecting group** temporarily converts a functional group into one that is unreactive under the conditions necessary for a step in the synthesis. Ketones, aldehydes, and alcohols can often be protected in the form of an acetal or ether. **(Section 21.2b)**

Problems

Problems that are related to synthesis are denoted (SYN).

Section 21.1 Considerations When a Synthesis Calls for a New Carbon–Carbon Bond

21.1 For each reaction, determine whether umpolung has taken place.

(a)
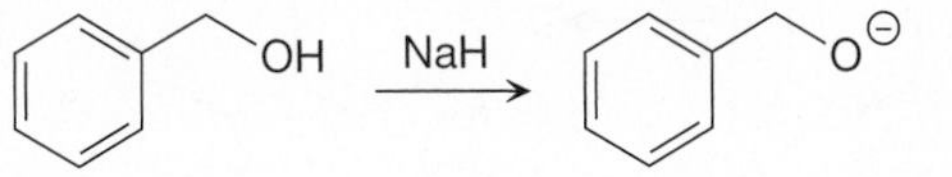

OH
NaH
O⊖

(b)

OH
PBr3
Br

(c)
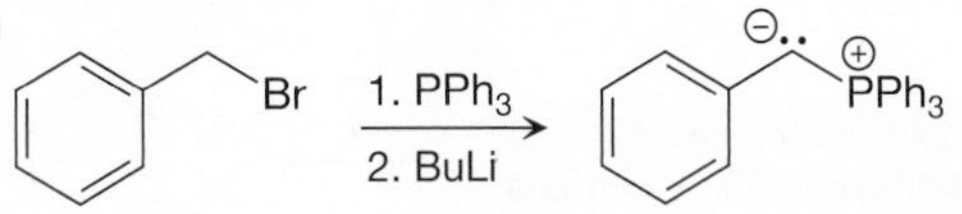

Br
1. PPh3
2. BuLi
PPh3

(d)
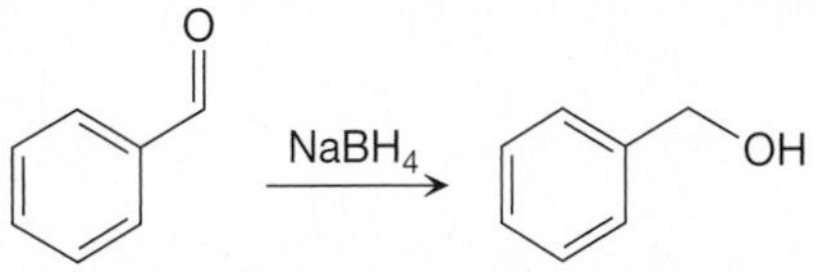

O
NaBH4
OH

(e)
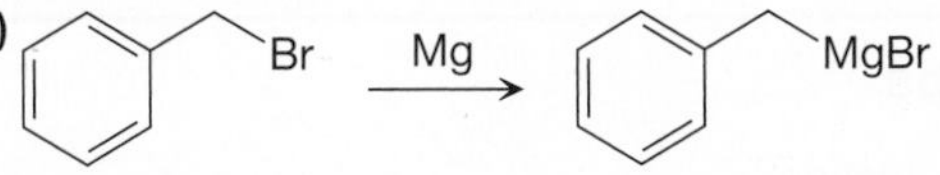

Br
Mg
MgBr

(f)
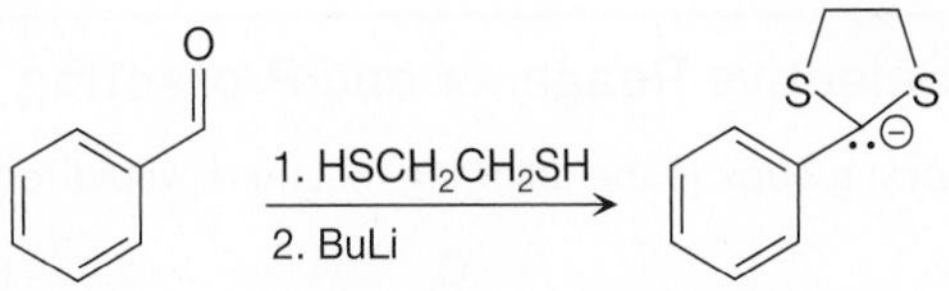

O
1. HSCH2CH2SH
2. BuLi
S
S

21.2 For each pair of molecules, determine whether umpolung (polarity reversal) should be considered to join the highlighted carbons together.

(a)
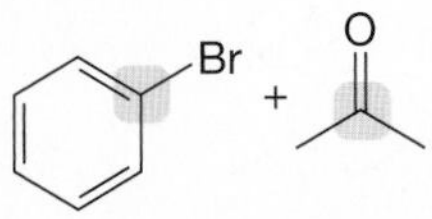

Br
+
O

(b)
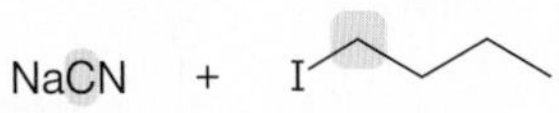

NaCN
+
I

(c)
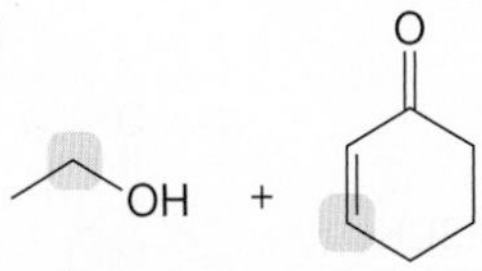

OH
+
O

21.3 **(SYN)** For each carbon–carbon bond formation that requires umpolung in Problem 21.2, design a synthesis that shows how to join the two carbons.

21.4 **(SYN)** Show how to carry out the following synthesis in which umpolung is carried out on **(a)** the alkyl halide or **(b)** the ketone. In each synthesis, identify the synthetic step in which umpolung takes place.

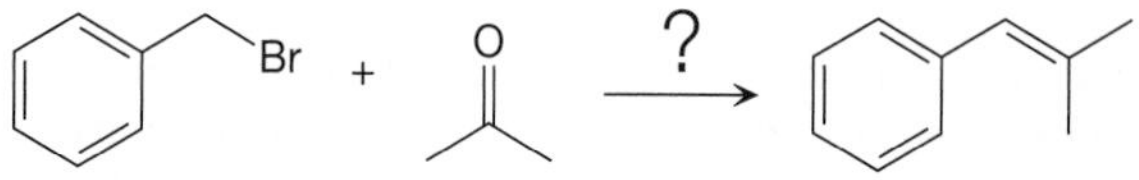

21.5 **(SYN)** Suppose that each compound shown here must be synthesized from compounds with six or fewer carbons. Which carbon–carbon bond-forming reaction(s) from Table 21-1 should you consider incorporating in each synthesis?

(a)
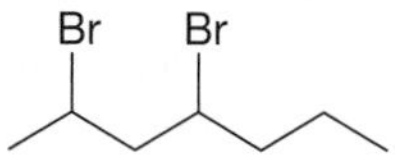
(b)
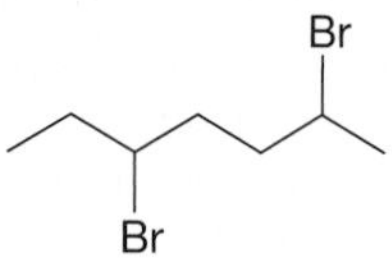
(c)
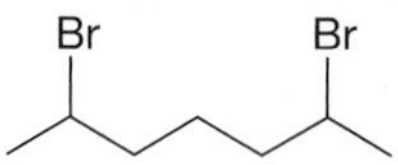
(d)
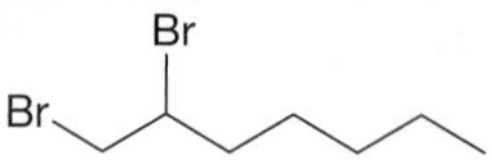

21.6 **(SYN)** Show how to synthesize each of the following compounds, beginning with pentan-2-one.

(a)
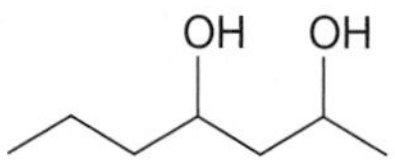
(b)
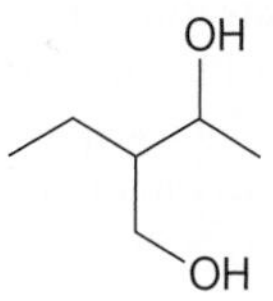
(c)
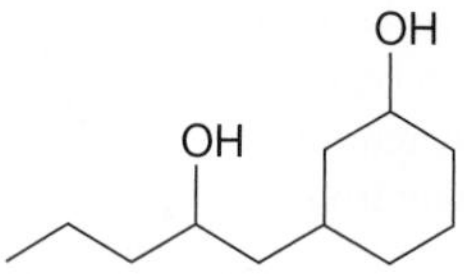

21.7 **(SYN)** Show how to carry out each of the following syntheses.

(a)
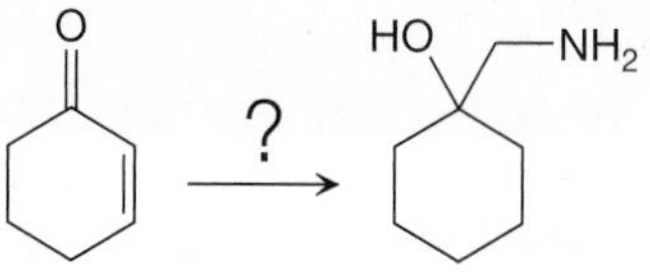
(b)
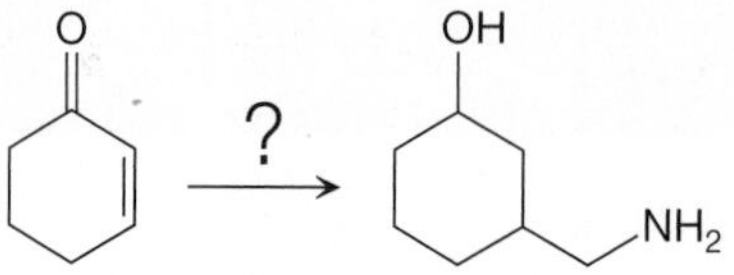

21.8 **(SYN)** Show how to carry out the transformation shown, using $CH_3CH_2CH_2Br$ as your only other carbon source.

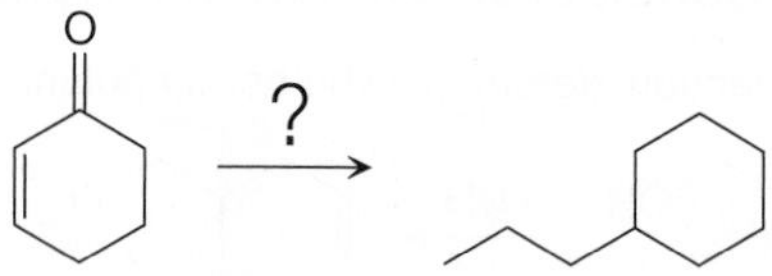

21.9 **(SYN)** Show how to carry out the transformation shown, using $CH_3CH_2CH_2Br$ as your only other carbon source.

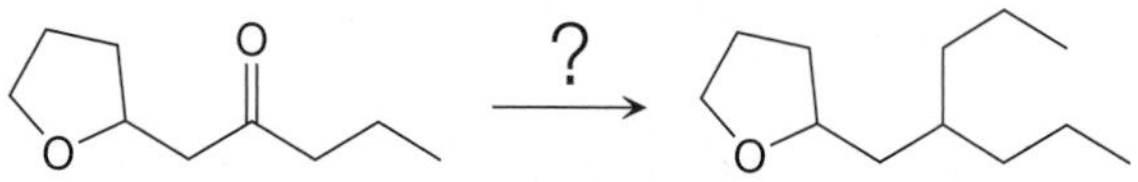

21.10 **(SYN)** Show how to synthesize the following compound from any carbon sources containing three carbons.

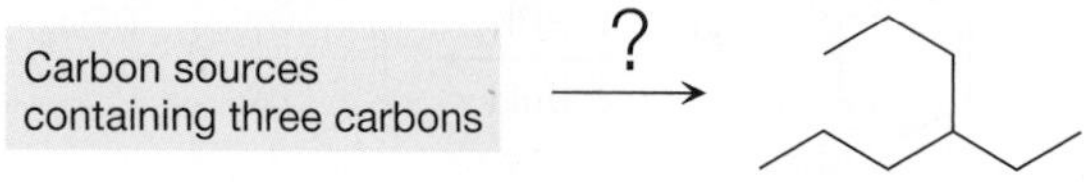
Carbon sources
containing three carbons

Section 21.2 Selective Reagents and Protecting Groups

21.11 Which carbonyl groups in the following reactions would require protection?

(a)
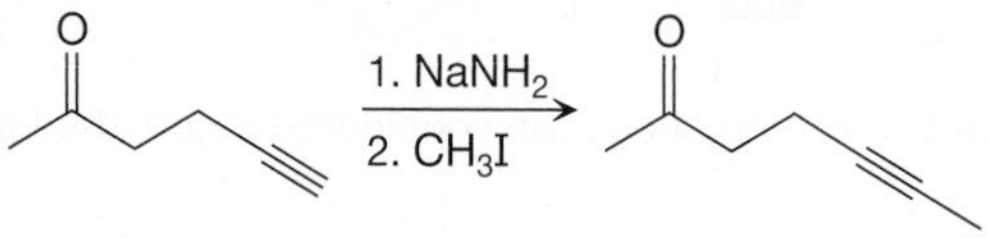
(b)
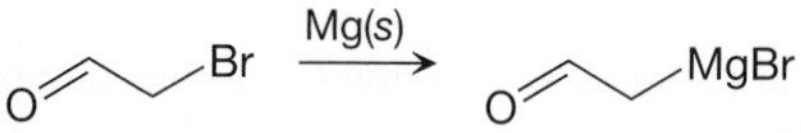
(c)
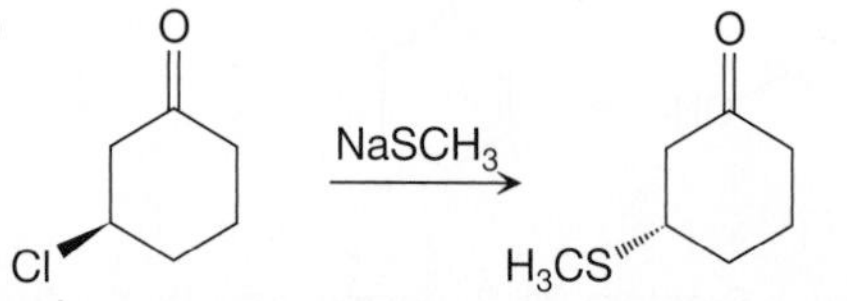
(d)
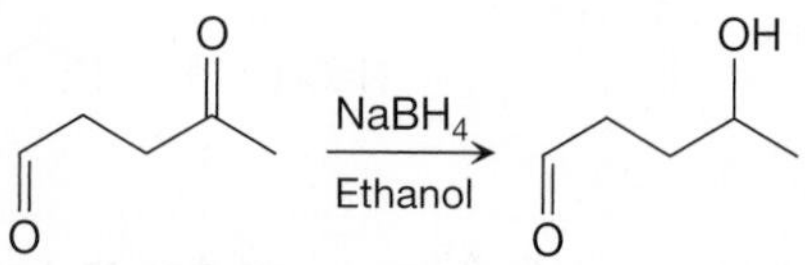

21.12 Which hydroxyl groups in the following reactions would require protection?

(a)

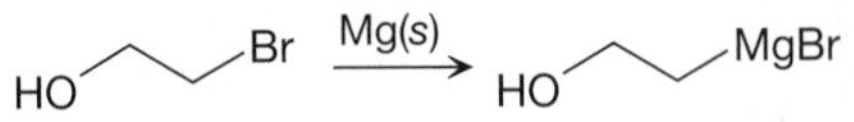
HO
Br
Mg(s)
HO
MgBr

(b)

Cl
HO
NaCN
HO
CN

(c)

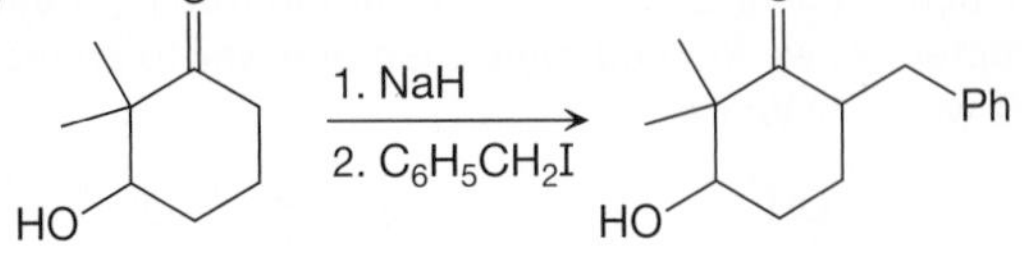
O
HO
1. NaH
2. C6H5CH2I
O
Ph
HO

(d)

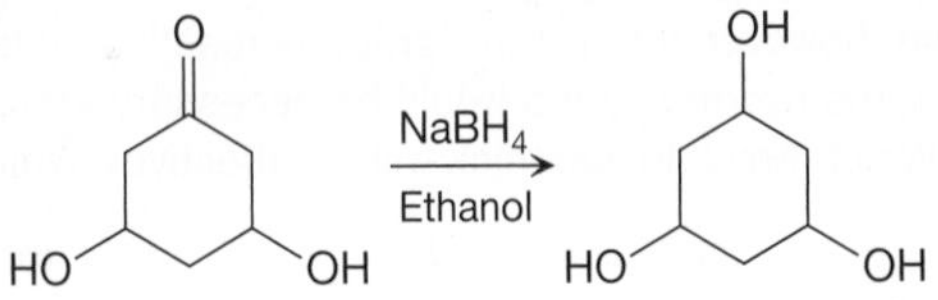
O
HO
OH
NaBH4
Ethanol
OH
HO
OH

21.13 Show how to carry out the following synthesis.

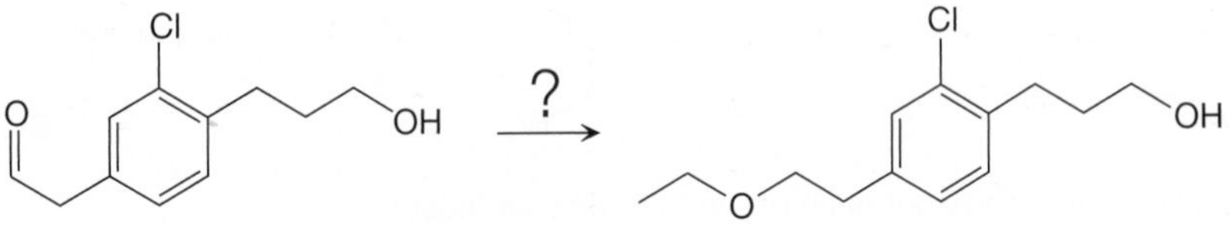
Cl
O
OH
?
Cl
OH
O

21.14 A student carried out the following sequence of reactions, using *tert*-butyldimethylsilyl chloride (TBDMS–Cl) to protect the hydroxyl group.

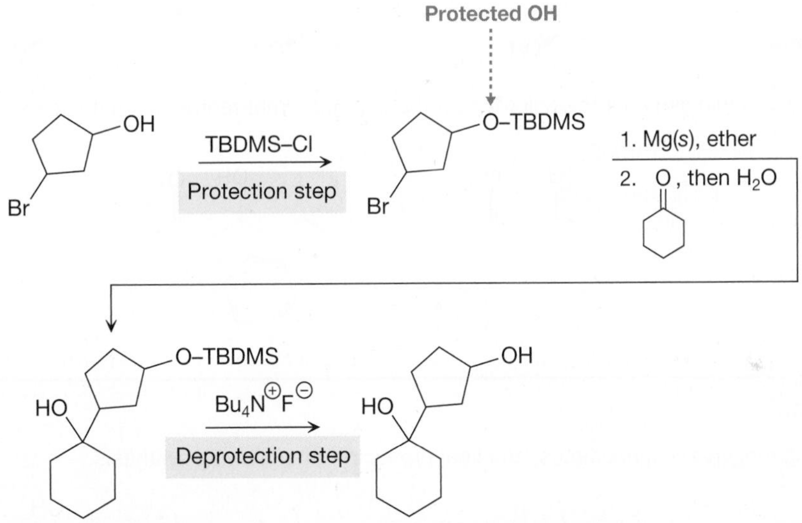
Protected OH
OH
Br
TBDMS–Cl
Protection step
O–TBDMS
Br
1. Mg(s), ether
2. O, then H2O
O–TBDMS
HO
Bu4N⊕F⊖
Deprotection step
OH
HO

(a) Could this synthesis be carried out without protecting the hydroxyl group? Why or why not?
(b) Which other protecting groups in Table 21-2 could have been used instead? Explain.

21.15 Propose how you would carry out this synthesis using a TBDMS protecting group.

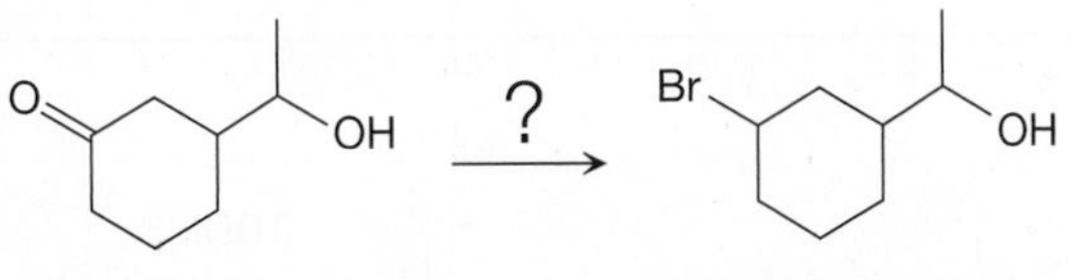
O
OH
?
Br
OH

21.16 Here in Chapter 21, we learned that converting a ketone or aldehyde to an acetal is a good way to protect the carbonyl group, because an acetal is composed of ether linkages. It is possible to convert a ketone or aldehyde into an epoxide (for example, see Problem 18.29, p. 920), which can be thought of as a three-membered-ring ether. Why would an epoxide be a poor choice as a protecting group?

21.17 **(SYN)** A student wants to carry out the reaction shown here. Explain the problem(s) associated with this synthesis scheme, and suggest a way to carry out the transformation efficiently.

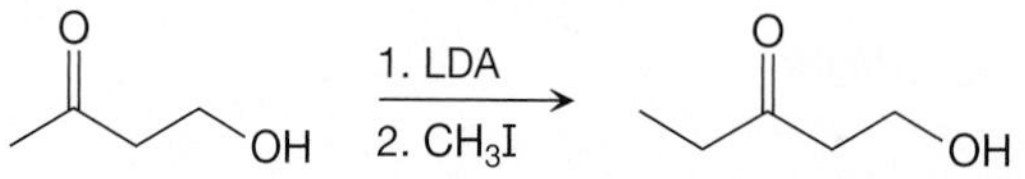

1. LDA
2. CH_3I

21.18 Suppose we want to carry out the following functional group conversions, in which group A is converted to group B. In each case, however, the hydroxyl group is reactive under the reaction conditions that carry out the transformation, so protecting the hydroxyl group would be necessary. Here in Chapter 21, we learned more than one way to protect hydroxyl groups. Which ways do you think will be effective? Which ones will not? Why?

(a)

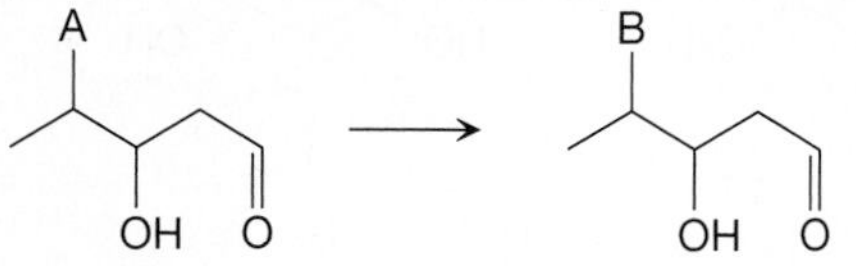

(b)

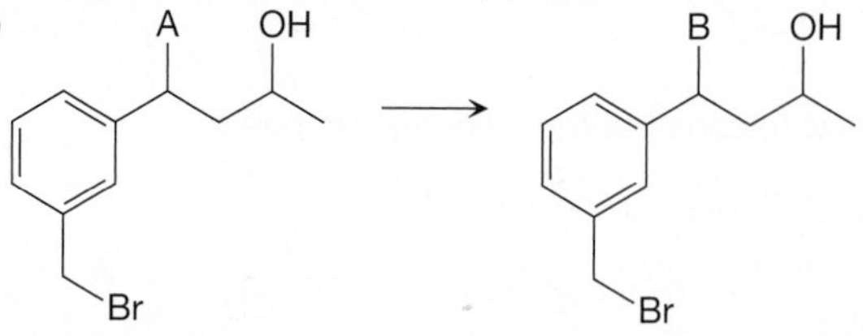

21.19 **(SYN)** Propose how you would carry out each of the following syntheses.

(a)

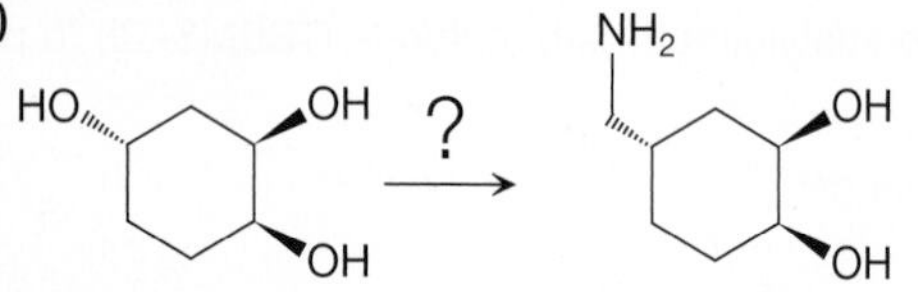

(b)

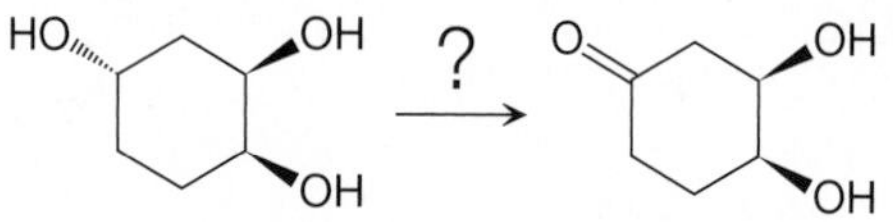

21.20 **(SYN)** Show how you would carry out the following synthesis. *Hint*: What rearrangement occurs when an enol is formed?

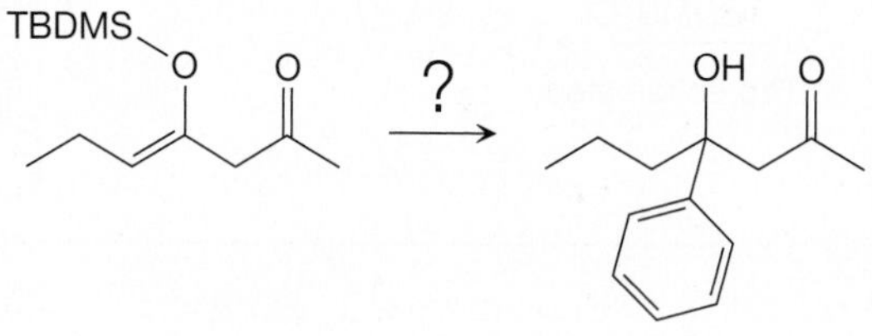

Integrated Problems

21.21 Supply the missing reagents, intermediates, and final product in the following synthesis.

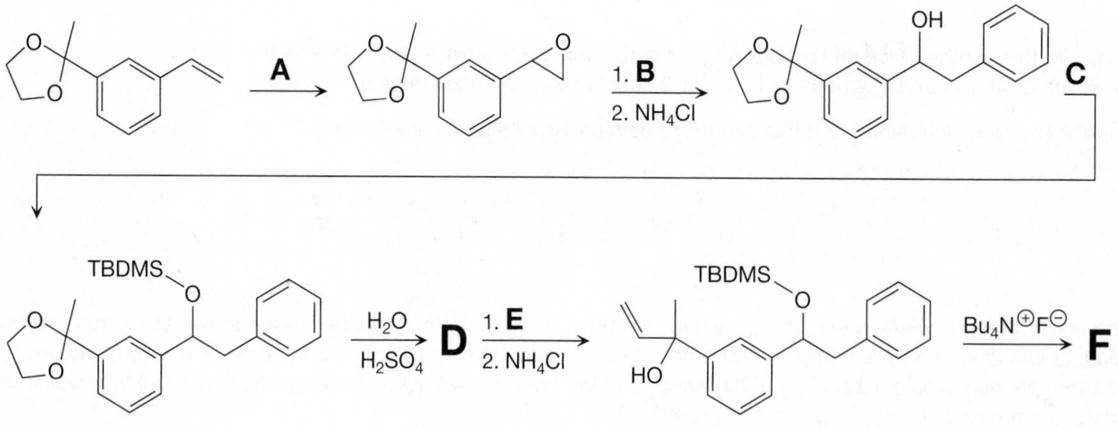

A
1. B
2. NH_4Cl
C
H_2O
H_2SO_4
D
1. E
2. NH_4Cl
$Bu_4N^{\oplus}F^{\ominus}$
F

21.22 **(SYN)** Show how to synthesize each of the following compounds, using propanal and any other ketone or aldehyde as your only starting materials containing carbon.

(a)

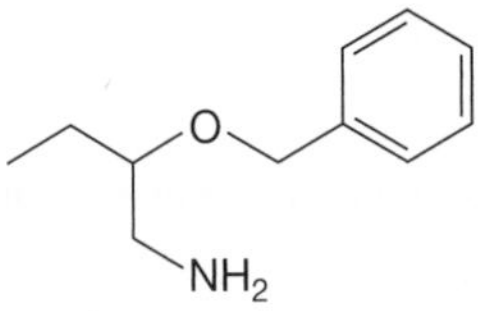

(b)

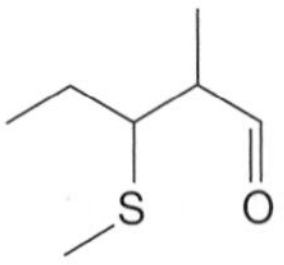

(c)

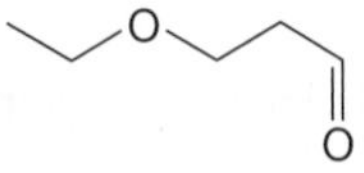

(d)

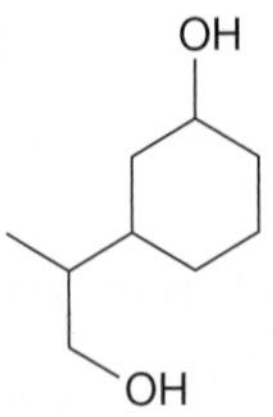

21.23 **(SYN)** Show how to synthesize each of the following compounds, using the given restrictions on the starting materials.

(a)

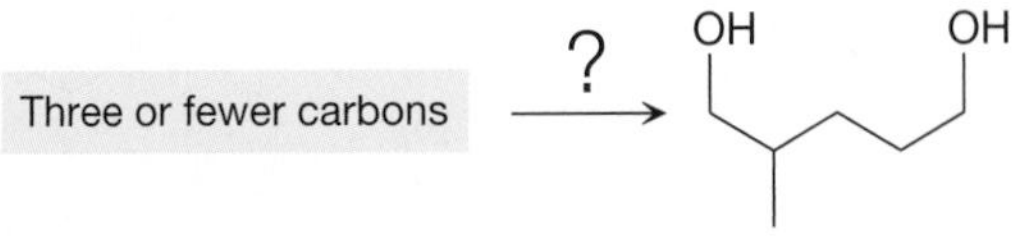
Three or fewer carbons
?

(b)

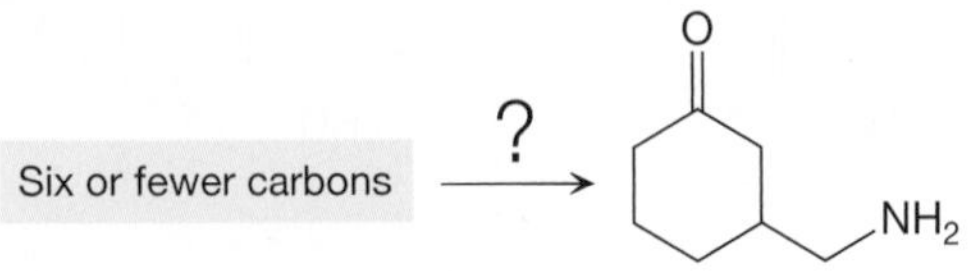
Six or fewer carbons
?

(c)

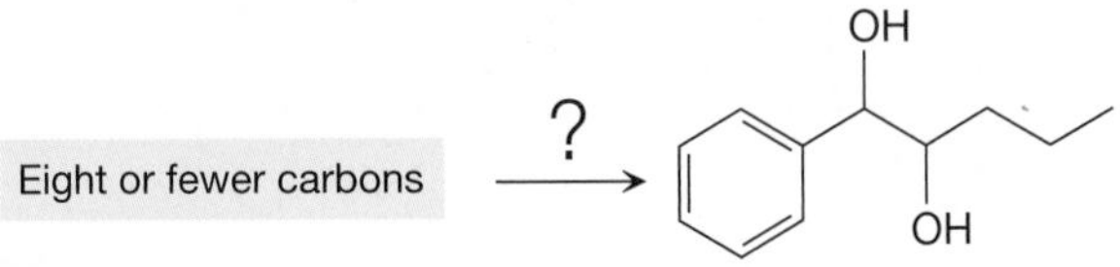
Eight or fewer carbons
?

(d)

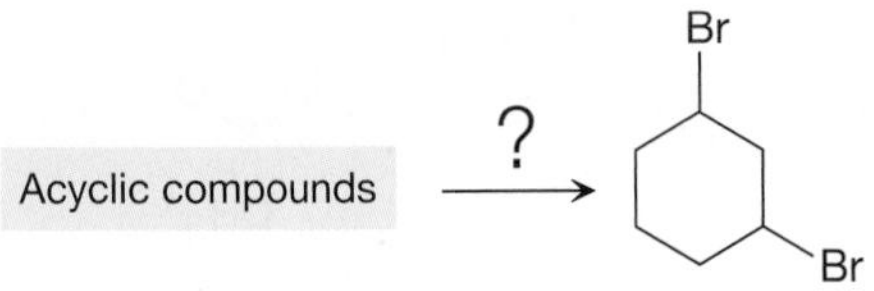
Acyclic compounds
?

21.24 **(SYN)** Show how to carry out the following synthesis, using any reagents necessary. *Hint*: The carbonyl group of a ketone or aldehyde is entirely removed.

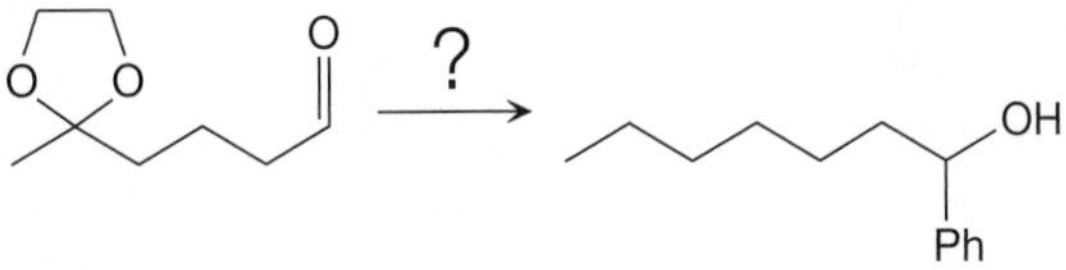

21.25 **(SYN)** 1,4-Cyclohexanedione monoethylene acetal is commercially available. **(a)** Show how you would use it to synthesize 4-ethylidenecyclohexanone. **(b)** What problems would arise if you tried to synthesize the same target from 1,4-cyclohexanedione?

1,4-Cyclohexanedione monoethylene acetal **4-Ethylidenecyclohexanone**

21.26 **(SYN)** Show how you would synthesize hexane-3,4-diol, using propanal as your only source of carbon atoms.

21.27 **(SYN)** Show how you would carry out each of the following syntheses.

(a)

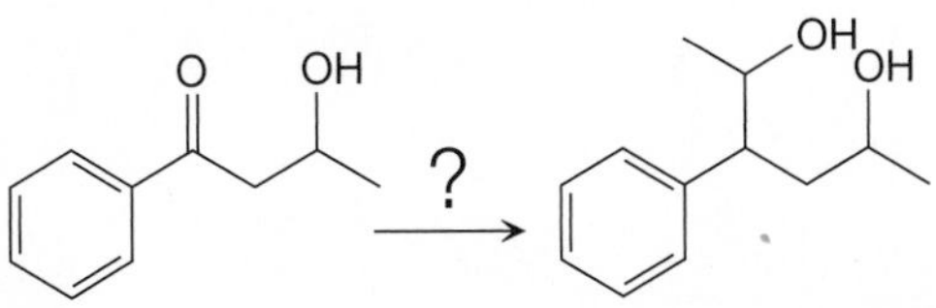

(b)

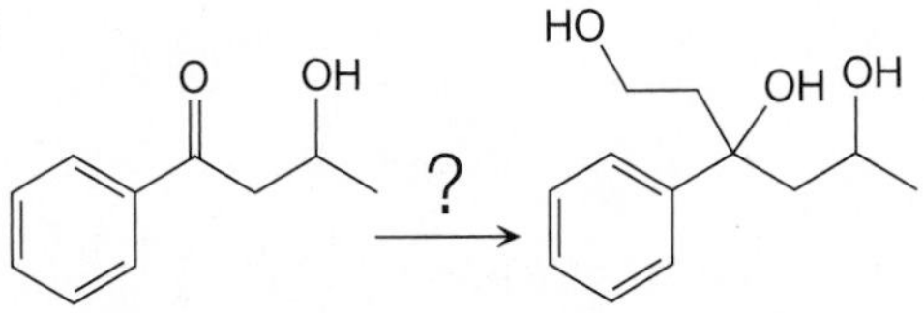

21.28 (SYN) Show how you would synthesize the compound shown, using propanal as your only carbon source.

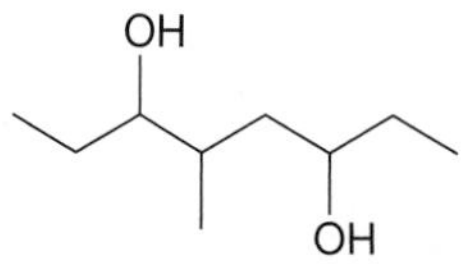
OH
OH

21.29 (SYN) Show how to carry out each of the following syntheses. *Hint*: You may need to use selective reagents or protecting groups.

(a)

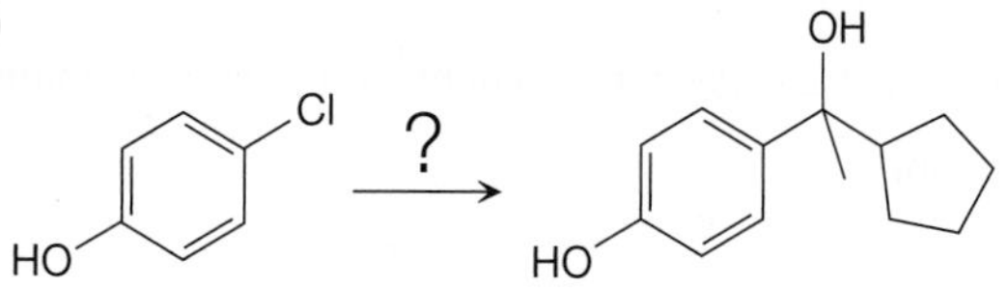
Cl
HO
?
OH
HO

(b)

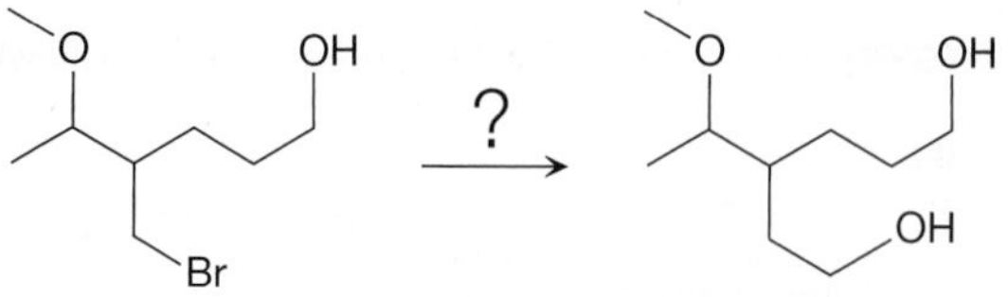
O
OH
Br
?
O
OH
OH

(c)

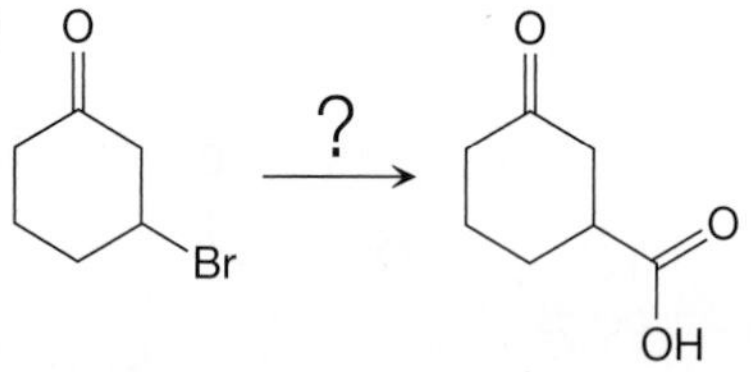
O
Br
?
O
O
OH

(d)

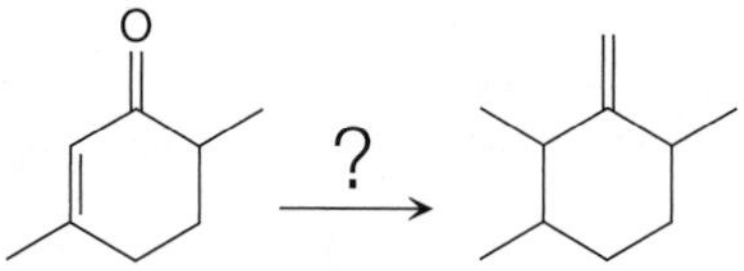
O
?

(e)

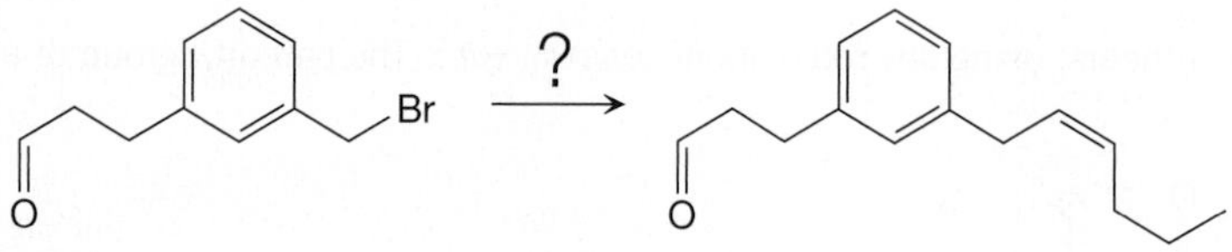
Br
O
?
O

22

A soap's cleansing properties derive from its ability to dissolve nonpolar substances and effectively make those substances soluble in water. Soaps are particularly effective at killing viruses because soaps dissolve the lipid membrane that coats a virus; the lipid membrane contains proteins that are vital for the normal functioning of the virus. The process for making soap involves one of the oldest organic reactions known, called saponification. Here in Chapter 22, we study saponification and other nucleophilic addition–elimination reactions.

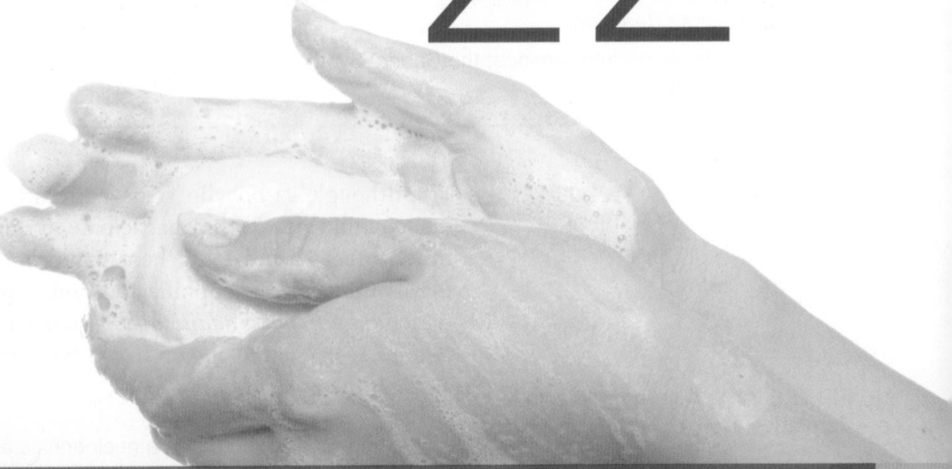

Nucleophilic Addition–Elimination Reactions 1

Reagents That Are Strongly Nucleophilic

Chapters 18 and 19 discuss reactions in which nucleophiles add to compounds containing polar π bonds, such as ketones, aldehydes, imines, and nitriles. Those nucleophilic addition reactions are driven, in large part, by the flow of electrons from the electron-rich nucleophile to the electron-poor (i.e., electrophilic) atom of the polar π bond.

A variety of other compound classes contain polar π bonds, too, and are therefore susceptible to nucleophilic attack. For example, carboxylic acids have the polar carbonyl group (highlighted in **Figure 22-1**), as do esters, amides, acid anhydrides, and acid halides—collectively known as **carboxylic acid derivatives**.

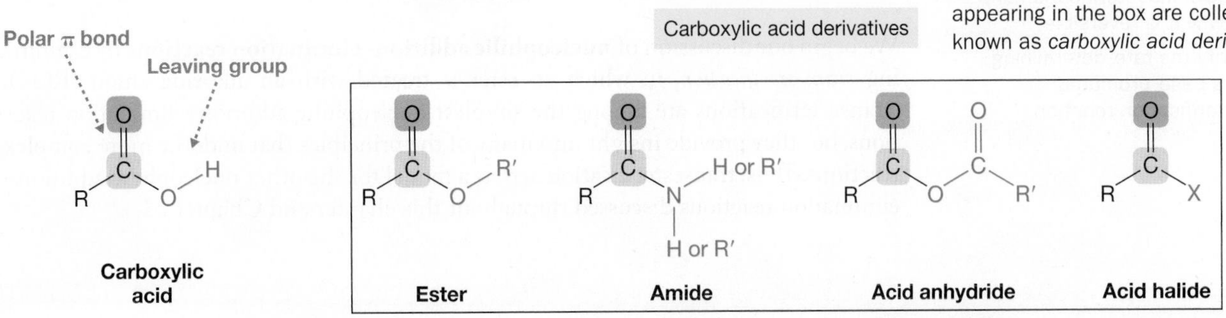

Polar π bond
Leaving group
Carboxylic acid derivatives
Carboxylic acid
Ester
Amide
Acid anhydride
Acid halide

FIGURE 22-1 Some compound classes that undergo nucleophilic addition–elimination These compounds contain a leaving group (shown in red type) attached to the electron-poor C atom of the polar π bond. The compound classes appearing in the box are collectively known as *carboxylic acid derivatives*.

Chapter Outline

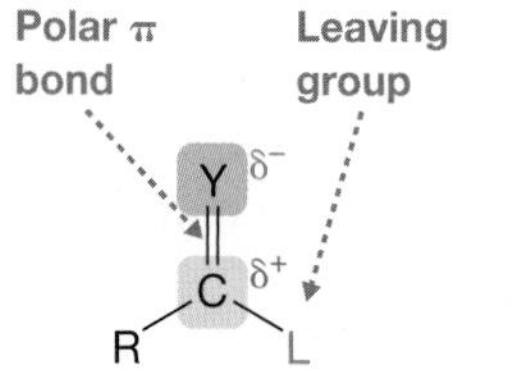

Polar π bond
Leaving group
Y
δ−
C
δ+
R
L

FIGURE 22-2 A carboxylic acid derivative

Although carboxylic acids and carboxylic acid derivatives are susceptible to nucleophilic attack, they participate in different *overall* reactions from what we saw in Chapters 18 and 19. Whereas the compound classes in Chapters 18 and 19 primarily undergo nucleophilic addition, carboxylic acids and their derivatives tend to undergo *nucleophilic addition–elimination* mechanisms. This is because they each contain a *leaving group* (shown in red type, Fig. 22-1) bonded to the electron-deficient atom of the polar π bond.

> A compound can undergo a nucleophilic addition–elimination reaction if it has a leaving group attached to the electron-poor atom of a polar π bond (**Figure 22-2**).

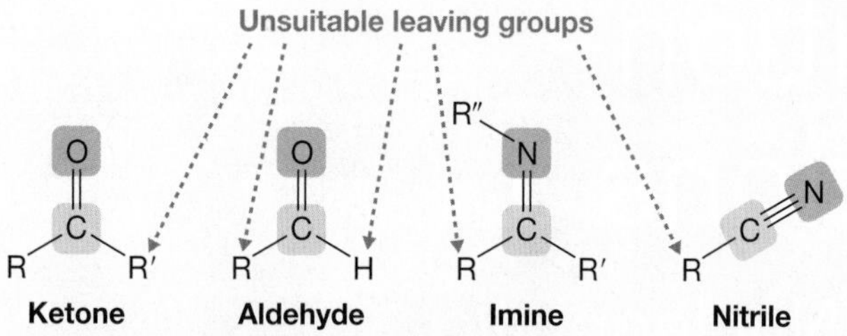

Unsuitable leaving groups
O
C
R
R′
Ketone
O
C
R
H
Aldehyde
R″
N
C
R
R′
Imine
N
C
R
Nitrile

FIGURE 22-3 Compound classes that tend to undergo nucleophilic addition only These compounds do not have a leaving group attached to the polar π bond. The H and R groups that are attached to the electron-poor C atom would have to depart as H^- or R^-, which are highly unstable.

By contrast, ketones, aldehydes, imines, and nitriles do *not* possess a suitable leaving group; the electron-deficient carbon is bonded to H or alkyl (R) groups only (**Figure 22-3**), so any leaving group would have to depart as H^- or R^-, which are too unstable to leave. Consequently, these compounds tend to undergo nucleophilic addition only.

As we will see throughout this chapter and Chapter 23, a wide variety of reactions proceed by a nucleophilic addition–elimination mechanism. Here in Chapter 22, we focus just on nucleophilic addition–elimination reactions in which one of the reagents added is strongly nucleophilic itself. These include the salts of alkoxide anions (RO^-), reducing agents that are sources of hydride (H^-), and organometallic reagents that are sources of alkyl anions (R^-). In Chapter 23, we examine reactions in which the reagents are weakly nucleophilic or non-nucleophilic, many of which require acid or base catalysis.

SECTION 22.1 OBJECTIVES

You will be able to:

1. Draw the mechanism for base-promoted transesterification and explain why it is reversible.
2. Identify the rate-determining step of a base-promoted transesterification reaction.

22.1 An Introduction to Nucleophilic Addition–Elimination Reactions: Transesterification

We begin our discussion of **nucleophilic addition–elimination reactions** by examining *transesterification*, in which an ester is treated with an alkoxide anion (RO^-). Transesterifications are among the simplest nucleophilic addition–elimination reactions, but they provide insight into many of the principles that underlie more complex reactions. Thus, transesterification acts as a model for the other nucleophilic addition–elimination reactions discussed throughout this chapter and Chapter 23.

22.1a The General Nucleophilic Addition–Elimination Mechanism

When a butyl ester such as the one shown in Equation 22-1 is treated with sodium methoxide, a different ester is produced:

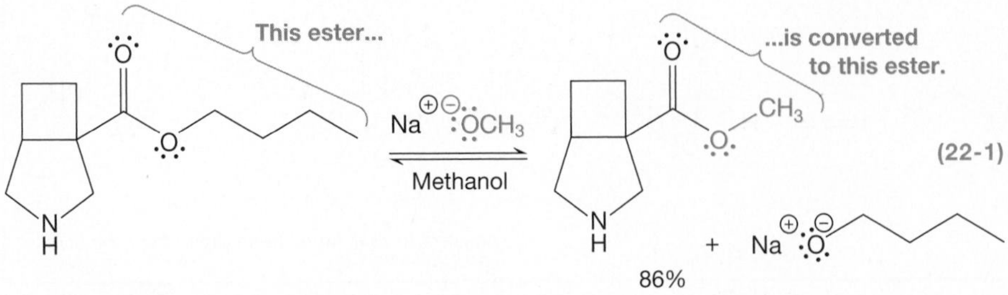

This ester...
...is converted to this ester.
Methanol
86%

(22-1)

This is an example of a **transesterification reaction**, so called because one ester is converted into another. It is further called *base-promoted* transesterification because $NaOCH_3$ (a reactant) is strongly basic.

The mechanism for this base-promoted transesterification, shown in Equation 22-2, is typical of reactions involving a nucleophile and a carboxylic acid derivative. It is called a *nucleophilic addition–elimination* mechanism because of the two steps that take place.

Mechanism for base-promoted transesterification (Eq. 22-1)

Nucleophilic addition–elimination mechanism

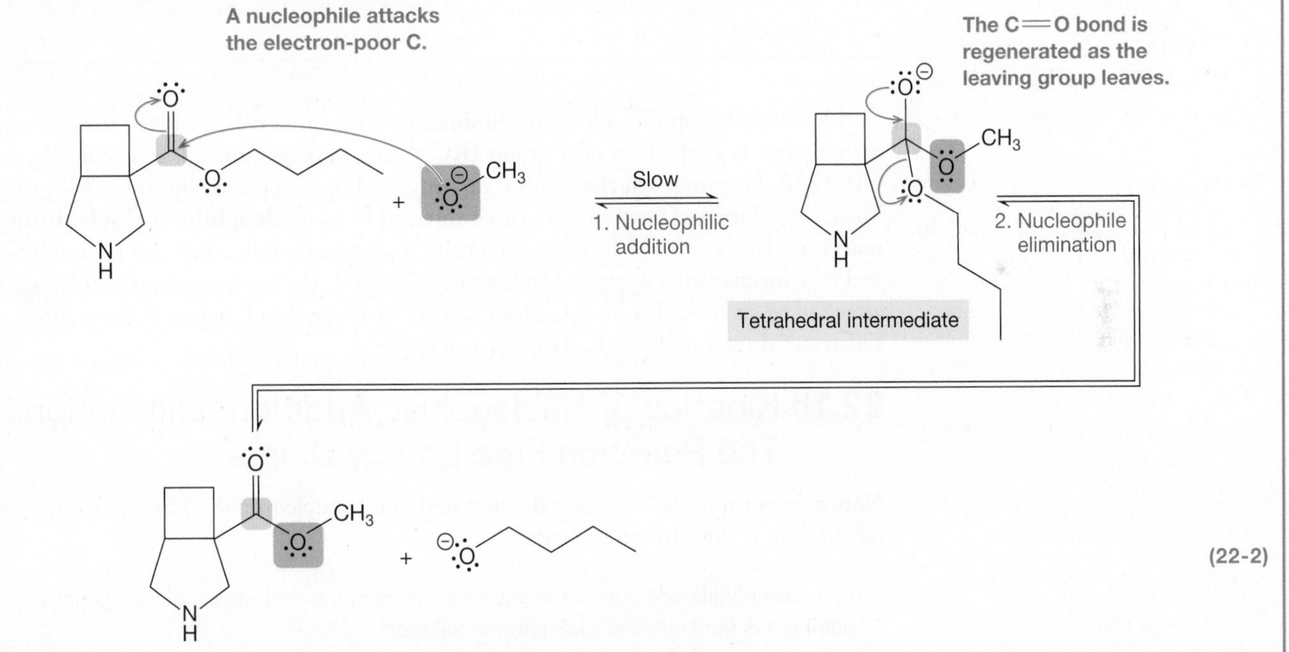

A nucleophile attacks the electron-poor C.
The C═O bond is regenerated as the leaving group leaves.
Slow
1. Nucleophilic addition
2. Nucleophile elimination
Tetrahedral intermediate

(22-2)

Step 1 is *nucleophilic addition* (Section 7.4), in which a nucleophile attacks the electron-poor carbonyl carbon. This forces the pair of electrons from the initial C═O π bond onto the O atom, which generates a negative charge on O. Because the carbonyl carbon was converted from a planar geometry to tetrahedral, the product of that step is a **tetrahedral intermediate**. In Step 2, the tetrahedral intermediate undergoes *nucleophile elimination* (Section 7.4). A lone pair of electrons on the negatively charged O atom is used to regenerate the C═O double bond, and the leaving group departs as $CH_3(CH_2)_3O^-$.

YOUR TURN 22.1

The following is the mechanism for another transesterification reaction, but the curved arrows have been omitted. Complete the mechanism by adding the necessary curved arrows and identify the tetrahedral intermediate. Below each reaction arrow, write the name of the elementary step that takes place.

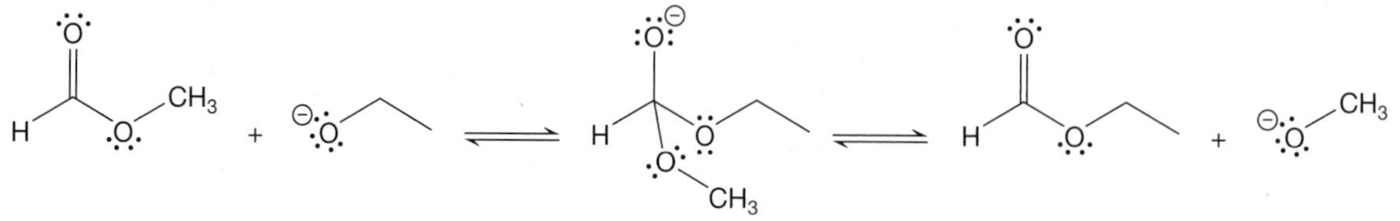

Answers to Your Turns are in the back of the book.

YOUR TURN 22.2

Draw the complete, detailed mechanism and the major product(s) for each of the following reactions.

(a)

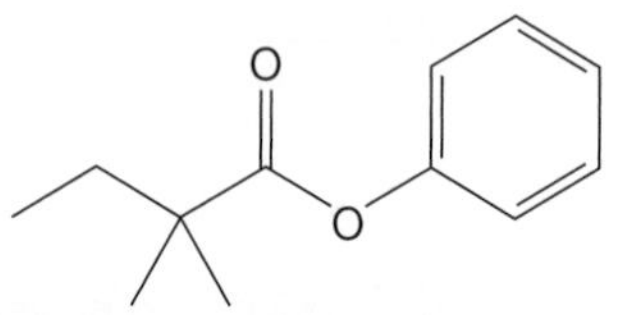

NaOCH2CH3
CH3CH2OH
?

(b)

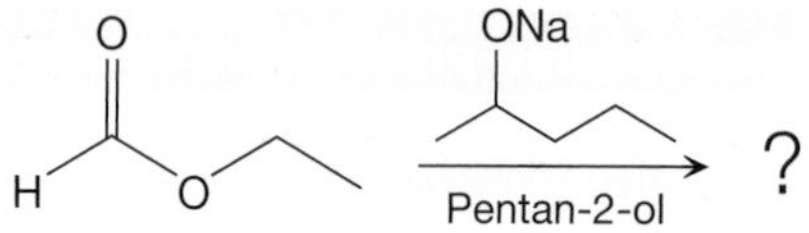

ONa
Pentan-2-ol
?

Overall, nucleophilic addition–elimination results in a *substitution* at the carbonyl carbon that is part of an acyl group (RC=O). In Equation 22-1 specifically, the $O(CH_2)_3CH_3$ group attached to the carbonyl carbon is replaced by an OCH_3 group. Thus, these kinds of reactions are often referred to as **nucleophilic acyl substitution reactions**. Keep in mind, however, that this mechanism is quite different from the S_N2 and S_N1 mechanisms described in Chapters 7 and 8. The leaving group in this case is attached to an sp^2-hybridized C atom and, as we learned in Chapter 9, these kinds of substrates do not undergo S_N2 or S_N1 reactions.

22.1b Kinetics of Nucleophilic Addition–Elimination: The Reaction Free Energy Diagram

Notice from Equation 22-2 that the first step of this nucleophilic addition–elimination mechanism is slow. In other words:

> In a nucleophilic addition–elimination mechanism, the first step (i.e., nucleophilic addition) is generally the rate-determining step.

The first step is slow because its transition state energy is so high, as shown in **Figure 22-4**.

The high transition state energy of the nucleophilic addition–elimination reaction is due in part to the loss of *resonance stabilization* in the ester reactant. Resonance in the ester involves the π bond of the carbonyl group and a lone pair of electrons from the leaving group, as shown in Figure 22-4. No such resonance stabilization exists in the tetrahedral intermediate, however, because it lacks the π bond. Similarly, the transition state, which closely resembles the tetrahedral intermediate, lacks resonance stabilization. When the products are formed, resonance stabilization is reestablished.

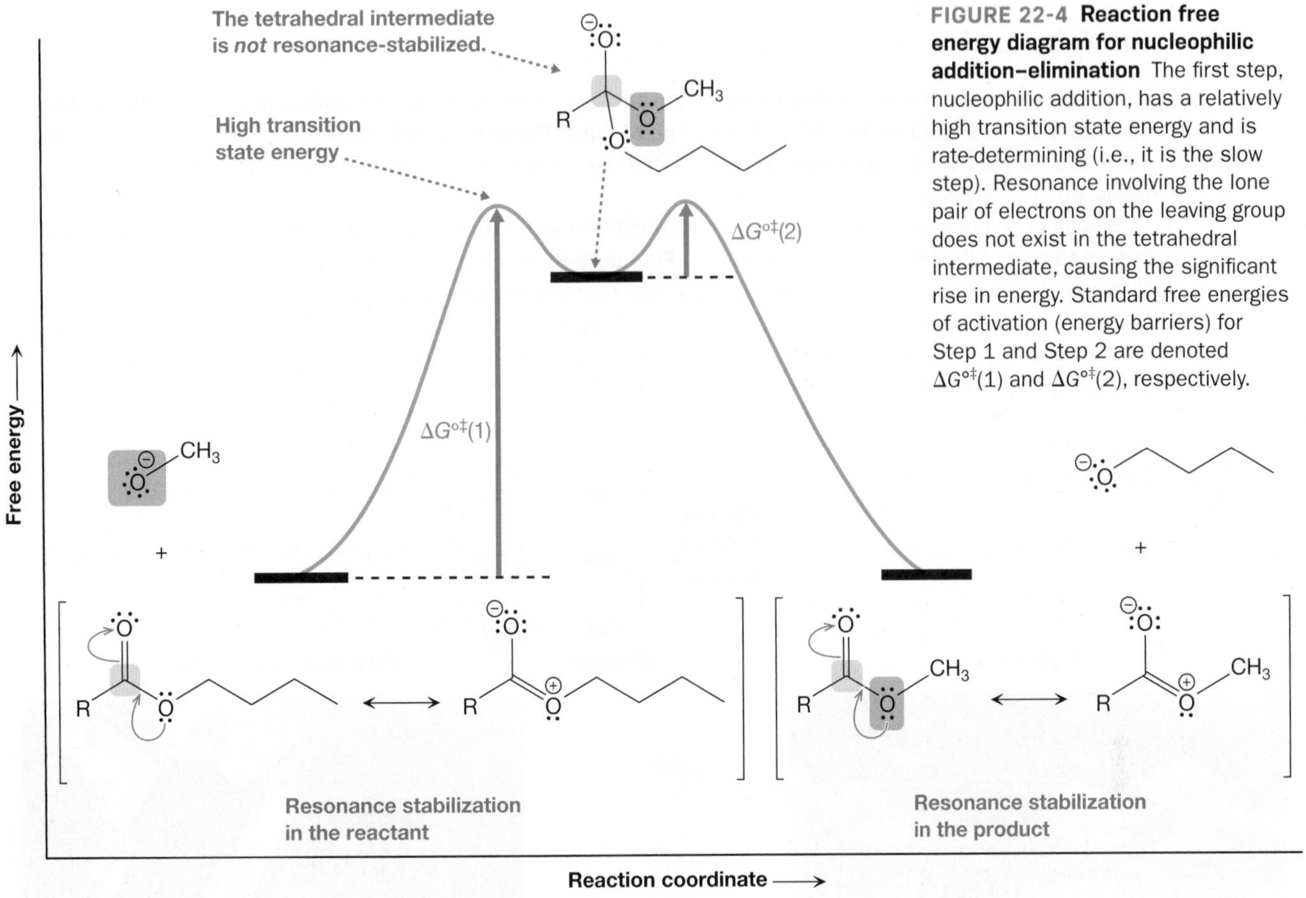

The tetrahedral intermediate is *not* resonance-stabilized.
High transition state energy
$\Delta G^{\circ\ddagger}(2)$
$\Delta G^{\circ\ddagger}(1)$
Free energy
Resonance stabilization in the reactant
Resonance stabilization in the product
Reaction coordinate

FIGURE 22-4 Reaction free energy diagram for nucleophilic addition–elimination The first step, nucleophilic addition, has a relatively high transition state energy and is rate-determining (i.e., it is the slow step). Resonance involving the lone pair of electrons on the leaving group does not exist in the tetrahedral intermediate, causing the significant rise in energy. Standard free energies of activation (energy barriers) for Step 1 and Step 2 are denoted $\Delta G^{\circ\ddagger}(1)$ and $\Delta G^{\circ\ddagger}(2)$, respectively.

YOUR TURN 22.3

Construct a free energy diagram for the reaction in Your Turn 22.1. Include and label the overall reactants, overall products, and the tetrahedral intermediate, and draw a vertical arrow to represent each step's energy barrier.

22.1c Thermodynamics and Reversibility

Looking back at Equation 22-1, notice that the reactants and products are connected by an equilibrium reaction arrow ($\rightleftharpoons$). In other words:

Transesterification is a *reversible* reaction.

Thus, if the methyl ester on the product side of Equation 22-1 is treated with $CH_3(CH_2)_3O^-$, the butyl ester on the reactant side of Equation 22-1 will be produced by nucleophilic addition–elimination (see Recall box).

◂ RECALL

According to Le Châtelier's principle (Section 6.2b), a reaction at equilibrium will shift toward reactants when a product is added. The equilibrium will shift toward products when a reactant is added.

YOUR TURN 22.4

Draw the detailed mechanism for the reverse of the reaction in Equation 22-1.

The reversibility of base-promoted transesterification is consistent with the reactants and products having similar energies, as shown previously in Figure 22-4. Therefore, the overall energy barrier that must be traversed in the reverse direction is roughly the same size as that in the forward direction. The reactants and products are similar

Biodiesel and Transesterification

Biodiesel is an attractive alternative to petroleum-based fuels for a variety of reasons, and it currently makes up roughly 1% of all fuel consumption in the United States. Some studies indicate that its use results in lower net production of CO_2, a greenhouse gas, than does use of petroleum diesel. Derived from plants, it can be produced domestically, and it is also *renewable*.

Biodiesel is produced from plant oils by essentially the same transesterification process as that discussed here in Chapter 22. Plant oils are triglycerides (**Figure 22-5**), which are fatty acid triesters of glycerol. Biodiesel, however, is a fatty acid monoester. To carry out the transesterification that produces the biodiesel, the triglyceride is treated with an alcohol under basic conditions. Methanol is the most popular alcohol used for this process, resulting in *fatty acid methyl esters*, though other alcohols can be used, depending on cost and the specific properties desired of the biodiesel.

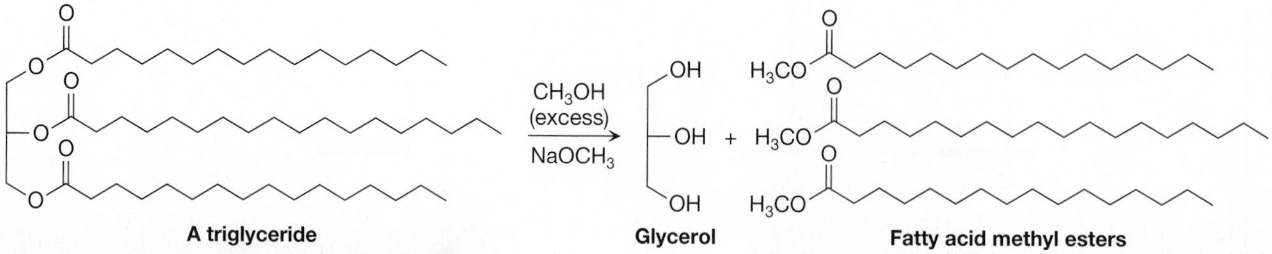

CH3OH
(excess)
NaOCH3
OH
OH
OH
H3CO
H3CO
H3CO
A triglyceride
Glycerol
Fatty acid methyl esters

Grown
for
Biofuel

Bio
Diesel

FIGURE 22-5

Biodiesel synthesis offers a creative solution to the billions of gallons of waste cooking oil produced each year by restaurants. McDonald's, for example, is partnering with renewable fuel companies to convert its waste cooking oil into biodiesel to power its delivery trucks.

Some issues surrounding biodiesel production still remain. One is that methanol is currently produced primarily from petroleum-based sources. However, ways of making renewable methanol are being developed and optimized. Another issue is that large amounts of glycerol are produced as a by-product, but researchers continue to find ways to put the compound to good use. Glycerol can potentially be used, for example, as the starting material in the large-scale production of other valuable compounds, such as ethanol, propylene glycol, acrolein, and hydrogen gas.

in energy because the negative charge that appears on either side of the reaction is stabilized comparably in the alkoxide anions:

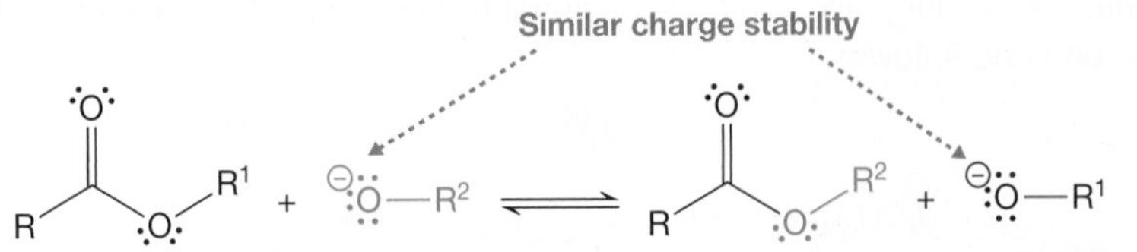

Similar charge stability

(22-3)

Although base-promoted transesterification reactions are reversible, this is *not* true of all nucleophilic addition–elimination reactions. As we will see, the relative stabilities of the nucleophile and the leaving group greatly affect the reversibility of the reaction.

SECTION 22.2 OBJECTIVES

You will be able to:

1. Establish the relative stabilities of various carboxylic acids and carboxylic acid derivatives.
2. Determine whether a given nucleophilic acyl substitution reaction is energetically favorable.

22.2 Acyl Substitution Involving Other Carboxylic Acid Derivatives: The Thermodynamics of Acyl Substitution

The transesterification reactions we examined in Section 22.1 are rather limited in scope, involving an ester as the carboxylic acid derivative and RO^- as the nucleophile. Numerous other acyl substitutions can be carried out, however, simply by using different combinations of carboxylic acid derivatives and nucleophiles. Equation 22-4 shows, for example, that CH_3O^- can displace Cl^- from an acid chloride such as benzoyl chloride to produce an ester:

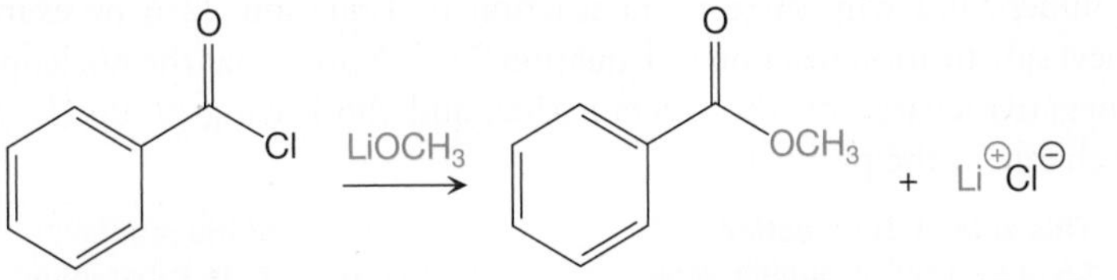

LiOCH3

Benzoyl chloride **Methyl benzoate** 84% (22-4)

The mechanism for this reaction is shown in Equation 22-5. It consists of the usual nucleophilic addition and elimination steps and proceeds through a tetrahedral intermediate.

CONNECTIONS 22.1

Got acne? Benzoyl chloride (Eq. 22-4) is used to produce benzoyl peroxide, which is an important oxidizing agent and radical initiator in chemistry. Benzoyl peroxide is an active ingredient in some topical acne treatments because it kills bacteria that cause acne and removes dead skin cells that clog pores.

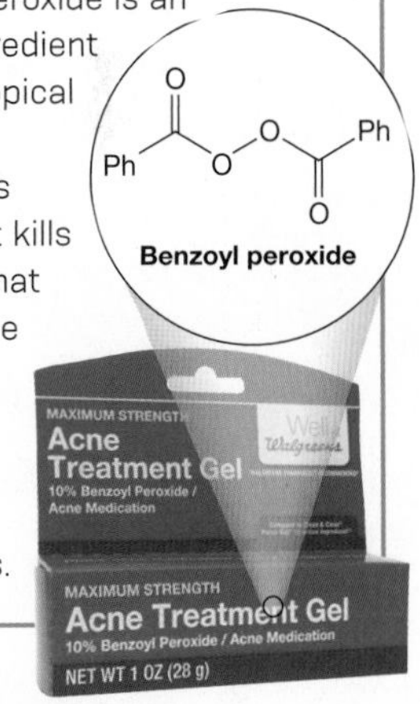

Benzoyl peroxide
MAXIMUM STRENGTH
Acne Treatment Gel
10% Benzoyl Peroxide / Acne Medication
NET WT 1 OZ (28 g)

Mechanism for the base-promoted conversion of an acid chloride into an ester (Eq. 22-4)

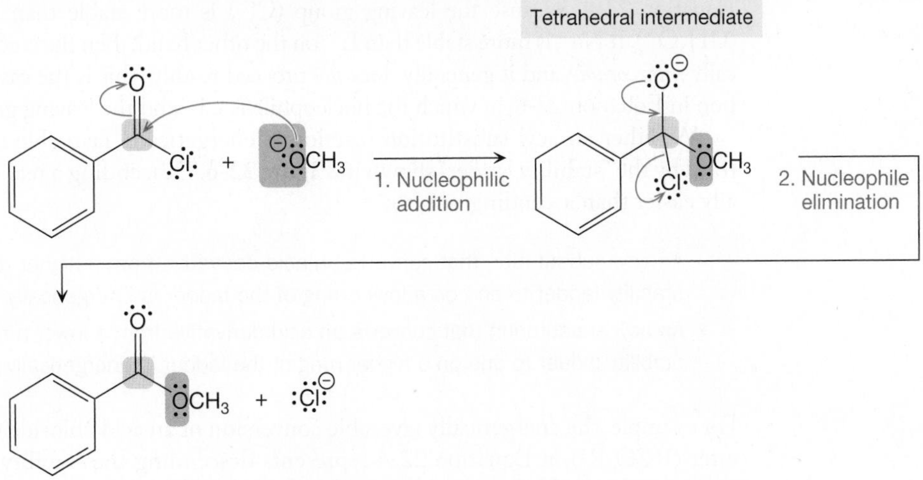

Tetrahedral intermediate
1. Nucleophilic addition
2. Nucleophile elimination

(22-5)

YOUR TURN **22.5**

An ester such as methyl acetate can react with $(CH_3)_2N^-$ to produce an amide. The nucleophilic addition–elimination mechanism that describes this reaction is as follows:

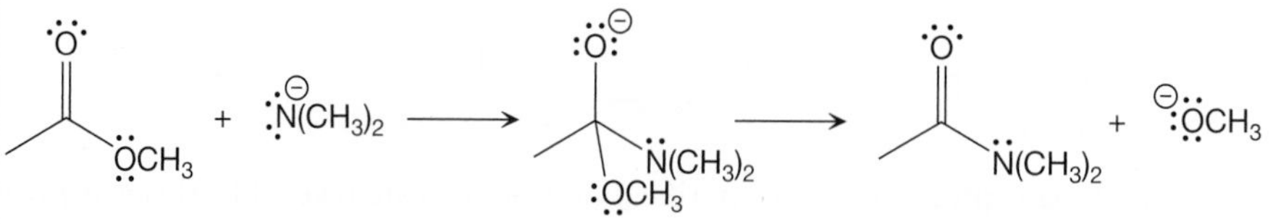

Complete the mechanism by adding the curved arrows to show the movement of the electrons. Under each reaction arrow, write the name of the elementary step taking place. Label the tetrahedral intermediate.

Not every combination of acid derivative and nucleophile leads to an effective acyl substitution reaction. Equation 22-6 shows, for example, that essentially no acyl substitution takes place when an ester is treated with chloride ion:

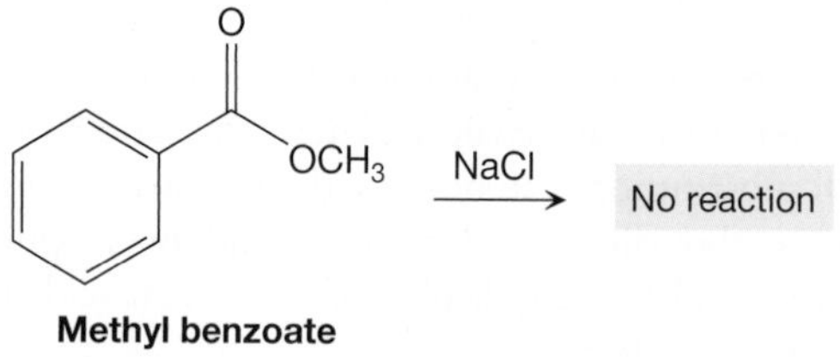
OCH3
NaCl
No reaction
Methyl benzoate

(22-6)

We can understand why there is no reaction in Equation 22-6 by examining the generic acyl substitution reaction in Equation 22-7. Notice that the nucleophile (Nu^-) bears a negative charge on the reactant side, and the leaving group (L^-) bears the negative charge in the products.

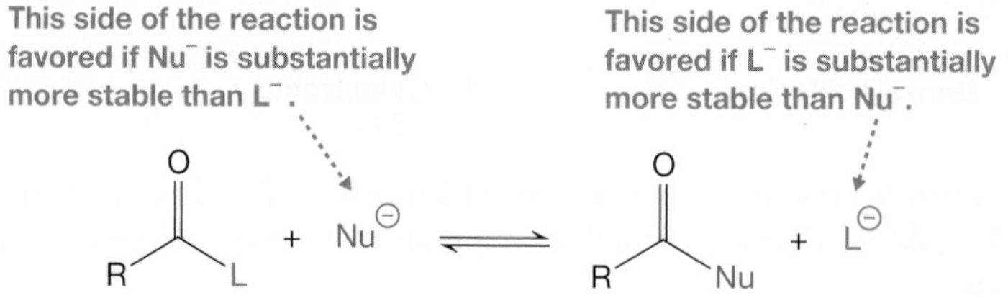
This side of the reaction is favored if Nu⁻ is substantially more stable than L⁻.
This side of the reaction is favored if L⁻ is substantially more stable than Nu⁻.

(22-7)

If L^- is more stable than Nu^- (reflected by the weaker basicity of L^-), then the reaction is energetically favorable and generally occurs readily. This is the case with the reaction in Equation 22-4, because the leaving group (Cl^-) is more stable than the nucleophile (CH_3O^-). If Nu^- is more stable than L^-, on the other hand, then the reaction is energetically *unfavorable*, and it generally does *not* proceed readily. This is the case with the reaction in Equation 22-6, in which the nucleophile is Cl^- and the leaving group is CH_3O^-.

Whether an acyl substitution reaction is energetically favorable can be summarized by the "stability ladder" shown in **Figure 22-6**. Descending a real ladder is generally easier than ascending one, so:

- An acyl substitution that converts an acid derivative from a higher rung on the stability ladder to one on a lower rung of the ladder is energetically *favorable*.
- An acyl substitution that converts an acid derivative from a lower rung on the stability ladder to one on a higher rung of the ladder is energetically *unfavorable*.

For example, the energetically favorable conversion of an acid chloride (RCOCl) to an ester (RCO_2R') in Equation 22-4 represents descending the stability ladder (in this case, two rungs). The opposite is true for the unfavorable conversion of an ester to an acid chloride in Equation 22-6.

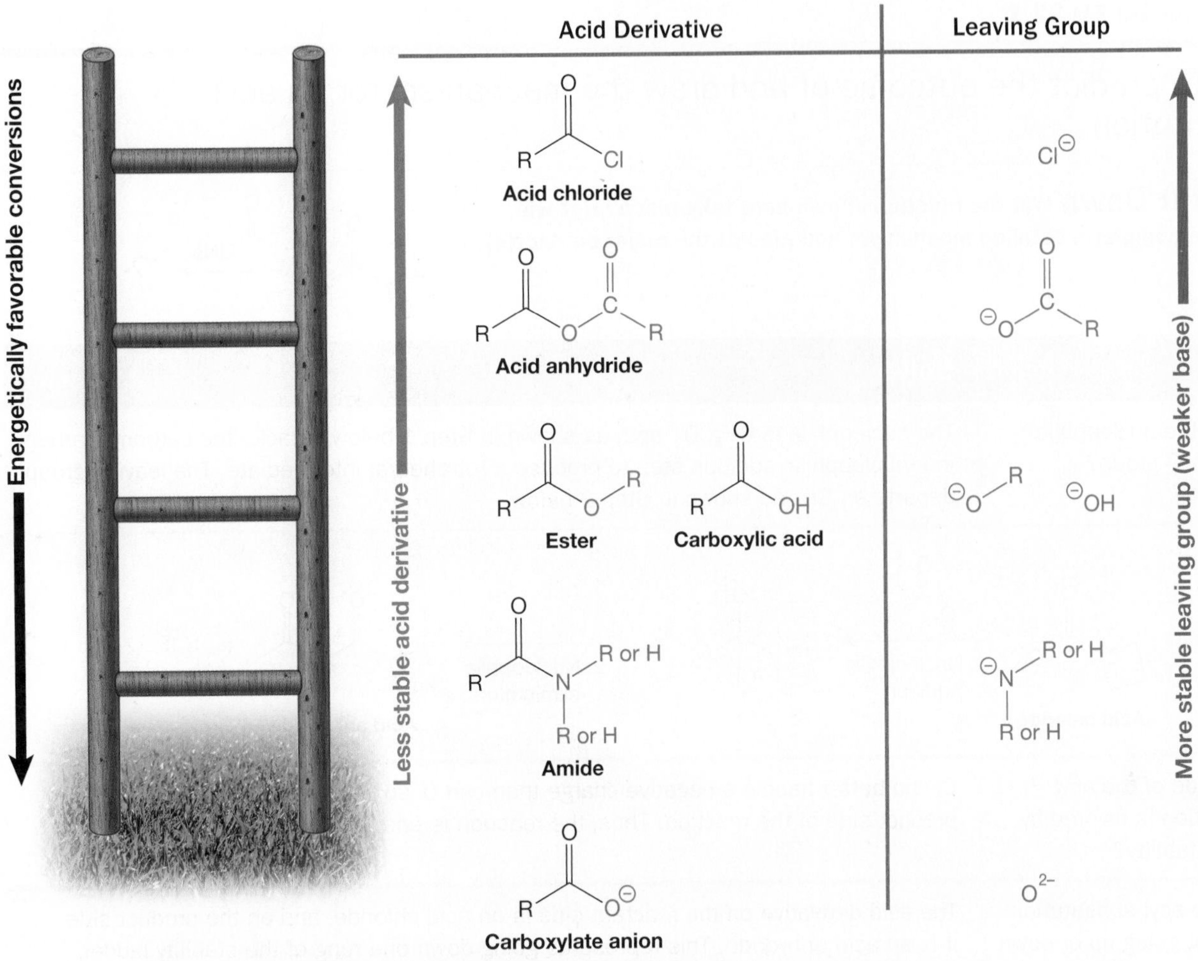

Energetically favorable conversions
Acid Derivative
Leaving Group
Less stable acid derivative
More stable leaving group (weaker base)
Acid chloride
Acid anhydride
Ester
Carboxylic acid
Amide
Carboxylate anion

FIGURE 22-6 The "stability ladder" for carboxylic acid derivatives A reaction that converts an acid derivative on a higher rung to one on a lower rung is energetically favorable and generally takes place readily. Going from a lower rung to a higher rung is unfavorable and is generally quite difficult to carry out.

YOUR TURN 22.6

Indicate whether each of the following conversions would be energetically favorable or unfavorable. Which reactions will likely occur readily?

(a)

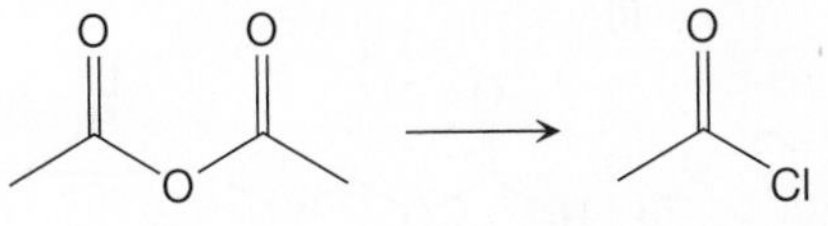

(b)

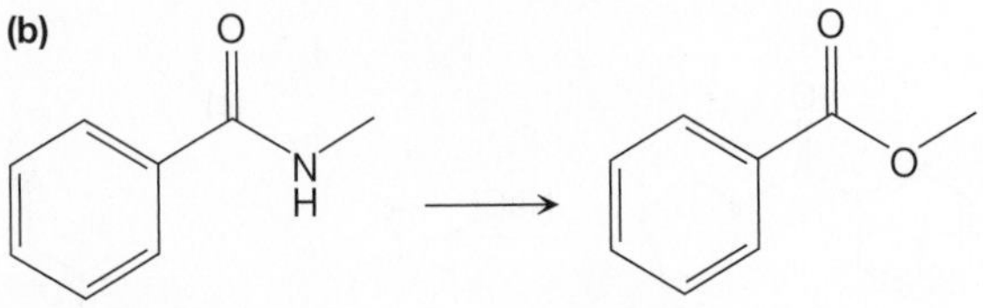

(c)

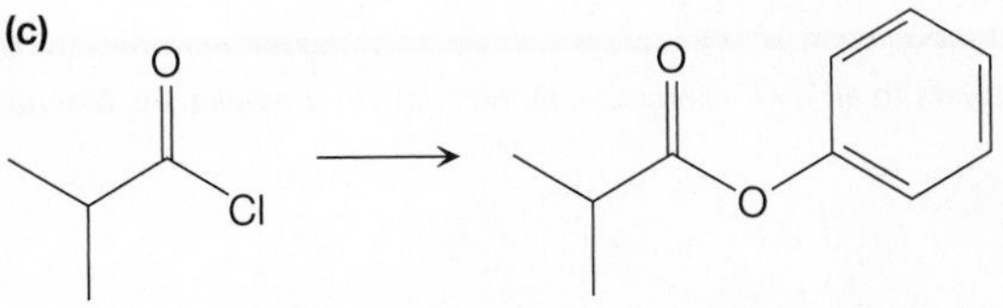

(d)

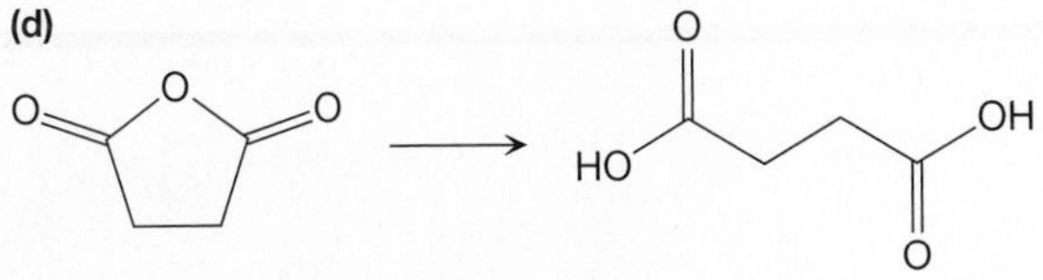

SOLVED PROBLEM **22.1**

How to predict the outcome of and draw the mechanism for an acyl substitution

Break It Down **Will the reaction shown here take place? If it will, draw the complete, detailed mechanism and predict the major product(s).**

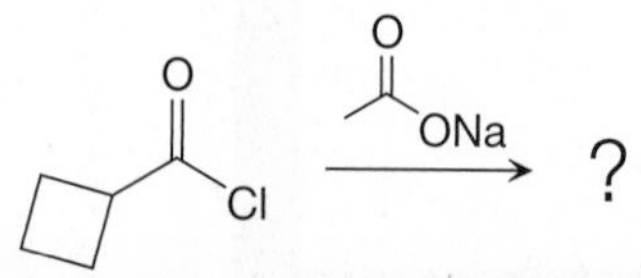

Think	Solve
What is the nucleophile? The leaving group?	The nucleophile is $CH_3CO_2^-$ and, as shown in Step 1 below, attacks the carbonyl carbon in a nucleophilic addition step to produce a tetrahedral intermediate. The leaving group departs as Cl^-, as shown in Step 2 below.

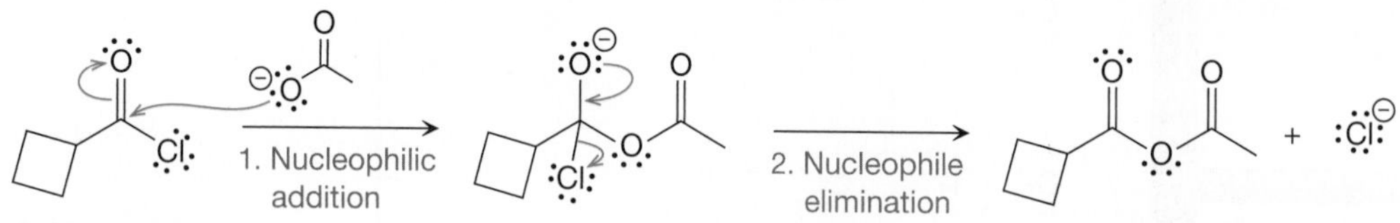
1. Nucleophilic addition
2. Nucleophile elimination
Acid chloride
Acid anhydride

Think	Solve
Which side of the acyl substitution is favored by charge stability?	Cl can better handle a negative charge than can O, so charge stability favors the product side of the reaction. Thus, the reaction is energetically favorable.
Does the acyl substitution represent going up or down the stability ladder?	The acid derivative on the reactant side is an acid chloride, and on the product side it is an acid anhydride. This represents going down one rung of the stability ladder, in agreement with our earlier conclusion that the reaction is energetically favorable. Therefore, we expect the reaction to take place.

Try It Draw the complete, detailed mechanism and predict the major product(s) for each of the following reactions. If no reaction takes place, write "no reaction."

(a)

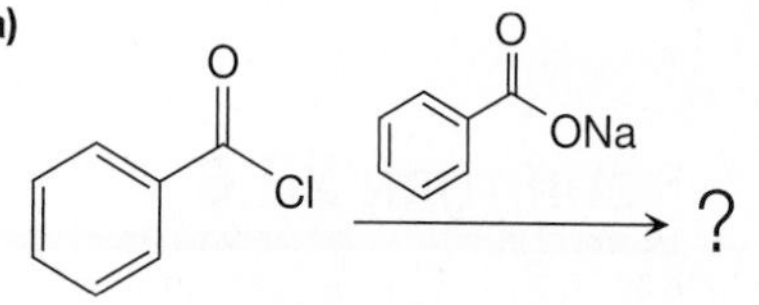

(b)

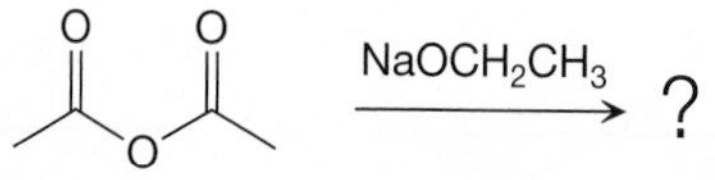
$NaOCH_2CH_3$

(c)

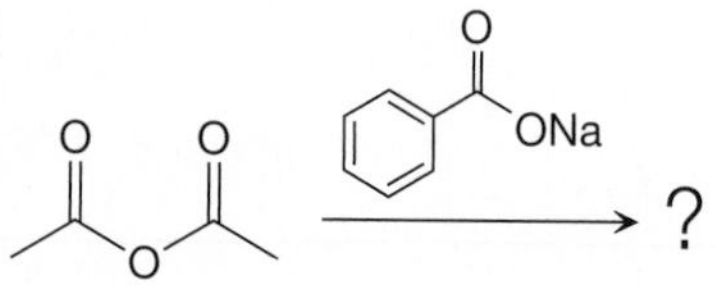

(d)

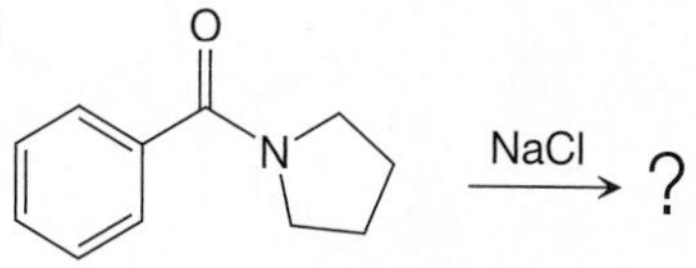
NaCl

(e)

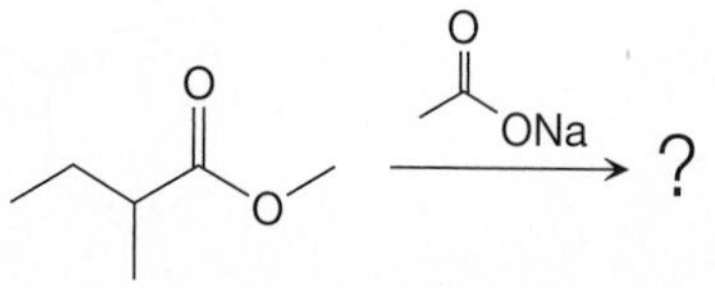

(f)

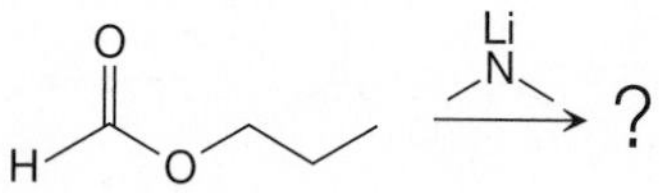

Answers to all Try It exercises can be found in the Solutions Manual.

22.3 Reaction of an Ester with Hydroxide (Saponification) and the Reverse Reaction

SECTION 22.3 OBJECTIVES

You will be able to:

1. Draw the mechanism for a saponification reaction, and explain why it is irreversible.
2. Explain why esters cannot be produced by treating a carboxylic acid with an alkoxide anion.

Hydroxide (HO^-) and alkoxide (RO^-) ions generally have similar nucleophile strengths and leaving group abilities, so you might expect that a carboxylic acid [R′CO—OH] would react with an alkoxide anion to produce an ester [R′CO—OR]. If such a reaction were to take place, RO^- would replace HO^-, much like we saw for transesterifications (Section 22.1), where one alkoxide ion replaces another. As shown in Equation 22-8, however, no such reaction occurs. Instead, the alkoxide anion, which is a strong base, deprotonates the carboxylic acid *rapidly* and *irreversibly* to produce a carboxylate anion, after which no further reaction takes place.

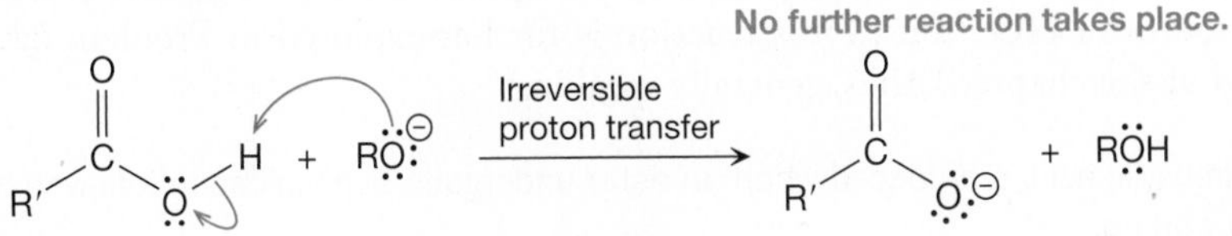
No further reaction takes place.
Irreversible proton transfer
(22-8)

YOUR TURN **22.7**

To convince yourself that the proton transfer reaction in Equation 22-8 is irreversible, use the appropriate pK_a values from Table 6-1 (p. 269) to determine which side of that proton transfer step is favored. To what extent is it favored?

No further reaction takes place because carboxylate anions are at the very bottom of the stability ladder. Therefore, any acyl substitution reaction that converts a carboxylate anion to another carboxylic acid derivative in the stability ladder would be highly unfavorable. Carboxylate anions are unreactive in large part because they have equivalent resonance structures, and the resulting electron delocalization heavily stabilizes the C═O group's π electrons (**Figure 22-7a**). Moreover, carboxylate anions are negatively charged, so they repel incoming nucleophiles (Fig. 22-7b).

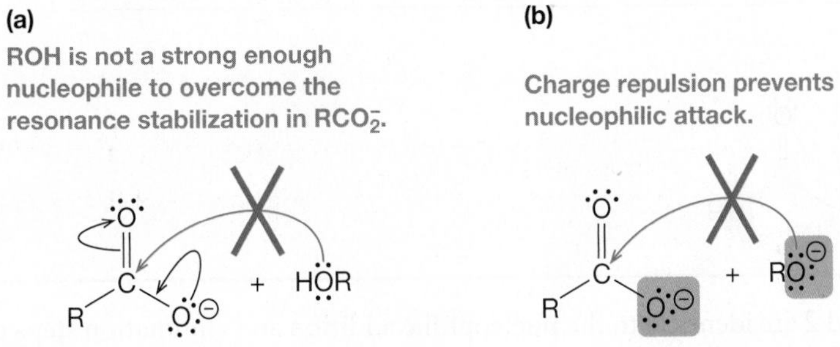
(a)
ROH is not a strong enough nucleophile to overcome the resonance stabilization in RCO_2^-.
(b)
Charge repulsion prevents nucleophilic attack.

FIGURE 22-7 The unreactive nature of carboxylate anions Nucleophiles tend not to add to the carbonyl C of a carboxylate anion. (a) Uncharged nucleophiles such as alcohols are not strong enough to overcome the resonance delocalization of the π electrons in the carboxylate anion. (b) Stronger nucleophiles, such as alkoxide anions, are repelled from the carboxylate anion because of the like charges.

YOUR TURN **22.8**

Draw the mechanism and product for the following reaction.

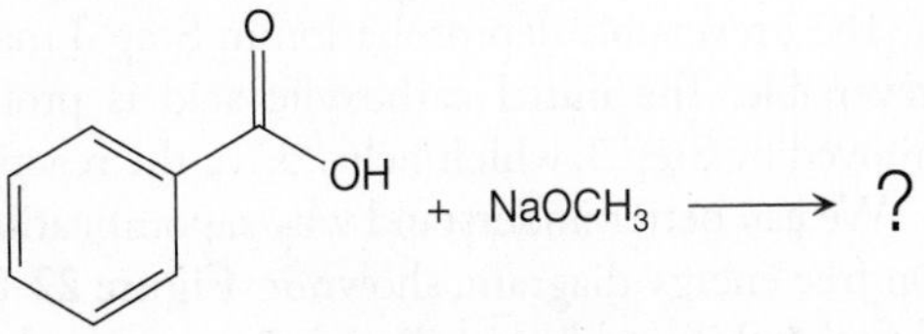

Although the deprotonation of a carboxylic acid prevents conversion of a carboxylic acid to an ester under basic conditions, this kind of deprotonation promotes conversion of

CONNECTIONS 22.2

Decaffeinating coffee Ethyl acetate (Eq. 22-9) is a common organic solvent used in liquid chromatography. It is also used as a decaffeinating agent for coffee because it can efficiently extract caffeine from the bean without excessively removing other compounds that would substantially alter the flavor of the coffee.

DECAFFEINATED COFFEE

an ester to a carboxylic acid. For example, if ethyl acetate is treated with KOH, followed by acid workup, ethanoic acid (acetic acid) is produced in relatively high yield:

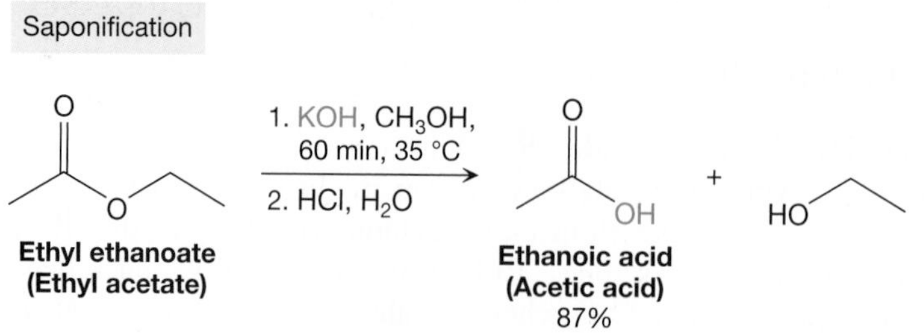

Saponification
1. KOH, CH_3OH, 60 min, 35 °C
2. HCl, H_2O
Ethyl ethanoate (Ethyl acetate)
Ethanoic acid (Acetic acid) 87%

(22-9)

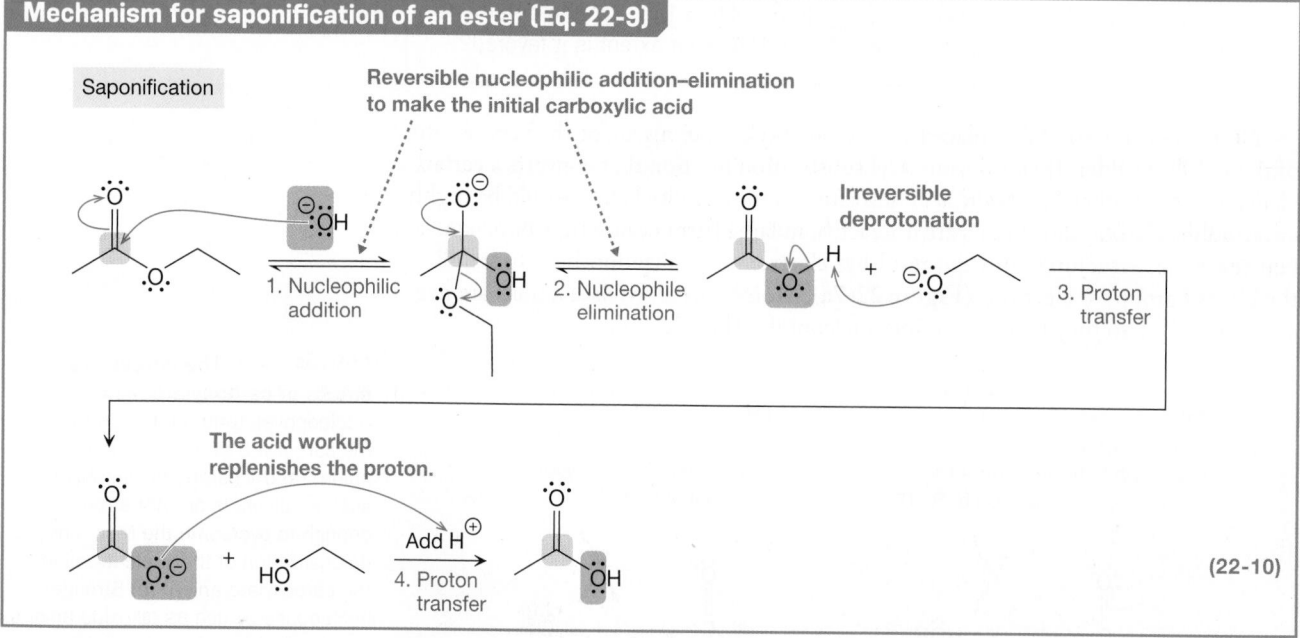

The first reaction in this sequence is known as **saponification**, which literally means "soap making" (*sapo* is the Latin root for "soap"). Ancient civilizations made crude soap by boiling animal fat (which is chiefly long-chain esters) together with wood ash, a source of HO^- ions. (This reaction is further explored in Problem 22.28 at the end of the chapter.) Thus, generally speaking:

A carboxylic acid is produced when an ester undergoes saponification followed by acid workup.

The mechanism for this sequence of reactions is shown in Equation 22-10:

Mechanism for saponification of an ester (Eq. 22-9)

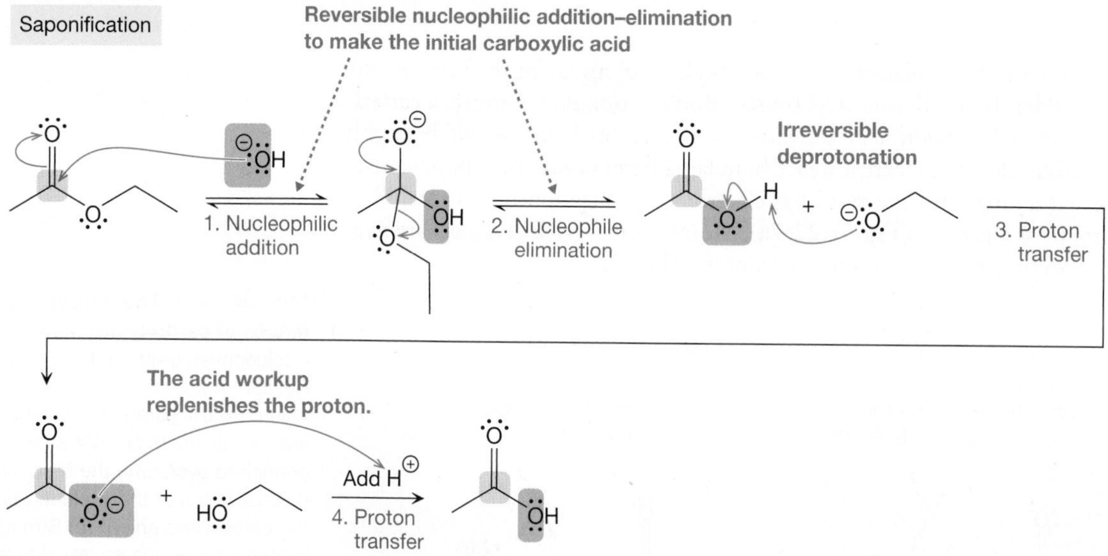

Saponification
Reversible nucleophilic addition–elimination to make the initial carboxylic acid
1. Nucleophilic addition
2. Nucleophile elimination
Irreversible deprotonation
3. Proton transfer
The acid workup replenishes the proton.
Add H⊕
4. Proton transfer

(22-10)

Steps 1 and 2 are identical to the nucleophilic addition and elimination steps in Equation 22-2 (p. 1053). Step 3 is the rapid, irreversible deprotonation of the newly formed carboxylic acid, similar to that in Equation 22-8 (p. 1061). Finally, in Step 4, the proton is replenished by adding a strong acid.

The irreversible deprotonation in Step 3 makes the *overall* saponification reaction irreversible. The initial carboxylic acid is produced reversibly, but it is continually removed by Step 3, which helps drive the reaction to completion.

We can better understand why saponification is irreversible by examining its reaction free energy diagram, shown in **Figure 22-8**. Notice that the immediate products of nucleophilic addition–elimination—namely, the carboxylic acid and the alkoxide

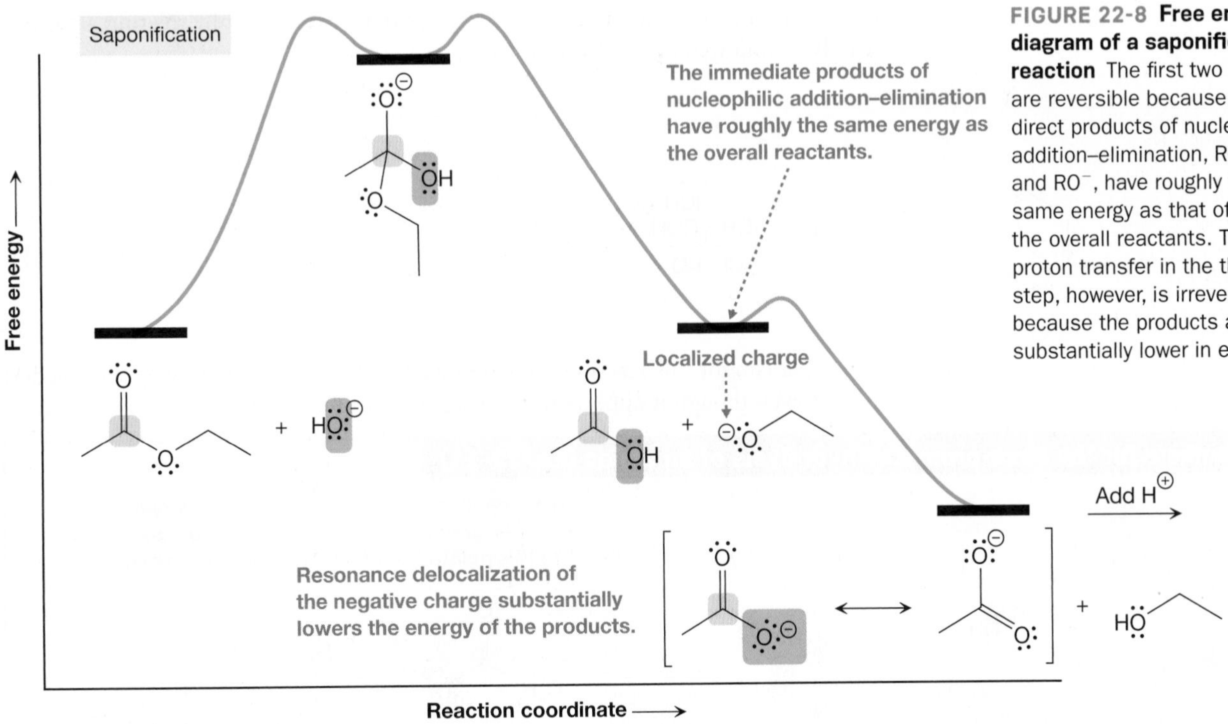
Saponification
The immediate products of nucleophilic addition–elimination have roughly the same energy as the overall reactants.
Localized charge
Add H
Resonance delocalization of the negative charge substantially lowers the energy of the products.
Free energy
Reaction coordinate

FIGURE 22-8 Free energy diagram of a saponification reaction The first two steps are reversible because the direct products of nucleophilic addition–elimination, RCO_2H and RO^-, have roughly the same energy as that of the overall reactants. The proton transfer in the third step, however, is irreversible because the products are substantially lower in energy.

anion—appear at roughly the same energy as the overall reactants. This is consistent with esters and carboxylic acids appearing on the same rung of the stability ladder in Figure 22-6. The subsequent deprotonation, however, rapidly converts the carboxylic acid into a carboxylate anion, which represents going down two rungs of the stability ladder—a very energetically favorable process.

YOUR TURN **22.9**

Draw the complete, detailed mechanism and predict the overall products for each of the following reactions.

(a)

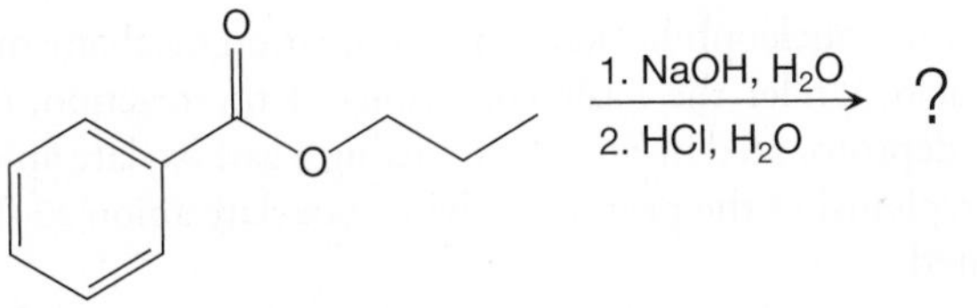
1. NaOH, H_2O
2. HCl, H_2O
?

(b)

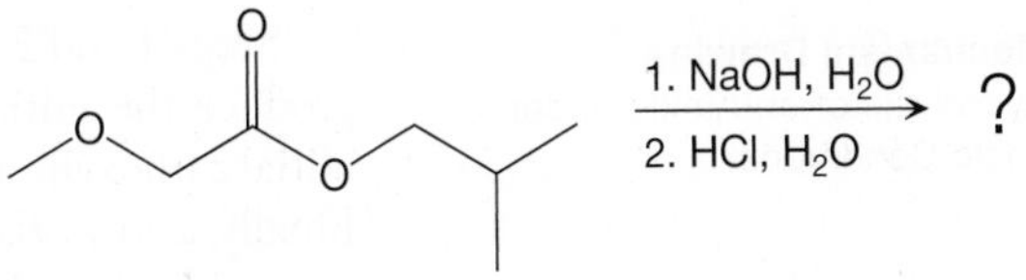
1. NaOH, H_2O
2. HCl, H_2O
?

22.4 Carboxylic Acids from Amides; the Gabriel Synthesis of Primary Amines

SECTION 22.4 OBJECTIVES

You will be able to:

1. Draw the mechanism for the base-promoted hydrolysis of an amide to produce a carboxylic acid.
2. Explain why a base-promoted amide hydrolysis is feasible even though a carboxylic acid is less stable than an amide.
3. Show how a primary amine can be produced from a Gabriel synthesis.

In Section 22.2, we saw that an amide ($RCONR_2$) is on a lower rung in the stability ladder relative to a carboxylic acid (RCO_2H) (Fig. 22-6, p. 1059), which means the conversion of an amide to a carboxylic acid is energetically *unfavorable*. However, this transformation, known as an *amide hydrolysis*, can be carried out by treating an amide with HO^-, followed by acid workup:

Amide hydrolysis

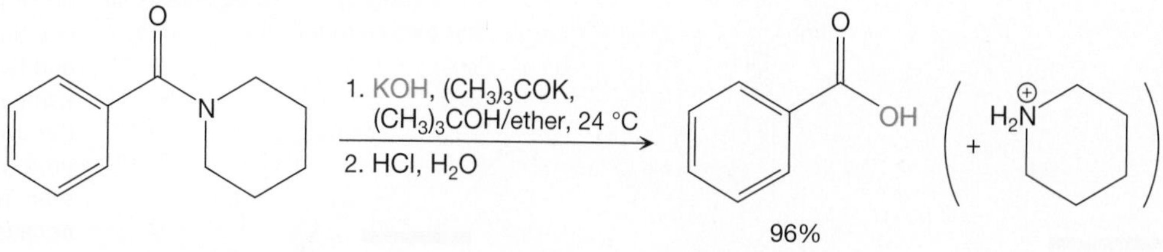
1. KOH, $(CH_3)_3COK$,
$(CH_3)_3COH$/ether, 24 °C
2. HCl, H_2O
N
OH
H_2N
96%

(22-11)

The mechanism for this reaction, shown in Equation 22-12, explains why the reaction proceeds even though it appears to be energetically unfavorable.

Mechanism for the base-promoted hydrolysis of an amide (Eq. 22-11)

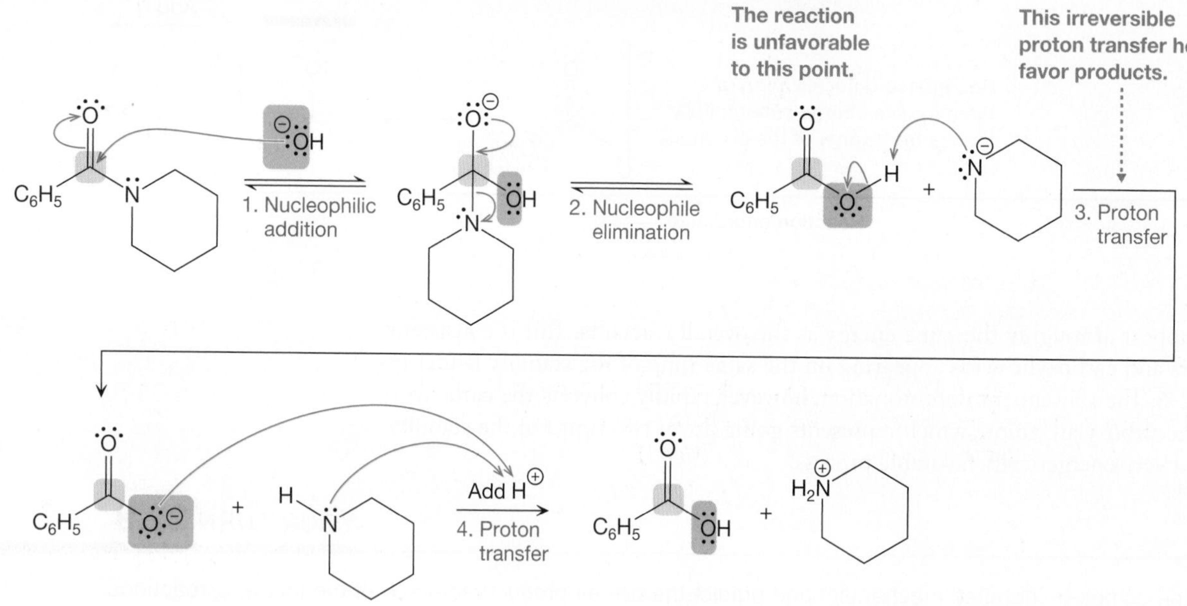
The reaction
is unfavorable
to this point.
This irreversible
proton transfer helps
favor products.
C_6H_5
1. Nucleophilic
addition
2. Nucleophile
elimination
3. Proton
transfer
Add H
4. Proton
transfer
H_2N

(22-12)

Mechanism Drawing
Hydrolysis of an Amide under Basic Conditions

Steps 1 and 2 make up the usual nucleophilic addition–elimination mechanism to produce the initial carboxylic acid. Under the basic conditions of the reaction, this initial carboxylic acid is quickly deprotonated in Step 3, producing a carboxylate anion. Finally, acid workup in Step 4 replenishes the proton on the carboxylate anion so that the carboxylic acid can be isolated.

As indicated in the mechanism, the direct formation of the carboxylic acid from the amide is energetically unfavorable because the negative charge on N in the leaving group is poorly stabilized. Therefore, the reaction is reversible through the second step. The proton transfer in Step 3 is irreversible, however, just as we saw in the saponification mechanism in Equation 22-10, so it is the critical step that drives the reaction toward products. *Without the proton transfer step, no appreciable amount of product would form.*

The reaction free energy diagram in **Figure 22-9** helps explain why amide hydrolysis takes place. Notice that the immediate products from nucleophilic addition and elimination are higher in energy than the overall reactants (carboxylic acids are one rung higher in the stability ladder than amides). Thus, direct acyl substitution to form

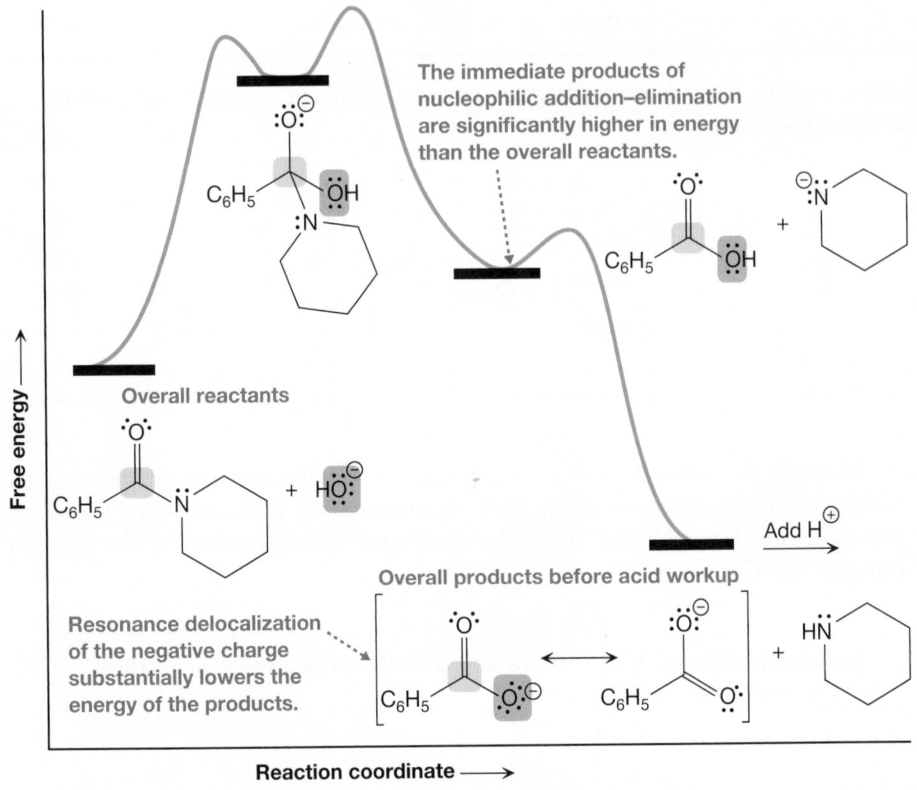

The immediate products of nucleophilic addition–elimination are significantly higher in energy than the overall reactants.
Overall reactants
Add H
Overall products before acid workup
Resonance delocalization of the negative charge substantially lowers the energy of the products.
Free energy
Reaction coordinate

FIGURE 22-9 Free energy diagram for base-promoted amide hydrolysis This diagram corresponds to the mechanism in Equation 22-12. The first two steps are reversible and unfavorable because the direct products of nucleophilic addition–elimination, RCO_2H and R_2N^-, are higher in energy than the overall reactants. The proton transfer in the third step is energetically very favorable, however, which drives the reaction toward products. The subsequent acid workup replenishes the proton on the carboxylate anion so that the carboxylic acid can be isolated.

the carboxylic acid is energetically unfavorable. The irreversible proton transfer in the third step, however, lowers the energy dramatically. Importantly, note that the product of deprotonation—a carboxylate anion—is one rung lower than the initial amide on the stability ladder.

YOUR TURN 22.10

The following mechanism, in which the curved arrows have been omitted, is for another amide hydrolysis. Complete the mechanism by drawing the missing curved arrows, and identify the tetrahedral intermediate. Below each reaction arrow, write the name of the elementary step that takes place, and indicate whether the step is reversible or irreversible.

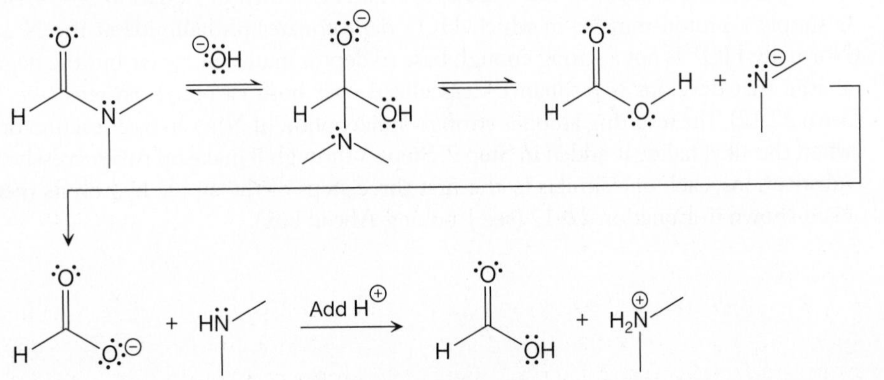

Add H

YOUR TURN 22.11

Draw the complete, detailed mechanism and predict the major product(s) for each of the following reactions.

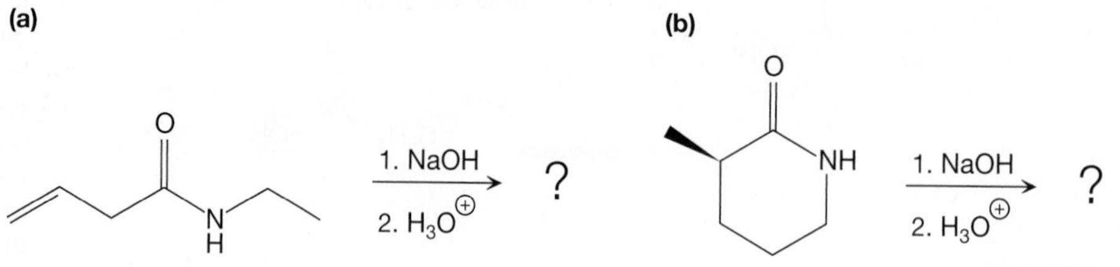

(a)
O
N
H
1. NaOH
2. $H_3O^{\oplus}$
?
(b)
O
NH
1. NaOH
2. $H_3O^{\oplus}$
?

◀ RECALL

Section 10.10 showed that a 1° amine can be produced by treating a 1° alkyl halide with NH_3. As we saw, however, such conversions are inefficient because 1° amines are more nucleophilic than NH_3, so 2° and higher alkylated amines tend to be produced along with the 1° amine.

Although the carboxylic acid is often the desired product when an amide is treated with hydroxide (as suggested in Eq. 22-11), sometimes the goal is to isolate the nitrogen-containing leaving group. This is the case for the *Gabriel synthesis*, as illustrated in Equation 22-13.

The **Gabriel synthesis** is an effective way to synthesize a primary amine (RNH_2) from an alkyl halide (see Recall box).

Gabriel synthesis

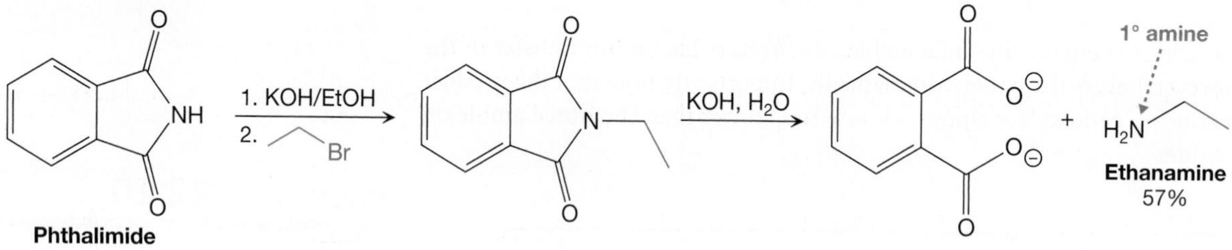

O
NH
O
Phthalimide
1. KOH/EtOH
2.
Br
O
N
O
KOH, H_2O
O
$O^{\ominus}$
$O^{\ominus}$
O
+
1° amine
H_2N
Ethanamine
57%

(22-13)

In the Gabriel synthesis, phthalimide is first treated with a strong base such as potassium hydroxide, followed by an alkyl halide. Subsequent hydrolysis using hydroxide then frees the primary amine.

A partial mechanism of the Gabriel synthesis is shown in Equation 22-14. Step 1 is simply a proton transfer in which HO^- deprotonates phthalimide at the N atom. Normally, HO^- is not a strong enough base to deprotonate a nitrogen, but the negative charge that develops is resonance-delocalized over both carbonyl oxygens (see Your Turn 22.12). The resulting anion is strongly nucleophilic at N, so an S_N2 reaction occurs when the alkyl halide is added in Step 2. Steps 3 through 8 make up two successive acyl substitutions, each one similar to the first three steps of the amide hydrolysis mechanism shown in Equation 22-12 (see Looking Ahead box).

▶ LOOKING AHEAD

In Section 23.7, we will see that amide hydrolysis can take place under acidic conditions, too. Therefore, the hydrolysis portion of a Gabriel synthesis can instead be carried out under acidic conditions.

Partial mechanism for the Gabriel synthesis of primary amines (Eq. 22-13)

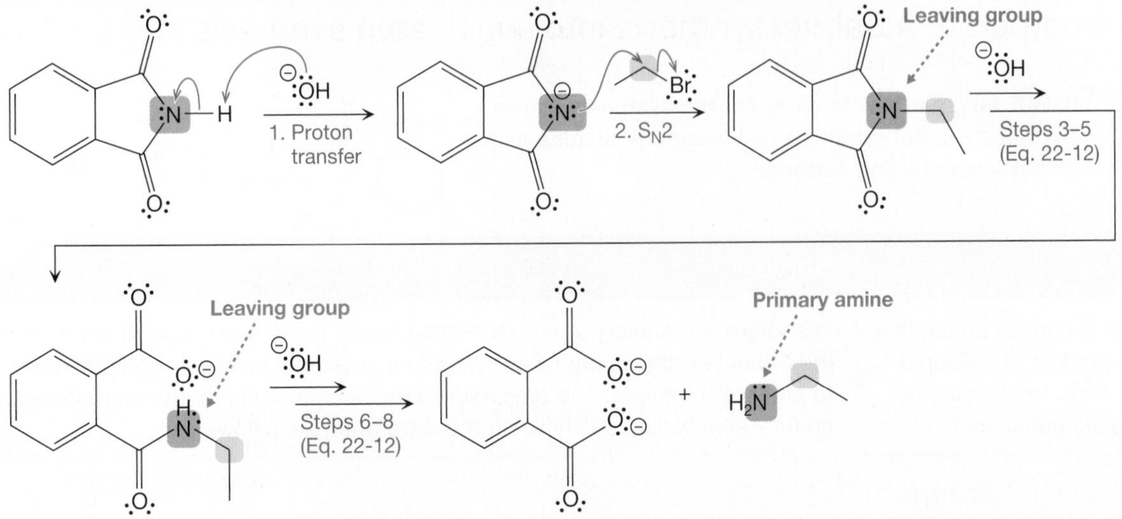

Leaving group
1. Proton transfer
2. S_N2
Steps 3–5 (Eq. 22-12)
Leaving group
Steps 6–8 (Eq. 22-12)
Primary amine

(22-14)

YOUR TURN 22.12

Draw the other two resonance structures of the anion produced in Step 1 of Equation 22-14.

YOUR TURN 22.13

Predict the product of the sequence of reactions shown here.

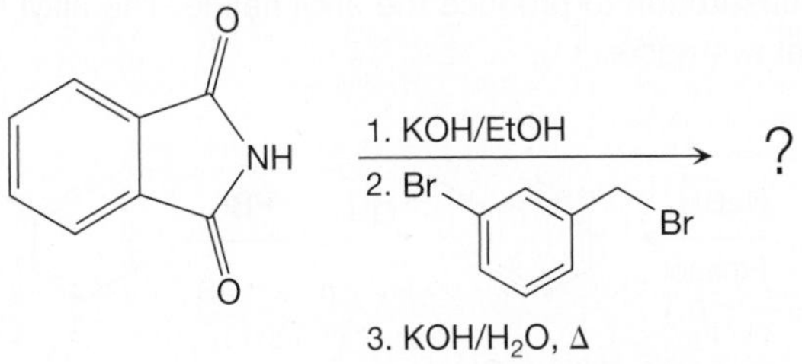

NH
1. KOH/EtOH
2. Br
Br
3. KOH/H2O, Δ
?

GREEN CHEMISTRY One of the by-products of the Gabriel synthesis, the phthalate dianion ($C_8H_4O_4^{2-}$), has a relatively high molecular weight of 164 g/mol. This means the Gabriel synthesis can suffer from low atom economy, making the reaction inefficient. Other ways of synthesizing amines, such as reductive amination (Section 19.5), tend to be substantially more efficient.

SOLVED PROBLEM **22.2**

How to incorporate a Gabriel synthesis into a multistep synthesis

Break It Down **Suggest how to carry out the synthesis shown here by incorporating a Gabriel synthesis and using phthalimide and the indicated aldehyde as starting materials.**

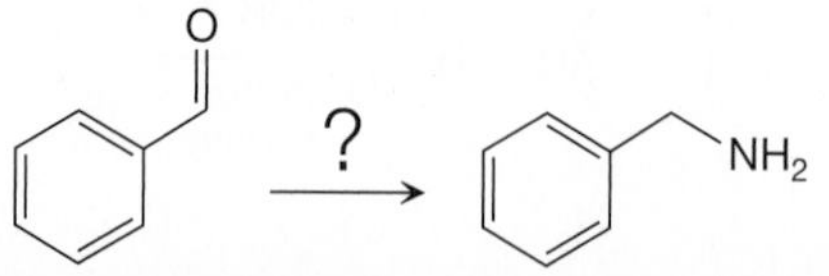

O
?
NH2

Think	Solve
Is the target a primary amine that can be the product of a Gabriel synthesis? If so, what would be the alkyl halide precursor?	The target is a primary amine (R—NH_2), which is the same type of amine that the Gabriel synthesis produces. Therefore, a Gabriel synthesis could be used to produce the target. The precursor to that amine would be the corresponding primary alkyl halide, as shown in the retrosynthesis below.

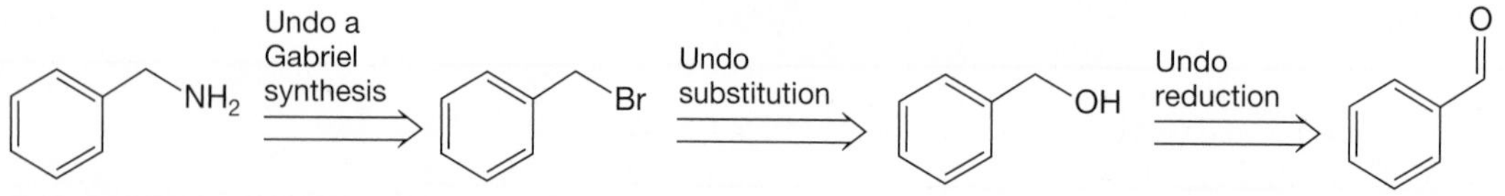

NH2
Undo a Gabriel synthesis
Br
Undo substitution
OH
Undo reduction
O

Think	Solve
Can the alkyl halide be made directly from the aldehyde starting material? If not, from what could the alkyl halide be made?	We haven't learned a reaction that will convert an aldehyde directly into an alkyl halide. However, as shown above, the alkyl halide could be made from the corresponding alcohol, which, in turn, could be made from the starting aldehyde.
How can we report the final synthesis?	To report the synthesis, we begin with the starting material and add the appropriate reagents, as shown here. The aldehyde is reduced to the alcohol, which then undergoes substitution to produce the alkyl halide. The alkyl halide is then used in the Gabriel synthesis.

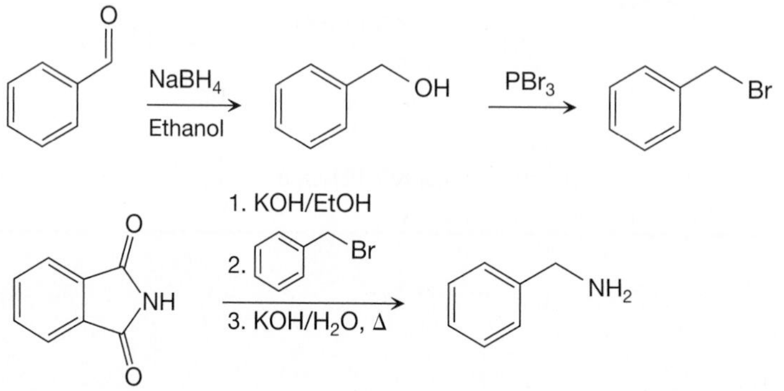

O
NaBH4
Ethanol
OH
PBr3
Br
O
NH
O
1. KOH/EtOH
2.
Br
3. KOH/H2O, Δ
NH2

Try It How would you carry out the transformation shown here using a Gabriel synthesis? [Note that both this synthesis and the one shown above can be carried out by a reductive amination instead (Section 19.5). Can you also design those transformations?]

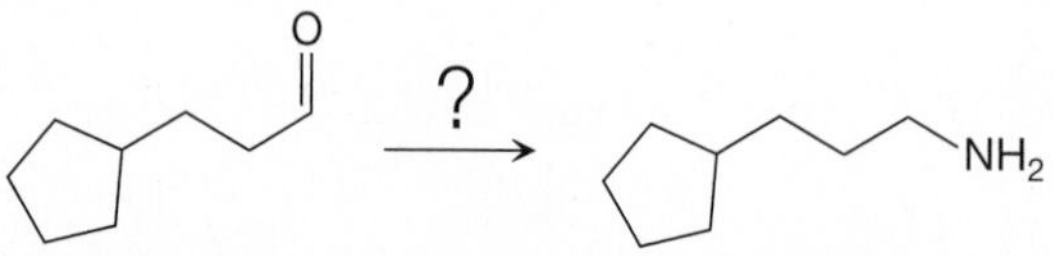

O
?
NH2

22.5 Haloform Reactions

SECTION 22.5 OBJECTIVES

You will be able to:

1. Identify compounds that can undergo a haloform reaction.
2. Draw the mechanism and product for a haloform reaction.
3. Explain how an iodoform reaction can be used to test for methyl ketones in the laboratory.

In all of the acyl substitution reactions we have discussed so far, one reactant is an acid derivative in which the carbonyl carbon is bonded to a leaving group. As shown in Equation 22-15, however, a methyl ketone ($RCOCH_3$) can undergo acyl substitution when treated with excess Br_2 in aqueous sodium hydroxide, followed by acid workup:

Haloform reaction

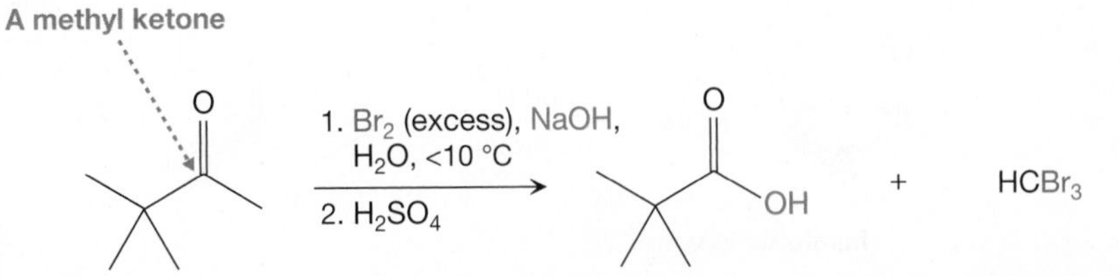

A methyl ketone
1. Br_2 (excess), NaOH, H_2O, <10 °C
2. H_2SO_4
OH
+
$HCBr_3$

(22-15)

3,3-Dimethylbutan-2-one **2,2-Dimethylpropanoic acid** 74% **Tribromomethane (Bromoform)**

One of the products, bromoform ($HCBr_3$), is an example of a **haloform**, which has the general formula HCX_3 (where X is a halogen atom). Such a reaction that produces a haloform is known as a **haloform reaction**. Haloform reactions can also take place when a methyl ketone is treated with Cl_2 or I_2, producing chloroform ($HCCl_3$) or iodoform (HCI_3), respectively. Thus:

> A methyl ketone ($RCOCH_3$) can undergo a haloform reaction when it is treated with a molecular halogen (X_2) under basic conditions, followed by acid workup, producing a carboxylic acid (RCO_2H) and a haloform (HCX_3) by-product.

GREEN CHEMISTRY The haloform products of haloform reactions have a number of health risks. Chloroform and bromoform, in particular, are probable human carcinogens. Here is a greener alternative that avoids the production of halogenated by-products.

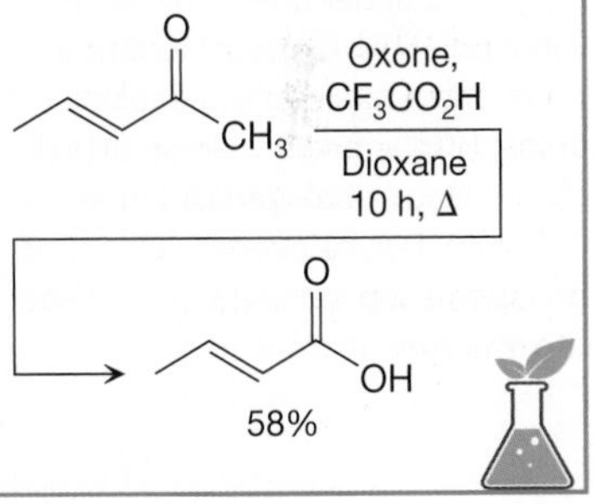

CH_3
Oxone, CF_3CO_2H
Dioxane
10 h, Δ
OH
58%

YOUR TURN **22.14**

The following reactions are the same as the one in Equation 22-15; only the halogen molecule is different. Draw the products in the boxes provided.

(a)

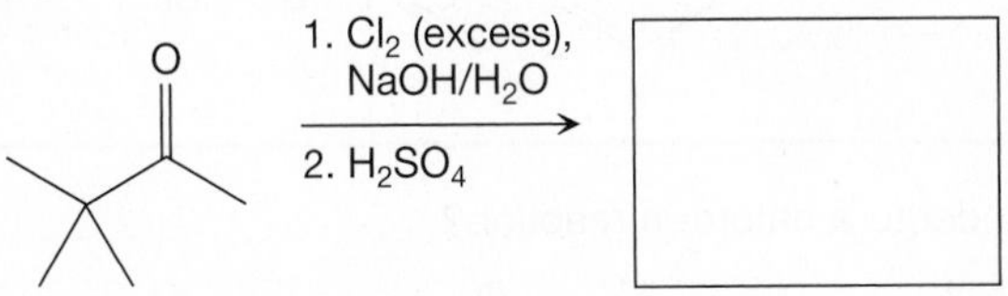

1. Cl_2 (excess), NaOH/H_2O
2. H_2SO_4

(b)

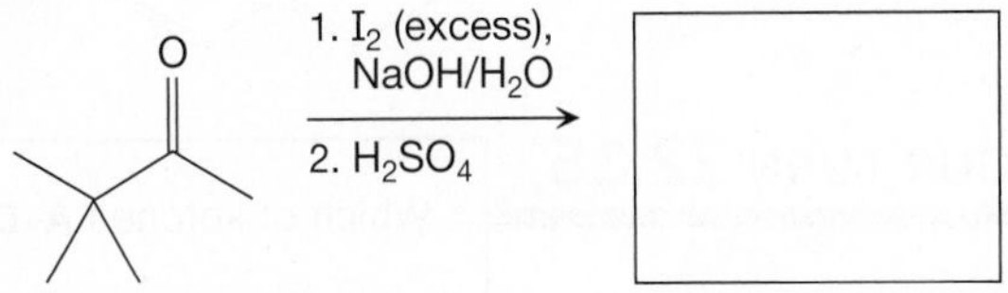

1. I_2 (excess), NaOH/H_2O
2. H_2SO_4

Note in the acyl substitution reaction shown in Equation 22-15 that HO^- appears to replace H_3C^-, a very poor leaving group. This peculiarity is explained by the reaction mechanism shown in Equation 22-16.

Partial mechanism for a haloform reaction (Eq. 22-15)

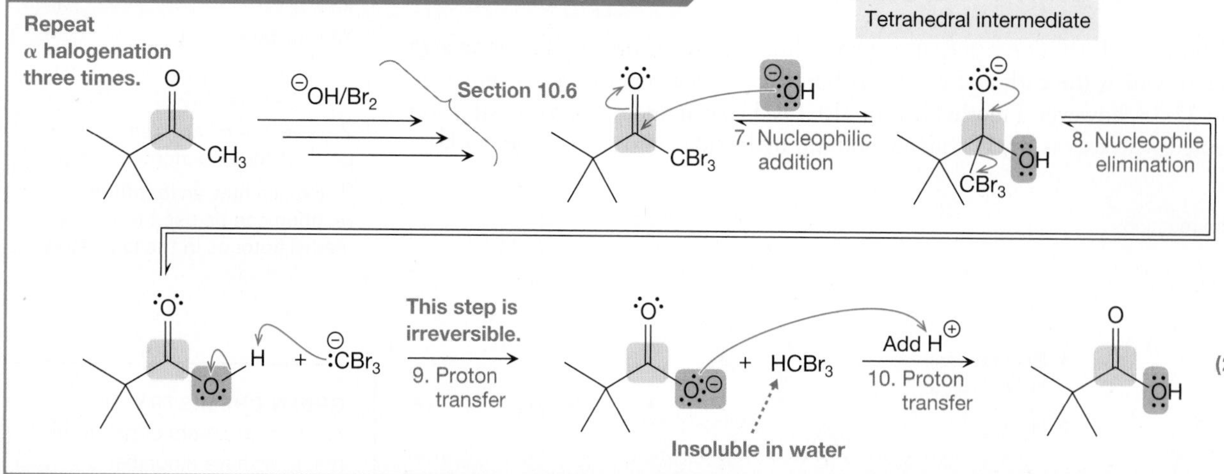

Repeat
α halogenation
three times.
O
CH3
⊖OH/Br2
Section 10.6
CBr3
7. Nucleophilic
addition
Tetrahedral intermediate
OH
CBr3
8. Nucleophile
elimination
H
+ :CBr3
This step is
irreversible.
9. Proton
transfer
+ HCBr3
Add H⊕
10. Proton
transfer
Insoluble in water
OH

(22-16)

In Steps 1–6 of this mechanism, the three α hydrogens on the methyl group are replaced by bromine atoms by the α-halogenation mechanism discussed in Section 10.6 (see Recall box). The resulting tribromomethyl ketone ($RCOCBr_3$) then undergoes attack by HO^- in Step 7 to produce a tetrahedral intermediate, which subsequently eliminates Br_3C^- in Step 8 to produce an initial carboxylic acid. In Step 9, that carboxylic acid is deprotonated by Br_3C^-, yielding a relatively stable carboxylate anion. In the acid workup in Step 10, the proton is replenished on the carboxylate anion to produce the final carboxylic acid product.

◂ RECALL

Each α halogenation proceeds by two steps under basic conditions (Section 10.6): (1) deprotonation produces a nucleophilic enolate anion; (2) the enolate anion attacks the molecular halogen (X_2) in an S_N2 step. Polyhalogenation occurs because each halogenation makes the α carbon more acidic.

Notice in Equation 22-16 that the leaving group is Br_3C^-, *not* H_3C^-. This is important, because H_3C^- is very unstable, making it unsuitable as a leaving group. Br_3C^- is a suitable leaving group, however, because the three Br atoms significantly stabilize the negative charge on C.

All three α-halogen atoms are necessary to make the carbanion a suitable leaving group. As shown in Equation 22-17, an ethyl ketone does not undergo acyl substitution because it gains only two α halogens.

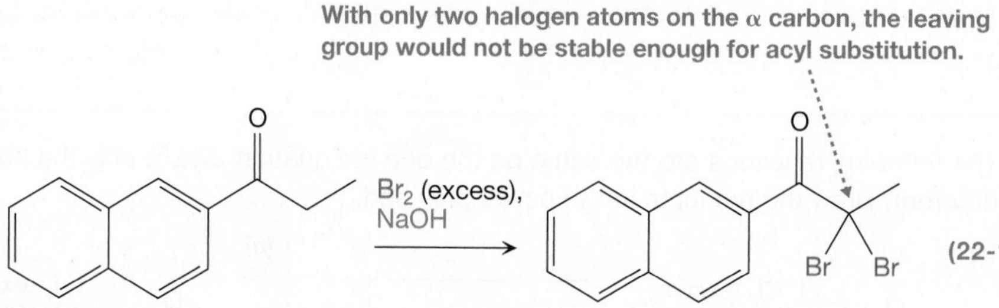

With only two halogen atoms on the α carbon, the leaving group would not be stable enough for acyl substitution.
O
Br2 (excess),
NaOH
O
Br
Br

(22-17)

YOUR TURN **22.15**

Which of ketones **A–D** can undergo a haloform reaction?

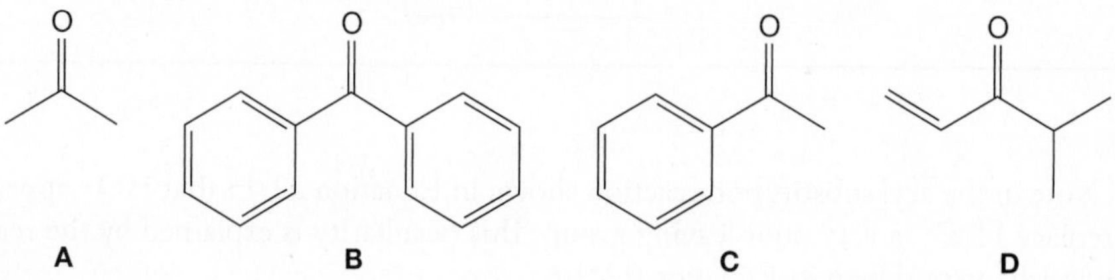

O
O
O
O
A
B
C
D

Draw the complete, detailed mechanism and the major product(s) for each of the following reactions.

(a)

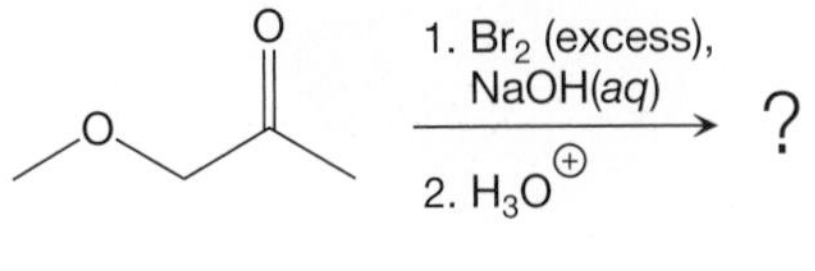
1. Br_2 (excess), NaOH(*aq*)
2. $H_3O^{\oplus}$
?

(b)

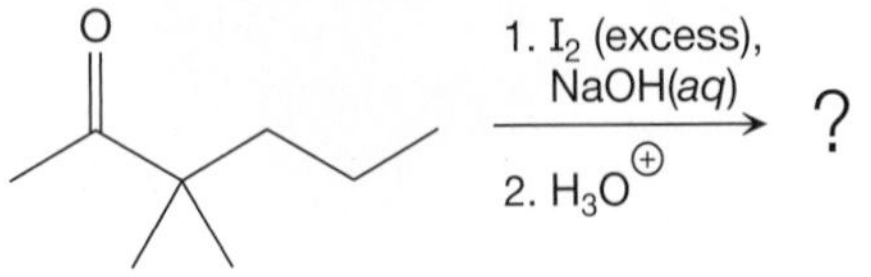
1. I_2 (excess), NaOH(*aq*)
2. $H_3O^{\oplus}$
?

SOLVED PROBLEM **22.3**

How to incorporate a haloform reaction into a synthesis

Break It Down **Show how to carry out the synthesis shown here.**

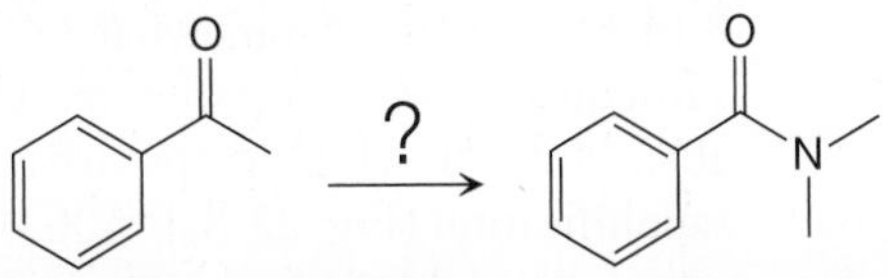
?

Think	Solve
Does the starting compound have a leaving group on the carbonyl carbon? How can that be changed?	The starting compound is a methyl ketone, which does not have a suitable leaving group. However, a haloform reaction can be used to convert that methyl ketone into a carboxylic acid. 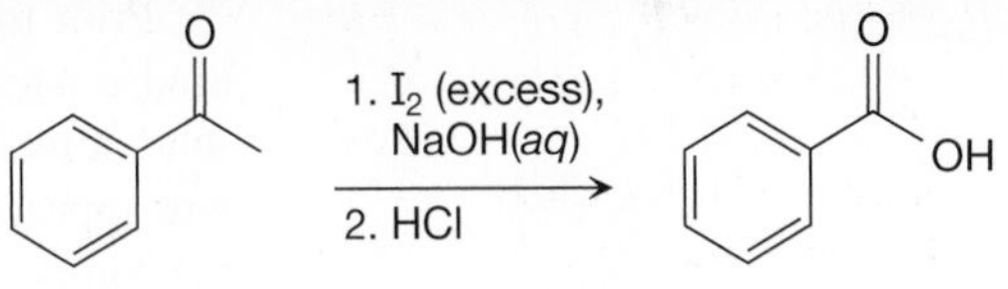
Have we learned a reaction that will convert a carboxylic acid directly into the amide target? If not, what other precursor could be used?	To convert the carboxylic acid into the amide directly, $(CH_3)_2N^-$ would need to act as a nucleophile to replace HO^-. However, $(CH_3)_2N^-$ is a strong base and would deprotonate the carboxylic acid instead. Rather, the amide can be produced from an ester by acyl substitution, as shown here. The ester, in turn, can be produced using diazomethane (Section 10.9). 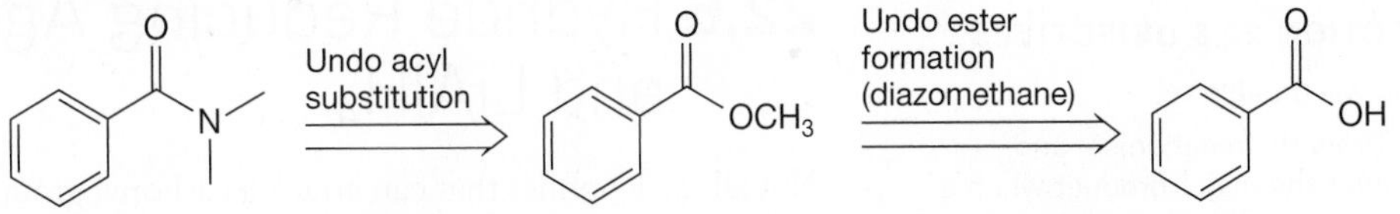
How can the final synthesis be reported?	To report the final synthesis, we begin with the starting carboxylic acid and supply the appropriate reagents and conditions, as shown below.

1. I_2 (excess), NaOH(*aq*)
2. HCl
OH

Undo acyl substitution
Undo ester formation (diazomethane)
OCH_3
OH

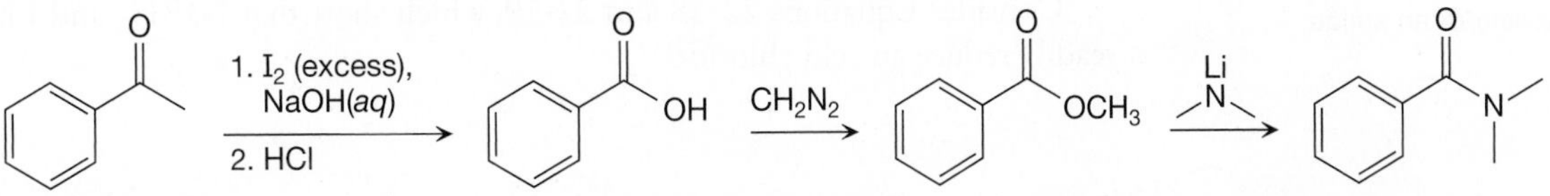
1. I_2 (excess), NaOH(*aq*)
2. HCl
OH
CH_2N_2
OCH_3
Li
N

Try It Show how to carry out this synthesis using any reagents necessary.

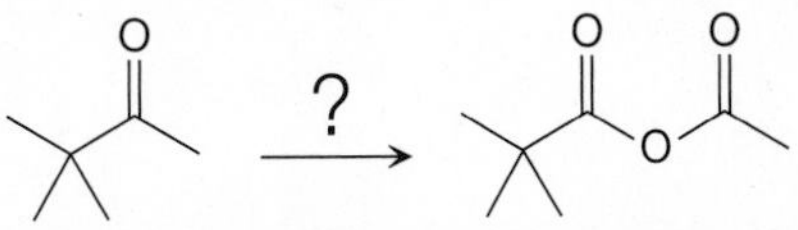
?

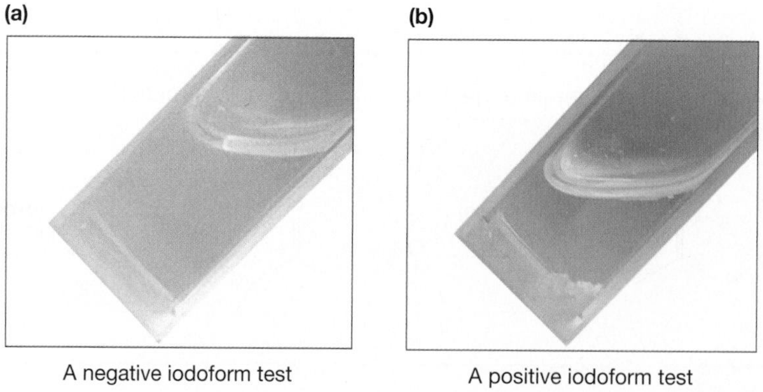
(a)
(b)
A negative iodoform test
A positive iodoform test

FIGURE 22-10 The iodoform test When sample (a) was treated with a basic solution of I_2, no yellow precipitate of iodoform formed. When a basic solution of I_2 was added to sample (b), however, iodoform precipitated, indicating that the sample contained a methyl ketone.

Despite the three Br atoms, the negative charge on Br_3C^- is less stabilized than that on HO^-, as reflected by the stronger basicity of Br_3C^- (pK_a of $Br_3CH \approx 20$; pK_a of $H_2O = 14$). Consequently, the acyl substitution that takes place (Steps 7 and 8 in Eq. 22-16) is somewhat unfavorable energetically and is thus reversible. The subsequent proton transfer step (Step 9 in Eq. 22-16) is energetically quite favorable, however, which helps drive the reaction toward products, just as we saw in saponification (Fig. 22-8, p. 1063). Moreover, the haloform that is produced in that step is insoluble in water, so it is effectively removed from the reaction mixture. According to Le Châtelier's principle, this drives the acyl substitution reaction even further toward products.

Prior to the advent of spectroscopy, the iodoform (HCI_3) reaction was commonly used as a test for methyl ketones. As shown in **Figure 22-10**, iodoform is a bright yellow solid at room temperature and is insoluble in water. Therefore, if a bright yellow precipitate appears on treating an organic compound with I_2 in basic solution, it is likely that the compound is a methyl ketone.

YOUR TURN **22.17**

Which of the ketones **A–D** in Your Turn 22.15 (p. 1070) will produce a yellow solid when treated with I_2 and sodium hydroxide, followed by acid workup?

SECTION 22.6 OBJECTIVES

You will be able to:

1. Draw the mechanism and predict the major product when a carboxylic acid or a carboxylic acid derivative is treated with either $NaBH_4$ or $LiAlH_4$.
2. Explain the role of the O—Al bond when $LiAlH_4$ reduces a carboxylic acid or an amide.

22.6 Hydride Reducing Agents: $NaBH_4$ and $LiAlH_4$

Not all nucleophiles that can attack a carbonyl group are capable of behaving as leaving groups. Hydride ions (H^-) from sources such as sodium borohydride ($NaBH_4$) and lithium aluminum hydride ($LiAlH_4$), for example, are excellent nucleophiles but are not practical leaving groups. These kinds of nucleophiles can still react with acid derivatives in nucleophilic addition–elimination reactions, but some key differences exist.

Consider Equations 22-18 and 22-19, which show that $NaBH_4$ and $LiAlH_4$ can readily reduce an acid chloride.

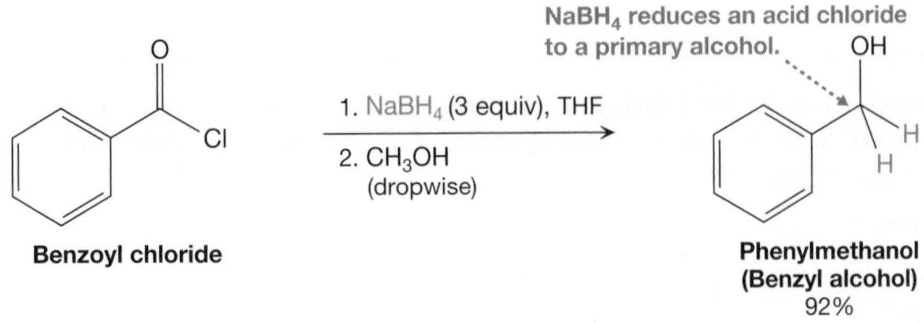
NaBH4 reduces an acid chloride to a primary alcohol.
O
Cl
1. NaBH4 (3 equiv), THF
2. CH3OH (dropwise)
OH
H
H
Benzoyl chloride
Phenylmethanol (Benzyl alcohol)
92%

(22-18)

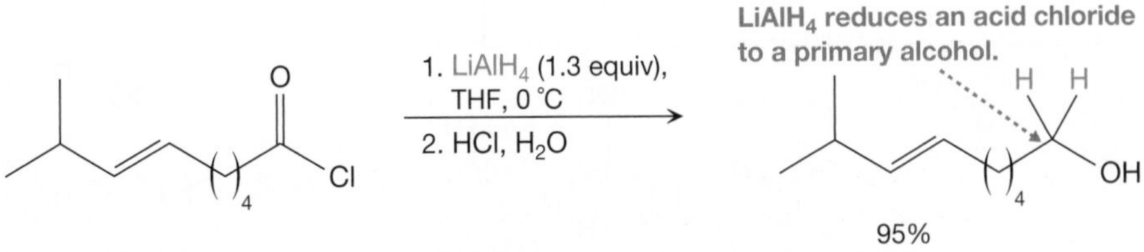
LiAlH4 reduces an acid chloride to a primary alcohol.
O
Cl
4
1. LiAlH4 (1.3 equiv), THF, 0 °C
2. HCl, H2O
H H
OH
4
95%

(22-19)

◂ RECALL

As explained in Section 7.1b, the H atoms in $NaBH_4$ and $LiAlH_4$ are part of polar covalent bonds: H—B and H—Al bonds, respectively. In each case, H bears a δ^- charge, but it behaves as H^- in a reduction reaction. In actuality, H^- is transferred from B or Al to a C=O carbon in a single step.

Notice that no carbonyl group is present in the product. Instead, a primary alcohol is produced. The simplified mechanism in Equation 22-20 shows how this occurs for the reduction by $NaBH_4$ and, as shown in Your Turn 22.18, the mechanism for the $LiAlH_4$ reduction is essentially the same. In each of these cases, we have represented $NaBH_4$ and $LiAlH_4$ as an H^- nucleophile (see Recall box), just as we did in Section 18.3 for the reductions of aldehydes, ketones, imines, and nitriles. In a more complete, detailed mechanism (review Section 18.3a), however, H^- is transferred directly from the Metal—H bond to the carbon atom.

Mechanism for the hydride reduction of an acid chloride to a primary alcohol (Eq. 22-18)

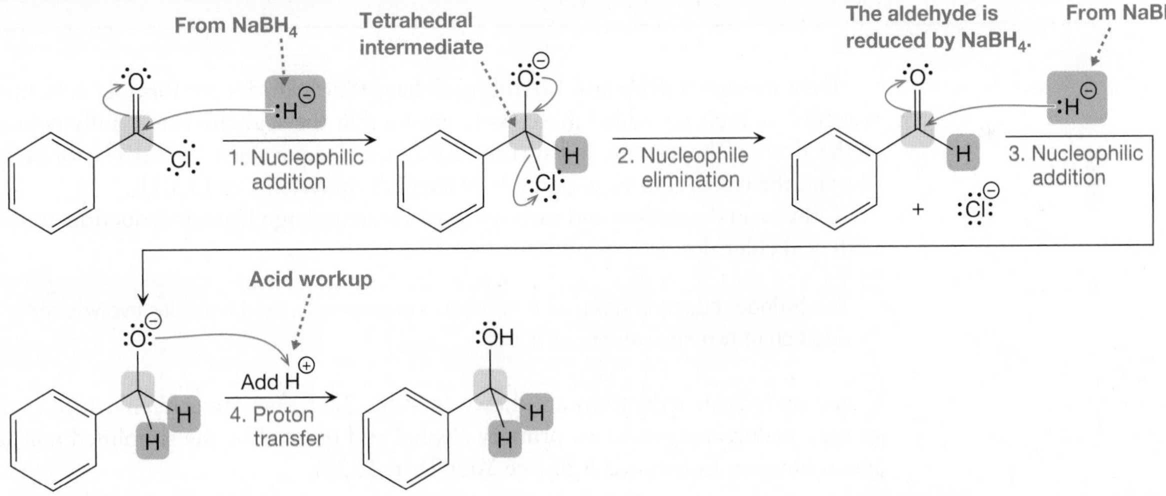
From NaBH4
Tetrahedral intermediate
The aldehyde is reduced by NaBH4.
From NaBH4
:H⊖
1. Nucleophilic addition
2. Nucleophile elimination
3. Nucleophilic addition
+ :Cl:⊖
Acid workup
Add H⊕
4. Proton transfer
:OH

(22-20)

Steps 1 and 2 make up the usual nucleophilic addition–elimination mechanism, producing an aldehyde as an intermediate. Under these reduction conditions, however, the aldehyde reacts rapidly with another equivalent of hydride (Section 18.3a) to produce an alkoxide anion. Subsequent acid workup yields the alcohol.

Mechanism Drawing
$NaBH_4$ Reduction of an Acid Chloride to a 1° Alcohol

YOUR TURN 22.18

The following scheme outlines the mechanism for the $LiAlH_4$ reduction of the acid chloride in Equation 22-19. Supply the appropriate curved arrows, write the name of the elementary step underneath each reaction arrow, and identify the tetrahedral intermediate.

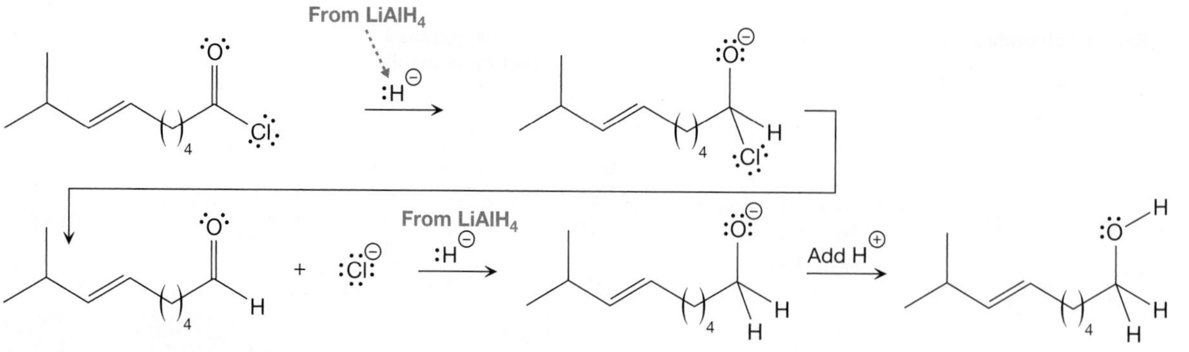

From LiAlH4
:H⊖
From LiAlH4
:H⊖
Add H⊕

YOUR TURN 22.19

Predict the major product and draw the complete, detailed mechanism for each of the following reactions.

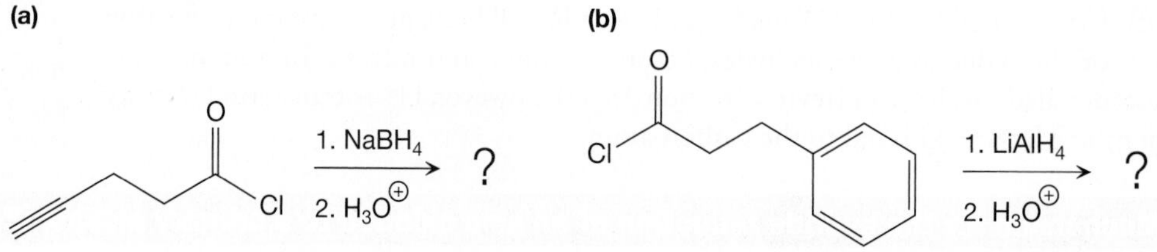

(a)
1. NaBH4
2. H3O⊕
?
(b)
1. LiAlH4
2. H3O⊕
?

Even though $NaBH_4$ and $LiAlH_4$ each have four hydrides per formula unit, these reagents are typically added in excess to ensure that the acid chloride is fully reduced to the alcohol. The reaction in Equation 22-18 uses 3 equivalents of $NaBH_4$, for example, and the reaction in Equation 22-19 uses 1.3 equivalents of $LiAlH_4$.

Other acid derivatives and carboxylic acids can undergo hydride reduction, too. As with acid chlorides:

> The hydride reduction of an acid derivative or carboxylic acid typically involves the addition of two equivalents of H^-.

Common hydride reductions are shown in Table 22-1. As with acid chlorides, many of these reductions produce a primary alcohol and proceed by the simplified mechanism shown in Equation 22-20 (see Your Turn 22.20).

YOUR TURN 22.20

Draw the complete, detailed mechanism for each generic reaction in Table 22-1 that converts an acid derivative to a primary alcohol.

The reactants in Table 22-1 appear in the same order as in the stability ladder (review Fig. 22-6, p. 1059), with the less stable species toward the top and the more stable species toward the bottom. Whereas all of those species are easily reduced by $LiAlH_4$, $NaBH_4$ does not readily reduce the more stable carboxylic acid derivatives. We will explore this distinction between $NaBH_4$ and $LiAlH_4$ in Sections 22.6a and 22.6b.

TABLE 22-1 Hydride Reductions of Acid Derivatives and Carboxylic Acids

Reductions with $NaBH_4$	Reductions with $LiAlH_4$

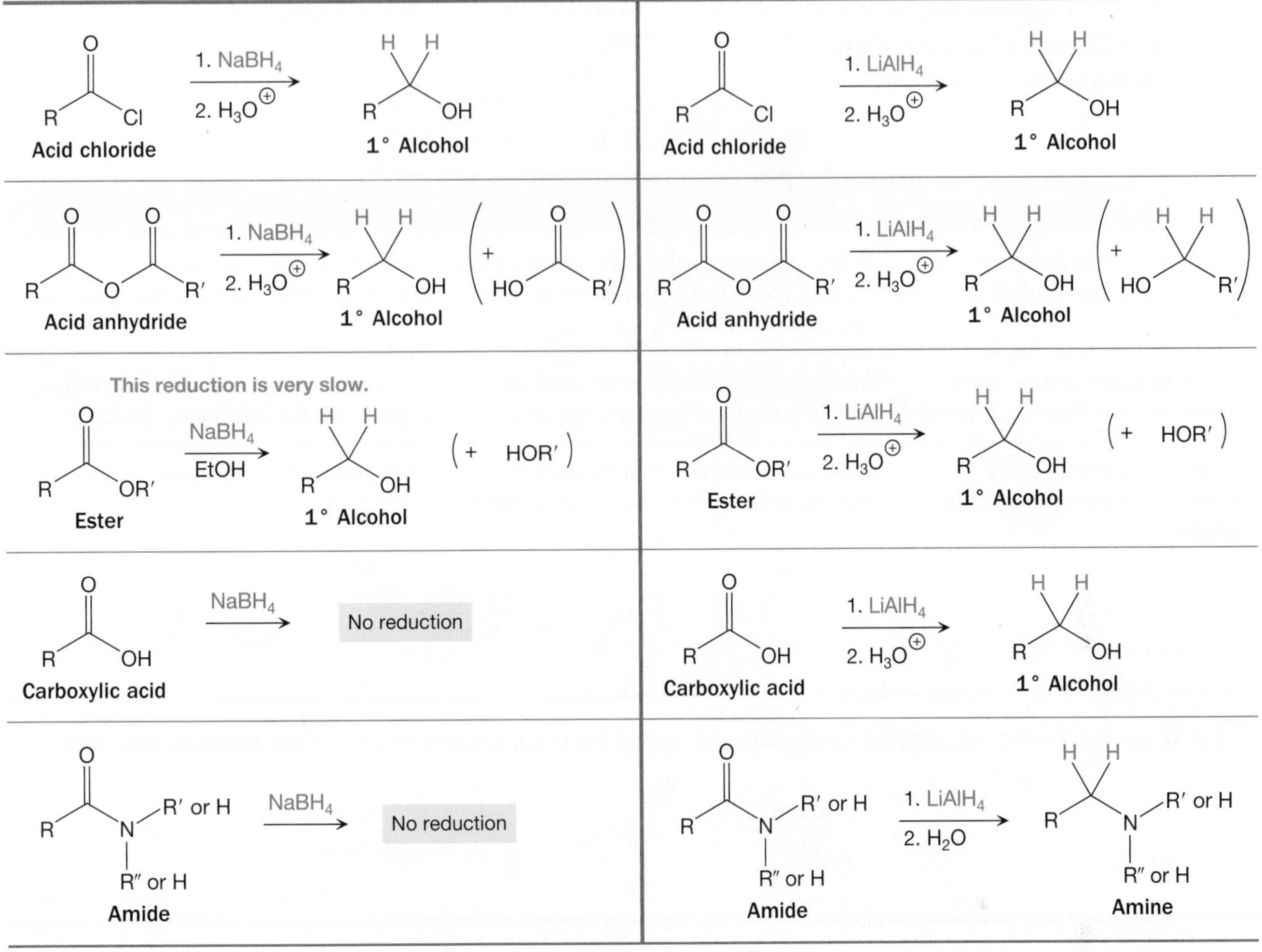

Acid chloride
1. NaBH4
2. H3O+
1° Alcohol
1. LiAlH4
Acid anhydride
This reduction is very slow.
NaBH4
EtOH
Ester
(+ HOR′)
Carboxylic acid
No reduction
Amide
R′ or H
R″ or H
2. H2O
Amine

22.6a The Selectivity of $NaBH_4$

Notice in Table 22-1 that $NaBH_4$ reduces esters very slowly and does not reduce amides at all. Esters are difficult to reduce by $NaBH_4$ because of the pronounced resonance stabilization of their carbonyl and leaving groups, shown previously in Figure 22-4 (p. 1055). The carbonyl group of an amide is stabilized even more, making amides unreactive toward $NaBH_4$ (see Looking Ahead box).

We can take advantage of the low reactivity of esters and amides to *selectively* reduce a more reactive acid derivative, such as an acid chloride or acid anhydride. As discussed in Section 18.3a, $NaBH_4$ readily reduces aldehydes and ketones, so $NaBH_4$ can be used to selectively reduce aldehydes and ketones relative to esters and amides. In the β-keto ester in Equation 22-21, for example, the carbonyl group that has two attached carbons, characteristic of a ketone, is readily reduced to the alcohol, but the ester group is unaffected.

> **▸ LOOKING AHEAD**
>
> In Chapter 23, we will examine resonance in carboxylic acid derivatives in greater detail. As we will see, resonance involving the π electrons of the carbonyl group and a lone pair on the leaving group plays an important role in the relative reaction rates of carboxylic acid derivatives.

Ketones are selectively reduced relative to esters.

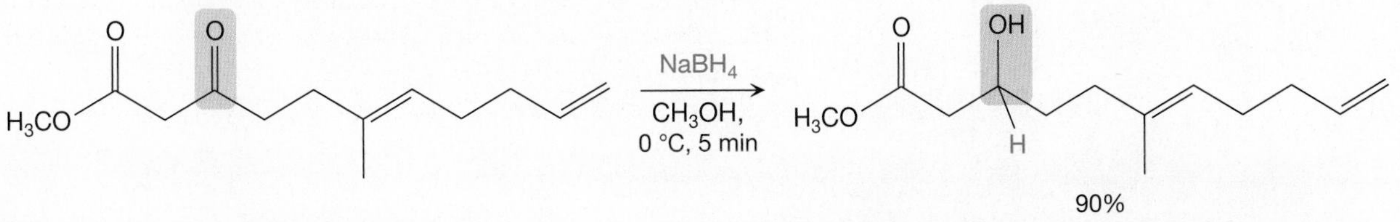

H3CO
NaBH4
CH3OH,
0 °C, 5 min
OH
90%

(22-21)

SOLVED PROBLEM **22.4**

How to predict the product of a selective hydride reduction by $NaBH_4$

Break It Down Predict the major product of the reaction shown here.

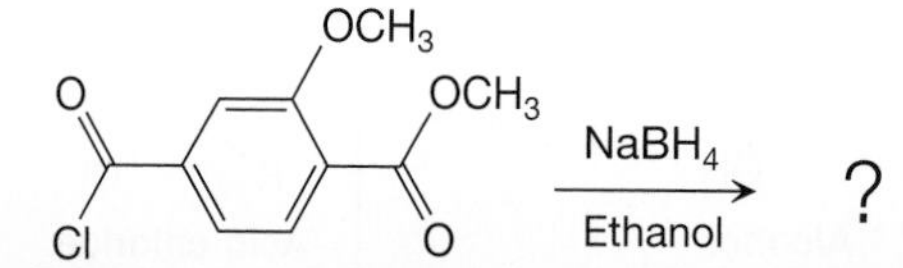

Think	Solve
Which functional groups in the reactant can be reduced by $NaBH_4$?	$NaBH_4$ can reduce the COCl group characteristic of an acid chloride and the CO_2CH_3 group characteristic of an ester. The aromatic ring and the ether group are not reduced by $NaBH_4$.
Is one of those groups more easily reduced than the others?	Table 22-1 indicates that an acid chloride is reduced much more rapidly by $NaBH_4$ than is an ester. Therefore, the acid chloride group will be selectively reduced.
What will be produced by reduction of the acid chloride group?	Table 22-1 indicates that an acid chloride will be reduced to a primary alcohol. The specific product of the reaction at hand is shown here. 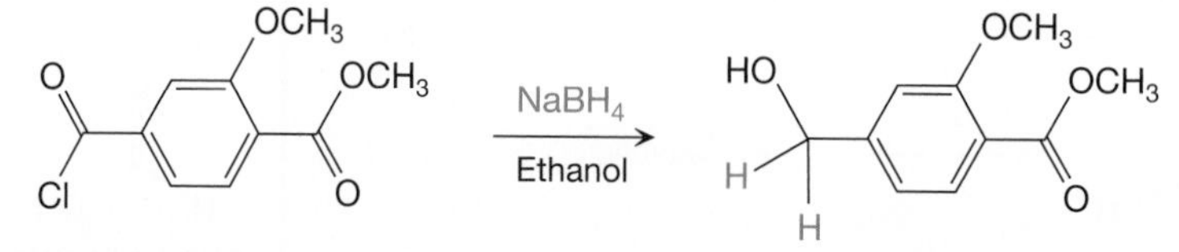

Try It Draw the complete, detailed mechanism and predict the major product for each of the following reactions.

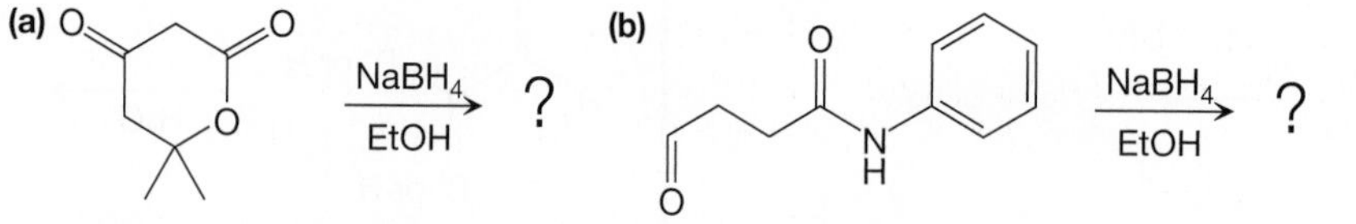

Why can't $NaBH_4$ reduce a carboxylic acid even though it can reduce esters (slowly)? Esters and carboxylic acids are on the same rung of the stability ladder (Fig. 22-6, p. 1059), but carboxylic acids are moderately acidic and $NaBH_4$ is somewhat basic. Therefore, as shown in Equation 22-22, a rapid proton transfer converts the carboxylic acid into its carboxylate anion, which is heavily stabilized by resonance. Because carboxylate anions are at the very bottom of the stability ladder, there is no further reaction once the carboxylate is formed under these conditions.

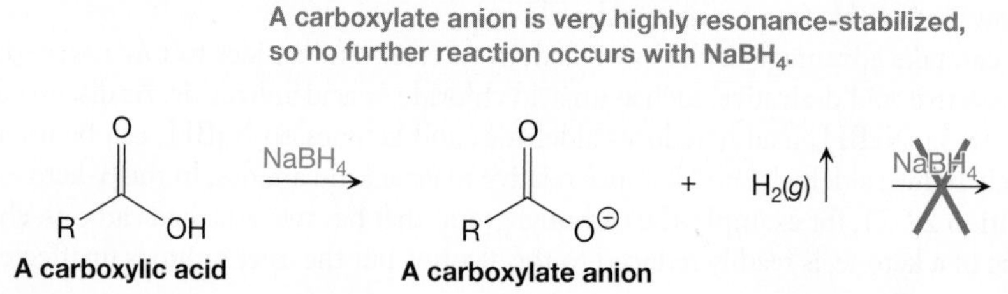
A carboxylate anion is very highly resonance-stabilized, so no further reaction occurs with NaBH4.
NaBH4
A carboxylic acid
A carboxylate anion
+ H2(g)
NaBH4
(22-22)

YOUR TURN 22.21

Show how this carboxylic acid can be converted into the corresponding alcohol using $NaBH_4$ as the reducing agent. *Hint*: Can you convert the carboxylic acid into a different acid derivative first?

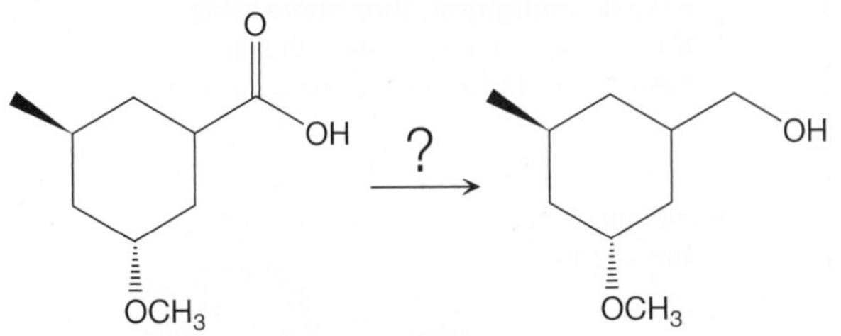

O
OH
?
OH
OCH3
OCH3

22.6b The Greater Reactivity of $LiAlH_4$

Whereas $NaBH_4$ cannot reduce carboxylic acids, *$LiAlH_4$ is a much stronger reducing agent* and will reduce a carboxylic acid to a primary alcohol:

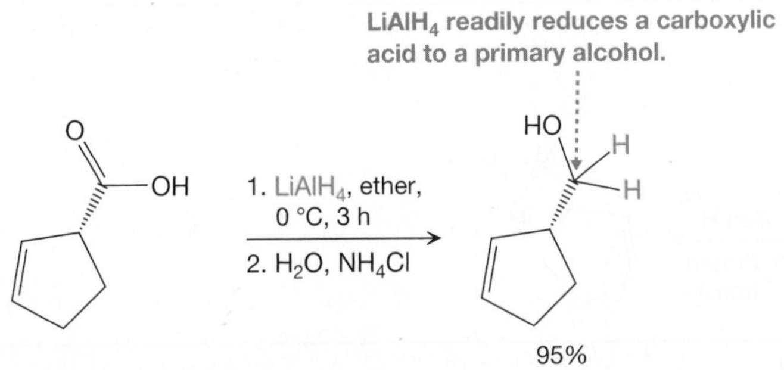

LiAlH4 readily reduces a carboxylic acid to a primary alcohol.
O
OH
1. LiAlH4, ether, 0 °C, 3 h
2. H2O, NH4Cl
HO
H
H
95%

(22-23)

The mechanism for the reduction of a carboxylic acid to a primary alcohol is shown in Equation 22-24. Step 1 is a rapid proton transfer that produces a carboxylate anion, just as we saw in Equation 22-22 when a carboxylic acid is treated with $NaBH_4$. At the same time, the negatively charged O atom of the carboxylate anion forms a relatively strong bond to the Al atom (analogous to the hydride transfer step described in Section 18.3a). Subsequent back-to-back hydride reductions occur in Steps 2–4 (review Eq. 22-20), and the acid workup in Step 5 supplies the proton to produce the final primary alcohol. For the nucleophilic addition steps in Steps 2 and 4, notice that we have simplified $LiAlH_4$ to a H^- nucleophile.

Mechanism for the reduction of a carboxylic acid to a primary alcohol with $LiAlH_4$ (Eq. 22-23)

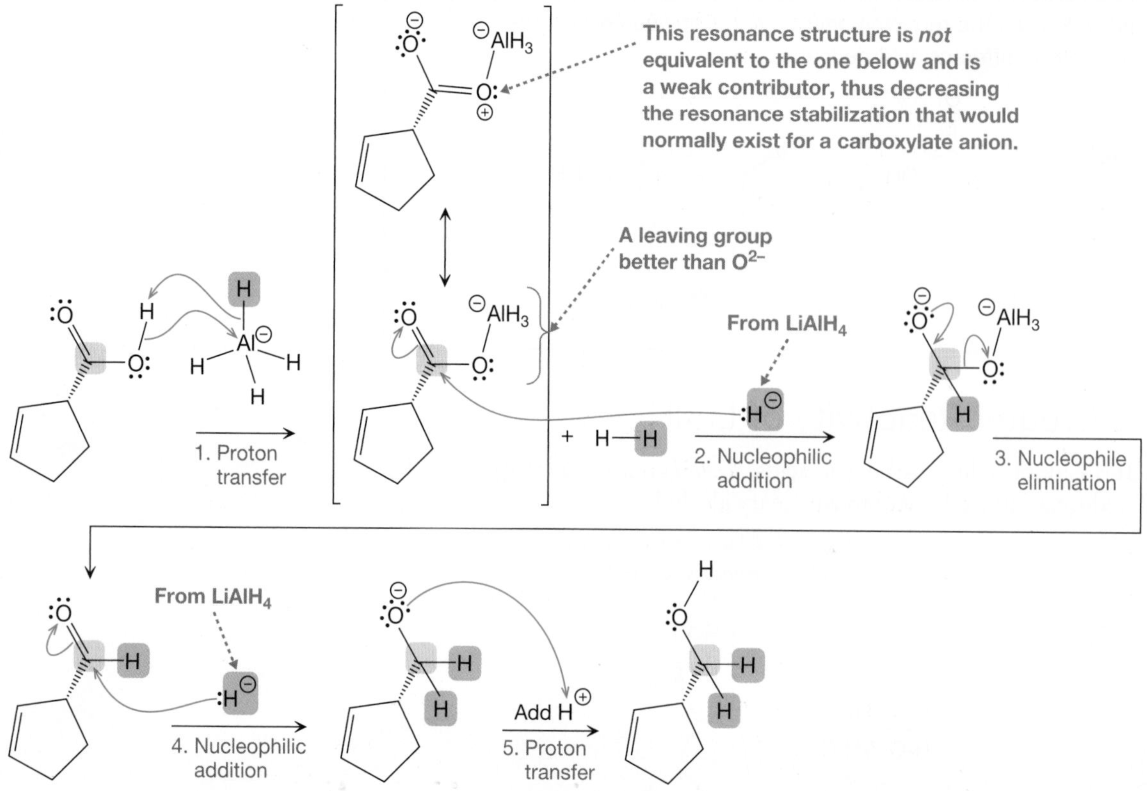
This resonance structure is *not* equivalent to the one below and is a weak contributor, thus decreasing the resonance stabilization that would normally exist for a carboxylate anion.
A leaving group better than O2–
From LiAlH4
1. Proton transfer
2. Nucleophilic addition
3. Nucleophile elimination
From LiAlH4
4. Nucleophilic addition
Add H⊕
5. Proton transfer

(22-24)

The formation of the O—Al bond in Step 1 of Equation 22-24 facilitates the $LiAlH_4$ reduction of a carboxylic acid in two ways. First, as indicated in Equation 22-24, this bond removes the equivalence that is normally observed for the resonance structures of a carboxylate anion (RCO_2^-). Thus, with the O—Al bond present, the C═O is not as highly resonance-stabilized as in a regular carboxylate anion and is therefore more susceptible to nucleophilic attack by H^-. Second, a better leaving group is generated when the O—Al bond forms; without the O—Al bond, the leaving group in a regular carboxylate anion would depart as an isolated oxygen atom bearing a −2 charge (review Fig. 22-6, p. 1059)—a species that is much too unstable to depart on its own.

Although not shown, the O—AlH_3^- group produced in Step 1 can be the source of H^- in Step 2, becoming O—AlH_2 before departing. Thus, the leaving group would depart as $^-$O—AlH_2, which carries just a single negative charge and is even more stable than the leaving group shown in Step 3 of Equation 22-24.

$LiAlH_4$ and $NaBH_4$ also differ in the way they react with an amide. Whereas $NaBH_4$ cannot reduce an amide, $LiAlH_4$ can, as shown in Equation 22-25.

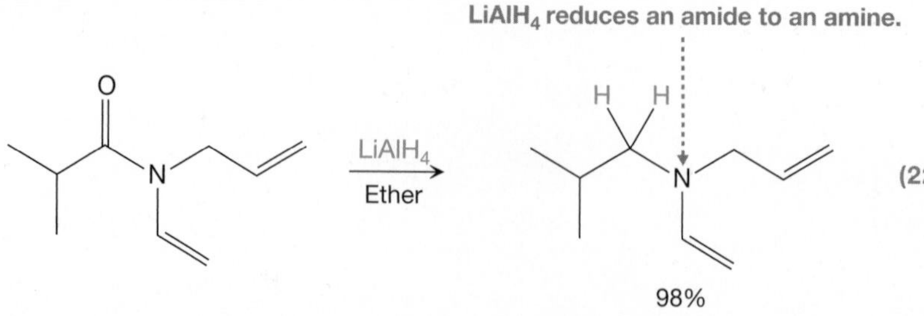
LiAlH4 reduces an amide to an amine.
LiAlH4
Ether
98%

(22-25)

More specifically:

> $LiAlH_4$ reduces an amide ($RCONR_2$) to an amine (RCH_2NR_2) without changing the structure of the carbon backbone.

It is particularly striking that the product is an amine, because $LiAlH_4$ reduces all of the other acid derivatives to primary alcohols. This difference stems, once again, from the relatively strong O—Al bond that forms, as shown in the mechanism in Equation 22-26:

Mechanism for the reduction of an amide to an amine with $LiAlH_4$ (Eq. 22-25)

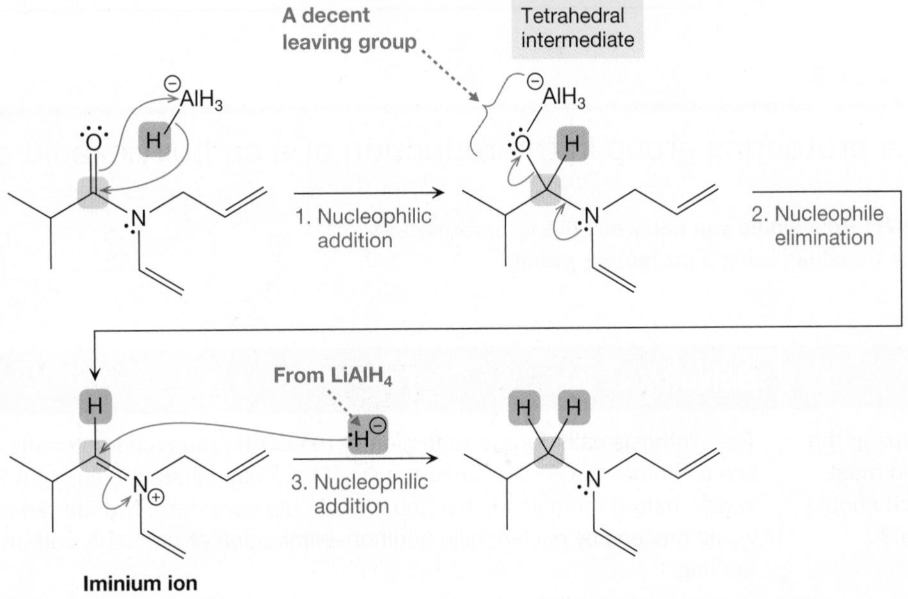
A decent leaving group
Tetrahedral intermediate
AlH3
H
1. Nucleophilic addition
2. Nucleophile elimination
From LiAlH4
3. Nucleophilic addition
Iminium ion

(22-26)

In Step 1, H^- adds to the carbonyl group of the amide, and the O—Al bond forms at the same time. The tetrahedral intermediate that is produced contains the same $O{-}AlH_3^-$ leaving group we saw in the mechanism describing the reduction of carboxylic acids (Eq. 22-24). In Step 2, the $O{-}AlH_3^-$ leaving group departs, yielding an iminium ion, which is subsequently attacked by H^- in Step 3 to yield the final product.

Similar to the lithium aluminum hydride reduction of a carboxylic acid, the $O{-}AlH_3^-$ group in the product of Step 1 can donate a H^- to become $O{-}AlH_2$. The leaving group in the subsequent nucleophilic addition–elimination, therefore, would be even more stable.

Mechanism Drawing
$LiAlH_4$ Reduction of an Amide to an Amine

YOUR TURN 22.22

The following mechanism is for the $LiAlH_4$ reduction of another amide, but the curved arrows have been omitted. Supply the missing curved arrows, and identify the tetrahedral intermediate. Below each reaction arrow, write the name of the elementary step that is taking place.

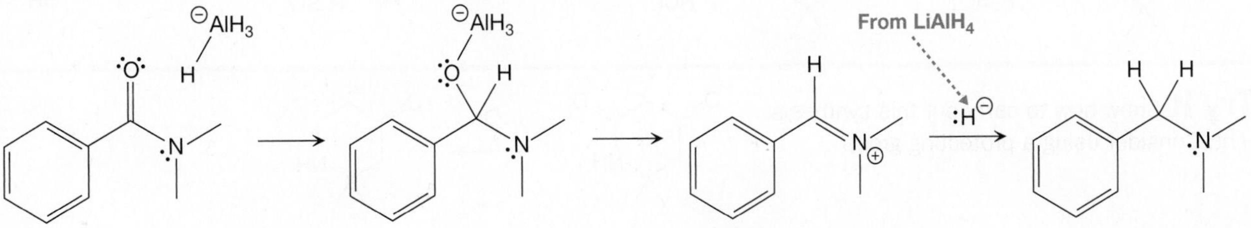
AlH3
H
From LiAlH4

YOUR TURN 22.23

Draw the complete, detailed mechanism and predict the major product for each of the following reactions.

(a)

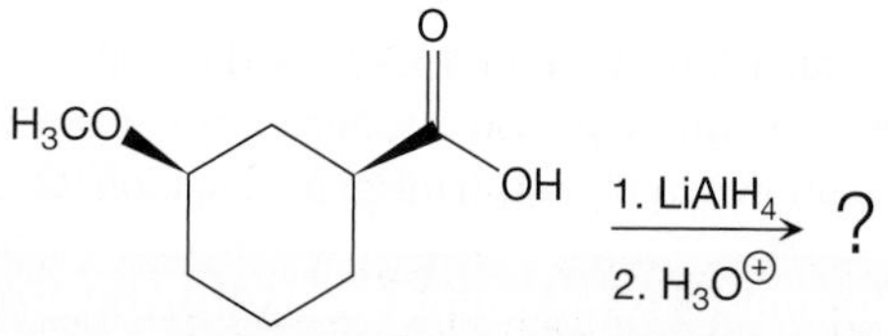

H3CO
O
OH
1. LiAlH4
2. H3O⊕
?

(b)

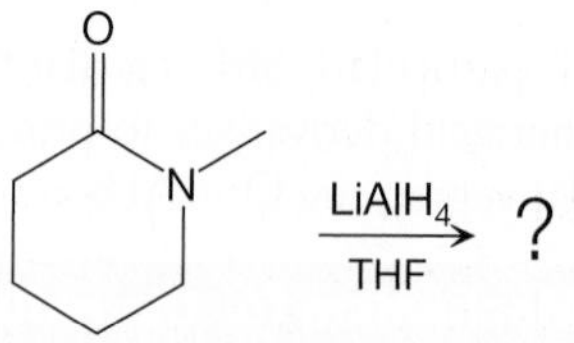

O
N
LiAlH4
THF
?

SOLVED PROBLEM 22.5

How to use a protecting group in the reduction of a carboxylic acid derivative

Break It Down **How would you carry out the transformation shown here? *Hint*: Consider using a protecting group.**

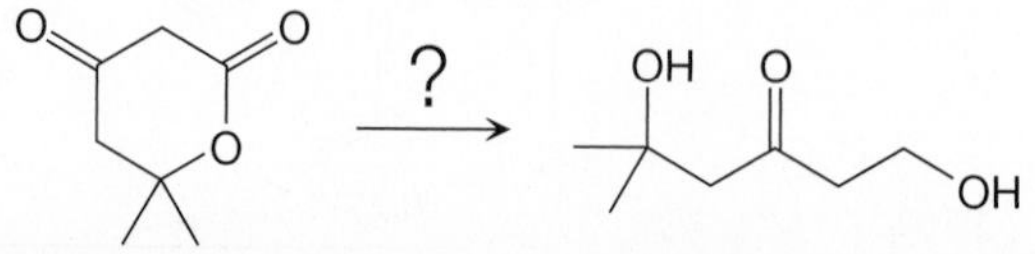

O
O
O
?
OH
O
OH

Think	Solve
Which of the groups in the starting compound must be reduced? Which should remain unchanged?	The synthesis calls for the reduction of the CO_2R group (characteristic of an ester, red screen below) to C—OH, while the O═CC_2 group (characteristic of a ketone, blue screen below) remains unchanged. We should consider a hydride reduction, which would proceed by nucleophilic addition–elimination at the CO_2R carbon and would open the ring.

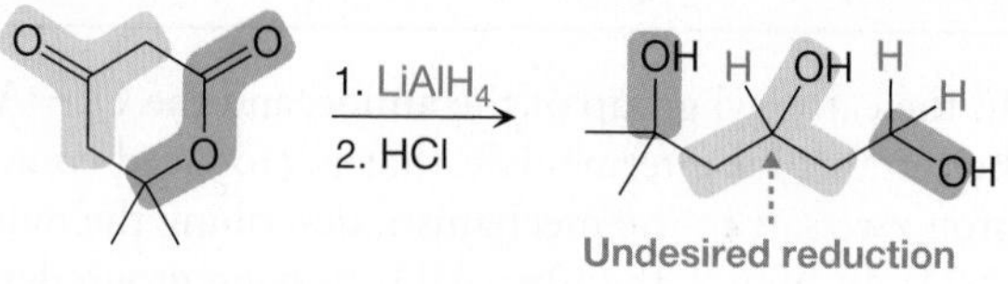

1. LiAlH4
2. HCl
OH
H
OH
H
H
OH
Undesired reduction

Think	Solve
Will the desired reduction also reduce the other functional group?	As shown above, reduction with $LiAlH_4$ would reduce the O═CC_2 group as well as the CO_2R group. The same would be true if we were to use $NaBH_4$.
How can you use a protecting group to prevent the undesired reduction?	Prior to adding the reducing agent, we could protect the O═CC_2 group by converting it to an acetal, as shown below (Section 21.2b). Then, after the ester has been reduced, we could deprotect using aqueous acid.

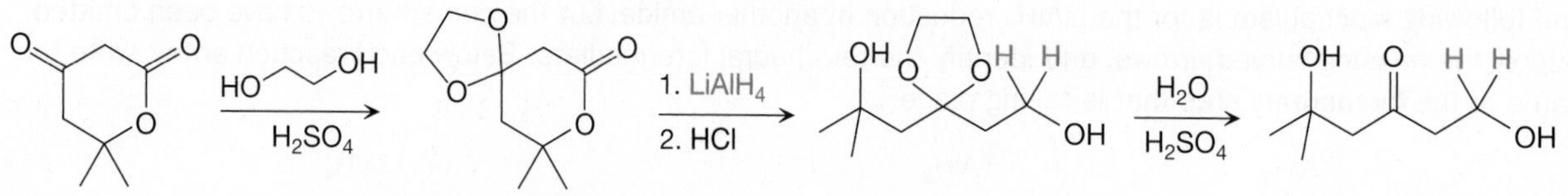

HO
OH
H2SO4
1. LiAlH4
2. HCl
OH
H
H
OH
H2O
H2SO4
OH
O
H
H
OH

Try It Show how to carry out this synthesis.
Hint: Consider using a protecting group.

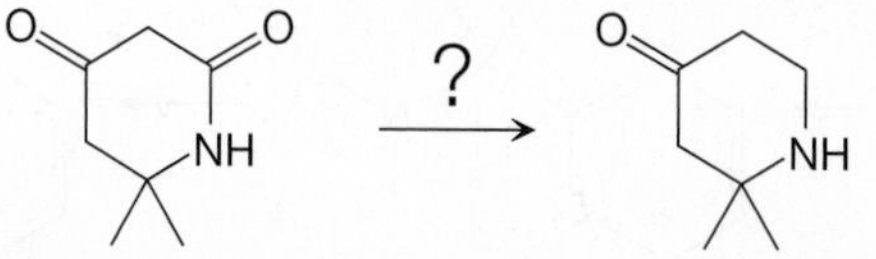

O
O
NH
?
O
NH

22.7 A Deeper Look: DIBAH and LTBA as Specialized Reducing Agents

The mechanism in Equation 22-20 (p. 1073), which describes the hydride reduction of an acid derivative to a primary alcohol, proceeds through an aldehyde intermediate. That is, once the aldehyde is formed, it quickly reacts with H^- in a second reduction. In some situations, however, it might be advantageous to stop at the aldehyde. Two specialized reducing agents are commonly used for such purposes: **lithium tri-*tert*-butoxyaluminum hydride (LTBA)** and **diisobutylaluminum hydride (DIBAH,** or **DIBAL-H)** (**Figure 22-11**). Both of these compounds possess an Al—H bond and thus are hydride anion (H^-) sources, much like $LiAlH_4$.

Examples of how these specialized reducing agents are used are shown in Equations 22-27 and 22-28:

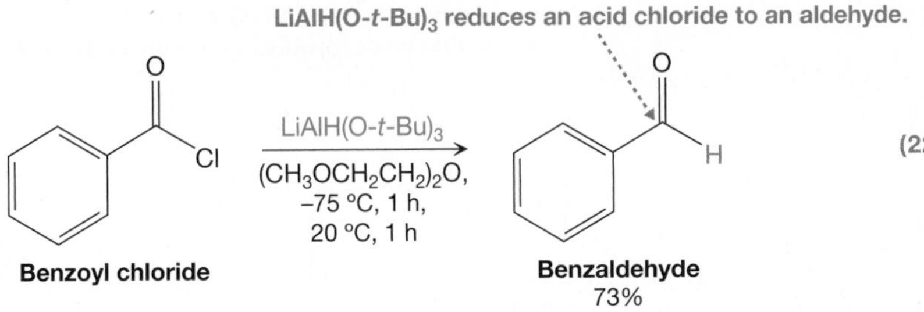
LiAlH(O-t-Bu)3 reduces an acid chloride to an aldehyde.
LiAlH(O-t-Bu)3
(CH3OCH2CH2)2O,
–75 °C, 1 h,
20 °C, 1 h
Benzoyl chloride
Benzaldehyde
73%

(22-27)

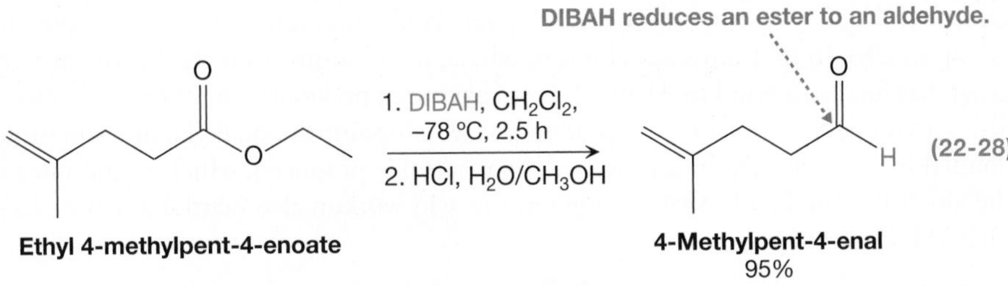
DIBAH reduces an ester to an aldehyde.
1. DIBAH, CH2Cl2,
–78 °C, 2.5 h
2. HCl, H2O/CH3OH
Ethyl 4-methylpent-4-enoate
4-Methylpent-4-enal
95%

(22-28)

Specifically:

- Lithium tri-*tert*-butoxyaluminum hydride (LTBA) is commonly used to reduce an acid chloride (RCOCl) to an aldehyde (RCH=O) at low temperature.
- Diisobutylaluminum hydride (DIBAH) is commonly used to reduce an ester (RCO_2R) to an aldehyde (RCH=O) at low temperature.

The mechanism by which LTBA (simplified to H^-) reduces an acid chloride to an aldehyde is shown in Equation 22-29:

Mechanism for the reduction of an acid chloride to an aldehyde with LTBA (Eq. 22-27)

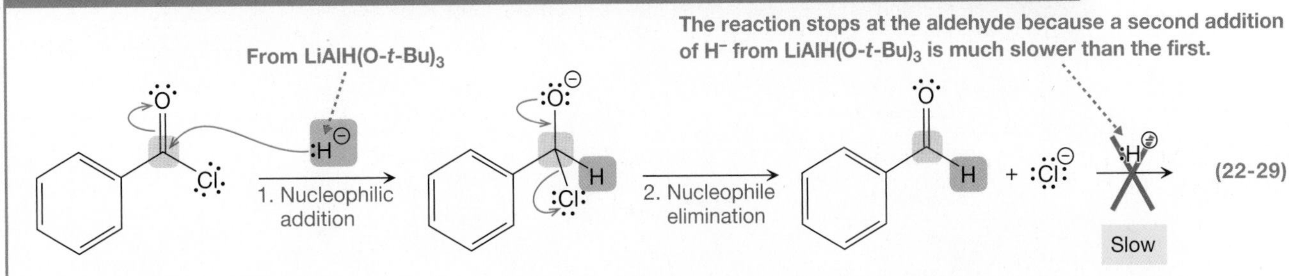
The reaction stops at the aldehyde because a second addition of H⁻ from LiAlH(O-t-Bu)3 is much slower than the first.
From LiAlH(O-t-Bu)3
1. Nucleophilic addition
2. Nucleophile elimination
Slow

(22-29)

SECTION 22.7 OBJECTIVES

You will be able to:

1. Explain why reductions by DIBAH or LTBA can produce an aldehyde.
2. Incorporate reductions by DIBAH or LTBA into a synthesis.

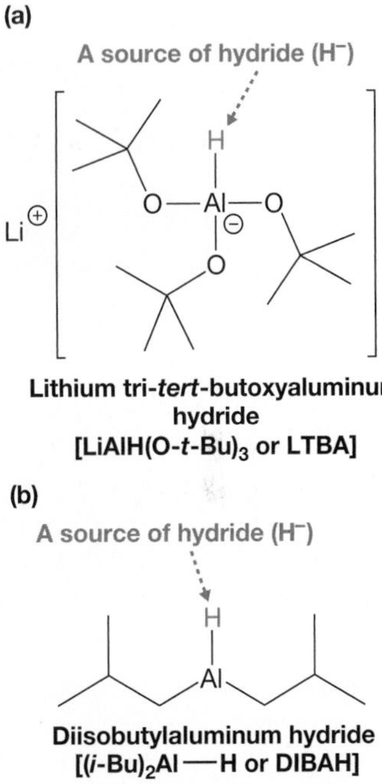
(a)
A source of hydride (H⁻)
Lithium tri-tert-butoxyaluminum hydride
[LiAlH(O-t-Bu)3 or LTBA]
(b)
A source of hydride (H⁻)
Diisobutylaluminum hydride
[(i-Bu)2Al—H or DIBAH]

FIGURE 22-11 Two specialized hydride reducing agents These hydride reducing agents can be used to reduce a carboxylic acid derivative to an aldehyde. (a) Lithium tri-*tert*-butoxyaluminum hydride can reduce an acid chloride to an aldehyde. (b) Diisobutylaluminum hydride can reduce an ester to an aldehyde.

This is essentially the same nucleophilic addition–elimination mechanism as the one by which $LiAlH_4$ operates, the only difference being the rate.

Reduction by LTBA occurs much more slowly than that by $LiAlH_4$, allowing the reaction to take place in a more controlled fashion.

Thus, because an aldehyde is less reactive than an acid chloride, the second reduction is slower than the first. Once the first reduction has come to completion, the reaction can be stopped before the second reduction can proceed.

There are two reasons why reduction with LTBA is significantly slower than reduction with $LiAlH_4$. One is the bulkiness of the *tert*-butoxy groups, which introduces significant steric hindrance in the nucleophilic addition step. The second reason is that the reaction is carried out at very cold temperatures (−75 °C in the case of Eq. 22-27). At room temperature, LTBA can rapidly reduce an acid chloride all the way to the alcohol, adding two equivalents of hydride:

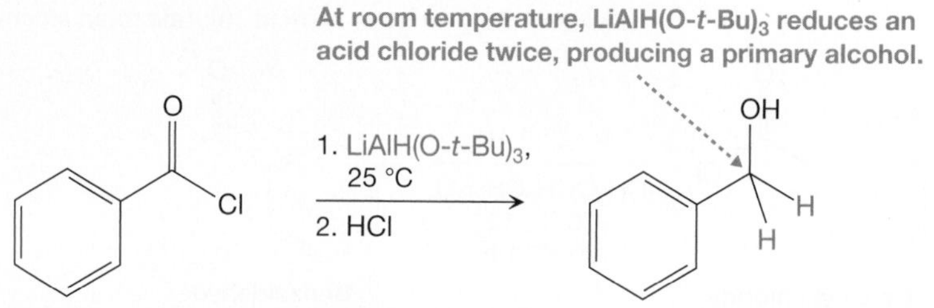
At room temperature, LiAlH(O-*t*-Bu)$_3$ reduces an acid chloride twice, producing a primary alcohol.
O
Cl
1. LiAlH(O-*t*-Bu)$_3$,
25 °C
2. HCl
OH
H
H

(22-30)

The reduction of an ester by DIBAH stops at the aldehyde stage *not* because the second reduction is slower than the first, but because the tetrahedral intermediate that is formed (Eq. 22-31) is relatively stable at very cold temperatures (−78 °C in the case of Eq. 22-28). In that tetrahedral intermediate, the O atom from the initial carbonyl group has formed a bond to Al, much as we have seen previously in other mechanisms. This species persists until H_3O^+ is added, at which point the dialkylaluminum group bonded to O is replaced by a proton. A hemiacetal is produced, which equilibrates to the aldehyde. The H_3O^+ that is added in the acid workup also neutralizes any excess DIBAH. Consequently:

In the DIBAH reduction of an ester, the aldehyde product and the reducing agent are *not* present in the reaction mixture at the same time, so the aldehyde cannot be further reduced to the alcohol.

Mechanism for the reduction of an ester with DIBAH (Eq. 22-28)

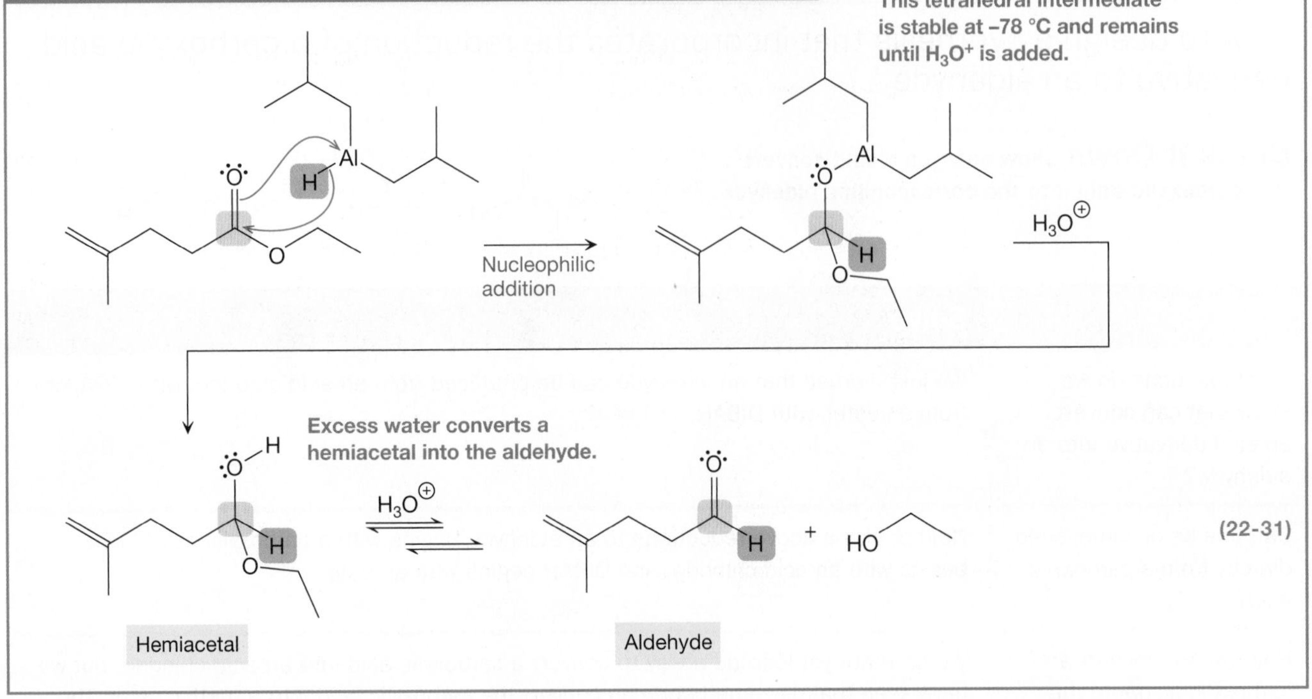
This tetrahedral intermediate is stable at −78 °C and remains until H_3O^+ is added.
Al
H
O
Nucleophilic addition
$H_3O^{\oplus}$
Excess water converts a hemiacetal into the aldehyde.
HO
Hemiacetal
Aldehyde

(22-31)

The relative stability of the tetrahedral intermediate in the DIBAH reduction of an ester can be rationalized in part by charge stability. As shown in Equation 22-32, elimination of the alkoxy leaving group from the tetrahedral intermediate would generate two additional charges: a negative charge on the O atom of the leaving group (RO^-) and a positive charge on the O atom bonded to Al. The small size of O does little to stabilize those charges, so the uncharged tetrahedral intermediate persists.

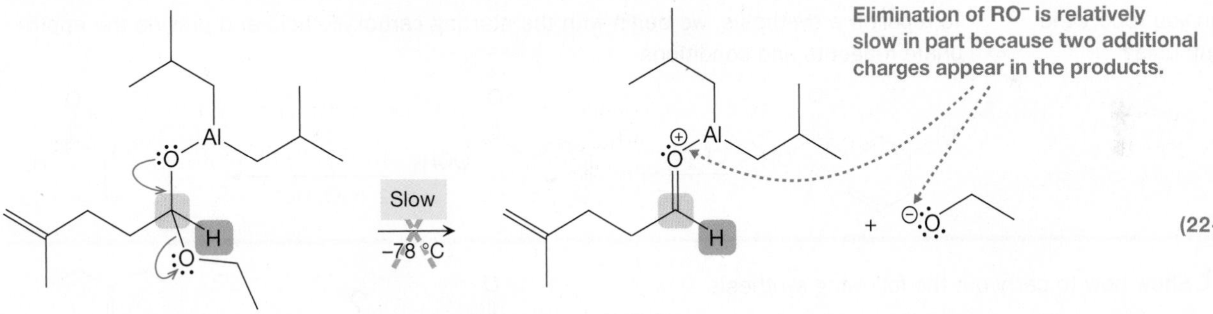
Elimination of RO^- is relatively slow in part because two additional charges appear in the products.
Al
H
O
Slow
−78 °C

(22-32)

SOLVED PROBLEM **22.6**

How to design a synthesis that incorporates the reduction of a carboxylic acid derivative to an aldehyde

Break It Down **Show how you would convert this carboxylic acid into the corresponding aldehyde.**

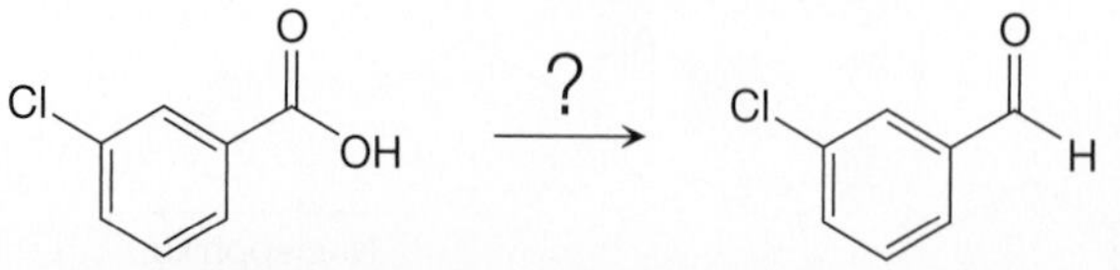

Think	Solve
What reactions do we know that can convert an acid derivative into an aldehyde?	We just learned that an aldehyde can be produced from an acid chloride, with LTBA, or from an ester, with DIBAH.
Can this be accomplished directly from a carboxylic acid?	Neither of the above reductions to an aldehyde begins with a carboxylic acid. LTBA begins with an acid chloride, and DIBAH begins with an ester.
How can we convert a carboxylic acid into the necessary acid derivative?	We have not yet learned a way to convert a carboxylic acid into an acid chloride, but we have seen that diazomethane can convert the carboxylic acid into a methyl ester. The complete retrosynthesis is shown here. 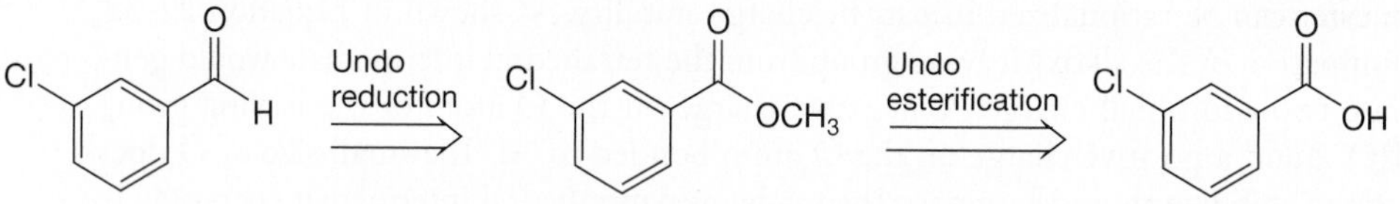
How can you report the final synthesis?	To report the synthesis, we begin with the starting carboxylic acid and provide the appropriate reagents and conditions. 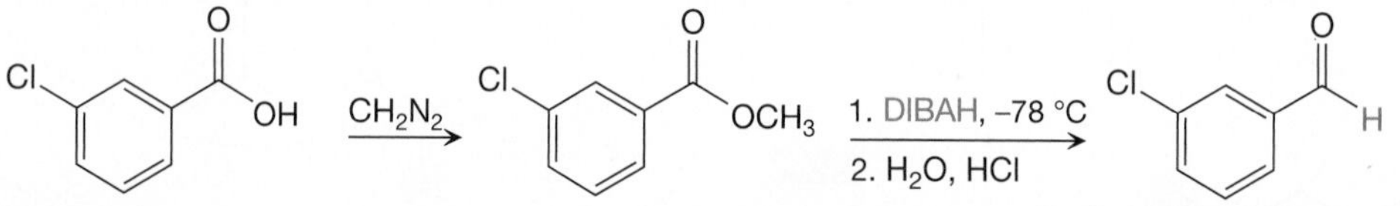

Try It Show how to carry out the following synthesis.

SECTION 22.8 OBJECTIVES

You will be able to:

1. Draw the mechanism and predict the product for reactions in which a carboxylic acid derivative is treated with a Grignard reagent or an alkyllithium reagent.
2. Show how a ketone can be produced by reacting an acid chloride with a lithium dialkylcuprate.

22.8 Organometallic Reagents

Like hydride anions (H^-), alkyl anions (R^-) can act as nucleophiles but not as leaving groups. As we have seen in previous chapters, sources of R^- are organometallic compounds such as alkyllithium reagents (RLi), Grignard reagents (RMgX), and lithium dialkylcuprates (R_2CuLi) (see Recall box, p. 1085). Therefore, as with hydride reagents, the product of a nucleophilic addition–elimination reaction involving one of these organometallic reagents is *not* an acid derivative. We can see this explicitly in Equations 22-33 and 22-34, in which an acid derivative is treated with an alkyllithium and a Grignard reagent, respectively:

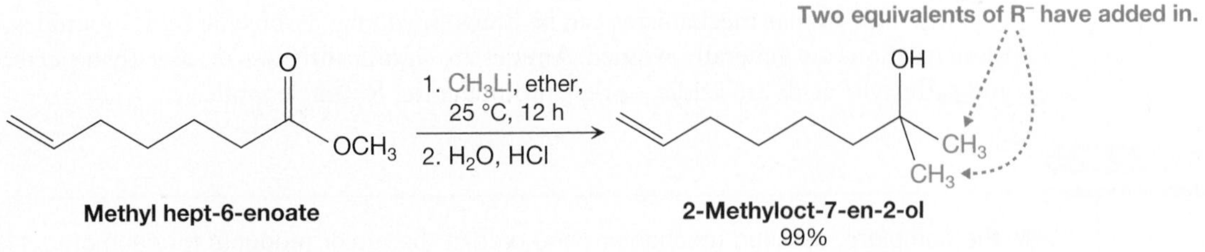

Two equivalents of R⁻ have added in.
1. CH3Li, ether, 25 °C, 12 h
2. H2O, HCl
OCH3
OH
CH3
CH3
Methyl hept-6-enoate
2-Methyloct-7-en-2-ol
99%

(22-33)

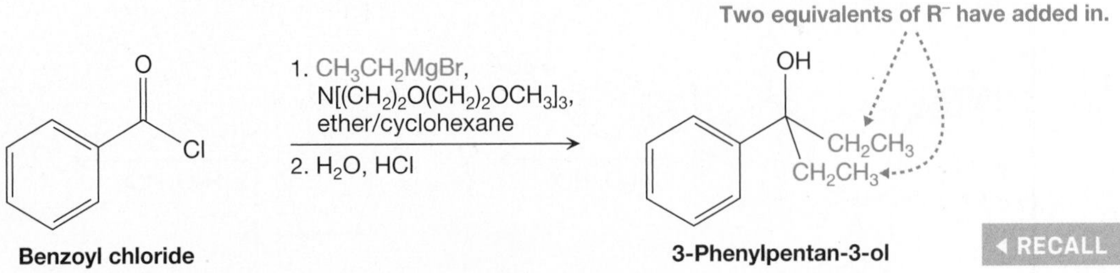

Two equivalents of R⁻ have added in.
1. CH3CH2MgBr, N[(CH2)2O(CH2)2OCH3]3, ether/cyclohexane
2. H2O, HCl
Cl
OH
CH2CH3
CH2CH3
Benzoyl chloride
3-Phenylpentan-3-ol

(22-34)

◀ RECALL

RLi and RMgX act as R^- nucleophiles when they add to ketones, aldehydes, imines, and nitriles (Section 18.4). R^- from R_2CuLi will undergo conjugate addition to α,β-unsaturated ketones and aldehydes (Section 18.9). These organometallic reagents are synthesized from corresponding alkyl halides (Section 20.6).

In general:

> Acid chlorides (RCOCl), acid anhydrides (RCO_2COR), and esters (RCO_2R) can be treated with an alkyllithium (R′Li) or a Grignard (R′MgX) reagent to produce a tertiary alcohol ($R_2'RCOH$).

In each case, two equivalents of the R'^- nucleophile must add to the acid derivative to produce a tertiary alcohol. This is explained by Equation 22-35, the simplified mechanism of the reaction in Equation 22-34.

Mechanism for the reaction of an acid chloride with a Grignard reagent (Eq. 22-34)

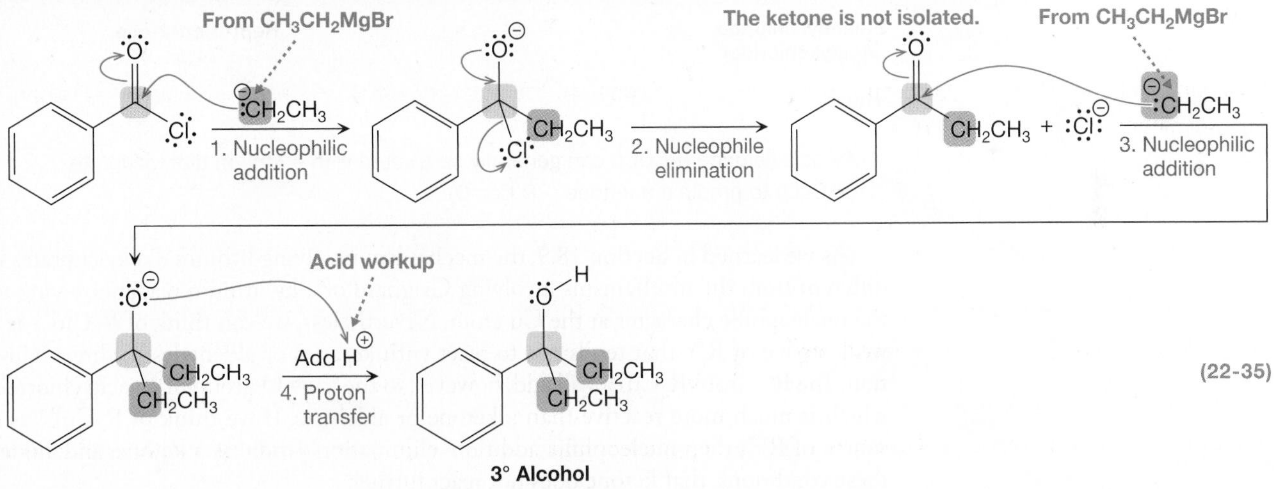

From CH3CH2MgBr
CH2CH3
1. Nucleophilic addition
CH2CH3
2. Nucleophile elimination
The ketone is not isolated.
From CH3CH2MgBr
CH2CH3 + :Cl:
CH2CH3
3. Nucleophilic addition
Acid workup
Add H+
4. Proton transfer
CH2CH3
CH2CH3
H
CH2CH3
CH2CH3
3° Alcohol

(22-35)

This mechanism is essentially the same as the one in Equation 22-20 (p. 1073), which describes the hydride reduction of an acid chloride to a primary alcohol. The first two steps make up the usual nucleophilic addition–elimination mechanism, which produces a ketone in this case. Once that ketone is produced, it reacts with a second equivalent of R^- in Step 3 to produce a tertiary alkoxide anion, R_3CO^-. Acid workup in Step 4 yields the tertiary alcohol as the final product. Notice that Steps 3 and 4 compose the mechanism for a typical alkyllithium or Grignard reaction involving a ketone, which we previously discussed in Section 18.4.

YOUR TURN 22.24

Draw the mechanism for the reaction in Equation 22-33.

Although similar mechanisms can be drawn involving carboxylic acids or amides, these reactions are generally avoided. Amides are significantly less reactive than esters, and carboxylic acids are acidic, so they protonate the R^- nucleophile.

YOUR TURN 22.25

Draw the complete, detailed mechanism and predict the major products for each of the following reactions.

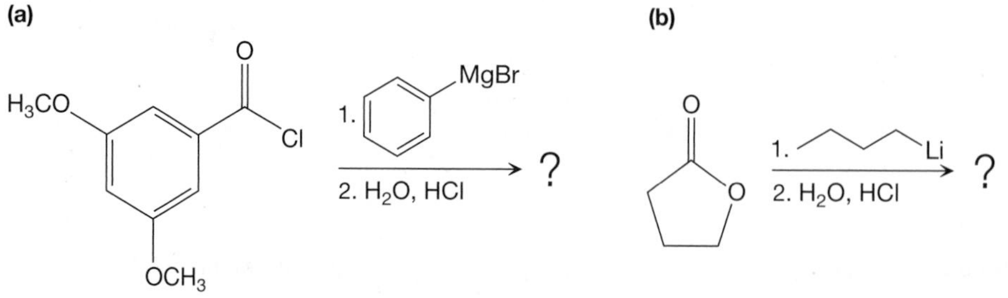

(a)
H3CO
O
Cl
OCH3
1.
MgBr
2. H2O, HCl
?
(b)
O
O
1.
Li
2. H2O, HCl
?

It can be advantageous to carry out reactions in which only one equivalent of R^- adds to an acid derivative, thus producing a ketone that can be isolated. One way to carry out this kind of a reaction involves lithium dialkylcuprates:

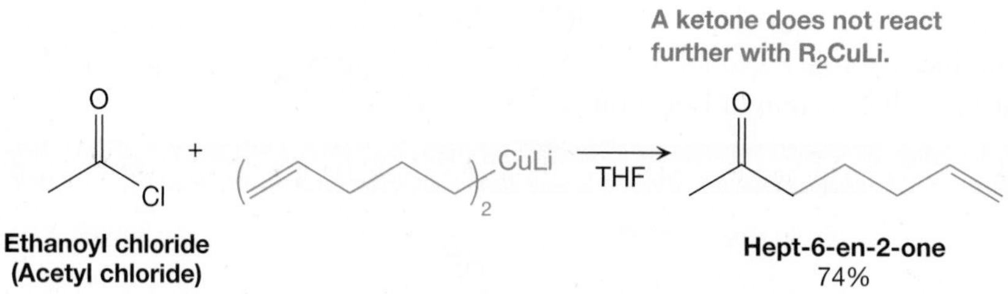

A ketone does not react further with R2CuLi.
O
Cl
+
CuLi
2
THF
O
Ethanoyl chloride (Acetyl chloride)
Hept-6-en-2-one
74%

(22-36)

Thus:

An acid chloride (RCOCl) can generally be treated with a lithium dialkylcuprate (R'_2CuLi) to produce a ketone ($RR'C{=}O$).

As we learned in Section 18.9, the mechanism involving lithium dialkylcuprates is different from the mechanisms involving Grignard or alkyllithium reagents, owing to the nucleophilic character at the Cu atom. Nevertheless, we can think of R'_2CuLi as a weak source of R'^- that tends not to react with ketones or aldehydes by direct addition. The R'^- from R'_2CuLi will add, however, to the $C{=}O$ group of an acid chloride, which is much more reactive than a ketone or aldehyde. If we think of R'_2CuLi as a source of R'^-, then nucleophilic addition–elimination produces a ketone, and, under these conditions, that ketone does not react further.

Lithium dialkylcuprates do not react with esters or amides, which are significantly more stable than acid chlorides. Thus, to convert an ester or amide into a ketone, we must first convert it into an acid chloride. We will discuss how to do so in Chapter 23.

YOUR TURN **22.26**

Draw the major organic product for each of the following reactions. If no reaction takes place, write "no reaction." For each reaction that does take place, draw its simplified mechanism, treating R_2CuLi as a weak source of R^-.

(a)

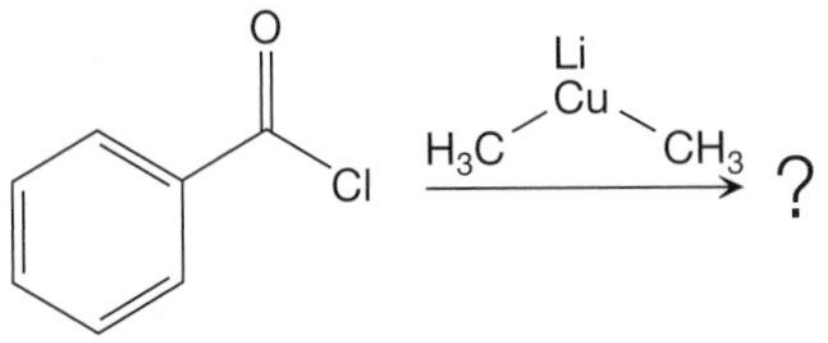
O
Cl
Li
Cu
H3C
CH3
?

(b)

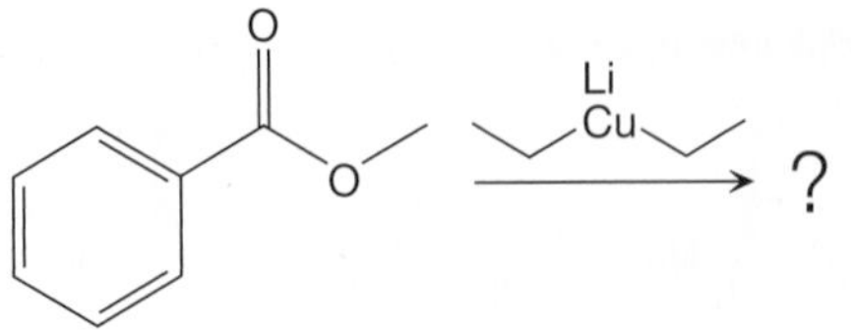
O
O
Li
Cu
?

(c)

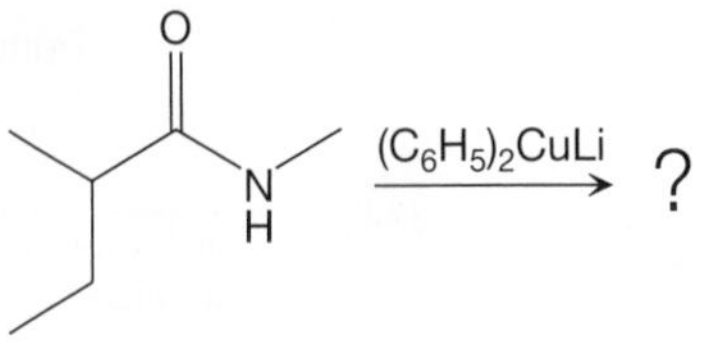
O
N
H
(C6H5)2CuLi
?

SOLVED PROBLEM **22.7**

How to carry out a synthesis that requires converting an acid derivative into a ketone

Break It Down **Show how to carry out this synthesis.**

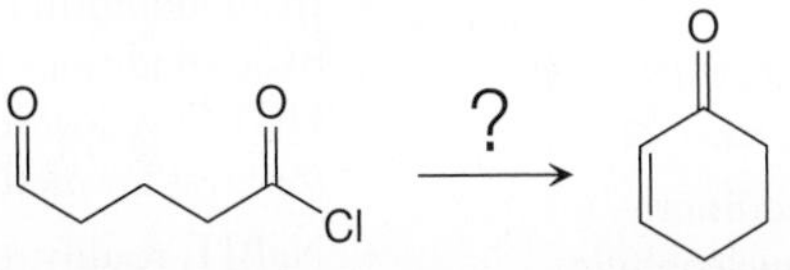
O
O
Cl
?
O

Think	Solve
What precursor can be used to produce the α,β-unsaturated ketone?	The α,β-unsaturated ketone can be produced from an aldol condensation (Section 19.9), as shown in the retrosynthetic analysis here. 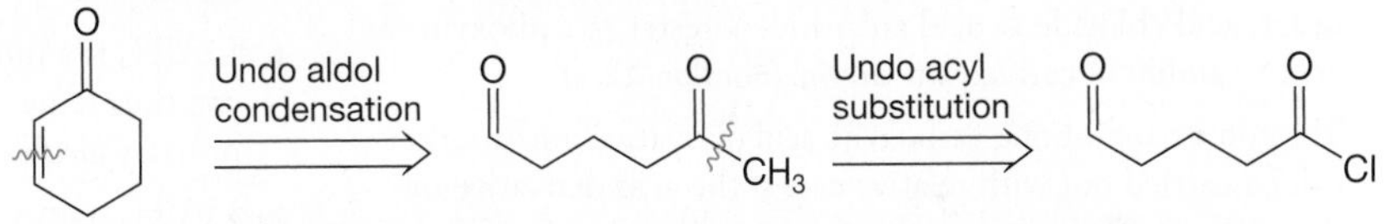 Undo aldol condensation Undo acyl substitution CH3 Cl
To make that precursor from the starting compound, which carbonyl-containing functional group must gain an additional carbon–carbon bond?	As shown above, there is a C—C bond in the precursor that does not exist in the starting material. To make that bond, H_3C^- must substitute for the Cl^- leaving group.
What reagent can you use to carry out a single addition of R^- to the acid chloride?	To ensure that there is only one R^- addition to the acid chloride, we must use a lithium dialkylcuprate, specifically $(CH_3)_2CuLi$, as shown here. If we were to use CH_3Li or CH_3MgX instead, two nucleophilic additions would instead lead to a tertiary alcohol. 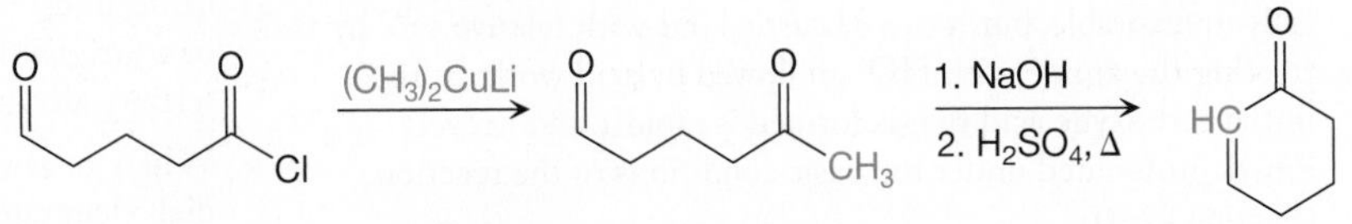 (CH3)2CuLi 1. NaOH 2. H2SO4, Δ Cl CH3 HC

Try It Show how to carry out this synthesis.

O
O
Cl
?
OH
OH

Chapter Summary and Key Terms

- The general mechanism of a **nucleophilic addition–elimination reaction** consists of two steps:

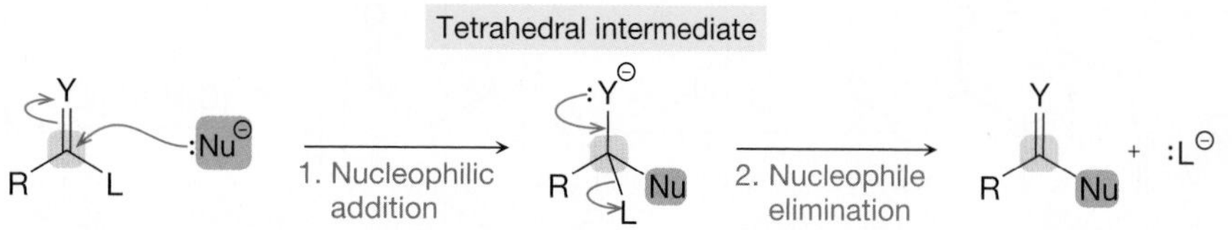

Tetrahedral intermediate
1. Nucleophilic addition
2. Nucleophile elimination

First a nucleophile (:Nu⁻) attacks the electron-poor atom of a polar π bond (Y is an electronegative atom) in a nucleophilic addition step, producing a high-energy **tetrahedral intermediate**. Second, the tetrahedral intermediate eliminates a leaving group (L⁻) initially bonded to the electron-poor atom of the polar π bond. (Sections 22.1 and 22.1a)

- When the leaving group is bonded to a carbonyl group, nucleophilic addition–elimination is called a **nucleophilic acyl substitution reaction**. (Section 22.1a)
- In a **transesterification reaction**, an ester reacts with an alkoxide anion (RO^-) to produce a new ester. (Section 22.1a)
- The rate-determining step of a nucleophilic addition–elimination reaction is usually the first step, nucleophilic addition. (Section 22.1b)
- A transesterification reaction is reversible because the reactants and products have roughly equal stabilities. (Section 22.1c)
- The stability of a carboxylic acid derivative decreases in the order: acid chloride > acid anhydride > ester ≈ carboxylic acid > amide > carboxylate anion. (Section 22.2)
- The conversion of one carboxylic acid derivative into another can be carried out with relative ease if the acid derivative on the product side is more stable (i.e., on a lower rung of the stability ladder) than the one on the reactant side. By contrast, the conversion is difficult if the acid derivative on the product side is higher in energy than the one on the reactant side. (Section 22.2)
- In a **saponification** reaction, an ester reacts with HO^- to produce an initial carboxylic acid that is rapidly and irreversibly deprotonated under the basic conditions of the reaction to yield the corresponding carboxylate anion. (Section 22.3)
- The conversion of an amide ($RCONR_2$) to a carboxylic acid (RCO_2H) by nucleophilic addition–elimination is energetically unfavorable, but it can be carried out with relative ease by treating the amide with HO^-, followed by acid workup. The initial carboxylic acid that is formed is rapidly and irreversibly deprotonated under the basic conditions of the reaction. (Section 22.4)
- The **Gabriel synthesis** produces a primary amine from a corresponding alkyl halide. (Section 22.4)
- A **haloform reaction** converts a methyl ketone ($RCOCH_3$) into a carboxylic acid (RCO_2H). The CH_3 group is an unsuitable leaving group, but under the conditions of the reaction, it is first converted into CX_3 (X = Cl, Br, or I), which is a suitable leaving group. Subsequent acyl substitution involving HO^- as the nucleophile produces an initial carboxylic acid that is rapidly and irreversibly deprotonated under the basic conditions of the reaction. (Section 22.5)
- In an iodoform reaction, I_2 reacts with a methyl ketone under basic conditions to produce a carboxylic acid and iodoform, HCI_3, a yellow solid. Thus, the iodoform reaction is a laboratory test for methyl ketones. (Section 22.5)
- $NaBH_4$ readily reduces high-energy acid derivatives, such as acid chlorides (RCOCl) and acid anhydrides (RCO_2COR), to primary alcohols. Esters, which are significantly more stable, are reduced to primary alcohols slowly. All of these reactions proceed through an aldehyde intermediate, which is reduced in a second reduction step to the alcohol. (Sections 22.6 and 22.6a)
- $LiAlH_4$ is a more powerful reducing agent than $NaBH_4$ and can thus reduce acid chlorides, acid anhydrides, and esters to primary alcohols. (Section 22.6b)
- $LiAlH_4$ reduces carboxylic acids (RCO_2H) to primary alcohols and reduces amides ($RCONR_2$) to amines (RCH_2NR_2). These reactions are facilitated by the strong O—Al bond that forms in the mechanism. (Section 22.6b)
- **Diisobutylaluminum hydride (DIBAH** or **DIBAL-H)** and **lithium tri-*tert*-butoxyaluminum hydride (LTBA)** are two specialized reducing agents that can be used to reduce an acid derivative to an aldehyde. DIBAH reduces an ester to an aldehyde, whereas LTBA reduces an acid chloride to an aldehyde. (Section 22.7)
- When an acid derivative such as an acid chloride, acid anhydride, or ester is treated with an alkyllithium reagent (RLi) or a Grignard reagent (R′MgX), R'^- adds twice to produce a tertiary alcohol. (Section 22.8)
- When an acid chloride (RCOCl) is treated with a lithium dialkylcuprate (R'_2CuLi), R'^- adds once to produce a ketone. (Section 22.8)

Reaction Tables

Functional group transformations introduced in this chapter are collected in Table 22-2, and reactions introduced in this chapter that alter the carbon skeleton are collected in Table 22-3.

TABLE 22-2 Functional Group Transformations

	Starting Compound Class	Typical Reagents and Reaction Conditions	Compound Class Formed	Key Electron-Rich Species	Key Electron-Poor Species	Comments	Discussed in Section
(1)	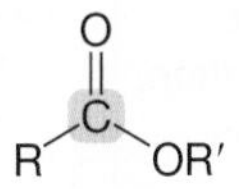 Ester	NaOR″ →	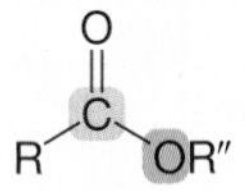 Ester	$^{\ominus}$OR″	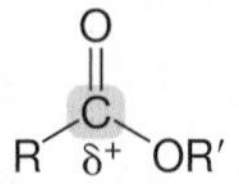	Nucleophilic addition–elimination (transesterification)	22.1a
(2)	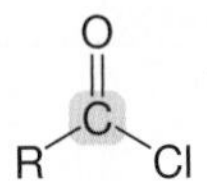 Acid chloride	LiOR′ →	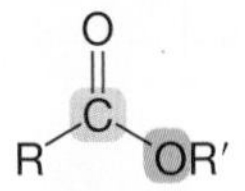 Ester	$^{\ominus}$OR′	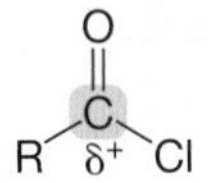	Nucleophilic addition–elimination	22.2
(3)	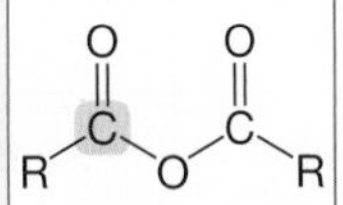 Acid anhydride	NaOR′ →	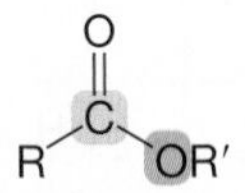 Ester	$^{\ominus}$OR′	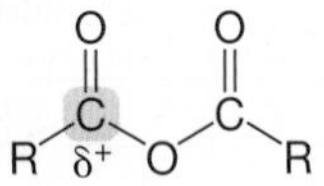	Nucleophilic addition–elimination	22.2
(4)	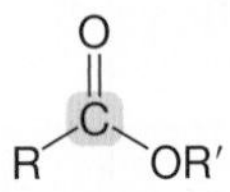 Ester	LiNR″$_2$ →	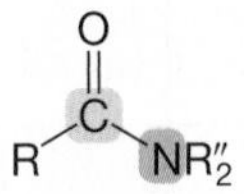 Amide	$^{\ominus}$NR″$_2$	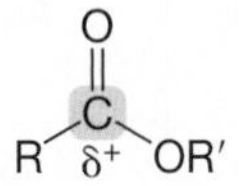	Nucleophilic addition–elimination	22.2
(5)	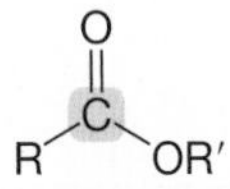 Ester	1. NaOH 2. HCl →	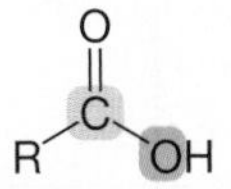 Carboxylic acid	$^{\ominus}$OH	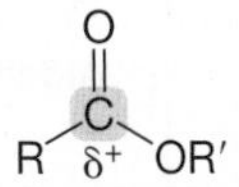	Nucleophilic addition–elimination (saponification)	22.3
(6)	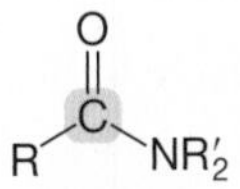 Amide	1. NaOH 2. HCl →	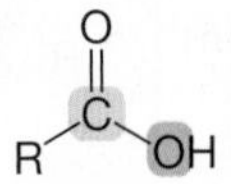 Carboxylic acid	$^{\ominus}$OH	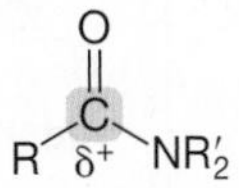	Nucleophilic addition–elimination	22.4
(7)	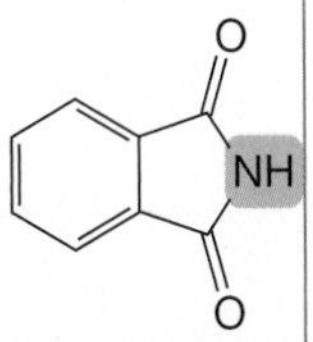 Phthalimide	1. KOH/EtOH 2. RBr 3. KOH/H_2O →	H_2N—R 1° Amine	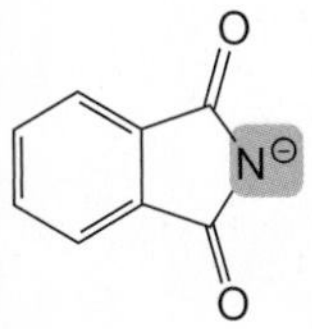	δ^+ R—Br	S_N2, then nucleophilic addition–elimination (Gabriel synthesis)	22.4
(8)	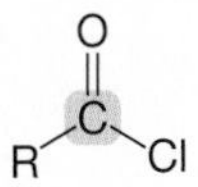 Acid chloride	1. $NaBH_4$ or $LiAlH_4$ 2. HCl →	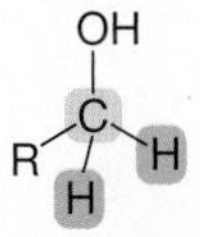 1° Alcohol	$^{\ominus}$H Hydride anion	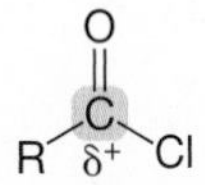	Nucleophilic addition–elimination, then addition (reduction)	22.6

(continued)

TABLE 22-2 Functional Group Transformations (continued)

	Starting Compound Class	Typical Reagents and Reaction Conditions	Compound Class Formed	Key Electron-Rich Species	Key Electron-Poor Species	Comments	Discussed in Section
(9)	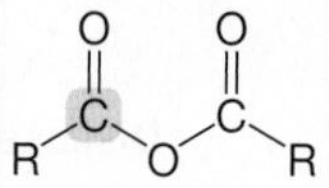 Acid anhydride	1. $NaBH_4$ or $LiAlH_4$ 2. HCl	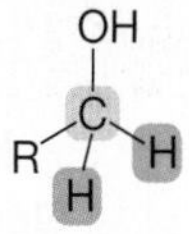 1° Alcohol	$^{\ominus}H$ Hydride anion	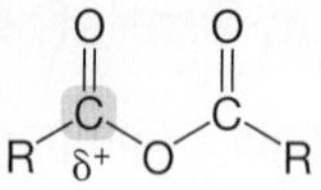	Nucleophilic addition–elimination, then addition (reduction)	22.6
(10)	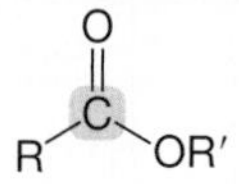 Ester	1. $NaBH_4$ or $LiAlH_4$ 2. HCl	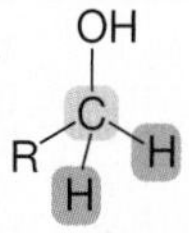 1° Alcohol	$^{\ominus}H$ Hydride anion	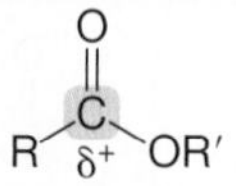	Nucleophilic addition–elimination, then addition (reduction); very slow with $NaBH_4$	22.6
(11)	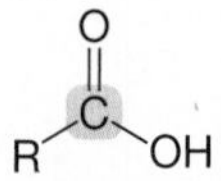 Carboxylic acid	1. $LiAlH_4$ 2. HCl	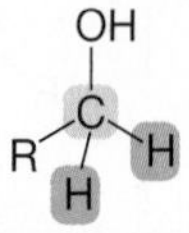 1° Alcohol	$^{\ominus}H$ Hydride anion	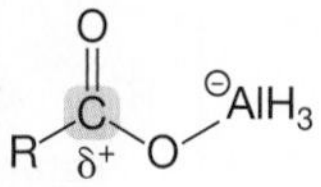	Nucleophilic addition–elimination, then addition (reduction)	22.6
(12)	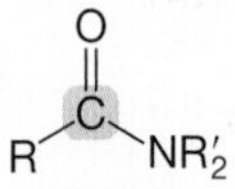 Amide	$LiAlH_4$ Ether	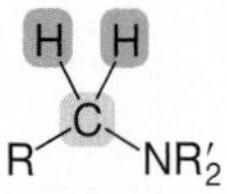 Amine	$^{\ominus}H$ Hydride anion	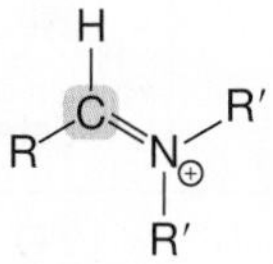	Nucleophilic addition–elimination, then addition (reduction)	22.6
(13)	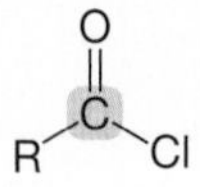 Acid chloride	$LiAlH(O\text{-}t\text{-}Bu)_3$ −75 °C	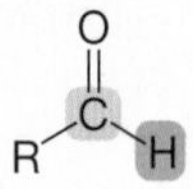 Aldehyde	$^{\ominus}H$ Hydride anion	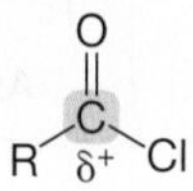	Nucleophilic addition–elimination (reduction); note cold *T*	22.7
(14)	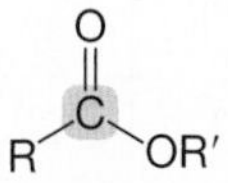 Ester	1. DIBAH −78 °C 2. HCl	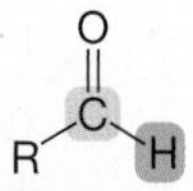 Aldehyde	$^{\ominus}H$ Hydride anion	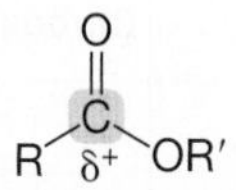	Nucleophilic addition–elimination (reduction); note cold *T*	22.7

TABLE 22-3 Reactions That Alter the Carbon Skeleton[a]

	Starting Compound Class	Typical Reagents and Reaction Conditions	Compound Class Formed	Key Electron-Rich Species	Key Electron-Poor Species	Comments	Discussed in Section
(1)	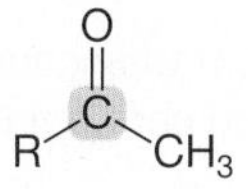 Methyl ketone	1. X_2 (excess), NaOH → 2. HCl	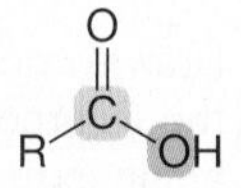 Carboxylic acid	$^{\ominus}OH$	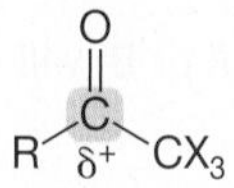	Halogenation, then nucleophilic addition–elimination (haloform reaction)	22.5
(2)	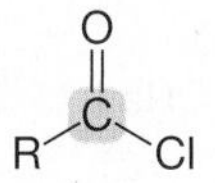 Acid chloride	1. R′—Li or R′—MgX → 2. HCl	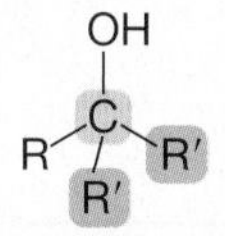 3° Alcohol	$^{\ominus}R'$	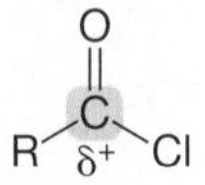	Nucleophilic addition–elimination, then addition (alkyllithium or Grignard reaction)	22.8
(3)	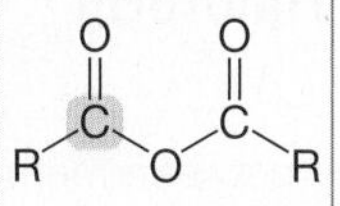 Acid anhydride	1. R′—Li or R′—MgX → 2. HCl	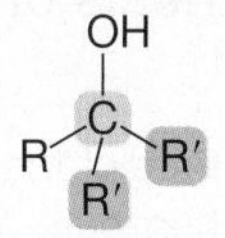 3° Alcohol	$^{\ominus}R'$	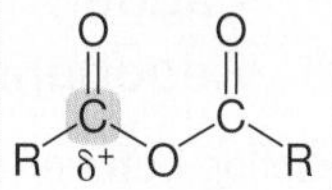	Nucleophilic addition–elimination, then addition (alkyllithium or Grignard reaction)	22.8
(4)	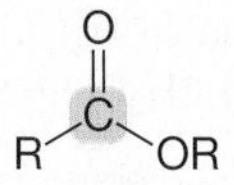 Ester	1. R′—Li or R′—MgX → 2. HCl	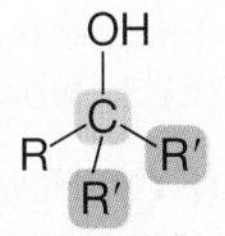 3° Alcohol	$^{\ominus}R'$	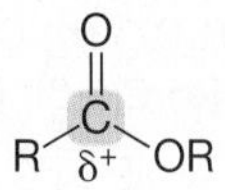	Nucleophilic addition–elimination, then addition (alkyllithium or Grignard reaction)	22.8
(5)	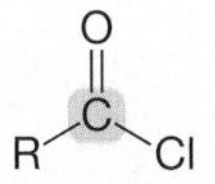 Acid chloride	R'_2CuLi →	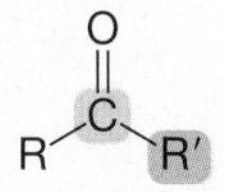 Ketone	$^{\ominus}R'$	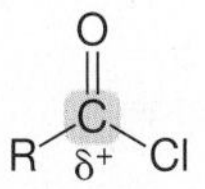	Nucleophilic addition–elimination	22.8

[a]X = Cl, Br, or I.

Problems

Problems that are related to synthesis are denoted (SYN).

Sections 22.1 and 22.3 Transesterification and Saponification

22.1 Predict the product for the reaction between methyl cyclohexylmethanoate and each of the following. If no reaction is expected to occur, write "no reaction." For each reaction that does occur, draw the complete, detailed mechanism. **(a)** NaOH, then H_3O^+; **(b)** $CH_3CH_2CH_2ONa$, $CH_3CH_2CH_2OH$; **(c)** C_6H_5OK, C_6H_5OH

22.2 Which products in Problem 22.1 will produce methyl cyclohexylmethanoate when treated with $NaOCH_3$?

22.3 Draw an energy diagram for each reaction in Problem 22.1, paying attention to the relative energies of the overall reactants, overall products, and any intermediates.

22.4 Draw the mechanism for each of the following reactions, and predict the major organic product in each.

(a)

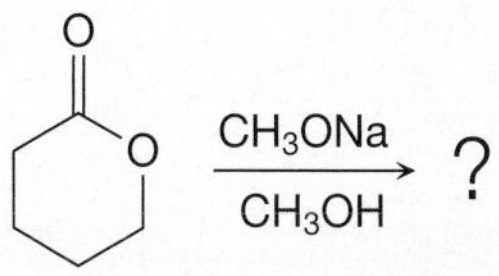
O
O
CH3ONa
CH3OH
?

(b)

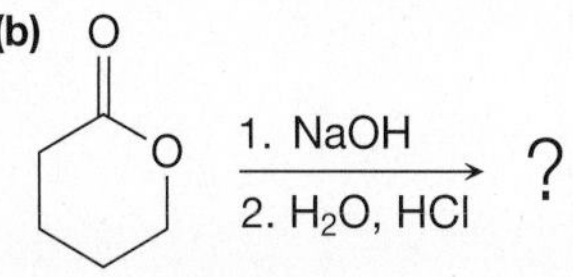
O
O
1. NaOH
2. H2O, HCl
?

22.5 **(SYN)** Show how to carry out each of the following transformations.

(a)

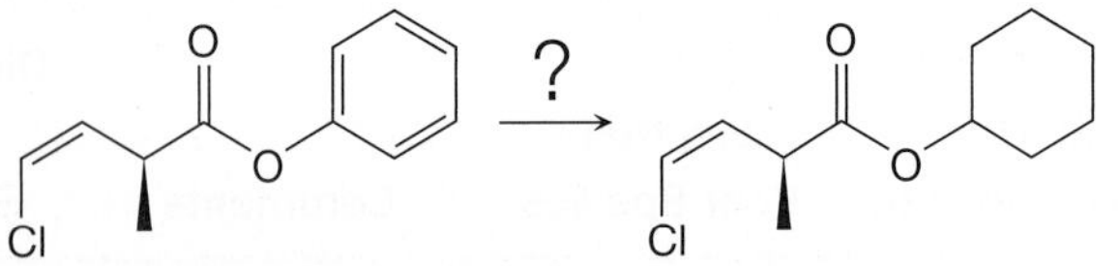

(b)

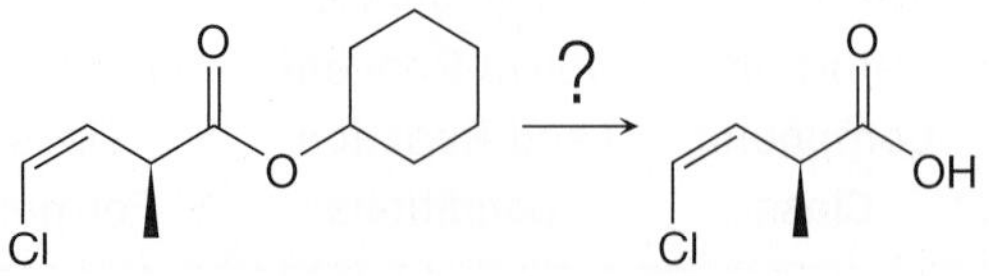

22.6 Which of the following esters, **A** or **B**, will undergo saponification faster? Why?

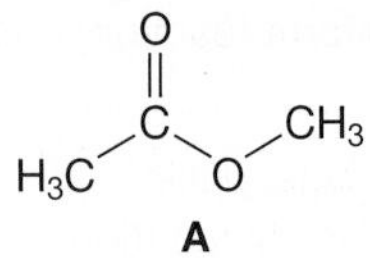

A

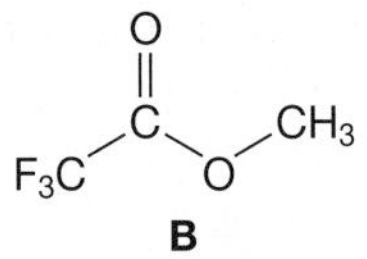

B

22.7 Draw a complete, detailed mechanism to account for the incorporation of ^{18}O twice into the carboxylate anion in the reaction shown here.

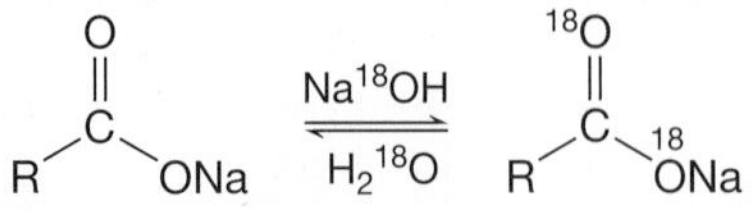

Sections 22.2, 22.4, and 22.5 Interconverting Carboxylic Acid Derivatives and the Stability Ladder; The Gabriel Synthesis of Primary Amines; Haloform Reactions

22.8 Predict the product for the reaction between *m*-ethylbenzoyl chloride and each of the following. Draw the complete, detailed mechanism for each reaction. If no reaction is expected to occur, write "no reaction." **(a)** NaOH, then H_3O^+; **(b)** CH_3NHLi; **(c)** CH_3CH_2OK; **(d)** $C_6H_5CO_2K$; **(e)** CH_3Cl; **(f)** CH_3OCH_3

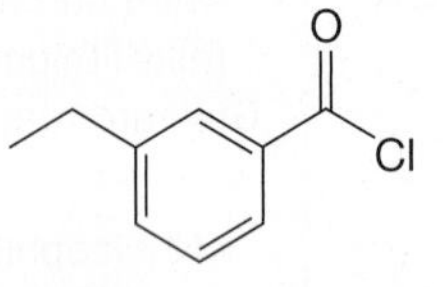

***m*-Ethylbenzoyl chloride**

22.9 Predict the product for the reaction between acetic anhydride and each of the following. If no reaction is expected to occur, write "no reaction." For those reactions that do occur, draw the complete, detailed mechanism. **(a)** NaOH, then H_3O^+; **(b)** CH_3NHLi; **(c)** CH_3CH_2OK; **(d)** $C_6H_5CO_2K$; **(e)** NaBr; **(f)** $CH_3CH_2OCH_2CH_3$; **(g)** 3-chloropentane; **(h)** hexanal

22.10 Predict the product for the reaction between methyl benzoate and each of the following. If no reaction is expected to occur, write "no reaction." For those reactions that do occur, draw the complete, detailed mechanism. **(a)** NaBr; **(b)** $NaN(CH_3)_2$; **(c)** 3-chloropentane; **(d)** hexanal; **(e)** CH_3Cl

22.11 **(SYN)** How would you carry out the following transformation?

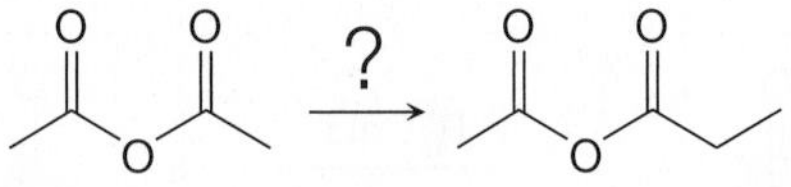

22.12 **(SYN)** Show how to carry out each of the following transformations.

(a)

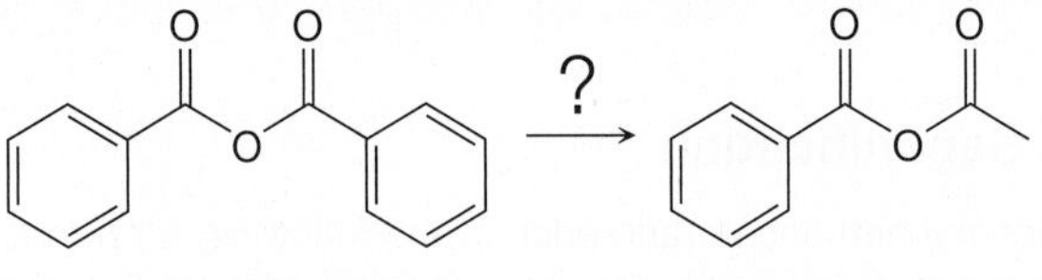

(b)

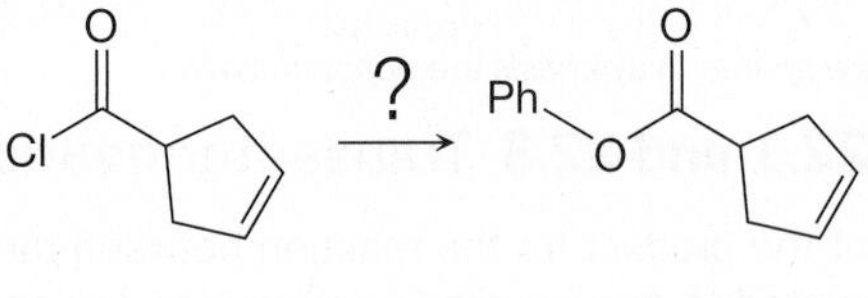

(c)

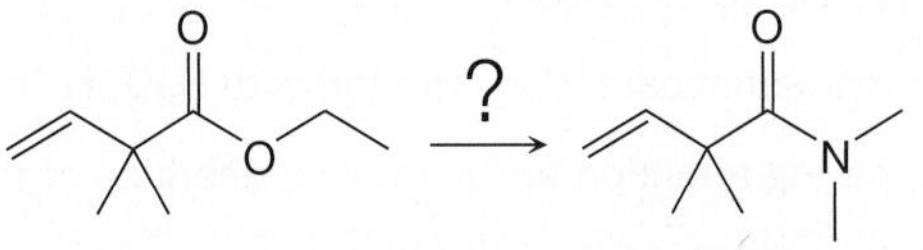

(d)

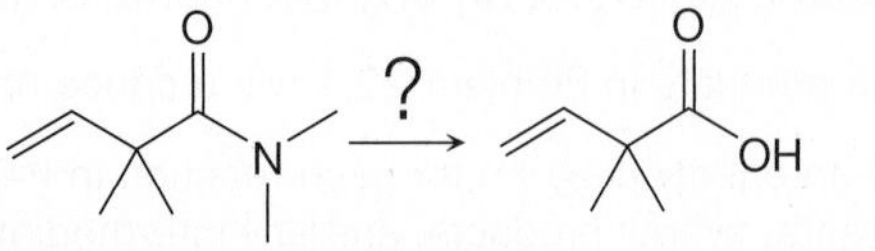

22.13 *N,N*-Diacylamides can be prepared by treating an acyl chloride with lithium nitride in a 3:1 ratio. Draw a complete, detailed mechanism for this reaction.

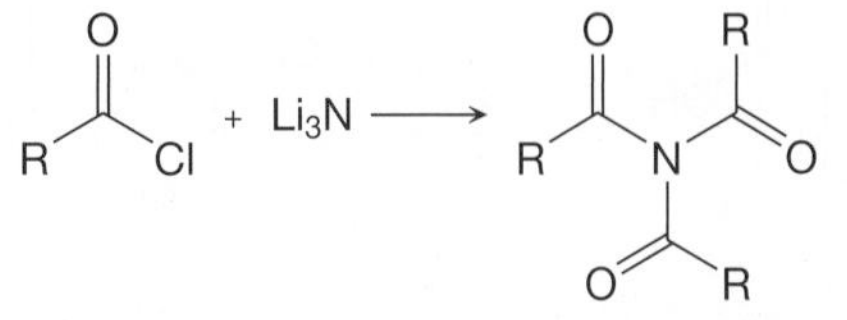
O
R
Cl
+ Li_3N
O
R
R
N
O
O
R

An *N,N*-diacylamide

22.14 Barbituric acid can be prepared from malonic ester and urea as follows. Provide a complete, detailed mechanism for this reaction.

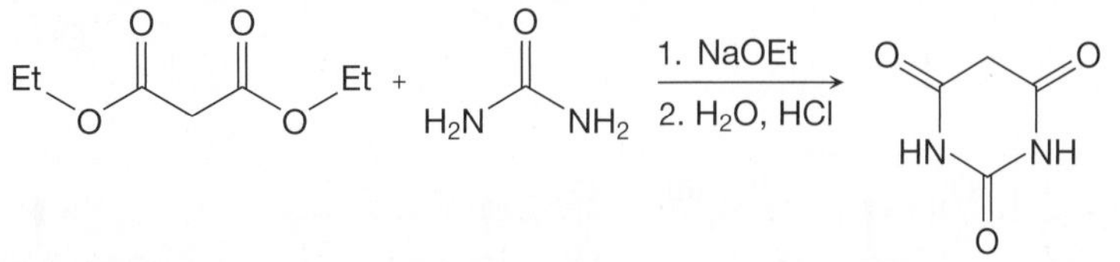
Et
O
O
O
O
Et
+
O
H_2N
NH_2
1. NaOEt
2. H_2O, HCl
O
O
HN
NH
O

Barbituric acid

22.15 Which of the following compounds will form a yellow solid when dissolved in a basic, aqueous solution of I_2? **(a)** butanoic acid; **(b)** pentan-2-one; **(c)** pentan-3-one; **(d)** cyclohexanone; **(e)** pentanal

22.16 **(SYN)** Show how to synthesize each of the following amines from an alkyl halide via a Gabriel synthesis.

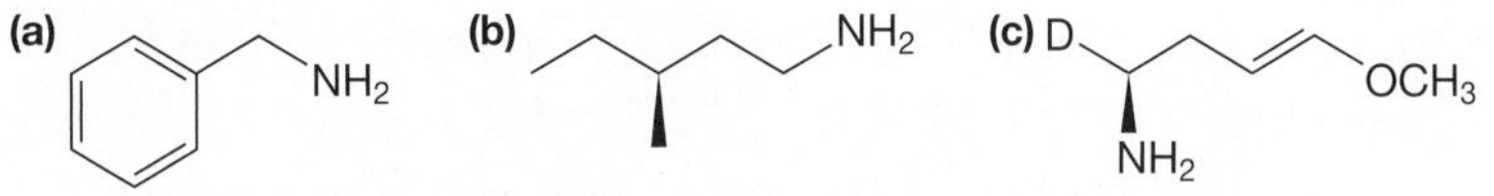
(a)
NH_2
(b)
NH_2
(c) D
OCH_3
NH_2

22.17 In a Gabriel synthesis, the yield of the amine can be compromised when hydrolysis is carried out under conditions that are too basic. The problem, in particular, is with the second hydrolysis (Steps 6–8 in Equation 22-14, p. 1067), not the first (Steps 3–5). Explain why.

Sections 22.6–22.8 Reactions with Hydride Reducing Agents and Organometallic Reagents

22.18 Predict the product for the reaction between *m*-ethylbenzoyl chloride (see Problem 22.8) and each of the following. Draw the complete, detailed mechanism for each reaction. If no reaction is expected to occur, write "no reaction." **(a)** $(CH_3CH_2)_2CuLi$; **(b)** $LiAlH(O\text{-}t\text{-}Bu)_3$, −75 °C; **(c)** $NaBH_4$, EtOH; **(d)** C_6H_5MgBr (excess), then H^+

22.19 Predict the product for the reaction between methyl benzoate and each of the following. If no reaction is expected to occur, write "no reaction." For those reactions that do occur, draw the complete, detailed mechanism. **(a)** $LiAlH_4$, then H_3O^+; **(b)** $CH_3CH_2CH_2Li$ (excess), then H_3O^+; **(c)** $(CH_3CH_2)_2CuLi$; **(d)** C_6H_5MgBr (excess), then H^+; **(e)** DIBAH, then H_3O^+

22.20 Predict the product for each of the following reactions. If no reaction is expected to occur, write "no reaction." For those reactions that do occur, draw the complete, detailed mechanism.

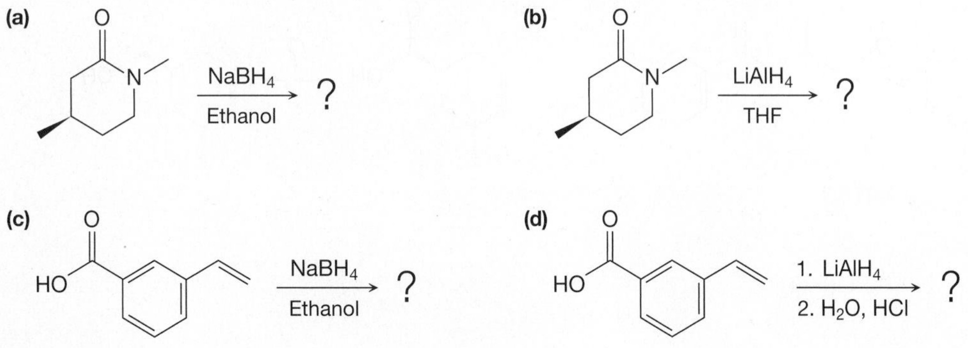
(a)
O
N
$NaBH_4$
Ethanol
?
(b)
O
N
$LiAlH_4$
THF
?
(c)
O
HO
$NaBH_4$
Ethanol
?
(d)
O
HO
1. $LiAlH_4$
2. H_2O, HCl
?

22.21 **(SYN)** Propose a synthesis for the following transformation.

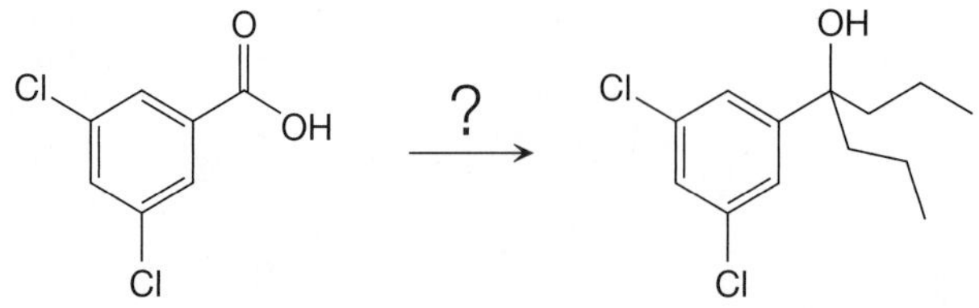

22.22 **(SYN)** Show how to carry out each of the following transformations.

(a)

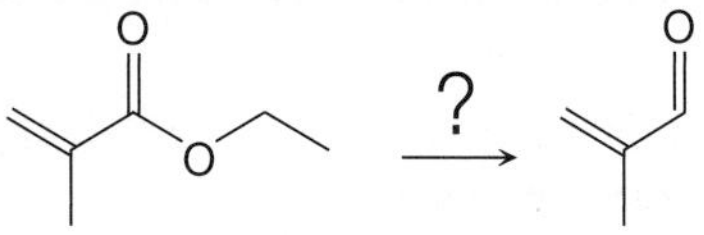

(b)

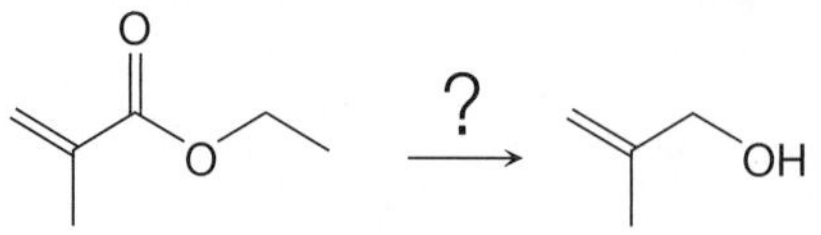

(c)

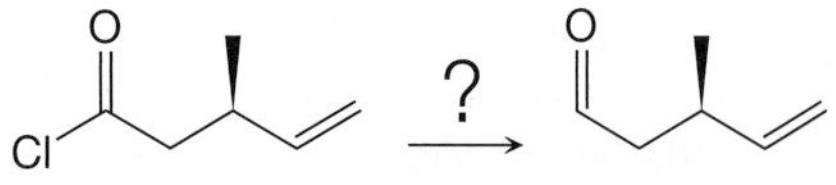

(d)

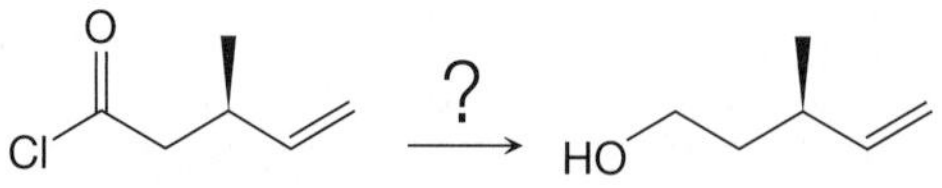

22.23 **(SYN)** Show how to carry out each of the following transformations.

(a)

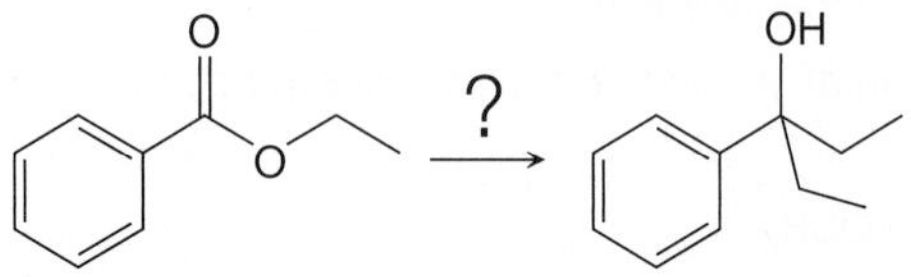

(b)

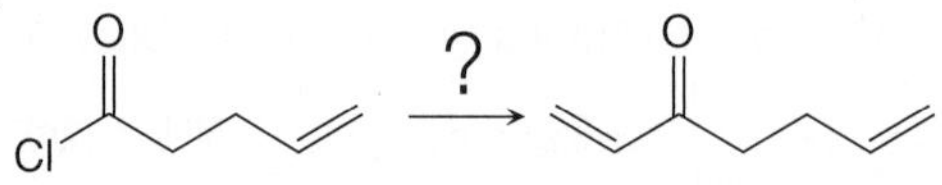

(c)

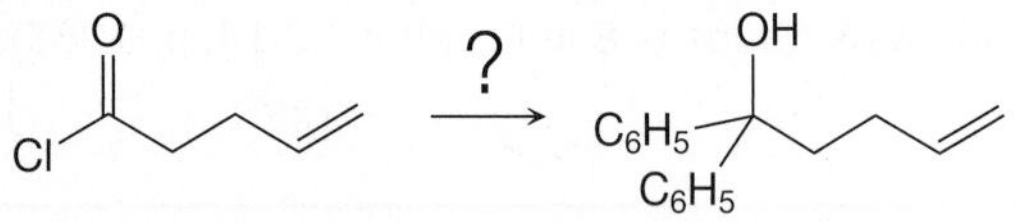

(d)

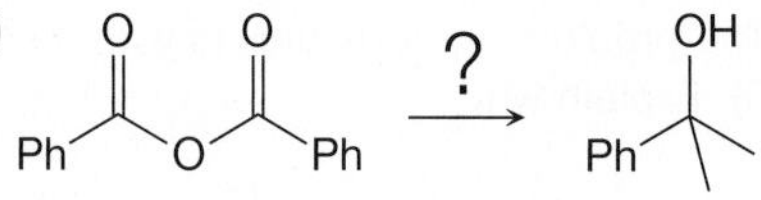

22.24 **(SYN)** How would you carry out the following transformation?

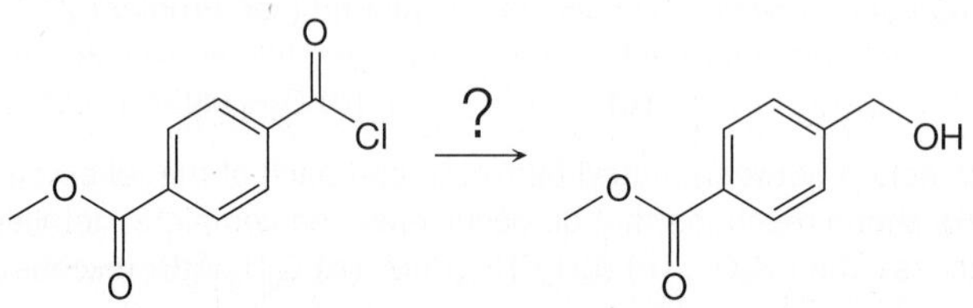

22.25 **(SYN)** How would you carry out each of the following transformations?

(a)

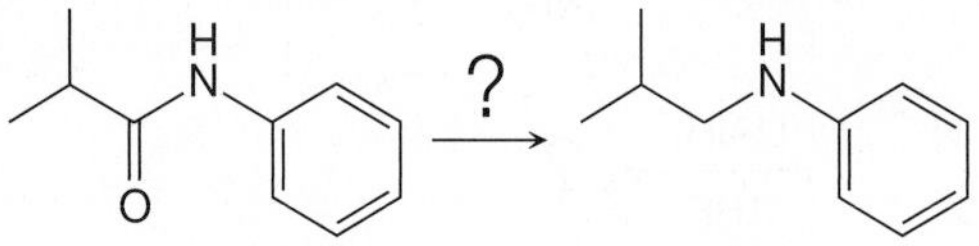

(b)

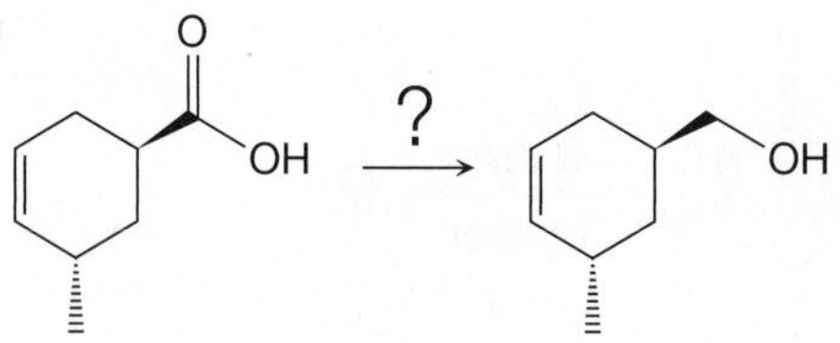

Integrated Problems

22.26 Predict the product of the following sequence of reactions.

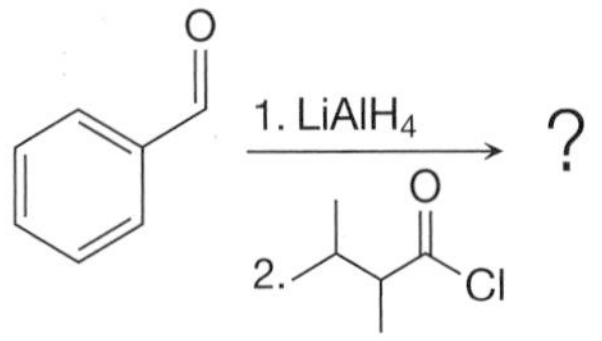

22.27 Shown here is a proposed synthesis of a thioester from an ester. **(a)** Draw the mechanism for this reaction. **(b)** Would this reaction be energetically favorable? Why or why not?

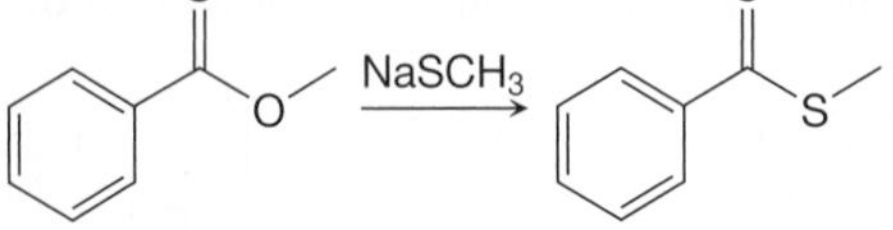

22.28 For thousands of years, civilizations have been synthesizing soap by heating animal fat with wood ash, a source of HO^-. Animal fat consists of triesters, known as triglycerides, an example of which is shown here on the left.

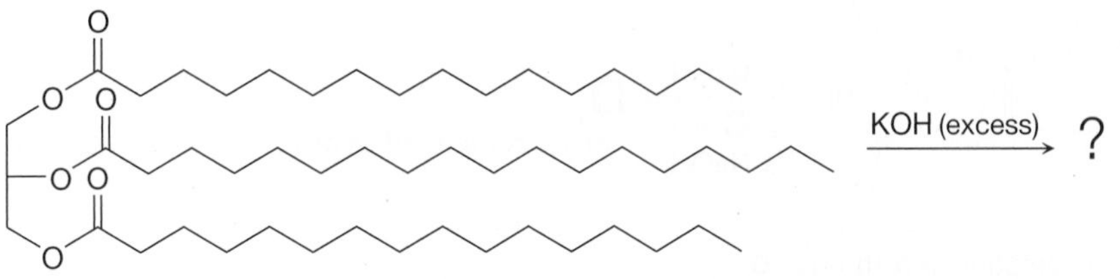

(a) Assuming that the triglyceride reacts completely with HO^-, what are the products of this reaction?
(b) Draw the complete, detailed mechanism that leads to those products.
(c) Explain how those products can serve as soap. *Hint*: See the special interest box on page 99.

22.29 Enamines can react with acyl chlorides via nucleophilic addition–elimination, such as in the synthesis of the following 1,3-diketone. Provide a complete, detailed mechanism for this transformation.

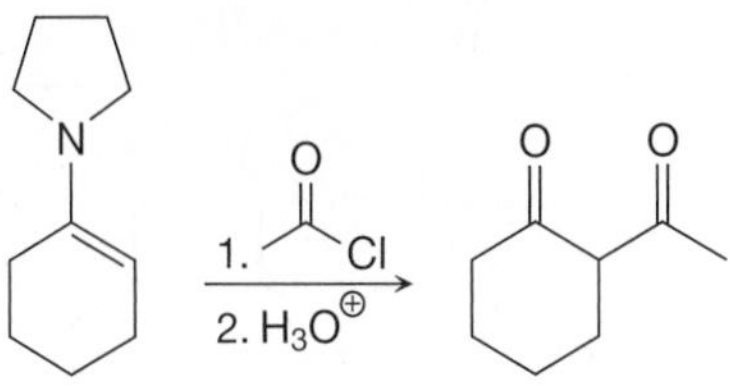

22.30 Amidines have the general form 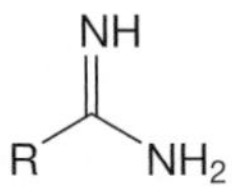, so they are nitrogen analogs of carboxylic acids. As shown here, they can be hydrolyzed under basic conditions to form amides. Propose a mechanism showing the conversion of an amidine to an amide.

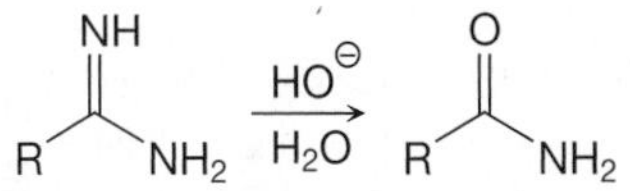

22.31 **(a)** Propose a mechanism for reaction **A**, which is a substitution reaction. **(b)** Explain why reaction **B** does not lead to a similar substitution.

A

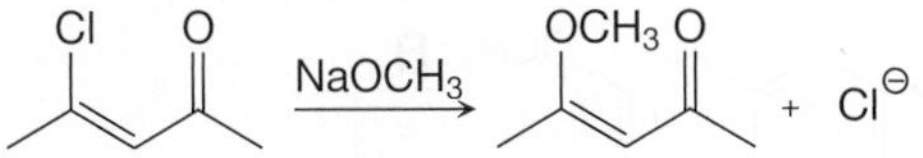

B

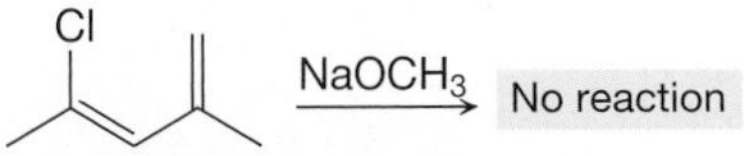

22.32 Propose a mechanism for the following reaction.

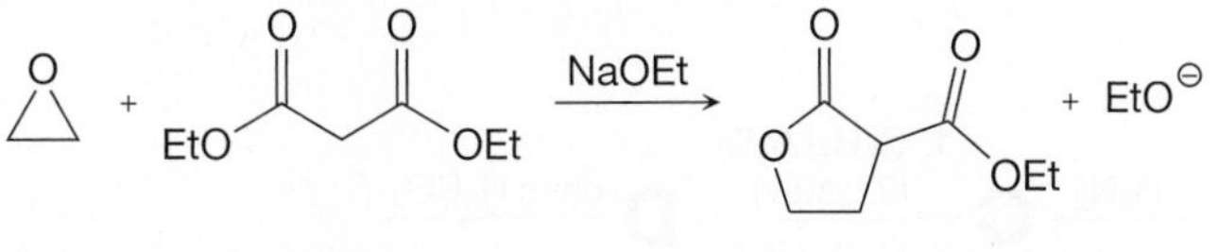

22.33 If a lactam (cyclic amide) contains an alkyl group with an amino group, treatment with lithium diisopropylamide (LDA) results in a ring-expanded lactam, as shown here. Provide a detailed mechanism for this reaction.

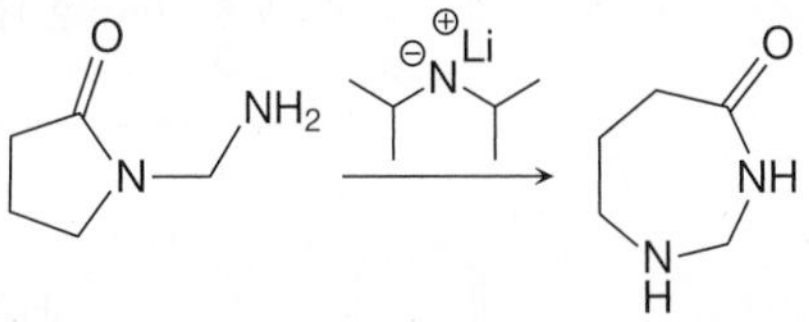

22.34 Draw the complete, detailed mechanism for the following reaction.

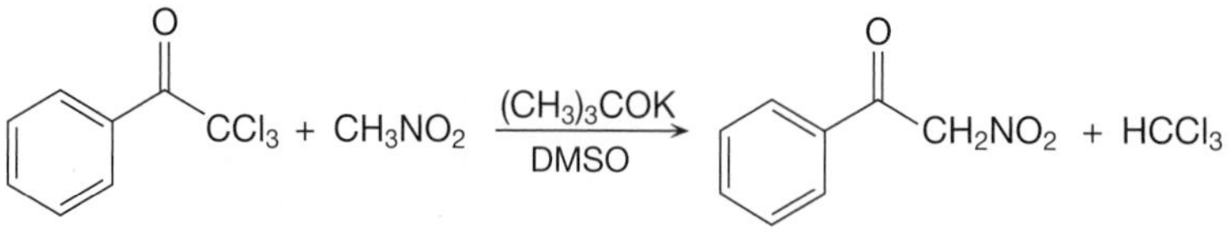

22.35 Supply the missing compounds **A** through **D**.

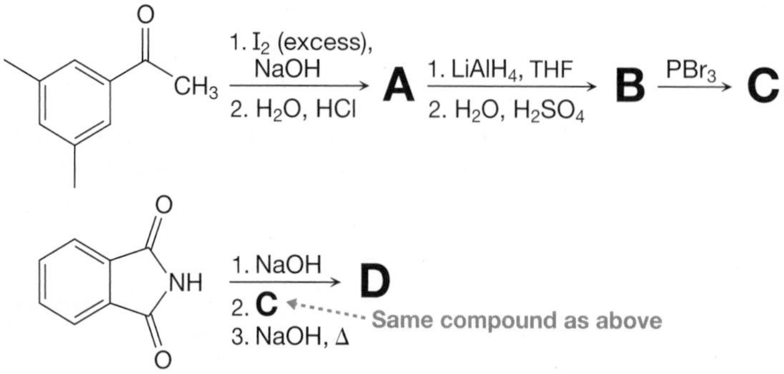

22.36 Supply the missing compounds **A** through **G**.

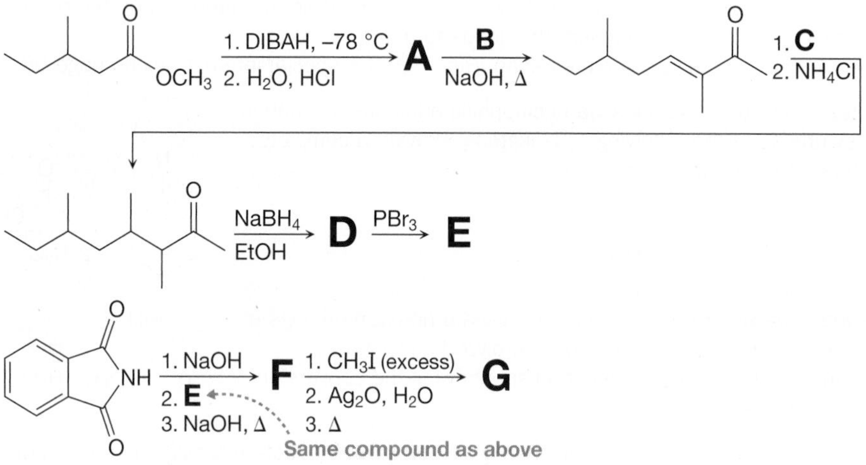

22.37 Supply the missing compounds **A** through **D**.

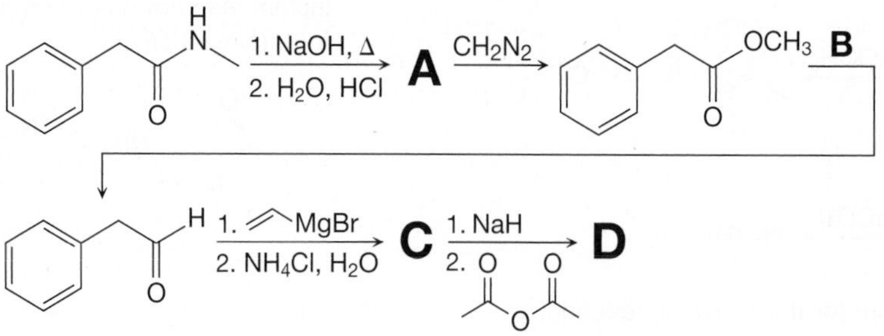

22.38 Supply the missing compounds **A** through **G**.

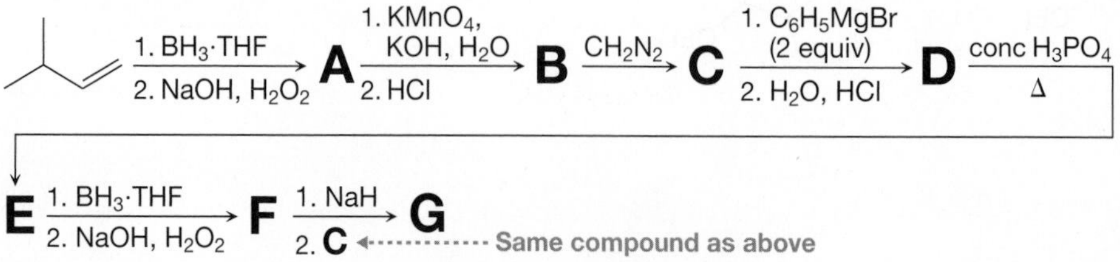

22.39 **(SYN)** Starting with acetyl chloride (CH_3COCl) and any other reagents necessary, how would you synthesize each of the following compounds?

(a)

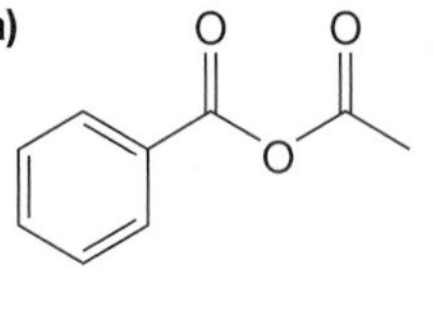

(b)

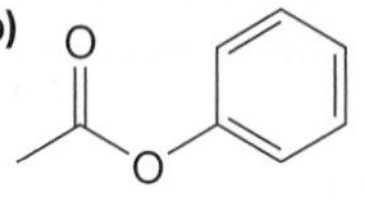

(c)

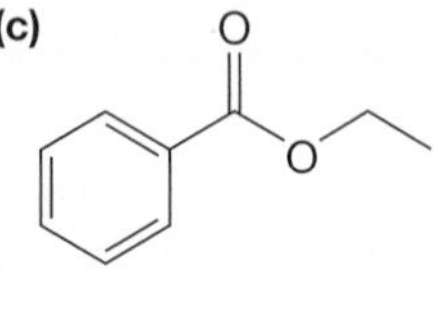

(d)

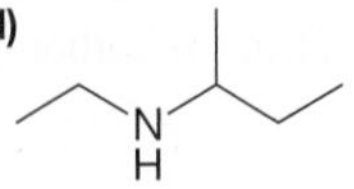

(e)

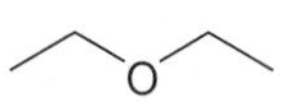

(f)

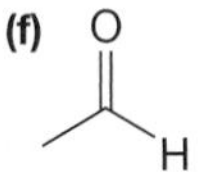

(g)

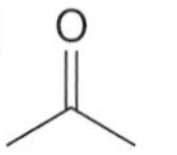

(h)

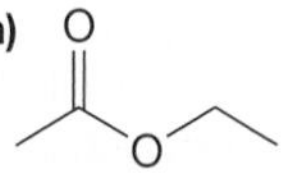

22.40 **(SYN)** Using acetyl chloride as your only source of carbon, propose a synthesis for each of the following compounds. You may use any inorganic reagents necessary. **(a)** butan-2-ol; **(b)** 3-methylpentan-3-ol; **(c)** butan-2-one; **(d)** ethanamine; **(e)** acetic anhydride

22.41 **(SYN)** Show how to synthesize the following molecule from any compounds containing two carbons. Draw the complete, detailed mechanism for the reaction.

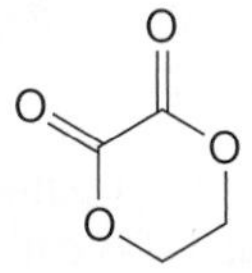

22.42 **(SYN)** Show how to synthesize 2,4-diphenylbut-2-ene using phenylethanoic acid (phenylacetic acid) as your only source of carbon atoms.

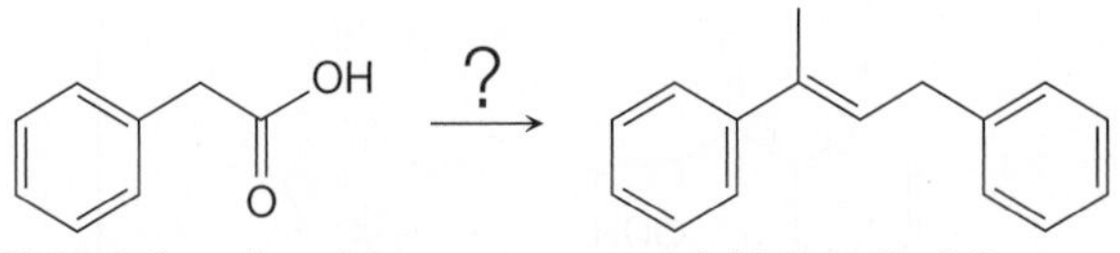
OH
?
O

Phenylethanoic acid (Phenylacetic acid) **2,4-Diphenylbut-2-ene**

22.43 A pain reliever has the formula $C_8H_9NO_2$. Its IR spectrum is as follows:

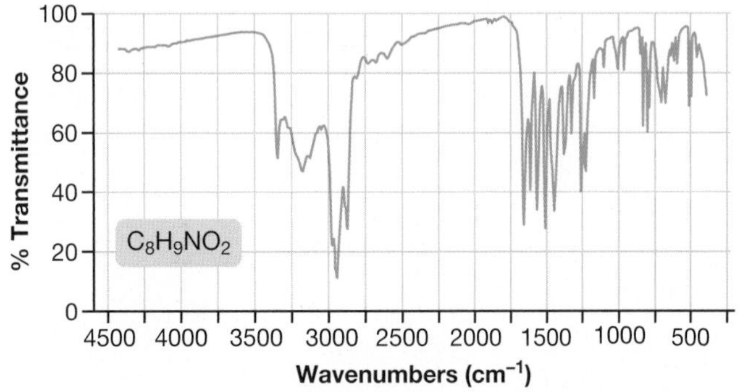
% Transmittance
100
80
60
40
20
0
$C_8H_9NO_2$
4500 4000 3500 3000 2500 2000 1500 1000 500
Wavenumbers (cm^{-1})

When it is heated in water under basic conditions, followed by an acid workup, two compounds are formed: acetic acid and a compound whose formula is C_6H_7NO and whose ^1H NMR spectrum is shown below. The ^{13}C NMR spectrum of C_6H_7NO has four signals. Draw the structure for this compound and for the pain reliever.

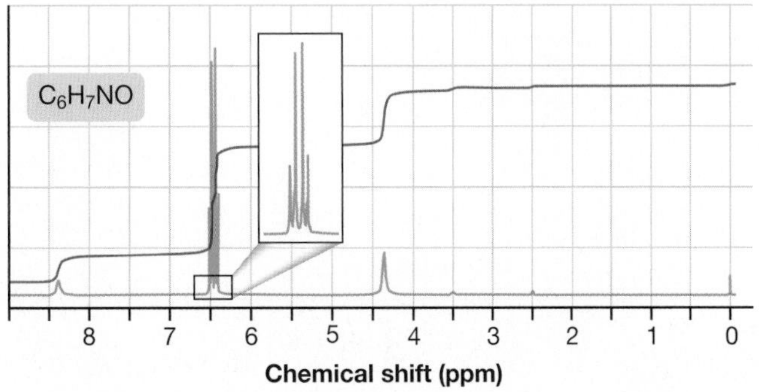
C_6H_7NO
8 7 6 5 4 3 2 1 0
Chemical shift (ppm)

22.44 When methyl 5-oxopentanoate is treated with vinyl Grignard, a compound is produced whose formula is $C_7H_{10}O_2$. In the IR spectrum of $C_7H_{10}O_2$, an intense absorption appears at 1740 cm^{-1}, and a weaker absorption appears at 1650 cm^{-1}. Seven signals appear in the ^{13}C NMR spectrum of $C_7H_{10}O_2$. The DEPT spectrum shows that there is one carbon that is bonded to no hydrogens, two CH carbons, and four CH_2 carbons. Draw the structure of $C_7H_{10}O_2$.

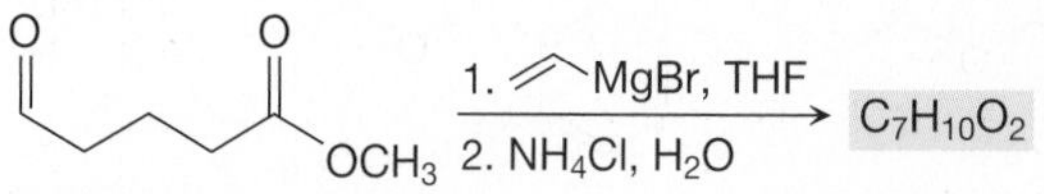

O
O
OCH3
1. MgBr, THF
2. NH4Cl, H2O
C7H10O2

Methyl 5-oxopentanoate

22.45 When dimethyl phthalate is treated with lithium aluminum hydride, a compound is produced whose ^1H NMR spectrum is shown below. Determine the product, and draw the complete, detailed mechanism of the reaction that produces it.

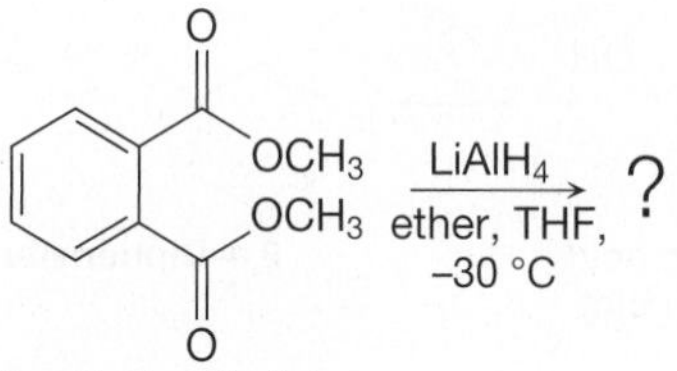

O
OCH3
OCH3
O
LiAlH4
ether, THF,
–30 °C
?

Dimethyl phthalate

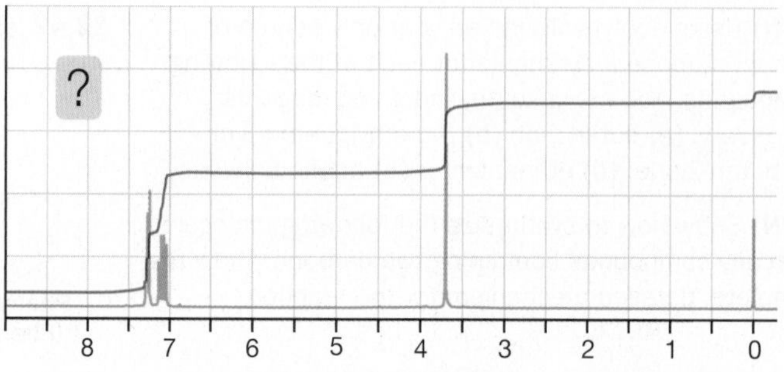

?
8
7
6
5
4
3
2
1
0
Chemical shift (ppm)

22.46 A compound whose molecular formula is $C_6H_{12}O$ produces a bright yellow solid when it is treated with excess iodine and a basic solution of water. The IR spectrum of the compound shows a distinct peak at 1708 cm^{-1}. Its ^1H NMR spectrum contains only two singlets: one at 1.2 ppm and one at 2.2 ppm. Integration shows that the upfield signal has three times the area of the downfield signal. **(a)** Draw the structure for this molecule. **(b)** Draw the products of the reaction that is described.

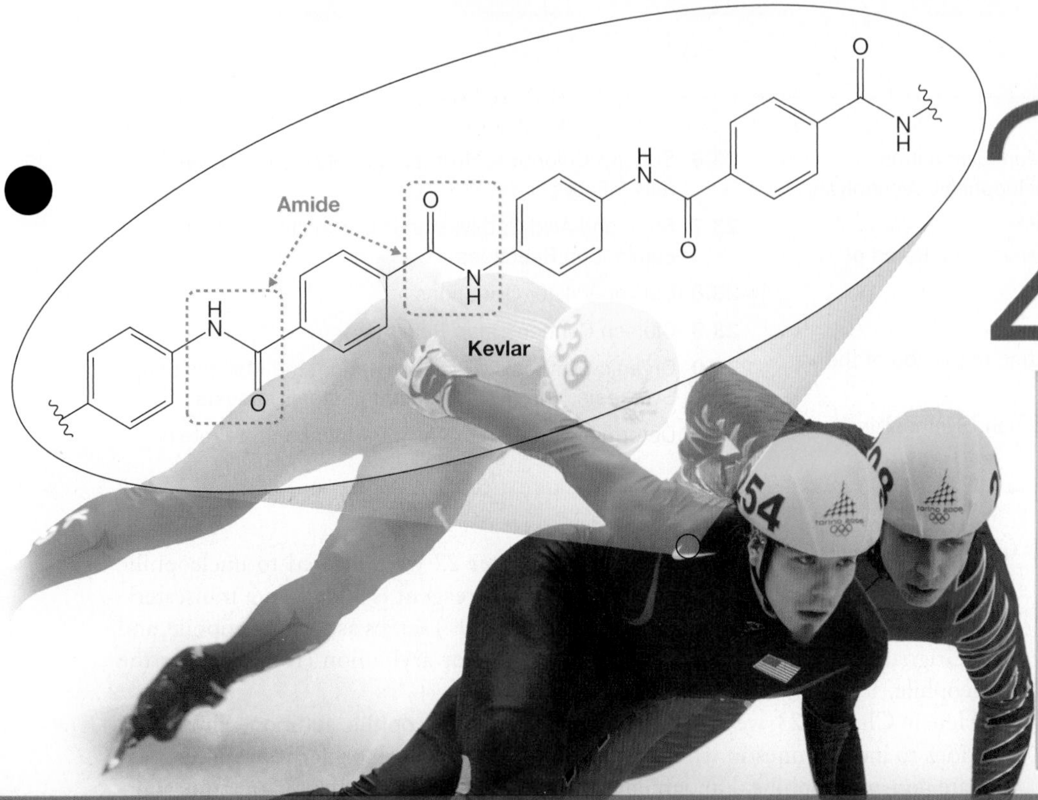
Amide
Kevlar

23

The blades used in speed skating are *very* sharp. To protect against being cut by the blade from another skater, skaters wear a cut-proof suit made of Kevlar—the same strong, lightweight flexible material commonly used to make body armor. Kevlar is produced from an aminolysis reaction, a type of nucleophilic addition–elimination reaction that leads to the formation of amide groups, which we discuss here in Chapter 23.

Nucleophilic Addition–Elimination Reactions 2

Reagents That Are Weakly Nucleophilic or Non-nucleophilic

Chapter 22 discussed reactions that proceed by the nucleophilic addition–elimination mechanism:

General mechanism for nucleophilic addition–elimination

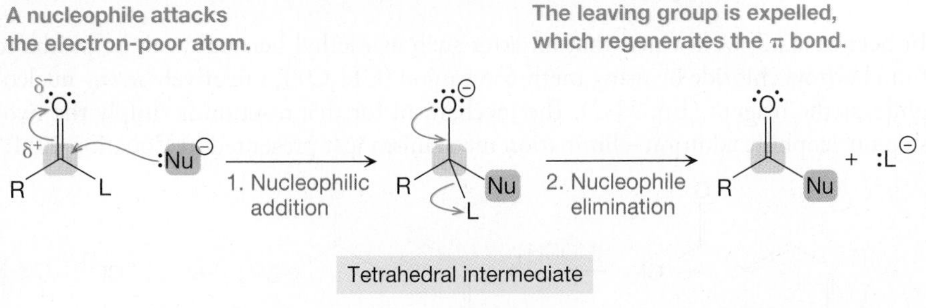
A nucleophile attacks the electron-poor atom.
The leaving group is expelled, which regenerates the π bond.
δ−
δ+
:Nu
R
L
1. Nucleophilic addition
Nu
2. Nucleophile elimination
+ :L
Tetrahedral intermediate
(23-1)

In Step 1, a nucleophile attacks the electrophilic atom of a polar π bond to generate an unstable tetrahedral intermediate. In Step 2, a leaving group is expelled from the tetrahedral intermediate, which regenerates the π bond.

Chapter Outline

The specific reactions we examined in Chapter 22 were limited to nucleophilic acyl substitutions in which a strongly nucleophilic reagent is added. In a transesterification reaction, for example, an alkoxide anion (RO^-) serves as the nucleophile, and in a Grignard reaction involving an ester, an alkyl or aryl anion (R^-) serves as the nucleophile.

Here in Chapter 23, we expand our discussion of nucleophilic addition–elimination reactions to include ones in which the nucleophiles are weak or derive from reagents that are non-nucleophilic. Fundamentally, the reactions in this chapter are quite similar to the ones in Chapter 22, but there are some key differences. For example, nucleophilic addition–elimination reactions involving weakly nucleophilic reagents tend to proceed much slower than ones involving strong nucleophiles, and as a result, they often require acid or base catalysis. Therefore, mechanisms that describe such reactions tend to consist of more steps.

Most of our discussion will concern reactions in which a nucleophile attacks the carbonyl carbon of a carboxylic acid derivative or a carboxylic acid, leading to acyl substitution. However, we will also examine reactions that involve nucleophilic attack at other polar bonds that have π character, such as S═O. Some reactions we will examine are functional group conversions, while others alter a molecule's carbon skeleton. Given this variety of reactions, it will be particularly important for you to maintain focus on the mechanism, so that you can see clearly how all of these reactions are related.

SECTION 23.1 OBJECTIVES

You will be able to:

1. Draw the mechanism and product for the reaction of an acid chloride with water or an alcohol.
2. Construct a free energy diagram for the reaction of an acid chloride with water or an alcohol.

23.1 The General Nucleophilic Addition–Elimination Mechanism Involving Weak Nucleophiles: Alcoholysis and Hydrolysis of Acid Chlorides

In Section 22.2, we learned that an ester such as methyl benzoate can be produced from benzoyl chloride by using methoxide anion (CH_3O^-), a relatively *strong* nucleophile, as the reagent (Eq. 23-2). The mechanism for this reaction is simply the two-step nucleophilic addition–elimination mechanism just presented in Equation 23-1:

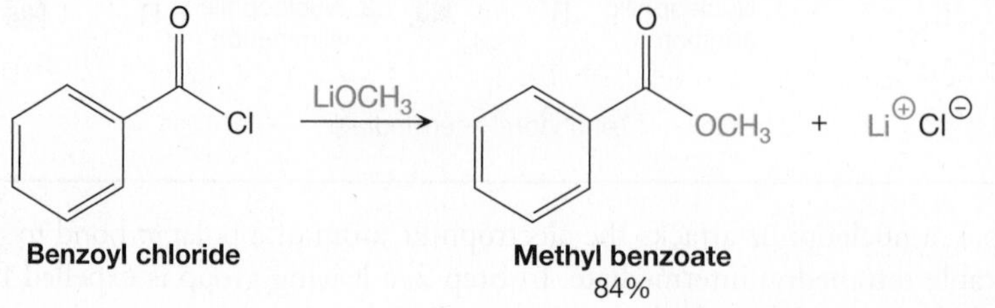

O
Cl
LiOCH3
OCH3
+ Li⊕Cl⊖
Benzoyl chloride
Methyl benzoate
84%

(23-2)

An ester can also be produced from an acid chloride by treating the acid chloride with an alcohol, a relatively *weak* nucleophile. An example is shown in Equation 23-3. Similarly, treating an acid chloride with water (another relatively weak nucleophile) produces a carboxylic acid, as shown in Equation 23-4.

An alcoholysis reaction

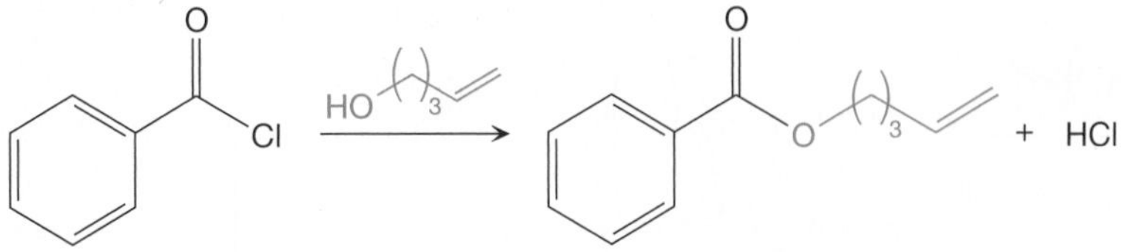

HO
3
3
+ HCl

(23-3)

Benzoyl chloride **4-Pentenyl benzoate** 71%

A hydrolysis reaction

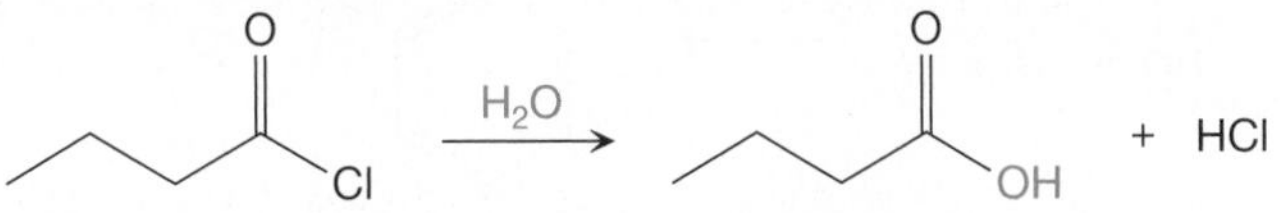

H_2O
+ HCl

(23-4)

Butanoyl chloride **Butanoic acid** 77%

> ◀ **RECALL**
>
> We have studied other reactions in which an alcohol or water is the species responsible for breaking bonds. Section 9.9 showed how an alcohol or water can serve as the nucleophile in an S_N1 reaction. Section 19.4 showed how acetals, imines, and enamines undergo hydrolysis when treated with aqueous acid.

Equation 23-3 is an example of **alcoholysis**, a reaction in which the addition of the alcohol results in the breaking of a bond (*lysis* in Greek means "breaking")—in this case, the C—Cl bond of the acid chloride. Equation 23-4 is an example of **hydrolysis** (see Recall box) because the bond in the acid chloride is broken as a result of the addition of water.

The mechanism for the hydrolysis of an acid chloride is shown in Equation 23-5. The mechanism for alcoholysis is essentially the same and is presented in Your Turn 23.1.

Mechanism for the hydrolysis of an acid chloride (Eq. 23-4)

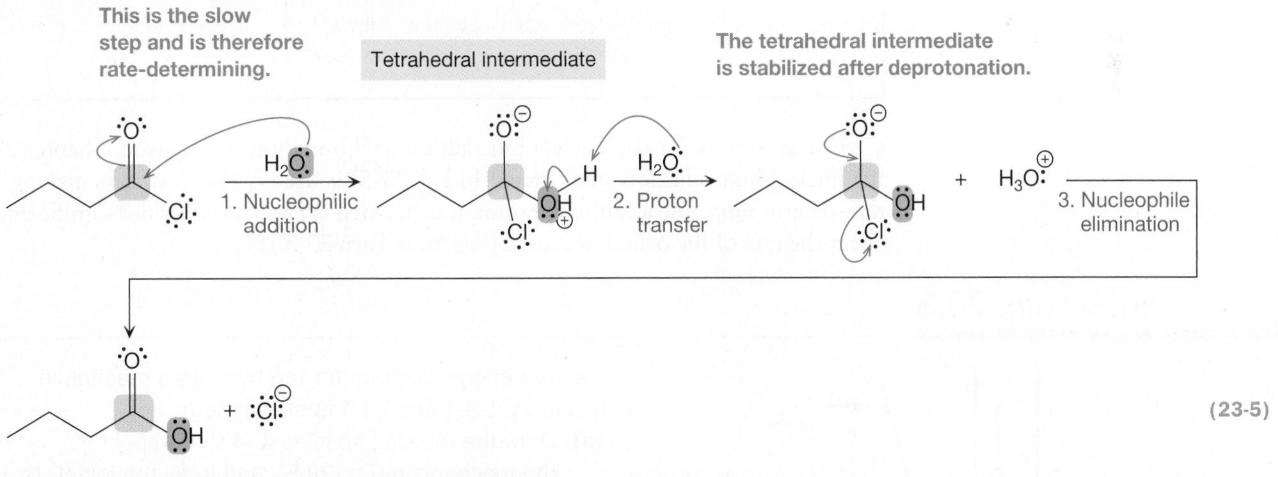

This is the slow step and is therefore rate-determining.
Tetrahedral intermediate
The tetrahedral intermediate is stabilized after deprotonation.
H_2O
1. Nucleophilic addition
H_2O
2. Proton transfer
+ H_3O^+
3. Nucleophile elimination

(23-5)

In Step 1 of Equation 23-5, H_2O attacks the carbonyl carbon to produce a tetrahedral intermediate. Unlike the general mechanism from Chapter 22, this tetrahedral intermediate contains an acidic proton that is rapidly deprotonated by another water molecule in Step 2. Finally, in Step 3, the Cl^- leaving group is expelled to re-form the carbonyl bond.

Notice that hydronium ion (H_3O^+) is produced in Step 2 of Equation 23-5, and chloride ion (Cl^-) is produced in Step 3. These species represent HCl appearing as a net product in water.

YOUR TURN 23.1

The mechanism for the alcoholysis reaction in Equation 23-3 is shown here, but the curved arrows have been omitted. Draw in the appropriate curved arrows, write the name of the elementary step below each reaction arrow, and identify the initial tetrahedral intermediate formed.

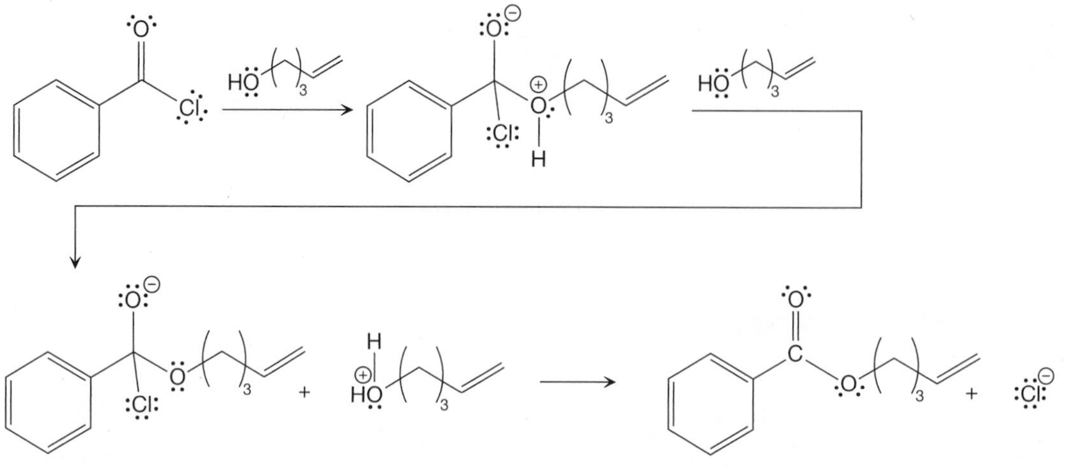

Answers to Your Turns are in the back of the book.

YOUR TURN 23.2

Draw the complete, detailed mechanism and predict the major organic product for each of the following reactions.

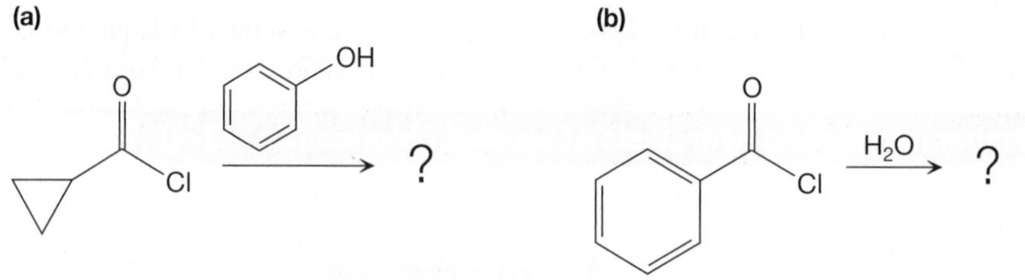

Just as we saw for the nucleophilic addition–elimination reactions in Chapter 22, the nucleophilic addition step (Step 1 in Eq. 23-5) is usually the slow step, making it rate-determining. The additional proton transfer step is fast, so it does not significantly affect the rate of the overall reaction. (See Your Turn 23.3.)

YOUR TURN 23.3

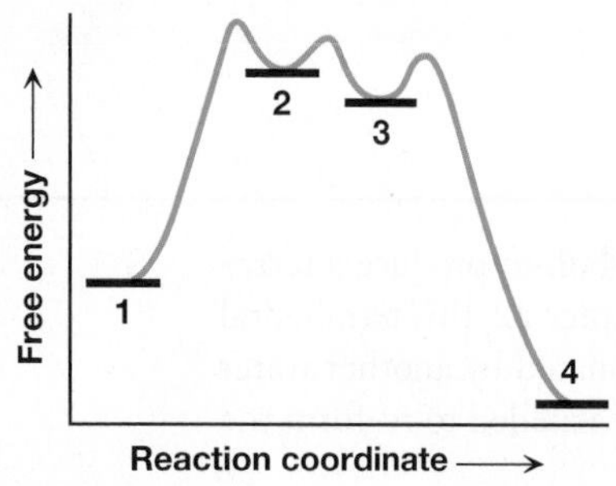
Free energy
Reaction coordinate
1
2
3
4

The free energy diagram for the hydrolysis reaction in Equations 23-4 and 23-5 is shown here.

(a) Draw the missing species **1–4** that appear in the mechanism (Eq. 23-5), and label the initial tetrahedral intermediate. *Hint*: Review Figure 22-4 (p. 1055).

(b) Explain how this diagram is consistent with the nucleophilic addition step being the slow step.

23.2 Relative Reactivities of Acid Derivatives: Rates of Hydrolysis

SECTION 23.2 OBJECTIVES

You will be able to:

1. Rank the carboxylic acid derivatives, aldehydes, and ketones in order of their reaction rate with a nucleophile.
2. Explain the relative reaction rates of carboxylic acid derivatives, aldehydes, and ketones.

Section 23.1 highlighted alcoholysis and hydrolysis reactions involving acid chlorides, but these reactions are not limited to just acid chlorides. As shown in Equations 23-6 and 23-7, acid anhydrides can readily undergo alcoholysis and hydrolysis, producing esters and carboxylic acids, respectively. The mechanisms for these reactions are essentially the same as the one in Equation 23-5 that describes the hydrolysis of an acid chloride.

Alcoholysis of an acid anhydride

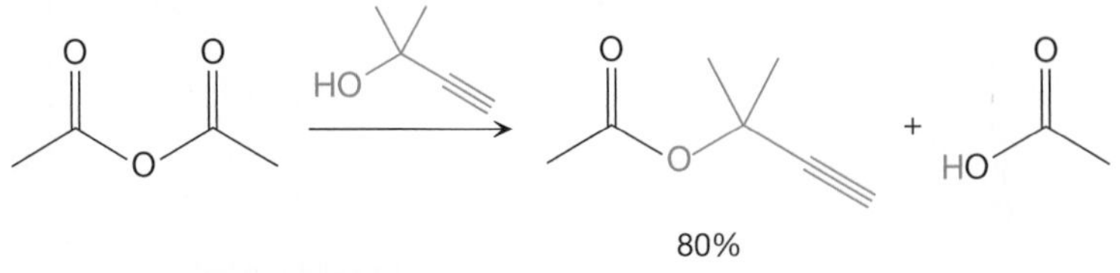

HO
80%
HO

(23-6)

Hydrolysis of an acid anhydride

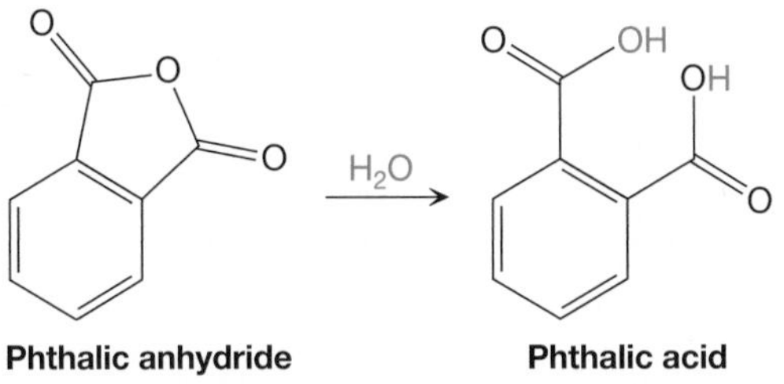

H_2O
OH
OH
Phthalic anhydride
Phthalic acid

(23-7)

YOUR TURN 23.4

Draw the complete, detailed mechanisms for the reactions in Equations 23-6 and 23-7.

CONNECTIONS 23.1

Controversial food dyes

Phthalic anhydride (Eq. 23-7) is a precursor to quinoline yellow, a dye used globally in food and cosmetics. The FDA restricts the use of the dye as a food colorant because of potential health risks.

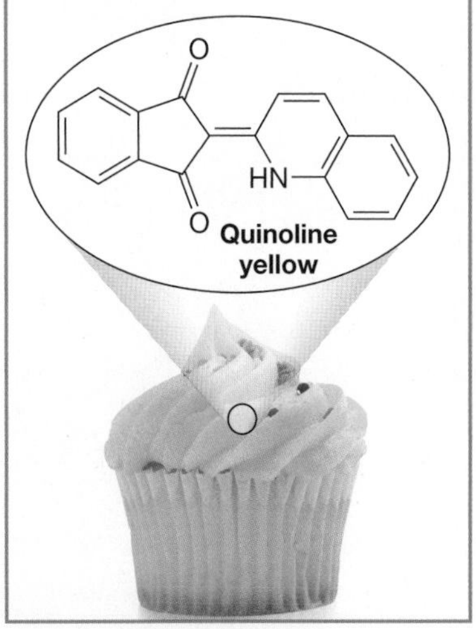

HN
Quinoline yellow

We can envision similar reactions taking place when other acid derivatives, such as esters or amides, are treated with water. As indicated in Table 23-1, however:

Ester hydrolysis and amide hydrolysis reactions are much too slow under neutral conditions to be useful for synthesis.

The relative hydrolysis rates of the species in Table 23-1 are essentially the rates of the rate-determining step: typically the nucleophilic addition of H_2O to the C=O group. Therefore, even though ketones and aldehydes don't undergo hydrolysis like the acid derivatives do (ketones and aldehydes don't have a suitable leaving group), they can still undergo the addition of H_2O to form a hydrate, and those rates of hydration establish the locations of ketones and aldehydes in Table 23-1. That is to say:

- Ketones and aldehydes are more reactive toward nucleophiles than are carboxylic acids, esters, amides, and carboxylates.
- Ketones and aldehydes are less reactive toward nucleophiles than are acid chlorides or acid anhydrides.

The hydrolysis rates in Table 23-1 tell us that the energy barrier for nucleophilic addition increases in the order: acid chlorides < acid anhydrides < carboxylic acids and esters < amides < carboxylate anions. This is explained by the increasing stability of the acid derivatives, as shown in **Figure 23-1** (next page), which is the same order we saw in the stability ladder in Figure 22-6 (p. 1059).

TABLE 23-1 Relative Reactivities of Various Carbonyl-Containing Species

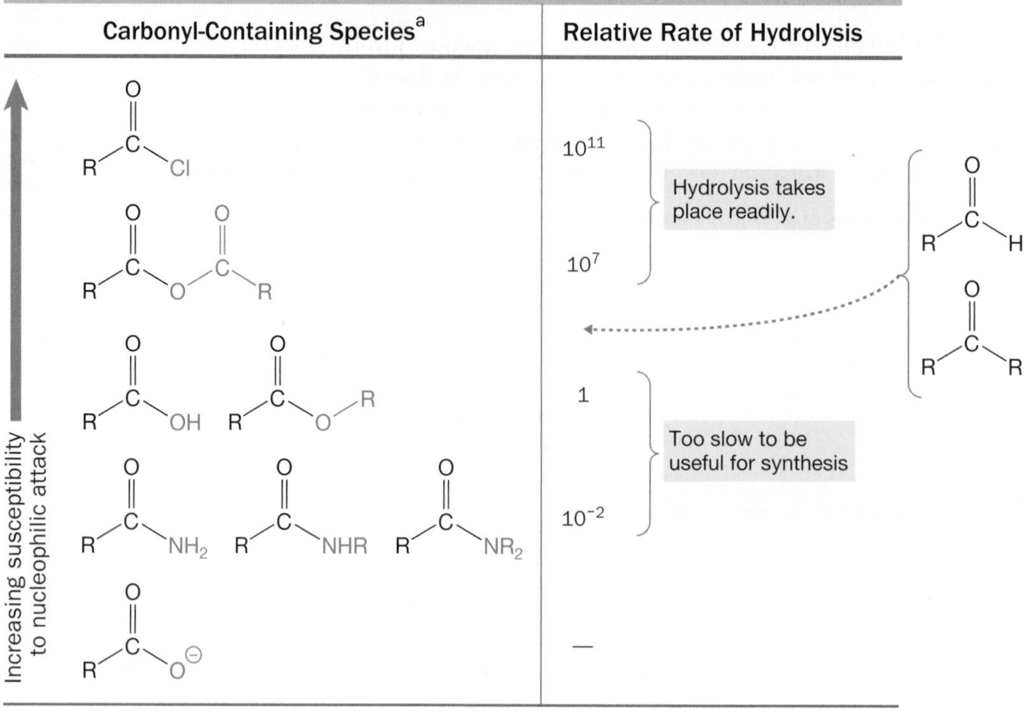
Carbonyl-Containing Species[a]
Relative Rate of Hydrolysis
Increasing susceptibility to nucleophilic attack
10^11
Hydrolysis takes place readily.
10^7
1
Too slow to be useful for synthesis
10^-2
—

[a]The leaving groups are indicated in red.

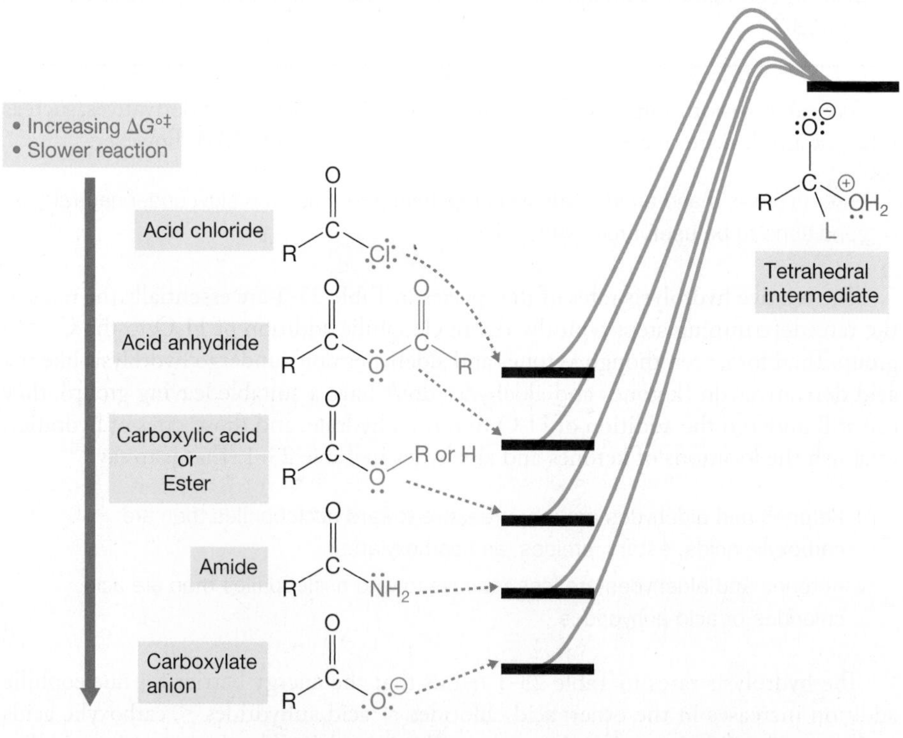
• Increasing ΔG°‡
• Slower reaction
Acid chloride
Acid anhydride
Carboxylic acid
or
Ester
Amide
Carboxylate
anion
Tetrahedral
intermediate

FIGURE 23-1 Relative reactivities of the acid derivatives Free energy diagrams for just the nucleophilic addition steps in the hydrolysis of various acid derivatives. A slower rate of hydrolysis (Table 23-1) reflects a larger energy barrier for nucleophilic addition.

The relative stabilities of the acid derivatives are an outcome of the extent to which the π electrons in the C=O group participate in resonance with a lone pair of electrons on the leaving group. As shown in **Figure 23-2a**, those π electrons are delocalized the most in a carboxylate anion because it has two equivalent resonance structures. For the uncharged carboxylic acid derivatives, the second resonance structure (exhibiting a C=L double bond) contributes less because it has both a positive and a negative formal charge, as shown in Figure 23-2b. Moreover, the contribution by the second resonance structure decreases in the order: amides > carboxylic acids ≈ esters > acid anhydrides > acid chlorides.

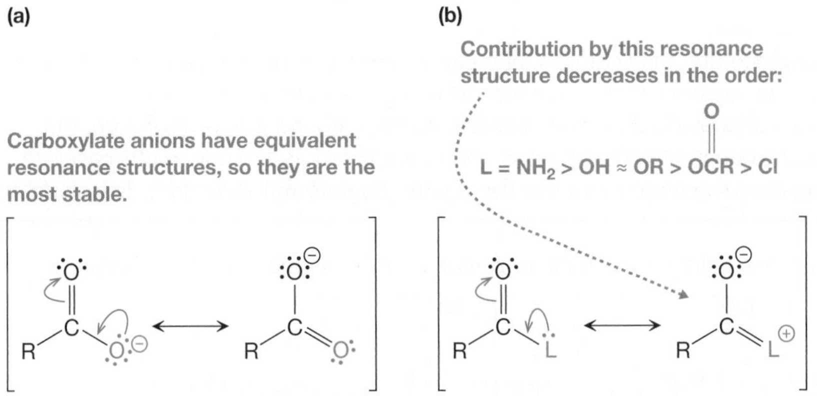
(a)
Carboxylate anions have equivalent resonance structures, so they are the most stable.
(b)
Contribution by this resonance structure decreases in the order:
L = NH2 > OH ≈ OR > OCR > Cl

FIGURE 23-2 Resonance stabilization in the carboxylic acid derivatives (a) Carboxylate anions (RCO_2^-) are stabilized the most because they have equivalent resonance structures. (b) For uncharged acid derivatives, the contribution by the resonance structure—and therefore the stability of the carboxylic acid derivative—decreases in the order: amides > carboxylic acids ≈ esters > acid anhydrides > acid chlorides.

The second resonance structure contributes less for an ester than an amide because O, being more electronegative than N, does not accommodate a positive charge as well as N. In an acid anhydride, that contribution is even smaller because the central O atom's lone pair is tied up in resonance with *the other* carbonyl group simultaneously. Finally, the contribution is smallest in an acid chloride because the lone pair on Cl belongs to a different shell ($n = 3$) than the valence electrons of the C and O atoms making up the C=O group ($n = 2$). This leads to relatively poor overlap among the valence orbitals, and thus diminishes any resulting stabilization.

CONNECTIONS 23.2

KHP and acid–base titrations

The monopotassium salt of phthalic acid (Eq. 23-7) is potassium hydrogen phthalate (KHP), a weak acid often used in analytical chemistry to standardize NaOH solutions to be used for titrations. KHP is a primary standard because it is an air-stable solid for which the number of moles can accurately be determined from its mass.

PHENOLPHTHALEIN

Potassium hydrogen phthalate (KHP)

SOLVED PROBLEM **23.1**

How to determine the relative reactivities of carboxylic acid derivatives

Break It Down Is the hydrolysis of phenyl acetate faster or slower than the hydrolysis of ethyl acetate? Explain.

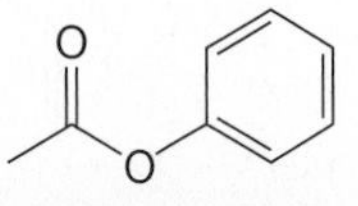

Phenyl acetate

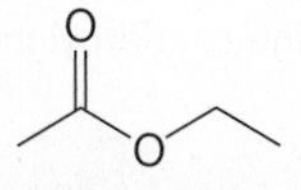

Ethyl acetate

Think	Solve
What role does resonance play in the reactivity of carboxylic acid derivatives?	As we saw in Figure 23-1, carboxylic acid derivatives become less reactive as the carbonyl group becomes more stabilized by resonance.

(continued)

What relevant resonance structures involve the carbonyl group?	Both molecules have a resonance structure of the form shown in Figure 23-2b, which involves the lone pair on the O atom of the leaving group. Phenyl acetate has the additional resonance structures shown here. 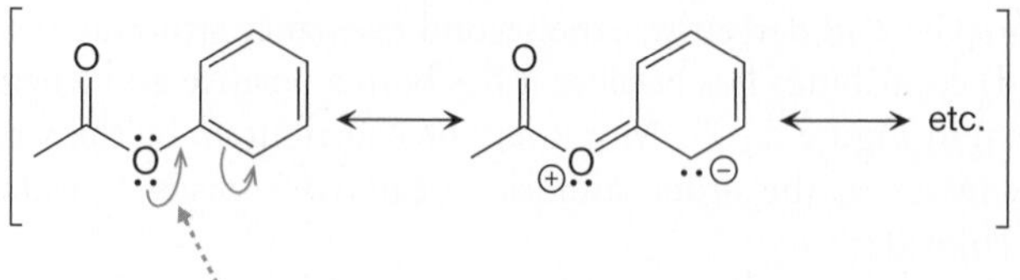 Resonance with the phenyl ring makes these electrons less available for resonance with the C=O group.
Are the carbonyl groups stabilized differently by resonance? How so?	In phenyl acetate, the O atom's lone pair is partly tied up in resonance with the phenyl ring, according the resonance structures shown above, which makes those electrons less available for resonance with the carbonyl group. Therefore, the carbonyl group in phenyl acetate is not as stabilized as the one in ethyl acetate, making phenyl acetate more reactive; phenyl acetate will undergo hydrolysis faster.

Try It Which acid derivative in each of these pairs do you think undergoes hydrolysis more quickly? Explain.

(a) (b) (c)

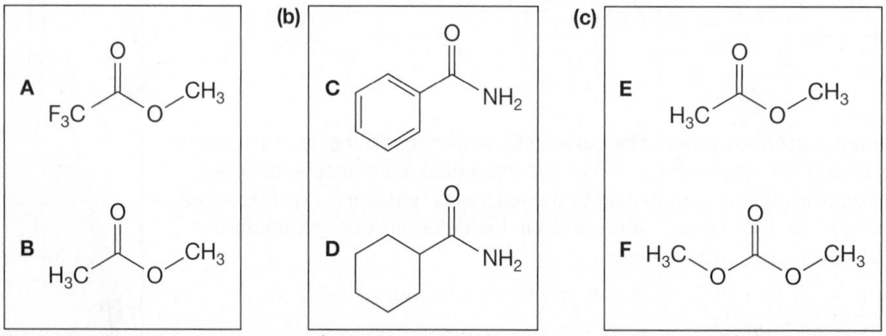

Answers to all Try It exercises can be found in the Solutions Manual.

SECTION 23.3 OBJECTIVES

You will be able to:

1. Draw the mechanism and product for the reaction of an acid chloride or an acid anhydride with an amine.
2. Explain why two equivalents of an amine are required for the reaction of an acid chloride or an acid anhydride with an amine, unless an equivalent of a base such as pyridine or triethylamine is added.

23.3 Aminolysis of Acid Derivatives

Amines are even more nucleophilic than water and alcohols, so they, too, will react with acid chlorides and acid anhydrides. As shown in Equations 23-8 and 23-9, these **aminolysis** reactions produce amides:

Aminolysis

An amide

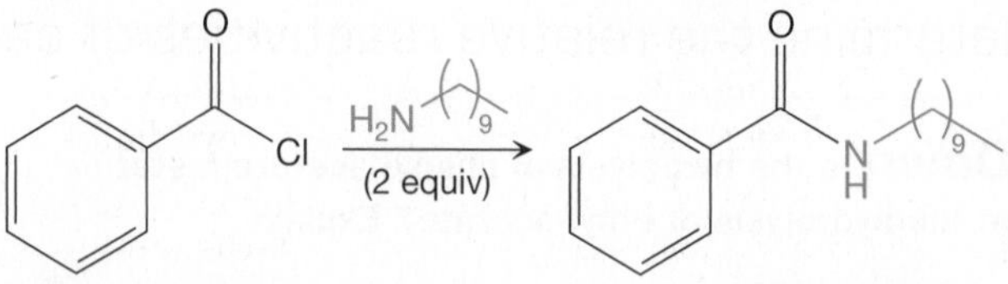

(23-8)

Benzoyl chloride **N-Decylbenzamide**

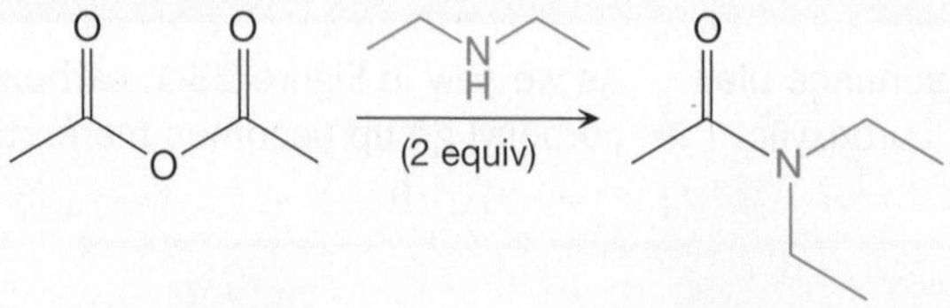

(23-9)

Acetic anhydride ***N,N*-Diethylethanamide**

The mechanisms for Equations 23-8 and 23-9 are similar to the one for the hydrolysis of an acid chloride, shown previously in Equation 23-5 (p. 1101). Equation 23-10 shows the mechanism for the aminolysis of an acid chloride. Step 1 is nucleophilic addition of the amine to produce the tetrahedral intermediate, followed by deprotonation of the positively charged N in Step 2. Finally, Cl^- is eliminated in Step 3.

Mechanism for the aminolysis of an acid chloride (Eq. 23-8)

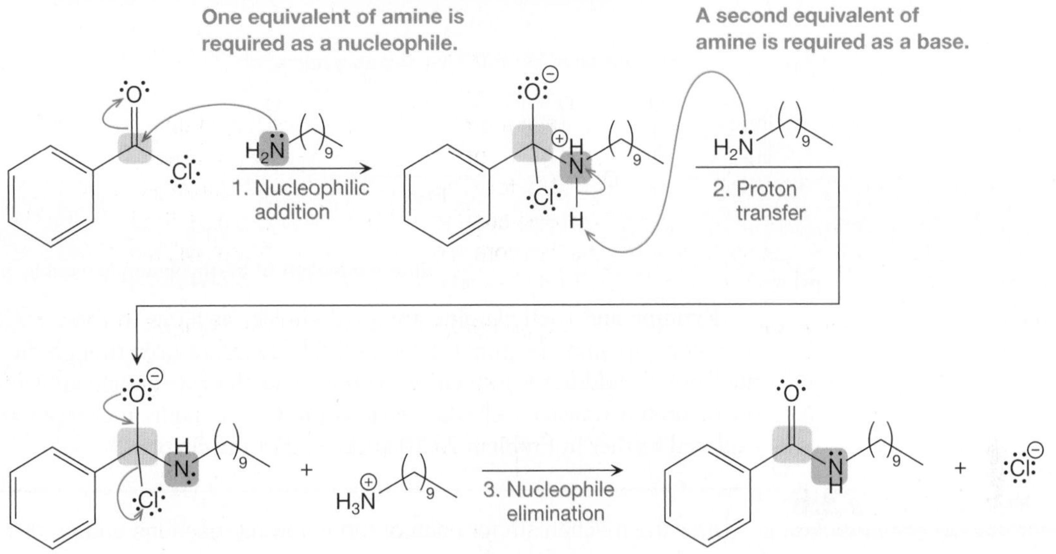

One equivalent of amine is required as a nucleophile.
A second equivalent of amine is required as a base.
1. Nucleophilic addition
2. Proton transfer
3. Nucleophile elimination

(23-10)

YOUR TURN 23.5

Draw the complete, detailed mechanism for the reaction in Equation 23-9.

An important consideration for aminolysis reactions is the number of equivalents of the amine required.

Aminolysis reactions require two equivalents of an amine.

According to the mechanism, the first equivalent is used in Step 1, in which the amine, acting as a nucleophile, attacks the carbonyl carbon of the acid chloride. The second equivalent is used in Step 2, where it acts as a base to deprotonate the positively charged N from the original nucleophile.

If the amine is readily available and inexpensive, it may be acceptable to carry out an aminolysis reaction that consumes two equivalents of the amine. If the amine is difficult to obtain or expensive, however, then it is advantageous to use only one equivalent. In these cases, another amine such as pyridine or triethylamine (**Figure 23-3**) can be added to the reaction mixture to act as a base, freeing up the desired amine to act as the nucleophile. For example, the aminolysis reaction in Equation 23-11 requires only one equivalent of the amine when one equivalent of pyridine is also present. Similarly, the aminolysis reaction in Equation 23-12 requires only one equivalent of the desired amine in the presence of one equivalent of triethylamine.

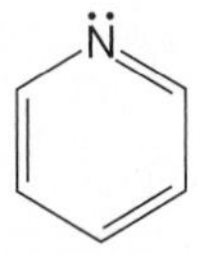
Pyridine

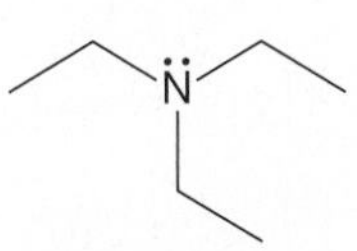
Triethylamine (Et_3N)

FIGURE 23-3

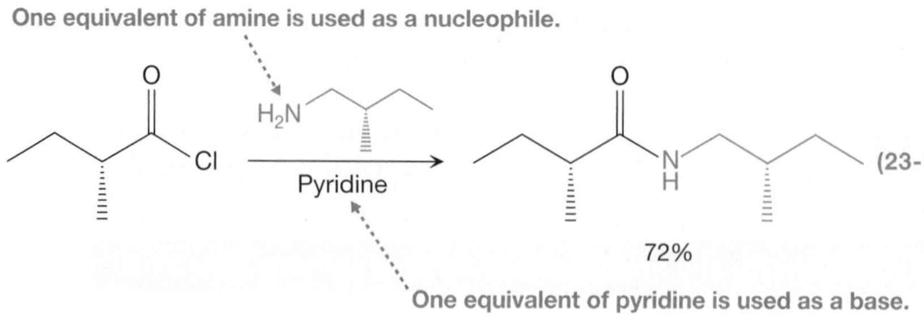

One equivalent of amine is used as a nucleophile.
Pyridine
72%
One equivalent of pyridine is used as a base.

(23-11)

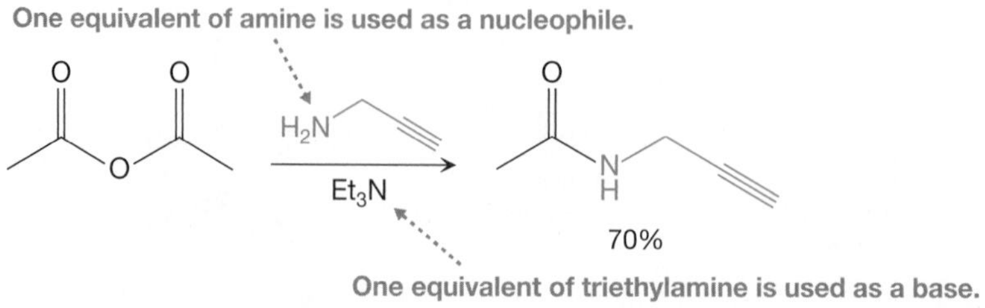

One equivalent of amine is used as a nucleophile.
Et3N
70%
One equivalent of triethylamine is used as a base.

(23-12)

Pyridine and triethylamine are good choices as bases in these reactions because neither compound's N atom is bonded to H. Therefore, even though they can undergo nucleophilic addition–elimination with an acid chloride or acid anhydride, no subsequent proton transfer can take place to produce a stable uncharged amide. (This is explored further in Problem 23.10 at the end of the chapter.)

YOUR TURN **23.6**

Draw the mechanism for each of the following reactions and predict the major product.

(a) **(b)**

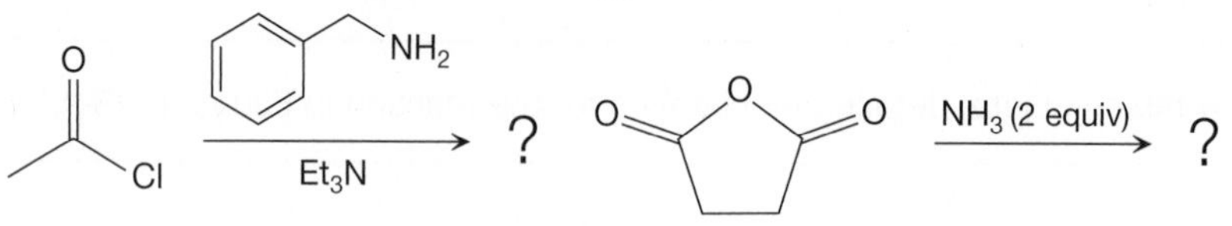

Et3N
?
NH3 (2 equiv)
?

The use of pyridine or triethylamine as a base is not limited only to aminolysis reactions. Looking back at the alcoholysis (Eq. 23-3) or hydrolysis (Eq. 23-4) of an acid chloride, notice that HCl is effectively a by-product. As the acid accumulates, the protonated form of the alcohol or water becomes more abundant, which can slow down the reaction and compromise yield. To combat this problem, an excess of alcohol or water can be used. Alternatively, pyridine or triethylamine can be added to neutralize the acid.

23.4 Synthesis of Acid Halides: Getting to the Top of the Stability Ladder

SECTION 23.4 OBJECTIVES

You will be able to:

1. Show how an acid chloride can be synthesized from a carboxylic acid.
2. Draw the mechanism for the synthesis of an acid chloride from a carboxylic acid, and explain the role of reversibility.

Recall from Section 22.2 that an acid chloride appears at the top of the stability ladder and can therefore be converted into any of the other acid derivatives with relative ease. In light of this, it can be extremely useful to produce acid chlorides from compounds that are more readily available.

As shown in Equations 23-13 and 23-14, **thionyl chloride** ($SOCl_2$) and phosphorus trichloride (PCl_3) can be used to convert carboxylic acids into acid chlorides. Of these, thionyl chloride is the more widely used reagent, largely because the two by-products, SO_2 and HCl, are gases that can bubble out of an organic solvent as they are produced, making the reaction irreversible.

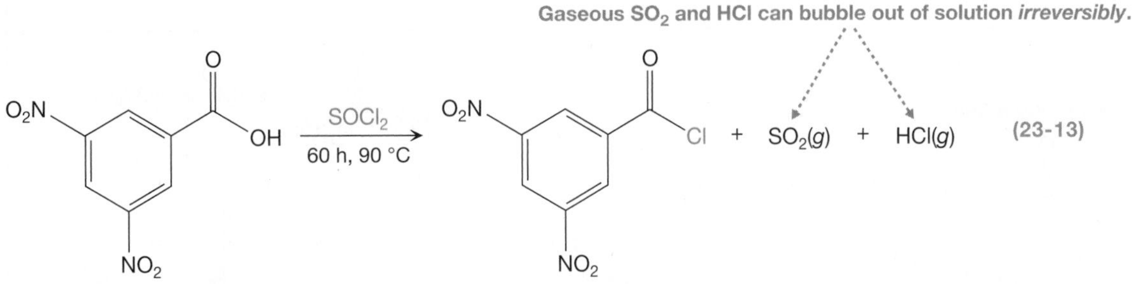

Gaseous SO2 and HCl can bubble out of solution irreversibly.
O2N
OH
SOCl2
60 h, 90 °C
O2N
Cl
+ SO2(g) + HCl(g)
NO2
NO2

(23-13)

3,5-Dinitrobenzoic acid **3,5-Dinitrobenzoyl chloride** 90%

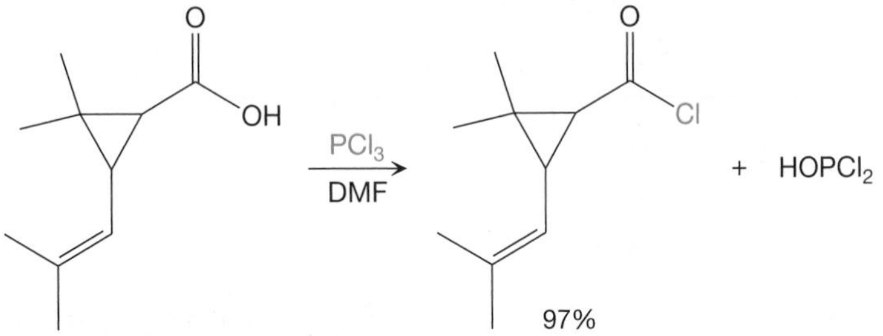

OH
PCl3
DMF
Cl
+ HOPCl2
97%

(23-14)

The reaction in Equation 23-13 is explained by the mechanism in Equation 23-15, which consists of back-to-back nucleophilic addition–elimination sequences. The first addition–elimination involves the carboxylic acid and $SOCl_2$. In Step 1, the carbonyl O of the carboxylic acid attacks the polar S=O bond of $SOCl_2$, producing a species in which the positive charge is resonance delocalized. In Step 2, a Cl^- leaving group is eliminated from S, thereby regenerating the S=O bond.

Mechanism for the conversion of a carboxylic acid into an acid chloride with $SOCl_2$ (Eq. 23-13)

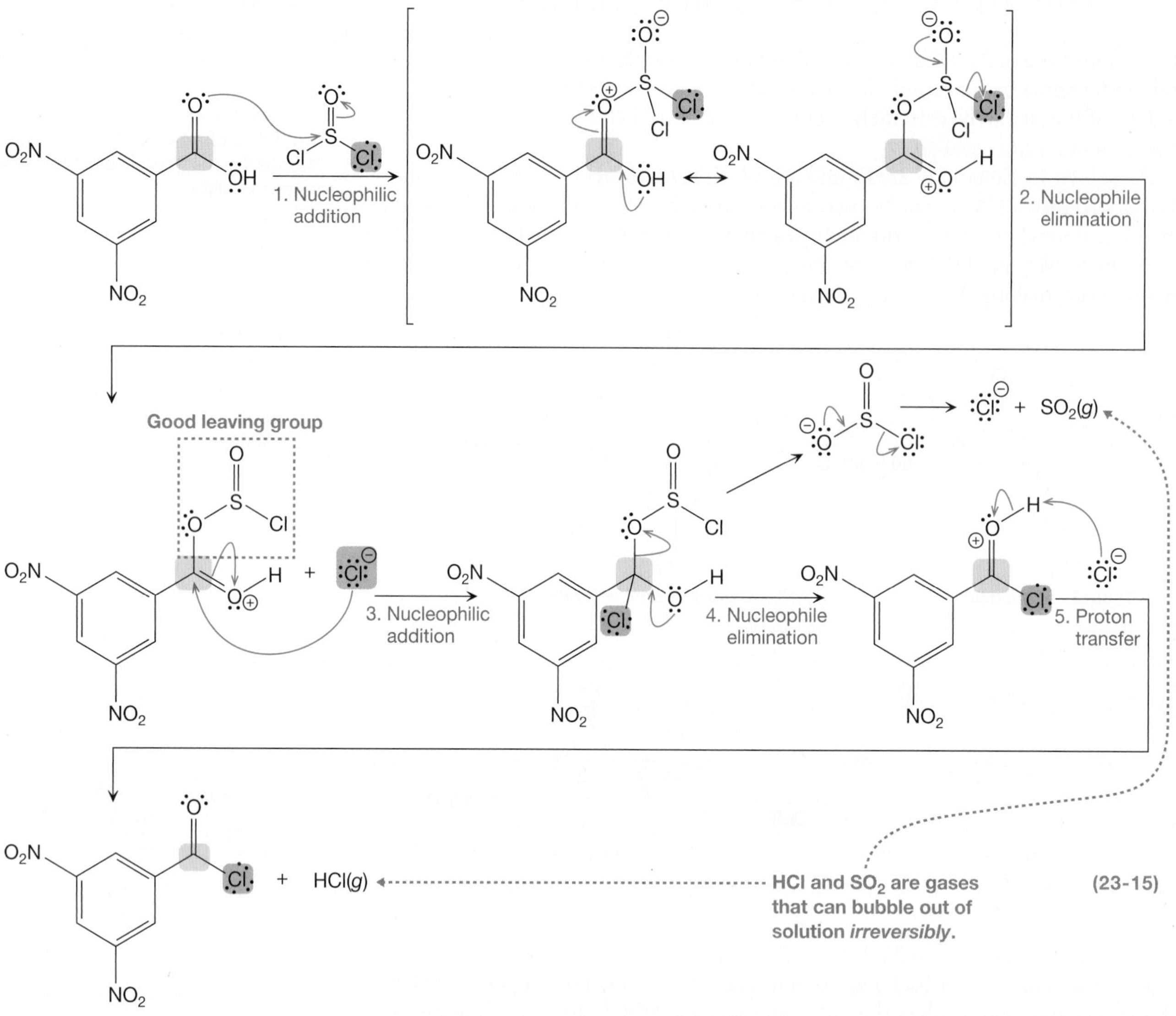

1. Nucleophilic addition
2. Nucleophile elimination
Good leaving group
3. Nucleophilic addition
4. Nucleophile elimination
5. Proton transfer
HCl and SO2 are gases that can bubble out of solution irreversibly.

(23-15)

Mechanism Drawing
$SOCl_2$ Conversion of a Carboxylic Acid to an Acid Chloride

The product of Step 2 contains a very good leaving group bonded to the carbonyl C, as indicated in the mechanism. This sets the stage for the second nucleophilic addition–elimination sequence (Steps 3 and 4), in which the Cl^- anion generated in Step 2 replaces $ClSO_2^-$. Finally, in Step 5, the carbonyl O is deprotonated.

The mechanism for the reaction involving PCl_3 (Eq. 23-14) is shown in Your Turn 23.7 and is similar to the one involving $SOCl_2$. The difference is that PCl_3 does not possess a polar π bond, so Cl^- is generated from an S_N2 step instead of an addition–elimination sequence. This is essentially the same way that Cl^- is generated when PCl_3 is used to convert an alcohol to an alkyl chloride (see Recall box).

◀ RECALL

Section 10.5 showed how PCl_3 or PBr_3 can be used to convert an alcohol into an alkyl halide by back-to-back S_N2 steps. In the first S_N2 step, the alcohol attacks P to displace Cl^- or Br^-. In the second S_N2 step, Cl^- or Br^- attacks the C atom of the C—O bond to produce the alkyl halide.

The mechanism for the reaction in Equation 23-14 is shown here, but the curved arrows have been omitted. Supply the missing curved arrows, and label each elementary step below its respective reaction arrow. Identify the leaving group in the product of the first step.

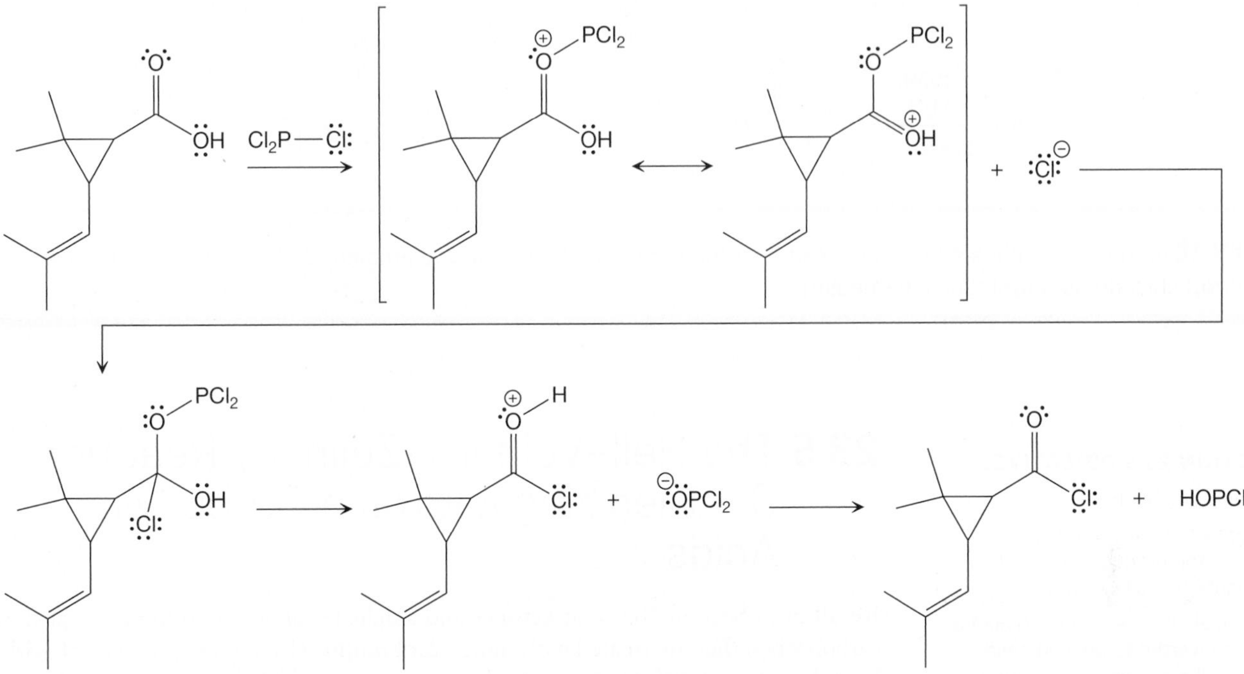

$Cl_2P—Cl$
PCl_2
OH
Cl
$OPCl_2$
$HOPCl_2$

SOLVED PROBLEM 23.2

How to design a synthesis that proceeds through an acid chloride intermediate

Break It Down **Propose how you would carry out the synthesis shown here, in which an amide is converted into an acid anhydride.**

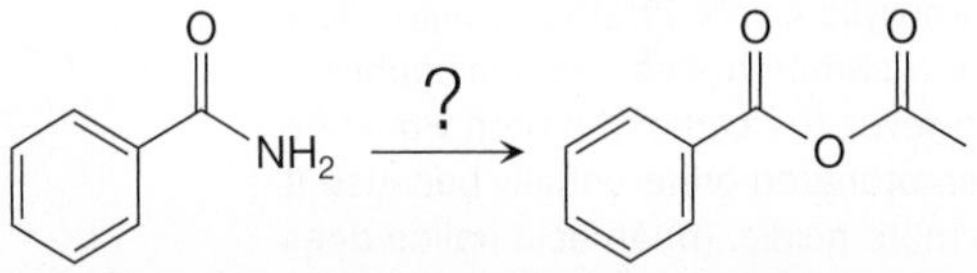

O
NH_2
?
O
O
O

Think	Solve
From what other acid derivative can we produce an acid anhydride?	The target is an acid anhydride, which appears near the top of the stability ladder. To make the anhydride, we can choose an acid derivative precursor appearing even higher on the stability ladder—an acid chloride—as shown in the first transform below.

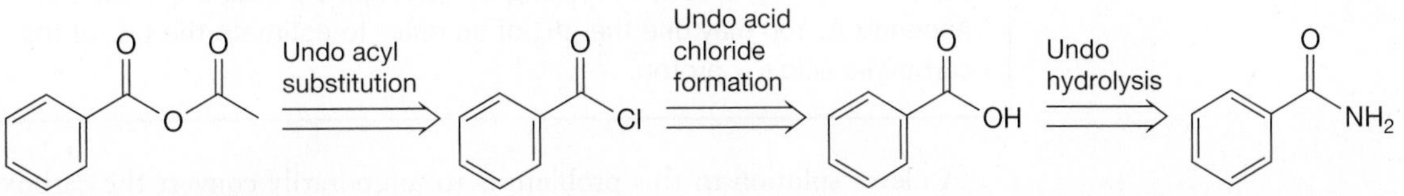

Undo acyl substitution
Undo acid chloride formation
Undo hydrolysis
Cl
OH
NH_2

Think	Solve
From what precursor can you synthesize an acid chloride?	Here in Section 23.4, we learned that an acid chloride can be made from the corresponding carboxylic acid, as shown in the second transform above.

(continued)

Can the carboxylic acid be made from the starting amide?	Section 22.4 showed that carboxylic acids can be made from amides by hydrolysis of the amide, as indicated in the third transform above.
How might you report the final synthesis?	To report the synthesis, we begin with the starting amide and supply the appropriate reagents and conditions, as shown below.

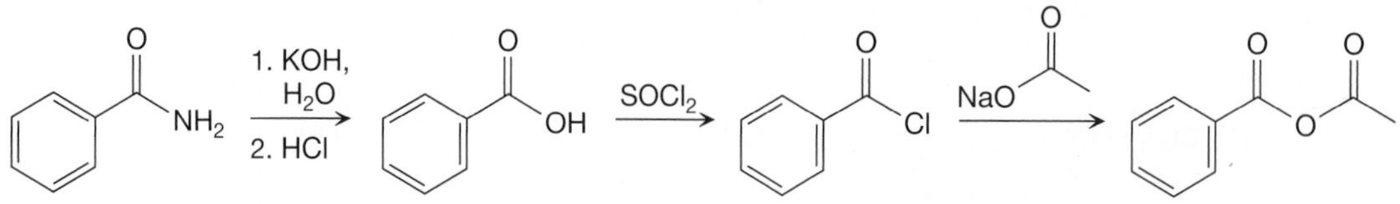

O
NH2
1. KOH, H2O
2. HCl
OH
SOCl2
Cl
NaO

Try It Propose a synthesis that would carry out the transformation in Solved Problem 23.2 but does *not* involve benzoyl chloride as a synthetic intermediate.

SECTION 23.5 OBJECTIVES

You will be able to:

1. Draw the mechanism and predict the product for a Hell–Volhard–Zelinsky reaction.
2. Explain why a carboxylic acid is first converted to an acid halide in Hell–Volhard–Zelinsky reactions.

23.5 The Hell–Volhard–Zelinsky Reaction: Synthesizing α-Bromo Carboxylic Acids

Recall from Section 10.6 that ketones and aldehydes undergo bromination at the α carbon when they are treated with molecular bromine (Br_2) in the presence of acid or base. For those reactions to work, the α carbon must be deprotonated to become nucleophilic. In a carboxylic acid, deprotonating the α carbon is unfeasible because the most acidic proton is the one that is part of the carboxyl group, as indicated in **Figure 23-4a**.

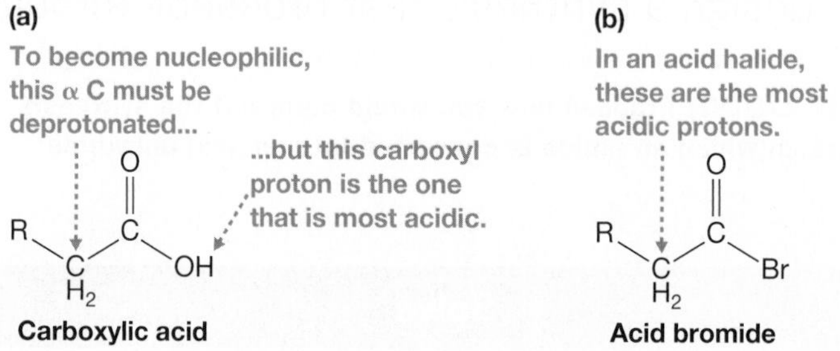

(a)
To become nucleophilic, this α C must be deprotonated...
...but this carboxyl proton is the one that is most acidic.
O
R
C
H2
OH
Carboxylic acid
(b)
In an acid halide, these are the most acidic protons.
O
R
C
H2
Br
Acid bromide

FIGURE 23-4 **Carboxylic acids, acid halides, and nucleophilicity at the α carbon** (a) Deprotonation of a carboxylic acid's α carbon would allow the α carbon to become nucleophilic. However, the carboxyl proton would be deprotonated preferentially because it is more acidic. (b) An acid halide does not have an acidic carboxyl proton, so the α carbon can be deprotonated to become nucleophilic.

YOUR TURN 23.8

Verify the above statement that the α proton in Figure 23-4a is less acidic than the carboxyl proton by looking up their approximate pK_a values in Appendix A. You may use the pK_a of an ester to estimate the pK_a of the carboxylic acid's α proton.

A clever solution to this problem is to temporarily convert the carboxylic acid into an acid halide and to carry out the bromination on the acid halide instead. Bromination works for an acid halide because, without the acidic carboxyl proton, the α protons are the most acidic (Fig. 23-4b). Incorporating bromination in this manner is the basis of a **Hell–Volhard–Zelinsky (HVZ) reaction**, examples of which are shown in Equations 23-16 and 23-17:

The Hell–Volhard–Zelinsky reaction

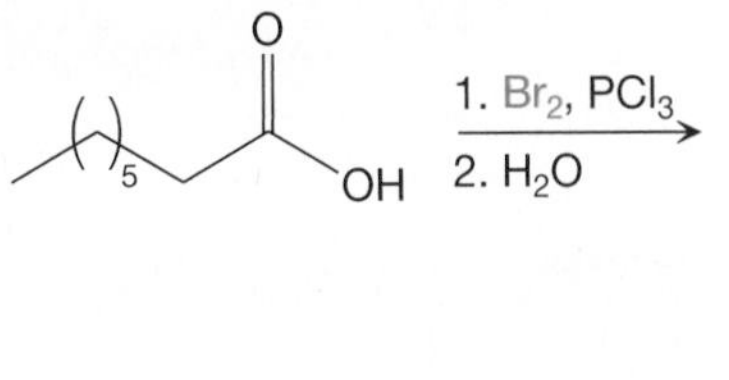

1. Br2, PCl3
2. H2O
OH
Br
95%

(23-16)

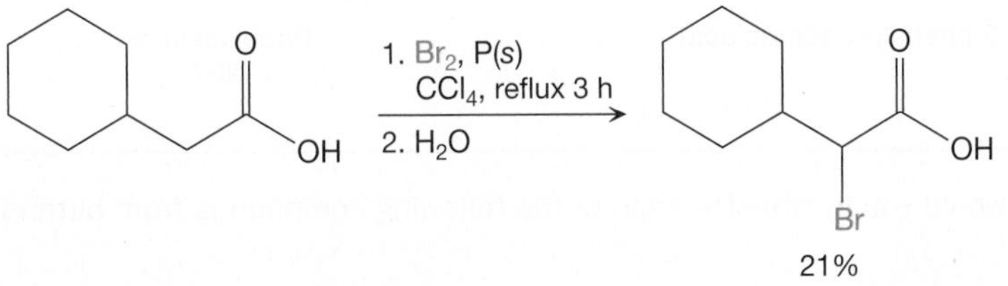

1. Br2, P(s)
CCl4, reflux 3 h
2. H2O
OH
Br
21%

(23-17)

In both cases, PBr_3 is produced [$Br_2 + PCl_3$ in Eq. 23-16 or $Br_2 + P(s)$ in Eq. 23-17]. As shown in the partial mechanism in Equation 23-18, PBr_3 is responsible for converting the carboxylic acid to an acid bromide (review Section 23.4):

◀ **RECALL**

The conversion from the keto form to the enol form takes place by back-to-back proton transfer steps (Section 7.10). As we saw in Section 10.6, the α carbon of an enol is nucleophilic and can attack Br_2 in an S_N2 step, resulting in bromination of the α carbon.

Partial mechanism for the Hell–Volhard–Zelinsky reaction (Eq. 23-16)

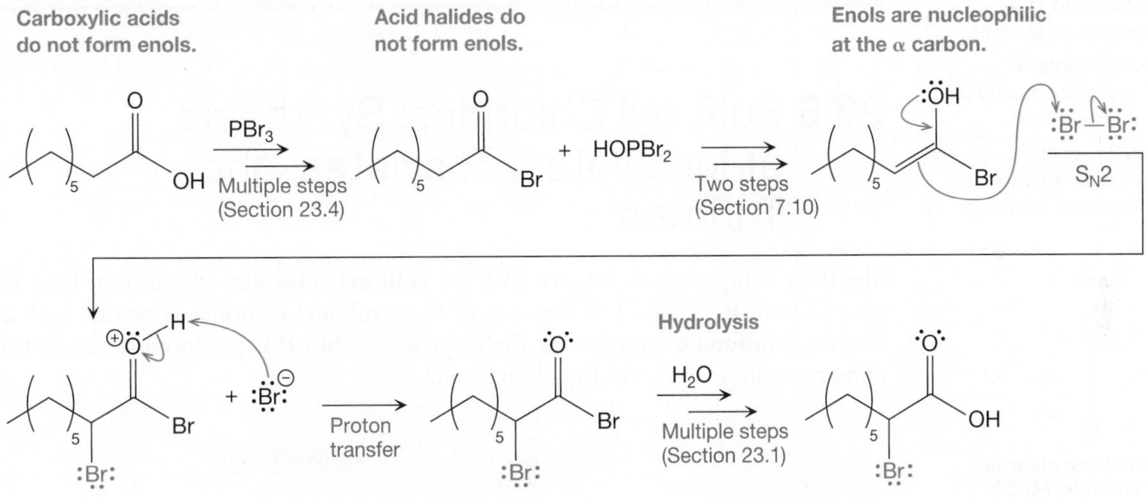

Carboxylic acids do not form enols.
Acid halides do not form enols.
Enols are nucleophilic at the α carbon.
PBr3
Multiple steps (Section 23.4)
+ HOPBr2
Two steps (Section 7.10)
SN2
Proton transfer
Hydrolysis
H2O
Multiple steps (Section 23.1)

(23-18)

The acid bromide then undergoes tautomerization to form the enol (see Recall box), and the enol acts as a nucleophile in a substitution reaction in the subsequent steps to produce the α-brominated acid bromide. Finally, treatment with water hydrolyzes the acid bromide to re-form the carboxylic acid (Section 23.1).

YOUR TURN **23.9**

Draw the missing steps of the partial mechanism shown in Equation 23-18.

YOUR TURN **23.10**

Draw the partial mechanism for the reaction in Equation 23-17, similar to Equation 23-18.

Because Br^- is an excellent leaving group, α-bromo acids are useful synthetic intermediates. For example, as shown in Equation 23-19, they can be used to synthesize α-amino acids, such as phenylalanine, by a nucleophilic substitution reaction with aqueous ammonia:

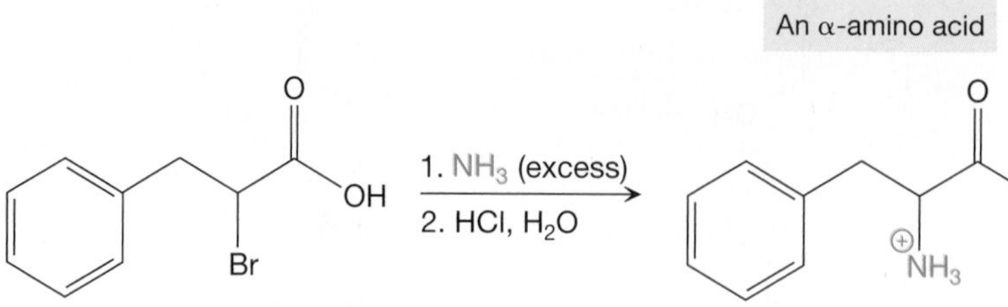

An α-amino acid
O
OH
Br
1. NH3 (excess)
2. HCl, H2O
O
OH
NH3
2-Bromo-3-phenylpropanoic acid
Phenylalanine
60%

(23-19)

YOUR TURN **23.11**

How would you synthesize each of the following compounds from butanoic acid?

(a) (b) (c)

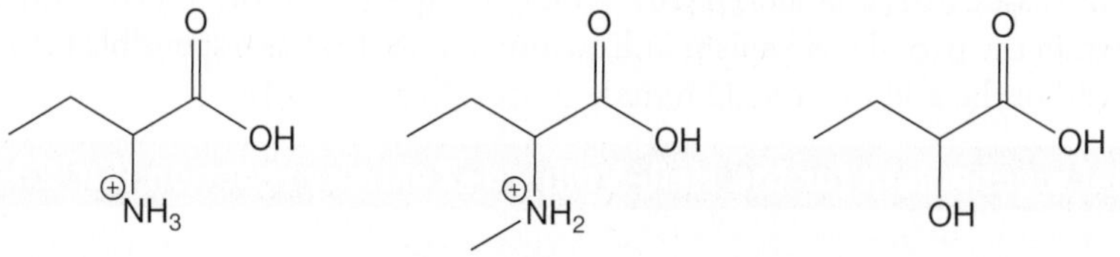

O
OH
NH3
O
OH
NH2
O
OH
OH

SECTION 23.6 OBJECTIVES

You will be able to:

1. Draw the mechanism and product for the reaction of a sulfonyl chloride with an alcohol.
2. Explain why the reaction between a sulfonyl chloride and an alcohol is useful in synthesis.
3. Design syntheses that incorporate a reaction between a sulfonyl chloride and an alcohol.

23.6 Sulfonyl Chlorides: Synthesis of Mesylates, Tosylates, and Triflates

The three compounds in **Figure 23-5** are **sulfonyl chlorides**, species that have the general form R—SO_2Cl. When one of these sulfonyl chlorides is treated with an alcohol, a **sulfonate ester** having the form R′O—SO_2R is produced by a sulfonylation reaction, as shown in Equation 23-20:

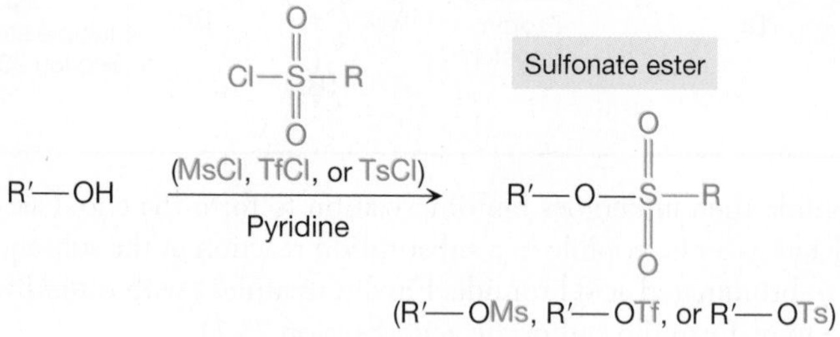

Cl—S—R
O
O
(MsCl, TfCl, or TsCl)
Pyridine
R′—OH
Sulfonate ester
R′—O—S—R
O
O
(R′—OMs, R′—OTf, or R′—OTs)

(23-20)

(a)

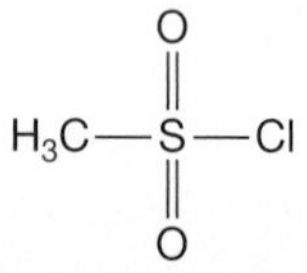

O
H3C—S—Cl
O

Methanesulfonyl chloride (Mesyl chloride, MsCl)

(b)

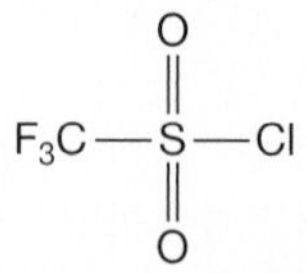

O
F3C—S—Cl
O

Trifluoromethanesulfonyl chloride (Triflyl chloride, TfCl)

(c)

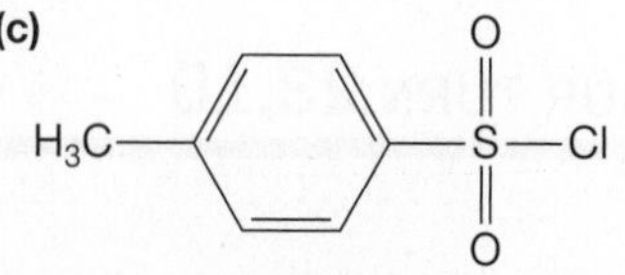

H3C
O
S—Cl
O

***p*-Toluenesulfonyl chloride (Tosyl chloride, TsCl)**

FIGURE 23-5 Some common sulfonyl chlorides
These sulfonyl chlorides can be used to make sulfonate esters, which have excellent leaving groups.

The mechanism in Equation 23-21 accounts for these sulfonylation reactions, where the alcohol attacks the sulfonyl chloride in a nucleophilic addition–elimination sequence:[1]

Mechanism for the sulfonylation of an alcohol (Eq. 23-20)

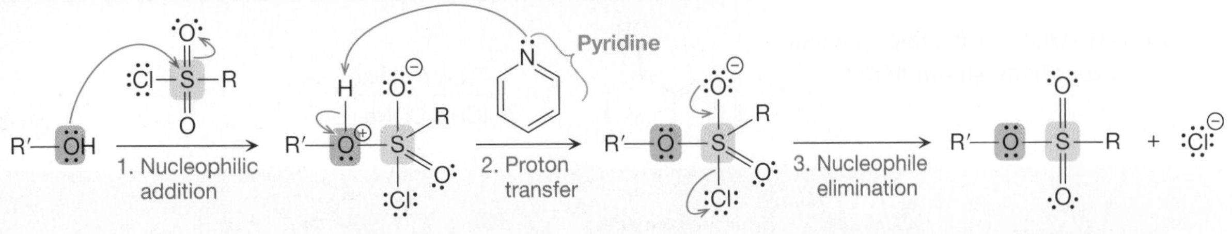
Pyridine
1. Nucleophilic addition
2. Proton transfer
3. Nucleophile elimination

(23-21)

This mechanism is essentially identical to the one shown previously in Equation 23-5 for the hydrolysis of acid chlorides, but in this case the nucleophilic OH group attacks the S═O group rather than a C═O group. Notice, too, that pyridine is added to the reaction to act as a base in Step 2. As we saw in Section 23.3, pyridine will not compromise the desired nucleophilic addition–elimination reaction because pyridine has no N—H proton that can be removed.

Recall from Section 9.5 that MsO^- (mesylate), TfO^- (triflate), and TsO^- (tosylate) are very good leaving groups for S_N2, S_N1, E2, and E1 reactions. Therefore:

> Sulfonylation of an alcohol converts a poor HO^- leaving group into a very good RSO_3^- leaving group.

Moreover, notice in Equation 23-21 that no bonds to the C—OH carbon are broken or formed. Consequently:

> Sulfonylation of an alcohol occurs with retention of configuration at the C—OH carbon.

A specific example is shown in Equation 23-22. Sulfonylation of an alcohol, therefore, complements the PBr_3 bromination of an alcohol (Section 10.5), which converts a poor HO^- leaving group into a good Br^- leaving group with *inversion* of configuration at the C—OH carbon.

CONNECTIONS 23.3

Essential soft drinks? The artificial sweetener aspartame is a source of phenylalanine (Eq. 23-19), which is highlighted on many food and drink labels. A small percentage of the population has a genetic disorder called phenylketonuria, in which individuals cannot metabolize phenylalanine.

LOW SODIUM
Nutrition Facts
Serv. Size 1 Bottle
Calories 0
Amount/Serving % DV*
Total Fat 0g 0%
Sodium 70mg 3%
Total Carb. 0g 0%
Protein 0g
PHENYLKETONURICS: CONTAINS PHENYLALANINE

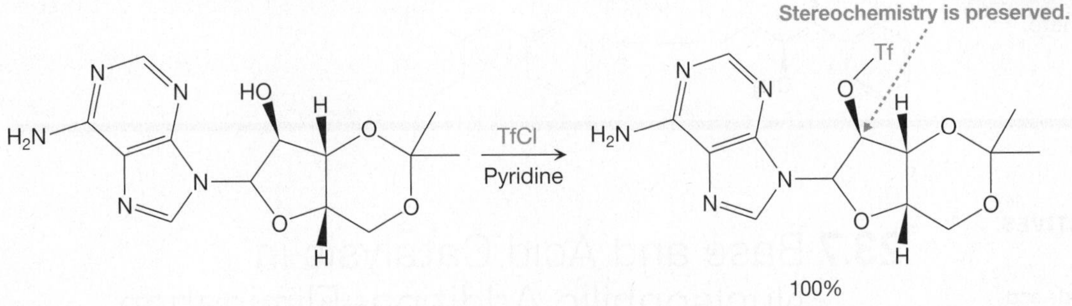
Stereochemistry is preserved.
TfCl
Pyridine
100%

(23-22)

[1]Although there is experimental evidence to support the mechanism in Equation 23-21, there is also evidence suggesting that the addition and elimination steps occur in a single S_N2 step instead. Neither mechanism has been established conclusively.

SOLVED PROBLEM **23.3**

How to implement the sulfonylation of an alcohol to generate a good leaving group

Break It Down **What is the major product of the sequence of reactions shown here?**

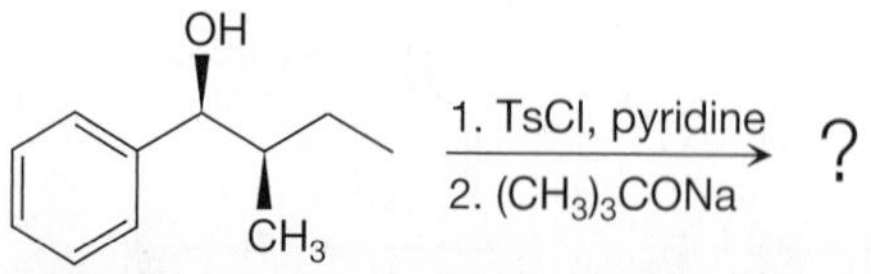

OH
1. TsCl, pyridine
2. $(CH_3)_3CONa$
?
CH_3

Think	Solve
What is the product of sulfonylation of an alcohol, and what stereochemistry is associated with that reaction?	The first reaction is a sulfonylation in which tosyl chloride (TsCl) converts the alcohol to an alkyl tosylate. This conversion does not involve the C—O bond, so the stereochemical configuration remains unchanged at that chiral carbon, as shown below.

The configuration is preserved in a sulfonylation reaction. The leaving group is anti to the adjacent H.

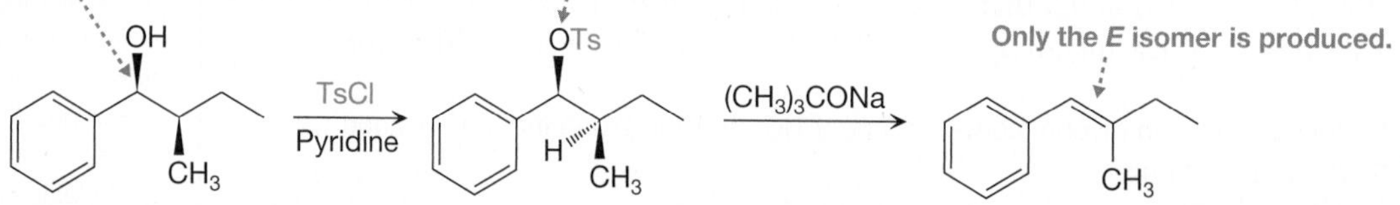

OH
CH_3
TsCl
Pyridine
OTs
H
CH_3
$(CH_3)_3CONa$
Only the *E* isomer is produced.
CH_3

Think	Solve
What type of reaction is promoted by a strong, bulky base in the second step of this synthesis?	Because the tosylate anion is an excellent leaving group, the presence of the strong, bulky base, $(CH_3)_3CONa$, promotes an E2 reaction (review Section 9.9).
What stereochemistry is associated with an E2 reaction?	The favored alkene product in an E2 reaction derives from the substrate conformation in which the H and the leaving group on adjacent carbons are anti to each other (i.e., anticoplanar; Section 8.5c). That conformation is the one shown above, which, in this case, leads to the *E* alkene as the major product.

Try It Show how to carry out the synthesis given here.

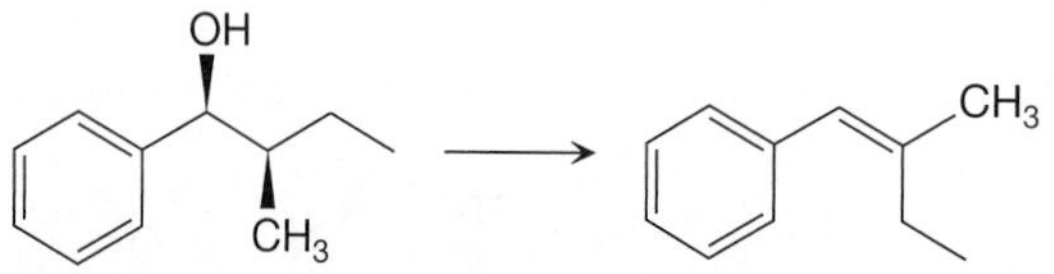

OH
CH_3
CH_3

SECTION 23.7 OBJECTIVES

You will be able to:

1. Explain the role of acids and bases in speeding up reactions of carboxylic acids, esters, and amides.
2. Draw the mechanism and product for an acid- or base-catalyzed transesterification.
3. Draw the mechanism and product for a Fischer esterification.
4. Draw the mechanism and product for the hydrolysis of an amide or ester under acidic or basic conditions.

23.7 Base and Acid Catalysis in Nucleophilic Addition–Elimination Reactions

Thus far, we have seen that weak nucleophiles, such as water, alcohols, and amines, react readily with acid halides, acid anhydrides, thionyl chloride, and sulfonyl chlorides. Even though the nucleophiles are weak, the polar π bonds (C=O and S=O) in these compounds are reactive enough to compensate. By contrast, we saw in Section 23.2 that esters are significantly less reactive at the carbonyl carbon because of resonance involving the leaving group. Thus, as Equation 23-23 shows, esters do *not* undergo nucleophilic addition–elimination under normal conditions with weak nucleophiles such as alcohols:

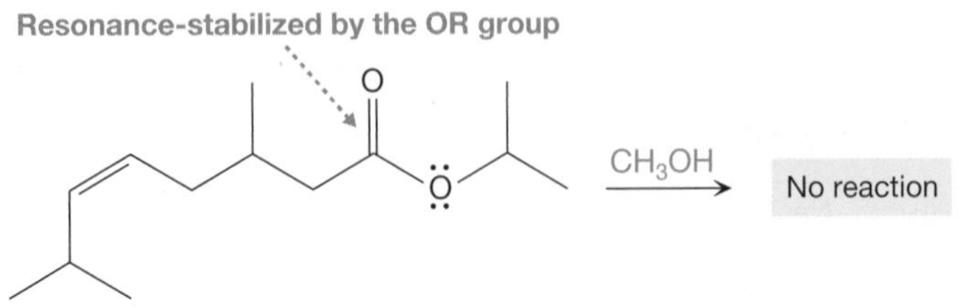

Resonance-stabilized by the OR group
CH_3OH
No reaction

(23-23)

> **◂ RECALL**
>
> Section 22.1 showed that transesterification can also be *base-promoted,* whereby 1 molar equivalent of the alkoxide salt reagent is consumed in the substitution reaction. The mechanism for such a reaction consists of just two steps: (1) nucleophilic addition and (2) nucleophile elimination.

Transesterification takes place readily, however, when a small amount (i.e., a catalytic amount) of a base (sodium methoxide, CH_3ONa, in Eq. 23-24) is added. Moreover, the base is not consumed overall in the reaction, so the reaction is *base-catalyzed* (see Recall box).

Base-catalyzed transesterification

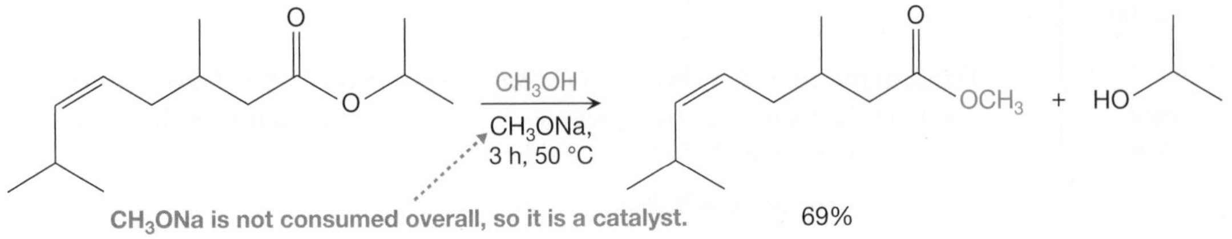

CH_3OH
CH_3ONa, 3 h, 50 °C
OCH_3 + HO
CH_3ONa is not consumed overall, so it is a catalyst.
69%

(23-24)

The mechanism for base-catalyzed transesterification, presented in Equation 23-25, shows why the reaction is catalyzed by the methoxide anion base:

Mechanism for base-catalyzed transesterification (Eq. 23-24)

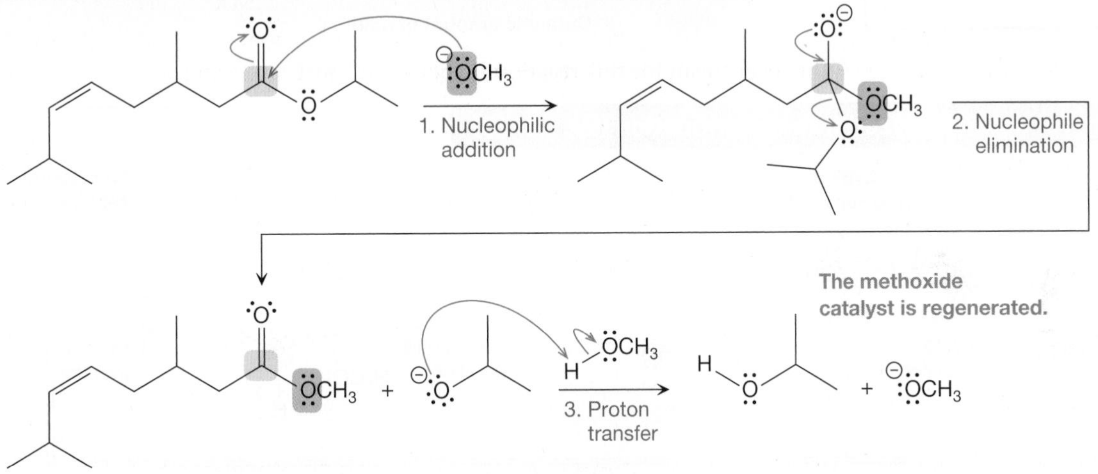

$:\ddot{O}CH_3$
1. Nucleophilic addition
2. Nucleophile elimination
The methoxide catalyst is regenerated.
3. Proton transfer

(23-25)

The reaction rate is increased because the nucleophile that attacks the carbonyl carbon in the nucleophilic addition step (Step 1, the rate-determining step) is CH_3O^-, a strong nucleophile. In the absence of CH_3O^- (e.g., in Eq. 23-23), the nucleophile would have to be methanol, a weak nucleophile. Moreover, there is no net consumption of CH_3O^- because it is regenerated in the proton transfer step (Step 3).

Because water and alcohols behave similarly, it might also seem that a base could be used to catalyze the conversion from esters to carboxylic acids. Indeed, as shown in Equation 23-26, hydrolysis takes place to produce the carboxylic acid initially, but that carboxylic acid is then rapidly and irreversibly deprotonated by the base. Thus, the base is consumed in the overall reaction, making it a *base-promoted* reaction instead of a base-catalyzed reaction. In fact, this is an example of a *saponification reaction*, discussed previously in Section 22.3. As shown in Equation 23-27, a similar proton transfer takes place when a carboxylic acid is treated with an alkoxide anion, making it unfeasible to convert a carboxylic acid into an ester under basic conditions.

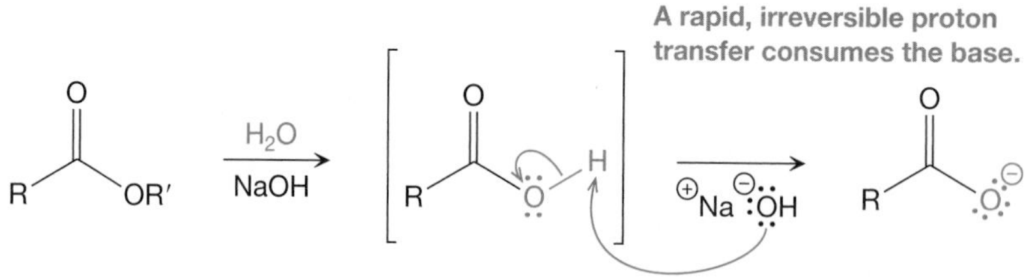
A rapid, irreversible proton transfer consumes the base.
R OR′
H_2O
NaOH
R O H
Na OH
R O

(23-26)

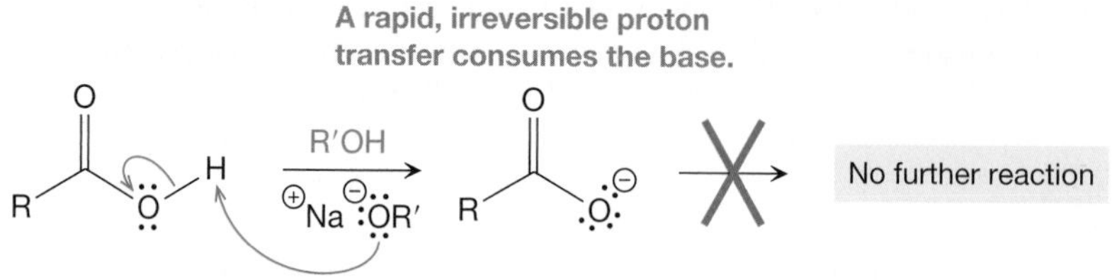
A rapid, irreversible proton transfer consumes the base.
R O H
R′OH
Na OR′
R O
No further reaction

(23-27)

CONNECTIONS 23.4

A fruity carboxylic acid ester
Hexyl acetate (Eq. 23-28)—commonly called hexyl caproate—has a bittersweet, fruity taste and is a flavoring agent, especially in gummy candies.

Transesterification can also be *acid-catalyzed*. Equation 23-28 shows, for example, that a catalytic amount of a strong acid, such as sulfuric acid, facilitates the production of hexyl acetate from methyl acetate and hexan-1-ol:

Acid-catalyzed transesterification

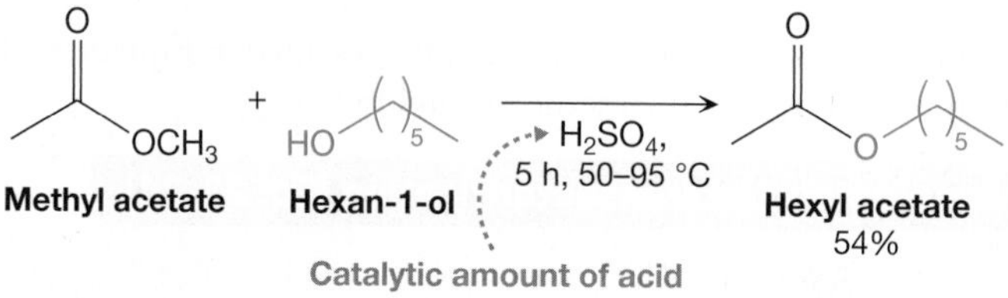
OCH_3
Methyl acetate
HO
Hexan-1-ol
H_2SO_4,
5 h, 50–95 °C
Catalytic amount of acid
Hexyl acetate
54%
+ $HOCH_3$

(23-28)

The mechanism for this reaction is shown in Equation 23-29:

Mechanism for acid-catalyzed transesterification (Eq. 23-28)

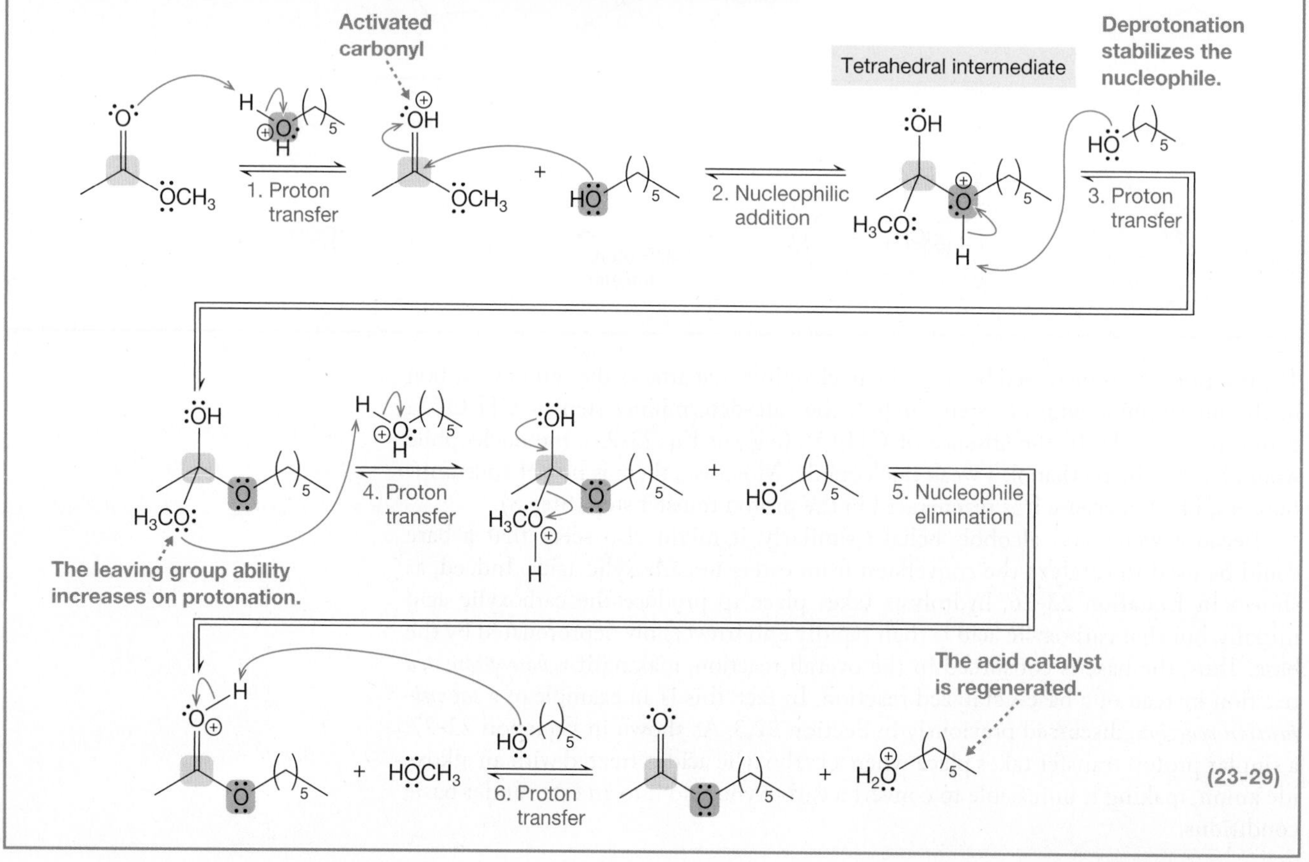
Activated carbonyl
1. Proton transfer
2. Nucleophilic addition
Tetrahedral intermediate
Deprotonation stabilizes the nucleophile.
3. Proton transfer
4. Proton transfer
5. Nucleophile elimination
The leaving group ability increases on protonation.
6. Proton transfer
The acid catalyst is regenerated.

(23-29)

Sulfuric acid is a strong acid, so the predominant acid in solution, according to the leveling effect, is the protonated alcohol, $CH_3(CH_2)_5OH_2^+$ (see top Recall box). In Step 1 of the mechanism, $CH_3(CH_2)_5OH_2^+$ protonates the ester's carbonyl group, and in Step 2, the alcohol attacks the carbonyl C atom, resulting in a tetrahedral intermediate. Steps 3 and 4 are proton transfers. In Step 3, the O atom from the original nucleophile becomes uncharged, and thus is stabilized. In Step 4, the singly bonded O atom of the original ester gains a positive charge, which increases its leaving group ability. In Step 5, the leaving group departs and the C=O bond is re-formed, and in Step 6, the carbonyl O is deprotonated, producing the overall uncharged product.

◀ RECALL

The leveling effect (Section 6.2a) states that the strongest acid that can exist in solution is the protonated solvent, and the strongest base that can exist is the deprotonated solvent. Therefore, an acid that is stronger than the protonated solvent will transfer its proton to the solvent.

Why does the presence of a strong acid catalyze this reaction? Notice in Step 2 (the rate-determining step) that the nucleophile (an alcohol) is relatively weak, but the rate of nucleophilic addition is enhanced because the carbonyl group has become *activated* (see bottom Recall box) by the proton transfer in Step 1; that is, the carbonyl C has become more electrophilic. Notice, too, that the strong acid used in Step 1 is regenerated in Step 6, so it is not consumed in the overall reaction.

◀ RECALL

Section 19.1 showed that two new charges (+1 and −1) are generated when a weak nucleophile adds to a carbonyl group that is not protonated. This makes the energy barrier large. The energy barrier is lower when a protonated carbonyl group is attacked by a weak nucleophile because no new charges appear.

Each step of the acid-catalyzed transesterification reaction in Equation 23-29 is reversible, so the overall reaction is reversible. Therefore, according to Le Châtelier's principle, the product yield can be increased by adding reactants or removing products. Often the product alcohol (CH_3OH in Eq. 23-28) is volatile and can be removed by distillation.

Unlike what we saw previously under basic conditions, the conversion of an ester to a carboxylic acid can also be acid-catalyzed. Equation 23-30 shows an example of this *ester hydrolysis*:

Acid-catalyzed ester hydrolysis

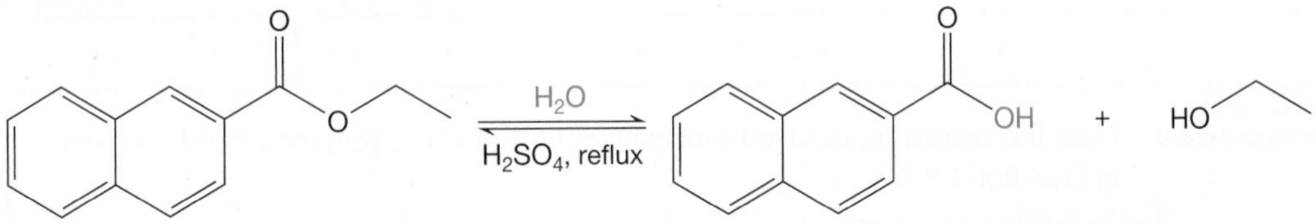

O
O
H2O
H2SO4, reflux
O
OH
+
HO

(23-30)

This reaction, like acid-catalyzed transesterifications, is reversible, so achieving a high yield of the product often requires manipulating Le Châtelier's principle. To avoid such complications, chemists generally prefer to carry out the hydrolysis of an ester irreversibly under basic conditions (saponification; Eq. 23-26), unless the basic conditions will lead to an undesirable side reaction.

The *esterification* of a carboxylic acid can be acid-catalyzed, too, in what is called a **Fischer esterification reaction**:

Fischer esterification

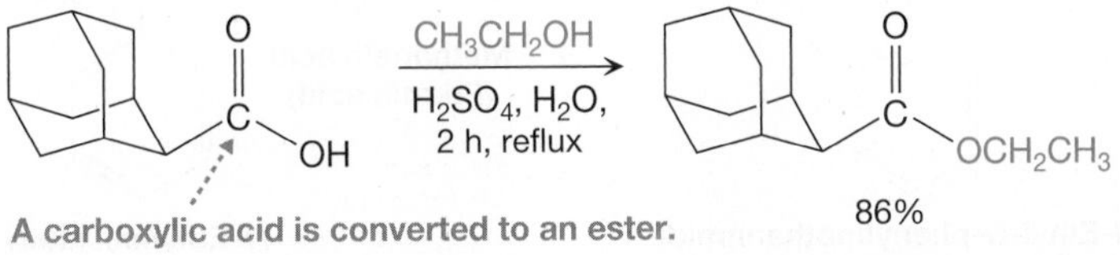

O
C
OH
CH3CH2OH
H2SO4, H2O,
2 h, reflux
O
C
OCH2CH3
86%
A carboxylic acid is converted to an ester.

(23-31)

Emil Fischer (1852–1919), the German chemist and Nobel laureate, was the first to report these kinds of reactions.

YOUR TURN 23.12

The mechanism for the Fischer esterification reaction in Equation 23-31 is shown here, but the curved arrows have been omitted. Supply the curved arrows for each step, and write the name of each elementary step below its reaction arrow.

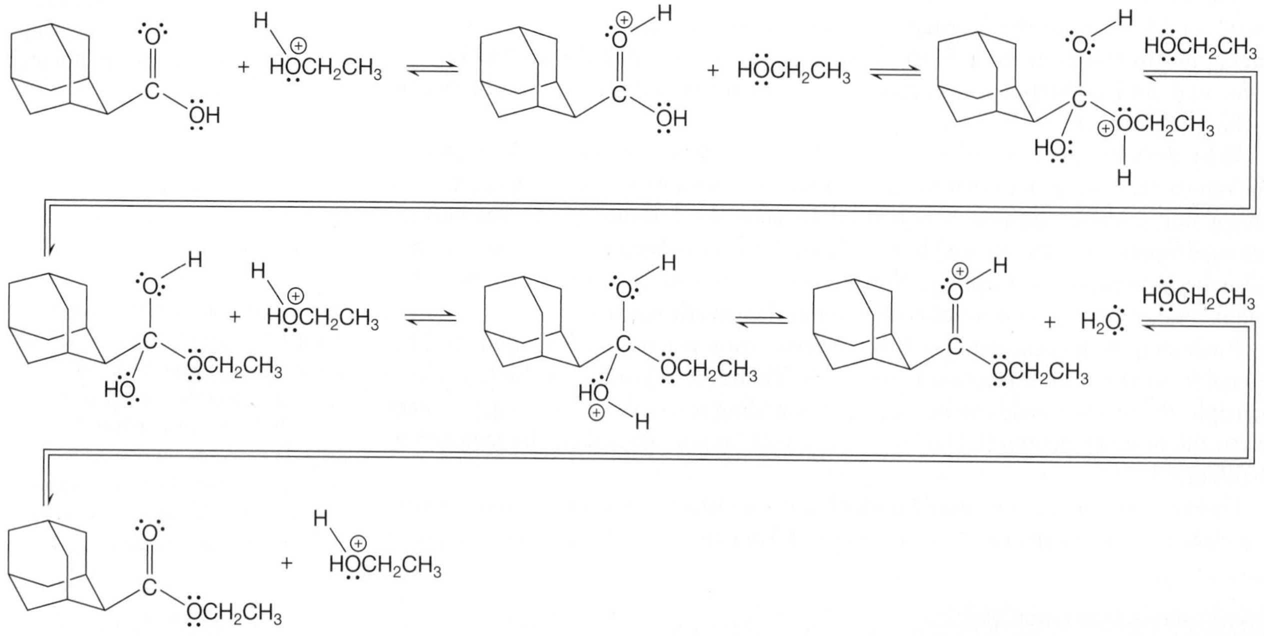

YOUR TURN 23.13

Draw the complete, detailed mechanism for the acid-catalyzed ester hydrolysis in Equation 23-30.

Acyl substitutions under acidic conditions are not limited to esters and carboxylic acids. Amides, which are even less reactive than esters or carboxylic acids, do not react with weak nucleophiles under normal conditions either. Under acidic conditions, however, amides can undergo hydrolysis to produce a carboxylic acid:

Amide hydrolysis

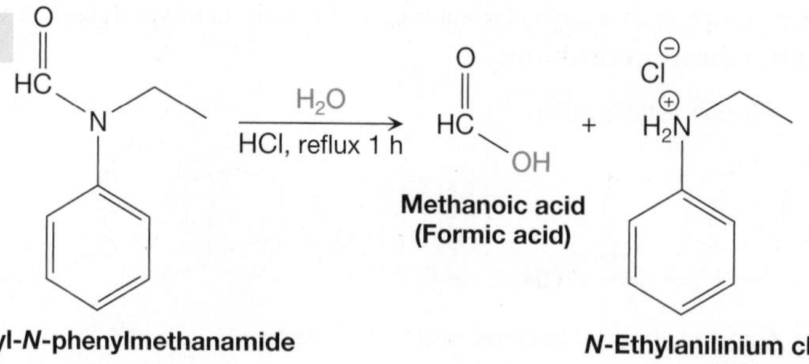

H_2O
HCl, reflux 1 h
Methanoic acid (Formic acid)
N-Ethyl-*N*-phenylmethanamide
N-Ethylanilinium chloride
88%

(23-32)

The mechanism for this reaction, presented in Equation 23-33, is essentially the same as the one that describes acid-catalyzed transesterification, shown previously in Equation 23-29.

Mechanism for amide hydrolysis under acidic conditions (Eq. 23-32)

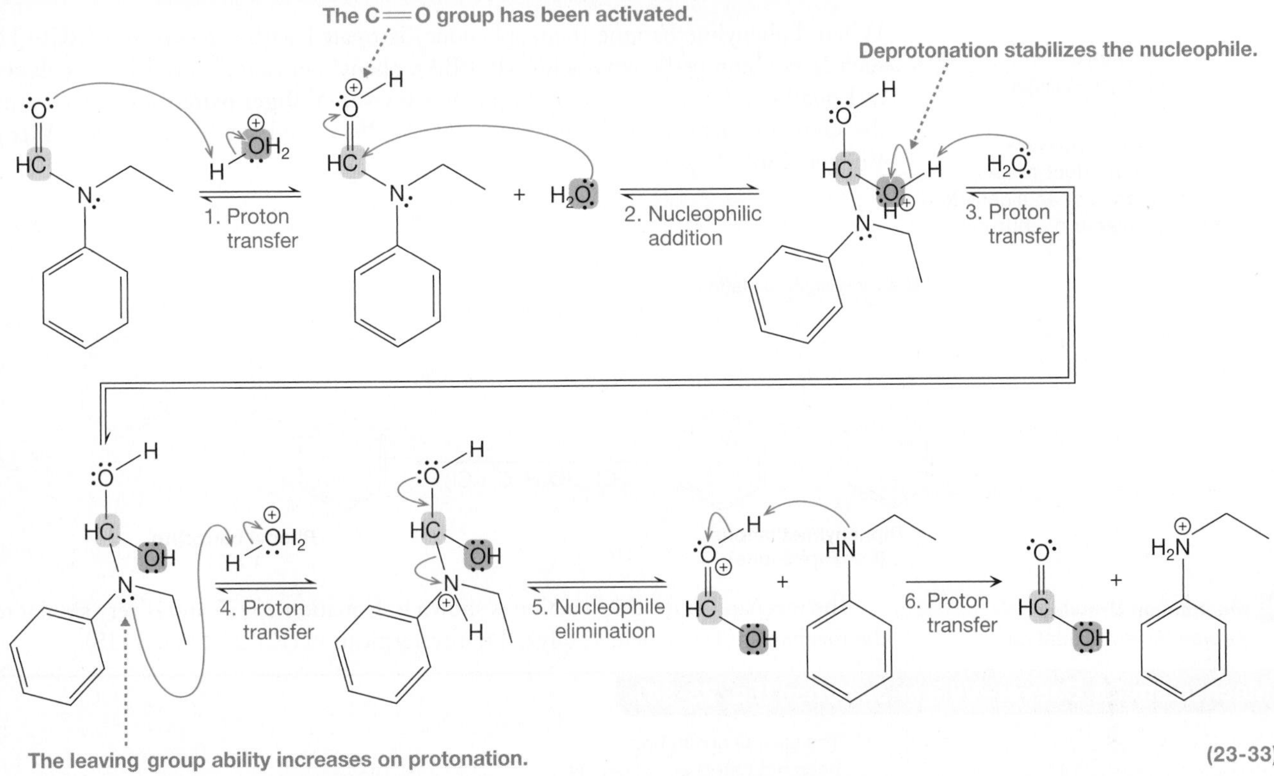
The C=O group has been activated.
Deprotonation stabilizes the nucleophile.
1. Proton transfer
2. Nucleophilic addition
3. Proton transfer
4. Proton transfer
5. Nucleophile elimination
6. Proton transfer
The leaving group ability increases on protonation.

(23-33)

The carbonyl group is activated in Step 1, which better facilitates nucleophilic addition of the weak nucleophile in Step 2. In Step 3, the charge on the O atom from the nucleophile goes from +1 to 0, so the O atom is stabilized. The reverse is true for the N atom of the leaving group in Step 4. In Step 5, the amine leaving group departs, and the C=O bond is simultaneously regenerated. Finally, in Step 6, the newly formed amine, which is weakly basic, irreversibly deprotonates the carbonyl O. This irreversible step consumes the acid, so the reaction is *acid-promoted* rather than acid-catalyzed.

YOUR TURN 23.14

Draw the complete detailed mechanism and the overall products for each of the following reactions.

(a)

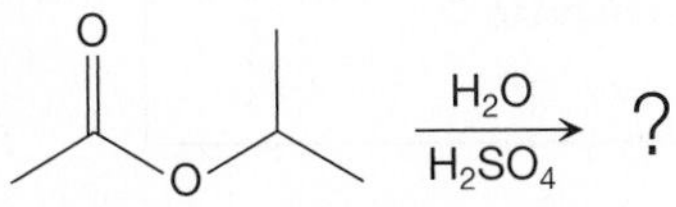
H2O
H2SO4
?

(b)

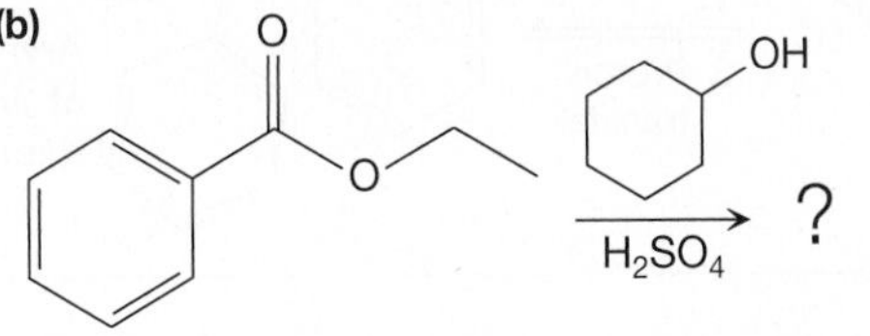
OH
H2SO4
?

(c)

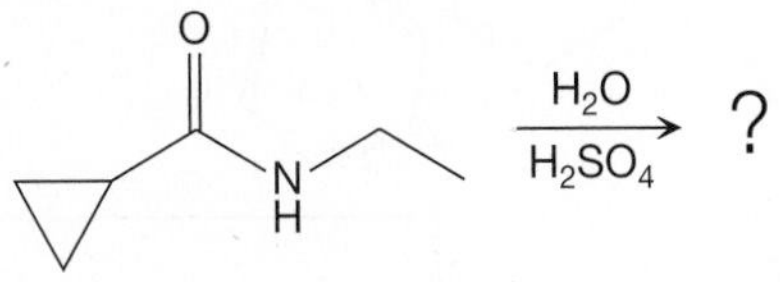
H2O
H2SO4
?

(d)

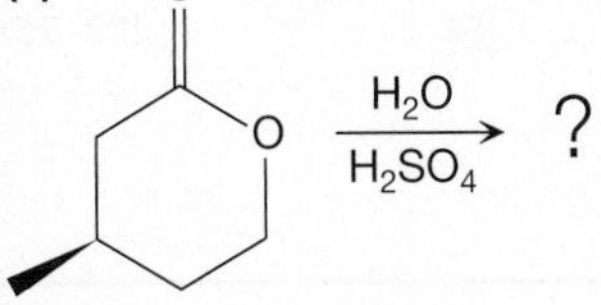
H2O
H2SO4
?

(e)

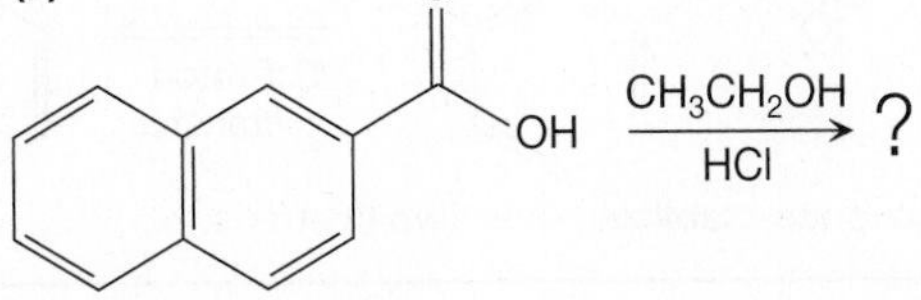
OH
CH3CH2OH
HCl
?

(f)

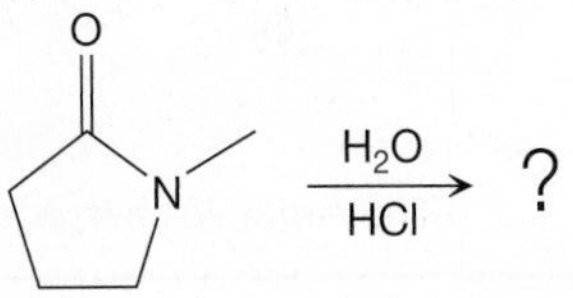
H2O
HCl
?

SECTION 23.8 OBJECTIVES

You will be able to:

1. Draw the mechanism and product for a Baeyer–Villiger oxidation reaction.
2. Predict the major Baeyer–Villiger oxidation product of an unsymmetric ketone or an aldehyde by considering migratory aptitude.

23.8 Baeyer–Villiger Oxidations

When diphenylmethanone (benzophenone) is treated with a *peroxy acid* (RCO_3H) such as *m*-chloroperbenzoic acid (MCPBA), phenyl benzoate is produced, as shown in Equation 23-34. This is an example of a **Baeyer–Villiger oxidation**, named after the German chemist Adolf von Baeyer (1835–1917) and the Swiss chemist Victor Villiger (1868–1934).

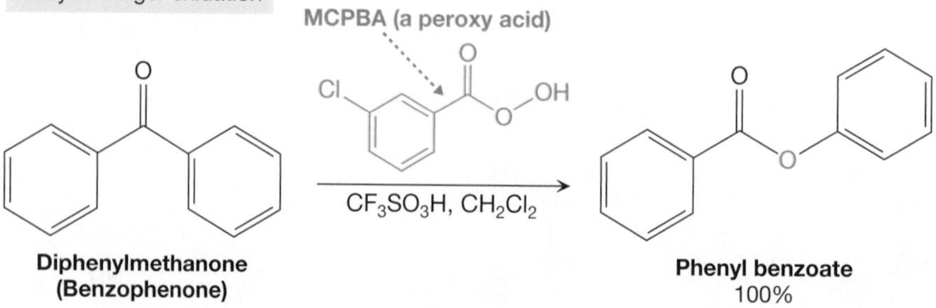

Baeyer–Villiger oxidation
MCPBA (a peroxy acid)
Cl
O
OH
O
CF3SO3H, CH2Cl2
Diphenylmethanone (Benzophenone)
Phenyl benzoate
100%

(23-34)

Mechanism Drawing
Baeyer–Villiger Oxidation

The mechanism for this reaction is shown in Equation 23-35 and is very similar to the mechanism for an acid-catalyzed transesterification (Eq. 23-29, p. 1118).

Mechanism for Baeyer–Villiger oxidation (Eq. 23-34)

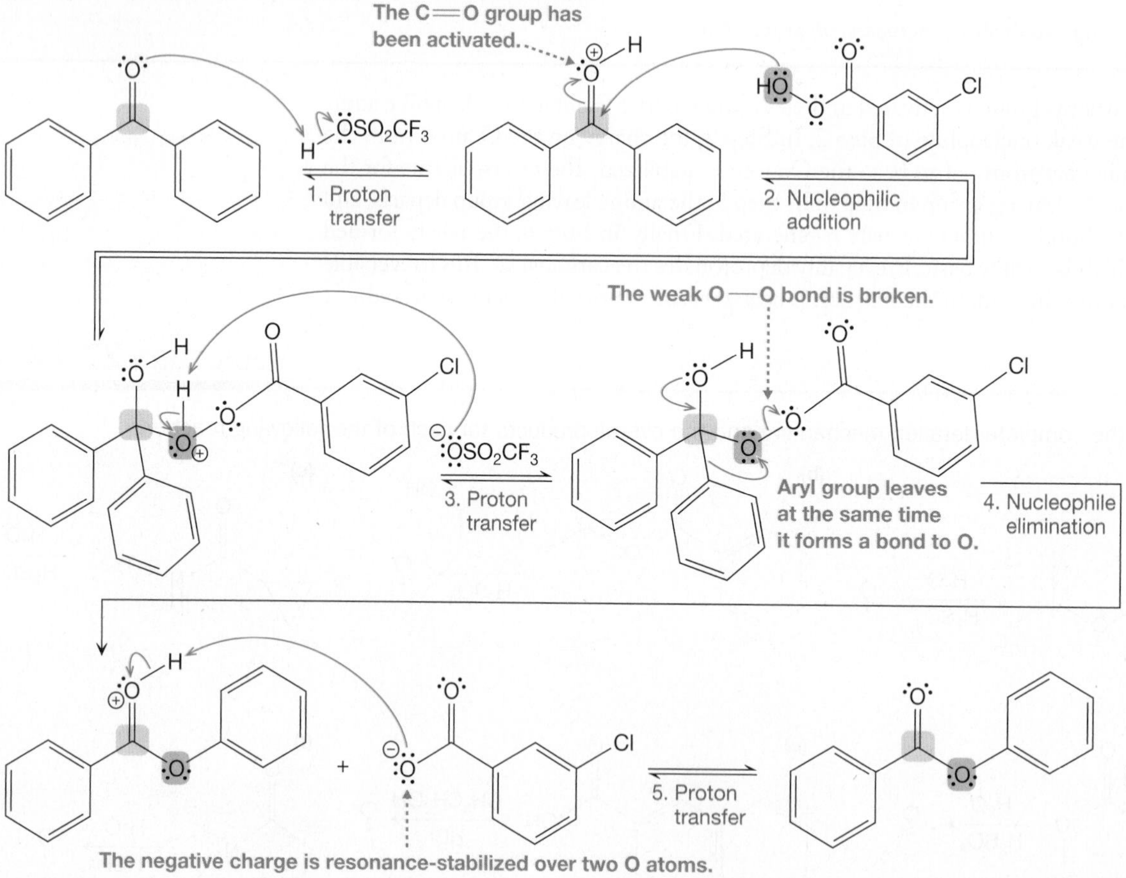

The C=O group has been activated.
OSO2CF3
1. Proton transfer
2. Nucleophilic addition
HO
Cl
The weak O—O bond is broken.
3. Proton transfer
Aryl group leaves at the same time it forms a bond to O.
4. Nucleophile elimination
+
5. Proton transfer
The negative charge is resonance-stabilized over two O atoms.

(23-35)

After the carbonyl group of the ketone has been activated by protonation in Step 1, the relatively weak peroxy acid nucleophile attacks the carbonyl C in Step 2. A proton is then removed from the peroxy acid's O atom in Step 3, and an aryl group departs from the carbonyl C in Step 4. Simultaneously, the aryl group forms a bond to an O atom from the peroxy acid, breaking the peroxy acid's O—O bond in the process. Finally, in Step 5, the ester's carbonyl group is deprotonated, yielding the overall uncharged ester product.

Even though ketones don't possess a good leaving group attached to the carbonyl carbon, the aryl group departs in Step 4 for two reasons. First, the O—O bond of the peroxy acid is weak and is replaced by a much stronger C—O bond (see Recall box). Second, the negative charge that is formed in that step appears on a carboxylate anion, RCO_2^-, so it is resonance-stabilized over two O atoms.

The ketone oxidized in Equation 23-34 is *symmetric*; that is, the carbonyl C is bonded to identical groups. If the groups bonded to the carbonyl C are different, as in an *unsymmetric* ketone or an aldehyde, then the major product depends on **migratory aptitude**: the ease with which each group attached to the carbonyl C can depart. Migratory aptitudes have been determined empirically for a variety of groups, as follows:

Migratory Aptitude in a Baeyer–Villiger Oxidation

Methyl group $<$ 1° Alkyl group $<$ 2° Alkyl group $\approx$ Aryl group $<$ 3° Alkyl group $<$ H

These migratory aptitudes roughly follow the order for cation stability. Indeed, the migrating group has been shown to acquire some cationic character in the transition state in the step in which it departs. This information is useful in predicting the major Baeyer–Villiger product, as shown in Solved Problem 23.4.

◂ RECALL

In Section 13.3, we saw how peroxy acids can be used to convert alkenes into epoxides. In those epoxide-formation reactions, the O atom of the OH group adds to the alkene, facilitated by the weak O—O bond of the peroxy acid.

GREEN CHEMISTRY

Traditionally, Baeyer–Villiger oxidations are carried out under conditions that are not very green. The CH_2Cl_2 solvent may be carcinogenic, and some of the common peroxy acids are toxic. One green alternative is shown here: it is solvent-free, incorporates hydrogen peroxide as the oxidizing agent, and is catalyzed by Fe_3O_4 nanoparticles that can be recycled.

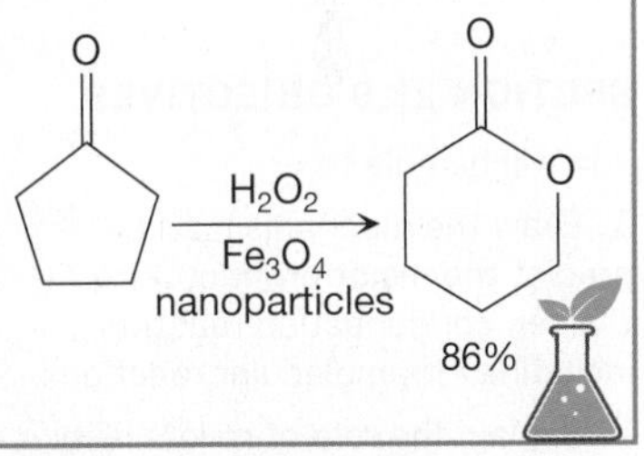

O
H₂O₂
Fe₃O₄
nanoparticles
O
O
86%

SOLVED PROBLEM **23.4**

How to predict the major product of a Baeyer–Villiger oxidation

Break It Down **Predict the major product of the reaction shown here. (CF_3CO_3H is relatively acidic.)**

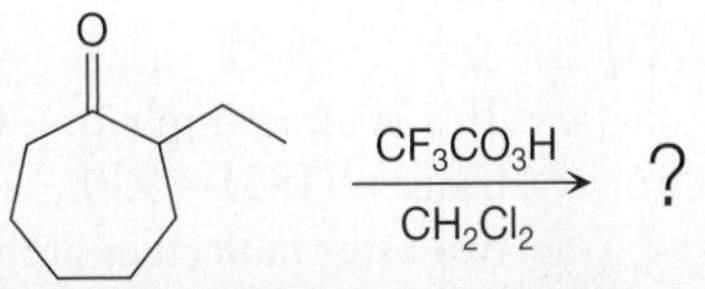

O
CF₃CO₃H
CH₂Cl₂
?

Think	Solve
What type of reagent is CF_3CO_3H? How does it tend to react with a ketone?	CF_3CO_3H is a peroxy acid and will react with a ketone in a Baeyer–Villiger oxidation. In such a reaction, an O atom from the peroxy acid is inserted between the carbonyl C and one of the groups initially bonded to the carbonyl C.

(continued)

Does one side of the ketone favor reaction over the other? If so, which side?	In this case, the carbonyl C is bonded to a primary and a secondary alkyl group. The secondary alkyl group has a greater migratory aptitude, so its bond will preferentially break, producing the lactone (cyclic ester) shown here.

A 2° alkyl group has a greater *migratory aptitude* than a 1° alkyl group.

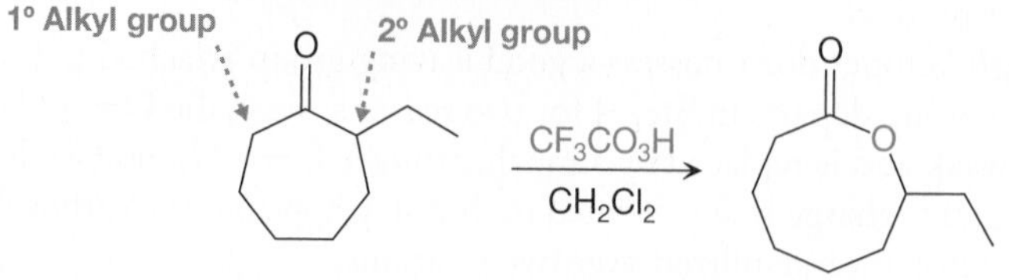
1° Alkyl group
2° Alkyl group
O
CF_3CO_3H
CH_2Cl_2
O
O

Try It Predict the major product of each of the following reactions.

(a)

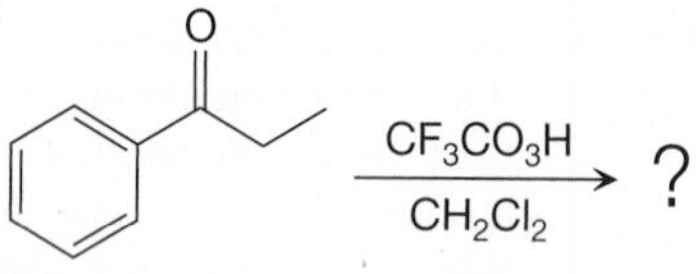
O
CF_3CO_3H
CH_2Cl_2
?

(b)

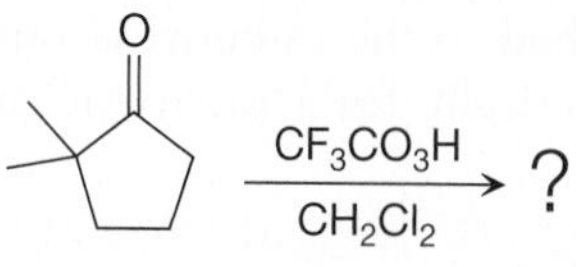
O
CF_3CO_3H
CH_2Cl_2
?

(c)

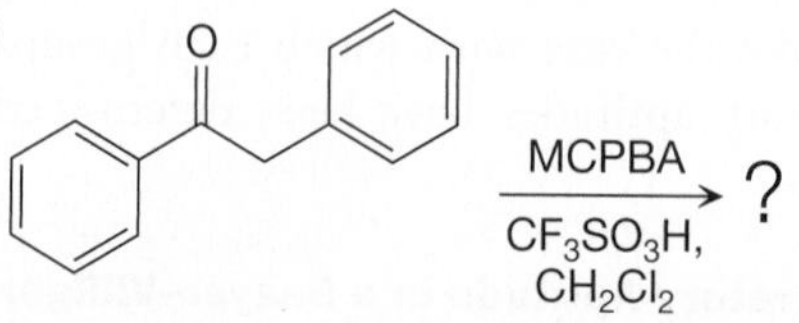
O
MCPBA
CF_3SO_3H,
CH_2Cl_2
?

SECTION 23.9 OBJECTIVES

You will be able to:

1. Draw the mechanism and predict the major product for a Claisen condensation reaction, including intramolecular reactions.
2. Explain the role of reversibility in Claisen condensation reactions.
3. Design an effective self-Claisen or crossed Claisen condensation reaction that uses an appropriate base and solvent.

23.9 Claisen Condensation Reactions

When ethyl ethanoate (ethyl acetate) is treated with sodium ethoxide, followed by acid workup, ethyl 3-oxobutanoate, a **β-keto ester**, is produced (Eq. 23-36):

Claisen condensation

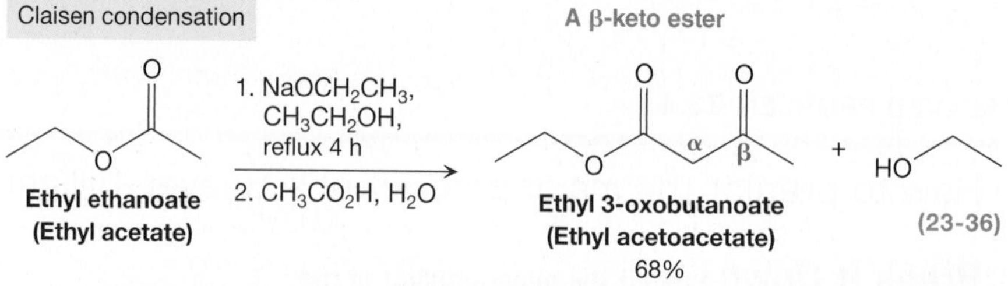
A β-keto ester
O
O
1. $NaOCH_2CH_3$,
CH_3CH_2OH,
reflux 4 h
2. CH_3CO_2H, H_2O
Ethyl ethanoate
(Ethyl acetate)
O
O
O
α
β
+
HO
Ethyl 3-oxobutanoate
(Ethyl acetoacetate)
68%

(23-36)

This is an example of a **Claisen condensation reaction**, named after Rainer Ludwig Claisen (1851–1930), who developed it. It is a *condensation* reaction because, overall, two ester molecules are fused together and a smaller molecule—in this case, a molecule of ethanol—is eliminated.

The mechanism for the Claisen condensation reaction in Equation 23-36, shown in Equation 23-37, is very similar to the mechanism for base-catalyzed transesterification (review Eq. 23-25, p. 1117). Normally an ester is not strongly nucleophilic, but because of the basic conditions of the reaction, $CH_3CH_2O^-$ deprotonates the ester at its α carbon in Step 1 to produce a strongly nucleophilic enolate anion. In Step 2, that enolate anion attacks the carbonyl carbon of a second molecule of the same ester, forming a new C—C bond. $CH_3CH_2O^-$ is then eliminated in Step 3, producing an initial β-keto ester, which is quickly deprotonated in Step 4. Acid workup in Step 5 replenishes the β-keto ester.

Mechanism for a Claisen condensation reaction (Eq. 23-36)

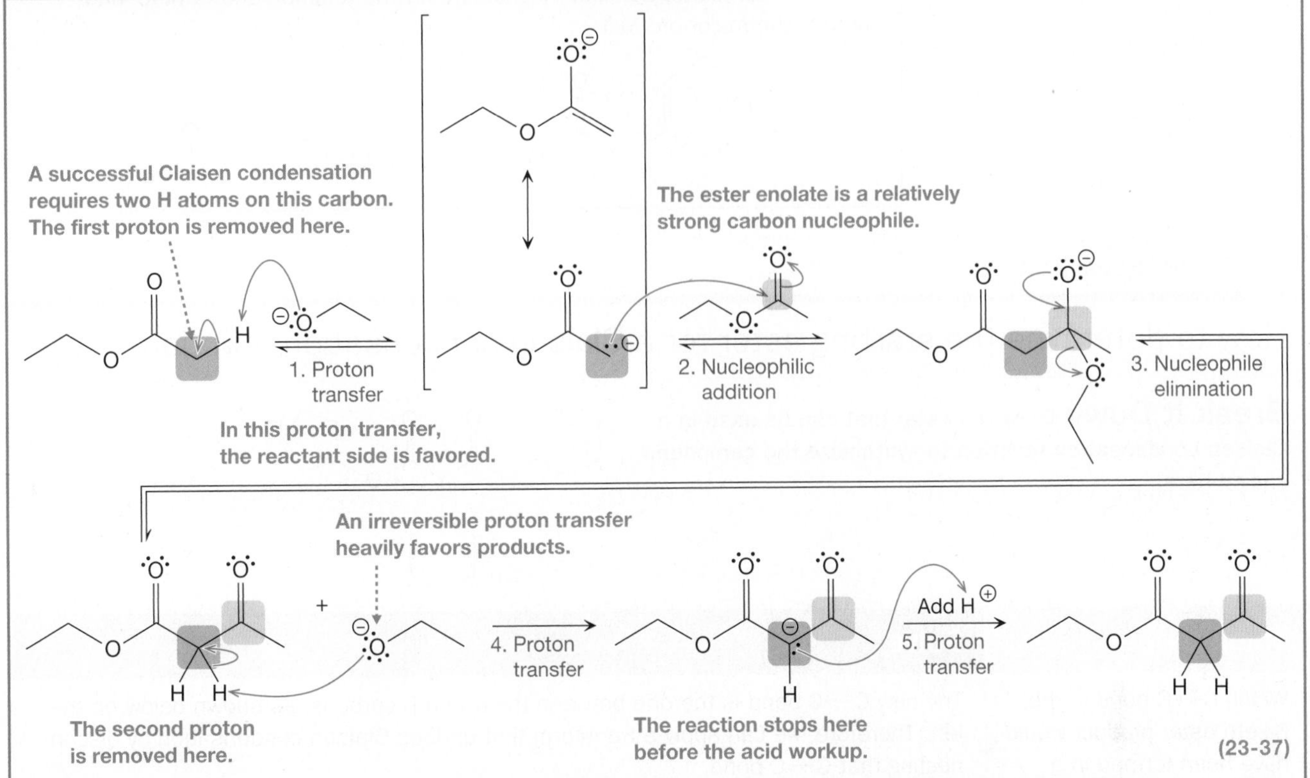

A successful Claisen condensation requires two H atoms on this carbon. The first proton is removed here.
1. Proton transfer
In this proton transfer, the reactant side is favored.
The ester enolate is a relatively strong carbon nucleophile.
2. Nucleophilic addition
3. Nucleophile elimination
An irreversible proton transfer heavily favors products.
4. Proton transfer
Add H
5. Proton transfer
The second proton is removed here.
The reaction stops here before the acid workup.

(23-37)

The first two proton transfer steps (i.e., Steps 1 and 4) play important roles in this mechanism. The first (Step 1) is reversible and favors the reactant side, much like we saw for aldol reactions (see Recall box). Thus, only a small fraction of the initial ester exists in the form of the enolate anion at any given time, leaving a substantial amount of the uncharged ester available to react with the enolate anion. The second proton transfer (Step 4) is *irreversible*, heavily favoring the product side. That step is irreversible because the β-keto ester is much more acidic ($pK_a = 11$) than a normal ester because of the substantial resonance delocalization of the negative charge in the enolate anion that is produced. It is important that Step 4 is irreversible because the reaction is reversible through the first three steps, favoring the overall reactants. The deprotonation in Step 4 effectively removes the β-keto ester product, and according to Le Châtelier's principle, the first three steps shift continually toward products.

The proton transfer steps in Equation 23-37 place a significant restriction on the esters that can participate in Claisen condensations:

Mechanism Drawing
Claisen Condensation

◂ RECALL

Enolate anions formed on deprotonation of an α carbon serve as nucleophiles in α halogenation (Section 10.6), α alkylation (Section 11.3), and aldol reactions (Section 19.8). In an aldol reaction, an enolate anion undergoes nucleophilic addition, as in a Claisen condensation, but no leaving group departs.

> A successful Claisen condensation generally requires at least two α protons on the initial ester.

Without the first α proton, the enolate anion could not be produced. Without the second α proton, the equilibrium would favor the overall reactants, and as shown in Equation 23-38, no significant amount of the β-keto ester would be isolated:

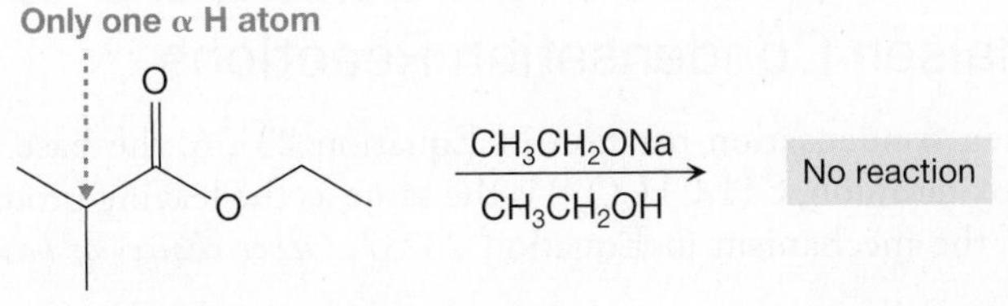

Only one α H atom
CH_3CH_2ONa
CH_3CH_2OH
No reaction

(23-38)

Ethyl 2-methylpropanoate

YOUR TURN **23.15**

Draw the complete, detailed mechanism for the reaction shown here, and predict the major product.

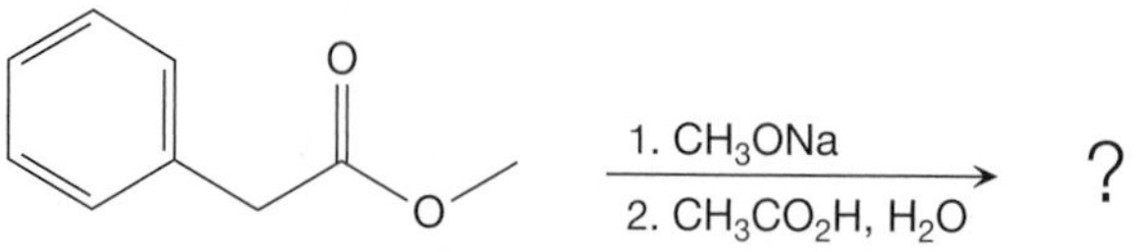
1. CH_3ONa
2. CH_3CO_2H, H_2O
?

SOLVED PROBLEM **23.5**

How to determine the starting ester for a Claisen condensation reaction

Break It Down **Draw the ester that can be used in a Claisen condensation reaction to synthesize the compound shown here.**

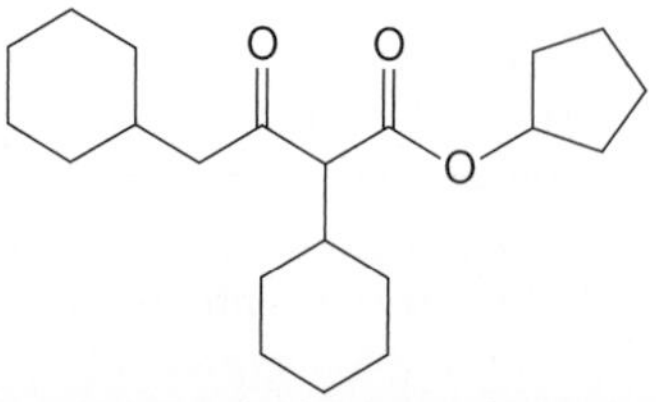

Think	Solve
Which C—C bond in the β-keto ester product would have been formed in a Claisen condensation?	The new C—C bond is the one between the α and β carbons, as shown below on the left. Therefore, we can apply a transform that undoes Claisen condensation by disconnecting that C—C bond.

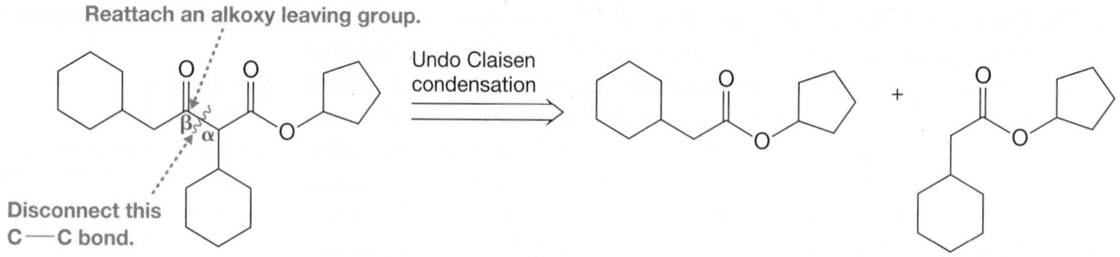
Reattach an alkoxy leaving group.
Disconnect this C—C bond.
Undo Claisen condensation

Which C atom would have been bonded to the alkoxy leaving group?	The leaving group would have been attached to the β C atom. When the leaving group is added back, as shown above on the right, both precursor molecules are identical esters.

Try It Draw the ester that can be used in a Claisen condensation reaction to synthesize the compound shown here.

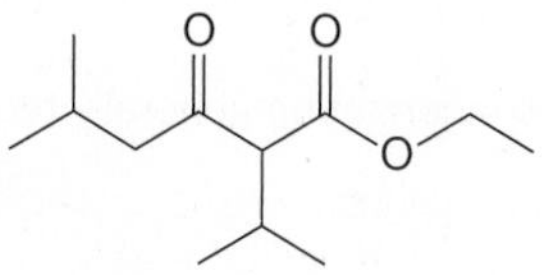

23.9a The Importance of the Solvent and Base in Claisen Condensation Reactions

In the Claisen condensation reaction in Equation 23-36, the base that is added (i.e., the ethoxide anion, $CH_3CH_2O^-$) is the same as the leaving group that departs in Step 3 of the mechanism in Equation 23-37. *Other choices of base could lead to undesired products*. If the base were an alkoxide other than ethoxide, for example, as in Equation 23-39, then transesterification would produce an ester that is different from the starting material (see Your Turn 23.16). Alternatively, if hydroxide were used as the base, as in Equation 23-40, then *saponification* (Section 22.3) would irreversibly convert the ester into a carboxylate anion (see Your Turn 23.17).

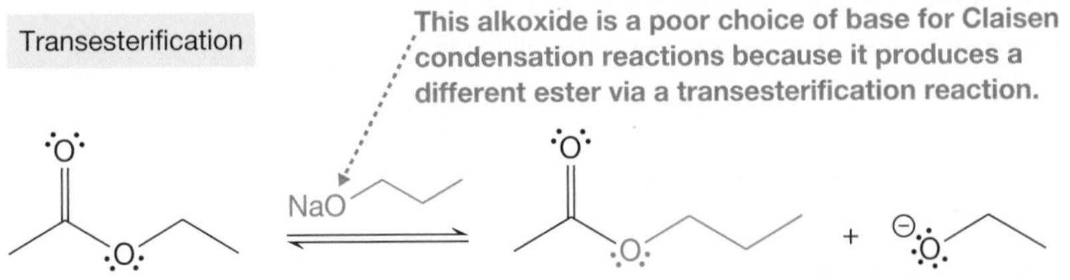
Transesterification
This alkoxide is a poor choice of base for Claisen condensation reactions because it produces a different ester via a transesterification reaction.
NaO

(23-39)

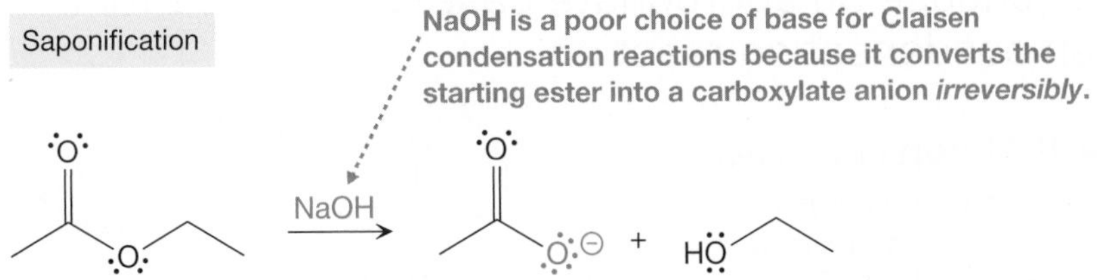
Saponification
NaOH is a poor choice of base for Claisen condensation reactions because it converts the starting ester into a carboxylate anion *irreversibly*.
NaOH
HO

(23-40)

These problems are avoided when ethoxide is the base. Transesterification still occurs, but the transesterification product is identical to the initial ester.

YOUR TURN 23.16

Draw the complete, detailed mechanism for the transesterification reaction that takes place among the species in Equation 23-39. Then draw the complete, detailed mechanism for the Claisen condensation reaction that would take place with the new ester. How does this Claisen condensation product compare to the one in Equation 23-36 (p. 1124)?

YOUR TURN 23.17

Draw the complete, detailed mechanism for the reaction in Equation 23-40.

Notice that the solvent in Equation 23-36 (i.e., ethanol, CH_3CH_2OH) is the conjugate acid of the base that is added. *Other choices of solvent can lead to an unwanted transesterification or saponification reaction*. If, for example, the solvent for the reaction in Equation 23-36 were another alcohol, such as propan-1-ol ($CH_3CH_2CH_2OH$), then the added ethoxide anion would deprotonate propan-1-ol to generate the 1-propoxide anion ($CH_3CH_2CH_2O^-$), thereby causing the transesterification reaction in Equation 23-39 to occur (see Your Turn 23.18). Alternatively, if water were used as the solvent, then HO^- would be produced, and the saponification reaction in Equation 23-40 would take place. With ethanol as the solvent, this kind of proton transfer still takes place, but that proton transfer is not a problem because the products are the same as the reactants.

YOUR TURN 23.18

Write the proton transfer equilibrium that would take place if propan-1-ol were used as the solvent for the reaction in Equation 23-36 (p. 1124). Do the same if water were used as the solvent and if ethanol were used as the solvent. What do you notice about the reactants and products of these proton transfer reactions?

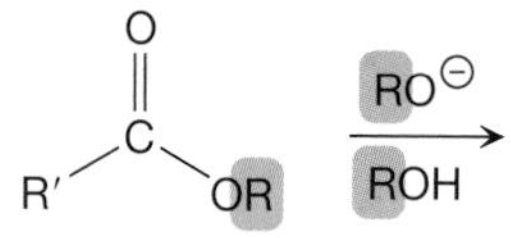
RO⊖
ROH
R′
OR
Same R groups

FIGURE 23-6 Choice of base and solvent for Claisen condensations Unwanted side reactions can be avoided for Claisen condensation reactions if the alkyl groups are the same in the leaving group, the alkoxide base, and the alcohol solvent.

In light of the issues that can arise with the wrong choice of base or solvent, Claisen condensation reactions are often carried out according to the following guideline:

For a Claisen condensation reaction, unwanted transesterification and saponification reactions can be avoided if:

- The base that is added is the same as the alkoxide leaving group on the ester.
- The alcohol solvent is the conjugate acid of that base.

These ideas are captured in **Figure 23-6**.

SOLVED PROBLEM **23.6**

How to choose an appropriate base and solvent for a Claisen condensation reaction

Break It Down Identify the appropriate base–solvent pair to accomplish a Claisen condensation with the ester shown here.

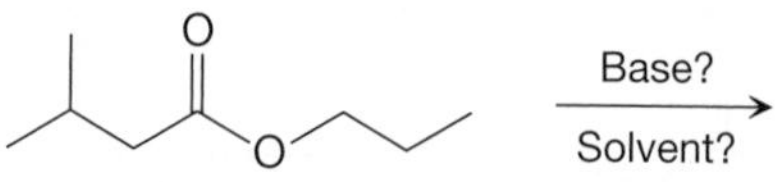
Base?
Solvent?

Think	Solve
What is the leaving group on the ester? What choice of base would ensure that a nucleophilic addition–elimination would leave us with the same ester?	The leaving group is $CH_3CH_2CH_2O^-$. Therefore, if we were to add $NaOCH_2CH_2CH_3$ as the base, then transesterification would leave us with the same ester.
What solvent, if deprotonated, would form the base that is added?	$CH_3CH_2CH_2OH$ should be the solvent, because if it were to be deprotonated, it would yield $CH_3CH_2CH_2O^-$, the same as the added base. The Claisen condensation reaction would be carried out as shown here. 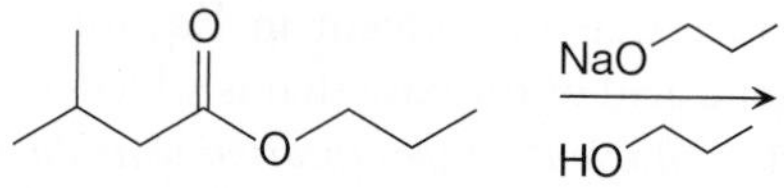

NaO
HO

Try It Identify the appropriate base–solvent pair to accomplish a Claisen condensation with each of the following esters.

(a)
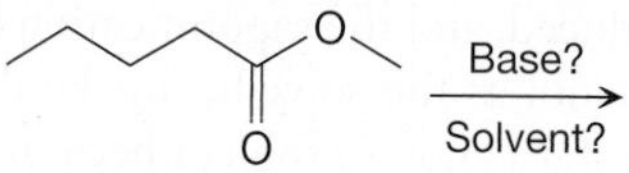
Base?
Solvent?

(b)
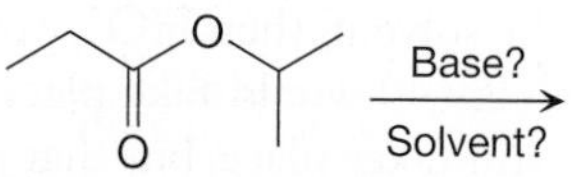
Base?
Solvent?

23.9b Crossed Claisen Condensation Reactions

The Claisen condensation reactions discussed in Section 23.9a involve two molecules of the same ester; that is, they are *self-condensations*. A Claisen condensation can also involve two *different* esters: this is called a **crossed Claisen condensation reaction**. These reactions require special considerations, however, because crossed Claisen reactions can potentially lead to a mixture of condensation products (just as we saw with crossed *aldol* reactions in Section 19.11).

The reaction in Equation 23-41, for example, would produce a mixture of four β-keto esters, because two different ester enolates can be generated as nucleophiles and two different, uncharged esters can be attacked by those nucleophiles:

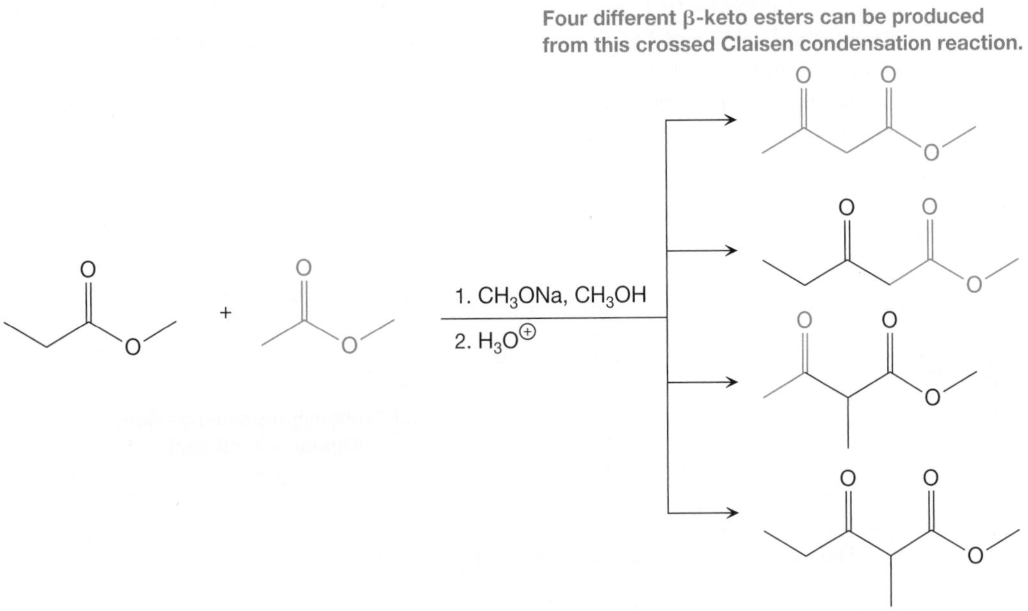
Four different β-keto esters can be produced from this crossed Claisen condensation reaction.
1. CH_3ONa, CH_3OH
2. $H_3O^{\oplus}$

(23-41a)

(23-41b)

(23-41c)

(23-41d)

YOUR TURN 23.19

Draw a complete, detailed mechanism for the formation of *each* product in Equation 23-41.

One way to avoid producing a mixture of condensation products in a crossed Claisen reaction is to ensure that one of the esters has no α hydrogens (see Recall box). Some common examples of such esters are shown in **Figure 23-7**.

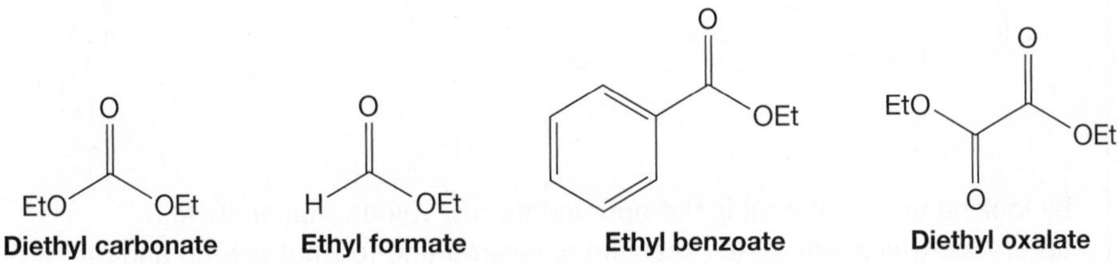
Diethyl carbonate
Ethyl formate
Ethyl benzoate
Diethyl oxalate

FIGURE 23-7 Esters with no α hydrogens Without α hydrogens, these esters will not produce enolate anions that would act as nucleophiles in Claisen condensation reactions.

Esters that do not have any α hydrogens can be dissolved in solution with an alkoxide base without initiating a Claisen condensation reaction. A second ester that has α hydrogens can then be added slowly to this solution. As the ester with α hydrogens comes in contact with the base, its enolate anion is produced, and the crossed Claisen condensation begins. An example is shown in Equation 23-42, which uses ethyl formate as the ester with no α hydrogens.

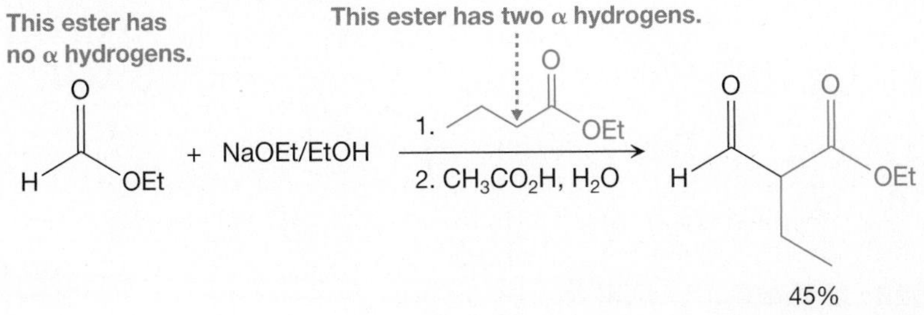
This ester has no α hydrogens.
This ester has two α hydrogens.
+ NaOEt/EtOH
1.
2. CH_3CO_2H, H_2O
45%

(23-42)

◂ RECALL

Attempts to carry out crossed aldol reactions (Section 19.11) can produce a mixture of aldol products, similar to the potential problem with crossed Claisen condensation reactions. As explained in Section 19.11, unwanted aldol products can be avoided if one aldehyde or ketone lacks α hydrogens.

Aldehyde and ketone enolate anions can also undergo nucleophilic addition–elimination with an ester, as shown for the examples involving ketones in Equations 23-43 and 23-44; the products are *1,3-dicarbonyl compounds*. The reaction in Equation 23-43 is synthetically useful because the ester has no α hydrogens. In Equation 23-44, the ester has α hydrogens, but the reaction is synthetically useful because an ester is significantly less acidic than a ketone. Therefore, when the ester is added to the ketone enolate that was first produced quantitatively by H_2N^-, the α protons largely remain on the ester. (See Your Turn 23.20.)

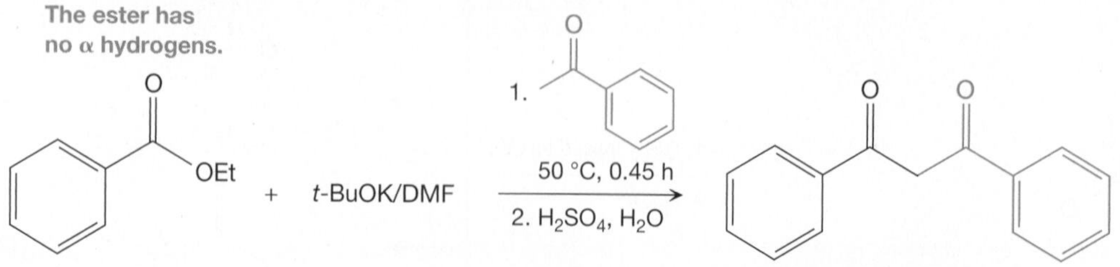
The ester has no α hydrogens.
OEt
+ t-BuOK/DMF
1.
50 °C, 0.45 h
2. H2SO4, H2O

(23-43)

1,3-Diphenylpropane-1,3,-dione
(Dibenzoylmethane)
80%

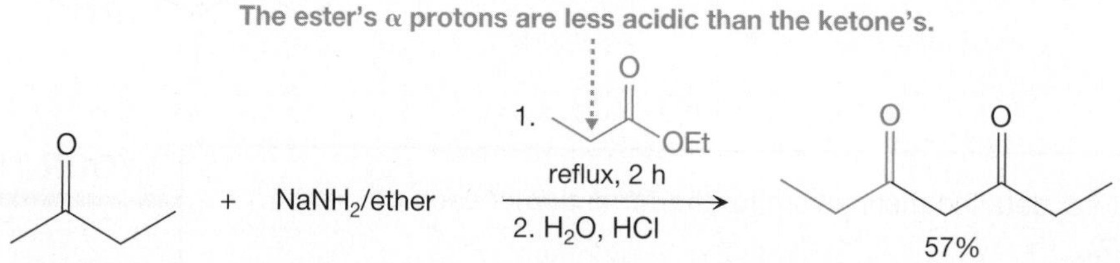
The ester's α protons are less acidic than the ketone's.
1.
OEt
reflux, 2 h
+ NaNH2/ether
2. H2O, HCl

(23-44)

57%

YOUR TURN 23.20

Once the ketone enolate anion is produced in the reaction in Equation 23-44, the following proton transfer reaction is possible when the ester is added and could result, therefore, in undesired condensation products.

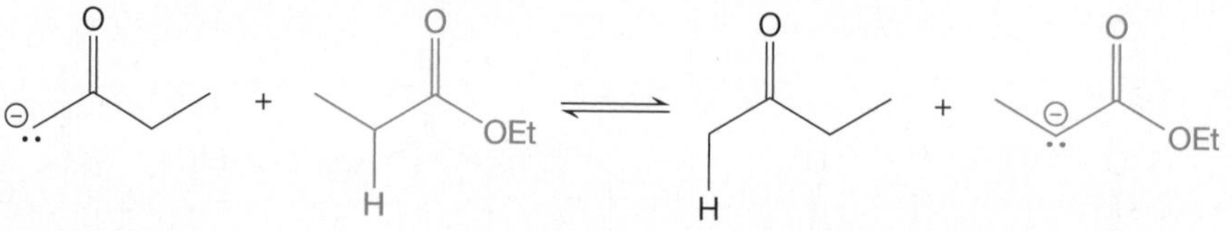
OEt
H
H
OEt

By looking up or estimating the appropriate pK_a values (Appendix A), determine which side of the reaction is favored and to what extent, and explain why this proton transfer reaction is not a major concern.

CONNECTIONS 23.5

Licorice root and your health
Licorice root (*Glycyrrhiza glabra*) is a widely used ancient Chinese herbal medicine. One of its components, 1,3-diphenylpropane-1,3-dione (Eq. 23-43), commonly called dibenzoylmethane, exhibits a variety of anticancer properties.

SOLVED PROBLEM **23.7**

How to design a crossed Claisen condensation reaction for synthesis

Break It Down **Show how you would synthesize this compound in a Claisen condensation reaction.**

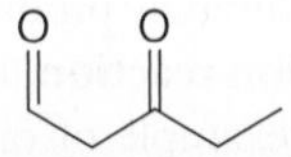

Think	Solve
Which C—C bond would have been formed in a Claisen condensation? Which C would have an attached OR group in the precursors?	The bond between the α and β carbons indicated below could have been formed in a Claisen condensation. To draw the precursors, we undo that C—C bond and add an OR group to the β carbon. 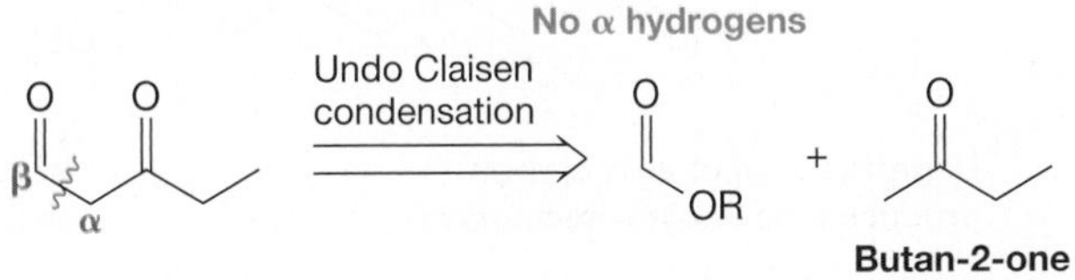 No α hydrogens Undo Claisen condensation β α OR **Butan-2-one**
Does this transform suggest a self-Claisen or a crossed Claisen condensation reaction?	The two carbonyl-containing precursors are not identical esters, so a crossed Claisen condensation reaction is in order.
Does one of the precursors lack α hydrogens? How does that help?	The precursor that is an ester has no α hydrogens, so it will not undergo a self-Claisen condensation.
Is the required enolate anion the result of deprotonation under kinetic control or thermodynamic control? Which base would be appropriate?	The required enolate anion is the result of deprotonating the less substituted α carbon, so deprotonation needs to take place under kinetic control (review Section 11.3). We should therefore choose a base that would deprotonate irreversibly, such as lithium diisopropylamide (LDA). The synthesis could be reported as shown here. 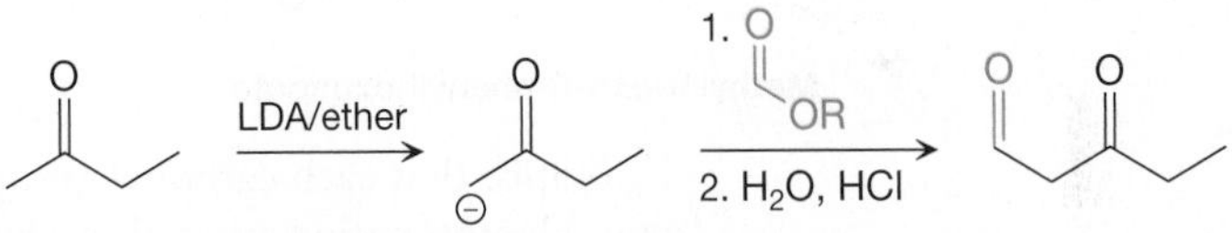 LDA/ether 1. OR 2. H_2O, HCl

Try It Devise another synthesis of the target in Solved Problem 23.7 without using an ester of the form:

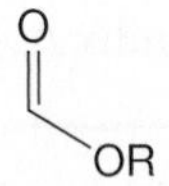
OR

23.9c Intramolecular Claisen Condensation: The Dieckmann Condensation Reaction

The Claisen condensation, like the aldol reaction, has the potential for an *intramolecular* reaction, ultimately producing a ring. When it does, the reaction is called a **Dieckmann condensation reaction**, named after the German chemist Walter Dieckmann (1869–1925). An example of one involving a diester is shown in Equation 23-45. As with most cyclization reactions, Dieckmann condensations occur most readily when the reaction leads to the formation of a five- or six-membered ring.

Dieckmann condensation

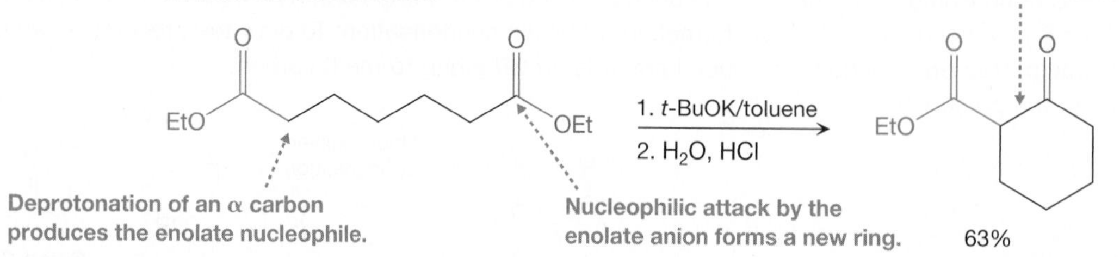
New C—C bond
EtO
OEt
1. t-BuOK/toluene
2. H2O, HCl
EtO
Deprotonation of an α carbon produces the enolate nucleophile.
Nucleophilic attack by the enolate anion forms a new ring.
63%

(23-45)

YOUR TURN 23.21

Draw the complete, detailed mechanism for the reaction in Equation 23-45.

An intramolecular nucleophilic addition–elimination reaction on an ester can also occur if the enolate anion derives from the portion of a molecule characteristic of a ketone or aldehyde. For example, methyl 6-oxo-6-phenylhexanoate cyclizes when treated with sodium amide to yield the five-membered ring product shown in Equation 23-46:

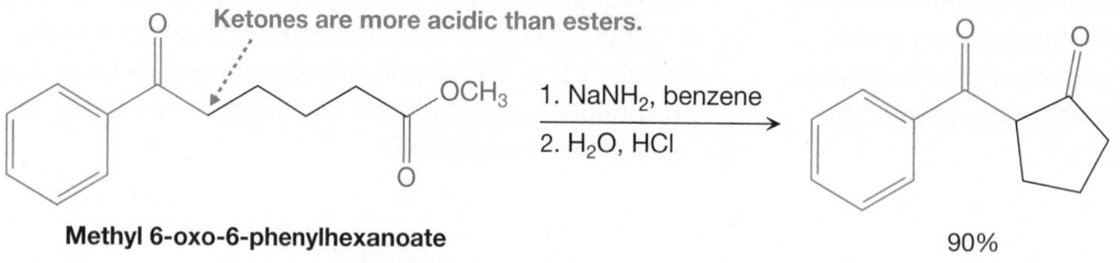
Ketones are more acidic than esters.
OCH3
1. NaNH2, benzene
2. H2O, HCl
90%

(23-46)

Methyl 6-oxo-6-phenylhexanoate

Notice that each carbonyl group in the reactant in Equation 23-46 has α hydrogens. Deprotonation takes place almost exclusively at the α carbon on the left because *ketones (and aldehydes) are substantially more acidic than esters.* (Compare their pK_a values in Appendix A.)

YOUR TURN 23.22

Draw the complete, detailed mechanism for the reaction shown here, and predict the major product.

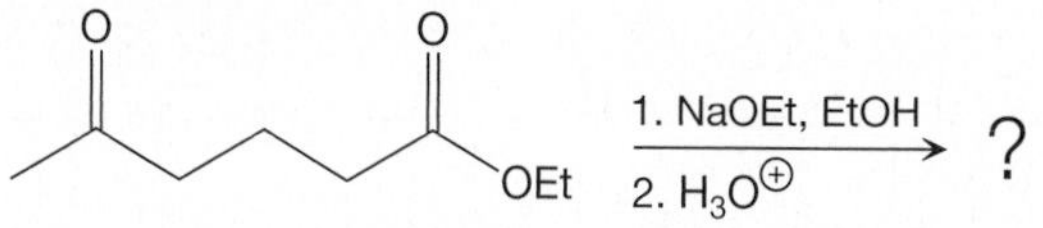
OEt
1. NaOEt, EtOH
2. H3O⊕
?

YOUR TURN 23.23

Draw the acyclic dicarbonyl compound that can be used to synthesize the cyclic β-keto aldehyde shown here.

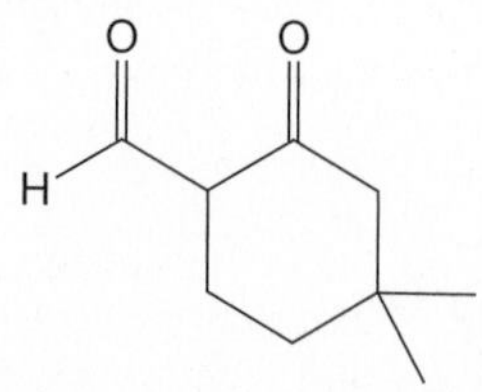
H

Biological Claisen Condensation Reactions

When people consume more calories in their diet than they burn, the excess fuel (typically from carbohydrates) is stored as fat. A fat is a triglyceride (Section 2.10a), which is a triester formed between glycerol (a triol) and three fatty acids. Each fatty acid is a carboxylic acid whose carbon chain has an even number of carbons, most commonly 14–20 carbons long. How do carbohydrates become converted to fat, and why do the carbon chains of fatty acids appear in increments of two carbons? The answer has to do with biological Claisen condensation reactions. An example between malonyl-acyl carrier protein (ACP) and acetyl synthase is shown in Steps 1 and 2 of the scheme in **Figure 23-8**. The acyl group indicated in malonyl-ACP is produced in glycolysis, the metabolic pathway that breaks down glucose for energy.

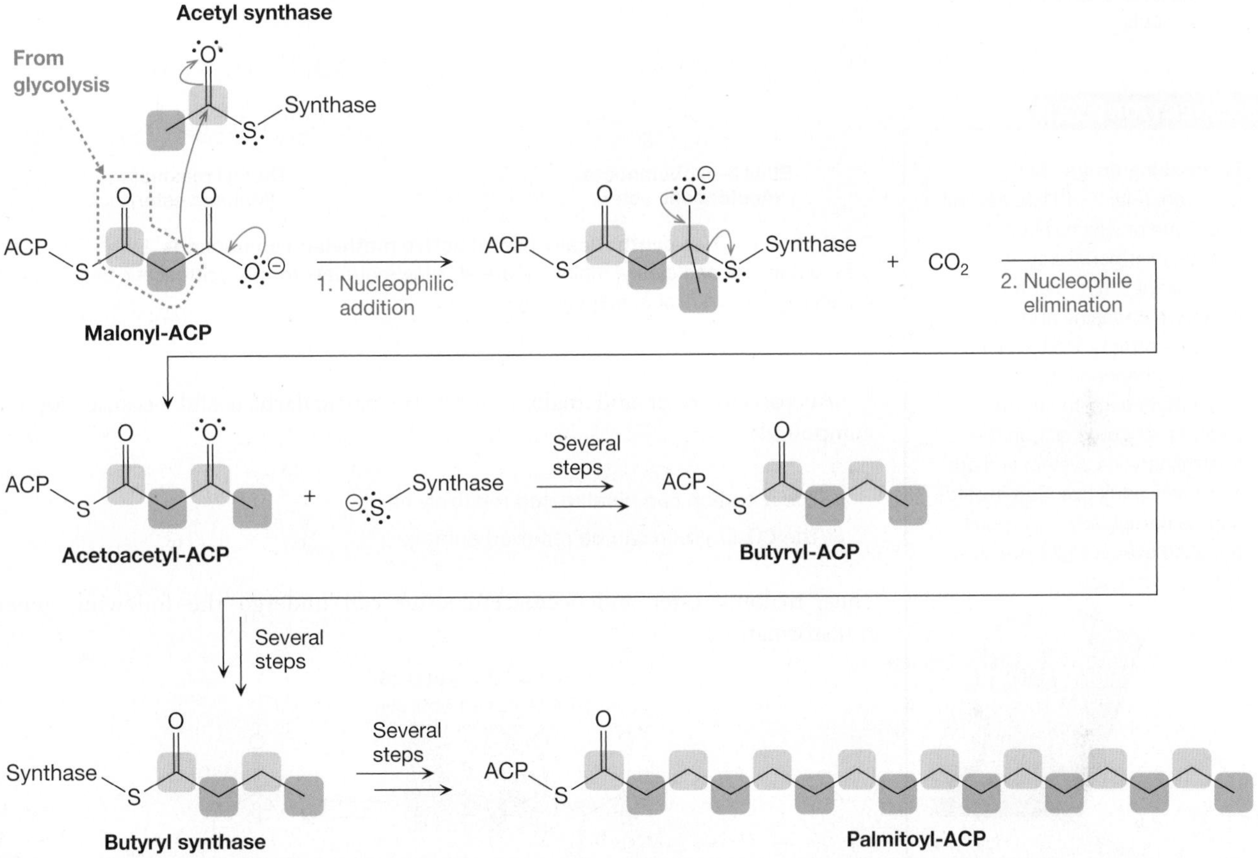

Acetyl synthase
From glycolysis
Synthase
ACP
Malonyl-ACP
1. Nucleophilic addition
+ CO_2
2. Nucleophile elimination
Acetoacetyl-ACP
Several steps
Butyryl-ACP
Several steps
Synthase
Butyryl synthase
Several steps
Palmitoyl-ACP

FIGURE 23-8

In Step 1, the α C of malonyl-ACP undergoes nucleophilic addition to the carbonyl C of acetyl synthase to produce a tetrahedral intermediate. In Step 2, the S—synthase leaving group is eliminated and the C═O bond is regenerated, producing acetoacetyl-ACP, a β-keto thioester. Through several subsequent steps, acetoacetyl-ACP is converted to butyryl-ACP, which is the sulfur analog to the fatty acid butyric acid. Butyryl-ACP is converted to butyryl synthase, which can participate in another Claisen condensation with malonyl-ACP. Each time this process is repeated, the carbon chain grows by two, which explains the even number of carbons.

This scheme is validated in part by an experiment in which organisms are fed ^{14}C-labeled acetic acid (CH_3CO_2H). A cell uses acetic acid to synthesize acetyl-coenzyme A, from which both malonyl-ACP and acetyl synthase are derived, so the ^{14}C label appears in the synthesized fatty acid. When the carbonyl C of acetic acid was labeled, the ^{14}C label appeared at the locations highlighted in blue in Figure 23-8. When the label was at the α C, the label appeared at the locations highlighted in red in the figure.

23.10 Organic Synthesis: Decarboxylation, the Malonic Ester Synthesis, and the Acetoacetic Ester Synthesis

SECTION 23.10 OBJECTIVES

You will be able to:

1. Identify species that can undergo decarboxylation, and draw the mechanism and major product for such a reaction.
2. Predict the major product of a malonic ester synthesis or an acetoacetic ester synthesis.
3. Design an effective malonic ester synthesis or an acetoacetic ester synthesis.

CONNECTIONS 23.6

Depressing drugs Diethyl malonate (Fig. 23-9) has several uses, one of which is in the synthesis of barbiturates, depressant drugs that have anxiety-decreasing and sleep-inducing effects. Barbiturates such as phenobarbital, a medication used to control epileptic seizures, act on the central nervous system and are extremely addictive. Barbiturates can be particularly dangerous because even a slight overdose can lead to death.

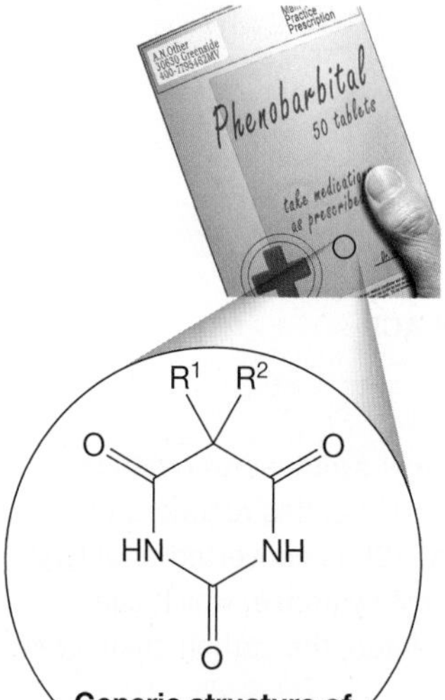

Phenobarbital
50 tablets
R^1 R^2
O
O
HN
NH
O

Generic structure of a barbiturate

The main focus of Section 23.9 was the production of β-keto esters by Claisen condensation reactions. Ethyl 3-oxobutanoate (acetoacetic ester), shown in **Figure 23-9**, is a β-keto ester that is particularly useful as a starting material in organic syntheses. Diethyl malonate (malonic ester), a β diester, is structurally similar to acetoacetic ester and is also quite useful synthetically.

Ethyl 3-oxobutanoate (Acetoacetic ester) **Diethyl malonate (Malonic ester)**

FIGURE 23-9 Two synthetically useful active methylene compounds Ethyl 3-oxobutanoate and diethyl malonate are starting materials for the acetoacetic ester and malonic ester syntheses, respectively.

Acetoacetic ester and malonic ester are particularly useful because, for both compounds:

- The α carbon can be alkylated relatively easily.
- The CO_2Et group can be removed entirely.

Thus, malonic ester and acetoacetic ester can undergo the following general transformation:

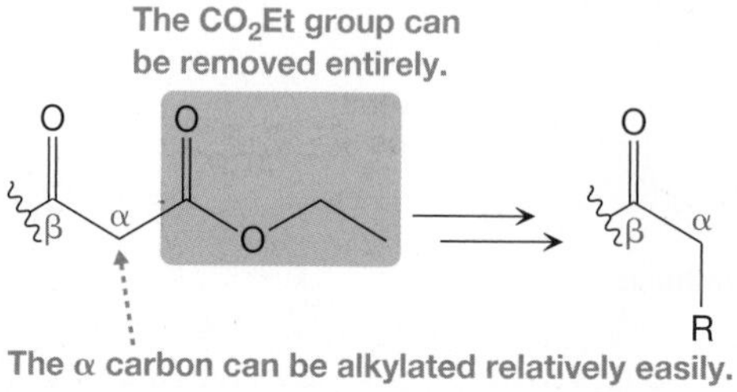

The CO_2Et group can be removed entirely.
The α carbon can be alkylated relatively easily.

(23-47)

Alkylation is relatively easy to carry out because the protons on the α CH_2 group are significantly more acidic than normal esters or ketones; malonic ester and acetoacetic ester are therefore called **active methylene compounds**. Each of the two C=O groups flanking the α CH_2 group significantly enhances the acidity by resonance and inductive stabilization in the enolate conjugate base. The α protons are sufficiently acidic that even a moderately strong base such as $CH_3CH_2O^-$ will produce the enolate anion *quantitatively* (Eq. 23-48). The negatively charged enolate anion is strongly nucleophilic and will react with an alkyl halide in an S_N2 reaction to produce the alkylated product.

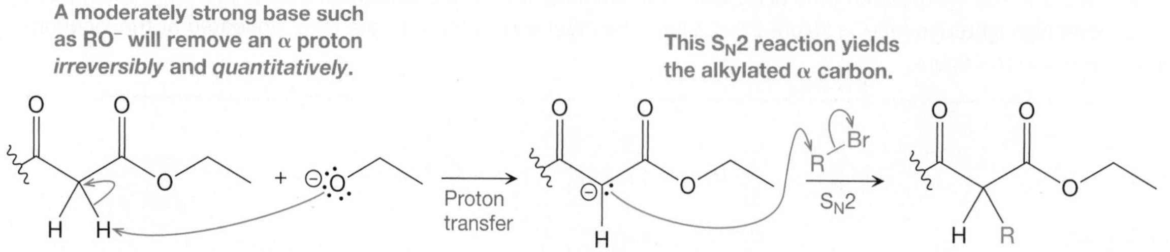

A moderately strong base such as RO^- will remove an α proton *irreversibly* and *quantitatively*.
This S_N2 reaction yields the alkylated α carbon.
Proton transfer
S_N2

(23-48)

As with any S_N2 reaction, these alkylation reactions are easiest with methyl and 1° substrates; 2° substrates are not very practical because of increased steric hindrance, and 3° substrates cannot be used at all.

YOUR TURN 23.24

To verify the preceding statement that an active methylene compound can be quantitatively deprotonated with an alkoxide base, use the appropriate pK_a values (Appendix A) to determine the side of the following reaction that is favored. To what extent is that side favored?

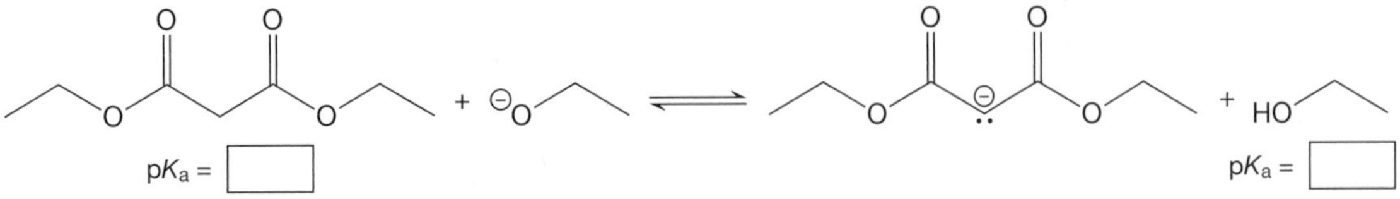

pKa =
pKa =

To remove the ester group entirely from a β-keto ester or a β diester, we can simply heat it under aqueous, acidic conditions, according to Equation 23-49:

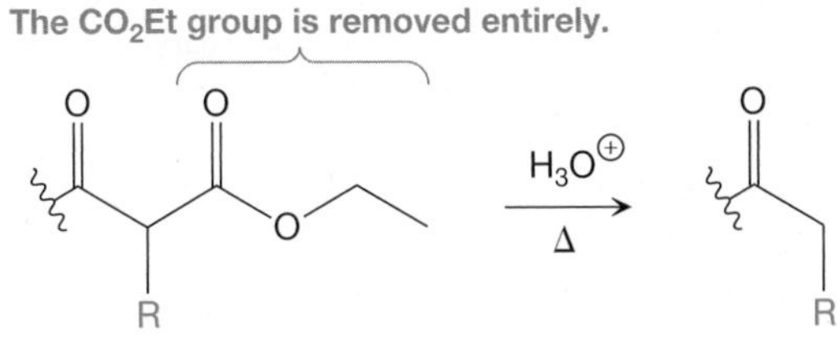

The CO2Et group is removed entirely.
H3O+
Δ
R
R

(23-49)

The partial mechanism for this reaction is shown in Equation 23-50 (see Looking Ahead box).

▸ LOOKING AHEAD

The curved arrow notation for decarboxylation shows that the transition state will have six electrons delocalized cyclically. These types of elementary steps are called pericyclic reactions and are the basis for the Diels–Alder reaction, which we will explore in Chapter 26.

Partial mechanism for the hydrolysis and decarboxylation of a β-keto ester or β diester (Eq. 23-49)

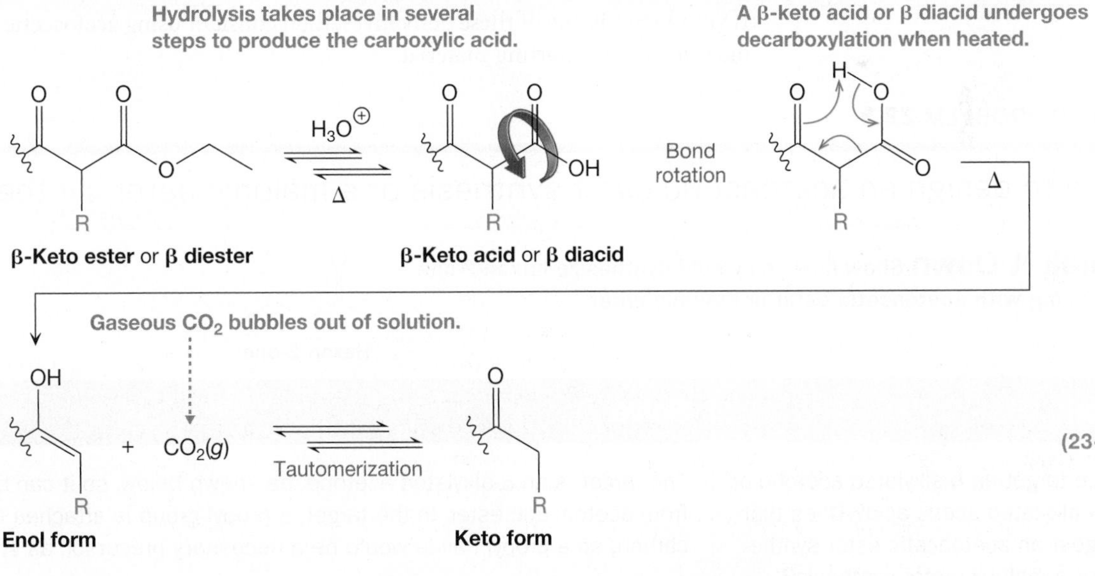

Hydrolysis takes place in several steps to produce the carboxylic acid.
A β-keto acid or β diacid undergoes decarboxylation when heated.
H3O+
Δ
Bond rotation
Δ
β-Keto ester or β diester
β-Keto acid or β diacid
Gaseous CO2 bubbles out of solution.
CO2(g)
Tautomerization
Enol form
Keto form

(23-50)

The acidic, aqueous conditions hydrolyze esters to carboxylic acids (review Section 23.7); more specifically, a β-keto ester is converted to a **β-keto acid**, and a β diester is converted to a **β diacid**. Heating the β-keto acid or β diacid drives a **decarboxylation** in which gaseous CO_2 is lost and an enol is formed. The enol rapidly tautomerizes to the keto form.

Beginning with acetoacetic ester, we can put all of these steps together in what is called an **acetoacetic ester synthesis,** as shown in Equation 23-51. Similarly, a **malonic ester synthesis** is shown in Equation 23-52.

Acetoacetic ester synthesis

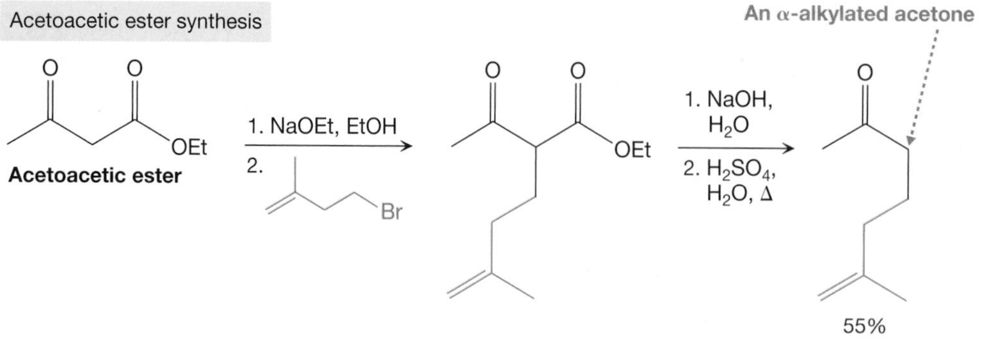

An α-alkylated acetone
OEt
Acetoacetic ester
1. NaOEt, EtOH
2.
Br
OEt
1. NaOH, H_2O
2. H_2SO_4, H_2O, Δ
55%

(23-51)

Malonic ester synthesis

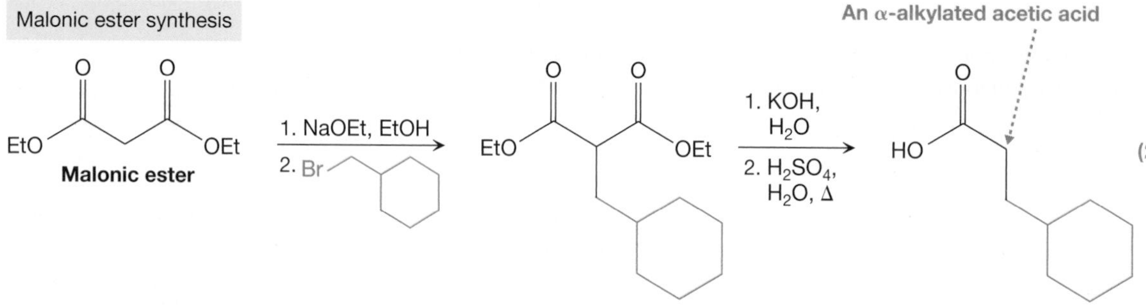

An α-alkylated acetic acid
EtO
OEt
Malonic ester
1. NaOEt, EtOH
2. Br
EtO
OEt
1. KOH, H_2O
2. H_2SO_4, H_2O, Δ
HO

(23-52)

The acetoacetic ester and malonic ester syntheses have characteristic products:

- An acetoacetic ester synthesis produces an α-alkylated acetone.
- A malonic ester synthesis produces an α-alkylated acetic acid.

If your target is one of these derivatives, then consider using acetoacetic ester or malonic ester as your starting material.

SOLVED PROBLEM **23.8**

How to design an acetoacetic ester synthesis or a malonic ester synthesis

Break It Down Show how you would synthesize hexan-2-one beginning with acetoacetic ester or malonic ester.

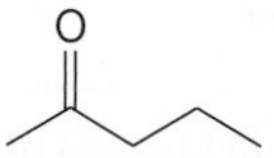

Hexan-2-one

Think

Is the target an α-alkylated acetone or an α-alkylated acetic acid? Does that suggest an acetoacetic ester synthesis or a malonic ester synthesis?

Solve

The target is an α-alkylated acetone, as shown below, so it can be made from acetoacetic ester. In the target, a propyl group is attached to the α carbon, so a propyl halide would be a necessary precursor, as shown here.

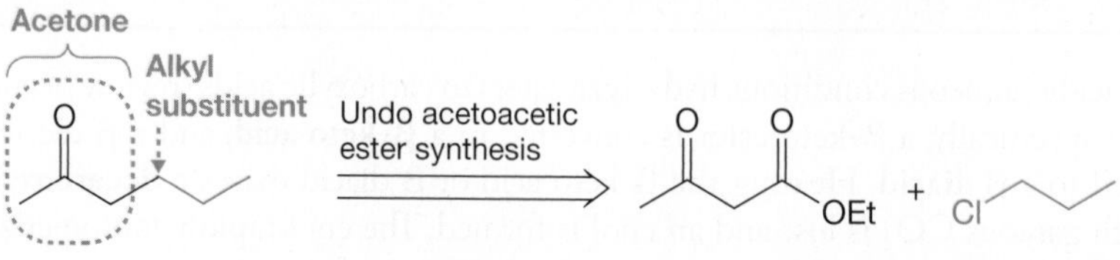

Acetone
Alkyl substituent
Undo acetoacetic ester synthesis
OEt
Cl

(continued)

Beginning with acetoacetic ester, how do you carry out the necessary alkylation? The hydrolysis and decarboxylation?

➤ As shown below, we carry out the alkylation by adding a base, followed by the propyl halide. Hydrolysis can be carried out by saponification, followed by acid workup. Finally, heating the β-keto acid causes decarboxylation.

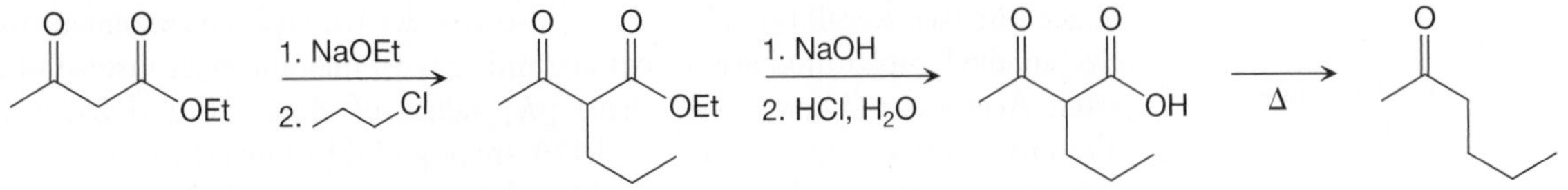

OEt
1. NaOEt
2. Cl
OEt
1. NaOH
2. HCl, H₂O
OH
Δ

Try It Outline a synthesis of pent-4-enoic acid from either acetoacetic ester or malonic ester.

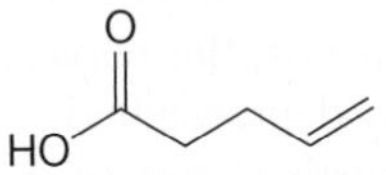

HO

Pent-4-enoic acid

Both the acetoacetic ester synthesis and the malonic ester synthesis also lend themselves to *dialkylation* of the active methylene group, given that there are two acidic hydrogens. Examples are shown in Equations 23-53 and 23-54. Notice that the two alkyl groups can be the same or different.

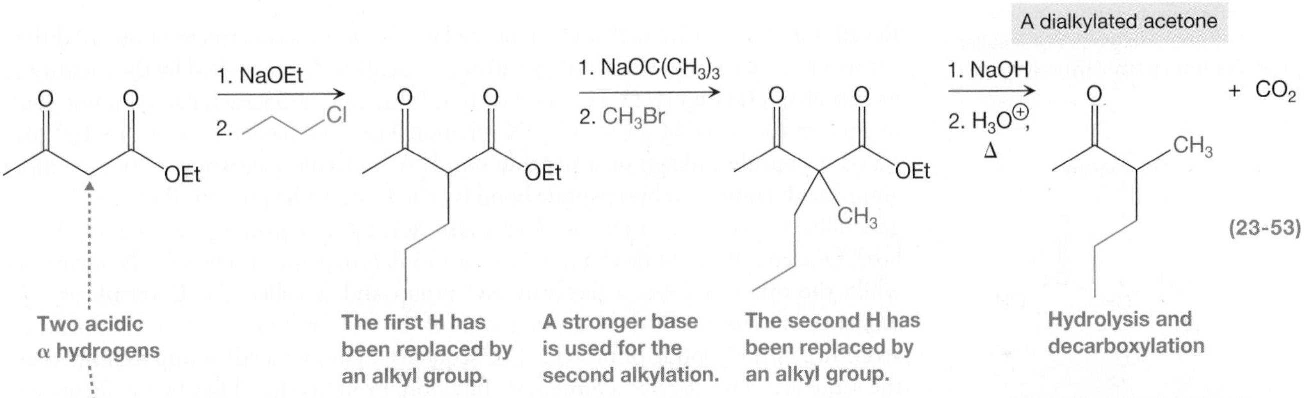

A dialkylated acetone
1. NaOEt
2. Cl
OEt
1. NaOC(CH₃)₃
2. CH₃Br
OEt
CH₃
OEt
1. NaOH
2. H₃O⊕, Δ
CH₃
+ CO₂
Two acidic α hydrogens
The first H has been replaced by an alkyl group.
A stronger base is used for the second alkylation.
The second H has been replaced by an alkyl group.
Hydrolysis and decarboxylation

(23-53)

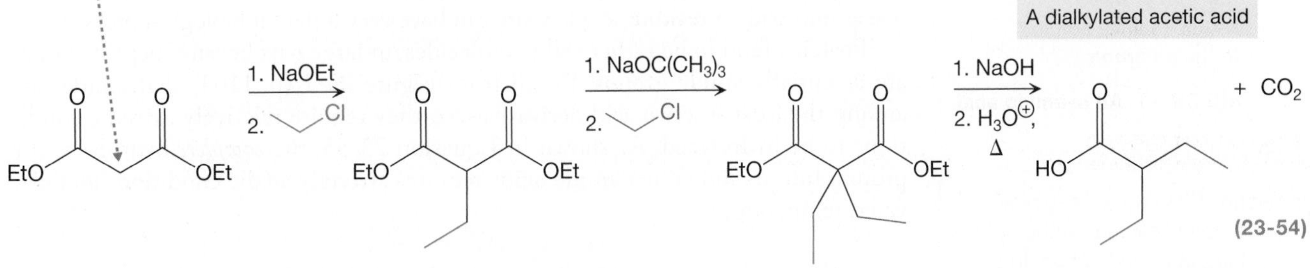

A dialkylated acetic acid
EtO
OEt
1. NaOEt
2. Cl
EtO
OEt
1. NaOC(CH₃)₃
2. Cl
EtO
OEt
1. NaOH
2. H₃O⊕, Δ
HO
+ CO₂

(23-54)

In both cases, alkylation of the methylene C is carried out twice prior to hydrolysis and decarboxylation. The base in the second alkylation is the *tert*-butoxide anion, $(CH_3)_3CO^-$, however, because the second deprotonation is more difficult than the first, so a stronger base compensates. The second deprotonation is more difficult because the alkyl group added in the first alkylation is electron-donating, as shown in **Figure 23-10**, and thus destabilizes the resulting enolate anion.

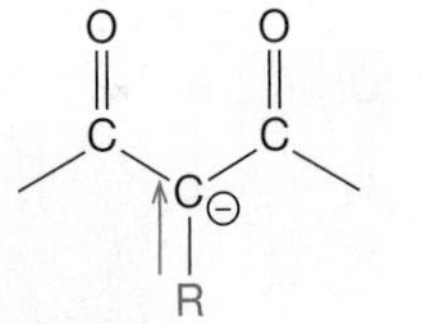

C
C
C⊖
R

The electron-donating R group destabilizes the enolate anion.

FIGURE 23-10 Second alkylation of a malonic ester or acetoacetic ester synthesis

YOUR TURN **23.25**

Show how you would synthesize 2-ethylhexanoic acid from malonic ester.

◂ RECALL

The α alkylation of a ketone or aldehyde (Section 11.3) involves (1) deprotonation of the ketone or aldehyde to produce an enolate anion and (2) an S_N2 reaction between the enolate anion and a substrate. Deprotonation is reversible with HO^- and RO^- and is irreversible with stronger bases such as NaH, $NaNH_2$, and LDA.

Because an acetoacetic ester synthesis produces an alkyl-substituted acetone, you might wonder what advantages an acetoacetic ester synthesis has over direct alkylation of acetone (see Recall box). You might also wonder why it is advantageous to synthesize an alkyl-substituted acetic acid beginning with malonic ester instead of a monoester. Acetone and monoesters have pK_a values of about 20 and 25, respectively. Therefore, very strong bases such as LDA are required to convert them to their enolate anions quantitatively. Moreover, their enolate anions are strongly basic, so when they are treated with an alkyl halide, E2 reactions will compete with the desired S_N2 reactions. By contrast, the enolate anions of acetoacetic ester and malonic ester can be quantitatively deprotonated by weaker bases such as HO^- or RO^-. The resulting enolate anions, furthermore, are not as strongly basic, which will help favor S_N2 reactions and maximize the yield for alkylation.

SECTION 23.11 OBJECTIVES

You will be able to:

1. Show how an Edman degradation is used to determine the sequence of a peptide.
2. Determine the sequence of a peptide if the sequences of smaller peptides from partial hydrolysis are known.

THE ORGANIC CHEMISTRY OF BIOMOLECULES

23.11 Determining the Amino Acid Sequence of a Protein

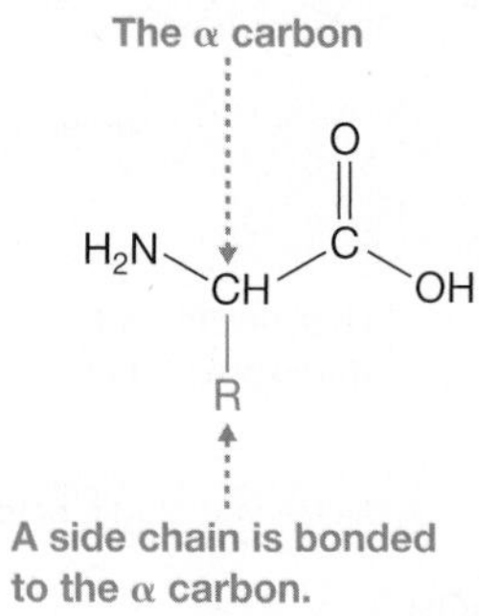
The α carbon
A side chain is bonded to the α carbon.

FIGURE 23-11 An α-amino acid

▸ LOOKING AHEAD

In Section 29.6, we will see how peptide bonds can be synthesized in the laboratory. In Section 30.5, we will examine how the body uses enzymatic pathways to construct such linkages to synthesize proteins.

Recall from Section 1.14a that proteins are large molecules constructed from 20 different α-amino acids, and each of these 20 amino acids is distinguished by the identity of its side chain, R (**Figure 23-11**). As shown in Equation 23-55, each pair of amino acids in a protein is joined by a O═C—N functional group (characteristic of amides), also called a **peptide linkage** or a **peptide bond**. A molecule consisting of two or more amino acids connected by a peptide bond is called a **peptide**; proteins (because they are generally long chains of amino acids) are also called **polypeptides** (see Looking Ahead box). One end of a peptide chain has a free amino group and is called the **N-terminus**, while the other end has a free carboxyl group and is called the **C-terminus**. The sequence of amino acids from the N-terminus to the C-terminus is called the **primary structure** of the peptide or protein. This sequence of amino acids is important because the sequence is what gives a protein its function. Proteins that differ by the identity of one amino acid, or **residue**, at a key site can have very different biological properties.

Proteins tend to be rather stable molecules, in large part because peptide bonds are essentially amide groups. Recall from Figure 23-1 (p. 1104) that amides are among the least reactive acid derivatives, so they require relatively extreme conditions to be hydrolyzed. As shown in Equation 23-55, the *complete* hydrolysis of a protein into its individual amino acids requires strongly acidic conditions and elevated temperatures.

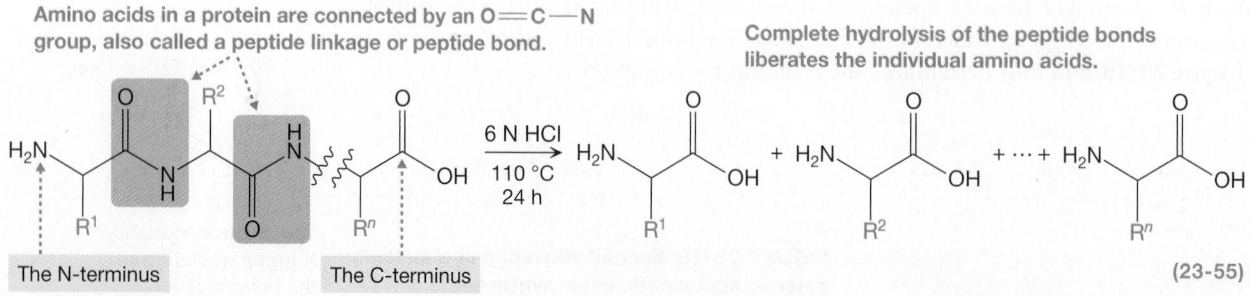
Amino acids in a protein are connected by an O═C—N group, also called a peptide linkage or peptide bond.
Complete hydrolysis of the peptide bonds liberates the individual amino acids.
6 N HCl
110 °C
24 h
The N-terminus
The C-terminus

(23-55)

A complete hydrolysis of a protein can be used to determine the relative amounts of each type of amino acid in a protein. The process entails injecting the sample (an amino acid mixture) into an *amino acid analyzer*. However, complete hydrolysis does not reveal the primary structure of the protein.

One way to determine the amino acid sequence of a protein is with an **Edman degradation**. The basis of an Edman degradation is to remove one amino acid at a time from the N-terminus and to convert it to a phenylthiohydantoin (PTH) derivative that can be analyzed by chromatographic or mass spectrometric techniques. Each cycle of the Edman degradation, summarized in **Figure 23-12**, takes place in three steps: (1) the peptide is treated with phenyl isothiocyanate (PhNCS), which converts the N-terminal amino acid into a phenylthiocarbamoyl (PTC) derivative; (2) the PTC derivative is treated with aqueous HCl to release the N-terminal amino acid in the form of a thiazolinone; and (3) the thiazolinone is extracted into an organic solvent, and when treated with HCl, it produces the PTH derivative.

The partial mechanism for each step of the Edman degradation is also shown in Figure 23-12. In Step 1, the free NH_2 group of the N-terminal amino acid adds to the polar C═N bond in a nucleophilic addition reaction. Step 2 involves one nucleophilic addition–elimination sequence, and Step 3 involves two such sequences.

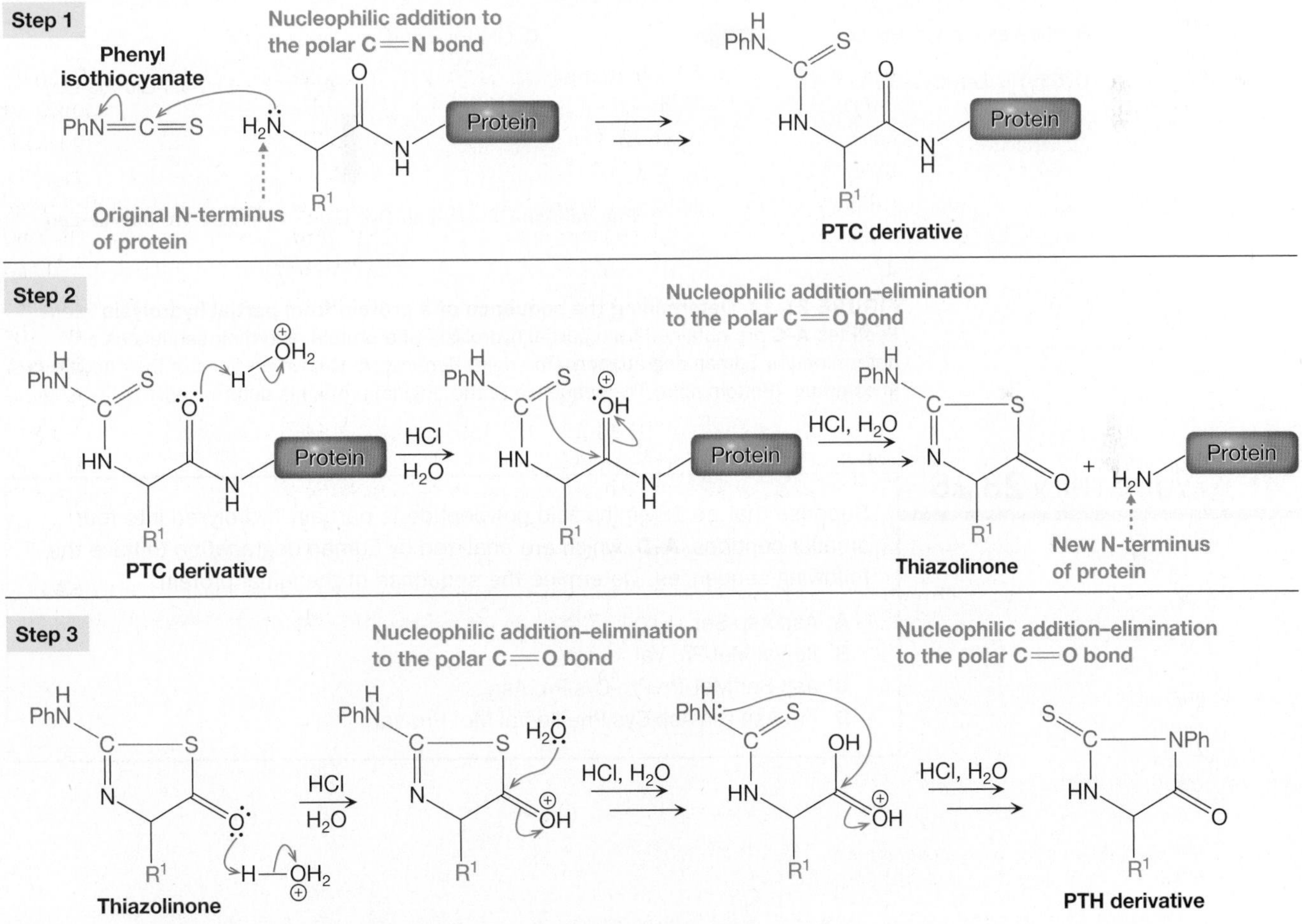
Step 1
Nucleophilic addition to the polar C═N bond
Phenyl isothiocyanate
PhN═C═S
Protein
Original N-terminus of protein
PTC derivative
Step 2
Nucleophilic addition–elimination to the polar C═O bond
HCl
H₂O
HCl, H₂O
Thiazolinone
New N-terminus of protein
Step 3
Nucleophilic addition–elimination to the polar C═O bond
Nucleophilic addition–elimination to the polar C═O bond
Thiazolinone
PTH derivative

FIGURE 23-12 Partial mechanism for the Edman degradation (*Step 1*) The amino group of the N-terminal amino acid undergoes nucleophilic addition to phenyl isothiocyanate to yield the corresponding phenylthiocarbamoyl (PTC) derivative. (*Step 2*) The PTC derivative cyclizes when treated with HCl to yield the corresponding thiazolinone. (*Step 3*) Treatment of the thiazolinone with HCl produces the corresponding phenylthiohydantoin (PTH) derivative, which can be detected using chromatography or spectroscopy. Steps 1–3 can be repeated with each new N-terminal amino acid.

> **▸ LOOKING AHEAD**
>
> In Section 29.5, we will see how enzymes called trypsin and chymotrypsin can be used to hydrolyze proteins at specific locations to aid in peptide sequencing.

Theoretically, the entire sequence of a protein can be determined in this manner. However, sequencing proteins by an Edman degradation becomes impractical when the protein exceeds roughly 30 amino acids, because side products accumulate and interfere with the results. In these cases, the protein can be *partially* hydrolyzed using dilute acid, in which case hydrolysis takes place at essentially random locations in the protein (see Looking Ahead box). The smaller polypeptides that are produced then can be sequenced by an Edman degradation, and the sequence of the original protein subsequently can be pieced together from the results.

Suppose, for example, that the partial hydrolysis of a 15-amino-acid polypeptide yielded three smaller polypeptides, **A–C**, whose sequences were determined to be the ones shown on the left of **Figure 23-13**. As shown on the top right of Figure 23-13, certain portions of the peptides have the same sequence; specifically, the Ser-His sequence in peptides **A** and **C** (red) and the Gln-His-Leu sequence in peptides **B** and **C** (blue). Assuming those sequences come from the same portions of the original protein, we can piece together the overall sequence, as shown at the bottom right of Figure 23-13.

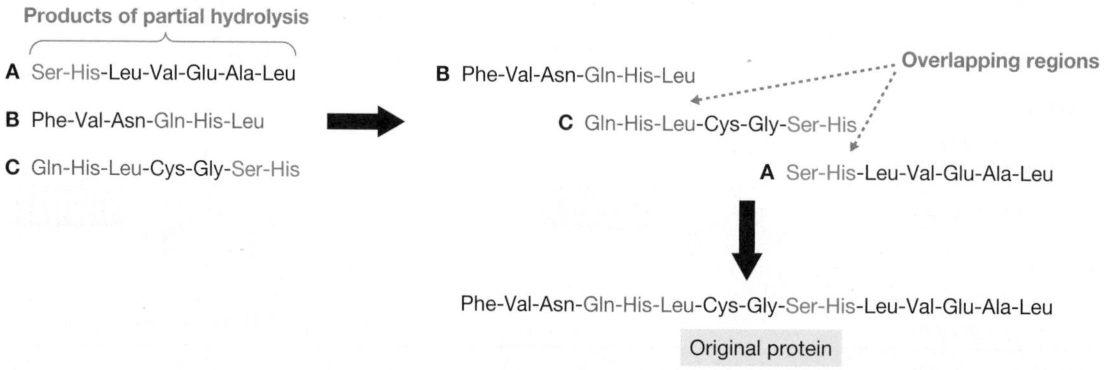

Products of partial hydrolysis
A Ser-His-Leu-Val-Glu-Ala-Leu
B Phe-Val-Asn-Gln-His-Leu
C Gln-His-Leu-Cys-Gly-Ser-His
B Phe-Val-Asn-Gln-His-Leu
C Gln-His-Leu-Cys-Gly-Ser-His
A Ser-His-Leu-Val-Glu-Ala-Leu
Overlapping regions
Phe-Val-Asn-Gln-His-Leu-Cys-Gly-Ser-His-Leu-Val-Glu-Ala-Leu
Original protein

FIGURE 21-13 Determining the sequence of a protein from partial hydrolysis (*Left*) Peptides **A–C** are obtained from partial hydrolysis of a protein, and their sequences are determined by Edman degradation. (*Top right*) Peptides **A–C** have portions of their sequences in common. (*Bottom right*) The sequence of the original protein is determined.

YOUR TURN 23.26

Suppose that an 18-amino-acid polypeptide is partially hydrolyzed into four smaller peptides, **A–D**, which are analyzed by Edman degradation to have the following sequences. Determine the sequence of the initial protein.

A Asp-Asp-Ser
B Ile-Val-Met-Pro-Val
C Asp-Ser-Met-Trp-Pro-Cys-Pro-Asn
D Pro-Asn-Gln-Asp-Cys-Phe-Ile-Val-Met-Pro-Val

Chapter Summary and Key Terms

- The general mechanism for nucleophilic addition–elimination involving a weak nucleophile (H—Nu) is similar to the one involving a strong nucleophile but includes a proton transfer step to produce an uncharged product. This mechanism describes the **hydrolysis**, **alcoholysis**, and **aminolysis** that acid chlorides and acid anhydrides undergo. (Sections 23.1 and 23.3)

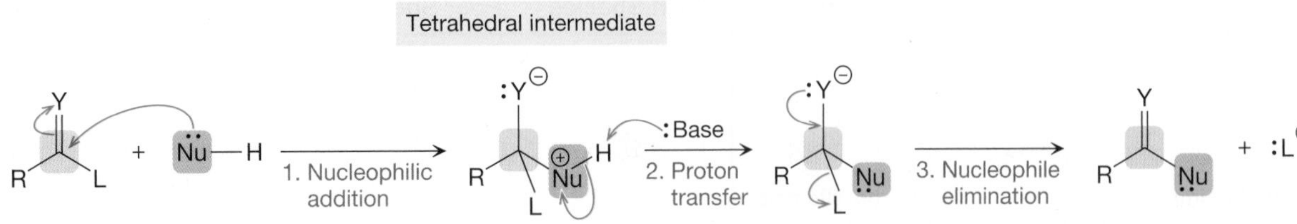

Tetrahedral intermediate
1. Nucleophilic addition
2. Proton transfer
3. Nucleophile elimination
:Base

- The reactivity of an acid derivative decreases as the resonance stabilization of the carbonyl group increases. Overall, the relative reactivities of acid derivatives decrease in the order: acid chloride > acid anhydride > ester ≈ carboxylic acid > amide. (Section 23.2)
- In the aminolysis of an acid chloride or acid anhydride, which produces an amide, two equivalents of an amine are required: one to act as a nucleophile and the other to act as a base. Only one equivalent of the amine is required if pyridine or triethylamine is added as the base. (Section 23.3)
- **Thionyl chloride** ($SOCl_2$) converts a carboxylic acid to an acid chloride (the acid derivative at the top of the stability ladder), from which any other carboxylic acid derivative can be produced. (Section 23.4)
- The **Hell–Volhard–Zelinsky (HVZ) reaction** produces an α-bromo carboxylic acid from a carboxylic acid. The key is to convert the carboxylic acid into an acid bromide, which can form an enol, making it nucleophilic at the α carbon. (Section 23.5)
- Treating an alcohol with a **sulfonyl chloride** (R—SO_2Cl) produces a **sulfonate ester** (R′O—SO_2R). Thus, a poor HO^- leaving group is converted into an excellent alkylsulfonate leaving group, such as mesylate (MsO^-), tosylate (TsO^-), or triflate (TfO^-), for nucleophilic substitution and elimination reactions. (Section 23.6)
- Carboxylic acids, esters, and amides are relatively stable and do not react readily with weak nucleophiles under normal conditions. However, nucleophilic acyl substitution can be base-catalyzed or acid-catalyzed. Base catalysis involves deprotonating the nucleophile to convert it into a strong nucleophile. Acid catalysis involves protonating the carbonyl oxygen to activate the carbonyl carbon. (Section 23.7)
- The **Fischer esterification reaction** produces an ester from a carboxylic acid under acidic conditions and is described by the acid-catalyzed acyl substitution mechanism. (Section 23.7)
- The **Baeyer–Villiger oxidation** produces carboxylic acids from aldehydes and esters from ketones. In these reactions, a hydrogen or alkyl group departs from the carbonyl carbon, facilitated by the breaking of the weak O—O bond from a *peroxy acid* (RCO_3H). (Section 23.8)
- In a **Claisen condensation reaction**, an ester with at least two α protons is treated with a strong base, followed by acid workup, to produce a **β-keto ester**. In these reactions, the base deprotonates the α carbon of one ester to produce an ester enolate anion, which acts as a nucleophile and attacks the carbonyl carbon of a second ester. (Section 23.9)
- If the base in a Claisen condensation is nucleophilic, it should be identical to the alkoxide leaving group on the ester. If the solvent can be deprotonated to become strongly nucleophilic, the conjugate acid of the base should be used as the solvent. (Section 23.9a)
- In a **crossed Claisen condensation reaction**, the enolate anion that acts as the nucleophile derives from an ester that is different from the ester it attacks. Crossed Claisen condensations are synthetically useful if only one ester enolate anion is present and only one uncharged ester can be attacked. (Section 23.9b)
- A **Dieckmann condensation reaction** is an intramolecular Claisen condensation and is favored when a five- or six-membered ring can be formed. (Section 23.9c)
- A **β-keto acid** or **β diacid** can undergo **decarboxylation** on heating under acidic conditions. The result is loss of CO_2, leaving behind a ketone or carboxylic acid. Decarboxylation is used in the **acetoacetic ester synthesis** to produce an alkyl-substituted acetone, as well as in the **malonic ester synthesis** to produce an alkyl-substituted acetic acid. (Section 23.10)
- In a protein, amino acids are linked together by **peptide bonds**, which are essentially amide groups. The **primary structure** of a peptide chain describes the amino acid sequence. An **Edman degradation** can be used to determine the primary structure by removing one N-terminal amino acid at a time for analysis. (Section 23.11)

Reaction Tables

Functional group transformations introduced in this chapter are collected in Table 23-2, and reactions introduced in this chapter that alter the carbon skeleton are collected in Table 23-3.

TABLE 23-2 Functional Group Transformations

	Starting Compound Class	Typical Reagents and Reaction Conditions	Compound Class Formed	Key Electron-Rich Species	Key Electron-Poor Species	Comments	Discussed in Section
(1)	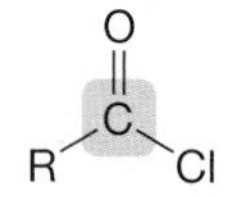 Acid chloride	$\xrightarrow{H_2O}$	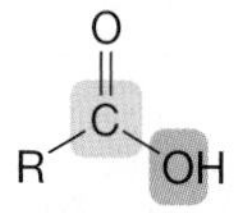 Carboxylic acid	$H_2\ddot{O}:^{\delta-}$	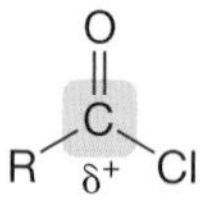	Nucleophilic addition–elimination (hydrolysis)	23.1
(2)	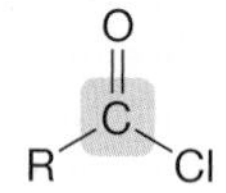 Acid chloride	$\xrightarrow{R'OH}$	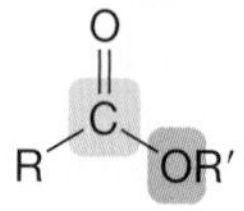 Ester	$R'\ddot{O}H^{\delta-}$	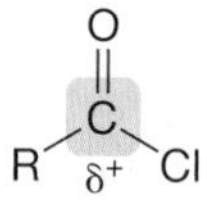	Nucleophilic addition–elimination (alcoholysis)	23.1
(3)	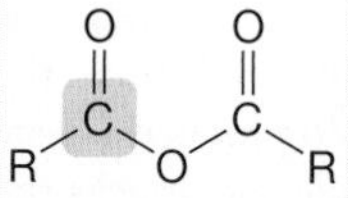 Acid anhydride	$\xrightarrow{H_2O}$	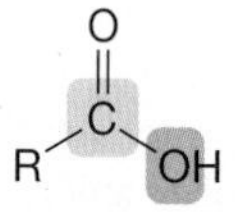 Carboxylic acid	$H_2\ddot{O}:^{\delta-}$	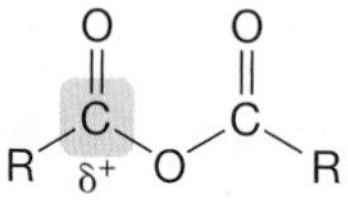	Nucleophilic addition–elimination (hydrolysis)	23.2
(4)	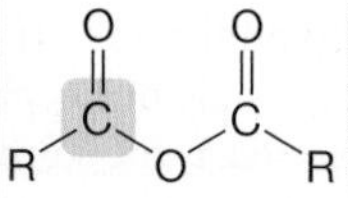 Acid anhydride	$\xrightarrow{R'OH}$	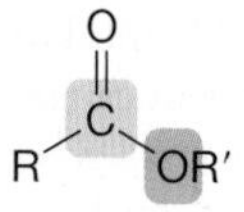 Ester	$R'\ddot{O}H^{\delta-}$	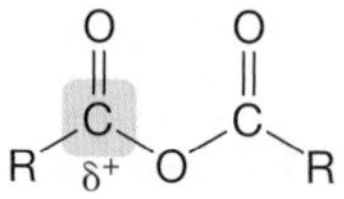	Nucleophilic addition–elimination (alcoholysis)	23.2
(5)	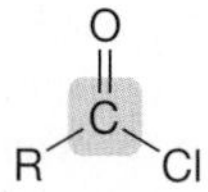 Acid chloride	$\xrightarrow[Et_3N \text{ or pyridine}]{R'_2NH}$	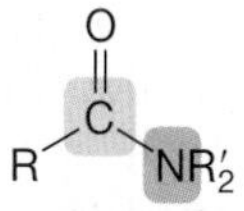 Amide	$R'_2\ddot{N}H^{\delta-}$	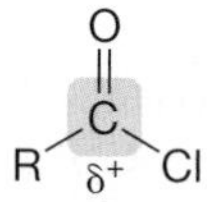	Nucleophilic addition–elimination (aminolysis)	23.3
(6)	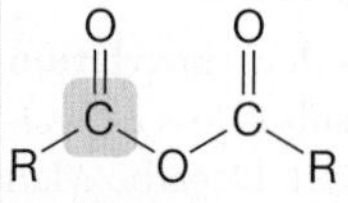 Acid anhydride	$\xrightarrow[Et_3N \text{ or pyridine}]{R'_2NH}$	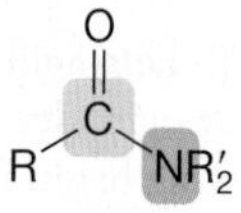 Amide	$R'_2\ddot{N}H^{\delta-}$	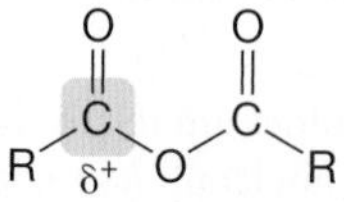	Nucleophilic addition–elimination (aminolysis)	23.3

TABLE 23-2 Functional Group Transformations (continued)

	Starting Compound Class	Typical Reagents and Reaction Conditions	Compound Class Formed	Key Electron-Rich Species	Key Electron-Poor Species	Comments	Discussed in Section
(7)	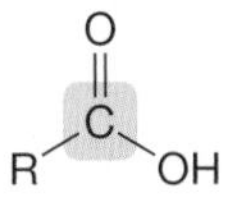 Carboxylic acid	$SOCl_2$ →	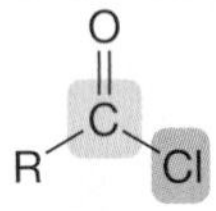 Acid chloride	$:\ddot{Cl}:^{-}$	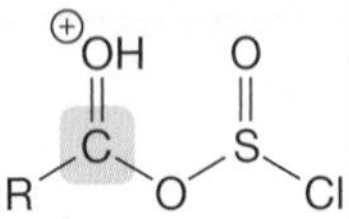	Back-to-back nucleophilic addition–elimination	23.4
(8)	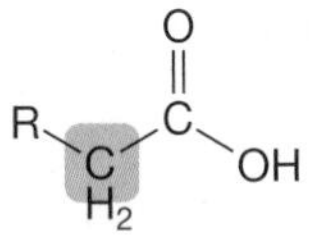 Carboxylic acid	Br_2, P →	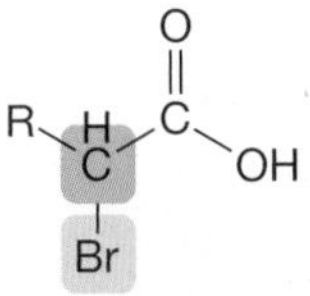 α-Bromo acid	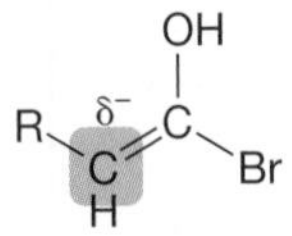	$\overset{\delta+}{Br}-\overset{\delta-}{Br}$	Hell–Volhard–Zelinsky reaction	23.5
(9)	R—OH Alcohol	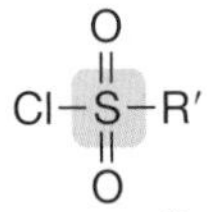 →	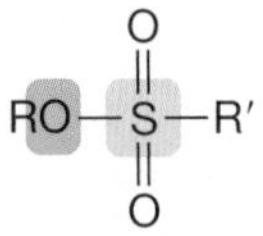 Sulfonate ester	$R\ddot{O}H^{\delta-}$	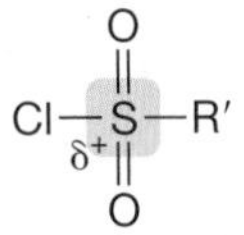	Nucleophilic addition–elimination	23.6
(10)	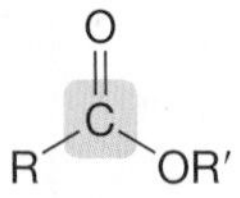 Ester	R″OH → R″ONa	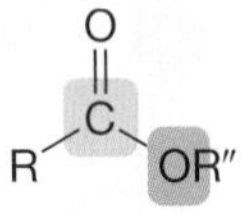 Ester	$^{-}:\ddot{O}R''$	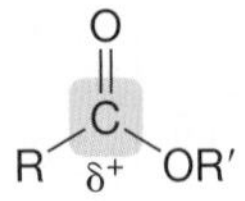	Base-catalyzed nucleophilic addition–elimination (transesterification)	23.7
(11)	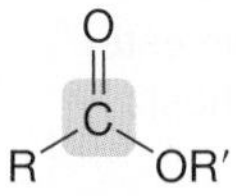 Ester	R″OH → H_2SO_4	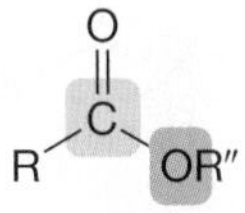 Ester	$R''\ddot{O}H^{\delta-}$	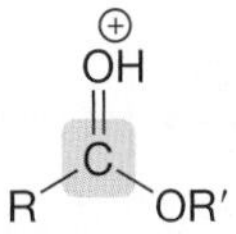	Acid-catalyzed nucleophilic addition–elimination (transesterification)	23.7
(12)	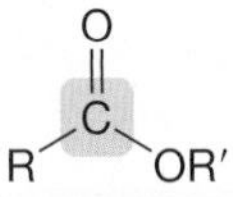 Ester	H_2O → H_2SO_4	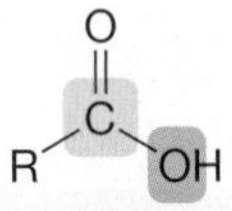 Carboxylic acid	$H_2\ddot{O}:^{\delta-}$	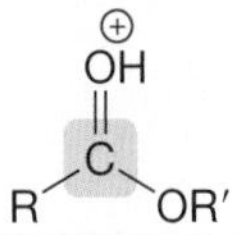	Acid-catalyzed nucleophilic addition–elimination (hydrolysis)	23.7
(13)	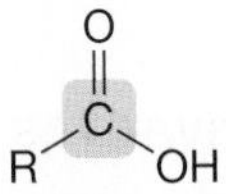 Carboxylic acid	R′OH → H_2SO_4	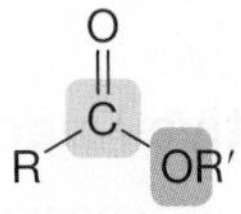 Ester	$R'\ddot{O}H^{\delta-}$	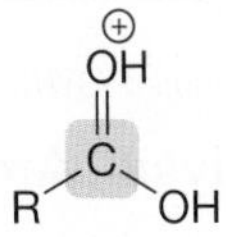	Acid-catalyzed nucleophilic addition–elimination (Fischer esterification)	23.7
(14)	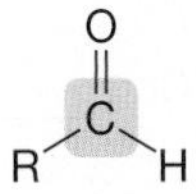 Aldehyde	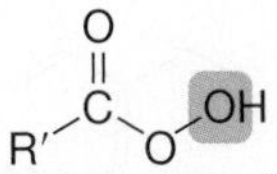 →	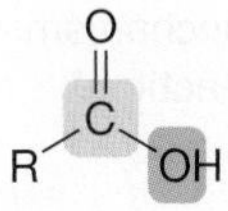 Carboxylic acid	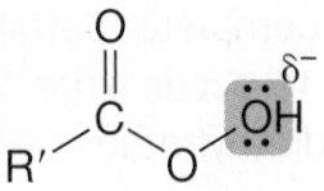	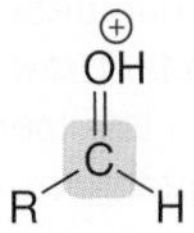	Acid-catalyzed nucleophilic addition–elimination (Baeyer–Villiger oxidation)	23.8

TABLE 23-3 Reactions That Alter the Carbon Skeleton[a]

	Starting Compound Class	Typical Reagents and Reaction Conditions	Compound Class Formed	Key Electron-Rich Species	Key Electron-Poor Species	Comments	Discussed in Section
(1)	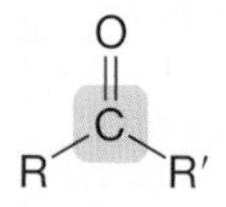 Ketone	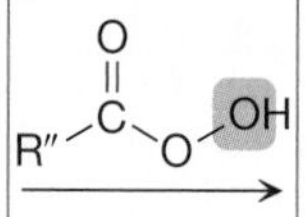	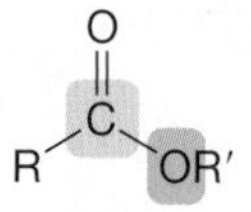 Ester	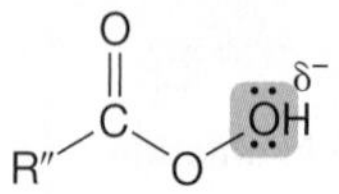	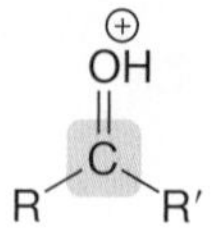	Acid-catalyzed nucleophilic addition–elimination (Baeyer–Villiger oxidation)	23.8
(2)	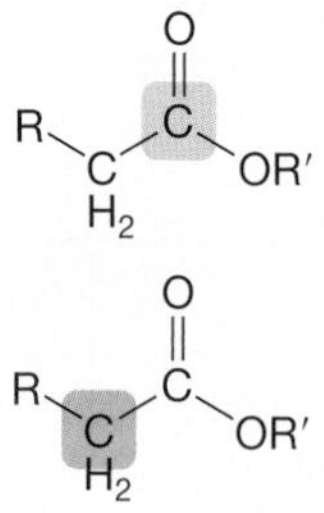 Ester	1. NaOR′ 2. CH_3CO_2H	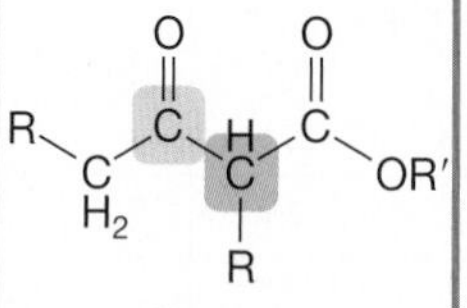 β-Keto ester	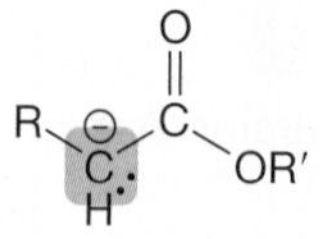	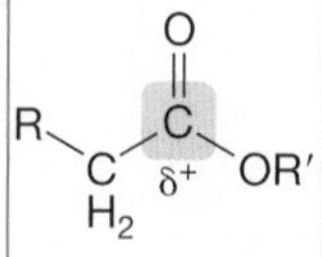	Base-promoted nucleophilic addition–elimination (Claisen condensation)	23.9
(3)	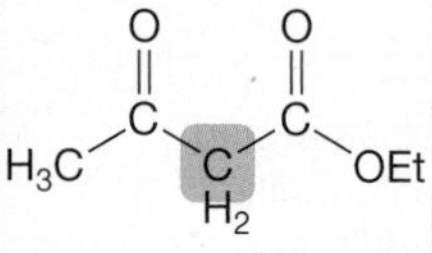 Acetoacetic ester	1. NaOEt 2. R–X 3. H_3O^+, Δ	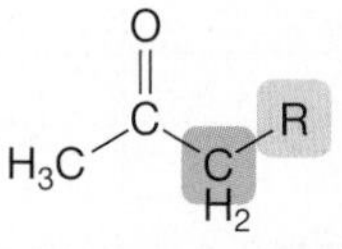 Alkyl-substituted acetone	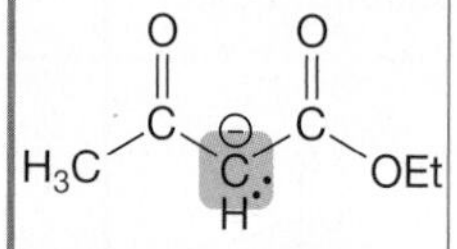	δ^+ R–X	Acetoacetic ester synthesis	23.10
(4)	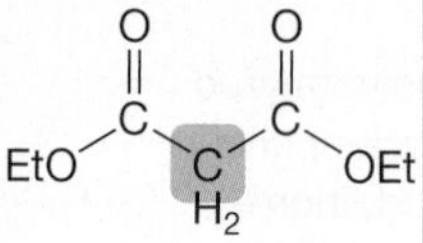 Malonic ester	1. NaOEt 2. R–X 3. H_3O^+, Δ	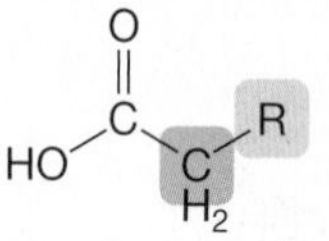 Alkyl-substituted acetic acid	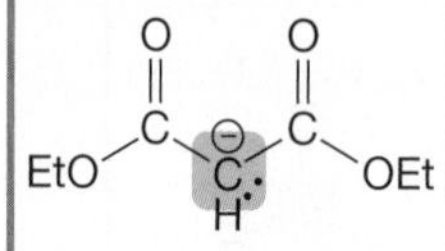	δ^+ R–X	Malonic ester synthesis	23.10

[a]X = Cl, Br, or I.

Problems

Problems that are related to synthesis are denoted (SYN).

Sections 23.1–23.3 Alcoholysis, Aminolysis, and Relative Reactivities of Acid Derivatives

23.1 Draw the free energy diagram for the alcoholysis reaction in Equation 23-3 (p. 1101). Include the species that appear in its mechanism (see Your Turn 23.1, p. 1102), and label the initial tetrahedral intermediate.

23.2 Predict the product of the reaction between *m*-ethylbenzoyl chloride and each of the following compounds. Draw the complete, detailed mechanism for each reaction. If no reaction is expected to occur, write "no reaction."
(a) H_2O; **(b)** CH_3NH_2; **(c)** (*S*)-butan-2-ol; **(d)** diethyl ether

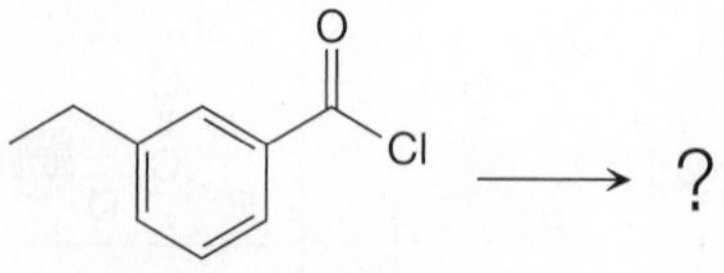

m-Ethylbenzoyl chloride

23.3 Predict the product of the reaction between acetic anhydride and each of the following compounds. If no reaction is expected to occur, write "no reaction." Draw the complete, detailed mechanism for each reaction that does occur. **(a)** H_2O; **(b)** CH_3NH_2, pyridine; **(c)** (*S*)-butan-2-ol; **(d)** diethyl ether

23.4 Aspirin (acetylsalicylic acid) is made by treating salicylic acid with acetic anhydride. Draw the complete, detailed mechanism for this reaction, and draw the product.

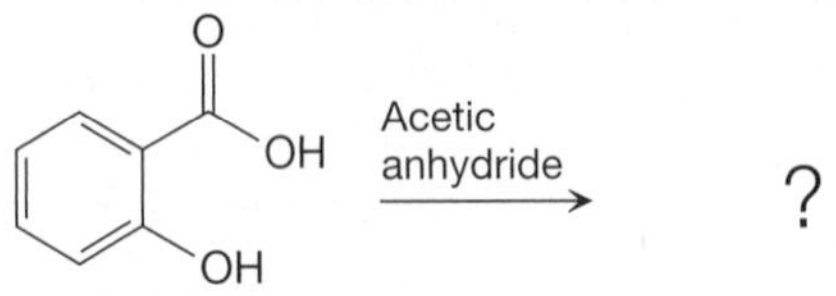
O
OH
OH
Acetic
anhydride
?

Salicylic acid **Acetylsalicylic acid**

23.5 Draw the complete, detailed mechanism and the products for each of the following reactions.

(a)

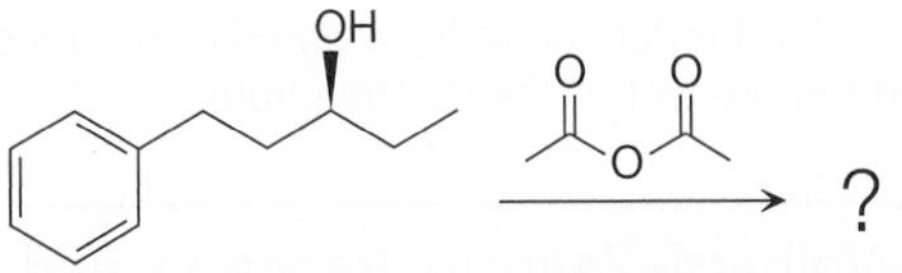
OH
O
O
O
?

(b)

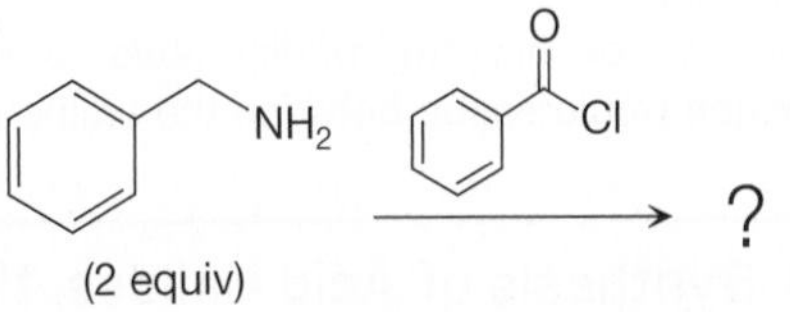
NH2
O
Cl
(2 equiv)
?

(c)

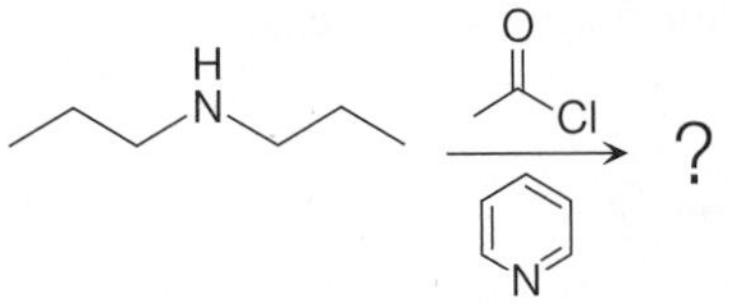
H
N
O
Cl
N
?

(d)

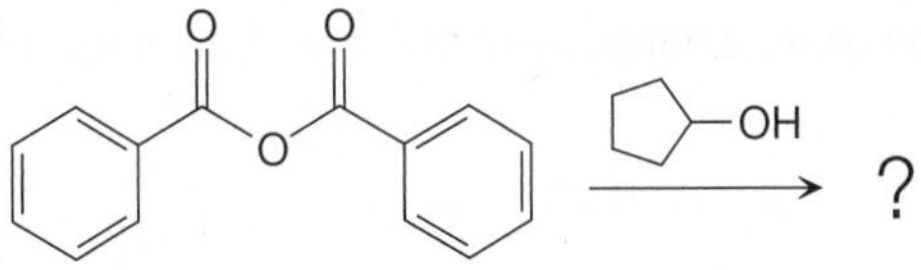
O
O
O
OH
?

23.6 **(SYN)** Show how each of the following compounds can be synthesized from an acid chloride and either water, an alcohol, or an amine. For each reaction, provide the complete, detailed mechanism.

(a)

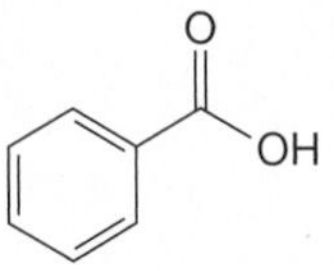
O
OH

(b)

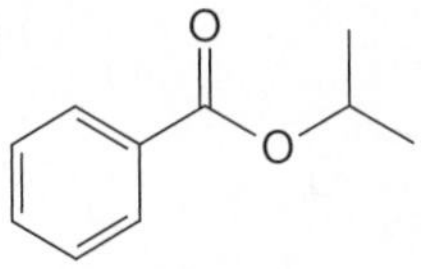
O
O

(c)

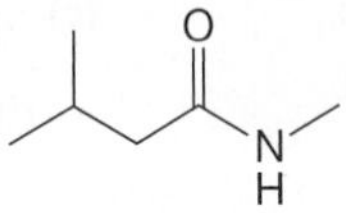
O
N
H

(d)

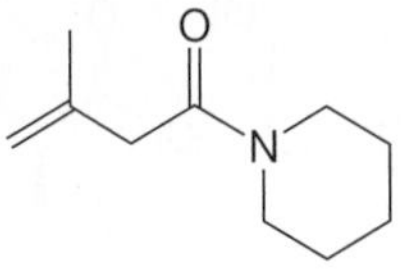
O
N

23.7 A *thioester* is the sulfur analog of an ester. Do you think a thioester would undergo hydrolysis faster or slower than an ester under normal conditions? Explain your reasoning.

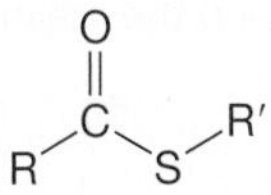
O
C
R
S
R′

A thioester

23.8 Treating a δ lactone (reaction **A**) with ammonia yields a hydroxyamide. If a β lactone is treated with ammonia (reaction **B**), however, then a β-amino acid is formed. Provide the complete, detailed mechanism for each of these reactions, and explain these observations.

A

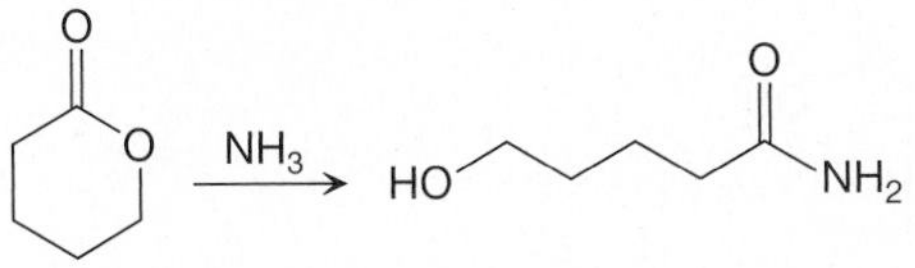
O
O
NH3
HO
O
NH2

B

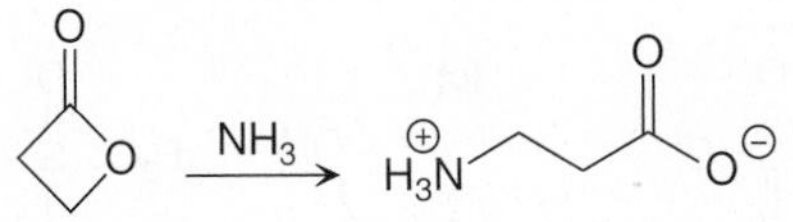
O
O
NH3
H3N
O
O

23.9 The reaction shown here is an example of the *Favorskii reaction*, which involves an R^- leaving group in a nucleophilic addition–elimination reaction.

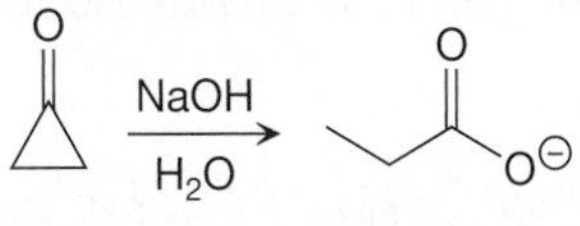
O
NaOH
H2O
O
O

(a) Draw the complete, detailed mechanism for this reaction, and explain why R^- can act as a leaving group.

(b) Suggest how you can synthesize an ester from cyclopropanone using only this reaction.

23.10 In an aminolysis of an acid chloride, pyridine is often used to minimize the amount of the amine that is required, as shown here. Pyridine is a moderately strong nucleophile, however, so it can react with an acid chloride through a nucleophilic addition–elimination mechanism. Nevertheless, this reaction involving pyridine does not interfere with the production of the desired amide.

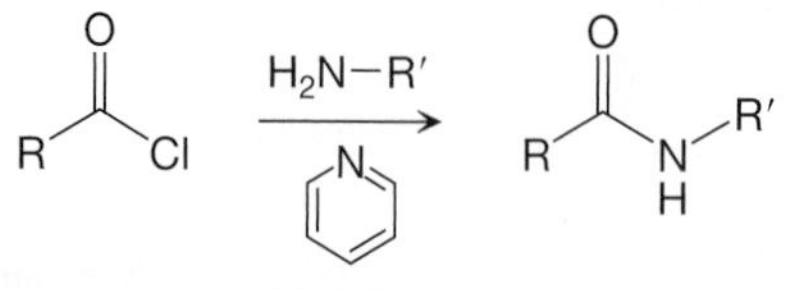

Pyridine

(a) Draw the complete, detailed mechanism and the product for the nucleophilic addition–elimination reaction of pyridine with an acid chloride.

(b) Explain why this reaction involving pyridine does not interfere with the production of the desired amide product. *Hint*: What reaction would ensue between the amine shown and the product of the reaction from part (a)?

Sections 23.4–23.6 Synthesis of Acid Halides, the Hell–Volhard–Zelinsky Reaction, and Sulfonyl Chlorides

23.11 Draw the complete, detailed mechanism and the major product for each of the following reactions.

(a)

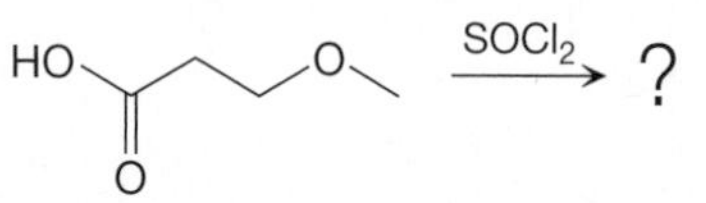

(b)

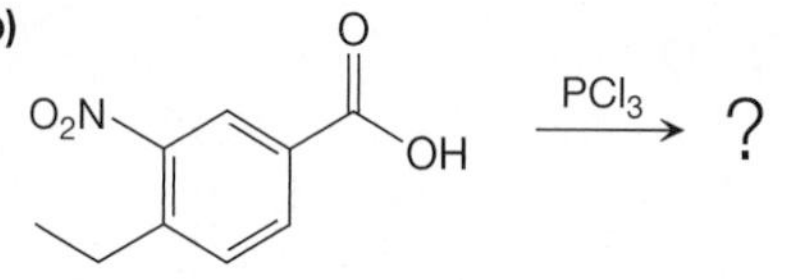

23.12 (SYN) For each acid chloride, draw the carboxylic acid that would produce it when treated with $SOCl_2$.

(a)

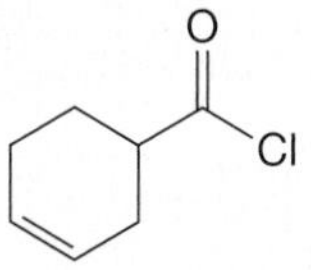

(b)

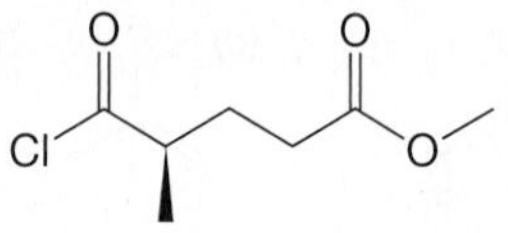

(c)

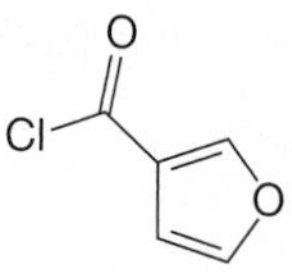

23.13 Draw the complete, detailed mechanism and the major product for each of the following reactions.

(a)

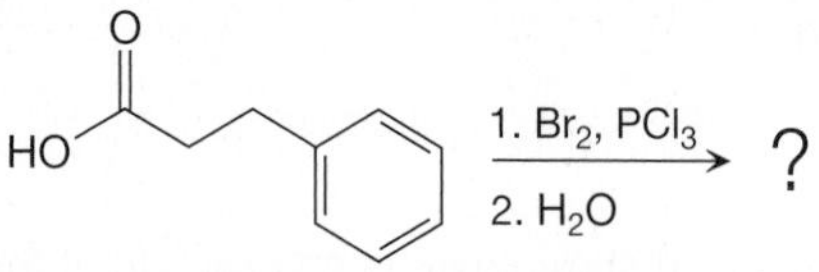

(b)

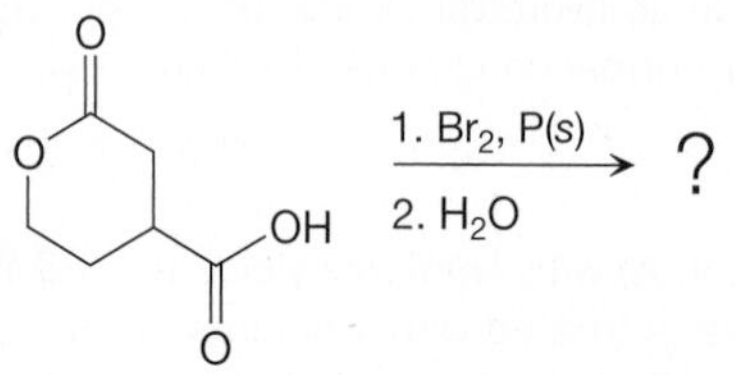

23.14 (SYN) Show how to synthesize each of the following compounds from 3-methylpentanoic acid.

(a)

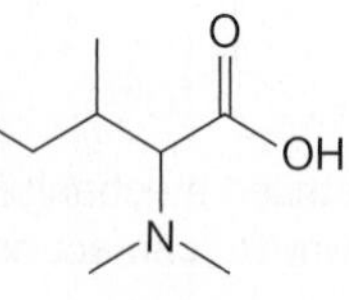

(b)

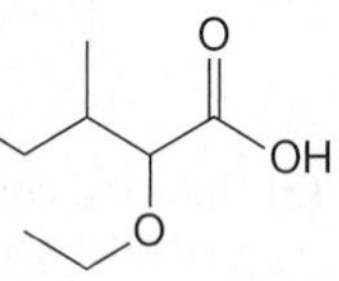

(c)

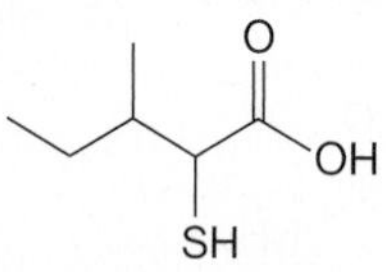

23.15 Draw the complete, detailed mechanism and the major product for each of the following reactions.

(a)

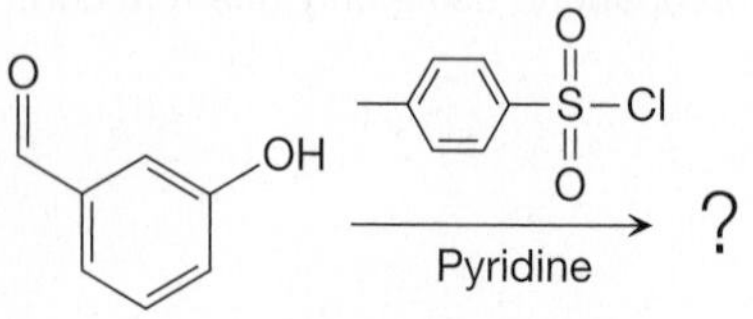

(b)

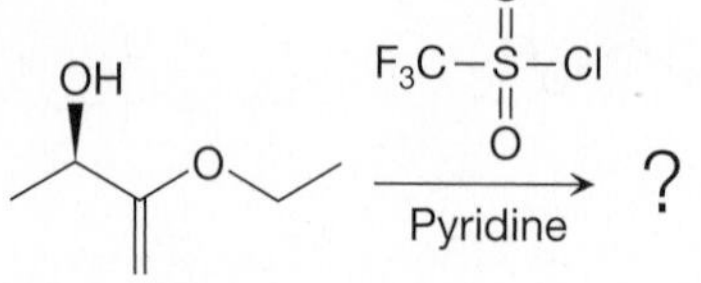

(c)

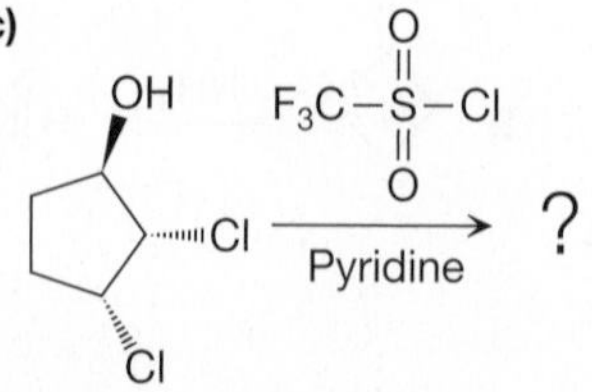

23.16 **(SYN)** Show how to carry out each of the following syntheses by first converting the alcohol into a sulfonyl chloride.

(a)

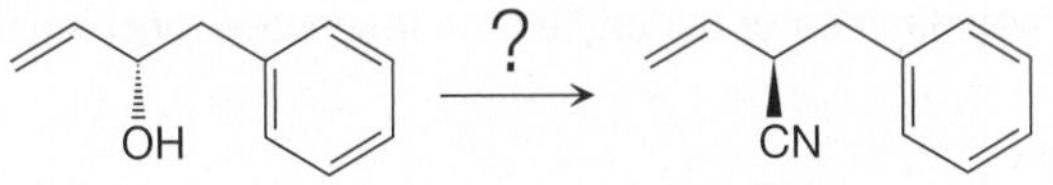

(b)

23.17 An imino chloride can be prepared from an amide according to the reaction shown here. Propose a mechanism for this reaction.

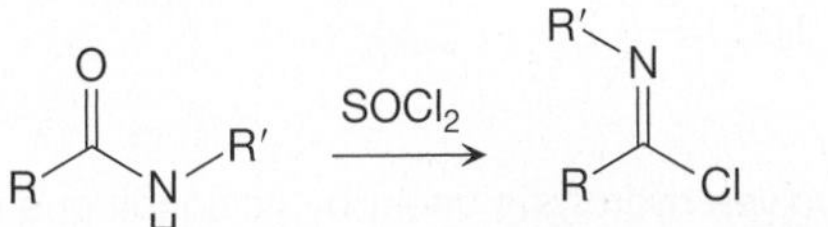

An imino chloride

23.18 A *sulfonamide* is produced when a sulfonyl chloride is treated with an amine, as shown here. This reaction is a key step in the synthesis of *sulfa drugs*, which constitute an important class of antibiotics. Draw a complete, detailed mechanism for this reaction.

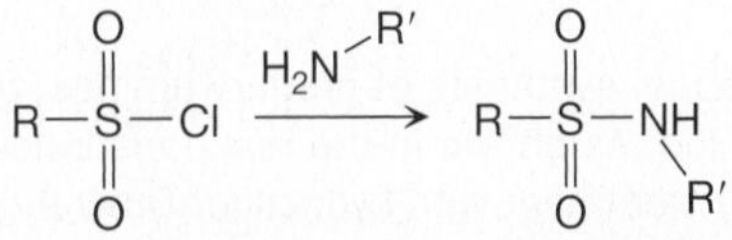

A sulfonamide

Sections 23.7 and 23.8 Base and Acid Catalysis in Nucleophilic Addition–Elimination Reactions; Baeyer–Villiger Oxidations

23.19 Predict the product of the reaction between methyl cyclohexylmethanoate and each of the following. If no reaction is expected to occur, write "no reaction." For those reactions that do occur, draw the complete, detailed mechanism. *Hint*: Pay attention to the reaction conditions. **(a)** H_2O, H^+; **(b)** H_2O, OH^-, then H_3O^+; **(c)** $CH_3CH_2CH_2OH$, $CH_3CH_2CH_2ONa$; **(d)** propan-2-ol, H^+; **(e)** propan-2-amine (excess), H^+; **(f)** propan-1-ol

23.20 Draw the complete, detailed mechanism and the major product for each of the following reactions.

(a)

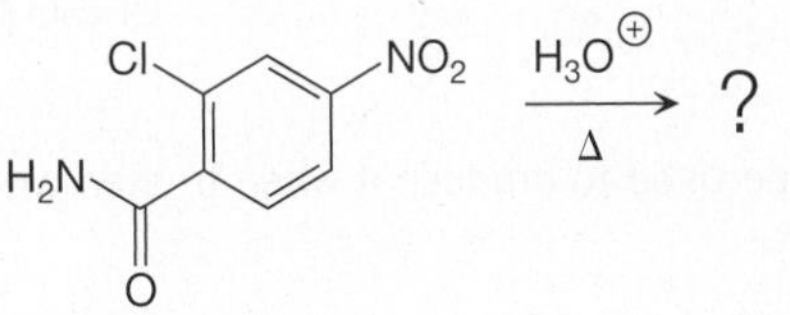

(b)

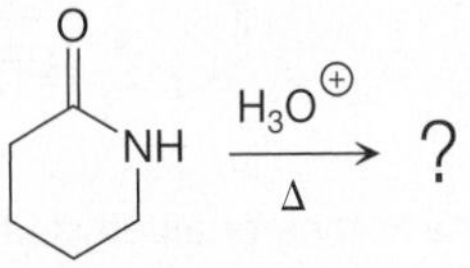

23.21 In each of the reactants shown here, a CO_2H group is separated from a OH group by the same number of carbons. When heated in the presence of acid, only the compound in the first reaction forms a lactone. Explain why.

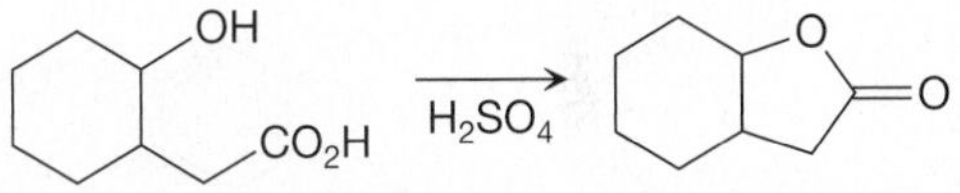

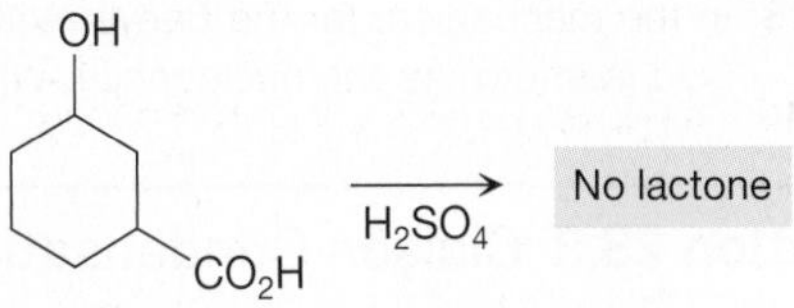
No lactone

23.22 The hydrolysis of an ester can be sped up by both acidic and basic conditions. Aminolysis of an ester can be sped up by acidic conditions but not by basic conditions. Explain why.

23.23 An acid anhydride can be formed under equilibrium conditions by reacting an ester with a carboxylic acid, as shown below. Reasonable yield is achieved if the equilibrium can be shifted by exploiting Le Châtelier's principle.

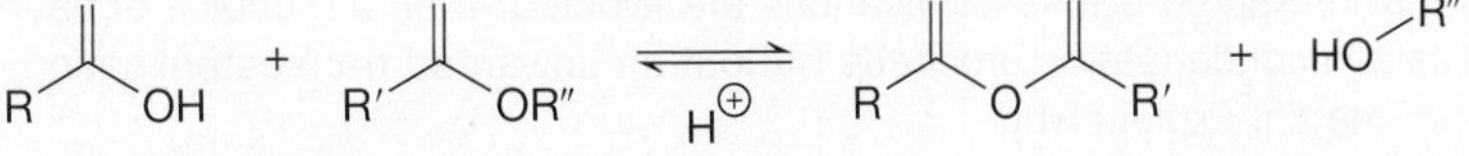

(a) Provide a complete, detailed mechanism for this reaction.

(b) In general, the above equilibrium favors the reactants. However, if the ester that is used is the one shown on the right, then the equilibrium favors the products. Explain why.

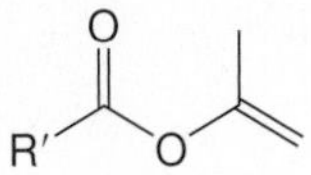

23.24 When a methyl ester is hydrolyzed under acidic conditions in $H_2{}^{18}O$, the ^{18}O isotope ends up in the carboxylic acid. When a *tert*-butyl ester is hydrolyzed under the same conditions, the labeled oxygen ends up in the alcohol product. **(a)** Propose mechanisms to account for these observations. **(b)** Explain why each ester undergoes the respective mechanism.

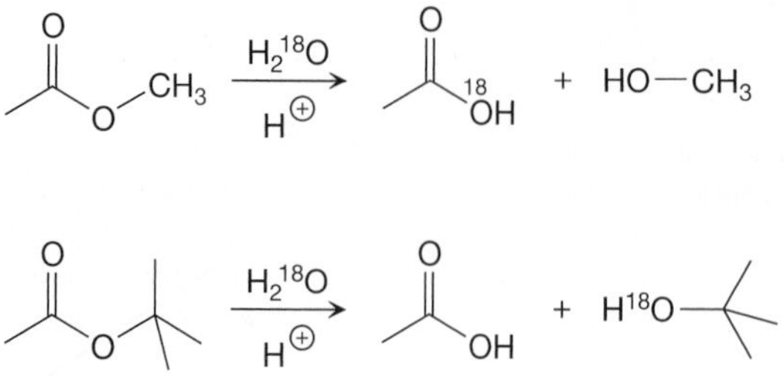

23.25 The Gabriel synthesis of primary amines, discussed in Chapter 22, involves hydrolysis under basic conditions to release the amine. As shown in the reactions below, the amine can also be released by **(a)** hydrolysis under acidic conditions and **(b)** treatment with hydrazine. Draw the complete, detailed mechanisms for these reactions.

(a)

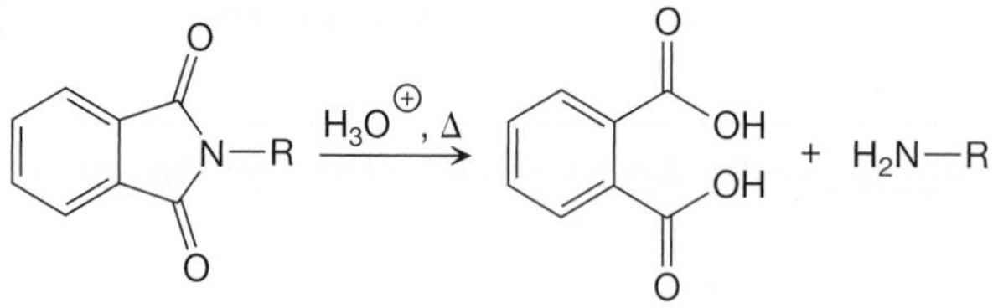

(b)

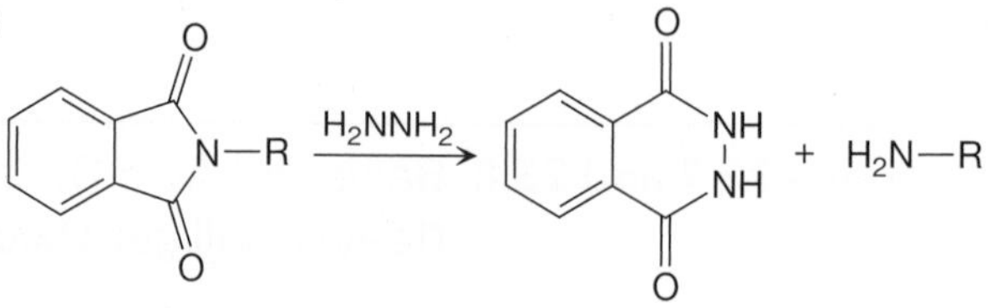

23.26 Draw the complete, detailed mechanism and the major product for each of the following reactions.

(a)

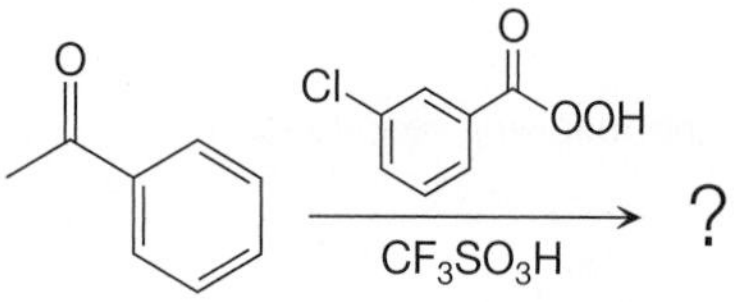

(b)

(c)

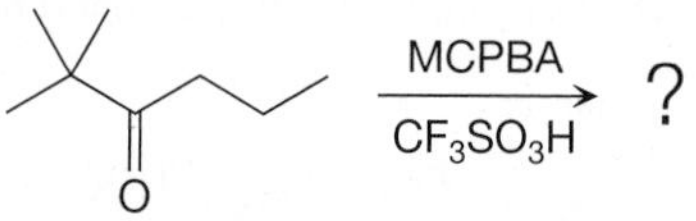

23.27 (SYN) For each compound below, draw the ketone or aldehyde that can be used to produce it when treated with *m*-chloroperbenzoic acid under acidic conditions.

(a)

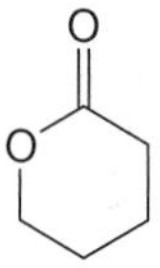

(b)

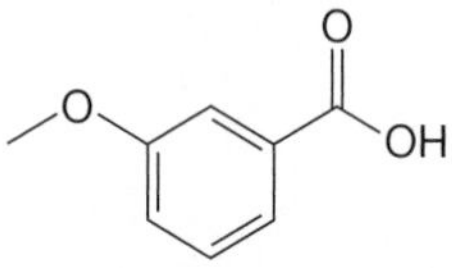

(c)

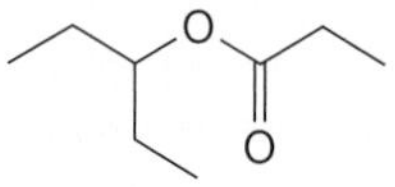

(d)

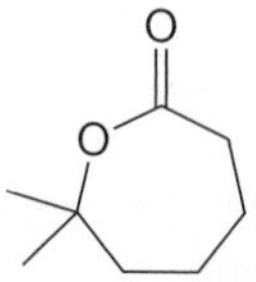

23.28 In the mechanism for the Baeyer–Villiger oxidation in Equation 23-35 (p. 1122), the hydroxyl (OH) oxygen of the peroxy acid is shown as the nucleophile. Why is that oxygen more nucleophilic than the adjacent oxygen?

Section 23.9 Claisen Condensation Reactions

23.29 Draw the complete, detailed mechanism for each of the following reactions, and predict the major product.

(a) Ethyl 3-methylbutanoate $\xrightarrow[\text{EtOH}]{\text{NaOEt}}$?

(b) Ethyl propanoate + Ethyl benzoate $\xrightarrow[\text{EtOH}]{\text{NaOEt}}$?

(c) Ethyl butanoate + Diethyl carbonate $\xrightarrow[\text{EtOH}]{\text{NaOEt}}$?

23.30 This chapter explains that unwanted transesterifications are avoided when the choice of base is the same as the leaving group. The following Claisen condensation proceeds without an unwanted transesterification, even though the base and the leaving group do not match. Explain why.

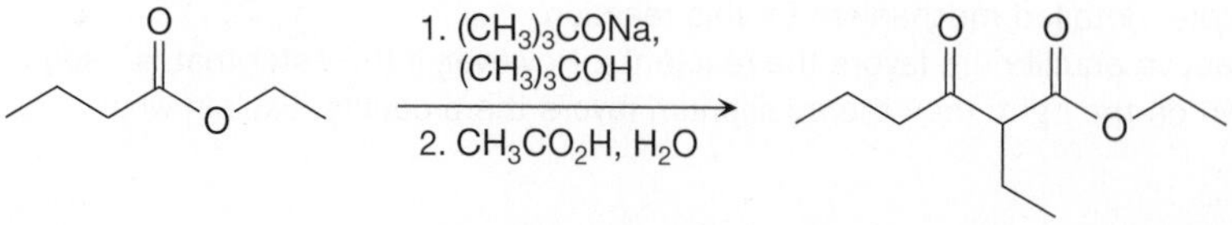

23.31 A crossed Claisen reaction between methylpropanoate and methyl acetate is not synthetically useful because it produces a mixture of products. The reaction between methyl 2-methylpropanoate and methyl acetate, however, is synthetically useful. Explain why.

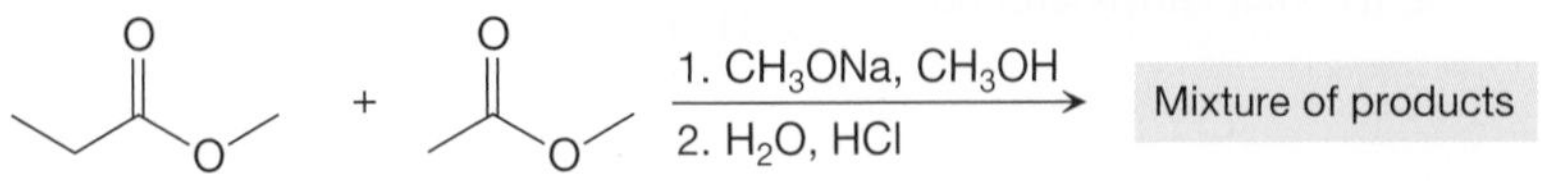
1. CH_3ONa, CH_3OH
2. H_2O, HCl
Mixture of products

Methyl propanoate

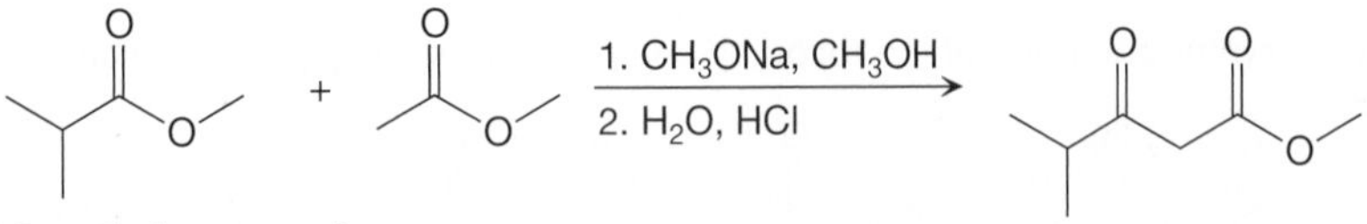
1. CH_3ONa, CH_3OH
2. H_2O, HCl

Methyl 2-methylpropanoate

78%

23.32 Draw the complete, detailed mechanism for each of the following reactions, and predict the major products.

(a)

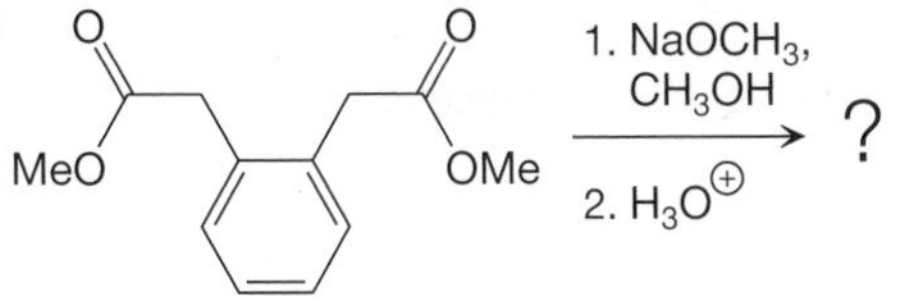
MeO
OMe
1. $NaOCH_3$, CH_3OH
2. $H_3O^{\oplus}$
?

(b)

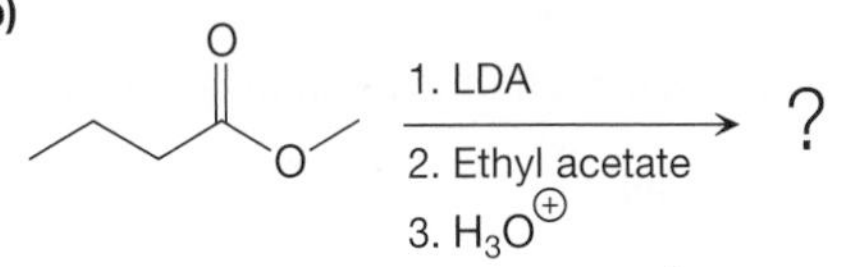
1. LDA
2. Ethyl acetate
3. $H_3O^{\oplus}$
?

23.33 Explain why the following Claisen condensation does *not* work.

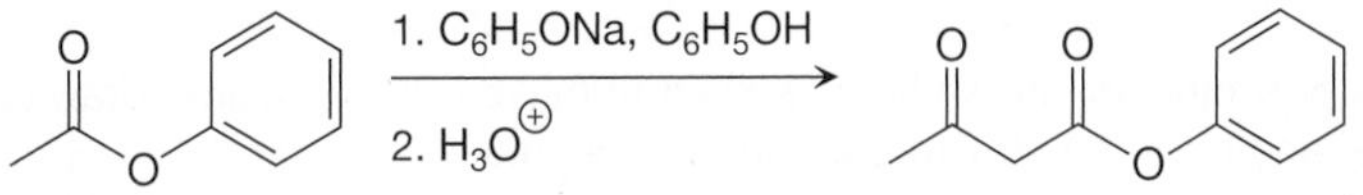
1. C_6H_5ONa, C_6H_5OH
2. $H_3O^{\oplus}$

23.34 Draw a complete, detailed mechanism for the reaction shown here.

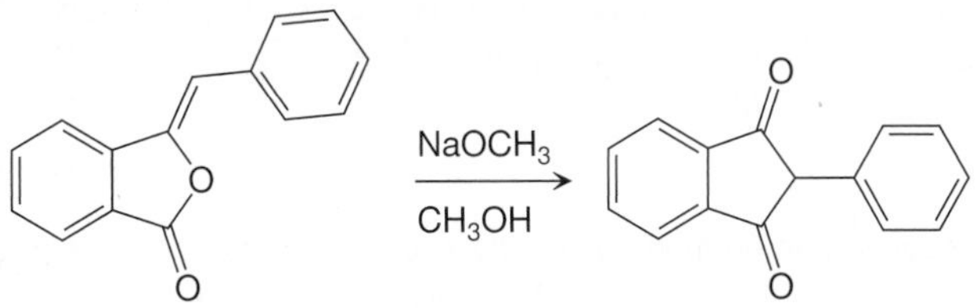
$NaOCH_3$
CH_3OH

23.35 **(SYN)** Show how to synthesize each of the following compounds by a Claisen or Dieckmann condensation.

(a)

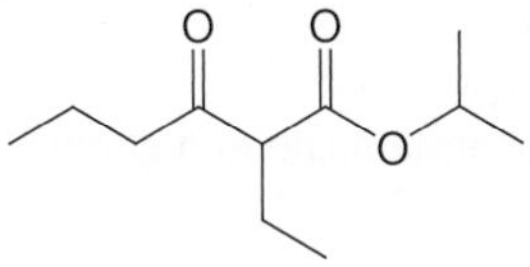

(b)

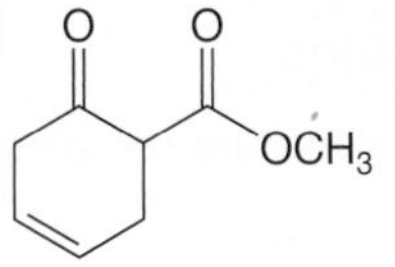
OCH_3

(c)

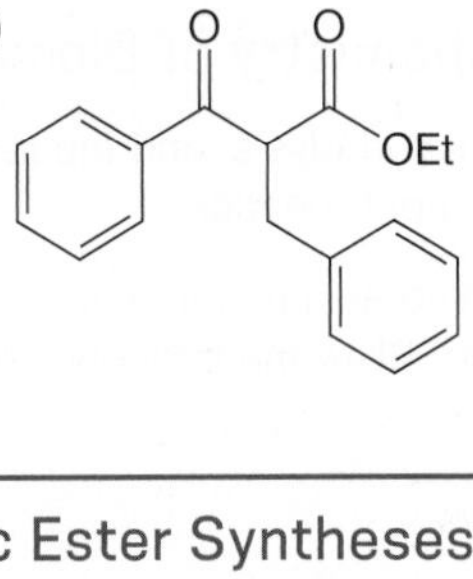
OEt

(d)

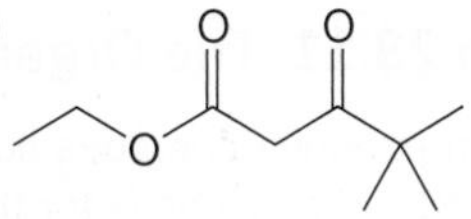

Section 23.10 The Malonic Ester and Acetoacetic Ester Syntheses

23.36 Draw structures for compounds **A** through **D**.

(a) Ethyl acetoacetate $\xrightarrow[\text{2. 1-Chloro-4-methylpentane}]{\text{1. NaOEt, EtOH}}$ **A** $\xrightarrow[\text{2. } H_3O^{\oplus}, \Delta]{\text{1. NaOH, } H_2O}$ **B**

Same as above

(b) **A** $\xrightarrow[\text{2. 1-Chloropropane}]{\text{1. NaOC(CH}_3)_3\text{, (CH}_3)_3\text{COH}}$ **C** $\xrightarrow[\text{2. } H_3O^{\oplus}, \Delta]{\text{1. NaOH, } H_2O}$ **D**

23.37 Draw structures for compounds **E** through **H**.

(a) Diethyl malonate $\xrightarrow[\text{2. (Bromomethyl)benzene}]{\text{1. NaOEt, EtOH}}$ **E** $\xrightarrow[\text{2. } H_3O^{\oplus}, \Delta]{\text{1. NaOH, } H_2O}$ **F**

Same as above

(b) **E** $\xrightarrow[\text{2. 1-Iodopentane}]{\text{1. NaOC(CH}_3)_3\text{, (CH}_3)_3\text{COH}}$ **G** $\xrightarrow[\text{2. } H_3O^{\oplus}, \Delta]{\text{1. NaOH, } H_2O}$ **H**

23.38 **(SYN)** Show how to synthesize each of the following compounds, beginning with malonic ester.

(a)

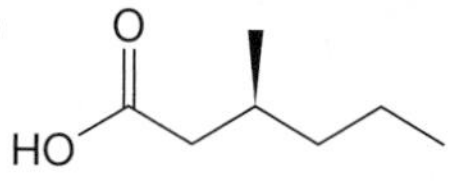

(b)

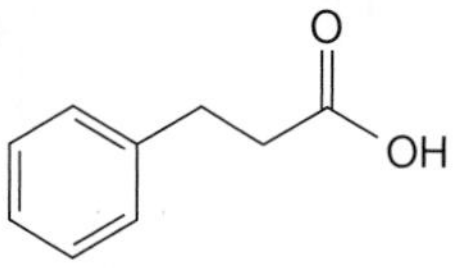

(c)

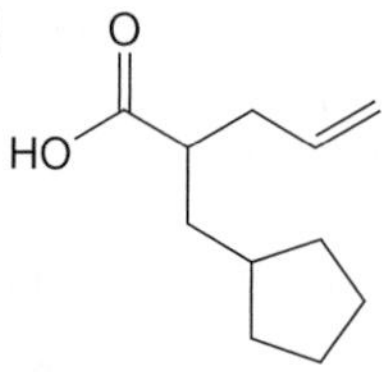

23.39 **(SYN)** Show how to synthesize each of the following compounds, beginning with acetoacetic ester.

(a)

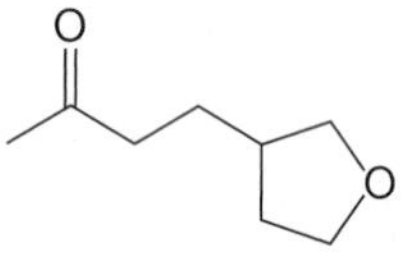

(b)

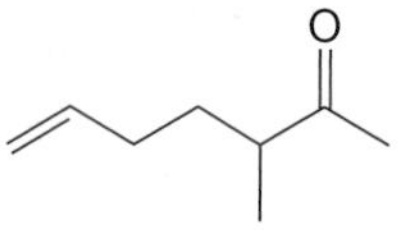

(c)

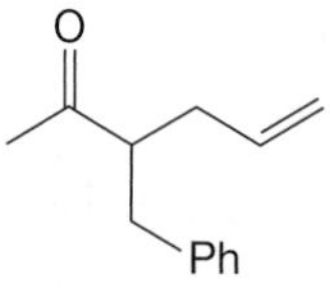

23.40 The Gabriel–malonic ester synthesis, shown here, is used to make α-amino acids. Draw complete, detailed mechanisms for this set of reactions, and draw the structure of the intermediate **I**.

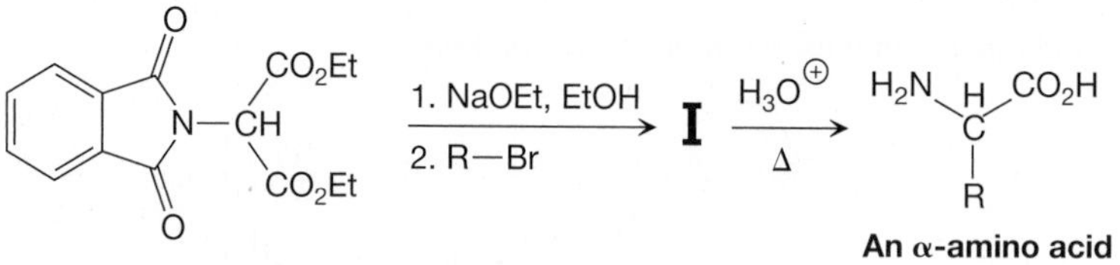

CO2Et
N—CH
CO2Et
1. NaOEt, EtOH
2. R—Br
I
H3O⊕
Δ
H2N H CO2H
C
R

An α-amino acid

23.41 **(SYN)** Do you think this compound can be made using the acetoacetic ester synthesis? Why or why not?

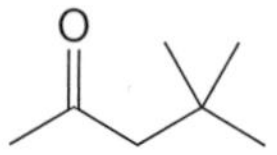

Section 23.11 The Organic Chemistry of Biomolecules

23.42 A tripeptide undergoes complete hydrolysis, and the resulting mixture contains only phenylalanine and glycine. Draw all possible sequences for the original tripeptide.

23.43 A polypeptide containing 18 amino acid residues in its sequence was partially hydrolyzed, and peptides **A–D** were detected in the resulting mixture. Draw the sequence of the original peptide.

A Phe-Gly-Ala
B Ser-Ser-Ser-Trp-Phe-Gly-Ala
C Phe-Phe-Met-Ala-Ala-Pro-Trp-Cys
D Met-Ala-Ala-Pro-Trp-Cys-Leu-Ile-Leu-Ser-Ser

23.44 During the hydrolysis of proteins, some amino acids, such as tryptophan, do not survive the reaction conditions. Other amino acids, such as asparagine and glutamine, are modified. Refer to Table 1-7 (p. 39), which shows the structures of the 20 common amino acids, and write the structures of the two amino acids that are formed when asparagine and glutamine decompose in hot, concentrated HCl.

23.45 *N,N'*-Dicyclohexylcarbodiimide (DCC), shown here, is a reagent used in the laboratory synthesis of peptides.

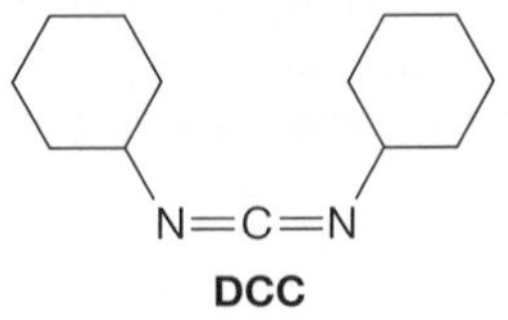
N=C=N
DCC

Specifically, when DCC is added to a mixture of a carboxylic acid and an amine, the carboxylic acid and the amide will be coupled together to produce an amide:

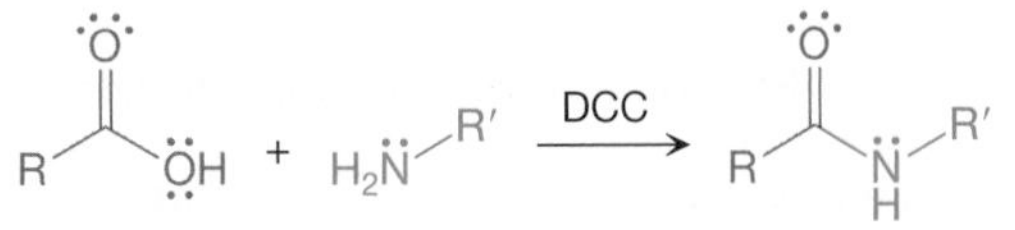
DCC

As shown below, a key intermediate in the mechanism is an *O*-acyl isourea, which has a good leaving group attached to the carbonyl carbon.

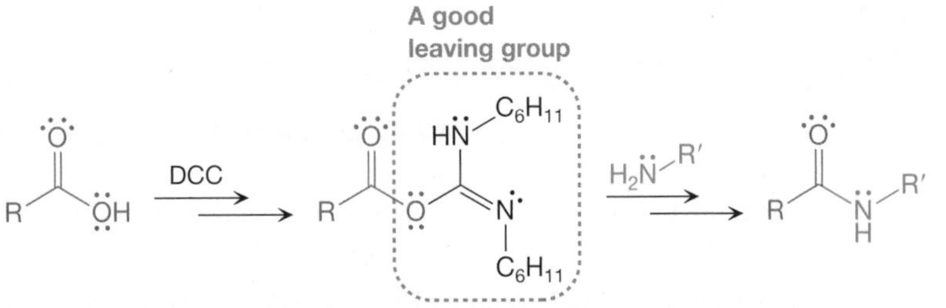
A good
leaving group
DCC
An O-acyl isourea

Draw the complete, detailed mechanism for this coupling reaction.

23.46 When DCC (see Problem 23.45) is added to a mixture of two peptides, whose side chains are represented by R^1 and R^2, four different dipeptides are produced. Draw the structures of all four dipeptides, and use the generic R^1 and R^2 notation for the side chains.

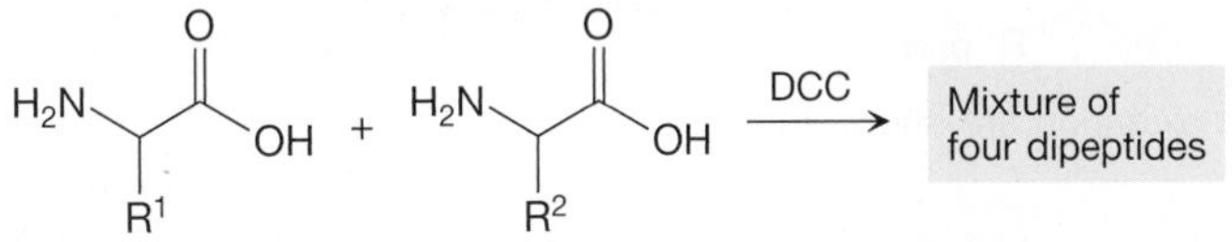
DCC
Mixture of
four dipeptides

23.47 To avoid producing mixtures of peptides when DCC is used to couple amino acids (see Problems 23.45 and 23.46), the carboxyl and amino groups that should *not* undergo coupling are protected prior to adding DCC. For example, a carboxyl group can be protected in the form of a *benzyl ester* (CO_2—Bn), and an amino group can be protected in the form of a *carbamate* (represented as Z—N). Both of these groups can be deprotected using H_2 with a Pd catalyst. With this in mind, draw the exclusive dipeptide that is produced in the following scheme.

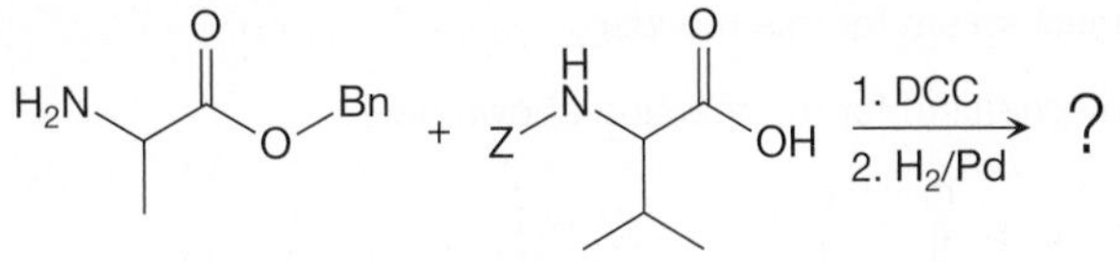
1. DCC
2. H2/Pd
?

Integrated Problems

23.48 Predict the product of the sequence of reactions shown here.

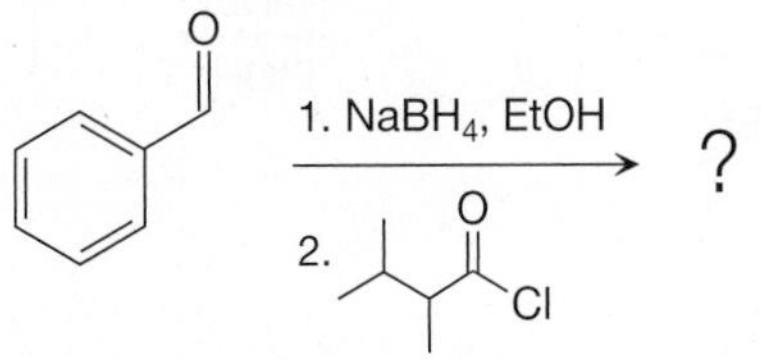
1. NaBH4, EtOH
2.
?

23.49 An example of the McFayden–Stevens reaction is shown below, in which an acyl chloride is converted to an aldehyde. First, benzoyl chloride is reacted with hydrazine, H_2NNH_2, and then that product is reacted with benzenesulfonyl chloride. The result is a 1-benzoyl-2-benzenesulfonylhydrazide, which, when heated under basic conditions, decomposes into the aldehyde. Provide the complete, detailed mechanism showing the conversion of benzoyl chloride into 1-benzoyl-2-benzenesulfonylhydrazide.

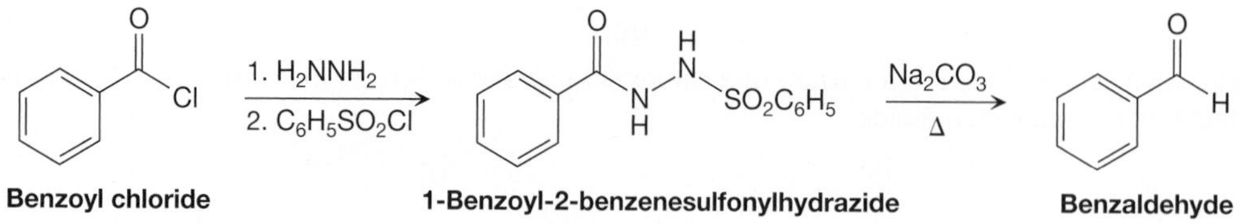
1. H2NNH2
2. C6H5SO2Cl
SO2C6H5
Na2CO3
Δ
Benzoyl chloride
1-Benzoyl-2-benzenesulfonylhydrazide
Benzaldehyde

23.50 One method for synthesizing lactones (cyclic esters) involves treating a hydroxy acid with 2-pyridinethiol, followed by heating under reflux. The mechanism proceeds through a 2-pyridinethiol ester, as indicated.

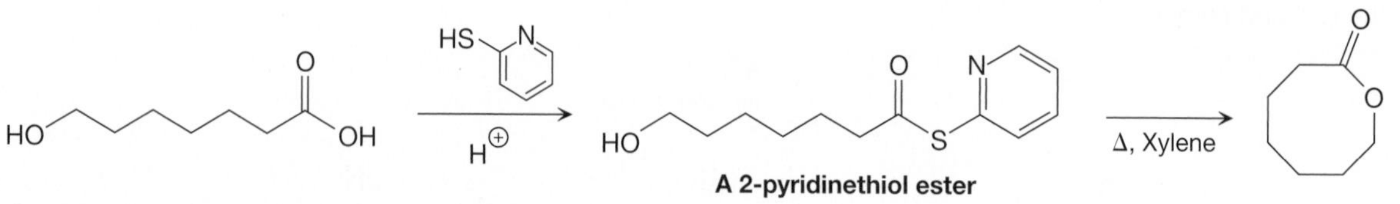
HS
HO
OH
H⊕
A 2-pyridinethiol ester
Δ, Xylene

(a) Provide a complete, detailed mechanism for this reaction.
(b) If benzenethiol (C_6H_5SH) is used instead of 2-pyridinethiol, the conversion is much less effective. This suggests the N atom is instrumental in the mechanism. Explain the role of the N atom.

23.51 A Swern oxidation can be used to oxidize a primary alcohol to an aldehyde or a secondary alcohol to a ketone. The alcohol is first treated with dimethyl sulfoxide (DMSO) and oxalyl chloride, followed by treatment with base:

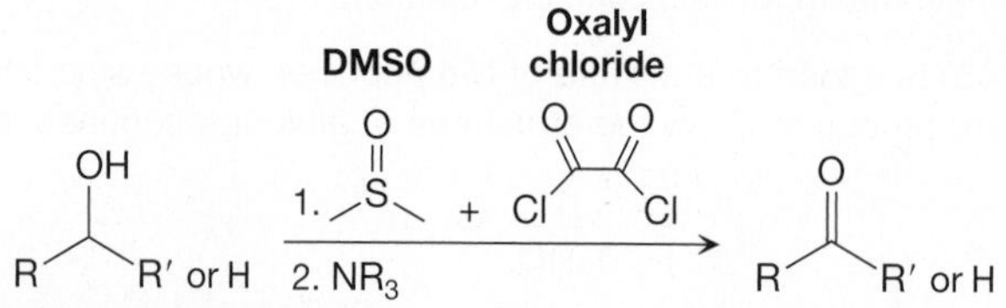
DMSO
Oxalyl chloride
1.
2. NR3
R' or H

Key intermediates of this oxidation are shown below.

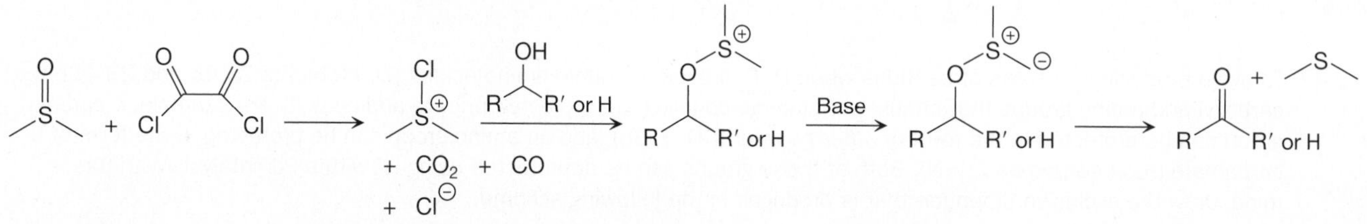
+ CO2 + CO
+ Cl⊖
R' or H
Base

Draw the complete, detailed mechanism for this reaction.

23.52 Draw the complete, detailed mechanism for the reaction shown here.

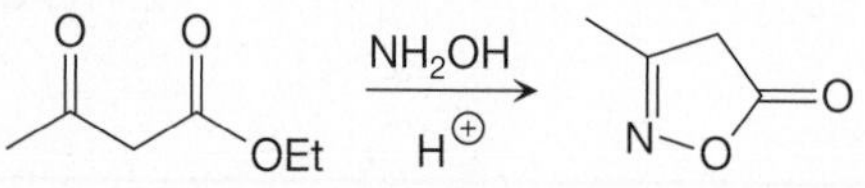
OEt
NH2OH
H⊕

23.53 Draw the complete, detailed mechanism for the following reaction.

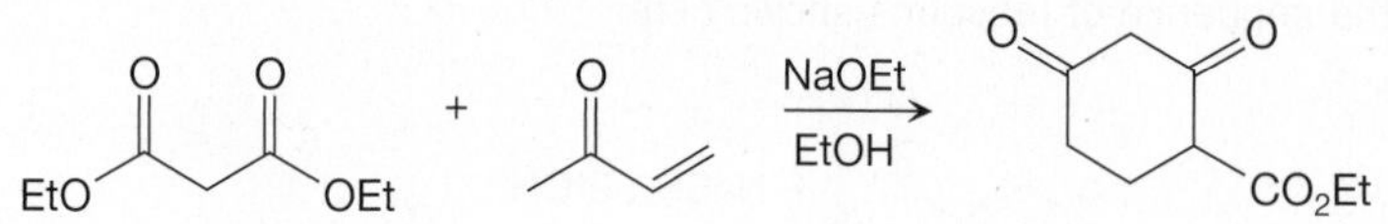
EtO
OEt
NaOEt
EtOH
CO2Et

23.54 Diazomethane can be used to bring about a *ring expansion* of a cyclic ketone, as shown here. **(a)** Propose a mechanism for this reaction. **(b)** Suggest why this reaction is capable of converting a more stable six-membered ring to a less stable seven-membered ring.

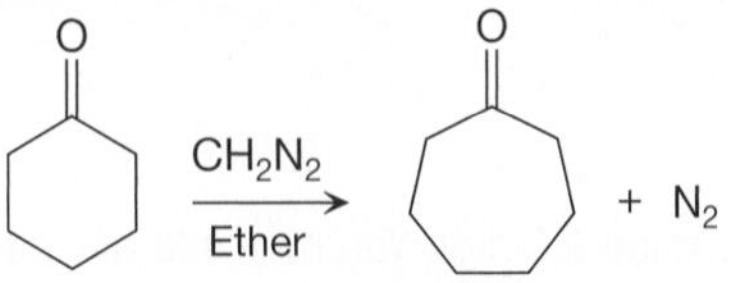

O
CH2N2
Ether
O
+ N2

23.55 **(SYN)** Starting with acetic acid and using any other reagents necessary, show how you would synthesize each of the following compounds.

(a)
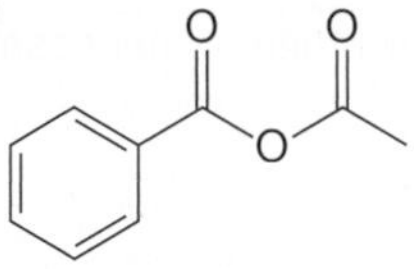
(b)
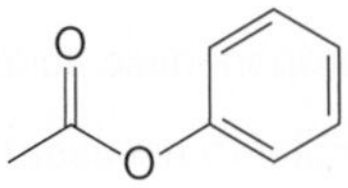
(c)
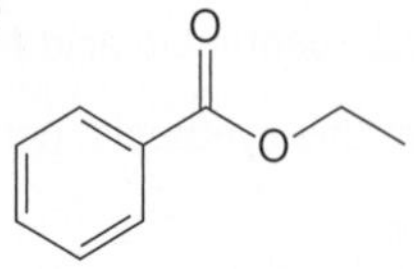

(d)
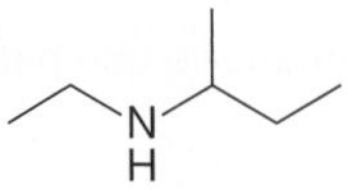
(e)
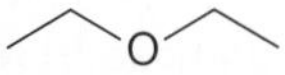
(f)
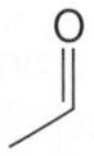
(g)
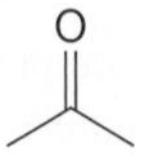

23.56 **(SYN)** Using acetic acid as your only source of carbon, propose a synthesis of each of the following compounds. You may use any inorganic reagent necessary. **(a)** ethyl acetate; **(b)** butan-2-ol; **(c)** 3-methylpentan-3-ol; **(d)** butan-2-one; **(e)** ethanamine; **(f)** *N*-ethylacetamide; **(g)** *N,N*-diethylacetamide.

23.57 Draw the structures of **A**, **B**, and **C** in the following sequence of reactions.

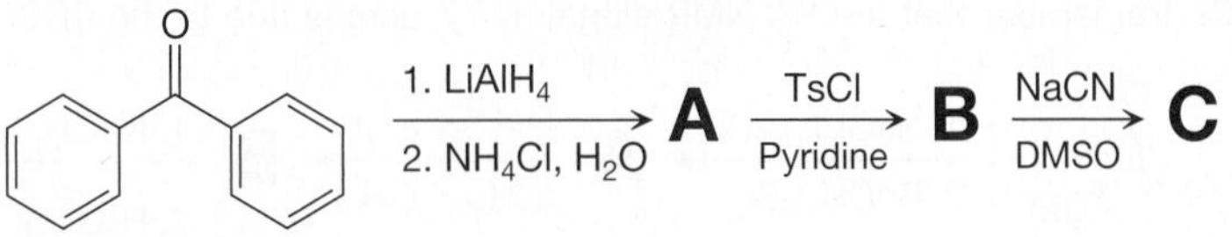

O
1. LiAlH4
2. NH4Cl, H2O
A
TsCl
Pyridine
B
NaCN
DMSO
C

23.58 Draw the major product of each of the following sequences of reactions.

(a)
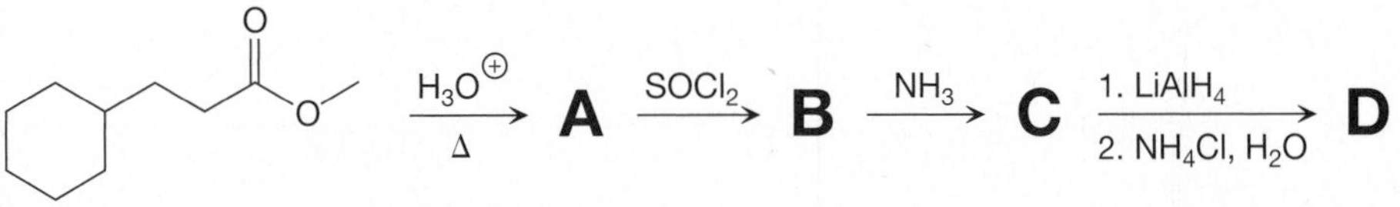

O
O
H3O+
Δ
A
SOCl2
B
NH3
C
1. LiAlH4
2. NH4Cl, H2O
D

(b)
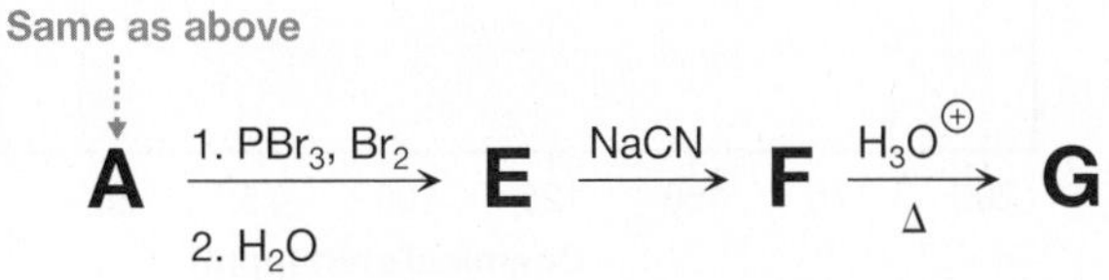

Same as above
A
1. PBr3, Br2
2. H2O
E
NaCN
F
H3O+
Δ
G

(c)
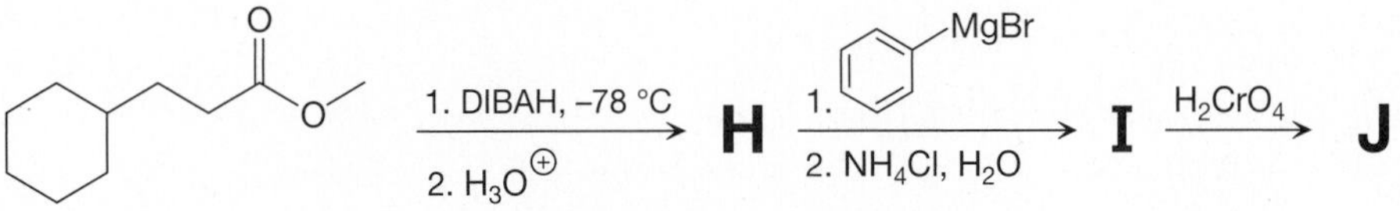

O
O
1. DIBAH, –78 °C
2. H3O+
H
MgBr
1.
2. NH4Cl, H2O
I
H2CrO4
J

(d)
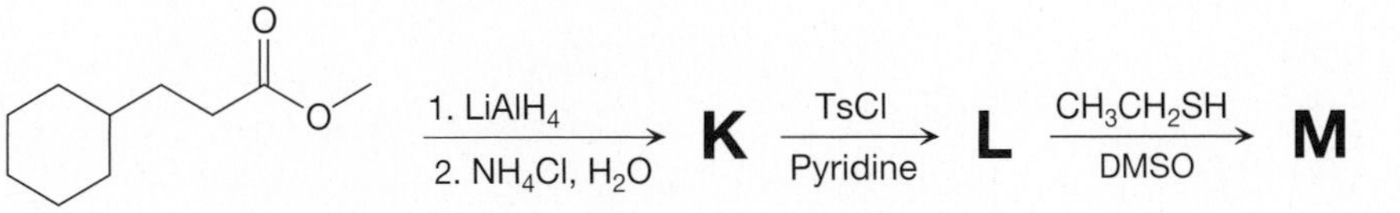

O
O
1. LiAlH4
2. NH4Cl, H2O
K
TsCl
Pyridine
L
CH3CH2SH
DMSO
M

23.59 **(SYN)** Suggest how you should carry out each of the following syntheses.

(a)

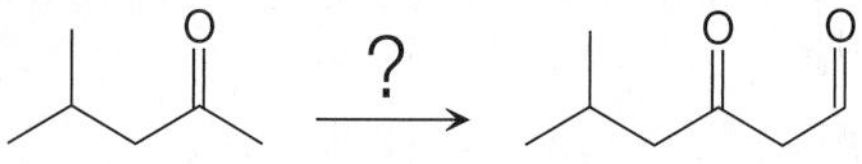

(b)

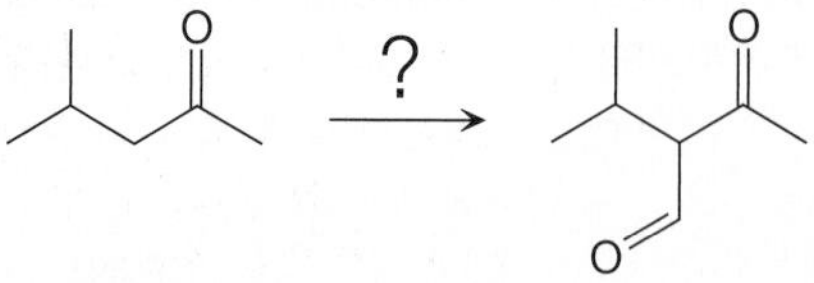

23.60 **(SYN)** Devise a synthesis of 2-methylpentane-1,3-diol. You may use any inorganic reagents, but your only carbon source must be alcohols containing three or fewer carbons.

23.61 **(SYN)** Show how you would synthesize 3-oxo-2-methylpentanal. You may use any inorganic reagents, but your only carbon source must be alcohols containing three or fewer carbons.

23.62 **(SYN)** Show how you would synthesize pentanoic acid from 1,3-propanedioic acid, using any reagents necessary.

23.63 **(SYN)** Show how you would carry out this synthesis, using any reagents necessary.

23.64 When phosgene is treated with excess methanol, a product is formed whose ^{1}H NMR spectrum shows one peak—a singlet at 3.8 ppm. Provide a complete, detailed mechanism for this reaction.

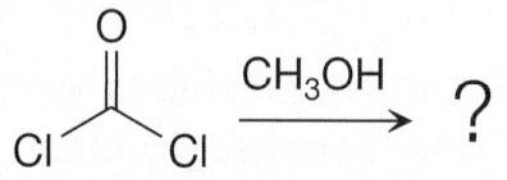
CH$_3$OH
Cl
Cl
?

Phosgene

23.65 A student carries out the following sequence of reactions. The IR and ^{13}C NMR spectra are shown for the product **C**. Draw structures for **A–C**. (Remember that the ^{13}C NMR signal at 77 ppm is due to the CDCl$_3$ solvent.)

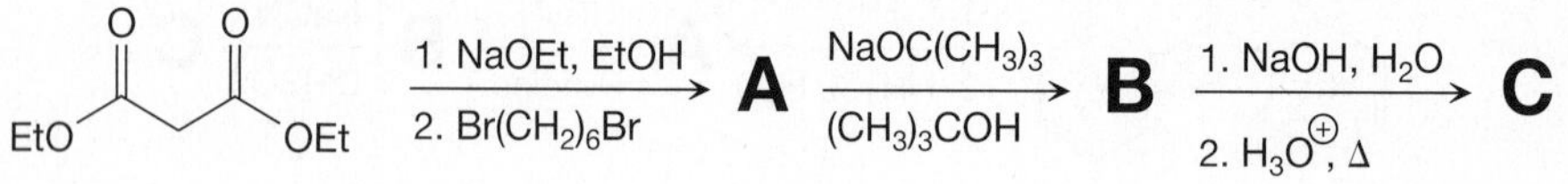
EtO
OEt
1. NaOEt, EtOH
2. Br(CH$_2$)$_6$Br
A
NaOC(CH$_3$)$_3$
(CH$_3$)$_3$COH
B
1. NaOH, H$_2$O
2. H$_3$O$^+$, Δ
C

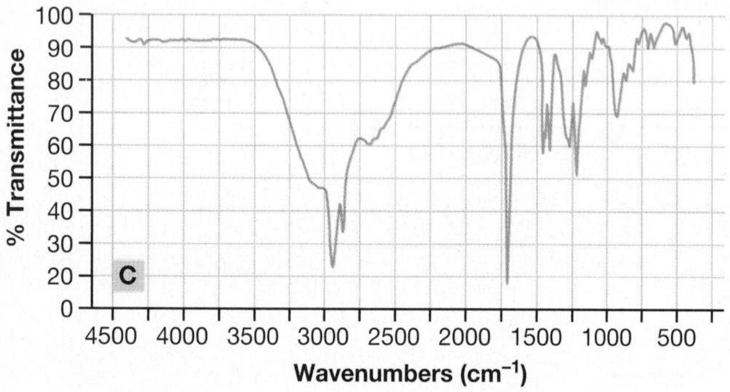
% Transmittance
C
Wavenumbers (cm^{-1})

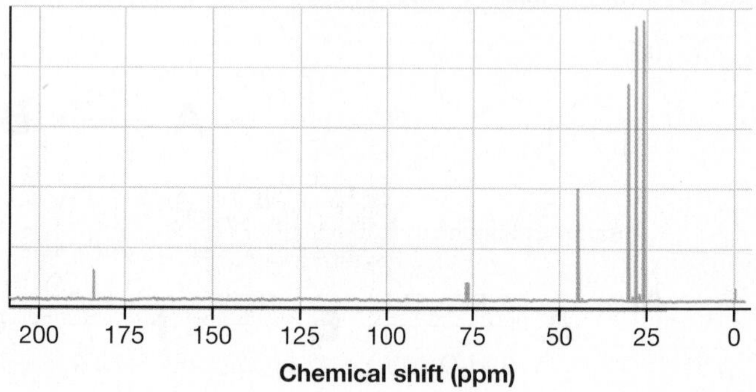
Chemical shift (ppm)

23.66 A student treated methyl 2-methylpropanoate with sodium methoxide dissolved in methanol. After the solution was refluxed for 2 hours, the mixture was analyzed, and its NMR, IR, and mass spectra are shown below.

(a) Draw the mechanism of the reaction the student was expecting, and draw the expected product.

(b) What do the spectra suggest occurred?

(c) Explain these results.

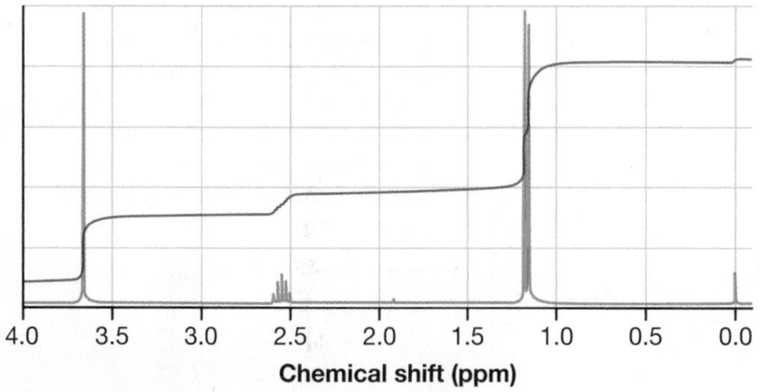
Chemical shift (ppm)

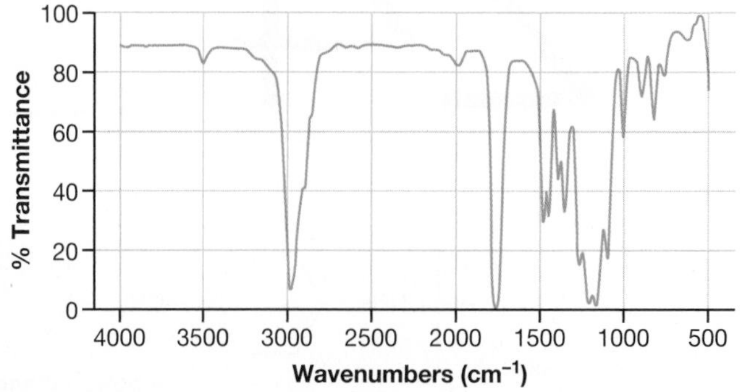
% Transmittance
Wavenumbers (cm⁻¹)

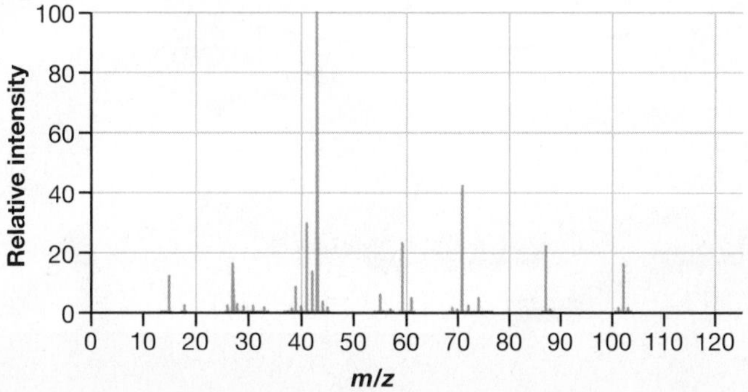
Relative intensity
m/z

23.67 A liquid, which is insoluble in water, reacts in acidic water to form an insoluble solid product. That product is soluble in water under basic conditions. The IR and ^{1}H NMR spectra of the reactant are shown below. Provide a structure for both the reactant and the product.

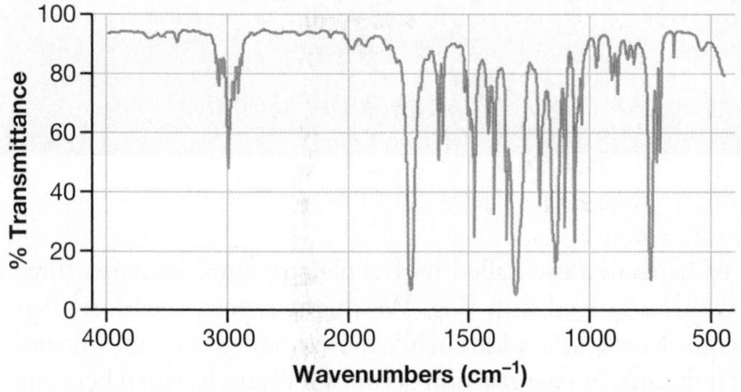
% Transmittance
Wavenumbers (cm⁻¹)

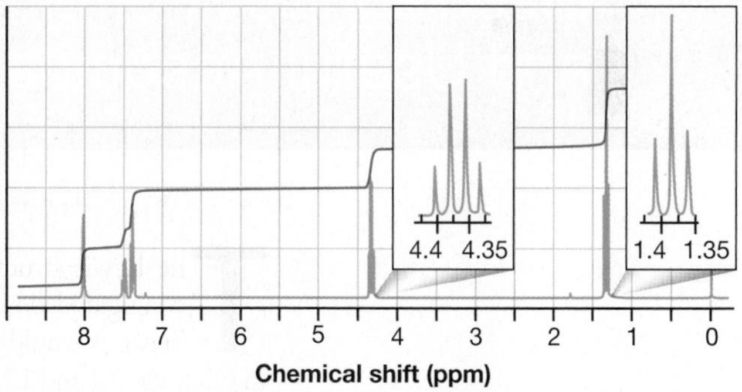
4.4 4.35
1.4 1.35
Chemical shift (ppm)

23.68 A compound that has no hydrogen atoms is treated with excess ethanol. The product is a compound whose formula is $C_6H_{10}O_4$. The IR and ^{1}H NMR spectra of the product are shown below. Draw structures for both the product and the reactant.

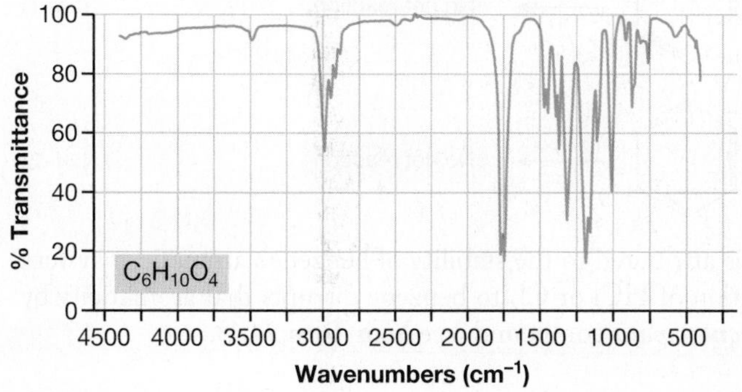
% Transmittance
C6H10O4
Wavenumbers (cm⁻¹)

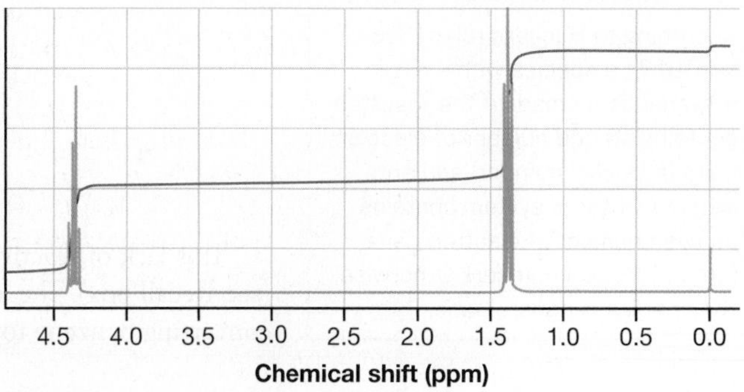
Chemical shift (ppm)

24

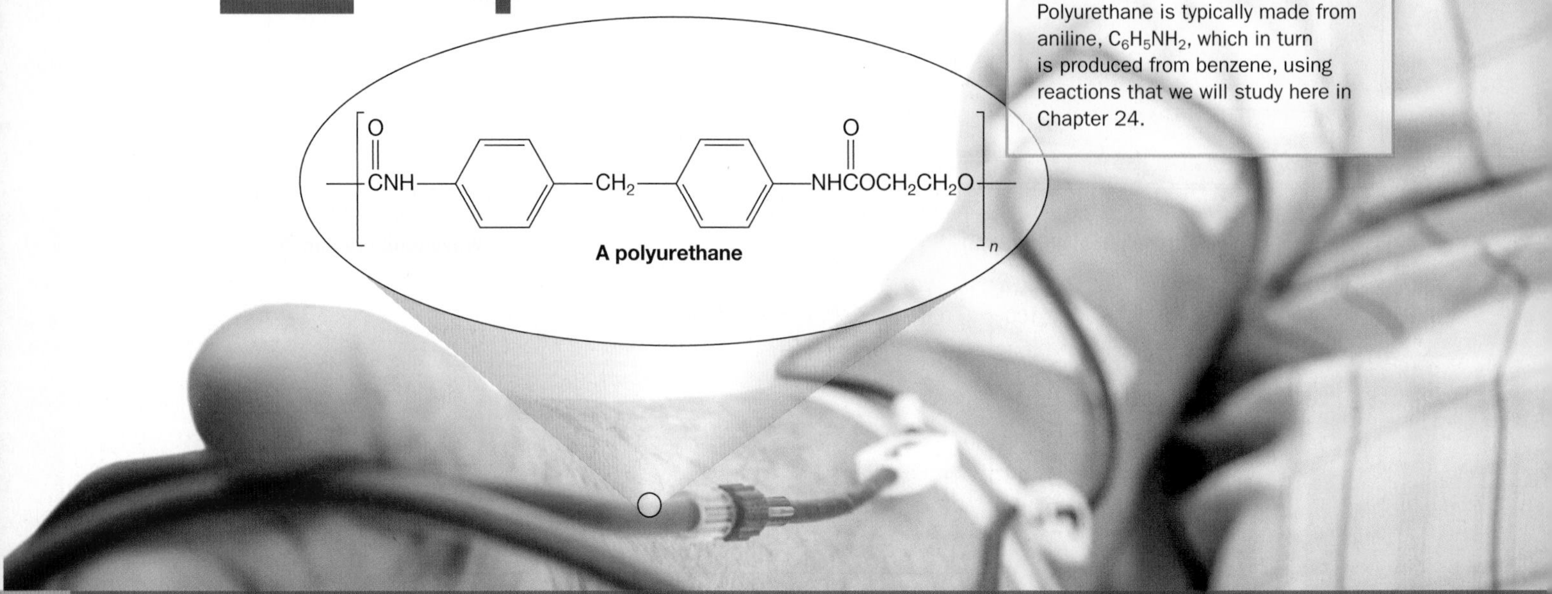
O
CNH
CH$_2$
O
NHCOCH$_2$CH$_2$O
n
A polyurethane

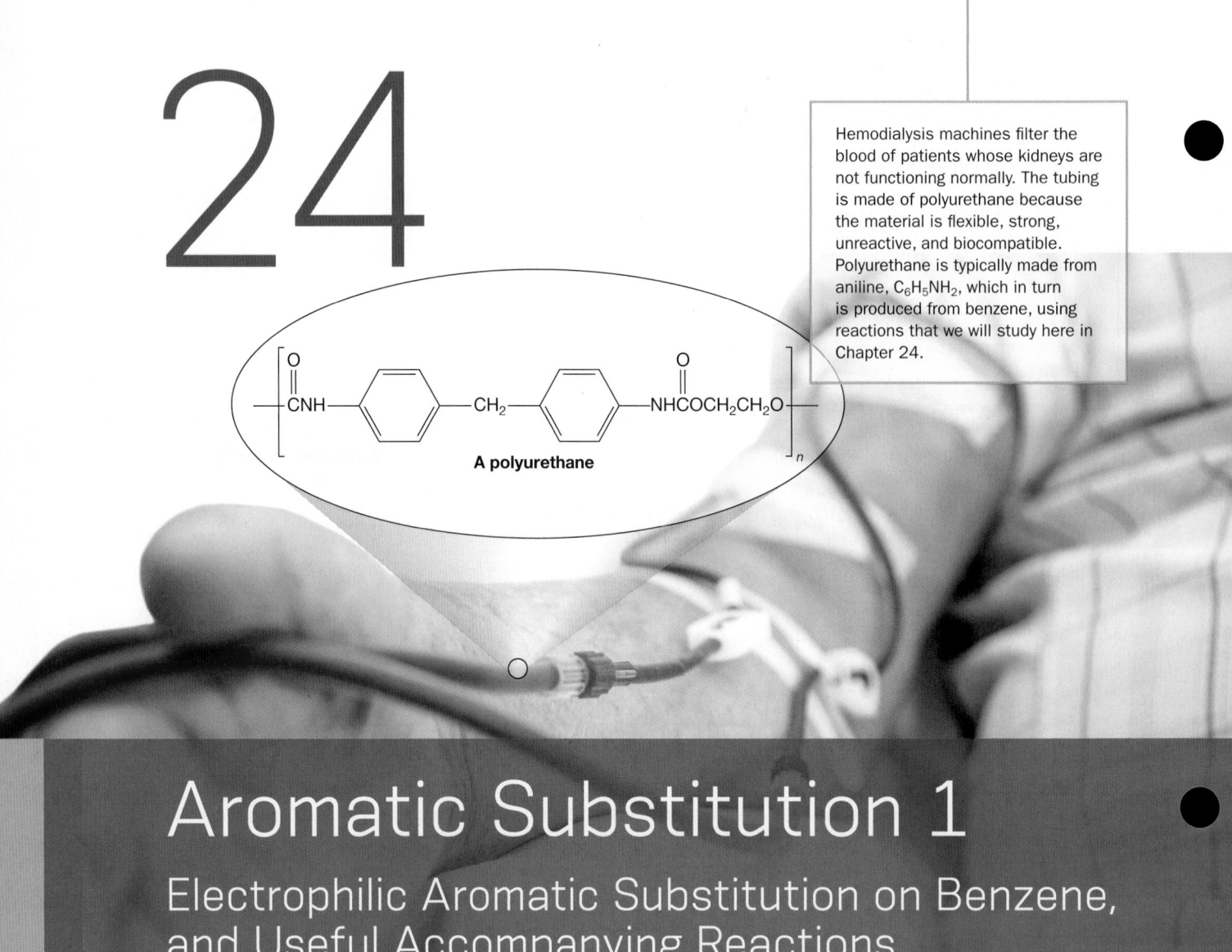

Hemodialysis machines filter the blood of patients whose kidneys are not functioning normally. The tubing is made of polyurethane because the material is flexible, strong, unreactive, and biocompatible. Polyurethane is typically made from aniline, $C_6H_5NH_2$, which in turn is produced from benzene, using reactions that we will study here in Chapter 24.

Aromatic Substitution 1

Electrophilic Aromatic Substitution on Benzene, and Useful Accompanying Reactions

The Lewis structure of benzene (also called its Kekulé structure) contains three conjugated double bonds arranged in a ring. We might expect, therefore, that benzene would undergo electrophilic addition like the various alkenes and alkynes in Chapters 12 and 13. But it doesn't. No net reaction occurs, for example, when benzene is treated with HCl (Eq. 24-1) or with Cl_2 (Eq. 24-2) under normal conditions:

> **◂ RECALL**
>
> According to Hückel's rules (Section 14.7), a species with a cyclic π system is aromatic if the π system contains an odd number of electron pairs (a Hückel number) and antiaromatic if the π system contains an even number of electron pairs (an anti-Hückel number). Otherwise, the species is nonaromatic.

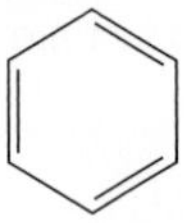 $\xrightarrow{\text{HCl}}$ No net reaction **(24-1)**

 $\xrightarrow{\text{Cl}_2}$ No net reaction **(24-2)**

This lack of reactivity is attributed to the stability of benzene's aromatic π system (see Recall box). The addition of HCl or Cl_2 to benzene disrupts that aromaticity by converting benzene to a *nonaromatic* compound (see Your Turn 24.1).

Chapter Outline

YOUR TURN 24.1

Draw the electrophilic addition products for the reactions in Equations 24-1 and 24-2 and show that they are, indeed, nonaromatic.

Answers to Your Turns are in the back of the book.

Electrophilic addition reactions that *permanently* disrupt benzene's aromaticity, such as those in Equations 24-1 and 24-2, are heavily disfavored. When metallic iron or iron(III) chloride ($FeCl_3$) is added to the reaction mixture, however, benzene does react with Cl_2, as shown in Equation 24-3:

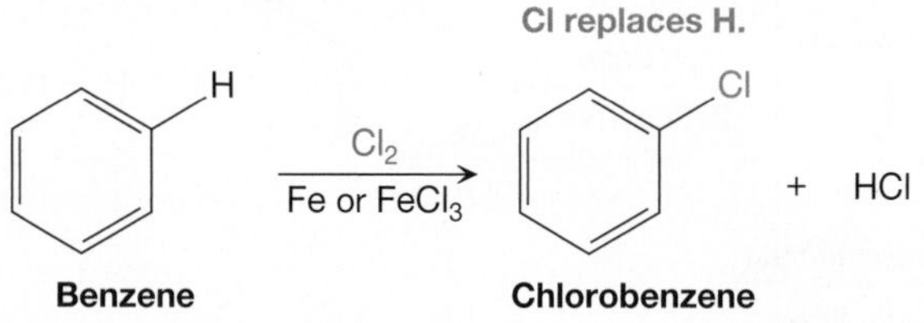

Cl replaces H.
H
Cl
Cl_2
Fe or $FeCl_3$
+ HCl
Benzene
Chlorobenzene

(24-3)

Because the Cl in the product appears where there was initially a H, the net reaction is a *substitution*, not an addition. More specifically, the reaction is called an **electrophilic aromatic substitution reaction** (EAS) because an electrophilic Cl and an aromatic species are involved.

Here in Chapter 24, we study the general mechanism for the reaction in Equation 24-3 and other electrophilic aromatic substitution reactions involving benzene. Although the reactions can include a variety of different reagents, they follow the same general mechanism.

Aromaticity is not limited to benzene. Other aromatic compounds we examined in Chapter 14 can also undergo electrophilic aromatic substitution. The mechanisms for the reactions involving other aromatic compounds are no different from the ones involving benzene, but they require additional consideration of reaction rates and regiochemistry, which will be discussed in Chapter 25. Here in Chapter 24, we focus on variations in reactions described by the electrophilic aromatic substitution mechanism. We will also consider organic synthesis, introducing reactions that are often used in conjunction with electrophilic aromatic substitution reactions.

24.1 The General Mechanism of Electrophilic Aromatic Substitution

SECTION 24.1 OBJECTIVES

You will be able to:

1. Draw the two-step sequence that characterizes the general electrophilic aromatic substitution mechanism.
2. Identify the rate-determining step in electrophilic aromatic substitution, and explain the importance of electrophile strength and concentration.

Like alkenes and alkynes, the π system of benzene is relatively electron-rich. In contrast, an electrophile is relatively electron-poor. Accordingly, we can write E^+ to represent a generic electrophile, where the positive charge emphasizes that the electrophile is electron-poor. Therefore, an electrophilic addition step between benzene and E^+ results in a new bond, using a pair of π electrons from benzene. This is shown in Step 1 of Equation 24-4, the general mechanism for electrophilic aromatic substitution (EAS).

It is the same first step we have seen previously in the addition of a Brønsted acid across an alkene (Chapter 12), in which the electrophile is a proton (H^+).

General mechanism for electrophilic aromatic substitution

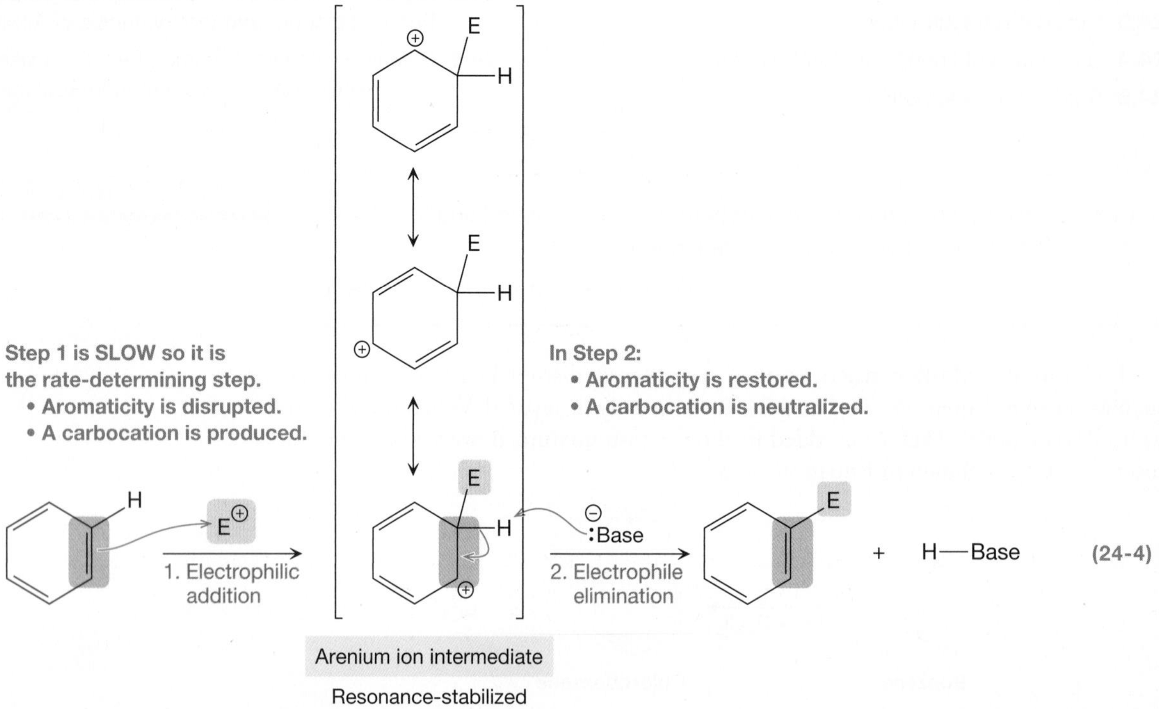

Step 1 is SLOW so it is
the rate-determining step.
• Aromaticity is disrupted.
• A carbocation is produced.
In Step 2:
• Aromaticity is restored.
• A carbocation is neutralized.
E
H
:Base
1. Electrophilic addition
2. Electrophile elimination
+ H—Base
(24-4)
Arenium ion intermediate
Resonance-stabilized

Mechanism Drawing
General Mechanism of Electrophilic Aromatic Substitution on Benzene

The product of Step 1 in Equation 24-4 is an **arenium ion intermediate** or a **Wheland intermediate**. It is a carbocation intermediate consisting of five sp^2-hybridized C atoms and one sp^3-hybridized C atom. This intermediate participates in an electrophile elimination step in Step 2 of the mechanism. In the electrophile elimination step, a proton (H^+) is eliminated, assisted by the formation of a bond to a base that is present. Overall, then, E^+ replaces H^+, converting benzene into a substituted benzene.

YOUR TURN **24.2**

Label the hybridization on each carbon atom in this arenium ion intermediate.

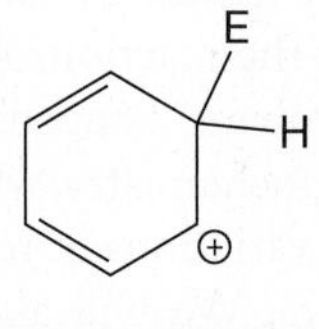

E
H

The arenium ion intermediate is not aromatic, and it possesses a positively charged carbon that lacks an octet. As a result, this intermediate is much less stable than benzene, the starting compound, as illustrated in the reaction energy diagram in **Figure 24-1**. Consequently, the first step of the EAS mechanism is highly unfavorable. By contrast, elimination of H^+ from the sp^3-hybridized C atom in Step 2 is highly favorable, because it restores aromaticity and neutralizes the carbocation.

Given the loss of aromaticity and the formation of a carbocation in Step 1, you might wonder why electrophilic aromatic substitution takes place at all. The arenium ion intermediate is stabilized by resonance delocalization of the positive charge (Eq. 24-4), so it is significantly more stable than it otherwise would be.

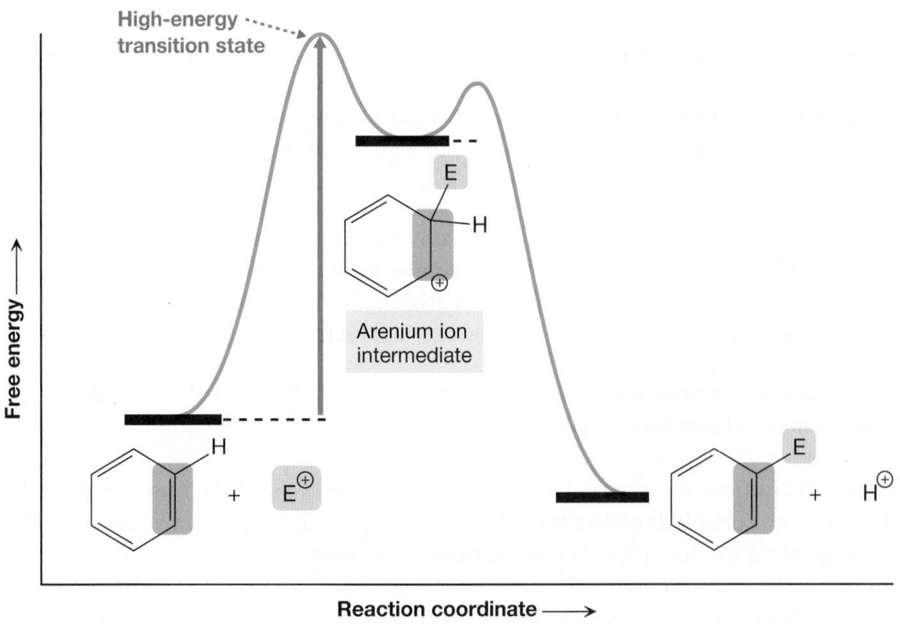
High-energy transition state
E
H
Arenium ion intermediate
Free energy
H
E
+
E
+
H
Reaction coordinate

FIGURE 24-1 Reaction energy diagram for an electrophilic aromatic substitution The arenium ion intermediate is significantly less stable than either the reactants or products, due to the loss of aromaticity and the formation of a positively charged C lacking an octet. As a result, Step 1 has a very high energy transition state and is the slow step.

YOUR TURN 24.3

Draw all of the resonance structures and the resonance hybrid of the arenium ion intermediate from Equation 24-4. Include curved arrows that show how each resonance structure is converted to the next one. In the resonance hybrid, how many C atoms share the positive charge?

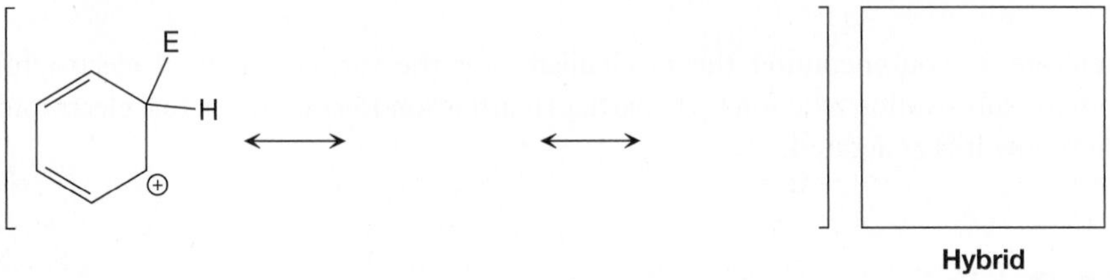
E
H
Hybrid

Notice in Figure 24-1 that the transition state for Step 1 is very high in energy and the energy barrier is quite large, which makes Step 1 the slow step of the mechanism. That is:

In electrophilic aromatic substitution, the electrophilic addition step (Step 1 in Eq. 24-4) is the rate-determining step.

Because benzene and the electrophile both appear as reactants in the rate-determining step, the rate of the overall reaction depends on the concentration of both species, as indicated in Equation 24-5:

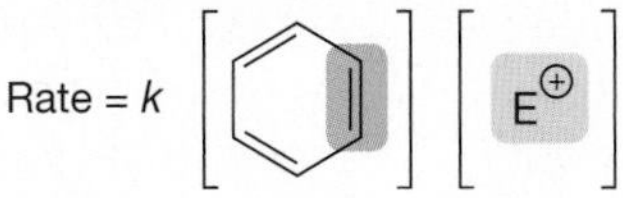
Rate = k
E

(24-5)

Specifically:

The general electrophilic aromatic substitution reaction is first-order with respect to the concentration of benzene and first-order with respect to the concentration of the electrophile.

YOUR TURN 24.4

Suppose an electrophilic aromatic substitution takes place between benzene and a particular electrophile, E^+. If the concentration of benzene is 1.0 M, which concentration of E^+ will lead to the faster reaction? **(a)** 0.01 M E^+; **(b)** 0.05 M E^+; **(c)** both reactions will proceed at the same rate

In situations where electrophilic aromatic substitution is involved in a competition, it is important to know whether that competition takes place under *kinetic control* or *thermodynamic control*. As indicated in Figure 24-1, the overall products appear significantly lower in energy than the reactants. Therefore:

Electrophilic aromatic substitution reactions are generally *irreversible* and take place under *kinetic control* (see Recall box).

◂ RECALL

Section 11.3 explained that a reaction is irreversible if the energy barrier for the reverse reaction is very large, such as when products are much more stable than reactants. The products of competing irreversible reactions do *not* equilibrate, so the major product is the one that is formed the fastest.

These substitutions tend to be highly favorable and irreversible because electrophiles (E^+) that are suitable for aromatic substitution tend to be very reactive and unstable to compensate for disrupting the aromaticity of the ring.

In the next few sections, we'll introduce some specific types of substitution reactions. Each of these reactions involves the same two-step electrophilic aromatic substitution mechanism, but the identity of E^+ differs from reaction to reaction. In most cases, the high reactivity required of each of these electrophiles generally makes it difficult or impossible to add them directly as reactants. Instead:

Electrophiles in electrophilic aromatic substitution reactions typically must be generated in situ from more stable precursors that can be added as starting materials.

Therefore, as you encounter the mechanisms for the various kinds of electrophilic aromatic substitution reactions, pay particular attention to what the actual electrophile is and how it is generated.

SECTION 24.2 OBJECTIVES

You will be able to:

1. Draw the mechanism for bromination and chlorination of benzene, and explain the role of the Lewis acid catalyst.
2. Incorporate the bromination or chlorination of benzene into a synthesis.

24.2 Halogenation

Recall from the introduction of this chapter that benzene does not react with molecular chlorine, Cl_2 (Eq. 24-2), under normal conditions. In the presence of Fe or $FeCl_3$, however, **chlorination** occurs, in which Cl replaces H to yield chlorobenzene (Eq. 24-3). Similarly, molecular bromine, Br_2, does not react with benzene under normal conditions (Eq. 24-6), but **bromination** will occur in the presence of Fe or $FeBr_3$ to produce bromobenzene (Eq. 24-7), whereby H is replaced by Br. Both of these reactions are examples of **aromatic halogenation** because a halogen replaces an aromatic hydrogen.

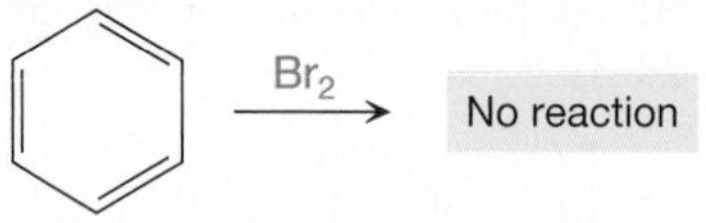

Br2
No reaction

(24-6)

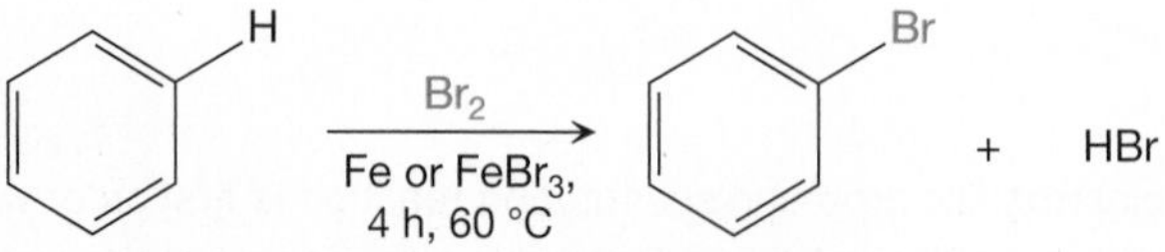

H
Br2
Fe or FeBr3,
4 h, 60 °C
Br
+
HBr

Bromobenzene
97%

(24-7)

To account for the bromination of benzene, it might seem that Br^+ acts as the electrophile in the two-step EAS sequence (shown previously in Eq. 24-4):

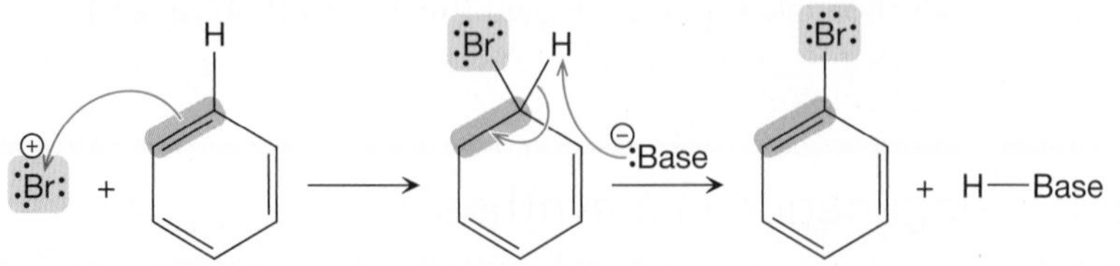

:Br:
H
:Br:
H
:Base
:Br:
+ H—Base

(24-8)

However, Br^+ does not actually form because it is too unstable. Instead, the reaction proceeds according to the mechanism in Equation 24-9:

Mechanism for aromatic halogenation (Eq. 24-7)

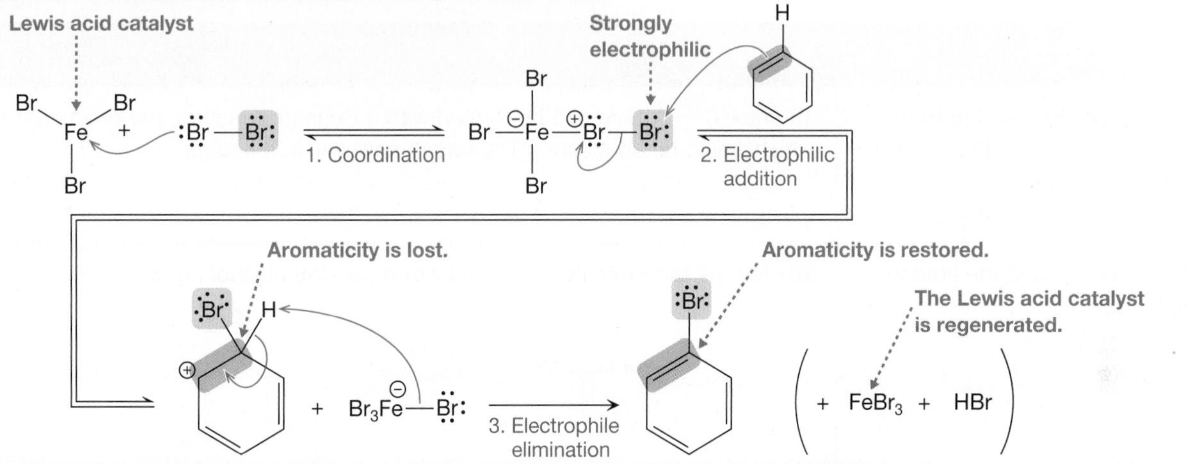

Lewis acid catalyst
Strongly electrophilic
1. Coordination
2. Electrophilic addition
Aromaticity is lost.
Aromaticity is restored.
The Lewis acid catalyst is regenerated.
3. Electrophile elimination
+ Br3Fe—Br:
+ FeBr3 + HBr

(24-9)

$FeBr_3$ acts as a Lewis acid in Step 1 when it complexes with Br_2 in a coordination step to produce a Lewis acid–base adduct. $FeBr_3$ can be added as a reagent directly, or it can be produced in situ by combining Fe and Br_2. Step 2 is electrophilic addition, in which the indicated Br is strongly electrophilic. Effectively, Br^+ adds to benzene at the same time it departs from the adduct. Finally, in Step 3, H^+ is eliminated from the arenium ion intermediate to form bromobenzene. In that step, $FeBr_4^-$ acts as a base and $FeBr_3$ is regenerated. Thus, $FeBr_3$ is not consumed overall and is an example of a **Lewis acid catalyst**.

YOUR TURN 24.5

The mechanism of the chlorination of benzene is as follows, but the curved arrows have been omitted. Supply the missing curved arrows, and below each reaction arrow, write the name of the elementary step that is taking place. Which two steps make up the electrophilic aromatic substitution mechanism presented earlier in Equation 24-4?

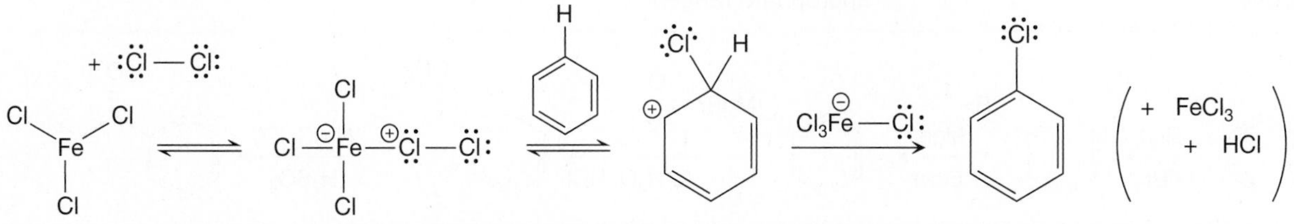

+ :Cl—Cl:
Cl3Fe—Cl:
+ FeCl3
+ HCl

Lewis acids other than $FeCl_3$ or $FeBr_3$ can be used to carry out aromatic chlorination and bromination reactions. Aluminum chloride ($AlCl_3$), for example, is another Lewis acid catalyst that can be used for these reactions.

The product of an aromatic halogenation, an aryl halide, could be the desired target in a synthesis. Alternatively, an aryl halide could be a useful synthetic intermediate, such as in the production of a Grignard reagent (see Solved Problem 24.1).

SOLVED PROBLEM **24.1**

How to incorporate an aromatic halogenation in a synthesis

Break It Down **Show how to carry out this synthesis using an aromatic halogenation reaction.**

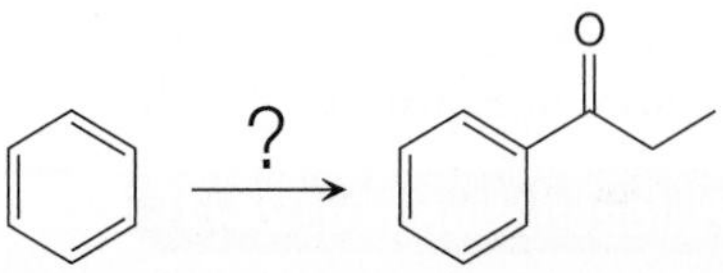
?
O

Think	Solve
What reaction can be used to form the necessary C—C bond? Does the product of that reaction contain the appropriate functional groups?	The new C—C bond can be formed with a Grignard reaction, the product of which would be an alcohol. The target, however, is a ketone.
From what alcohol could the ketone target be made?	The ketone target could be made by oxidizing the alcohol shown here.

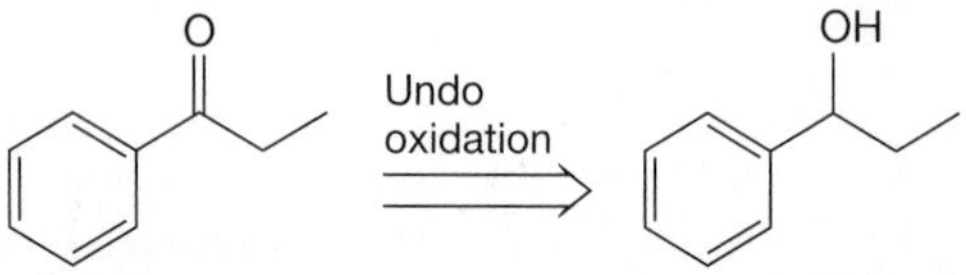
O
Undo
oxidation
OH

Think	Solve
From what Grignard reagent and carbonyl compound could the alcohol be made? From what alkyl halide could the Grignard reagent be made?	To arrive at the precursors for a Grignard reaction, we can disconnect the C—C bond between the COH carbon and the adjacent carbon, as shown below. The Grignard reagent can be made from bromobenzene, which can be made by the halogenation of benzene.

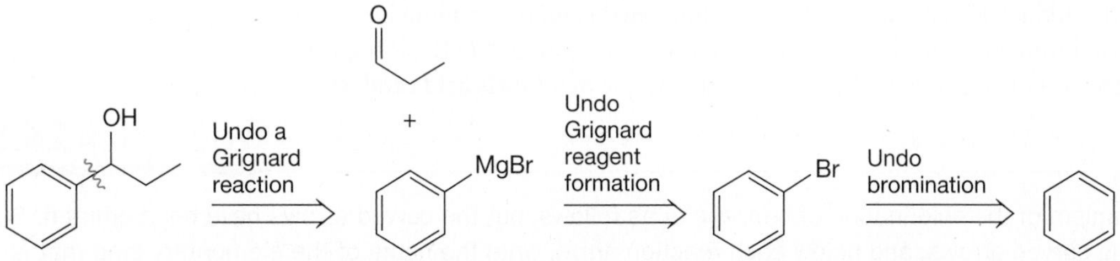
OH
Undo a
Grignard
reaction
O
+
MgBr
Undo
Grignard
reagent
formation
Br
Undo
bromination

Think	Solve
How might you present the final synthesis?	To present the synthesis, we begin with the starting materials and add the appropriate reagents.

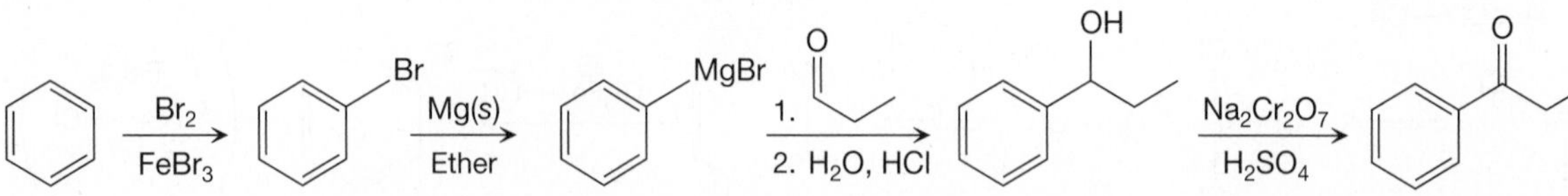
Br_2
$FeBr_3$
Br
Mg(s)
Ether
MgBr
1.
O
2. H_2O, HCl
OH
$Na_2Cr_2O_7$
H_2SO_4
O

Try It Show how to carry out the following synthesis using an aromatic halogenation reaction as one step.

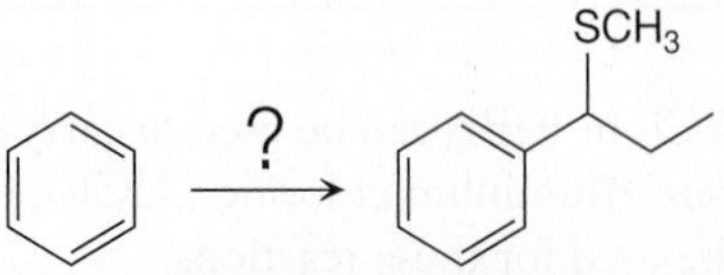
?
SCH_3

Answers to all Try It exercises can be found in the Solutions Manual.

The fluorination and iodination of benzene can proceed through a similar mechanism. However, as we saw with the addition of molecular halogens across double bonds (Chapter 13), fluorine is very highly reactive, so other reagents are generally used to carry out aromatic fluorination. Iodination with one of the above Lewis acids, on the other hand, is too slow, but it can be carried out in the presence of an oxidizing agent like Cu^{2+} or hydrogen peroxide (Eq. 24-10). Oxidation of I_2 generates I^+, which can then enter into the electrophilic aromatic substitution mechanism.

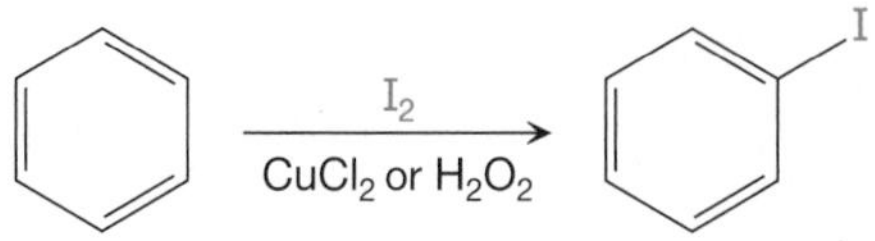

I2
CuCl2 or H2O2
I

(24-10)

YOUR TURN **24.6**

With the understanding that the reaction conditions in Equation 24-10 generate a small amount of I^+, draw the two-step electrophilic aromatic substitution mechanism that leads to the formation of iodobenzene.

24.3 Friedel–Crafts Alkylation

SECTION 24.3 OBJECTIVES

You will be able to:

1. Draw the mechanism for a Friedel–Crafts alkylation, and explain the role of the Lewis acid catalyst.
2. Incorporate a Friedel–Crafts alkylation into a synthesis.

In 1877, Charles Friedel (1832–1899) and James Crafts (1839–1917) reported that *alkylation* can take place when benzene is treated with an alkyl chloride in the presence of $AlCl_3$, which is a strong Lewis acid catalyst (Eqs. 24-11 and 24-12). In **Friedel–Crafts alkylation** reactions such as these, the electrophile is a carbocation, R^+. In Equation 24-11, the electrophile is a *tert*-butyl cation, $(CH_3)_3C^+$; in Equation 24-12, it is the cyclohexyl cation, $C_6H_{11}^+$.

Friedel–Crafts alkylations

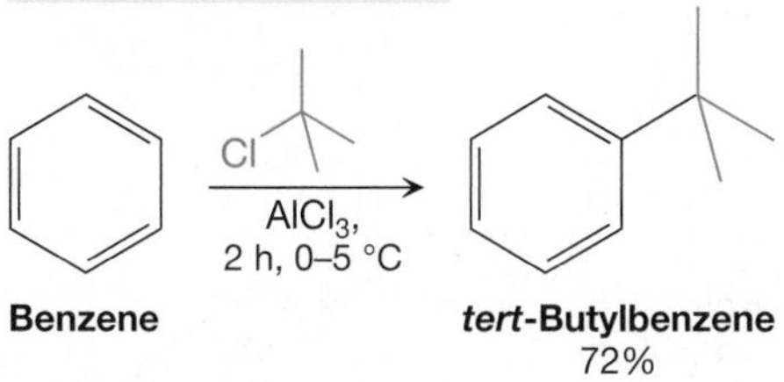

Cl
AlCl3,
2 h, 0–5 °C
Benzene
tert-Butylbenzene
72%

(24-11)

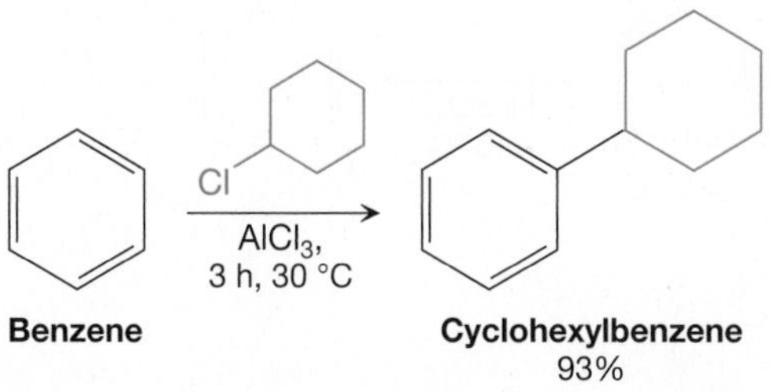

Cl
AlCl3,
3 h, 30 °C
Benzene
Cyclohexylbenzene
93%

(24-12)

The production of these carbocation electrophiles is illustrated in Equation 24-13, which shows the mechanism of the alkylation in Equation 24-11. In Step 1, the alkyl halide coordinates to the Al atom of $AlCl_3$. In Step 2, the Cl—C bond breaks in a heterolysis step to produce the carbocation electrophile. The final two steps make up the EAS sequence originally shown in Equation 24-4 (p. 1158).

GREEN CHEMISTRY The $AlCl_3$ catalyst used in Friedel–Crafts alkylation can react violently with water, forming toxic HCl gas, and can damage the lungs if inhaled. When used for alkylation, the Al-containing waste can lead to water contamination. One green alternative, developed by J. P. Hallett, P. Pollet, C. L. Liotta, and C. A. Eckert, enables Friedel–Crafts alkylation to take place without any catalyst! The reaction is carried out in near-critical water (NCW), where the high temperature causes the properties of water to become significantly different from room temperature water.

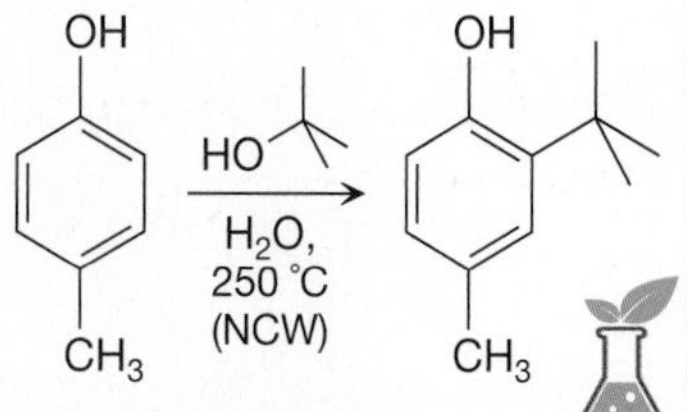

OH
HO
H2O,
250 °C
(NCW)
CH3
OH
CH3

Mechanism for Friedel–Crafts alkylation (Eq. 24-11)

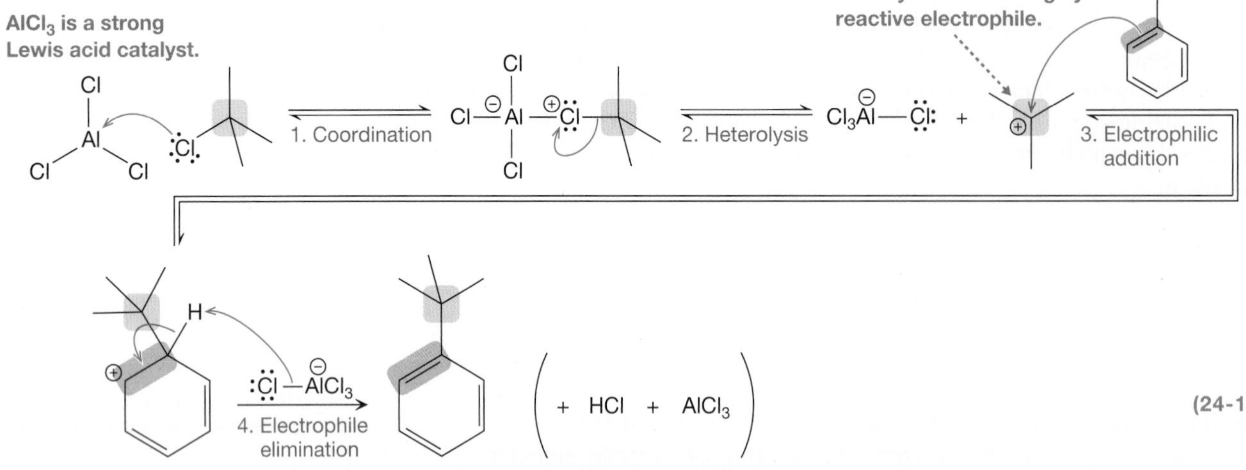
AlCl3 is a strong Lewis acid catalyst.
1. Coordination
2. Heterolysis
An alkyl cation is a highly reactive electrophile.
3. Electrophilic addition
4. Electrophile elimination
+ HCl + AlCl3

(24-13)

Notice how similar the Friedel–Crafts alkylation mechanism is to the mechanism for aromatic halogenation shown previously in Equation 24-9 (p. 1161). The only difference is that, in Equation 24-13, the electrophile (a 3° carbocation) is stable enough to depart from the Lewis acid–base adduct in a heterolysis step before adding to benzene.

Friedel–Crafts alkylation reactions can take place in the presence of other Lewis acid catalysts, such as $FeCl_3$ and $FeBr_3$. They can also take place under other conditions that generate carbocation intermediates. Examples are shown in Equations 24-14 and 24-15. In Equation 24-14, the acidic conditions convert the OH group into an excellent leaving group, which departs as H_2O. The carbocation is produced on loss of the water leaving group. In Equation 24-15, on the other hand, protonation of the double bond produces a carbocation intermediate directly. These are the same steps that make up the beginnings of the S_N1/E1 and electrophilic addition reactions, respectively.

CONNECTIONS 24.1

Long live your battery
Cyclohexylbenzene (Eqs. 24-12 and 24-15) has been studied as an overcharge protection agent for lithium ion batteries, which can help extend the life of these batteries.

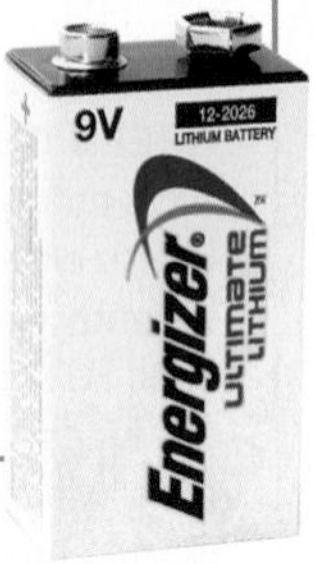
9V
Energizer
ULTIMATE LITHIUM

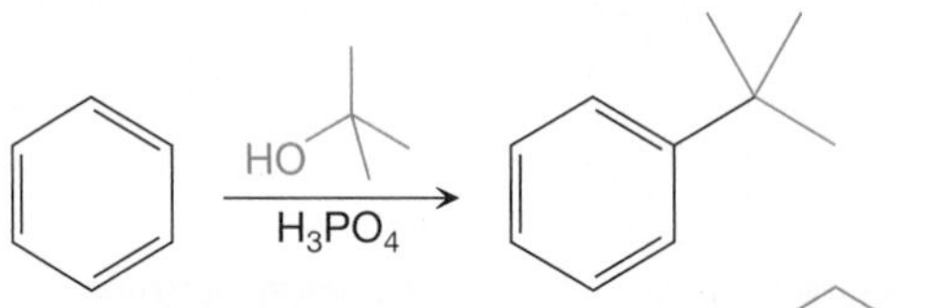
HO
H3PO4

(24-14)

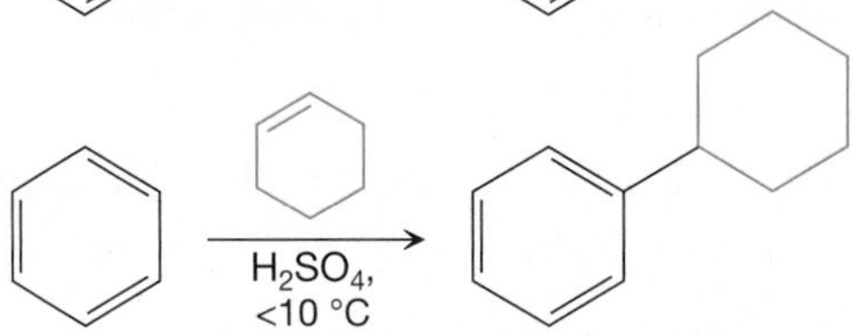
H2SO4,
<10 °C

68%

(24-15)

YOUR TURN **24.7**

The mechanism of the reaction in Equation 24-12 is as follows, but the curved arrows have been omitted. Supply the missing curved arrows, and below each reaction arrow, write the name of the elementary step taking place. Identify the two steps that make up the general EAS sequence shown previously in Equation 24-4 (p. 1158).

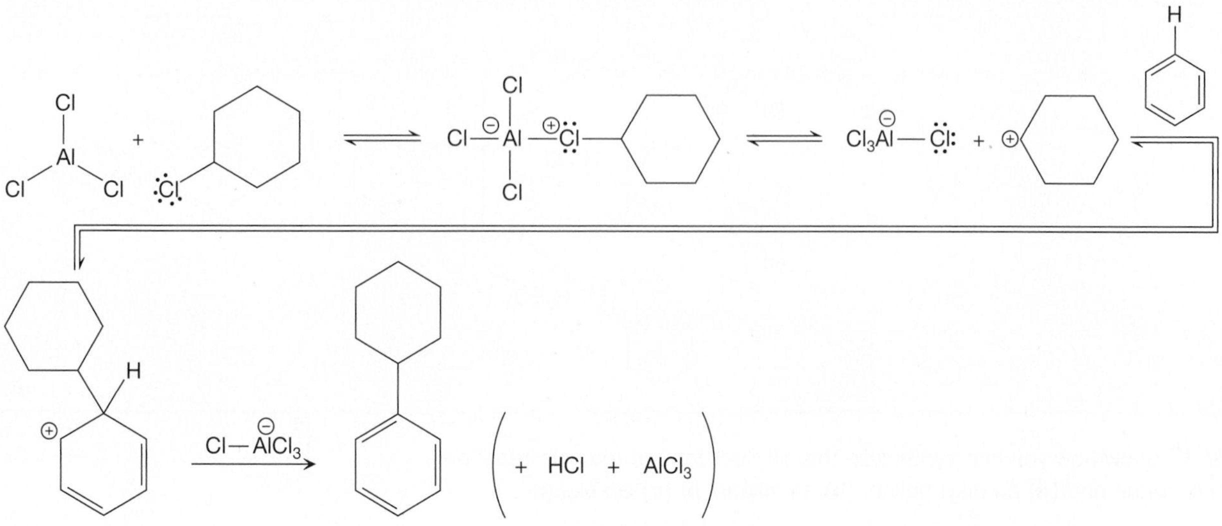

Cl
Al
Cl
Cl
+
:Cl
Cl
Cl—Al—Cl
Cl
Cl₃Al—Cl:
+
H
H
Cl—AlCl₃
+ HCl + AlCl₃

YOUR TURN **24.8**

Propose a mechanism for the reaction in Equation 24-14 and for the reaction in Equation 24-15.

SOLVED PROBLEM **24.2**

How to incorporate Friedel–Crafts alkylation in a synthesis

Break It Down **Show how to synthesize the following compound in a single reaction, using benzene as one reagent and (a) an alkyl halide, (b) an alkene, or (c) an alcohol as the other reagent.**

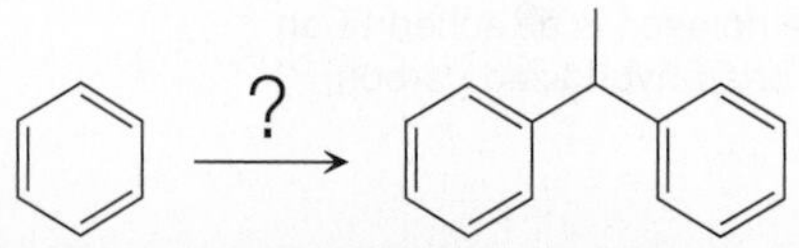

?

Think	Solve
Which bond must be formed in the target? What electrophile would be necessary as a precursor?	One of the C—C bonds to the aromatic ring must be formed. That bond can be made from a carbocation as the electrophile in an electrophilic aromatic substitution:

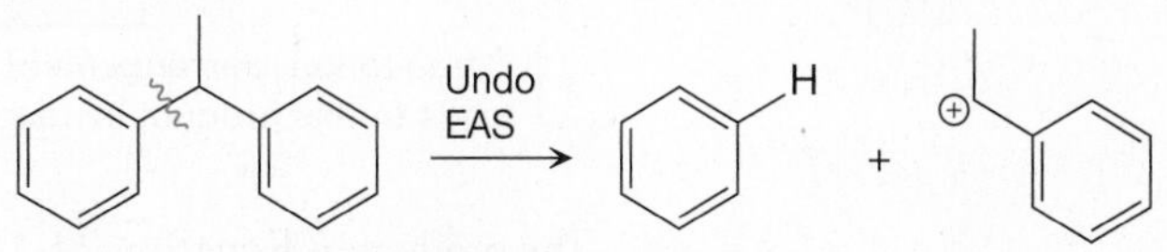

Undo
EAS
H
+

(continued)

How can that electrophile be produced from an alkyl halide, an alkene, or an alcohol?	The carbocation can be produced from **(a)** an alkyl halide with $AlCl_3$ as a strong Lewis acid catalyst or from **(b)** an alkene or **(c)** an alcohol under acidic conditions.

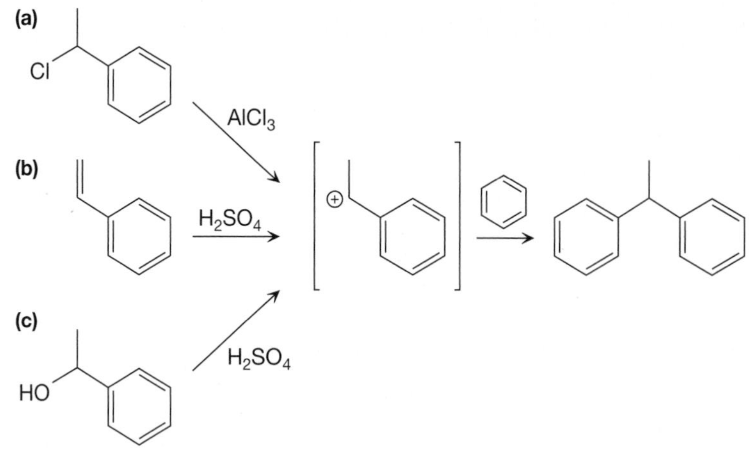

(a)
Cl
AlCl3
(b)
H2SO4
(c)
HO
H2SO4

Try It Show how you can synthesize this alkylbenzene in a single reaction from benzene and **(a)** an alkyl halide, **(b)** an alkene, or **(c)** an alcohol.

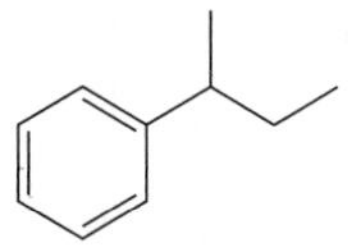

SECTION 24.4 OBJECTIVES

You will be able to:

1. Determine whether a particular Friedel–Crafts alkylation will undergo carbocation rearrangement.
2. Explain why Friedel–Crafts alkylation tends to be unfeasible if the halogen is attached to an sp^2- or sp-hybridized carbon.

24.4 Limitations of Friedel–Crafts Alkylation

In the Friedel–Crafts alkylation below, you might expect the product in Equation 24-16a to be produced, in which the new bond has replaced the C—Cl bond. However, the major product in Equation 24-16b is produced instead:

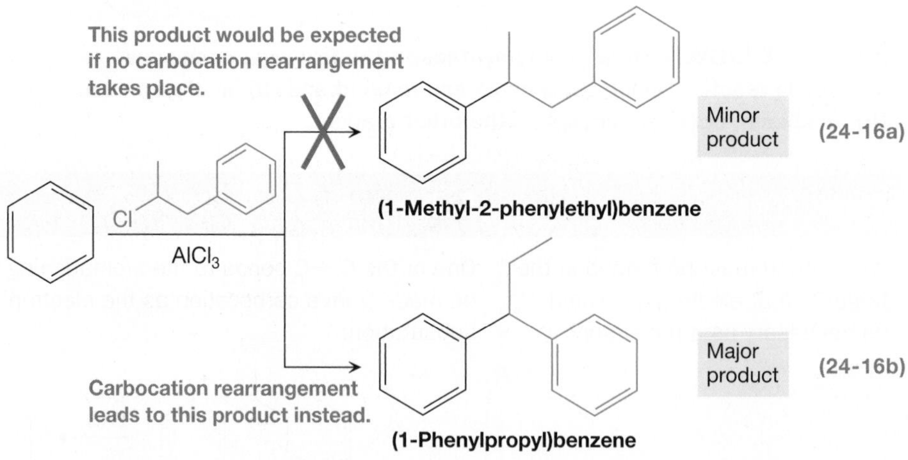

This product would be expected if no carbocation rearrangement takes place.
Minor product
(24-16a)
(1-Methyl-2-phenylethyl)benzene
Cl
AlCl3
Major product
(24-16b)
Carbocation rearrangement leads to this product instead.
(1-Phenylpropyl)benzene

The product in Equation 24-16a is not produced substantially because, as with any reaction in which a carbocation is produced:

Friedel–Crafts alkylation reactions are susceptible to carbocation rearrangements.

As shown in the partial mechanism in Equation 24-17, the carbocation that is initially formed in Equation 24-16 is a secondary carbocation in which the positive charge is localized. A 1,2-hydride shift rapidly produces a more stable carbocation in which the positive charge is resonance-delocalized onto the benzene ring. The product of that carbocation rearrangement is the actual electrophile that enters the electrophilic aromatic substitution mechanism.

Partial mechanism for Friedel–Crafts alkylation, with carbocation rearrangement (Eq. 24-16)

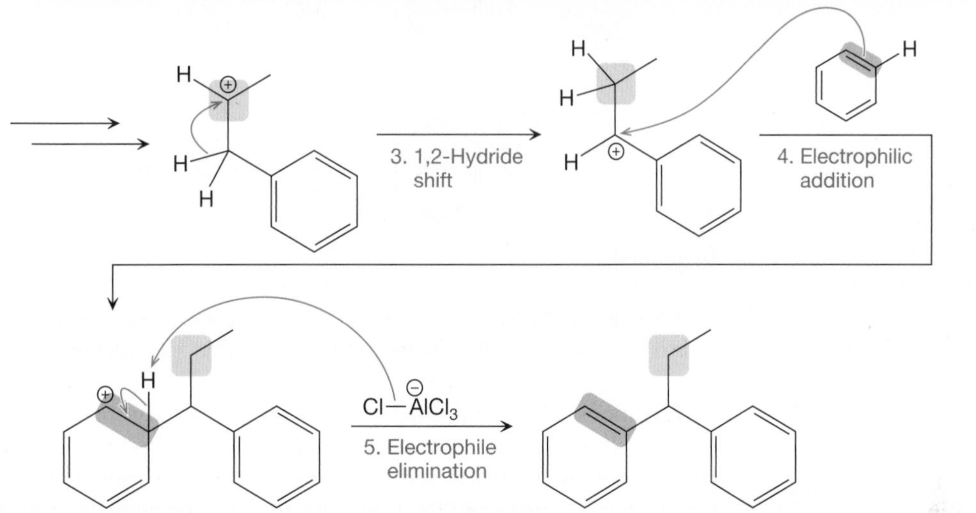
3. 1,2-Hydride shift
4. Electrophilic addition
Cl—AlCl3
5. Electrophile elimination

(24-17)

Equation 24-18 shows another example of a rearrangement in a Friedel–Crafts alkylation:

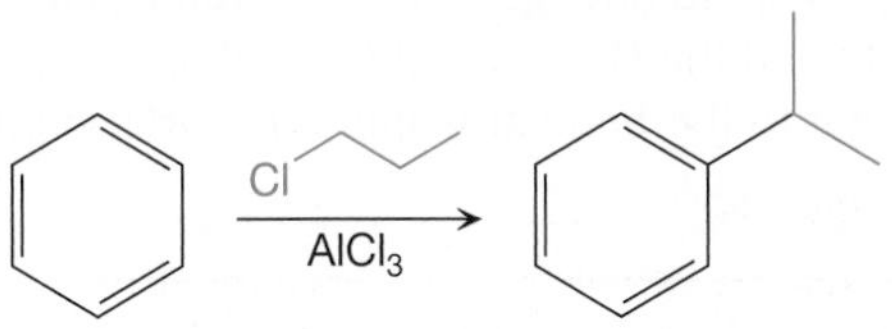
Cl
AlCl3

(24-18)

(1-Methylethyl)benzene

The product of this reaction is what we would expect if the C—Cl bond undergoes heterolysis to form a primary carbocation that then rapidly rearranges to a more stable secondary carbocation. However, as we learned in Section 9.6b, a primary carbocation with a localized positive charge is not a reasonable intermediate because it is too unstable. Instead, the hydride shift and heterolysis can occur together in the same step, as shown in the partial mechanism in Equation 24-19:

CONNECTIONS 24.2

Helping you shred the slopes
(1-Methylethyl)benzene (Eq. 24-18), more commonly called cumene, is used industrially to produce phenol, C_6H_5OH, a starting material for polycarbonate plastics like the one used for the screen in this ski mask.

Partial mechanism for Friedel–Crafts alkylation involving a primary alkyl halide (Eq. 24-18)

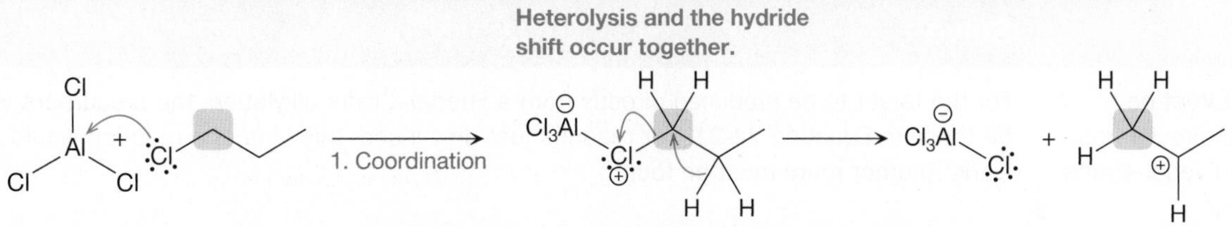
Heterolysis and the hydride shift occur together.
1. Coordination
Cl3Al

(24-19)

Even though a carbocation is not *actually* produced in this reaction, it can be helpful to *think* of the reaction as first producing a primary carbocation before rearranging to the secondary carbocation shown in Equation 24-19.

In some cases, no Friedel–Crafts reaction takes place at all, as shown in Equations 24-20 and 24-21:

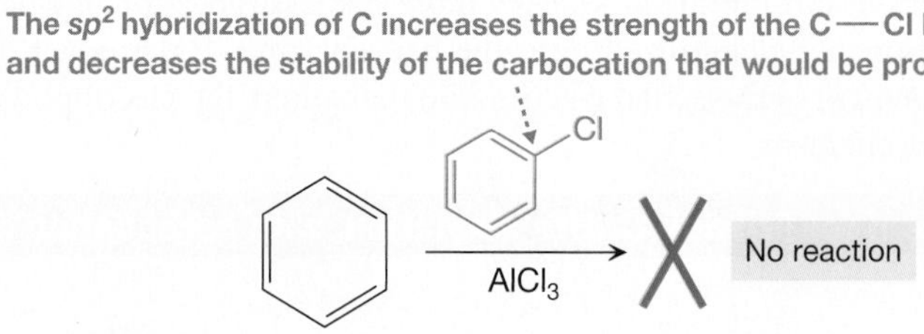
The sp^2 hybridization of C increases the strength of the C—Cl bond and decreases the stability of the carbocation that would be produced.
Cl
$AlCl_3$
No reaction

(24-20)

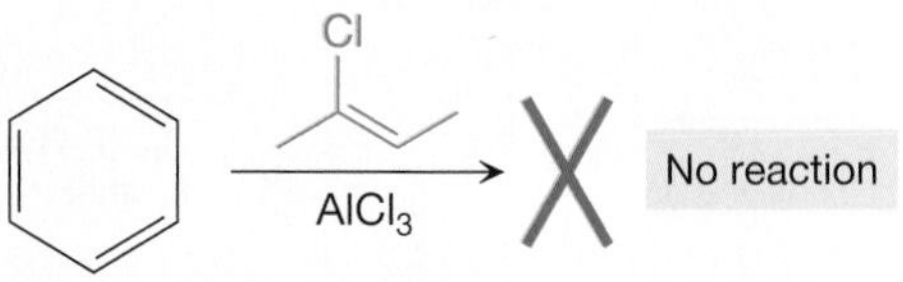
Cl
$AlCl_3$
No reaction

(24-21)

In general:

A Friedel–Crafts alkylation reaction does not occur readily unless the halogen atom of the alkyl halide is bonded to an sp^3-hybridized carbon.

In Equations 24-20 and 24-21, which involve an aryl halide and a vinylic halide, respectively, the halogen atom is bonded to an sp^2-hybridized C. With the increased *s* character of an sp^2-hybridized C relative to an sp^3-hybridized C, the strength of the C—Cl bond is greater and so is the effective electronegativity of the C atom. Thus, the carbocation that would be produced would be excessively unstable (see Recall box).

◂ RECALL

Section 3.9 showed that an atom forms stronger bonds and has a higher effective electronegativity as its hybridization goes from sp^3 to sp^2 to sp. This is why aryl halides and vinylic halides are resistant to nucleophilic substitution and elimination reactions, as we saw in Section 9.6a.

YOUR TURN **24.9**

Verify the dependence of bond strength on atom hybridization by looking in Figure 3-28 (p. 133) to find the C—H bond strength of an sp^3-hybridized carbon and comparing it to the bond strength of an sp^2-hybridized carbon.

sp^3 ______________ sp^2 ______________

SOLVED PROBLEM **24.3**

How to synthesize a vinylic benzene from benzene

Break It Down **Show how you can synthesize 2-phenylbut-2-ene from benzene. (Do not worry about stereochemistry in this case.)**

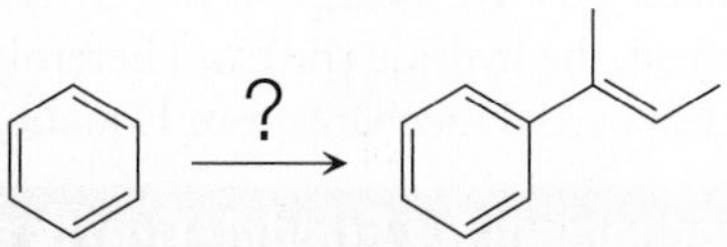
?

Think	Solve
Can the target be produced directly from a simple Friedel–Crafts alkylation?	For the target to be produced directly from a Friedel–Crafts alkylation, the precursors would be those in Equation 24-21. For reasons just discussed, this kind of a reaction would not work. Another route must be found.

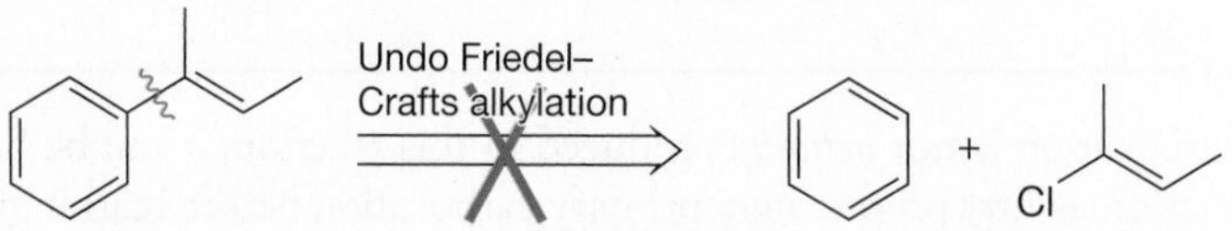
Undo Friedel–Crafts alkylation
+
Cl

(continued)

What other reaction could we use to form the appropriate C—C bond? Can the target be made from the product of that reaction?

We can consider using a Grignard reaction to form the new C—C bond, the product of which would be an alcohol. As shown here, dehydration of the alcohol would produce the target.

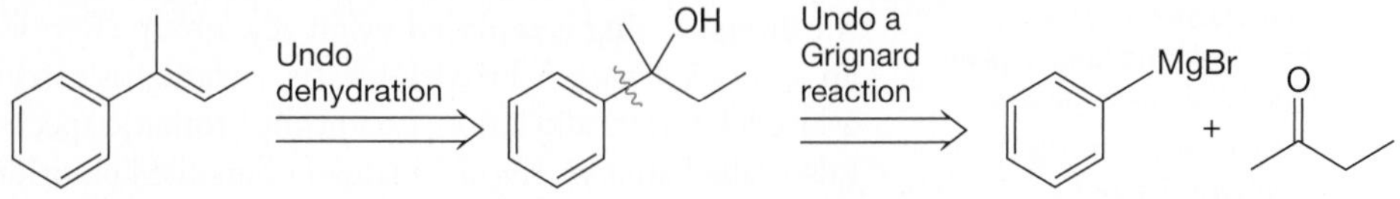

Undo dehydration
OH
Undo a Grignard reaction
MgBr
+
O

How can the Grignard reagent be made from benzene?

The Grignard reagent can be made from bromobenzene, which can be made from benzene.

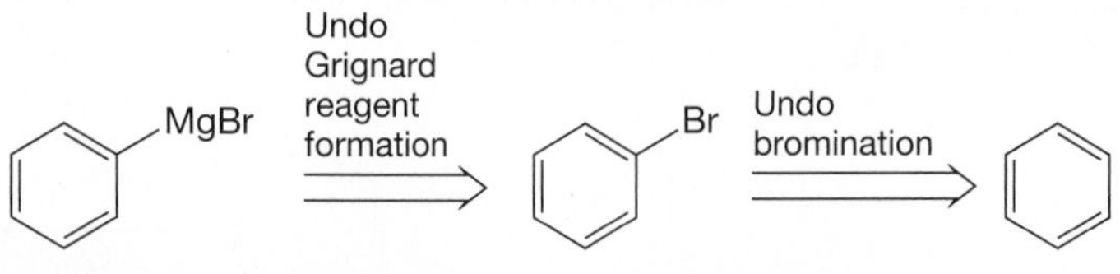

MgBr
Undo Grignard reagent formation
Br
Undo bromination

How can we report the final synthesis?

To report the synthesis, we begin with the starting materials and add the appropriate reagents, as shown here.

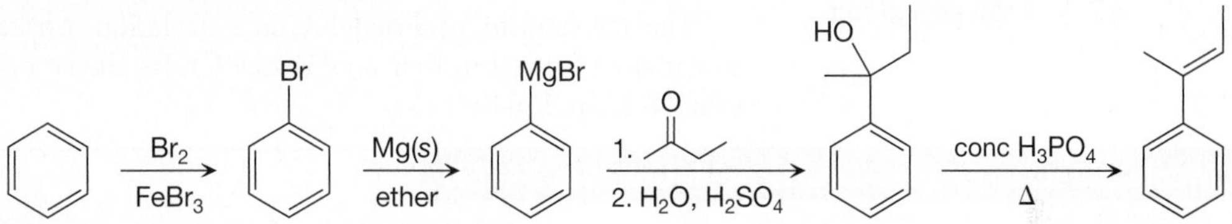

Br_2
$FeBr_3$
Br
Mg(s)
ether
MgBr
1.
O
2. H_2O, H_2SO_4
HO
conc H_3PO_4
Δ

Try It Butylbenzene cannot be synthesized in good yield directly from benzene using a Friedel–Crafts alkylation. Why not? Propose an alternate synthesis of butylbenzene that does not use a Friedel–Crafts reaction.

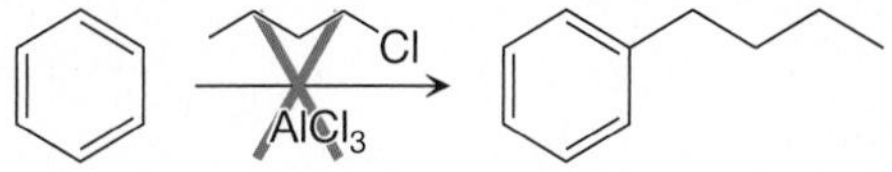

Cl
$AlCl_3$

One additional limitation of Friedel–Crafts alkylation arises because each alkyl group attached to the aromatic ring makes the ring even *more* reactive toward electrophilic aromatic substitution. As shown in Equation 24-22, this could result in a mixture of products:

Friedel–Crafts alkylation can result in polyalkylation.

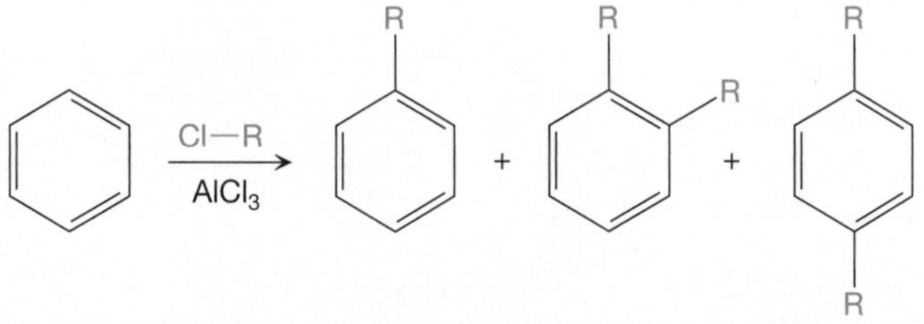

Cl—R
$AlCl_3$
R
R
R
+
+
R
R

(24-22)

In general:

Friedel–Crafts alkylation reactions are susceptible to *polyalkylation* (see Looking Ahead box).

▸ LOOKING AHEAD

Section 25.4 will explain how and why the electron-donating nature of alkyl groups is responsible for polyalkylation occurring when a Friedel–Crafts alkylation is carried out.

SECTION 24.5 OBJECTIVES

You will be able to:

1. Draw the mechanism for a Friedel–Crafts acylation, and explain the role of the Lewis acid catalyst.
2. Explain why Friedel–Crafts acylation reactions are not susceptible to carbocation rearrangements.
3. Incorporate a Friedel–Crafts acylation reaction into a synthesis.

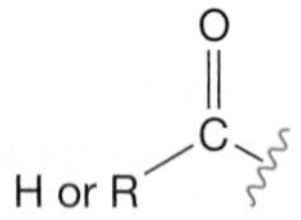

O
C
H or R

FIGURE 24-2 An acyl group

24.5 Friedel–Crafts Acylation

Equation 24-23 shows a **Friedel–Crafts acylation** of benzene, in which a H atom on the aromatic ring is replaced by an acyl group (R—C=O, **Figure 24-2**) to produce an *aromatic ketone*. A Friedel–Crafts acylation is carried out in much the same way as a Friedel–Crafts alkylation, except the aromatic species is treated with an *acid chloride* (also called an *acyl chloride*) instead of an alkyl chloride.

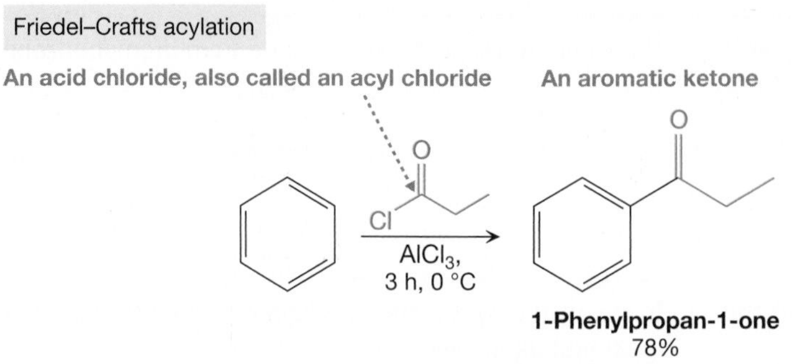

Friedel–Crafts acylation
An acid chloride, also called an acyl chloride
An aromatic ketone
O
Cl
$AlCl_3$,
3 h, 0 °C
1-Phenylpropan-1-one
78%

(24-23)

The mechanism of Friedel–Crafts acylation, presented in Equation 24-24, is essentially identical to that for Friedel–Crafts alkylation, shown previously in Equation 24-13 (p. 1164):

Mechanism for Friedel–Crafts acylation (Eq. 24-23)

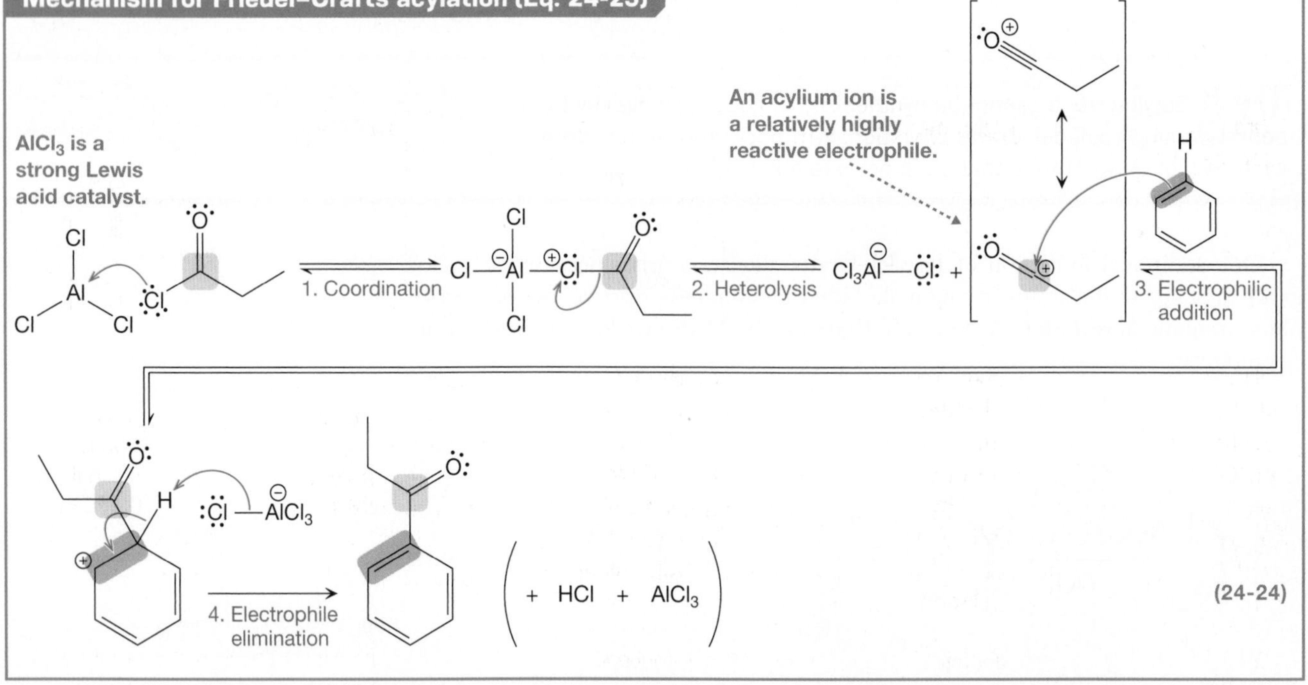

$AlCl_3$ is a strong Lewis acid catalyst.
1. Coordination
2. Heterolysis
An acylium ion is a relatively highly reactive electrophile.
Cl_3Al—Cl: +
3. Electrophilic addition
H
Cl—AlCl$_3$
4. Electrophile elimination
+ HCl + $AlCl_3$

(24-24)

The strong Lewis acid catalyst, $AlCl_3$, is responsible for generating the cationic electrophile, called an **acylium ion**, in the first two steps. In Step 1, the Cl atom of the acyl chloride coordinates to the electron-deficient Al atom. In Step 2, the C—Cl bond undergoes heterolysis. Step 3 is electrophilic addition of the acylium ion to the benzene ring, producing the arenium ion intermediate. Finally, in Step 4, removal of the proton from the arenium ion yields the aromatic ketone product.

YOUR TURN **24.10**

The mechanism for Friedel–Crafts acylation involving acetyl chloride is as follows, but most of the curved arrows have been omitted, as have the overall products. Supply the missing curved arrows and draw the overall products. Also, write the name of each elementary step below the appropriate reaction arrow and label the acylium ion.

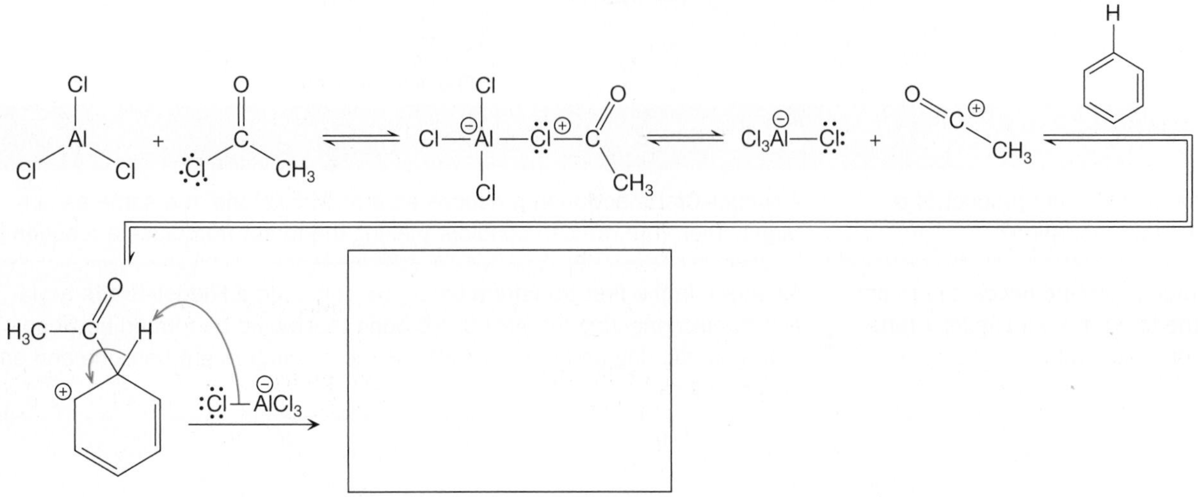

YOUR TURN **24.11**

Draw the mechanism and the major product for the following reaction.

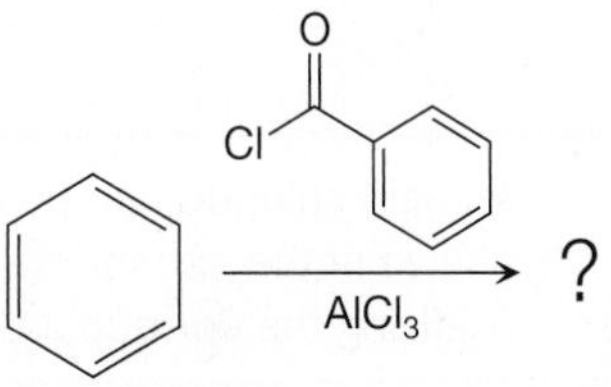
AlCl3
?

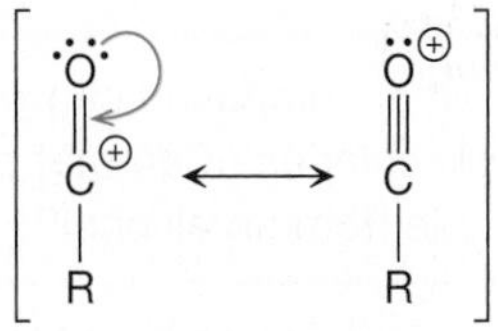

An acylium ion

FIGURE 24-3 Resonance stabilization of the acylium ion The lone pair of electrons on O participates in resonance to delocalize the positive charge over O and C.

It might seem peculiar that Friedel–Crafts acylation can take place at all, given that the Cl atom in the acid chloride reactant is bonded to an sp^2-hybridized C. (Recall from Section 24.4 that this, in fact, prevents a Friedel–Crafts *alkylation* from taking place.) The acylium ion that is produced in Friedel–Crafts acylation, however, is *resonance-stabilized* by a lone pair of electrons on the adjacent oxygen (**Figure 24-3**). With this additional stability, the cationic electrophile can be produced and enter into the electrophilic aromatic substitution mechanism.

Unlike Friedel–Crafts alkylation reactions:

Friedel–Crafts acylation reactions are *not* susceptible to carbocation rearrangements.

The acylium ion does not rearrange because its positive charge is already delocalized by resonance and because it has a resonance structure in which all non-hydrogen atoms have an octet.

Friedel–Crafts acylation reactions can be used with a variety of acyl halides to produce different aromatic ketones. However:

Friedel–Crafts acylation as a means of *formylation* (replacing H by a formyl group, HC=O) requires in situ formation of the very unstable Cl—CH=O.

See Problem 24.8 at the end of the chapter for an example.

CONNECTIONS 24.3

What's in a walnut?

1-Phenylbutan-1-one (Solved Problem 24.4) is found in significant amounts in peanuts, almonds, and walnuts. Haloperidol, a commonly used antipsychotic drug, is a derivative of 1-phenylbutan-1-one.

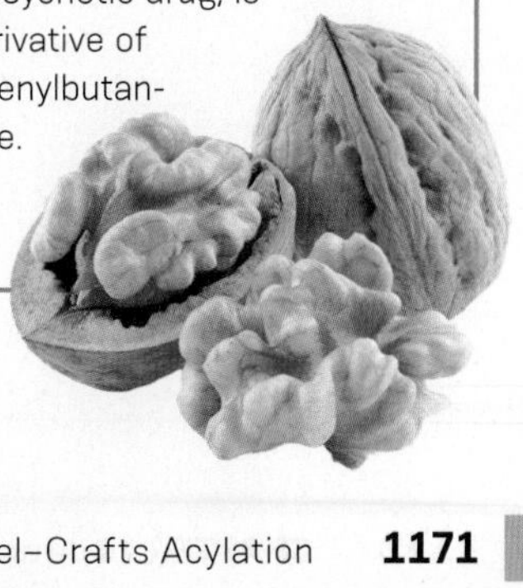

SOLVED PROBLEM **24.4**

How to incorporate a Friedel–Crafts acylation into a synthesis

Break It Down **Show how to synthesize 1-phenylbutan-1-one from benzene and an alcohol, using a Friedel–Crafts acylation.**

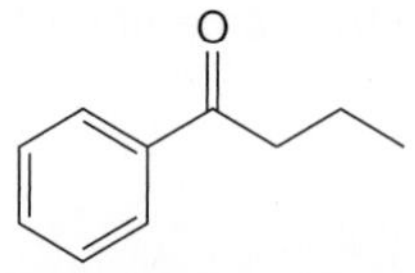

1-Phenylbutan-1-one

Think	Solve
Can the target be the product of a Friedel–Crafts acylation?	A Friedel–Crafts acylation produces an aromatic ketone, the same as our target. Therefore, we can consider making the target from such a reaction.
What precursors are necessary to produce the target from a Friedel–Crafts acylation reaction?	As shown in the first transform below, we can undo a Friedel–Crafts acylation by disconnecting the new C—C bond that would be formed between that aromatic ring and the acyl carbon. The precursors are benzene and an acid chloride.

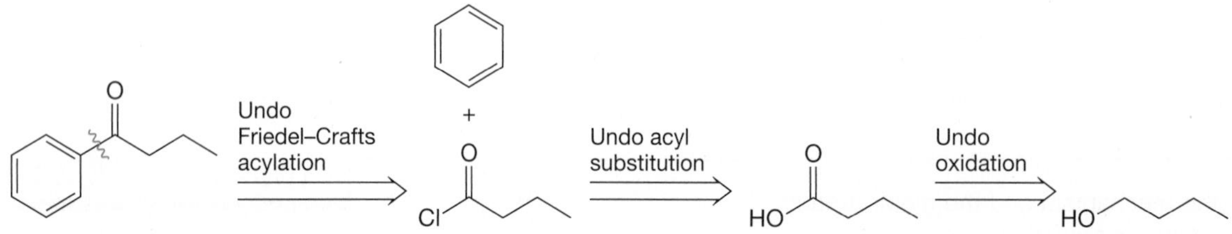

O
Undo
Friedel–Crafts
acylation
+
O
Cl
Undo acyl
substitution
O
HO
Undo
oxidation
HO

Think	Solve
From what compound can we produce an acid chloride? Can that precursor be made from an alcohol?	An acid chloride can be made from the corresponding carboxylic acid, as shown in the second transform above. The carboxylic acid can be made by oxidizing the corresponding primary alcohol.
How can we report the final synthesis?	To report the final synthesis, we begin with the starting materials and show the appropriate reagents and reaction conditions.

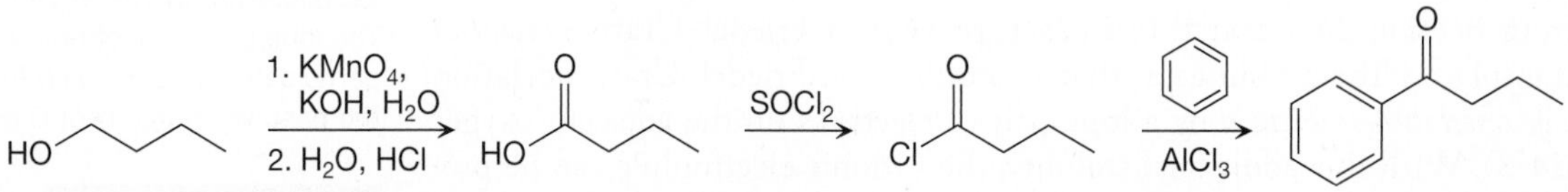

HO
1. KMnO4,
KOH, H2O
2. H2O, HCl
O
HO
SOCl2
O
Cl
AlCl3
O

Try It Show how to synthesize benzophenone from benzene and any alcohol.

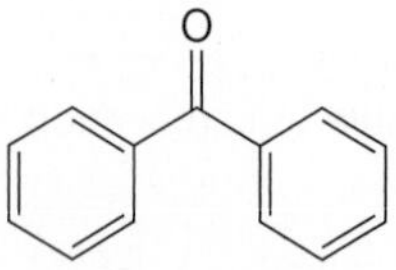

Benzophenone

24.6 Nitration

Equation 24-25 shows that benzene reacts with concentrated nitric acid to produce nitrobenzene. In such a **nitration** reaction, a H on the aromatic ring is replaced by a nitro (NO_2) group:

Nitration

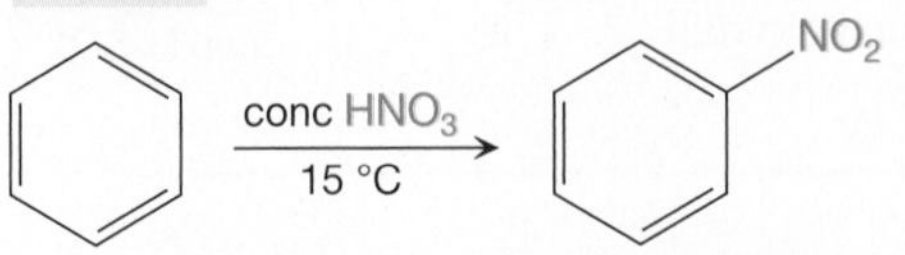

NO2
conc HNO3
15 °C

(24-25)

Nitrobenzene
83%

The mechanism for aromatic nitration is presented in Equation 24-26:

Mechanism for nitration of an aromatic ring (Eq. 24-25)

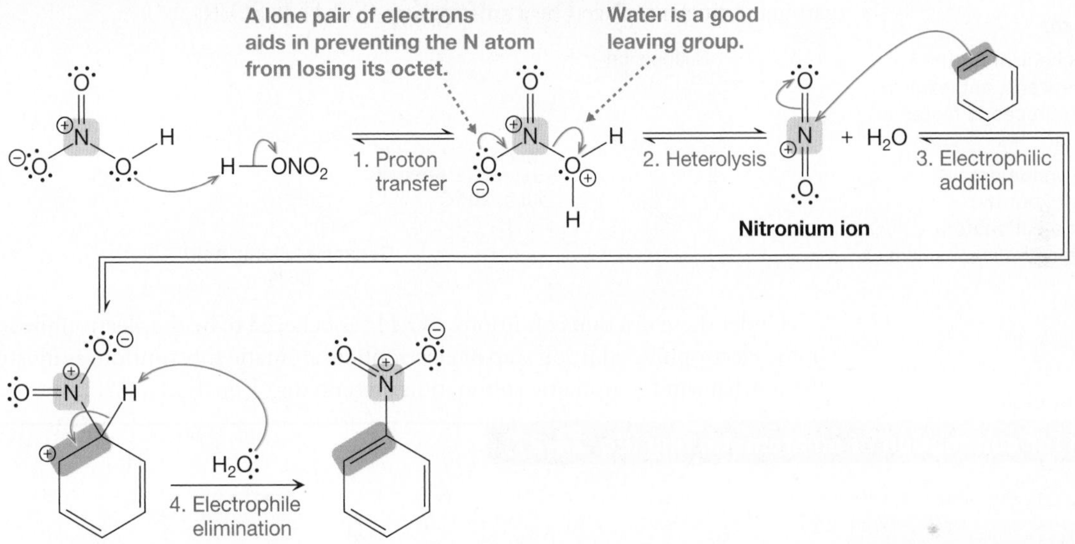

A lone pair of electrons aids in preventing the N atom from losing its octet.
Water is a good leaving group.
H—ONO2
1. Proton transfer
2. Heterolysis
+ H2O
3. Electrophilic addition
Nitronium ion
H2O:
4. Electrophile elimination

(24-26)

SECTION 24.6 OBJECTIVES

You will be able to:

1. Draw the mechanism for the nitration of benzene.
2. Explain why nitration reactions proceed faster when sulfuric acid is present.

Steps 1 and 2 of the mechanism are responsible for generating the powerful NO_2^+ electrophile, called the **nitronium ion**. First, HNO_3 is protonated to create a good H_2O leaving group. Next, H_2O departs by heterolysis. During the heterolysis step, an additional N═O double bond is formed, using a lone pair of electrons from an O atom. This aids the elimination of the water leaving group by preventing the N atom from losing its octet. Once the NO_2^+ electrophile is created, it enters into the two-step EAS sequence, as shown in Steps 3 and 4.

Although the nitration reaction in Equation 24-25 is effective, it can be slow:

> With concentrated nitric acid alone, the nitration of benzene tends to proceed relatively slowly.

The rate is slow because the amount of NO_2^+ present in concentrated HNO_3 is small, about 4%, and as we saw in Equation 24-5 (p. 1159), *the rate of electrophilic aromatic substitution is directly proportional to the concentration of the electrophile.*

To increase the rate of nitration, the reaction can be run at high temperatures. Alternatively:

> The rate of nitration increases when concentrated sulfuric acid is added.

CONNECTIONS 24.4

Benzenesulfonic acid and pharmaceutical drugs

Benzenesulfonic acid (Eq. 24-27) is strongly acidic and produces a salt, called a besylate salt, when it is treated with a weakly basic compound. Some pharmaceutical drugs are sold as besylate salts, including amlodipine besylate (trade name Norvasc), which is used to treat angina.

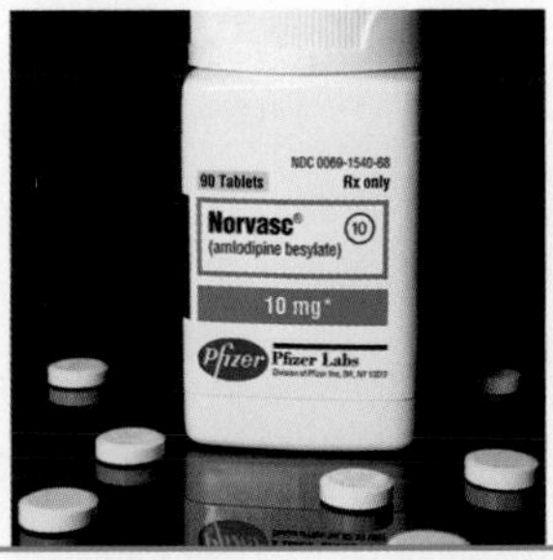

90 Tablets
Rx only
Norvasc®
(amlodipine besylate)
10 mg*
Pfizer Labs

Sulfuric acid (H_2SO_4; $pK_a = -9$) is much more acidic than HNO_3 ($pK_a = -1.3$), so when H_2SO_4 acts as the acid (see Your Turn 24.12), a substantially higher concentration of the active electrophile NO_2^+ is generated.

YOUR TURN 24.12

Draw the complete mechanism for the nitration of benzene in which concentrated sulfuric acid has been added.

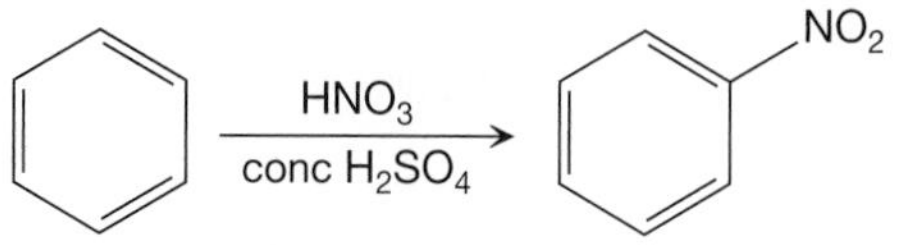
HNO3
conc H2SO4
NO2

24.7 Sulfonation

SECTION 24.7 OBJECTIVES

You will be able to:

1. Draw the mechanism for the sulfonation of benzene, and explain why the reaction proceeds faster when SO_3 is added.
2. Describe the conditions necessary to carry out the desulfonation of a sulfonated benzene, and draw the mechanism.

As shown in Equation 24-27, benzene reacts with concentrated sulfuric acid to produce benzenesulfonic acid. This is a **sulfonation** reaction, in which a H atom on the aromatic ring is replaced by a **sulfo group** (SO_3H or SO_3R).

Sulfonation

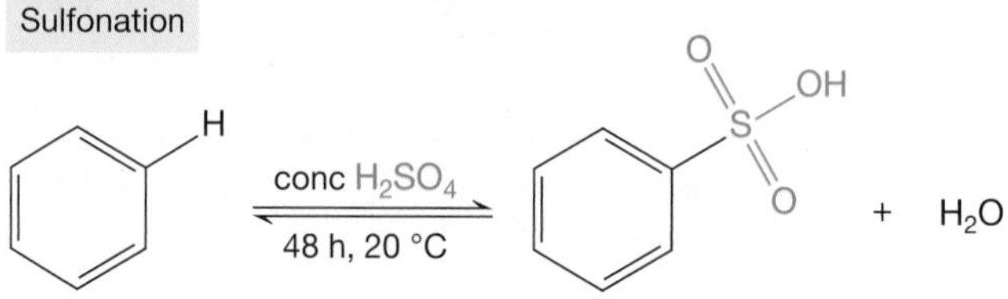
H
conc H2SO4
48 h, 20 °C
O
S
OH
O
+ H2O

Benzenesulfonic acid
66%

(24-27)

Under these reaction conditions, SO_3H^+ is believed to be the electrophile involved in the electrophilic addition step of electrophilic aromatic substitution, as illustrated in the mechanism for aromatic sulfonation presented in Equation 24-28:

Mechanism for sulfonation of an aromatic ring (Eq. 24-27)

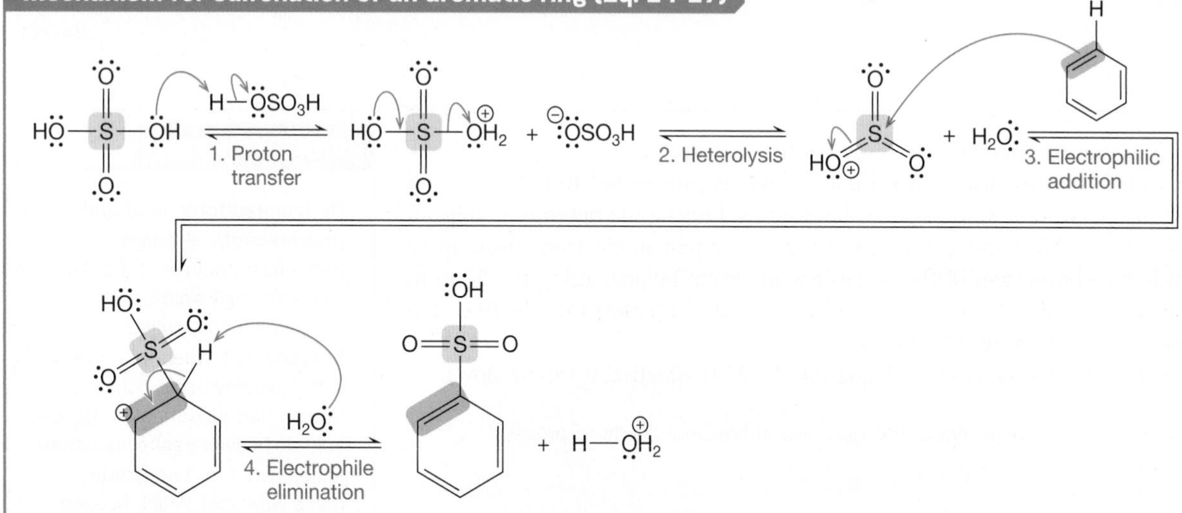
H—OSO3H
1. Proton transfer
+ OSO3H
2. Heterolysis
+ H2O
3. Electrophilic addition
H2O
4. Electrophile elimination
+ H—OH2

(24-28)

Concentrated H_2SO_4 contains a small amount of SO_3H^+ at equilibrium. It is produced in much the same way as NO_2^+ is generated in concentrated HNO_3 (Eq. 24-26, p. 1173): an OH group is protonated in Step 1 to generate a very good H_2O leaving group, and then H_2O leaves in Step 2. The resulting HSO_3^+ electrophile enters into the two-step EAS sequence, as shown in Steps 3 and 4.

As we saw with nitration, sulfonation can be slow because the concentration of the HSO_3^+ electrophile in concentrated H_2SO_4 is rather small. Sulfonation can be sped

Aromatic Sulfonation in Antibiotics and Detergents

Sulfa drugs, discovered in 1932, were among the first clinically useful antibiotics, and they ultimately sparked a revolution in medicine. The general structure of these antibiotics, shown in **Figure 24-4a**, is characterized by sulfonamide (SO_2NHR') and amino groups that are para to one another on the phenyl ring. To synthesize the sulfonamide portion, a sulfo group (SO_3H) is first attached to the aromatic ring by sulfonation, in a reaction similar to the one presented here in Chapter 24. The sulfo group is then converted to a sulfonyl chloride (SO_2Cl), which is condensed with an amine (H_2NR') to produce the final sulfonamide.

Sulfa drugs resemble *p*-aminobenzoic acid (PABA, $H_2N—C_6H_4—CO_2H$), and this resemblance is believed to be responsible for their antimicrobial properties. Bacteria, like humans, need folic acid to synthesize nucleic acids and proteins. Bacteria synthesize their folic acid from PABA in an enzymatic reaction. Sulfa drugs compete with PABA for the active site of that enzyme, and in this way they inhibit the synthesis of folic acid in bacteria. Because humans do not synthesize folic acid but must instead acquire it as an essential vitamin in our diets, we can tolerate sulfa drugs.

Several detergents are synthesized by aromatic sulfonation reactions. Detergents have the general structure $RSO_3^-Na^+$, where R is a relatively large, nonpolar group. Like soaps (see the special interest box on p. 99), one end of a detergent is very hydrophilic, and the other end is very hydrophobic. In some common detergents, a benzene ring separates an alkyl group from the $SO_3^-Na^+$ group, as shown in Figure 24-4b. The alkyl group can be linear or branched but typically consists of 12 carbons in total, and thus the compound is called a sodium dodecylbenzenesulfonate.

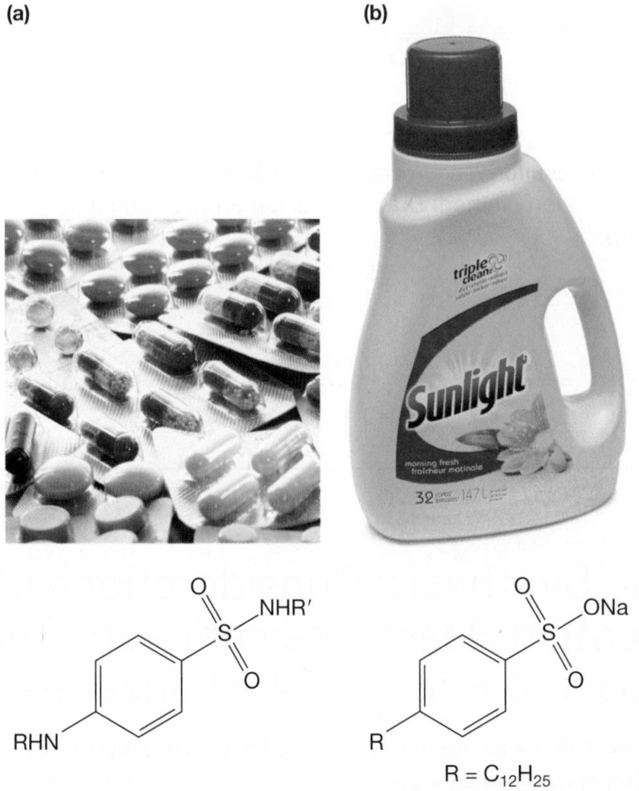
(a)
(b)
NHR′
RHN
ONa
R
R = $C_{12}H_{25}$

A sulfa drug

A sodium dodecylbenzenesulfonate

FIGURE 24-4

up, however, by using **fuming sulfuric acid**, which is concentrated sulfuric acid infused with SO_3. Under these acidic conditions, SO_3 is protonated to produce HSO_3^+, according to the equilibrium in Equation 24-29:

The concentration of the SO_3H^+ electrophile increases in fuming sulfuric acid.

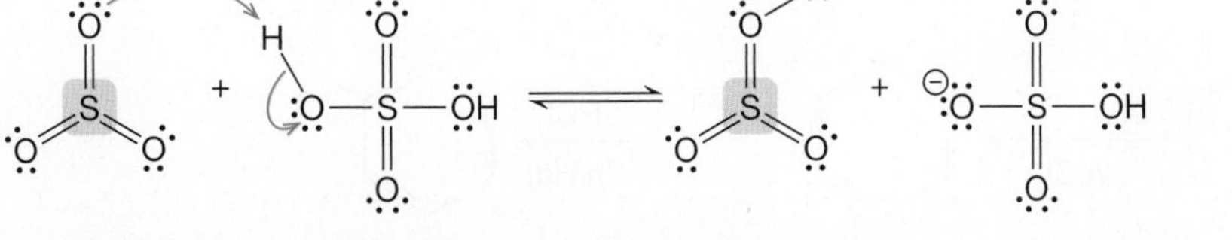

(24-29)

Although electrophilic aromatic substitution reactions are generally irreversible, sulfonation is an exception:

The sulfonation of an aromatic ring is *reversible*.

> **▸ LOOKING AHEAD**
>
> Here you have seen how a SO_3H group can be added or removed from an aromatic ring. In Section 25.12 you will learn how sulfonation can be used as a *protecting group* to block a specific site on the benzene ring where substitution is not desired.

Notice that water is a product in the sulfonation reaction in Equation 24-27. The reverse of a sulfonation reaction, called **desulfonation** (Eq. 24-30), can therefore be carried out by treating an arenesulfonic acid with large amounts of water under acidic conditions (see Your Turn 24.13 and Looking Ahead box):

Desulfonation

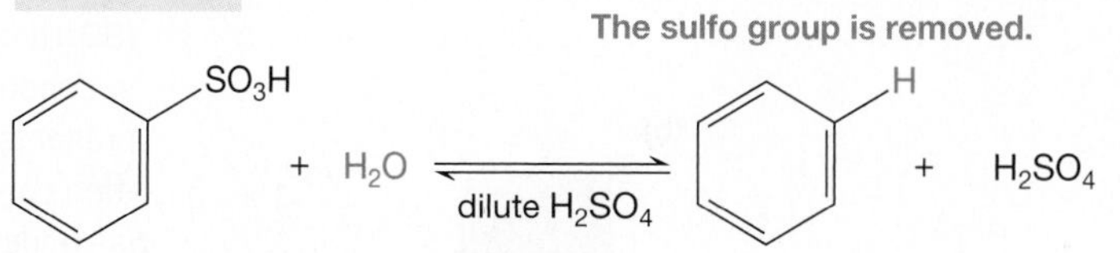

The sulfo group is removed.
SO3H
+ H2O
dilute H2SO4
H
+ H2SO4

(24-30)

YOUR TURN **24.13**

> The mechanism for the desulfonation in Equation 24-30 is shown here, but the curved arrows have been omitted. Draw the curved arrows and name each elementary step.
>
> 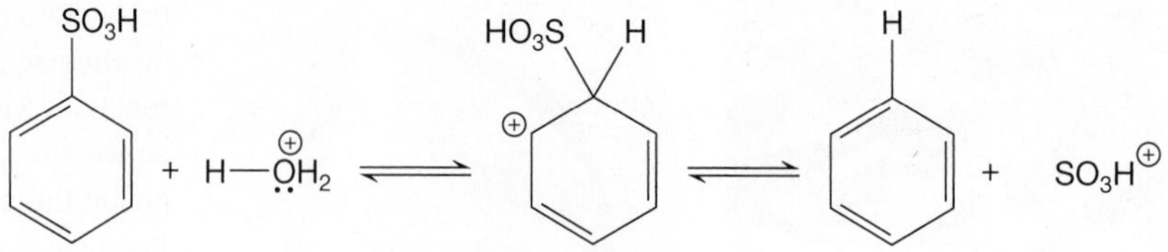
>
> SO3H
> + H—OH2
> HO3S H
> H
> + SO3H
>

> **SECTION 24.8 OBJECTIVES**
>
> You will be able to:
>
> 1. Explain why carbocation rearrangements are a concern when synthesizing primary alkylbenzenes.
> 2. Design the synthesis of a primary alkylbenzene that circumvents the problem of carbocation rearrangements.

24.8 Organic Synthesis: Considerations of Carbocation Rearrangements and the Synthesis of Primary Alkylbenzenes

Recall from Section 24.4 that one limitation of Friedel–Crafts alkylation is the potential for carbocation rearrangements. As we saw in Equations 24-18 and 24-19 (p. 1167), for example, propylbenzene cannot be synthesized directly in good yield by Friedel–Crafts alkylation because rearrangement of the cationic intermediate leads to (1-methylethyl)benzene instead.

To avoid this problem, we can use Friedel–Crafts *acylation* instead, which forms a C—C bond to the aromatic ring without competing carbocation rearrangements (Section 24.5). Because the immediate product of an acylation reaction is an aromatic ketone, the carbonyl group must be reduced to produce an alkylbenzene. An example using the Clemmensen reduction (Section 20.4) is shown in Equation 24-31:

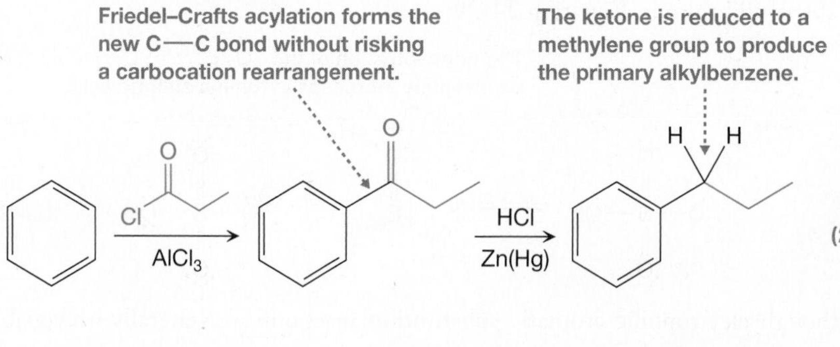

Friedel–Crafts acylation forms the new C—C bond without risking a carbocation rearrangement.
The ketone is reduced to a methylene group to produce the primary alkylbenzene.
O
Cl
AlCl3
O
HCl
Zn(Hg)
H H

(24-31)

SOLVED PROBLEM **24.5**

How to synthesize a primary alkylbenzene from benzene

Break It Down **Show how you would synthesize this compound, using benzene as the only aromatic starting compound.**

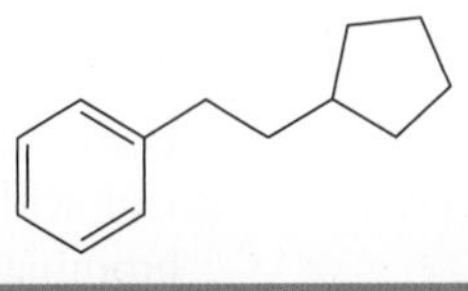

Think	Solve
Can a Friedel–Crafts alkylation be used to form the C—C bond to benzene? If not, why not?	A Friedel–Crafts alkylation would require the equivalent of a primary carbocation intermediate, as shown here. This is unfeasible, however, because a primary carbocation intermediate, if produced, would rearrange to a more stable secondary carbocation.

A primary carbocation, if produced, would undergo rearrangement.

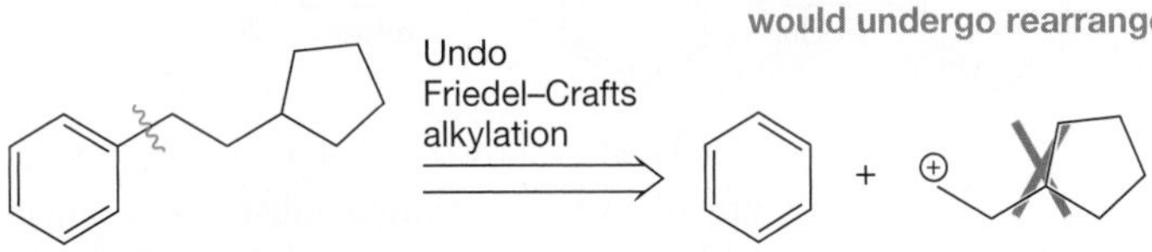

Undo
Friedel–Crafts
alkylation
+

Think	Solve
What advantage does Friedel–Crafts acylation have to form the intended C—C bond? How could such a reaction be incorporated?	When a Friedel–Crafts acylation is used to form a new C—C bond to an aromatic ring, no carbocation rearrangements occur. We can produce the target from the product of Friedel–Crafts acylation (an aromatic ketone), as shown below.

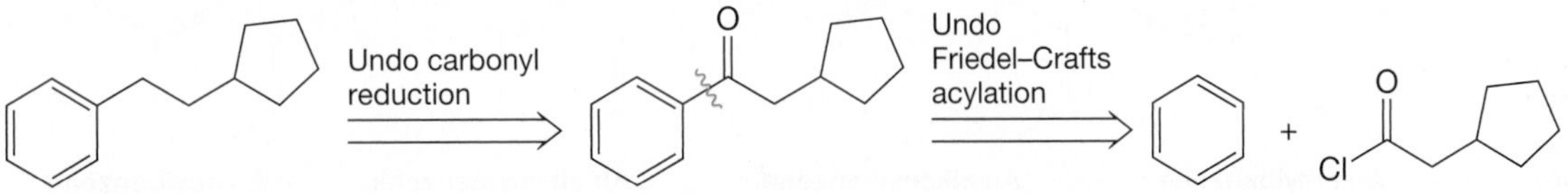

Undo carbonyl
reduction
O
Undo
Friedel–Crafts
acylation
+
O
Cl

Think	Solve
How might you report the final synthesis?	To report the final synthesis, begin with the starting materials and supply the appropriate reagents and reaction conditions.

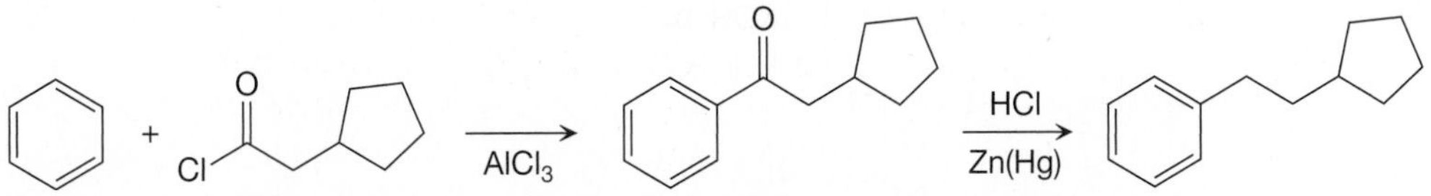

+
O
Cl
AlCl3
O
HCl
Zn(Hg)

Try It Show how you would synthesize this compound, using benzene as the only aromatic starting compound.

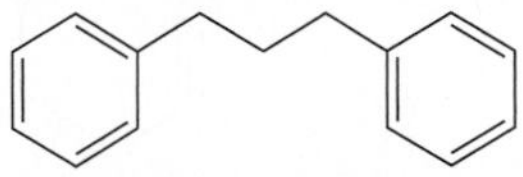

SECTION 24.9 OBJECTIVES

You will be able to:

1. Design a synthesis that results in a new carboxyl or amino group attached to a benzene ring.
2. Show how to synthesize a benzenediazonium ion and how various substituted benzenes can be produced from such an intermediate.

24.9 Organic Synthesis: Common Reactions Used Along with Electrophilic Aromatic Substitution Reactions

Electrophilic aromatic substitution reactions allow us to incorporate a variety of substituents onto an aromatic ring, but several substituents cannot be put in place directly by an electrophilic aromatic substitution reaction. Here we discuss how an electrophilic aromatic substitution reaction can be used to incorporate a *different* substituent that can be subsequently transformed into the desired substituent.

24.9a Oxidation of Carbon Side Chains: Synthesis of Benzoic Acids

Using the reactions we have learned thus far, how would you incorporate a carboxylic acid group into a benzene ring? Equation 24-32 shows that benzene can be brominated, and the resulting bromobenzene can be treated with Mg to produce a Grignard reagent. Bubbling carbon dioxide through the mixture (review Eq. 18-23, p. 893) leads to a Grignard reaction that produces the carboxylate anion, which is protonated in an acid workup.

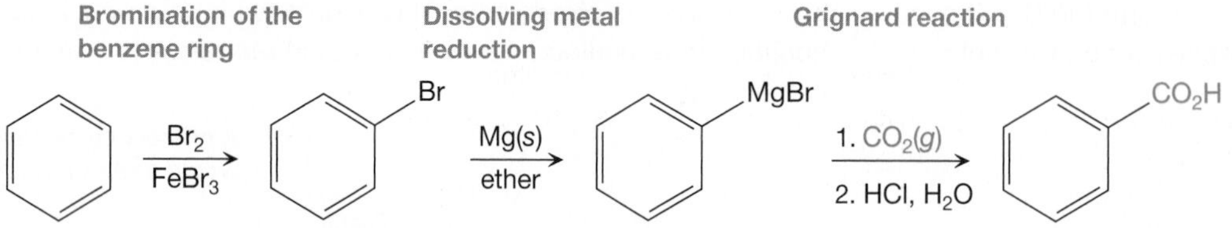

Bromination of the benzene ring
Dissolving metal reduction
Grignard reaction
Br
MgBr
CO2H
Br2
FeBr3
Mg(s)
ether
1. CO2(g)
2. HCl, H2O

(24-32)

An alternative way to incorporate a carboxylic acid group into the ring begins with any of a variety of monosubstituted benzenes in which a C atom from the substituent is directly bonded to the ring, as shown in Equation 24-33a through 24-33e. Oxidation of substituted benzenes using $KMnO_4$ (potassium permanganate) heated in a basic solution produces benzoic acid after acid workup. Several precursors for this oxidation could be produced by Friedel–Crafts reactions.

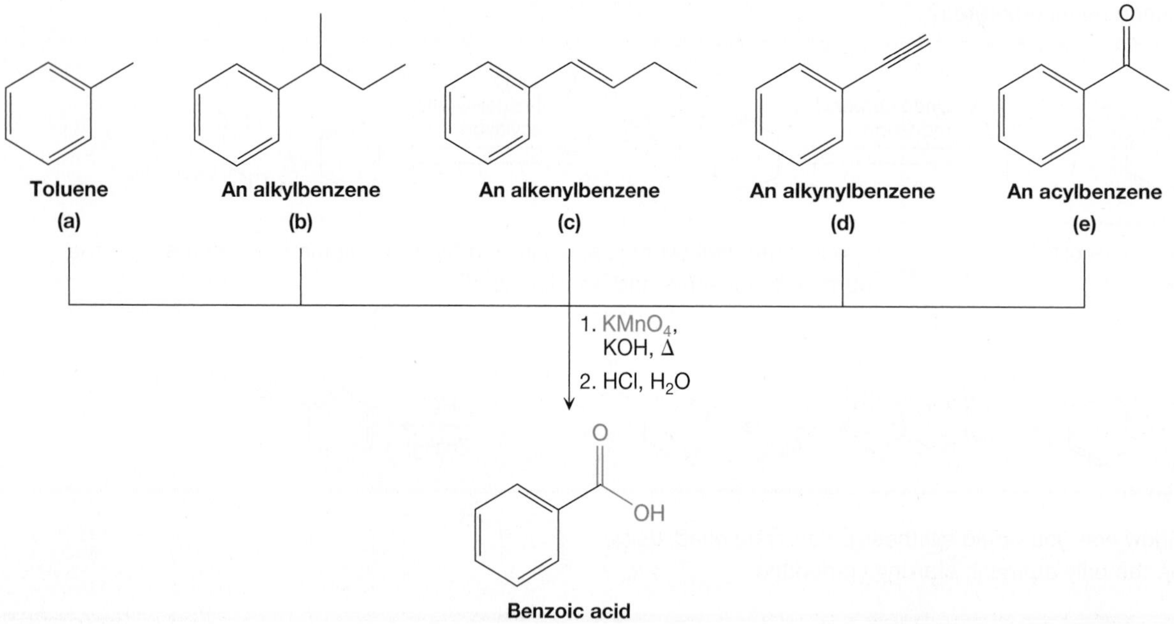

Toluene
(a)
An alkylbenzene
(b)
An alkenylbenzene
(c)
An alkynylbenzene
(d)
An acylbenzene
(e)
O
1. KMnO4,
KOH, Δ
2. HCl, H2O
O
OH
Benzoic acid

(24-33)

The permanganate oxidation reactions shown in Equation 24-33 are believed to proceed through *radical intermediates* (see Looking Ahead box). The C atom bonded directly to the phenyl ring, known as the **benzylic carbon**, is particularly reactive under these conditions. This is why the product of each reaction in Equation 24-33 is the same, essentially independent of the group that is bonded to the benzylic carbon.

▸ LOOKING AHEAD

A *radical* is a species that possesses at least one unpaired electron. Radicals are generally very unstable and highly reactive, so they usually cannot be isolated for any substantial length of time. Chapter 27 discusses the formation of various kinds of radicals and the types of reactions they undergo.

This permanganate oxidation fails, however, when the benzylic C is *quaternary* (i.e., bonded to four other C atoms). (1,1-Dimethylethyl)benzene, for example, is *not* oxidized to benzoic acid (Eq. 24-34):

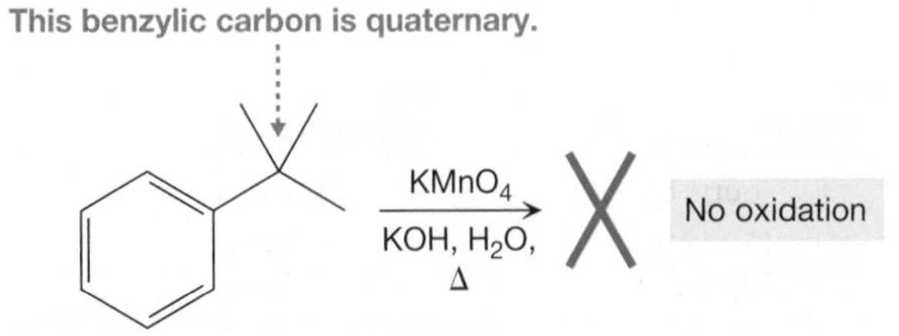
This benzylic carbon is quaternary.
KMnO4
KOH, H2O, Δ
No oxidation

(24-34)

(1,1-Dimethylethyl)benzene

Thus:

When a substituent on a phenyl ring is attached by a carbon atom, $KMnO_4$ oxidation requires the benzylic C to be bonded to at least one H atom or be part of a π bond.

YOUR TURN **24.14**

A student proposed the following synthesis. Why does it not work?

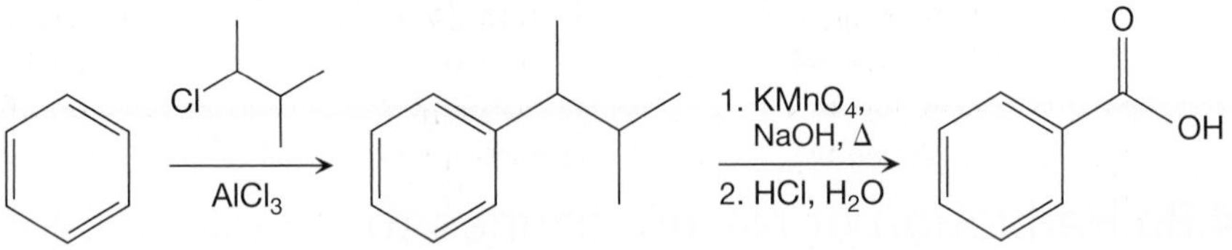
Cl
AlCl3
1. KMnO4, NaOH, Δ
2. HCl, H2O
O
OH

In a synthesis, the CO_2H group might not appear in the target molecule. Instead, as Solved Problem 24.6 demonstrates, the CO_2H group can be transformed into other functional groups, such as esters.

SOLVED PROBLEM **24.6**

How to design the synthesis of a benzoic acid derivative from benzene

Break It Down **Propose a synthesis of ethyl benzoate from benzene and any other compounds containing two or fewer carbon atoms.**

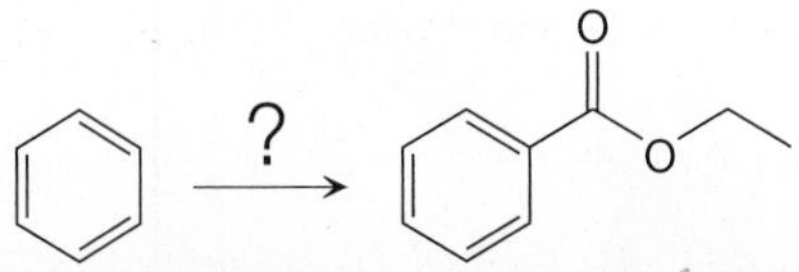
?
O
O

Think	Solve
How can an ester be synthesized from a precursor with fewer carbons?	In Chapter 23 we learned that an ester can be synthesized from a carboxylic acid and an alcohol. Here, the necessary alcohol is ethanol, which contains two C atoms. 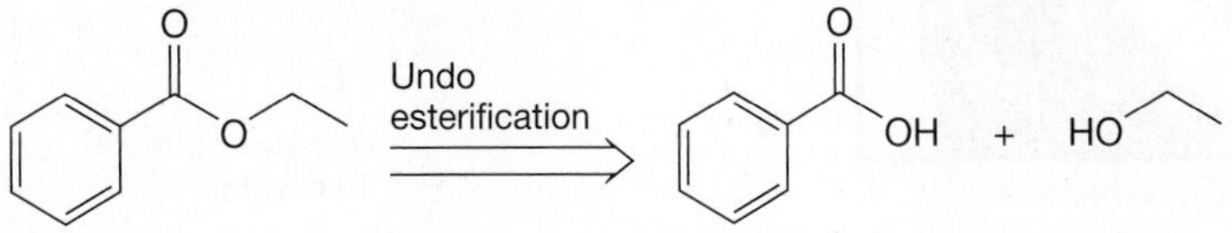 O O Undo esterification O OH + HO

(continued)

How can you make benzoic acid from benzene?

Benzoic acid can be made by oxidizing one of the types of compounds in Equation 24-33. As shown here, for example, we can make it from an aromatic ketone, which can be made by Friedel–Crafts acylation.

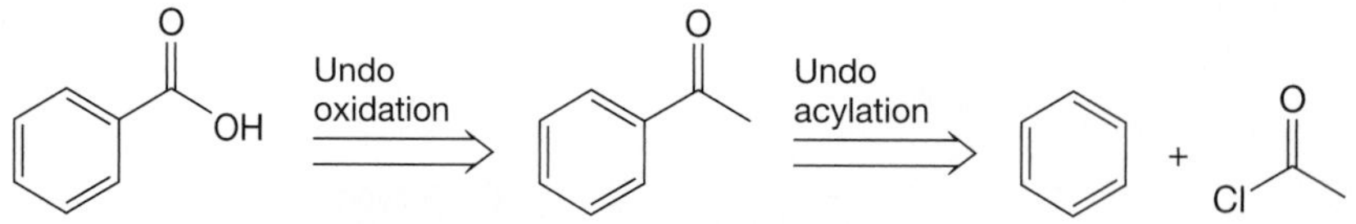

O
OH
Undo oxidation
O
Undo acylation
+
O
Cl

How might you report the final synthesis?

To report the final synthesis, we begin with the starting materials and supply the appropriate reagents and reaction conditions.

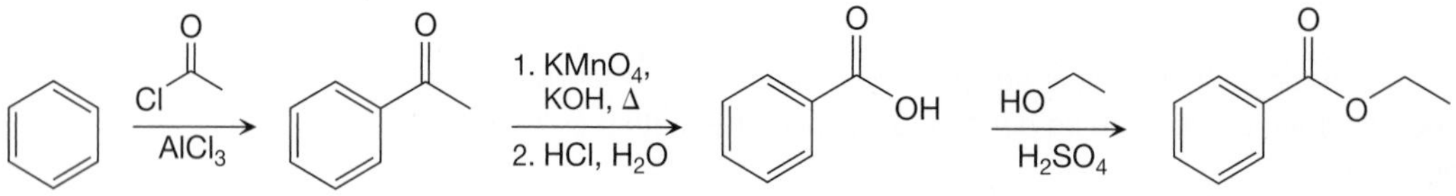

O
Cl
AlCl3
O
1. KMnO4, KOH, Δ
2. HCl, H2O
O
OH
HO
H2SO4
O
O

Try It Show how you could synthesize benzoic anhydride using benzene as the only aromatic starting compound.

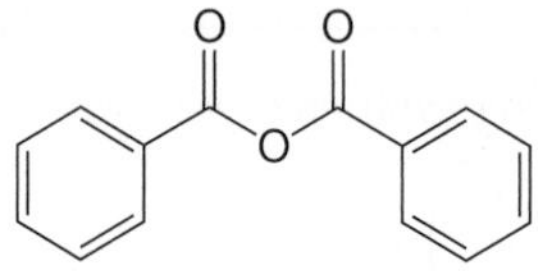

O
O
O

CONNECTIONS 24.5

Clear arteries

N-Phenylbenzamide (Solved Problem 24.7), commonly called benzanilide, is believed to counter the effects of atherosclerosis, or artery hardening, by lowering cholesterol levels in the blood. Atherosclerosis results from the buildup of fats and cholesterol, and it is the leading cause of heart attacks and strokes.

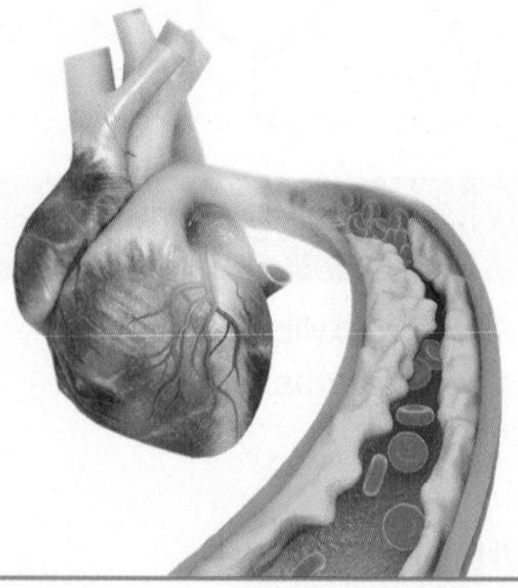

24.9b Reduction of Nitrobenzenes to Aromatic Amines

An amino group (NH_2) is typically not incorporated into a benzene ring directly by electrophilic aromatic substitution. Instead, the benzene ring is often nitrated first (Eq. 24-25, p. 1173), followed by reduction of the NO_2 group to an NH_2 group. This reduction can be carried out either by catalytic hydrogenation (Eq. 24-33a) or by treatment with a metal (e.g., Fe or Sn) under acidic conditions, followed by NaOH to neutralize the acid (Eq. 24-33b). Reduction with a metal under acidic conditions resembles the Clemmensen reduction introduced in Chapter 20, in which the C=O group of a ketone or aldehyde is reduced to a methylene (CH_2) group by treatment with a Zn(Hg) amalgam in HCl.

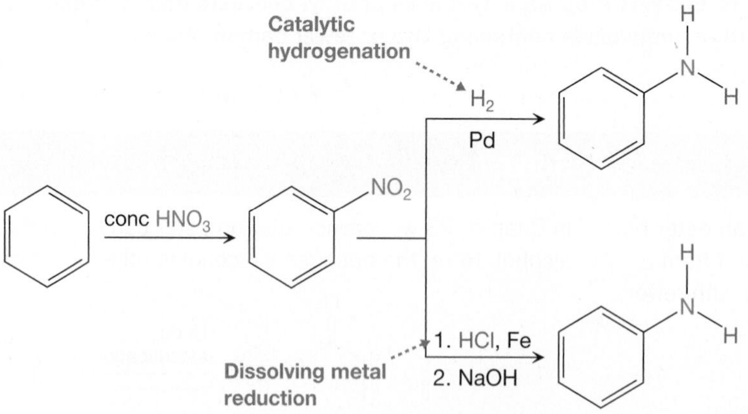

Catalytic hydrogenation
H2
Pd
H
N
H
conc HNO3
NO2
H
N
H
1. HCl, Fe
2. NaOH
Dissolving metal reduction

(24-35a)

(24-35b)

The reduction of a nitro substituent to an amino group should be considered if the target is an aromatic amine. Moreover, the aromatic amine could be used as a synthetic intermediate toward the synthesis of a different target (see Looking Ahead box). An example is shown in Solved Problem 24.7.

> **▸ LOOKING AHEAD**
>
> Aromatic amines are important in synthesis. In Section 24.9c, we will see that aromatic amines are precursors to arenediazonium ions (Ar—N_2^+), which can be transformed into a variety of functionalized aromatic species. In Chapter 25, we will see that amino groups can be important in influencing the incorporation of additional groups onto the aromatic ring.

SOLVED PROBLEM **24.7**

How to design a synthesis with an aromatic amine as an intermediate

Break It Down Show how to synthesize *N*-phenylbenzamide, using benzene as the only aromatic starting compound.

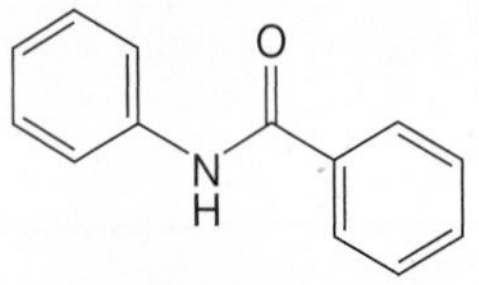

N-Phenylbenzamide

Think	Solve
From what acid derivative and amine can the target be made?	An *N*-substituted amide can be produced from an amine and an acid chloride: in this case, aniline and benzoyl chloride. 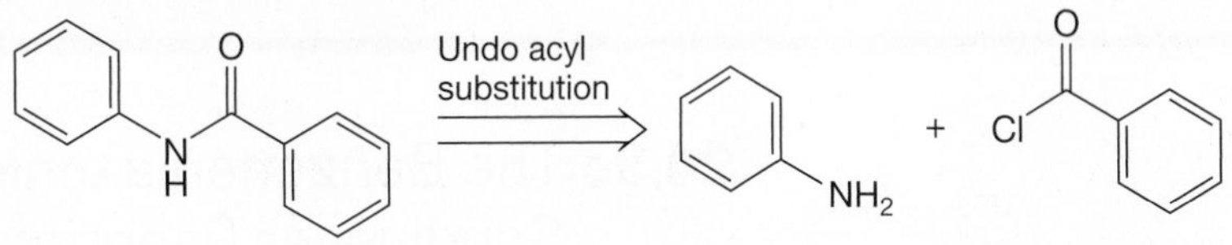 Undo acyl substitution
How can aniline be synthesized from benzene?	Aniline can be made from nitrobenzene, which can be made from benzene, as shown here. 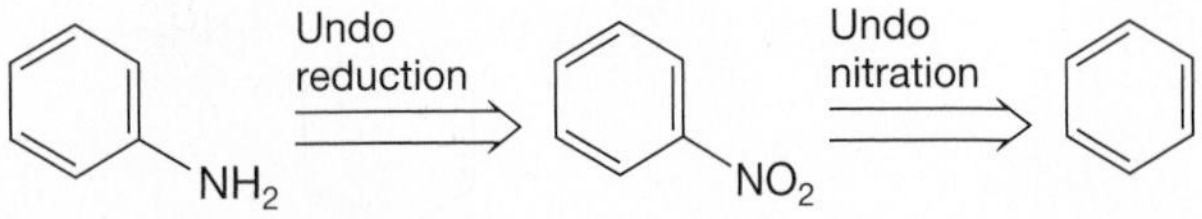 Undo reduction Undo nitration
From what carboxylic acid can benzoyl chloride be made? How can that carboxylic acid be made from benzene?	As shown below, benzoyl chloride can be made from benzoic acid. Benzoic acid can be made by oxidation of a substituent attached by carbon, such as an acyl group. The aromatic ketone can be made from benzene by Friedel–Crafts acylation.

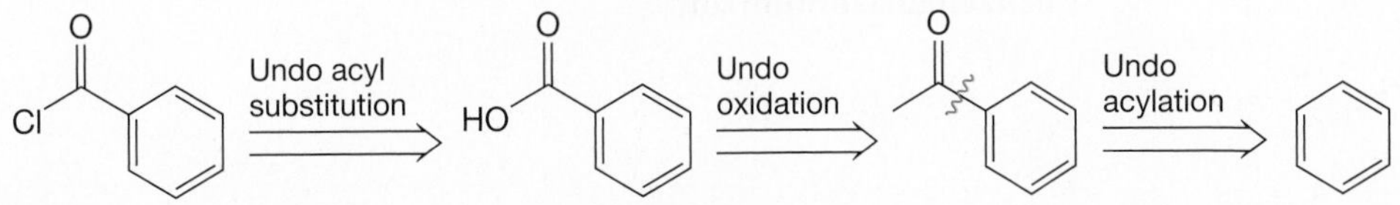
Undo acyl substitution
Undo oxidation
Undo acylation

(continued)

How might you report the final synthesis?	To report the final synthesis, we begin with the starting materials and supply the appropriate reagents and reaction conditions.

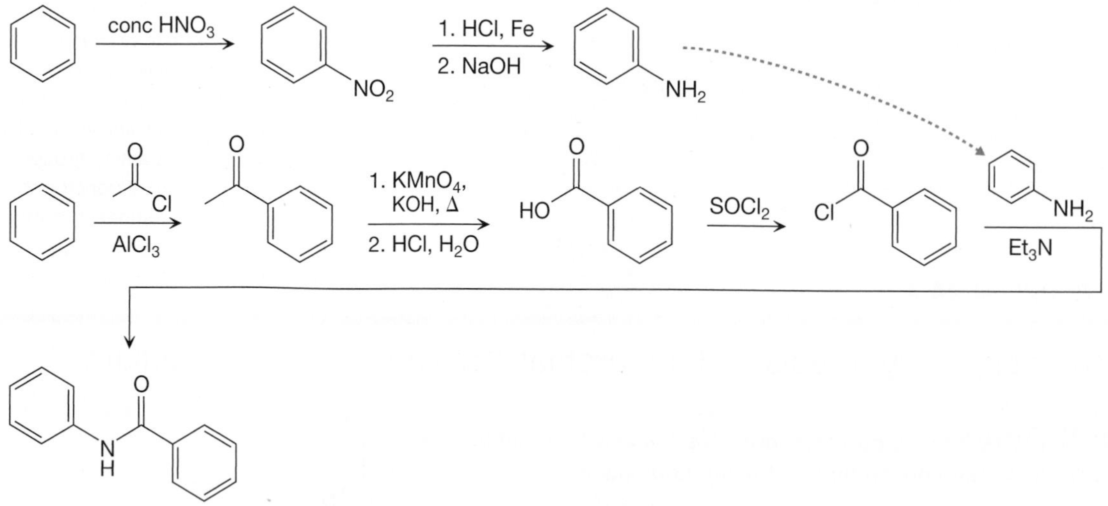

conc HNO_3
NO_2
1. HCl, Fe
2. NaOH
NH_2
O
Cl
$AlCl_3$
O
1. $KMnO_4$, KOH, Δ
2. HCl, H_2O
HO
O
$SOCl_2$
Cl
O
NH_2
Et_3N
O
N
H

Try It Show how to synthesize each of these compounds, using benzene as the only aromatic starting compound.

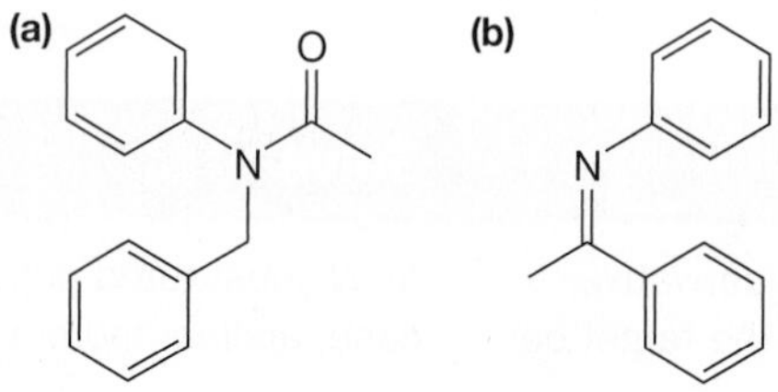

(a)
O
N
(b)
N

24.9c The Benzenediazonium Ion and Sandmeyer Reactions

Bromobenzene is produced when aniline is treated with sodium nitrite ($NaNO_2$) under acidic conditions, followed by copper(I) bromide (CuBr) (Eq. 24-36):

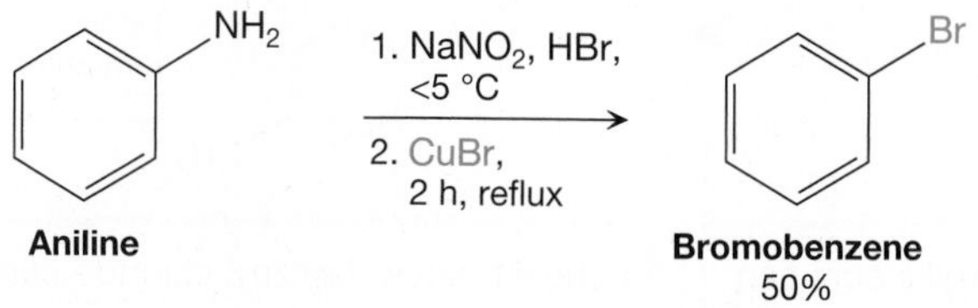

NH_2
1. $NaNO_2$, HBr, <5 °C
2. CuBr, 2 h, reflux
Br
Aniline
Bromobenzene
50%

(24-36)

Overall, Br has replaced NH_2, but the mechanism is not a simple electrophilic aromatic substitution. As shown in Equation 24-37, the first of the two reactions, called **diazotization**, is a multistep mechanism, which ultimately produces the **benzenediazonium ion**:

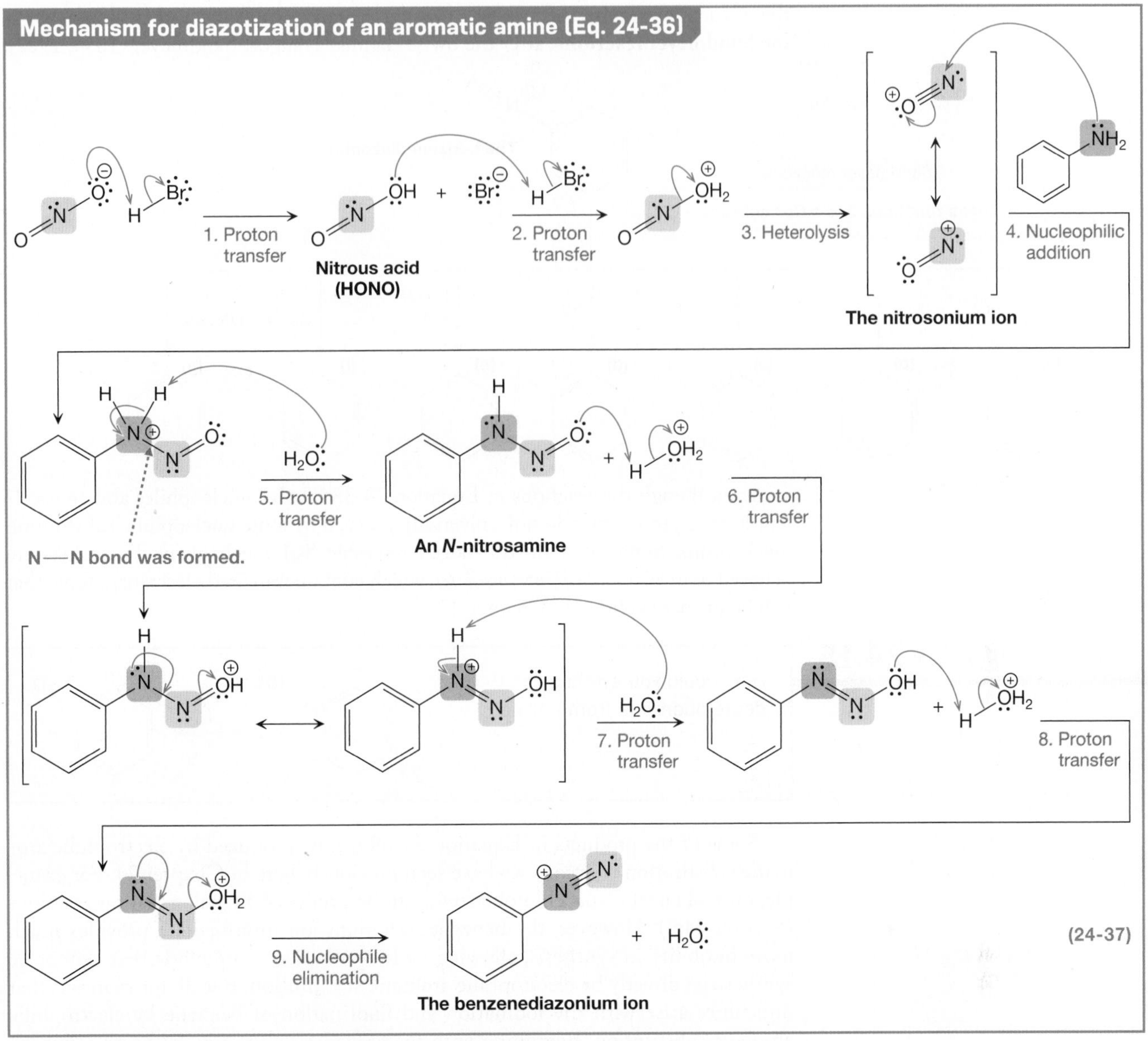
Mechanism for diazotization of an aromatic amine (Eq. 24-36)
1. Proton transfer
Nitrous acid (HONO)
2. Proton transfer
3. Heterolysis
The nitrosonium ion
4. Nucleophilic addition
5. Proton transfer
N—N bond was formed.
An N-nitrosamine
6. Proton transfer
7. Proton transfer
8. Proton transfer
9. Nucleophile elimination
The benzenediazonium ion

(24-37)

In Step 1, the nitrite anion is protonated, which produces nitrous acid, HONO. Protonation in Step 2 converts a poor hydroxide leaving group into an excellent H_2O leaving group, which departs in Step 3 to produce the nitrosonium ion, NO^+. The aromatic amine attacks the nitrosonium ion in Step 4, in which a N—N bond is formed. Steps 5–8 are proton transfers that serve to remove protons from the initial amino N and to produce an excellent H_2O leaving group on the adjacent N, analogous to how protons are shuttled in a keto–enol tautomerization (Section 7.10). Finally, in Step 9, the H_2O leaving group departs, producing the benzenediazonium ion.

The benzenediazonium ion possesses the N_2^+ group, which can behave as an excellent leaving group and depart as $N_2(g)$. The ion is highly reactive and must be kept below ~10 °C to prevent decomposition or explosion.

At the same time, the high reactivity of the benzenediazonium ion makes it possible to carry out a subsequent substitution reaction simply by choosing the appropriate nucleophile. Examples are shown in Equation 24-38a through 24-38g. Some of these reactions require the presence of a Cu^+ catalyst; collectively, they are known as the **Sandmeyer reactions**, after the Swiss chemist Traugott Sandmeyer (1854–1922).

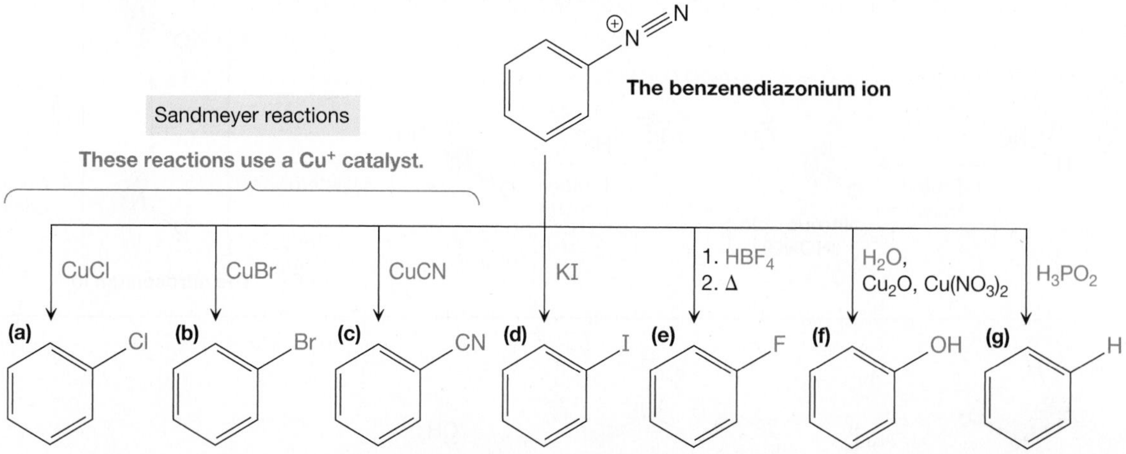

N
The benzenediazonium ion
Sandmeyer reactions
These reactions use a Cu⁺ catalyst.
CuCl
CuBr
CuCN
KI
1. HBF4
2. Δ
H2O,
Cu2O, Cu(NO3)2
H3PO2
(a)
Cl
(b)
Br
(c)
CN
(d)
I
(e)
F
(f)
OH
(g)
H

(24-38)

Even though the reactions in Equation 24-38 involve nucleophiles and an excellent leaving group, they do not universally proceed by ionic nucleophilic substitution mechanisms. Some of them do indeed resemble S_N1 mechanisms, but others are believed to involve *radical intermediates*, which contain unpaired electrons, a topic that will be further explored in Chapter 27.

YOUR TURN **24.15**

How would you synthesize deuterobenzene from aniline?

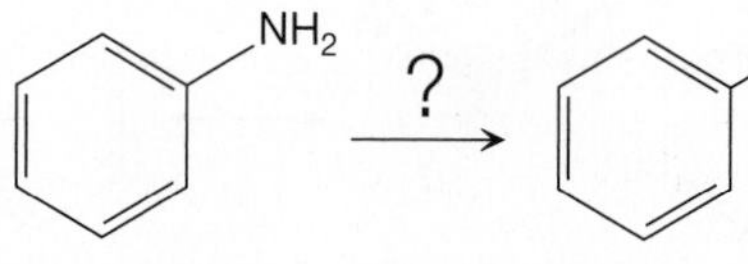

NH2
?
D

Some of the products in Equation 24-38 can be produced by electrophilic aromatic substitution reactions we have seen previously here in Chapter 24. For example, bromobenzene and chlorobenzene can be produced by halogenation reactions (Section 24.2). However, the benzenediazonium ion intermediate provides much more flexibility in synthesis, allowing us to synthesize compounds that cannot be synthesized directly by electrophilic aromatic substitution. Recall, for example, that difficulties arise with the iodination and fluorination of benzene by electrophilic aromatic substitution. Beginning with the arenediazonium ion, however, iodobenzene (Eq. 24-38d) and fluorobenzene (Eq. 24-38e) can be synthesized rather straightforwardly. Similarly, benzonitrile (C_6H_5CN) and phenol (C_6H_5OH) cannot be produced directly from benzene by electrophilic aromatic substitution, but they can be produced by incorporating the benzenediazonium ion as a synthetic intermediate. This is exemplified in Solved Problem 24.8.

How to design a synthesis involving a benzenediazonium ion as an intermediate

Break It Down **Show how to synthesize benzonitrile from benzene.**

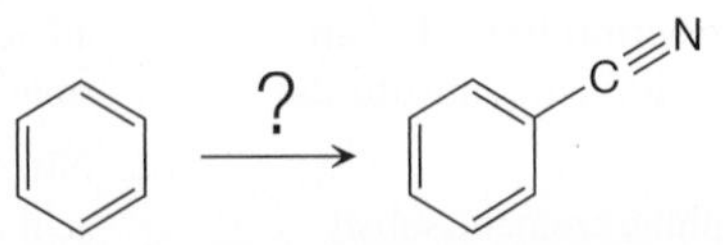
?
Benzonitrile

Think	Solve
Can a cyano group replace H on a benzene ring directly? If not, what precursor is required?	We have not encountered a reaction in which a cyano group directly replaces a H^+ on benzene. However, as we saw in Equation 24-38c, benzonitrile can be made from a benzenediazonium ion precursor, $C_6H_5—N_2^+$, as shown in the first transform here.
From what precursor can the benzenediazonium ion be made? How can that precursor be made from benzene?	The precursor to the benzenediazonium ion is an aromatic amine, as shown in the second transform above. The aromatic amine, in turn, can be made by reducing nitrobenzene. Finally, nitrobenzene can be made directly from benzene by nitration.
How might you report the final synthesis?	To report the synthesis, begin with benzene as the starting material and supply the appropriate reagents and reaction conditions.

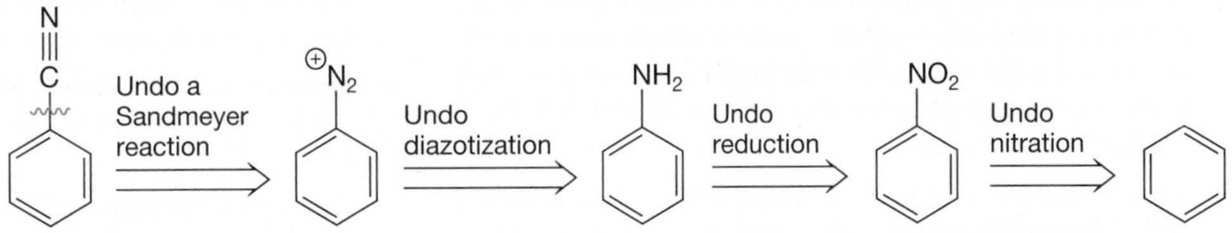
Undo a Sandmeyer reaction
Undo diazotization
Undo reduction
Undo nitration
NH2
NO2

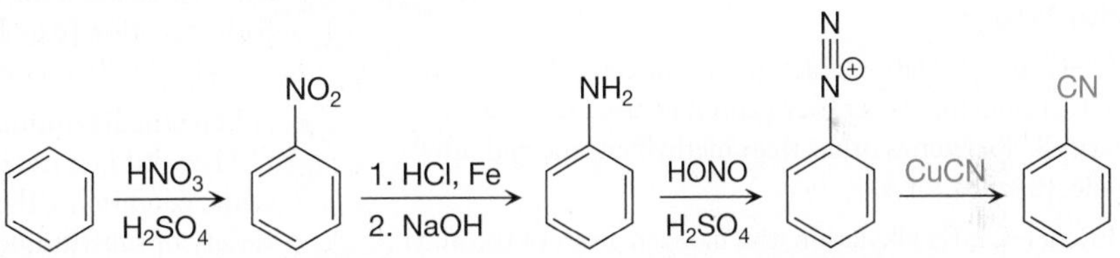
NO2
NH2
CN
HNO3
H2SO4
1. HCl, Fe
2. NaOH
HONO
H2SO4
CuCN

Try It Show how to synthesize phenol from benzene.

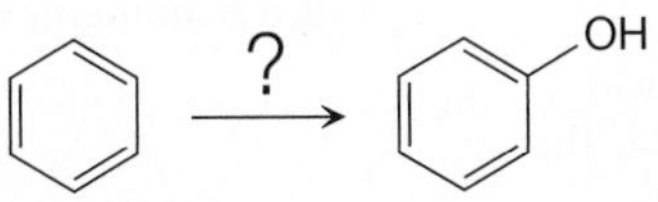
?
OH

Chapter Summary and Key Terms

- Aromatic species tend to react with electrophiles (E^+) in an **electrophilic aromatic substitution reaction** instead of an addition reaction, because electrophilic aromatic substitution preserves aromaticity. (Section 24.1)
- The general mechanism for an electrophilic aromatic substitution reaction on benzene consists of two steps. First, E^+ undergoes electrophilic addition to the aromatic ring to produce an **arenium ion intermediate** or **Wheland intermediate**, which temporarily disrupts aromaticity in the ring. Second, a proton (H^+) undergoes electrophile elimination, which restores aromaticity and results in a substituted aromatic ring. (Section 24.1)
- To temporarily disrupt aromaticity in the ring, electrophiles that participate in electrophilic aromatic substitution tend to be very strong (in which case they must be generated in situ), so the reactions are generally very product-favored and irreversible. (Section 24.1)
- The first step of electrophilic aromatic substitution, addition of the electrophile, is slow, so it is the rate-determining step of the reaction. Thus, the reaction is first-order with respect to both the aromatic species and the electrophile. (Section 24.1)
- **Aromatic halogenation** typically requires a molecular halogen, Br_2 or Cl_2, in the presence of a strong **Lewis acid catalyst**, such as $FeBr_3$ or $FeCl_3$. These reactions behave as if Br^+ or Cl^+ is the electrophile. (Section 24.2)
- **Friedel–Crafts alkylation** involves a carbocation (R^+) electrophile, which can be produced from an alkyl halide in the presence of a strong Lewis acid catalyst, such as $AlCl_3$. (Section 24.3)
- Friedel–Crafts alkylation reactions are susceptible to carbocation rearrangements, so they cannot be used to produce primary alkylbenzenes other than methylbenzene and ethylbenzene. (Section 24.4)
- In a Friedel–Crafts alkylation, the halogen atom of the alkyl halide must be bonded to an sp^3-hybridized carbon atom. (Section 24.4)
- A **Friedel–Crafts acylation** requires an acid halide or acid anhydride in the presence of a strong Lewis acid catalyst. The catalyst is responsible for the production of the electrophile, an **acylium ion**, $R{-}C{\equiv}O^+$. These reactions are not susceptible to carbocation rearrangement. (Section 24.5)
- **Nitration** of an aromatic ring requires concentrated nitric acid (HNO_3), which produces the **nitronium ion** (NO_2^+) as the electrophile. The addition of concentrated sulfuric acid (H_2SO_4) increases the concentration of the nitronium ion and therefore increases the rate of the electrophilic aromatic substitution reaction. (Section 24.6)
- **Sulfonation** of an aromatic ring involves SO_3H^+ as the electrophile, which is present in small amounts in concentrated H_2SO_4. The rate of sulfonation is greater with **fuming sulfuric acid**, which is H_2SO_4 enriched with SO_3, because it increases the concentration of SO_3H^+. (Section 24.7)
- Sulfonation is *reversible*. A SO_3H group on an aromatic ring can be replaced by a hydrogen atom on treatment with H_3O^+. (Section 24.7)
- Although most primary alkylbenzenes cannot be produced directly from a Friedel–Crafts alkylation, they can be produced by Friedel–Crafts acylation followed by a reduction of the ketone's carbonyl group to a methylene (CH_2) group. (Section 24.8)
- A variety of carbon side chains on an aromatic ring can be oxidized to a CO_2H group by heating the aromatic compound in the presence of basic $KMnO_4$, followed by acid workup. (Section 24.9a)
- An aromatic amine can be produced by reducing a nitro-substituted aromatic ring, by incorporating either catalytic hydrogenation [e.g., $H_2(g)$, Pd] or dissolving metal reduction (e.g., Fe, HCl). (Section 24.9b)
- A **benzenediazonium ion** ($C_6H_5{-}N_2^+$) is produced when $C_6H_5{-}NH_2$ is treated with sodium nitrite ($NaNO_2$) under acidic conditions. The benzenediazonium ion can undergo a variety of substitution reactions readily, due to the excellent $N_2(g)$ leaving group. Reactions involving a Cu^+ catalyst are called **Sandmeyer reactions**. (Section 24.9c)

Reaction Tables

Functional group transformations introduced in this chapter are collected in Table 24-1, and reactions introduced in this chapter that alter the carbon skeleton are collected in Table 24-2.

TABLE 24-1 Functional Group Transformations

	Starting Compound Class	Typical Reagents and Reaction Conditions	Compound Class Formed	Key Electron-Rich Species	Key Electron-Poor Species	Comments	Discussed in Section
(1)	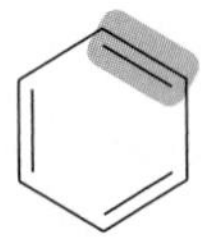 Arene	Br_2 → $FeBr_3$	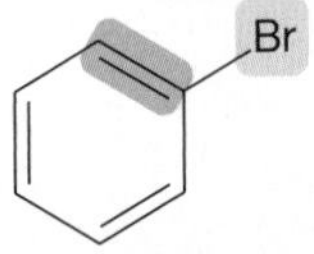 Aryl bromide	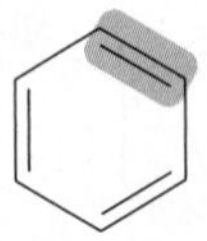	:Br:—$\overset{\oplus}{FeBr_3}$	Electrophilic aromatic substitution	24.2
(2)	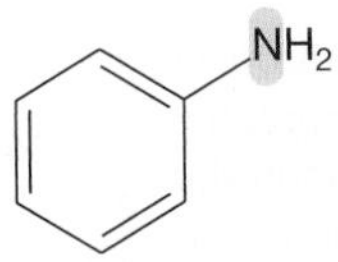 Arylamine	1. $NaNO_2$, H_2SO_4 → 2. CuBr	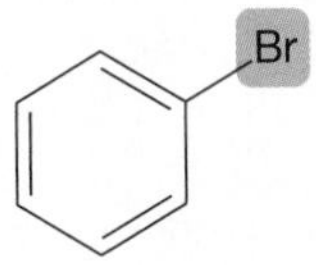 Aryl bromide	CuBr	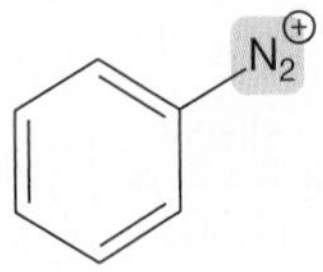	Proceeds through a diazonium ion; Sandmeyer reaction	24.9c
(3)	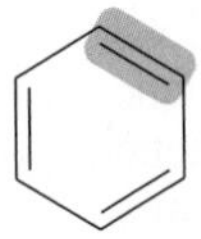 Arene	Cl_2 → $FeCl_3$	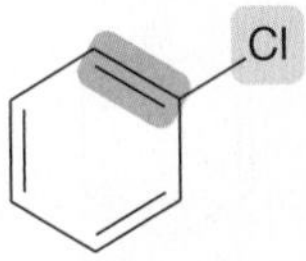 Aryl chloride	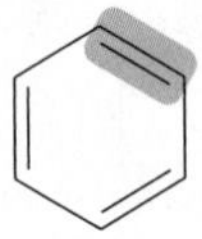	:Cl:—$\overset{\oplus}{FeCl_3}$	Electrophilic aromatic substitution	24.2
(4)	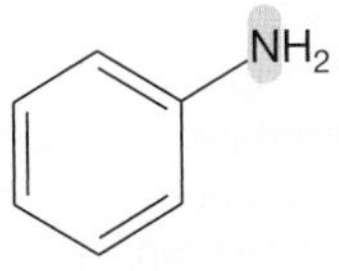 Arylamine	1. $NaNO_2$, H_2SO_4 → 2. CuCl	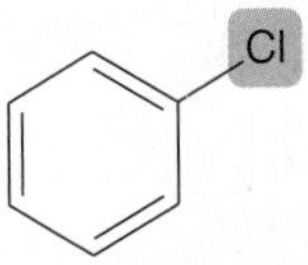 Aryl chloride	CuCl	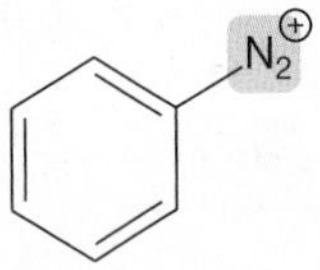	Proceeds through a diazonium ion; Sandmeyer reaction	24.9c
(5)	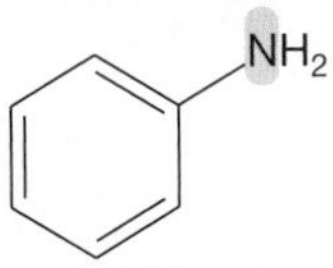 Arylamine	1. $NaNO_2$, H_2SO_4 → 2. KI	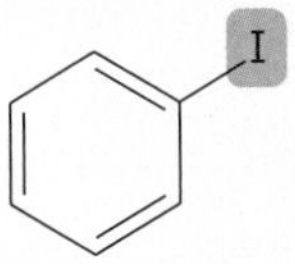 Aryl iodide	KI	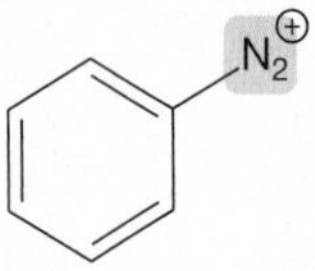	Proceeds through a diazonium ion	24.9c
(6)	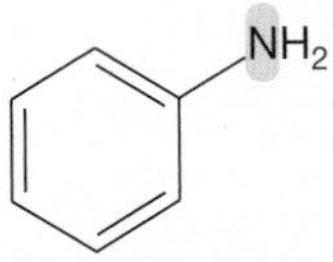 Arylamine	1. $NaNO_2$, H_2SO_4 → 2. HBF_4, then Δ	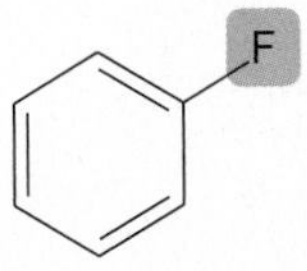 Aryl fluoride	HBF_4	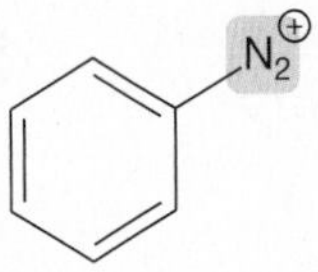	Proceeds through a diazonium ion	24.9c
(7)	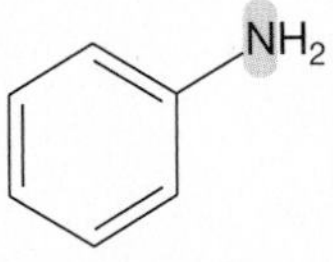 Arylamine	1. $NaNO_2$, H_2SO_4 → 2. H_2O, Cu_2O, $Cu(NO_3)_2$	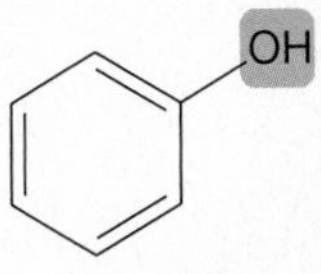 Aryl alcohol	H_2O	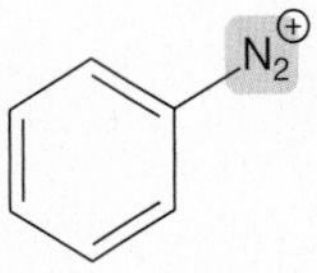	Proceeds through a diazonium ion; Sandmeyer reaction	24.9c

(continued)

TABLE 24-1 Functional Group Transformations (continued)

	Starting Compound Class	Typical Reagents and Reaction Conditions	Compound Class Formed	Key Electron-Rich Species	Key Electron-Poor Species	Comments	Discussed in Section
(8)	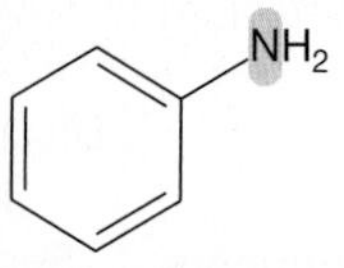NH_2 Arylamine	1. $NaNO_2$, H_2SO_4 → 2. H_3PO_2	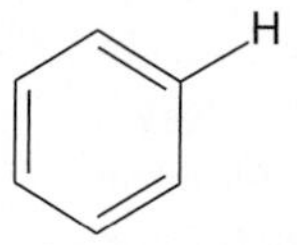H Arene	—	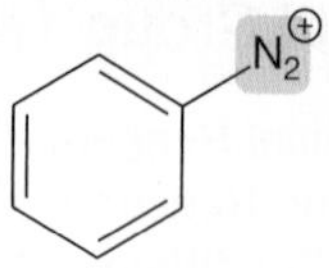$N_2^{\oplus}$	Proceeds through a diazonium ion	24.9c
(9)	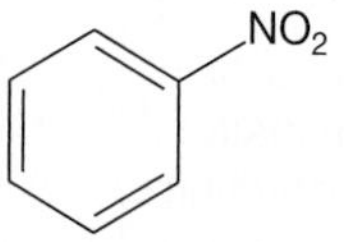NO_2 Nitroarene	1. HCl, Fe → 2. NaOH	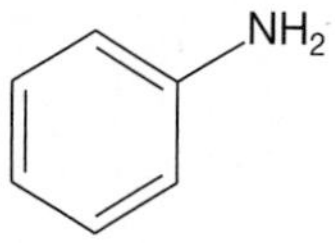NH_2 Arylamine	—	—	Reduction	24.9b
(10)	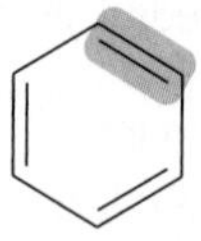 Arene	HNO_3 → H_2SO_4	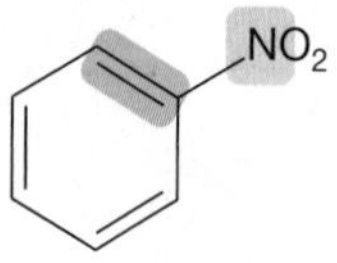NO_2 Nitroarene	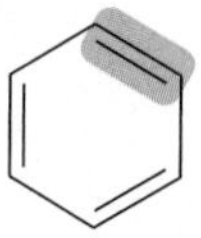	$^{\oplus}NO_2$	Electrophilic aromatic substitution; nitration	24.6
(11)	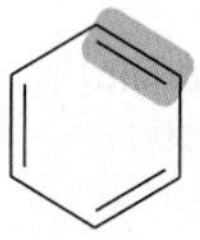 Arene	SO_3 → H_2SO_4	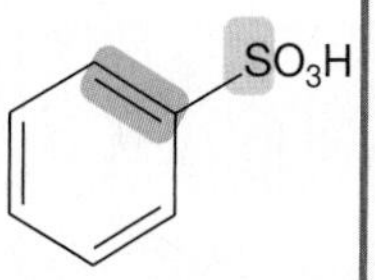SO_3H Arenesulfonic acid	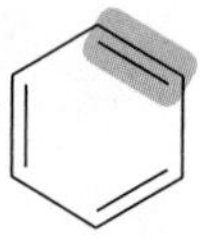	$SO_3H^{\oplus}$	Electrophilic aromatic substitution; sulfonation	24.7
(12)	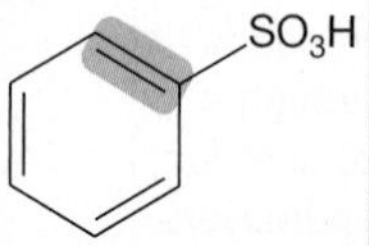SO_3H Arenesulfonic acid	$H_3O^{\oplus}$ →	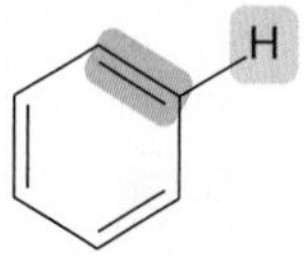H Arene	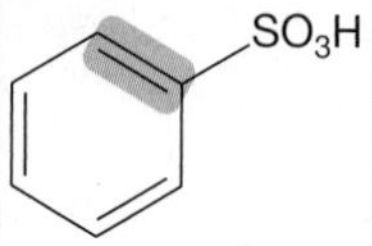SO_3H	$H—\overset{\oplus}{O}H_2$	Electrophilic aromatic substitution; desulfonation	24.7

TABLE 24-2 Reactions That Alter the Carbon Skeleton

	Starting Compound Class	Typical Reagents and Reaction Conditions	Compound Class Formed	Key Electron-Rich Species	Key Electron-Poor Species	Comments	Discussed in Section
(1)	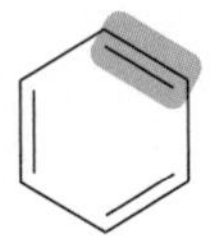 Arene	R—Cl, $AlCl_3$	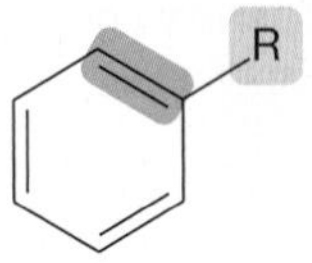 Alkylarene	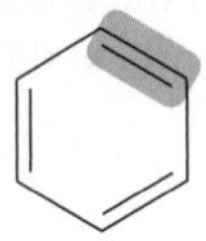	$R^{\oplus}$	Electrophilic aromatic substitution; Friedel–Crafts alkylation	24.3
(2)	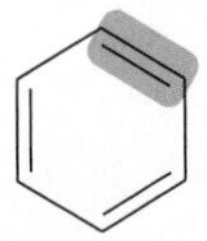 Arene	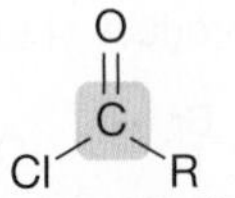 $AlCl_3$	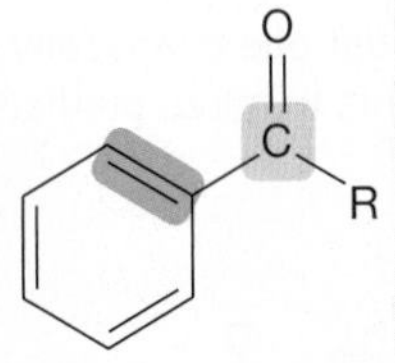 Aromatic ketone	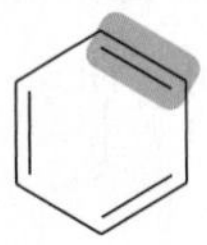	 Acylium ion	Electrophilic aromatic substitution; Friedel–Crafts acylation	24.5
(3)	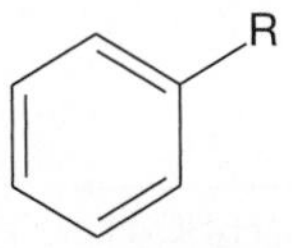 Alkylarene	1. $KMnO_4$, KOH, Δ 2. HCl, H_2O	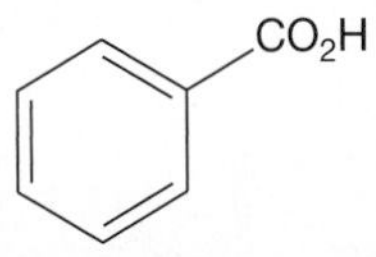 Aromatic carboxylic acid	—	—	Oxidation	24.9a
(4)	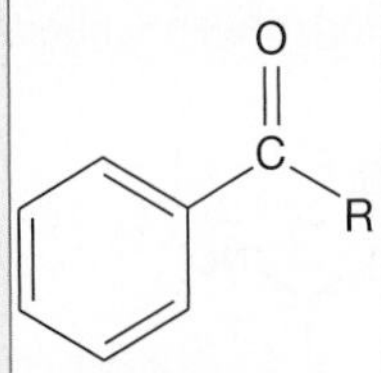 Aromatic ketone/aldeyde	1. $KMnO_4$, KOH, Δ 2. HCl, H_2O	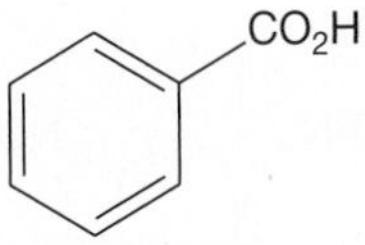 Aromatic carboxylic acid	—	—	Oxidation	24.9a
(5)	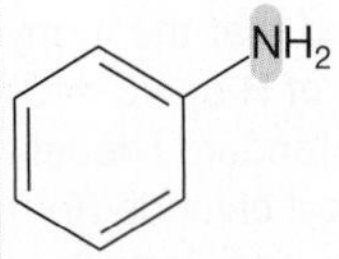 Arylamine	1. $NaNO_2$, H_2SO_4 2. CuCN	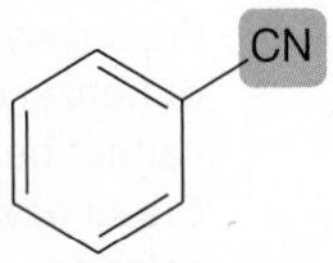 Arylnitrile	CuCN	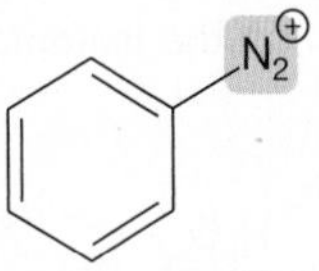	Proceeds through a diazonium ion; Sandmeyer reaction	24.9c

Problems

Problems that are related to synthesis are denoted (SYN).

Sections 24.1–24.5 The General Mechanism, Halogenation, and Friedel–Crafts Reactions

24.1 Which of these isomers of trimethylbenzene will produce exclusively one monobrominated product when treated with Br_2 and $FeBr_3$? Explain.

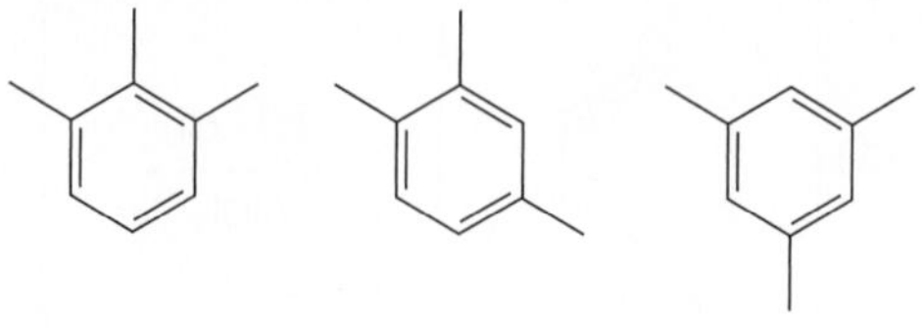

A **B** **C**

24.2 In each of the following reactions, the aromatic ring has just one chemically distinct, aromatic H, so a single electrophilic aromatic substitution will lead to a single product. With this in mind, predict the product of each reaction.

(a)

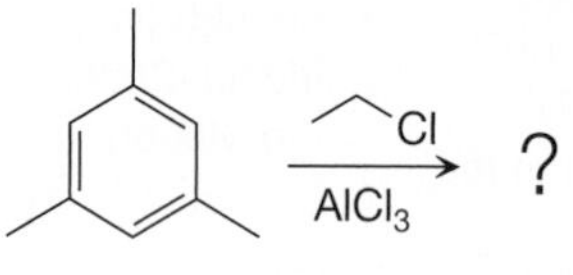

(b)

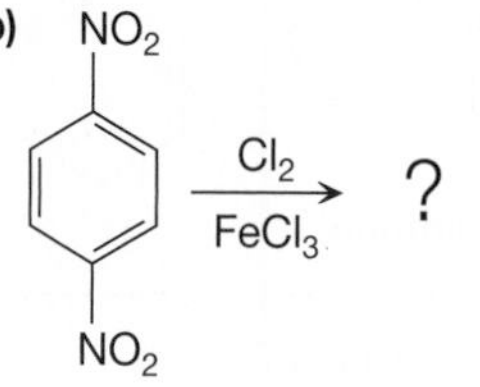

(c)

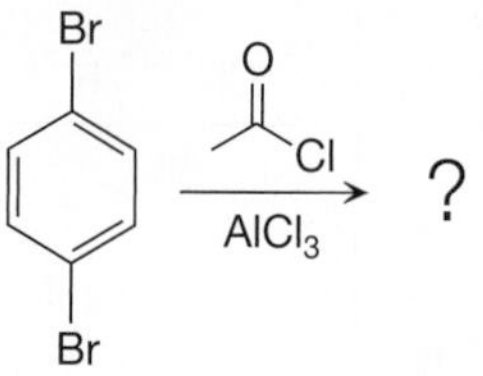

24.3 When a mixture of benzyl alcohol and benzene is treated with *p*-$MeC_6H_4SO_3H$, a strong acid, a compound with the molecular formula $C_{13}H_{12}$ is produced. Draw the mechanism for this reaction and the structure of $C_{13}H_{12}$.

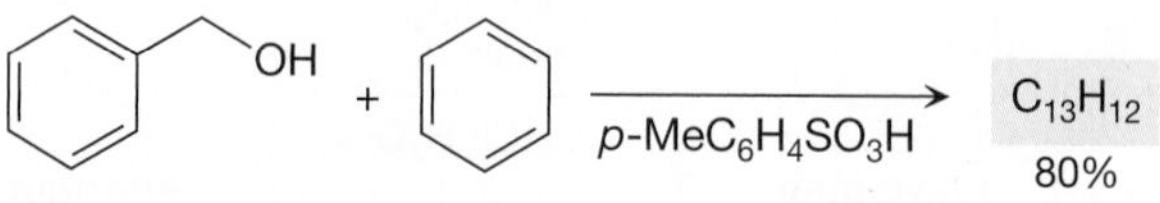

24.4 **(SYN)** In each of the following reactions, the aromatic ring has just one chemically distinct, aromatic H, so a single electrophilic aromatic substitution will lead to a single product. With this in mind, supply the missing reagents needed to carry out each transformation.

(a)

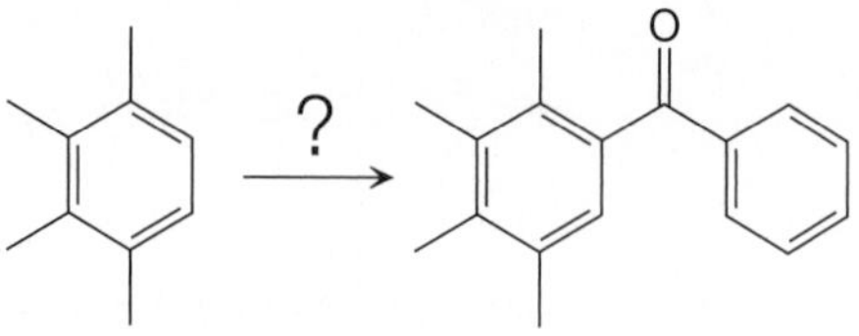

(b)

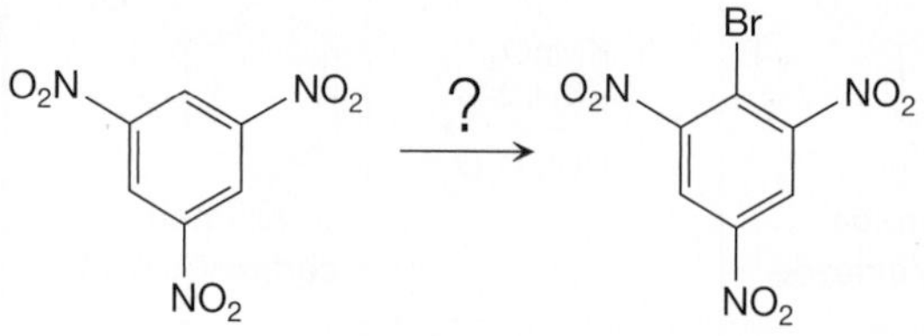

24.5 Propose a mechanism for the isotopic exchange reaction shown here.

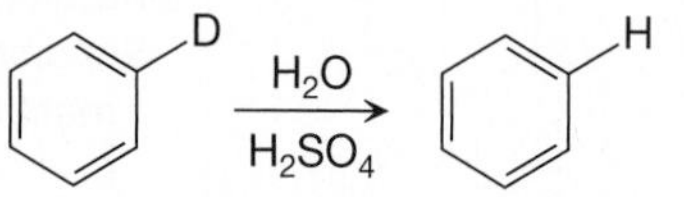

24.6 Halogenation with the mixed halogen ICl can feasibly lead to two different products, as shown here. Draw the complete, detailed mechanism for the formation of each product. Which do you think is the major product? Why?

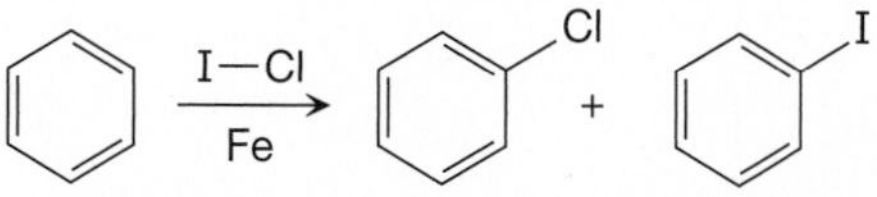

24.7 Draw the complete, detailed mechanism for the reaction shown here. Will the product be optically active? Explain.

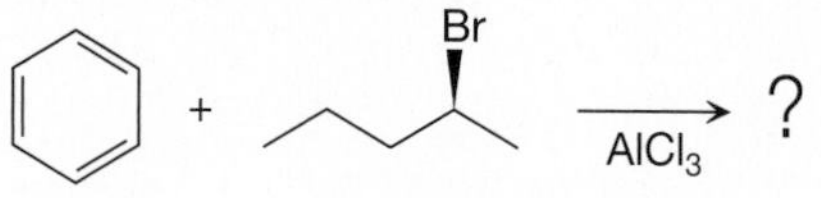

24.8 Previously (p. 1171), we mentioned that the formylation of benzene (i.e., the replacement of H by HC═O) cannot be carried out through a standard Friedel–Crafts acylation because methanoyl chloride (formyl chloride) cannot be added directly. The *Gattermann–Koch synthesis* circumvents this problem by making methanoyl chloride in situ (shown in the box), using a gaseous mixture of carbon monoxide and hydrochloric acid at high pressures. With this in mind, draw the detailed mechanism for the electrophilic aromatic substitution that takes place in the bottom reaction.

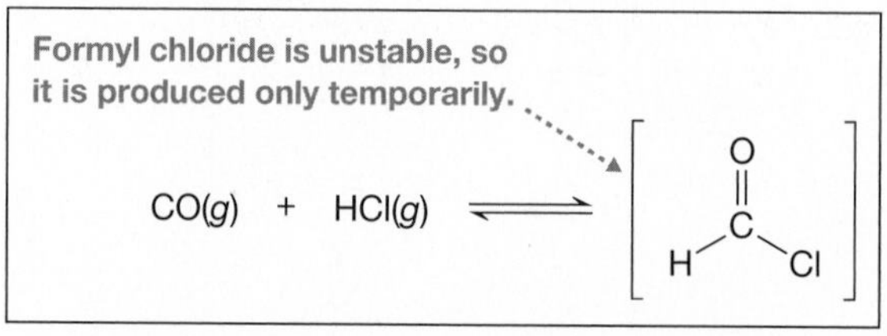
Formyl chloride is unstable, so
it is produced only temporarily.
CO(g) + HCl(g)

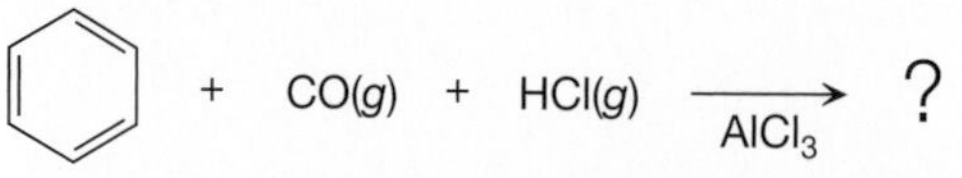

24.9 The reactant in the reaction shown here is aromatic and will undergo electrophilic aromatic substitution in much the same way that benzene does. This reaction leads to a single product only. Explain why. Predict the product of the reaction and draw the complete, detailed mechanism for its formation.

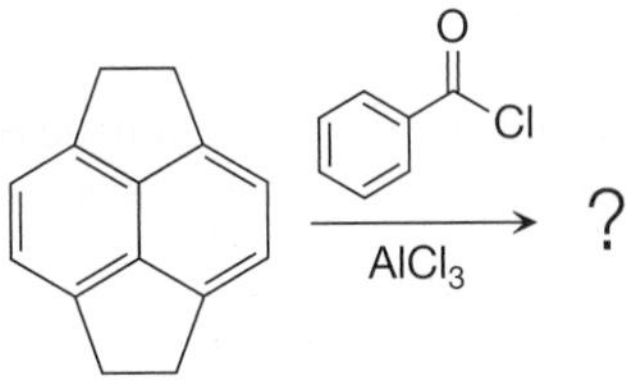

O
Cl
AlCl3
?

24.10 In the acid-catalyzed aromatic alkylation involving 1-methylcyclohexene and benzene, two isomeric products are possible but only one is formed, as shown here. Draw the complete mechanism that would lead to each product, and explain why only one isomer is formed.

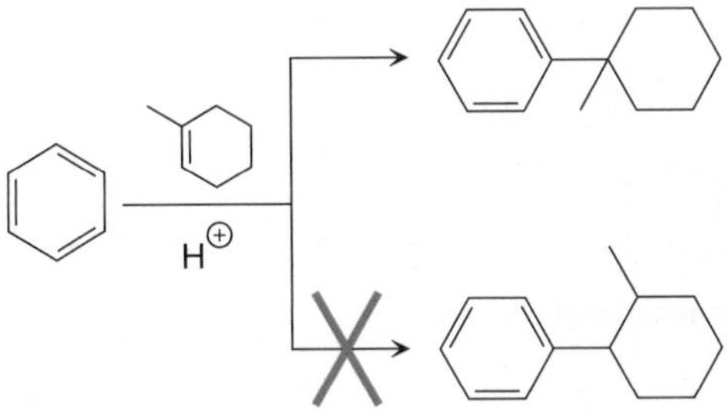

H⊕

24.11 Two isomeric products can be produced from the reaction shown here. **(a)** Draw the complete, detailed mechanism showing the formation of each of those products. **(b)** Which product will be formed in greater abundance?

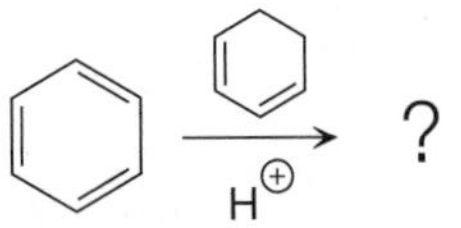

H⊕
?

24.12 As we learned in Chapters 22 and 23, carboxylic acid chlorides behave quite similarly to carboxylic acid anhydrides. Not surprisingly, then, aromatic acylation can be carried out with an acid anhydride in the presence of $AlCl_3$, analogous to the Friedel–Crafts acylation reaction in Equation 24-23 (p. 1170). The example here shows the reaction of benzene with acetic anhydride to produce phenylethanone. Propose a mechanism for this reaction.

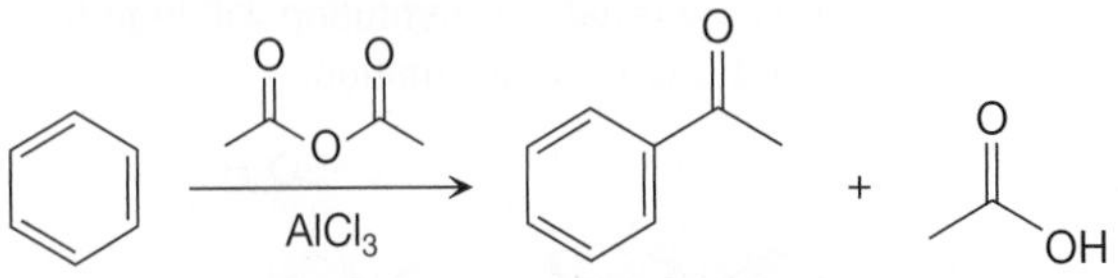

O
O
O
AlCl3
O
+
O
OH

Phenylethanone (Acetophenone)

24.13 The compound shown here can be synthesized from benzene and a carboxylic acid anhydride in a single Friedel–Crafts reaction. What acid anhydride must be used? *Hint*: See Problem 24.12. The two phenyl rings come from two different compounds.

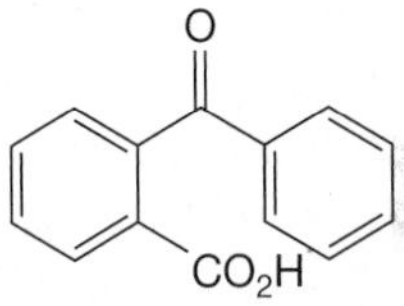

O
CO2H

24.14 When benzene is treated with sulfur dichloride (SCl_2) in the presence of a Friedel–Crafts catalyst like $AlCl_3$, diphenyl sulfide is produced, as shown here. Propose a mechanism for this reaction.

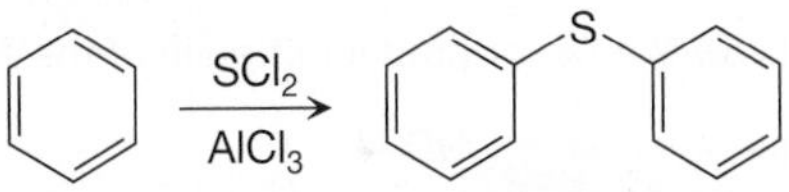

SCl2
AlCl3
S

Diphenyl sulfide

Sections 24.6 and 24.7 Nitration and Sulfonation

24.15 An isomer of tetramethylbenzene undergoes nitration to yield a single product. Based on this information, which isomer(s) of tetramethylbenzene could the starting material have been?

24.16 Compounds **A**, **B**, and **C** are isomers of xylene (dimethylbenzene). When each of these isomers undergoes a single nitration, compound **A** produces just one product, **B** produces a mixture of two products, and **C** produces a mixture of three products. Identify which of compounds **A**, **B**, and **C** is the ortho isomer, which is the meta isomer, and which is the para isomer.

24.17 In each of the following reactions, the aromatic ring has just one chemically distinct, aromatic H, so a single electrophilic aromatic substitution will lead to a single product. With this in mind, predict the product of each reaction.

(a)

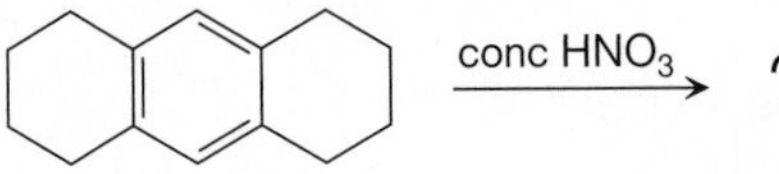

conc HNO3
?

(b)

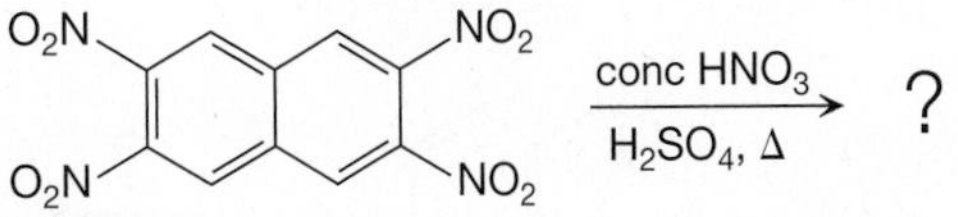

O2N
NO2
O2N
NO2
conc HNO3
H2SO4, Δ
?

24.18 Draw the mechanism and the major product for each of the following reactions.

(a)

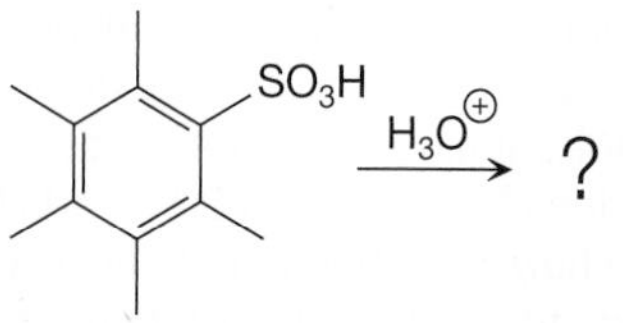
SO3H
H3O⊕
?

(b)

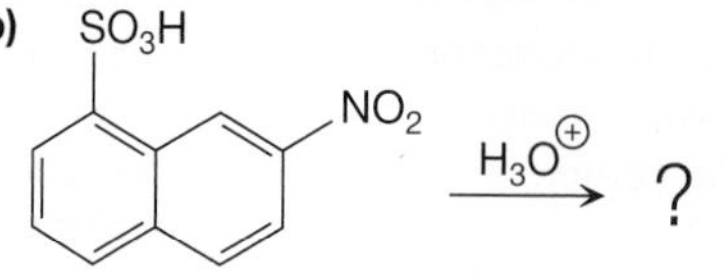
SO3H
NO2
H3O⊕
?

24.19 **(SYN)** In each of the following reactions, the aromatic ring has just one chemically distinct, aromatic H, so a single electrophilic aromatic substitution will lead to a single product. With this in mind, supply the missing reagents needed to carry out each transformation.

(a)

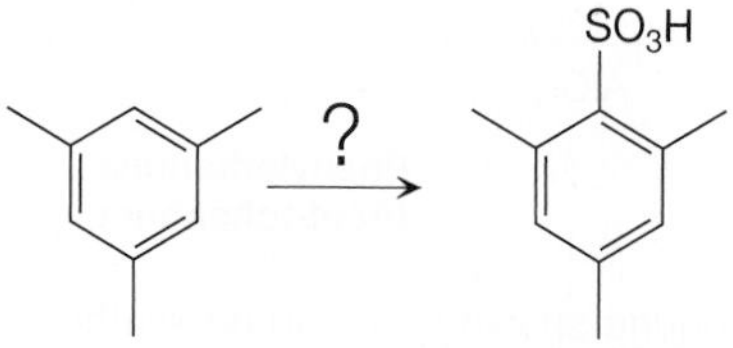
?
SO3H

(b)

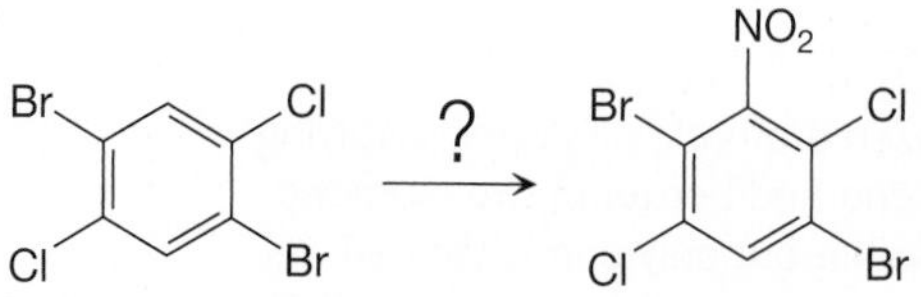
Br
Cl
Cl
Br
?
NO2
Br
Cl
Cl
Br

24.20 The reaction shown here is a halosulfonation, which is a useful variation of the sulfonation reaction. Draw the complete, detailed mechanism for this reaction.

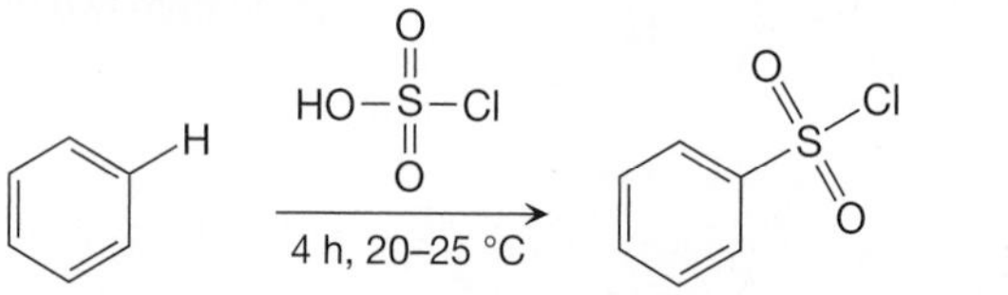
H
HO–S–Cl
4 h, 20–25 °C
Cl

Benzenesulfonyl chloride
77%

Sections 24.8 and 24.9 Avoiding Carbocation Rearrangements; Common Reactions Used Along with Electrophilic Aromatic Substitution

24.21 Draw the major product of each of the following reactions.

(a)

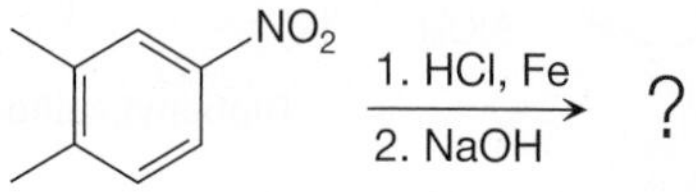
NO2
1. HCl, Fe
2. NaOH
?

(b)

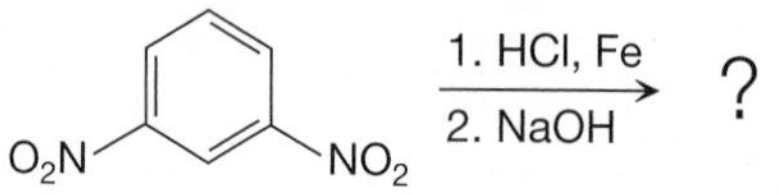
O2N
NO2
1. HCl, Fe
2. NaOH
?

24.22 Draw the major product of each of the following reactions.

(a)

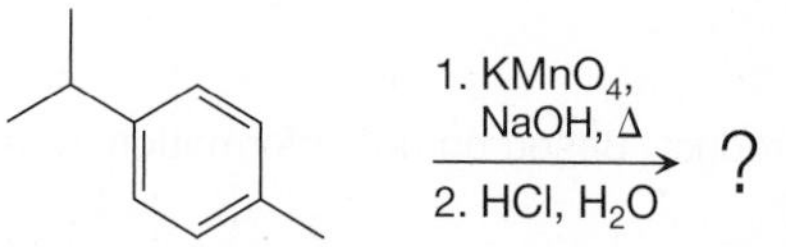
1. KMnO4,
NaOH, Δ
2. HCl, H2O
?

(b)

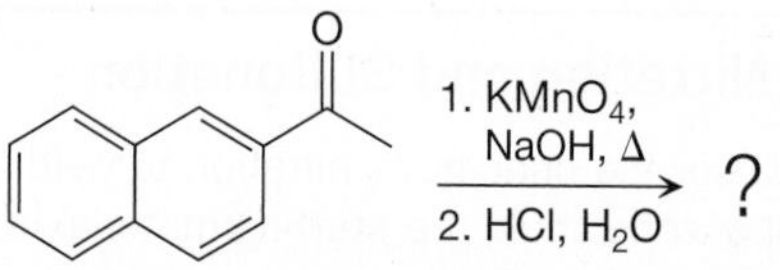
O
1. KMnO4,
NaOH, Δ
2. HCl, H2O
?

24.23 A dialkyl-substituted benzene, $C_{14}H_{22}$, is treated with basic potassium permanganate, followed by acid workup. The same dialkyl-substituted benzene was recovered afterward from the reaction mixture. Draw the structure of the compound.

24.24 **(SYN)** In the reaction shown here, the aromatic ring has just one chemically distinct, aromatic H, so a single electrophilic aromatic substitution will lead to a single product. With this in mind, supply the missing reagents needed to carry out the transformation.

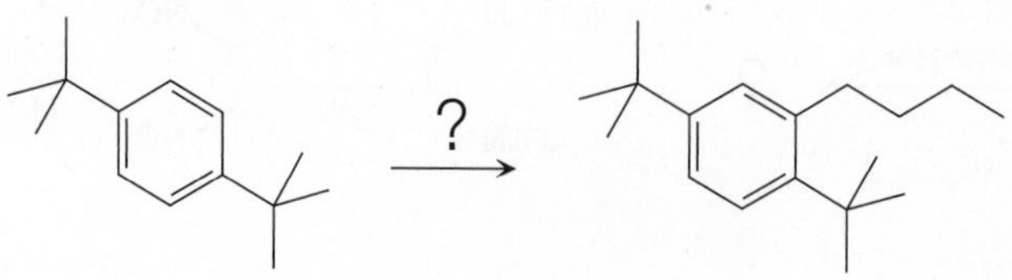
?

24.25 **(SYN)** In each of the following reactions, the aromatic ring has just one chemically distinct, aromatic H, so a single electrophilic aromatic substitution will lead to a single product. With this in mind, show how to carry out each transformation. (Multiple synthetic steps may be necessary for each.)

(a)
Br
Cl
Cl
Br
?
NH2
Br
Cl
Cl
Br
(b)
Br
Cl
Cl
Br
?
CO2H
Br
Cl
Cl
Br

24.26 **(a)** Predict the product of the set of reactions shown here. **(b)** Draw the complete, detailed mechanism for the formation of the synthetic intermediate that is not shown.

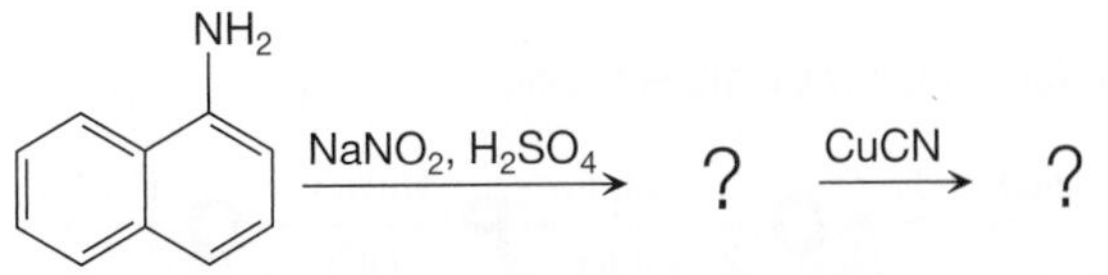

NH2
NaNO2, H2SO4
?
CuCN
?

24.27 Diazonium ions can be produced from primary alkylamines, R—NH_2, when they are treated with $NaNO_2$ under acidic conditions, but the resulting alkyldiazonium ions are generally much too reactive to be useful intermediates in Sandmeyer reactions. Draw the alkyldiazonium ion that would be produced from $(CH_3)_2CHNH_2$. Why do you think it is less stable than the benzenediazonium ion?

Integrated Problems

24.28 No reaction occurs when benzene is treated with Br_2 in CCl_4. When anthracene is treated with Br_2 in CCl_4, however, addition of Br_2 occurs, as shown here. Explain why.

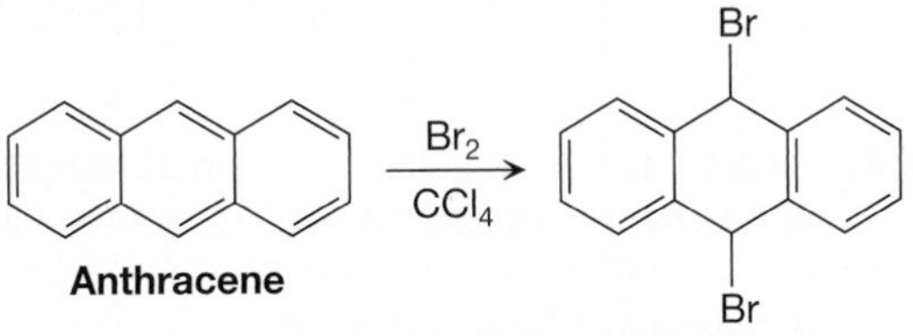

Br2
CCl4
Br
Br
Anthracene

24.29 The reaction shown here is an example of a *deiodination*. Without $AlCl_3$ present, no reaction occurs. Draw a complete, detailed mechanism for this reaction.

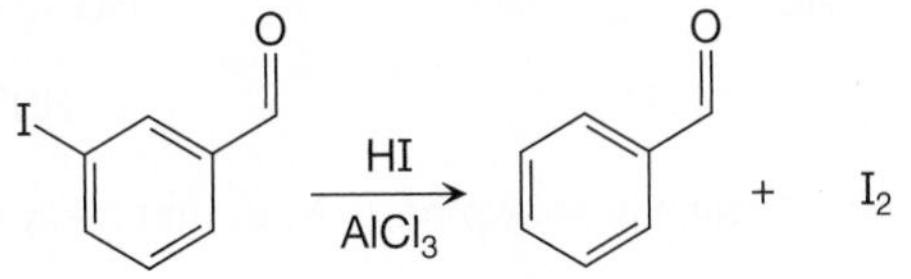

I
O
HI
AlCl3
O
+
I2

24.30 An example of a deiodination reaction is provided in Problem 24.29. Halogens other than iodine may be replaced on a benzene ring, but the reaction rates are slower; rates of substitution are observed to be Ar—F < Ar—Cl < Ar—Br < Ar—I. Explain.

24.31 Propose a mechanism for the reaction shown here. Note that the reaction does *not* take place without the presence of $AlCl_3$.

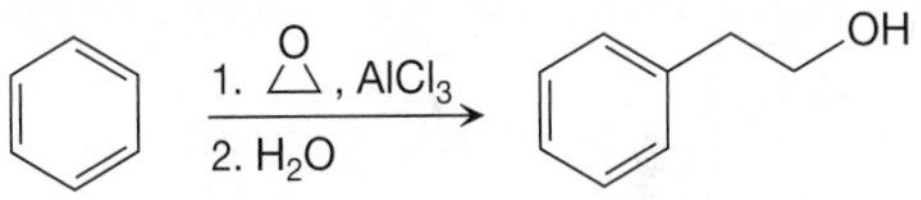

1. O, AlCl3
2. H2O
OH

24.32 Propose a mechanism for the following reaction.

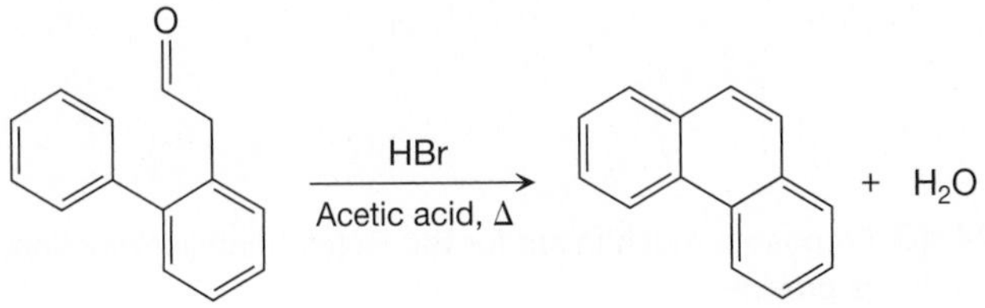

O
HBr
Acetic acid, Δ
+ H2O

24.33 Identify compounds **A–G** in the following synthesis scheme.

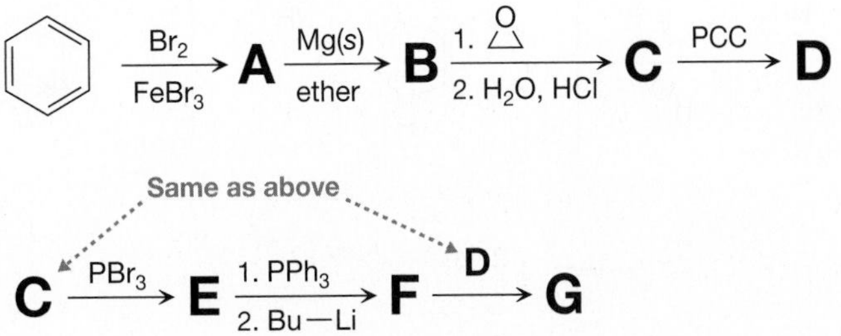

Br2
FeBr3
A
Mg(s)
ether
B
1. O
2. H2O, HCl
C
PCC
D
Same as above
C
PBr3
E
1. PPh3
2. Bu—Li
F
D
G

24.34 Identify compounds **H–N** in the following synthesis scheme.

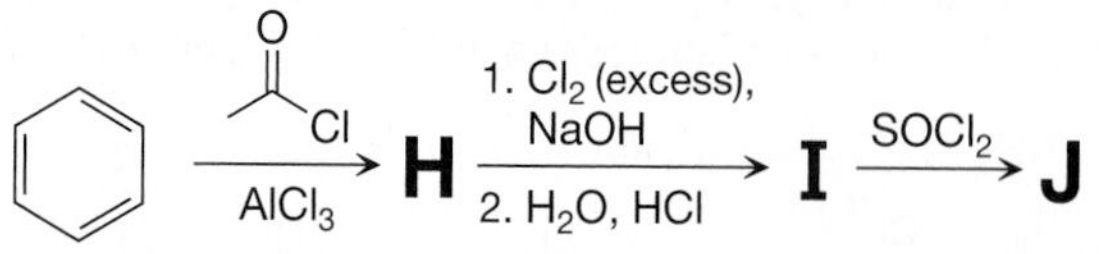

AlCl$_3$
H
1. Cl$_2$ (excess), NaOH
2. H$_2$O, HCl
I
SOCl$_2$
J

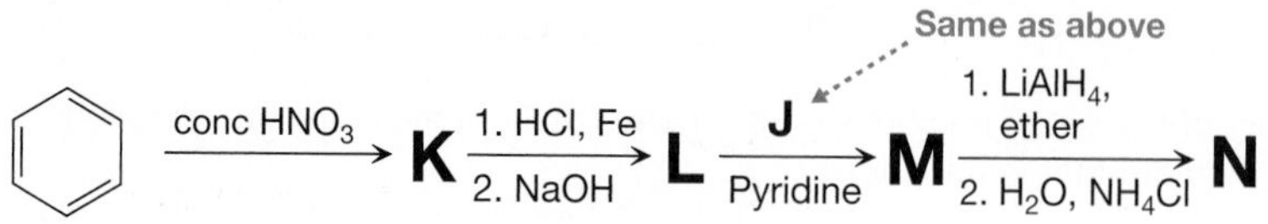

Same as above
conc HNO$_3$
K
1. HCl, Fe
2. NaOH
L
J
Pyridine
M
1. LiAlH$_4$, ether
2. H$_2$O, NH$_4$Cl
N

24.35 Identify compounds **O–W** in the following synthesis scheme.

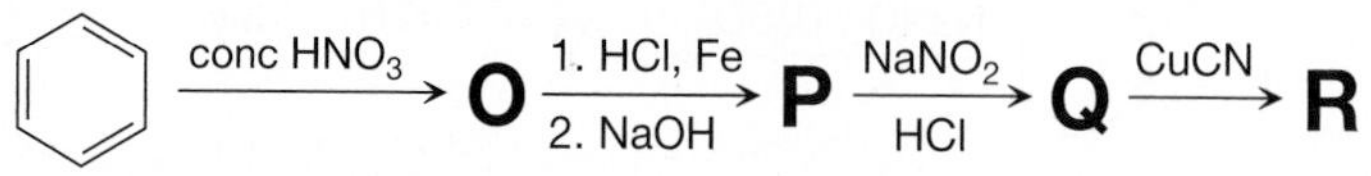

conc HNO$_3$
O
1. HCl, Fe
2. NaOH
P
NaNO$_2$
HCl
Q
CuCN
R

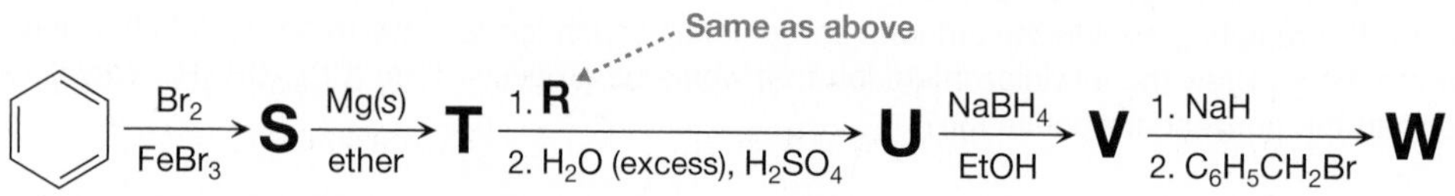

Same as above
Br$_2$
FeBr$_3$
S
Mg(s)
ether
T
1. R
2. H$_2$O (excess), H$_2$SO$_4$
U
NaBH$_4$
EtOH
V
1. NaH
2. C$_6$H$_5$CH$_2$Br
W

24.36 Predict the product of the following reaction.

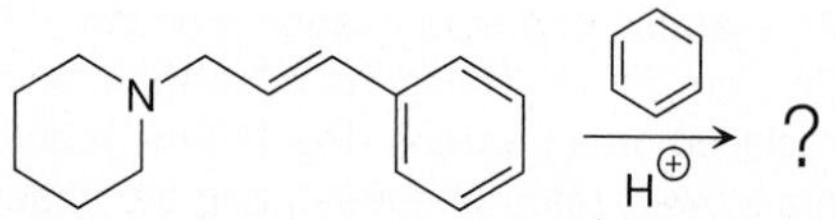

24.37 Draw the complete, detailed mechanism for the following reaction.

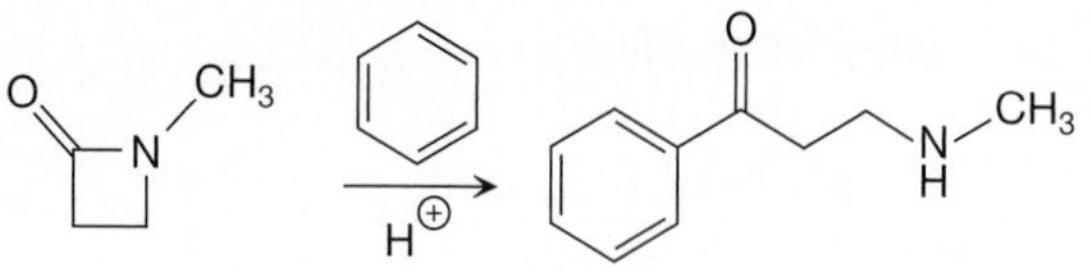

24.38 Benzene can be *hydroxylated* by treating it with hydrogen peroxide and a strong acid such as trifluoromethanesulfonic acid (TfOH). Propose a mechanism for this reaction.

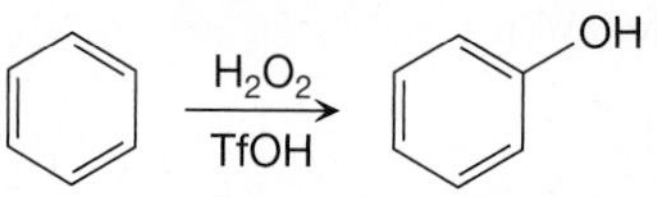

H$_2$O$_2$
TfOH
OH

24.39 An aromatic imine is formed when 3,5-dihydroxyphenol is treated with ethanenitrile (CH_3CN) in HCl in the presence of a $ZnCl_2$ catalyst, as shown here. Propose a mechanism for this reaction.

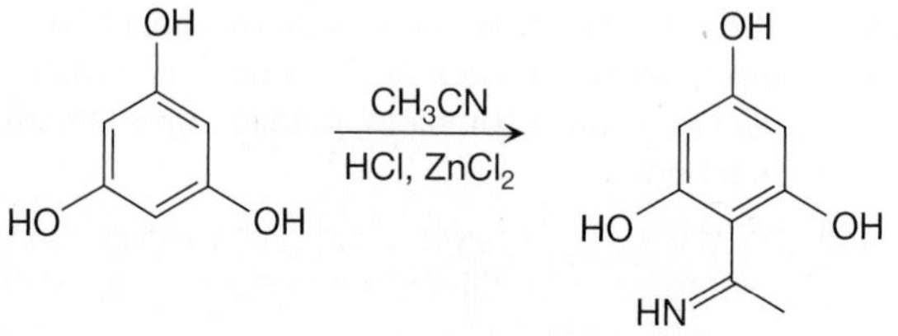

CH$_3$CN
HCl, ZnCl$_2$

24.40 Propose a mechanism for the *Pictet–Spengler reaction*, an example of which is shown here. Note that a key intermediate is provided.

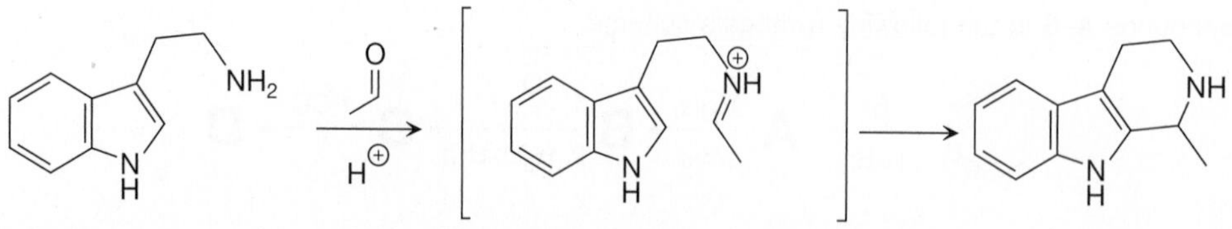

24.41 (SYN) Show how to carry out this synthesis, using benzene and any alcohol as your only sources of carbon.

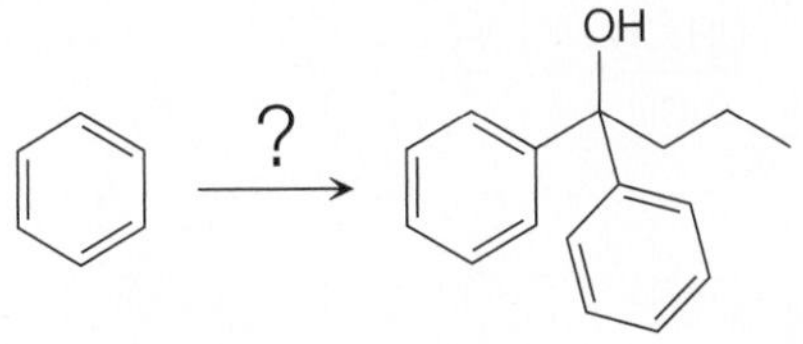

24.42 (SYN) Dibenzyl ether is used as a flavor and fragrance agent. Show how to synthesize dibenzyl ether, using benzene and any ketone or aldehyde as your only sources of carbon.

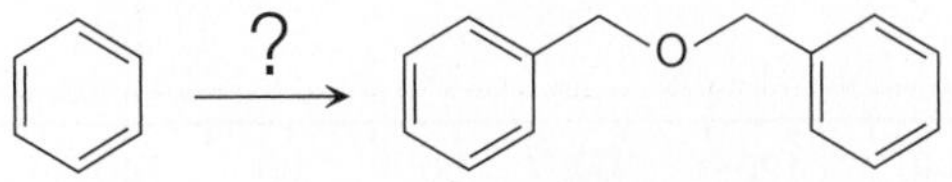

Dibenzyl ether

24.43 (SYN) Stilbene is used in the manufacture of dyes and also has estrogenic activity. Show how to synthesize stilbene, using benzene and any carboxylic acid as your only sources of carbon.

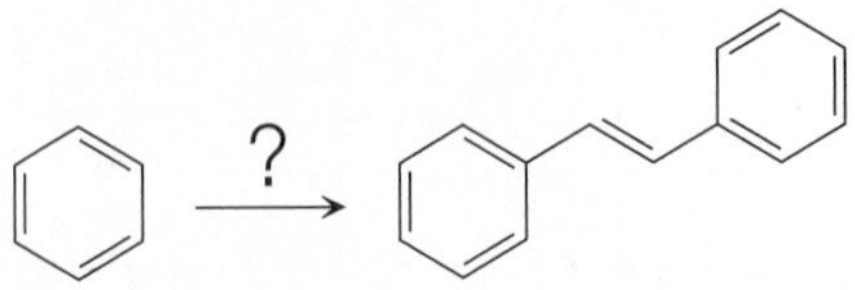

Stilbene

24.44 When diphenyl ether is reacted under the same conditions as in Problem 24.14 (SCl_2 and $AlCl_3$), a compound is produced whose ^{13}C NMR spectrum shows six signals. Draw that product.

24.45 When the following acid chloride is treated with $AlCl_3$, followed by HCl and Zn(Hg), a product is formed whose ^{1}H NMR and IR spectra are shown here. Draw the product and propose a complete, detailed mechanism for the first of these two reactions.

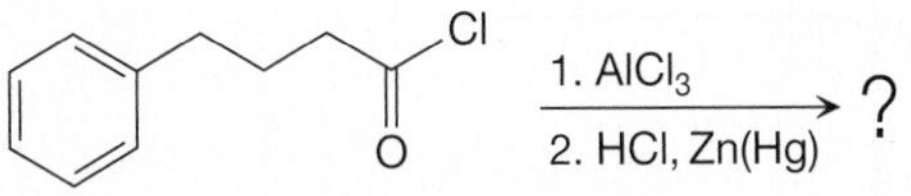

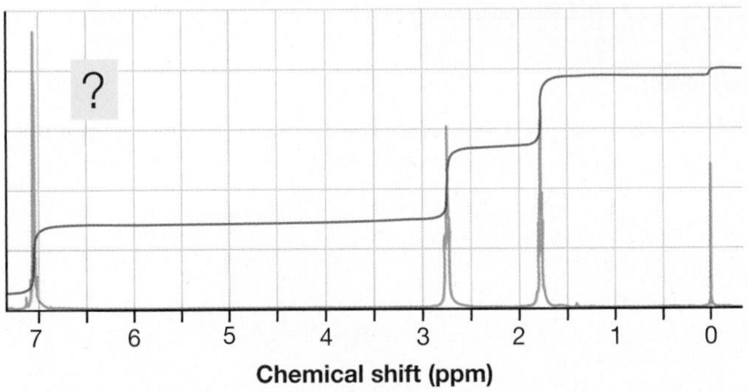
?
7
6
5
4
3
2
1
0
Chemical shift (ppm)

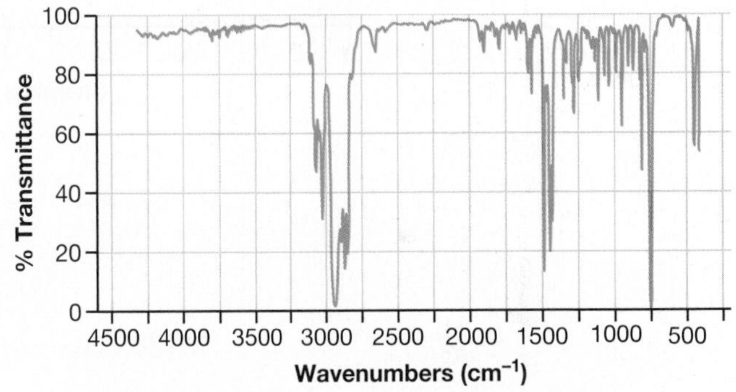
100
80
60
40
20
0
% Transmittance
4500
4000
3500
3000
2500
2000
1500
1000
500
Wavenumbers (cm^{-1})

24.46 The product of the set of reactions shown here exhibits eight signals in its ^{13}C NMR spectrum. Draw a complete, detailed mechanism for the formation of that product.

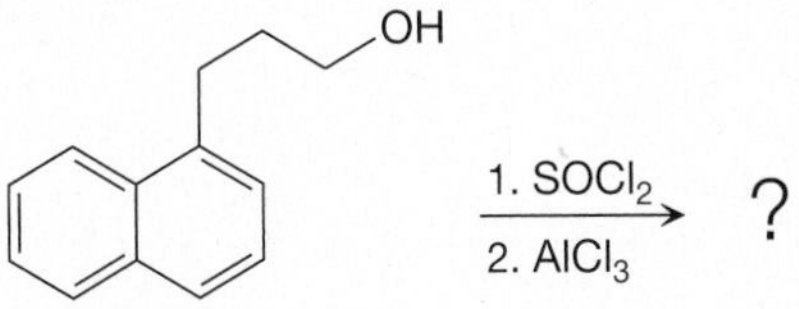

24.47 When benzene is treated with dichloromethane in the presence of aluminum trichloride, as shown here, a product is formed whose IR, ^{13}C NMR, and ^{1}H NMR spectra are shown below. Draw the product and propose a mechanism for this reaction.

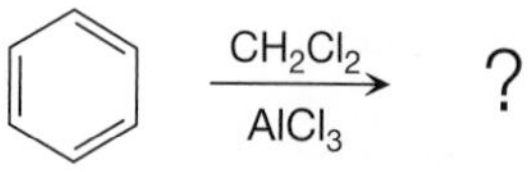
CH2Cl2
AlCl3
?

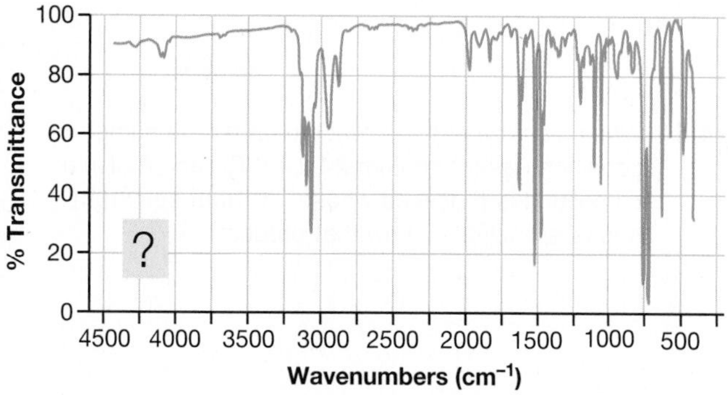
100
80
60
40
20
0
% Transmittance
?
4500
4000
3500
3000
2500
2000
1500
1000
500
Wavenumbers (cm−1)

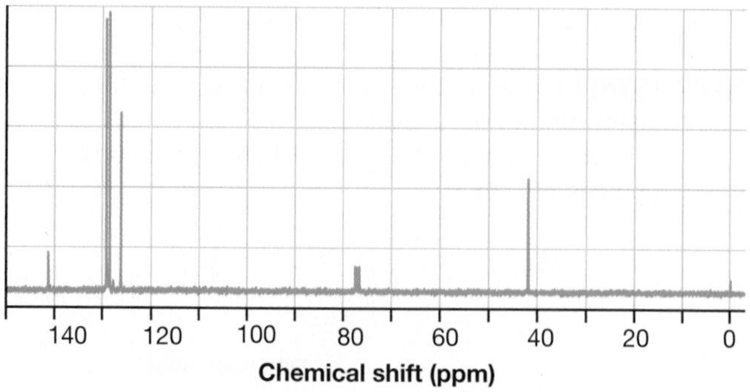
140
120
100
80
60
40
20
0
Chemical shift (ppm)

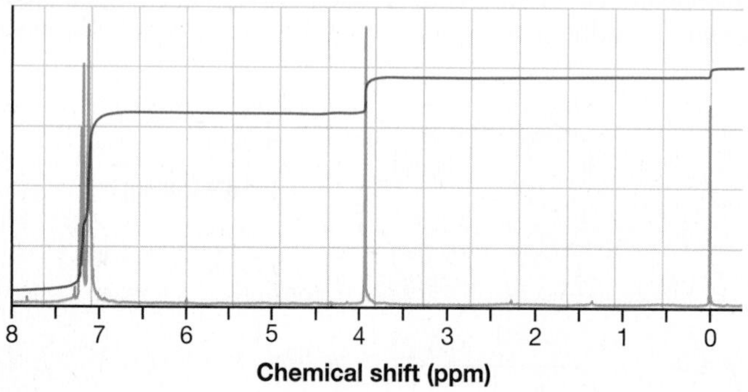
8
7
6
5
4
3
2
1
0
Chemical shift (ppm)

25

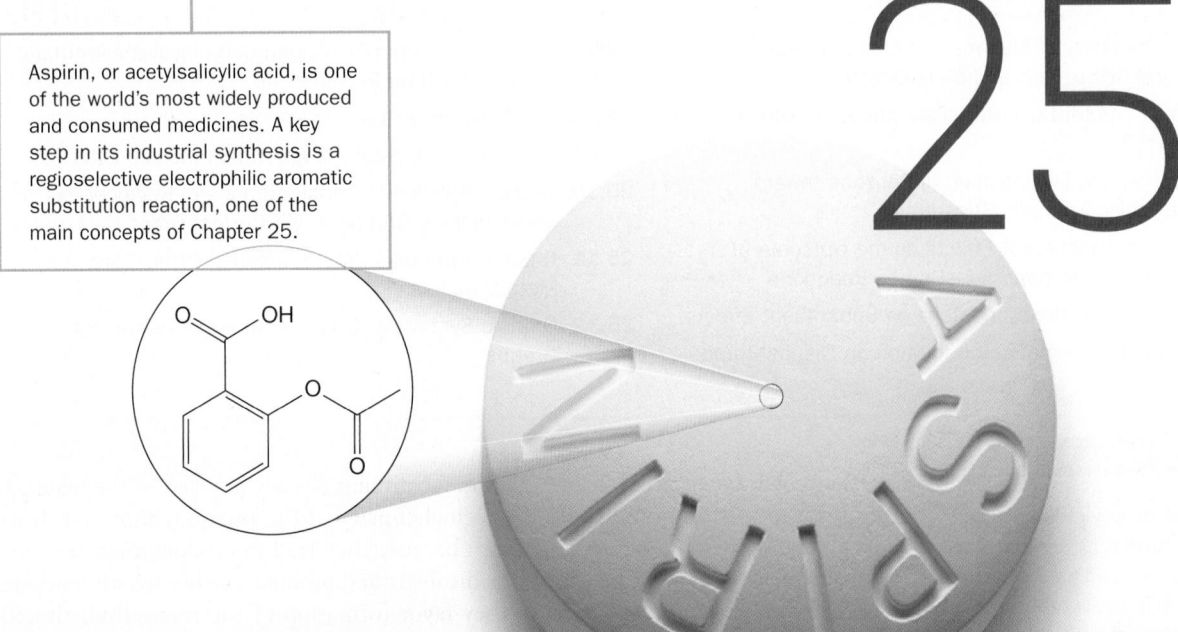

Aspirin, or acetylsalicylic acid, is one of the world's most widely produced and consumed medicines. A key step in its industrial synthesis is a regioselective electrophilic aromatic substitution reaction, one of the main concepts of Chapter 25.

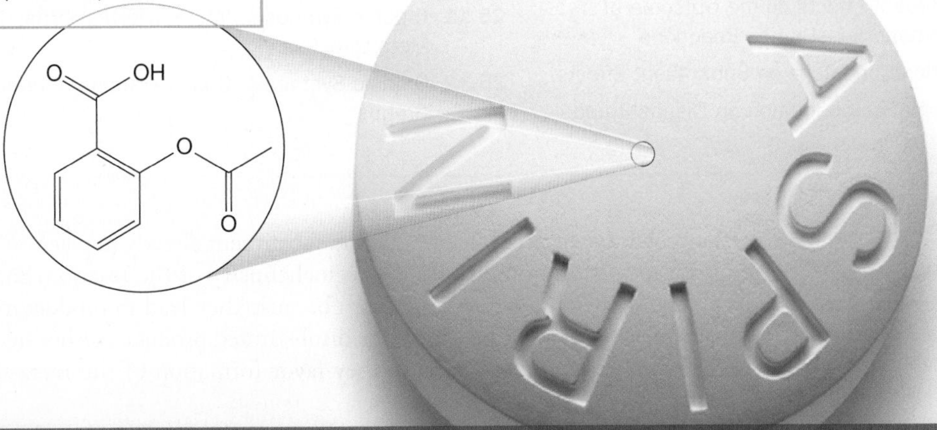
O
OH
O
O
ASPIRIN

Aromatic Substitution 2

Reactions of Substituted Benzenes and Other Rings

In Chapter 24, we examined a variety of *electrophilic aromatic substitution* reactions, focusing primarily on substitution involving benzene (C_6H_6), which has no substituents. Electrophilic aromatic substitution on a **monosubstituted benzene** (C_6H_5—Sub), however, involves additional issues.

One of those issues is *regiochemistry*. In benzene itself, all six hydrogen atoms are equivalent, so substitution of any one of them leads to precisely the same product. A monosubstituted benzene, however, has three chemically distinct hydrogens: the ortho, meta, and para hydrogens. Substitution, therefore, can lead to three different possible products—the ortho-, meta-, and para-disubstituted benzenes (Eq. 25-1)—depending on which hydrogen is replaced. (*Notice in the equation the convention that is used to denote a generic disubstituted benzene without designating the specific isomer.*)

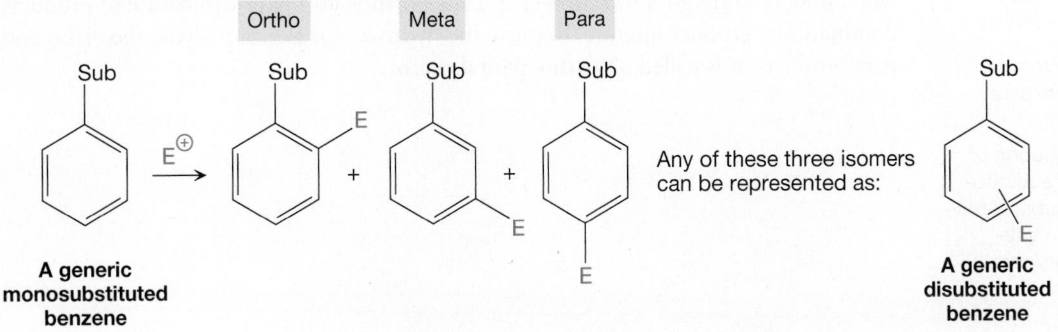
Ortho
Meta
Para
Sub
Sub
Sub
Sub
Sub
$E^{\oplus}$
E
E
E
E
+
+
Any of these three isomers can be represented as:
A generic monosubstituted benzene
A generic disubstituted benzene

(25-1)

Chapter Outline

CONNECTIONS 25.1

Increasing crop yields and reducing fevers Nitrophenols (Eq. 25-2) are used as the starting material in the synthesis of a wide variety of pesticides and herbicides. *p*-Nitrophenol is an intermediate in the synthesis of acetaminophen (also known as paracetamol), a medicine marketed under the trade name Tylenol, which is used to treat fever and pain.

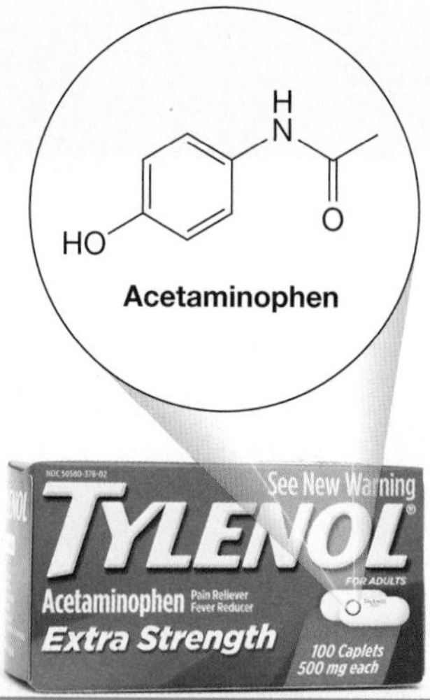
HO
H
N
O
Acetaminophen
See New Warning
TYLENOL
Acetaminophen
Extra Strength
100 Caplets
500 mg each

As we will see here in Chapter 25, the substituent already in place on the benzene ring prior to substitution dictates the regiochemistry of the reaction. Some substituents are designated as *ortho/para directors* because they lead to product mixtures consisting primarily of the ortho- and para-disubstituted products. Other substituents are designated as *meta directors* because they favor formation of the meta-disubstituted product.

A second issue with monosubstituted benzenes is the effect the substituent has on the *rate* of electrophilic aromatic substitution. Some substituents slow the reaction and therefore are called *deactivating groups*, whereas other substituents, called *activating groups*, cause the reaction to speed up.

The substituents attached to an aromatic ring can even alter the reaction mechanism involving the ring, making the ring susceptible to reaction with nucleophiles rather than electrophiles. Here in Chapter 25, we study two such *nucleophilic aromatic substitution reactions.*

Finally, we consider how the characteristics of the substituents on an aromatic ring factor into organic synthesis. Ultimately, you should be able to design efficient syntheses of targets with multiple substituents attached to an aromatic ring.

25.1 Regiochemistry of Electrophilic Aromatic Substitution: Defining Ortho/Para and Meta Directors

SECTION 25.1 OBJECTIVES

You will be able to:

1. Explain what it means for a substituent to be an ortho/para director or a meta director.
2. Use the product distribution of an electrophilic aromatic substitution reaction on a monosubstituted benzene to characterize a substituent as either an ortho/para director or a meta director.

Phenol (C_6H_5—OH) has two H atoms that are ortho to the hydroxy (OH) group, two H atoms that are meta, and one H atom that is para. If each of those H atoms were equally likely to be replaced in an electrophilic aromatic substitution reaction, then the ortho-disubstituted product would make up 40% of the products (2 out of 5), another 40% would be meta (2 out of 5), and 20% would be para (1 out of 5). However, when phenol undergoes nitration (Eq. 25-2), ortho- and para-disubstituted products dominate the product mixture. Because the hydroxy (OH) group favors the ortho and para products, it is called an **ortho/para director**.

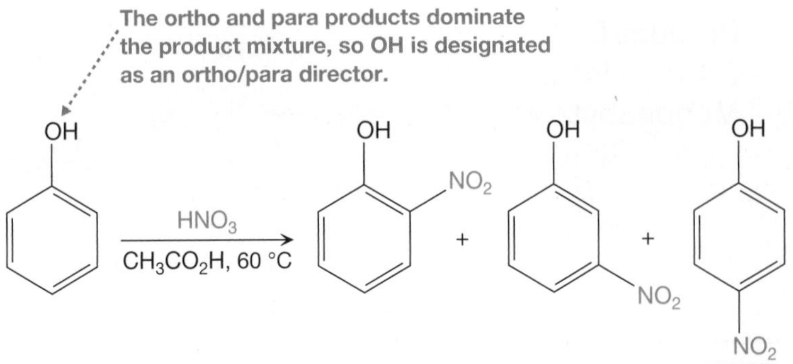
The ortho and para products dominate the product mixture, so OH is designated as an ortho/para director.
OH
HNO$_3$
CH$_3$CO$_2$H, 60 °C
NO$_2$

(25-2)

Phenol Distribution of products: **Ortho** 50% **Meta** ~0% **Para** 50%

When nitrobenzene undergoes nitration, on the other hand, *m*-dinitrobenzene is the major product (Eq. 25-3). Because the NO_2 group initially attached to the ring favors the production of the meta product, it is called a **meta director**.

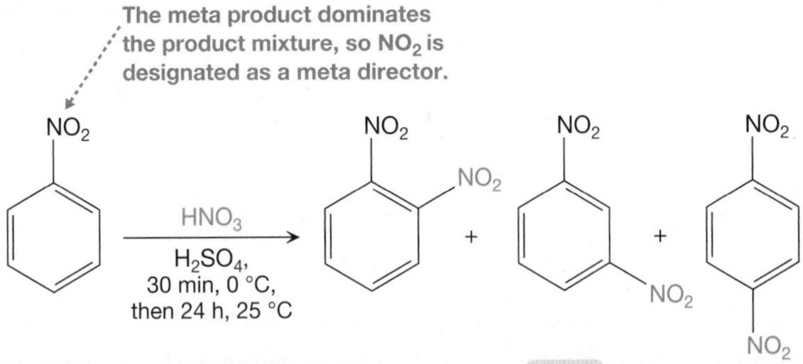
The meta product dominates the product mixture, so NO$_2$ is designated as a meta director.
NO$_2$
HNO$_3$
H$_2$SO$_4$,
30 min, 0 °C,
then 24 h, 25 °C

(25-3)

Nitrobenzene Distribution of products: **Ortho** 7% **Meta** 91% **Para** 2%

The results from these and other nitration reactions are summarized in Table 25-1. The OH group and other ortho/para-directing substituents appear on the left side of the table; the NO_2 group and other meta-directing substituents appear on the right. To help illustrate which type of director each substituent is, the sum of the percentages of ortho and para products ($o + p$) is also listed in the table.

In the next section, we will examine why these substituents have the effects on regiochemistry that they do.

CONNECTIONS 25.2

Not too hot to handle

Dinitrobenzenes (Eq. 25-3) are converted by hydrogenation to their corresponding phenylenediamines ($H_2N—C_6H_4—NH_2$), which are starting materials for aramid fibers. Aramid fibers have high melting points and are quite strong, which is why they are used to manufacture heat- and flame-resistant products such as these gloves.

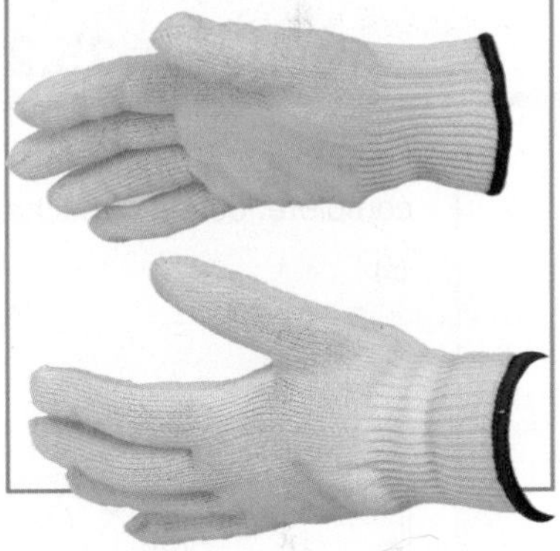

YOUR TURN 25.1

The iodo (I) and formyl (CHO) groups are not listed in Table 25-1. The relative amounts of ortho and meta nitration products obtained for each substituent are shown here.

Substituent	*o*	*m*	*p*	*o* + *p*	Type of Director
—I	45	1			
—CHO	19	72			

(a) Supply the missing information pertaining to the relative amounts of the para isomers that are produced, as well as the sum of the ortho and para products.

(b) On the basis of that information, determine whether each substituent is an ortho/para director or a meta director.

Answers to Your Turns are in the back of the book.

TABLE 25-1 Product Distribution for the Nitration of Various Monosubstituted Benzenes

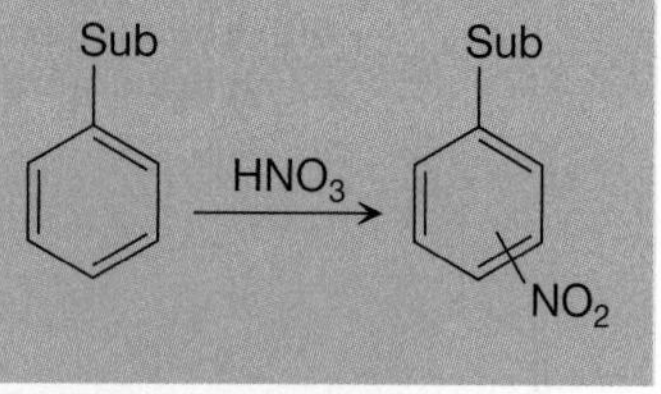

Sub
HNO3
Sub
NO2

ORTHO/PARA-DIRECTING					META-DIRECTING				
Substituent	*o*	*m*	*p*	*o* + *p*	Substituent	*o*	*m*	*p*	*o* + *p*
—OH	**50**	0	**50**	100	$—NO_2$	7	**91**	2	9
$—NHCOCH_3$	**19**	2	**79**	98	$—\overset{\oplus}{N}(CH_3)_3$	2	**87**	11	13
$—CH_3$	**63**	3	**34**	97	$—CO_2H$	22	**76**	2	24
—F	**13**	1	**86**	99	—CN	17	**81**	2	19
—Cl	**35**	1	**64**	99	$—CO_2Et$	28	**66**	6	34
—Br	**43**	1	**56**	99	$—COCH_3$	26	**72**	2	28

YOUR TURN 25.2

From the information in Table 25-1, predict the major product(s) for each of the following reactions. Draw the complete, detailed mechanism that leads to the formation of each major product.

(a)

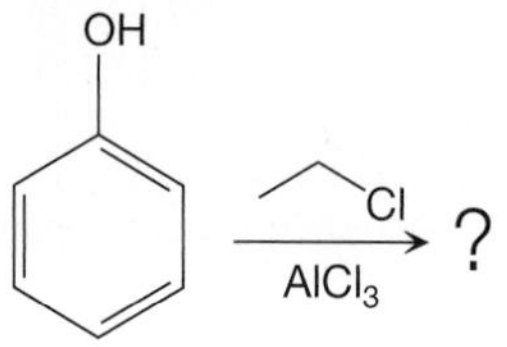

OH
Cl
AlCl3
?

(b)

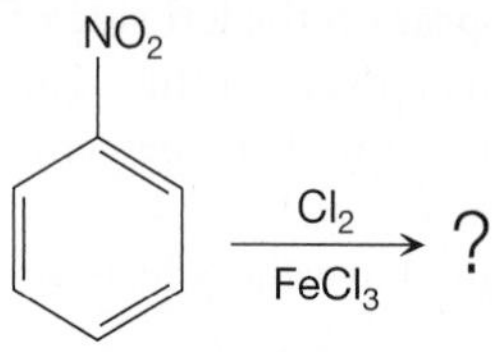

NO2
Cl2
FeCl3
?

(c)

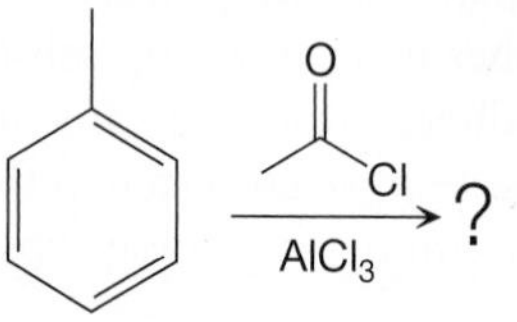

O
Cl
AlCl3
?

(d)

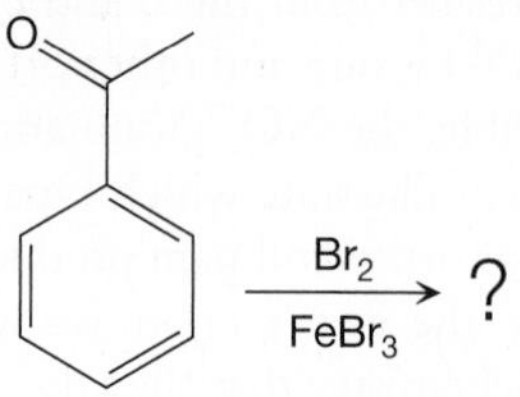

O
Br2
FeBr3
?

SECTION 25.2 OBJECTIVES

You will be able to:

1. Use the structure of a substituent to characterize the substituent as an ortho/para director or a meta director.
2. Explain the role that resonance and inductive effects have in governing whether a substituent is an ortho/para director or a meta director.

25.2 What Characterizes Ortho/Para and Meta Directors, and Why?

Look back at Table 25-1 and note the following structural features for ortho/para and meta directors:

1. Substituents attached by an atom with at least one lone pair of electrons are ortho/para directors.
2. Substituents attached by an atom with no lone pairs of electrons are:
   a. Ortho/para directors if they are alkyl groups.
   b. Meta directors if the atom at the point of attachment is electronegative or if it is bonded to highly electronegative atoms.

YOUR TURN 25.3

The OCH_3 and CH_2CH_3 groups do not appear in Table 25-1. Identify which of the above structural features each substituent has (i.e., Feature 1, 2a, or 2b), and on that basis, determine whether the substituent is an ortho/para director or a meta director.

Why should these characteristics dictate the type of director? To begin to answer this question, recall from Section 24.1 that electrophilic aromatic substitution reactions usually run under *kinetic control.* Therefore:

The relative amounts of ortho-, meta-, and para-disubstituted products produced in an electrophilic aromatic substitution reaction are proportional to the *rates* at which they are produced.

Recall, too, that the first step in an electrophilic aromatic substitution reaction, the formation of the arenium ion intermediate, is highly endothermic and is rate-determining. Thus, as the arenium ion intermediate becomes more stable, the reaction rate increases (see Recall box). This idea leads to a very useful generalization:

The major product of electrophilic aromatic substitution is the one produced from the most stable arenium ion intermediate.

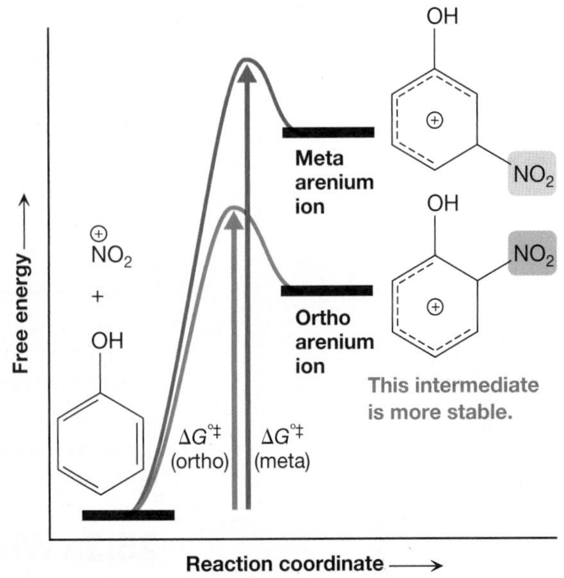

Free energy
Reaction coordinate
$\overset{\oplus}{NO_2}$
+
OH
Meta arenium ion
Ortho arenium ion
OH
NO_2
This intermediate is more stable.
$\Delta G^{\circ\ddagger}$ (ortho)
$\Delta G^{\circ\ddagger}$ (meta)

FIGURE 25-1 Energy diagrams for the rate-determining step in nitration of phenol Nitration at the ortho position is represented by the red curve, and nitration at the meta position is represented by the blue curve. Because the ortho product is produced in greater abundance than the meta product (Table 25-1), we can say that the $\Delta G^{\circ\ddagger}$ leading to the ortho intermediate is smaller.

In the nitration of phenol (C_6H_5—OH), for example, the distribution of products is 50% ortho, ~0% meta, and 50% para. Because much more ortho isomer than meta isomer is produced, we know that the ortho arenium ion intermediate is lower in energy (more stable) than the meta intermediate, as shown in **Figure 25-1**. What can we say about the relative energies of the meta and para intermediates? (See Your Turn 25.4.)

YOUR TURN 25.4

In the nitration of phenol (C_6H_5—OH), which arenium ion intermediate is formed faster: meta or para? Which one is lower in energy?

The conclusions we have just drawn about the OH group, which is an ortho/para director, can be generalized to other ortho/para directors as well:

When an ortho/para director is attached to benzene, the ortho and para arenium ion intermediates are lower in energy (more stable) and are formed faster than the meta intermediate.

The opposite is true for meta directors, which lead predominantly to the meta-disubstituted product:

When a meta director is attached to benzene, the meta arenium ion intermediate is lower in energy (more stable) and is formed faster than the ortho or para intermediate.

◂ RECALL

According to the Hammond postulate (Section 9.3a), the transition state for an endothermic step resembles products more than reactants. Thus, factors that stabilize the products tend to stabilize the transition state and lower the energy barrier.

YOUR TURN 25.5

Consider these arenium ion intermediates that are formed in the nitration of fluorobenzene. Using Table 25-1 (p. 1200), determine which one is formed the fastest. Which is formed the slowest? Which is the most stable? Which is the least stable? Repeat this problem for the nitration of benzonitrile, in which F has been replaced by CN in each arenium ion intermediate.

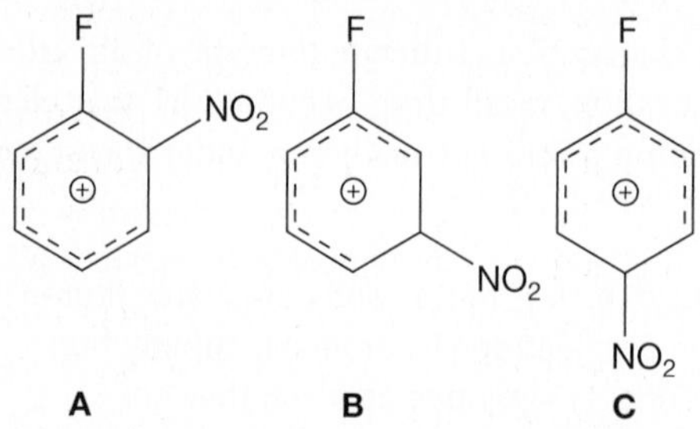

F
NO2
A
B
C

To this point, we have learned how to identify ortho/para and meta directors *empirically* and how to use that information to determine the relative energies of the ortho, meta, and para arenium ion intermediates. However, we have yet to explain *why* ortho/para and meta directors influence the stability of the arenium ion intermediates in the ways that they do, which is the focus of the following sections.

25.2a Why Are Ortho and Para Arenium Ion Intermediates Lower in Energy When an Ortho/Para Director Is Attached?

We have encountered two kinds of ortho/para directors: (1) groups attached by an atom having at least one lone pair of electrons and (2) alkyl groups. When either of these groups is attached to benzene, we know that the ortho and para arenium ion intermediates are lower in energy than the meta intermediate. To see why this is true for the first type of ortho/para director, let's carefully examine the ortho and meta intermediates that are produced in the nitration of phenol, C_6H_5—OH:

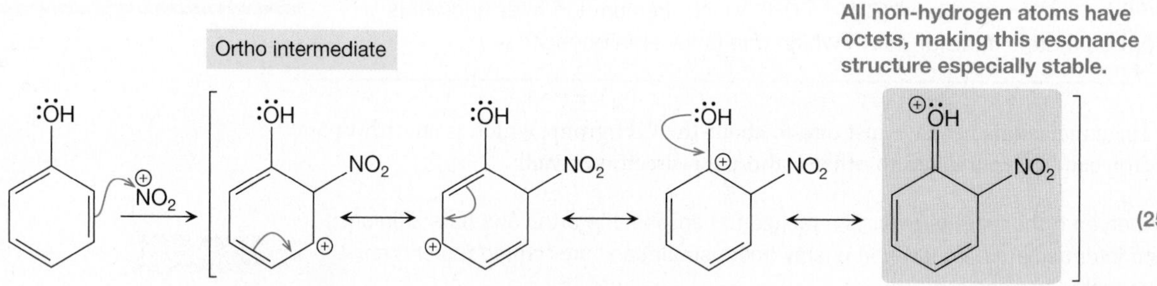

Ortho intermediate
All non-hydrogen atoms have octets, making this resonance structure especially stable.
:ÖH
NO2

(25-4)

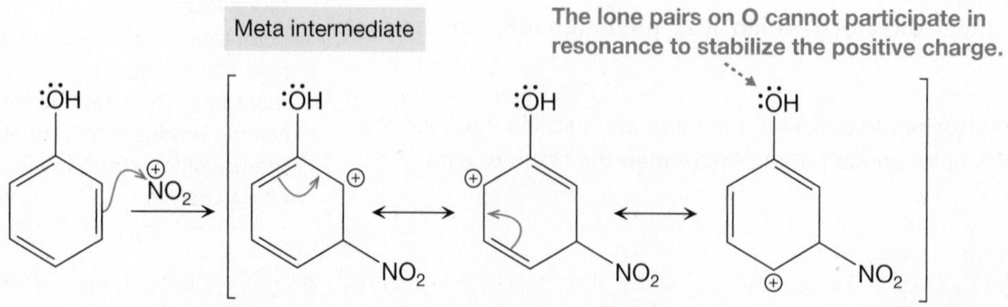

Meta intermediate
The lone pairs on O cannot participate in resonance to stabilize the positive charge.
:ÖH
NO2

(25-5)

When nitration occurs at the ortho position (Eq. 25-4), the arenium ion that is produced has four resonance structures, allowing the positive charge to be delocalized over four separate atoms. By contrast, when nitration occurs at the meta position (Eq. 25-5), the arenium ion intermediate has just three total resonance structures. The ortho arenium ion intermediate, with its additional resonance structure, is therefore lower in energy (more stable) than the meta intermediate.

The additional resonance structure for the ortho intermediate (highlighted in Eq. 25-4) is due to the involvement of the lone pair of electrons from the OH group. The involvement of that lone pair is not possible for the meta intermediate (Eq. 25-5) because the meta intermediate has no resonance structure in which C^+ is directly attached to OH.

All non-hydrogen atoms have an octet in the highlighted resonance structure in Equation 25-4, which is not true of the other three resonance structures. The additional stability provided by that single resonance structure is extremely important.

Similar reasoning allows us to rationalize why the para arenium intermediate in the nitration of phenol is lower in energy than the meta intermediate (see Solved Problem 25.1). The para intermediate has four resonance structures, including one in which all non-hydrogen atoms have an octet.

SOLVED PROBLEM **25.1**

How to determine relative stabilities of arenium ions with an o/p director

Break It Down Draw a diagram similar to Figure 25-1 that illustrates the formation of the para and meta intermediates during the nitration of phenol. Which of those two arenium ions is more stable, and why?

Think	Solve
Which isomeric product, meta or para, is formed faster? What does that say about the stabilities of the respective intermediates?	According to Table 25-1 (p. 1200), the para arenium ion is formed faster than the meta, so the para intermediate must be more stable. This gives rise to the energy diagram shown here:
How many resonance structures does each intermediate have? Are any of them particularly stable?	Whereas the meta intermediate has only three resonance structures (Eq. 25-5), the para intermediate has four, as shown below (similar to the ortho intermediate, Eq. 25-4). Furthermore, the highlighted structure is the most important of the four, because all of its non-hydrogen atoms have complete octets.

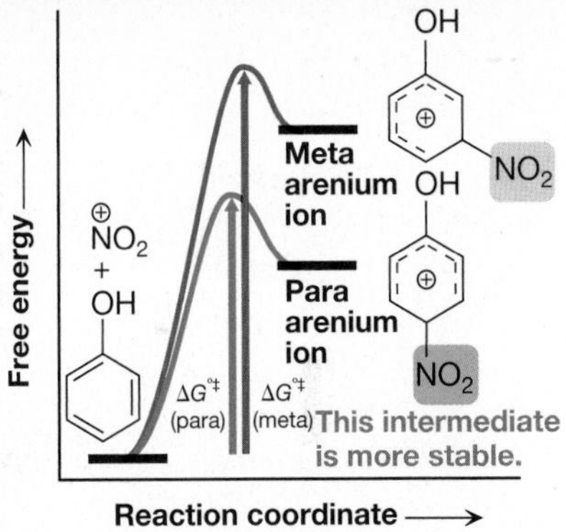
OH
Meta
arenium
ion
NO2
OH
NO2
+
OH
Para
arenium
ion
NO2
ΔG‡ (para)
ΔG‡ (meta)
This intermediate is more stable.
Free energy
Reaction coordinate

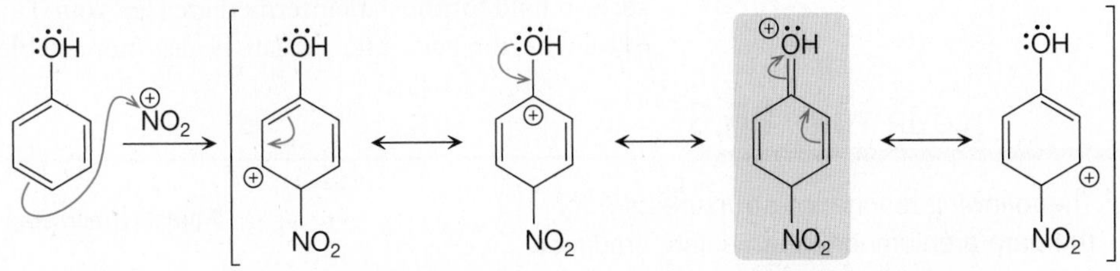
:ÖH
NO2
:ÖH
NO2
:ÖH
NO2
ÖH
NO2
:ÖH
NO2

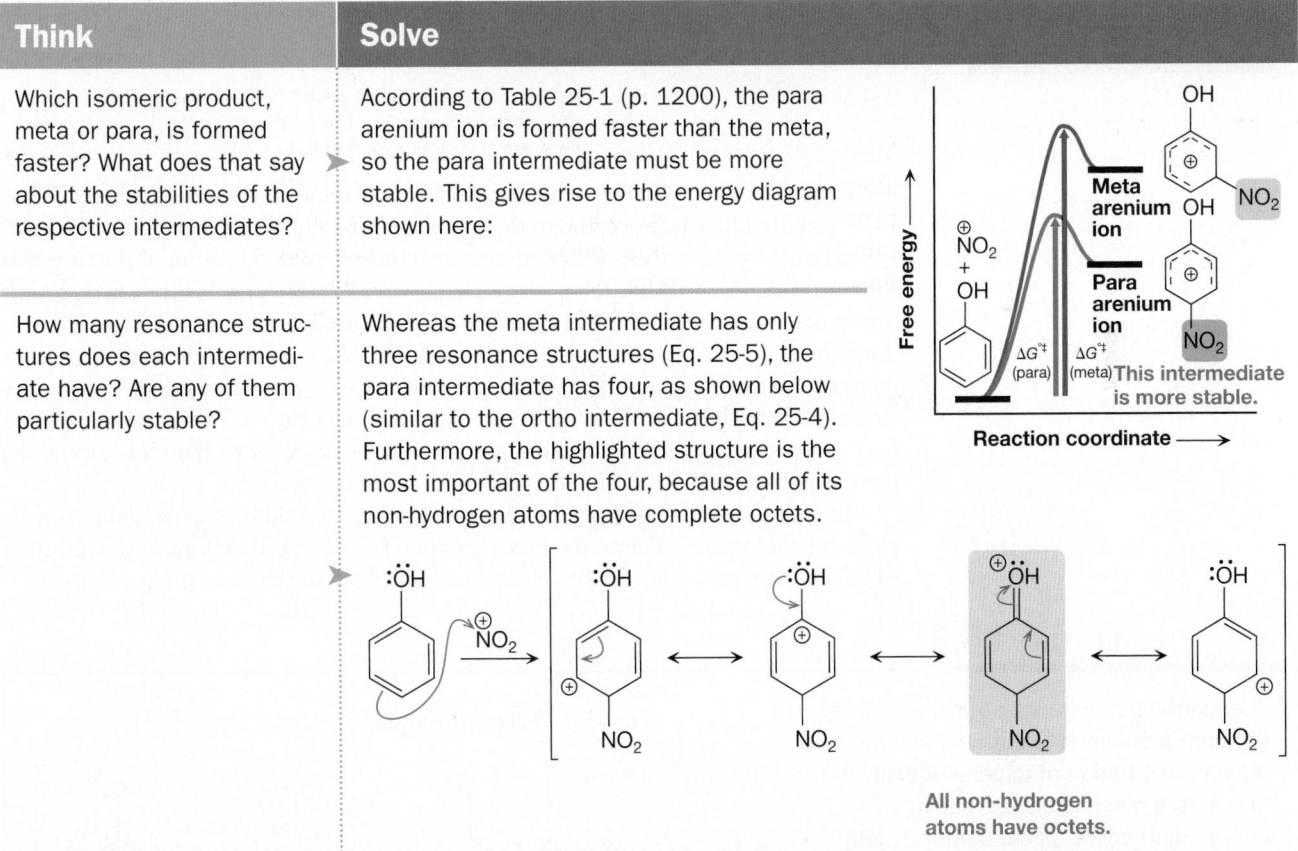

All non-hydrogen atoms have octets.

Try It Draw a plot similar to Figure 25-1 that shows the formation of the ortho and meta intermediates during the nitration of fluorobenzene. Use resonance arguments to explain the relative stabilities of the two isomeric intermediates. *Hint*: See Your Turn 25.5.

Answers to all Try It exercises can be found in the Solutions Manual.

CONNECTIONS 25.3

Weed killers The reduction of *o*-nitrotoluene (a product of the nitration of toluene, Eq. 25-6) produces *o*-toluidine, a precursor in the manufacture of the herbicides metolachlor and acetochlor.

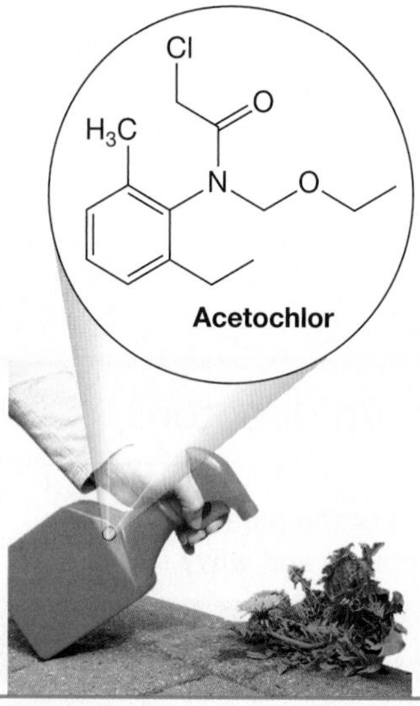
Cl
O
H3C
N
O
Acetochlor

Let's now turn to the second kind of ortho/para directors: alkyl groups. An alkyl group is attached by a C atom that has no lone pairs of electrons, so alkyl groups do not participate in resonance with the arenium ion intermediate. Why, then, should alkyl groups cause the ortho and para arenium ion intermediates to be lower in energy than the meta intermediate? To answer this question, let's carefully examine the resonance structures of the ortho and meta intermediates in the nitration of toluene, $C_6H_5—CH_3$:

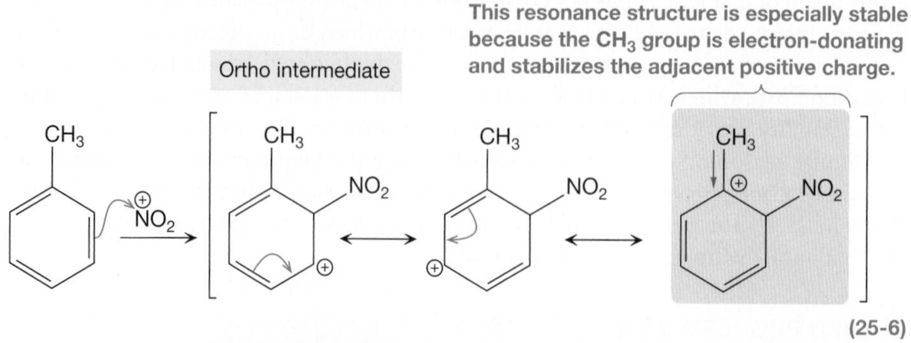
This resonance structure is especially stable because the CH3 group is electron-donating and stabilizes the adjacent positive charge.
Ortho intermediate
CH3
NO2

(25-6)

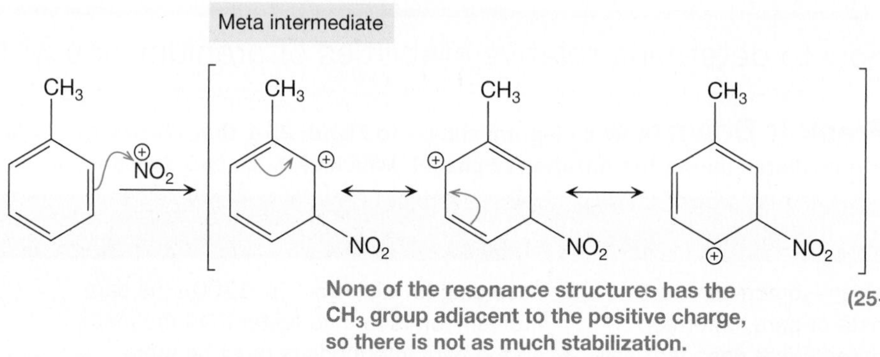
Meta intermediate
CH3
NO2
None of the resonance structures has the CH3 group adjacent to the positive charge, so there is not as much stabilization.

(25-7)

There are three resonance structures for each of the isomeric intermediates. If the NO_2^+ electrophile attaches ortho to the methyl group (Eq. 25-6), then two of the resonance structures have the positive charge on an unsubstituted C atom of the ring, and the third (highlighted) has the positive charge on a C atom attached to a CH_3 group. The positive charge in the third resonance structure is stabilized by the electron-donating ability of the attached CH_3 group. If the NO_2^+ electrophile instead attaches meta to the methyl group (Eq. 25-7), then all three of the intermediate's resonance structures have the positive charge on an unsubstituted C atom. Without contribution from a resonance structure with the positive charge adjacent to the CH_3 group, the meta arenium ion is not as stable as the ortho arenium ion.

As with the nitration of phenol, the arguments that hold for the ortho intermediate also hold for the para intermediate (see Your Turn 25.6). Therefore, in the nitration of toluene, the para intermediate is also more stable than the meta intermediate.

YOUR TURN 25.6

The following resonance structures are for the para arenium ion intermediate produced during the nitration of toluene. Identify the one that is responsible for making this intermediate more stable than the meta arenium ion intermediate.

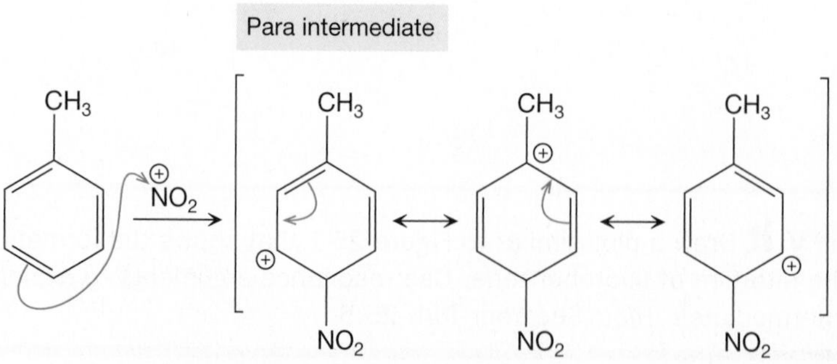
Para intermediate
CH3
NO2

Iodized Salt and Electrophilic Aromatic Substitution

When table salt (NaCl) is sold as "iodized," it contains a small amount of potassium iodide (KI). Have you ever wondered why? What is the importance of iodide in our diet?

Your body needs trace amounts of iodide for proper growth and development. A deficiency in iodide can result in goiter (a condition that is characterized by an enlarged thyroid gland) and other symptoms related to hypothyroidism (a deficiency in the production of thyroid hormone), including fatigue, increased sensitivity to cold, and unexplained weight gain. A deficiency of iodide in someone who is pregnant or nursing puts the child at risk for brain damage.

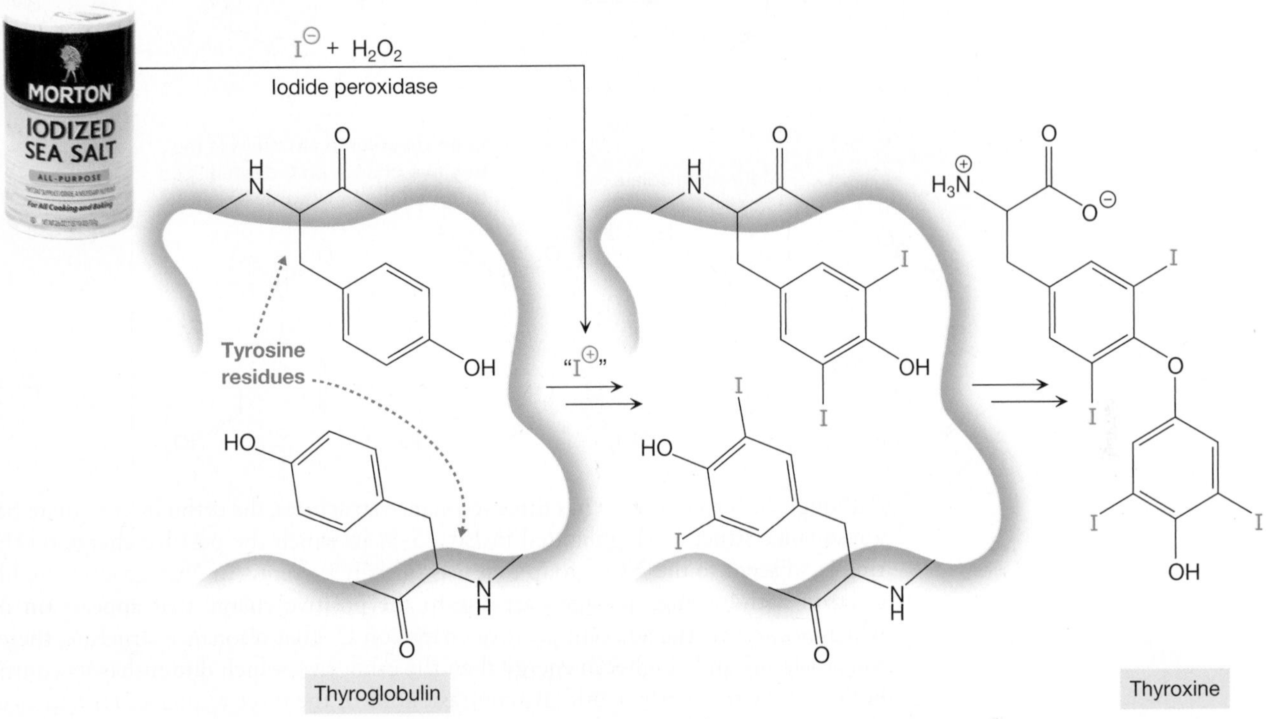

MORTON
IODIZED SEA SALT
ALL-PURPOSE
$I^{\ominus}$ + H_2O_2
Iodide peroxidase
Tyrosine residues
"$I^{\oplus}$"
Thyroglobulin
Thyroxine

FIGURE 25-2

Iodide is important in our diets because it is necessary for the biosynthesis of thyroxine, a thyroid hormone, which is shown on the right in **Figure 25-2**. The biosynthesis of thyroxine begins with the iodination of phenolic rings of tyrosine residues in the protein thyroglobulin. First, the enzyme iodide peroxidase catalyzes the oxidation of I^- to produce an electrophile that behaves as I^+. Then the "I^+" electrophile participates in electrophilic aromatic substitution at the available ortho positions of the phenolic rings, as expected by the ortho/para-directing capability of the OH groups already attached.

25.2b Why Are Meta Arenium Ion Intermediates Lower in Energy When a Meta Director Is Attached?

Recall that when a meta director is attached to benzene, electrophilic aromatic substitution forms predominantly the meta-disubstituted product. In such cases, the meta arenium ion intermediate must be lower in energy than the ortho or para intermediates. Why?

We can answer this question by examining the ortho and meta intermediates in the nitration of nitrobenzene, $C_6H_5—NO_2$:

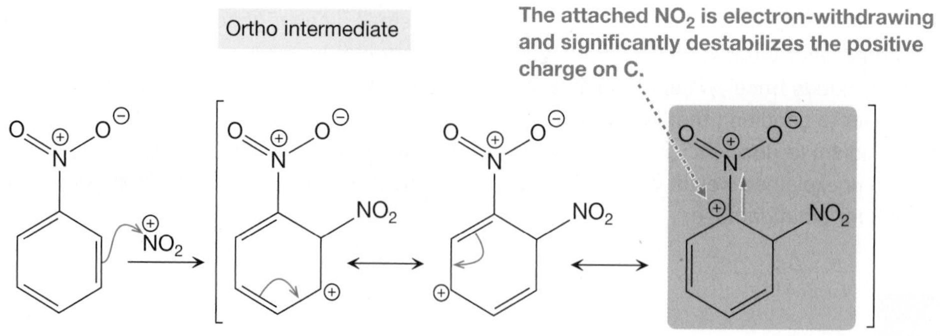
Ortho intermediate
The attached NO2 is electron-withdrawing and significantly destabilizes the positive charge on C.

(25-8)

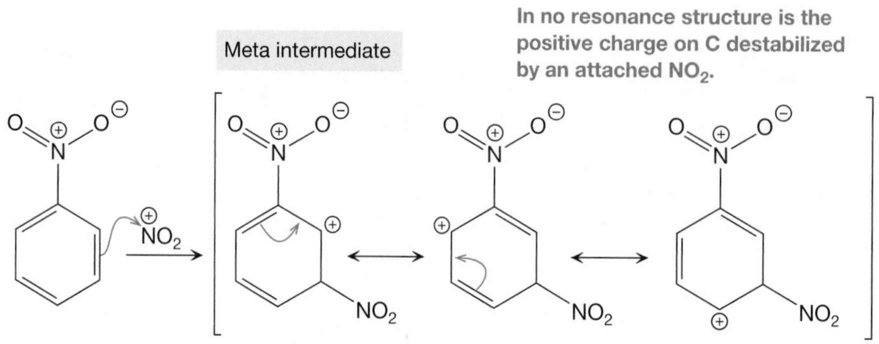
Meta intermediate
In no resonance structure is the positive charge on C destabilized by an attached NO2.

(25-9)

Although each arenium ion has three resonance structures, the ortho intermediate has a resonance structure (highlighted in Eq. 25-8) in which the positive charge on the ring is adjacent to the NO_2 group that was initially present. An NO_2 group is highly electron-withdrawing, in large part due to the positive charge that appears on N, which *destabilizes* the adjacent positive charge on C. That resonance structure, therefore, is significantly higher in energy than the other two, which diminishes its contribution to the resonance hybrid. By contrast, none of the three resonance structures of the meta intermediate has the positive charge of the ring adjacent to the NO_2 group. Consequently, there is greater delocalization of the charge in the resonance hybrid of the meta intermediate, resulting in a lower energy.

Similar arguments explain why a meta director causes the para arenium ion intermediate to be higher in energy than the meta intermediate (see Your Turn 25.7).

YOUR TURN 25.7

Nitration of nitrobenzene at the para C atom proceeds through an arenium ion intermediate that has the following three resonance structures. Identify the *least* stable resonance structure.

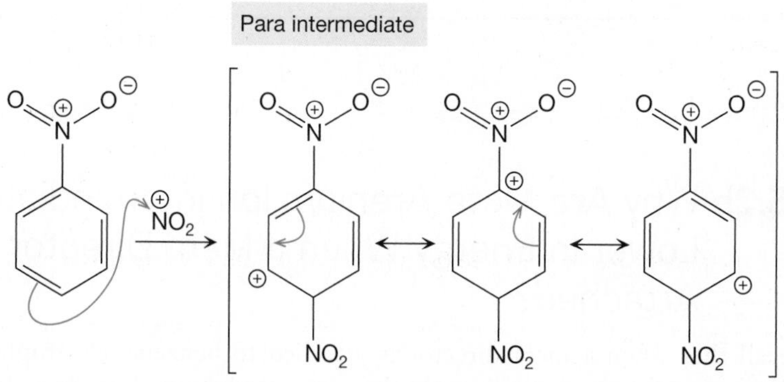
Para intermediate

SOLVED PROBLEM **25.2**

How to determine whether a substituent is an ortho/para or a meta director

Break It Down **The trifluoromethyl group (CF_3) is not listed in Table 25-1. Predict whether CF_3 is an ortho/para director or a meta director.**

Think	Solve
What resonance structures can be drawn for the ortho intermediate?	When an electrophile (E^+) adds to the ortho position of the benzene ring, we can draw three resonance structures (shown here). 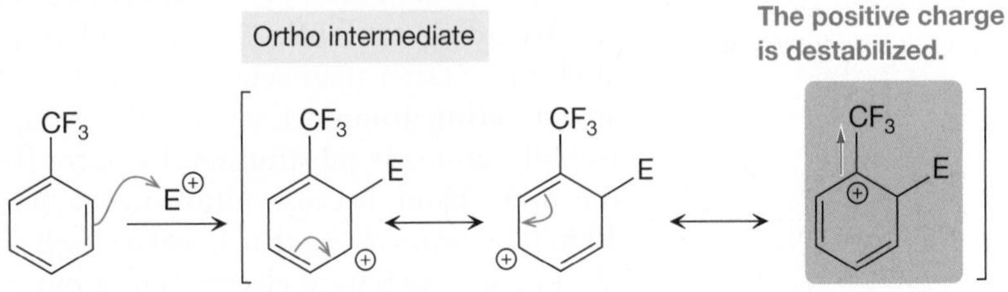 Ortho intermediate The positive charge is destabilized. CF3 E
What resonance structures can be drawn for the meta intermediate?	We can draw three resonance structures (shown here) for the meta arenium ion intermediate. 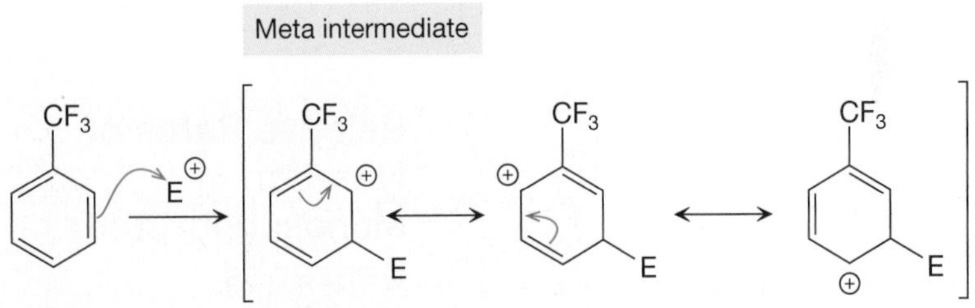 Meta intermediate CF3 E
In which resonance structure does the positive charge appear on the C attached to the CF_3 group?	Of the six resonance structures drawn above, only the highlighted structure has the positive charge on a C that is directly attached to the CF_3 group.
What is the impact on the energy of that resonance structure? On the energy of the intermediate?	The CF_3 group is electron-withdrawing, so it destabilizes the adjacent positive charge in the highlighted resonance structure. Therefore, the ortho intermediate is higher in energy (less stable) than the meta intermediate.
Which product is formed faster? How can you extend these arguments to the para intermediate?	Because the ortho intermediate is higher in energy than the meta intermediate, the ortho product will be formed more slowly than the meta product. Applying the same arguments, we can say that the para product will be formed more slowly than the meta product, too. Therefore, the meta product is the major product, and the CF_3 group is a meta director.

Try It Verify the statement in Solved Problem 25.2 that the para product will be formed more slowly than the meta product. Begin by drawing all resonance structures of the para intermediate, and note the relative stability of each structure.

SECTION 25.3 OBJECTIVES

You will be able to:

1. Define the terms *activating group* and *deactivating group* as they pertain to electrophilic aromatic substitution reactions.
2. Use the structure of a substituent to characterize the substituent as an activating group or a deactivating group.
3. Explain the role of resonance and inductive effects in governing whether a substituent is an activating group or a deactivating group.

25.3 Activation and Deactivation of Benzene toward Electrophilic Aromatic Substitution

The discussion to this point in the chapter has focused on how a substituent affects the rates of formation of the ortho, meta, and para products, *relative to one another*, for a single electrophilic aromatic substitution reaction. We have yet to discuss how substituents affect the *overall* rate of an electrophilic aromatic substitution reaction: that is, the rate of disappearance of the substituted aromatic reactant relative to unsubstituted benzene. Let's begin by examining Table 25-2, which lists the relative overall rates of nitration for a variety of monosubstituted benzenes.

According to Table 25-2, phenol (C_6H_5—OH) undergoes nitration about 1000 times faster than benzene itself. Consequently, the OH group is classified as an **activating group**; we say that the group *activates the benzene ring* toward electrophilic aromatic substitution. The nitro (NO_2) group is a **deactivating group**, on the other hand, because nitrobenzene (C_6H_5—NO_2) undergoes nitration over 10 million times *slower* than benzene itself. Relative to H, the NO_2 group *deactivates the benzene ring* toward electrophilic aromatic substitution.

Why is the OH group so strongly activating? When the electrophile adds to phenol, a lone pair of electrons from the O atom of the OH group participates in

TABLE 25-2 Relative Rates of Nitration of Monosubstituted Benzenes

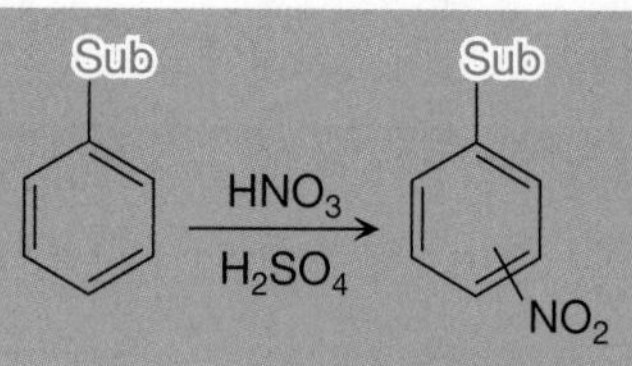

Sub
HNO3
H2SO4
Sub
NO2

Substituent	Relative Rate	Type of Group
—NH_2	—[a]	Strongly activating
—OH	1000	Strongly activating
—CH_3	25	Weakly activating
—H (benzene)	1 (reference)	—
—F	0.84	Weakly deactivating
—I	0.45	Weakly deactivating
—Cl	0.15	Weakly deactivating
—Br	0.11	Weakly deactivating
—CO_2Et	0.0037	Moderately deactivating
—NO_2	6×10^{-8}	Strongly deactivating
—$\overset{\oplus}{N}(CH_3)_3$	1.2×10^{-8}	Strongly deactivating

Increasing rate of reaction (↑)

[a]Aromatic amines are susceptible to protonation and oxidation under nitration conditions. The NH_2 group is determined to be a strongly activating group using other electrophilic aromatic substitution reactions.

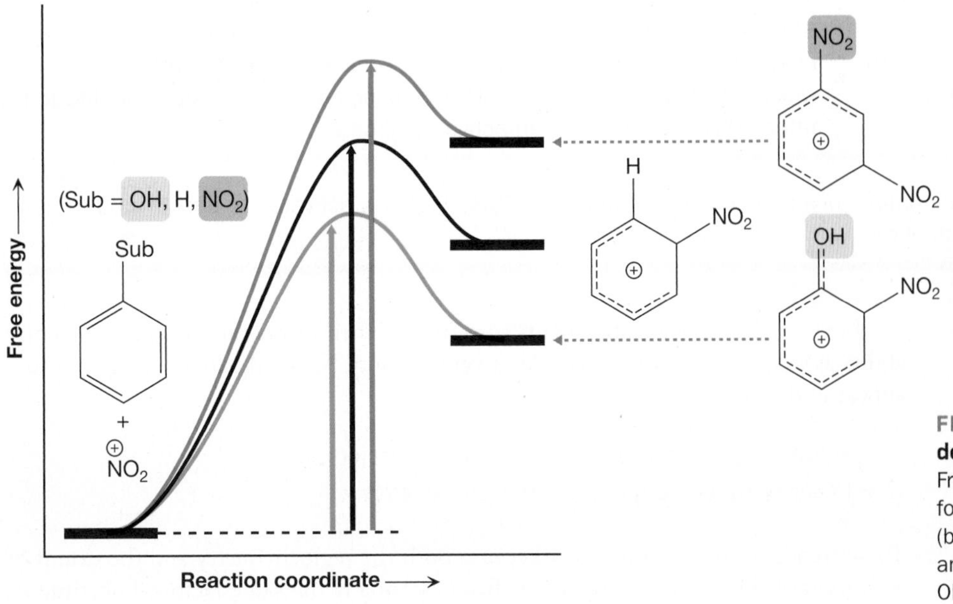

Free energy
(Sub = OH, H, NO2)
Sub
+
NO2
Reaction coordinate
H
NO2
NO2
NO2
OH
NO2
Formed the slowest
The NO2 group destabilizes the arenium ion intermediate and raises the energy barrier.
Formed the fastest
Resonance involving the OH group stabilizes the arenium ion intermediate and lowers the energy barrier.

FIGURE 25-3 Activation and deactivation of an aromatic ring Free energy diagrams are shown for the addition of NO_2^+ to benzene (black curve), phenol (green curve), and nitrobenzene (red curve). The OH group in phenol stabilizes the arenium ion intermediate by involving the lone pair of electrons on the O atom in resonance. This stabilization increases the rate of formation of the arenium ion intermediate, making OH an *activating group*. A nitro group, on the other hand, destabilizes the arenium ion intermediate. This destabilization slows the rate of formation of the arenium ion, making the nitro group a *deactivating group*.

resonance to stabilize the arenium ion intermediate (it is stabilized the most when the electrophile adds ortho or para). As shown in **Figure 25-3** (green curve), this stabilization lowers the energy barrier for formation of the arenium ion, and the arenium ion is formed faster.

Conversely, when the electrophile adds to nitrobenzene, the NO_2 group destabilizes the arenium ion intermediate that is formed (it is destabilized the most when the electrophile adds ortho or para). This destabilization increases the energy barrier for formation of the arenium ion (Fig. 25-3, red curve), which slows the overall reaction rate. As a result, the NO_2 group is *deactivating*.

YOUR TURN **25.8**

For the nitration of ethyl benzoate ($C_6H_5—CO_2Et$), where would you expect the arenium ion intermediate to appear in Figure 25-3? *Hint*: What is the relative rate of nitration listed in Table 25-2?

SOLVED PROBLEM **25.3**

How to identify an activating or deactivating substituent for electrophilic aromatic substitution

Break It Down Why does toluene ($C_6H_5—CH_3$) undergo electrophilic aromatic substitution faster than benzene, thereby making CH_3 an *activating group*?

Think	Solve
Are toluene's arenium ion intermediates more stable or less stable than those of benzene?	The CH_3 group is electron-donating, so it stabilizes the arenium ion intermediate. **The arenium ion is stabilized by the electron donation of CH_3.** 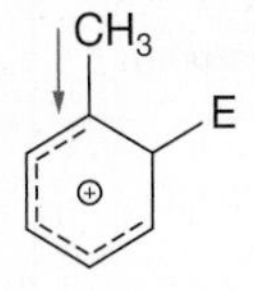

CH3
E

(continued)

How does stability of the arenium ion intermediates affect the energy barriers for formation of the arenium ions and, hence, the rates of reaction?	Stabilization of toluene's arenium ion intermediates lowers the activation energy for formation of the intermediates, which increases the rate at which they form. Therefore, a CH_3 group increases the overall substitution rates, which defines it as an activating group.

Try It Determine whether the aromatic ring in trifluoromethylbenzene (C_6H_5—CF_3) is activated or deactivated toward electrophilic aromatic substitution.

Table 25-3 organizes substituents according to their ortho/para- or meta-directing ability as well as their activating or deactivating ability. Notice the following trends that appear in the table:

- Activating groups are generally ortho/para directors.
- Deactivating groups are generally meta directors.

These trends break down this way because both the regiochemistry and the extent of activation of the aromatic ring derive from essentially the same factors. Substituents that are electron-donating (due to either resonance or inductive effects) stabilize the

TABLE 25-3 Comparison of the Activating or Deactivating Nature and the Ortho/Para- or Meta-Directing Nature of Substituents

Substituent	Activating or Deactivating	Ortho/Para- or Meta-Directing	Substituent	Activating or Deactivating	Ortho/Para- or Meta-Directing
—$O^{\ominus}$	Strongly activating	Ortho/para	—C(=O)OR (or OH)	Moderately deactivating	Meta
—NH_2 —NR_2	Strongly activating	Ortho/para	—C(=O)R (or H)	Moderately deactivating	Meta
—OH —OR	Strongly activating	Ortho/para	—C≡N	Strongly deactivating	Meta
—N(H)—C(=O)R (or H)	Moderately activating	Ortho/para	—S(=O)(=O)—OH	Strongly deactivating	Meta
—O—C(=O)R (or H)	Moderately activating	Ortho/para	—$N^{\oplus}$(=O)$O^{\ominus}$	Strongly deactivating	Meta
—R	Weakly activating	Ortho/para	—$N^{\oplus}$R (or H)(R (or H))(R (or H))	Strongly deactivating	Meta
—H (Benzene)	—	—			
—Cl —Br —I	Weakly deactivating	Ortho/para			

Increasing rate of reaction ↑

arenium ion intermediate and increase the overall reaction rate, so they are activating. These groups also stabilize the ortho and para arenium ion intermediates more than they do the meta intermediate, so they are ortho/para directors. By the same token, substituents that destabilize the arenium ion intermediate by withdrawing electron density are deactivating groups. These groups destabilize the ortho and para intermediates more than they do the meta intermediate, making them meta directors.

The lone exceptions in Table 25-3 are the halogen atoms:

Halogen substituents are weakly deactivating, but they are ortho/para directors.

Halogens are ortho/para directors because, like the OH group, halogens possess a lone pair of electrons and are electron-donating through resonance. Consequently, a halogen atom substituent stabilizes the arenium ion intermediate substantially when an electrophile attaches to either the ortho or para position. Conversely, halogens are deactivators because they are inductively electron-withdrawing groups.

YOUR TURN 25.9

The ortho/para-directing and deactivating characteristics of a Cl substituent can be understood by considering the resonance structures and the resonance hybrid of the ortho arenium ion intermediate below. **(a)** Supply the curved arrow notation to the first resonance structure to show how a lone pair of electrons on Cl helps stabilize the intermediate. **(b)** Draw a straight arrow along the C—Cl bond in the resonance hybrid to represent the inductive effect by Cl. How does that inductive effect impact the stability of the positive charge in the intermediate?

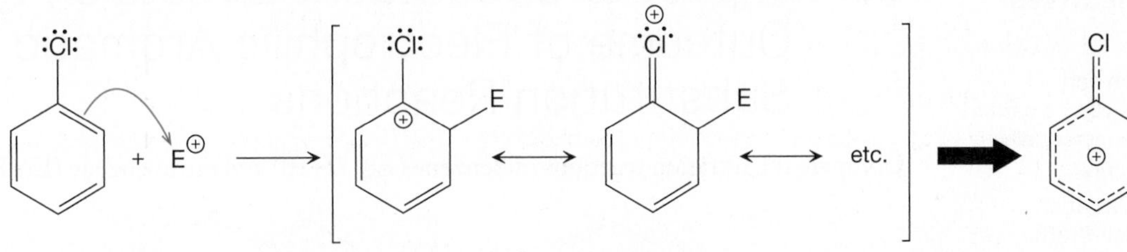

:Cl:
+ E⊕
:Cl:
E
⊕
Cl
E
etc.
Cl
E
⊕

We can gain more insight into the activating or deactivating character of a substituent by examining the effect of the substituent on the electron density of the aromatic ring prior to the reaction. As examples, the electrostatic potential maps of benzene, aniline, and nitrobenzene are shown in **Figure 25-4**.

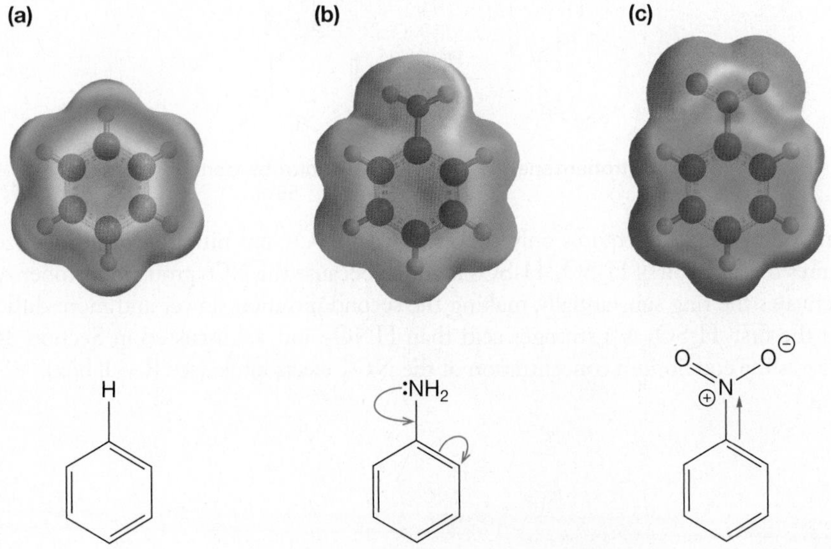

(a)
(b)
(c)
H
:NH2
O
O
N

FIGURE 25-4 Effects of activating and deactivating groups on electron density in the benzene ring Electrostatic potential maps of (a) benzene, (b) aniline, and (c) nitrobenzene are shown. The electron-donating ability of the NH_2 group, through resonance, increases the electron density of the aromatic ring (shown as more red) and, hence, activates the ring toward electrophilic aromatic substitution. Conversely, the electron-withdrawing ability of the NO_2 group decreases electron density in the ring (shown as more blue/green) and, hence, deactivates the ring toward electrophilic aromatic substitution.

The aromatic ring of aniline, which has an NH_2 activating group, has *greater* electron density (depicted as more red) than the aromatic ring of benzene. The NH_2 group donates electron density to the ring through resonance, making it more electron-rich than benzene itself and giving it greater driving force for attack of an incoming electrophile (E^+). This greater driving force increases the overall rate of substitution compared to benzene.

Conversely, the aromatic ring of nitrobenzene, which has a NO_2 deactivating group, is less electron-rich (depicted as more blue/green) than benzene itself. The NO_2 group withdraws electron density from the ring, so the driving force for the aromatic ring to attack the electrophile is diminished relative to benzene, causing nitrobenzene to react more slowly.

YOUR TURN 25.10

The electrostatic potential maps of benzene and a monosubstituted benzene are shown here. **(a)** Is the aromatic ring of the monosubstituted compound activated or deactivated relative to benzene? **(b)** On the basis of its impact on the electron density in the ring, is the substituent more likely CH_3 or CF_3? Explain.

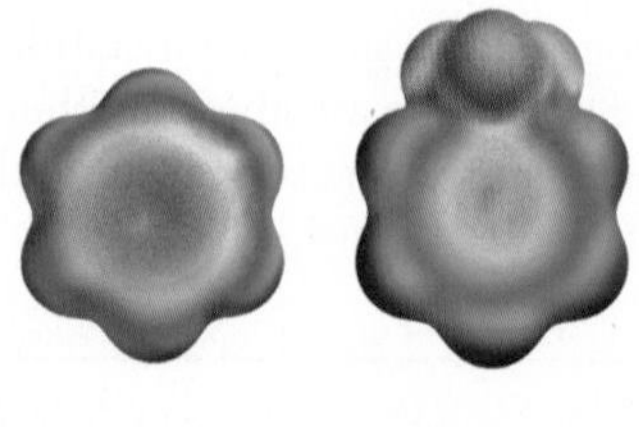

SECTION 25.4 OBJECTIVES

You will be able to:

1. Show how nitration and sulfonation reactions can be carried out effectively on a substantially deactivated aromatic ring.
2. Explain why polyalkylation is a problem with Friedel–Crafts alkylation reactions.
3. Determine when a Friedel–Crafts reaction is unfeasible for a particular aromatic ring.

25.4 Impact of Substituent Effects on the Outcome of Electrophilic Aromatic Substitution Reactions

Compare the nitration reactions of benzene (Eq. 25-10) and nitrobenzene (Eq. 25-11):

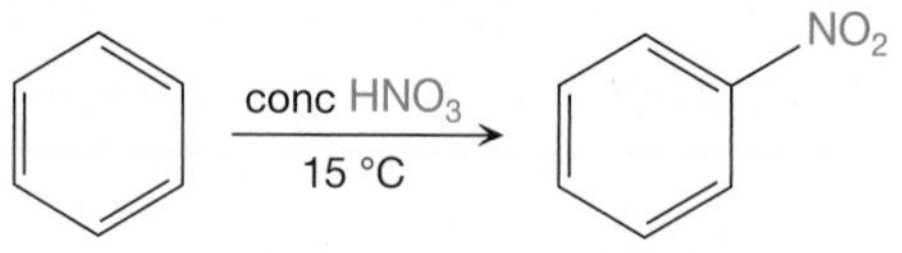

NO2
conc HNO3
15 °C

Benzene **Nitrobenzene** 83% (25-10)

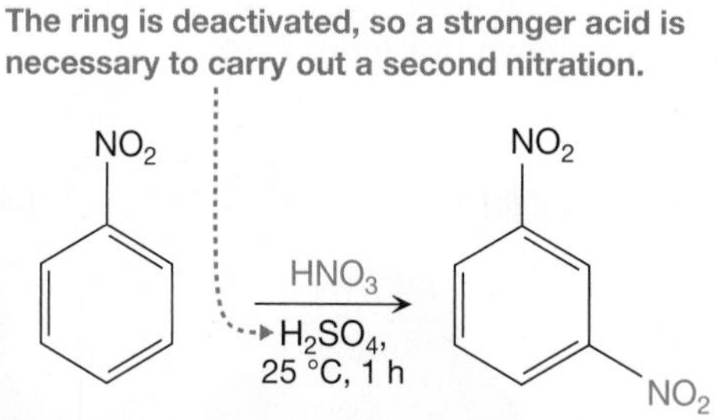

The ring is deactivated, so a stronger acid is necessary to carry out a second nitration.
NO2
NO2
HNO3
H2SO4,
25 °C, 1 h
NO2

Nitrobenzene ***m*-Dinitrobenzene** 58% (25-11)

◂ RECALL

In Section 24.1, we saw that addition of the electrophile to an aromatic ring is the rate-determining step of electrophilic aromatic substitution. Therefore, the rate of the overall reaction increases with increasing concentration of the electrophile.

Nitration of benzene requires only concentrated HNO_3, but nitration of nitrobenzene requires the addition of H_2SO_4. H_2SO_4 is added because the NO_2 group in nitrobenzene deactivates the ring substantially, making the second nitration slower and more difficult than the first. H_2SO_4 is a stronger acid than HNO_3 and, as discussed in Section 24.6, increases the equilibrium concentration of the NO_2^+ electrophile (see Recall box).

Explain why a single sulfonation of benzene can be carried out with just concentrated H_2SO_4 (left), but fuming sulfuric acid is needed to produce the disulfonated product (right). *Hint*: Review Section 24.7.

SO3H
conc H2SO4
48 h, 20 °C
Benzenesulfonic acid
66%
HO3S
SO3H
conc H2SO4
SO3,
4 h, <90 °C
1,3-Benzenedisulfonic acid
90%

Many electrophilic aromatic substitution reactions can be carried out despite the presence of a moderately or strongly deactivating group on the ring, but this is not true for Friedel–Crafts reactions:

Friedel–Crafts reactions do not readily take place on moderately or strongly deactivated aromatic rings (review Table 25-3, p. 1210).

When the ring is deactivated, the cationic electrophile that is generated in a Friedel–Crafts reaction tends to degrade or polymerize before it can be attacked by the ring. So, for example, no alkylation takes place in Equation 25-12 because the C═O group is moderately deactivating:

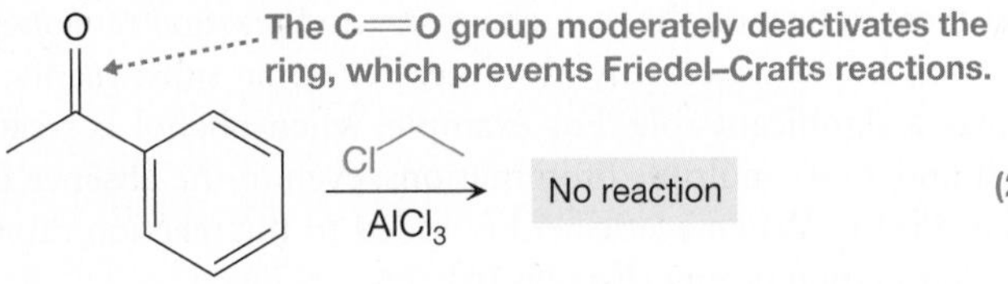
O
The C═O group moderately deactivates the ring, which prevents Friedel–Crafts reactions.
Cl
AlCl3
No reaction

(25-12)

When a Friedel–Crafts alkylation is carried out on benzene itself, we run into a different problem: the enhanced reactivity of the product.

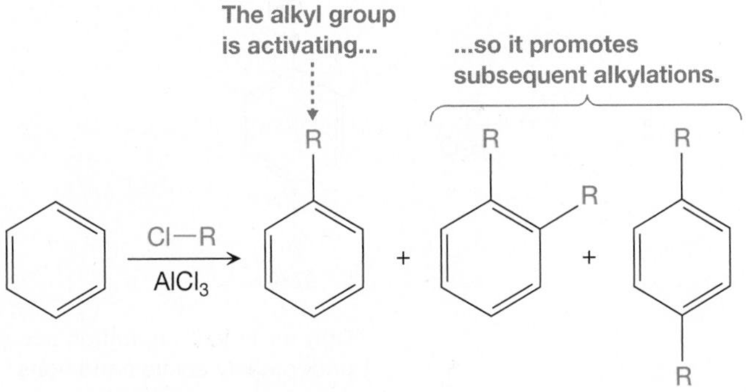
The alkyl group is activating...
...so it promotes subsequent alkylations.
Cl—R
AlCl3
R
R
R
R
R
+
+

(25-13)

Each alkyl group activates the aromatic ring toward electrophilic aromatic substitution, so with an alkyl group having been added in the first alkylation, subsequent alkylations become faster. Thus, as we first mentioned in Section 24.4:

Friedel–Crafts alkylations are subject to polyalkylation.

To avoid polyalkylation, it is often better to add an alkyl group by first acylating the ring and then reducing the C═O group to a CH_2 group, as we saw previously in Section 24.8 and as shown in Equation 25-14:

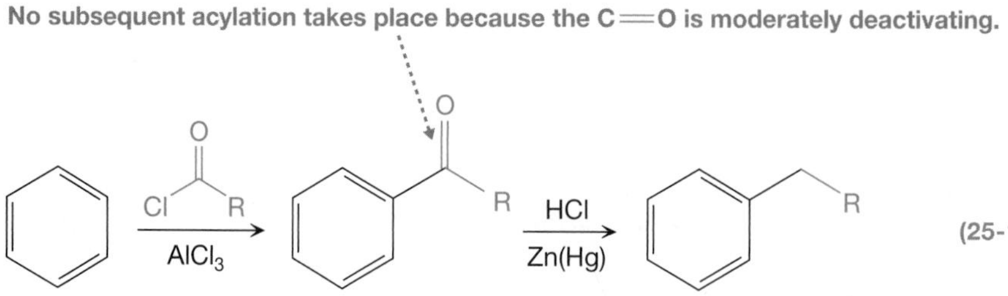

No subsequent acylation takes place because the C═O is moderately deactivating.
O
Cl
R
AlCl3
O
R
HCl
Zn(Hg)
R

(25-14)

We are not concerned about multiple acylations because the aromatic ring in the product of the first acylation is substantially deactivated.

YOUR TURN 25.12

Show how to synthesize butylbenzene from benzene.

SECTION 25.5 OBJECTIVES

You will be able to:

1. Explain how the pH of a solution can impact the substituent effects by hydroxyl and amino groups.
2. Justify why the substituent effects by an amino group can change in the presence of a strong Lewis acid.

25.5 Impact of Reaction Conditions on Substituent Effects

A substituent's effect on the regiochemistry and reaction rate of electrophilic aromatic substitution is not necessarily absolute. For some substituents, the reaction conditions play a significant role. For example, when phenol is treated with bromine in water, it undergoes multiple brominations, even in the absence of a Lewis acid catalyst (Eq. 25-15). When acetic acid is added to the reaction mixture, however, only a single bromination occurs (Eq. 25-16):

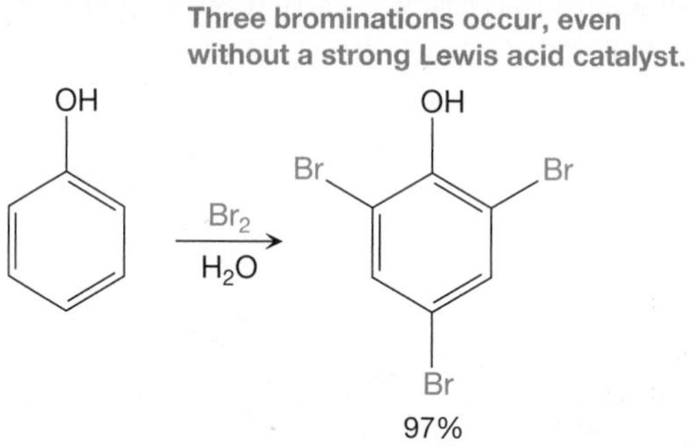

Three brominations occur, even without a strong Lewis acid catalyst.
OH
Br2
H2O
OH
Br
Br
Br
97%

(25-15)

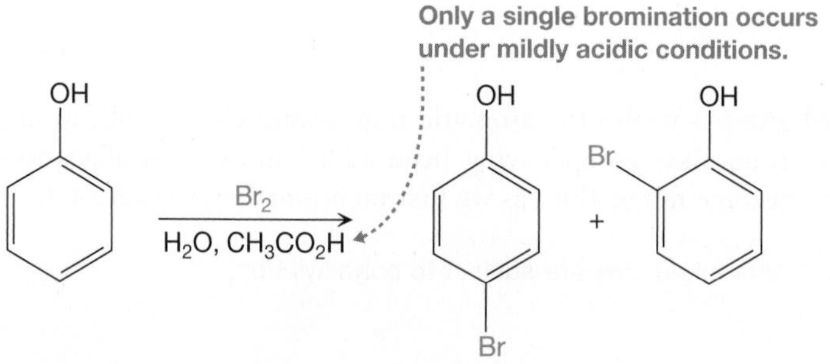

Only a single bromination occurs under mildly acidic conditions.
OH
Br2
H2O, CH3CO2H
OH
Br
+
OH
Br

(25-16)

These results are observed because the nature of the substituent is affected by the pH of the solution. Phenol is a weak acid ($pK_a = 10.0$), so in the absence of acetic acid, phenol is in equilibrium with a small amount of its conjugate base, the phenoxide anion (C_6H_5—O^-), as shown in Equation 25-17. Even though very little of

CONNECTIONS 25.4

Fighting fire with brominated epoxy resins

2,4,6-Tribromophenol (the product of Eq. 25-15) is used as a precursor in the manufacture of some flame-retardant chemicals, such as brominated epoxy resins. Heavy use of these chemicals in fighting wildfires has elevated the need for bioremediation studies of the risks they pose to the environment.

the phenoxide anion is present, the O^- substituent is a *very* powerful activating group, far better than the OH group, so it dramatically increases the rate of electrophilic aromatic substitution. As a result, the phenoxide anion is the dominant reactant in the reaction.

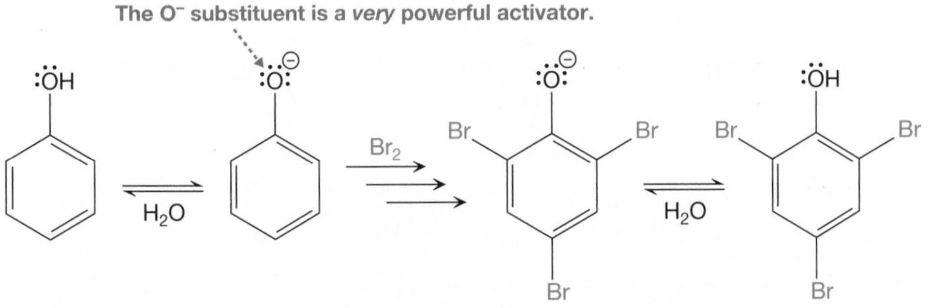

The O⁻ substituent is a *very* powerful activator.
:ÖH
:Ö:
Br₂
H₂O
Br

(25-17)

The presence of acetic acid decreases the pH of the solution. The resulting increased concentration of H^+ substantially decreases the concentration of the phenoxide anion (Le Châtelier's principle), effectively cutting off the route by which the phenoxide anion participates in electrophilic aromatic substitution. The only route available is the one in which the electrophile reacts with the uncharged phenol itself: a much slower reaction that can be easily stopped after just a single bromination.

YOUR TURN 25.13

Draw the complete, detailed mechanism for the reaction in Equation 25-17.

The pH can also dramatically affect the nitration of *N,N*-dimethylaniline. If *N,N*-dimethylaniline is treated with HNO_3 in acetic acid (Eq. 25-18), then the ortho and para nitro products are predominantly formed. This is as expected, since the lone pair on the substituent's N atom makes it an ortho/para director and an activator. However, if nitration is carried out in sulfuric acid (i.e., at a much lower pH), then the major product is the meta isomer (Eq. 25-19):

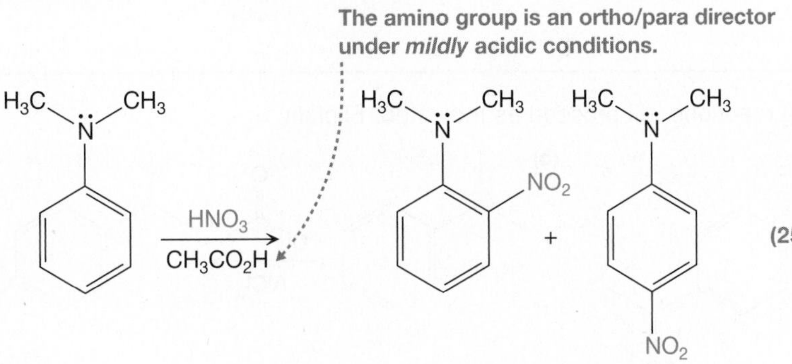

The amino group is an ortho/para director under *mildly* acidic conditions.
H₃C
CH₃
N
HNO₃
CH₃CO₂H
NO₂
+

(25-18)

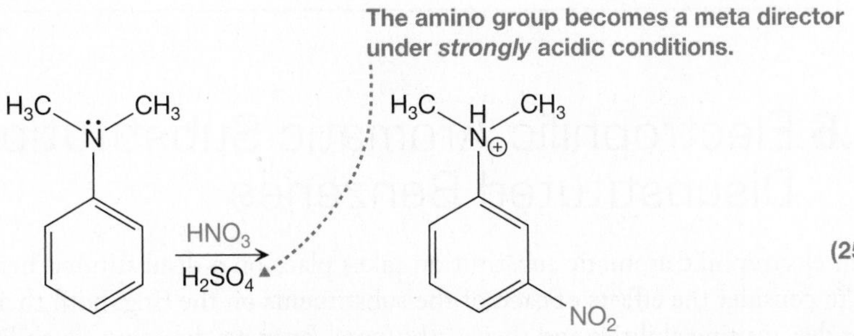

The amino group becomes a meta director under *strongly* acidic conditions.
H₃C
CH₃
N
HNO₃
H₂SO₄
H
NO₂

(25-19)

Sulfuric acid is much stronger than acetic acid, so it *quantitatively* protonates the amino group, generating an anilinium ion in which a +1 formal charge exists on N

(Eq. 25-20). In this form, the substituent is highly electron-withdrawing, much like an NO_2 group, so it is a meta director and a deactivator:

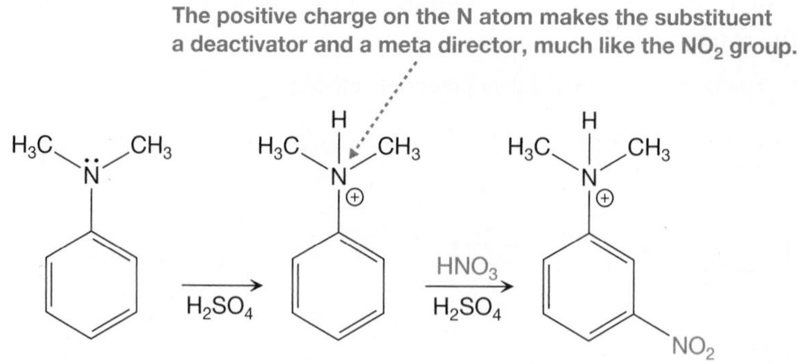
The positive charge on the N atom makes the substituent a deactivator and a meta director, much like the NO2 group.
H3C
CH3
N
H
HNO3
H2SO4
NO2

(25-20)

A similar phenomenon can occur when a strong Lewis acid is present. For example, even though aniline possesses a highly activating NH_2 group, it is incompatible with Friedel–Crafts reactions, as shown in Equation 25-21. The amino group is a relatively strong Lewis base, so it readily coordinates to the $AlCl_3$ Lewis acid. In that complexed form, the N atom possesses a +1 formal charge, making it a highly *deactivating* group that makes Friedel–Crafts reactions unfeasible (Section 25.4).

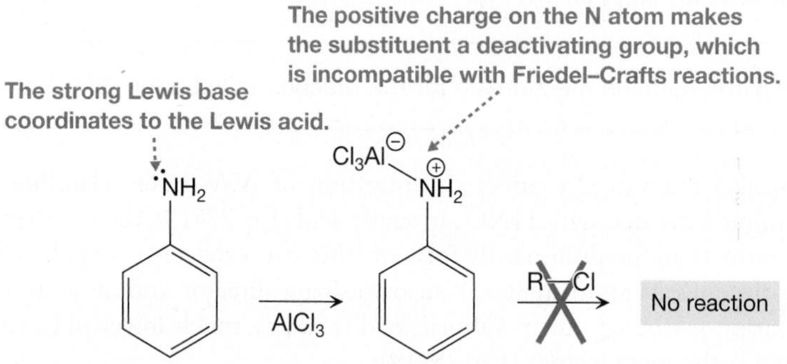
The positive charge on the N atom makes the substituent a deactivating group, which is incompatible with Friedel–Crafts reactions.
The strong Lewis base coordinates to the Lewis acid.
NH2
Cl3Al
AlCl3
R—Cl
No reaction

(25-21)

YOUR TURN 25.14

Determine whether each of the following reactions will proceed as indicated. Explain.

(a)

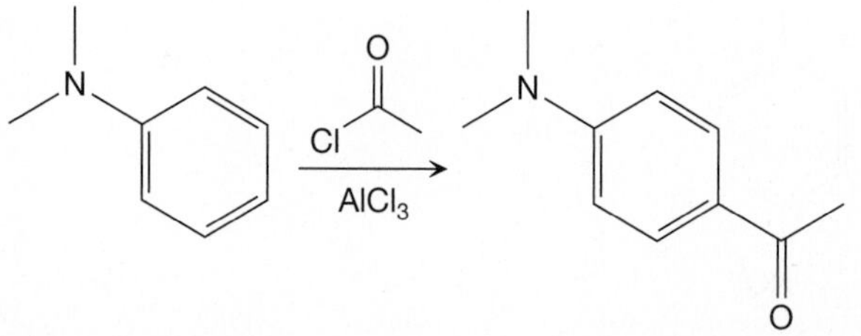
N
O
Cl
AlCl3

(b)

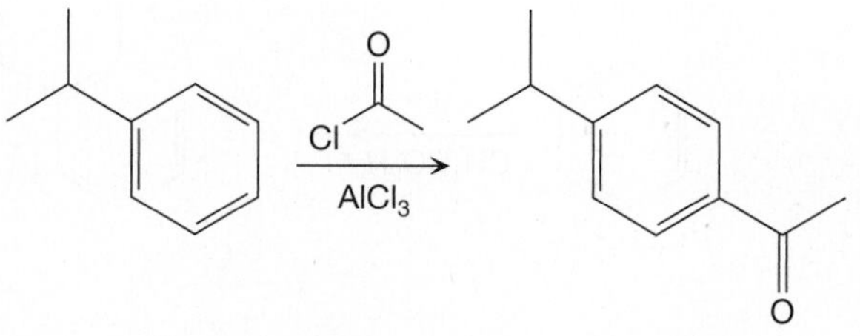
O
Cl
AlCl3

SECTION 25.6 OBJECTIVES

You will be able to:

1. Predict the major products for an electrophilic aromatic substitution reaction on a disubstituted benzene.
2. Rank the relative rates of electrophilic aromatic substitution on the basis of the number and type of substituents on the ring.

25.6 Electrophilic Aromatic Substitution on Disubstituted Benzenes

When electrophilic aromatic substitution takes place on a disubstituted benzene, we need to consider the effects of each of the substituents on the ring: both their activating or deactivating abilities and their ortho/para- or meta-directing capabilities.

The regiochemistry of these reactions is straightforward if the two substituents are "in agreement," meaning that they favor substitution at the same positions on the ring.

For nitration of *p*-nitrotoluene (Eq. 25-22), for example, both substituents are in agreement, and the reaction produces almost exclusively 2,4-dinitrotoluene:

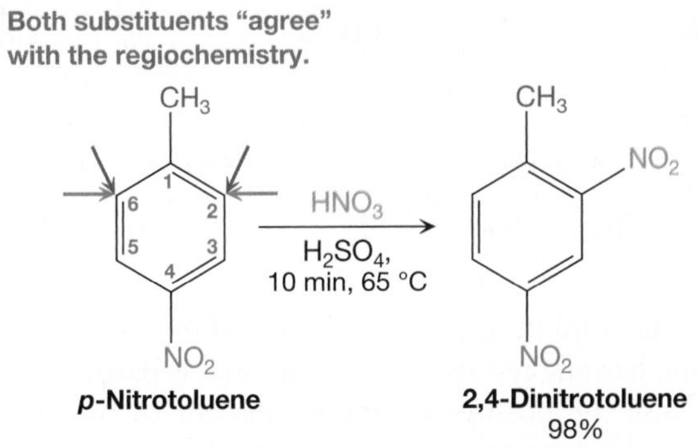
Both substituents "agree"
with the regiochemistry.
CH3
1
2
3
4
5
6
NO2
HNO3
H2SO4,
10 min, 65 °C
CH3
NO2
NO2
p-Nitrotoluene
2,4-Dinitrotoluene
98%

(25-22)

The methyl group at C-1 is an ortho/para director, so it favors substitution at the available positions ortho or para to itself, in this case at C-2 or C-6 (indicated by the blue arrows). The nitro group at C-4 is a meta director, so it favors substitution at the available positions meta to itself, in this case at C-2 or C-6 (indicated by the red arrows). With agreement like this, we observe substitution primarily at the C atom ortho to the CH_3 group.

Without agreement among the substituents, regiochemistry is not as clear-cut, but the following rule is helpful:

> When two substituents attached to an aromatic ring "disagree" about where to direct the incoming electrophile, regiochemistry is usually dictated by the substituent that is the stronger activating group: that is, the group that appears nearer the beginning of Table 25-3 (p. 1210).

For example, when *m*-nitrotoluene undergoes nitration (Eq. 25-23), the methyl group at C-1 directs substitution ortho and para to itself (at C-2, C-4, and C-6, indicated by the blue arrows), whereas the NO_2 group directs substitution meta to itself (at C-5, indicated by the red arrow):

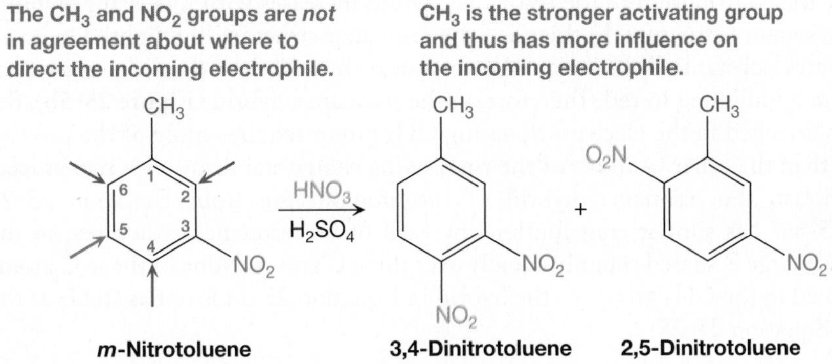
The CH3 and NO2 groups are not
in agreement about where to
direct the incoming electrophile.
CH3 is the stronger activating group
and thus has more influence on
the incoming electrophile.
CH3
1
2
3
4
5
6
NO2
HNO3
H2SO4
CH3
NO2
NO2
+
CH3
O2N
NO2
m-Nitrotoluene
3,4-Dinitrotoluene
2,5-Dinitrotoluene

(25-23)

CH_3 is a stronger activating group than NO_2, so the above rule would suggest substitution at C-2, C-4, and C-6. Notice in Equation 25-23, however, that substitution is observed at C-4 and C-6 but is *not* observed at C-2, due to the following rule:

> Electrophilic aromatic substitution is disfavored at positions that are ortho to two different substituents due to steric hindrance.

Why the more activating group dictates the regiochemistry can be understood by examining the resonance contributors and resonance hybrids of the various possible arenium ion intermediates. When the electrophile attaches meta to the methyl group (Eq. 25-24), then all resonance contributors of the resulting arenium ion have similar stabilities; in each case, the positive charge appears on an unsubstituted carbon.

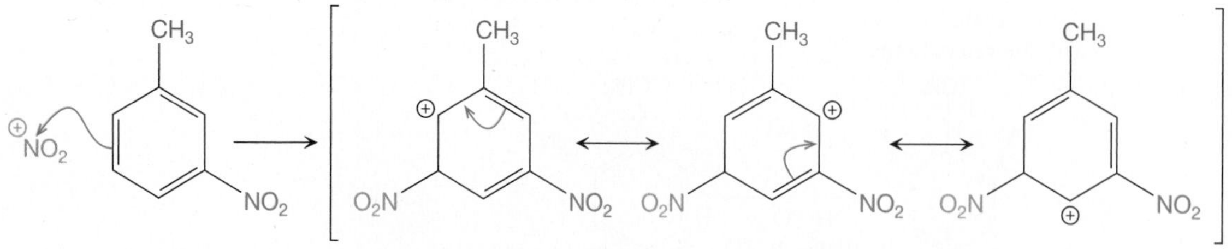

CH3
NO2
NO2
CH3
O2N
NO2
CH3
O2N
NO2
CH3
O2N
NO2

(25-24)

When the electrophile attaches para to the CH_3 group (Eq. 25-25), the resulting arenium ion has one resonance structure that is particularly stable (highlighted in green) because the positive charge is adjacent to the electron-donating CH_3 group. There is also one resonance structure that is particularly unstable (highlighted in red) because the positive charge is adjacent to the electron-withdrawing NO_2 group:

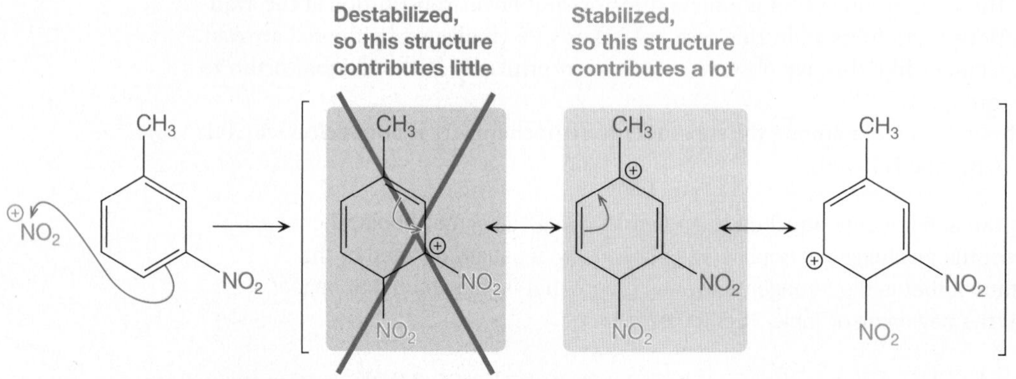

Destabilized, so this structure contributes little
Stabilized, so this structure contributes a lot
CH3
NO2
NO2
CH3
NO2
NO2
CH3
NO2
NO2
CH3
NO2
NO2

(25-25)

It is tempting to think that the destabilization in the first resonance structure in Equation 25-25 might counter the effects from the stabilization in the second resonance structure. However, resonance theory (Chapters 1 and 6) tells us otherwise, because the contribution to the resonance hybrid increases with increasing stability of the resonance structure. In this case, the resonance structure highlighted in green contributes substantially more to the resonance hybrid than does the resonance structure highlighted in red. Therefore, in the resonance hybrid (**Figure 25-5b**), the C atom attached to the electron-donating CH_3 group acquires more of the positive charge than the other C atoms of the ring, so the charge stabilization is maximized. By contrast, the resonance hybrid of the arenium ion from Equation 25-24 (Fig. 25-5a) has similar contributions by each of its resonance structures, so the positive charge is shared roughly equally over three C atoms. None of those C atoms is attached to the CH_3 group, so the hybrid in Equation 25-24 is not as stable as the one in Equation 25-25.

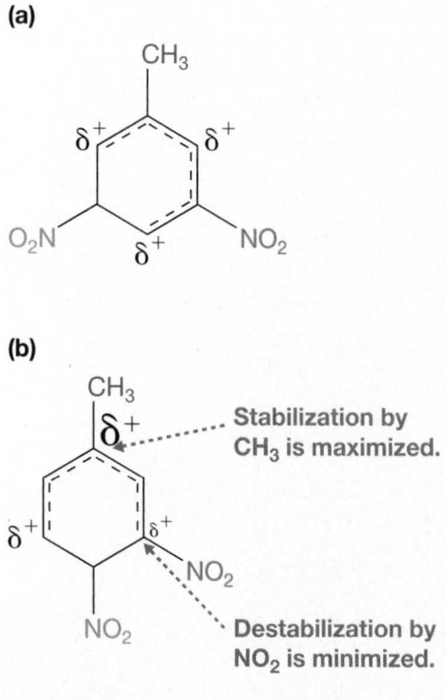

(a)
CH3
δ+
δ+
O2N
δ+
NO2
(b)
CH3
δ+
Stabilization by CH3 is maximized.
δ+
δ+
NO2
NO2
Destabilization by NO2 is minimized.

FIGURE 25-5 Substituent effects on resonance hybrids Resonance hybrids of the arenium ions from (a) Equation 25-24 and (b) Equation 25-25 are shown. (a) When NO_2 adds meta to CH_3, the positive charge is roughly equally distributed over the three C atoms of the ring, and there is no special stabilization or destabilization by the attached groups. (b) When NO_2 adds para to CH_3, the greatest accumulation of the partial positive charge is on the C atom attached to the CH_3 group, which maximizes the stabilization of the charge. The hybrid in (b) is therefore more stable than the hybrid in (a).

YOUR TURN **25.15**

The following resonance structures are for the arenium ion produced when NO_2^+ attaches ortho to the CH_3 group in *m*-nitrotoluene. Identify the most stable and least stable resonance structures. Overall, is this arenium ion more stable or less stable than the one in Equation 25-24?

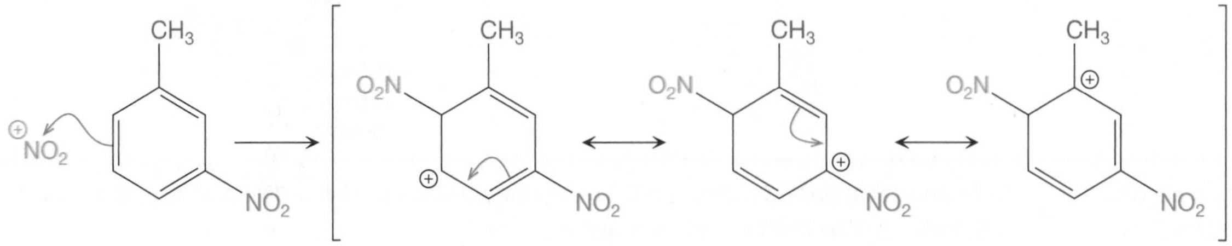

CH3
NO2
NO2
O2N
CH3
NO2
O2N
CH3
NO2
O2N
CH3
NO2

What happens if the two substituents on benzene disagree with the placement of the incoming electrophile *and* have roughly the same activating or deactivating ability: that is, if they are in roughly the same location in Table 25-3 (p. 1210)? This is the case when *p*-ethyltoluene undergoes electrophilic aromatic substitution, because the two alkyl groups have about the same activating capabilities. As indicated in Equation 25-26, a mixture of isomers is produced because the two alkyl groups have nearly equal influence when it comes to directing the incoming electrophile:

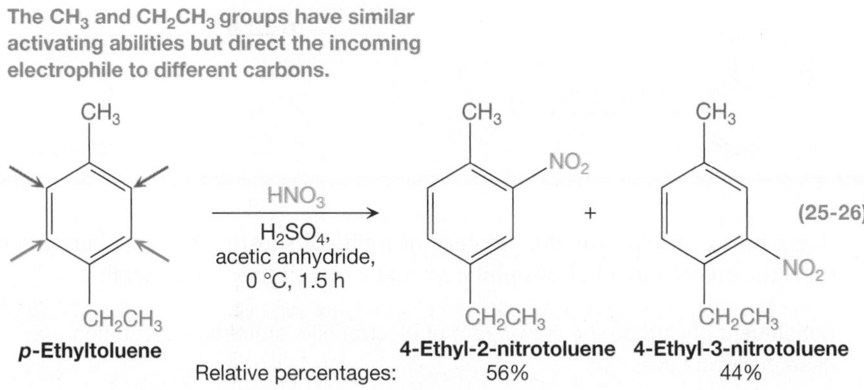

The CH3 and CH2CH3 groups have similar activating abilities but direct the incoming electrophile to different carbons.
CH3
CH2CH3
p-Ethyltoluene
HNO3
H2SO4,
acetic anhydride,
0 °C, 1.5 h
CH3
NO2
CH2CH3
4-Ethyl-2-nitrotoluene
56%
+
CH3
NO2
CH2CH3
4-Ethyl-3-nitrotoluene
44%
Relative percentages:

(25-26)

SOLVED PROBLEM **25.4**

How to predict the major product(s) in the electrophilic aromatic substitution of a disubstituted benzene

Break It Down **Predict the major product(s) of the following reaction.**

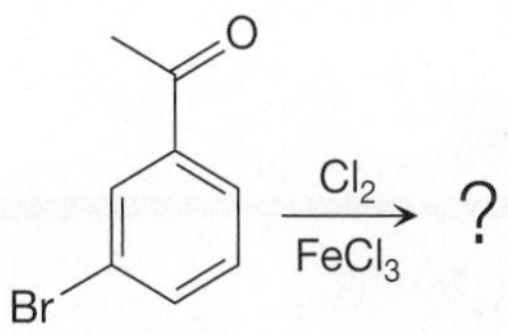

O
Br
Cl2
FeCl3
?

(continued)

Think	Solve
Is the C(=O)CH_3 group an ortho/para director or a meta director? Which positions on the ring does it favor?	The C(=O)CH_3 group is a meta director and favors substitution of the proton at C-5, indicated by the red arrow at the right. 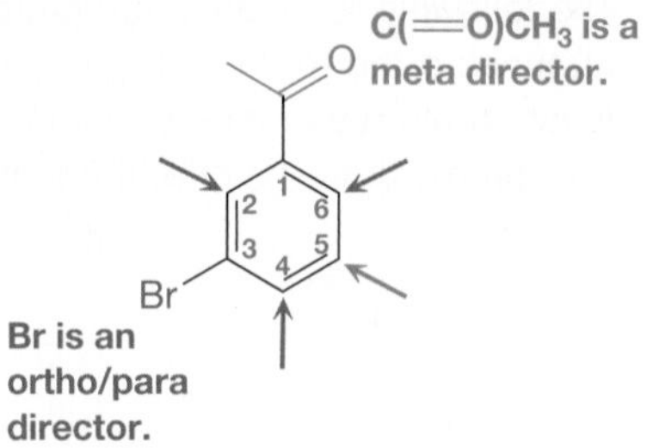 C(=O)CH3 is a meta director. Br is an ortho/para director.
Is Br an ortho/para director or a meta director?	Br is an ortho/para director, so it favors substitution of the protons at C-2, C-4, and C-6, indicated by the blue arrows above.
Are the substituents in agreement? If not, which one wins out?	The two substituents disagree on where to direct the incoming electrophile. Br wins out because it appears nearer the beginning of Table 25-3 (p. 1210); it is more activating.
How do we take into account steric hindrance?	C-2 is disfavored by steric hindrance because that position is ortho to two substituents. Therefore, chlorination is favored at just C-4 and C-6, as shown here. 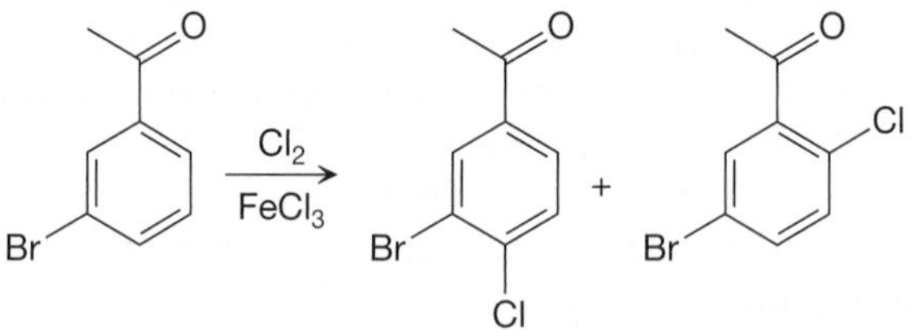 Cl2 FeCl3

Try It Predict the major product(s) of the following reaction.

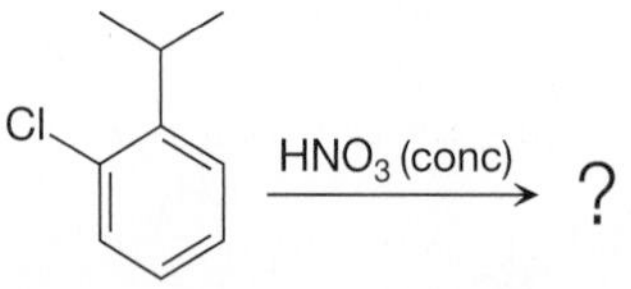
HNO3 (conc)
?

Let's now consider how the presence of multiple substituents on a benzene ring impacts the *overall* rate of electrophilic aromatic substitution. In general:

> Substituent effects on the *overall* rate of electrophilic aromatic substitution are essentially additive.
> - Each activating group increases the reaction rate, and each deactivating group decreases the reaction rate.
> - The extent to which the rate is increased or decreased by each substituent depends on how strongly activating or deactivating that substituent is.

Figure 25-6 shows the rates of chlorination for several methylated benzenes. Each methyl group is *activating*, so as the number of methyl groups increases, so does the

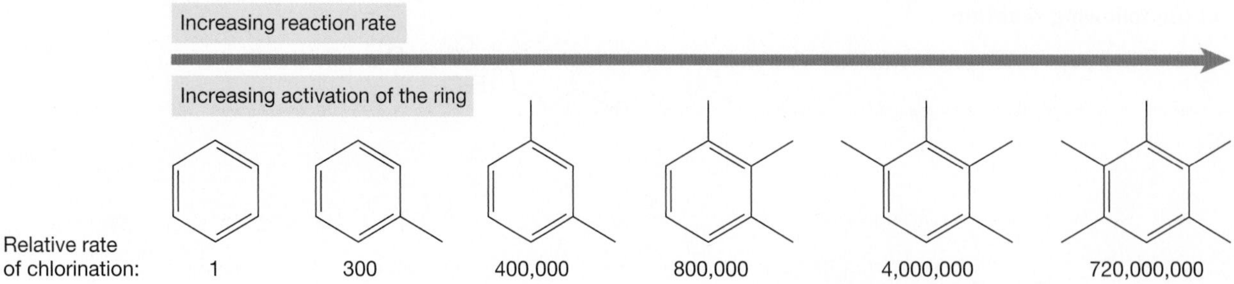
Increasing reaction rate
Increasing activation of the ring
Relative rate of chlorination:
1
300
400,000
800,000
4,000,000
720,000,000

FIGURE 25-6 Additivity of substituent effects on reaction rate With each additional alkyl group, the ring becomes increasingly activated toward electrophilic aromatic substitution, which causes the reaction rate to increase.

reaction rate. (As explored further in Problem 25.14 at the end of the chapter, the reaction rates are also sensitive to the particular locations of the substituents relative to one another about the ring.)

SOLVED PROBLEM **25.5**

How to predict the relative rates of electrophilic aromatic substitution for various substituted benzenes

Break It Down Rank the rate of electrophilic aromatic substitution from slowest to fastest for the following aromatic rings.

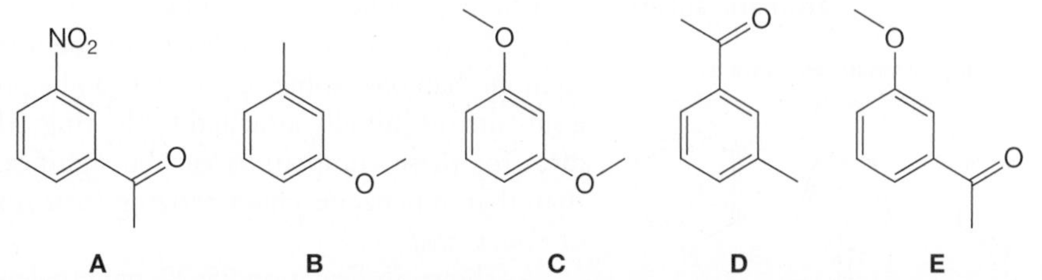

NO2
O
O
O
O
O
O
O
A
B
C
D
E

Think	Solve
Are the substituents on the ring activating or deactivating? How strongly?	According to Table 25-3 (p. 1210), the substituents have the following characteristics: NO_2 is strongly deactivating (in **A** only) C(=O)CH_3 is moderately deactivating (in **A**, **D**, and **E**) CH_3 is weakly activating (in **B** and **D**) OCH_3 is strongly activating (in **B**, **C**, and **E**)
How can these effects be added together to arrange the rings from most deactivated to most activated?	**Most deactivated** **A:** strongly deactivating (NO_2) + moderately deactivating [C(=O)CH_3] **D:** moderately deactivating [C(=O)CH_3] + weakly activating (CH_3) **E:** moderately deactivating [C(=O)CH_3] + strongly activating (OCH_3) **B:** weakly activating (CH_3) + strongly activating (OCH_3) **C:** strongly activating (OCH_3) + strongly activating (OCH_3) **Most activated**
How does the activation or deactivation of the rings correspond to relative reaction rates?	The more deactivated the ring is, the slower the rate of electrophilic aromatic substitution will be. The more activated the ring is, the faster the reaction will be. Therefore, the rate of reaction will increase in the order **A** < **D** < **E** < **B** < **C**.

Try It Rank the rate of electrophilic aromatic substitution from slowest to fastest for the following aromatic rings.

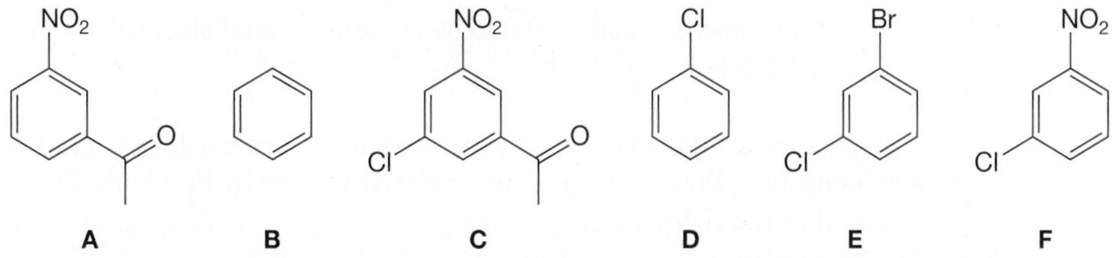

NO2
NO2
Cl
Br
NO2
O
Cl
O
Cl
Cl
A
B
C
D
E
F

SECTION 25.7 OBJECTIVES

You will be able to:

1. Draw the possible isomers produced when naphthalene, furan, pyrrole, or pyridine undergoes electrophilic aromatic substitution.
2. Predict the major products when furan, pyrrole, or pyridine undergoes electrophilic aromatic substitution.
3. Explain why furan, pyrrole, and pyridine are either activated or deactivated toward electrophilic aromatic substitution.

25.7 Electrophilic Aromatic Substitution Involving Aromatic Rings other than Benzene

Benzene is but one of many aromatic compounds. Recall from Section 14.7 that naphthalene is an aromatic hydrocarbon consisting of two fused rings, whereas furan, pyrrole, and pyridine are *heterocyclic* aromatic compounds (**Figure 25-7**).

Like benzene, the aromatic compounds in Figure 25-7 are resistant to electrophilic addition. When treated with electrophiles, these compounds instead tend to undergo substitution to preserve their aromaticity.

Naphthalene, furan, pyrrole, and pyridine undergo many of the same electrophilic aromatic substitution reactions as benzene. Unlike benzene, however, each of these aromatic compounds has at least two chemically distinct C atoms, so more than one isomeric product can be produced even without a substituent initially attached to the ring. Moreover, the reaction rates for these compounds can be significantly faster or slower than that of benzene, characterizing their rings as either *activated* or *deactivated*.

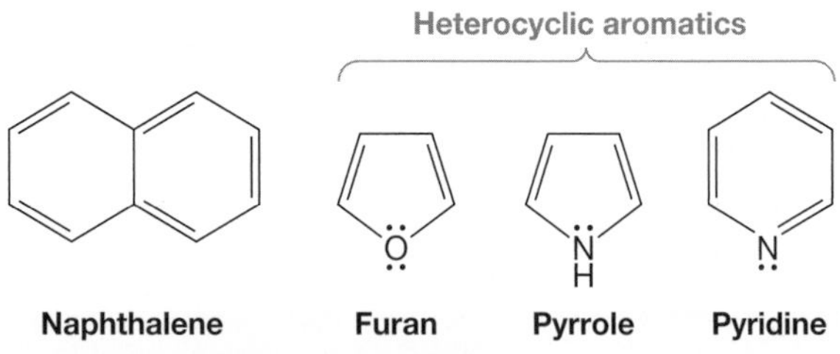

Heterocyclic aromatics
O
N
H
N
Naphthalene
Furan
Pyrrole
Pyridine

FIGURE 25-7 Some aromatic rings other than benzene These compounds can undergo electrophilic aromatic substitution because they have aromatic rings.

As shown in Equation 25-27, naphthalene has two chemically distinct H atoms, one designated α and the other β, and the substitution of each yields a different product:

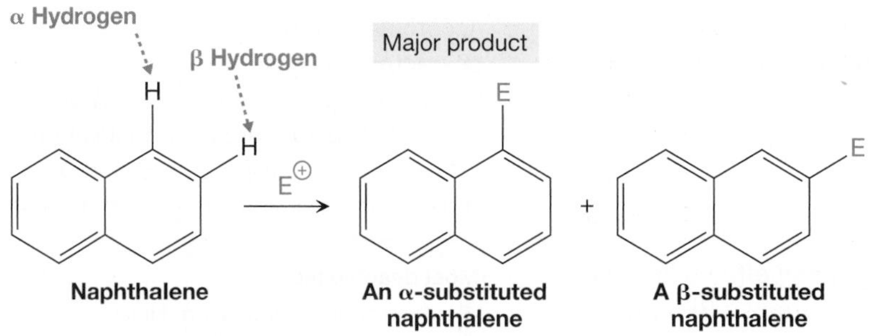

α Hydrogen
β Hydrogen
H
H
Major product
E
E
$E^{\oplus}$
+
Naphthalene
An α-substituted naphthalene
A β-substituted naphthalene

(25-27)

As indicated in Equation 25-27:

> Electrophilic aromatic substitution on naphthalene generally favors the α product over the β product.

Because the α product is favored, the arenium ion produced when an electrophile attaches to the α position must be more stable than that produced when an electrophile attaches to the β position.

Electrophilic aromatic substitution reactions of naphthalene are generally faster than those of benzene. Therefore:

> Naphthalene is considered to be activated toward electrophilic aromatic substitution.

This means the arenium ion intermediate of naphthalene is more stable than that of benzene. (These outcomes are explored further in Problems 25.28 and 25.29 at the end of the chapter.)

YOUR TURN **25.16**

Draw the mechanism that leads to the formation of each product in Equation 25-27.

Like naphthalene, pyrrole has two chemically distinct H atoms and can undergo electrophilic aromatic substitution to produce two isomeric products, as shown in Equation 25-28. Pyridine has three chemically distinct H atoms and can undergo electrophilic aromatic substitution to produce three isomeric products, as shown in Equation 25-29:

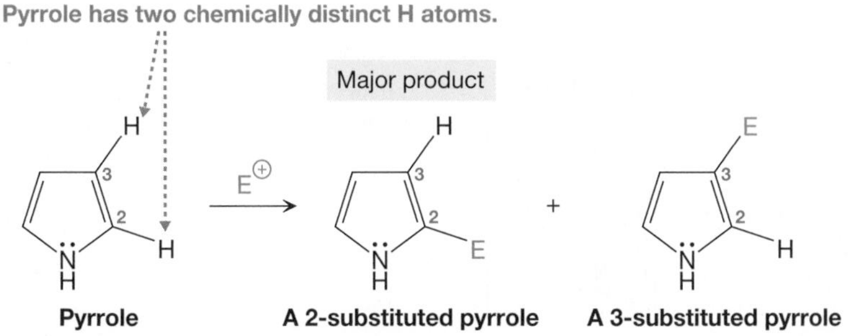

Pyrrole has two chemically distinct H atoms.
Major product
Pyrrole
A 2-substituted pyrrole
A 3-substituted pyrrole

(25-28)

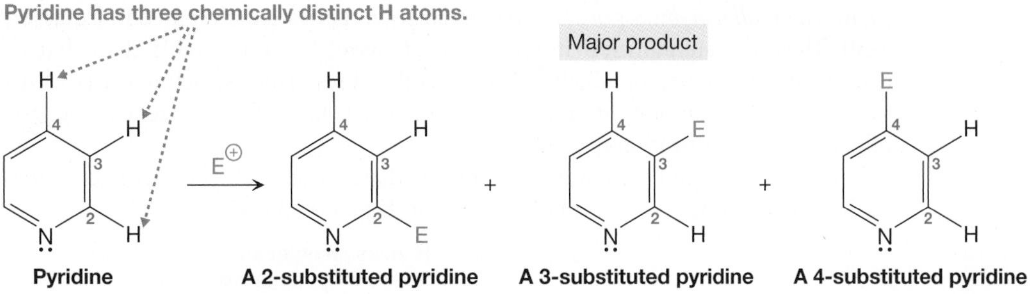

Pyridine has three chemically distinct H atoms.
Major product
Pyridine
A 2-substituted pyridine
A 3-substituted pyridine
A 4-substituted pyridine

(25-29)

YOUR TURN **25.17**

Draw the mechanism that leads to the formation of each product in Equations 25-28 and 25-29.

As indicated in Equations 25-28 and 25-29:

- Electrophilic aromatic substitution of pyrrole takes place primarily at C-2.
- Electrophilic aromatic substitution of pyridine occurs primarily at C-3.

Moreover, electrophilic aromatic substitution of pyrrole is typically faster than that of benzene, whereas electrophilic aromatic substitution of pyridine is typically slower than that of benzene. That is:

- Pyrrole is *activated* toward electrophilic aromatic substitution.
- Pyridine is *deactivated* toward electrophilic aromatic substitution.

Why should the regiochemistry and reaction rates differ so much as a result of different ring sizes? As we saw with the reactions involving substituted benzenes, the answer lies with the relative stabilities of the arenium ion intermediates.

Equation 25-30 shows the arenium ion intermediates produced when an electrophile attaches to pyrrole at C-2 or C-3. The arenium ion intermediate produced when the electrophile attaches to C-2 (Eq. 25-30a) has three total resonance structures, whereas the intermediate produced when the electrophile attaches to C-3 has just two resonance structures (Eq. 25-30b). Consequently, the arenium ion intermediate is more stable when substitution occurs at C-2, which is why the 2-substituted pyrrole is the major product.

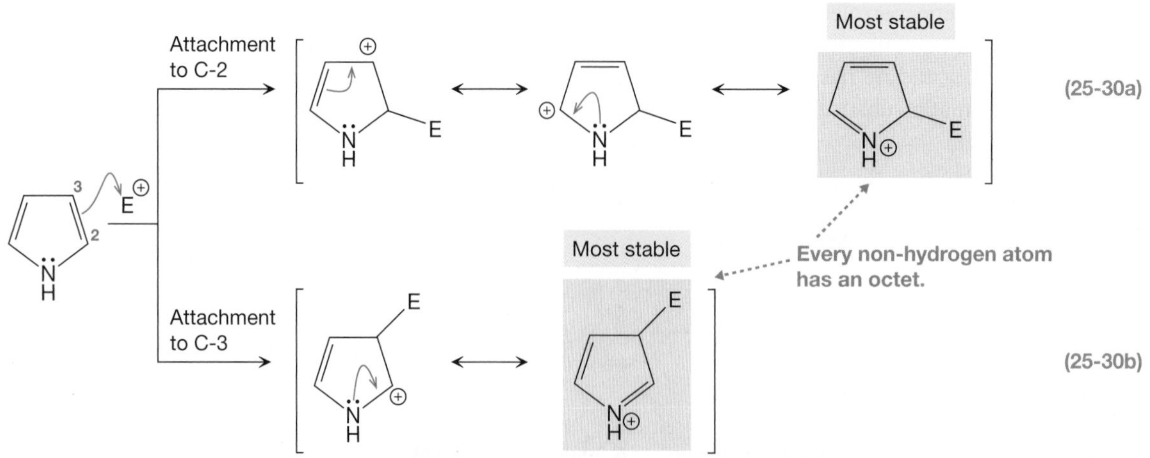

Most stable
Attachment to C-2
(25-30a)
Most stable
Every non-hydrogen atom has an octet.
Attachment to C-3
(25-30b)

Notice, too, that each of pyrrole's arenium ion intermediates has a resonance structure in which *all non-hydrogen atoms have their octet*: these are highlighted in Equation 25-30. Thus, the arenium ion intermediate of pyrrole is more stable than that of unsubstituted benzene, for which no such stabilized resonance structure exists. With a more stable arenium ion intermediate, pyrrole reacts faster than benzene in electrophilic aromatic substitution reactions.

Now let's examine the arenium ion intermediates produced when an electrophile attaches to C-2 or C-3 of pyridine, as shown in Equation 25-31:

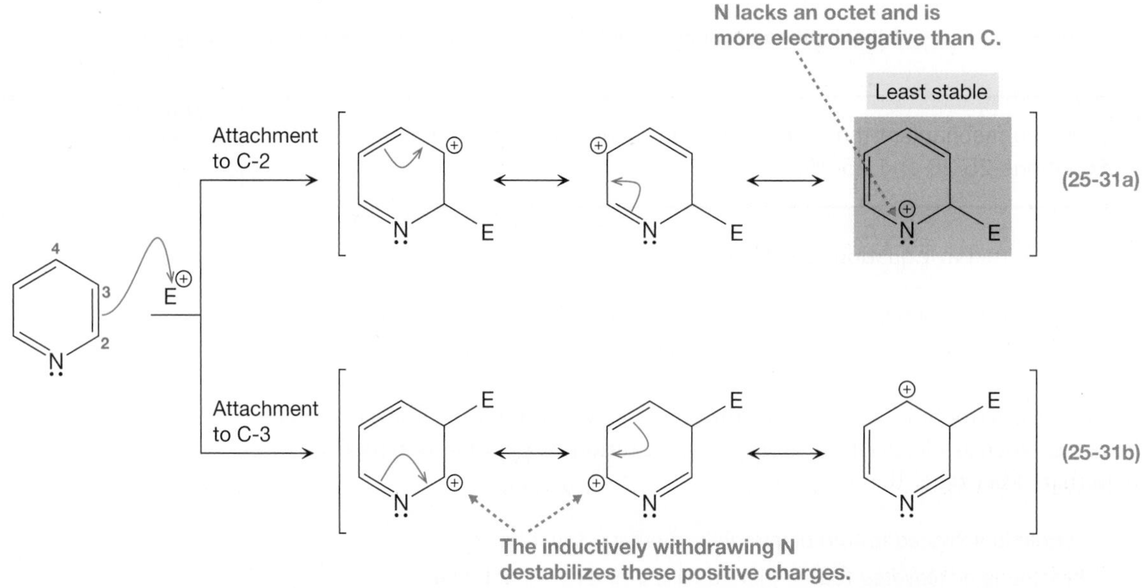

N lacks an octet and is more electronegative than C.
Least stable
Attachment to C-2
(25-31a)
Attachment to C-3
(25-31b)
The inductively withdrawing N destabilizes these positive charges.

Both arenium ion intermediates have three resonance structures, and each resonance structure has one positively charged atom lacking an octet. The resonance structure highlighted in Equation 25-31a, however, is *much* less stable than the others because the atom lacking an octet is N. In the other resonance structures, the atom lacking an octet is C, which is less electronegative and can therefore better accommodate a positive charge.

The most stable arenium ion intermediate of pyridine (Eq. 25-31b) is still less stable than that of benzene. In the arenium ion intermediate of pyridine, the N atom is electron-withdrawing and destabilizes the adjacent positive charge in two of the resonance structures. With a less stable arenium ion intermediate, pyridine undergoes electrophilic aromatic substitution more slowly than benzene.

YOUR TURN **25.18**

Using E^+ as a generic electrophile, draw the mechanism for electrophilic aromatic substitution of pyridine at C-4. Using resonance arguments, determine whether the corresponding arenium ion intermediate is more stable or less stable than the one in Equation 25-31b.

SECTION 25.8 OBJECTIVES

You will be able to:

1. Show how to use azo coupling to connect one aromatic ring to another, and identify which ring should be activated.
2. Explain how a compound with aromatic rings that are connected by an azo group can function as a dye.

25.8 Azo Coupling and Azo Dyes

Recall from Section 24.9c that an arenediazonium ion can be produced from the corresponding aromatic amine, as shown in Equation 25-32 for the conversion of aniline to the benzenediazonium ion:

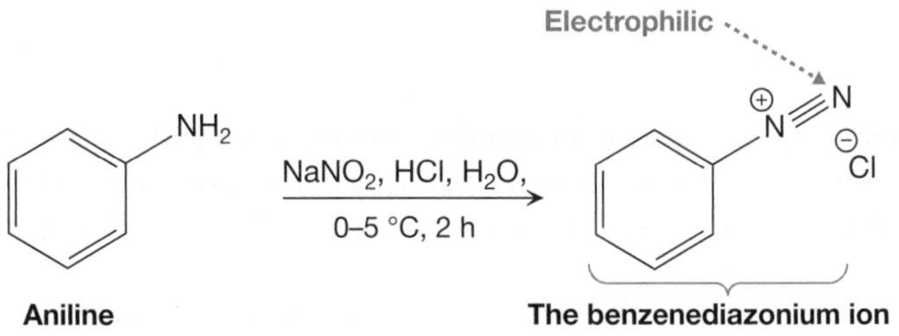

Electrophilic
NH2
NaNO2, HCl, H2O,
0–5 °C, 2 h
N
N
Cl
Aniline
The benzenediazonium ion

(25-32)

In Section 24.9c, we saw that such arenediazonium ions can undergo a wide variety of substitution reactions because of the excellent leaving group ability of $N_2(g)$. With the N_2^+ group still attached, however, the arenediazonium ion is electrophilic and can undergo electrophilic aromatic substitution with another aromatic ring, as shown in Equation 25-33:

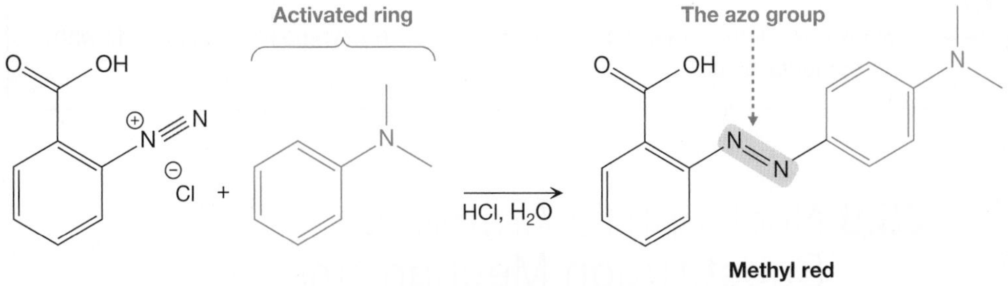

Activated ring
The azo group
O
OH
N
N
Cl
+
N
HCl, H2O
Methyl red

(25-33)

In the product, the —N=N— group, called the **azo group**, connects the two aromatic rings together, so this type of reaction is called **azo coupling**.

YOUR TURN **25.19**

Draw the mechanism for the azo coupling reaction in Equation 25-33.

Arenediazonium ions are not very stable, so they are usually kept at relatively low temperatures to prevent them from degrading. These low temperatures slow the electrophilic aromatic substitution reaction, so to compensate, the aromatic ring that reacts with the arenediazonium ion is generally activated.

Notice that the azo group allows one aromatic ring to be conjugated to the other. Such extended conjugation can enable molecules to absorb visible light, which gives the compound a color that is detectable by the human eye (see Recall box). The product of Equation 25-33, for example, is methyl red, which is a pH indicator that is red when the solution's pH is less than about 4.4 and is yellow when the pH is above about 6.2 (**Figure 25-8**).

◀ RECALL

As we learned in Section 16.10, π electrons absorb photons in the UV and visible regions of the spectrum. As conjugation of the π system increases, the wavelengths of the absorbed photons become longer because the energy between the highest occupied and lowest unoccupied molecular orbitals (HOMO and LUMO) decreases.

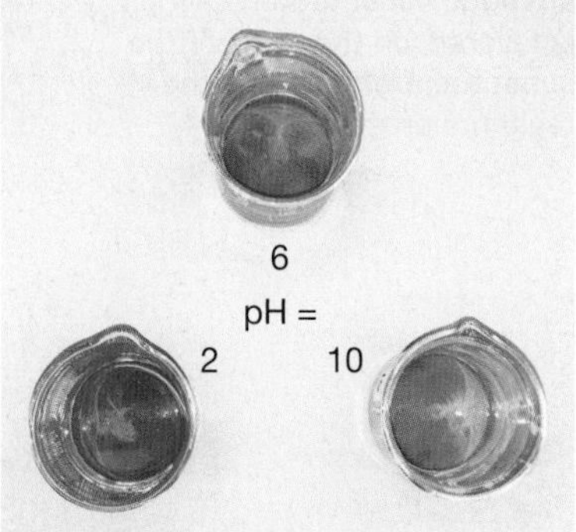

6
pH =
2
10

FIGURE 25-8 **Methyl red**

CONNECTIONS 25.5

A life-saving dye Prontosil, the azo dye shown here, was the first example discovered of a sulfa drug, a class of antibiotics. Prontosil is more accurately classified as a prodrug, meaning that it is a precursor that is metabolized into the active form of the drug (in this case, sulfanilamide).

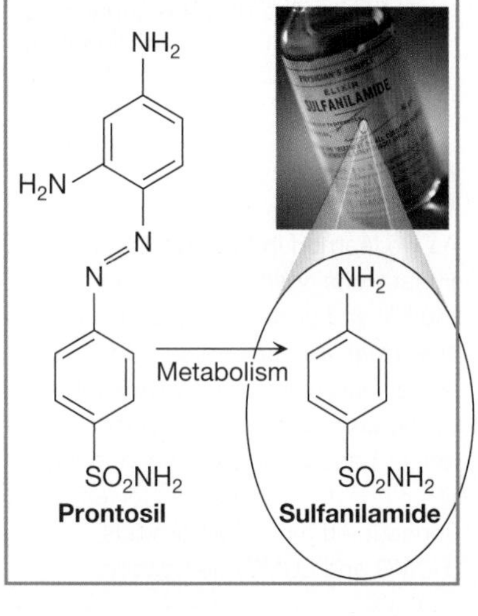

NH2
H2N
N
N
Metabolism
NH2
SO2NH2
SO2NH2
Prontosil
Sulfanilamide

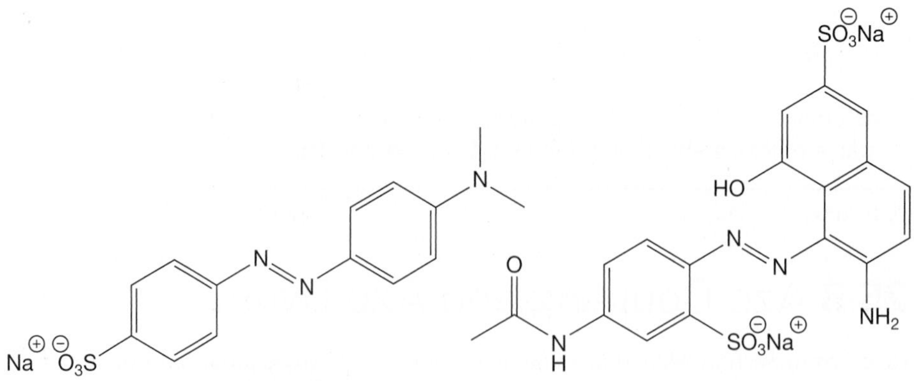

Methyl orange

Acid red 37

FIGURE 25-9 Azo dyes used in clothing

Methyl red is an example of an **azo dye**: a compound with a distinct color that results from the azo coupling of aromatic rings. The particular color of the dye depends on the identities of the aromatic rings as well as the substituents that are attached.

Many of the dyes used in the clothing industry are azo dyes, often having one or more sulfonate groups, as illustrated in **Figure 25-9**. A sulfonate group serves two purposes. First, it enables the dye to be soluble in water. Second, the ionic character of the sulfonate group allows the dye to bind to the polymer molecules that make up the fabric. Thus, the dye is *colorfast*, meaning that it does not bleed substantially when the dyed item is washed.

YOUR TURN 25.20

Show how methyl orange and acid red 37 can be synthesized, beginning with an arenediazonium ion.

SECTION 25.9 OBJECTIVES

You will be able to:

1. Draw the mechanism for a nucleophilic aromatic substitution reaction that proceeds through a Meisenheimer complex or a benzyne intermediate.
2. Determine which type of aromatic substitution reaction is favored, on the basis of the substituent effects and the reagents present.

25.9 Nucleophilic Aromatic Substitution Mechanisms

The aromatic substitution reactions examined in Chapter 24 and thus far here in Chapter 25 proceed by mechanisms involving an aromatic ring attacking an electrophile: so-called *electrophilic aromatic substitution* reactions. In this section, we examine **nucleophilic aromatic substitution reactions** in which the aromatic ring is attacked by a nucleophile. We explore two types of such reactions: one that proceeds by a *nucleophilic addition–elimination* mechanism and the other by an *elimination–nucleophilic addition* mechanism.

Nucleophilic aromatic substitution reactions are fundamentally different from electrophilic aromatic substitution reactions. However, nucleophilic aromatic substitution reactions are presented here because they can be used in syntheses in conjunction with, or as an alternative to, electrophilic aromatic substitution reactions.

25.9a Nucleophilic Aromatic Substitution by the Addition–Elimination Mechanism: The Meisenheimer Complex

When 1-chloro-2-nitrobenzene is treated with excess ethanamine ($CH_3CH_2NH_2$), *N*-ethyl-2-nitroaniline is produced (Eq. 25-34). Overall, Cl is replaced by an ethylamino group ($NHCH_2CH_3$):

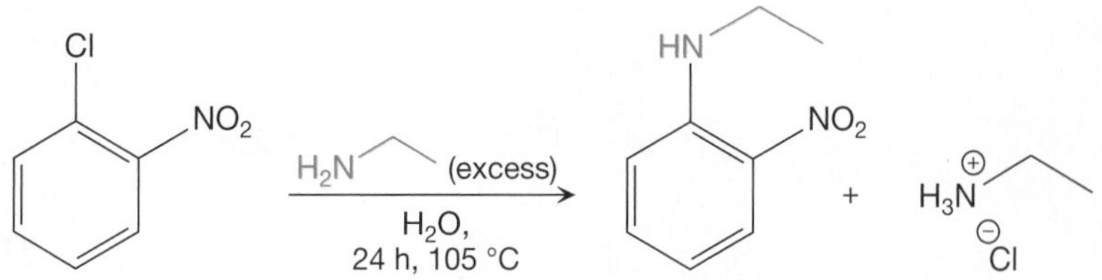
Cl
NO2
H2N (excess)
H2O,
24 h, 105 °C
HN
NO2
+
H3N
Cl

1-Chloro-2-nitrobenzene *N*-Ethyl-2-nitroaniline 99% (25-34)

The mechanism for this aromatic substitution reaction is shown in Equation 25-35:

Mechanism for nucleophilic aromatic substitution via a Meisenheimer complex (Eq. 25-34)

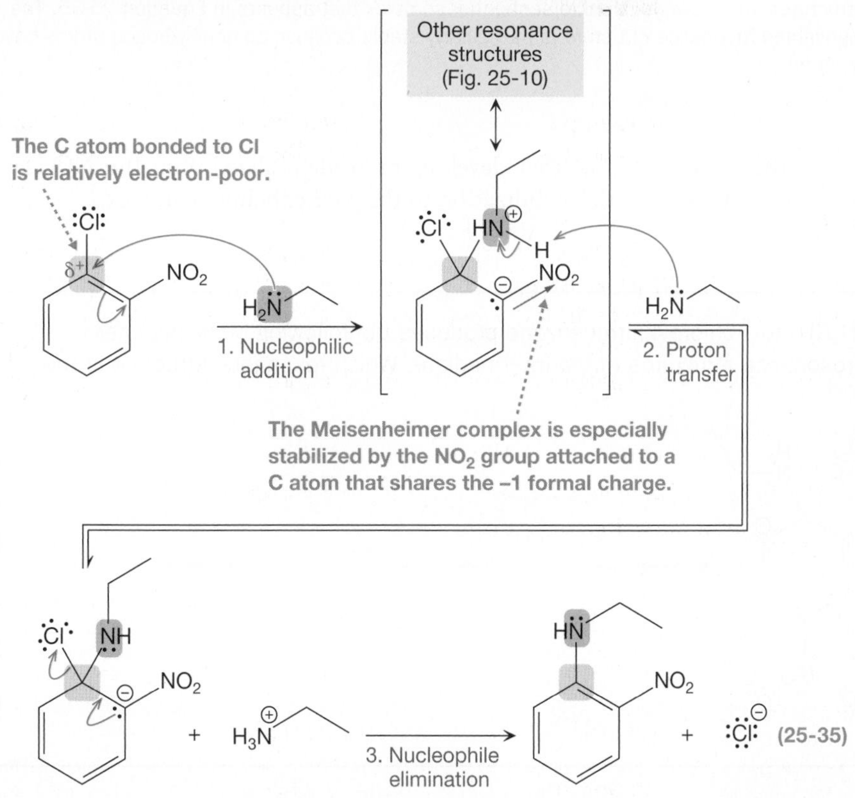
Other resonance structures (Fig. 25-10)
The C atom bonded to Cl is relatively electron-poor.
Cl
δ+
NO2
H2N
1. Nucleophilic addition
Cl
HN
H
NO2
H2N
2. Proton transfer
The Meisenheimer complex is especially stabilized by the NO2 group attached to a C atom that shares the –1 formal charge.
Cl
NH
NO2
+
H3N
3. Nucleophile elimination
HN
NO2
+
Cl
(25-35)

In Step 1, the amine acts as a nucleophile, attacking the C atom bonded to Cl. This nucleophilic addition step is the slow step (and is therefore rate-determining) because aromaticity is disrupted and two new charges appear. Step 2 is a proton transfer, and in Step 3, Cl^- departs as a leaving group and aromaticity is restored.

As we can see in Equation 25-35, Step 1 is assisted by the partial positive charge on the carbon atom to which the leaving group is attached, which sets up the electron-rich-to-electron-poor driving force. Step 1 is also assisted by the resonance delocalization of the negative charge in the intermediate, called a **Meisenheimer complex**, as shown in **Figure 25-10** (next page).

Not every nucleophilic aromatic substitution reaction is feasible:

> Nucleophilic aromatic substitution that proceeds through a Meisenheimer complex generally requires at least one moderately or strongly electron-withdrawing group ortho or para to the leaving group.

Notice that this is indeed the case with the reaction shown in Equation 25-34. As we can see in the resonance structures in Figure 25-10, this relative positioning

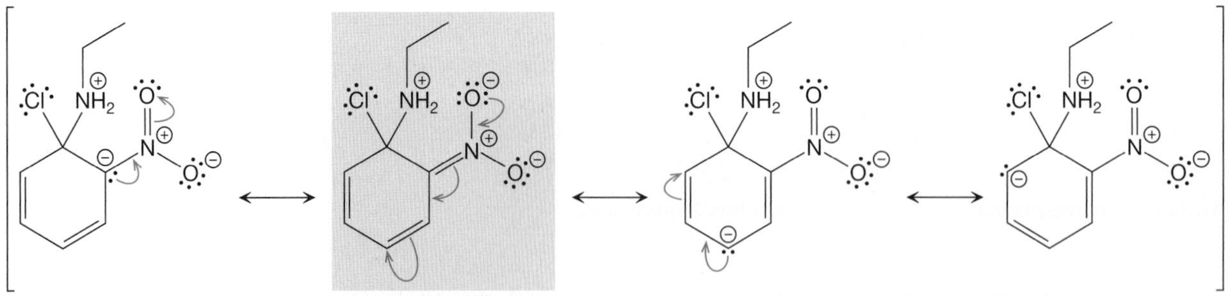
The negative charge is delocalized onto the NO_2 substituent.

FIGURE 25-10 Resonance stabilization in a Meisenheimer complex Resonance structures are shown for the Meisenheimer complex that appears in Equation 25-35. The highlighted resonance structure is particularly stable because all non-hydrogen atoms have an octet.

allows the negative charge that develops to be delocalized onto the NO_2 group, which provides substantial stabilization to the Meisenheimer complex.

YOUR TURN 25.21

Nucleophilic addition of $CH_3CH_2NH_2$ to 1-chloro-4-nitrobenzene produces the following Meisenheimer complex. Draw the additional resonance structures of the intermediate. Which resonance structure is the most stable? Why?

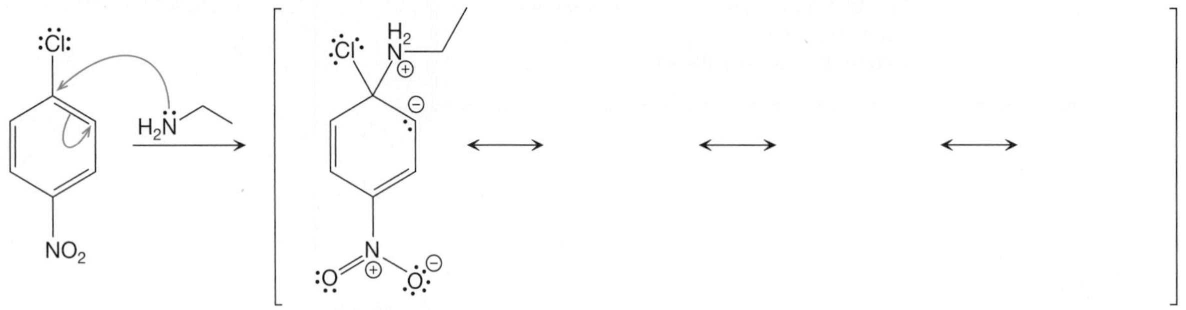

The importance of the number and locations of the strongly electron-withdrawing groups relative to the leaving group is demonstrated by the reaction in Equation 25-36, which is a substitution similar to the one in Equation 25-34. The reaction requires less heat because the leaving group is ortho to one NO_2 group and para to the other:

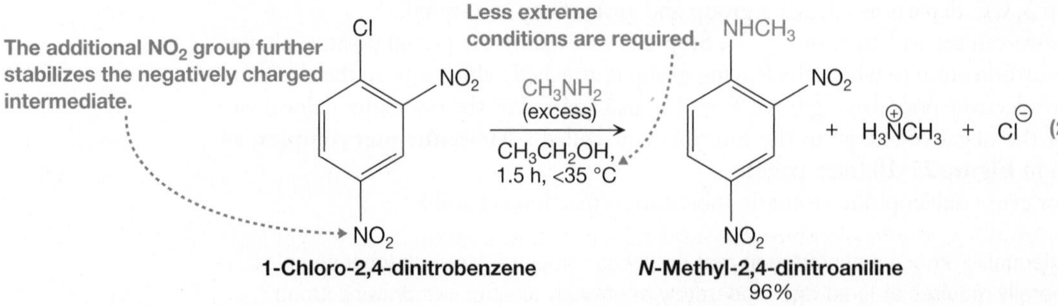
The additional NO_2 group further stabilizes the negatively charged intermediate.
Less extreme conditions are required.
CH_3NH_2 (excess)
CH_3CH_2OH, 1.5 h, <35 °C
1-Chloro-2,4-dinitrobenzene
N-Methyl-2,4-dinitroaniline
96%

(25-36)

YOUR TURN 25.22

Draw the complete, detailed mechanism for this reaction and predict the major product. Will this reaction be faster or slower than the one in Equation 25-36?

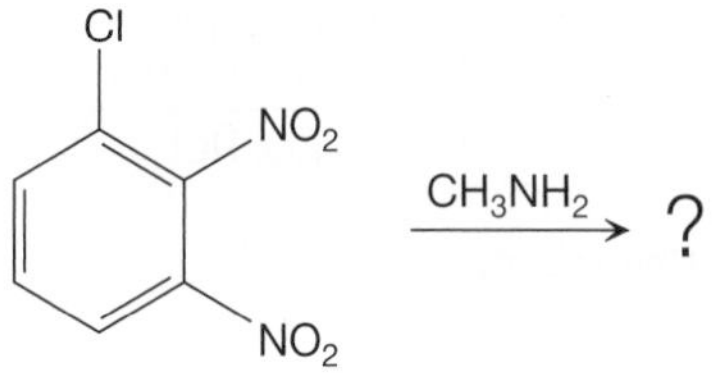
Cl
NO2
NO2
CH3NH2
?

Nucleophilic aromatic substitution can be carried out with a variety of leaving groups, even F^- (Eq. 25-37). The major restriction is that the leaving group needs to be more stable (i.e., less basic) than the incoming nucleophile, because the more stable of the two will depart in the elimination step.

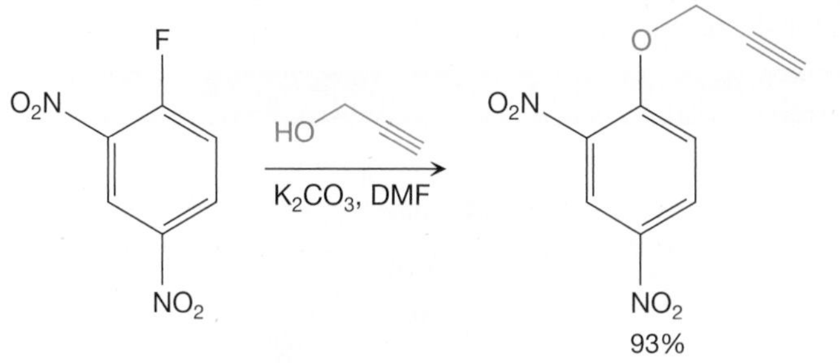
F
O2N
NO2
HO
K2CO3, DMF
O
O2N
NO2
93%

(25-37)

GREEN CHEMISTRY

I. Gallardo and G. Guirado of Barcelona have shown that nucleophilic aromatic substitution reactions can be carried out electrochemically, using a room-temperature ionic liquid (called BMIM • BF_4) as the solvent and conducting electrolyte. These alternative reactions significantly reduce waste and decrease risks associated with high-temperature reactions.

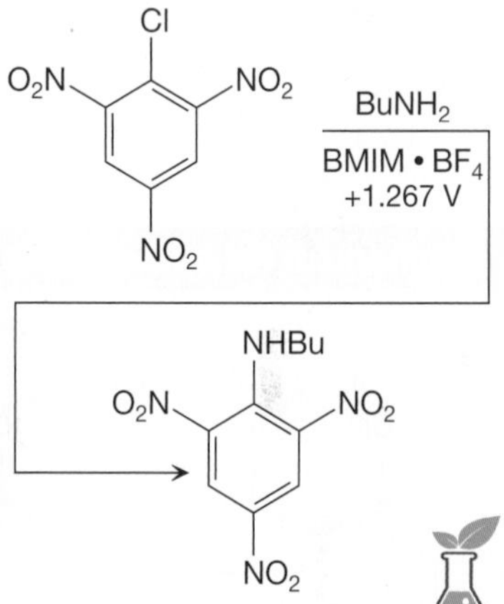
Cl
O2N
NO2
NO2
BuNH2
BMIM • BF4
+1.267 V
NHBu
O2N
NO2
NO2

YOUR TURN 25.23

Draw the complete, detailed mechanism and the major product of each of the following reactions.

(a)

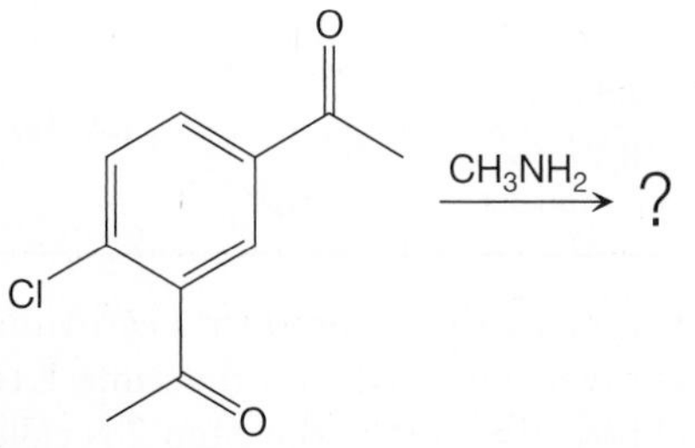
O
Cl
O
CH3NH2
?

(b)

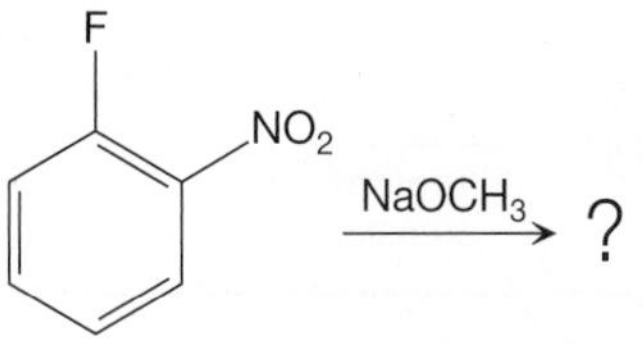
F
NO2
NaOCH3
?

(c)

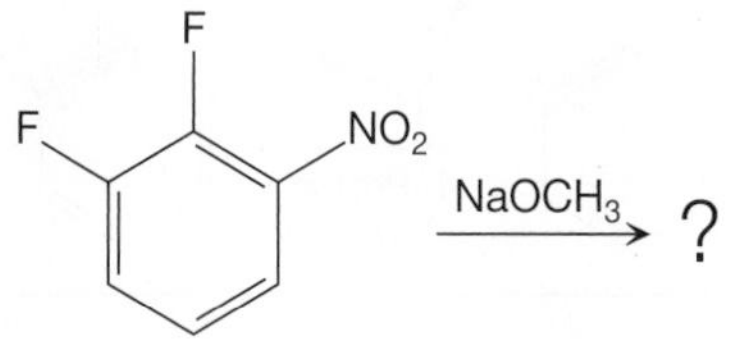
F
F
NO2
NaOCH3
?

25.9b Nucleophilic Aromatic Substitution by the Elimination–Addition Mechanism: The Benzyne Intermediate

Even without a strongly electron-withdrawing group attached to the ring, a halobenzene can still undergo nucleophilic substitution. For example, chlorobenzene can react with sodium hydroxide to produce phenol (Eq. 25-38), or it can react with potassium amide to produce aniline (Eq. 25-39). These reactions typically require extreme conditions, however, such as the presence of a very strong base, high temperatures, or both.

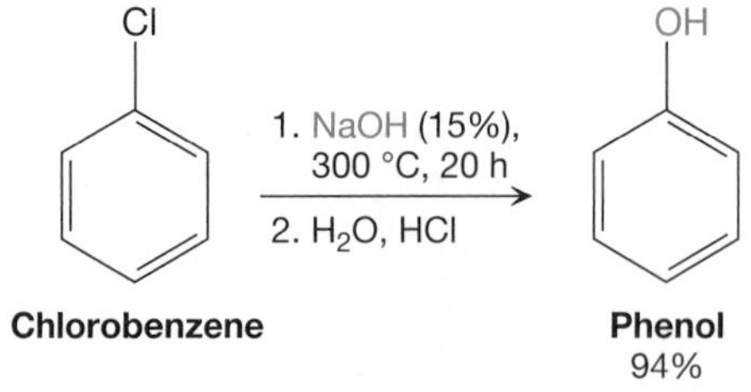
Cl
1. NaOH (15%), 300 °C, 20 h
2. H_2O, HCl
OH
Chlorobenzene
Phenol
94%

(25-38)

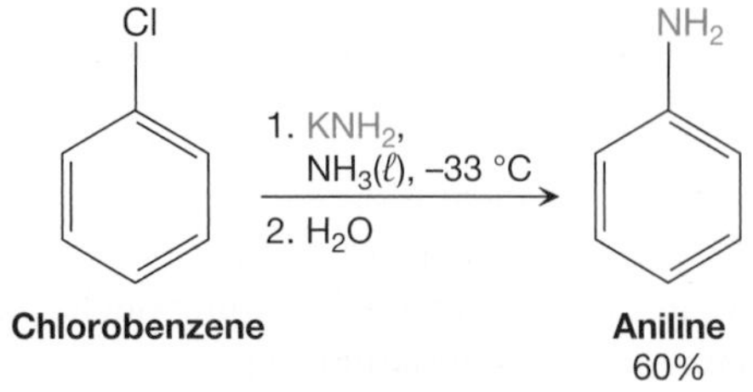
Cl
1. KNH_2, $NH_3(\ell)$, −33 °C
2. H_2O
NH_2
Chlorobenzene
Aniline
60%

(25-39)

◀ RECALL

E1cb stands for *elimination, unimolecular, conjugate base*, and it describes a β elimination that consists of a deprotonation followed by nucleophile elimination. In Section 19.9, we saw that the product of an aldol addition undergoes E1cb to lose H_2O and complete an aldol condensation.

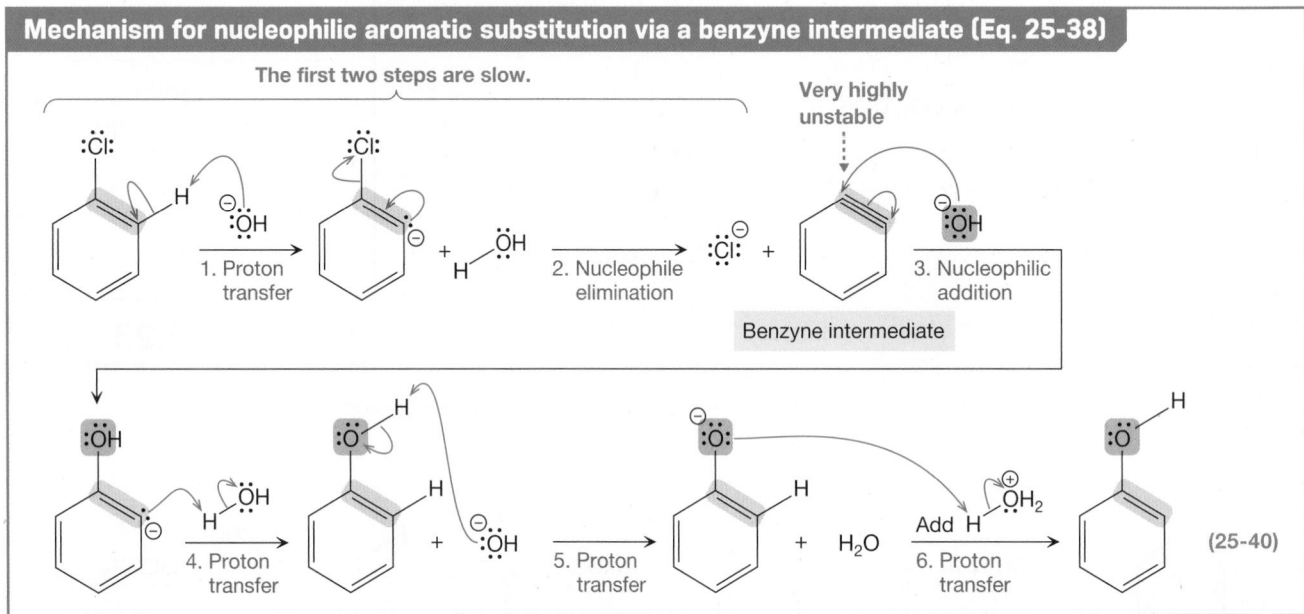

The requirement for these extreme conditions is explained by Equation 25-40, the mechanism for the reaction in Equation 25-38:

Mechanism for nucleophilic aromatic substitution via a benzyne intermediate (Eq. 25-38)

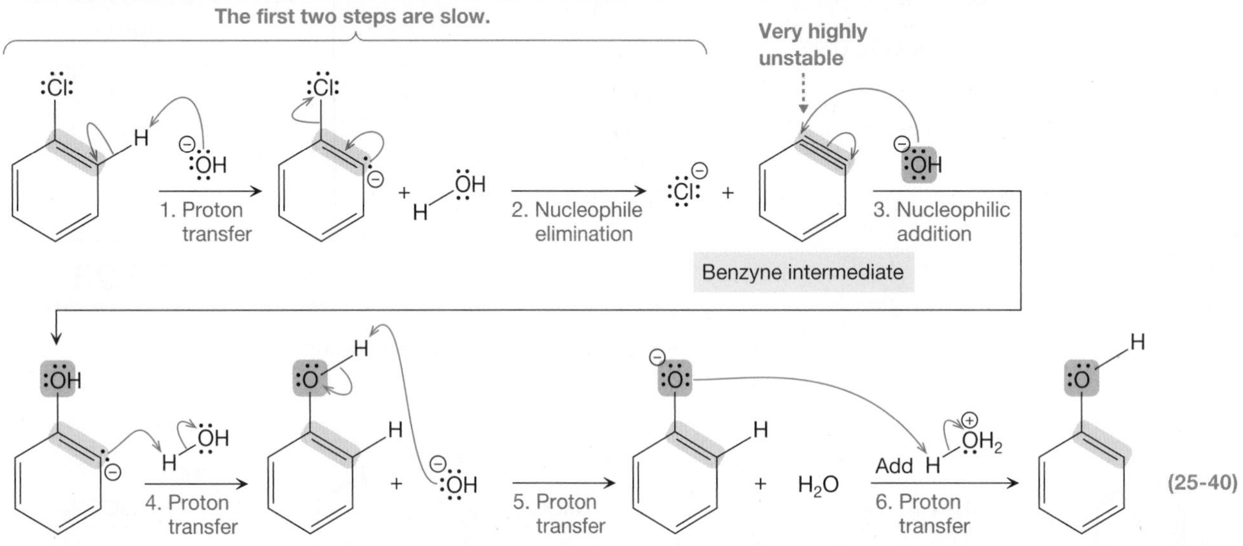
The first two steps are slow.
Very highly unstable
1. Proton transfer
2. Nucleophile elimination
3. Nucleophilic addition
Benzyne intermediate
4. Proton transfer
5. Proton transfer
Add H
6. Proton transfer

(25-40)

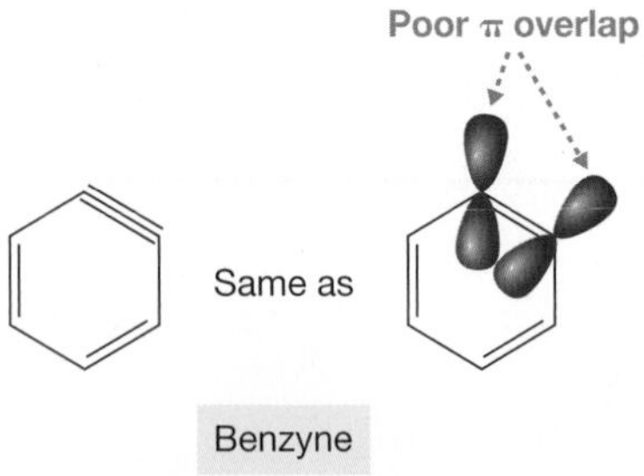
Poor π overlap
Same as
Benzyne

FIGURE 25-11 Instability of the benzyne intermediate The *p* orbitals in the plane of the ring intersect at ~60°. Thus, their overlap is less than ideal and the resulting π bond is rather weak, making benzyne highly reactive.

In Step 1, the base removes a proton from the aromatic ring to produce a carbanion, and in Step 2, the leaving group departs. These two steps make up the same E1cb mechanism we saw in Section 19.9 (see Recall box). The product of Step 2 is called a **benzyne intermediate**, because it has a C≡C triple bond in its Lewis structure. In Step 3, the benzyne intermediate undergoes nucleophilic addition to produce a deprotonated form of phenol. In Step 4, a proton from H_2O adds to produce phenol, whose OH group is irreversibly deprotonated in Step 5 due to the basic conditions. Acid workup in Step 6 replenishes that proton to produce the overall uncharged product.

Both Steps 1 and 2 are relatively slow. Step 1 is slow because a very unstable carbanion is produced, which is why a strong base is required. Step 2 is slow because the benzyne product is highly unstable due to the large amount of angle strain caused by the triple bond. The ideal bond angle for each triply bonded C atom is 180°, but the constraints of the ring require it to be ~120°. This has a major effect on the strength of the π bond that is in the plane of the ring, as indicated in **Figure 25-11**. Adjacent *p* orbitals are parallel in a normal π bond, but they are ~60° apart in this case. As a result, the overlap of those adjacent p orbitals is significantly decreased, making the π bond abnormally weak and benzyne highly reactive.

YOUR TURN 25.24

The mechanism for the reaction in Equation 25-39 is as follows, but the curved arrows have been omitted. Supply the missing curved arrows, and write the name of the elementary step below each reaction arrow.

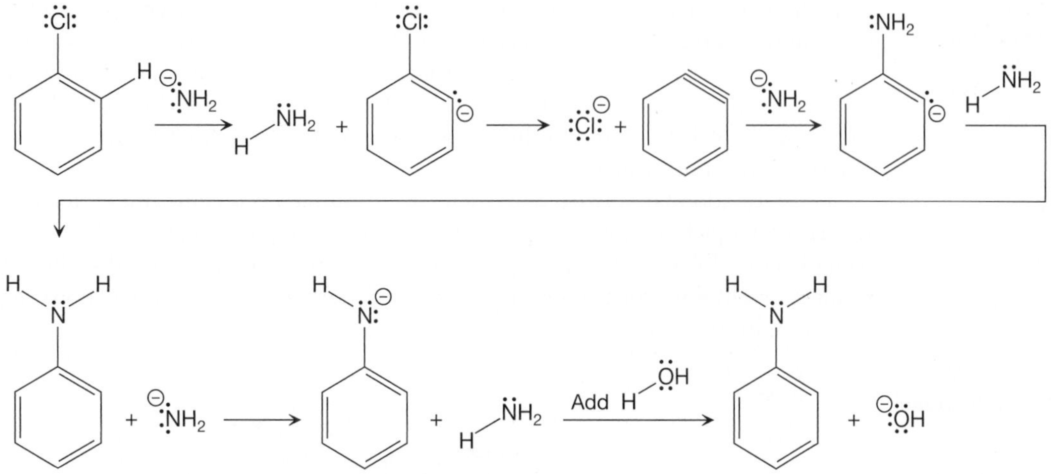

Add H–OH

Because benzyne is highly reactive, it has not been isolated and purified, though some experiments indirectly support its existence. One of the most compelling is a carbon-14 labeling experiment, shown in Equation 25-41. When the Cl atom in chlorobenzene is bonded to a ^{14}C atom, reaction with KNH_2 produces a roughly equal mixture of two isomers of aniline, where the NH_2 group is bonded to the ^{14}C atom in one isomer and to a ^{12}C atom in the other.

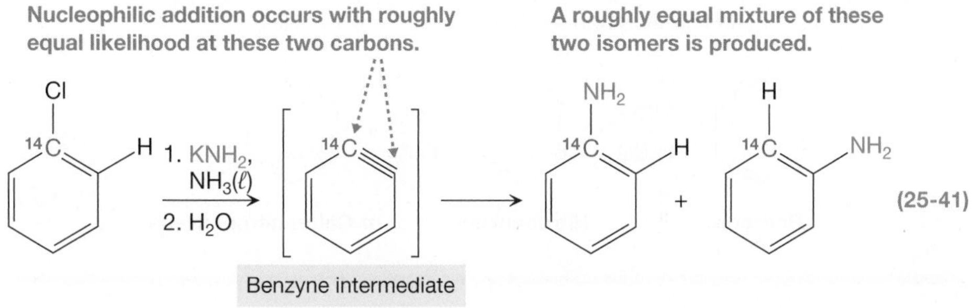

Nucleophilic addition occurs with roughly equal likelihood at these two carbons.
A roughly equal mixture of these two isomers is produced.
1. KNH2, NH3(ℓ)
2. H2O
Benzyne intermediate

(25-41)

These results are consistent with benzyne's symmetry about the triple bond. Thus, nucleophilic addition to benzyne occurs with essentially equal likelihood at both alkyne C atoms. Addition to the alkyne ^{14}C atom produces one isomer, and addition to the alkyne ^{12}C atom produces the other.

YOUR TURN 25.25

(a) Draw the mechanism for the formation of phenol from bromobenzene and sodium hydroxide shown in the first reaction.
(b) Suppose, instead, that the deuterium-labeled bromobenzene shown in the second reaction were used. What percentage of the product would you expect to contain the deuterium atom? Explain.

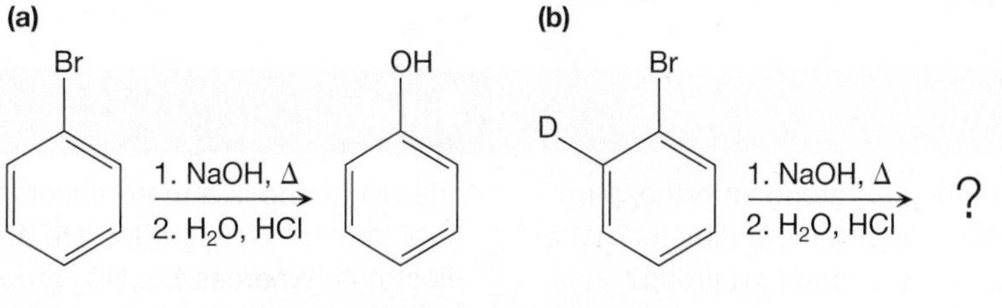

(a)
1. NaOH, Δ
2. H2O, HCl
(b)
1. NaOH, Δ
2. H2O, HCl
?

SECTION 25.10 OBJECTIVES

You will be able to:

1. Explain how the order in which substituents are attached to benzene by consecutive electrophilic aromatic substitution reactions can impact the outcome.
2. Design the synthesis of a disubstituted benzene from benzene so that the relative positioning of the substituents matches the ortho/para- or meta-directing ability of one of the substituents.

25.10 Organic Synthesis: Considerations of Regiochemistry, and Attaching Groups in the Correct Order

As discussed in Section 25.1, a substituent that is already on the aromatic ring greatly influences the site of reaction in a subsequent electrophilic aromatic substitution. In a synthesis that requires successive substitutions, then, we must choose wisely the order in which the reactions are carried out. For example, how would you synthesize *m*-chloronitrobenzene from benzene (**Figure 25-12**)? Benzene can be nitrated by treating it with concentrated HNO_3 in H_2SO_4, and it can be chlorinated with Cl_2 in the presence of $FeCl_3$. The synthesis therefore must involve both a nitration and a chlorination, but in which order?

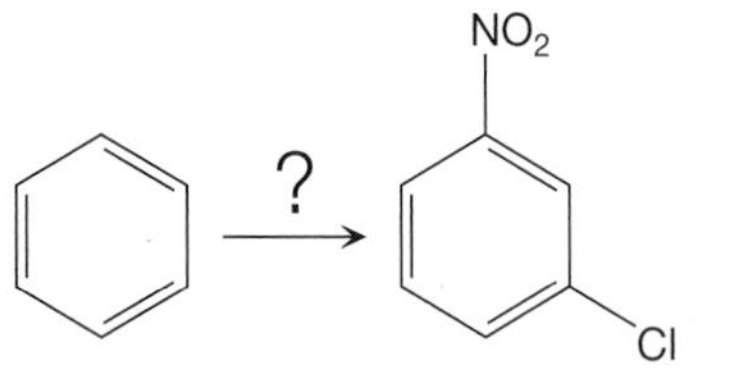

NO2
?
Cl
Benzene
m-Chloronitrobenzene

FIGURE 25-12 How can we synthesize *m*-chloronitrobenzene from benzene?

If chlorination takes place first, then we encounter a problem with regiochemistry, as shown in Equation 25-42. The Cl substituent in chlorobenzene is an ortho/para director (Table 25-1, p. 1200), so a subsequent nitration would yield as the major products *o*-chloronitrobenzene and *p*-chloronitrobenzene. Our target, however, is *m*-chloronitrobenzene.

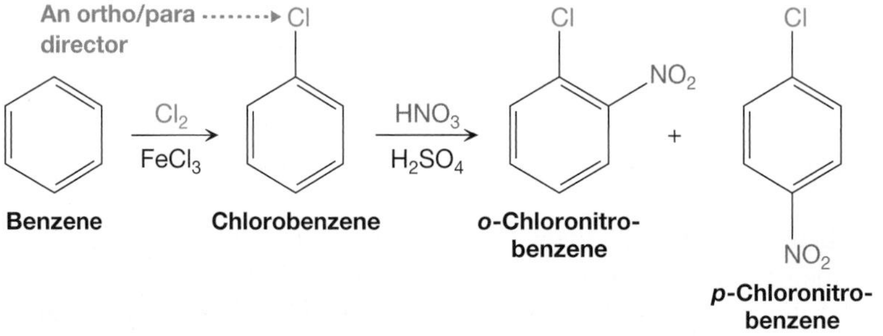

An ortho/para director
Cl
Cl2
FeCl3
HNO3
H2SO4
Cl
NO2
+
Cl
NO2
Benzene
Chlorobenzene
o-Chloronitro-benzene
p-Chloronitro-benzene

(25-42)

If the nitration of benzene is carried out first (Eq. 25-43), the correct isomer will then be produced as the major product, because the nitro group in nitrobenzene is a meta director.

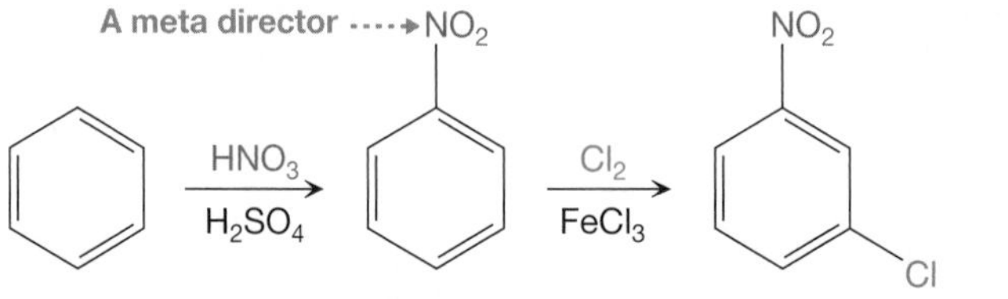

A meta director
NO2
HNO3
H2SO4
Cl2
FeCl3
NO2
Cl
Benzene
Nitrobenzene
m-Chloronitrobenzene

(25-43)

SOLVED PROBLEM **25.6**

How to design the synthesis of a disubstituted benzene

Break It Down How would you synthesize *p*-isopropylnitrobenzene from benzene?

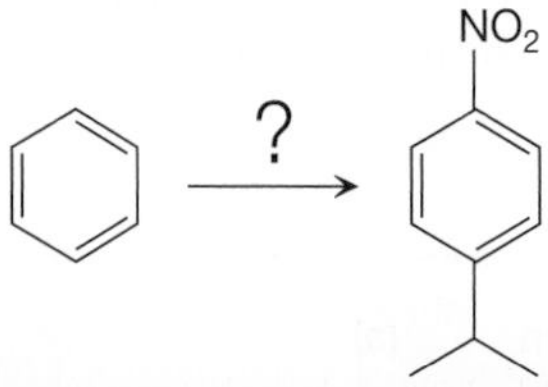

NO2
?

Think	Solve
Is the NO_2 group an ortho/para director or a meta director? What about the isopropyl group?	The NO_2 group is a meta director, whereas the isopropyl group is an ortho/para director. Both groups are attached by an atom that has no lone pairs of electrons. Whereas the NO_2 group is electron-withdrawing, the isopropyl group is electron-donating.

(continued)

Which group should be on the ring prior to the second substitution?

The target is the para isomer, so when the second substitution occurs, an ortho/para director should already be attached to the ring. Therefore, the isopropyl group should be attached first, as shown here.

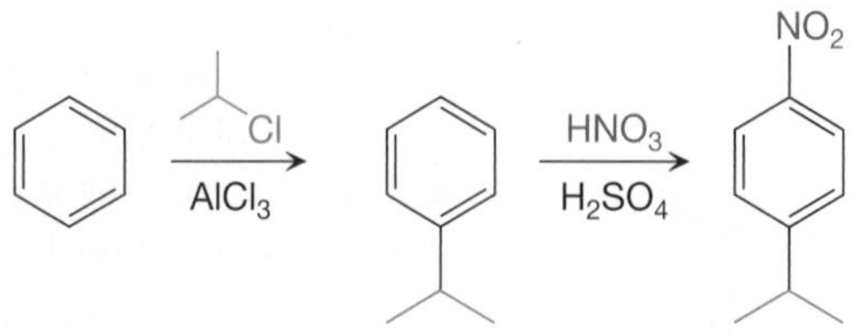

Cl
AlCl3
HNO3
H2SO4
NO2

Try It Show how to synthesize this compound from benzene.

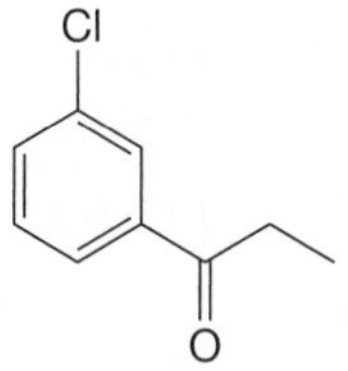

Cl
O

The order in which substitutions are carried out can be an issue, too, because some substituents on the ring make certain electrophilic aromatic substitution reactions unfeasible. Friedel–Crafts reactions, for example, do not occur with moderately or highly deactivated rings (Section 25.4). Therefore, we must avoid placing these kinds of deactivating groups on the ring prior to carrying out a Friedel–Crafts reaction. How, then, would you synthesize *m*-nitroacetophenone from benzene (**Figure 25-13**)?

This synthesis requires two substitutions: a nitration and a Friedel–Crafts acylation. Because both the NO_2 group and the acetyl group are meta directors (Table 25-1), regiochemistry will not depend on the order in which these substitutions are carried out. We do need to avoid attempting a Friedel–Crafts reaction on nitrobenzene, however, because the benzene ring would be highly deactivated by the nitro substituent (Eq. 25-44):

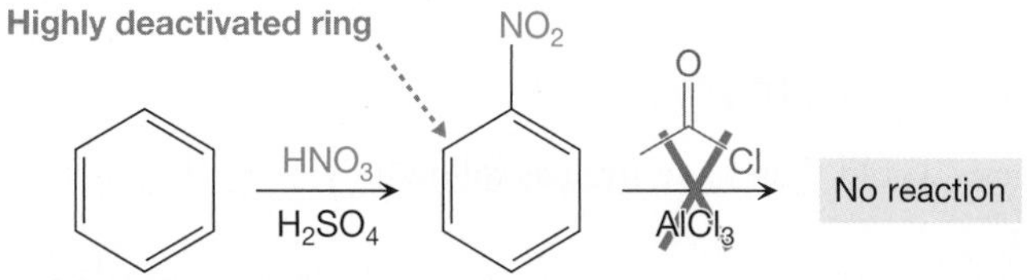

Highly deactivated ring
NO2
HNO3
H2SO4
O
Cl
AlCl3
No reaction

(25-44)

Instead, nitration should be the final step, leaving the Friedel–Crafts acylation as the first step. Equation 25-45 shows the best way to carry out this synthesis:

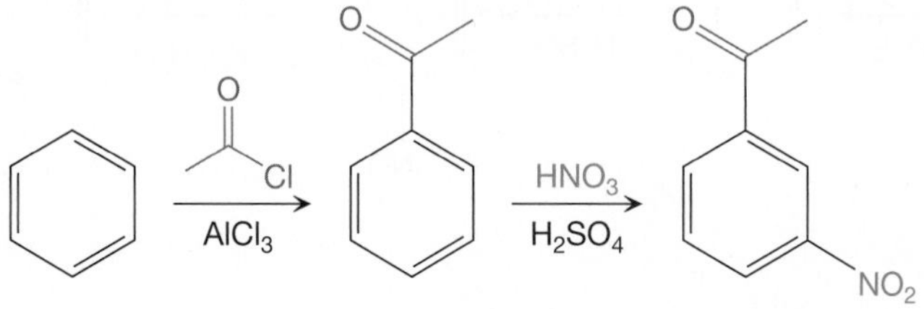

O
Cl
AlCl3
O
HNO3
H2SO4
O
NO2

(25-45)

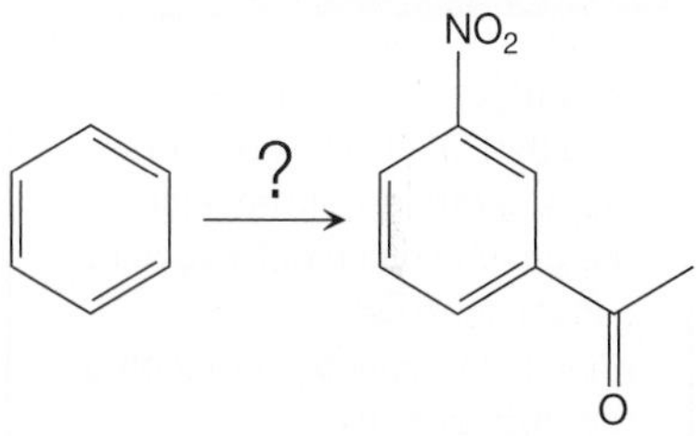

?
NO2
O

Benzene **m-Nitroacetophenone**

FIGURE 25-13 How can we synthesize *m*-nitroacetophenone from benzene?

25.11 Organic Synthesis: Interconverting Ortho/Para and Meta Directors

SECTION 25.11 OBJECTIVES

You will be able to:

1. Identify disubstituted benzenes in which the relative positioning of the substituents does not match the ortho/para- or meta-directing abilities of either substituent.
2. Design an effective synthesis of disubstituted benzenes from benzene that involves interconverting ortho/para and meta directors.

Section 25.10 showed that, when devising a synthesis that requires carrying out successive electrophilic aromatic substitution reactions, the order in which ortho/para- and meta-directing groups are added to the ring can impact whether the synthesis is

These substituents are para to each other but are both meta directors.

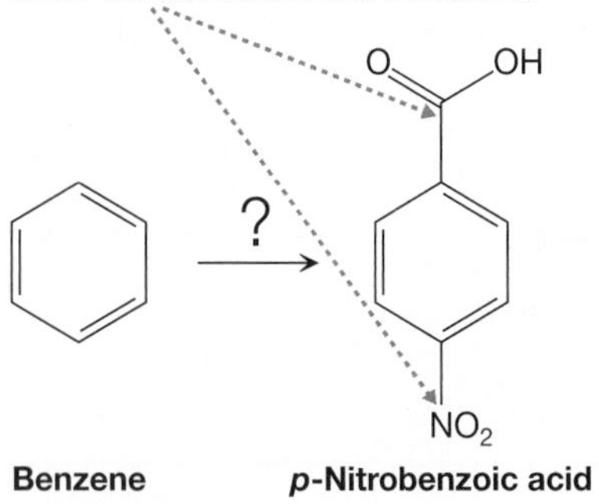

OH
O
?
NO_2
Benzene
p-Nitrobenzoic acid

FIGURE 25-14 How can we synthesize *p*-nitrobenzoic acid from benzene?

successful. With this in mind, we revisit some reactions presented in Chapter 24 that can be used to interconvert ortho/para- and meta-directing substituents. Thus, the regiochemistry of a substitution that takes place later in a synthesis is not automatically predetermined by the ortho/para- or meta-directing ability of a substituent added earlier.

Recall from Section 24.9a, for example, that treating an alkylbenzene with a hot, basic solution of $KMnO_4$ yields benzoic acid on acid workup (Eq. 25-46). The substituent in the reactant is an alkyl group, which is an ortho/para director, but the substituent in the product is a CO_2H group, which is a meta director.

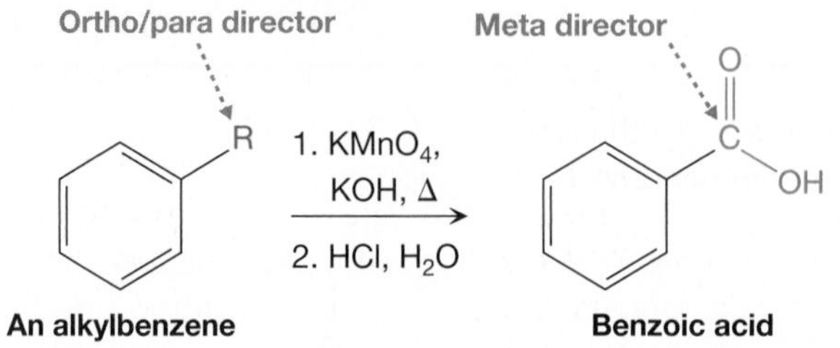

Ortho/para director
Meta director
R
1. $KMnO_4$,
KOH, Δ
2. HCl, H_2O
O
C
OH
An alkylbenzene
Benzoic acid

(25-46)

How can we use this reaction in the synthesis of *p*-nitrobenzoic acid from benzene (**Figure 25-14**)? The CO_2H substituent and the NO_2 substituent are both meta directors (Table 25-1), but the desired product is the para isomer. We can work around this problem by making sure that the second substituent is added after an ortho/para director is already on the ring, such as an alkyl group. With that in mind, the target could be made from oxidation of the *p*-nitroalkylbenzene, as shown in the following retrosynthetic analysis:

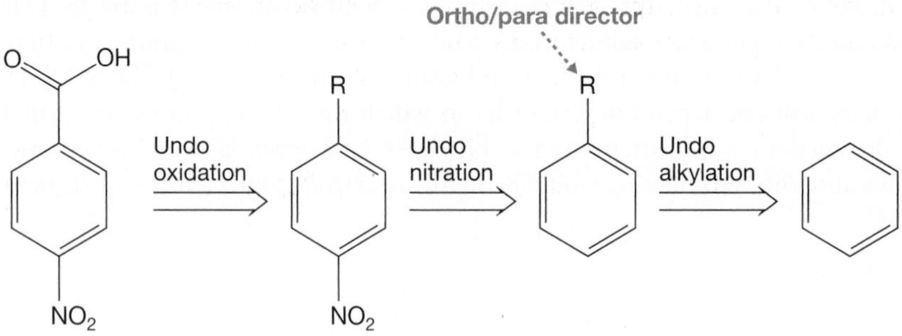

Ortho/para director
O
OH
R
R
Undo oxidation
Undo nitration
Undo alkylation
NO_2
NO_2

(25-47)

The final synthesis would then be written as follows:

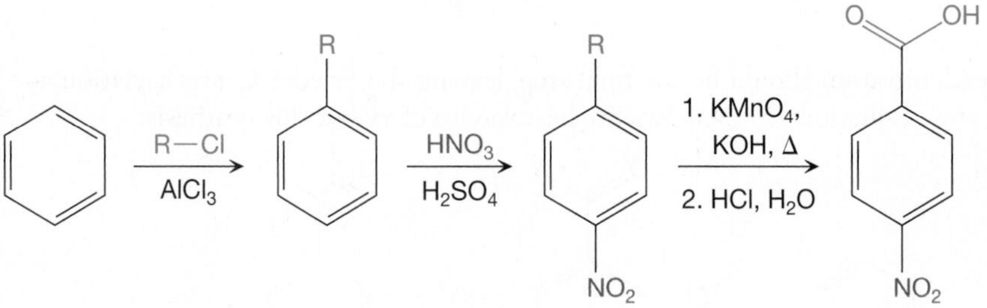

R
R
O
OH
R—Cl
$AlCl_3$
HNO_3
H_2SO_4
1. $KMnO_4$,
KOH, Δ
2. HCl, H_2O
NO_2
NO_2

(25-48)

CONNECTIONS 25.6

Numb gum *p*-Nitrobenzoic acid (Fig. 25-14) is a precursor in the synthesis of procaine, the generic name of Novocain, a local anesthetic that was popular in dentistry for much of the 20th century.

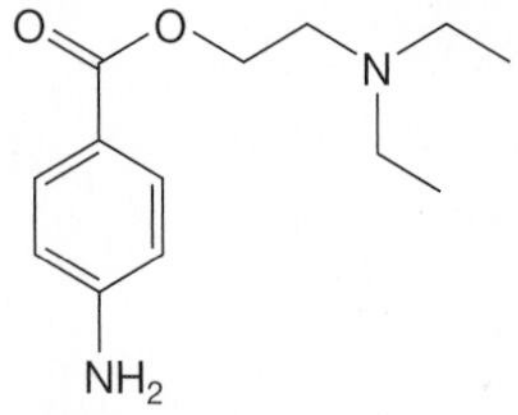

O
O
N
NH_2

Procaine

YOUR TURN 25.26

Can you reorder the steps in the synthesis in Equation 25-48 to produce *m*-nitrobenzoic acid instead?

YOUR TURN 25.27

Show how to synthesize benzene-1,4-dicarboxylic acid ($HO_2C—C_6H_4—CO_2H$) from benzene, using ethanol as your only other source of carbon.

We can achieve even greater flexibility in synthesis with the ability to convert a meta director into an ortho/para director. We have already encountered two types of reductions that accomplish this. One, which was discussed in Section 24.9b, is the reduction of a nitro (NO_2) group to an amino (NH_2) group. The second is the reduction of a carbonyl (C=O) group on a ketone or aldehyde to a methylene (CH_2) group. Recall from Section 20.4 that this carbonyl reduction can be done in either acidic conditions (Clemmensen reduction), basic conditions (Wolff–Kishner reduction), or neutral conditions (Raney-nickel reduction).

The utility of these reactions is demonstrated when *m*-bromoethylbenzene is synthesized from benzene (**Figure 25-15**). The substituents in the target are meta to each other, so the second of two electrophilic aromatic substitution reactions must be carried out with a meta director already on the ring. Both the Br and the CH_2CH_3 substituents are ortho/para directors (Table 25-1), however, so a meta director must be converted into an ortho/para director after the second substitution reaction is carried out.

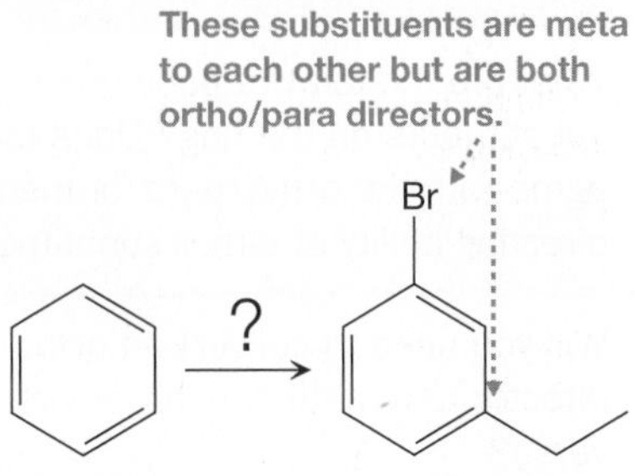
These substituents are meta to each other but are both ortho/para directors.
Br
?
Benzene
m-Bromoethylbenzene

FIGURE 25-15 How can we synthesize *m*-bromoethylbenzene from benzene?

Thinking retrosynthetically, the meta director could be an acetyl group that is reduced to the ethyl group, as in Equation 25-49:

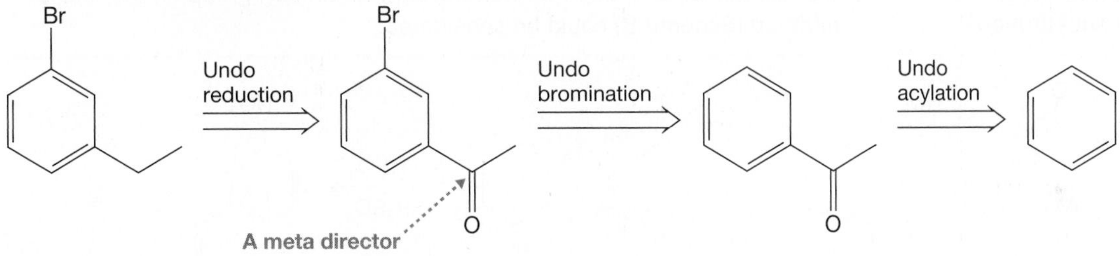
Br
Undo reduction
Br
Undo bromination
Undo acylation
O
O
A meta director

(25-49)

In the forward direction, the synthesis would be written as in Equation 25-50:

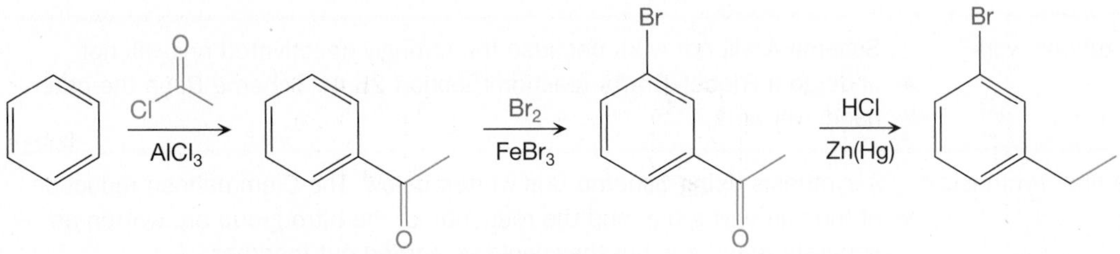
O
Cl
AlCl3
Br2
FeBr3
Br
O
HCl
Zn(Hg)
O
Br

(25-50)

SOLVED PROBLEM **25.7**

How to design the synthesis of a disubstituted benzene that calls for interconverting ortho/para and meta directors

Break It Down **Show how to synthesize *m*-(2-methylpropyl)aniline from benzene.**

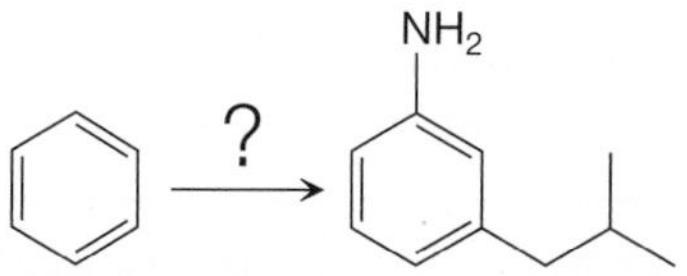

?
NH_2

Think	Solve
What are the relative positions of the substituents on the ring? Does that agree with the ortho/para- or meta-directing ability of either substituent?	The substituents are meta to each other on the ring. The NH_2 group is an ortho/para director, and so is the alkyl group.
Will you need to convert an ortho/para director to a meta director or vice versa?	Because neither substituent is a meta director, the second substitution requires a meta director on the ring that can then be converted to an ortho/para director.
What meta director can be converted into the NH_2 group? What meta director can be converted into the alkyl group?	The NO_2 group can be converted to an NH_2 group (Section 24.9b), and an acyl group [C(=O)R] can be converted into an alkyl group (Section 20.4).
With one of those meta-directing groups already on the ring, what would be the appropriate second substitution?	With a nitro group on the ring, a Friedel–Crafts acylation could be considered (Scheme A, below). Alternatively, with an acyl group on the ring, a nitration (Scheme B) could be considered.

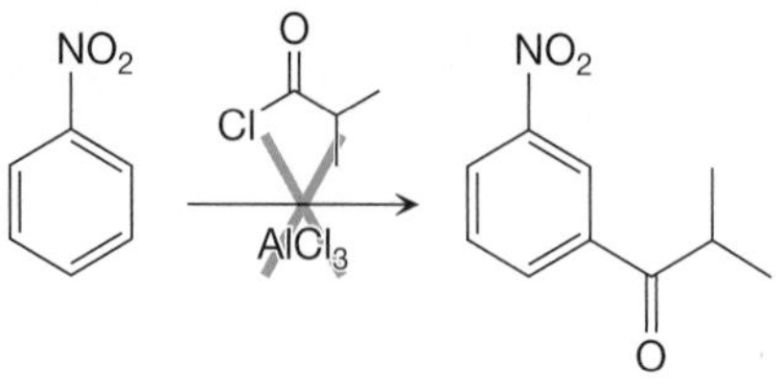

NO_2
O
Cl
$AlCl_3$
NO_2
O

Scheme A

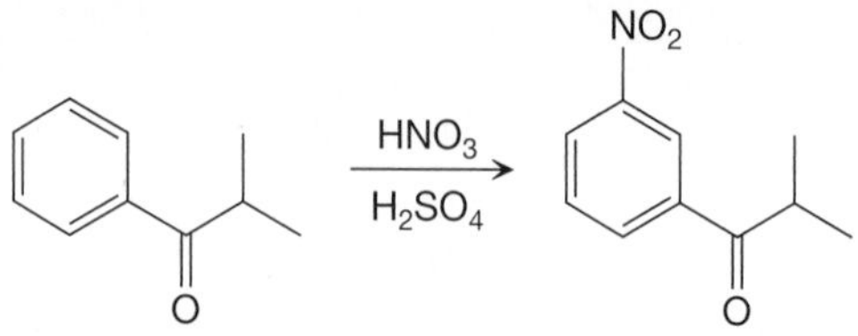

O
HNO_3
H_2SO_4
NO_2
O

Scheme B

Think	Solve
Will both of these substitutions work?	Scheme A will not work because the strongly deactivated ring will not undergo a Friedel–Crafts reaction (Section 25.4). Scheme B, on the other hand, will work.
How might we report the final synthesis?	A synthesis using Scheme B is written below. The Clemmensen reduction of the carbonyl group and the reduction of the nitro group are written as separate reactions, but they could be carried out together.

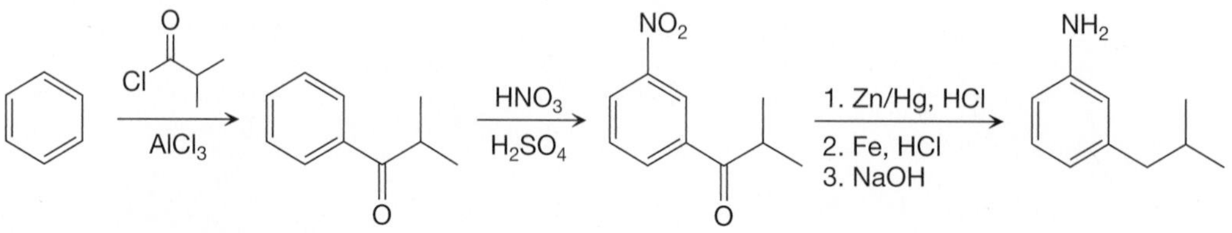

O
Cl
$AlCl_3$
O
HNO_3
H_2SO_4
NO_2
O
1. Zn/Hg, HCl
2. Fe, HCl
3. NaOH
NH_2

(continued)

Try It Show how to synthesize *m*-chloroaniline from benzene.

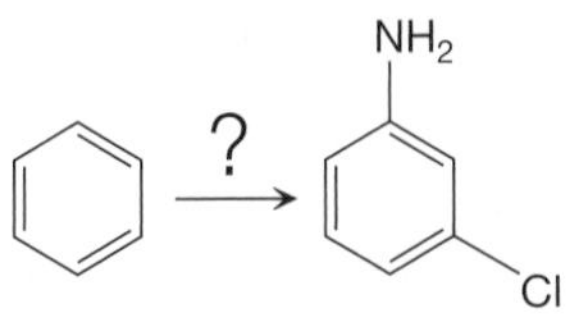

NH2
?
Cl

25.12 Organic Synthesis: Considerations of Protecting Groups

SECTION 25.12 OBJECTIVES

You will be able to:

1. Identify situations in which a protecting group would be beneficial in an electrophilic aromatic substitution reaction.
2. Design a synthesis of a substituted benzene that calls for a protecting group.

There are two ways to incorporate a protecting group into an aromatic substitution reaction. One is to temporarily lower the reactivity of a substituent attached to the ring, by reversibly converting it to a different functional group. The second is to block a particular site on the ring where substitution is not desired.

To illustrate the first scenario, how would you carry out the transformation in **Figure 25-16**, where aniline is acylated at the para position? A simple Friedel–Crafts acylation would seem to be required, given that the NH_2 group on aniline is an ortho/para director. As we learned in Section 25.5, however, the reaction conditions that are required would convert the activating amino substituent into a strongly deactivating group (Eq. 25-51), thereby making a direct Friedel–Crafts acylation unfeasible:

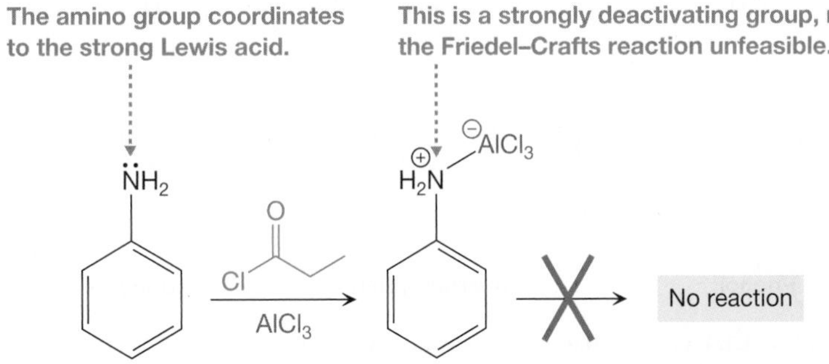

The amino group coordinates to the strong Lewis acid.
This is a strongly deactivating group, making the Friedel–Crafts reaction unfeasible.
NH2
O
Cl
AlCl3
AlCl3
H2N
No reaction

(25-51)

The problem here is that the NH_2 group is a good Lewis base; its lone pair of electrons is available to form a bond to $AlCl_3$, a strong Lewis acid. To avoid this problem, the amino group can be converted *temporarily* into a different functional group (e.g., an O═C—N group, characteristic of an amide) in which the lone pair of electrons is less available (see top Recall box).

Treating aniline with an acid chloride or an acid anhydride in the *absence* of a strong Lewis acid catalyst converts it to the amide (Eq. 25-52; see bottom Recall box). Even in the protected form, the substituent on the ring is an ortho/para director and a moderate activator (Table 25-3, p. 1210), due to the presence of the lone pair of electrons on N. (It would be undesirable for a protecting group to alter the regiochemistry of the reaction or to strongly deactivate the ring.) In the protected form, acylation can then be carried out. Afterward, the amino group is deprotected by hydrolysis.

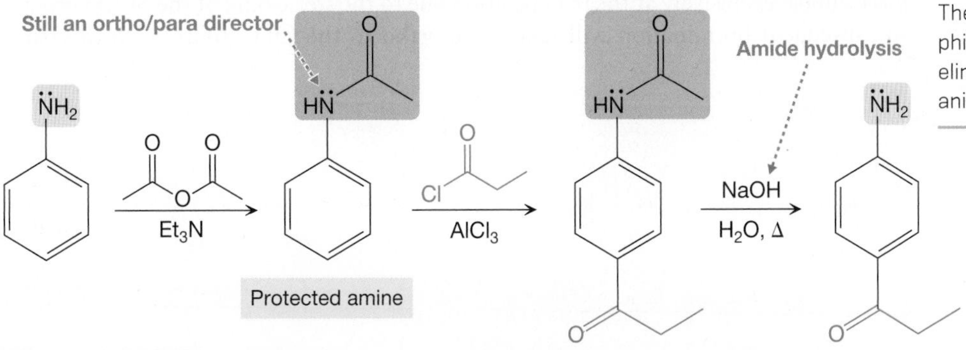

Still an ortho/para director
NH2
O
O
O
Et3N
HN
O
Protected amine
O
Cl
AlCl3
HN
O
O
Amide hydrolysis
NaOH
H2O, Δ
NH2
O

(25-52)

◂ RECALL

As we learned in Chapters 22 and 23, amides are relatively unreactive, due in large part to the resonance of the lone pair on the N atom with the adjacent carbonyl group.

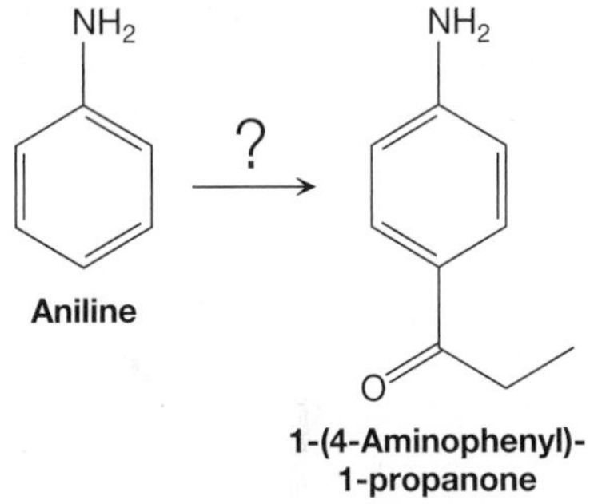

NH2
?
NH2
Aniline
O
1-(4-Aminophenyl)-1-propanone

FIGURE 25-16 How can we carry out acylation of aniline at the para position?

◂ RECALL

Section 23.3 discussed *aminolysis* reactions, in which an acid chloride or acid anhydride is converted to an amide when treated with an amine. The mechanism involves nucleophilic addition of the amine and elimination of Cl^- or an alkanoate anion as the leaving group.

YOUR TURN **25.28**

Show how to carry out this synthesis.

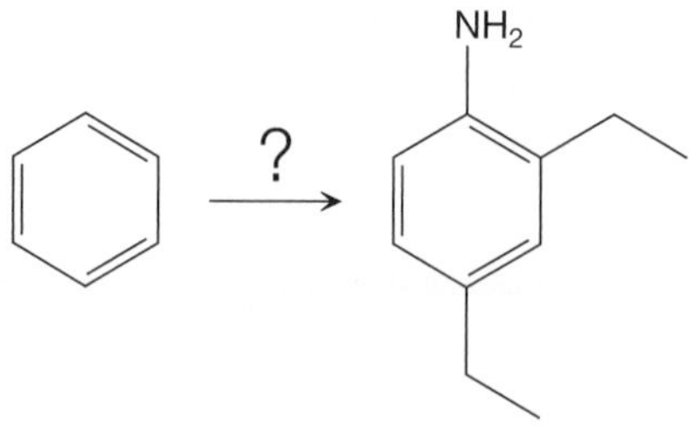

?
NH_2

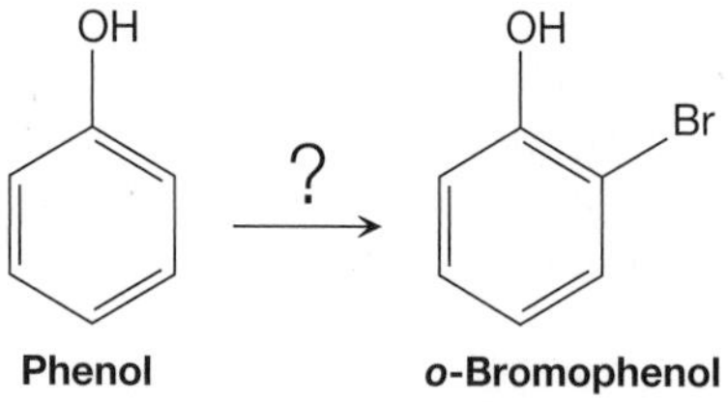

OH
?
OH
Br
Phenol
o-Bromophenol

FIGURE 25-17 How can we synthesize *o*-bromophenol from phenol?

The para product is undesired.

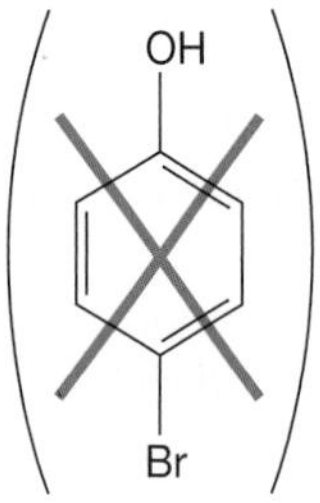

OH
Br

In some instances, the reaction we want to carry out leads to possible substitution at two or more sites on the ring. This demonstrates the second use of protecting groups in electrophilic aromatic substitution: namely, we can guide the regiochemistry by protecting one of those sites. For example, how would you convert phenol into *o*-bromophenol, if the para product is undesired (**Figure 25-17**)?

The OH group is an ortho/para director, so simple bromination will yield a substantial amount of both the ortho and para isomers, as shown in Equation 25-53:

Simple bromination will produce a mixture of both the ortho and para isomers.

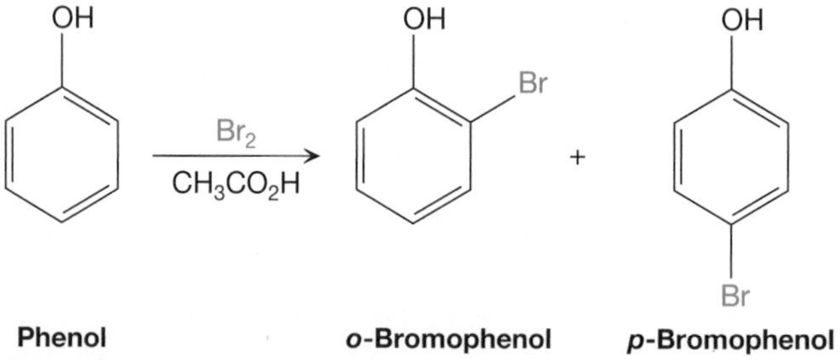

OH
Br_2
CH_3CO_2H
OH
Br
+
OH
Br
Phenol
o-Bromophenol
p-Bromophenol

(25-53)

One method that can be used to protect the para position is to place an SO_3H group there temporarily (Eq. 25-54):

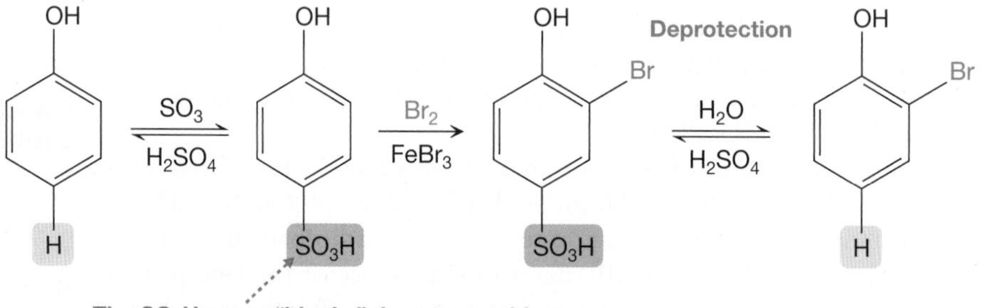

OH
H
SO_3
H_2SO_4
OH
SO_3H
Br_2
$FeBr_3$
OH
Br
SO_3H
Deprotection
H_2O
H_2SO_4
OH
Br
H
The SO_3H group "blocks" the para position.

(25-54)

As emphasized in Section 24.7, sulfonation is *reversible*. Furthermore, it will take place almost exclusively at the para position due to the steric bulk of the SO_3H group, so subsequent bromination will take place ortho to the OH group (an ortho/para director). The OH group dictates regiochemistry because it is the more activating group on the ring. It can't direct Br to the para position because the SO_3H group is already there, blocking the para position. After bromination, the SO_3H group is removed with aqueous acid.

An NH_2 group can also be used as a blocking group, as shown in the synthesis of *m*-chlorotoluene from *p*-methylaniline (Eq. 25-55):

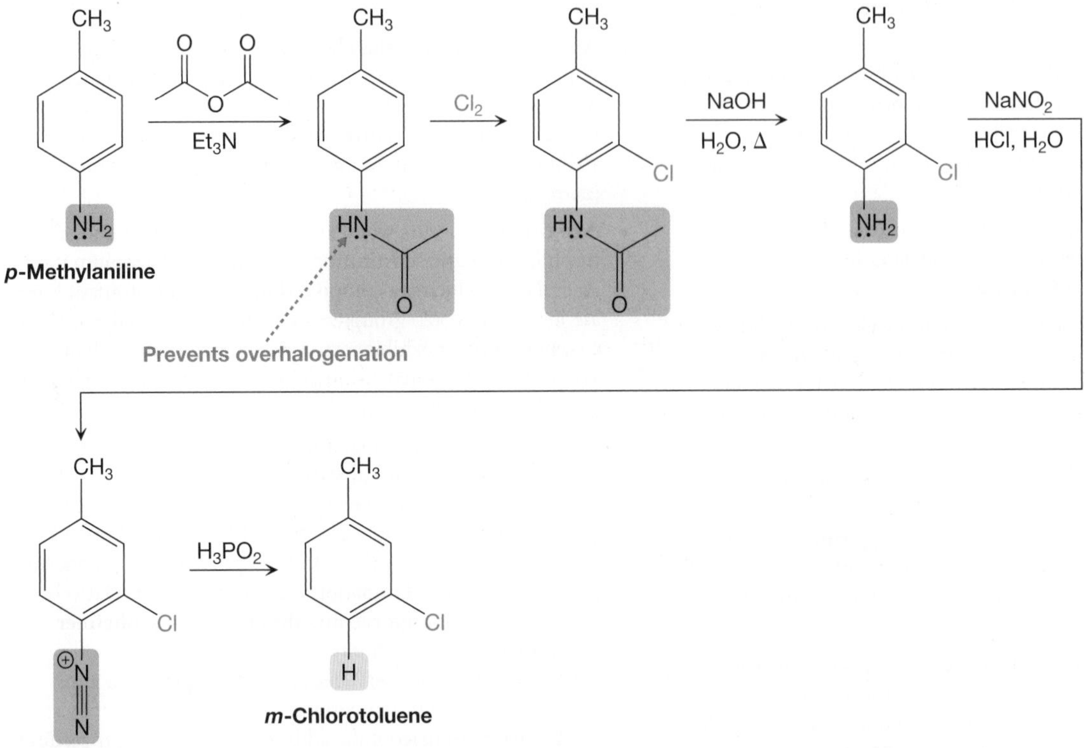

CH3
O O
O
Et3N
Cl2
NaOH
H2O, Δ
NaNO2
HCl, H2O
Cl
NH2
HN
O
p-Methylaniline
Prevents overhalogenation
H3PO2
N
H
m-Chlorotoluene

(25-55)

In the first step, the NH_2 group (a strongly activating group) is converted to the $NHCOCH_3$ group (a moderately activating group) to prevent overhalogenation. In the second step, halogenation takes place ortho to the $NHCOCH_3$ group (an ortho/para director), given that $NHCOCH_3$ is more activating than the CH_3 group. Next, the NH_2 group is deprotected by hydrolysis. Diazotization followed by treatment with H_3PO_2 converts the NH_2 group into an H (Section 24.9c). Therefore, even though the original NH_2 group is not in the final product, it was instrumental in directing the regiochemistry of chlorination.

YOUR TURN 25.29

Show how you can carry out this synthesis without generating any of the para isomer.

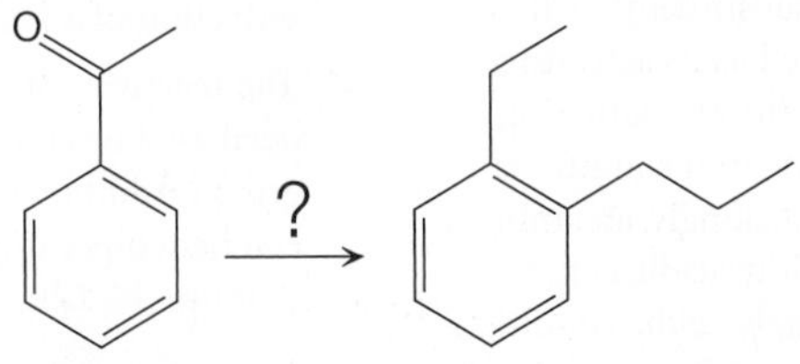

O
?

Chapter Summary and Key Terms

- In electrophilic aromatic substitution reactions, certain substituents attached to a phenyl ring, called **ortho/para directors**, favor reaction at the ortho and para positions. Substituents called **meta directors** favor reaction at the meta position. (Section 25.1)
- A substituent attached to a phenyl ring by an atom possessing a lone pair of electrons tends to be an ortho/para director. When the incoming electrophile attaches to a carbon at the ortho or para position of the ring, the resulting arenium ion intermediate is stabilized by resonance. (Section 25.2)
- Alkyl groups are ortho/para directors because they stabilize ortho and para arenium ion intermediates by electron-donating effects. (Section 25.2)
- Meta directors such as the nitro group are electron-withdrawing and are attached to the aromatic ring by an atom that has no lone pair of electrons. Meta directors destabilize the arenium ion intermediate when the incoming electrophile attaches to the ortho or para position. (Section 25.2)
- In general, ortho/para directors act as **activating groups** that increase the rate of electrophilic aromatic substitution. Conversely, meta directors act as **deactivating groups** that tend to slow the reaction rate. Halogen substituents are exceptions; halogen substituents are ortho/para directors but function as deactivating groups. (Section 25.3)
- Activating groups speed up an electrophilic aromatic substitution reaction because they *stabilize* the arenium ion intermediate that is produced. Deactivating groups *destabilize* the arenium ion intermediate. (Section 25.3)
- To compensate for the presence of a deactivating group on an aromatic ring, nitration can be sped up by adding H_2SO_4, and sulfonation can be sped up by adding SO_3. (Section 25.4)
- Friedel–Crafts reactions do not readily take place on moderately or strongly deactivated aromatic rings. The electron-donating ability of an alkyl group makes polyalkylation a potential problem in Friedel–Crafts alkylation reactions. (Section 25.4)
- The conditions under which an electrophilic aromatic substitution reaction takes place can alter a substituent's ortho/para- or meta-directing capabilities, as well as its activating or deactivating capabilities. For example, the aromatic ring of phenol is much more activated under neutral conditions than it is under acidic conditions. More strikingly, an amino group is an ortho/para director under mildly acidic conditions, but it is a meta director under strongly acidic conditions. (Section 25.5)
- When multiple substituents are attached to a phenyl ring, their activating or deactivating qualities are additive, and the regiochemistry tends to be governed by the most activating of those substituents. (Section 25.6)
- Aromatic rings other than benzene can also undergo electrophilic aromatic substitution. These include naphthalene, furan, pyrrole, and pyridine. Just as in substituted benzenes, the regiochemistry and relative reaction rates are governed by the stabilities of the arenium ion intermediates that are produced. (Section 25.7)
- **Azo coupling** occurs when an aromatic ring undergoes electrophilic aromatic substitution with an arenediazonium ion, $Ar{-}N_2^+$, producing a compound in which the aromatic rings are joined by an azo group, $-N{=}N-$. An **azo dye** is such a compound that exhibits extended conjugation involving the azo group and absorbs visible light, giving it a characteristic color. (Section 25.8)
- Aromatic rings with halogen substituents can undergo **nucleophilic aromatic substitution reactions**, whereby the halogen atom is replaced by a nucleophile. (Section 25.9)
  - Rings that are strongly deactivated toward reaction with an electrophile (and thus electron-poor) react by a nucleophilic addition–elimination mechanism under relatively mild conditions, proceeding through a **Meisenheimer complex**. (Section 25.9a)
  - Rings that are not very electron-poor typically require strong bases, high temperatures, or both, and react by an elimination–nucleophilic addition mechanism, proceeding through a **benzyne intermediate**. (Section 25.9b)
- It is important to consider the order in which successive electrophilic aromatic substitution reactions in a synthesis are carried out. The incorrect order could lead to undesired regiochemistry or could make some desired reactions unfeasible. (Section 25.10)
- Reactions that transform an ortho/para director into a meta director, and vice versa, can be instrumental in synthesis. An example of the former is the $KMnO_4$ oxidation of an alkyl side chain to a CO_2H group. An example of the latter is the reduction of a NO_2 group to an NH_2 group. (Section 25.11)
- The reactivity of an aromatic amine can be temporarily decreased by converting the NH_2 group into an $O{=}C{-}N$ group. Additionally, the para position of a phenyl ring can be temporarily blocked by sulfonating that position. (Section 25.12)

Reaction Table

Functional group transformations introduced in this chapter are collected in Table 25-4.

TABLE 25-4 Functional Group Transformations[a,b]

	Starting Compound Class	Typical Reagents and Reaction Conditions	Compound Class Formed	Key Electron-Rich Species	Key Electron-Poor Species	Comments	Discussed in Section(s)
(1)	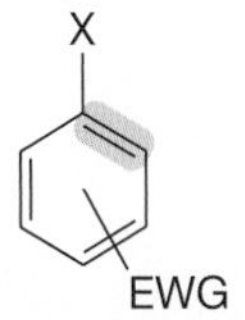X EWG Electron-poor aromatic halide	$\xrightarrow{H_2NR}$	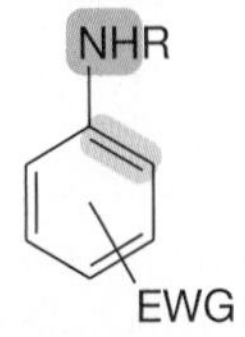NHR EWG Substituted aromatic amine	$H_2\ddot{N}R$ (δ−)	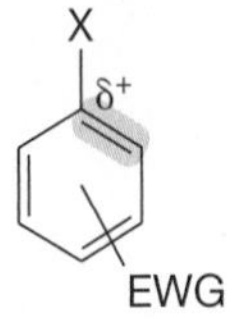X δ+ EWG	Nucleophilic addition–elimination mechanism; EWG ortho or para to X	25.9a
(2)	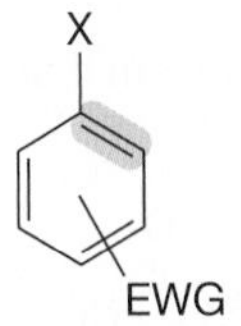X EWG Electron-poor aromatic halide	$\xrightarrow{NaOR}$	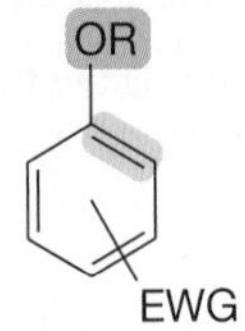OR EWG Substituted aromatic ether	$^{\ominus}:\ddot{O}R$	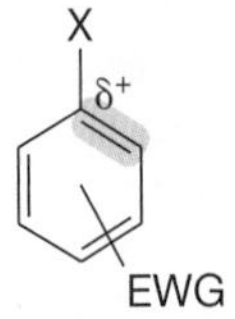X δ+ EWG	Nucleophilic addition–elimination mechanism; EWG ortho or para to X	25.9a
(3)	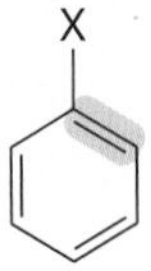X Aromatic halide	1. NaOH, Δ 2. H_2O, HCl	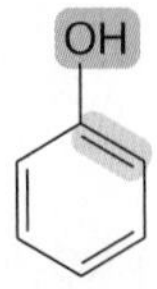OH Phenol	$^{\ominus}:\ddot{O}H$	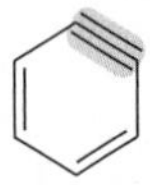	Proceeds through benzyne intermediate	25.9b
(4)	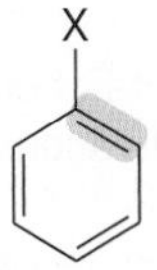X Aromatic halide	1. KNH_2, $NH_3(\ell)$ 2. H_2O	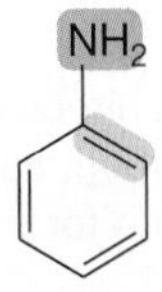NH2 Aniline	$^{\ominus}:\ddot{N}H_2$	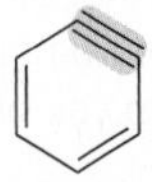	Proceeds through benzyne intermediate	25.9b

[a]X = F, Cl, Br, or I.
[b]EWG = electron-withdrawing group.

Problems

Problems that are related to synthesis are denoted (SYN).

Sections 25.1 and 25.2 Ortho/Para and Meta Directors in Electrophilic Aromatic Substitution on Monosubstituted Benzenes

25.1 Draw the complete, detailed mechanism that leads to the ortho-, meta-, and para-disubstituted products for each of the following reactions, and identify the major products.

(a)

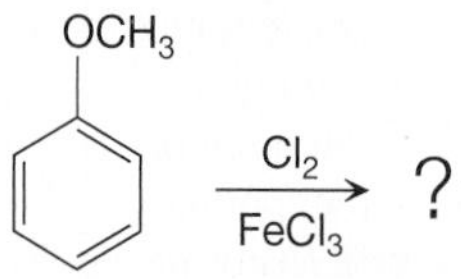
OCH3
Cl2
FeCl3
?

(b)

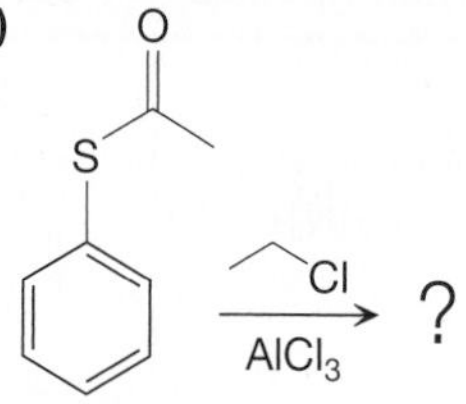
O
S
Cl
AlCl3
?

25.2 Draw all resonance structures for the ortho, meta, and para arenium ion intermediates that are formed during the bromination of ethylbenzene. Which arenium ion intermediate is the least stable? Explain.

25.3 Predict the major product(s) for each of the following reactions. Draw the complete, detailed mechanism that leads to the formation of each product.

(a)

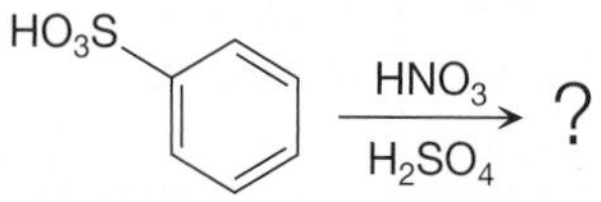
HO3S
HNO3
H2SO4
?

(b)

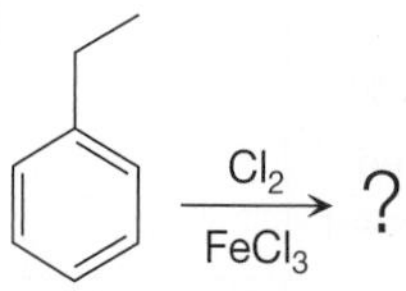
Cl2
FeCl3
?

(c)

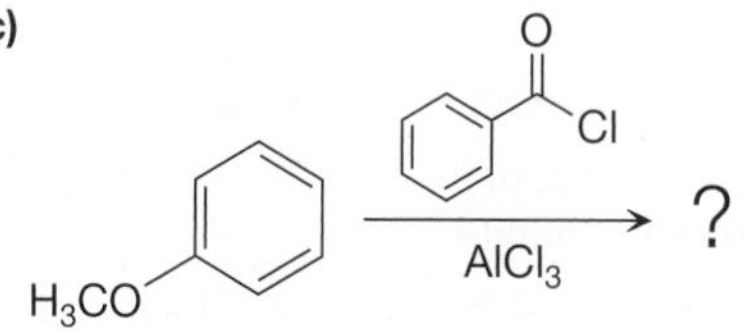
O
Cl
H3CO
AlCl3
?

(d)

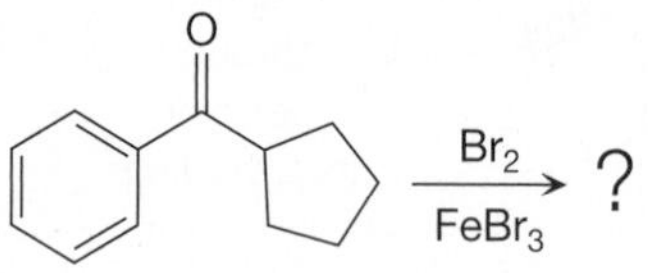
O
Br2
FeBr3
?

(e)

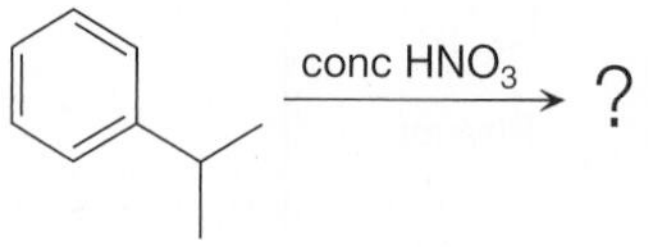
conc HNO3
?

25.4 In Section 25.2, we learned that all alkyl groups are ortho/para directors. However, the relative amounts of ortho and para products depend on the specific identity of the alkyl group, as shown here for the nitration of various alkylbenzenes. What trend do you observe? What factor accounts for that trend?

	CH_3	CH_2CH_3	$CH(CH_3)_2$	$C(CH_3)_3$
% Ortho	63	45	30	16
% Meta	3	6	8	11
% Para	34	49	62	73

25.5 According to Table 25-1, the nitration of phenol results in a product mixture that is 50% ortho and 50% para. What would the major products be if one of the ortho positions of phenol were labeled with deuterium (D)? What would you expect the relative amounts of each of those products to be?

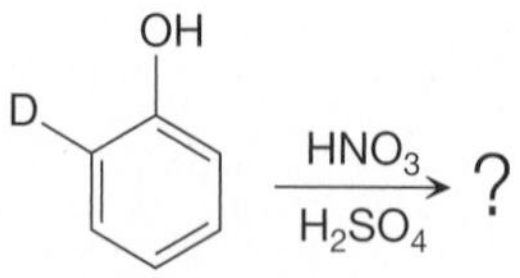
OH
D
HNO3
H2SO4
?

25.6 A Br substituent is an ortho/para director, so the halogenation of bromobenzene predominantly yields the ortho and para products, as shown in the following bromination and chlorination reactions:

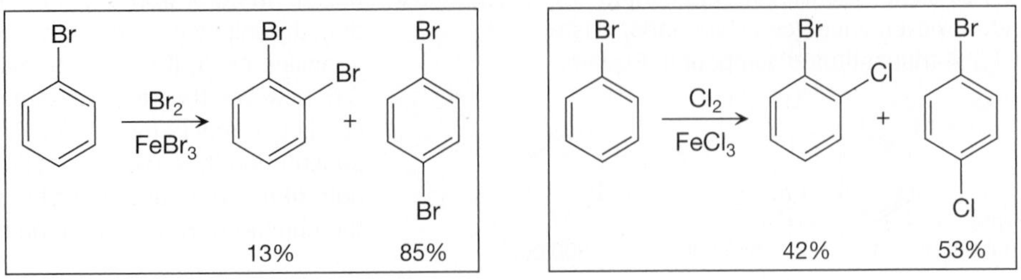

Br
Br_2
$FeBr_3$
Br
Br
+
Br
Br
13%
85%
Br
Cl_2
$FeCl_3$
Br
Cl
+
Br
Cl
42%
53%

Explain why bromination yields more of the para product than chlorination.

25.7 Which of the reactions shown here do you think will produce the para product in the greater amount? Explain. *Hint*: See Problem 25.6.

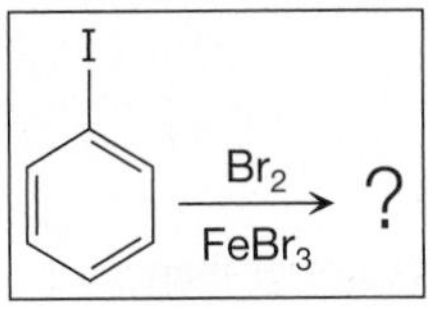

I
Br_2
$FeBr_3$
?

Reaction A

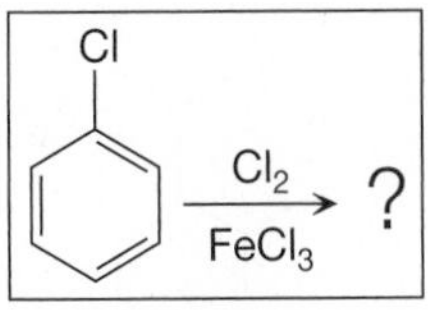

Cl
Cl_2
$FeCl_3$
?

Reaction B

25.8 Predict the most likely site of electrophilic aromatic substitution in the compound shown here. *Hint*: How do you determine whether the substituent is an ortho/para-directing group or a meta-directing group?

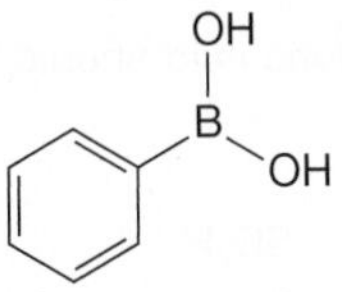

OH
B
OH

25.9 Predict whether the nitroso group (—N═O) is an ortho/para or meta director.

25.10 The phenyl group, C_6H_5, is known to be an ortho/para-directing group. **(a)** With that in mind, predict the product of the reaction shown here. **(b)** Justify why it is an ortho/para director by examining the ortho, meta, and para arenium ion intermediates that would be formed during the course of the reaction.

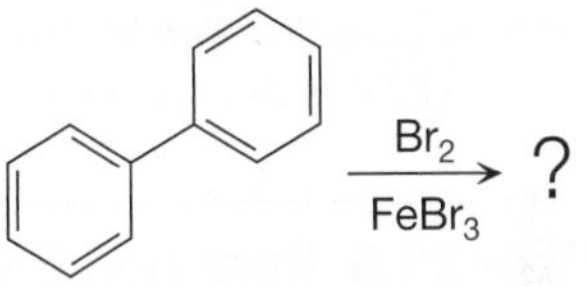

Br_2
$FeBr_3$
?

Section 25.3 Activation and Deactivation of Benzene toward Electrophilic Aromatic Substitution

25.11 The NHCOR group of an amide is an activating group, but it is not as strongly activating as NH_2. **(a)** Explain why it is an activating group. **(b)** Explain why it is less activating than NH_2.

25.12 For each pair of aromatic compounds, determine which one will undergo electrophilic aromatic substitution faster.

(a)

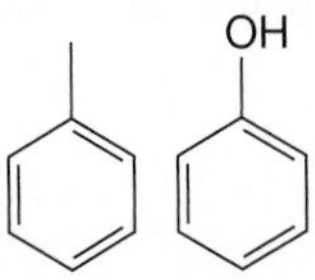

OH

(b)

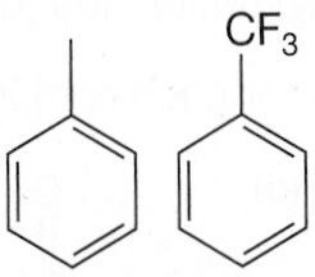

CF_3

(c)

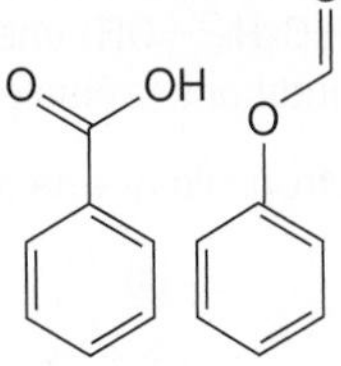

O
OH
O
O

(d)

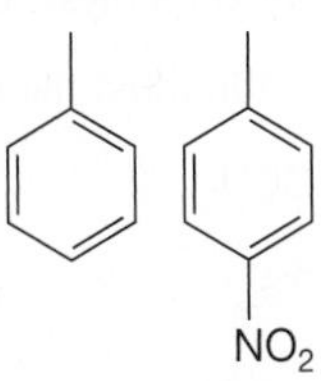

NO_2

(e)

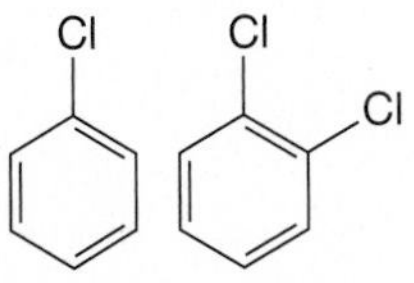

Cl
Cl
Cl

(f)

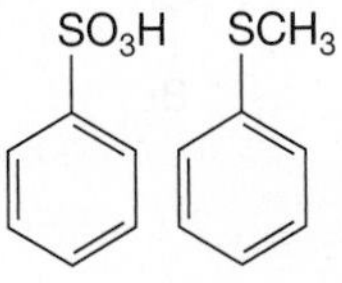

SO_3H
SCH_3

(g)

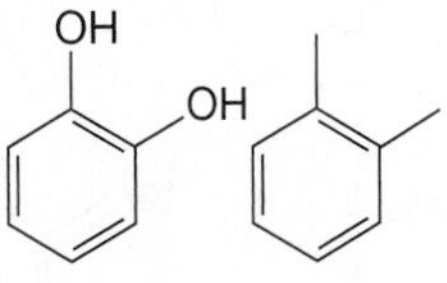

OH
OH

(h)

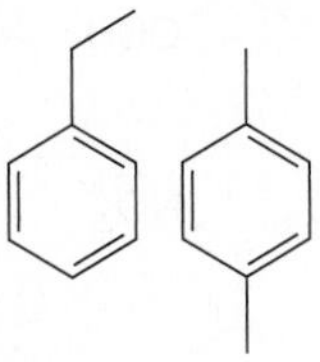

25.13 The OH group on phenol (C_6H_5—OH) is an activating group, but the ring in phenylmethanol (C_6H_5—CH_2OH) is deactivated. Explain.

25.14 Alkyl groups are activating, so both trisubstituted benzenes shown here undergo chlorination much faster than benzene. The 1,2,3-trisubstituted compound, however, undergoes chlorination faster than the 1,2,4-trisubstituted compound. Explain.

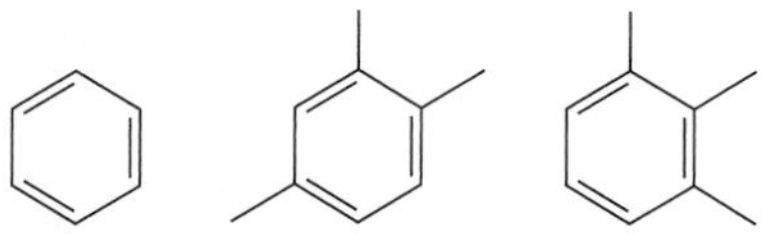

Relative rate of chlorination: 1 680,000 800,000

25.15 For each pair of isomers, determine which one will undergo electrophilic aromatic substitution faster and explain why. *Hint*: See Problem 25.14.
(a) *o*-Dimethylbenzene or *m*-dimethylbenzene;
(b) *m*-dimethylbenzene or *p*-dimethylbenzene;
(c) 1,2,3,4-tetramethylbenzene or 1,2,3,5-tetramethylbenzene

25.16 We learned that halogen atoms are one of the few substituents that are ortho/para-directing but deactivating. The nitroso group (—N═O) is ortho/para directing (see Problem 25.9) and deactivating, too. Explain why it is deactivating.

25.17 As shown below, electrophilic aromatic substitution on *N,N*-dimethylaniline is faster than on the unsubstituted aniline. In other words, the aromatic ring in *N,N*-dimethylaniline is more activated than the ring is in aniline itself. If the ring is methylated at C-2 and C-6, however, then the *N,N*-dimethyl-substituted compound reacts more slowly in electrophilic aromatic substitution than the unsubstituted compound. Explain both of these results. *Hint*: It does *not* have to do with the number of H atoms on the ring.

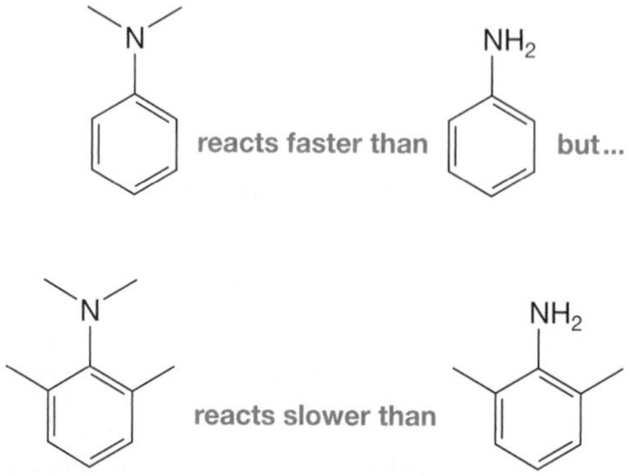
N
reacts faster than
NH2
but...
N
reacts slower than
NH2

Sections 25.4–25.6 Reaction Conditions and Disubstituted Benzenes in Electrophilic Aromatic Substitution Reactions

25.18 **(SYN)** For each of the following substituted benzenes, determine whether sulfuric acid should be added to concentrated nitric acid to carry out a nitration.

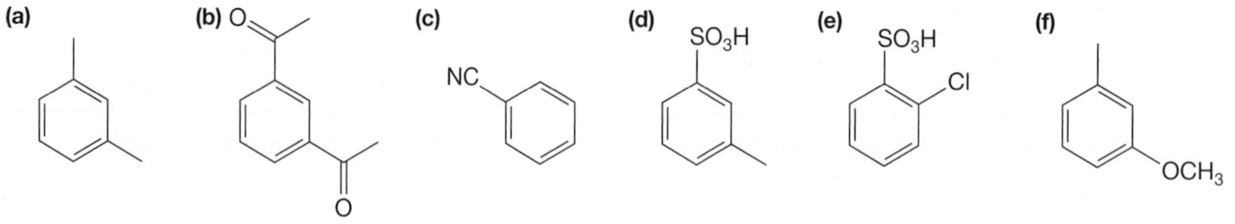
(a)
(b) O
O
(c)
NC
(d)
SO3H
(e)
SO3H
Cl
(f)
OCH3

25.19 **(SYN)** For each compound in Problem 25.18, determine whether fuming sulfuric acid should be added to concentrated sulfuric acid to carry out a sulfonation.

25.20 **(SYN)** Which compounds in Problem 25.18 can undergo a Friedel–Crafts reaction? Explain.

25.21 In Section 25.5, we saw that phenol (C_6H_5—OH) undergoes three rapid, successive brominations, even without a strong Lewis acid catalyst. Under similar conditions, anisole (C_6H_5—OCH_3) undergoes just a single bromination. Explain why.

25.22 Predict the most likely site(s) of electrophilic aromatic substitution for each compound.

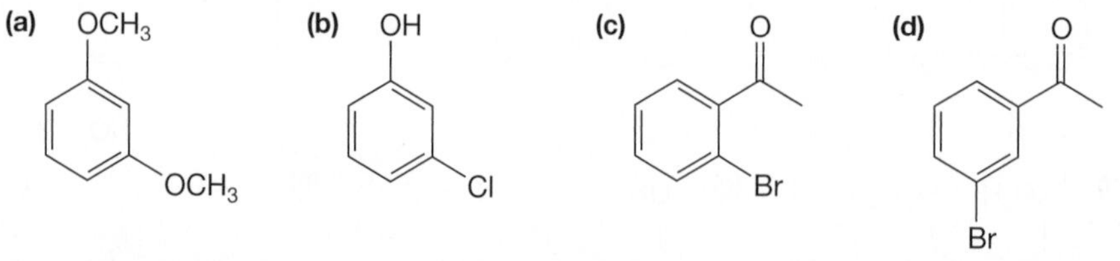
(a)
OCH3
OCH3
(b)
OH
Cl
(c)
O
Br
(d)
O
Br

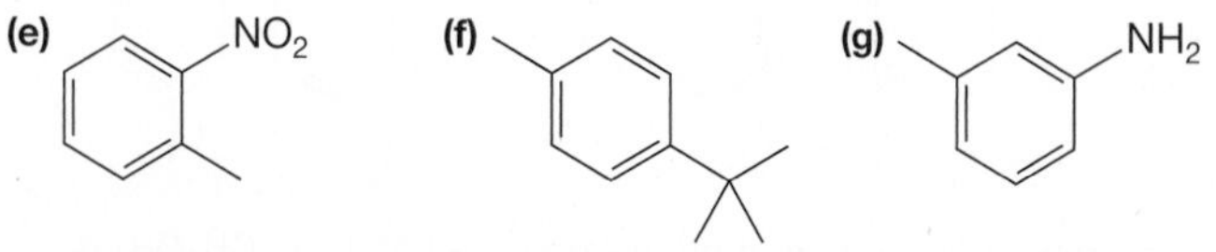
(e)
NO2
(f)
(g)
NH2

25.23 For each of the following reactions, draw the complete, detailed mechanism and the major product(s).

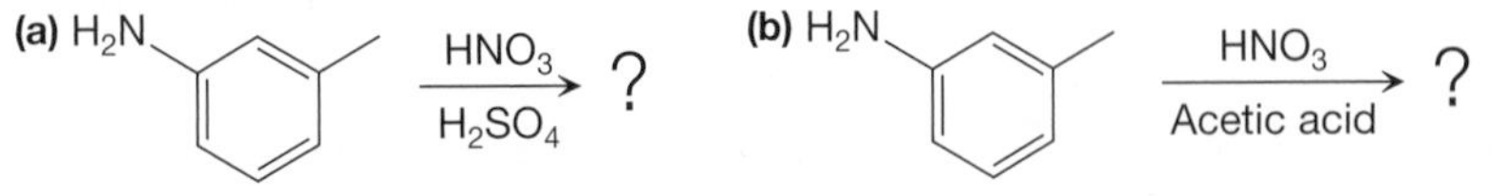

25.24 (SYN) Show how to synthesize each of the following trisubstituted benzenes from a disubstituted benzene.

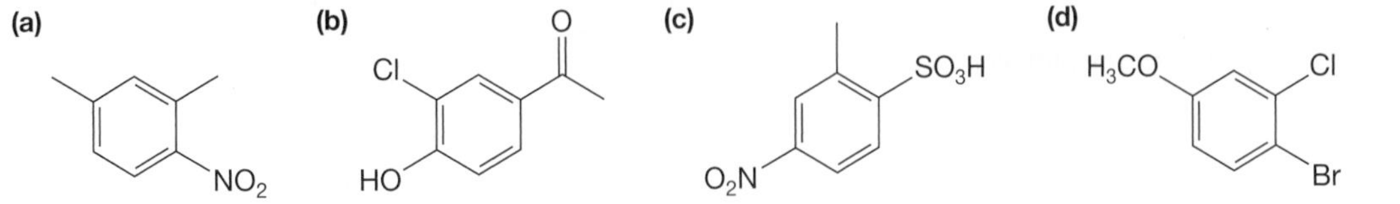

Section 25.7 Electrophilic Aromatic Substitution Involving Aromatic Rings other than Benzene

25.25 The electrostatic potential maps of benzene and pyridine are shown here. Is the map of pyridine consistent with the ring being activated or deactivated relative to benzene? Explain.

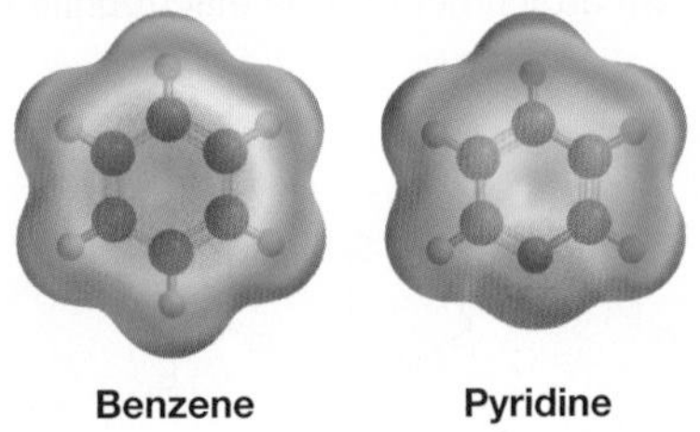

25.26 The electrostatic potential maps of benzene and pyrrole are shown here. Is the map of pyrrole consistent with the ring being activated or deactivated relative to benzene? Explain.

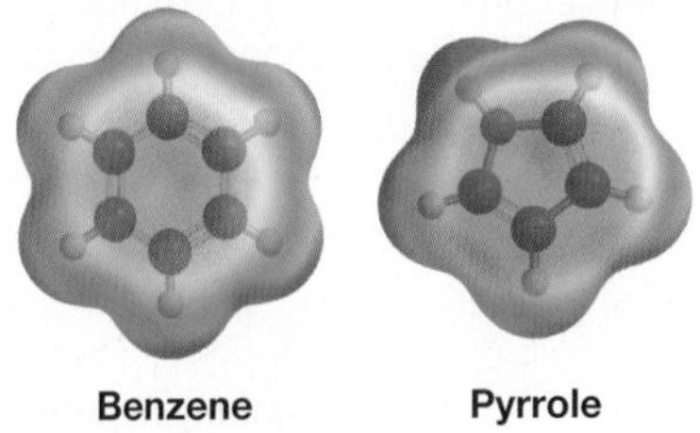

25.27 Here in Chapter 25, we learned that aniline becomes highly deactivated in the presence of a strong Lewis acid, due to coordination of the N atom to the Lewis acid. Thus, as shown below at the left, Friedel–Crafts reactions involving aniline are unfeasible. As shown at the right, though, this does not appear to be a problem with the N atom in pyrrole. Explain why.

25.28 When naphthalene undergoes an irreversible electrophilic aromatic substitution, such as a Friedel–Crafts acylation, the major product is the kinetic product, which proceeds through the most stable arenium ion intermediate. In Section 25.7, we mentioned that substitution is generally favored at the α position over the β position, which means that the arenium ion is more stable when the electrophile attaches to the α position. Explain this difference in arenium ion stabilities. *Hint*: Draw out all resonance structures for each arenium ion intermediate. Does each one have the same number of resonance structures? How many resonance structures of each intermediate preserve the aromaticity?

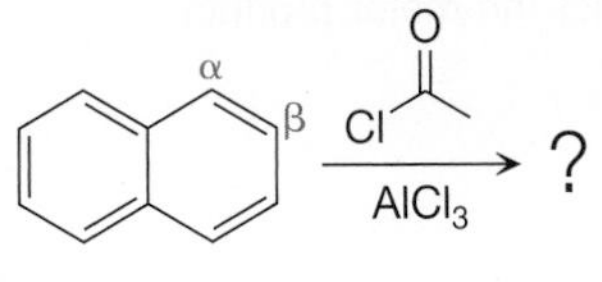

25.29 The bromination of benzene requires a Lewis acid catalyst such as $FeBr_3$, but the bromination of naphthalene does not. Explain why.

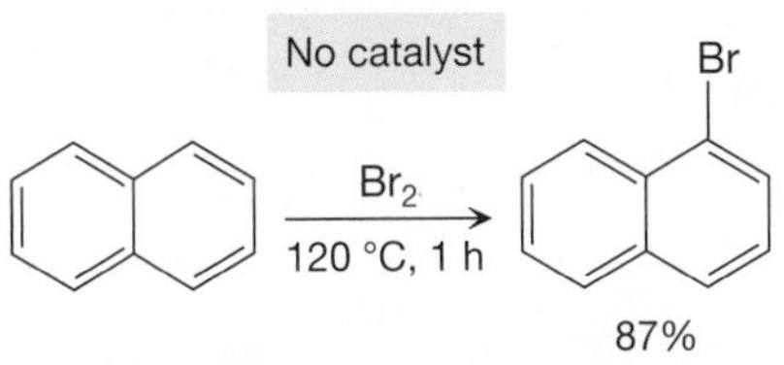

25.30 When an electrophilic aromatic substitution reaction on naphthalene is reversible, such as in a sulfonation reaction, the major product is the one that is most stable. With this in mind, predict the major product of the reaction shown here.

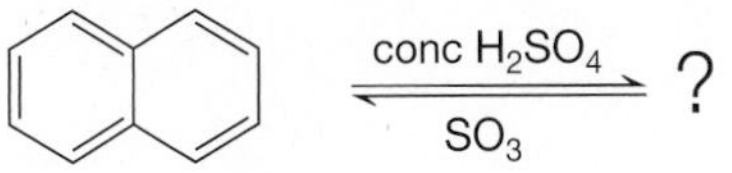

25.31 Electrophilic aromatic substitution on a monosubstituted naphthalene tends to take place on the substituted ring when the substituent is an activator, like CH_3, and tends to take place on the unsubstituted ring when the substituent is a deactivator, like NO_2. Explain why.

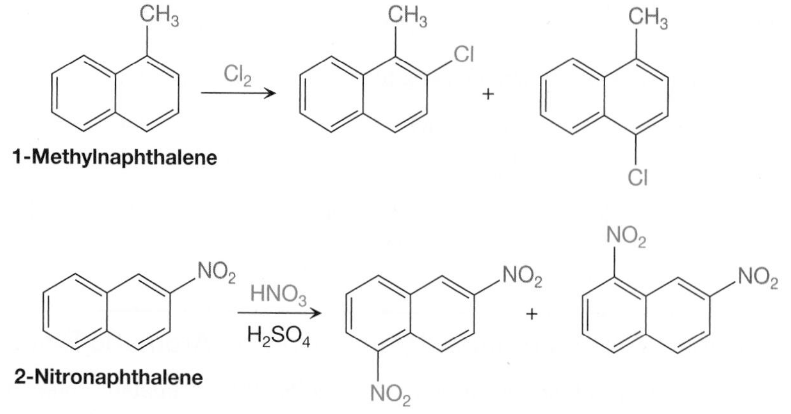

CH3
Cl2
CH3
Cl
+
CH3
1-Methylnaphthalene
Cl
NO2
HNO3
H2SO4
NO2
+
NO2
NO2
2-Nitronaphthalene
NO2

25.32 When 2-methylnaphthalene undergoes an irreversible electrophilic aromatic substitution, the electrophile predominantly attaches to C-1 instead of C-3, as shown here. This suggests that the arenium ion that is formed from attachment of the electrophile to C-1 is more stable than the arenium ion formed from attachment of the electrophile to C-3. Explain why. *Hint*: Simple resonance theory can explain why.

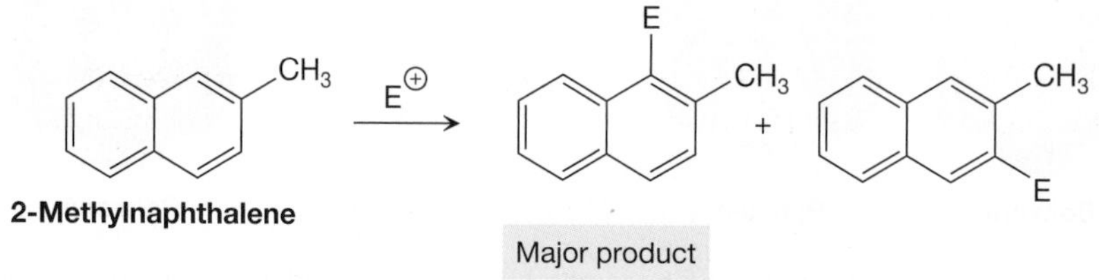

CH3
E⊕
E
CH3
+
CH3
E
2-Methylnaphthalene
Major product

25.33 Draw the complete, detailed mechanism for the reaction shown here and predict the major product. *Hint*: See Problems 25.31 and 25.32.

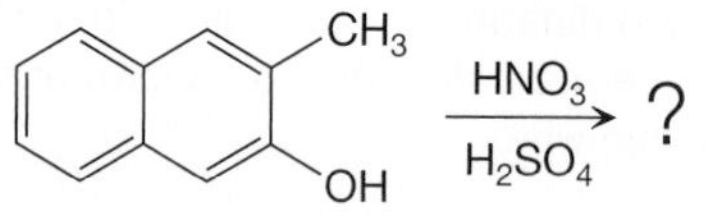

CH3
OH
HNO3
H2SO4
?

25.34 Draw the complete, detailed mechanism and predict the major product for each of the following reactions. *Hint*: See Problems 25.31 and 25.32.

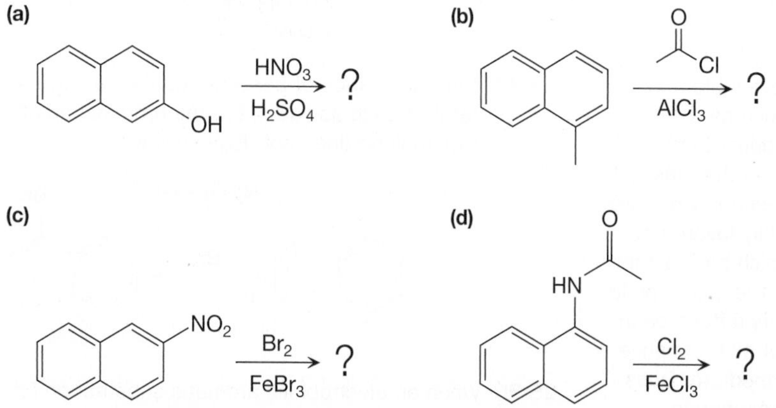

(a)
OH
HNO3
H2SO4
?
(b)
O
Cl
AlCl3
?
(c)
NO2
Br2
FeBr3
?
(d)
O
HN
Cl2
FeCl3
?

25.35 Using E^+ as a generic electrophile, draw the complete, detailed mechanisms for electrophilic aromatic substitution of furan at both C-2 and C-3 of the ring. Determine which of those reactions will proceed through the more stable arenium ion intermediate and predict the major product.

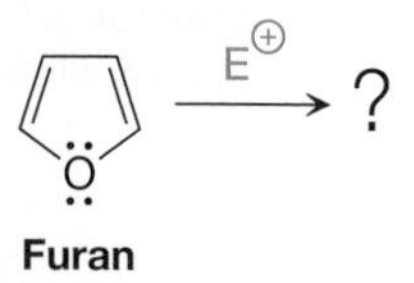

E⊕
?
Furan

25.36 **(a)** For which aromatic compound do you expect nitration to take place faster: furan or thiophene? **(b)** For each of these compounds, at which C atom do you expect electrophilic aromatic substitution to predominantly take place? Explain your reasoning.

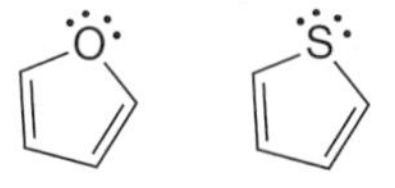

O
S

Furan **Thiophene**

25.37 A thiophene ring is sufficiently activated that bromination may take place without the presence of a Lewis acid catalyst. With this in mind, draw the complete, detailed mechanism for the reaction shown here and predict the major product.

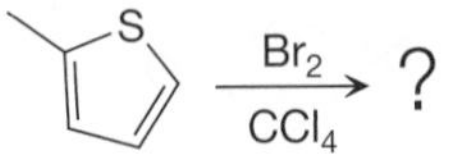

S
Br_2
CCl_4
?

25.38 Draw the complete, detailed mechanism and predict the major product for each of the following reactions.

(a)

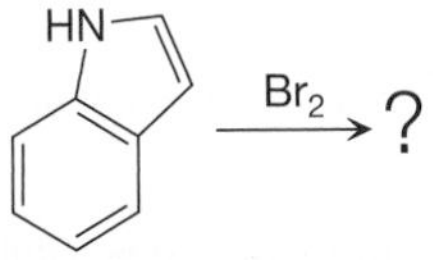

HN
Br_2
?

(b)

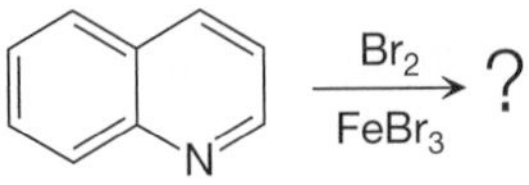

N
Br_2
$FeBr_3$
?

(c)

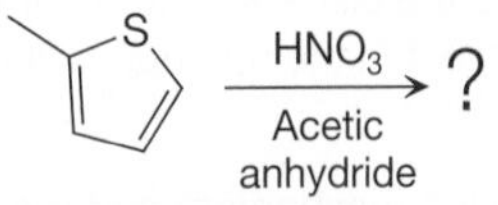

S
HNO_3
Acetic anhydride
?

(d)

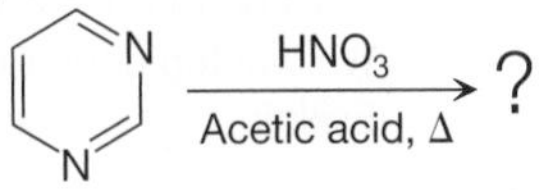

N
N
HNO_3
Acetic acid, Δ
?

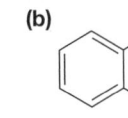

25.39 Predict the site on each molecule that is most likely to undergo electrophilic aromatic substitution.

(a)

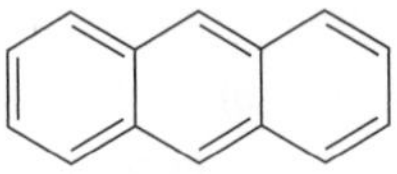

(b)

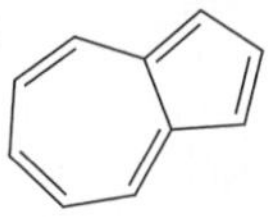

Section 25.8 Azo Coupling and Azo Dyes

25.40 Butter yellow is an azo dye produced from the following reaction. Draw the complete, detailed mechanism for this reaction. Would you expect a significant amount of the meta product? Why or why not?

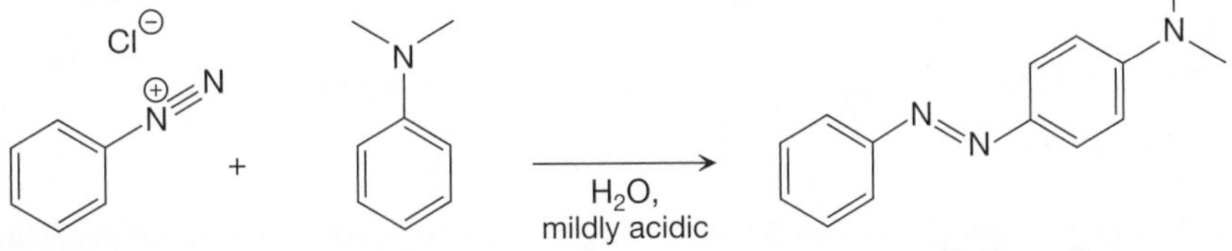

Cl⊖
⊕N≡N
+
N
H_2O,
mildly acidic
N
N
N

Benzenediazonium chloride ***N,N*-Dimethylaniline** **Butter yellow (An azo dye)**

25.41 **(SYN)** Tartrazine is an azo dye that is primarily used as a lemon-yellow food coloring. Draw the arenediazonium ion and the separate aromatic compound that would react to form the dye, and draw the complete, detailed mechanism for that reaction.

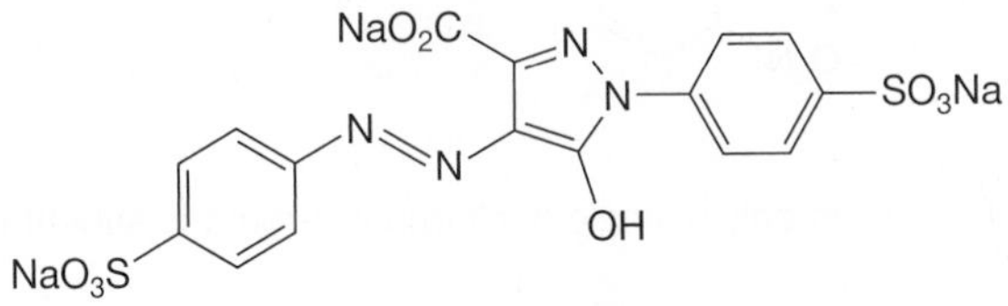

NaO_2C
N
N
SO_3Na
N
N
OH
NaO_3S

Tartrazine

25.42 **(SYN)** Sunset Yellow FCF is an azo dye that, when used as a food coloring in the United States, is called FD&C Yellow 6. Draw the arenediazonium ion and the separate aromatic compound that would react to form the dye, and draw the complete, detailed mechanism for that reaction.

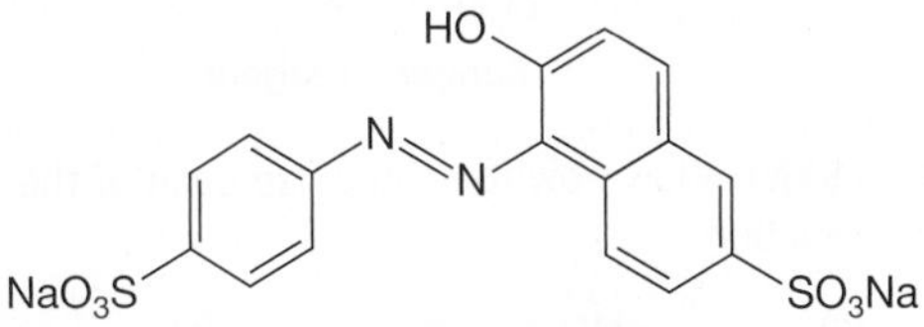

HO
N
N
NaO_3S
SO_3Na

Sunset yellow FCF

25.43 The reaction shown here is used to synthesize an azo dye called azo violet. Draw the complete, detailed mechanism for this reaction and the structure of azo violet.

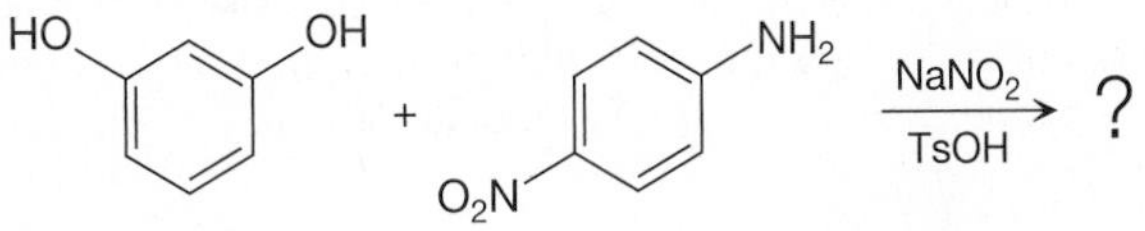

HO
OH
+
NH_2
O_2N
$NaNO_2$
TsOH
?

Section 25.9 Nucleophilic Aromatic Substitution Mechanisms

25.44 Draw the complete, detailed mechanism and the major product for each of the following reactions.

(a)
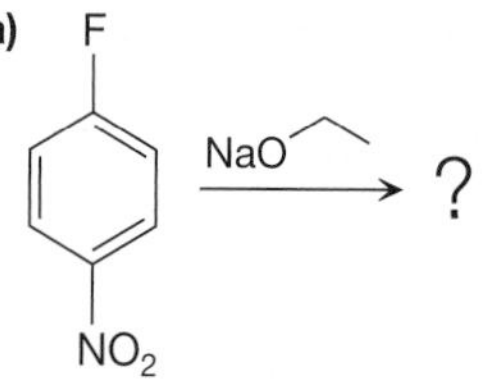
F
NaO
?
NO2

(b)
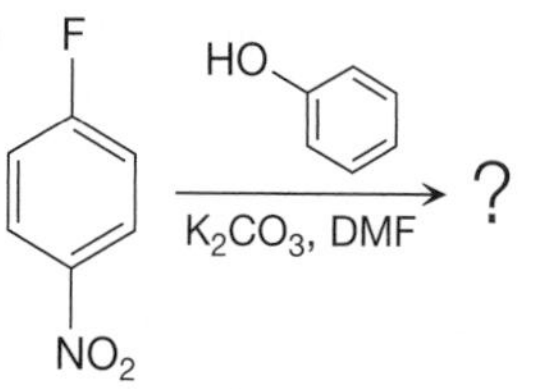
F
HO
K2CO3, DMF
?
NO2

(c)
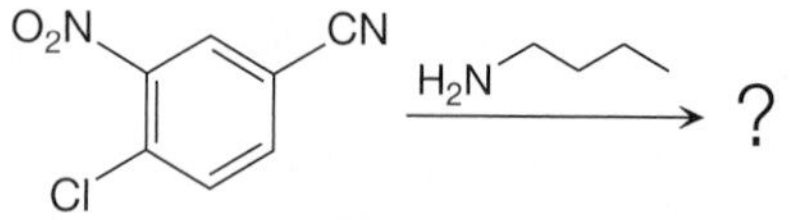
O2N
CN
Cl
H2N
?

25.45 In nucleophilic aromatic substitution reactions that proceed by the nucleophilic addition–elimination mechanism, the reaction rate increases as the electronegativity of the halogen leaving group increases: Ar—I < Ar—Br < Ar—Cl < Ar—F. Which step does this suggest is the rate-determining step of the mechanism: the addition step or the elimination step? Explain.

25.46 Draw the complete, detailed mechanism and predict the major product for each of the following reactions. *Hint*: See Problem 25.45.

(a)
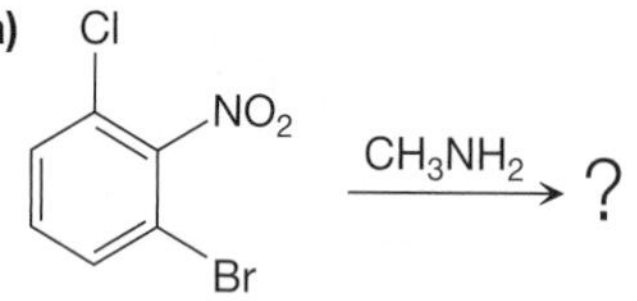
Cl
NO2
Br
CH3NH2
?

(b)
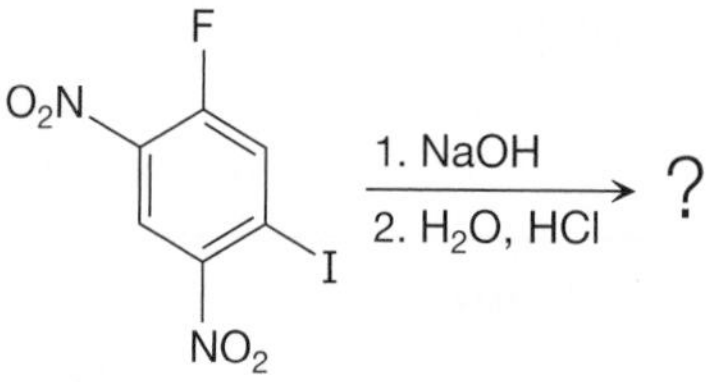
F
O2N
I
NO2
1. NaOH
2. H2O, HCl
?

25.47 Draw the complete, detailed mechanism leading to the major product(s) for each of the following reactions.

(a)
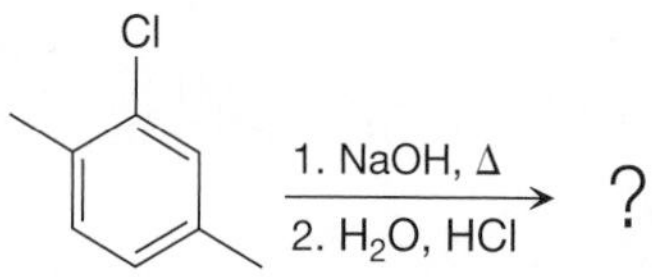
Cl
1. NaOH, Δ
2. H2O, HCl
?

(b)
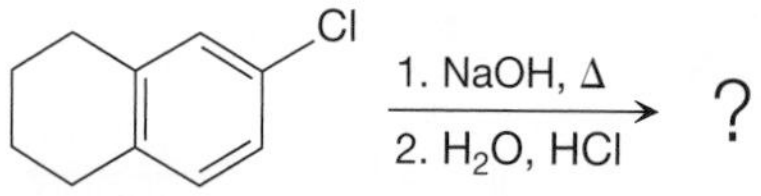
Cl
1. NaOH, Δ
2. H2O, HCl
?

(c)
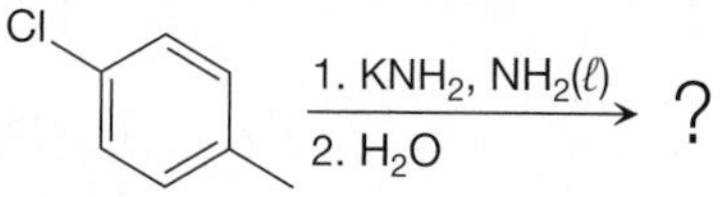
Cl
1. KNH2, NH2(ℓ)
2. H2O
?

25.48 1-Fluoro-2,4-dinitrobenzene, known as Sanger's reagent, can be used to determine the N-terminal amino acid of a protein. As shown here, the protein is treated with Sanger's reagent to produce a dinitrophenyl (DNP)-substituted amino group on the N-terminal amino acid. When the protein is subsequently hydrolyzed, the DNP-amino acid can be recovered and identified through chromatography. Draw the complete, detailed mechanism for the formation of the DNP-amino acid.

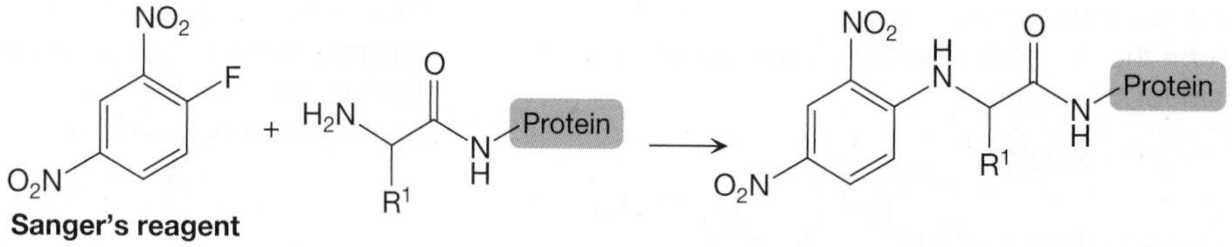
NO2
F
O2N
+
H2N
O
N
H
Protein
R1
NO2
H
N
O
N
H
Protein
R1
O2N

Sanger's reagent

25.49 **(SYN)** Show how to synthesize each of the following compounds from only a single nucleophilic aromatic substitution reaction.

(a)
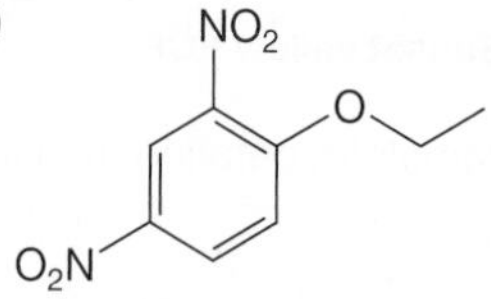
NO2
O
O2N

(b)
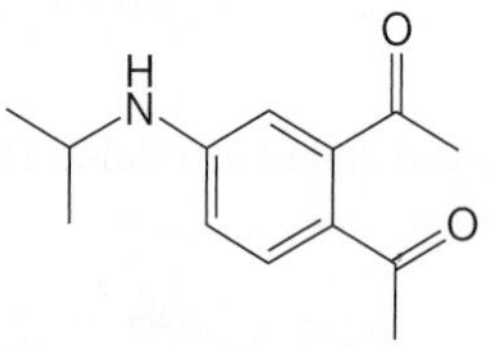
H
N
O
O

(c)
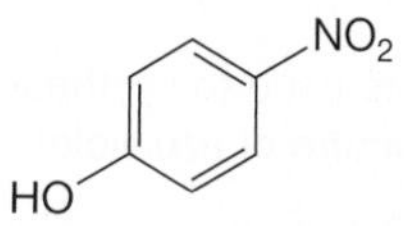
NO2
HO

25.50 **(SYN)** Show how to synthesize each of the following compounds from only a single nucleophilic aromatic substitution reaction.

(a)
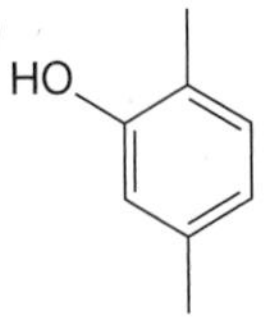
(b)
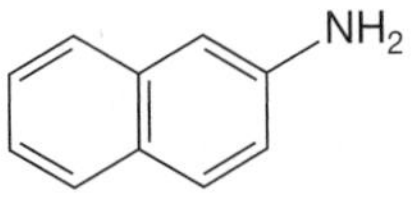
(c)
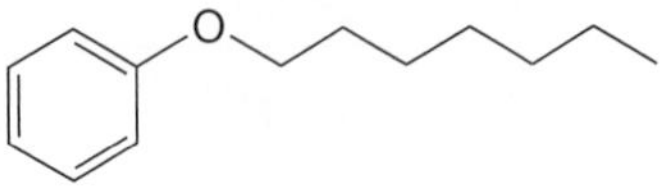

Sections 25.10–25.12 Organic Synthesis

25.51 **(SYN)** Show how you would synthesize each of the following compounds from benzene.

(a)
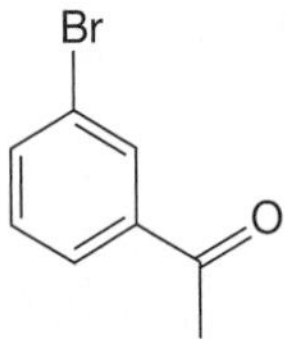
(b)
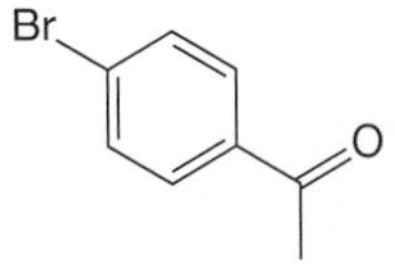
(c)
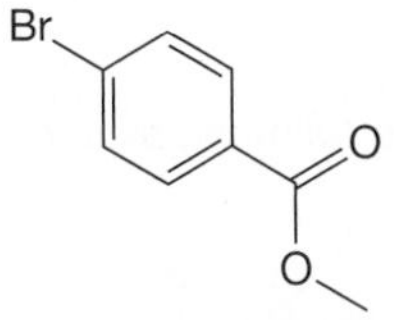
(d)
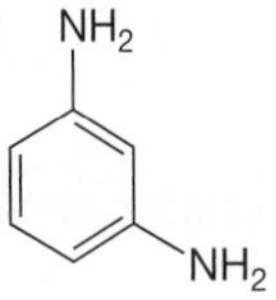
(e)
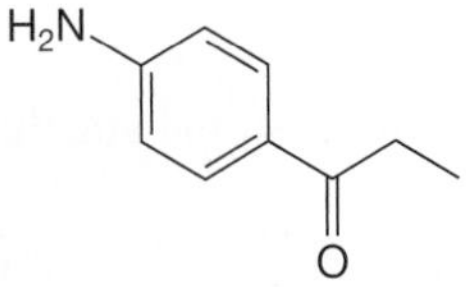

25.52 **(SYN)** Show how you would synthesize each of the following compounds from benzene.

(a)
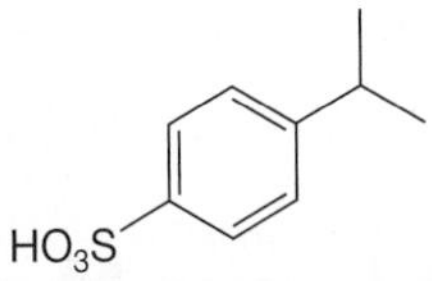
(b)
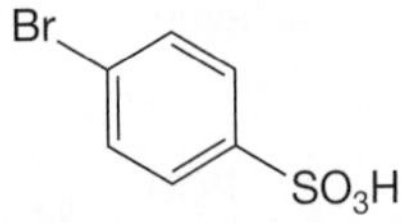
(c)
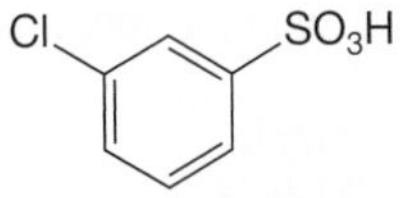

25.53 **(SYN)** Show how you would carry out each of the following transformations.

(a)
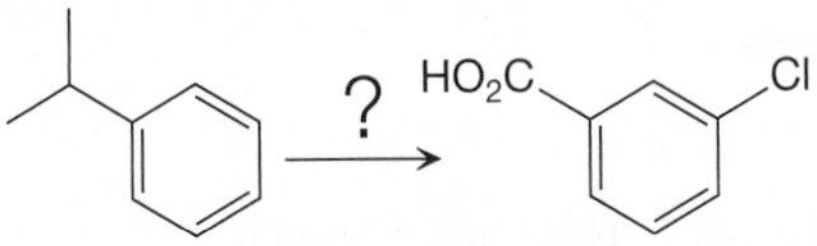
(b)
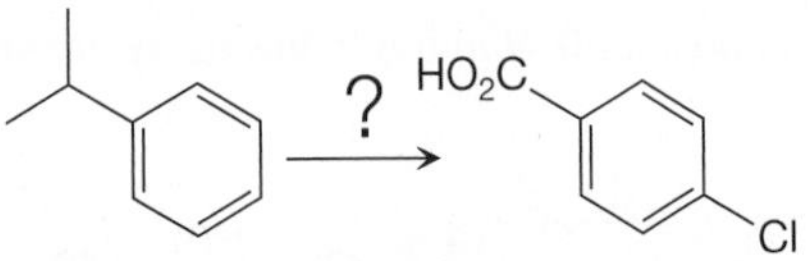

25.54 **(SYN)** Show how you would carry out each of the following transformations.

(a)
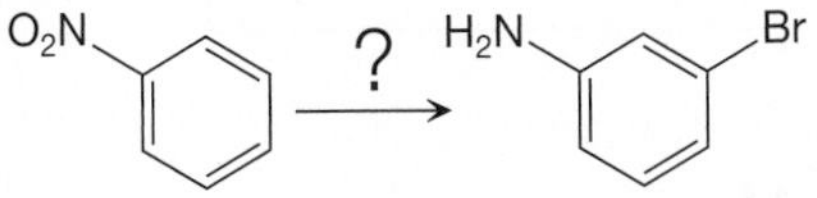
(b)
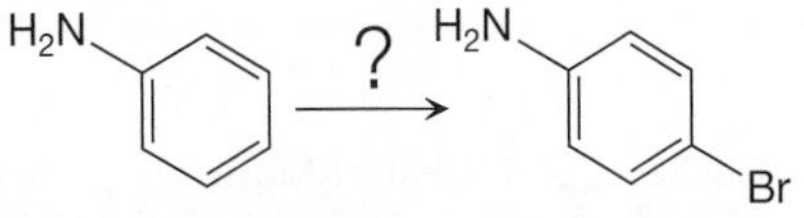

25.55 **(SYN)** Show how you would carry out this synthesis.

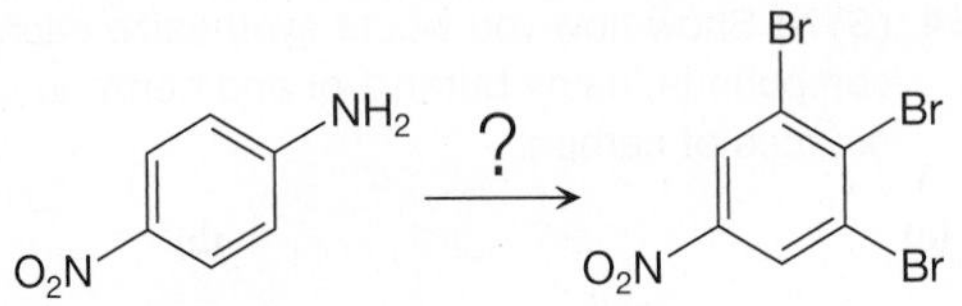

25.56 **(SYN)** Show how you would synthesize each of these compounds from benzene.

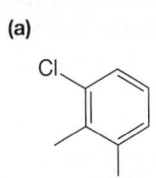

(a)
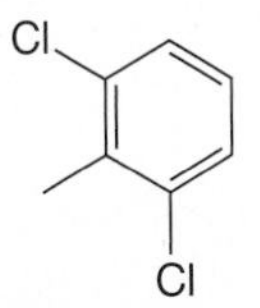
(b)
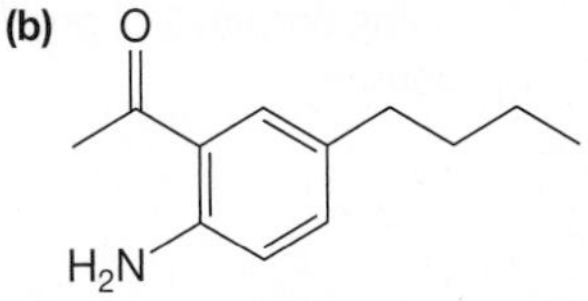

Integrated Problems

25.57 Predict the most likely sites of electrophilic aromatic substitution in each of the following molecules.

(a)
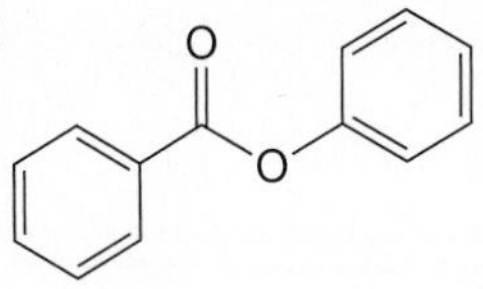
(b)
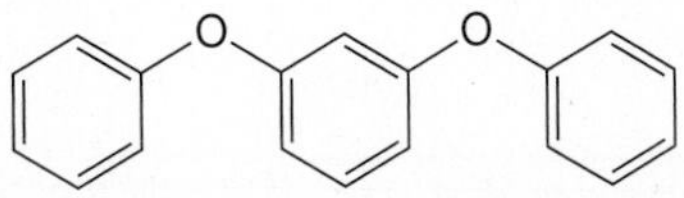
(c)
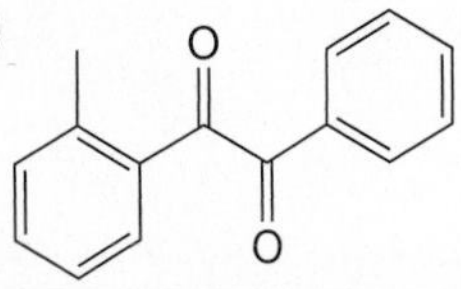
(d)
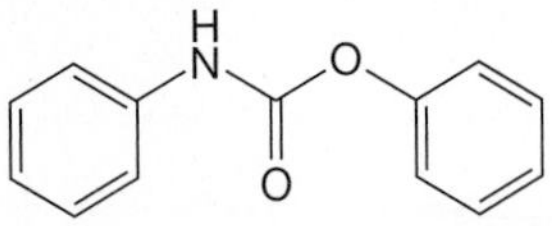

25.58 Draw a complete, detailed mechanism for this reaction.

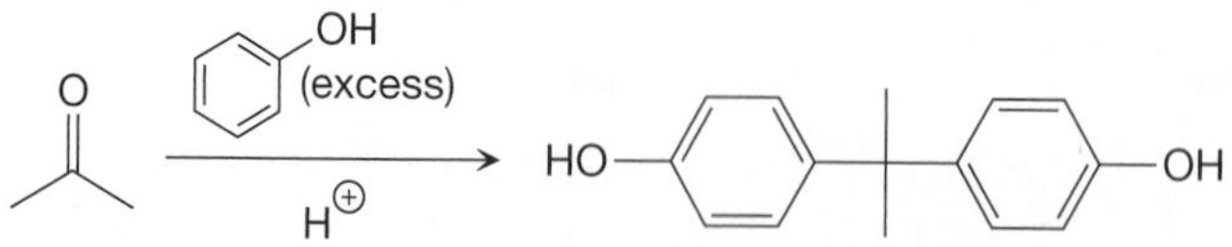

25.59 Draw a complete, detailed mechanism for the following reaction. A key intermediate is provided.

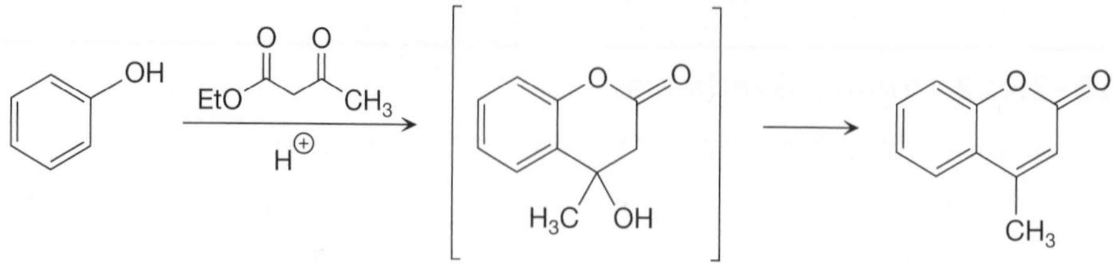

25.60 Draw the structures of compounds **A–F** in the following synthesis scheme.

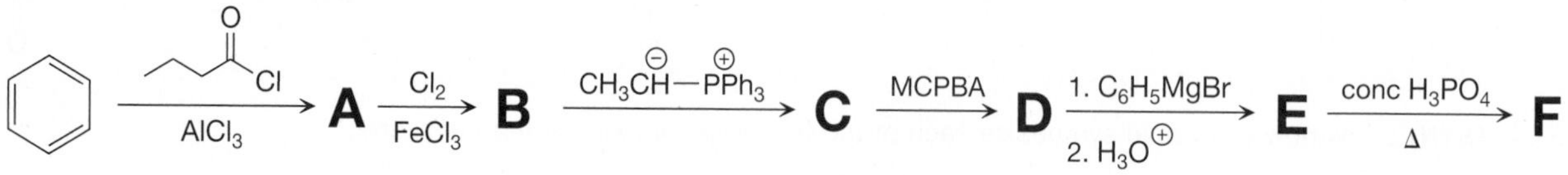

25.61 Draw the structures of compounds **G–N** in the following synthesis scheme.

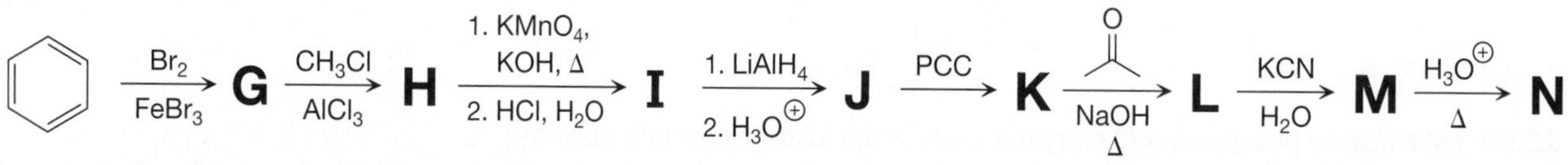

25.62 Draw the structures of compounds **O–V** in the following synthesis scheme.

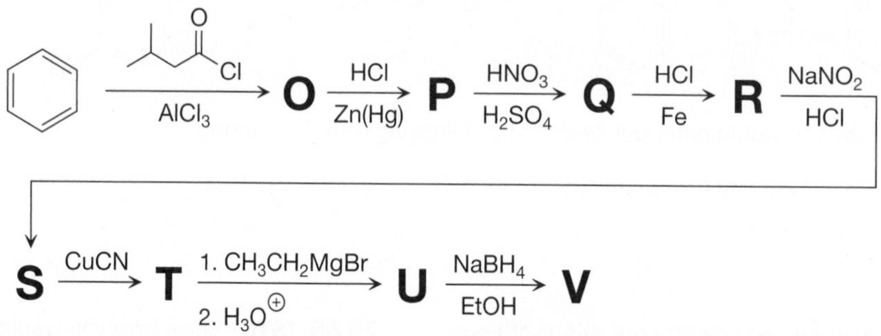

25.63 (SYN) Show how you would synthesize this compound, using propan-1-ol and benzene as your only sources of carbon.

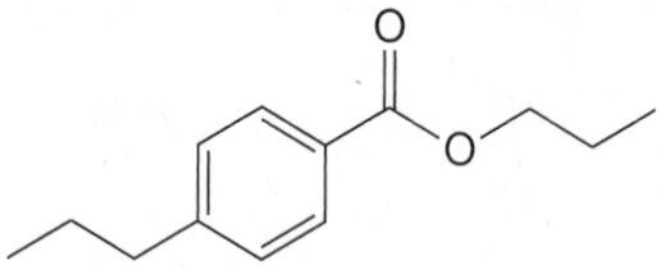

25.64 (SYN) Show how you would synthesize each of these compounds, using butan-1-ol and benzene as your only sources of carbon.

(a)

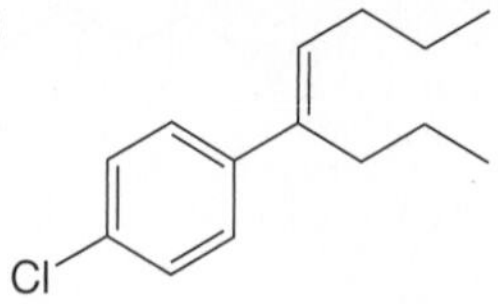

(b)

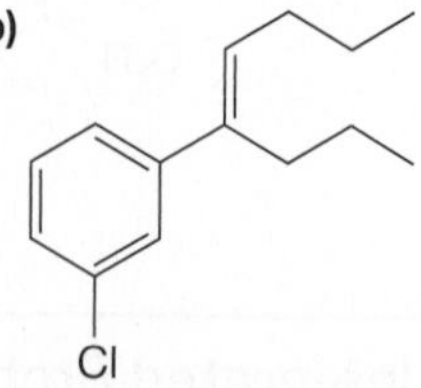

25.65 **(SYN)** Aspirin, or acetylsalicylic acid, is one of the world's most widely produced medications. Show how to synthesize aspirin from benzene.

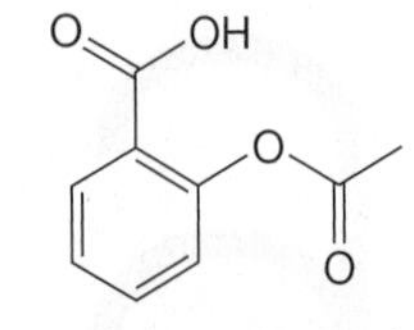

Acetylsalicylic acid (Aspirin)

25.66 The reaction shown here yields a compound whose molecular formula is $C_7H_6O_4$. The ^1H NMR and ^{13}C NMR spectra of $C_7H_6O_4$ are shown below. Draw the product and the complete, detailed mechanism for this reaction.

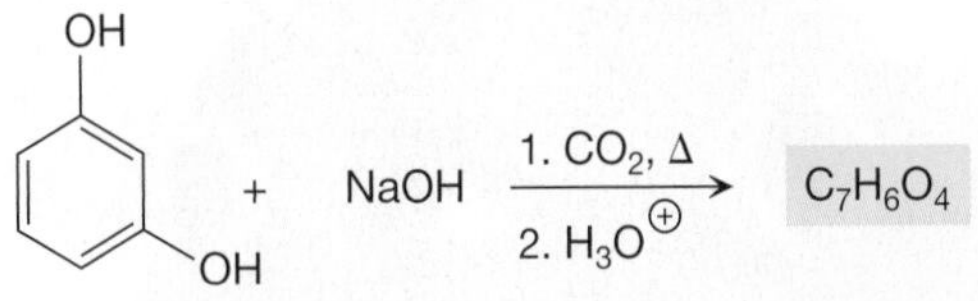
OH
OH
+ NaOH
1. CO_2, Δ
2. $H_3O^{\oplus}$
$C_7H_6O_4$

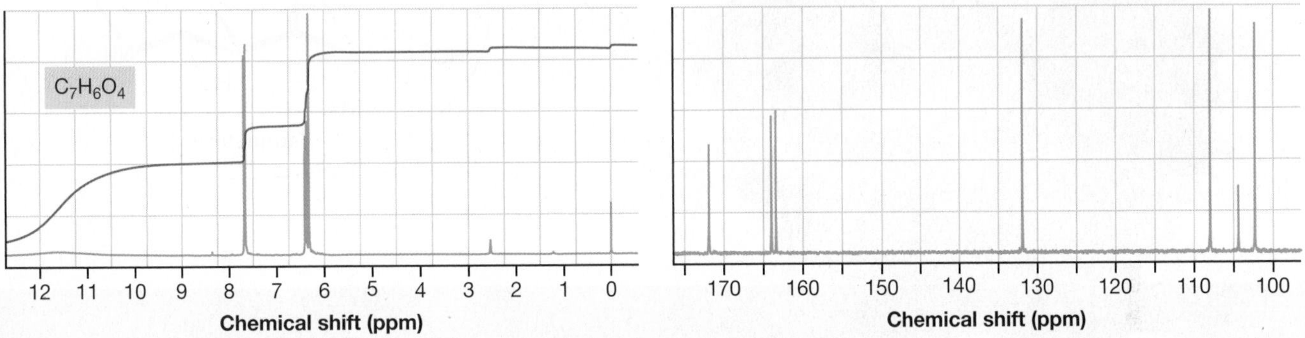
$C_7H_6O_4$
12 11 10 9 8 7 6 5 4 3 2 1 0
Chemical shift (ppm)
170 160 150 140 130 120 110 100
Chemical shift (ppm)

25.67 Compound **X**, whose formula is C_9H_{10}, dimerizes in the presence of acid to produce the compound shown here. The ^1H NMR and ^{13}C NMR spectra of **X** are shown below. Determine the structure of **X** and draw the complete, detailed mechanism for the reaction. (In the ^{13}C NMR spectrum, there are two signals >130 ppm.)

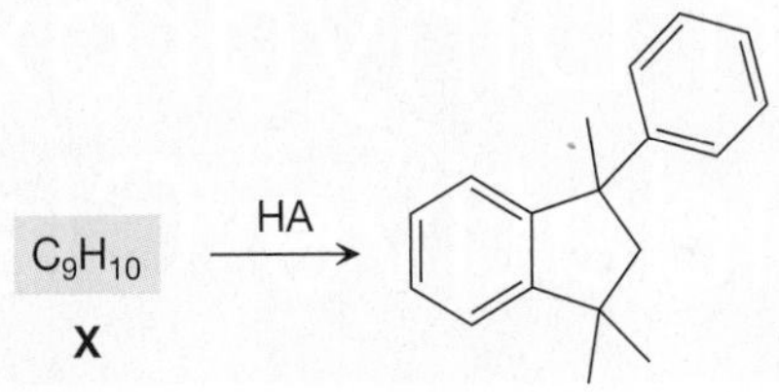
C_9H_{10}
X
HA

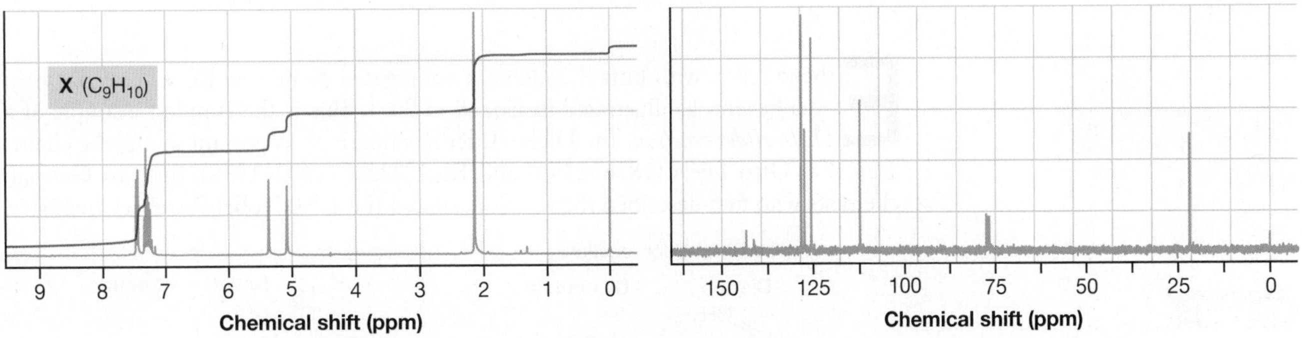
X (C_9H_{10})
9 8 7 6 5 4 3 2 1 0
Chemical shift (ppm)
150 125 100 75 50 25 0
Chemical shift (ppm)

25.68 Heating compound **Y** under acidic conditions produces compound **Z**, whose formula is $C_{15}H_{12}$. The ^{13}C NMR spectrum of **Z** exhibits one signal near 20 ppm and 14 signals between 120 and 140 ppm. The ^1H NMR spectrum exhibits one signal at 2.7 ppm and several overlapping signals between 7 and 9 ppm. The integrations of the two sets of signals are in a 1 : 3 ratio. Determine the structure of **Z** and draw the complete, detailed mechanism for the reaction.

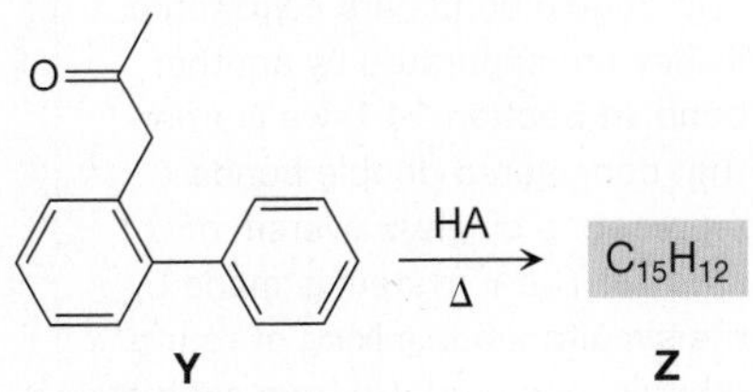
O
HA
Δ
$C_{15}H_{12}$
Y
Z

26

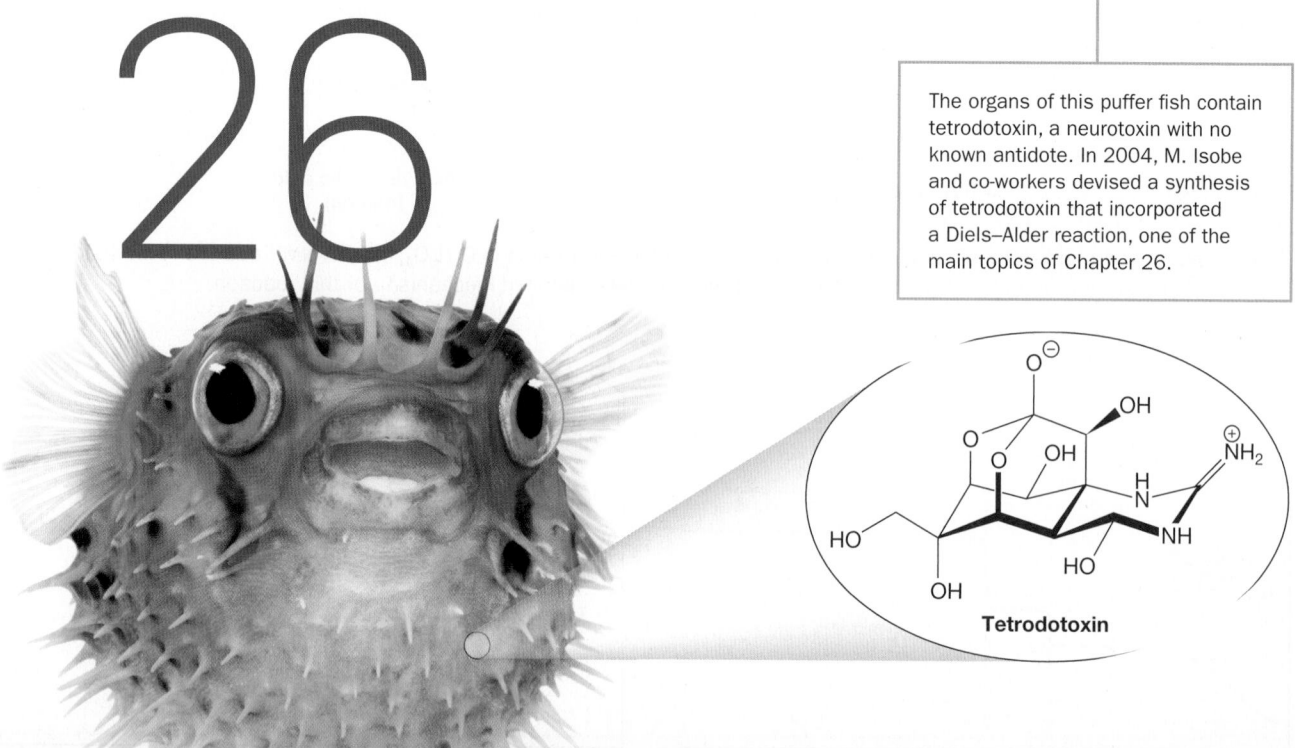

The organs of this puffer fish contain tetrodotoxin, a neurotoxin with no known antidote. In 2004, M. Isobe and co-workers devised a synthesis of tetrodotoxin that incorporated a Diels–Alder reaction, one of the main topics of Chapter 26.

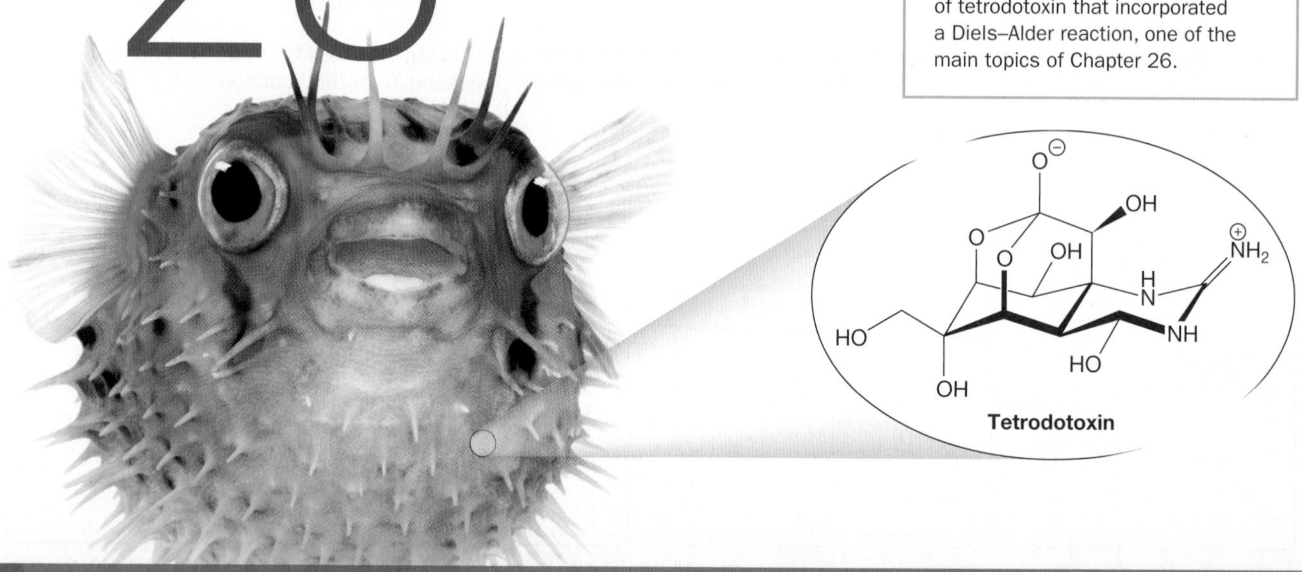

Tetrodotoxin

The Diels–Alder Reaction, Syn Dihydroxylation, and Oxidative Cleavage

Ethene reacts with buta-1,3-diene, a conjugated diene (see Recall box), to form cyclohexene, as illustrated in Equation 26-1. This is the simplest example of a *Diels–Alder reaction*. The Diels–Alder reaction is so important in organic chemistry that Otto Diels (1876–1954) and Kurt Alder (1902–1958), the two German chemists who first described the reaction, shared the 1950 Nobel Prize in Chemistry.

◂ RECALL

Two double bonds are *conjugated* if they are separated by another bond. In Section 14.1, we learned that conjugated double bonds represent a single π system of orbitals. The π system is made by the simultaneous mixing of four *p* orbitals, one *p* orbital from each of the doubly bonded atoms.

The Diels–Alder reaction

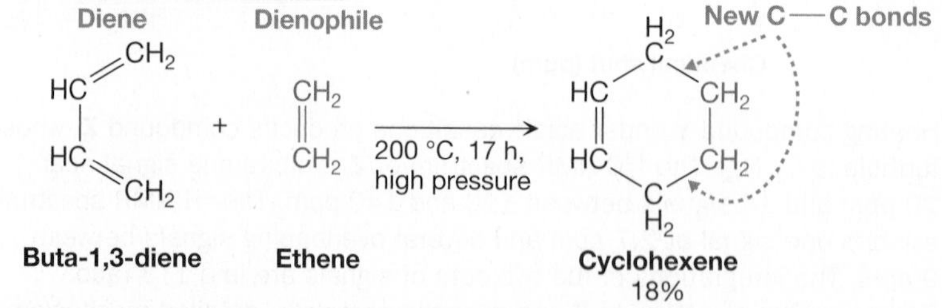

Diene
Dienophile
New C—C bonds
200 °C, 17 h, high pressure
Buta-1,3-diene
Ethene
Cyclohexene
18%

(26-1)

The Diels–Alder reaction is especially useful because it forms two new carbon–carbon σ bonds. (As we stressed in Chapters 10 and 11, these are *extremely* important types of reactions in organic synthesis.) Moreover, the Diels–Alder reaction produces

Chapter Outline

a six-membered ring of carbons, which is common in natural products. The reaction is also quite robust; it can be carried out with a variety of other functional groups present, and many Diels–Alder reactions can be carried out under mild conditions. Finally, the reaction is *stereospecific* and often *regioselective*, which can provide chemists with substantial control over the products that are formed.

The mechanism of the Diels–Alder reaction cannot be described by the elementary steps we learned in Chapters 6 and 7. Therefore, we introduce a new elementary step here in Chapter 26, which we will explore with the same systematic approach taken in introducing other elementary steps. We will begin by presenting the curved arrow notation and examples. Then we will investigate factors that affect the reaction's rate, and we will examine the stereochemistry and regiochemistry of the reaction.

After we discuss the Diels–Alder reaction, we will consider syn dihydroxylation and oxidative cleavage reactions—important reactions that involve elementary steps closely related to the elementary step that describes the Diels–Alder reaction. Oxidative cleavage reactions are particularly useful because of their ability to *break* carbon–carbon bonds regiospecifically.

GREEN CHEMISTRY

Diels–Alder reactions can be very green, owing to their high atom economy (Section 11.6c), thus minimizing waste. Notice that every atom in the starting material ends up in the desired product. Many Diels–Alder reactions can be carried out at low temperatures and in nontoxic solvents such as water, and many can take place with high yield, too, making them even greener.

26.1 Curved Arrow Notation and Examples of Diels–Alder Reactions

SECTION 26.1 OBJECTIVES

You will be able to:

1. Draw the mechanism and product for a Diels–Alder reaction, identifying one reactant as the diene and the other as the dienophile.
2. Explain why a Diels–Alder reaction is thermally allowed.

Mechanism Drawing
Mechanism for the Diels–Alder Reaction

The reaction shown previously in Equation 26-1 is the simplest possible Diels–Alder reaction, and it serves as the prototype for all other Diels–Alder reactions. The mechanism for that reaction is provided in Equation 26-2 (see Looking Ahead box).

Mechanism for the Diels–Alder reaction (Eq. 26-1)

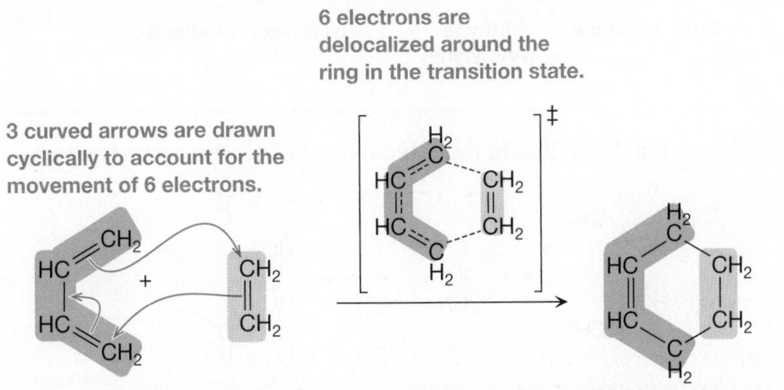

6 electrons are delocalized around the ring in the transition state.
3 curved arrows are drawn cyclically to account for the movement of 6 electrons.

(26-2)

▸ LOOKING AHEAD

Section 26.7 will show how molecular orbital theory is applied to describe the electron flow in a Diels–Alder reaction.

The entire reaction takes place in a *single step*. In other words:

The Diels–Alder reaction is concerted, whereby all of the bonds are formed and broken simultaneously.

To depict this concerted process, we draw three curved arrows in a cyclic fashion. Thus, the reaction proceeds through a *cyclic transition state*, which makes it a **pericyclic reaction**. More specifically, because the electron movement is responsible for joining together two separate species to form a ring, it is also called a **cycloaddition reaction**. (Other examples of pericyclic reactions are explored in Problem 26.13 at the end of the chapter.)

In Equation 26-2, the curved arrows depict a clockwise movement of the electrons. It would be equally correct, however, if the curved arrows were drawn to depict a counterclockwise movement of those electrons.

YOUR TURN **26.1**

Redraw the elementary step in Equation 26-2 to depict a counterclockwise movement of the electrons. Does this alternate way of drawing the curved arrows lead to the same product shown in Equation 26-2?

Answers to Your Turns are in the back of the book.

The Diels–Alder reaction in Equation 26-1 is the simplest one, but it is not the only possible one. In general, a **Diels–Alder reaction** joins a *diene* and a *dienophile* to form a new six-membered ring:

- A **diene** contributes four π electrons from a pair of *conjugated* π bonds.
- A **dienophile** (meaning "diene-loving") contributes two π electrons from a single π bond.

Therefore, buta-1,3-diene in Equation 26-1 acts as the diene and ethene acts as the dienophile. Moreover, a Diels–Alder reaction can be described as a **[4+2] cycloaddition**, where the numbers indicate the number of π electrons contributed by each species involved.

The dienophile of the Diels–Alder reaction can be an alkene, as depicted in Equation 26-2, or it can be an alkyne, as shown in Equation 26-3. In Equation 26-3, two electrons are contributed from one π bond of the triple bond, leaving the other π bond intact in the product:

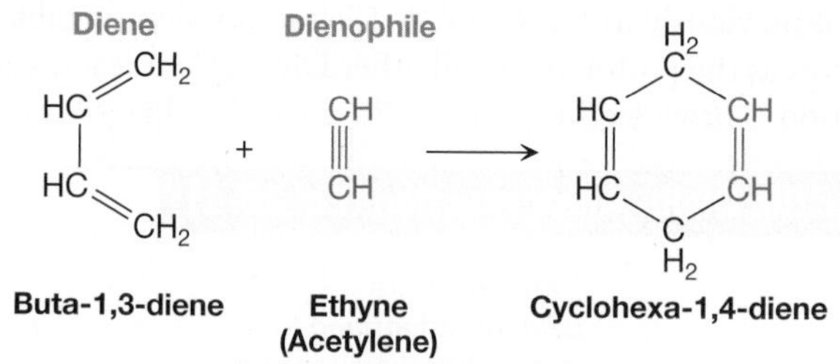
Diene
Dienophile
CH2
HC
HC
CH2
+
CH
CH
H2
C
HC
CH
HC
CH
C
H2
Buta-1,3-diene
Ethyne
(Acetylene)
Cyclohexa-1,4-diene

(26-3)

YOUR TURN **26.2**

The reaction in Equation 26-3 is repeated here. Supply the curved arrows.

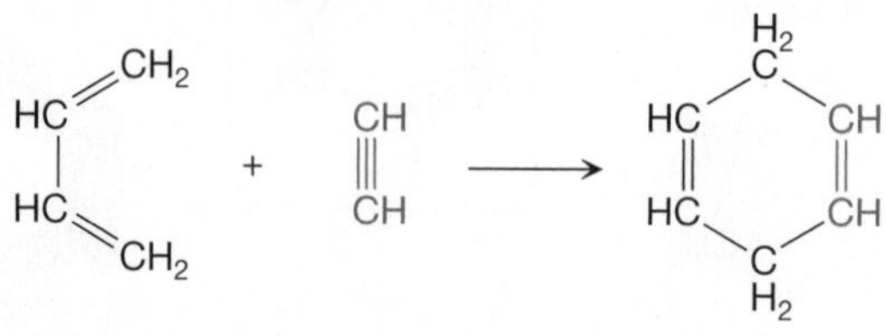
CH2
HC
HC
CH2
+
CH
CH
H2
C
HC
CH
HC
CH
C
H2

All Diels–Alder reactions involve the flow of six π electrons. The number of electrons is important, because six is a Hückel number and those electrons are delocalized over a complete ring in the transition state. Therefore, according to Hückel's rules (see Recall box):

The Diels–Alder reaction proceeds through an *aromatic transition state* (**Figure 26-1**).

Aromaticity in the transition state substantially lowers the reaction's energy barrier, which helps make the reaction feasible. We say that the reaction is **thermally allowed**, meaning that it can proceed at a reasonable rate with the reactants in their ground state (i.e., most stable) electron configurations (see Looking Ahead box).

For comparison, let's examine two other possible cycloaddition reactions. In Equation 26-4, two molecules of ethene combine in a **[2+2] cycloaddition**, and in Equation 26-5, a molecule of hexa-1,3,5-triene and a molecule of ethene combine in a **[6+2] cycloaddition**. Both of these reactions would have to proceed through an *antiaromatic transition state*, because an even number of pairs (an anti-Hückel number) of electrons is delocalized over an entire ring: two pairs for the [2+2] cycloaddition and four pairs for the [6+2] cycloaddition. The antiaromatic nature of the transition state creates a large energy barrier; such reactions are **thermally forbidden** because they do *not* take place readily with the reactants in their ground state electron configurations.

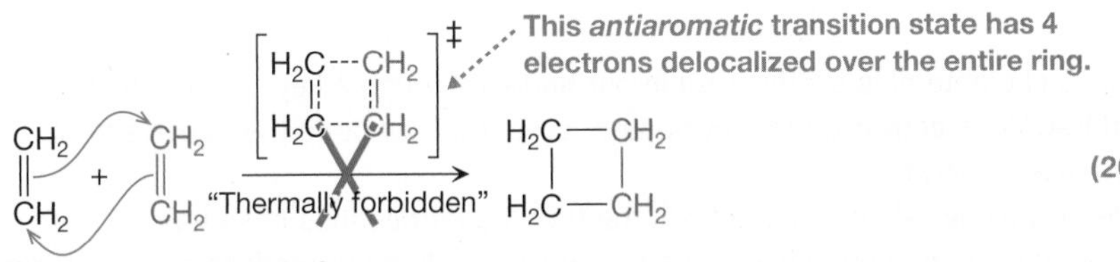

This *antiaromatic* transition state has 4 electrons delocalized over the entire ring.
"Thermally forbidden"

Ethene Ethene (26-4)

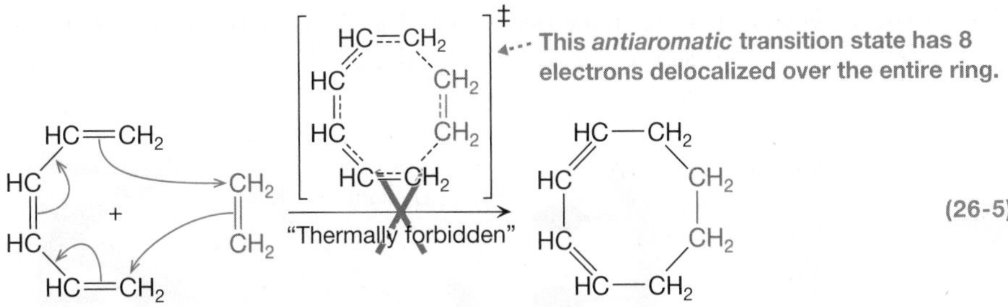

This *antiaromatic* transition state has 8 electrons delocalized over the entire ring.
"Thermally forbidden"

Hexa-1,3,5-triene Ethene (26-5)

6 electrons delocalized

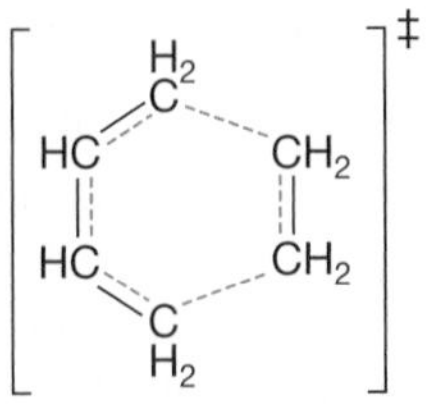

"Thermally allowed"

FIGURE 26-1 An aromatic transition state

◂ RECALL

Hückel's rules (Section 14.7) state that a compound is *aromatic* if it has a cyclic, planar π system that contains an odd number of pairs (a Hückel number) of π electrons. An *antiaromatic* compound has a cyclic, planar π system that contains an even number of pairs (an anti-Hückel number) of π electrons.

▸ LOOKING AHEAD

Section 26.7c will distinguish *thermally allowed* cycloaddition reactions from *photochemically allowed* reactions. As we will see, photochemically allowed reactions do not take place readily without one of the reactants in an excited electron configuration (e.g., the result of photon absorption).

YOUR TURN **26.3**

If the cycloaddition reaction involving two molecules of cyclopentene were to occur, it would appear as follows:

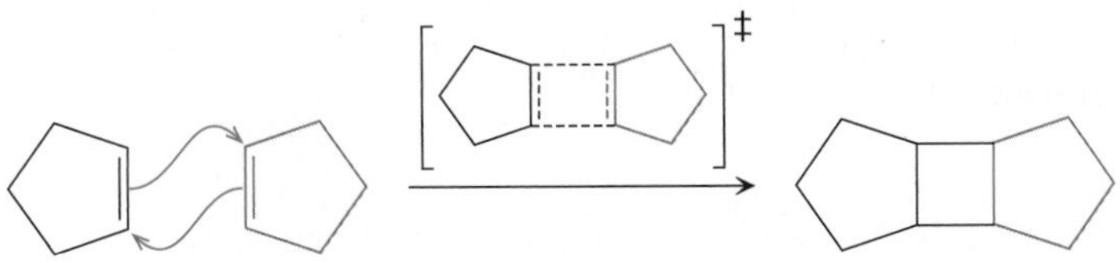

Is the transition state *aromatic* or *antiaromatic*? Is this reaction *thermally allowed* or *thermally forbidden*?

Biological Cycloaddition Reactions

The Diels–Alder reaction was first documented in 1928, but nature has been using the reaction since long before then. One example is in the biosynthesis of lovastatin, a cholesterol-lowering natural product produced by the fungus *Aspergillus terreus* and marketed under the trade name Mevacor. The Diels–Alder step is shown in **Figure 26-2**, and it is believed to be catalyzed by an enzyme called Diels–Alderase. The bicyclic product of the Diels–Alder reaction then goes on to form lovastatin.

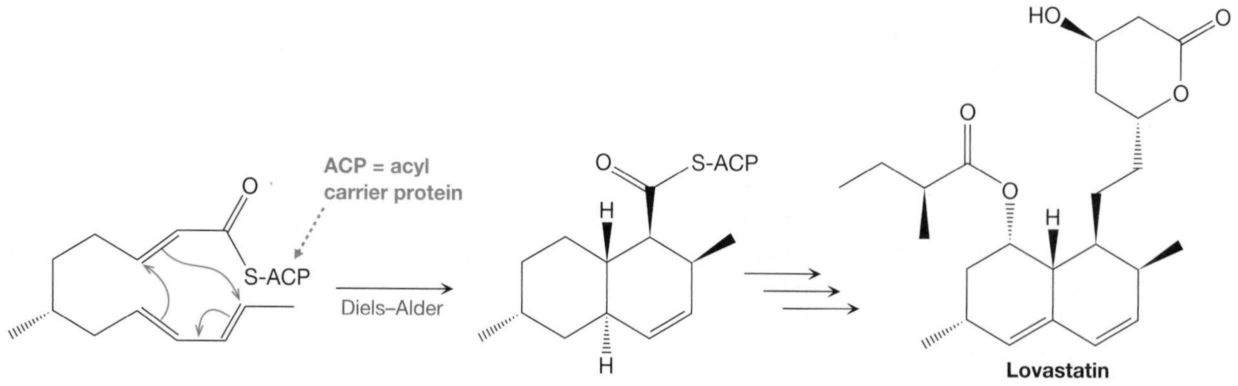
ACP = acyl carrier protein
S-ACP
Diels–Alder
Lovastatin

FIGURE 26-2

Lovastatin can lower cholesterol because cholesterol is synthesized in our bodies through a key step in which 3-hydroxy-3-methylglutaryl-coenzyme A (HMG-CoA) is converted to mevalonate. Lovastatin binds to the active site of HMG-CoA reductase, which inhibits its enzymatic activity.

Cycloaddition reactions also play a role in causing skin cancer. In DNA, the thymine nitrogenous base has a C=C double bond, so two adjacent thymine nucleotides can feasibly undergo a [2+2] cycloaddition to produce a *thymine dimer* (**Figure 26-3**, left). As we saw in Section 26.1, this kind of [2+2] cycloaddition is *thermally forbidden*. However, when one of the molecules absorbs a photon of UV light (such as from the sun), the reaction becomes *allowed*. (This is discussed in detail in Section 26.7c.) The resulting thymine dimer causes a kink in the DNA strand (Fig. 26-3, right), which interferes with the normal function of DNA.

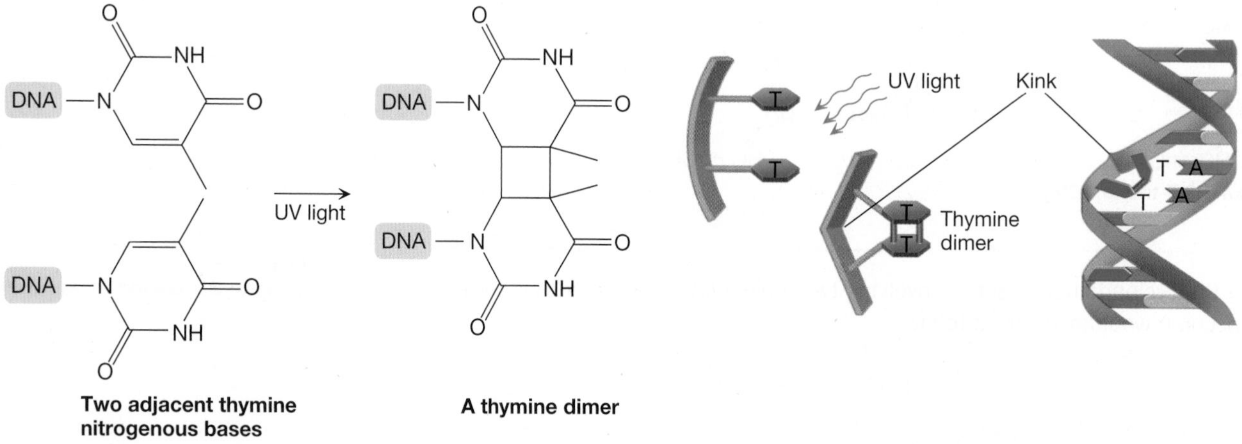
DNA
UV light
Two adjacent thymine nitrogenous bases
A thymine dimer
UV light
Kink
Thymine dimer

FIGURE 26-3

Fortunately, our bodies can remove these thymine dimers through a process called nucleotide excision repair. Once the thymine dimer is recognized, a short segment of damaged single-stranded DNA is removed. DNA polymerase uses the remaining undamaged, complementary single-stranded DNA as a template to produce a replacement segment without flaws, which is inserted by an enzyme called DNA ligase.

SOLVED PROBLEM **26.1**

How to determine if a cycloaddition is thermally allowed or forbidden

Break It Down **Is this cycloaddition reaction thermally allowed or forbidden?**

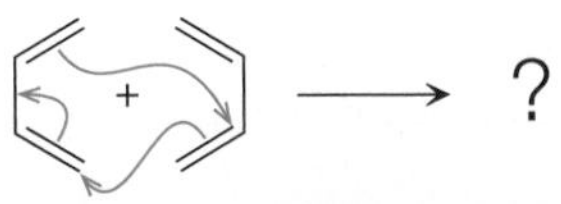

Think	Solve
In the transition state, are electrons delocalized over a complete ring? If so, how many electrons?	The transition state is drawn by taking a rough average of the reactants and products, as shown here. Each curved arrow represents two electrons. Six electrons are delocalized over a complete ring in the transition state. 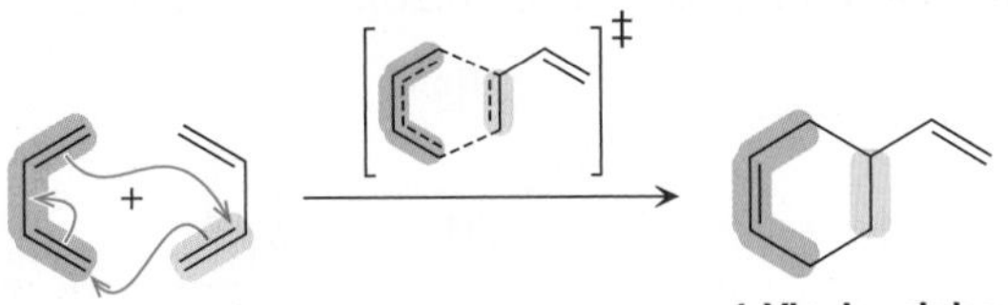 **4-Vinylcyclohexene**
Does that number of electrons represent a Hückel number or an anti-Hückel number? How does that correspond to whether the reaction is allowed or forbidden?	Six is a Hückel number of electrons (an odd number of pairs of electrons), so the transition state is aromatic, making the reaction thermally allowed.

Try It Draw the transition state for the cycloaddition reaction shown here. Does this reaction take place readily? Why or why not?

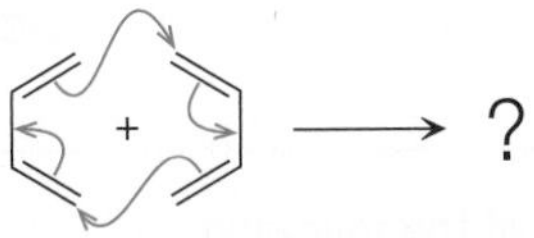

Answers to all Try It exercises can be found in the Solutions Manual.

CONNECTIONS 26.1

Transmitting power safely 4-Vinylcyclohexene (Solved Problem 26.1) is used to make 4-vinylcyclohexene dioxide, which is a cross-linking agent in the production of cycloaliphatic epoxy resins. Cycloaliphatic epoxy resins are used to make these overhead power-line insulators, which electrically separate power lines from each other and from the supporting structure.

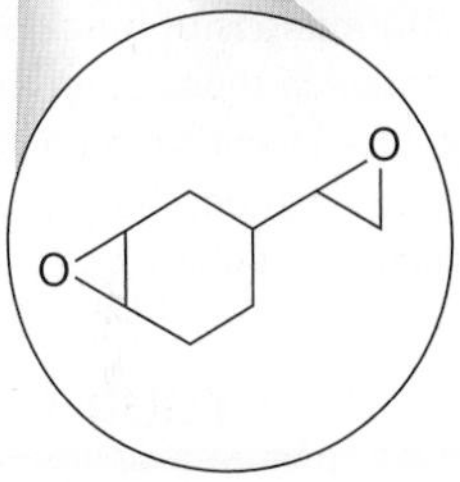

Vinylcyclohexene dioxide

26.2 Conformation of the Diene in Diels–Alder Reactions

SECTION 26.2 OBJECTIVES

You will be able to:

1. Explain why the *s*-cis conformation of the diene is required for a Diels–Alder reaction.
2. Determine the relative rates of Diels–Alder reactions on the basis of the diene achieving the *s*-cis conformation.

The concerted nature of the Diels–Alder reaction means that both of the new carbon–carbon σ bonds form simultaneously. Therefore, both ends of the diene must be relatively close to the dienophile in the transition state. The appropriate distances are achieved only if the diene attains a geometry in which the two ends of the π system are pointing in nearly the same direction—the so-called ***s*-cis conformation** (**Figure 26-4a**, next page). (The *s* indicates that the cis designation describes the orientation of groups about a single bond rather than a double bond or the plane of a ring.) In the ***s*-trans conformation** (Fig. 26-4b), the ends of the two reacting species are

(a)
With the diene in the s-cis conformation, the ends of the diene are at the appropriate distance from the dienophile to produce two new C—C bonds.

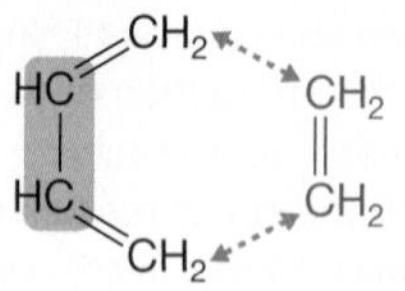

CH2
HC
CH2
HC
CH2
CH2

s-Cis conformation

(b)
With the diene in the s-trans conformation, the ends of the diene are too far from the dienophile.

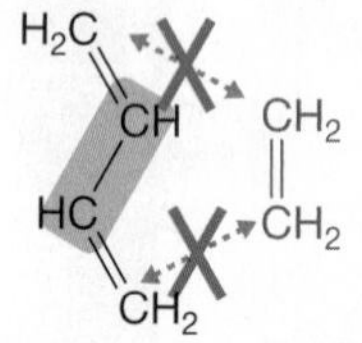

H2C
CH
CH2
HC
CH2
CH2

s-Trans conformation

FIGURE 26-4 The diene conformation in Diels–Alder reactions (a) In the s-cis conformation of a diene, both double bonds appear on the same side of the single bond connecting them (highlighted in red). (b) In the s-trans conformation, the double bonds appear on opposite sides of the single bond. Diels–Alder reactions are feasible only when the diene is s-cis.

◂ **RECALL**

The *s*-trans and the *s*-cis conformations are the relatively stable conformations of buta-1,3-diene because in those conformations the four valence *p* atomic orbitals are conjugated; that is, parallel and adjacent (Section 14.1).

farther apart, which raises the energy of the transition state and makes the Diels–Alder reaction unfeasible. Thus:

For a Diels–Alder reaction to take place, the diene must be in the s-cis conformation.

For buta-1,3-diene, the *s*-cis and *s*-trans conformations rapidly interchange through rotation about the C—C bond. The *s*-cis conformation is about 10 kJ/mol higher in energy than the *s*-trans conformation (see Recall box), so 98% of the molecules are in the *s*-trans conformation at equilibrium (Eq. 26-6a), and the remaining 2% are in the *s*-cis conformation (Eq. 26-6b). As the *s*-cis conformation undergoes the Diels–Alder reaction, it is continually replenished by its equilibrium with the *s*-trans conformation (Le Châtelier's principle, Section 6.2b).

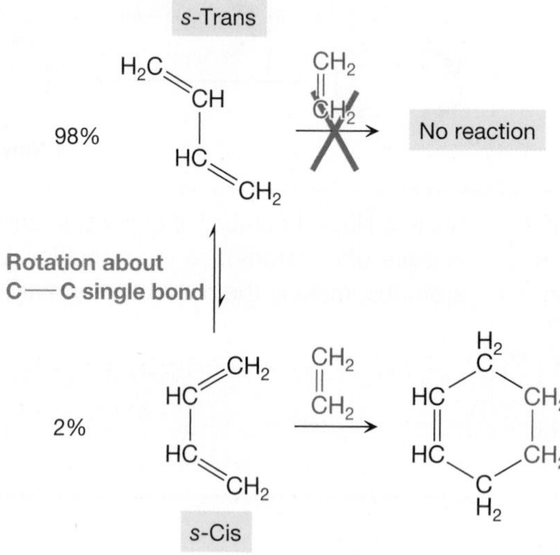

s-Trans
H2C
CH
HC
CH2
CH2
CH2
98%
No reaction
Rotation about
C—C single bond
2%
CH2
HC
HC
CH2
CH2
CH2
H2
C
HC
CH2
HC
CH2
C
H2
s-Cis

(26-6a)

(26-6b)

YOUR TURN **26.4**

Which of the following conformations is s-cis and which is s-trans? Which can undergo a Diels–Alder reaction?

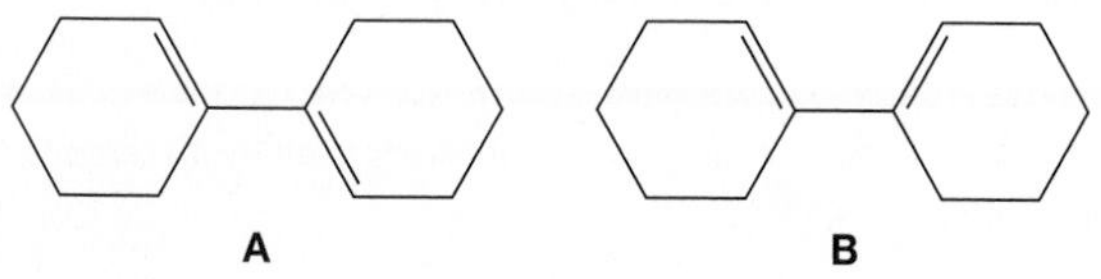

A
B

The requirement for the *s*-cis conformation makes the Diels–Alder reactions in Equations 26-7 and 26-8 unfeasible.

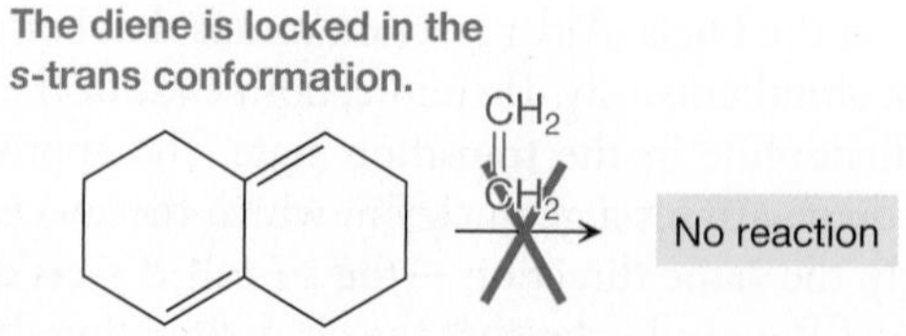

The diene is locked in the s-trans conformation.
CH2
CH2
No reaction

(26-7)

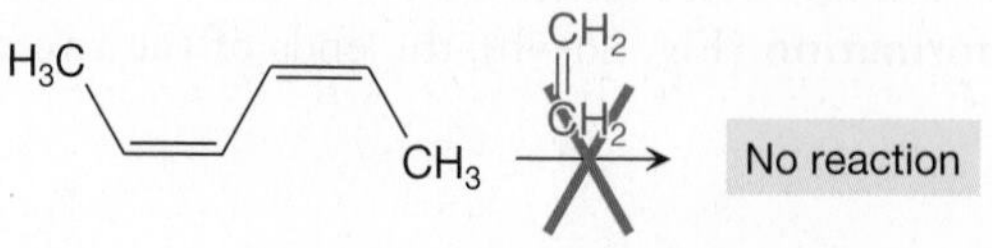

H3C
CH3
CH2
CH2
No reaction

(26-8)

The diene in Equation 26-7 is locked in the *s*-trans conformation by the fused ring system. The diene in Equation 26-8 is *not* locked in the *s*-trans conformation, but it is unable to attain the *s*-cis conformation because of severe steric strain, as illustrated in Equation 26-9:

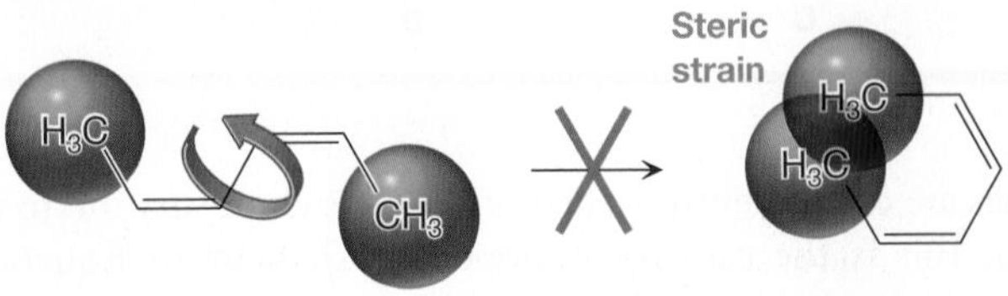

Steric strain
H_3C
CH_3
H_3C
H_3C

(26-9)

s-Trans **s-Cis**

YOUR TURN **26.5**

Draw this diene as it would appear in its s-cis conformation.

SOLVED PROBLEM **26.2**

How to assess a Diels–Alder reaction from the diene's ability to attain *s*-cis

Break It Down **Which molecule, A or B, will react faster with ethene in a Diels–Alder reaction? Explain.**

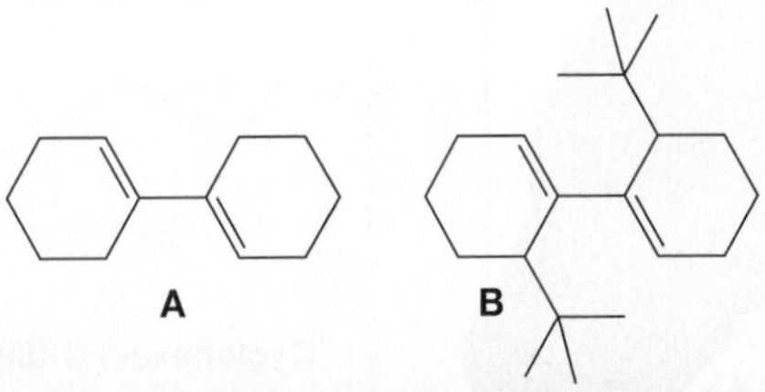

A B

Think	Solve
Are the dienes in an s-cis conformation? If not, can they undergo bond rotation to attain an s-cis conformation?	Neither diene is in the s-cis conformation as written, but the single bond in each molecule that connects the two double bonds can rotate. 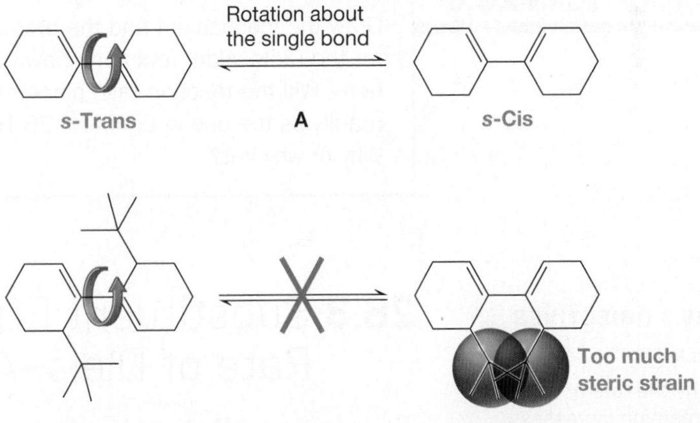 Rotation about the single bond s-Trans A s-Cis s-Trans B Too much steric strain s-Cis
How does steric strain factor into each s-cis conformation?	No substantial strain exists in the s-cis conformation of molecule **A**. By contrast, severe steric strain from the overlapping *tert*-butyl groups prevents molecule **B** from attaining the s-cis conformation.
How does the diene's ability to attain the s-cis conformation affect the Diels–Alder reaction?	The Diels–Alder reaction cannot occur unless the diene is in the s-cis conformation. Therefore, diene **A** will undergo a Diels–Alder reaction with ethene, whereas diene **B** will not.

(continued)

Try It Which molecule, **C** or **D**, will react faster with ethene in a Diels–Alder reaction? Explain.

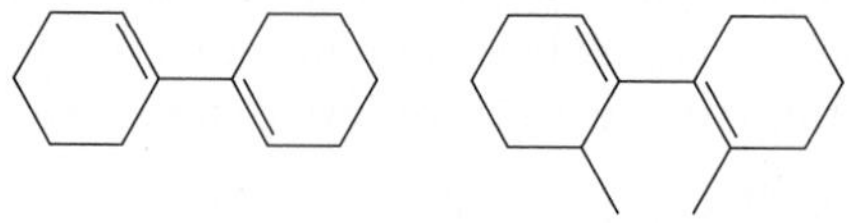

C **D**

Some dienes are conveniently locked in the *s*-cis conformation to allow a Diels–Alder reaction. This is the case for cyclopenta-1,3-diene in Equation 26-10 and cyclohexa-1,3-diene in Equation 26-11.

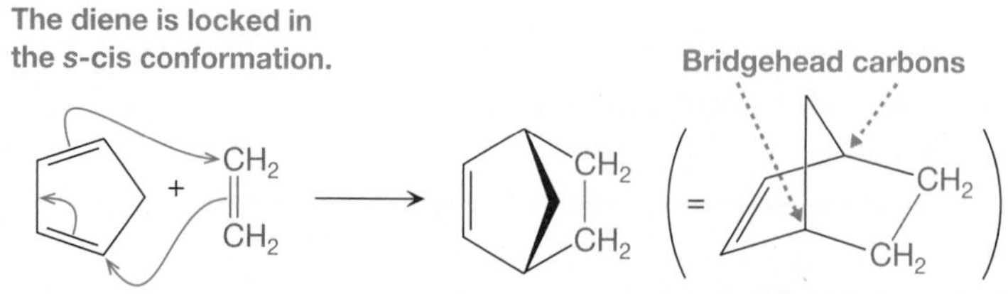

The diene is locked in the s-cis conformation.
Bridgehead carbons
+
CH2
CH2
=

(26-10)

Cyclopenta-1,3-diene **Bicyclo[2.2.1]hept-2-ene**

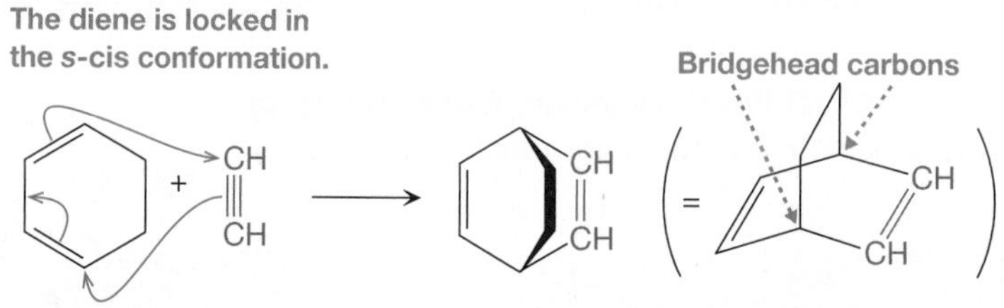

The diene is locked in the s-cis conformation.
Bridgehead carbons
+
CH
CH
=

(26-11)

Cyclohexa-1,3-diene **Bicyclo[2.2.2]octadiene**

CONNECTIONS 26.2

Helping keep motorcycle riders safe Bicyclo[2.2.1]hept-2-ene (Eq. 26-10), commonly called norbornene, is polymerized to produce polynorbornene. Polynorbornene is a high-impact-resistant rubber used to make this back protector insert used by motorcycle riders, which helps prevent serious injury in an accident.

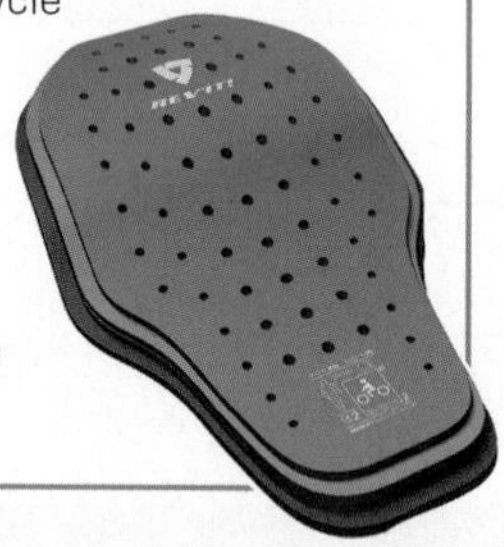

Equations 26-10 and 26-11 each produce a **bicyclic compound**, in which two **bridgehead carbons** are part of multiple rings. Notice that the bridgehead carbons are the C atoms from the reactant diene that form new bonds to the dienophile.

YOUR TURN **26.6**

Draw the mechanism and the product for the Diels–Alder reaction shown here. Will the reaction take place as readily as the one in Equation 26-10? Why or why not?

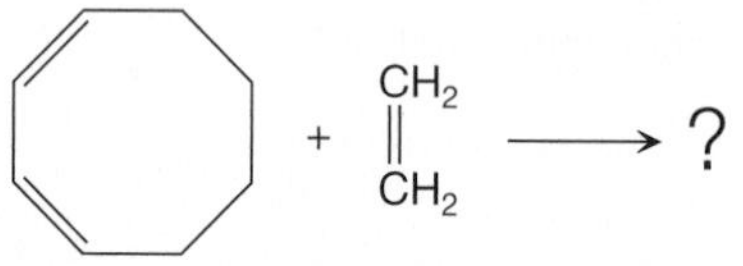

+
CH2
CH2
?

SECTION 26.3 OBJECTIVES

You will be able to:

1. Explain why the rate of a Diels–Alder reaction increases when an electron-donating group is attached to the diene or an electron-withdrawing group is attached to the dienophile.
2. Predict the relative rates of Diels–Alder reactions on the basis of the electron-donating or electron-withdrawing abilities of the substituents attached to the diene and dienophile.

26.3 Substituent Effects on the Reaction Rate of Diels–Alder Reactions

The prototypical Diels–Alder reaction (Eq. 26-1, p. 1252) between ethene and buta-1,3-diene is quite sluggish, requiring temperatures around 200 °C to proceed at a reasonable rate. Even then, the yield is only 18%. Much of the difficulty with that reaction occurs because there is no well-established flow of electrons from an electron-rich site to an electron-poor site. In fact, as we saw in Chapter 12, both buta-1,3-diene and ethene often react as electron-rich species. One of those species can be made more electron-rich, however, by attaching electron-donating groups, whereas the other species can be made electron-poor by attaching electron-withdrawing groups. Thus, the flow of electrons is more clearly established, which increases the reaction rate (see Looking Ahead box, p. 1261).

In a *standard* Diels–Alder reaction, the diene is electron-rich and the dienophile is electron-poor:

- Electron-donating substituents bonded directly to the diene carbons (**Figure 26-5**) facilitate standard Diels–Alder reactions. These are the same substituents that were classified as *activating* groups in electrophilic aromatic substitution (Table 25-3, p. 1210).
- Electron-withdrawing substituents bonded directly to the dienophile carbons (**Figure 26-6**) facilitate standard Diels–Alder reactions. These are the same substituents that were classified as *deactivating* groups in electrophilic aromatic substitution.

▶ LOOKING AHEAD

The effects that electron-donating and electron-withdrawing substituents have on the rate of a Diels–Alder reaction are discussed in the context of molecular orbital theory in Section 26.7a.

In the reaction in Equation 26-12, for example, two electron-donating CH_3 groups are attached directly to the diene. The reaction takes place at a slightly lower temperature than the one in Equation 26-1, and the yield is much higher.

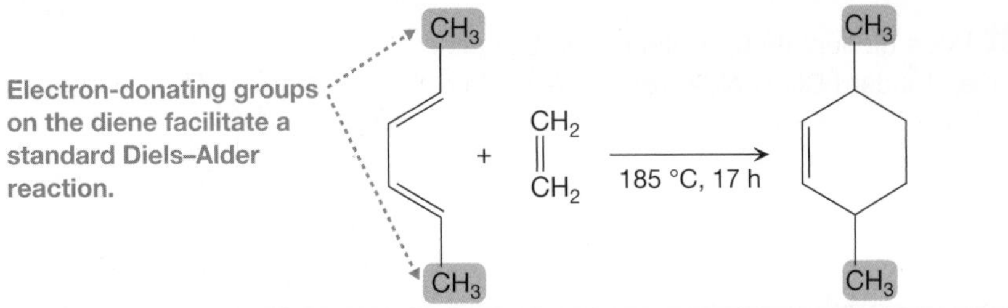
Electron-donating groups on the diene facilitate a standard Diels–Alder reaction.
CH3
CH2
CH2
185 °C, 17 h
CH3

(26-12)

3,6-Dimethylcyclohexene
60%

A similar outcome is observed with the reaction in Equation 26-13, in which a highly electron-withdrawing NO_2 group is attached to the dienophile:

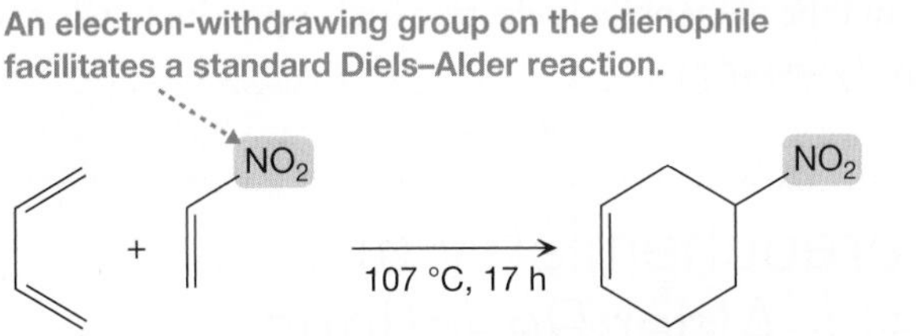
An electron-withdrawing group on the dienophile facilitates a standard Diels–Alder reaction.
NO2
107 °C, 17 h
NO2

(26-13)

4-Nitrocyclohexene
84%

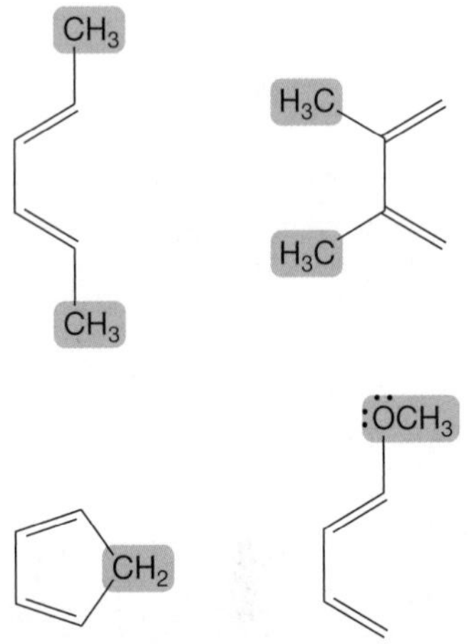
CH3
H3C
H3C
CH3
:ÖCH3
CH2

FIGURE 26-5 Electron-donating groups on the diene Electron-donating groups (highlighted in red) make the diene more electron-rich, which facilitates standard Diels–Alder reactions.

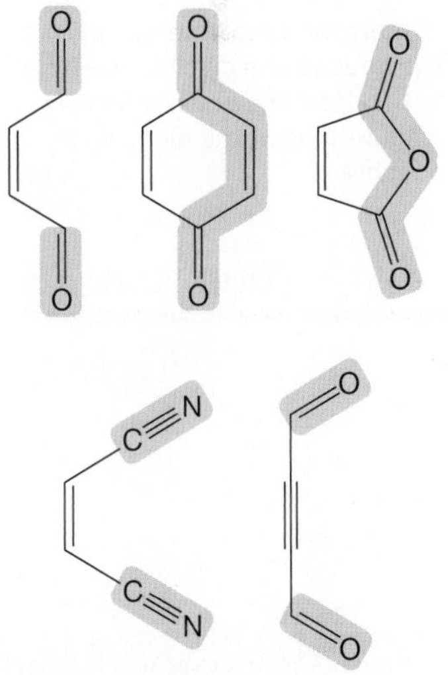
O
O
O
O
O
O
O
C≡N
C≡N
O
O

FIGURE 26-6 Electron-withdrawing groups on the dienophile Electron-withdrawing groups (highlighted in blue) make the dienophile electron-poor, which facilitates standard Diels–Alder reactions.

SOLVED PROBLEM **26.3**

How to predict relative Diels–Alder reaction rates from substituent effects

Break It Down Does diene A or diene B react faster in a standard Diels–Alder reaction? Explain.

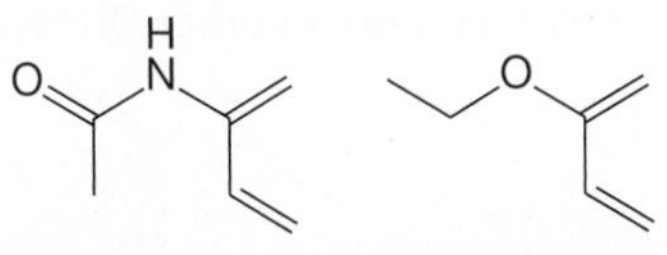
H
N
O
O

A **B**

Think	Solve
Should the diene be relatively electron-rich or electron-poor in a standard Diels–Alder reaction?	The diene should be relatively electron-rich in a standard Diels–Alder reaction, so the more electron-donating a substituent is, the faster the reaction will be.

(continued)

Does each diene have an attached electron-donating or electron-withdrawing substituent? Does that make the diene more electron-rich or electron-poor?	In both dienes **A** and **B**, the substituent is electron-donating, because each is attached to the diene by an atom with a lone pair of electrons. Therefore, each substituent serves to make the diene more electron-rich.
How can you tell which substituent is more effective?	According to Table 25-3 (p. 1210), the alkoxy group in **B** is more strongly activating than the acylamino group (NHCOR) in **A** (because of the presence of the carbonyl group). Therefore, diene **B** is more electron-rich than diene **A**, and **B** will react faster.

Try It Does dienophile **C** or dienophile **D** react faster in a standard Diels–Alder reaction? Explain.

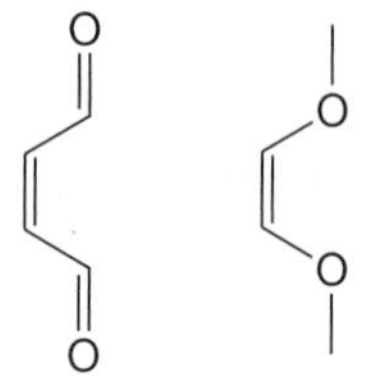

C **D**

In addition to standard Diels–Alder reactions, the reaction rate can be increased by attaching electron-withdrawing groups to the diene and electron-donating groups to the dienophile. In these *inverse electron demand* Diels–Alder reactions, the diene is electron-poor and the dienophile is electron-rich, opposite to what we saw with standard Diels–Alder reactions.

SECTION 26.4 OBJECTIVES

You will be able to:

1. Identify which atoms in a diene or dienophile become chiral centers in the product.
2. Determine which stereoisomers are produced in a given Diels–Alder reaction from the stereochemical configurations of the diene and dienophile.

26.4 Stereochemistry of Diels–Alder Reactions

In the prototypical Diels–Alder reaction between buta-1,3-diene and ethene, four carbon atoms rehybridize from sp^2 to sp^3: two from the diene and two from the dienophile (see Your Turn 26.7). These atoms, therefore, have the potential to become chiral centers in the product.

YOUR TURN **26.7**

In the prototypical Diels–Alder reaction shown here, identify the C atoms in the product that have rehybridized from sp^2 to sp^3, making them *potential* chiral centers in other Diels–Alder reactions.

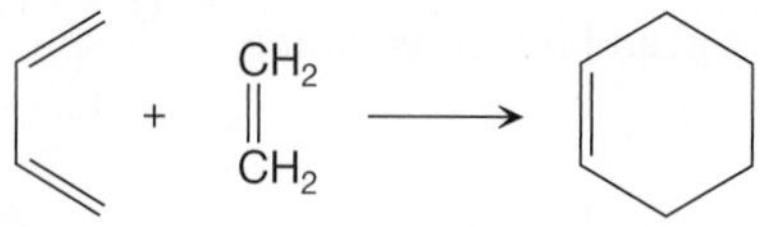
CH2
+
CH2

Two chiral centers are produced, for example, in each of the following reactions:

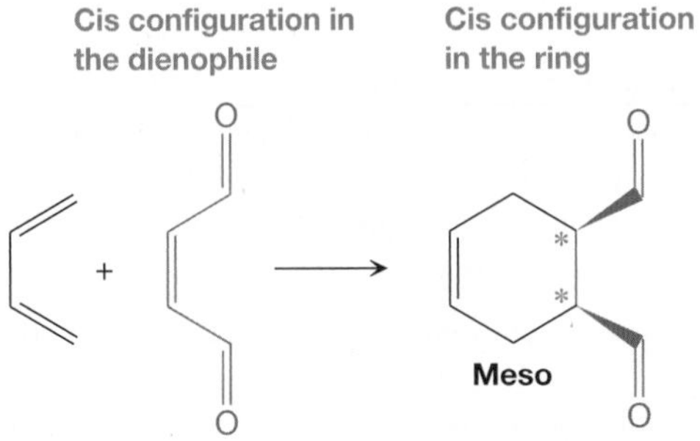
Cis configuration in the dienophile
Cis configuration in the ring
O
O
O
O
Meso

(26-14)

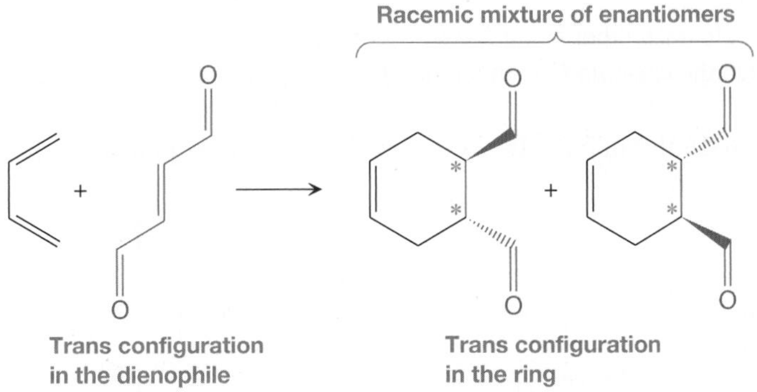
Racemic mixture of enantiomers
O
O
O
O
O
O
Trans configuration in the dienophile
Trans configuration in the ring

(26-15)

Only the cis configuration (meso) is produced in Equation 26-14, whereas only the trans configuration (a racemic mixture of enantiomers) is produced in Equation 26-15. Note that these stereochemical outcomes reflect the configurations of the C=C double bonds in the dienophiles. In general:

> Substituents that are cis to each other with respect to the double bond in the dienophile become cis to each other with respect to the new ring in the Diels–Alder product.

Thus, Diels–Alder reactions are *stereospecific*: the stereochemistry of the product is dictated by the stereochemistry of the reactants.

YOUR TURN 26.8

Predict the product of the Diels–Alder reaction shown here, paying particular attention to the configuration of the C=C double bond from the dienophile.

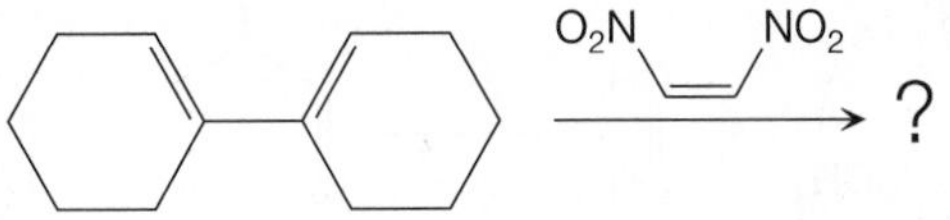
O2N
NO2
?

Similarly, the stereochemistry in the diene leads to specific stereochemical configurations in the products, which we can predict using the following method.

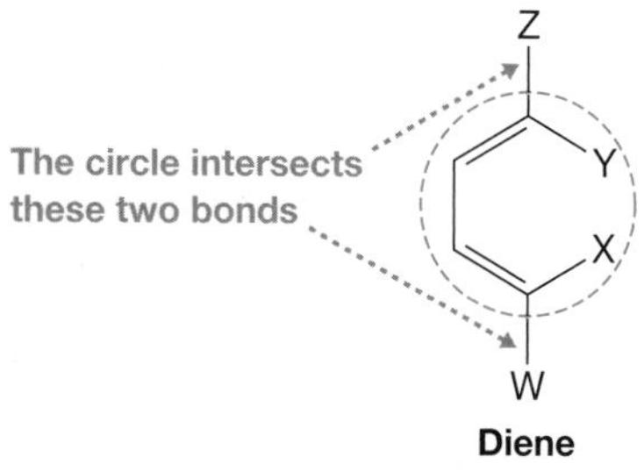

Z
The circle intersects
these two bonds
Y
X
W
Diene

FIGURE 26-7

Mechanism Drawing
Mechanism and Stereochemistry for the Diels–Alder Reaction

Elementary Step
Diels–Alder

Determining the stereochemical outcome of a Diels–Alder reaction from the diene

1. Draw a circle around the diene in its s-cis conformation.
   - Make sure the circle encompasses both double bonds of the diene.
   - The circle should intersect two of the four single bonds that attach the substituents W, X, Y, and Z, as shown in **Figure 26-7**. (Bonds to H atoms might not be explicitly drawn in line structures.)
2. Identify where the bonds to the substituents W, X, Y, and Z are located with respect to the circle you drew. Any two of those substituents will be:
   - Cis to each other in the Diels–Alder product if their bonds in the diene are either both inside the circle (X and Y) or both intersected by the circle (W and Z).
   - Trans to each other in the Diels–Alder product if one bond in the diene is inside the circle and the other intersects the circle (e.g., W and Y, or X and Z).

Equations 26-16 through 26-18 show how this method is applied:

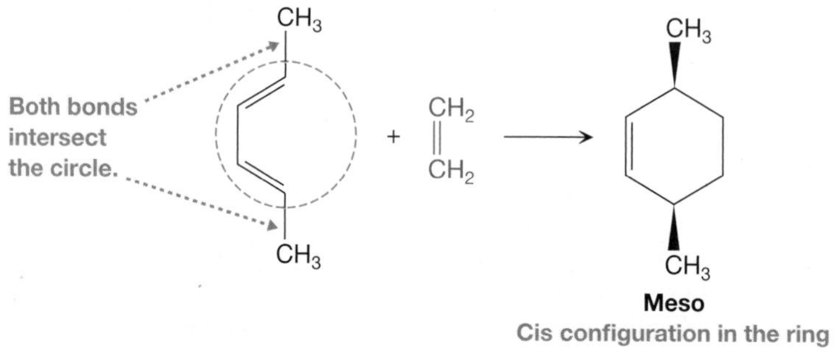

CH_3
Both bonds
intersect
the circle.
CH_3
+
CH_2
CH_2
CH_3
CH_3
Meso
Cis configuration in the ring

(26-16)

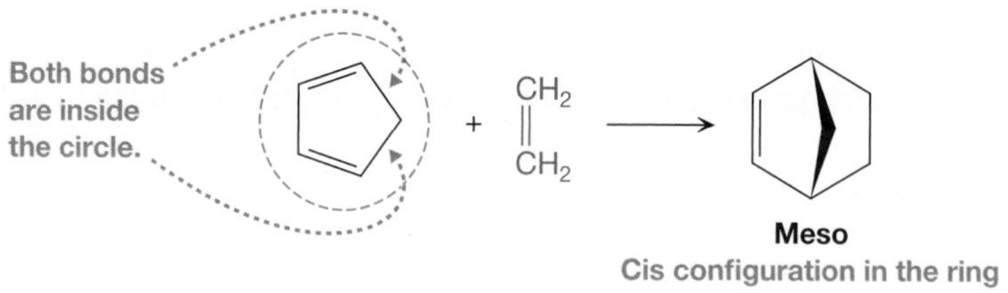

Both bonds
are inside
the circle.
+
CH_2
CH_2
Meso
Cis configuration in the ring

(26-17)

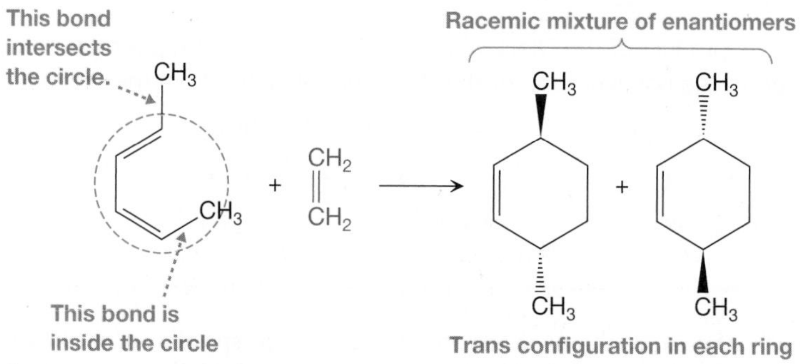

This bond
intersects
the circle.
CH_3
CH_3
This bond is
inside the circle
+
CH_2
CH_2
Racemic mixture of enantiomers
CH_3
CH_3
+
CH_3
CH_3
Trans configuration in each ring

(26-18)

We obtain the stereochemical outcomes in Equations 26-14 through 26-18 when the dienophile approaches the diene from below, as shown in Equation 26-19 (alternatively, the dienophile can approach from above the diene). The Diels–Alder reaction is concerted—the two σ bonds that form at each end of the diene and dienophile are formed *simultaneously*—so the substituents about the dienophile (A, B, C, and D in Eq. 26-19) cannot rotate relative to each other to scramble the stereochemistry. This explains our observations in Equations 26-14 and 26-15.

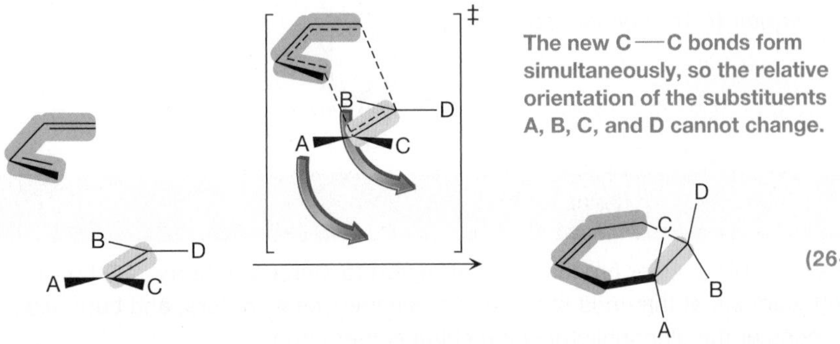

The new C—C bonds form simultaneously, so the relative orientation of the substituents A, B, C, and D cannot change.
A
B
C
D
‡

(26-19)

The concerted nature of the Diels–Alder reaction also explains the stereochemistry observed in Equations 26-16 through 26-18, as shown in Equation 26-20 for the generic diene with substituents W, X, Y, and Z attached to the terminal carbon atoms. For the new six-membered ring to relax into its equilibrium geometry, the terminal carbon atoms from the initial diene must rotate in *opposite directions*. Viewed from the right in Equation 26-20, the C atom bonded to W and X would rotate counterclockwise and the C atom bonded to Y and Z would rotate clockwise. If substituents W and Z are both CH_3 groups and X and Y are both H atoms, for example, then both CH_3 groups will be cis to each other in the product, just as we saw previously in Equation 26-16.

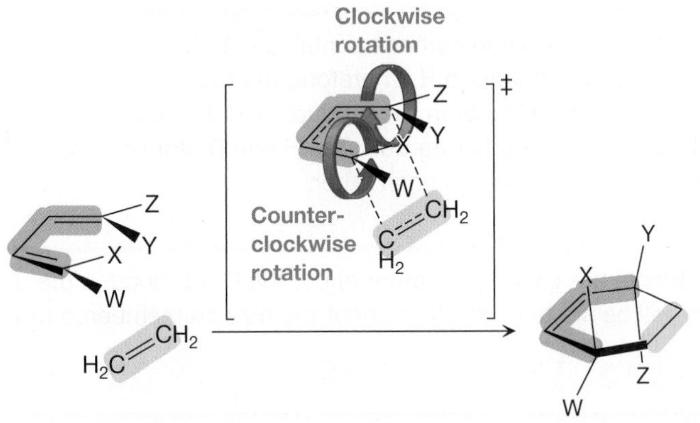

Clockwise rotation
Counter-clockwise rotation
W
X
Y
Z
H_2C=CH_2
‡

(26-20)

YOUR TURN **26.9**

Match the generic groups (W, X, Y, and Z) on the diene in Equation 26-20 to the specific groups on the diene in Equation 26-18. Do the cis–trans relationships among the substituents in the product in Equation 26-20 agree with those in Equation 26-18?

SOLVED PROBLEM **26.4**

How to predict the stereochemical outcome of a Diels–Alder reaction

Break It Down **Predict the product(s) of the Diels–Alder reaction shown here, paying particular attention to stereochemistry.**

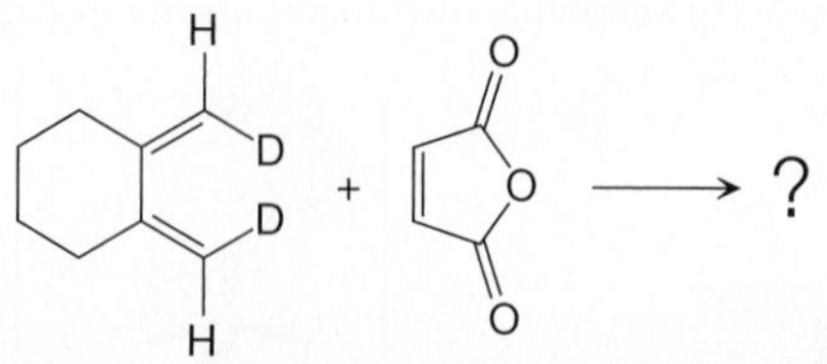

H
D
D
H
O
O
O
+
?

Think	Solve
Do the carbons at the ends of the diene become chiral centers in the products? Do the alkene carbons of the dienophile become chiral centers?	Draw the Diels–Alder product without regard to stereochemistry. As shown here, both carbons at the ends of the diene become chiral centers, and both alkene carbons of the dienophile become chiral centers, too. 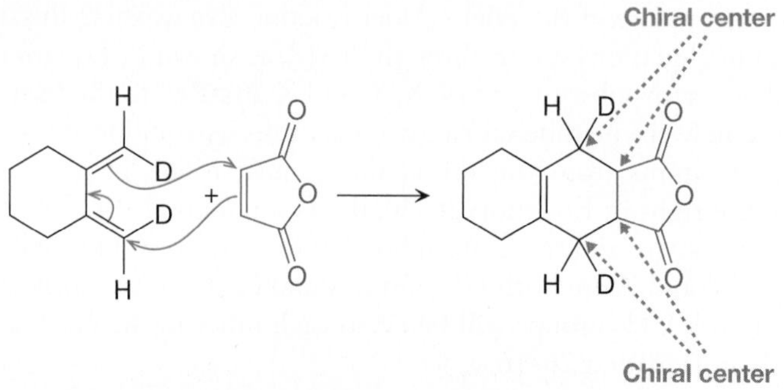
How should a circle be drawn around the diene carbons (in black above) to determine the cis–trans relationships of the indicated H and D atoms in the product?	A circle drawn around the diene carbons contains both bonds to D and intersects both bonds to H. Therefore, the two D atoms will be cis to each other in the product, and the two H atoms will be cis to each other as well. The H and D atoms, on the other hand, will be trans to each other. 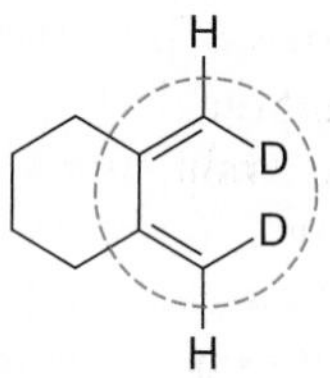
Are the substituents attached to the C=C carbons of the dienophile (in blue above) cis or trans to each other?	Those substituents are cis to each other about the C=C bond in the dienophile, so they will be cis to each other about the new six-membered ring in the product.
Given these stereochemical requirements, what combinations of dash and wedge bonds should be drawn for the product? Are any redundant?	Four possible structures—**A** through **D** below—result from the above stereochemical requirements. Because of the plane of symmetry that exists, structure **C** is redundant with **B**, and structure **D** is redundant with **A**.

Chiral center
Chiral center

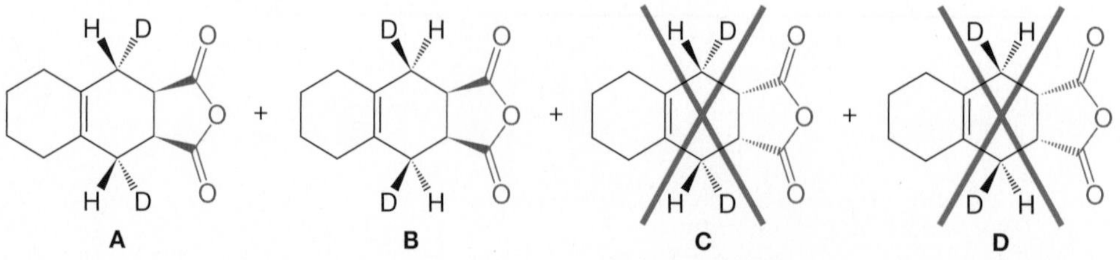

A
B
C
Redundant with B
D
Redundant with A

(continued)

Try It Predict the Diels–Alder products for each of the following reactions in which the diene is isotopically labeled. Pay particular attention to stereochemistry.

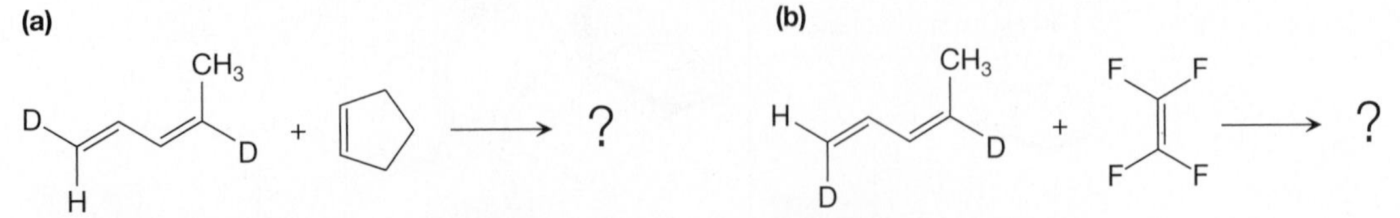

(a)
CH_3
D
D
H
+
?
(b)
CH_3
H
D
D
+
F
F
F
F
?

So far, the stereochemical aspects we have considered for the Diels–Alder reaction deal with the diene and dienophile independently. Another aspect of stereochemistry to consider pertains to the configurations of the carbon atoms from the diene *relative* to those from the dienophile. This is shown in Equation 26-21, in which a mixture of *diastereomers* is produced:

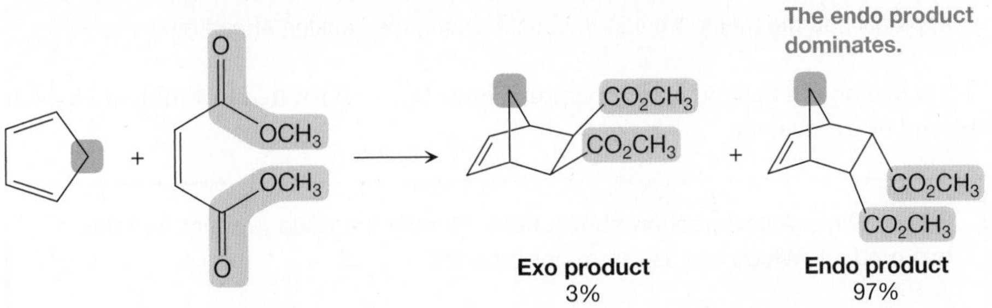

The endo product dominates.
O
OCH_3
OCH_3
O
+
CO_2CH_3
CO_2CH_3
+
CO_2CH_3
CO_2CH_3
Exo product
3%
Endo product
97%

(26-21)

Equations 26-22 and 26-23 show that these two products result from the two different approaches possible for the dienophile: one with the substituents pointed toward the diene and the other with the substituents pointed away. In an **endo approach**, the dienophile's substituents point toward the diene (Eq. 26-22), producing an **endo product**. Conversely, in an **exo approach** the dienophile's substituents point away from the diene (Eq. 26-23), resulting in an **exo product**. As indicated in Equations 26-22 and 26-23, endo and exo products can generally be recognized by the cis–trans relationship of substituents from the diene and dienophile on the new six-membered ring in the product:

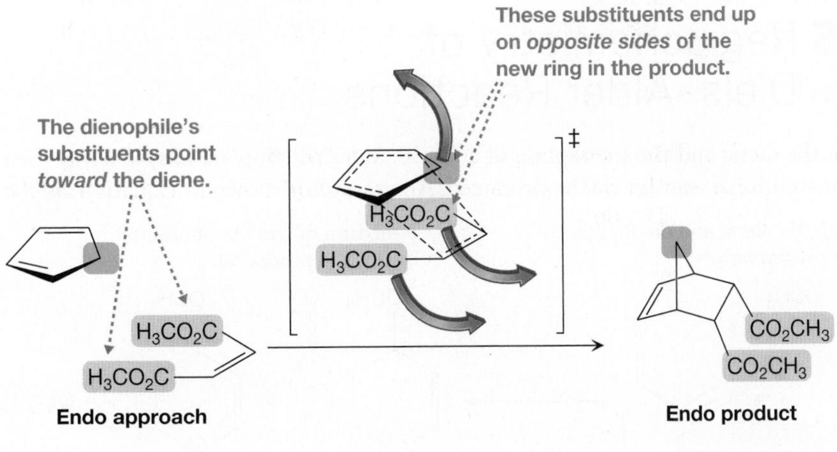

These substituents end up on *opposite sides* of the new ring in the product.
The dienophile's substituents point *toward* the diene.
‡
H_3CO_2C
H_3CO_2C
H_3CO_2C
H_3CO_2C
Endo approach
CO_2CH_3
CO_2CH_3
Endo product

(26-22)

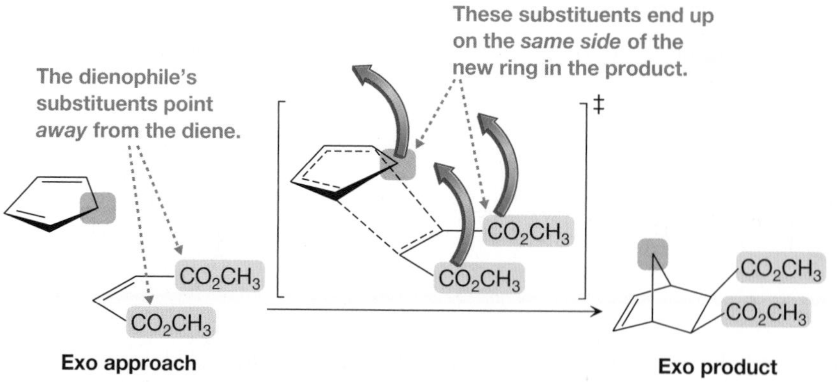

These substituents end up on the *same side* of the new ring in the product.
The dienophile's substituents point *away* from the diene.
‡
CO_2CH_3
CO_2CH_3
CO_2CH_3
CO_2CH_3
CO_2CH_3
CO_2CH_3
Exo approach
Exo product

(26-23)

> ▶ LOOKING AHEAD
>
> The endo rule is explained with molecular orbital theory in Section 26.7b. As we will see, the transition state for the endo approach is stabilized as a result of favorable mixing of orbitals from the diene and dienophile.

Although both endo and exo approaches are feasible, the product mixture is usually dominated by one product, according to the **endo rule** (also called the **Alder rule**):

> In a Diels–Alder reaction, the endo approach is generally favored over the exo approach, so the major product is usually endo (see Looking Ahead box).

This outcome can depend on temperature, however, as illustrated in Problem 26.24 at the end of the chapter.

YOUR TURN **26.10**

For the Diels–Alder reaction shown here, identify the endo product and the exo product. Which one is the major product?

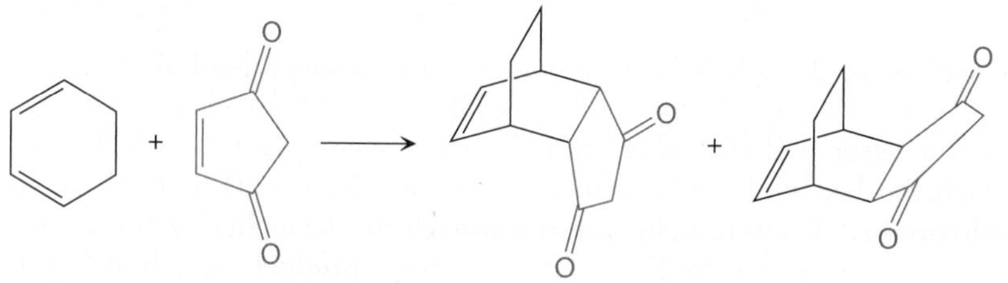

O
O
+
O
O
+
O
O

> **SECTION 26.5 OBJECTIVES**
>
> You will be able to:
>
> 1. Identify when regiochemistry should be considered in predicting a given Diels–Alder reaction.
> 2. Predict the major constitutional isomer of a Diels–Alder reaction when regiochemistry applies.

26.5 Regiochemistry of Diels–Alder Reactions

If both the diene and the dienophile of a Diels–Alder reaction are *unsymmetric*, then two constitutional isomers can be produced. An example is shown in Equation 26-24:

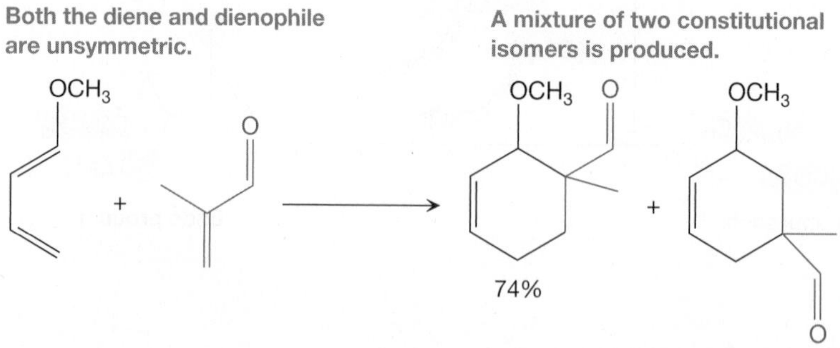

Both the diene and dienophile are unsymmetric.
A mixture of two constitutional isomers is produced.
OCH_3
O
+
OCH_3
O
+
OCH_3
O
74%

(26-24)

The isomers are produced from different relative orientations of the two reactants when they approach each other, as shown in Equations 26-25 and 26-26. The reaction is *regioselective*, and the major product is produced from the approach in Equation 26-25.

One isomer is produced from this approach.

Major product

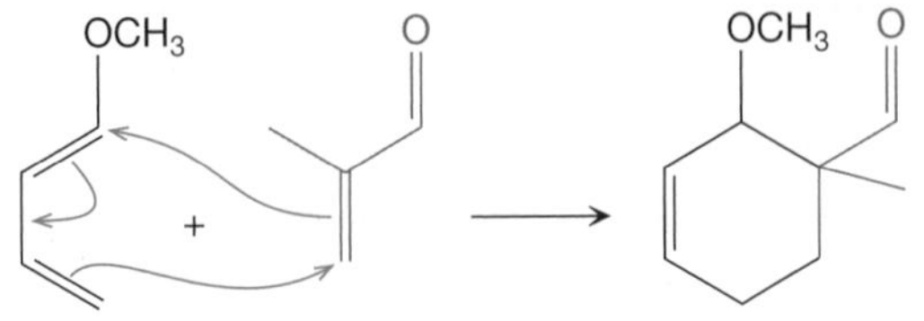
OCH3
O
+
OCH3
O

(26-25)

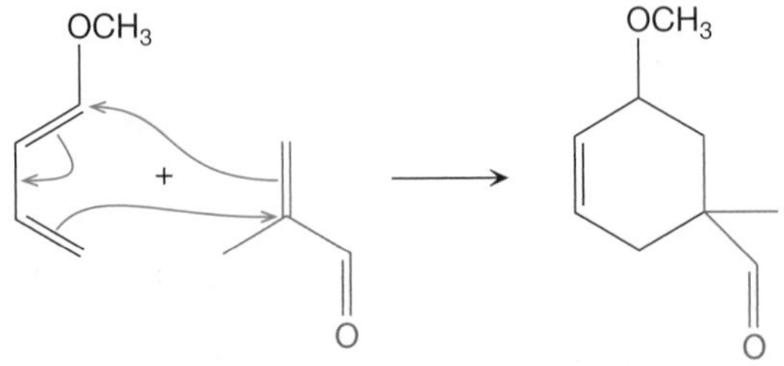
OCH3
+
O
OCH3
O

(26-26)

The other isomer is produced from this approach.

Minor product

One way to understand this regiochemistry is to draw the resonance hybrids of the diene and dienophile and apply the following rule:

> When the diene and the dienophile of a Diels–Alder reaction are both unsymmetric, the major isomeric product is the one produced by the approach that exhibits the more favorable electrostatic attraction among atoms undergoing bond formation (see Looking Ahead box).

For the diene and dienophile in Equation 26-24, the resonance structures and the resonance hybrids are shown in **Figure 26-8a**, and their two possible approaches are shown

> **▸ LOOKING AHEAD**
>
> According to molecular orbital (MO) theory (Section 26.10), Diels–Alder reactions are driven by stabilizing overlap of MOs in the transition state. The major isomeric product is the one that derives from the transition state in which that orbital overlap is more extensive, which is dictated by the substituents.

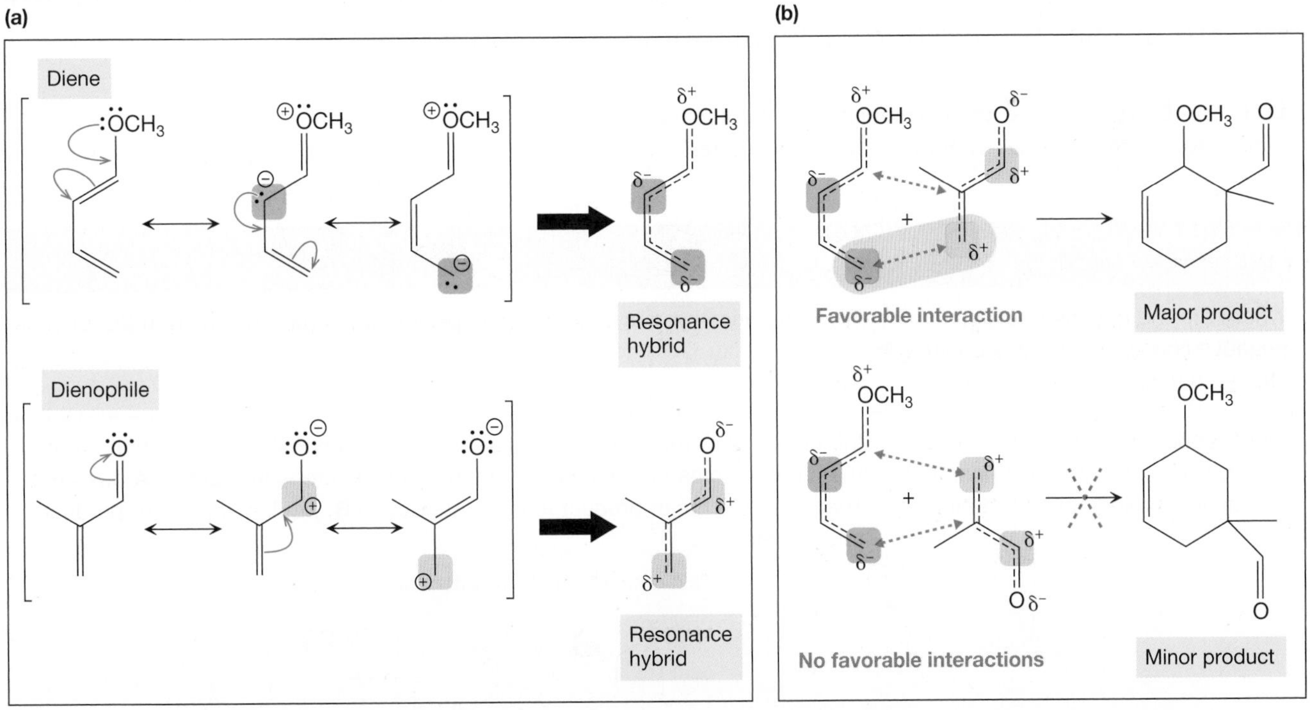
(a)
Diene
:ÖCH3
⊕ÖCH3
⊕ÖCH3
δ+
OCH3
δ−
δ−
Resonance hybrid
Dienophile
:Ö:
:Ö:⊖
:Ö:⊖
δ−
O
δ+
δ+
Resonance hybrid
(b)
δ+
OCH3
δ−
O
δ+
δ−
δ+
δ−
+
OCH3
O
Favorable interaction
Major product
δ+
OCH3
δ−
δ+
+
δ+
δ−
Oδ−
OCH3
O
No favorable interactions
Minor product

FIGURE 26-8 Predicting the regiochemistry in Diels–Alder reactions (a) Resonance structures and resonance hybrids of the diene and dienophile from Equation 26-24 are shown. Regions of excess negative charge are highlighted in red, and regions of excess positive charge are highlighted in blue. (b) Two approaches of the diene and dienophile are shown. The approach shown at the top exhibits favorable electrostatic interaction between atoms undergoing bond formation and thus leads to the major product.

in Figure 26-8b. Notice that the approach shown at the top of Figure 26-8b exhibits favorable electrostatic interaction between the atoms undergoing bond formation and leads to the major product. The approach shown at the bottom of Figure 26-8b lacks such favorable interactions.

YOUR TURN **26.11**

The following resonance structures and resonance hybrid are of a diene that is an isomer of the one in Figure 26-8.

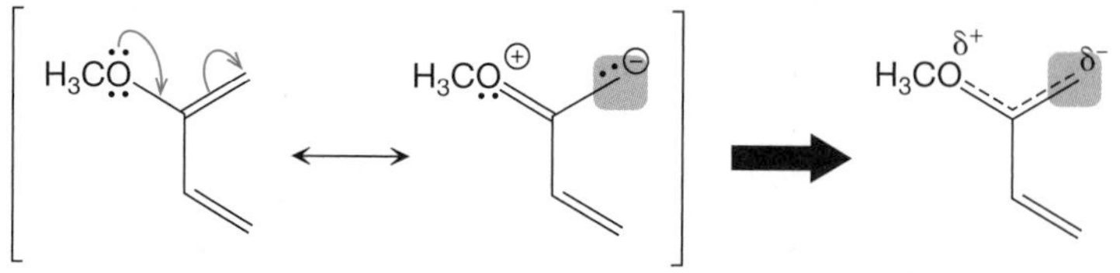

H_3CO
H_3CO
H_3CO
δ+
δ−

A and **B** represent the two ways this diene can approach the dienophile from Figure 26-8.

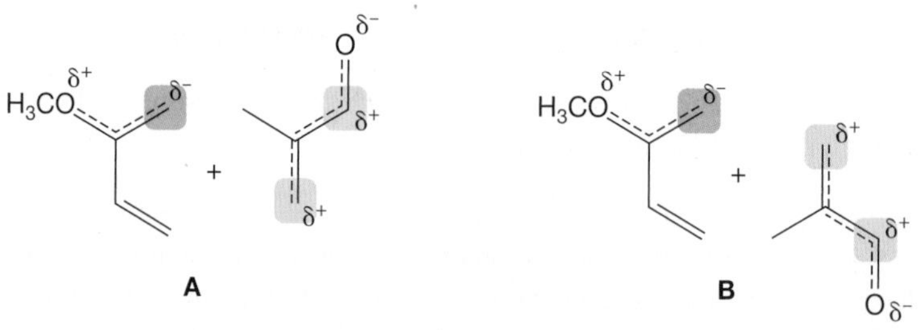

H_3CO
δ+
δ−
A
B

Which of these interactions will lead to the major Diels–Alder product?

SOLVED PROBLEM **26.5**

How to predict the major regioisomer of a Diels–Alder reaction

Break It Down Draw the mechanism and predict the major product for the Diels–Alder reaction shown here.

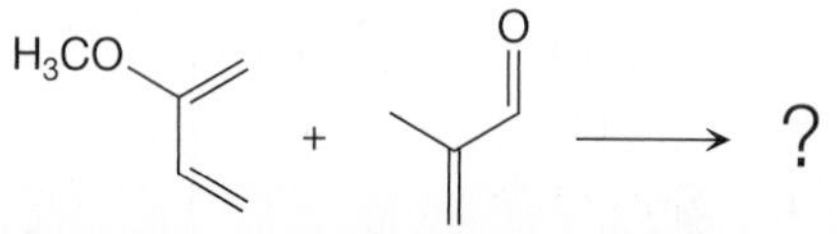

H_3CO
O
?

Think	Solve
Where are the regions of excess negative charge and excess positive charge in each resonance hybrid?	The resonance hybrids of these two species are shown in Your Turn 26.11 above.
Which approach leads to favorable electrostatic interactions among the atoms undergoing bond formation?	Interaction **B** in Your Turn 26.11 has favorable electrostatic interaction among the carbon atoms undergoing bond formation, whereas interaction **A** does not. Therefore, the major product is from interaction **B**, yielding the major product shown here. **Favorable electrostatic interaction** 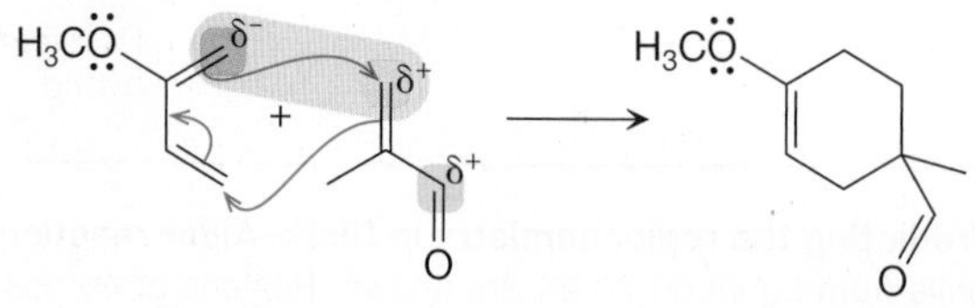

H_3CO
δ−
δ+
O

(continued)

Try It Without taking stereochemistry into account, draw the mechanism and major product of each of these reactions.

(a)

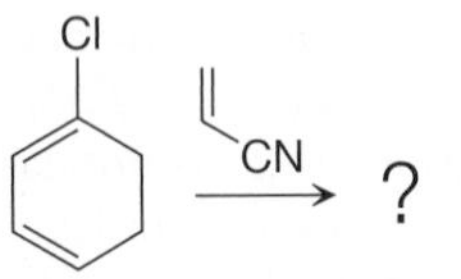
Cl
CN
?

(b)

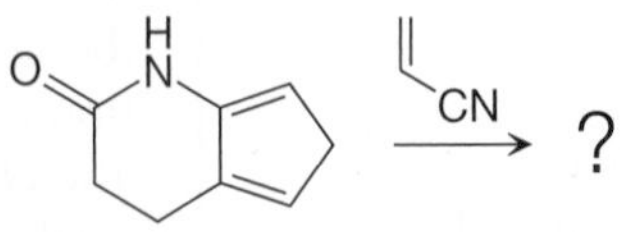
O
H
N
CN
?

26.6 A Deeper Look: The Reversibility of Diels–Alder Reactions; the Retro Diels–Alder Reaction

SECTION 26.6 OBJECTIVES

You will be able to:

1. Explain why a retro Diels–Alder reaction typically requires substantially elevated temperatures.
2. Draw the curved arrows and product for a retro Diels–Alder reaction.

Under normal conditions, the prototypical Diels–Alder reaction in Equation 26-1 (shown again in Eq. 26-27) has a substantially negative change in standard free energy ($\Delta G^\circ_{rxn} = -113$ kJ/mol), giving it a very large equilibrium constant ($K_{eq} = 3.5 \times 10^{19}$). As a result, this reaction is *irreversible* (see Recall box).

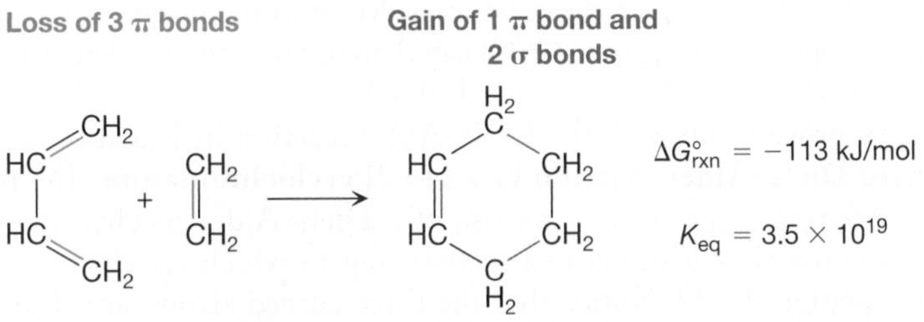
Loss of 3 π bonds
Gain of 1 π bond and 2 σ bonds
CH2
HC
HC
CH2
+
CH2
CH2
H2
C
HC
CH2
HC
CH2
C
H2
ΔG°rxn = −113 kJ/mol
Keq = 3.5 × 10^19

(26-27)

RECALL

As we saw in Section 11.3, a reaction that is very exergonic in the forward direction tends to be irreversible because the energy barrier for the reverse reaction is very large, which makes the rate for the reverse reaction excessively small.

As with any reaction, ΔG°_{rxn} can be broken down into a ΔH°_{rxn} term and a $T\Delta S^\circ_{rxn}$ term (i.e., $\Delta G^\circ_{rxn} = \Delta H^\circ_{rxn} - T\Delta S^\circ_{rxn}$). For the Diels–Alder reaction in Equation 26-27, $\Delta H^\circ_{rxn} = -168$ kJ/mol and $T\Delta S^\circ_{rxn} = -55$ kJ/mol at 25 °C. Therefore, the large, negative ΔH°_{rxn} term dominates to make ΔG°_{rxn} substantially negative.

The large, negative ΔH° for this reaction stems primarily from how the bond energies in the product differ from those in the reactants. Notice in Equation 26-27 that there are three C═C double bonds and one C—C single bond in the reactants, whereas there are five C—C single bonds and one C═C double bond in the product. In essence, three π bonds are converted into two σ bonds and one π bond, and, as we learned in Chapter 3, σ bonds are stronger than their corresponding π bonds.

YOUR TURN 26.12

To estimate ΔH°_{rxn} in Equation 26-27 quantitatively, complete and solve the following equation, which accounts for the changes in the numbers of C—C and C═C bonds. Use the average C—C and C═C bond energies in Table 1-3 (p. 11).

Three C═C bonds → 3(____ kJ/mol); One C—C bond → 1(____ kJ/mol); Five C—C bonds → 5(____ kJ/mol); One C═C bond → 1(____ kJ/mol)

ΔH°_{rxn} = [3(____kJ/mol) + 1(____kJ/mol)] − [5(____kJ/mol) + 1(____kJ/mol)] = −____kJ/mol

How does this estimate of ΔH°_{rxn} compare to the experimentally measured value of −168 kJ/mol?

CONNECTIONS 26.3

Need plastic?
Cyclopentadiene (Eq. 26-28) is used to make zirconocene dichloride (shown here), an important catalyst in the production of polyethylene, the most common plastic in use.

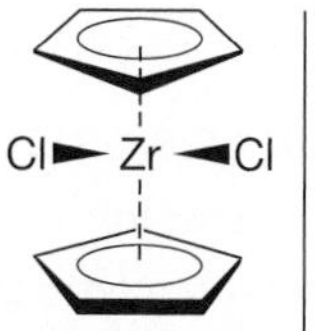
Cl
Zr
Cl

Catalyst

CONNECTIONS 26.4

Making trucks with dicyclopentadiene Dicyclopentadiene (Eq. 26-29) can be polymerized to produce polydicyclopentadiene, which is used as an alternative to fiberglass/polyester composites in the manufacture of heavy-vehicle exterior components, as on this one.

The entropy term in a Diels–Alder reaction is negative because the reaction decreases the number of independent molecules (i.e., the reaction leads to less "disorder"). This means increasing the temperature makes ΔG°_{rxn} less negative (because $\Delta G^\circ_{rxn} = \Delta H^\circ_{rxn} - T\Delta S^\circ_{rxn}$). Even at 200 °C, however, the prototypical reaction in Equation 26-27 is not easily reversible because of its large, negative ΔH°_{rxn}. The Diels–Alder reaction in Equation 26-28, on the other hand, has a significantly smaller value of ΔH°_{rxn} (−77 kJ/mol), so it is easily reversible at moderately high temperatures.

This Diels–Alder reaction is *reversible*.

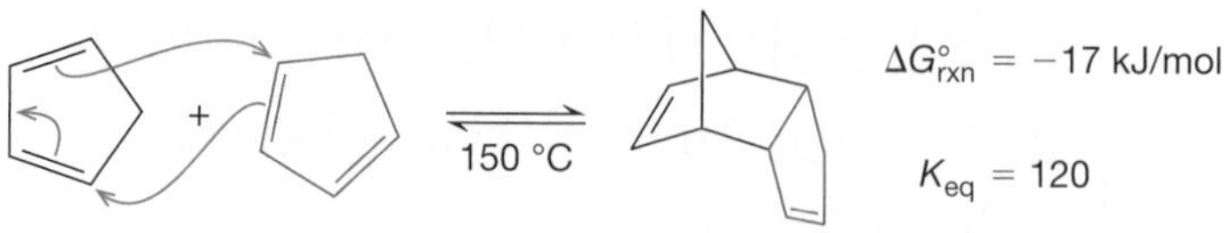
150 °C
$\Delta G^\circ_{rxn} = -17$ kJ/mol
$K_{eq} = 120$

Cyclopentadiene **Dicyclopentadiene** (26-28)

Chemists take advantage of the reversibility of the Diels–Alder reaction in Equation 26-28 to prepare a fresh sample of cyclopentadiene. At room temperature, K_{eq} heavily favors the dicyclopentadiene product, and over about 1 week's time, cyclopentadiene *dimerizes* entirely into dicyclopentadiene. When a sample of dicyclopentadiene is heated to 150 °C or higher, the reaction is driven in the reverse direction. The lower-boiling cyclopentadiene (bp = 42 °C) can then be collected by distillation from the higher-boiling dicyclopentadiene (bp = 170 °C).

Because this process "undoes" the Diels–Alder reaction in Equation 26-28, it is called a **retro Diels–Alder reaction** or a **[4+2] cycloelimination**. The mechanism for this reaction is simply the reverse of a Diels–Alder mechanism, so the entire reaction consists of a single (concerted) step in which six electrons move, as shown in Equation 26-29. Notice that the three curved arrows are all oriented in the same direction about the six-membered ring, and one curved arrow originates from the double bond. These curved arrows were drawn clockwise, but as we saw with cycloaddition reactions, it would be equally correct if they were drawn counterclockwise.

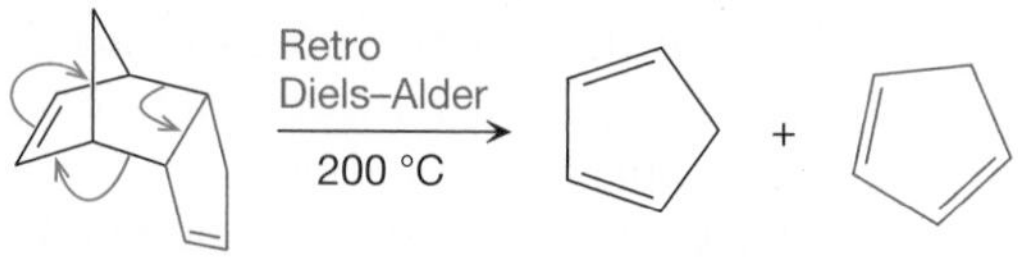
Retro
Diels–Alder
200 °C

Dicyclopentadiene **Cyclopentadiene** 70% (26-29)

YOUR TURN **26.13**

For the Diels–Alder reaction shown here, $\Delta H^\circ_{rxn} = -121$ kJ/mol. Do you think this reaction would be easily reversible at 150 °C? *Hint*: Compare ΔH°_{rxn} of this reaction to the one in Equation 26-27.

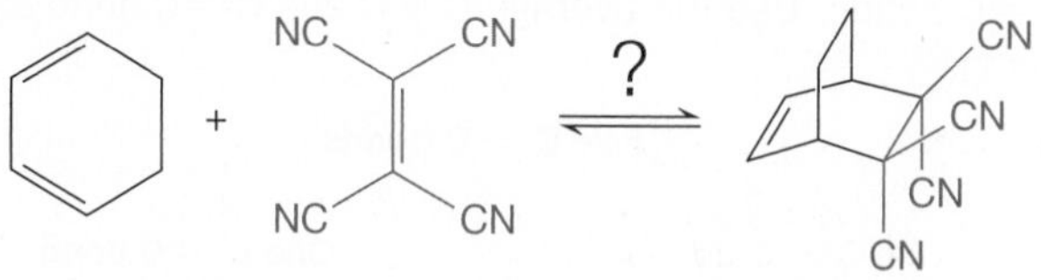
NC
CN
NC
CN
?
CN
CN
CN
CN

YOUR TURN **26.14**

When the compound shown here is heated, a single product with the formula C_6H_8 is produced. Draw the product and the curved arrows necessary to produce it.

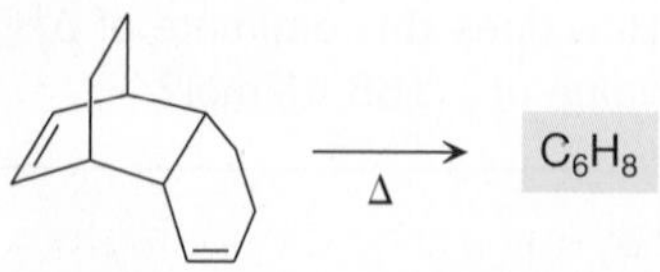
Δ
C_6H_8

26.7 A Deeper Look: A Molecular Orbital Picture of the Diels–Alder Reaction

SECTION 26.7 OBJECTIVES

You will be able to:

1. Use MO theory to explain why a Diels–Alder reaction is thermally allowed, whereas [2+2] cycloadditions are photochemically allowed.
2. Use MO theory to explain how substituents on the diene and dienophile affect the rate of a Diels–Alder reaction.
3. Explain how MO theory accounts for the endo rule pertaining to the stereochemistry of a Diels–Alder reaction.

In our treatment of Diels–Alder reactions so far, we have relied exclusively on Lewis structures and resonance theory. Those ideas can describe the Diels–Alder reaction quite well, but they alone cannot account for some aspects of the reaction, such as the *endo rule* for stereochemistry. Moreover, the presence of UV light changes the outcome of the Diels–Alder reaction, and this, too, cannot be explained simply by Lewis structures and resonance theory. These results can be accounted for, however, by *frontier molecular orbital (FMO) theory*.

As we saw in Interchapter C, FMO theory focuses on the interaction between the HOMO and LUMO of the reactants. A reaction is *allowed* if the HOMO and LUMO have significant interaction in the transition state and is *forbidden* if they do not (see Recall box).

◂ RECALL

In Interchapter C, we identified frontier molecular orbitals as the HOMO (the highest-energy MO containing electrons) and LUMO (the lowest-energy MO that is empty) of the reactants. Substantial interaction between FMOs leads to significant stabilization of the transition state.

Figure 26-9 shows the π MO energy diagrams for both buta-1,3-diene and ethene in their ground state electron configurations and highlights one frontier orbital interaction between the HOMO of buta-1,3-diene and the LUMO of ethene.

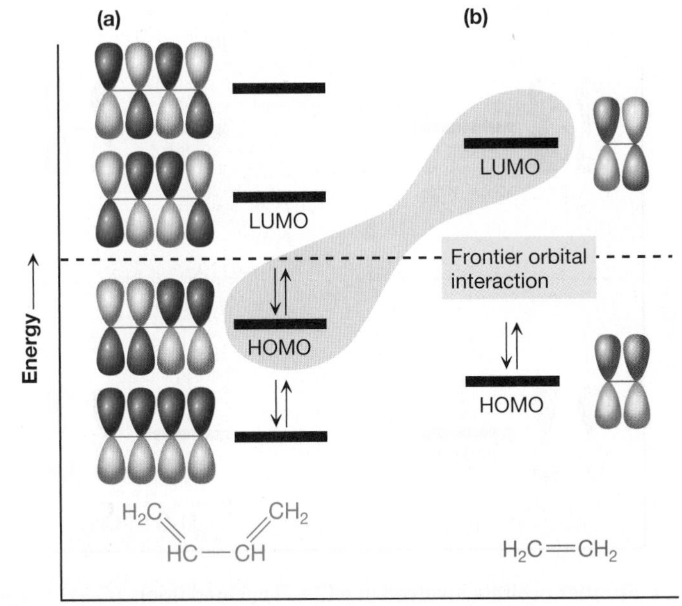

(a)
(b)
Energy
LUMO
HOMO
LUMO
HOMO
Frontier orbital interaction
H_2C CH_2 HC—CH
$H_2C{=}CH_2$

FIGURE 26-9 Frontier orbitals involved in a Diels–Alder reaction (a) MO energy diagram for buta-1,3-diene. (b) MO energy diagram for ethene. Shading highlights the HOMO–LUMO interaction of interest.

As illustrated in **Figure 26-10**, as the diene and dienophile approach each other, the ends of the HOMO and LUMO π systems begin to overlap. Each region of overlap results in constructive interference. Therefore:

> The frontier orbitals involved in a Diels–Alder reaction have the appropriate symmetries to interact when the diene and dienophile are in their ground states, so the reaction is *thermally allowed*.

This is in agreement with our analysis in Section 26.1, where we justified the Diels–Alder reaction being thermally allowed because it proceeds through an aromatic transition state.

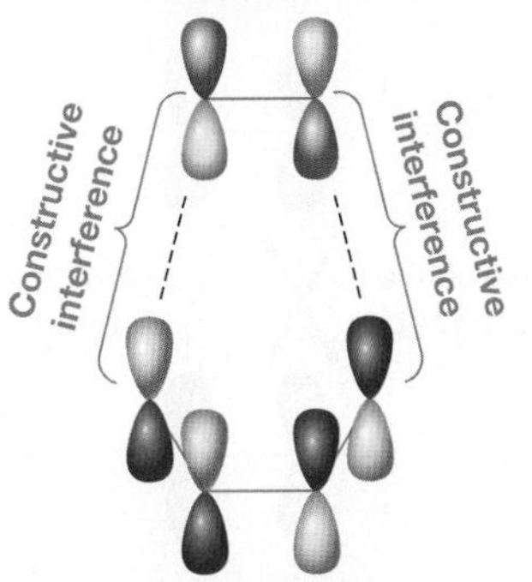

LUMO of dienophile
Constructive interference
Constructive interference
HOMO of diene

FIGURE 26-10 Frontier orbital interaction in a Diels–Alder reaction The HOMO of buta-1,3-diene (red) and the LUMO of ethene (blue) have the appropriate symmetries to result in significant net overlap. In the example shown, both regions of overlap result in constructive interference.

YOUR TURN 26.15

Figure 26-10 highlights one of two possible frontier orbital interactions, which involves the HOMO of buta-1,3-diene and the LUMO of ethene. The drawing shown here highlights the other, involving the HOMO of ethene and the LUMO of buta-1,3-diene.

Determine each type of interference resulting from the indicated regions of overlap. Are they both the same or are they different? Do the orbitals have the appropriate symmetries to interact?

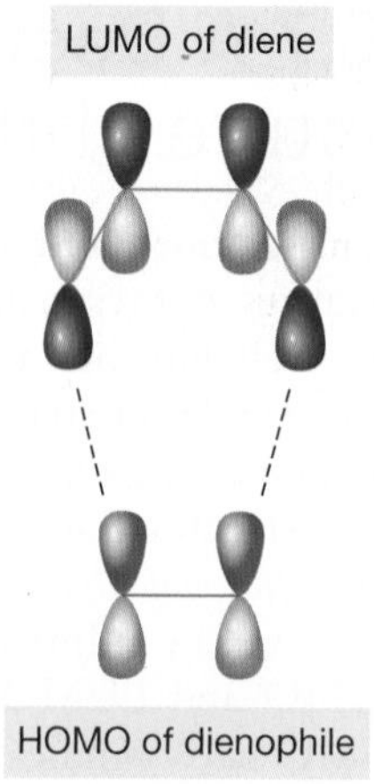
LUMO of diene
HOMO of dienophile

The story is quite different for the [2+2] cycloaddition reaction between two molecules of ethene. **Figure 26-11** shows the MOs of π symmetry for each reactant and highlights one possible frontier orbital interaction.

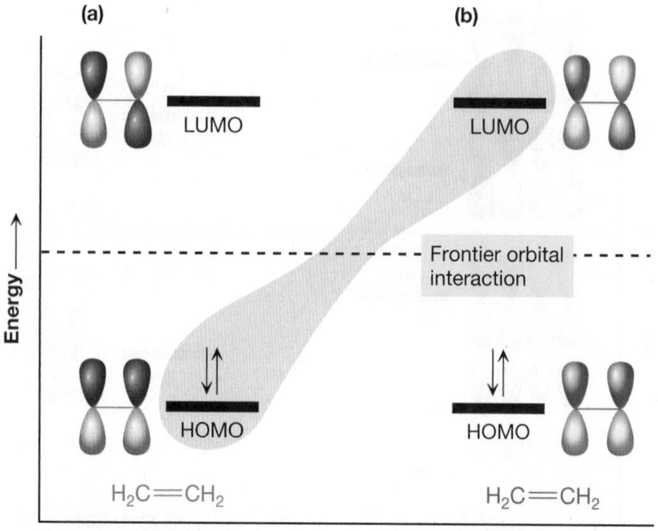
(a)
(b)
LUMO
LUMO
Energy
Frontier orbital interaction
HOMO
HOMO
$H_2C{=}CH_2$
$H_2C{=}CH_2$

FIGURE 26-11 Frontier orbitals involved in a [2+2] cycloaddition (a) MO energy diagram for one molecule of ethene. (b) MO energy diagram for the second molecule of ethene. Shading indicates a HOMO–LUMO interaction.

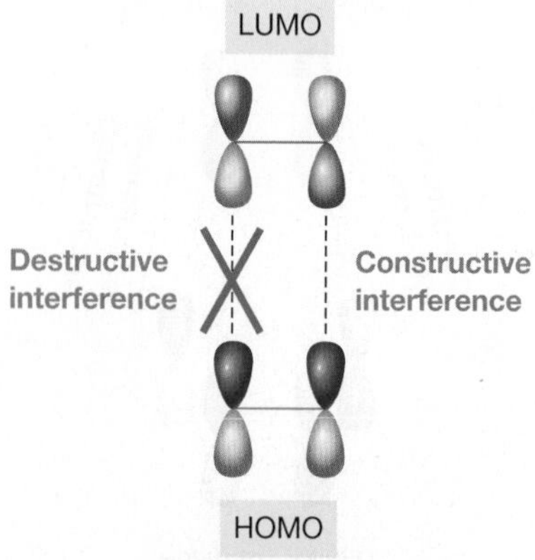
LUMO
Destructive interference
Constructive interference
HOMO

FIGURE 26-12 Frontier orbital interaction in a [2+2] cycloaddition reaction The net HOMO–LUMO interaction is zero. Whereas overlap on the right leads to constructive interference, overlap on the left leads to destructive interference. The two effects cancel each other.

The overlap that takes place with these orbitals is illustrated in **Figure 26-12.** Unlike the Diels–Alder reaction (a [4+2] cycloaddition; Fig. 26-10), symmetry prevents the orbitals of the [2+2] cycloaddition from having a net interaction. Overlap on one end leads to constructive interference, but overlap on the other end leads to destructive interference.

Because the frontier orbitals in a [2+2] cycloaddition do not have the appropriate symmetries to interact when the reactants are in their ground states, the reaction is *thermally forbidden*.

This outcome is consistent with the fact that a [2+2] cycloaddition proceeds through an antiaromatic transition state, as we saw in Section 26.1.

YOUR TURN 26.16

The second possible HOMO–LUMO interaction in Figure 26-11 involves the HOMO of the blue molecule and the LUMO of the red one. The overlap of those orbitals is shown here. Determine whether the overlap will lead to constructive or destructive interference. Do the orbitals have the appropriate symmetries to interact?

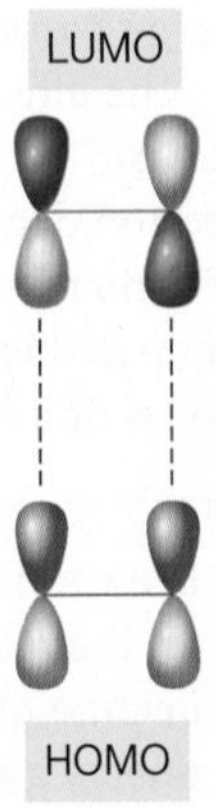

LUMO
HOMO

26.7a Substituent Effects on the Reaction Rate

Recall from Section 26.3 that standard Diels–Alder reactions are facilitated by electron-donating groups attached to the diene and electron-withdrawing groups attached to the dienophile. How does FMO theory account for these results?

Figure 26-13a shows the energies of the MOs of buta-1,3-diene and ethene (reproduced from Fig. 26-9, p. 1273). Figure 26-13b shows how the picture changes when an electron-donating group (EDG) is attached to buta-1,3-diene and an electron-withdrawing group (EWG) is attached to ethene. Notice specifically that:

- An electron-donating group *raises* the orbital energies of the diene.
- An electron-withdrawing group *lowers* the orbital energies of the dienophile.

Consequently, the difference in energy between the HOMO of the diene and the LUMO of the dienophile has diminished. With a smaller HOMO–LUMO energy

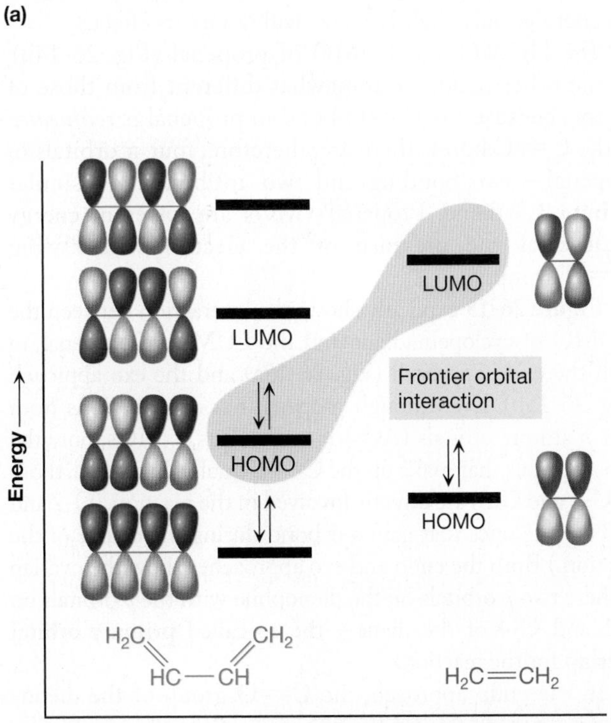

(a)
Energy
LUMO
HOMO
LUMO
HOMO
Frontier orbital interaction
H_2C CH_2 HC—CH
$H_2C{=}CH_2$

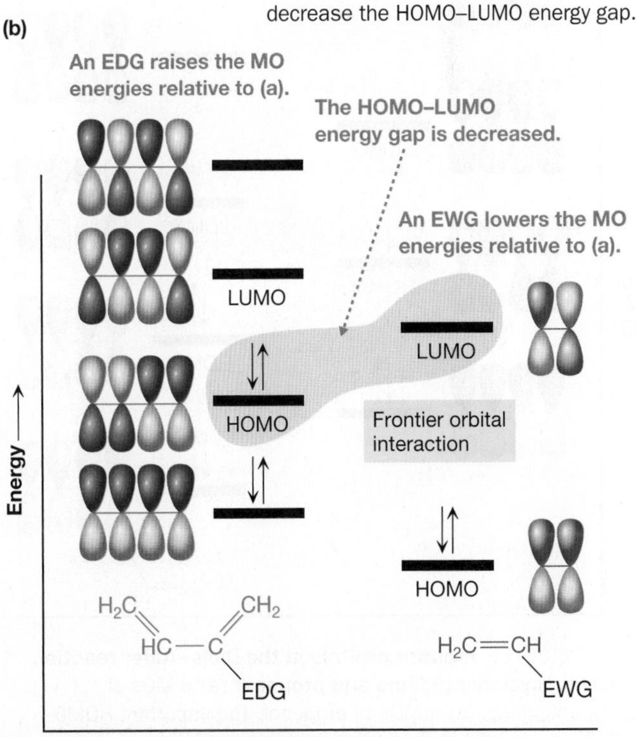

(b)
An EDG raises the MO energies relative to (a).
The HOMO–LUMO energy gap is decreased.
An EWG lowers the MO energies relative to (a).
Energy
LUMO
HOMO
LUMO
HOMO
Frontier orbital interaction
H_2C CH_2 HC—C EDG
$H_2C{=}CH$ EWG

FIGURE 26-13 Substituent effects on a frontier orbital interaction (a) MO energy diagrams for unsubstituted buta-1,3-diene and ethene. (b) MO energy diagrams for buta-1,3-diene with an attached electron-donating group (EDG) and ethene with an attached electron-withdrawing group (EWG). The EDG raises the MO energies of the diene, and the EWG lowers the MO energies of the dienophile. Both effects decrease the HOMO–LUMO energy gap.

gap, the orbitals interact to a greater extent in the transition state, which lowers the energy barrier between reactants and products.

The effects of electron-donating and electron-withdrawing groups on MO energies can be understood in terms of charge repulsion between electrons. Increased electron density from a nearby electron-donating group results in increased electron–electron repulsion, which raises the energy. Conversely, a nearby electron-withdrawing group reduces electron–electron repulsion by removing electron density from the orbital of interest, which lowers the energy.

YOUR TURN 26.17

Draw a diagram similar to Figure 26-13b, but assume that an EWG is placed on the diene and an EDG is placed on the dienophile (thus establishing an inverse electron demand Diels–Alder reaction). How does the HOMO–LUMO energy gap compare to the one in Figure 26-13a?

26.7b The Endo Rule for Stereochemistry

When both endo and exo products can be made in a Diels–Alder reaction, the endo products tend to dominate (Section 26.4). Simple resonance theory cannot account for these results, but FMO theory can.

The Diels–Alder reaction between cyclopentadiene and propenal can produce both endo and exo products (Eq. 26-30):

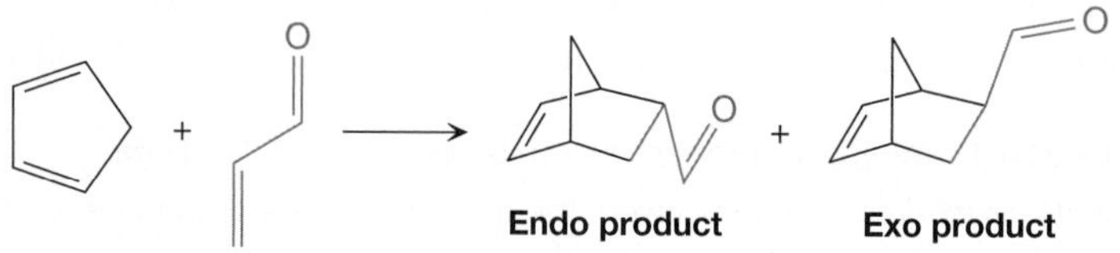

O
O
O
Endo product
Exo product

(26-30)

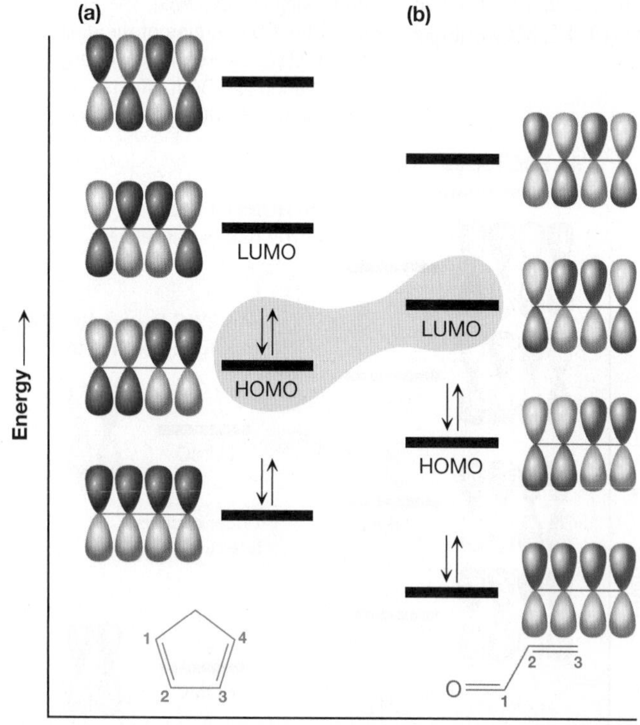

(a)
(b)
Energy
LUMO
HOMO
LUMO
HOMO
1
4
2
3
O
1
2
3

FIGURE 26-14 Frontier orbitals in the Diels–Alder reaction involving cyclopentadiene and propenal (a) π MOs of cyclopentadiene. (b) π MOs of propenal. The important HOMO–LUMO interaction between them is shaded.

The π MOs of the two molecules are shown in **Figure 26-14**. Notice that the HOMO and LUMO of cyclopentadiene (Fig. 26-14a) are essentially the same as those of buta-1,3-diene. (The presence of the extra CH_2 group modifies the energies only slightly, so we will ignore its effect.)

The HOMO and LUMO of propenal (Fig. 26-14b), on the other hand, are somewhat different from those of ethene, because the C═O bond in propenal is *conjugated* to the C═C bond. There are, therefore, four π orbitals in propenal—two bonding and two antibonding—similar to buta-1,3-diene. Propenal's MOs are lower in energy because of the presence of the electron-withdrawing C═O group.

Figure 26-15 explicitly shows the interaction between the HOMO of cyclopentadiene and the LUMO of propenal, in both the endo approach (Fig. 26-15a) and the exo approach (Fig. 26-15b). Even though propenal has contributions from four *p* atomic orbitals (AOs) in each of its π MOs, only the two *p* orbitals that make up the C═C double bond (i.e., those on C-2 and C-3) are directly involved in the reaction. (C-2 and C-3 are the ones that gain a σ bond during the course of the reaction.) Both the endo and exo approaches show the overlap of these two *p* orbitals on the dienophile with the *p* orbitals on C-1 and C-4 of the diene—the so-called **primary orbital overlap** for the reaction.

In the endo approach, the C═O group of the dienophile is oriented toward the π system of the diene, allowing

(a)

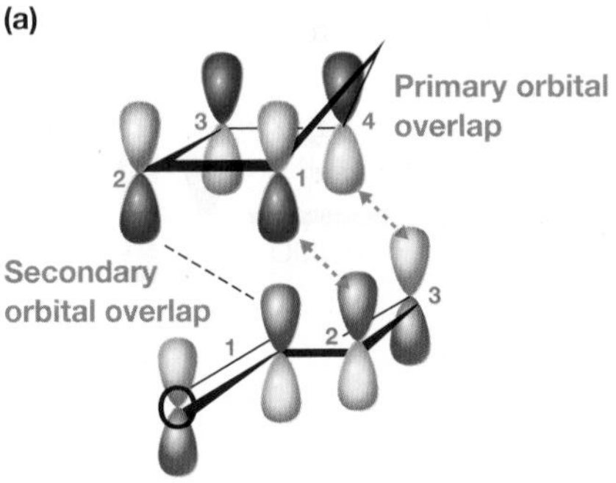

Primary orbital overlap
Secondary orbital overlap
Endo approach

(b)

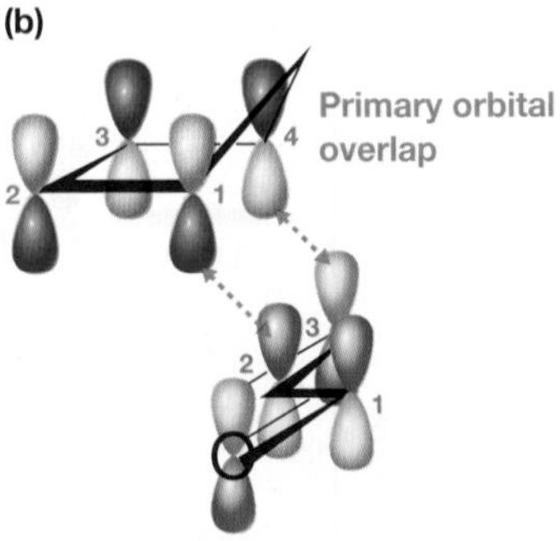

Primary orbital overlap
Exo approach

FIGURE 26-15 Primary and secondary orbital overlap in a Diels–Alder reaction Interaction between the HOMO of cyclopentadiene and the LUMO of propenal when propenal approaches in (a) an endo fashion and (b) an exo fashion. Both approaches exhibit primary overlap of the orbitals forming the two new σ bonds in the reaction, but only the endo approach exhibits secondary orbital overlap (dashed line), using a *p* orbital on the dienophile that is not directly involved in bond formation or bond breaking. This lowers the energy for the transition state, thereby favoring the endo approach over the exo approach.

the *p* orbital on the carbonyl carbon to interact with an unused *p* orbital on the diene (indicated by the dashed line in Fig. 26-15a). This interaction among orbitals *not* forming a bond is called **secondary orbital overlap**, and it is not possible in the exo approach. Even though secondary overlap does not specifically lead to bond breaking or bond formation in the reaction, it does provide stabilization.

In a Diels–Alder reaction, the transition state produced from the endo approach tends to be lower in energy than the one produced from the exo approach. Therefore, the endo product usually is the major product.

YOUR TURN **26.18**

Figure 26-15b is reproduced here. Identify the two *p* orbitals that, in Figure 26-15a, are involved in secondary orbital overlap. Are those *p* orbitals closer together in Figure 26-15a or Figure 26-15b?

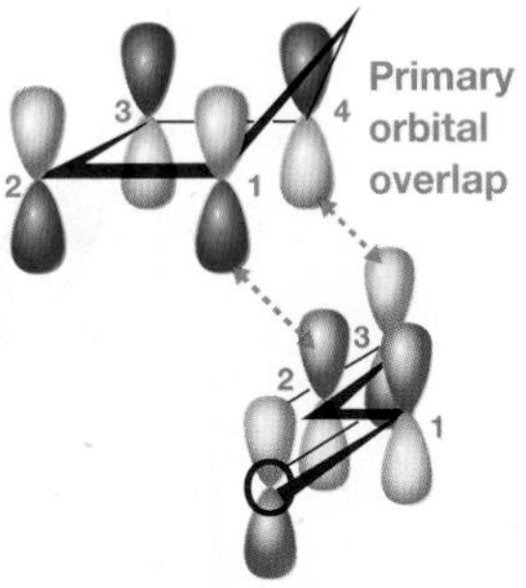

Primary orbital overlap

26.7c Thermal versus Photochemical Reactions

In all of the cycloaddition reactions we have examined thus far, we have considered only *thermal* conditions, in which the reactants are in their ground state (i.e., lowest energy) electron configurations. We have seen that the Diels–Alder reaction, a [4+2] cycloaddition reaction, is *thermally allowed* because of the favorable frontier orbital interactions. By contrast, the [2+2] cycloaddition is *thermally forbidden* because the frontier orbital interactions do not lead to net stabilization (see again Figs. 26-10 and 26-12).

It turns out, though, that [2+2] cycloaddition reactions, such as the one between two molecules of ethene, take place readily when irradiated with UV light (Eq. 26-31):

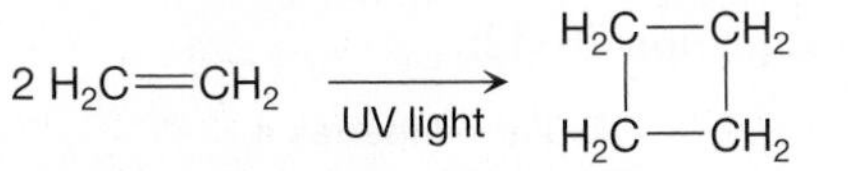

2 H2C=CH2
UV light
H2C—CH2
H2C—CH2

(26-31)

When ethene absorbs a photon with sufficient energy, an electron is promoted from the HOMO to the LUMO (see Recall box), thereby generating an **excited electronic state** (**Figure 26-16**, next page).

The new HOMO in that excited state is the π^* MO. Therefore, when an excited molecule of ethene encounters another ethene molecule still in the ground electronic

◀ RECALL

The HOMO–LUMO transition shown in Figure 26-16, which takes place on absorption of a UV photon, is the same transition that corresponds to the longest-wavelength λ_{max} that appears in the UV–vis spectrum of the molecule (Section 16.11).

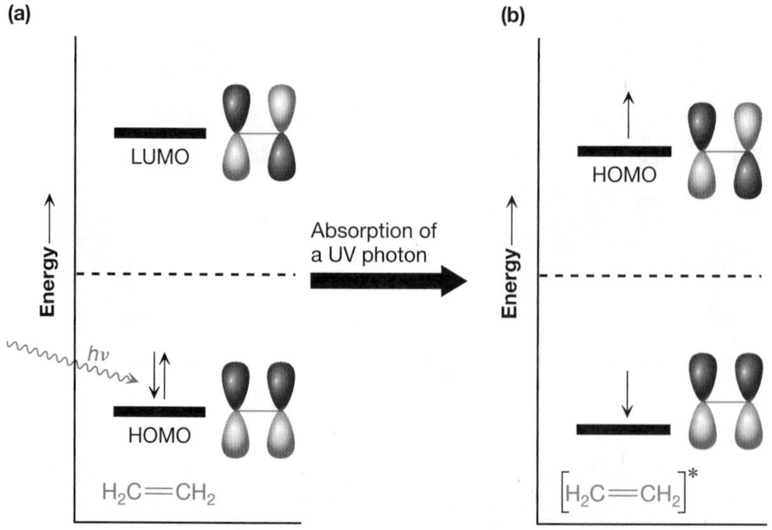
(a)
LUMO
HOMO
Energy
$H_2C{=}CH_2$
hν
Absorption of
a UV photon
(b)
HOMO
Energy
$[H_2C{=}CH_2]^*$

FIGURE 26-16 Impact of UV photon absorption on the identities of the HOMO and LUMO (a) Ground state electron configuration of ethene. (b) Excited electronic state of ethene, denoted by *. A UV photon with sufficient energy ($h\nu$) is capable of promoting an electron from ethene's HOMO to its LUMO to generate the excited state. The excited state's HOMO is the ground state's LUMO.

state, the frontier orbital interaction involves the π^* MO from each species (**Figure 26-17**). These HOMO and LUMO orbitals do, indeed, have the appropriate symmetries to interact, as illustrated in **Figure 26-18**, which makes the [2+2] cycloaddition *allowed*. More specifically, the reaction is **photochemically allowed** because the proper interaction between the frontier MOs requires at least one of the reactants to be in an excited electronic state.

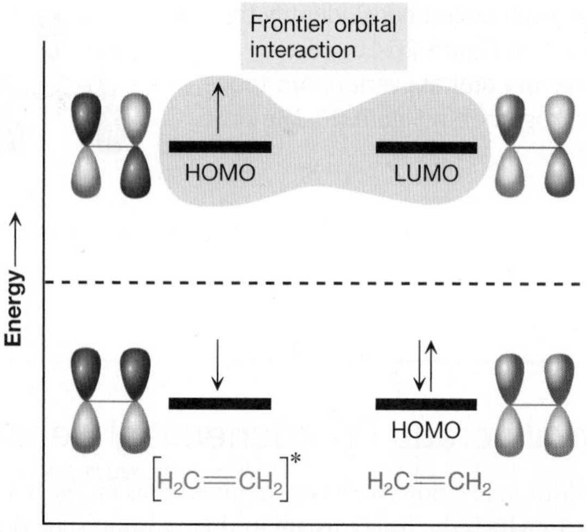
Frontier orbital
interaction
HOMO
LUMO
Energy
HOMO
$[H_2C{=}CH_2]^*$
$H_2C{=}CH_2$

FIGURE 26-17 Frontier orbitals in a photochemical [2+2] cycloaddition reaction The π MOs of ethene in an excited state are shown in red, and the π MOs of ethene in its ground state are shown in blue. The resulting frontier orbital interaction is between the π^* MO in each species.

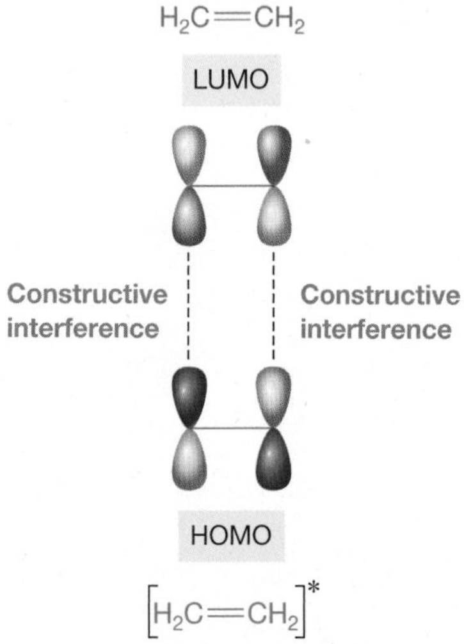
$H_2C{=}CH_2$
LUMO
Constructive
interference
Constructive
interference
HOMO
$[H_2C{=}CH_2]^*$

FIGURE 26-18 Frontier orbital interaction in a photochemical [2+2] cycloaddition reaction Both ends of the π systems exhibit the same type of interference; in this case, it is constructive interference. Therefore, the orbitals have the appropriate symmetries to interact, making this reaction *photochemically allowed*.

Unlike the [2+2] cycloaddition reaction, the Diels–Alder reaction is impeded by UV light, as indicated in Equation 26-32:

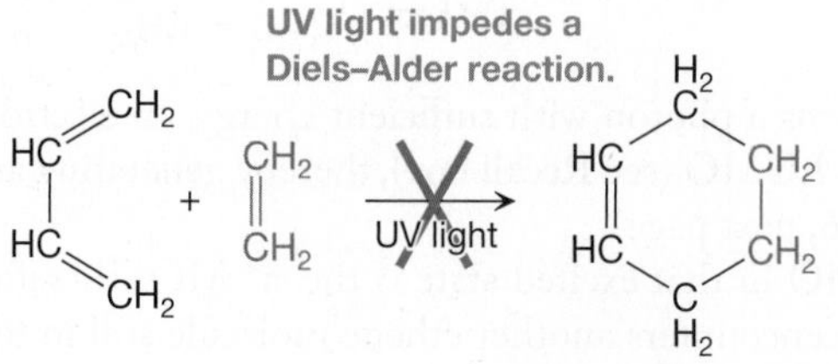
UV light impedes a
Diels–Alder reaction.
UV light

(26-32)

When a molecule of buta-1,3-diene absorbs a photon with sufficient energy, an excited state of buta-1,3-diene is generated, in which an electron from what was originally the HOMO now occupies what was originally the LUMO. When this excited state species encounters a molecule of ethene in the ground state, the HOMO and LUMO no longer have the appropriate symmetries to interact, making the reaction forbidden. Consequently, the Diels–Alder reaction is **photochemically forbidden** because the frontier MOs lack the proper symmetry to interact when one of the reactants is in an excited electronic state. The same is true when a molecule of ethene in its excited state and buta-1,3-diene in its ground state (see Your Turn 26.19).

YOUR TURN **26.19**

Redraw Figure 26-9 (p. 1273) for buta-1,3-diene in its excited state and ethene in its ground state. Do the same for buta-1,3-diene in its ground state and ethene in its excited state. Are these results consistent with a Diels–Alder reaction being photochemically forbidden?

SECTION 26.8 OBJECTIVES

You will be able to:

1. Draw the mechanism and product for the syn dihydroxylation reaction involving OsO_4 or $KMnO_4$.
2. Explain why the two hydroxyl groups end up syn to each other in the product.

26.8 Syn Dihydroxylation of Alkenes and Alkynes with OsO_4 or $KMnO_4$

The Diels–Alder reaction we have studied extensively in this chapter is characterized by an elementary step in which three curved arrows depict the cyclic movement of six electrons. However, the Diels–Alder reaction is not the only reaction with that kind of elementary step. Another reaction that has a similar elementary step is the **syn dihydroxylation** of an alkene or alkyne, in which two OH groups appear to add across a C═C double bond or a C≡C triple bond in a syn fashion. An example is shown in Equation 26-33:

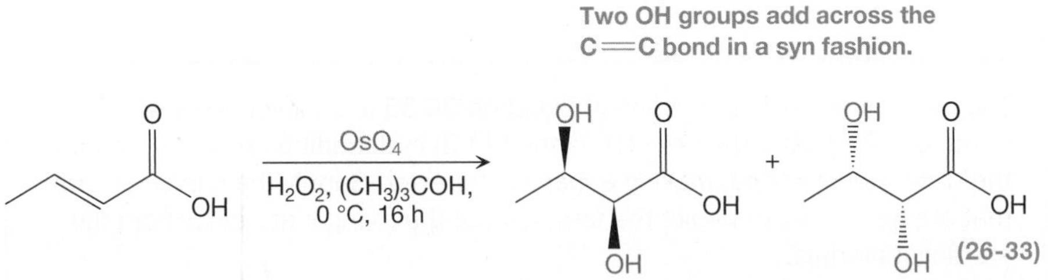

Two OH groups add across the C═C bond in a syn fashion.
O
OH
OsO4
H2O2, (CH3)3COH, 0 °C, 16 h
OH
O
OH
OH
+
OH
O
OH
OH

(26-33)

(*E*)-But-2-enoic acid **(2*S*,3*R*)- and (2*R*,3*S*)-2,3-Dihydroxybutanoic acid** 53%

A partial mechanism for this reaction is shown in Equation 26-34:

Partial mechanism for the syn dihydroxylation of an alkene (Eq. 26-33)

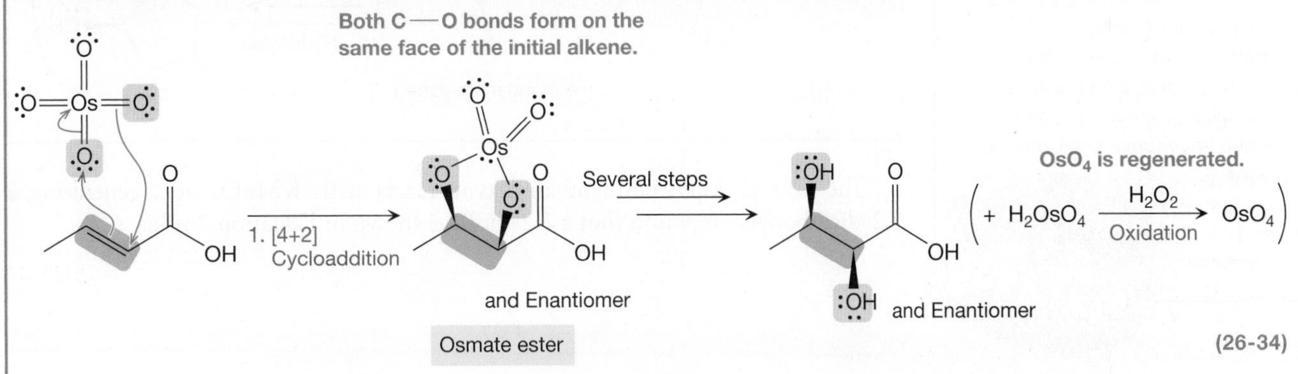

Both C—O bonds form on the same face of the initial alkene.
O=Os=O
O
OH
1. [4+2] Cycloaddition
Os
and Enantiomer
Osmate ester
Several steps
:OH
:OH
OH
and Enantiomer
OsO4 is regenerated.
+ H2OsO4
H2O2
Oxidation
OsO4

(26-34)

CONNECTIONS 26.5

A marker for Type 1 diabetes (2*R*,3*S*)-2,3-Dihydroxybutanoic acid (Eq. 26-33), also called 4-deoxythreonic acid, is a naturally occurring metabolite in humans. Significantly elevated levels of the compound are found in the urine of patients with Type 1 diabetes, who can monitor their blood sugar levels with devices like this one.

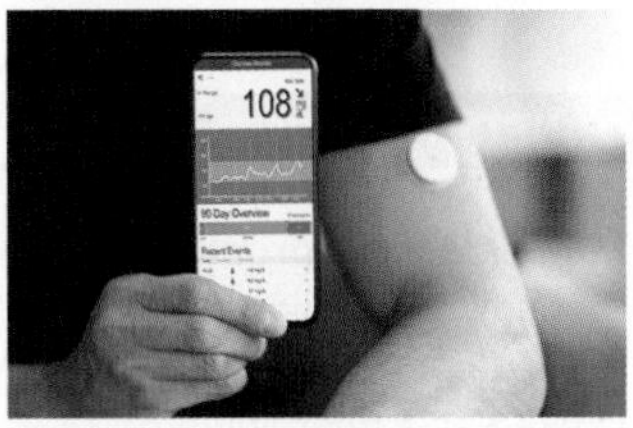

108

GREEN CHEMISTRY OsO_4 is toxic and, when used as a heterogeneous catalyst in syn dihydroxylation reactions, can contaminate the products. One green alternative is to use elemental osmium confined inside a zeolite (a porous inorganic mineral) as the catalyst, with hydrogen peroxide as a co-oxidant. The zeolite-confined catalyst is easily removed and reused.

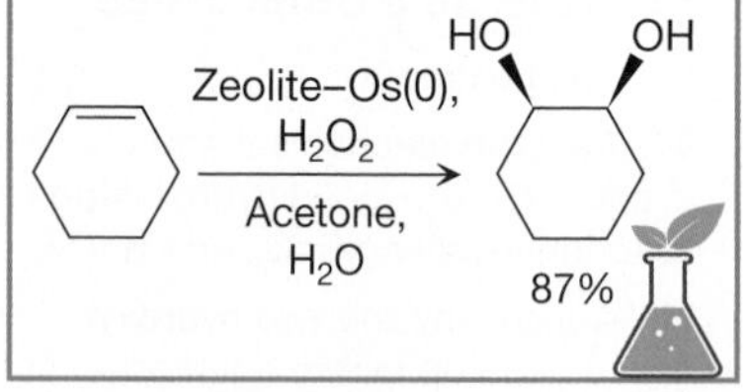

HO
OH
Zeolite–Os(0), H2O2
Acetone, H2O
87%

GREEN CHEMISTRY Even though $KMnO_4$ is not as synthetically useful as OsO_4, $KMnO_4$ is much less toxic and less expensive, too. Therefore, when yield is not a high priority, $KMnO_4$ may be considered to carry out syn dihydroxylation rather than OsO_4, in order to avoid generating highly toxic waste.

Step 1 is the cycloaddition of OsO_4 across the C=C double bond in a syn fashion, producing an **osmate ester**. Then, over the course of several steps, the O—Os bonds are replaced by O—H bonds, ultimately producing a cis-1,2-diol and a reduced form of the osmium. Hydrogen peroxide, H_2O_2, oxidizes the reduced form of osmium back to OsO_4, making OsO_4 a *catalyst* because it is not consumed overall.

Step 1 is key in this mechanism because it attaches the two O atoms syn to the initial alkene C atoms. This step involves the concerted movement of six electrons through a cyclic transition state, so all bond formation and all bond breaking occur simultaneously; it is, therefore, a type of *pericyclic reaction*. In particular, the step involves four π electrons from OsO_4 and two π electrons from the alkene, resulting in a new ring, so it is a [4+2] cycloaddition, much like the Diels–Alder reaction. Moreover, the concerted movement of the electrons requires the new bonds to the alkene to form on the same side, also like the Diels–Alder reaction.

In contrast to a Diels–Alder reaction, the electron movement in this [4+2] cycloaddition involves just five atoms: three atoms from OsO_4 and two atoms from the alkene. As a result, two of the six electrons that move end up as a lone pair on the Os atom from OsO_4.

An older method of producing cis-1,2-diols involves treating an alkene with a cold, basic solution of potassium permanganate ($KMnO_4$), as shown in Equation 26-35. It is not very synthetically useful, however, because the yields are typically low, and the diol product can be further oxidized by $KMnO_4$ (see Section 26.9).

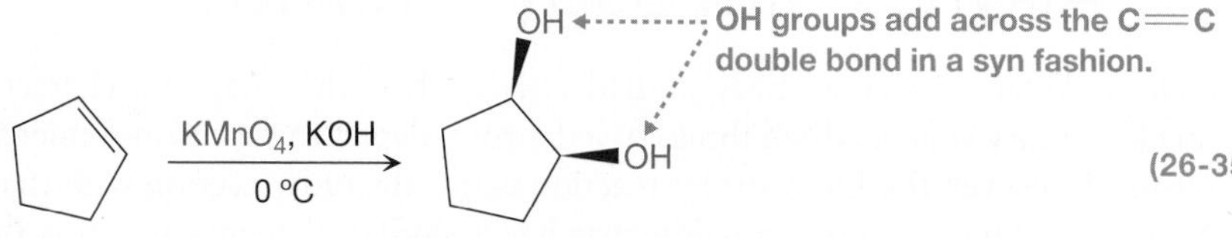

OH
OH groups add across the C=C double bond in a syn fashion.
KMnO4, KOH
0 °C
OH
Cyclopentene
cis-Cyclopentane-1,2-diol
31%

(26-35)

YOUR TURN 26.20

The mechanism for the reaction in Equation 26-35 is believed to be similar to the one for OsO_4. The key step is the [4+2] cycloaddition of MnO_4^- across the C=C double bond, making a *manganate ester*. Supply the curved arrows that are necessary to depict the formation of the manganate ester from the starting materials.

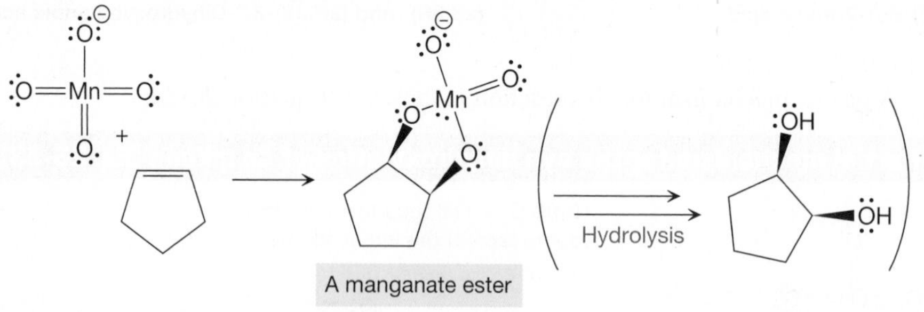

Mn
+
Hydrolysis
A manganate ester

CONNECTIONS 26.6

Making acrylic products
Diphenylethanedione (Eq. 26-36), commonly called benzil, is used as a photoinitiator (which initiates reactions on absorption of a photon) in the production of some polymers, such as poly(methyl methacrylate). Poly(methyl methacrylate), also known as Plexiglas or acrylic, is used to make aquariums, solar panels, bone implants, and dentures.

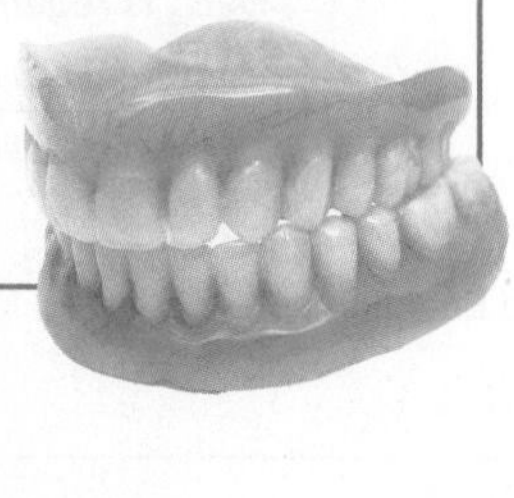

The C≡C triple bond of an alkyne reacts with $KMnO_4$, too, generating a 1,2-dicarbonyl compound (not a 1,2-diol), as shown in Equation 26-36:

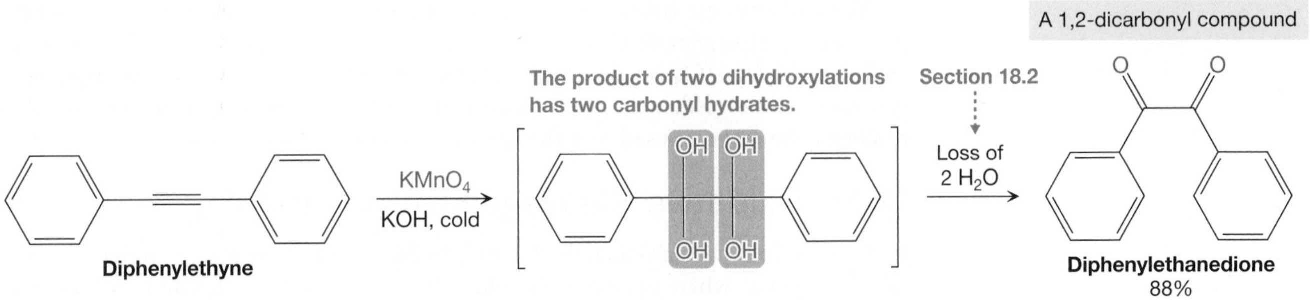
A 1,2-dicarbonyl compound
The product of two dihydroxylations has two carbonyl hydrates.
Section 18.2
KMnO4
KOH, cold
OH
OH
Loss of 2 H2O
O
Diphenylethyne
Diphenylethanedione
88%

(26-36)

We can envision the alkyne as having undergone two syn dihydroxylations to yield a 1,1,2,2-tetraol intermediate. This intermediate has two adjacent hydrates (each characterized by two OH groups attached to the same carbon atom). Recall from Section 18.2 that hydrates equilibrate with their C=O forms through the loss of H_2O, so the dihydrate would go on to form the dicarbonyl product.

YOUR TURN 26.21

Which of the following diols can be produced from an alkene by using either OsO_4 or $KMnO_4$? For each one that can, draw the alkene that can be used to produce it.

(a) (b) (c) (d) (e)

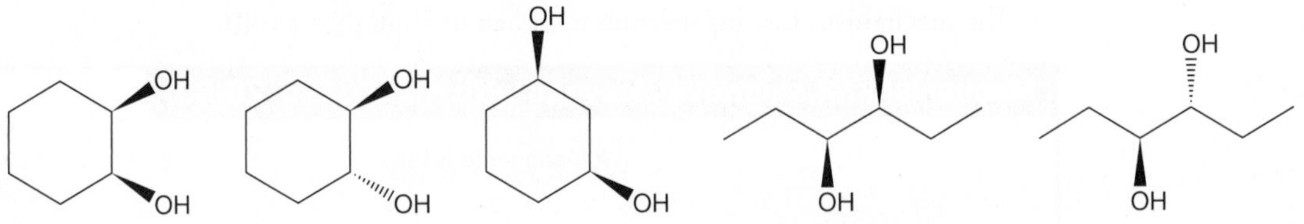
OH
OH

26.9 Oxidative Cleavage of Alkenes and Alkynes

SECTION 26.9 OBJECTIVES

You will be able to:

1. Draw the mechanism and product for oxidative cleavage reactions involving $KMnO_4$, IO_4^-, and ozonolysis.
2. Determine whether the conditions for oxidative cleavage of alkenes or alkynes will produce aldehydes, carboxylic acids, or CO_2.

As we saw with Diels–Alder and syn dihydroxylation reactions, *oxidative cleavage* reactions have at least one elementary step that exhibits the movement of six electrons to proceed through a cyclic transition state. In an **oxidative cleavage** reaction, the C=C bond of an alkene or the C≡C bond of an alkyne is broken, and the initial alkene or alkyne carbons are oxidized in the process. The general process is illustrated in Equations 26-37 and 26-38:

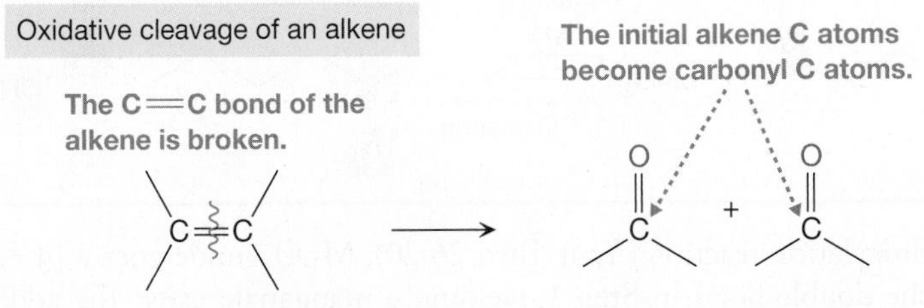
Oxidative cleavage of an alkene
The C=C bond of the alkene is broken.
The initial alkene C atoms become carbonyl C atoms.
C
O
+

(26-37)

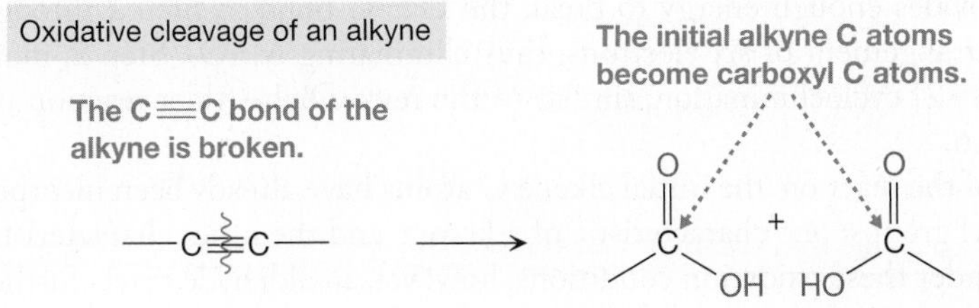
Oxidative cleavage of an alkyne
The C≡C bond of the alkyne is broken.
The initial alkyne C atoms become carboxyl C atoms.
C
O
+
OH
HO

(26-38)

We will examine oxidative cleavage reactions involving three different reagents: potassium permanganate ($KMnO_4$; Section 26.9a), periodate anion (IO_4^-; Section 26.9b), and ozone (O_3; Section 26.9c). As we will see, oxidative cleavage reactions can generate ketones, aldehydes, carboxylic acids, or carbon dioxide, depending on the reactants, the reagents used, and the exact conditions of the reaction.

26.9a Oxidative Cleavage Involving $KMnO_4$

In Section 26.8, we saw that the C═C double bond of an alkene undergoes syn dihydroxylation when treated with cold (often <0 °C), basic $KMnO_4$. When the $KMnO_4$ solution is concentrated and the reaction mixture is heated significantly above room temperature, however, *oxidative cleavage* of the C═C bond takes place, as shown in Equation 26-39.

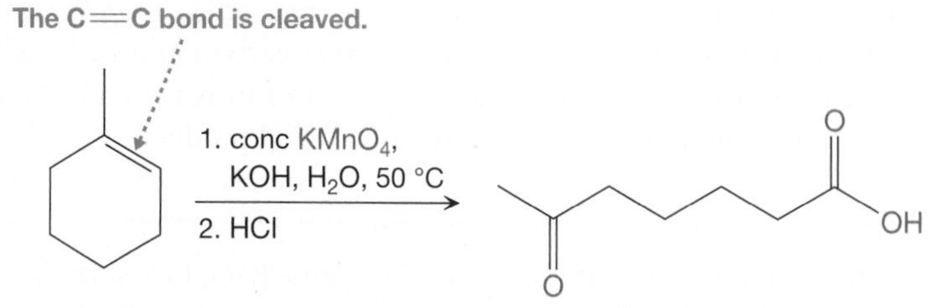

The C═C bond is cleaved.
1. conc KMnO4, KOH, H2O, 50 °C
2. HCl
O
OH
O

1-Methylcyclohexene

6-Oxoheptanoic acid 61%

(26-39)

The mechanism for this reaction is shown in Equation 26-40:

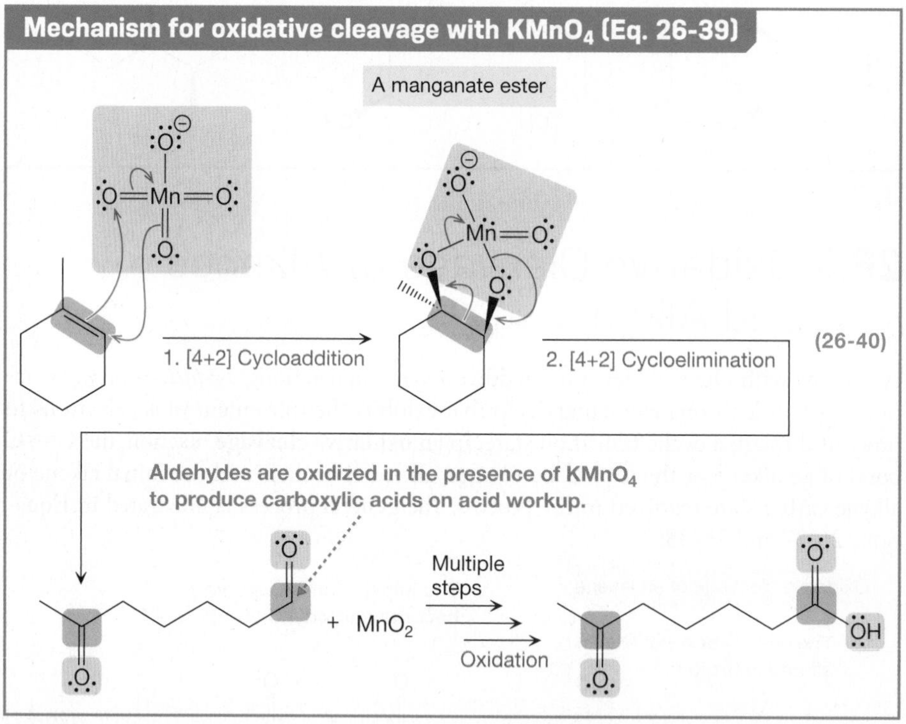

Mechanism for oxidative cleavage with KMnO4 (Eq. 26-39)
A manganate ester
Mn
O
1. [4+2] Cycloaddition
2. [4+2] Cycloelimination
Aldehydes are oxidized in the presence of KMnO4 to produce carboxylic acids on acid workup.
+ MnO2
Multiple steps
Oxidation
OH

(26-40)

Just like the dihydroxylation reaction (Your Turn 26.20), MnO_4^- undergoes a [4+2] cycloaddition to the double bond in Step 1, yielding a manganate ester. The added heat, however, provides enough energy to break the C—C bond in Step 2 through another cyclic rearrangement of six electrons, thus eliminating MnO_2. Step 2, more specifically, is a [4+2] cycloelimination, similar to the retro Diels–Alder reaction we saw in Section 26.6.

At this stage of the reaction, the initial alkene C atoms have already been incorporated into carbonyl groups: one characteristic of a ketone and the other characteristic of an aldehyde. Under these oxidation conditions, however, an aldehyde reacts further to produce a carboxylic acid that is rapidly deprotonated under the basic conditions to produce a carboxylate anion, RCO_2^- (Section 20.5b). Subsequent acid workup produces the final carboxylic acid.

When one of the alkene carbons is part of a CH_2 group (i.e., when the alkene is terminal), then cleavage of the C═C double bond initially produces formaldehyde, $H_2C{=}O$, as shown in Equation 26-41. Further oxidation in the presence of basic $KMnO_4$, followed by acid workup, produces carbonic acid, which degrades into H_2O and CO_2.

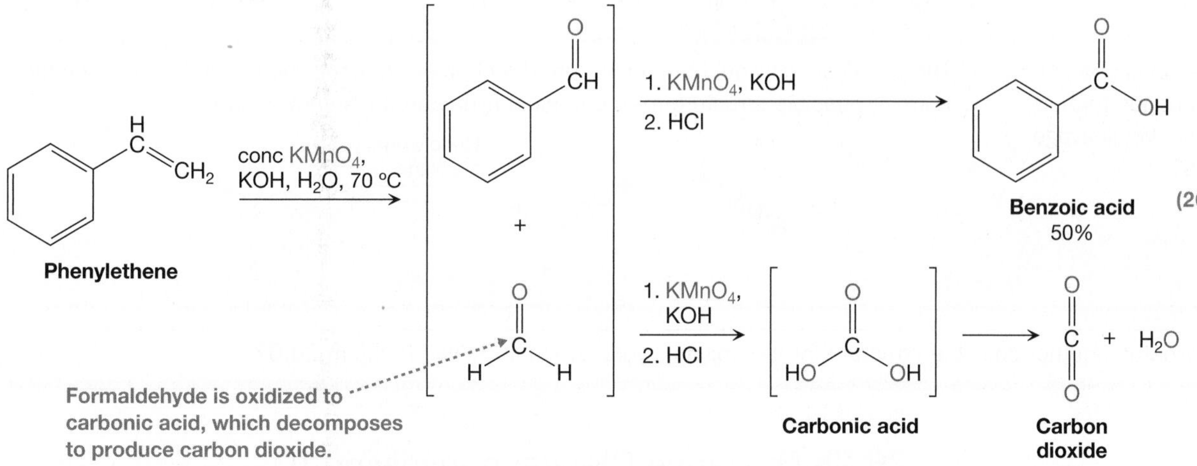

Phenylethene
conc KMnO4, KOH, H2O, 70 °C
1. KMnO4, KOH
2. HCl
Benzoic acid
50%
1. KMnO4, KOH
2. HCl
Formaldehyde is oxidized to carbonic acid, which decomposes to produce carbon dioxide.
Carbonic acid
Carbon dioxide

(26-41)

Alkynes are also susceptible to oxidative cleavage with $KMnO_4$. In this case, though, oxidative cleavage followed by acid workup produces only carboxylic acids and (in the case of a terminal alkyne) CO_2, as shown in Equation 26-42:

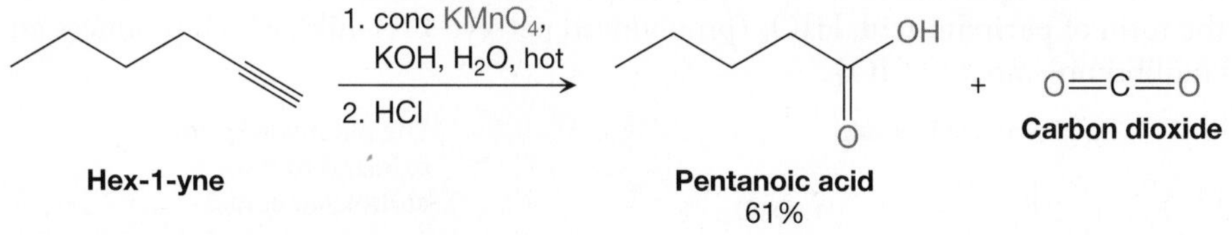

1. conc KMnO4, KOH, H2O, hot
2. HCl
Carbon dioxide
Hex-1-yne
Pentanoic acid
61%

(26-42)

Ketones cannot be formed from alkynes under these conditions because, after cleavage, each of the original C atoms from the C≡C bond can be bonded to, at most, one alkyl group.

SOLVED PROBLEM **26.6**

How to determine the starting material from oxidative cleavage products

Break It Down A hydrocarbon having the formula C_8H_{14} is treated with hot, basic, concentrated $KMnO_4$, followed by acid workup. Bubbling is observed, and the compounds shown here are recovered. What is a possible structure for the original hydrocarbon?

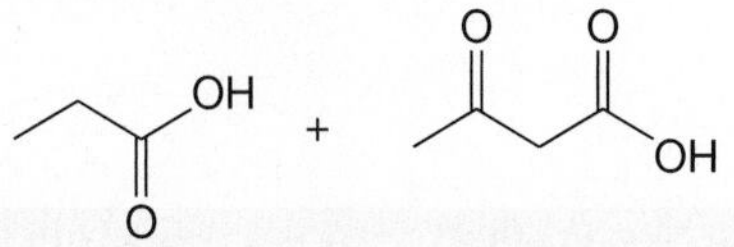

Think	Solve
Is the number of C atoms in the product compounds the same as in the reactant?	A total of seven C atoms appear in the two compounds that were recovered, whereas there are eight C atoms in the original hydrocarbon.
How is that difference accounted for by the bubbling that is observed?	Bubbling suggests the production of CO_2. When CO_2 gas escapes, it is not detected in the product mixture.

(continued)

What is the precursor to a CO_2H group under oxidative cleavage conditions? What is the precursor to CO_2?	As shown below, the two CO_2H functional groups must have come from the initial formation of HC=O groups, and CO_2 must have come from formaldehyde ($H_2C{=}O$).

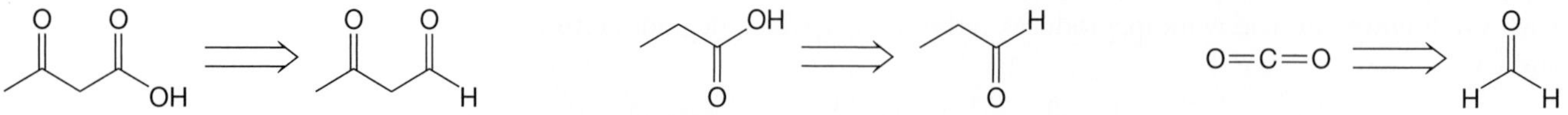

From what functional groups are C=O bonds formed under oxidative cleavage conditions?	The C=O bonds would be made from the cleavage of C=C bonds under these conditions. A possible structure for the original hydrocarbon is shown below.

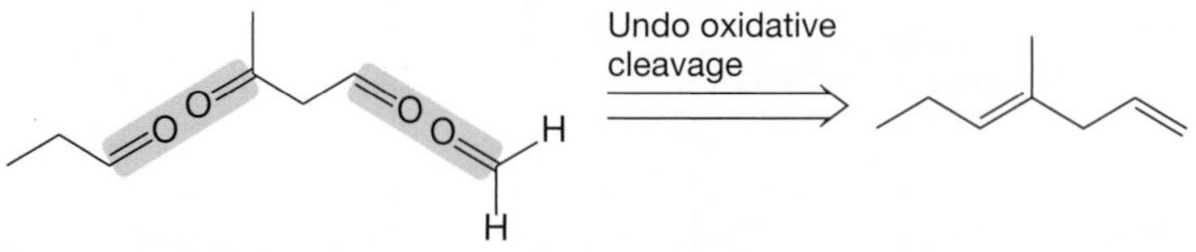

Undo oxidative cleavage

Try It What is another possible structure for the original hydrocarbon in Solved Problem 26.6?

26.9b Oxidative Cleavage Involving IO_4^-

An alkene can also undergo oxidative cleavage by treatment with OsO_4, followed by the **periodate anion**, IO_4^- (pronounced per-EYE-oh-date). The periodate anion is most commonly introduced as $NaIO_4$ (Eq. 26-43), but it can also be introduced in the form of **periodic acid**, HIO_4 (pronounced per-eye-OH-dik), which produces an equilibrium amount of IO_4^-.

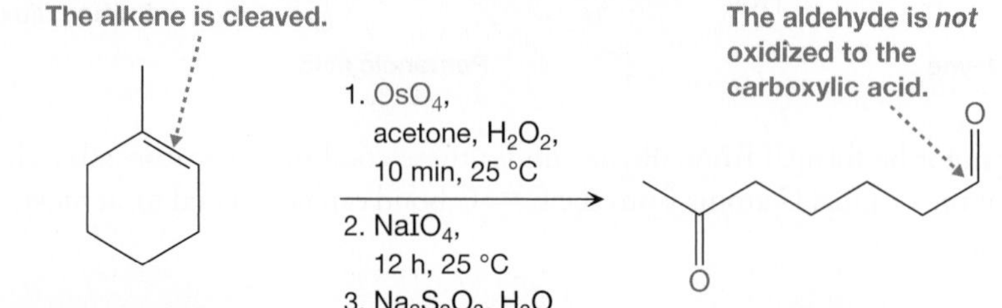

The alkene is cleaved.
The aldehyde is not oxidized to the carboxylic acid.
1. OsO_4, acetone, H_2O_2, 10 min, 25 °C
2. $NaIO_4$, 12 h, 25 °C
3. $Na_2S_2O_3$, H_2O

1-Methylcyclohexene **6-Oxoheptanal** (26-43)

Unlike oxidative cleavage involving $KMnO_4$, however:

> Aldehydes that are produced on oxidative cleavage involving IO_4^- are *not* oxidized further.

A partial mechanism for this reaction is shown in Equation 26-44:

Partial mechanism for oxidative cleavage with IO_4^- (Eq. 26-43)

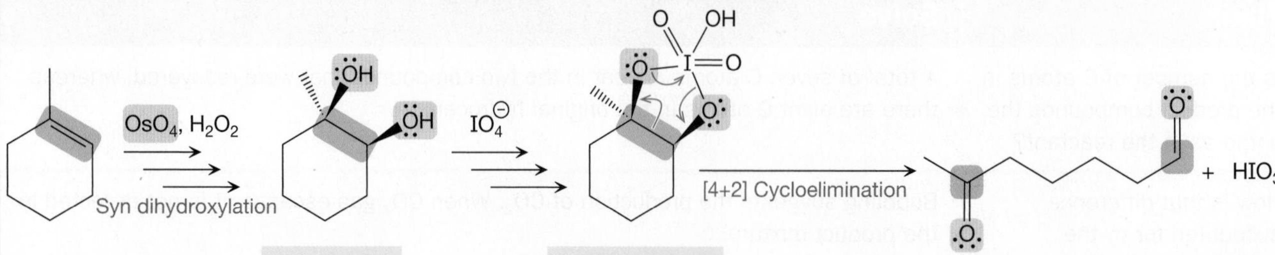

OsO_4, H_2O_2
Syn dihydroxylation
IO_4^-
[4+2] Cycloelimination
+ HIO_3

A cis-1,2-diol A periodate ester (26-44)

The first several steps make up the syn dihydroxylation mechanism from Equation 26-34 (Section 26.8), thus producing a cis-1,2-diol. Then, the addition of IO_4^- produces a cyclic **periodate ester**. The final step in the mechanism is key, because it cleaves the C—C bond and produces the two carbonyl groups. This step is a [4+2] cycloelimination, much like Step 2 in Equation 26-40 (p. 1282).

Notice in Equation 26-44 that the mechanism proceeds through a 1,2-diol. Therefore:

> Periodate oxidative cleavage can be carried out directly on a 1,2-diol.

Examples are shown in Equations 26-45 and 26-46:

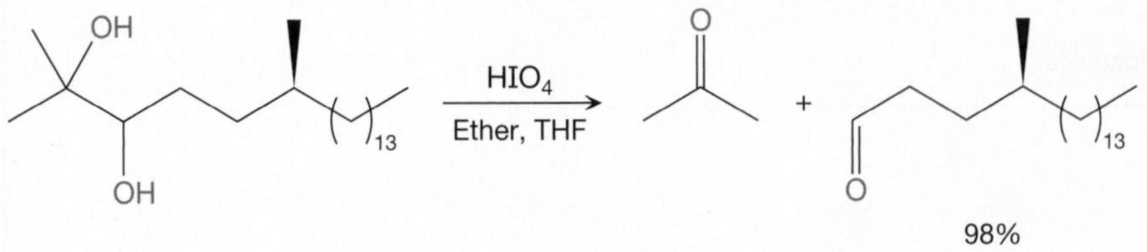

OH
OH
13
HIO4
Ether, THF
O
+
13
O
98%

(26-45)

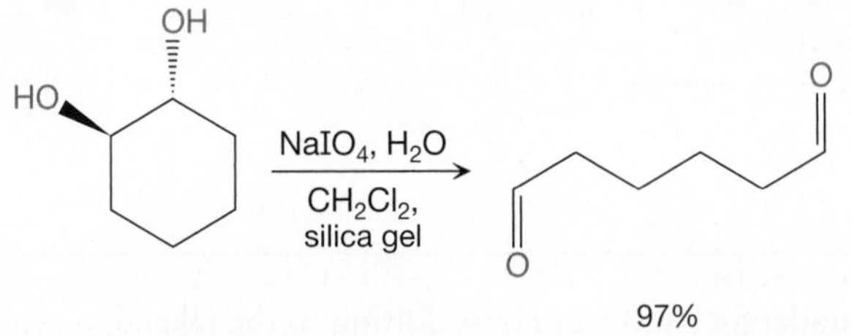

OH
HO
NaIO4, H2O
CH2Cl2,
silica gel
O
O
97%

(26-46)

A variety of 1,2-diols can undergo this reaction; the major requirement is the ability of the 1,2-diol to produce a cyclic periodate ester as in Equation 26-44. (See Your Turn 26.22.)

YOUR TURN 26.22

Explain why **A** will undergo periodate oxidative cleavage but **B** will not. Draw the product of the reaction between **A** and HIO_4, including stereochemistry.
Hint: It is not due to steric hindrance involving HIO_4.

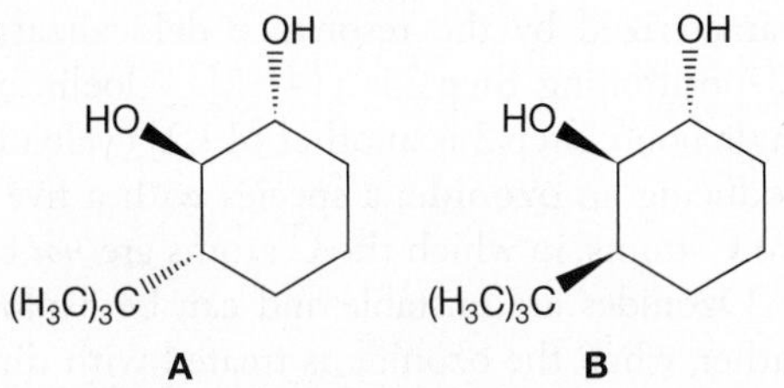

OH
HO
(H3C)3C
A
OH
HO
(H3C)3C
B

26.9c Oxidative Cleavage Involving Ozone: Ozonolysis

Oxidative cleavage with **ozone**, O_3, a process called **ozonolysis**, is shown in Equation 26-47 for 1-methylcyclohexene. Treatment with ozone is followed by dimethyl sulfide, CH_3SCH_3, though zinc metal in acetic acid could be used instead of CH_3SCH_3. The double bond is cleaved to yield precisely the same product as oxidative cleavage with IO_4^-, shown previously in Equation 26-44.

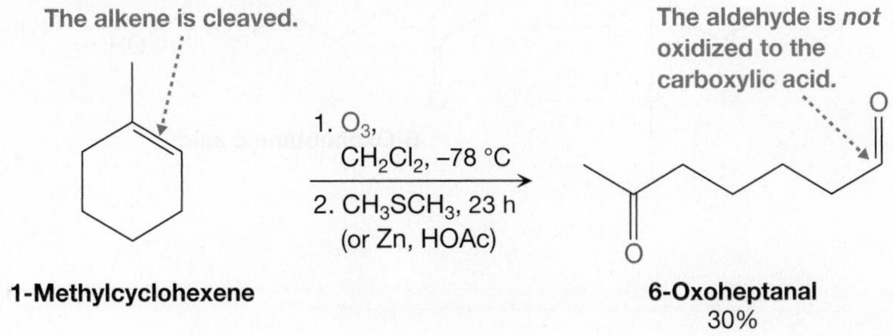

The alkene is cleaved.
The aldehyde is *not* oxidized to the carboxylic acid.
1. O3,
CH2Cl2, –78 °C
2. CH3SCH3, 23 h
(or Zn, HOAc)
O
O
1-Methylcyclohexene
6-Oxoheptanal
30%

(26-47)

The mechanism for this reaction is shown in Equation 26-48:

Mechanism for oxidative cleavage by ozonolysis (Eq. 26-47)

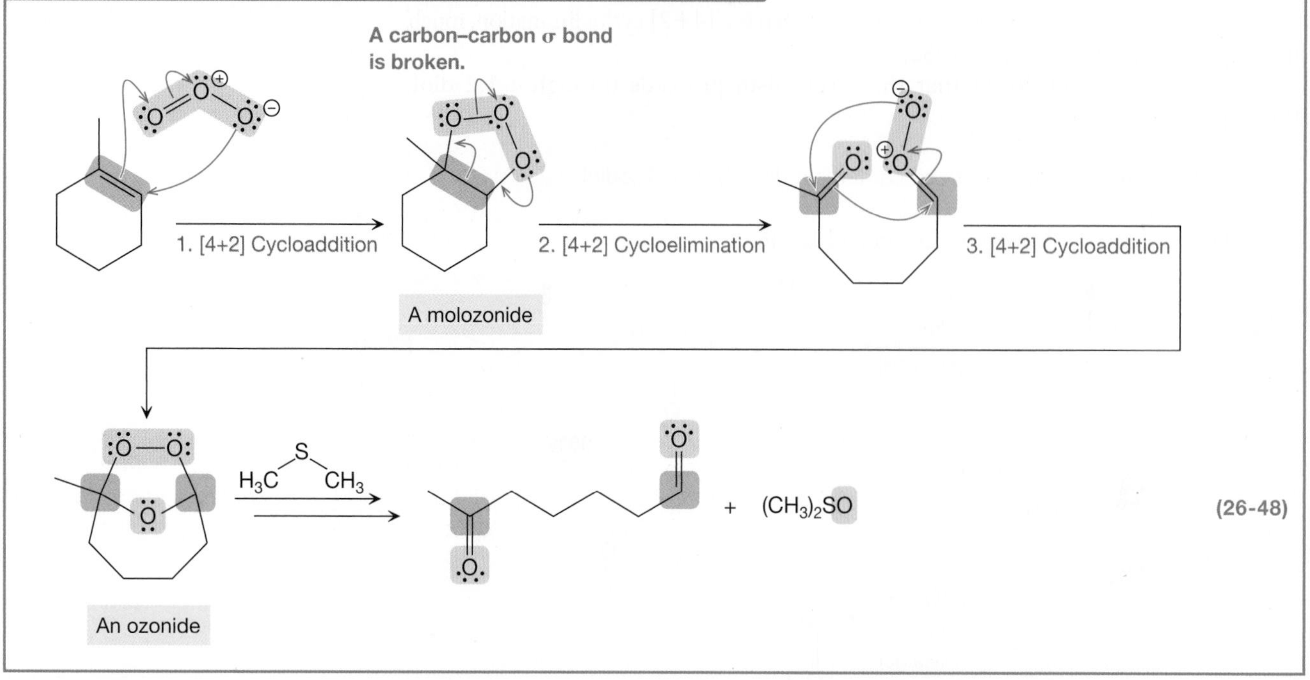
A carbon–carbon σ bond is broken.
1. [4+2] Cycloaddition
2. [4+2] Cycloelimination
3. [4+2] Cycloaddition
A molozonide
An ozonide
+ (CH3)2SO

(26-48)

In Step 1, ozone undergoes a [4+2] cycloaddition to the alkene to produce a **molozonide**, which has a characteristic five-membered ring consisting of three sequential O atoms and two connected C atoms. That step is much like the addition of OsO_4 to an alkene to produce an osmate ester (Eq. 26-34, p. 1279) or the addition of MnO_4^- to an alkene to produce a manganate ester (Eq. 26-40, p. 1282). Step 1, more specifically, is called a **1,3-dipolar cycloaddition** because ozone is a 1,3-dipolar compound, characterized by the resonance delocalization of charge over atoms that have a 1,3-positioning. Step 2 is a [4+2] cycloelimination, which breaks the carbon–carbon single bond. Step 3 is another [4+2] cycloaddition, also a 1,3-dipolar cycloaddition, producing an **ozonide**: a species with a five-membered ring of three O atoms and two C atoms, in which the C atoms are *not* connected to each other.

Ozonides are unstable and can be explosive, so they are generally not isolated. Rather, when the ozonide is treated with dimethyl sulfide, the ozonide decomposes into the final product. Dimethyl sulfide is a reducing agent, moreover, so it prevents aldehydes in the product from being oxidized to carboxylic acids.

If oxidizing the aldehyde product to a carboxylic acid is desired, then hydrogen peroxide (an oxidizing agent) can be used in the ozonolysis reaction instead of dimethyl sulfide, as indicated in Equation 26-49:

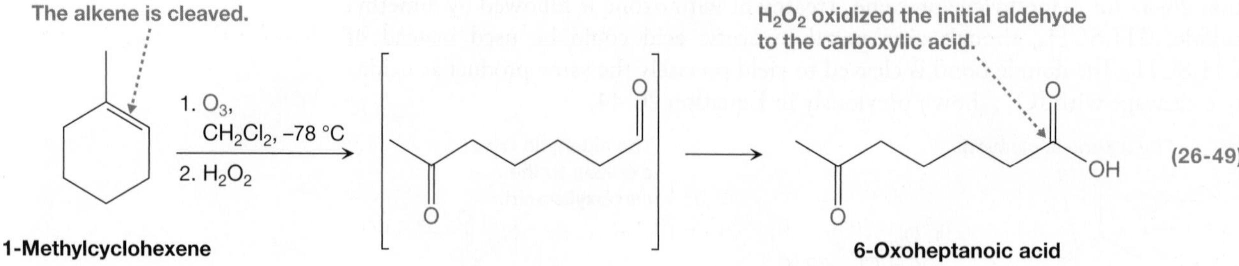
The alkene is cleaved.
1. O3, CH2Cl2, –78 °C
2. H2O2
H2O2 oxidized the initial aldehyde to the carboxylic acid.
OH

(26-49)

1-Methylcyclohexene

6-Oxoheptanoic acid

YOUR TURN **26.23**

Draw the molozonide, the ozonide, and the products that are formed in each of these reactions.

(a) (b)

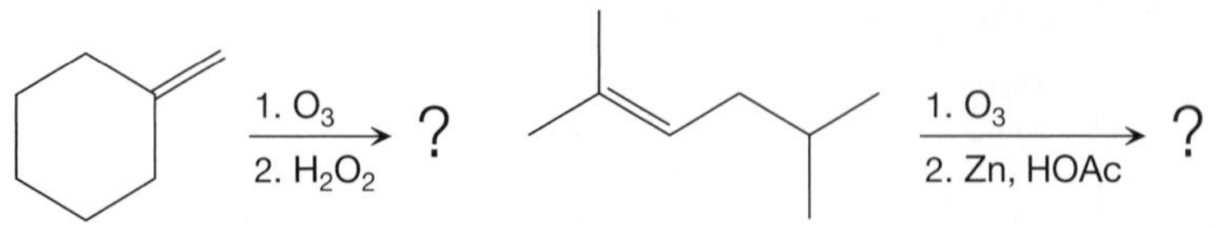
1. O3
2. H2O2
?
1. O3
2. Zn, HOAc
?

26.10 Organic Synthesis: The Diels–Alder Reaction in Synthesis

SECTION 26.10 OBJECTIVES

You will be able to:

1. Explain why the Diels–Alder reaction is such a valuable reaction for synthesis.
2. Identify when a synthesis might call for incorporating a Diels–Alder reaction.

As we have emphasized throughout Chapter 26, the Diels–Alder reaction is a valuable asset to organic synthesis, in large part because it makes it possible to synthesize a six-membered carbon ring from acyclic precursors. The prototypical Diels–Alder reaction between buta-1,3-diene and ethene is repeated in Equation 26-50; the fundamental characteristic of the product is a cyclohexene ring.

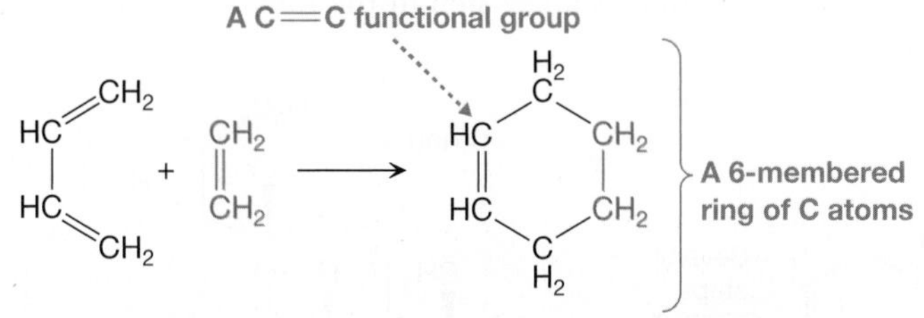
A C=C functional group
CH2
HC
HC
CH2
+
CH2
CH2
H2
C
HC
CH2
HC
CH2
C
H2
A 6-membered
ring of C atoms

(26-50)

The alkene functionality that is left in the product is an important feature of the Diels–Alder reaction, because it allows further reaction to take place specifically at that site. For example, the C=C double bond can be hydrogenated (Section 13.9) to produce a cyclohexane ring. Or, it can undergo electrophilic addition to produce a new functional group that can be used further (Chapters 12 and 13); an example is provided in Equation 26-51, in which the Diels–Alder product is converted into a Grignard reagent:

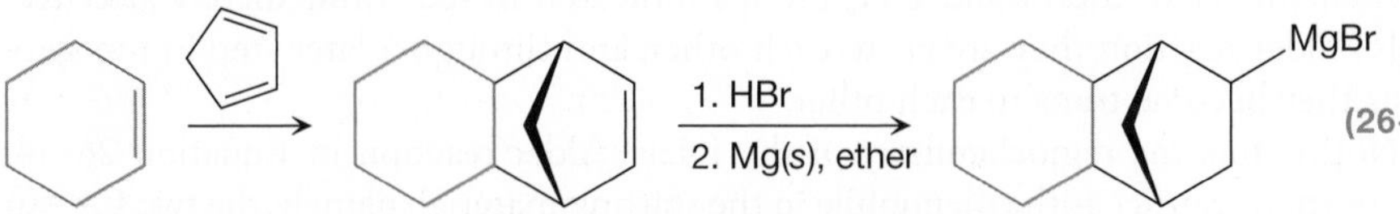
1. HBr
2. Mg(s), ether
MgBr

(26-51)

Another option is to alter the size of the ring, as shown in Equation 26-52:

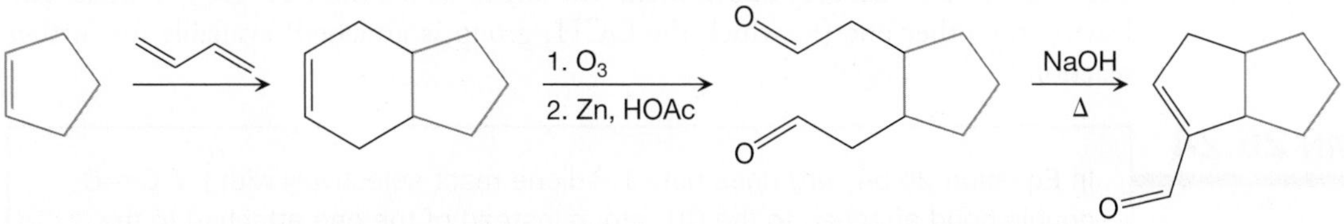
1. O3
2. Zn, HOAc
O
O
NaOH
Δ
O

(26-52)

Oxidative cleavage (Section 26.9) opens the six-membered ring at the C=C double bond. An intramolecular aldol condensation (Section 19.12) follows, producing a five-membered ring.

◀ RECALL

Section 19.13 showed that the mechanism for a Robinson annulation is the conjugate addition of an enolate anion to an α,β-unsaturated ketone, followed by an intramolecular aldol condensation.

The Diels–Alder reaction is not the first reaction we have encountered that can produce a six-membered carbon ring. In Section 19.13 we used the Robinson annulation reaction, which is shown again in Equation 26-53 (see Recall box). The immediate product is an unsaturated cyclohexenone, but the carbonyl group can be selectively reduced to produce the cyclohexene ring.

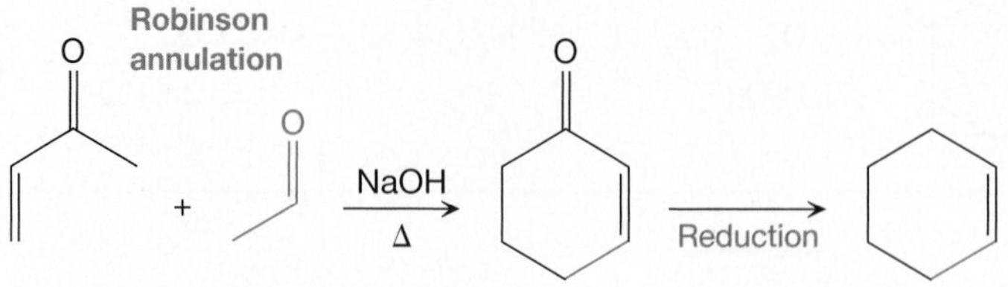
Robinson annulation
O
O
O
+
NaOH
Δ
Reduction

(26-53)

Although a cyclohexene ring can be produced by the Robinson annulation, the Diels–Alder reaction generally offers numerous advantages. One advantage is the relatively mild conditions under which many Diels–Alder reactions can be run; by contrast, the Robinson annulation requires significantly basic conditions that may interfere with other functional groups present. Furthermore, reduction of a carbonyl group to a methylene (CH_2) group in the second step in Equation 26-53 can require harsh conditions, such as the presence of strong acid or strong base (see again Section 20.4).

Other advantages include the *stereospecificity* and the *regioselectivity* of the Diels–Alder reaction. In 1952, for example, R. B. Woodward and co-workers pioneered the use of the Diels–Alder reaction as a key step in the total synthesis of cholesterol, as indicated in Equation 26-54:

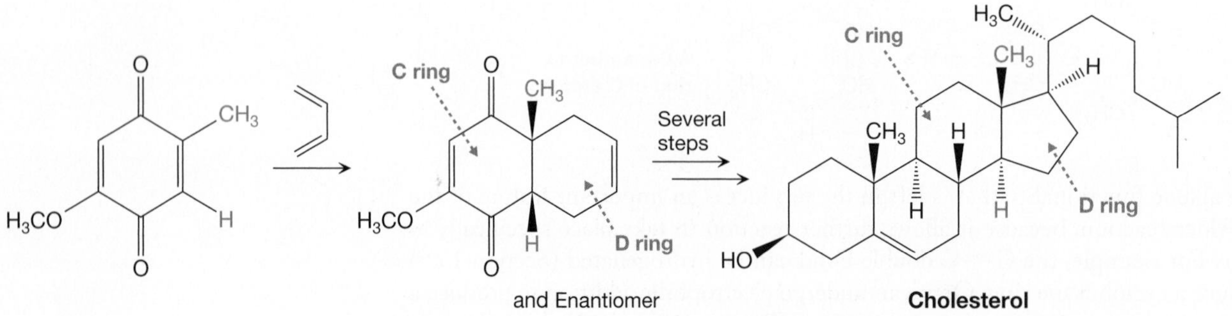
O
CH3
H3CO
H
O
C ring
O
CH3
H3CO
H
O
D ring
and Enantiomer
Several steps
C ring
H3C
CH3
H
CH3
H
H
H
D ring
HO
Cholesterol

(26-54)

The Diels–Alder reaction was used to generate the six-membered ring that later becomes the D ring in the target. It was also used to establish the initial relative stereochemistry of the H and CH_3 groups indicated in red: Immediately after the Diels–Alder reaction they are cis to each other, and through a later step in the synthesis they become trans to each other.

Notice, too, the regiochemistry of the Diels–Alder reaction in Equation 26-54. Two portions can act as the dienophile in the starting material: namely, the two C=C double bonds on either side of the six-membered ring. Nevertheless, buta-1,3-diene selectively reacts with only one of them (the one to which the CH_3 group is attached), leaving the other one (to which the OCH_3 group is attached) available for further reaction.

YOUR TURN 26.24

In Equation 26-54, why does buta-1,3-diene react selectively with the C=C double bond attached to the CH_3 group instead of the one attached to the OCH_3 group?

Equation 26-54 provides a glimpse of the utility of the Diels–Alder reaction in total synthesis. Indeed, as we mentioned at the outset of this chapter, the utility of the

Diels–Alder reaction is captured by the fact that Otto Diels and Kurt Alder were awarded the 1950 Nobel Prize in Chemistry.

SOLVED PROBLEM **26.7**

How to incorporate a Diels–Alder reaction in synthesis

Break It Down Show how to carry out the following synthesis, in which acetaldehyde is your only source of carbon. Do not be concerned with stereochemistry in this case.

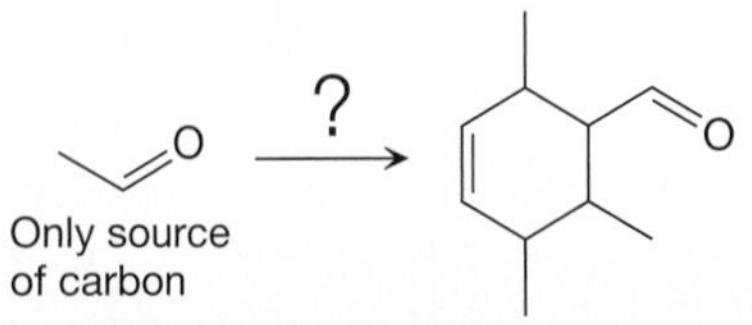
O
?
O
Only source
of carbon

Think	Solve
What reaction can produce a six-membered ring of carbons? What are the necessary precursors for that reaction?	A six-membered ring of carbons can be produced from a Diels–Alder reaction. The following transform shows the necessary diene and dienophile precursors.

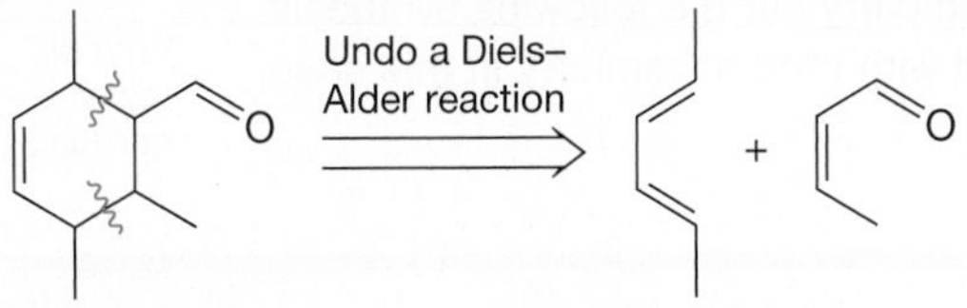
Undo a Diels–
Alder reaction
O
+
O

Think	Solve
To make the dienophile from the starting material, which carbon–carbon bond should be formed? What reaction will produce that bond?	The dienophile is an α,β-unsaturated aldehyde that can be produced from an aldol condensation reaction (Section 19.9). To arrive at the precursors for such a reaction, disconnect the bond between the α and β carbons, as shown.

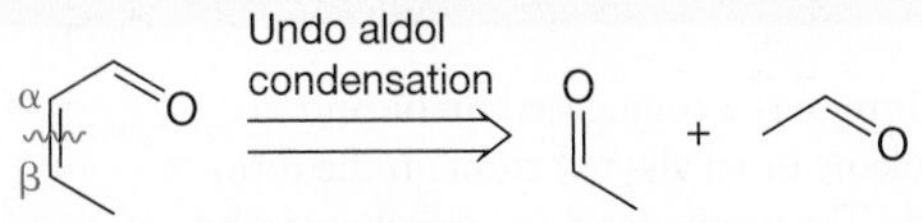
α
β
O
Undo aldol
condensation
O
+
O

Think	Solve
To make the diene from the starting material, which carbon–carbon bond should be formed? What reaction will produce that bond?	The diene has six carbons, whereas the starting material has two carbons. We should therefore consider formation of the bond between C-2 and C-3. As shown, that bond can be formed from a Grignard reaction (Section 18.4).

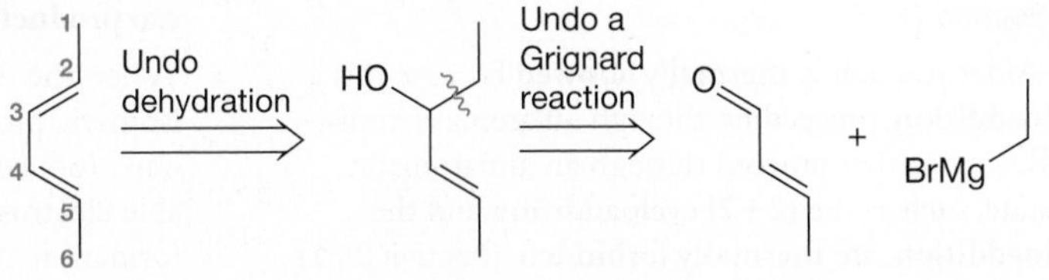
1
2
3
4
5
6
Undo
dehydration
HO
Undo a
Grignard
reaction
O
+
BrMg

Think	Solve
How can the precursors for the diene be made from the starting material?	The α,β-unsaturated aldehyde precursor is the same as the dienophile, which we already showed how to make. The Grignard reagent can be made from the starting material as shown.

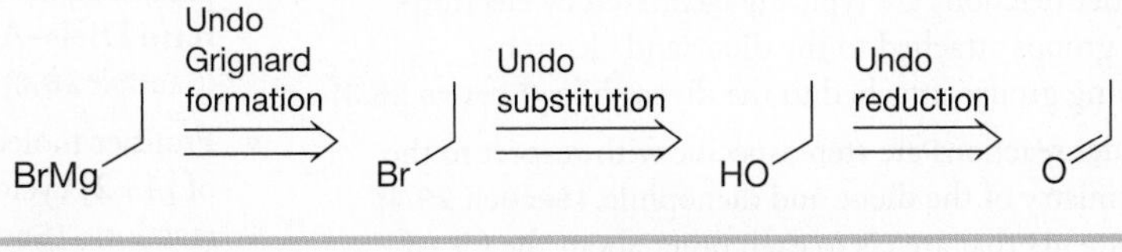
Undo
Grignard
formation
BrMg
Br
Undo
substitution
HO
Undo
reduction
O

(continued)

How can the final synthesis be reported?	To report the final synthesis, reverse the direction of the retrosynthetic analysis and add the appropriate reagents, as shown below.

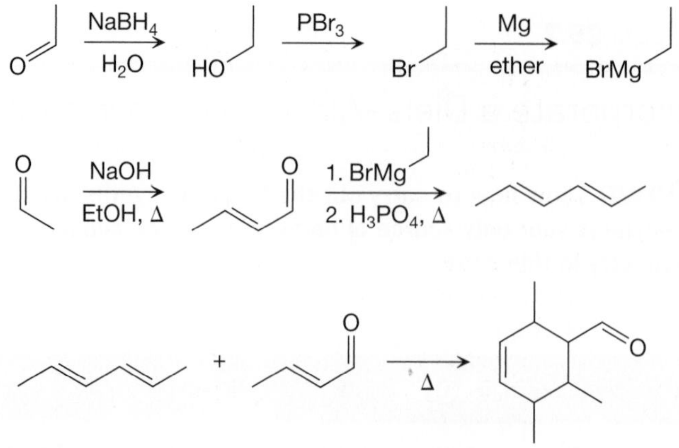
NaBH4
H2O
HO
PBr3
Br
Mg
ether
BrMg
O
NaOH
EtOH, Δ
O
1. BrMg
2. H3PO4, Δ
+
O
Δ
O

Try It Show how to carry out the following synthesis. Do not be concerned with stereochemistry in this case.

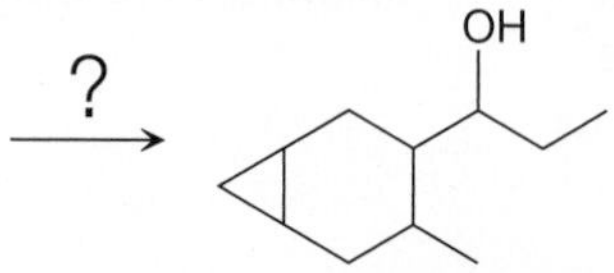
Four or
fewer
carbons
?
OH

Chapter Summary and Key Terms

- The **Diels–Alder reaction** joins a conjugated **diene** and a **dienophile** (either an alkene or an alkyne) through the formation of two new σ bonds. The product is a six-membered ring of carbon atoms. **(Introduction and Section 26.1)**
- The Diels–Alder reaction is concerted; all bonds that are formed and broken do so simultaneously. It requires the cyclic movement of electrons, so it is classified as a **pericyclic reaction**. **(Section 26.1)**
- The Diels–Alder reaction is **thermally allowed** because it is a **[4+2] cycloaddition**, proceeding through an aromatic transition state. Reactions that proceed through an antiaromatic transition state, such as the **[2+2] cycloaddition** and the **[6+2] cycloaddition**, are **thermally forbidden**. **(Section 26.1)**
- For a Diels–Alder reaction to take place, the diene must be able to attain the ***s*-cis conformation**. Diels–Alder reactions cannot take place with the diene in the ***s*-trans conformation**. **(Section 26.2)**
- Diels–Alder reactions are typically facilitated by electron-donating groups attached to the diene and electron-withdrawing groups attached to the dienophile. **(Section 26.3)**
- Diels–Alder reactions are stereospecific with respect to the stereochemistry of the diene and dienophile. **(Section 26.4)**
  - Substituents that are cis to each other about the C═C double bond of the dienophile end up cis to each other in the new ring that is produced. Otherwise, the substituents end up trans to each other in the ring.
  - One way to determine whether the substituents attached to the terminal carbons of the diene will end up cis or trans to each other in the new ring is to draw a circle that encompasses the diene in its *s*-cis conformation and then observe which substituents are attached by bonds entirely inside the circle or intersected by it.
- Diels–Alder reactions tend to favor an **endo product** over an **exo product**. **(Section 26.4)**
- When the diene and dienophile are both unsymmetric, two isomeric products can be produced. The major product is the one produced by the approach that exhibits the most favorable electrostatic attraction among atoms undergoing bond formation. **(Section 26.5)**
- Enthalpy tends to heavily favor the products of a Diels–Alder reaction, whereas entropy favors reactants. Therefore, under normal conditions, Diels–Alder reactions tend to be irreversible and proceed under kinetic control. At high temperatures, though, some can undergo the reverse reaction—a **retro Diels–Alder reaction** or **[4+2] cycloelimination**. **(Section 26.6)**
- Frontier molecular orbital theory accounts for key outcomes of [4+2] cycloaddition reactions and [2+2] cycloaddition reactions. **(Section 26.7)**
  - A [4+2] cycloaddition is thermally allowed because the HOMO and LUMO have the appropriate symmetries to interact when the reactants are in their ground state

electron configurations. Such a reaction is **photochemically forbidden** because the HOMO and LUMO lack the proper symmetry to interact when one reactant is in an excited state.

- A [2+2] cycloaddition is thermally forbidden because the HOMO and LUMO lack the appropriate symmetries to interact when the reactants are in their ground state electron configurations. Such a reaction is **photochemically allowed** because the HOMO and LUMO have the proper symmetry to interact when one reactant is in an excited state.
- The rate of a Diels–Alder reaction increases when substituents on the diene and dienophile decrease the HOMO–LUMO energy gap.
- **Secondary orbital overlap** in a Diels–Alder reaction stabilizes the transition state in the endo approach of the diene and dienophile, which favors the endo product.

- An alkene can undergo **syn dihydroxylation** with OsO_4 or $KMnO_4$ (cold), resulting in a cis-1,2-diol. An alkyne that undergoes such a reaction results in a 1,2-dicarbonyl compound. **(Section 26.8)**
- **Oxidative cleavage** of an alkene or alkyne completely breaks the C=C double bond or C≡C triple bond, with the initial alkene or alkyne carbons becoming part of C=O groups in the final products. **(Section 26.9)**
  - Aldehydes produced from oxidative cleavage are further oxidized to carboxylic acids when cleavage is initiated with a hot, concentrated solution of $KMnO_4$ followed by workup with acid **(Section 26.9a)** or with **ozonolysis** followed by workup with H_2O_2 **(Section 26.9c)**.
  - Aldehydes produced from oxidative cleavage are *not* oxidized further when cleavage involves the treatment of a 1,2-diol with $NaIO_4$ or HIO_4 **(Section 26.9b)** or is initiated with ozonolysis followed by workup with CH_3SCH_3 or Zn/HOAc **(Section 26.9c)**.

Reaction Tables

Functional group transformations introduced in this chapter are collected in Table 26-1, and reactions introduced in this chapter that alter the carbon skeleton are collected in Table 26-2.

TABLE 26-1 Functional Group Transformations

	Starting Compound Class	Typical Reagents and Reaction Conditions	Compound Class Formed	Key Electron-Rich Species	Key Electron-Poor Species	Comments	Discussed in Section
(1)	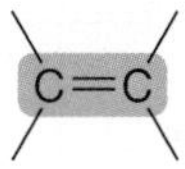 Alkene	OsO_4 → H_2O_2	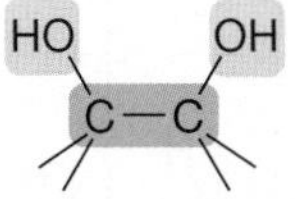 Syn 1,2-diol	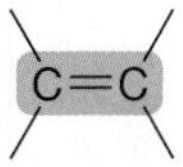	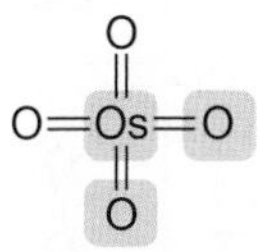	An alternate method uses a cold, basic solution of $KMnO_4$	26.8
(2)	 Alkyne	OsO_4 → H_2O_2	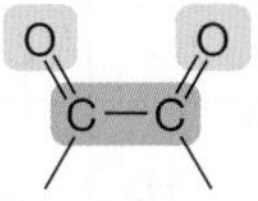 1,2-Dione		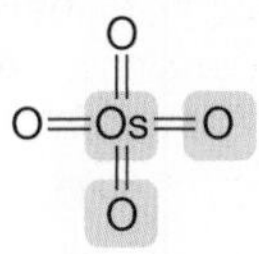	An alternate method uses a cold, basic solution of $KMnO_4$	26.8

TABLE 26-2 Reactions That Alter the Carbon Skeleton

	Starting Compound Class	Typical Reagents and Reaction Conditions	Compound Class Formed	Key Electron-Rich Species	Key Electron-Poor Species	Comments	Discussed in Section(s)
(1)	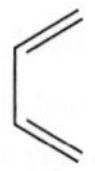 **Conjugated diene**	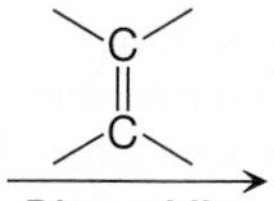 **Dienophile**	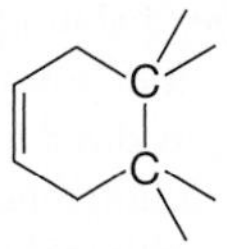 **Substituted cyclohexene**	N/A	N/A	Standard Diels–Alder reactions are facilitated by an electron-donating group on the diene and an electron-withdrawing group on the dienophile	26.1–26.6
(2)	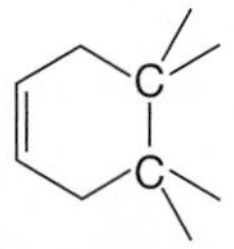 **Substituted cyclohexene**	→ Δ	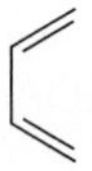 **Conjugated diene** + 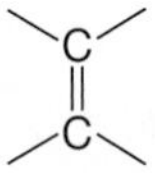 **Alkene**	N/A	N/A	Retro Diels–Alder reaction	26.6
(3)	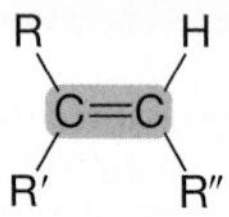 **Alkene**	1. conc $KMnO_4$, KOH, H_2O, Δ 2. HCl	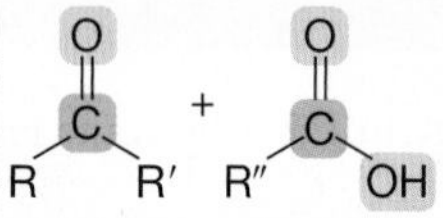 **Ketone and/or carboxylic acid**	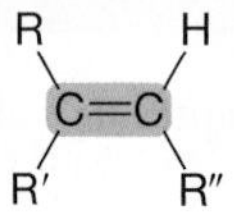	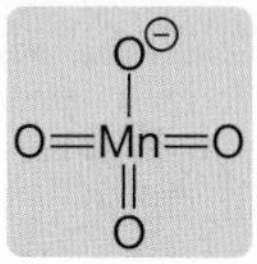	Oxidative cleavage; formic acid product (R″ = H) oxidizes to CO_2	26.9a
(4)	R—C≡C—R′ **Alkyne**	1. conc $KMnO_4$, KOH, H_2O, Δ 2. HCl	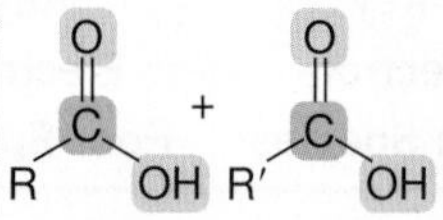 **Carboxylic acid**	R—C≡C—R′	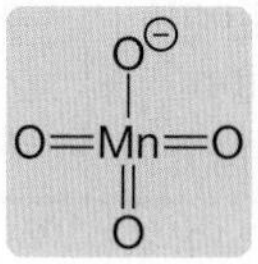	Oxidative cleavage; formic acid product (R′ = H) oxidizes to CO_2	26.9a
(5)	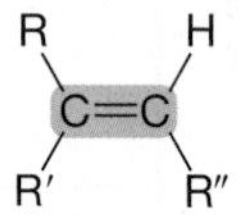 **Alkene**	1. O_3 2. CH_3SCH_3 or Zn, HOAc	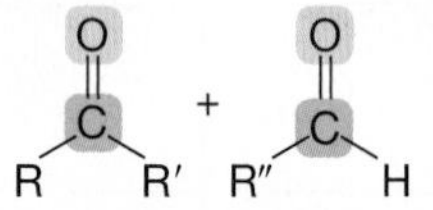 **Ketone and/or aldehyde**	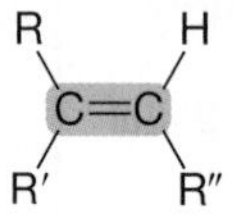	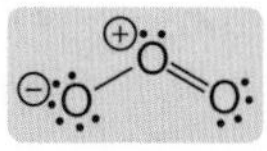	Ozonolysis	26.9c
(6)	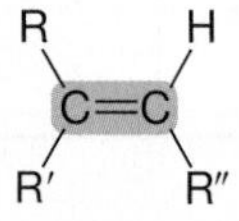 **Alkene**	1. O_3 2. H_2O_2	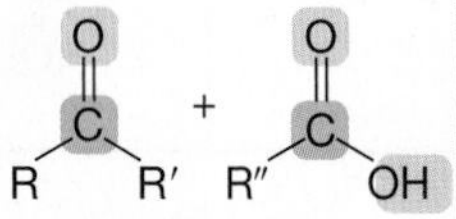 **Ketone and/or carboxylic acid**	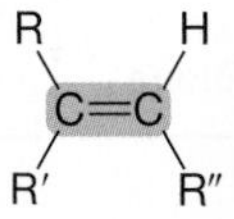	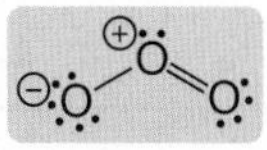	Ozonolysis; oxidative cleavage; formic acid product (R″ = H) oxidizes to CO_2	26.9c
(7)	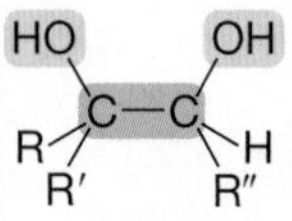 **1,2-Diol**	$NaIO_4$ or HIO_4 →	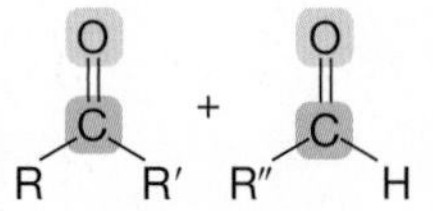 **Ketone and/or aldehyde**	—	—	Oxidative cleavage	26.9b

Problems

Problems that are related to synthesis are denoted (SYN).

Sections 26.1 and 26.2 The Diels–Alder Reaction and the *s*-Cis Conformation of the Diene

26.1 We mentioned in the chapter opener (p. 1252) that tetrodotoxin has been synthesized using a Diels–Alder reaction. The one incorporated in the synthesis by M. Isobe involved the following diene and dienophile. Draw the curved arrow notation for this reaction.

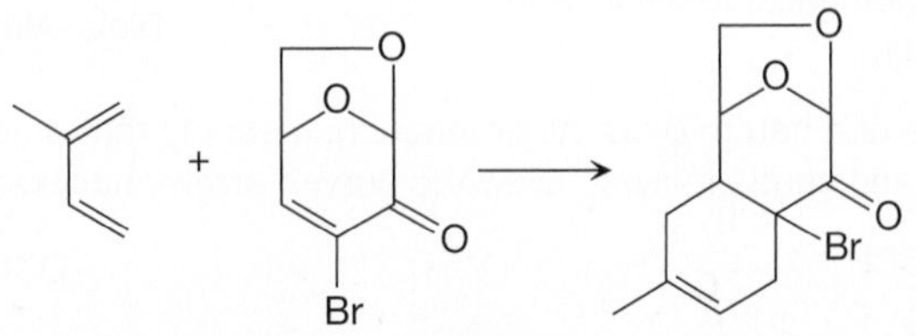

O
O
Br
O
O
O
Br
O

26.2 Draw the complete, detailed mechanism and the major product for each of the following Diels–Alder reactions.

(a)

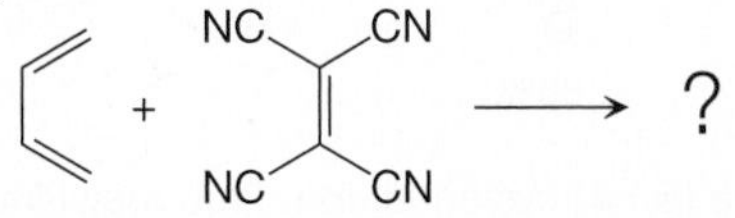

NC
CN
NC
CN
?

(b)

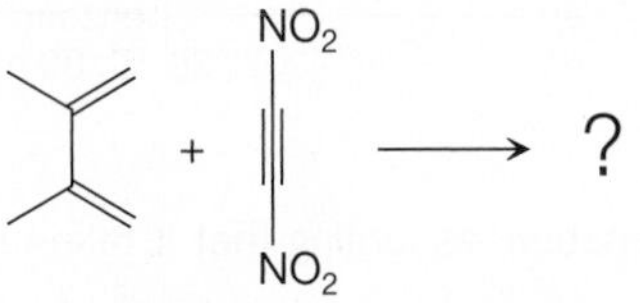

NO_2
NO_2
?

26.3 **(SYN)** Draw the diene that would react with ethene to produce each of the following compounds.

(a)

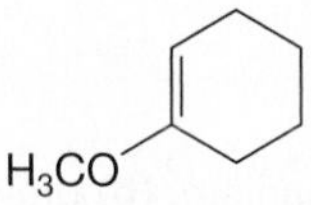

H_3CO

(b)

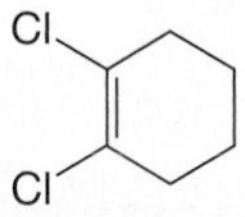

Cl
Cl

(c)

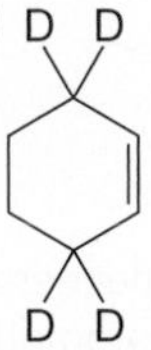

D D
D D

(d)

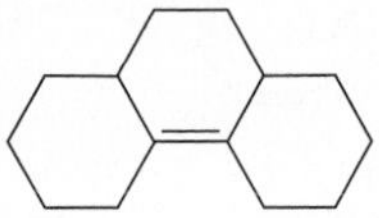

26.4 **(SYN)** Draw the dienophile that would react with buta-1,3-diene to produce each of the following compounds.

(a)

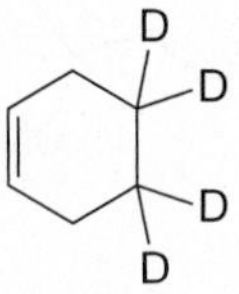

D
D
D
D

(b)

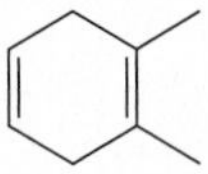

(c)

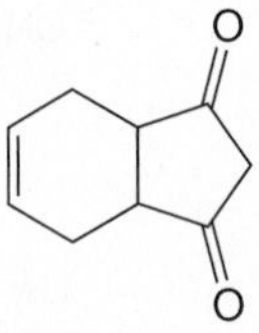

O
O

26.5 The following are several isomers of $C_{10}H_{14}$ with two fused six-membered rings.

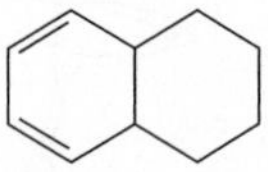

A

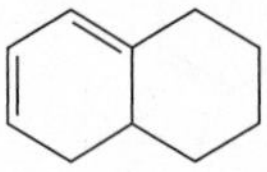

B

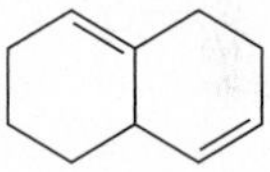

C

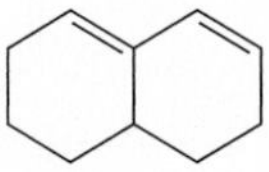

D

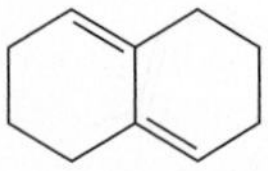

E

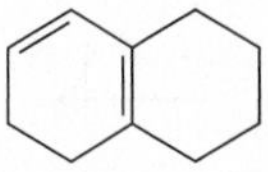

F

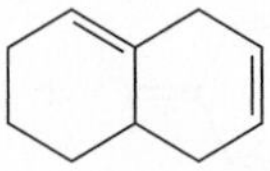

G

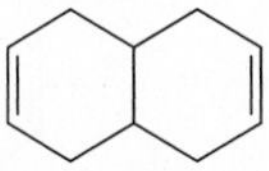

H

(a) Identify which will react with ethene in a Diels–Alder reaction and which will not.

(b) Draw one more isomer with two fused six-membered rings that *will* react with ethene in a Diels–Alder reaction.

26.6 Rank the following compounds in order from slowest to fastest rate of reaction in a Diels–Alder reaction with ethene.

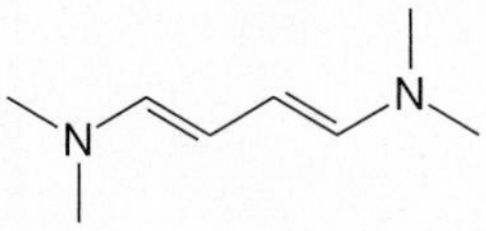

N
N

I

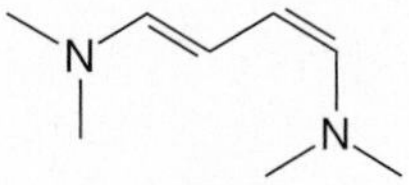

N
N

J

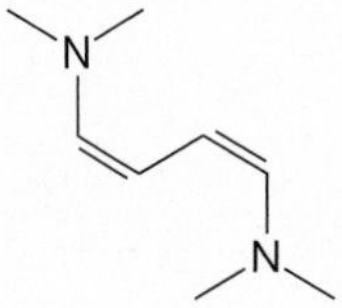

N
N

K

26.7 Which of the molecules shown here will react faster as a diene in a Diels–Alder reaction with ethene? Explain.

L **M**

26.8 Although benzene's Lewis structure exhibits a pair of conjugated double bonds locked in the s-cis conformation, benzene does *not* react with ethene. Draw the product of this hypothetical reaction, and explain why it does not occur.

26.9 Anthracene readily undergoes a Diels–Alder reaction with tetracyanoethene, even though anthracene is aromatic.

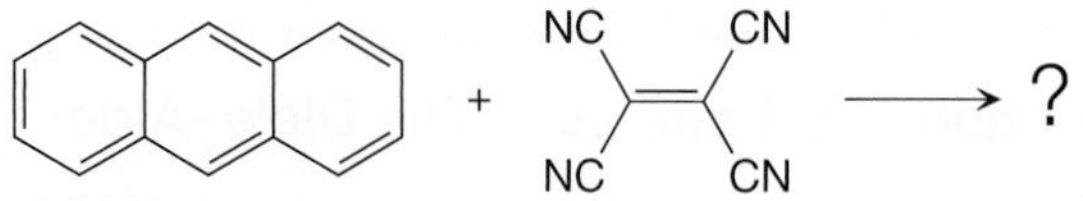
NC
CN
NC
CN
+
?

(a) Draw two possible products that can form from this reaction.

(b) Explain why anthracene can readily undergo a Diels–Alder reaction, whereas benzene does not.

26.10 The following is an example of a hetero Diels–Alder reaction, meaning that a non-carbon atom (in this case, a N atom) is involved in bond formation and bond breaking. Draw the curved arrows necessary to account for this transformation.

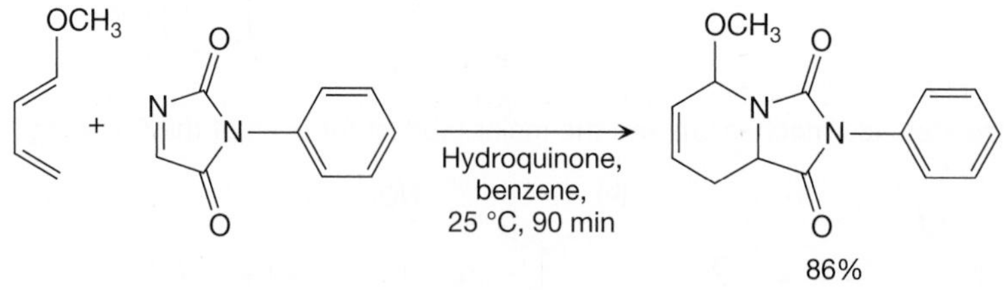
OCH3
O
N
N
O
+
Hydroquinone,
benzene,
25 °C, 90 min
OCH3
O
N
N
O
86%

26.11 Draw the product of the following reaction, assuming that it takes place by a [6+4] cycloaddition. (You may ignore stereochemistry.)

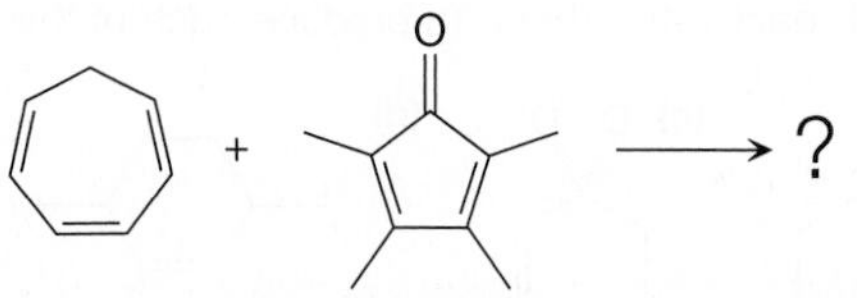
O
+
?

26.12 For each of the following reactions, **(a)** draw the curved arrows necessary for a concerted mechanism, **(b)** draw the transition state, **(c)** determine whether each transition state is aromatic or antiaromatic, and **(d)** on the basis of your answer to part (c), determine whether the reaction is thermally allowed or thermally forbidden.

(1)

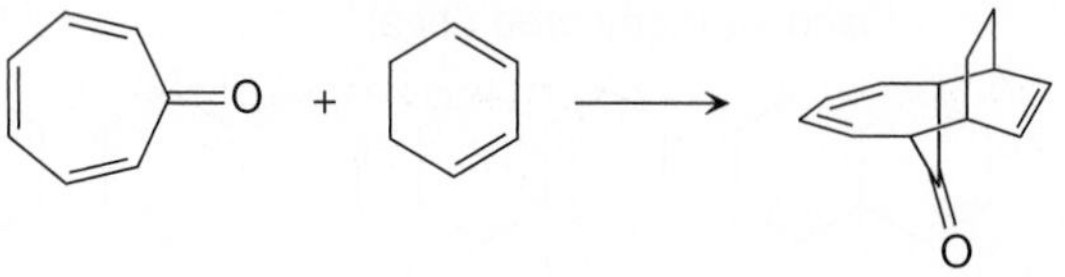
O
+
O

(2)

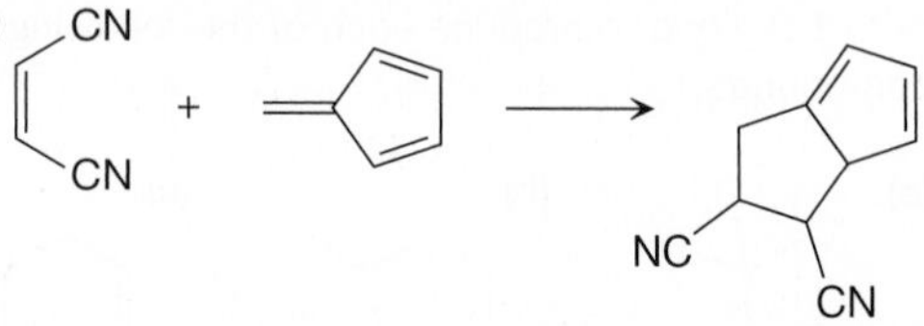
CN
CN
+
NC
CN

(3)

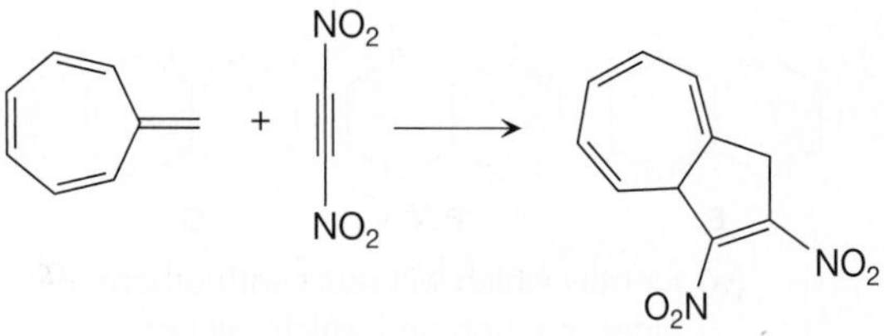
NO2
+
NO2
NO2
O2N

26.13 The Diels–Alder reaction is not the only pericyclic reaction involving the cyclic flow of six electrons over six atoms. Other examples include *electrocyclic reactions*, *Cope rearrangements*, and *Claisen rearrangements*, the curved arrow notations for which are shown here. Complete each of these reactions by drawing the product.

(a)

Electrocyclic reaction

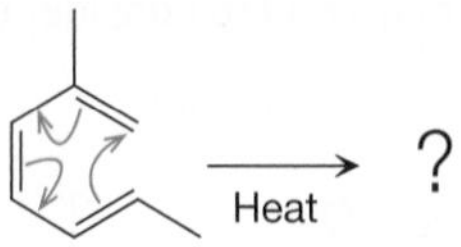
Heat
?

(b)

Cope rearrangement

Heat
?

(c)

Claisen rearrangement

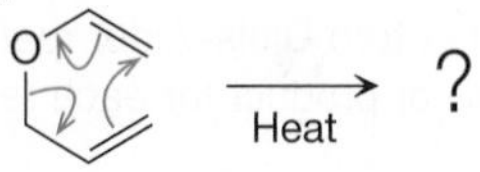
O
Heat
?

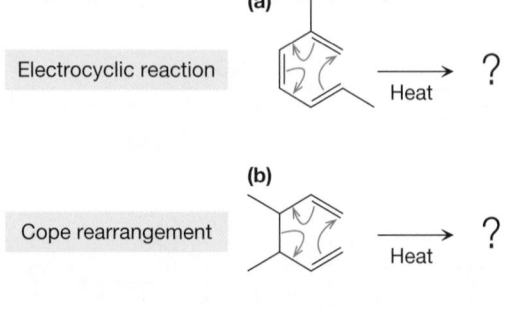

Section 26.3 Substituent Effects on the Reaction Rate

26.14 Rank the following in order from slowest to fastest rate of reaction in a Diels–Alder reaction with buta-1,3-diene.

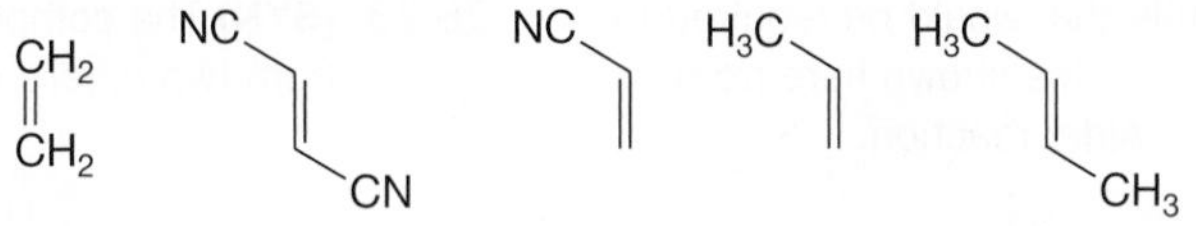
CH2
CH2
NC
CN
NC
H3C
H3C
CH3

N O P Q R

26.15 Consider the following dienes in a Diels–Alder reaction with ethene. Which will react the fastest? Which will react the slowest? Explain.

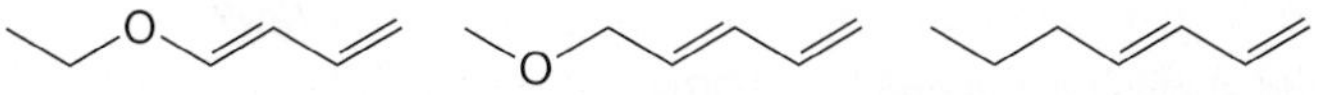
O
O

S T U

26.16 Which of the molecules shown here will react faster as a dienophile in a Diels–Alder reaction with buta-1,3-diene? Explain.

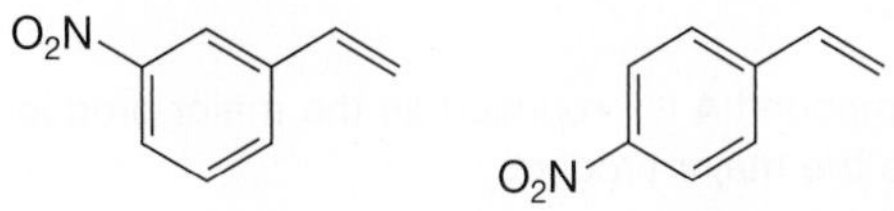
O2N
O2N

V W

26.17 Which of the molecules shown here will react faster as a dienophile in a Diels–Alder reaction with buta-1,3-diene? Explain.

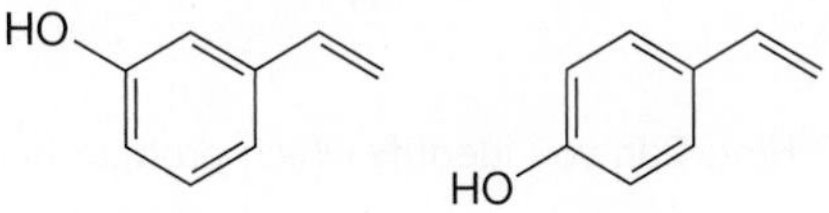
HO
HO

X Y

26.18 **(SYN)** The compound shown here can be produced from two *different* Diels–Alder reactions.

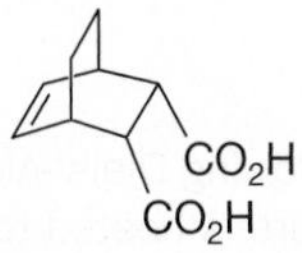
CO2H
CO2H

(a) Draw the reactants that can be used for each Diels–Alder reaction.

(b) Which would be the better route? Why?

Sections 26.4 and 26.5 Stereochemistry and Regiochemistry of Diels–Alder Reactions

26.19 Draw the complete, detailed mechanism and major product for each of the following Diels–Alder reactions. Pay attention to stereochemistry. *Hint*: You may need to consider conformations and orientations other than the ones shown.

(a)

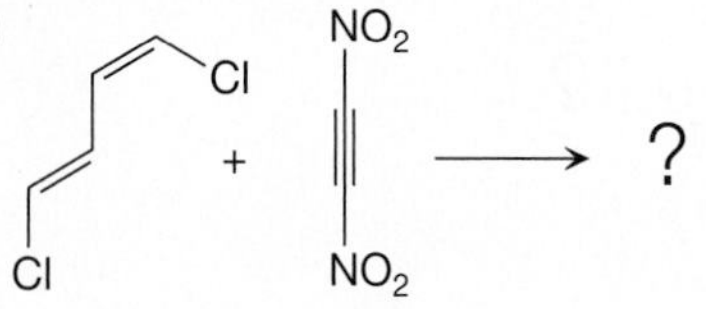

Cl
NO2
+
NO2
Cl
?

(b)

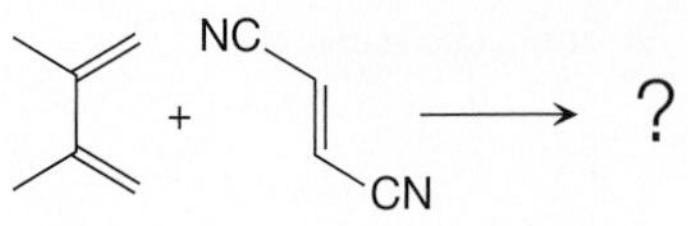

NC
+
CN
?

(c)

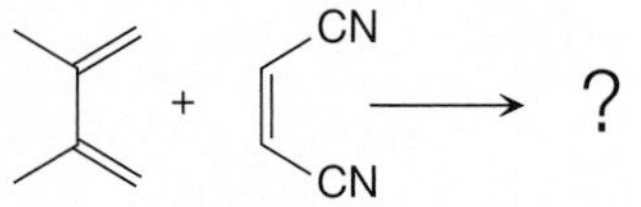

CN
+
CN
?

(d)

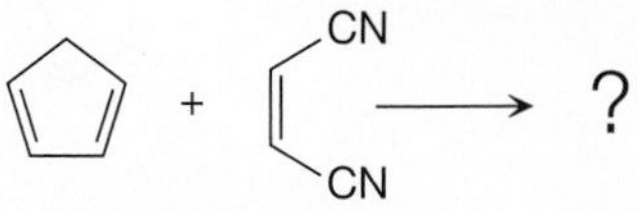

CN
+
CN
?

26.20 The following are examples of hetero Diels–Alder reactions (see Problem 26.10). Draw the complete, detailed mechanism and predict the major product for each reaction, paying particular attention to stereochemistry.

(a)

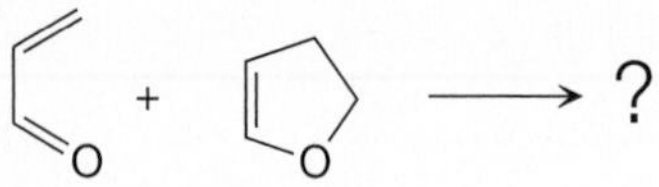

+
O
O
?

(b)

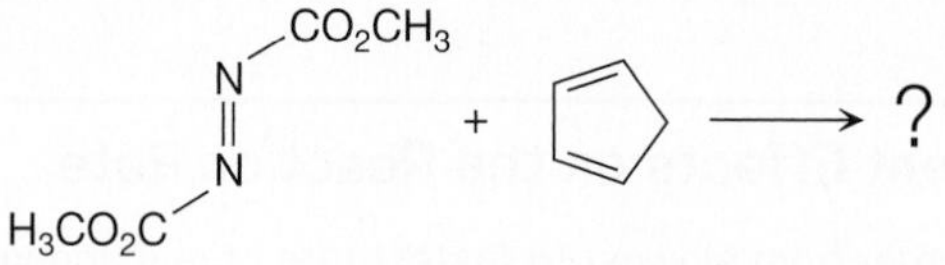

CO2CH3
N
N
H3CO2C
+
?

26.21 **(SYN)** Draw the dienophile that would be required to generate each of the molecules shown here from buta-1,3-diene in a Diels–Alder reaction.

(a)

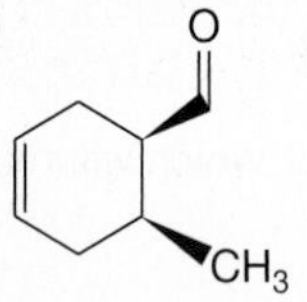

O
CH3

(b)

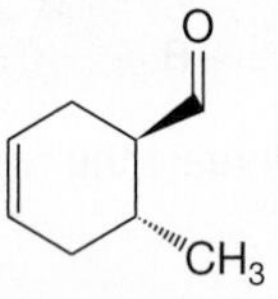

O
CH3

26.22 **(SYN)** If the compound shown here is one of two enantiomers produced from a Diels–Alder reaction with ethene, then what is the structure of the diene that would have been required?

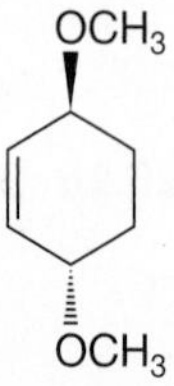

OCH3
OCH3

26.23 **(SYN)** The compound shown here can be produced from two different Diels–Alder reactions.

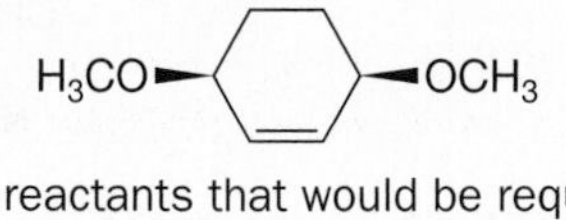

H3CO
OCH3

(a) Draw the reactants that would be required for each reaction.

(b) Which set of reactants would be the better choice? Why?

26.24 When the following Diels–Alder reaction takes place at 0 °C, compound **A** is produced as the major product. When the product mixture is heated to 60 °C, compound **B** is produced as the major product.

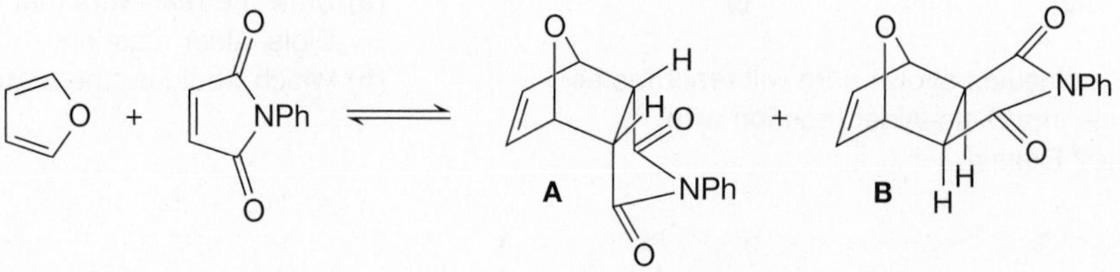

O
+
O
NPh
O
O
H
H
O
A
NPh
O
+
O
O
NPh
O
B
H
H

(a) Which product is produced faster in this Diels–Alder reaction? *Hint*: Can you identify which product is endo and which one is exo?

(b) Which product is more stable? Why? *Hint*: It might help to build a model.

26.25 Draw the complete, detailed mechanism and major product for each of the following Diels–Alder reactions. Pay attention to regiochemistry. *Hint*: You may need to consider conformations and orientations other than the ones shown.

(a)

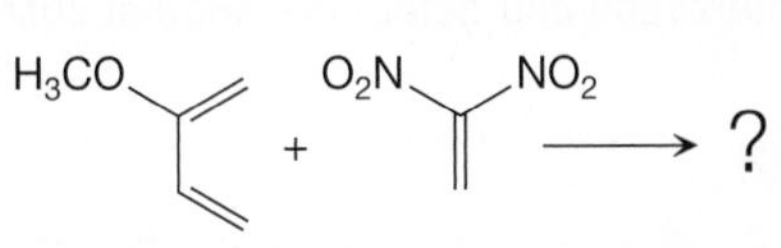

(b)

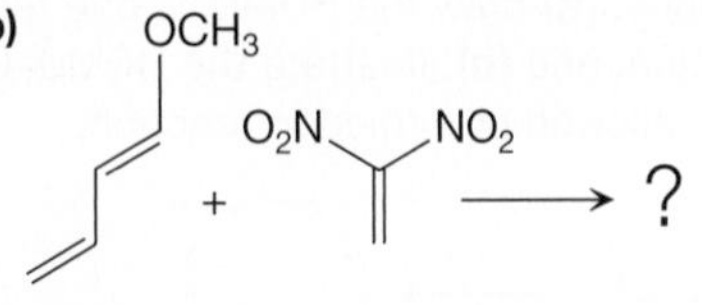

26.26 Two constitutional isomers can be produced from this Diels–Alder reaction.

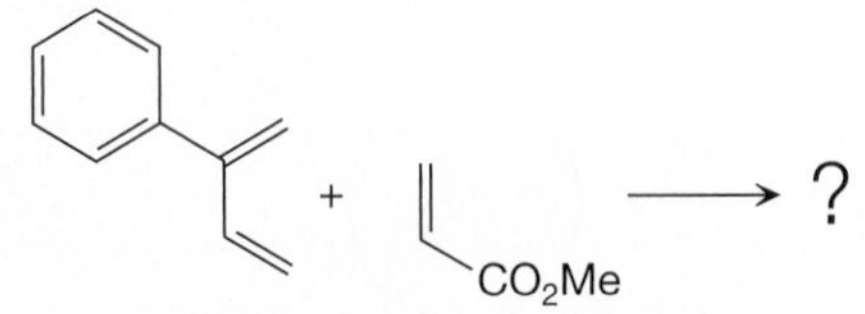

(a) Draw the complete, detailed mechanism for the formation of each isomer.
(b) Determine which isomer is the major product. *Hint*: Is a phenyl ring electron-rich or electron-poor?

Section 26.6 The Reversibility of Diels–Alder Reactions; the Retro Diels–Alder Reaction

26.27 What temperature would be required to achieve $K_{eq} = 120$ for the prototypical Diels–Alder reaction in Equation 26-27 (p. 1271)? (The values of $\Delta H°$ and $\Delta S°$ can be obtained from the text.)

26.28 When cyclohexene is heated to *very* high temperatures, a retro Diels–Alder reaction takes place. Draw the curved arrows and the products for this reaction.

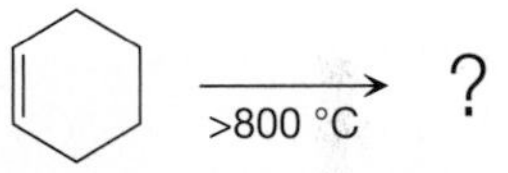

26.29 Consider the Diels–Alder reaction below, for which $\Delta H°_{rxn} = -54$ kJ/mol and $\Delta S°_{rxn} = -151$ J/mol·K. **(a)** Is this reaction reversible at room temperature? **(b)** Estimate the temperature at which the equilibrium constant equals 1.

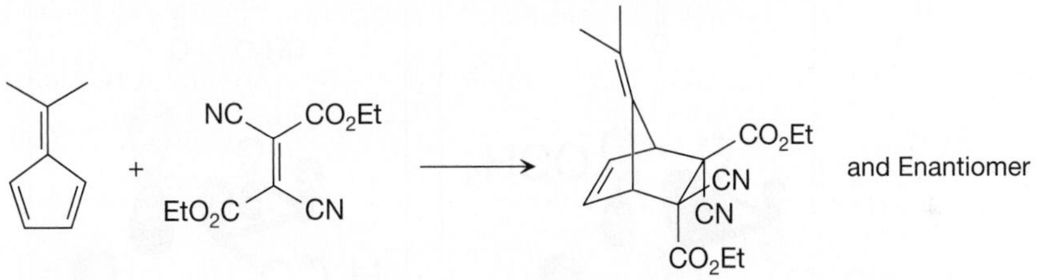

26.30 Draw the retro Diels–Alder mechanism for the product shown in Problem 26.29.

26.31 Draw the retro Diels–Alder mechanism and product for each of the compounds shown here. Which retro Diels–Alder reaction would require the lower temperature? Why?

(a)

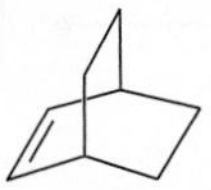

(b)

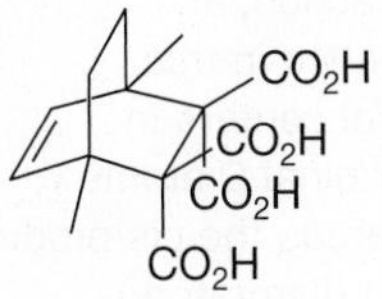

26.32 Draw a complete, detailed mechanism to account for the reaction shown here, which scrambles the isotopic labeling.

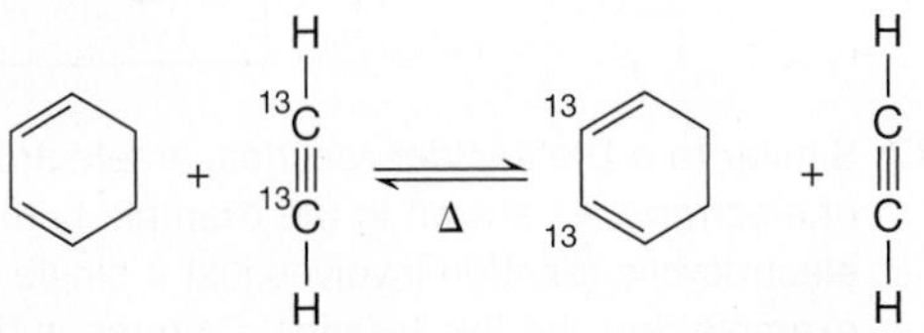

26.33 Using the reaction shown in Problem 26.24, draw the mechanism that converts **A** to **B** when the product is heated.

Section 26.7 A Molecular Orbital Picture of the Diels–Alder Reaction

26.34 For each of the following reactions, **(a)** draw the HOMO of one reactant and the LUMO of the other, assuming that both reactants are in their ground state, and **(b)** illustrate the HOMO–LUMO interaction and determine whether such an interaction leads to a thermally allowed or forbidden reaction.

(1)

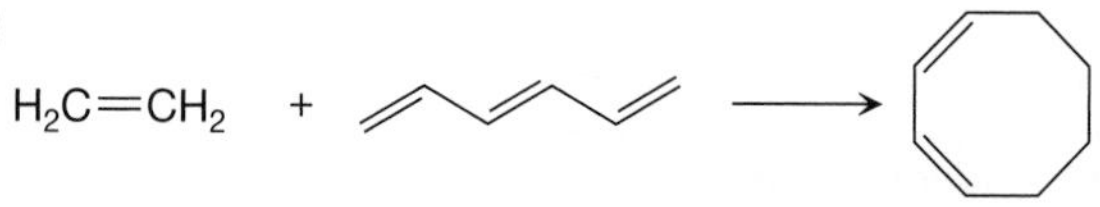

H2C=CH2
+

(2)

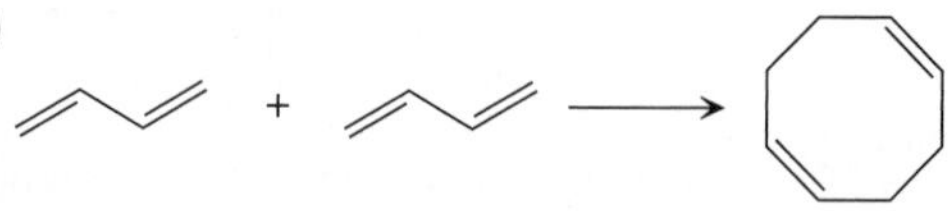

(3)

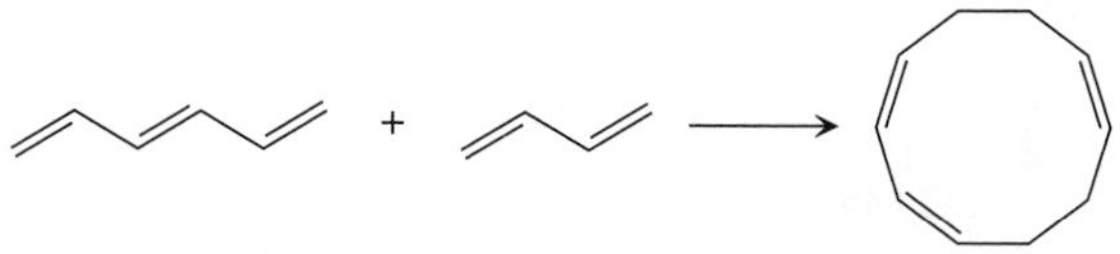

26.35 Repeat Problem 26.34, assuming that *one* of the reactants is in its lowest excited state. On the basis of your answers, which of the reactions are photochemically allowed?

26.36 In Section 26.5, we learned how to use resonance hybrids to understand the regiochemistry of Diels–Alder reactions. Frontier MO theory, on the other hand, explains the regiochemistry by taking into account the extent of orbital overlap between the frontier MOs. Consider the diene and dienophile shown here having the two different approaches indicated. In both cases, the *p* orbital contributions are shown for the pertinent frontier MOs. The relative contributions by the *p* AOs to the frontier MOs are indicated by the *p* AO sizes. Use this information to explain which approach is favored.

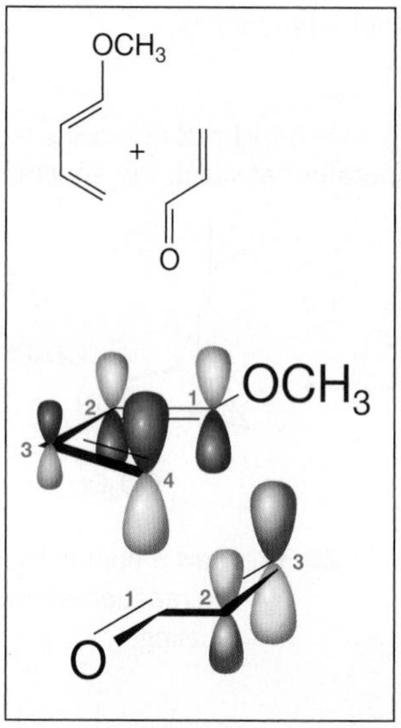

OCH3
+
O
OCH3
1
2
3
4
1
2
3
O

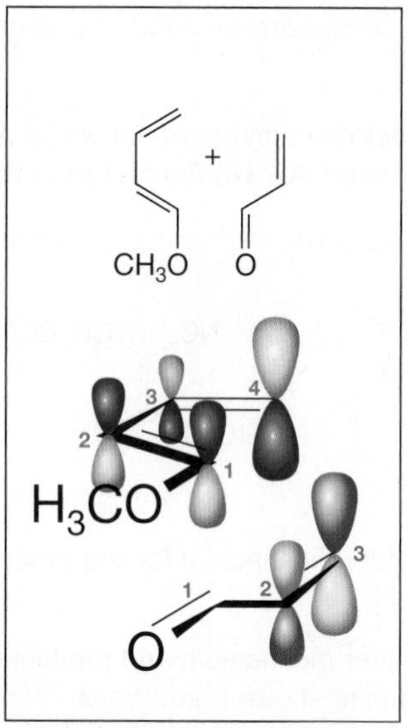

+
CH3O
O
H3CO
1
2
3
4
1
2
3
O

26.37 Similar to a Diels–Alder reaction, an electrocyclic reaction involves a cyclic flow of electrons, as shown in the example here. Unlike a Diels–Alder reaction, an electrocyclic reaction involves just a single conjugated π system. Notice in this example that the two terminal C atoms in the reactant become chiral centers in the product. As shown, the trans product would be formed if the terminal C atoms rotate in the same direction (i.e., conrotatory) to close the ring, whereas the cis product would be formed if those C atoms rotate in opposite directions (i.e., disrotatory).

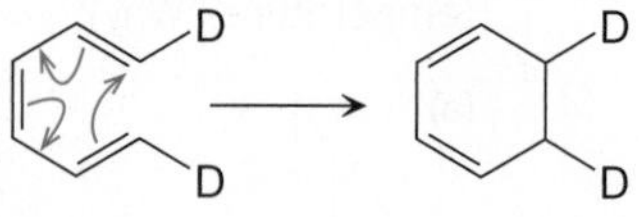

D
D
D
D

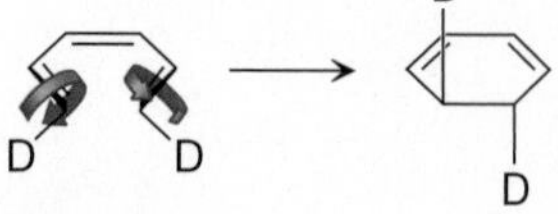

D
D
D
D

Conrotatory

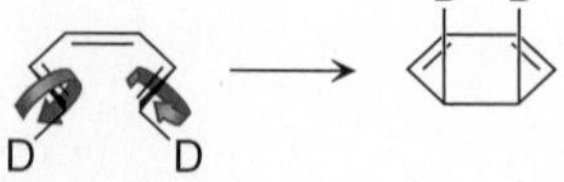

D
D
D
D

Disrotatory

The favored mechanism (conrotatory or disrotatory) is the one for which the HOMO, during rotation, exhibits constructive interference among the contributing *p* AOs on the terminal C atoms. With this information, determine whether the cis or trans product is favored **(a)** thermally and **(b)** photochemically.

26.38 Repeat Problem 26.37 for the electrocyclic reaction shown here.

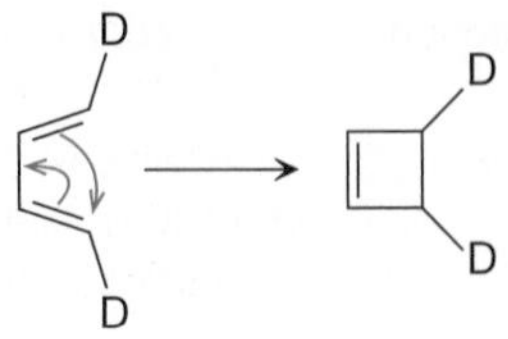
D
D
D
D

Sections 26.8 and 26.9 Syn Dihydroxylation and Oxidative Cleavage of Alkenes and Alkynes

26.39 Draw the organic products of each of the following reactions.

(a)
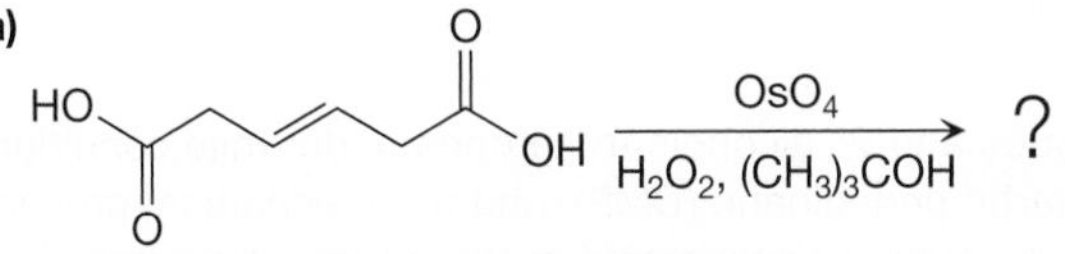
HO
O
O
OH
OsO_4
H_2O_2, $(CH_3)_3COH$
?

(b)
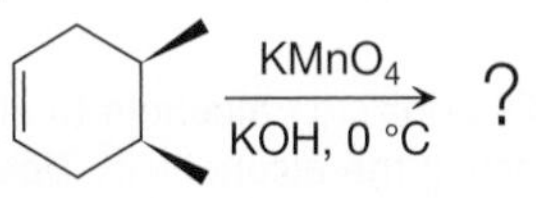
$KMnO_4$
KOH, 0 °C
?

(c)
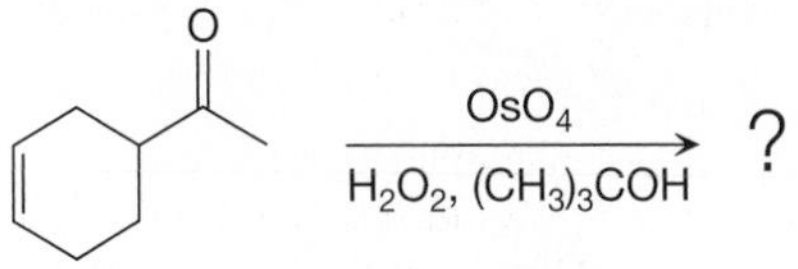
O
OsO_4
H_2O_2, $(CH_3)_3COH$
?

(d)
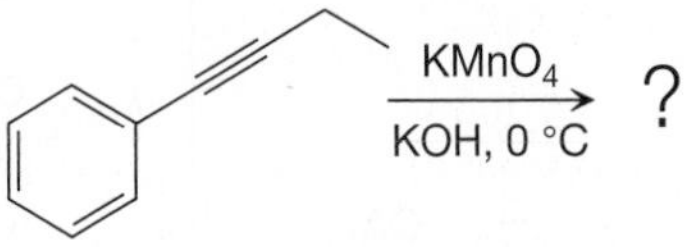
$KMnO_4$
KOH, 0 °C
?

26.40 **(SYN)** Show how each of the following compounds can be produced from an alkene or alkyne.

(a)
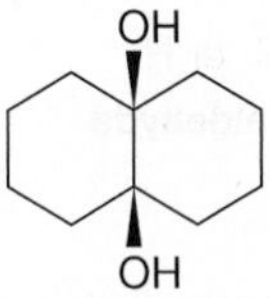
OH
OH

(b)
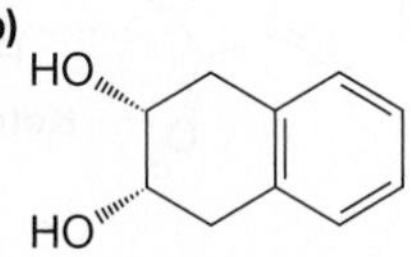
HO
HO

(c)
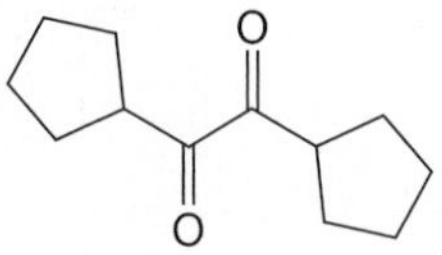
O
O

(d)
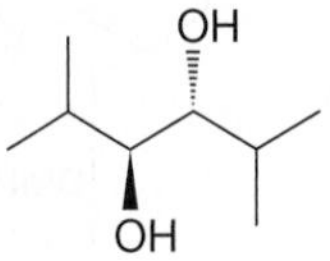
OH
OH

26.41 Draw the major products of each of the following reactions.

(a)
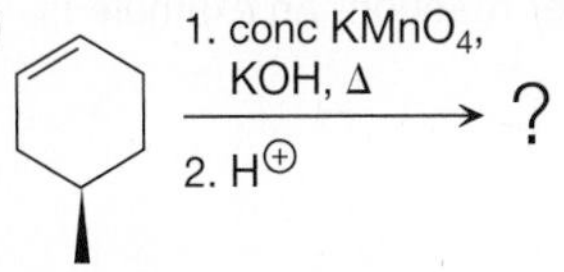
1. conc $KMnO_4$,
KOH, Δ
2. $H^{\oplus}$
?

(b)
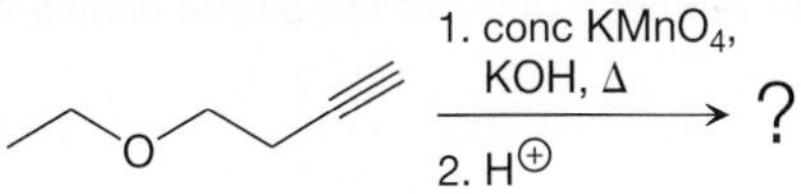
O
1. conc $KMnO_4$,
KOH, Δ
2. $H^{\oplus}$
?

(c)
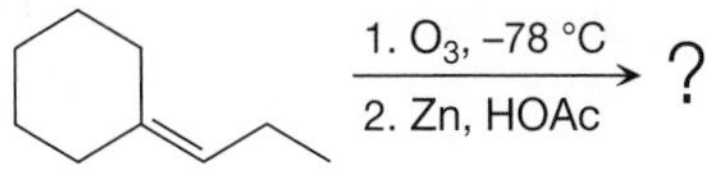
1. O_3, −78 °C
2. Zn, HOAc
?

(d)
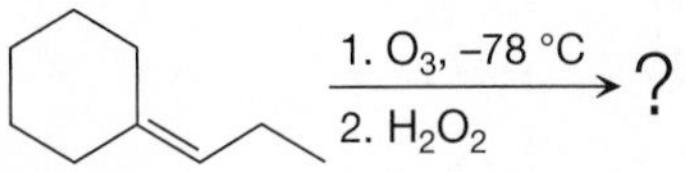
1. O_3, −78 °C
2. H_2O_2
?

(e)
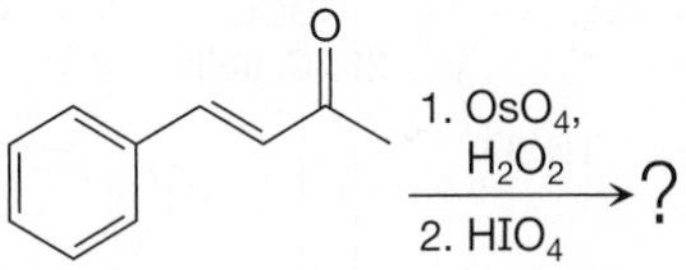
O
1. OsO_4,
H_2O_2
2. HIO_4
?

(f)
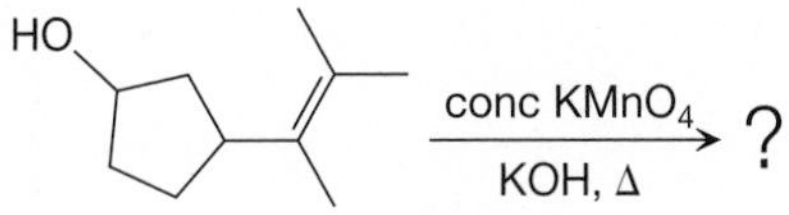
HO
conc $KMnO_4$
KOH, Δ
?

26.42 Draw the structure of the reactant that produces the molecules shown for each of the following reactions.

(a)
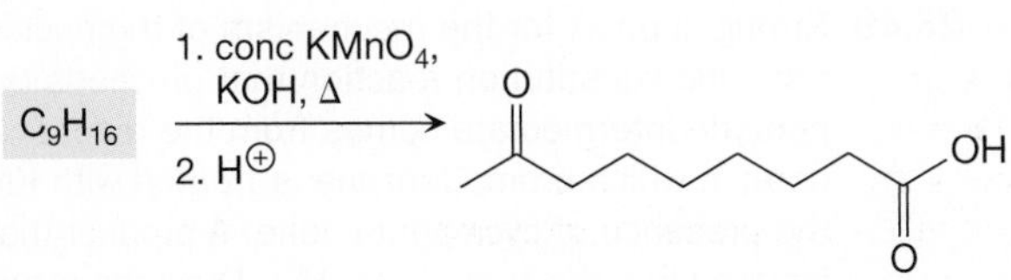
C_9H_{16}
1. conc $KMnO_4$,
KOH, Δ
2. $H^{\oplus}$
O
OH
O

(b)
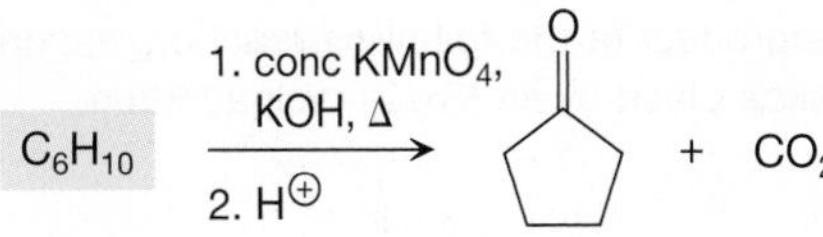
C_6H_{10}
1. conc $KMnO_4$,
KOH, Δ
2. $H^{\oplus}$
O
+ CO_2

(c)
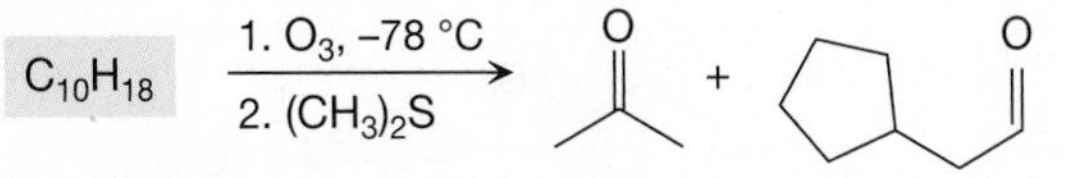
$C_{10}H_{18}$
1. O_3, −78 °C
2. $(CH_3)_2S$
O
+
O

(d)
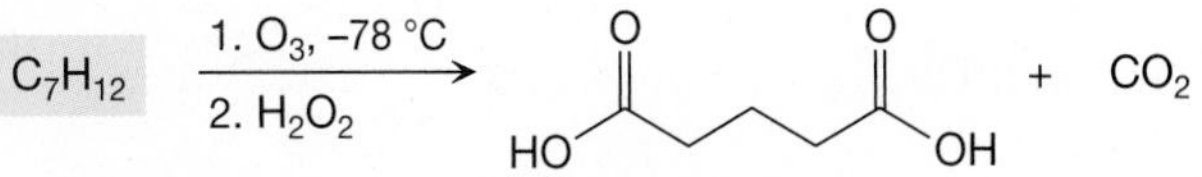
C_7H_{12}
1. O_3, −78 °C
2. H_2O_2
O
O
HO
OH
+ CO_2

26.43 Draw the major product of the following reaction.

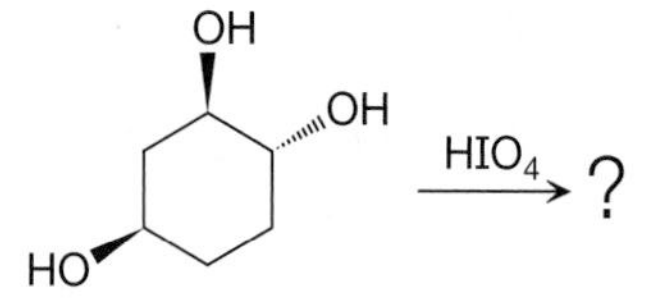
OH
OH
HO
HIO_4
?

26.44 Rubber degrades when it is exposed to ozone for an extended time—a phenomenon called ozone cracking. Rubber is a natural polymer (a long-chain molecule with a regular repeating structural unit), a portion of which is shown here. Explain why ozone cracking occurs.

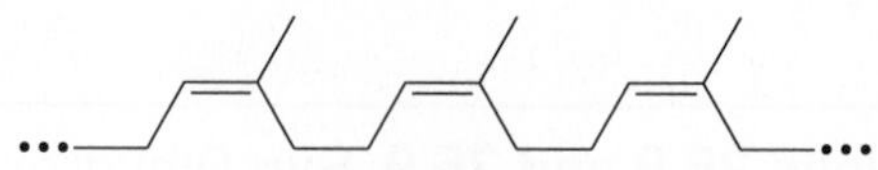

Rubber

Integrated Problems

26.45 The Dess–Martin oxidation will oxidize 1° alcohols to aldehydes and 2° alcohols to ketones under mild conditions. The oxidation is carried out by reacting the alcohol with Dess–Martin periodinane (DMP), and the mechanism proceeds through the key intermediate shown. Draw the curved arrow notation for conversion of the intermediate into products.

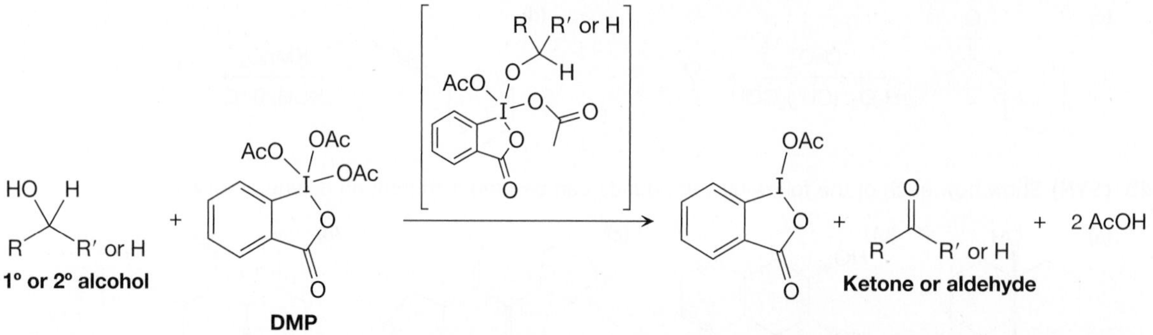
HO H
R R′ or H
1° or 2° alcohol
AcO OAc OAc
DMP
R R′ or H
AcO
H
OAc
+ 2 AcOH
R R′ or H
Ketone or aldehyde

26.46 A reaction takes place when *cis*-1,3,9-decatriene is heated. The product of that reaction, when treated with excess Br_2 in CCl_4, yields a compound whose formula is $C_{10}H_{16}Br_2$. What is the product of the first reaction?

26.47 T. R. Hoye and co-workers reported the synthetic utility of the alkyne analog of a Diels–Alder reaction. An example is shown below.

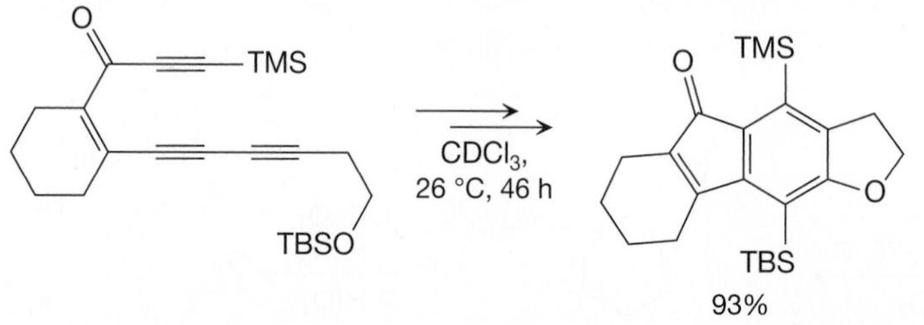
TMS
TBSO
$CDCl_3$,
26 °C, 46 h
TMS
TBS
93%

A [4+2] cycloaddition is believed to produce a benzyne intermediate that is quickly "trapped." Show the benzyne intermediate that would be produced in the above reaction.

26.48 Draw the product of the following reaction, assuming that it takes place by an [8+2] cycloaddition.

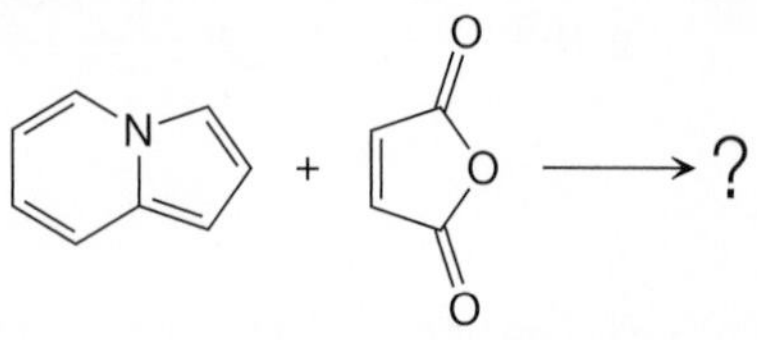
N
?

26.49 Strong support for the mechanism of the nucleophilic aromatic substitution reaction that proceeds through a benzyne intermediate comes from the reaction shown here, in which bromobenzene is treated with KNH_2 in the presence of cyclopentadiene. A product that is isolated has the formula $C_{11}H_{10}$. Draw the structure of that product, and explain how it validates the production of a benzyne intermediate.

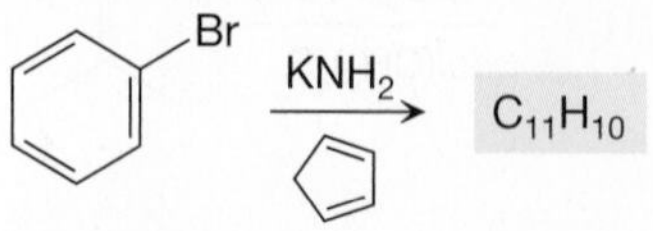
Br
KNH_2
$C_{11}H_{10}$

26.50 **(SYN)** Show how you would synthesize this compound beginning with benzene. *Hint*: See Problem 26.49.

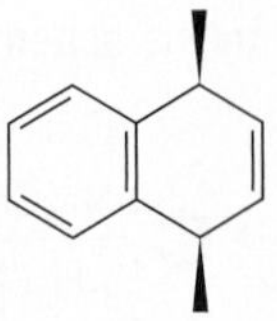

26.51 **(SYN)** The compound shown here cannot be synthesized *directly* from a Diels–Alder reaction.

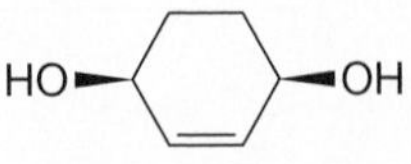

HO
OH

(a) Why not? *Hint*: Examine the reactants that would be required.

(b) What change(s) can be made to the synthesis to get around this problem?

26.52 **(SYN)** Show how to carry out this transformation using any reagents necessary.

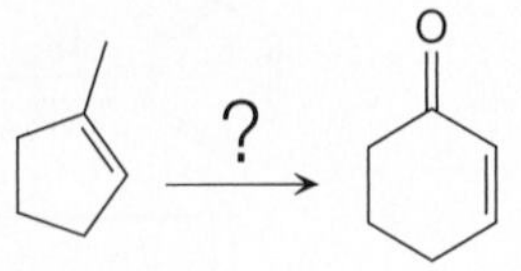

?
O

26.53 Gibberellic acid is a plant hormone that controls the development of plants. At various points in their synthesis of gibberellic acid, E. J. Corey and co-workers incorporated the Diels–Alder reactions below. Draw the complete, detailed mechanism and the major product of each of these reactions. *Hint*: In the first reaction, which C═C bond of the dienophile is more electron-poor?

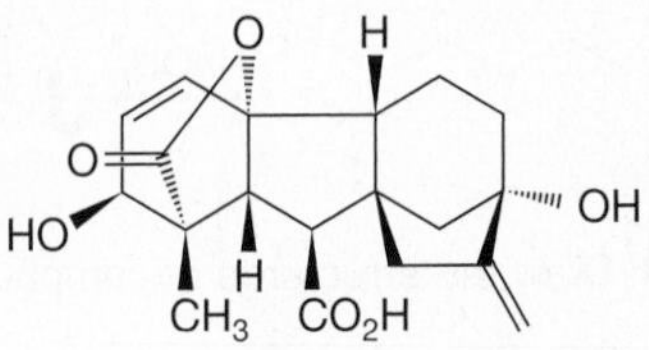

O
H
O
HO
H
OH
CH_3
CO_2H

Gibberellic acid

(a)

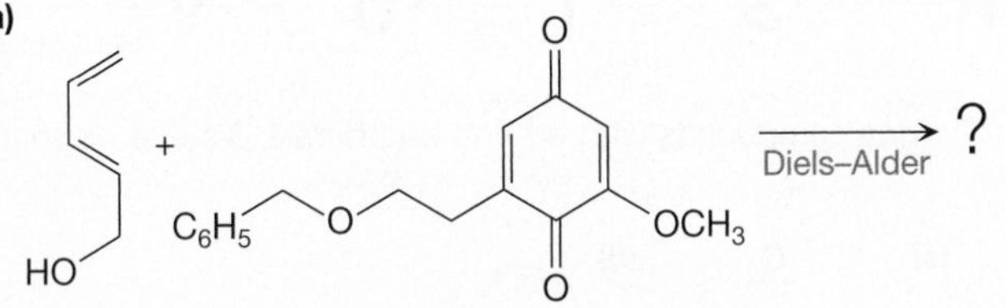

O
+
C_6H_5
O
OCH_3
HO
O
Diels–Alder
?

(b)

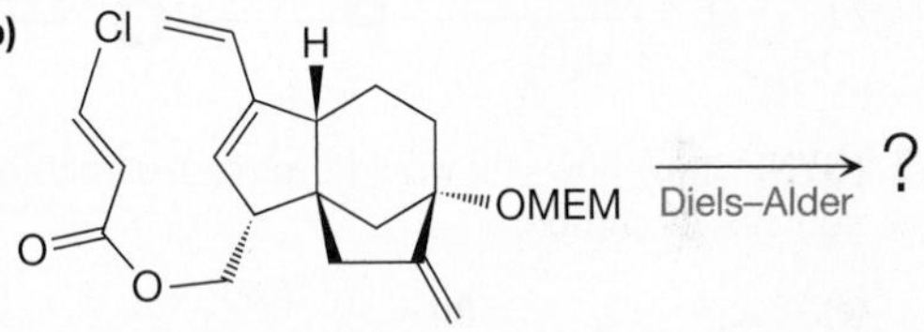

Cl
H
OMEM
O
O
Diels–Alder
?

26.54 Myrocin C is an antitumor antibiotic. In their synthesis of myrocin C, S. J. Danishefsky and co-workers incorporated the Diels–Alder reactions below. Draw the complete, detailed mechanism and the major product of each of these reactions.

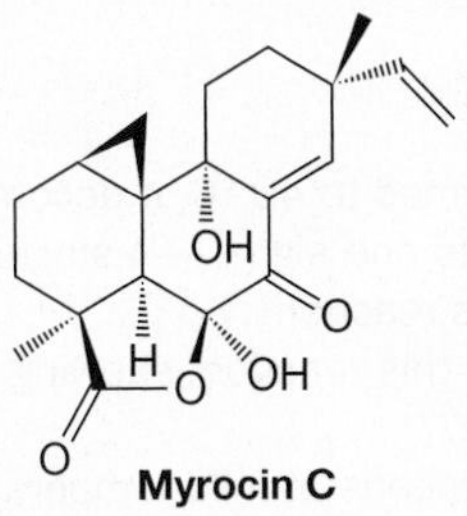

OH
O
H
O
OH
O

Myrocin C

(a)

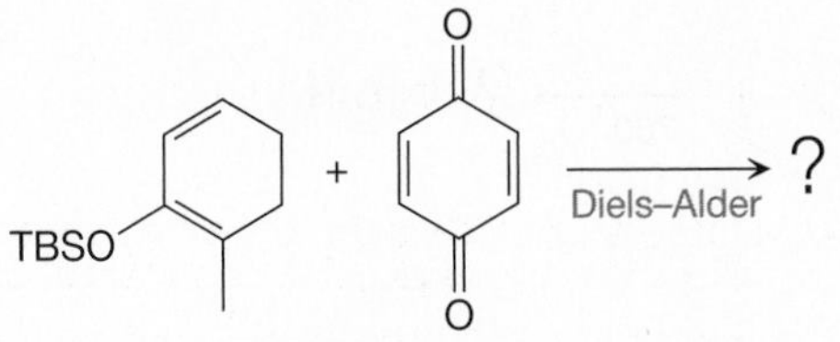

TBSO
+
O
O
Diels–Alder
?

(b)

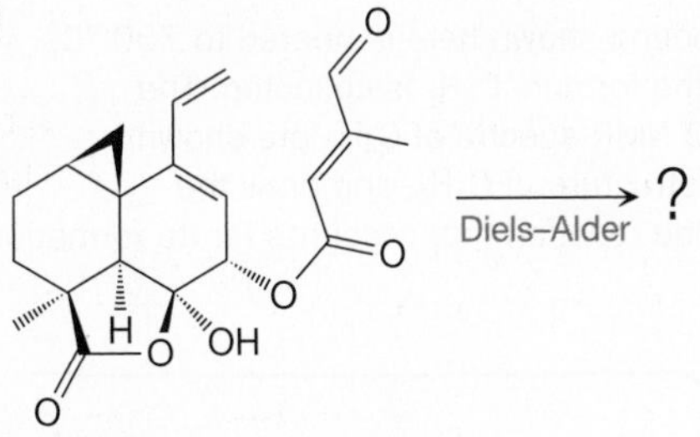

O
O
O
H
O
OH
O
Diels–Alder
?

26.55 Draw the structures of compounds **A–I** in the following synthesis scheme.

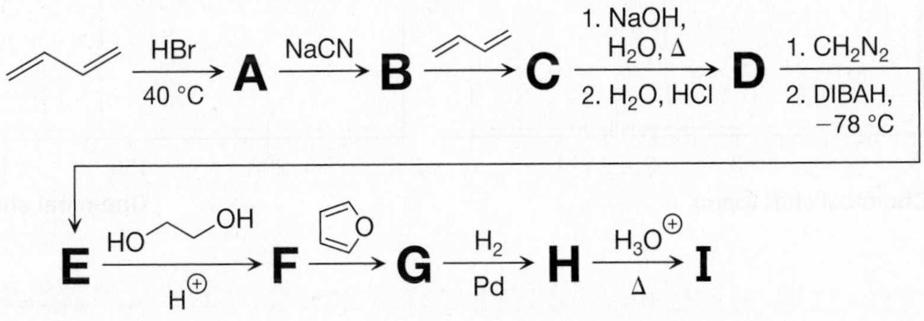

HBr
40 °C
A
NaCN
B
C
1. NaOH, H_2O, Δ
2. H_2O, HCl
D
1. CH_2N_2
2. DIBAH, −78 °C
E
HO
OH
$H^{\oplus}$
F
O
G
H_2
Pd
H
$H_3O^{\oplus}$
Δ
I

26.56 Draw the structures of compounds **A–I** in the following synthesis scheme.

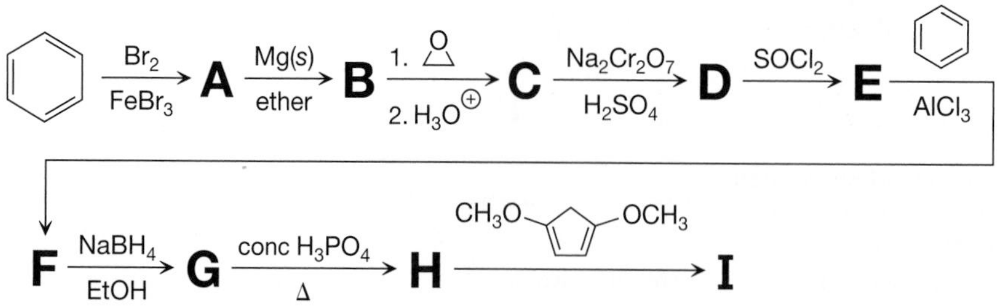
Br2
FeBr3
A
Mg(s)
ether
B
1.
2. H3O⊕
C
Na2Cr2O7
H2SO4
D
SOCl2
E
AlCl3
F
NaBH4
EtOH
G
conc H3PO4
Δ
H
CH3O
OCH3
I

26.57 Draw the structures of compounds **J–O** in the following synthesis scheme.

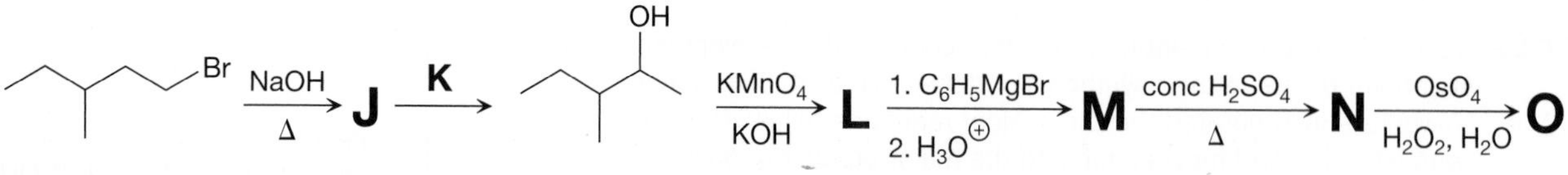
Br
NaOH
Δ
J
K
OH
KMnO4
KOH
L
1. C6H5MgBr
2. H3O⊕
M
conc H2SO4
Δ
N
OsO4
H2O2, H2O
O

26.58 Draw the structures of compounds **P–W** in the following synthesis scheme.

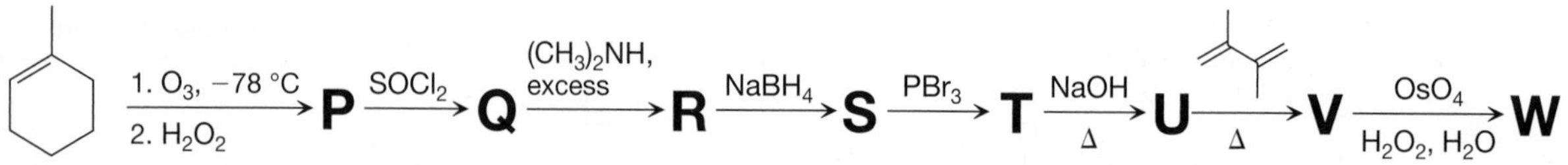
1. O3, −78 °C
2. H2O2
P
SOCl2
Q
(CH3)2NH,
excess
R
NaBH4
S
PBr3
T
NaOH
Δ
U
Δ
V
OsO4
H2O2, H2O
W

26.59 **(SYN)** Show how you would synthesize each of the following compounds with ethene and buta-1,3-diene as your only sources of carbon.

(a)

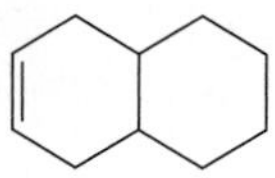

(b)

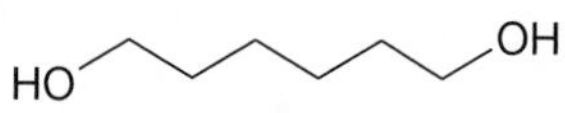
HO
OH

(c)

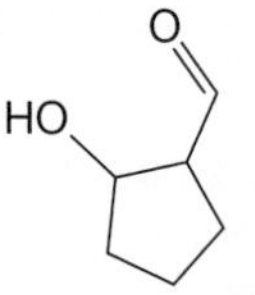
O
HO

(d)

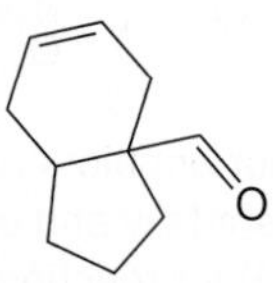
O

26.60 When the reactant shown is warmed to 40 °C, it decomposes into a compound whose ^1H NMR spectrum exhibits one signal—a singlet at 7.3 ppm.

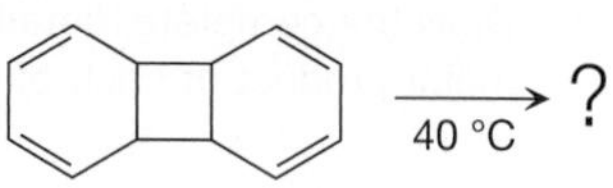
40 °C
?

(a) Draw the mechanism for this reaction.

(b) Draw the transition state for this reaction, showing that it proceeds through an antiaromatic transition state.

(c) Explain why this reaction proceeds at mild temperatures, even though it proceeds through an antiaromatic transition state.

26.61 When the compound shown here is heated to 700 °C, a product with the formula C_4H_6 is collected. The ^1H NMR and ^{13}C NMR spectra of C_4H_6 are shown here. Draw the structure of C_4H_6, and draw the mechanism of the reaction that accounts for its formation.

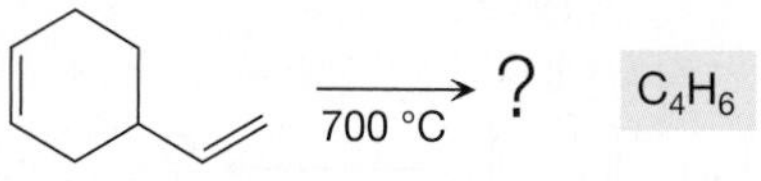
700 °C
?
C4H6

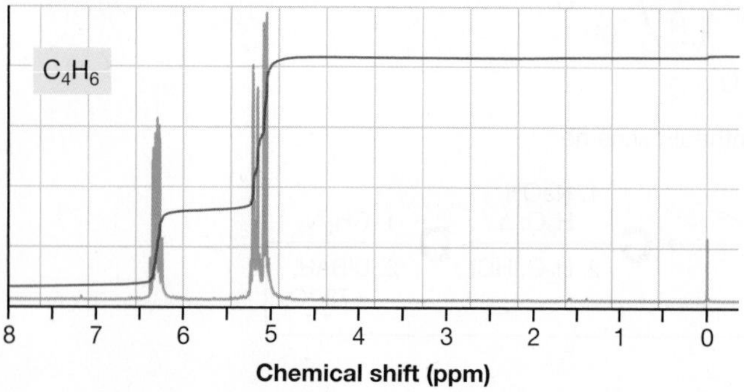
C4H6
8
7
6
5
4
3
2
1
0
Chemical shift (ppm)

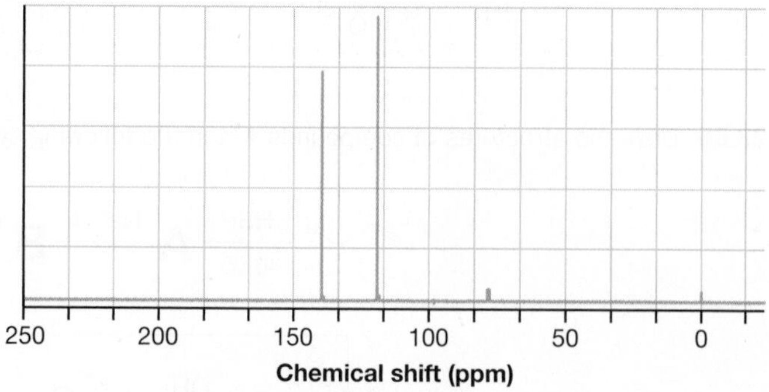
250
200
150
100
50
0
Chemical shift (ppm)

26.62 When the compound shown here is heated, ethene gas is evolved, and a product with the formula $C_{14}H_8O_2$ is formed. The ^1H NMR and ^{13}C NMR spectra of $C_{14}H_8O_2$ are shown. (There are two signals >150 ppm in the ^{13}C NMR spectrum. Recall that the ^{13}C NMR signal at 77 ppm is from the $CDCl_3$ solvent.)

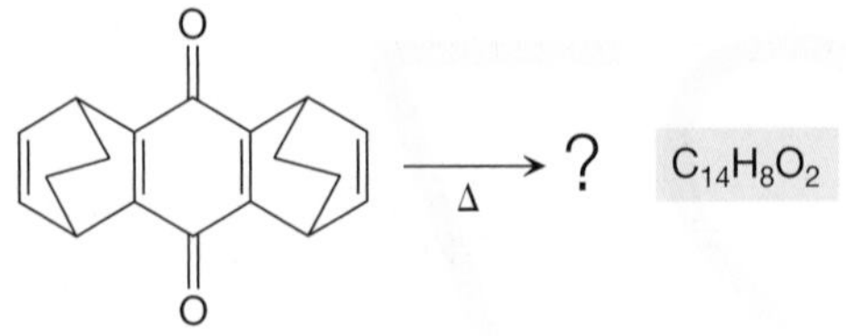

Δ
?
C14H8O2

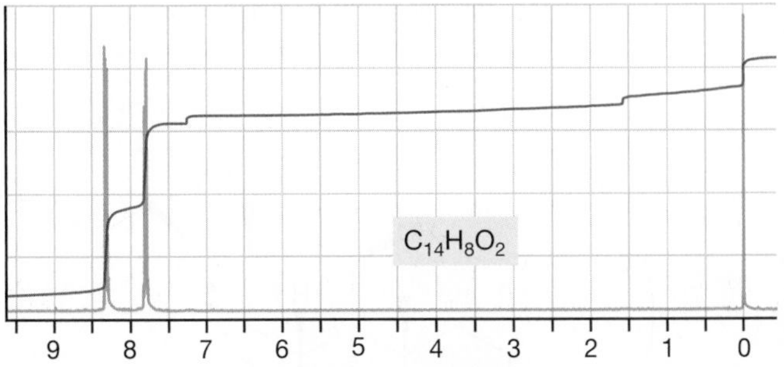

C14H8O2
9 8 7 6 5 4 3 2 1 0
Chemical shift (ppm)

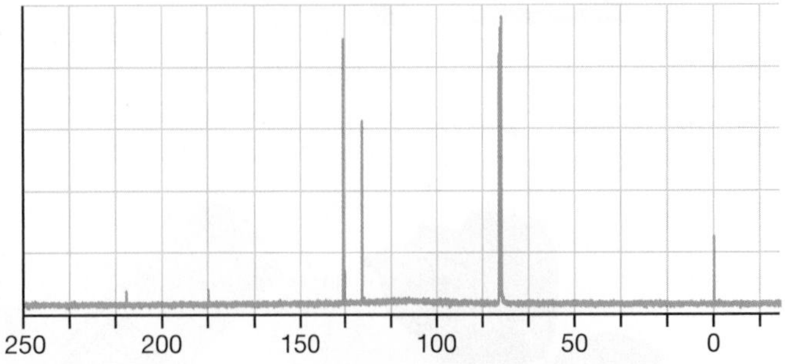

250 200 150 100 50 0
Chemical shift (ppm)

(a) Draw the structure of $C_{14}H_8O_2$.
(b) Draw the complete, detailed mechanism that accounts for its formation.
(c) What is the main driving force that favors the products of this reaction?

26.63 A compound with the formula C_6H_{10} is known to react with 1 molar equivalent of Br_2 in carbon tetrachloride. When C_6H_{10} was treated with a hot, basic solution of potassium permanganate, followed by acid workup, a product was formed whose IR spectrum exhibits a broad absorption of medium intensity from 2500 to 3300 cm^{-1} and a sharp, intense absorption near 1700 cm^{-1}. The ^1H NMR and ^{13}C NMR spectra of the product are shown. (The multiplet at 39 ppm is from the solvent, DMSO-d_6.) Draw the structure of C_6H_{10}.

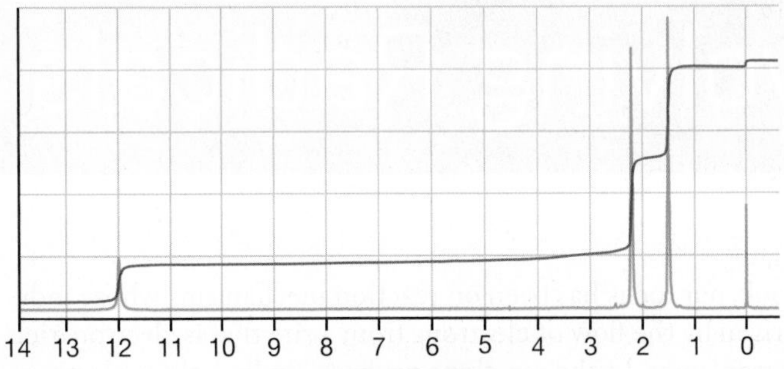

14 13 12 11 10 9 8 7 6 5 4 3 2 1 0
Chemical shift (ppm)

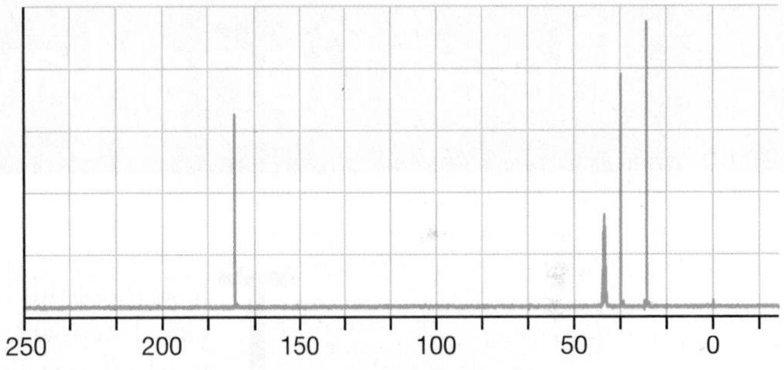

250 200 150 100 50 0
Chemical shift (ppm)

26.64 Heating the compound shown here at 225–235 °C for 8 h produced a new compound with the formula $C_{23}H_{16}N_2O$. The mechanism for this reaction is believed to consist of a [4+2] cycloaddition followed by a [4+2] cycloelimination. The ^1H NMR spectrum of the product contained the following signals: δ 8.33–8.25 and 7.58–6.97 (m, 14 H), 5.46 (s, 2 H).
(a) Draw the complete, detailed mechanism for this reaction.
(b) Draw the product.

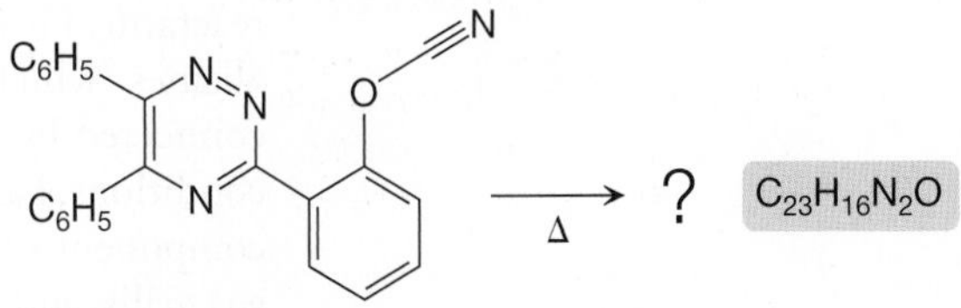

C6H5
C6H5
N
N
N
O
N
Δ
?
C23H16N2O

27

Hydrocortisone is a steroid hormone that is used to provide relief from itching, such as that resulting from exposure to poison ivy. The biosynthesis of hydrocortisone involves a radical reaction, the type of reaction we examine here in Chapter 27.

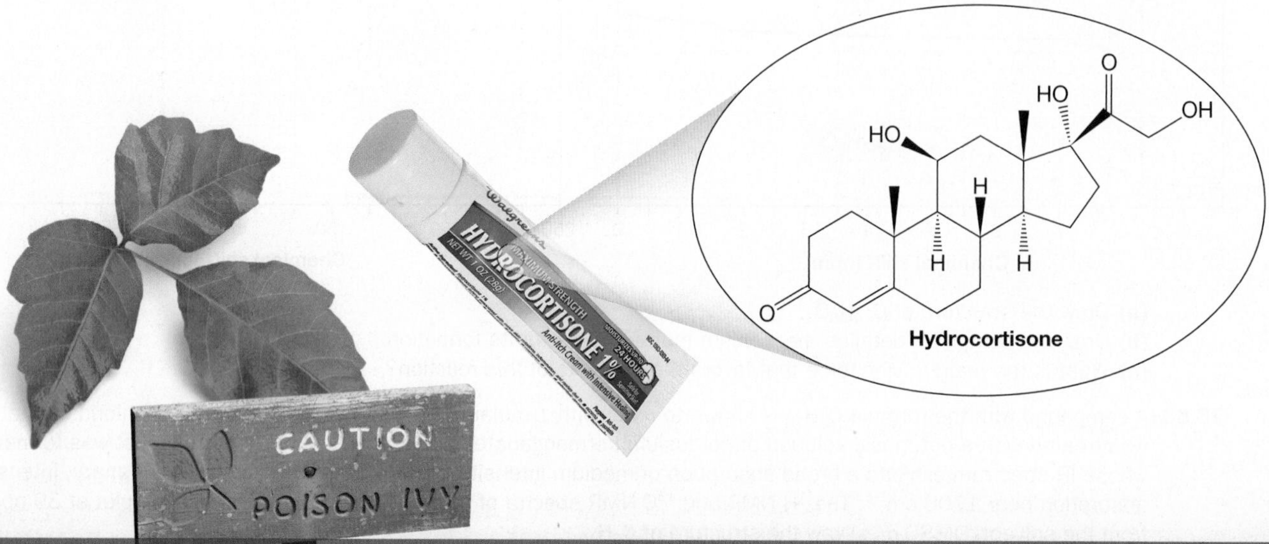

CAUTION
POISON IVY
HYDROCORTISONE 1%
HO
O
OH
H
Hydrocortisone

Reactions Involving Radicals

Throughout this book, our focus has been on reaction mechanisms whose individual steps are driven by the flow of electrons from a site that is electron-rich to one that is electron-poor. In the reactions we have studied, these electron-rich and electron-poor sites are established by the functional groups contained in the reactants. However, not all reactions are driven by such electron flow. For example, alkanes (which lack functional groups) consist of only carbon and hydrogen atoms connected by relatively nonpolar single bonds, yet alkanes will react under certain conditions. Familiarly, alkanes react *violently* in combustion: methane is the primary component of the natural gas used to heat homes; propane is burned in furnaces, gas grills, and camp stoves; and a mixture of relatively small hydrocarbons makes up the gasoline used in car engines. Without a well-defined electron-rich-to-electron-poor driving force in the reactants, it should be no surprise that these combustion reactions proceed by mechanisms that differ from the ones we have encountered thus far.

Although combustion reactions are important for energy use, we will focus on related reactions that are important in synthesis: halogenation of alkanes, alkene additions, and dissolving metal reductions. All of these reactions involve very highly reactive intermediates called *radicals*.

A **radical** is a species that possesses at least one unpaired electron.

Examples include the bromine atom and the methyl radical (**Figure 27-1**).

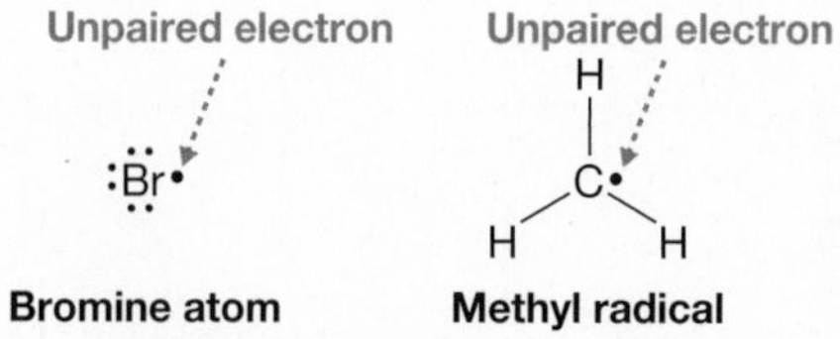

Unpaired electron
Unpaired electron
:Br•
C•
H
Bromine atom
Methyl radical

FIGURE 27-1 Examples of radicals Each of these species is a radical because it has one unpaired electron.

Chapter Outline

Radicals such as Br• and H_3C• behave somewhat differently from **closed-shell species**, in which all electrons are paired. Therefore, we will begin this chapter by looking at radical structure and stability, and then we will examine the most common elementary steps that radicals undergo. Finally, we will delve into the mechanisms of radical reactions that are useful for synthesis.

In addition to presenting new elementary steps, this chapter also introduces a new type of mechanism associated with radicals: the *chain reaction*. As we will see in Chapter 28, radical chain reactions are often used to synthesize *polymers* (very large molecules that have repeating subunits) such as plastics.

27.1 Homolysis: Curved Arrow Notation and Radical Initiators

SECTION 27.1 OBJECTIVES

You will be able to:

1. Determine the most likely bond that would undergo homolysis for a given molecule, and draw the corresponding curved arrow notation and products for the reaction.
2. Explain why radicals must typically be generated from radical initiators, and recognize common radical initiators.

Because radicals contain an unpaired electron, it is impossible for all of their atoms to have a complete octet. Therefore:

> Radicals are generally very unstable compared to analogous closed-shell species and are highly reactive, so they usually cannot be isolated for any substantial length of time.

Once a radical is produced, it will typically react very quickly with other species present, including the solvent.

By and large, radicals are produced from uncharged, closed-shell precursors by *homolytic bond dissociation*, or *homolysis*.

> **Homolytic bond dissociation**, or **homolysis**, is the breaking of a covalent bond, whereby the electrons making up that bond are distributed equally to the atoms that are disconnected.

Two bromine radicals (Br•), for example, can be produced from molecular bromine, Br_2, by homolysis of the Br—Br bond (Eq. 27-1). Homolysis of a C—H bond in methane (Eq. 27-2), on the other hand, produces a methyl radical (H_3C•) and a hydrogen radical (H•).

Elementary Step
Homolysis Elementary Step

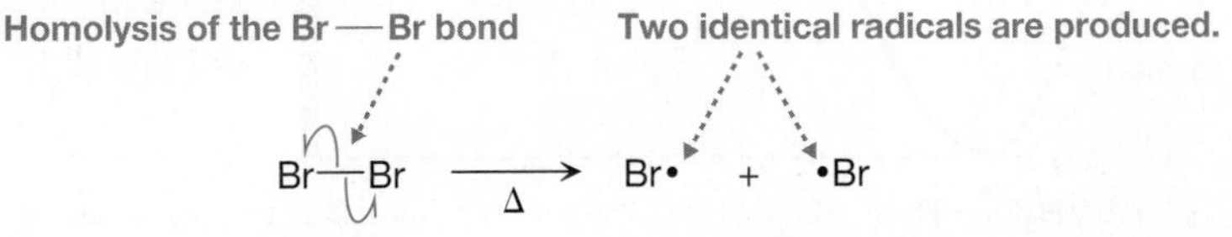

Homolysis of the Br—Br bond
Two identical radicals are produced.
Br—Br
Δ
Br•
+
•Br

(27-1)

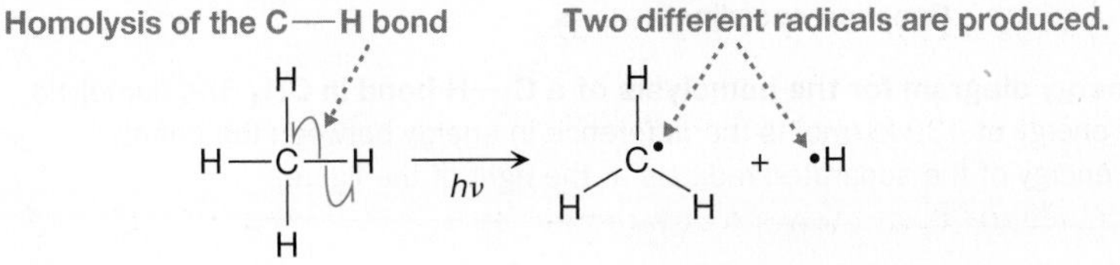

Homolysis of the C—H bond
Two different radicals are produced.
H—C—H
hν
+
•H

(27-2)

The curved arrow notation used to describe homolysis differs from that used in previous chapters to describe elementary steps. Specifically, *single-barbed arrows* are used for homolysis.

A **single-barbed arrow** ( ) represents the movement of a *single electron*.

The curved arrow notation in Equations 27-1 and 27-2 explicitly shows that one electron from the covalent bond moves to one atom and the second electron moves to the other atom. In contrast, we have used *double-barbed arrows* ( ) in previous elementary steps to show the movement of *pairs* of electrons in closed-shell species.

YOUR TURN **27.1**

The homolysis of Cl_2 produces two chlorine radicals:

$$Cl{-}Cl \longrightarrow Cl\bullet + \bullet Cl$$

Add the appropriate curved arrows to depict this reaction.

Answers to Your Turns are in the back of the book.

YOUR TURN **27.2**

Draw the appropriate curved arrows and draw the products for the homolysis of each of the following bonds. **(a)** the C—C bond in ethane; **(b)** a C—H bond in ethane; **(c)** the C—Br bond in 2-bromopropane; **(d)** a C—H bond in benzene

CONNECTIONS 27.1

Keeping water safe to drink
Cl_2 (Your Turn 27.1) is often used to protect drinking water supplies from harmful bacteria because Cl_2 reacts with water to produce HOCl, a bactericide. In 1905 in Lincoln, England, this type of chlorination process helped stop a typhoid fever epidemic that was traced back to a contaminated water supply.

Figure 27-2 shows that it takes 439 kJ/mol of energy for a C—H bond in CH_4 to undergo homolysis and thereby produce H• and $H_3C\bullet$. This corresponds to a vanishingly small equilibrium constant of $<10^{-77}$ and should give you some idea of just how unstable these radicals are.

Many single bonds have similar homolytic bond dissociation energies, as shown in Tables 27-1 and 27-2. Table 27-1 lists bond dissociation energies of bonds involving hydrogen, whereas Table 27-2 lists bond dissociation energies of bonds that involve atoms other than hydrogen.

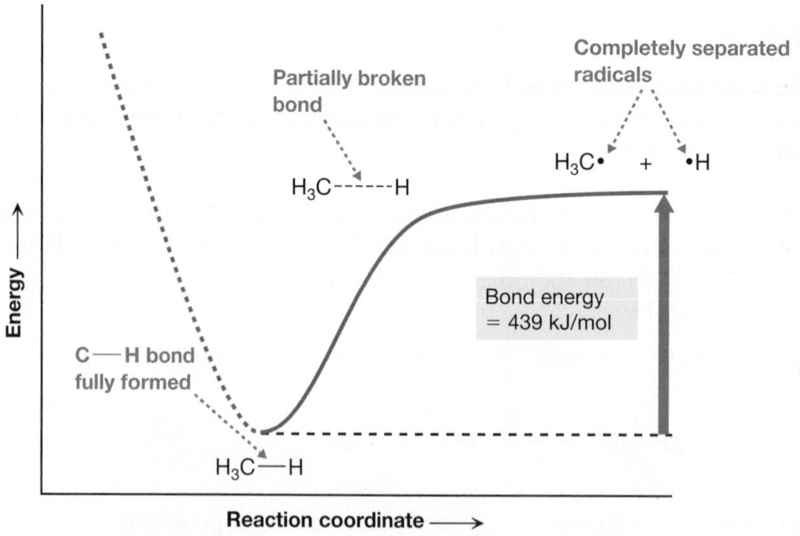
Completely separated radicals
Partially broken bond
H3C• + •H
H3C------H
Energy
Bond energy = 439 kJ/mol
C—H bond fully formed
H3C—H
Reaction coordinate

FIGURE 27-2 Energy diagram for the homolysis of a C—H bond in CH_4 The homolytic bond dissociation energy of 439 kJ/mol is the difference in energy between the energy minimum and the energy of the separated radicals at the right of the figure.

Because homolysis requires large amounts of energy, the concentration of radicals in solution is essentially zero under normal conditions for most species.

To produce any reasonable concentration of radicals from a closed-shell species, energy can be supplied in the form of heat (Δ) or UV light ($h\nu$).

Note how the notations Δ and $h\nu$ are used in Equations 27-1 and 27-2.

For a molecule with only one type of covalent bond, such as Br_2 or CH_4, only one set of homolysis products is possible. Molecules with more than one type of covalent bond, however, can lead to more than one set of homolysis products, but one homolysis reaction generally dominates.

The major products of homolysis derive from breaking the weakest bond in the molecule; that is, the bond with the smallest bond dissociation energy.

For example, bromomethane (CH_3Br) has three C—H bonds and one C—Br bond. The C—Br bond (294 kJ/mol) is weaker than the C—H bond (427 kJ/mol), so homolysis leads almost exclusively to Br• and H_3C•, as shown in Equation 27-3.

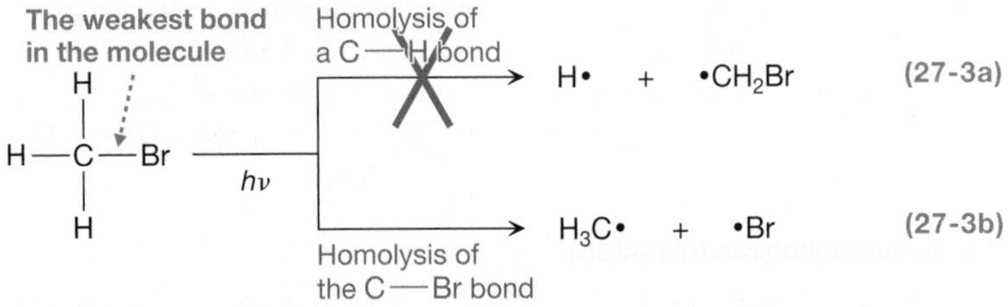
The weakest bond in the molecule
Homolysis of a C—H bond
H• + •CH₂Br
(27-3a)
hν
H₃C• + •Br
(27-3b)
Homolysis of the C—Br bond

SOLVED PROBLEM **27.1**

How to predict the major homolysis products of a compound with only single bonds

Break It Down **Predict the major homolysis products of ethane.**

$$CH_3CH_3 \xrightarrow[h\nu]{} ?$$

Think	Solve
What types of bonds are found in the molecule?	There are two distinct types of bonds. One is H—CH_2CH_3, and the other is H_3C—CH_3.
From the tables of bond dissociation energies, which bond is the weakest?	The bond dissociation energy of H—CH_2CH_3 is 421 kJ/mol (Table 27-1), and that of H_3C—CH_3 is 377 kJ/mol (Table 27-2). Therefore, H_3C—CH_3 is the weaker bond.
What products are produced by homolysis of the weakest bond?	Homolysis of the H_3C—CH_3 bond is shown here. 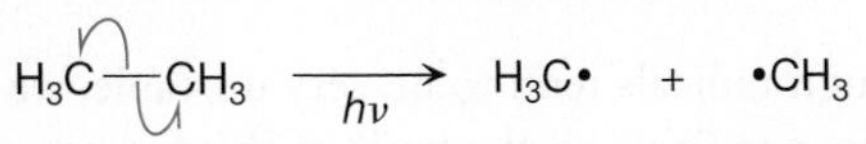

Try It Predict the major homolysis products of methanol.

$$CH_3OH \xrightarrow[h\nu]{} ?$$

Answers to all Try It exercises can be found in the Solutions Manual.

TABLE 27-1 Homolytic Bond Dissociation Energies Involving Bonds to Hydrogen[a]

Bond	Bond Energy (kJ/mol)
H—H	436
H—F	569
H—Cl	431
H—Br	368
H—I	297
H—OCH_3	440
H—SCH_3	366
H—CH_3	439
H—CH_2CH_3	421
H—$CH_2CH_2CH_3$	422
H—$CH(CH_3)_2$	410
H—$C(CH_3)_3$	400
H—CH=CH_2	464
H—C≡CH	558
H—CH_2—CH=CH_2	369
H—CH_2—C_6H_5	376
H—CH_2Br	427
H—CH_2OH	402

[a]Adapted from Luo, Y-R. *Comprehensive Handbook of Chemical Bond Energies*; CRC Press: New York, 2007.

TABLE 27-2 Homolytic Bond Dissociation Energies of Bonds Involving Atoms other than Hydrogen[a]

Bond	Bond Energy (kJ/mol)
$H_3C—CH_3$	377
$F—CH_3$	460
$Br—CH_3$	294
$HO—CH_3$	385
HO—OH	211
F—F	159
Cl—Cl	243
Br—Br	192
I—I	151

[a]Adapted from Luo, Y-R. *Comprehensive Handbook of Chemical Bond Energies*; CRC Press: New York, 2007.

Radicals can in theory be produced from the homolysis of a covalent bond in virtually any molecule, but in practice, some precursors, called **radical initiators**, are particularly well suited to producing radicals. Examples of radical initiators include molecular halogens (Cl_2, Br_2, and I_2), peroxides (RO—OR), ***N*-bromosuccinimide (NBS)** (Eq. 27-4), and **2,2′-azobisisobutyronitrile (AIBN)** (Eq. 27-5). Radical initiators are often added to a reaction mixture to initiate a reaction that proceeds by a radical mechanism (more on this in Section 27.4).

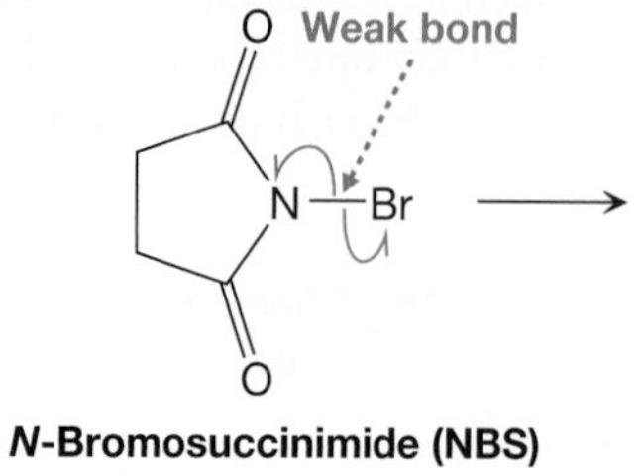

Weak bond
N
Br
N•
+
•Br
N-Bromosuccinimide (NBS)

(27-4)

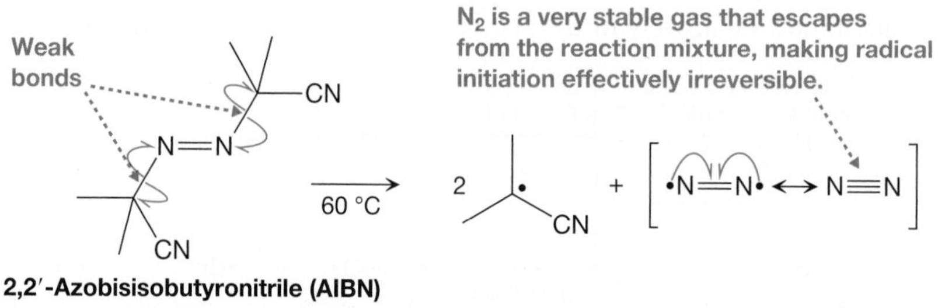

Weak bonds
CN
N=N
CN
60 °C
2
CN
+
•N=N• ↔ N≡N
N₂ is a very stable gas that escapes from the reaction mixture, making radical initiation effectively irreversible.
2,2′-Azobisisobutyronitrile (AIBN)

(27-5)

Radical initiators generally have a rather weak bond that is relatively easy to break.

The bond dissociation energy of the N—Br bond in NBS, for example, is 276 kJ/mol, which is a little over half the strength of a C—H bond in CH_4. AIBN is advantageous for another reason as well: homolysis of the two C—N single bonds produces gaseous N_2, which permanently leaves the reaction mixture, making homolysis effectively irreversible.

YOUR TURN 27.3

Verify that halogens and peroxides have weak bonds by comparing the bond energies of the following bonds to that of a typical C—H bond.

Cl—Cl ___________ Br—Br ___________ I—I ___________

HO—OH ___________ Compare to $H_3C—H$ ___________

SECTION 27.2 OBJECTIVES

You will be able to:

1. Rank the stabilities of alkyl radicals from their structures.
2. Determine when an alkyl radical has resonance structures, and draw the resonance structures of such a species.
3. Explain why the carbon atom bearing the unpaired electron in an alkyl radical tends to be planar.

27.2 Structure and Stability of Alkyl Radicals

Although radicals tend to be very unstable, we can assign different *relative* stabilities to various radicals on the basis of the energy required to produce them by homolysis (Tables 27-1 and 27-2). For example, Equation 27-6 shows the C—H homolysis reactions of a variety of alkanes, yielding the H• atom and an alkyl radical (R•) as the products:

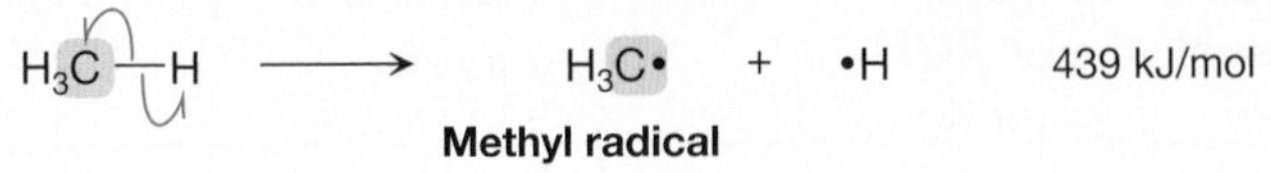

H3C—H → H3C• + •H 439 kJ/mol
Methyl radical

(27-6a)

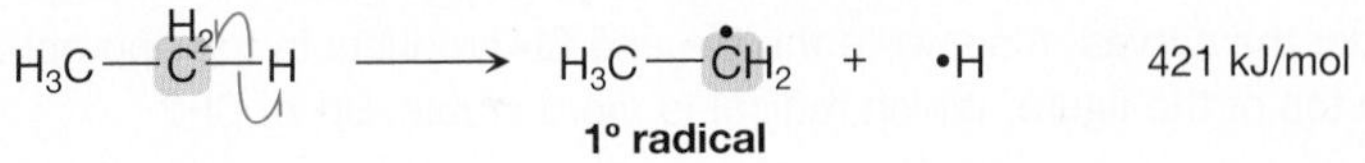

421 kJ/mol
1° radical

(27-6b)

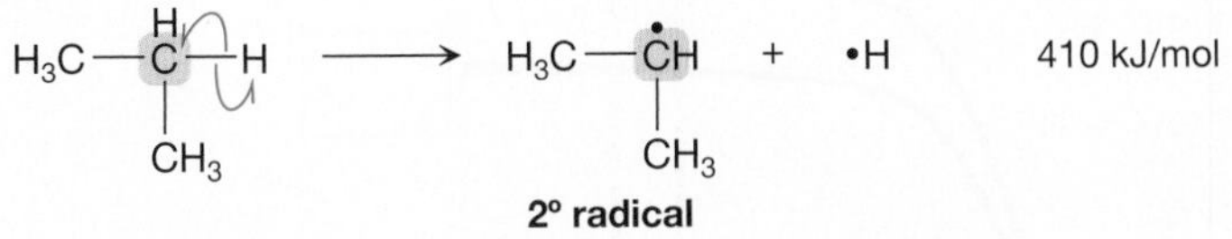

410 kJ/mol
2° radical

(27-6c)

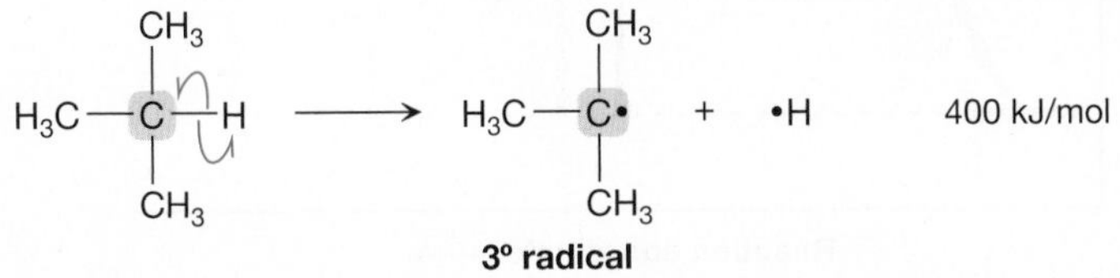

400 kJ/mol
3° radical

(27-6d)

The free energy diagrams for these homolysis steps are shown in **Figure 27-3**. With the various alkanes placed at the same energy, we can focus on differences in stability of the radicals.

A H• radical is produced in all four reactions, so any difference in product energy must come from the different stabilities of the alkyl radicals that are produced. For example, it takes 18 kJ/mol more energy to produce a methyl radical than it does to

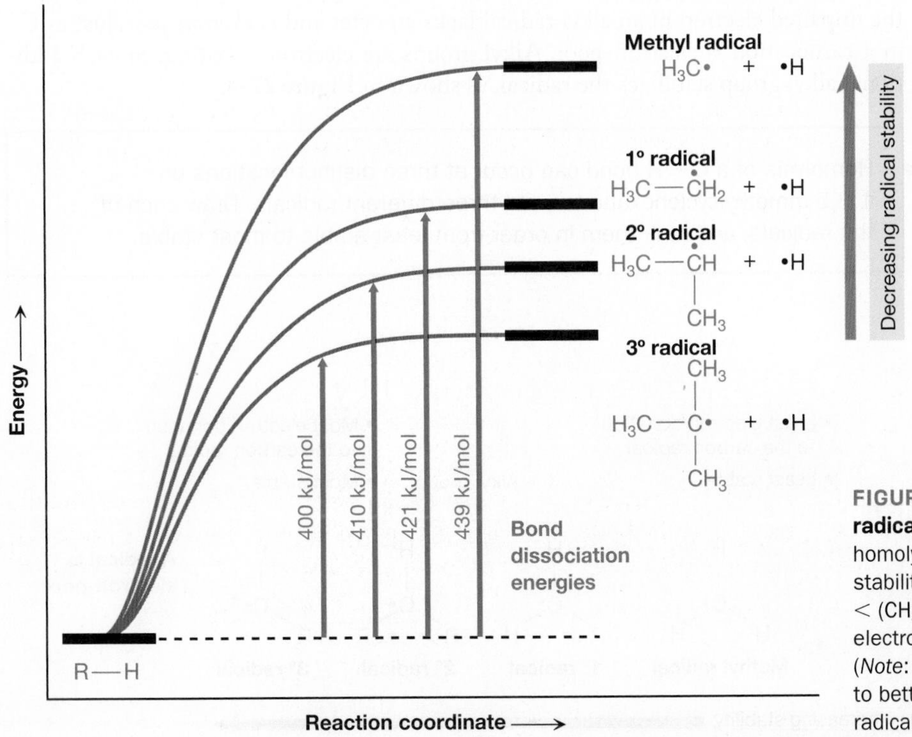

Methyl radical
1° radical
2° radical
3° radical
Decreasing radical stability
400 kJ/mol
410 kJ/mol
421 kJ/mol
439 kJ/mol
Bond dissociation energies
R—H
Energy
Reaction coordinate

FIGURE 27-3 Relative stabilities of alkyl radicals Reaction energy diagrams for C—H homolysis in a variety of alkanes. Alkyl radical stability increases in the order $CH_3\bullet < CH_3CH_2\bullet < (CH_3)_2CH\bullet < (CH_3)_3C\bullet$, where the unpaired electron is on a carbon atom in each case. (*Note*: Alkanes are placed at the same energy to better highlight the relative stabilities of the radicals.)

CONNECTIONS 27.2

Time-sensitive chemicals

Like peroxides, ether hydroperoxides have a weak O—O bond. Ether hydroperoxides are produced by a radical oxidation when ethers (common organic solvents) are exposed to oxygen in the atmosphere (see Problem 27.42). Ether hydroperoxides react to produce ether peroxides, which are somewhat unstable and potentially explosive. Therefore, you should avoid working with ethers that have been exposed to air for a prolonged time.

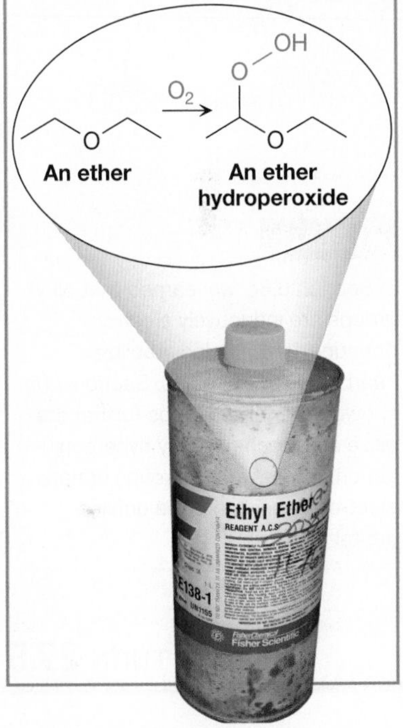

O2
An ether
An ether hydroperoxide
Ethyl Ether

produce an ethyl radical (439 vs. 421 kJ/mol), so •CH_3 is 18 kJ/mol higher in energy than •CH_2CH_3 in Figure 27-3. In other words, •CH_3 is 18 kJ/mol less stable than •CH_2CH_3. In turn, •CH_2CH_3 is 11 kJ/mol less stable than •$CH(CH_3)_2$, which is 10 kJ/mol less stable than •$C(CH_3)_3$.

YOUR TURN 27.4

The following figure represents homolysis for the H—Cl and H—Br bonds, but it is incomplete. Write the homolytic bond dissociation energies in the boxes provided under the curves. Also, write the Br• and Cl• products in the appropriate boxes at the top of the figure. Which radical is more stable, Br• or Cl•?

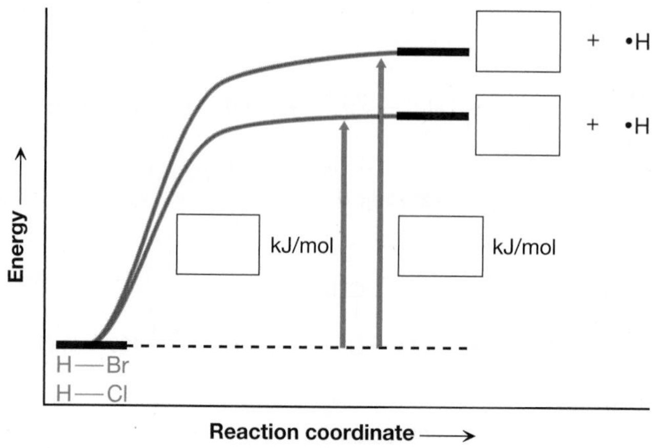

+ •H
+ •H
kJ/mol
kJ/mol
Energy
H—Br
H—Cl
Reaction coordinate

◂ RECALL

In Section 6.8e, we learned that alkyl groups are inductively electron-donating, which helps stabilize nearby positive charges. Section 7.9a showed that alkyl groups further stabilize an attached C^+ by hyperconjugation, whereby alkyl groups donate electron density into the unfilled orbital on C^+.

The relative stabilities shown in Figure 27-3 reveal the following trend:

Alkyl radical stability increases in the order:

(Least stable) Methyl < 1° < 2° < 3° (Most stable)

The stability of alkyl radicals follows the same order as the stability of *carbocations* (R^+) (see Recall box). The orders of stability are the same because the carbon atom that has the unpaired electron in an alkyl radical lacks an octet and is *electron-poor*, just as C^+ in a carbocation is electron-poor. Alkyl groups are electron-donating, so each additional alkyl group stabilizes the radical, as shown in **Figure 27-4**.

YOUR TURN 27.5

Homolysis of a C—H bond can occur at three distinct locations on 1,3,5-trimethylcyclohexane to yield three different radicals. Draw each of the radicals, and rank them in order from least stable to most stable.

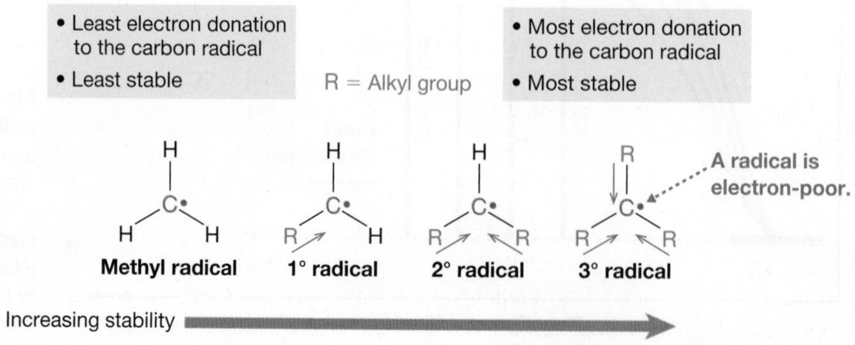

• Least electron donation to the carbon radical
• Least stable
R = Alkyl group
• Most electron donation to the carbon radical
• Most stable
A radical is electron-poor.
Methyl radical
1° radical
2° radical
3° radical
Increasing stability

FIGURE 27-4 Relative stabilities of alkyl radicals A radical carbon (in blue) is stabilized by the electron-donating effect of attached alkyl groups (in red), so alkyl radical stability increases in the order: methyl radical < 1° radical < 2° radical < 3° radical.

Effective electronegativity (see Recall box) also affects the stability of an alkyl radical. Notice in Table 27-1 (p. 1307) that the C—H bond dissociation energies for CH_3CH_3, $H_2C{=}CH_2$, and $HC{\equiv}CH$ are 421, 464, and 558 kJ/mol, respectively. According to these data, the ethyl radical ($\bullet CH_2CH_3$) is more stable than the ethenyl radical ($\bullet CH{=}CH_2$), which is more stable than the ethynyl radical ($\bullet C{\equiv}CH$). Therefore:

Alkyl radical stability decreases as the effective electronegativity of the carbon atom that gains the unpaired electron increases.

◂ RECALL

Section 3.9 showed that effective electronegativity derives from the *s*-character the atom has in its hybrid orbitals. An *s* orbital is more compact than a *p* orbital, so with greater *s*-character, the atom's electrons are held closer to the nucleus as if the atom's electronegativity were increasing.

Just as the atom's ability to accommodate a positive charge decreases with increasing effective electronegativity (Section 6.8c), so, too, does its ability to accommodate an unpaired electron.

The similarities between alkyl radicals and carbocations are further demonstrated with the allyl ($CH_2{=}CH{-}CH_2\bullet$) and benzyl ($C_6H_5{-}CH_2\bullet$) radicals. Recall that the allyl cation and the benzyl cation are more stable than ordinary primary carbocations because of resonance delocalization of the positive charge, as shown in Equations 27-7 and 27-8:

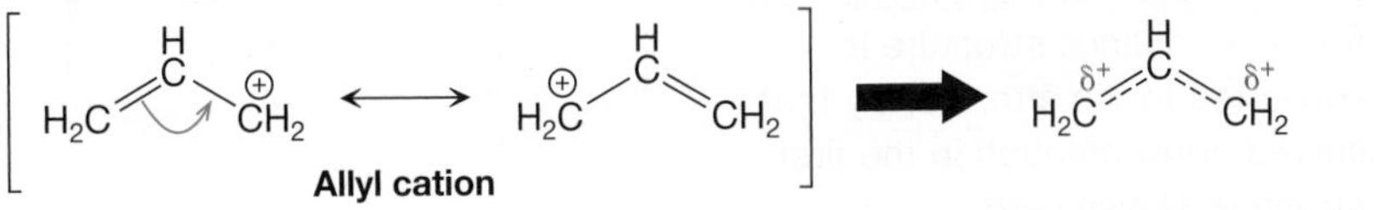

Allyl cation

(27-7)

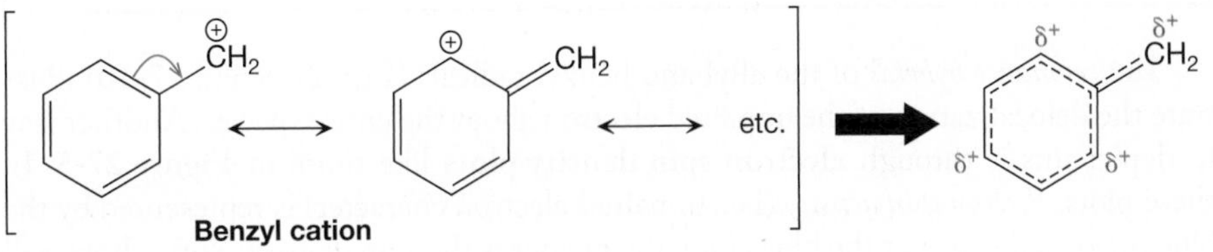

etc.
Benzyl cation

(27-8)

YOUR TURN **27.6**

Complete Equation 27-8 by drawing the three missing resonance structures, including curved arrow notation.

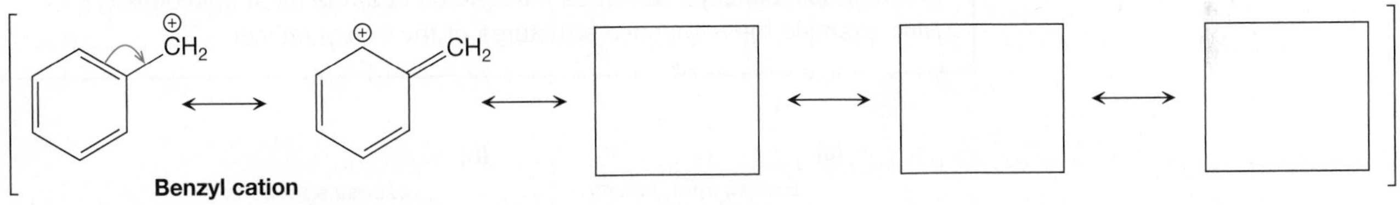

Benzyl cation

The allyl radical and the benzyl radical are more stable than ordinary primary alkyl radicals, too. Thus, the methyl C—H bonds in $CH_2{=}CH{-}CH_2{-}H$ and $C_6H_5{-}CH_2{-}H$ are weaker than those in ethane by 52 and 45 kJ/mol, respectively.

YOUR TURN **27.7**

Draw a plot similar to that in Figure 27-3 (p. 1309) and Your Turn 27.4 (p. 1310), illustrating the relative stabilities of the ethyl radical ($CH_3{-}CH_2\bullet$) and the allyl radical. What conclusion can you make from your plot regarding the stabilities of the two radicals?

Equations 27-9 and 27-10 show that the allyl and benzyl radicals are stabilized by resonance, similar to the allyl and benzyl cations (see Your Turn 27.8). For each radical, notice how single-barbed curved arrows depict the electron movement to arrive at the next resonance structure. Additionally, notice that the unpaired electron in each radical is shared among the same carbon atoms as the positive charge is in the analogous carbocations.

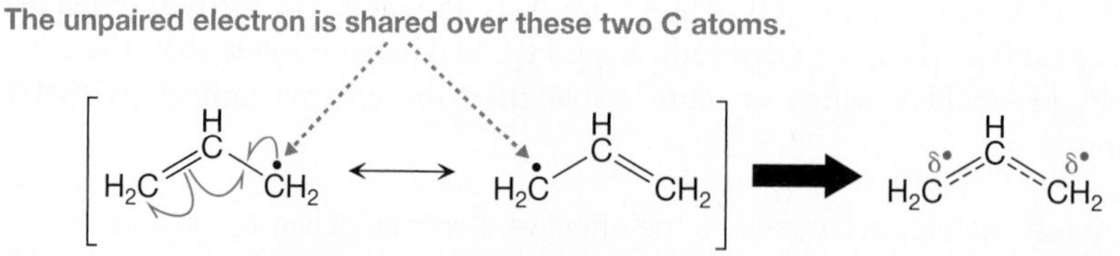

The unpaired electron is shared over these two C atoms.
H
H₂C
CH₂
δ•

(27-9)

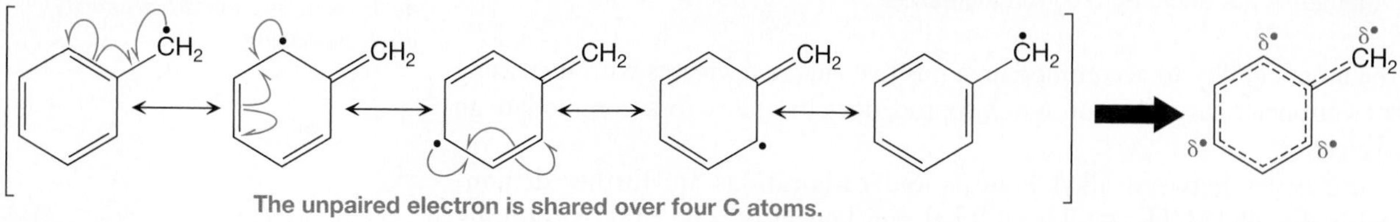

CH₂
δ•
The unpaired electron is shared over four C atoms.

(27-10)

YOUR TURN 27.8

Equation 27-10 is missing the curved arrow notation that shows how the fourth resonance structure is converted to the fifth. Supply that curved arrow notation in the first structure shown here.

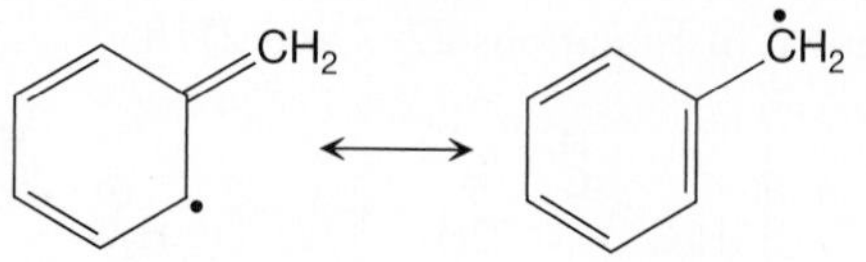

CH₂
CH₂

The *resonance hybrids* of the allyl and benzyl radicals (Eqs. 27-9 and 27-10) illustrate the delocalization of the unpaired electron about the entire species. Another way to depict this is through **electron spin density plots** like those in **Figure 27-5**. In these plots, *electron spin density* (i.e., unpaired electron character) is represented by the blue regions; the deeper the blue color, the greater is the spin density. Notice how well the electron spin density plots match the resonance hybrids.

YOUR TURN 27.9

Which carbon atom in the benzyl radical in Figure 27-5 possesses the greatest spin density? Why does that carbon bear the most spin density? *Hint*: Examine the resonance structures of the benzyl radical.

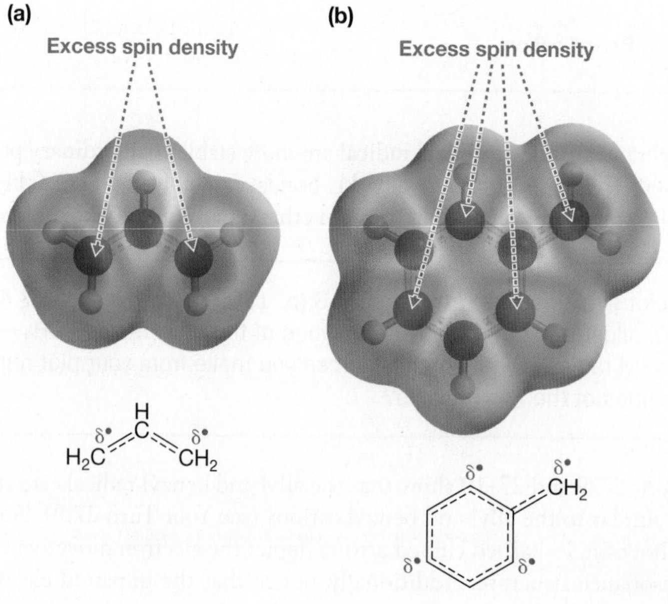

(a)
Excess spin density
(b)
Excess spin density
H
H₂C
CH₂
δ•
CH₂

FIGURE 27-5 Electron spin density plots Electron spin density plots of (a) the allyl radical and (b) the benzyl radical are shown. The deeper the blue, the greater the electron spin density. Spin density in the allyl radical is delocalized over the two terminal carbon atoms. Spin density in the benzyl radical is delocalized over four carbon atoms.

SOLVED PROBLEM **27.2**

How to predict relative strengths of single bonds involving carbon

Break It Down **Which is the weakest C—C single bond in the molecule shown here?**

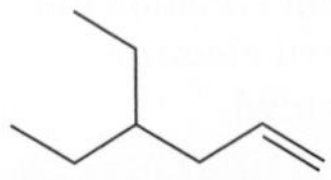

Think	Solve
What are the distinct types of C—C bonds?	There are four distinct C—C single bonds, labeled **A–D** here on the left. 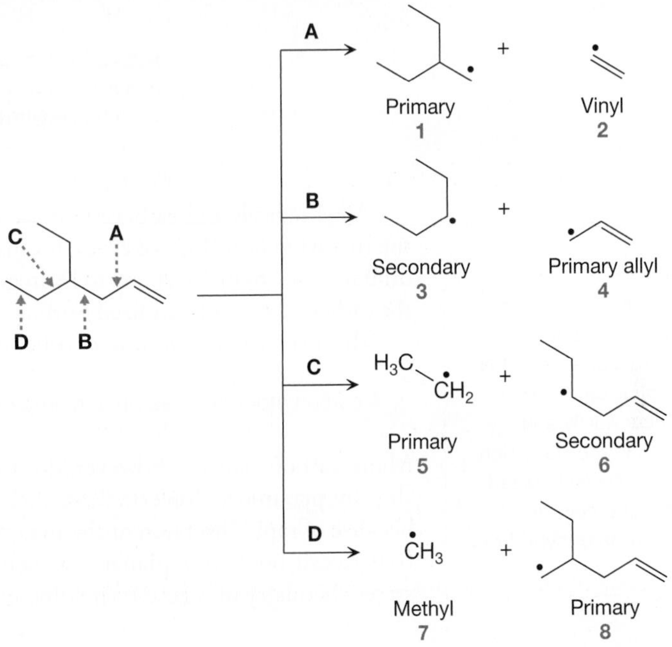 A B C D Primary 1 Vinyl 2 Secondary 3 Primary allyl 4 H_3C $\dot{C}H_2$ Primary 5 Secondary 6 $\dot{C}H_3$ Methyl 7 Primary 8
What are the products of homolysis for each of those bonds?	The homolysis products of bonds **A** through **D** are shown above on the right, numbered **1** through **8**.
Which products exhibit the most alkyl substitution on C•? How does that affect the stabilities of the products?	Homolysis products **B** and **C** have the most alkyl substitution on C•. In both cases, one radical is secondary and the other is primary. In products **A** and **D**, the radicals are primary or methyl. Therefore, products **B** and **C** are more stable than products **A** and **D**.
Can products **B** and **C** be distinguished on the basis of resonance?	Products **B** and **C** each include one secondary radical in which the unpaired electron is localized: radicals **3** and **6**. Thus, radicals **3** and **6** are similar in stability. Radical **4** is an allylic radical, so the unpaired electron is resonance-delocalized. In radical **5**, the unpaired electron is localized. Therefore, radical **4** is more stable than radical **5**.
Which set of products is most stable? How does that affect bond energy?	The alkyl substitution and the resonance delocalization of the unpaired electron make homolysis products **B** the most stable, so the homolysis of bond **B** is the easiest. That is, bond **B** is the weakest.

Try It Which is the weakest C—H bond in the molecule shown here?

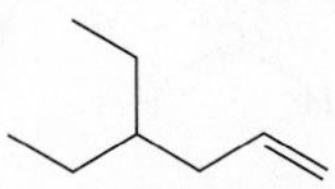

FIGURE 27-6 Structural similarities between the methyl radical and the methyl cation The three-dimensional structures of (a) $H_3C\bullet$ and (b) H_3C^+ are shown. Both structures are planar, indicating that the C atom is sp^2-hybridized. The single, unpaired electron in $H_3C\bullet$ resides, therefore, in an unhybridized *p* orbital. The corresponding *p* orbital in H_3C^+ is empty.

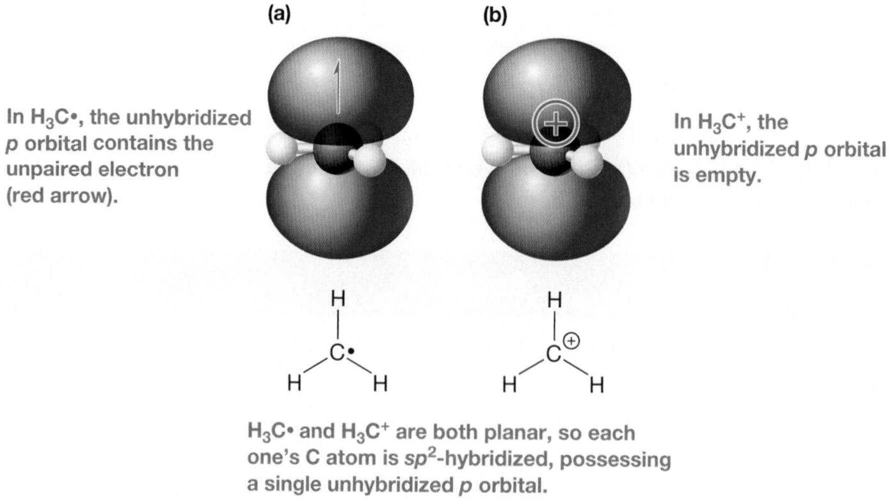
(a)
(b)
In H₃C•, the unhybridized p orbital contains the unpaired electron (red arrow).
In H₃C⁺, the unhybridized p orbital is empty.
H₃C• and H₃C⁺ are both planar, so each one's C atom is sp²-hybridized, possessing a single unhybridized p orbital.

◀ RECALL

Section 5.7 showed that the three groups bonded to a pyramidal N atom can flip from one side of N to the other. This nitrogen inversion tends to occur easily and rapidly because N in the transition state is planar and sp^2-hybridized, which allows the lone pair on N to temporarily occupy an unhybridized *p* orbital.

Alkyl radicals and carbocations are structurally similar, too. The methyl cation and the methyl radical (**Figure 27-6**), for instance, are both *planar*. Because each sp^2 hybrid orbital is used to make a bond to hydrogen, the unpaired electron in $H_3C\bullet$ must reside in the carbon atom's unhybridized *p* orbital. By comparison, that *p* orbital is empty in H_3C^+.

This planarity is common to other carbon radicals, too.

A carbon atom that has an unpaired electron tends to be planar and sp^2-hybridized.

Many carbon radicals, however, do not achieve complete planarity but are instead slightly pyramidal. Nevertheless, such radicals often behave as if they were planar because of rapid inversion of the pyramid, much like we saw with nitrogen inversion (see Recall box). This planar-like behavior of carbon radicals is important in the stereochemistry of reactions involving radicals (Section 27.6).

SECTION 27.3 OBJECTIVES

You will be able to:

1. Determine whether a set of reacting species can undergo a radical coupling, S_H2, or radical addition step.
2. Draw the curved arrows and products for a radical coupling, S_H2, or radical addition step.

27.3 Common Elementary Steps That Radicals Undergo

Just as there are a small number of common elementary steps for closed-shell species (Chapters 6 and 7), radicals also tend to participate in relatively few elementary steps. We examine those steps briefly here in Section 27.3, in particular looking at each step's curved arrow notation and aspects of its driving force. We will then be better equipped to tackle the mechanisms of the synthetically useful reactions introduced throughout the rest of this chapter.

27.3a Radical Coupling

Elementary Step
Radical Coupling Elementary Step

Perhaps the simplest of steps that a radical can undergo is *radical coupling*, also called *radical recombination*, an example of which is shown in Equation 27-11:

Radical coupling

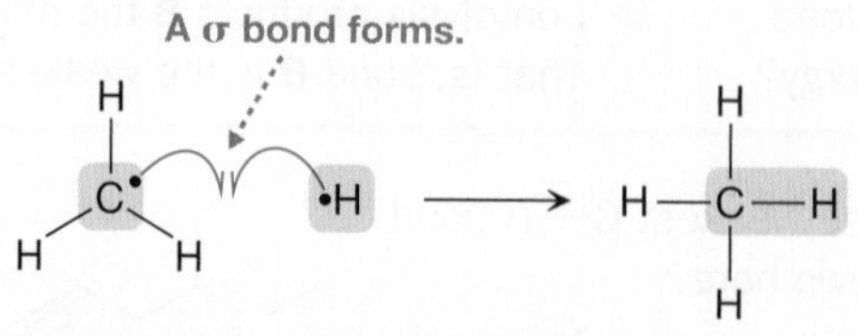
A σ bond forms.

(27-11)

Radical coupling involves two radicals. In this case, the unpaired electron on C joins the unpaired electron on H to form a new C—H σ bond. The formation of the σ bond is indicated by the two single-barbed arrows pointing to the bond-forming region. (Just as with double-barbed arrows, the atoms are assumed to follow their own electrons.) In general:

In a **radical coupling** (or **radical combination**) step, an unpaired electron from one atom joins an unpaired electron from a second atom, forming a new σ bond that connects the two atoms.

YOUR TURN **27.10**

Supply the missing curved arrows for the following radical coupling step involving two $H_3C•$ radicals.

$$H_3C• \quad + \quad •CH_3 \longrightarrow H_3C—CH_3$$

Radical coupling is essentially the reverse of homolysis: Whereas homolysis produces two new radicals by *breaking* a σ bond, radical coupling removes two radicals by *forming* a new σ bond. Thus, in contrast to homolysis being very unfavorable:

Radical coupling is usually very favorable and, therefore, *irreversible*.

Because radical coupling is the reverse of homolysis, the free energy diagram for a radical coupling step is precisely the reverse of one for homolysis. For example, the free energy diagram for the radical coupling of a methyl radical and a hydrogen radical, shown in **Figure 27-7**, is the reverse of CH_4 homolysis, shown previously in Figure 27-2 (p. 1306).

Notice at every distance that the two radicals are separated, shortening that distance (i.e., moving to the right in the figure) results in a lower energy. In other words, *radical coupling steps generally have no energy barrier!* The absence of an energy barrier distinguishes radical coupling from every other elementary step we have studied thus far, offering further evidence of just how reactive and unstable radicals are.

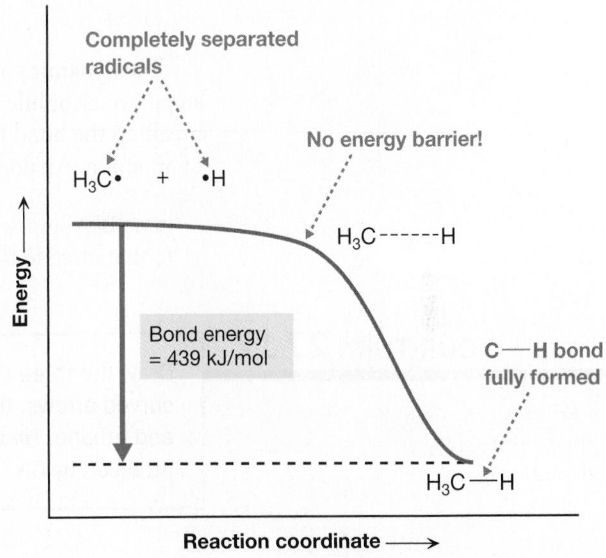

Completely separated radicals
No energy barrier!
H3C• + •H
H3C------H
Energy
Bond energy = 439 kJ/mol
C—H bond fully formed
H3C—H
Reaction coordinate

FIGURE 27-7 **Reaction energy diagram for radical coupling** The completely separated $H_3C•$ and $H•$ radicals appear on the left, and the fully formed C—H bond appears on the right. This energy diagram is essentially the mirror image of the one for homolysis, shown previously in Figure 27-2 (p. 1306). Unlike other reaction steps we have seen, radical coupling typically proceeds with no energy barrier between reactants and products.

27.3b Bimolecular Homolytic Substitution (S_H2)

As we have just seen, radical coupling involves one radical reacting with another. A radical can react with a closed-shell species as well. One example is the **bimolecular homolytic substitution (S_H2) step** shown in Equation 27-12, which involves Br• and a molecule of methane, CH_4.

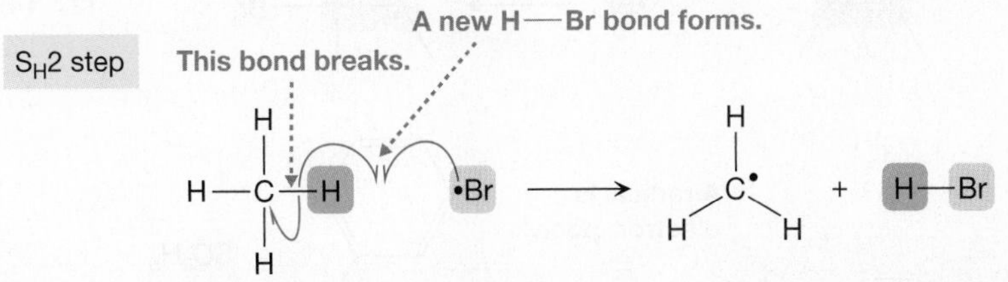

SH2 step
This bond breaks.
A new H—Br bond forms.
•Br
H—Br

(27-12)

The curved arrows show that the C—H bond is broken, and that one of the two electrons from that bond ends up on the C atom. The other electron joins the unpaired electron on Br• to form a new H—Br bond. Because a H atom is transferred from the C atom to the Br atom, the S_H2 step in Equation 27-12 is more specifically called a **hydrogen atom abstraction** (Br has *abstracted* a H atom).

YOUR TURN 27.11

Supply the missing curved arrows for the following hydrogen atom abstraction step.

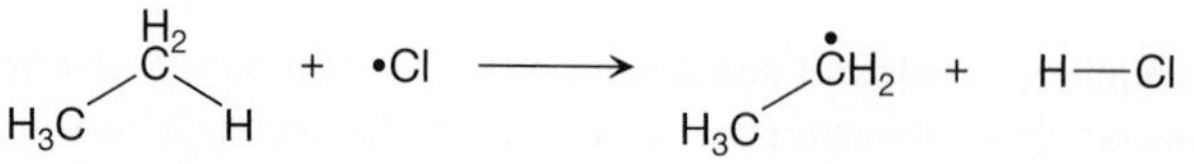

H2
C
H3C
H
+ •Cl
CH2
H3C
+ H—Cl

Elementary Step
S_H2 Elementary Step

Equation 27-13 provides another example of an S_H2 step. In this case, a chlorine radical (Cl•) is abstracted from a molecule of Cl_2, which makes the elementary step a *chlorine atom abstraction.*

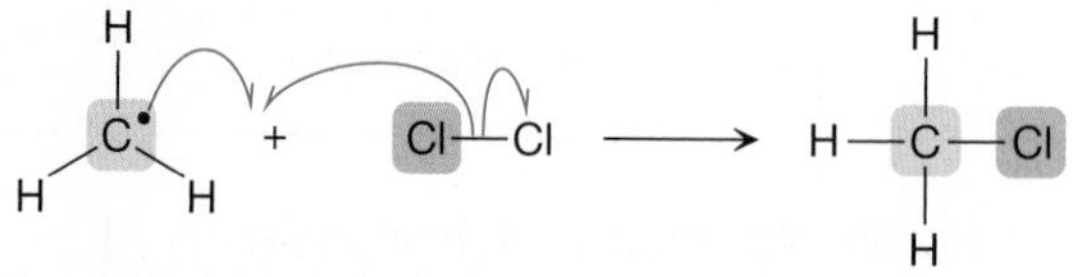

H
C
H
H
+
Cl—Cl
H—C—Cl
H
H
+ •Cl

(27-13)

The dynamics of an S_H2 step are essentially the same as in an S_N2 step. In an S_N2 step, a nucleophile forms a new bond to an atom attached to a leaving group, thus breaking the bond to the leaving group. The leaving group typically leaves in the form of an anion. Analogously:

> In an S_H2 step, a radical forms a new bond to an atom and causes another bond to that atom to break, which displaces a new radical from that atom.

YOUR TURN 27.12

Draw the three possible S_H2 steps, including curved arrows, that can occur between Cl• and ethane. *Hint*: Which atom(s) can be attacked by Cl•? Which bond(s) can be broken?

$$C_2H_6 + \bullet Cl \longrightarrow ?$$

27.3c Radical Addition to an Alkene or Alkyne

Elementary Step
Radical Addition

Recall from Chapter 12 that the C=C double bond of an alkene and the C≡C triple bond of an alkyne are relatively *electron-rich*. Because a radical is electron-poor, an alkene or alkyne can react with a radical in a *radical addition* step such as the one shown in Equation 27-14 or 27-15:

Radical addition

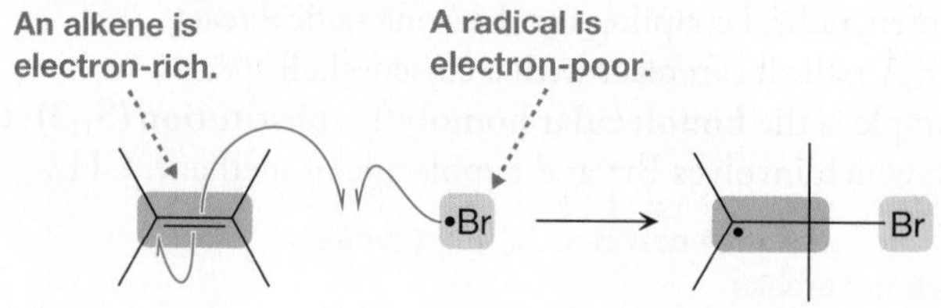

An alkene is electron-rich.
A radical is electron-poor.
•Br
Br

(27-14)

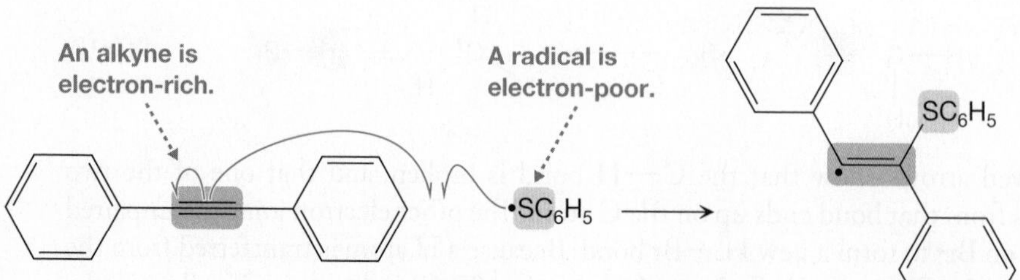

An alkyne is electron-rich.
A radical is electron-poor.
•SC6H5
SC6H5

(27-15)

One electron from the multiple bond of an alkene or alkyne joins the unpaired electron from the radical, and a second electron from the multiple bond ends up as an unpaired electron on carbon. Thus:

> In a **radical addition step**, one atom involved in a double or triple bond forms a new σ bond to a radical, and the other atom of the double or triple bond gains an unpaired electron.

YOUR TURN 27.13

Supply the curved arrows necessary for the following radical addition step.

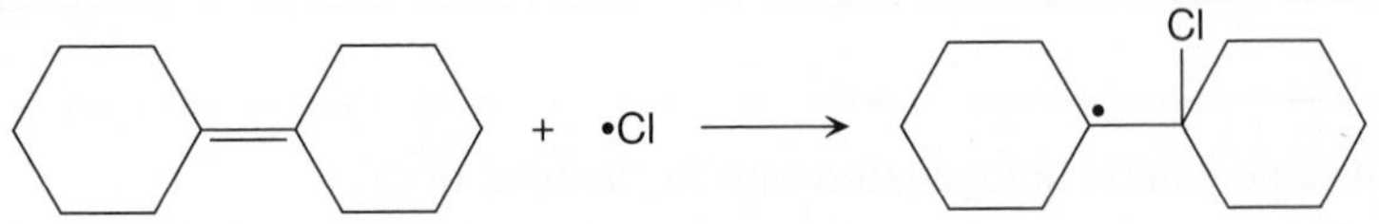

+ •Cl
Cl

27.4 Radical Halogenation of Alkanes: Synthesis of Alkyl Halides

SECTION 27.4 OBJECTIVES

You will be able to:

1. Identify the conditions for radical halogenation of an alkane.
2. Draw the mechanism for radical halogenation of an alkane, characterizing it as a chain reaction, and predict the major product.
3. Explain how the rate of radical halogenation depends on the identity of the halogen, and explain why bromination is more selective than chlorination.
4. Determine when NBS—rather than Br_2—should be used to carry out radical bromination, and predict the major product of such a reaction.

When an alkane such as cyclohexane is treated with a molecular halogen such as Cl_2, no reaction occurs (Eq. 27-16). However, if the same mixture is irradiated with UV light, *halogenation* takes place, producing chlorocyclohexane and HCl (Eq. 27-17).

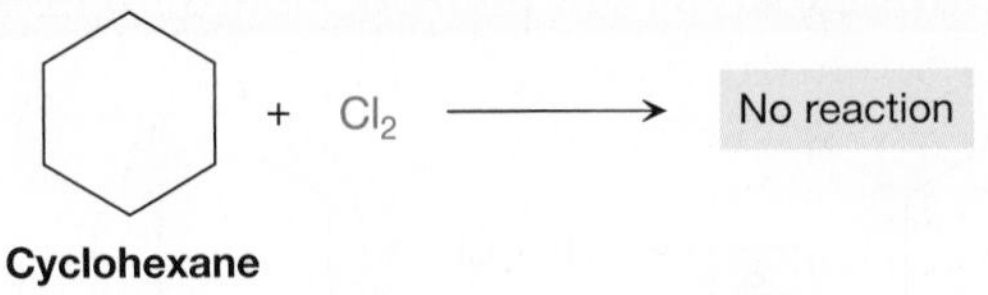

+ Cl2
No reaction
Cyclohexane

(27-16)

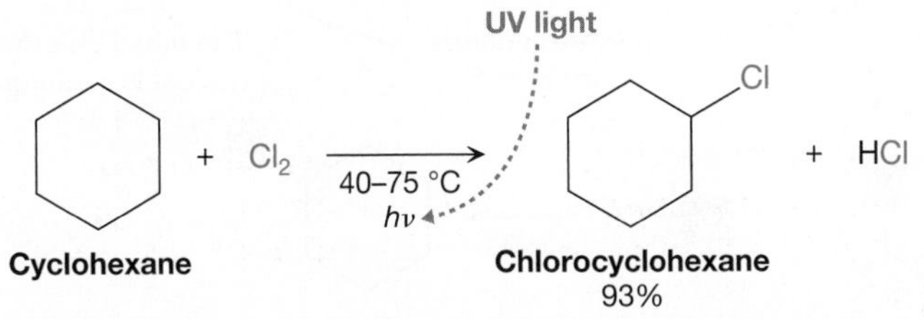

+ Cl2
UV light
40–75 °C
hν
Cl
+ HCl
Cyclohexane
Chlorocyclohexane
93%

(27-17)

Because its mechanism involves radical intermediates (as will be explained in Section 27.4a), the reaction in Equation 27-17 is more specifically called a *radical halogenation*. Radical halogenation can take place with a variety of alkanes, as well as other molecular halogens. In general:

> **Radical halogenation** of an alkane replaces a hydrogen atom with a halogen atom from a molecular halogen, X_2, to produce an alkyl halide, RX.

We will explore radical halogenation throughout the rest of Section 27.4. We begin by examining the mechanism. Then we will consider the choice of halogen, including its effect on kinetics, thermodynamics, and selectivity.

27.4a The Mechanism of Radical Halogenation: An Introduction to Chain-Reaction Mechanisms

The mechanism for radical halogenation involves radicals, but no radicals appear in the overall reaction in Equation 27-17. At what point do radicals arise, and how are they involved? Recall from Section 27.1 that Cl_2 is a radical initiator, and UV light can induce homolysis to produce radicals. In particular, as shown in Equation 27-18, homolysis of Cl_2 produces two Cl• radicals. Equation 27-18 is called the **initiation step** of the mechanism because it is responsible for generating the radicals necessary for the reaction to proceed:

Mechanism Drawing
Radical Chlorination of an Alkane

Partial mechanism for radical halogenation: Initiation (Eq. 27-17)

UV light brings about homolysis of the Cl—Cl bond.

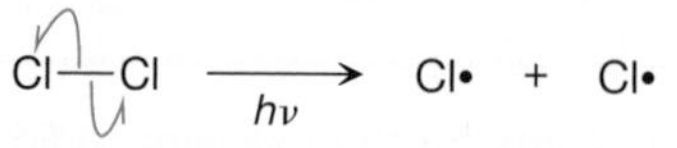

Cl—Cl
hν
Cl• + Cl•

(27-18)

YOUR TURN **27.14**

Cyclohexane can be halogenated with Br_2 instead of Cl_2:

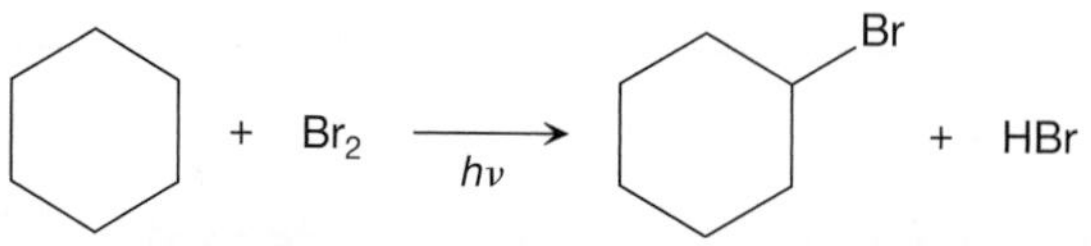

+ Br2
hν
Br
+ HBr

Draw the initiation step, including the necessary curved arrows.

The next two steps of the mechanism, shown in Equation 27-19a and 27-19b, are responsible for producing the overall products:

Partial mechanism for radical halogenation: Propagation (Eq. 27-17)

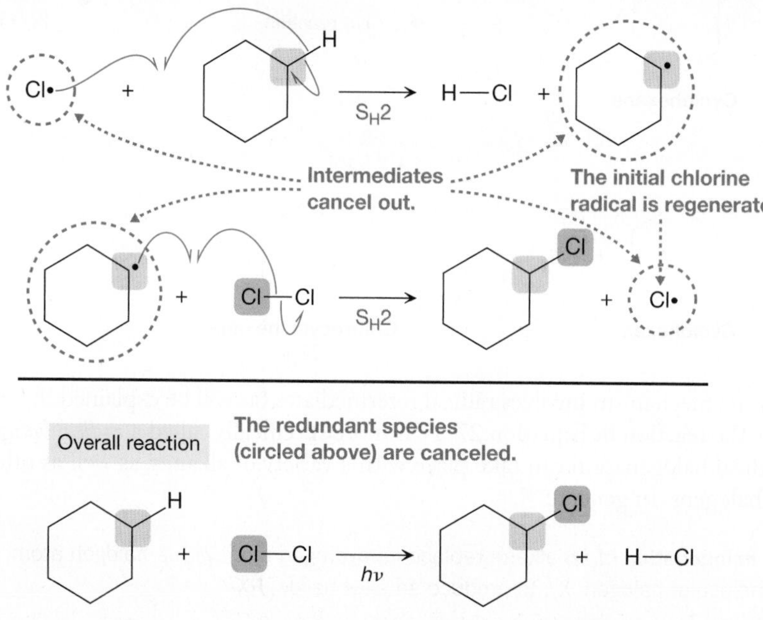

Cl•
+
H
SH2
H—Cl +
Intermediates cancel out.
The initial chlorine radical is regenerated.
+
Cl—Cl
SH2
Cl
+ Cl•
Overall reaction
The redundant species (circled above) are canceled.
H
+ Cl—Cl
hν
Cl
+ H—Cl

(27-19a)

(27-19b)

(27-19c)

Equation 27-19a is an S_H2 step in which Cl• (formed by the homolysis in Eq. 27-18) abstracts a H atom from cyclohexane (an overall reactant), producing a molecule of HCl (an overall product) and a cyclohexyl radical. Then, in Equation 27-19b, the cyclohexyl radical abstracts a Cl• from Cl_2 (an overall reactant) in another S_H2 step, producing a molecule of chlorocyclohexane (an overall product) and leaving behind another Cl•.

The Cl• that is produced in Equation 27-19b is available to react with another molecule of cyclohexane, so Equation 27-19a and 27-19b can be repeated many times. Each time these two elementary steps take place, one molecule of cyclohexane and one molecule of Cl_2 are converted to one molecule of chlorocyclohexane and one molecule of HCl. We can see this more clearly in Equation 27-19c, which is the sum of Equation 27-19a and 27-19b (the redundant radical intermediates have been canceled), and is also the same conversion that is represented by the balanced *overall* reaction shown previously in Equation 27-17. In other words, the steps in Equation 27-19a and 27-19b are responsible for *propagating* the overall reaction and are therefore called **propagation steps**; together they make up a repeating process called the **propagation cycle** of the mechanism.

YOUR TURN **27.15**

Draw the propagation steps for the reaction in Your Turn 27.14. *Hint*: They are very similar to the ones in Equation 27-19.

There are two ways for a propagation cycle to end. One is for the overall reactants to be completely consumed, as is the case for any chemical reaction. The second is for the radicals involved in the propagation steps to be destroyed.

Any reaction that is responsible for decreasing the number of radicals that participate in the propagation cycle is called a **termination step**.

Equation 27-20 shows three possible termination steps for the radical chlorination of cyclohexane. All of these are *radical coupling* steps that convert radicals from the propagation cycle into closed-shell molecules.

Partial mechanism for radical halogenation: Termination (Eq. 27-17)

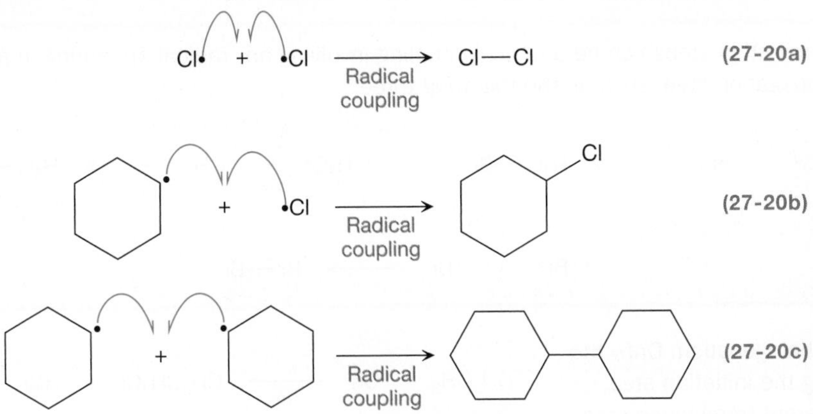

Cl•
+
•Cl
Radical coupling
Cl—Cl
(27-20a)
Cl
Radical coupling
(27-20b)
Radical coupling
(27-20c)

YOUR TURN **27.16**

Draw three termination steps for the reaction in Your Turn 27.14. *Hint*: They are similar to the ones in Equation 27-20.

SOLVED PROBLEM **27.3**

How to draw the mechanism for radical halogenation of an alkane

Break It Down **Methane can undergo radical halogenation:**

$$CH_4 + Br_2 \xrightarrow[h\nu]{} H_3C{-}Br + H{-}Br$$

Draw the mechanism for this reaction, including the initiation step, the propagation steps, and three different termination steps.

Think	Solve
For the initiation step, what is the weakest bond in the reactants that can undergo homolysis?	The Br—Br bond is the weakest bond in the reactants, so it will undergo homolysis in an initiation step to produce two Br• radicals.

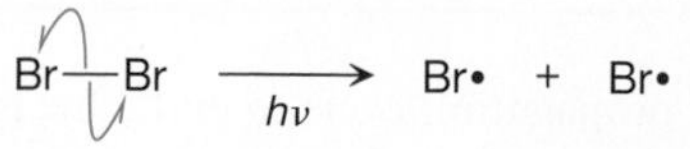

Br—Br
hν
Br•
+
Br•

Think	Solve
For the propagation steps, what S_H2 step can the initial radical undergo to produce the HBr product? What S_H2 step can the resulting radical undergo to produce the CH_3Br product and regenerate the initial radical?	In the first of two propagation steps, Br• abstracts a hydrogen from CH_4 to produce one overall product, HBr, and a methyl radical, H_3C•. In the second propagation step, the H_3C• abstracts a Br atom from Br_2 to produce the second overall product, CH_3Br, and regenerate another Br•.

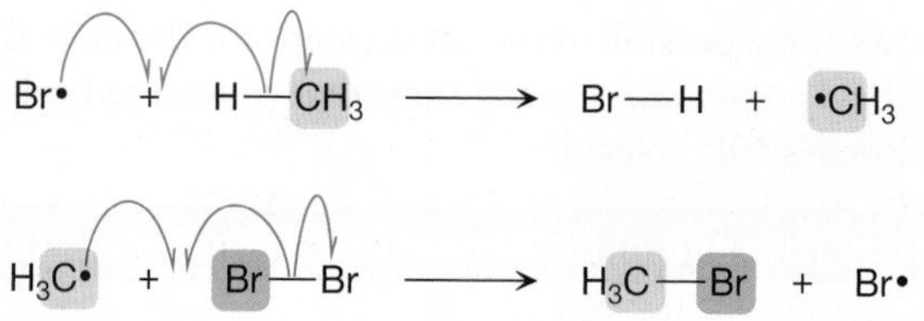

Br•
+
H—CH3
Br—H
+
•CH3
H3C•
+
Br—Br
H3C—Br
+
Br•

Think	Solve
For the termination steps, what possible radical coupling steps can take place?	Termination steps can be a radical coupling involving any radical appearing in a propagation step, such as the following three:

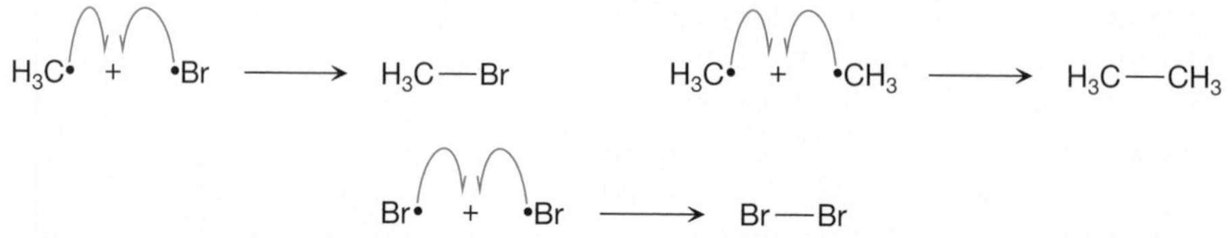

H3C•
+
•Br
H3C—Br
H3C•
+
•CH3
H3C—CH3
Br•
+
•Br
Br—Br

Try It Ethane can undergo radical halogenation. Draw the mechanism for this reaction, including the initiation step, the propagation steps, and three different termination steps.

$$CH_3CH_3 + Cl_2 \xrightarrow[h\nu]{} CH_3CH_2Cl + HCl$$

The termination steps in a radical halogenation mechanism are often quite favorable energetically, so the radical intermediates that are produced generally exist for only short times. Radical halogenation reactions can have high yields, however, because a single radical that enters a propagation cycle can lead to many thousands of conversions of reactants to products. This is possible because there is no net consumption of radicals in a complete propagation cycle—an idea that is captured in **Figure 27-8**, a schematic representation of the mechanism for the radical chlorination reaction in Equation 27-17.

YOUR TURN **27.17**

Study the diagram in Figure 27-8 and match the initiation and propagation steps to either Equation 27-18, 27-19a, 27-19b, 27-20a, 27-20b, or 27-20c.

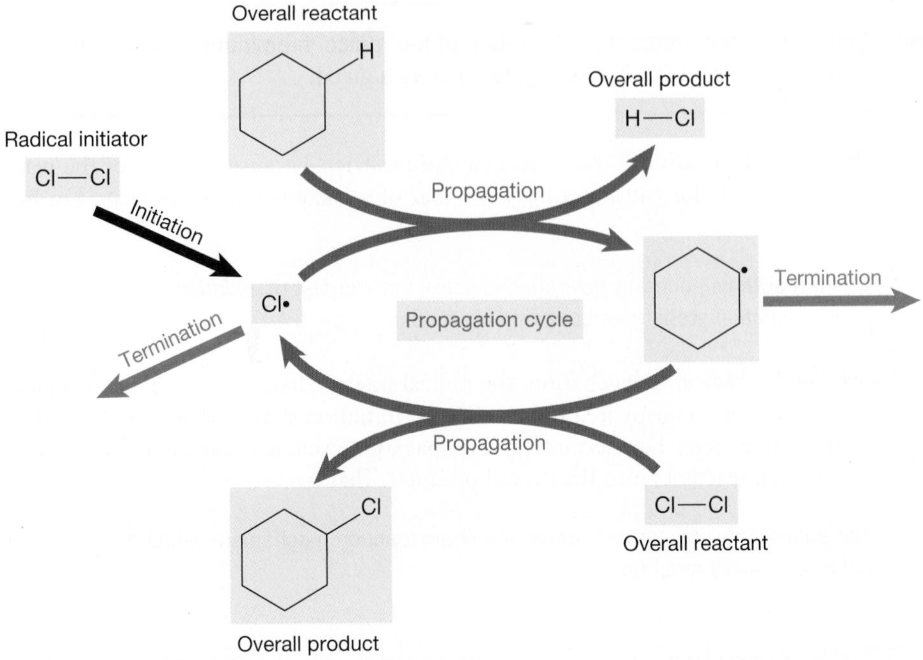
Overall reactant
Overall product
H—Cl
Radical initiator
Cl—Cl
Initiation
Propagation
Termination
Cl•
Propagation cycle
Termination
Propagation
Cl
Cl—Cl
Overall reactant
Overall product

FIGURE 27-8 Schematic representation of the radical chlorination mechanism The initiation step (black arrow) represents the introduction of radicals into the propagation cycle (blue arrows). Each time a full propagation cycle is completed, one molecule of cyclohexane (*top left*) and one molecule of Cl_2 (*bottom right*) are converted to one molecule of HCl (*top right*) and one molecule of chlorocyclohexane (*bottom left*). Termination steps (red arrows) represent the destruction of the radicals that participate in the propagation cycle.

Halogenated Alkanes and the Ozone Layer: Radical Chain Reactions in Nature

Earth is constantly bombarded by harmful UV radiation from the sun, but a very small amount (<10 ppm) of gaseous ozone (O_3), located roughly 10–20 miles above sea level (in the region of the atmosphere called the stratosphere), protects us from much of that radiation. Ozone is believed to convert UV photons into heat by the mechanism depicted in Scheme A in **Figure 27-9**.

In the 1970s, however, the total amount of stratospheric ozone began to decrease an average of about 5% per decade, and that trend continued until the year 2000. Moreover, each year from mid-August to late November (i.e., winter/spring in the Southern Hemisphere), there is a dramatic decrease in the amount of ozone over Antarctica. This "ozone hole" is depicted in red in Figure 27-9.

Chlorofluorocarbons (CFCs) receive much of the blame. In 1928, certain CFCs, such as CCl_2F_2 and CCl_3F, were patented as types of Freon and became the dominant coolants used in refrigerators and air conditioners throughout the 20th century. The problem with CFCs is that they are *very* stable. Therefore, as M.J. Molina and F.S. Rowland showed in their 1974 *Nature* article, when CFCs are released in the atmosphere, they eventually migrate to the stratosphere, where UV light causes homolysis of a C—Cl bond to produce Cl•. Cl• can then enter the propagation cycle shown in Scheme B (Fig. 27-9), the sum of which (shown on the third line) is the catalytic breakdown of O_3 to O_2.

The Montreal Protocol was established in 1987 to combat the problem by phasing out the production of CFCs and other ozone-depleting substances. Thanks to these measures, the ozone hole has shrunk more than 5% since it peaked in size in the year 2000, but it still poses a problem today. Indeed, in 2020 the ozone hole was the 12th largest in 40 years. However, if the Montreal Protocol can be adhered to, then stratospheric ozone is projected to reach pre-1980 levels by 2050, which would be a great success story about the cooperative efforts of science and politics.

Scheme A

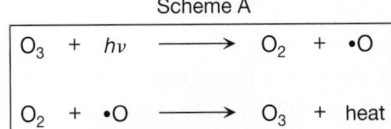

$$O_3 + h\nu \longrightarrow O_2 + \cdot O$$
$$O_2 + \cdot O \longrightarrow O_3 + \text{heat}$$

September 2020

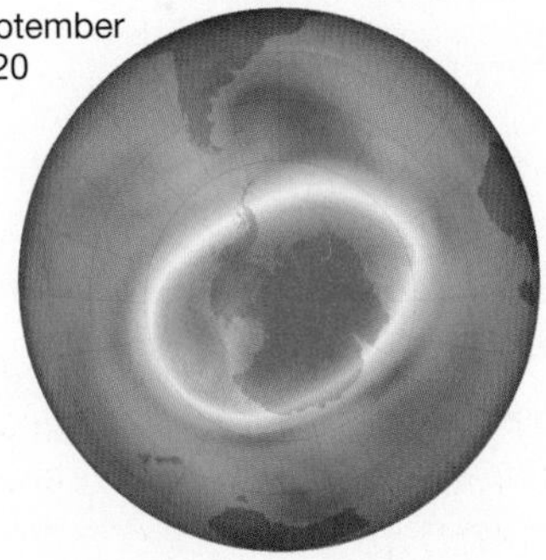

$$Cl\cdot + O_3 \longrightarrow ClO\cdot + O_2$$
$$ClO\cdot + \cdot O \longrightarrow O_2 + Cl\cdot$$
$$\overline{O_3 + \cdot O \longrightarrow 2\,O_2}$$

Scheme B

FIGURE 27-9

YOUR TURN 27.18

Construct a schematic representation of the radical bromination of methane in Solved Problem 27.3. Use Figure 27-8 as a guide.

Radical halogenation is classified as a *chain reaction*, because one step of the reaction is responsible for causing a large number of subsequent steps to occur. For our purposes:

Chain reactions generally have mechanisms that consist of *initiation*, *propagation*, and *termination* steps (see Looking Ahead box).

> **▸ LOOKING AHEAD**
>
> In Section 27.5, we will study the radical addition of HBr to alkenes, which proceeds by a chain-reaction mechanism. Many polymers, such as plastics, are produced by chain-reaction mechanisms as well, as we will see in Chapter 28.

As we saw for radical halogenation, the radical intermediates that participate in any chain-reaction mechanism are produced by the initiation steps and are diminished by the termination steps. Furthermore, the propagation cycle is responsible for converting the overall reactants into the overall products. That is:

The sum of the propagation steps of a chain-reaction mechanism yields the balanced overall reaction.

27.4b Kinetics, Thermodynamics, and Selectivity of Radical Halogenation

Although the mechanism of halogenation is the same regardless of the identity of the molecular halogen used, some halogenations are more feasible to carry out than others. One important aspect to consider is the relative reaction rates, which exhibit a periodic table trend, as shown in Equation 27-21a through 27-21d:

Explosive

Decreasing reaction rate

$$CH_4 + F_2 \xrightarrow[h\nu]{} CH_3F + HF \qquad \textbf{(27-21a)}$$

$$CH_4 + Cl_2 \xrightarrow[h\nu]{} CH_3Cl + HCl \qquad \textbf{(27-21b)}$$

$$CH_4 + Br_2 \xrightarrow[h\nu]{} CH_3Br + HBr \qquad \textbf{(27-21c)}$$

$$CH_4 + I_2 \xrightarrow[h\nu]{} CH_3I + HI \qquad \textbf{(27-21d)}$$

Extremely slow

Namely:

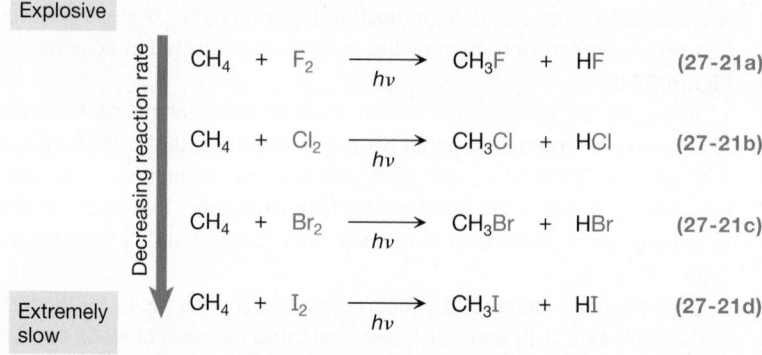

The rate of radical halogenation decreases in the order: $F_2 > Cl_2 > Br_2 > I_2$.

Fluorination is explosive, even with dilute concentrations. Chlorination is slower than fluorination but is still potentially explosive. Bromination is slower still and therefore quite controllable. Iodination is so slow that the reaction has to have energy added, such as heat, for it to proceed at a reasonable rate.

To understand this trend, examine **Figure 27-10**, which gives the energy diagram for each halogenation reaction in Equation 27-21. Each of those energy diagrams was constructed from the energies of the bonds broken and formed in the two steps that make up the propagation cycle. (In Section 27.4c, we will examine the details of how those energy diagrams are constructed from the relevant bond energies.) Notice in Figure 27-10 that the size of the energy barrier for halogenation decreases in the order: $I_2 > Br_2 > Cl_2 > F_2$. As that energy barrier decreases, the reaction rate increases, which is consistent with fluorination being the fastest of the halogenation reactions and iodination being the slowest.

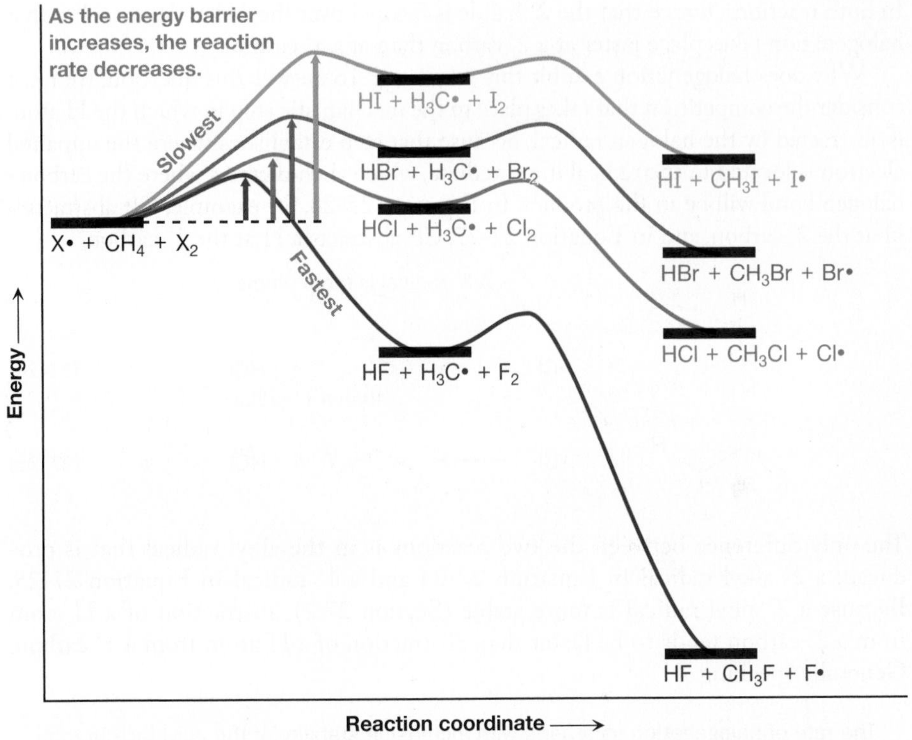
As the energy barrier increases, the reaction rate decreases.
Slowest
Fastest
X• + CH_4 + X_2
HI + H_3C• + I_2
HBr + H_3C• + Br_2
HCl + H_3C• + Cl_2
HF + H_3C• + F_2
HI + CH_3I + I•
HBr + CH_3Br + Br•
HCl + CH_3Cl + Cl•
HF + CH_3F + F•
Energy
Reaction coordinate

FIGURE 27-10 Energy diagrams for the halogenation of CH_4 The purple curve represents fluorination, the red curve represents chlorination, the blue curve represents bromination, and the green curve represents iodination. The arrows indicate the energy barriers for the first propagation step, which also represent the overall energy barriers between reactants and products. Fluorination has the smallest energy barrier, followed by chlorination, bromination, and iodination.

Another major factor contributing to the differences in halogenation rates is the *overall* ΔH°_{rxn}; that is, the energy difference between species at the very left of the energy diagram and the species at the very right. Notice that fluorination is very exothermic. Having so much heat generated in each propagation cycle raises the temperature of the reaction mixture, which further increases the reaction rate and contributes to making fluorination explosive. Iodination, on the other hand, is endothermic overall, which is why it must have energy added to proceed.

YOUR TURN 27.19

Which of these halogenation reactions will proceed faster? Explain.

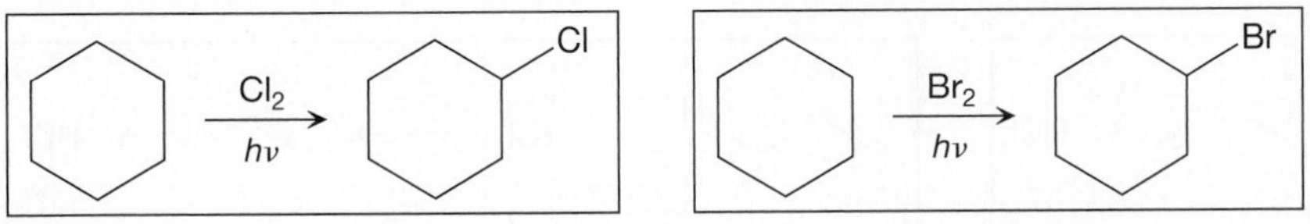
Cl_2
$h\nu$
Cl
Br_2
$h\nu$
Br

A **B**

In addition to the choice of halogen having a substantial impact on the rate of halogenation, the type of carbon undergoing halogenation can have a significant impact, too. For example, as shown in Equations 27-22 and 27-23, halogenation of propane can take place at either the central carbon or a terminal carbon, producing a mixture of both the 2° and 1° alkyl halides:

Slightly selective

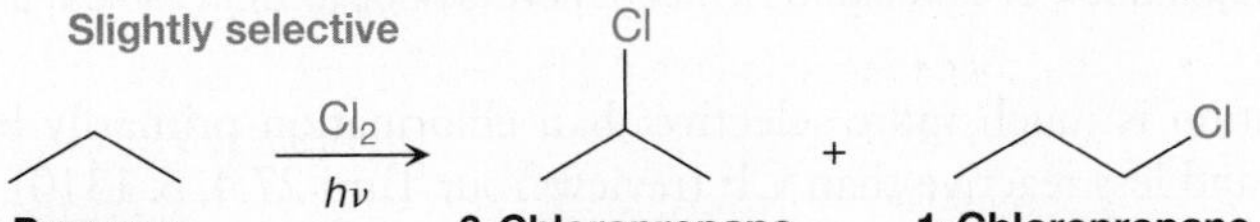
Cl
Cl_2
$h\nu$
+
Cl

(27-22)

Propane **2-Chloropropane** **1-Chloropropane**

Percentage of product: ~60% ~40%

Highly selective

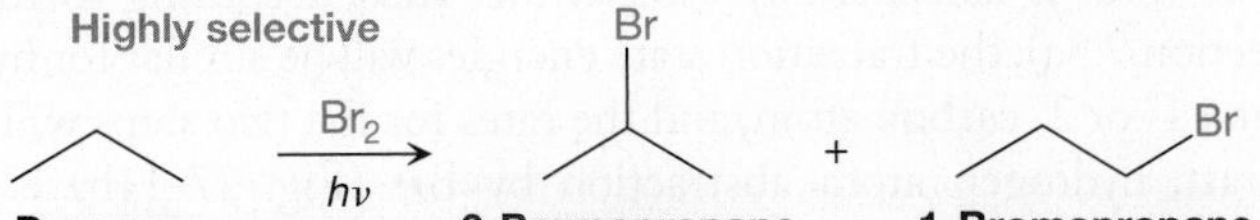
Br
Br_2
$h\nu$
+
Br

(27-23)

Propane **2-Bromopropane** **1-Bromopropane**

Percentage of product: ~96% ~4%

In both reactions, notice that the 2° halide is favored over the 1° halide, meaning that halogenation takes place faster at a 2° carbon than at a 1° carbon.

Why does halogenation exhibit this *selectivity*? To answer this question, we must consider the competition that takes place in the mechanistic step in which the H atom is abstracted by the halogen radical, because that step establishes where the unpaired electron is located in the radical intermediate, which then dictates where the carbon–halogen bond will be in the product. In Equation 27-24, for example, Cl• abstracts a H at the 2° carbon, and in Equation 27-25, Cl• abstracts a H at the 1° carbon.

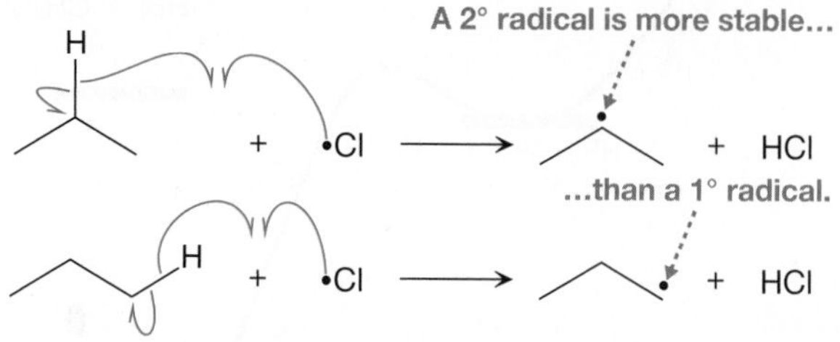

A 2° radical is more stable...
H
+ •Cl
+ HCl
...than a 1° radical.
H
+ •Cl
+ HCl

(27-24)

(27-25)

The only difference between the two reactions is in the alkyl radical that is produced: a 2° alkyl radical in Equation 27-24 and a 1° radical in Equation 27-25. Because a 2° alkyl radical is more stable (Section 27.2), abstraction of a H atom from a 2° carbon tends to be faster than abstraction of a H atom from a 1° carbon. Generally speaking:

> The rate of halogenation increases with increasing stability of the alkyl radical that is produced on hydrogen abstraction (see Recall box).

◂ RECALL

The Hammond postulate (Section 9.3a) states that as an elementary step becomes more exothermic (less endothermic), the transition state increasingly resembles the reactant. Thus, as an elementary step becomes more exothermic (less endothermic), its rate tends to increase.

Thus, not only does radical halogenation tend to be faster at 2° carbons than at 1° carbons, but it also tends to be faster at 3° carbons than at 2° carbons. Halogenation is particularly favored when hydrogen abstraction produces a resonance-stabilized alkyl radical (see Your Turn 27.20).

YOUR TURN 27.20

Which of the following hydrogen atom abstraction steps will proceed faster? Explain your reasoning.

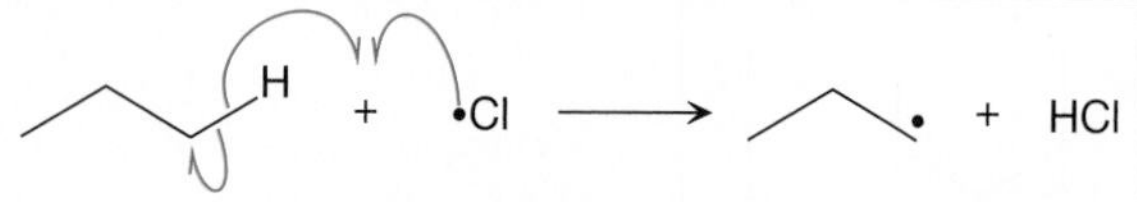

H
+ •Cl
+ HCl

A

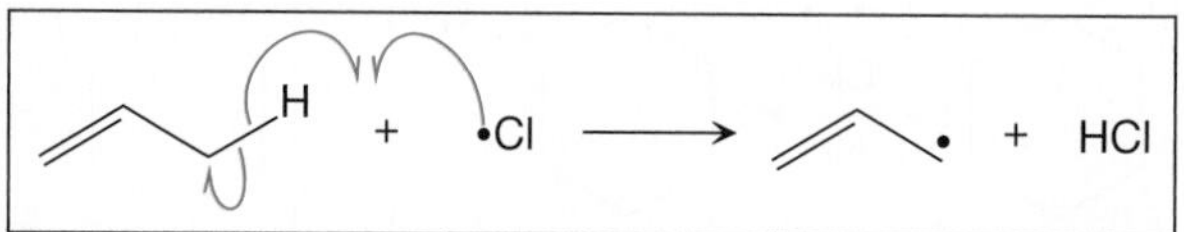

H
+ •Cl
+ HCl

B

Looking back at Equations 27-22 and 27-23, notice that the *extent* to which the 2° alkyl halide product is favored is much greater for bromination than it is for chlorination. In other words:

> Radical bromination of an alkane is much more selective than radical chlorination.

Bromination is much more selective than chlorination primarily because Br• is more stable and less reactive than Cl• (review Your Turn 27.4, p. 1310). As shown in **Figure 27-11**, the greater stability of Br• than that of Cl• significantly affects the hydrogen abstraction step of the mechanism. Notice that hydrogen atom abstraction by Cl• (Fig. 27-11a) is considerably exothermic. Thus, according to the Hammond postulate (Section 9.3a), the transition state energies will be similar for hydrogen atom abstraction at a 1° or 2° carbon atom, and the rates for the two steps will also be similar. By contrast, hydrogen atom abstraction by Br• (Fig. 27-11b) is considerably

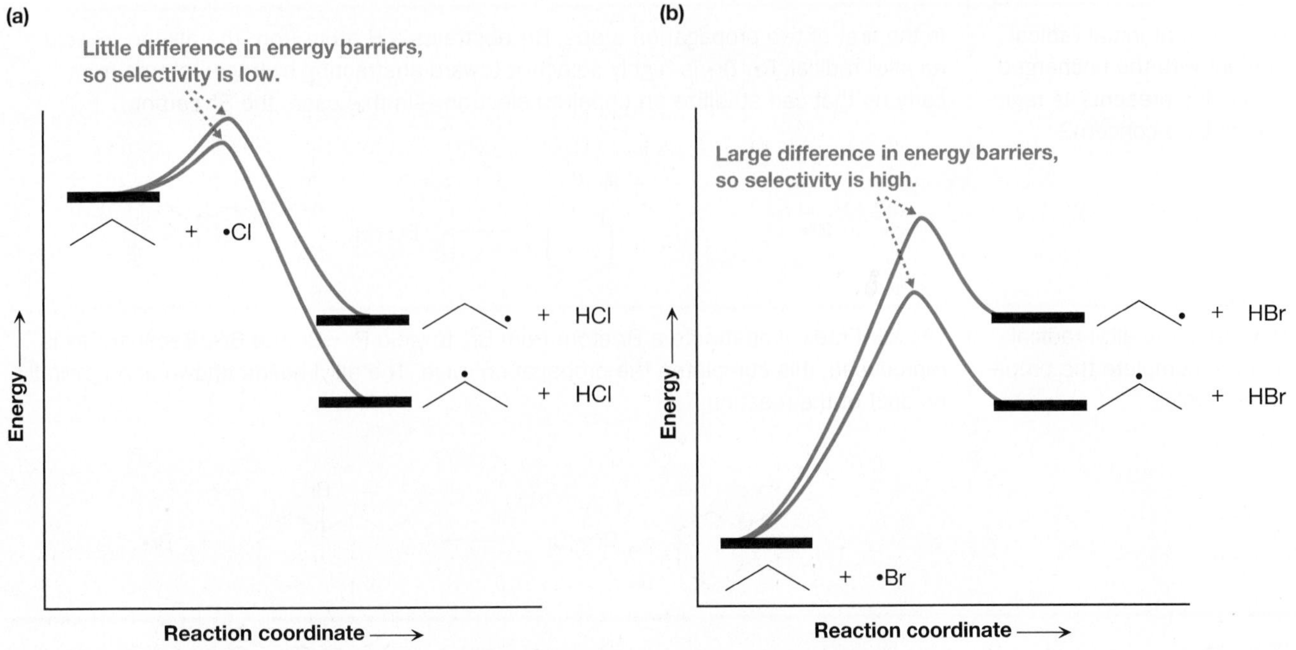
(a)
Little difference in energy barriers, so selectivity is low.
+ •Cl
+ HCl
+ HCl
Energy
Reaction coordinate
(b)
Large difference in energy barriers, so selectivity is high.
+ HBr
+ HBr
+ •Br
Energy
Reaction coordinate

FIGURE 27-11 Selectivity in radical halogenation reactions (a) Hydrogen abstraction by Cl• at a 2° and a 1° carbon atom. (b) Hydrogen abstraction by Br• at a 2° and a 1° carbon atom. The energy barriers are similar in size in (a), so there is little selectivity in chlorination. The energy barriers are significantly different in size in (b), so bromination occurs with high selectivity.

endothermic, so the transition state energies for hydrogen atom abstraction at a 1° or 2° carbon atom will be significantly different. Consequently, the rates for hydrogen atom abstraction at the two types of carbon atoms will be significantly different.

YOUR TURN **27.21**

Construct energy diagrams similar to the ones in Figure 27-11 with 2-methylpropane instead of propane. Consider that the abstraction of a hydrogen from 2-methylpropane can take place at either a 1° or 3° carbon. How do the energy diagrams you drew differ from the ones in Figure 27-11?

SOLVED PROBLEM **27.4**

How to draw the mechanism and major product for radical bromination of an alkane

Break It Down Predict the major product of the reaction shown here, and draw the complete, detailed mechanism. Include all initiation and propagation steps.

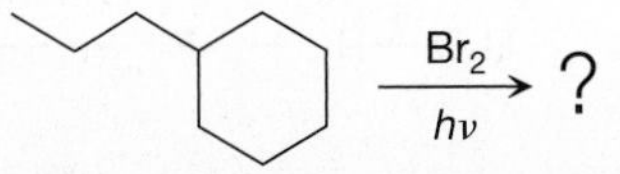
Br2
hν
?

Think	Solve
What initial radical is formed? How is it formed?	Br_2 will undergo homolysis in the presence of UV light, producing the initial radical, Br•. 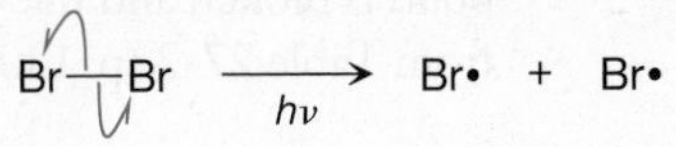

Br—Br
hν
Br• + Br•

(continued)

How will that initial radical interact with the uncharged molecules present? Is regiochemistry a concern?

In the first of two propagation steps, Br• abstracts a H atom from the alkane to yield an alkyl radical, R•. Br• is highly selective toward abstracting hydrogen atoms from carbons that can stabilize an unpaired electron—in this case, the 3° carbon.

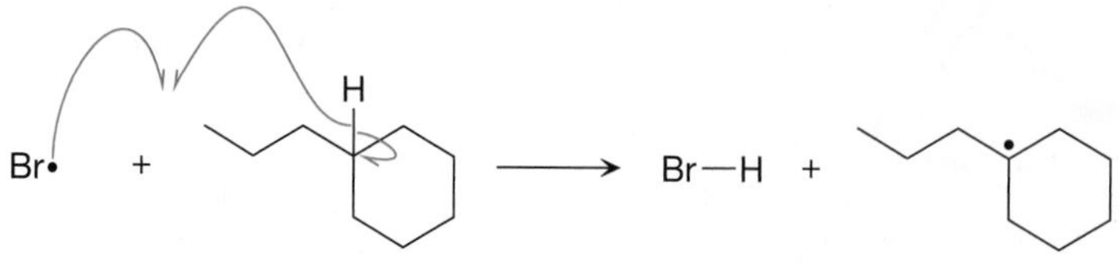

Br•
+
H
Br—H
+

How does the alkyl radical react to complete the propagation cycle?

The alkyl radical abstracts a Br atom from Br_2 to yield R—Br and Br•. Because Br• is reproduced, this completes the propagation cycle. The alkyl halide shown is an overall product of the reaction.

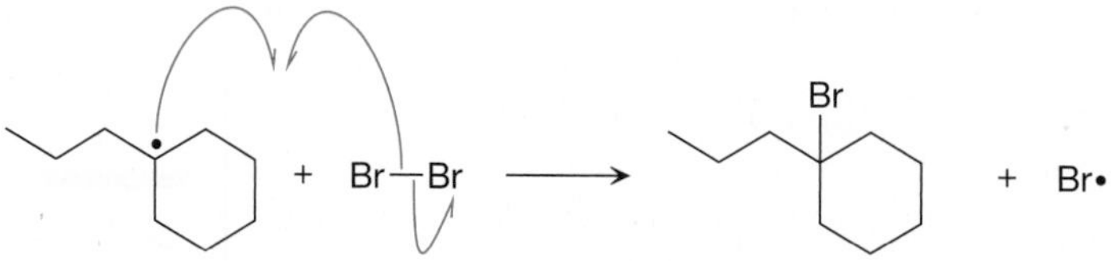

+
Br—Br
Br
+
Br•

Try It Predict the major product of the reaction shown here, and draw the complete, detailed mechanism. Include all initiation and propagation steps. Draw two plausible termination steps as well.

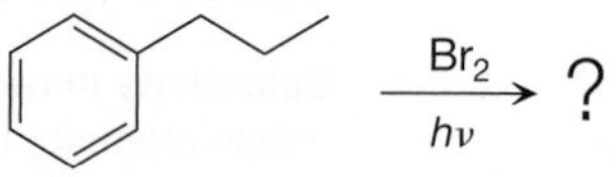

Br2
hν
?

27.4c A Deeper Look: A Quantitative Look at Radical Halogenation

In Section 27.4b, we saw how the rate of halogenation of methane (Eq. 27-21a through 27-21d, p. 1322) depends on the identity of the halogen, decreasing in the order: $F_2 > Cl_2 > Br_2 > I_2$. This outcome is consistent with the energy diagrams shown in Figure 27-10 (p. 1323), in which each reaction's pair of propagation steps establishes an energy barrier that decreases in the order: $I_2 > Br_2 > Cl_2 > F_2$.

The energy diagrams in Figure 27-10 were constructed by calculating the value of ΔH°_{rxn} for each propagation step, which calls for subtracting the energy of the bond formed from the energy of the bond broken. For example, in the first propagation step in the fluorination of methane (Eq. 27-26), a C—H bond of methane is broken and the H—F bond is formed. Substituting the values of bond energy from Table 27-1 (p. 1307), we find ΔH°_{rxn} for that step to be −130 kJ/mol.

Bond broken = 439 kJ/mol; Bond formed = 569 kJ/mol

$$H_3C{-}H + \cdot F \longrightarrow H_3C\cdot + H{-}F \qquad \Delta H^\circ_{rxn} = \text{Bond broken} - \text{Bond formed} = 439\ \text{kJ/mol} - 569\ \text{kJ/mol}; \quad \boxed{\Delta H^\circ_{rxn} = -130\ \text{kJ/mol}} \qquad (27\text{-}26)$$

Therefore, the products of this step are 130 kJ/mol more stable than the reactants, which is why Figure 27-10 shows that the first step of fluorination leads to a substantial energy lowering.

Similarly, in the second propagation step of the reaction (Eq. 27-27), the F—F bond is broken and the C—F bond is formed. Substituting the values of bond energy from Table 27-2 (p. 1308), we find ΔH°_{rxn} for that step to be −301 kJ/mol.

Bond broken = 159 kJ/mol ; Bond formed = 460 kJ/mol

$$H_3C\bullet + F{-}F \longrightarrow H_3C{-}F + \bullet F \qquad \Delta H^\circ_{rxn} = \text{Bond broken} - \text{Bond formed} = 159\ \text{kJ/mol} - 460\ \text{kJ/mol}, \quad \boxed{\Delta H^\circ_{rxn} = -301\ \text{kJ/mol}} \tag{27-27}$$

Again, this is consistent with Figure 27-10, which shows a substantial lowering of energy in the second fluorination step.

Summing the ΔH°_{rxn} values of the two propagation steps, we calculate ΔH°_{rxn} for the entire propagation cycle (and therefore the overall reaction) to be (−130 kJ/mol) + (−301 kJ/mol) = −431 kJ/mol. This indicates a highly exothermic overall reaction, which, as we mentioned in Section 27.4b, helps explain why fluorination reactions tend to be explosive.

We can carry out this exercise on the chlorination, bromination, and iodination of methane, as well, by calculating ΔH°_{rxn} for each propagation step and for the overall reaction (see Your Turn 27.22). All three ΔH°_{rxn} values for each such halogenation reaction are listed in Table 27-3. Notice that, just as we saw in Figure 27-10, ΔH°_{rxn} for each propagation step and for the overall reaction become more negative in the order: $I_2 > Br_2 > Cl_2 > F_2$.

TABLE 27-3 Reaction Enthalpies for the Propagation Steps of $CH_4 + X_2 \longrightarrow CH_3X + HX$

	ΔH°_{rxn} (kJ/mol)			
Reaction	**X• = F•**	**X• = Cl•**	**X• = Br•**	**X• = I•**
$X\bullet + CH_4 \rightarrow HX + CH_3\bullet$	−130	+4	+71	+138
$CH_3\bullet + X_2 \rightarrow CH_3X + X\bullet$	−301	−107	−102	−88
$CH_4 + X_2 \rightarrow CH_3X + HX$	−431	−103	−31	+50

YOUR TURN 27.22

Complete the following table to obtain the ΔH°_{rxn} values shown in Table 27-3 for the propagation steps that make up the bromination of methane. Then sum the values to calculate the value of ΔH°_{rxn} for the overall reaction. Bond energies can be found in Tables 27-1 (p. 1307) and 27-2 (p. 1308). How do the values you determined here compare to the ones in Table 27-3?

Reaction	Energy of Bond Broken	Energy of Bond Formed	(Energy of Bond Broken) − (Energy of Bond Formed)
$Br\bullet + CH_4 \longrightarrow HBr + CH_3\bullet$	H—CH_3 =	H—Br =	
$CH_3\bullet + Br_2 \longrightarrow CH_3Br + Br\bullet$	Br—Br =	Br—CH_3 =	

Now let's further consider the *selectivity* in radical halogenation. We learned in Section 27.4b that *radical bromination is much more selective than chlorination.* To help us understand why, we examined the energy diagrams in Figure 27-11 (p. 1325), which depict propane undergoing competing 1° or 2° hydrogen atom abstractions by Cl• (Fig. 27-11a) or Br• (Fig. 27-11b). As we saw, those competing steps are exothermic in chlorination, whereas they are endothermic in bromination.

As we did for Figure 27-10, we can use bond energies to construct the free energy diagrams shown in Figures 27-11a and 27-11b. The relevant elementary steps and bond energies (Table 27-1, p. 1307) for chlorination are shown in Equations 27-28 and 27-29:

Bond broken = 422 kJ/mol; Bond formed = 431 kJ/mol

$$Cl\bullet + H{-}CH_2CH_2CH_3 \longrightarrow Cl{-}H + \bullet CH_2CH_2CH_3 \qquad \begin{aligned}\Delta H^\circ_{rxn} &= \text{Bond broken} - \text{Bond formed}\\ &= 422\text{ kJ/mol} - 431\text{ kJ/mol}\\ \Delta H^\circ_{rxn} &= -9\text{ kJ/mol}\end{aligned} \qquad (27\text{-}28)$$

Bond broken = 410 kJ/mol; Bond formed = 431 kJ/mol

$$Cl\bullet + H{-}CH(CH_3)_2 \longrightarrow Cl{-}H + \bullet CH(CH_3)_2 \qquad \begin{aligned}\Delta H^\circ_{rxn} &= \text{Bond broken} - \text{Bond formed}\\ &= 410\text{ kJ/mol} - 431\text{ kJ/mol}\\ \Delta H^\circ_{rxn} &= -21\text{ kJ/mol}\end{aligned} \qquad (27\text{-}29)$$

Notice that both steps for chlorination are exothermic. By contrast, the relevant steps in bromination are endothermic:

Bond broken = 422 kJ/mol; Bond formed = 368 kJ/mol

$$Br\bullet + H{-}CH_2CH_2CH_3 \longrightarrow Br{-}H + \bullet CH_2CH_2CH_3 \qquad \begin{aligned}\Delta H^\circ_{rxn} &= \text{Bond broken} - \text{Bond formed}\\ &= 422\text{ kJ/mol} - 368\text{ kJ/mol}\\ \Delta H^\circ_{rxn} &= +54\text{ kJ/mol}\end{aligned} \qquad (27\text{-}30)$$

Bond broken = 410 kJ/mol; Bond formed = 368 kJ/mol

$$Br\bullet + H{-}CH(CH_3)_2 \longrightarrow Br{-}H + \bullet CH(CH_3)_2 \qquad \begin{aligned}\Delta H^\circ_{rxn} &= \text{Bond broken} - \text{Bond formed}\\ &= 410\text{ kJ/mol} - 368\text{ kJ/mol}\\ \Delta H^\circ_{rxn} &= +42\text{ kJ/mol}\end{aligned} \qquad (27\text{-}31)$$

YOUR TURN 27.23

Use Table 27-1 to calculate ΔH°_{rxn} for the competing hydrogen abstractions in the fluorination of propane. On the basis of those values, should fluorination be more selective or less selective than chlorination or bromination? Repeat this exercise for the iodination of propane.

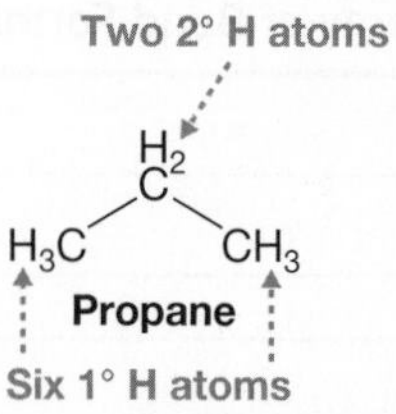

Two 2° H atoms
H_2
C
H_3C
CH_3
Propane
Six 1° H atoms

FIGURE 27-12 Equivalent protons in propane The six 1° H atoms are equivalent and the two 2° H atoms are equivalent.

We can quantify the selectivity of halogenation by comparing the experimentally measured product distribution of each reaction to what the distributions would be if the reactions were completely nonselective (i.e., if all positions were favored equally). Propane, for example, has two equivalent 2° H atoms and six equivalent 1° H atoms, as shown in **Figure 27-12**. If there were equal likelihood for each of the eight H atoms to be replaced in a chlorination reaction, then there would be a 25% chance (two of eight) that the reaction would replace a 2° H atom to produce 2-chloropropane, and there would be a 75% chance (six of eight) that the reaction would replace a 1° H atom to produce 1-chloropropane. In other words, a completely nonselective chlorination reaction would produce 25% 2-chloropropane and 75% 1-chloropropane, giving a ratio of 1:3, not the observed ratio of 60:40 (i.e., 3:2) we saw previously in Equation 27-22 (p. 1323).

To compute the selectivity of chlorination at the 2° carbon relative to the 1° carbon, we divide the projected nonselective ratio (i.e., 1:3) into the one that is actually observed (i.e., 60:40):

$$\text{Chlorination selectivity } (2°:1°) = \frac{60:40}{1:3} = \frac{60}{1}:\frac{40}{3} = 60:13\tfrac{1}{3} = 4.5:1$$

This selectivity of 4.5:1 means that if a molecule had the same number of 1° and 2° hydrogens, then the product mixture would have 4.5 times more of the secondary alkyl chloride than of the primary alkyl chloride.

Repeating this calculation for the bromination in Equation 27-23, and using the 96:4 ratio of 2°-to-1° alkyl halide products, we obtain:

$$\text{Bromination selectivity } (2°:1°) = \frac{96:4}{1:3} = \frac{96}{1}:\frac{4}{3} = 96:\tfrac{4}{3} = 72:1$$

On the basis of the two ratios for halogenation at a 2° versus a 1° carbon, bromination is about $\frac{72}{4.5} = 16$ times more selective than chlorination.

Experimentally determined product distributions from other halogenation reactions have enabled us to determine the relative selectivities of halogenating 2° versus 3° carbons. These results can be combined with the ones from above to give the following relative selectivities for 3°, 2°, and 1° carbons:

Relative selectivities of halogenation at 3°, 2°, and 1° carbon atoms:

- Chlorination = 6:4.5:1
- Bromination = 1600:72:1

Notice how selective bromination is toward a 3° carbon!

27.4d Radical Bromination Using *N*-Bromosuccinimide

If an alkene undergoes radical bromination, substitution will most likely take place at the allylic position because of the resonance stabilization in the allylic radical that would be produced on hydrogen abstraction. Thus, radical bromination of cyclohexene would produce 3-bromocyclohexene, as shown in Equation 27-32a:

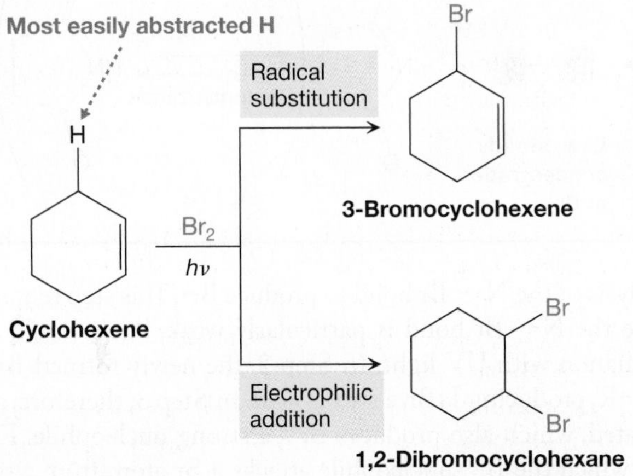
Most easily abstracted H
H
Cyclohexene
Br2
hν
Radical substitution
Br
3-Bromocyclohexene
Electrophilic addition
Br
Br
1,2-Dibromocyclohexane

(27-32a)

(27-32b)

A problem arises, however, if we carry out a bromination by simply treating the alkene with molecular bromine and UV light. As we learned in Section 13.4a, Br_2 will also add to the C=C double bond in an *electrophilic addition* reaction (Eq. 27-32b). To avoid this problem, chemists carry out radical brominations with *N*-bromosuccinimide

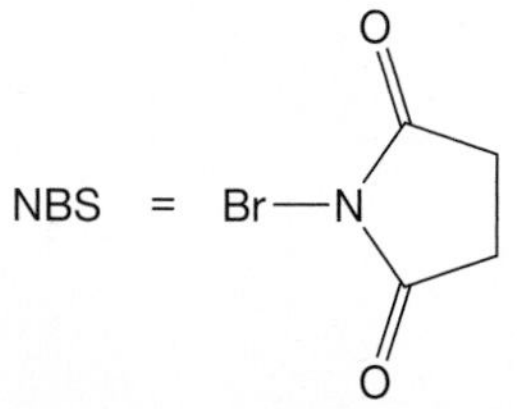
NBS
Br
N
O
O

FIGURE 27-13 ***N*-Bromosuccinimide and bromination** NBS is often used to carry out radical bromination at allylic positions without producing unwanted electrophilic addition products.

(NBS; **Figure 27-13**). As shown in Equation 27-33, NBS reacts with cyclohexene to give only the allylic bromide:

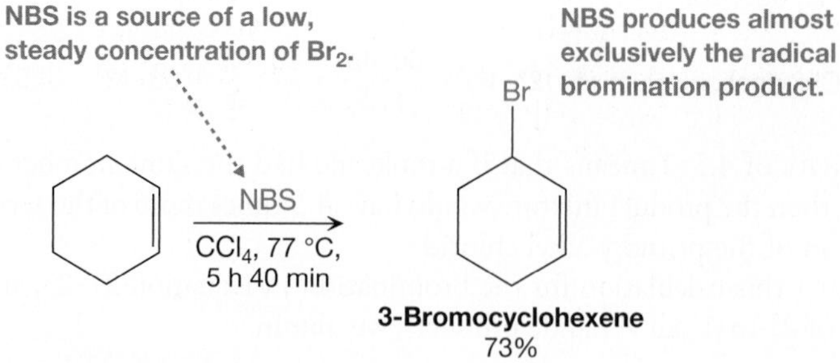
NBS is a source of a low, steady concentration of Br2.
NBS produces almost exclusively the radical bromination product.
Br
NBS
CCl4, 77 °C,
5 h 40 min
3-Bromocyclohexene
73%

(27-33)

N-Bromosuccinimide does not alter the mechanism of radical bromination, but it controls the rates of the competing reactions in Equation 27-32 by controlling the concentration of Br_2 (and, thus, the concentration of Br•).

> In radical halogenation reactions, *N*-bromosuccinimide (NBS) is the source of a low, steady concentration of Br_2.

The mechanism by which Br_2 is produced from NBS is shown in Equation 27-34:

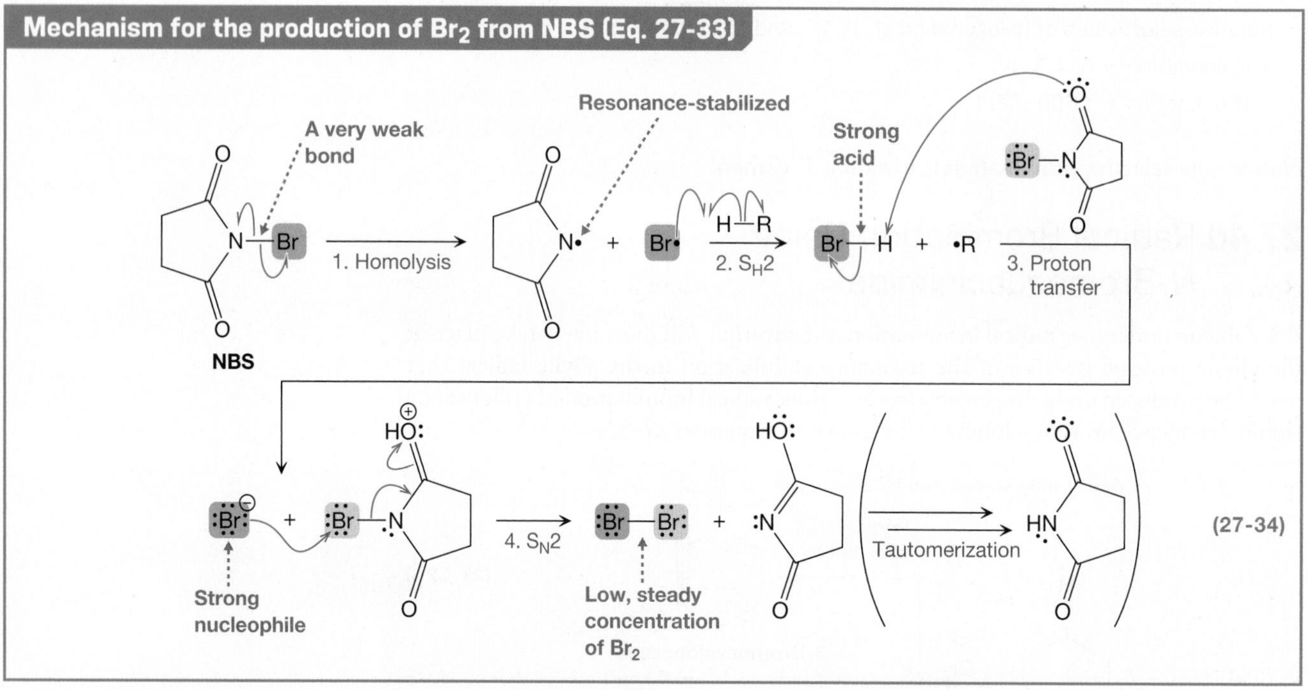
Mechanism for the production of Br2 from NBS (Eq. 27-33)
A very weak bond
Resonance-stabilized
Strong acid
NBS
1. Homolysis
2. SH2
H—R
Br—H + •R
3. Proton transfer
4. SN2
Tautomerization
Strong nucleophile
Low, steady concentration of Br2
(27-34)

Step 1 is homolysis of the N—Br bond to produce Br•. This step requires only modest heating because the N—Br bond is particularly weak, but it could also be accomplished by irradiation with UV light. In Step 2, the newly formed Br• abstracts a H atom from H—R, producing HBr, a strong acid. In Step 3, therefore, a carbonyl O on NBS is protonated, which also produces Br^-, a strong nucleophile. Finally, Step 4 is an S_N2 step, in which the Br^- nucleophile attacks a Br atom from a second molecule of NBS, yielding Br_2.

YOUR TURN **27.24**

In Step 1 of Equation 27-34, homolysis of NBS produces a resonance-stabilized radical. In the space provided here, draw the additional resonance structures involving the unpaired electron, and include the appropriate curved arrows. Also, complete the mechanism by explicitly drawing the two proton transfer steps that make up the tautomerization in Equation 27-34. *Hint*: Are the conditions acidic or basic?

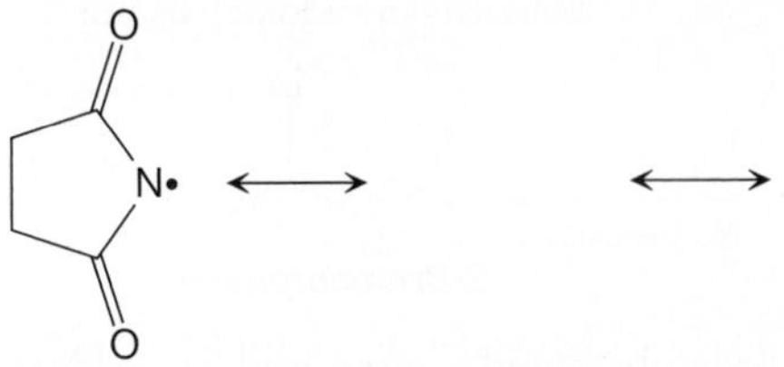

The low concentration of Br_2 maintained by NBS favors radical bromination over alkene addition because the rate of alkene addition is slowed more dramatically than the rate of radical bromination. To see why, recall from Section 13.4a that electrophilic addition of Br_2 to an alkene proceeds through a bromonium ion intermediate (Eq. 27-35):

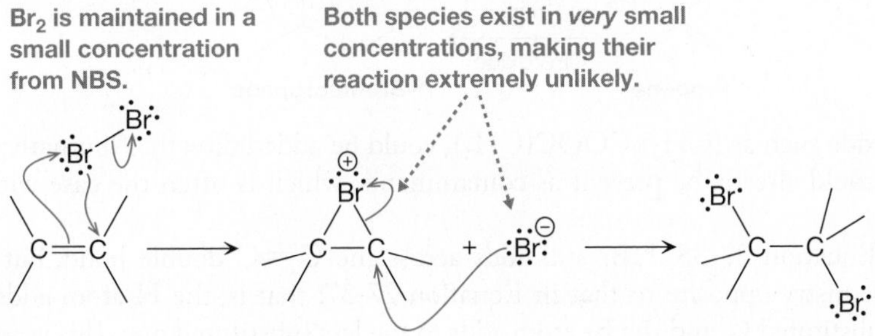

Br2 is maintained in a small concentration from NBS.
Both species exist in very small concentrations, making their reaction extremely unlikely.

(27-35)

Because of the low abundance of Br_2, the bromonium ion and Br^- intermediates that derive from Br_2 are both present in *very low* concentrations, making it *extremely unlikely* that they will encounter each other to complete the reaction.

The story is somewhat different for radical bromination using NBS, whose initiation and propagation steps are shown in Equation 27-36:

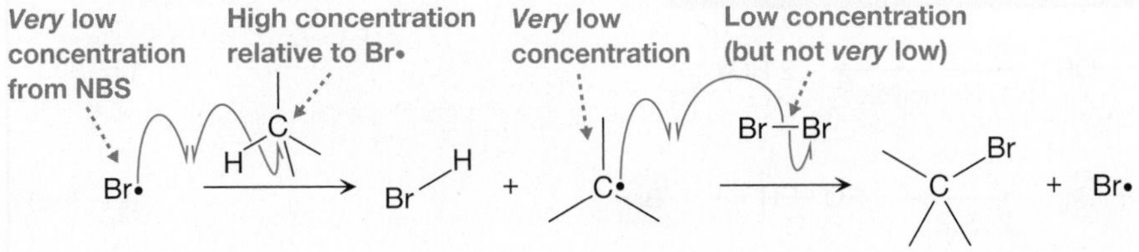

Very low concentration from NBS
High concentration relative to Br•
Very low concentration
Low concentration (but not very low)

(27-36)

None of these steps requires the reaction between two species produced from Br_2, so there are no steps that require the reaction between two species whose concentrations are excessively low.

YOUR TURN **27.25**

Predict the major product of the reaction shown here.

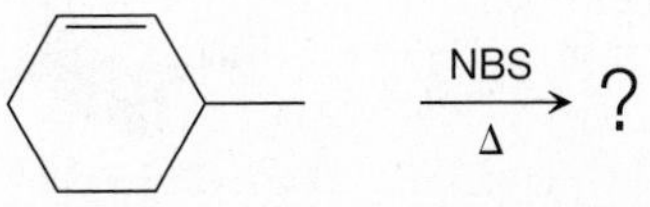

NBS
Δ
?

27.5 Radical Addition of HBr: Anti-Markovnikov Addition

SECTION 27.5 OBJECTIVES

You will be able to:

1. Draw the mechanism for the radical addition of HBr to an alkene, and predict the major product.
2. Explain why the radical addition of HBr to an alkene takes place with anti-Markovnikov regiochemistry.

Recall from Section 12.3 that a hydrogen halide adds across the double bond of an alkene. For example, HBr will add to propene to produce 2-bromopropane, as shown in Equation 27-37:

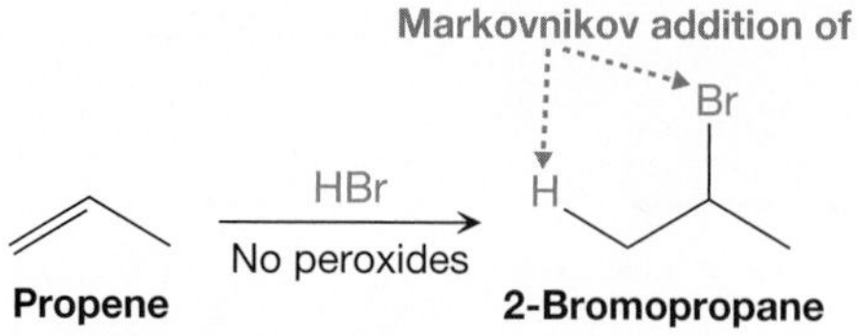

Markovnikov addition of HBr
Br
H
HBr
No peroxides
Propene
2-Bromopropane

(27-37)

◂ RECALL

Section 12.3 showed that in the Markovnikov addition of HBr to an alkene, the major product derives from the more stable carbocation intermediate produced on addition of H^+. The more stable carbocation is produced when H^+ adds to the less substituted C atom of the C=C bond.

Overall, H^+ adds to the less alkyl-substituted C atom, and Br^- adds to the more alkyl-substituted C atom, an example of *Markovnikov addition* (see top Recall box). If a small amount of peroxide (RO—OR) is present, however, 1-bromopropane will be the major product instead, as indicated in Equation 27-38:

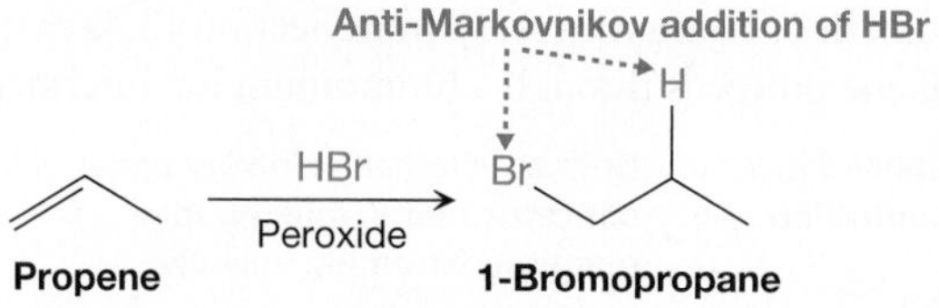

Anti-Markovnikov addition of HBr
H
Br
HBr
Peroxide
Propene
1-Bromopropane

(27-38)

◂ RECALL

Sections 13.6 and 13.7 showed how hydroboration–oxidation leads to the anti-Markovnikov addition of H_2O across the C=C bond of an alkene or the C≡C bond of an alkyne.

A peroxide such as $(CH_3)_3COOC(CH_3)_3$ could be added directly. Alternatively, peroxides could already be present as contaminants, which is often the case with ether solvents.

In Equation 27-38, HBr still adds across the C=C double bond, but with a regiochemistry opposite to that in Equation 27-37; that is, the H atom adds to the more substituted C, and the Br atom adds to the less substituted one. This is an example of an *anti-Markovnikov addition* (see bottom Recall box).

Mechanism Drawing
Radical Addition of HBr to an Alkene

Peroxides are radical initiators because they contain a weak O—O bond. Consequently, the reaction in Equation 27-38 proceeds by the radical mechanism in Equation 27-39:

Mechanism for radical addition of HBr to an alkene (Eq. 27-38)

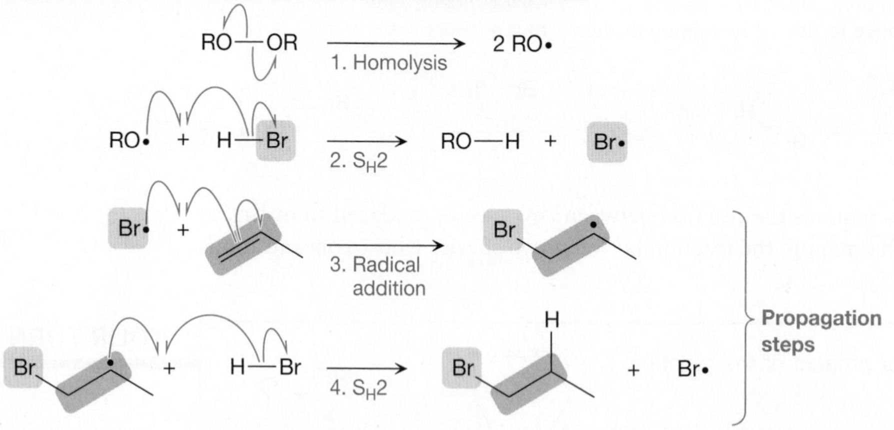

RO—OR
2 RO•
1. Homolysis
RO• + H—Br
RO—H + Br•
2. S_H2
Br• +
Br
3. Radical addition
H
Br + H—Br
4. S_H2
Br + Br•
Propagation steps

(27-39a)

(27-39b)

(27-39c)

(27-39d)

Step 1 (Eq. 27-39a) is homolysis of the peroxide to produce two alkoxy radicals (RO•). In Step 2, RO• abstracts a H atom from HBr to produce Br•. Br• then adds to the alkene in Step 3, and the resulting alkyl radical abstracts a H atom from HBr in Step 4, yielding the overall product. This is a *chain reaction*, because Steps 3 and 4 make up a propagation cycle; that is, the Br• radical that reacts in Step 3 is regenerated as a product in Step 4. Summing Steps 3 and 4 yields the net reaction (see Your Turn 27.26).

The propagation steps from Equation 27-39 are as follows. Cross out the redundant species, and sum the two steps to arrive at the net reaction.

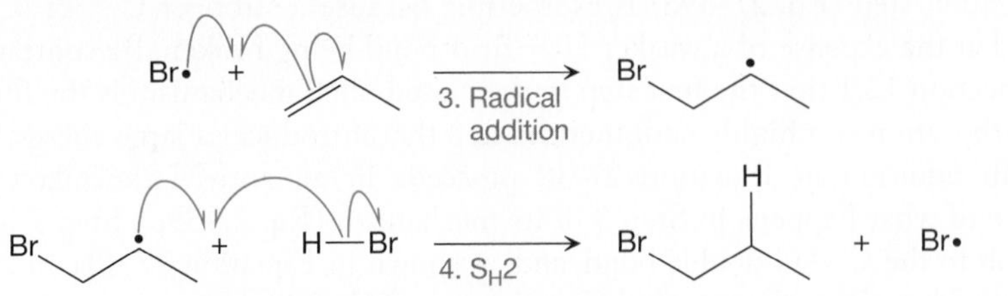

Br•
+
3. Radical addition
Br
H
+
H—Br
4. S_H2
Br•

YOUR TURN **27.26**

The initial Br• that is used in the propagation steps in Equation 27-39 is produced by the sequence of Steps 1 and 2, so Steps 1 and 2 can be viewed as a *set* of initiation steps. As usual, a termination step is any step that removes a radical from the propagation cycle (see Your Turn 27.27).

Draw three plausible termination steps for the reaction in Equation 27-38.

YOUR TURN **27.27**

The mechanism for the radical addition of HBr is represented schematically in **Figure 27-14**. Two steps (black arrows) are required to introduce Br• into the propagation cycle (blue arrows). With each completion of the propagation cycle, one molecule of propene and one molecule of HBr are converted to one molecule of 1-bromopropane. Termination steps (red arrows) remove radicals from the propagation cycle.

Study the diagram in Figure 27-14 and match the initiation and propagation steps to either Equation 27-39a, 27-39b, 27-39c, or 27-39d.

YOUR TURN **27.28**

Two important questions are yet to be answered: (1) Why is the radical mechanism for the addition of HBr faster than the closed-shell mechanism that proceeds through a carbocation intermediate, and (2) why does the radical mechanism favor the anti-Markovnikov addition of HBr? The radical mechanism is faster because

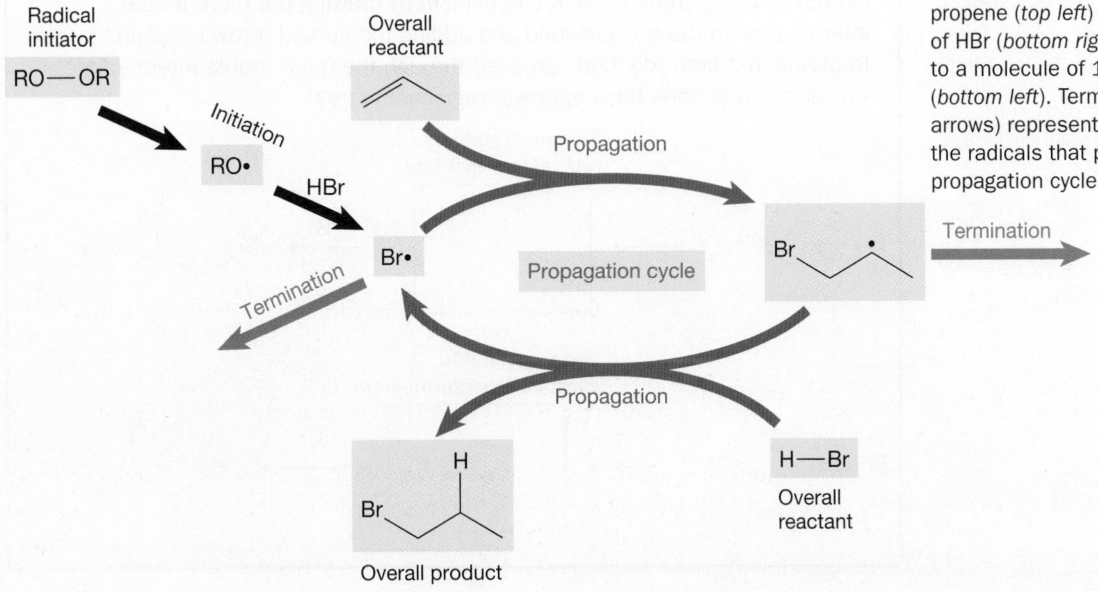

Radical initiator
RO—OR
Initiation
RO•
HBr
Overall reactant
Propagation
Br•
Propagation cycle
Br
Termination
Termination
Propagation
H
Br
Overall product
H—Br
Overall reactant

FIGURE 27-14 Schematic representation of the mechanism for the radical addition of HBr The initiation steps (black arrows) represent the introduction of radicals into the propagation cycle (blue arrows). Each time a full propagation cycle is completed, one molecule of propene (*top left*) and one molecule of HBr (*bottom right*) are converted to a molecule of 1-bromopropane (*bottom left*). Termination steps (red arrows) represent the destruction of the radicals that participate in the propagation cycle.

each of the two propagation steps (Eq. 27-39c and 27-39d) is exothermic. The first propagation step (Eq. 27-39c) is exothermic because a stronger C—Br σ bond is formed at the expense of a weaker carbon–carbon π bond being broken. The second propagation step (Eq. 27-39d) is exothermic because a stronger C—H σ bond is formed at the expense of a weaker H—Br σ bond being broken. By contrast, recall from Section 12.1 that the first step in the closed-shell mechanism is the formation of a carbocation—a highly endothermic step that introduces a large energy barrier.

HBr addition in Equation 27-38 proceeds in an anti-Markovnikov fashion because of what happens in Step 3 of its mechanism (Eq. 27-39c). Step 3 is radical addition to the C=C double bond, and, as shown in Equation 27-40a and 27-40b, Br• can add to either the terminal C or the central C:

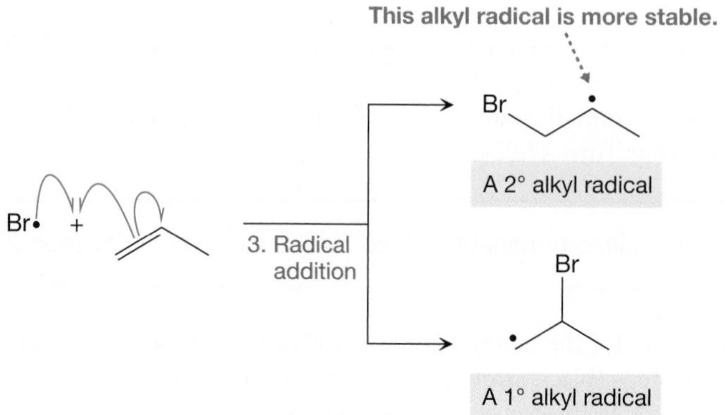
This alkyl radical is more stable.
Br•
+
3. Radical addition
Br
A 2° alkyl radical
Br
A 1° alkyl radical

(27-40a)

(27-40b)

When Br• adds to a terminal C (Eq. 27-40a), a 2° alkyl radical is produced, and when it adds to the central C (Eq. 27-40b), a 1° alkyl radical is produced. The greater stability of the 2° radical provides more driving force.

Radical addition to an alkene generally takes place so as to produce the more stable alkyl radical intermediate.

A similar concept explains why HBr addition to an alkene involving only closed-shell species (Section 12.3) takes place with Markovnikov regiochemistry (see Your Turn 27.29).

YOUR TURN 27.29

The radical and closed-shell mechanisms for the addition of HBr to propene are shown below, but the curved arrow notation and intermediate are omitted in both cases. Complete each mechanism by drawing the more stable intermediate in the box provided and adding the curved arrow notation. Realizing that both reactions proceed through the more stable intermediate, why do the reactions have opposite regiochemistry?

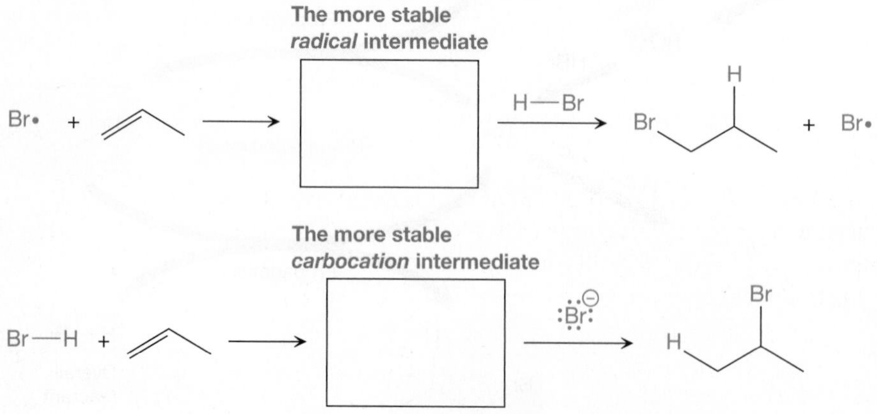
The more stable
radical intermediate
Br•
+
H—Br
Br
H
+
Br•
The more stable
carbocation intermediate
Br—H
+
:Br:⊖
H
Br

Predict the major product of each of the following reactions.

(a)

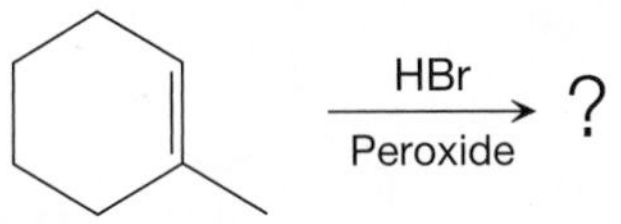

HBr
Peroxide
?

(b)

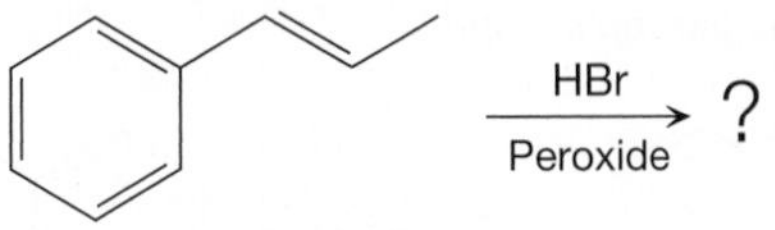

HBr
Peroxide
?

YOUR TURN **27.30**

27.6 Stereochemistry of Radical Halogenation and HBr Addition

SECTION 27.6 OBJECTIVES

You will be able to:

1. Identify radical reactions for which stereochemistry is an issue.
2. Draw the products of radical reactions, taking stereochemistry into account.

In the radical reactions we have seen thus far, stereochemistry can be an issue if the reaction takes place at a carbon atom that is a chiral center in the reactants or becomes one in the products. In the radical halogenation in Equation 27-41, for example, a new chiral center appears in the products and both configurations are produced, resulting in a mixture of enantiomers:

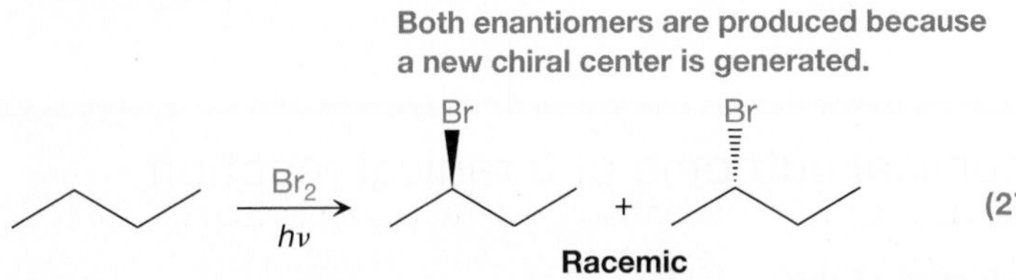

Both enantiomers are produced because a new chiral center is generated.
Br_2
$h\nu$
Br
Br
+
Racemic

(27-41)

The reaction results in a mixture of enantiomers because the chiral center is produced directly from the S_H2 step shown in Equation 27-42 (review Eq. 27-19, p. 1318).

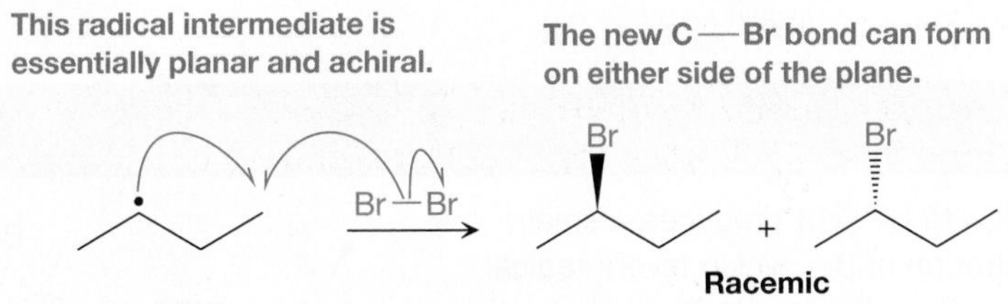

This radical intermediate is essentially planar and achiral.
The new C—Br bond can form on either side of the plane.
Br—Br
Br
Br
+
Racemic

(27-42)

Equation 27-43 shows an example in which halogenation takes place at a C atom that is initially a chiral center:

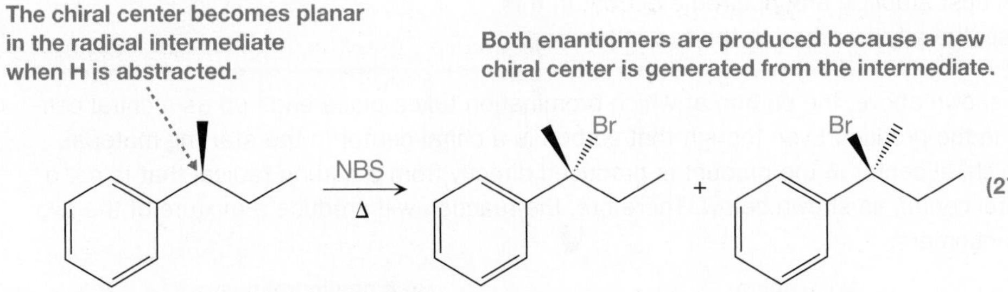

The chiral center becomes planar in the radical intermediate when H is abstracted.
Both enantiomers are produced because a new chiral center is generated from the intermediate.
NBS
Δ
Br
Br
+

(27-43)

Once again, the reaction produces a mixture of enantiomers, because the C atom that undergoes halogenation becomes a chiral center. Even though the C atom is initially a chiral center, it becomes a planar radical intermediate after the H atom is abstracted.

Similarly, if radical addition of HBr to an alkene results in a new chiral center, then both enantiomers will be produced. An example is shown in Equation 27-44.

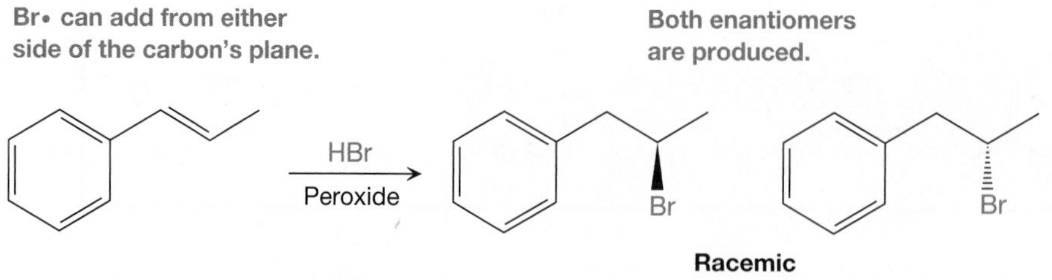

Br• can add from either side of the carbon's plane.
Both enantiomers are produced.
HBr
Peroxide
Br
Br
Racemic

(27-44)

In this case, the chiral center is produced when Br• adds to the alkene C (review Eq. 27-39, p. 1332). The alkene C is planar, and Br• can add to the carbon from either side of the plane.

The lessons we learn from the stereochemistry of radical halogenation and HBr addition reactions can be extended to other radical reactions as well:

> In general, reactions that proceed by radical chain-reaction mechanisms tend not to be stereoselective.

SOLVED PROBLEM **27.5**

How to predict the stereochemical outcome of a radical reaction

Break It Down Draw the major product(s) of this reaction, taking stereochemistry into account.

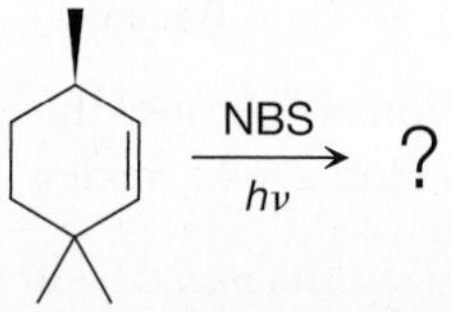

NBS
hν
?

Think	Solve
Temporarily ignoring stereochemistry, what is the major product of the reaction?	Irradiating NBS with UV light produces a small, steady concentration of Br_2, which favors radical bromination over Br_2 addition. Radical bromination will replace a H atom with a Br atom, and the favored site of the reaction will be at a carbon that can best stabilize an unpaired electron; in this case, the allylic carbon at the top of the ring. 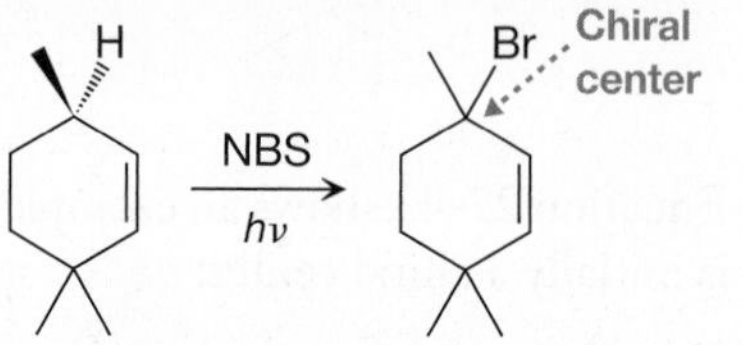 H NBS hν Br Chiral center
Do any atoms involved in the reaction end up as chiral centers in the product? If so, is the chiral center produced directly from an atom that is or is not a chiral center?	As shown above, the carbon at which bromination takes place ends up as a chiral center in the product. Even though that carbon is a chiral center in the starting material, the chiral center in the product is produced directly from a carbon radical that is *not* a chiral center, as shown below. Therefore, the reaction will produce a mixture of the two enantiomers. 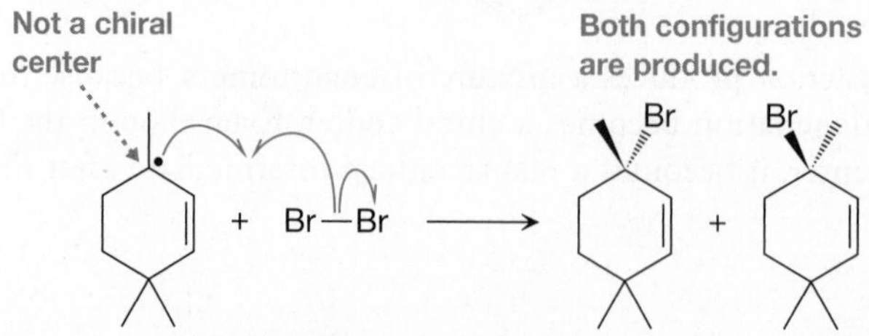 Not a chiral center Both configurations are produced. + Br—Br Br + Br

(continued)

Try It Draw the major product of each of the following reactions, paying attention to stereochemistry. *Hint*: How many chiral centers does each reaction produce?

(a) 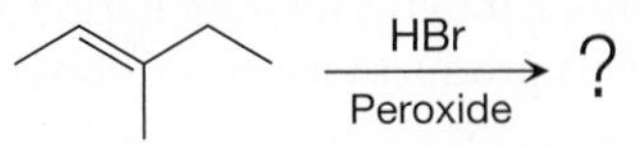
HBr
Peroxide
?

(b) 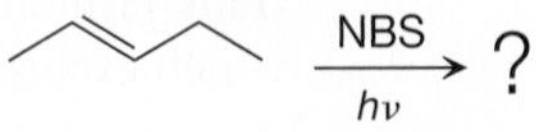
NBS
hν
?

27.7 Dissolving Metal Reductions: Hydrogenation of Alkenes and Alkynes

To this point in Chapter 27, we have examined only radical reactions that proceed by chain-reaction mechanisms. Here in Section 27.7, we study two types of hydrogenation reactions that have radical mechanisms but do not proceed by a chain reaction, known as *dissolving metal reductions*.

Hydrogenation by a dissolving metal reduction takes place under conditions that are different from those of the catalytic hydrogenation reactions discussed in Section 13.9 (see Recall box). In catalytic hydrogenation, a solid *insoluble* metal such as Pt(*s*), Pd(*s*), or Ni(*s*) acts as a catalyst, and the reactants are dissolved in solution. Thus, the catalyst is in a different phase from that of the reactants, making catalytic hydrogenation an example of *heterogenous catalysis*.

In a **dissolving metal reduction**, on the other hand, a metal such as Na(*s*) or Li(*s*) acts as a reducing agent and is *dissolved* in solution along with the reactants. When this takes place in a solvent such as liquid ammonia, $NH_3(\ell)$, the metal loses an electron, and the ammonia solvent stabilizes the electron through extensive solvation. The result, called a **solvated electron**, is depicted in Equation 27-45. Notably, solvated electrons absorb visible light, making the solution appear dark blue, as shown in **Figure 27-15**.

$$\text{Na}\bullet \xrightarrow[\text{NH}_3(\ell)]{} \text{Na}^{\oplus} + \text{e}^{\ominus}\ \text{(solvated)} \qquad (27\text{-}45)$$

In light of this:

> The active radical species in a dissolving metal reduction involving $NH_3(\ell)$/Na(s) is simply an electron that does not formally belong to any atom.

In the discussion that follows, we will see examples of how this solvated electron is involved in the reduction of a multiple bond. Section 27.7a discusses the reduction of alkynes to trans alkenes, and Section 27.7b discusses the Birch reduction of benzene rings.

27.7a Anti-Hydrogenation: Synthesis of Trans Alkenes

When oct-4-yne is treated with sodium metal dissolved in liquid ammonia (−78 °C), the triple bond is reduced to a double bond:

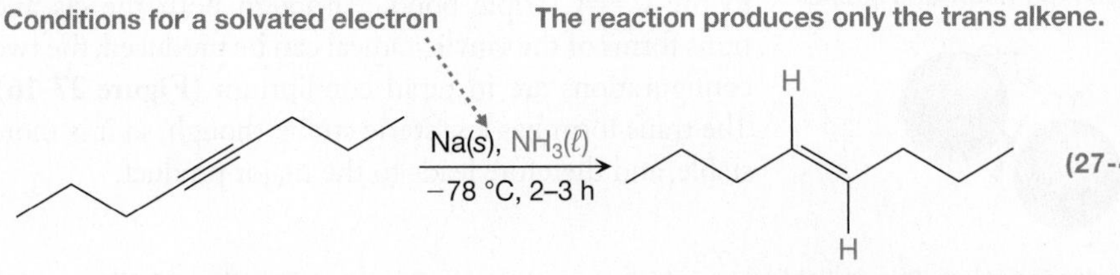
Conditions for a solvated electron
The reaction produces only the trans alkene.
Na(s), NH3(ℓ)
−78 °C, 2–3 h
H
H

(27-46)

Oct-4-yne

(*E*)-Oct-4-ene
>80%

SECTION 27.7 OBJECTIVES

You will be able to:

1. Identify the conditions that facilitate the dissolving metal reduction of an alkyne and the Birch reduction of a benzene ring.
2. Draw the mechanism and major product for the dissolving metal reduction of an alkyne and for the Birch reduction.

◂ RECALL

Catalytic hydrogenation (Section 13.9) takes place on the surface of a metal catalyst that has bound H atoms. When an alkene or alkyne adsorbs to the metal, a C=C or C≡C π bond effectively breaks. C—H σ bond formation occurs when the adsorbed alkene or alkyne encounters a surface-bound H atom.

Solvated electrons being produced in liquid ammonia

FIGURE 27-15 Solvated electrons Whereas liquid ammonia is clear and colorless, the solution turns dark blue when Na(s) is dissolved to produce solvated electrons.

A dissolving metal reduction of an alkyne is highly regioselective, producing the E alkene almost exclusively. Thus, Equation 27-46 is an example of an **anti-hydrogenation** reaction because two H atoms, overall, add to the triple bond in a trans fashion. It complements catalytic hydrogenation using a poisoned catalyst, which exclusively forms the cis product (see Recall box).

YOUR TURN **27.31**

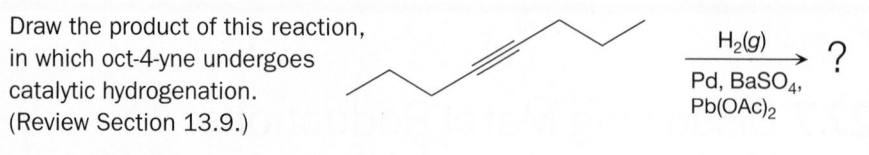

Draw the product of this reaction, in which oct-4-yne undergoes catalytic hydrogenation. (Review Section 13.9.)

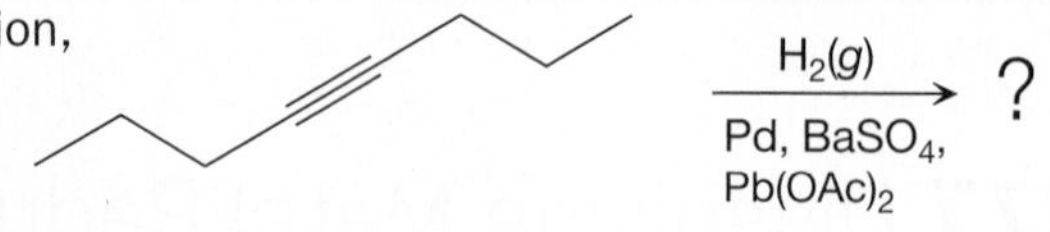

$H_2(g)$
Pd, $BaSO_4$, $Pb(OAc)_2$
?

◂ RECALL

As we saw in Section 13.9, catalytic hydrogenation of an alkyne will produce an alkane on addition of 2 equivalents of H_2. A poisoned catalyst is used to slow the reaction so the reduction can be stopped after the first addition. In such cases, both H atoms add to the same side of the C≡C bond to make a cis alkene.

The mechanism for the dissolving metal reduction is shown in Equation 27-47. It begins with a solvated electron, which was produced on dissolving solid sodium in liquid ammonia. In Step 1, a solvated electron adds to an alkyne C, thus converting the triple bond into a double bond. One of the initial alkyne C atoms gains an unpaired electron and the other gains a negative charge. The carbanion is a very strong base and deprotonates NH_3 in Step 2 (notice the double-barbed curved arrows). This produces an uncharged vinylic radical, which, in Step 3, undergoes radical coupling with a second solvated electron to produce a carbanion. Finally, in Step 4, the carbanion deprotonates a second molecule of NH_3, yielding the overall product.

Mechanism for the dissolving metal reduction of an alkyne (Eq. 27-46)

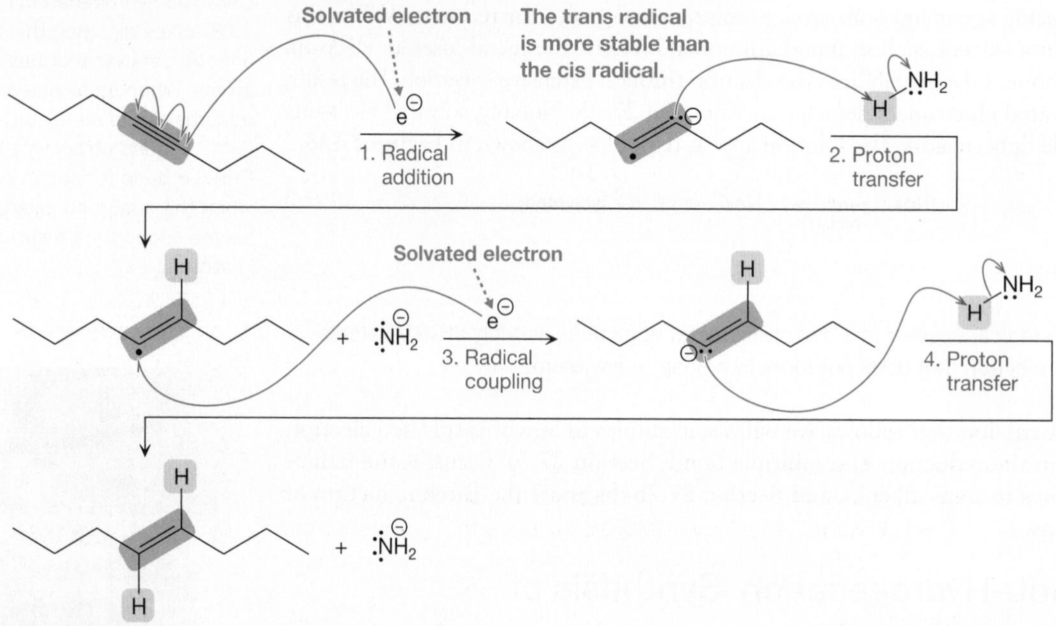

Solvated electron
The trans radical is more stable than the cis radical.
1. Radical addition
2. Proton transfer
Solvated electron
3. Radical coupling
4. Proton transfer

(27-47)

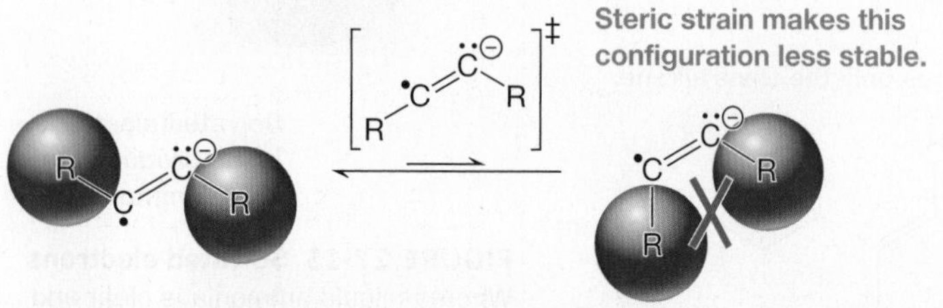

Steric strain makes this configuration less stable.

The stereochemistry of this reaction is established in the first step, which is the addition of a solvated electron to the C≡C triple bond. Although both the cis and trans forms of the vinylic radical can be produced, the two configurations are in rapid equilibrium (**Figure 27-16**). The trans form has less steric strain, though, so it is more stable, and therefore leads to the major product.

FIGURE 27-16 Stereoselectivity of anti-hydrogenation This radical anion, which is produced in Step 1 of Equation 27-47, exists in rapid equilibrium between the cis and trans forms. The trans form is more stable, which is why the reaction produces the trans alkene almost exclusively.

Dissolving metal reductions are much more sluggish with alkenes than with alkynes, in part because of charge stability. In the reduction of an alkyne, the C atom that gains the negative charge is *sp*-hybridized, whereas in the reduction of an alkene, the C atom that gains the negative charge is sp^2-hybridized. Therefore, the alkene C has a lower effective electronegativity (see Recall box), so it does not readily accommodate gaining a negative charge. As a result:

> A dissolving metal reduction will selectively reduce an alkyne over an alkene.

An example is shown in Equation 27-48. This kind of selectivity can be very useful in synthesis.

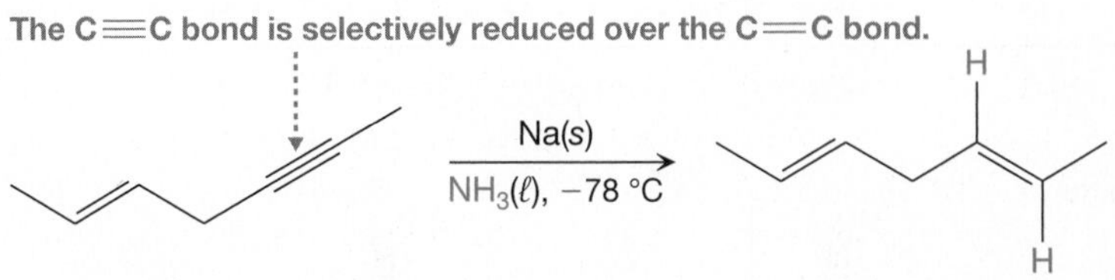

The C≡C bond is selectively reduced over the C=C bond.
Na(s)
NH3(ℓ), −78 °C
H
H

(27-48)

◀ RECALL

Section 3.9 explained that effective electronegativity derives from the *s*-character an atom has in its hybrid orbitals. An *s* orbital is more compact than a *p* orbital, so with greater *s*-character, the atom's electrons are held closer to the nucleus, as would be expected for an atom with higher electronegativity.

YOUR TURN 27.32

Draw the alkyne from which the compound shown here can be produced by a dissolving metal reduction.

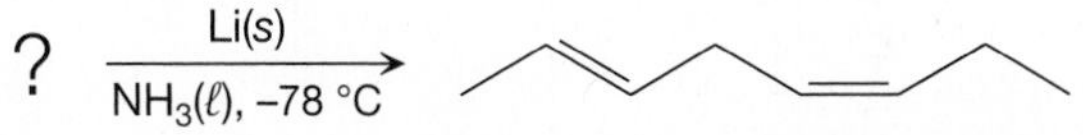

?
Li(s)
NH3(ℓ), −78 °C

27.7b The Birch Reduction

Benzene can be reduced to cyclohexane using catalytic hydrogenation under high temperature and pressure, as shown in Equation 27-49. These extreme conditions are necessary because aromaticity makes benzene's π system quite stable.

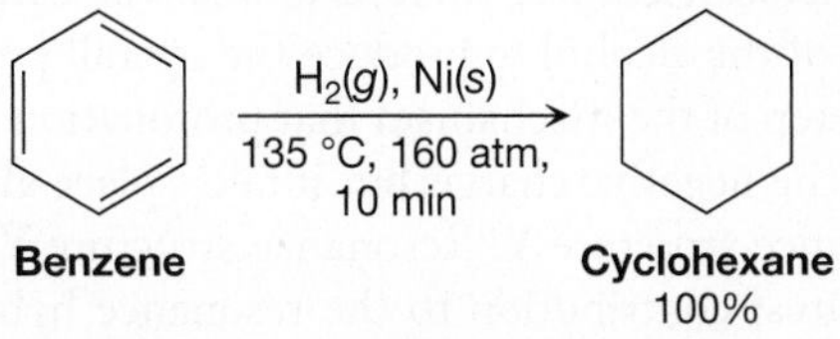

H2(g), Ni(s)
135 °C, 160 atm,
10 min
Benzene
Cyclohexane
100%

(27-49)

Under extreme conditions, it is impractical to stop the catalytic hydrogenation of benzene at an intermediate stage of reduction—that is, at a diene or an alkene—because the second and third reductions, which involve alkenes that are no longer aromatic, are faster than the first. However, a **Birch reduction** (Eq. 27-50), named after the Australian chemist Arthur Birch (1915–1995), reduces benzene to cyclohexa-1,4-diene. Not only does the reaction stop after just a single hydrogenation, but also reduction takes place *regioselectively*, yielding the 1,4-diene.

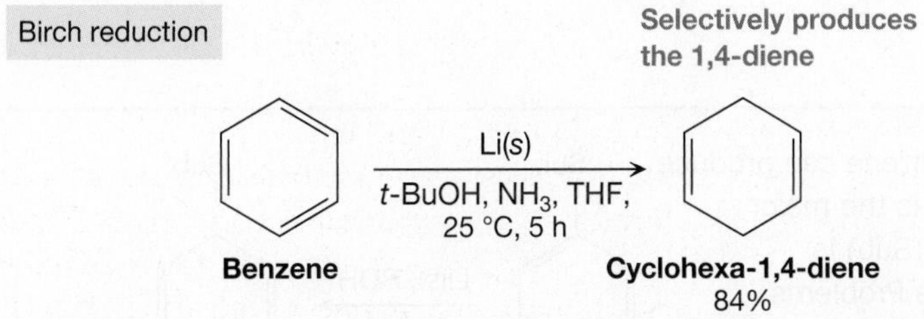

Birch reduction
Selectively produces
the 1,4-diene
Li(s)
t-BuOH, NH3, THF,
25 °C, 5 h
Benzene
Cyclohexa-1,4-diene
84%

(27-50)

The conditions for a Birch reduction are similar to those for the dissolving metal reductions discussed in Section 27.7a. One difference is that a small amount of an alcohol [typically *tert*-butyl alcohol, $(CH_3)_3COH$] is added to act as the proton source. As a result, the mechanism for the Birch reduction, shown in Equation 27-51, is

GREEN CHEMISTRY In dissolving metal reductions such as the one in Equation 27-46, both sodium metal and ammonia (the source of protons) are consumed as reactants. Moreover, ammonia is toxic and requires very cold temperatures to act as a liquid solvent, making it difficult to handle. A greener alternative, developed by Li-Biao Han at Hunan University (China), uses $NiCl_2Ph_2P(CH_2)_3PPh_2$ (abbreviated $NiCl_2dppp$) as *a catalyst* and H_3PO_2 as the proton source. Thus, waste is reduced, and the reagents are easier to handle.

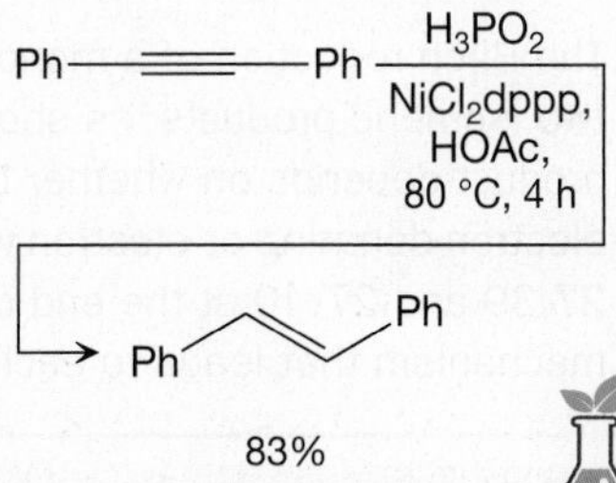

Ph
Ph
H3PO2
NiCl2dppp,
HOAc,
80 °C, 4 h
Ph
Ph
83%

similar to that for the dissolving metal reduction of an alkyne, shown previously in Equation 27-47.

Mechanism for the Birch reduction (Eq. 27-50)

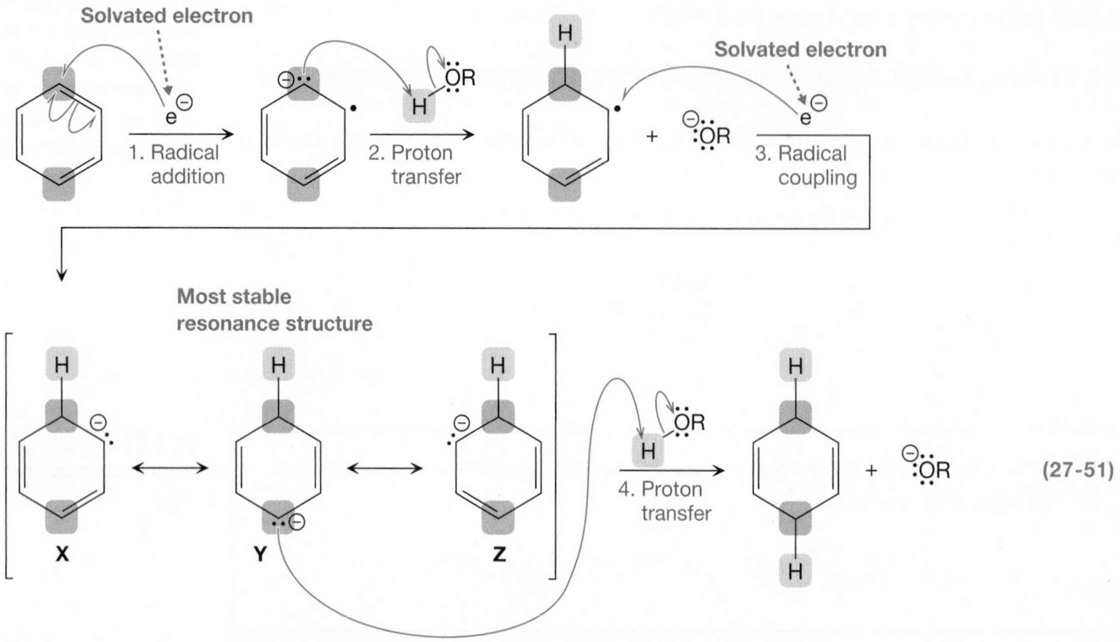
Solvated electron
1. Radical addition
2. Proton transfer
Solvated electron
3. Radical coupling
Most stable resonance structure
X
Y
Z
4. Proton transfer
(27-51)

Step 1 is radical addition of a solvated electron to a C═C double bond of the benzene ring. The resulting radical anion intermediate is strongly basic, so it deprotonates the alcohol in Step 2 to produce an uncharged alkyl radical. Radical coupling takes place in Step 3, this time producing a closed-shell carbanion species in which the negative charge is delocalized over three C atoms. The carbanion then deprotonates a second molecule of the alcohol to produce the overall product.

Notice in the final step of the mechanism that protonation can occur at any of the three C atoms sharing the negative charge, but it takes place almost exclusively at the one indicated in resonance structure **Y**. Resonance structure **Y** is more stable than **X** or **Z**, giving **Y** the greatest contribution to the resonance hybrid. In **Y**, the negative charge is stabilized by two adjacent sp^2-hybridized C atoms, each of which has a relatively high effective electronegativity (Section 3.9). Thus, the C atom at the bottom of the ring has the greatest concentration of negative charge and will most strongly attract the proton from H—OR. Moreover, notice that the major product resembles resonance structure **Y** more than it does **X** or **Z**. Therefore, in the final step of the mechanism, **Y** is favored by the *principle of least nuclear motion*, which states: When there are multiple species that could form in an elementary step, the major product tends to be the one that requires the least change in geometry.

YOUR TURN 27.33

The Birch reduction of a monosubstituted benzene can produce two isomeric products, as shown. Which one is the major product depends on whether the substituent (Sub) is electron-donating or electron-withdrawing (see Problems 27.39 and 27.40 at the end of the chapter). Draw the mechanism that leads to each product.

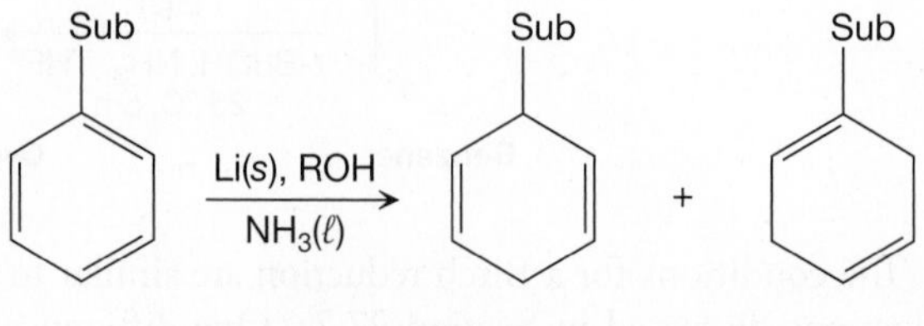
Sub
Li(s), ROH
NH3(ℓ)
Sub
Sub

27.8 Organic Synthesis: Radical Reactions in Synthesis

SECTION 27.8 OBJECTIVES

You will be able to:

1. Identify whether a synthesis might call for a radical reaction presented in this chapter.
2. Effectively incorporate radical reactions in synthesis.

The radical reactions we have examined in Chapter 27 are valuable synthetically for two main reasons. First, they allow us to carry out transformations that are impractical with reactions whose mechanisms involve only closed-shell species. Second, they allow us to carry out transformations we have seen in previous chapters, but with different regiochemistry or stereochemistry.

Radical halogenation, for example, is one of the few practical reactions that can *functionalize* (i.e., add a functional group to) the 3 position of cyclohexene, as indicated in Equation 27-52, and it is the only reaction we have discussed in this book that does so.

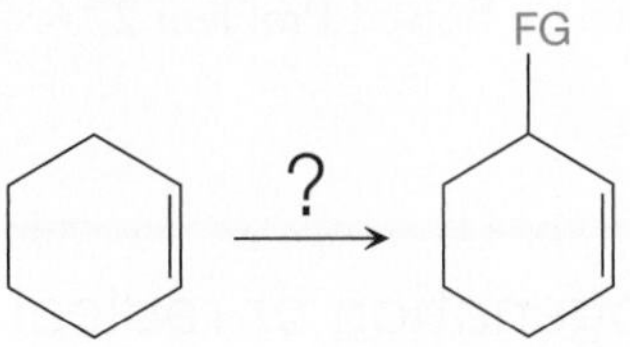
FG
?

(27-52)

This transformation can be achieved, in particular, by bromination with NBS (Eq. 27-53), similar to what we previously saw in Equation 27-33 (p. 1330).

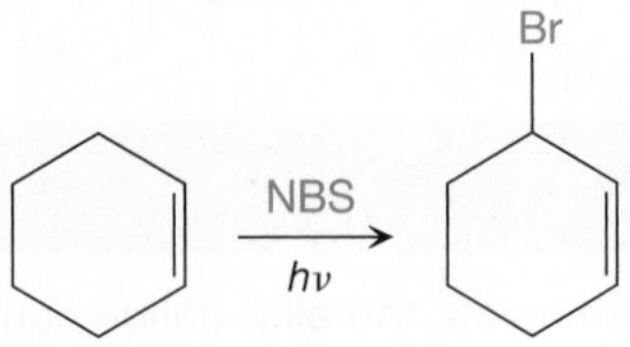
Br
NBS
hν

(27-53)

Allylic bromination such as this is used in the synthesis of the natural product (+)-koninginin D, an antibiotic. A key step in the synthesis is shown in Equation 27-54.[1]

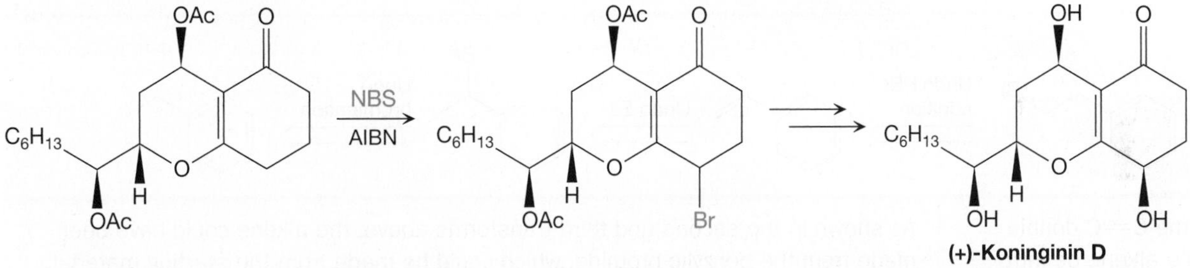
OAc
O
C6H13
H
OAc
NBS
AIBN
Br
OH
(+)-Koninginin D

(27-54)

Under these relatively mild conditions, other functional groups present are unaffected.

Radical bromination with NBS is also a popular method to functionalize the benzylic position of aromatic compounds in synthesis. Equation 27-55[2] shows how it is used in a key step in the synthesis of flavones, which are compounds that can contribute to plant pigments.

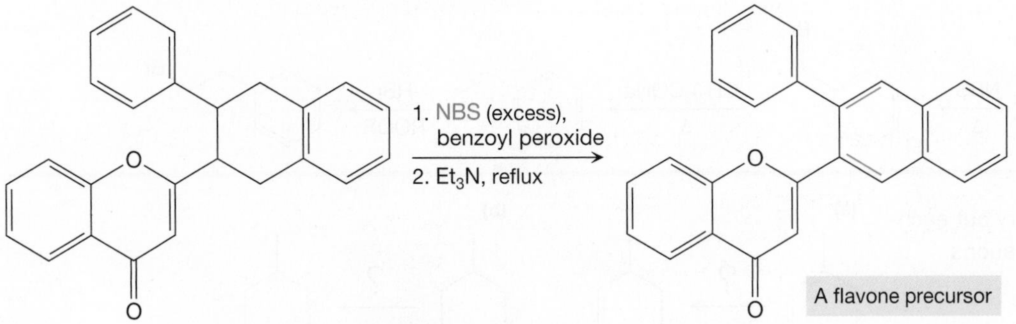
O
1. NBS (excess), benzoyl peroxide
2. Et3N, reflux
A flavone precursor

(27-55)

[1]Liu, G.; Wang, Z. *Chem. Commun.* **1999**, *12*, 1129-1130.
[2]Silva, A. M. S.; Silva, A. M. G.; Tomé, A. C.; Cavaleiro, J. A. S. *Eur. J. Org. Chem.* **1999**, *1*, 135-139.

YOUR TURN **27.34**

(a) Draw a product that could form in Equation 27-55 after reaction with excess NBS, which could go on to produce the flavone precursor on addition of Et_3N.
(b) What kind of reaction takes place in the second reaction in Equation 27-55?

In synthesis, we can also take advantage of the *regiochemistry* of radical reactions, which often differs from that of other reactions we have encountered. An example is the hydrohalogenation of an alkene. In the absence of a radical initiator, HBr adds across a C=C double bond in a Markovnikov fashion, proceeding through the more stable carbocation intermediate (Section 12.1). The addition of HBr in the presence of a radical initiator (such as peroxides), however, takes place in an *anti*-Markovnikov fashion, proceeding through the more stable *radical* intermediate. The importance of this difference is demonstrated in Solved Problem 27.6.

SOLVED PROBLEM **27.6**

How to design a synthesis with radical halogenation or radical addition of HBr

Break It Down Show how you would carry out this transformation using at least one radical chain reaction.

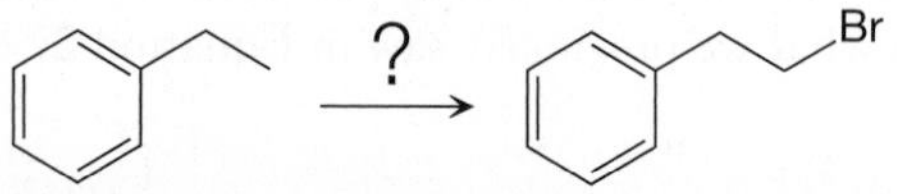
?
Br

Think	Solve
What functional group can be used to introduce a halogen on a carbon that is two carbons away from a phenyl ring?	As shown in the first transform below, the alkyl halide could have been made from an alkene. The reaction would require the anti-Markovnikov addition of HBr.

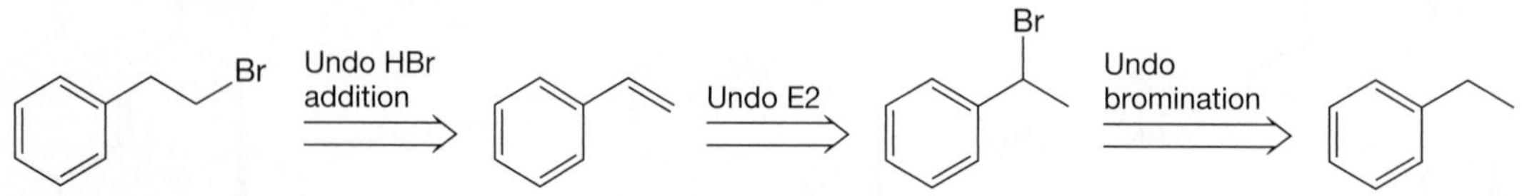
Br
Undo HBr addition
Undo E2
Br
Undo bromination

Think	Solve
How can the C=C double bond of the alkene be introduced on a carbon that initially is not functionalized?	As shown in the second and third transforms above, the alkene could have been made from the benzylic bromide, which could be made from the starting material. As we have seen, bromination is a way to functionalize a carbon.
How can we report the final synthesis?	To report the final synthesis, we begin with the starting material and supply the appropriate reagents and reaction conditions, as shown below.

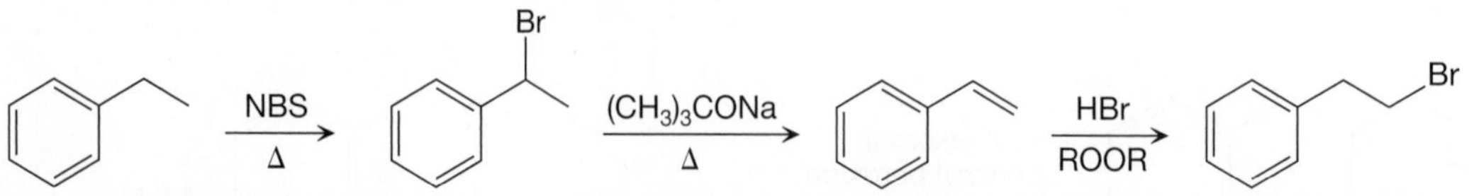
NBS
Δ
Br
(CH3)3CONa
Δ
HBr
ROOR
Br

Try It Show how to carry out each of the following transformations.

(a)

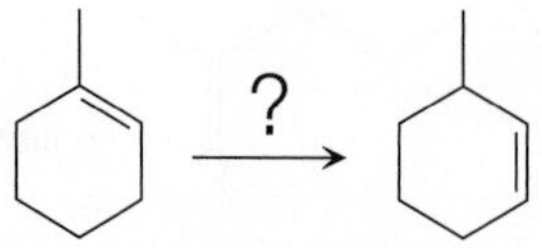
?

(b)

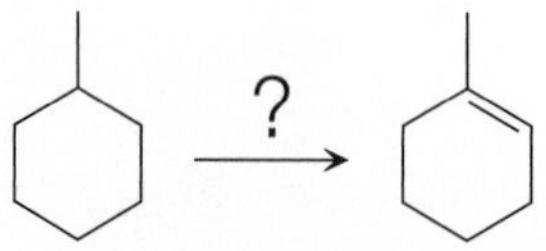
?

Finally, radical reactions might allow us to take advantage of *stereochemistry* that differs from other reactions. Consider, for example, the dissolving metal reduction of an alkyne to produce a trans alkene:

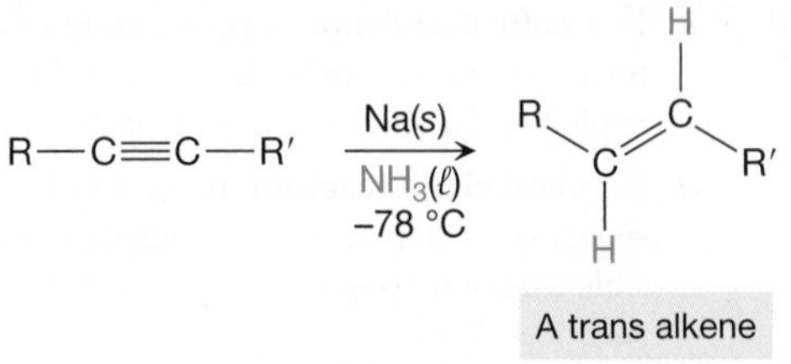
R—C≡C—R′
Na(s)
NH3(ℓ)
−78 °C
A trans alkene

(27-56)

Catalytic hydrogenation with a poisoned catalyst (Section 13.9), on the other hand, reduces an alkyne to a cis alkene:

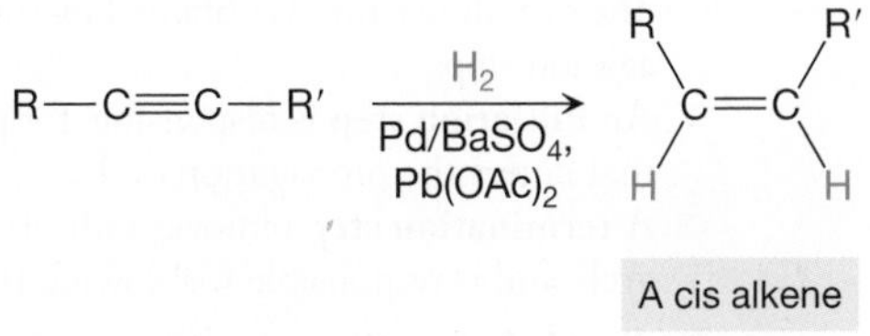
R—C≡C—R′
H2
Pd/BaSO4,
Pb(OAc)2
A cis alkene

(27-57)

An application of the dissolving metal reduction of an alkyne is shown in Equation 27-58.[3] This is a step in the total synthesis of sphingosine, which undergoes phosphorylation in vivo to produce a potent signaling lipid. (Notice in Eq. 27-58 that the reaction conditions also remove a protecting group.)

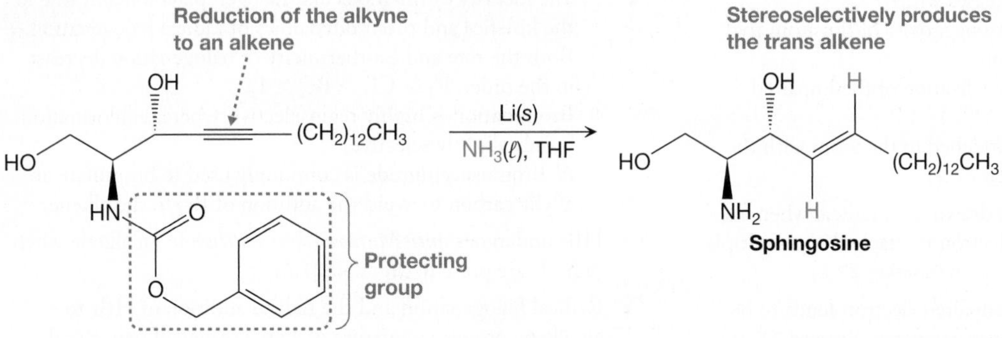
Reduction of the alkyne to an alkene
Stereoselectively produces the trans alkene
Li(s)
NH3(ℓ), THF
(CH2)12CH3
Protecting group
Sphingosine

(27-58)

[3]Boutin, R. H.; Rapoport, H. J. *Org. Chem.* **1986**, *51*, 5320-5327.

Chapter Summary and Key Terms

- A species that possesses at least one unpaired electron is called a **radical**. In a **closed-shell species**, all electrons are paired. **(Introduction)**
- Radicals lack an octet, so they are usually very unstable and highly reactive. They are generally introduced in a sample by **homolysis** of a covalent bond in a closed-shell precursor. **(Section 27.1)**
- Homolysis generally breaks the weakest bond in the compound. **(Section 27.1)**
- A **single-barbed arrow** (⌒) describes the movement of a single electron in an elementary step. **(Section 27.1)**
- A **radical initiator** is a precursor from which a radical is produced and generally possesses a relatively weak covalent bond. Common initiators are molecular halogens, ***N*-bromosuccinimide (NBS)**, **2,2-azobisisobutyronitrile (AIBN)**, and peroxides (RO—OR). **(Section 27.1)**
- Radical stability can be determined from homolytic bond dissociation energies. In general, the greater the energy required to produce the radical by homolysis, the more unstable the radical is. **(Section 27.2)**
- The stability of a radical increases with:
  - Decreasing effective electronegativity of the atom that gains the unpaired electron.
  - Increasing resonance delocalization of the unpaired electron.
  - Additional alkyl groups attached to the atom with the unpaired electron. **(Section 27.2)**
- Resonance structures can be drawn for a radical when the atom having the unpaired electron is attached to a multiple bond or an atom with a lone pair. **(Section 27.2)**
- A carbon atom that has an unpaired electron tends to be sp^2-hybridized and has a planar geometry. **(Section 27.2)**
- In a **radical coupling** step, an unpaired electron from a radical joins an unpaired electron from a second radical to produce a new covalent bond. **(Section 27.3a)**
  - Radical coupling is typically irreversible and proceeds to products with no energy barrier.
- In a **bimolecular homolytic substitution (S_H2) step**, a radical forms a bond to an atom of a closed-shell species and displaces another radical from that atom. **(Section 27.3b)**
- In a **radical addition step**, one atom of a double or triple bond forms a bond to a radical, and the other atom of the double or triple bond gains an unpaired electron. **(Section 27.3c)**
- A radical **chain reaction** involves radicals in a repeating sequence of steps, called **propagation steps**, which are responsible for converting overall reactants into overall products. **(Section 27.4a)**
  - Throughout the sequence of propagation steps, also called the **propagation cycle**, there is no net consumption of radicals.
  - The overall reaction is obtained by summing just the propagation steps.
  - An **initiation step** is responsible for producing the radical that enters the propagation cycle.
  - A **termination step** removes radicals from the propagation cycle and is responsible for slowing the overall reaction.
- **Radical halogenation** is a chain reaction that replaces the H of a C—H bond with a halogen atom. It takes place when radicals are generated in the presence of a molecular halogen and a compound containing a reactive C—H bond. **(Section 27.4)**
  - The identity of the molecular halogen plays a major role in the kinetics and thermodynamics of radical halogenation. Both the rate and exothermicity of halogenation decrease in the order: $F_2 > Cl_2 > Br_2 > I_2$.
  - Bromination is highly regioselective, whereas chlorination is only slightly selective.
  - *N*-Bromosuccinimide is commonly used to brominate an allylic carbon to avoid the addition of Br_2 to the alkene.
- HBr undergoes *anti-Markovnikov addition* to an alkene when radicals are present. **(Section 27.5)**
- Radical halogenation and the radical addition of HBr to an alkene produce a mixture of stereoisomers if new chiral centers are produced. **(Section 27.6)**
- In a **dissolving metal reduction**, a **solvated electron** behaves as the radical species. **(Section 27.7)**
  - The dissolving metal reduction of an alkyne produces a trans alkene. **(Section 27.7a)**
  - The dissolving metal reduction of a benzene ring, called a **Birch reduction**, produces a cyclohexa-1,4-diene. **(Section 27.7b)**

Reaction Table

The reactions introduced in this chapter are all functional group transformations; they are collected in Table 27-4.

TABLE 27-4 Functional Group Transformations[a]

	Starting Compound Class	Typical Reagents and Reaction Conditions	Compound Class Formed	Key Electron-Rich Species	Key Electron-Poor Species	Comments	Discussed in Section
(1)	R—H Alkane	$\xrightarrow[h\nu]{X_2}$	R—X Alkyl halide	X—X	R•	Radical halogenation	27.4
(2)	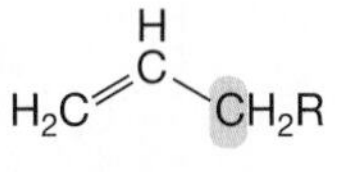 Alkene with allylic H	$\xrightarrow[\Delta \text{ or } h\nu]{\text{NBS}}$	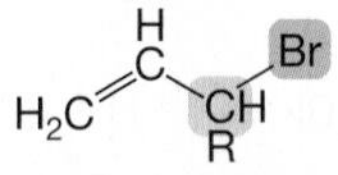 Allylic bromide	Br—Br	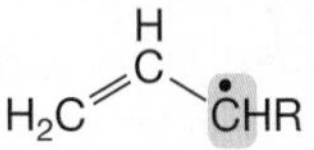	Radical bromination of the allylic carbon favored over addition of Br_2 to the C=C	27.4d
(3)	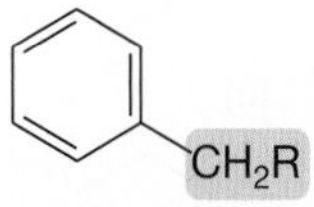 Alkylbenzene with benzylic H	$\xrightarrow[\Delta \text{ or } h\nu]{\text{NBS}}$	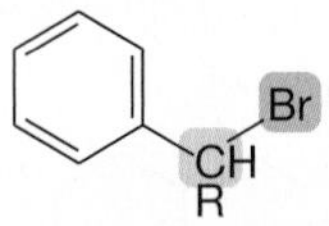 Benzylic bromide	Br—Br	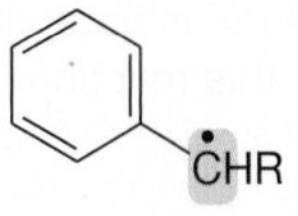	Radical bromination of the benzylic carbon	27.4d
(4)	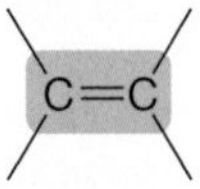 Alkene	$\xrightarrow[\text{Peroxide}]{\text{HBr}}$	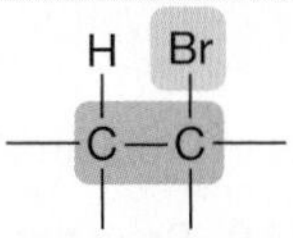 Alkyl bromide	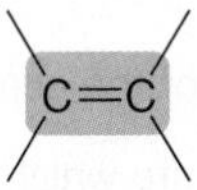	Br•	Anti-Markovnikov regiochemistry	27.5
(5)	R—C≡C—R Alkyne	$\xrightarrow[NH_3(\ell),\ -78\ °C]{\text{Na(s) or Li(s)}}$	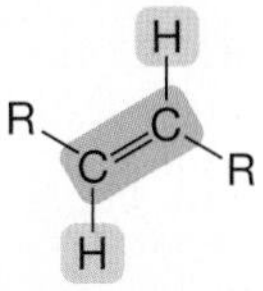 Trans alkene	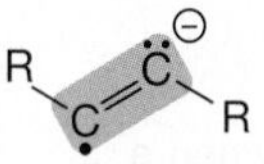	H—NH_2	Dissolving metal reduction	27.7a
(6)	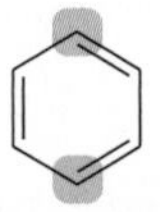 Benzene	$\xrightarrow[NH_3(\ell)]{\text{Li(s), ROH}}$	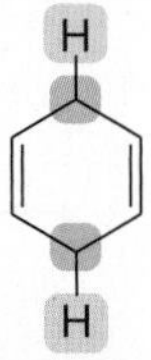 Cyclohexa-1,4-diene	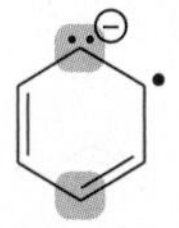	H—OR	Birch reduction; 1,4-positioning of the double bonds	27.7b

[a]X = Cl or Br

Problems

Problems that are related to synthesis are denoted (SYN).

Sections 27.1–27.3 Radical Initiators and Curved Arrow Notation; Structure and Stability of Radicals; Common Elementary Steps That Radicals Undergo

27.1 The elementary step shown here is an example of a *McLafferty rearrangement*, an important fragmentation pathway in mass spectrometry. Section 15.6d showed the electron flow in a McLafferty rearrangement with double-barbed curved arrows. Show how the electron flow could instead be depicted using single-barbed curved arrows.

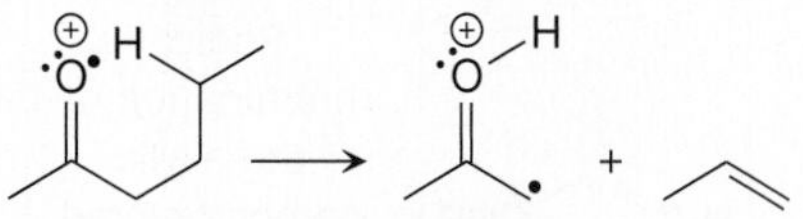

27.2 The radical cation product in Problem 27.1 has another resonance structure. Draw that resonance structure and include the proper curved arrow notation.

27.3 Acyl peroxides can be used to initiate alkyl radicals. Propose a mechanism for this reaction.

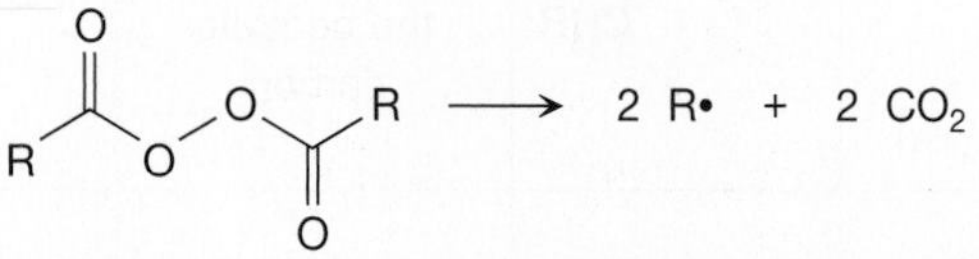
2 R• + 2 CO2

27.4 The energy barrier for rotation of a CH_2 group in an allyl radical ($H_2C{=}CH{-}CH_2\bullet$) is about 66 kJ/mol. The energy barrier for rotation of a CH_3 group in propane is about 14 kJ/mol. Explain this difference.

27.5 Add the curved arrow notation for this elementary step. Classify the step as either homolysis, radical coupling, S_H2, or radical addition.

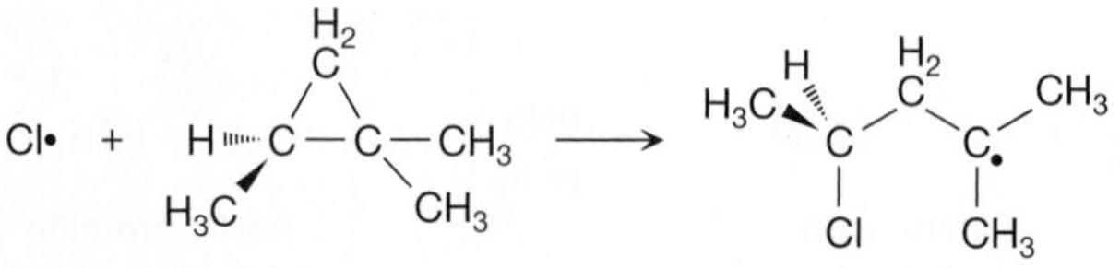

27.6 Determine the weakest C—H bond in each of the following compounds.

(a) 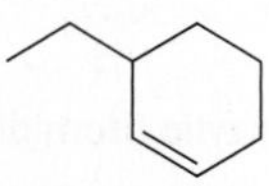

(b) 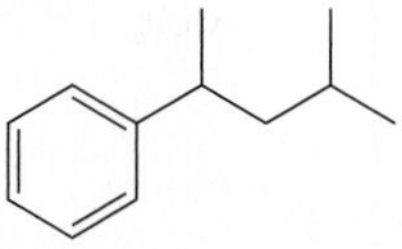

(c) 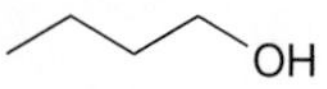

27.7 Determine the weakest C—C bond in each of the compounds in Problem 27.6.

27.8 For each of the molecules shown here, indicate which C—H bond is the weakest. Which do you think is the weaker of those two C—H bonds? Explain.

(a) 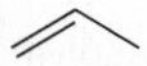 (b) 

27.9 Predict the most likely homolysis product when a *mixture* of cyclohexene, HBr, and hydrogen peroxide (H_2O_2) is heated.

27.10 Draw the major homolysis products when the compound shown here is irradiated with UV light.

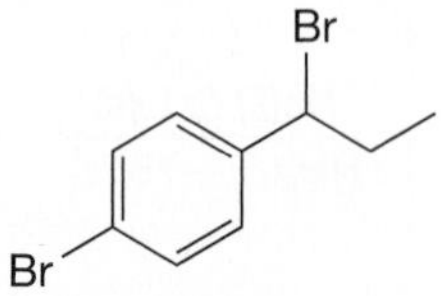

27.11 Draw the curved arrow notation and product for each reaction when it undergoes an S_H2 step.

(a) 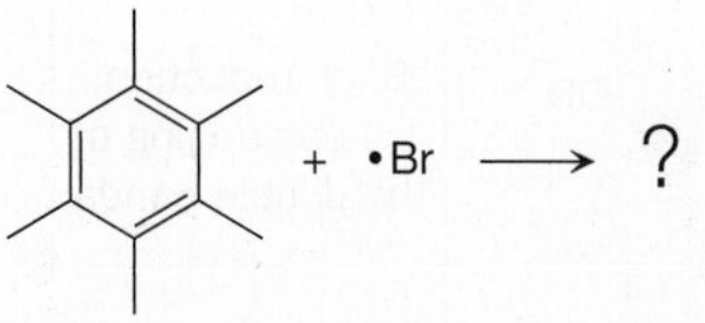

(b) 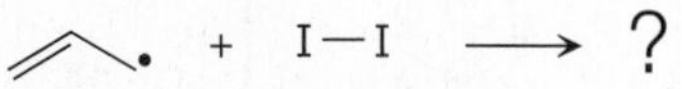

27.12 For each reaction shown, there are two possible radical addition steps. In each case, draw the curved arrow notation and product for both radical additions, and predict the more stable product.

(a) 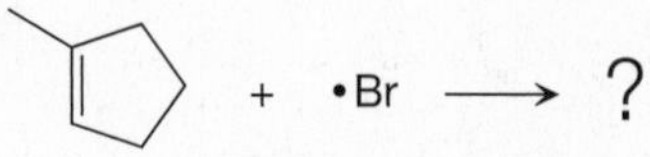

(b) 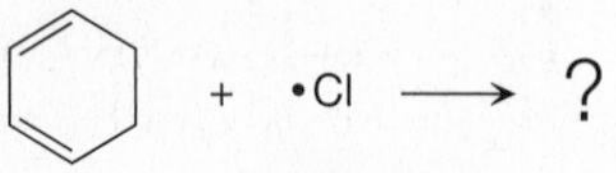

27.13 In the chapter, we mentioned that radical coupling tends to be very product-favored and irreversible. However, two diphenylamino radicals undergo radical coupling *reversibly* to produce tetraphenylhydrazine. Explain why this reaction is an exception.

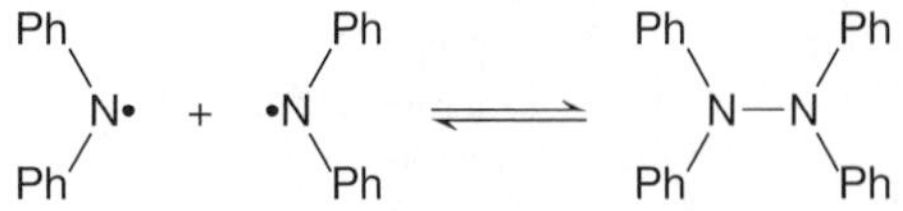

27.14 In the body, the hydroxyl radical (HO•) can lead to unwanted side reactions that damage or kill cells. One damaging process is called lipid peroxidation. A key step in lipid peroxidation is the abstraction of a hydrogen from a lipid's hydrocarbon tail, producing a lipid radical intermediate that can be represented as R•. α-Tocopherol (a form of vitamin E) is a natural antioxidant that terminates lipid peroxidation by donating H to a lipid radical. This hydrogen abstraction step is shown below. Why do you suppose α-tocopherol is so effective at terminating lipid peroxidation?

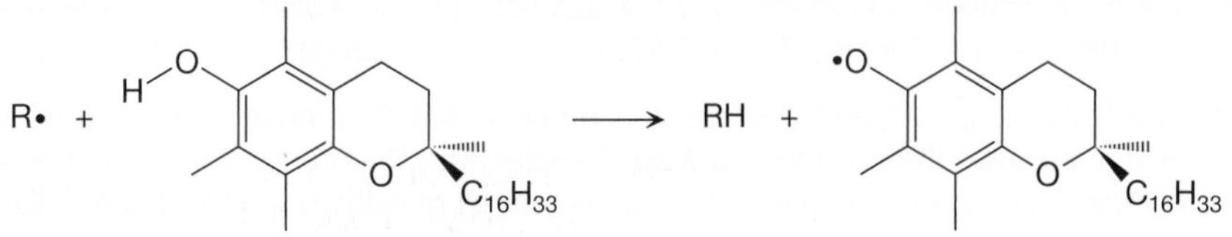

α-Tocopherol (Vitamin E)

Section 27.4 Radical Halogenation of Alkanes: Synthesis of Alkyl Halides

27.15 In each of the following compounds, which H would most likely be abstracted by a bromine radical, Br•?

(a) 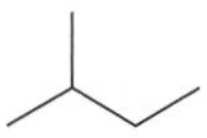
(b) 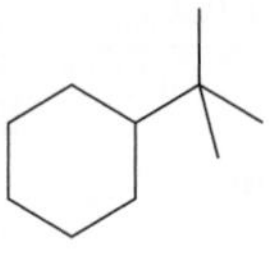
(c) 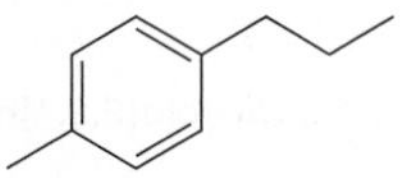
(d) 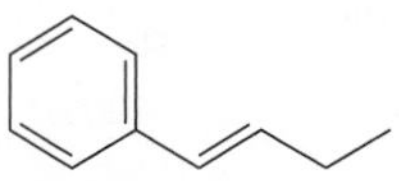

27.16 On treatment with $Cl_2/h\nu$, a compound with the formula C_9H_{12} yields only a single monochloride. What is a possible structure of the compound?

27.17 At which carbon in the molecule shown here will radical substitution predominantly take place? Explain. 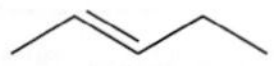

27.18 Predict the major product of each of the following reactions, and provide the complete, detailed mechanism.

(a) 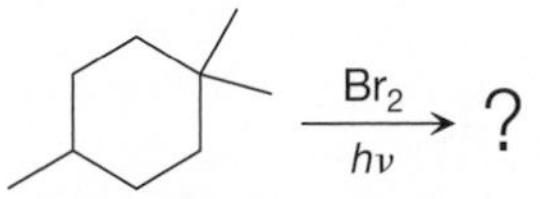
(b) 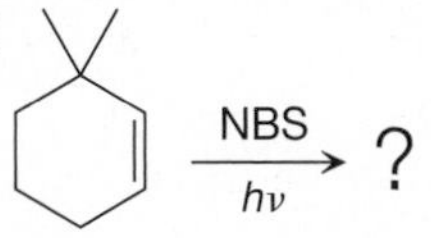
(c) 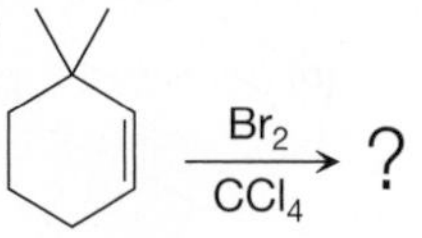

27.19 **(SYN)** Show how to produce each of the following compounds from a hydrocarbon that has the formula indicated.

(a) 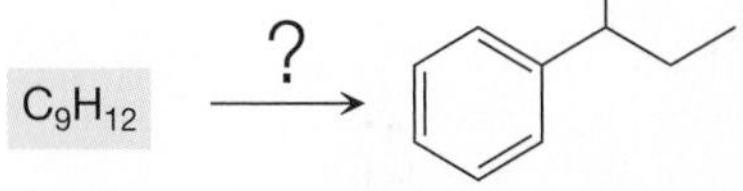
(b) 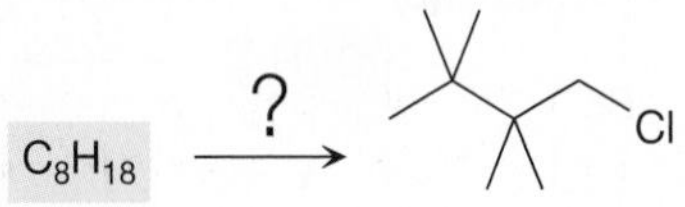

27.20 A hydrogen radical, H•, is known to abstract a hydrogen atom from an alkane in the same manner that halogen atoms do. Like halogen atoms, H• will more likely abstract a hydrogen atom from a secondary carbon than from a primary carbon, in this case with a selectivity of 5:1.

(a) Draw the two isomeric propyl radicals that are formed on hydrogen abstraction from propane by H•.

(b) Draw the curved arrow notation for the formation of each of those isomeric radicals.

(c) Compute the percentage of each propyl radical that is formed, taking into account the different numbers of each type of hydrogen on propane.

27.21 For each of the following reactions, draw the complete mechanisms leading to the two major products and determine whether the product mixture will be optically active.

(a)

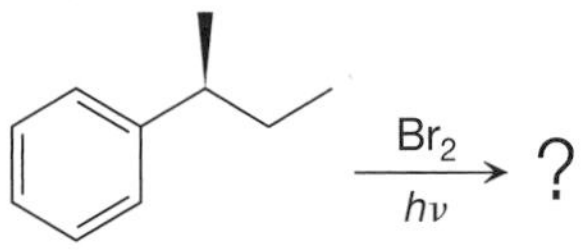

Br_2
$h\nu$
?

(b)

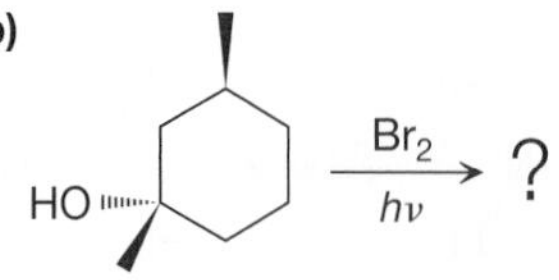

HO
Br_2
$h\nu$
?

27.22 Similar to alkanes, hydrogen gas can undergo radical halogenation according to the following reaction, where X = F, Cl, Br, or I. Propose a chain-reaction mechanism for this reaction, including an initiation step, propagation steps, and two plausible termination steps.

$$\text{H—H} + \text{X—X} \xrightarrow[h\nu]{} 2\ \text{H—X}$$

27.23 In the halogenation of H_2, described in Problem 27.22, which halogen will react fastest? Defend your answer by using the appropriate bond energies from Tables 27-1 (p. 1307) and 27-2 (p. 1308).

27.24 The selectivity of chlorination at 1°, 2°, and 3° carbons is about 1:4.5:6 in most solvents. If the reaction takes place in benzene, however, it is believed that Cl_2 forms a weak complex with the aromatic ring, thereby stabilizing the chlorine molecule. Does this lead to an increased selectivity or a decreased selectivity in chlorination? Explain.

27.25 Both bicyclo[3.3.1]nonane and bicyclo[2.2.1]heptane are saturated hydrocarbons composed of only 2° and 3° carbons. Recall that radical substitution generally takes place preferentially at a 3° carbon. Indeed, when bicyclo[3.3.1]nonane is treated with bromotrichloromethane under irradiation, substitution takes place 100% at the 3° carbon. Under the same conditions, however, no substitution is observed at the 3° carbon in bicyclo[2.2.1]heptane. Explain. *Hint*: Build molecular models of each of these compounds.

$BrCCl_3$
$h\nu$
Br
$BrCCl_3$
$h\nu$
Br

Bicyclo[3.3.1]nonane 100% **Bicyclo[2.2.1]heptane** 0%

27.26 Propose a mechanism for the chain reaction in Problem 27.25, including initiation and propagation steps. Provide two plausible termination steps.

Section 27.5 Radical Addition of HBr: Anti-Markovnikov Addition

27.27 Predict the major product of each of the reactions shown here, and provide the complete, detailed mechanism.

(a)

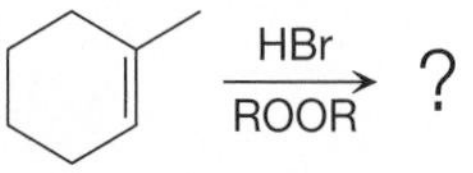

HBr
ROOR
?

(b)

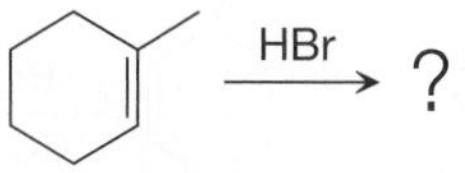

HBr
?

27.28 **(SYN)** Show how to produce each of the following from a hydrocarbon that has the formula indicated.

(a)

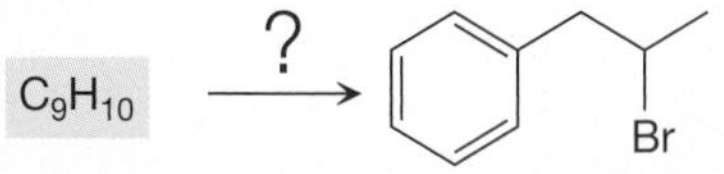

C_9H_{10}
?
Br

(b)

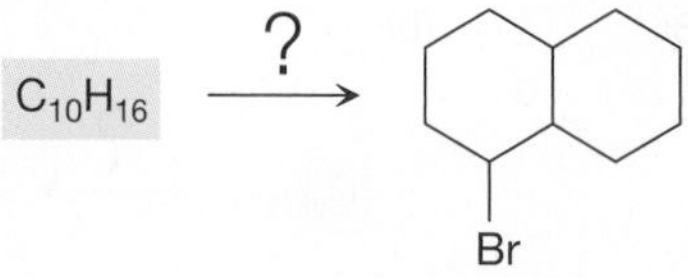

$C_{10}H_{16}$
?
Br

27.29 This addition of HBr to (*Z*)-2-bromobut-2-ene takes place regioselectively, with the Br preferentially adding to the alkene C that does *not* already possess a Br atom. **(a)** Provide a detailed mechanism for this reaction, including initiation and propagation steps. **(b)** Explain why this regiochemistry is observed.

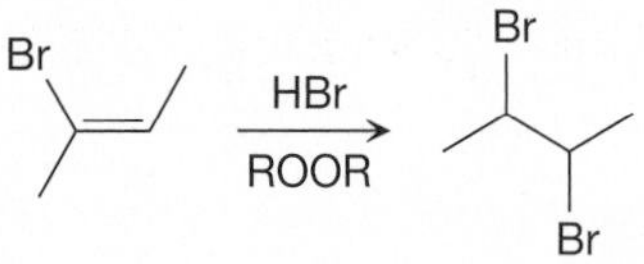

Br
HBr
ROOR
Br
Br

27.30 The radical addition of HBr can be used to cyclize a carbon chain. Provide a detailed mechanism for this reaction. Include an initiation step, propagation steps, and two plausible termination steps.

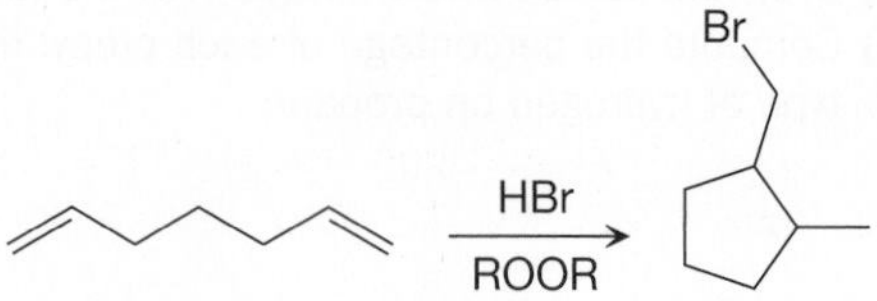

HBr
ROOR
Br

27.31 Provide a detailed mechanism to account for the following reaction. Include an initiation step, propagation steps, and two plausible termination steps. *Hint*: Consult Problem 27.30.

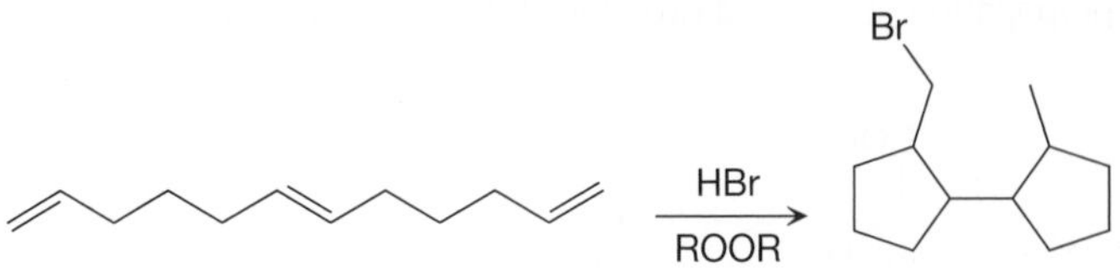
Br
HBr
ROOR

27.32 Propose a mechanism for the reaction shown here, which proceeds by a radical chain reaction. Include an initiation step, propagation steps, and two plausible termination steps.

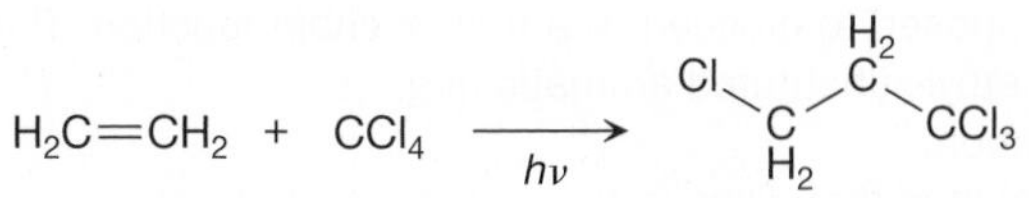
H2C=CH2 + CCl4
hν
Cl
H2
C
C
H2
CCl3

27.33 Propose a chain-reaction mechanism for the elimination of HI to form an alkene, showing reasonable initiation, propagation, and termination steps. *Hint*: Consider the mechanism for the reverse reaction.

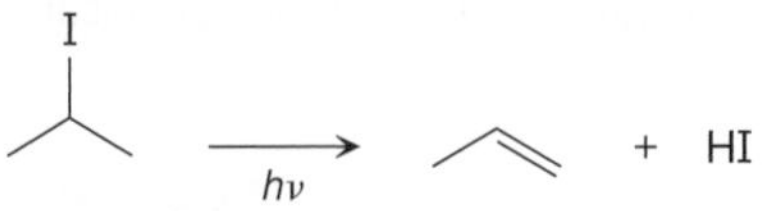
I
hν
+ HI

27.34 The conversion of *cis*-1,2-diphenylethene to *trans*-1,2-diphenylethene is catalyzed when I_2 is added and the reaction mixture is irradiated with UV light. Provide a detailed mechanism for this reaction.

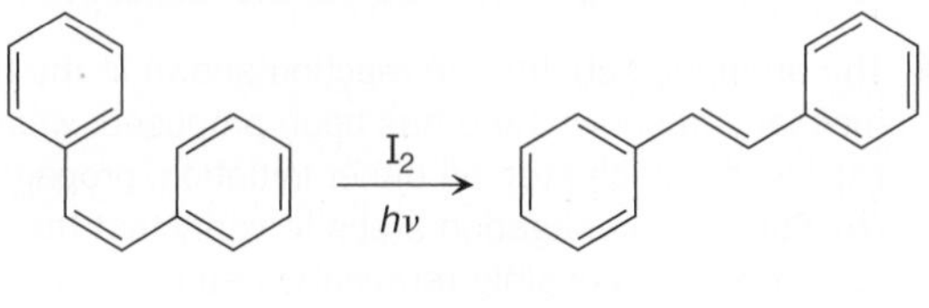
I2
hν

Section 27.7 Dissolving Metal Reductions: Hydrogenation of Alkenes and Alkynes

27.35 Predict the major product of each of the following reactions, and provide the complete, detailed mechanisms.

(a) 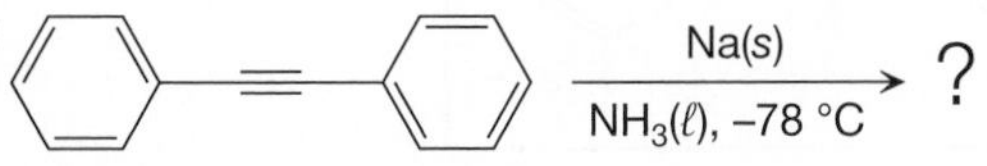
Na(s)
NH3(ℓ), –78 °C
?

(b) 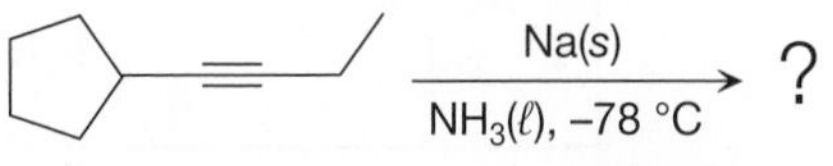
Na(s)
NH3(ℓ), –78 °C
?

27.36 **(SYN)** Show how to produce each of the compounds shown here from 1-phenylprop-1-yne.

(a) 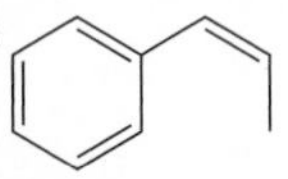

(b) 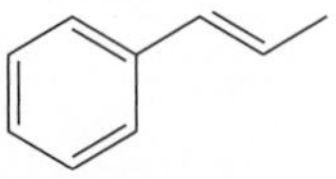

27.37 As we saw in this chapter, dissolving metal reductions reduce alkynes to trans alkenes. Why, then, do those reactions fail with a terminal alkyne? *Hint*: What species appear as intermediates in the mechanism?

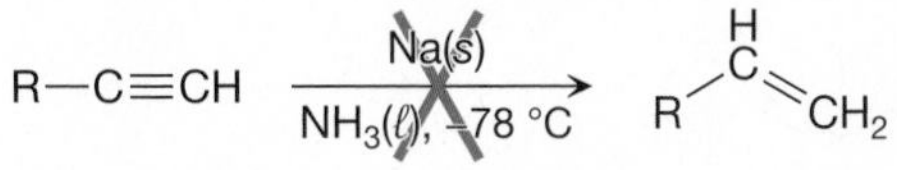
R—C≡CH
Na(s)
NH3(ℓ), –78 °C
H
C
R
CH2

27.38 A dissolving metal reduction can be used to reduce a ketone to an alcohol, as shown in the reduction here. Draw a complete, detailed mechanism for this reaction.

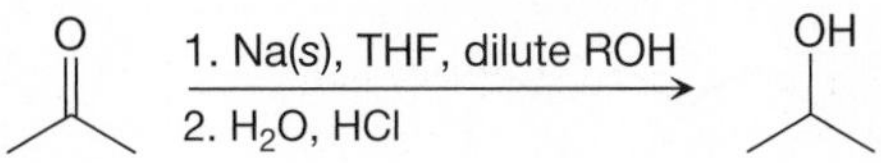
O
1. Na(s), THF, dilute ROH
2. H2O, HCl
OH

27.39 There are two isomeric cyclohexa-1,4-diene products when benzoic acid undergoes the Birch reduction (see Your Turn 27.33, p. 1340). **(a)** Draw the mechanism that leads to the formation of the major product. **(b)** Will the Birch reduction of benzoic acid occur faster or slower than the Birch reduction of benzene itself? *Hint*: Is CO_2H an electron-donating or an electron-withdrawing group?

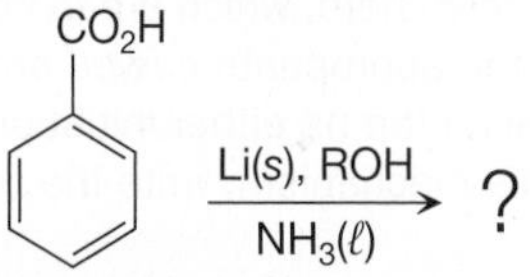
CO2H
Li(s), ROH
NH3(ℓ)
?

27.40 There are two isomeric cyclohexa-1,4-diene products when toluene undergoes the Birch reduction (see Your Turn 27.33). **(a)** Draw the mechanism that leads to the formation of the major product. **(b)** Will the Birch reduction of toluene occur faster or slower than the Birch reduction of benzene itself? *Hint*: Is CH_3 an electron-donating or an electron-withdrawing group?

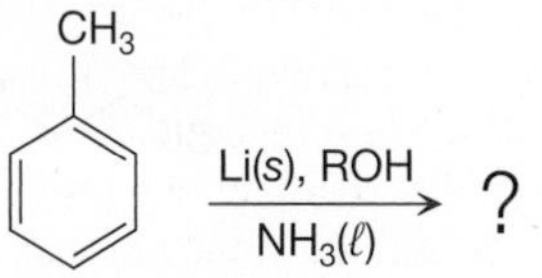
CH3
Li(s), ROH
NH3(ℓ)
?

27.41 Why does a Birch reduction require ROH as the proton source, whereas a dissolving metal reduction of an alkyne uses NH_3 as the proton source? *Hint*: Which acid is stronger?

Integrated Problems

27.42 When an ether is exposed to air for a prolonged time, it undergoes a radical chain reaction with oxygen gas to form explosive *hydroperoxides*. The overall reaction between diethyl ether and O_2 is shown here. Provide a complete, detailed mechanism for this reaction, including an initiation step, propagation steps, and two plausible termination steps. *Hint*: In its ground state, O_2 is a diradical.

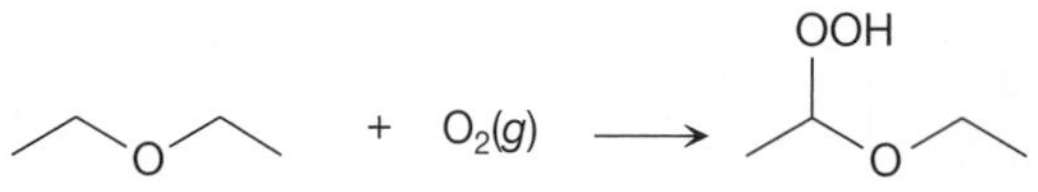
OOH
O
+ O2(g)
O

A hydroperoxide of diethyl ether

27.43 Notice in Problem 27.42 that the hydroperoxide forms at the C atom that is α to the O atom and not at the one that is β to it. Explain why. *Hint*: Write out the respective radicals that are formed on hydrogen abstraction.

27.44 The aromatic substitution reaction shown in the box has been proposed to proceed by a radical chain reaction. The mechanism shown here has been proposed, where Ar is the trimethyl-substituted aromatic ring.
(a) Identify each step as either initiation, propagation, or termination.
(b) Sum the propagation steps to verify that the net equation matches that given in the problem statement.
(c) Propose a possible termination step.

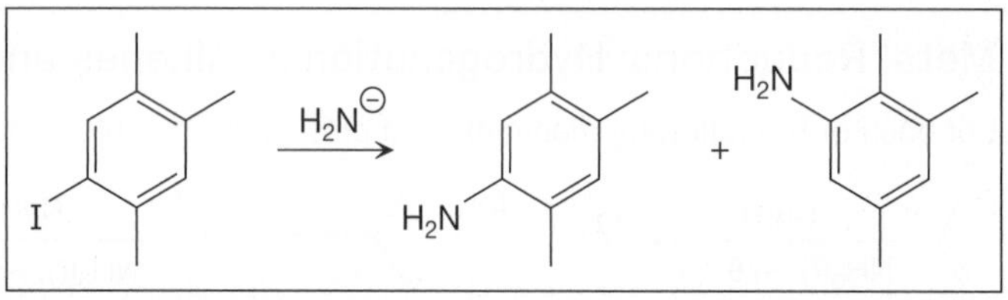
I
H2N
H2N
+
H2N

$$\mathrm{ArI} + e^{\ominus} \longrightarrow \mathrm{ArI}^{\bullet\ominus}$$
$$\mathrm{ArI}^{\bullet\ominus} \longrightarrow \mathrm{Ar}\bullet + \mathrm{I}^{\ominus}$$
$$\mathrm{Ar}\bullet + \mathrm{H_2N}^{\ominus} \longrightarrow \overset{\bullet}{\mathrm{Ar}}\mathrm{NH_2}^{\ominus}$$
$$\overset{\bullet}{\mathrm{Ar}}\mathrm{NH_2}^{\ominus} + \mathrm{ArI} \longrightarrow \mathrm{ArNH_2} + \mathrm{ArI}^{\bullet\ominus}$$

27.45 The steps shown here, which are in no particular order, have been proposed for a radical chain-reaction mechanism.
(a) Draw in the appropriate curved arrows for each step.
(b) Label each step as either initiation, propagation, or termination.
(c) Using this mechanism, write the balanced net reaction.

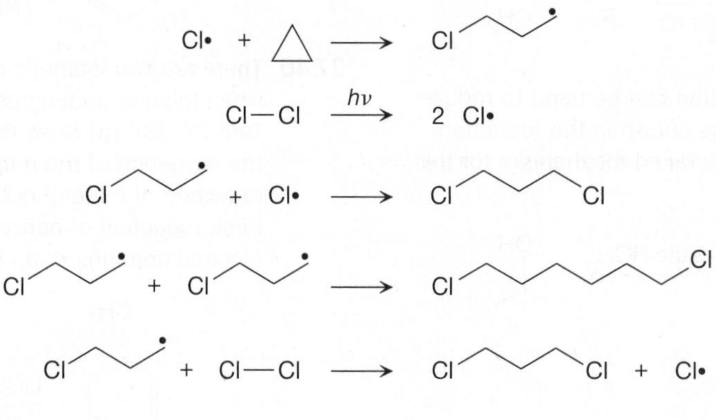
Cl• +
Cl
Cl—Cl
hν
2 Cl•
Cl
+ Cl•
Cl
Cl
Cl
+ Cl
Cl
Cl
Cl
+ Cl—Cl
Cl
Cl + Cl•

27.46 The steps shown here, which are in no particular order, have been proposed for the initiation and propagation of a radical chain-reaction mechanism.

(a) Draw in the appropriate curved arrows for each step.
(b) Label each step as either initiation or propagation.
(c) Write the balanced net reaction.
(d) Provide two plausible termination steps, including curved arrows.

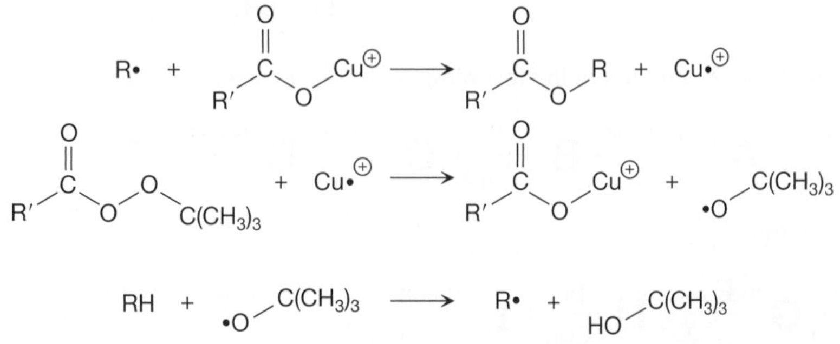

27.47 The following steps, which are in no particular order, have been proposed for the initiation and propagation of a radical chain-reaction mechanism.

(a) Draw in the appropriate curved arrows for each step.
(b) Label each step as either initiation or propagation.
(c) Write the balanced net reaction.
(d) Provide two plausible termination steps, including curved arrows.

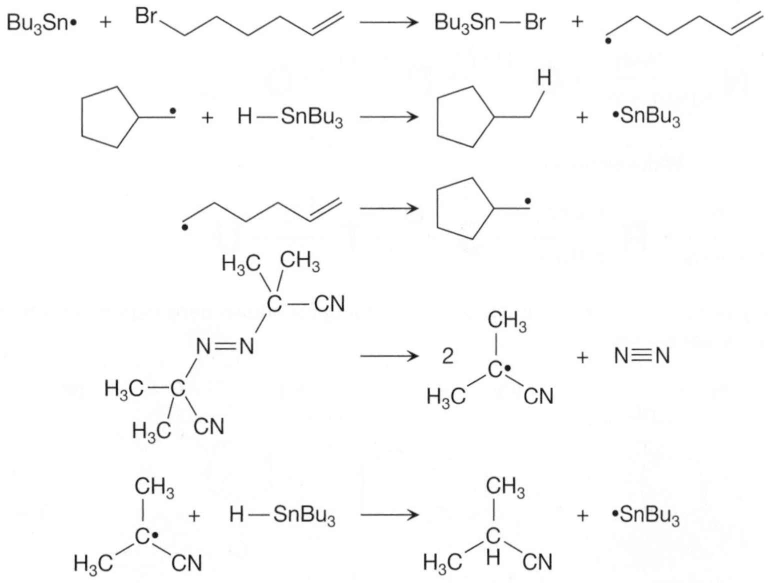

27.48 Propose a chain-reaction mechanism for the decomposition of dimethyl ether to form methane and formaldehyde.

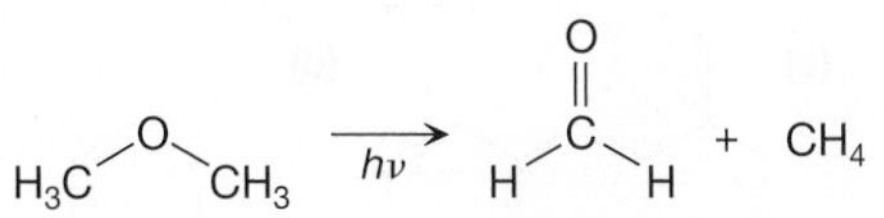

27.49 The following reaction proceeds by a chain-reaction mechanism. Propose an initiation step, propagation steps, and two plausible termination steps.

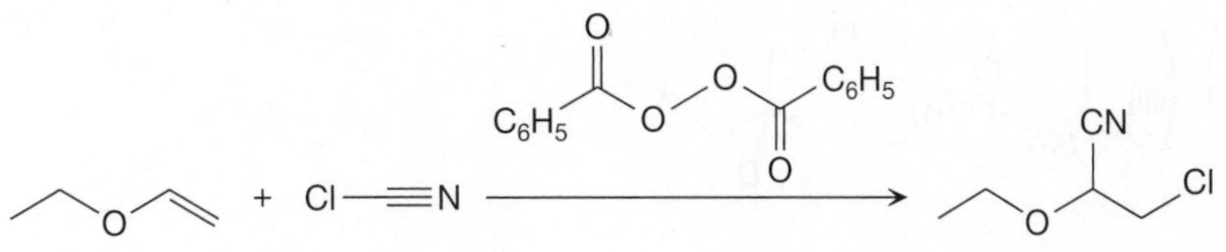

27.50 Radical halogenation generally yields a mixture of stereoisomers. When a Br atom is adjacent to the site of hydrogen abstraction, however, the reaction is stereospecific, as shown here. Provide a detailed mechanism for this reaction, and propose a key intermediate that accounts for the reaction's stereochemistry. With that key intermediate, explain why this stereochemistry is observed.

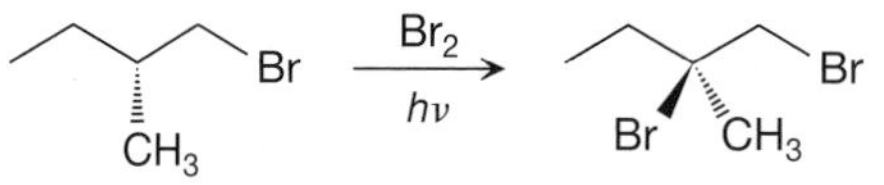
Br
CH3
Br2
hν
Br
Br
CH3

27.51 Supply the structures of compounds **A–I** in the following synthesis scheme.

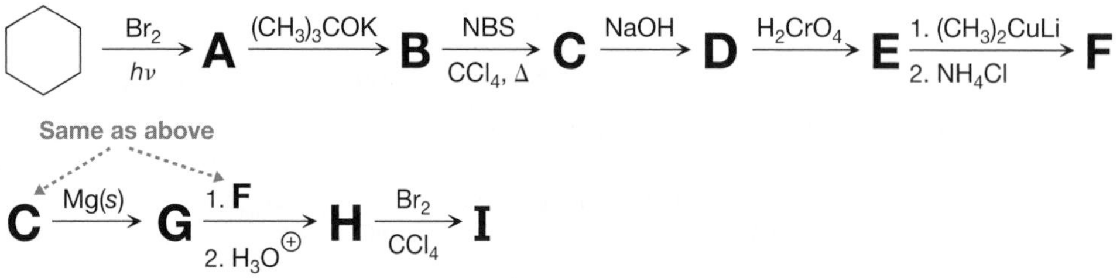
Br2
hν
A
(CH3)3COK
B
NBS
CCl4, Δ
C
NaOH
D
H2CrO4
E
1. (CH3)2CuLi
2. NH4Cl
F
Same as above
C
Mg(s)
G
1. F
2. H3O+
H
Br2
CCl4
I

27.52 Supply the structures of compounds **J–U** in the following synthesis scheme.

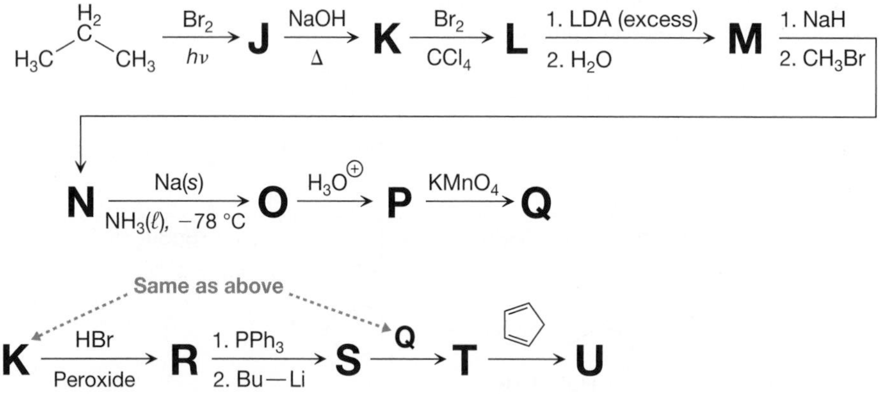
H2
C
H3C
CH3
Br2
hν
J
NaOH
Δ
K
Br2
CCl4
L
1. LDA (excess)
2. H2O
M
1. NaH
2. CH3Br
N
Na(s)
NH3(ℓ), −78 °C
O
H3O+
P
KMnO4
Q
Same as above
K
HBr
Peroxide
R
1. PPh3
2. Bu—Li
S
Q
T
U

27.53 **(SYN)** Suggest how you would synthesize each of the compounds shown here beginning with propylbenzene. You may use any other reagents necessary.

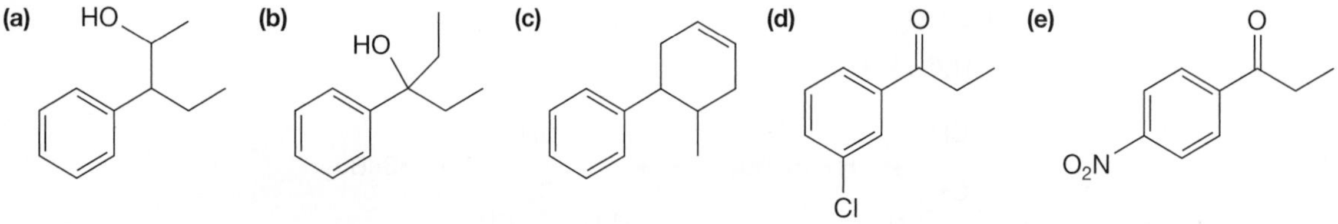
(a)
HO
(b)
HO
(c)
(d)
O
Cl
(e)
O
O2N

27.54 **(SYN)** How would you synthesize each of the following compounds beginning with 2-methylpropane? You may use any other reagents necessary.

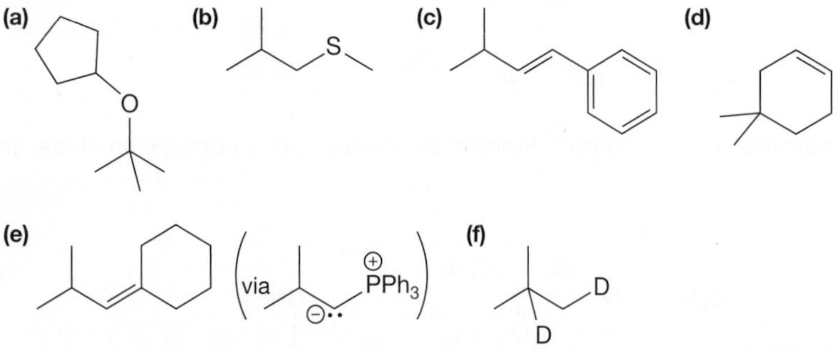
(a)
O
(b)
S
(c)
(d)
(e)
via
PPh3
(f)
D
D

27.55 **(SYN)** Show how you would synthesize each of the following from 1-cyclopentylprop-1-yne. You may use any other reagents necessary. You may assume that each chiral target is produced as a racemic mixture.

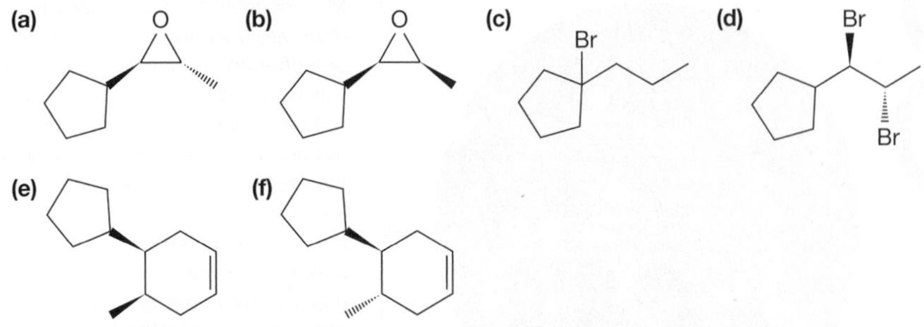

(a)
O
(b)
O
(c)
Br
(d)
Br
Br
(e)
(f)

27.56 A student wanted to determine whether alkyl radicals rearrange, so the student ran the reaction below.

(a) Why is it plausible to think that radical rearrangement might take place in this reaction? To help answer this question, draw the mechanism of the radical reaction that would potentially take place.

(b) The student acquired a ^{1}H NMR spectrum of the product, which is shown below. What should the student conclude regarding alkyl radical rearrangements? Explain.

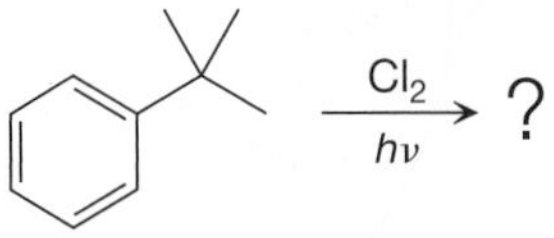

Cl_2
$h\nu$
?

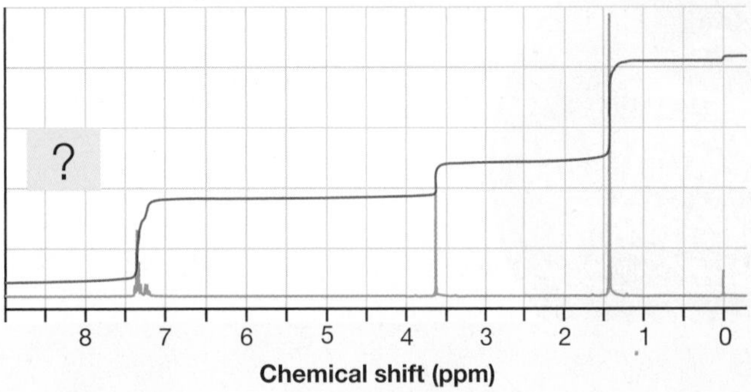

?
8
7
6
5
4
3
2
1
0
Chemical shift (ppm)

28

UNITED STATES OF AMERICA
ONE CENT

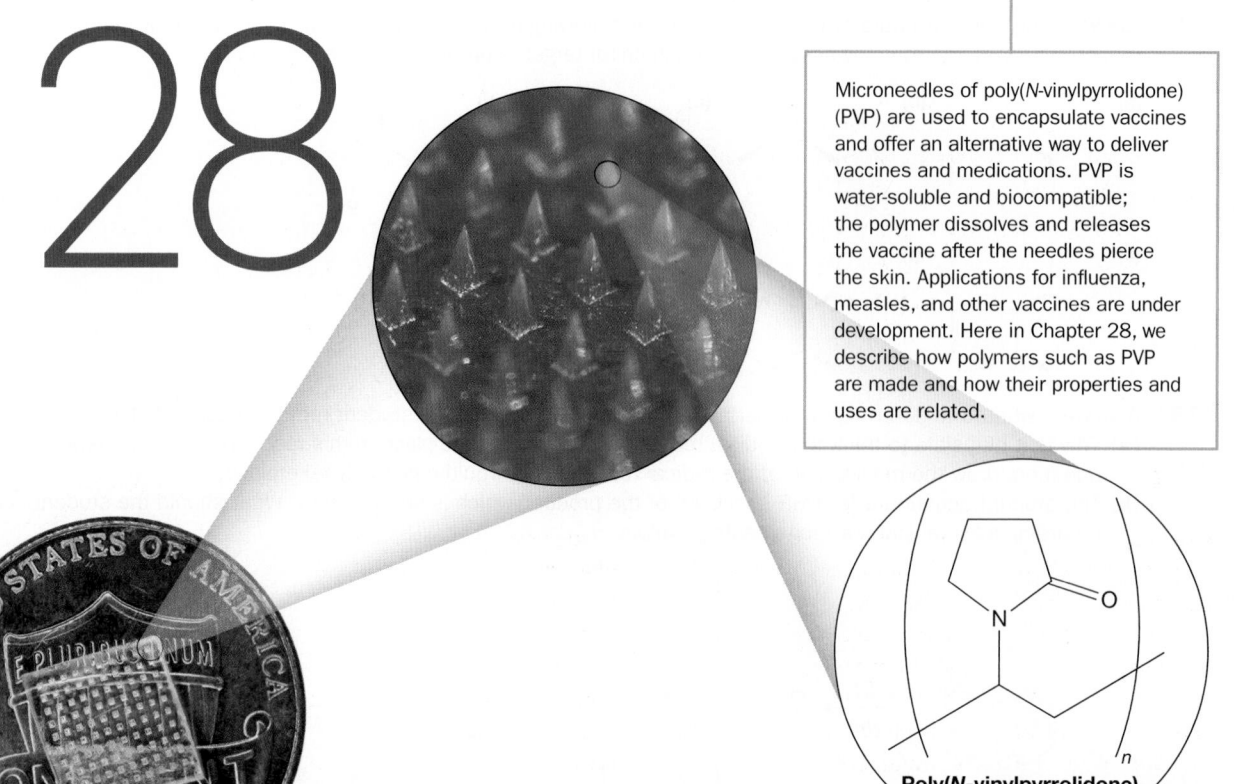

Microneedles of poly(*N*-vinylpyrrolidone) (PVP) are used to encapsulate vaccines and offer an alternative way to deliver vaccines and medications. PVP is water-soluble and biocompatible; the polymer dissolves and releases the vaccine after the needles pierce the skin. Applications for influenza, measles, and other vaccines are under development. Here in Chapter 28, we describe how polymers such as PVP are made and how their properties and uses are related.

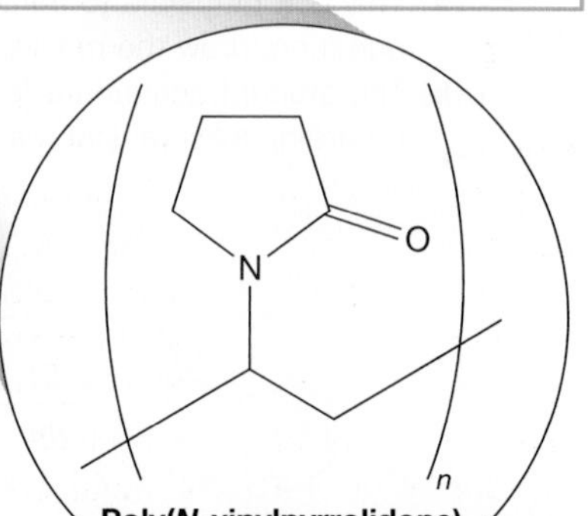

N
O
n

Poly(*N*-vinylpyrrolidone) (PVP)

Polymers

Polymers are large molecules that are produced from relatively small molecules, and they exhibit some kind of regular repetition in their structures. You are probably most familiar with polymers as *plastics*, which are in such widespread use that it is difficult to imagine the world without them! Drinking bottles, storage containers, pipes for plumbing, and synthetic fibers in your clothes are all polymers. So, too, are trademarked products such as Plexiglas, Kevlar, and Teflon, each with special properties that make them desirable for specific uses, as shown in **Figure 28-1**.

Many thousands of different polymers exist. How are they synthesized? How is one polymer distinguished from another? What factors contribute to the specific properties of a polymer? These are the kinds of questions we will tackle here in Chapter 28.

As it turns out, polymers can be made by a wide variety of reactions we have studied throughout this book, and polymer structure can be quite diverse. We will begin by investigating how polystyrene (PS), a very common plastic, is made by a radical chain reaction, one of the main topics of Chapter 27. Using polystyrene as a model, we will explore aspects of polymer structure, including regiochemistry, stereochemistry, and size distribution. We'll then study how polymers can be made using other types of

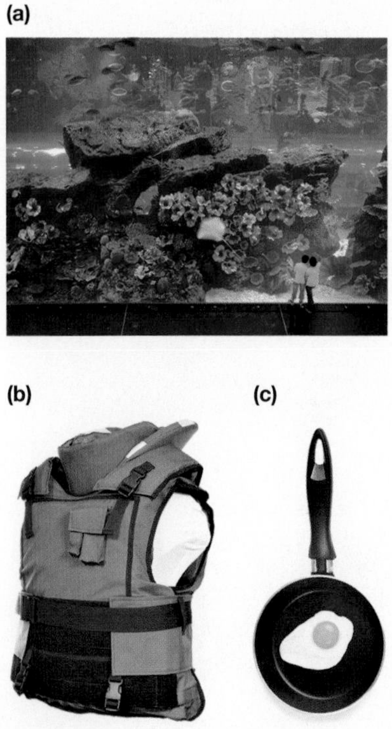

(a)
(b)
(c)

FIGURE 28-1 **Examples of commercially available polymers** (a) The Dubai Mall aquarium walls are made of Plexiglas sheets. (b) Body armor made from Kevlar fiber. (c) A nonstick skillet with a Teflon lining. Teflon is the only known substance that geckos cannot climb (see p. 86).

Chapter Outline

reactions, and how polymers can be chemically modified after they are formed. In doing so, we can begin to appreciate the diversity in structure that polymers can offer.

After having examined a handful of polymers, we will consider how a polymer's structure relates to its properties, such as solubility and melting point. Then we will see how the properties of a polymer make it suited for particular uses (especially food and beverage storage), before discussing some introductory aspects of recycling.

At the end of the chapter, we will revisit proteins and polysaccharides—familiar biomolecules—in the context of polymers. Specifically, we will see how those biomolecules can be viewed as biopolymers, in which case we can apply some of the lessons about polymer properties from earlier in the chapter.

The field of polymers and polymer chemistry is immense, too much for one chapter. The goal of this chapter is to provide a foundation of some key aspects of polymers, which you can build on should you choose to pursue further studies of polymers.

28.1 Radical Polymerization: Polystyrene as a Model

SECTION 28.1 OBJECTIVES

You will be able to:

1. Describe polymers and how they relate to monomers.
2. Draw the mechanism for the radical polymerization of a vinyl monomer, and show how the vinyl polymer's repeating unit and monomer structure are related.
3. Explain the relevance of regiochemistry and stereochemistry in the production of vinyl polymers.
4. Discuss the relevance of size distribution in a polymer sample.

Expanded polystyrene (**Figure 28-2**), the material used to make "packing peanuts" and insulated, disposable coffee cups, is a foam made from the synthetic polymer polystyrene (see Looking Ahead box).

FIGURE 28-2 Uses of expanded polystyrene (a) Cups for hot beverages and (b) pellets for preventing damage to fragile objects during shipping.

▸ LOOKING AHEAD

In Section 28.9 we will learn how polymers are classified according to their chemical makeup, and we will also learn how polymers are named.

Polystyrene was discovered in the 19th century when several chemists found that styrene, a liquid at room temperature, can react to produce a jelly-like substance:

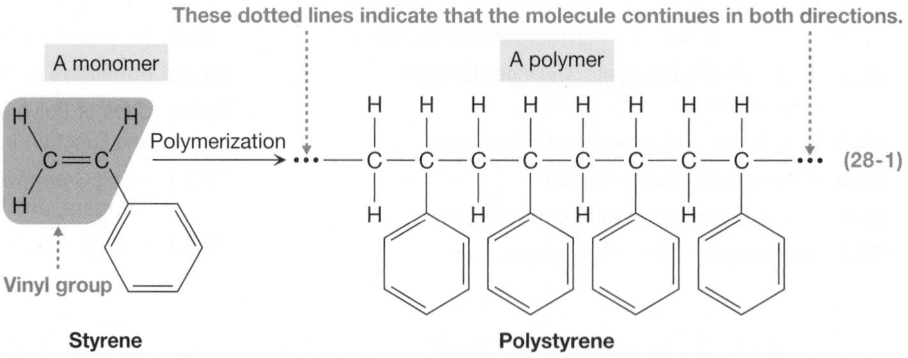
These dotted lines indicate that the molecule continues in both directions.
A monomer
A polymer
Polymerization
Vinyl group
Styrene
Polystyrene

(28-1)

Only a partial structure of polystyrene is shown in Equation 28-1; the dotted lines (· · ·) indicate that the structure continues in both directions. A typical molecule of polystyrene is so large, in fact, that it would require the width of about 200 pages to depict the entire structure using the size scale shown!

Notice the repetition in the structure of polystyrene, which arises because the polymer is produced from a large number of the same molecule: styrene. Styrene, therefore, is a *monomer* (Greek: *mono* = one; *meros* = part) because many of them are required to construct polystyrene, the *polymer* ("many parts"). In general, a **monomer** is a molecule that undergoes reaction to produce a polymer, and it is responsible for the repeating structure of the polymer. A reaction that links monomers together to produce a polymer is a **polymerization**.

Throughout the rest of this section, we will discuss polymerization in greater detail, with polystyrene as our model. We will see how the reaction mechanism for polymerization leads to the structure of the polymer, and the lessons we learn will be applied to other polymers and polymerization reactions later in the chapter.

28.1a Vinyl Polymers: Monomers, Repeating Units, and Degree of Polymerization

For the polymerization shown in Equation 28-1, we have already identified styrene as the monomer and polystyrene as the polymer. More specifically, polystyrene is a type of **vinyl polymer** because atoms that characterize the *vinyl group* (i.e., the C═C bond) of the monomer are linked together on polymerization.

Most polymers contain a long, continuous chain of atoms, known as the **polymer chain** (also called the **main chain** or **polymer backbone**), which extends from one end of the polymer to the other. In polystyrene and other vinyl polymers, the main chain consists of only carbon atoms, as highlighted in **Figure 28-3**. In other polymers, heteroatoms may be included in the main chain, as we will see in some examples later in this chapter.

Non-hydrogen atoms or groups attached to the main chain are called **side groups**, or **pendant groups**. Pendant means "hanging," so it appropriately describes these

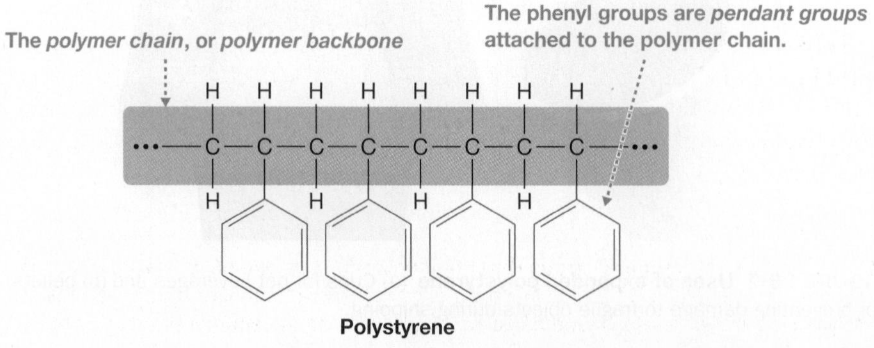
The *polymer chain*, or *polymer backbone*
The phenyl groups are *pendant groups* attached to the polymer chain.
Polystyrene

FIGURE 28-3 Polymer chains and pendant groups The polymer chain of polystyrene is screened in red, and the phenyl pendant groups are drawn in blue.

groups that are hanging off the polymer chain. In polystyrene, for example, the phenyl groups (blue in Fig. 28-3) are the polymer's pendant groups.

YOUR TURN **28.1**

Identify the pendant groups in the partial structure of polypropylene shown here. What term, similar to *phenyl*, can you use to describe the pendant groups?

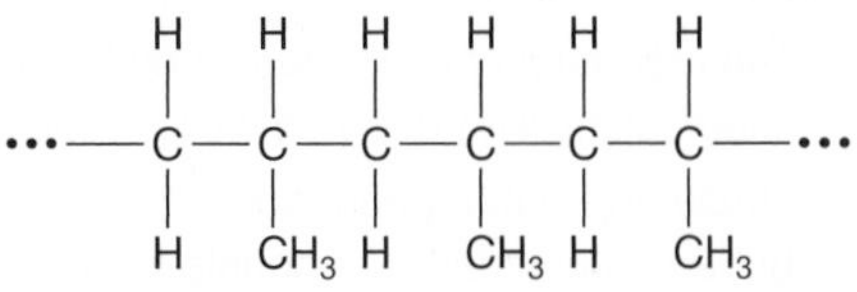

Answers to Your Turns are in the back of the book.

You can see the relationship between styrene and polystyrene more clearly by mentally cutting the main chain of the polymer into two-carbon units, as shown on the left in **Figure 28-4**. This gives you the **repeating unit** of the polymer, which is the basis of the polymer's *condensed formula* on the right of the figure. The number of repeating units determines the **degree of polymerization (DP)**, which is designated in Figure 28-4 with the subscript *n*.

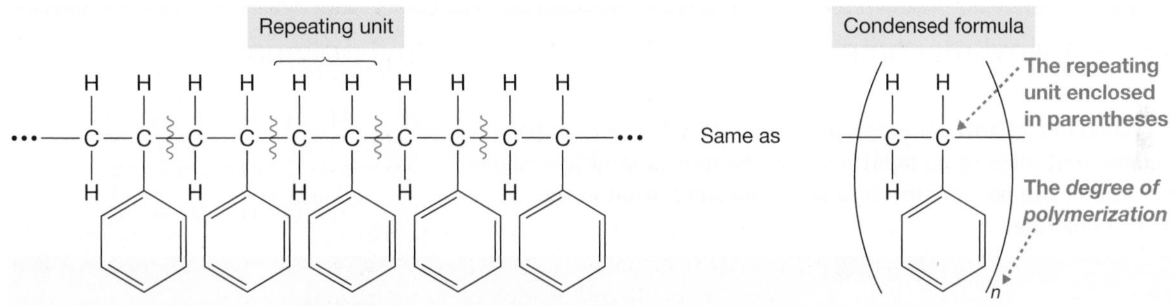

Repeating unit
Same as
Condensed formula
The repeating unit enclosed in parentheses
The *degree of polymerization*
n
Polystyrene

FIGURE 28-4 The repeating unit and condensed formula of polystyrene Mentally cutting the backbone of polystyrene, as indicated on the left, reveals the repeating unit. In the condensed formula on the right, the repeating unit is enclosed in parentheses, and the subscript *n* indicates repetition of the unit. The value of *n* is called the *degree of polymerization*.

If you know the molar mass of a polymer, you can calculate the approximate DP, as shown in Equation 28-2:

$$\text{DP} \approx \frac{\text{Molar mass of the polymer}}{\text{Molar mass of the repeating unit}} \qquad \textbf{(28-2)}$$

For example, the atoms shown on the left in Figure 28-4 can be represented as $C_{40}H_{40}$, which has a molar mass of 520 g/mol. The repeating unit's formula is C_8H_8, whose molar mass is 104 g/mol. Dividing 520 g/mol by 104 g/mol, we arrive at a DP of 5, the same as the number of repeating units depicted on the left of the figure. (The number is exact in this example, but in general a calculated DP will be an approximation because of variables we will discuss shortly.)

Polystyrene's monomer and repeating unit are similar but not identical, as illustrated in **Figure 28-5**. Notice the repeating unit lacks the double bond that is present in the monomer, and each C atom in the repeating unit has an additional single bond. As we will explain later, the π electrons of the C=C double bond are used to form the σ bonds that join the monomers together.

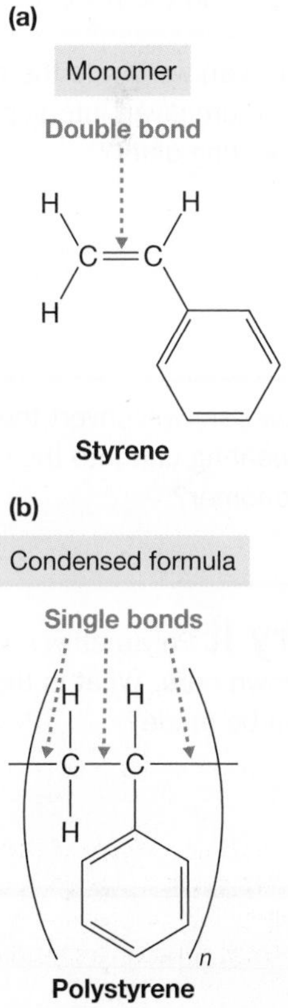

(a)
Monomer
Double bond
Styrene
(b)
Condensed formula
Single bonds
n
Polystyrene

FIGURE 28-5 Monomers versus repeating units (a) A double bond makes up the vinyl group in styrene, the monomer. (b) The double bond does not appear in the repeating unit of polystyrene, the polymer, as shown inside parentheses. Each C atom along the polymer backbone gains a single bond.

The exercises we just carried out for polystyrene can be applied to other vinyl polymers, too.

For vinyl polymers:

- The repeating unit is established by two adjacent carbon atoms of the main chain, along with the atoms or groups attached to them.
- Those adjacent carbon atoms are involved only in single bonds in the polymer, but are connected by a double bond in the vinyl monomer.

YOUR TURN **28.2**

Given the partial structure of polypropylene shown here, draw its condensed formula. How many repeating units are shown in the structure given?

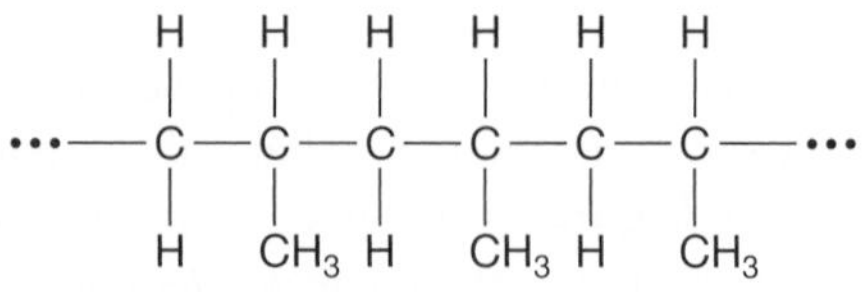

SOLVED PROBLEM **28.1**

How to draw a vinyl monomer from the structure of a vinyl polymer

Break It Down Poly(vinyl chloride), abbreviated PVC, is a vinyl polymer used for plumbing materials (e.g., pipe) and has the partial structure shown here. On the basis of the partial structure of the polymer, what is the structure of vinyl chloride?

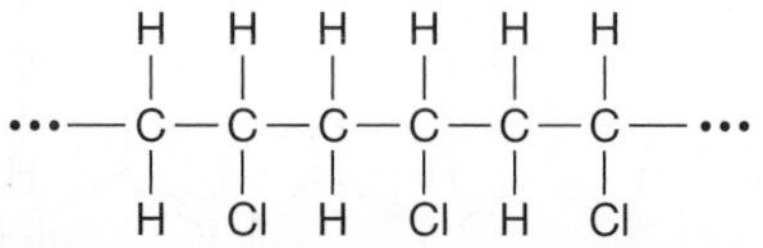

Think	Solve
What atoms make up the main chain and the pendant groups?	The main chain is the chain of carbon atoms, and the Cl atoms are the pendant groups, or side groups, analogous to the phenyl rings in polystyrene.
How can we divide the partial structure given into separate repeating units?	The polymer repeats every two carbons in the main chain, as shown here on the left, giving us the repeating unit depicted inside the parentheses of the condensed formula shown on the right. 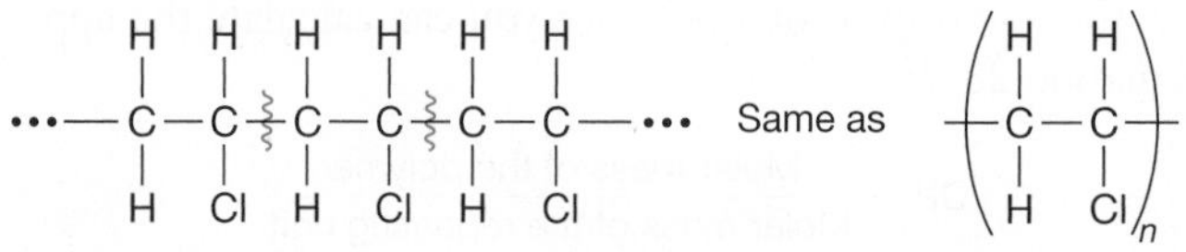
How can we convert the repeating unit into the vinyl monomer?	We remove the single bonds on the left and right of the repeating unit and change the C—C single bond to a C=C double bond, as shown here. 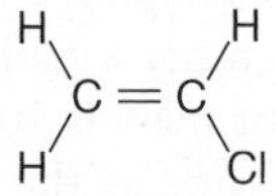 **Vinyl chloride**

Try It Poly(methyl methacrylate), or Plexiglas, has the partial structure shown here. What is the structure of the vinyl monomer from which Plexiglas can be made?

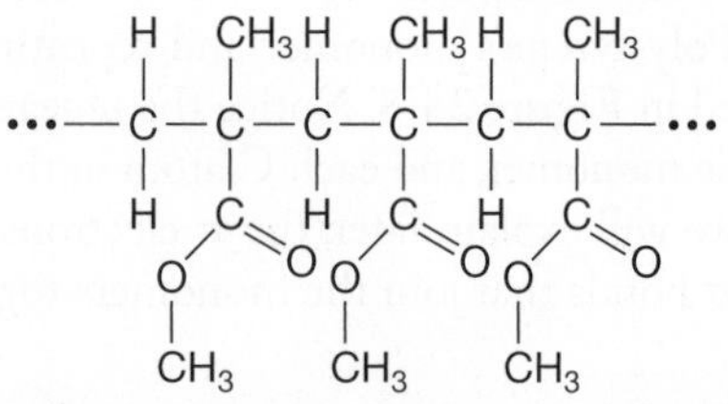

Answers to all Try It exercises can be found in the Solutions Manual.

28.1b Radical Polymerization of Styrene and Other Vinyl Monomers

Manufacturers create polystyrene from styrene (the monomer) by means of **radical polymerization**, which is a polymerization that proceeds by a radical chain-reaction mechanism. An example is shown in Equation 28-3, in which styrene is warmed in the presence of benzoyl peroxide, $C_6H_5CO_2—O_2CC_6H_5$.

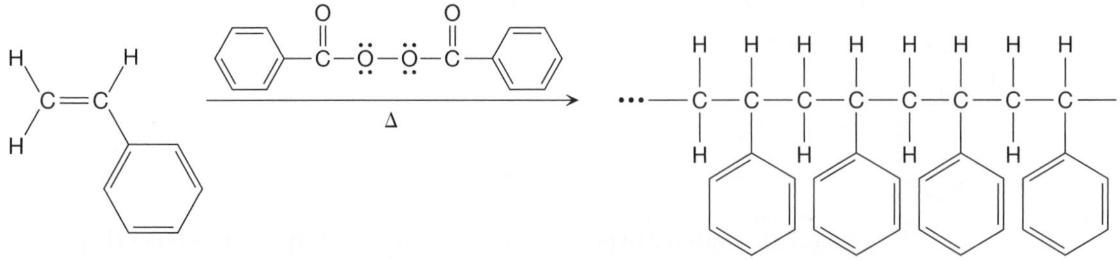

(28-3)

The mechanistic steps of this reaction are essentially the same types of initiation, propagation, and termination steps you studied in Section 27.4a. *Initiation* is needed to create the radicals. Monomers such as styrene do not produce radicals readily, so we use benzoyl peroxide, a radical initiator (see Recall box). Because oxygen–oxygen single bonds are particularly weak (see Table 27-2, p. 1308), heating benzoyl peroxide results in homolysis of the bond between the two O atoms to produce the benzoyloxyl radical:

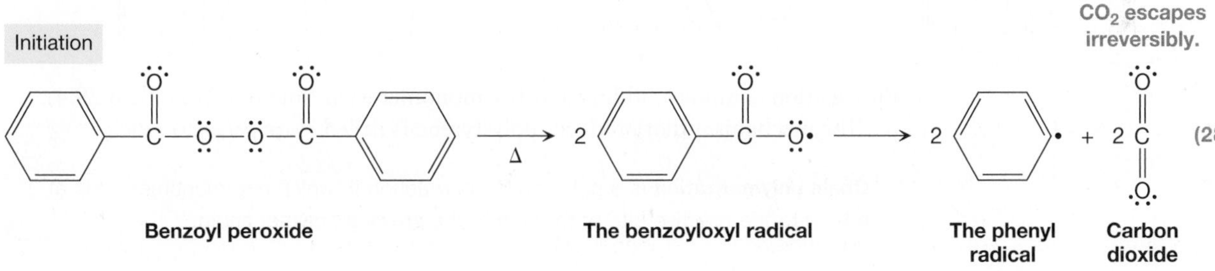
Initiation
CO2 escapes irreversibly.
Benzoyl peroxide
The benzoyloxyl radical
The phenyl radical
Carbon dioxide

(28-4)

This initiation step is further driven by the irreversible loss of CO_2 from the benzoyloxyl radical, leaving the phenyl radical available for further reaction.

YOUR TURN 28.3

Draw in the curved arrows that show the movement of electrons in both steps of Equation 28-4.

◀ RECALL

As we saw in Section 27.1, radicals have at least one unpaired electron and are generally quite unstable. Therefore, radicals typically need to be generated from closed-shell radical initiators. Good radical initiators have a weak bond that will readily undergo homolysis to produce radicals.

After initiation, *propagation* occurs by radical addition (Section 27.4a). In this case, the phenyl radical adds to a styrene monomer, as shown in Equation 28-5. (The regiochemistry of this step will be discussed in Section 28.1c.)

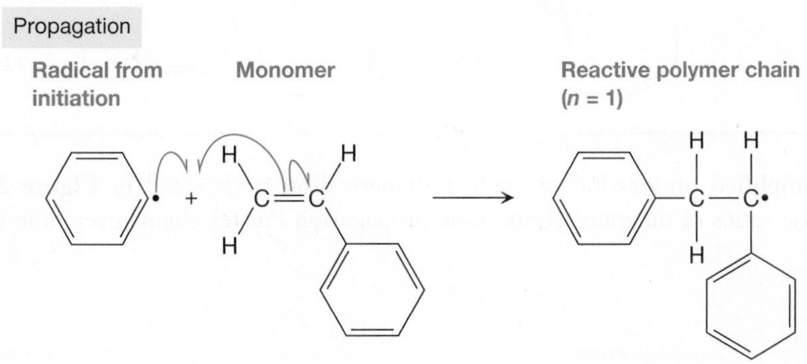
Propagation
Radical from initiation
Monomer
Reactive polymer chain
(n = 1)

(28-5)

What occurs next explains how the polymer chain grows: The radical on the product side of Equation 28-5 adds to another monomer of styrene, increasing the length of the carbon chain, as shown in Equation 28-6:

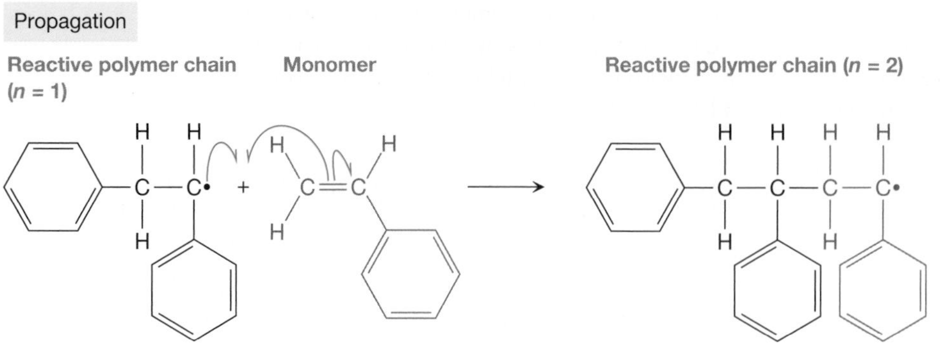

Propagation
Reactive polymer chain (n = 1)
Monomer
Reactive polymer chain (n = 2)

(28-6)

This radical can continue to propagate, adding to a third styrene monomer (Eq. 28-7):

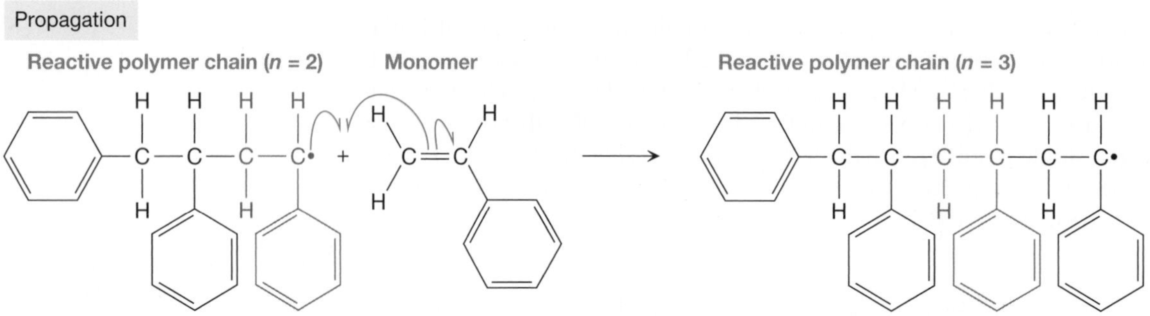

Propagation
Reactive polymer chain (n = 2)
Monomer
Reactive polymer chain (n = 3)

(28-7)

Propagation continues, adding another monomer each time (see Your Turn 28.4). The mechanism that produces polystyrene is called *chain polymerization*.

Chain polymerization is a polymerization reaction in which one monomer adds at a time to the reactive site at the end of the growing polymer chain.

When all atoms of the monomer end up in the repeating unit after each propagation step, as we see in Equations 28-5 through 28-7, this type of reaction is further classified as **addition polymerization**.

YOUR TURN **28.4**

Add the curved arrows, and draw the product of the next propagation step in the polymerization reaction, using Equations 28-5 through 28-7 as a guide.

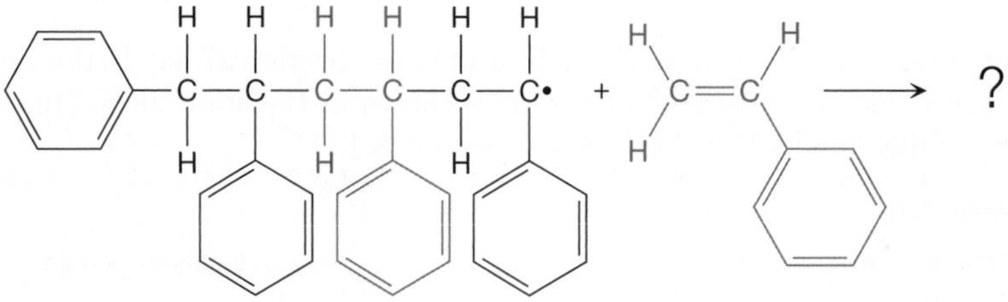

A simplified progression of chain polymerization is depicted in **Figure 28-6**, where the series of diagrams shows how propagation creates chains over time (it is

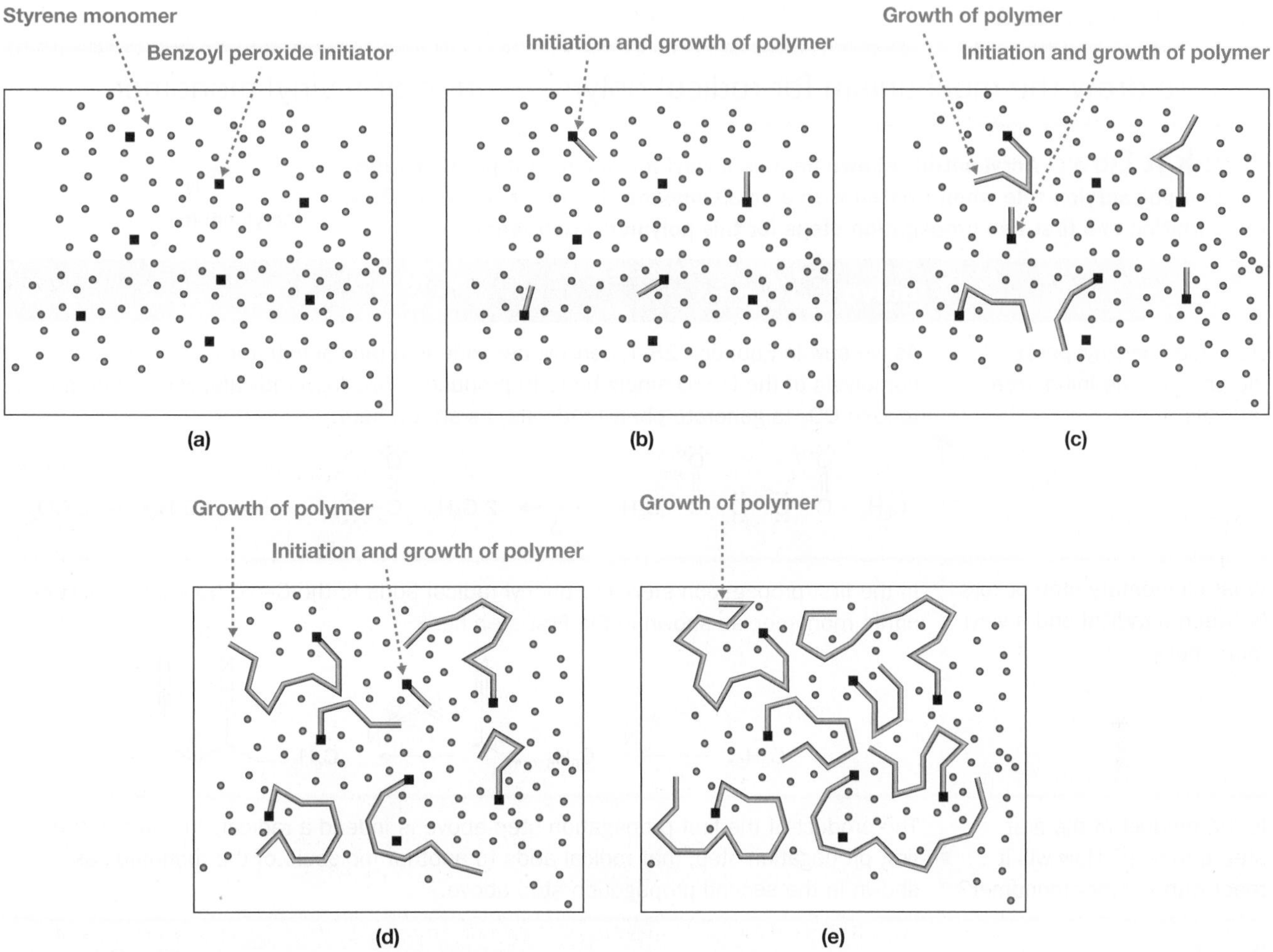
Styrene monomer
Benzoyl peroxide initiator
Initiation and growth of polymer
Growth of polymer
Initiation and growth of polymer
(a)
(b)
(c)
Growth of polymer
Initiation and growth of polymer
Growth of polymer
(d)
(e)

FIGURE 28-6 Chain polymerization of styrene over time (a) A solution of styrene (red dots) and benzoyl peroxide (blue squares) prior to heating. (b) During heating, the benzoyl peroxide molecules undergo homolysis (initiation) and propagation. The gray lines represent bonds formed between an initiated radical and a styrene molecule. (c) Propagation continues for each growing chain. Initiation continues, but at a slower rate than propagation. (d) Propagation continues, and each chain increases in length. Benzoyl peroxide molecules that remain also initiate chain growth. (e) Later in the reaction, initiation is minimal. Propagation continues, and polymer chains grow longer.

simplified in that it represents two dimensions, whereas the polymers actually grow three-dimensionally). The diagram begins with unreacted starting material in (a), proceeds to initiation and growth in (b), and then shows how propagation and initiation continue in (c) through (e).

YOUR TURN 28.5

In Figure 28-6e, draw a line (similar to the ones in Fig. 28-6b) indicating the initiation and growth of a new polymer chain. Also draw a line indicating the propagation of two existing chains.

SOLVED PROBLEM **28.2**

How to draw the mechanism for radical polymerization of a vinyl monomer

Break It Down Acrylonitrile, shown here, is a vinyl monomer that produces the polymer polyacrylonitrile when treated with a small amount of benzoyl peroxide. Draw the initiation and first two propagation steps for this polymerization reaction.

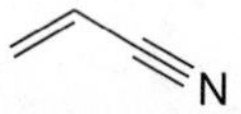

Acrylonitrile

Think	Solve
How does benzoyl peroxide produce the initial free radicals?	As we saw in Equation 28-4, benzoyl peroxide is a radical initiator that undergoes homolysis of the O—O single bond to produce benzoyloxyl radicals, which then go on to lose CO_2 to generate phenyl radicals, as shown here. 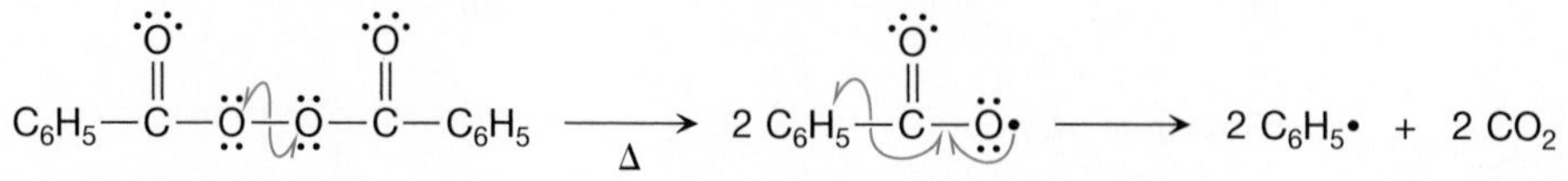 C_6H_5—C—O—O—C—C_6H_5 Δ 2 C_6H_5—C—O• 2 C_6H_5• + 2 CO_2
What elementary step occurs between a radical and a vinyl monomer?	In the first propagation step, the phenyl radical adds to the C═C bond of an acrylonitrile monomer, as shown in the first step here. 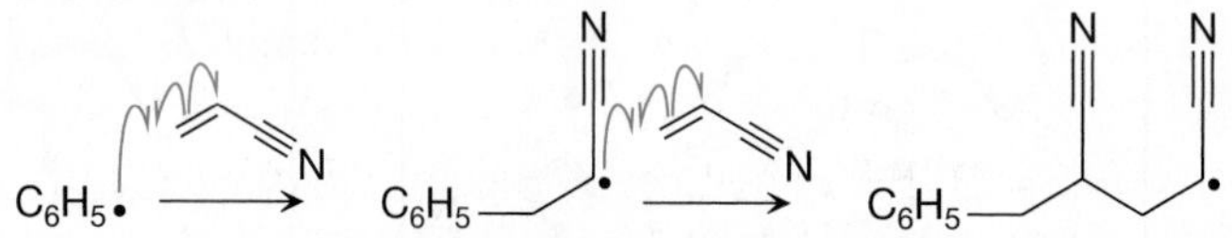 C_6H_5• N C_6H_5 N N N N C_6H_5
Is the product of the first step a radical? How will it react with another monomer?	The product of the first propagation step above is indeed a radical. Just like in the first propagation step, that radical adds to another molecule of the monomer, as shown in the second propagation step above.

Try It But-1-ene, commonly called butylene, is a vinyl monomer that, when treated with benzoyl peroxide, produces polybutylene, a polymer used to manufacture the pipes that carry modern municipal water supplies. Draw the initiation step and the first two propagation steps for this polymerization reaction.

But-1-ene (Butylene)

Propagation could continue, in theory, until there are no remaining molecules of monomer. In reality, though, the growth of the chain usually ends by *termination*, of which there are two basic types: *combination* and *disproportionation*.

Combination, shown in Equation 28-8 for two reactive PS chains, is another term for radical coupling (see Recall box).

◂ RECALL

Radical coupling, presented in Section 27.3a, is the joining of an unpaired electron from one radical to an unpaired electron from a second radical to form a new σ bond. As we saw, radical coupling typically proceeds with no energy barrier.

Termination by combination

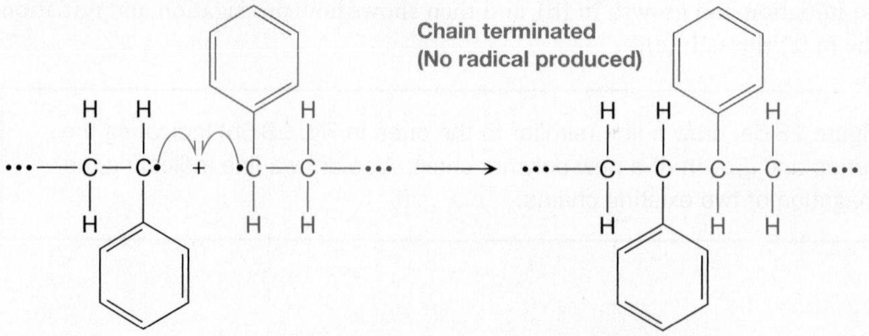
Chain terminated
(No radical produced)

(28-8)

Disproportionation, shown in Equation 28-9, describes any reaction in which two of the same species react to produce two different products.

Termination by disproportionation

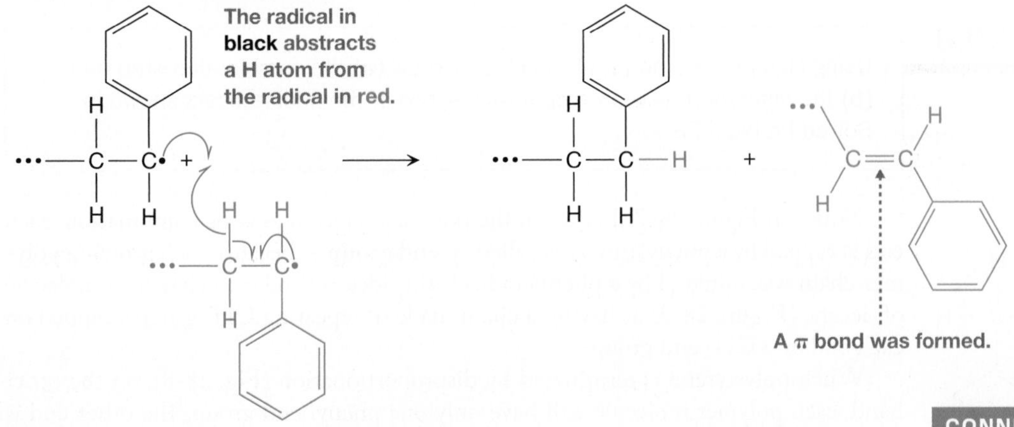

The radical in black abstracts a H atom from the radical in red.
A π bond was formed.

(28-9)

In the case of polystyrene, disproportionation occurs when one of the radicals abstracts a hydrogen atom from another radical. One electron from the C—H bond that is broken is used to form a new C—H bond, whereas the other electron joins with the unpaired electron on the adjacent carbon to form a C=C double bond.

Both combination and disproportionation produce closed-shell species from radicals, so these steps are typically quite rapid. Which step dominates can depend on the nature of the monomer and the reaction conditions.

Figure 28-7 shows how a particular polystyrene molecule might appear after a combination step. Two growing polymer chains—one with n repeating units and the

CONNECTIONS 28.1

Water, water everywhere . . . Polyacrylonitrile (Solved Problem 28.2) is used to make ultrafiltration membranes for wastewater treatment and is also used to make hollow fiber membranes for reverse osmosis, a technique that removes contaminants from water to make fresh drinking water. Polyacrylonitrile is ideally suited for these purposes because it is strong, stable, and hydrophilic.

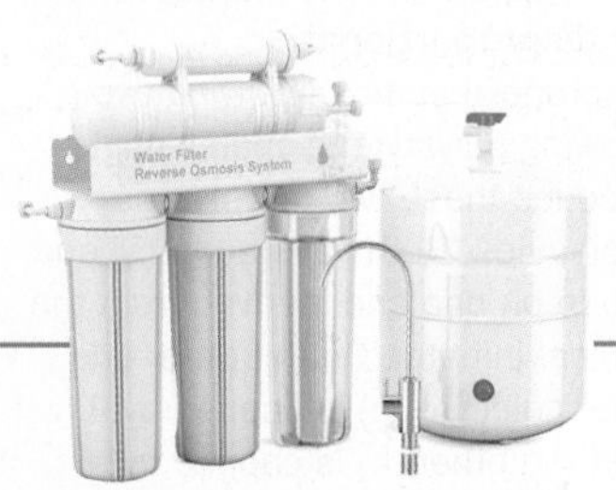

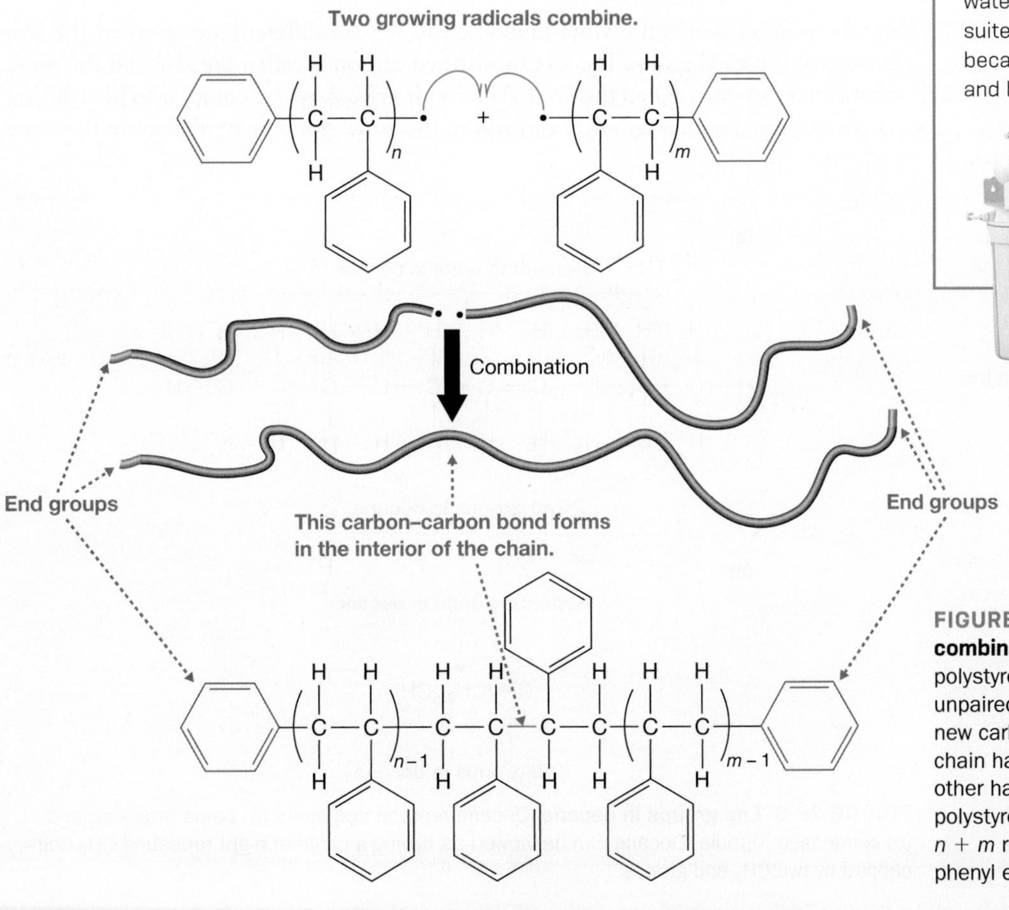

Two growing radicals combine.
Combination
End groups
This carbon–carbon bond forms in the interior of the chain.
End groups

FIGURE 28-7 Termination by combination (*Top*) Two growing polystyrene chains meet, and the unpaired electrons join to produce a new carbon–carbon bond. One growing chain has n repeating units, and the other has m. (*Bottom*) The terminated polystyrene molecule has a total of $n + m$ repeating units and has two phenyl end groups (blue).

other with m repeating units—join to produce a longer chain with $n + m$ total repeating units (in the product, one repeating unit from each reactant chain is drawn separately from the other $n - 1$ or $m - 1$ units). **Figure 28-8** shows the two polystyrene molecules that might be produced after disproportionation.

YOUR TURN **28.6**

Using Figures 28-7 and 28-8 as guides, draw **(a)** the combination step and **(b)** the disproportionation step involving two of the final radicals shown in Solved Problem 28.2.

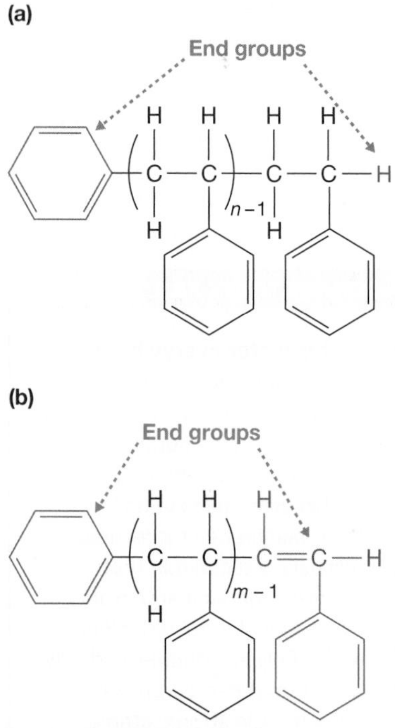

(a)
End groups
H H H H
C C C C H
n−1
H H
(b)
End groups
H H H
C C C C H
m − 1
H

FIGURE 28-8 Termination by disproportionation A disproportionation involving two growing polystyrene chains might produce these two polystyrene molecules. Both have a phenyl end group on one end, derived from the radical initiator. On the other end, one molecule (a) is capped by H and the other (b) is capped by a vinylic group, both resulting from the disproportionation reaction.

Notice in Figure 28-7 that when the polymer is terminated by combination, each end is capped by a phenyl group—called an **end group**—because each growing polymer chain was initiated by a phenyl radical. This idea is similar to viewing a molecule of decane (**Figure 28-9**) as having a chain made of repeating CH_2 groups, capped on each end by a CH_3 end group.

When polystyrene is terminated by disproportionation (Fig. 28-8), on the other hand, each polymer molecule will have only one phenyl end group. The other end is capped by either a hydrogen atom or a vinylic group.

Unlike in a molecule of decane, the end groups of a polymer are variable and contribute little to the polymer's overall structure: two units out of >1900 (i.e., $< \sim 0.1\%$) in a typical molecule in commercial polystyrene. Therefore:

Only the repeating unit of a polymer (not its end groups) is used to evaluate the polymer's structure.

Consequently, most representations of polymers omit the end groups.

28.1c Regiochemistry of Radical Polymerization

Styrene is an unsymmetric vinyl monomer, so we can differentiate between the two carbons of the vinyl group. The less substituted carbon is called the *tail*, and the more substituted carbon is called the *head*. As a result, *regiochemistry* comes into play during polymerization because a radical can add to the vinyl group of styrene more than one

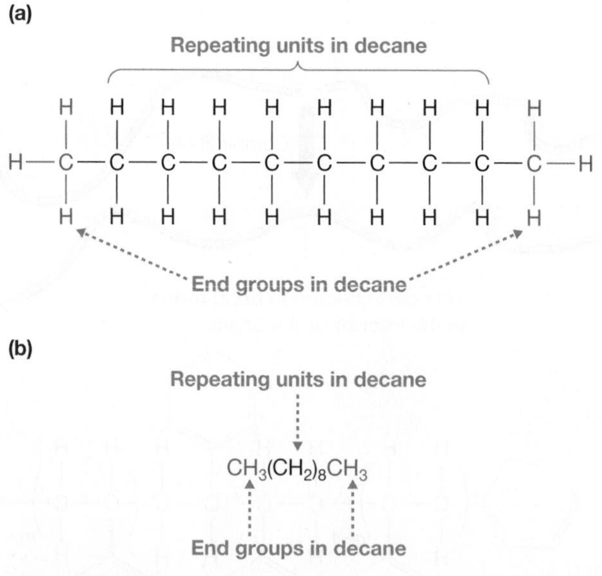

(a)
Repeating units in decane
H H H H H H H H H H
H C C C C C C C C C C H
H H H H H H H H H H
End groups in decane
(b)
Repeating units in decane
CH3(CH2)8CH3
End groups in decane

FIGURE 28-9 End groups in decane Decane represented as its (a) Lewis structure and (b) condensed formula. Decane can be viewed as having a chain of eight repeating CH_2 units, capped by two CH_3 end groups.

way: Equation 28-10 shows **head-to-tail** addition, and Equation 28-11 shows **head-to-head** addition. (Tail-to-tail addition is also possible; see Your Turn 28.7.)

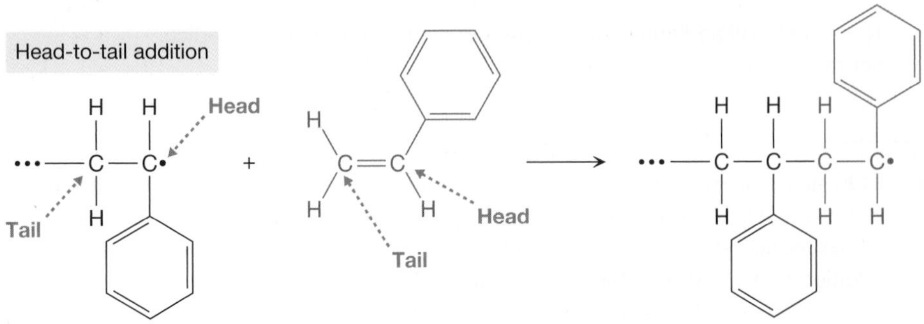

Head-to-tail addition
Head
Tail
Head
Tail

(28-10)

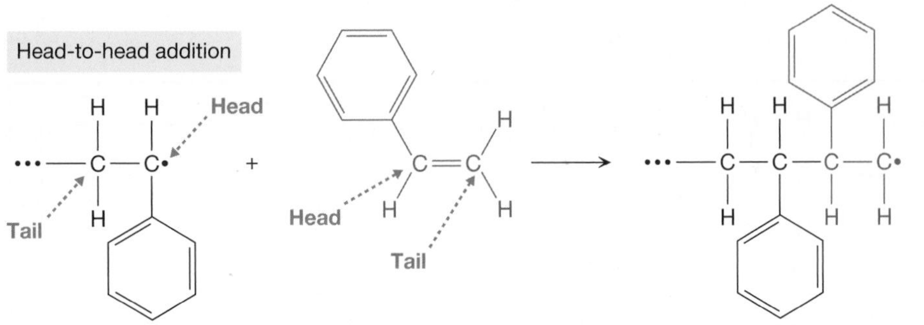

Head-to-head addition
Head
Tail
Head
Tail

(28-11)

Head-to-tail addition (i.e., Eq. 28-10) is favored in the polymerization of polystyrene for two reasons, as shown in **Figure 28-10**. First, steric repulsion between the two phenyl groups (one at the end of the propagating radical and one in the monomer) leads to a rise in energy, making it less likely that a head-to-head collision will bring the reactive carbons close enough to form a bond. Second, the radical formed in the head-to-tail addition is lower in energy (more stable): The radical produced from head-to-tail addition is resonance-stabilized, whereas the radical produced from head-to-head addition is not.

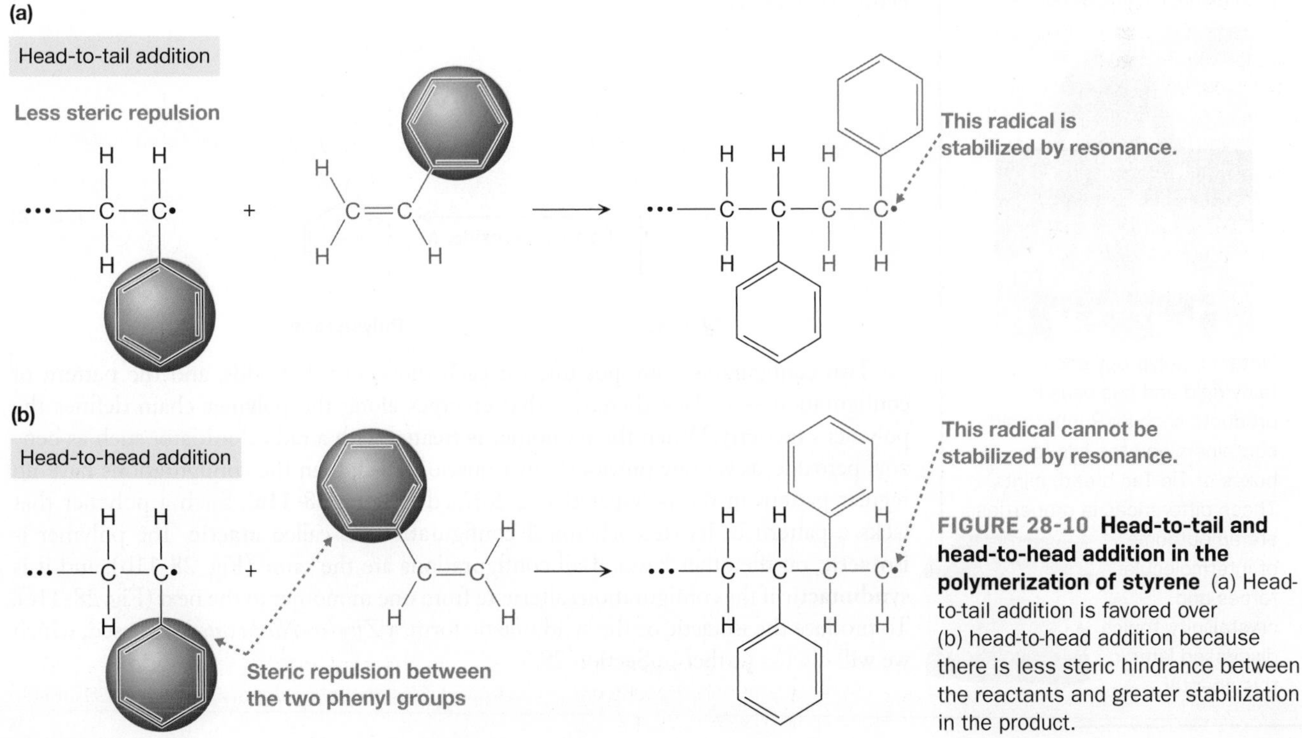

(a)
Head-to-tail addition
Less steric repulsion
This radical is stabilized by resonance.
(b)
Head-to-head addition
Steric repulsion between the two phenyl groups
This radical cannot be stabilized by resonance.

FIGURE 28-10 Head-to-tail and head-to-head addition in the polymerization of styrene (a) Head-to-tail addition is favored over (b) head-to-head addition because there is less steric hindrance between the reactants and greater stabilization in the product.

The energy contributions toward the propagation steps that form polystyrene (Fig. 28-10) have similar roles in other polymerizations. In general:

> The head-to-tail addition of vinyl monomers is usually favored in radical polymerization.

YOUR TURN 28.7

Draw all resonance structures for the product of head-to-tail addition shown in Figure 28-10. Then write the elementary step for tail-to-tail addition, and draw all resonance structures for the tail-to-tail product. Explain why head-to-tail addition is favored over tail-to-tail addition.

YOUR TURN 28.8

Use curved arrow notation to show the movement of electrons in the head-to-tail addition of a growing chain of poly(ethyl acrylate) to a molecule of ethyl acrylate. Draw resonance structures to explain why head-to-tail addition occurs instead of head-to-head addition.

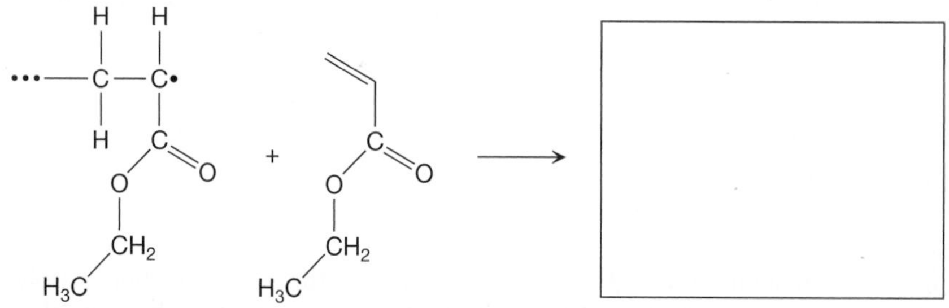

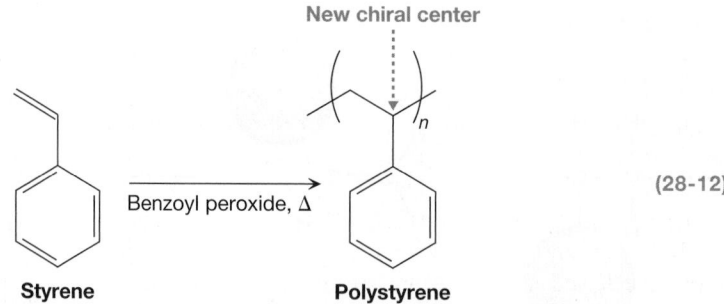

Propagating chain of poly(ethyl acrylate) + **Ethyl acrylate** → **Product of head-to-tail addition**

CONNECTIONS 28.2

Widely different uses of polypropylene Atactic polypropylene (Your Turn 28.9) has use as roofing adhesive.

Isotactic polypropylene is fairly rigid and has uses in products such as Rubbermaid containers and the lids for boxes of Tic Tac breath mints. These differences in properties are an outcome of intermolecular forces and crystallinity, topics discussed later in this chapter.

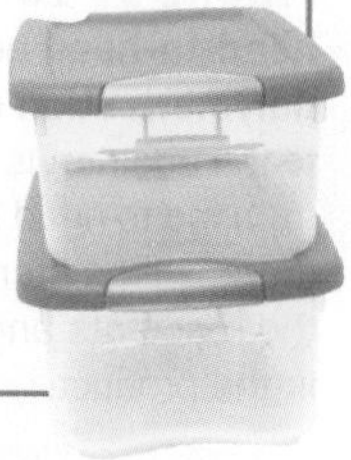

28.1d Stereochemistry of Radical Polymerization

When styrene polymerizes, the sp^2-hybridized C atoms of the vinyl group become sp^3-hybridized, and the C atom attached to the phenyl ring becomes a new chiral center (Eq. 28-12):

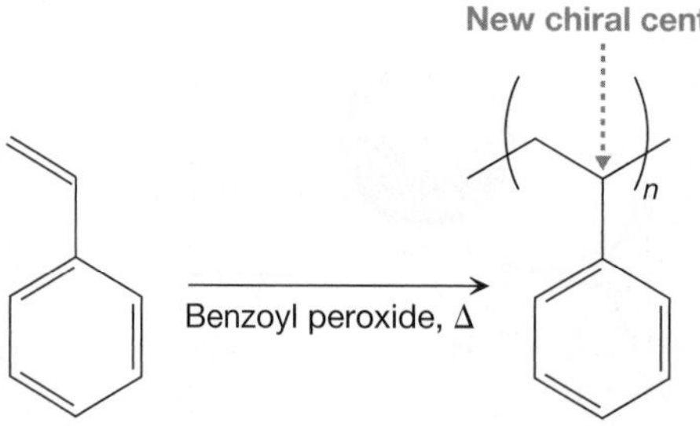
New chiral center
n
Benzoyl peroxide, Δ

Styrene **Polystyrene** **(28-12)**

Two configurations are possible for each monomer that adds, and the pattern of configurations—or lack thereof—that emerges along the polymer chain defines the polymer's **tacticity**. When the monomer is treated with a radical initiator such as benzoyl peroxide, as we saw previously in Equation 28-3, then the configurations have no regular pattern in the polymer that is formed (**Figure 28-11a**). Such a polymer that lacks a pattern in its stereochemical configurations is called **atactic**. The polymer is **isotactic**, on the other hand, if all configurations are the same (Fig. 28-11b), and it is **syndiotactic** if the configurations alternate from one monomer to the next (Fig. 28-11c). To produce the isotactic or the syndiotactic form, a *Ziegler–Natta catalyst* is used, which we will discuss further in Section 28.3.

The three forms of polystyrene have different properties and, consequently, different uses. Atactic polystyrene is malleable and easily molded into solid objects, such as the yogurt container in Figure 28-11a. The syndiotactic form is rigid and can withstand relatively high temperatures. It is used to manufacture some of the components for the rice cooker shown in Figure 28-11c. Isotactic polystyrene is rather crystalline and does not have commercial use but is studied in thin films, such as the one shown in Figure 28-11b. The reasons for these different properties will become clearer in Section 28.10.

YOUR TURN 28.9

Polypropylene, whose condensed formula is shown here, has been synthesized in atactic and isotactic forms. Draw each polymer; use the ones shown in Figure 28-11 as a guide.

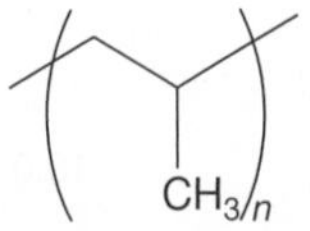

CH_3 n

Polypropylene

28.1e Size Distribution of Polymers

The goal of most organic syntheses is to make a single product in high yield. In the synthesis of a polymer such as polystyrene, however, this is difficult or impossible because of variations that exist in the chain-polymerization mechanism (Section 28.1b). Therefore, the lengths of the chains that are produced cannot be precisely controlled. Instead, a polymer is a mixture (a distribution) of chains of different lengths and can be described with an *average* molar mass or, alternatively, an average degree of polymerization. Commercial-grade polystyrene, for example, has an average molar mass of >200,000 g/mol (i.e., an average degree of polymerization of >1920).

How do we know the distributions of polymer size within a sample? One method to determine this information is **gel permeation chromatography (GPC)**, which works by size exclusion. Polymer samples in solution pass through a porous gel inside a column. Smaller polymer molecules spend more time interacting with the gel, so they pass through the column more slowly and elute from the column at later times. The amount of polymer eluting at a given time registers as a signal. Consider **Figure 28-12** (next page), for example, which shows the GPC results of a sample of polystyrene with an average molar mass of 24,000 g/mol, or an average degree of polymerization of 230. Molecular size varies widely, from ~2000 g/mol (DP ~19) to ~520,000 g/mol (DP ~5000), and the sample consists of two separate distributions, one centered at ~8000 g/mol (DP ~77) and the other at ~130,000 g/mol (DP ~1250).

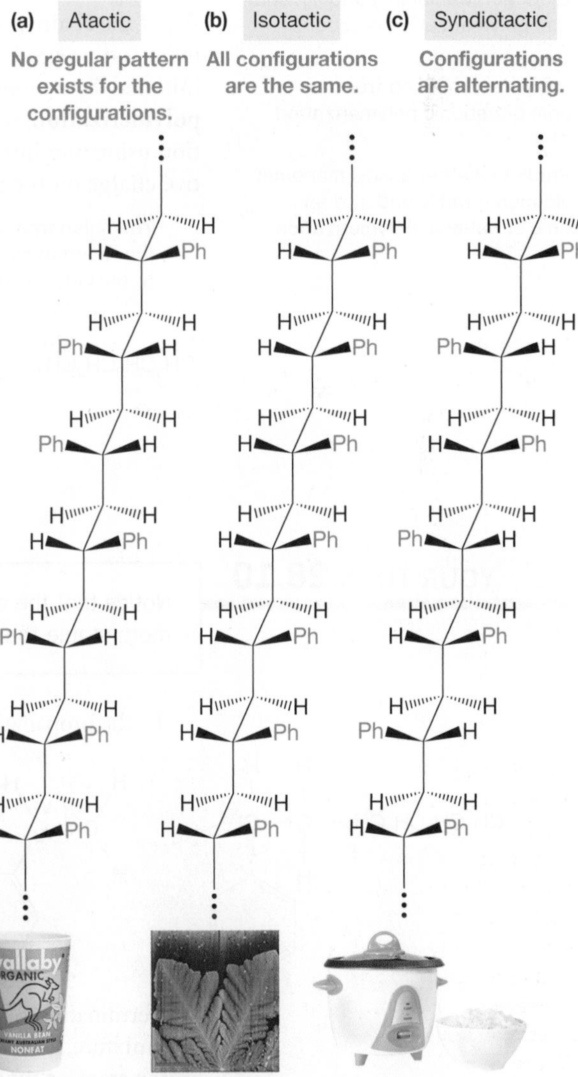

(a) Atactic
No regular pattern exists for the configurations.
(b) Isotactic
All configurations are the same.
(c) Syndiotactic
Configurations are alternating.
H
Ph
wallaby
ORGANIC
VANILLA BEAN
NONFAT

FIGURE 28-11 Tacticity in polystyrene (a) In atactic polystyrene, the stereochemical configurations do not establish a regular pattern. (b) In isotactic polystyrene, all stereochemical configurations are the same. (c) In syndiotactic polystyrene, the stereochemical configurations alternate.

FIGURE 28-12 Gel permeation chromatogram of a polystyrene sample with average molar mass of ~24,000 g/mol (DP = 230) Elution time on the x axis is correlated with molar mass. The magnitude of the signal on the y axis is proportional to the number of molecules that elute (i.e., exit from) the gel at a particular time.

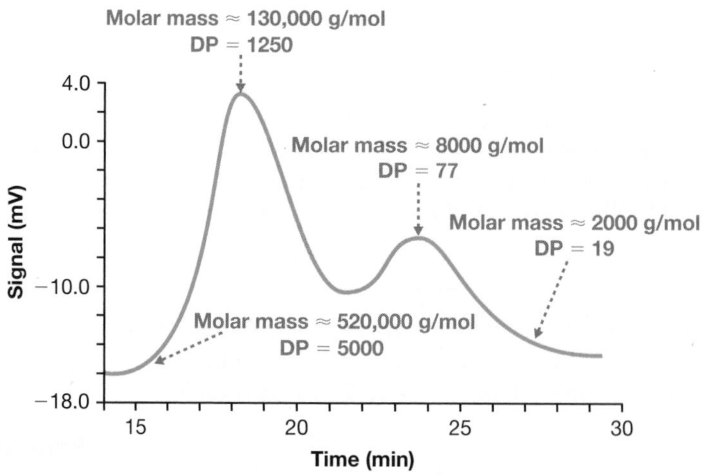

Molar mass ≈ 130,000 g/mol
DP = 1250
Molar mass ≈ 8000 g/mol
DP = 77
Molar mass ≈ 2000 g/mol
DP = 19
Molar mass ≈ 520,000 g/mol
DP = 5000
4.0
0.0
−10.0
−18.0
Signal (mV)
15
20
25
30
Time (min)

SECTION 28.2 OBJECTIVES

You will be able to:

1. Distinguish anionic, cationic, and radical polymerization reactions.
2. Draw the mechanism for, and the polymer produced from, an anionic or cationic polymerization reaction.
3. Predict whether a vinyl monomer would more readily undergo an anionic or cationic polymerization.

28.2 Anionic and Cationic Polymerization Reactions

All of the chain-polymerization reactions we have studied so far involve vinyl monomers and proceed through a radical mechanism. Chain polymerizations can also be initiated by anions or cations, resulting in **anionic polymerization** or **cationic polymerization**, respectively. For example, styrene can undergo anionic polymerization using butyllithium ($CH_3CH_2CH_2CH_2Li$) as the initiator, which forms a negative charge on the growing chain instead of an unpaired electron (Eq. 28-13).

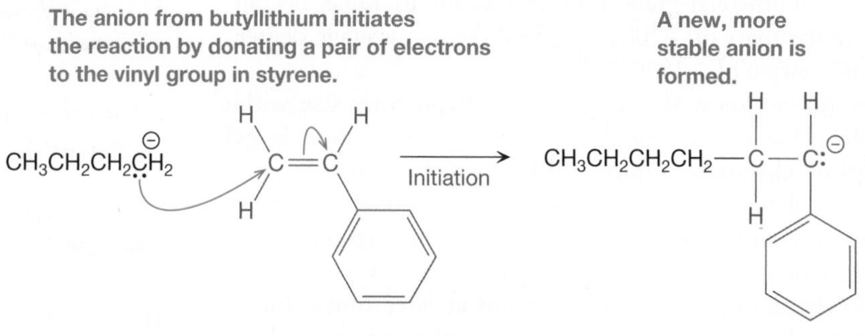

The anion from butyllithium initiates the reaction by donating a pair of electrons to the vinyl group in styrene.
A new, more stable anion is formed.
CH3CH2CH2CH2
Initiation
CH3CH2CH2CH2—C—C:

(28-13)

YOUR TURN **28.10**

Notice that the anion on the product side of the reaction in Equation 28-13 is more stable than the anion on the reactant side. Explain why.

In the propagation steps, the reactive intermediates are anions, too, not radicals:

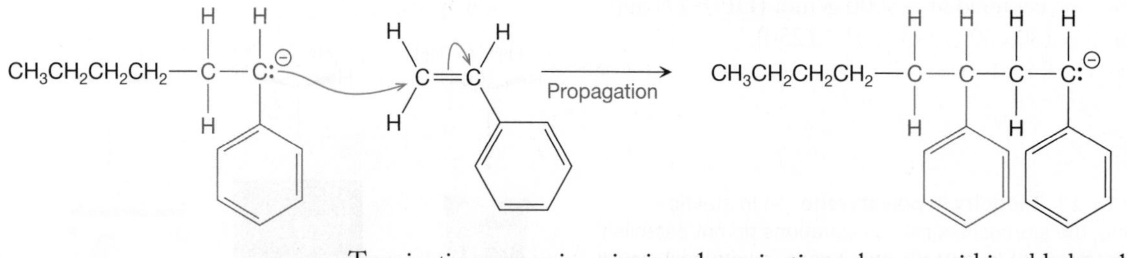

CH3CH2CH2CH2—C—C:
Propagation
CH3CH2CH2CH2—C—C—C—C:

(28-14)

Termination occurs in anionic polymerization when an acid is added to the reaction mixture, as shown in Equation 28-15. The anion is neutralized in the resulting proton transfer, which ends the propagation cycle:

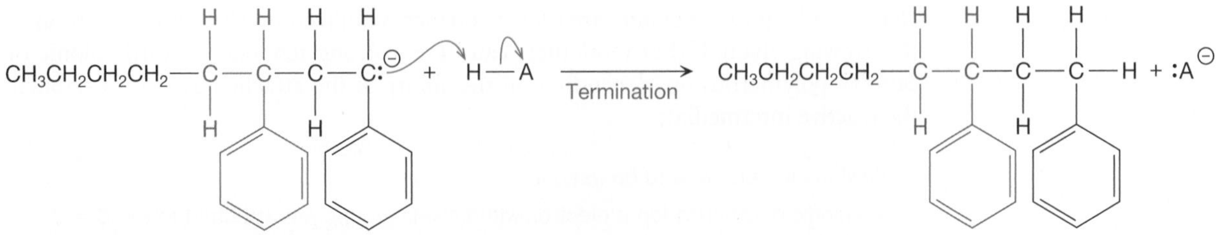
(28-15)

YOUR TURN **28.11**

Combination and disproportionation are not feasible termination steps for the anionic polymerization of styrene. Why not?

In cationic polymerization, the reactive intermediates are positively charged. For example, the polymerization of styrene can be initiated by treatment with $BCl_3 \cdot H_2O$ in a non-nucleophilic solvent such as CH_2Cl_2 (Eq. 28-16). The $BCl_3 \cdot H_2O$ complex acts as a Brønsted acid to protonate the C=C bond of styrene, which produces the first carbocation intermediate:

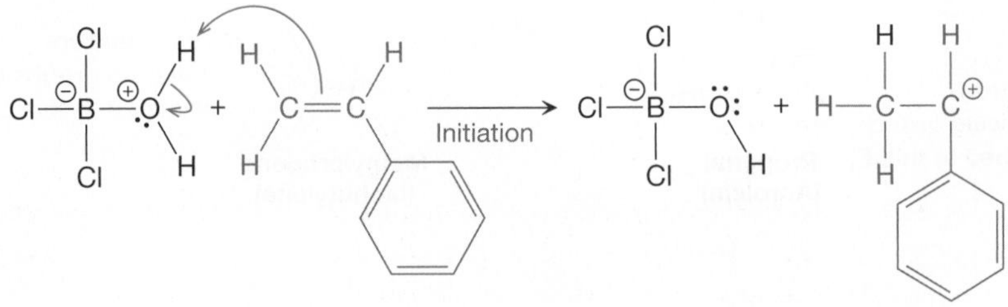
(28-16)

Propagation occurs when the carbocation of the growing chain undergoes electrophilic addition to another monomer:

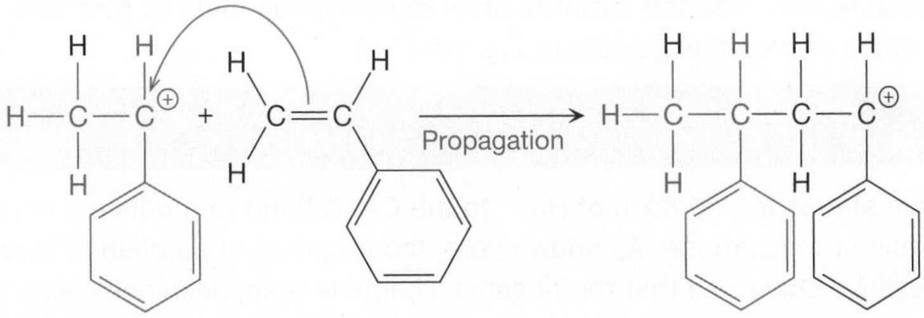
(28-17)

Polymerization of the chain terminates when all of its atoms have a complete octet. In this case, as shown in Equation 28-18, Cl^- can be donated by the conjugate base that was produced in the initiation step, probably through an addition–elimination sequence:

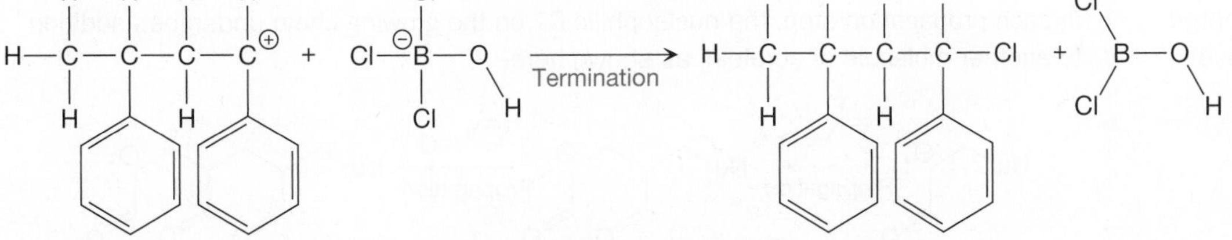
(28-18)

As we have seen, polystyrene can be produced from a chain polymerization that proceeds through a radical, anionic, or cationic mechanism. All three types of mechanisms are available for this polymerization because an unpaired electron, a negative charge, and a positive charge are each resonance-stabilized on the benzylic carbon of the growing chain. Other monomers can have a strong tendency toward anionic or cationic polymerization, depending on the ability of the attached groups to stabilize the reactive intermediate.

> Vinyl monomers tend to be used in:
> - Anionic polymerization if electron-withdrawing groups are attached to the C═C bond.
> - Cationic polymerization if electron-donating groups are attached to the C═C bond.

The electron-withdrawing C═O group in propenal (acrolein; **Figure 28-13a**), for example, will facilitate anionic polymerization, whereas the electron-donating methyl groups in methylpropene (isobutylene; Fig. 28-13b) will facilitate cationic polymerization.

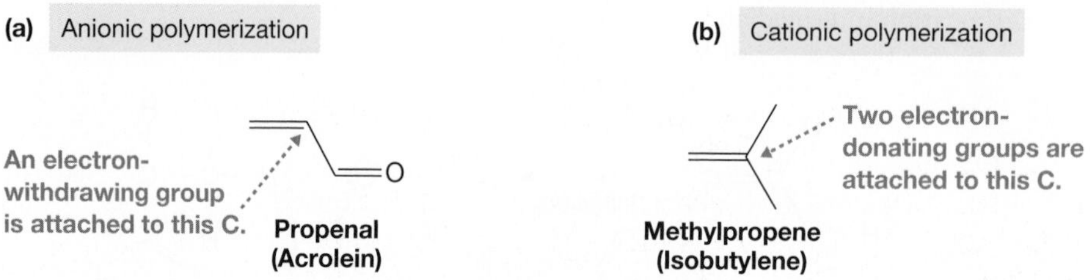

(a) Anionic polymerization
An electron-withdrawing group is attached to this C.
O
Propenal (Acrolein)
(b) Cationic polymerization
Two electron-donating groups are attached to this C.
Methylpropene (Isobutylene)

FIGURE 28-13 Vinyl monomers for anionic and cationic polymerization (a) A vinyl monomer with electron-withdrawing substituents tends to be used for anionic polymerization because electron-withdrawing groups stabilize negative charges. (b) A vinyl monomer with electron-donating groups tends to be used for cationic polymerization because electron-donating groups stabilize positive charges.

SOLVED PROBLEM **28.3**

How to determine the product of anionic or cationic polymerization

Break It Down Using a generic nucleophile, Nu:⁻, as the initiator, draw the initiation and the first two propagation steps for the anionic polymerization of propenal (acrolein; Fig. 28-13a).

Think	Solve
What type of elementary step will take place between Nu:⁻ and acrolein? Which vinylic carbon can better handle the resulting negative charge?	The initiation step is the addition of Nu:⁻ to the C═C bond to produce a negative charge on one of the carbons. As shown here, the α carbon of acrolein is favored to gain the negative charge so that the negative charge is resonance-delocalized. 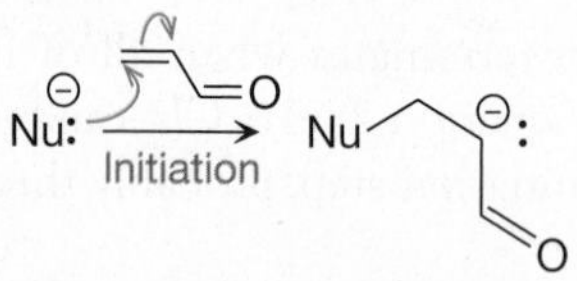 Nu: Initiation Nu O O
Can that step be repeated with another molecule of acrolein?	In each propagation step, the nucleophilic C⁻ on the growing chain undergoes addition to another molecule of acrolein, as shown here. 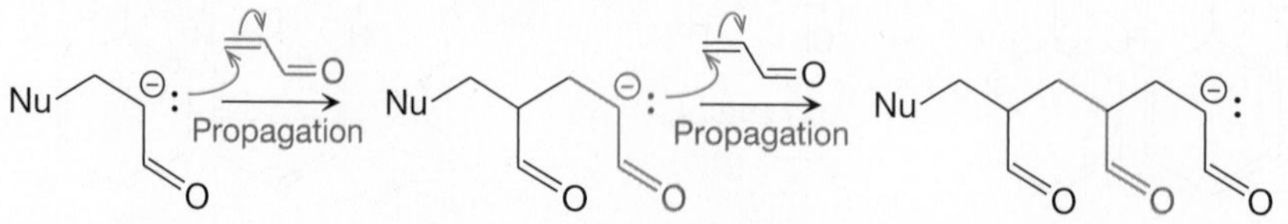 Nu Propagation Nu Propagation Nu O

Try It Using a generic strong Brønsted acid, HA, as the initiator, draw the initiation step and the first two propagation steps for the cationic polymerization of methylpropene (isobutylene; Fig. 28-13b).

28.3 Ziegler–Natta Catalysts and Coordination Polymerization

SECTION 28.3 OBJECTIVES

You will be able to:

1. Draw the mechanism for a Ziegler–Natta polymerization, and characterize it as a coordination polymerization.
2. Describe the benefits that Ziegler–Natta catalysts can offer.

Section 28.1 discussed how vinyl polymers can be produced by radical polymerization, and Section 28.2 discussed how such polymers can be produced by anionic or cationic polymerization. In the early 1950s, German chemist Karl Ziegler (1898–1973) and Italian chemist Giulio Natta (1903–1979) pioneered catalysts that promote the polymerization of vinyl polymers by *coordination polymerization*. Such catalysts, which have come to be known as Ziegler–Natta catalysts, can carry out vinyl polymerization at remarkable rates under mild conditions, and they can be used to produce some vinyl polymers that are unattainable with other polymerization mechanisms. For their work, Ziegler and Natta shared the 1963 Nobel Prize in Chemistry.

Ziegler–Natta catalysts are typically mixtures of transition metal halides (such as those of Ti, V, Zr, and Cr) with organoaluminum compounds. Equation 28-19, for example, shows how ethylene can be polymerized with $TiCl_4$ and $Al(CH_2CH_3)_2Cl$ to produce polyethylene:

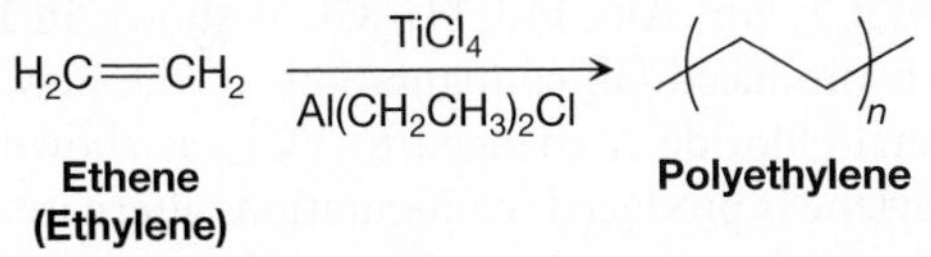

H2C=CH2
TiCl4
Al(CH2CH3)2Cl
n
Ethene
(Ethylene)
Polyethylene

(28-19)

The partial mechanism for this reaction is shown in Equation 28-20. $TiCl_4$ and $Al(CH_2CH_3)_2Cl$ combine to generate the species shown at the top-left of the mechanism. In that species, Al maintains partial bonds to the C atom and one of the Cl atoms bonded to Ti, and Ti has an open site for coordination. In Step 1, $H_2C{=}CH_2$ uses a pair of π electrons to coordinate with Ti. Then, Step 2 is addition across the C=C bond, similar to what occurs in hydroboration (Section 13.6a) when BH_3 adds across a C=C bond. Thus, the growing polymer has increased in size by one monomer, and Ti has regained an open coordination site. In Step 3, the growing polymer chain migrates, and the catalyst is ready for the coordination of another ethylene monomer. Steps 1–3 therefore make up the propagation cycle for the mechanism.

Partial mechanism for Ziegler–Natta polymerization (Eq. 28-19)

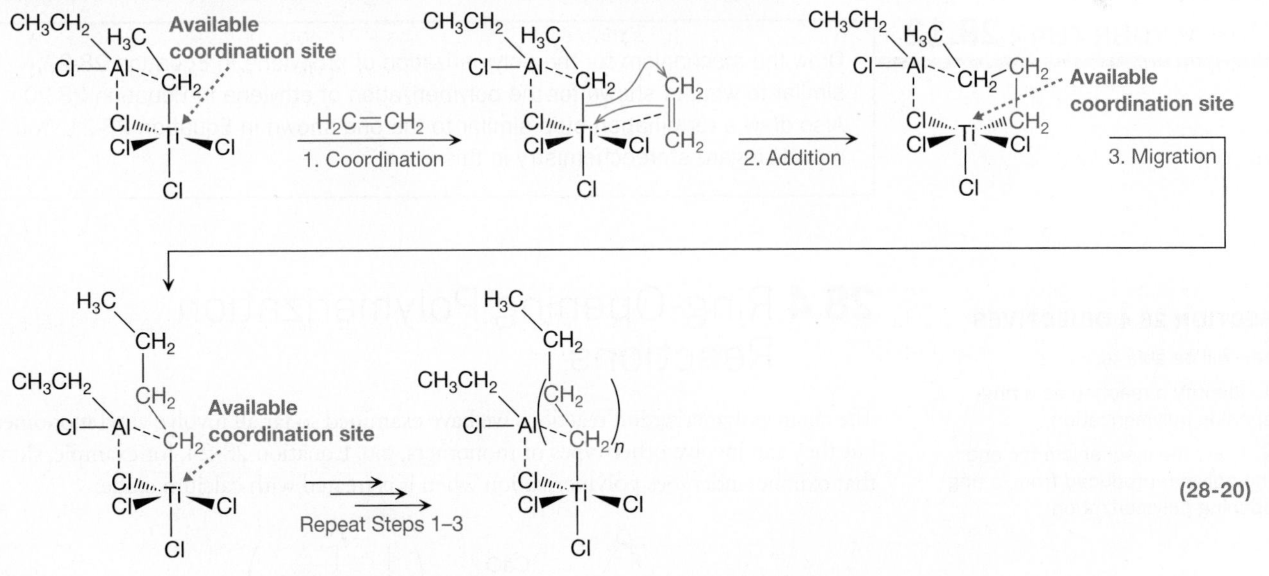

CH3CH2
H3C
Available coordination site
Cl
Al
CH2
Ti
Cl
H2C=CH2
1. Coordination
CH2
2. Addition
Available coordination site
3. Migration
Repeat Steps 1–3
n

(28-20)

A variety of termination steps is possible. One such termination is β-elimination, as shown in Equation 28-21:

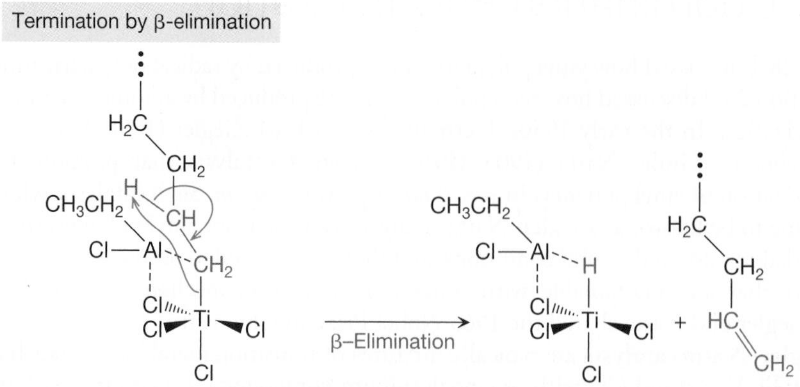

Termination by β-elimination
β-Elimination

(28-21)

A remarkable aspect of Ziegler–Natta polymerization is the ability to control the *tacticity* of the resulting polymer. For example, when propene (propylene) undergoes polymerization with $TiCl_4$ and $Al(CH_2CH_3)_2Cl$, as shown in Equation 28-22, isotactic polypropylene is produced (all configurations of the new chiral center are the same). When the metal chloride is changed to VCl_4, as shown in Equation 28-23, syndiotactic polypropylene is produced (configurations alternate along the chain). The details behind how the catalyst controls tacticity are beyond the scope of this book.

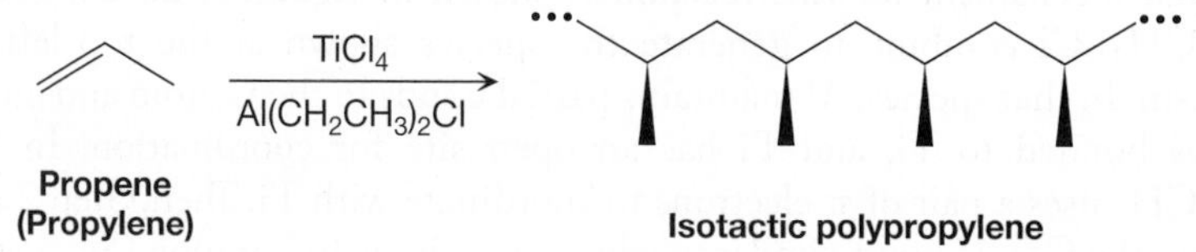

$TiCl_4$
$Al(CH_2CH_3)_2Cl$
Propene (Propylene)
Isotactic polypropylene

(28-22)

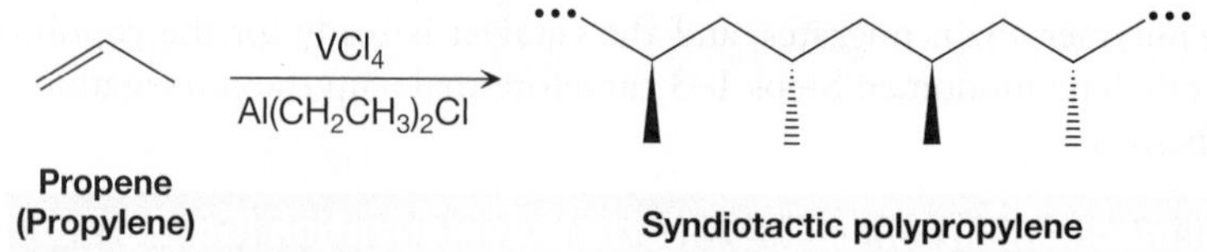

VCl_4
$Al(CH_2CH_3)_2Cl$
Propene (Propylene)
Syndiotactic polypropylene

(28-23)

YOUR TURN **28.12**

Draw the mechanism for the polymerization of propylene in Equation 28-22, similar to what is shown for the polymerization of ethylene in Equation 28-20. Also draw a termination step similar to the one shown in Equation 28-21. You may disregard stereochemistry in this case.

SECTION 28.4 OBJECTIVES

You will be able to:

1. Identify a reaction as a ring-opening polymerization.
2. Draw the mechanism for, and the polymer produced from, a ring-opening polymerization.

28.4 Ring-Opening Polymerization Reactions

The chain-polymerization reactions we have examined so far all involve vinyl monomers, but they can involve other types of monomers, too. Equation 28-24, for example, shows that oxirane undergoes polymerization when it is treated with calcium oxide:

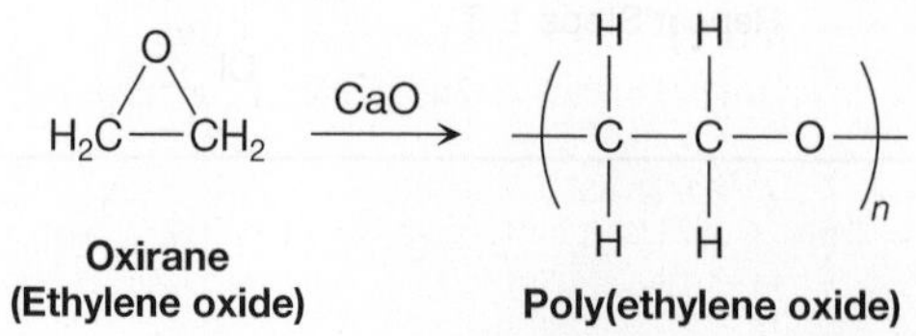

CaO
Oxirane (Ethylene oxide)
Poly(ethylene oxide)

(28-24)

The monomer is cyclic, whereas the polymer is acyclic, so this is a type of **ring-opening polymerization**.

Equation 28-25 shows that the oxide anion in calcium oxide initiates polymerization, acting as a nucleophile (see top Recall box).

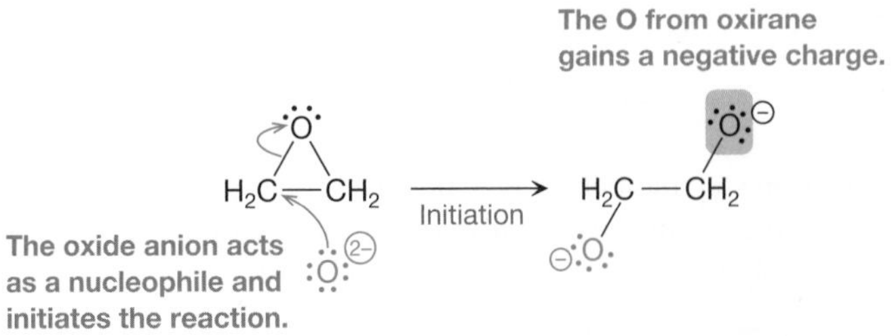

The O from oxirane gains a negative charge.
Initiation
The oxide anion acts as a nucleophile and initiates the reaction.

(28-25)

◂ RECALL

In Section 10.7, we learned that the ring opening of an epoxide under basic conditions is an S_N2 step. Even though the leaving group is of the form RO^-, which is normally unsuitable for S_N2 steps, the relief of ring strain compensates to allow the reaction to occur.

The O atom from oxirane gains a negative charge, so it becomes strongly nucleophilic and can be the site of chain growth, as shown in Equation 28-26 (note that the O^- at the other end of the chain can be the site of chain growth as well). The reaction, therefore, is a type of anionic polymerization.

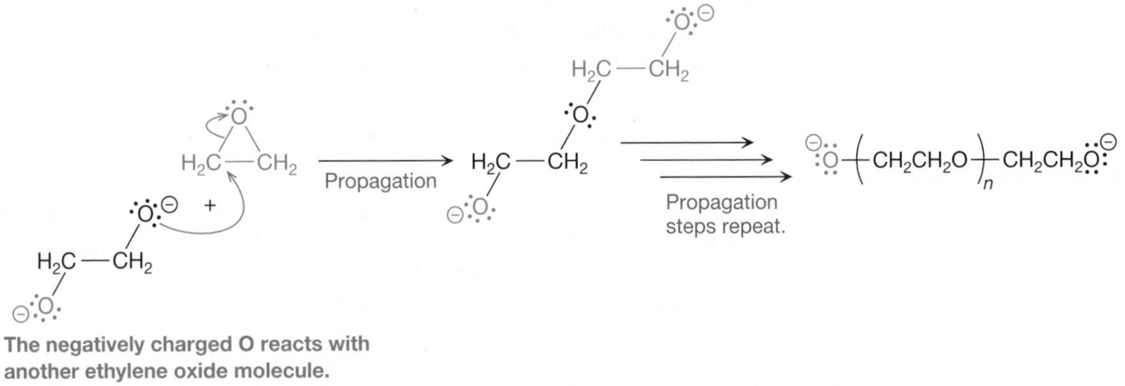

Propagation
Propagation steps repeat.
The negatively charged O reacts with another ethylene oxide molecule.

(28-26)

Termination occurs when an acid is added to the reaction mixture and protonates the alkoxide anion, similar to the termination step we saw previously in Equation 28-15 (p. 1369).

YOUR TURN **28.13**

The polymer chain that is produced in Equation 28-26 will undergo two steps to complete its termination. Write the mechanism for these two steps.

Like oxirane, oxetane (a four-membered-ring ether) is strained and can undergo anionic ring-opening polymerization (see Problem 28.14 at the end of the chapter), but anionic polymerization is generally unfeasible for larger cyclic ethers because they lack sufficient ring strain (see bottom Recall box). Cationic mechanisms are feasible for those monomers, however. For example, as shown in Equation 28-27, tetrahydrofuran undergoes ring-opening polymerization when treated with trimethylsilyl trifluoromethanesulfonate, $CF_3SO_3Si(CH_3)_3$.

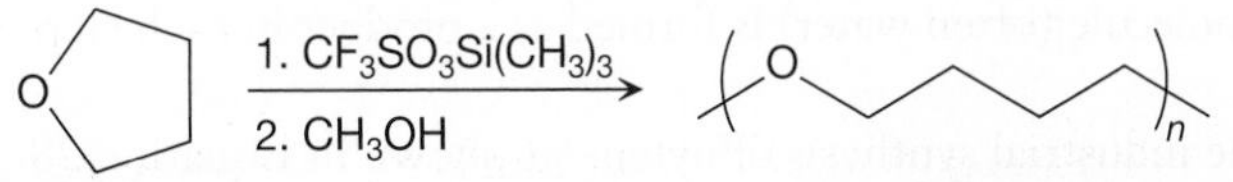

1. CF3SO3Si(CH3)3
2. CH3OH

(28-27)

Tetrahydrofuran **Poly(tetrahydrofuran)**

Initiation occurs when the nucleophilic O atom of tetrahydrofuran attacks the Si atom of $CF_3SO_3Si(CH_3)_3$ in an S_N2 step (Eq. 28-28). Thus, the O atom of the ring becomes positively charged, which creates a good leaving group.

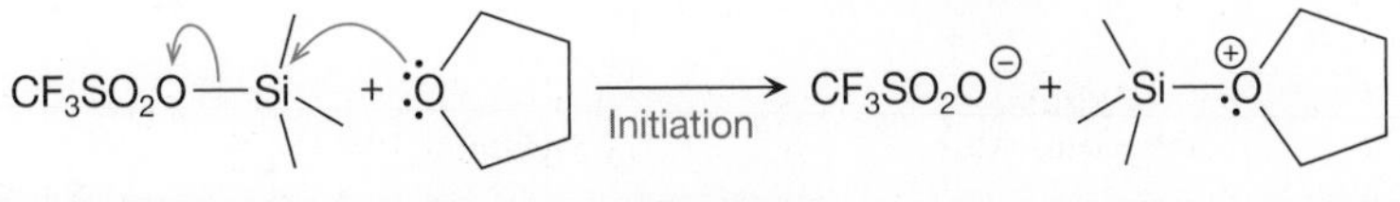

Initiation

(28-28)

◂ RECALL

In Section 4.3, we learned that cyclopentane has little ring strain and cyclohexane is strain-free. Cycloheptane and larger cycloalkanes have a small amount of ring strain. Similarly, cyclic ethers whose rings are five-membered or larger have little ring strain.

Propagation occurs when an uncharged molecule of tetrahydrofuran attacks the positively charged ring:

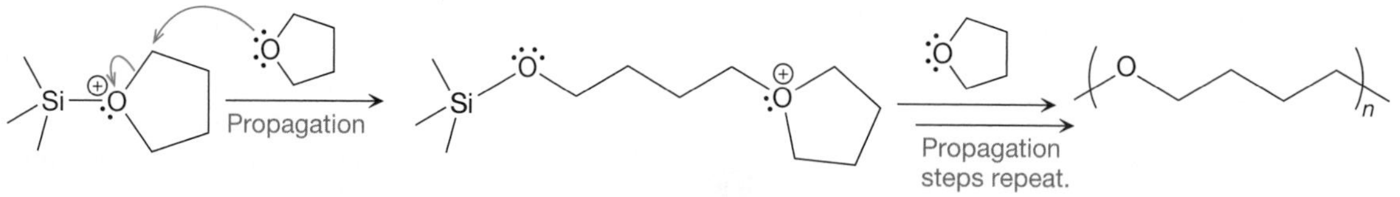

Si
Propagation
Si
Propagation
steps repeat.
n

(28-29)

Each time a propagation step happens, a new positively charged O appears in the ring at the end of the growing chain until, finally, methanol is added to the reaction mixture to terminate the polymerization. (See Your Turn 28.14.)

YOUR TURN **28.14**

Draw the curved arrows and product for the second propagation step in Equation 28-29. Also, draw the mechanism for the termination that would occur if methanol were to react with the product you drew.

The cationic ring-opening polymerization in Equation 28-27 is initiated by an S_N2 step, but it could also have been initiated using a strong Brønsted or Lewis acid. (See Your Turn 28.15.)

YOUR TURN **28.15**

Draw the initiation step and the first two propagation steps for the cationic ring-opening polymerization reaction that takes place when oxetane is treated with a Lewis acid such as BF_3. Also, draw the condensed formula of the resulting polymer.

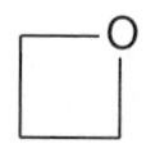
Oxetane

Ring-opening polymerization reactions are not limited to cyclic ethers for monomers. We explore these kinds of reactions involving other functional groups in Problems 28.15, 28.16, and 28.17 at the end of the chapter.

SECTION 28.5 OBJECTIVES

You will be able to:

1. Distinguish step-growth polymerization from chain polymerization.
2. Draw the mechanism for, and the polymer that is produced from, a step-growth polymerization reaction.
3. Determine whether a step-growth polymerization is also a condensation polymerization.

28.5 Step-Growth Polymerization

All of the polymerization reactions we have studied so far have been *chain polymerizations*, in which one monomer adds at a time to the reactive site at the end of the growing polymer chain. Polymerization can also occur through *step-growth polymerization*.

Step-growth polymerization occurs when molecules throughout a mixture join with any other molecule that has an appropriate functional group available to react, whether it is a monomer unit or another polymer molecule.

Step-growth polymerization is referred to as **condensation polymerization** in cases where a small molecule (often water) is formed as a product in each step in which the polymer grows.

Consider the industrial synthesis of nylon-6,6 shown in Equation 28-30, which is an example of both a step-growth polymerization and a condensation polymerization (notice H_2O is a product).

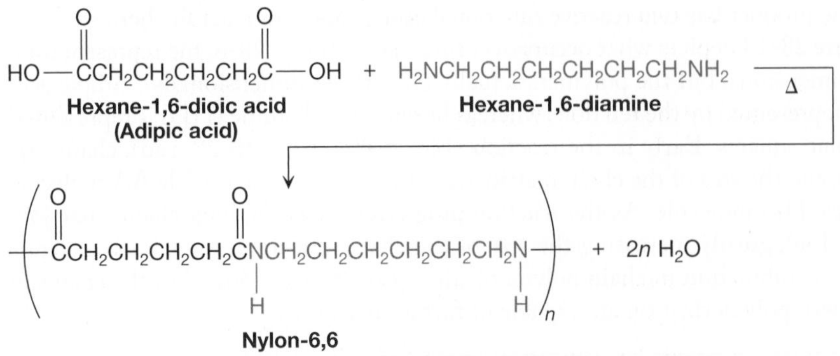
Hexane-1,6-dioic acid
(Adipic acid)
Hexane-1,6-diamine
Nylon-6,6

(28-30)

The reaction mixture contains two different monomers, adipic acid and hexane-1,6-diamine, each of which has two reactive functional groups. A CO_2H group from adipic acid reacts with an NH_2 group from hexane-1,6-diamine to form an O═C—N group (characteristic of an amide) and a molecule of water, as shown in Equation 28-31:

The first steps in the growth of the polymer chain

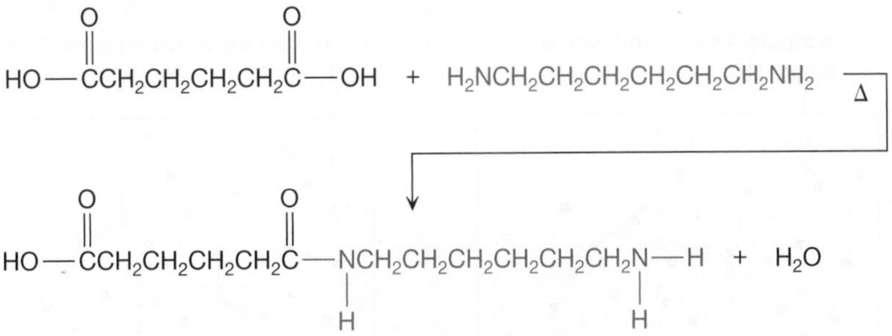

(28-31)

This reaction proceeds by a nucleophilic addition–elimination mechanism, similar to the ones we saw in Section 23.7, and forms a new C—N bond that links the monomers together.

YOUR TURN 28.16

Equation 28-31 can be represented by the generic reaction shown here. Review Section 23.7 and then draw the complete mechanism for this reaction. You may assume that it is acid-catalyzed.

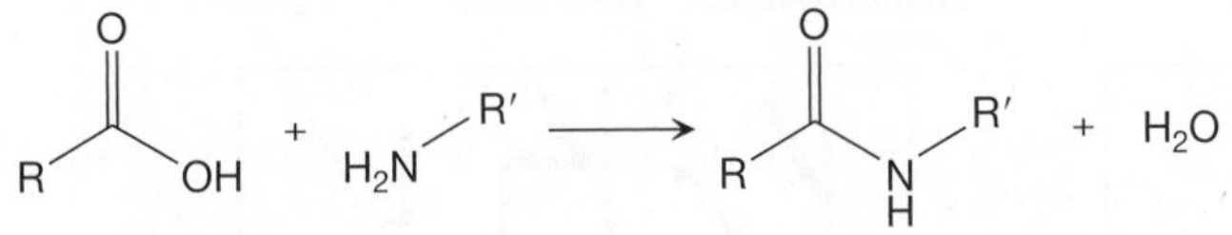

The reaction in Equation 28-31 continues and the chain length increases because the product has two reactive functional groups. Each of those functional groups can therefore produce yet another O═C—N group. One possible way for this to occur is shown in Equation 28-32:

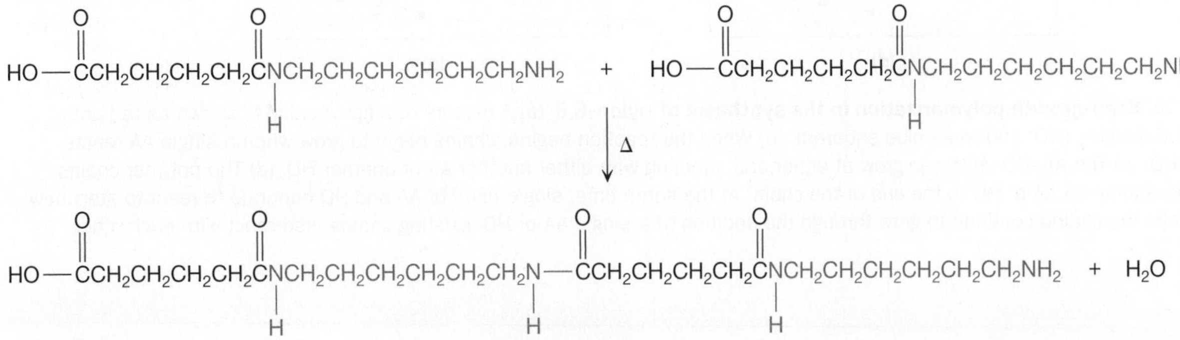

(28-32)

Again the product has two reactive functional groups and can react further.

Figure 28-14 depicts what occurs over time (as with Fig. 28-6, the representation is two-dimensional but the polymers actually grow three-dimensionally). Adipic acid (AA) is represented by the red dots, whereas hexane-1,6-diamine (HD) is represented by the blue squares. Early in the reaction (Fig. 28-14a through 28-14d), chains are initiated, and the size of the chain may increase by the length of a single AA molecule or a single HD molecule. As the reaction progresses, however, long chains may join (Fig. 28-14e), greatly increasing the size of the chain in a single step. Such a step is similar to combination in chain polymerization (Eq. 28-8, p. 1362), but the chains in step-growth polymerization are capable of further reactions.

YOUR TURN **28.17**

In Figure 28-14e, draw **(a)** a new line indicating two monomers linking together, **(b)** a new line indicating an existing polymer chain linking to a monomer, and **(c)** a new line indicating two existing chains linking together.

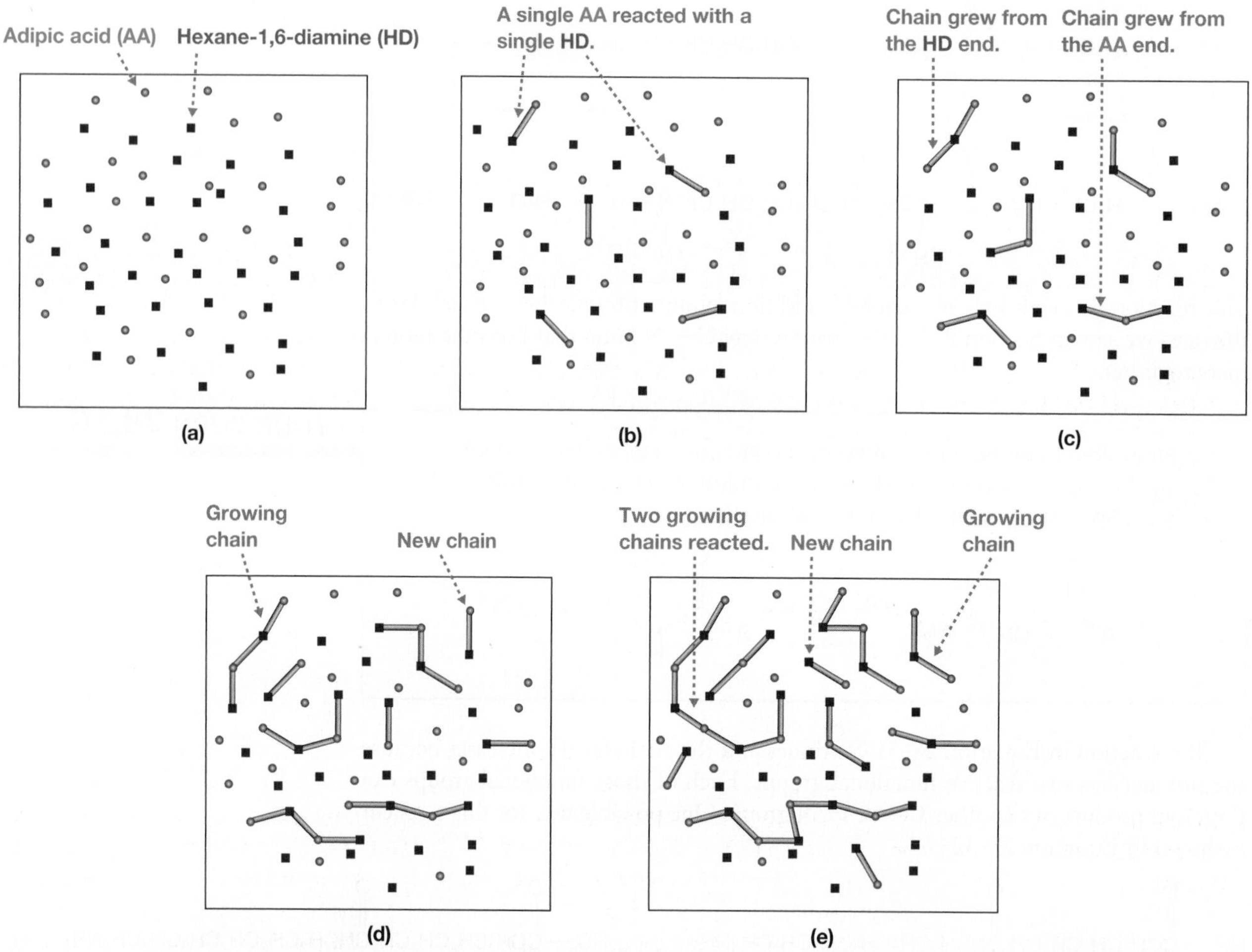

Adipic acid (AA)
Hexane-1,6-diamine (HD)
(a)
A single AA reacted with a single HD.
(b)
Chain grew from the HD end.
Chain grew from the AA end.
(c)
Growing chain
New chain
(d)
Two growing chains reacted.
New chain
Growing chain
(e)

FIGURE 28-14 Step-growth polymerization in the synthesis of nylon-6,6 (a) A mixture of adipic acid (AA; shown as red dots) and hexane-1,6-diamine (HD; shown as blue squares). (b) When the reaction begins, chains begin to grow when a single AA reacts with a single HD. (c) The AA–HD units can grow at either end, reacting with either another AA or another HD. (d) The polymer chains grow stepwise, adding an AA or HD to the end of the chain. At the same time, single units of AA and HD continue to react to start new chains. (e) While the chains continue to grow through the addition of a single AA or HD, existing chains also react with each other.

The distinctions between step-growth polymerization and chain polymerization are important. Chain polymerizations are typically fast, irreversible reactions, generating products that are thermodynamically very favored. Step-growth polymerizations are typically slower, and, because the reactions are often reversible, removal of water or other products can be necessary for the polymer to reach a high degree of polymerization. In the synthesis of nylon-6,6, for example, the reaction is reversible and so slow that heat is required to drive the reaction to proceed at a reasonable rate.

SOLVED PROBLEM **28.4**

How to draw a condensation polymer from its monomers

Break It Down Kevlar is a high-strength polymer used in body armor and bicycle tires. It is a condensation polymer synthesized from benzene-1,4-diamine (*para*-phenylenediamine) and benzene-1,4-dicarbonyl chloride (terephthaloyl chloride). Draw the condensed formula for Kevlar.

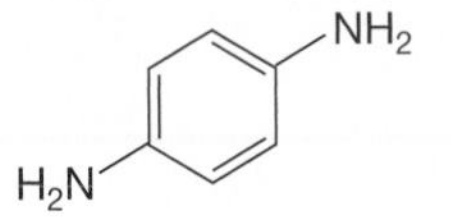

NH2
H2N

Benzene-1,4-diamine (*para*-Phenylene-diamine)

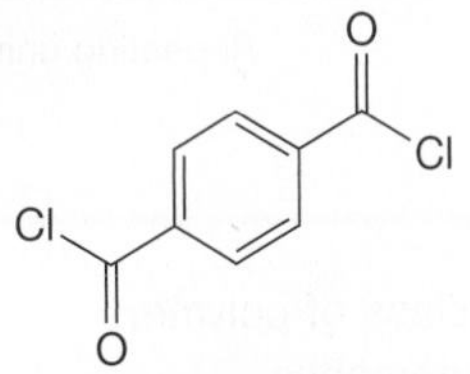

O
Cl
Cl
O

Benzene-1,4-dicarbonyl chloride (Terephthaloyl chloride)

Think	Solve
What functional groups do benzene-1,4-diamine and benzene-1,4-dicarbonyl chloride contain? When those functional groups react, what functional group is produced?	Benzene-1,4-diamine has NH_2 functional groups, and benzene-1,4-dicarbonyl chloride has COCl functional groups. Molecules with these functional groups react to produce an amide that connects the two molecules together (Section 23.3), so these two monomers will produce a dimer, as shown below.

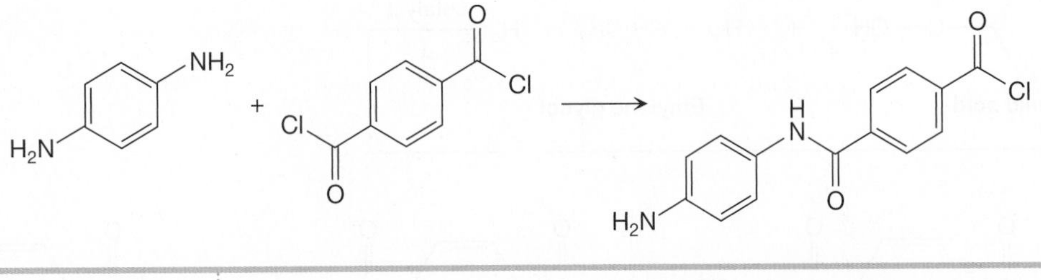

NH2
H2N
+
O
Cl
Cl
O
H
N
H2N
O
Cl
O

Think	Solve
Does that product contain other reactive sites for polymerization to continue?	Each end of the dimer has an unreacted functional group that can react further. It can react with another monomer, or, as shown below, two dimers can react to increase the chain length. In the resulting tetramer, the repeating unit becomes evident, which includes two different types of phenyl rings: one that has two attached N atoms and the other that has two attached carbonyl groups. To draw the condensed formula, enclose the repeating unit inside parentheses and write a subscript *n*.

(continued)

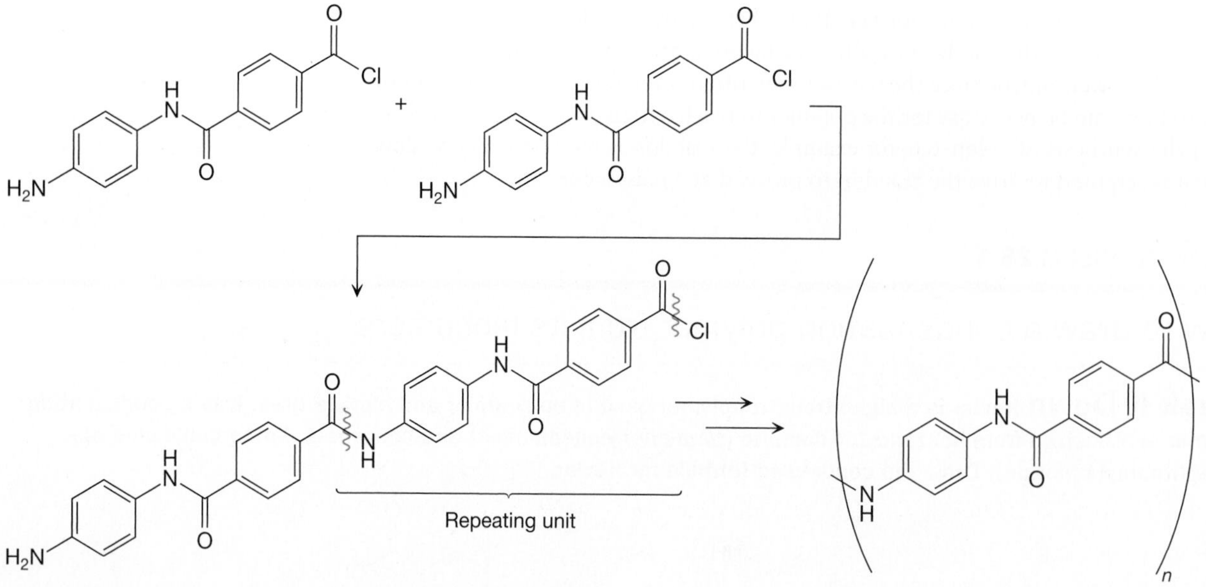
Repeating unit

Try It Polyphthalamides are a class of polymers used in several components of automobile engines and are produced from an aliphatic diamine and benzene-1,4-dioic acid. Draw the condensed formula for the polyphthalamide synthesized from hexane-1,6-diamine.

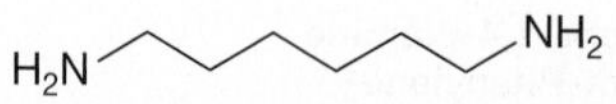

Hexane-1,6-diamine

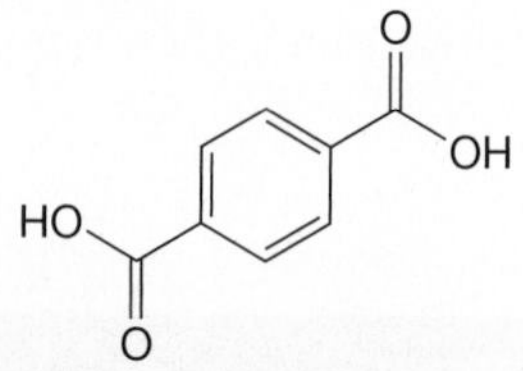

Benzene-1,4-dioic acid

Many nucleophilic addition–elimination reactions can be used to make step-growth polymers. For example, the Fischer esterification (see Recall box, next page) of terephthalic acid and ethylene glycol may be used to make polyesters, such as poly(ethylene terephthalate) (PET), as shown in Equation 28-33.

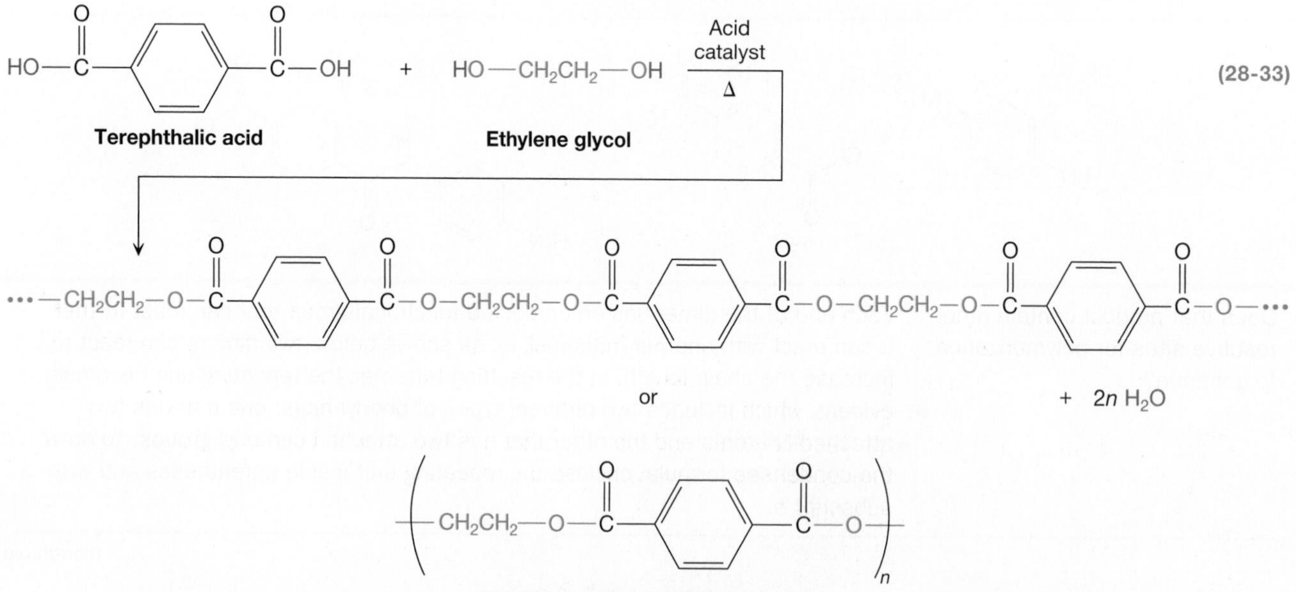
Acid
catalyst
Δ
Terephthalic acid
Ethylene glycol
or
+ 2n H₂O

(28-33)

Poly(ethylene terephthalate) or **PET**
An ester of terephthalic acid and ethylene glycol

Alternatively, transesterification can be used to make PET from the dimethyl ester of terephthalic acid, as shown in Equation 28-34.

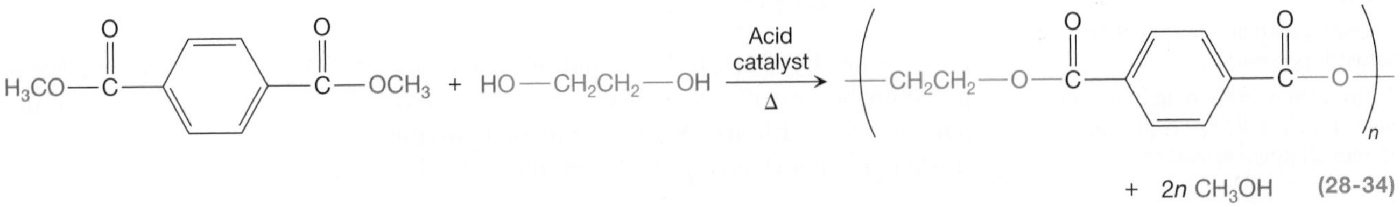

H3CO—C
C—OCH3 + HO—CH2CH2—OH
Acid catalyst
Δ
CH2CH2—O—C
C—O
n
+ 2n CH3OH

(28-34)

YOUR TURN 28.18

In a third reaction for the synthesis of PET, the reactants are a diacid chloride and ethylene glycol. Provide the structures of the reactants and products for this reaction.

◀ RECALL

In a Fischer esterification (Section 23.7), a carboxylic acid ($R—CO_2H$) reacts with an alcohol (HO—R′) under acidic conditions to produce an ester ($R—CO_2—R'$) and H_2O. In the nucleophilic addition–elimination mechanism, HO—R′ is the nucleophile and H_2O is the leaving group.

In the three step-growth polymerizations we have examined, water (Eqs. 28-30 and 28-33) or methanol (Eq. 28-34) is a product of the reaction, and each must be removed from the product mixture to isolate the polymer. Some step-growth polymerizations, however, do *not* produce a second product, as shown for the polyurethanes in Equation 28-35.

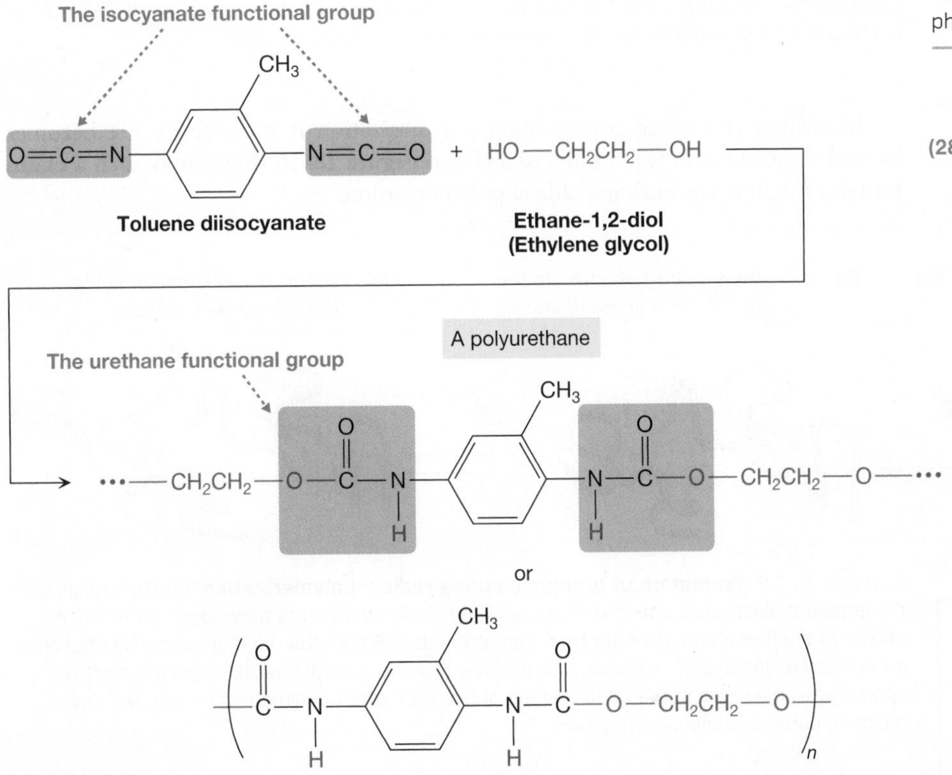

The isocyanate functional group
CH3
O=C=N
N=C=O + HO—CH2CH2—OH
Toluene diisocyanate
Ethane-1,2-diol
(Ethylene glycol)
A polyurethane
The urethane functional group
CH2CH2—O—C—N
N—C—O—CH2CH2—O
H
or
n

(28-35)

YOUR TURN 28.19

The steps in the reaction in Equation 28-35 are: addition of a nucleophile to a polar double bond and two proton transfer steps. Draw the mechanism for this reaction.

SECTION 28.6 OBJECTIVES

You will be able to:

1. Distinguish linear, branched, and network polymers.
2. Show how branching can occur when a vinyl polymer is produced by radical polymerization.

28.6 Linear, Branched, and Network Polymers

Polystyrene (Eq. 28-1, p. 1356) and nylon-6,6 (Eq. 28-30, p. 1375) are called **linear polymers** because the monomers are linked end to end along the entire length of the polymer chain (**Figure 28-15a**). **Branched polymers** can also be produced, in which smaller polymer chains split off from the main chain (Fig. 28-15b).

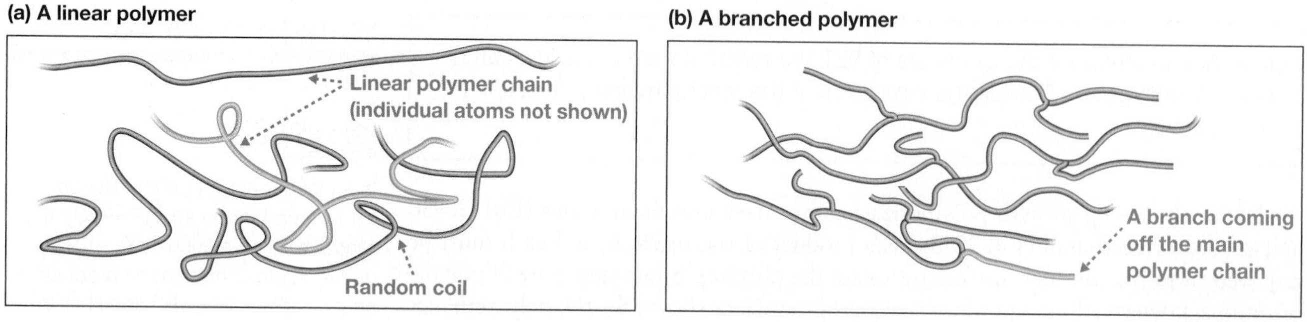

(a) A linear polymer
Linear polymer chain (individual atoms not shown)
Random coil
(b) A branched polymer
A branch coming off the main polymer chain

FIGURE 28-15 Branching in polymers (a) A linear polymer has one continuous chain that contains the pendant groups. Linear polymer chains usually exist as random coils. (b) In a branched polymer, multiple smaller chains split off from the main chain.

Branching can occur during chain polymerization if the reactive site becomes located somewhere in the middle of a chain. **Figure 28-16** shows how such a **chain transfer** might occur during a radical polymerization.

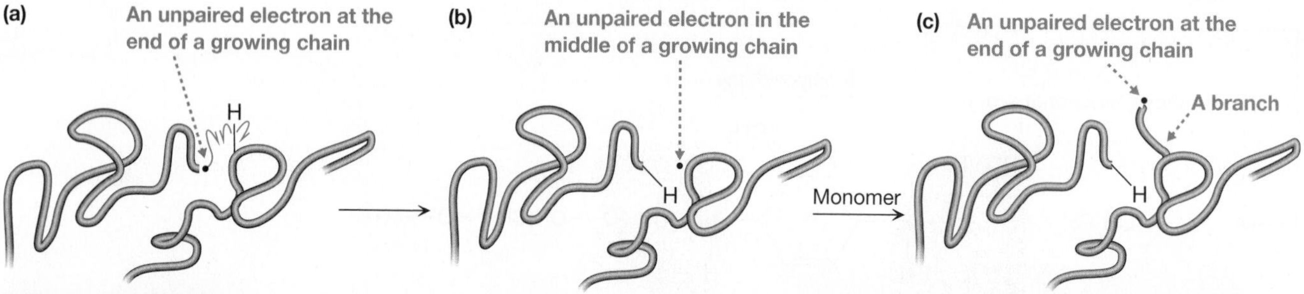

(a)
An unpaired electron at the end of a growing chain
H
(b)
An unpaired electron in the middle of a growing chain
H
Monomer
(c)
An unpaired electron at the end of a growing chain
A branch
H

FIGURE 28-16 Formation of branches during radical polymerization (a) The radical with the unpaired electron at one end of one growing chain encounters a hydrogen atom in the middle of another chain. (b) After hydrogen atom abstraction, the original radical has become a terminated closed-shell species, and the new reactive radical has the unpaired electron appearing somewhere in the middle of the chain. (c) Further polymerization with the new radical creates a branch in the chain.

CONNECTIONS 28.3

How old is that plastic?
Bakelite (pronounced BAKE-uh-light) (Eq. 28-36) was one of the first synthetic plastics, developed in 1907. Because it is very rigid, electrically nonconductive, and quite heat-resistant, Bakelite found a wide variety of uses, including in telephones, electrical components, kitchenware, and even billiard balls.

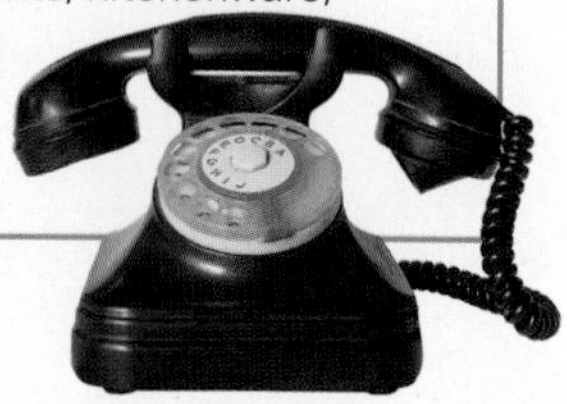

YOUR TURN 28.20

The following two steps show polyethylene (PE) undergoing chain transfer. Use curved arrows to show the movement of electrons in both steps.

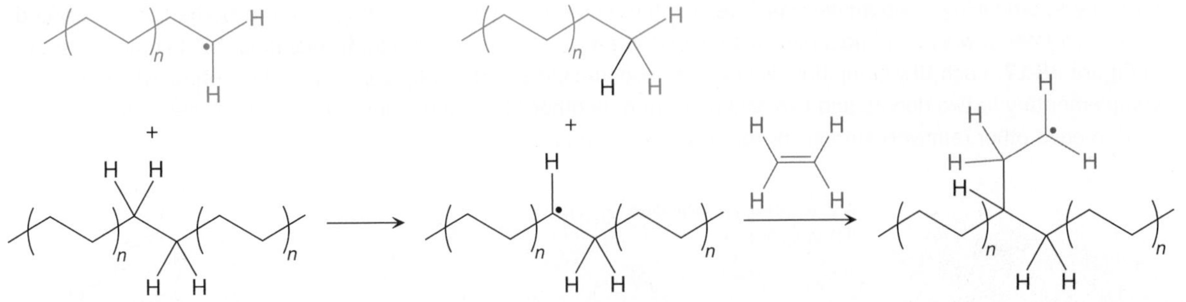

Branching can also occur during polymerization when a monomer has multiple reactive sites, such as in the reaction of phenol with formaldehyde to produce the hard material known as Bakelite:

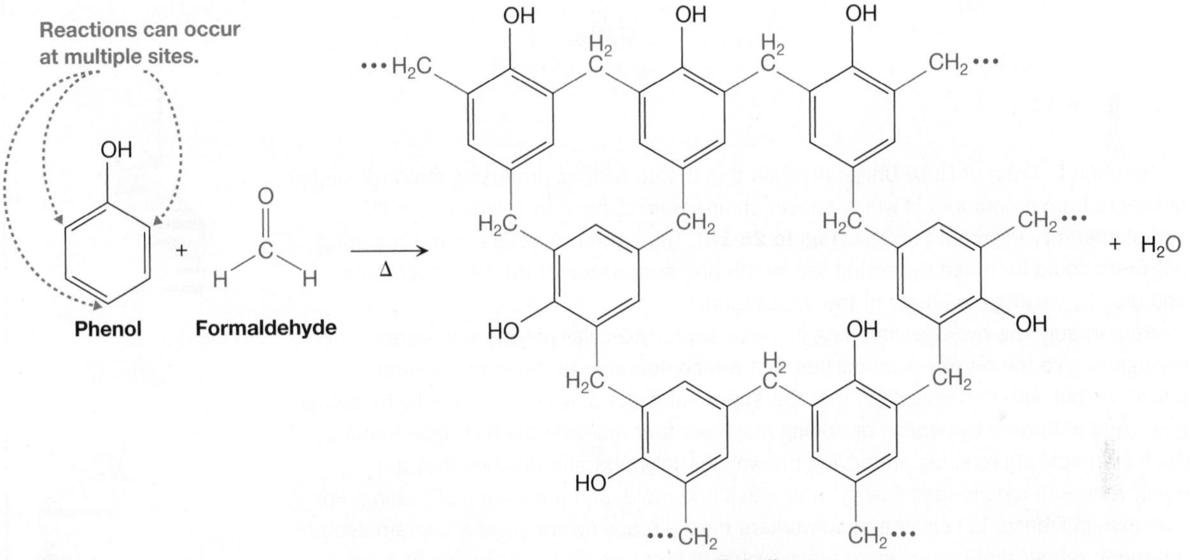

Reactions can occur at multiple sites.
OH
O
C
H
H
+
Phenol
Formaldehyde
Δ
OH
OH
OH
•••H$_2$C
H_2C
H_2C
CH$_2$•••
H_2C
CH$_2$
H_2C
CH$_2$•••
HO
OH
OH
H_2C
H_2C
CH$_2$
HO
•••CH$_2$
CH$_2$•••
+ H$_2$O
Bakelite

(28-36)

The extent of branching in Bakelite is so high, in fact, that the polymer has no recognizable linearity. Bakelite, therefore, is a **network polymer** because a sample of it can be described as a single, *very* large molecule.

YOUR TURN 28.21

In Bakelite, what do you notice about the substitution pattern on the phenyl rings? What explains that pattern? *Hint*: The mechanism for the formation of Bakelite involves electrophilic aromatic substitution; see Problem 28.50 at the end of the chapter.

Supramolecular Polymers: Polymers That Can Heal Themselves

All of the polymers we have discussed in this chapter are produced by the formation of *covalent* bonds between monomers. But similarly long arrangements of atoms can be built through *noncovalent* interactions among monomers, producing a *supramolecular* ("beyond the molecular") polymer. Chemists in the Netherlands produced such a polymer in which the monomer was capped at each end with a 2-ureidopyrimidinone (UPy) group, as shown in **Figure 28-17**. Each UPy group has two hydrogen-bond donors and two hydrogen-bond acceptors, which are complementary to two donors and two acceptors from another UPy group. Therefore, a pair of these groups can bind to each other relatively strongly by four hydrogen bonds.

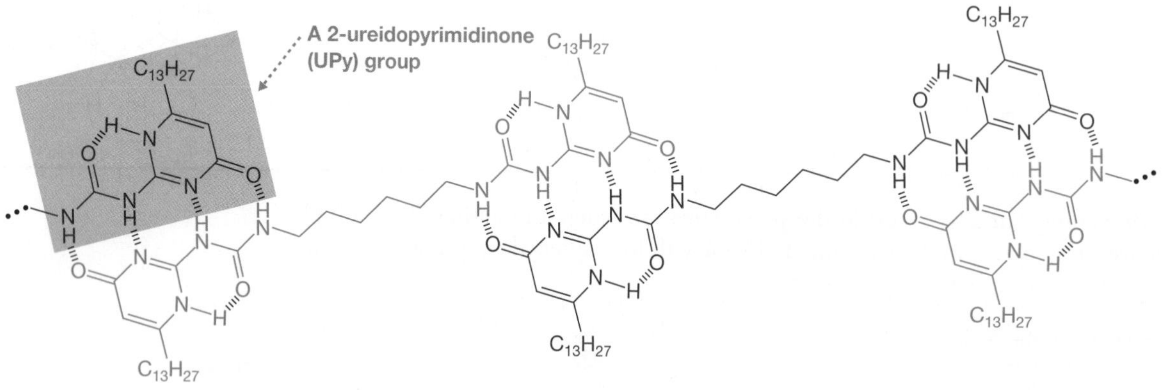
A 2-ureidopyrimidinone (UPy) group

FIGURE 28-17

Stephen L. Craig of Duke University took this a step further, producing supramolecular polymers from monomers in which spacer chains were capped by relatively small, complementary segments of DNA (**Figure 28-18**). Thus, the properties of the resulting polymers could be tuned by varying the length and sequences of the DNA segments, and also by varying the length of the spacer chain.

Remarkably, the hydrogen bonding in these supramolecular polymers is strong enough to give the polymers properties that are comparable to those of covalent polymers, but with the advantage that the supramolecular polymers can easily be broken down and re-formed by heating or adding a solvent that disrupts the hydrogen bonding. Such chemical approaches are paving the way for polymers and plastics that are easily recycled, require less energy to process and mold, and are even *self-healing*! For example, in France, L. Leibler and co-workers have already synthesized a supramolecular polymeric rubber that can undergo many cycles of breaking and self-healing at room temperature, and you can imagine how this strategy could be applied to new types of adhesives and other materials.

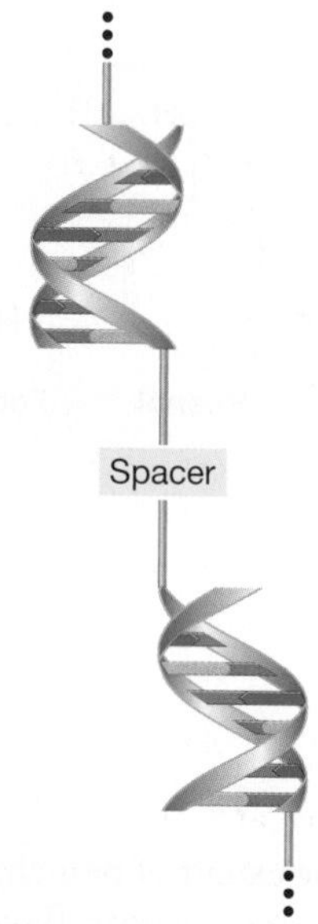
Spacer

FIGURE 28-18

SECTION 28.7 OBJECTIVES

You will be able to:

1. Explain how the properties of a polymer can be changed by chemical modification of its pendant groups after polymerization is complete.
2. Describe how chemical modification of pendant groups after polymerization can be used as a strategy to synthesize a polymer that cannot be made directly by polymerization.

28.7 Modification of Pendant Groups

Once synthesized, many polymers can be reacted further, in a *post-synthesis modification*, to give the polymer significantly different properties. Consider Equation 28-37, for example, which shows that the pendant groups of poly(vinyl acetate) (PVAc) can undergo transesterification when treated with a basic solution of methanol. Effectively, poly(vinyl acetate) is converted to poly(vinyl alcohol) (PVA):

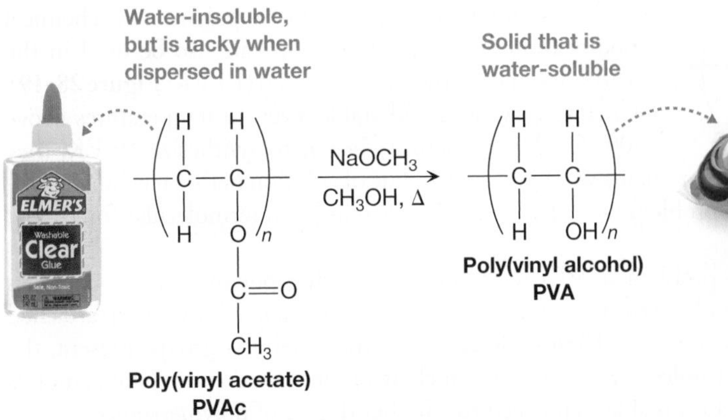
Water-insoluble, but is tacky when dispersed in water
Solid that is water-soluble
NaOCH3
CH3OH, Δ
Poly(vinyl acetate)
PVAc
Poly(vinyl alcohol)
PVA

(28-37)

PVAc is the principal component of Elmer's glue; it is insoluble in water but becomes tacky when dispersed in water. PVA is solid and is soluble in water, which makes it ideal as the casing for laundry detergent pods; in a washing machine, the solid casing dissolves in water and releases the detergent (see Looking Ahead box).

▸ LOOKING AHEAD

In Section 28.10, we will discuss physical properties of polymers in greater detail, including solubility and melting point.

YOUR TURN 28.22

Draw the mechanism for the reaction in Equation 28-37. What is the second product of the reaction, which is not shown? *Hint*: Review Section 22.1.

More than simply providing a way to convert one polymer into another, Equation 28-37 turns out to be an important part of the synthesis of PVA, because PVA cannot be synthesized directly by vinyl polymerization. Vinyl alcohol ($H_2C{=}CH{-}OH$) would be the monomer required for polymerization but, as shown in Equation 28-38, it is an enol that heavily favors its keto form, ethanal (see Recall box). Therefore, vinyl alcohol is not feasible as a starting material.

◂ RECALL

In Section 7.10, we learned that keto and enol tautomers exist in rapid equilibrium through back-to-back proton transfer steps. The keto form is usually favored quite heavily because it has significantly greater total bond energy.

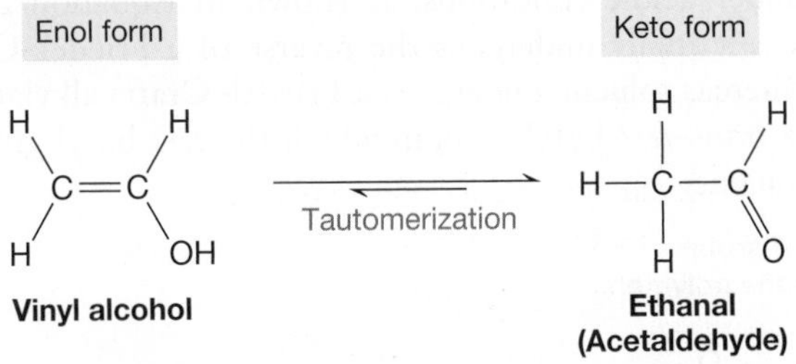
Enol form
Keto form
Tautomerization
Vinyl alcohol
Ethanal
(Acetaldehyde)

(28-38)

Vinyl acetate, on the other hand, is available as a starting material. Therefore, as shown in Equation 28-39, vinyl acetate can undergo radical polymerization to produce PVAc, which can subsequently be converted to PVA.

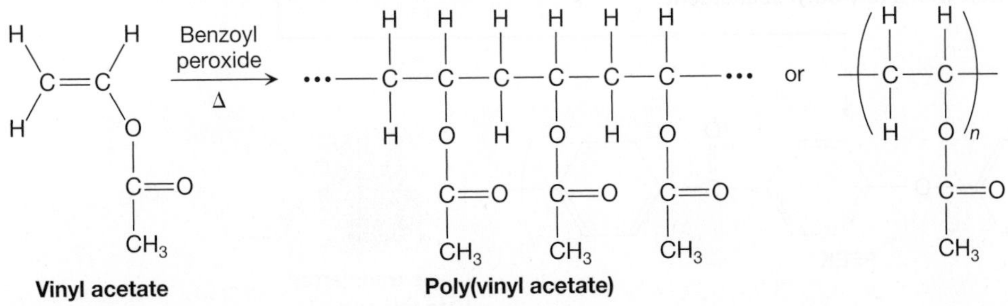
Benzoyl peroxide
Δ
or
Vinyl acetate
Poly(vinyl acetate)

(28-39)

YOUR TURN 28.23

Draw the mechanism for the tautomerization shown in Equation 28-38. You can assume acidic conditions.

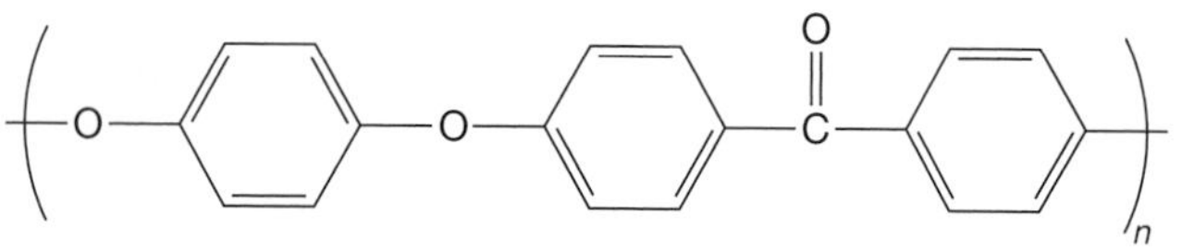

FIGURE 28-19 Poly(ether ether ketone), or PEEK

The strategy of synthesizing a polymer by chemical modification after polymerization can also be used in the synthesis of poly(ether ether ketone) (PEEK; **Figure 28-19**), which is very rigid and stable, even to temperatures above 500 °C. When chemists began to synthesize PEEK, they found that the polymer chains would crystallize out of solution before reaching a substantial length. The problem was PEEK's rigidity, leading to intermolecular forces that were too great.

To address the problem of PEEK crystallizing during polymerization, chemists instead carried out polymerization with a monomer that has a *tert*-butyl group attached to the aryl ring, as shown in **Figure 28-20**. With the *tert*-butyl groups present, the strength of the intermolecular forces between chains is decreased and crystallization is avoided, so the reaction is able to proceed to a higher degree of polymerization.

CONNECTIONS 28.4

A skull cap? Poly(ether ether ketone), or PEEK (Fig. 28-19), is biocompatible and has mechanical properties similar to human bone, which is why it can be used for joint replacement and to surgically repair defects in the skull.

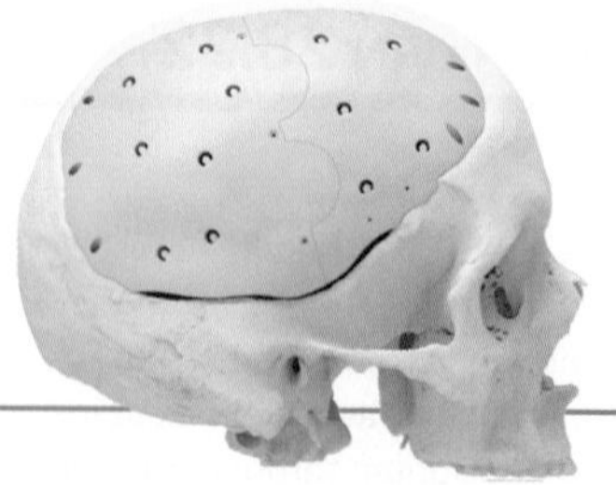

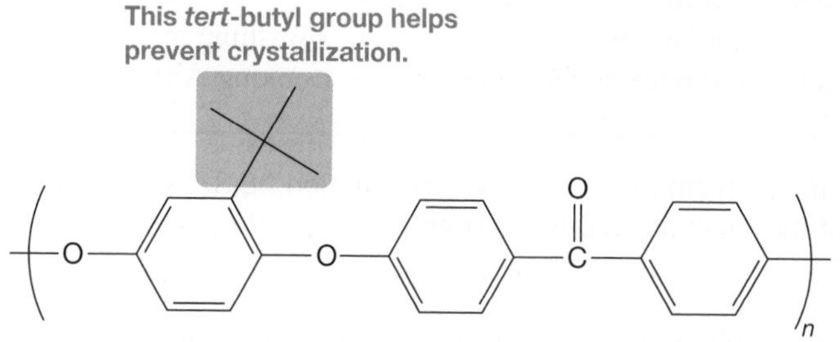
This tert-butyl group helps prevent crystallization.

FIGURE 28-20 PEEK with a *tert*-butyl substituent The *tert*-butyl group can be removed to produce PEEK.

To isolate PEEK, the *tert*-butyl groups must be removed. This is done by adding excess toluene under acidic conditions, as shown in Equation 28-40. The *tert*-butylated PEEK essentially undergoes the reverse of a Friedel–Crafts alkylation (Section 24.3), whereas toluene undergoes a Friedel–Crafts alkylation. The overall reaction is thus a trans-*tert*-butylation, in which the *tert*-butyl group moves from the polymer to toluene.

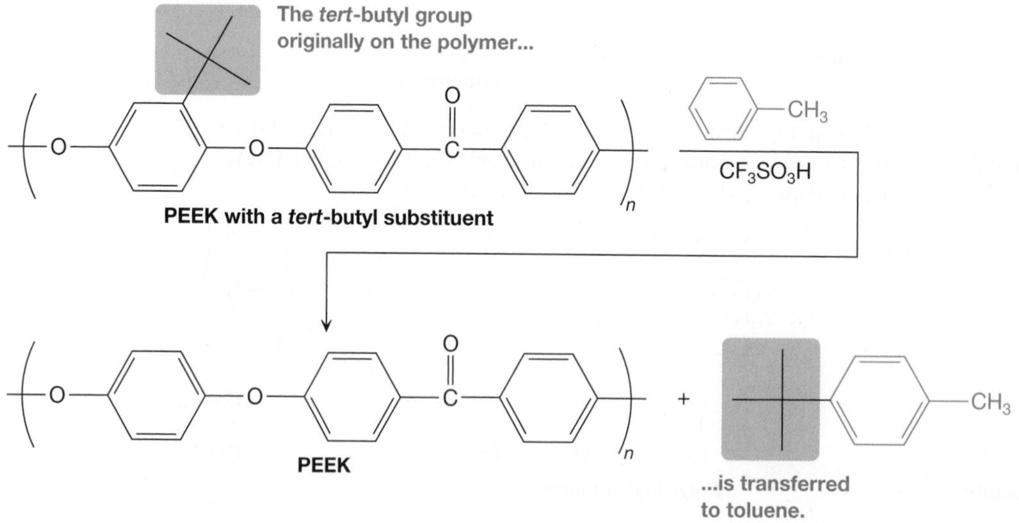
The tert-butyl group originally on the polymer...
PEEK with a tert-butyl substituent
CH_3
CF_3SO_3H
PEEK
CH_3
...is transferred to toluene.

(28-40)

YOUR TURN **28.24**

Propose a mechanism for the reaction that occurs in Equation 28-40. Do you think the reaction would be as successful if the *tert*-butyl group were a linear butyl group instead? Why or why not?

28.8 Cross-linking

In Section 28.7, we discussed chemical reactions that change the structure and properties of linear polymers without affecting their linearity. Many polymers, however, can undergo reactions that produce connections, or **cross-links**, between linear polymer chains. Such cross-linked polymers can have dramatically different properties from their linear forms.

Consider poly(vinyl alcohol), or PVA, which is water-soluble because of the large number of OH groups along the polymer chain. In fact, a dilute aqueous solution of PVA is sold commercially as lubricating eyedrops. Borax ($Na_2B_4O_7$), however, can react with OH groups from different chains of PVA to produce a form of cross-linked PVA that we call "slime," as shown in **Figure 28-21**. Cross-linking holds the polymer chains together, so instead of the PVA molecules separating to dissolve in water, the water molecules now act as a solute in the cross-linked polymer. The result is the dispersion of a liquid (water) throughout a solid medium (cross-linked PVA), which defines a *gel*. Moreover, the particular cross-links that are produced when borax reacts with PVA are continually formed and broken, which allows the polymer chains to slide past one another and helps give the substance its "slime" characteristics.

The reaction between borax and alcohol OH groups is not the only way to create cross-links. Cross-linking reactions can involve a wide variety of functional groups and a wide variety of mechanisms, many of which we have studied in this book. Moreover, the same linear polymer can often be cross-linked by more than one cross-linking agent. **Figure 28-22** (next page) shows a second way to cross-link PVA, using formaldehyde to form acetal groups that act as cross-links (see Your Turn 28.25).

SECTION 28.8 OBJECTIVES

You will be able to:

1. Distinguish a cross-linked polymer from a linear polymer by their structures.
2. Explain how cross-linking can change the properties of a polymer.

YOUR TURN **28.25**

Draw the mechanism for the cross-linking reaction shown in Figure 28-22. Assume some acid, HA, is present to catalyze the reaction.

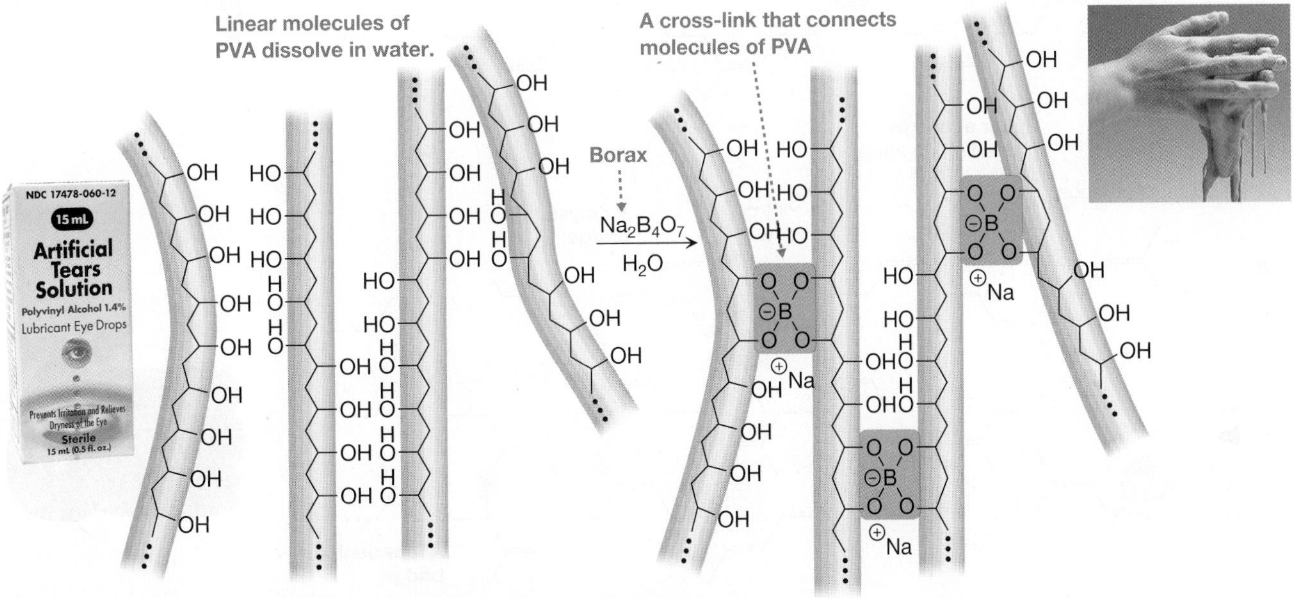

Linear molecules of PVA dissolve in water.
A cross-link that connects molecules of PVA
Borax
$Na_2B_4O_7$
H_2O
NDC 17478-060-12
15 mL
Artificial Tears Solution
Polyvinyl Alcohol 1.4%
Lubricant Eye Drops
Sterile
15 mL (0.5 fl. oz.)

FIGURE 28-21 Cross-linking PVA to make "slime" (*Left*) Linear PVA is water-soluble because the hydrophilic polymer chains can separate in solution. (*Right*) The cross-links made by reaction with borax prevent the polymer chains from separating in water. Instead, water can be taken up by cross-linked PVA, and the cross-links are continually broken and formed, giving the material characteristics of "slime."

FIGURE 28-22 Cross-linking PVA with acetal links (a) Two OH groups from different chains of linear PVA can react with acetaldehyde to form (b) an acetal cross-link.

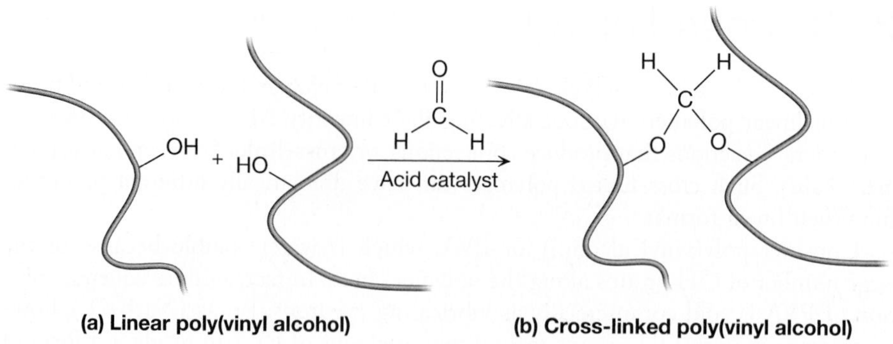
OH
HO
Acid catalyst
(a) Linear poly(vinyl alcohol)
(b) Cross-linked poly(vinyl alcohol)

Rubber provides one particularly notable example of cross-linking. In the 19th century, natural rubber had limited uses because it became brittle at low temperatures and shapeless at high temperatures. When Charles Goodyear (1800–1860) accidentally dropped some natural rubber mixed with sulfur on a hot stove, however, he discovered a product that had the desired elasticity and did not lose its properties at extreme temperatures. The key to this transformation of rubber—a process called **vulcanization**—is the introduction of *sulfur bridges* that act as cross-links between the rubber chains, as shown in **Figure 28-23**. Unlike the cross-links that join PVA chains to make "slime," these

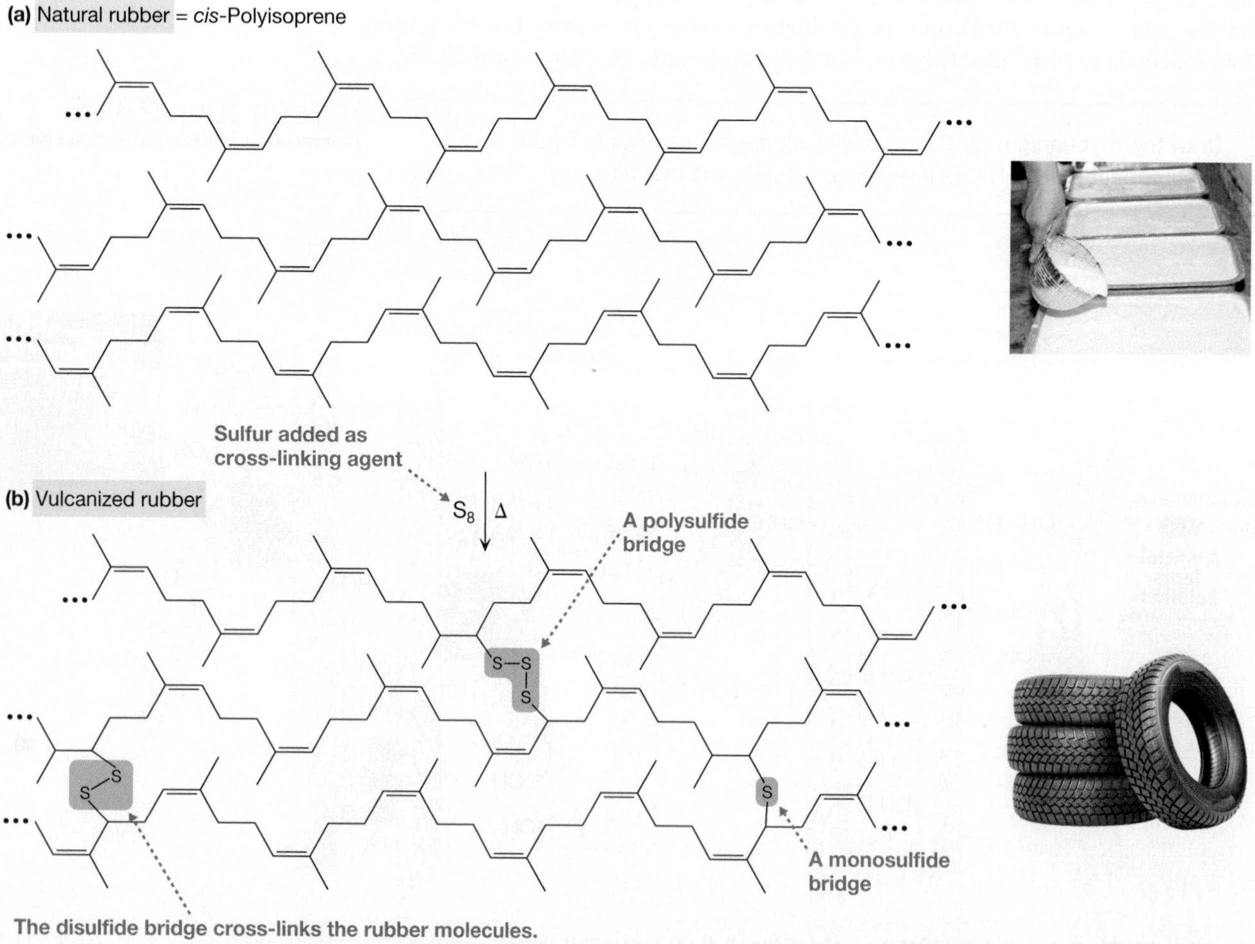
(a) Natural rubber = *cis*-Polyisoprene
Sulfur added as cross-linking agent
S_8 | Δ
(b) Vulcanized rubber
A polysulfide bridge
A monosulfide bridge
The disulfide bridge cross-links the rubber molecules.

FIGURE 28-23 Vulcanization of rubber (a) Natural rubber consists of independent polymer molecules. The addition of sulfur (S_8) results in cross-linking among the main chains to produce (b) vulcanized rubber. The cross-links can consist of monosulfide, disulfide, or polysulfide bridges. Natural rubber has high elasticity but minimal durability. Modern tires made of vulcanized rubber (19% natural rubber and 24% synthetic rubber), on the other hand, are less elastic but much more durable.

sulfur bridges are fixed. Therefore, when vulcanized rubber is stretched and released, the polymer chains will slide past one another, but their original locations will largely be restored; thus, the sample of rubber regains its original shape (see Looking Ahead box).

▸ LOOKING AHEAD

In Section 28.10a, we will discuss how the characteristics of rubber depend on temperature.

28.9 General Aspects of Polymer Structure

SECTION 28.9 OBJECTIVES

You will be able to:

1. Classify a polymer according to the type of chain, the functional group(s) in the chain, and the monomer(s) used to make the polymer.
2. Distinguish a homopolymer from a copolymer.
3. Determine the IUPAC name for a polymer.

We have seen a variety of polymerization mechanisms and a variety of polymers. What structural characteristics distinguish one type of polymer from another? On the basis of their structures, how are polymers named? Here in Section 28.9, we begin to answer these questions, learning how to classify polymers and how to name simple ones.

28.9a Classes of Polymers

Polymers can be classified according to a variety of criteria: type of main chain, type of functional group in the main chain, type of monomer, and the number of different monomers. We will discuss each such classification here.

Classification by type of main chain

When polymers are classified by type of chain, we distinguish polymers having only carbons in the main chain (**carbon-chain polymers**) from those with heteroatoms in the chain (**heterochain polymers**). Polystyrene (**Figure 28-24a**) is a carbon-chain polymer, whereas nylon-6,6 (Fig. 28-24b) is a heterochain polymer.

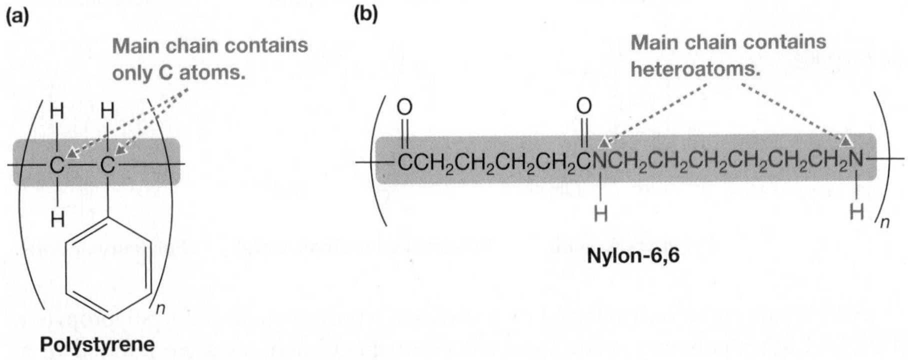

(a)
Main chain contains
only C atoms.
Polystyrene
(b)
Main chain contains
heteroatoms.
CCH2CH2CH2CH2CNCH2CH2CH2CH2CH2CH2N
Nylon-6,6

FIGURE 28-24 Carbon-chain versus heterochain polymers (a) Polystyrene is a carbon-chain polymer because its main chain contains only carbon atoms. (b) Nylon-6,6 is a heterochain polymer because its main chain contains heteroatoms (N in this case).

Classification by type of functional group in the main chain

Heterochain polymers can be classified by the functional groups that are responsible for linking the monomers together to make the main chain. **Poly(ethylene terephthalate) (PET)**, for example, which is used to make bottles for carbonated beverages, is a **polyester**. A portion of the PET molecule is shown in **Figure 28-25a** (next page), and its condensed formula is shown in Figure 28-25b. Notice that the repeating unit that appears in the condensed formula for PET contains two ester groups; the one on the left is a complete ester group, and the one on the right is incomplete but is completed by a carbon atom from an adjacent repeating unit.

YOUR TURN 28.26

On the basis of its functional groups, to what class of polymers does nylon-6,6 (Fig. 28-24b) belong? How many times does the functional group appear in the repeating unit?

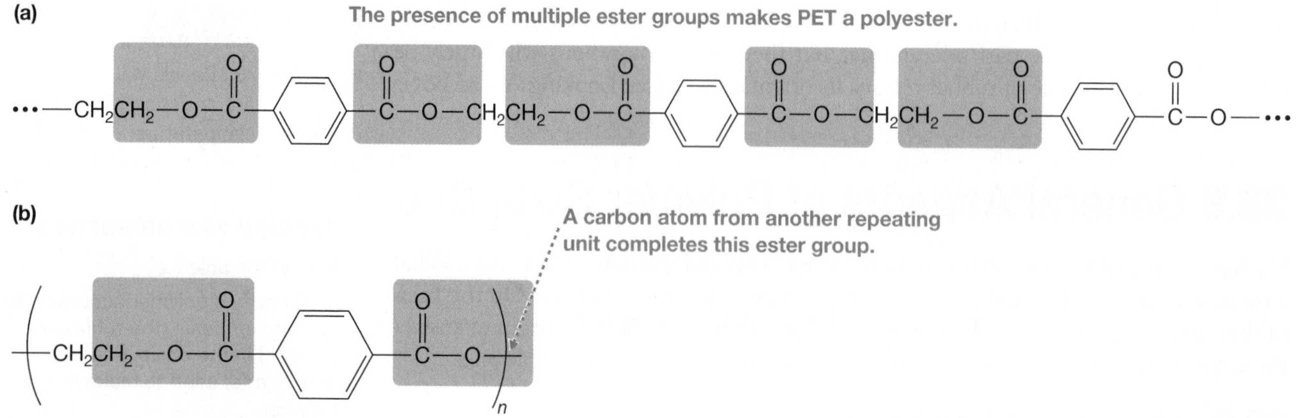
(a)
The presence of multiple ester groups makes PET a polyester.
(b)
A carbon atom from another repeating unit completes this ester group.

FIGURE 28-25 Poly(ethylene terephthalate), or PET (a) A portion of PET and (b) its condensed formula. PET is a polyester because of the repeating ester groups in the main chain, screened in red.

Classification by type of monomer

Carbon-chain polymers are usually classified according to the monomer used to make them. For example, the polymers in **Figure 28-26** are classified as **polyacrylates**, or **acrylics**, because the monomers are derivatives of acrylic acid.

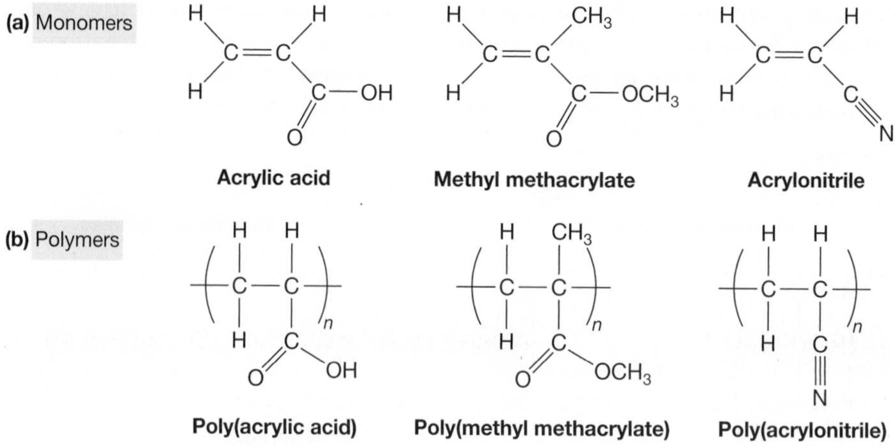
(a) Monomers
Acrylic acid
Methyl methacrylate
Acrylonitrile
(b) Polymers
Poly(acrylic acid)
Poly(methyl methacrylate)
Poly(acrylonitrile)

FIGURE 28-26 Polyacrylates (a) Acrylic acid and its derivatives can polymerize to form (b) the corresponding polyacrylate (or acrylic) polymers.

Alkenes are commonly referred to as **olefins**, so polyethylene (PE), polypropylene (PP), and other polymers made from alkene or diene monomers are referred to as **polyolefins**. Some examples are shown in **Figure 28-27**.

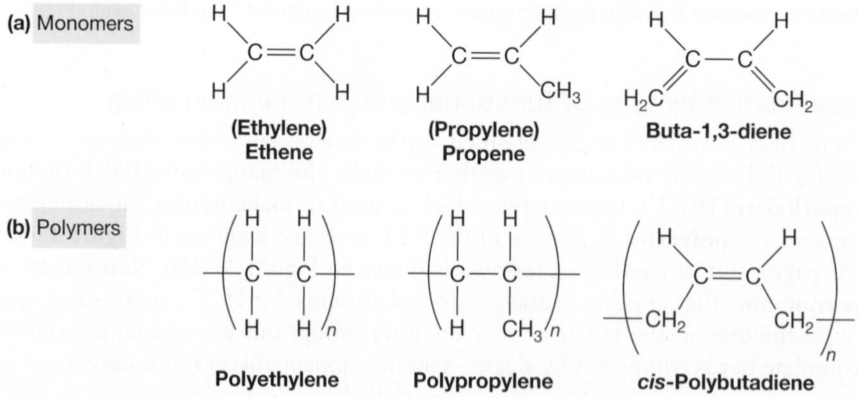
(a) Monomers
(Ethylene)
Ethene
(Propylene)
Propene
Buta-1,3-diene
(b) Polymers
Polyethylene
Polypropylene
cis-Polybutadiene

FIGURE 28-27 Polyolefins (a) These alkene (or olefin) monomers can polymerize to form (b) the corresponding polyolefins.

Classification by number of different monomers

Polymers such as polystyrene and polyethylene are said to be **homopolymers** because each is synthesized from one monomer (i.e., styrene or ethylene, respectively). Other homopolymers are shown in Table 28-1 for comparison.

TABLE 28-1 Comparison of Homopolymers and Their Descriptions

Monomer(s)	Polymer	Carbon–Chain or Heterochain Polymer	Description Based on Monomer	Description Based on Functional Group in Polymer
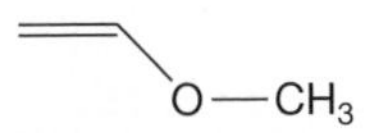 (Methyl vinyl ether) Methoxyethene	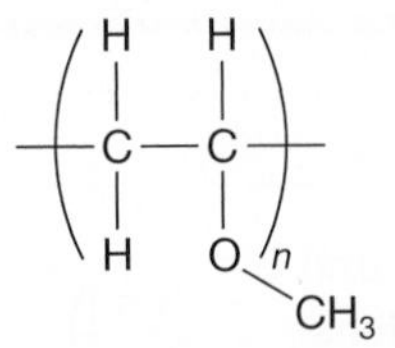 Poly(methyl vinyl ether)	Carbon–chain polymer	A poly(vinyl ether)	—
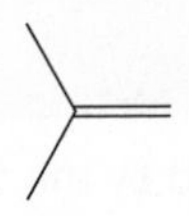 (Isobutylene) 2-Methylpropene	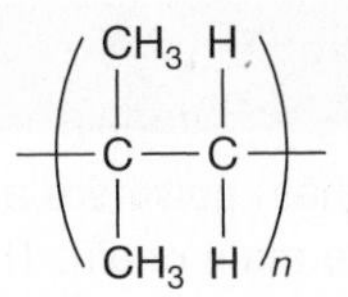 Polyisobutylene	Carbon–chain polymer	A polyolefin	—
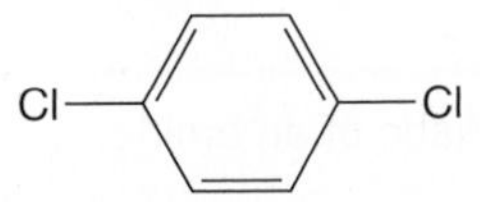 1,4-Dichlorobenzene + Na_2S Sodium sulfide	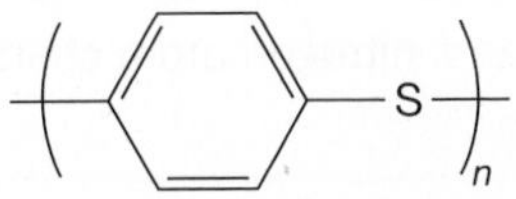 Poly(phenylene sulfide)	Heterochain polymer	—	A polysulfide

If two different monomers are polymerized together, and each monomer is capable of undergoing self-polymerization, then the resulting polymer is called a **copolymer**. For example, styrene and buta-1,3-diene can each form a homopolymer. When the two monomers polymerize together, as shown in Equation 28-41, a copolymer called styrene–butadiene rubber (SBR) is produced:

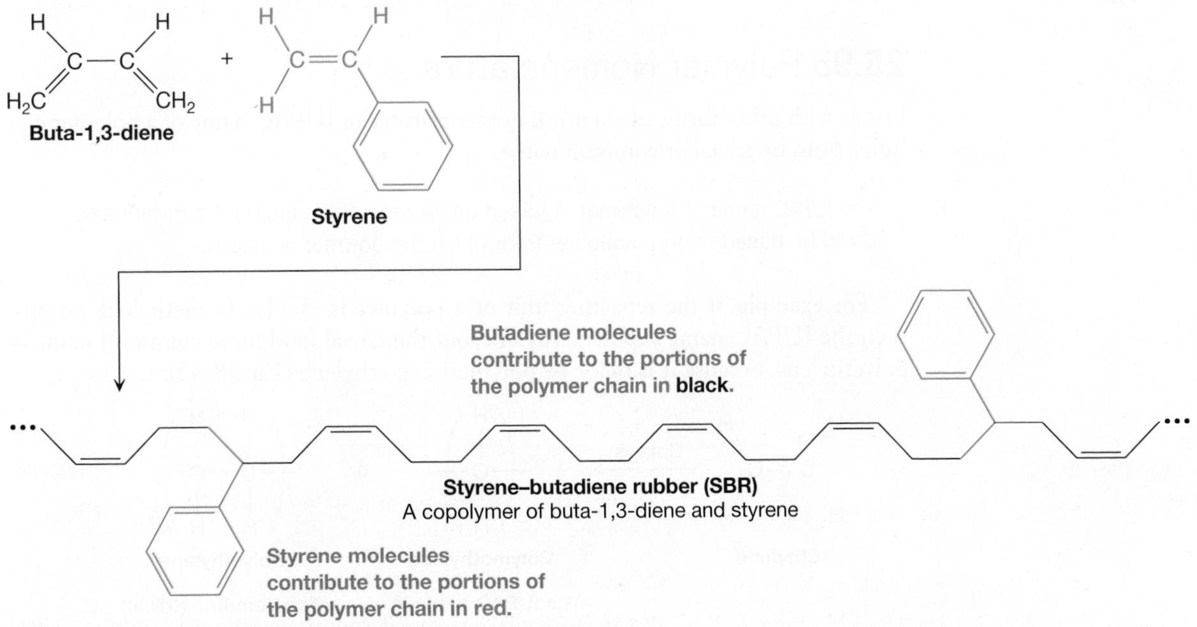

Buta-1,3-diene
Styrene
Butadiene molecules contribute to the portions of the polymer chain in black.
Styrene–butadiene rubber (SBR)
A copolymer of buta-1,3-diene and styrene
Styrene molecules contribute to the portions of the polymer chain in red.

(28-41)

SBR was used during World War II as a suitable replacement for natural rubber, which was in limited supply.

Nylon-6,6 (Eq. 28-30, p. 1375) is synthesized from two different reactants (adipic acid and hexane-1,6-diamine), but it is *not* a copolymer. That is because neither adipic acid nor hexane-1,6-diamine is capable of forming a polymer in the absence of the other reactant.

SOLVED PROBLEM **28.5**

How to classify polymers

Break It Down The condensed formulas of polymers A and B are shown here. Determine each one's polymeric classifications according to Table 28-1.

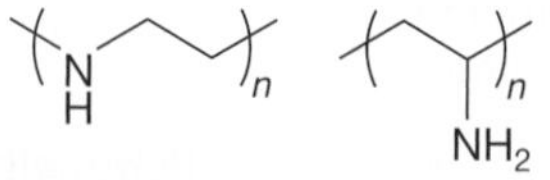

A **B**

Think	Solve
How is a carbon-chain polymer distinguished from a heterochain polymer?	Carbon-chain and heterochain polymers are distinguished by the types of atoms that make up the main chain. The main chain of polymer **A** has a nitrogen atom, so it is a heterochain polymer. Polymer **B** is a carbon-chain polymer because it has only carbon atoms in the main chain.
What functional group is present in each repeating unit?	Each repeating unit has a nitrogen atom characteristic of an amine.
Should the polymer be classified according to the functional group in the polymer or according to the monomer?	Polymer **A**, being a heterochain polymer, should be classified according to the functional group, so it is a polyamine. Polymer **B**, on the other hand, being a carbon-chain polymer, should be classified according to its monomer, making it a poly(vinyl amine).

Try It How would you classify polyglycine, the polymer made from the amino acid glycine?

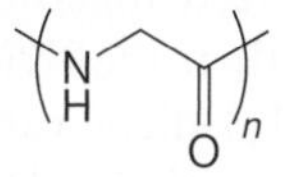

Polyglycine

28.9b Polymer Nomenclature

Just as with other forms of chemical nomenclature, an IUPAC name of a polymer can differ from its trivial or common name.

> The IUPAC name of a polymer is based on its repeating unit, but its trivial name could be based on the monomer from which the polymer is made.

For example, if the repeating unit of a polymer is $-CH_2-$ (a methylene group), then the IUPAC name is polymethylene, but the trivial (and more common) name is polyethylene, because it is made by polymerizing ethylene (Eq. 28-42):

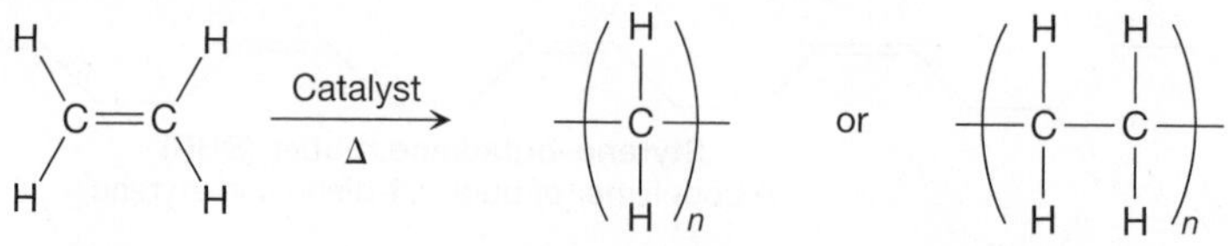

(28-42)

Ethylene **Polymethylene** **Polyethylene**

The IUPAC name is based on the simplest repeating unit.

The common (trivial) name is based on the name of the monomer.

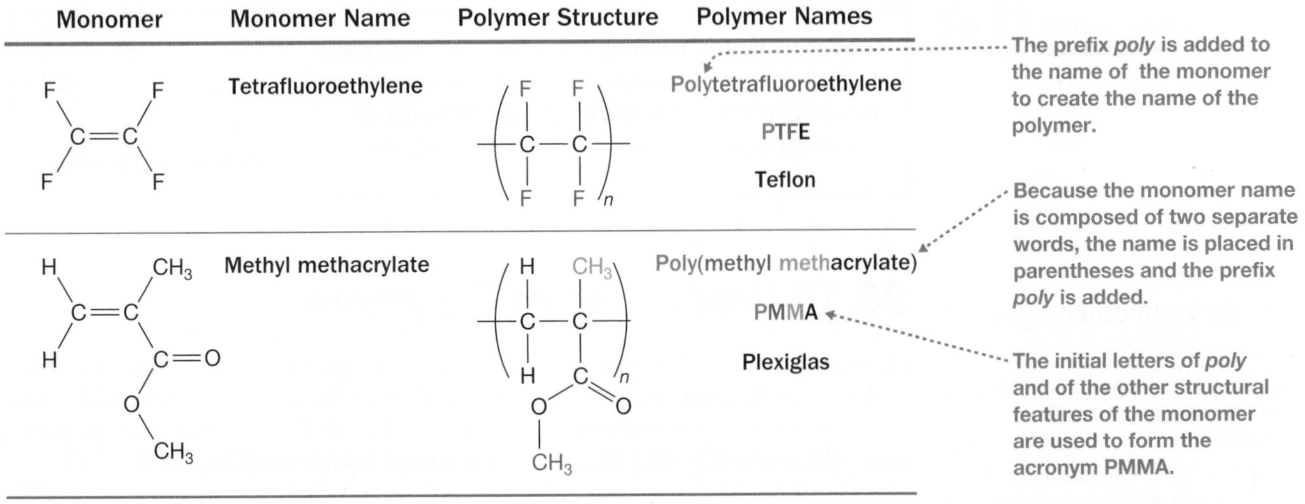
Monomer
Monomer Name
Polymer Structure
Polymer Names
Tetrafluoroethylene
Polytetrafluoroethylene
PTFE
Teflon
Methyl methacrylate
Poly(methyl methacrylate)
PMMA
Plexiglas
The prefix poly is added to the name of the monomer to create the name of the polymer.
Because the monomer name is composed of two separate words, the name is placed in parentheses and the prefix poly is added.
The initial letters of poly and of the other structural features of the monomer are used to form the acronym PMMA.

FIGURE 28-28 Nomenclature of homopolymers In these examples, the name of a polymer is related to the name of the monomer.

IUPAC recognizes the trivial names for approximately 20 common polymers. We use these trivial names in this text because you are more likely to encounter them in everyday life and because they help establish the relationship between the polymer and the monomer from which it is made.

In general, as shown in **Figure 28-28**:

- The names for homopolymers follow a *polymonomer* format.
- If the name of the monomer consists of two or more words, then the name of the monomer appears in parentheses in the name of the polymer.

Therefore, the name *polystyrene* does not contain parentheses, but *poly(methyl methacrylate)* does.

In addition to IUPAC and trivial names, there are trademarked names for polymers. As shown in Figure 28-28, Teflon is the trademarked name for polytetrafluoroethylene and Plexiglas is the trademarked name for poly(methyl methacrylate). These trademarked names, however, provide no information about the structure of the repeating unit.

Some polymers are referred to by their acronyms:

A polymer's acronym is usually derived from the prefix *poly* and the initial letters of the different portions of the monomer.

Teflon, for example, is also known as PTFE, an abbreviation derived from polytetrafluoroethylene.

Some polymers use the name of the repeating unit as the basis for the name of the polymer. For example, the most common polyester is poly(ethylene terephthalate), or PET (Section 28.5). In PET, the repeating unit is named as an ester of terephthalic acid and the ethylene group:

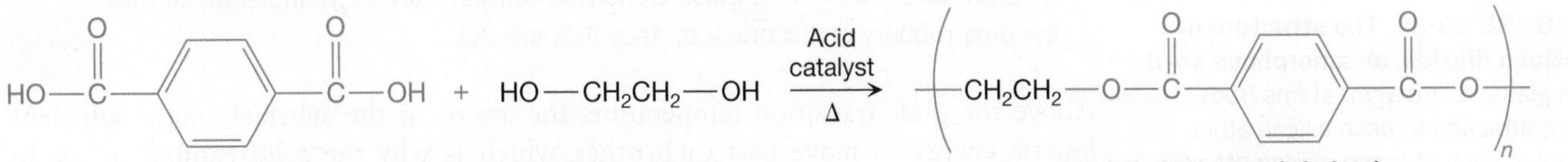
Acid catalyst
Δ

Terephthalic acid — Ethylene glycol — **Poly(ethylene terephthalate)** **PET** An ester of terephthalic acid and ethylene glycol

(28-43)

YOUR TURN **28.27**

The derivative of acrylic acid shown here undergoes radical polymerization to make a vinyl polymer that is water-soluble. Draw the condensed formula for the polymer, and provide its name and acronym.

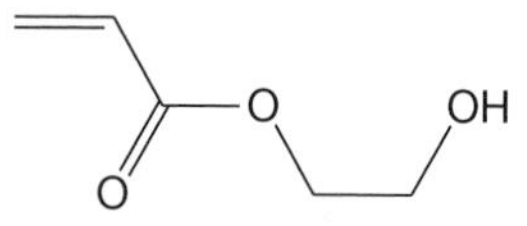

O
OH
O

2-Hydroxyethyl acrylate

SECTION 28.10 OBJECTIVES

You will be able to:

1. Distinguish a polymer's melting point from its glass transition temperature.
2. Explain how the crystallinity of a polymer can affect the polymer's glass transition temperature.
3. Explain differences in melting points, glass transition temperatures, or solubilities of polymers on the basis of their structures.

28.10 Properties of Polymers

Many polymers are "designed" to have specific properties, as are drugs and other molecules, with a specific function in mind. Here in Section 28.10, we consider two properties of polymers—thermal transitions and solubility—as they relate to intermolecular forces (Chapter 2) and conformational isomerism (Chapter 4).

28.10a Thermal Transitions in Polymers

There are two fundamental types of solids: *crystalline* and *amorphous*. **Crystalline solids** are ones in which the molecules are arranged in a highly ordered repeating pattern called the **crystal lattice**. An example of the crystal lattice of solid benzene is shown in **Figure 28-29**, with two different representations of the benzene molecule.

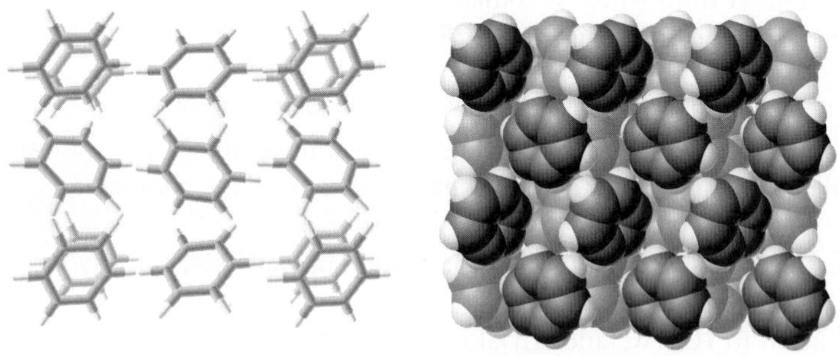

(a)
(b)

FIGURE 28-29 A crystal lattice of solid benzene Solid benzene is depicted with (a) stick models and (b) space-filling models.

Because of the high degree of order in a crystal lattice:

> Crystalline solids have a well-defined **melting point (T_m)**, above which they become liquids.

In contrast to crystalline solids, the species that make up an **amorphous solid** have no long-range order to their arrangement. The most common example of an amorphous solid is glass, which is composed primarily of silicon dioxide (SiO_2), as shown in **Figure 28-30**.

Amorphous solids do not have a well-defined melting point. Instead:

> Amorphous solids have a **glass transition temperature (T_g)**, above which they become rubbery or viscous (i.e., they flow slowly).

Above the glass transition temperature, the atoms in the substance have sufficient kinetic energy to move past each other, which is why the solid exhibits a loss in mechanical strength.

Polymers range from being completely amorphous to being highly crystalline. They are rarely entirely crystalline, however, because polymer chains are generally very

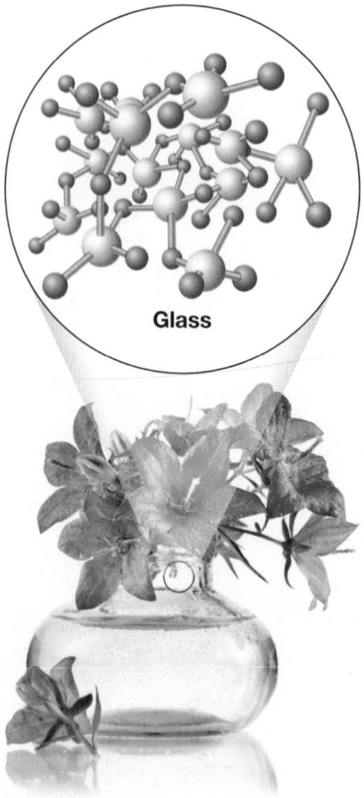

Glass

FIGURE 28-30 The structure of silicon dioxide, an amorphous solid In glass, four oxygen atoms (red) are attached to each silicon atom (gray); each of those oxygen atoms is attached to two different silicon atoms. Note the lack of a regular or repeating arrangement of atoms.

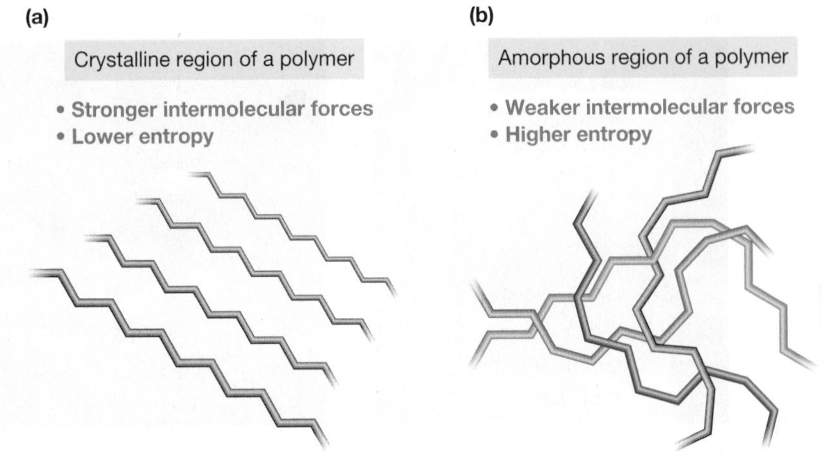
(a)
Crystalline region of a polymer
• Stronger intermolecular forces
• Lower entropy
(b)
Amorphous region of a polymer
• Weaker intermolecular forces
• Higher entropy

FIGURE 28-31 A comparison of a polymer's crystalline and amorphous regions (a) Polymer molecules in a crystalline region require significant kinetic energy to overcome intermolecular forces to convert to liquid. (b) For polymer molecules in an amorphous region, the intermolecular forces are not maximized, so less energy is required for the molecules to flow past each other.

long, making it difficult for a single molecule to arrange itself entirely in an orderly fashion. Moreover, because polymers are mixtures that vary in length, it is difficult for polymer molecules to establish an ordered crystal lattice.

Some polymers can have crystalline *regions* (**Figure 28-31a**), as well as amorphous regions (Fig. 28-31b). These types of polymers can therefore have both a T_m that characterizes the crystalline regions and a T_g that characterizes the amorphous regions.

As Figure 28-31 indicates, a crystalline region of a polymer generally has stronger intermolecular forces than an amorphous region, so the energy required to melt a crystalline region is greater than the energy required for an amorphous region to undergo a glass transition. Therefore:

A polymer's T_g is lower than its T_m.

The value of T_g increases, moreover, as the *degree of crystallinity* of the polymer increases. T_g increases with the polymer's crystallinity because, as shown in **Figure 28-32**, the crystalline regions "anchor" the amorphous regions and impede the movement of the chains in the amorphous regions.

The T_m and the T_g of polymers are important data to know because polymers are generally heated before they are formed into a particular shape. In addition, T_m and T_g determine the range of temperatures over which the polymer can perform without losing its shape or function.

At room temperature, for example, the rubber in a rubber band or a racquetball is an **elastomer** because it can experience large deformations yet return to its original shape.

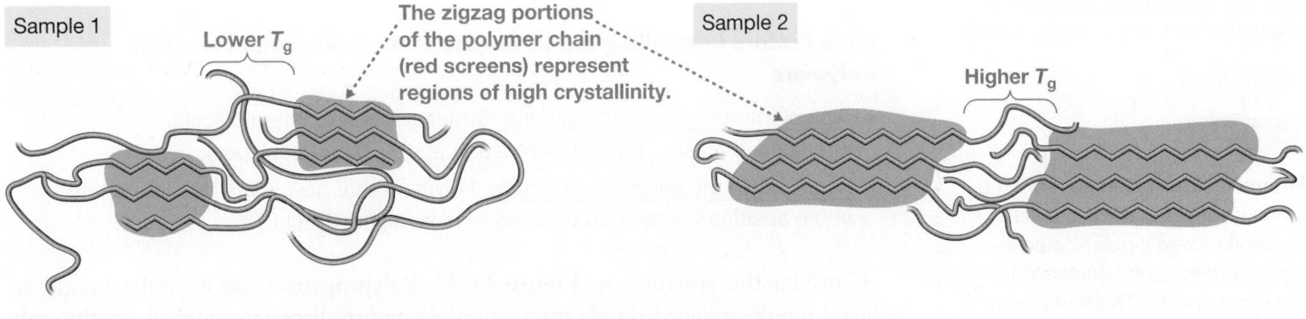
Sample 1
Lower T_g
The zigzag portions of the polymer chain (red screens) represent regions of high crystallinity.
Sample 2
Higher T_g

FIGURE 28-32 The effect of crystallinity on T_g Sample 2 has a greater degree of crystallinity than Sample 1. The noncrystalline regions in Sample 2 have a higher T_g than the noncrystalline regions in Sample 1, because the crystalline regions in Sample 2 constrain the noncrystalline regions, which increases the amount of energy needed for those segments to flow.

(a) (b) (c)

FIGURE 28-33 A comparison of a racquetball's performance as an elastomer at high and low temperatures (a) At room temperature, the racquetball has its normal elastic quality. (b) A ball immersed in liquid nitrogen is cooled below its T_g. (c) The polymer molecules in the chilled ball no longer bend or deform as easily; the ball shatters when thrown against a wall.

A racquetball is deformed when it impacts a racquet or a wall, yet it resumes its shape and, in the process, forces itself away from the racquet or the wall (**Figure 28-33a**). Rubber can do this because room temperature is well above its T_g. A frozen racquetball, on the other hand, shatters like glass when thrown against a wall, because the molecules no longer have the mobility they had at room temperature (Fig. 28-33b and 28-33c).

28.10b Factors Affecting Thermal Transitions in Polymers

FIGURE 28-34 Injection molding of thermoplastic polymers These plastic toy bricks are produced when plastic that has been heated above its glass transition temperature is injected into molds and then cooled.

Synthetic polymers can be molded into useful objects. **Thermoplastic** polymers (often shortened to just *plastics*) can be heated above their T_g or T_m and then forced into molds (**Figure 28-34**) or pushed through slots to form films or threads.

Recall from Chapter 2 that a substance undergoes a phase transition (from solid to liquid, or liquid to gas) given sufficient energy to overcome the intermolecular interactions present. As intermolecular interactions become more difficult to overcome, the melting point and boiling point increase. Similarly:

> As the intermolecular interactions between polymer molecules become more difficult to overcome, the polymer's T_g and T_m increase.

Two main factors control how difficult it is to overcome the intermolecular interactions for a polymer, and thus control T_g and T_m:

Main Factors Controlling the Strengths of Intermolecular Forces in Polymers

- Type of intermolecular interactions. Stronger types of intermolecular interactions present tend to increase T_g and T_m (see Recall box).
- Regularity in the polymer's structure. Polymers that have more regular patterns in the positions of their atoms tend to have higher T_g and T_m.

◀ RECALL

Intermolecular forces generally become stronger in the order: induced dipole–induced dipole < dipole–dipole < hydrogen bonding < ion–ion (Section 2.6). Therefore, compounds with ion–ion interactions tend to have higher melting and boiling points than those of compounds with only hydrogen bonding, and so on.

Consider the polymers in **Figure 28-35**. Polypropylene has no polar bonds, so induced dipole–induced dipole interactions (London dispersion forces) are the only intermolecular interactions present. Poly(vinyl chloride) has polar C—Cl bonds, so dipole–dipole interactions are present. Hydrogen bonding is present in poly(acrylic acid), and ion–ion interactions are present in poly(sodium acrylate). Therefore, going left to right in Figure 28-35, the type of intermolecular interaction becomes stronger, and T_g increases.

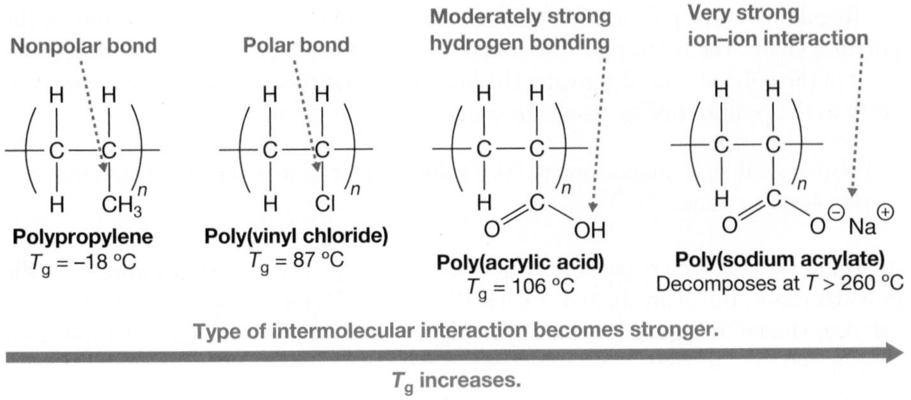

Nonpolar bond
Polar bond
Moderately strong hydrogen bonding
Very strong ion–ion interaction
Polypropylene
T_g = −18 °C
Poly(vinyl chloride)
T_g = 87 °C
Poly(acrylic acid)
T_g = 106 °C
Poly(sodium acrylate)
Decomposes at T > 260 °C
Type of intermolecular interaction becomes stronger.
T_g increases.

FIGURE 28-35 Types of intermolecular interactions and thermal transitions The dominant intermolecular interactions in the four polymers going from left to right are: induced dipole–induced dipole interactions, dipole–dipole interactions, hydrogen bonding, and ion–ion interactions. This is the order in which the type of intermolecular interaction becomes stronger and is also the order in which T_g for the corresponding polymer increases.

When compounds have similar types of intermolecular interactions, differences in induced dipole–induced dipole interactions can have a significant effect on T_g and T_m. Recall from Chapter 2 that induced dipole–induced dipole interactions become stronger as the size of the molecule increases (see Recall box). Similarly:

> An increase in the chain length of linear polymers raises T_g and T_m.

◂ RECALL

As we saw in Section 2.6d, the strength of induced dipole–induced dipole interactions increases as a species' electron cloud becomes easier to distort; that is, as the species becomes more polarizable. Such polarizability increases as the total number of electrons in a species increases.

By contrast, induced dipole–induced dipole interactions become weaker as the contact surface area between molecules decreases, which happens when a polymer becomes more branched or when longer pendant groups force the polymer chains farther apart. Thus:

> - Polymers with more branching tend to have lower T_g and T_m.
> - Polymers with longer pendant groups tend to have lower T_g and T_m.

Notice in **Figure 28-36**, for example, that poly(vinyl *n*-butyl ether) has longer pendant groups than those of poly(vinyl methyl ether) and has a lower T_g, too.

Figure 28-37 shows how regularity in polymer structure can impact T_m. Isotactic polypropylene (Fig. 28-37a) has a very regular structure (all stereochemical configurations are the same) and has a relatively well-defined melting point that is well above room temperature. Atactic polypropylene (Fig. 28-37b), on the other hand, lacks regularity in its configurations, lacks a well-defined melting point, and is tacky at room temperature.

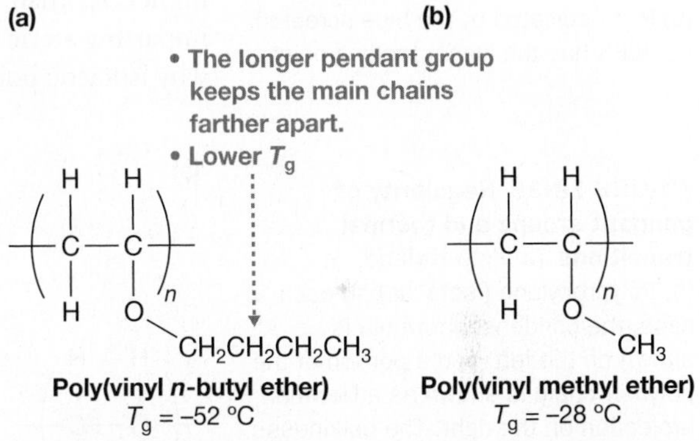

(a)
(b)
• The longer pendant group keeps the main chains farther apart.
• Lower T_g
Poly(vinyl *n*-butyl ether)
T_g = −52 °C
Poly(vinyl methyl ether)
T_g = −28 °C

FIGURE 28-36 Pendant group length and thermal transitions Because the butyl group is longer than the methyl group, the chains of (a) poly(vinyl *n*-butyl ether) are kept farther apart than those of (b) poly(vinyl methyl ether), which diminishes intermolecular attractions and lowers the T_g.

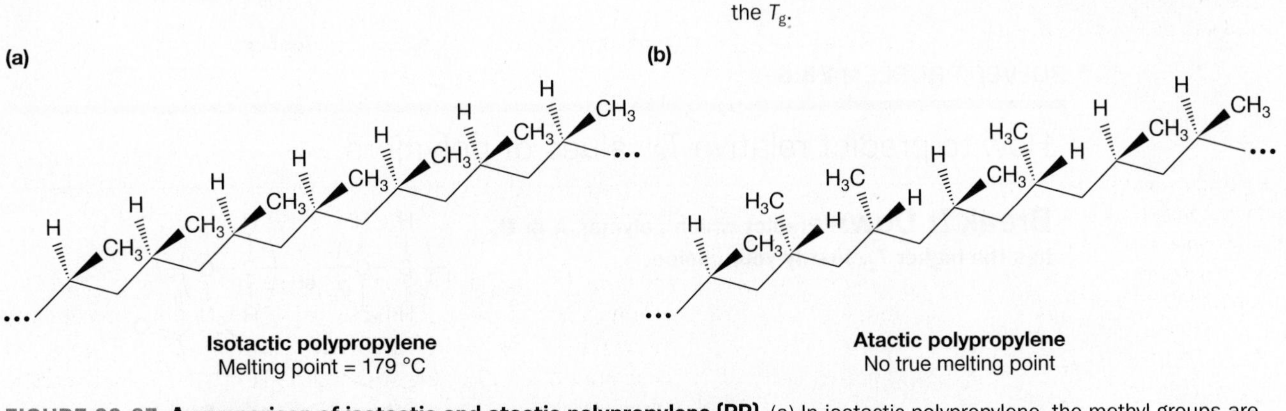

(a)
(b)
Isotactic polypropylene
Melting point = 179 °C
Atactic polypropylene
No true melting point

FIGURE 28-37 A comparison of isotactic and atactic polypropylene (PP) (a) In isotactic polypropylene, the methyl groups are all on the same side of the chain. Isotactic PP has a melting point of 179 °C. (b) In atactic polypropylene, the positions of the methyl groups are random, so atactic PP is not crystalline and has no true melting point.

Regularity in the positions of a polymer's atoms is influenced by the rigidity of the polymer chain. The more rigid the polymer chain, the fewer the possible conformations of the polymer, and the greater the likelihood that the polymer will achieve regularity in the positions of its atoms. In short:

> Polymers with rigid chains tend to have higher T_g and T_m than those of polymers with flexible chains.

Rigidity is characteristic of polymers in which conjugation exists throughout the polymer chain. The main chain of PEEK (Section 28.7), for example, is entirely conjugated, as shown in **Figure 28-38a**. PET (Fig. 28-38b), on the other hand, has portions of the main chain that are conjugated and portions that are not. Thus, PEEK has a higher T_m than PET. Bulky pendant groups can also make a polymer more rigid by imparting steric strain during rotations about the single bonds of the chain, which is why isotactic polypropylene has a higher T_m than that of polyethylene (**Figure 28-39**).

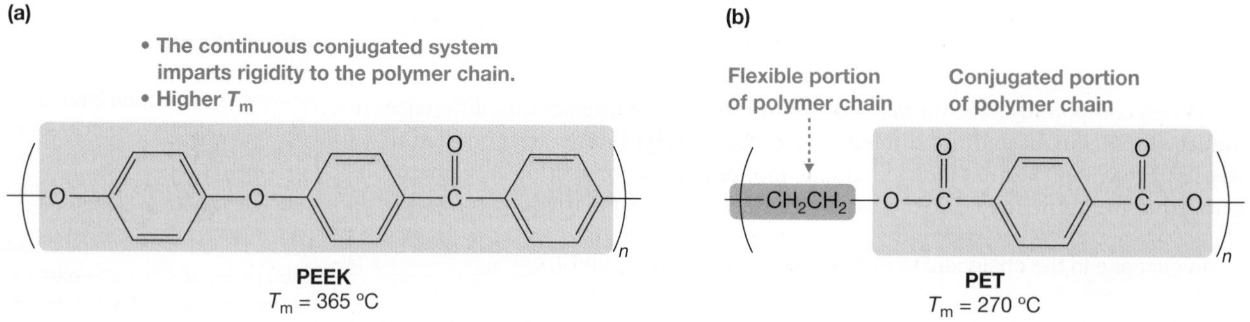

(a)
• The continuous conjugated system imparts rigidity to the polymer chain.
• Higher T_m
PEEK
T_m = 365 °C
(b)
Flexible portion of polymer chain
Conjugated portion of polymer chain
PET
T_m = 270 °C

FIGURE 28-38 Chain rigidity and thermal transitions The chain of (a) PEEK is more rigid than that of (b) PET (indicated by the blue screens), so PEEK has the higher melting point.

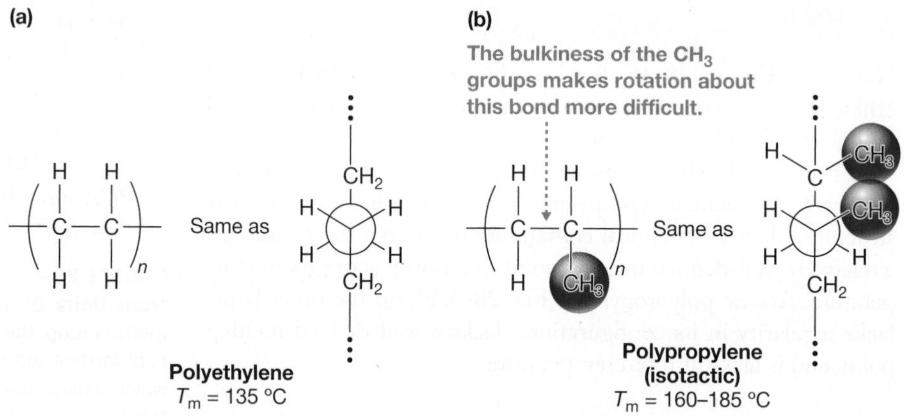

(a)
Same as
Polyethylene
T_m = 135 °C
(b)
The bulkiness of the CH_3 groups makes rotation about this bond more difficult.
Same as
Polypropylene (isotactic)
T_m = 160–185 °C

FIGURE 28-39 Regularity of pendant groups and thermal transitions (a) Polyethylene. (b) Polypropylene (isotactic). In each case, the condensed formula is shown on the left, and a portion of the polymer chain is shown as a Newman projection on the right. The bulkiness of the CH_3 group in polypropylene hinders rotation about the single bonds in the polymer's main chain, which makes the polymer more rigid and results in a significantly higher melting point.

SOLVED PROBLEM **28.6**

How to predict relative T_g values of polymers

Break It Down Predict which polymer, A or B, has the higher T_g. Justify your choice.

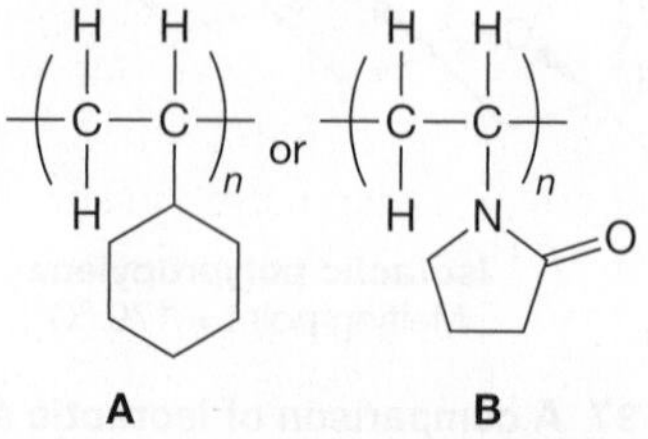

or
A
B

(continued)

Think	Solve
Do the polymers participate in the same or different types of intermolecular interactions?	Polymer **A** consists of only nonpolar C—H and C—C bonds, so induced dipole–induced dipole interactions dominate. In **B**, the polar O═C—N group characteristic of an amide introduces dipole–dipole interactions that contribute to a higher T_g for **B**.
Do the pendant groups in **A** or **B** cause the polymer chains to be substantially farther apart?	The pendant groups in **A** and **B** are similar in size, so they will cause similar separations between polymer chains and will not have a major effect on the relative values of T_g.
Is there a substantial difference in the rigidity of each polymer on the basis of conjugation along the main chain? On the basis of the bulkiness of the pendant groups?	Neither polymer exhibits conjugation along its main chain that might contribute to rigidity. The pendant groups have similar bulkiness, so they should contribute similarly to the rigidity of the polymer chain. Differences in polymer rigidity are not very significant and are unlikely to contribute to a substantial difference in T_g.
What factor dictates the difference in T_g for these polymers?	The main factor affecting T_g in this example is the type of intermolecular interactions present. Because the intermolecular interactions are stronger for **B**, we expect **B** to have the higher T_g.

Try It For each pair of polymers, predict which one has the higher T_g. Justify your choice.

(a)

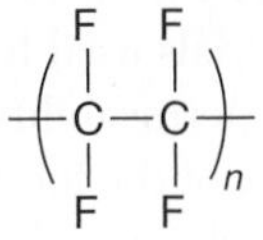

or

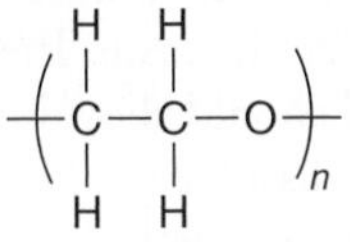

C D

(b)

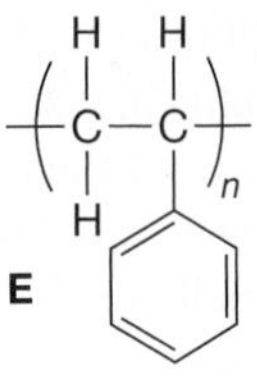

or

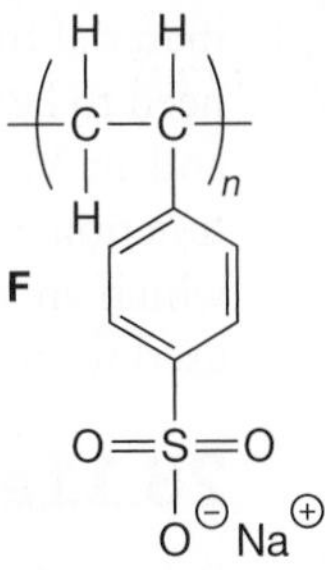

E F

(c)

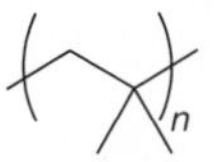

or

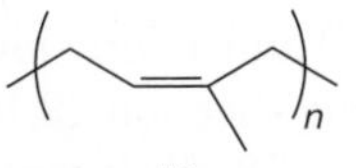

G H

(d)

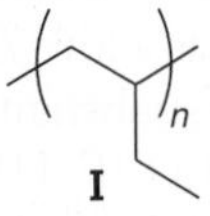

or

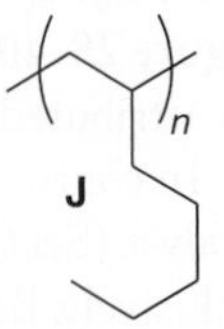

I J

28.10c Solubility

The solubility of polymers generally follows the same patterns discussed in Chapter 2. When the intermolecular interactions involving the solvent molecules are similar to those involving the polymer molecules, the polymer tends to dissolve. For example, polystyrene (Eq. 28-1, p. 1356), a nonpolar aromatic polymer, dissolves in toluene ($C_6H_5CH_3$), a nonpolar aromatic solvent. Poly(vinyl alcohol) (Eq. 28-37, p. 1383) dissolves in water because its hydroxyl groups can hydrogen bond with water. Polymers with ionic side groups, such as poly(sodium acrylate) (Fig. 28-35, p. 1395), dissolve even more readily in water due to ion–dipole interactions.

Cross-linking tends to limit the interactions between the solvent molecules and the polymer, which decreases the polymer's solubility. Linear poly(vinyl alcohol), PVA, is soluble in water and is used as an eye lubricant. Cross-linked PVA (Section 28.8) retains its ability to hydrogen bond with water, but with enough cross-linking it becomes insoluble in water. Network polymers (Section 28.6) are insoluble for similar reasons.

Highly crystalline polymers also have lower solubilities. Crystalline regions tend to have strong polymer–polymer interactions, making it difficult to establish solvent–polymer interactions. We saw this in the discussion of PEEK in Section 28.7.

YOUR TURN 28.28

Among the polymers shown in Solved Problem 28.6 and the accompanying Try It exercise, three are water-soluble and are used in pharmaceutical applications. Which polymers are they? Justify your choices.

SECTION 28.11 OBJECTIVES

You will be able to:

1. Describe how the molecular structures of common polymers used for food storage lead to the desired properties of those polymers.
2. Explain how the crystallinity of poly(ethylene terephthalate) can be modified to improve its desired properties.

28.11 Uses of Polymers: The Relationship between Structure and Function in Materials for Food Storage

Historically, food products were shipped in glass, metal, or ceramic containers. In an effort to improve shelf life, lower costs, and expand the range of foods that can be packaged, industry has turned to synthetic polymers for food packaging. Materials for food storage must be chemically unreactive, because we don't want to store food in a material that will react with it and affect its taste. The materials used for food storage need to be insoluble in water, too, and should show limited permeability toward water and air. We don't want the material to dissolve on the surface of the food, and it should function to prevent spoilage. Polyolefins such as polyethylene and polypropylene, which are essentially really long alkanes, meet these requirements and are commonly used for food storage.

28.11a Polyethylene

Polyethylene, the simplest polyolefin, comes in three types: low-density polyethylene (LDPE), linear low-density polyethylene (LLDPE), and high-density polyethylene (HDPE). LDPE is a flexible polymer that is used for packaging foods. As shown in **Figure 28-40**, it has a low T_g (−120 °C) and a fairly low T_m (112 °C), properties that are attributed to its substantial branching (Section 28.10b).

In contrast to LDPE, HDPE (**Figure 28-41**) is synthesized using a Ziegler–Natta catalyst (Section 28.3) that prevents branching, so linear polymer is produced almost exclusively. Because of its increased crystallinity, HDPE has a higher T_m (135 °C) and higher tensile strength (resistance to breaking when stretched) than those of LDPE. This makes HDPE suitable for applications in which LDPE would fail, such as milk jugs and other containers for liquids.

Linear low-density polyethylene (LLDPE). **Figure 28-42** combines properties of both LDPE and HDPE. LLDPE is made by copolymerizing ethylene and a small percentage of 1-alkenes such as but-1-ene. The copolymerization takes place with a catalyst that produces a linear polymer. The linearity of the polymer increases intermolecular forces, leading to a higher T_m (T_m = 125 °C) and greater strength than

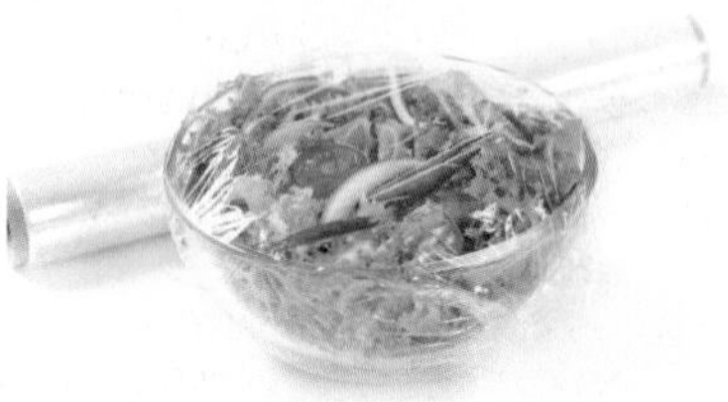

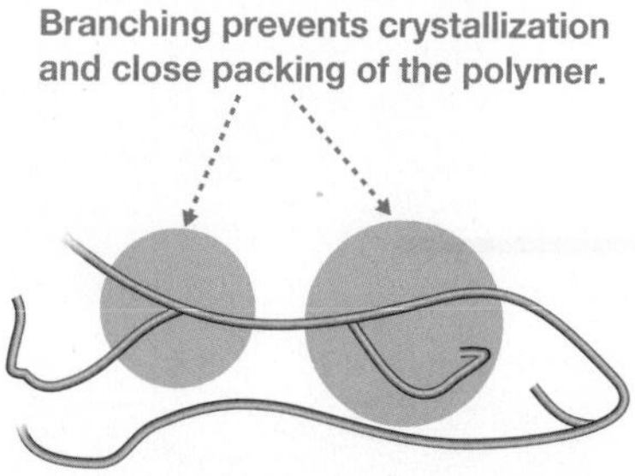
Branching prevents crystallization and close packing of the polymer.

Low-density polyethylene (LDPE)

Density (g/cm^3)	T_g (°C)	T_m (°C)
0.92	−120	112

FIGURE 28-40 Structure, properties, and use of LDPE The branching of the polymer prevents crystallization, which results in a relatively low density, low T_g, and low T_m. It also makes the plastic flexible, making it ideal for use as plastic wrap.

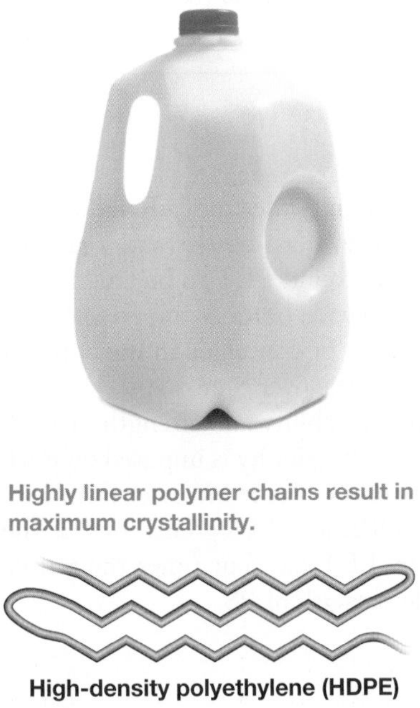
Highly linear polymer chains result in maximum crystallinity.
High-density polyethylene (HDPE)

Density (g/cm^3)	T_g (°C)	T_m (°C)
0.94	~−120	135

FIGURE 28-41 Structure, properties, and use of HDPE The polymer is relatively highly crystalline, so HDPE is more rigid than LDPE. The high crystallinity of the plastic also gives it a higher density and T_m than those of LDPE. This makes HDPE ideal as a material for containers such as milk jugs.

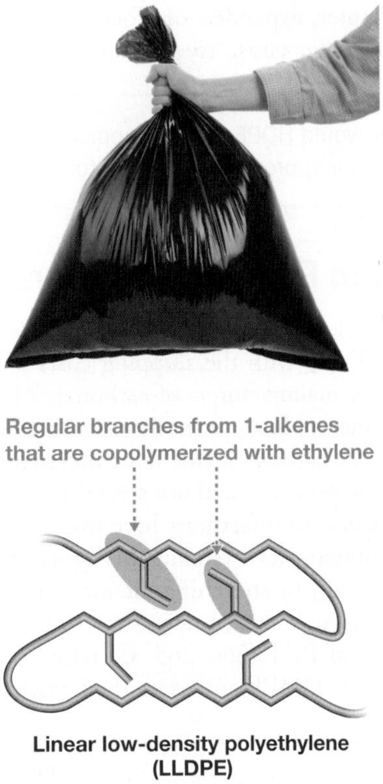
Regular branches from 1-alkenes that are copolymerized with ethylene
Linear low-density polyethylene (LLDPE)

Density (g/cm^3)	T_g (°C)	T_m (°C)
0.92	~−120	125

FIGURE 28-42 Structure, properties, and use of LLDPE The incorporation of 1-alkenes pushes the polymer chains apart, which leads to lower density than in HDPE. The absence of random branches of different lengths, however, leads to higher crystallinity, which is reflected in a melting point that is higher than that of LDPE. The regular branching of the polymer allows for more crystallinity in LLDPE and, consequently, a stronger plastic, making it ideal for use as garbage bags.

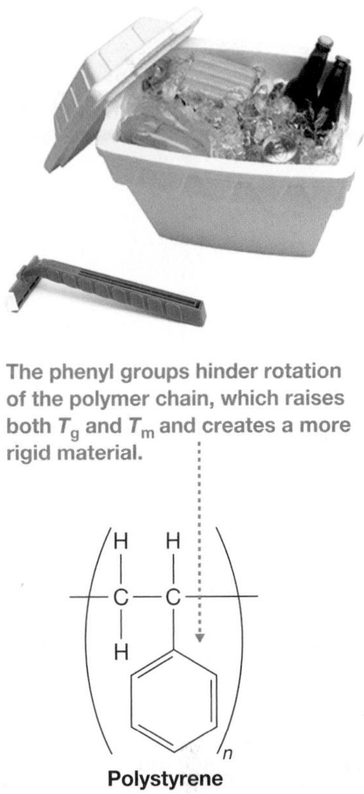
The phenyl groups hinder rotation of the polymer chain, which raises both T_g and T_m and creates a more rigid material.
H
H
C
C
H
n
Polystyrene

Density (g/cm^3)	T_g (°C)	T_m (°C)
1.05	100	—

FIGURE 28-43 Structure, properties, and uses of polystyrene The large pendant groups limit the flexibility of the polymer and make it rigid. Polystyrene is used to make disposable razors, and expanded or "foamed" polystyrene is used to make insulated containers.

those of LDPE. The alkyl pendant groups, however, keep the polymer chains apart, giving LLDPE a lower T_m than that of HDPE (Section 28.10b). LLDPE is used extensively in the manufacture of garbage bags, which need to be flexible and also need to have high tensile strength to prevent ripping.

28.11b Polystyrene

Whereas polyethylene (PE) is extremely flexible, polystyrene (PS) is not, due largely to the phenyl rings that increase the barrier to rotation around the main chain. Consequently (Section 28.10b), the T_g of PS (100 °C) is much higher than that of PE (−120 °C).

The mass of the phenyl groups makes PS denser (1.05 g/cm^3) than HDPE (0.94 g/cm^3). The rigidity and low cost of PS make it a good choice for a variety of applications, such as disposable razors (**Figure 28-43**). As we discussed earlier in the chapter, expanded or "foamed" PS is also used for insulated food packaging such as coffee cups, "to-go" containers, and egg cartons.

YOUR TURN **28.29**

Why would HDPE be an inappropriate material for a disposable razor? Why is PS an inappropriate material for a milk jug?

28.11c Poly(ethylene terephthalate)

Poly(ethylene terephthalate), PET, is the material used in bottles for carbonated beverages. Faced with the shipping costs of relatively heavy glass bottles and loss from breakage, manufacturers of carbonated beverages have found PET to be an effective replacement. However, an important requirement for a soda bottle is impermeability; that is, the carbon dioxide in carbonated beverages must be contained in the bottle at moderate pressures and not seep through the plastic bottle over time.

Plastics manufacturers have maximized the impermeability and strength of PET by maximizing its crystallinity (**Figure 28-44**). When crystallinity is imposed on PET mechanically by stretching the material, the density of the plastic increases from 1.33 to 1.39 g/cm^3. This compares to 0.94 g/cm^3 for HDPE and 1.05 g/cm^3 for PS. The high T_m of PET (260–265 °C) reflects its strength. PET has four times the tensile strength of HDPE and more than twice the tensile strength of PS.

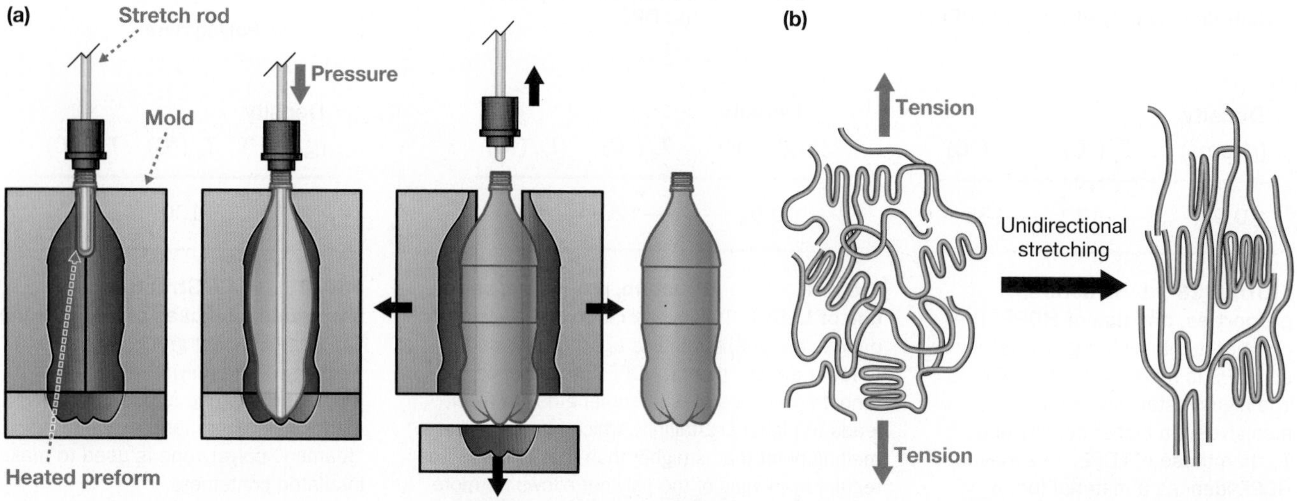

(a)
Stretch rod
Pressure
Mold
Heated preform
(b)
Tension
Unidirectional stretching
Tension

FIGURE 28-44 Molding of poly(ethylene terephthalate) bottles (a) Process for the manufacture of PET bottles. In the first stage, the heated plastic is stretched into the mold. In the second stage, pressure is used to expand the PET to take the shape of the mold, which stretches the polymer chains and facilitates crystallization. In the third stage, the plastic is cooled and the mold is opened. (b) Depiction of the crystallization that occurs when PET is stretched.

SECTION 28.12 OBJECTIVES

You will be able to:

1. Describe the general process for recycling of plastics, and distinguish mechanical recycling from chemical recycling.
2. List some of the obstacles that make recycling of plastics challenging, and describe how those challenges are being met.
3. Explain why it is important to develop polymers that can be made from renewable sources.

28.12 Going Green with Polymers: Recycling, Biodegradable Polymers, and Renewable Sources

There is no question that plastics have had a tremendous impact on the world: keeping food safe, advancing medical technology, making construction more efficient, and adding convenience to our lives. Much of the widespread usage of plastics has to do with how durable and long-lasting they are, so it's no wonder that more than 300 million tons of plastic is produced every year! Unfortunately, these attractive properties of plastics also pose a serious environmental problem, as many plastics take dozens or even hundreds of years to decompose.

Recycling is one way to tackle this problem. On many plastic consumer products you will find a *resin identification code (RIC)*, which was developed in 1988 by the Society of the Plastics Industry (they have since become the Plastics Industry Association). The RIC is a number 1–7 that identifies the type of plastic that went into making the particular product, and the numbers are arranged in order of how difficult the plastic is to recycle: 1 is the easiest, and 7 is the most difficult. In Table 28-2, you can see the type of plastic that each RIC number represents.

TABLE 28-2 Resin Identification Codes (RICs)

RIC Symbol	Polymer
01 PET	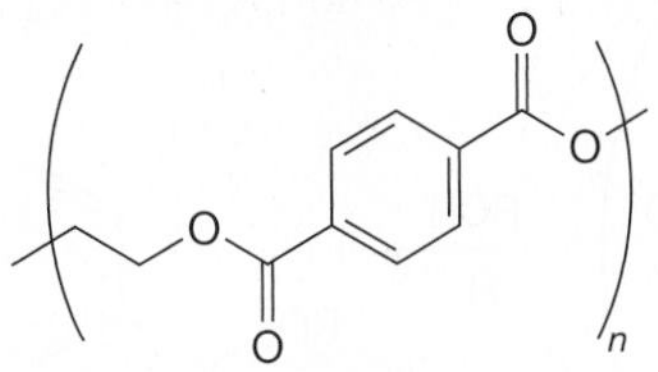 Poly(ethylene terephthalate)
02 PE-HD	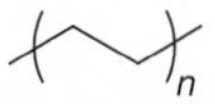 High-density polyethylene
03 PVC	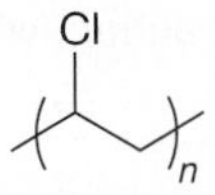 Poly(vinyl chloride)
04 PE-LD	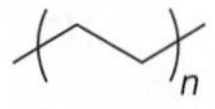 Low-density polyethylene
05 PP	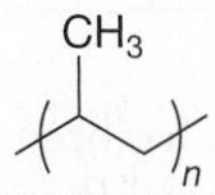 Polypropylene
06 PS	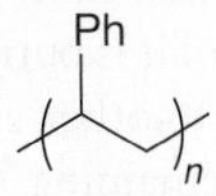 Polystyrene
07 O	Other plastics including nylon, polycarbonate, and acrylic

Before plastic is recycled, it is first sorted. Historically, this sorting was done only manually, using the RIC. Today, manual sorting is often used in combination with automated processes that rely on the density and spectroscopic characterization of the plastic. Once sorted, the plastic is cleaned to remove impurities and debris, such as paper labels, adhesives, and food residue. After the plastic has been properly prepared, it can undergo one of two basic types of recycling: (1) mechanical recycling or (2) chemical recycling.

In *mechanical recycling*, the cleaned plastic is shredded or ground into small pieces, which are then melted and formed into pellets. The pellets can then be used to manufacture new products. Mechanical recycling therefore leaves the molecular structure of the plastic essentially intact throughout the process.

Chemical recycling, by contrast, incorporates reactions that chemically modify the polymer. As one example, poly(ethylene terephthalate), PET, can undergo alcoholysis when treated with an acid catalyst to produce a dialkyl terephthalate diester (Eq. 28-44) and ethylene glycol, which are monomers of the polymer. Alcoholysis is a *depolymerization* reaction, and the resulting monomers can be collected, purified, and used in a subsequent polymerization reaction to produce new polymer.

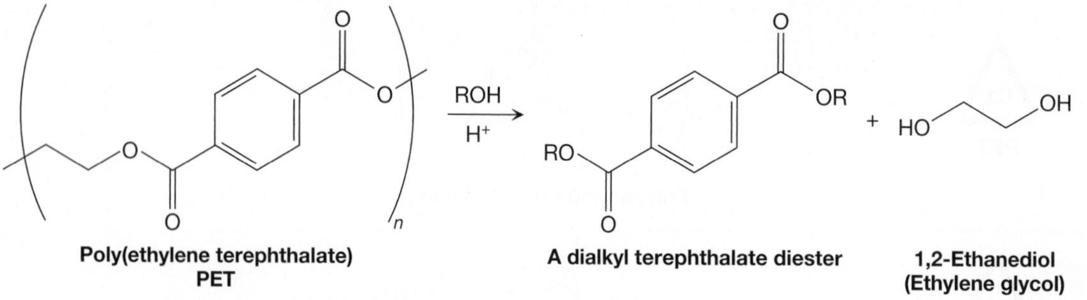

ROH
H+
RO
OR
HO
OH
Poly(ethylene terephthalate)
PET
A dialkyl terephthalate diester
1,2-Ethanediol
(Ethylene glycol)

(28-44)

YOUR TURN **28.30**

Draw the mechanism for the following reaction, which is the same mechanism that describes the depolymerization in Equation 28-44.

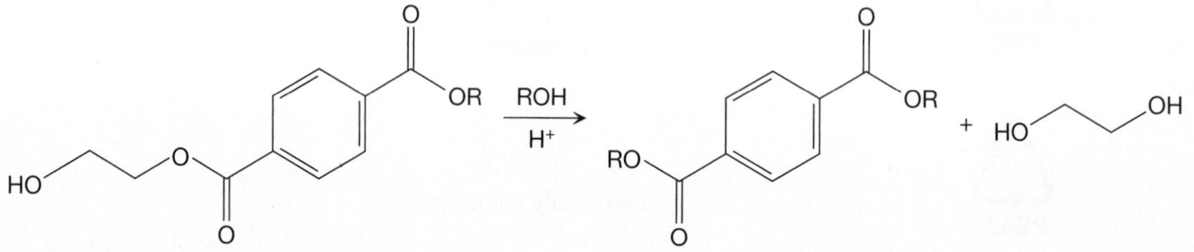

HO
OR
ROH
H+
RO
OR
HO
OH

A lot of progress has been made in recycling over the past few decades. According to the U.S. Environmental Protection Agency, only about 0.3% of plastic waste was recycled in 1980, and that number has climbed to roughly 9% today. Despite the improvements, you can see that more than 90% of discarded plastic is still not being recycled. Instead, about 15% of it is burned to produce electricity, similar to how coal is burned for energy, which leads to other environmental issues such as air pollution and greenhouse gas emissions. The remaining 76% of discarded plastic ends up in landfills and the ocean.

The relatively low percentage of plastic waste that ends up being recycled is, in part, a reflection of some significant obstacles. For example, when plastic is recycled mechanically, residual impurities (including other types of plastic) tend to result in a lower-quality plastic; the plastic becomes unusable after being recycled only two or three times. To compensate, new plastic material is blended with the recycled plastic before being used again in manufacturing. This is particularly problematic because polypropylene (PP) and polyethylene (PE) are recycled mechanically, and they account for about half of the annual production of all plastics.

Chemical recycling is viewed as the more sustainable approach because the monomers that are obtained from the depolymerization process can go on to produce recycled plastic that is essentially identical to the original plastic. Therefore, plastics that are recycled chemically can be recycled numerous times. However, not all polymers lend themselves to efficient depolymerization reactions like we saw for PET.

Biodegradable plastics offer another way to tackle the problem of accumulating plastic waste. A *biodegradable plastic* is one that is broken down naturally by enzymes from bacteria and other organisms, often in a matter of just months. Unfortunately, most polymers are not biodegradable, but ones that are tend to be polyesters, polyamides, or polyethers. An example is poly(3-hydroxybutyric acid) shown in **Figure 28-45.**

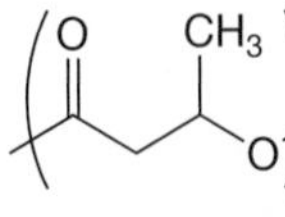
O
CH3
n

FIGURE 28-45 Poly(3-hydroxybutyric acid), PHB This polyester is a biodegradable polymer.

Separate from the issue of accumulating plastic waste, most synthetic polymers are currently produced from monomers that derive from petroleum sources. Petroleum is a nonrenewable resource, so making plastics from petroleum is unsustainable. Fortunately, much progress has been made in recent decades in the development of polymers that are synthesized from renewable sources. One such polymer is poly(lactic acid), PLA, which is made from corn! The most common synthesis begins with lactide, a dimer of lactic acid that is found in corn starch (Eq. 28-45). PLA has the added benefit that it is also biodegradable.

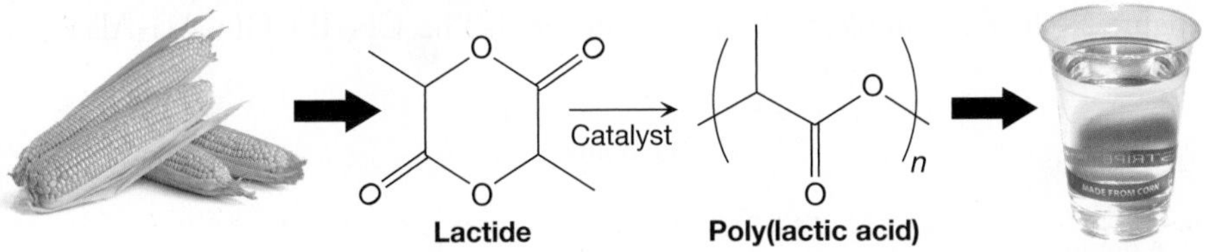
Catalyst
Lactide
Poly(lactic acid)
n

(28-45)

YOUR TURN **28.31**

The polymerization reaction in Equation 28-45 can be initiated by a nucleophile undergoing addition–elimination with a carbonyl group of lactide. The ring-opened product can then react with a second molecule of lactide by nucleophilic addition–elimination. Draw the four steps just described to show the formation of a dimer.

THE ORGANIC CHEMISTRY OF BIOMOLECULES

28.13 Biological Polymers

SECTION 28.13 OBJECTIVES

You will be able to:

1. Characterize a protein as a polypeptide and a large carbohydrate as a polysaccharide.
2. Distinguish a protein's primary, secondary, tertiary, and quaternary structures.
3. Identify disulfide bonds, α-helices, and β-sheets in a protein.
4. Explain how the glycosidic linkages in polysaccharides affect their physical properties and their use as either a storage polysaccharide or a structural polysaccharide.

Recall from Section 1.14 that proteins, carbohydrates (saccharides), and nucleic acids are constructed from relatively small molecular building blocks. Proteins are constructed from amino acids, carbohydrates from monosaccharides, and nucleic acids from nucleotides. Thus proteins, carbohydrates, and nucleic acids can be thought of as **biopolymers** made up of amino acid, monosaccharide, and nucleotide monomers. More specifically, a protein is a **polyamino acid** or **polypeptide** (due to the peptide bond that links together amino acids), a large carbohydrate is a **polysaccharide**, and a nucleic acid is a **polynucleotide**.

In Section 9.13, we saw how bonds between monosaccharides, called glycosidic linkages, can be formed and broken, and in Section 23.11 we discussed bonds that connect amino acids, so-called peptide linkages. Here in Section 28.13, we turn our attention to the macroscopic properties of these biopolymers. Just as we saw with synthetic polymers, the structures and properties of biopolymers are governed by the nature of their monomers. We will see how this applies to polypeptides in

Sections 28.13a–28.13d, and we will see how it applies to polysaccharides throughout Section 28.13e.

28.13a Primary Structures of Proteins

The specific function of a protein is governed by its structure. There are four distinct levels of protein structure: *primary*, *secondary*, *tertiary*, and *quaternary*. The **primary structure** of a protein is its specific sequence of amino acids:

> A protein is defined by its primary structure; different proteins have different primary structures.

We will discuss secondary, tertiary, and quaternary structures in the next few sections.

As we explained in Section 23.11, the amide functional group (O═C—N) serves to connect adjacent amino acids along a protein's main chain; the connection formed by an amide group is called a **peptide linkage** or **peptide bond** (highlighted in red in **Figure 28-46**). When connected by a peptide linkage, the amino acids are referred to as **residues**. The side chains attached to the α carbons of amino acid residues typically remain intact, so the protein's primary sequence can be "read" by identifying the side chains in order from the N-terminus to the C-terminus. In the hexapeptide shown in Figure 28-46, for example, the primary sequence is Phe-Cys-Thr-Gln-Ala-Ala.

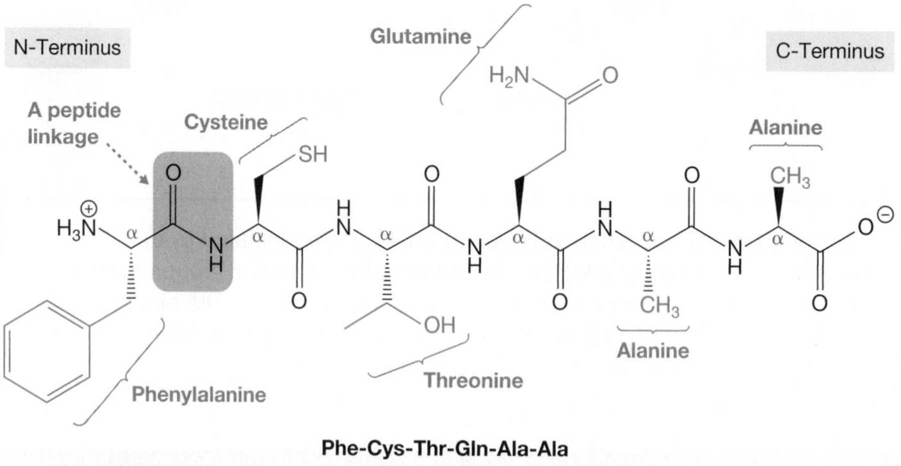
N-Terminus
Glutamine
C-Terminus
A peptide linkage
Cysteine
Alanine
SH
H_2N
O
CH_3
H_3N
OH
CH_3
Alanine
Threonine
Phenylalanine
Phe-Cys-Thr-Gln-Ala-Ala

FIGURE 28-46 Primary structure In this hexapeptide, the peptide linkage that connects the first and second amino acids is highlighted in red. The side chains on the α carbons identify the amino acids, so the primary structure, which is read from the N-terminus to the C-terminus, is Phe-Cys-Thr-Gln-Ala-Ala.

YOUR TURN 28.32

Identify all the peptide linkages in the hexapeptide in Figure 28-46. How many are there in all?

Some amino acids can form cross-links (Section 28.8), whereby one portion of the protein's backbone is covalently bonded to another portion of the backbone. The most common and important cross-linking in a protein occurs when the thiol (SH) groups of two cysteine residues are oxidized, creating a **disulfide bond** (also called a **disulfide bridge**), as shown in Equation 28-46:

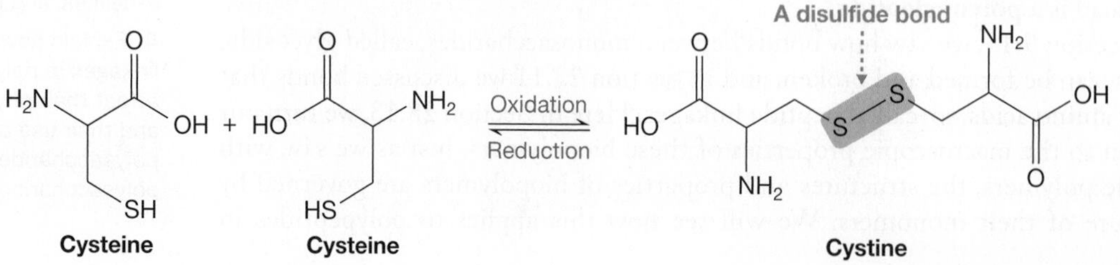
A disulfide bond
Oxidation
Reduction
Cysteine
Cysteine
Cystine

(28-46)

YOUR TURN **28.33**

Glutathione is an antioxidant that helps prevent cell damage from radicals. Under oxidizing conditions, glutathione forms a dimer through a disulfide bond. Draw the structure of that dimer.

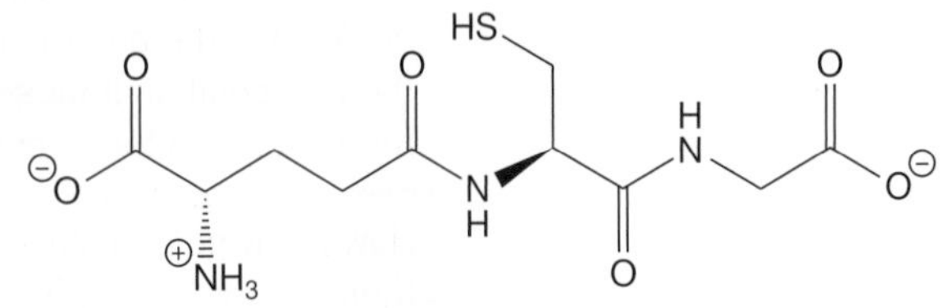

Glutathione

Vasopressin, a hormone protein that is involved in the fight-or-flight response of mammals, has a disulfide bond. The sequence of amino acids that characterizes vasopressin is Cys-Tyr-Phe-Gln-Asn-Cys-Pro-Arg-Gly-NH_2. When oxidized, the two cysteine residues form a disulfide bond, giving rise to the structure in **Figure 28-47**.

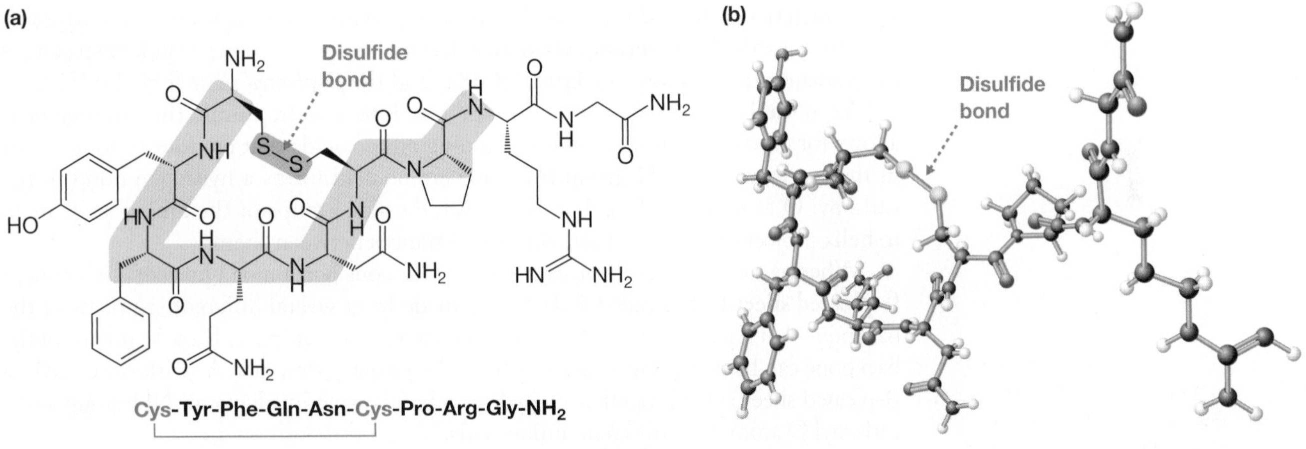

(a)
Disulfide bond
Cys-Tyr-Phe-Gln-Asn-Cys-Pro-Arg-Gly-NH2
(b)
Disulfide bond

FIGURE 28-47 **A disulfide bond in vasopressin** (a) Vasopressin is represented as a line structure (*top*) and in its abbreviated form (*bottom*). The backbone of the protein is highlighted in blue in the line structure. In both representations, the disulfide bond is highlighted in red. (b) Vasopressin is shown in a ball-and-stick representation. In the disulfide bond, the sulfur atoms (yellow) are connected by a single bond.

CONNECTIONS 28.5

Why does alcohol make you pee? Vasopressin (Fig. 28-47) is responsible for the body's retention of water. Drinking alcohol inhibits the release of vasopressin, and the suppression of vasopressin leads to the kidneys releasing water rather than retaining it.

SOLVED PROBLEM **28.7**

How to determine the number of primary structures possible for a polypeptide

Break It Down **Determine how many different primary structures are possible for a tripeptide constructed from the naturally occurring amino acids.**

Think	Solve
How many possible amino acids could be located at the first position in the tripeptide?	There are 20 naturally occurring amino acids, and any one of them can be at the first position of the tripeptide.

(continued)

How many possibilities are there for the second position? Does the amino acid at the first position impose any restrictions on the second?	Any amino acid could occupy the second position, so there are 20 possible choices for the second position, giving $20 \times 20 = 20^2 = 400$ possible combinations in the first two positions.
How many possibilities are there for the third position?	Any of the 20 amino acids could occupy the third position. The total possible combinations for a tripeptide is calculated as $20^3 = 8000$.

Try It Determine how many different polypeptides 300 amino acids long (a modest number for a protein) can be constructed from the naturally occurring amino acids. How does that number compare to Avogadro's number?

28.13b Secondary Structures of Proteins

A characteristic three-dimensional pattern involving local segments of a protein's backbone is called a **secondary structure**. The two most common secondary structures for proteins are the *α-helix* (**Figure 28-48a**) and the *β-pleated sheet* (Fig. 28-48b).

An **α-helix** winds the protein's backbone into a tight spiral. This arrangement allows for efficient hydrogen bonding among amino acids that are four residues apart in the sequence; the NH group from one amino acid forms a hydrogen bond to the carbonyl O atom from the other. Moreover, the side groups of the amino acids in an α-helix project outward, maximizing the distances between them.

Whereas each α-helix involves a single continuous portion of a protein's backbone, a **β-pleated sheet** (often called a *β-sheet*) is made from several different segments of the backbone that align next to each other in the same region of space. These segments of the backbone can be many amino acids apart in the primary structure. As with the α-helix, a β-pleated sheet is held together by hydrogen bonds, each involving an NH group and a carbonyl O atom from different amino acids.

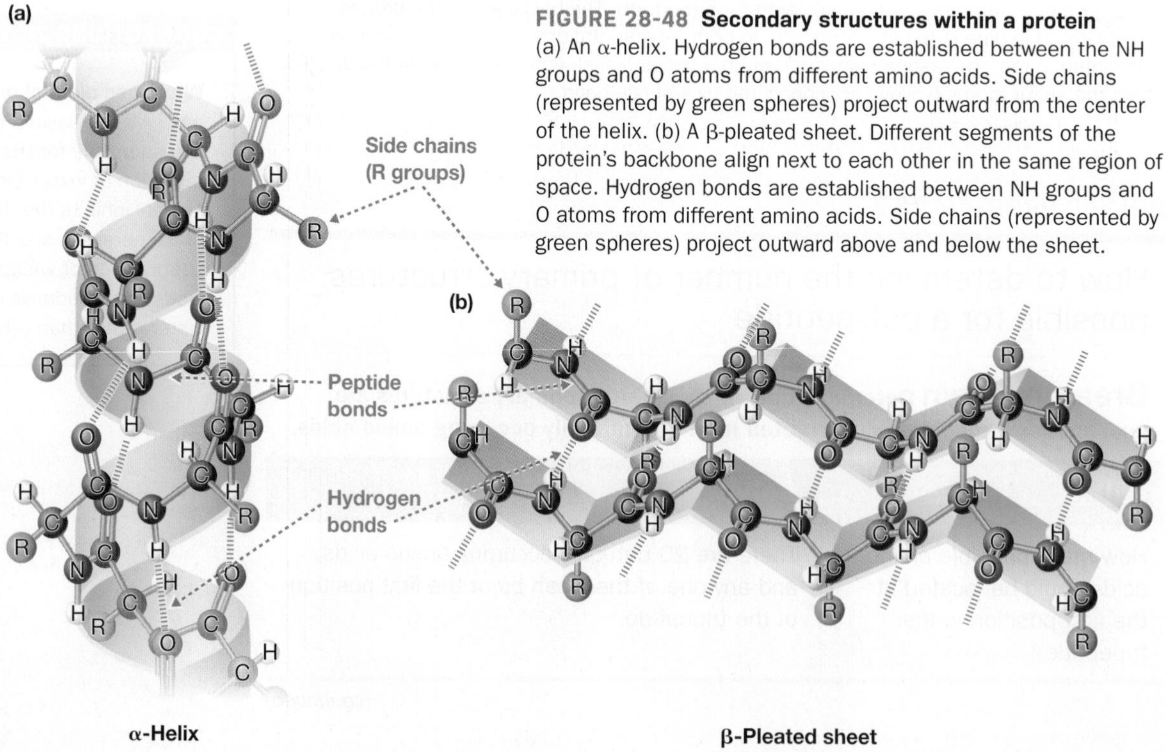

(a)
Side chains
(R groups)
Peptide
bonds
Hydrogen
bonds
(b)
α-Helix
β-Pleated sheet

FIGURE 28-48 Secondary structures within a protein (a) An α-helix. Hydrogen bonds are established between the NH groups and O atoms from different amino acids. Side chains (represented by green spheres) project outward from the center of the helix. (b) A β-pleated sheet. Different segments of the protein's backbone align next to each other in the same region of space. Hydrogen bonds are established between NH groups and O atoms from different amino acids. Side chains (represented by green spheres) project outward above and below the sheet.

FIGURE 28-49 Planarity of a peptide bond (a) In a β-pleated sheet, the planarity of each peptide linkage is maintained, and the rotation of one plane relative to the other establishes the kink that gives rise to the "pleats." (b) Resonance structures of an amide, showing the double-bond character of the C—N bond.

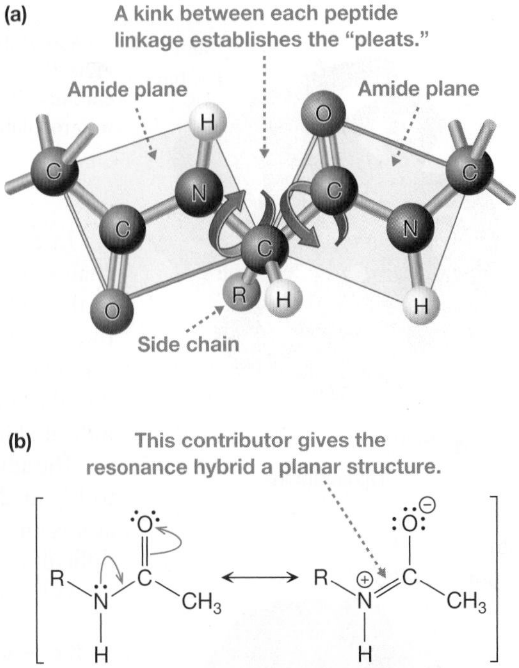

(a)
A kink between each peptide linkage establishes the "pleats."
Amide plane
Amide plane
Side chain
(b)
This contributor gives the resonance hybrid a planar structure.

The pleats, or folds, in a β-pleated sheet arise because each peptide linkage is planar, and adjacent planes are slightly rotated relative to each other, as shown in **Figure 28-49a**. The planarity of a peptide linkage results from the contribution of a resonance structure that gives the C—N bond significant double-bond character, as shown in Figure 28-49b.

The nature of the amino acid side chains determines whether an α-helix or β-pleated sheet is favored:

- An α-helix tends to be disrupted when adjacent or nearby amino acids in a protein's sequence (within about three or four residues) have side chains that are either bulky or carry the same charge (remember, like charges repel).
- A β-pleated sheet tends to be disrupted if it requires bulky or like-charged side chains from different segments of the primary structure to occupy similar locations in space.

YOUR TURN **28.34**

Suggest whether alanine or isoleucine should be found more commonly in an α-helix. Explain why. (Consult Table 1-7 on p. 39 for structures.)

28.13c Tertiary Structures of Proteins

Even after a protein has been assembled with a definite primary structure and segments of the protein have adopted specific secondary structures, the protein may still lack proper biological activity. That's because the function of a protein depends critically on its **tertiary structure**, which is the location of all of its atoms in space. Achieving the proper tertiary structure requires the protein to fold in a particular way.

A **ribbon structure** is typically used to depict the tertiary structure of a protein, as shown in **Figure 28-50a** for triose-phosphate isomerase (also called phosphotriose isomerase), an enzyme used in glycolysis to catalyze the isomerization of three-carbon sugars with an attached phosphate group (see the box on p. 349, *Sugar Transformers*).

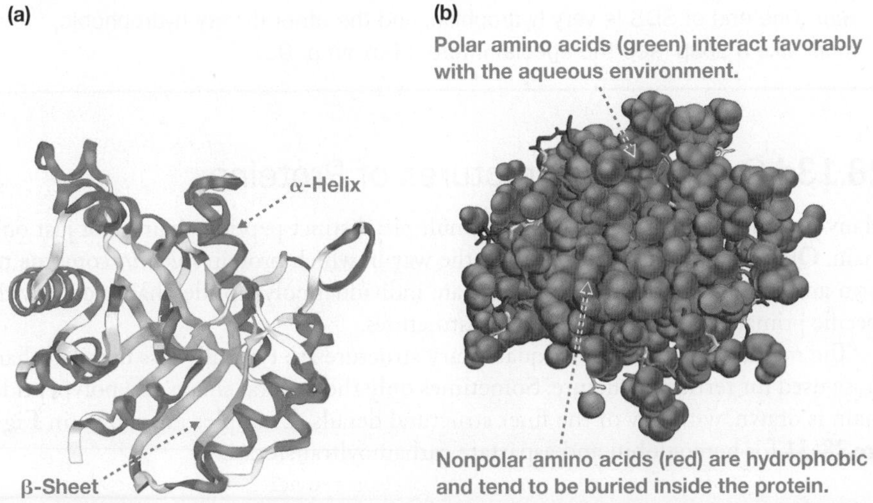

(a)
α-Helix
β-Sheet
(b)
Polar amino acids (green) interact favorably with the aqueous environment.
Nonpolar amino acids (red) are hydrophobic and tend to be buried inside the protein.

FIGURE 28-50 Tertiary structure of triose-phosphate isomerase (a) Ribbon structure of triose-phosphate isomerase. Magenta indicates an α-helix, and gold indicates a β-sheet. (b) Cross section of a space-filling model of triose-phosphate isomerase. Red indicates nonpolar amino acids, and green indicates polar amino acids.

(a)

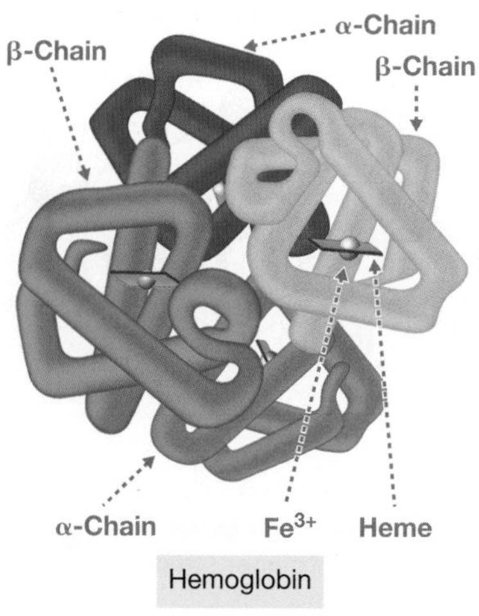

β-Chain
α-Chain
β-Chain
α-Chain
Fe^{3+}
Heme
Hemoglobin

(b)

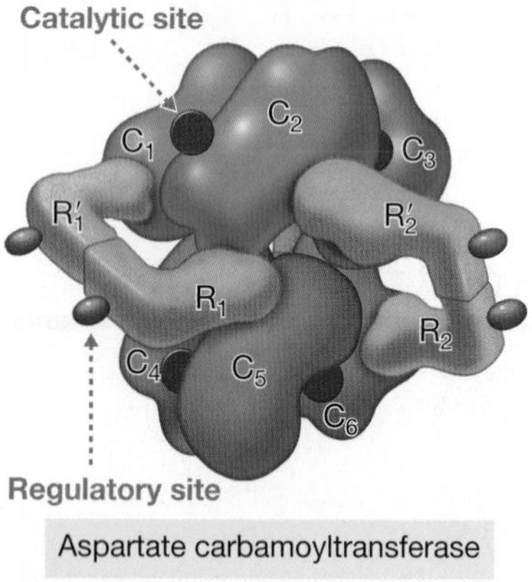

Catalytic site
C1
C2
C3
R′1
R′2
R1
R2
C4
C5
C6
Regulatory site
Aspartate carbamoyltransferase

FIGURE 28-51 Quaternary structures The quaternary structures of (a) hemoglobin and (b) aspartate carbamoyltransferase are shown. Four distinct peptide chains are associated in hemoglobin (two α- and two β-chains, each chain with a Fe^{3+}–heme group). Aspartate carbamoyltransferase contains 10 peptide chains: six with catalytic roles (C_1–C_6) and four with regulatory roles (R_1, R_1', R_2, and R_2').

In a ribbon structure, a trace of the backbone is shown explicitly, and the side chains are generally omitted. Regions of secondary structure are represented by coils in the ribbon (for α-helices) and by arrows (for β-sheets), where the arrows point in the direction from the N-terminal amino acid to the C-terminal amino acid. Secondary structures are further highlighted by using a consistent color scheme. In Figure 28-50a, for example, the α-helices are indicated in magenta and the β-sheets are indicated in gold.

The advantage of using a ribbon structure can be seen by comparing Figure 28-50a to Figure 28-50b, which is a cross section of triose-phosphate isomerase in which all atoms are shown explicitly in a space-filling model. The space-filling model makes it difficult to distinguish the secondary structures from the rest of the enzyme.

Why do proteins adopt particular tertiary structures?

The tertiary structure of a protein tends to be the one that gives the lowest possible free energy, *G*.

Factors such as intermolecular forces and steric crowding among amino acids contribute to a protein's overall free energy. Another very important factor is the **hydrophobic effect**: the tendency of hydrophobic species to aggregate to minimize their contact with water. Proteins typically reside in an aqueous environment, so amino acids that are polar, such as serine and aspartic acid (Table 1-7, p. 39), are *hydrophilic* and tend to reside on the exterior of a protein. By contrast, nonpolar amino acids, such as valine and phenylalanine, are *hydrophobic* and tend to reside in the protein's interior (Fig. 28-50b).

The hydrophobic effect is largely driven by entropy. Hydrophobic amino acids at the surface of a protein have very weak interactions with the surrounding water molecules, in which case the water molecules at the protein–water interface would favor strong hydrogen bonding among themselves. The water molecules would become highly ordered, causing an unfavorable decrease in entropy. Hydrophilic amino acids on the protein's surface, on the other hand, interact favorably with the water molecules, so the substantial decrease in the entropy of water doesn't occur.

YOUR TURN **28.35**

For some laboratory analyses, proteins are first denatured (i.e., unfolded) by treatment with a detergent called sodium dodecyl sulfate (SDS), $CH_3(CH_2)_{11}OSO_3Na$. Explain why detergents such as SDS have this effect. *Hint*: One end of SDS is very hydrophilic, and the other is very hydrophobic, much like a soap (see the special interest box on p. 99).

28.13d Quaternary Structures of Proteins

Many proteins in living cells consist of multiple, distinct peptide chains, not just one chain. **Quaternary structure** describes the way in which protein *subunits* combine to form an even larger structure. Subunits are individual polypeptide chains, each with specific primary, secondary, and tertiary structures.

The methods used to depict quaternary structure are typically less detailed than those used for tertiary structure. Sometimes only the general shape of a polypeptide chain is drawn, with few of the finer structural details. Examples are shown in **Figure 28-51** for hemoglobin and aspartate carbamoyltransferase.

Polypeptide subunits are often distinguished in the depiction of a quaternary structure. Notice in the quaternary structure of hemoglobin (Fig. 28-51a) how the α-chain subunits are distinguished from β-chain subunits. In aspartate carbamoyltransferase (Fig. 28-51b), the catalytic subunits (which are responsible for enzymatically catalyzing a particular reaction) are denoted C_1–C_6, and the regulatory subunits (responsible for promoting or inhibiting catalytic activity) are denoted R_1, R_1', R_2, and R_2'.

YOUR TURN 28.36

Would you expect the surface of each subunit of hemoglobin to have a relatively large or small number of nonpolar amino acids? Explain your reasoning. *Hint*: Consider the interactions that the amino acids at the surface of the subunits have with water.

28.13e Structures of Polysaccharides

As we saw in Section 1.14b, carbohydrate monomers (simple sugars) join to form carbohydrate polymers called *polysaccharides*. Some polysaccharides, such as *starch* and *glycogen*, are used to store energy and are called **storage polysaccharides**. Others, such as cellulose, are responsible for maintaining the structure of organisms and are called **structural polysaccharides**.

Starch, a main component of foods such as rice, potatoes, corn, and wheat, is actually a mixture of two different polysaccharides: namely, *amylose* (~20%) and *amylopectin* (~80%). Amylose consists of *unbranched* chains of D-glucose, which, as shown in **Figure 28-52**, are connected by α-1,4′-glycosidic linkages (see Recall box). That is, the glycosidic linkage involves C-1 of one glucose unit and C-4 of the next unit, and the substituent on C-1 is axial. Terminal glycosidic linkages are hydrolyzed readily by α-glucosidase, an enzyme that is found in every known mammal. Hydrolysis of the glycosidic linkage releases a molecule of glucose, which is subsequently broken down for energy.

◂ RECALL

In Section 9.13, we saw that glycosidic linkages that connect sugar units contain the acetal functional group in which two alkoxy (OR) groups are attached to the same carbon: RO—C—OR. In a polysaccharide, the alkoxy groups belong to separate sugar units.

The α configuration of the anomeric carbon affects the physical properties of amylose. In particular, the α configuration causes amylose to adopt a helical form, as shown in **Figure 28-53a** (next page), which is reminiscent of the α-helix adopted by proteins. The cross section of amylose in Figure 28-53b shows that numerous hydroxyl groups reside on the exterior of the helix, where they are available for extensive hydrogen bonding with water. Amylose, therefore, is highly soluble in water.

Amylopectin is very similar to amylose, having a main chain that consists of glucose units joined by α-1,4′-glycosidic linkages. The essential difference between the

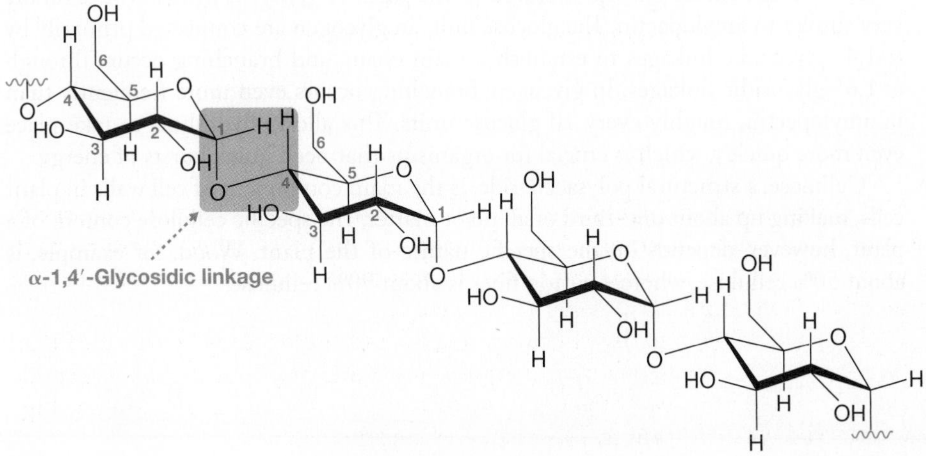

α-1,4′-Glycosidic linkage

FIGURE 28-52 Partial structure of amylose Amylose consists of a large number of D-glucose units that are connected by α-1,4′-glycosidic linkages. One glycosidic linkage is highlighted in red, and the numbering systems for the rings are shown in blue.

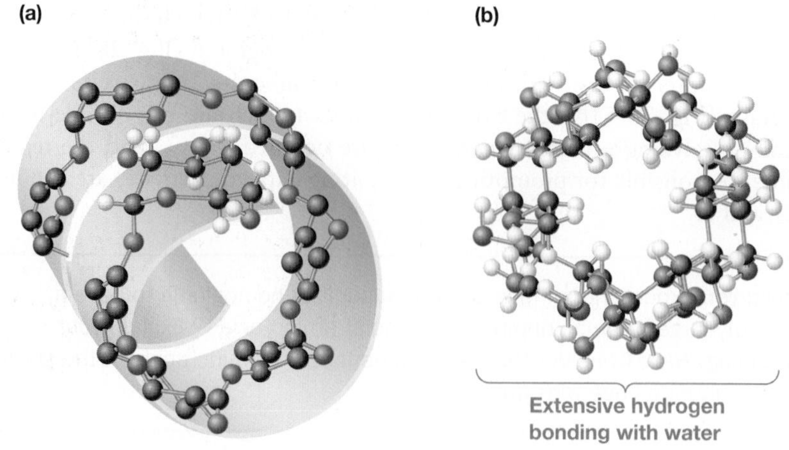
(a)
(b)
Extensive hydrogen bonding with water

FIGURE 28-53 Helical structure of amylose (a) A partial view of amylose as a helix (black spheres represent C atoms; red spheres, O atoms; and white spheres, H atoms). Most H atoms have been omitted in this view. (b) Cross section of amylose, showing numerous OH groups on the exterior of the helix, where they can form hydrogen bonds with water.

two is that amylopectin's chain is relatively highly branched. Branching takes place through α-1,6′-glycosidic linkages (**Figure 28-54**), which occur roughly every 25–30 glucose units. This branching results in more terminal glycosidic linkages than are found in amylose, so α-glucosidase is capable of releasing glucose units relatively quickly: a benefit when energy is needed.

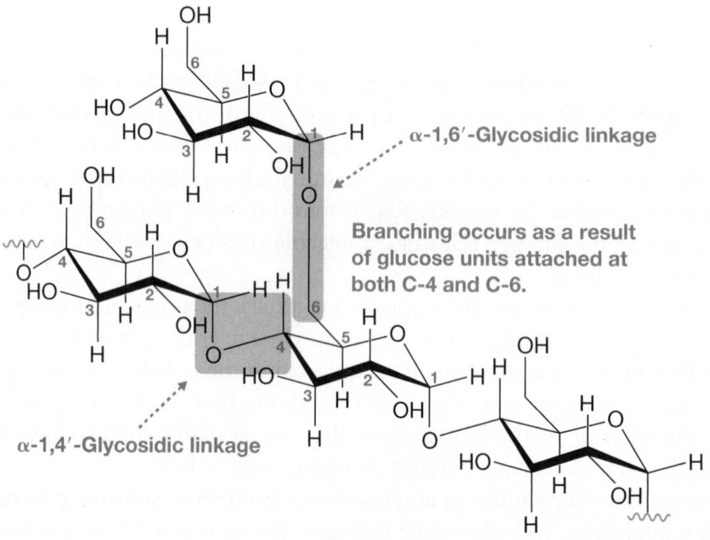
α-1,6′-Glycosidic linkage
Branching occurs as a result of glucose units attached at both C-4 and C-6.
α-1,4′-Glycosidic linkage

FIGURE 28-54 Partial structure of amylopectin Glucose units in the main chain are joined by α-1,4′-glycosidic linkages, whereas glucose units at the branch points are joined by α-1,6′-glycosidic linkages.

In animals, excess glucose is stored in the form of *glycogen*, which is structurally very similar to amylopectin. The glucose units in glycogen are connected primarily by α-1,4′-glycosidic linkages to establish a main chain, and branching occurs through α-1,6′-glycosidic linkages. In glycogen, branching occurs even more frequently than in amylopectin, roughly every 10 glucose units. This allows hydrolysis to take place even more quickly, which is crucial for organisms that need quick bursts of energy.

Cellulose, a structural polysaccharide, is the main component of cell walls in plant cells, making up about one-third of all plant matter. The specific cellulose content of a plant, however, depends on the specific nature of the plant. Wood, for example, is about 50% cellulose, whereas cotton fiber is about 90% cellulose.

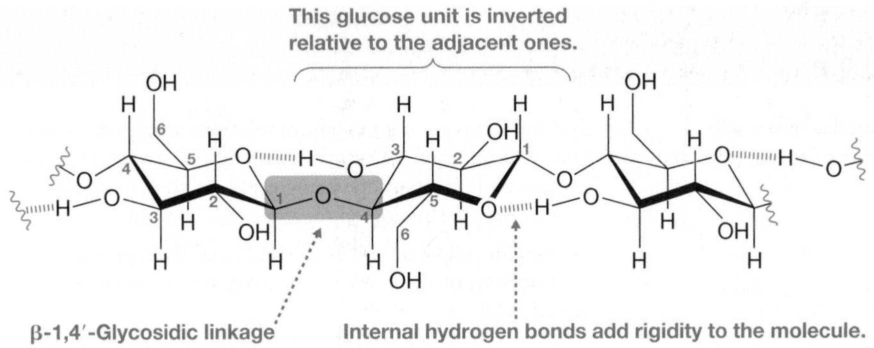
This glucose unit is inverted relative to the adjacent ones.
β-1,4′-Glycosidic linkage
Internal hydrogen bonds add rigidity to the molecule.

FIGURE 28-55 Partial structure of cellulose Glucose units are connected by β-1,4′-glycosidic linkages.

Cellulose consists of long, unbranched chains of D-glucose. How, then, is cellulose different from amylose? The glucose units in amylose are connected by α-1,4′-glycosidic linkages, whereas the glucose units in cellulose are connected by β-1,4′-glycosidic linkages: that is, the substituent attached to C-1 is equatorial in each unit, as shown in **Figure 28-55**.

YOUR TURN 28.37

There is one glycosidic linkage not highlighted in Figure 28-54 and another in Figure 28-55. Identify each one and classify what kind of glycosidic linkage it is.

Although the difference between an α linkage and a β linkage may seem slight on the small scale, the differences are dramatic on the large scale. As shown in Figure 28-55, the β linkage makes extensive intramolecular hydrogen bonding possible, which makes cellulose more rigid than amylose. Moreover, the free OH groups are situated for hydrogen bonding with other cellulose chains to create a stable polymer network. This is what makes cellulose such a useful structural polysaccharide.

Another difference between cellulose and amylose is that cellulose is insoluble in water. Whereas the helical shape of amylose allows its OH groups to remain free for hydrogen bonding with water, the OH groups in cellulose are tied up in hydrogen bonding with adjacent glucose units of the same chain or with OH groups from a separate chain. Without substantial hydrogen bonding with water, there are not enough favorable interactions to make cellulose soluble.

Yet another difference between cellulose and amylose is that mammals cannot digest cellulose directly. Mammals lack β-glucosidase, the enzyme required for hydrolyzing the β-1,4′-glycosidic linkages of cellulose. The digestive tracts of ruminants (a class of grazing animals such as horses and cows) contain certain bacteria that do have the enzyme and are therefore capable of breaking down cellulose. In this way, grazing animals can obtain glucose from grass and hay.

YOUR TURN 28.38

The exoskeletons of insects and arthropods incorporate chitin, which is structurally almost identical to, but stronger than, cellulose. The difference between the two polymers is that in chitin, the 2-position on each ring has an $NHCOCH_3$ group instead of an OH group. Explain why this makes chitin stronger.

Chapter Summary and Key Terms

- **Polymers** are large molecules made from relatively small molecules, and they exhibit some kind of regular repetition in their structures. (Introduction)
- The relatively small molecules that react to form polymers are called **monomers**. (Section 28.1)
- Polymers contain a **main chain** and often have **pendant groups**. Polymers are usually depicted by showing their **repeating units** in a condensed formula, because the chains are so large that a full structure is impractical to draw. (Section 28.1a)
- The number of monomers making up a polymer's chain is its **degree of polymerization (DP)**. (Section 28.1a)
- Numerous polymers are made by **radical polymerization**, involving *initiation*, *propagation*, and *termination* steps. Termination can occur by **combination** or **disproportionation**. Most monomers add in a **head-to-tail** fashion during propagation. (Sections 28.1b and 28.1c)
- **Tacticity** describes the regularity in a polymer's stereochemical configurations. The configurations are all the same in an **isotactic** polymer, and they alternate in a **syndiotactic** polymer. In an **atactic** polymer, there is no regular pattern. (Section 28.1d)
- Polymers are generally mixtures with different molecular sizes but can be characterized by an average molar mass or average degree of polymerization. (Section 28.1e)
- **Anionic polymerization** and **cationic polymerization** proceed through mechanisms that involve negatively and positively charged intermediates, respectively. (Section 28.2)
- **Ziegler–Natta catalysts** promote coordination polymerization and can be used to synthesize isotactic and syndiotactic polymers. (Section 28.3)
- In a **ring-opening polymerization**, cyclic monomers produce an acyclic polymer. (Section 28.4)
- Radical polymerization is an example of **chain polymerization**, one general class of polymerization reactions. The other class of reactions is **step-growth polymerization**. (Sections 28.1b and 28.5)
    - In chain polymerization, reaction occurs at the end of the growing chain, and each reaction lengthens the polymer chain by a single repeating unit.
    - In step-growth polymerization, reaction occurs between the ends of molecules—either monomers or polymer chains—and the increase in chain size depends on the size of the two molecules that react.
- Polymers can be classified according to the type of chain (**carbon-chain** or **heterochain polymers**), the type of functional group in the chain, the type of monomer used to make the polymer, and the number of different kinds of monomers used to make the polymer (**homopolymers** vs. **copolymers**). Polymers can also be classified by the types of chain (**linear** vs. **branched polymers**) and the degree of cross-linking (**cross-linked** and **network polymers**). (Sections 28.6, 28.8, and 28.9a)
- Polymers can undergo chemical reactions after polymerization is terminated. Most involve modifications to the pendant groups, an important one being **cross-linking**, in which polymer chains are joined together. (Sections 28.8)
- Names for polymers can be derived from the repeating unit or from the monomer used to create the polymer. (Section 28.9b)
- The **melting point (T_m)** and **glass transition temperature (T_g)** are thermal properties that quantify the crystalline and amorphous character of a polymer. (Section 28.10a)
- Thermal transitions and the solubility properties of a polymer depend on the strengths of the intermolecular interactions at play and on the ability of the polymer to achieve regularity in the positions of its atoms. (Sections 28.10b and 28.10c)
- The structure of a polymer determines its function; that is, its properties dictate its uses.
    - Polymers with low T_g, such as LDPE, are flexible and can be used as packaging films. (Section 28.11a)
    - Polymers with higher T_g are more rigid and are used for objects that need to retain their shapes. (Section 28.11b)
    - Introducing crystallinity increases rigidity and density, often with retention of flexibility, so HDPE is suitable for milk jugs and PET is suitable for carbonated beverage bottles. (Sections 28.10a, 28.11a, and 28.11c)
- Most plastics are not biodegradable, so mechanical and chemical recycling help reduce the accumulation of plastics in landfills and in nature. Advances are being made toward manufacturing polymers that are biodegradable and are produced from renewable sources. (Section 28.12)
- Proteins (polypeptides) and polysaccharides are **biopolymers**. (Section 28.13)
    - A protein is defined by its **primary structure**, which is the specific sequence of amino acids linked by **peptide bonds**. Primary structures include **disulfide bridges**, which can link one part of a peptide chain to another. (Section 28.13a)
    - **Secondary structures** of proteins describe local patterns of folding in the peptide chain; they include the **α-helix** and the **β-pleated sheet**. (Section 28.13b)
    - **Tertiary structures** of proteins describe the three-dimensional location of every atom of the protein. The **hydrophobic effect** explains why nonpolar amino acids tend to reside on the interior of a folded protein. (Section 28.13c)
    - The **quaternary structure** of a protein describes how multiple polypeptides aggregate together to form a larger structure. (Section 28.13d)
    - In a polysaccharide, individual sugar units are linked together by glycosidic linkages, which consist of acetal functional groups. The functions and properties of polysaccharides are dictated in part by the types of glycosidic linkages and the degree of branching. (Section 28.13e)

Problems

Problems that are related to synthesis are denoted (SYN).

Section 28.1 Radical Polymerization: Polystyrene as a Model

28.1 Given the condensed formulas shown here, draw the partial structure of each polymer by explicitly showing three repeating units. *Hint*: Each polymer should look similar to the representation in Your Turn 28.2 (p. 1358).

(a)

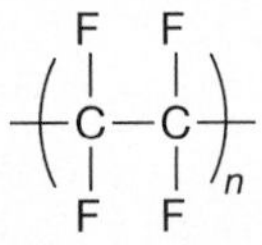

(b)

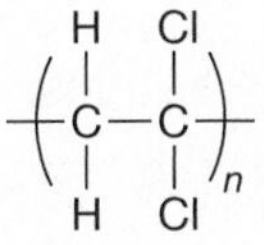

28.2 Each of the monomers shown here can undergo radical polymerization. For each polymerization:

(a) Show the mechanism for the initiation and the first two propagation steps, using benzoyl peroxide as the initiator.

(b) Draw the condensed formula for the polymer, showing the repeating unit.

(c) Provide a name for the polymer.

(1)

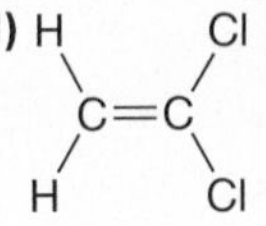

Vinylidene chloride

(2)

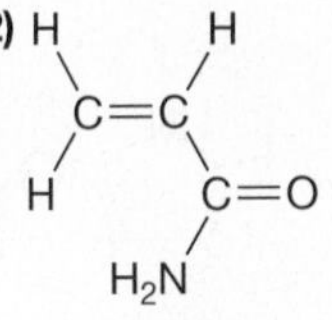

Acrylamide

(3)

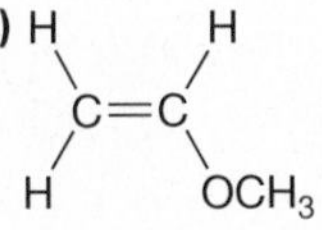

Methyl vinyl ether

28.3 **(SYN)** From the representation of each of the following polymers,

(a) Draw the condensed formula for the polymer.

(b) Propose a structure for the monomer from which the polymer was synthesized.

(1)

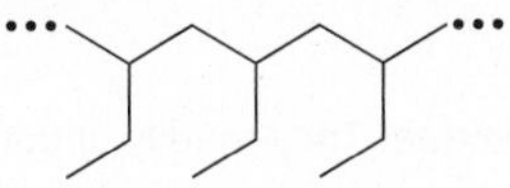

(2)

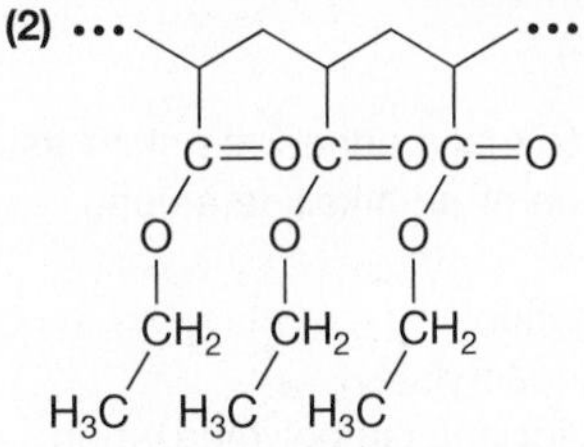

(3)

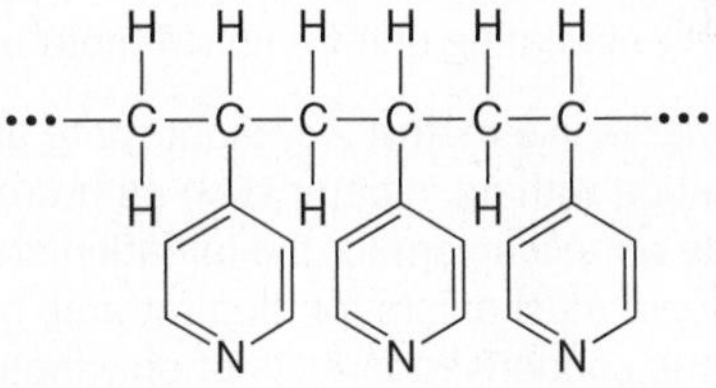

28.4 **(SYN)** Poly(*N*-vinylpyrrolidone), whose condensed formula is shown in the chapter opener on page 1354, can be synthesized by heating the monomer in the presence of a small amount of H_2O_2. **(a)** Draw the condensed formula of *N*-vinylpyrrolidone. **(b)** Draw the initiation step and the first two propagation steps of this polymerization mechanism.

28.5 Teflon can be made from tetrafluoroethylene by radical polymerization. In the reaction, termination occurs only by combination and not by disproportionation. Explain this observation.

28.6 Propylene does not undergo radical polymerization readily because there are two competing steps after initiation: propagation and hydrogen atom abstraction.

(a) Using a generic radical R• as a reactant with propylene, draw the mechanism and products for the two competing steps.

(b) Which step produces the more stable product?

(c) How do your results explain propylene's poor reactivity in radical polymerization?

28.7 Using a generic radical R• as the initial radical, draw the first two propagation steps in the polymerization of crotonic acid, paying close attention to regiochemistry. Do the same for acrylic acid. Explain why crotonic acid polymerizes much more slowly than acrylic acid.

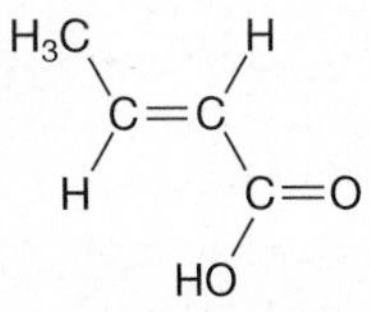

Crotonic acid

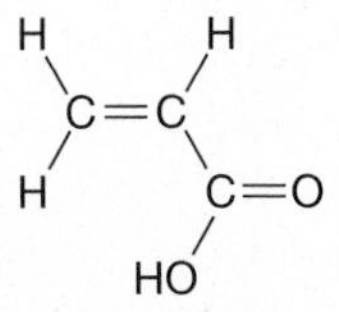

Acrylic acid

Section 28.2 Anionic and Cationic Polymerization Reactions

28.8 **(a)** Which monomer would most readily undergo anionic polymerization? Justify your choice. **(b)** Which one would most readily undergo cationic polymerization? Justify your choice.

Ethyl vinyl ether **But-1-ene** **Nitroethylene**

28.9 *N*-Vinylcarbazole undergoes cationic polymerization to produce poly(*N*-vinylcarbazole), or PVK, which is a photoconducting material used in laser printers. Explain why the monomer readily undergoes cationic polymerization.

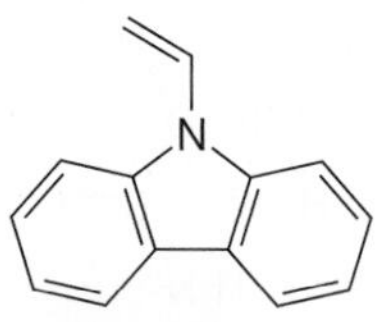

***N*-Vinylcarbazole**

28.10 Do you think that 4-methoxystyrene will more easily undergo anionic or cationic polymerization? Explain your answer.

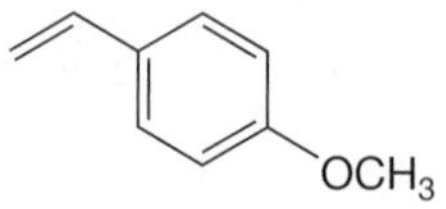

4-Methoxystyrene

28.11 For the polymerization you chose in Problem 28.10,

(a) Propose a mechanism for the initiation step, using either a generic Brønsted acid (HA) or a generic nucleophile (Nu:$^-$) as the initiator.

(b) Propose a mechanism for the first two propagation steps.

(c) Draw the repeating unit for poly(4-methoxystyrene).

28.12 Cyanoacrylates like methyl 2-cyanoacrylate are used to make adhesives such as superglue. They readily undergo polymerization with an initiator such as hydroxide anion or an alkoxide anion.

(a) Provide a mechanism for the initiation step.

(b) Propose a mechanism for the first step of propagation.

(c) Draw the condensed formula of poly(methyl 2-cyanoacrylate).

(d) Why is methyl 2-cyanoacrylate a better candidate for anionic polymerization than methyl acrylate?

(e) Do you think methyl 2-cyanoacrylate would be a good candidate for cationic polymerization? Why or why not?

(f) Notice that the ester group can undergo hydrolysis with HO$^-$. Why do you think this unwanted side reaction is not a severe issue in this case?

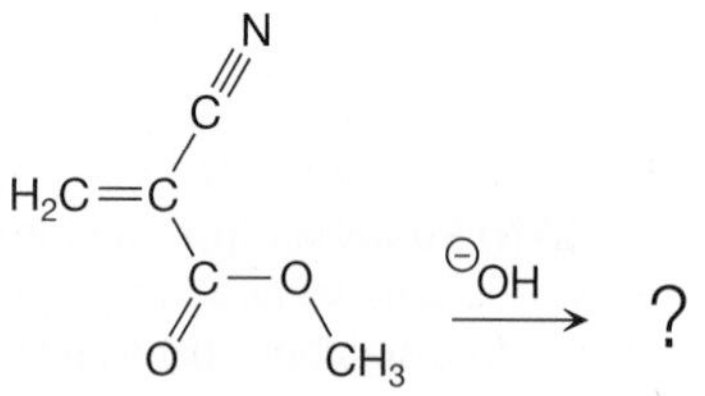

Methyl 2-cyanoacrylate

Sections 28.3 and 28.4 Coordination Polymerization and Ring-Opening Polymerization Reactions

28.13 **(SYN)** **(a)** Show how poly(propylene oxide) can be synthesized by anionic ring-opening polymerization. **(b)** Draw the mechanism for the initiation and first two propagation steps.

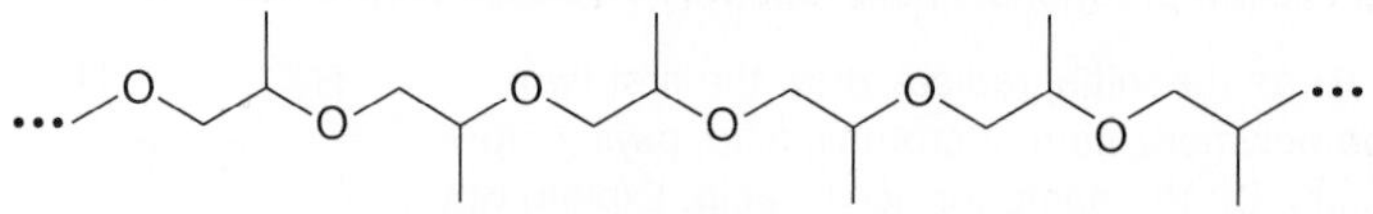

Poly(propylene oxide)

28.14 **(SYN)** The Your Turn 28.15 exercise (p. 1374) highlighted the cationic ring-opening polymerization of oxetane, producing polyoxetane. Polyoxetane can be synthesized by anionic polymerization, too.

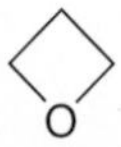

Oxetane

(a) Propose a synthesis of polyoxetane by anionic polymerization, and show the mechanism for the first two propagation steps.

(b) Draw a condensed formula for polyoxetane.

(c) Do you expect polyoxetane to be more or less soluble in water than poly(ethylene oxide)? Justify your answer.

(d) Do you expect polyoxetane to have a higher or lower melting point than poly(ethylene oxide)? Justify your answer.

28.15 Lactones (cyclic esters) can undergo anionic ring-opening polymerization when treated with an alkoxide anion, as shown here. Draw the mechanism for the initiation and first two propagation steps for this polymerization, and draw the condensed formula of the resulting polymer.

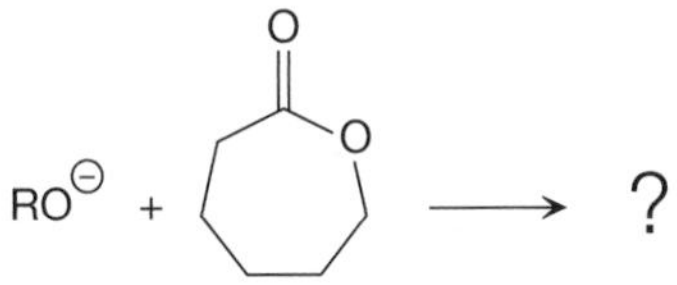

28.16 Lactams (cyclic amides) can undergo anionic ring-opening polymerization when treated with a small amount of a strong base such as NaH, as shown here. Draw the mechanism for the initiation and first two propagation steps for this polymerization, and draw the condensed formula of the resulting polymer.

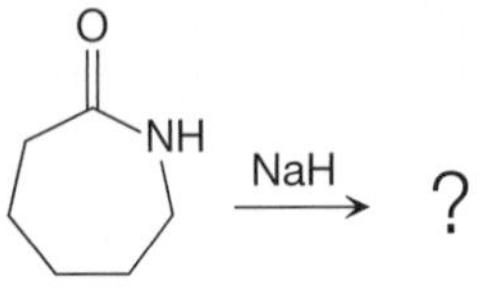

28.17 A ketene acetal can undergo radical ring-opening polymerization, as shown below. After the initial radical, R•, is produced, the catalytic cycle that adds each monomer to the growing chain consists of two steps. Draw the mechanism for those two steps, and draw the condensed formula for the resulting polymer.

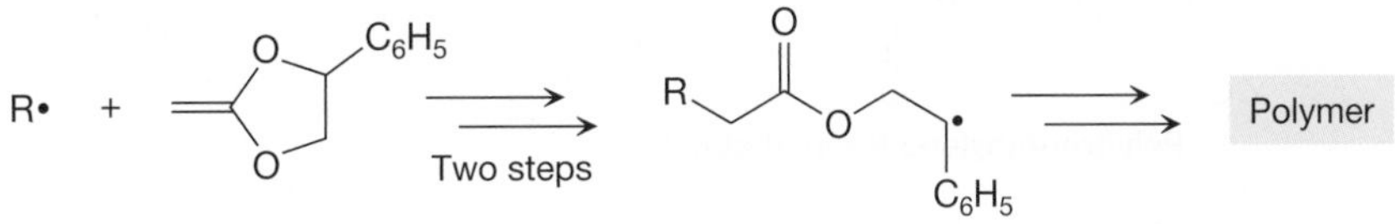

28.18 In Section 20.7c, we learned that alkene metathesis produces an equilibrium mixture of alkenes, according to this general reaction:

$$R^1CH{=}CHR^2 \xrightleftharpoons{\text{Catalyst}} R^1CH{=}CHR^1 + R^2CH{=}CHR^2$$

When the C=C bond is part of a strained ring, this kind of reaction leads to polymerization, according to the following general reaction:

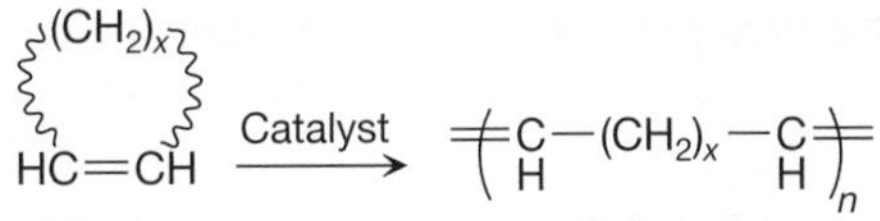

Monomer **Polymer**

Equilibrium favors opening the strained cycloalkene ring and joining the monomers with new C=C bonds. Such a reaction is called *ring-opening metathesis polymerization* (*ROMP*). With this in mind, draw the condensed formula for the polymer produced from each of these monomers undergoing ROMP.

(a) **(b)** **(c)**

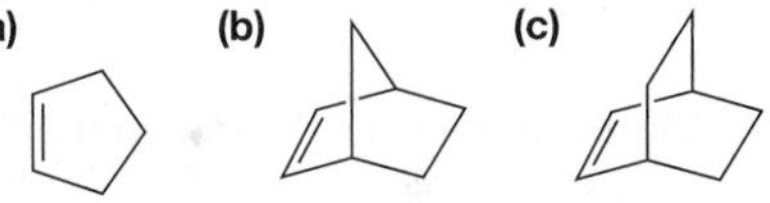

28.19 As discussed in Section 28.3, polymerization of propene with a Ziegler–Natta catalyst can produce isotactic or syndiotactic polypropylene. Do you expect either of these polymers to be optically active? Why or why not?

28.20 Propene can undergo polymerization with a Ziegler–Natta catalyst to produce isotactic or syndiotactic forms (Section 28.3). Polymerization of 2-methylpropene [$CH_2{=}C(CH_3)_2$], however, does not produce isotactic or syndiotactic forms. Explain why not.

28.21 Draw the product of each of the following Ziegler–Natta polymerization reactions. The specific form of each polymer product is indicated. You may assume that monomers alternate in a copolymer.

(a)

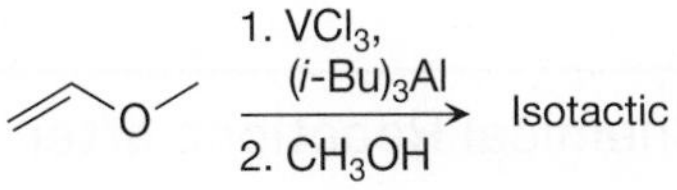

(b)

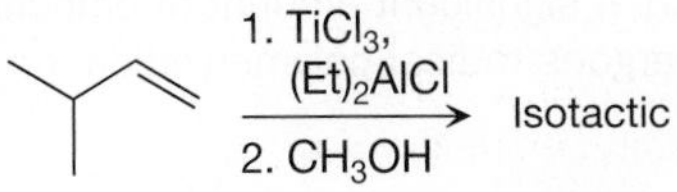

(c)

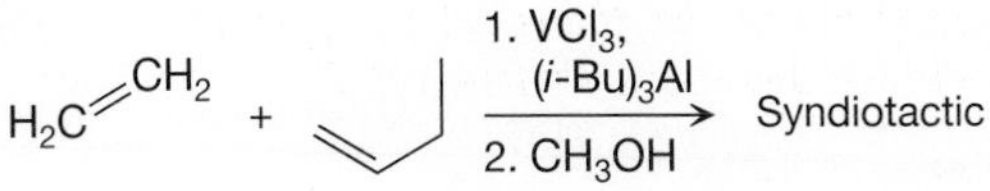

Section 28.5 Step-Growth Polymerization

28.22 **(SYN)** Propose a synthesis for each of the following polymers.

(a)

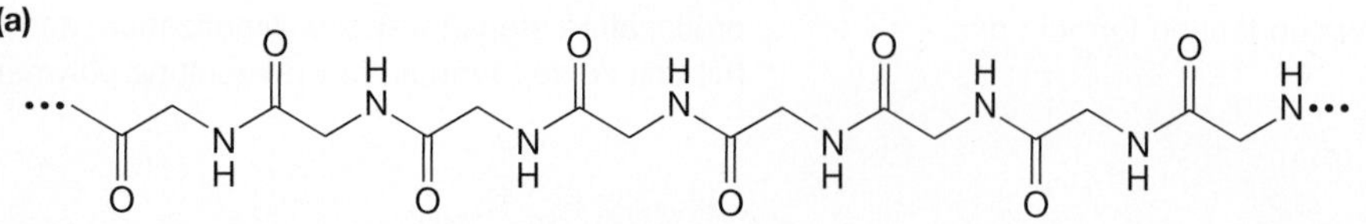

Polyglycine

(b)

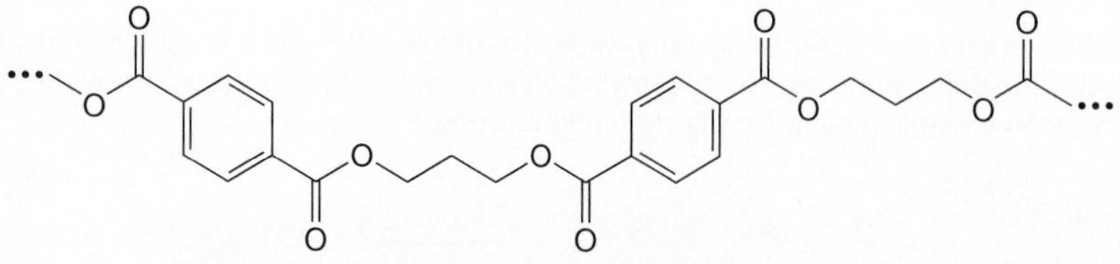

Poly(trimethylene terephthalate)

28.23 Nylon-6,6 (see Eq. 28-30, p. 1375) can also be synthesized from adipoyl chloride and hexane-1,6-diamine, as shown below. What are the two products of this reaction?

$$Cl-\overset{O}{\overset{\|}{C}}CH_2CH_2CH_2CH_2\overset{O}{\overset{\|}{C}}-Cl \; + \; H_2NCH_2CH_2CH_2CH_2CH_2CH_2NH_2 \longrightarrow \; ?$$

28.24 **(SYN)** The polymer shown is an example of a polycarbonate, and it can be made by transesterification. Show how this polymer can be synthesized from its monomers.

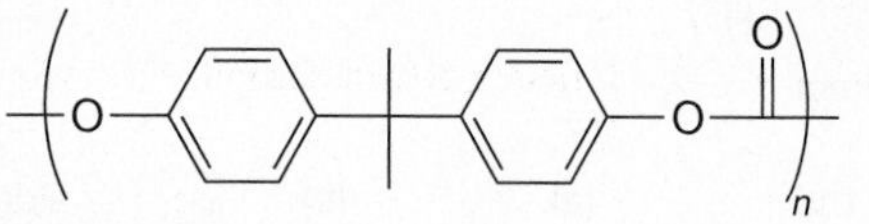

28.25 Nylon-11 can be synthesized by polymerization of 11-aminoundecanoic acid. Draw the condensed formula for nylon-11.

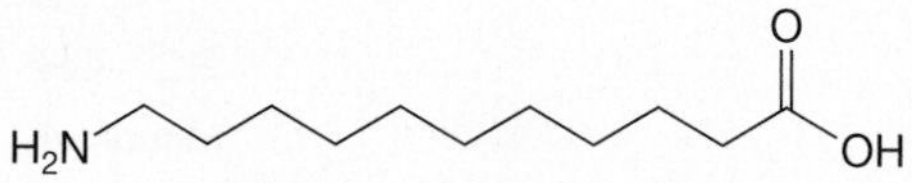

11-Aminoundecanoic acid

28.26 Draw the condensed formula of the polymer produced from each reaction.

(a)

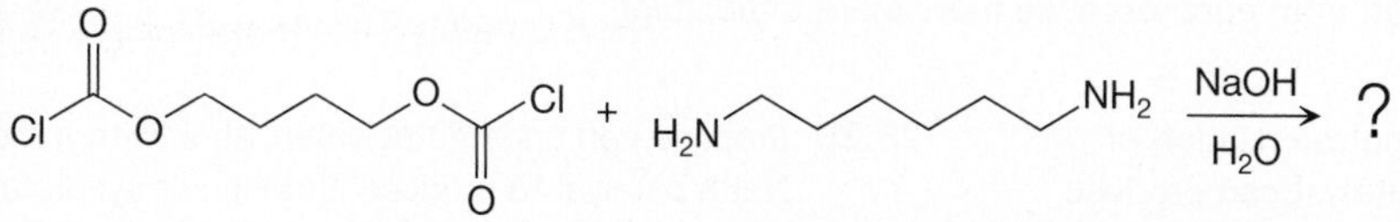
NaOH
H2O

(b)

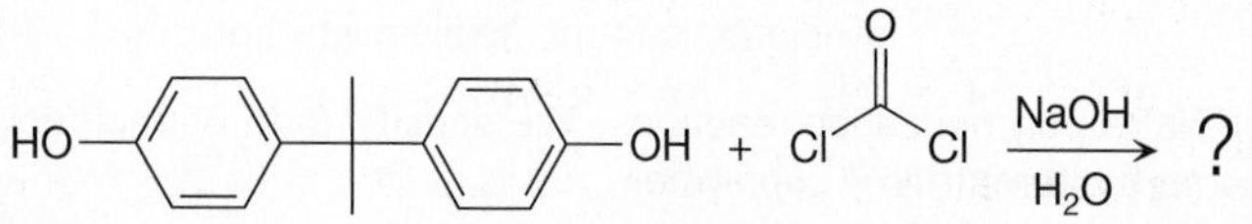
NaOH
H2O

Sections 28.6–28.8 Linear, Branched, and Network Polymers; Chemical Reactions after Polymerization

28.27 When polyethylene is made by radical polymerization, the resulting polymer has a significant amount of branching, resulting in low-density polyethylene (see Section 28.11a). When styrene undergoes radical polymerization, on the other hand, very little branching occurs. Explain this phenomenon.

28.28 When treated with acid, aziridine will undergo ring-opening polymerization to produce branched polyethylenimine. Draw the mechanism that shows how a tetramer can be produced, in which three monomers form a chain and the fourth forms a branch.

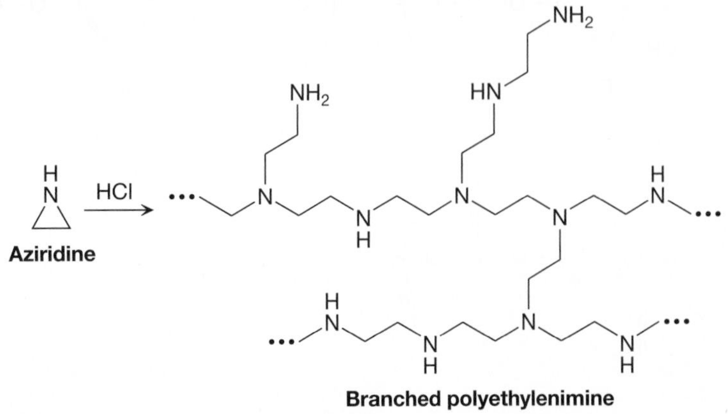

HCl
Aziridine
Branched polyethylenimine

28.29 **(SYN)** Poly(ethylene terephthalate) is a linear polyester that can be synthesized from the condensation polymerization between terephthalic acid and ethylene glycol, as shown previously in Equation 28-33 (p. 1378). What alcohol would you react with terephthalic acid to produce a *branched* polyester? Draw a portion of the resulting polymer that shows a main chain and one branching point.

28.30 **(SYN)** To synthesize linear polyethylenimine instead of the branched form (see Problem 28.28), 2-ethyl-2-oxazoline can undergo ring-opening polymerization followed by a chemical modification of the side groups. Propose how to carry out the chemical modification after polymerization.

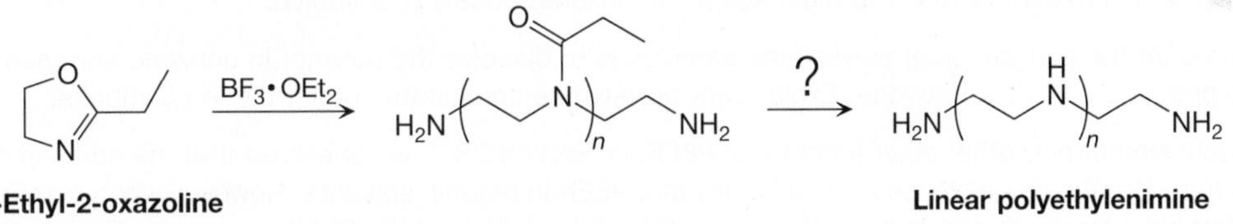

$BF_3 \cdot OEt_2$
?
2-Ethyl-2-oxazoline
Linear polyethylenimine

28.31 **(SYN)** Propose a synthesis of poly(vinyl amine) that involves the polymerization of *N*-vinylformamide. Can poly(vinyl amine) be produced by polymerizing vinyl amine ($H_2C{=}CH{-}NH_2$)? Explain.

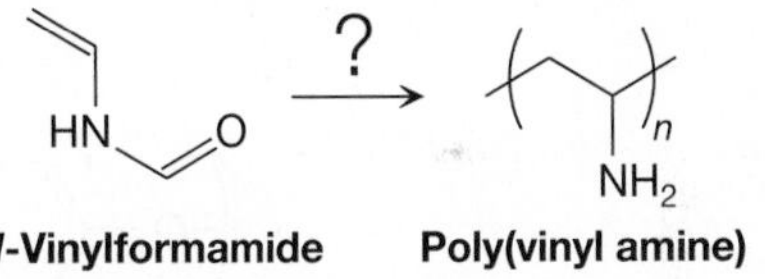

?
N-Vinylformamide
Poly(vinyl amine)

Sections 28.9 and 28.10 General Aspects of Polymer Structure; Properties of Polymers

28.32 Classify the molecules in Problems 28.13 (p. 1414) and 28.22 (p. 1416) as either carbon-chain or heterochain polymers. Identify the repeating unit in each polymer, and draw the condensed formula.

28.33 On the basis of functional groups, identify the class of polymer for the polymers in Problems 28.13 and 28.22.

28.34 Consider the following series of poly(phenylene oxide) polymers **A–D** and their glass transition temperatures. Explain how the differences in structure can account for the differences in T_g.

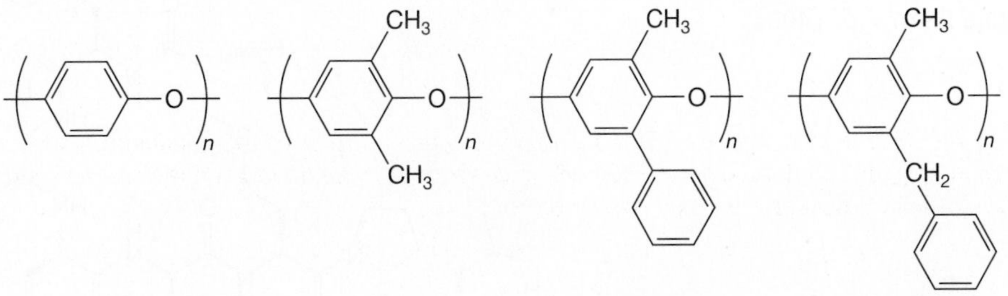

A T_g = 82 °C   **B** T_g = 211 °C   **C** T_g = 169 °C   **D** T_g = 99 °C

28.35 Consider polycarbonate polymers **E–G**. **(a)** Which one has the highest T_g? **(b)** Which one has the lowest T_g?

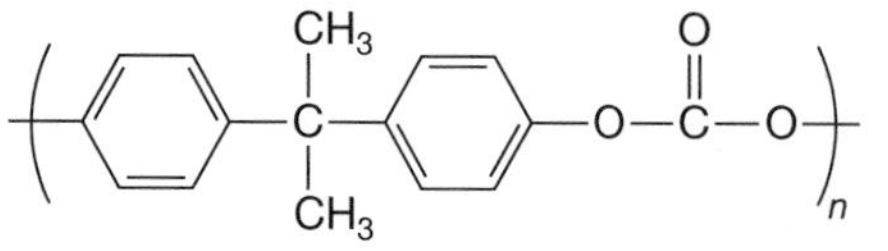

E

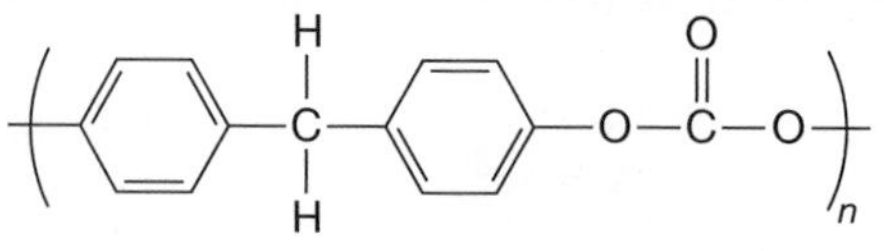

F

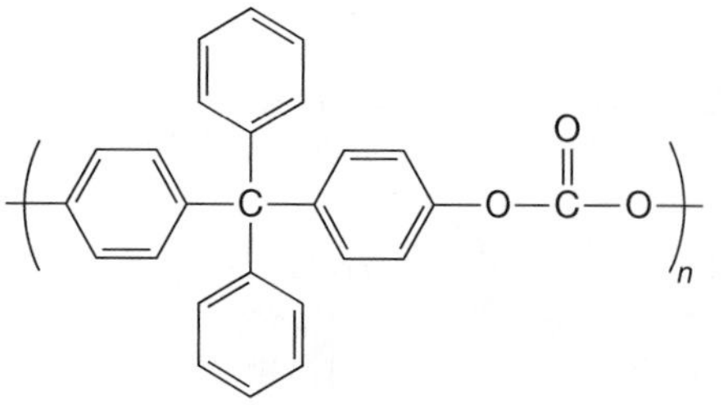

G

28.36 Which polymer do you think has the higher T_g, Kevlar (see Solved Problem 28.4, p. 1377) or the polyphthalamide described in the accompanying Try It exercise? Explain your reasoning.

28.37 Poly(vinyl alcohol), PVA, is produced from poly(vinyl acetate) by converting the acetate groups into hydroxyl groups (Section 28.7). As the number of hydroxyl groups in PVA increases, the solubility of the polymer in water decreases. How do you explain this behavior?

28.38 Which polymer in Problem 28.3 (p. 1413) is the most soluble in ethanol? Justify your choice.

28.39 Which polymer in Problem 28.3 is the most soluble in hexane? Justify your choice.

28.40 One method for the purification of polystyrene samples is to dissolve the polymer in benzene and then add methanol slowly to precipitate solid polystyrene. Explain why polystyrene precipitates under these conditions.

28.41 In the discussion of poly(ether ether ketone), or PEEK, in Section 28.7, we observed that the addition of a *tert*-butyl group to the aromatic ring increases the solubility of a PEEK in organic solvents. However, when researchers added a second *tert*-butyl group, as shown here, they found that the solubility of the PEEK decreased. Explain this observation.

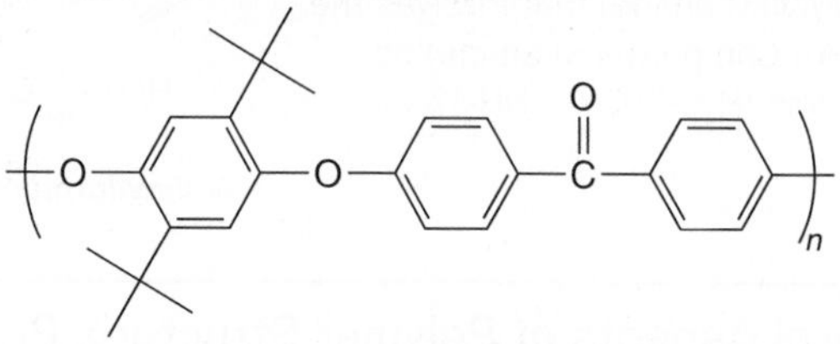

A PEEK with two *tert*-butyl groups per repeating unit

Section 28.13 The Organic Chemistry of Biomolecules

28.42 The line structure of oxytocin, a hormone that regulates childbirth and breastfeeding, is shown here. **(a)** Identify the disulfide bond, and **(b)** write the primary structure of oxytocin in abbreviated form, similar to Figure 28-47a (p. 1405).

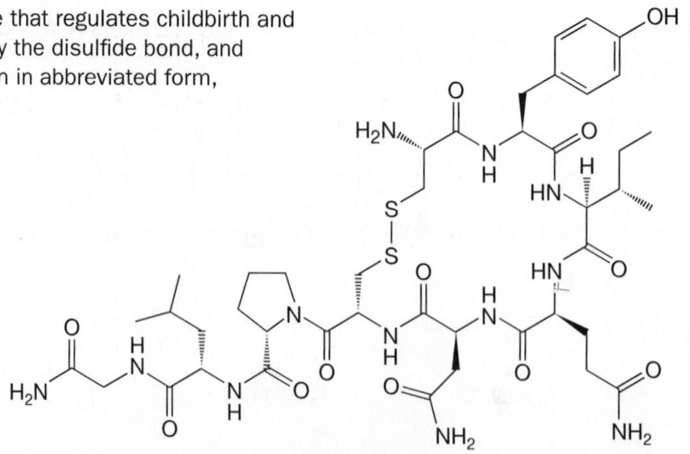

Oxytocin

28.43 Some polypeptides can dimerize to form a coiled coil, a structural motif where one α-helix wraps around another (shown here). Typically the primary structure of each polypeptide has a seven-amino-acid repeating pattern, in which the first and third amino acids are hydrophobic. As a result, a stripe of hydrophobic side chains extends down the length of each α-helix. Explain how this stabilizes the coiled coil in an aqueous environment.

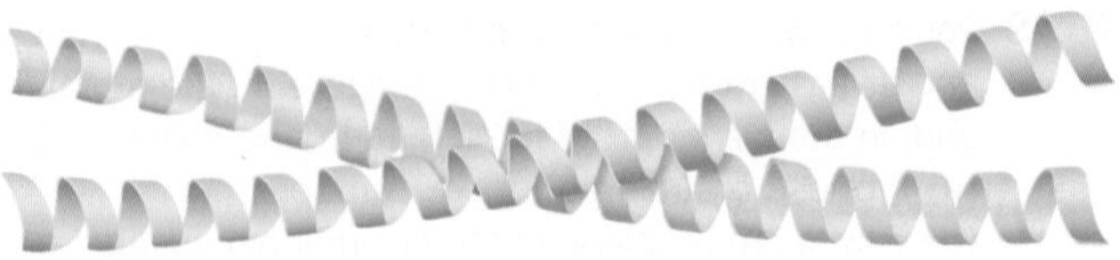

28.44 Much of the strength of silk, a natural protein fiber, is attributed to β-pleated sheets stacking to form a crystalline structure. The sequence within those sheets exhibits a repeating pattern, Gly-Ser-Gly-Ala-Gly-Ala. Why do you think these amino acids are prevalent in those crystalline structures?

28.45 Arabinoxylan is a copolymer of arabinose and xylose, two five-carbon sugars. A portion of the polysaccharide is shown here. **(a)** Identify and classify each glycosidic linkage. **(b)** On the basis of the structure, do you think arabinoxylan functions as a storage polysaccharide or a structural polysaccharide? Explain your reasoning.

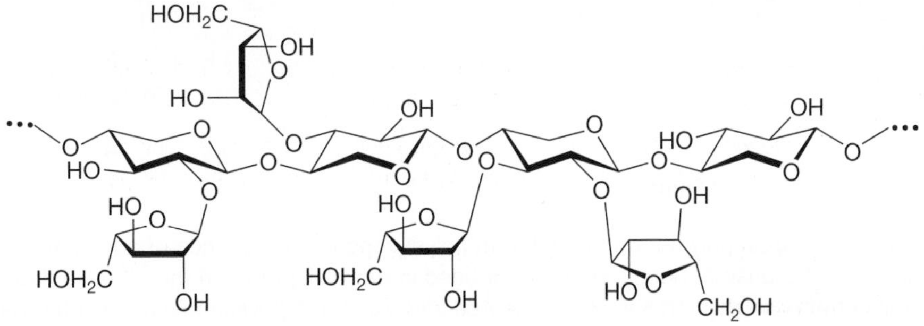

Integrated Problems

28.46 Methyl acrylate and methyl methacrylate react with radical initiators (R•) as shown here. The difference in their reactivities in radical polymerizations is dramatic. For example, methyl acrylate is less reactive with radicals than is methyl methacrylate, but radicals formed from methyl acrylate are more reactive than those formed from methyl methacrylate. In other words, **C** is more reactive than **A**, and **B** is more reactive than **D**. Explain these observations. *Hint*: Draw an energy diagram for the two reactions.

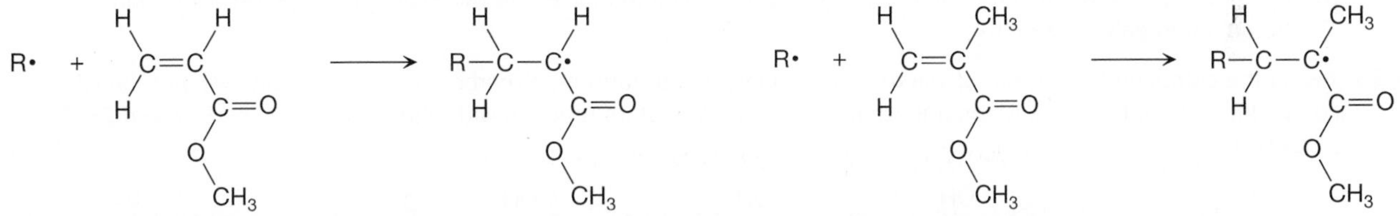

Methyl acrylate **A** | **B** | **Methyl methacrylate** **C** | **D**

28.47 A polymer closely related to PET is PBT, which is made from terephthalic acid and butane-1,4-diol.
(a) Propose a structure for PBT, and write the condensed formula for the structure.
(b) What does PBT stand for? That is, what do you expect the trivial name of PBT to be?
(c) Would you expect PBT to have a higher or lower melting point than PET? Justify your answer.
(d) PBT, rather than PET, is used in molding because it crystallizes faster. Explain why PBT crystallizes more quickly than PET.

28.48 Propose a mechanism for the following reaction, which is a synthesis of PEEK (see Section 28.7).

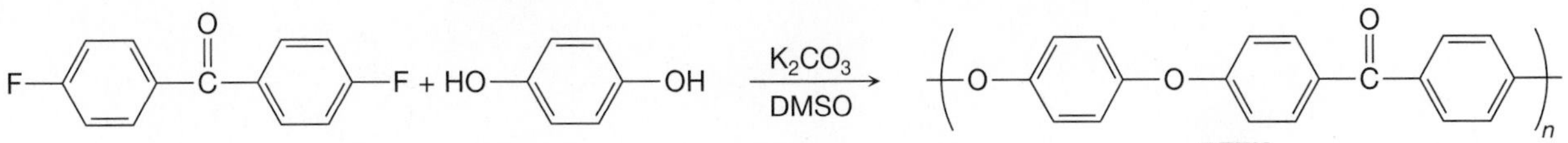

PEEK

28.49 Polycarbophil is a dietary fiber supplement. It is the calcium salt of a copolymer of acrylic acid and divinyl glycol, a cross-linking agent. In the stomach, the calcium ions exchange for protons and, in the higher pH of the intestine, the polymer absorbs 70 times its mass in water.
(a) Propose a structure for polycarbophil.
(b) Why is cross-linking of the polymer necessary for this application?
(c) Why is polycarbophil effective at providing bulk in the intestine? That is, what occurs on a molecular level to polycarbophil?

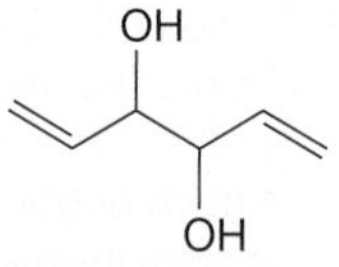
OH
OH
Divinyl glycol

28.50 Bakelite, one of the first synthetic plastics, was briefly discussed in the chapter (see Equation 28-36, p. 1381). Draw the mechanism showing how the "dimer" and "trimer" below are formed. (You may assume acidic conditions.)

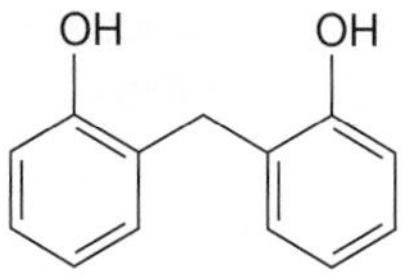
OH
OH
"Dimer"

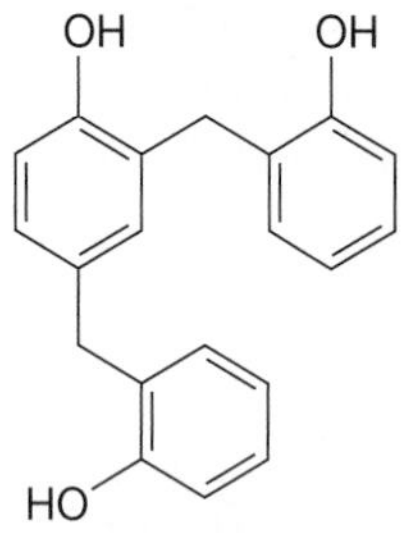
OH
OH
HO
"Trimer"

28.51 Dry-erase boards, or whiteboards, in classrooms consist of a network polymer similar to Bakelite that is made from formaldehyde and melamine.
(a) Propose a structure for the polymer formed.
(b) Why is this type of polymer suitable for use in whiteboards?

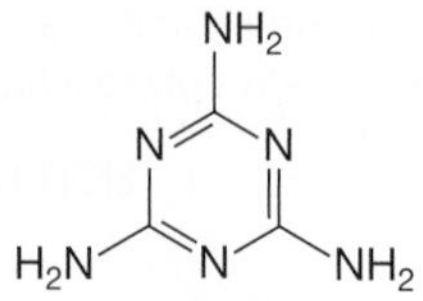
NH_2
N
N
H_2N
N
NH_2
Melamine

28.52 Styrene can *autoinitiate* radical polymerization and form polystyrene in the absence of an initiator. At temperatures >100 °C, radicals form because of homolysis of the π bond in the vinyl group. In the study of this reaction, researchers have found 1,2-diphenylcyclobutane in samples of heated styrene. The following mechanism for the formation of 1,2-diphenylcyclobutane has been proposed:

Step 1: Homolysis of the vinyl π bond in a styrene molecule
Step 2: Homolysis of the vinyl π bond in a second styrene molecule
Step 3: Tail-to-tail addition of the radicals from Steps 1 and 2
Step 4: Radical coupling of the diradical formed in Step 3

(a) Use curved arrow notation to show the steps in this mechanism.
(b) Are the steps in this mechanism consistent with those for radical polymerization?
(c) Why is the use of an initiator such as benzoyl peroxide more efficient in the synthesis of polystyrene than autoinitiated polymerization?

28.53 Two of the compounds **X**, **Y**, and **Z** will react with phosgene to form a polycarbonate; the third one will not. Which compound will *not* form a polymer, and what will the product of its reaction with phosgene be? (See Problem 28.23, p. 1416.)

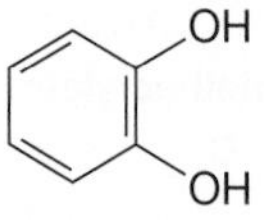
OH
OH
X

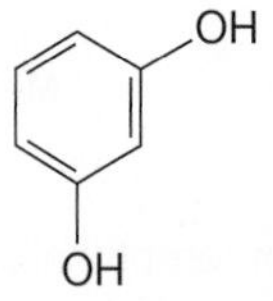
OH
OH
Y

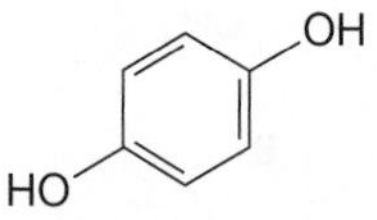
OH
HO
Z

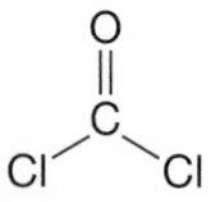
O
C
Cl
Cl
Phosgene

28.54 **(SYN)** Urea has the structure shown here. Polyureas are used to make truck bed liners. Examine the synthesis of polyurethanes in Section 28.5 (Eq. 28-35, p. 1379), then **(a)** propose a synthesis of a polyurea, and **(b)** draw the condensed formula for the polymer.

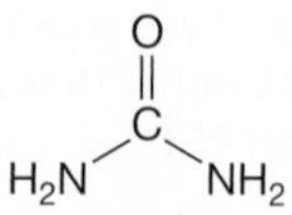
O
C
H_2N
NH_2
Urea

28.55 Poly(vinyl chloride), PVC, degrades under heat to eliminate HCl, according to the reaction below. Once the double bonds begin to form, subsequent eliminations of HCl from the polymer chain occur more readily, and the molecule "unzips" to form a polyene.

(a) Provide a mechanism for the reaction that forms the first double bond. You may assume it is the one on the very left of the structure below.

(b) Explain why subsequent eliminations of HCl occur more readily after the first elimination.

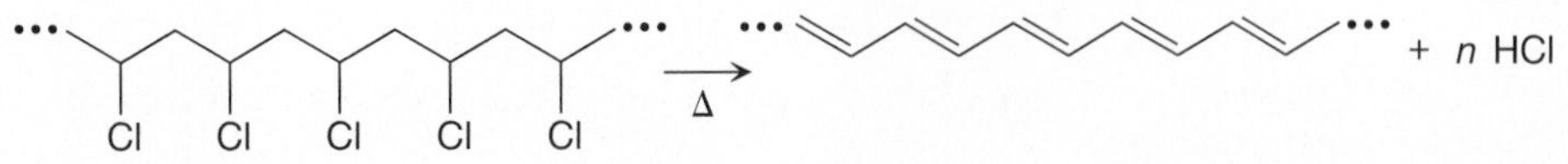

Cl
Cl
Cl
Cl
Cl
Δ
+ n HCl

28.56 Research in the "unzipping" of poly(vinyl chloride) (see Problem 28.55) indicates that certain defects in the polymer contribute to the rate of unzipping. These defects are arrangements of atoms that are different from the arrangements in the repeating unit shown in the condensed formula. Researchers have found that defects involving allylic chlorides and tertiary chlorides, specifically, promote the reaction. Review the mechanism for the unzipping and explain this observation.

28.57 Explain how IR spectroscopy could be used to monitor the conversion of poly(vinyl acetate) to poly(vinyl alcohol). That is, how can a chemist use IR to tell if poly(vinyl acetate) has been converted to $>$99% poly(vinyl alcohol)?

APPENDIX A

Values of pK_a for Various Acids[a]

Acid	Conjugate Base	pK_a
$F_3C-S(=O)_2-OH$ Trifluoromethanesulfonic acid (TfOH)	$F_3C-S(=O)_2-O^{\ominus}$	–13
HI Hydroiodic acid	$I^{\ominus}$	–10
$HO-S(=O)_2-OH$ Sulfuric acid	$HO-S(=O)_2-O^{\ominus}$	–9
HBr Hydrobromic acid	$Br^{\ominus}$	–9
HCl Hydrochloric acid	$Cl^{\ominus}$	–7
$p\text{-}CH_3C_6H_4-S(=O)_2-OH$ *p*-Toluenesulfonic acid (TsOH)	$p\text{-}CH_3C_6H_4-S(=O)_2-O^{\ominus}$	–2.8
$H_3C-S(=O)_2-OH$ Methanesulfonic acid (MsOH)	$H_3C-S(=O)_2-O^{\ominus}$	–2
$H_3O^{\oplus}$ Hydronium ion	H_2O	0.0[b]
$F_3C-C(=O)-OH$ Trifluoroethanoic acid (Trifluoroacetic acid)	$F_3C-C(=O)-O^{\ominus}$	0.0
$Cl_3C-C(=O)-OH$ Trichloroethanoic acid (Trichloroacetic acid)	$Cl_3C-C(=O)-O^{\ominus}$	0.77
$H_2ClC-C(=O)-OH$ Chloroethanoic acid (Chloroacetic acid)	$H_2ClC-C(=O)-O^{\ominus}$	2.87
HF Hydrofluoric acid	$F^{\ominus}$	3.2
$H-C(=O)-OH$ Methanoic acid (Formic acid)	$H-C(=O)-O^{\ominus}$	3.75
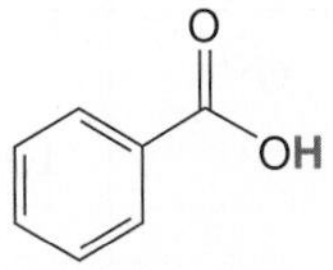 Benzoic acid	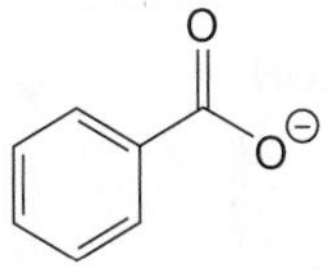	4.2
$CH_3-C(=O)-OH$ Ethanoic acid (Acetic acid)	$CH_3-C(=O)-O^{\ominus}$	4.75
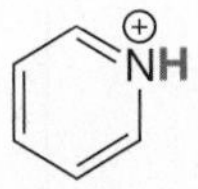 Pyridinium ion	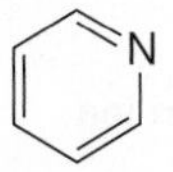	5.2
$HO-C(=O)-OH$ Carbonic acid	$^{\ominus}O-C(=O)-O^{\ominus}$	6.3

(continued)

Acid	Conjugate Base	pK_a
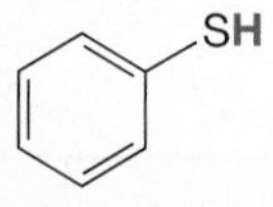 Thiophenol	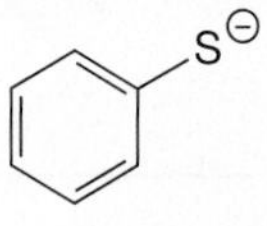	6.6
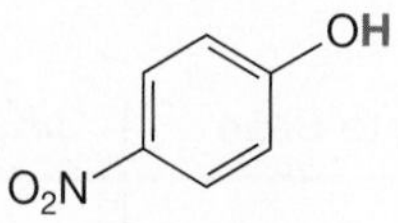 4-Nitrophenol	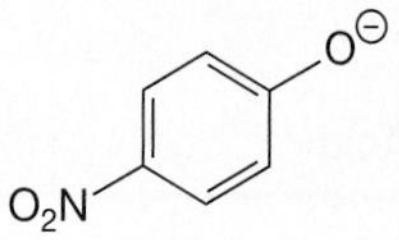	7.2
H_2S Hydrogen sulfide	$HS^{\ominus}$	7.2
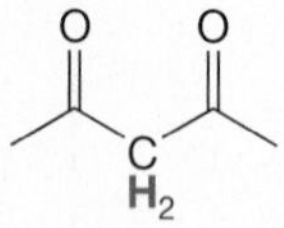 2,4-Pentanedione	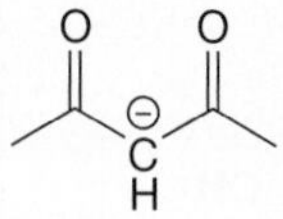	8.9
N≡C—H Hydrocyanic acid	$N{\equiv}C^{\ominus}$	9.2
$H_4N^{\oplus}$ Ammonium ion	NH_3	9.4
$(CH_3)_3\overset{\oplus}{N}H$ Trimethylammonium ion	$(CH_3)_3N$	9.8
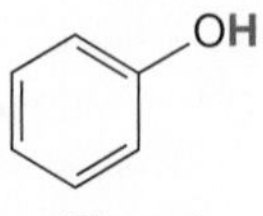 Phenol	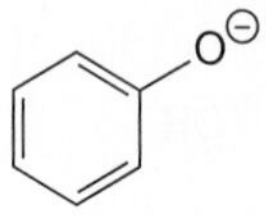	10.0
$O_2N—CH_3$ Nitromethane	$O_2N—\overset{\ominus}{C}H_2$	10.2
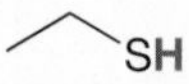 Ethanethiol	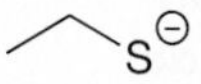	10.6
$H_3C—\overset{\oplus}{N}H_3$ Methylammonium ion	$H_3C—NH_2$	10.63
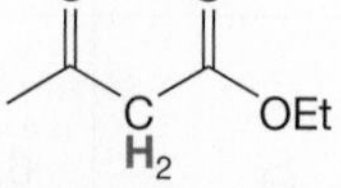 Ethyl 3-oxobutanoate (Acetoacetic ester)	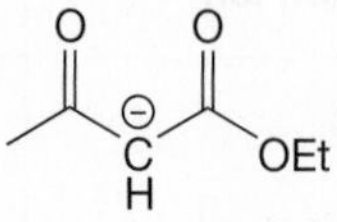	11
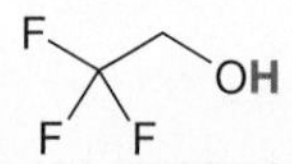 2,2,2-Trifluoroethanol	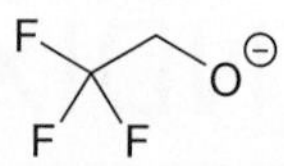	12.4
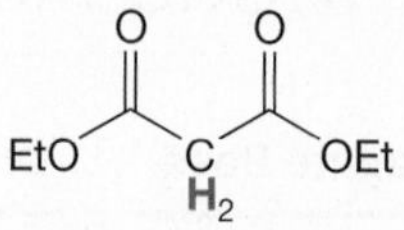 Diethyl propanedioate (Diethyl malonate)	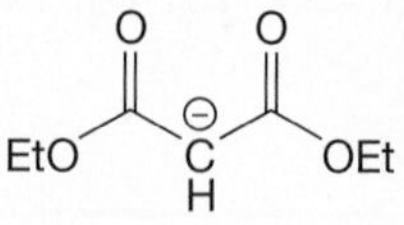	13.5
H_2O Water	$HO^{\ominus}$	14.0[b]
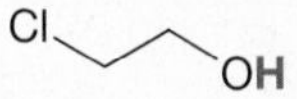 2-Chloroethanol	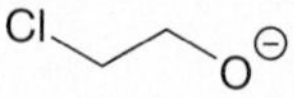	14.3
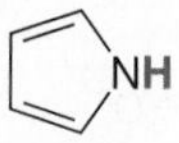 Pyrrole	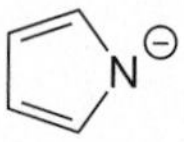	15
CH_3OH Methanol	$CH_3O^{\ominus}$	15.5
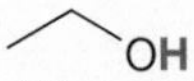 Ethanol	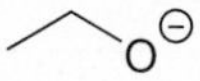	16
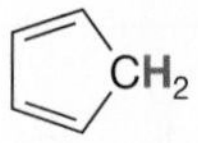 Cyclopentadiene	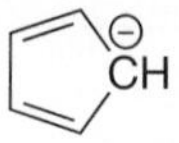	16
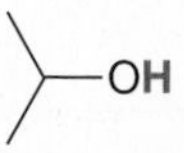 Propan-2-ol (Isopropyl alcohol)	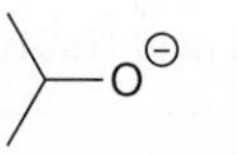	16.5
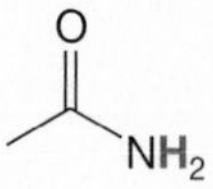 Ethanamide (Acetamide)	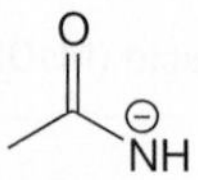	17
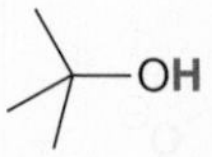 Methylpropan-2-ol (*tert*-Butyl alcohol)	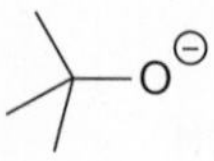	19

Acid	Conjugate Base	pK_a	Acid	Conjugate Base	pK_a
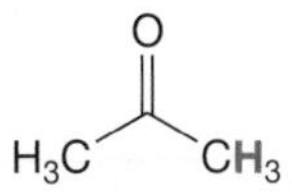 **Propanone (Acetone)**	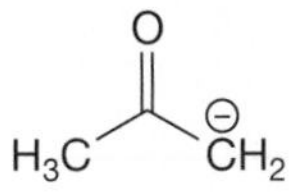	20	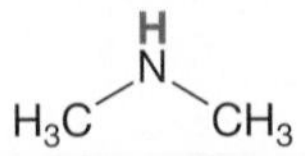 ***N*-Methylmethanamine (Dimethylamine)**	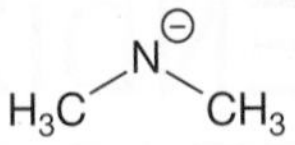	38
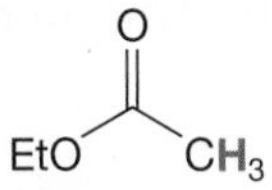 **Ethyl ethanoate (Ethyl acetate)**	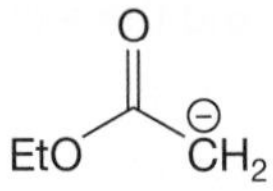	25	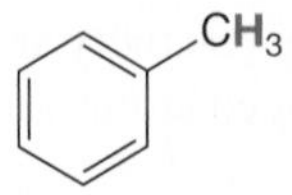 **Toluene (Methylbenzene)**	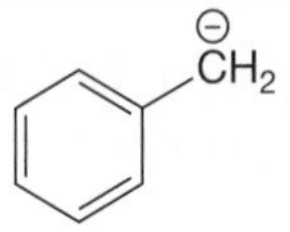	40
$N\equiv C-CH_3$ **Ethanenitrile (Acetonitrile)**	$N\equiv C-\overset{\ominus}{C}H_2$	25	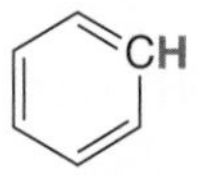 **Benzene**	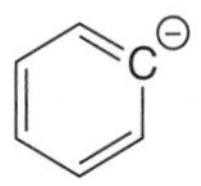	43
$HC\equiv CH$ **Ethyne (Acetylene)**	$HC\equiv C^{\ominus}$	25	$H_2C=CH_2$ **Ethene (Ethylene)**	$H_2C=\overset{\ominus}{C}H$	44
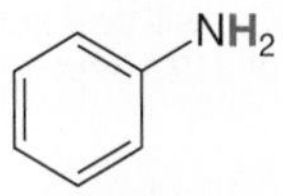 **Aniline (Phenylamine)**	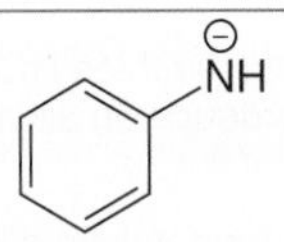	27	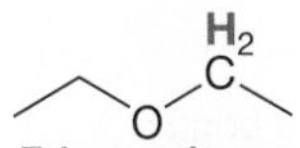 **Ethoxyethane (Diethyl ether)**	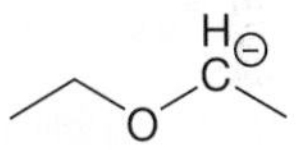	45
H_2 **Hydrogen gas**	$H^{\ominus}$	35	CH_3 **Methane**	$H_3C^{\ominus}$	48
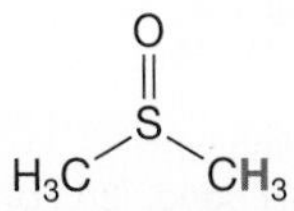 **Dimethyl sulfoxide**	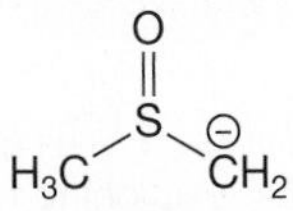	35	CH_3CH_3 **Ethane**	$CH_3\overset{\ominus}{C}H_2$	50
NH_3 **Ammonia**	$H_2N^{\ominus}$	36			

[a]pK_a = –log K_a. The less positive (or more negative) the pK_a value, the stronger the acid relative to another acid.
[b]In older textbooks, the pK_a values of H_3O^+ and H_2O are reported to be –1.7 and 15.7, respectively, but by definition they are 0 and 14.

APPENDIX B

Characteristic Reactivities of Particular Compound Classes

For each compound class, distinct types of reactivity are highlighted in blue, and the sections in which the types of reactivity are discussed appear in parentheses. Halogen atoms are represented by X.

Alkanes

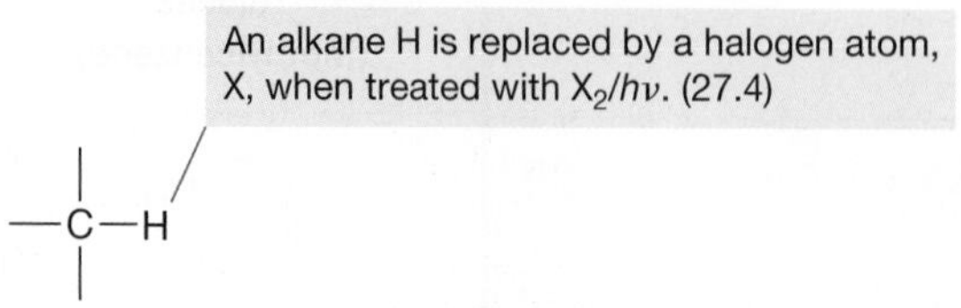
An alkane H is replaced by a halogen atom, X, when treated with $X_2/h\nu$. (27.4)
C
H

Alkenes

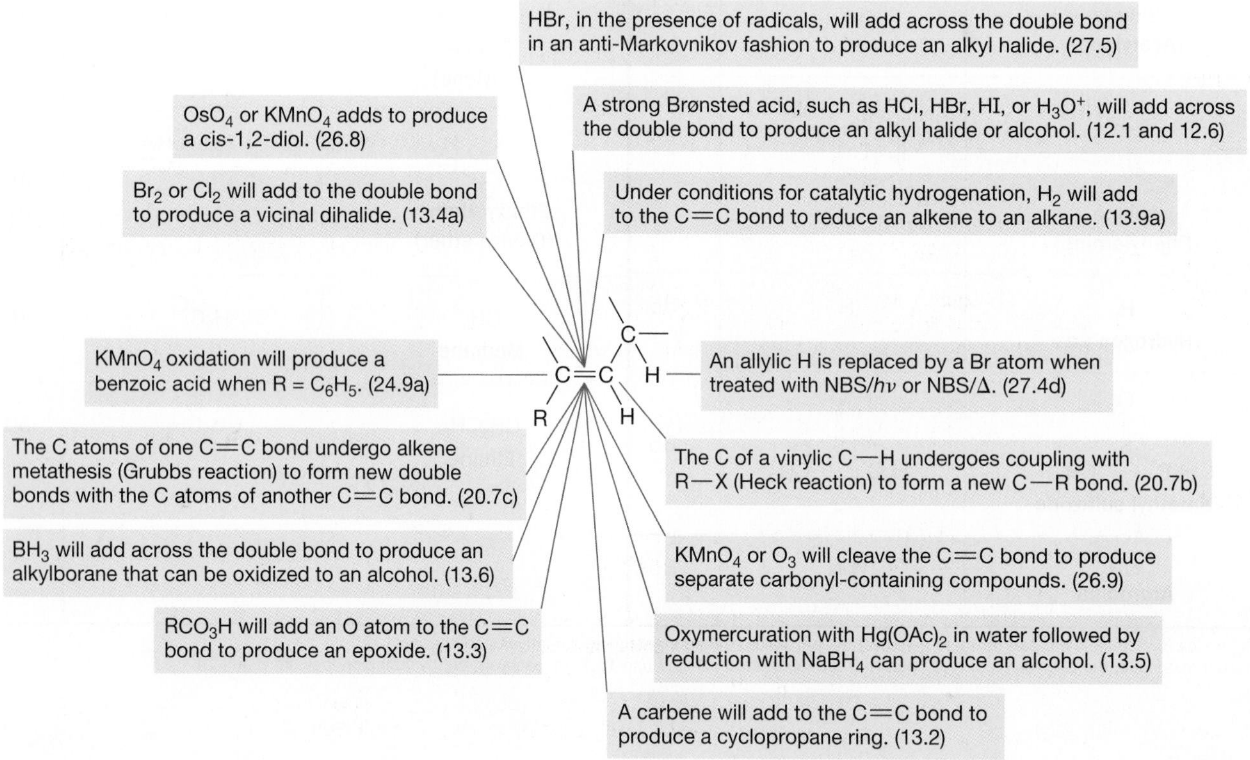
HBr, in the presence of radicals, will add across the double bond in an anti-Markovnikov fashion to produce an alkyl halide. (27.5)
OsO_4 or $KMnO_4$ adds to produce a cis-1,2-diol. (26.8)
A strong Brønsted acid, such as HCl, HBr, HI, or H_3O^+, will add across the double bond to produce an alkyl halide or alcohol. (12.1 and 12.6)
Br_2 or Cl_2 will add to the double bond to produce a vicinal dihalide. (13.4a)
Under conditions for catalytic hydrogenation, H_2 will add to the C=C bond to reduce an alkene to an alkane. (13.9a)
$KMnO_4$ oxidation will produce a benzoic acid when R = C_6H_5. (24.9a)
An allylic H is replaced by a Br atom when treated with NBS/$h\nu$ or NBS/Δ. (27.4d)
C=C
C
H
R
H
The C atoms of one C=C bond undergo alkene metathesis (Grubbs reaction) to form new double bonds with the C atoms of another C=C bond. (20.7c)
The C of a vinylic C—H undergoes coupling with R—X (Heck reaction) to form a new C—R bond. (20.7b)
BH_3 will add across the double bond to produce an alkylborane that can be oxidized to an alcohol. (13.6)
$KMnO_4$ or O_3 will cleave the C=C bond to produce separate carbonyl-containing compounds. (26.9)
RCO_3H will add an O atom to the C=C bond to produce an epoxide. (13.3)
Oxymercuration with $Hg(OAc)_2$ in water followed by reduction with $NaBH_4$ can produce an alcohol. (13.5)
A carbene will add to the C=C bond to produce a cyclopropane ring. (13.2)

Alkynes

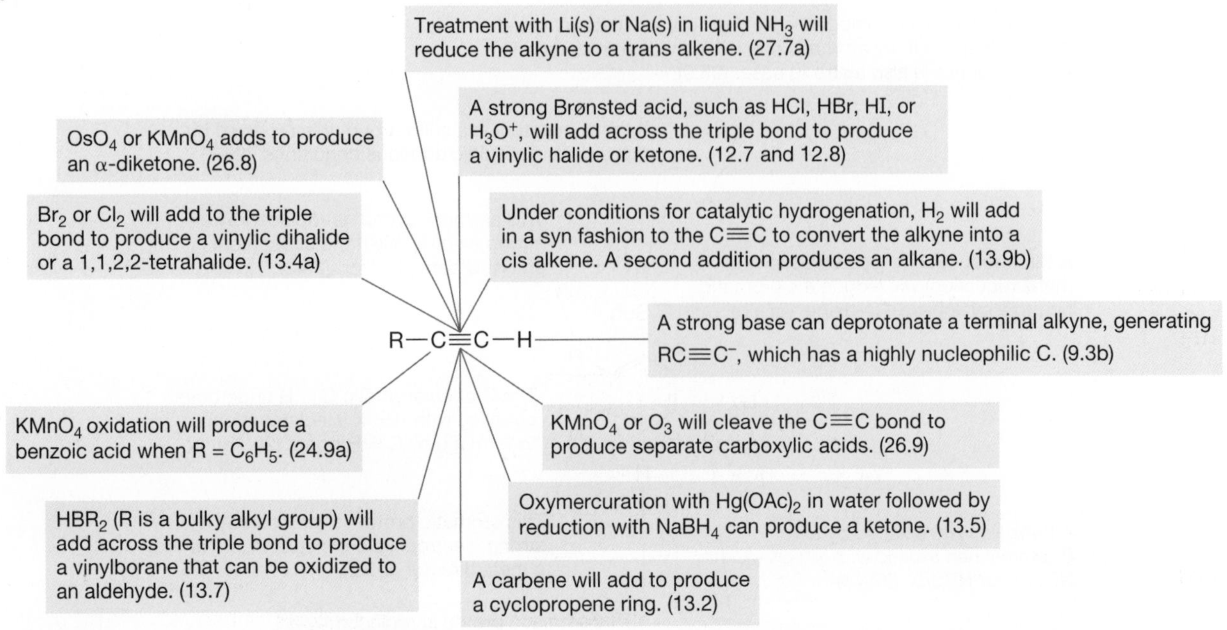
Treatment with Li(s) or Na(s) in liquid NH_3 will reduce the alkyne to a trans alkene. (27.7a)
OsO_4 or $KMnO_4$ adds to produce an α-diketone. (26.8)
A strong Brønsted acid, such as HCl, HBr, HI, or H_3O^+, will add across the triple bond to produce a vinylic halide or ketone. (12.7 and 12.8)
Br_2 or Cl_2 will add to the triple bond to produce a vinylic dihalide or a 1,1,2,2-tetrahalide. (13.4a)
Under conditions for catalytic hydrogenation, H_2 will add in a syn fashion to the C≡C to convert the alkyne into a cis alkene. A second addition produces an alkane. (13.9b)
R—C≡C—H
A strong base can deprotonate a terminal alkyne, generating $RC{\equiv}C^-$, which has a highly nucleophilic C. (9.3b)
$KMnO_4$ oxidation will produce a benzoic acid when R = C_6H_5. (24.9a)
$KMnO_4$ or O_3 will cleave the C≡C bond to produce separate carboxylic acids. (26.9)
HBR_2 (R is a bulky alkyl group) will add across the triple bond to produce a vinylborane that can be oxidized to an aldehyde. (13.7)
Oxymercuration with $Hg(OAc)_2$ in water followed by reduction with $NaBH_4$ can produce a ketone. (13.5)
A carbene will add to produce a cyclopropene ring. (13.2)

Alkyl halides

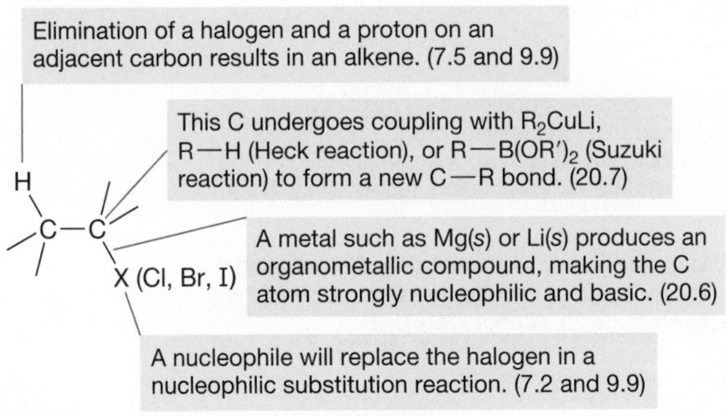
Elimination of a halogen and a proton on an adjacent carbon results in an alkene. (7.5 and 9.9)
This C undergoes coupling with R_2CuLi, R—H (Heck reaction), or R—B(OR′)$_2$ (Suzuki reaction) to form a new C—R bond. (20.7)
H
C
C
X (Cl, Br, I)
A metal such as Mg(s) or Li(s) produces an organometallic compound, making the C atom strongly nucleophilic and basic. (20.6)
A nucleophile will replace the halogen in a nucleophilic substitution reaction. (7.2 and 9.9)

Ethers

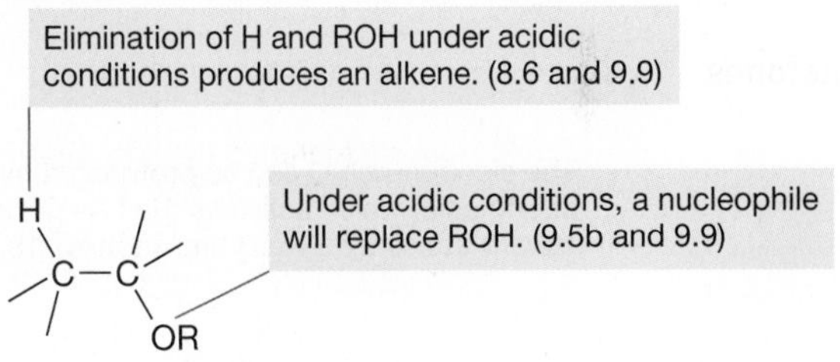
Elimination of H and ROH under acidic conditions produces an alkene. (8.6 and 9.9)
H
C
C
OR
Under acidic conditions, a nucleophile will replace ROH. (9.5b and 9.9)

Alcohols

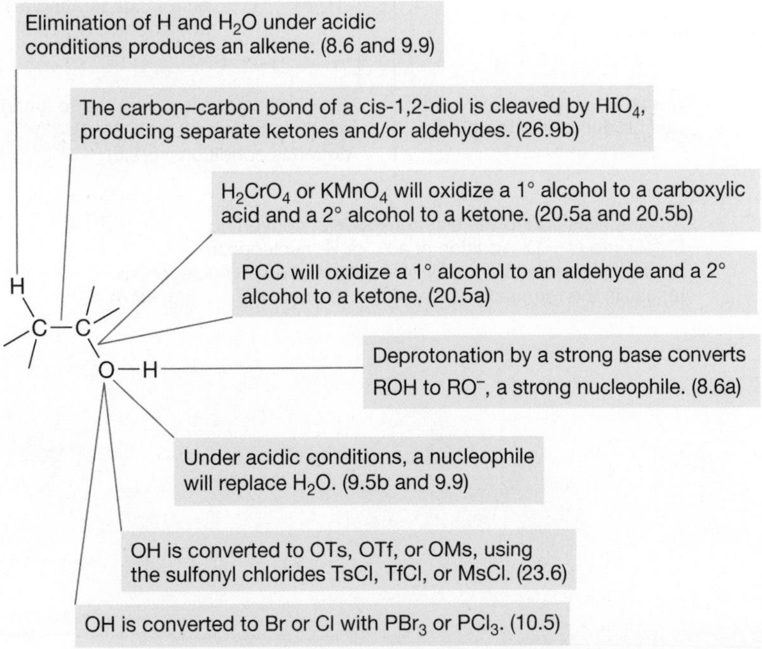
Elimination of H and H_2O under acidic conditions produces an alkene. (8.6 and 9.9)
The carbon–carbon bond of a cis-1,2-diol is cleaved by HIO_4, producing separate ketones and/or aldehydes. (26.9b)
H_2CrO_4 or $KMnO_4$ will oxidize a 1° alcohol to a carboxylic acid and a 2° alcohol to a ketone. (20.5a and 20.5b)
PCC will oxidize a 1° alcohol to an aldehyde and a 2° alcohol to a ketone. (20.5a)
H
C
C
O—H
Deprotonation by a strong base converts ROH to RO^-, a strong nucleophile. (8.6a)
Under acidic conditions, a nucleophile will replace H_2O. (9.5b and 9.9)
OH is converted to OTs, OTf, or OMs, using the sulfonyl chlorides TsCl, TfCl, or MsCl. (23.6)
OH is converted to Br or Cl with PBr_3 or PCl_3. (10.5)

Aromatic rings

If the substituent is a halogen leaving group, it can be replaced by a nucleophile if the aromatic ring is highly deactivated or if the nucleophile is also a strong base. (25.9)

If the subsitutent is a sulfo group, it is replaced by a proton under acidic aqueous conditions. (24.7)

This aromatic proton is replaced by a strong electrophile if the substituent is an ortho/para director. (25.2)

A Birch reduction (a type of dissolving metal reduction) will reduce the aromatic ring to a cyclohexa-1,4-diene. (27.7b)

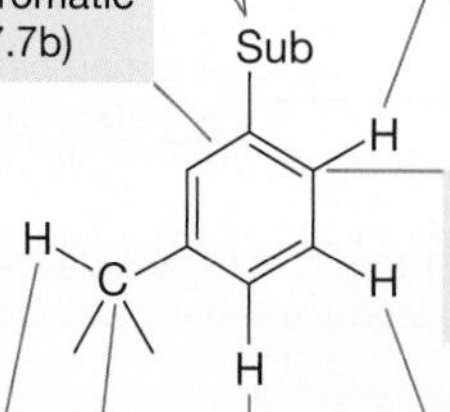
Sub
H
H
C
H
H

The C of an aromatic C—H undergoes coupling with R—X (Heck reaction) to form a new C—R bond. (20.7b)

This aromatic proton is replaced by a strong electrophile if the substituent is a meta director. (25.2)

A benzylic H is replaced by a Br atom when treated with NBS/$h\nu$ or NBS/Δ. (27.4d)

A benzylic C is oxidized to a benzoic acid using $KMnO_4$. (24.9)

This aromatic proton is replaced by a strong electrophile if the substituent is an ortho/para director. (25.2)

Ketones

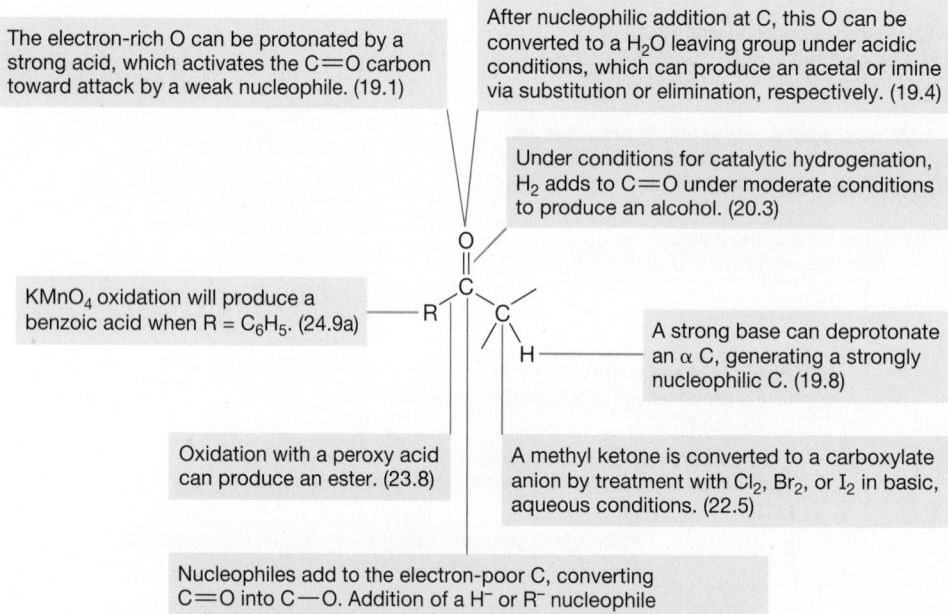

The electron-rich O can be protonated by a strong acid, which activates the C═O carbon toward attack by a weak nucleophile. (19.1)

After nucleophilic addition at C, this O can be converted to a H_2O leaving group under acidic conditions, which can produce an acetal or imine via substitution or elimination, respectively. (19.4)

Under conditions for catalytic hydrogenation, H_2 adds to C═O under moderate conditions to produce an alcohol. (20.3)

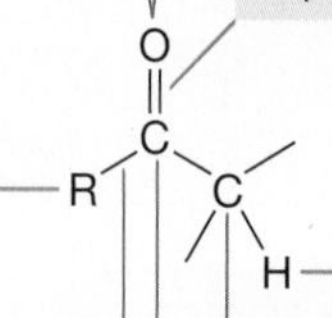
O
C
R
C
H

$KMnO_4$ oxidation will produce a benzoic acid when R = C_6H_5. (24.9a)

A strong base can deprotonate an α C, generating a strongly nucleophilic C. (19.8)

Oxidation with a peroxy acid can produce an ester. (23.8)

A methyl ketone is converted to a carboxylate anion by treatment with Cl_2, Br_2, or I_2 in basic, aqueous conditions. (22.5)

Nucleophiles add to the electron-poor C, converting C═O into C—O. Addition of a H^- or R^- nucleophile reduces a ketone to an alcohol. Addition of an R^- nucleophile results in the formation of a new C—C bond. (18.1, 18.3, 18.4)

Aldehydes

The electron-rich O can be protonated by a strong acid, which activates the C═O carbon toward attack by a weak nucleophile. (19.1)

After nucleophilic addition at C, this O can be converted to a H_2O leaving group under acidic conditions, which can produce an acetal or imine via substitution or elimination, respectively. (19.4)

Under conditions for catalytic hydrogenation, H_2 adds to C═O under mild conditions to produce an alcohol. (20.3)

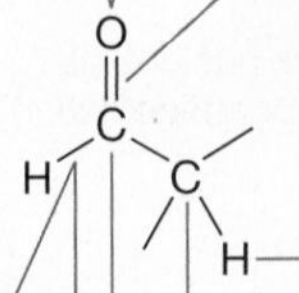
O
C
H
C
H

A strong base can deprotonate an α C, generating a strongly nucleophilic C. (19.8)

In the presence of H_2O, the hydrate is oxidized to a carboxylic acid by H_2CrO_4 or $KMnO_4$. (20.5)

Ethanal (O═CH—CH_3) is converted to the methanoate anion (HCO_2^-) by treatment with Cl_2, Br_2, or I_2 in basic, aqueous conditions. (22.5)

Oxidation with a peroxy acid can produce a carboxylic acid. (23.8)

Nucleophiles add to the electron-poor C, converting C═O into C—O. Addition of a H^- or R^- nucleophile reduces an aldehyde to an alcohol. Addition of an R^- nucleophile results in the formation of a new C—C bond. (18.1, 18.3, 18.4)

α,β-Unsaturated carbonyls

Direct addition is favored by nucleophiles that add irreversibly to the C═O. (18.8)

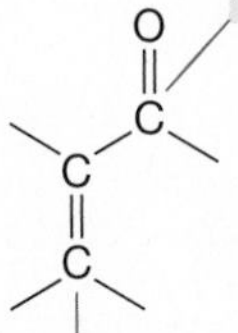
O
C
C
C

Conjugate addition is favored by nucleophiles that add reversibly to the C═O. (18.8)

Amines

Elimination of the H and the N-containing group can take place in the presence of a base when N is quaternary. (10.11)

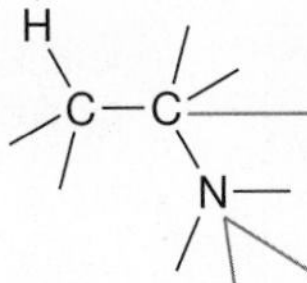
H
C
C
N

Aromatic Ar—NH_2 produces an arenediazonium ion when treated with $NaNO_2/H^+$. (24.9c)

N is moderately nucleophilic. (9.3)

N is weakly basic. (6.2)

Acid halides

Attack by R^- from an alkyllithium or Grignard reagent produces a 3° alcohol. (22.8)

Attack by H^- from $NaBH_4$ or $LiAlH_4$ produces a 1° alcohol. (22.6)

Attack by R^- from a lithium dialkylcuprate produces a ketone. (22.8)

Attack by H^- from LiAl(O-*t*-Bu)$_3$ produces an aldehyde. (22.7)

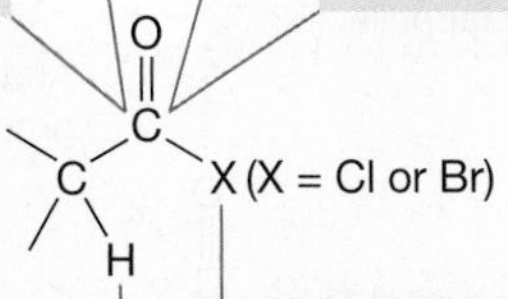
O
C
C
X (X = Cl or Br)
H

Acyl substitution by a strong or weak nucleophile produces an acid anhydride, ester, carboxylic acid, or amide. (23.1)

α Halogenation takes place with the enol form. (23.5)

Acid anhydrides

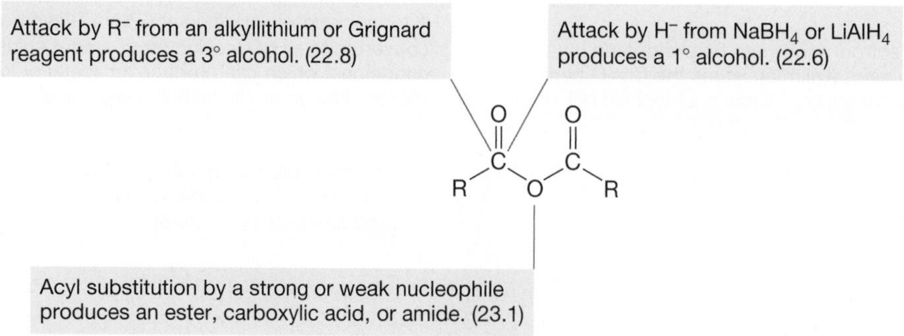
Attack by R⁻ from an alkyllithium or Grignard reagent produces a 3° alcohol. (22.8)
Attack by H⁻ from $NaBH_4$ or $LiAlH_4$ produces a 1° alcohol. (22.6)
O
O
C
C
R
O
R
Acyl substitution by a strong or weak nucleophile produces an ester, carboxylic acid, or amide. (23.1)

Esters

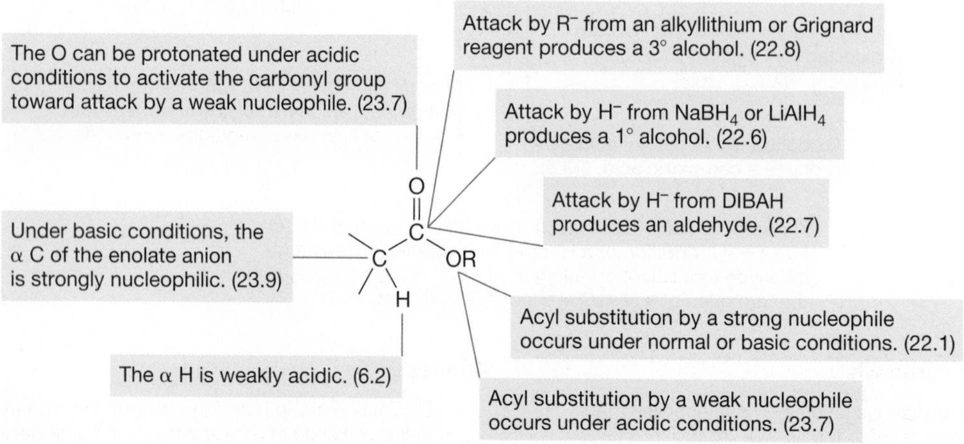
The O can be protonated under acidic conditions to activate the carbonyl group toward attack by a weak nucleophile. (23.7)
Attack by R⁻ from an alkyllithium or Grignard reagent produces a 3° alcohol. (22.8)
Attack by H⁻ from $NaBH_4$ or $LiAlH_4$ produces a 1° alcohol. (22.6)
Attack by H⁻ from DIBAH produces an aldehyde. (22.7)
Under basic conditions, the α C of the enolate anion is strongly nucleophilic. (23.9)
O
C
C
OR
H
Acyl substitution by a strong nucleophile occurs under normal or basic conditions. (22.1)
The α H is weakly acidic. (6.2)
Acyl substitution by a weak nucleophile occurs under acidic conditions. (23.7)

Carboxylic acids

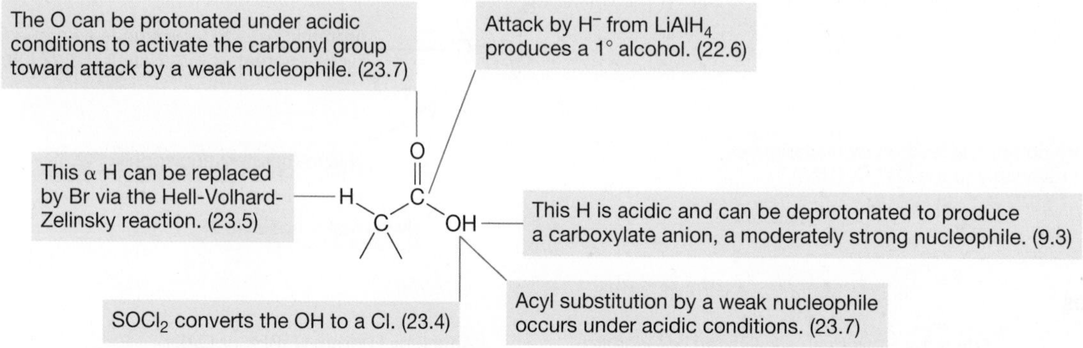
The O can be protonated under acidic conditions to activate the carbonyl group toward attack by a weak nucleophile. (23.7)
Attack by H⁻ from $LiAlH_4$ produces a 1° alcohol. (22.6)
This α H can be replaced by Br via the Hell-Volhard-Zelinsky reaction. (23.5)
H
O
C
C
OH
This H is acidic and can be deprotonated to produce a carboxylate anion, a moderately strong nucleophile. (9.3)
$SOCl_2$ converts the OH to a Cl. (23.4)
Acyl substitution by a weak nucleophile occurs under acidic conditions. (23.7)

Amides

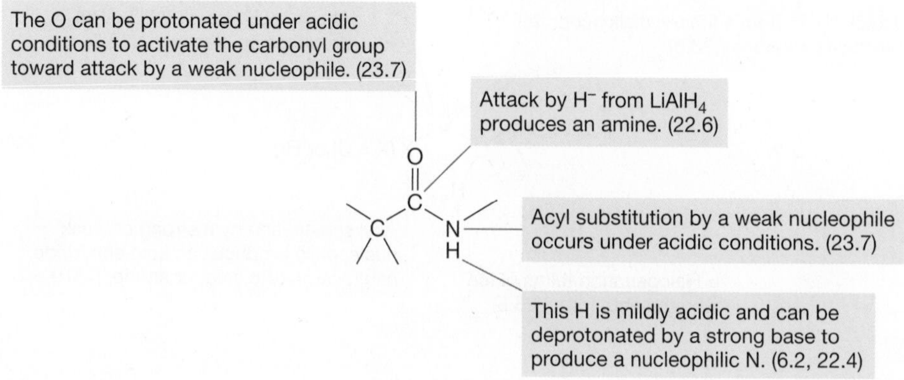
The O can be protonated under acidic conditions to activate the carbonyl group toward attack by a weak nucleophile. (23.7)
Attack by H⁻ from $LiAlH_4$ produces an amine. (22.6)
O
C
C
N
H
Acyl substitution by a weak nucleophile occurs under acidic conditions. (23.7)
This H is mildly acidic and can be deprotonated by a strong base to produce a nucleophilic N. (6.2, 22.4)

APPENDIX C

Reactions That Alter the Carbon Skeleton

	Starting Compound Class	Typical Reagents and Reaction Conditions	Compound Class Formed	Key Electron-Rich Species	Key Electron-Poor Species	Comments	Discussed in Section(s)
(1)	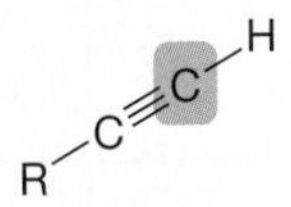 Alkyne	1. NaH → 2. R′—X (X = Cl, Br, or I)	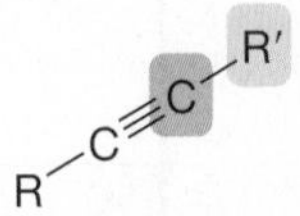 Alkyne	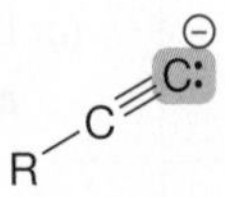 Alkynide anion	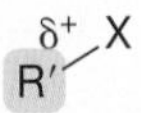 Alkyl halide	S_N2	7.2, 8.3, 8.5, 9,3b, 9.9
(2)	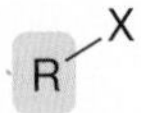 Alkyl halide (X = Cl, Br, or I)	NaCN →	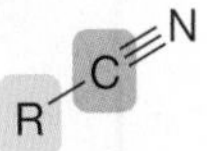 Nitrile	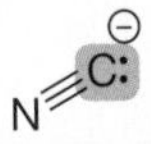 Cyanide anion	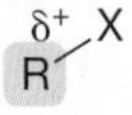 Alkyl halide	S_N2	7.2, 8.3, 8.5, 9.9
(3)	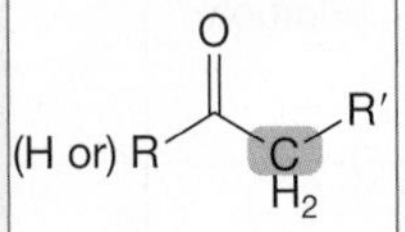 Ketone or aldehyde	1. Base$^{\ominus}$ → 2. R″—X (X = Cl, Br, or I)	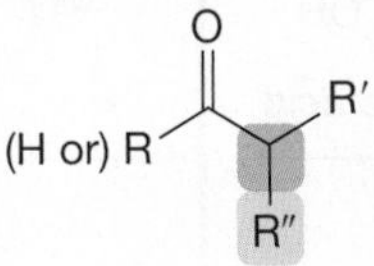 α-Alkylated ketone or aldehyde	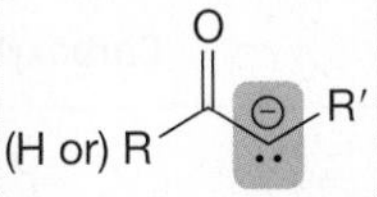 Enolate anion	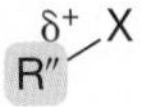 Alkyl halide	S_N2	11.3
(4)	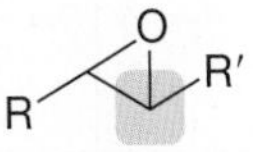 Epoxide	1. R″—Li or R″—MgX → 2. $H_3O^{\oplus}$ (X = Cl or Br)	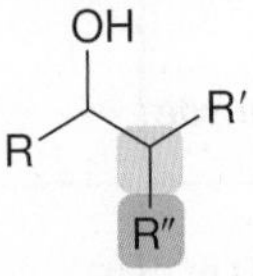 Alcohol		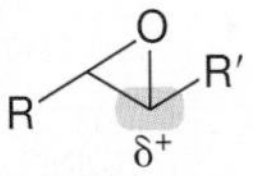	S_N2	11.2
(5)	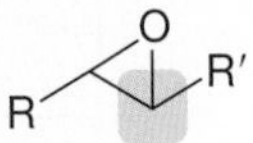 Epoxide	NaCN → H_2O	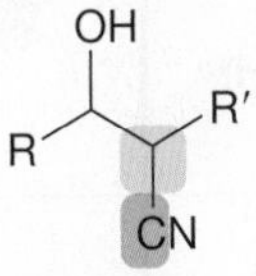 Nitrile (β-hydroxy)		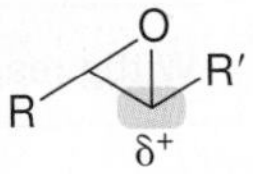	S_N2	11.2
(6)	R″C≡CH Alkyne (terminal)	1. NaH → 2. 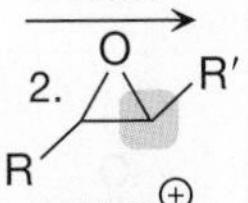 3. $H_3O^{\oplus}$	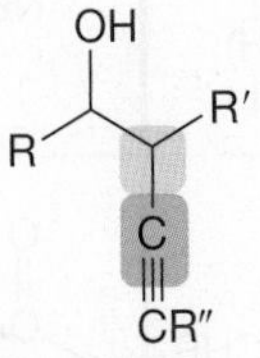 Alcohol (3-alkyn-1-ol)	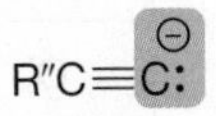	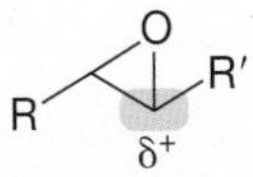	S_N2	11.2

(continued)

	Starting Compound Class	Typical Reagents and Reaction Conditions	Compound Class Formed	Key Electron-Rich Species	Key Electron-Poor Species	Comments	Discussed in Section(s)
(7)	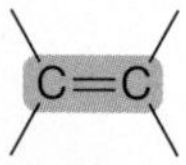 Alkene	CH_2N_2 → Δ or $h\nu$	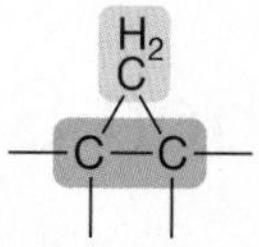 Cyclopropane ring	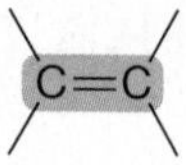	$:CH_2$	Syn addition; retention of cis/trans configuration; not very useful in synthesis	13.2
(8)	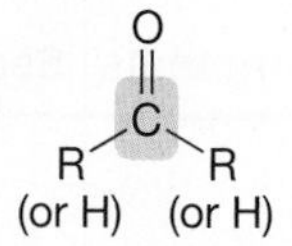 Ketone or aldehyde	1. R′—Li or R′—MgX → 2. H_2O, H_2SO_4 (X = Cl or Br)	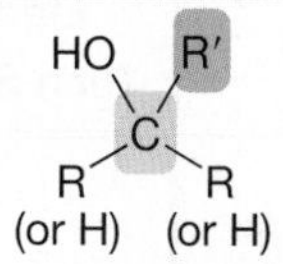 Alcohol	:R′⊖	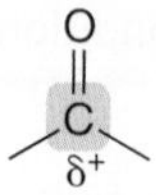	Nucleophilic addition	18.4
(9)	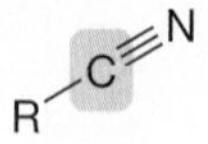 Nitrile	1. R′—MgX → 2. CH_3OH (X = Cl or Br)	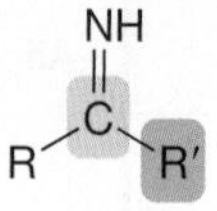 Imine	:R′⊖	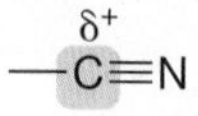	Nucleophilic addition	18.4
(10)	 Grignard reagent (X = Cl or Br)	1. $CO_2(s)$ → 2. H_2O, H_2SO_4	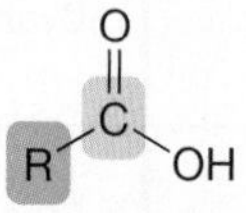 Carboxylic acid	:R⊖	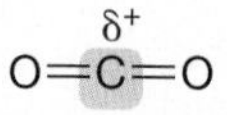	Nucleophilic addition	18.4
(11)	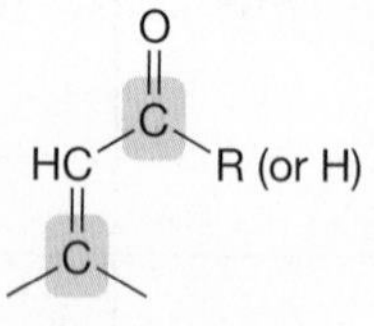 α,β-Unsaturated ketone or aldehyde	1. R'_2CuLi, THF → 2. NH_4Cl, H_2O	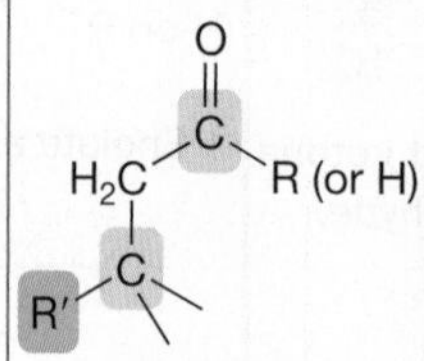 Ketone or aldehyde	:R′⊖	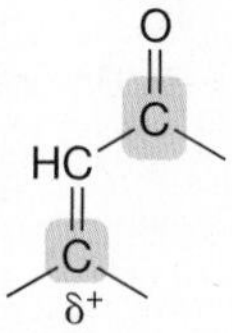	Conjugate nucleophilic addition	18.9
(12)	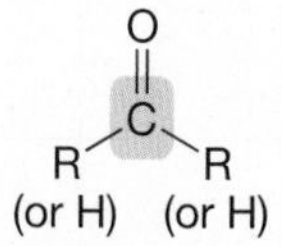 Ketone or aldehyde	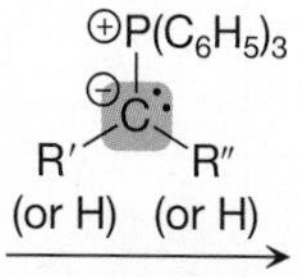 Wittig reagent	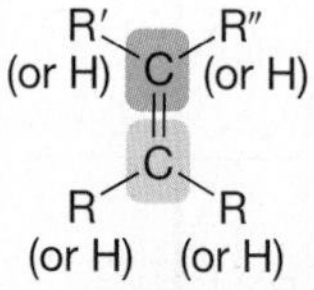 Alkene	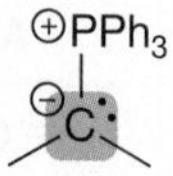	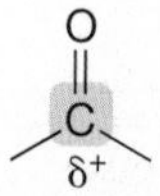	Wittig reaction	18.6
(13)	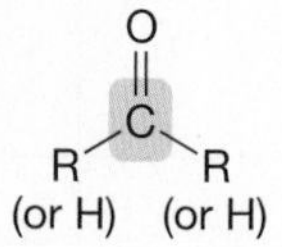 Ketone or aldehyde	H—CN → NaOH or KCN	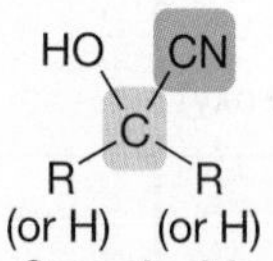 Cyanohydrin	NC:⊖	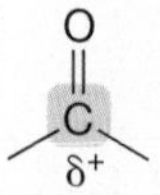	Nucleophilic addition	19.2
(14)	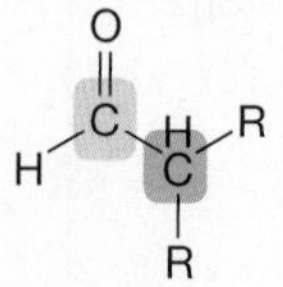 Aldehyde	NaOH →	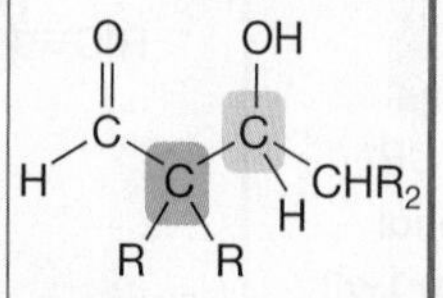 β-Hydroxy aldehyde	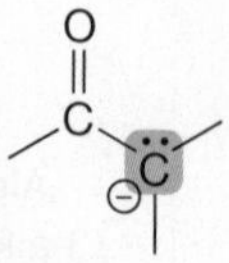 Enolate anion	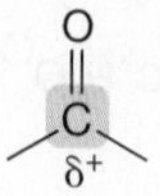	Aldol addition; nucleophilic addition	19.8

	Starting Compound Class	Typical Reagents and Reaction Conditions	Compound Class Formed	Key Electron-Rich Species	Key Electron-Poor Species	Comments	Discussed in Section(s)
(15)	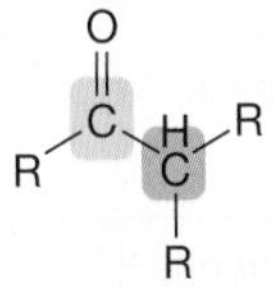 Ketone	NaOH →	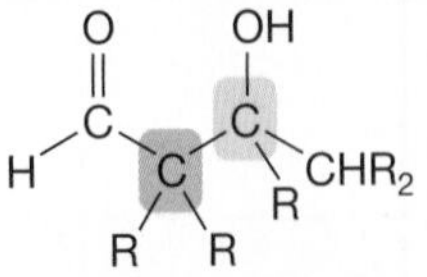 β-Hydroxy ketone	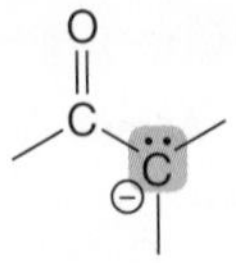 Enolate anion	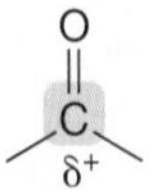	Aldol addition; nucleophilic addition	19.10
(16)	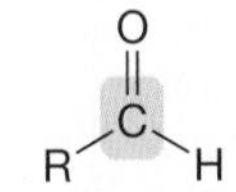 (or H) Aldehyde	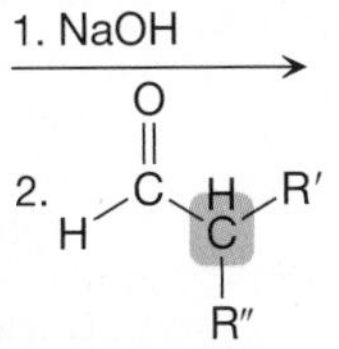	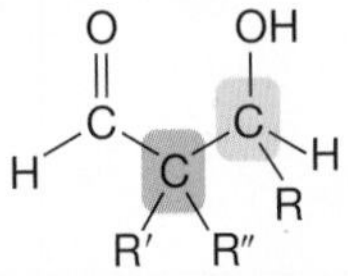 β-Hydroxy aldehyde	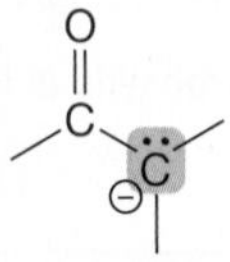 Enolate anion	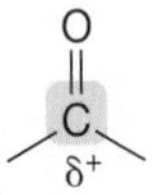	Crossed aldol addition; nucleophilic addition	19.11
(17)	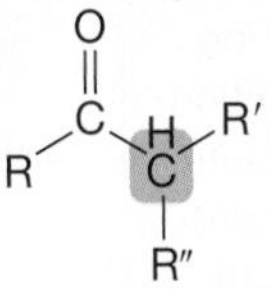 Ketone	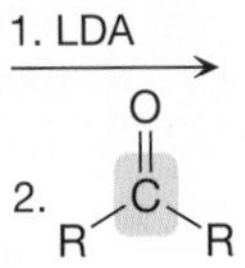	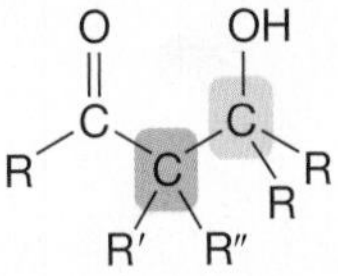 β-Hydroxy ketone	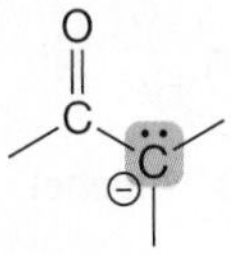 Enolate anion	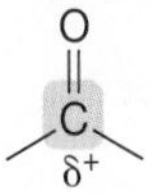	Crossed aldol addition; nucleophilic addition	19.11
(18)	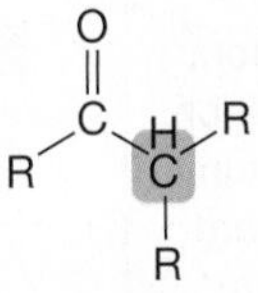 Ketone	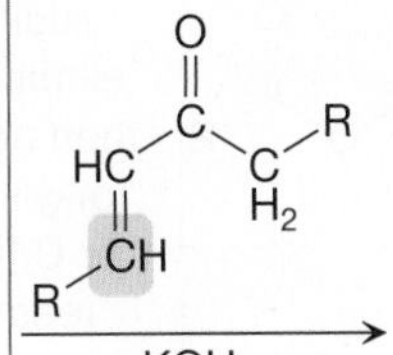 KOH	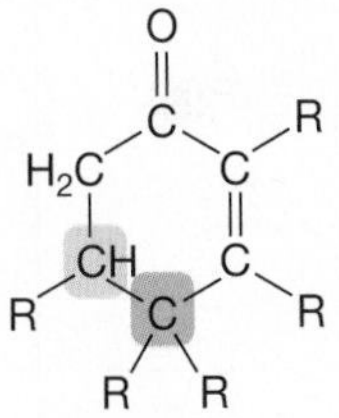	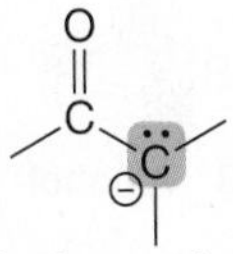 Enolate anion	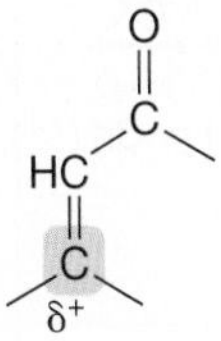	Robinson annulation	19.13
(19)	R–X **Alkyl, vinylic, or aryl halide** (X = Cl, Br, or I)	R'_2CuLi →	R—R′	–	–	Coupling reaction	20.7a
(20)	R–X **Vinylic or aryl halide** (X = Cl, Br, or I)	R′—B(OR″)$_2$ → PdL$_n$, base	R—R′	–	–	Suzuki reaction	20.7b
(21)	R–X **Vinylic or aryl halide** (X = Cl, Br, or I)	H—R′ → PdL$_2$, base	R—R′	–	–	Heck reaction	20.7b

(continued)

	Starting Compound Class	Typical Reagents and Reaction Conditions	Compound Class Formed	Key Electron-Rich Species	Key Electron-Poor Species	Comments	Discussed in Section(s)
(22)	R—CH=CH_2 **Terminal alkene**	Grubbs catalyst →	R—CH=CH—R **Alkene**	—	—	Alkene metathesis	20.7c
(23)	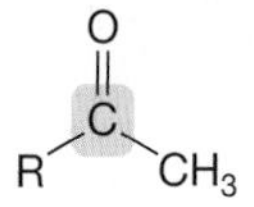 **Methyl ketone**	1. X_2 (excess), NaOH → 2. HCl (X = Cl, Br, or I)	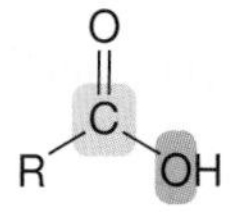 **Carboxylic acid**	⊖:ÖH	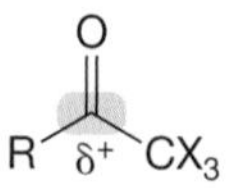	Halogenation, then nucleophilic addition–elimination (haloform reaction)	22.5
(24)	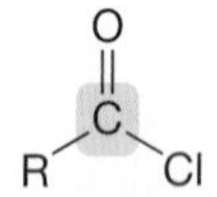 **Acid chloride**	1. R′—Li or R′—MgX → 2. HCl (X = Cl or Br)	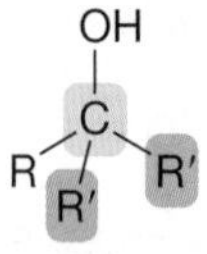 **3° Alcohol**	⊖:R′	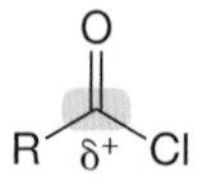	Nucleophilic addition–elimination, then addition (alkyllithium or Grignard reaction)	22.8
(25)	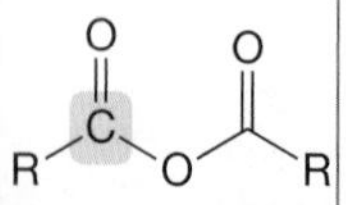 **Acid anhydride**	1. R′—Li or R′—MgX → 2. HCl (X = Cl or Br)	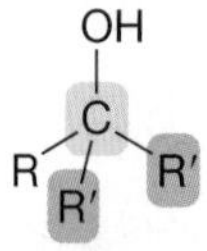 **3° Alcohol**	⊖:R′	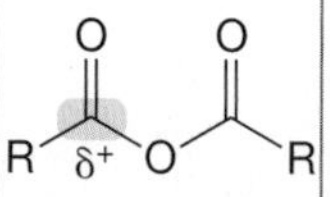	Nucleophilic addition–elimination, then addition (alkyllithium or Grignard reaction)	22.8
(26)	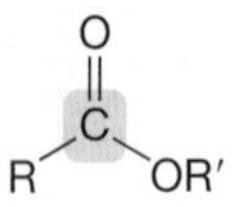 **Ester**	1. R′—Li or R′—MgX → 2. HCl (X = Cl or Br)	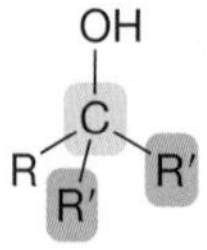 **3° Alcohol**	⊖:R′	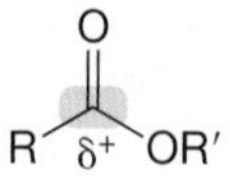	Nucleophilic addition–elimination, then addition (alkyllithium or Grignard reaction)	22.8
(27)	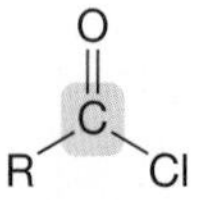 **Acid chloride**	R'_2CuLi →	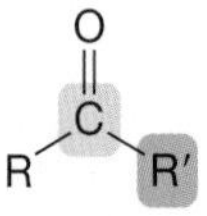 **Ketone**	⊖:R′	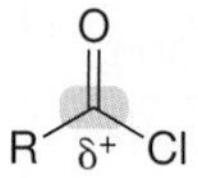	Nucleophilic addition–elimination	22.8
(28)	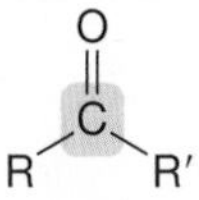 **Ketone**	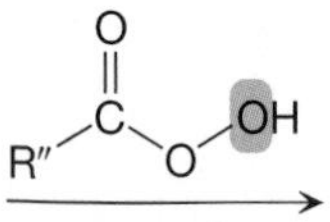	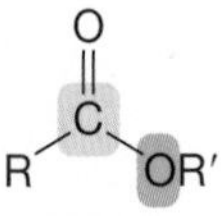 **Ester**	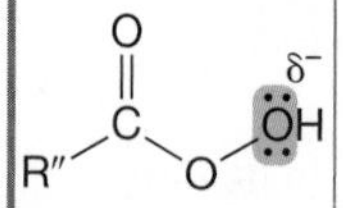	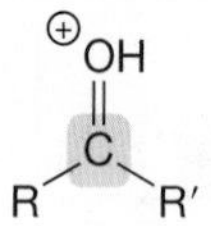	Acid-catalyzed nucleophilic addition–elimination (Baeyer–Villiger oxidation)	23.8
(29)	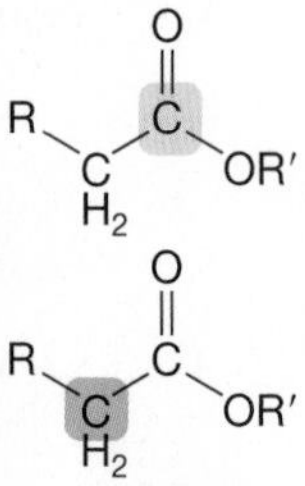 **Ester**	1. NaOR″ → 2. CH_3CO_2H	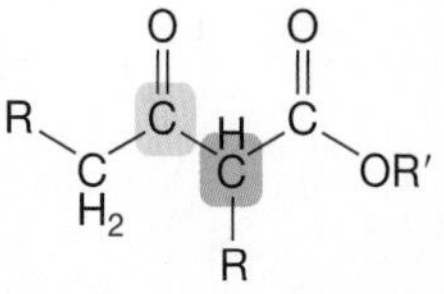 **β-Keto ester**	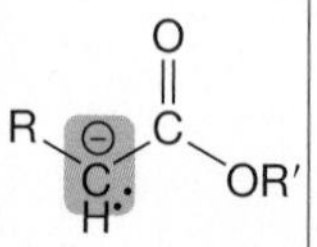	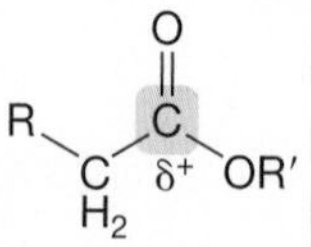	Base-promoted nucleophilic addition–elimination (Claisen condensation)	23.9

	Starting Compound Class	Typical Reagents and Reaction Conditions	Compound Class Formed	Key Electron-Rich Species	Key Electron-Poor Species	Comments	Discussed in Section(s)
(30)	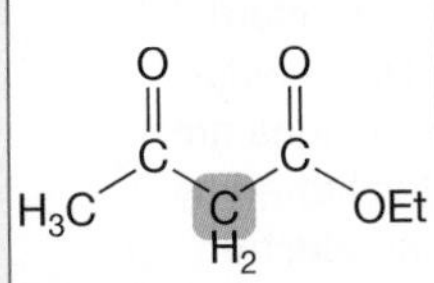 **Acetoacetic ester**	1. NaOEt 2. R—X 3. $H_3O^{\oplus}$, Δ (X = Cl or Br)	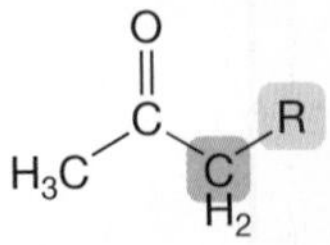 **Alkyl-substituted acetone**	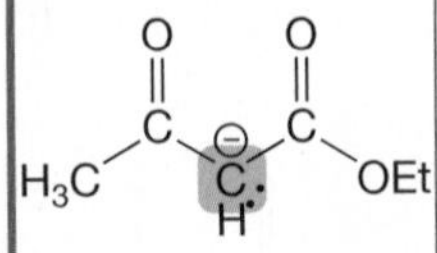	δ^+ R—X	Acetoacetic ester synthesis	23.10
(31)	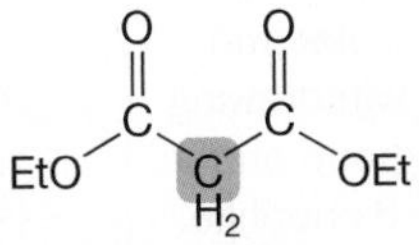 **Malonic ester**	1. NaOEt 2. R—X 3. $H_3O^{\oplus}$, Δ (X = Cl or Br)	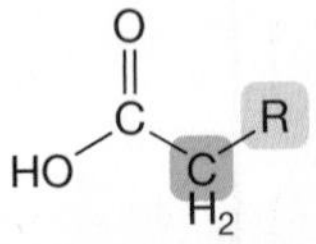 **Alkyl-substituted acetic acid**	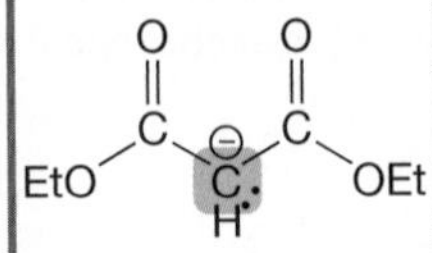	δ^+ R—X	Malonic ester synthesis	23.10
(32)	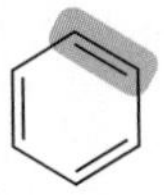 **Arene**	R—Cl $AlCl_3$	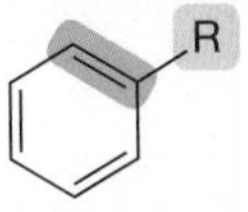 **Alkylarene**	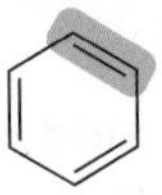	$R^{\oplus}$	Electrophilic aromatic substitution; Friedel–Crafts alkylation	24.3
(33)	 **Arene**	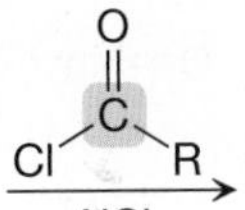 $AlCl_3$	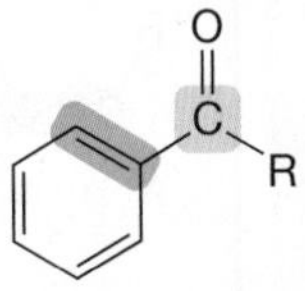 **Aromatic ketone**	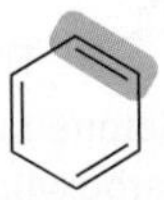	 **Acylium ion**	Electrophilic aromatic substitution; Friedel–Crafts acylation	24.5
(34)	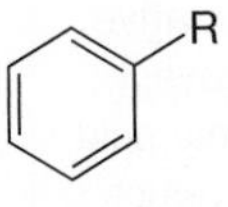 **Alkylarene**	1. $KMnO_4$, KOH, Δ 2. HCl, H_2O	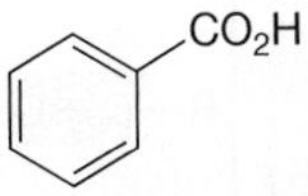 **Aromatic carboxylic acid**	—	—	Oxidation	24.9a
(35)	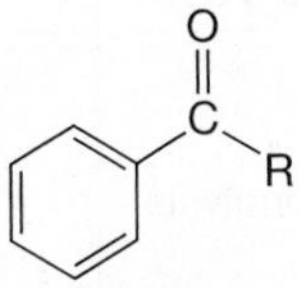 **Aromatic ketone/aldehyde**	1. $KMnO_4$, KOH, Δ 2. HCl, H_2O	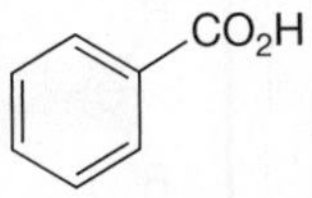 **Aromatic carboxylic acid**	—	—	Oxidation	24.9a
(36)	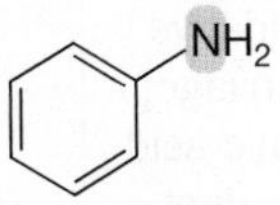 **Arylamine**	1. $NaNO_2$, H_2SO_4 2. CuCN	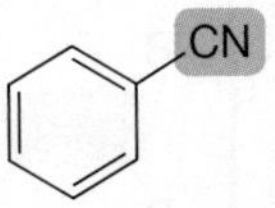 **Arylnitrile**	CuCN	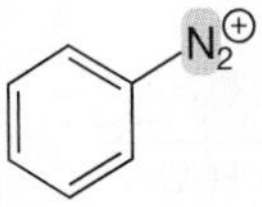	Proceeds through a diazonium ion; Sandmeyer reaction	24.9c

(continued)

	Starting Compound Class	Typical Reagents and Reaction Conditions	Compound Class Formed	Key Electron-Rich Species	Key Electron-Poor Species	Comments	Discussed in Section(s)
(37)	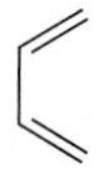 **Conjugated diene**	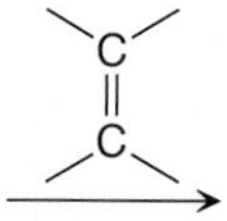 **Dienophile**	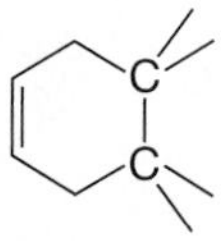 **Substituted cyclohexene**	—	—	Standard Diels–Alder reactions are facilitated by an electron-donating group on the diene and an electron-withdrawing group on the dienophile.	26.1–26.6
(38)	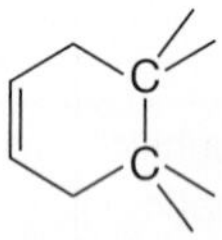 **Substituted cyclohexene**	$\xrightarrow[\Delta]{}$	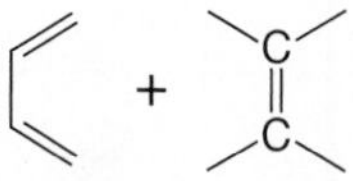 **Conjugated diene** **Alkene**	—	—	Retro Diels–Alder reaction	26.6
(39)	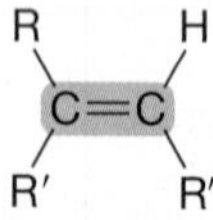 **Alkene**	1. conc $KMnO_4$, KOH, H_2O, Δ 2. HCl	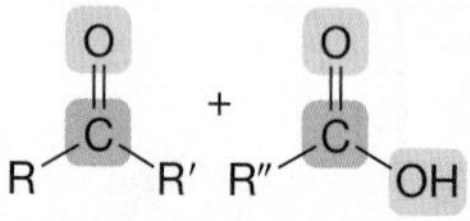 **Ketone and/or carboxylic acid**	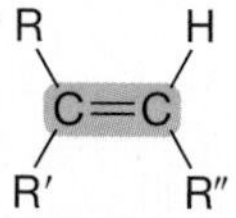	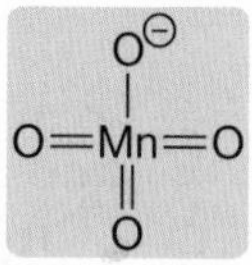	Oxidative cleavage; formic acid product (R″ = H) oxidizes to CO_2	26.9a
(40)	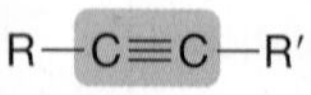 **Alkyne**	1. conc $KMnO_4$, KOH, H_2O, Δ 2. HCl	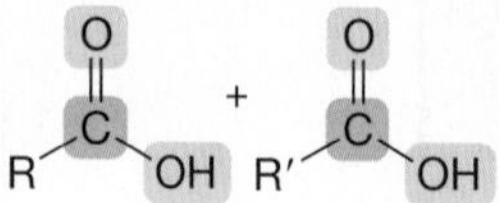 **Carboxylic acid**	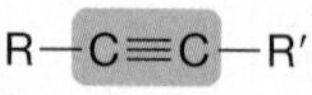	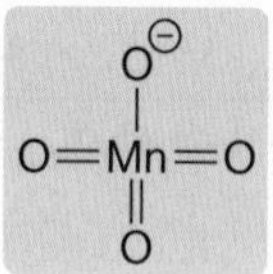	Oxidative cleavage; formic acid product (R′ = H) oxidizes to CO_2	26.9a
(41)	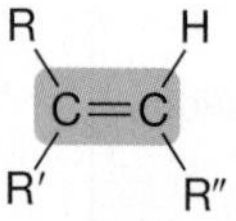 **Alkene**	1. O_3 2. CH_3SCH_3 or Zn, HOAc	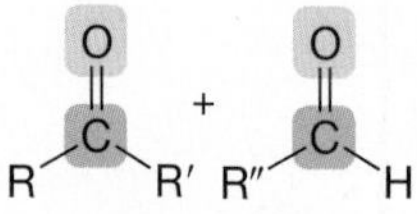 **Ketone and/or aldehyde**	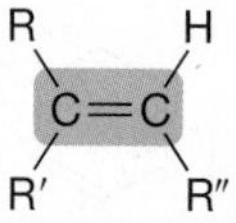	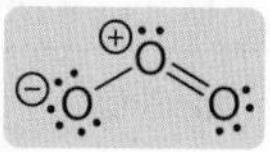	Ozonolysis	26.9c
(42)	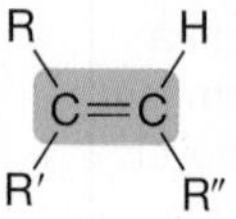 **Alkene**	1. O_3 2. H_2O_2	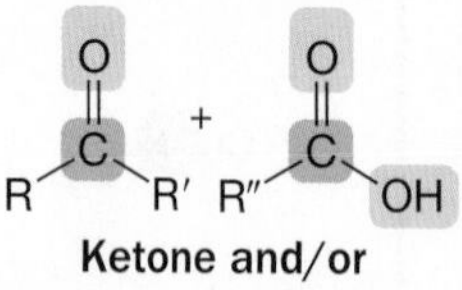 **Ketone and/or carboxylic acid**	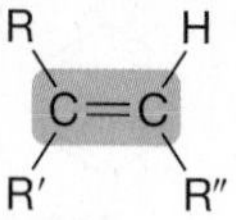	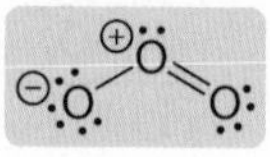	Ozonolysis; oxidative cleavage; formic acid product (R″ = H) oxidizes to CO_2	26.9c
(43)	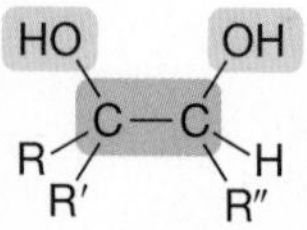 **1,2-Diol**	$NaIO_4$ or HIO_4	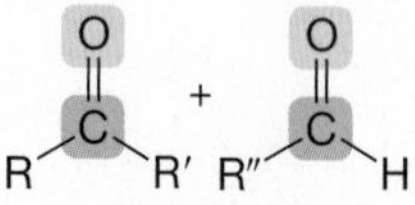 **Ketone and/or aldehyde**	—	—	Oxidative cleavage	26.9b

APPENDIX D

Synthesizing Particular Compound Classes via Functional Group Transformations

TABLE AppD-1 Reactions That Produce or Alter Alkenes and Alkynes

	Starting Compound Class	Typical Reagents and Reaction Conditions	Compound Class Formed	Key Electron-Rich Species	Key Electron-Poor Species	Comments	Discussed in Section(s)
(1)	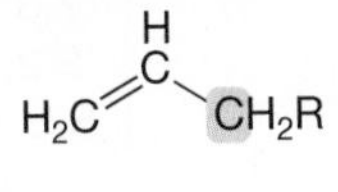 Alkene with allylic H	NBS → Δ or $h\nu$	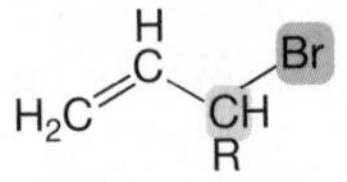 Allylic bromide	Br—Br	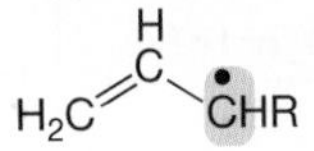	Favors allylic substitution over bromination of C=C	27.4d
(2)	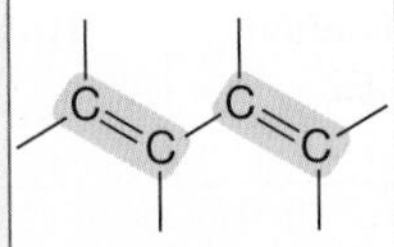 Conjugated diene	HX (1 equiv), cold → (X = Cl, Br, or I)	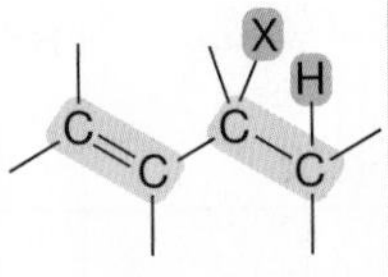 Allylic halide (1,2-adduct)		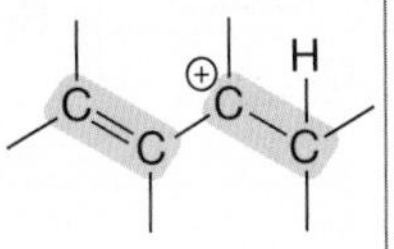	Kinetic control; 1,2-addition	12.9, 12.10
(3)	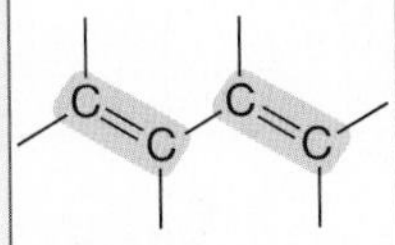 Conjugated diene	HX (1 equiv), warm → (X = Cl, Br, or I)	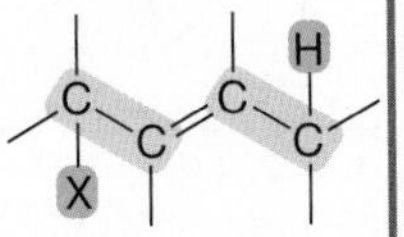 Allylic halide (1,4-adduct)		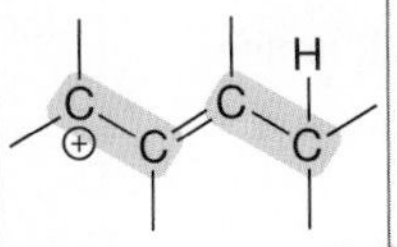	Thermodynamic control; 1,4-addition	12.9, 12.10
(4)	 Benzene	Li(s), ROH → $NH_3(\ell)$	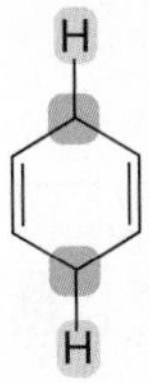 Cyclohexa-1,4-diene	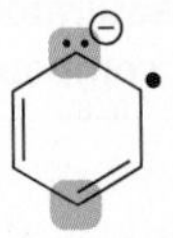	H—OR	Birch reduction; 1,4-positioning of the double bonds	27.7b
(5)	R—C≡C—R Alkyne	H_2 → Lindlar catalyst	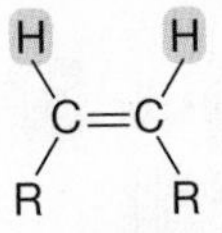 Cis alkene	—	—	Catalytic hydrogenation; poisoned catalyst	13.9b
(6)	R—C≡C—R Alkyne	Na(s) or Li(s) → $NH_3(\ell)$, –78 °C	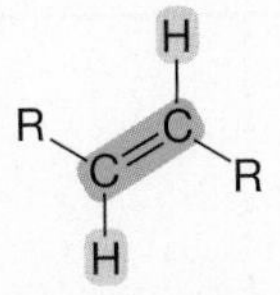 Trans alkene	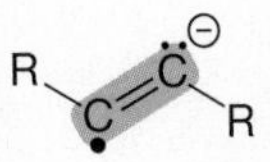	H—NH_2	Dissolving metal reduction	27.7a

(continued)

TABLE AppD-1 Reactions That Produce or Alter Alkenes and Alkynes (continued)

	Starting Compound Class	Typical Reagents and Reaction Conditions	Compound Class Formed	Key Electron-Rich Species	Key Electron-Poor Species	Comments	Discussed in Section(s)
(7)	—C≡C— Alkyne	HX (1 equiv) (X = Cl, Br, or I)	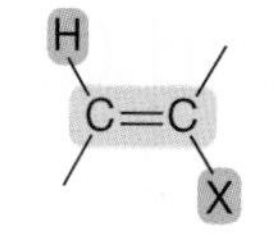 Vinylic halide	$:\ddot{X}:^{\ominus}$	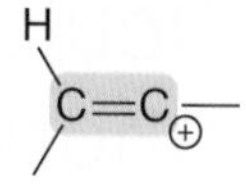	Markovnikov addition, predominantly trans; not useful for synthesis	12.7
(8)	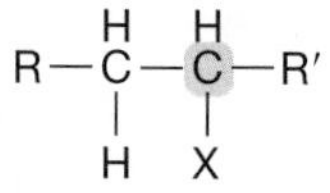 Alkyl halide	$(CH_3)_3CONa$, Δ	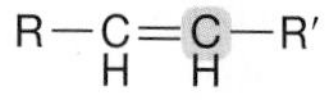 Alkene	$(CH_3)_3C\ddot{O}:^{\ominus}$	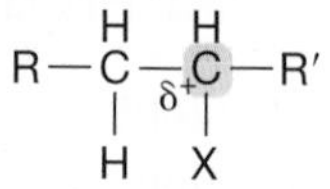	E2	7.5, 8.3, 8.5, 9.3d, 9.9
(9)	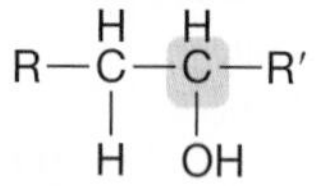 Alcohol	H_3PO_4 or H_2SO_4, Δ	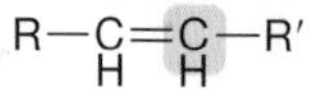 Alkene	$H_2\ddot{O}$ δ−	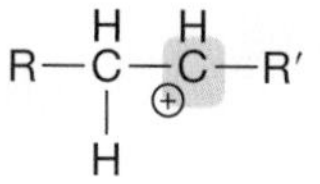	E1	7.3, 7.6, 8.2, 8.3, 8.5, 9.5a, 9.9
(10)	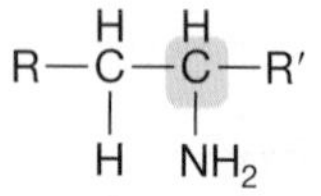 Amine	1. CH_3I (excess) 2. Ag_2O 3. Δ	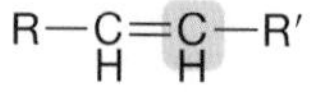 Alkene	$^{\ominus}:\ddot{O}H$	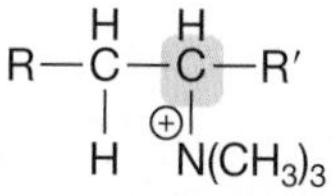	Hofmann elimination, E2	10.11
(11)	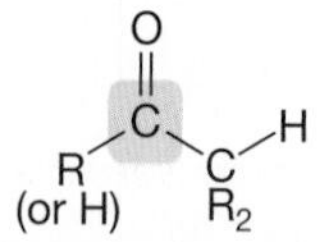 Ketone or aldehyde	R'_2NH (excess), $H^{\oplus}$; 2° amine	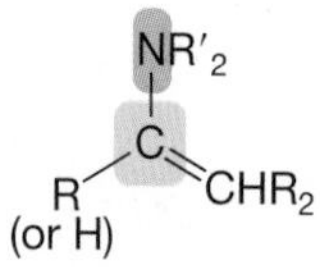 Enamine	$R'_2\ddot{N}H$ δ−	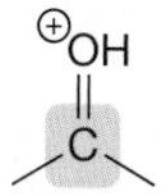	Nucleophilic addition, then E1	19.4b
(12)	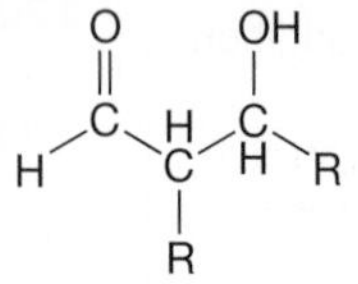 β-Hydroxy carbonyl compound	H_2SO_4 or NaOH, Δ	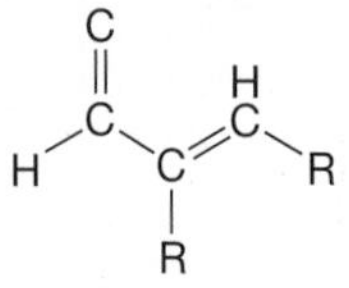 α,β-Unsaturated carbonyl compound	—	—	E1 or E1cb	19.9
(13)	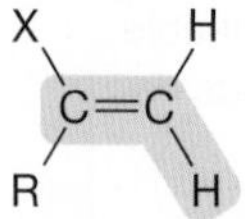 Vinylic halide	1. $NaNH_2$ or NaH 2. H_2O	R—C≡CH Terminal alkyne	$^{\ominus}:\ddot{N}H_2$ or $^{\ominus}:H$	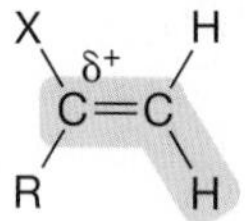	E2	10.12
(14)	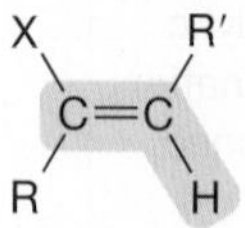 Vinylic halide	$NaNH_2$ or NaH or NaOH, Δ	R—C≡C—R′ Internal alkyne	$^{\ominus}:\ddot{N}H_2$ or $^{\ominus}:H$ or $^{\ominus}:\ddot{O}H$	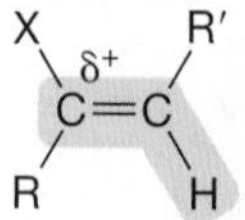	E2	10.12

TABLE AppD-2 Reactions That Produce Alkyl and Aryl Halides

	Starting Compound Class	Typical Reagents and Reaction Conditions	Compound Class Formed	Key Electron-Rich Species	Key Electron-Poor Species	Comments	Discussed in Section(s)
(1)	R—H Alkane	$\xrightarrow[h\nu]{X_2}$	R—X Alkyl halide	X—X	R•	X = Cl or Br	27.4
(2)	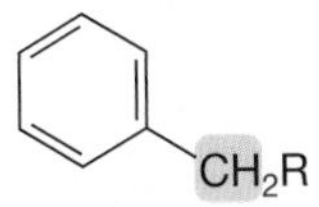 Alkylbenzene with benzylic H	$\xrightarrow[\Delta \text{ or } h\nu]{\text{NBS}}$	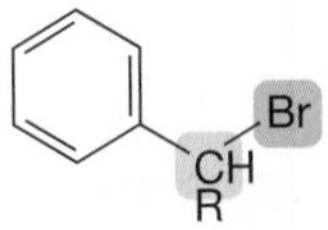 Benzylic bromide	Br—Br	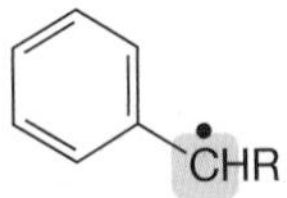	Functionalizes a relatively unreactive carbon	27.4d
(3)	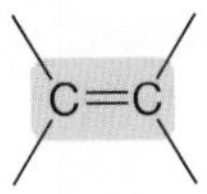 Alkene	$\xrightarrow[\text{(X = Cl, Br, or I)}]{HX}$	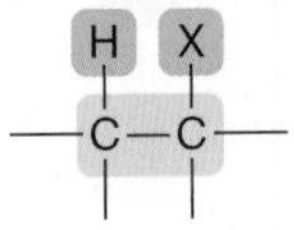 Alkyl halide	$:\ddot{X}:^{\ominus}$	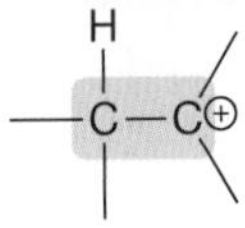	Markovnikov addition	12.1
(4)	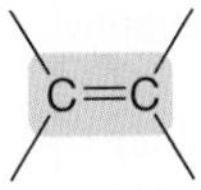 Alkene	$\xrightarrow[CCl_4]{X_2 \text{ (X = Cl or Br)}}$	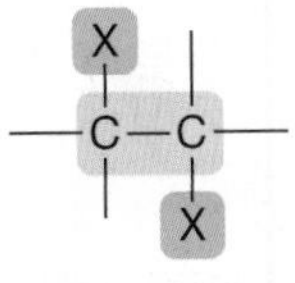 Vicinal dihalide	$:\ddot{X}:^{\ominus}$	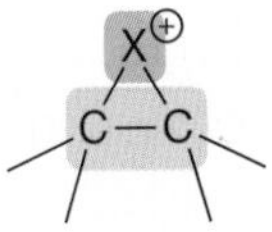	Anti addition	13.4a
(5)	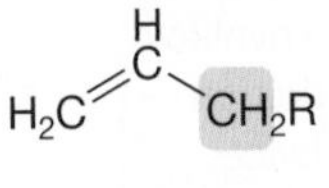 Alkene with allylic H	$\xrightarrow[\Delta \text{ or } h\nu]{\text{NBS}}$	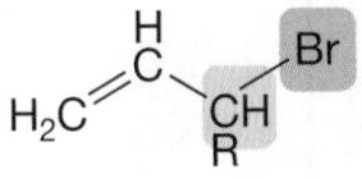 Allylic bromide	Br—Br	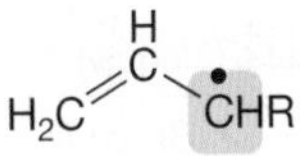	Favors allylic substitution over bromination of C=C	27.4d
(6)	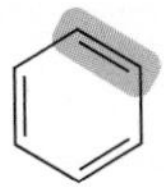 Arene	$\xrightarrow[FeCl_3]{Cl_2}$	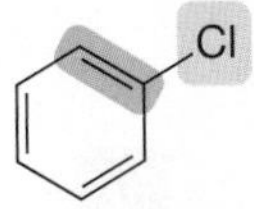 Aryl chloride	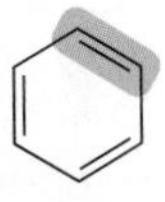	$:\ddot{Cl}—\overset{\oplus}{Fe}Cl_3$	Electrophilic aromatic substitution	24.2
(7)	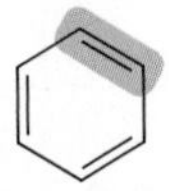 Arene	$\xrightarrow[FeBr_3]{Br_2}$	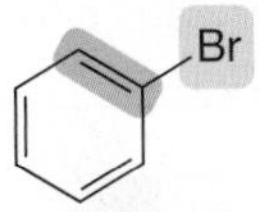 Aryl bromide	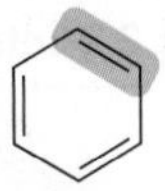	$:\ddot{Br}—\overset{\oplus}{Fe}Br_3$	Electrophilic aromatic substitution	24.2
(8)	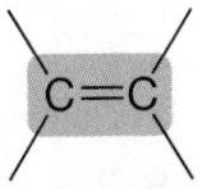 Alkene	$\xrightarrow[\text{Peroxide}]{HBr}$	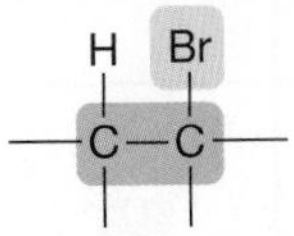 Alkyl bromide	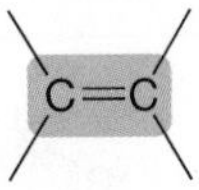	Br•	Anti-Markovnikov regiochemistry	27.5

(continued)

TABLE AppD-2 Reactions That Produce Alkyl and Aryl Halides (continued)

	Starting Compound Class	Typical Reagents and Reaction Conditions	Compound Class Formed	Key Electron-Rich Species	Key Electron-Poor Species	Comments	Discussed in Section(s)
(9)	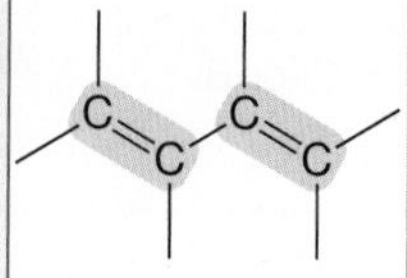 Conjugated diene	HX (1 equiv), cold → (X = Cl, Br, or I)	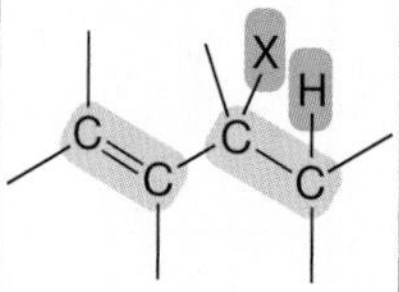 Allylic halide (1,2-adduct)	$:X:^{\ominus}$	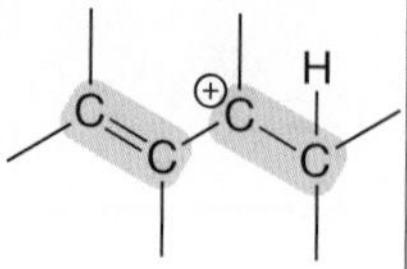	Kinetic control; 1,2-addition	12.9, 12.10
(10)	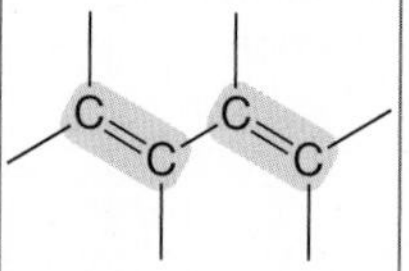 Conjugated diene	HX (1 equiv), warm → (X = Cl, Br, or I)	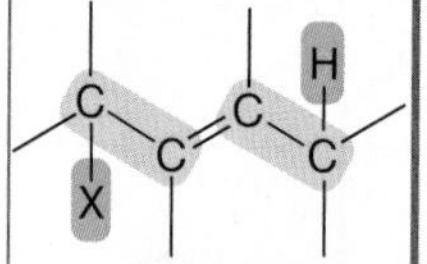 Allylic halide (1,4-adduct)	$:X:^{\ominus}$	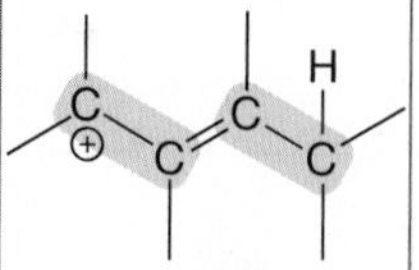	Thermo-dynamic control; 1,4-addition	12.9, 12.10
(11)	—C≡C— Alkyne	HX (1 equiv) → (X = Cl, Br, or I)	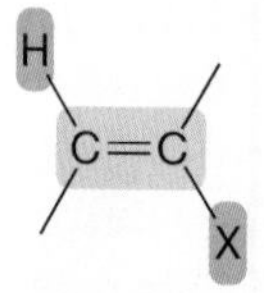 Vinylic halide	$:X:^{\ominus}$	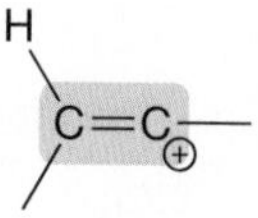	Markovnikov addition, predominantly trans; not useful for synthesis	12.7
(12)	—C≡C— Alkyne	HX (2 equiv) → (X = Cl, Br, or I)	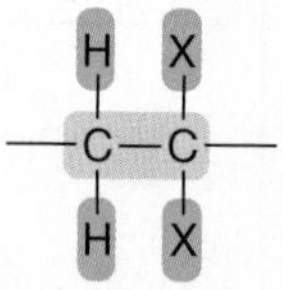 Geminal dihalide	$:X:^{\ominus}$	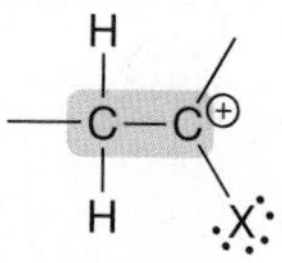	Markovnikov addition twice	12.7
(13)	—C≡C— Alkyne	X_2 (2 equiv) → CCl_4 (X = Cl, Br, or I)	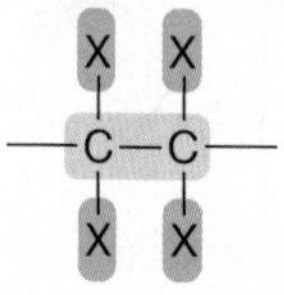 1,1,2,2-Tetrahalide	$:X:^{\ominus}$	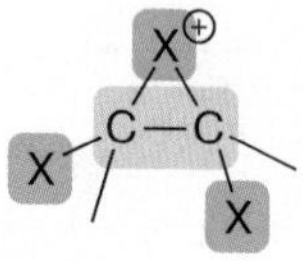	2 equiv of halogen	13.4a
(14)	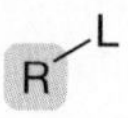 L = Cl, Br, I, OTs, OMs, or OTf	NaX →	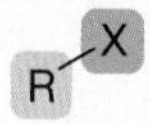 Alkyl halide	$:X:^{\ominus}$	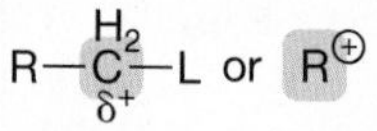	S_N1 or S_N2	7.2, 7.3, 8.1, 8.3, 8.5, 9.9
(15)	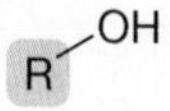 Alcohol	HX →	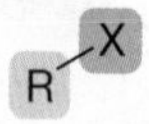 Alkyl halide	$:X:^{\ominus}$	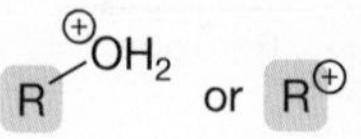	S_N1 or S_N2	7.2, 7.3, 8.1, 8.3, 8.5, 9.5b

TABLE AppD-2 Reactions That Produce Alkyl and Aryl Halides (continued)

	Starting Compound Class	Typical Reagents and Reaction Conditions	Compound Class Formed	Key Electron-Rich Species	Key Electron-Poor Species	Comments	Discussed in Section(s)
(16)	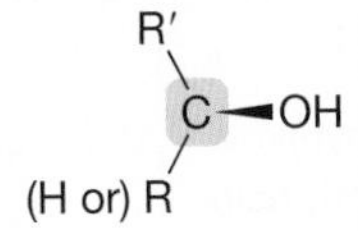 1° or 2° Alcohol	PBr_3 →	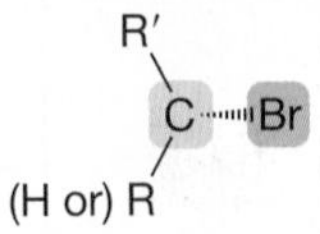 1° or 2° Alkyl halide	$:Br:^{\ominus}$	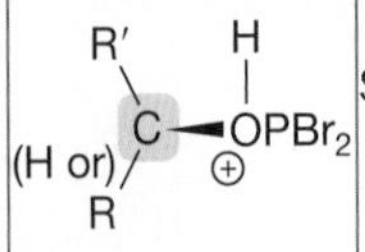	Back-to-back S_N2 reactions; overall inversion of stereo-chemistry	10.5
(17)	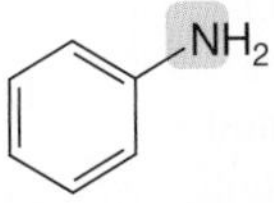 Arylamine	1. $NaNO_2$, H_2SO_4 2. CuBr →	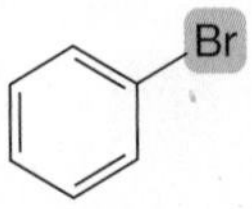 Aryl bromide	CuBr	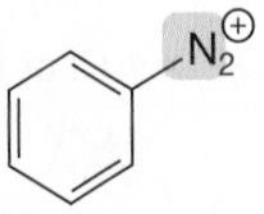	Proceeds through a diazonium ion; Sandmeyer reaction	24.9c
(18)	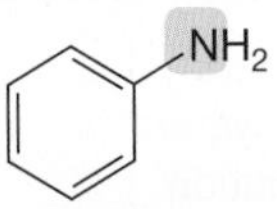 Arylamine	1. $NaNO_2$, H_2SO_4 2. CuCl →	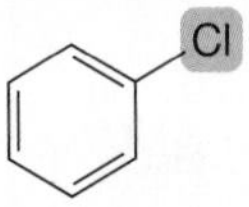 Aryl chloride	CuCl	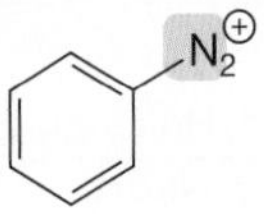	Proceeds through a diazonium ion; Sandmeyer reaction	24.9c
(19)	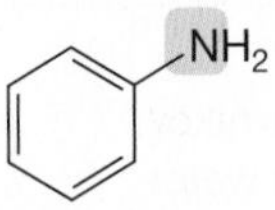 Arylamine	1. $NaNO_2$, H_2SO_4 2. KI →	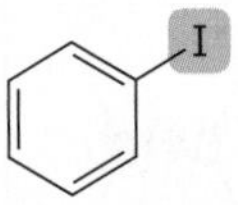 Aryl iodide	KI	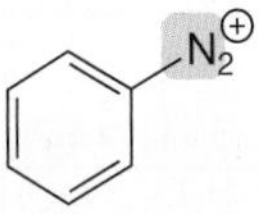	Proceeds through a diazonium ion	24.9c
(20)	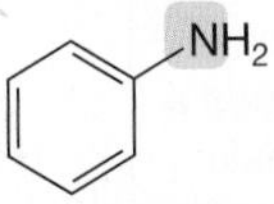 Arylamine	1. $NaNO_2$, H_2SO_4 2. HBF_4, then Δ →	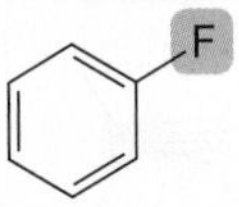 Aryl fluoride	HBF_4	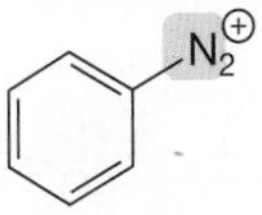	Proceeds through a diazonium ion	24.9c
(21)	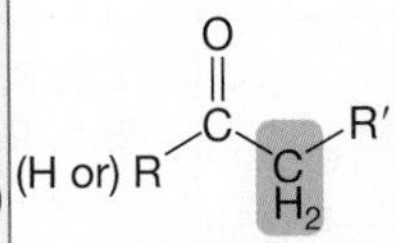 Ketone or aldehyde	X_2 (X = Cl, Br, or I) → NaOH	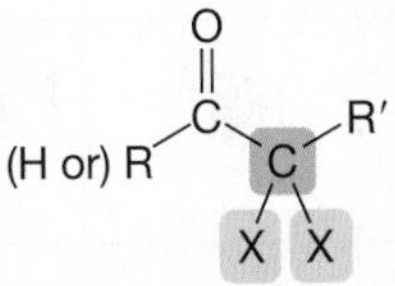 α-Halogenated ketone or aldehyde	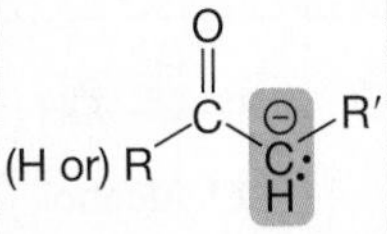 Enolate anion	$\overset{\delta+}{X}-\overset{\delta-}{X}$	Multiple S_N2 reactions	10.6
(22)	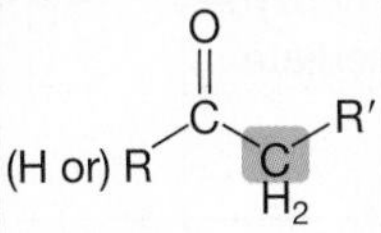 Ketone or aldehyde	X_2 (X = Cl, Br, or I) → $H^{\oplus}$	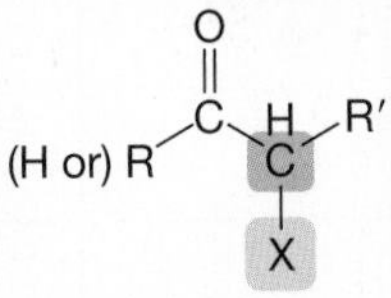 α-Halogenated ketone or aldehyde	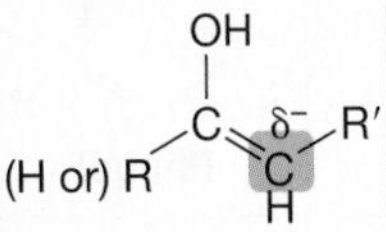 Enol	$\overset{\delta+}{X}-\overset{\delta-}{X}$	Single S_N2 reaction	10.6
(23)	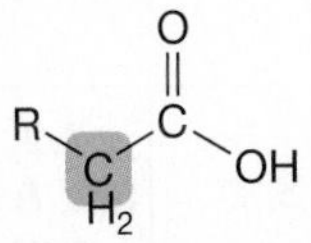 Carboxylic acid	Br_2, P →	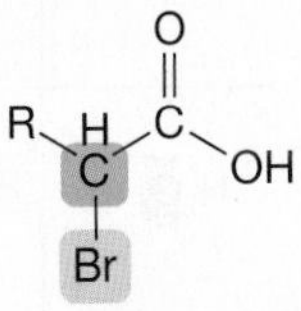 α-Bromo acid	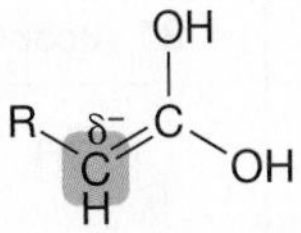 Enol	$\overset{\delta+}{Br}-\overset{\delta-}{Br}$	Hell–Volhard–Zelinsky reaction	23.5

TABLE AppD-3 Reactions That Produce Alcohols and Phenols

	Starting Compound Class	Typical Reagents and Reaction Conditions	Compound Class Formed	Key Electron-Rich Species	Key Electron-Poor Species	Comments	Discussed in Section(s)
(1)	C=C Alkene	H_2O / $H^{\oplus}$	H, OH on C—C Alcohol	$H_2\ddot{O}:$	H—C—$C^{\oplus}$	Markovnikov addition, acid catalysis	12.6
(2)	C=C Alkene	X_2 (X = Cl or Br) / H_2O	X, OH on C—C Halohydrin	$H_2\ddot{O}:$	$X^{\oplus}$ bridging C—C	OH bonds to more substituted carbon; anti addition	13.4b
(3)	C=C Alkene	1. $Hg(OAc)_2$, H_2O 2. $NaBH_4$	H, OH on C—C Alcohol	$H_2\ddot{O}:$	OAc—$Hg^{\oplus}$ bridging C—C	Markovnikov addition of water; no carbocation rearrangements	13.5
(4)	C=C Alkene	1. B_2H_6 or BH_3·THF 2. H_2O_2, NaOH, H_2O	H, OH on C—C Alcohol	C=C	BH_3	Anti-Markovnikov addition of water	13.6
(5)	C=C Alkene	OsO_4 / H_2O_2	HO, OH on C—C Syn 1,2-diol	C=C	O=Os(=O)(=O)=O	An alternate method uses a cold, basic solution of $KMnO_4$.	26.8
(6)	R—CH_2—X 1° Alkyl halide	NaOH	R—CH_2—OH 1° Alcohol	$H\ddot{O}:^{\ominus}$	R—$CH_2^{\delta+}$—X	S_N2	7.2, 8.4, 8.5, 9.9
(7)	(X = F, Cl, Br, or I) X on benzene ring Aromatic halide	1. NaOH, Δ 2. H_2O, HCl	OH on benzene ring Phenol	$H\ddot{O}:^{\ominus}$	benzyne	Proceeds through benzyne intermediate	25.9b
(8)	R_3C—X 3° Alkyl halide	H_2O	R_3C—OH 3° Alcohol	$H_2\ddot{O}$	$R_3C^{\oplus}$	S_N1	7.3, 8.1, 8.3, 8.5, 9.5a, 9.9
(9)	R—O—R Ether	H_2O / $H^{\oplus}$	R—OH Alcohol	$H_2\ddot{O}$	$R^{\oplus}$ or R—$\overset{\oplus}{O}$(H)R	S_N1 or S_N2	7.2, 7.3, 8.1, 8.3, 8.5, 9.5a, 9.9

TABLE AppD-3 Reactions That Produce Alcohols and Phenols (continued)

	Starting Compound Class	Typical Reagents and Reaction Conditions	Compound Class Formed	Key Electron-Rich Species	Key Electron-Poor Species	Comments	Discussed in Section(s)
(10)	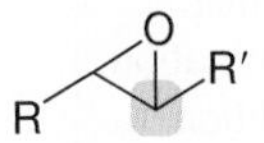 Epoxide	$:Nu^{\ominus}$ → Neutral or basic	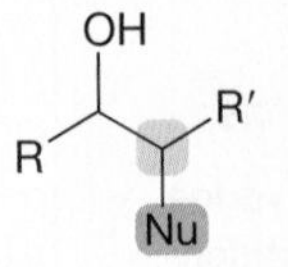 Alcohol (2-substituted)	$:Nu^{\ominus}$	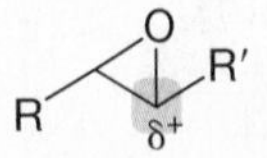	S_N2	10.7a
(11)	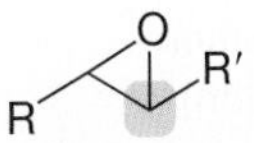 Epoxide	H—Nu → Acidic	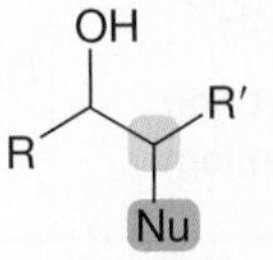 Alcohol (2-substituted)	$:Nu^{\ominus}$	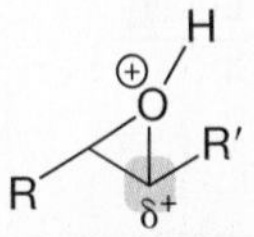	S_N2	10.7b
(12)	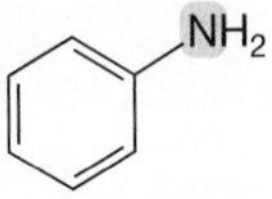 Arylamine	1. $NaNO_2$, H_2SO_4 2. H_2O, Cu_2O, $Cu(NO_3)_2$	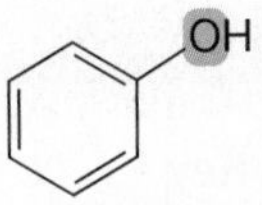 Aryl alcohol	$H_2\ddot{O}$	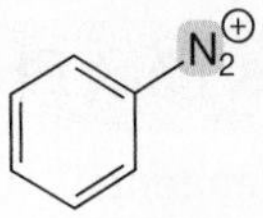	Proceeds through a diazonium ion; Sandmeyer reaction	24.9c
(13)	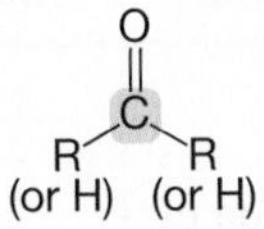 Ketone or aldehyde	1. $NaBH_4$, or $LiAlH_4$ 2. H_2O, H_2SO_4	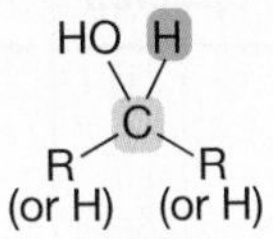 Alcohol	$:H^{\ominus}$ Hydride anion	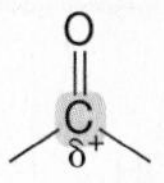	Nucleophilic addition	18.3
(14)	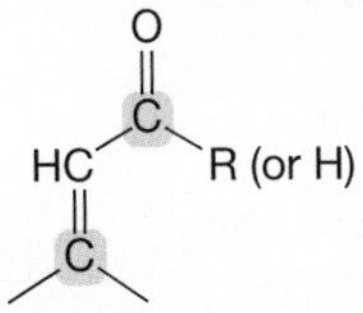 α,β-Unsaturated ketone or aldehyde	1. $NaBH_4$ or $LiAlH_4$ 2. NH_4Cl, H_2O	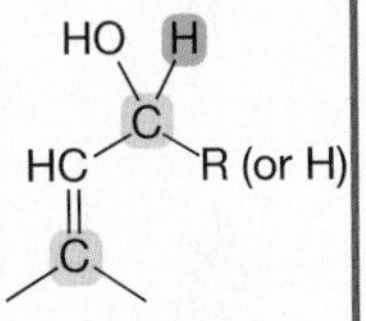 Alcohol	$:H^{\ominus}$ Hydride anion	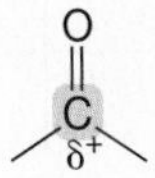	Nucleophilic addition	18.8
(15)	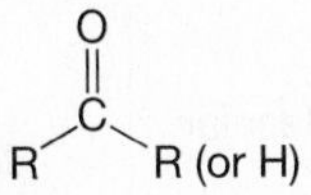 Ketone or aldehyde	H_2 → Pt, Pd, or Ni	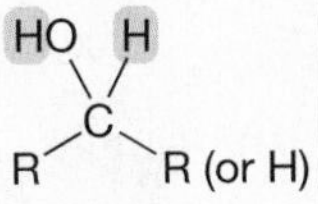 Alcohol	—	—	Catalytic hydrogenation	20.3
(16)	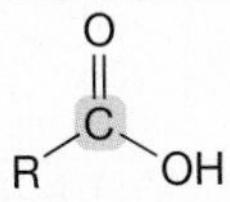 Carboxylic acid	1. $LiAlH_4$ 2. HCl	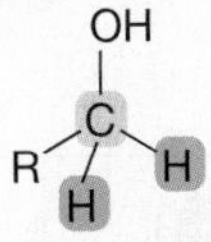 1° Alcohol	$:H^{\ominus}$ Hydride anion	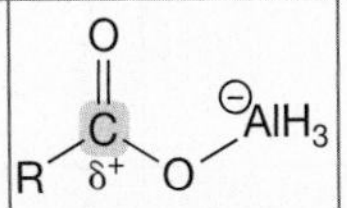	Nucleophilic addition–elimination, then addition (reduction)	22.6
(17)	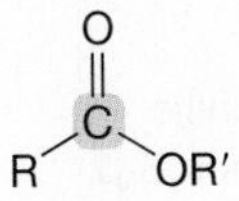 Ester	1. $NaBH_4$ or $LiAlH_4$ 2. HCl	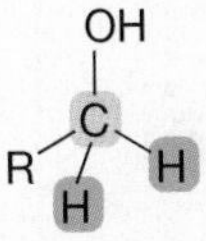 1° Alcohol	$:H^{\ominus}$ Hydride anion	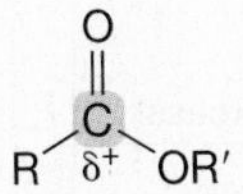	Nucleophilic addition–elimination, then addition (reduction); very slow with $NaBH_4$	22.6

(continued)

TABLE AppD-3 Reactions That Produce Alcohols and Phenols (continued)

	Starting Compound Class	Typical Reagents and Reaction Conditions	Compound Class Formed	Key Electron-Rich Species	Key Electron-Poor Species	Comments	Discussed in Section(s)
(18)	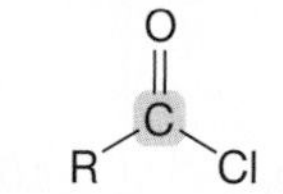 Acid chloride	1. $NaBH_4$ or $LiAlH_4$ 2. HCl →	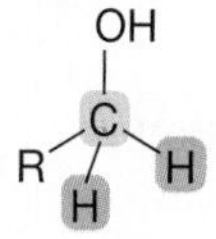 1° Alcohol	:H⊖ Hydride anion	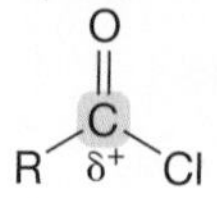	Nucleophilic addition–elimination, then addition (reduction)	22.6
(19)	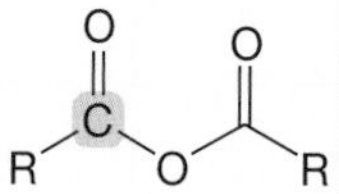 Acid anhydride	1. $NaBH_4$ or $LiAlH_4$ 2. HCl →	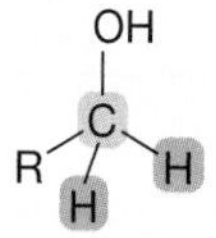 1° Alcohol	:H⊖ Hydride anion	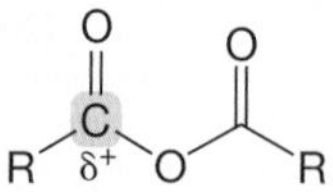	Nucleophilic addition–elimination, then addition (reduction)	22.6

TABLE AppD-4 Reactions That Produce Ethers, Epoxides, and Acetals

	Starting Compound Class	Typical Reagents and Reaction Conditions	Compound Class Formed	Key Electron-Rich Species	Key Electron-Poor Species	Comments	Discussed in Section(s)
(1)	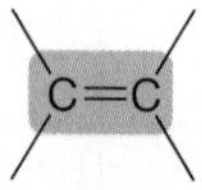 Alkene	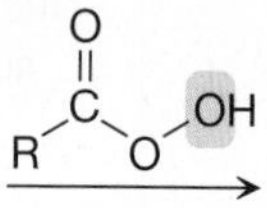	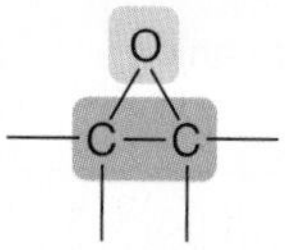 Epoxide	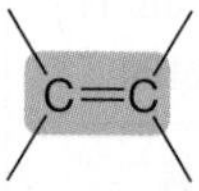	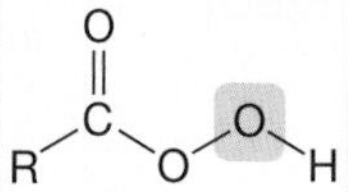	Conservation of cis/trans configurations	13.3
(2)	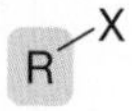 Alkyl halide (X = Cl, Br, or I)	NaOR′ →	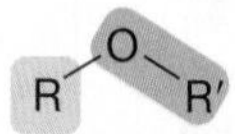 Ether (symmetric or unsymmetric)	R′Ö:⊖	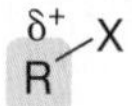	Williamson ether synthesis, S_N2	10.4
(3)	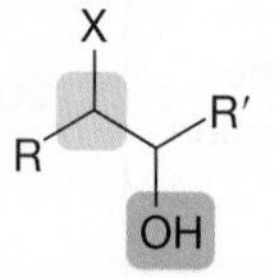 Halohydrin (X = Cl, Br, or I)	NaOH →	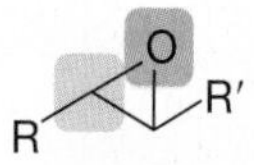 Epoxide	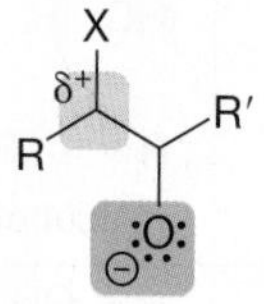		Intramolecular S_N2	10.8
(4)	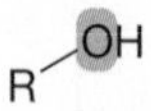 Alcohol	$H^{\oplus}$, Δ →	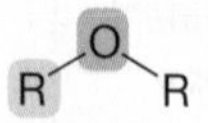 Ether (symmetric)	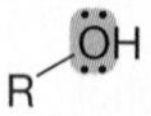	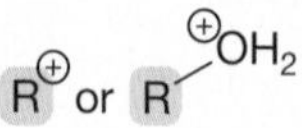	S_N1 or S_N2 (dehydration)	7.2, 7.3, 8.1, 8.3, 8.4, 10.4
(5)	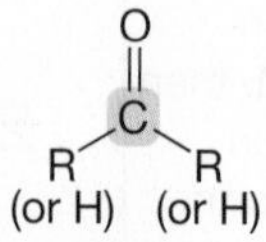 Ketone or aldehyde	R′OH (excess), H_2SO_4 →	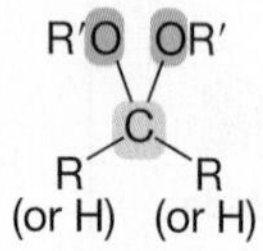 Acetal	R′—ÖH (δ^-)	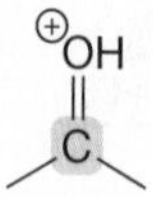	Nucleophilic addition, then S_N1	19.4a

TABLE AppD-5 Reactions That Produce Amines

	Starting Compound Class	Typical Reagents and Reaction Conditions	Compound Class Formed	Key Electron-Rich Species	Key Electron-Poor Species	Comments	Discussed in Section
(1)	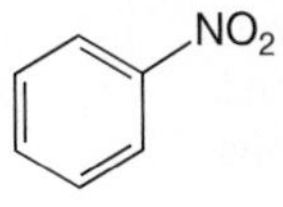 Nitroarene	1. HCl, Fe 2. NaOH	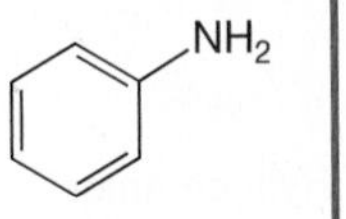 Arylamine	—	—	Reduction	24.9b
(2)	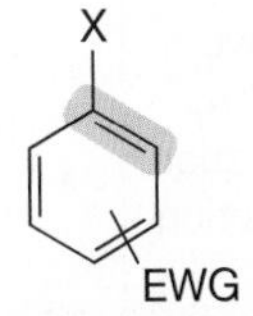 Electron-poor aromatic halide (X = F, Cl, Br, or I)	H_2NR (or H)	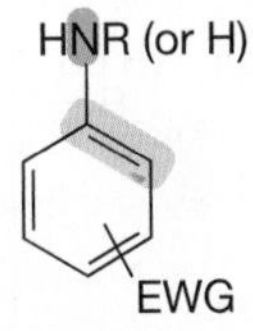 Aromatic amine	δ− $H_2\ddot{N}R$ (or H)	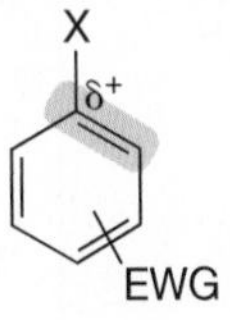	Nucleophilic addition–elimination mechanism; EWG ortho or para to X (EWG = electron-withdrawing group)	25.9a
(3)	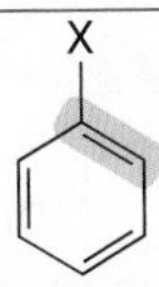 Aromatic halide (X = F, Cl, Br, or I)	LiNHR	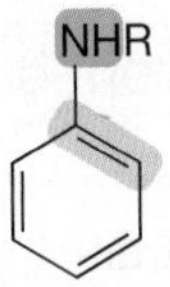 Aromatic amine	$\ominus$ $H\ddot{N}R$	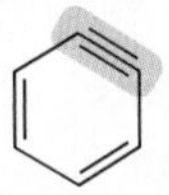	Proceeds through benzyne intermediate	25.9b
(4)	R—X 1° Alkyl halide	1 equiv of NH_3	R—NH_2 + other amines 1° Amine	δ− $:NH_3$	δ+ R—X	S_N2 reaction; not synthetically useful	10.10
(5)	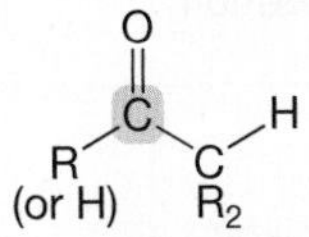 Ketone or aldehyde	R'_2NH (excess) $H^{\oplus}$ 2° Amine	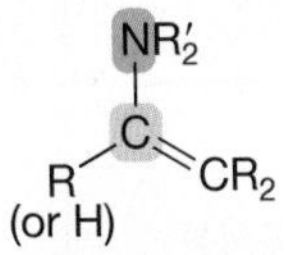 Enamine	δ− $R'_2\ddot{N}H$	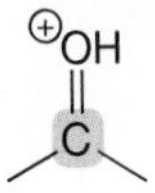	Nucleophilic addition, then E1	19.4b
(6)	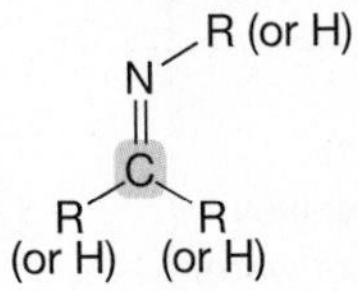 Imine	1. $LiAlH_4$ 2. H_2O	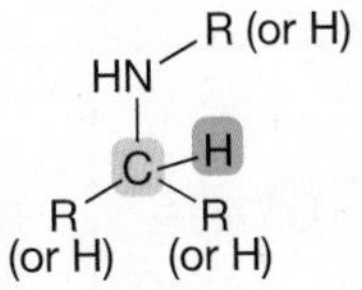 Amine	$:H^{\ominus}$ Hydride anion	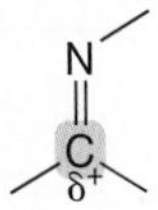	Nucleophilic addition	18.3
(7)	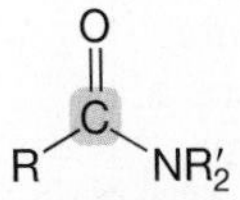 Amide	$LiAlH_4$ Ether	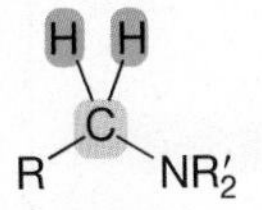 Amine	$:H^{\ominus}$ Hydride anion	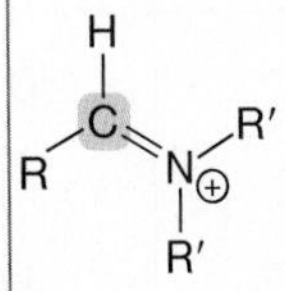	Nucleophilic addition–elimination, then addition (reduction)	22.6
(8)	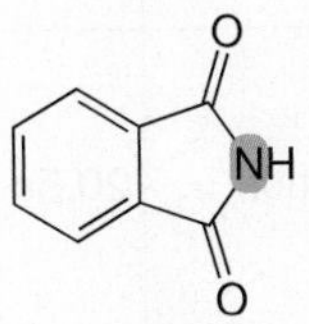 Phthalimide	1. KOH/EtOH 2. RBr 3. KOH/H_2O	H_2N—R 1° Amine	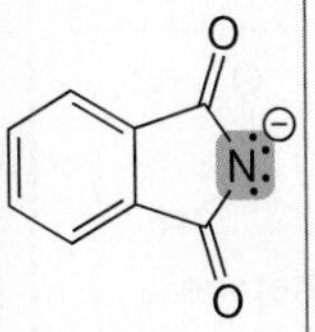	δ+ R—Br	S_N2, then nucleophilic addition–elimination (Gabriel synthesis)	22.4

(continued)

TABLE AppD-5 Reactions That Produce Amines (continued)

	Starting Compound Class	Typical Reagents and Reaction Conditions	Compound Class Formed	Key Electron-Rich Species	Key Electron-Poor Species	Comments	Discussed in Section
(9)	R—C≡N **Nitrile**	1. $LiAlH_4$ 2. H_2O	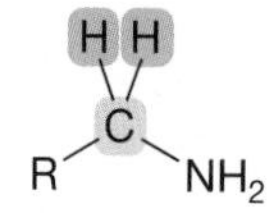 **1° Amine**	:$H^{\ominus}$ **Hydride anion**	$R—\overset{\delta+}{C}≡N$	Sequential nucleophilic additions	18.3
(10)	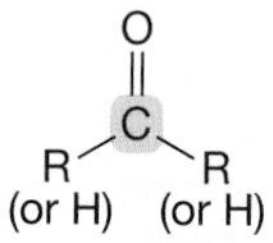 **Ketone or aldehyde**	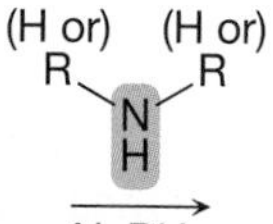 $NaBH_4$	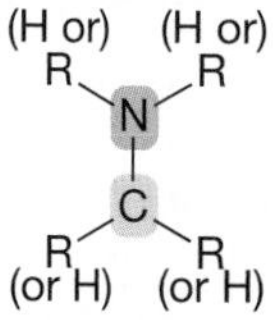 **Amine**	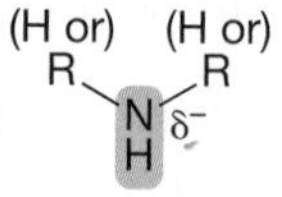	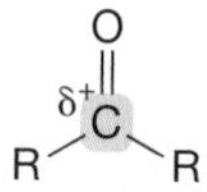	Reductive amination; imine formation, then reduction	19.5

TABLE AppD-6 Reactions That Produce or Alter Ketones and Aldehydes

	Starting Compound Class	Typical Reagents and Reaction Conditions	Compound Class Formed	Key Electron-Rich Species	Key Electron-Poor Species	Comments	Discussed in Section(s)
(1)	—C≡C— **Alkyne**	H_2O → H_2SO_4, Δ or TfOH, CF_3CH_2OH	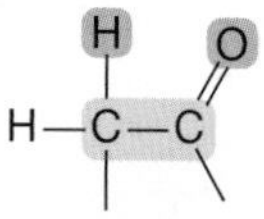 **Ketone**	$H_2\ddot{O}$:	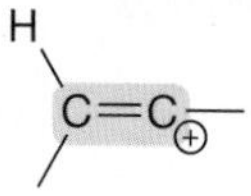	Markovnikov addition of H_2O, keto–enol tautomerization	12.8
(2)	—C≡C— **Alkyne**	$Hg(OAc)_2$, H_2O →	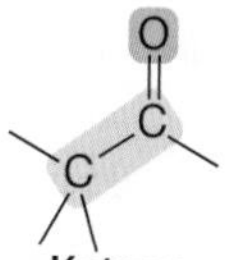 **Ketone**	$H_2\ddot{O}$:	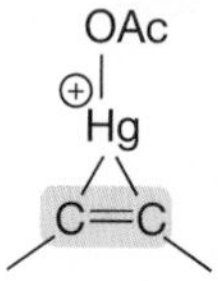	Markovnikov addition of water	13.5
(3)	—C≡C— **Alkyne**	1. $(C_5H_{11})_2BH$ 2. H_2O_2, NaOH, H_2O	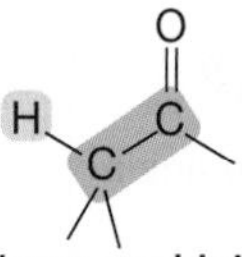 **Ketone or aldehyde**	—C≡C—	$(C_5H_{11})_2BH$	Anti-Markovnikov addition of water	13.7
(4)	—C≡C— **Alkyne**	OsO_4 → H_2O_2	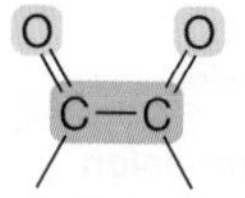 **1,2-Dione**	—C≡C—	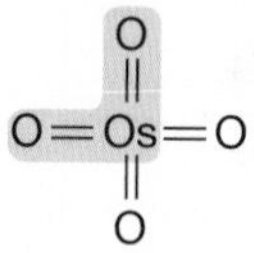	An alternate method uses a cold, basic solution of $KMnO_4$.	26.8
(5)	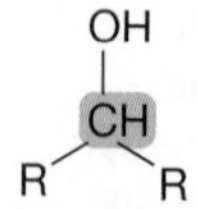 **2° Alcohol**	H_2CrO_4 → or $KMnO_4$, KOH →	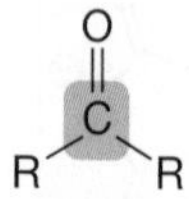 **Ketone**	—	—	Oxidation	20.5a, 20.5b

TABLE AppD-6 Reactions That Produce or Alter Ketones and Aldehydes (continued)

	Starting Compound Class	Typical Reagents and Reaction Conditions	Compound Class Formed	Key Electron-Rich Species	Key Electron-Poor Species	Comments	Discussed in Section(s)
(6)	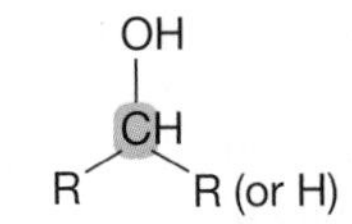 1° or 2° Alcohol	PCC →	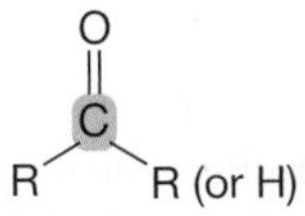 Aldehyde or ketone	—	—	Oxidation	20.5a
(7)	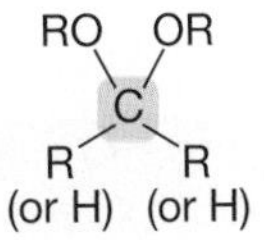 Acetal	H_2O (excess) → H_2SO_4	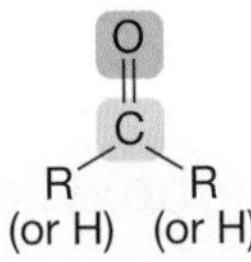 Ketone or aldehyde	$H_2\overset{\delta-}{\ddot{O}}:$	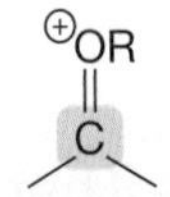	S_N1, then E1	19.4a
(8)	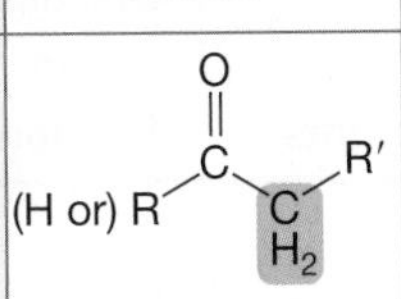 Ketone or aldehyde	X_2 (X = Cl, Br, or I) → NaOH	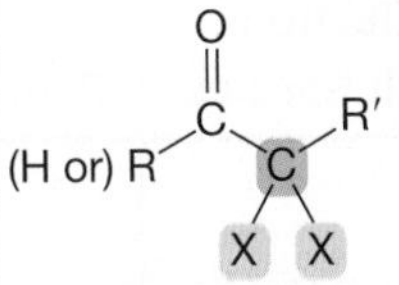 α-Halogenated ketone or aldehyde	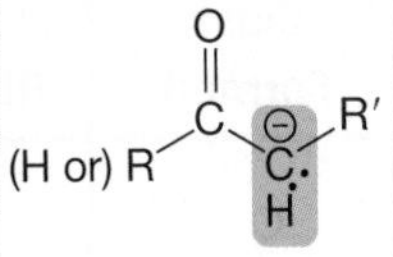 Enolate anion	$\overset{\delta+}{X}-\overset{\delta-}{X}$	Multiple S_N2 reactions	10.6
(9)	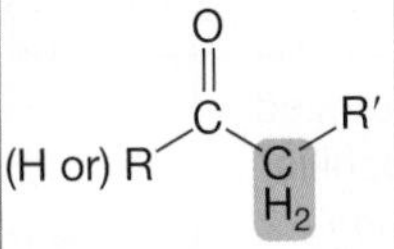 Ketone or aldehyde	X_2 (X = Cl, Br, or I) → Acid	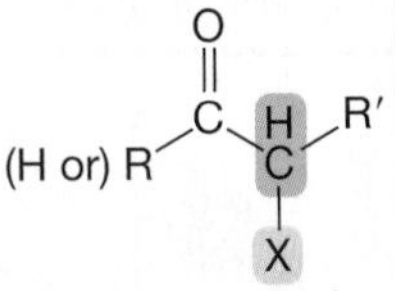 α-Halogenated ketone or aldehyde	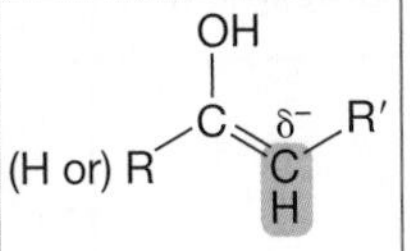 Enol	$\overset{\delta+}{X}-\overset{\delta-}{X}$	Single S_N2 reaction	10.6
(10)	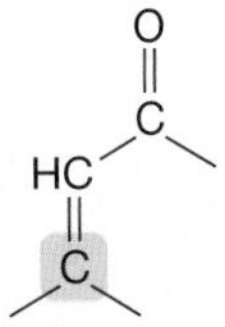 α,β-Unsaturated ketone or aldehyde	H—Nu → Nu = OR, SR, or NR_2	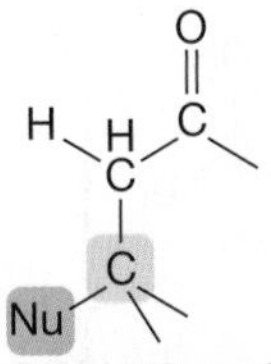 β-Substituted ketone or aldehyde	$H-\overset{\delta-}{\ddot{N}u}:$	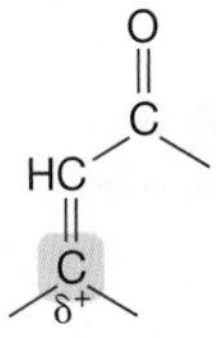	Conjugate nucleophilic addition	19.3
(11)	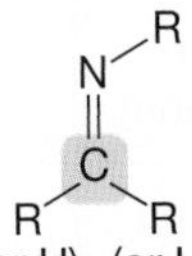 Imine	H_2O (excess) → HCl	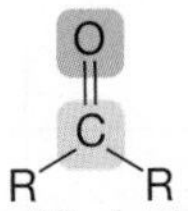 Ketone or aldehyde	$H_2\overset{\delta-}{\ddot{O}}:$	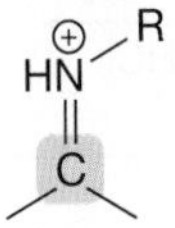	Nucleophilic addition, then E1	19.4b
(12)	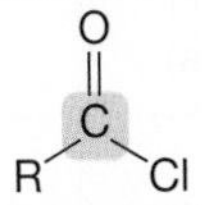 Acid chloride	$LiAlH(O\text{-}t\text{-}Bu)_3$ → –75 °C	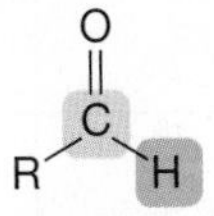 Aldehyde	$:H^{\ominus}$ Hydride anion	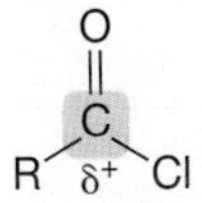	Nucleophilic addition–elimination (reduction); note cold *T*	22.7

(continued)

TABLE AppD-6 Reactions That Produce or Alter Ketones and Aldehydes (continued)

	Starting Compound Class	Typical Reagents and Reaction Conditions	Compound Class Formed	Key Electron-Rich Species	Key Electron-Poor Species	Comments	Discussed in Section(s)
(13)	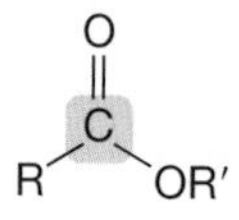 Ester	1. DIBAH, −78 °C 2. HCl	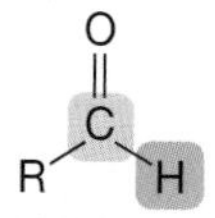 Aldehyde	$:H^{\ominus}$ Hydride anion	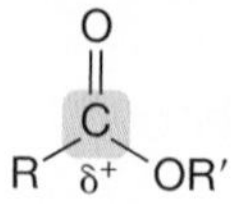	Nucleophilic addition–elimination (reduction); note cold *T*	22.7

TABLE AppD-7 Reactions That Produce or Alter Carboxylic Acids

	Starting Compound Class	Typical Reagents and Reaction Conditions	Compound Class Formed	Key Electron-Rich Species	Key Electron-Poor Species	Comments	Discussed in Section(s)
(1)	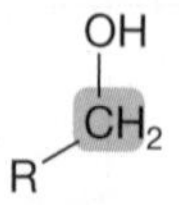 1° Alcohol	H_2CrO_4 or 1. $KMnO_4$, KOH 2. H_2O, HCl	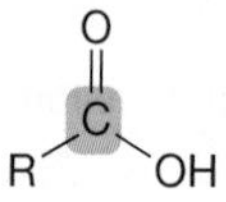 Carboxylic acid	—	—	Oxidation	20.5a, 20.5b
(2)	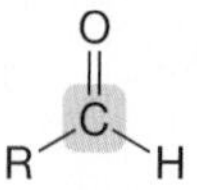 Aldehyde	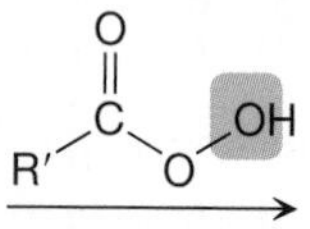	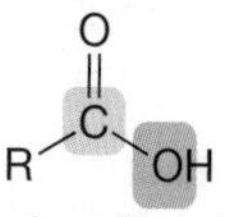 Carboxylic acid	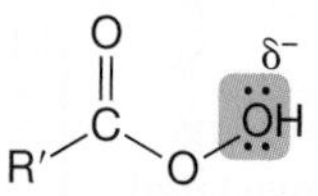	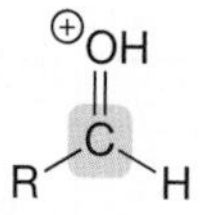	Acid-catalyzed nucleophilic addition–elimination (Baeyer–Villiger oxidation)	23.8
(3)	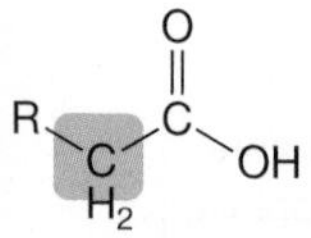 Carboxylic acid	Br_2, P	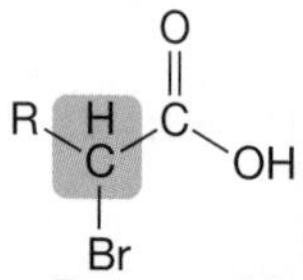 α-Bromo acid	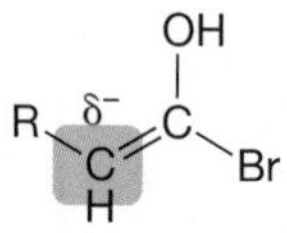	δ^+ δ^- Br—Br	Hell–Volhard–Zelinsky reaction	23.5
(4)	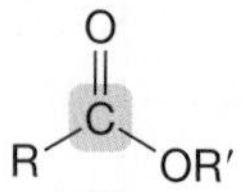 Ester	1. NaOH 2. HCl	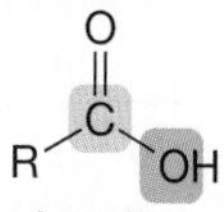 Carboxylic acid	$^{\ominus}$:ÖH	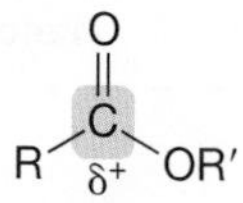	Nucleophilic addition–elimination (saponification)	22.3
(5)	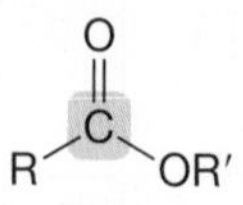 Ester	H_2O H_2SO_4	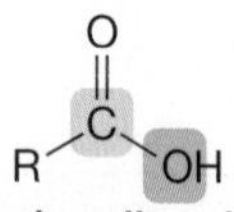 Carboxylic acid	$H_2\ddot{O}$: δ^-	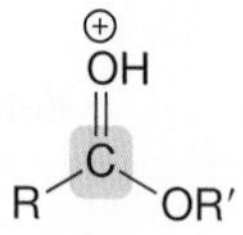	Acid-catalyzed nucleophilic addition–elimination (hydrolysis)	23.7
(6)	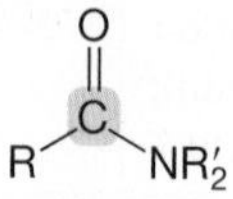 Amide	1. NaOH 2. HCl	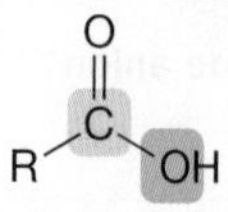 Carboxylic acid	$^{\ominus}$:ÖH	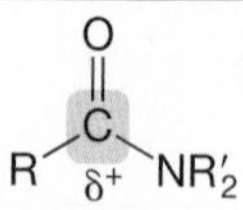	Nucleophilic addition–elimination	22.4

TABLE AppD-7 Reactions That Produce or Alter Carboxylic Acids (continued)

	Starting Compound Class	Typical Reagents and Reaction Conditions	Compound Class Formed	Key Electron-Rich Species	Key Electron-Poor Species	Comments	Discussed in Section(s)
(7)	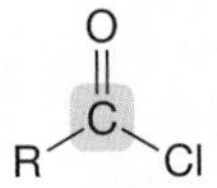 Acid chloride	H_2O →	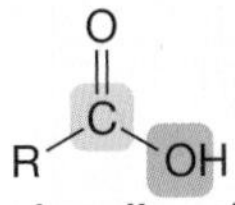 Carboxylic acid	$H_2\ddot{O}:^{\delta-}$	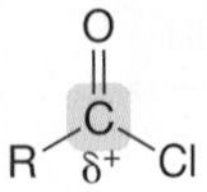	Nucleophilic addition–elimination (hydrolysis)	23.1
(8)	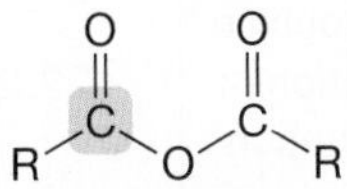 Acid anhydride	H_2O →	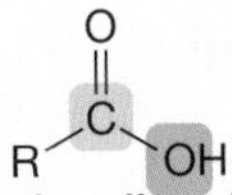 Carboxylic acid	$H_2\ddot{O}:^{\delta-}$	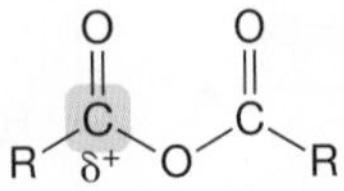	Nucleophilic addition–elimination (hydrolysis)	23.2

TABLE AppD-8 Reactions That Produce or Alter Esters

	Starting Compound Class	Typical Reagents and Reaction Conditions	Compound Class Formed	Key Electron-Rich Species	Key Electron-Poor Species	Comments	Discussed in Section(s)
(1)	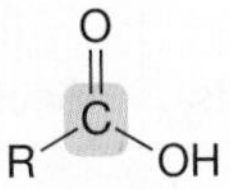 Carboxylic acid	R′OH → H_2SO_4	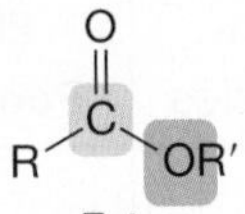 Ester	$R'\ddot{O}H^{\delta-}$	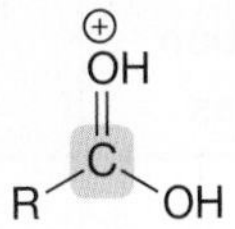	Acid-catalyzed nucleophilic addition–elimination (Fischer esterification)	23.7
(2)	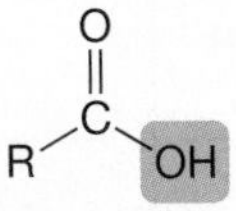 Carboxylic acid	CH_2N_2 →	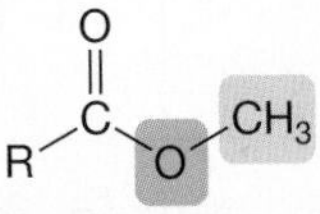 Methyl ester	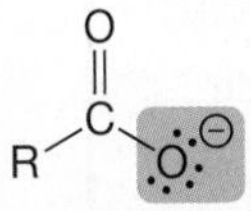 Carboxylate anion	$H_3C—N_2^{\oplus}$	S_N2	10.9
(3)	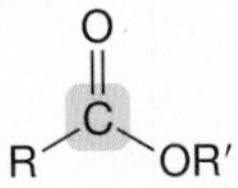 Ester	R″OH → R″ONa	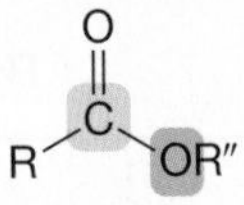 Ester	$^{\ominus}:\ddot{O}R''$	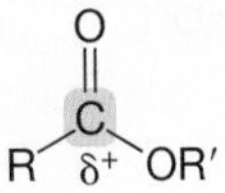	Base-catalyzed nucleophilic addition–elimination (transesterification)	22.1a, 23.7
(4)	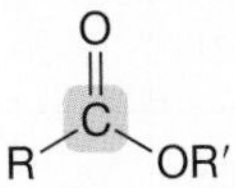 Ester	R″OH → H_2SO_4	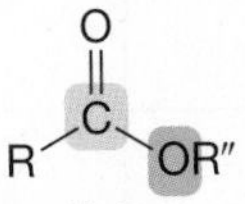 Ester	$R''\ddot{O}H^{\delta-}$	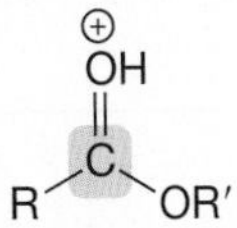	Acid-catalyzed nucleophilic addition–elimination (transesterification)	23.7
(5)	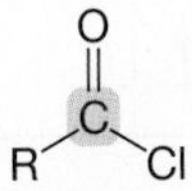 Acid chloride	LiOR′ →	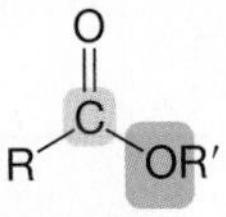 Ester	$^{\ominus}:\ddot{O}R'$	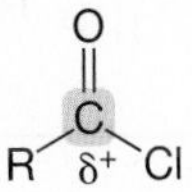	Nucleophilic addition–elimination	22.2

(continued)

TABLE AppD-8 Reactions That Produce or Alter Esters (continued)

	Starting Compound Class	Typical Reagents and Reaction Conditions	Compound Class Formed	Key Electron-Rich Species	Key Electron-Poor Species	Comments	Discussed in Section
(6)	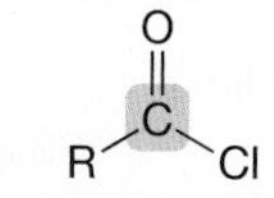 Acid chloride	$\xrightarrow{R'OH}$	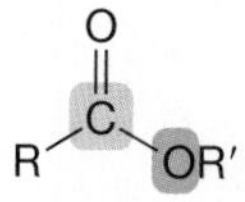 Ester	$R'\ddot{O}H$ $\delta-$	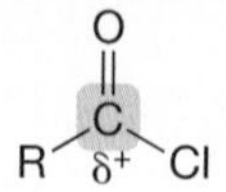	Nucleophilic addition–elimination (alcoholysis)	23.1
(7)	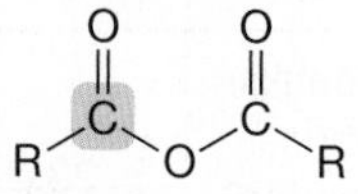 Acid anhydride	$\xrightarrow{NaOR'}$	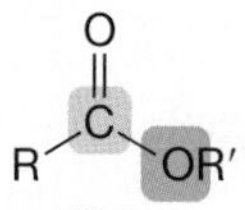 Ester	$^{\ominus}:\ddot{O}R'$	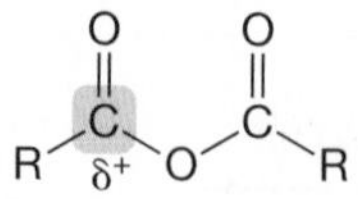	Nucleophilic addition–elimination	22.2
(8)	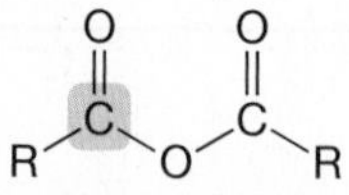 Acid anhydride	$\xrightarrow{R'OH}$	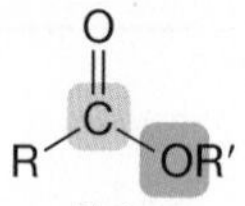 Ester	$R'\ddot{O}H$ $\delta-$	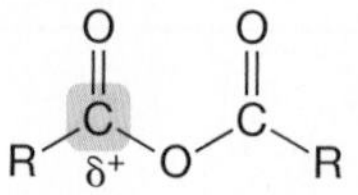	Nucleophilic addition–elimination (alcoholysis)	23.2

TABLE AppD-9 Reactions That Produce Amides

	Starting Compound Class	Typical Reagents and Reaction Conditions	Compound Class Formed	Key Electron-Rich Species	Key Electron-Poor Species	Comments	Discussed in Section
(1)	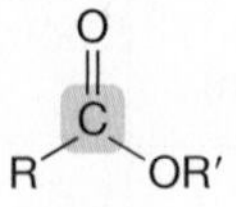 Ester	$\xrightarrow{LiNR''_2}$	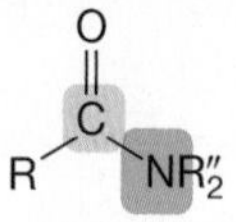 Amide	$^{\ominus}:NR''_2$	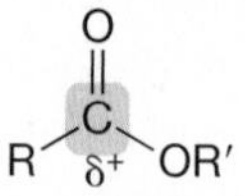	Nucleophilic addition–elimination	22.2
(2)	R—C≡N Nitrile	$\xrightarrow[H_2SO_4 \text{ or } NaOH]{H_2O \text{ (1 equiv)}}$	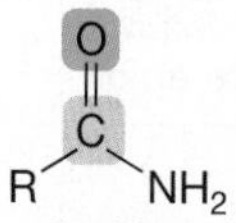 Amide	$\delta-$ $H_2\ddot{O}:$ or $^{\ominus}:\ddot{O}H$	R—C≡$\overset{\oplus}{N}$H or $\delta+$ R—C≡N	Nucleophilic addition	19.7
(3)	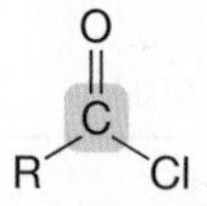 Acid chloride	$\xrightarrow[Et_3N \text{ or pyridine}]{R'_2NH}$	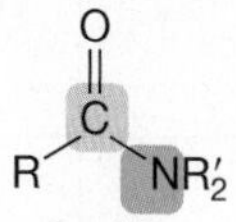 Amide	$R'_2\ddot{N}H$ $\delta-$	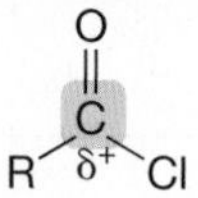	Nucleophilic addition–elimination (aminolysis)	23.3
(4)	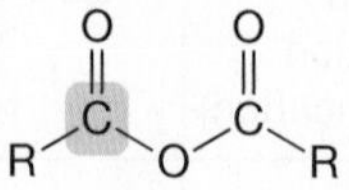 Acid anhydride	$\xrightarrow[Et_3N \text{ or pyridine}]{R'_2NH}$	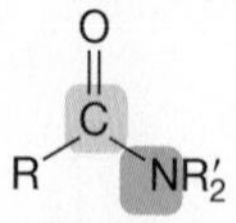 Amide	$R'_2\ddot{N}H$ $\delta-$	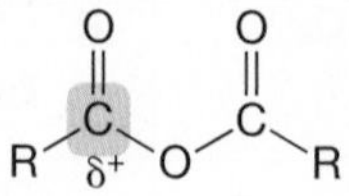	Nucleophilic addition–elimination (aminolysis)	23.3

TABLE AppD-10 Reactions That Alter Aromatic Compounds

	Starting Compound Class	Typical Reagents and Reaction Conditions	Compound Class Formed	Key Electron-Rich Species	Key Electron-Poor Species	Comments	Discussed in Section
(1)	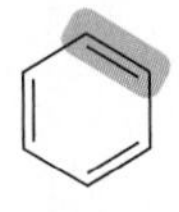 Arene	Br_2, $FeBr_3$ →	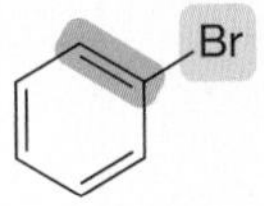 Br Aryl bromide	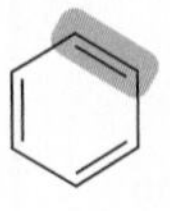	$:\ddot{Br}^{\oplus}—FeBr_3$	Electrophilic aromatic substitution	24.2
(2)	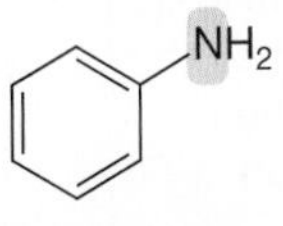 NH2 Arylamine	1. $NaNO_2$, H_2SO_4 2. CuBr →	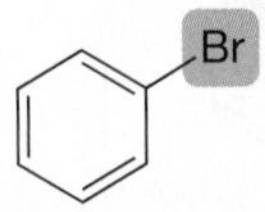 Br Aryl bromide	CuBr	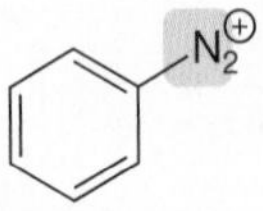 N2⊕	Proceeds through a diazonium ion; Sandmeyer reaction	24.9c
(3)	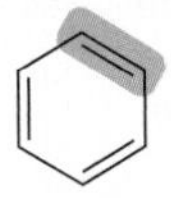 Arene	Cl_2, $FeCl_3$ →	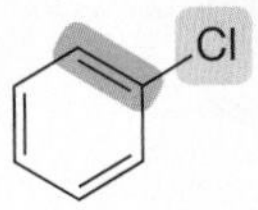 Cl Aryl chloride	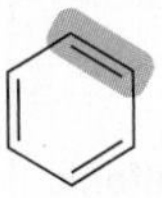	$:\ddot{Cl}^{\oplus}—FeCl_3$	Electrophilic aromatic substitution	24.2
(4)	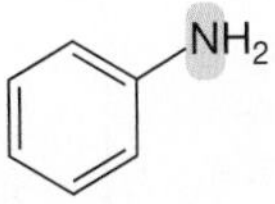 NH2 Arylamine	1. $NaNO_2$, H_2SO_4 2. CuCl →	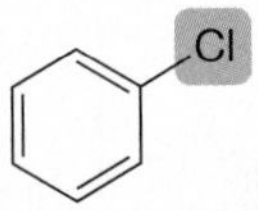 Cl Aryl chloride	CuCl	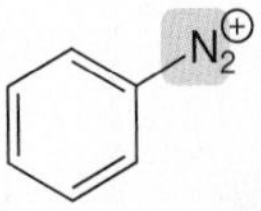 N2⊕	Proceeds through a diazonium ion; Sandmeyer reaction	24.9c
(5)	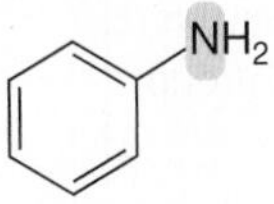 NH2 Arylamine	1. $NaNO_2$, H_2SO_4 2. KI →	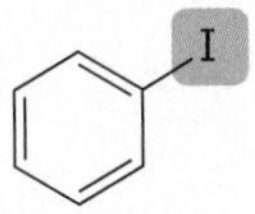 I Aryl iodide	KI	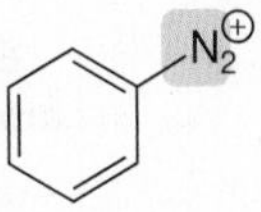 N2⊕	Proceeds through a diazonium ion	24.9c
(6)	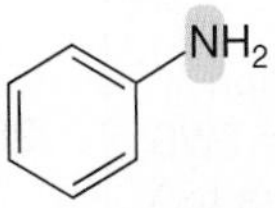 NH2 Arylamine	1. $NaNO_2$, H_2SO_4 2. HBF_4, then Δ →	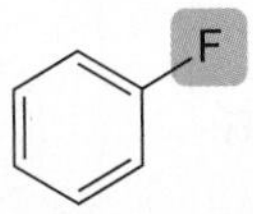 F Aryl fluoride	HBF_4	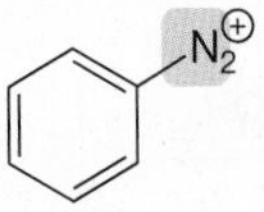 N2⊕	Proceeds through a diazonium ion	24.9c
(7)	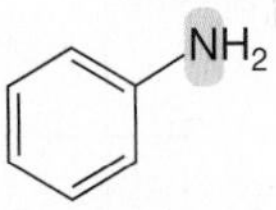 NH2 Arylamine	1. $NaNO_2$, H_2SO_4 2. H_2O, Cu_2O, $Cu(NO_3)_2$ →	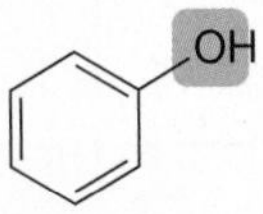 OH Aryl alcohol	H_2O	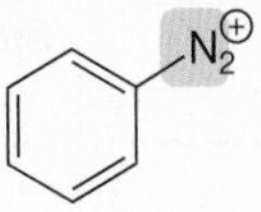 N2⊕	Proceeds through a diazonium ion; Sandmeyer reaction	24.9c
(8)	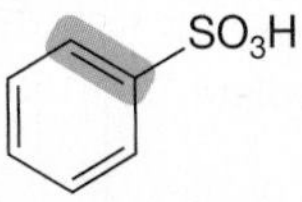 SO3H Arenesulfonic acid	$H_3O^{\oplus}$ →	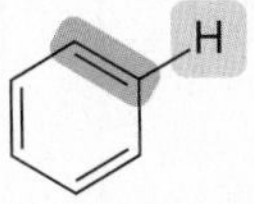 H Arene	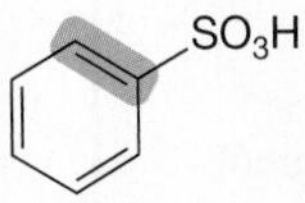 SO3H	$H—\overset{\oplus}{O}H_2$	Electrophilic aromatic substitution; desulfonation	24.7
(9)	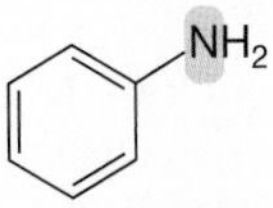 NH2 Arylamine	1. $NaNO_2$, H_2SO_4 2. H_3PO_2 →	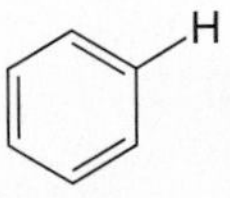 H Arene	—	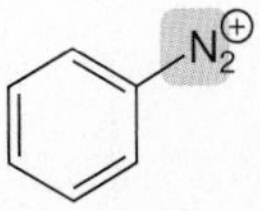 N2⊕	Proceeds through a diazonium ion	24.9c

(continued)

TABLE AppD-10 Reactions That Alter Aromatic Compounds (continued)

	Starting Compound Class	Typical Reagents and Reaction Conditions	Compound Class Formed	Key Electron-Rich Species	Key Electron-Poor Species	Comments	Discussed in Section
(10)	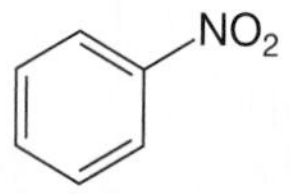 NO2 Nitroarene	1. HCl, Fe → 2. NaOH	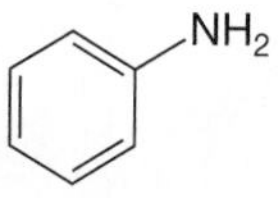 NH2 Arylamine	—	—	Reduction	24.9b
(11)	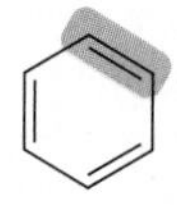 Arene	HNO_3 → H_2SO_4	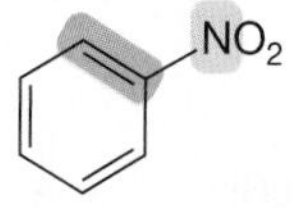 NO2 Nitroarene	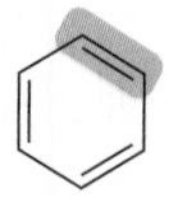	$^{\oplus}NO_2$	Electrophilic aromatic substitution; nitration	24.6
(12)	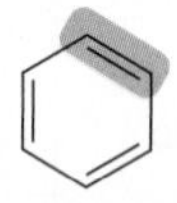 Arene	SO_3 → H_2SO_4	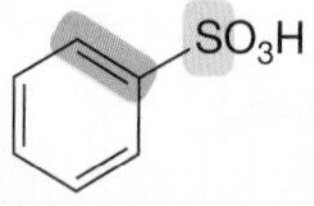 SO3H Arenesulfonic acid	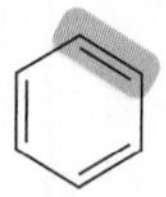	$SO_3H^{\oplus}$	Electrophilic aromatic substitution	24.7
(13)	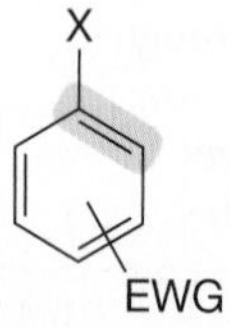 X EWG Electron-poor aromatic halide (X = F, Cl, Br, or I)	H_2NR →	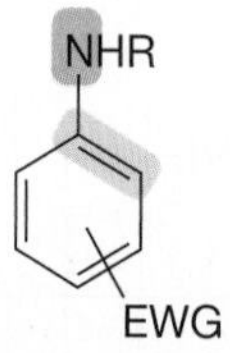 NHR EWG Substituted aromatic amine	$H_2\ddot{N}R$ δ^-	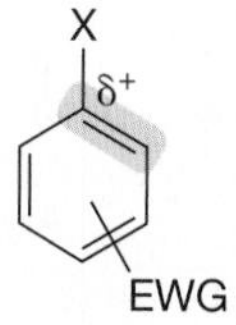 X δ+ EWG	Nucleophilic addition–elimination mechanism; EWG ortho or para to X (EWG = electron-withdrawing group)	25.9a
(14)	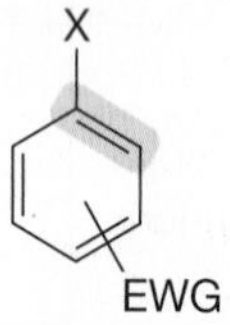 X EWG Electron-poor aromatic halide (X = F, Cl, Br, or I)	NaOR →	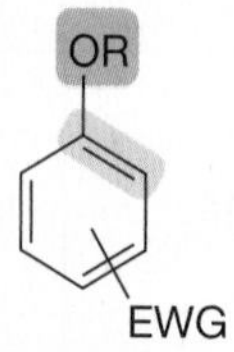 OR EWG Substituted aromatic ether	$^{\ominus}:\ddot{O}R$	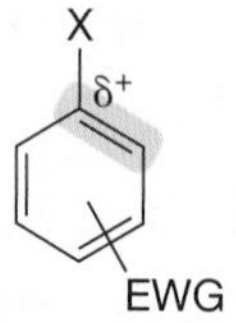 X δ+ EWG	Nucleophilic addition–elimination mechanism; EWG ortho or para to X (EWG = electron-withdrawing group)	25.9a
(15)	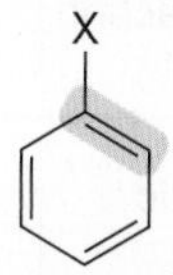 X Aromatic halide (X = F, Cl, Br, or I)	1. NaOH, Δ → 2. H_2O, HCl	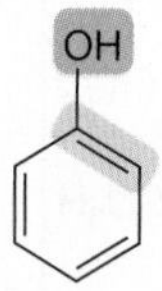 OH Phenol	$^{\ominus}:\ddot{O}H$	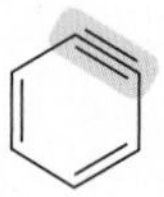	Proceeds through benzyne intermediate	25.9b

TABLE AppD-10 Reactions That Alter Aromatic Compounds (continued)

	Starting Compound Class	Typical Reagents and Reaction Conditions	Compound Class Formed	Key Electron-Rich Species	Key Electron-Poor Species	Comments	Discussed in Section
(16)	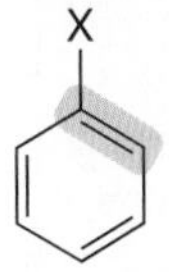 Aromatic halide (X = F, Cl, Br, or I)	1. KNH_2, $NH_3(\ell)$ H_2SO_4 → 2. H_2O	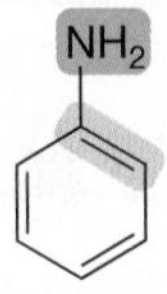 Aniline	$^{\ominus}\ddot{N}H_2$	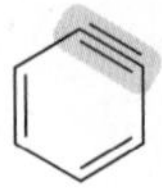	Proceeds through benzyne intermediate	25.9b
(17)	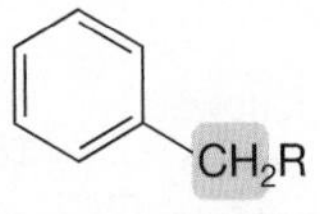 Alkylbenzene with allylic H	NBS → Δ or $h\nu$	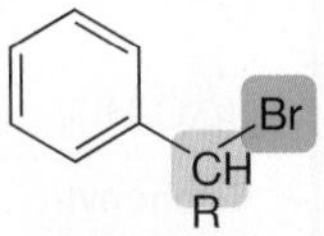 Benzylic bromide	Br—Br	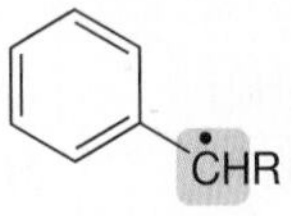	Functionalizes a relatively unreactive carbon	27.4d

TABLE AppD-11 Reactions That Produce Alkanes

	Starting Compound Class	Typical Reagents and Reaction Conditions	Compound Class Formed	Key Electron-Rich Species	Key Electron-Poor Species	Comments	Discussed in Section
(1)	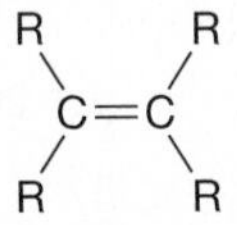 Alkene	H_2 → Pt, Pd, or Ni	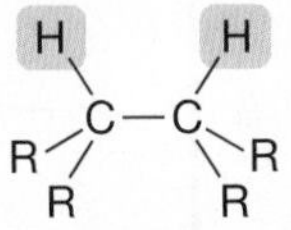 Alkane	—	—	Catalytic hydrogenation	13.9a
(2)	R—C≡C—R Alkyne	H_2 (excess) → Pt, Pd, or Ni	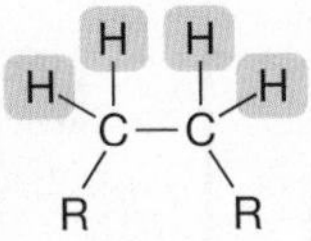	—	—	Catalytic hydrogenation	13.9b
(3)	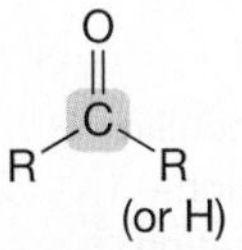 Ketone or aldehyde	1. H_2N—NH_2, $H^{\oplus}$ → 2. KOH/diethylene glycol, Δ	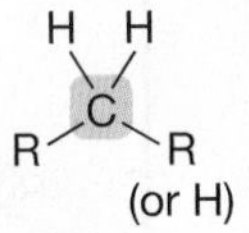 Alkane	$\delta-$ $H_2\ddot{N}NH_2$	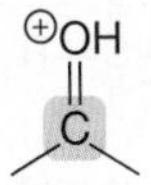	Wolff–Kishner reduction: nucleophilic addition, then E1, then E2	19.6
(4)	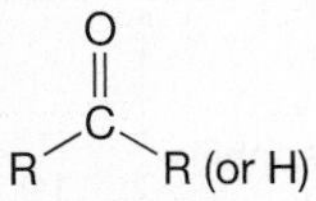 Ketone or aldehyde	Zn/Hg, HCl → H_2O, reflux	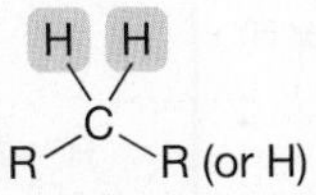 Alkane	—	—	Clemmensen reduction	20.4
(5)	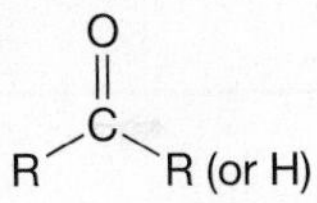 Ketone or aldehyde	1. $HSCH_2CH_2SH$, $H^{\oplus}$ → 2. Raney nickel (H_2)	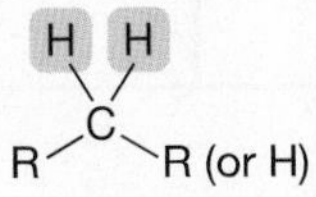 Alkane	—	—	Raney-nickel reduction	20.4

TABLE AppD-12 Reactions That Produce Other Species

	Starting Compound Class	Typical Reagents and Reaction Conditions	Compound Class Formed	Key Electron-Rich Species	Key Electron-Poor Species	Comments	Discussed in Section
(1)	R—NH_2 Amine	excess R′—X → (X = Cl, Br, or I)	$X^{\ominus}$ $R—N^{\oplus}R'_3$ Quaternary ammonium salt	R—$\ddot{N}H_2$ (δ−)	R′—X (δ+ on R′)	Multiple S_N2 reactions	10.10
(2)	H, Br on C with R, R (or H) (or H) Alkyl halide	1. $P(C_6H_5)_3$ 2. R—Li →	$^{\oplus}P(C_6H_5)_3$ on $^{\ominus}\ddot{C}$ with (H or) R, R (or H) Wittig reagent	$:P(C_6H_5)_3$ (δ−) Triphenylphosphine	H, Br on C (δ+) with R, R (or H) (or H)	S_N2 followed by proton transfer	18.6
(3)	R—X Alkyl halide (X = Cl or Br)	Mg(s), Ether →	R—MgX Grignard reagent	—	—	Dissolving metal reduction	20.6
(4)	R—X Alkyl halide (X = Cl or Br)	Li(s), Ether →	R—Li Alkyllithium reagent	—	—	Dissolving metal reduction	20.6
(5)	R—Li Alkyllithium reagent	CuI, Ether →	R—Cu(Li)—R Lithium dialkylcuprate	—	—	—	20.6
(6)	R—C(=O)—OH Carboxylic acid	$SOCl_2$ →	R—C(=O)—Cl Acid chloride	$:\ddot{Cl}:^{\ominus}$	R—C(=$^{\oplus}$OH)—O—S(=O)—Cl	Back-to-back nucleophilic addition–eliminations	23.4
(7)	R—OH Alcohol	Cl—S(=O)₂—R′ →	RO—S(=O)₂—R′ Sulfonate ester	R$\ddot{O}$H (δ−)	Cl—S(=O)₂—R′ (δ+ on S)	Nucleophilic addition–elimination	23.6
(8)	R—C(=O)—R (or H) (or H) Ketone or aldehyde	NH_3 or R′NH_2 (excess) → $H^{\oplus}$ Ammonia or 1° amine	R′ (or H)—N=C(R)(R) (or H) (or H) Imine	R′—$\ddot{N}H_2$ (δ−) (or H)	$^{\oplus}$OH=C<	Nucleophilic addition, then E1	19.4b

APPENDIX E

Trivial Names or Common Names

Prior to the establishment of the IUPAC system of nomenclature, the names of many organic compounds were based on their properties or their natural source. Some naming systems based on structure had been developed for certain compound classes, but the rules were not the same from one compound class to another. Compound names that were in use before the IUPAC system but not adopted by the IUPAC are today called **trivial names** or **common names**. Here in Appendix E, we examine various aspects of trivial names in the order they were presented in the nomenclature interchapters earlier in the text; each section in Appendix E is devoted to one compound class or a group of related compound classes. As we have done throughout this book, IUPAC names appearing in figures will be presented without parentheses, whereas trivial names will be presented within parentheses.

Chapter Outline

AppE.1 Alkanes and Alkyl Groups

IUPAC rules for naming alkanes were presented in Section A.2 (p. 53). Historically, to differentiate straight-chain alkanes such as butane and pentane from their branched counterparts, straight-chain alkanes were given the prefix *n*-, which stands for *normal*. Common branched alkanes with the same number of carbon atoms were given the same root but a different prefix. As shown in **Figure AppE-1**, for example, *n*-butane is the trivial name for butane, whereas isobutane, the only branched alkane with four carbon atoms, is the trivial name for methylpropane. Similarly, *n*-pentane, isopentane, and neopentane all have five carbon atoms and are the trivial names for pentane, methylbutane, and dimethylpropane, respectively.

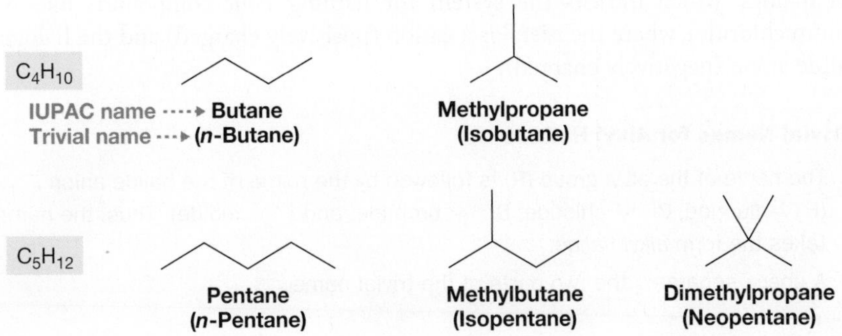

C_4H_{10}
IUPAC name ····▸ Butane
Trivial name ···▸ (n-Butane)
Methylpropane
(Isobutane)
C_5H_{12}
Pentane
(n-Pentane)
Methylbutane
(Isopentane)
Dimethylpropane
(Neopentane)

FIGURE AppE-1 **Trivial names of alkanes**

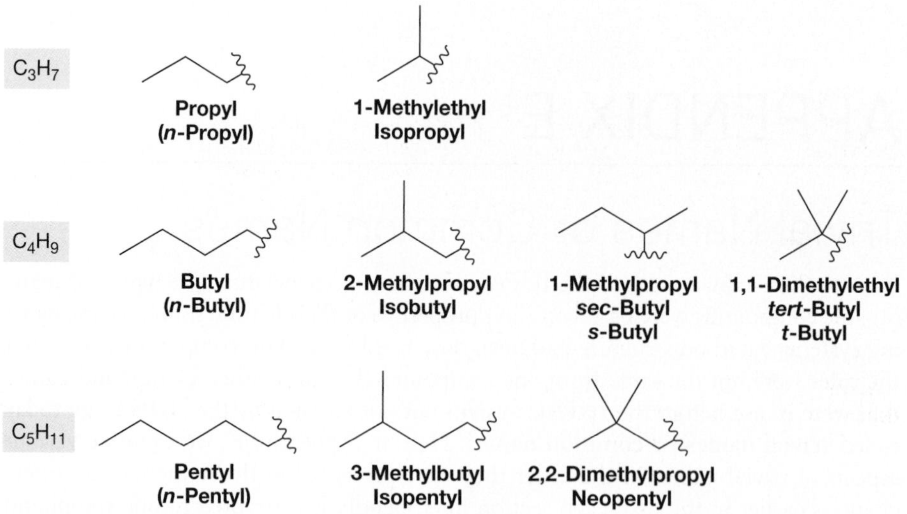
C_3H_7
Propyl
(*n*-Propyl)
1-Methylethyl
Isopropyl
C_4H_9
Butyl
(*n*-Butyl)
2-Methylpropyl
Isobutyl
1-Methylpropyl
sec-Butyl
s-Butyl
1,1-Dimethylethyl
tert-Butyl
t-Butyl
C_5H_{11}
Pentyl
(*n*-Pentyl)
3-Methylbutyl
Isopentyl
2,2-Dimethylpropyl
Neopentyl

FIGURE AppE-2 Trivial names of alkyl substituents

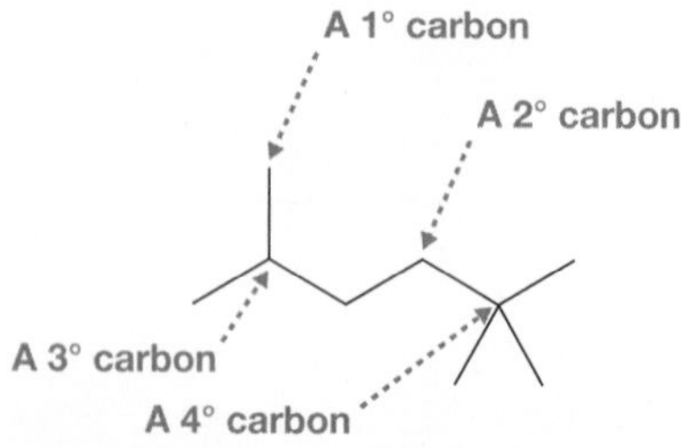
A 1° carbon
A 2° carbon
A 3° carbon
A 4° carbon

FIGURE AppE-3 Types of carbon Carbons in a molecule are classified by the number of other carbons that are directly attached.

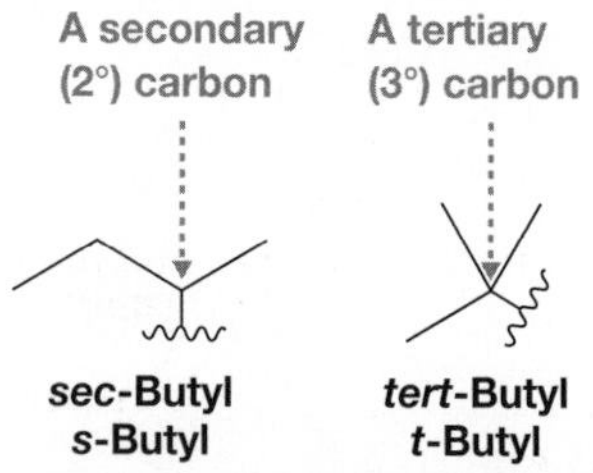
A secondary
(2°) carbon
A tertiary
(3°) carbon
sec-Butyl
s-Butyl
tert-Butyl
t-Butyl

FIGURE AppE-4 Distinguishing C_4H_9 groups A *sec*-butyl group is attached by a secondary carbon. A *tert*-butyl group is attached by a tertiary carbon.

A much more common use of trivial names involves branched alkyl substituents, whose IUPAC names were discussed in Section A.4 (p. 59). The examples shown in **Figure AppE-2** appear frequently and should be committed to memory. In fact, the branched alkyl groups in Figure AppE-2 (isopropyl, isobutyl, *sec*-butyl, *tert*-butyl, isopentyl, and neopentyl) appear so frequently that they have become accepted IUPAC names.

In learning the trivial names for the alkyl substituents in Figure AppE-2, it helps to know that the prefixes *sec* and *tert* stand for secondary and tertiary, respectively, and reflect the type of carbon atom at the point of attachment. As illustrated in **Figure AppE-3**, we generally distinguish carbon atoms by the number of *other* carbon atoms to which they are directly bonded:

- A *primary carbon* (abbreviated 1°) is directly bonded to one other carbon atom.
- A *secondary carbon* (abbreviated 2°) is directly bonded to two other carbon atoms.
- A *tertiary carbon* (abbreviated 3°) is directly bonded to three other carbon atoms.
- A *quaternary carbon* (abbreviated 4°) is directly bonded to four other carbon atoms.

For example, examine the *sec*-butyl and *tert*-butyl groups in **Figure AppE-4**. Notice in the *sec*-butyl group that the C atom at the point of attachment is a secondary (2°) carbon, whereas the *tert*-butyl group is attached by a tertiary (3°) carbon.

AppE.2 Haloalkanes (Alkyl Halides)

IUPAC rules for naming haloalkanes (R—X, where X is a halogen) were presented in Section A.3 (p. 55). **Figure AppE-5** shows the trivial names for a variety of haloalkanes. Some of these names derive from an older system of naming haloalkanes as alkyl halides, which mirrors the system for naming *ionic* compounds like NaCl (sodium chloride), where the metal is a cation (positively charged) and the halogen is a halide anion (negatively charged):

Trivial Names for Alkyl Halides

- The name of the alkyl group (R) is followed by the name of the halide anion (F^- = fluoride, Cl^- = chloride, Br^- = bromide, and I^- = iodide). Thus, the name takes the form *alkyl halide*.
- A space separates the two parts of the trivial name.

$H_3C—I$

Iodomethane
(Methyl iodide)

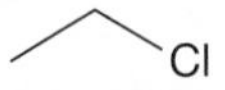

Chloroethane
(Ethyl chloride)

Dichloromethane
(Methyl dichloride)
(Methylene chloride)

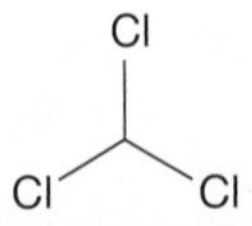

Trichloromethane
(Methyl trichloride)
(Chloroform)

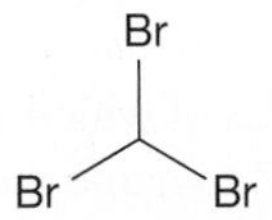

Tribromomethane
(Methyl tribromide)
(Bromoform)

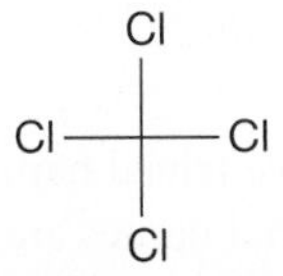

Tetrachloromethane
(Methyl tetrachloride)
(Carbon tetrachloride)

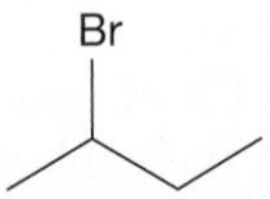

2-Bromobutane
(*sec*-Butyl bromide)
(*s*-Butyl bromide)

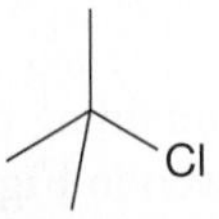

2-Chloro-2-methylpropane
(*tert*-Butyl chloride)
(*t*-Butyl chloride)

FIGURE AppE-5 Trivial names of haloalkanes

Under this system, the alkyl group can be one that has been incorporated into the IUPAC system, as is the case for methyl iodide (CH_3I), *sec*-butyl bromide, and *tert*-butyl chloride.

In addition to the trivial names derived from the above system, some haloalkanes have other trivial names as well. Important ones include methylene chloride (CH_2Cl_2), chloroform ($CHCl_3$), bromoform ($CHBr_3$), and carbon tetrachloride (CCl_4).

AppE.3 Ethers

IUPAC rules for naming ethers were presented in Section A.6 (p. 63). Trivial names for ethers (R—O—R′) primarily come from a naming system that simply identified the alkyl groups to which the oxygen atom is attached (i.e., R and R′):

Trivial Names for Ethers

- Write the name of each alkyl group attached to O in alphabetical order, followed by "ether." The name has the form *alkyl alkyl ether*, with each word separated by a space.
- If the alkyl groups are identical, the prefix *di* is used.

The trivial name for 1-methoxypropane ($CH_3CH_2CH_2OCH_3$), for example, is methyl propyl ether, and the trivial name for ethoxyethane ($CH_3CH_2OCH_2CH_3$) is diethyl ether. Other examples are shown in **Figure AppE-6**.

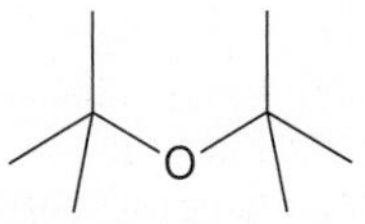

(Di-*tert*-butyl ether)

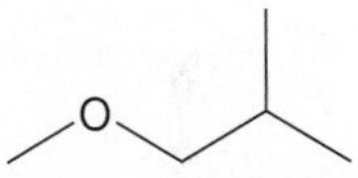

1-Methoxy-2-methylpropane
(Isobutyl methyl ether)

FIGURE AppE-6 Trivial names of ethers

AppE.4 Alkenes, Alkynes, and Benzene Derivatives

IUPAC rules for naming alkenes and alkynes were presented in Sections B.1 (p. 150) and B.2 (p. 153). Trivial names for some common alkenes (containing C═C) and an alkyne (containing C≡C) are given in **Figure AppE-7**. Several substituents

$H_2C═CH_2$

Ethene
(Ethylene)

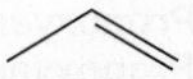

Propene
(Propylene)

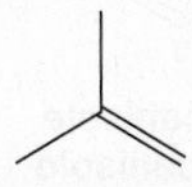

Methylpropene
(Isobutylene)

HC≡CH

Ethyne
(Acetylene)

FIGURE AppE-7 Trivial names of alkenes and alkynes

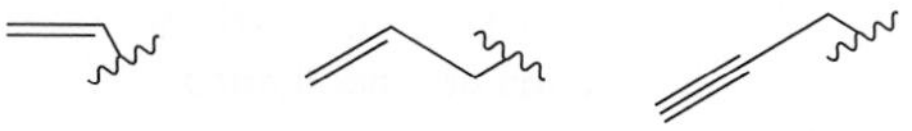

Ethenyl (Vinyl) | 2-Propenyl (Allyl) | 2-Propynyl (Propargyl)

FIGURE AppE-8 Trivial names of common substituents containing C═C or C≡C bonds

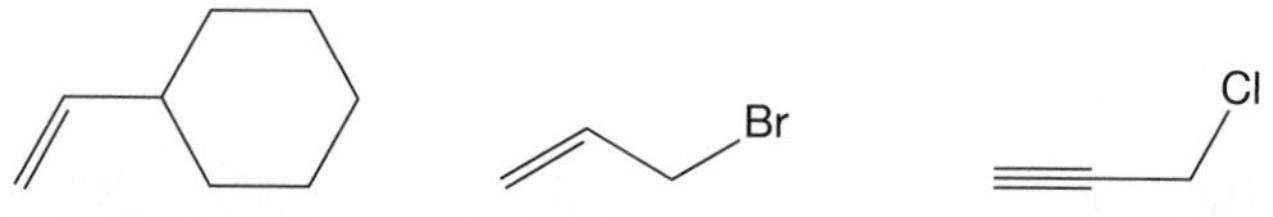

Br
Cl

Cyclohexylethene (Vinylcyclohexane) | 3-Bromoprop-1-ene (Allyl bromide) | 3-Chloroprop-1-yne (Propargyl chloride)

FIGURE AppE-9 Trivial names of molecules treating C═C or C≡C as a substituent

containing the C═C or C≡C group also have trivial names, examples of which are given in **Figure AppE-8**. These substituent trivial names are often used to name molecules, as shown in **Figure AppE-9**.

IUPAC rules for naming benzene derivatives were presented in Section B.3 (p. 155). Because of the rich history of aromatic compounds in chemistry, several of their trivial names are in widespread use. Some of them are given in **Figure AppE-10**. A handful of these trivial names, such as toluene and anisole, have been adopted by the IUPAC system, which is why those two names are not in parentheses in Figure AppE-10. In such cases, the entire substituted benzene molecule establishes the root, and C-1 is assigned to the carbon that is attached to the substituent on which the molecule's name is based (methyl in the case of toluene, and methoxy in the case of anisole). Examples of how to name substituted toluenes and substituted anisoles are shown in **Figure AppE-11**.

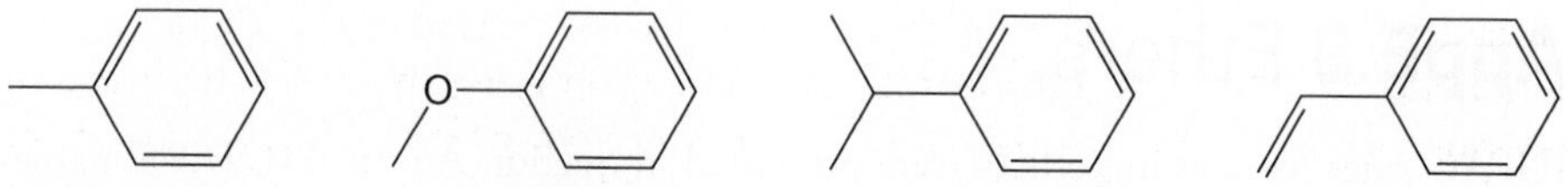

O

Methylbenzene or toluene | Methoxybenzene or anisole | Isopropylbenzene (Cumene) | Vinylbenzene (Styrene)

FIGURE AppE-10 Trivial names of molecules containing the phenyl ring

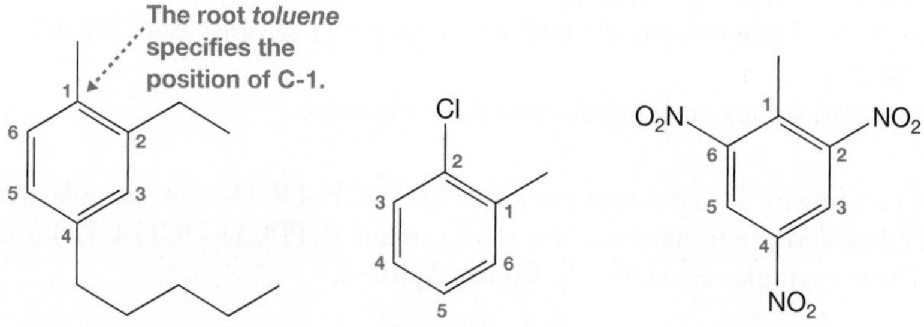

The root *toluene* specifies the position of C-1.
1
2
3
4
5
6
Cl
O_2N
NO_2
NO_2

2-Ethyl-4-pentyltoluene | 2-Chlorotoluene *o*-Chlorotoluene | 2,4,6-Trinitrotoluene (TNT)

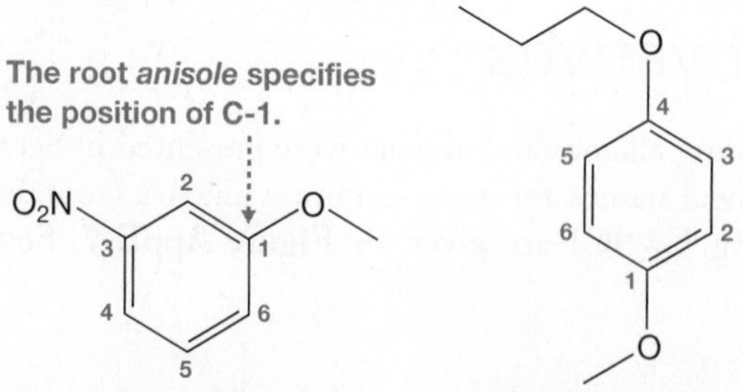

The root *anisole* specifies the position of C-1.
O_2N
O
O
O
1
2
3
4
5
6

3-Nitroanisole *m*-Nitroanisole | 4-Propoxyanisole *p*-Propoxyanisole

FIGURE AppE-11 Names of substituted toluenes and substituted anisoles

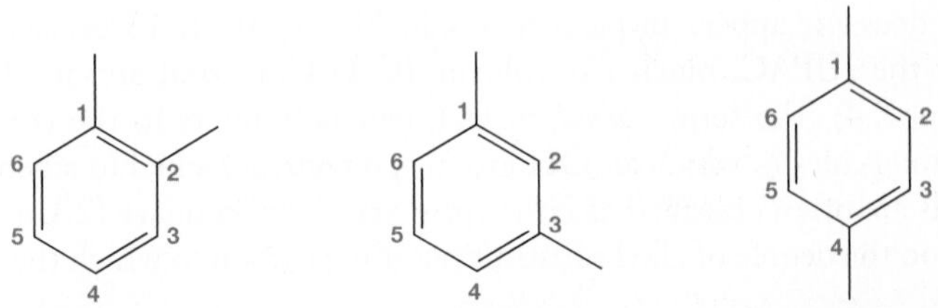

1,2-Dimethylbenzene
***ortho*-Dimethylbenzene**
***o*-Dimethylbenzene**
(*o*-Xylene)

1,3-Dimethylbenzene
***meta*-Dimethylbenzene**
***m*-Dimethylbenzene**
(*m*-Xylene)

1,4-Dimethylbenzene
***para*-Dimethylbenzene**
***p*-Dimethylbenzene**
(*p*-Xylene)

FIGURE AppE-12 **Isomers of xylene**

Some trivial names describe two substituents on benzene, not just one. The most common of these is xylene, the trivial name for dimethylbenzene, which can have either an ortho, meta, or para positioning of the methyl substituents, as shown in **Figure AppE-12**.

AppE.5 Alcohols

IUPAC rules for naming alcohols (ROH) were presented in Section D.2 (p. 372). Because alcohols consist of an alkyl group attached to a hydroxyl (OH) group, many trivial names of alcohols are derived simply by identifying the specific alkyl group present and adding the separate word *alcohol* (**Figure AppE-13**). For example, methanol (sometimes referred to as wood alcohol because it was first isolated from the pyrolysis of wood) consists of a methyl group attached to OH, so its trivial name is methyl alcohol. Similarly, the trivial name of ethanol (sometimes called grain alcohol because of its production during the fermentation of grains) is ethyl alcohol, and the trivial name of propan-1-ol is propyl alcohol. Examples that incorporate trivial names for the alkyl group include isopropyl alcohol (also known as rubbing alcohol) and *tert*-butyl alcohol. Phenol and benzyl alcohol represent examples that contain a phenyl ring.

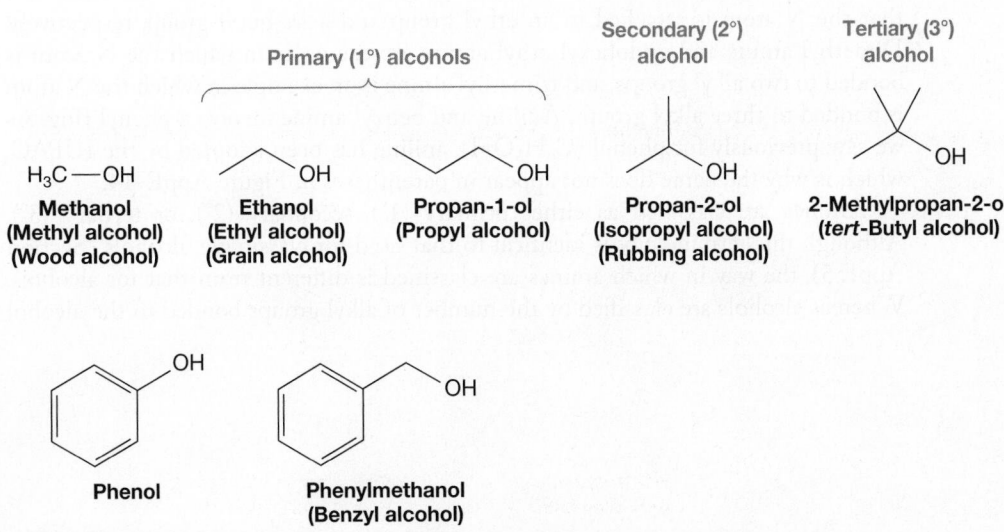

Primary (1°) alcohols | Secondary (2°) alcohol | Tertiary (3°) alcohol

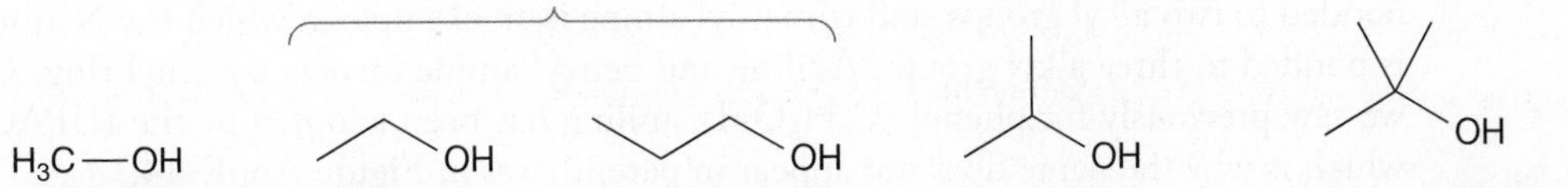

Methanol (Methyl alcohol) (Wood alcohol) | **Ethanol (Ethyl alcohol) (Grain alcohol)** | **Propan-1-ol (Propyl alcohol)** | **Propan-2-ol (Isopropyl alcohol) (Rubbing alcohol)** | **2-Methylpropan-2-ol (*tert*-Butyl alcohol)**

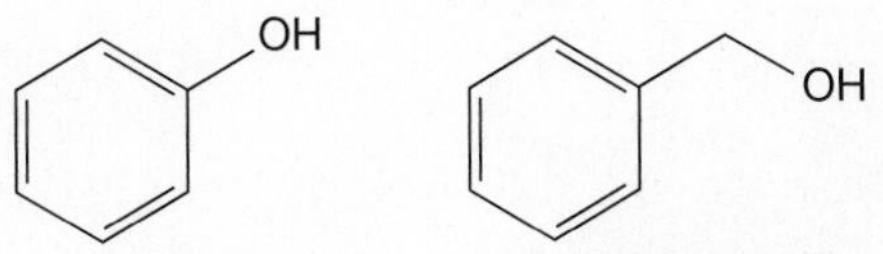

Phenol | **Phenylmethanol (Benzyl alcohol)**

FIGURE AppE-13 **Trivial names of alcohols**

Phenol does *not* appear in parentheses in Figure AppE-13 because it has been adopted by the IUPAC, much like toluene ($C_6H_5CH_3$) and anisole ($C_6H_5OCH_3$) (Section AppE.4). The term *phenol*, in fact, generally refers to the compound class describing molecules in which an OH group is directly attached to a benzene ring.

Alcohols are often classified as either primary (1°), secondary (2°), or tertiary (3°), depending on the degree of alkyl substitution of the carbon to which the OH group is attached:

- In a *primary* (1°) alcohol, the OH group is attached to a primary carbon.
- In a *secondary* (2°) alcohol, the OH group is attached to a secondary carbon.
- In a *tertiary* (3°) alcohol, the OH group is attached to a tertiary carbon.

Recall from Section AppE.1 that a carbon's degree of substitution is defined by the number of alkyl or aryl groups to which it is bonded. Therefore, as indicated in Figure AppE-13, ethanol (ethyl alcohol) and propan-1-ol (propyl alcohol) are primary alcohols, whereas propan-2-ol (isopropyl alcohol) and methylpropan-2-ol (*tert*-butyl alcohol) are secondary and tertiary alcohols, respectively.

AppE.6 Amines

IUPAC rules for naming amines were presented in Section D.2 (p. 372). Trivial names for amines are constructed in much the same way as they are for alcohols. The alkyl groups attached to the amine N are named first, followed by the suffix *amine*. The main difference between naming amines and naming alcohols is in the number of alkyl groups that must be identified. Whereas an alcohol oxygen is bonded to only one alkyl group, the nitrogen atom of an amine can be bonded to one, two, or three alkyl groups.

Trivial Names for Amines

- Write the name of each alkyl group attached to N in alphabetical order, each separated by a space, followed by "amine."
- If the alkyl groups are identical, the prefix *di* or *tri* is used.

Examples of trivial names for amines are shown in **Figure AppE-14**. In methyl amine, for example, the N atom is bonded to just a methyl group, so the other two bonds to N are N—H bonds. The names ethyl amine and *sec*-butyl amine indicate that the N atom is attached to an ethyl group and a *sec*-butyl group, respectively. Dimethyl amine and cyclohexyl ethyl amine are examples in which the N atom is bonded to two alkyl groups, and trimethyl amine is an example in which the N atom is bonded to three alkyl groups. Aniline and benzyl amine involve a phenyl ring. As we saw previously for phenol (C_6H_5OH), aniline has been adopted by the IUPAC, which is why the name does not appear in parentheses in Figure AppE-14.

Amines are classified as either primary (1°), secondary (2°), or tertiary (3°). Although this terminology is identical to that used for classifying alcohols (Section AppE.5), the way in which amines are classified is different from that for alcohols. Whereas alcohols are classified by the number of alkyl groups bonded to the alcohol

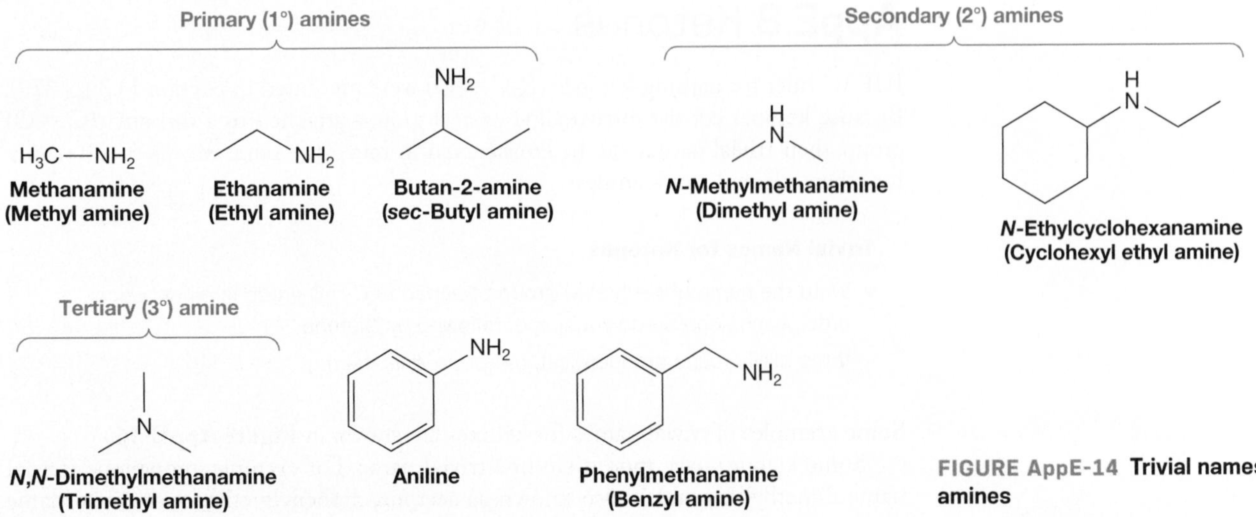

Primary (1°) amines
Secondary (2°) amines
H3C—NH2
Methanamine
(Methyl amine)
NH2
Ethanamine
(Ethyl amine)
NH2
Butan-2-amine
(sec-Butyl amine)
H
N
N-Methylmethanamine
(Dimethyl amine)
H
N
N-Ethylcyclohexanamine
(Cyclohexyl ethyl amine)
Tertiary (3°) amine
N
N,N-Dimethylmethanamine
(Trimethyl amine)
NH2
Aniline
NH2
Phenylmethanamine
(Benzyl amine)

FIGURE AppE-14 Trivial names of amines

carbon, an amine is classified by the number of alkyl groups to which the N atom is attached:

- In a *primary* (1°) amine, the N atom is bonded to one alkyl or aryl group.
- In a *secondary* (2°) amine, the N atom is bonded to two alkyl or aryl groups.
- In a *tertiary* (3°) amine, the N atom is bonded to three alkyl or aryl groups.

Therefore, methyl amine, ethyl amine, and *sec*-butyl amine are all primary amines, whereas dimethyl amine and cyclohexyl ethyl amine are secondary amines, and trimethyl amine is a tertiary amine.

AppE.7 Aldehydes

IUPAC rules for naming aldehydes were presented in Section D.3 (p. 379). Some of the more frequently encountered trivial names for aldehydes are shown in **Figure AppE-15**. Many of these trivial names derive from trivial names for the analogous carboxylic acids, which will be discussed in Section AppE.9. For example, the trivial name for methanal, which has one carbon atom, is formaldehyde. This is analogous to formic acid, the carboxylic acid that contains just one carbon atom. Similarly acetaldehyde, the trivial name for the two-carbon aldehyde, derives from acetic acid, the two-carbon carboxylic acid.

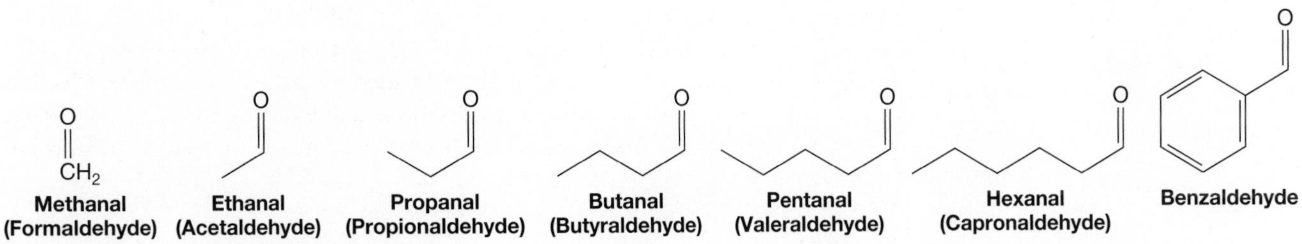

O
CH2
Methanal
(Formaldehyde)
O
Ethanal
(Acetaldehyde)
O
Propanal
(Propionaldehyde)
O
Butanal
(Butyraldehyde)
O
Pentanal
(Valeraldehyde)
O
Hexanal
(Capronaldehyde)
O
Benzaldehyde

FIGURE AppE-15 Trivial names of aldehydes

AppE.8 Ketones

IUPAC rules for naming ketones ($R_2C{=}O$) were presented in Section D.3 (p. 379). Because ketones consist of two alkyl or aryl groups attached to a carbonyl ($C{=}O$) group, their trivial names can be constructed in much the same way as trivial names for ethers, alcohols, and amines:

Trivial Names for Ketones

- Write the name of each alkyl group attached to C=O group in alphabetical order, each separated by a space, followed by "ketone."
- If the alkyl groups are identical, the prefix *di* is used.

Some examples of trivial names for ketones are shown in **Figure AppE-16**.

Some ketones have more than one trivial name. For example, propanone (trivial name dimethyl ketone) is also known as acetone, diphenylmethanone (trivial name diphenyl ketone) is also known as benzophenone, and phenylethanone (trivial name methyl phenyl ketone) is also known as acetophenone.

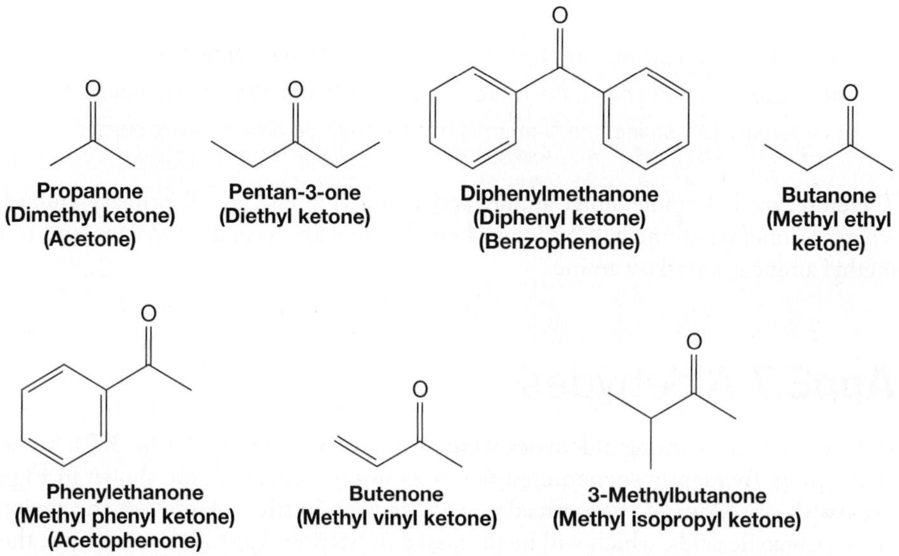

Propanone
(Dimethyl ketone)
(Acetone)
Pentan-3-one
(Diethyl ketone)
Diphenylmethanone
(Diphenyl ketone)
(Benzophenone)
Butanone
(Methyl ethyl ketone)
Phenylethanone
(Methyl phenyl ketone)
(Acetophenone)
Butenone
(Methyl vinyl ketone)
3-Methylbutanone
(Methyl isopropyl ketone)

FIGURE AppE-16 **Trivial names of ketones**

AppE.9 Carboxylic Acids

IUPAC rules for naming carboxylic acids were presented in Section D.4 (p. 381). Trivial names of some common monocarboxylic acids (containing one CO_2H group) are shown in **Figure AppE-17**, and trivial names of some dicarboxylic acids (containing two CO_2H groups) are shown in **Figure AppE-18**.

Trivial names of several carboxylic acids are used almost to the exclusion of their IUPAC names. Acetic acid, the principal component of vinegar, is one example. Another is formic acid, a main constituent of ant venom (*formica* is the Latin word for ant). The name *benzoic acid*, in fact, has been accepted by IUPAC, which is why it appears without parentheses.

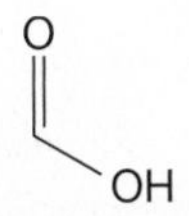

O
OH

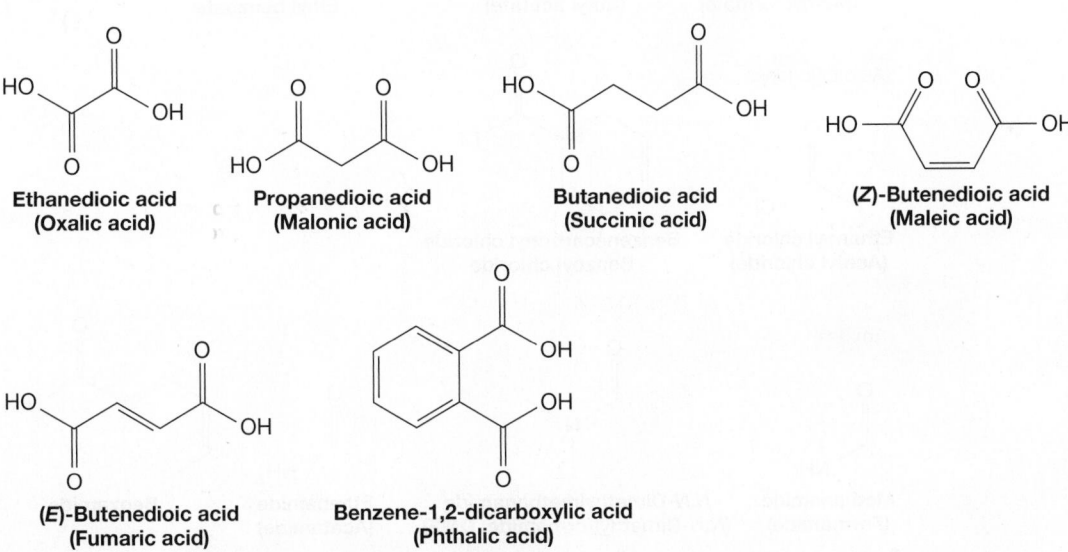

Methanoic acid (Formic acid)

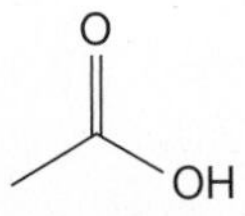

O
OH

Ethanoic acid (Acetic acid)

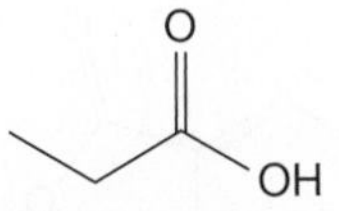

O
OH

Propanoic acid (Propionic acid)

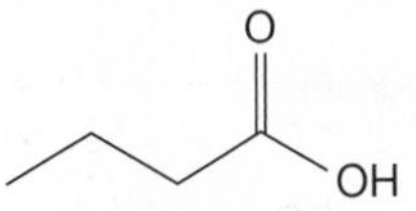

O
OH

Butanoic acid (Butyric acid)

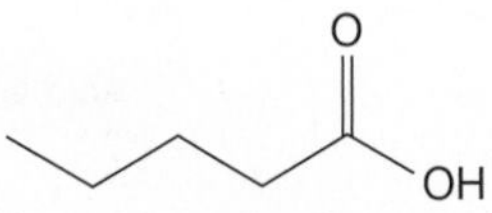

O
OH

Pentanoic acid (Valeric acid)

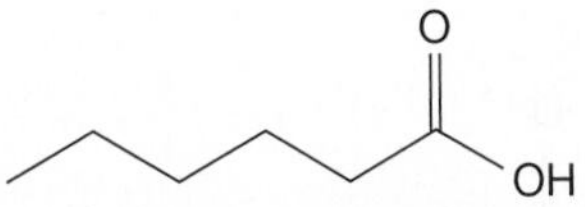

O
OH

Hexanoic acid (Caproic acid)

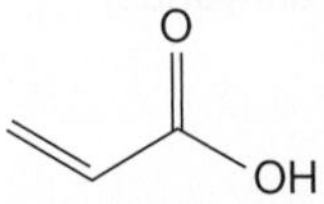

O
OH

Propenoic acid (Acrylic acid)

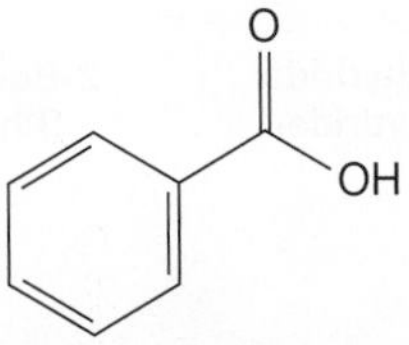

O
OH

Benzenecarboxylic acid
Benzoic acid

FIGURE AppE-17 Trivial names of monocarboxylic acids

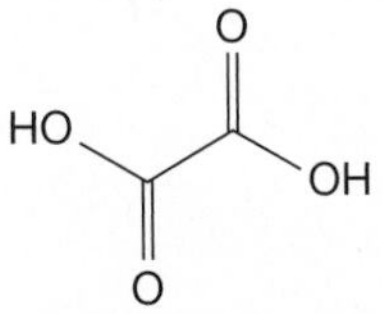

HO
O
OH
O

Ethanedioic acid (Oxalic acid)

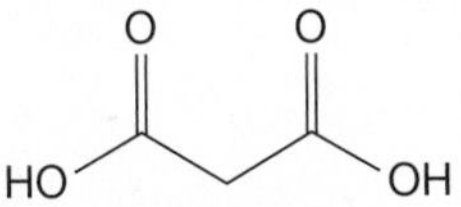

O
O
HO
OH

Propanedioic acid (Malonic acid)

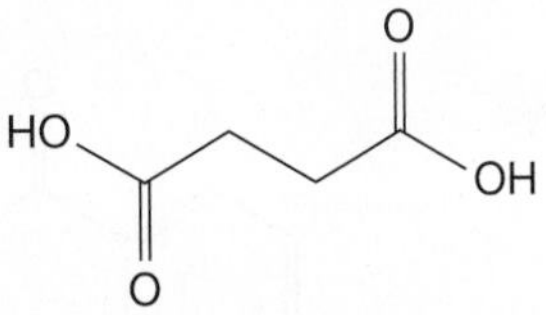

HO
O
OH
O

Butanedioic acid (Succinic acid)

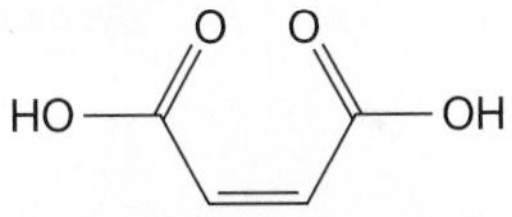

O
O
HO
OH

(*Z*)-Butenedioic acid (Maleic acid)

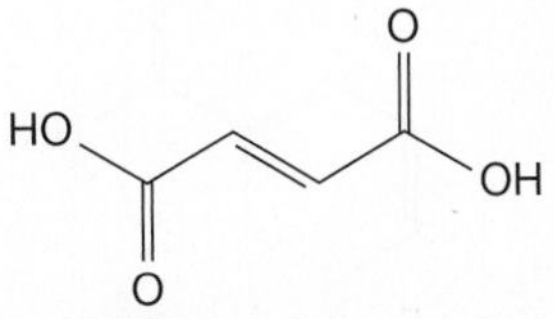

HO
O
OH
O

(*E*)-Butenedioic acid (Fumaric acid)

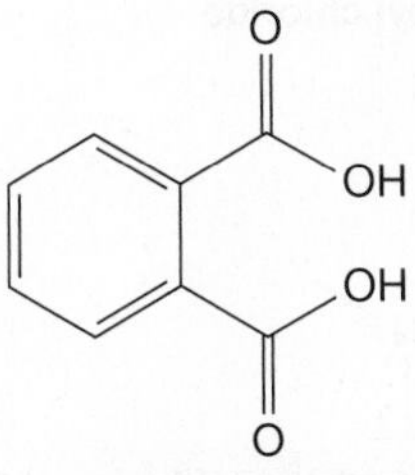

O
OH
OH
O

Benzene-1,2-dicarboxylic acid (Phthalic acid)

FIGURE AppE-18 Trivial names of dicarboxylic acids

AppE.10 Carboxylic Acid Derivatives

IUPAC rules for naming carboxylic acid derivatives were presented in Sections D.4 (p. 381) and D.5 (p. 385). These include acid anhydrides, esters, acid chlorides, amides, and nitriles. The trivial names of many carboxylic acid derivatives are derived from the trivial names of the analogous carboxylic acids. Examples are shown in **Figure AppE-19**. Notice, in particular, the prevalence of the roots *form*, *acet*, and *benz*, which derive from formic acid, acetic acid, and benzoic acid, respectively. As is the case with other compound classes, some of these trivial names have been accepted by the IUPAC, such as ethyl benzoate, benzoyl chloride, benzamide, and benzonitrile.

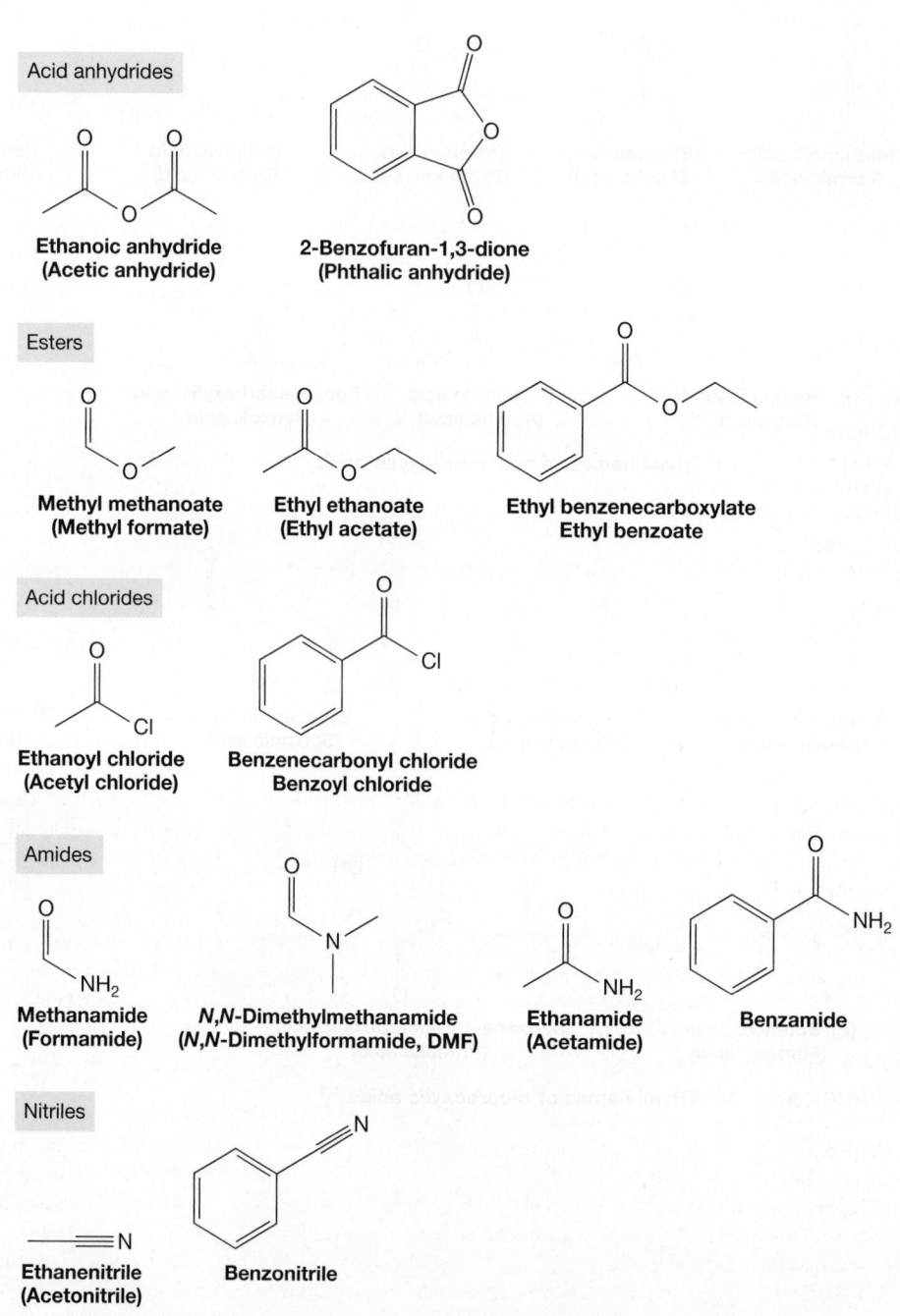

Acid anhydrides

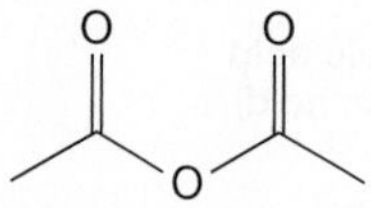
O
O
O

Ethanoic anhydride
(Acetic anhydride)

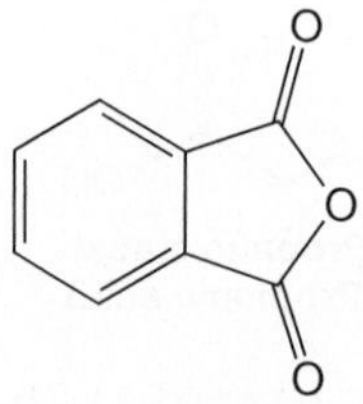
O
O
O

2-Benzofuran-1,3-dione
(Phthalic anhydride)

Esters

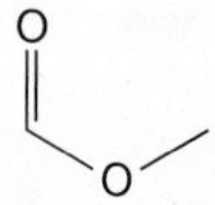
O
O

Methyl methanoate
(Methyl formate)

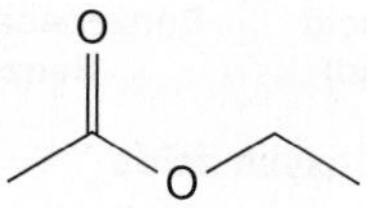
O
O

Ethyl ethanoate
(Ethyl acetate)

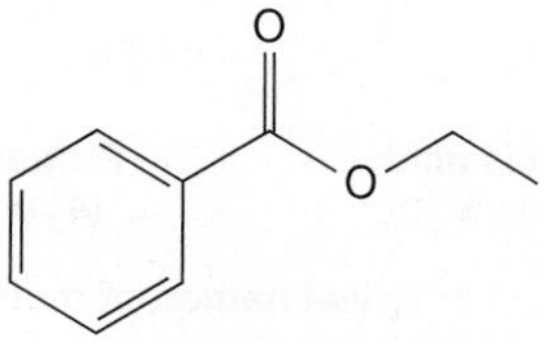
O
O

Ethyl benzenecarboxylate
Ethyl benzoate

Acid chlorides

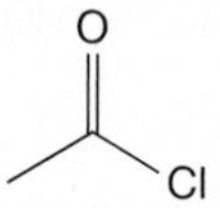
O
Cl

Ethanoyl chloride
(Acetyl chloride)

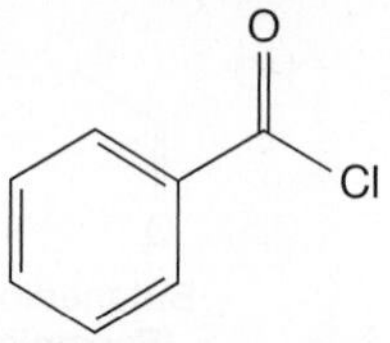
O
Cl

Benzenecarbonyl chloride
Benzoyl chloride

Amides

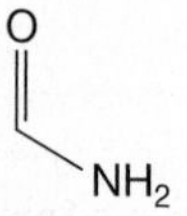
O
NH2

Methanamide
(Formamide)

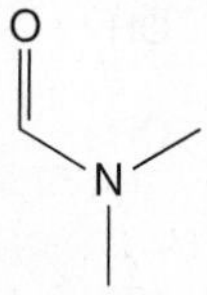
O
N

***N,N*-Dimethylmethanamide**
(*N,N*-Dimethylformamide, DMF)

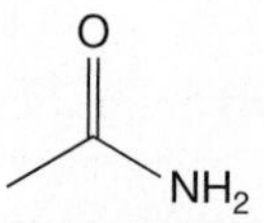
O
NH2

Ethanamide
(Acetamide)

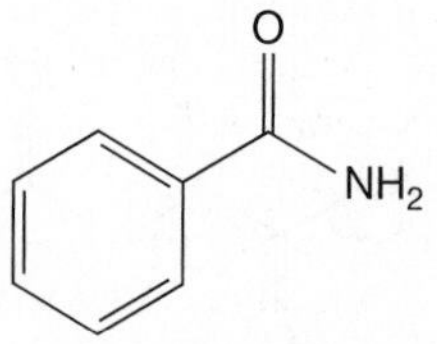
O
NH2

Benzamide

Nitriles

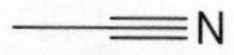
N

Ethanenitrile
(Acetonitrile)

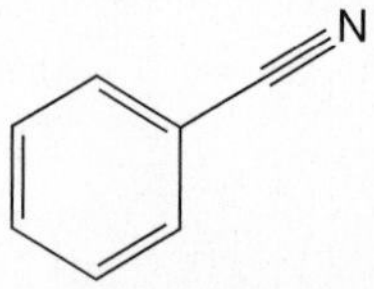
N

Benzonitrile

FIGURE AppE-19 Trivial names of carboxylic acid derivatives

GLOSSARY

[E] = online chapter only

A

Absorbance (*A*) a measure of light absorbed by a sample for *spectroscopy*, ranging from 0 (no absorption) to infinity (complete absorption): $A = -\log\left(\frac{I_{\text{detected}}}{I_{\text{source}}}\right) = -\log\left(\frac{\%T}{100}\right)$. (Ch. 16)

Absorption band (also known as *peak*) a feature of a spectrum where absorbance is high. (Ch. 16)

Acetal a compound that contains the bonding arrangement $C(OR)_2$, in which two alkoxy groups are attached to the same carbon atom. (Ch. 1)

Acetoacetic ester synthesis a synthesis scheme that converts acetoacetic ester into an alkyl- or dialkyl-substituted acetone. (Ch. 23)

Achiral describes a molecule that does not have an *enantiomer*; that is, the molecule's mirror image is superimposable on itself. (Ch. 5)

Achiral environment an environment that is superimposable on its mirror image, in which enantiomers have exactly the same physical and chemical properties. (Ch. 5)

Acid-catalyzed describes a reaction that speeds up in the presence of a small amount of acid, without the acid being consumed by the reaction. (Ch. 19)

Acid-catalyzed alkoxylation reaction a reaction in which an alcohol adds across a C═C or C≡C bond, catalyzed by acid. (Ch. 12)

Acid-catalyzed hydration reaction a reaction in which water adds across a C═C or C≡C bond, catalyzed by acid. (Ch. 12)

Acidity constant (K_a) an experimentally obtained constant that reflects the strength of an acid (i.e., an acid's propensity to donate a proton). (Ch. 6)

Acid workup a synthetic step in which acid is added to protonate a product or remove leftover basic components (e.g., extra Grignard or alkyllithium reagent) after the main reaction is completed. (Ch. 10)

Acrylic see *polyacrylate*. (Ch. 28)

Activating group a substituent that increases the reactivity of a molecule in a particular reaction; often refers to a substituent that makes an aromatic ring more susceptible to an *electrophilic aromatic substitution reaction*. (Ch. 25)

Active methylene compound a CH_2 group with two adjacent C═O groups; can be converted into a highly nucleophilic enolate anion relatively easily. (Ch. 23)

Active site a specific pocket of an *enzyme* where the reaction involving substrates occurs. (Ch. 30) [E]

Acylium ion a cation of the form $R—C≡O^+$. (Ch. 24)

1,2-Addition a type of reaction in which two substituents add to two adjacent atoms. (Ch. 12)

1,4-Addition a type of reaction in which two substituents add to two atoms that have 1,4 relative positioning. (Ch. 12)

Addition polymerization a *polymerization* reaction in which all atoms of the monomer end up in the repeating unit after each *propagation step*. (Ch. 28)

Adduct the addition product of two molecules. (Ch. 12)

Alcohol a compound that contains the bonding arrangement C—OH. (Ch. 1)

Alcoholysis a reaction in which an alcohol reactant is responsible for breaking bonds; used to convert a carboxylic acid derivative into an ester. (Ch. 23)

Aldehyde a compound that contains the bonding arrangement HC═O. (Ch. 1)

Alder rule see *endo rule*. (Ch. 26)

Aldohexose a six-carbon sugar in which the carbonyl group involves a terminal C, characteristic of an aldehyde. (Ch. 4, 29)

Aldol a β-hydroxy aldehyde, characterized by an OH group that is beta to a HC═O group. (Ch. 19)

Aldol addition a reaction in which an enolate anion adds to the carbonyl group of a ketone or an aldehyde to produce a *β-hydroxy carbonyl compound*. (Ch. 19)

Aldol condensation a reaction consisting of an *aldol addition* followed by the elimination of water, resulting in the production of an *α,β-unsaturated carbonyl compound*. (Ch. 19)

Aldopentose a five-carbon sugar in which the carbonyl group involves a terminal C, characteristic of an aldehyde. (Ch. 4, 29)

Aldose a sugar whose carbonyl group involves a terminal C, characteristic of an aldehyde. (Ch. 4, 29)

Alkane an acyclic compound consisting of only C—C and C—H single bonds. (Ch. 1)

Alkanoate group an RCO_2 group containing a carbonyl (C═O) that has a singly bound O atom. (Int. D)

Alkene a compound that contains the bonding arrangement C═C; sometimes called an *olefin*. (Ch. 1)

Alkene metathesis (also known as *olefin metathesis*) a reaction in which portions of molecules joined by C═C bonds in the products were part of a different C═C bond in the reactant. (Ch. 20)

Alkoxy group the group OR. (Int. A)

Alkoxymercuration–reduction the sequence of reactions in which a Hg^{2+} species adds to an alkene or alkyne, followed by reduction (typically with $NaBH_4$), resulting in the *Markovnikov addition* of an alcohol. (Ch. 13)

Alkylation a reaction in which a hydrogen atom is replaced by an alkyl group. (Ch. 10)

Alkylborane a compound, $R—BH_2$, in which an alkyl group has replaced hydrogen on borane, BH_3. (Ch. 13)

Alkyl group a portion of a molecule that consists only of C—C and C—H single bonds. (Ch. 1, Int. A)

Alkyl halide a compound that contains the bonding arrangement C—X, where X is a halogen atom. (Ch. 1)

1,2-Alkyl shift a carbocation rearrangement wherein an alkyl group migrates to an adjacent atom. (Ch. 7)

Alkyne a compound that contains the bonding arrangement $C{\equiv}C$. (Ch. 1)

Alkynide anion the species $RC{\equiv}C^-$, a strong nucleophile. (Ch. 9)

All-anti conformation (also known as *zigzag conformation*) the lowest-energy conformation of an alkyl chain, in which it has the *anti conformation* at each C—C bond. (Ch. 4)

Allosteric activator an effector molecule whose binding favors the state of the enzyme with high substrate binding affinity and high catalytic efficiency. (Ch. 30)

Allosteric inhibitor an effector molecule whose binding favors the state of the enzyme with low substrate binding affinity and low catalytic efficiency. (Ch. 30)

Allosteric regulation a situation where an effector molecule binds to a *regulatory site* in an enzyme, away from the *active site*; this causes the enzyme to undergo a significant conformational change that alters its catalytic efficiency. (Ch. 30)

Allyl substrate a compound of the form $L{-}CH_2{-}CH{=}CH_2$, where L is a *leaving group*. (Ch. 9)

α-Amino acid one of the relatively few types of small organic molecules from which proteins are constructed; it contains an amino group (NH_2), a carboxyl group (CO_2H), and a side chain (R) that are all attached to the α carbon. (Ch. 1, 29)

α Anomer a diastereomeric form of a cyclic sugar in which the OH group attached to the anomeric carbon atom is on the opposite side of the ring from the substituent attached by C. (Ch. 19, 29)

α,β-Unsaturated carbonyl compound a ketone or aldehyde that has a double or triple bond connecting the α and β carbons. (Ch. 18)

α Carbon a carbon atom that is attached to a carbonyl (C=O) carbon. (Ch. 1, 7, 29)

α Cleavage a fragmentation pathway in *mass spectrometry* in which a C—C bond adjacent to the atom with the unpaired electron is cleaved. (Ch. 15)

α Halogenation the reaction that occurs when a ketone or aldehyde with an α hydrogen is treated with a molecular halogen (Cl_2, Br_2, or I_2) under basic or acidic conditions. (Ch. 10)

α-Helix a type of *secondary structure* in a protein characterized by a tight winding of the protein's backbone around an axis. (Ch. 28, 29)

α Spin state describes a nucleus that has a spin of $+\frac{1}{2}$ au. (Ch. 17)

Amide a compound that contains the bonding arrangement C(=O)N. (Ch. 1)

Amine a compound that contains the bonding arrangement C—N. (Ch. 1)

Aminolysis a reaction in which an amine reactant is responsible for breaking bonds; used to convert a carboxylic acid derivative into an amide. (Ch. 23)

Amorphous solid a solid that does not have a well-defined crystal structure. (Ch. 28)

Anabolic describes a *metabolic pathway* that builds up molecules and requires energy. (Ch. 30)

Angle strain an increase in energy that arises when the actual bond angles differ significantly from the ideal bond angles predicted by *VSEPR theory*. (Ch. 4)

Anion a negatively charged ion. (Ch. 1)

Anionic polymerization a *polymerization* reaction in which the *propagation steps* involve anionic species. (Ch. 28)

[*n*]Annulene one of a class of compounds that are monocyclic, fully *conjugated*, and contain only carbon and hydrogen; has the condensed formula $(CH)_n$. (Ch. 14)

Anode the positively charged pole of an electrochemical cell, such as one used in *electrophoresis*. (Ch. 29)

Anomeric carbon the carbon atom of a cyclic sugar that is part of an acetal or a hemiacetal and is the carbonyl carbon of the sugar in its acyclic form. Depending on the stereochemical configuration of the anomeric carbon, the cyclic sugar can exist as one of two diastereomers called *anomers*. (Ch. 19, 29)

Anomers diastereomers of a cyclic sugar that differ in the stereochemical configuration at the *anomeric carbon*. A cyclic sugar can exist as the α or β anomer. (Ch. 19, 29)

Antiaromatic describes compounds with cyclic π systems that are unusually unstable; the cyclic π system contains an *anti-Hückel number* of electrons. Compare with *aromatic* and *nonaromatic*. (Ch. 14)

Antibonding interaction overlapping of atomic orbitals with the opposite phase, which raises the energy of the molecular orbital to which they contribute. Compare with *bonding interaction*. (Ch. 14)

Antibonding MO a *molecular orbital* that is significantly higher in energy than its contributing atomic orbitals. Compare with *bonding MO* and *nonbonding MO*. (Ch. 3)

Anticodon a three-nucleotide sequence in transfer RNA that is recognized by the *codon* in messenger RNA. (Ch. 30)

Anti conformation a *staggered conformation* wherein bulky groups are 180° apart in a *Newman projection*. (Ch. 4)

Anticoplanar (also known as *antiperiplanar*) the conformation where the H and *leaving group* on adjacent atoms are anti to each other and all four atoms reside in the same plane (that is, they are coplanar). (Ch. 8)

Anti-Hückel number a number in the set {4, 8, 12, 16, ...}, which can be described as an even number of pairs or as a number that is consistent with $4n$, where n is a positive integer. (Ch. 14)

Anti-hydrogenation a reaction in which two H atoms, overall, add to a triple bond in a trans fashion. (Ch. 27)

Anti-Markovnikov addition *or* anti-Markovnikov regiochemistry a reaction in which the product of addition to an alkene or alkyne appears to have been formed from the less stable carbocation intermediate. The regiochemistry describing these reactions is opposite the regiochemistry describing reactions that undergo *Markovnikov addition*. (Ch. 13)

Antiperiplanar see *anticoplanar*. (Ch. 8)

Anti-Zaitsev product (also known as *Hofmann product*) the less highly alkyl-substituted alkene product of an elimination reaction, produced when the reaction does not follow *Zaitsev's rule*. (Ch. 9)

Aprotic solvent a solvent that does not possess a *hydrogen-bond donor*. (Ch. 2)

Arene (also known as *aromatic compound*) a compound that contains an aromatic ring. (Ch. 1)

Arenium ion intermediate (also known as *Wheland intermediate*) a cationic intermediate in an *electrophilic aromatic substitution reaction*, produced by the addition of an electrophile to an aromatic ring. (Ch. 24)

Aromatic describes compounds with cyclic π systems that are unusually stable; the cyclic π system contains a *Hückel number* of electrons. Compare with *antiaromatic* and *nonaromatic*. (Ch. 14)

Aromatic compound see *arene*. (Ch. 1)

Aromatic halogenation an *electrophilic aromatic substitution reaction* that replaces an aromatic hydrogen with a halogen. (Ch. 24)
Arrow pushing see *curved arrow notation*. (Ch. 6)
Asymmetric atom see *chiral center*. (Ch. 5)
Asymmetric stretching vibrational motion involving two bonds within a molecule, in which one bond lengthens while the other bond shortens. (Ch. 16)
Atactic describes a *polymer* that has no regularity in the stereochemical configurations along its main chain. (Ch. 28)
Atomic number (*Z*) the number of protons in the nucleus. (Ch. 1)
Atomic orbital an *orbital* that is assigned to a single atom, such as an *s* orbital, a *p* orbital, or a hybrid orbital. (Ch. 3)
Attacking species any species that can act as a nucleophile or base to displace a *leaving group* from an atom. (Ch. 9)
Aufbau principle states that each successive electron must fill the available orbital with the lowest energy. (Ch. 1)
Axial describes a bond that is perpendicular to the plane roughly defined by the ring to which it is attached. Compare with *equatorial*. (Ch. 4)
2,2′-Azobisisobutyronitrile (AIBN) the molecule $(CH_3)_2C(CN)N{=}NC(CN)(CH_3)_2$, a common radical initiator. (Ch. 27)
Azo coupling a reaction that connects two aromatic rings by the N═N group. (Ch. 25)
Azo dye a compound with a distinct color that contains the *azo group*. (Ch. 25)
Azo group the N═N group. (Ch. 25)

B

Backside attack the spatial arrangement describing a *nucleophile* approaching the substrate from the side opposite the *leaving group*, leading to an inversion of stereochemical configuration at the attacked carbon; occurs in all S_N2 reactions. (Ch. 8)
Baeyer–Villiger oxidation a reaction in which a peroxy acid (RCO_3H) converts a ketone or an aldehyde into an ester or a carboxylic acid. (Ch. 23)
Base-catalyzed describes a reaction that speeds up in the presence of a small amount of base, without the base being consumed by the reaction. (Ch. 19)
Base peak the peak with the greatest intensity in a *mass spectrum*; it is assigned a relative abundance of 100% and is used as a reference to assign the *relative abundances* of other peaks. (Ch. 15)
Beer–Lambert law states the direct relationship of absorbance (*A*) to sample concentration (*C*), molar absorptivity (ε), and light path length (*l*) in *spectroscopy*: $A = \varepsilon lC$. (Ch. 16)
B_{eff} see *effective magnetic field*. (Ch. 17)
Bending one of two basic, independent types of vibrational motion, in which an angle (either a bond angle or a dihedral angle) becomes larger and smaller throughout one vibrational cycle. Compare with *stretching*. (Ch. 16)
Benzene C_6H_6, a nonpolar, aromatic ring; a six-carbon annulene. (Int. B)
Benzene derivative a relatively simple molecule with one or more substituents attached to benzene. (Int. B)
Benzenediazonium ion the reactive species $C_6H_5N_2^+$, used to produce a variety of substituted benzenes. (Ch. 24)
Benzyl (Bn) (also known as *phenylmethyl*) a $CH_2C_6H_5$ group. (Int. B)
Benzylic carbon a carbon atom attached directly to a phenyl ring. (Ch. 24)
Benzyl substrate a substrate of the form L—$CH_2C_6H_5$, where L is a *leaving group*. (Ch. 9)
Benzyne intermediate a six-membered carbon ring whose Lewis structure exhibits two C═C bonds and one C≡C bond; an intermediate in a type of *nucleophilic aromatic substitution reaction*. (Ch. 25)
β Anomer a diastereomeric form of a cyclic sugar in which the OH group attached to the anomeric carbon atom is on the same side of the ring as the substituent attached by C. (Ch. 19, 29)
β Carbon a carbon atom located two bonds away from an atom or group of interest, usually a C═O group. (Ch. 18)
β-Diacid a species having two carboxyl (CO_2H) groups separated by a single carbon atom: HO_2C—C—CO_2H. (Ch. 23)
β Elimination a reaction in which substituents on adjacent atoms are eliminated from a molecule, resulting in a new π bond between those atoms. (Ch. 7)
β-Hydroxy carbonyl compound a species in which a hydroxyl (OH) group is bonded to the carbon that is beta to a carbonyl functional group. (Ch. 19)
Betaine a species in which a positive and a negative charge are separated by two uncharged atoms and in which the positively charged atom has no attached hydrogens. (Ch. 18)
β-Keto acid a species in which the β carbon of a carboxylic acid is part of a carbonyl group that is characteristic of a ketone or aldehyde. (Ch. 23)
β-Keto ester a species in which the β carbon of an ester is part of a carbonyl group that is characteristic of a ketone or aldehyde. (Ch. 23)
β-Oxidation pathway a fatty acid oxidation pathway that takes place inside the mitochondrion. (Ch. 30) E
β-Pleated sheet a type of *secondary structure* in a protein in which several segments of the backbone align next to each other in the same region of space. (Ch. 28, 29)
β Spin state describes a nucleus that has a spin of $-\frac{1}{2}$ au. (Ch. 17)
B_{ext} see *external magnetic field*. (Ch. 17)
Bicyclic compound a compound consisting of two rings. (Ch. 26)
Bimolecular describes an *elementary step* that involves two separate reactant species. (Ch. 7, 8)
Bimolecular elimination (E2) step an *elementary step* wherein a proton and a *leaving group* are eliminated from adjacent atoms, and a double bond or triple bond is formed. (Ch. 7)
Bimolecular homolytic substitution (S_H2) step an *elementary step* in which a radical forms a bond to an atom in a closed-shell species and displaces another radical from that atom. (Ch. 27)
Bimolecular nucleophilic substitution (S_N2) step an *elementary step* wherein a nucleophile forms a bond to an atom that is attached to a *leaving group* and displaces the leaving group from that atom. (Ch. 7)
Biomolecule a particular organic molecule found almost exclusively in or produced by living organisms. (Ch. 1, 29)
Biopolymer a *polymer* that is produced biosynthetically; examples include polypeptides (proteins), polysaccharides (carbohydrates), and polynucleotides (nucleic acids) such as DNA and RNA. (Ch. 28)
Birch reduction a *dissolving metal reduction* that reduces a benzene ring to a cyclohexa-1,4-diene. (Ch. 27)
B_{loc} see *local magnetic field*. (Ch. 17)
Bond dipole a separation of partial positive and negative charges along a covalent bond. (Ch. 1)
Bond energy see *bond strength*. (Ch. 1)

Bonding interaction overlapping of atomic orbitals with the same phase, which lowers the energy of the molecular orbital to which they contribute. Compare with *antibonding interaction.* (Ch. 14)

Bonding MO a *molecular orbital* that is significantly lower in energy than its contributing atomic orbitals. Compare with *antibonding MO* and *nonbonding MO*. (Ch. 3)

Bonding pair a pair of electrons that makes up a covalent bond. (Ch. 1)

Bond length the internuclear distance at which energy is a minimum. (Ch. 1)

Bond strength (also known as *bond energy*) the energy that would be required to increase the distance between two bonded atoms from the bond length to infinity. (Ch. 1)

9-Borabicyclo[3.3.1]nonane (9-BBN) a reagent used in the *hydroboration–oxidation* of alkynes to produce aldehydes or ketones. (Ch. 13)

Borate ester a class of compounds or functional groups that have the structure $B(OR)_3$. (Ch. 13)

Branched describes a molecule in which additional carbon chains or alkyl groups are attached to the main chain. (Int. A)

Branched polymer a *polymer* in which hydrogens or substituents on the main chain of the polymer are replaced by other chains of the polymer. (Ch. 28)

Bridgehead carbon a carbon atom that is simultaneously part of more than one ring. (Ch. 26)

Broadband decoupling a technique used to "turn off" the coupling between ^{13}C and ^{1}H nuclei so that carbon signals are not split by attached protons in *NMR spectroscopy*. In this method, *radio frequency* radiation forces protons to rapidly switch between α and β spin states, resulting in a zero average magnetic field produced by each proton. (Ch. 17)

Bromination a reaction that adds bromine atoms to a molecule; can be accomplished by substituting a bromine atom for a hydrogen atom or by adding molecular bromine (Br_2) to a C═C or C≡C bond. (Ch. 24)

Bromohydrin a compound in which a bromine atom and a hydroxyl group (OH) are attached to two adjacent carbons. (Ch. 13)

Bromonium ion intermediate a positively charged species containing a three-membered ring composed of two carbon atoms and a bromine atom. (Ch. 13)

***N*-Bromosuccinimide (NBS)** a radical initiator with a particularly weak Br—N bond, which is the source of a small, steady concentration of Br_2. Commonly, NBS is used to brominate allylic and benzylic carbons. (Ch. 27)

Brønsted–Lowry acid a species that donates a proton in a *proton transfer reaction*. (Ch. 6)

Brønsted–Lowry acid–base reaction see *proton transfer reaction*. (Ch. 6)

Brønsted–Lowry base a species that accepts a proton in a *proton transfer reaction*. (Ch. 6)

C

^{13}C NMR spectroscopy a method in which *radio frequency* electromagnetic radiation is used to cause *spin flips* in the nuclei of carbon-13 atoms. (Ch. 17)

Cahn–Ingold–Prelog system a set of tie-breaking rules applied to substituents to determine their relative priorities in establishing stereochemical configurations. (Ch. 5)

Carbanion an *anion* in which a negative formal charge appears on carbon. (Ch. 7)

Carbene an uncharged species containing a carbon atom that possesses two bonds and nonbonded electrons. (Ch. 13)

Carbocation a species that contains a positively charged carbon atom (C^+); carbocations are key reactive intermediates in a variety of chemical reactions. (Ch. 1)

Carbocation rearrangement an *elementary step* in which the *connectivity* changes within a carbocation. Examples include a *1,2-hydride shift* and a *1,2-methyl shift*. (Ch. 7)

Carbohydrate (also known as *saccharide*) a compound with the formula $C_xH_{2y}O_y$. (Ch. 1, 29)

Carbon-chain polymer a *polymer* in which the main chain consists only of carbon atoms. (Ch. 28)

Carbon skeleton the bonding arrangement (*connectivity*) of carbon atoms. (Ch. 10)

Carbonyl group the functional group having the bonding arrangement C═O. (Ch. 1)

Carboxylation a reaction in which a substrate gains a carboxyl group (CO_2H). (Ch. 18)

Carboxylic acid a compound that contains the bonding arrangement CO_2H. (Ch. 1)

Carboxylic acid derivative a compound that can be produced relatively easily from a carboxylic acid; generally characterized by the presence of a *leaving group* attached to a carbonyl (C═O) carbon. (Int. D, Ch. 22)

Catabolic describes a *metabolic pathway* that breaks down molecules and generates energy. (Ch. 30)

Catalyst a species that speeds up a reaction but is not consumed overall. (Ch. 12)

Catalytic hydrogenation a reaction in which hydrogen atoms are added to a molecule in the presence of a catalyst. (Ch. 13)

Catalytic triad three characteristic amino acids situated in the active site of an enzyme such as a *serine protease*; the three amino acids are critical to the proper functioning of the enzyme. (Ch. 30)

Cathode the negatively charged pole of an electrochemical cell, such as one used in *electrophoresis*. (Ch. 29)

Cation a positively charged ion. (Ch. 1)

Cationic polymerization a *polymerization* reaction in which the *propagation steps* involve cationic species. (Ch. 28)

Cell signaling a means by which chemical information outside the cell is converted to a different type of chemical information inside the cell. (Ch. 30)

Chain polymerization a *polymerization* reaction in which the polymer grows one monomer at a time and the reaction takes place at specific sites on the growing polymer. (Ch. 28)

Chain reaction a reaction whose mechanism consists of initiation, propagation, and termination steps and whose net reaction is the sum of its *propagation steps*. (Ch. 27)

Chain transfer a step in *chain polymerization* in which the site of reaction on a polymer chain changes; changing the site of reaction to the middle of a polymer chain can result in a *branched polymer*. (Ch. 28)

Chair conformation a cyclohexane geometry in which all bond angles of the ring are about 111° and all C—C bonds are staggered. (Ch. 4)

Chair flip (also known as *ring flip*) the process of single-bond rotations that converts one chair conformation of cyclohexane (or a substituted cyclohexane) into the other. (Ch. 4)

Chemical distinction test a protocol used to determine whether atoms in a molecule are chemically distinct. (Ch. 17)

Chemical environment the electron distribution surrounding a particular location in space, governing the chemical behavior of an atom. (Ch. 17)

Chemically distinct (also known as *heterotopic*) describes nuclei surrounded by different electron distributions; that is, they reside in different chemical environments and so absorb at different frequencies in *NMR spectroscopy*. (Ch. 17)

Chemically equivalent (also known as *homotopic)* describes nuclei surrounded by identical electron distributions; that is, they reside in identical chemical environments and so absorb at the same frequency in *NMR spectroscopy*. (Ch. 17)

Chemical reaction the transformation of one substance (the reactant) into another substance (the product), typically through changes in chemical bonds. (Ch. 6)

Chemical shift (δ) in *NMR spectroscopy*, a measure of the extent to which a signal's frequency differs from that of a reference compound, usually tetramethylsilane (TMS). (Ch. 17)

Chiral describes a molecule that has an *enantiomer.* (Ch. 5)

Chiral center (also known as *stereocenter* or *asymmetric atom*) a tetrahedral atom bonded to four different groups. (Ch. 5)

Chiral environment an environment that is nonsuperimposable on its mirror image, in which *enantiomers* must have different physical and chemical properties. (Ch. 5)

Chlorination a reaction that adds chlorine atoms to a molecule; can be accomplished by substituting a chlorine atom for a hydrogen atom or by adding molecular chlorine (Cl_2) to a C=C or C≡C bond. (Ch. 24)

Chlorohydrin a compound in which a chlorine atom and a hydroxyl group (OH) are attached to two adjacent carbons. (Ch. 13)

Chloronium ion intermediate a positively charged species containing a three-membered ring composed of two carbon atoms and a chlorine atom. (Ch. 13)

***m*-Chloroperbenzoic acid (MCPBA)** a *peroxy acid* used in epoxidation reactions. (Ch. 13)

Chromate ester a compound characterized by the arrangement O=Cr—OR; an intermediate in the chromium oxidation of alcohols and aldehydes. (Ch. 20)

Chromic acid the compound H_2CrO_4, which is used to oxidize secondary alcohols to ketones and primary alcohols to carboxylic acids. (Ch. 20)

Cis describes the configuration wherein two atoms are on the same side of a double bond or plane of a ring. Compare with *trans*. (Ch. 3)

Claisen condensation reaction a reaction in which an enolate anion undergoes nucleophilic addition–elimination with an ester, producing a β-keto ester. (Ch. 23)

Clemmensen reduction a reaction that uses a zinc amalgam under acidic conditions to reduce the C=O group of a ketone or an aldehyde to a methylene (CH_2) group. (Ch. 20)

Closed-shell species a molecule or ion in which all electrons are paired. (Ch. 27)

Codon a three-nucleotide sequence in messenger RNA that serves as the "instruction" for adding a specific amino acid to a protein. (Ch. 30) E

Coenzyme an organic non-protein molecule that is recruited to the active site of an enzyme to facilitate the reaction. Unlike *cofactors*, coenzymes generally are not considered to be part of the enzyme's structure. (Ch. 30) E

Cofactor a metal ion or non-protein molecule required for an enzyme to function properly. Cofactors are often considered as part of the enzyme structure during the course of the reaction. (Ch. 30) E

Common name see *trivial name*. (Int. A)

Competitive inhibition the situation where an inhibitor molecule binds to the active site of an enzyme to form an enzyme–inhibitor complex (EI). While the active site is occupied by an inhibitor, the substrate cannot undergo the proper reaction to form the product. (Ch. 30) E

Complementary describes two DNA or RNA strands when their facing nitrogenous bases pair, forming strong hydrogen bonds and a characteristic double helix. In DNA, adenine pairs with thymine, and guanine pairs with cytosine; in RNA, adenine pairs with uracil, and guanine pairs with cytosine. (Ch. 14, 29)

Complex splitting in *NMR spectroscopy*, splitting that arises when a nucleus is coupled to more than one distinct type of nuclei. (Ch. 17)

Concerted describes the fact that breaking of bonds and forming of bonds during an *elementary step* occur simultaneously. (Ch. 6)

Condensation polymerization a type of *step-growth polymerization* in which a small molecule is eliminated when two monomers or growing polymer chains bond together. (Ch. 28)

Condensation reaction a reaction in which two larger molecules are joined at the expense of the loss of a smaller molecule. (Ch. 10)

Condensed formula a way of representing molecules as a line of text, with hydrogens written immediately to the right of the atom to which they are bonded. (Ch. 1)

Configuration see *stereochemical configuration*. (Ch. 5)

Configurational isomers molecular species that have the same *connectivity* but differ in a way other than by rotations about single bonds. See the two types: *enantiomers* and *diastereomers*. (Ch. 5)

Conformational analysis a plot of a molecule's energy as a function of one or more of its dihedral angles. (Ch. 4)

Conformers nonsuperimposable molecules that have the same *connectivity* (see *stereoisomers*) but differ by rotations about single bonds. (Ch. 4)

Conjugate acid the species that results after a base acquires a proton. (Ch. 6)

Conjugate addition a reaction that takes place by nucleophilic attack at the β carbon of an *α,β-unsaturated carbonyl compound*; sometimes referred to by the more general term *1,4-addition*. (Ch. 18)

Conjugate base the species that results after an acid loses a proton. (Ch. 6)

Conjugated describes double or triple bonds that are separated by another bond; also describes *p* atomic orbitals or π molecular orbitals that are adjacent and overlap in a side-by-side fashion. (Ch. 12, 14)

Connectivity information that conveys which atoms are bonded together and by what types of bonds (single, double, or triple). (Ch. 1)

Conservation of number of orbitals the generalized concept that when *n* orbitals are mixed, *n* unique orbitals must be produced. See *molecular orbital theory*. (Ch. 3)

Constitutional isomers (also known as *structural isomers*) compounds that share the same molecular formula but differ in their *connectivity*. (Ch. 4)

Constructive interference the mixing that occurs when waves or orbitals overlap with the same phase. Constructive interference produces a new wave or orbital that has been built up by the addition of the amplitudes from the contributing waves. (Ch. 3)

Convergent synthesis a method of synthesizing molecules, wherein portions of the *target* are synthesized separately and then assembled at a later stage, usually resulting in a higher yield than a corresponding *linear synthesis*. (Ch. 11)

Coordination step an *elementary step* in which a single bond is formed using two electrons from the same atom and no bonds are broken. (Ch. 7)

Copolymer a *polymer* that is produced from two different monomers that can each undergo self-polymerization. (Ch. 28)

Core electron a lower energy inner-shell electron that is not used for bonding. (Ch. 1)

COSY abbreviation for **homonuclear correlation spectroscopy**. (Ch. 17)

Coupled describes two or more atoms that exhibit *spin–spin coupling* in *NMR spectroscopy*. (Ch. 17)

Coupling constant (J) in *NMR spectroscopy*, the frequency difference between peaks of a split NMR signal; this property is independent of the external magnetic field (B_{ext}). (Ch. 17)

Coupling reaction a reaction in which two groups are joined together and a new C—C bond is formed. (Ch. 20)

Covalent bond one of the two types of fundamental bonds in chemistry; it is characterized by the sharing of *valence electrons* between two or more atoms. Compare with *ionic bond*. (Ch. 1)

Crossed aldol reaction an *aldol addition* reaction in which the carbonyl-containing reactants that join together are different. (Ch. 19)

Crossed Claisen condensation reaction a specific type of *Claisen condensation reaction* in which the carbonyl-containing reactants that join together are different. (Ch. 23)

Cross-link a portion of a *polymer* that is responsible for joining two separate main chains. (Ch. 28)

Crystal lattice the three-dimensional pattern into which ions or molecules in a solid are arranged. (Ch. 1, 28)

Crystalline solid a solid that has a well-defined *crystal lattice*. (Ch. 28)

C-terminus the end of a polypeptide (protein) chain that is part of a carboxyl group. (Ch. 23, 29)

Curved arrow the symbol (↷) or (⇀) that illustrates the electron movement necessary to change one resonance structure into another or to form or break bonds in an *elementary step* of a mechanism. (Ch. 1)

Curved arrow notation (also known as *arrow pushing*) the notation used by organic chemists to describe the movement of electrons necessary to change one resonance structure into another or to form or break bonds in an *elementary step* of a mechanism. (Ch. 6)

Cyanohydrin a compound characterized by a hydroxyl (OH) and a cyano (C≡N) group attached to the same carbon. (Ch. 19)

Cyclic π system a group of molecular orbitals derived from a set of *p* orbitals that are all *conjugated* and make a complete ring. (Ch. 14)

Cycloaddition reaction a concerted reaction in which two separate species come together to produce a new ring. (Ch. 26)

[2+2] Cycloaddition a specific type of *cycloaddition reaction* in which two electrons are supplied by each species. (Ch. 26)

[4+2] Cycloaddition a specific type of *cycloaddition reaction* in which four electrons are supplied by one species and two electrons are supplied by the other species. (Ch. 26)

[6+2] Cycloaddition a specific type of *cycloaddition reaction* in which six electrons are supplied by one species and two electrons are supplied by the other species. (Ch. 26)

Cycloalkane a cyclic molecule consisting of only carbon and hydrogen atoms and only single bonds. (Int. A)

Cycloalkyl group a substituent consisting of a cyclic arrangement of only carbon and hydrogen atoms and only single bonds. (Int. A)

[4+2] Cycloelimination (also known as *retro Diels–Alder reaction*) a concerted reaction in which a cyclic molecule is cleaved into two separate species; one species receives four electrons and the other species receives two electrons. (Ch. 26)

D

Dash–wedge notation a system of drawing to represent three-dimensional molecules that uses dashes for bonds that point away from the viewer and wedges for bonds that point toward the viewer. (Ch. 2)

Deactivating group a substituent that decreases the reactivity of a molecule in a particular reaction; often refers to a substituent that makes an aromatic ring less susceptible to an *electrophilic aromatic substitution reaction*. (Ch. 25)

Debye (D) conventional unit for the magnitude of a dipole. (Ch. 2)

Decarboxylation a reaction that removes a carboxyl (CO_2H) group from a molecule. (Ch. 23)

Degenerate orbital one of a set of orbitals that have identical energies. (Ch. 14)

Degree of polymerization (DP) the number of *repeating units* in a polymer. (Ch. 28)

Degree of unsaturation see *index of hydrogen deficiency (IHD)*. (Ch. 4)

Dehydration the removal of water from a substance; often describes a reaction in which water is a product. (Ch. 9)

Delocalization the phenomenon of electrons or charges being less confined to a particular location within a species. Delocalization is generally stabilizing. (Ch. 1)

Delocalization energy see *resonance energy*. (Ch. 1)

Delocalized describes an electron or charge that is not confined to a particular location within a species. (Ch. 1)

Deoxyribonucleic acid (DNA) a double-helical pair of intertwined nucleic acid strands that stores genetic information. (Ch. 1)

Deprotection step a reaction used in synthesis to selectively convert a protected functional group back to the original functional group. (Ch. 21)

Deshielded in *NMR spectroscopy*, describes nuclei whose shielding (see *shielded*) becomes diminished by nearby electronegative atoms or by magnetic anisotropy. Deshielded nuclei have higher signal frequencies, and thus larger *chemical shifts*. (Ch. 17)

Destructive interference the mixing that occurs when waves or orbitals overlap with opposite phase. Destructive interference between two orbitals produces a new orbital that is diminished in size. (Ch. 3)

Desulfonation a reaction that removes a sulfo group (SO_3H or SO_3R) from a molecule. (Ch. 24)

Dextrorotatory (from Latin, meaning "rotating to the right") describes chiral compounds that rotate plane-polarized light clockwise (in the + direction). Compare with *levorotatory*. (Ch. 5)

Dialkylborane a compound that has the structure R_2BH, with two alkyl groups attached to boron. (Ch. 13)

Diastereomers a type of *configurational isomer* where the molecules are not mirror images of each other. (Ch. 5)

1,3-Diaxial interaction interaction between atoms or groups separately attached to a cyclohexane ring, at relative positions numbered 1 and 3, and occupying axial positions. (Ch. 4)

Diazomethane the compound CH_2N_2; it is used as a reagent to produce a methyl ester from a carboxylic acid or to produce a cyclopropane ring from an alkene. (Ch. 10)

Diazotization a reaction that forms a compound with the diazo group (N═N). (Ch. 24)

Diborane (B_2H_6) an explosive, gaseous dimer of borane (BH_3) that contains three-center, two-electron bonds. (Ch. 13)

Dicyclohexylborane a bulky dialkylborane that has the formula $(C_6H_{11})_2BH$, used in the *hydroboration* of an alkyne to help ensure that the alkyne undergoes a single addition. (Ch. 13)

Dicyclohexylcarbodiimide (DCC) the molecule $(C_6H_{11})N{=}C{=}N(C_6H_{11})$, which is used as a reagent to couple a carboxylic acid and an amine to produce an amide. (Ch. 29)

Dieckmann condensation reaction a specific type of *Claisen condensation reaction* that occurs intramolecularly. (Ch. 23)

Diels–Alder reaction a reaction between a conjugated *diene* and a *dienophile* that produces a cyclohexene ring. (Ch. 26)

Diene a compound with a pair of conjugated π bonds that contributes four π electrons in a *Diels–Alder reaction*. (Ch. 26)

Dienophile a compound that contributes a single π bond (two π electrons) in a *Diels–Alder reaction*. (Ch. 26)

Diglyceride a fatty acid diester of glycerol. (Ch. 2, 29)

Dihedral angle (θ) the angle between a bond on the front atom and a bond on the rear atom of a *Newman projection*; each angle of rotation defines a particular dihedral angle. (Ch. 4)

Diisobutylaluminum hydride (DIBAH or DIBAL-H) the compound $(i\text{-Bu})_2Al{-}H$, which is used to reduce esters to aldehydes. (Ch. 22)

Dipeptide a molecule consisting of two *amino acid* residues linked by a *peptide bond*. (Ch. 29)

1,3-Dipolar cycloaddition a concerted reaction in which two separate species come together to produce a new ring and in which one species is characterized by resonance delocalization of charge over atoms that have 1,3-positioning. (Ch. 26)

Dipole arrow a labeling arrow (+⟶) depicting the direction from excess positive charge (the origin) to excess negative charge (the point). (Ch. 1)

Dipole–dipole interaction the attraction between the positive end of one molecule's *net dipole* and the negative end of another molecule's net dipole. (Ch. 2)

Direct addition a reaction that takes place by nucleophilic attack at the carbonyl carbon of an *α,β-unsaturated carbonyl compound*; sometimes referred to by the more general term *1,2-addition*. (Ch. 18)

Disaccharide a molecule consisting of two *monosaccharides* joined by a *glycosidic linkage*. (Ch. 29)

Disiamylborane a bulky dialkylborane that has the formula$(C_5H_{11})_2BH$, used in the *hydroboration* of an alkyne to help ensure that the alkyne undergoes a single addition. (Ch. 13)

Disproportionation a reaction in which two of the same species react to form two different products. (Ch. 28)

Dissolving metal reduction a reaction during which a metal dissolves in solution, commonly used to reduce alkynes to trans alkenes. (Ch. 20, 27)

Distortionless enhancement by polarization transfer (DEPT) a technique used in *^{13}C NMR spectroscopy* to determine the type of carbon (CH_3, CH_2, CH, or C) responsible for producing a particular signal. (Ch. 17)

Disubstituted having two substituents. (Ch. 4)

Disubstituted benzene a benzene ring that has two substituents attached. (Int. B)

Disulfide bond *or* disulfide bridge a link characterized by two sulfur atoms singly bonded together (i.e., S—S); often found in proteins, linking two cysteine residues. (Ch. 28, 29)

DNA polymerase an enzyme that catalyzes the incorporation of each nucleotide into the growing DNA strand during *DNA replication*. (Ch. 30)

DNA replication the process of making identical copies of the parent cell's DNA. (Ch. 30)

Doublet (d) the splitting pattern of an NMR *signal* into two peaks of essentially equal height; occurs when $N = 1$, according to the *$N + 1$ rule*. (Ch. 17)

Doublet of doublets the splitting pattern of an NMR *signal* when each peak in a doublet is split again into a doublet by a second coupling, resulting in a total of four peaks. (Ch. 17)

Downfield in an NMR spectrum, appearing in a region of higher chemical shift. (Ch. 17)

Driving force a thermodynamic concept (not an actual force) describing the extent to which a reaction favors products over reactants under a particular set of conditions; it tends to increase with increasing stability (lower energy) of products relative to reactants, and charge stability and total bond energy are important contributors. (Ch. 7)

Duet a set of two electrons in the $n = 1$ shell of an atom. (Ch. 1)

E

E1 abbreviation for **unimolecular elimination reaction**. (Ch. 8)

E1cb abbreviation for **unimolecular elimination of conjugate base mechanism**. (Ch. 19)

E2 abbreviation for **bimolecular elimination step**. (Ch. 7)

Eclipsed conformation a rotational geometry in which the bonds to the front atom in a *Newman projection* cover, or "eclipse," the bonds to the rear atom. Compare with *staggered conformation*. (Ch. 4)

***E* configuration** describes a double bond in which the higher-priority substituents attached to the ends of the double bond appear on opposite sides of the double bond. Compare with *Z configuration*. (Ch. 5)

Edman degradation a cycle of three reactions that removes the N-terminal amino acid from a polypeptide for analysis. (Ch. 23, 29)

Effective electronegativity property describing the tendency of an atom to hold electrons more tightly as an outcome of the atom's hybridization. (Ch. 3)

Effective magnetic field (B_{eff}) the net magnetic field that is "felt" by the nucleus; the sum of external (B_{ext}) and local (B_{loc}) magnetic fields. (Ch. 17)

Elastomer a *polymer* that has the ability to retain its original shape after large deformations; vulcanized rubber is a common example. (Ch. 28)

Electromagnetic radiation a form of energy that has characteristics of both waves and particles. Behaving as a wave, electromagnetic radiation exhibits oscillating electric and magnetic fields. Behaving as a particle, electromagnetic radiation exists as *photons*. (Ch. 16)

Electron configuration the way in which electrons are arranged in atomic or molecular orbitals. (Ch. 1)

Electron-donating describes a substituent that adds electron density to an atom to which it is bonded; electron-donating ability is considered relative to hydrogen. (Ch. 6)

Electronegativity (EN) the ability of an atomic nucleus to attract electrons in a covalent bond. (Ch. 1)

Electron geometry the orientation of the electron groups about a particular atom. (Ch. 2)

Electron impact ionization (EI) the process of producing a molecular ion by colliding an electron beam with a gaseous molecule; used in *mass spectrometry*. (Ch. 15)

Electron spin density plot a plot of the electron cloud about a molecule, color-coded to show regions where there is high probability of finding an unpaired electron. (Ch. 27)

Electron-withdrawing describes a substituent that removes electron density from an atom to which it is bonded; electron-withdrawing ability is considered relative to hydrogen. (Ch. 6)

Electrophile an electron-deficient species. (Ch. 7)

Electrophile elimination step an *elementary step* in which an electrophile is eliminated from a carbocation, generating a new π bond; the reverse of an *electrophilic addition step*. (Ch. 7)

Electrophilic addition reaction a reaction whose mechanism involves an *electrophilic addition step* as a key step. (Ch. 12)

Electrophilic addition step an *elementary step* in which electrons from a nonpolar π bond (as part of a double or triple bond) are used to form a new σ bond to an electrophile; the reverse of an *electrophile elimination step*. (Ch. 7)

Electrophilic aromatic substitution reaction a reaction in which an electrophile is attached to an aromatic ring; it proceeds by an *electrophilic addition step* followed by an *electrophile elimination step*, resulting in a net substitution. (Ch. 24)

Electrophoresis a common way of separating a mixture of amino acids or proteins (often at a given pH) by using an electric field; it is often done in a gel-like medium (known as gel electrophoresis). (Ch. 29)

Electrostatic force the interaction by which opposite charges attract one another and like charges repel one another. (Ch. 1)

Electrostatic potential map the depiction of a molecule's electron cloud in colors that indicate its relative charge; one way to illustrate the distribution of charge along a covalent bond. (Ch. 1)

Elementary step a reaction that occurs in a single event and does not proceed through an intermediate; all bonds that break or form in an elementary step do so essentially simultaneously. (Ch. 6)

Empirical rate law an experimentally determined relationship that describes how the rate of a reaction depends on reactant and product concentrations. (Ch. 8)

Enamine a compound characterized by the bonding arrangement C=C—N. (Ch. 19)

Enantiomeric excess (ee) the fraction of a mixture of *enantiomers* that is not racemic and contributes to the rotation of plane-polarized light. (Ch. 5)

Enantiomers a type of *configurational isomer* where the molecules are mirror images of each other. (Ch. 5)

Endergonic describes a reaction that gains free energy on producing products (i.e., $\Delta G^\circ_{rxn} > 0$) and is generally nonspontaneous. (Ch. 6)

End group the collection of atoms that characterizes the end of the main chain of a polymer. (Ch. 28)

Endo approach in a *Diels–Alder reaction*, the orientation of the dienophile in which the substituents on the dienophile point toward the diene, resulting in the *endo product*. (Ch. 26)

Endo product the diastereomeric product resulting from *endo approach* in a *Diels–Alder reaction*. (Ch. 26)

Endo rule (also known as *Alder rule*) description of the tendency of a Diels–Alder reaction to favor the *endo product* over the *exo product*. (Ch. 26)

Endothermic describes a reaction or process that absorbs heat; $\Delta H^\circ_{rxn} > 0$. (Ch. 6)

Enolate anion a deprotonated *enol*, bearing a negative charge. (Ch. 7)

Enol form a compound that has the bonding arrangement C=C—OH; the enol form of a molecule is the tautomer of its *keto form*. (Ch. 7)

Entropy a thermodynamic quantity that increases with the number of equivalent ways the energy in a system can be arranged. Many people like to think of entropy as a measure of disorder; a system with greater entropy (i.e., one that is more disordered) tends to be more likely to occur than a system with less entropy. (Ch. 2)

Envelope conformation the lowest-energy geometry of cyclopentane, where four of its five carbon atoms lie essentially in one plane, with the fifth carbon outside that plane; the geometry resembles an envelope. (Ch. 4)

Enzyme a catalyst for biological reactions; that is, an enzyme facilitates biological reactions but is not consumed while doing so. (Ch. 1, 30)

Enzyme–product complex (EP) a species in which the product of an enzyme-catalyzed reaction is bound to the enzyme. (Ch. 30)

Enzyme–substrate complex (ES) a species formed on the binding of an enzyme and its substrate immediately prior to the enzyme-catalyzed reaction. (Ch. 30)

Epimers compounds that differ in stereochemical configuration at only one chiral center. (Ch. 5, 29)

Epoxidation reaction a reaction wherein an epoxide is produced, often involving an alkene and a peroxy acid like *m*-chloroperbenzoic acid (MCPBA). (Ch. 13)

Epoxide a compound that contains a three-membered ring made of two C atoms and one O atom. (Ch. 1)

Equatorial describes bonds in a cyclic molecule that lie almost in the plane roughly defined by the ring (i.e., the equator of the molecule) and point outward from the center of the ring. Compare with *axial*. (Ch. 4)

Equilibrium a condition in which the rate of reaction in the forward direction (reactants forming products) equals the rate of reaction in the reverse direction (products forming reactants), so that the concentrations of reactants and products do not change. (Ch. 6)

Equilibrium constant (K_{eq}) an experimentally obtained constant that describes the tendency of a reaction to form products. (Ch. 6)

Essential fatty acid one of the naturally occurring fatty acids that cannot be synthesized in the human body by any known chemical pathway; instead, it must be consumed. (Ch. 4, 29)

Ester a compound that contains the bonding arrangement C—CO_2C. (Ch. 1)

Ether a compound that contains the bonding arrangement C—O—C. (Ch. 1)

Ethoxy group the group OCH_2CH_3; also written as OEt. (Int. A)

Ethylene glycol the compound $HOCH_2CH_2OH$, often used to protect a ketone or aldehyde. (Ch. 21)

Ethyl group the group CH_2CH_3; also written as Et. (Int. A)

Excited electronic state an electron configuration that is not the lowest-energy configuration or *ground state*. (Ch. 26)

Exergonic describes a reaction that releases free energy on producing products (i.e., $\Delta G^\circ_{rxn} < 0$) and is generally spontaneous. (Ch. 6)

Exo approach in a *Diels–Alder reaction*, the orientation of the dienophile in which the substituents on the dienophile point away from the diene, resulting in the *exo product*. (Ch. 26)

Exo product the diastereomeric product from *exo approach* in a *Diels–Alder reaction*. (Ch. 26)

Exothermic describes a reaction or process that releases heat; $\Delta H^\circ_{rxn} < 0$. (Ch. 6)

Expanded octet a group of more than eight *valence electrons* belonging to a single atom; only atoms in the third row of the periodic table and below can have an expanded octet. (Ch. 1)

External magnetic field (B_{ext}) a magnetic field applied to a sample by a magnet, such as a superconducting magnet in *NMR spectroscopy*. (Ch. 17)

F

Fat one of a subclass of lipids whose most common biological function is to store energy. Fats contain three adjacent ester groups, each of which can be produced from a *fatty acid* and one of the three hydroxyl groups of *glycerol*. Thus, a fat or oil is often described as a *triacylglycerol* or a *triglyceride*. (Ch. 2, 29)

Fatty acid a long-chain carboxylic acid. (Ch. 2, 29)

Fingerprint region the region of a sample's infrared spectrum below ~1400 cm^{-1}. A fingerprint region is often difficult to analyze but is unique to each compound. (Ch. 16)

Fischer esterification reaction an acid-catalyzed reaction between an alcohol and a carboxylic acid that produces an ester. (Ch. 23)

Fischer projection a relatively convenient, two-dimensional representation of configurations about chiral centers in a given molecule; for each stereocenter represented in a Fischer projection, horizontal bonds point toward the viewer and vertical bonds point away from the viewer. (Ch. 5)

Fischer proof the logical reasoning by which Emil Fischer used results from specific chemical reactions and polarimetry to establish the relative configurations at the four chiral centers in glucose. (Ch. 29)

Flagpole interaction the steric strain resulting from atoms or groups attached to C-1 and C-4 of cyclohexane in its boat conformation. (Ch. 4)

Flavin adenine dinucleotide a common *coenzyme* used in redox reactions. It exists in either the oxidized form, FAD, or the reduced form, $FADH_2$. (Ch. 30)

Force constant (k) a characteristic of a spring, often thought of as the spring stiffness; according to *Hooke's law*, vibrational frequency is proportional to $\sqrt{k}$. (Ch. 16)

Formal charge one of two methods used to assign charge to atoms involved in covalent bonds. Lone pairs are assigned to the atom on which they appear in the Lewis structure. In a given covalent bond, half the electrons are assigned to each atom involved in the bond. Compare with *oxidation state*. (Ch. 1)

Fourier transform a mathematical algorithm used in *NMR spectroscopy* that decomposes a *free induction decay* into its individual frequencies, or signals. (Ch. 17)

Fragmentation the process of breaking molecules into smaller pieces, as with an electron beam for *mass spectrometry*. (Ch. 15)

Fragmentation pathways the reactions that account for breaking the molecular ion ($M^{+\bullet}$) into smaller pieces in *mass spectrometry*. (Ch. 15)

Free energy of activation ($\Delta G^{\circ\ddagger}$) the energy barrier that must be surmounted for reactants to form products; the difference in *standard Gibbs free energy* between the reactants and the transition state. (Ch. 6)

Free induction decay (FID) in *NMR spectroscopy*, a digitized record of amplitude versus time for *radio frequency* radiation reemitted by a sample. (Ch. 17)

Frequency (ν) the number of complete wave oscillations that occur in a given time. Frequency is given in units of hertz (Hz) or cycles/second or s^{-1}, all of which are equivalent. (Ch. 16)

Friedel–Crafts acylation an *electrophilic aromatic substitution reaction* in which a proton on an aromatic ring is replaced by an acylium ion ($R—C{\equiv}O^+$). (Ch. 24)

Friedel–Crafts alkylation an *electrophilic aromatic substitution reaction* in which a proton on an aromatic ring is replaced by a carbocation (R^+). (Ch. 24)

Frontier molecular orbital the *highest occupied molecular orbital (HOMO)* or *lowest occupied molecular orbital (LUMO)* of a reacting species in an *elementary step*. (Int. C)

Frontier molecular orbital (FMO) theory a framework that invokes HOMO–LUMO interactions in the reacting species to establish whether an *elementary step* is allowed or forbidden. (Int. C)

Frontside attack the spatial arrangement describing a nucleophile approaching the substrate from the same side as the *leaving group*, leading to retention of stereochemical configuration. (Ch. 8)

Frost method a method to derive the relative energies of the π molecular orbitals in an [*n*]annulene. (Ch. 14)

Fuming sulfuric acid concentrated H_2SO_4 infused with SO_3 liquid. (Ch. 24)

Functional group conversion *or* functional group transformation a reaction that changes one functional group into another. (Ch. 10)

Functional group a common bonding arrangement of relatively few atoms. Functional groups dictate the behavior of entire molecules; that is, molecules with the same functional groups tend to behave similarly. (Ch. 1)

Furanose cyclic form of a *monosaccharide* characterized by a five-membered ring. (Ch. 19, 29)

Fused rings rings that have bonds in common. (Ch. 14)

G

Gabriel synthesis a synthesis scheme that involves the reaction of phthalimide and an alkyl halide (RX) to produce a primary amine (RNH_2). (Ch. 22)

Gauche conformation a *staggered conformation* wherein bulky groups are 60° apart in a *Newman projection*. (Ch. 4)

Gel permeation chromatography (GPC) a technique used to analyze the distribution of molecular size within a sample; smaller molecules are detected later in the analysis because they interact more strongly with the gel. (Ch. 28)

Geminal dihalide a molecule in which two halide substituents are attached to the same carbon atom. (Ch. 12)

Gene a segment of DNA containing a sequence of nucleotides that code for a specific protein. (Ch. 30)

General acid–base catalysis a means by which a reaction is catalyzed by acids or bases, and in which a proton transfer is part of the rate-determining step. Compare with *specific acid–base catalysis*. (Ch. 30)

Genome the complete set of genetic information defined by an organism's DNA. (Ch. 30)

Gilman reagent see *lithium dialkylcuprate*. (Ch. 18)

Glass transition temperature (T_g) the temperature above which the species that make up an *amorphous solid* begin to flow past each other. (Ch. 28)

Glucagon a peptide hormone that signals the need to increase the glucose concentration in the blood. (Ch. 30)

Gluconeogenesis a *metabolic pathway* responsible for synthesizing D-glucose. (Ch. 30)

Glycolysis a metabolic pathway that breaks down simple carbohydrates for their energy. (Ch. 30)

Glycosidation a reaction in which an OH from a sugar molecule has been replaced by an alkoxy group. This product is called a *glycoside*. (Ch. 9, 29)

Glycoside one of a class of compounds characterized by sugars with *glycosidic linkages* to other groups. (Ch. 9, 29)

Glycosidic linkage the C—O—C group that connects a sugar unit to another group, often another sugar. (Ch. 9, 29)

G protein-coupled receptor (GPCR) one of a large class of proteins that is embedded in the cell membrane and recognizes messenger molecules in *cell signaling*. (Ch. 30)

G proteins see *guanine nucleotide-binding proteins*. (Ch. 30)

Green alternative an innovative reaction, technique, or technology to avoid the production and accumulation of hazardous materials. (Ch. 11)

Green chemistry a set of guiding principles to prevent pollution and other health hazards associated with organic synthesis and the chemical industry. (Ch. 11)

Grignard reaction a reaction in which a Grignard reagent adds in as a nucleophile to the electrophilic atom of a group containing a polar π bond. (Ch. 18)

Grignard reagent an alkylmagnesium halide (R—MgX, where X = Cl, Br, or I) nucleophile that favors direct addition to a polar π bond over conjugate addition. Grignard reagents are often used to make new carbon–carbon bonds. (Ch. 7)

Ground state the most stable (i.e., the lowest energy) electron configuration. (Ch. 1)

Grubbs catalyst a compound that has the bonding arrangement $Cl_2Ru{=}C$, used in *alkene metathesis* reactions. (Ch. 20)

Guanine nucleotide-binding proteins (also known as *G proteins*) a family of proteins that are involved in *cell signaling*. (Ch. 30)

Gyromagnetic ratio (γ) a value that relates the energy separation between the spin states of a nucleus and an applied magnetic field. (Ch. 17)

H

^{1}H NMR spectroscopy see *proton NMR spectroscopy*. (Ch. 17)

Haloalkane an alkane with a halogen substituent (F, Cl, Br, or I). (Int. A)

Haloform a compound having the general form HCX_3, where X = F, Cl, Br, or I. (Ch. 22)

Haloform reaction the reaction of a methyl ketone or an aldehyde with a molecular halogen (e.g., Cl_2, Br_2, or I_2) under basic conditions, producing a *haloform* and a carboxylate anion that can be protonated to a form a carboxylic acid. (Ch. 22)

Halogenation a chemical reaction that increases the number of halogen atoms in a molecule. See *α halogenation* (Ch. 10), *aromatic halogenation* (Ch. 24), *polyhalogenation* (Ch. 10), and *radical halogenation* (Ch. 27). See also *bromination* and *chlorination* (Ch. 24), *bromonium ion intermediate* and *chloronium ion intermediate* (Ch. 13), and *geminal dihalide*. (Ch. 12).

Halohydrin one of a class of molecules in which a halogen atom and a hydroxyl group are on adjacent carbon atoms. (Ch. 10)

Hammond postulate in a *reaction free energy diagram*, the notion that if two species lie near each other along the reaction coordinate (the *x*-axis) and are similar in energy, then they will have very similar structures. (Ch. 9)

Haworth projection a two-dimensional representation wherein a ring is depicted as being planar, occupying the plane perpendicular to the page, and substituents are drawn perpendicular to that plane. This projection illustrates cis and trans relationships well, but it does not accurately convey three-dimensional relationships or steric strain. (Ch. 4)

Head-to-head in a *polymerization reaction*, describes the orientation in which the heads of two monomers are facing each other. (Ch. 28)

Head-to-tail in a *polymerization reaction*, describes the orientation in which the head of one monomer faces the tail of another monomer. (Ch. 28)

Heat of combustion the amount of energy released as heat (ΔH°_{comb}) during a combustion reaction. (Ch. 4)

Heat of hydrogenation the amount of energy released as heat (ΔH°_{hyd}) when $H_2(g)$ adds to double or triple bonds. It is used to gain a sense of the stability of π systems. (Ch. 14)

Heck reaction a *coupling reaction*, similar to the Suzuki reaction, in which one vinylic or aryl group joins with another in the presence of a palladium catalyst (PdL_2). (Ch. 20)

Hell–Volhard–Zelinsky (HVZ) reaction a reaction in which the α carbon of a carboxylic acid is brominated to produce an α-bromo acid. (Ch. 23)

Hemiacetal a compound that contains the bonding arrangement in which one hydroxy group (OH) and one alkoxy group (OR) are attached to the same carbon atom. (Ch. 1, 19)

Henderson–Hasselbalch equation the mathematical expression that relates the pH of a solution to the ratio of the concentration of an acid's conjugate base to that of the acid: $pH = pK_a + \log\left(\frac{[A^-]}{[HA]}\right)$. (Ch. 6)

HETCOR abbreviation for **heteronuclear correlation spectroscopy**. (Ch. 17)

Heteroatom an atom that is not carbon or hydrogen. (Ch. 1)

Heterochain polymer a *polymer* in which the main chain consists of both carbon and non-carbon atoms. (Ch. 28)

Heterocyclic aromatic compound one of a class of aromatic compounds that have heteroatoms incorporated into their aromatic ring structures. (Ch. 14)

Heterogeneous catalyst a catalyst that is in a different phase from the rest of the reaction mixture. (Ch. 13)

Heterolysis step *or* heterolytic bond dissociation step an *elementary step* in which only a single bond is broken and both electrons from that bond end up on one of the atoms initially involved in the bond. (Ch. 7)

Heteronuclear correlation (HETCOR) spectroscopy a two-dimensional NMR method in which the ^{13}C NMR spectrum is shown on the *x* axis and the ^{1}H NMR spectrum is shown on the *y* axis. Each cross peak provides information about which protons are attached to which carbons. (Ch. 17)

Heterotopic see *chemically distinct.* (Ch. 17)

Hexose a six-carbon sugar. (Ch. 4, 29)

Highest occupied molecular orbital (HOMO) the highest energy *molecular orbital* that contains an electron. (Ch. 3)

Hofmann elimination reaction a reaction that creates a double bond and leads to a product that has the less stable, less highly alkyl-substituted alkene, which is contrary to *Zaitsev's rule.* (Ch. 10)

Hofmann product (also known as *anti-Zaitsev product*) the product resulting from the *Hofmann elimination reaction*; the less highly alkyl-substituted product. (Ch. 10)

HOMO–LUMO transition promotion of an electron from the *highest occupied molecular orbital (HOMO)* to the *lowest unoccupied molecular orbital (LUMO)*, which corresponds to the lowest energy transition possible (and to the longest-wavelength λ_{max}) for a species in its *ground state* electron configuration. (Ch. 16)

Homolysis *or* homolytic bond dissociation an *elementary step* in which only a single bond is broken and the two electrons from that bond are split evenly between the atoms that were initially bonded together. (Ch. 27)

Homonuclear correlation spectroscopy (COSY) a two-dimensional NMR method in which the proton NMR spectrum is shown on both the *x* and *y* axes. Peaks that appear off the diagonal, called cross peaks, indicate which protons are coupled. (Ch. 17)

Homopolymer a *polymer* made from a single type of monomer. (Ch. 28)

Homotopic see *chemically equivalent.* (Ch. 17)

Hooke's law a mathematical representation of the behavior of a spring, used to model molecular vibrations: $\nu_{spring} = \sqrt{(k/\mu)}$, where ν_{spring} is the vibrational frequency of the spring, k is a constant that describes the spring stiffness, and μ is the reduced mass of the objects undergoing vibration. (Ch. 16)

Hückel number a number in the set {2, 6, 10, 14, ...}, which can be described as an odd number of pairs or as a number that is consistent with $4n + 2$, where n is a nonnegative integer. (Ch. 14)

Hückel's rules a set of criteria for predicting the aromaticity of a species. (Ch. 14)

Hund's rule states that all orbitals at the same energy must contain a single electron before a second electron can be paired in one of these orbitals. (Ch. 1)

Hybrid orbital an orbital that results from mixing two or more pure orbitals from the valence shell of a single atom. (Ch. 3)

Hydrazone a compound characterized by the bonding arrangement C=N—N. (Ch. 19)

Hydride anion ($H{:}^-$) an anion with a hydrogen nucleus and two electrons. (Ch. 7)

Hydride reagent a reagent that contains or has the tendency to donate hydride. Common hydride reducing agents include lithium aluminum hydride ($LiAlH_4$) and sodium borohydride ($NaBH_4$). Sodium hydride (NaH) is a strong base but a poor nucleophile. (Ch. 7)

1,2-Hydride shift a *carbocation rearrangement* wherein a hydride ion (H^-) migrates to an adjacent atom. (Ch. 7)

Hydroboration the net addition of BH_3 across a double or triple bond; hydrogen adds to one atom of the multiple bond and BH_2 adds to the other. (Ch. 13)

Hydroboration–oxidation a sequence of reactions (hydroboration followed by oxidation) that results in the *anti-Markovnikov addition* of water to an alkene or alkyne. (Ch. 13)

Hydrogen atom abstraction an *elementary step* in which a hydrogen atom is removed from a molecule; a type of S_H2 step in which a radical forms a bond to a hydrogen atom in a molecule and the initial bond to hydrogen is broken, generating a new radical. (Ch. 27)

Hydrogen bond (sometimes called H bond) an intermolecular interaction that involves a *hydrogen-bond donor* (NH, FH, or OH) and a *hydrogen-bond acceptor* (typically N, O, or F). (Ch. 2)

Hydrogen-bond acceptor any atom with a large concentration of negative charge and a lone pair of electrons, such as N, O, or F. (Ch. 2)

Hydrogen-bond donor a hydrogen atom covalently bonded to either F, O, or N. (Ch. 2)

Hydrolysis a type of reaction in which water is a reactant that facilitates the breaking of bonds; water is generally a nucleophile in these reactions. (Ch. 19, 23)

Hydroperoxide ion the HOO^- anion, a key nucleophile in the oxidation of a trialkylborane to produce an alcohol. (Ch. 13)

Hydrophilic "water-loving"; tending to dissolve in water. (Ch. 2)

Hydrophobic "water-fearing"; not tending to dissolve in water. (Ch. 2)

Hydrophobic effect the tendency of hydrophobic side chains to reside in the interior of a folded protein to minimize interactions of those side chains with an aqueous environment. (Ch. 28, 29)

Hydroxyl group the functional group having the bonding arrangement O—H. (Ch. 1)

Hyperconjugation the delocalization of electrons in a σ bonding molecular orbital into an adjacent orbital of π symmetry. (Ch. 7)

I

Ideal bond angle the theoretical bond angle predicted by valence shell electron pair repulsion (VSEPR) theory. (Ch. 4)

Imine (also known as *Schiff base*) a compound characterized by the bonding arrangement —C=N—R (or H). (Ch. 19)

Index of hydrogen deficiency (IHD) (also known as *degree of unsaturation*) half the number of hydrogen atoms missing from a molecule compared to an analogous, completely saturated molecule. (Ch. 4)

Induced dipole a temporary dipole that arises within a molecule as a result of the electron distribution being altered by a nearby full or partial charge. (Ch. 2)

Induced dipole–induced dipole interactions (also known as *London dispersion forces*) the source of attraction between nonpolar molecules resulting from the temporary distortion of their electron distributions. (Ch. 2)

Induced fit model a description of how, during the binding of an enzyme to its substrate, the active site's shape and the functional groups located there undergo conformational changes that enhance the interactions even further. (Ch. 30)

Induction the distortion of electron density along covalent bonds, brought about by the replacement of a hydrogen atom with another substituent. (Ch. 6)

Inductive effect the effect that *induction* has on stability or another property of a species. (Ch. 6)

Infrared (IR) spectroscopy study of the interaction of a sample with radiation from the infrared region of the electromagnetic spectrum; absorbance of this radiation increases the energy in molecular vibrations. (Ch. 16)

Initiation step the step in a *chain reaction* mechanism that produces the type of intermediate found in the *propagation cycle*. (Ch. 27)

Inorganic compound a compound that is not organic; that is, a compound that is not composed primarily of carbon and hydrogen. (Ch. 1)

In-plane bending vibrational motion of a molecule in which bond angles change but the atoms involved in the vibration all remain in the same plane. (Ch. 16)

Instantaneous dipole a temporary dipole that arises when there are more electrons on one side of a molecule than there are on the other at some instant. (Ch. 2)

Integral trace the line overlaid on an NMR spectrum that corresponds to the cumulative area under the peaks in the spectrum. The size of a stairstep in an integral trace is proportional to the number of nuclei that give rise to the corresponding peak. (Ch. 17)

Integration the operation of calculating the area under a curve, such as a peak in a spectrum; used to generate an *integral trace* in an NMR spectrum. (Ch. 17)

Intermediate a transitory species that appears in a reaction mechanism but does not appear in the *overall reaction*. (Ch. 8)

Intermolecular describes the involvement of two separate species. (Ch. 9)

Intermolecular force *or* intermolecular interaction attraction or repulsion that arises between molecules due to their charge distributions. (Ch. 2)

International Union of Pure and Applied Chemistry (IUPAC) an authoritative group that standardizes chemical nomenclature, constants, and processes. (Int. A)

Intramolecular describes the involvement of separate portions of a single species. (Ch. 9)

Intramolecular proton transfer a reaction that results in the loss of a proton from one part of a species and the gain of a proton at another part of the same species. (Ch. 8)

Ion a species that bears a net charge. (Ch. 1)

Ion–dipole interaction attraction between a positive or negative ion and a net molecular dipole; the intermolecular interaction whereby free ions can interact with the molecules of a polar solvent like water. (Ch. 2)

Ionic bond one of the two types of fundamental bonds in chemistry; in an ionic bond, the more electronegative atom acquires electrons given up by the less electronegative atom, forming oppositely charged ions. Electrostatic attraction between the positively charged cation and the negatively charged anion constitutes the ionic bond. Compare with *covalent bond*. (Ch. 1)

Ion–ion interaction the attraction between two oppositely charged ions. (Ch. 2)

Ionizable describes a species that is able to gain or lose a proton to become charged. (Ch. 6, 29)

Ion pair a pair of interacting, oppositely charged ions. (Ch. 8)

Irreversible describes a reaction that does not readily take place in the reverse direction. (Ch. 11)

IR spectrum a plot of *transmittance* (%T) of infrared radiation for a sample, on the y axis, against *wavenumbers* (cm^{-1}), a unit of frequency, on the x axis. (Ch. 16)

Isoelectric focusing a type of *electrophoresis* experiment in which amino acids or proteins are separated by charge using a pH gradient. (Ch. 29) ▣

Isoelectric pH *or* isoelectric point (pI) the pH at which a substance (usually an amino acid or protein) has an average charge of zero. (Ch. 29) ▣

Isomer a molecular species that has the same formula as another molecular species but is different in some way. See *constitutional isomers*, *stereoisomers*, *conformers*, *configurational isomers*, *diastereomers*, and *enantiomers*. (Ch. 4)

Isoprene unit a five-carbon unit into which a terpene's carbon backbone can be divided; each carbon atom in a *terpene* can be assigned to a distinct isoprene unit within the molecule. (Ch. 12, 29)

Isotactic describes a *polymer* in which all chiral centers along the main chain have the same configuration. (Ch. 28)

J

Jones oxidation a reaction in which aqueous chromic acid (H_2CrO_4) oxidizes a primary alcohol to a carboxylic acid and a secondary alcohol to a ketone. (Ch. 20)

K

K_a see *acidity constant*. (Ch. 6)

K_{eq} see *equilibrium constant*. (Ch. 6)

Kekulé structure a specific *resonance structure* of a species, usually referring to benzene. (Ch. 14)

Keto–enol tautomerization the transformation of one keto or enol *tautomer* (isomeric form) into the other; usually the process is an equilibrium. (Ch. 7)

Keto form a carbonyl compound that has an α hydrogen; the keto form of a molecule is the tautomer of its *enol form*. (Ch. 7)

Ketohexose a six-carbon sugar in which the carbonyl group involves an internal C, characteristic of a ketone. (Ch. 4, 29)

Ketone a compound that contains the bonding arrangement $C_2C{=}O$. (Ch. 1)

Ketopentose a five-carbon sugar in which the carbonyl group involves an internal C, characteristic of a ketone. (Ch. 4, 29)

Ketose a sugar whose carbonyl group involves an internal C, characteristic of a ketone. (Ch. 4, 29)

Kinetic control a reaction condition in which the major product is the one produced the fastest. (Ch. 11)

Kinetic enolate anion the enolate ion that is produced fastest by deprotonation of the corresponding ketone. (Ch. 11)

L

Labile describes a species that is reactive under a given set of conditions. (Ch. 21)

Lagging strand during DNA replication, the strand on which the *replication fork* moves in the $5' \rightarrow 3'$ direction, in which the parent DNA must be read and copied discontinuously, in a series of *Okazaki fragments*. (Ch. 30) ▣

λ_{max} the wavelength of light at which the *absorbance* of a particular peak is a maximum. (Ch. 16)

Leading strand during DNA replication, the strand on which the *replication fork* moves in the $3' \rightarrow 5'$ direction, in which the parent DNA can be read and copied continuously. (Ch. 30) ▣

Leaving group the substituent displaced or eliminated from the substrate in a reaction. (Ch. 7)

Leaving group ability the relative rate at which a *leaving group* will depart from its substrate in a reaction. (Ch. 9)

Le Châtelier's principle states that if a reaction at *equilibrium* experiences a change in reaction conditions (e.g., concentrations, temperature, pressure, or volume), then the equilibrium will shift to counteract that change. (Ch. 6)

Leveling effect the phenomenon dictating the maximum strength of an acid or base that can exist in solution; the strongest acid is the protonated solvent, and the strongest base is the deprotonated solvent. (Ch. 6)

Levorotatory (from Latin, meaning "rotating to the left") describes chiral compounds that rotate plane-polarized light counterclockwise (i.e., in the − direction). Compare with *dextrorotatory*. (Ch. 5)

Lewis acid an electron-pair acceptor. (Ch. 7)

Lewis acid catalyst a species that catalyzes a reaction by virtue of its ability to undergo coordination with a reactant; used in electrophilic aromatic halogenation reactions and Friedel–Crafts reactions. (Ch. 24)

Lewis adduct the product of a coordination step. (Ch. 7)

Lewis base an electron-pair donor. (Ch. 7)

Lewis dot structure *or* Lewis structure a representation of a molecule that conveys *connectivity* and depicts all *valence electrons*. (Ch. 1)

Ligand a messenger molecule that binds to a receptor during *cell signaling*. (Ch. 30)

Lindlar catalyst a catalyst prepared by treating palladium with calcium carbonate and a small amount of quinoline and a lead salt; it is a type of *poisoned catalyst* that is used to reduce an alkyne to a cis alkene. (Ch. 13)

Linear alkane see *straight-chain alkane*. (Int. A)

Linear combination of atomic orbitals (LCAO) the addition and subtraction of various atomic orbitals to generate *molecular orbitals*. (Ch. 3)

Linear polymer a *polymer* that consists of a single main chain with no branching. (Ch. 28)

Linear synthesis a method of synthesizing molecules, composed of sequential synthetic steps. (Ch. 11)

Line structure a standard chemical representation method wherein carbons are implied at the end of a line and at each intersection of two or more lines, hydrogens bonded to carbon are not drawn but hydrogens bonded to another atom are drawn, and heteroatoms are drawn. (Ch. 1)

Lipase one of a class of enzymes that can hydrolyze *triacylglycerols* to release free *fatty acids*. (Ch. 30)

Lipid a biomolecule that is relatively insoluble in water. Most lipids are highly nonpolar, consisting primarily of carbon and hydrogen, with very little oxygen or nitrogen content. Consequently, they tend to be soluble in relatively nonpolar organic solvents, such as ether. (Ch. 2, 29)

Lipid bilayer the double-layer structure into which phospholipids organize in an aqueous environment; the basis of cell membranes. (Ch. 2, 29)

Lithium dialkylcuprate (also known as *Gilman reagent*) one of a class of reagents with the formula R_2CuLi, which are sources of weak R^- nucleophiles that tend to favor conjugate addition over direct addition. (Ch. 18)

Lithium tri-*tert*-butoxyaluminum hydride (LTBA) the compound $LiAlH(O{-}t\text{-}Bu)_3$, commonly used to reduce a carboxylic acid chloride to an aldehyde. (Ch. 22)

Localized describes an electron or charge that is confined to a particular location within a molecular species. (Ch. 1)

Local magnetic field (B_{loc}) magnetic field lines, created by moving electrons, that add to or subtract from an external magnetic field (B_{ext}). (Ch. 17)

Local minimum a location along a curve in a plot where the value on the *y*-axis (often energy) rises on an increase or decrease of the value on the *x*-axis. (Ch. 8)

Locant *or* locator number a numerical index to identify sequential carbons in a main chain or ring. (Int. A)

London dispersion forces see *induced dipole–induced dipole interactions*. (Ch. 2)

Lone pair a pair of nonbonding electrons confined to a particular atom. (Ch. 1)

Long-range coupling in *NMR spectroscopy*, the situation in which nuclei separated by more than three bonds exhibit weak coupling. (Ch. 17)

Lowest unoccupied molecular orbital (LUMO) the lowest energy molecular orbital that is empty. (Ch. 3)

M

M + 1 peak a peak in a *mass spectrum* representing a molecular ion containing a heavy isotope whose mass is 1 u heavier than the most abundant isotope. The relative intensity of this peak can be used to estimate the number of carbon atoms in a sample molecule. (Ch. 15)

M + 2 peak a peak in a *mass spectrum* representing a molecular ion containing a heavy isotope whose mass is 2 u heavier than the most abundant isotope. The relative intensity of this peak can be used to determine the presence of atoms such as Br, Cl, and S. (Ch. 15)

m/z abbreviation for **mass-to-charge ratio**. (Ch. 15)

Magnetic anisotropy in *NMR spectroscopy*, the phenomenon resulting from ring current in double bonds and aromatic rings that contributes to the local magnetic field of nearby nuclei; it causes substantial deshielding of hydrogen and carbon nuclei associated with simple alkenes, aromatic rings, and aldehydes. (Ch. 17)

Main chain **1.** (also called *parent chain*) in a relatively small organic molecule, the longest continuous chain of carbon atoms that establishes the *root* of the IUPAC name (Int. A). **2.** see *polymer backbone* or *polymer chain*. (Ch. 28)

Malonic ester synthesis a synthesis scheme that converts malonic ester (diethyl malonate) into an alkyl- or dialkyl-substituted acetic acid. (Ch. 23)

Markovnikov addition a reaction in which the incoming halide in H—X adds to an alkene or alkyne at the more substituted carbon and the proton adds to the adjacent alkene or alkyne carbon with more hydrogens. (Ch. 12)

Markovnikov's rule an empirical description of the *regiochemistry* of addition of a Brønsted acid across a C═C bond: The addition of a hydrogen halide to an alkene favors the product in which the proton adds to the alkene carbon that is initially bonded to the greater number of hydrogen atoms. (Ch. 12)

Mass peak a bar in a *mass spectrum* representing an ion that is detected by the mass spectrometer. (Ch. 15)

Mass spectrometry an experimental process that provides insight into the mass of a molecule and the fragments that compose it; this information is obtained by interpreting a *mass spectrum*. (Ch. 15)

Mass spectrum a plot of the *relative abundances* of gaseous ions produced from a sample against their *mass-to-charge ratios, m/z.* (Ch. 15)

Mass-to-charge ratio (*m/z*) the ratio of a particle's mass to its charge; the property that a mass spectrometer distinguishes. (Ch. 15)

McLafferty rearrangement a type of *fragmentation pathway* in mass spectrometry, exhibited by molecular ions of compounds that have a carbonyl-containing functional group. (Ch. 15)

MCPBA abbreviation for ***m*-chloroperbenzoic acid**. (Ch. 13)

Measured angle of rotation (α) the angle by which plane-polarized light is rotated on passing through a sample of a chiral compound. (Ch. 5)

Mechanism the precise sequence of *elementary steps* resulting in conversion of the original reactants to the final products in a chemical reaction. (Ch. 6)

Meisenheimer complex a reactive intermediate in *nucleophilic aromatic substitution reactions* that proceed by the nucleophilic addition–elimination mechanism. (Ch. 25)

Melting point (T_m) the temperature above which the species that form a *crystal lattice* begin to flow past each other and behave as a liquid. (Ch. 28)

Mercurinium ion intermediate a positively charged, three-membered ring intermediate in which the ring consists of two carbon atoms and a mercury atom. (Ch. 13)

Merrifield synthesis the solid-phase synthesis of a peptide or protein; named after R. B. Merrifield. (Ch. 29)

Meso describes a molecule that contains at least two chiral centers but has a plane of symmetry that makes it *achiral* overall. (Ch. 5)

Metabolite an intermediate or end product in a *metabolic pathway*. (Ch. 30)

Metabolic pathway a biochemical pathway in the body that is responsible for building up or breaking down molecules. (Ch. 30)

Meta director a substituent attached to a benzene ring that directs an incoming electrophile to the meta carbon of the ring. (Ch. 25)

Methoxy group the group OCH_3; also written as OMe. (Int. A)

Methyl cation the carbocation H_3C^+ that has only hydrogen atoms attached to the positively charged carbon. (Ch. 7)

Methyl group the group CH_3; also written as Me. (Int. A)

1,2-Methyl shift a *carbocation rearrangement* wherein a methyl group migrates to an adjacent atom. (Ch. 7)

Michael addition *or* Michael reaction a reaction in which a carbon nucleophile adds by *conjugate addition* to form a carbon–carbon bond; sometimes used as a general description of conjugate additions involving any nucleophile. (Ch. 18)

Migratory aptitude the tendency of a bond between a H or alkyl group and a carbonyl carbon to be broken in a *Baeyer–Villiger oxidation*. (Ch. 23)

Molar absorptivity (ε) an experimentally derived quantity that is characteristic of a given species' probability of absorbing a photon at a given wavelength of *electromagnetic radiation*. (Ch. 16)

Molecular geometry the arrangement of atoms or groups of bonding electrons about a particular atom. (Ch. 2)

Molecular ion, $M^{\cdot+}(g)$ an ion formed when an electron is ejected from a gaseous molecule, often by *electron impact ionization* for mass spectrometry. (Ch. 15)

Molecularity **1.** the number of separate reacting species in an *elementary step*. (Ch. 7). **2.** the number of reactant species in the *rate-determining step* of a multistep mechanism. (Ch. 8).

Molecular modeling kit a collection of parts representing atoms and bonds, with which you can construct real models of molecules and manipulate them in your hands. (Ch. 2)

Molecular orbital (MO) an orbital resulting from a *linear combination of atomic orbitals* (LCAO), delocalized over the entire molecule; each molecular orbital accommodates up to two electrons. (Ch. 3)

Molecular orbital theory the theory whose central concept is that all electrons in a molecule can be thought of as occupying *molecular orbitals*, which are delocalized over the entire molecule. (Ch. 3)

Molozonide the product of cycloaddition of 1 molar equivalent of ozone (O_3) to an alkene or alkyne in a *[4+2] cycloaddition*, characterized by a five-membered ring consisting of three adjacent O atoms and two adjacent C atoms. In an *ozonolysis* reaction, it is reacted further to produce ketones, aldehydes, and carboxylic acids from an initial alkene. (Ch. 26)

Monomer one of the small reactant molecules that make up polymers. (Ch. 28)

Monosaccharide (also known as *simple sugar*) a carbohydrate in which the number of oxygen atoms is the same as the number of carbon atoms, giving it the general formula $C_xH_{2x}O_x$. *Polysaccharides* are constructed from monosaccharides. (Ch. 1, 29)

Monosubstituted benzene a benzene ring that is bonded to one substituent, having the form C_6H_5—Sub. (Ch. 25)

Monosubstituted cyclohexane the result when one of the hydrogen atoms in cyclohexane is replaced by another substituent. (Ch. 4)

Monounsaturated describes a molecule that has just one C=C double bond; often used to describe *fatty acids*. (Ch. 4, 29)

Multiplet (m) the splitting pattern of an NMR *signal* when there is a large number of coupled protons (typically more than five). (Ch. 17)

Multistep mechanism a mechanism composed of two or more *elementary steps*. (Ch. 8)

Mutarotation a change in the rotation of plane-polarized light due to the equilibration between *epimers*; observable when one anomer of a particular sugar equilibrates with its other anomer when dissolved in water. (Ch. 29)

N

***N* + 1 Rule** states that if a proton is coupled to *N* protons that are distinct from itself but equivalent to each other, then the NMR *signal* produced by that proton will be split into *N* + 1 separate peaks. (Ch. 17)

n → π^* Transition promotion of an electron from a nonbonding orbital to a π^* antibonding molecular orbital; the *HOMO–LUMO transition* for species that possess a lone pair of electrons and a double or triple bond. (Ch. 16)

NBS abbreviation for ***N*-bromosuccinimide**. (Ch. 27)

Net molecular dipole (also known as *permanent dipole*) a separation of partial positive charge and partial negative charge that sums to zero; the dipole is said to point from the center of positive charge to the center of negative charge. (Ch. 2)

Net reaction see *overall reaction*. (Ch. 8)

Network polymer a *polymer* that is so highly branched it has no recognizable linearity and can be viewed as a single, very large molecule. (Ch. 28)

Newman projection a two-dimensional representation of a molecule viewed down the bond of interest; it is a convenient way to illustrate *rotational conformations*. (Ch. 4)

Nicotinamide adenine dinucleotide a common *coenzyme* used in redox reactions. It exists in either the oxidized form, NAD^+, or the reduced form, NADH. (Ch. 30)

Nicotinamide adenine dinucleotide phosphate a common *coenzyme* used in redox reactions: it is a phosphorylated form of *nicotinamide adenine dinucleotide*. It exists in either the oxidized form, $NADP^+$, or the reduced form, NADPH. (Ch. 30)

Nitration a type of *electrophilic aromatic substitution reaction* in which a proton is replaced by a nitronium ion ($^+NO_2$). (Ch. 24)

Nitrile a compound that contains the bonding arrangement C—C≡N. (Ch. 1)

Nitroalkane an alkane with the substituent NO_2. (Int. A)

Nitrogen inversion the process (an umbrella flip) by which the configurations about nitrogen interconvert in the species NR R′R″. (Ch. 5)

Nitrogenous base one of several nitrogen-containing heterocyclic compounds (see *purine base* and *pyrimidine base*) found in nucleic acids. The nitrogenous base determines the identity of the *nucleotide*, and the sequence of nucleotides determines the genetic information encoded by the nucleic acid. (Ch. 29)

Nitrogen rule states that a compound tends to have an odd molecular mass if it contains an odd number of nitrogen atoms and an even molecular mass if it contains an even number of nitrogen atoms or none at all. (Ch. 15)

Nitronium ion the ion $^+NO_2$, which is the strong electrophile that replaces a proton in a *nitration* reaction. (Ch. 24)

NMR-active nucleus a nucleus that possesses spin and can be studied with *NMR spectroscopy*; such nuclei have an odd number of protons, or an odd number of neutrons, or both. (Ch. 17)

Noble gas an element in group 8A, characterized by completely filled valence shells that provide substantial stability. (Ch. 1)

Node a location where electron density is zero. (Ch. 3)

Nomenclature the naming of atoms and molecules. (Int. A)

Nonaromatic a catchall term describing compounds that are neither *aromatic* nor *antiaromatic*; that is, they do not have unusually stable or unusually unstable π systems. (Ch. 14)

Nonbonding MO a *molecular orbital* that is similar in energy to its contributing atomic orbitals. Compare with *antibonding MO* and *bonding MO*. (Ch. 3)

Nonpolar describes a molecule having no net dipole. (Ch. 2)

Nonpolar covalent bond a type of covalent bond between atoms that have the same electronegativity, such that the electrons that make up the bond are shared equally. (Ch. 1)

Nonreducing sugar a sugar that does not exhibit a hemiacetal in its cyclic form and is unable to equilibrate with its acyclic form; these sugars are not able to reduce a weak *oxidizing agent* such as Cu^{2+}. (Ch. 29)

Nonsuperimposable describes two molecules for which there is no orientation such that all atoms of both molecules can be superimposed (i.e., lined up perfectly). (Ch. 5)

N-terminus the end of a polypeptide (protein) chain that is part of an amino group. (Ch. 23, 29)

Nuclear magnetic resonance (NMR) spectroscopy an experimental process used for structure determination, in which *radio frequency* radiation is used to cause *spin flips* in the nuclei of atoms that have an odd number of protons, an odd number of neutrons, or both. (Ch. 17)

Nuclear spin a property of some atomic nuclei, which generates a small magnetic field, an outcome expected of a spinning charge. (Ch. 17)

Nucleic acid a large molecular chain that is primarily associated with the storage and transfer of genetic information; it is constructed from relatively small molecular units called *nucleotides*. (Ch. 1, 29)

Nucleophile a "nucleus-loving" species (usually with a lone pair of electrons) that seeks a substrate with a full or partial positive charge to stabilize its full or partial negative charge. (Ch. 7)

Nucleophile elimination step an *elementary step* wherein a new π bond is produced and the eliminated *leaving group*, in turn, has the characteristics of a nucleophile; the reverse of a *nucleophilic addition step*. (Ch. 7)

Nucleophilic acyl substitution reaction a reaction in which a nucleophile replaces the *leaving group* attached to a C═O carbon; it proceeds by a nucleophilic addition–elimination mechanism. (Ch. 22)

Nucleophilic addition–elimination reaction a sequence of steps in which a nucleophile is substituted for a leaving group; it proceeds by a *nucleophilic addition step* followed by a *nucleophile elimination step*. (Ch. 22)

Nucleophilic addition reaction a reaction whose mechanism involves a *nucleophilic addition step* as a key step. (Ch. 18)

Nucleophilic addition step an *elementary step* in which a nucleophile forms a bond to the electron-deficient atom of a polar π bond; the reverse of a *nucleophile elimination step*. (Ch. 7)

Nucleophilic aromatic substitution reaction a reaction in which a nucleophile replaces a leaving group attached to an aromatic ring. It could proceed by a nucleophilic addition–elimination mechanism with a *Meisenheimer complex* as the intermediate, or it could proceed by an elimination–nucleophilic addition mechanism with a *benzyne intermediate*. (Ch. 25)

Nucleophilicity (sometimes called nucleophile strength) the tendency of a nucleophile to promote an S_N2 reaction; typically determined by the rate of an S_N2 reaction between the nucleophile and a methyl halide. (Ch. 9)

Nucleotide a relatively small molecular unit from which *nucleic acids* are constructed. All nucleotides have three distinct components: an inorganic phosphate group (—OPO_3), a cyclic *monosaccharide* (or sugar), and a nitrogenous base. (Ch. 1, 29)

O

Octet a group of eight *valence electrons*; a complete valence shell of atoms in the second row of the periodic table. (Ch. 1)

Oil a *triglyceride* that is liquid at room temperature; typically produced from plants. (Ch. 2, 29)

Okazaki fragments during DNA replication, short fragments on the *lagging strand* that are read and copied by *DNA polymerase* in the 3′ → 5′ direction and then joined together. (Ch. 30)

Olefin another name for an *alkene*. (Ch. 28)

Olefin metathesis see *alkene metathesis*. (Ch. 20)

Oligopeptide a molecule consisting of two to about 25 *amino acid* residues linked by *peptide bonds*. (Ch. 29)

Operating frequency (ν_{op}) the frequency at which a bare (unshielded) proton absorbs *electromagnetic radiation* when subjected to an NMR spectrometer's magnetic field. (Ch. 17)

Optically active describes a sample that rotates plane-polarized light. *Chiral* species are optically active. (Ch. 5)

Optically inactive describes a sample that does not rotate plane-polarized light. *Achiral* species are optically inactive, as are *racemic mixtures* of enantiomers. (Ch. 5)
Orbital a description of the particular state of an electron in an atom or molecule. An electron that belongs to a particular orbital has a high probability of being located in a region of space whose size and shape are characteristic of that orbital. (Ch. 1)
Order the exponent to which a reactant (or product) concentration is raised in the rate law of a reaction. (Ch. 8)
Organic chemistry the branch of chemistry involving *organic compounds* (those containing carbon and hydrogen atoms). (Ch. 1)
Organic compound a compound composed primarily of carbon and hydrogen. (Ch. 1)
Organometallic describes compounds that contain a metal atom bonded directly to a carbon atom. (Ch. 7)
Ortho/para director a substituent attached to a benzene ring that directs an incoming electrophile to the ortho and para carbons of the ring. (Ch. 25)
Osmate ester a compound having the bonding arrangement RO—Os═O. A cyclic osmate ester is an intermediate in the oxidation of an alkene with osmium tetroxide (OsO_4). (Ch. 26)
Out-of-plane bending vibrational motion of a molecule in which the vibrating set of atoms occupies different planes throughout an oscillation. (Ch. 16)
Overall product a species that appears as a product in the overall (i.e., net) reaction; it is generally a product that can be isolated on the completion of the reaction. (Ch. 8)
Overall reactant a species that appears as a reactant in the overall (i.e., net) reaction; it is generally a *starting material* that is added to a reaction. (Ch. 8)
Overall reaction (also known as *net reaction*) the reaction that includes only the reactants that are added as *starting materials* and the products that are present when the reaction is complete; the sum of the *elementary steps* of the mechanism. (Ch. 8)
Oxaphosphetane an intermediate in a *Wittig reaction*, characterized by a four-membered ring consisting of two carbon atoms, one phosphorus atom, and one oxygen atom. (Ch. 18)
Oxidation part of a *redox reaction* in which a species loses one or more electrons and becomes oxidized, accompanied by the reduction of another species. (Ch. 20)
Oxidation state one of two methods used to assign charge to atoms involved in covalent bonds. Lone pairs are assigned to the atom on which they appear in the Lewis structure. In a given covalent bond, all electrons are assigned to the more electronegative atom; if the two atoms are identical, the electrons are split evenly. Compare with *formal charge*. (Ch. 20)
Oxidative cleavage an oxidation reaction that results in the severing of C═C or C≡C bonds into separate carbonyl-containing functional groups. (Ch. 26)
Oxidized describes a species that has lost one or more electrons in a *redox reaction*, resulting in the increase of an atom's oxidation state. (Ch. 20)
Oxidizing agent a reagent used to accept electrons, thereby causing another species to be *oxidized*. (Ch. 20)
Oxymercuration–demercuration *or* oxymercuration–reduction the sequence of reactions in which a Hg^{2+} species adds to an alkene or alkyne, followed by reduction (typically with $NaBH_4$), resulting in the *Markovnikov addition* of water. (Ch. 13)
Ozone the compound O_3, which is a key reagent in *ozonolysis* reactions. (Ch. 26)
Ozonide a key intermediate in an *ozonolysis* reaction, characterized by a five-membered ring consisting of three O atoms and two C atoms, and in which only two of the O atoms are adjacent. An ozonide is reacted further to produce ketones, aldehydes, and carboxylic acids from an initial alkene. (Ch. 26)
Ozonolysis a reaction in which an alkene is reacted with *ozone* to cleave the C═C bond, producing two separate carbonyl-containing functional groups. (Ch. 26)

P

Parent chain see *main chain*. (Int. A)
Pascal's triangle a pattern that describes the ratios of the relative peak heights in splitting patterns of NMR *signals*, in accordance with the *N + 1 rule*. (Ch. 17)
Pauli exclusion principle states that no more than two electrons (i.e., zero, one, or two electrons) can occupy a single orbital; two electrons in the same orbital must have opposite spins. (Ch. 1)
***p*-Character** the resemblance of an orbital's characteristics (e.g., shape and energy) to those of a *p* orbital; the fraction of a *hybrid orbital* that comes from a *p* orbital. (Ch. 3)
Peak see *absorption band*. (Ch. 16)
Pendant group (also known as *side group*) a non-hydrogen atom or group that is bonded to an atom of a *polymer* main chain. (Ch. 28)
Pentose a five-carbon sugar. (Ch. 4, 29)
Peptide a short chain of *amino acid* residues (up to about 50) linked by *peptide bonds*. (Ch. 23)
Peptide bond *or* peptide linkage the O═C—N group, characteristic of amides, that connects two *amino acid* residues together in a peptide or protein. (Ch. 23, 28, 29)
Percent atom economy measure of the inherent efficiency of a reaction; in general, as the percent atom economy increases, the amount of accumulated waste decreases. It is calculated as follows: $\%\ \text{Atom economy} = \frac{\text{Mass of atoms in the desired product}}{\text{Mass of atoms in all reagents}} \times 100\%$. (Ch. 11)
Pericyclic reaction a concerted reaction in which all of the electrons involved in bond breaking and bond formation are delocalized in a ring in the transition state. (Ch. 26)
Periodate anion the species IO_4^-, used as a reagent in the *oxidative cleavage* of 1,2-diols to produce aldehydes and ketones. (Ch. 26)
Periodate ester a compound characterized by the bonding arrangement RO—I═O. A cyclic periodate ester is a key intermediate in the reaction between a 1,2-diol and the *periodate anion* (IO_4^-) to produce ketones and aldehydes. (Ch. 26)
Periodic acid the reagent HIO_4, used to introduce *periodate anion* in the oxidative cleavage of 1,2-diols. (Ch. 26)
Permanent dipole see *net molecular dipole*. (Ch. 2)
Peroxy acid a molecule that has the structure RCO_3H. (Ch. 13)
Phase (of an electron) an immeasurable quantity that plays an important role in how orbitals interact with one another by *constructive interference* or *destructive interference*. (Ch. 3)
Phenol a compound that contains an O—H group attached to a phenyl ring. (Ch. 1)
Phenyl (Ph) the substituent C_6H_5. (Int. B)
Phenylmethyl see *benzyl (Bn)*. (Int. B)
Phospholipid one of a subclass of lipids; it can efficiently store energy and is integral in the formation of cell membranes. Whereas a fat or an oil has three fatty acids, making it a *triglyceride*, a phospholipid has only two fatty acids, making it a *diglyceride*. (Ch. 2, 29)

Phosphonium ylide see *Wittig reagent.* (Ch. 18)
Phosphorylation a covalent modification in which a phosphate group is added to an amino acid's side chain, usually one bearing an OH group. (Ch. 30)
Photochemically allowed describes a reaction that proceeds at a reasonable rate when irradiated with ultraviolet light; one or more of the reactants have an *excited electron configuration.* (Ch. 26)
Photochemically forbidden describes a reaction that does not take place readily when one or more of the reactants have an *excited electron configuration.* (Ch. 26)
Photon a particle that makes up light, which carries a specific quantity of energy associated with its frequency and wavelength. (Ch. 5)
Physiologic pH the pH of the human body, which is around 7.4. (Ch. 29)
π Bond a bond in which a pair of electrons occupies a bonding molecular orbital of *π symmetry*; that is, a *molecular orbital* in which the overlap of *atomic orbitals* takes place on opposite sides of a bonding axis. A double bond in a Lewis structure is generally a σ bond plus a π bond, and a triple bond is one σ bond plus two π bonds. (Ch. 3)
π Bonding MO a bonding molecular orbital that has *π symmetry*; that is, a *molecular orbital* that is lower in energy than its contributing *atomic orbitals* that overlap on opposite sides of a bonding axis. (Ch. 3)
$\pi \rightarrow \pi^*$ Transition promotion of an electron from a π bonding molecular orbital to a π^* antibonding molecular orbital; the *HOMO–LUMO transition* in an alkene or alkyne. (Ch. 16)
π Stacking the interaction (believed to be stabilizing) that takes place when the face of one π system is in close proximity to the face of another, separate π system. (Ch. 14, 29)
π^* Antibonding MO an antibonding molecular orbital that has *π symmetry*; that is, a *molecular orbital* that is higher in energy than its contributing *atomic orbitals* that overlap on opposite sides of a bonding axis. (Ch. 3)
π Symmetry the symmetry of a *molecular orbital* that is generated by the overlap of *atomic orbitals* on opposite sides of the bonding axis; the bonding axis itself lies in a node. (Ch. 3)
π System A group of molecular orbitals derived from a set of *p* orbitals that are all *conjugated.* (Ch. 14)
pK_a the negative logarithm of the *acidity constant*: $pK_a = -\log K_a$. (Ch. 6)
Planck's constant (*h*) the constant of proportionality that appears in the dependence of a photon's energy on its frequency: 6.626×10^{-34} J·s. (Ch. 16)
Plane of symmetry a plane that bisects a molecule in such a way that one half of the molecule is the mirror image of the other half. (Ch. 5)
Plane-polarized describes light whose photons have their electric fields oscillating in the same plane. (Ch. 5)
Poisoned catalyst a specially treated catalyst that prevents a reaction from occurring at the rate at which it would occur with an untreated catalyst. A poisoned Pd catalyst is often used to reduce an alkyne to a cis alkene. (Ch. 13)
Polar describes a molecule having a net dipole. (Ch. 2)
Polar covalent bond a type of covalent bond between atoms that have different electronegativities, such that the electrons that make up the bond are shared unequally. (Ch. 1)
Polarimetry an experimental technique that measures the optical activity of a sample. (Ch. 5)
Polarizability the ease with which the electron cloud of a species is distorted; it tends to increase with the total number of electrons in that species. (Ch. 2)
Polarizable describes the ability of the electron cloud of a species to be distorted. (Ch. 2)
Polarizer a device that generates plane-polarized light by allowing through only photons whose electric field is oscillating in a specified plane, effectively filtering out light whose electric field oscillates in any other plane. (Ch. 5)
Polyacrylate (also known as *acrylic*) a *polymer* derived from monomers that are derivatives of acrylic acid. (Ch. 28)
Polyamino acid see *polypeptide.* (Ch. 28)
Polyatomic ion a charged species that contains more than one atom; it typically consists only of nonmetals, and the atoms are held together by covalent bonds. (Ch. 1)
Polycyclic aromatic hydrocarbon (PAH) one of a class of molecules characterized by fused, unsubstituted, aromatic rings and often having a single π system. PAHs are known atmospheric pollutants. (Ch. 14)
Polycyclic compound a compound with two or more rings. (Ch. 14)
Polyester a *heterochain polymer* with a repeating unit containing ester linkages. (Ch. 28)
Poly(ethylene terephthalate) (PET) a polyester with the repeating unit $(CH_2CH_2O_2C{-}C_6H_4{-}CO_2)_n$; commonly used in 2-liter bottles for carbonated beverages. (Ch. 28)
Polyhalogenation the process of replacing multiple hydrogens on a single molecule with halogen atoms. (Ch. 10)
Polymer a large molecule that is made from relatively small monomers and that typically has a recognizable repeating unit. (Ch. 28)
Polymer backbone *or* polymer chain (also known as *main chain*) the chain of atoms bonded together in a polymer, to which *pendant groups* are attached. (Ch. 28)
Polymerization a reaction that produces a polymer from monomers. (Ch. 28)
Polynucleotide a large biomolecule made up of *nucleotide* monomers. In a completed polynucleotide, nucleotide residues are linked by *phosphodiester bonds.* (Ch. 28, 29)
Polyolefin a carbon-chain *polymer* made by the polymerization of alkene (i.e., olefin) monomers. (Ch. 28)
Polypeptide (also known as *polyamino acid*) a large biomolecule made up of *amino acid* monomers. In a completed polypeptide, amino acid residues are linked by *peptide bonds.* (Ch. 28, 29)
Polysaccharide a large biomolecule made up of *monosaccharide* (or *simple sugar*) monomers. In a completed polysaccharide, sugar residues are linked by *acetal* groups. (Ch. 1, 28, 29)
Polyunsaturated describes a molecule that has more than one C=C double bond; often used to describe *fatty acids.* (Ch. 4, 29)
1,2-Positioning describes substituents that are connected to adjacent atoms. (Ch. 21)
Potassium permanganate the compound $KMnO_4$, used principally as an *oxidizing agent.* $KMnO_4$ can be used in the oxidation of primary alcohols and aldehydes to carboxylic acids and of secondary alcohols to ketones, and it can cleave alkenes, alkynes, and C—C bonds to a benzylic carbon. (Ch. 20)
Precursor the preceding species from which a *synthetic target* can be synthesized. (Ch. 11)
Primary (1°) carbocation a carbocation that has one alkyl group directly attached to C^+. (Ch. 7)

Primary orbital overlap an overlap among orbitals that are directly involved in bond formation in a *Diels–Alder reaction.* (Ch. 26)

Primary structure the sequence of amino acids in a *protein*; it determines a protein's identity. (Ch. 23, 28, 29)

Principal quantum number (*n*) the number that defines a shell in an atom; *n* can assume any integer value from 1 to infinity. (Ch. 1)

Principle of microscopic reversibility the notion that a reaction has the same *reaction free energy diagram* in the forward direction and in the reverse direction. (Int. C)

Proenzyme an inactive enzyme precursor that is metabolized to produce the active form of the enzyme. (Ch. 30)

Propagation cycle in a *chain reaction*, the collection of *propagation steps* that sum to the net reaction. (Ch. 27)

Propagation steps in a *chain reaction*, the *elementary steps* that are principally responsible for converting the overall reactants into the overall products. (Ch. 27)

Prostaglandins a class of *lipids* that help control processes involved with illness or injury, such as inflammation, blood flow, and blood clotting; they are produced at the sites of infection or tissue damage in response to certain triggers. (Ch. 29)

Protecting group a modification that makes a functional group unreactive under the conditions for a desired chemical reaction. The original functional group is restored by removal of the protecting group. (Ch. 21)

Protection step a reaction used in *synthesis* to selectively change a *labile* group to another functional group that will not react under certain conditions. (Ch. 21)

Protein a biomolecule constructed from *amino acids*. Proteins can be hundreds or thousands of amino acids long and play diverse roles in biological systems. (Ch. 1, 29)

Proteolysis protein cleavage. (Ch. 30)

Protic solvent a solvent that possesses a *hydrogen-bond donor*. (Ch. 2)

Proton NMR spectroscopy (also known as *^{1}H NMR spectroscopy*) a method of generating a spectrum whereby *radio frequency* electromagnetic radiation is used to cause *spin flips* in the nuclei of hydrogen atoms. (Ch. 17)

Proton transfer reaction (also known as *Brønsted–Lowry acid–base reaction*) a reaction in which a proton is transferred from a *Brønsted–Lowry acid* to a *Brønsted–Lowry base* in a single *elementary step*; that is, one bond is broken and another is formed simultaneously. (Ch. 6)

Purine base a *nitrogenous base* with a two-ring system that resembles the compound purine; the most common examples are guanine and adenine. (Ch. 29)

Pyranose cyclic form of a *monosaccharide* characterized by a six-membered ring. (Ch. 19, 29)

Pyridinium chlorochromate (PCC) a specialized *oxidizing agent* that can be used in organic solvents and, therefore, can oxidize a primary alcohol to an aldehyde or a secondary alcohol to a ketone. (Ch. 20)

Pyrimidine base a *nitrogenous base* with a single ring that resembles the compound pyrimidine; the most common examples are cytosine, thymine, and uracil. (Ch. 29)

Q

Quantum mechanics a branch of chemistry and physics whose central idea is that very small particles, like electrons, have traits that are characteristic of both particles and waves. (Ch. 3)

Quartet (q) the splitting pattern of an NMR *signal* into four peaks with a 1:3:3:1 height ratio; occurs when $N = 3$, according to the *N + 1 rule*. (Ch. 17)

Quaternary ammonium ion a species in which four alkyl groups are attached to a N atom, having the general form R_4N^+. (Ch. 10)

Quaternary ammonium salt an ionic compound in which the cation is of the form R_4N^+. (Ch. 10)

Quaternary structure the arrangement of multiple folded *protein* subunits that form a complex. (Ch. 28, 29)

Quintet (qn) the splitting pattern of an NMR *signal* into five peaks; occurs when $N = 4$, according to the *N + 1 rule*. (Ch. 17)

R

Racemic mixture a mixture that contains equal amounts of the (+) and (−) *enantiomers* of a chiral molecule. (Ch. 5)

Radical a species that contains at least one *unpaired electron*. (Ch. 1, 27)

Radical addition step an *elementary step* in which a *radical* adds to an atom of a π bond. (Ch. 27)

Radical cation a positively charged ion that has an unpaired electron. (Ch. 15)

Radical combination *or* radical coupling an *elementary step* in which unpaired electrons from two *radicals* join to make a new covalent bond. (Ch. 27)

Radical halogenation a reaction that results in the addition of a halogen atom to a molecule and proceeds by a mechanism that involves *radicals*. (Ch. 27)

Radical initiator a compound that has especially weak covalent bonds and can be used to produce *radicals* by heating or irradiation with ultraviolet light. (Ch. 27)

Radical polymerization a *polymerization* reaction in which the *propagation steps* involve radical species. (Ch. 28)

Radio frequency (RF) the region of the electromagnetic spectrum with wavelengths between $\sim10^{-3}$ m and 10^5 m. This radiation is used in *NMR spectroscopy* to cause *spin flips* among nuclei. (Ch. 17)

Raney nickel a specialized catalyst used in the *Raney-nickel reduction* of ketones and aldehydes to convert the carbonyl group to a methylene. It is produced by treating a 50:50 alloy of aluminum and nickel with hot sodium hydroxide, followed by treatment with hydrogen gas. (Ch. 20)

Raney-nickel reduction a reaction that reduces the carbonyl group of a ketone or aldehyde to a methylene group using *Raney nickel* as a catalyst. (Ch. 20)

Rate constant the constant of proportionality that relates the concentrations of reactants or products (raised to certain exponents) to the rate of a given reaction. (Ch. 8)

Rate-determining step the *elementary step* that establishes the rate of an *overall reaction*; usually identified as the slow step of a mechanism. (Ch. 8)

***R* configuration** a *chiral center* where the substituents having priorities 1 through 3 are arranged clockwise when the priority 4 substituent points away. Compare with *S configuration*. (Ch. 5)

Reaction coordinate a variable that corresponds to geometric changes, on a molecular level, of the species involved in a reaction as reactants are transformed into products. As the reaction coordinate increases, the geometries of the species involved in the reaction increasingly resemble those of the products. (Ch. 6)

Reaction free energy diagram a plot of Gibbs free energy as a function of the *reaction coordinate*. (Ch. 6)

Reciprocal centimeter see *wavenumber*. (Ch. 16)
Redox reaction stands for reduction–oxidation reaction, in which at least one species is *oxidized* and at least one species is *reduced*. (Ch. 20)
Reduced describes a species that has gained one or more electrons in a *redox reaction*, resulting in the decrease of an atom's oxidation state. (Ch. 20)
Reduced mass (μ) the quantity $\frac{m_1 m_2}{(m_1 + m_2)}$ that relates the masses of two objects connected to a spring; according to *Hooke's law*, vibrational frequency is inversely proportional to $\sqrt{\mu}$. (Ch. 16)
Reducing agent a reagent used to donate electrons, thereby causing another species to be *reduced*. (Ch. 20)
Reducing sugar a sugar that exhibits a hemiacetal in its cyclic form, which enables it to equilibrate with its acyclic form; these sugars are able to reduce a weak *oxidizing agent* such as Cu^{2+}. (Ch. 29)
Reduction part of a *redox reaction* in which a species gains one or more electrons and becomes reduced, accompanied by the oxidation of another species. (Ch. 20)
Reductive amination formation of an amine from a ketone or aldehyde by *reduction* of an imine intermediate. (Ch. 19)
Regioselectivity the tendency of a reaction to take place at one site within a molecule over another. (Ch. 9)
Regulatory site a location in an enzyme, away from the *active site*, where an effector molecule can bind; this causes the enzyme to undergo a significant conformational change that alters its catalytic efficiency. (Ch. 30)
Relative abundance the amount of a species that is present relative to a standard; in *mass spectrometry*, the quantity that is plotted on the *y* axis. (Ch. 15)
Repeating unit the bonding scenario that occurs over and over within a *polymer*. (Ch. 28)
Replication fork the point where the two strands of a parent DNA molecule are separated from each other, or "unzipped," during *DNA replication*, thus exposing the nitrogenous bases in each strand. (Ch. 30)
Replisome a complex of multiple proteins involved in *DNA replication*; it is responsible for carrying out a highly coordinated set of enzymatic processes. (Ch. 30)
Residue a specific monomer within the polymer chain of a *biopolymer*. (Ch. 23, 28, 29)
Resolved describes items that are separated; *enantiomers* that are separated are said to be resolved, and peaks in a spectrum that are separated are also said to be resolved. (Ch. 17)
Resonance arrow a double-headed straight arrow (⟷) that is placed between two molecule structures to indicate that they are *resonance structures*. (Ch. 1)
Resonance contributor see *resonance structure*. (Ch. 1)
Resonance effect the impact that delocalization through resonance has on a property of a molecule or ion, such as stability or acid/base strength. (Ch. 6)
Resonance energy (also known as *delocalization energy*) the extent by which a species is stabilized due to the delocalization of electrons or charge. (Ch. 1)
Resonance hybrid a weighted average of all *resonance structures* that can be drawn for a species. (Ch. 1)
Resonance structure (also known as *resonance contributor*) one of two or more valid Lewis structures that represent a species. Resonance structures are imaginary and are related by the movement of *valence electrons*, not atoms; the one, true species is represented by the *resonance hybrid*. (Ch. 1)
Resonance theory the theory that reconciles the differences between multiple *Lewis structures* of a species and its observed characteristics. Resonance exists when two or more valid Lewis structures can be drawn for a given molecular species. (Ch. 1)
Retro Diels–Alder reaction see *[4+2]cycloelimination*. (Ch. 26)
Retrosynthetic analysis the strategy for designing a synthesis in which the chemist begins by focusing on the *target* and asks questions pertaining to feasible *precursors* that can be used to produce the target. Each precursor becomes the new target until the chemist arrives at precursors that can be used as *starting materials*. (Ch. 11)
Retrosynthetic arrow an open arrow (⟹) used to indicate a *transform* in retrosynthetic analysis; it is drawn from the *target* to the *precursor* and can be interpreted to mean "can be made from." (Ch. 11)
Reversible describes reactions that proceed in the reverse direction at a rate that is comparable to or faster than the rate in the forward direction. (Ch. 11)
R group see *side chain*. (Ch. 1, 29)
Ribbon structure a trace of a three-dimensional protein's backbone that highlights *secondary structures* such as α-helixes and β-pleated sheets. (Ch. 28, 29)
Ribonucleic acid (RNA) a nucleic acid strand that participates in protein synthesis. (Ch. 1)
Ribosome a complex that consists of ribosomal RNA molecules and various proteins, in which *translation* takes place. (Ch. 30)
Ring-closing metathesis a type of *alkene metathesis* reaction that forms a new ring. (Ch. 20)
Ring current the motion of π electrons along a circular path parallel to the plane of the π system to which they belong, giving rise to *magnetic anisotropy*; the motion is driven by forces from an external magnetic field. (Ch. 17)
Ring flip see *chair flip*. (Ch. 4)
Ring-opening polymerization a *polymerization* reaction in which the *propagation steps* involve the breaking of a bond that is part of a ring in the monomer. (Ch. 28)
Ring strain the increase in energy due to geometric constraints of the bonds and substituents involved in a ring; it is partly responsible for the instability of rings other than five- and six-membered ones. Ring strain can be quantified by using *heats of combustion*. (Ch. 4)
RNA polymerase an enzyme that catalyzes the synthesis of messenger RNA from DNA during *transcription*. (Ch. 30)
Robinson annulation a reaction, made up of a *Michael addition* followed by *aldol condensation*, that results in the formation of a new cyclohexenone ring. (Ch. 19)
Root the name of the alkane containing the same number of carbon atoms as the *main chain* for nomenclature. (Int. A)
Rotational conformation the distinct angle of rotation about a single bond. (Ch. 4)
Rotational energy barrier the amount of energy needed to convert one *conformer* into another by rotation about a specified bond. (Ch. 4)

S

Saccharide see *carbohydrate*. (Ch. 1)
Sandmeyer reaction one of several reactions in which a nucleophile replaces the N_2 *leaving group* in an arenediazonium ion and in which a Cu^+ catalyst is involved. (Ch. 24)

Saponification a reaction between hydroxide (HO^-) and an ester, resulting in the formation of a carboxylate anion. This is the same type of reaction used by ancient civilizations to make soap from animal fat. (Ch. 22)

Saturated describes a molecule that has the maximum number of hydrogen atoms possible, consistent with the number and type of each non-hydrogen atom in the molecule, the octet rule, and the duet rule. A saturated molecule has no double bonds, triple bonds, or rings. (Ch. 4)

***s*-Character** the resemblance of a hybrid orbital's characteristics (e.g., shape and energy) to those of an *s* orbital; the fraction of a *hybrid orbital* that comes from an *s* orbital. (Ch. 3)

Schiff base see *imine*. (Ch. 19)

***s*-Cis conformation** a rotational conformation in which substituents are on the same side of a single bond. (Ch. 26)

***S* configuration** a *chiral center* where the substituents having priorities 1 through 3 are arranged counterclockwise when the priority 4 substituent points away. Compare with *R configuration*. (Ch. 5)

Secondary (2°) carbocation a carbocation that has two alkyl groups attached directly to C^+. (Ch. 7)

Secondary orbital overlap in a *Diels–Alder reaction*, overlap among orbitals that are not directly involved in bond formation. (Ch. 26)

Secondary structure a characteristic three-dimensional pattern involving local segments of a protein's backbone; the most common examples are the *α-helix* and the *β-pleated* sheet. (Ch. 28, 29)

Selective reaction a reaction in which multiple products can be produced but one product is favored over the others. (Ch. 21)

Selective reagent a reagent that is used to favor the production of one product over another. (Ch. 21)

Self-aldol addition an *aldol addition* reaction in which the reactants that join together are the same carbonyl compound. (Ch. 19)

Serine protease one of a family of *enzymes* that can hydrolyze a peptide bond; in this reaction, the OH group of a serine residue in the active site of the enzyme acts as the nucleophile. (Ch. 30)

S_H2 abbreviation for **bimolecular homolytic substitution step**. (Ch. 27)

Shell the principal quantum number (*n*) associated with an atomic orbital; also referred to as the energy level of the orbital. (Ch. 1)

Shielded in *NMR spectroscopy*, describes nuclei in a molecule that have a local magnetic field that opposes an external magnetic field. Shielded nuclei have smaller *chemical shifts*. (Ch. 17)

Side chain (also known as *R group*) a group connected to an α carbon(s) in an amino acid or protein, which gives the amino acid its identity. (Ch. 1, 29)

Side group see *pendant group*. (Ch. 28)

σ Bond a bond in which a pair of electrons occupies a bonding molecular orbital of *σ symmetry*; that is, a *molecular orbital* in which the overlap of *atomic orbitals* takes place along a bonding axis. A single bond in a Lewis structure is generally a σ bond. (Ch. 3)

σ Bonding MO a bonding molecular orbital that has *σ symmetry*; that is, a *molecular orbital* that is lower in energy than its contributing *atomic orbitals* that overlap along a bonding axis. (Ch. 3)

σ → σ* Transition promotion of an electron from a σ bonding molecular orbital to a σ* antibonding molecular orbital; the *HOMO–LUMO transition* in an alkane. (Ch. 16)

σ* Antibonding MO an antibonding molecular orbital that has *σ symmetry*; that is, a *molecular orbital* that is higher in energy than its contributing *atomic orbitals* that overlap along a bonding axis. (Ch. 3)

σ Symmetry the symmetry of a *molecular orbital* that is generated by the overlap of *atomic orbitals* along a bonding axis. A *σ bond* occurs when two electrons occupy a *σ bonding MO*. (Ch. 3)

Signals in *NMR spectroscopy*, the frequencies of radiation emitted by *NMR-active nuclei*, which are converted into peaks in the NMR spectrum. (Ch. 17)

Signal splitting the separation of an NMR *signal* into multiple peaks due to the *spin–spin coupling* between the nucleus giving rise to the signal and nuclei of nearby atoms. (Ch. 17)

Simple sugar see *monosaccharide*. (Ch. 1)

Single-barbed arrow a curved arrow () used to show the movement of a single electron. (Ch. 27)

Singlet (s) the splitting pattern of an NMR *signal* when there are no coupled protons; it appears as just a single peak. (Ch. 17)

S_N1 abbreviation for **unimolecular nucleophilic substitution reaction**. (Ch. 8)

S_N2 abbreviation for **bimolecular nucleophilic substitution step**. (Ch. 7)

Solvated electron an electron that is stabilized by solvent molecules and, therefore, does not formally belong to any one atom. Solvated electrons are used in *dissolving metal reductions*. (Ch. 27)

Solvation the phenomenon wherein an individual ion participates in multiple ion–dipole interactions with its solvent. When this occurs, the ion is said to be solvated. (Ch. 2)

Solvent-mediated proton transfer the transfer of a proton from one site to another, assisted by a sufficiently acidic or basic solvent. (Ch. 8)

Solvolysis a reaction in which the solvent participates as a reactant in breaking a bond (lysis); an S_N1 reaction in which the solvent is a nucleophile is an example. (Ch. 9)

Species a particular collection of protons, neutrons, and electrons. (Ch. 1)

Specific acid–base catalysis a means by which a reaction is catalyzed by acids or bases, and in which proton transfer steps occur separately from the rate-determining step. Compare with *general acid–base catalysis*. (Ch. 30)

Specific rotation a constant term that is unique for a given *chiral* compound and describes the compound's propensity for rotating *plane-polarized* light; denoted $[\alpha]_\lambda^T$, it is the angle of rotation (α) of plane-polarized light of a given wavelength (λ) in nanometers, if it passes through a sample whose concentration is 1 g/mL, whose length is 1 decimeter (dm), and whose temperature is T°C. (Ch. 5)

Spectator ion an ion that is relatively inert in solution and tends not to react. (Ch. 7)

Spectroscopy the study of the interaction of *electromagnetic radiation* with matter. (Ch. 16)

***sp* Hybridization** the mixing of the single *s* orbital and one of the three *p* orbitals (p_x, p_y, or p_z) from the valence shell to form *sp* hybrid orbitals. (Ch. 3)

***sp*-Hybridized** describes an atom in which the valence *s* orbital mixes with one valence *p* orbital to produce two *sp* hybrid orbitals. Atoms that have a linear electron geometry are *sp*-hybridized. (Ch. 3)

***sp* Hybrid orbital** a *hybrid orbital* that results from *sp* hybridization. (Ch. 3)

***sp*^{2} Hybridization** the mixing of the single *s* orbital and two of the three *p* orbitals (p_x, p_y, or p_z) from the valence shell to form sp^2 hybrid orbitals. (Ch. 3)

***sp*^{2}-Hybridized** describes an atom in which the valence *s* orbital mixes with two valence *p* orbitals to produce three sp^2 hybrid orbitals. Atoms that have a trigonal planar electron geometry are sp^2-hybridized. (Ch. 3)

***sp*^{2} Hybrid orbital** a *hybrid orbital* that results from sp^2 hybridization. (Ch. 3)

***sp*^{3} Hybridization** the mixing of the single *s* orbital and all three *p* orbitals (p_x, p_y, and p_z) from the valence shell to form sp^3 hybrid orbitals. (Ch. 3)

***sp*^{3}-Hybridized** describes an atom in which the valence *s* orbital mixes with all three valence *p* orbitals to produce four sp^3 hybrid orbitals. Atoms that have a tetrahedral electron geometry are sp^2-hybridized. (Ch. 3)

***sp*^{3} Hybrid orbital** a *hybrid orbital* that results from sp^3 hybridization. (Ch. 3)

Spin flip a change from one spin state to another (e.g., from the α spin state to the β spin state, or vice versa). (Ch. 17)

Spin–spin coupling interaction between nearby nuclei that have spin; the cause of *signal splitting* in NMR spectroscopy. (Ch. 17)

Splitting diagram a schematic that illustrates the complex splitting of an NMR *signal* in a stepwise fashion. (Ch. 17)

Staggered conformation a geometry in which each single bond on the front carbon atom in a *Newman projection* bisects a pair of single bonds on the rear carbon. Compare with *eclipsed conformation*. (Ch. 4)

Standard biochemical free energy change the change in free energy for a process that takes place at pH 7, 298 K, 1 atm, and 1 M concentrations for all reactants and products. (Ch. 30)

Standard enthalpy difference the enthalpy difference between reactants and products under standard conditions, denoted ΔH°_{rxn}; associated with a reaction's tendency to absorb or release heat. (Ch. 6)

Standard entropy difference the entropy difference between reactants and products under standard conditions, denoted ΔS°_{rxn}; related to the gain or loss of the number of different states available to a system. (Ch. 6)

Standard Gibbs free energy (*G*°) the property of a species that relates to stability under standard conditions (all pure substances are in their most stable states at 298 K, the partial pressures of all gases are 1 atm, and the concentrations of all solutions are 1 mol/L). A lower standard Gibbs free energy corresponds to greater stability. (Ch. 6)

Standard Gibbs free energy difference the Gibbs free energy difference between reactants and products under standard conditions, denoted ΔG°_{rxn}; associated with a reaction's tendency to favor products at equilibrium (i.e., to be spontaneous). (Ch. 6)

Starting material one of the reactants that is available to use in a *synthesis*. (Ch. 10)

Step-growth polymerization a *polymerization* reaction in which molecules throughout a mixture join with any other molecules that have appropriate functional groups available to react, whether they are monomer units or other polymer molecules. (Ch. 28)

Stereocenter see *chiral center*. (Ch. 5)

Stereochemical configuration (also known as *configuration*) the classification of the three-dimensional arrangement of substituents attached to a chiral center or a double bond. The configuration of a chiral center is designated as *R* or *S*, and that of a double bond is designated as *E* or *Z*. (Ch. 5)

Stereochemistry the aspects of chemistry associated with the arrangement of atoms in space. (Ch. 8)

Stereoisomers molecular species that have the same *connectivity* but are not superimposable. Stereoisomers are *conformers* if they differ by rotations about single bonds and are *configurational isomers* if they do not. (Ch. 5)

Stereospecific describes reactions that produce one *stereochemical configuration* or arrangement of atoms exclusively, which is dictated by the stereochemistry of the reactant. (Ch. 8)

Steric hindrance the spatial restriction of movement (in rotation or of an incoming reacting species) due to bulky substituents on a molecule. (Ch. 2)

Steric strain an increase in energy that results from electron repulsion between atoms or groups of atoms that are not directly bonded together but occupy the same space. (Ch. 4)

Steroid a type of *lipid* with four fused carbon rings (three six-membered rings and one five-membered ring) that has a biological function (e.g., cholesterol regulates cell membrane permeability in mammals). (Ch. 2, 29)

Storage polysaccharide a *polysaccharide*, such as starch, whose main function is to store energy. (Ch. 28, 29)

Straight-chain alkane (also known as *linear alkane*) an alkane, containing only C—C and C—H single bonds with no functional groups, that has no branching along the chain. (Int. A)

***s*-Trans conformation** a rotational conformation in which substituents are on opposite sides of a single bond. (Ch. 26)

Stretching one of two basic, independent types of vibrational motion, in which the distance between two atoms in a chemical bond grows longer and shorter throughout one vibrational cycle. Compare with *bending*. (Ch. 16)

Strong absorption an absorption whose *transmittance* is near zero (near the bottom of the spectrum if %*T* is plotted on the *y* axis). (Ch. 16)

Structural isomers see *constitutional isomers*. (Ch. 4)

Structural polysaccharide a *polysaccharide*, such as cellulose, whose main function is to provide structural integrity. (Ch. 28, 29)

Substituent an atom or group of atoms attached to a molecule in place of hydrogen. (Int. A)

Substrate a molecular species that undergoes a particular reaction with an *attacking species*. In nucleophilic substitution or elimination, a substrate is the species that contains the *leaving group*. In enzyme-catalyzed reactions, substrates are the principal reactant molecules. (Ch. 7, 30)

Sulfo group a group with the bonding arrangement SO_3H or SO_3R. (Ch. 24)

Sulfonate a species of the form RSO_3^-, which has excellent *leaving group* ability. (Ch. 9)

Sulfonate ester a functional group with the bonding arrangement R′O—SO_2R. Sulfonate esters typically possess very good *leaving groups* for nucleophilic substitution and elimination reactions. (Ch. 23)

Sulfonation a type of *electrophilic aromatic substitution reaction* in which a proton is replaced by a sulfo group (SO_3H or SO_3R). (Ch. 24)

Sulfonyl chloride one of a class of compounds with the general formula R—SO_2Cl. (Ch. 23)

Suzuki reaction a *coupling reaction* that joins the carbon-containing group of a vinylic or aryl halide with that of an organoboron compound on treatment with a palladium catalyst (PdL_n) under basic conditions. (Ch. 20)

Symmetric stretching vibrational motion in which two or more bonds within a molecule stretch simultaneously and compress simultaneously. (Ch. 16)

Syn conformation the geometry of a species in which two substituents attached to atoms that are bonded together appear on the same side of that bond. (Int. C)

Syn dihydroxylation a reaction in which two OH groups add across a C═C or a C≡C bond in syn fashion. (Ch. 26)

Syndiotactic describes a *polymer* in which *stereochemical configurations* alternate from one monomer to the next along its main chain. (Ch. 28)

Synthesis a specific sequence of chemical reactions that converts *starting materials* into a desired compound, called the target of the synthesis (or the *synthetic target*). (Ch. 10)

Synthetic intermediate a compound that is produced in one *synthetic step* and later used as a reactant in another step. (Ch. 10)

Synthetic step a reaction that is carried out in a *synthesis*. (Ch. 10)

Synthetic target (also known as *target*) the desired end product of a *synthesis*. (Ch. 10)

Synthetic trap a difficulty preventing the execution of a *synthesis* in the forward direction as planned. (Ch. 11)

T

Tacticity the pattern of *stereochemical configurations*, or lack thereof, along a *polymer chain*. (Ch. 28)

Target see *synthetic target*. (Ch. 10)

Tautomer one form of a pair of *isomers* that exist together in equilibrium. (Ch. 7)

Termination step an *elementary step* in a *chain reaction* that results in a decrease in the number of reactive intermediates involved in the *propagation cycle*. (Ch. 27)

Termolecular describes an *elementary step* that involves three separate reactant species simultaneously. (Ch. 8)

Terpene a naturally produced hydrocarbon whose carbon backbone can be divided into separate and distinct five-carbon units called *isoprene units*. (Ch. 12, 29)

Terpenoid a natural product that is produced from chemical modifications to a *terpene*, in which the carbon backbone is altered or atoms other than carbon or hydrogen are introduced. (Ch. 12, 29)

Tertiary (3°) carbocation a carbocation that has three alkyl groups attached directly to C^+. (Ch. 7)

Tertiary structure the three-dimensional location of the amino acid residues that make up a particular *protein*. (Ch. 28, 29)

Tesla (T) the SI unit for the strength of a magnetic field. (Ch. 17)

Tetrahedral intermediate a transient species formed in a *nucleophilic addition–elimination reaction*; the product of a nucleophilic addition step and the reactant in the subsequent nucleophile elimination step. (Ch. 22)

Tetramethylsilane (TMS) the compound $(CH_3)_4Si$, commonly added to samples to provide a reference signal in *NMR spectroscopy*. (Ch. 17)

Tetrapeptide a molecule consisting of four *amino acid* residues linked by *peptide bonds*. (Ch. 29) E

T_g abbreviation for **glass transition temperature.** (Ch. 28)

Theoretical rate law an equation, derived from a proposed *mechanism*, that relates the rate of a reaction to the concentrations of the species involved in the reaction. (Ch. 8)

Thermal energy the average energy available through molecular collisions, which increases as temperature increases. (Ch. 4)

Thermally allowed describes a reaction that takes place readily when the reactants are in their *ground state* electron configurations. (Ch. 26)

Thermally forbidden describes a reaction that does not take place readily when the reactants are in their *ground state* electron configurations. (Ch. 26)

Thermodynamic control the execution of a chemical reaction under *equilibrium* conditions, such that the major product is the most stable one. (Ch. 11)

Thermodynamic enolate anion the more stable enolate ion that can be produced by deprotonation of the corresponding ketone. (Ch. 11)

Thermoplastic describes a *polymer* that, when heated above its glass transition or melting temperature, can be forced into molds or pushed through slots to form films or threads. (Ch. 28)

Thiol a compound that contains the bonding arrangement C—SH. (Ch. 1)

Thionyl chloride the compound $SOCl_2$, used as a reagent to convert alcohols to alkyl chlorides and carboxylic acids to carboxylic acid chlorides. (Ch. 23)

Three-center, two-electron bond a bond formed by two electrons and shared by three atoms; such bonds are found in *diborane*, for example. (Ch. 13)

Thymine dimer a structure produced when the nitrogenous bases of adjacent thymine nucleotides are fused together. (Ch. 30) E

T_m abbreviation for **melting point.** (Ch. 28)

Torsional stain an increase in energy (i.e., decrease in stability) that appears in an *eclipsed conformation*. (Ch. 4)

Trans describes the configuration wherein two atoms are on opposite sides of a double bond or plane of a ring. Compare with *cis*. (Ch. 3)

Transcription the stage in protein synthesis in which *RNA polymerase* uses the DNA sequence of a gene to produce a complementary segment of messenger RNA. (Ch. 30) E

Transesterification reaction a reaction that converts one ester into another. (Ch. 22)

Transfer RNA a molecule of ribonucleic acid that carries an amino acid to the *ribosome* to be incorporated into a newly synthesized *protein*. (Ch. 30) E

Transform in a *retrosynthetic analysis*, the proposed undoing of a single reaction or set of reactions to arrive at a potential *precursor*. (Ch. 11)

Transition state a high-energy species that corresponds to an energy maximum along the reaction coordinate on a *reaction free energy diagram*. (Ch. 6)

Transition state theory the model that relates the *free energy of activation* of a reaction to its rate constant. (Ch. 8)

Translation the stage in protein synthesis in which a *ribosome* "reads" the information from messenger RNA and constructs the corresponding protein one amino acid at a time. (Ch. 30) E

Transmetalation a reaction in which one metal of a C—Metal bond is replaced by another metal. (Ch. 20)

Transmittance (%*T*) in *spectroscopy*, the portion of light sent through a sample that reaches a detector: $\%T = \frac{I_{detected}}{I_{source}} \times 100\%$. (Ch. 16)

Triacylglycerol (also known as *triglyceride*) a fat or oil that contains three adjacent ester groups, each of which can be produced from a *fatty acid* and one of the three hydroxyl groups of *glycerol.* (Ch. 2, 29)

Trialkylborane a compound that has the structure R_3B, with three alkyl groups attached to boron. (Ch. 13)

Trialkylborate ester a compound that has the structure $(RO)_3B$, with three alkoxy groups attached to boron. (Ch. 13)

Triglyceride see *triacylglycerol.* (Ch. 2, 29)

Tripeptide a molecule consisting of three *amino acid* residues linked by *peptide bonds.* (Ch. 29)

Triplet (t) the splitting pattern of an NMR *signal* into three peaks in a 1:2:1 height ratio; occurs when $N = 2$, according to the *$N + 1$ rule.* (Ch. 17)

Triplet of doublets the splitting pattern of an NMR *signal* when each peak of a *triplet* is split into a *doublet* by a second coupling, resulting in a total of six peaks. (Ch. 17)

Trivial name (also known as *common name*) a nonsystematic name given to a molecule on the basis of its properties or origin. (Int. A)

Tropylium ion the aromatic cation $C_7H_7^+$, which has a seven-membered ring. The benzylic cation ($C_6H_5CH_2^+$) rearranges into $C_7H_7^+$ as part of a *fragmentation pathway* in mass spectrometry. (Ch. 15)

2-D NMR spectrum in *nuclear magnetic resonance spectroscopy*, a spectrum in which there are two frequency axes (the x and y axes), and the third axis (the z axis) corresponds to amplitude. Examples include *homonuclear correlation spectroscopy* and *heteronuclear correlation spectroscopy.* (Ch. 17)

U

Ultraviolet–visible (UV–vis) spectroscopy study of the interaction of a sample with light from the ultraviolet and visible regions of the electromagnetic spectrum; absorbance of this radiation typically causes electron transitions between orbitals. (Ch. 16)

Umpolung a German word that means "polarity reversal"; it describes the conversion of an electron-poor carbon atom into an electron-rich one or vice versa. (Ch. 21)

Unimolecular describes an *elementary step* in which there is one reactant species. (Ch. 8)

Unimolecular elimination of conjugate base (E1cb) mechanism a reaction sequence of steps that results in *β elimination*, in which the first step is deprotonation and the second step is departure of a leaving group. (Ch. 19)

Unimolecular elimination (E1) reaction a two-step sequence consisting of a *heterolysis step* followed by an *electrophile elimination step*, resulting in the net loss of a proton and a leaving group and the production of a new π bond. (Ch. 8)

Unimolecular nucleophilic substitution (S_N1) reaction a two-step sequence consisting of a *heterolysis step* followed by a *coordination step*, in which a leaving group is replaced by a nucleophile. (Ch. 8)

Unpaired electron an electron occupying an orbital without the presence of a second electron in that orbital. Unpaired electrons are found on species called *radicals.* (Ch. 1)

Unpolarized describes light whose photons travel in the same direction but have their electric fields oscillating in different planes. (Ch. 5)

Unsaturated describes a molecule that has fewer than the maximum number of hydrogen atoms possible; such molecules have double bonds, triple bonds, or rings. (Ch. 4)

Upfield in an NMR spectrum, appearing in a region of lower *chemical shift.* (Ch. 17)

UV–vis spectrum a plot of *absorbance* of ultraviolet and visible light for a sample, on the y axis, against the wavelength of light, on the x axis, showing *absorption bands* or *peaks.* (Ch. 16)

V

Valence bond (VB) theory a theory that describes orbitals in molecules as being produced by mixing just two *atomic orbitals* at a time, one from each of two adjacent atoms; often one or both of the orbitals involved in each mixing is a *hybrid orbital.* (Ch. 3)

Valence electron an electron available to participate in bonding interactions, occupying the highest (outermost) energy shell. (Ch. 1)

Valence shell electron pair repulsion (VSEPR) theory a model used to predict the geometry about an atom, based on the idea that the lowest-energy geometry about an atom is achieved by minimizing the electrostatic repulsions among the electron groups to which *valence electrons* can be assigned. (Ch. 2)

Vector a geometric entity that has both magnitude and direction. (Ch. 2)

Vinyl polymer a *polymer* made from linking monomers that contain vinyl groups (C=C) together. (Ch. 28)

Vitalism the outdated belief that organic compounds could not be made in the laboratory; instead, it was thought that only living systems could summon up a mysterious "vital force" needed to synthesize them. (Ch. 1)

Vulcanization the reaction of natural rubber with sulfur that results in cross-linking of the *polymer chains.* (Ch. 28)

W

Walden inversion the phenomenon that occurs on nucleophilic attack in an S_N2 reaction and causes inversion of stereochemistry. (Ch. 8)

Wavelength (λ) the distance between two successive maxima or minima in a wave's oscillation. (Ch. 16)

Wavenumber (also known as *reciprocal centimeter*) a unit of frequency that is calculated by taking the reciprocal of the wavelength in centimeters: that is, dividing 1 by the wavelength in centimeters. Physically, a wavenumber corresponds to the number of waves that fit in 1 cm. (Ch. 16)

Wax a secretion from plants or animals that is solid at room temperature but melts at relatively low temperatures; often a long-chain hydrocarbon or ester. (Ch. 2, 29)

Weak absorption an absorption whose *transmittance* is near 100% (near the top of the spectrum if $\%T$ is plotted on the y axis). (Ch. 16)

Wheland intermediate see *arenium ion intermediate.* (Ch. 24)

Williamson ether synthesis a reaction used to synthesize either symmetrical or unsymmetrical ethers by an S_N2 reaction between an alkoxide anion (RO^-) and an alkyl halide (R—X) under basic conditions. (Ch. 10)

Wittig reaction a reaction in which the negatively charged carbon of a *Wittig reagent* forms a C=C bond with the carbonyl carbon of a ketone or aldehyde to produce an alkene. (Ch. 18)

Wittig reagent (also known as *phosphonium ylide*) one of a class of compounds having a $^+$P—C:$^-$ bond, used to synthesize alkenes; characteristically, it is highly nucleophilic at the negatively charged carbon. (Ch. 18)

Wolff–Kishner reduction a reaction that reduces the carbonyl group of a ketone or an aldehyde to a methylene (CH_2) group through treatment with hydrazine followed by heating under basic conditions. (Ch. 19, 20)

Z

Zaitsev product the most highly alkyl-substituted alkene that can be produced in an elimination reaction. (Ch. 9)

Zaitsev's rule an empirical rule for elimination reaction regioselectivity, producing the *Zaitsev product*: The major elimination product is the one produced by deprotonating the carbon atom initially attached to the fewest hydrogen atoms. In other words, elimination usually takes place so as to produce the most highly alkyl-substituted alkene. (Ch. 9)

***Z* configuration** describes a double bond in which the higher-priority substituents attached to the ends of the double bond appear on the same side of the double bond. Compare with *E configuration*. (Ch. 5)

Ziegler–Natta catalyst a catalyst used to produce *isotactic* or *syndiotactic* forms of polymers. Ziegler–Natta catalysts are typically mixtures of transition metal halides (such as those of Ti, V, Zr, and Cr) with organoaluminum compounds. (Ch. 28)

Zigzag conformation see *all-anti conformation*. (Ch. 4)

Zinc amalgam an alloy of zinc and mercury, which is a key reactant in the *Clemmensen reduction*. (Ch. 20)

Zwitterion a species that has both a positive and a negative formal charge, but a net charge of zero. (Ch. 6)

ANSWERS TO YOUR TURNS

Chapter 1

Your Turn 1.1

The 2*s* and 2*p* orbitals are in the second shell. The 3*s* and 3*p* orbitals are in the third shell. Box electrons (3)–(10) in Figure 1-8, and circle electrons (11)–(18).

Your Turn 1.2

The valence electrons are in the second shell, $2s^2$ and $2p^2$, and the core electrons are in the first shell, $1s^2$.

Your Turn 1.3

Bond energy of $H_2 \approx 450$ kJ/mol $- 0$ kJ/mol $= 450$ kJ/mol.

Your Turn 1.4

(a) 586 kJ/mol. **(b)** The Si—F bond. **(c)** 138 kJ/mol. **(d)** The O—O bond. **(e)** 1072 kJ/mol. **(f)** The C≡O bond.

Your Turn 1.5

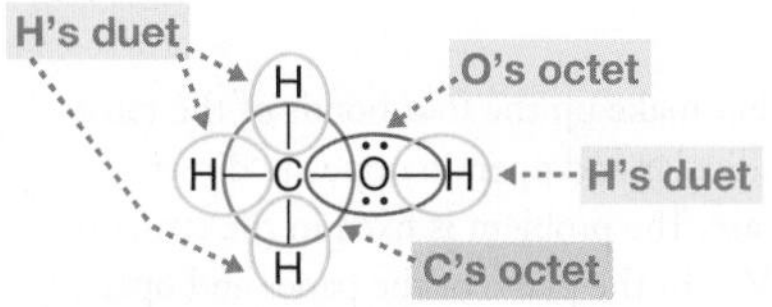

H's duet
O's octet
H's duet
C's octet

Your Turn 1.6

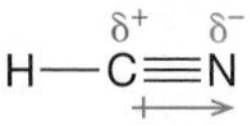

Your Turn 1.7

ΔEN for $MgBr_2$ is $2.96 - 1.31 = 1.65$, and ΔEN for CH_4 is $2.55 - 2.20 = 0.35$. ΔEN is large for ionic compounds and small for covalent ones.

Your Turn 1.8

Number of valence electrons (total number of electrons, number of protons, charge): 3 (5, 6, +1); 4 (6, 6, 0); 5 (7, 6, −1)

Your Turn 1.9

Sum of formal charges: $0 + 0 + 0 + (-1) = -1$. Sum equals the overall charge on HCO_2^- ion, −1.

Your Turn 1.10

(a) Feature 2

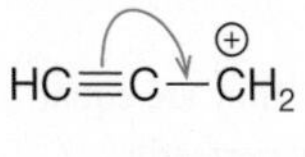

(b) Feature 3

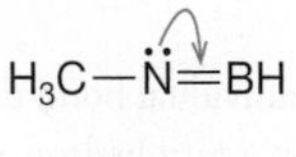

(c) Feature 1

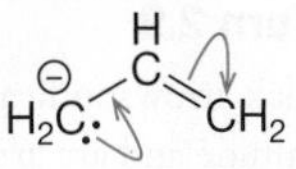

Your Turn 1.11

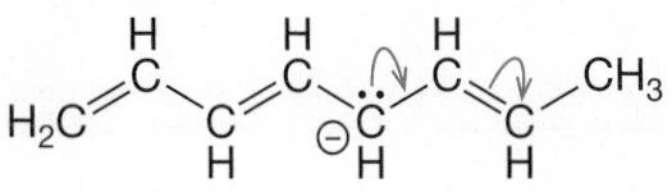

Your Turn 1.12

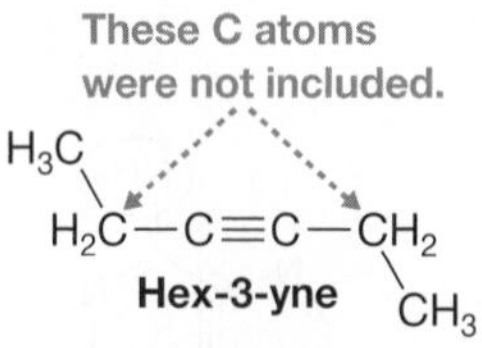

These C atoms
were not included.
Hex-3-yne

Your Turn 1.13

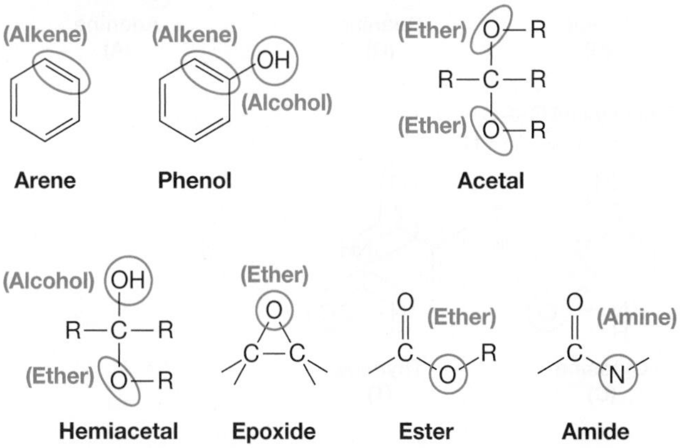

(Alkene)
(Alkene)
(Alcohol)
(Ether)
(Ether)
Arene
Phenol
Acetal
(Alcohol)
(Ether)
(Ether)
(Ether)
(Amine)
Hemiacetal
Epoxide
Ester
Amide

Your Turn 1.14

Each compound has a carbonyl (C═O) functional group and is classified as a ketone.

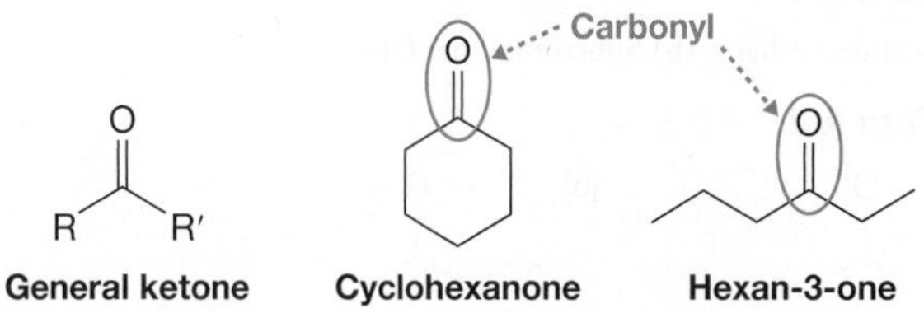

Carbonyl
General ketone
Cyclohexanone
Hexan-3-one

Your Turn 1.15

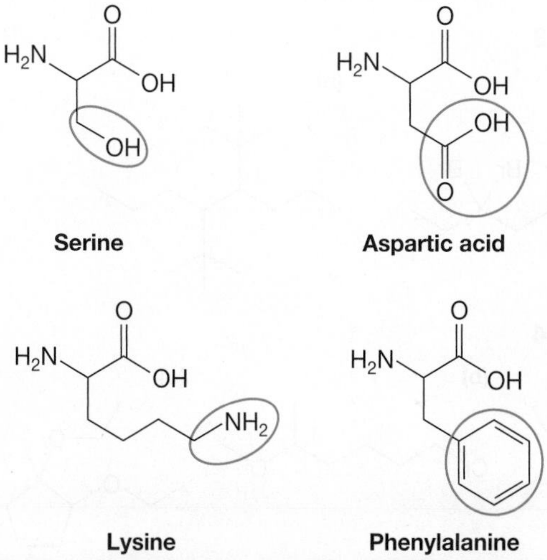

Serine
Aspartic acid
Lysine
Phenylalanine

Your Turn 1.16

The C=O group is part of RCH=O, characteristic of an aldehyde. Each OH group is part of R—OH, characteristic of an alcohol.

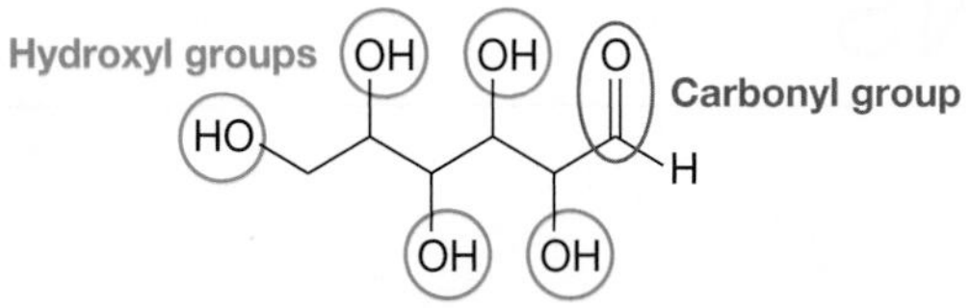
Hydroxyl groups
Carbonyl group

Glucose $C_6H_{12}O_6$

Your Turn 1.17

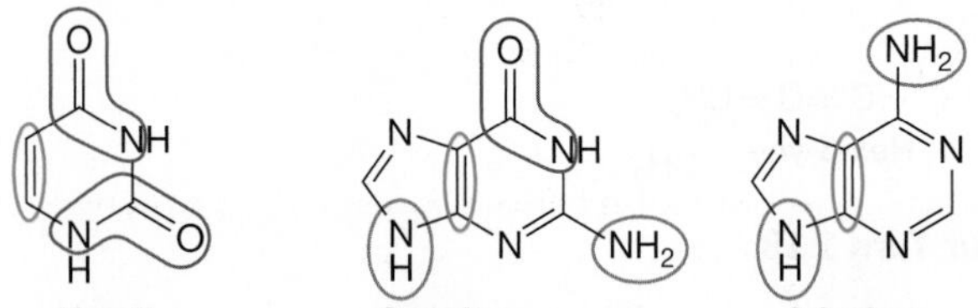

Uracil (U) **Guanine (G)** **Adenine (A)**

Alkene (red) C=C
Amide (blue) O=C—N
Amine (purple) C—N

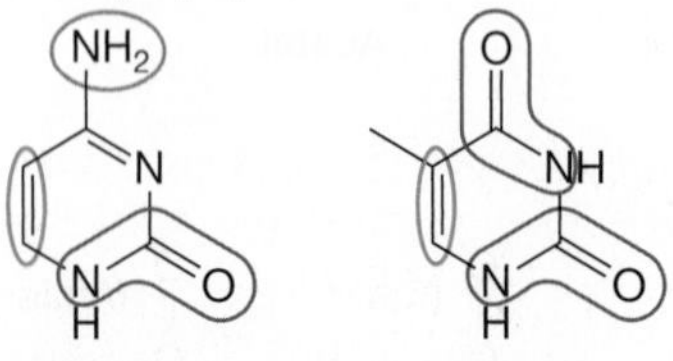

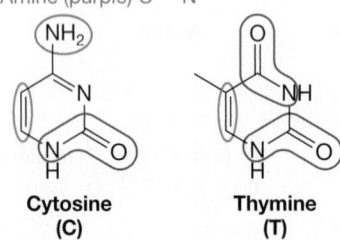

Cytosine (C) **Thymine (T)**

Interchapter A

Your Turn A.1

(a) Substituted ethane. **(b)** Substituted pentane.

Your Turn A.2

(a)

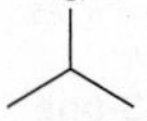

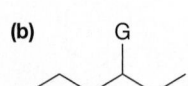

Substituted propane

(b)

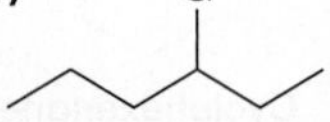

Substituted hexane

Note: Other substituted structures are possible.

Your Turn A.3

(a)

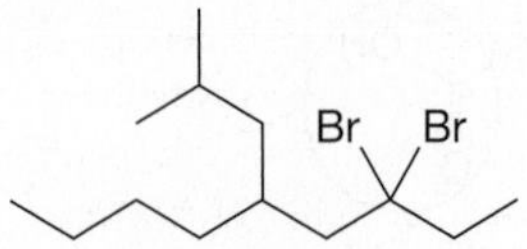

(b)

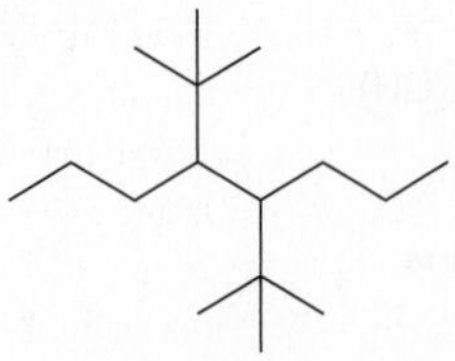

Your Turn A.4

(a)

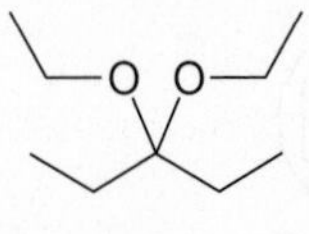

(b)

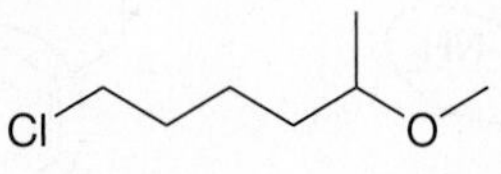

(c)

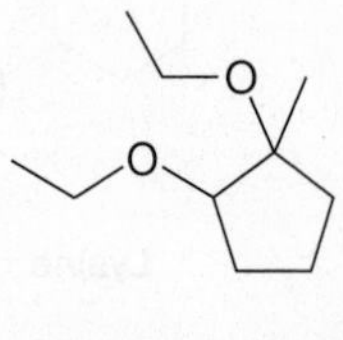

Chapter 2

Your Turn 2.1

(a) Two groups of electrons. **(b)** Three groups of electrons. **(c)** Four groups of electrons.

Your Turn 2.2

Electron geometry = tetrahedral. Molecular geometry = tetrahedral. Bond angle ≈ 109.5°.

Your Turn 2.3

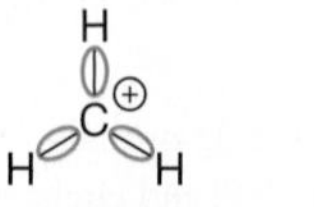

3 e^- groups

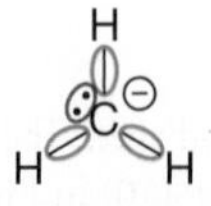

4 e^- groups

Your Turn 2.4

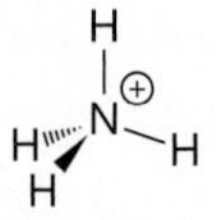

First structure

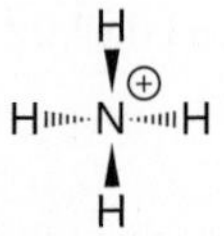

Second structure

Your Turn 2.5

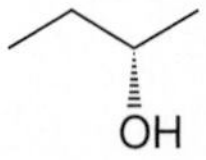

Your Turn 2.6

The two Vs (red and blue) that make up the four bonds of the tetrahedral atom must be perpendicular and open in opposite directions. On the left, that is not the case. The problem is fixed in the structure on the right, where the red V is in the plane of the paper and opens upward, and the blue V is perpendicular and opens downward.

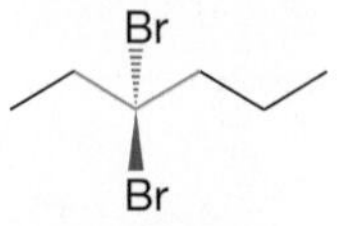

Incorrect

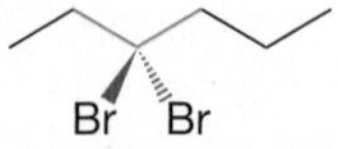

Correct

Your Turn 2.7

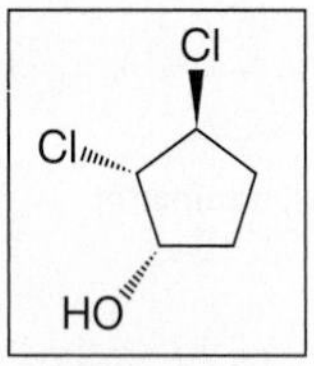

After first flip

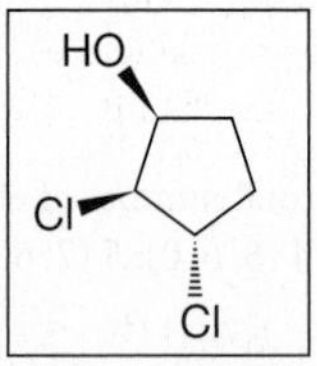

After second flip

Your Turn 2.8

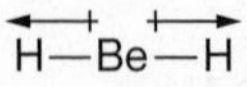

Your Turn 2.9

Thin black arrows indicate the individual bond dipoles. They are equal in magnitude and are arranged in a tetrahedron, so they perfectly cancel. The molecule is nonpolar.

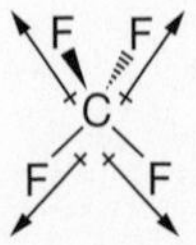

Your Turn 2.10

Methanoic acid has a CO_2H group and is a carboxylic acid (and sodium methanoate is a deprotonated form of this carboxylic acid); ethanol has an OH group and is an alcohol; ethanal has a C═O group and is an aldehyde; dimethyl ether has a C—O—C group and is an ether; propene has a C═C group and is an alkene; propane and ethane have no functional groups.

Your Turn 2.11

Dipole–dipole interactions are the dominant intermolecular interaction for both CH_3CH_2F and $CH_3CH{=}O$. $CH_3CH{=}O$ has a higher boiling point than CH_3CH_2F (+20 °C vs. −37.1 °C), so $CH_3CH{=}O$ must be more polar.

Your Turn 2.12

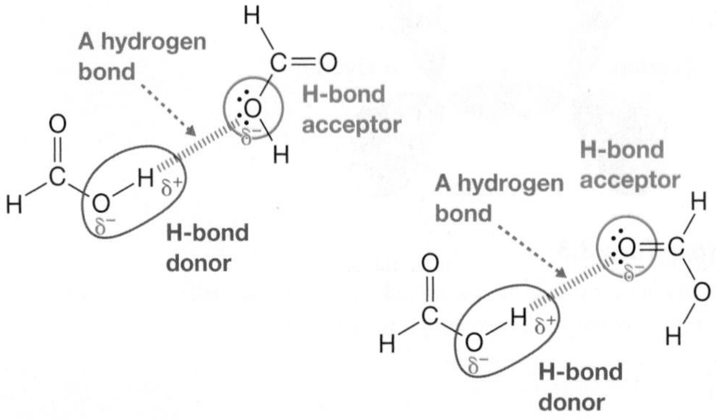

A hydrogen bond
H-bond acceptor
H-bond donor
A hydrogen bond
H-bond acceptor
H-bond donor

Your Turn 2.13

Functional groups that possess at least one H-bond acceptor but no H-bond donors include the ones characteristic of alkyl fluorides (but not other alkyl halides), ethers, acetals, epoxides, nitriles, ketones, aldehydes, and esters. Also included are the functional groups in amines and amides if no H atoms are bonded to the N atom. Functional groups that contain at least one H-bond donor and one H-bond acceptor include the groups characteristic of alcohols, phenols, hemiacetals, and carboxylic acids. Also included are the functional groups in amines and amides if at least one H atom is bonded to the N atom. Functional groups that contain no H-bond donors and no H-bond acceptors include the ones characteristic of alkyl halides other than fluoride, alkenes, alkynes, arenes, and thiols.

Your Turn 2.14

The F—H‖‖F hydrogen bond should be stronger than the N—H‖‖N hydrogen bond because F is more electronegative than N. Therefore, the attraction between opposite charges is stronger in the F—H‖‖F hydrogen bond.

Your Turn 2.15

As the total number of electrons increases, so does boiling point and the strength of the London dispersion forces.

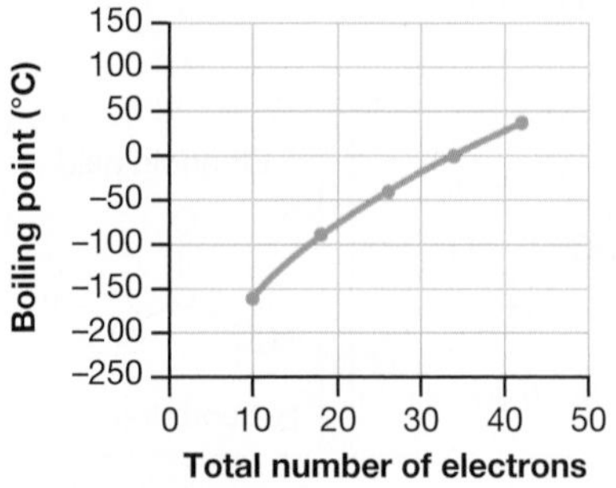

Boiling point (°C)
150
100
50
0
−50
−100
−150
−200
−250
0
10
20
30
40
50
Total number of electrons

Your Turn 2.16

As shown in red, pentane has a greater intermolecular contact surface area than dimethylpropane.

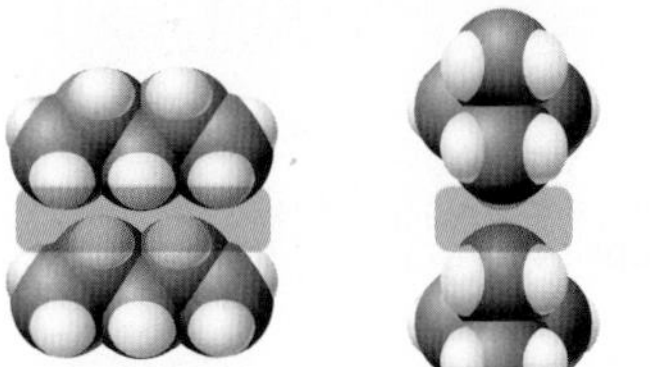

(a) Pentane

(b) Dimethylpropane

Your Turn 2.17

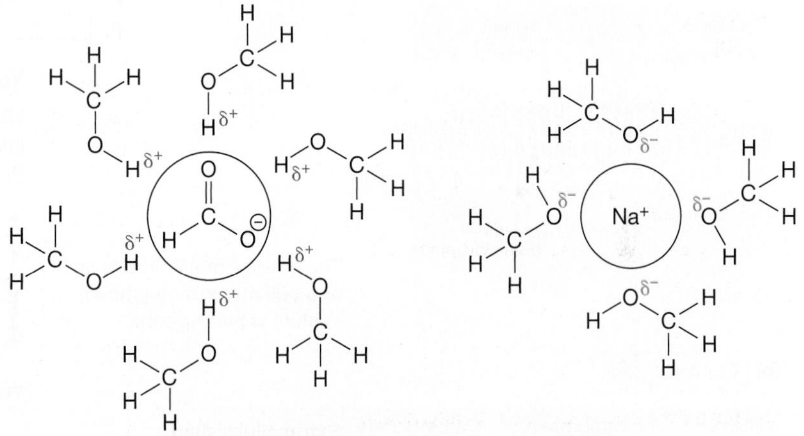

Na+

Your Turn 2.18

Hydrophilic functional groups include the ones characteristic of alkyl fluorides, alcohols, hemiacetals, nitriles, ketones, aldehydes, and carboxylic acids. They also include the functional groups in amines and amides if at least one H atom is bonded to the N atom. Hydrophobic functional groups include the ones characteristic of alkenes, alkynes, arenes, phenols, alkyl halides other than fluorides, thiols, ethers, acetals, epoxides, and esters. They also include the functional groups in amines and amides if no H atoms are bonded to the N atom.

Your Turn 2.19

Boiling point is directly related to the strength of the intermolecular interactions, so the compounds arranged from lowest to highest boiling point are as follows: **K** < **J** < **H** < **L** < **I**.

Your Turn 2.20

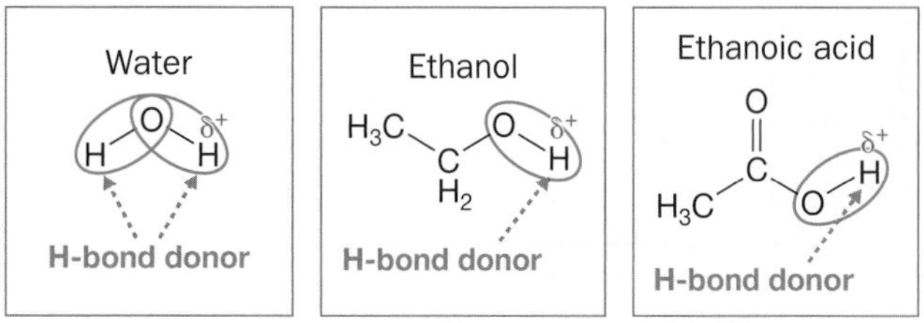

Water
H-bond donor
Ethanol
H-bond donor
Ethanoic acid
H-bond donor

Your Turn 2.21

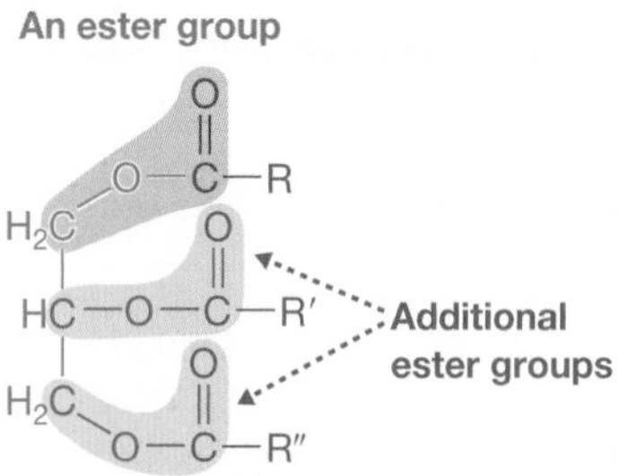

An ester group
Additional ester groups

Your Turn 2.22

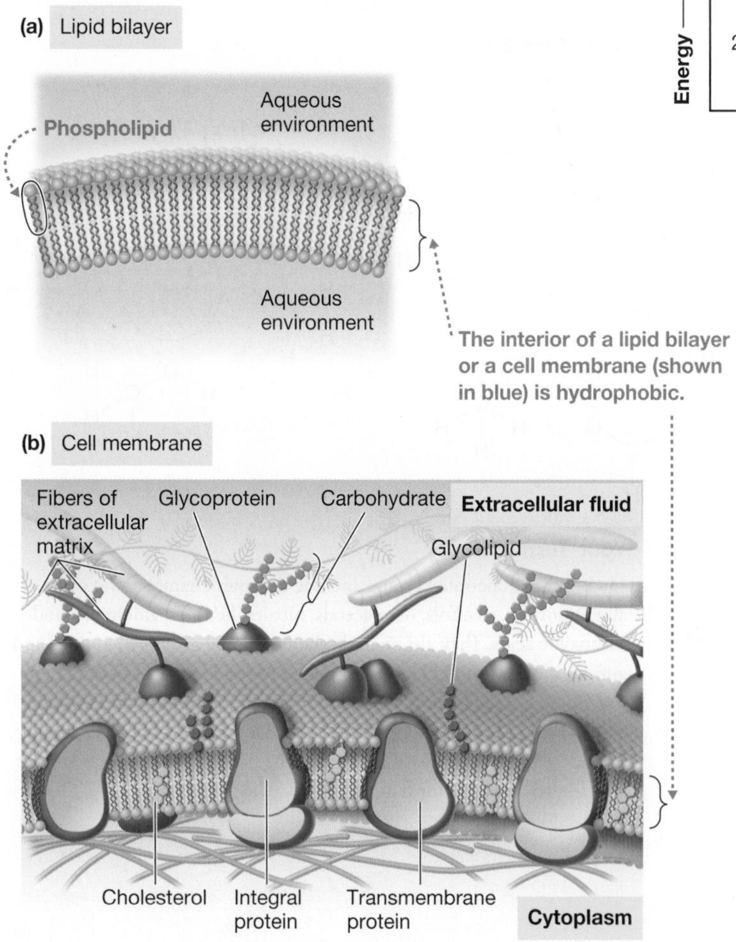

(a) Lipid bilayer
Phospholipid
Aqueous environment
Aqueous environment
The interior of a lipid bilayer or a cell membrane (shown in blue) is hydrophobic.
(b) Cell membrane
Fibers of extracellular matrix
Glycoprotein
Carbohydrate
Extracellular fluid
Glycolipid
Cholesterol
Integral protein
Transmembrane protein
Cytoplasm

Chapter 3

Your Turn 3.1

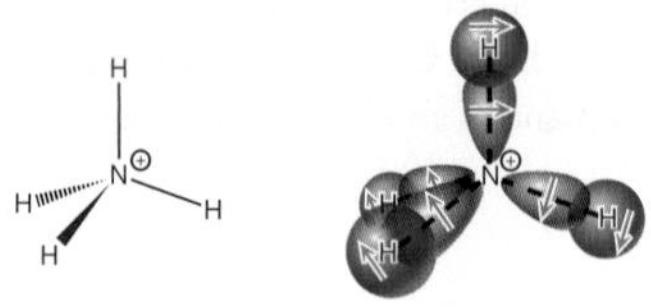

Your Turn 3.2

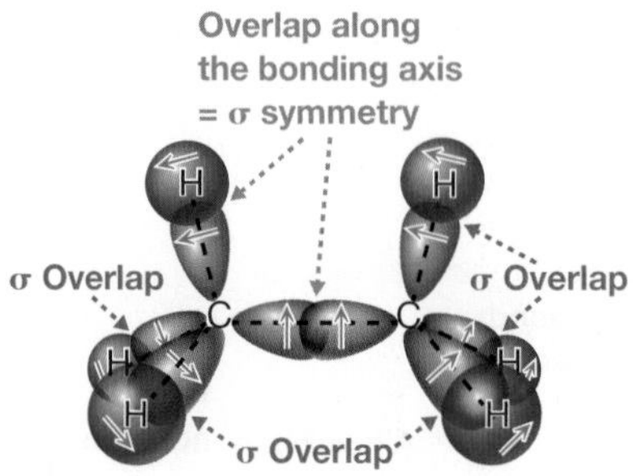

Overlap along the bonding axis = σ symmetry
σ Overlap
σ Overlap
σ Overlap

Your Turn 3.3

Two hybrid orbitals are completely filled, two are half-filled, and no orbitals are empty, in agreement with Figure 3-9a.

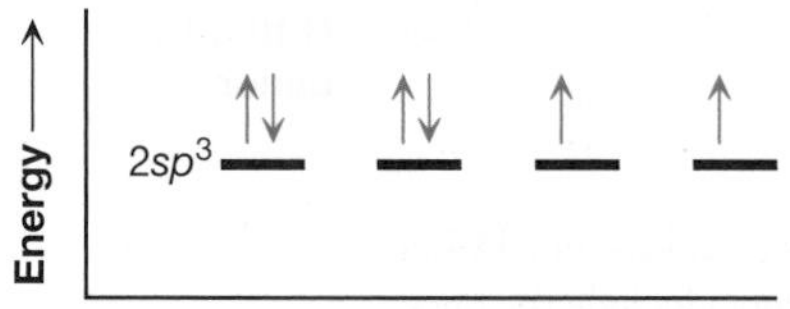

Energy
2sp³

Your Turn 3.4

One hybrid orbital is completely filled, three are half-filled, and no orbitals are empty, in agreement with Solved Problem 3.3.

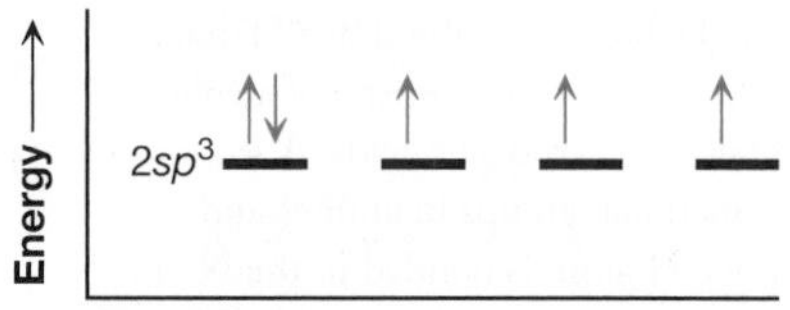

Energy
2sp³

Your Turn 3.5

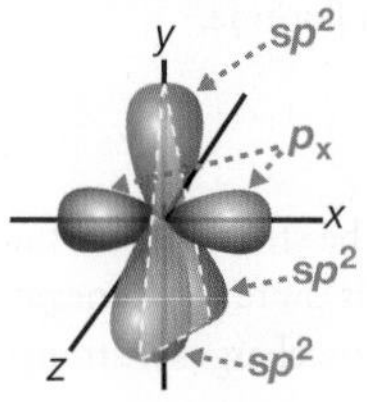

y
sp²
pₓ
x
sp²
z
sp²

Your Turn 3.6

Two hybrid orbitals are completely filled, one hybrid orbital and one unhybridized orbital are half-filled, and no orbitals are empty, in agreement with Solved Problem 3.4.

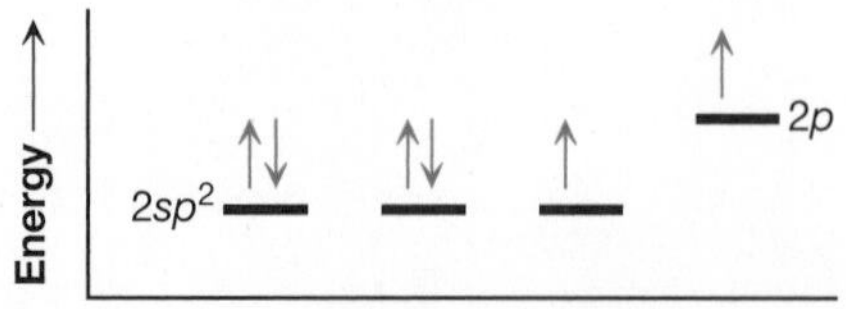

Energy
2sp²
2p

Your Turn 3.7

One electron occupies each sp^2 hybrid orbital and the p orbital is empty, in agreement with the statements made about C^+.

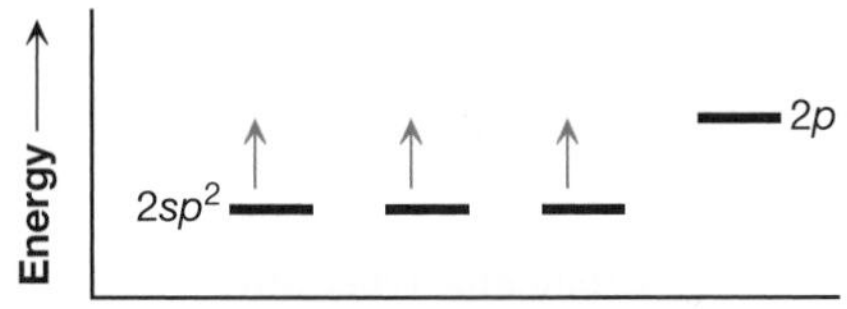
Energy
2sp²
2p

Your Turn 3.8

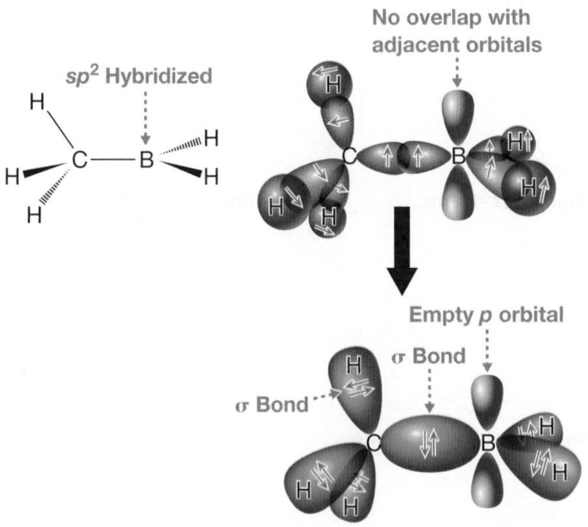
sp² Hybridized
No overlap with adjacent orbitals
Empty p orbital
σ Bond
σ Bond

Your Turn 3.9

One hybrid orbital is completely filled and one is half-filled, both unhybridized p orbitals are half-filled, and no orbitals are empty, in agreement with Solved Problem 3.5.

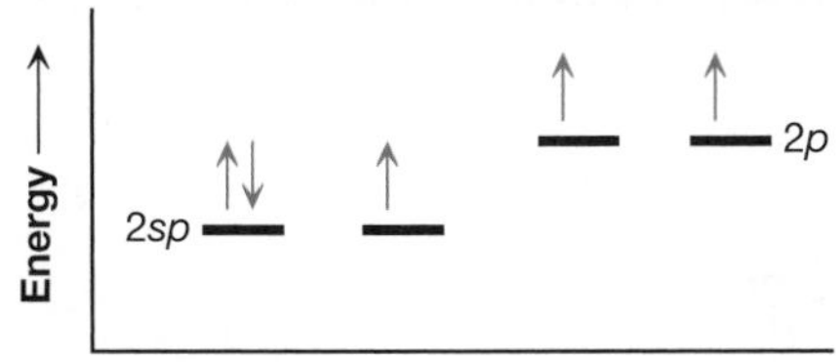
Energy
2sp
2p

Your Turn 3.10

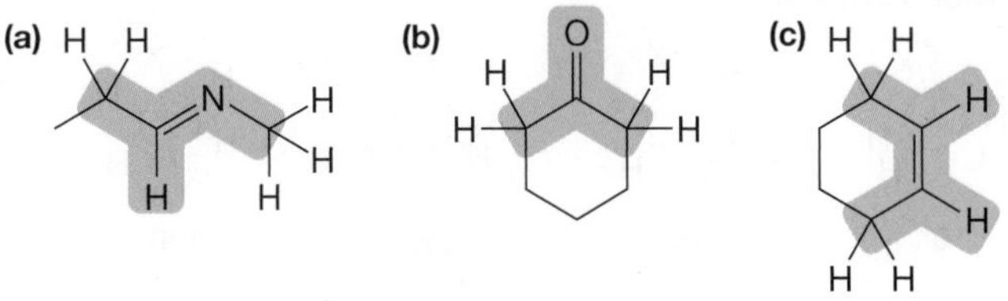
(a)
(b)
(c)

Your Turn 3.11

Flipping the molecule on the left vertically 180° shows it is the same as the molecule on the right.

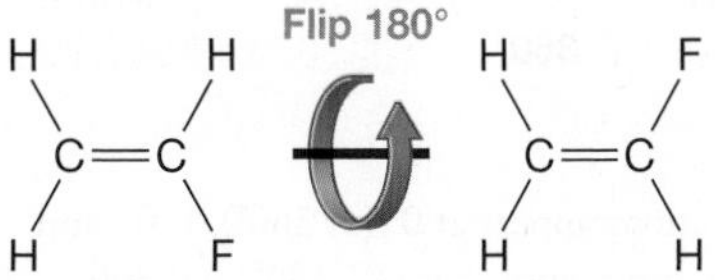
Flip 180°

Your Turn 3.12

(a) Cis. **(b)** Trans.

Your Turn 3.13

(a) $H_2C{=}C{=}C{=}CH_2$ is planar (top image).
(b) $H_2C{=}C{=}C{=}C{=}CH_2$ is not planar; one CH_2 group is perpendicular to the other (bottom image).

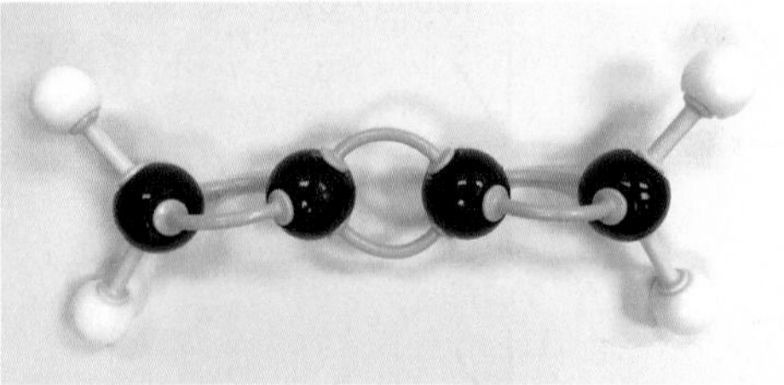

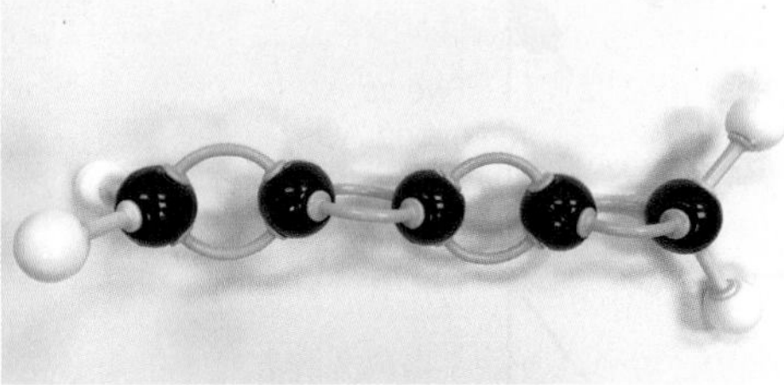

Your Turn 3.14

sp^3 orbitals are 25% s, sp^2 orbitals are 33.3% s, and sp orbitals are 50% s.

Your Turn 3.15

(a)

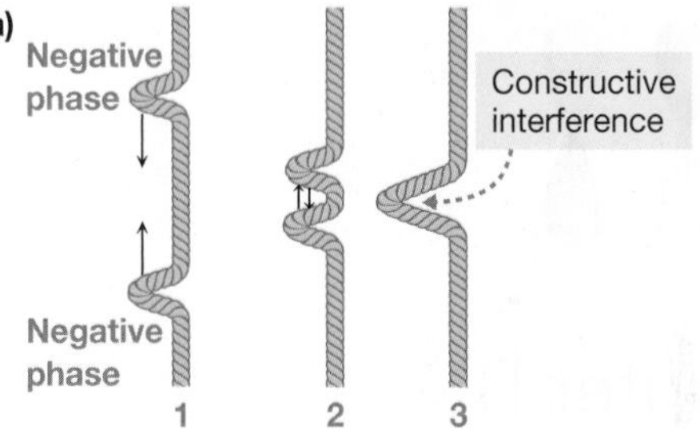
Negative phase
Negative phase
Constructive interference
1
2
3

(b)

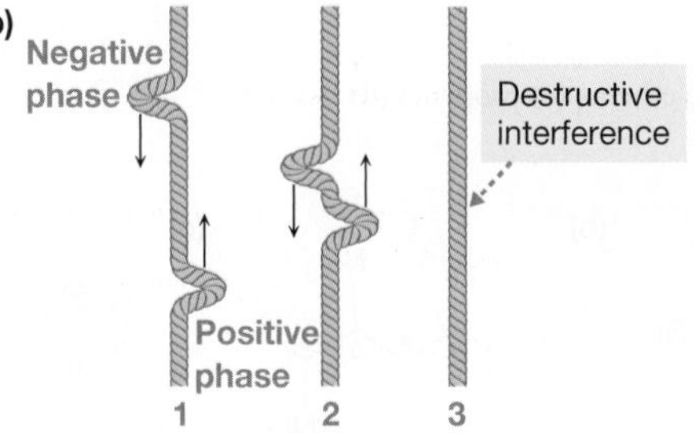
Negative phase
Positive phase
Destructive interference
1
2
3

Your Turn 3.16

The σ MO is the HOMO and the σ* MO is the LUMO.

Your Turn 3.17

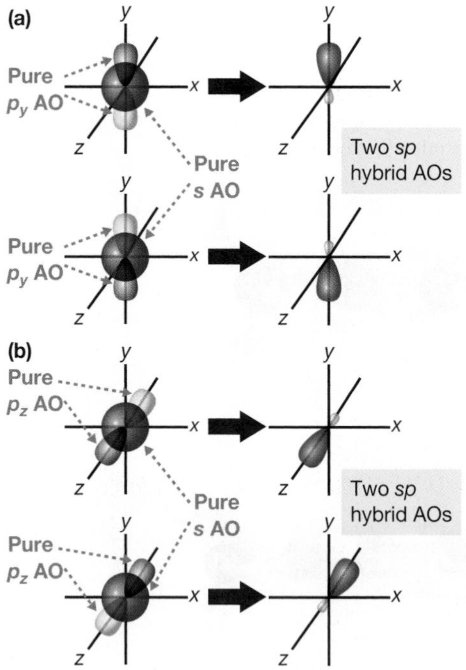

(a)
Pure p_y AO
Pure s AO
Two sp hybrid AOs
(b)
Pure p_z AO
Pure s AO
Two sp hybrid AOs

Your Turn 3.18

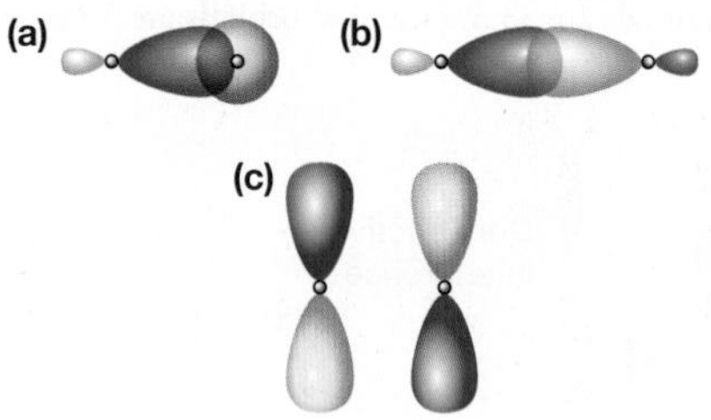

(a)
(b)
(c)

Interchapter B

Your Turn B.1

(a) Cyclohexene; **(b)** ethene; **(c)** propyne; **(d)** hexene.

Your Turn B.2

(a)

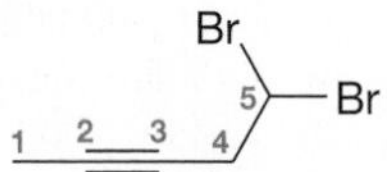

5,5-Dibromopent-2-yne

(b)

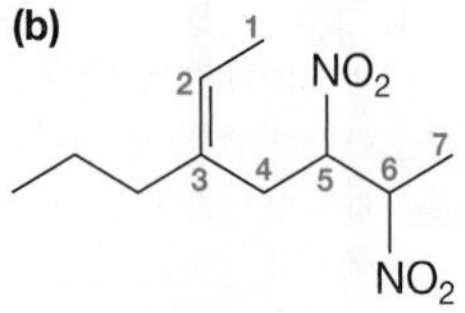

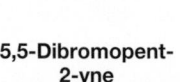

5,6-Dinitro-3-propylhept-2-ene

(c)

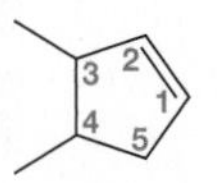

3,4-Dimethylcyclopentene

Your Turn B.3

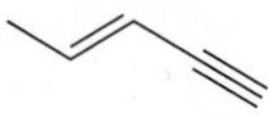

Pent-3-en-1-yne

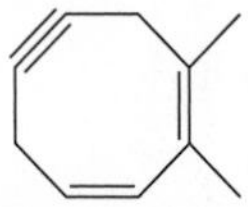

1,2-Dimethylcycloocta-1,3-dien-6-yne

Your Turn B.4

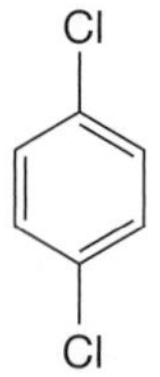

***p*-Dichlorobenzene**
1,4-Dichlorobenzene

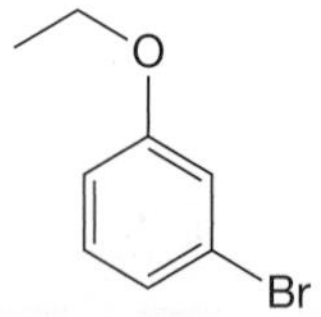

***m*-Bromoethoxybenzene**
1-Bromo-3-ethoxybenzene

Your Turn B.5

(a)

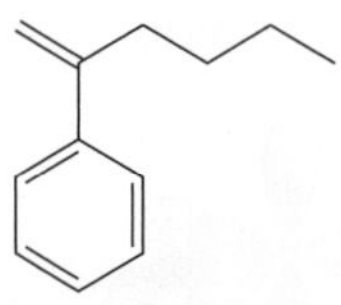

2-Phenylhex-1-ene

(b)

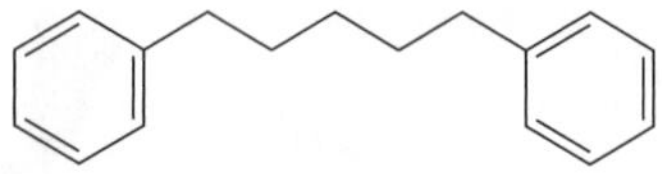

1,5-Diphenylpentane

(c)

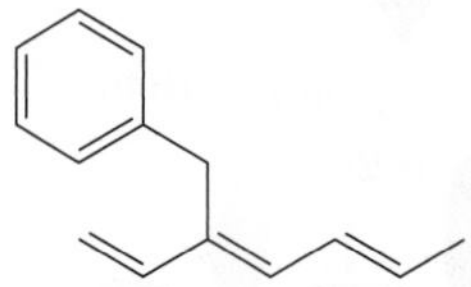

3-Benzylhepta-1,3,5-triene

Chapter 4

Your Turn 4.1

The C atom on the left is in front in the Newman projection, and the C atom on the right is in back in the Newman projection.

Your Turn 4.2

60°

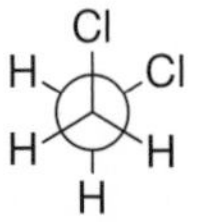

120°

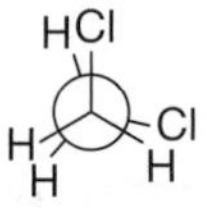

Your Turn 4.3

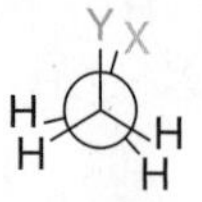

0°

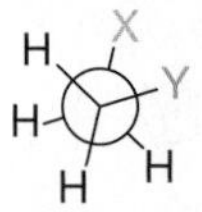

60°

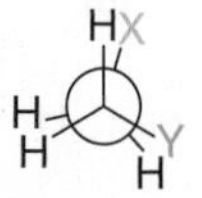

120°

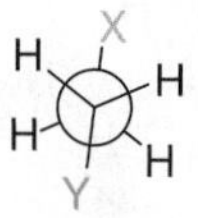

180°

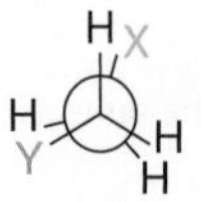

240°

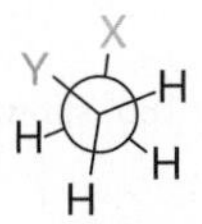

300°

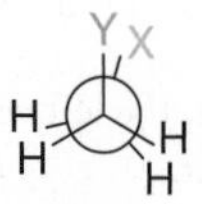

360°

Your Turn 4.4

In Figure 4-4, eclipsed conformations appear at 0° (or 360°), 120°, and 240°, whereas staggered conformations appear at 60°, 180°, and 300°.

Your Turn 4.5

The torsional strain is about 12 kJ/mol.

Your Turn 4.6

In Figure 4-7, eclipsed conformations appear at 0° (or 360°), 120°, and 240°, whereas staggered conformations appear at 60°, 180°, and 300°.

Your Turn 4.7

Conformation **A** is gauche. Conformation **B** is anti and is more stable.

Your Turn 4.8

The rotational energy barrier to go from anti to gauche is about 26 kJ/mol for 1,2-dibromoethane (Fig. 4-7). This is twice the size of the barrier in ethane (Fig. 4-4), which is about 12 kJ/mol, and it is due to greater steric strain from the larger size of Br compared to H.

Your Turn 4.9

1,2-Dibromoethane will have the larger rotational barrier because Br is much larger than F and will induce more steric strain.

Your Turn 4.10

(a) 

(b) In the zigzag conformation, steric interactions are minimized because every dihedral angle is in the anti conformation.

Your Turn 4.11

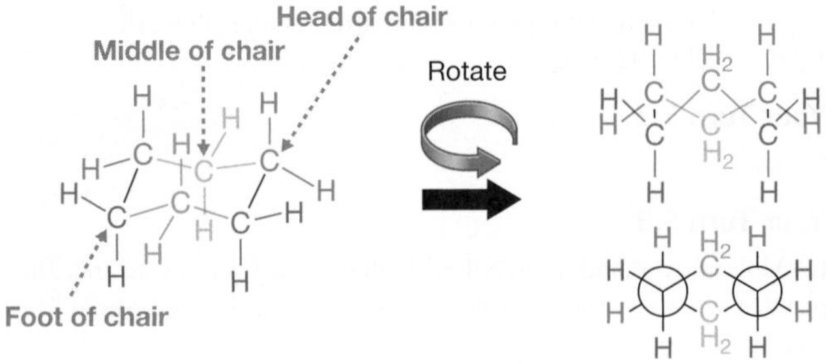
Head of chair
Middle of chair
Foot of chair
Rotate

Your Turn 4.12

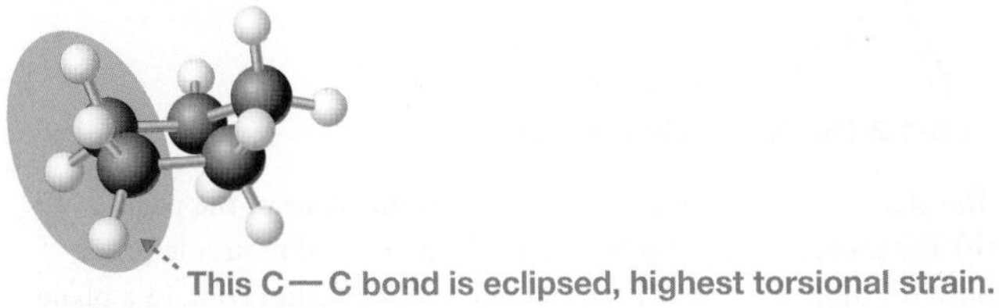
This C—C bond is eclipsed, highest torsional strain.

Your Turn 4.13

The ΔH° per CH_2 group in cyclopropane is (1961.0 kJ/mol)/(3 CH_2 groups) = 653.7 kJ/mol. Ring strain per CH_2 group in cyclopropane is 653.7 kJ/mol − 615.1 kJ/mol = 38.6 kJ/mol. Total ring strain for cyclopropane is 38.6 kJ/mol × 3 CH_2 groups = 115.8 kJ/mol.

Your Turn 4.14

All of the C—C bonds undergo rotation as axial and equatorial groups change their positions. Every pair of adjacent C—C bonds undergoes rotation in the opposite direction. The "head" of the chair (C′, shaded in blue) rotates to become the foot of the chair, and the foot of the chair (C″, shaded in blue) rotates to become the head of the chair.

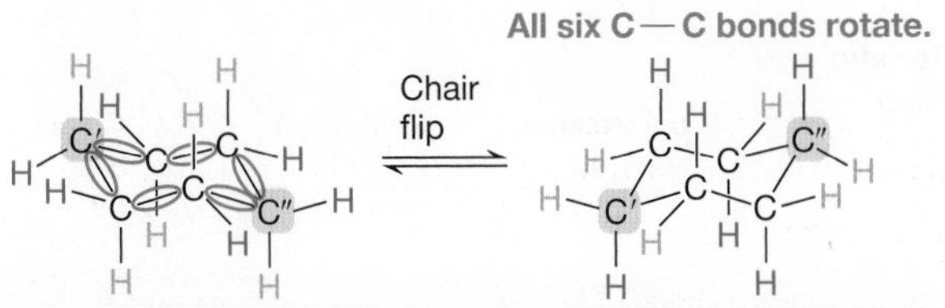
All six C—C bonds rotate.
Chair flip

Your Turn 4.15

Angle strain comes from the sp^3-hybridized C atoms having bond angles of ~120° instead of 109.5°. Torsional strain comes from eclipsed conformations. These strains are not present in the chair conformation, which is why the half-chair conformation is higher in energy.

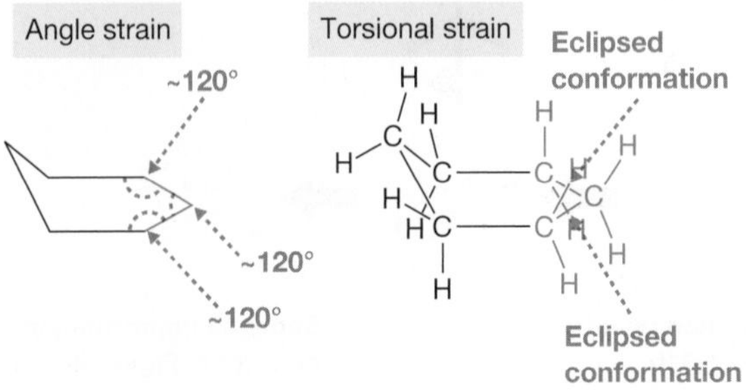
Angle strain
~120°
~120°
~120°
Torsional strain
Eclipsed conformation
Eclipsed conformation

Your Turn 4.16

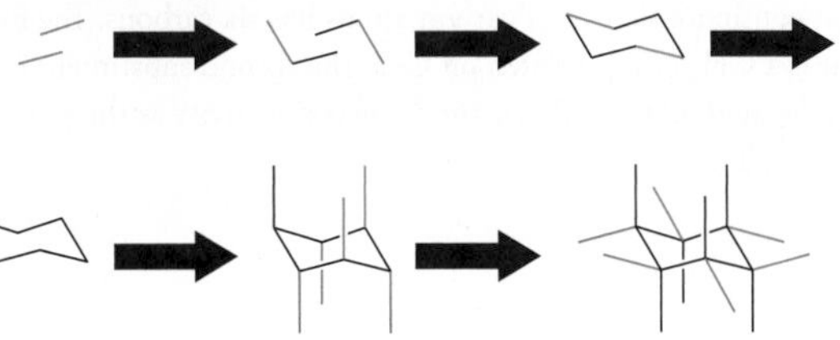

Your Turn 4.17

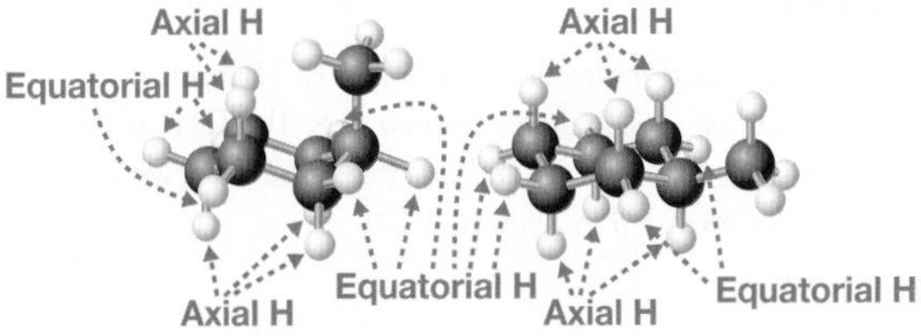
Axial H
Axial H
Equatorial H
Axial H
Equatorial H
Axial H
Equatorial H

Your Turn 4.18

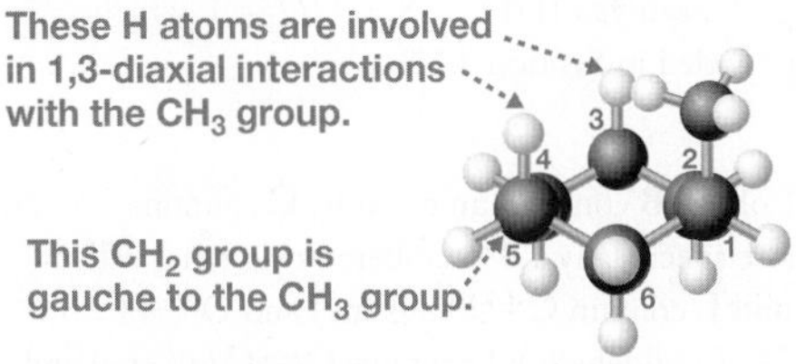
These H atoms are involved in 1,3-diaxial interactions with the CH3 group.
This CH2 group is gauche to the CH3 group.

Your Turn 4.19

Trifluoromethylcyclohexane will have a greater percentage of molecules with the substituent in the axial position. The CI_3 group is bulkier than CF_3, so the CI_3 group has a stronger preference for the equatorial position than does the CF_3 group.

Your Turn 4.20

(a) 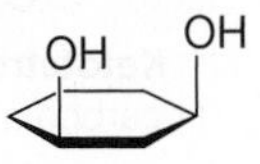
OH
OH

(b) 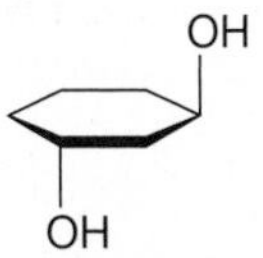
OH
OH

(c) 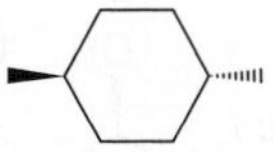

(d) 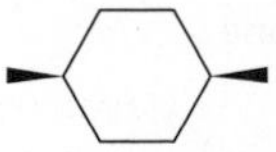

Your Turn 4.21

To translate the conformation of *trans*-1,3-dimethylcyclohexane on the left into the conformation on the right, without flipping the chair, carry out the following rotations of the molecule.

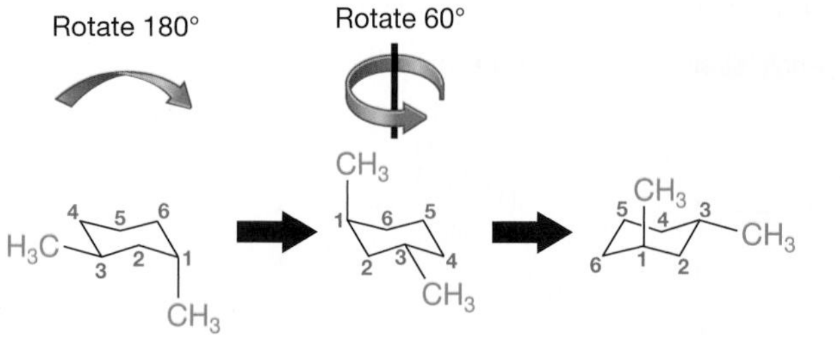

Rotate 180°
Rotate 60°
H_3C
CH_3
CH_3
CH_3
CH_3
CH_3

Conformation on left of Figure 4-31b

Same as conformation on right in Figure 4-31b

Your Turn 4.22

The longest continuous chain of carbon atoms has six carbons. The first substituent is a CH_3 group located on C-2. The second substituent is a CH_3 group located on C-4. This is the same connectivity as the previous two molecules.

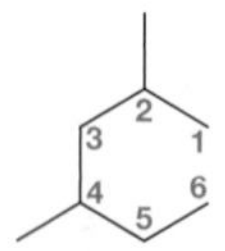

Your Turn 4.23

In the analogous saturated molecule, the number of H atoms is $2(4) + 2 + 0$ (N atoms) $- 2$ (halogen atoms) $= 8$. The IHD is half the number of missing H atoms, so IHD $= (8 - 8)/2 = 0$, which matches the number provided in Section 4.12a.

Your Turn 4.24

In the analogous saturated molecule, the number of H atoms is $2(3) + 2 + 0$ (N atoms) $- 0$ (halogen atoms) $= 8$. The IHD is half the number of missing H atoms, so IHD $= (8 - 6)/2 = 1$, which matches the number provided in Section 4.12b.

Your Turn 4.25

A contains O—H (alcohol); **B** contains an epoxide; **C** contains C—O—C (ether, more specifically a 4-membered ring ether called an *oxetane*); **G, H, K,** and **L** contain C═C (alkene) and O—H (alcohol); **I** contains C═O (aldehyde); **J** contains C═C (alkene) and C—O—C (ether); **M** contains C═O (ketone).

Your Turn 4.26

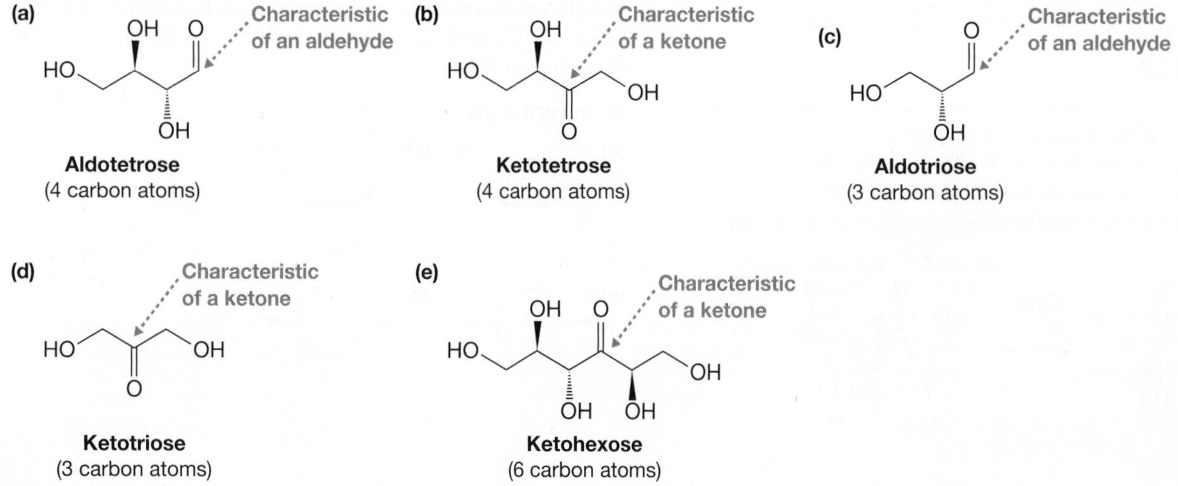

(a)
Characteristic of an aldehyde
Aldotetrose
(4 carbon atoms)
(b)
Characteristic of a ketone
Ketotetrose
(4 carbon atoms)
(c)
Characteristic of an aldehyde
Aldotriose
(3 carbon atoms)
(d)
Characteristic of a ketone
Ketotriose
(3 carbon atoms)
(e)
Characteristic of a ketone
Ketohexose
(6 carbon atoms)

Chapter 5

Your Turn 5.1

The two molecules are nonsuperimposable. Cl appears in the top box, and H appears in the bottom box.

Your Turn 5.2

After the mirror image structure in Figure 5-3b is rotated, every one of its atoms lines up perfectly with the corresponding atoms in Figure 5-3a; the molecule and its mirror image are superimposable.

Your Turn 5.3

(a) and **(b)** Superimposable; **(c)** nonsuperimposable.

Your Turn 5.4

The resulting mirror image is identical to the one in frame 4 of Figure 5-4.

Your Turn 5.5

The two mirror images are superimposable.

Your Turn 5.6

(a) and **(c)** Nonsuperimposable; **(b)** superimposable; **(d)** nonsuperimposable initially, but superimposable after rotation about the $F_2HC—CH_2CH_3$ bond.

Your Turn 5.7

Chiral.

Your Turn 5.8

(a) Molecules (a) and (b) in Solved Problem 5.2, Try It are achiral. The plane of symmetry for molecule (a) is indicated by the blue dotted line:

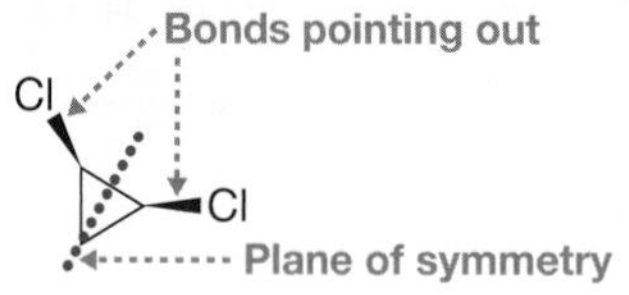

Bonds pointing out
Cl
Cl
Plane of symmetry

***cis*-1,2-Dichlorocyclopropane**

The plane of symmetry for molecule (b) is the plane of the page. **(b)** The molecule given in Solved Problem 5.2 and molecule (c) in Solved Problem 5.2, Try It are achiral, so they do not contain a plane of symmetry.

Your Turn 5.9

(a), (c), and **(e)** These molecules have no chiral centers and are achiral. **(b)** and **(d)** Each molecule has exactly one chiral center (indicated by * below) and must be chiral.

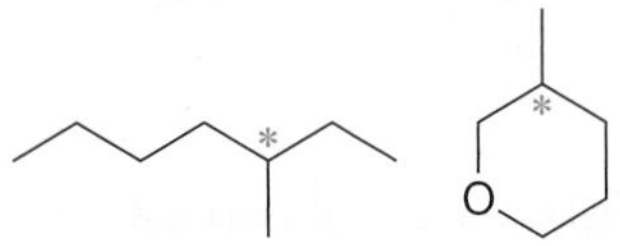

Your Turn 5.10

(a) F. **(b)** P. **(c)** ^{13}C.

Your Turn 5.11

(a) Br, Cl, F, CH_3. **(b)** I, Br, CH_3, H. **(c)** F, O, NH_2, CH_3.

Your Turn 5.12

(a) *S*. **(b)** *R*.

Your Turn 5.13

(a) and **(c)** Achiral; **(b)** chiral.

Your Turn 5.14

(a) Not meso; **(b)** meso.

Your Turn 5.15

Use molecular models to verify.

Your Turn 5.16

(a), (b), (d), and **(e)** Achiral; **(c)** chiral.

Your Turn 5.17

(a), (c), and **(d)** These molecules have no chiral centers. **(b)** This molecule has two chiral centers as shown below:

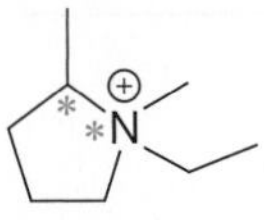

Your Turn 5.18

(a) *Z*. **(b)** *E*. **(c)** *E*. **(d)** *Z*.

Your Turn 5.19

The two molecules are diastereomers.

Your Turn 5.20

Molecule **A** has three chiral centers. Molecule **H** is the enantiomer, and all of the other molecules **B–G** are diastereomers of **A**. Molecules **B, C,** and **E** have one chiral center reversed, while **D, F,** and **G** have two and **H** has three.

Your Turn 5.21

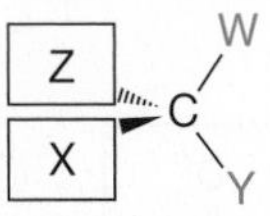

Your Turn 5.22

The stereochemical configurations differ only at C-3 (numbering begins at the top carbon for each structure in Fig. 5-36).

Your Turn 5.23

(a) D-Allose and L-glucose are diastereomers, as three of the four chiral centers are reversed: at C-2, C-4, and C-5. **(b)** The enantiomer is L-allose, shown below.

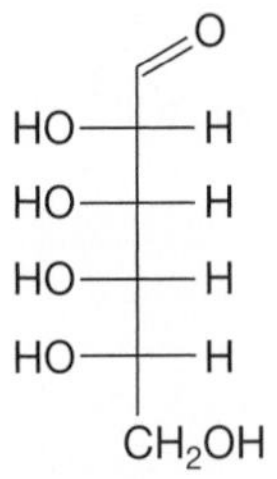

L-Allose

Your Turn 5.24

(a) *S*. **(b)** Top chiral center is *R*, bottom chiral center is *S*.

Your Turn 5.25

Construct molecular models and perform the rotations from Figure 5-39.

Your Turn 5.26

(a)

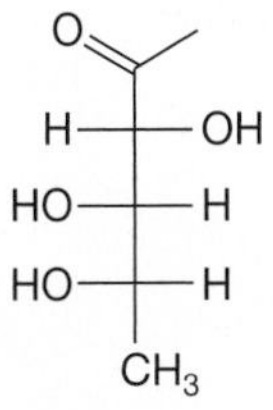

(b)

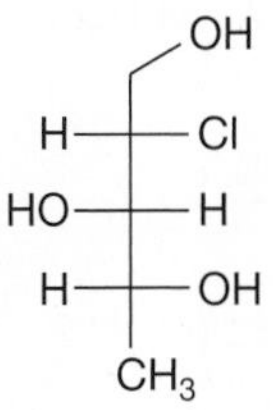

(c)

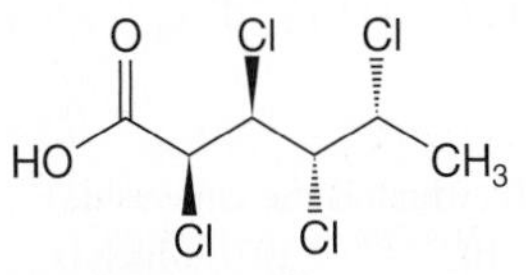

(d)

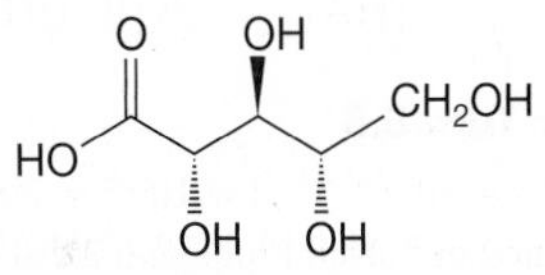

Your Turn 5.27

The solution's enantiomeric excess is 90% **A**.

Your Turn 5.28

(a) D-Mannose; **(b)** D-idose; **(c)** D-mannose; **(d)** D-ribose.

Your Turn 5.29

(a)

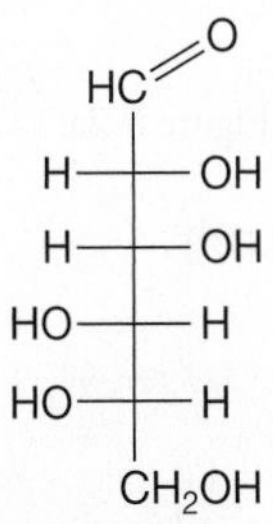

L-Mannose

(b)

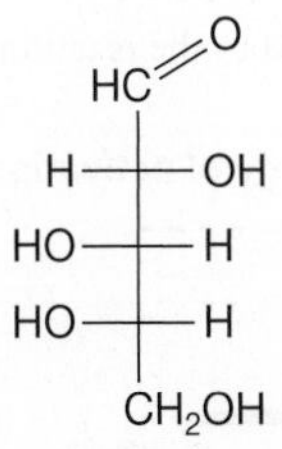

L-Arabinose

(c)

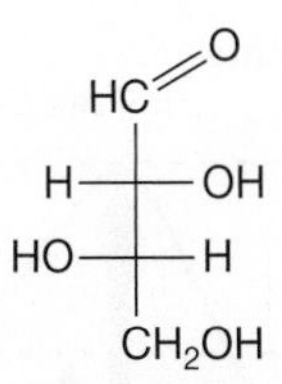

L-Threose

(d)

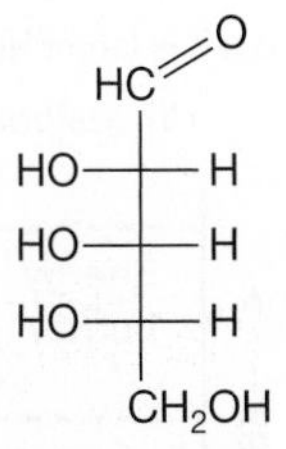

C-2 epimer of L-arabinose

Chapter 6

Your Turn 6.1

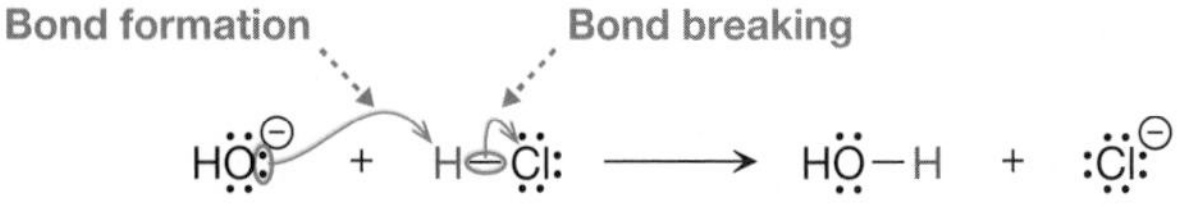
Bond formation
Bond breaking
HO: + H–Cl: ⟶ HO–H + :Cl:

Your Turn 6.2

4-Methylphenol (pK_a = 10.26) < phenol (pK_a = 10.0) < 4-chlorophenol (pK_a = 9.43).

Your Turn 6.3

(a) CH_3NH_2; **(b)** NH_3; **(c)** $CH_3CH_2O^-$.

Your Turn 6.4

HCl (pK_a = −7) has a lower pK_a than H_3O^+ (pK_a = 0), making it the stronger acid.

Your Turn 6.5

H_2O (pK_a = 14) has a lower pK_a than $(CH_3)_2NH$ (pK_a = 38) by 24 pK_a units, making H_2O the stronger acid by a factor of 10^{24}.

Your Turn 6.6

The second reaction has the larger K_{eq} and forms more products.

Your Turn 6.7

$$K_{eq} = \frac{K_a(\text{HA})}{K_a(\text{HB})} = \frac{\left(\dfrac{[\text{A}^-]_{eq}[\text{H}_3\text{O}^+]_{eq}}{[\text{HA}]_{eq}}\right)}{\left(\dfrac{[\text{B}^-]_{eq}[\text{H}_3\text{O}^+]_{eq}}{[\text{HB}]_{eq}}\right)}$$

$$= \left(\frac{[\text{A}^-]_{eq}[\text{H}_3\text{O}^+]_{eq}}{[\text{HA}]_{eq}}\right)\left(\frac{[\text{HB}]_{eq}}{[\text{B}^-]_{eq}[\text{H}_3\text{O}^+]_{eq}}\right) = \frac{[\text{A}^-]_{eq}[\text{HB}]_{eq}}{[\text{HA}]_{eq}[\text{B}^-]_{eq}}$$

Your Turn 6.8

(a) $K_{eq} = 10^{[10.63-4.75]} = 10^{5.88} = 7.6 \times 10^5$, which is the same value obtained in Solved Problem 6.2. **(b)** $K_{eq} = 10^{[19-20]} = 10^{-1}$, which is the same value obtained in the Try It exercise.

Your Turn 6.9

The reactant side is more stable and has the lower standard Gibbs free energy. $\Delta G^\circ_{rxn} > 0$.

Your Turn 6.10

The distance between Cl and H *decreases*, and the distance between HO and H *increases*.

Your Turn 6.11

$\Delta G^{\circ\ddagger}$ is larger in Figure 6-2b compared to the reaction in Figure 6-2a.

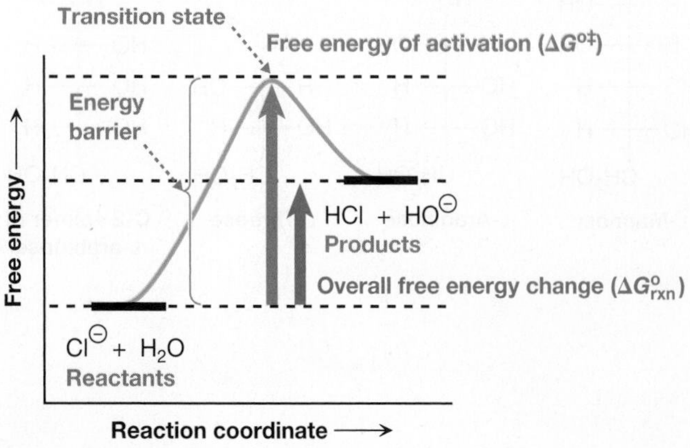
Transition state
Free energy of activation (ΔG°‡)
Energy barrier
HCl + HO⁻
Products
Overall free energy change (ΔG°rxn)
Cl⁻ + H2O
Reactants
Free energy ⟶
Reaction coordinate ⟶

Your Turn 6.12

(a) Reactant-favored because $\Delta G^\circ = +170$ kJ/mol; **(b)** product-favored because $\Delta G^\circ = -20$ kJ/mol.

Your Turn 6.13

(a) $\Delta S^\circ_{rxn} > 0$; **(b)** $\Delta S^\circ_{rxn} < 0$; **(c)** $\Delta S^\circ_{rxn} \approx 0$.

Your Turn 6.14

The reactants for the blue curve are higher energy as the charged species, NH_4^+, is less stable than the uncharged counterpart, NH_3. The products for the blue curve are lower energy as the uncharged species, NH_3, is more stable than the charged counterpart, NH_2^-.

Your Turn 6.15

H_3O^+ is a stronger acid, consistent with the much lower pK_a of H_3O^+ than of H_2O.

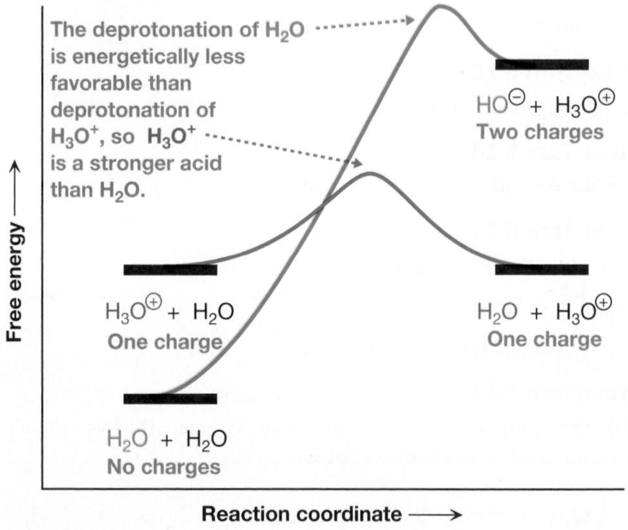
The deprotonation of H2O is energetically less favorable than deprotonation of H3O+, so H3O+ is a stronger acid than H2O.
HO⁻ + H3O⁺
Two charges
H3O⁺ + H2O
One charge
H2O + H3O⁺
One charge
H2O + H2O
No charges
Free energy ⟶
Reaction coordinate ⟶

Your Turn 6.16

H_2S is the stronger acid because S is to the right of P in the periodic table, which suggests that HS^- is more stable than H_2P^-.

Your Turn 6.17

H_3S^+ is the stronger acid because S is to the right of P in the periodic table, which suggests that H_3S^+ is less stable than H_4P^+.

Your Turn 6.18

The pK_a of $H_3C{-}CH_3$ is ~50 (highest), that of $H_2C{=}CH_2$ is ~44, and that of $HC{\equiv}CH$ is ~25 (lowest).

Your Turn 6.19

The pK_a of ethanoic acid (acetic acid) is 4.75, lower than that of ethanol (pK_a = 16).

Your Turn 6.20

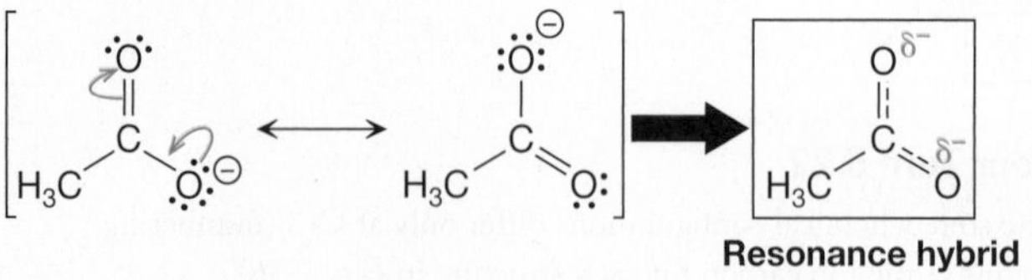
H3C
H3C
H3C
Resonance hybrid

Your Turn 6.21

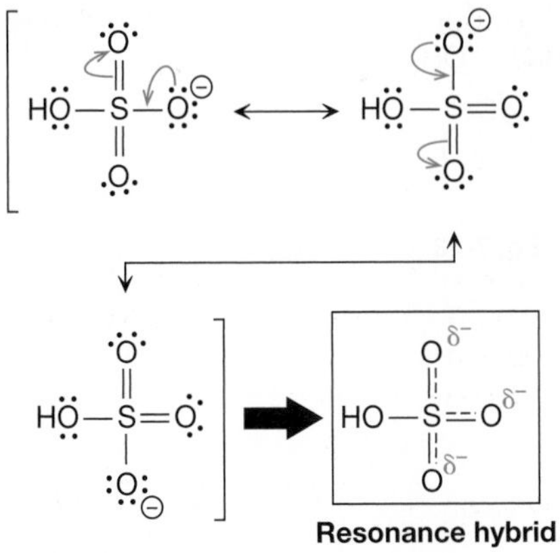

Resonance hybrid

Your Turn 6.22

The stronger acid is **B** because the electron-withdrawing Cl atom destabilizes the positive charge.

Your Turn 6.23

The N^+ in $CH_3NH_3^+$ has the smaller concentration of positive charge: $H_3C \rightarrow \overset{\oplus}{N}H_3$

Your Turn 6.24

The stronger acid is **B**, because the attached alkyl group in **A** will destabilize the negative charge that develops on S when the proton is removed.

Your Turn 6.25

Pair **A**: (a) $\Delta pK_a = 11$; (b) resonance favors deprotonation of the first molecule; (c) agrees.
Pair **B**: (a) $\Delta pK_a = 3.6$; (b) inductive effects favor deprotonation of the first molecule; (c) agrees.
Pair **C**: (a) $\Delta pK_a = 14.2$; (b) atom type favors deprotonation of HCl; (c) agrees.
Pair **D**: (a) $\Delta pK_a = 14$; (b) charge of the atom favors deprotonation of H_3O^+; (c) agrees.

Your Turn 6.26

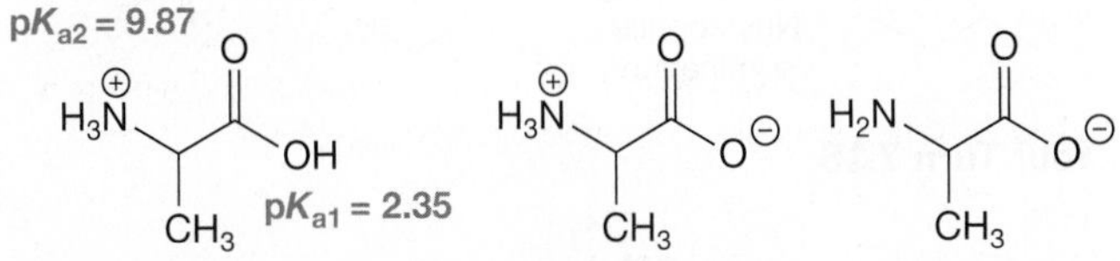
pKa2 = 9.87
pKa1 = 2.35

pH = 1 **pH = 4 and 8** **pH = 11**

Your Turn 6.27

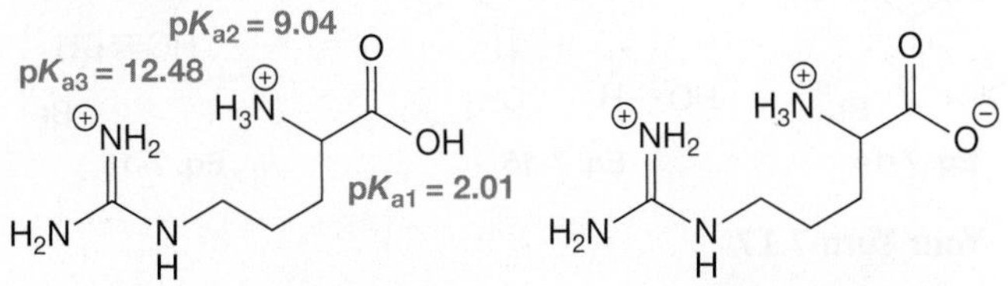
pKa2 = 9.04
pKa3 = 12.48
pKa1 = 2.01

pH = 1 **pH = 4 and 8**

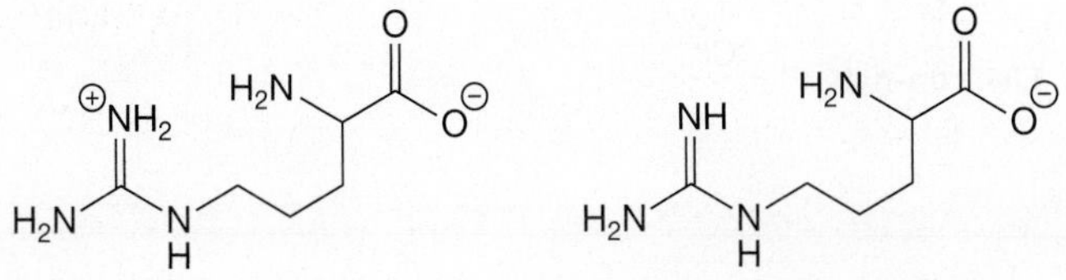

pH = 10 **pH = 14**

Chapter 7

Your Turn 7.1

(a)

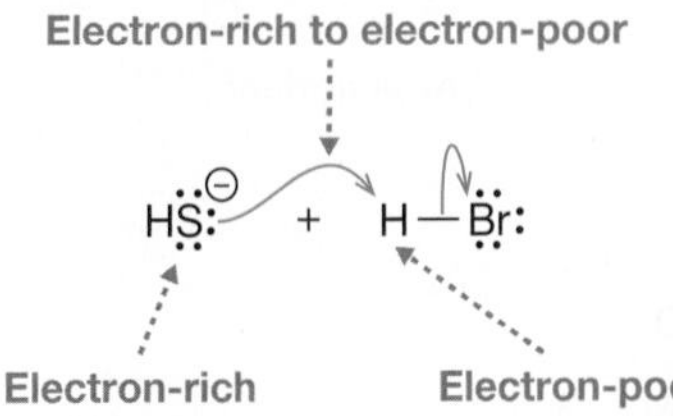
Electron-rich to electron-poor
Electron-rich
Electron-poor

(b) Without the curved arrow on the right, the H—Br bond would remain unbroken and H would have two bonds, exceeding its duet.

Your Turn 7.2

$LiAlH_4$ and $NaBH_4$ have been simplified to $:H^-$.

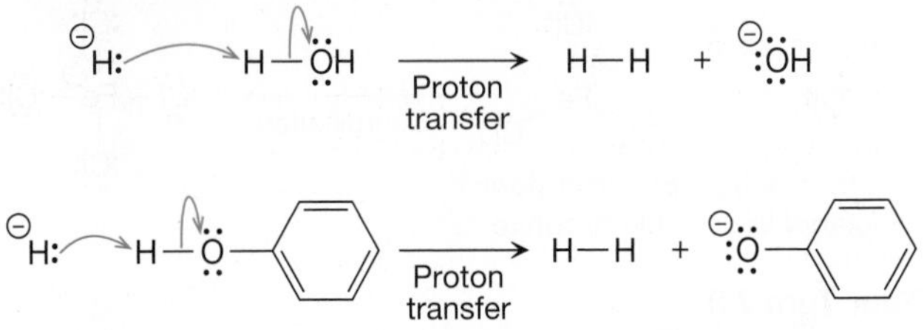
Proton transfer
Proton transfer

Your Turn 7.3

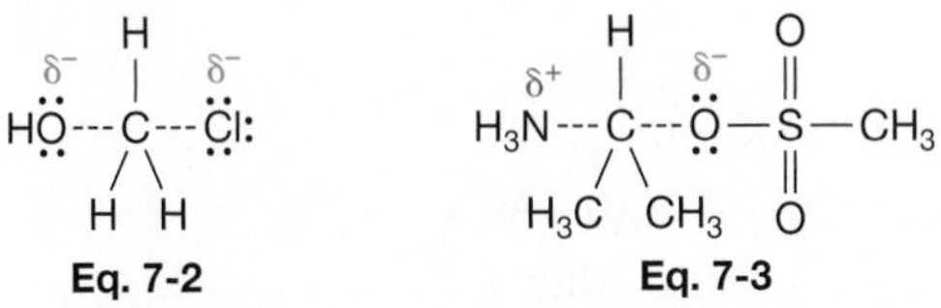
Eq. 7-2
Eq. 7-3

Your Turn 7.4

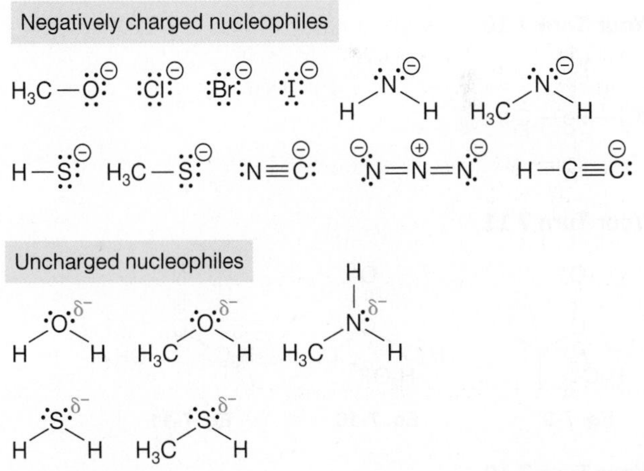
Negatively charged nucleophiles
Uncharged nucleophiles

Your Turn 7.5

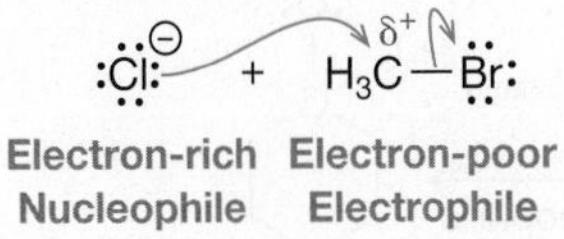
Electron-rich Nucleophile
Electron-poor Electrophile

Your Turn 7.6

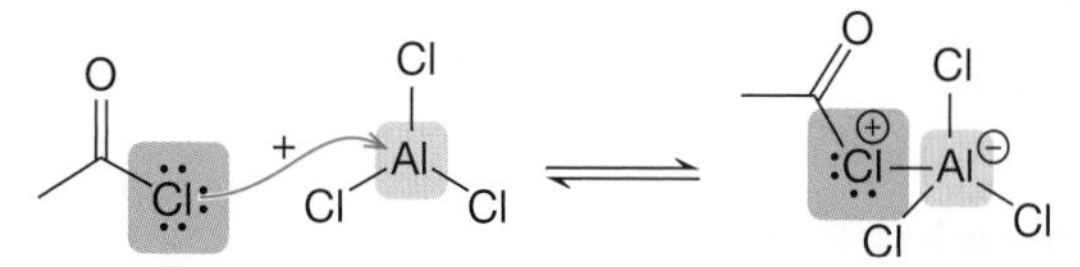

Lewis base
Nucleophile
Lewis acid
Electrophile
Lewis adduct

Your Turn 7.7

δ^- δ^+
Br --- $C(CH_3)_3$

Eq. 7-5

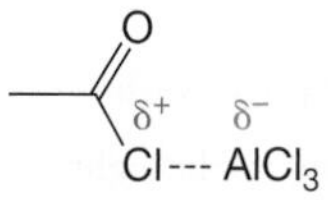

Eq. 7-6

Your Turn 7.8

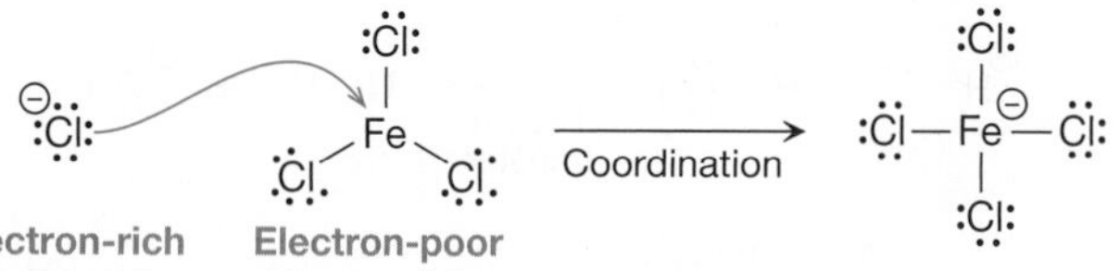

Coordination

Electron-rich
Nucleophile
Electron-poor
Electrophile

Your Turn 7.9

The positively charged carbon in the product is the only atom lacking an octet in each reaction. The transition states are shown below.

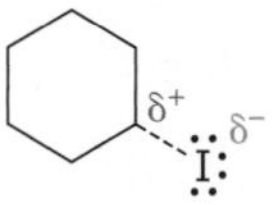

Eq. 7-7

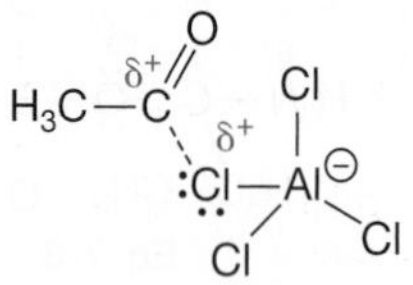

Eq. 7-8

Your Turn 7.10

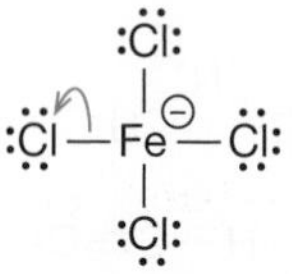

Your Turn 7.11

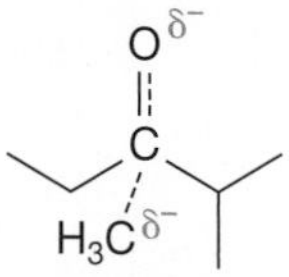

Eq. 7-9

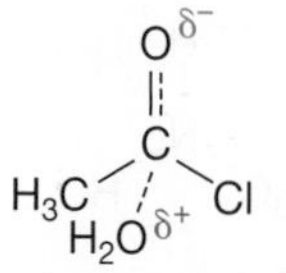

Eq. 7-10

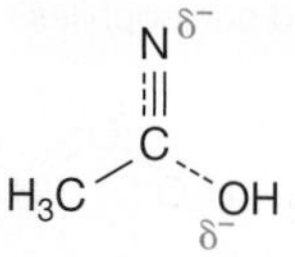

Eq. 7-11

Your Turn 7.12

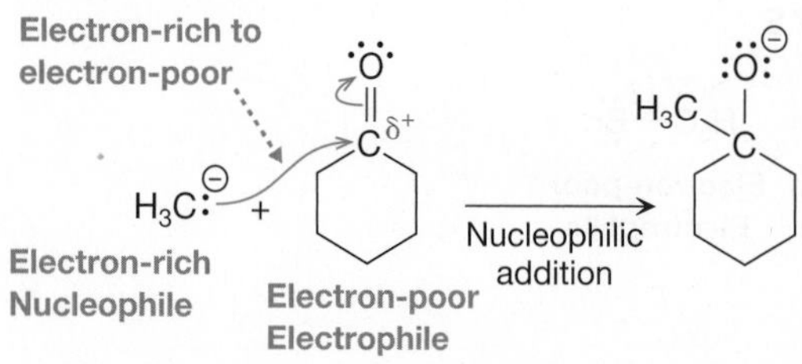

Electron-rich to electron-poor
Nucleophilic addition
Electron-rich Nucleophile
Electron-poor Electrophile

Your Turn 7.13

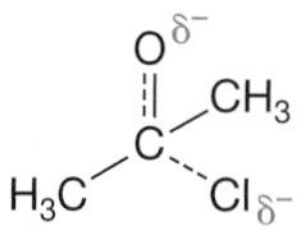

Eq. 7-12

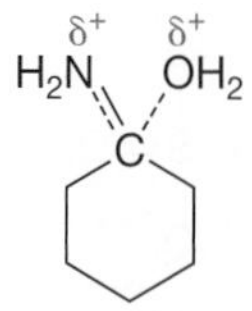

Eq. 7-13

Your Turn 7.14

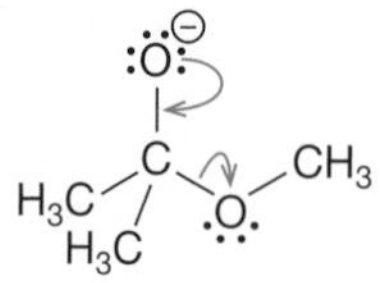

Your Turn 7.15

(a)

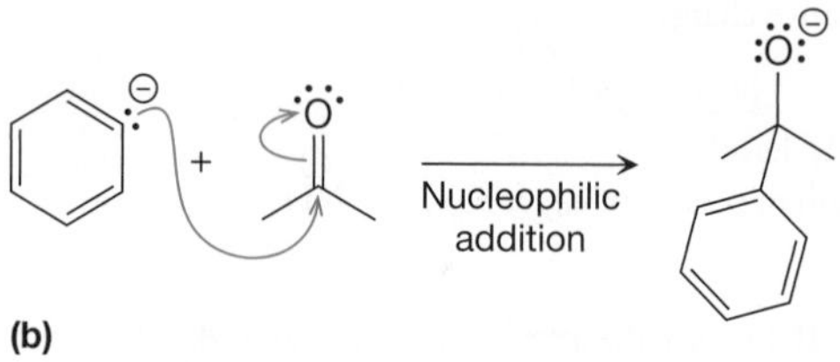

Nucleophilic addition

(b)

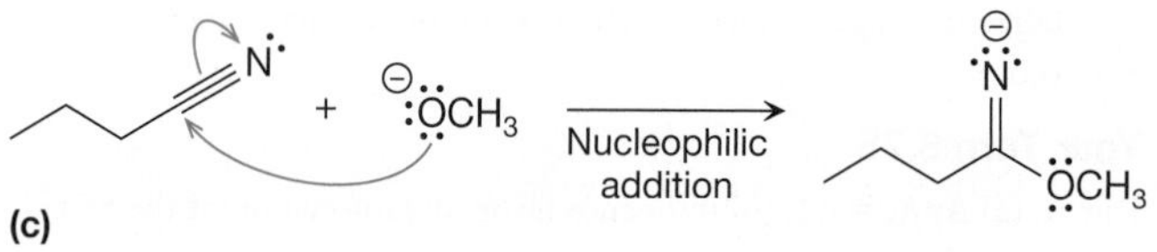

Nucleophilic addition

(c)

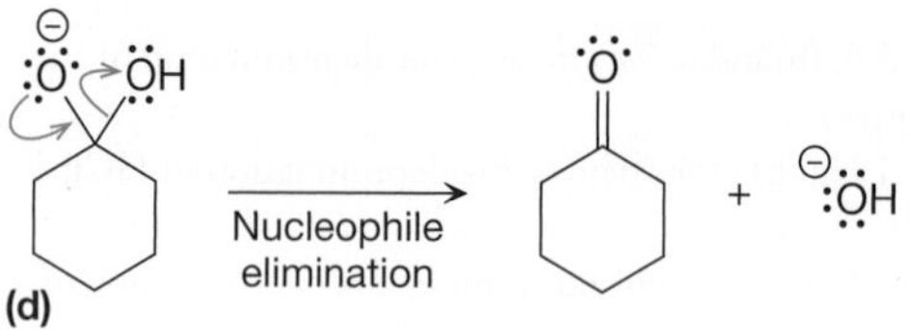

Nucleophile elimination

(d)

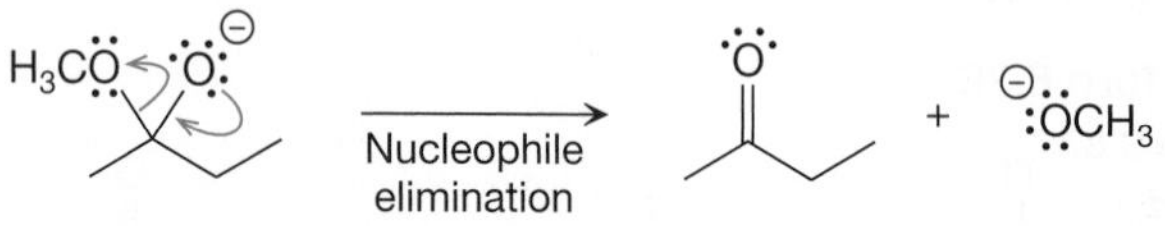

Nucleophile elimination

Your Turn 7.16

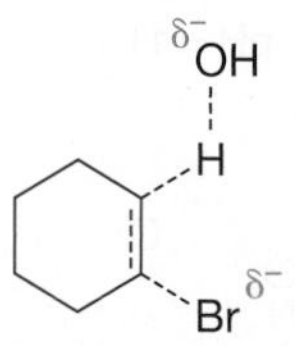

Eq. 7-14

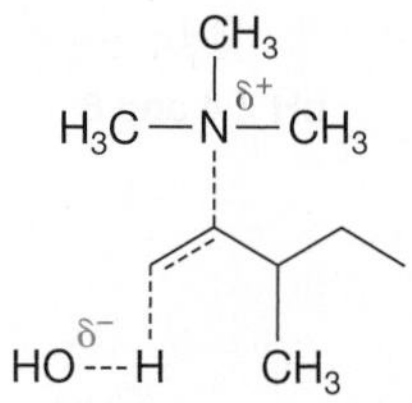

Eq. 7-15

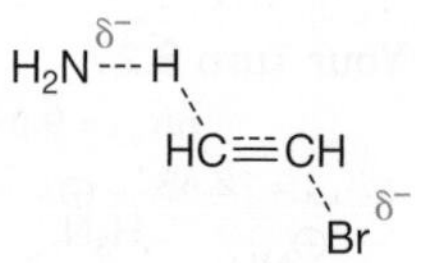

Eq. 7-16

Your Turn 7.17

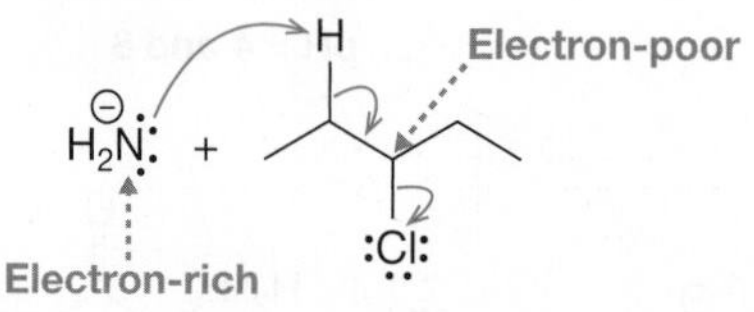

Electron-poor
Electron-rich

Your Turn 7.18

(a)

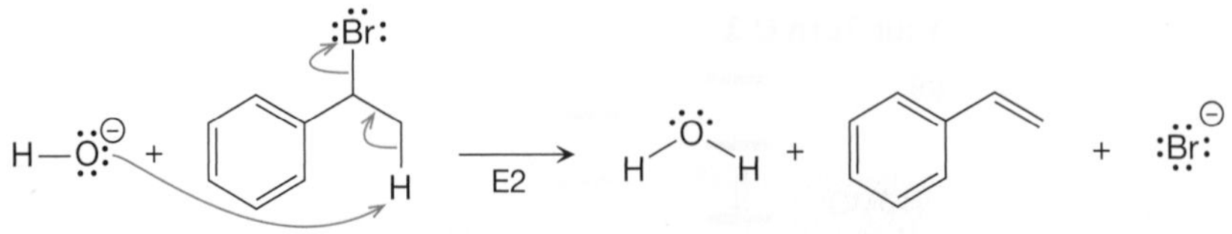
E2

(b)

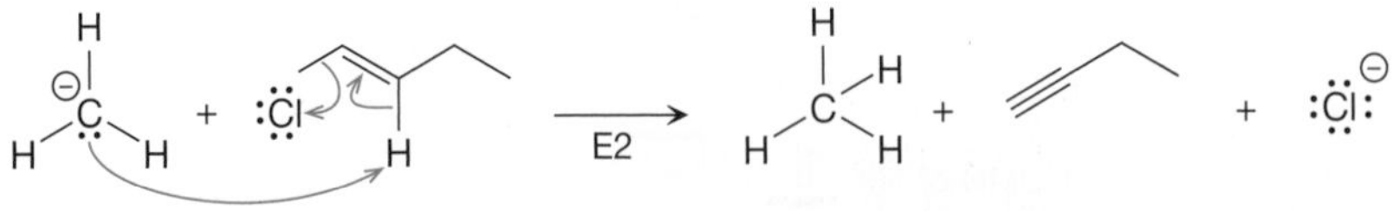
E2

Your Turn 7.19

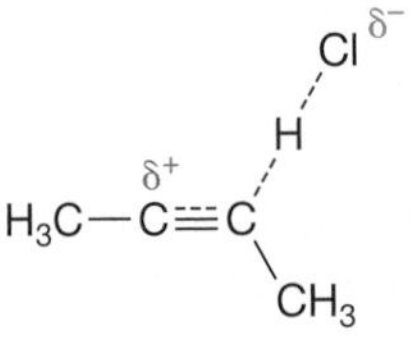

Eq. 7-18

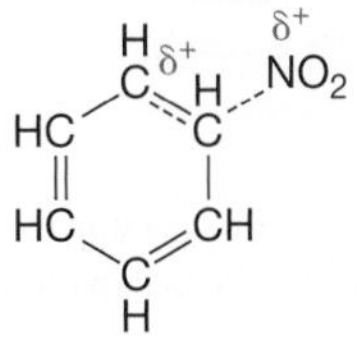

Eq. 7-19

Your Turn 7.20

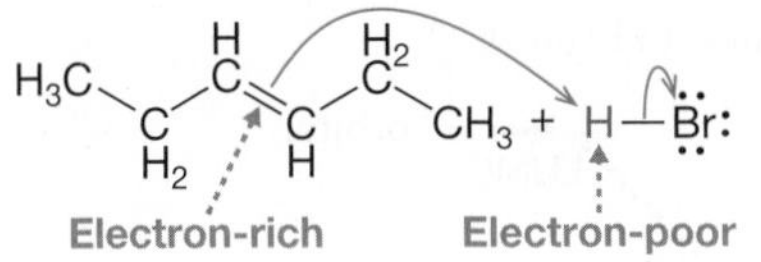
Electron-rich
Electron-poor

Your Turn 7.21

See answer to Your Turn 7.20.

Your Turn 7.22

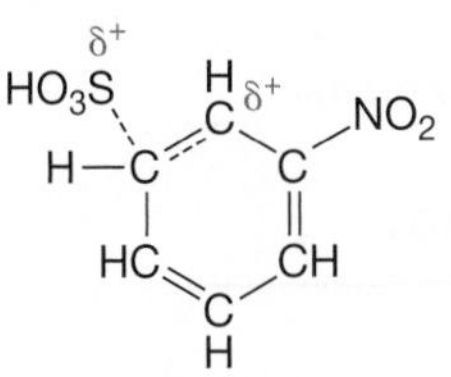

Eq. 7-22

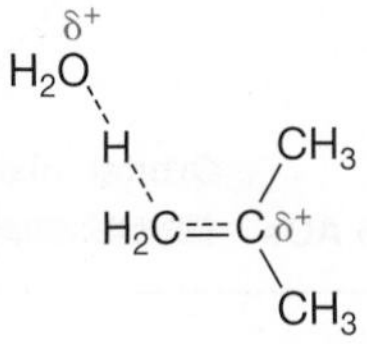

Eq. 7-23

Your Turn 7.23

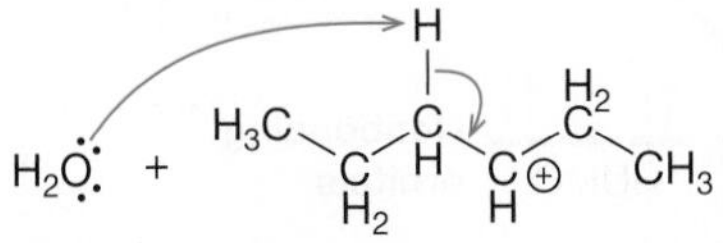

Your Turn 7.24

(a)

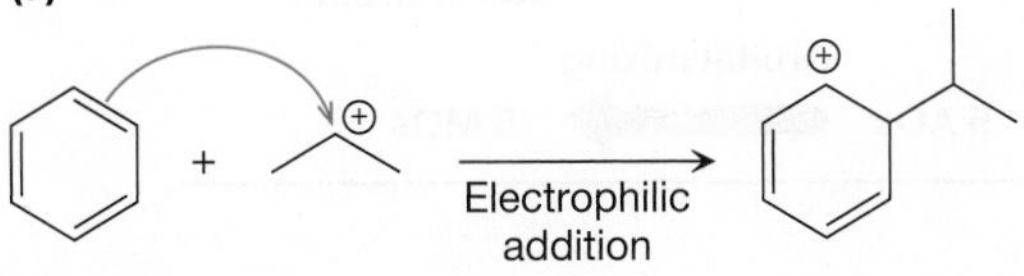
Electrophilic addition

(b)

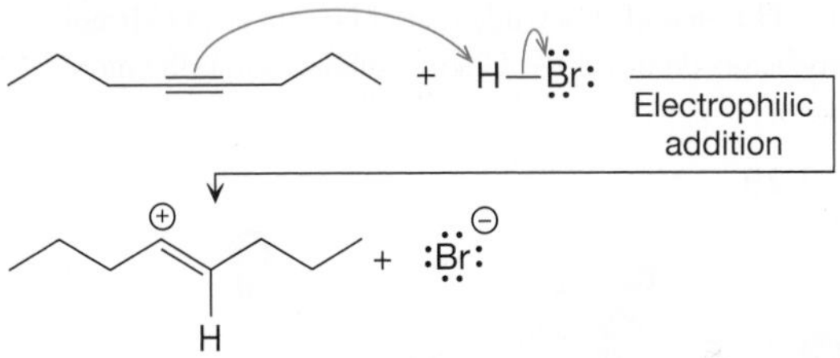
Electrophilic addition

(c)

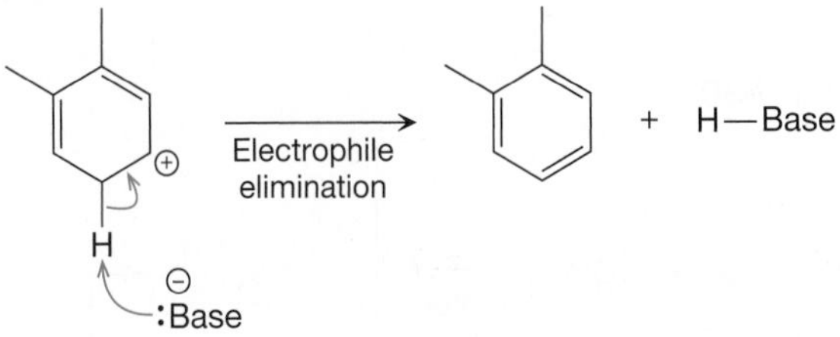
Electrophile elimination

(d)

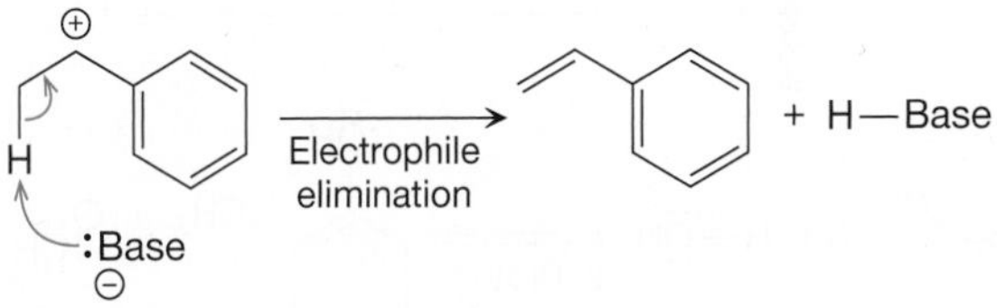
Electrophile elimination

Your Turn 7.25

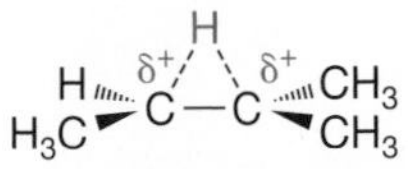

Eq. 7-24

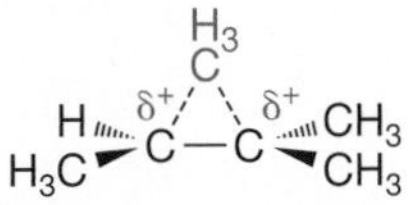

Eq. 7-25

Your Turn 7.26

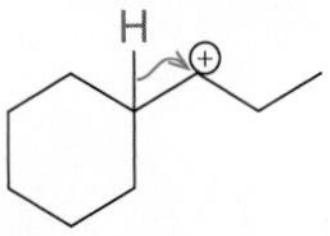

Your Turn 7.27

(a)

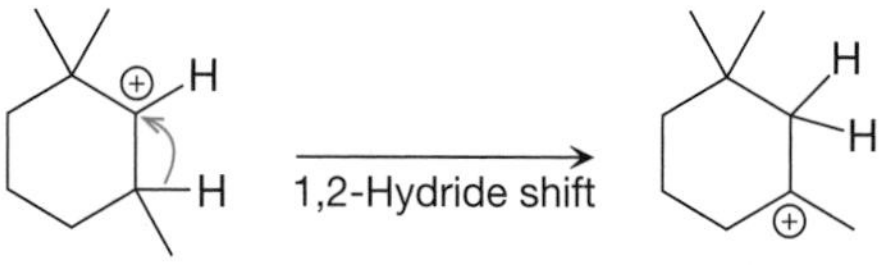
H
H
1,2-Hydride shift
H
H

(b)

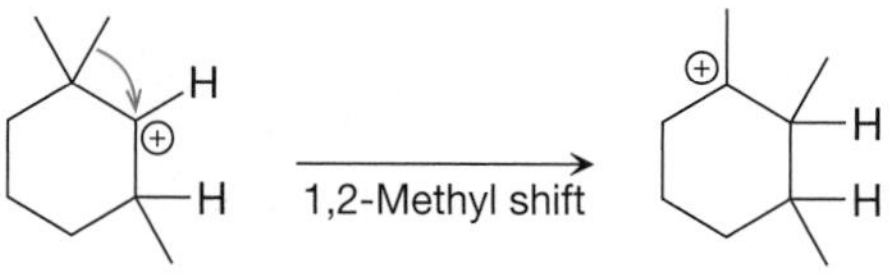
H
H
1,2-Methyl shift
H
H

Your Turn 7.28

(a) The product side, because O is more electronegative than N and can better handle a negative charge. **(b)** The reactant side, because the bond energy of O—H is 460 kJ/mol while that of N—H is 389 kJ/mol. **(c)** These two factors do not agree. Charge stabilization is the more important factor.

Your Turn 7.29

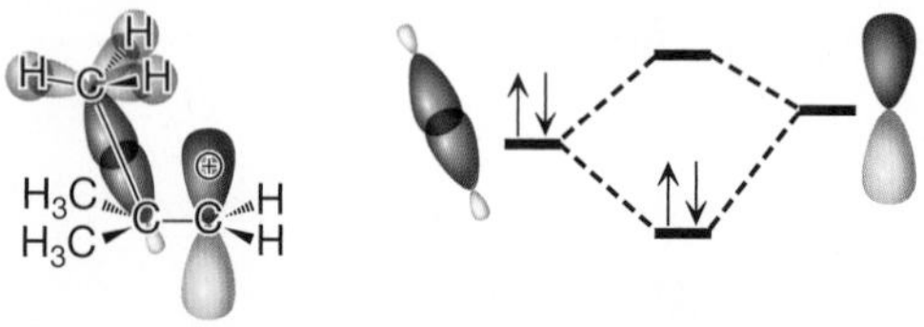
H
H—C—H
H_3C
H_3C
H
H

Your Turn 7.30

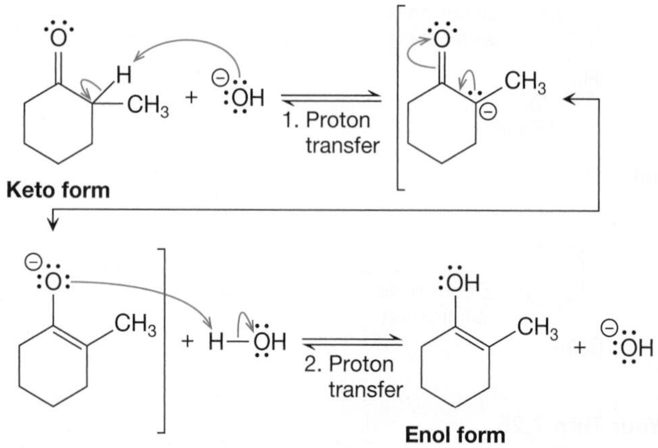
H
CH_3
+
:ÖH
1. Proton transfer
CH_3
Keto form
CH_3
+ H—ÖH
2. Proton transfer
:ÖH
CH_3
+
:ÖH
Enol form

Your Turn 7.31

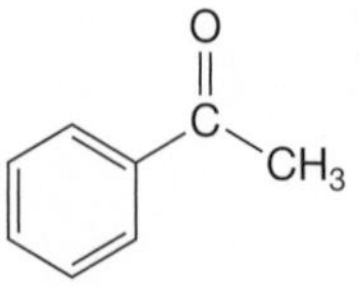
O
C
CH_3

Keto form

Interchapter C

Your Turn C.1

(a)

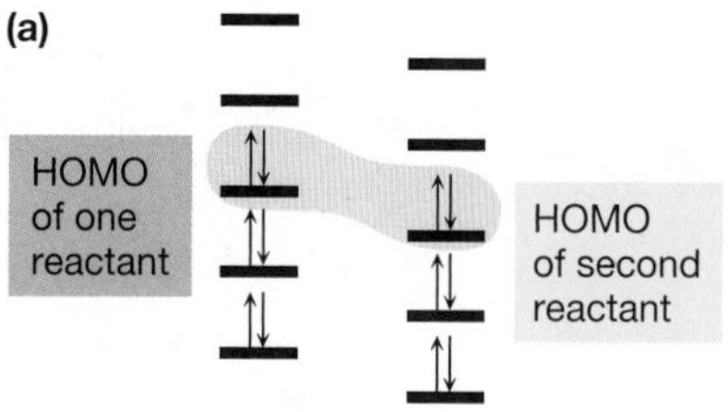
HOMO of one reactant
HOMO of second reactant

(b)

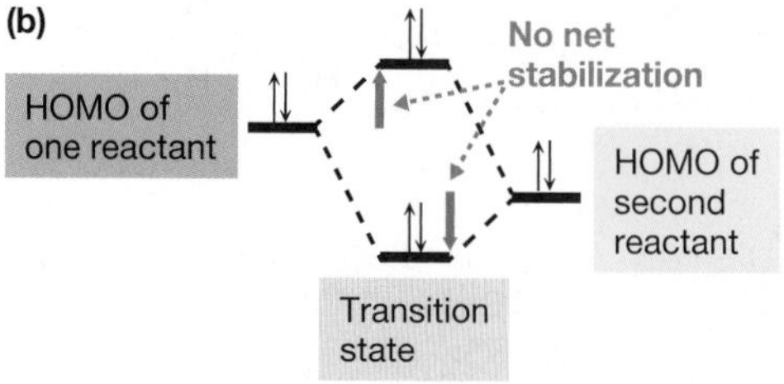
No net stabilization
HOMO of one reactant
HOMO of second reactant
Transition state

(c) The stabilization gained by occupying the lower-energy transition state orbital is canceled by the occupation of the higher-energy transition state orbital.

Your Turn C.2

The HOMO from HO^- is a nonbonding orbital, and the LUMO from HCl is a σ* MO, in agreement with Figure C-3.

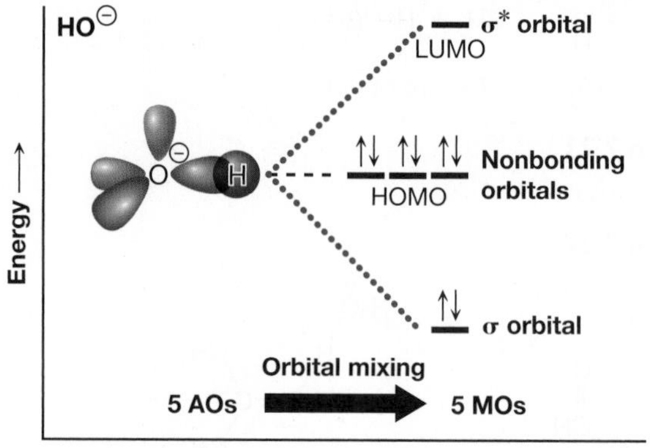
$HO^{\ominus}$
σ* orbital
LUMO
Nonbonding orbitals
HOMO
σ orbital
Energy
Orbital mixing
5 AOs
5 MOs

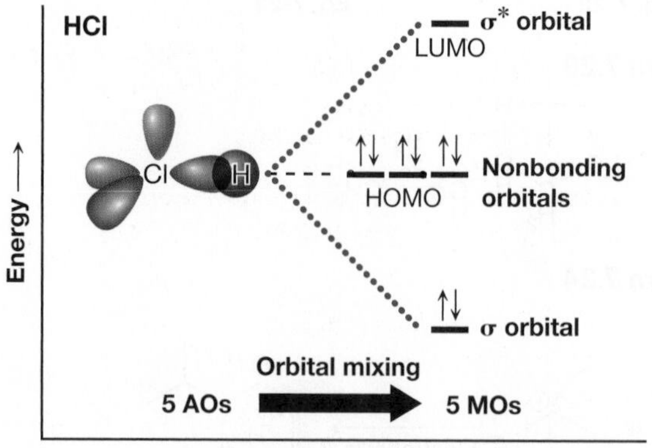
HCl
σ* orbital
LUMO
Nonbonding orbitals
HOMO
σ orbital
Energy
Orbital mixing
5 AOs
5 MOs

Your Turn C.3

(a)

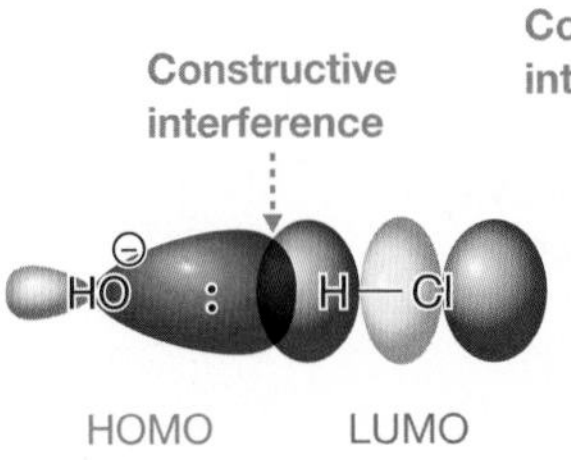

Constructive interference
HO
H—Cl
HOMO
LUMO

(b)

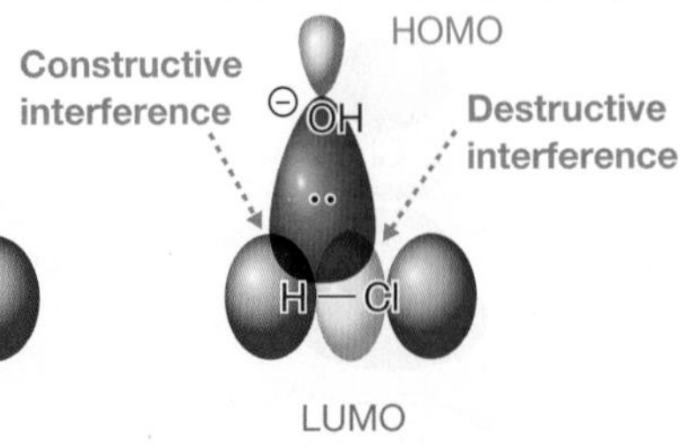

HOMO
Constructive interference
OH
Destructive interference
H—Cl
LUMO

Your Turn C.4

The LUMO is a σ* MO, in agreement with Figure C-4.

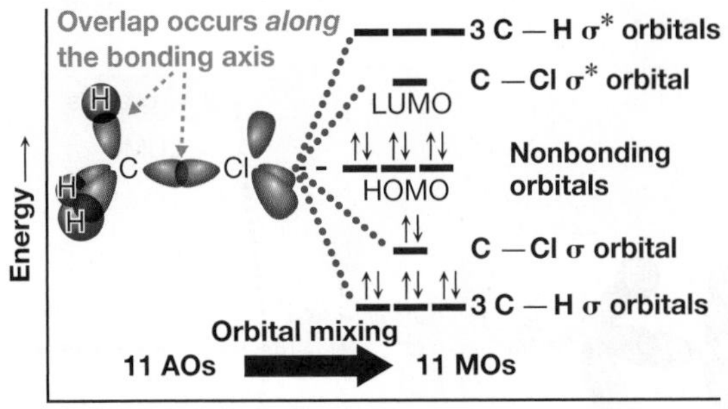

Overlap occurs *along* the bonding axis
3 C — H σ* orbitals
C — Cl σ* orbital
LUMO
Nonbonding orbitals
HOMO
C — Cl σ orbital
3 C — H σ orbitals
Energy ⟶
Orbital mixing
11 AOs
11 MOs

Your Turn C.5

(a)

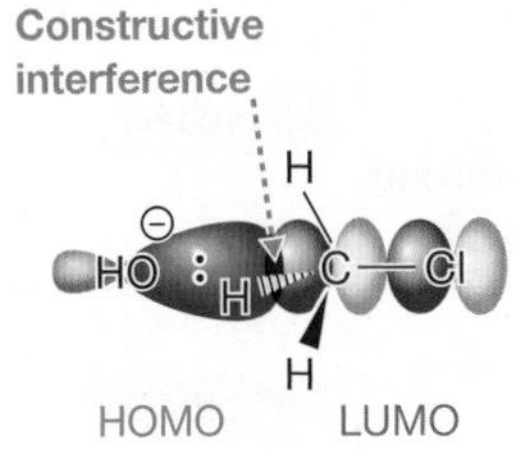

Constructive interference
HO
H
C—Cl
HOMO
LUMO

(b)

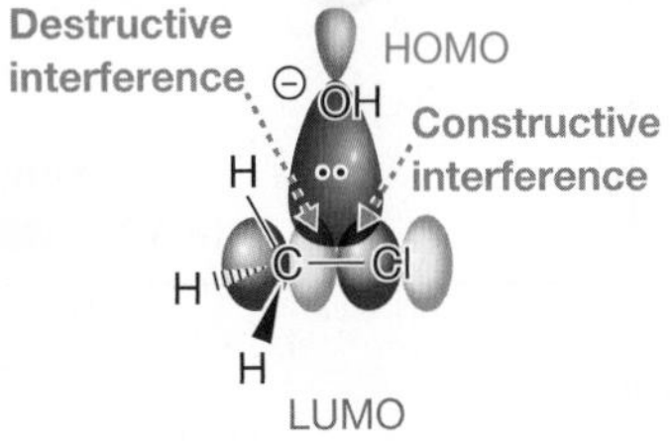

Destructive interference
HOMO
OH
Constructive interference
C—Cl
LUMO

Your Turn C.6

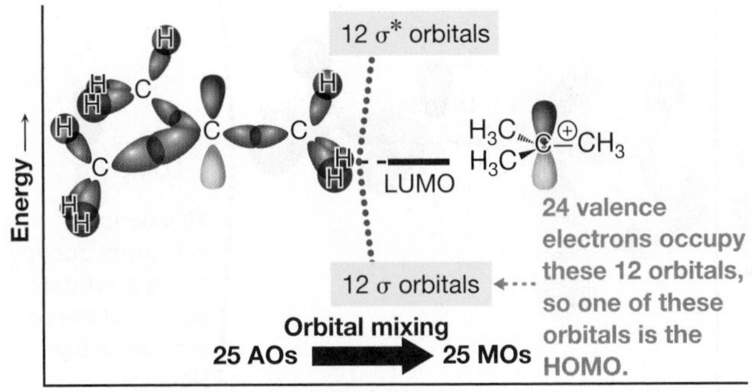

12 σ* orbitals
LUMO
H_3C
CH_3
24 valence electrons occupy these 12 orbitals, so one of these orbitals is the HOMO.
12 σ orbitals
Energy ⟶
Orbital mixing
25 AOs
25 MOs

The LUMO of $(CH_3)_3C^+$ is the empty unhybridized *p* orbital on the central carbon, in agreement with Figure C-5.

Your Turn C.7

(a)

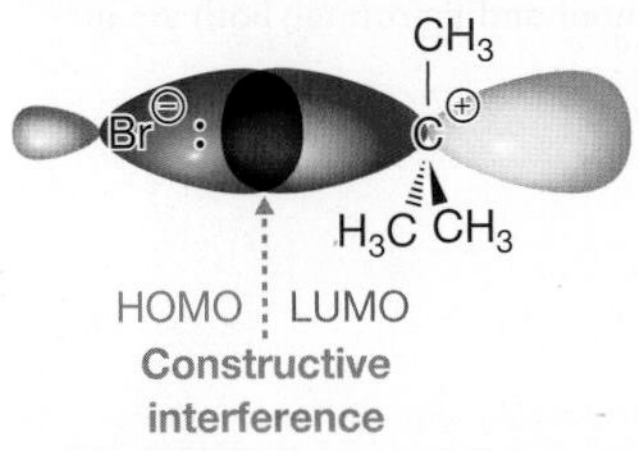

CH_3
Br
C
H_3C CH_3
HOMO LUMO
Constructive interference

(b)

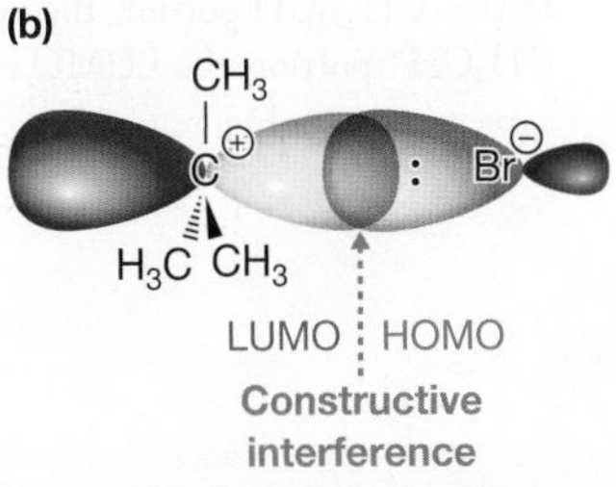

CH_3
C
Br
H_3C CH_3
LUMO HOMO
Constructive interference

Your Turn C.8

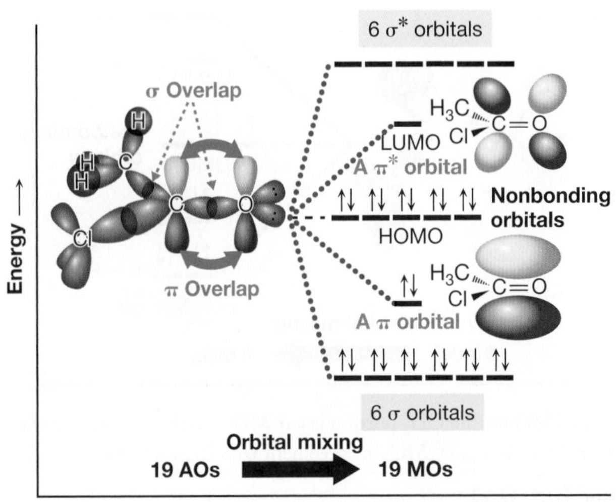

6 σ* orbitals
σ Overlap
LUMO
A π* orbital
Nonbonding orbitals
HOMO
π Overlap
A π orbital
6 σ orbitals
Energy ⟶
Orbital mixing
19 AOs
19 MOs

The LUMO is the π* MO, in agreement with Figure C-6a.

Your Turn C.9

(a)

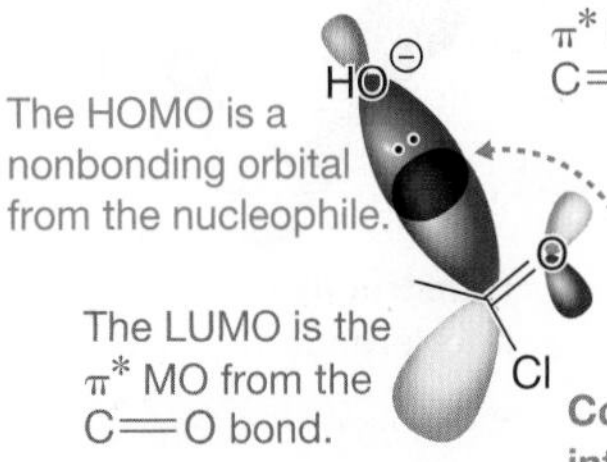

HO
The HOMO is a nonbonding orbital from the nucleophile.
The LUMO is the π* MO from the C=O bond.
Cl

(b)

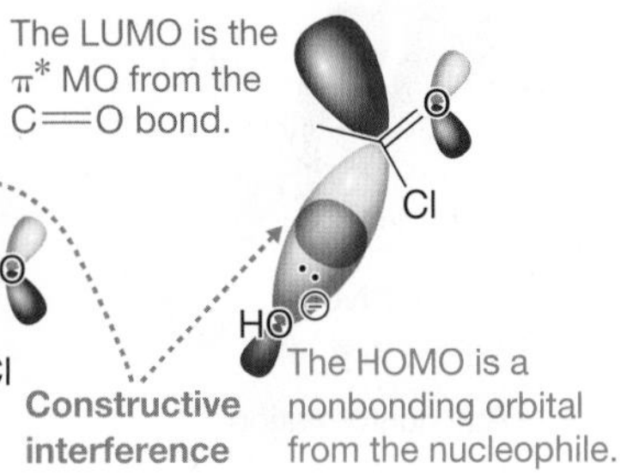

The LUMO is the π* MO from the C=O bond.
Cl
HO
Constructive interference
The HOMO is a nonbonding orbital from the nucleophile.

Your Turn C.10

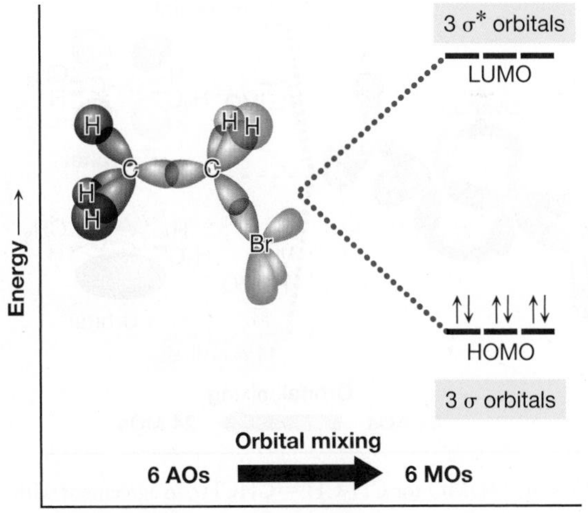

3 σ* orbitals
LUMO
Br
HOMO
3 σ orbitals
Energy ⟶
Orbital mixing
6 AOs
6 MOs

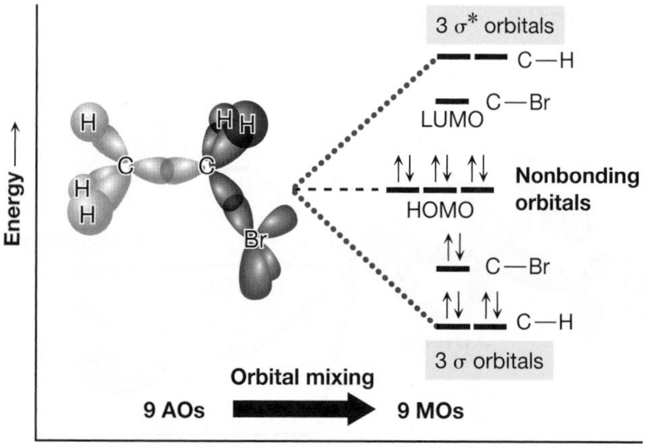
Energy ⟶
3 σ* orbitals
C—H
C—Br
LUMO
Nonbonding orbitals
HOMO
C—Br
C—H
3 σ orbitals
Orbital mixing
9 AOs
9 MOs

The HOMO for the CH_3 portion is a σ MO, and the LUMO for the CH_2Br portion is a σ* MO, in agreement with Figure C-8a.

Your Turn C.11

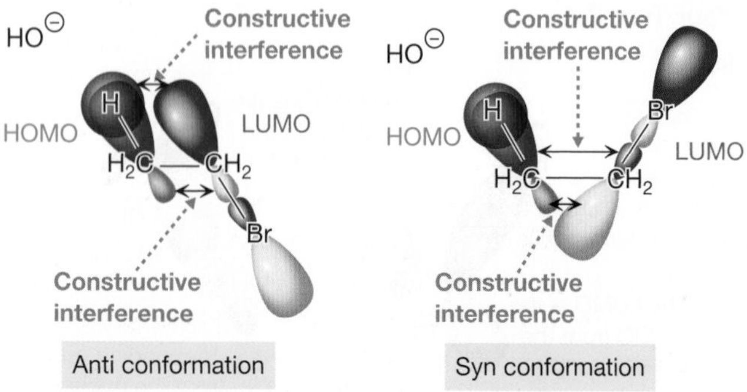
(a)
(b)
HO⊖
Constructive interference
HOMO
LUMO
Constructive interference
Anti conformation
HO⊖
Constructive interference
HOMO
LUMO
Constructive interference
Syn conformation

Your Turn C.12

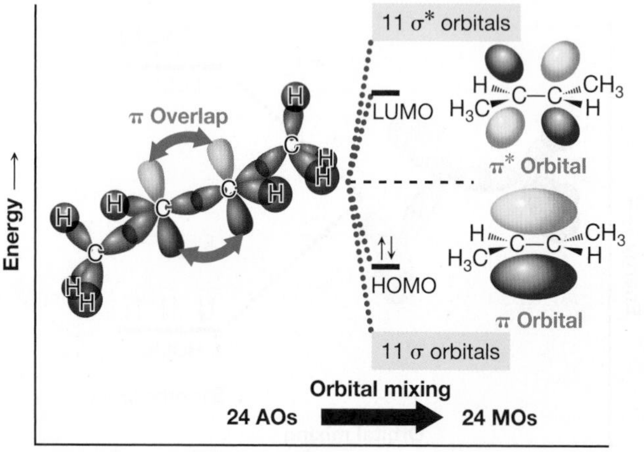
Energy ⟶
π Overlap
11 σ* orbitals
LUMO
π* Orbital
HOMO
π Orbital
11 σ orbitals
Orbital mixing
24 AOs
24 MOs

The π MO is the HOMO for $CH_3CH{=}CHCH_3$, in agreement with Figure C-9.

Your Turn C.13

The LUMO of HCl is a σ* MO.

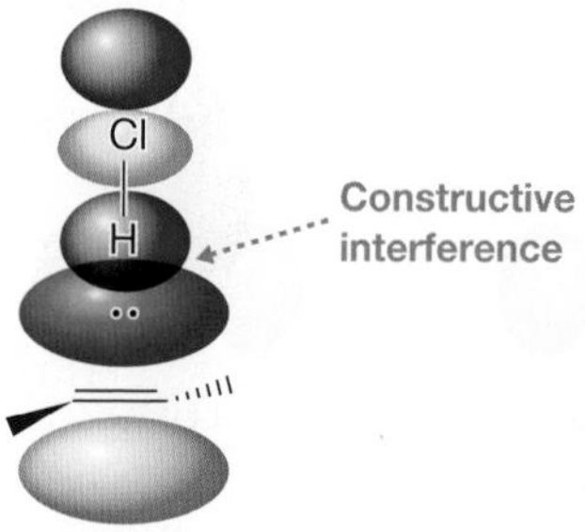
Cl
H
Constructive interference

The HOMO of an alkene is a π MO.

Your Turn C.14

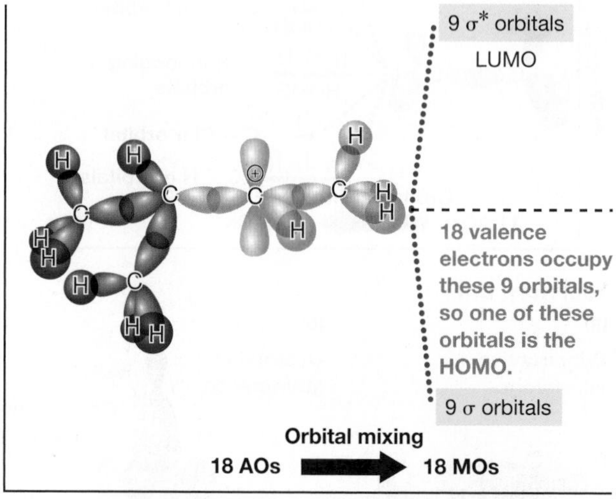
Energy ⟶
9 σ* orbitals
LUMO
18 valence electrons occupy these 9 orbitals, so one of these orbitals is the HOMO.
9 σ orbitals
Orbital mixing
18 AOs
18 MOs

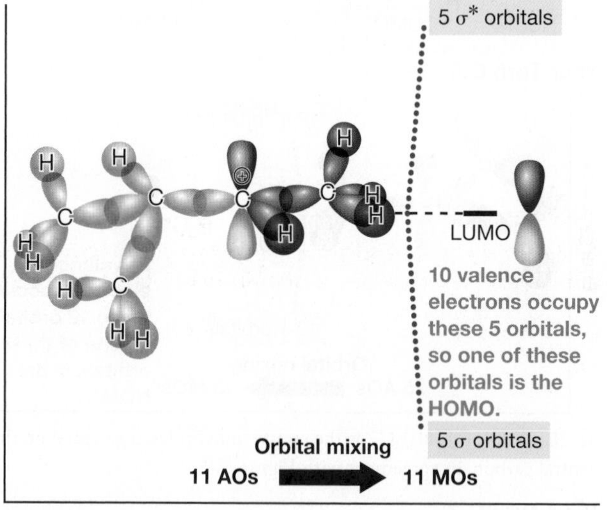
Energy ⟶
5 σ* orbitals
LUMO
10 valence electrons occupy these 5 orbitals, so one of these orbitals is the HOMO.
5 σ orbitals
Orbital mixing
11 AOs
11 MOs

In the $(CH_3)_2CH$ portion, the HOMO is a σ MO, and in the CH_3CH^+ portion, the LUMO is a nonbonding orbital; both are in agreement with Figure C-10.

Your Turn C.15

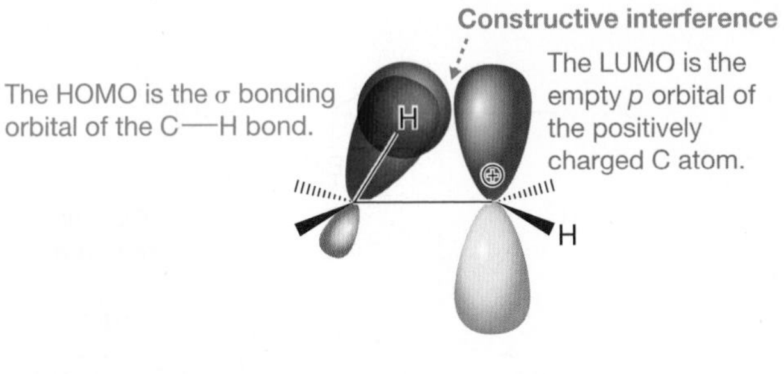
Constructive interference
The HOMO is the σ bonding orbital of the C—H bond.
The LUMO is the empty p orbital of the positively charged C atom.
H
H

Interchapter D

Your Turn D.1

(a) Butan-2-ol; **(b)** butan-1-ol; **(c)** cyclopropanol.

Your Turn D.2

(a)

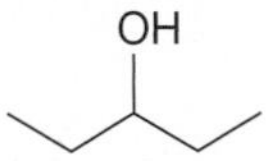
OH

(b)

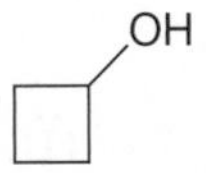
OH

(c)

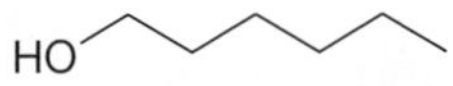
HO

Your Turn D.3

(a) 4,4-Dichlorobutan-2-amine; **(b)** 2-methoxyethanamine; **(c)** 3,4-diethylcyclohexanamine.

Your Turn D.4

(a)

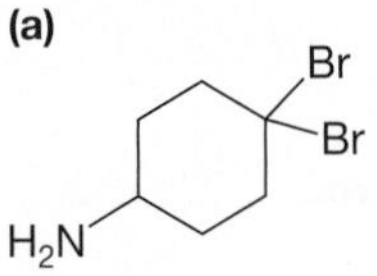
Br
Br
H2N

(b)

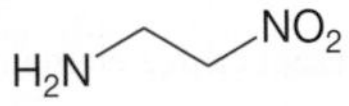
H2N
NO2

(c)

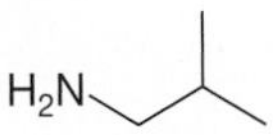
H2N

(d)

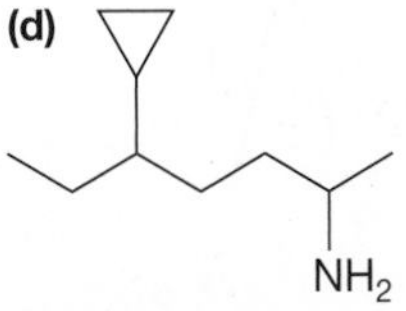
NH2

Your Turn D.5

(a) 2-Methoxycyclopent-2-en-1-amine; **(b)** 6,6-dichlorocyclohexa-2,4-dien-1-ol; **(c)** 3-ethylpent-3-en-1-ol; **(d)** 3-methylhex-4-yn-2-amine.

Your Turn D.6

(a)

H2N

(b)

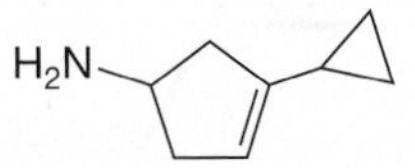
H2N

(c)

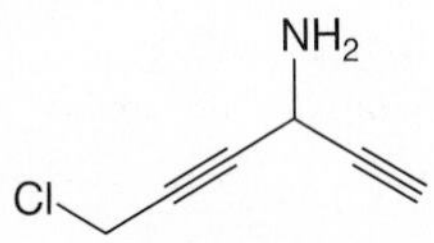
NH2
Cl

(d)

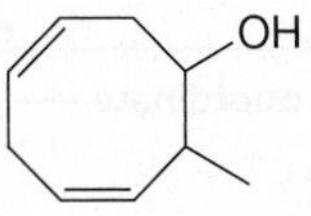
OH

Your Turn D.7

(a) 1-Amino-4-chlorobutan-2-ol; **(b)** 2-amino-5-ethyl-3-methylcyclopent-3-en-1-ol; **(c)** 2-aminohex-5-yn-1-ol.

Your Turn D.8

(a)

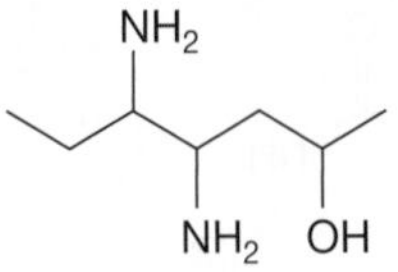
NH2
NH2
OH

(b)

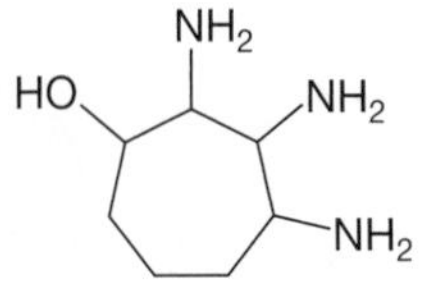
NH2
HO
NH2
NH2

Your Turn D.9

(a)

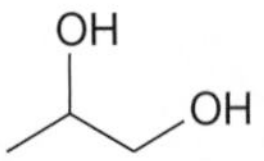
OH
OH

(b)

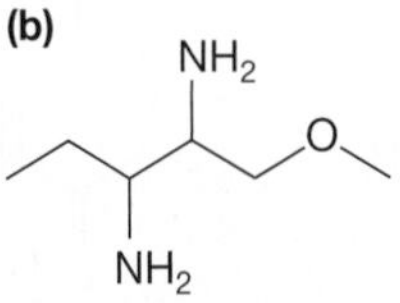
NH2
O
NH2

(c)

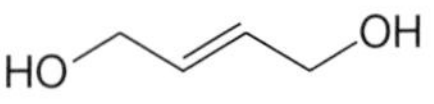
HO
OH

Your Turn D.10

(a) *N,N*-Dimethylcyclohex-2-en-1-amine; **(b)** *N,N*-dipropylpropan-1-amine; **(c)** 3-chloro-*N*,2-diethylpent-4-yn-1-amine.

Your Turn D.11

(a)

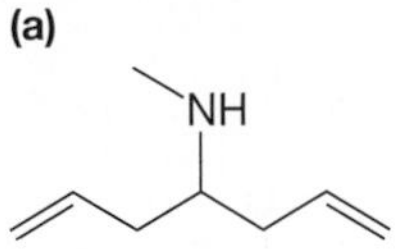
NH

(b)

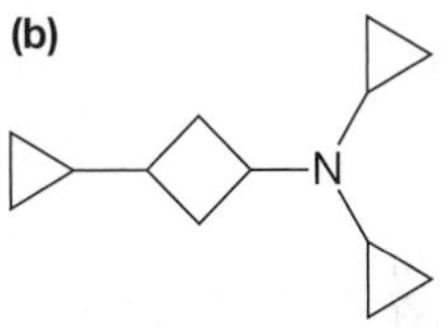
N

Your Turn D.12

(a) 4-Oxoheptanal; **(b)** 2-hydroxycyclohexanecarbaldehyde; **(c)** 1-amino-3-propylpentane-2,4-dione; **(d)** 3-methoxycyclohex-3-en-1-one.

Your Turn D.13

(a)

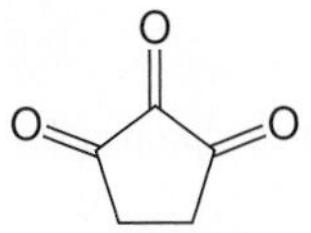
O
O
O

(b)

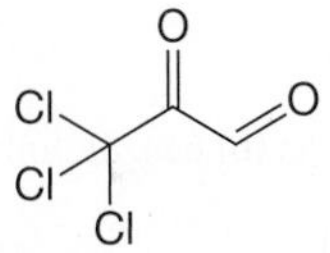
O
Cl
O
Cl
Cl

(c)

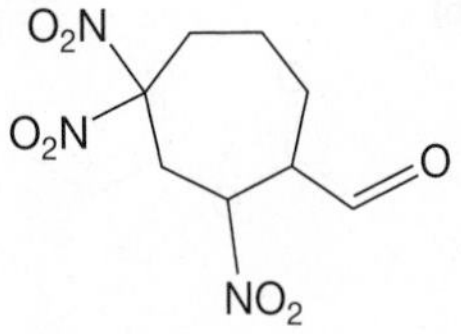
O2N
O2N
O
NO2

(d)

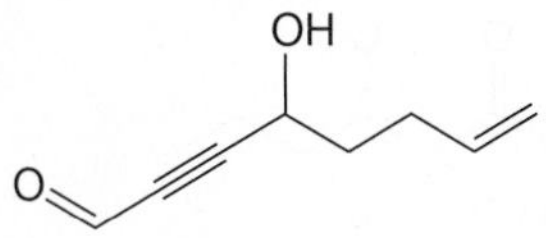
OH
O

Your Turn D.14

(a)

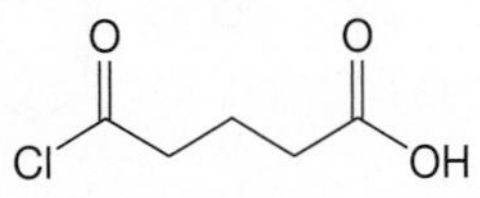
O
O
Cl
OH

(b)

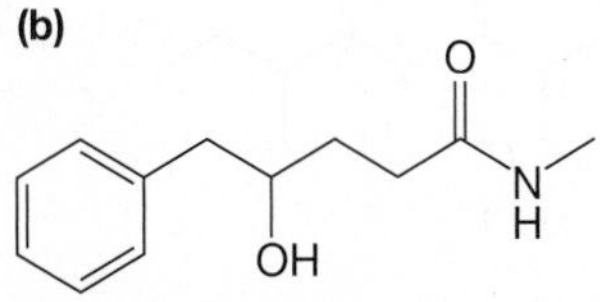
O
N
H
OH

(c)

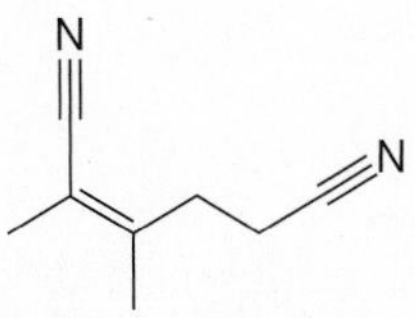
N
N

(d)

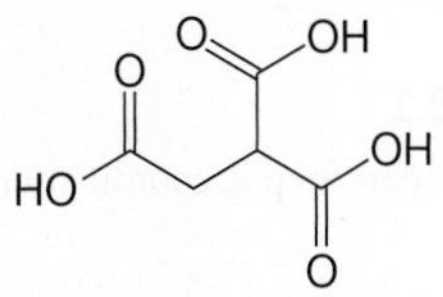
O
OH
O
OH
HO
O

Your Turn D.15

(a)

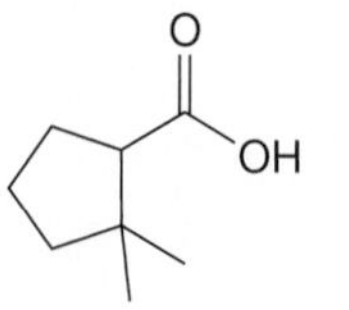
O
OH

(b)

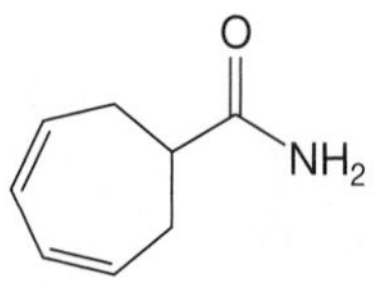
O
NH2

(c)

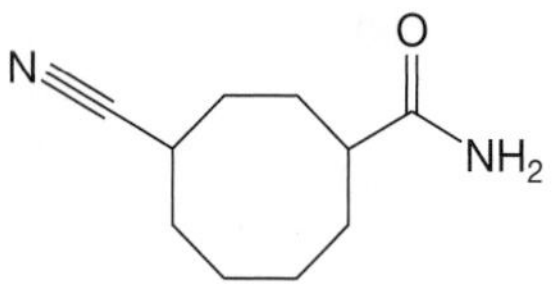
N
O
NH2

(d)

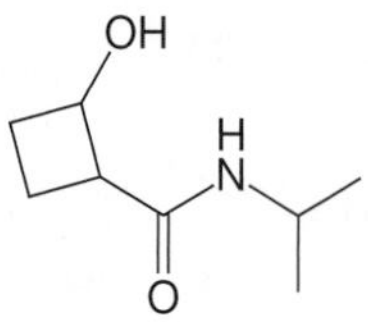
OH
H
N
O

(e)

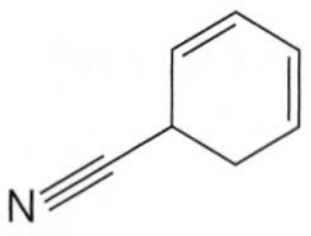
N

Your Turn D.16

(a)

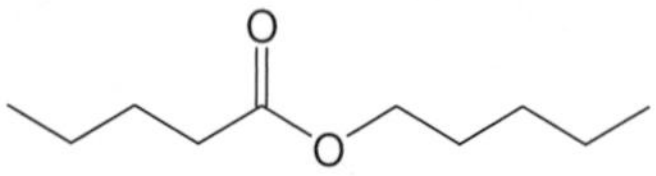
O
O

(b)

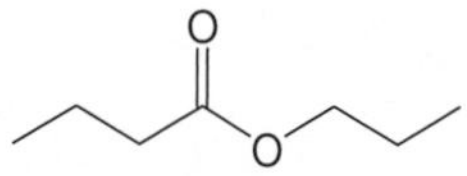
O
O

(c)

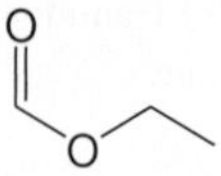
O
O

(d)

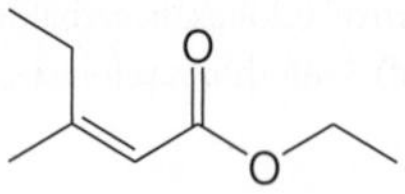
O
O

(e)

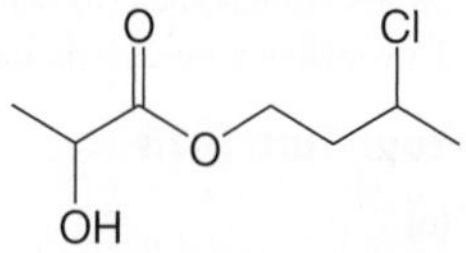
O
Cl
O
OH

Your Turn D.17

(a) Ethanoic anhydride; **(b)** benzoic anhydride; **(c)** 2-methylpropanoic propanoic anhydride.

Your Turn D.18

(a)

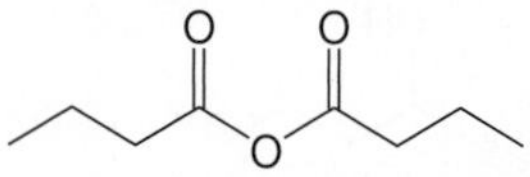
O
O
O

(b)

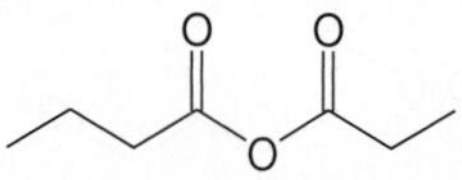
O
O
O

(c)

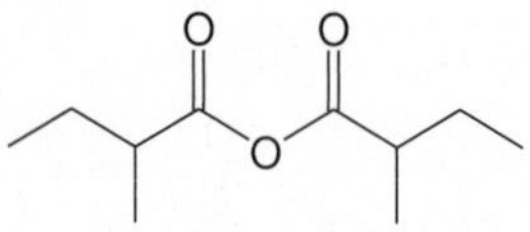
O
O
O

(d)

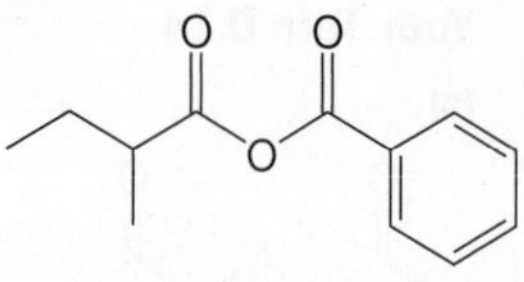
O
O
O

Chapter 8

Your Turn 8.1

Step 1, heterolysis; Step 2, coordination.

Your Turn 8.2

(a) S_N2

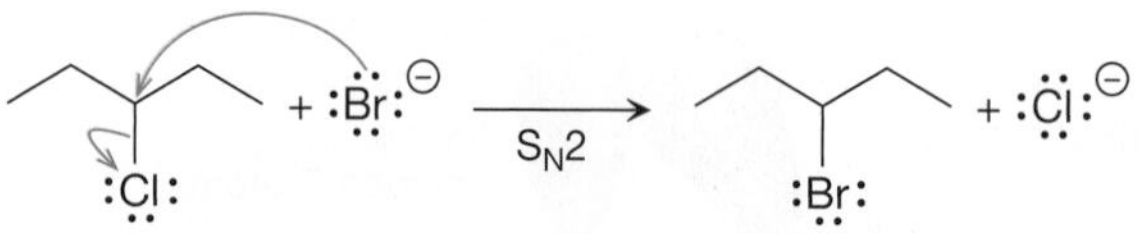
+ :Br:
:Cl:
SN2
:Br:
+ :Cl:

(b) S_N1

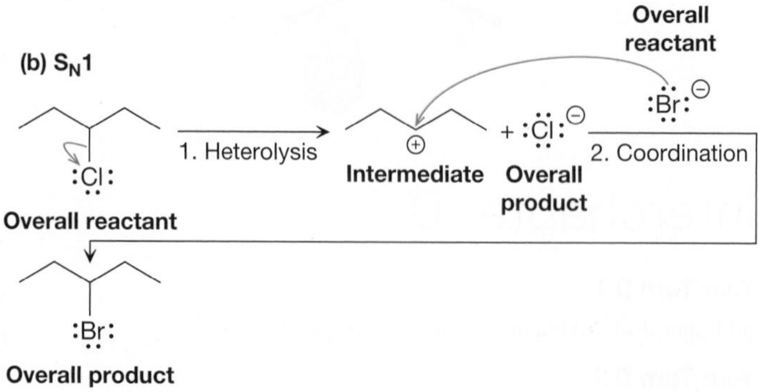
Overall reactant
:Br:
:Cl:
1. Heterolysis
Intermediate
+ :Cl:
Overall product
2. Coordination
Overall reactant
:Br:
Overall product

Your Turn 8.3

(a)

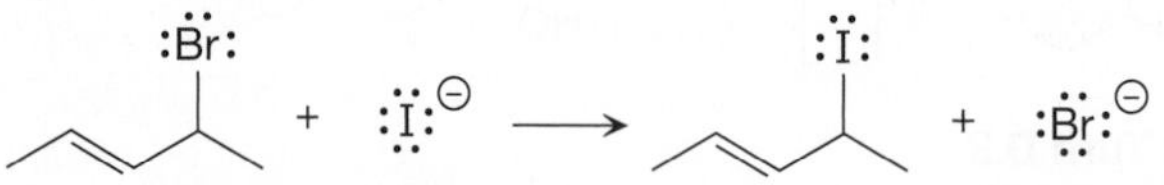
:Br:
+
:I:
:I:
+
:Br:

(b) Overall reactants are the alkyl bromide and I^-; overall products are the alkyl iodide and Br^-; the intermediate is the carbocation.

Your Turn 8.4

See labels in Your Turn 8.2 answer.

Your Turn 8.5

The energy diagram represents three elementary steps.

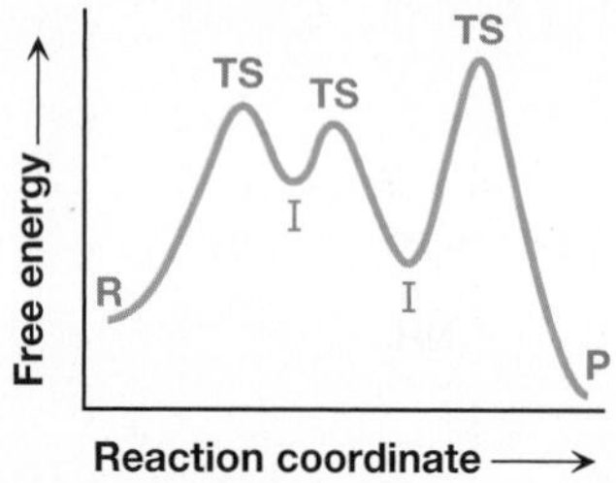
TS
TS
TS
I
I
R
P
Free energy
Reaction coordinate

Your Turn 8.6

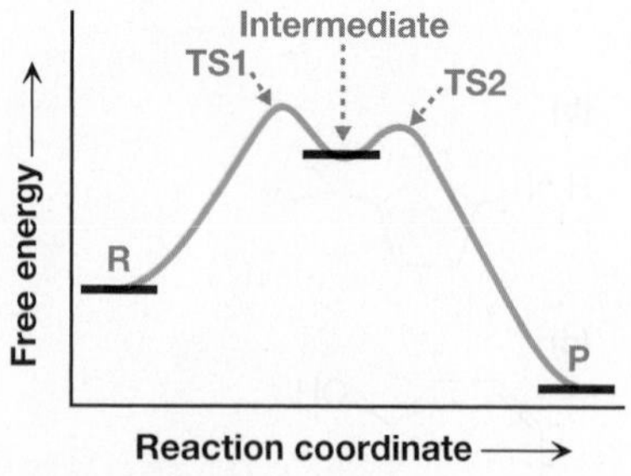
Intermediate
TS1
TS2
R
P
Free energy
Reaction coordinate

Your Turn 8.7

Step 1: heterolysis; Step 2: electrophile elimination.

Your Turn 8.8

The result of adding the steps of Equation 8-4 is shown in the following figure, which is in agreement with Equation 8-5.

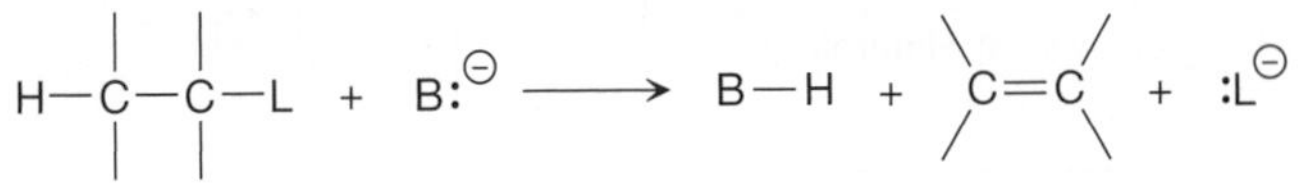

H—C—C—L + B:⊖ ⟶ B—H + C=C + :L⊖

Your Turn 8.9

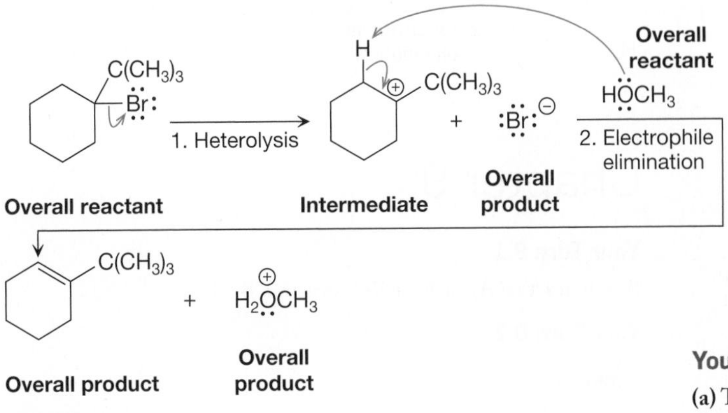

C(CH3)3
Br:
1. Heterolysis
Overall reactant
H
C(CH3)3
:Br:
Intermediate
Overall product
Overall reactant
HOCH3
2. Electrophile elimination
C(CH3)3
H2OCH3
Overall product
Overall product

Your Turn 8.10

The energy diagram is qualitatively the same as the one shown for the answer to Your Turn 8.6.

Your Turn 8.11

Doubling the concentration of $NaSCH_3$ would double the rate of the reaction.

Your Turn 8.12

(a) ~2%. **(b)** ~0.1%.

Your Turn 8.13

(a) <0.1%. **(b)** ~0.4%.

Your Turn 8.14

Molecule **B**.

Your Turn 8.15

The starting molecule and both product molecules are chiral. The carbocation intermediate is achiral.

Your Turn 8.16

(a) Equal mixture of enantiomers. **(b)** Unequal mixture of diastereomers. **(c)** Single, achiral product.

Your Turn 8.17

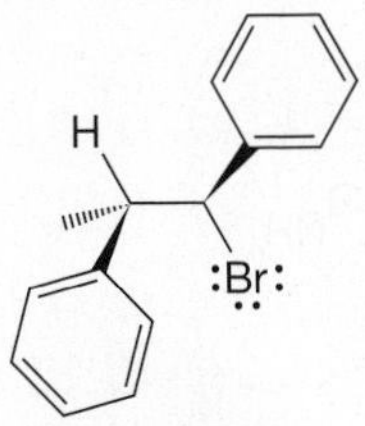

H
:Br:

Your Turn 8.18

In **A**, only the H on the top C is anticoplanar with the leaving group. In **B**, only the H on the bottom right C is anticoplanar with the leaving group.

Your Turn 8.19

Only **(a)** produces a mixture of diastereomers. The diastereomer in greater abundance would be the one shown here, in which the bulky *t*-butyl group is on the side of the double bond opposite the propyl group.

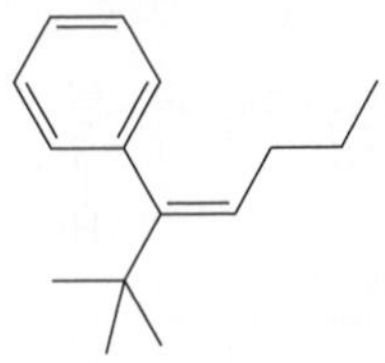

Your Turn 8.20

The pK_a for $CH_3OH_2^+$ (based on it being of similar acid strength as H_3O^+) is ~0, and thus it is a strong acid. The pK_a for $CH_3NH_3^+$ is 10.63, which is greater than 0, and thus it is a weak acid. The pK_a of H_2 (the conjugate acid of H^-) is 35, which is greater than 14, and thus H^- is a strong base. The pK_a of HCl (the conjugate acid of Cl^-) is −7, which is less than 14, and thus Cl^- is a weak base.

Your Turn 8.21

(a) The first step yields a strong acid, R_2OH^+, which would be incompatible with the basic HO^- conditions.

(b) Reasonable mechanism

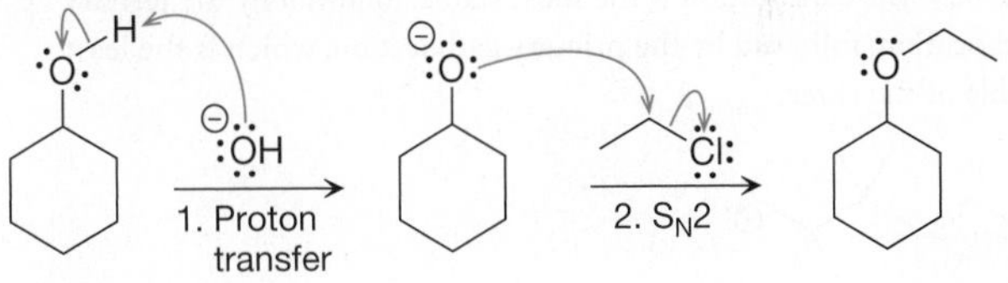

H
:O:
:OH
1. Proton transfer
:O:
Cl:
2. SN2
:O

Your Turn 8.22

(a) The first step yields a strong base, RO^-, which would be incompatible with the acidic H_3O^+ conditions.

(b) Reasonable mechanism

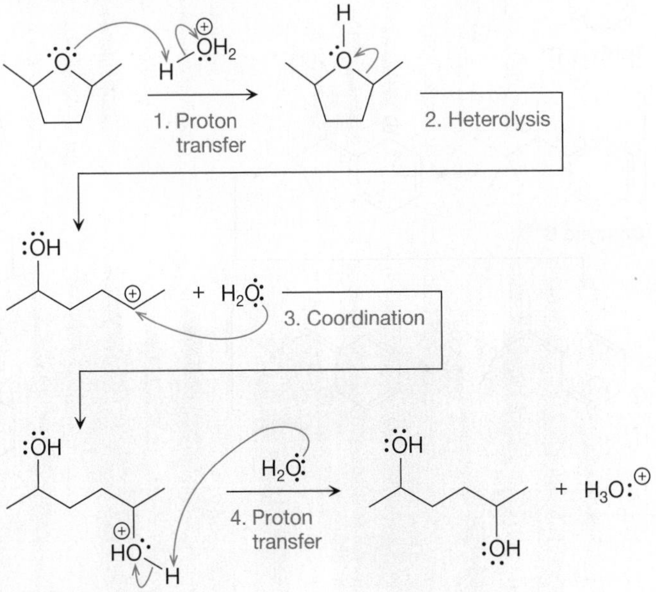

:O:
H
OH2
1. Proton transfer
H
:O
2. Heterolysis
:OH
+ H2O:
3. Coordination
:OH
HO:
H
H2O:
4. Proton transfer
:OH
:OH
+ H3O:

Your Turn 8.23

(a) The second step is unreasonable because it is an intramolecular proton transfer. A reasonable mechanism is shown below.

(b) Reasonable mechanism

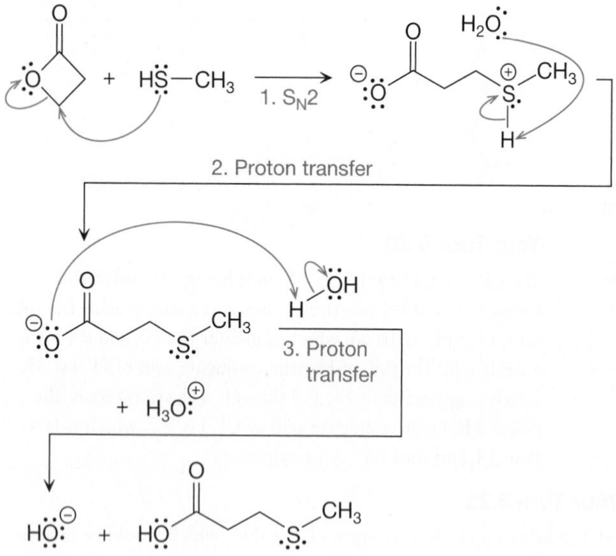

1. S_N2
2. Proton transfer
3. Proton transfer

Your Turn 8.24

The benzylic carbocation is the most stable, followed by the tertiary carbocation, followed by the primary carbocation, which is the least stable of the three.

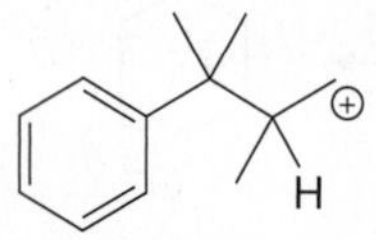

Primary C⁺

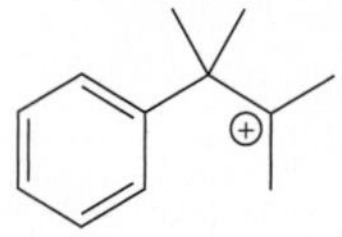

Tertiary C⁺

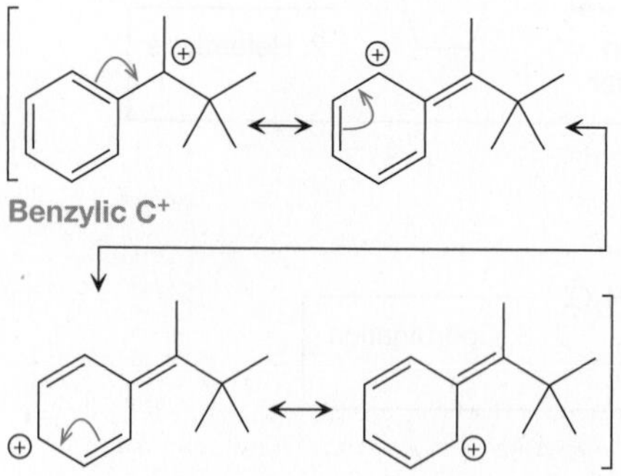

Benzylic C⁺

Your Turn 8.25

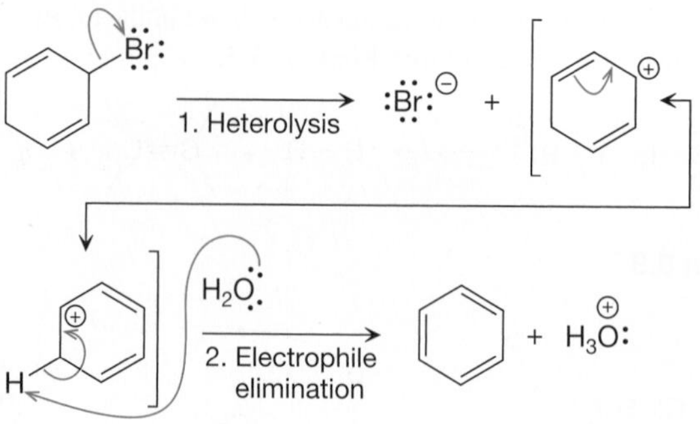

1. Heterolysis
2. Electrophile elimination

Chapter 9

Your Turn 9.1

Base in reaction **A,** nucleophile in reaction **B.**

Your Turn 9.2

S_N2

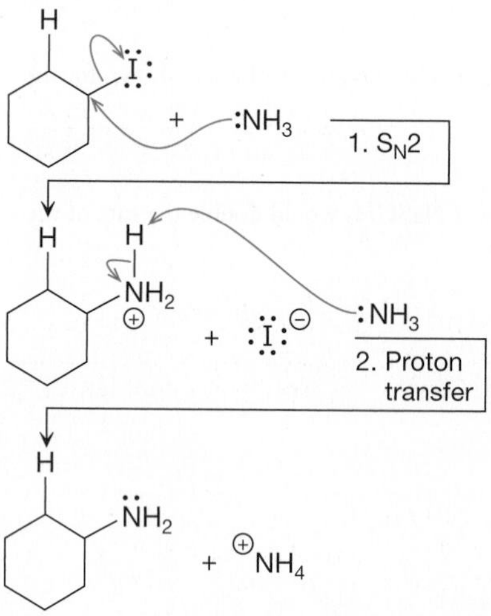

1. S_N2
2. Proton transfer

S_N1

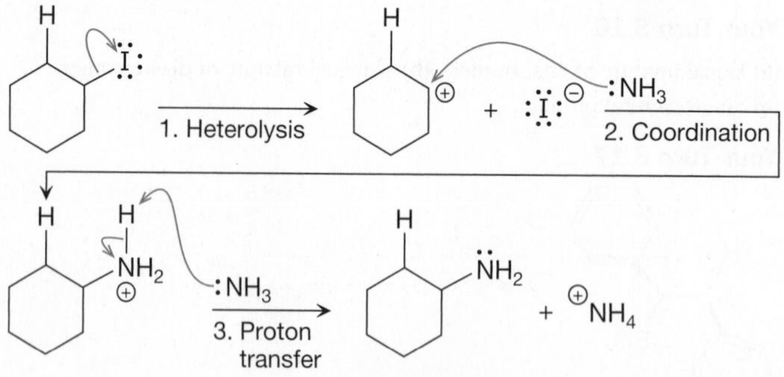

1. Heterolysis
2. Coordination
3. Proton transfer

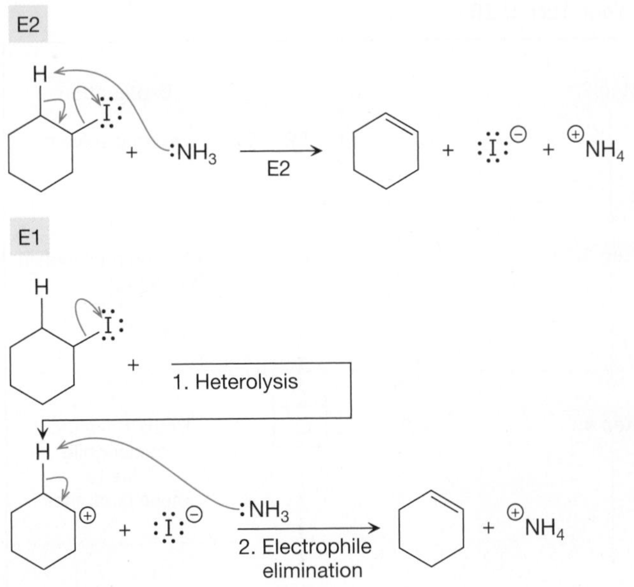
E2
E2
E1
1. Heterolysis
2. Electrophile elimination

Your Turn 9.3

The exergonic reaction in Figure 9-1a has a smaller energy barrier than the endergonic reaction in Figure 9-1b, and thus the reaction is faster.

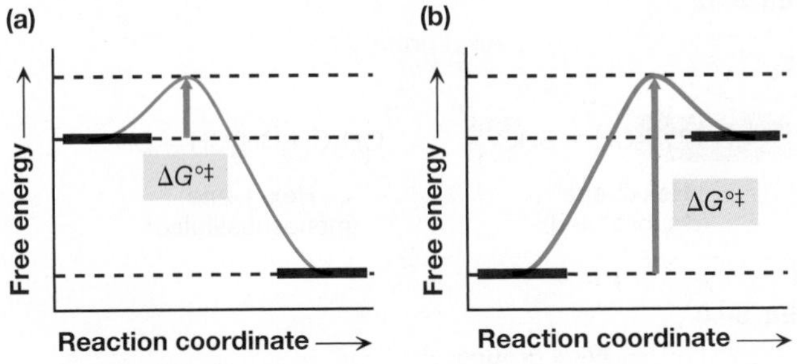
(a)
(b)
Free energy
ΔG°‡
Reaction coordinate

Your Turn 9.4

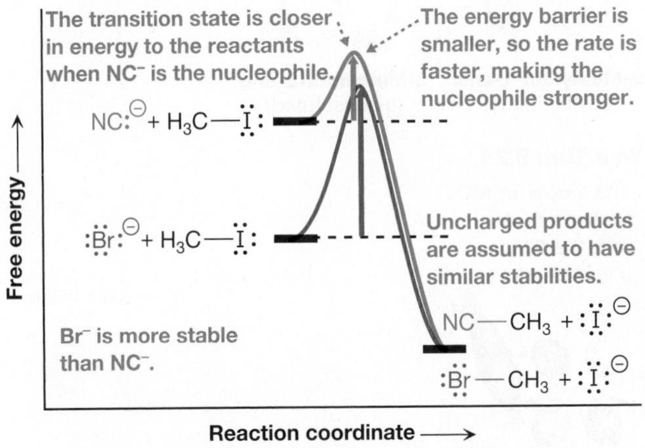
The transition state is closer in energy to the reactants when NC⁻ is the nucleophile.
The energy barrier is smaller, so the rate is faster, making the nucleophile stronger.
Uncharged products are assumed to have similar stabilities.
Br⁻ is more stable than NC⁻.
Free energy
Reaction coordinate

Your Turn 9.5

H_2P^- is a strong nucleophile, because it has a negative charge localized on a single atom (resonance is not possible). Therefore, it will favor the S_N2 mechanism.

Your Turn 9.6

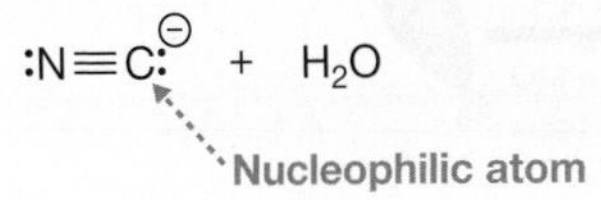
Nucleophilic atom

Your Turn 9.7

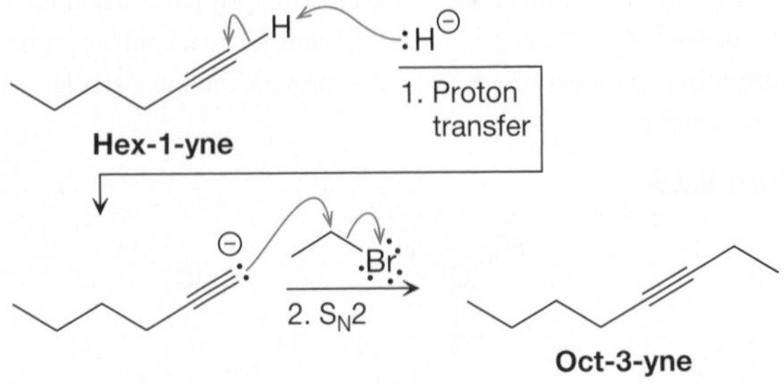
Hex-1-yne
1. Proton transfer
2. S_N2
Oct-3-yne

Your Turn 9.8

Faster, because the pK_a values of the conjugate acids indicate that HS^- is a stronger base than $CH_3CO_2^-$.

Your Turn 9.9

The reaction rate increases in the order **B** < **A** < **C**.

Your Turn 9.10

(a) None of the reactions are feasible. **(b)** All of the reactions are feasible. **(c)** S_N2 and E2 are feasible.

Your Turn 9.11

(a) TfO^- is the weakest base. **(b)** The S_N1 reaction with TfO^- as the leaving group has the fastest rate.

(c)

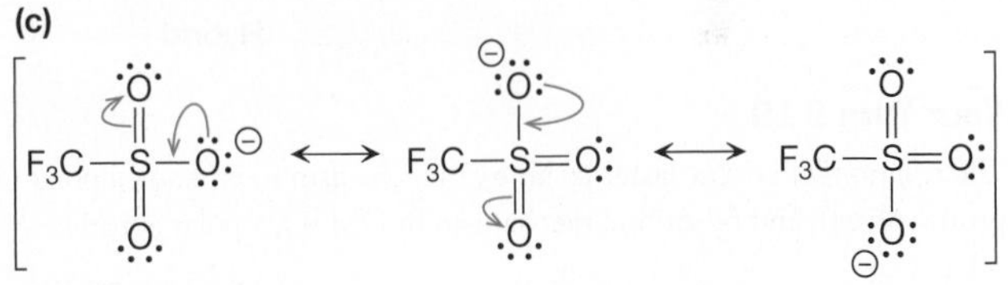

Your Turn 9.12

HCO_2^- is the better leaving group because it is the weaker base.

Your Turn 9.13

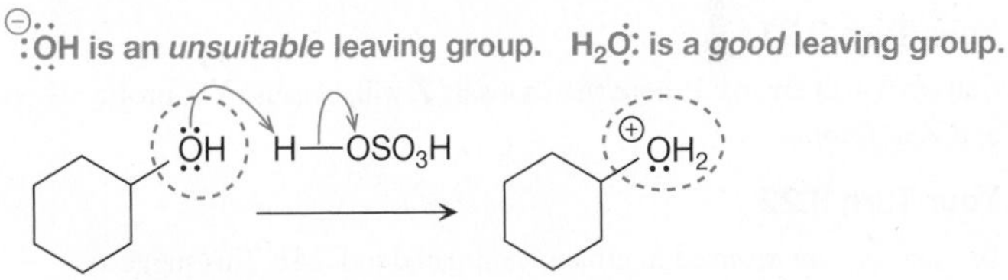
:OH is an *unsuitable* leaving group.
H_2O: is a *good* leaving group.

Your Turn 9.14

sp^3 C—H = 421 kJ/mol; sp^2 C—H = 464 kJ/mol; and sp C—H = 558 kJ/mol.

Your Turn 9.15

Nucleophilic substitution will occur most readily at the sp^3-hybridized C with a Br leaving group, which is the one in the middle. The other Br leaving groups are on sp^2- and sp-hybridized C atoms, which tend not to undergo nucleophilic substitution or elimination.

Your Turn 9.16

E2 reactions require a H and a leaving group attached to adjacent atoms. With a substrate of the form CH_3–L, there is no such adjacent C atom, so no double bond can be formed.

Your Turn 9.17

X reacts fastest by an S_N2 mechanism, because the primary carbon is the least hindered. **Z** reacts fastest by an S_N1 and E1 mechanism (same rate-determining step), because it proceeds through the most stable tertiary carbocation.

Your Turn 9.18

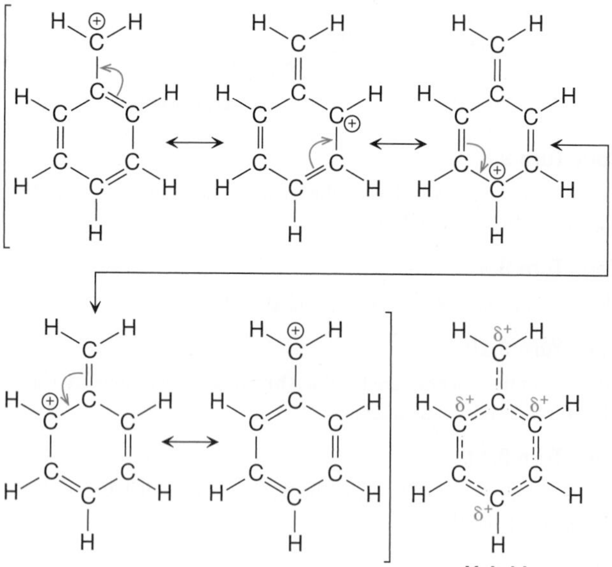

Hybrid

Your Turn 9.19

The reaction will occur faster by an S_N1 mechanism in ethanol, a polar protic solvent, and by an S_N2 mechanism in DMSO, a polar aprotic solvent.

Your Turn 9.20

The reaction will proceed faster in acetone, a polar aprotic solvent, because ethanol, a polar protic solvent, will solvate (and, therefore, weaken) the nucleophile to a greater degree.

Your Turn 9.21

Solvent **Y** will favor E1 more than solvent **Z** will, because **Y** is protic and **Z** is aprotic.

Your Turn 9.22

Br^- and N_3^- are reversed in ethanol compared to DMF. This suggests that N_3^- is more strongly solvated by ethanol than Br^- is. Similarly, $CH_3CO_2^-$ is a stronger nucleophile in DMF than either Br^- or Cl^-, but in ethanol, the opposite is true, suggesting that the ethanol solvates $CH_3CO_2^-$ more strongly than it solvates Br^- or Cl^-.

Your Turn 9.23

The nucleophiles are uncharged, so solvation is not a huge factor. Thus, the relative nucleophile strengths should be the same in both solvents; H_2S is a stronger nucleophile than H_2O in ethanol.

Your Turn 9.24

Greater entropy exists in the elimination products (bottom reaction) than the substitution products (top reaction).

Your Turn 9.25

Raising the temperature will favor the bottom E2 reaction. Lowering the temperature will favor the top S_N2 reaction.

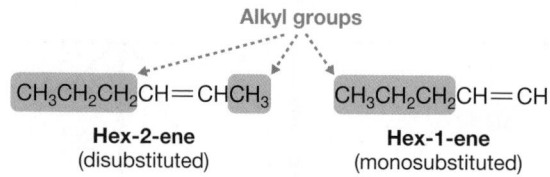

Your Turn 9.26

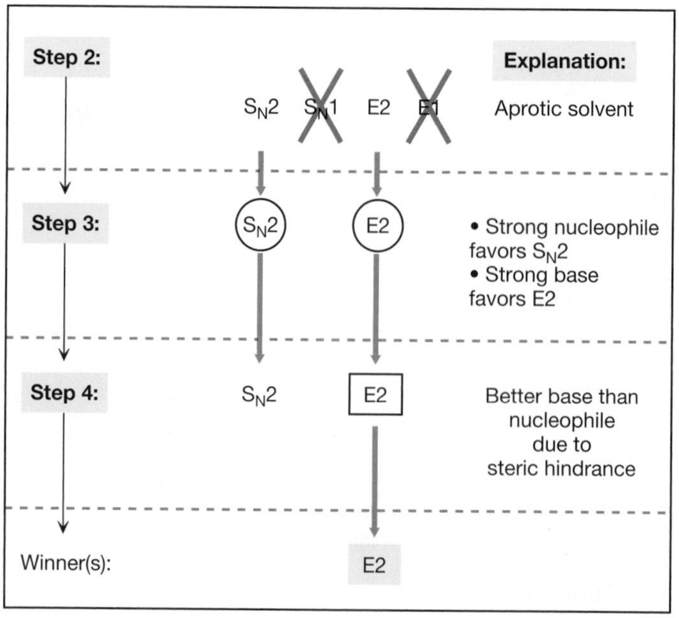

Step 2:
Step 3:
Step 4:
Winner(s):
Explanation:
S_N2 S_N1 E2 E1
Aprotic solvent
S_N2
E2
• Strong nucleophile favors S_N2
• Strong base favors E2
S_N2
E2
Better base than nucleophile due to steric hindrance
E2

Your Turn 9.27

Eq. 9-42

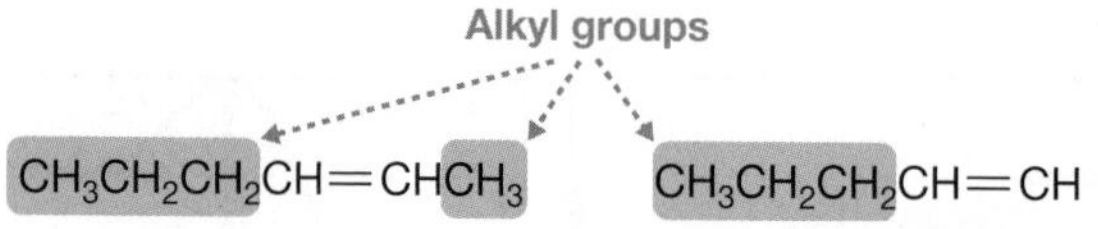

Alkyl groups
CH3CH2CH2CH=CHCH3
CH3CH2CH2CH=CH

Hex-2-ene (disubstituted) **Hex-1-ene** (monosubstituted)

Eq. 9-43

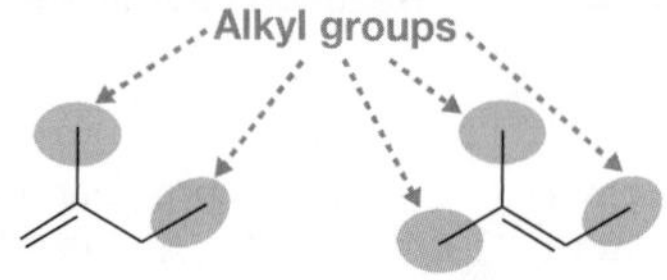

Alkyl groups

2-Methylbut-1-ene (disubstituted) **2-Methylbut-2-ene** (trisubstituted)

Your Turn 9.28

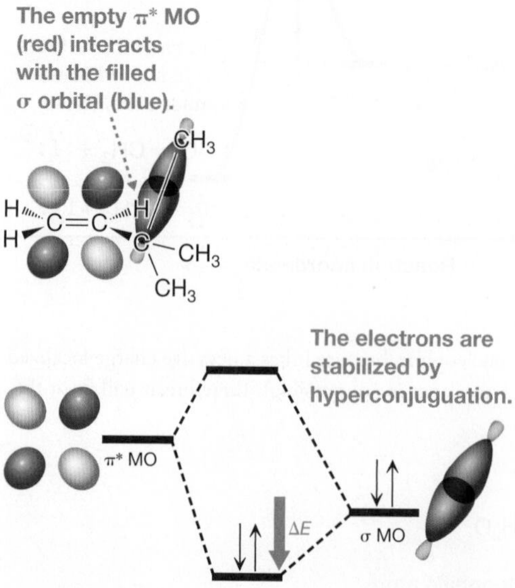

The empty π* MO (red) interacts with the filled σ orbital (blue).
The electrons are stabilized by hyperconjugation.
π* MO
ΔE
σ MO

Your Turn 9.29

An acetal carbon is an sp^3-hybridized carbon that is attached to two OR groups and either an R or H group at the other two bonds. In cellulose, amylose, and amylopectin, C-1 in each ring is an acetal carbon.

Chapter 10

Your Turn 10.1

There are five synthetic steps (reaction arrows) and four synthetic intermediates (compounds **A–D**).

Your Turn 10.2

(a)

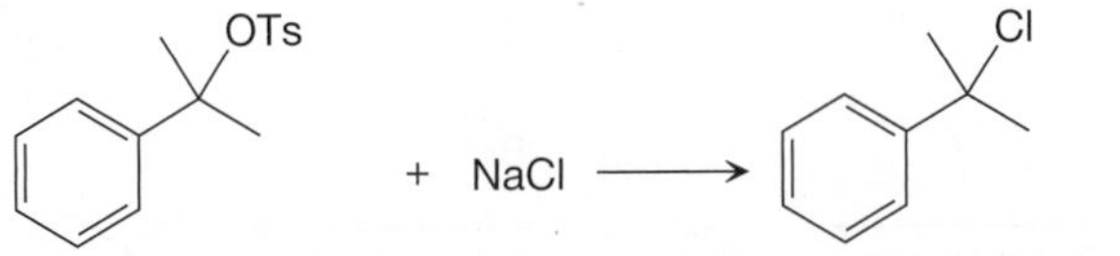
OTs
+ NaCl
Cl

2-Phenyl-2-tosyloxypropane **2-Chloro-2-phenylpropane**

(b)

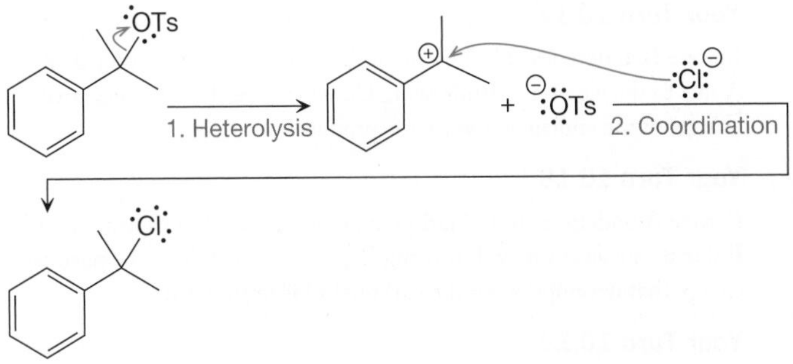
OTs
1. Heterolysis
OTs
Cl
2. Coordination
Cl

Your Turn 10.3

Write H_2O and 70 °C below the reaction arrow; for example:

$$\xrightarrow[H_2O,\ 70\ °C]{}$$

Your Turn 10.4

First, butanoic acid is treated with sodium hydroxide. Once that reaction has finished, bromoethane is added to yield ethyl butanoate.

Your Turn 10.5

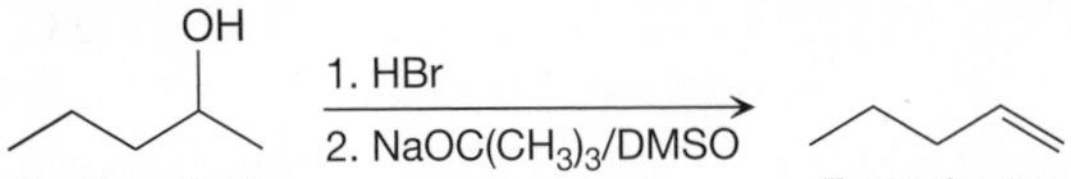
OH
1. HBr
2. NaOC(CH3)3/DMSO

Pentan-2-ol **Pent-1-ene**

Your Turn 10.6

(a) A strong bulky base, such as sodium *tert*-butoxide, with heating will accomplish this transformation. **(b)** An alkyl halide, RX, is the appropriate starting material.

Your Turn 10.7

The first, second, and fourth synthetic steps are functional group conversions. The third and fifth synthetic steps alter the carbon skeleton.

Your Turn 10.8

(A) Appendix D, Table AppD-4, Reactions That Produce Ethers, Epoxides, and Acetals, entry 1.
(B) Appendix C, Reactions That Alter the Carbon Skeleton, entry 4.
(C) Appendix D, Table AppD-2, Reactions That Produce Alkyl and Aryl Halides, entry 16.
(D) Appendix C, Reactions That Alter the Carbon Skeleton, entry 2.

Your Turn 10.9

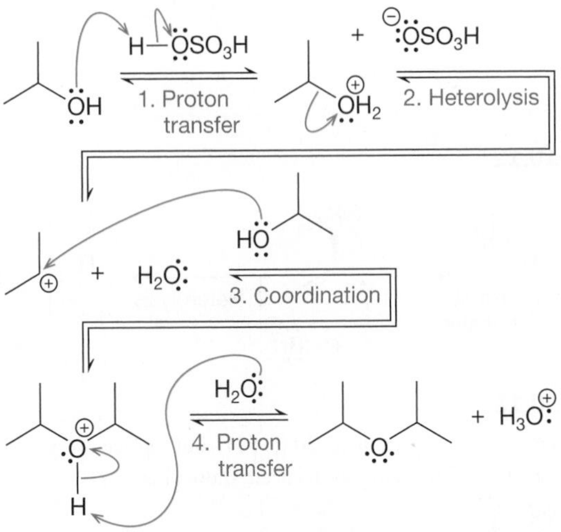
H—OSO3H
OH
1. Proton transfer
OSO3H
OH2
2. Heterolysis
HO
H2O
3. Coordination
H2O
O
H
4. Proton transfer
O
H3O

Your Turn 10.10

The first (desired) product can be produced by an S_N2 or S_N1 mechanism. For the S_N2 mechanism, draw the mechanism in Equation 10-14 (p. 518), but replace the alcohol in Step 1 with CH_3CH_2OH, and replace the alcohol in Step 2 with $(CH_3)_2CHOH$. For the S_N1 mechanism, draw the mechanism in the answer to Your Turn 10.9, but replace the alcohol in Step 3 with CH_3CH_2OH. For the second (undesired) product, draw the mechanism in Equation 10-14 (p. 518), but replace both alcohol molecules with CH_3CH_2OH.

Your Turn 10.11

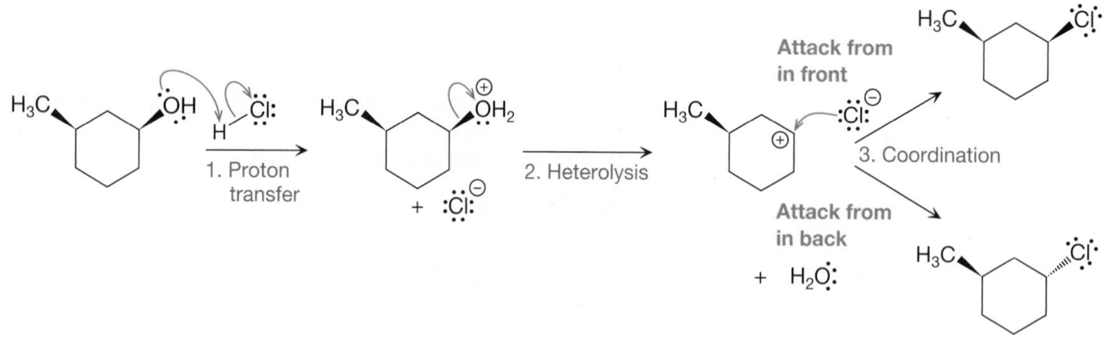
1. Proton transfer
2. Heterolysis
Attack from in front
3. Coordination
Attack from in back

Your Turn 10.12

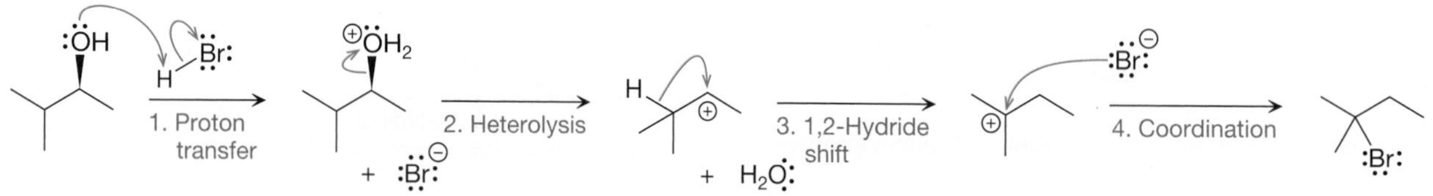
1. Proton transfer
2. Heterolysis
3. 1,2-Hydride shift
4. Coordination

Your Turn 10.13

Draw the mechanism in Equation 10-30 (p. 525), but replace every instance of Br with Cl. The major products are shown here:

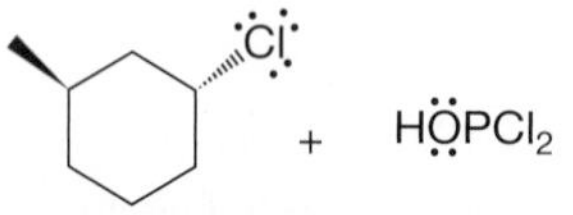

Your Turn 10.14

For each reaction, draw the mechanism in Equation 10-30 (p. 525), but **(a)** replace the alcohol with the one given in the problem and replace PBr_3 with PCl_3, and **(b)** replace the alcohol with the one given in the problem. The major products are shown here:

(a)

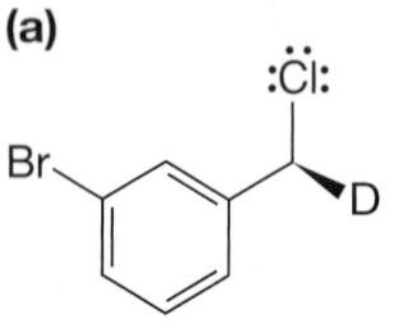

(b)

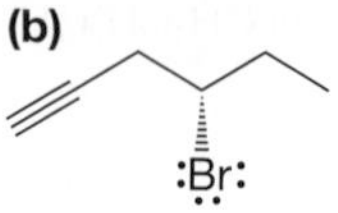

Your Turn 10.15

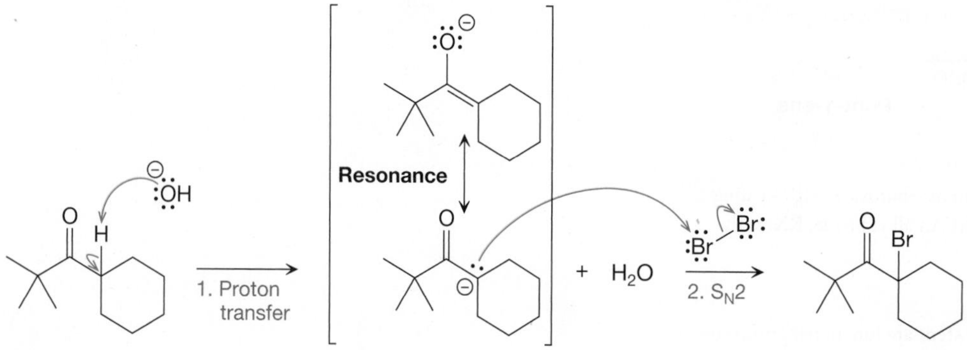
Resonance
1. Proton transfer
2. S_N2

Your Turn 10.16

Step 1 in Equation 10-39 is proton transfer; Step 2 is S_N2; Step 3 is proton transfer; Step 4 is S_N2.

Your Turn 10.17

Ketone **B** undergoes chlorination under basic conditions faster than **A** due to the electron-withdrawing Cl, which stabilizes the negative charge on the enolate anion that is produced.

Your Turn 10.18

Ketone **A** undergoes bromination under acidic conditions faster than **B** due to the electron-withdrawing Br, which destabilizes the positive charge that develops when the carbonyl O is protonated.

Your Turn 10.19

Draw the mechanism in Equation 10-41 (p. 533), but replace the ketone with the one given in the problem, and replace every instance of Cl with I. In this case, the α carbon on the right has the reactive proton. The major product is shown here:

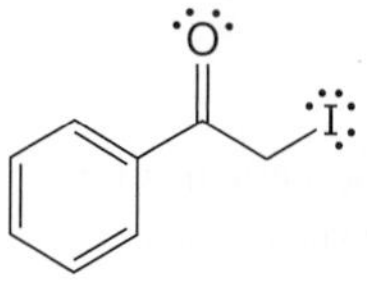

Your Turn 10.20

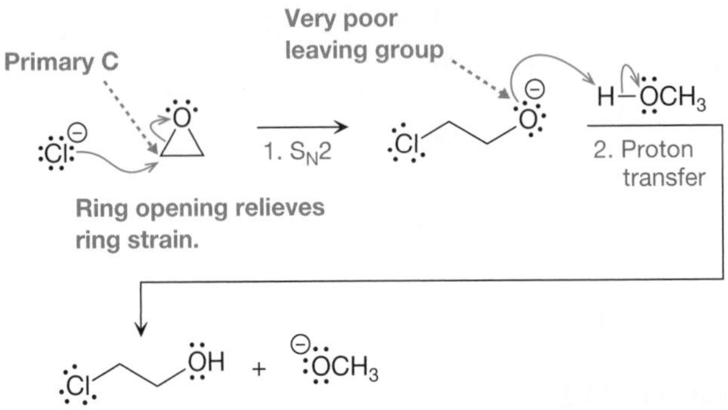

Primary C
Very poor leaving group
1. S$_N$2
2. Proton transfer
Ring opening relieves ring strain.

Your Turn 10.21

$NaSC_6H_5$ is the missing reagent. Draw the mechanism in Equation 10-45 (p. 534), but replace CH_3O^- with $^-SC_6H_5$, and replace $HOCH_3$ with H_2O.

Your Turn 10.22

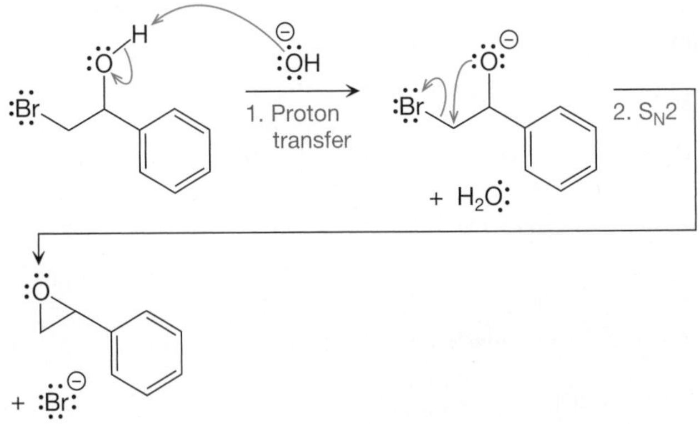

1. Proton transfer
2. S$_N$2

Your Turn 10.23

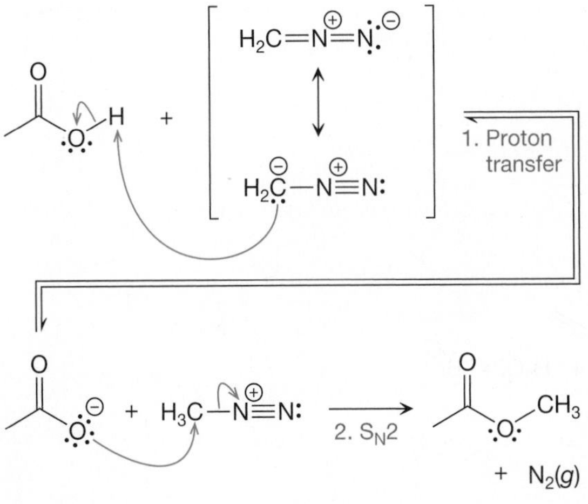

1. Proton transfer
2. S$_N$2

Your Turn 10.24

(a) Draw the mechanism in Equation 10-53 (p. 541), but replace the carboxylic acid with the one given in this problem. The major product is shown here:

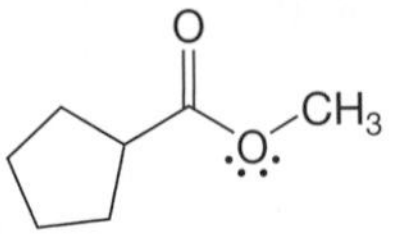

(b) Draw the mechanism in Equation 10-53 (p. 541), but replace the carboxylic acid with the dicarboxylic acid given in this problem. Draw the mechanism once for each of the carboxyl groups in the molecule. The major product is shown here:

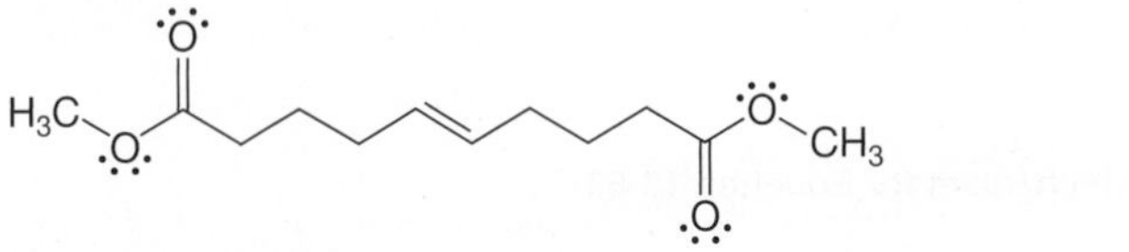

Your Turn 10.25

NH_3 (relative nucleophilicity 320,000) is a stronger nucleophile than Cl^- (relative nucleophilicity 23,000) in ethanol.

Your Turn 10.26

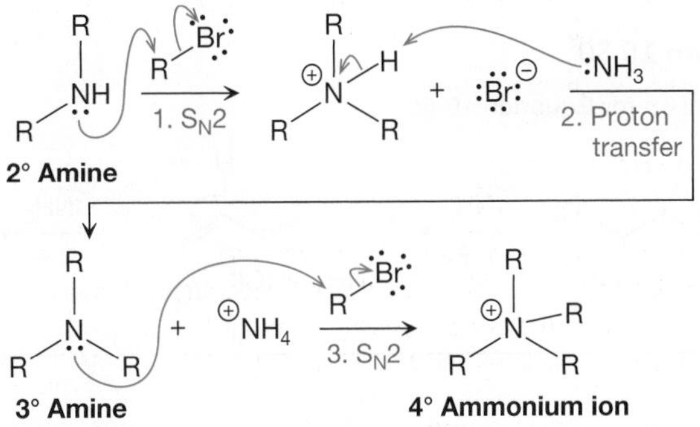

1. S$_N$2
2. Proton transfer
3. S$_N$2
2° Amine
3° Amine
4° Ammonium ion

Your Turn 10.27

There is less steric strain in **B** than in **A**.

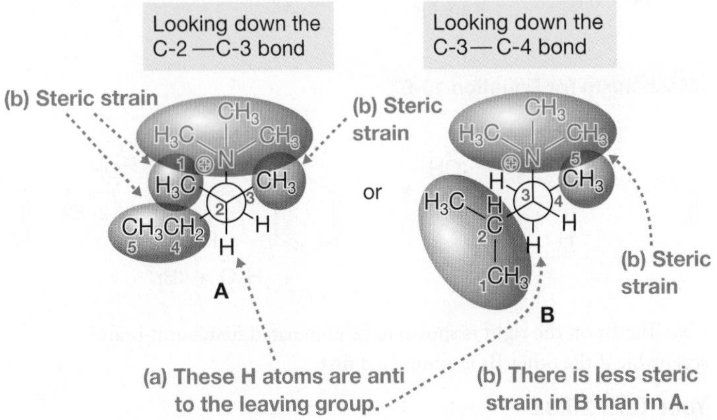

Looking down the C-2—C-3 bond
Looking down the C-3—C-4 bond
(b) Steric strain
(b) Steric strain
or
(b) Steric strain
A
B
(a) These H atoms are anti to the leaving group.
(b) There is less steric strain in B than in A.

(c)

Hofmann product, less substituted alkene

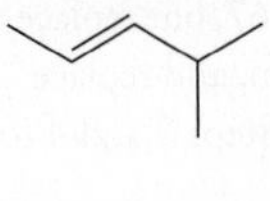

Your Turn 10.28

The pK_a of H_2 is 35, and the pK_a of RC≡CH is about the same as that of HC≡CH, which is 25. A lower pK_a indicates a stronger acid; therefore, RC≡CH is the stronger acid. The side opposite the terminal alkyne (the product side) is favored by a factor of 10^{10}.

Your Turn 10.29

Mechanism for Equation 10-62

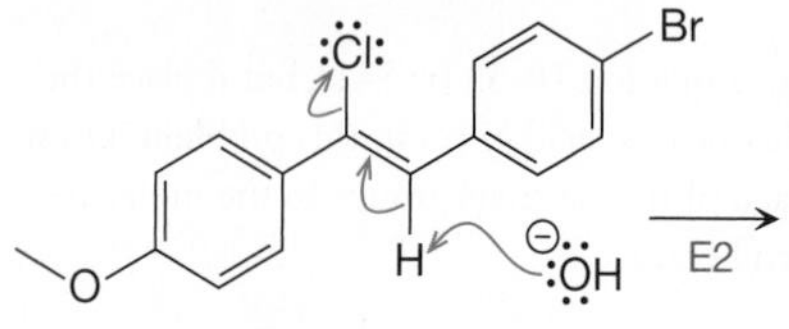
E2

Mechanism for Equation 10-63

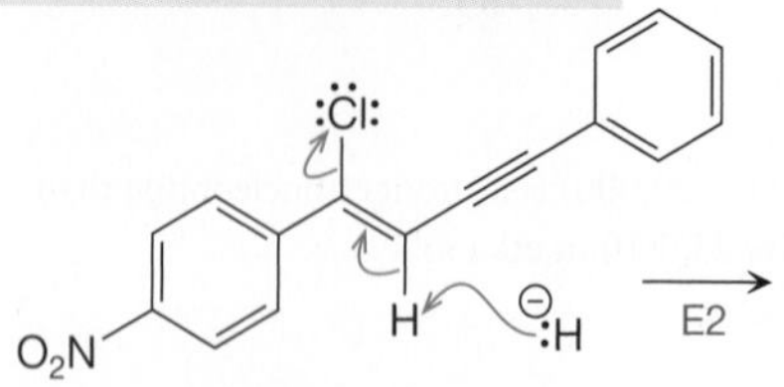
E2

Your Turn 10.30

Mechanism for Equation 10-66

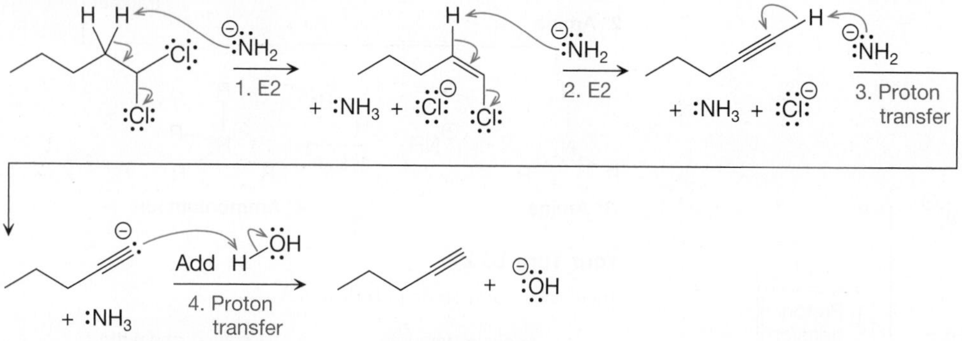
1. E2
2. E2
3. Proton transfer
Add H–OH
4. Proton transfer

Mechanism for Equation 10-67

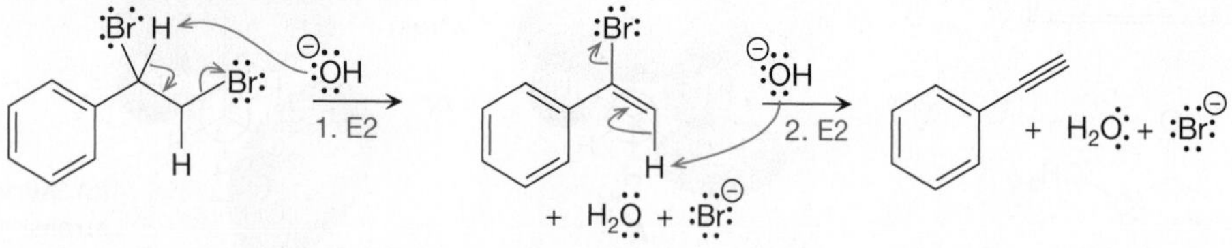
1. E2
2. E2

Note: The Br on the right is shown to be eliminated first, but it is also acceptable if the other Br is eliminated first.

Your Turn 10.31

(a) Draw the mechanism shown in the answer to Your Turn 10.30 for Equation 10-66, but replace the dichloride with the dibromide given in this problem. **(b)** For Steps 1 and 2, draw the mechanism shown in the answer to Your Turn 10.30 for Equation 10-67, but replace the dibromide with the dichloride given in this problem, and replace $^-$OH with $^-NH_2$. Then, with the resulting alkyne, draw Steps 3 and 4 for the mechanism shown in the answer to Your Turn 10.30 for Equation 10-66. The major products are shown here:

(a)

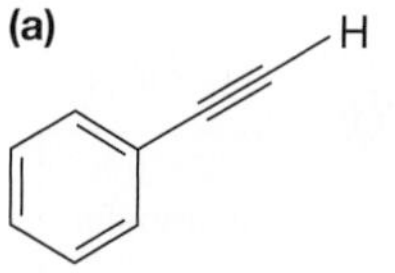

(b)

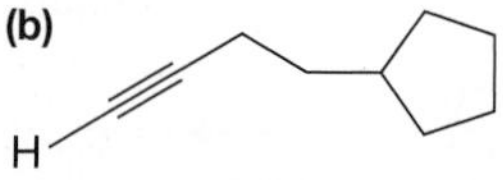

Chapter 11

Your Turn 11.1

The precursors for each transform are shown here.

(a)

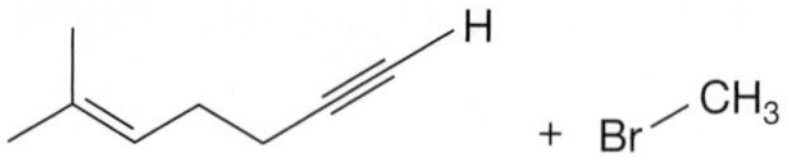

(b)

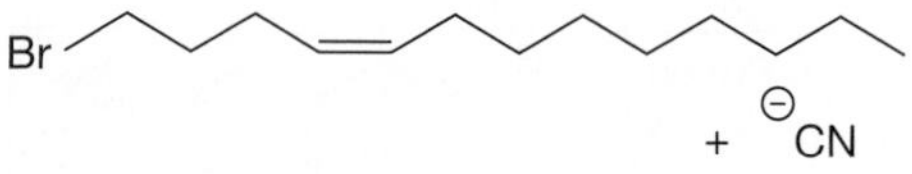

Your Turn 11.2

Transforms

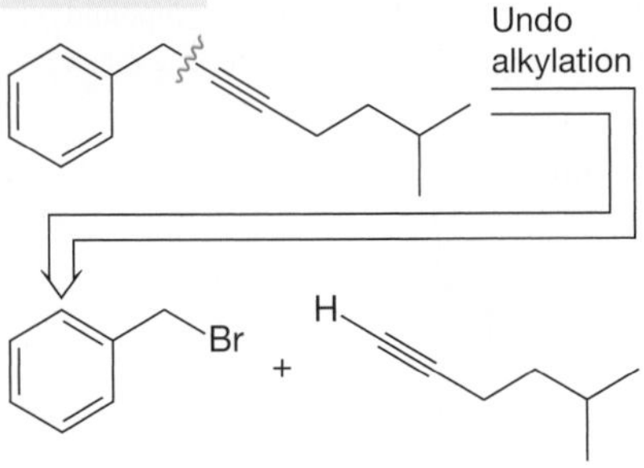
Undo
alkylation
Br
+
H

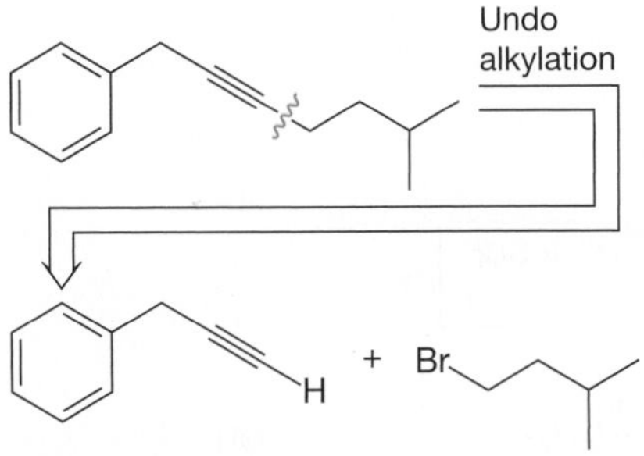
Undo
alkylation
H
+
Br

Syntheses

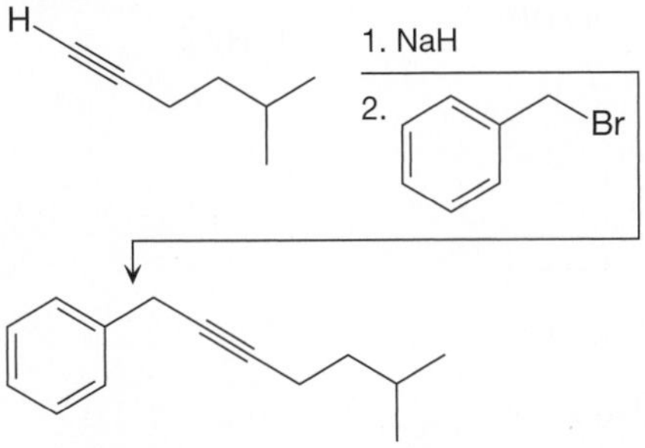
H
1. NaH
2.
Br

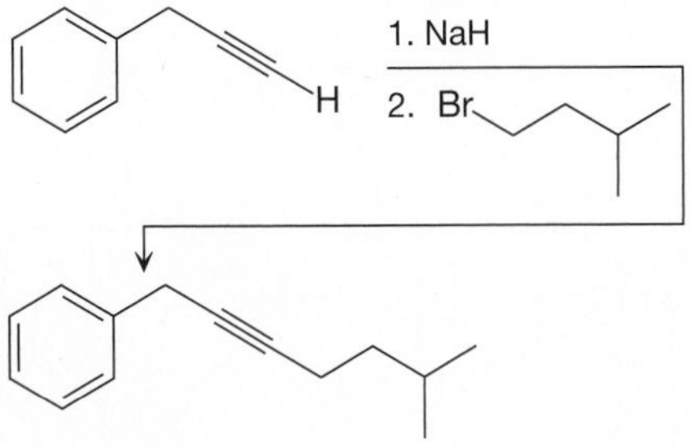
H
1. NaH
2. Br

Mechanisms

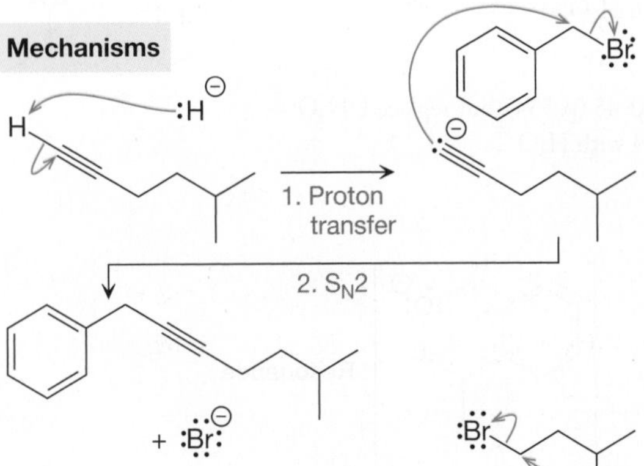
H
:H
1. Proton
transfer
Br
2. S_N2
+ :Br:

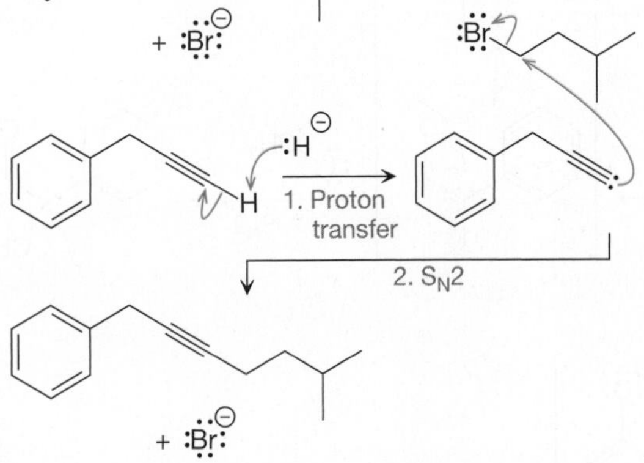
:Br
:H
H
1. Proton
transfer
2. S_N2
+ :Br:

Your Turn 11.3

Transform

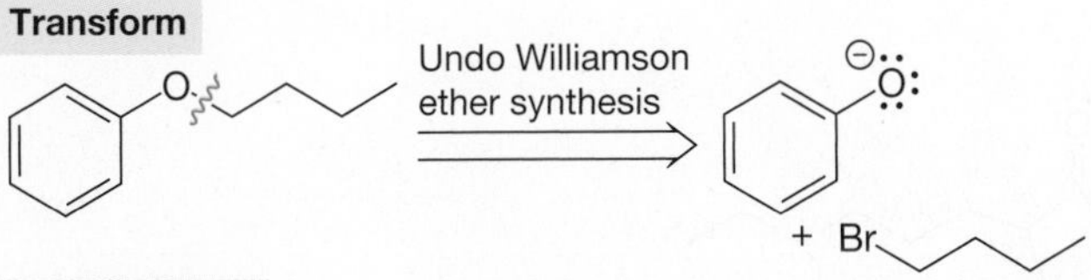
O
Undo Williamson
ether synthesis
O:
+ Br

Mechanism

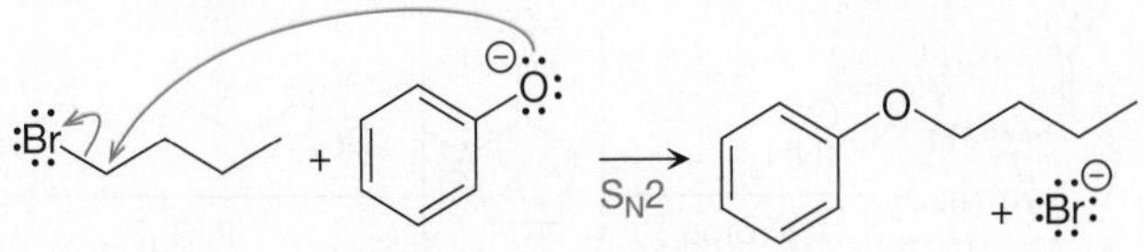
:Br
+
O:
S_N2
O
+ :Br:

Synthetic step

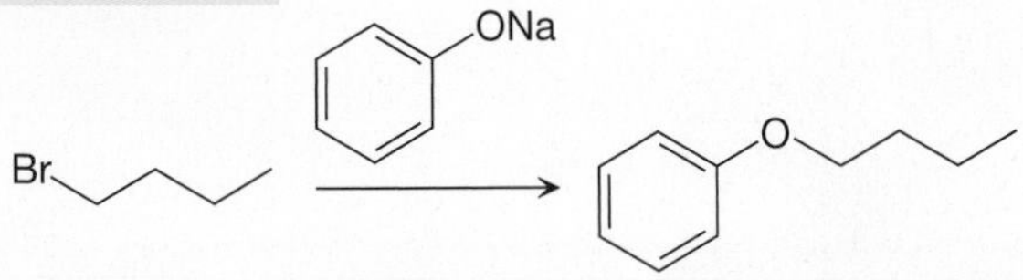
ONa
Br
O

Your Turn 11.4

Transform

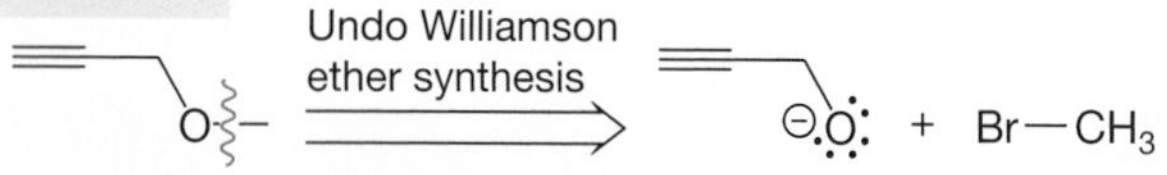
Undo Williamson ether synthesis
+ Br—CH3

Synthesis

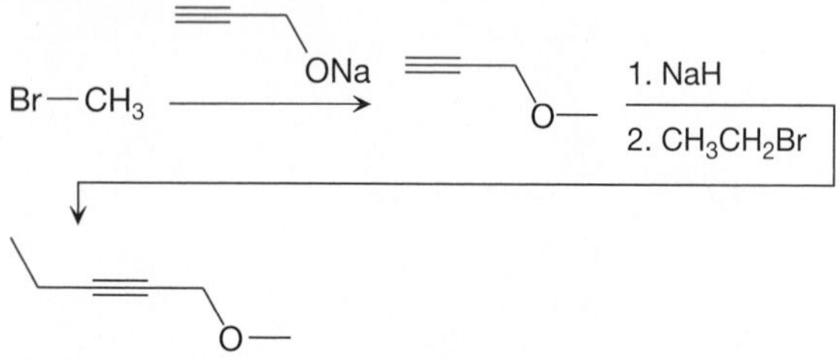
ONa
Br—CH3
1. NaH
2. CH3CH2Br

Your Turn 11.5

Draw the mechanism in Equation 10-45 (p. 534).

Your Turn 11.6

Draw the mechanism in Equation 10-45 (p. 534), but replace CH_3O^- with NC^-, and replace CH_3OH with H_2O.

Your Turn 11.7

Draw the mechanism in Equation 10-45 (p. 534), but replace CH_3O^- with $CH_3CH_2^-$, and replace CH_3OH with H_3O^+.

Your Turn 11.8

Mechanism for Eq. 11-31

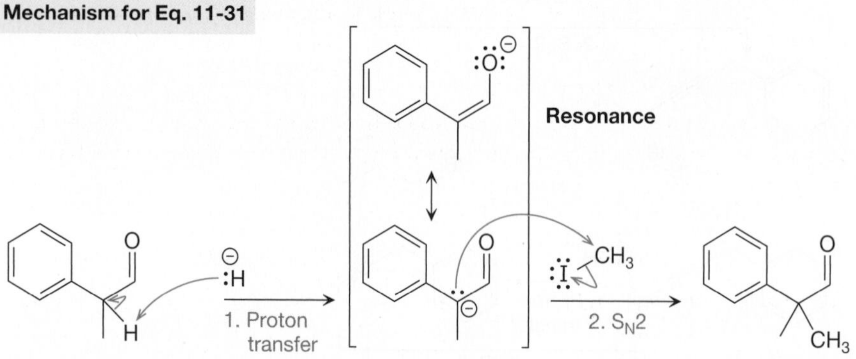
Resonance
1. Proton transfer
2. SN2
CH3

Mechanism for Eq. 11-32

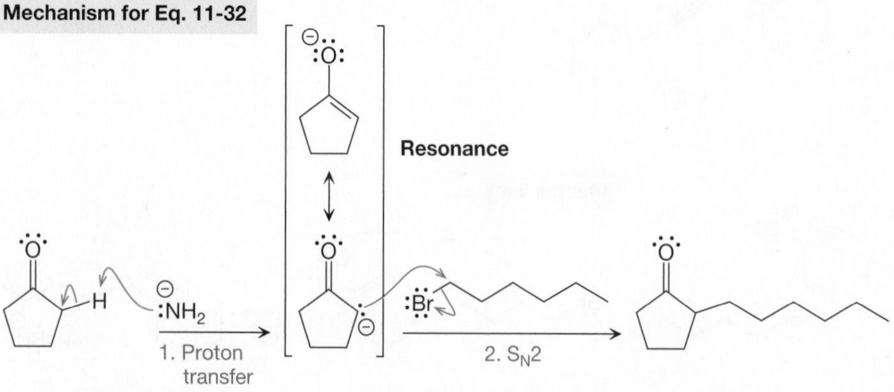
Resonance
:NH2
1. Proton transfer
:Br
2. SN2

Your Turn 11.9

For each reaction, draw the mechanism shown in the answer to Your Turn 11.8 for Equation 11-32, but replace the carbonyl compound and the alkyl halide with the ones given in this problem. The major products are shown here:

(a) **(b)**

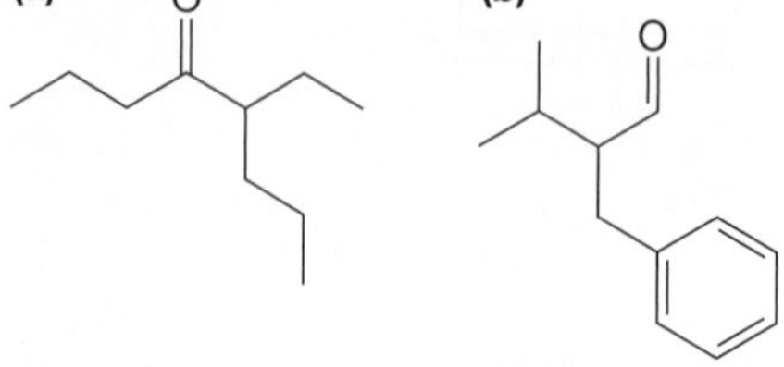

Your Turn 11.10

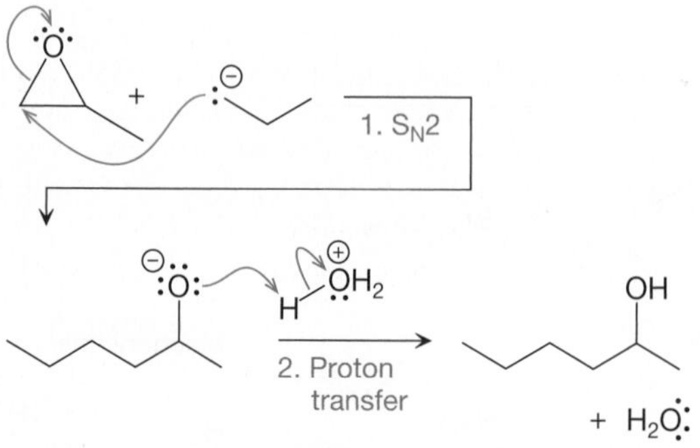
1. SN2
OH2
2. Proton transfer
OH
+ H2O

Your Turn 11.11

The first three proposed transforms can proceed as planned. **(a)** NaCN can be used as a nucleophile for an S_N2 reaction. **(b)** NaSH can be used as a nucleophile for an S_N2 reaction. **(c)** The conversion can take place with PBr_3. **(d)** This is a synthetic trap. We could attempt to convert the OH group to Br using PBr_3, but both OH groups could be converted, as both are attached to sp^3-hybridized carbons. **(e)** This is a synthetic trap. We could attempt to open the epoxide with a methyl Grignard reagent, but under basic conditions the less substituted C will be attacked, not the more substituted C as shown in this transform. **(f)** The conversion can proceed as planned. CH_3MgBr will work under basic conditions and the nucleophile will attack the less substituted C of the epoxide, opening the ring and forming a new C—C bond. Acid workup yields the desired alcohol.

Your Turn 11.12

DMF is a highly toxic solvent that is thought to be a carcinogen, is linked to liver disease, and is suspected to be a reproductive toxin that can harm a fetus. DMSO, conversely, does not display any of the above risks. Both solvents are polar aprotic, are miscible with water, and have high boiling points. Therefore, DMSO or mixtures of DMSO with other solvents are a suitable replacement for DMF.

Your Turn 11.13

If each step's yield is 80%, the overall yield of a six-step synthesis would be $(0.80)^6 = 0.26$, or 26%.

Your Turn 11.14

Overall yield in a linear synthesis like this is simply the product of the yields for each step.
Overall yield $= (0.90)(0.81)(0.85)(0.98)(0.82)(0.72)(0.94) = 0.337$, or 33.7%

Your Turn 11.15

(a) Scheme 1 is a convergent synthesis, and Scheme 2 is a linear synthesis. **(b)** In Scheme 1, the longest branch of the convergent synthesis is three steps, so the overall yield would be $(0.90)^3 = 0.73$, or 73%. In Scheme 2, five steps are required, so the overall yield is $(0.90)^5 = 0.59$, or 59%.

Chapter 12

Your Turn 12.1

HBr adds across the C=C double bond of (*E*)-but-2-ene to produce 2-bromobutane.

Your Turn 12.2

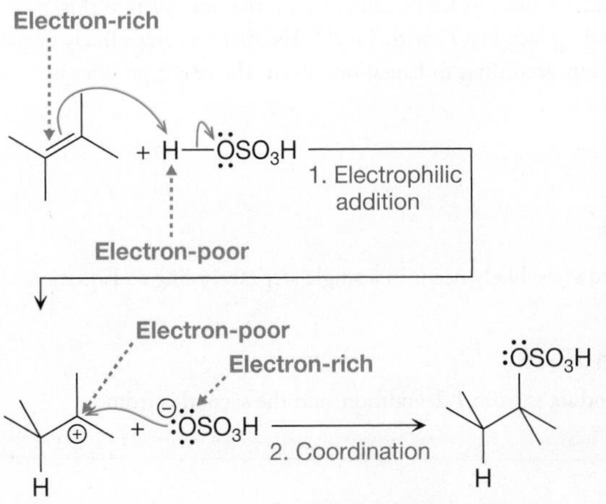
Electron-rich
+ H—ÖSO3H
1. Electrophilic addition
Electron-poor
Electron-poor
Electron-rich
+ :ÖSO3H
2. Coordination
:ÖSO3H
H
H

Your Turn 12.3

Draw the mechanism in Equation 12-3 (p. 606), but replace the alkene and acid with the ones given in the problem. The major products are shown here:

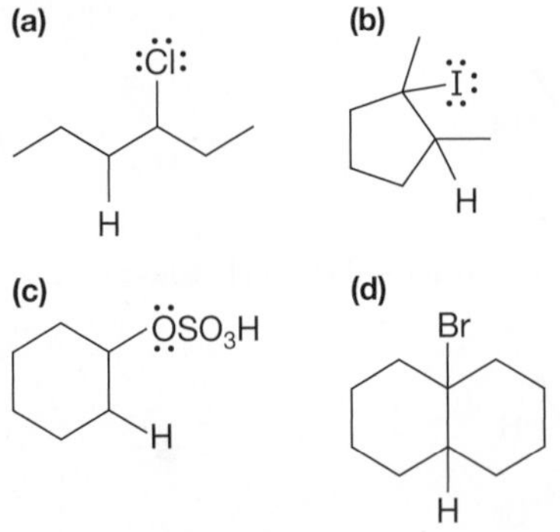
(a)
:Cl:
H
(b)
I:
H
(c)
ÖSO3H
H
(d)
Br
H

Your Turn 12.4

Draw the mechanism in Equation 12-3 (p. 606), but replace the alkene with the one given in the problem. The central C=C reacts, and the major product is shown here:

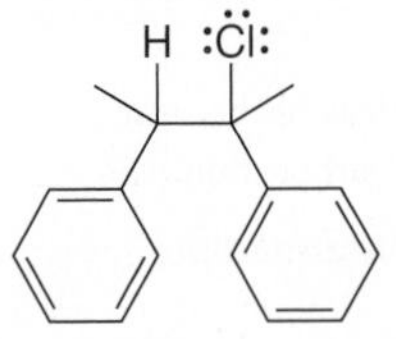
H :Cl:

Note: The C=C bonds of benzene rings are especially stable due to aromaticity and are not reactive under these reaction conditions.

Your Turn 12.5

The secondary carbocation is less stable (higher energy) and goes in the top box (red line). The tertiary carbocation is more stable (lower energy) and goes in the bottom box (blue line).

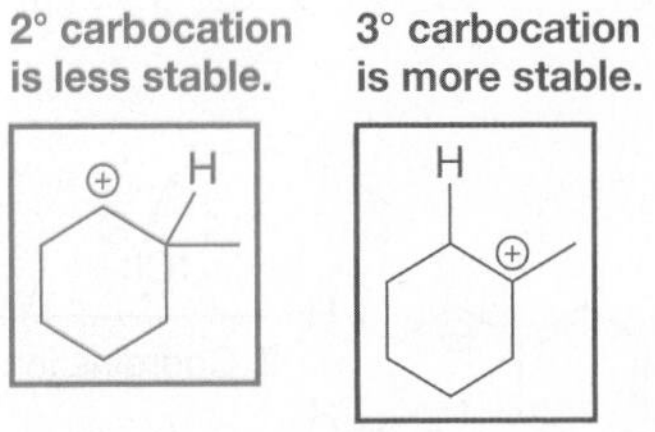
2° carbocation is less stable.
3° carbocation is more stable.
H
H

Your Turn 12.6

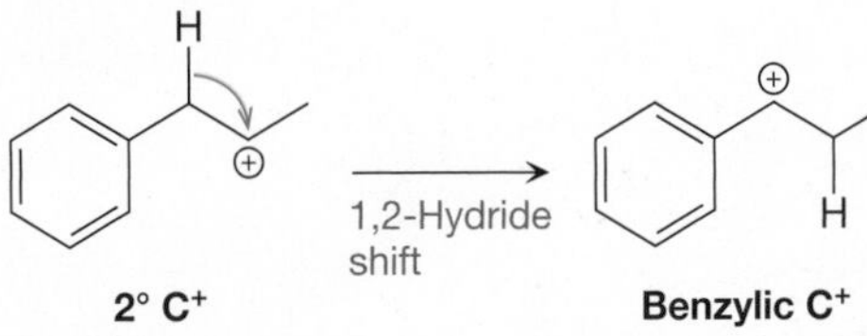
H
1,2-Hydride shift
H
2° C+
Benzylic C+

Your Turn 12.7

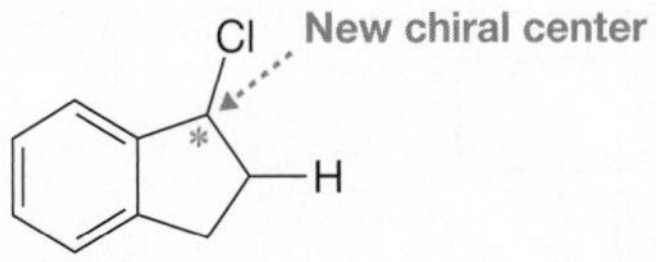
Cl
New chiral center
H

Your Turn 12.8

Draw the mechanism in Equation 12-12 (p. 616), but replace the alkene with the one given in the problem. The C=C bond is unsymmetric. The following two major products are formed when H^+ adds to the bottom alkene C.

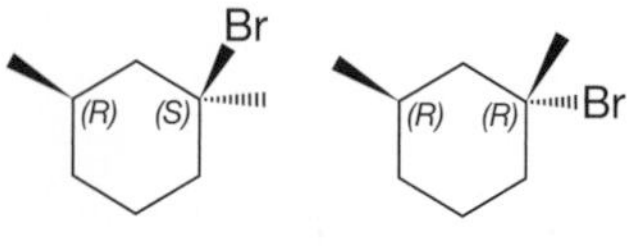

Br
(R) (S)
(R) (R)
Br

The following four minor products are formed when H^+ adds to the top alkene C.

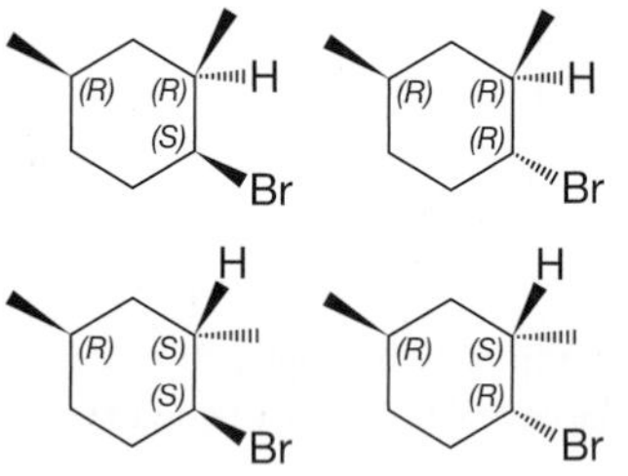

(R) (R) (S) H Br
(R) (R) (R) H Br
(R) (S) (S) H Br
(R) (S) (R) H Br

Your Turn 12.9

The hypothetical mechanism (shown below) is unfeasible because HO^- is too unstable to be produced along with a carbocation.

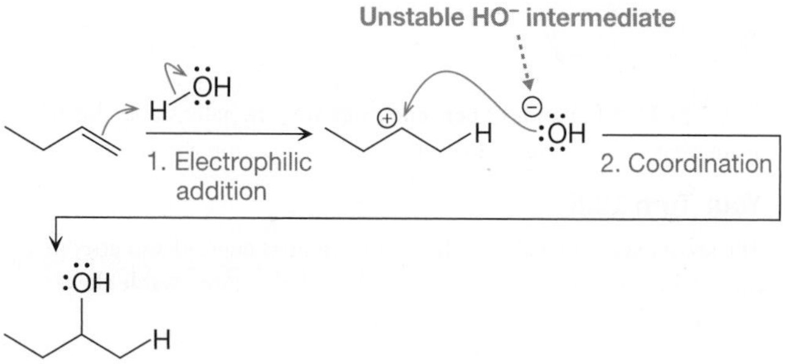

Unstable HO⁻ intermediate
1. Electrophilic addition
2. Coordination

Your Turn 12.10

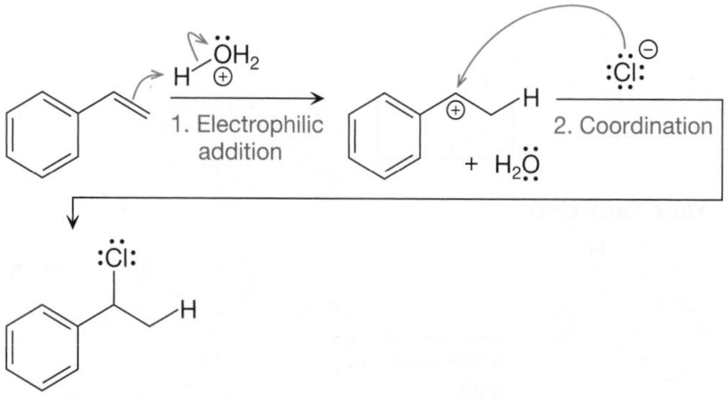

1. Electrophilic addition
2. Coordination

Your Turn 12.11

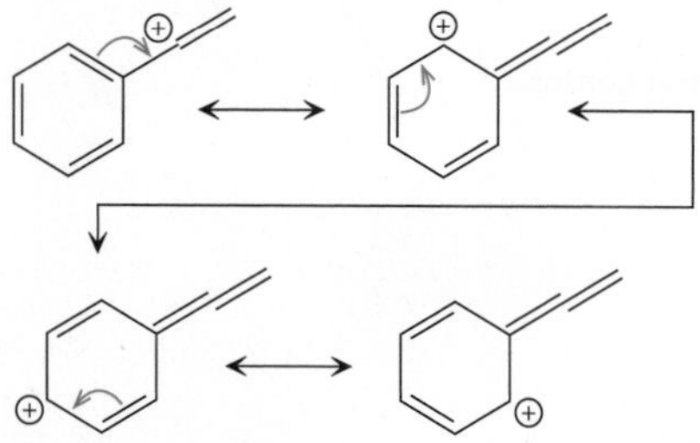

Your Turn 12.12

(a) Draw the mechanism in Equation 12-18 (p. 621), but replace the alkyne with the one given in the problem. **(b)** Draw Steps 3 and 4 of the mechanism in Equation 12-18 (p. 621), but replace the vinylic halide with the one given in the problem, and replace HCl with HBr. The major products are shown here:

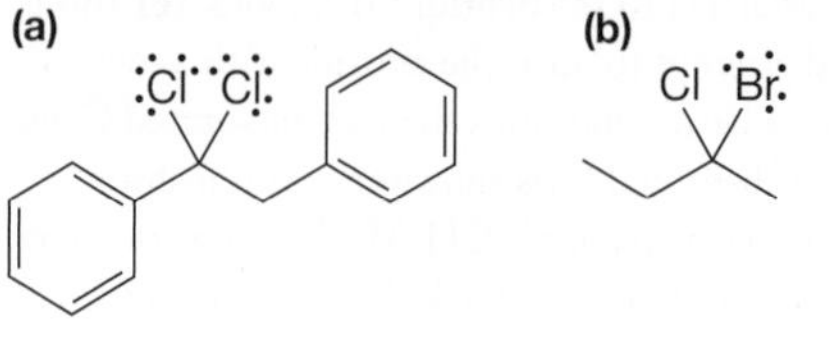

(a)
(b)

Your Turn 12.13

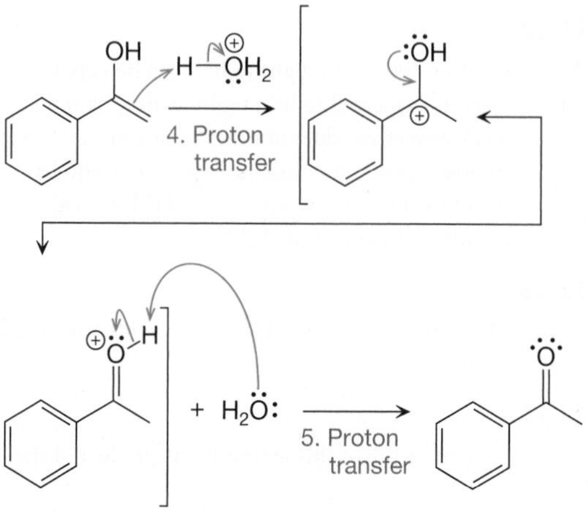

4. Proton transfer
5. Proton transfer

Your Turn 12.14

A less stable, vinylic carbocation would have to be generated, as shown below. This carbocation has the formal charge on a primary C rather than a secondary C, as in the more stable vinylic carbocation in Equation 12-22.

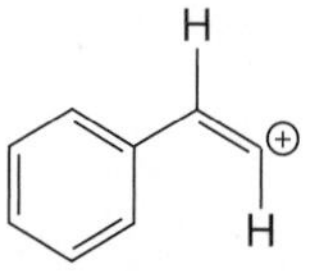

Less stable vinylic C⁺

Your Turn 12.15

Draw the mechanism in Equation 12-22 (p. 623) and the answer to Your Turn 12.13, but replace the alkyne with the one given in this problem, and replace H_3O^+ with TfOH. The first two steps likely occur in a single step, according to Equation 12-20. The major product is shown here:

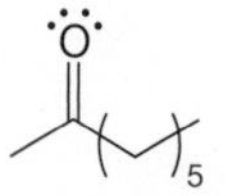

The first two steps likely occur in a single step, according to Equation 12-20.

Your Turn 12.16

The first product is from 1,2-addition, and the second is from 1,4-addition.

Your Turn 12.17

The first product is the thermodynamic product, as it is the more stable alkene (tetrasubstituted vs. trisubstituted) and is the result of 1,4-addition. The second product is the kinetic product, as it is the result of the faster 1,2-addition.

Your Turn 12.18

(a)

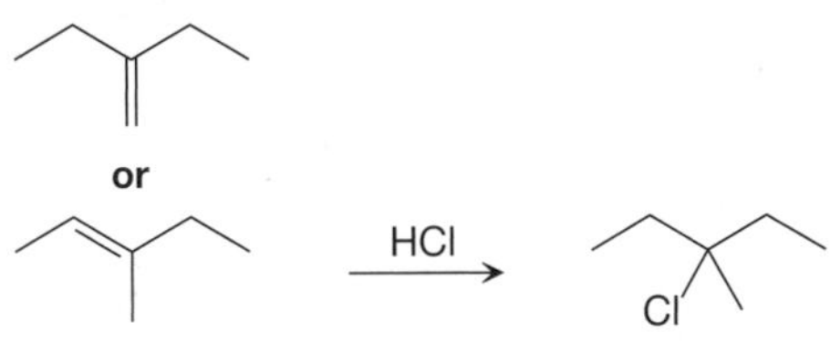
or
HCl
Cl

(b)

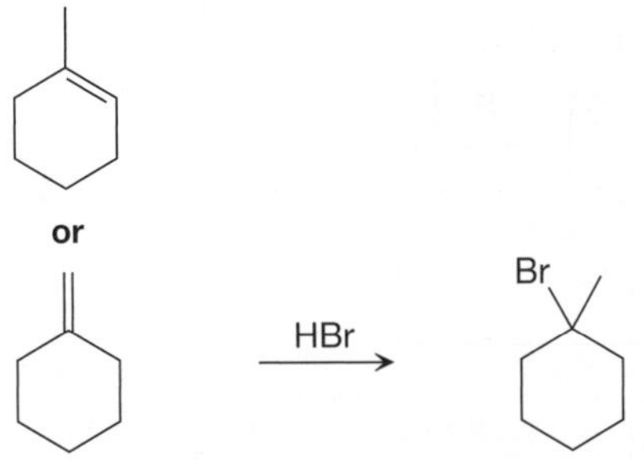
or
HBr
Br

(c)

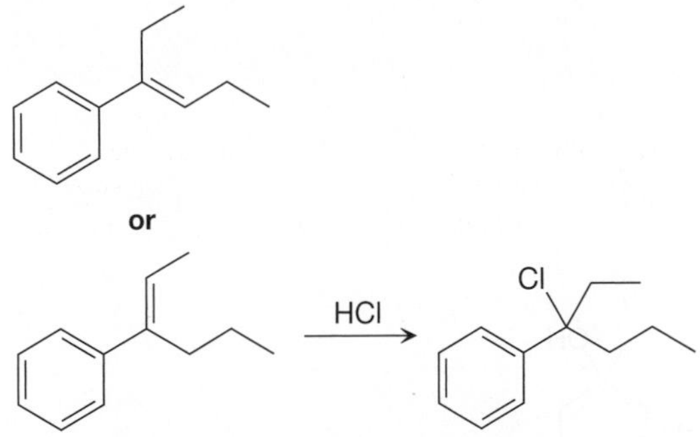
or
HCl
Cl

Your Turn 12.19

(a)

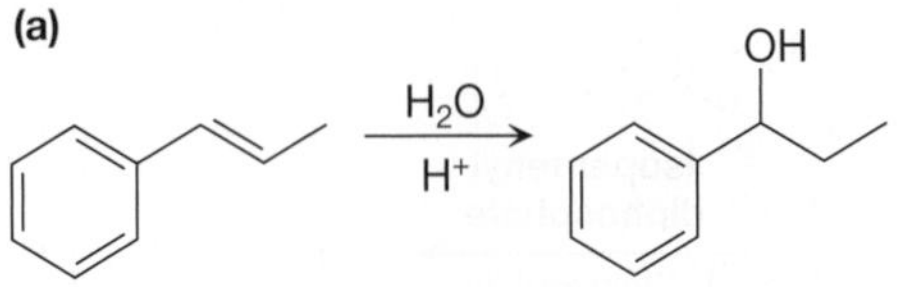
H2O
H+
OH

(b)

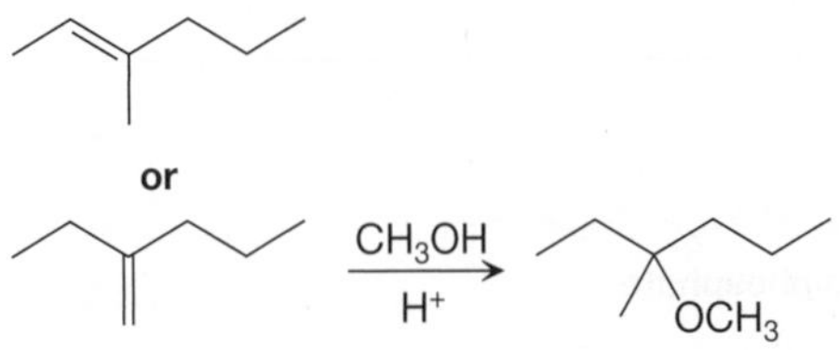
or
CH3OH
H+
OCH3

(c)

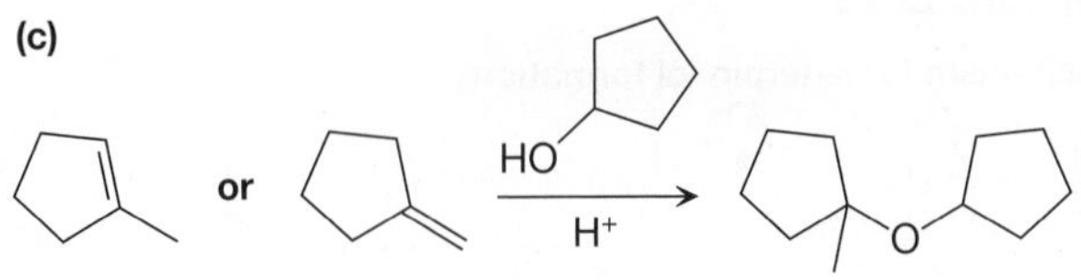
or
HO
H+
O

Your Turn 12.20

(a)

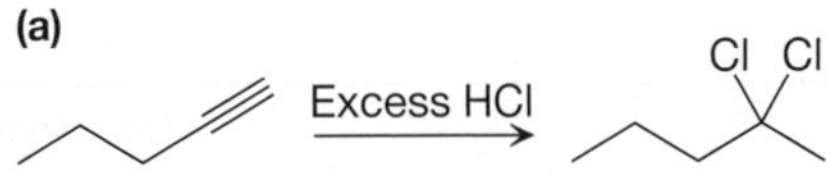
Excess HCl
Cl Cl

(b)

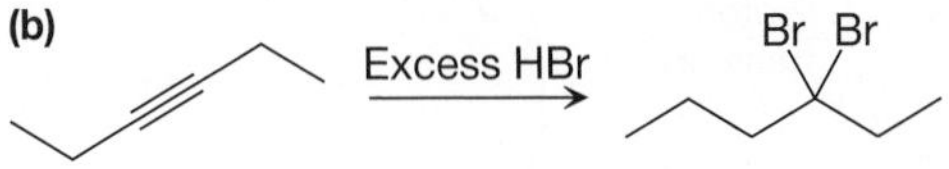
Excess HBr
Br Br

(c)

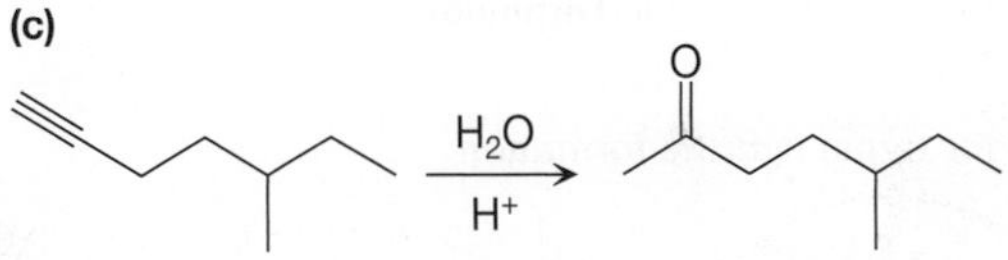
H2O
H+
O

Your Turn 12.21

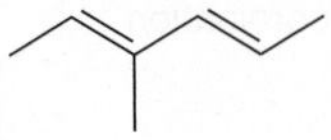

Your Turn 12.22

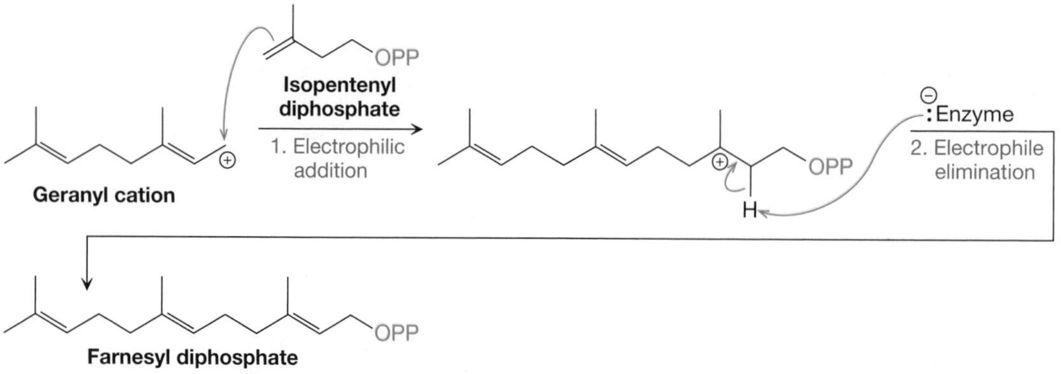
Isopentenyl diphosphate
OPP
1. Electrophilic addition
Geranyl cation
OPP
Enzyme
2. Electrophile elimination
H
OPP
Farnesyl diphosphate

Your Turn 12.23

Mechanism for α-terpineol formation

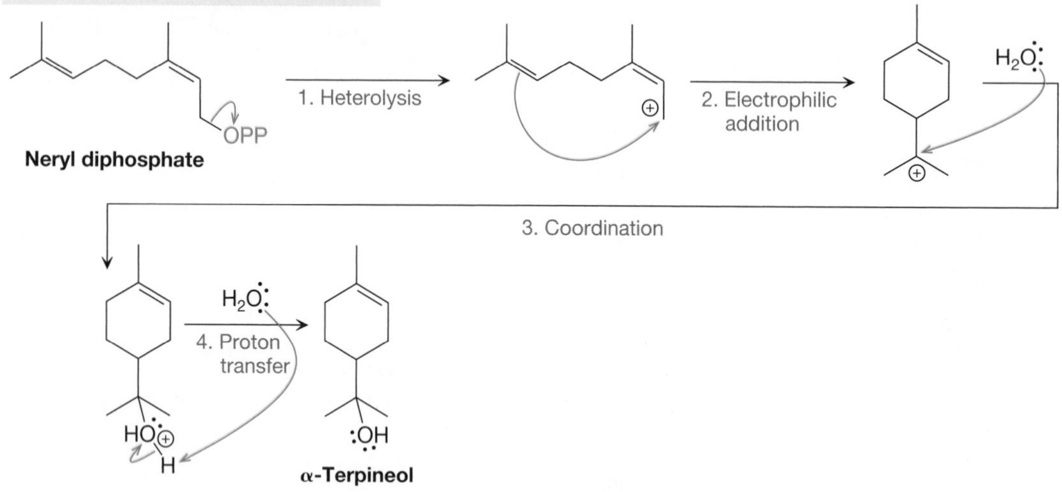
Neryl diphosphate
OPP
1. Heterolysis
2. Electrophilic addition
H_2O
3. Coordination
H_2O
4. Proton transfer
HO
H
:OH
α-Terpineol

Mechanism for terpin hydrate formation

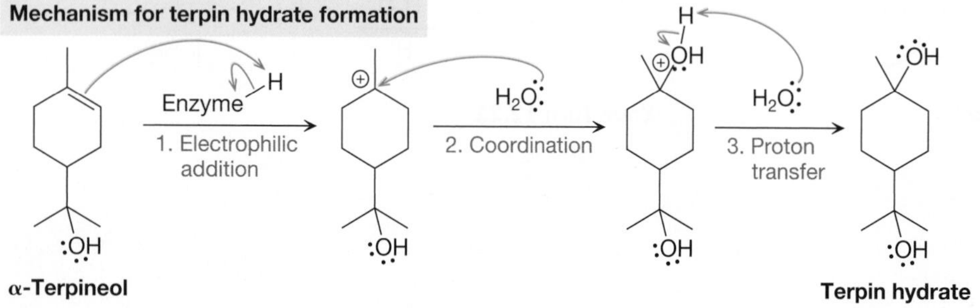
Enzyme
H
1. Electrophilic addition
H_2O
2. Coordination
H
OH
H_2O
3. Proton transfer
OH
:OH
α-Terpineol
Terpin hydrate

Chapter 13

Your Turn 13.1

Each highlighted C atom that is uncharged has four bonds, the same as in the initial alkene. The highlighted C^+ has three bonds, one fewer bond than in the initial alkene.

Your Turn 13.2

B matches **X** and **A** matches **Y**. The reaction product mixture in **Y** is racemic.

Your Turn 13.3

The carbene C is assigned one electron from each of its two bonds, and it is assigned both electrons in the lone pair. Thus, the carbene C is assigned four valence electrons, the same as in an isolated C atom, so the formal charge is 0.

Your Turn 13.4

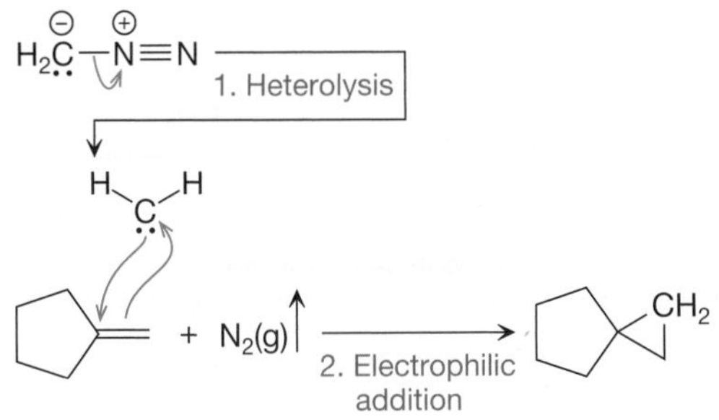
1. Heterolysis
2. Electrophilic addition

Your Turn 13.5

O—O bond = 138 kJ/mol; C—C bond = 339 kJ/mol.

Your Turn 13.6

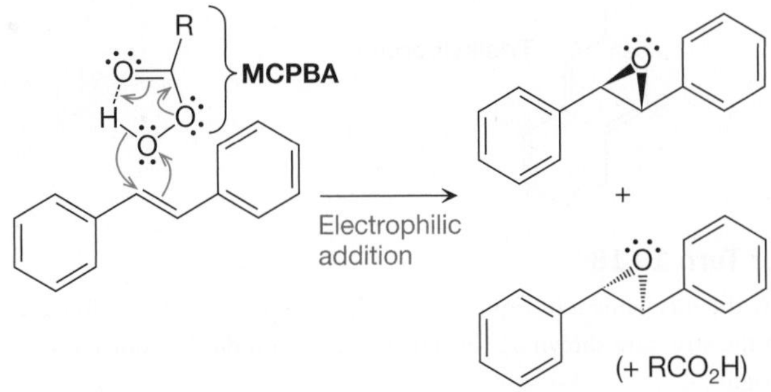
MCPBA
Electrophilic addition
(+ RCO_2H)

Your Turn 13.7

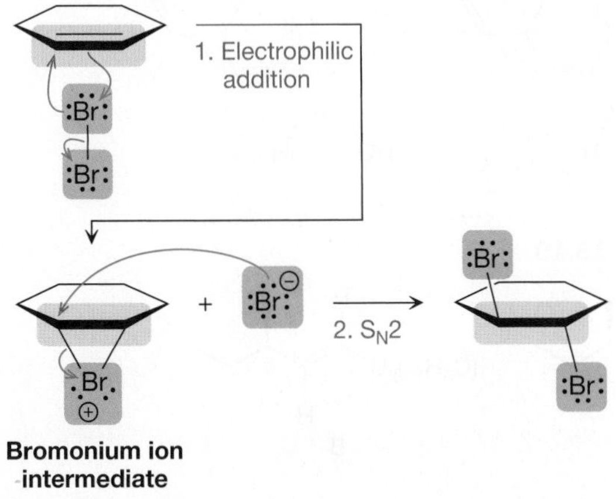
1. Electrophilic addition
2. S_N2
Bromonium ion intermediate

Your Turn 13.8

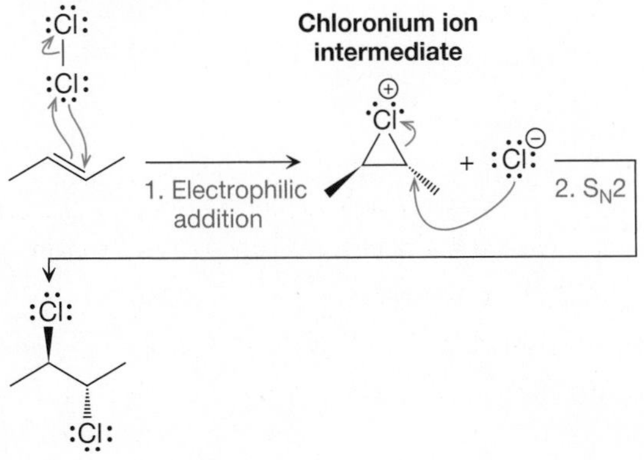
Chloronium ion intermediate
1. Electrophilic addition
2. S_N2

Your Turn 13.9

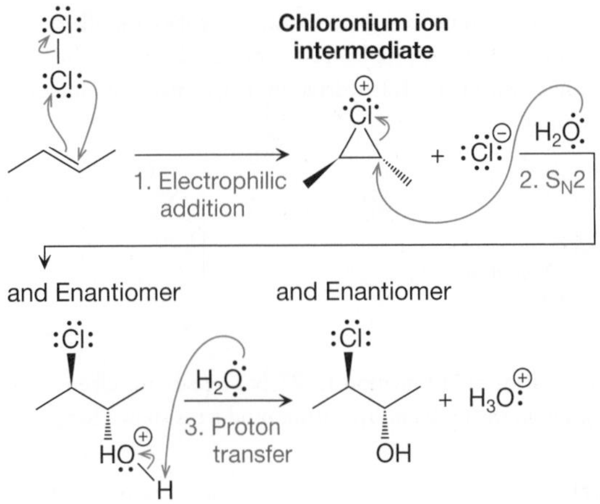
Chloronium ion intermediate
1. Electrophilic addition
2. S_N2
and Enantiomer
and Enantiomer
3. Proton transfer

Your Turn 13.10

Draw the mechanism in Equation 13-18, but in Step 2, H_2O attacks the alkene C on the right instead, as shown here.

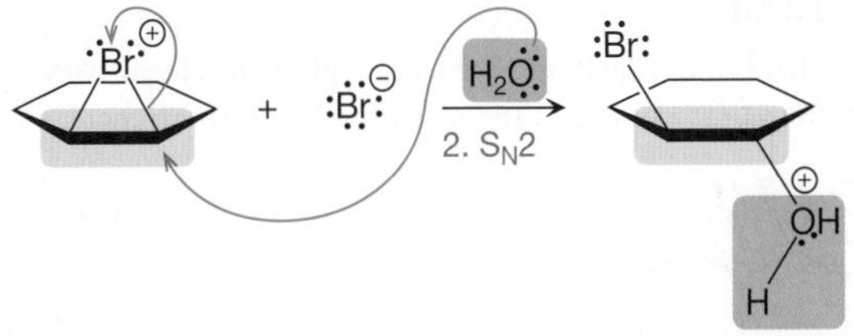
2. S_N2

Your Turn 13.11

Draw the mechanism in Equation 13-20, but replace the alkene with the structure on the left and replace Br_2 with Cl_2. The major products are shown on the right.

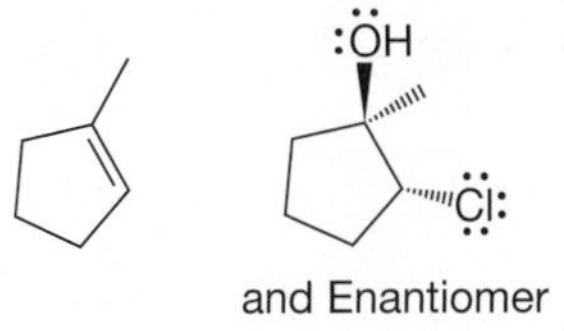
and Enantiomer

Your Turn 13.12

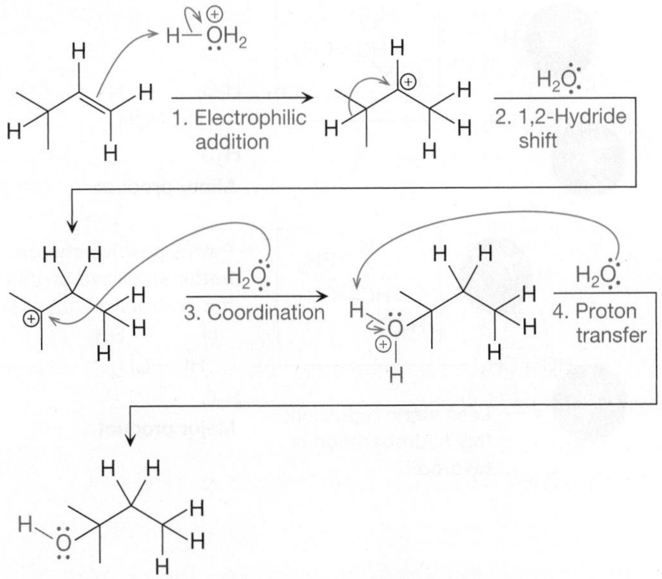
1. Electrophilic addition
2. 1,2-Hydride shift
3. Coordination
4. Proton transfer

Your Turn 13.13

(a) Draw the mechanism in Your Turn 13.12, but replace the alkene with the reactant given in the problem, and draw a 1,2-methyl shift as shown on the left instead of a 1,2-hydride shift. The major product is shown on the right.

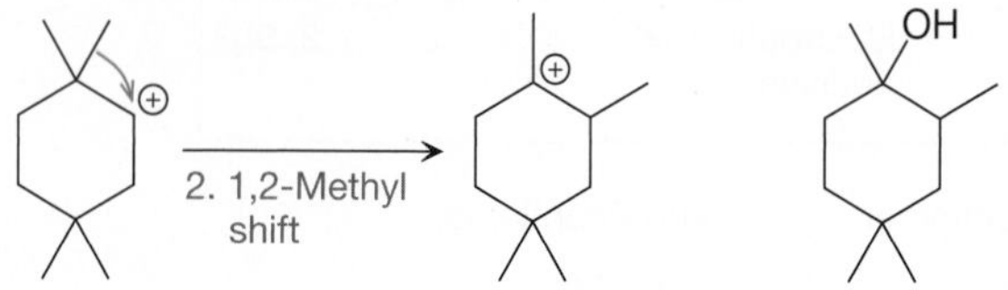
2. 1,2-Methyl shift
OH

(b) Draw the mechanism in Equation 13-23, but replace the alkene with the reactant given in the problem. The major product is shown here.

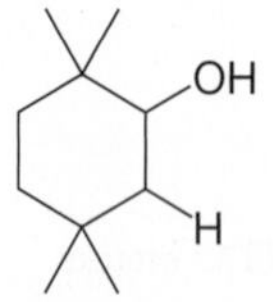
OH
H

Your Turn 13.14

Draw the mechanism in Equation 13-23, but replace the alkene with the reactant given in the problem. The major product is shown here.

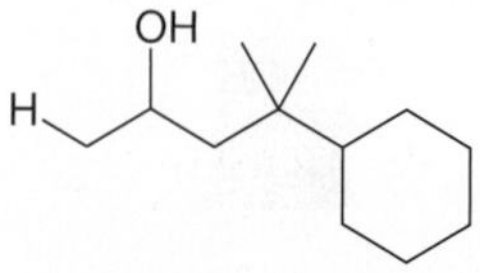
OH
H

Your Turn 13.15

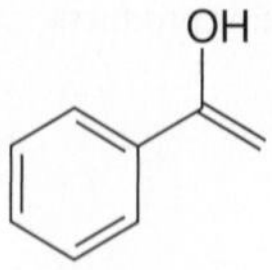
OH

Eq. 13-27

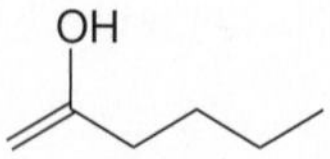
OH

Eq. 13-28

Your Turn 13.16

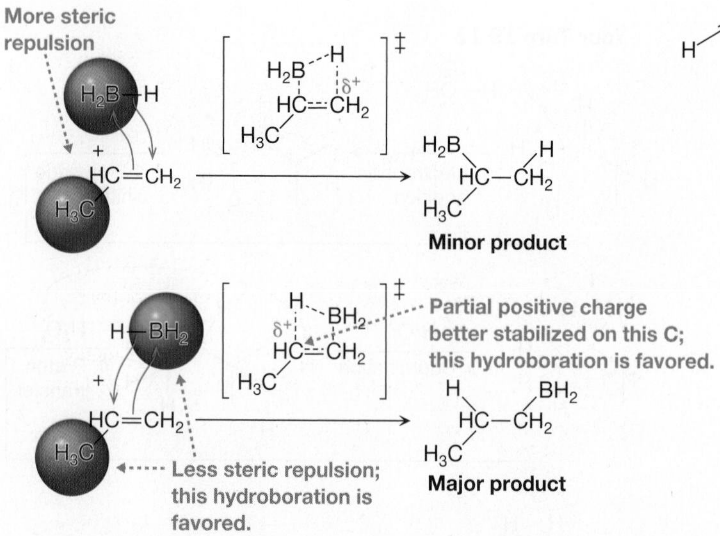
More steric repulsion
Minor product
Partial positive charge better stabilized on this C; this hydroboration is favored.
Less steric repulsion; this hydroboration is favored.
Major product

Your Turn 13.17

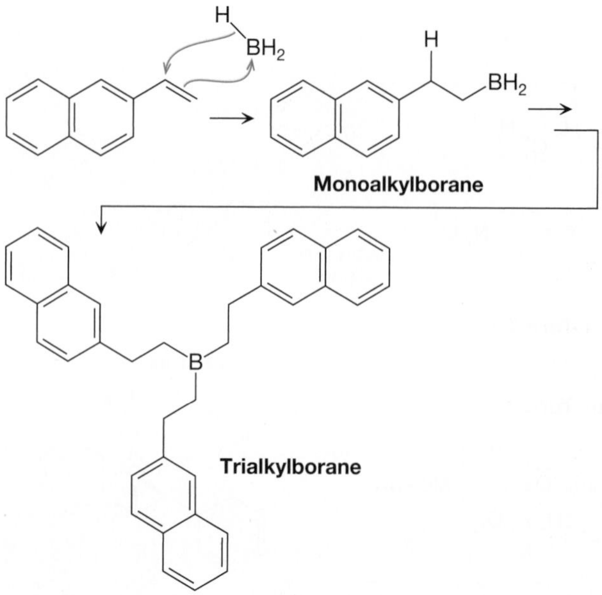
Monoalkylborane
Trialkylborane

Your Turn 13.18

Draw the mechanism in Equation 13-37, but replace the trialkylborane with the structure shown on the left. The major product is shown on the right.

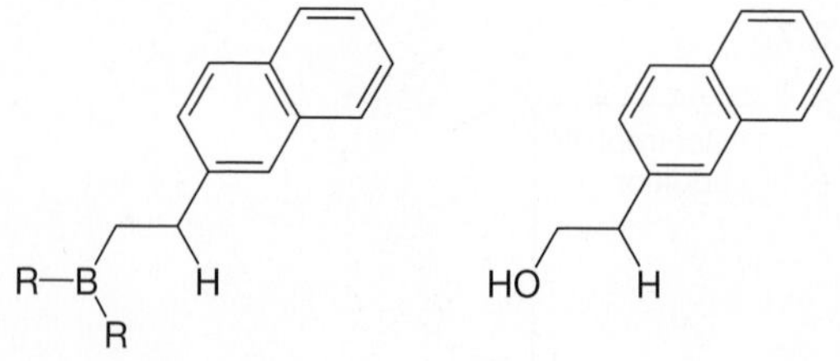

Your Turn 13.19

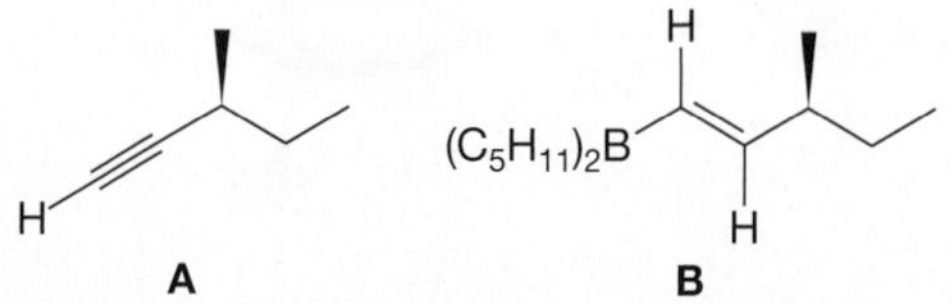
A
B

Your Turn 13.20

(a)

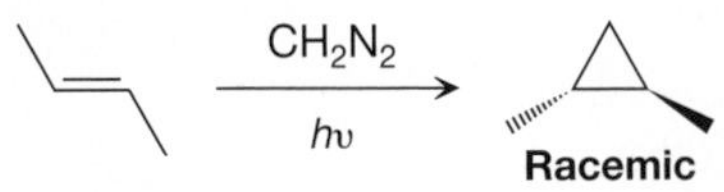

CH2N2
hυ
Racemic

(b)

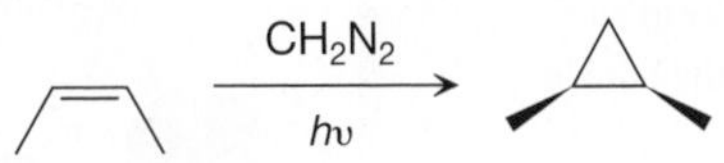

CH2N2
hυ

(c)

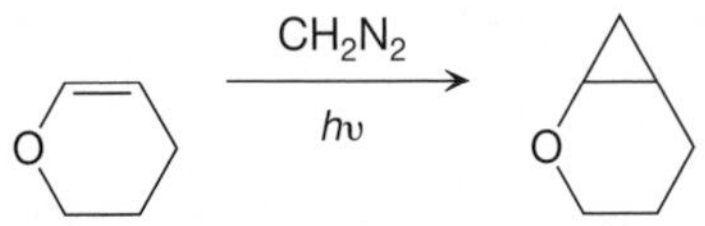

CH2N2
hυ
O

Your Turn 13.21

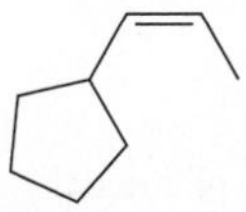

Your Turn 13.22

(a)

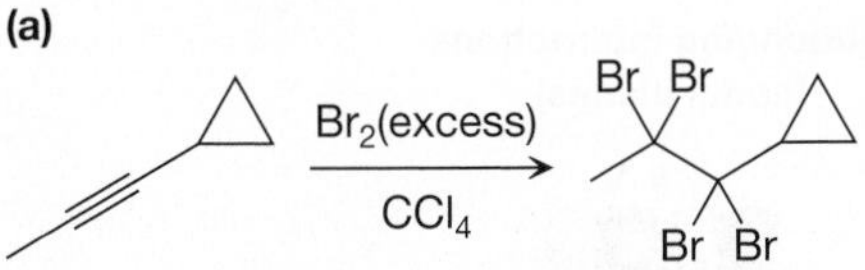

Br2(excess)
CCl4
Br Br
Br Br

(b)

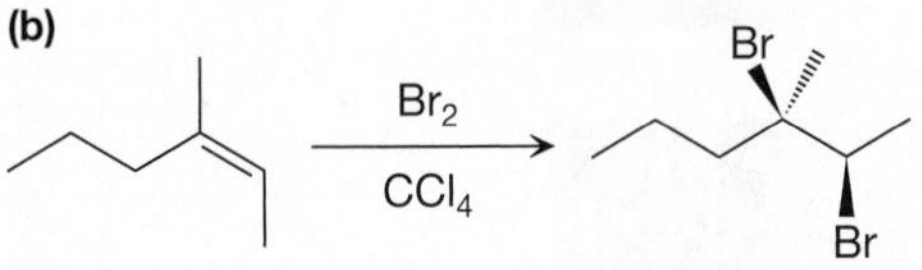

Br2
CCl4
Br
Br

(c)

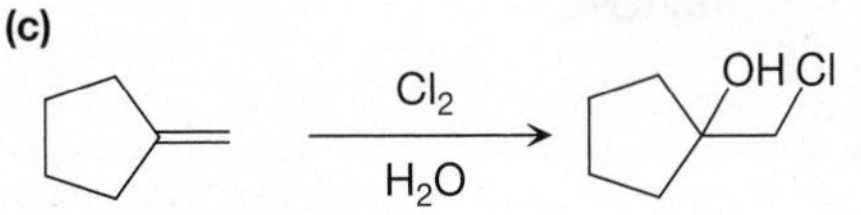

Cl2
H2O
OH Cl

Your Turn 13.23

(a) 1. $Hg(OAc)_2$, H_2O/THF; 2. $NaBH_4$. **(b)** 1. $BH_3 \cdot THF$; 2. H_2O_2, $NaOH$, H_2O; **(c)** $Hg(OAc)_2$, H_2O, acetic acid. **(d)** 1. Disiamylborane, 2. H_2O_2, NaOH, H_2O.

Your Turn 13.24

(a)

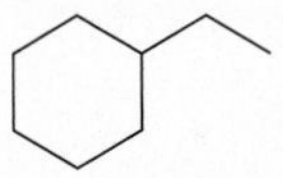

(b)

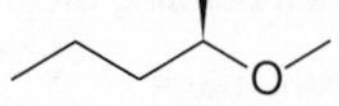

O

Your Turn 13.25

Only **B**, because it is a cis alkene.

Your Turn 13.26

The double bonds in the starting material are part of a benzene ring whose π system is aromatic and exceptionally stable.

Chapter 14

Your Turn 14.1

(a) (b)

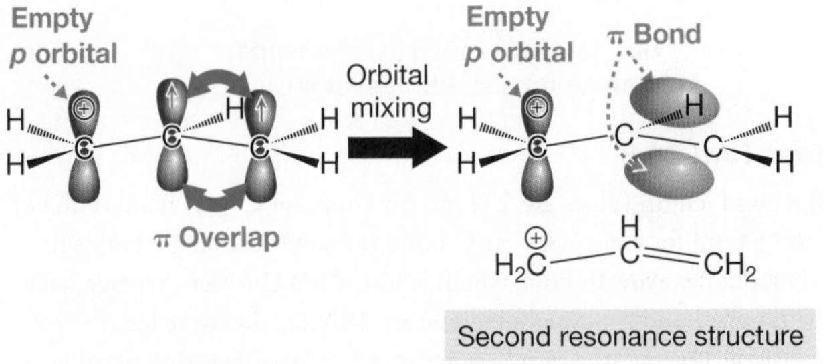

Empty
p orbital
π Overlap
Orbital
mixing
Empty
p orbital
π Bond
Second resonance structure

Your Turn 14.2

The C=O bond in **B** is longer. **B** has a conjugated π system in which electrons are delocalized over four atoms, which lengthens the two double bonds and shortens the single bond that is between the two double bonds.

Your Turn 14.3

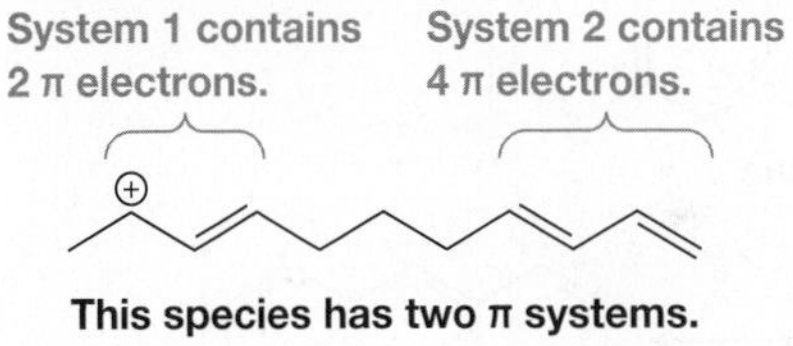

System 1 contains
2 π electrons.
System 2 contains
4 π electrons.
This species has two π systems.

Your Turn 14.4

The elimination product shown on the left is favored because it is the more stable product. It is more stable because the two π bonds are conjugated.

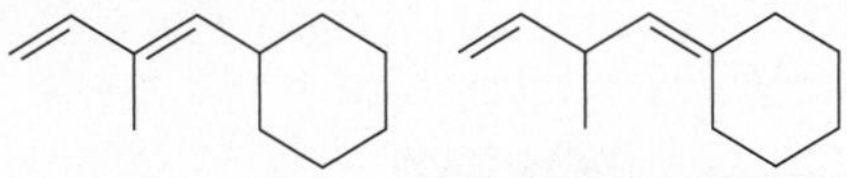

Your Turn 14.5

The π bond between C-1 and C-2, one of the π bonds of the triple bond, and the π bond between C-5 and C-6 make up one π system. The second set of *p* orbitals (second π bond) of the triple bond is perpendicular to the first set and so it is a second, separate π system.

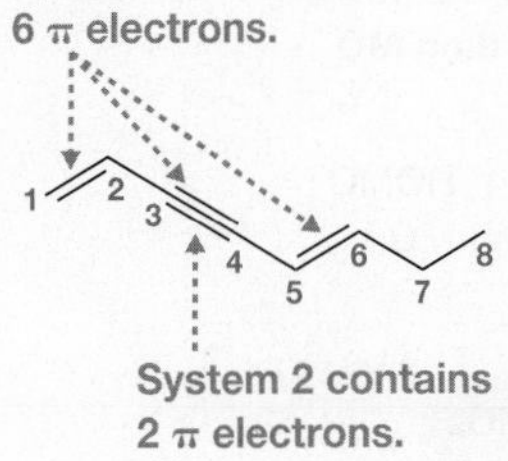

System 1 contains
6 π electrons.
System 2 contains
2 π electrons.

Your Turn 14.6

Cycloocta-1,5-diene has a heat of hydrogenation that is 17 kJ/mol more negative, meaning its double bonds are 17 kJ/mol higher in energy than the double bonds in cycloocta-1,3-diene. Thus, the double bonds in cycloocta-1,3-diene are more stable by 17 kJ/mol.

Your Turn 14.7

This species has one π system that extends from C-2 to C-6, indicated by the simultaneous movement of electrons over those atoms when going from one resonance structure to the other. Six electrons are moved, four from the two double bonds and two from the carbanion lone pair, so the π system contains six electrons.

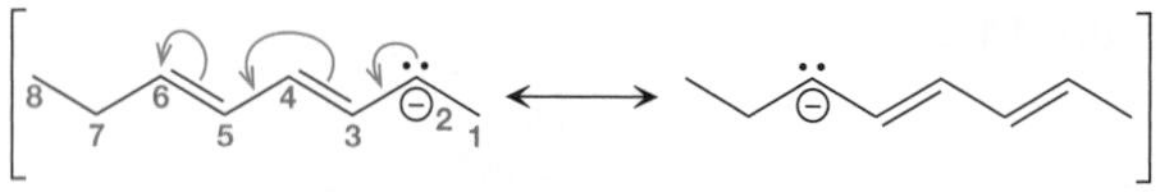

8
7
6
5
4
3
2
1

Six electrons move in resonance, making up a single π system.

Your Turn 14.8

The bond length values are 132 pm for a normal C=C bond (ethene) and 154 pm for a normal C—C bond (ethane). The single bonds in cyclobutadiene are 160 pm, which is just 4% longer than average, and the double bonds in cyclobutadiene are 132 pm, the same length as in ethene. Overall, the numbers are very similar, suggesting that the electrons are *not* significantly resonance-delocalized.

Your Turn 14.9

The resonance energy of 150 kJ/mol is 0.442, or 44.2%, as strong as the average C—C single bond energy of 339 kJ/mol (from Table 1-2).

Your Turn 14.10

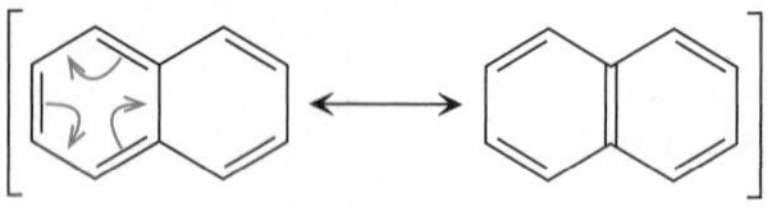

Naphthalene

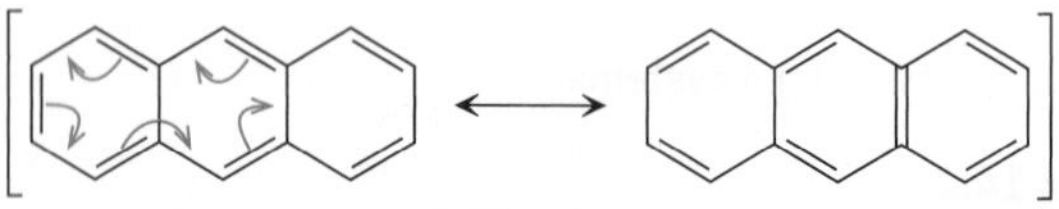

Anthracene

Each C atom is sp^2-hybridized and contains one unhybridized p orbital, so the resonance structures do not affect the locations of the p orbitals in Figure 14-20.

Your Turn 14.11

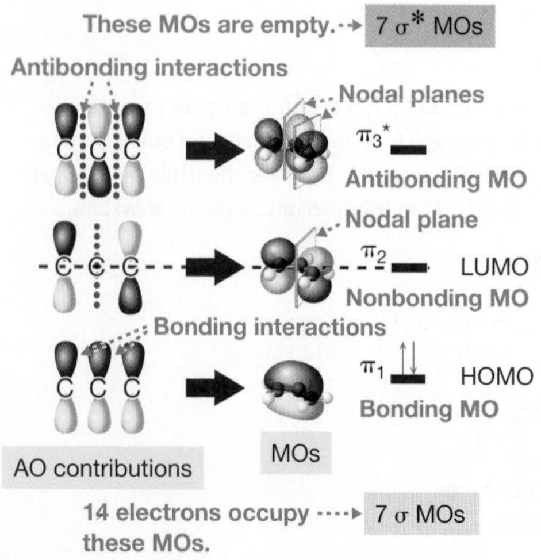

These MOs are empty.
7 σ* MOs
Antibonding interactions
Nodal planes
π3*
Antibonding MO
Nodal plane
π2
LUMO
Nonbonding MO
Bonding interactions
π1
HOMO
Bonding MO
AO contributions
MOs
14 electrons occupy these MOs.
7 σ MOs

Your Turn 14.12

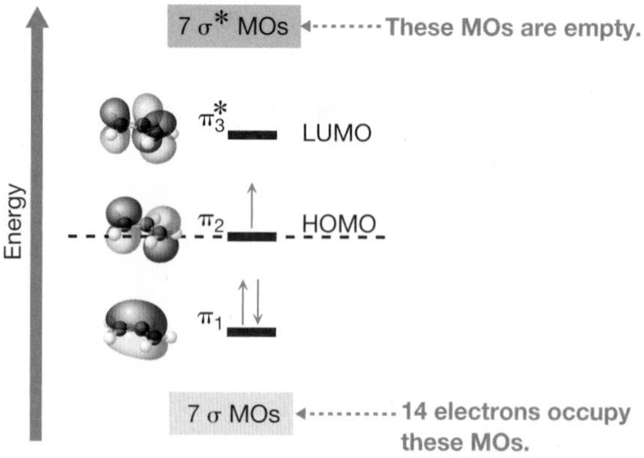

7 σ* MOs
These MOs are empty.
π3*
LUMO
Energy
π2
HOMO
π1
7 σ MOs
14 electrons occupy these MOs.

Your Turn 14.13

The antibonding interactions are indicated by the presence of a nodal plane (dotted line). The bonding interactions are indicated below by dashed ovals.

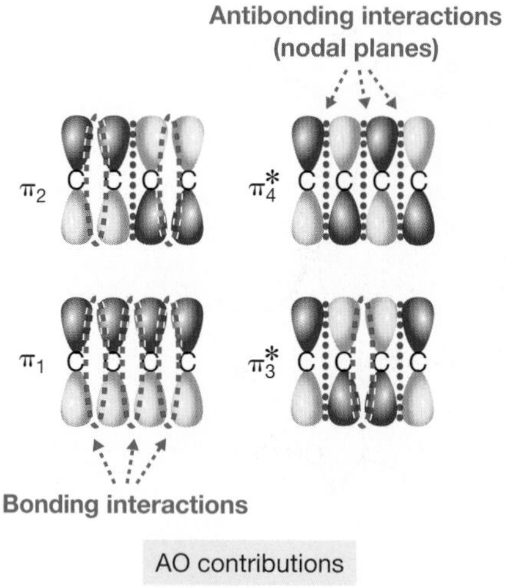

Antibonding interactions (nodal planes)
π2
π4*
π1
π3*
Bonding interactions
AO contributions

Your Turn 14.14

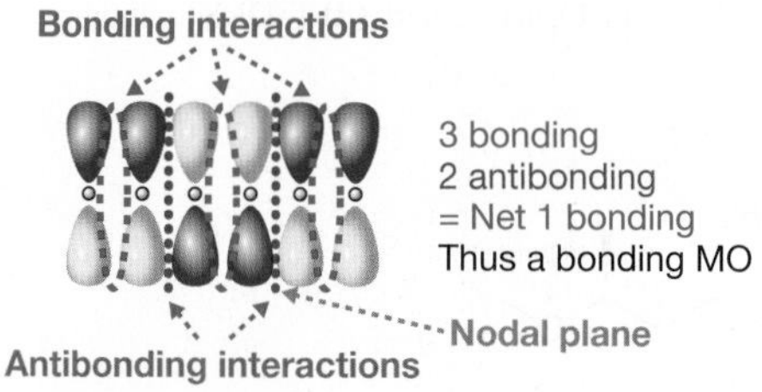

Bonding interactions
3 bonding
2 antibonding
= Net 1 bonding
Thus a bonding MO
Nodal plane
Antibonding interactions

Your Turn 14.15

The orbitals for the butadienyl dication are identical to the ones for buta-1,3-diene in Figure 14-25. The butadienyl dication has two fewer electrons, however, so its π_2 MO will remain unfilled. Therefore, the HOMO is π_1 and the LUMO is π_2.

Your Turn 14.16

The π_2 and π_3 MOs are degenerate; the π_4 and π_5 MOs are degenerate.

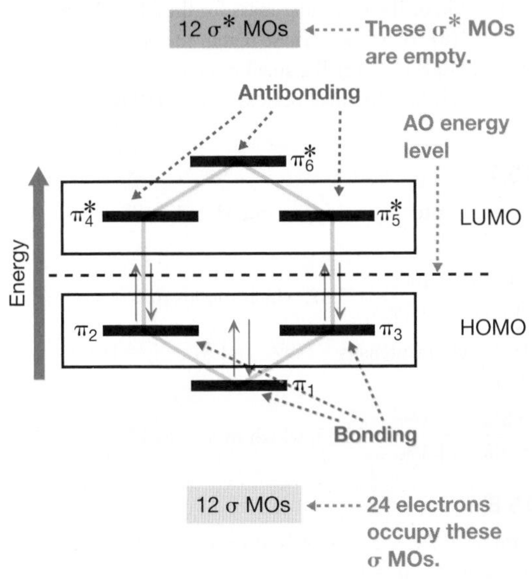

12 σ* MOs
These σ* MOs are empty.
Antibonding
AO energy level
LUMO
HOMO
Energy
Bonding
12 σ MOs
24 electrons occupy these σ MOs.

Your Turn 14.17

The π_6^* MO has three nodal planes perpendicular to the bonding axes.

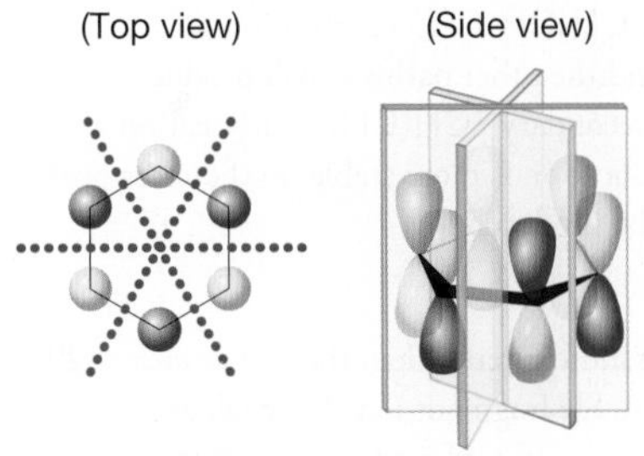

(Top view)
(Side view)

Your Turn 14.18

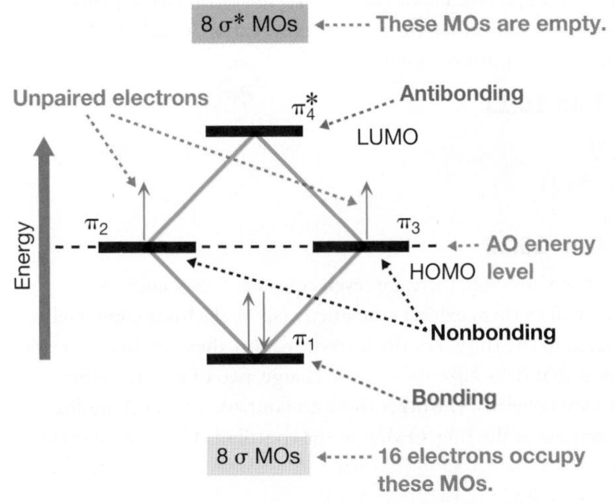

8 σ* MOs
These MOs are empty.
Unpaired electrons
Antibonding
LUMO
AO energy level
HOMO
Energy
Nonbonding
Bonding
8 σ MOs
16 electrons occupy these MOs.

Your Turn 14.19

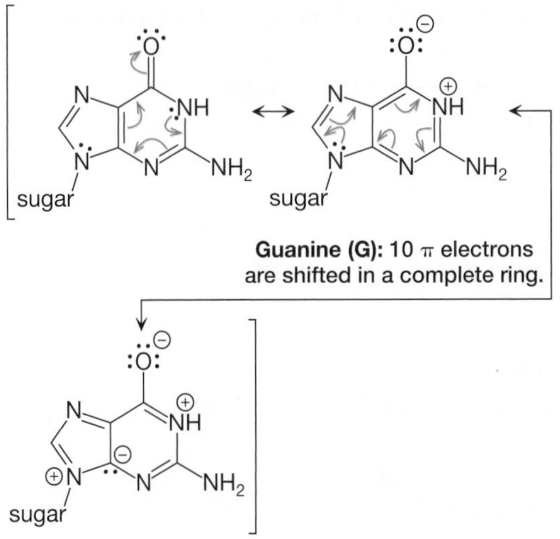

sugar
NH
NH2

Guanine (G): 10 π electrons are shifted in a complete ring.

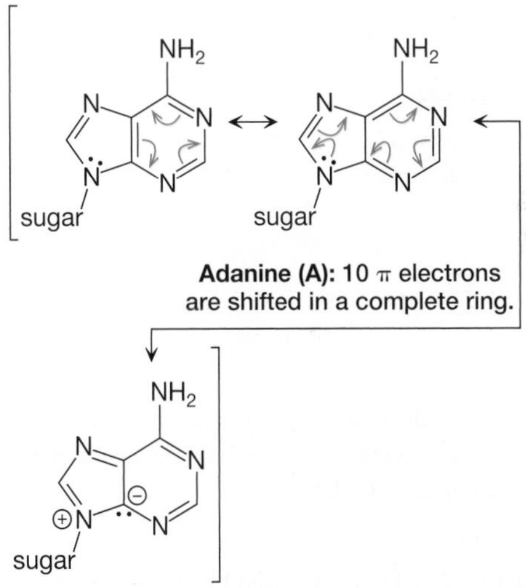

NH2
sugar

Adanine (A): 10 π electrons are shifted in a complete ring.

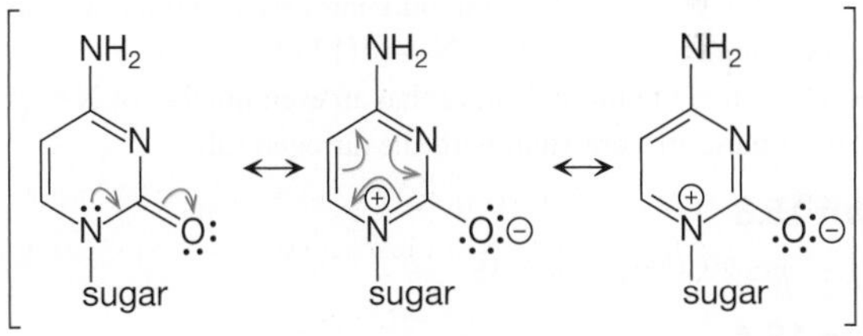

NH2
sugar

Cytosine (C): 6 π electrons are shifted in a complete ring.

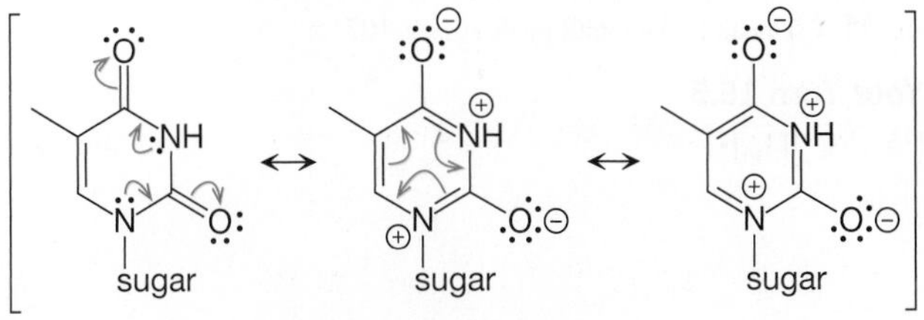

NH
sugar

Thymine (T): 6 π electrons are shifted in a complete ring.

Your Turn 14.20

The G–T base pair forms only one hydrogen bond, fewer than the three formed by the G–C base pair.

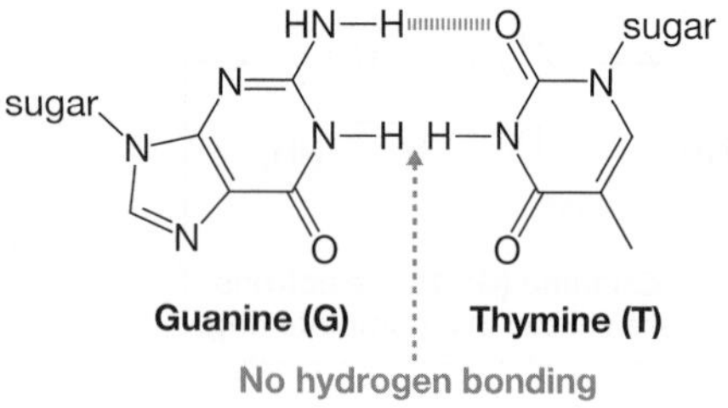
Guanine (G)
Thymine (T)
No hydrogen bonding

Your Turn 14.21

Hydrogen bonding is maximized when both G and C are in their keto forms (Figure 14-33a).

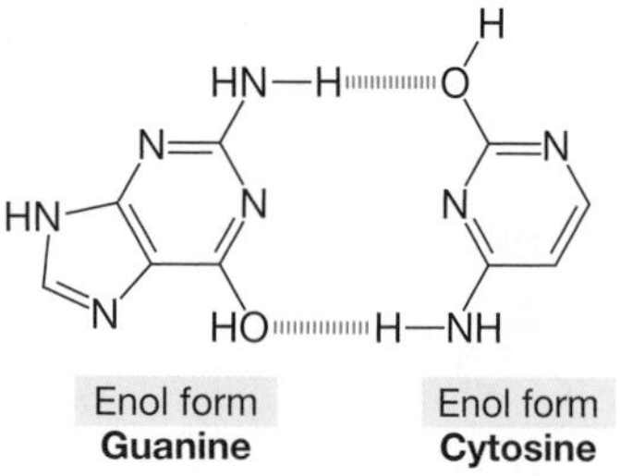
Enol form
Guanine
Enol form
Cytosine

Chapter 15

Your Turn 15.1

The fragment ions are lighter than the molecular ion and will be deflected too much to reach the detector; they will follow a path similar to the least massive ions in Figure 15-1.

Your Turn 15.2

The mass of CH_3—CO—$N(CH_3)_2$ = C_4H_9NO = 4(12 u) + 9(1 u) + 1(14 u) + 1(16 u) = 87 u (an odd number), and it has an odd number of N atoms. The mass of CH_2N_2 = 1(12 u) + 2(1 u) + 2(14 u) = 42 u (an even number), and it has an even number of N atoms. Both of these are consistent with the nitrogen rule.

Your Turn 15.3

$CH_3CH_2^+$ = *m/z* 29; CH_3^+ = *m/z* 15.

Your Turn 15.4

The M + 1 peak in Figure 15-2 is the small peak at *m/z* 87. The $M^{+\bullet}$ peak for ethylbenzene in Solved Problem 15.1 is at *m/z* 106, so the M + 1 peak is the small peak at *m/z* 107.

Your Turn 15.5

$[{}^{12}C_7{}^{13}C_1{}^{1}H_{10}]^{+\bullet}$.

Your Turn 15.6

(a) $[C_6H_5{}^{81}Br]^{+\bullet}$. **(b)** The molecular mass for the $M^{+\bullet}$ ion = 6(12 u) + 5(1 u) + 1(79 u) = 156 u. The molecular mass for the M + 2 ion = 6(12 u) + 5(1 u) + 1(81 u) = 158 u. These match the *m/z* values in the spectrum in Figure 15-7. **(c)** The small peak at *m/z* = 157 is from $[{}^{12}C_5{}^{13}CH_5{}^{79}Br]^{+\bullet}$, and the small peak at *m/z* = 159 is from $[{}^{12}C_5{}^{13}CH_5{}^{81}Br]^{+\bullet}$.

Your Turn 15.7

Hexane: $M^{+\bullet}$ = 86 u (intensity ~15.5%) and M + 1 = 87 u (intensity ~1.0%).

$$\frac{1.0\%}{15.5\%} \times \frac{100\%}{1.1\%} = 5.87\text{, which rounds to 6}$$

Dodecane: $M^{+\bullet}$ = 160 u (intensity ~5.9%) and M + 1 = 161 u (intensity ~0.8%).

$$\frac{0.8\%}{5.9\%} \times \frac{100\%}{1.1\%} = 12.33\text{, which rounds to 12}$$

Your Turn 15.8

Number of H atoms = $2n$ + 2 + (# of N atoms) − (# of halogen atoms) = 2(7) + 2 + 1 − 0 = 17.

Your Turn 15.9

When $[CH_3CH_2CH_2CH_2—CH(CH_3)_2]^{+\bullet}$ fragments, one pathway will produce the primary $CH_3CH_2CH_2CH_2^+$ carbocation at *m/z* = 57 and •$CH(CH_3)_2$, and the other pathway will produce $CH_3CH_2CH_2CH_2$• and the secondary ${}^+CH(CH_3)_2$ carbocation at *m/z* = 43. The secondary carbocation is more stable, so the mass peak at *m/z* = 43 will more likely be produced.

Your Turn 15.10

The mass peak at *m/z* = 71 is more intense than the one at *m/z* = 29 and corresponds to the more stable fragment ion. The peak at *m/z* = 29 is from an ethyl cation, $CH_3CH_2^+$, and the peak at *m/z* = 71 is from the fragmentation of the methyl group to give the 2-pentyl cation, $CH_3CH^+CH_2CH_2CH_3$. The secondary 2-pentyl cation is more stable than the primary ethyl cation, which is why the peak at *m/z* = 71 is more intense.

Your Turn 15.11

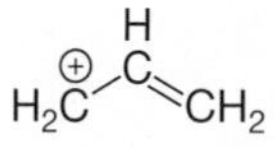

Your Turn 15.12

For the tropylium ion, there are seven equivalent resonance structures, and all of them exhibit aromaticity (six π electrons completely conjugated in the ring). For the benzylic cation, there are five resonance structures that delocalize the positive charge, two of which exhibit aromaticity (labeled). The other three do not have a Hückel number of π electrons in the ring. Owing to the contribution of the especially stable aromatic resonance structures and the delocalization of the positive charge over more atoms, the tropylium cation is more stable than the benzylic cation.

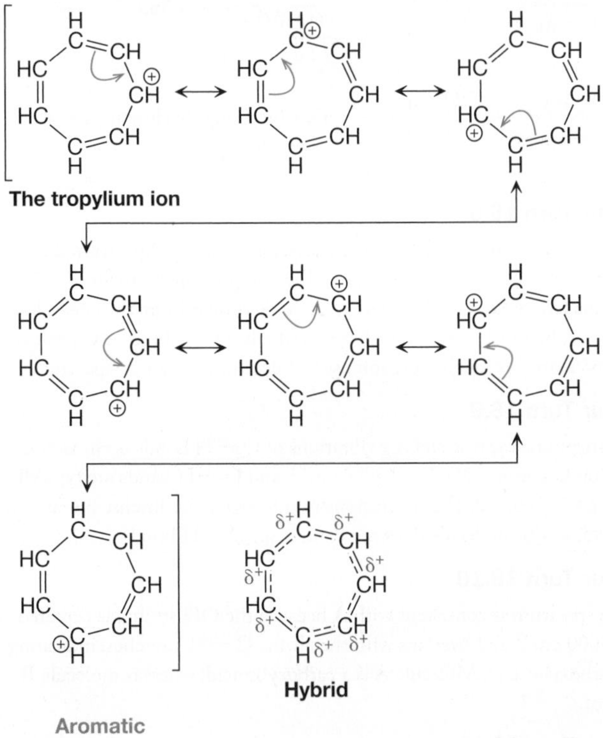
The tropylium ion
Hybrid
Aromatic

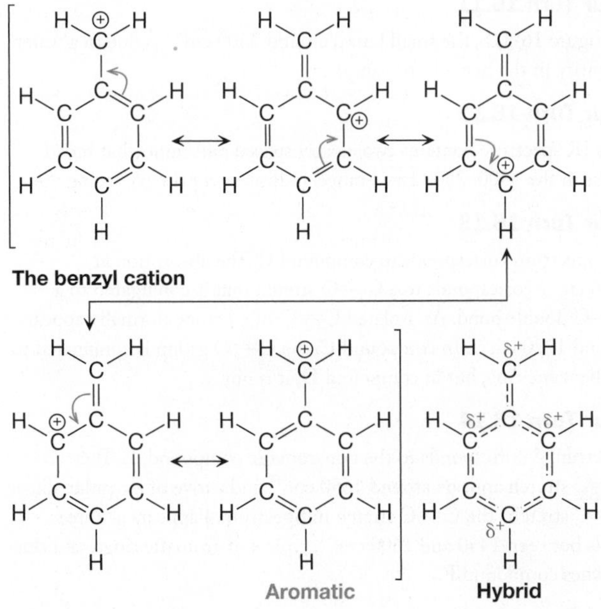
The benzyl cation
Aromatic
Hybrid

Your Turn 15.13

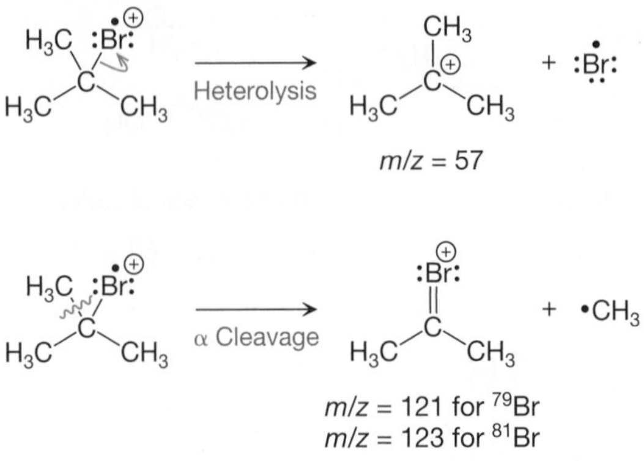
Heterolysis
m/z = 57
α Cleavage
m/z = 121 for 79Br
m/z = 123 for 81Br

Your Turn 15.14

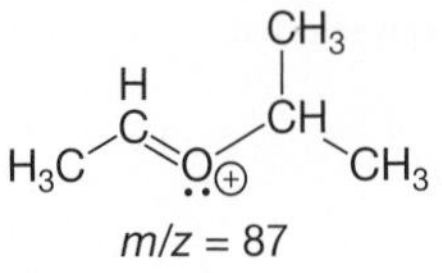
m/z = 87

Your Turn 15.15

α Cleavage of the molecular ion of pentan-1-ol, $CH_3CH_2CH_2CH_2—CH_2OH^{+\bullet}$, produces the $H_2C{=}OH^+$ fragment ion, and so does α cleavage of the molecular ion of hexan-1-ol, $CH_3CH_2CH_2CH_2CH_2—CH_2OH^{+\bullet}$. That fragment ion will appear at $m/z = 31$ in both cases.

Your Turn 15.16

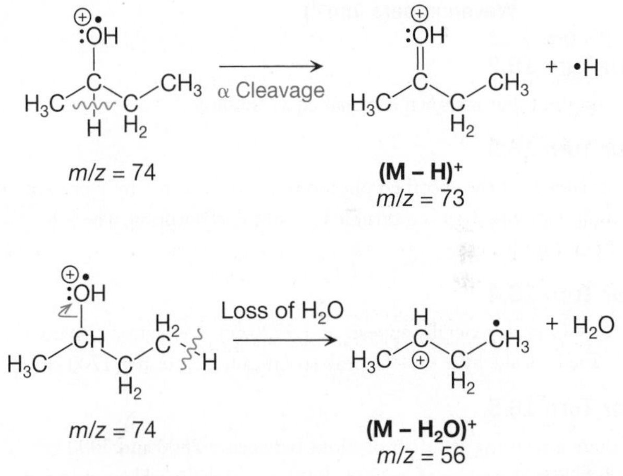
α Cleavage
m/z = 74
(M – H)+
m/z = 73
Loss of H2O
m/z = 74
(M – H2O)+
m/z = 56

Your Turn 15.17

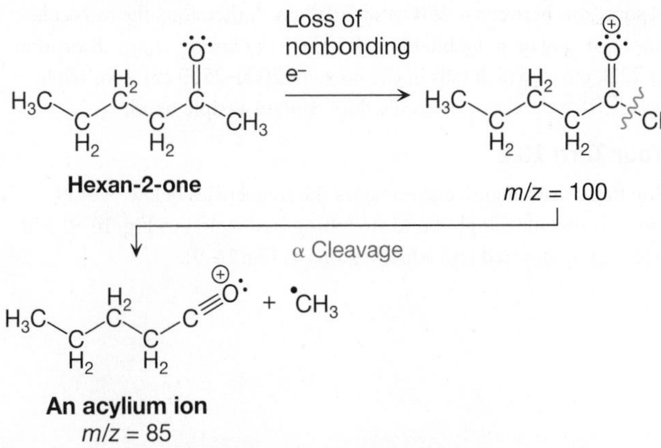
Loss of
nonbonding
e−
Hexan-2-one
m/z = 100
α Cleavage
An acylium ion
m/z = 85

Your Turn 15.18

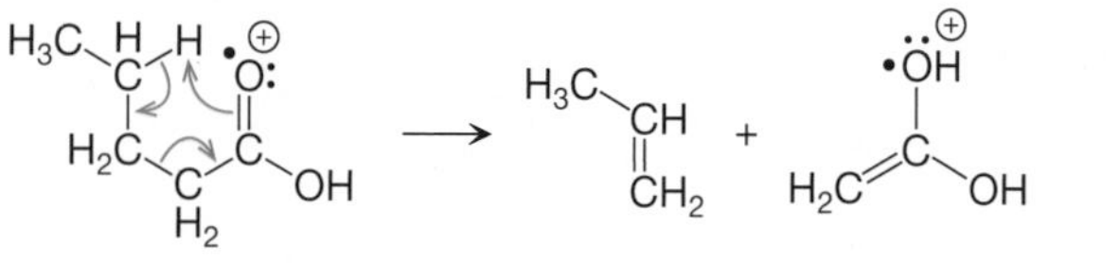

Pentanoic acid $m/z = 102$

An enol radical cation $m/z = 60$

Chapter 16

Your Turn 16.1

Two additional peaks at 1320 and 1167 cm^{-1} are labeled in red. However, several other peaks could also have been selected.

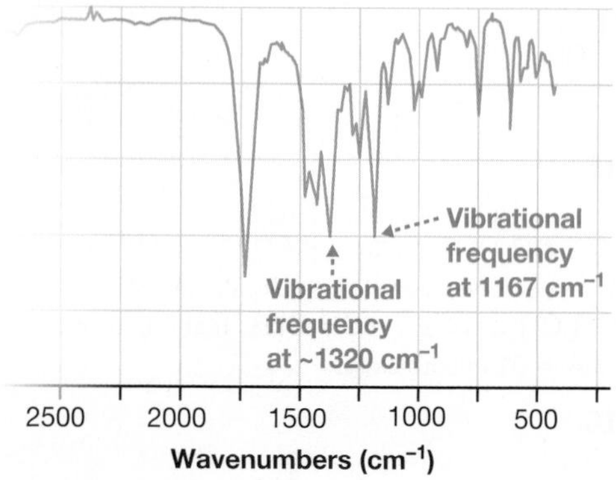

Vibrational frequency at 1167 cm^{-1}
Vibrational frequency at ~1320 cm^{-1}
2500
2000
1500
1000
500
Wavenumbers (cm^{-1})

Your Turn 16.2

The vibration that is shown is classified as bending.

Your Turn 16.3

The frequency of the absorbed photon is the same as the frequency of the molecular vibration responsible for photon absorption, which is 1167 cm^{-1} in this case.

Your Turn 16.4

The C=O peak generally appears at ~1720 cm^{-1} as a strong, sharp peak. The benzaldehyde C=O peak specifically occurs at ~1700 cm^{-1}.

Your Turn 16.5

(a) There is a strong set of absorptions between ~2800 and 3000 cm^{-1}, which falls in the range of ~2500–4000 cm^{-1} for Q—H single bonds. Therefore, this molecule does contain a Q—H bond. **(b)** There are no absorptions between ~1500 and 2000 cm^{-1}; therefore, the molecule does not contain a double bond. **(c)** There is a strong, sharp absorption at 2250 cm^{-1}, which falls in the range of 2000–2500 cm^{-1} for triple bonds. Therefore, this molecule does contain a triple bond.

Your Turn 16.6

The fingerprint region encompasses the frequencies below ~1400 cm^{-1}. It includes single-bond stretching (red region in Fig. 16-9) and bending modes (red and white regions in Fig. 16-9).

Your Turn 16.7

(a) $$\frac{\nu_{\text{C–H (Hooke)}}}{\nu_{\text{C–D (Hooke)}}} = \sqrt{\frac{\mu_{\text{C–D}}}{\mu_{\text{C–H}}}} = \sqrt{\frac{\dfrac{(12\text{ u})(2\text{ u})}{12\text{ u} + 2\text{ u}}}{\dfrac{(12\text{ u})(1\text{ u})}{12\text{ u} + 1\text{ u}}}} = 1.36.$$

(b) $$\frac{\nu_{\text{C–H (actual)}}}{\nu_{\text{C–D (actual)}}} = \frac{2900\text{ cm}^{-1}}{2150\text{ cm}^{-1}} = 1.35,$$ which is quite close to the ratio in part **(a)**.

Your Turn 16.8

Spectrum 1 corresponds to 1-methylcyclohexene and Spectrum 2 corresponds to methylenecyclohexane. The two portions of the molecule connected by the C=C bond are more dissimilar in methylenecyclohexane than in 1-methylcyclohexene, which is why the C=C peak at ~1650 cm^{-1} is much more intense in Spectrum 2 than in Spectrum 1.

Your Turn 16.9

Absorptions from stretching vibrations of Q—H bonds occur in the region between ~2500 and 4000 cm^{-1}, and O—H bands are typically intense and broad. The absorptions in this region are intense but are *not* broad, so this molecule does not contain an O—H bond.

Your Turn 16.10

The spectrum is consistent with **A** because the OH stretch is centered at 3000 cm^{-1} and overlaps with the alkane C—H stretches, indicating a carboxylic acid. Molecule **A** is a carboxylic acid, whereas molecule **B** is not.

Your Turn 16.11

In Figure 16-11b, the small bump around 3300 cm^{-1} is due to a water impurity in the hept-3-ene sample.

Your Turn 16.12

This IR spectrum contains two closely spaced and somewhat broad peaks in the 3300–3500 cm^{-1} range, indicating a primary amine.

Your Turn 16.13

The spectrum corresponds to compound **C**. The absorption at 1686 cm^{-1} corresponds to a C=O stretch that is conjugated to a C=C double bond. An isolated C=O of a ketone normally appears around 1720 cm^{-1}. In compound **C**, the C=O group is conjugated to the benzene ring, but in compound **D**, it is not.

Your Turn 16.14

Spectrum 3 corresponds to the nonaromatic compound, **E**. The C=C stretch appears around 1650 cm^{-1}, indicative of a regular alkene C=C stretch. The C=C stretch in Spectrum 4 appears as three peaks between 1450 and 1600 cm^{-1}, typical of aromatic rings, and thus matches compound **F**.

Your Turn 16.15

(a) The intense absorption at ~2250 cm^{-1} in Spectrum 5 corresponds to a nitrile, due to its large bond dipole. By contrast, the weak absorption at ~2100 cm^{-1} in Spectrum 6 is likely a C≡C triple bond, which often has a relatively small bond dipole. **(b)** There is no alkyne C—H peak at ~3300 cm^{-1}, indicating the alkyne is internal. Also, the intensity of the C≡C peak would be much greater if the C≡C were terminal because, being of the form RC≡CH, the two ends would be rather dissimilar and have a larger dipole.

Your Turn 16.16

Spectrum 7 indicates the presence of a C═C double bond. It has a clear C—H stretch above 3000 cm^{-1}, a C═C stretch at 1650 cm^{-1}, and strong C—H bending bands near 1000 cm^{-1}. Spectrum 8, although it has a peak that is consistent with a C═C stretch at ~1650 cm^{-1}, does not have a C—H stretch above 3000 cm^{-1}.

Your Turn 16.17

Alkene sp^2 C—H stretches are weak and present around 3100 cm^{-1}; no alkane sp^3 C—H stretches are present, but they would normally appear between 3000 and 2800 cm^{-1}.

Your Turn 16.18, 16.19, and 16.20

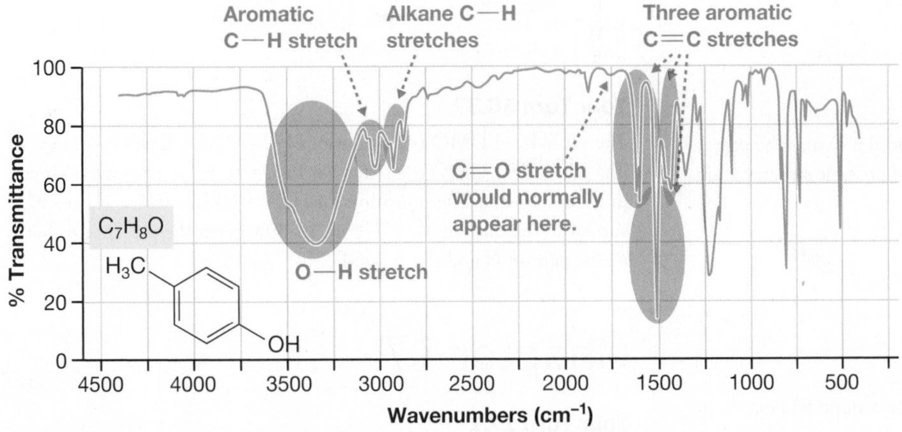
Aromatic
C—H stretch
Alkane C—H
stretches
Three aromatic
C═C stretches
C═O stretch
would normally
appear here.
O—H stretch
C7H8O
H3C
OH
% Transmittance
Wavenumbers (cm−1)
100
80
60
40
20
0
4500
4000
3500
3000
2500
2000
1500
1000
500

Your Turn 16.21

This molecule has an aromatic ring and an ether group. There is a peak between 1050 and 1150 cm^{-1} for the C—O bond, and the peaks for the aromatic ring are present in Figure 16-24. However, the broad stretching band centered at 3300 cm^{-1} is indicative of an O—H bond, which this molecule does not have. Therefore, this molecule is *not* consistent with Figure 16-24.

Your Turn 16.22, 16.23, and 16.24

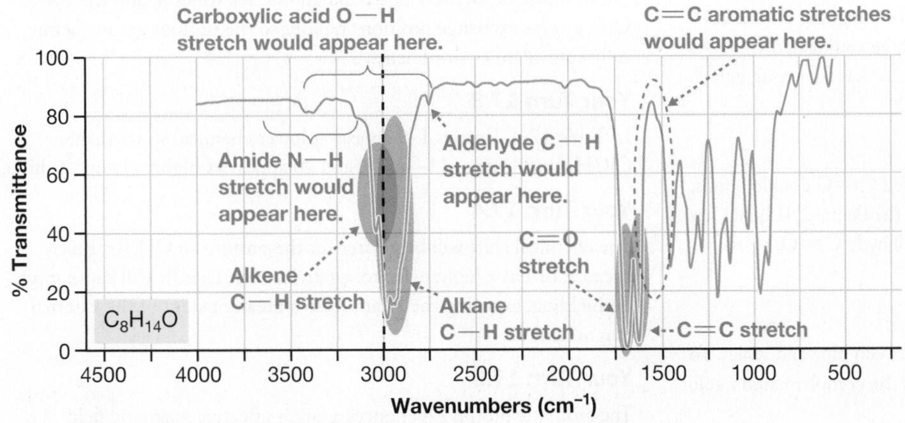
Carboxylic acid O—H
stretch would appear here.
C═C aromatic stretches
would appear here.
Amide N—H
stretch would
appear here.
Aldehyde C—H
stretch would
appear here.
C═O
stretch
Alkene
C—H stretch
Alkane
C—H stretch
C═C stretch
C8H14O
% Transmittance
Wavenumbers (cm−1)
100
80
60
40
20
0
4500
4000
3500
3000
2500
2000
1500
1000
500

Your Turn 16.25

For a saturated molecule corresponding to $C_7H_{13}NO$,
(# of H atoms) = $2n + 2$ + (# of N atoms) − (# of halogen atoms) = $2(7) + 2 + 1 - 0 = 17$.

$$\text{IHD} = \frac{17 - 13}{2} = 2$$, consistent with Unknown 3.

Your Turn 16.26

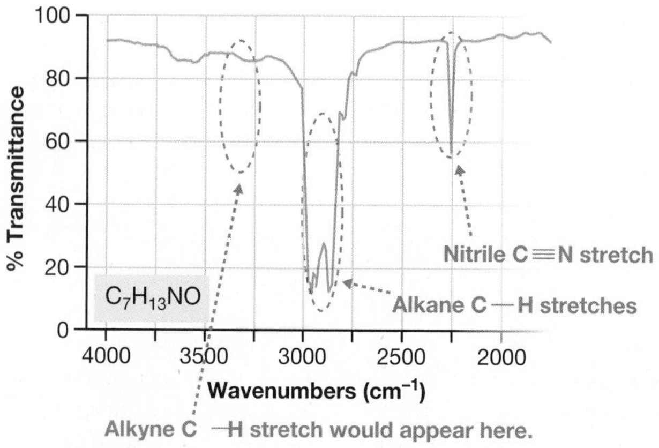
100
80
60
40
20
0
% Transmittance
4000
3500
3000
2500
2000
Wavenumbers (cm^{-1})
$C_7H_{13}NO$
Nitrile C≡N stretch
Alkane C—H stretches
Alkyne C—H stretch would appear here.

Your Turn 16.27

The molecule must contain a C≡N group and the O must be part of an ether group, C—O—C. Two additional possible structures are shown here, and there are others as well.

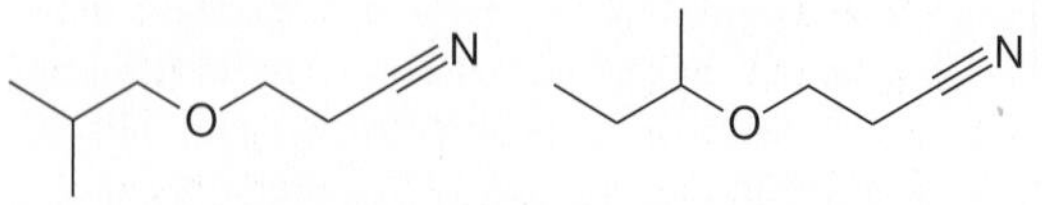
O
N
O
N

Your Turn 16.28

Structure **J**, because there is a strong absorption around 830 cm^{-1}, characteristic of a para-disubstituted benzene ring.

Your Turn 16.29

Structures **K** and **L**, because there are two strong absorptions around 910 and 990 cm^{-1}, characteristic of RCH=CH_2.

Your Turn 16.30

(a) $\%T = 20\%$. **(b)** $A = 0.750$.

Your Turn 16.31

The range for λ_{max} for one C=C or C≡C π bond (no conjugation) is 161–185 nm, and the range for λ_{max} for two conjugated C=C π bonds is 217–256 nm. Only one species has three conjugated C=C π bonds, with $\lambda_{max} = 274$ nm, and only one species has four conjugated C=C π bonds, with $\lambda_{max} = 290$ nm.

Your Turn 16.32

(a) Deca-1,3,5,7,9-pentaene has five conjugated C=C double bonds, so we should expect λ_{max} to be about 300 nm. **(b)** Penta-2,4-dienal has two C=C double bonds conjugated to an aldehyde C=O, so we estimate that λ_{max} would be 380 nm.

Your Turn 16.33

According to Figure 16-2, 420-nm light is between blue and violet. To our eyes, the solution at pH −1 will appear as the complementary color in Figure 16-35, which is yellow.

Your Turn 16.34

If molar absorptivity decreases by a factor of 3, absorbance also decreases by a factor of 3.

Your Turn 16.35

The result indicates that the rate of the elimination reaction is independent of the concentration of base, which is consistent with the E1 mechanism, not E2.

Your Turn 16.36

Additional transitions are shown in gray. All the arrows are longer than the one representing the HOMO–LUMO transition, and thus they are higher-energy transitions.

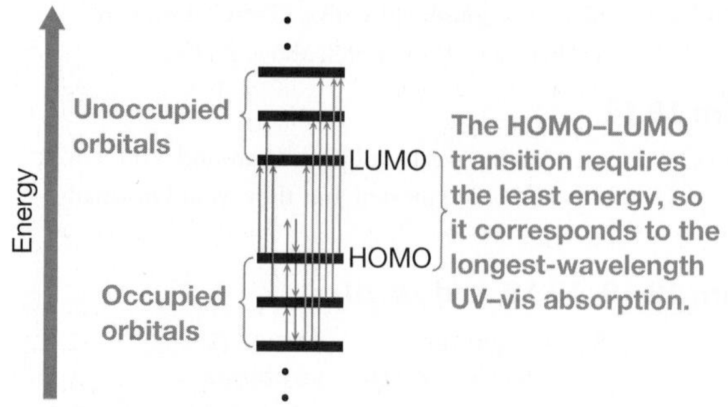
Energy
Unoccupied orbitals
Occupied orbitals
LUMO
HOMO
The HOMO–LUMO transition requires the least energy, so it corresponds to the longest-wavelength UV–vis absorption.

Your Turn 16.37

The HOMO–LUMO transition for H_2C=NH is lower in energy. The HOMO–LUMO transition for H_2C=CH_2 is $\pi \rightarrow \pi^*$, as shown in Figure 16-39a. The transition for H_2C=NH, however, is $n \rightarrow \pi^*$, similar to the one shown in Figure 16-39b, given the presence of both a lone pair on N and the π bond.

Chapter 17

Your Turn 17.1

No, the protons in propynoic acid are chemically distinct from those in TMS. We know this because the protons from the two compounds have different chemical shifts: 11.2 and 3.0 ppm for propynoic acid and 0.0 ppm for TMS.

Your Turn 17.2

The double bond in molecule **A** fixes the positions of the two CH_3 groups relative to the Cl, so the chemical environment for one set of CH_3 protons is different from the chemical environment for the other set. In molecule **B**, the single bond allows free rotation and the two CH_3 groups exchange positions rapidly, so the protons are in chemically equivalent environments.

Your Turn 17.3

In Table 17-1, Entries 1–9 appear at lower chemical shifts than $ClCH_3$, and Entries 11–16, 19, and 20 appear at higher chemical shifts.

Your Turn 17.4

The chemical shift will be greater for the protons in CH_3Br. This is because Br has a higher electronegativity than I, so Br will cause more deshielding, exposing the H atoms to a greater extent of the external magnetic field.

Your Turn 17.5

The aromatic proton experiences a larger effective magnetic field ($B_{eff} = B_{ext} + B_{loc}$) than the CH_2 protons do. B_{ext} is the same for both. The π electrons of the aromatic ring generate a ring current that creates a local magnetic field (B_{loc}) in the same direction as the external magnetic field (B_{ext}) outside the ring. The aromatic proton is closer to the ring, so its B_{loc} will be greater than that for the CH_2 protons.

Your Turn 17.6

The protons attached to the double bond experience a larger effective magnetic field ($B_{eff} = B_{ext} + B_{loc}$) than does the proton attached to the triple bond. In the double bond, B_{loc} from the ring current of the π electrons is aligned with B_{ext} at the positions of the protons. In the triple bond, the π electrons have cylindrical symmetry about the bonding axis and generate a B_{loc} that opposes the external magnetic field (B_{ext}) at the position of the proton.

Your Turn 17.7

(a) The proton on the right has the higher chemical shift because the three Cl atoms inductively remove more electron density from the nearby proton, causing it to be more deshielded. **(b)** The protons on the left have the higher chemical shift because the two O atoms inductively remove more electron density from the nearby protons, causing them to be more deshielded.

Your Turn 17.8

From lowest to highest chemical shift, the sets of protons are ranked A < B < C. Deshielding increases as the number of bonds separating the proton from the electron-withdrawing chlorine atom decreases.

Your Turn 17.9

From Equation 17-2 (p. 838), the energy difference for a bare proton can be calculated:

$$\Delta E_{\text{spin, bare proton}} = \frac{\gamma h B_{ext}}{2\pi} =$$

$$= \frac{(2.67512 \times 10^8\ \text{T}^{-1}\text{s}^{-1})(6.626 \times 10^{-34}\ \text{J} \cdot \text{s})(7.046\ \text{T})}{2\pi} =$$

$$= 1.988 \times 10^{-25}\ \text{J}$$

The units for seconds (s) and teslas (T) both cancel, leaving energy in units of joules (J).

Your Turn 17.10

From Equation 17-4 (p. 838), the operating frequency can be calculated:

$$\nu_{op} = \frac{\gamma B_{ext}}{2\pi} = \frac{(2.67512 \times 10^8\ \text{T}^{-1}\ \text{s}^{-1})(11.74\ \text{T})}{2\pi} =$$

$$= 500 \times 10^6\ \text{s}^{-1} = 500\ \text{MHz}$$

The unit tesla (T) cancels, leaving the frequency units of reciprocal seconds (s^{-1}); this unit is equivalent to hertz (Hz) and can be converted to megahertz (MHz).

Your Turn 17.11

From Equation 17-4 (p. 838), the operating frequency can be calculated:

$$\nu_{op} = \frac{\gamma B_{ext}}{2\pi} = \frac{(2.67512 \times 10^8\ \text{T}^{-1}\ \text{s}^{-1})(7.046\ \text{T})}{2\pi} =$$

$$= 300 \times 10^6\ \text{s}^{-1} = 300\ \text{MHz}$$

The operating frequency is 300 MHz, or 3×10^8 Hz. Because the signal of the proton of interest is 2200 Hz higher than those in TMS, ($\nu_{sample} - \nu_{TMS}$) = 2200 Hz. Using Equation 17-5 (p. 839), we can solve for the chemical shift in parts per million (ppm):

$$\delta = \frac{\nu_{sample} - \nu_{TMS}}{\nu_{op}} \times 10^6 = \frac{2200\ \text{Hz}}{3 \times 10^8\ \text{Hz}} \times 10^6 = 7.33\ \text{ppm}$$

Your Turn 17.12

The signal at 1.9 ppm represents the most H atoms, and the signal at 6.2 ppm represents the fewest. The signal at 1.9 ppm represents 3 times as many protons as the signal at 6.2 ppm.

Your Turn 17.13

The ratio of the stair-step heights, and thus the number of the corresponding protons, is roughly 3:2:1. If the molecule contains a total of 6 protons, the signals at 6.2, 3.9, and 1.9 ppm are due to 1, 2, and 3 H atoms, respectively. On the other hand, if the molecule has a total of 12 H atoms, these signals would be due to 2, 4, and 6 H atoms, respectively.

Your Turn 17.14

The proton on C-1 should be circled, and the two protons on C-2 should be boxed.

Your Turn 17.15

When a proton is coupled to N protons that are distinct from itself, the resulting splitting pattern has $N + 1$ peaks. **(a)** Two peaks (doublet) means $N + 1 = 2$, so $N = 1$ coupled proton. **(b)** Five peaks (quintet) means $N + 1 = 5$, so $N = 4$ coupled protons. **(c)** One peak (singlet) means $N + 1 = 1$, so $N = 0$ coupled protons.

Your Turn 17.16

In both compounds, we would expect the aromatic H atoms to have similar chemical shifts and similar splitting patterns because both rings are para-disubstituted, and the ring has an attached O and an attached alkene carbon in both cases. The CH_3 signals would be slightly different in chemical shift and would also be different in splitting, because in **A**, the CH_3 carbon is bonded to an alkene CH, whereas in **B**, it is bonded to an O. The alkene H signals would have different splitting patterns, because alkene **B** consists of CH═CH_2 and alkene **A** consists of CH═CH—CH_3. A major difference is that in the first molecule, the OH signal will be a broad singlet, and no such signal exists for the second molecule. If D_2O were added, a portion of molecules would have OD instead of OH, so the OH signal would diminish in size. With enough H/D exchange, the OH signal would disappear entirely.

Your Turn 17.17

The protons that generate signals E and G are coupled, and the protons that generate signals F and H are coupled.

Your Turn 17.18

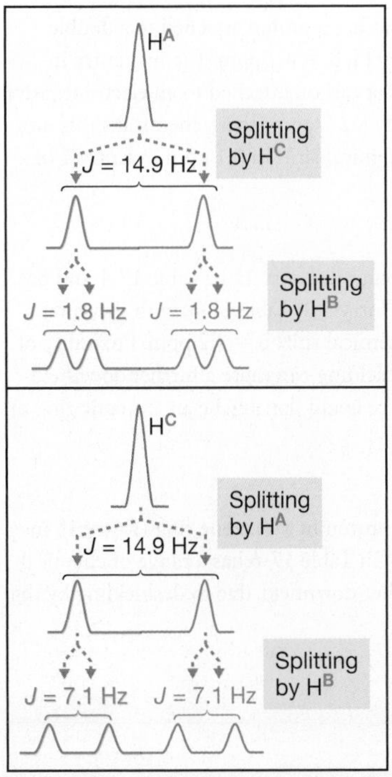

H^A
Splitting by H^C
J = 14.9 Hz
Splitting by H^B
J = 1.8 Hz
J = 1.8 Hz
H^C
Splitting by H^A
J = 14.9 Hz
Splitting by H^B
J = 7.1 Hz
J = 7.1 Hz

Your Turn 17.19

The CH would split the CH_2 signal into a doublet with a coupling constant of ~2 Hz. The CH_3 would split the CH_2 signal into a quartet with a coupling constant value of ~6 Hz. Therefore, the signal is a quartet of doublets.

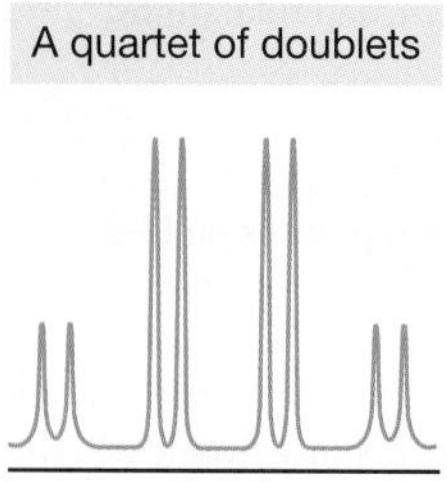
A quartet of doublets

Your Turn 17.20

The compound gives rise to six signals (there are also signals from solvent and TMS), so the compound has six chemically distinct C atoms.

Your Turn 17.21

Several examples are possible. For example, CH_3R has a proton chemical shift of 0.9 ppm and a carbon chemical shift of 10–25 ppm. CH_2R_2 has a proton chemical shift of 1.3 ppm and a carbon chemical shift of 20–45 ppm. Thus, CH_3R and CH_2R_2 have the same order for H and C chemical shifts (different scales). Other examples include $BrCH_3$ and $ClCH_3$, and alkenes and alkynes. The trends are the same because the factors that dictate the order of chemical shifts in ^1H nuclei—inductive effects and magnetic anisotropy—are the same factors that dictate the order of chemical shifts for ^{13}C nuclei.

Your Turn 17.22

As we can see in Table 17-5, aromatic carbons have chemical shifts around 130 ppm, whereas alkyl halide carbons have chemical shifts of 35–55 ppm. Not all the aromatic carbons have the same chemical shift, however. The one closest to the Cl atom will be most deshielded, due to inductive effects, so its signal will be the most downfield-shifted, and it will have the highest chemical shift.

Your Turn 17.23

The first entry in Table 17-1 that has a proton attached to a double bond is Entry 13, $R_2C{=}CH{-}H$, $\delta = 4.7$ ppm. The first entry in Table 17-1 that has a proton on a carbon attached to an electronegative atom is Entry 9, $BrCH_2{-}H$, $\delta = 2.7$ ppm. These chemical shifts are significantly higher than the chemical shift of 1.1 ppm in Entry 1 of Table 17-6.

Your Turn 17.24

The fragment H—C—O is found in Entry 11 in Table 17-1 and has a chemical shift $\delta = 3.3$ ppm. Entry 3 in Table 17-6, with the same fragment H—C—O, has a chemical shift $\delta = 4.2$ ppm. Proximity of protons to other sources of deshielding can cause a further downfield shift. In this unknown, the source could possibly be an aromatic ring or an additional oxygen.

Your Turn 17.25

The normal chemical shift of a proton in a benzene ring (Entry 15 in Table 17-1) is 7.3 ppm. Entry 4 in Table 17-6 has a range of chemical shifts, 7.4–8.1 ppm. This is farther downfield, due to deshielding by the carbonyl group.

Your Turn 17.26

Protons A correspond to the signals near 7.4–8.1 ppm; protons B correspond to the signal at ~4.3 ppm; protons C correspond to the signal at ~1.8 ppm; and protons D correspond to the signal at ~1.0 ppm.

Your Turn 17.27

Compound $CH_3CH_2CH_2CO_2C_6H_5$ will have a 3 H signal split into a triplet, a 2 H signal split into a multiplet, and a 2 H signal split into a triplet. Compound $CH_3CH_2OCH_2(C{=}O)C_6H_5$ will have a 3 H signal split into a triplet, a 2 H signal split into a quartet, and a 2 H signal as a singlet. The spectrum shown in Figure 17-41 matches the splitting patterns and integrations we would see with $CH_3CH_2CH_2CO_2C_6H_5$. However, the chemical shift of the CH_2 triplet signal in $CH_3CH_2CH_2CO_2C_6H_5$ does not match what is given in the spectrum very well. In $CH_3CH_2CH_2CO_2C_6H_5$, the chemical shift would be around 2.1 ppm (Entry 6 in Table 17-1, p. 832) or higher, whereas the triplet in the spectrum appears at 4.3 ppm. The chemical shift of 4.3 ppm is more consistent with protons of the form H—C—O (Entry 11 in Table 17-1, p. 832) that typically appear at 3.3 ppm or higher.

Your Turn 17.28

The first entry that has a carbon part of a double bond is C=C (Entry 11 in Table 17-5), $\delta = 105$–150 ppm. The first entry that has a carbon attached to an oxygen atom is C—OH (Entry 9 in Table 17-5), $\delta = 55$–70 ppm. These chemical shifts are higher than the chemical shift of ~26 ppm in Entry 1 of Table 17-7.

Your Turn 17.29

The chemical shift range for an alkyne carbon, RC≡CR (Entry 10 in Table 17-5), is 65–85 ppm. The chemical shift range for a carbon singly bonded to an oxygen, $R_3C{-}OH$ (Entry 9 in Table 17-5), is 55–70 ppm. Both of these ranges are close to the chemical shift value of ~73 ppm. The chemical shift range for a carbon that is part of a double bond (105–150 ppm) is much farther downfield than 73 ppm.

Your Turn 17.30

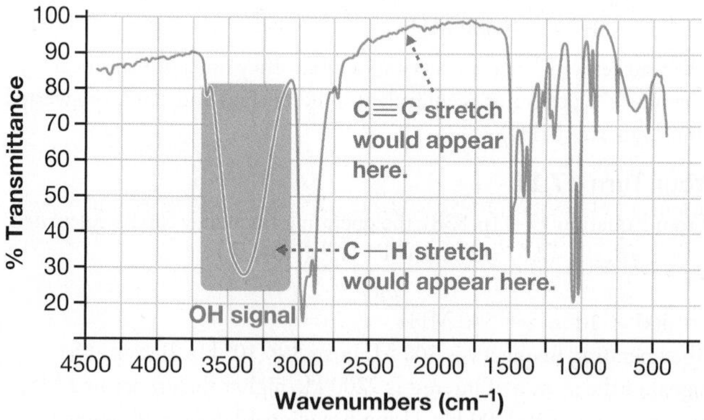

% Transmittance
100
90
80
70
60
50
40
30
20
C≡C stretch would appear here.
C—H stretch would appear here.
OH signal
4500 4000 3500 3000 2500 2000 1500 1000 500
Wavenumbers (cm⁻¹)

Chapter 18

Your Turn 18.1

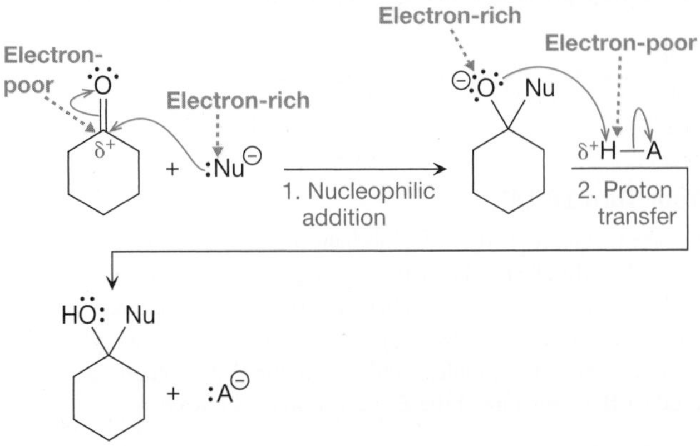
Electron-poor
Electron-rich
Electron-rich
Electron-poor
1. Nucleophilic addition
2. Proton transfer

Your Turn 18.2

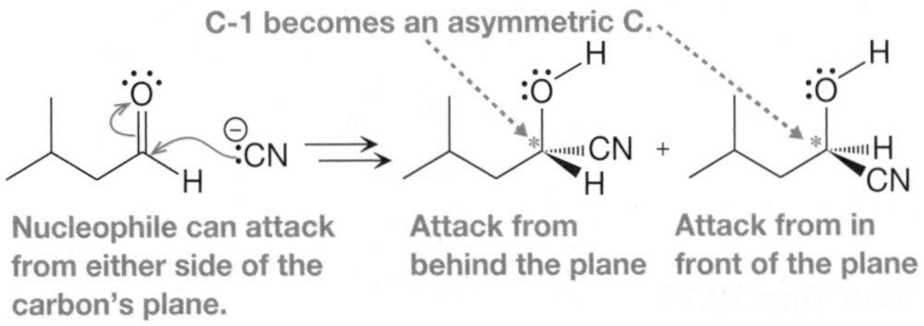
C-1 becomes an asymmetric C.
Nucleophile can attack from either side of the carbon's plane.
Attack from behind the plane
Attack from in front of the plane

Your Turn 18.3

The mechanism for Entry 1 in Table 18-1, with $H_2C{=}O$, is shown here. The mechanisms for Entries 2 and 3 in Table 18-1, with $CH_3CH{=}O$ and $(CH_3)_2C{=}O$, are the same as shown here but with one or both of the H atoms attached to the carbonyl C replaced by CH_3.

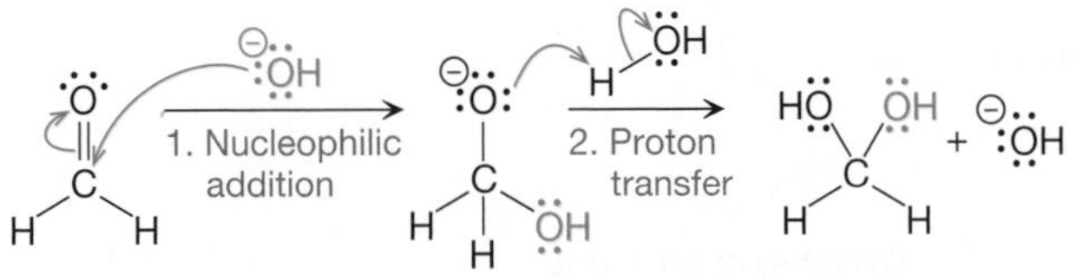
1. Nucleophilic addition
2. Proton transfer

Your Turn 18.4

Imine **B** has the greatest concentration of positive charge at the C═N carbon, and imine **C** has the least. The most reactive imine is **B**, and the least reactive is **C**.

Your Turn 18.5

For the ketone reaction in Equation 18-4, draw the mechanism in Equation 18-7 (p. 885), but in Step 2 replace H—OH with $H{-}NH_3^+$ and replace HO^- with NH_3. For the aldehyde reaction in Equation 18-5, draw the mechanism in Equation 18-8 (p. 885), but in Step 2 replace $H{-}OH_2^+$ with glycerol, which can be represented as H—OR, and replace H_2O with RO^-.

Your Turn 18.6

Draw the mechanism in Equation 18-9 (p. 885), but replace B with Al.

Your Turn 18.7

Mechanism for Eq. 18-12

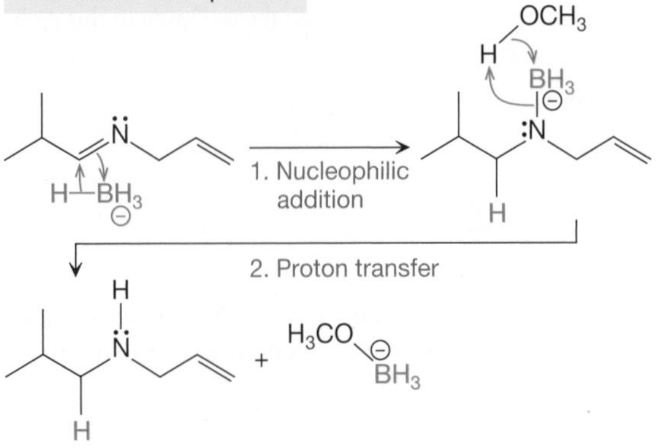
1. Nucleophilic addition
2. Proton transfer

Mechanism for Eq. 18-13

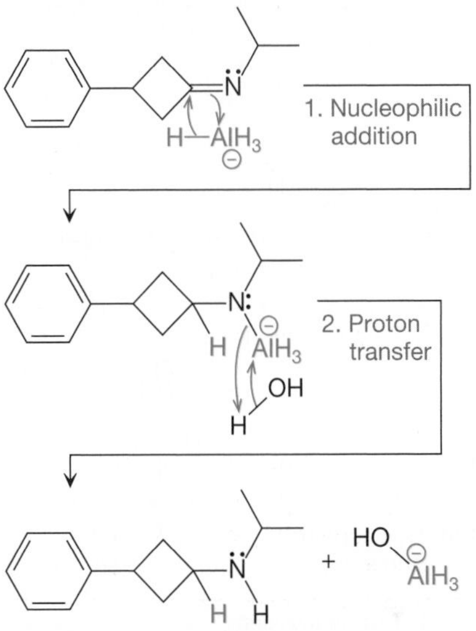
1. Nucleophilic addition
2. Proton transfer

Mechanism for Eq. 18-14

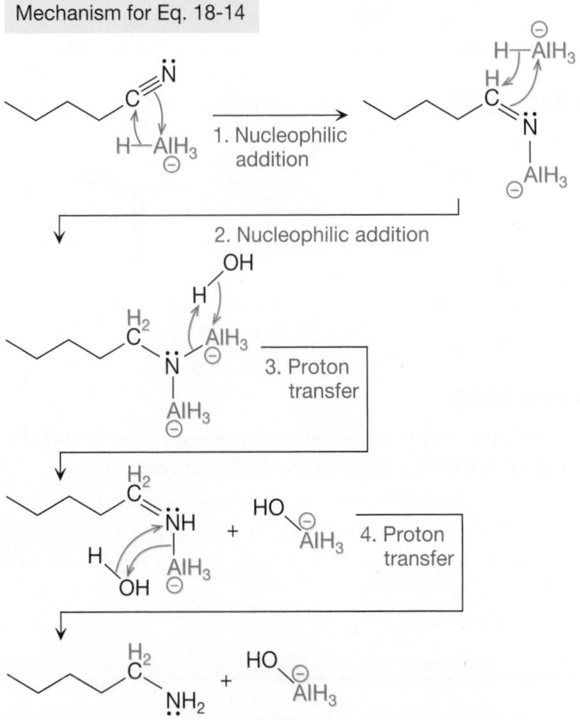
1. Nucleophilic addition
2. Nucleophilic addition
3. Proton transfer
4. Proton transfer

Your Turn 18.8

(a) Draw the mechanism shown in the answer to Your Turn 18.7 for Equation 18-14, but replace the nitrile with the one given in this problem. The major product is shown here.

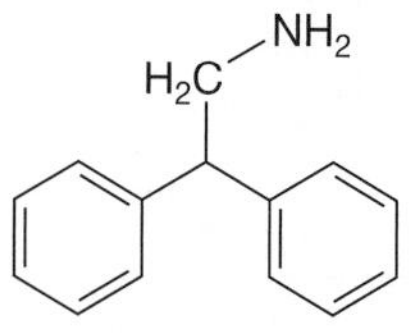

(b) Draw the mechanism shown in the answer to Your Turn 18.7 for Equation 18-13, but replace the imine with the one given in this problem. The major product is shown here.

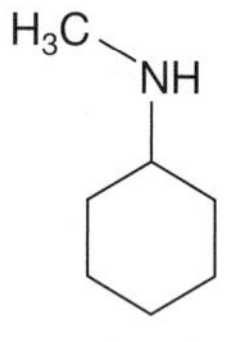

Your Turn 18.9

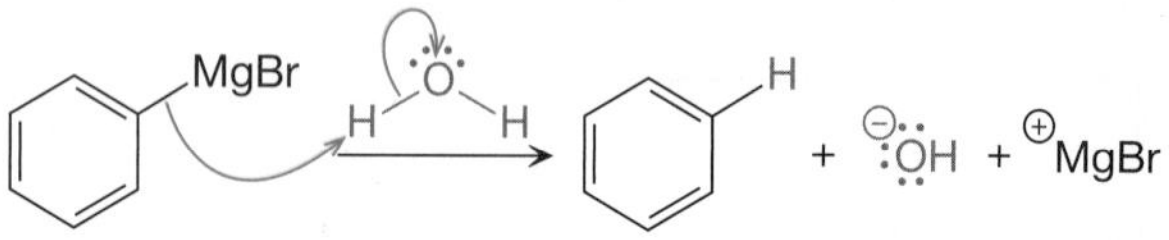

Your Turn 18.10

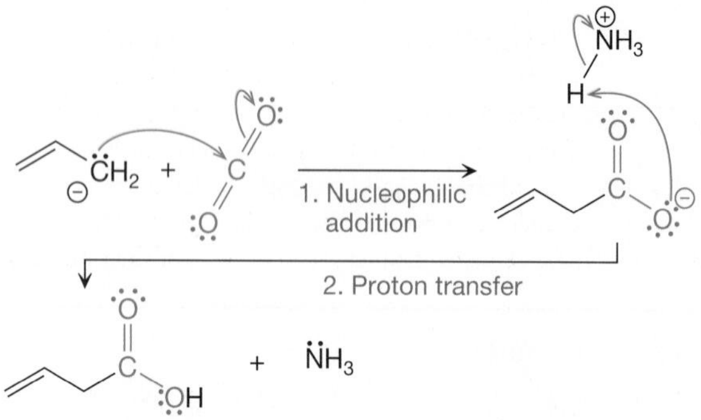
1. Nucleophilic addition
2. Proton transfer

Your Turn 18.11

(a)

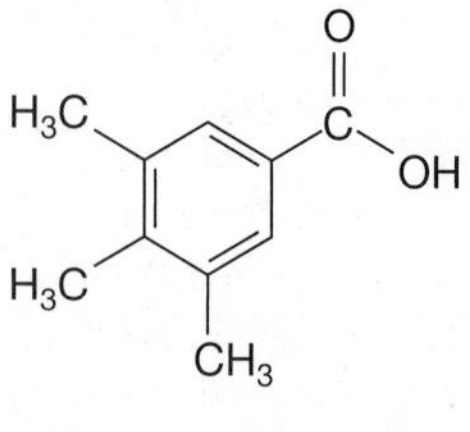

(b)

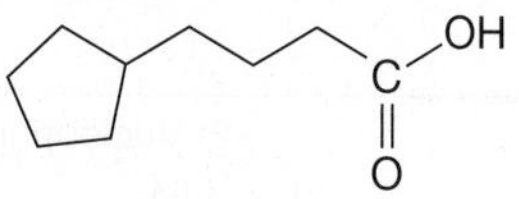

Your Turn 18.12

Only reaction **(b)** will proceed without interference. In reaction **(a)**, the epoxide group is incompatible with the alkyllithium reagent.

Your Turn 18.13

Draw the mechanism in Equation 18-25 (p. 896), but replace the aldehyde and Wittig reagent with the ones given in this problem. The reaction produces a mixture of the *E* and *Z* isomers shown here.

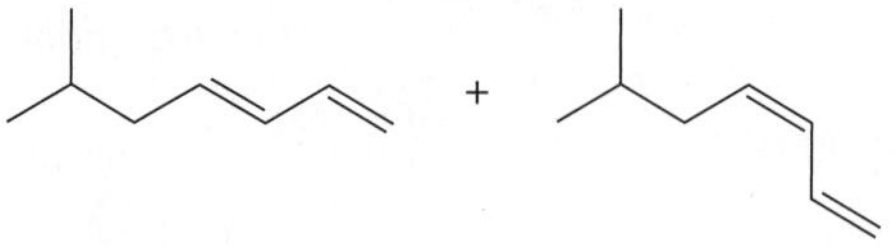

Your Turn 18.14

For the first reaction, draw the mechanism in Equation 18-28 (p. 897), but replace the alkyl halide with the one given in this problem. Product **A** is the Wittig reagent shown here. For the second reaction, draw the mechanism in Equation 18-25 (p. 896), but replace the aldehyde with the one given in this problem, and replace the Wittig reagent with **A**. Product **B** is a mixture of the *E* and *Z* isomers shown here.

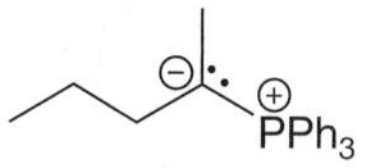

A

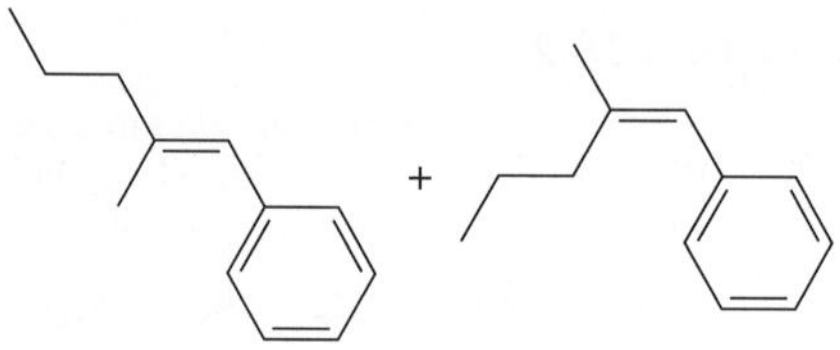

B

Your Turn 18.15

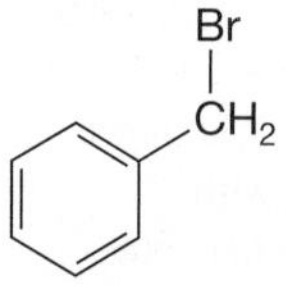

Your Turn 18.16

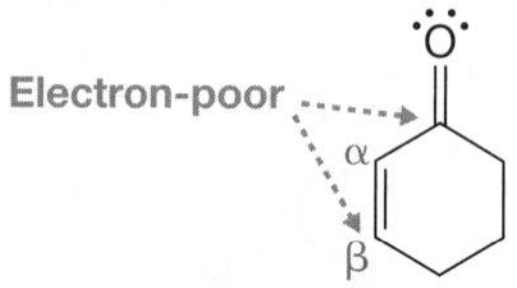
Electron-poor
α
β

Cyclohex-2-en-1-one

Your Turn 18.17

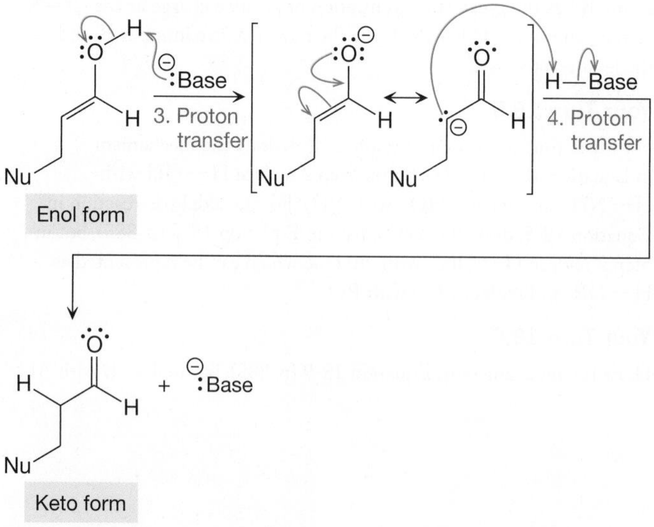
3. Proton transfer
4. Proton transfer
Enol form
Keto form

Your Turn 18.18

(a) For 1,2-addition, draw the mechanism in Equation 18-30 (p. 901), and for 1,4-addition, draw the mechanism in Equation 18-31 (p. 901). In both cases, replace the aldehyde with cyclohexenone as given in this problem, replace Nu^- with HO^-, and replace H—A with H—OH. The product of each reaction is shown here.

Direct addition (1,2-addition) | Conjugate addition (1,4-addition)

HO: :OH
O
HO

(b) For 1,2-addition, draw the mechanism in Equation 18-30 (p. 901), and for 1,4-addition, draw the mechanism in Equation 18-31 (p. 901). In both cases, replace the aldehyde with butenone as given in this problem, replace Nu^- with NC^-, and replace H—A with H—OH_2^+. The product of each reaction is shown here.

Direct addition (1,2-addition) | Conjugate addition (1,4-addition)

HO: CN
O
NC

Your Turn 18.19

The first product results from conjugate addition and is the thermodynamic product. The second product results from direct addition and is the kinetic product.

Your Turn 18.20

Synthesis for Eq. 18-38a

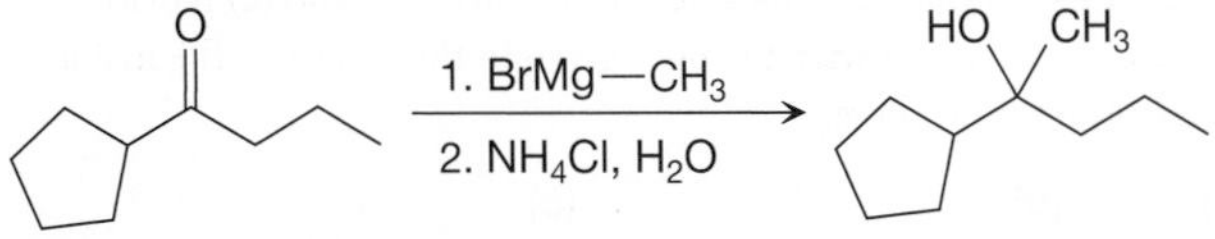
O
1. BrMg—CH3
2. NH4Cl, H2O
HO CH3

Synthesis for Eq. 18-38b

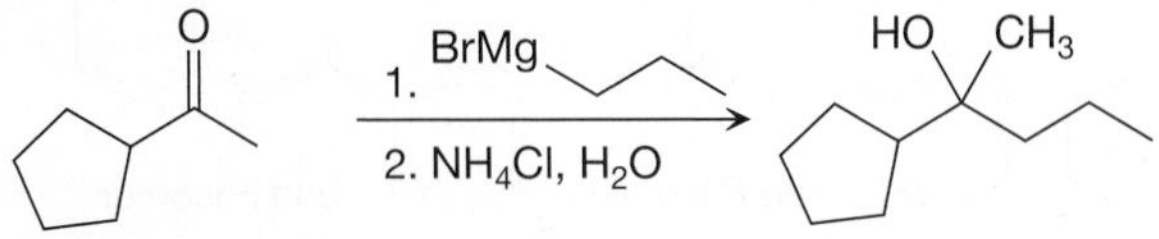
O
BrMg
1.
2. NH4Cl, H2O
HO CH3

Synthesis for Eq. 18-38c

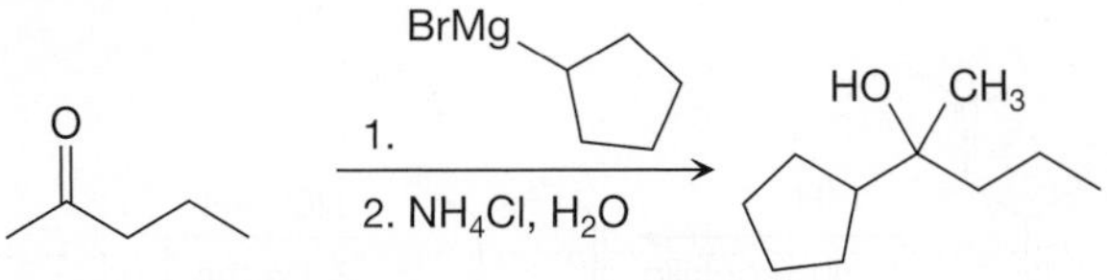
O
BrMg
1.
2. NH4Cl, H2O
HO CH3

Your Turn 18.21

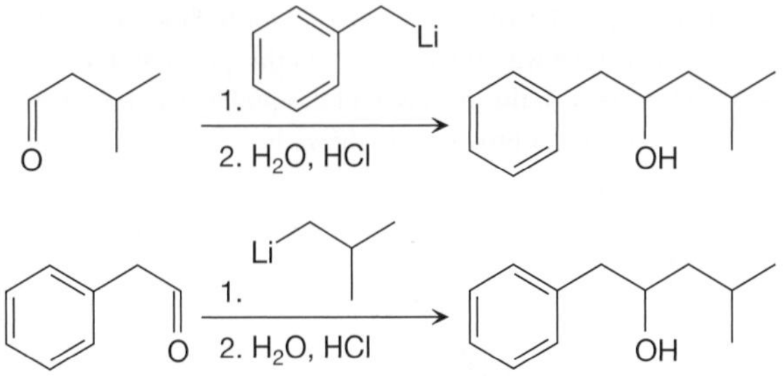
Li
O
1.
2. H2O, HCl
OH
Li
1.
O
2. H2O, HCl
OH

Your Turn 18.22

(a) Conjugate addition. **(b)** Direct addition.

Chapter 19

Your Turn 19.1

Draw the mechanism in Equation 19-2 (p. 927), but replace the ketone and alcohol with the ones given in the problem. The product is shown here.

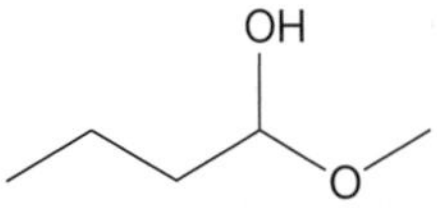
OH
O

Your Turn 19.2

Equation 19-2 has 0 charges initially, 2 charges after Step 1, 2 charges after Step 2, and 2 charges after Step 3 ($CH_3CH_2O^-$ produced in Step 2 is not shown after Step 3 but remains in solution); for Equation 19-4, the numbers of charges are 1, 1, 1, and 1; and for Equation 19-5 the numbers of charges are 1, 1, 1, and 1. The uncatalyzed reaction has a step that increases the number of charges by 2, whereas the number of charges remains the same for each step of the catalyzed reactions.

Your Turn 19.3

The positively charged species on the right will undergo a faster nucleophilic addition with water. It has a resonance structure that puts a positive charge on the C atom, making that C atom more susceptible to nucleophilic attack.

Your Turn 19.4

HCN has $pK_a = 9.2$, H_3O^+ has $pK_a = 0$, and H_2O has $pK_a = 14$. In Equation 19-7, the stronger acid (lower pK_a) is on the product side, so the reactants are favored. The difference in pK_a values is 9.2, so the reactant side is favored by $10^{9.2} = 1.6 \times 10^9$. In Equation 19-8, the stronger acid (lower pK_a) is on the reactant side, so the products are favored. The difference in pK_a between the reactant and product acids is $14 - 9.2 = 4.8$, so the product side is favored by $10^{4.8} = 6.3 \times 10^4$. This large extent to which the product side is favored means that the acid will be deprotonated quantitatively.

Your Turn 19.5

Draw the mechanism in Equation 19-7 (p. 932) for both reactions, but **(a)** replace the ketone with the one given in this problem, and **(b)** replace the ketone with the one given in this problem and replace H_2O with HO^-. The major products are shown here.

(a)

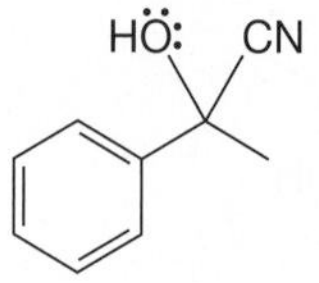

(b)

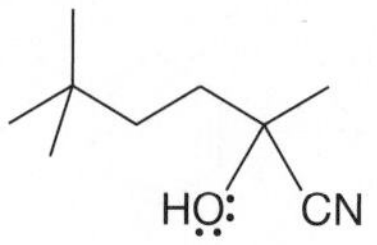

Your Turn 19.6

Your Turn 19.7

Draw the mechanism in Equation 19-13 (p. 936), but replace the aldehyde with the ketone given in this problem and replace $H—^{+}OHCH_3$ with $H—^{+}OHCH_2CH_3$. The major product is shown here.

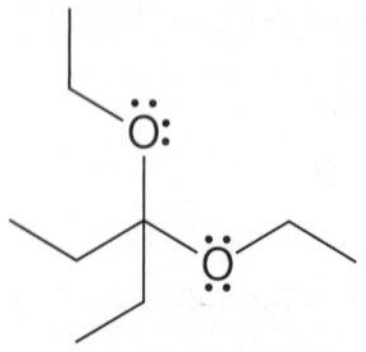

Your Turn 19.8

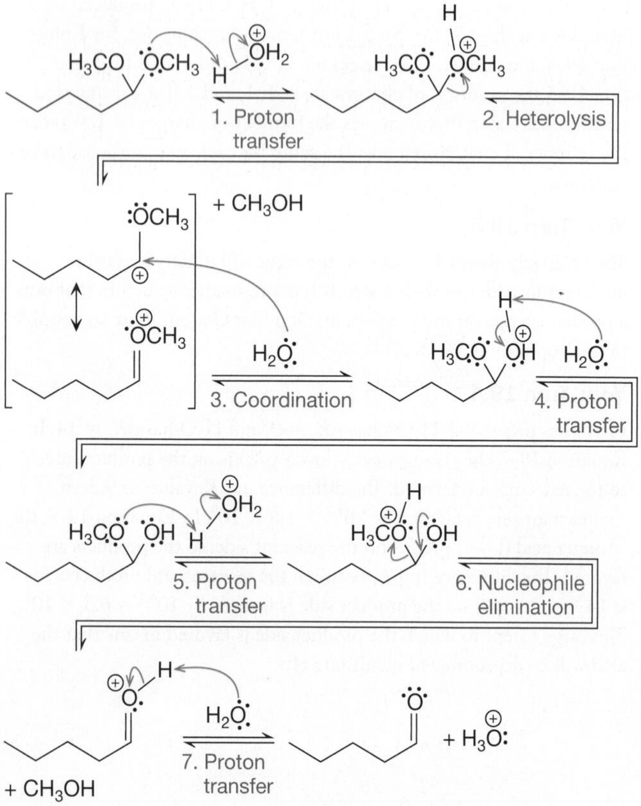
1. Proton transfer
2. Heterolysis
+ CH3OH
3. Coordination
4. Proton transfer
5. Proton transfer
6. Nucleophile elimination
7. Proton transfer
+ CH3OH

Your Turn 19.9

(a) Draw the mechanism for acetal formation in Equation 19-13 (p. 936), but replace the aldehyde with the ketone given in this problem, and replace $H—^{+}OHCH_3$ with $H—^{+}OHCH_2CH_3$. The major product is shown below. **(b)** NR. Acetals do *not* undergo hydrolysis in basic conditions, as there is no suitable leaving group. **(c)** Draw the mechanism for hemiacetal formation in Equation 19-4 (p. 929), but replace the ketone with the aldehyde given in this problem and use HO^- as the base. The major product is shown below. **(d)** Draw the mechanism in the answer to Your Turn 19.8, but replace the acetal with the one given in this problem. The major products are shown below.

(a)

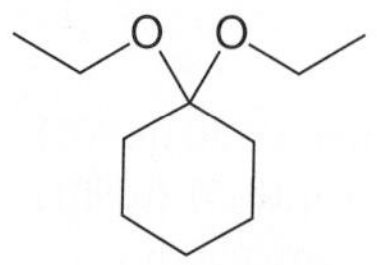

(c)

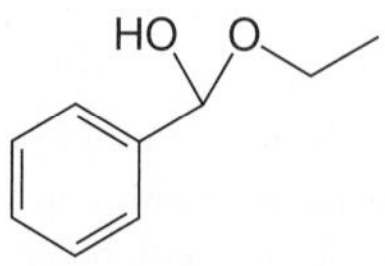

(d)

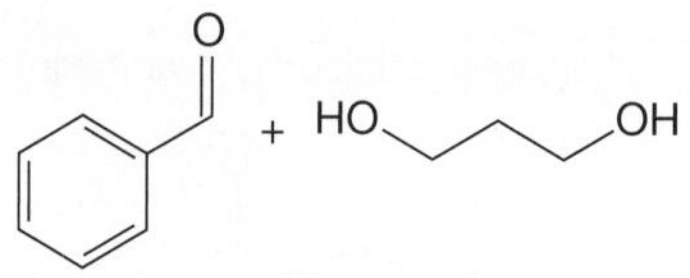

Your Turn 19.10

Draw the mechanism in Equation 19-20 (p. 940), but replace the ketone with the aldehyde given in Equation 19-19 and replace NH_3 with $H_2NCH_2CH_3$.

Your Turn 19.11

For each reaction, draw the mechanism in Equation 19-23 (p. 942), but **(a)** replace the amine with the one given in the problem; **(b)** replace the ketone with the aldehyde given in the problem; and **(c)** replace the ketone and amine with the ones given in the problem. The major products are shown here.

(a)

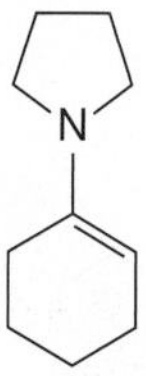

(b)

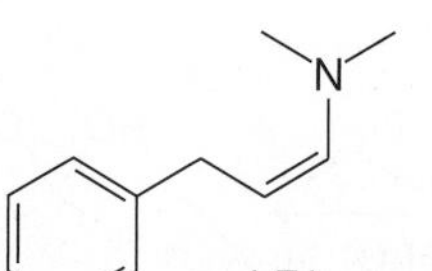

and *E* isomer

(c)

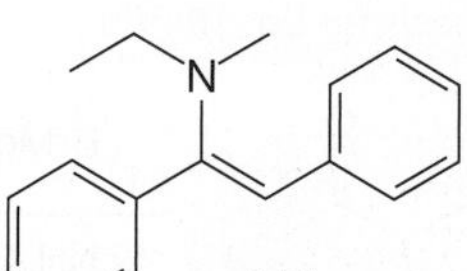

and *E* isomer

Your Turn 19.12

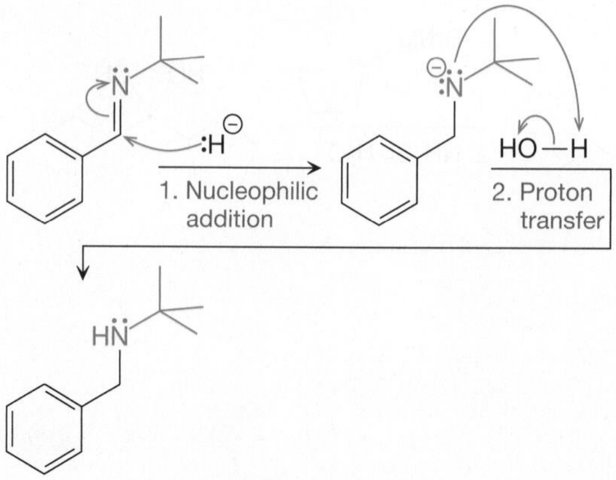
1. Nucleophilic addition
2. Proton transfer

Your Turn 19.13

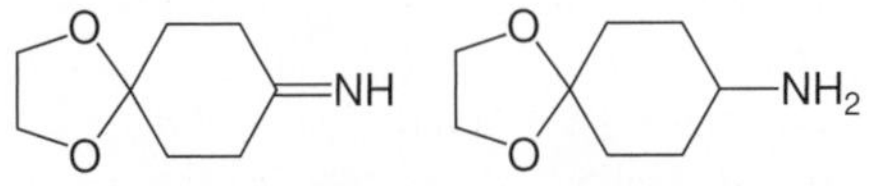
=NH
-NH2
O
O

Imine **Product**

Your Turn 19.14

(a)

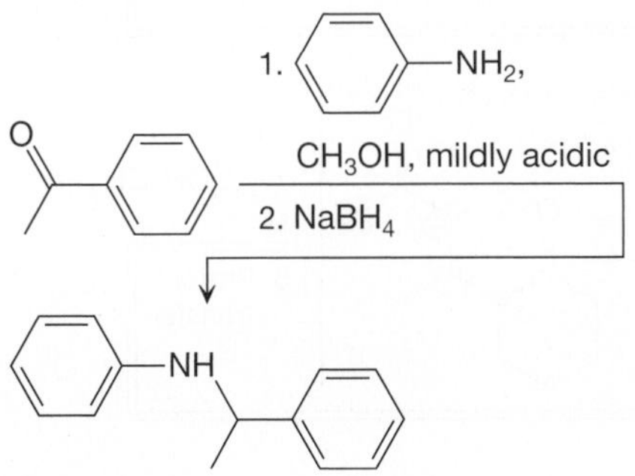
1. NH2,
CH3OH, mildly acidic
2. NaBH4
O
NH

(b)

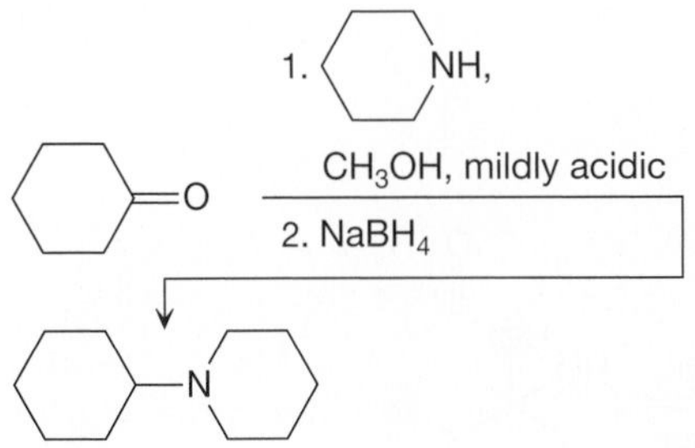
1. NH,
CH3OH, mildly acidic
2. NaBH4
O
N

(c)

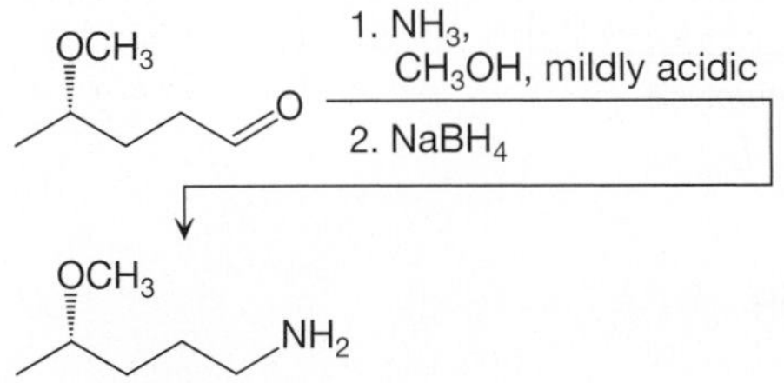
OCH3
1. NH3,
CH3OH, mildly acidic
2. NaBH4
O
OCH3
NH2

Your Turn 19.15

For each reaction, draw the mechanism in Equation 19-20 (p. 940) and Equation 19-28 (p. 946), but replace the amine with the one given in the problem. The major products are shown here.

(a) **(b)**

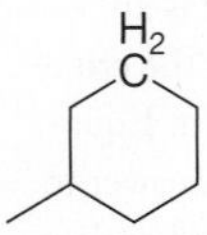
H2
C

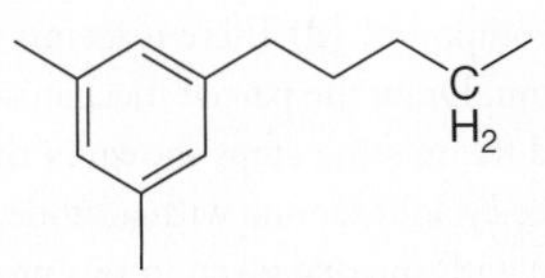
C
H2

Your Turn 19.16

(a) Draw the mechanism in Equation 19-33 (p. 948), but replace the nitrile with the one given in the problem. **(b)** Draw the mechanism in Equation 19-32 (p. 948), but replace the nitrile with the one given in the problem. The major products are shown here.

(a) **(b)**

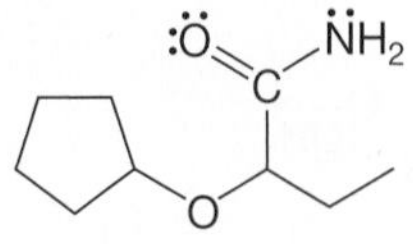
:O
NH2
C
O

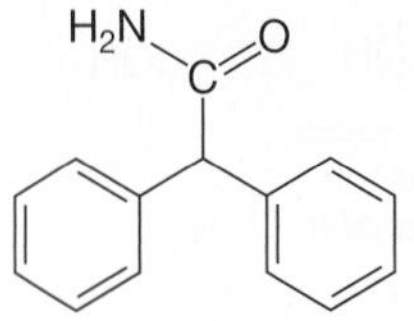
H2N
C
O

Your Turn 19.17

The product of every aldol addition is a β-hydroxy carbonyl compound. The only β-hydroxy carbonyl compound shown is molecule **(b)**.

Your Turn 19.18

The pK_a of $CH_3CH{=}O$ is similar to that of propanone (acetone), for which pK_a = 20, and H_2O has pK_a = 14. The stronger acid (lower pK_a) is on the product side, so the reactants are favored. The difference in pK_a between the reactant and product acids is 20 − 14 = 6, so the reactant side is favored by 10^6.

Your Turn 19.19

Reactant (two molecules of propanal): C = 6, H = 12, O = 2. Product (2-methylpent-2-enal): C = 6, H = 10, O = 1. The difference is two H and one O = H_2O, which is eliminated during condensation.

Your Turn 19.20

Although a mechanism analogous to the reaction in Equation 19-37 (E1cb) can be written for pent-4-en-2-ol, the first step would be very unfavorable. In Equation 19-37, it is feasible because the α hydrogen is reasonably acidic, with a pK_a of ~20. But the analogous proton in pent-4-en-2-ol has a pK_a of ~40. Because the conjugate acid of HO^- (i.e., H_2O) has a pK_a of 14, the equilibrium favors the reactants by ~10^{26}, making the reaction unfeasible.

Your Turn 19.21

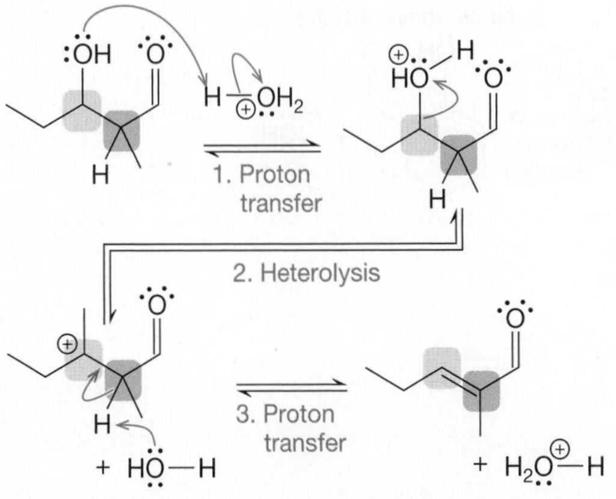
:OH
O
H
OH2
H
1. Proton
transfer
HO
H
O
H
2. Heterolysis
O
H
3. Proton
transfer
O
+ HO—H
+ H2O—H

Your Turn 19.22

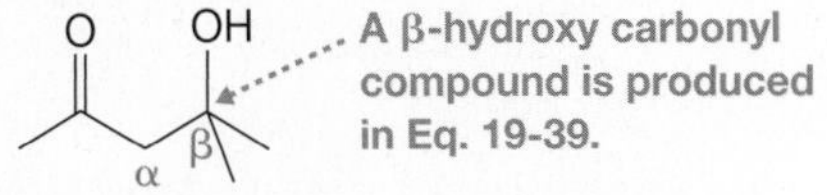
O
OH
α
β
A β-hydroxy carbonyl
compound is produced
in Eq. 19-39.

4-Hydroxy-4-methylpentan-2-one

Your Turn 19.23

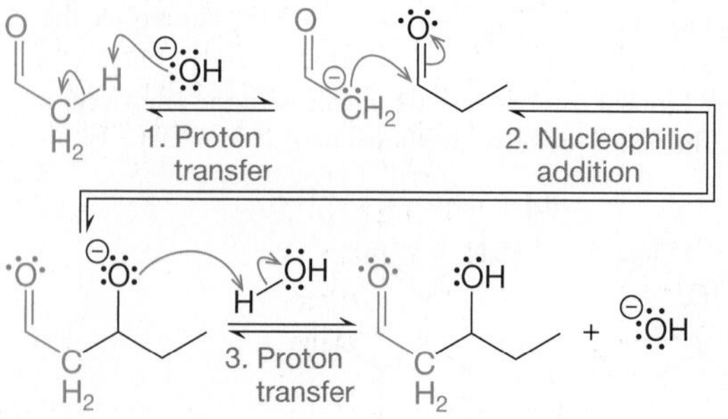
1. Proton transfer
2. Nucleophilic addition
3. Proton transfer

Your Turn 19.24

Compound **A** is best, because it is the only choice with no α protons.

Your Turn 19.25

NaOH is a proper choice of base in the first reaction, where the more highly substituted α C is deprotonated. LDA is a proper choice of base in the second reaction, where the less highly substituted α C is deprotonated.

Your Turn 19.26

The product of an aldol condensation is an α,β-unsaturated carbonyl compound.

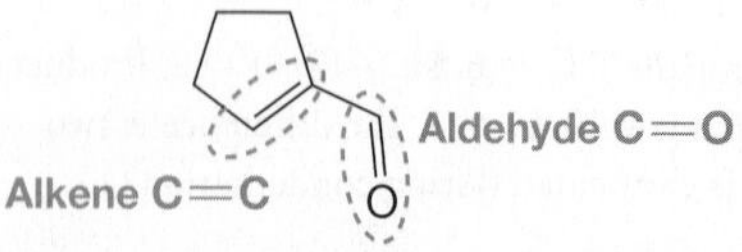
Aldehyde C=O
Alkene C=C

Your Turn 19.27

The intramolecular aldol reaction is favorable because it produces a six-membered ring.

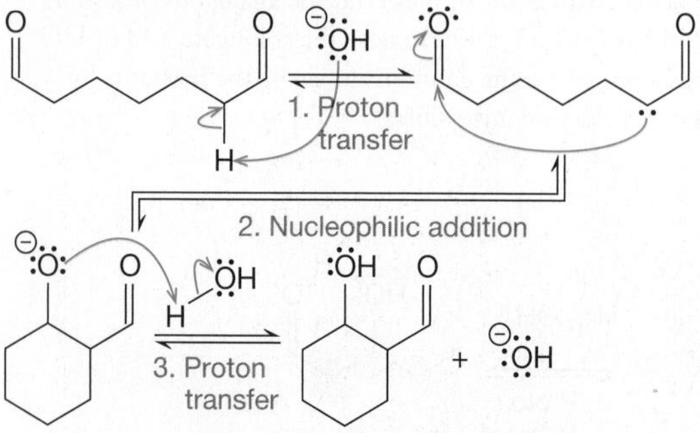
1. Proton transfer
2. Nucleophilic addition
3. Proton transfer

Your Turn 19.28

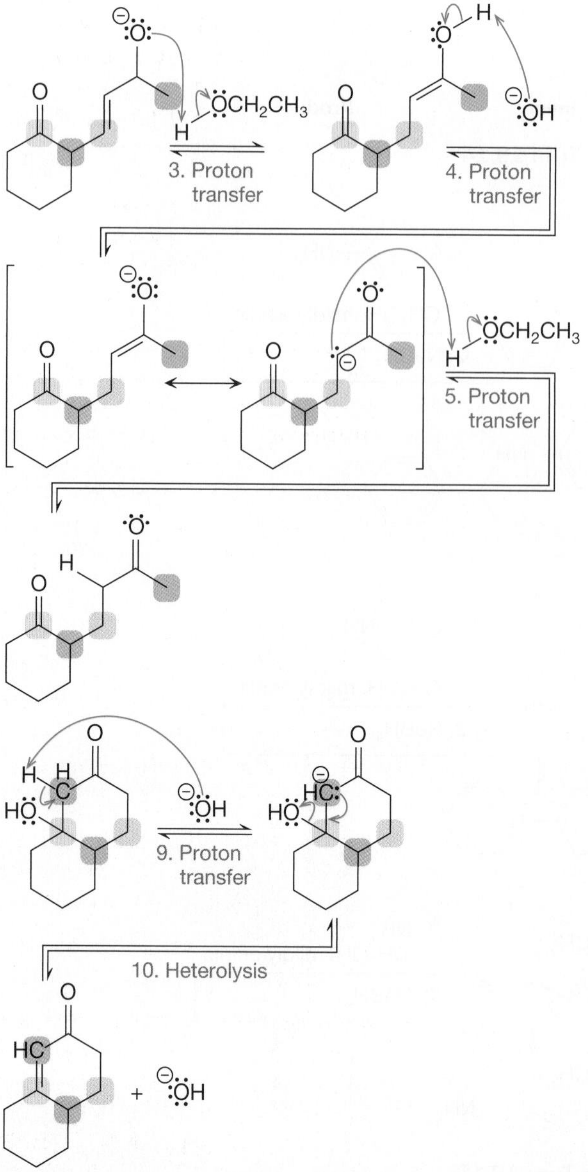
3. Proton transfer
4. Proton transfer
5. Proton transfer
9. Proton transfer
10. Heterolysis

Your Turn 19.29

(a) These reactants will not work because benzaldehyde does not have any α protons. **(b)** These reactants will not work because the α,β-unsaturated carbonyl does not have two acidic α protons. **(c)** These reactants will not work because neither compound is an α,β-unsaturated carbonyl compound. **(d)** These reactants fit the criteria for a Robinson annulation. Draw the partial mechanism in Equation 19-55 (p. 965) and add the missing steps shown in the answer to Your Turn 19.28, but replace cyclohexanone with acetone, and replace the α,β-unsaturated ketone with the one given in this problem. The major product is shown here.

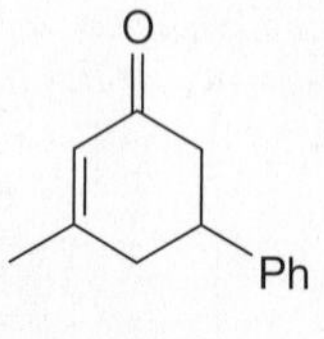
Ph

Your Turn 19.30

(a)

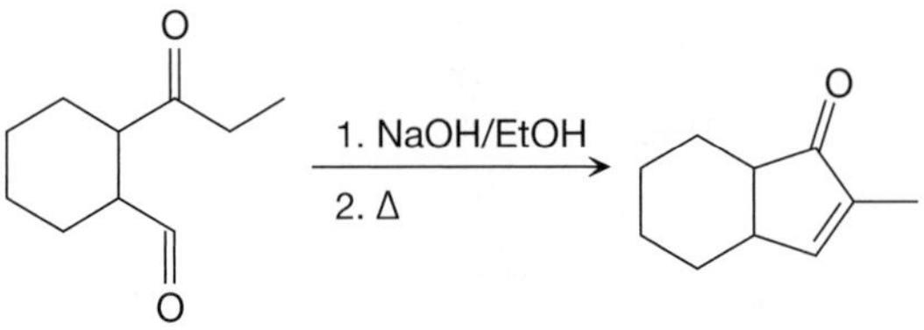

1. NaOH/EtOH
2. Δ

(b)

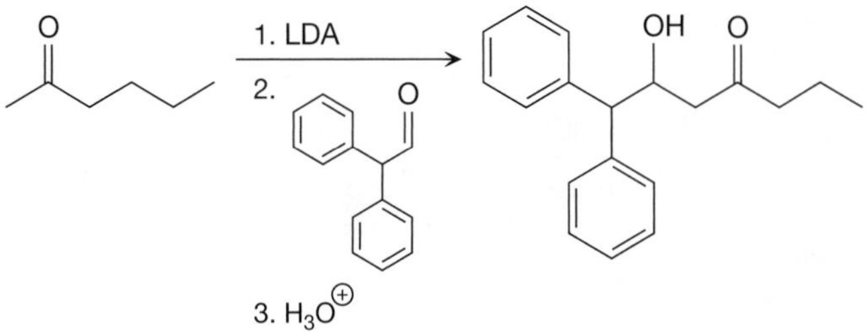

1. LDA
2.
3. $H_3O^{\oplus}$

Your Turn 19.31

(a)

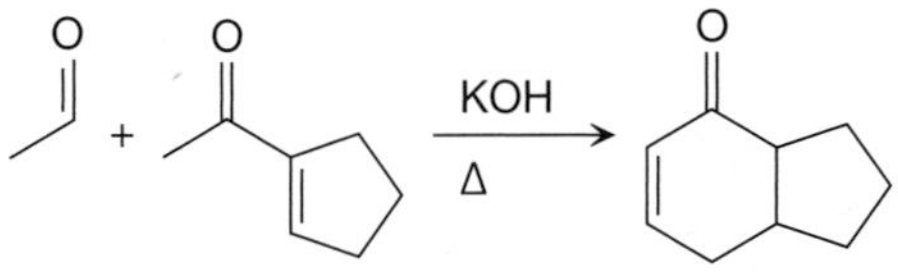

KOH
Δ

(b)

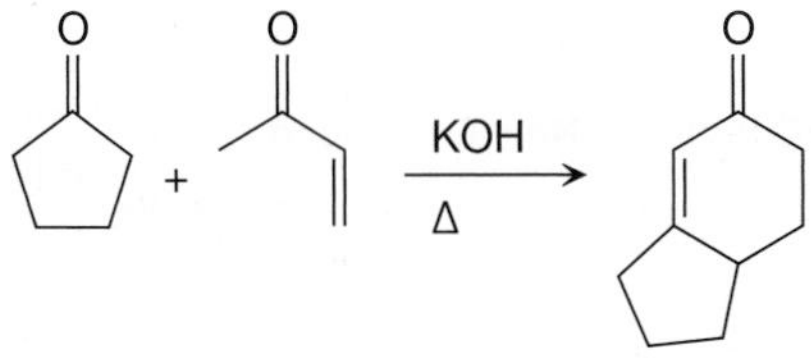

KOH
Δ

Your Turn 19.32

(a)

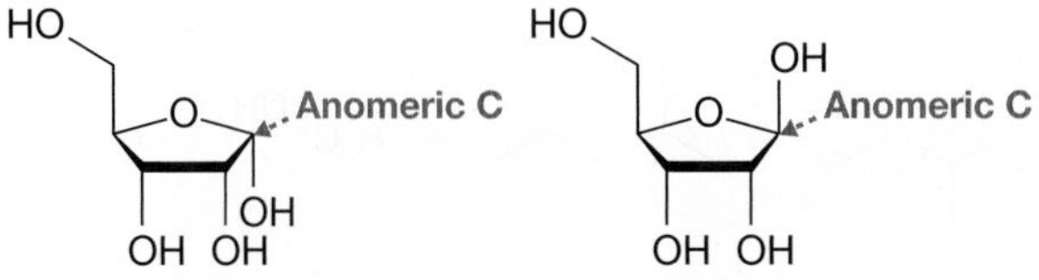

Anomeric C
Anomeric C

α-D-Ribofuranose **β-D-Ribofuranose**

(b)

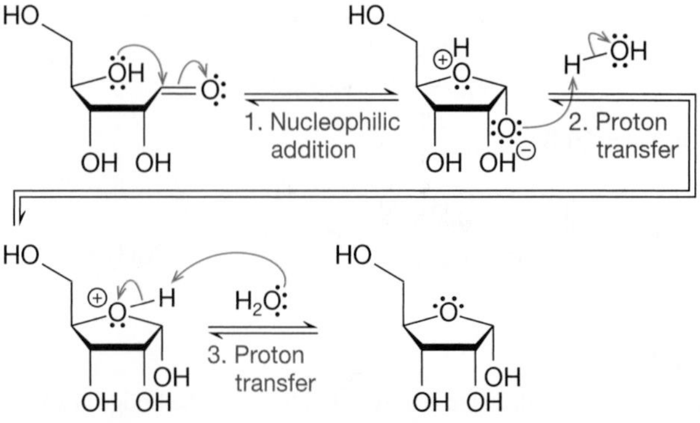

1. Nucleophilic addition
2. Proton transfer
3. Proton transfer

α-D-Ribofuranose

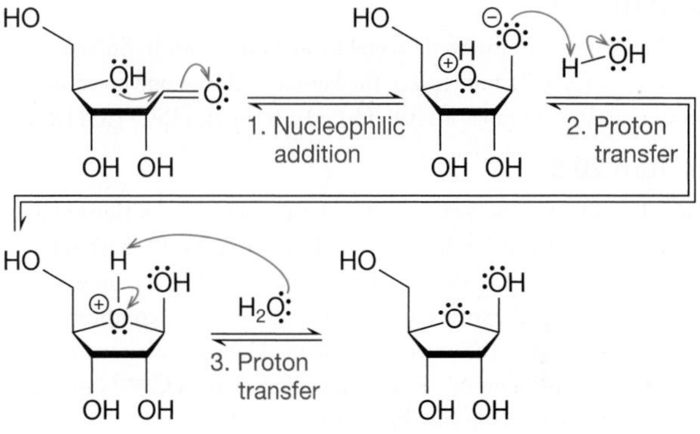

1. Nucleophilic addition
2. Proton transfer
3. Proton transfer

β-D-Ribofuranose

Your Turn 19.33

(a) α-D-Mannopyranose. **(b)** β-D-Talopyranose.

Chapter 20

Your Turn 20.1

The mechanism for Equation 20-1 is shown in Equation 18-7 (p. 885). The mechanism for Equation 20-2 is shown in Equation 18-8 (p. 885). In both mechanisms, Step 1 is responsible for increasing the number of C—H bonds and decreasing the number of C—O bonds.

Your Turn 20.2

The number of C—H bonds has increased by two (the two that are explicitly shown) and the number of C—EN bonds (C—N bonds in this case) has decreased by two. Both are indicative of a reduction reaction.

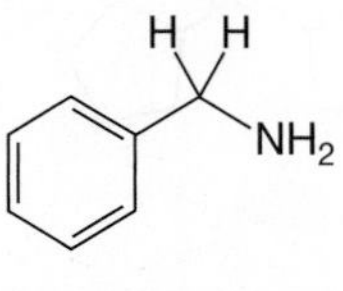

Your Turn 20.3

In Figure 20-1a and 20-1b, the oxidation state of the O atom is −2. In each case, O is assigned eight electrons, which is two more than its group number.

Your Turn 20.4

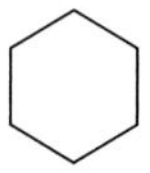

Your Turn 20.5

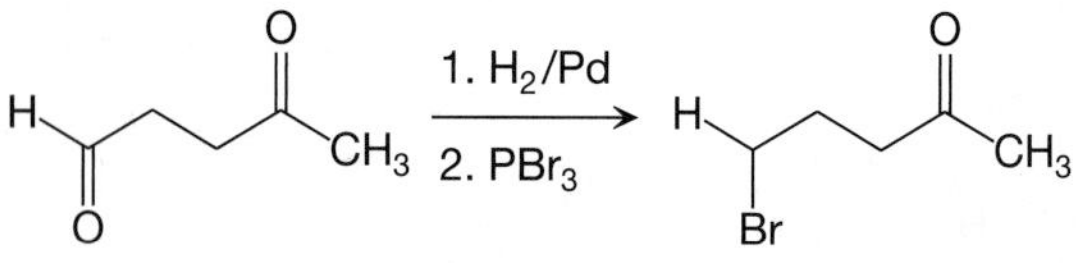
O
H
CH3
1. H2/Pd
2. PBr3
Br

Your Turn 20.6

Product **A** is favored, due to the steric hindrance of the bridged carbon and its methyl groups.

Your Turn 20.7

Draw the mechanism for cyclic acetal formation shown in Solved Problem 19.3 (p. 938), but replace the ketone with the one given in Equation 20-16, and replace $HOCH_2CH_2OH$ with $HSCH_2CH_2SH$.

Your Turn 20.8

The nitrile is likely to be hydrolyzed under the acidic conditions of a Clemmensen reduction or the basic conditions of a Wolff–Kishner reduction, so those reactions should be avoided. Table 20-1 shows that Raney nickel will hydrolyze a nitrile under extreme conditions (80 °C, 75 atm), so the carbonyl group of an aldehyde or ketone could be reduced with a Raney-Ni reduction, while leaving a C≡N group unaltered, if these extreme conditions are avoided.

Your Turn 20.9

Draw the mechanism in Equation 19-5 (p. 929), but replace the ketone with the aldehyde shown in Equation 20-21, and replace $H—^{+}OHCH_2CH_3$ with $H—^{+}OH_2$.

Your Turn 20.10

A, PCC. **B**, chromic acid.

Your Turn 20.11

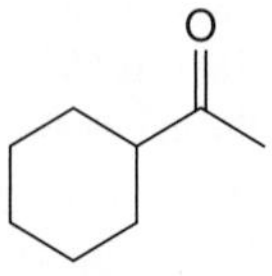

A

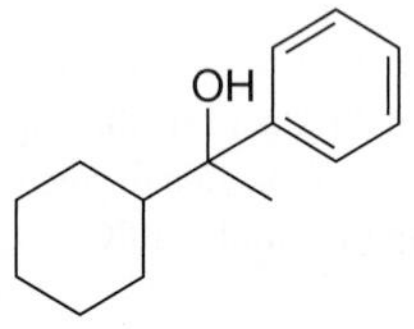
OH

B

Your Turn 20.12

(a)

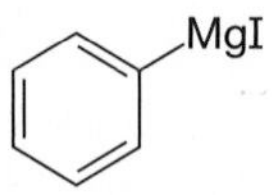
MgI

(b)

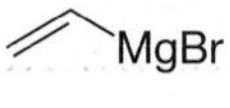
MgBr

(c)

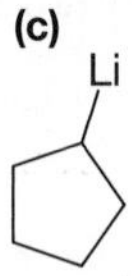
Li

(d)

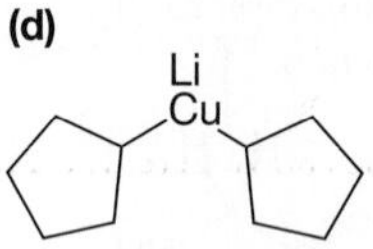
Li
Cu

Your Turn 20.13

(a)

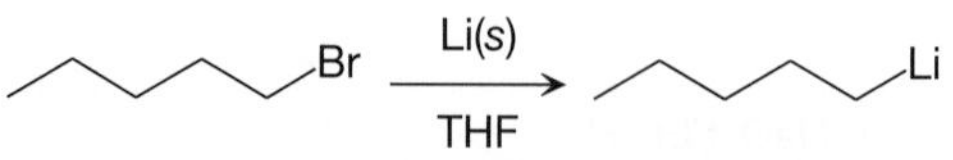
Br
Li(s)
THF
Li

(b)

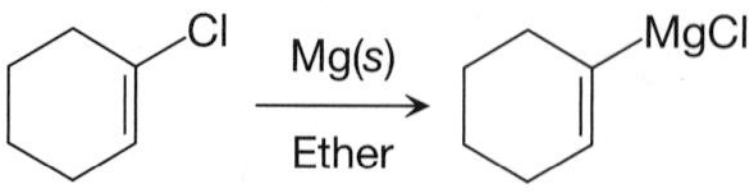
Cl
Mg(s)
Ether
MgCl

(c)

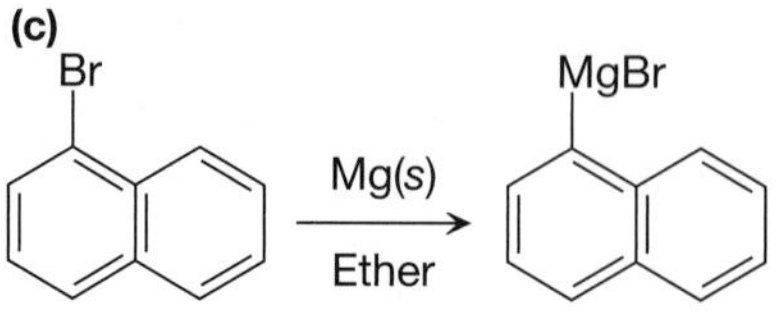
Br
Mg(s)
Ether
MgBr

(d)

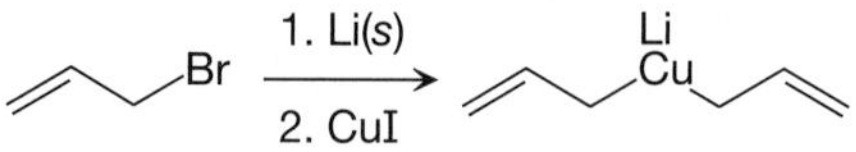
Br
1. Li(s)
2. CuI
Li
Cu

Your Turn 20.14

(a)

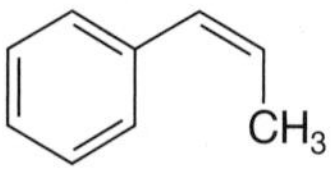
CH3

(b)

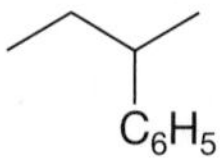
C6H5

Your Turn 20.15

(a)

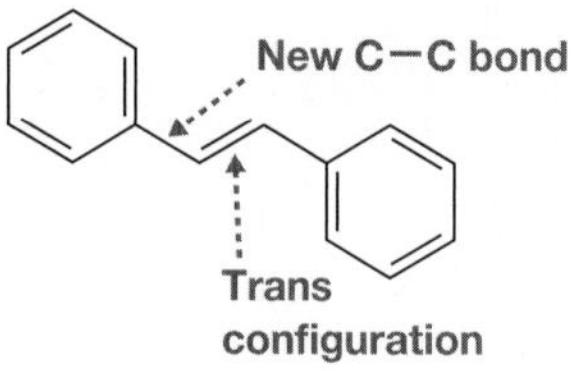
New C—C bond
Trans
configuration

(b)

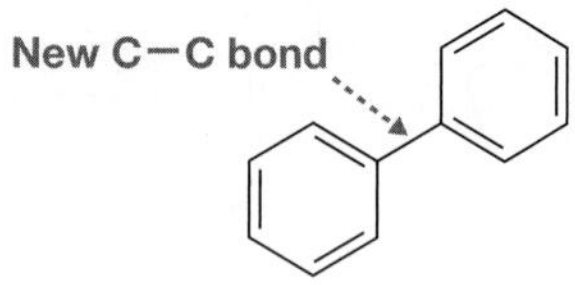
New C—C bond

Your Turn 20.16

(a)

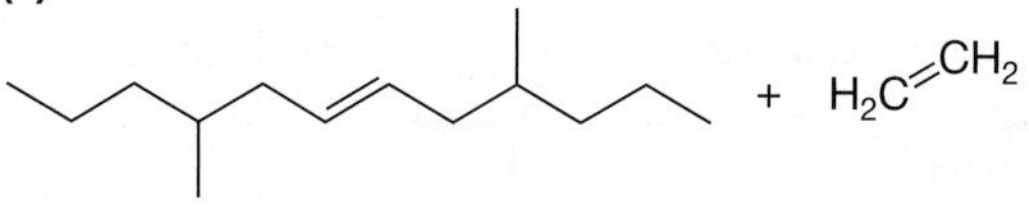
+ H2C=CH2

(b)

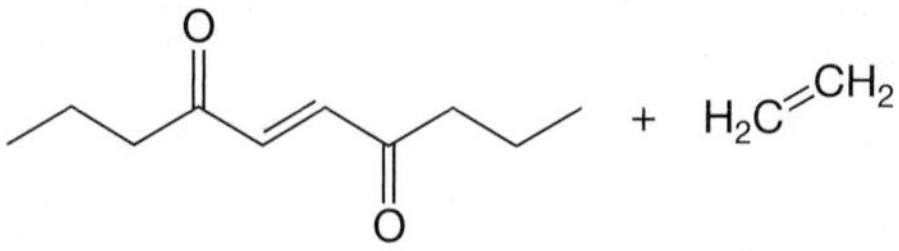
O
O
+ H2C=CH2

(c)

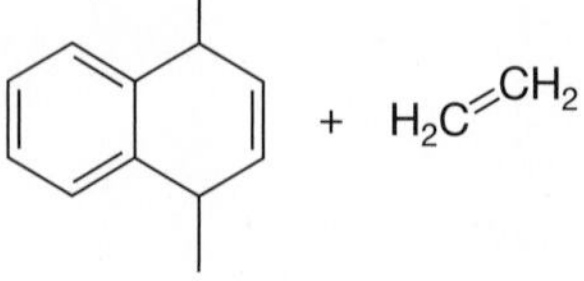
+ H2C=CH2

Chapter 21

Your Turn 21.1

In both cases, the charge on C has changed, indicating that umpolung has occurred.

(a)

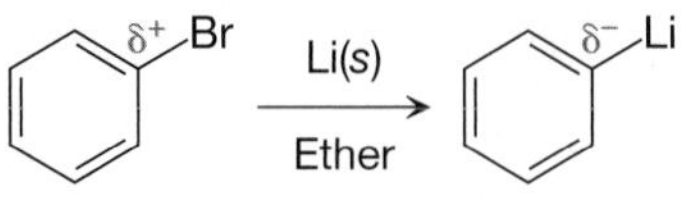

δ+ Br
Li(s)
Ether
δ− Li

(b)

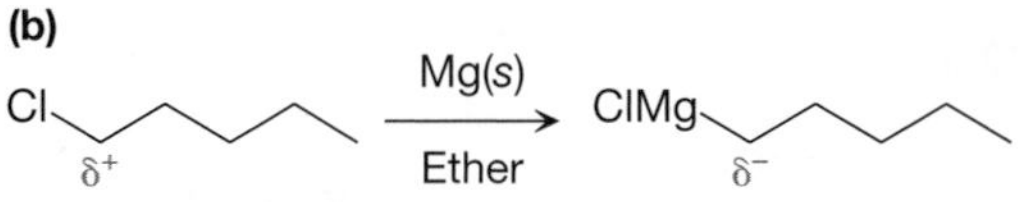

Cl
δ+
Mg(s)
Ether
ClMg
δ−

Your Turn 21.2

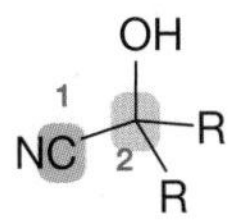

OH
NC
R
R

1,2-positioning

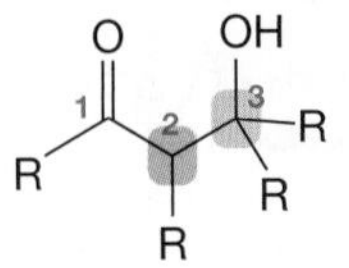

O
OH
R
R
R

1,3-positioning

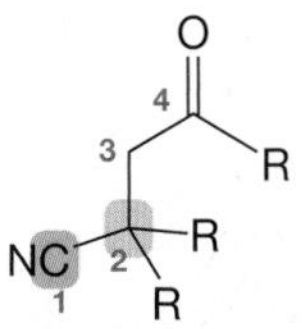

O
R
NC
R
R

1,4-positioning

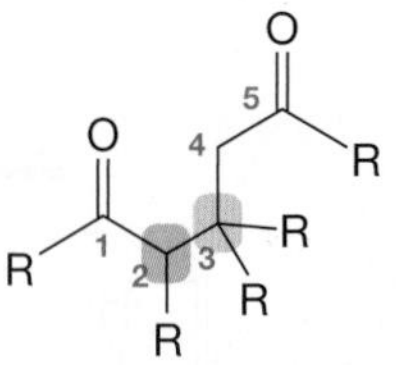

O
O
R
R
R
R

1,5-positioning

Your Turn 21.3

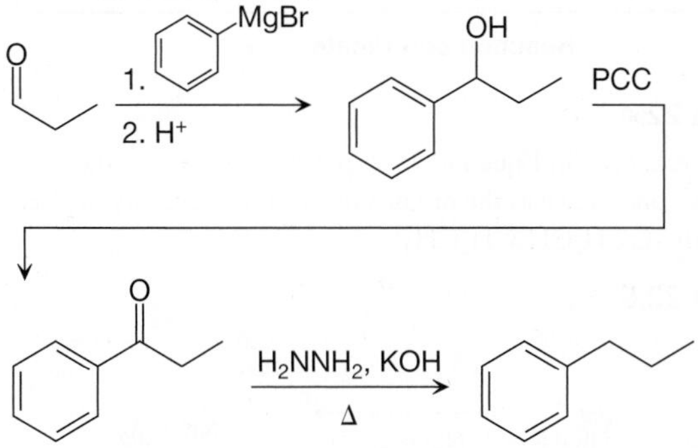

MgBr
1.
2. H+
OH
PCC
H2NNH2, KOH
Δ

Your Turn 21.4

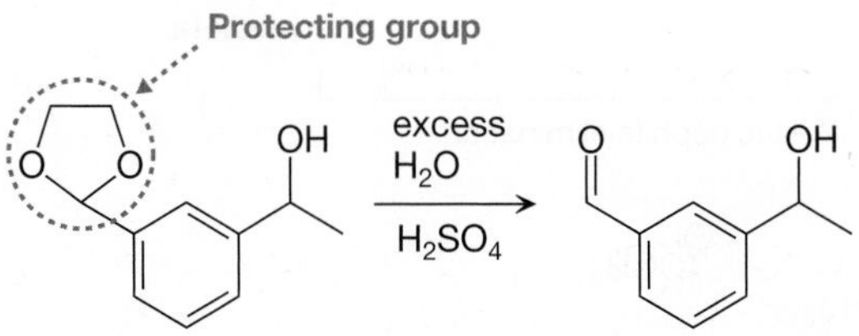

Protecting group
OH
excess
H2O
H2SO4
OH

Your Turn 21.5

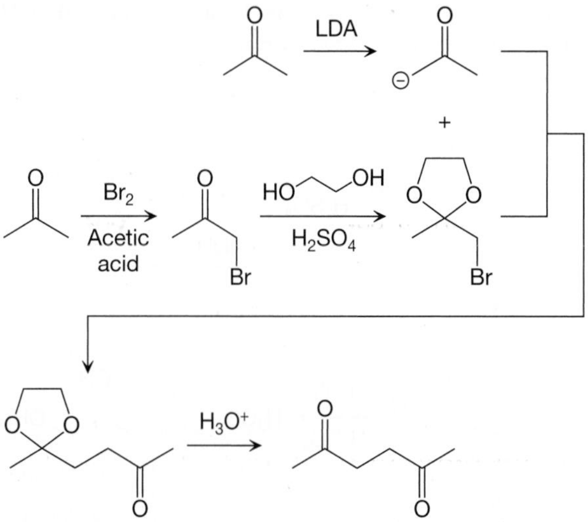

LDA
Br2
Acetic acid
HO OH
H2SO4
Br
Br
H3O+

Your Turn 21.6

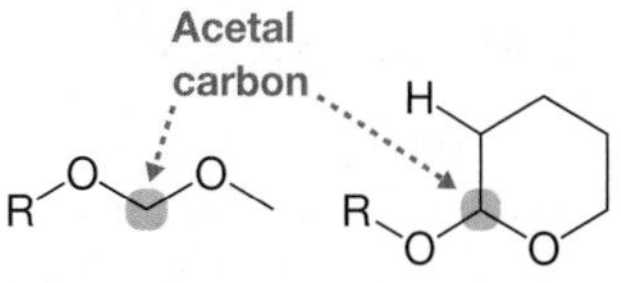

Acetal carbon

Entry 1 **Entry 2**

Your Turn 21.7

The mechanism for the protection step of Entry 1 is shown here. For the deprotection step of Entry 1, draw the mechanism shown in the answer to Your Turn 19.8, but replace the acetal with the one shown here. The two alkoxy leaving groups are circled in red.

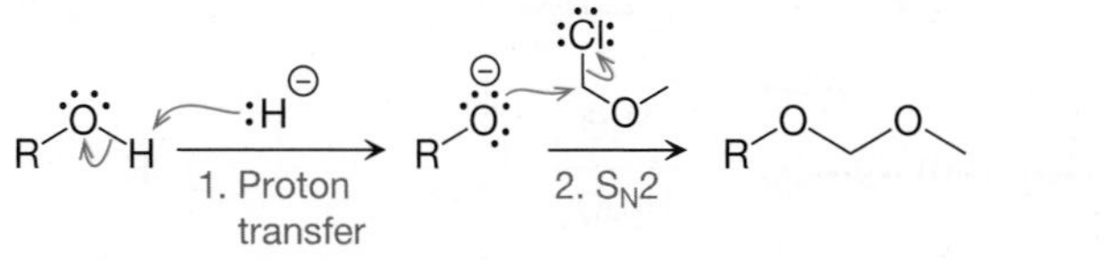

:Cl:
1. Proton transfer
2. SN2

For the protection step of Entry 2, draw the mechanism shown in Equation 12-15 (p. 617), but replace the alkene with dihydropyran (DHP) as shown in Entry 2, and replace H—$^{+}OH_2$ with H—^{+}OHR. For the deprotection step of Entry 2, draw Steps 1–4 of the mechanism shown in the answer to Your Turn 19.8, but replace the acetal with the one shown here. The alkoxy leaving group is circled in red.

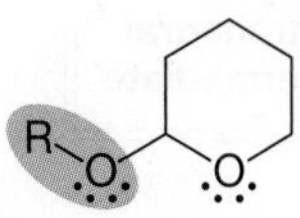

Your Turn 21.8

In both cases, in order to modify only the OH at position C-5, the OH groups at C-1 and C-2 have to be protected.

(a)

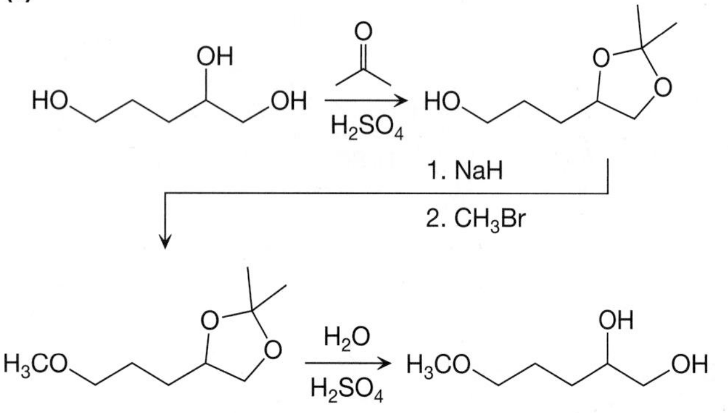

H_2SO_4
1. NaH
2. CH_3Br
H_2O
H_2SO_4

(b)

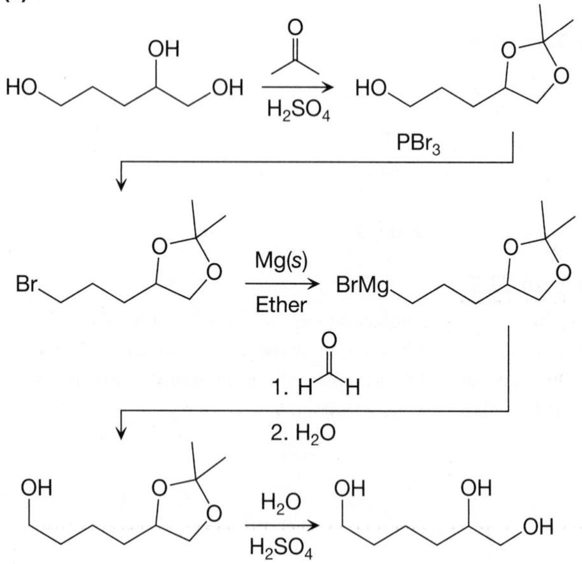

H_2SO_4
PBr_3
Mg(s)
Ether
1.
2. H_2O
H_2O
H_2SO_4

Chapter 22

Your Turn 22.1

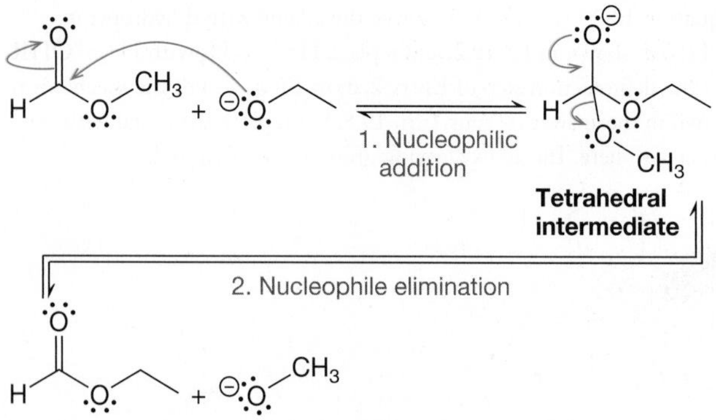

1. Nucleophilic addition
Tetrahedral intermediate
2. Nucleophile elimination

Your Turn 22.2

For each reaction, draw the mechanism in Equation 22-2 (p. 1053), but replace the ester with the one given in the problem, and replace $^-OCH_3$ with **(a)** $^-OCH_2CH_3$ and **(b)** $^-OCH(CH_3)CH_2CH_2CH_3$. The major products are shown here.

(a)

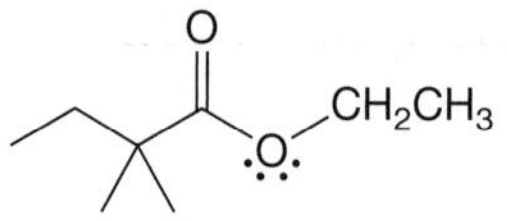

(b)

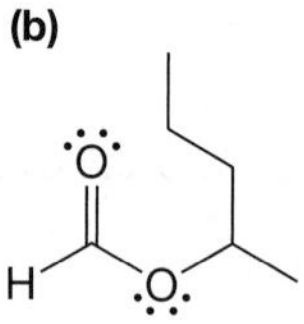

Your Turn 22.3

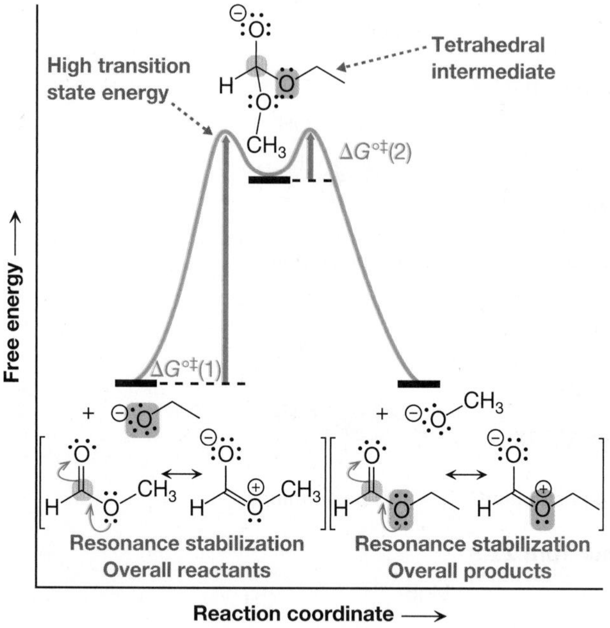

High transition state energy
Tetrahedral intermediate
$\Delta G^{\circ\ddagger}(2)$
$\Delta G^{\circ\ddagger}(1)$
Free energy
Resonance stabilization
Overall reactants
Resonance stabilization
Overall products
Reaction coordinate

Your Turn 22.4

Draw the mechanism in Equation 22-2 (p. 1053), but replace the ester with the one shown as the product of Equation 22-2, and replace $^-OCH_3$ with $^-OCH_2CH_2CH_2CH_3$.

Your Turn 22.5

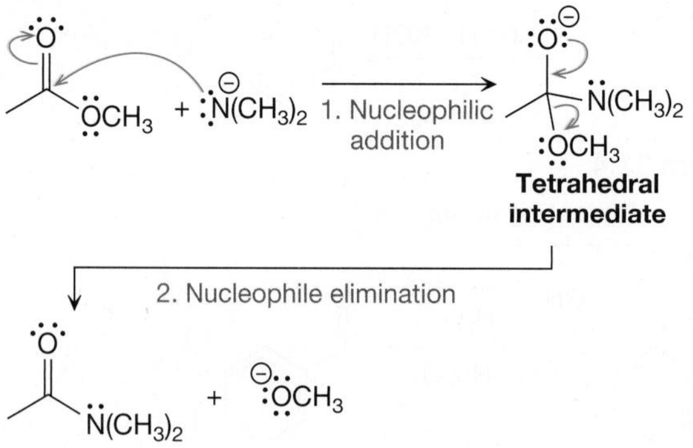

1. Nucleophilic addition
Tetrahedral intermediate
2. Nucleophile elimination

Your Turn 22.6

(a) Acid anhydride to acid chloride = up = unfavorable; **(b)** amide to ester = up = unfavorable; **(c)** acid chloride to ester = down = favorable; **(d)** acid anhydride to carboxylic acid = down = favorable. Reactions **(c)** and **(d)** are likely to occur readily because they involve going down rungs on the stability ladder.

Your Turn 22.7

CH_3CO_2H has pK_a = 4.75 and CH_3CH_2OH has pK_a = 16. The stronger acid (lower pK_a) is on the reactant side, so the products are favored. The difference in pK_a values is 16 − 4.75 = 11.25, so the products are favored by $10^{11.25} = 1.8 \times 10^{11}$.

Your Turn 22.8

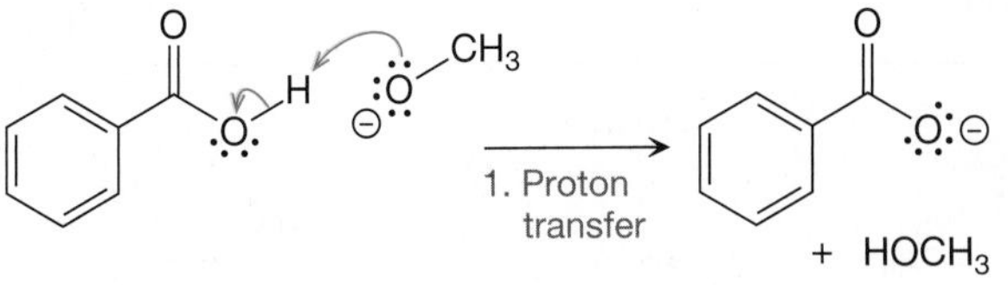
1. Proton transfer
+ HOCH3

Your Turn 22.9

For each reaction, draw the mechanism in Equation 22-10 (p. 1062), but replace the ester with the one given in the problem. The major products are shown here. Note that in part **(b)** the ether group remains unreacted.

(a)

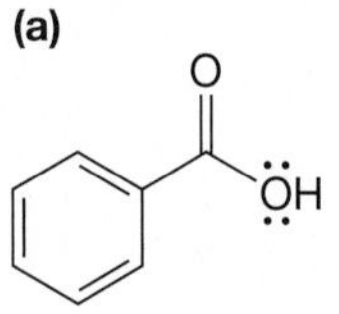

(b)

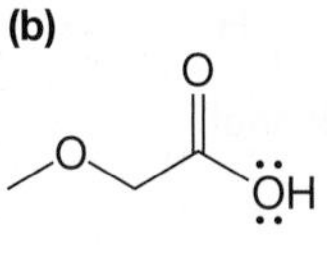

Your Turn 22.10

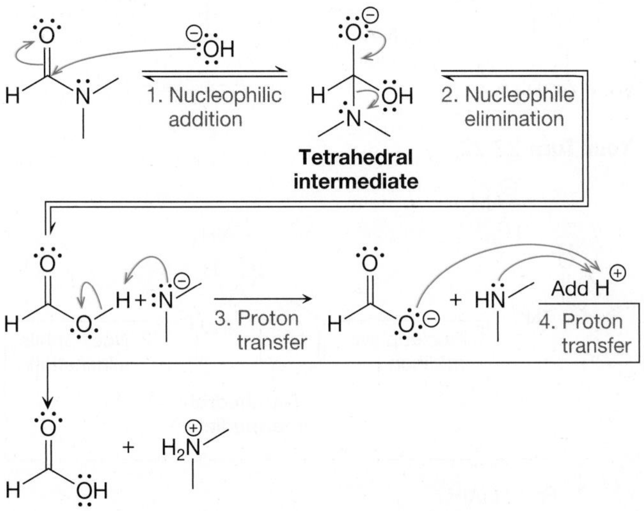
1. Nucleophilic addition
Tetrahedral intermediate
2. Nucleophile elimination
3. Proton transfer
Add H+
4. Proton transfer

Steps 1 and 2 are reversible; Steps 3 and 4 are irreversible.

Your Turn 22.11

For each reaction, draw the mechanism in Equation 22-12 (p. 1064), but replace the amide with the one given. The major products are shown here.

(a)

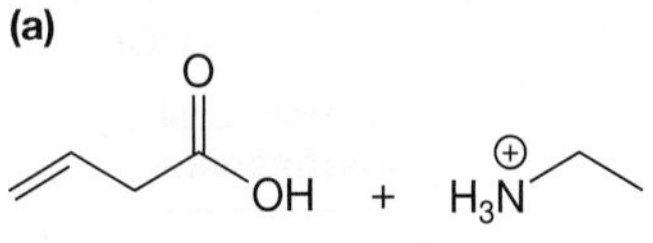

(b)

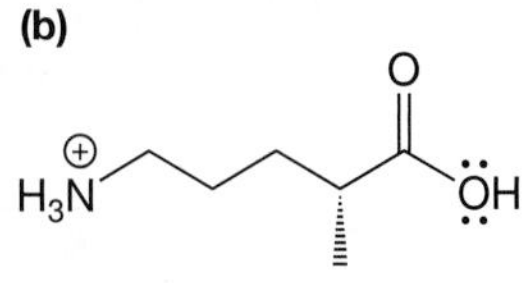

Your Turn 22.12

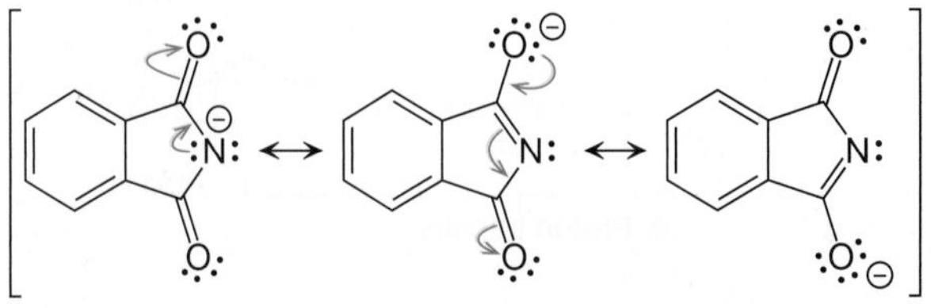

Your Turn 22.13

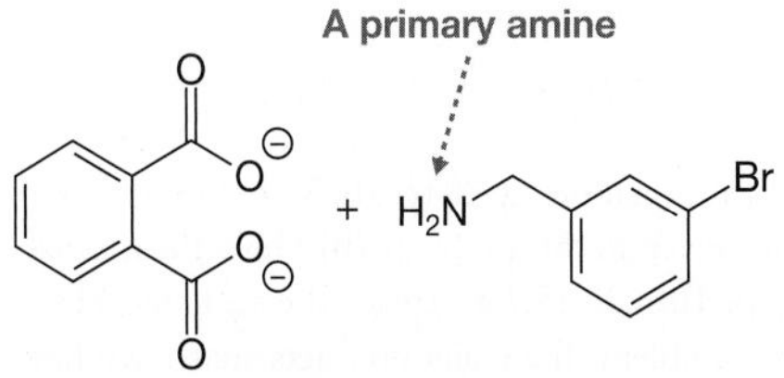
A primary amine

Your Turn 22.14

(a)

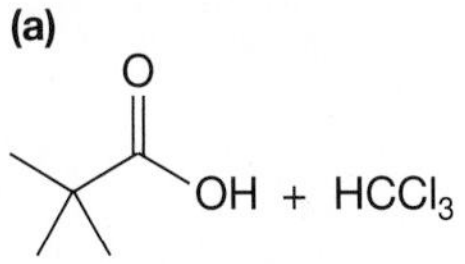

(b)

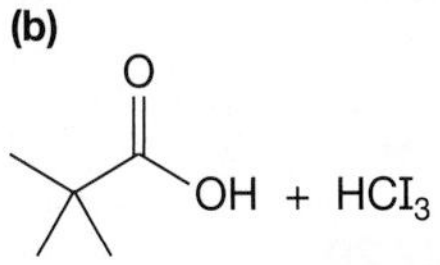

Your Turn 22.15

Compounds **A** and **C** can undergo a haloform reaction because they are methyl ketones.

Your Turn 22.16

For each reaction, draw the mechanism in Equation 22-16 (p. 1070) and Equation 10-35 (p. 528), but replace the methyl ketone with the one given in the problem, and for part **(b)**, replace Br_2 with I_2. The major products are shown here.

(a)

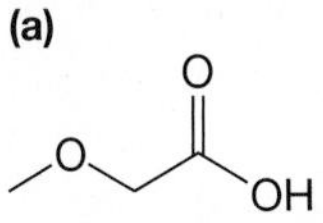

(b)

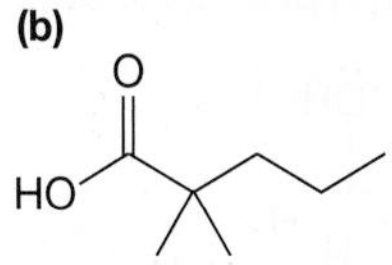

Your Turn 22.17

Compounds **A** and **C** will produce a yellow solid (positive iodoform test).

Your Turn 22.18

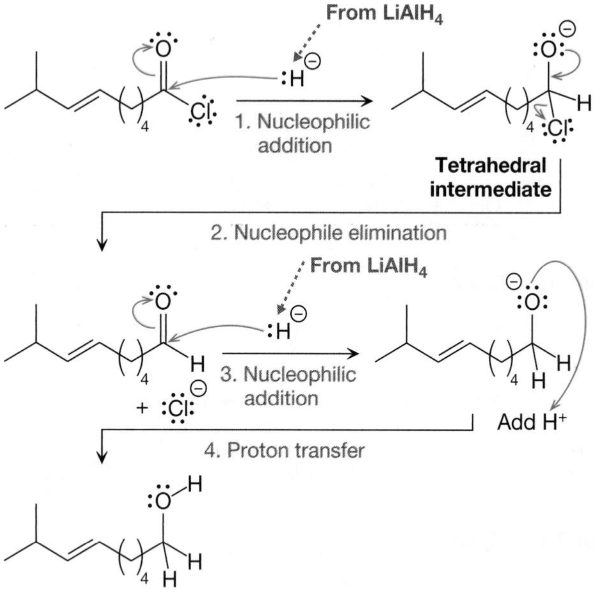

From LiAlH$_4$
1. Nucleophilic addition
Tetrahedral intermediate
2. Nucleophile elimination
From LiAlH$_4$
3. Nucleophilic addition
Add H$^+$
4. Proton transfer

Your Turn 22.19

(a) Draw the mechanism in Equation 22-20 (p. 1073), but replace the acid chloride with the one given in this problem. **(b)** Draw the mechanism in the answer to Your Turn 22.18, but replace the acid chloride with the one given in this problem. The major products are shown here.

(a) **(b)**

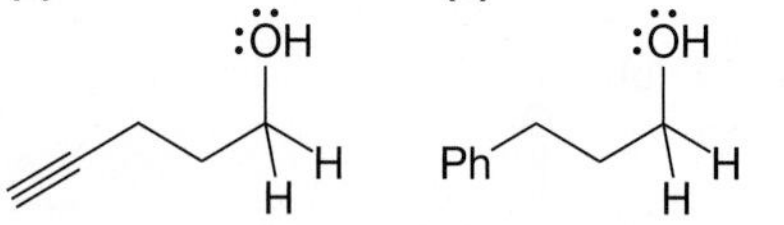

Your Turn 22.20

The reactions in rows 1–3 of Table 22-1 (hydride reductions of acid chlorides, acid anhydrides, and esters) proceed by the following general mechanism, in which $NaBH_4$ or $LiAlH_4$ is simplified to H^-.

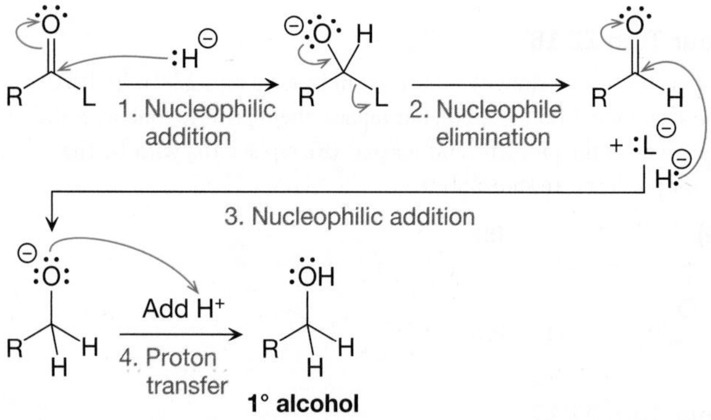

1. Nucleophilic addition
2. Nucleophile elimination
3. Nucleophilic addition
Add H$^+$
4. Proton transfer
1° alcohol

The leaving groups represented by L are circled in red here.

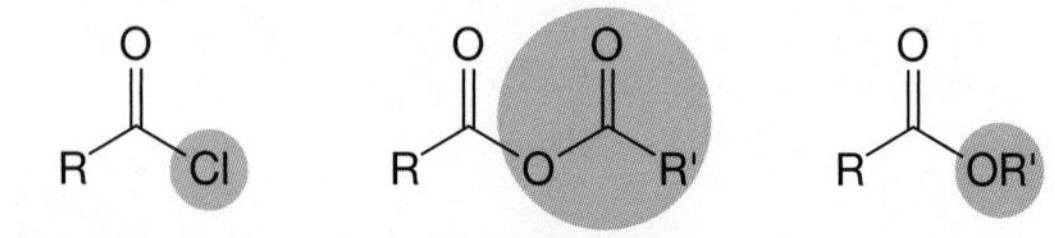

Acid chloride **Acid anhydride** **Ester**

The mechanism for reduction of a carboxylic acid with $LiAlH_4$ is shown here.

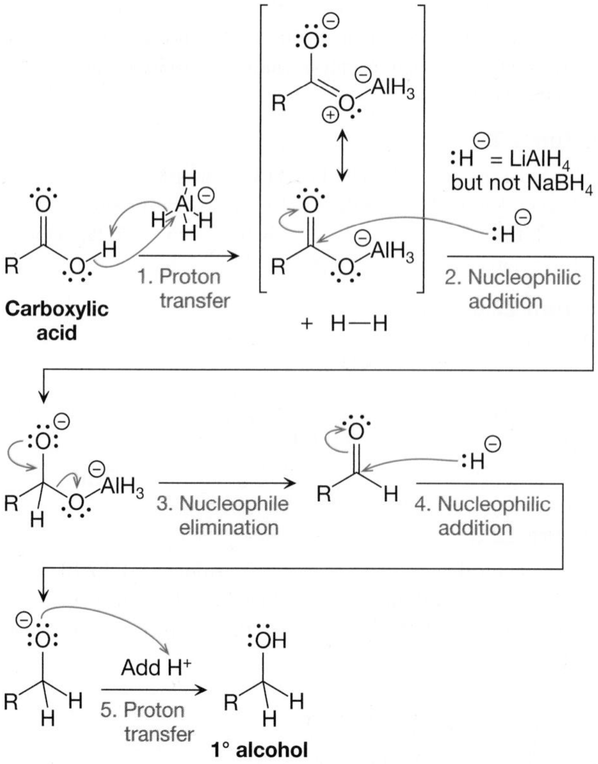

:H$^-$ = LiAlH$_4$ but not NaBH$_4$
Carboxylic acid
1. Proton transfer
+ H—H
2. Nucleophilic addition
3. Nucleophile elimination
4. Nucleophilic addition
Add H$^+$
5. Proton transfer
1° alcohol

Your Turn 22.21

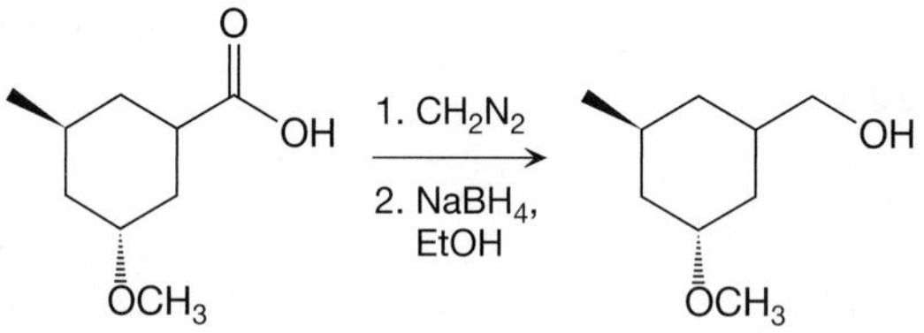

1. CH$_2$N$_2$
2. NaBH$_4$, EtOH

Your Turn 22.22

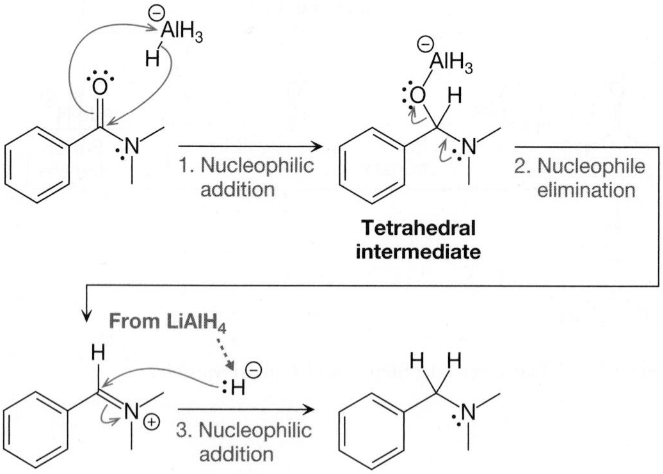

1. Nucleophilic addition
Tetrahedral intermediate
2. Nucleophile elimination
From LiAlH$_4$
3. Nucleophilic addition

Your Turn 22.23

(a) Draw the mechanism for the reaction in Equation 22-24 (p. 1078), but replace the carboxylic acid with the one given in this problem. **(b)** Draw the mechanism for the reaction in Equation 22-26 (p. 1079), but replace the amide with the one given in this problem. The major products are shown here.

(a)

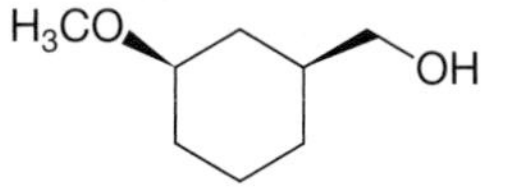

H_3CO
OH

(b)

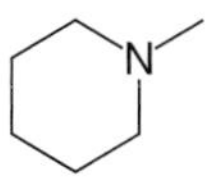

N

Your Turn 22.24

Draw the mechanism for the reaction in Equation 22-35 (p. 1085), but replace the acid chloride with the ester given in this problem, and replace $^-CH_2CH_3$ with $^-CH_3$. The leaving group in Step 2 is $^-OCH_3$ instead of ^-Cl.

Your Turn 22.25

(a) Draw the mechanism for the reaction in Equation 22-35 (p. 1085), but replace the acid chloride with the one given in this problem, and replace $^-CH_2CH_3$ with $^-C_6H_5$. **(b)** Draw the mechanism for the reaction in Equation 22-35 (p. 1085), but replace the acid chloride with the ester given in this problem, and replace $^-CH_2CH_3$ with $^-CH_2CH_2CH_2CH_3$. The major products are shown here.

(a)

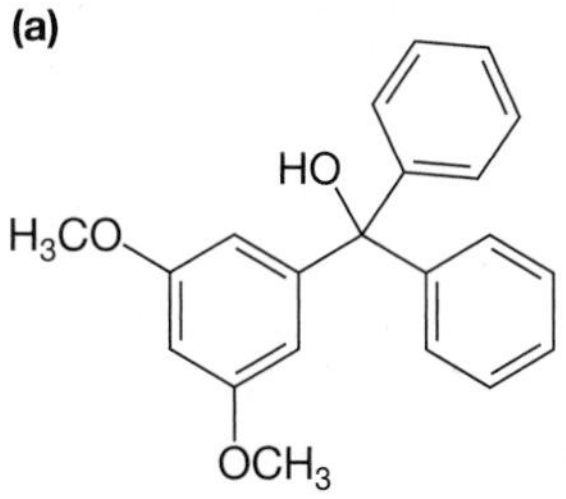

HO
H_3CO
OCH_3

(b)

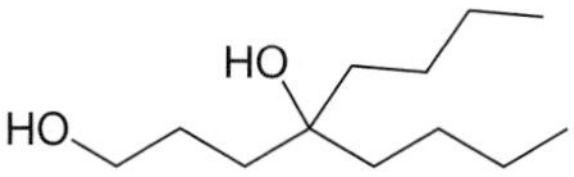

HO
HO

Your Turn 22.26

(a)

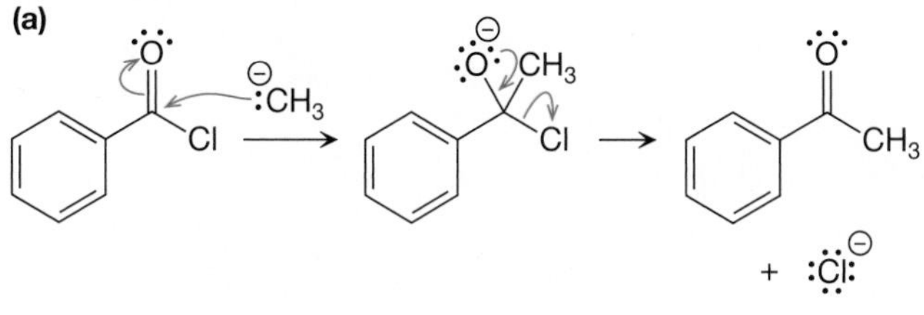

CH_3
Cl
OCH_3
Cl
CH_3

(b) and **(c)** No reaction.

Chapter 23

Your Turn 23.1

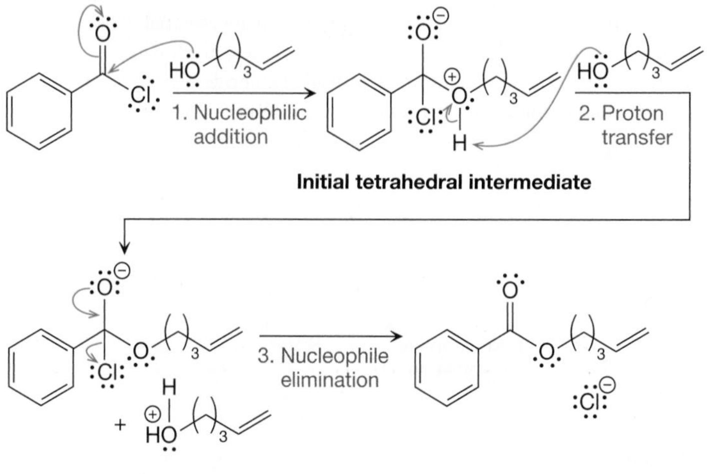

1. Nucleophilic addition
2. Proton transfer
Initial tetrahedral intermediate
3. Nucleophile elimination

Your Turn 23.2

(a) Redraw the mechanism in the answer to Your Turn 23.1, but replace the acid chloride with the one given in this problem, and replace the alcohol with phenol. The major product is shown here.

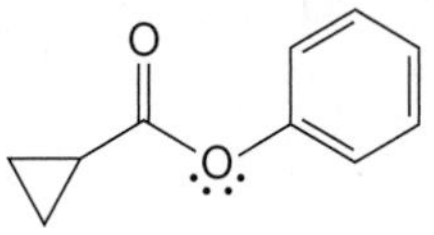

(b) Redraw the mechanism in Equation 23-5 (p. 1101), but replace the acid chloride with the one given in this problem. The major product is shown here.

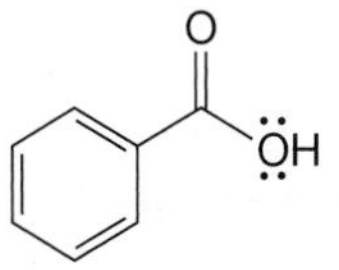

OH

Your Turn 23.3

(a)

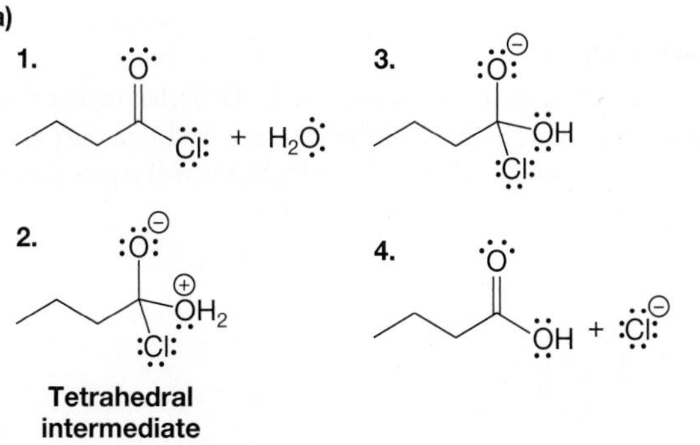

1.
2.
3.
4.
Tetrahedral intermediate

(b) Step 1 (nucleophilic addition) has the highest-energy transition state, which is consistent with it being the slow step.

Your Turn 23.4

For Equation 23-6, Steps 1–3 are essentially the same as in the answer to Your Turn 23.1, but as shown here, the leaving group in Step 3 is acetate anion instead of chloride anion. Step 4 is protonation of acetate anion by the solvent. For Equation 23-7, Steps 1–3 are essentially the same as in Equation 23-5 (p. 1101), but as shown here, the leaving group in Step 3 is a carboxylate anion instead of chloride anion. Step 4 is protonation of the carboxylate anion by the solvent.

Eq. 23-6

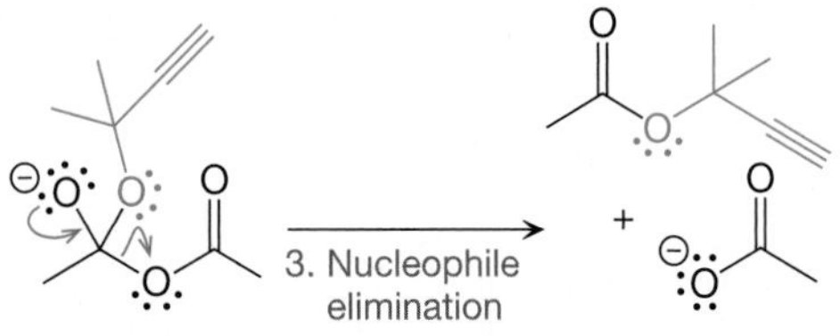
3. Nucleophile elimination

Eq. 23-7

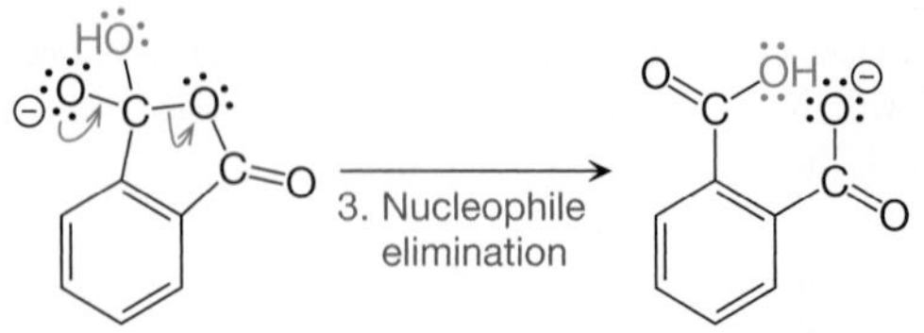
3. Nucleophile elimination

Your Turn 23.5

The mechanism is essentially the same as Equation 23-10 (p. 1107), but as shown here, the leaving group in Step 3 is acetate anion instead of chloride anion.

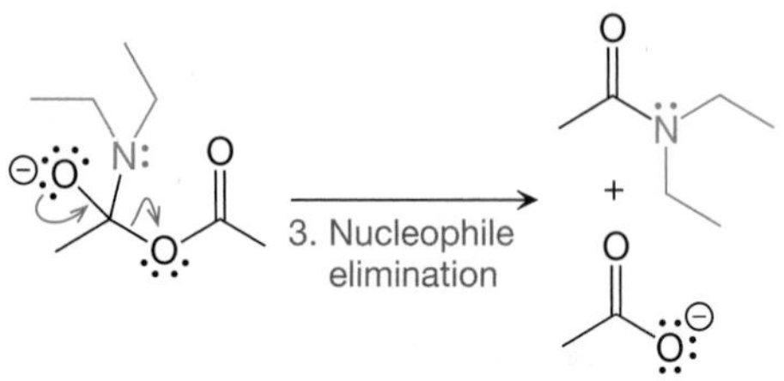
3. Nucleophile elimination

Your Turn 23.6

(a) Draw the mechanism in Equation 23-10 (p. 1107), but replace the acid chloride and amine in Step 1 with the ones provided in the problem, and replace the amine in Step 2 with Et_3N. The major product is shown here.

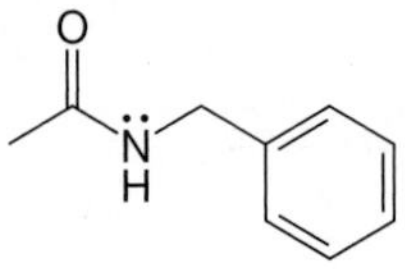

(b) Draw the mechanism in the answer to Your Turn 23.5, but replace the acid anhydride with the one provided in the problem, and replace the amine with NH_3. The major product is shown here.

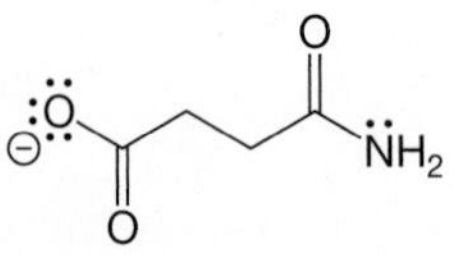

Your Turn 23.7

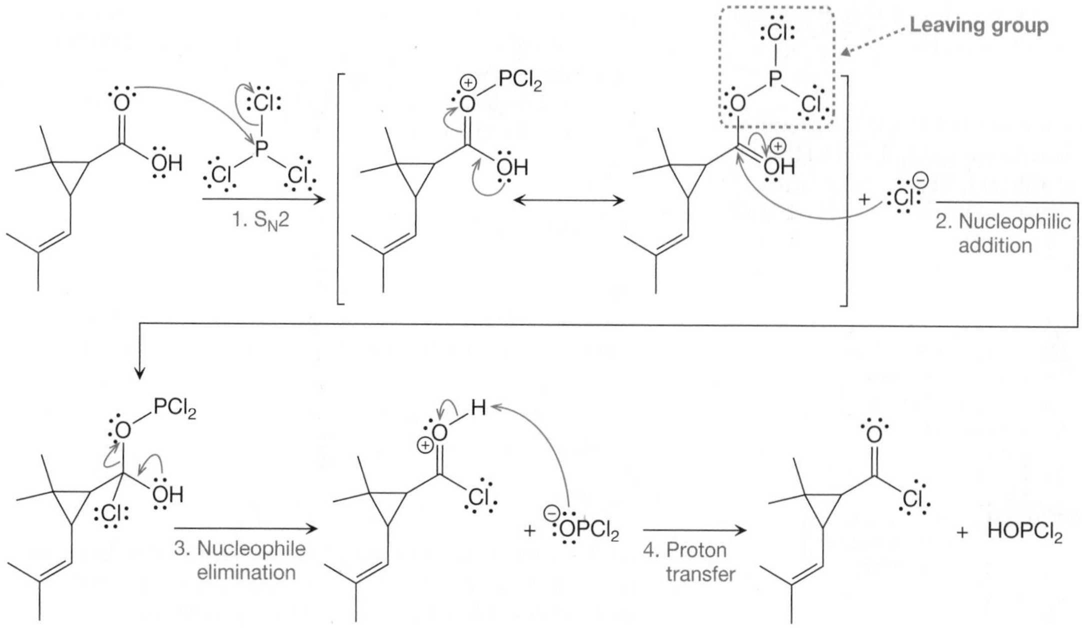

Leaving group
1. S_N2
2. Nucleophilic addition
3. Nucleophile elimination
4. Proton transfer
+ $HOPCl_2$

Your Turn 23.8

The carboxyl proton (acetic acid, $pK_a = 4.75$) is more acidic than the α proton (ethyl acetate, $pK_a = 25$).

Your Turn 23.9

Mechanism for "Multiple steps (Section 23.4)" in Eq. 23-18

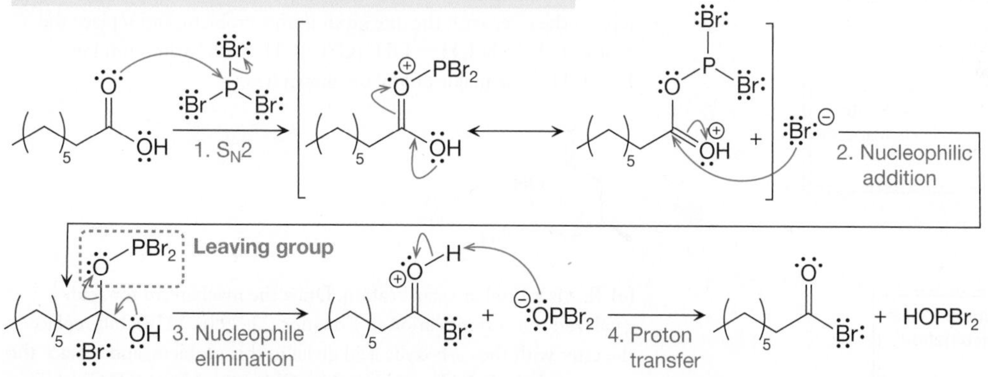

1. S_N2
2. Nucleophilic addition
Leaving group
3. Nucleophile elimination
4. Proton transfer
+ $HOPBr_2$

Mechanism for "Two steps (Section 7.10)" in Eq. 23-18

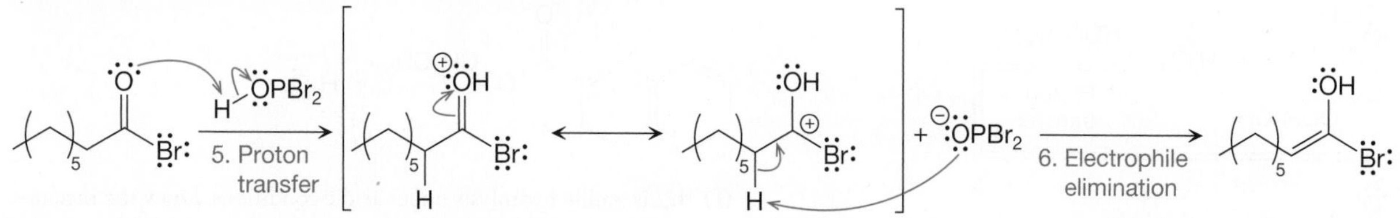

5. Proton transfer
6. Electrophile elimination

Mechanism for "Multiple steps (Section 23.1)" in Eq. 23-18

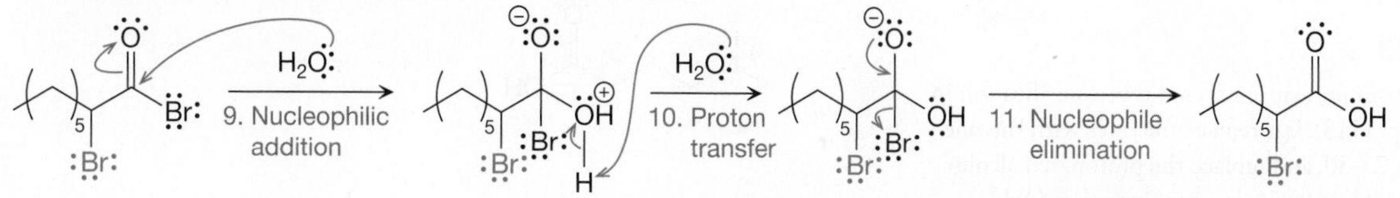

9. Nucleophilic addition
10. Proton transfer
11. Nucleophile elimination

Your Turn 23.10

Redraw Equation 23-18 (p. 1113), but replace $CH_3(CH_2)_5$ in each structure with a cyclohexyl substituent, C_6H_{11}.

Your Turn 23.11

For each synthesis, begin by treating $CH_3CH_2CH_2CO_2H$ with 1. Br_2, PCl_3 / 2. H_2O to produce the α-bromo acid, $CH_3CH_2CHBrCO_2H$. Then treat the α-bromo acid with **(a)** 1. NH_3 (excess) / 2. HCl, H_2O; **(b)** 1. CH_3NH_2 (excess) / 2. HCl, H_2O; or **(c)** 1. NaOH / 2. H_3O^+.

Your Turn 23.12

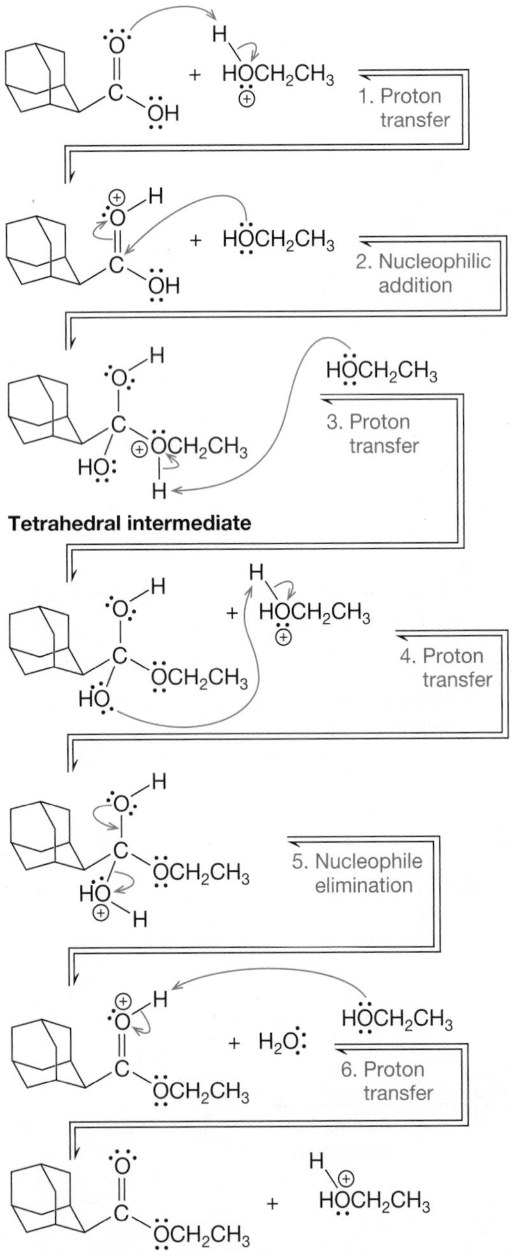
1. Proton transfer
2. Nucleophilic addition
3. Proton transfer
Tetrahedral intermediate
4. Proton transfer
5. Nucleophile elimination
6. Proton transfer

Your Turn 23.13

Draw the mechanism for acid-catalyzed transesterification in Equation 23-29 (p. 1118), but replace the ester with the one given in Equation 23-30, and replace the protonated alcohol, $H—OH^+(CH_2)_5CH_3$, with hydronium ion, $H—OH_2^+$.

Your Turn 23.14

(a) This is acid-catalyzed ester hydrolysis. Draw the mechanism for acid-catalyzed transesterification in Equation 23-29 (p. 1118), but replace the ester with the one given in this problem, and replace the protonated alcohol, $H—OH^+(CH_2)_5CH_3$, with hydronium ion, $H—OH_2^+$. The major products are shown here.

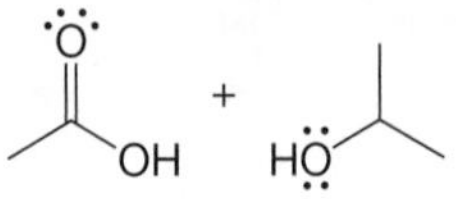

(b) This is acid-catalyzed transesterification. Draw the mechanism in Equation 23-29 (p. 1118), but replace the ester and protonated alcohol with the ones given in this problem. The major products are shown here.

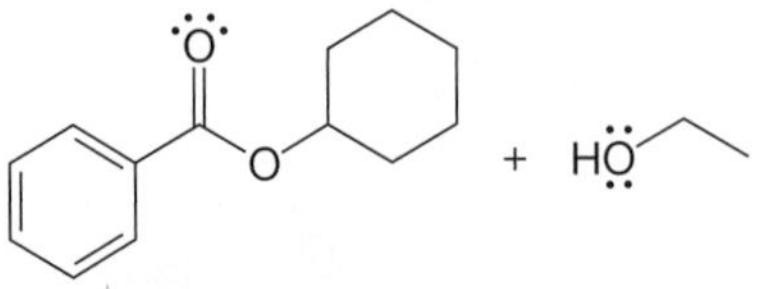

(c) This is amide hydrolysis under acidic conditions. Draw the mechanism in Equation 23-33 (p. 1121), but replace the amide with the one given in this problem. The major products are shown here.

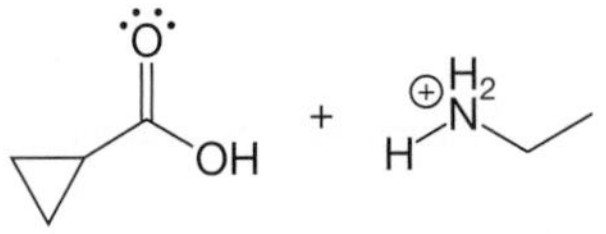

(d) This is acid-catalyzed ester hydrolysis. Draw the mechanism for acid-catalyzed transesterification in Equation 23-29 (p. 1118), but replace the ester with the one given in this problem, and replace the protonated alcohol, $H—OH^+(CH_2)_5CH_3$, with hydronium ion, $H—OH_2^+$. The major product is shown here.

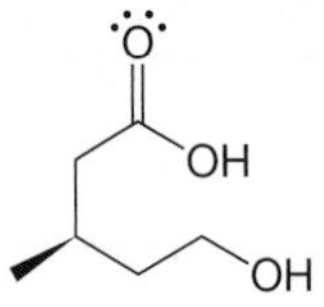

(e) This is a Fischer esterification. Draw the mechanism for acid-catalyzed transesterification in Equation 23-29 (p. 1118), but replace the ester with the carboxylic acid given in this problem, and replace the protonated alcohol, $H—OH^+(CH_2)_5CH_3$, with $H—OH^+CH_2CH_3$. The major product is shown here.

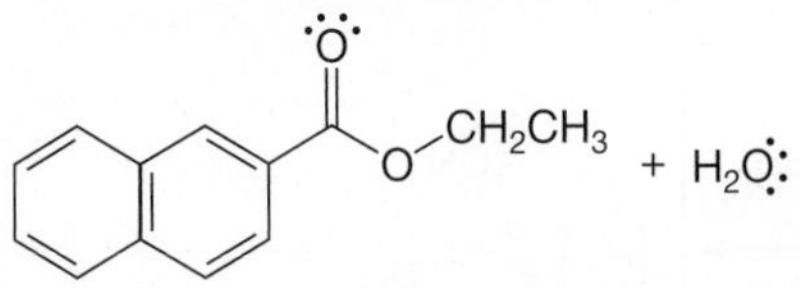

(f) This is amide hydrolysis under acidic conditions. Draw the mechanism in Equation 23-33 (p. 1121), but replace the amide with the one given in this problem. The major product is shown here.

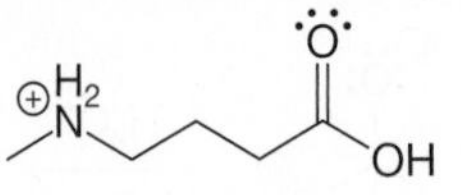

Your Turn 23.15

This is a Claisen condensation. Draw the mechanism in Equation 23-37 (p. 1125), but replace the ester molecule with the one given in this problem. The major product is shown here.

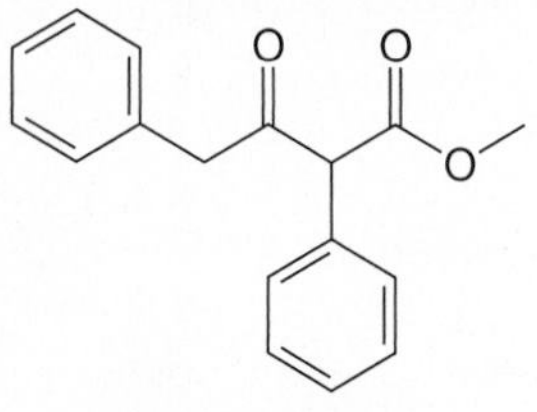

Your Turn 23.16

Mechanism for Transesterification (Eq. 23-39)

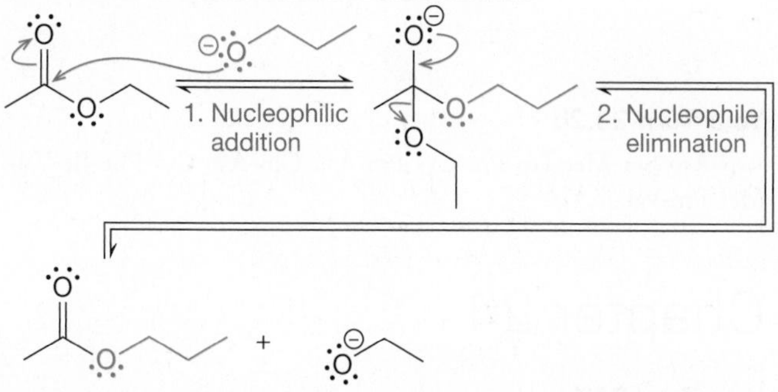

1. Nucleophilic addition
2. Nucleophile elimination

For the Claisen condensation with the new ester, draw the Claisen condensation mechanism in Equation 23-37 (p. 1125), but replace the ester molecule with the new ester product shown above. The resulting product, shown below, has an additional C atom on the alkoxy group compared to Equation 23-36.

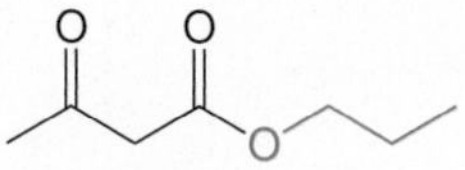

Your Turn 23.17

Mechanism for Saponification (Eq. 23-40)

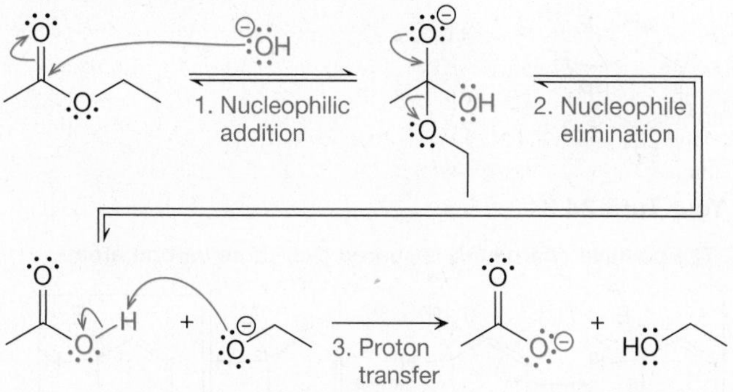

1. Nucleophilic addition
2. Nucleophile elimination
3. Proton transfer

Your Turn 23.18

In each case, $CH_3CH_2O^-$ is the base and it picks up a proton from the uncharged acid. The products are different from the reactants unless ethanol is the acid.

Propan-1-ol

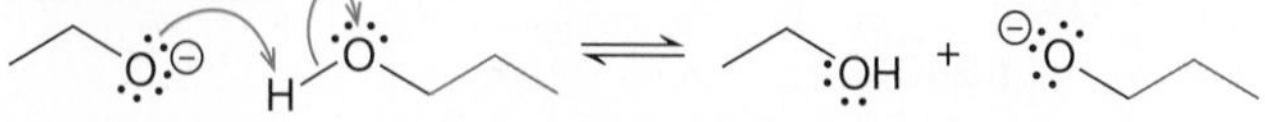

Water

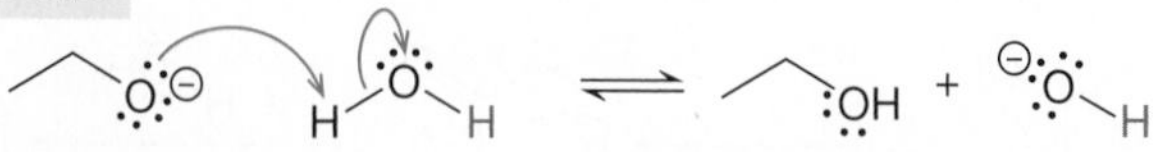

Ethanol

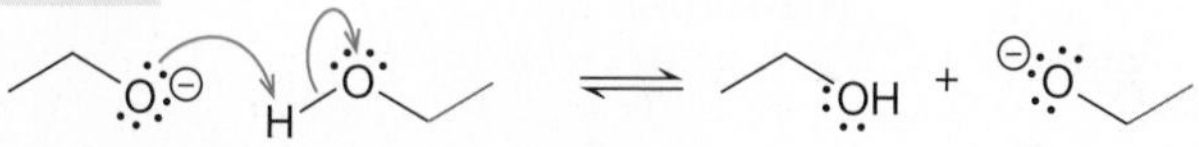

Your Turn 23.19

In each case, draw the Claisen condensation mechanism in Equation 23-37 (p. 1125), but replace $CH_3CH_2O^-$ with CH_3O^- and make the following replacements from Equation 23-41 (p. 1129):

(a) Replace both the ester in Step 1 and the ester in Step 2 with the ester shown in red in Equation 23-41.

(b) Replace the ester in Step 1 with the ester shown in red in Equation 23-41, and replace the ester in Step 2 with the ester shown in black in Equation 23-41.

(c) Replace the ester in Step 1 with the ester shown in black in Equation 23-41, and replace the ester in Step 2 with the ester shown in red in Equation 23-41.

(d) Replace both the ester in Step 1 and the ester in Step 2 with the ester shown in black in Equation 23-41.

Your Turn 23.20

The pK_a for an ester is 25, and the pK_a for a ketone is 20. Therefore, the reactant side of the proton transfer reaction is favored by 10^5. Consequently, this reaction will not interfere with the intended Claisen condensation reaction.

Your Turn 23.21

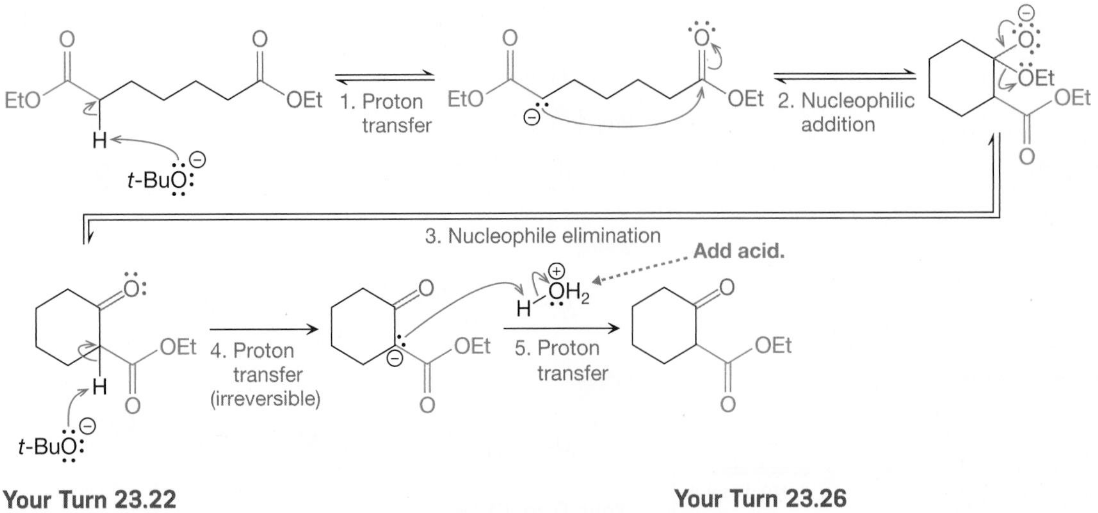

EtO
OEt
1. Proton transfer
t-BuO:
2. Nucleophilic addition
OEt
3. Nucleophile elimination
Add acid.
4. Proton transfer (irreversible)
5. Proton transfer

Your Turn 23.22

The mechanism is the same as the one in the answer to Your Turn 23.21 with the following modifications.

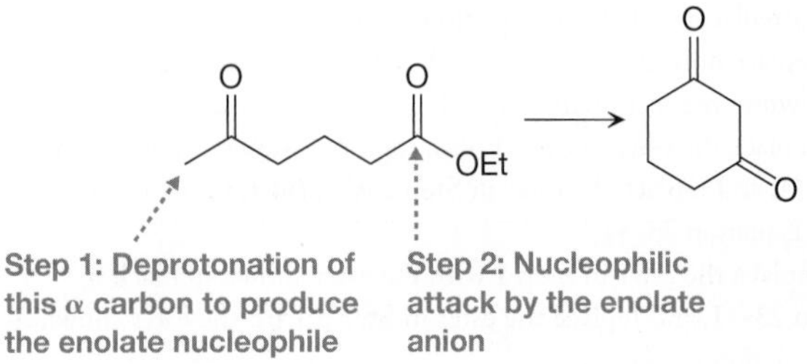

OEt
Step 1: Deprotonation of this α carbon to produce the enolate nucleophile
Step 2: Nucleophilic attack by the enolate anion

Your Turn 23.23

OR

Your Turn 23.24

Malonic ester (diethyl malonate) has a pK_a of 13.5, and the pK_a of ethanol is 16. The product side is favored by $10^{2.5}$.

Your Turn 23.25

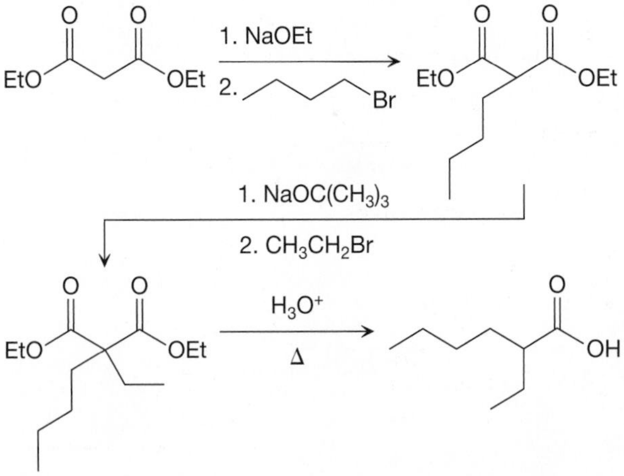

EtO
OEt
1. NaOEt
2.
Br
1. NaOC(CH3)3
2. CH3CH2Br
H3O+
Δ
OH

Your Turn 23.26

Asp-Asp-Ser-Met-Trp-Pro-Cys-Pro-Asn-Gln-Asp-Cys-Phe-Ile-Val-Met-Pro-Val.

Chapter 24

Your Turn 24.1

In each product, the sp^3-hybridized atoms prevent the π system from being cyclic.

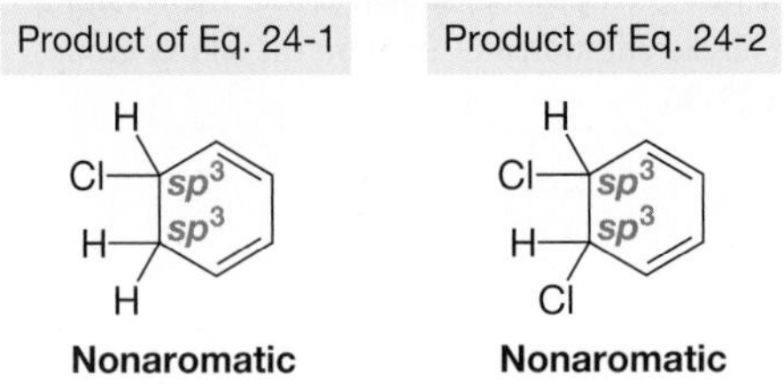

Product of Eq. 24-1
Product of Eq. 24-2
Nonaromatic
Nonaromatic

Your Turn 24.2

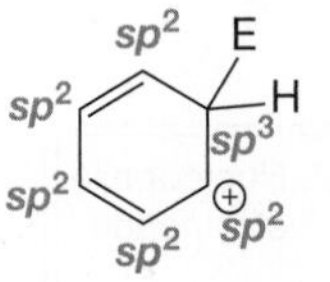

sp2
E
H
sp3

Your Turn 24.3

The positive charge (δ⁺) is shared over three carbon atoms.

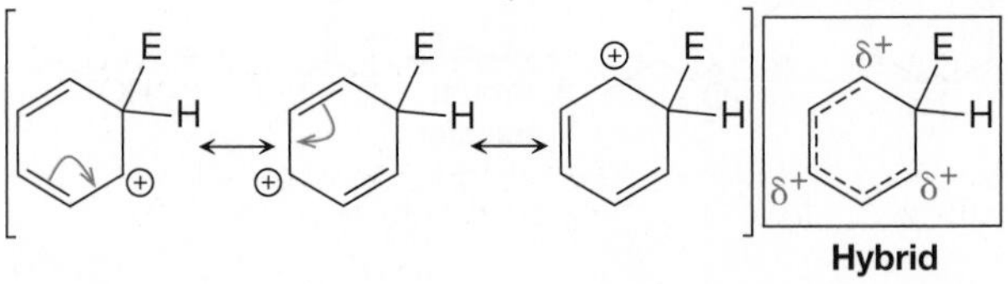

E
H
Hybrid

Your Turn 24.4

(b) is faster because a higher concentration of electrophile leads to a faster reaction.

Your Turn 24.5

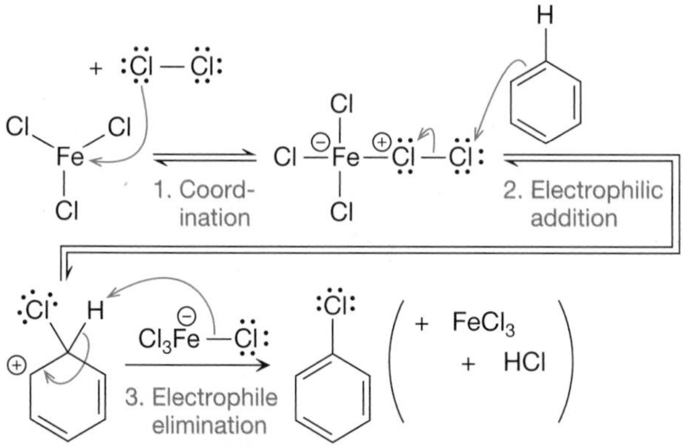
1. Coord-ination
2. Electrophilic addition
3. Electrophile elimination
+ FeCl3
+ HCl

Steps 2 and 3 formally make up the EAS mechanism, with Cl^+ as the electrophile.

Your Turn 24.6

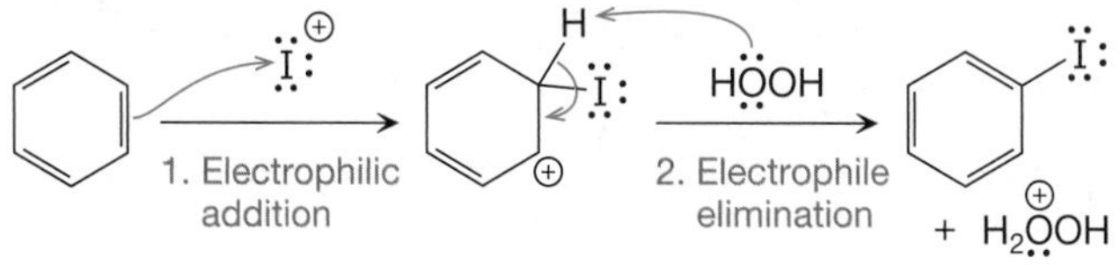
1. Electrophilic addition
2. Electrophile elimination

Your Turn 24.7

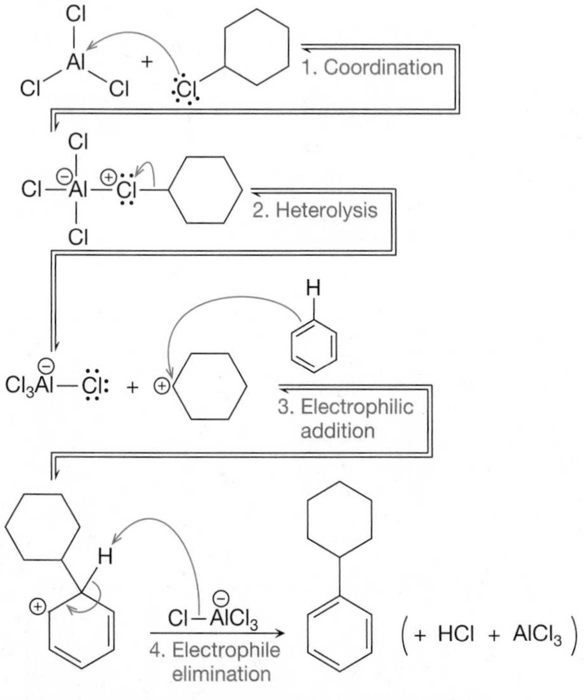
1. Coordination
2. Heterolysis
3. Electrophilic addition
4. Electrophile elimination
(+ HCl + AlCl3)

Steps 3 and 4 formally make up the EAS mechanism, with the cyclohexyl C^+ as the electrophile.

Your Turn 24.8

Mechanism for Eq. 24-14

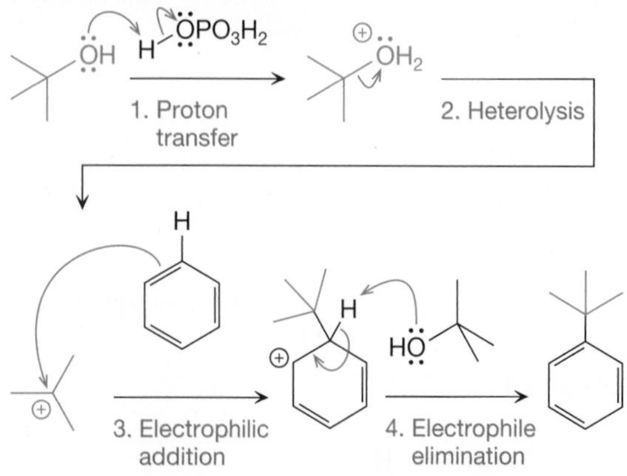
1. Proton transfer
2. Heterolysis
3. Electrophilic addition
4. Electrophile elimination

Mechanism for Eq. 24-15

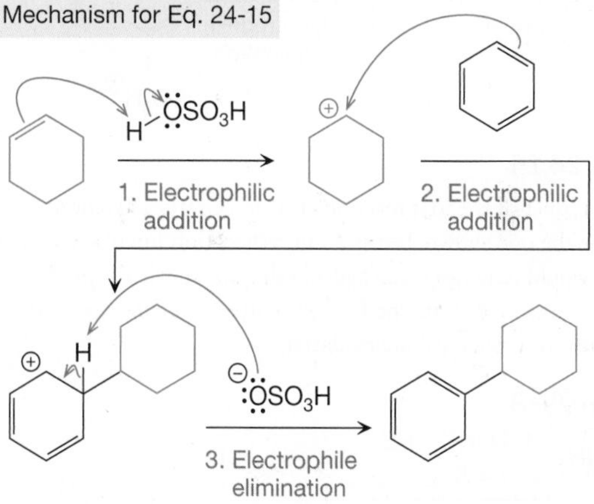
1. Electrophilic addition
2. Electrophilic addition
3. Electrophile elimination

Your Turn 24.9

sp^3, 421 kJ/mol; *sp*^{2}, 464 kJ/mol.

Your Turn 24.10

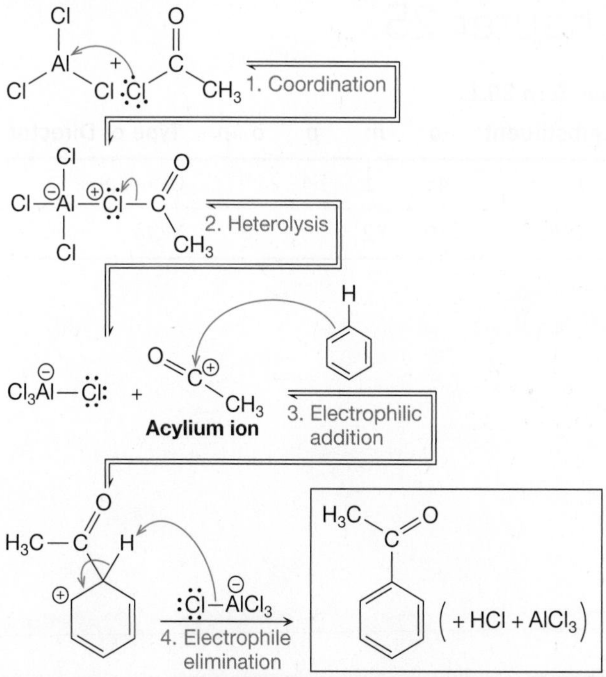
1. Coordination
2. Heterolysis
Acylium ion
3. Electrophilic addition
4. Electrophile elimination
(+ HCl + AlCl3)

Your Turn 24.11

Draw the mechanism in Equation 24-24 (p. 1170), but replace the acid chloride with the one given in the problem. The major product is shown here.

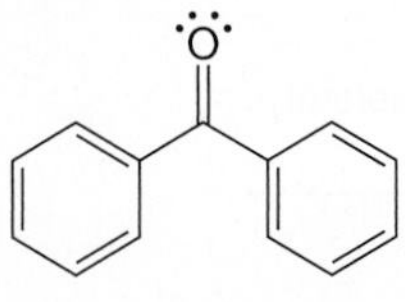

Your Turn 24.12

Draw the mechanism in Equation 24-26 (p. 1173), but replace H—ONO_2 in Step 1 with H—OSO_3H.

Your Turn 24.13

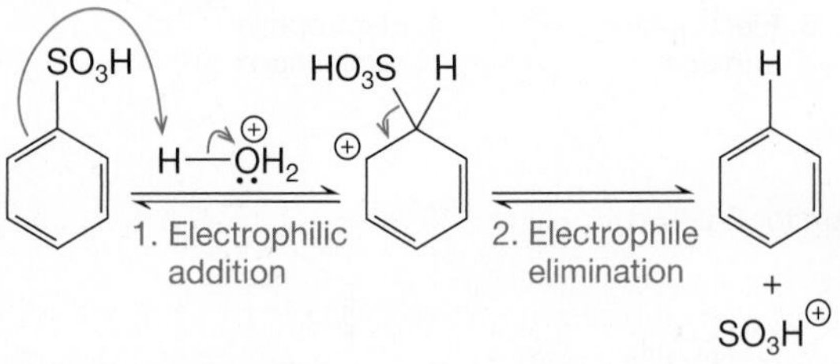

SO_3H
H—OH_2
1. Electrophilic addition
HO_3S H
2. Electrophile elimination
H
+
$SO_3H^{\oplus}$

Your Turn 24.14

The major product of the first reaction (Friedel–Crafts alkylation) would not be the one shown, because the carbocation intermediate that is produced would undergo a 1,2-hydride shift. In the actual product of the Friedel–Crafts alkylation, the benzylic carbon is *quaternary* and is unreactive toward permanganate oxidation.

Your Turn 24.15

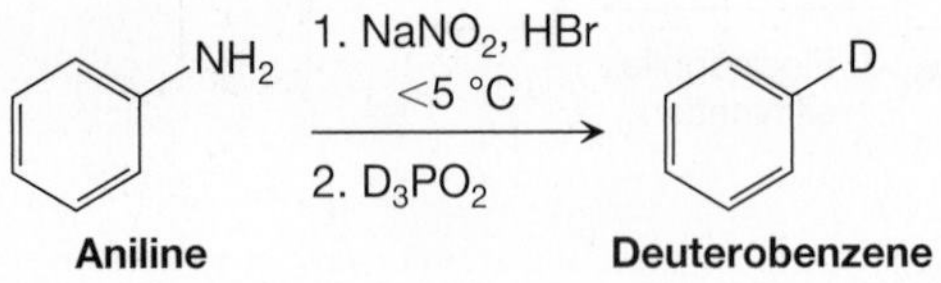

NH_2
1. $NaNO_2$, HBr
<5 °C
2. D_3PO_2
D
Aniline
Deuterobenzene

Chapter 25

Your Turn 25.1

Substituent	*o*	*m*	*p*	*o*+*p*	Type of Director
—I	45	1	54	99	Ortho/para
—CHO	19	72	9	28	Meta

Your Turn 25.2

(a) An OH substituent is an ortho/para director.

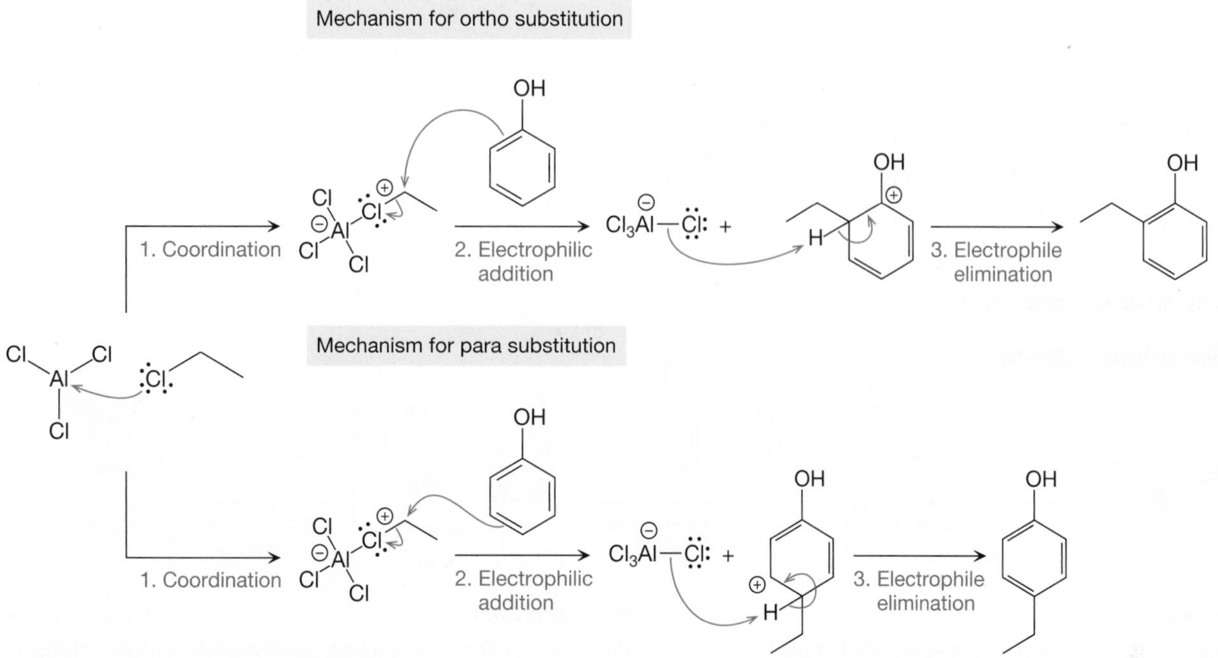
Mechanism for ortho substitution
1. Coordination
2. Electrophilic addition
3. Electrophile elimination
Mechanism for para substitution
1. Coordination
2. Electrophilic addition
3. Electrophile elimination

(b) A nitro substituent is a meta director.

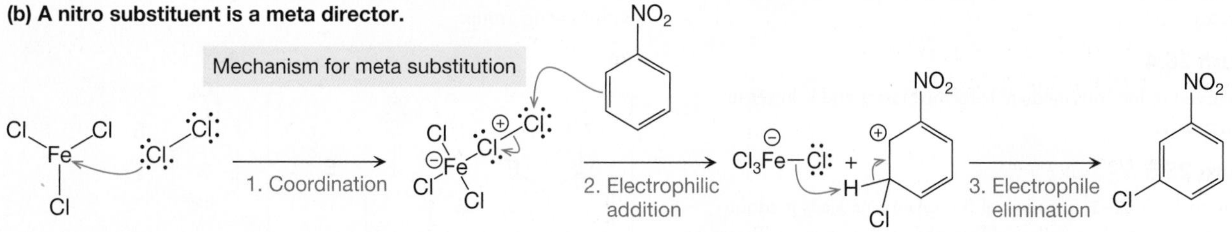
Mechanism for meta substitution
1. Coordination
2. Electrophilic addition
3. Electrophile elimination

(c) A methyl substituent is an ortho/para director.

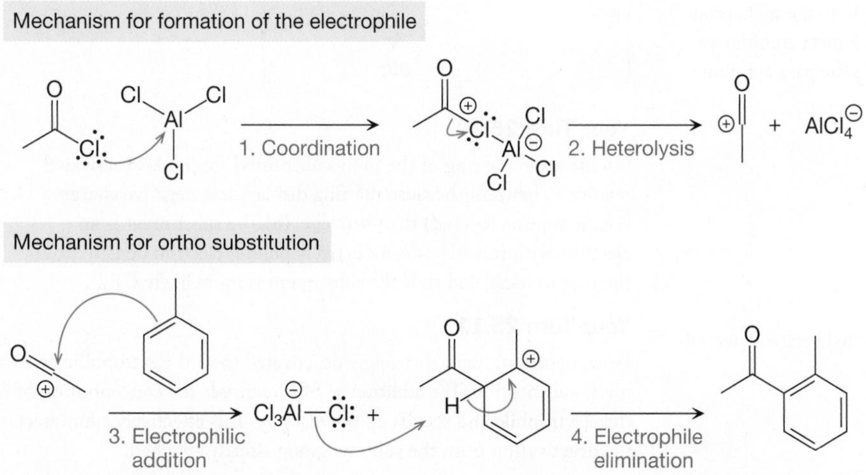
Mechanism for formation of the electrophile
1. Coordination
2. Heterolysis
Mechanism for ortho substitution
3. Electrophilic addition
4. Electrophile elimination

Mechanism for para substitution

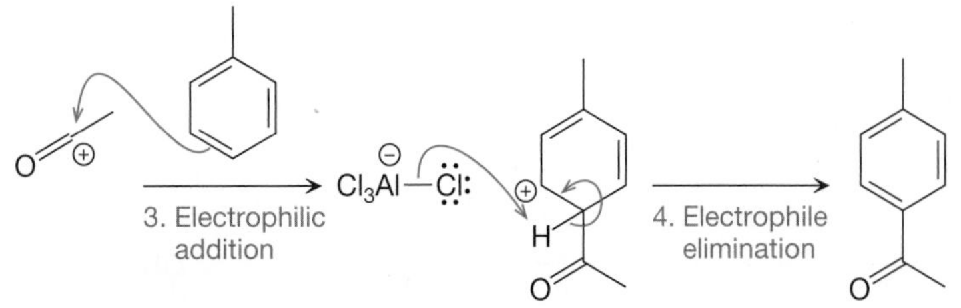
3. Electrophilic addition
4. Electrophile elimination

(d) An acetyl group is a meta director.

Mechanism for meta substitution

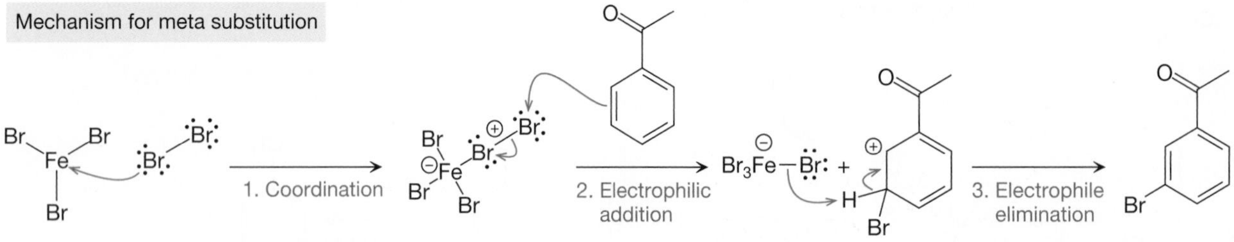
1. Coordination
2. Electrophilic addition
3. Electrophile elimination

Your Turn 25.3

The OCH_3 group is an ortho/para director, as it has Feature 1. The CH_2CH_3 group is an alkyl group (Feature 2a) and is thus an ortho/para director.

Your Turn 25.4

The para arenium ion intermediate is formed faster and is lower in energy.

Your Turn 25.5

According to Table 25-1, nitration of fluorobenzene leads predominantly to the para product, followed by ortho, and then meta. Therefore, the para arenium ion (**C**), is produced the fastest and is the most stable, while the meta arenium ion (**B**) is produced the slowest and is the least stable. Nitration of benzonitrile leads predominantly to the meta product, followed by ortho, and then para. Therefore, the meta arenium ion is produced the fastest and is the most stable, while the para arenium ion is produced the slowest and is the least stable.

Your Turn 25.6

The second resonance structure is especially stable.

Your Turn 25.7

The second resonance structure is the least stable.

Your Turn 25.8

In Figure 25-3, the arenium ion intermediate for ethyl benzoate would appear between that of benzene and nitrobenzene.

Your Turn 25.9

The inductive effect leads to a larger concentration of positive charge in the intermediate and decreases stability, because Cl is an electron-withdrawing group.

(a)

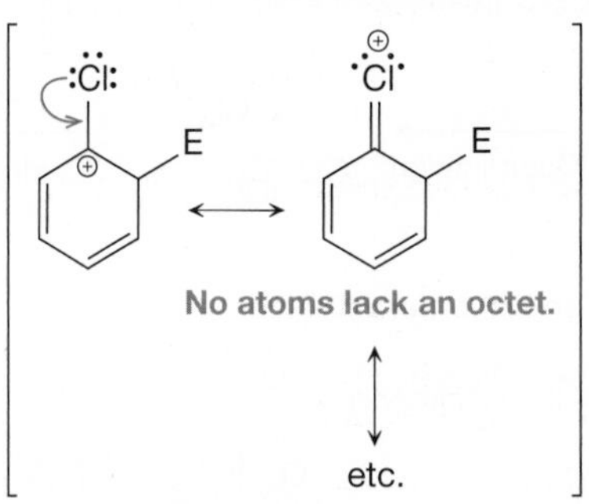
No atoms lack an octet.
etc.

(b)

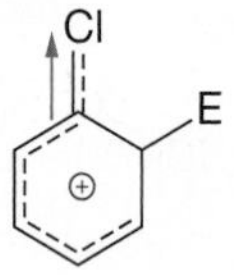

Your Turn 25.10

(a) The aromatic ring of the monosubstituted species is deactivated relative to benzene, because the ring displays less negative charge (i.e., it appears less red) than benzene. **(b)** The substituent is an electron-withdrawing one, inductively pulling electron density from the ring to itself, and thus the substituent is more likely CF_3.

Your Turn 25.11

Benzenesulfonic acid is strongly deactivated toward electrophilic aromatic substitution. The addition of SO_3 increases the concentration of the electrophile and speeds up the reaction. This effectively counteracts the deactivation from the sulfonyl group already attached.

Your Turn 25.12

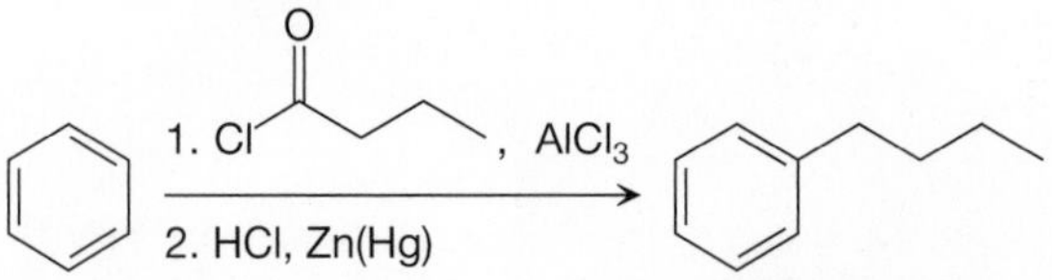
1. Cl
, AlCl3
2. HCl, Zn(Hg)

Butylbenzene

Your Turn 25.13

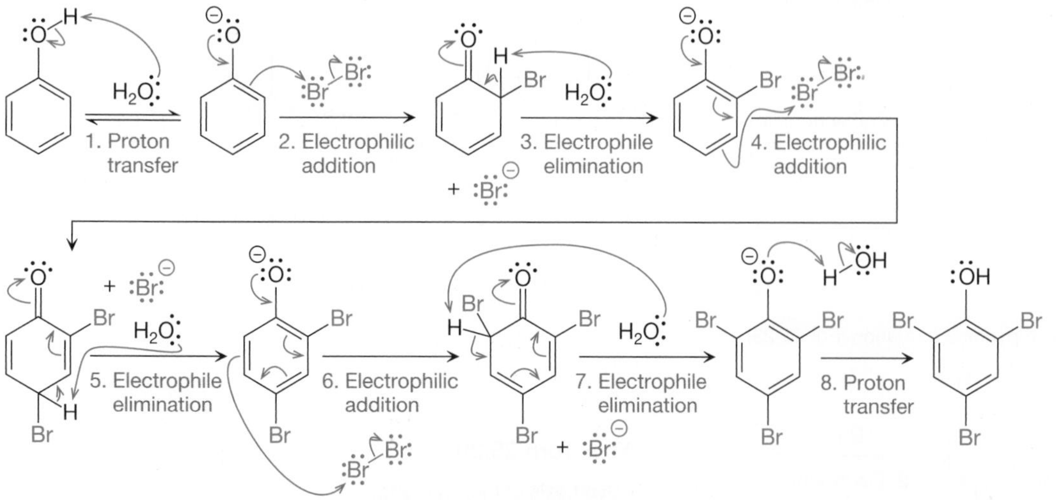
1. Proton transfer
2. Electrophilic addition
3. Electrophile elimination
4. Electrophilic addition
5. Electrophile elimination
6. Electrophilic addition
7. Electrophile elimination
8. Proton transfer

Your Turn 25.14

(a) No. The amino group is a relatively strong Lewis base, so it readily coordinates to the $AlCl_3$ Lewis acid. In that complexed form, the N atom possesses a +1 formal charge, making it a highly deactivating group that precludes Friedel–Crafts reactions altogether. **(b)** Yes. The $CH(CH_3)_2$ isopropyl alkyl group is inert to the $AlCl_3$ acid and, therefore, will undergo the indicated Friedel–Crafts reaction.

Your Turn 25.15

The second resonance structure is the least stable, and the third resonance structure is the most stable. Overall, this intermediate is more stable than the one in Equation 25-24.

Your Turn 25.16

Mechanism for α-substituted naphthalene formation

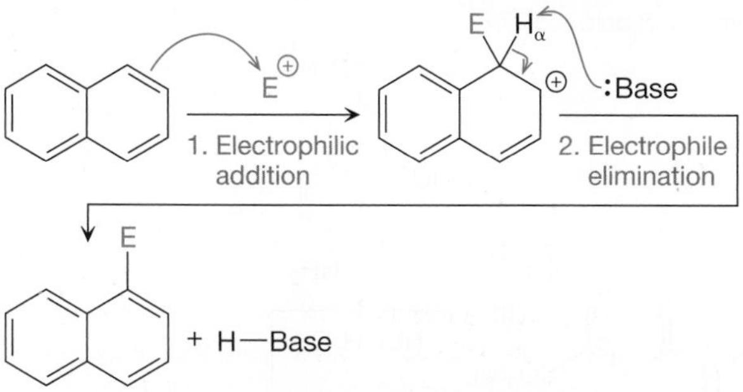
1. Electrophilic addition
2. Electrophile elimination
:Base
+ H—Base

Mechanism for β-substituted naphthalene formation

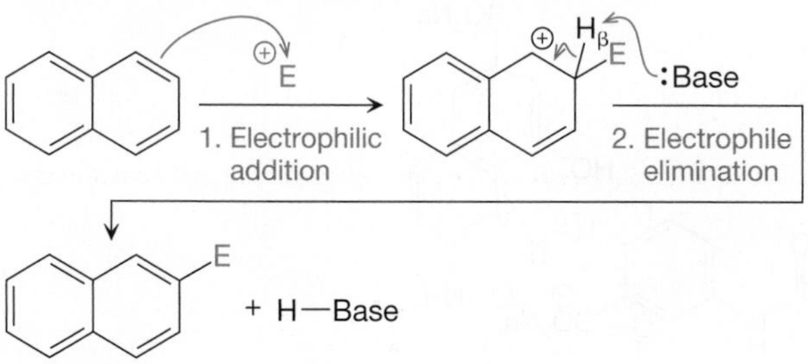
1. Electrophilic addition
2. Electrophile elimination
:Base
+ H—Base

Your Turn 25.17

Mechanism for 2-substituted pyrrole formation (Eq. 25-28)

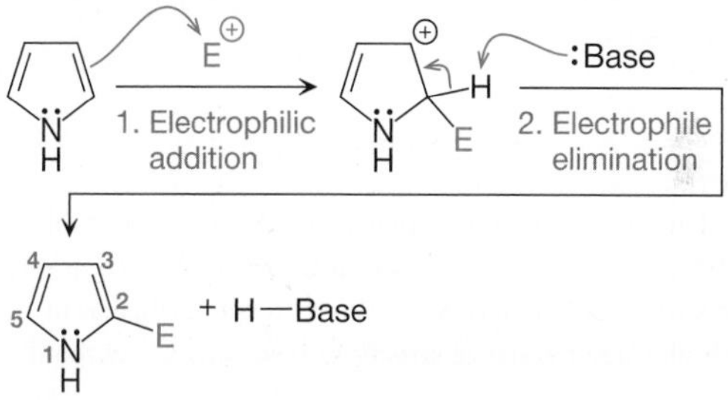
1. Electrophilic addition
2. Electrophile elimination
:Base
+ H—Base

Mechanism for 3-substituted pyrrole formation (Eq. 25-28)

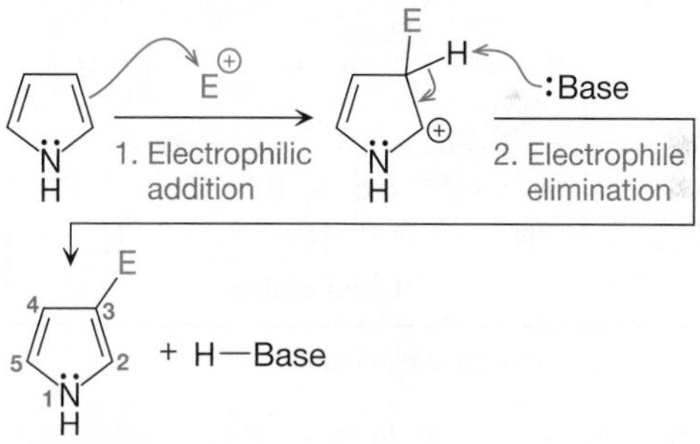
1. Electrophilic addition
2. Electrophile elimination
:Base
+ H—Base

Mechanism for 2-substituted pyridine formation (Eq. 25-29)

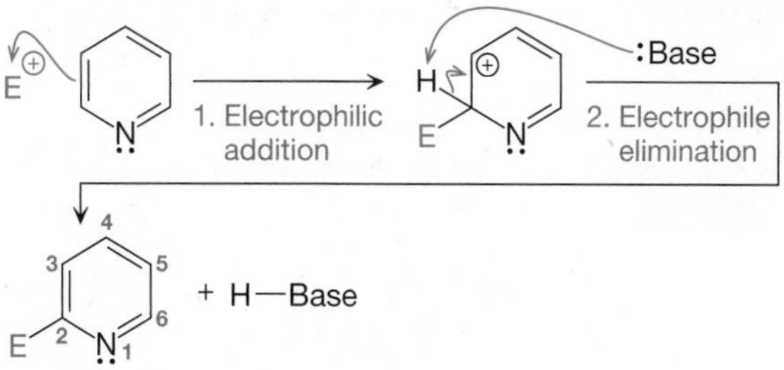
1. Electrophilic addition
2. Electrophile elimination
:Base
+ H—Base

Mechanism for 3-substituted pyridine formation (Eq. 25-29)

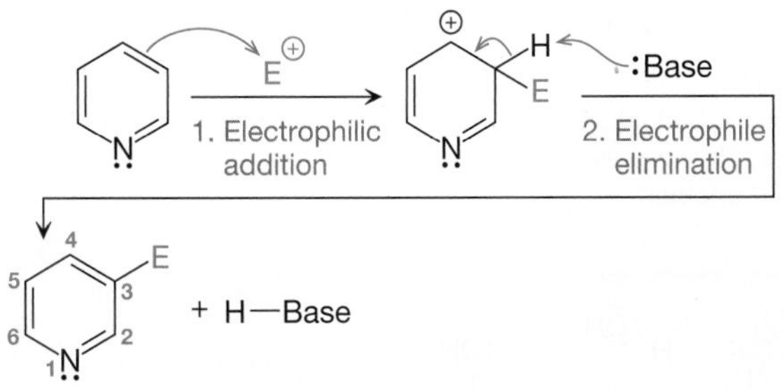
1. Electrophilic addition
:Base
2. Electrophile elimination
+ H—Base

Mechanism for 4-substituted pyridine formation (Eq. 25-29)

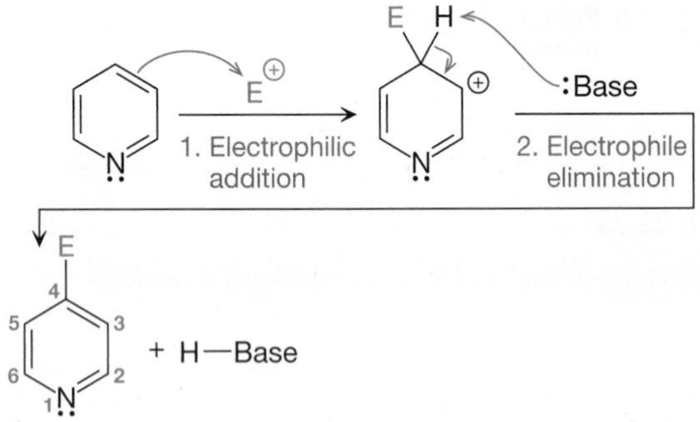
1. Electrophilic addition
:Base
2. Electrophile elimination
+ H—Base

Your Turn 25.18

The 4-substituted arenium ion intermediate formed here is less stable than the 3-substituted intermediate formed in Equation 25-31b, as one of the resonance structures here has N^+ without an octet, whereas in Equation 25-31b, all three resonance structures have only C^+ without an octet.

Mechanism for electrophilic aromatic substitution of pyridine at C-4

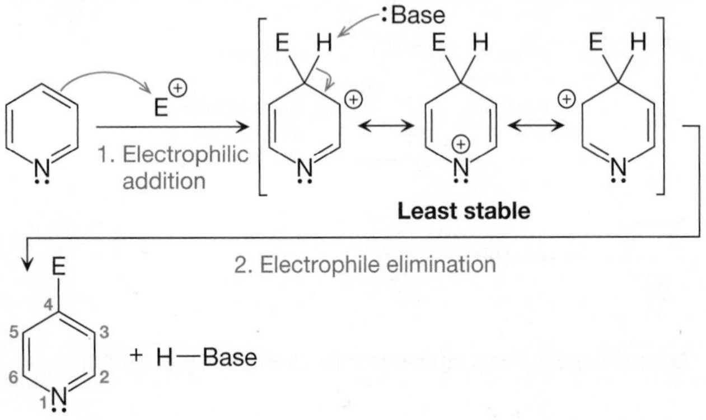
:Base
1. Electrophilic addition
Least stable
2. Electrophile elimination
+ H—Base

Your Turn 25.19

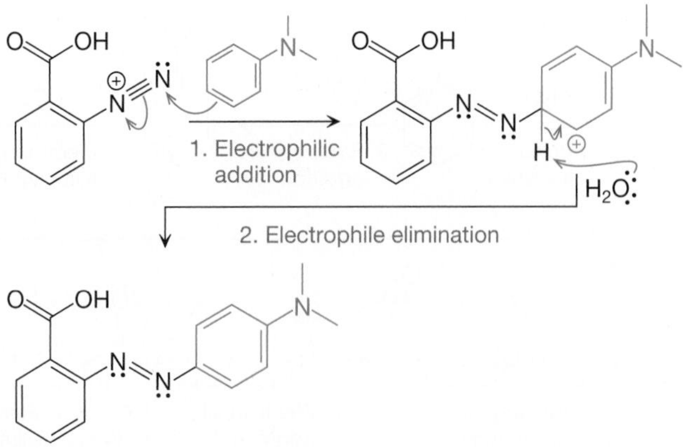
1. Electrophilic addition
2. Electrophile elimination

Your Turn 25.20

Synthesis of methyl orange

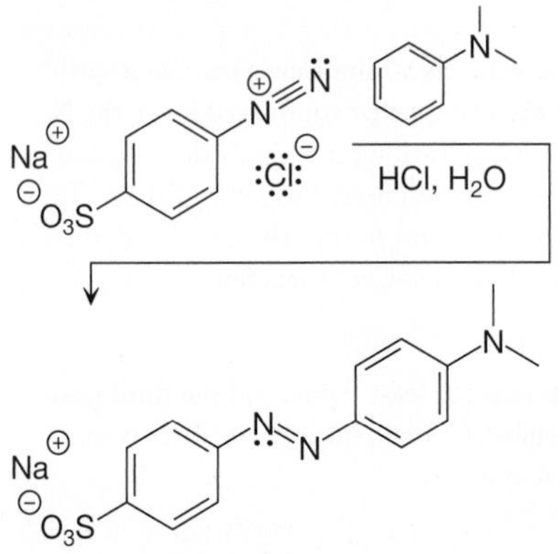
HCl, H_2O

Methyl orange

Synthesis of acid red 37

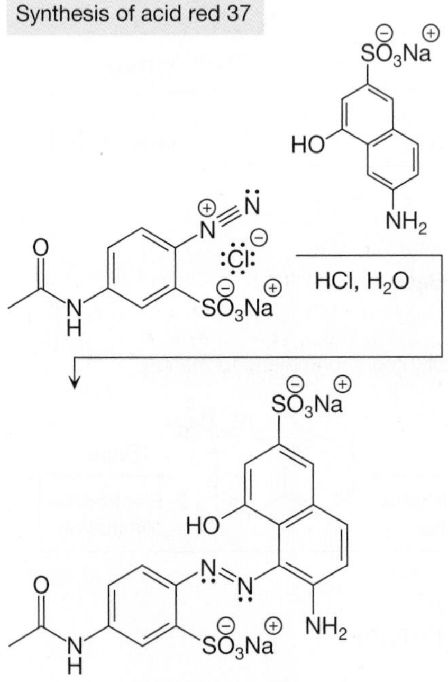
HCl, H_2O

Acid red 37

Your Turn 25.21

The final structure is the most stable, because the negative charge is on an electronegative O atom, whereas the negative charge is on a less electronegative C atom in the other three resonance structures.

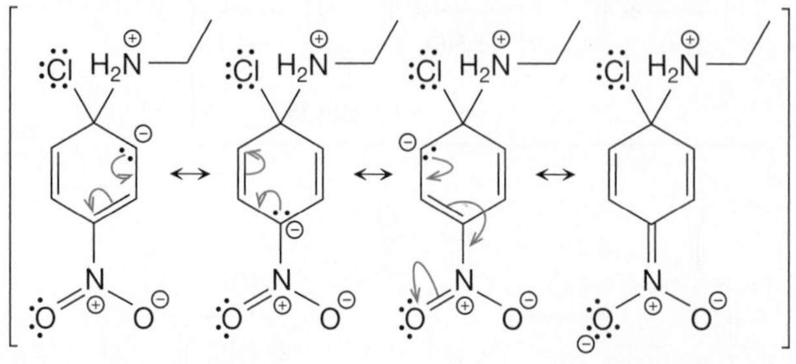

Most stable

Your Turn 25.22

Draw the mechanism in Equation 25-35 (p. 1227), but replace the aromatic compound and the amine with the ones given in this problem; the major product is shown here. This reaction is *slower* than the one shown in Equation 25-36, because the strongly electron-withdrawing groups are in ortho and meta positions and not ortho and para positions.

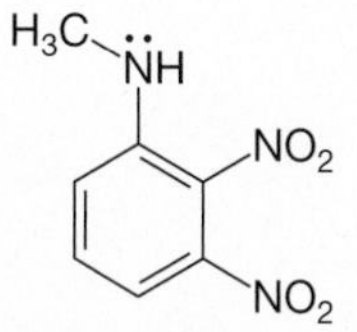

Your Turn 25.23

(a) Draw the mechanism in Equation 25-35 (p. 1227), but replace the aromatic compound and the amine with the ones given in this problem. The major product is shown here.

(a)

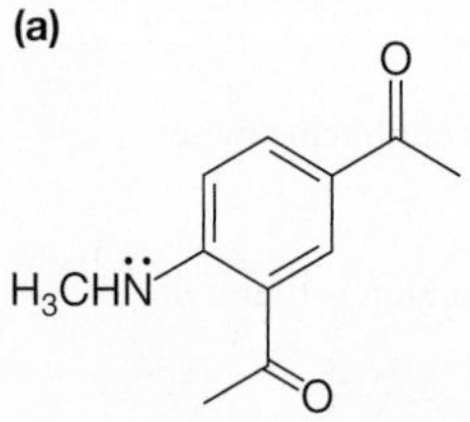

(b) Draw just the nucleophilic addition and nucleophile elimination steps (Steps 1 and 3) of the mechanism in Equation 25-35 (p. 1227), but replace the aromatic compound with the one given in this problem and replace the amine nucleophile with CH_3O^-. The leaving group is F^-. The major product is shown here.

(b)

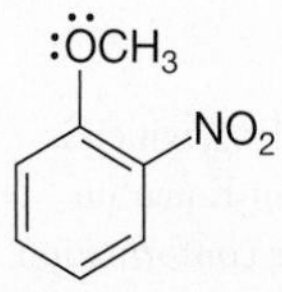

(c) Draw just the nucleophilic addition and nucleophile elimination steps (Steps 1 and 3) of the mechanism in Equation 25-35 (p. 1227), but replace the aromatic compound with the one given in this problem and replace the amine nucleophile with CH_3O^-. The leaving group is F^- attached to the top carbon of the ring. The major product is shown here.

(c)

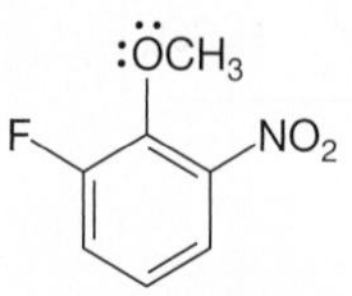

Your Turn 25.24

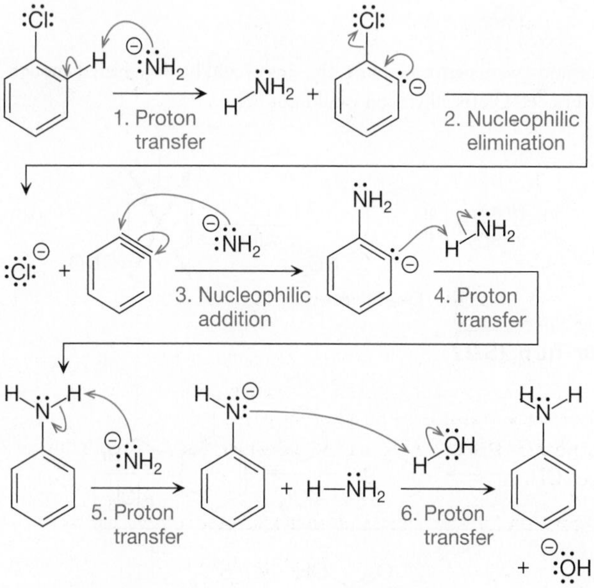

Your Turn 25.25

(a)

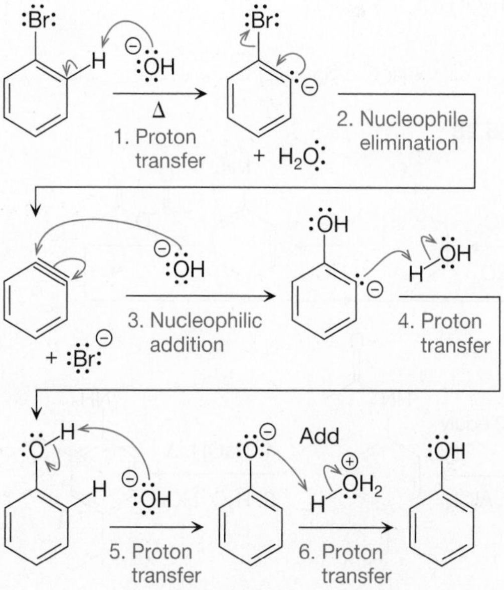

(b) H and D can both be eliminated with essentially equal likelihood; therefore, 50% of the product is expected to contain D.

Your Turn 25.26

The CO_2H group is meta-directing, and oxidation of the alkyl group prior to nitration will direct the NO_2 group to the meta position.

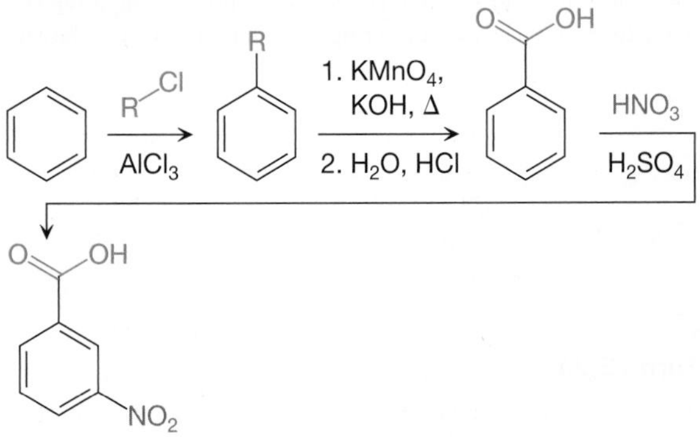

R
Cl
AlCl3
1. KMnO4, KOH, Δ
2. H2O, HCl
O
OH
HNO3
H2SO4
NO2

If nitration were performed first, the ring would be deactivated enough that Friedel–Crafts alkylation would not occur.

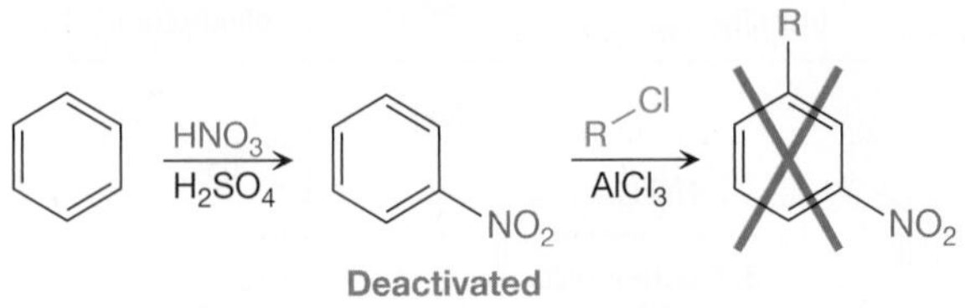

HNO3
H2SO4
NO2
Deactivated
R
Cl
AlCl3

Your Turn 25.27

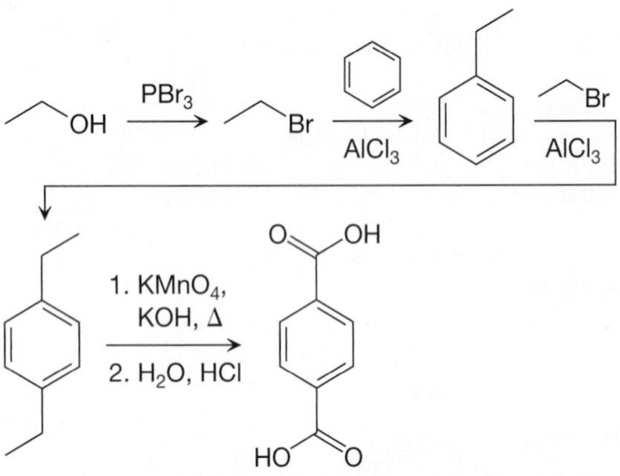

OH
PBr3
Br
AlCl3
1. KMnO4, KOH, Δ
2. H2O, HCl
O
OH
HO

Your Turn 25.28

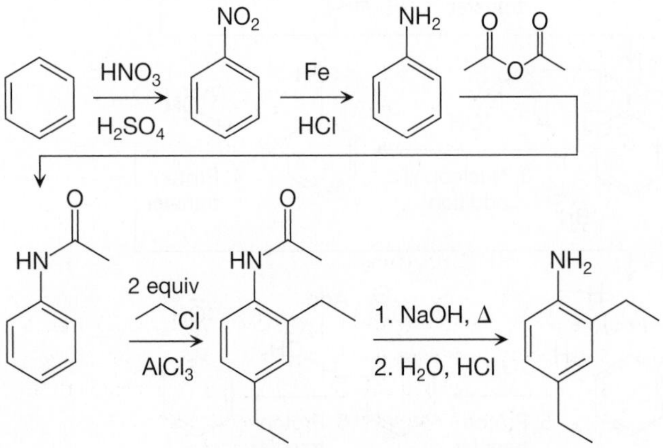

HNO3
H2SO4
NO2
Fe
HCl
NH2
O
HN
2 equiv
Cl
AlCl3
1. NaOH, Δ
2. H2O, HCl

Your Turn 25.29

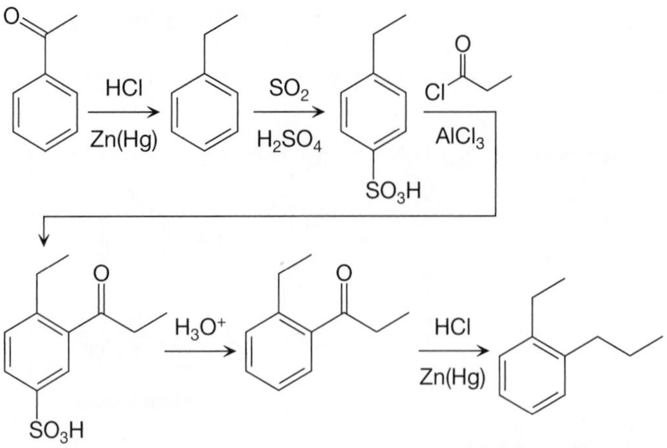

O
HCl
Zn(Hg)
SO2
H2SO4
SO3H
Cl
AlCl3
H3O+

Chapter 26

Your Turn 26.1

The product is the same as in Equation 26-2.

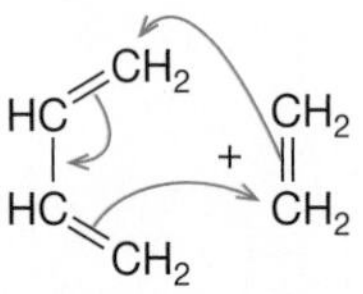

HC
CH2
+

Your Turn 26.2

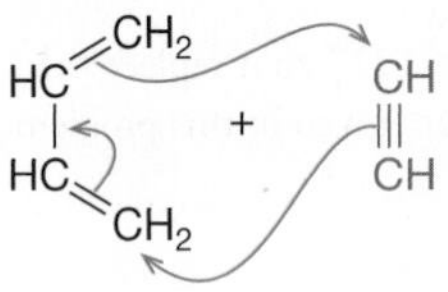

HC
CH2
+
CH

The three curved arrows could also be drawn counterclockwise.

Your Turn 26.3

The transition state is antiaromatic and the reaction is thermally forbidden.

Your Turn 26.4

Conformation **B** is *s*-cis and can undergo a Diels–Alder reaction. Conformation **A** is *s*-trans and cannot undergo a Diels–Alder reaction.

Your Turn 26.5

***s*-Cis**

Your Turn 26.6

The diene in this reaction is part of an eight-membered ring, which is significantly more flexible than the five-membered ring in Equation 26-10. Therefore, the diene will not be locked in the *s*-cis conformation as rigidly as is the dienophile in Equation 26-10, making the reaction slower.

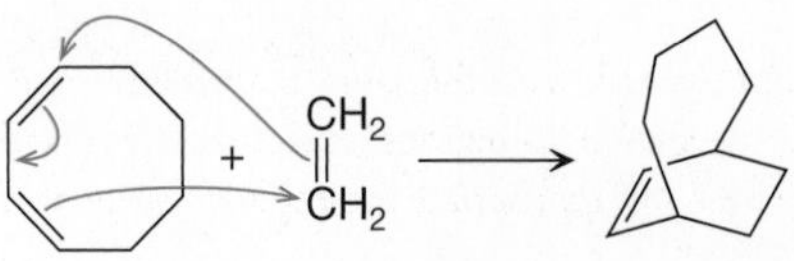

CH2
+

Your Turn 26.7

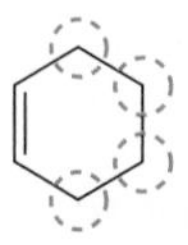

Your Turn 26.8

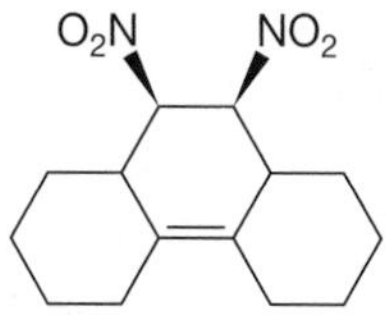
O2N
NO2

Your Turn 26.9

Yes, the cis–trans relationships among the substituents agree (Eqs. 26-18 and 26-20), as shown.

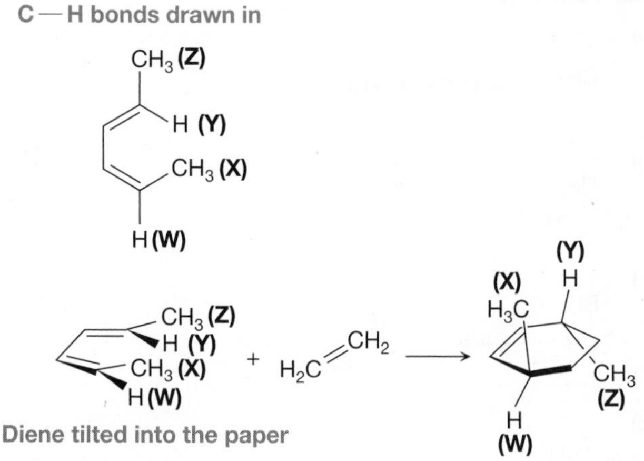
C—H bonds drawn in
CH3 (Z)
H (Y)
CH3 (X)
H (W)
CH3 (Z)
H (Y)
CH3 (X)
H (W)
+
H2C
CH2
(Y)
H
(X)
H3C
CH3
(Z)
H
(W)
Diene tilted into the paper

Your Turn 26.10

The first product is endo and is the major product. The second product is exo.

Your Turn 26.11

B will lead to the major Diels–Alder product.

Your Turn 26.12

From Table 1-3, [3(619 kJ/mol) + 1(339 kJ/mol)] − [5(339 kJ/mol) + 1(619 kJ/mol)] = −118 kJ/mol. This estimate is 50 kJ/mol more positive than the measured value of −168 kJ/mol.

Your Turn 26.13

This reaction has a large negative value for ΔH°_{rxn} (−121 kJ/mol), as does Equation 26-27 (−168 kJ/mol). Therefore, similar to the reaction in Equation 26-27, this reaction will have a substantially negative ΔG°_{rxn} and will be irreversible.

Your Turn 26.14

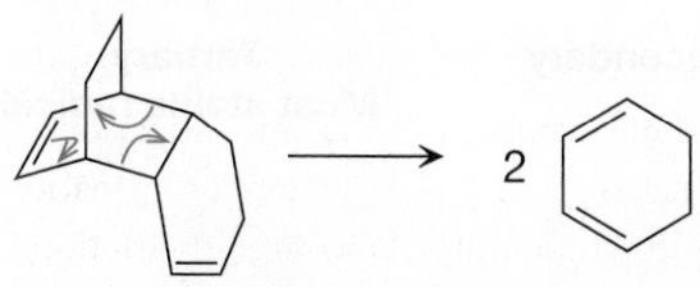
2

Your Turn 26.15

In both regions of overlap, the orbitals have the same phase, which leads to constructive interference. Because both regions exhibit the same kind of interference, the orbitals have the appropriate symmetries to interact.

Your Turn 26.16

On the left, the orbitals have opposite phases, resulting in destructive interference. On the right, the orbitals have the same phase, resulting in constructive interference. Therefore, there is no net overlap, and the orbitals do not have the appropriate symmetries to interact.

Your Turn 26.17

Relative to the unsubstituted molecules (Fig. 26-13a), the energies of the diene's MOs are lowered by the EWG, and the energies of the dienophile's MOs are raised by the EDG. This makes the HOMO of the dienophile and the LUMO of the diene closer in energy. Thus, the HOMO–LUMO energy gap is decreased.

Your Turn 26.18

In Figure 26-15a, the *p* orbital on C-1 of the dienophile (blue) is involved in secondary orbital overlap with the *p* orbital on C-2 of the diene (red), but that is not the case in Figure 26-15b. Those orbitals are closer together in Figure 26-15a than they are in Figure 26-15b.

Your Turn 26.19

When buta-1,3-diene is in its excited state, one electron occupies π_3^*, making it the HOMO of the diene, shown in red here. The LUMO of the dienophile, shown in blue here, is the same as in Figure 26-9.

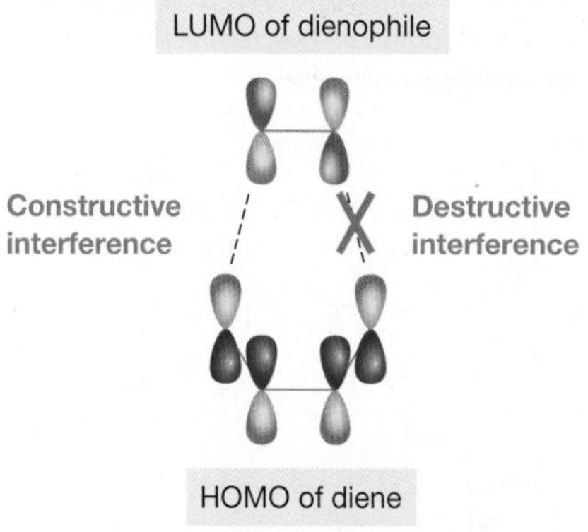
LUMO of dienophile
Constructive interference
Destructive interference
HOMO of diene

When ethene is in its excited state, one electron occupies π_2^*, making it the HOMO of the dienophile, shown in blue here. The LUMO of the diene, shown in red here, is the same as in Figure 26-9.

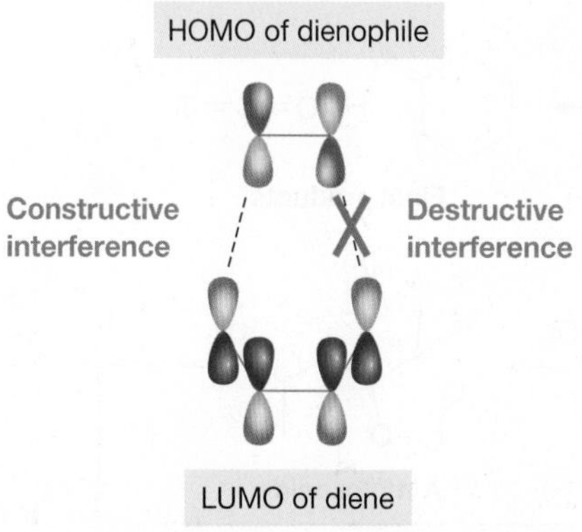
HOMO of dienophile
Constructive interference
Destructive interference
LUMO of diene

In both cases, the overlap between the HOMO and LUMO orbitals has constructive interference on one end and destructive interference on the other, leading to no net interaction. This is consistent with the [4+2] cycloaddition reaction being photochemically forbidden.

Your Turn 26.20

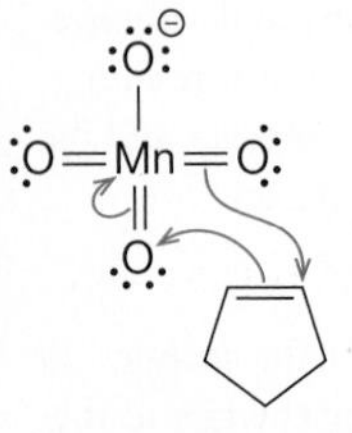

Your Turn 26.21

Molecules **(a)**, **(d)**, and **(e)** can be produced by syn dihydroxylation of the alkenes shown here.

(a) **(d)** **(e)**

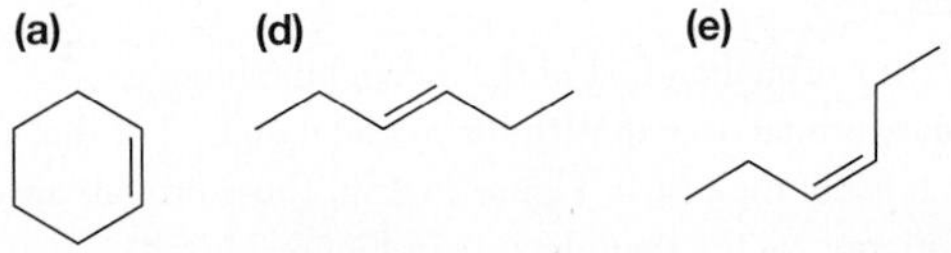

Your Turn 26.22

In both structures, the most stable chair conformation of the cyclohexane ring has the *t*-butyl group in the equatorial position. In **A**, the OH groups are also equatorial and are close enough to each other to form the cyclic periodate ester on treatment with IO_4^-, leading to the product shown here. In **B**, the OH groups occupy axial positions and are too far apart to form the cyclic periodate ester.

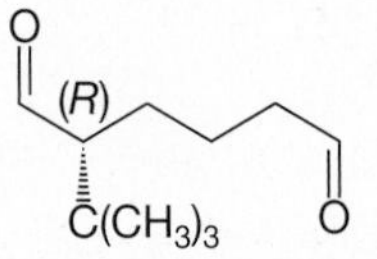

Your Turn 26.23

(a)

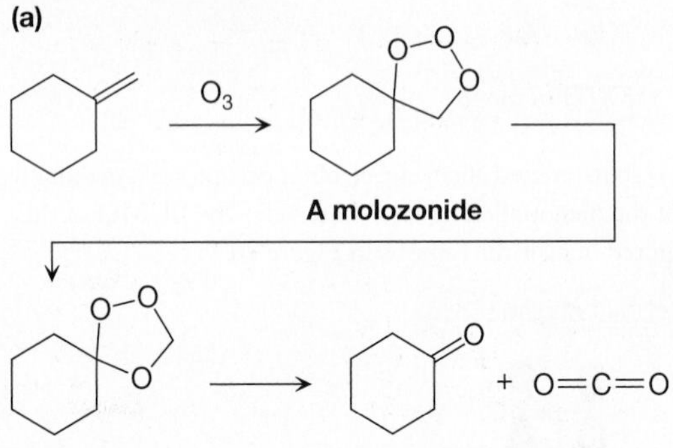
A molozonide
An ozonide
Final products

(b)

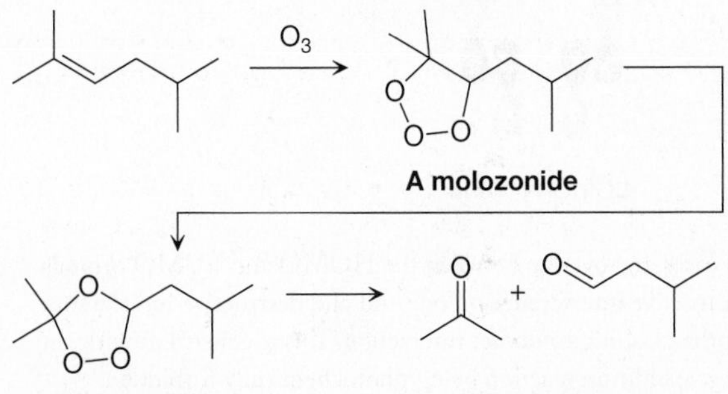
A molozonide
An ozonide
Final products

Your Turn 26.24

The standard Diels–Alder reaction is favored when the dienophile is electron-poor: namely, when electron-withdrawing groups are on the dienophile. The OCH_3 and CH_3 are both electron-donating groups (EDGs), but CH_3 is a weaker EDG compared to the OCH_3. Given the choice, the diene will react with the dienophile that has the weaker EDG.

Chapter 27

Your Turn 27.1

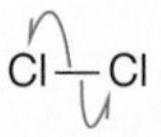

Your Turn 27.2

(a)

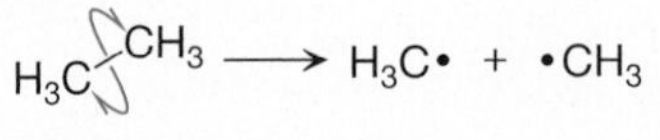

(b)

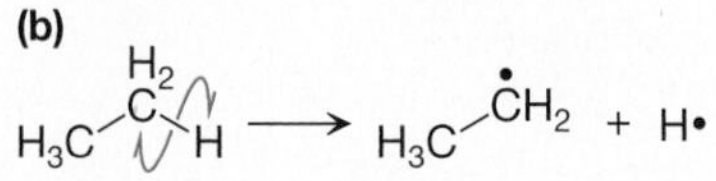

(c)

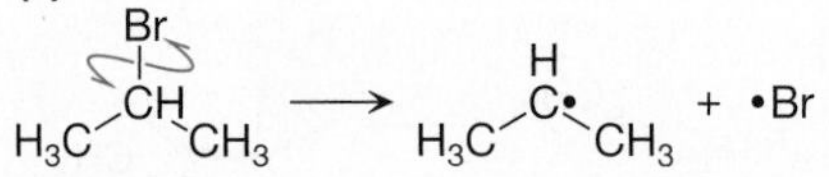

(d)

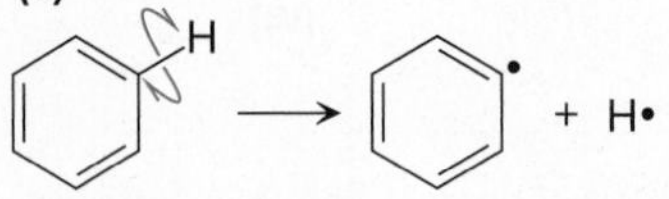

Your Turn 27.3

From Table 27-2, Cl—Cl = 243 kJ/mol, Br—Br = 192 kJ/mol, I—I = 151 kJ/mol, and HO—OH = 211 kJ/mol; from Table 27-1, H_3C—H = 439 kJ/mol.

Your Turn 27.4

Left energy box = 368 kJ/mol, and right energy box = 431 kJ/mol. Top product box = •Cl, and bottom product box = •Br. The bromine radical (•Br) is more stable.

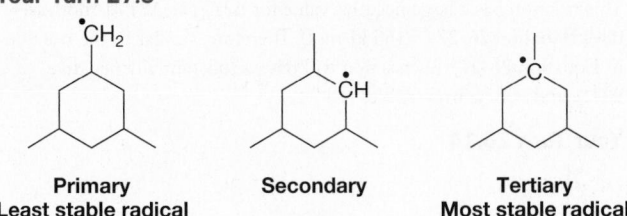

Your Turn 27.5

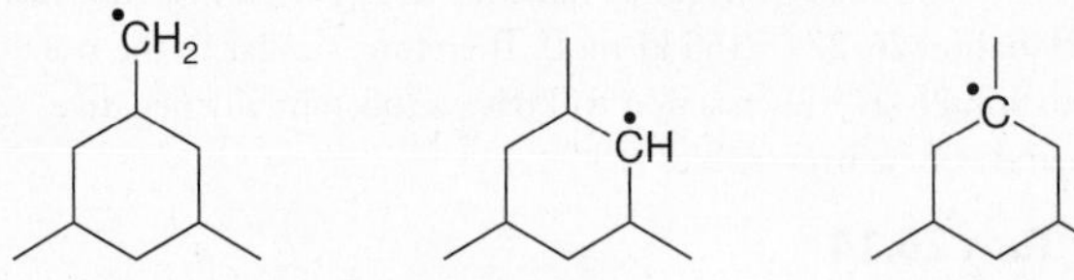

Primary
Least stable radical

Secondary

Tertiary
Most stable radical

Your Turn 27.6

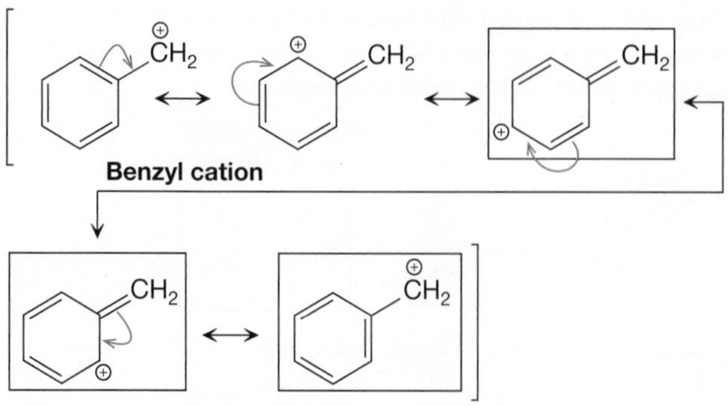
Benzyl cation

Your Turn 27.7

The figure will be essentially the same as the one shown in Your Turn 27.4 (p. 1310) with the following differences: (1) Replace H—Br and H—Cl at the bottom left with CH_3CH_3 and $CH_2{=}CHCH_3$; (2) the box at the top should contain $CH_3CH_2^{\bullet}$, while the box below it should contain $CH_2{=}CHCH_2^{\bullet}$; and (3) the box to the left of the shorter red arrow should show 369 kJ/mol, while the box to the right of the longer red arrow should show 421 kJ/mol. The allyl radical is more stable owing to resonance delocalization of the unpaired electron over two C atoms.

Your Turn 27.8

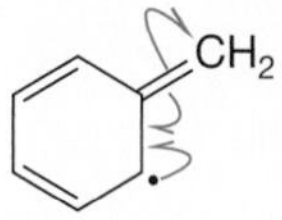

Your Turn 27.9

The primary (CH_2) carbon possesses the most spin density (it has the deepest blue color in Fig. 27-5). Examination of the resonance contributors (Eq. 27-10, p. 1312) shows that the first radical retains the aromatic character of the benzene ring, whereas the others do not. This contributor is more stable and contributes more to the resonance hybrid.

Your Turn 27.10

H3C• + •CH3

Your Turn 27.11

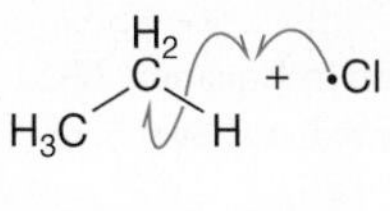

Your Turn 27.12

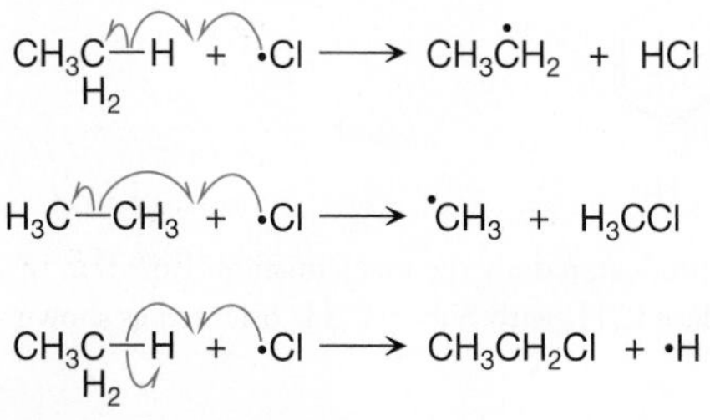
CH3CH2—H + •Cl ⟶ CH3ĊH2 + HCl
H3C—CH3 + •Cl ⟶ •CH3 + H3CCl
CH3CH2—H + •Cl ⟶ CH3CH2Cl + •H

Your Turn 27.13

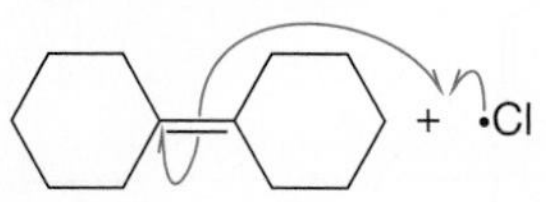

Your Turn 27.14

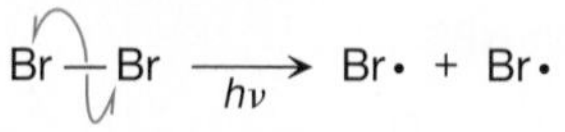
Br—Br ⟶ hν Br• + Br•

Your Turn 27.15

Redraw Equation 27-19a and 27-19b (p. 1318), but replace the six instances of Cl with Br.

Your Turn 27.16

Redraw Equation 27-20a, 27-20b, and 27-20c (p. 1319), but replace the six instances of Cl with Br.

Your Turn 27.17

The initiation step matches Equation 27-18, the top propagation step matches Equation 27-19a, and the bottom propagation step matches Equation 27-19b.

Your Turn 27.18

Redraw Figure 27-8 (p. 1321) but change the blue screened structures as follows: replace Cl—Cl with Br—Br, replace cyclohexane with methane, replace H—Cl with H—Br, replace Cl• with Br•, replace cyclohexyl radical ($C_6H_{11}^{\bullet}$) with H_3C•, replace chlorocyclohexane ($C_6H_{11}Cl$) with bromomethane (CH_3—Br), and replace Cl—Cl with Br—Br.

Your Turn 27.19

A (radical chlorination) is the faster of the two reactions, because it has a smaller energy barrier and is more exothermic.

Your Turn 27.20

The radical abstraction in **B** will proceed faster because the allyl radical is stabilized by resonance.

Your Turn 27.21

The 3° radical is more stable than a 2° or 1° radical. This is reflected in a larger energy difference between 3° and 1° radicals here, compared to the energy difference between 2° and 1° radicals in Figure 27-11.

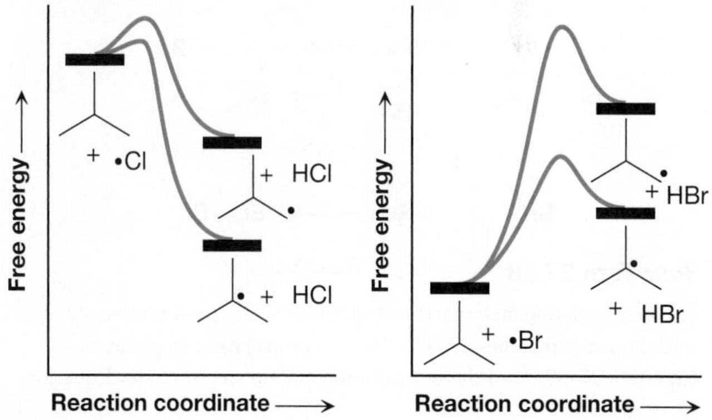
Free energy
+ •Cl
+ HCl
+ HCl
Reaction coordinate
Free energy
+ HBr
+ HBr
+ •Br
Reaction coordinate

Your Turn 27.22

From Table 27-1, H—CH_3 = 439 kJ/mol and H—Br = 368 kJ/mol, so ΔH°_{rxn} = 71 kJ/mol. From Table 27-2, Br—Br = 192 kJ/mol and Br—CH_3 = 294 kJ/mol, so ΔH°_{rxn} = −102 kJ/mol. Both values match the ones in Table 27-3.

Your Turn 27.23

In the fluorination of propane for formation of 1° and 2° alkyl radicals, ΔH°_{rxn} = −147 and −159 kJ/mol, respectively. In the iodination of propane, ΔH°_{rxn} = 125 and 113 kJ/mol for the corresponding reactions. Fluorination is less selective, and iodination is more selective.

Your Turn 27.24

Resonance stabilization of radical from NBS

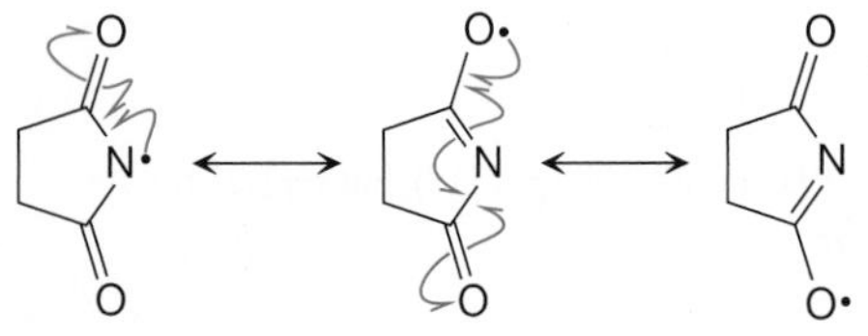

Tautomerization mechanism

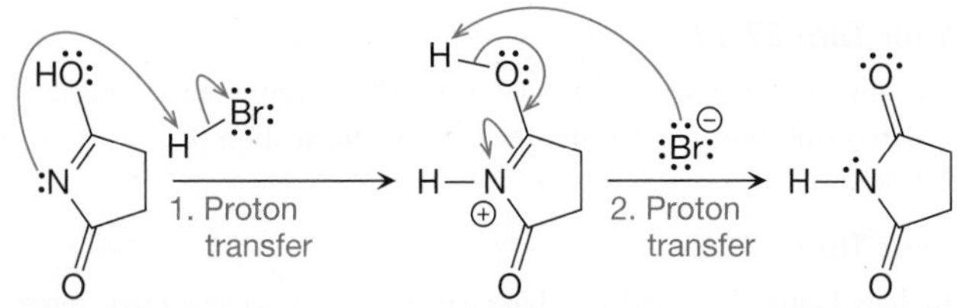
1. Proton transfer
2. Proton transfer

Your Turn 27.25

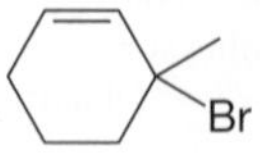

Your Turn 27.26

Cross out Br• (reactant in Step 3 and product in Step 4) and $BrCH_2CH{\bullet}CH_3$ (reactant in Step 4 and product in Step 3). Summing the two steps results in the net reaction shown here.

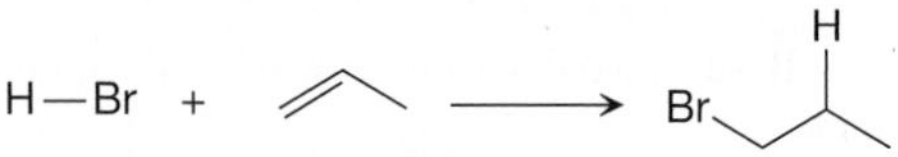

Your Turn 27.27

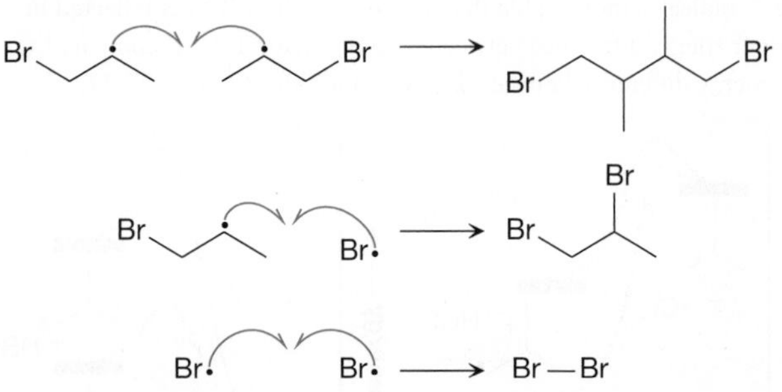

Your Turn 27.28

The first initiation step matches Equation 27-39a, and the second initiation step matches 27-39b. The top propagation step matches Equation 27-39c, and the bottom propagation step matches Equation 27-39d.

Your Turn 27.29

In both cases, a 2° reactive intermediate forms in the first step. The difference is the species that adds in the first step: Br• in the radical mechanism and H^+ in the closed-shell mechanism.

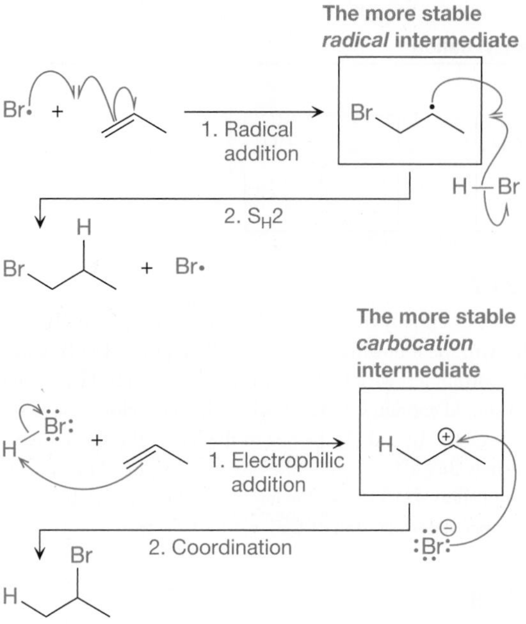
The more stable
radical intermediate
1. Radical
addition
2. SH2
The more stable
carbocation
intermediate
1. Electrophilic
addition
2. Coordination

Your Turn 27.30

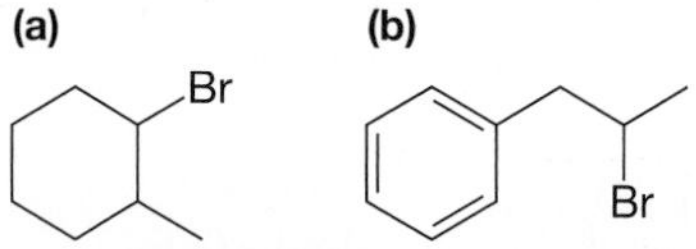
(a)
(b)

Your Turn 27.31

Cis alkene

Your Turn 27.32

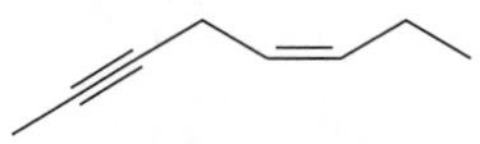

Your Turn 27.33

To arrive at the first product, redraw the mechanism in Equation 27-51 (p. 1340) but replace C_6H_6 with Sub—C_6H_5 oriented as shown here.

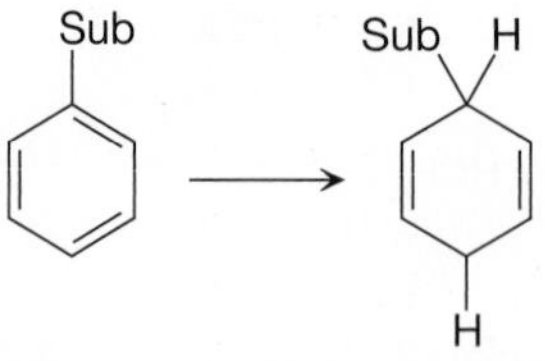

To arrive at the second product, redraw the mechanism in Equation 27-51 (p. 1340) but replace C_6H_6 with Sub—C_6H_5 oriented as shown here.

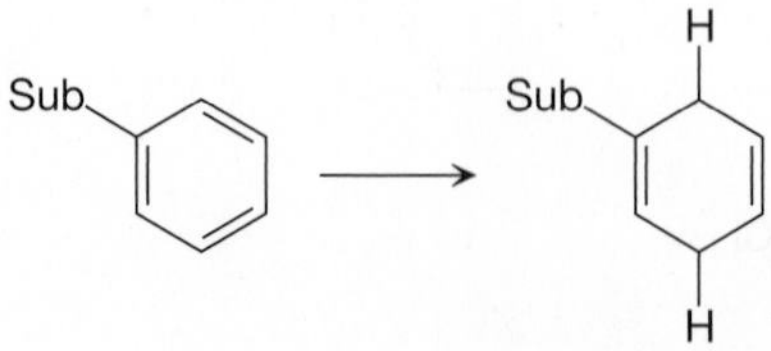

Your Turn 27.34

(a) Bromination occurs at two benzylic positions. The following are possible isomers that can form.

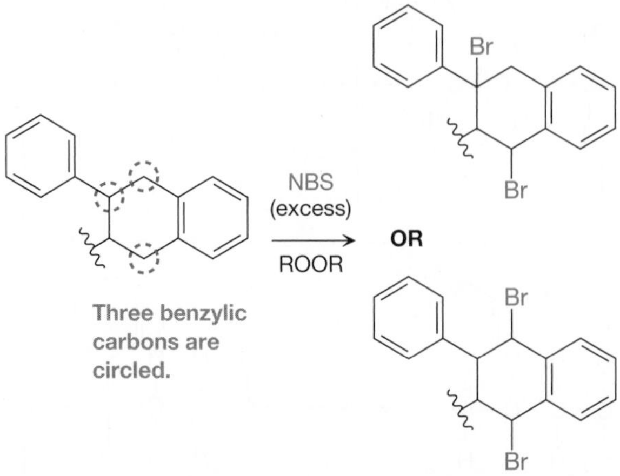

Br
Br
NBS
(excess)
ROOR
OR
Br
Br
Three benzylic
carbons are
circled.

(b) Both isomers undergo E2 or E1 reactions twice to form two new C═C bonds. The amine serves as the base for such reactions. The resulting product has a new naphthalene ring.

Chapter 28

Your Turn 28.1

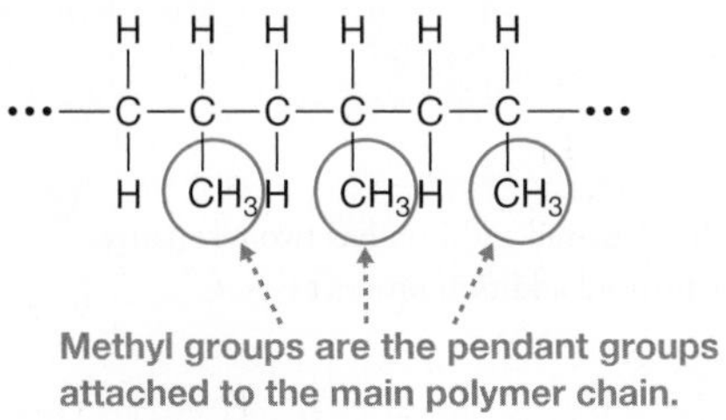

Methyl groups are the pendant groups
attached to the main polymer chain.

Your Turn 28.2

The condensed formula is shown here. For the structure given, three repeating units are shown.

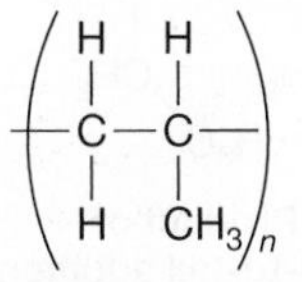

Your Turn 28.3

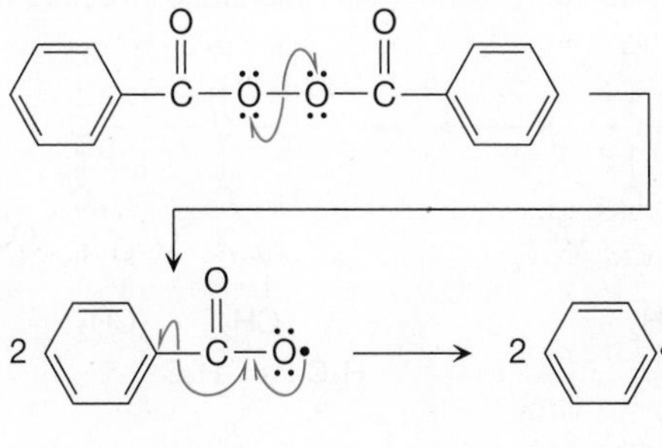

Your Turn 28.4

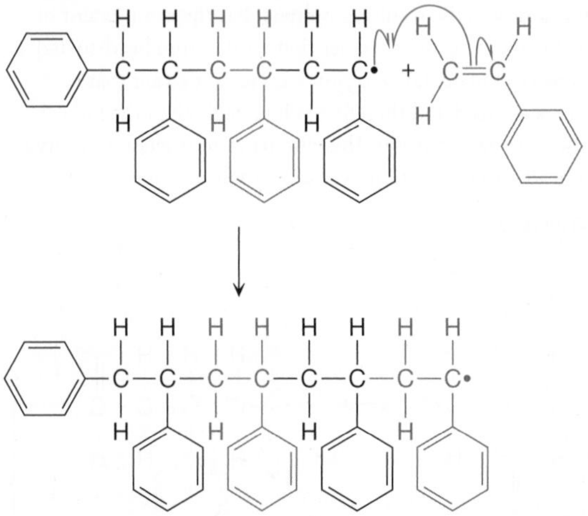

Your Turn 28.5

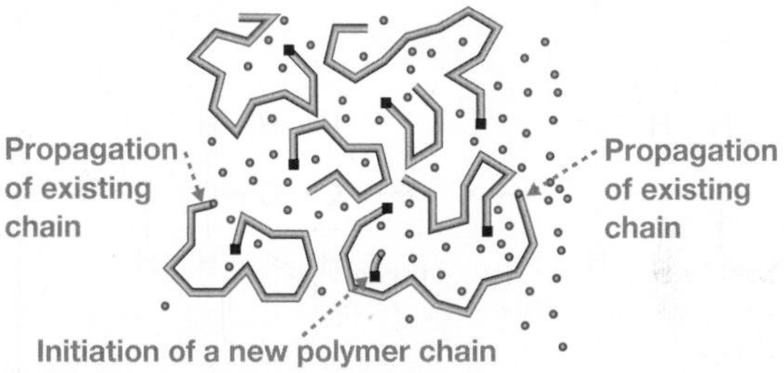

Propagation
of existing
chain
Propagation
of existing
chain
Initiation of a new polymer chain

Your Turn 28.6

(a)

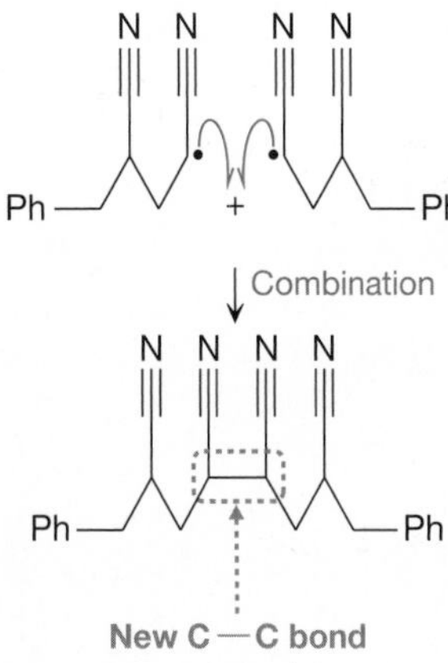

Combination
New C—C bond

(b)

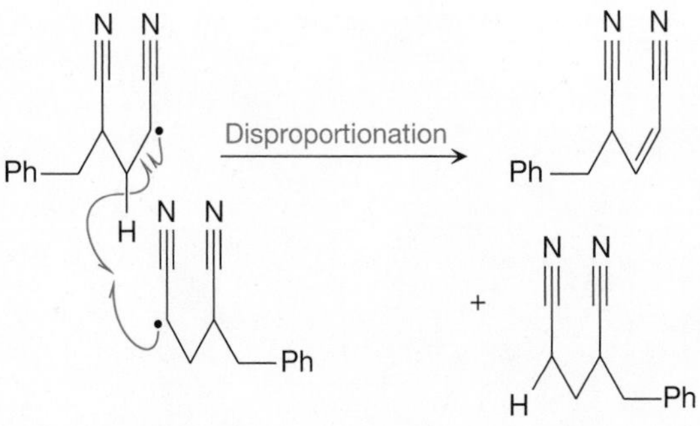

Disproportionation

Your Turn 28.7

In tail-to-tail addition, the resulting polymer has the same extent of resonance stabilization as the polymer that results from head-to-tail addition. However, tail-to-tail addition requires a reactant that is not resonance-stabilized and therefore is less stable than the radical reactant in head-to-tail addition. This difference in reactant stability is what favors head-to-tail addition over tail-to-tail addition.

Head-to-Tail Addition

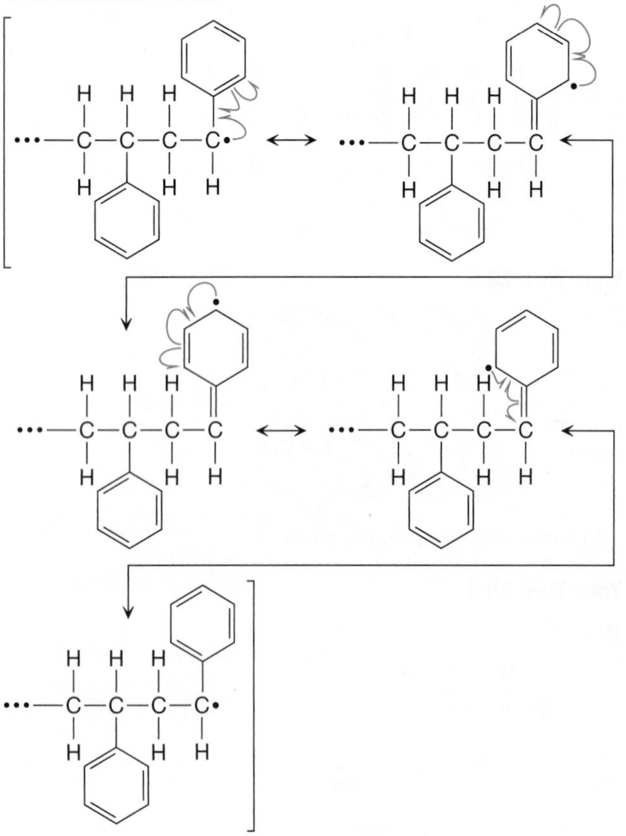

Tail-to-Tail Addition

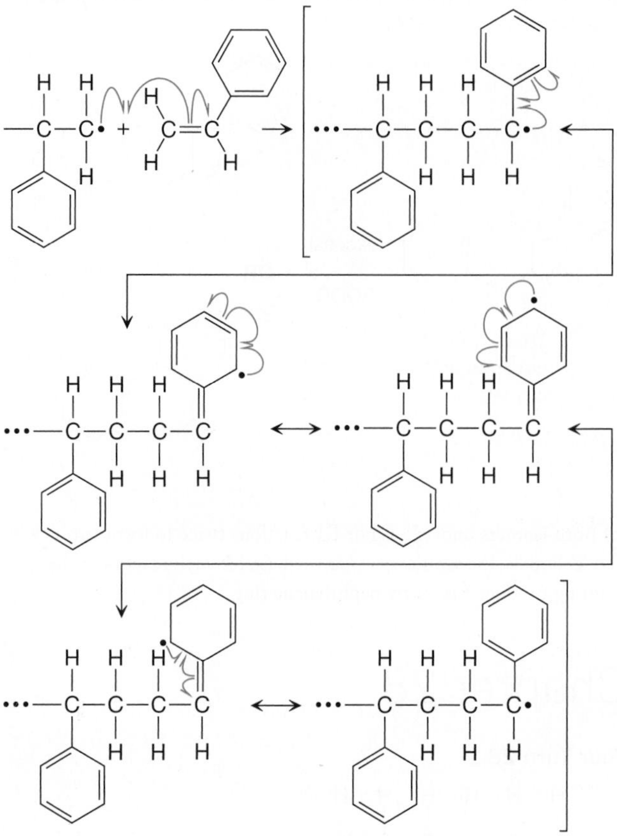

Your Turn 28.8

The product radical from head-to-tail addition has two resonance structures, while the head-to-head addition product is not resonance-stabilized.

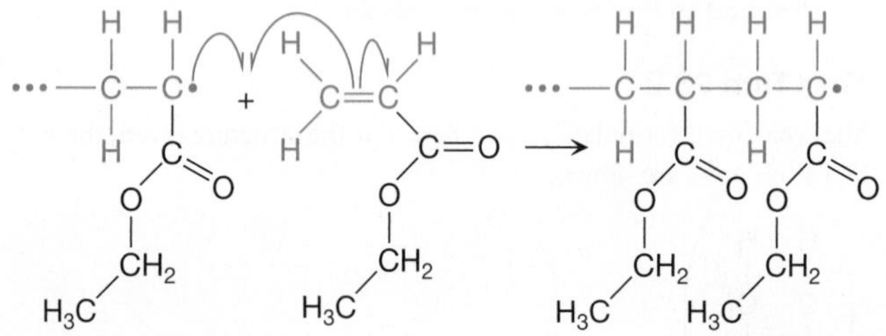

Propagating chain of poly(ethyl acrylate) **Ethyl acrylate** **Product of head-to-tail addition**

The product radical has the following two resonance structures:

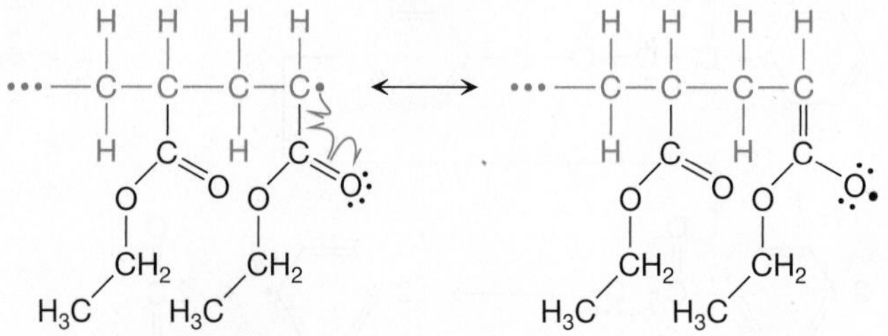

Product of head-to-tail addition

Your Turn 28.9

Redraw the atactic and isotactic forms in Figure 28-11 (p. 1367), but replace every instance of Ph with CH_3.

Your Turn 28.10

The product anion in Equation 28-13 is resonance-stabilized owing to the presence of π bond next to the C^- electron pair. Resonance is possible around the entire benzene ring. No such resonance exists in the reactant anion.

Your Turn 28.11

In a radical mechanism, combination and disproportionation each require two radicals reacting. The analogous reactive intermediates in an anionic mechanism are anions. Neither of these steps is likely, because the like charges of the two anions would repel each other.

Your Turn 28.12

Redraw the mechanism in Equation 28-20 (p. 1371), but replace $H_2C{=}CH_2$ with $H_2C{=}CHCH_3$. In the product of Step 1 and in each subsequent structure, replace the blue CH_2 group on top with $CHCH_3$ to yield the structure shown here.

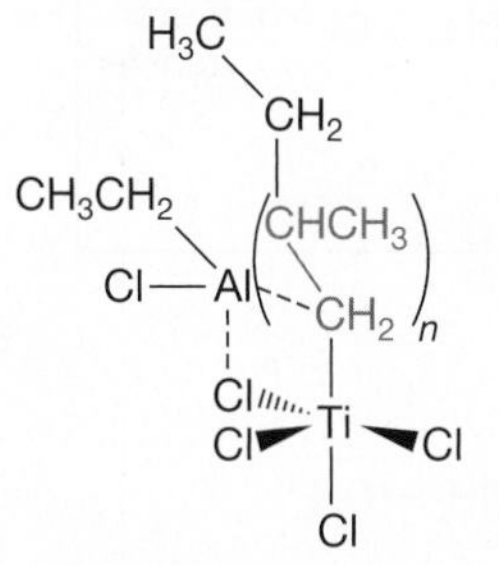

The termination step is shown here.

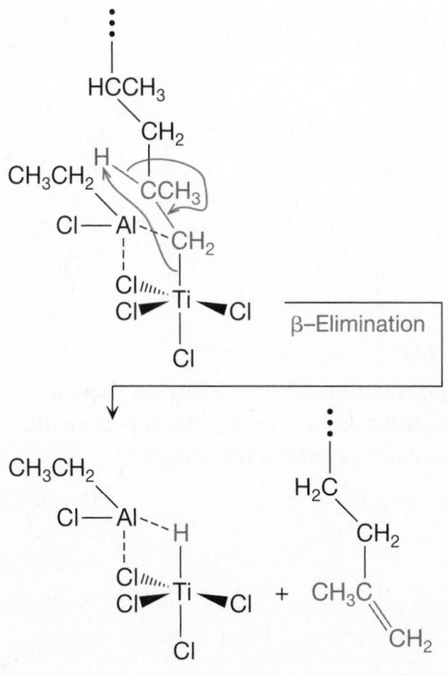
β–Elimination

Your Turn 28.13

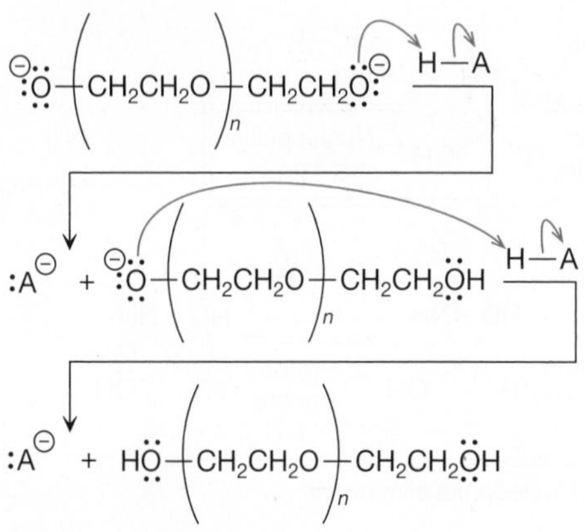

Your Turn 28.14

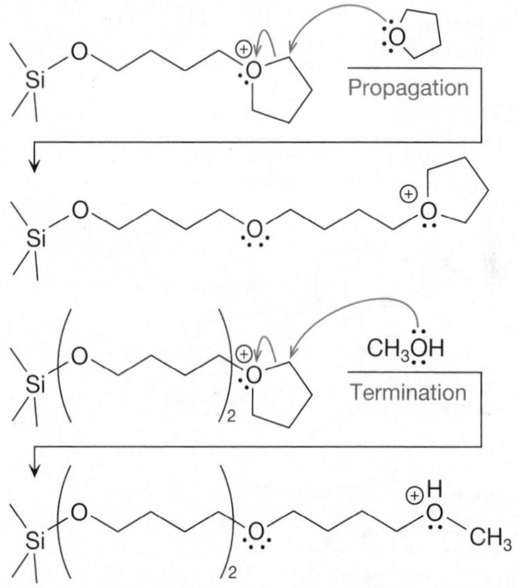
Propagation
Termination

Your Turn 28.15

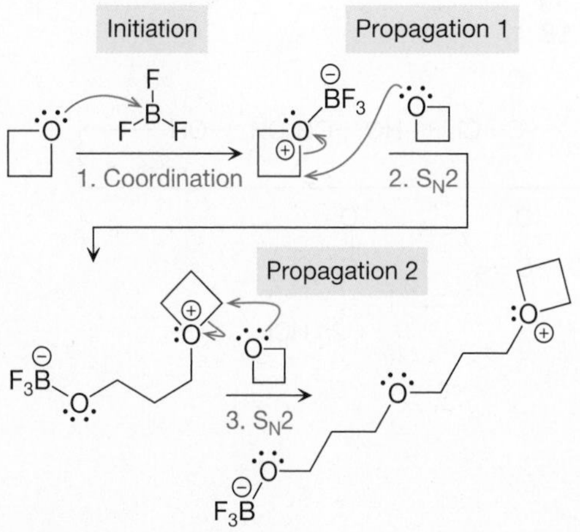
Initiation
Propagation 1
1. Coordination
2. S_N2
Propagation 2
3. S_N2

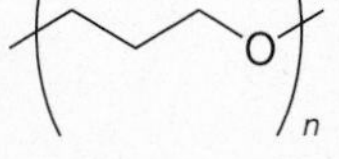

Condensed formula

Your Turn 28.16

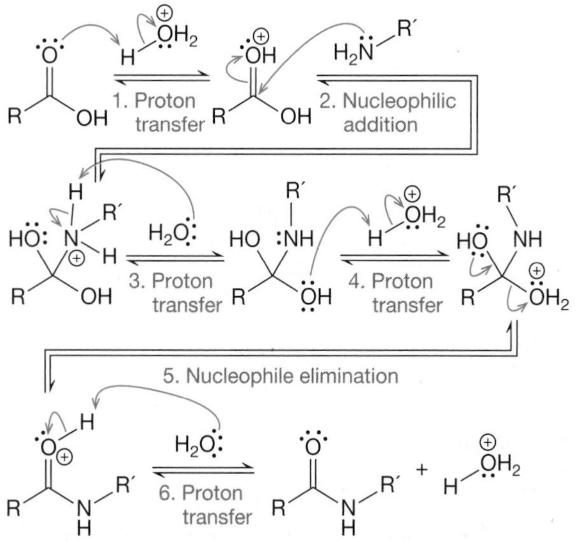
1. Proton transfer
2. Nucleophilic addition
3. Proton transfer
4. Proton transfer
5. Nucleophile elimination
6. Proton transfer

Your Turn 28.17

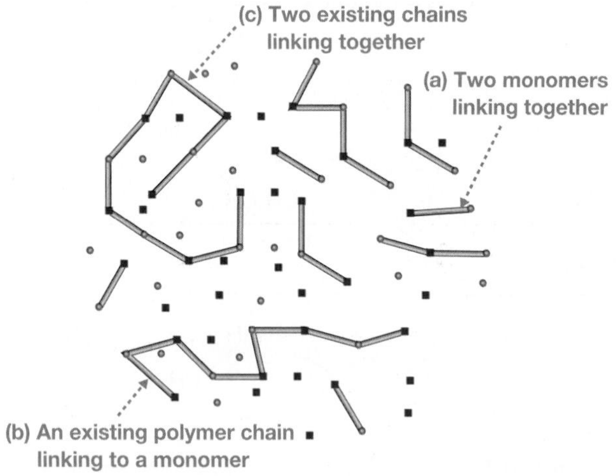
(c) Two existing chains linking together
(a) Two monomers linking together
(b) An existing polymer chain linking to a monomer

Your Turn 28.18

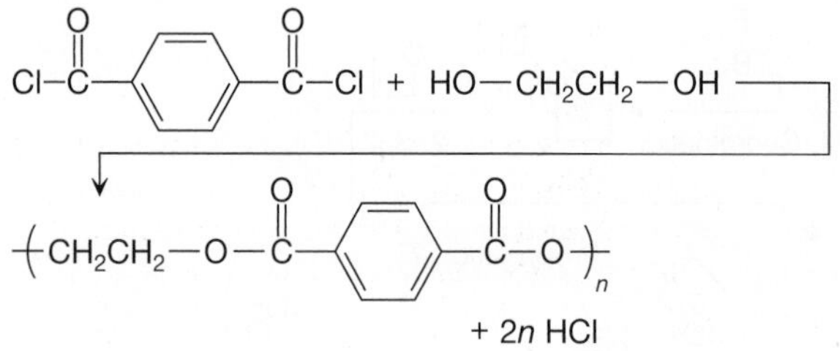
+ 2n HCl

Your Turn 28.19

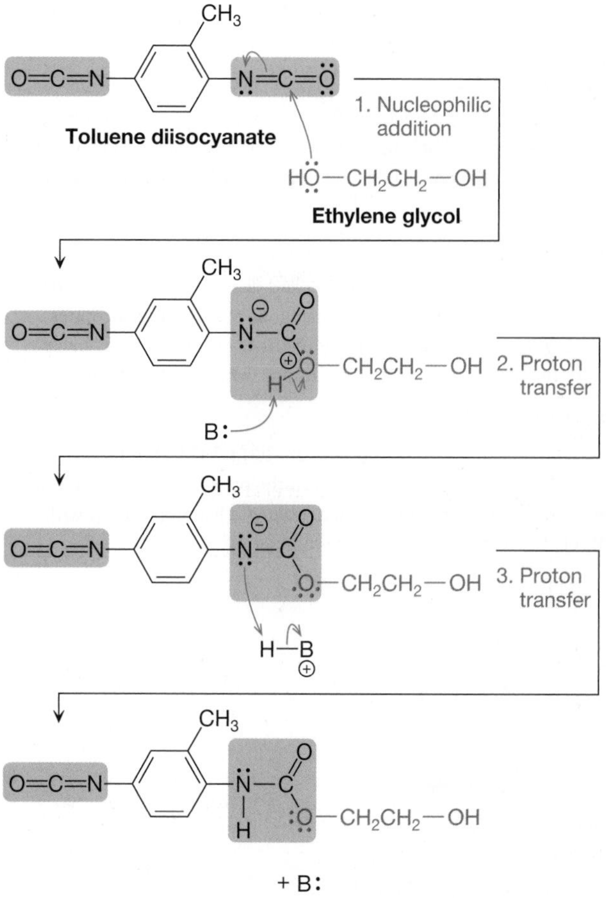
Toluene diisocyanate
1. Nucleophilic addition
Ethylene glycol
2. Proton transfer
3. Proton transfer

Your Turn 28.20

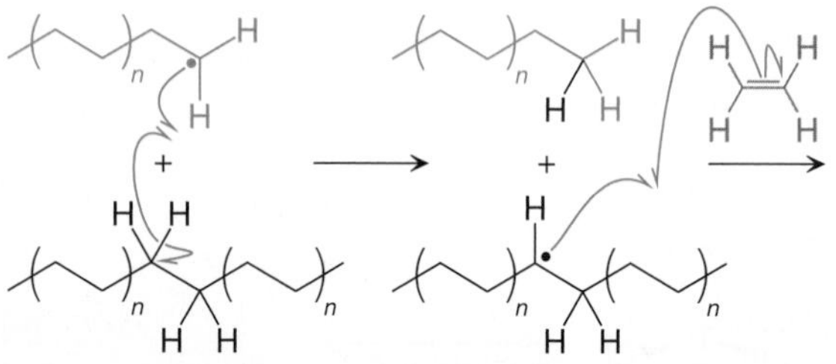

Your Turn 28.21

In Bakelite, the starting monosubstituted benzene ring is a phenol, and substitution takes place at the ortho or para positions because the hydroxyl substituent is an ortho/para director (Section 25.1).

Your Turn 28.22

The second product will be methyl acetate.

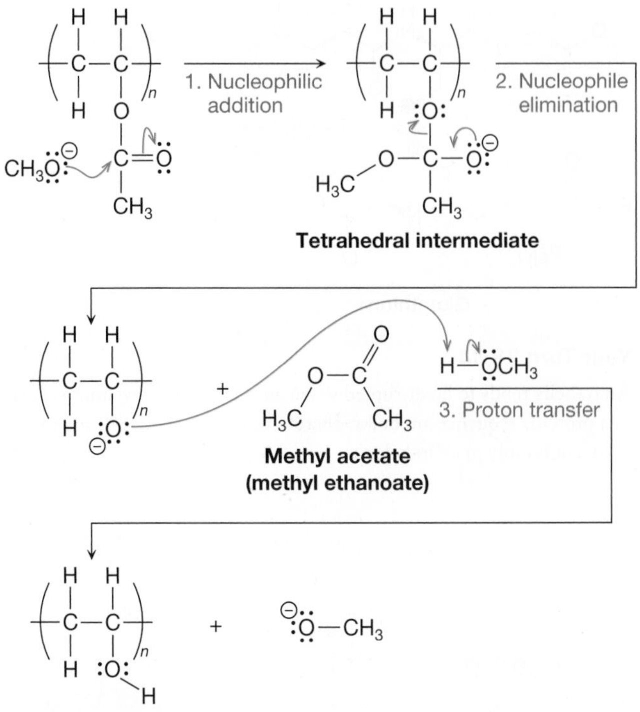

1. Nucleophilic addition
2. Nucleophile elimination
Tetrahedral intermediate
3. Proton transfer
Methyl acetate
(methyl ethanoate)

Your Turn 28.23

The mechanism is the same as Equation 7-33 (p. 346), with a H atom at the end of each open bond.

Your Turn 28.24

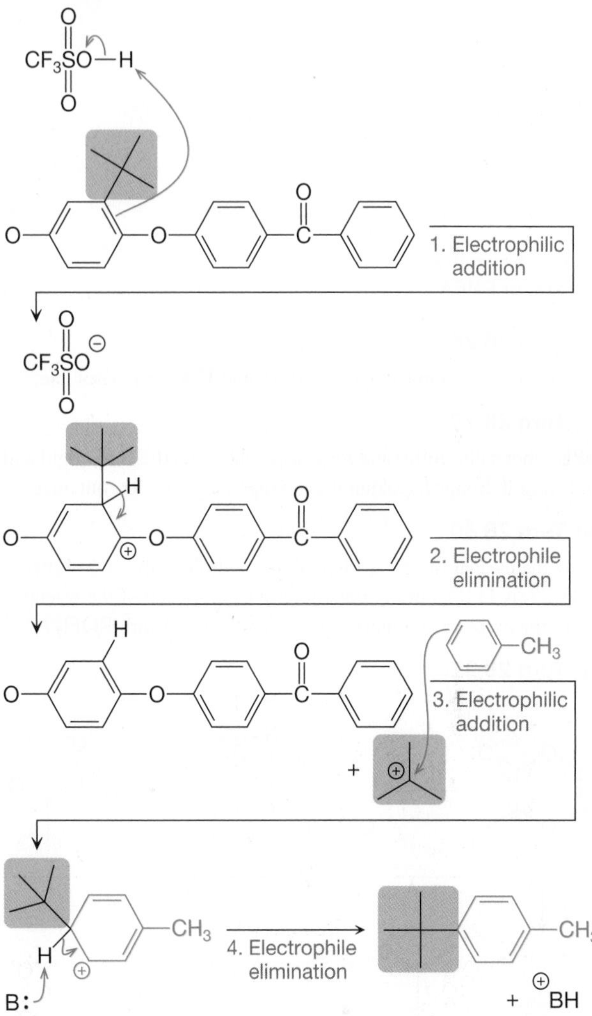

1. Electrophilic addition
2. Electrophile elimination
3. Electrophilic addition
4. Electrophile elimination

This trans *tert*-butylation would not be as successful if the *tert*-butyl group were a linear butyl group, because the electrophile to be eliminated in the second step would be a primary carbocation. A primary carbocation is far less stable than a tertiary carbocation.

Your Turn 28.25

Redraw the mechanism for acetal formation shown in Equation 19-13 (p. 936), but replace the aldehyde in Equation 19-13 with formaldehyde, and replace the protonated alcohol with the protonated form of the representation of linear poly(vinyl alcohol) given in the problem.

Your Turn 28.26

Nylon-6,6 is a polyamide. The O═C—N group, characteristic of an amide, appears twice in the repeating unit. One complete amide group appears in the center of the repeating unit. The second amide group is split between two repeating units: the N at the right of one repeating unit is connected to a C═O group that is part of the next repeating unit (represented by the C═O at the far left).

Your Turn 28.27

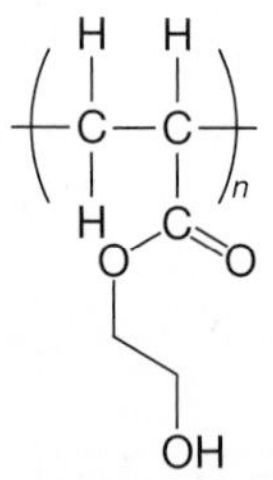

Poly(2-hydroxyethyl acrylate) or PHEA

Your Turn 28.28

The more polar and ionic polymers (**B**, **D**, and **F**) are water-soluble.

Your Turn 28.29

HDPE is not sufficiently rigid for a disposable razor. PS is too rigid and would crack if dropped, making it inappropriate for a milk container.

Your Turn 28.30

Redraw the mechanism for acid-catalyzed hydrolysis shown in Equation 23-29 (p. 1118), but use the ester group on the left of the reactant given in the problem and replace protonated hexanol with ROH_2^+.

Your Turn 28.31

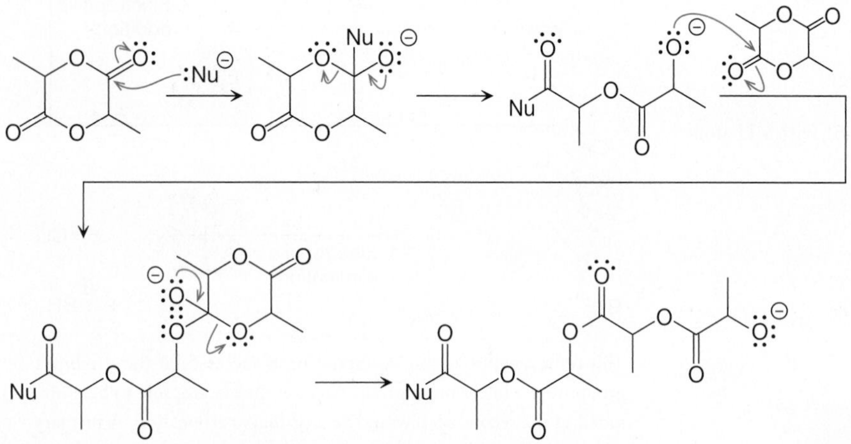

Your Turn 28.32

There are five peptide linkages, as shown by the red screens.

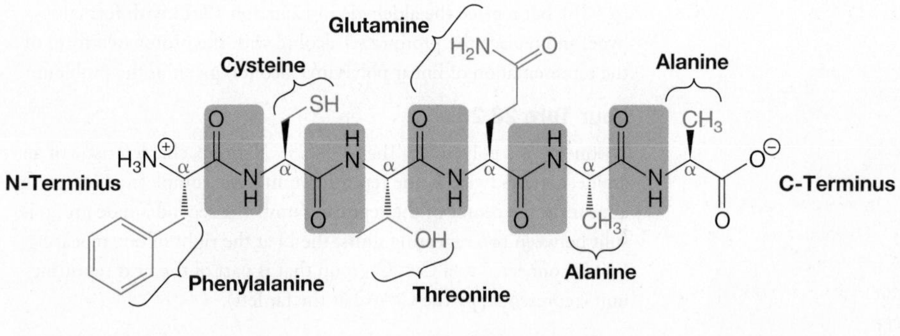
Glutamine
Cysteine
Alanine
N-Terminus
C-Terminus
Phenylalanine
Threonine
Alanine

Phe-Cys-Thr-Gln-Ala-Ala

Your Turn 28.33

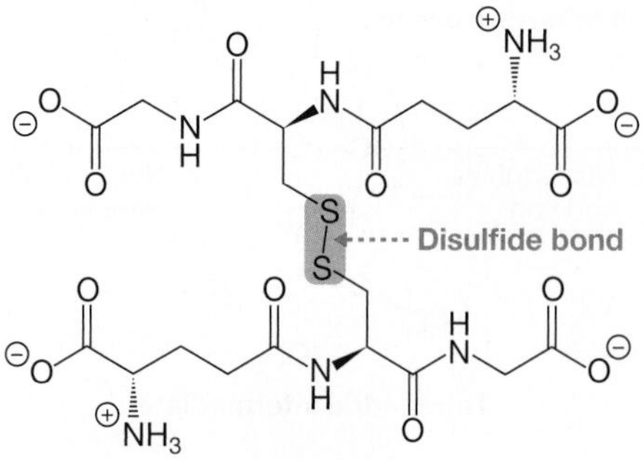
Disulfide bond

Glutathione

Your Turn 28.34

An α-helix tends to be disrupted when adjacent or nearby amino acids in a protein's sequence are bulky. Therefore, alanine should be found more commonly in an α-helix.

Your Turn 28.35

The hydrophobic end of SDS interacts favorably with the hydrophobic portions of a protein, while the hydrophilic end of SDS interacts favorably with the aqueous environment. This disrupts the attractive forces that a protein normally exhibits between its various portions when it is properly folded, and it diminishes the driving force by the hydrophobic effect for the hydrophobic portions of the protein to be buried.

Your Turn 28.36

Hemoglobin is more soluble in blood if hydrophilic or polar amino acids are on the surface. Blood is a water-based liquid, and having a greater number of polar groups on the exterior of the protein makes the protein more soluble in the polar medium. Nonpolar amino acids are found at the surfaces where the subunits bind together, however, because those regions largely exclude water.

Your Turn 28.37

The missing glycosidic linkage in Figure 28-54 is α-1,4′, and that in Figure 28-55 is β-1,4′. These linkages involve C-1 of one glucose unit and C-4 of the next, and the substituent on C-1 is axial in Figure 28-54 and equatorial in Figure 28-55.

Figure 28-54

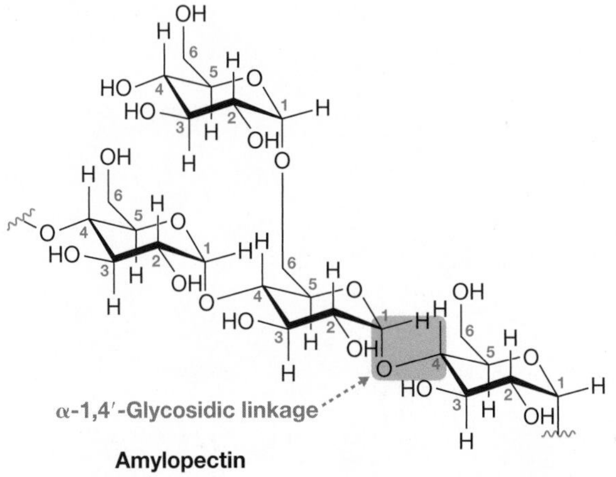
α-1,4′-Glycosidic linkage

Amylopectin

Figure 28-55

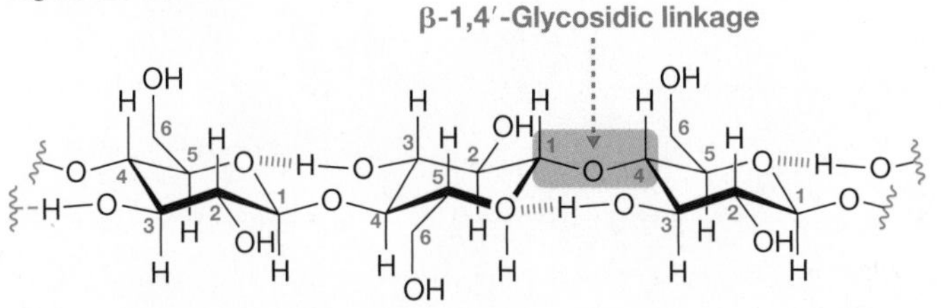
β-1,4′-Glycosidic linkage

Cellulose

Your Turn 28.38

The amide group has a resonance structure that increases the concentration of positive charge on N and increases the concentration of negative charge on O (see Fig. 28-49b, p. 1407). With greater magnitudes for the opposite charges that attract between the hydrogen-bond donor (the N—H bond) and the hydrogen-bond acceptor (the O atom), the strength of the hydrogen bond increases.

CREDITS

Front Matter

Photos: p. iii: GlobalP/Getty Images; **p. vii:** Courtesy of Joshua Karty and Jacob Karty; **p. xi:** Paul Hakimata Photography/Shutterstock; **p. xiii:** Skyhobo/Getty Images; **p. xv:** Spencer Platt/Getty Images; **p. xviii:** SPL / Science Source; **p. xx:** Mopic/Shutterstock; **p. xxi:** SimpleFoto/Depositphoto; **p. xxiii:** exyne/Getty Images; **p. xxv:** GlobalP/Getty Images; **p. xxvii:** Rudolf Vlcek/Getty Images; **p. xiv:** schankz/Depositphotos; **p. lix:** Dr. Jeremy Burgess/Science Source; **p. lx** (top, left to right) Pavel Ilyukhin/Shutterstock; Phanie/Science Source; Martin Brayley/Alamy Stock Photo; one-image photography/Alamy Stock Photo; (middle) Lukmanazis/Shutterstock; (bottom) Reprinted (adapted) with permission from Molecular Electronic Devices Based on Single-Walled Carbon Nanotube Electrodes, by Alina K. Feldman, Michael L. Steigerwald, Xuefeng Guo, et al. Copyright 2008 American Chemical Society; **p. lxi:** (a) age fotostock/Alamy Stock Photo; (b) NASA Earth Observatory image by Joshua Stevens, using data courtesy of NASA Ozone Watch and GEOS-5 data from the Global Modeling and Assimilation Office at NASA GSFC; (c) Sunpix Travel/Alamy Stock Photo

Chapter 1

Photos: p. 1: (sign) petrmalinak/Shutterstock; (hands) Paul Hakimata Photography/Shutterstock; **p. 3:** INTERFOTO/Alamy Stock Photo; **p. 4:** Charles D. Winters/Science Source; **p. 10:** ART Collection/Alamy Stock Photo; **p. 12:** (top) NASA; (bottom) Leo Mason/Popperfoto/Getty Images; **p. 13:** The Photo Works/Alamy Stock Photo; **p. 23:** (duck) PetStockBoys/Alamy Stock Photo; (otter) David & Micha Sheldon/Mediabakery; (platypus) Dave Watts/Alamy Stock Photo; **p. 25:** (top) PhiveT/Alamy Stock Photo; (bottom) The Photo Works/Alamy Stock Photo; **p. 32:** Roberto Machado Noa/LightRocket via Getty Images; **p. 34:** Alexander Chelmodeev/Shutterstock

Interchapter A

Photos: p. 53: (a) Daniel Hurst Photography/Getty Images; (b) Ken Welsh/Design Pics/Getty Images; (c) NicksPlace/Getty Images; (d) Blue Jeans Images/Media Bakery; **p. 56:** pierredesvarre/Getty Images; **p. 57:** Picsfive/Shutterstock

Chapter 2

Photos: p. 68: (left) Michel Gunther/Science Source; (middle) Perennou Nuridsany/Science Source; (right) Eye of Science/Science Source; **p. 70:** Dusan Jankovic/Shutterstock; **p. 75:** (both) Courtesy of Joel Karty; **p. 76:** studiomode/Alamy Stock Photo; **p. 77:** tam_odin/Shutterstock; **p. 78:** (top) Praethip Docekalova/Alamy Stock Photo; (bottom) Triduza Studio/Shutterstock; p. 81: Mlle Sonyah/Alamy Stock Photo; **p. 85:** dlewis33/Getty Images; **p. 86:** Defense Advanced Research Projects Agency; **p. 88:** CreVis2/Getty Images; **p. 97:** Mike Cullen; **p. 103:** (a) Valentina Proskurina/Shutterstock; (b) BrazilPhotos/Alamy Stock Photo; (c) Digital Zoo/Getty Images; (d) Qrt/Alamy Stock Photo

Chapter 3

Photos: p. 112: SciePro/Shutterstock; **p. 114:** Tramino/Getty Images; **p. 116:** (top) Tony Anderson/Getty Images; (bottom) Thomas Baker/Alamy Stock Photo; **p. 121:** Editorial Image/Science Source; **p. 125:** (top) ampolsonthong/Depositphotos; (bottom) Steve Lovegrove/Shutterstock; **p. 131:** (top) Karl Martin/Alamy Stock Photo; (bottom) Africa Studio/Shutterstock; **p. 132:** Courtesy of Joel Karty

Chapter 4

Photos: p. 162: Skyhobo/Getty Images; **p. 168:** Papilio/Alamy Stock Photo; **p. 177:** Elnur/Shutterstock; **p. 179:** Andrey_Kuzmin/Shutterstock; **p. 185:** (Model kits and chair flips) Courtesy of Joel Karty; (Pipes) Courtesy of Mike Jaquish Realty Arts; **p. 189:** shironosov/Getty Images

Chapter 5

Photos: p. 205: vesilvio/iStockphoto; **p. 211:** (a) Courtesy of Valerie Karty; (b) IvancoVlad/Getty Images; (c) Lawrence Lawry/Science Source; **p. 226:** The Photo Works; **p. 227:** Gregory James Van Raalte/Shutterstock; **p. 241:** Mtsaride/Shutterstock; **p. 242:** (all) John Kelly Green Photography; **p. 245:** (sunglasses) Mike Cullen; (profile) BLACKDAY/Shutterstock; **p. 246:** BLACKDAY/Shutterstock; **p. 247:** Take Photo/Shutterstock

Chapter 6

Photos: p. 264: Spencer Platt/Getty Images; **p. 266:** The Photo Works/Alamy Stock Photo; **p. 268:** anopdesignstock/Getty Images; **p. 270:** (top) James Jones/RiverRat Antiques; (bottom) Matjaz Corel/Alamy Stock Photo; **p. 275:** (left) The Photo Works/Alamy Stock Photo; (right) Sherry Yates Young/Shutterstock; **p. 282:** Editorial Image, LLC/Alamy Stock Photo; **p. 298:** Marilyn Howell/Stockimo/Alamy Stock Photo; **p. 300:** Elnur/Shutterstock

Chapter 7

Photos: p. 318: Alexander Zinovoy/123RF.com; **p. 322:** schankz/Depositphotos; **p. 337:** Chiyacat/Shutterstock

Interchapter D

Photos: p. 374: evemilla/Getty Images; **p. 375:** Gary Bell/OceanwideImages.com; **p. 376:** Syda Productions/Shutterstock; **p. 380:** Olga Popova/Shutterstock; **p. 381:** WIN-Initiative/Getty Images; **p. 383:** blickwinkel/Alamy Stock Photo; **p. 384:** eye35.pix/Alamy Stock Photo; **p. 386:** Grafner/Getty Images; **p. 388:** The Photo Works

Chapter 8

Photos: p. 393: Zerbor/Shutterstock; **p. 401:** The Photo Works; **p. 427:** Mariusz Szczygiel/Shutterstock; **p. 429:** Image Point Fr/Shutterstock; **p. 431:** Everett Collection/Shutterstock; **p. 435:** D. Kucharski K. Kucharska/Shutterstock

Chapter 9

Photos: p. 444: Whitebox Media/Alamy Stock Photo; **p. 454:** Milos Luzanin/Shutterstock; **p. 455:** Vikram Prasad Denis Semwogerere and Eric R Weeks Confocal microscopy of colloids. J. Phys.: Condens. Matter 19 (2007) 113102 (25pp). ©IOP Publishing LTD.; **p. 465:** Juan Medina/REUTERS/Newscom; **p. 472:** SHSPhotography/Getty Images; **p. 480:** winnond/Shutterstock; **p. 488:** Kongsky/Shutterstock; **p. 492:** Leonard Lessin / Science Source; **p. 496:** (top) xiaorui/Shutterstock; (bottom) chakkrachai nicharat/Shutterstock

Chapter 10

Photos: p. 508: Adam Berry/Getty Images; **p. 514:** digidreamgrafix/FeaturePics; **p. 519:** M. Unal Ozmen/Shutterstock; **p. 526:** vz maze/Shutterstock; **p. 535:** Jaromir Chalabala/Shutterstock; **p. 542:** Dusan Jankovic/Shutterstock

Chapter 11

Photos: p. 562: Sally Scott/Shutterstock; **p. 570:** Vladimir Godnik/Getty Images; **p. 571:** kolesniks/Shutterstock; **p. 584:** AP Photo

Chapter 12

Photos: p. 604: Virojt Changyencham/Getty Images; **p. 604:** SPL/Science Source; **p. 613:** Fidel/Shutterstock; **p. 616:** Mike Flippo/Shutterstock; **p. 619:** Irina_iris/Shutterstock; **p. 622:** Natali _ Mis/Shutterstock; **p. 625:** Westend61/Getty Images

Chapter 13

Photos: p. 647: Hurst Photo/Shutterstock; **p. 654:** Jody Ann/Shutterstock; **p. 662:** (top) Andrew J. Martinez/Science Source; (bottom) Dr. D.P. Wilson/Science Source; **p. 666:** Igor Normann/Shutterstock; **p. 668:** Chaikom/Shutterstock; **p. 669:** Bret Hartman/AP Images for Hyundai; **p. 674:** Robyn Mackenzie/Shutterstock; **p. 683:** Mike Cullen

Chapter 14

Photos: p. 693: LONG WEI/FEATURECHINA/Newscom; **p. 697:** zhudifeng/Getty Images; **p. 711:** Jiri Hera/Newscom; **p. 712:** karandaev/Getty Images; **p. 713:** Eye of Science/Science Source; **p. 714:** (top) Grafner/Getty Images; (bottom) Dan Kitwood/Getty Images; **p. 716:** Crevis/Shutterstock

Chapter 15

Photos: p. 739: kmls/Shutterstock; **p. 749:** Mitch Fuqua/USAF/Getty Images; **p. 754:** Getty Images

Drawn Art: TI15.1, TI15.2, TI15.3, TI15.4, P15.6, P15.11, P15.12, P15.13, P15.30: Reprinted by permission. SDBSWeb: https://sdbs.db.aist.go.jp (National Institute of Advanced Industrial Science and Technology, date of access)

Chapter 16

Photos: p. 769: PandaWild/Shutterstock; **p. 771:** Courtesy of Meg Healy, Anna Sheinberg, and Rachel Goldstein; **p. 787:** Courtesy of Heinrich Pniok; **p. 788:** PureRadiancePhoto/Shutterstock; **p. 791:** BlueRingMedia/Shutterstock; **p. 792:** studiovin/Shutterstock; **p. 802:** The Photo Works; **p. 804:** (top) -oqlpo-/Getty Images; (bottom) Steve Cavalier/Alamy Stock Photo; **p. 809:** PlanilAstro/Shutterstock

Drawn Art: Fig. 16-28, YT16.12, P16.4, P16.5, P16.28, P16.29: Reprinted by permission. SDBSWeb : https://sdbs.db.aist.go.jp (National Institute of Advanced Industrial Science and Technology, date of access); **Fig. 16-4, Fig. 16-8 a-b, YT16.4, SP 16.1, YT16.8, Fig. 16-12, Fig. 16-13, YT16.10, Fig. 16-16, Fig. 16-17 a-c, YT16.12, YT16.14, YT16.15, Fig. 16-21, YT16.16, Fig. 16-22a-c, Fig. 16-24, Fig. 16-26, P16.21, P16.23, P16.24, P16.25, P16.26, P16.27, P16.45, P16.46, P16.49, P16.50, P16.51, P16.52:** © Sigma-Aldrich Co. LLC. Used with permission of Sigma-Aldrich Co. LLC.

Chapter 17

Photos: p. 819: SimpleFoto/Depositphoto; **p. 827:** Rasmus Loeth Petersen/Alamy Stock Photo; **p. 828:** visivastudio/Shutterstock; **p. 836:** bluestocking/Getty Images; **p. 841:** hudiemm/Getty Images; **p. 850:** Donna Beeler/Shutterstock; **p. 851:** The Photo Works/Alamy Stock Photo; **p. 864:** TaLaNoVa/Shutterstock

Drawn Art: Fig. 17-8: Reprinted by permission. SDBSWeb: https://sdbs.db.aist.go.jp (National Institute of Advanced Industrial Science and Technology, date of access); **Fig. 17-40**: Reprinted by permission of Nanalysis Corp.; **P17.33, P17.34:** © Sigma-Aldrich Co. LLC. Used with permission of Sigma-Aldrich Co. LLC;

Chapter 18

Photos: p. 878: Ted Kinsman; **p. 882:** Petr Goskov/Alamy Stock Photo; **p. 891:** Contrail/Shutterstock; **p. 892:** Panther

Media GmbH/Alamy Stock Photo; **p. 900:** Jack Jelly/Shutterstock; **p. 906:** Panther Media GmbH/Alamy Stock Photo

Chapter 19

Photos: p. 926: Sergiy Bykhunenko/Shutterstock; **p. 935:** Pressmaster/Shutterstock; **p. 949:** Peter Dazeley/Getty Images; **p. 954:** Melinda Lee Patelli; **p. 957:** govindji/Shutterstock

Chapter 20

Photos: p. 987: Mopic/Shutterstock; **p. 996:** ntstudio/Shutterstock; **p. 1004:** TRL ltd./Science Source; **p. 1006:** FUN FUN PHOTO/Shutterstock; **p. 1008:** tadamichi/Shutterstock

Chapter 21

Photos: p. 1025: LUIS PADILLA-Fotografia/Shutterstock; **p. 1042:** Melinda Lee Patelli; **p. 1044:** Perry Correll/Shutterstock

Chapter 22

Photos: p. 1051: exyne/Getty Images; **p. 1056:** (left) All Canada Photos/Alamy Stock Photo; (right) Sean Gallup/Getty Images; **p. 1058:** The Photo Works/Alamy Stock Photo; **p. 1062:** Lew Robertson/StockFood; **p. 1072:** (both) Courtesy of Joel Karty

Chapter 23

Photos: p. 1099: Paolo Bona/Shutterstock; **p. 1104:** Michael Flippo/Alamy Stock Photo; **p. 1105:** Turtle Rock Scientific/Science Source; **p. 1108:** The Photo Works/Alamy Stock Photo; **p. 1118:** domnitsky/Shutterstock; **p. 1130:** O.Bellini/Shutterstock; **p. 1134:** DWD-Comp/Alamy Stock Photo
Drawn Art: P23.65, P23.66, P23.67, P23.68: © Sigma-Aldrich Co. LLC. Used with permission of Sigma-Aldrich Co. LLC.

Chapter 24

Photos: p. 1156: mailsonpignata/Shutterstock; **p. 1164:** The Photo Works/Alamy Stock Photo; **p. 1167:** CSP_drohn/AgeFotostock; **p. 1171:** Tim UR/Shutterstock; **p. 1173:** Bloomberg/Getty Images; **p. 1175:** (left) Andrey Kiselev/Fotolia; (right) Helen Sessions/Alamy Stock Photo; **p. 1180:** Explode/Shutterstock
Drawn Art: P24.45, P22.47: © Sigma-Aldrich Co. LLC. Used with permission of Sigma-Aldrich Co. LLC

Chapter 25

Photos: p. 1197: Last Resort/Getty Images; **p. 1198:** The Photo Works/Alamy Stock Photo; **p. 1199:** Melinda Lee Patelli; **p. 1202:** Dean Clarke/Shutterstock; **p. 1205:** Kenneth Sponsler/Shutterstock; **p. 1214:** USDA Photo/Alamy Stock Photo; **p. 1225:** Courtesy of Dan Wright and Ashley Moreno; **p. 1226:** 2020 Images/Alamy Stock Photo; **p. 1234:** Nejron Photo/Shutterstock

Chapter 26

Photos: p. 1252: GlobalP/Getty Images; **p. 1257:** Lorne Chapman/Alamy Stock Photo; **p. 1260:** Jantz/Shutterstock; **p. 1272:** (top) StanislauV/Shutterstock; (bottom) Art Konovalov/Shutterstock; **p. 1278:** Panther Media GmbH/Alamy Stock Photo; **p. 1280:** Sotnikov Misha/Shutterstock
Drawn Art: P26.61b, P26.62b, P26.63: © Sigma-Aldrich Co. LLC. Used with permission of Sigma-Aldrich Co. LLC

Chapter 27

Photos: p. 1304: (Poison ivy) Melinda Fawver/Shutterstock; (Sign) raksyBH/Depositphotos; (Hydrocortisone) Science History Images/Alamy Stock Photo; **p. 1306:** imageBROKER/Alamy Stock Photo; **p. 1309:** Courtesy of Patrick Ryan - CIH, CSP, CHMM; **p. 1321:** NASA Earth Observatory image by Joshua Stevens, using data courtesy of NASA Ozone, Watch and GEOS-5 data from the Global Modeling and Assimilation Office at NASA GSFC; **p. 1337:** Courtesy of Joel Karty
Drawn Art: P27.56: © Sigma-Aldrich Co. LLC. Used with permission of Sigma-Aldrich Co. LLC.

Chapter 28

Photos: p. 1354: (Penny and needles) Courtesy of Jeong-Woo Lee, Georgia Tech; (a) Jan Wlodarczyk/Alamy Stock Photo; (b) risteski goce/Shutterstock; (c) Oksana Shufrych/Shutterstock; **p. 1355:** (left) bluestocking/Getty Images; (right) DonNichols/Getty Images; **p. 1363:** AlexLMX/Shutterstock; **p. 1366:** (top) Dmitry Kalinovsky/Shutterstock; (bottom) Duplass/Shutterstock; **p. 1367:** (left) The Photo Works/Alamy Stock Photo; (middle) László Gránásy Tamás Pusztai Tamás Börzsönyi James A. Warren and Jack F. Douglas. A general mechanism of polycrystalline growth, Nature Materials 3 645–650 (2004). doi:10.1038/nmat1190. ©2004 Nature Publishing Group; (right) oneclearvision/Getty Images; **p. 1380:** Milen Gagov/Alamy Stock Photo; **p. 1383:** (left) Keith Homan/Shutterstock; (right) Roman Samokhin/Shutterstock; **p. 1384:** Oral and maxillofacial surgery, Deutsche Gesellschaft fur Mund-, Kiefer-, und Gesichtschirurgie 01/01/2008; **p. 1385:** (left) Melinda Lee Patelli; (right) oliver leedham/Alamy Stock Photo; **p. 1386:** (top) PhilipYb Studio/Shutterstock; (bottom) Dmitry Kalinovsky/Shutterstock; **p. 1392:** Madlen/Shutterstock; **p. 1394:** (left) Bill Oxford/Getty Images; (middle and right) D. Dockstader/M. Noble/S. Pruett; (lego mold) LNS Technologies; **p. 1398:** Basilios1/Getty Images; **p. 1399:** (milk) Michael Flippo/Alamy Stock Photo; (bag) Feng Yu/Alamy Stock Photo; (razor) The Photo Works/Alamy Stock Photo; (cooler) C Squared Studios/Getty Images; **p. 1403:** (left) Nataly Studio/Shutterstock; (right) GIPhotoStock X/Alamy Stock Photo
Drawn Art: Fig. 28-18: Reprinted with permission from Xu, J.; Fogleman, E. A.; Craig, S. L. Structure and Properties of DNA-Based Reversible Polymers. Macromolecules 2004, 37 (5), 1863–1870. Copyright © 2004 American Chemical Society.

Chapter 29

Photos: p. 1422: Rudolf Vlcek/Getty Images; **p. 1426:** Darryl Brooks/Shutterstock; **p. 1440:** imageBROKER/Alamy Stock Photo; **p. 1447:** CDC/Science Source; **p. 1466:** Sinhyu/Getty Images; **p. 1467:** xiaorui/Shutterstock; **p. 1469:** The Photo Works/Alamy Stock Photo; **p. 1475:** A. Barrington Brown/ Science Source; **p. 1476:** Courtesy of Rockefeller University; **p. 1477:** (top) Courtesy of Vittorio Luzzati; (middle) University Archives and Records Center, University of Pennsylvania; (bottom) AP Photo/Anthony Camerano; **p. 1487:** (top) Ian Dagnall/Alamy Stock Photo; (a) Valentina Proskurina/ Shutterstock; (b) BrazilPhotos/Alamy Stock Photo; (c) Digital Zoo/Getty Images; (d) Qrt/Alamy Stock Photo

Chapter 30

Photos: p. 1497: Talaj/Shutterstock; **p. 1527:** V.S.Anandhakrishna/Shutterstock; **p. 1529:** Drizzyphotographyja/Shutterstock; **p. 1538:** Kumar Sriskandan/Alamy Stock Photo; **p. 1542:** Melinda Lee Patelli

(Beaker icon used for Green Chemistry boxes throughout): Shutterstock

INDEX

Note: Page numbers in *italic* indicate material in figures and tables. The [e] icon refers to content in online chapters.

B

D

E

H

N